LITERARY MARKET PLACE™

# LMP 2014

*Literary Market Place™*
74th Edition

**Publisher**
*Thomas H. Hogan*

**Vice President, Content**
*Dick Kaser*

**Senior Director, ITI Reference Group**
*Owen O'Donnell*

**Managing Editor**
*Karen Hallard*

**Senior Editor**
*Mitra Purkayastha*

**Assistant Editor**
*Vivian Sposobiec*

**Tampa Operations:**

**Manager, Tampa Editorial Operations**
*Debra James*

**Project Coordinator, Tampa Editorial**
*Carolyn Victor*

**Graphics & Production:**

**Vice President**
*Heide Dengler*

**Production**
*Dana Stevenson*
*Jackie Crawford*

LITERARY MARKET PLACE™

# LMP 2014

THE DIRECTORY OF THE AMERICAN BOOK PUBLISHING INDUSTRY WITH INDUSTRY INDEXES

Volume

*Published by*

**Information Today, Inc.**
**143 Old Marlton Pike**
**Medford, NJ 08055-8750**
**Phone: (609) 654-6266**
**Fax: (609) 654-4309**
**E-mail (Orders): custserv@infotoday.com**
**Web site: www.infotoday.com**

ISSN 0000-1155
ISBN 978-1-57387-473-1 (set)
978-1-57387-471-7 (Vol. 1)
978-1-57387-472-4 (Vol. 2)
Library of Congress Catalog Card Number 41-51571



Information Today, Inc.
143 Old Marlton Pike
Medford, NJ 08055-8750
Phone: 800-300-9868 (Customer Service)
800-409-4929 (Editorial)
Fax: 609-654-4309
E-mail (orders): custserv@infotoday.com
Web Site: www.infotoday.com

Printed in the United States of America

# CONTENTS

## VOLUME 1

## VOLUME 2

## SERVICES & SUPPLIERS



## INDEXES

# Preface

The 2014 edition marks the 74[th] annual publication of *Literary Market Place*™—the leading directory of the American and Canadian book publishing industry. Covering publishers and literary agents to manufacturers and shipping services, *LMP* is the most comprehensive directory of its kind. Completely revised, *LMP* 2014 contains over 9,800 entries. Of these listings 2,808 are publishers—including Canadian houses and small presses. Together with its companion publication, *International Literary Market Place*™, these directories cover the global book publishing industry.

**Organization & Content**

Volume 1 covers core publishing industry information: Book Publishers; Editorial Services and Agents; Associations, Events, Courses and Awards; and Books and Magazines for the Trade.

Volume 2 contains information on service providers and suppliers to the publishing industry. Advertising, Marketing and Publicity; Book Manufacturing; Sales and Distribution; and Services and Suppliers can be found in this volume.

Entries generally contain name, address, telephone and other telecommunications data, key personnel, company reportage, branch offices, brief statistics and descriptive annotations. Where applicable, Standard Address Numbers (SANs) have been included. SANs are unique numbers assigned to the addresses of publishers, wholesalers and booksellers. Publishers' entries also contain their assigned ISBN prefixes. Both the SAN and ISBN systems are administered by R.R. Bowker LLC, 630 Central Avenue, New Providence, NJ 07974.

**Indexes**

In addition to the numerous section-specific indexes appearing throughout, each volume of *LMP* contains four indexes that reference listings appearing in that volume. The Industry Indexes cover two distinct areas of data: a Company Index that includes the name, address, communications information and page reference for company listings and a separate Personnel Index that includes the main personnel associated with each entry as well as the page reference. Other indexes include the Index to Sections for quickly finding specific categories of information and the Index to Advertisers.

**A Note to Authors**

Prospective authors seeking a publisher should be aware that there are publishers who, as a condition for publishing and marketing an individual's work, may require a significant sum of money be paid to the publisher. This practice is known by a number of terms including author subsidized publishing, author investment, and co-operative publishing. Before entering an agreement involving such a payment, the author is advised to make a careful investigation to determine the standing of the publisher's imprint in the industry.

Similarly, authors seeking literary representation are advised that some agents request a nominal reading fee that may be applied to the agent's commission upon representation. Other agencies may charge substantially higher fees which may not be applicable to a future commission and which are not refundable. The recommended course is to first send a query letter with an outline, sample chapter, and a self-addressed stamped envelope (SASE). Should an agent express interest in handling the manuscript, full details of fees and commissions should be obtained in writing before the complete manuscript is sent. Should an agency require significant advance payment from an author, the author is cautioned to make a careful investigation to determine the agency's standing in the industry before entering an agreement. The author should always retain a copy of the manuscript in his or her possession.

Occasionally, the editors of *LMP* will receive complaints against publishers or agents listed in the work. If, after investigation and review, the editors determine that the complaints are significant and justified, we may exclude the company or individual in question. However, the absence of a listing in *LMP* for any particular publisher or agent should not be construed as a judgment on the legitimacy or integrity of that organization or individual.

**Compilation**

*LMP* is updated throughout the year via a number of methods. A request for updated information is sent to every current entrant at least once each year to corroborate and update the information contained on our database. All updates received are edited for the next product release. Those entrants who do not respond to our request are verified through telephone interviews. Entrants who cannot be verified or who fall short of entry criteria are dropped from the current edition.

Information on new listings is gathered in a similar method. Possible new listings are identified through ongoing research, or nominations for listings may come from the organization itself or from a third party. A data collection form is then sent to gather the essential listing information. Unless we receive information directly from the organization, the new listing will not be included in *LMP*.

Updated information or suggestions for new listings can also be submitted by using the form that follows this preface. Simply fill in the information requested and send the form to:

*Literary Market Place*
Information Today, Inc.
630 Central Ave
New Providence, NJ 07974
Fax: 908-219-0192

**An updating method using the Internet is also available for *LMP* listings:**

Visit the *Literary Market Place* web site to update an *LMP* listing. **Literarymarketplace.com** allows you the opportunity to provide new information for a listing by clicking on the "Update or Correct Your Entry" option. The Feedback option on the home page of the web site can be used to suggest new entries as well.

**Related Services**

*Literary Market Place*, along with its companion volume *International Literary Market Place*, is available through the Internet at **www.literarymarketplace.com**. Designed to give users simple, logical access to the information they require, the site offers users the choice of searching for data alphabetically, geographically, by type, or by subject. Continuously updated by Information Today's team of editors, this is a truly enhanced version of the *LMP* and *ILMP* databases, incorporating features that make "must-have" information easily available.

Arrangements for placing advertisements in *LMP* can be coordinated through Lauri Rimler by telephone at 908-219-0088, by fax at 908-219-0192, or by e-mail at lwrimler@infotoday.com.

Your feedback is important to us. We strongly encourage you to contact us with suggestions or comments on the print edition of *LMP*, or its web site. Our editorial office can be reached at 800-409-4929, or by e-mail at khallard@infotoday.com.

The editors would like to thank those entrants who took the time to respond to our requests for current information.

# Abbreviations & Acronyms

The following is a list of acronyms & abbreviations used throughout *LMP*.

AAP - Association of American Publishers
AAR - Association of Authors' Representatives
AB - Alberta
ABA - American Booksellers Association
Acct(s) - Account(s)
Acctg - Accounting
Acq(s) - Acquisition(s)
Ad - Advertising
Admin - Administrative, Administration
Aff - Affairs
AK - Alaska
AL - Alabama
ALA - American Library Association
ALTA - American Literary Translators Association
APA - American Photographic Artists
appt - appointment
Apt - Apartment
AR - Arkansas
ASMP - American Society of Media Photographers
ASPP - American Society of Picture Professionals
Assoc(s) - Associate(s)
Asst(s) - Assistant(s)
ATA - American Translators Association
AV - Audiovisual
Ave - Avenue
AZ - Arizona

B&W - Black & White
BC - British Columbia
Bd - Board
bio - biography
BISAC - Book Industry Standards & Communications
BISG - Book Industry Study Group
Bldg - Building
Blvd - Boulevard
BMI - Book Manufacturers' Institute
Br - Branch
Busn - Business

CA - California
CEO - Chief Executive Officer
CFO - Chief Financial Officer
Chmn - Chairman
Chpn - Chairperson
CIO - Chief Information Officer
Circ - Circulation
CN - Canada
CO - Colorado
Co(s) - Company(-ies)
Co-edns - Co-editions
Coll(s) - College(s)
Comm - Committee
Commun(s) - Communication(s)
Comp - Compiler
Compt - Comptroller
Cont - Controller
Contrib - Contributing
COO - Chief Operating Officer
Coord(s) - Coordinator(s)
Corp - Corporate, Corporation
Coun - Counsel
CT - Connecticut
Ct - Court
CTO - Chief Technical / Technology Officer
Ctr - Center
Curr - Current
Cust - Customer
CZ - Canal Zone

DC - District of Columbia
DE - Delaware
Dept - Department
Devt - Development
Dir(s) - Director(s)
Dist - Distributed, Distribution, Distributor
Div - Division
Dom - Domestic
Dr - Drive

ed - edition
Ed(s) - Editor(s)
Edit - Editorial
Educ - Education, Educational
El-hi - Elementary-High School
Elem - Elementary
Ency - Encyclopedia
Eng - English
Engg - Engineering
Engr - Engineer
Equip - Equipment
ESL - English as a Second Language
Est - Established
EVP - Executive Vice President
exc - except
Exec(s) - Executive(s)
Expwy - Expressway
ext - extension

Fed - Federal
Fin - Finance, Financial
fl - floor
FL - Florida
Freq - Frequency
Fwy - Freeway

GA - Georgia
Gen - General
Govt - Government
GU - Guam

HI - Hawaii
HR - Human Resources
HS - High School
Hwy - Highway

IA - Iowa
ID - Idaho
IL - Illinois
Illus - Illustrator
IN - Indiana
indiv(s) - individual(s)
Indus - Industrial, Industry
Info - Information
Instl - Institutional
Instn(s) - Institution(s)
Instrl - Instructional
Intl - International
ISBN - International Standard Book Number
ISSN - International Standard Serial Number
IT - Information Technology

Jt - Joint
Jr - Junior
Juv - Juvenile

K - Kindergarten
KS - Kansas
KY - Kentucky

LA - Louisiana
Lang(s) - Language(s)
Lib(s) - Library(-ies)
Libn(s) - Librarian(s)
Lit - Literature

MA - Massachusetts
MB - Manitoba
MD - Maryland
Mdse - Merchandise
Mdsg - Merchandising
ME - Maine
Med - Medical
Memb(s) - Member(s)
Metro - Metropolitan
Mfg - Manufacturing
Mgmt - Management
Mgr(s) - Manager(s)
MI - Michigan
Mkt(s) - Market(s)
Mktg - Marketing
MLA - Modern Language Association
MN - Minnesota
Mng - Managing
MO - Missouri
MS - Mississippi
ms(s) - manuscript(s)
MT - Montana

Natl - National
NB - New Brunswick
NC - North Carolina
ND - North Dakota
NE - Nebraska
NH - New Hampshire

NJ - New Jersey
NL - Newfoundland and Labrador
NM - New Mexico
No - Number
NS - Nova Scotia
NT - Northwest Territories
NU - Nunavut
NV - Nevada
NY - New York

Off(s) - Office(s)
Offr - Officer
OH - Ohio
OK - Oklahoma
ON - Ontario
Oper(s) - Operation(s)
OR - Oregon

PA - Pennsylvania
Pbk(s) - Paperback(s)
PE - Prince Edward Island
Perms - Permissions
Photo - Photograph
Photog - Photographer, Photography
Pkwy - Parkway
pp - pages
PPA - Professional Photographers of America
PR - Public Relations
PR - Puerto Rico
Pres - President
Proc - Processing
Prod(s) - Product(s)
Prodn - Production
Prodr - Producer
Prof - Professional
Prog(s) - Program(s)
Proj(s) - Project(s)
Promo(s) - Promotion(s)
Prop - Proprietor
Pub Aff - Public Affairs
Publg - Publishing
Publr - Publisher
Pubn(s) - Publication(s)
Purch - Purchasing

QC - Quebec

R&D - Research & Development
Rd - Road
Ref - Reference
Reg - Region
Regl - Regional
Rel - Relations
Rep(s) - Representative(s)
Res - Research
RI - Rhode Island
Rm - Room
Rte - Route
Rts - Rights

SAN - Standard Address Number
SASE - Self-Addressed Stamped Envelope
SATW - Society of American Travel Writers
SC - South Carolina
Sci - Science
SD - South Dakota
Secy - Secretary
Serv(s) - Service(s)
SK - Saskatchewan
SLA - Special Libraries Association
Soc - Social, Sociology
Spec - Special
Sq - Square
Sr - Senior
St - Saint, Street
Sta - Station
Ste - Sainte
Subn(s) - Subscription(s)
Subs - Subsidiary
Supv - Supervisor
SVP - Senior Vice President
Synd - Syndicated, Syndication

Tech - Technical
Technol - Technology
Tel - Telephone
Terr - Terrace
TN - Tennessee
Tpke - Turnpike
Treas - Treasurer
TX - Texas

UK - United Kingdom
Univ - University
unsol - unsolicited
UT - Utah

V - Vice
VA - Virginia
VChmn - Vice Chairman
VI - Virgin Islands
vol(s) - volume(s)
VP - Vice President
VT - Vermont

WA - Washington
WI - Wisconsin
WV - West Virginia
WY - Wyoming

yr - year
YT - Yukon Territory

# Book Publishers

## U.S. Publishers

Listed in alphabetical order are those U.S. publishers that have reported to *LMP* that they produce an average of three or more books annually. Publishers that have appeared in a previous edition of *LMP*, but whose output currently does not meet our defined rate of activity, will be reinstated when their annual production reaches the required level. It should be noted that this rule of publishing activity does not apply to publishers of dictionaries, encyclopedias, atlases and braille books or to university presses.

The definition of a book is that used for *Books in Print* (Grey House Publishing, PO Box 56, Amenia, NY 12501-0056) and excludes charts, pamphlets, folding maps, sheet music and material with stapled bindings. Publishers that make their titles available only in electronic or audio format are included if they meet the stated criteria. In the case of packages, the book must be of equal or greater importance than the accompanying piece. With few exceptions, new publishers are not listed prior to having published at least three titles within a year.

§ before the company name indicates publishers involved in electronic publishing.

The following indexes can be found immediately after the publishers' listings:

U.S. Publishers–Geographic Index
U.S. Publishers–Type of Publications Index
U.S. Publishers–Subject Index

See **Imprints, Subsidiaries & Distributors** for additional information on the companies listed herein. This section should also be checked for apparently active companies that are no longer listed in the U.S. Publishers section. In many cases, they have been acquired as an imprint or subsidiary of a larger entity and no longer have a discrete listing.

**A Better Be Write Publishing LLC**
9001 Ridge Hill St, Kernersville, NC 27284
Mailing Address: PO Box 914, Kernersville, NC 27285
*Tel:* 336-354-7173 *Fax:* 336-993-2497
*Web Site:* www.abetterbewrite.com
*Key Personnel*
Mng Ed: William J Connor, Jr *E-mail:* profin@triad.rr.com
Founded: 2005
Subjects include the paranormal.
ISBN Prefix(es): 978-0-9767732; 978-0-9771971; 978-0-9788985
Number of titles published annually: 30 Print
Total Titles: 150 Print
Membership(s): AAP; IBPA, the Independent Book Publishers Association

**A Cappela Publishing**
PO Box 3691, Sarasota, FL 34230-3691
*Tel:* 941-351-2050 *Fax:* 941-351-4735
*E-mail:* acappub@aol.com
*Web Site:* www.acappela.com
*Key Personnel*
Pres: Patrika Vaughn
Admin: Lilo Weidinger
Book Editing: Bonita Chambers
Book Promos: Ashley Grant
Founded: 1996
One-stop-shop for authors: consulting, classes, critiques, editing, ghost writing, publishing, marketing & promoting.
This publisher has indicated that 25% of their product line is author subsidized.
ISBN Prefix(es): 978-0-9656309; 978-0-9724979; 978-0-9779139; 978-0-9818933
Number of titles published annually: 10 Print; 2 CD-ROM; 10 Online; 10 E-Book; 2 Audio
Total Titles: 110 Print; 2 CD-ROM; 20 Online; 20 E-Book; 2 Audio
Imprints: Advocate House
*Editorial Office(s):* 913 Tennessee Lane, Sarasota, FL 34234-5712
Foreign Rights: E-Lit Agent.com (Worldwide)
*Orders to:* 913 Tennessee Lane, Sarasota, FL 34234-5712
Membership(s): IBPA, the Independent Book Publishers Association

**A Cappella Books**, see Chicago Review Press

**§A K Peters Ltd**
Division of CRC Press LLC
5 Commonwealth Rd, Suite 2-C, Natick, MA 01760-1526
Mailing Address: 6000 Broken Sound Pkwy, Suite 300, Boca Raton, FL 33487
*E-mail:* editorial@akpeters.com
*Web Site:* www.akpeters.com
*Key Personnel*
SVP, Publg: John Lavender *Tel:* 561-998-2579 *E-mail:* john.lavender@taylorandfrancis.com
VP, Mktg: Stacey Mironov *E-mail:* stacey.mironov@taylorandfrancis.com
Founded: 1992
Scientific-technical publisher specializing in mathematics, computer science & computer game programming from undergraduate textbooks to research monographs & professional books.
ISBN Prefix(es): 978-1-56881
Number of titles published annually: 35 Print
Total Titles: 308 Print; 2 CD-ROM
*Warehouse:* Taylor & Francis, 7625 Empire Dr, Florence, KY 41042-2919 *Tel:* 859-727-5000
*Distribution Center:* Taylor & Francis, 7625 Empire Dr, Florence, KY 41042-2919 *Tel:* 859-727-5000

**§A-R Editions Inc**
8551 Research Way, Suite 180, Middleton, WI 53562
*Tel:* 608-836-9000 *Toll Free Tel:* 800-736-0070 (US book orders only) *Fax:* 608-831-8200
*E-mail:* info@areditions.com
*Web Site:* www.areditions.com
*Key Personnel*
CEO & Pres: Patrick Wall *Tel:* 608-203-2575 *E-mail:* patrick.wall@areditions.com
Dir, Sales & Mktg: James L Zychowicz *Tel:* 608-203-2580 *E-mail:* james.zychowicz@areditions.com
Founded: 1962
Scholarly critical editions of music for performance & study; computer music & digital audio professional books, electronics & Internet technology, online music anthology (www.armusicanthology.com) & co-published series with MLA: Index & Bibliography, Basic Manual & Technical Reports Series.
ISBN Prefix(es): 978-0-89579
Number of titles published annually: 25 Print
Total Titles: 500 Print
Distributor for AIM (American Institute of Musicology)

**§AAAI Press**
Imprint of Association for the Advancement of Artificial Intelligence
2275 E Bayshore Rd, Suite 160, Palo Alto, CA 94303
*Tel:* 650-328-3123 *Fax:* 650-321-4457
*E-mail:* press12@aaai.org
*Web Site:* www.aaaipress.org; www.aaai.org
*Key Personnel*
Exec Dir: Carol Hamilton
Pubns Dir: Mike Hamilton
Ed-in-Chief: Anthony G Cohn
Founded: 1989
Publishing books on all aspects of artificial intelligence.
ISBN Prefix(es): 978-0-929280; 978-1-57735

Number of titles published annually: 30 Print; 4 CD-ROM; 2 Online
Total Titles: 400 Print; 30 CD-ROM; 2 Online

**AACC**, see Community College Press

**AACC International**
3340 Pilot Knob Rd, St Paul, MN 55121
*Tel:* 651-454-7250 *Fax:* 651-454-0766
*E-mail:* aacc@scisoc.org
*Web Site:* www.aaccnet.org
*Key Personnel*
EVP: Steven C Nelson *Tel:* 651-994-3832 *E-mail:* snelson@scisoc.org
VP, Fin: Barbara Mock *Tel:* 651-994-3829 *E-mail:* bmock@scisoc.org
VP, Opers: Amy Hope *Tel:* 651-994-3827 *E-mail:* ahope@scisoc.org
Dir, Pubns: Greg Grahek *Tel:* 651-994-3841 *E-mail:* ggrahek@scisoc.org
Founded: 1920
Source for cereal science information.
ISBN Prefix(es): 978-1-891127; 978-0-9624407
Number of titles published annually: 5 Print; 1 CD-ROM
Total Titles: 100 Print; 1 CD-ROM; 1 Online; 1 E-Book
*See separate listing for:*
**Eagan Press**

**AAPC Publishing**, see Autism Asperger Publishing Co

**§AAPG (American Association of Petroleum Geologists)**
1444 S Boulder Ave, Tulsa, OK 74119
Mailing Address: PO Box 979, Tulsa, OK 74101-0979
*Tel:* 918-584-2555 *Toll Free Tel:* 800-364-AAPG (364-2274) *Fax:* 918-580-2665 *Toll Free Fax:* 800-898-2274
*E-mail:* publications@aapg.org
*Web Site:* www.aapg.org
*Key Personnel*
Mng Ed, Tech Pubns: Beverly Molyneux *Tel:* 918-560-2670 *E-mail:* molyneux@aapg.org
Founded: 1917
Peer-reviewed geological science tomes.
ISBN Prefix(es): 978-0-89181; 978-1-58861
Number of titles published annually: 10 Print; 10 CD-ROM
Total Titles: 100 Print; 80 CD-ROM
Distributed by Affiliated East - West Press Private Ltd; Canadian Society of Petroleum Geologists; Geological Society of London
Distributor for Geological Society of London
*Shipping Address:* 125 W 15 St, Tulsa, OK 74119

**AAVIM**, see American Association for Vocational Instructional Materials

**§Abacus**
3413 Roger B Chaffee SE, Suite 101, Grand Rapids, MI 49546
*Tel:* 616-241-3404 *Fax:* 616-698-0325
*E-mail:* info@abacuspub.com
*Web Site:* www.abacuspub.com
*Key Personnel*
Pres & Mktg Mgr: Arnie Lee
VP & Publr: James Oldfield, Jr
Founded: 1978
Publish computer books, hardware & software user guides for IBM & compatibles users.
ISBN Prefix(es): 978-1-55755; 978-0-916439
Number of titles published annually: 6 Print; 3 E-Book
Total Titles: 12 Print; 7 CD-ROM; 3 E-Book
Imprints: Stay Focused Press

**Abaris Books**
Division of Opal Publishing Corp
70 New Canaan Ave, Norwalk, CT 06850
*Tel:* 203-838-8402 *Fax:* 203-857-0730
*E-mail:* abaris@abarisbooks.com
*Web Site:* abarisbooks.com
*Key Personnel*
Dir & Mng Ed: J C West *Tel:* 203-838-8625
Publr: Anthony S Kaufmann
Ed: Miriam West
Founded: 1973
Art, art history, art reference, philosophy & metaphysics.
ISBN Prefix(es): 978-0-913870; 978-0-89835
Number of titles published annually: 7 Print
Total Titles: 185 Print
Imprints: The Illustrated Bartsch; Janus Library

**Abbeville Press**
Imprint of Abbeville Publishing Group
137 Varick St, Suite 504, New York, NY 10013-1105
*Tel:* 212-366-5585 *Toll Free Tel:* 800-ARTBOOK (278-2665) *Fax:* 212-366-6966
*E-mail:* abbeville@abbeville.com
*Web Site:* www.abbeville.com
*Key Personnel*
Sr Ed: Joan Strasbaugh
Cust Serv Mgr: Nadine Winns
Mktg & Publicity Mgr: Diana Griffin
Founded: 1977
A fine arts publisher.
ISBN Prefix(es): 978-0-89659; 978-1-55859; 978-0-7892
Number of titles published annually: 25 Print

**Abbeville Publishing Group**
137 Varick St, Suite 504, New York, NY 10013
SAN: 211-4755
*Tel:* 212-366-5585 *Toll Free Tel:* 800-ART-BOOK (278-2665) *Fax:* 212-366-6966
*E-mail:* abbeville@abbeville.com; marketing@abbeville.com; sales@abbeville.com; rights@abbeville.com
*Web Site:* www.abbeville.com
*Key Personnel*
Pres & Publr: Robert E Abrams
Edit Dir: David Fabricant
Dir, Fin Analysis: John Olivieri
Warehouse Dir: Arthur Goldberg
Cust Serv Mgr: Nadine Winns *E-mail:* nwinns@abbeville.com
Publicist: Erin Dress
Mktg: Stephanie Gomory
Founded: 1977
Publishers of high-quality, fine art books, nonfiction illustrated books, children's books, limited editions, prints, gift line.
ISBN Prefix(es): 978-0-89659; 978-1-55859; 978-0-89660; 978-0-7892
Number of titles published annually: 40 Print
Total Titles: 700 Print
Imprints: Abbeville Kids; Abbeville Press; Artabras; Modern Masters
Foreign Rep(s): Angell Eurosales (Benelux, Scandinavia); Bookport Associates (Greece, Italy, Malta, Portugal, Spain); CBL Marketing Services (Albania, Bosnia and Herzegovina, Bulgaria, Croatia, Czech Republic, Hungary, Macedonia, Montenegro, Poland, Romania, Serbia, Slovakia, Slovenia); European Marketing Services (Anselm Robinson) (Austria, Germany, Switzerland); Celine Khoury (Lebanon); Peribo Pty Ltd (Eddie Coffey) (Australia); Steimatzky House (Arlette Perl) (Israel); Ralph & Sheila Summers (Hong Kong, Korea, Malaysia, Philippines, Singapore, Taiwan, Thailand)
Foreign Rights: Bookbank, SA (Latin America, Mexico, Spain); Motovun Tokyo (Japan); Ultreya srl (Italy)
*Warehouse:* Client Distribution Services, 193 Edwards Dr, Jackson, TN 38301 *Toll Free Tel:* 800-343-4499 *Toll Free Fax:* 800-351-5073
*See separate listing for:*
**Abbeville Press**

**§ABC-CLIO**
130 Cremona Dr, Santa Barbara, CA 93117
Mailing Address: PO Box 1911, Santa Barbara, CA 93116-1911
*Tel:* 805-968-1911 *Toll Free Tel:* 800-368-6868 *Fax:* 805-685-9685 *Toll Free Fax:* 866-270-3856
*E-mail:* sales@abc-clio.com; customerservice@abc-clio.com
*Web Site:* www.abc-clio.com
*Key Personnel*
CEO & Academic Publr: Ronald Boehm
Pres: Becky Snyder *Tel:* 805-968-1911 ext 306
Founded: 1955
A privately held corporation which has for many years enjoyed an international reputation for high quality & innovation. As an educational reference publisher the company has received critical acclaim for its computer assisted abstracting & indexing services, world renowned book program & cutting-edge online products.
ISBN Prefix(es): 978-0-87436; 978-1-57607
Number of titles published annually: 300 Print; 100 E-Book
Total Titles: 900 Print; 100 Online; 150 E-Book
Imprints: Greenwood Press; Libraries Unlimited/Linworth Publishing; Praeger
Subsidiaries: ABC-CLIO Ltd
*Warehouse:* ABC-CLIO Inc, c/o Sheridan Books, 617 E Industrial Dr, Chelsea, MI 48818
*See separate listing for:*
**Libraries Unlimited**

**ABDO Publishing Group**
Subsidiary of Abdo Consulting Group Inc (ACGI)
8000 W 78 St, Suite 310, Edina, MN 55439
Mailing Address: PO Box 398166, Minneapolis, MN 55439-8166
*Tel:* 952-831-2120 (ext 223) *Toll Free Tel:* 800-800-1312 *Toll Free Fax:* 800-862-3480
*E-mail:* info@abdopublishing.com
*Web Site:* www.abdopub.com
*Key Personnel*
Pres & Dir: Jill Hansen *E-mail:* jhansen@abdopublishing.com
Dir, Mktg: Dan Verdick *Tel:* 952-698-2404 *E-mail:* dverdick@abdopublishing.com
Dir, Sales: Paul Skaj *Tel:* 952-698-2403 *E-mail:* pskaj@abdopublishing.com
Publr & Natl Sales Mgr: Jim Abdo
Ed-in-Chief: Paul Abdo *E-mail:* pabdo@abdopublishing.com
Founded: 1985
Children's books for the library market.
ISBN Prefix(es): 978-1-56239; 978-1-57765
Number of titles published annually: 350 Print; 350 Online
Total Titles: 3,000 Print; 2,000 Online; 500 E-Book
Imprints: A&D Xtreme; Abdo & Daughters Publishing (grades 4 & up); Big Buddy Books; Buddy Books (grades 1-2); The Checkerboard Library (grades 2-4); Cool Trash to Treasure; Core Library; Essential Library (grades 6-8); Sandcastle (grades pre-K-2); SportsZONE; Super Sandcastle (grades K-3)
Distributed by Rockbottom Book Co
*Warehouse:* 1920 Lookout Dr, North Mankato, MN 56003

**Aberdeen Bay**
Imprint of Champion Writers Inc
9301 Maple St, Manassas, VA 20110
*Tel:* 703-473-1392
*E-mail:* editor@aberdeenbay.com
*Web Site:* www.aberdeenbay.com

*Key Personnel*
Acqs Dir: Ross Murphy
Founded: 2007
Traditional publisher that strives to publish quality books.
ISBN Prefix(es): 978-0-981
Number of titles published annually: 20 Print; 1 Online
Total Titles: 60 Print; 1 Online
Distributed by Champion Writers Inc

**§Abingdon Press**
Imprint of The United Methodist Publishing House
201 Eighth Ave S, Nashville, TN 37203-3919
SAN: 201-0046
Mailing Address: PO Box 801, Nashville, TN 37202-0801
*Toll Free Tel:* 800-251-3320 *Toll Free Fax:* 800-836-7802 (orders)
*E-mail:* orders@abingdonpress.com
*Web Site:* www.abingdonpress.com
*Key Personnel*
Pres & Publr: Neil M Alexander
Exec Dir, Mktg: Tamara Crabtree
Assoc Publr, Christian Fiction: Pamela Clements
Ed-in-Chief: Mary Catherine Dean
Sr Acqs Ed: Lil Copan; Ramona Richards
Mktg Mgr: Hampton Ryan
Regl Sales Mgr: Bryan C Williams
Mature Years Ed: Marvin Cropsey
Founded: 1789
Religion/ecumenical Christianity; general interest, children's, family, church professional, academic, reference, lay spiritual; United Methodist history, doctrine, polity.
ISBN Prefix(es): 978-0-687
Number of titles published annually: 175 Print
Total Titles: 270 Print; 10 CD-ROM; 3 Online
Imprints: Upper Room Books
*Branch Office(s)*
Academic Books Office, 201 Eighth Ave, Nashville, TN 37203 *Tel:* 615-749-6000 *Fax:* 615-749-6056
*Sales Office(s):* Ingram Publisher Services, One Ingram Blvd, La Vergne, TN 37086 *Tel:* 615-793-5000 *Web Site:* www.ingrampublisherservices.com
Distributor for Church Publishing Inc; Judson Press; Upper Room Books
Foreign Rep(s): Alban Books (Europe, Ireland, UK); Ausburg Fortress (Canada); Canaanland Distributors Sdn Bhd (Malaysia); Cross Communications Co (Hong Kong); KCBS Inc (Korea); Koorong (Australia); MediaCom (Australia, New Zealand); Methodist Publishing House (South Africa); Rainbow Books (Australia); SKS Books (Singapore); Soul Distributors (New Zealand)
*Warehouse:* 341 Great Circle Dr, Nashville, TN 37228-1703
*Distribution Center:* Ingram Publisher Services, One Ingram Blvd, La Vergne, TN 37086 *Tel:* 615-793-5000 *Web Site:* www.ingrampublisherservices.com

**Harry N Abrams Inc**
Subsidiary of La Martiniere Groupe
115 W 18 St, 6th fl, New York, NY 10011
SAN: 200-2434
*Tel:* 212-206-7715 *Toll Free Tel:* 800-345-1359 *Fax:* 212-519-1210
LOD *E-mail:* abrams@abramsbooks.com
*Web Site:* www.abramsbooks.com
*Key Personnel*
CEO & Pres: Michael Jacobs
Chief Mktg & Busn Devt Offr: Steve Tager
Exec Dir, Adult Mktg & Publicity: Michelle Montague
Exec Dir, Publicity: Katrina Weidknecht *Tel:* 212-229-8812
VP & Ed-in-Chief: Eric Himmel
VP & Publr, Adult Trade Group: Deborah Aaronson
VP, Worldwide Sales: Mary Wowk
Assoc Publr, Adult Group: Elisa Urbanelli
Dir & Mng Ed: David Blatty
Creative Dir, Adult: John Gall
Dir, Children's Mktg & Publicity, Abrams Children's, Amulet & Appleseed: Nicole Russo
Dir, Digital Mktg: Jeffrey Yamaguchi
Dir, Natl Accts: Erica Warshal
Dir, Spec Mkts: Jody Mosley
Dir, Trade Sales: Elisa Garcia
Assoc Art Dir, Abrams Children's: Maria Middleton
Assoc Dir, Mktg, Opers, Licenses & Brands: Veronica Wasserman
Sr Mktg Mgr: Nancy Lambert
Sr Mktg Mgr, Adult: Erin Hotchkiss
Mktg Mgr, Adult Trade: Paul Colarusso
Mktg Mgr & Soc Media Specialist: Ellie Levine
Assoc Mktg & Publicity Mgr, Abrams Children's: Laura Mihalick
Publicity & Mktg Assoc, Abrams Children's: Morgan Dubin
Mktg Coord: Nico Cassanetti
Sr Publicist, Abrams Children's: Mary Ann Zissimos
Assoc Publicist: Maya Bradford
Exec Ed, Cookbooks-Stewart, Tabori & Chang: Holly Dolce
Sr Ed: Dervla Kelly
Ed: Laura Dozier
Asst Ed: Samantha Weiner
Founded: 1949
Art & architecture, photography, natural sciences, performing arts & children's books.
ISBN Prefix(es): 978-0-8109
Number of titles published annually: 250 Print
Total Titles: 2,000 Print
Imprints: Abrams Appleseed; Abrams Books; Abrams Books for Young Readers; Abrams ComicArts; Abrams Image; Amulet Books; SelfMadeHero; STC Craft; Stewart, Tabori & Chang
Distributed by Editions Alain
Distributor for Booth-Clibborn Editions; 5 Continents Editions; Royal Academy Publications; Tate Publishing; V&A Publishing; The Vendome Press
Foreign Rep(s): Canadian Manda; Thames & Hudson
*Shipping Address:* Hachette Book Group USA, 322 S Enterprise Blvd, Lebanon, IN 46052-8193
Membership(s): AAP
*See separate listing for:*
**Stewart, Tabori & Chang**

**§Abrams Learning Trends**
Subsidiary of Learning Trends LLC
16310 Bratton Lane, Suite 250, Austin, TX 78728-2403
*Toll Free Tel:* 800-227-9120 *Toll Free Fax:* 800-737-3322
*E-mail:* customerservice@abramslearningtrends.com (orders, cust serv)
*Web Site:* www.abramslearningtrends.com (orders, cust serv)
*Key Personnel*
CEO & Pres: Roy Mayers
CFO & EVP, Fin: Peter Dunn
EVP, Opers & Gen Mgr: William Thomas
EVP, Prod Devt & Publr: Erin Kinard
EVP, Sales: Gunnar Voltz
VP, Sales: Bruce Warren
Founded: 2008
PreK-5 educational materials.
ISBN Prefix(es): 978-0-7665; 978-0-7664
Number of titles published annually: 100 Print; 6 CD-ROM; 15 Audio
Total Titles: 1,000 Print; 36 CD-ROM; 36 Audio
Imprints: The Letter People®
Distributor for General Education Services (New Zealand)

**Absey & Co Inc**
23011 Northcrest Dr, Spring, TX 77389
*Tel:* 281-257-2340 *Toll Free Tel:* 888-41-ABSEY (412-2739) *Fax:* 281-251-4676
*E-mail:* info@absey.biz
*Web Site:* www.absey.biz
*Key Personnel*
Publr: Edward E Wilson
Founded: 1996
Small publishing house catering to the author & illustrator. We encourage end-to-end participation, e.g. author may select his or her illustrator, type of paper & type style. Queries or information about submissions can be found online. If a cover letter does not utilize conventional grammar/usage, then the ms will definitely be rejected.
ISBN Prefix(es): 978-1-888842
Number of titles published annually: 3 Print; 1 CD-ROM; 26 Online
Total Titles: 36 Print; 1 CD-ROM; 26 Online
*Branch Office(s)*
45 W 21 St, Suite 5, New York, NY 10010, Contact: Edward E Wilson *Tel:* 212-277-8028
Membership(s): Southwest Booksellers Association

**§Academic Press**
Imprint of Elsevier
525 "B" St, Suite 1800, San Diego, CA 92101
*Tel:* 619-231-6616 *Toll Free Tel:* 800-321-5068 (cust serv) *Fax:* 619-699-6715
*E-mail:* firstinitial.lastname@elsevier.com
*Web Site:* www.elsevier.com
*Key Personnel*
VP & Dir, Sales & Mktg: Salvatore Gelardi
ISBN Contact: Connie Smeyres
Perms: Jackie Garrett
Founded: 1942
Scientific, technical & professional information in multiple media formats
ISBN Prefix(es): 978-0-12
Number of titles published annually: 375 Print; 8 E-Book
Total Titles: 4,700 Print; 14 CD-ROM; 175 E-Book
Imprints: Morgan Kaufmann Publishers

**Academica Press LLC**
PO Box 60728, Cambridge Sta, Palo Alto, CA 94306
*Tel:* 650-329-0685 *Fax:* 650-329-0685
*E-mail:* academicapress@aol.com
*Web Site:* www.academicapress.com
*Key Personnel*
Dir: Robert Redfern-West
Founded: 2002
Publish scholarly research, monographs & collections in humanities, social sciences, education & law.
ISBN Prefix(es): 978-1-933146; 978-1-930901
Number of titles published annually: 40 Print
Total Titles: 250 Print; 50 Online
Imprints: Maunsel & Co Publishers (Dublin); W B Sheridan (law books)
Foreign Rep(s): Eurospan Group (London) (Europe, Middle East, UK)
*Orders to:* Books International Inc, 22883 Quicksilver Dr, Dulles, VA 20166 *Tel:* 703-661-1500 *Fax:* 703-661-1501 *E-mail:* todd@booksintl.com
*Returns:* Books International Inc, 22883 Quicksilver Dr, Dulles, VA 20166 *Tel:* 703-661-1500 *Fax:* 703-661-1501 *E-mail:* todd@booksintl.com
*Shipping Address:* Books International Inc, 22883 Quicksilver Dr, Dulles, VA 20166 *Tel:* 703-

661-1500 *Fax:* 703-661-1501 *E-mail:* todd@booksintl.com
*Warehouse:* Books International Inc, 22883 Quicksilver Dr, Dulles, VA 20166 *Tel:* 703-661-1500 *Fax:* 703-661-1501 *E-mail:* todd@booksintl.com
*Distribution Center:* Books International Inc, 22883 Quicksilver Dr, Dulles, VA 20166 *Tel:* 703-661-1500 *Fax:* 703-661-1501 *E-mail:* todd@booksintl.com
Membership(s): American Conference on Irish Studies

**Academy Chicago Publishers**
363 W Erie St, Suite 4-W, Chicago, IL 60654
SAN: 213-2001
*Tel:* 312-751-7300 *Toll Free Tel:* 800-248-READ (248-7323) *Fax:* 312-751-7306
*E-mail:* info@academychicago.com
*Web Site:* www.academychicago.com
*Key Personnel*
Pres & Sr Ed: Anita Miller
VP & Publicity: Jordan Miller
Founded: 1975
Fiction, nonfiction, history, mysteries, women's studies; emphasis on neglected classics & books for women.
ISBN Prefix(es): 978-0-915864; 978-0-89733
Number of titles published annually: 12 Print
Total Titles: 367 Print
Distributor for Wicker Park Press
Foreign Rep(s): Eurospan Group (Africa, Asia, Australia, Continental Europe, Middle East, UK); Transnet Contracts Ltd (Austria, Germany)
Foreign Rights: Scholarly Book Services Inc (Laura Rust) (Canada); Susan Schulman Literary Agency (USA)
*Orders to:* Chicago Distribution Ctr, 11030 S Langkey Ave, Chicago, IL 60628 *Tel:* 773-702-7000 *Toll Free Tel:* 800-621-2736

**Academy of Nutrition & Dietetics**
120 S Riverside Plaza, Suite 2000, Chicago, IL 60606-6995
*Tel:* 312-899-0040 *Toll Free Tel:* 800-877-1600 *Fax:* 312-899-4757
*E-mail:* sales@eatright.org
*Web Site:* www.eatright.org
*Key Personnel*
Dir: Cathy Iammartino *E-mail:* ciammartino@eatright.org
Acqs Ed: Laura Pelehach
Founded: 1917
Information on food, nutrition & fitness for dieticians & other allied health professionals.
ISBN Prefix(es): 978-0-88091; 978-0-9837255 (Eat Right Press)
Number of titles published annually: 12 Print; 4 Online
Total Titles: 70 Print
*Branch Office(s)*
1120 Connecticut Ave NW, Suite 480, Washington, DC 20036 *Tel:* 202-775-8277 *Toll Free Tel:* 800-877-0877
Distributed by Small Press United (Eat Right Press)

**§Acanthus Publishing**
Division of The Ictus Group LLC
343 Commercial St, Unit 214, Boston, MA 02109
*Tel:* 617-230-2167 *Fax:* 215-243-7495
*E-mail:* info@acanthuspublishing.com
*Web Site:* www.acanthuspublishing.com
*Key Personnel*
CEO & Pres: Paige Stover Hague, Esq *Tel:* 508-577-0271
CTO: George Kasparian, Esq
Founded: 2004
This publisher has indicated that 100% of their product line is author subsidized.
ISBN Prefix(es): 978-0-9754810; 978-1-933631; 978-0-9815589
Number of titles published annually: 5 Print; 10 E-Book; 2 Audio
Total Titles: 18 Print; 70 E-Book; 2 Audio
*Advertising Agency:* The Ictus Initiative

**Accent Publications**
Subsidiary of Cook Communications Ministries
4050 Lee Vance View, Colorado Springs, CO 80918
SAN: 208-5100
*Tel:* 719-536-0100 *Toll Free Tel:* 800-708-5550; 800-535-2905 (cust serv); 800-323-7543 (main); 800-426-6596 (sales) *Fax:* 719-535-2928 *Toll Free Fax:* 800-430-0726
*Web Site:* www.davidcook.com
Founded: 1947
Sunday School curriculum & church resources.
ISBN Prefix(es): 978-0-89636; 978-0-916406
Number of titles published annually: 15 Print
Total Titles: 193 Print
*Returns:* 850 N Grove, Elgin, IL 60120

**§Accuity, a SourceMedia Co**
4709 W Golf Rd, Suite 600, Skokie, IL 60076-1253
*Tel:* 847-676-9600 *Toll Free Tel:* 800-321-3373 *Fax:* 847-933-8101
*E-mail:* custserv@accuitysolutions.com; support@accuitysolutions.com; sales@accuitysolutions.com; general@accuitysolutions.com
*Web Site:* www.accuitysolutions.com
*Key Personnel*
CEO & Pres: Hugh Jones
Mng Dir: Brent Newman
Sr Dir, HR: Patty Pickett
Founded: 1876
Leading worldwide provider of information on depository financial institutions throughout the world; specialize in Internet references/directories; software; databases.
ISBN Prefix(es): 978-1-56310
Number of titles published annually: 30 Print; 1 CD-ROM; 2 E-Book
Total Titles: 30 Print; 4 CD-ROM; 3 E-Book
*Foreign Office(s):* 4 Young St, Neutral Bay, Suite 333, Sydney, NSW 2089, Australia *Tel:* (02) 80060584 *Fax:* (02) 99536426
Xi Cheng District, Cheng Ming Mansion, Bldg B, No 2, Rm C, S Xi Zhi Men St, Beijing 100035, China *Tel:* (010) 8260 9619 *E-mail:* chinese@accuitysolutions.com
7 Bassein Rd, No 06-06, Pastoral View 309837, Singapore *Tel:* 9067 2236
Level 41 Emirates Towers, Sheikh Zaye Rd, PO Box 31303, Dubai, United Arab Emirates *Tel:* 4421 0286 *E-mail:* middle-east@accuitysolutions.com
One Quality Ct, Chancery Lane, London WC2A 1HR, United Kingdom, Gen Mgr: Susan McGregor *Tel:* (020) 7014 3480 *Fax:* (020) 7061 6478 *E-mail:* susan.mcgregor@accuitysolutions.com

**Acres USA**
Division of Acres USA Inc
4031 Guadalupe St, Austin, TX 78751
SAN: 270-6555
Mailing Address: PO Box 301209, Austin, TX 78703-0021
*Tel:* 512-892-4400 *Toll Free Tel:* 800-355-5313 *Fax:* 512-892-4448
*E-mail:* orders@acresusa.com; editor@acresusa.com
*Web Site:* www.acresusa.com
Founded: 1970
Books & a monthly periodical on organic & sustainable agriculture.
ISBN Prefix(es): 978-0-911311
Number of titles published annually: 6 Print; 1 Audio
Total Titles: 80 Print; 2 Audio
Imprints: Halcyon House Publishers

**ACTA Publications**
4848 N Clark St, Chicago, IL 60640
*Tel:* 773-271-1030 *Toll Free Tel:* 800-397-2282 *Fax:* 773-271-7399 *Toll Free Fax:* 800-397-0079
*E-mail:* info@actapublications.com
*Web Site:* www.actapublications.com
*Key Personnel*
Owner & Publr: John Dewan; Gregory Pierce
Founded: 1957
Books, audio & video tapes for the Christian market & baseball statistics market.
ISBN Prefix(es): 978-0-87946; 978-0-914070; 978-0-915388
Number of titles published annually: 15 Print; 2 Audio
Total Titles: 150 Print; 20 Audio
Distributor for Grief Watch; Veritas
Foreign Rep(s): John Garratt Publishing (Australia); Veritas (Ireland, UK)
Membership(s): Association of Catholic Publishers Inc

**ACU Press**
Affiliate of Abilene Christian University
1626 Campus Ct, Abilene, TX 79601
SAN: 207-1681
*Tel:* 325-674-2720 *Toll Free Tel:* 877-816-4455 *Fax:* 325-674-6471
*Web Site:* www.acupressbooks.com; www.leafwoodpublishers.com
*Key Personnel*
Dir: Dr Leonard Allen *E-mail:* leonard.allen@acupressbooks.com
Dir, Opers: Duane Anderson
Founded: 1984
Religion & ethics.
ISBN Prefix(es): 978-0-915547; 978-0-89112
Number of titles published annually: 12 Print
Total Titles: 200 Print

**Adam Hill Publications**
Division of Adam Hill Advertising Corp
2699 Stirling Rd, Suite B-301, Fort Lauderdale, FL 33312
*Tel:* 954-680-7639
*E-mail:* books@adamhilldesign.com
*Web Site:* www.adamhilldesign.com
*Key Personnel*
Founding Partner: Nick Aiossa *Tel:* 954-983-5005 *E-mail:* nick@adamhilldesign.com
Off Mgr: Melodee Putt *E-mail:* melodee@adamhilldesign.com
Founded: 2005
Designs & publishes children's books, general trade, juvenile & young adult books.
This publisher has indicated that 100% of their product line is author subsidized.
ISBN Prefix(es): 978-0-9769360
Number of titles published annually: 16 Print
Total Titles: 20 Print

**Adams & Ambrose Publishing**
PO Box 259684, Madison, WI 53725-9684
SAN: 655-5624
*Tel:* 608-257-5700 *Fax:* 608-257-5700
*E-mail:* info@adamsambrose.com
*Key Personnel*
Mktg Dir & Intl Rts: Joyce Harrington *E-mail:* jharrington@adamsambrose.com
Sr Ed: Jill Robinson Wren *E-mail:* jrwren@adamsambrose.com
Edit: Roger B Oakes *E-mail:* rboakes@adamsambrose.com
Founded: 1983
Publication of nonfiction books. Specialize in academic, professional & how-to books.
ISBN Prefix(es): 978-0-916951
Number of titles published annually: 6 Print

Total Titles: 6 Print
*Returns:* c/o United Parcel Service, 8350 Murphy Dr, Middleton, WI 53562 (hold for pick up)

**§Adams-Blake Publishing**
8041 Sierra St, Suite 102, Fair Oaks, CA 95628
*Tel:* 916-962-9296
*E-mail:* info@adams-blake.com
*Web Site:* www.adams-blake.com
*Key Personnel*
VP: Alan N Canton
Founded: 1990
Ebook titles on business, finance, career, sales, occupations, technology. No fiction, no poetry.
ISBN Prefix(es): 978-1-883422
Number of titles published annually: 3 Print; 4 E-Book
Total Titles: 9 Print; 4 E-Book

**§Adams Media**
Imprint of F+W Media Inc
57 Littlefield St, Avon, MA 02322
*Tel:* 508-427-7100 *Fax:* 508-427-6790 *Toll Free Fax:* 800-872-5627
*E-mail:* orders@adamsmedia.com
*Web Site:* www.adamsmedia.com
*Key Personnel*
Publr: Karen Cooper
Natl Sales Dir: Karen Patterson
Publicity Dir: Beth Gissinger *E-mail:* beth.gissinger@fwmedia.com
Founded: 1980
General nonfiction, including business, self-help, inspiration, careers, teen nonfiction, women's issues, cooking, parenting, reference, relationships, weddings, pets.
ISBN Prefix(es): 978-1-55850; 978-1-58062; 978-1-59337
Number of titles published annually: 200 Print
Total Titles: 800 Print; 20 CD-ROM
Imprints: Adams Business (busn); Everything (series); F+W Media Business Now; Platinum Press (mgmt & leadership); Polka Dot Press (women's nonfiction); Provenance Press (new age)
Foreign Rep(s): Advantage Quest (Malaysia); David Bateman Ltd (New Zealand); Michelle Morrow Curreri (Asia, Middle East); F & W Intl (Europe); IMA/Intermediaamericana (David Williams) (Caribbean, Latin America); Manda Group (Canada); Pearson Education; Peribo (Australia)
Foreign Rights: Bardon-Chinese Media Agency (China, Hong Kong, Taiwan); Graal Literary Agency (Zbigniew Kanski) (Poland); The Harris/Elon Agency (Efrat Lev) (Israel); Imprima Korea Agency (Korea); Japan Uni Agency (Japan); Alexander Korzhenevski Agency (Russia); Michael Meller Literary Agency GmbH (Germany); The Rights Agency (France); Silkroad Publishers Agency (Jane Vejjajiva) (Thailand); Julio F Yanez, Agencia Literaria S L (Spain)
*Warehouse:* 1140 Airport Rd, Fall River, MA 02720

**ADASI Publishing Co**
6 Dover Point Rd, Suite B, Dover, NH 03820-4698
*Tel:* 603-866-9426
*E-mail:* info@adasi.com
*Web Site:* www.adasi.com
*Key Personnel*
Mktg Dir: Parvaneh Ghavami
Physics, math & history of those subjects.
ISBN Prefix(es): 978-0-9641295
Number of titles published annually: 6 Print
Total Titles: 12 Print
Distributor for Wall & Thompson

**ADD Warehouse**
300 NW 70 Ave, Suite 102, Plantation, FL 33317
SAN: 251-6977
*Tel:* 954-792-8100 *Toll Free Tel:* 800-233-9273 *Fax:* 954-792-8545
*E-mail:* websales@addwarehouse.com
*Web Site:* addwarehouse.com
*Key Personnel*
CEO & Intl Rts: Harvey Parker *E-mail:* hparker@addwarehouse.com
Founded: 1990
Selections related to children with special needs.
ISBN Prefix(es): 978-0-9621629; 978-1-886941
Number of titles published annually: 3 Print
Total Titles: 40 Print; 4 E-Book
Distributed by Boys Town Press; Child Play; MHS
Distributor for Bantam; Guilford Press; Plenum; Simon & Schuster; Slossen; Woodbine House

**Addicus Books Inc**
PO Box 45327, Omaha, NE 68145
*Tel:* 402-330-7493 *Toll Free Tel:* 800-352-2873 (orders) *Fax:* 402-330-1707
*E-mail:* info@addicusbooks.com; addicusbks@aol.com
*Web Site:* www.addicusbooks.com
*Key Personnel*
Pres & Publr: Rod Colvin *E-mail:* rod@addicusbooks.com
Assoc Publr: Jack Kusler *E-mail:* jackaddicusbks@aol.com
Mng Ed: Susan Adams
Founded: 1994
Independent press, publishing high-quality trade paperbacks. Submissions by mail only, no phone inquiries.
ISBN Prefix(es): 978-1-886039
Number of titles published annually: 9 Print; 10 E-Book
Total Titles: 200 Print; 200 Online; 36 E-Book
*Billing Address:* IPG Books, 814 Franklin St, Chicago, IL 60610 *Tel:* 312-337-0747 *Toll Free Tel:* 800-888-4741 *Fax:* 312-337-5985 *Web Site:* ipgbook.com
*Returns:* IPG Warehouse, 600 N Pulaski, Chicago, IL 60624, Contact: Tom Greene
*Warehouse:* IPG Warehouse, 600 N Pulaski, Chicago, IL 60624, Contact: Tom Greene
*Distribution Center:* IPG Books, 814 Franklin St, Chicago, IL 60610 *Tel:* 312-337-0747 *Toll Free Tel:* 800-888-4741 *Fax:* 312-337-5985 *Web Site:* ipgbook.com
Membership(s): IBPA, the Independent Book Publishers Association

**Adirondack Mountain Club**
814 Goggins Rd, Lake George, NY 12845-4117
SAN: 204-7691
*Tel:* 518-668-4447 *Toll Free Tel:* 800-395-8080 *Fax:* 518-668-3746
*E-mail:* adkinfo@adk.org
*Web Site:* www.adk.org
*Key Personnel*
Pubns & Mktg Dir: John Kettlewell *Tel:* 518-668-4447 ext 23 *E-mail:* john@adk.org
Founded: 1922
Calendar (wall) - trade, hiking, canoeing, skiing & climbing guidebooks & maps for New York State; natural history field guides; cultural & literary works on the Adirondacks, members journals, *Adirondac.*
ISBN Prefix(es): 978-0-935272
Number of titles published annually: 4 Print
Total Titles: 39 Print

**Adler Publishing Inc**
PO Box 2948, Parker, CO 80134
*Toll Free Tel:* 800-660-5107 (sales & orders) *Fax:* 303-688-4388
*E-mail:* mail@adlerpublishing.com
*Web Site:* 4wdbooks.com
*Key Personnel*
Mktg Dir: Jeanne Massey *E-mail:* jmassey@adlerpublishing.com
Publr: Peter Massey
Founded: 1999
ISBN Prefix(es): 978-0-930657; 978-0-9665675; 978-1-930193
Number of titles published annually: 5 Print
Total Titles: 70 Print
Imprints: Outdoor Books & Maps; Swagman Publishing

**Advance Publishing Inc**
6950 Fulton St, Houston, TX 77022
SAN: 263-9572
*Tel:* 713-695-0600 *Toll Free Tel:* 800-917-9630 *Fax:* 713-695-8585
*E-mail:* info@advancepublishing.com
*Web Site:* www.advancepublishing.com
*Key Personnel*
VP: John Sommer
Founded: 1984
Publish children's picture books, junior biographies & general nonfiction, technical books & current events.
ISBN Prefix(es): 978-1-57537; 978-0-9610810
Number of titles published annually: 20 Print
Total Titles: 150 Print; 23 CD-ROM; 75 Online
Imprints: Another Great Achiever Series
Membership(s): IBPA, the Independent Book Publishers Association

**Adventure House**
914 Laredo Rd, Silver Spring, MD 20901
*Tel:* 301-754-1589
*Web Site:* www.adventurehouse.com
*Key Personnel*
Publr & Ed: John P Gunnison *E-mail:* gunnison@adventurehouse.com
Founded: 1985
Special reprints; fiction from the pulp fiction era.
ISBN Prefix(es): 978-1-886937; 978-1-59798
Number of titles published annually: 60 Print
Total Titles: 300 Print

**Adventure Publications**
820 Cleveland St, Cambridge, MN 55008
SAN: 212-7199
*Tel:* 763-689-9800 *Toll Free Tel:* 800-678-7006 *Fax:* 763-689-9039 *Toll Free Fax:* 877-374-9016
*E-mail:* custservice@adventurepublications.net
*Web Site:* www.adventurepublications.net
*Key Personnel*
Pres: Gordon Slabaugh *E-mail:* gordon@adventurepublications.net
VP & Gen Mgr: Gerri Slabaugh *E-mail:* gerri@adventurepublications.net
Sales Mgr: Julie Arthur *E-mail:* julie@adventurepublications.net
Founded: 1988
General trade & regional.
ISBN Prefix(es): 978-0-934860; 978-1-885061; 978-1-59193
Number of titles published annually: 30 Print
Total Titles: 435 Print; 12 CD-ROM
Distributor for Blacklock Nature Photography; Kollath-Stensaas; Nodin Press; Pocket Guides Publishing

**Adventures Unlimited Press**
One Adventure Place, Kempton, IL 60946
Mailing Address: PO Box 74, Kempton, IL 60946-0074
*Tel:* 815-253-6390 *Fax:* 815-253-6300
*E-mail:* auphq@frontiernet.net; info@adventuresunlimitedpress.com
*Web Site:* www.adventuresunlimitedpress.com
*Key Personnel*
Pres & Intl Rts Contact: David H Childress
Mng Dir: Jennifer Bolm
Founded: 1983

Eclectic variety of books on mysteries of the past, alternative technologies & conspiracy theories.
ISBN Prefix(es): 978-0-932813; 978-1-931882
Number of titles published annually: 11 Print
Total Titles: 175 Print
*Foreign Office(s):* Frontier Sciences Foundation, Pannewal 22, Enkhuizen 1602-KS, Netherlands
Distributor for Eagle Wing Books; EDFU Books; Yelsraek Publishing
Foreign Rep(s): Brumby Books (Australia); Speaking Tree (UK)
Foreign Rights: Il Caduceo (Italy)

**Aegean Park Press**
PO Box 2120, Walnut Creek, CA 94595
*Tel:* 925-947-2533 *Toll Free Tel:* 800-736-3587 (orders only)
*E-mail:* aegeanparkpress@earthlink.net
*Web Site:* www.aegeanparkpress.com
*Key Personnel*
Pres: Wayne G Barker
Founded: 1973
Technical books in contract bridges, computers, cryptology, Mayan studies, history, intelligence, communications & genealogy.
ISBN Prefix(es): 978-0-89412
Number of titles published annually: 10 Print
Total Titles: 145 Print

**Aegean Publishing Co**
PO Box 6790, Santa Barbara, CA 93160
*Tel:* 805-964-6669 *Fax:* 805-683-4798
*E-mail:* info@aegeanpublishing.com
*Web Site:* aegeanpublishing.com
*Key Personnel*
Gen Mgr: Mary Morgan
Founded: 1993
Book publisher.
ISBN Prefix(es): 978-0-9636178
Number of titles published annually: 3 Print
Total Titles: 4 Print
Foreign Rights: Japan UNI Agency Inc (Japan)
Membership(s): IBPA, the Independent Book Publishers Association

**The AEI Press**
Division of American Enterprise Institute
1150 17 St NW, Washington, DC 20036
SAN: 202-4527
*Tel:* 202-862-5800 *Fax:* 202-862-7177
*Web Site:* www.aei.org
*Key Personnel*
Chmn of the Bd: Kevin Rollins
Pres: Arthur Brooks
Sr Ed: Christy Sablar *Tel:* 202-862-5800 ext 5916
Ed: Hilary Waterman
Founded: 1943
Public policy economics, foreign affairs & defense, government & politics, law; research on education, energy, government regulation & tax policy.
ISBN Prefix(es): 978-0-8447
Number of titles published annually: 15 Print
Total Titles: 300 Print
Distributed by MIT (selected titles)
Foreign Rep(s): Eurospan
*Orders to:* c/o National Book Network, 4501 Forbes Blvd, Suite 200, Lantham, MD 20706 *Toll Free Tel:* 800-462-6420 *Toll Free Fax:* 800-338-4550 *E-mail:* custserv@nbnbooks.com
*Distribution Center:* Client Distribution Services, 193 Edwards Dr, Jackson, TN 38301 *Toll Free Tel:* 800-343-4499 *Toll Free Fax:* 800-351-5073 *Web Site:* cdsbooks.com

**Aerial Photography Services Inc**
2511 S Tryon St, Charlotte, NC 28203
*Tel:* 704-333-5143 *Fax:* 704-333-4911
*E-mail:* aps@aps-1.com
*Web Site:* www.aps-1.com
*Key Personnel*
Off Mgr: Gregg Balkcum *E-mail:* gregg@aps-1.com
Founded: 1960
Publish travel & tourist books.
ISBN Prefix(es): 978-0-933672; 978-1-880970
Number of titles published annually: 3 Print
Total Titles: 36 Print

**Africa World Press Inc**
541 W Ingham Ave, Suite B, Trenton, NJ 08638
*Tel:* 609-695-3200 *Fax:* 609-695-6466
*E-mail:* customerservice@africaworldpressbooks.com
*Web Site:* www.africaworldpressbooks.com
*Key Personnel*
Pres: Kassahun Checole
Administrator: Senait Kassahun
Founded: 1983
Research on Latin America, the Caribbean, Africa, Afrocentric children's books.
ISBN Prefix(es): 978-0-86543; 978-1-59221
Number of titles published annually: 100 Print
Total Titles: 1,400 Print; 10 Online; 10 E-Book
*Foreign Office(s):* East Africa, PO Box 48, Asmara, Eritrea *Tel:* (01) 120707 *Fax:* (01) 123369
Foreign Rights: Turnaround Publisher Services Ltd (Europe, London)

**§African American Images**
PO Box 1799, Chicago Heights, IL 60412
*Tel:* 708-672-4909 (cust serv) *Toll Free Tel:* 800-552-1991 (orders) *Fax:* 708-672-0466
*E-mail:* customer@africanamericanimages.com
*Web Site:* www.africanamericanimages.com
*Key Personnel*
Pres & Intl Rts: Dr Jawanza Kunjufu, PhD
Founded: 1983
Publish & distribute books of an Africentric nature that promote self-esteem, collective values, liberation & skill development.
ISBN Prefix(es): 978-0-913543
Number of titles published annually: 8 Print
Total Titles: 130 Print; 2 CD-ROM

**Africana Homestead Legacy Publishers Inc**
811 Church Rd, Suite 105, Cherry Hill, NJ 08002
SAN: 941-4811
*Tel:* 856-773-0694 *Toll Free Tel:* 866-250-8477 *Fax:* 856-486-1135 *Toll Free Fax:* 866-289-8681
*E-mail:* customer-service@ahlpub.com; sales@ahlpub.com (ordering info); editors@ahlpub.com (edit inquiries); public-relations@ahlpub.com
*Web Site:* www.ahlpub.com
*Key Personnel*
CEO & Publr: Carolyn C Williams *Tel:* 856-382-0335 *E-mail:* publisher@ahlpub.com
Assoc Publr: E Lama Wonkeryor, PhD *Tel:* 856-382-0335 *E-mail:* ewonkeryor@ahlpub.com
Dir, Prodn & Design: Brian Lancaster *Tel:* 856-382-0335 *E-mail:* blancaster@ahlpub.com
Founded: 1996
Small independent book publisher of scholary nonfiction, literary fiction, autobiography & memoirs, popular fiction & nonfiction & poetry for all ages about black history, culture & experience worldwide. As a royalty publisher, we use both traditional & emerging business models to build our publishing program.
ISBN Prefix(es): 978-0-9653308; 978-0-9770904; 978-0-9799537; 978-0-9818939; 978-0-9825842; 978-0-9831151
Number of titles published annually: 8 Print; 7 E-Book
Total Titles: 36 Print; 3 E-Book
Imprints: AHLP Books; AHLP Communications; Nefu Books; Oyinde Publishing
Membership(s): IBPA, the Independent Book Publishers Association

**§Ageless Press**
3759 Collins St, Sarasota, FL 34232
SAN: 297-830X
*Tel:* 941-365-1367 *Fax:* 941-365-1367
*E-mail:* irishope@comcast.net
*Key Personnel*
Owner: Hope Day
Ed: Iris Forrest
Founded: 1992
Publish short stories by various authors.
ISBN Prefix(es): 978-0-9635177
Number of titles published annually: 6 Print
Total Titles: 3 Print; 1 Online

**AGU**, see American Geophysical Union (AGU)

**AHA Press**
Subsidiary of Health Forum Inc
155 N Wacker, Suite 400, Chicago, IL 60606
*Tel:* 312-893-6800 *Toll Free Tel:* 800-242-4890 *Toll Free Fax:* 866-516-5817 (orders)
*Web Site:* www.healthforum.com
*Key Personnel*
Edit Dir: Richard Hill *E-mail:* rhill@healthforum.com
Founded: 1984
Professional references for healthcare managers & textbooks for HIM programs.
ISBN Prefix(es): 978-1-55648
Number of titles published annually: 4 Print
Total Titles: 20 Print
*Orders to:* AHA Services Inc, PO Box 933283, Atlanta, GA 31193-3283 *Toll Free Tel:* 800-242-2626
*Returns:* AHA Services Inc, Customer Returns Section, 3280 Summit Ridge Pkwy, Duluth, GA 30096 *Toll Free Tel:* 800-242-2626
Membership(s): American Hospital Association; Association Media & Publishing

**Ahsahta Press**
Boise State University, Mail Stop 1525, 1910 University Dr, Boise, ID 83725-1525
*Tel:* 208-426-4373 *Fax:* 208-426-4373
*E-mail:* ahsahta@boisestate.edu
*Web Site:* ahsahtapress.boisestate.edu
*Key Personnel*
Dir & Ed: Prof Janet Holmes *Tel:* 208-426-3134 *E-mail:* jholmes@boisestate.edu
Founded: 1974
Trade paperback books. Specialize in American poetry, Accept editorial submissions through our Submissions Manager.
ISBN Prefix(es): 978-0-916272; 978-1-934103
Number of titles published annually: 7 Print
Total Titles: 108 Print
Distributed by Small Press Distribution
*Orders to:* Small Press Distribution, 1341 Seventh St, Berkeley, CA 94710-1409, Contact: Clay Banes *Tel:* 510-524-1668 *Toll Free Tel:* 800-869-7553 *Fax:* 510-524-0852 *E-mail:* spd@spdbooks.org *Web Site:* www.spdbooks.org
Membership(s): Council of Literary Magazines & Presses

**§AICPA Professional Publications**
Subsidiary of American Institute of Certified Public Accountants
220 Leigh Farm Rd, Durham, NC 27707
SAN: 202-4578
*Tel:* 919-402-4500 *Toll Free Tel:* 888-777-7077 *Fax:* 919-402-4505
*E-mail:* acquisitions@aicpa.org
*Web Site:* www.aicpa.org
*Key Personnel*
CEO & Pres: Barry C Melancon *E-mail:* bmelancon@aicpa.org
VP, Prof Pubns: Linda Cohen *Tel:* 919-402-4854 ext 3 *E-mail:* lcohen@aicpa.org
Founded: 1959
Technical guidance for accountants & auditors, books on practice management & specialized topics, research & practice development tools,

magazines, newsletters, online & downloadable products.
ISBN Prefix(es): 978-0-87051
Number of titles published annually: 150 Print; 10 CD-ROM; 20 Online; 100 E-Book
Total Titles: 600 Print; 20 CD-ROM; 50 Online; 200 E-Book
*Branch Office(s)*
1455 Pennsylvania Ave NW, Washington, DC 20004-1081 *Tel:* 202-737-6600
Princeton South Corporate Ctr, Suite 200, 100 Princeton S, Ewing, NJ 08628 *Tel:* 609-671-2902
1211 Avenue of the Americas, New York, NY 10036-8775 *Tel:* 212-596-6200
Distributed by CCH; Practitioners Publishing Co; Thomson Reuters
Distributor for Wiley
Membership(s): American Society for Training & Development; EBSCO; ISO

**AIMS Education Foundation**
1595 S Chestnut Ave, Fresno, CA 93702-4706
Mailing Address: PO Box 8120, Fresno, CA 93747-8120
*Tel:* 559-255-4094 *Toll Free Tel:* 888-733-2467 *Fax:* 559-255-6396
*E-mail:* aimsed@aimsedu.org
*Web Site:* www.aimsedu.org
*Key Personnel*
Systems Administrator & Webmaster: Johann Weber
Founded: 1985
Provides educational enrichment for grades K-9 through hands-on activities that integrate mathematics, science, technology & other disciplines; curriculum writing for K-9.
ISBN Prefix(es): 978-1-881431
Number of titles published annually: 6 Print
Total Titles: 75 Print; 1 CD-ROM; 3 Audio
*Shipping Address:* 5391 E Home Ave, Fresno, CA 93727

**AK Press Distribution**
Subsidiary of AK Press Inc
674-A 23 St, Oakland, CA 94612
*Tel:* 510-208-1700 *Fax:* 510-208-1701
*E-mail:* info@akpress.org; sales@akpress.org; orders@akpress.org
*Web Site:* www.akpress.org
*Key Personnel*
Ed: Zach Blue *Tel:* 510-208-1700 ext 4; Kate Khatib
Founded: 1990
Specialize in publishing & distribution of radical & small press nonfiction.
ISBN Prefix(es): 978-1-873176; 978-1-902593; 978-1-904859
Number of titles published annually: 20 Print; 3 Audio
Total Titles: 500 Print; 30 Audio
Distributor for AK Press; Crimethinc; Freedom Press; Payback Press; Phoenix Press; Rebel Inc; Rebel Press

**Akashic Books**
232 Third St, Suite A-115, Brooklyn, NY 11215
Mailing Address: PO Box 1456, New York, NY 10009
*Tel:* 718-643-9193 *Fax:* 718-643-9195
*E-mail:* info@akashicbooks.com
*Web Site:* www.akashicbooks.com
*Key Personnel*
Publr: Johnny Temple
Mng Ed: Johanna Ingalls
Founded: 1997
Specialize in urban literary fiction & political nonfiction.
ISBN Prefix(es): 978-1-888451; 978-0-9719206
Number of titles published annually: 30 Print
Total Titles: 300 Print
Imprints: RDV Books
*Orders to:* Consortium Book Sales & Distribution, The Keg House, Suite 101, 34 13 Ave NE, Minneapolis, MN 55413 *Tel:* 612-746-2600 *Toll Free Tel:* 800-283-3572 (cust serv) *Fax:* 612-746-2606 *Web Site:* www.cbsd.com
*Returns:* Consortium Book Sales & Distribution, The Keg House, Suite 101, 34 13 Ave NE, Minneapolis, MN 55413 *Tel:* 612-746-2600 *Toll Free Tel:* 800-283-3572 (cust serv) *Fax:* 612-746-2606 *Web Site:* www.cbsd.com
*Warehouse:* Consortium Book Sales & Distribution, c/o Perseus, 210 American Dr, Jackson, TN 38301 *Toll Free Tel:* 800-283-3572 *Toll Free Fax:* 800-351-5073
*Distribution Center:* Consortium Book Sales & Distribution, The Keg House, Suite 101, 34 13 Ave NE, Minneapolis, MN 55413 *Tel:* 612-746-2600 *Toll Free Tel:* 800-283-3572 (cust serv) *Fax:* 612-746-2606 *Web Site:* www.cbsd.com

**ALA**, see The American Library Association (ALA)

**Aladdin**, see Simon & Schuster Children's Publishing

**Alaska Native Language Center**
Division of University of Alaska Fairbanks
PO Box 757680, Fairbanks, AK 99775-7680
SAN: 692-9796
*Tel:* 907-474-7874 *Fax:* 907-474-6586
*E-mail:* fyanlp@uaf.edu (orders)
*Web Site:* www.uaf.edu/anlc/
*Key Personnel*
Dir: Lawrence D Kaplan
Ed: Leon Unruh *Tel:* 907-474-6577
Founded: 1972
Publish books in & about Alaska's 20 indigenous languages, including dictionaries, grammars & collections of folktales & oral history, language maps.
ISBN Prefix(es): 978-1-55500; 978-0-933769
Number of titles published annually: 4 Print
Total Titles: 200 Print; 3 Audio

**Alban Publishing**
Division of The Alban Institute Inc
2121 Cooperative Way, Suite 100, Herndon, VA 20171
*Tel:* 703-964-2700 *Toll Free Tel:* 800-486-1318 *Fax:* 703-964-0370
*E-mail:* infocenter@alban.org
*Web Site:* www.alban.org
*Key Personnel*
Dir, Publg: Richard Bass
Publg Assoc: Lauren Belen *Tel:* 703-964-2700 ext 273
Founded: 1974
Nonprofit organization which publishes Ecumenical, research based publications for congregations. Produce Congregations magazine.
ISBN Prefix(es): 978-1-56699
Number of titles published annually: 12 Print
Total Titles: 250 Print

**Albert Whitman & Co**
250 S Northwest Hwy, Suite 320, Park Ridge, IL 60068
SAN: 201-2049
*Tel:* 847-232-2800 *Toll Free Tel:* 800-255-7675 *Fax:* 847-581-0039
*E-mail:* mail@awhitmanco.com
*Web Site:* www.albertwhitman.com
*Key Personnel*
Pres, Prodn & Rts & Perms: John Quattrocchi
VP: Pat McPartland
Edit Dir: Kelly Barrales-Saylor
Dir, Mktg: Michelle F Bayuk *Tel:* 847-232-2800 ext 2811
Founded: 1919
Juveniles, language arts, fiction & nonfiction.
ISBN Prefix(es): 978-0-8075
Number of titles published annually: 50 Print
Total Titles: 800 Print
Distributed by Open Road

**The Alexander Graham Bell Association for the Deaf & Hard of Hearing**
3417 Volta Place NW, Washington, DC 20007-2778
SAN: 203-6924
*Tel:* 202-337-5220 *Toll Free Tel:* 866-337-5220 (orders) *Fax:* 202-337-8314
*E-mail:* info@agbell.org; publications@agbell.org
*Web Site:* www.agbell.org
*Key Personnel*
Mgr, Ad & Exhibit Sales: Gary Yates *Tel:* 202-204-4683 *E-mail:* gyates@agbell.org
Mgr, Memb Servs: Robin Bailey *Tel:* 202-204-4670 *E-mail:* rbailey@agbell.org
Founded: 1890
Resource, support network & advocate for listening, learning, talking & living independently with hearing loss. Through publications, outreach, training, scholarships & financial aid, AG Bell promotes the use of spoken language & hearing technology. Headquarted in Washington, DC with chapters located in the US & Canada & a network of international affiliates. AG Bell's global presence provides its members & the public with the support they need close to home. With over a century of service, AG Bell supports it's mission, advocating independence through listening & talking.
ISBN Prefix(es): 978-0-88200
Number of titles published annually: 5 Print
Total Titles: 70 Print

**Alexander Street Press LLC**
3212 Duke St, Alexandria, VA 22314
SAN: 858-5512
*Tel:* 703-212-8520 *Toll Free Tel:* 800-889-5937 *Fax:* 703-940-6584
*E-mail:* sales@alexanderstreet.com; marketing@alexanderstreet.com
*Web Site:* www.alexanderstreet.com
*Key Personnel*
COO: Tim Lloyd *E-mail:* tlloyd@alexanderstreet.com
Pres: Stephen Rhind-Tutt *E-mail:* rhindtutt@alexanderstreet.com
SVP, Edit & Devt: Andrea Eastman-Mullins *E-mail:* aeastmanmullins@alexanderstreet.com
VP, Sales & Mktg: Eileen Lawrence *E-mail:* lawrence@alexanderstreet.com
Founded: 2000
Publish large electronic collections of works in the humanities & social sciences.
Number of titles published annually: 30 Print; 6 Online; 2,000 E-Book; 4 Audio
Total Titles: 34 Online; 10,000 E-Book; 6 Audio
*Foreign Office(s):* 2123 Pudong Ave, Rm 805, Shanghai 200135, China
Business & Technology Ctr, G04, Bessemer Dr, Stevenage SG1 2DX, United Kingdom *Tel:* (01438) 310193
Foreign Rep(s): Julie Atkins (Ireland, UK); Calvin Chee (Asia); Dan Hamid (Australia, New Zealand); Robert Iannello (Africa, Europe); Eileen Lawrence (Latin America); Julie Stevens (Middle East)
Membership(s): ALA

**§Alfred Publishing Company Inc**
PO Box 10003, Van Nuys, CA 91410-0003
*Tel:* 818-891-5999 *Toll Free Tel:* 800-292-6122 (dealer sales) *Fax:* 818-892-9239; 818-893-5560 *Toll Free Fax:* 800-632-1928 (dealer sales)
*E-mail:* customerservice@alfred.com; sales@alfred.com
*Web Site:* www.alfred.com

*Key Personnel*
Owner & CEO: Ron Manus
Founded: 1922
Publisher of music education; music books & software, performance & instructional.
ISBN Prefix(es): 978-0-88284; 978-0-87487; 978-0-7390; 978-1-58951
Number of titles published annually: 500 Print; 4 CD-ROM
Total Titles: 18,000 Print; 20 CD-ROM
*Foreign Office(s):* Bankstown M5 Business Park, Units 3 & 4, 17 Willfox St, Condell Park, NSW 2200, Australia *Tel:* 8707 3600 *Fax:* 8707 3601
Lutzerathstr 127, 51107 Cologne, Germany *Tel:* 221 93 35 39 0 *Fax:* 221 93 35 3916 *E-mail:* info@alfredverlag.de *Web Site:* www.alfredverlag.de
20 Sin Ming Lane, 5th fl, 05-54 Midview City 573968, Singapore, SE Asia Mktg Mgr: Larry Bong *Tel:* 6659 8919 *Fax:* 6659 8908 *E-mail:* enquiries@alfred.com.sg
Burnt Mill, Elizabeth Way, Harlow, Essex CM20 2HX, United Kingdom *Tel:* (01279) 828960 *Fax:* (01279) 828961 *E-mail:* music@alfred.uk.com
Distributor for Dover; Faber Music; Myklas Music Press; National Guitar Workshop
Foreign Rep(s): Dave Bolden (Australia, New Zealand); Larry Bong (Asia); Gerry Mooney (UK); Thomas Petzold (Europe)
Membership(s): Magazine Publishers of America

**Algonquin Books of Chapel Hill**
Division of Workman Publishing Co Inc
400 Silver Cedar Ct, Suite 300, Chapel Hill, NC 27514-1585
SAN: 282-7506
Mailing Address: PO Box 2225, Chapel Hill, NC 27515-2225
*Tel:* 919-967-0108 *Fax:* 919-933-0272
*E-mail:* inquiry@algonquin.com
*Web Site:* www.workman.com/algonquin
*Key Personnel*
Mktg Dir: Craig Popelars *E-mail:* craig@algonquin.com
Publicity Dir: Kelly Bowen
Publr, Young Adult & Middle Grade: Elise Howard
Publr: Elisabeth Scharlatt
Assoc Publr: Ina Stern
Mktg Mgr: Katie Ford
Online Mktg Mgr: Debra Linn
Exec Ed: Chuck Adams
Mng Ed & ISBN Contact: Brunson Hoole *Tel:* 919-967-0108 ext 22 *E-mail:* brunson@algonquin.com
Design & Prodn: Anne Winslow *Tel:* 919-967-0108 ext 29
Publicity: Emma Boyer
Intl Rts: Kendra Poster
Founded: 1982
Trade books, fiction & nonfiction.
ISBN Prefix(es): 978-0-912697; 978-0-945575; 978-1-56512
Number of titles published annually: 38 Print
Imprints: Algonquin Young Readers; Artisan; HighBridge Audio; Shannon Ravenel Books; Storey Publishing; Timber Press
*Sales Office(s):* Workman Publishing Co Inc, 225 Varick St, New York, NY 10014-4381 *Tel:* 212-254-5900 *Fax:* 212-254-8098
Distributed by Workman Publishing Co Inc
Distributor for Black Dog & Lenventhal; Fearless Critic Media; Greenwich Workshop Press
Foreign Rep(s): Thomas Allen & Son Ltd (Canada)
Foreign Rights: Big Apple Agency Inc (China, Taiwan); Graal Literary Agency (Poland); Japan UNI Agency Inc (Japan); JLM Literary Agency (Greece); Katai & Bolza Literary Agency (Hungary); Korea Copyright Center Inc (KCC) (Korea); Leonhardt & Hoier (Scandinavia); Kristin Olson Literary Agency SRO (Czech Republic); I Pikarski Ltd (Israel); Plima Literary Agency (Bulgaria, Croatia, Macedonia, Serbia, Slovenia); Sebes & Gelderen Literary Agency (Netherlands); Julio F Yanez Agencia Literaria SL (Portugal, Spain)
*Billing Address:* Workman Publishing Co Inc, 225 Varick St, New York, NY 10014-4381 *Tel:* 212-254-5900 *Fax:* 212-254-8098
*Orders to:* Workman Publishing Co Inc, 225 Varick St, New York, NY 10014-4381 *Tel:* 212-254-5900 *Toll Free Tel:* 800-722-7202 *Fax:* 212-254-8098
*Returns:* Workman Publishing Co Inc, c/o George Banta Co, 677 Brighton Beach Rd, Menasha, WI 54952-2998
*Warehouse:* Workman Publishing Co Inc, c/o George Banta Co, 677 Brighton Beach Rd, Menasha, WI 54952-2998

**Algora Publishing**
222 Riverside Dr, Suite 16-D, New York, NY 10025-6809
*Tel:* 212-678-0232 *Fax:* 212-666-3682
*E-mail:* editors@algora.com
*Web Site:* www.algora.com
*Key Personnel*
Publr: Claudiu A Secara *E-mail:* claudiu@algora.com
Ed: Martin De Mers
Author Rel: Andrea Secara
Founded: 1992
Books on subjects of history, international affairs, current issues, political economy, philosophy, etc in the tradition of independent progressive thinking.
ISBN Prefix(es): 978-0-87586; 978-0-9646073; 978-1-892941
Number of titles published annually: 25 Print; 25 E-Book
Total Titles: 400 Print; 100 E-Book
Imprints: Agathon Press
Membership(s): AAP; IBPA, the Independent Book Publishers Association

**§ALI-ABA Continuing Professional Education**
Affiliate of American Bar Association & American Law Institute
4025 Chestnut St, Philadelphia, PA 19104
*Tel:* 215-243-1600 *Toll Free Tel:* 800-CLE-NEWS (253-6397) *Fax:* 215-243-1664; 215-243-1683
*Web Site:* www.ali-aba.org
*Key Personnel*
Exec Dir: Julene Franki
Deputy Exec Dir: Larry Meehan
Dir, Off of Courses of Study: Nancy A Kane
Dir, Off of Mktg: Amy Shapiro
Dir, Off of Periodicals: Mark T Carroll
Dir, Off of R&D: Leslie Belasco
Dir, Off of Topical Seminars: Nancy Mulloy-Bonn
Libn: Harry Kyriakodis
Founded: 1947
Publish law books & legal periodicals.
ISBN Prefix(es): 978-0-8318
Number of titles published annually: 4 Print; 5 CD-ROM; 5 E-Book
Total Titles: 300 Print; 20 CD-ROM; 5 Online; 20 E-Book; 380 Audio

**Alice James Books**
Division of Alice James Poetry Cooperative Inc
238 Main St, Farmington, ME 04938
SAN: 201-1158
*Tel:* 207-778-7071 *Fax:* 207-778-7766
*E-mail:* info@alicejamesbooks.org
*Web Site:* www.alicejamesbooks.org
*Key Personnel*
Exec Dir: Carey Salerno
Mng Ed: Frank Giampietro
Edit Asst: Andrew Thompson; Meg Willing
Founded: 1973
ISBN Prefix(es): 978-0-914086; 978-1-882295
Number of titles published annually: 6 Print
Total Titles: 115 Print; 3 Audio
*Distribution Center:* Consortium Book Sales & Distribution, The Keg House, Suite 101, 34 13 Ave NE, Minneapolis, MN 55413 *Tel:* 612-746-2600 *Toll Free Tel:* 800-283-3572 (cust serv) *Fax:* 612-746-2606 *Web Site:* www.cbsd.com

**All About Kids Publishing**
PO Box 159, Gilroy, CA 95020
*Tel:* 408-337-1866
*E-mail:* mail@aakp.com
*Web Site:* www.aakp.com
*Key Personnel*
Publr: Mike G Guevara
Ed: Linda L Guevara *E-mail:* lguevara@aakp.com
Founded: 2000
Strives to set the standards in children's book publishing by creating innovative books of the highest quality with beautiful art work for children of all walks of life. See submission guidelines at aakp.com.
ISBN Prefix(es): 978-0-9700863; 978-0-9710278; 978-0-9744446
Number of titles published annually: 6 Print
Total Titles: 20 Print; 5 E-Book
Membership(s): IBPA, the Independent Book Publishers Association

**§All Things That Matter Press**
79 Jones Rd, Somerville, ME 04348
*E-mail:* allthingsthatmatterpress@gmail.com
*Web Site:* www.allthingsthatmatterpress.com
*Key Personnel*
CEO: Debra Harris
Founded: 2008
Number of titles published annually: 20 Print; 30 E-Book; 10 Audio
Total Titles: 140 Print; 140 E-Book; 18 Audio

**Allen D Bragdon Publishers Inc**
252 Great Western Rd, South Yarmouth, MA 02664-2210
SAN: 208-5623
*Tel:* 508-398-4440 *Toll Free Tel:* 877-876-2787 *Fax:* 508-760-2397
*E-mail:* admin@brainwaves.com
*Web Site:* www.brainwaves.com
*Key Personnel*
Pres: Allen D Bragdon *E-mail:* abragdon@brainwaves.com
Cust Rel & Admin: Donna McGovern
Founded: 1977
Self-improvement, brain development books, puzzles, tests, mental exercises.
ISBN Prefix(es): 978-0-916410
Number of titles published annually: 1 CD-ROM; 5 E-Book
Total Titles: 10 Print; 10 E-Book
Membership(s): ABA; NEBA

**§Allium Press of Chicago**
1530 Elgin Ave, Forest Park, IL 60130
SAN: 858-3331
*Tel:* 708-689-9323
*E-mail:* info@alliumpress.com
*Web Site:* www.alliumpress.com
*Key Personnel*
Publr: Emily Victorson
Founded: 2009
Small independent press publishing fiction with a Chicago connection. Publish literary fiction, historical fiction, mysteries, thrillers & young adult fiction.
ISBN Prefix(es): 978-0-9840676; 978-0-9831938
Number of titles published annually: 5 Print; 5 E-Book
Total Titles: 8 Print; 8 E-Book
Membership(s): The Association of Publishers for Special Sales; Historical Novel Society; IBPA,

the Independent Book Publishers Association; Midwest Independent Booksellers Association; Midwest Independent Publishers Association

**Alloy Entertainment**
Division of Alloy Online
151 W 26 St, 11th fl, New York, NY 10001
*Tel.* 212-244-4307
~~*E-mail:* nycassistant@alloyentertainment.com~~
*Web Site:* www.alloyentertainment.com
*Key Personnel*
Pres: Leslie Morgenstein
EVP: Josh Bank *Tel:* 212-244-4307 ext 8375
VP & Edit Dir: Sara Shandler
Ed, Book Div: Joelle Hobeika
Assoc Ed: Emilia Rhodes
Founded: 1987
Hardcover, trade, mass market juvenile & young adult fiction & nonfiction; adult trade fiction & mass market fiction.
ISBN Prefix(es): 978-0-533; 978-0-590; 978-0-06; 978-0-14; 978-0-931497
Number of titles published annually: 50 Print
*Branch Office(s)*
6300 Wilshire Blvd, Suite 2150, Los Angeles, CA 90048 *Tel:* 323-801-1373 *E-mail:* laassistant@alloyentertainment.com
Distributed by Avon Books; HarperCollins; Hyperion; Little, Brown & Co; Penguin Group (USA) LLC; Random House Inc; Scholastic Books; Simon & Schuster
Foreign Rep(s): Rights People (UK)

**§Allworth Press**
Imprint of Skyhorse Publishing Inc
307 W 36 St, 11th fl, New York, NY 10018
*Tel:* 212-643-6816
*E-mail:* crawford@allworth.com
*Web Site:* www.allworth.com
*Key Personnel*
Publr: Tad Crawford
Publicity & Mktg Assoc: Cindy Peng
Assoc Publr: Robert Porter *E-mail:* bporter@allworth.com
Asst Ed: Delia Casa
Busn Mgr: Marrissa Jones *E-mail:* mjones@allworth.com
Founded: 1989
Business & self-help books for artists, crafters, designers, photographers, authors & film & performing artists; books about business & law for the general public.
ISBN Prefix(es): 978-0-927629; 978-0-9607118; 978-1-880559; 978-1-58115
Number of titles published annually: 40 Print; 3 CD-ROM; 30 E-Book
Total Titles: 400 Print; 15 CD-ROM; 38 E-Book
Imprints: Helios Press
Distributed by W W Norton
Foreign Rep(s): Bookwise International (Australia, New Zealand); CKK Ltd (Theo Philips) (Hong Kong, Philippines, Singapore, Thailand); Windsor Books (Geoff Cowen) (Europe, UK)
Foreign Rights: Jean V Naggar Literary Agency; Jennifer Weltz (foreign lang rts)
Membership(s): IBPA, the Independent Book Publishers Association

**AllWrite Advertising & Publishing**
260 Peachtree St NW, Suite 2200, Atlanta, GA 30303
Mailing Address: PO Box 1071, Atlanta, GA 30301
*Tel:* 678-691-9005 *Fax:* 530-689-6980
*E-mail:* questions@allwritepublishing.com; support@allwritepublishing.com (orders & returns)
*Web Site:* www.allwritepublishing.com
*Key Personnel*
Pres & Publr: Annette R Johnson *E-mail:* annette@allwritepublishing.com
Founded: 1995
A conventional small press. Books that we do not decide to publish are given thorough feedback.
ISBN Prefix(es): 978-0-9744935
Number of titles published annually: 5 Print; 5 E-Book
Total Titles: 20 E-Book
Membership(s): Writers Guild of America East

**Allyn & Bacon**
Imprint of Pearson Higher Education
75 Arlington St, Suite 300, Boston, MA 02116
*Tel:* 617-848-6000 *Toll Free Tel:* 800-526-0485 *Fax:* 617-848-6016
*Web Site:* www.pearsonhighered.com
Founded: 1868
A college textbook publisher focusing on a select number of social science, education & humanities disciplines.
ISBN Prefix(es): 978-0-205; 978-0-321
Number of titles published annually: 310 Print
Total Titles: 2,300 Print

**Alpha**
Imprint of Penguin Group (USA) LLC
375 Hudson St, New York, NY 10014
*Tel:* 212-366-2000
*Key Personnel*
Publr: Michael Sanders
Dir, Mktg & Publicity: Dawn Werk
Founded: 2003
ISBN Prefix(es): 978-1-61564
Number of titles published annually: 88 Print
Total Titles: 580 Print

**ALPHA Publications of America Inc**
Affiliate of Alpha Legal Forms & More
1830 E Broadway, Suite 124, Tucson, AZ 85719
*Tel:* 520-795-7100 *Toll Free Tel:* 800-528-3494 *Toll Free Fax:* 800-770-4329
*E-mail:* alphapublications@aol.com
*Web Site:* www.alphapublications.com
*Key Personnel*
Pres: Kermit Burton
Founded: 1976
Non-lawyer self-help legal kits (books & packets).
ISBN Prefix(es): 978-0-937434; 978-1-57164
Number of titles published annually: 109 Print
Total Titles: 128 Print; 160 Online; 4 E-Book
Membership(s): IBPA, the Independent Book Publishers Association

**Alpine Publications Inc**
38262 Linman Rd, Crawford, CO 81415
*Tel:* 970-921-5005 *Toll Free Tel:* 800-777-7257 *Fax:* 970-921-5081
*E-mail:* editorial@alpinepub.com; customerservice@alpinepub.com
*Web Site:* www.alpinepub.com
*Key Personnel*
Publr: Betty McKinney
Founded: 1975
Dog & horse nonfiction titles.
ISBN Prefix(es): 978-0-931866; 978-0-87714; 978-1-57779
Number of titles published annually: 6 Print; 15 E-Book
Total Titles: 70 Print; 1 CD-ROM; 7 E-Book
*Advertising Agency:* Artline
Membership(s): ABA; The Association of Publishers for Special Sales; IBPA, the Independent Book Publishers Association

**AltaMira Press**
Imprint of Rowman & Littlefield Publishing Group
4501 Forbes Blvd, Suite 200, Lanham, MD 20706
*Tel:* 301-459-3366 *Toll Free Tel:* 800-462-6420 (cust serv) *Fax:* 301-429-5748
*E-mail:* custserv@rowman.com
*Web Site:* www.altamirapress.com
*Key Personnel*
Publr: Marcus Boggs *Tel:* 301-459-3366 ext 304 *E-mail:* mboggs@rowman.com
Exec Ed: Wendi Schnaufer *Tel:* 301-459-3366 ext 5320 *E-mail:* wschnaufer@rowman.com
Founded: 1995
Academic & professional materials, anthropology, museum & cultural studies, religion, archeology, history & humanities.
New titles to be released under the Rowman & Littlefield imprint.
ISBN Prefix(es): 978-0-8039; 978-0-7619 (shared with Sage Publications); 978-0-930390; 978-0-910050; 978-0-942063; 978-0-7425 (shared with Rowman & Littlefield); 978-0-8039 (shared with Sage Publications)
Number of titles published annually: 75 Print; 1 CD-ROM
Total Titles: 500 Print; 3 CD-ROM
Distributor for American Association for State & Local History
Foreign Rep(s): Oxford Publicity Partnership (Europe, UK)
*Shipping Address:* National Book Network/University Press of America, 15200 NBN Way, PO Box 191, Blue Ridge Summit, PA 17214 *Toll Free Tel:* 800-462-6420 *Toll Free Fax:* 800-338-4550 *E-mail:* customercare@rowman.com
*Distribution Center:* National Book Network/University Press of America, 15200 NBN Way, PO Box 191, Blue Ridge Summit, PA 17214 *Toll Free Tel:* 800-462-6420 *Toll Free Fax:* 800-338-4550 *E-mail:* customercare@rowman.com
Membership(s): AAP

**Althos Publishing**
1500 Piney Plains Rd, Suite 200, Carey, NC 27518
*Tel:* 919-557-2260 *Fax:* 919-557-2261
*E-mail:* info@althos.com
*Web Site:* www.althosbooks.com
*Key Personnel*
Pres & Publr: Lawrence Harte *E-mail:* lharte@althos.com
Dir: Carolyn Luck *E-mail:* carolyn@althos.com
Founded: 2002
ISBN Prefix(es): 978-0-9650658; 978-0-87288; 978-0-87288; 978-0-917845
Number of titles published annually: 50 Print; 45 Online; 45 E-Book
Total Titles: 140 Print; 130 Online; 130 E-Book

**§AMACOM Books**
Division of American Management Association
1601 Broadway, New York, NY 10019-7420
SAN: 201-1670
*Tel:* 212-586-8100; 518-891-5510 (orders) *Toll Free Tel:* 800-250-5308 (cust serv) *Fax:* 212-903-8083; 518-891-2372 (orders)
*E-mail:* pubservice@amanet.org
*Web Site:* www.amacombooks.org
*Key Personnel*
Pres & Publr: Hank Kennedy *E-mail:* hkennedy@amanet.org
Dir, Publicity: Irene Majuk *Tel:* 212-903-8087 *E-mail:* imajuk@amanet.org
Dir, Subs Rts & Intl Sales: Therese Mausser *E-mail:* tmausser@amanet.org
Dir, Trade Sales & Mktg: Jenny Wesselmann Schwartz *Tel:* 212-903-8448 *E-mail:* jwesselmann@amanet.org
Exec Ed: Ellen Kadin; Christina Parisi
Sr Ed: Robert Nirkind
Founded: 1972
Publish books on business management, career growth, current events, technology & personal finance. AMACOM books help readers enhance their personal & professional growth & reach into the future to understand emerging trends & cutting-edge thinking.
ISBN Prefix(es): 978-0-8144; 978-0-7612

Number of titles published annually: 60 Print; 30 E-Book
Total Titles: 500 Print; 150 E-Book; 54 Audio
Distributed by McGraw-Hill International
Foreign Rep(s): McGraw-Hill International Distribution (Worldwide exc Canada)
*Returns:* 600 Ama Way, Saranac Lake, NY 12983
*Warehouse:* 600 Ama Way, Saranac Lake, NY 12983, Contact: William McIntyre *Toll Free Tel:* 800-250-5308 *E-mail:* wmintyre@amanet.org

**Amadeus Press/Hal Leonard Performing Arts Publishing Group**
Imprint of Hal Leonard Performing Arts Publishing Group
33 Plymouth St, Suite 302, Montclair, NJ 07042
*Tel:* 973-337-5034 *Toll Free Tel:* 800-524-4425
*E-mail:* info@halleonardbooks.com
*Web Site:* www.amadeuspress.com; www.halleonardbooks.com
*Key Personnel*
Group Publr: John Cerullo *Tel:* 973-337-5034 ext 210 *E-mail:* jcerullo@amadeuspress.com
Founded: 1987
Full-service trade publisher that produces books, book/CDs & DVDs about classical music & opera.
ISBN Prefix(es): 978-1-57467
Number of titles published annually: 20 Print
Total Titles: 150 Print

**Frank Amato Publications Inc**
4040 SE Wister St, Portland, OR 97222
Mailing Address: PO Box 82112, Portland, OR 97282
*Tel:* 503-653-8108 *Toll Free Tel:* 800-541-9498 *Fax:* 503-653-2766
*E-mail:* customerservice@amatobooks.com; info@amatobooks.com
*Web Site:* www.amatobooks.com
*Key Personnel*
Publr: Frank W Amato
Founded: 1967
Fishing books & magazines, some outdoor sport titles.
ISBN Prefix(es): 978-0-936608; 978-1-878175; 978-1-57188
Number of titles published annually: 40 Print; 1 CD-ROM
Total Titles: 800 Print; 1 CD-ROM
Distributed by Angler's Book Supply

**Amber Lotus Publishing**
PO Box 11329, Portland, OR 97211
SAN: 247-6819
*Tel:* 503-284-6400 *Toll Free Tel:* 800-326-2375 (orders only) *Fax:* 503-284-6417
*E-mail:* info@amberlotus.com
*Web Site:* www.amberlotus.com
*Key Personnel*
CEO & Pres: Lawson Day
Founded: 1988
Calendars, greeting cards, journals & books.
ISBN Prefix(es): 978-1-885394; 978-1-56937; 978-1-60237
Number of titles published annually: 65 Print
Imprints: Bluestar
*Returns:* Ware-Pak, Amber Lotus Publishing returns, 2427 Bond St, University Park, IL 60466

**Amber Quill Press LLC**
PO Box 265, Indian Hills, CO 80454
SAN: 255-3872
*E-mail:* business@amberquill.com
*Web Site:* www.amberquill.com; www.amberheat.com (imprint); www.amberallure.com (imprint)
*Key Personnel*
Owner & Creative Dir: Trace Edward Zaber *E-mail:* tezaber@earthlink.net
Owner & Cust Serv Dir: J Kathe
Owner & Mktg Dir: E J Gilmer *E-mail:* ej_gilmer@amberquill.com
Owner & Prodn/Tech Dir: Ingrid Arbaiza *E-mail:* ilandr@earthlink.net
Owner & Fin Mgr: Karin Story *E-mail:* karin-aqp@earthlink.net
Mng Ed: Catherine Snodgrass
Mktg & Promos Coord: Theresa Gallup
Founded: 2002
An independent, royalty-paying publisher offering a varied list of fiction: young adult, romance (& all sub-genres), erotica (straight & GLBT), science fiction, mystery, thriller, suspense, horror, fantasy, vampire, historical & romantic; e-book &/or print-on-demand. Not open for submissions.
Accepts no returns.
ISBN Prefix(es): 978-1-59279
Number of titles published annually: 60 Print; 300 E-Book
Total Titles: 350 Print; 840 E-Book
Imprints: Amber Allure (GLBT); Amber Heat (erotic romance)
*Shipping Address:* Booksurge LLC, 7290-B Investment Dr, Charleston, SC 29418 *Tel:* 843-789-5000 *Toll Free Tel:* 866-308-6235 *E-mail:* customerservice@booksurge.com *Web Site:* www.booksurge.com
Membership(s): IBPA, the Independent Book Publishers Association

**America West Publishers**
Subsidiary of Global Insights Inc
PO Box 599, Hayden, ID 83835
*Tel:* 775-885-0700 *Toll Free Tel:* 800-729-4131
*Web Site:* www.nohoax.com
*Key Personnel*
Pres: George Green *E-mail:* geo@nohoax.com
Founded: 1986
New science, UFO's, healing, metaphysics, spiritual, political & economic.
ISBN Prefix(es): 978-0-922356
Number of titles published annually: 5 Print; 1 CD-ROM
Total Titles: 100 Print; 20 CD-ROM; 5 Audio
*Billing Address:* Global Insights Inc, 1805 N Carson St, Carson City, NV 89701
*Orders to:* Global Insights Inc, 1805 N Carson St, Carson City, NV 89701
*Returns:* Global Insights Inc, 1805 N Carson St, Carson City, NV 89701
*Warehouse:* 5872 Government Way, Bldg 1, No 10, Dalton Gardens, ID 83815 *E-mail:* geo@nohoax.com

**American Academy of Environmental Engineers**
130 Holiday Ct, Suite 100, Annapolis, MD 21401
*Tel:* 410-266-3311 *Fax:* 410-266-7653
*E-mail:* info@aaee.net
*Web Site:* www.aaee.net
*Key Personnel*
Exec Dir: Joseph S Cavarretta *E-mail:* jcava@aaee.net
Founded: 1955
Journals & textbooks for the environmental engineering & science professions.
ISBN Prefix(es): 978-1-883767
Number of titles published annually: 5 Print
Total Titles: 49 Print
Distributor for The ABS Group; CRC Press; McGraw-Hill; Pearson Education; Prentice Hall; John Wiley & Sons Inc

**§American Academy of Orthopaedic Surgeons**
6300 N River Rd, Rosemont, IL 60018-4262
SAN: 228-2097
*Tel:* 847-823-7186 *Toll Free Tel:* 800-346-2267 *Fax:* 847-823-8125 *Toll Free Fax:* 800-999-2939
*Web Site:* www.aaos.org
*Key Personnel*
Dir, Dept of Pubns: Marilyn L Fox *E-mail:* fox@aaos.org
Fin Analyst: Tricia Keesey *Tel:* 847-384-4160
Mgr, Pubns & Licensing: Joan Golembiewski *Tel:* 847-384-4144 *Fax:* 847-823-8033 *E-mail:* golembiewski@aaos.org
Founded: 1933
Scientific & technical books, including annual updates on orthopaedic procedures; home study programs & examinations; symposium volumes; monographs on scientific, clinical, practice management & socioeconomic topics in orthopaedics; clinical review journal.
ISBN Prefix(es): 978-0-89203
Number of titles published annually: 15 Print; 12 CD-ROM; 2 Online; 1 Audio
Total Titles: 100 Print; 38 CD-ROM; 5 Online; 5 Audio
Distributed by Jones & Bartlett Publishers
Foreign Rep(s): Eurospan (Europe, Middle East); Nankodo Co Inc (Japan)
*Warehouse:* Dearborn Distribution Center, 940 Enterprise St, Aurora, IL 60504 *Toll Free Fax:* 800-823-8025 *E-mail:* custserv@aaos.org

**American Academy of Pediatrics**
141 NW Point Blvd, Elk Grove Village, IL 60007-1098
*Tel:* 847-434-4000 *Toll Free Tel:* 888-227-1770 *Fax:* 847-434-8000
*E-mail:* pubs@aap.org
*Web Site:* www.aap.org
*Key Personnel*
Pres: Dr Robert W Block
Dir, Mktg & Pubns: Maureen De Rosa
Dir, Prod Devt Div: Mark Grimes *Tel:* 847-434-7822 *E-mail:* mgrimes@aap.org
Founded: 1930
Patient educational material, medical textbooks, professional textbook, patient education & practice management materials; pediatrics; family & emergency medicine.
ISBN Prefix(es): 978-0-910761; 978-0-87493; 978-0-915473; 978-0-87553; 978-0-553; 978-0-89707; 978-1-56055; 978-1-58110
Number of titles published annually: 40 Print; 5 CD-ROM; 10 Online; 120 E-Book
Total Titles: 400 Print; 10 CD-ROM; 10 Online; 120 E-Book
*Branch Office(s)*
601 13 St NW, Suite 400-N, Washington, DC 20005 *Tel:* 202-347-8600 *Fax:* 202-393-6137
Foreign Rights: John Scott & Co

**The American Alpine Club Press**
Division of The American Alpine Club
710 Tenth St, Suite 100, Golden, CO 80401
*Tel:* 303-384-0110 *Fax:* 303-384-0111
*Web Site:* www.americanalpineclub.org
*Key Personnel*
Opers Dir: Penn Burris *Tel:* 303-384-0110 ext 11 *E-mail:* pburris@americanalpineclub.org
Founded: 1902
Mountaineering: general, regional guides, safety, medical & scientific, annual journals & historical.
ISBN Prefix(es): 978-0-930410
Number of titles published annually: 3 Print
Total Titles: 57 Print
Distributed by Mountaineers Books
Foreign Rep(s): Mountaineers Books (Worldwide)
Foreign Rights: Mountaineers Books (Worldwide)

**§American Anthropological Association (AAA)**
Publications Dept, Suite 600, 2200 Wilson Blvd, Arlington, VA 22201
*Tel:* 703-528-1902 *Fax:* 703-528-3546
*Web Site:* www.aaanet.org
*Key Personnel*
Dir, Publg: Oona Schmid *Tel:* 703-528-1902 ext 1174 *E-mail:* oschmid@aaanet.org

Mng Ed: Amy Goldenberg *Tel:* 703-528-1902 ext 1184 *E-mail:* agoldenberg@aaanet.org
Asst Mgr, Membership Servs: Dion Dears *E-mail:* ddears@aaanet.org
Founded: 1902
Publish scholarly journals.
ISBN Prefix(es): 978-0-913167
Number of titles published annually: 100 Print
Total Titles: 27 Print
Distributed by Wiley-Blackwell
Membership(s): AAP; World Council of Anthropological Association

**§American Association for Vocational Instructional Materials**
220 Smithonia Rd, Winterville, GA 30683-9527
*Tel:* 706-742-5355 *Toll Free Tel:* 800-228-4689 *Fax:* 706-742-7005
*E-mail:* sales@aavim.com
*Web Site:* www.aavim.com
*Key Personnel*
Dir: Gary Farmer
Founded: 1949
Consortium formed for development, publishing & distribution of instructional materials for vocational education.
ISBN Prefix(es): 978-0-89606
Number of titles published annually: 4 Print
Total Titles: 182 Print; 10 CD-ROM
Distributor for Southeastern Cooperative Wildlife Disease Study

**§American Association of Blood Banks**
8101 Glenbrook Rd, Bethesda, MD 20814-2749
*Tel:* 301-907-6977 *Toll Free Tel:* 866-222-2498 (sales) *Fax:* 301-907-6895
*E-mail:* aabb@aabb.org; sales@aabb.org (ordering)
*Web Site:* www.aabb.org
*Key Personnel*
Dir, Pubns: Laurie Munk *Tel:* 301-215-6595 *E-mail:* laurie@aabb.org
Founded: 1947
Texts in blood banking standards, transfusion medicine, transplantation & cellular therapy.
ISBN Prefix(es): 978-0-915355
Number of titles published annually: 20 Print; 14 Audio
Total Titles: 100 Print; 2 CD-ROM; 5 Online; 60 Audio
Distributed by Karger
*Distribution Center:* Login Brothers Canada

**American Association of Cereal Chemists**, see AACC International

**American Association of Colleges for Teacher Education (AACTE)**
1307 New York Ave NW, Suite 300, Washington, DC 20005-4701
*Tel:* 202-293-2450 *Fax:* 202-457-8095
*E-mail:* aacte@aacte.org
*Web Site:* www.aacte.org
*Key Personnel*
CEO & Pres: Sharon P Robinson *Tel:* 202-478-4505
COO & CFO: Jerry D Wirth *Tel:* 202-478-4570
Ed & Mktg Communs Assoc: Kristin McCabe *Tel:* 207-899-1309 *E-mail:* kmccabe@aacte.org
Founded: 1948
Teacher education related works.
ISBN Prefix(es): 978-0-89333
Number of titles published annually: 3 Print
Total Titles: 85 Print

**American Association of Collegiate Registrars & Admissions Officers (AACRAO)**
One Dupont Circle NW, Suite 520, Washington, DC 20036-1135
*Tel:* 202-293-9161 *Fax:* 202-872-8857
*E-mail:* info@aacrao.org
*Web Site:* www.aacrao.org
*Key Personnel*
Exec Dir: Jerry Sullivan *E-mail:* sullivanj@aacrao.org
Dir, Pubns: Martha Henebry *Tel:* 202-263-0285 ext 6812 *E-mail:* henebrym@aacrao.org
Founded: 1910
Periodicals, monograph series, higher education-general, international, technology & higher education.
ISBN Prefix(es): 978-0-929851; 978-0-910054
Number of titles published annually: 4 Print
Total Titles: 118 Print
*Distribution Center:* AACRAO Distribution Center, PO Box 231, Annapolis Junction, MD 20701 *Tel:* 301-490-7651 *Fax:* 301-206-9789

**American Atheist Press**
PO Box 158, Cranford, NJ 07016
*Tel:* 908-276-7300 *Fax:* 908-276-7402
*E-mail:* info@atheists.org
*Web Site:* www.atheists.org
*Key Personnel*
Pres: David Silverman *Tel:* 908-276-7300 ext 5 *E-mail:* dsilverman@atheists.org
Mng Ed: Frank R Zindler *Tel:* 614-447-3600 ext 3361 *E-mail:* fzindler@atheists.org
PR Dir: Teresa MacBain *Tel:* 908-276-7300 ext 7
Founded: 1963
Specialize in atheism, religious criticism, atheist history, religious intolerance.
ISBN Prefix(es): 978-0-910309; 978-0-911826; 978-1-57884
Number of titles published annually: 5 Print
Total Titles: 40 Print
Imprints: Gustav Broukal Press
*Editorial Office(s):* 1352 Hunter Ave, Columbus, OH 43201
*Shipping Address:* 225 Cristiani St, Cranford, NJ 07016-3214

**American Bar Association**
321 N Clark St, Chicago, IL 60654
*Tel:* 312-988-5000 *Toll Free Tel:* 800-285-2221 (orders) *Fax:* 312-988-6281
*E-mail:* orders@abanet.org
*Web Site:* www.ababooks.org
*Key Personnel*
Dir, New Prod Devt: Timothy Brandhorst *Tel:* 312-988-6082 *E-mail:* tim.brandhorst@americanbar.org
Founded: 1878
Books, magazines, journals, newsletters & AV materials.
ISBN Prefix(es): 978-1-57073; 978-1-59031; 978-1-60442
Number of titles published annually: 170 Print; 25 CD-ROM; 100 Online; 100 E-Book
Total Titles: 1,000 Print; 150 CD-ROM; 250 Online; 250 E-Book
*Branch Office(s)*
1800 "M" St NW, Washington, DC 20036
*Warehouse:* PBD, 905 Carlow Dr, Unit B, Bolingbrook, IL 60490
*Distribution Center:* National Book Network, 4501 Forbes Blvd, Suite 200, Lanham, MD 20706
Membership(s): IBPA, the Independent Book Publishers Association

**American Bible Society**
1865 Broadway, New York, NY 10023-7505
SAN: 203-5189
*Tel:* 212-408-1200 *Toll Free Tel:* 800-322-4253 *Fax:* 212-408-1512
*E-mail:* info@americanbible.org
*Web Site:* www.americanbible.org
*Key Personnel*
Dir, Print & Prodn: John Greco
Dir, Publg Servs: Tom Durakis
Founded: 1816
Publisher, producer & distributor of Bibles, books, audio, video & software products emphasizing Christian, inspirational & family values.
ISBN Prefix(es): 978-1-58516
Number of titles published annually: 20 Print
Total Titles: 800 Print
*Branch Office(s)*
1550 Liberty Ridge Dr, Suite 330, Wayne, PA 19087 *Tel:* 610-647-8080 *Fax:* 484-654-3503
14120 Parke Long Ct, Suite 204, Chantilly, VA 20151 *Tel:* 703-621-2000 *Fax:* 703-621-2001

**American Biographical Institute**
Division of Historical Preservations of America Inc
5126 Bur Oak Circle, Raleigh, NC 27612
Mailing Address: PO Box 31226, Raleigh, NC 27622-1226
*Tel:* 919-781-8710 *Fax:* 919-781-8712
*E-mail:* abiinfo@abiworldwide.com
*Web Site:* www.abiworldwide.com
*Key Personnel*
Chmn: Arlene S Calhoun *E-mail:* ascalhoun@abiworldwide.com
Founded: 1967
Publish biographical reference books: regional, national & international.
ISBN Prefix(es): 978-0-934544
Number of titles published annually: 6 Print
Total Titles: 300 Print

**American Book Publishing**
14435-C Big Basin Way, No 155, Saratoga, CA 95070
*Tel:* 415-935-5082 *Toll Free Tel:* 800-684-8746
*E-mail:* info@american-book.com; orders@american-book.com
*Web Site:* www.americanbookpublishing.com
*Key Personnel*
Dir, Opers: Kathleen Brooks Montgomery
Book Orders: Michelle Grace
Founded: 1985
To support, document & disseminate through book publication, great works & teachings of talented authors, scholars & professionals.
ISBN Prefix(es): 978-1-58982
Number of titles published annually: 70 Print
Total Titles: 360 Print
Imprints: American Book Business Press; American Book Classics; American University & Colleges Press; Bedside Books; Millennial Mind Publishing

**§American Carriage House Publishing**
PO Box 1130, Nevada City, CA 95959
*Tel:* 530-432-8860 *Toll Free Tel:* 866-986-2665 *Fax:* 530-432-7379
*E-mail:* editor@carriagehousepublishing.com
*Web Site:* www.americancarriagehousepublishing.com
Founded: 2003
Focused on providing traditional & family values in a new fresh approach. Distribution Centers: Baker & Taylor, Inc, FaithWorks Books, Ingram Book Group & Quality Books Inc.
ISBN Prefix(es): 978-0-970
Number of titles published annually: 8 Print; 20 CD-ROM; 8 Online; 14 E-Book; 68 Audio
Total Titles: 16 E-Book; 240 Audio
Distributed by Faith Works Books
*Shipping Address:* 17860 Cattle Dr, Rough & Ready, CA 95975
*Warehouse:* 17860 Cattle Dr, Rough & Ready, CA 95975
Membership(s): The Association of Publishers for Special Sales; IBPA, the Independent Book Publishers Association

**American Catholic Press (ACP)**
16565 S State St, South Holland, IL 60473
SAN: 162-4989

*Tel:* 708-331-5485 *Fax:* 708-331-5484
*E-mail:* acp@acpress.org
*Web Site:* www.acpress.org
*Key Personnel*
Exec Dir: Rev Michael Gilligan, PhD
Devt Dir: Peter Ruhl
Subscriber Serv Dir: Michael Yukich
Founded: 1967
Christian liturgy, especially in the Roman Catholic Church including music resources for churches. No poetry or fiction.
ISBN Prefix(es): 978-0-915866
Number of titles published annually: 5 Print; 1 Audio
Total Titles: 25 Print; 1 CD-ROM; 4 Audio

**§The American Ceramic Society**
600 N Cleveland Ave, Suite 210, Westerville, OH 43082
*Tel:* 240-646-7054 *Toll Free Tel:* 866-721-3322 *Fax:* 614-794-5892
*E-mail:* customerservice@ceramics.org
*Web Site:* www.ceramics.org
*Key Personnel*
Exec Dir: Charles Spahr *E-mail:* cspahr@ceramics.org
Dir, Mktg & Membership: Megan Bricker *E-mail:* mbricker@ceramics.org
Dir, Tech Pubns: Mark Mecklenborg *Tel:* 240-646-7054 ext 5829 *E-mail:* mmecklenborg@ceramics.org
Founded: 1898
Dedicated to the advancement of ceramics, serving more than 8,000 members & subscribers. Members include engineers, scientists, researchers & others in the ceramics & materials industry. Provides the latest technical, scientific & educational information.
ISBN Prefix(es): 978-0-944904; 978-1-57498; 978-0-916094
Number of titles published annually: 25 Print
Total Titles: 250 Print; 8 CD-ROM

**The American Chemical Society**
1155 16 St NW, Washington, DC 20036
SAN: 201-2626
*Tel:* 202-872-4600 *Fax:* 202-872-6067
*E-mail:* help@acs.org
*Web Site:* www.acs.org
*Key Personnel*
Pres: Bassam Z Shakhashiri *E-mail:* president@acs.org
Exec Dir: Madeleine Jacobs
Asst Dir: Joseph Graham *E-mail:* j_graham@acs.org
Founded: 1876
Serials, proceedings, reprint collections, monographs & other professional & reference books; specializes in food chemistry, environmental sciences & green chemistry, analytical, inorganic, medicinal, organic & physical chemistries, biochemistry, polymer & materials science & nanotechnology.
ISBN Prefix(es): 978-0-8412
Number of titles published annually: 31 Print
Total Titles: 500 Print; 1 CD-ROM
Distributed by Oxford University Press
Distributor for Royal Society of Chemistry
Foreign Rep(s): Maruzen Co Ltd (Japan); Sonya Nickson (UK); Andrew Pitts (UK)
Membership(s): AAP

**American College**
270 S Bryn Mawr Ave, Bryn Mawr, PA 19010
SAN: 240-5822
*Tel:* 610-526-1000 *Toll Free Tel:* 888-263-7265 *Fax:* 610-526-1310
*Web Site:* www.theamericancollege.edu
*Key Personnel*
CEO & Pres: Laurence Barton, PhD
VP & Dean, Academic Div: Walt Woerheide, PhD
Founded: 1927
An independent, accredited nonprofit educational institution offering financial services texts & course guides online & life insurance for students in financial services programs at colleges & universities including American College programs: CLU, ChFC, CLF, LUTCF, RHU, REBC, CASL & CFP certification curriculum & MSFS degree for professionals in the financial services industry. Subject specialties: business, finance, insurance & securities.
ISBN Prefix(es): 978-0-943590; 978-1-57996; 978-1-932819
Number of titles published annually: 42 Print; 60 Online; 11 Audio
Total Titles: 42 Print; 15 CD-ROM; 60 Online; 11 Audio

**§American College of Physician Executives**
400 N Ashley Dr, Suite 400, Tampa, FL 33602
SAN: 688-7449
*Tel:* 813-287-2000 *Toll Free Tel:* 800-562-8088 *Fax:* 813-287-8993
*E-mail:* acpe@acpe.org
*Web Site:* www.acpe.org
*Key Personnel*
Communs Ed: Bill Steiger *E-mail:* bsteiger@acpe.org
Founded: 1975
Publishes books & journals.
ISBN Prefix(es): 978-0-9605218; 978-0-924674
Number of titles published annually: 6 Print; 1 CD-ROM
Total Titles: 50 Print; 6 CD-ROM; 1 Audio
*Distribution Center:* BrightKey, 1780 Crossroads Dr, Odenton, MD 21113 *Tel:* 301-604-3305 *Fax:* 301-543-9052 *E-mail:* cjones@pmds.com

**American College of Surgeons**
633 N Saint Clair St, Chicago, IL 60611-3211
*Tel:* 312-202-5000 *Fax:* 312-202-5001
*E-mail:* postmaster@facs.org
*Web Site:* www.facs.org
*Key Personnel*
Mgr, Public Info Electronic Publg, Integrated Communs Div: Sally Garneski *Tel:* 312-202-5409 *Fax:* 312-202-5021 *E-mail:* sgarneski@facs.org
Founded: 1913
Publishes CD-ROMs, reference books & manuals. Specialize in surgery, trauma, cancer & professional liability. Also publishes the *Journal of the American College of Surgeons* (monthly) & the *Bulletin of the American College of Surgeons* (monthly).
ISBN Prefix(es): 978-0-9620370
Number of titles published annually: 5 Print
Total Titles: 20 Print; 6 CD-ROM
Distributed by Cine-Med Inc; Scientific American Medicine

**American Correctional Association**
206 N Washington St, Suite 200, Alexandria, VA 22314
*Tel:* 703-224-0000 *Toll Free Tel:* 800-222-5646 *Fax:* 703-224-0040
*Web Site:* www.aca.org
*Key Personnel*
Dir, Pubns: Susan Clayton *Tel:* 703-224-0180 *E-mail:* susanc@aca.org
Mgr, Pubns & Res: Alice Heiserman *Tel:* 703-224-0194 *E-mail:* aliceh@aca.org
Founded: 1870
Corrections professionals.
ISBN Prefix(es): 978-1-56991
Number of titles published annually: 8 Print; 1 Audio
Total Titles: 200 Print; 1 Audio

**American Council on Education**
One Dupont Circle NW, Washington, DC 20036-1193
*Tel:* 202-939-9300; 301-632-6757 (orders) *Fax:* 202-939-9302
*E-mail:* pubs@acenet.edu
*Web Site:* www.acenet.edu
*Key Personnel*
Pres: Molly Corbett Broad
Ed: Megan Stevens *Tel:* 202-939-9477 *E-mail:* megan_stevens@ace.nche.edu
Pubns Coord: Don Hoyt *Tel:* 202-939-9380
Founded: 1917
Books, directories & handbooks in higher education, monographs.
ISBN Prefix(es): 978-0-8268; 978-0-89774
Number of titles published annually: 70 Print
Total Titles: 200 Print
Imprints: ACE/Oryx
Distributed by Rowman & Littlefield

**American Counseling Association**
5999 Stevenson Ave, Alexandria, VA 22304
*Tel:* 703-823-9800 (ext 222, book orders) *Toll Free Tel:* 800-422-2648 (ext 222, book orders); 800-347-6647 *Fax:* 703-823-0252 *Toll Free Fax:* 800-473-2329
*E-mail:* membership@counseling.org (book orders)
*Web Site:* www.counseling.org
*Key Personnel*
Dir, Pubns: Carolyn C Baker *Tel:* 703-823-9800 ext 356 *Fax:* 703-823-4786 *E-mail:* cbaker@counseling.org
Edit Asst & Rts & Perms Ed: Catherine Brumley *Tel:* 703-823-9800 ext 330 *Fax:* 703-823-4786 *E-mail:* cbrumley@counseling.org
Founded: 1952
More than 45,000 members from the school counseling, mental health & human development professions at all educational levels. Publishes 11 scholarly journals, a newspaper & approximately 8-10 new professional book titles a year for members & nonmembers.
ISBN Prefix(es): 978-1-55620
Number of titles published annually: 10 Print; 1 CD-ROM
Total Titles: 150 Print; 2 CD-ROM
Imprints: ACA
Distributed by Counseling Outfitters; Mental Health Resources; Paperbacks for Educators; ProEd; Self-Esteem Shop; Social Sciences School Services
Distributor for Association for Assessment in Counseling & Education; Association for Counselor Education & Supervision

**§American Diabetes Association**
1701 N Beauregard St, Alexandria, VA 22311
*Toll Free Tel:* 800-342-2383
*E-mail:* booksinfo@diabetes.org
*Web Site:* www.diabetes.org
*Key Personnel*
Dir, Book Publg: Abe Ogden
Mgr, Mktg: Carrie Engel
Acqs Ed: Victor Van Beuren
Founded: 1945
Books, handouts & collateral materials pertaining to diabetes for patients & health-care professionals.
ISBN Prefix(es): 978-1-58040; 978-0-94544
Number of titles published annually: 17 Print; 10 E-Book
Total Titles: 180 Print; 80 E-Book
Distributed by Publishers Group West

**American Federation of Arts**
305 E 47 St, 10th fl, New York, NY 10017
*Tel:* 212-988-7700 *Toll Free Tel:* 800-232-0270 *Fax:* 212-861-2487
*E-mail:* pubinfo@afaweb.org
*Web Site:* www.afaweb.org
*Key Personnel*
Dir, Pubns & Communs: Michaelyn Mitchell *Tel:* 212-988-7700 ext 228
Founded: 1909

Publisher of exhibition catalogues (books) that accompany art exhibitions organized by the AFA.
ISBN Prefix(es): 978-0-917418; 978-1-885444
Number of titles published annually: 4 Print
Total Titles: 47 Print
Distributed by Harry N Abrams Inc; Distributed Art Publishers; Hudson Hills Press Inc; Scala Publishers; University of Washington Press; Yale University Press

**American Federation of Astrologers Inc**
6535 S Rural Rd, Tempe, AZ 85283-3746
*Tel:* 480-838-1751 *Toll Free Tel:* 888-301-7630 *Fax:* 480-838-8293
*Web Site:* www.astrologers.com
*Key Personnel*
Exec Dir: Kris Brandt Riske
Founded: 1938
Astrology book publisher & membership organization.
ISBN Prefix(es): 978-0-86690
Number of titles published annually: 25 Print
Total Titles: 250 Print

**American Fisheries Society**
5410 Grosvenor Lane, Suite 110, Bethesda, MD 20814-2199
*Tel:* 301-897-8616; 703-661-1570 (book orders) *Fax:* 301-897-8096; 703-996-1010 (book orders)
*E-mail:* main@fisheries.org
*Web Site:* www.fisheries.org
*Key Personnel*
Dir, Pubns: Aaron Lerner *E-mail:* alerner@fisheries.org
Off Mgr: Denise Spencer
Founded: 1870
Fisheries science, aquaculture & management materials, aquatic ecology, fisheries law, fisheries history, conservation biology & publishing.
ISBN Prefix(es): 978-0-913235; 978-1-888569; 978-1-934874
Number of titles published annually: 12 Print
Total Titles: 100 Print
Foreign Rep(s): USACO (Japan)
*Advertising Agency:* Media West Inc, 230 Kings Hwy E, Suite 316, Haddonfield, NJ 08033, Contact: Steve West *Tel:* 856-432-1501 *Fax:* 856-494-1455 *E-mail:* steve@afs-fisheries.com

**§American Foundation for the Blind (AFB Press)**
2 Penn Plaza, Suite 1102, New York, NY 10001
*Tel:* 212-502-7600; 412-741-1398 (orders) *Toll Free Tel:* 800-232-3044 (orders) *Fax:* 917-210-3979; 412-741-0609 (orders) *Toll Free Fax:* 888-545-8331
*E-mail:* press@afb.net; afborder@afb.net (orders); afbinfo@afb.net
*Web Site:* www.afb.org
*Key Personnel*
Dir & Ed-in-Chief, Books: Natalie Hilzen *Tel:* 212-502-7653 *E-mail:* nhilzen@afb.net
Sales & Mktg Mgr: Anne Durham *Tel:* 304-710-3026 *E-mail:* adurham@afb.net
Founded: 1921
Text & professional books in the fields of visual impairment & blindness.
ISBN Prefix(es): 978-0-89128
Number of titles published annually: 8 Print; 4 Online
Total Titles: 200 Print; 17 Online; 5 Audio
*Branch Office(s)*
AFB National Employment Center, 50 California St, Suite 1500, San Francisco, CA 94111 *Tel:* 415-392-4845 *Fax:* 415-439-5299 *E-mail:* sanfran@afb.net
AFB Public Policy Center, 1660 "L" St NW, Suite 513, Washington, DC 20036, Contact: Paul Schroeder *Tel:* 202-822-0830 *Fax:* 646-478-9260 *E-mail:* afbgov@afb.net
AFB National Literacy Center, 100 Peachtree St, Suite 620, Atlanta, GA 30303 *Tel:* 404-525-2303 *Fax:* 646-478-9260 *E-mail:* literacy@afb.net
AFB Center on Vision Loss, 11030 Ables Lane, Dallas, TX 75229, Contact: Judy Scott *Tel:* 214-352-7222 *Fax:* 646-478-9260 *E-mail:* dallas@afb.net
AFB Tech, 1000 Fifth Ave, Suite 350, Huntington, WV 25701, Contact: Mark Uslan *Tel:* 304-523-8651 *Fax:* 646-478-9260 *E-mail:* wv@afb.net
*Orders to:* AFB Press Customer Service, PO Box 1020, Sewickley, PA 15143-1020 *Tel:* 412-741-1398 *Toll Free Tel:* 800-232-3044 *Fax:* 412-741-0609 *E-mail:* afborder@abdintl.com *Web Site:* www.afb.org/store
*Warehouse:* Associations Book Distributors International Inc, Buncher Commerce Park, Avenue A, Bldg 16, Leetsdale, PA 15056-1304 *Tel:* 412-741-1398 *Toll Free Tel:* 800-232-3044 *Fax:* 412-741-0609 *E-mail:* afborder@abdintl.com
Membership(s): AAP

**§American Geological Institute (AGI)**
4220 King St, Alexandria, VA 22302-1502
*Tel:* 703-379-2480 *Fax:* 703-379-7563
*E-mail:* pubs@agiweb.org
*Web Site:* www.agiweb.org
*Key Personnel*
Cont: Patrick C Burks *Tel:* 703-379-2480 ext 209 *E-mail:* pburks@agiweb.org
Exec Dir: P Patrick Leahy, PhD
Dir, Educ, Outreach & Devt: Ann E Benbow *Tel:* 703-379-2480 ext 245 *E-mail:* aeb@agiweb.org
Environmental Affs Dir: Travis L Hudson *Tel:* 360-582-1844 *Fax:* 360-582-1845 *E-mail:* ageology@olypen.com
Info Systems Dir: Sharon Tahirkheli *Tel:* 703-379-2480 ext 231 *E-mail:* snt@agiweb.org
Mktg Dir: John P Rasnin *Tel:* 703-379-2480 ext 224 *E-mail:* jr@agiweb.org
Technol & Communs Dir: Christopher Keane *Tel:* 703-379-2480 ext 219 *E-mail:* cmk@agiweb.org
Founded: 1948
Geoscience reference books.
ISBN Prefix(es): 978-0-922152; 978-0-913312
Number of titles published annually: 5 Print; 3 E-Book
Total Titles: 60 Print; 10 CD-ROM; 2 Online; 5 E-Book
Distributed by W H Freeman; It's About Time Inc; Prentice Hall
*Orders to:* AGI Book Center *Web Site:* www.agiweb.org/pubs

**American Geophysical Union (AGU)**
2000 Florida Ave NW, Washington, DC 20009-1277
SAN: 202-4489
*Tel:* 202-462-6900 *Toll Free Tel:* 800-966-2481 (North America) *Fax:* 202-328-0566
*E-mail:* service@agu.org
*Web Site:* www.agu.org
Founded: 1919
International scientific society with more than 50,000 members in over 135 countries. For over 80 years, AGU researchers, teachers & science administrators have dedicated themselves to advancing the understanding of earth & its environment in space. AGU now stands as a leader in the increasingly interdisciplinary global endeavor that encompasses the geophysical sciences.
ISBN Prefix(es): 978-0-87590
Number of titles published annually: 15 Print
Total Titles: 500 Print
Membership(s): AAP; Society for Scholarly Publishing

**American Girl Publishing**
Subsidiary of Mattel
8400 Fairway Place, Middleton, WI 53562
Mailing Address: PO Box 620497, Middleton, WI 53562-0497
*Tel:* 608-836-4848; 608-360-1861 (US & CN); 608-831-5210 (outside US & CN) *Toll Free Tel:* 800-233-0264; 800-360-1861 *Fax:* 608-836-1999
*Web Site:* www.americangirl.com
*Key Personnel*
Pres: Ellen L Brothers
Intl Rts: Jeff Meterval
Founded: 1986
Children's fiction & nonfiction.
ISBN Prefix(es): 978-0-937295; 978-1-56247; 978-1-58485
Number of titles published annually: 40 Print; 1 CD-ROM; 6 Audio
Total Titles: 350 Print; 3 CD-ROM; 18 Audio
Imprints: A G Fiction™; American Girl Library®; The American Girls Collection®
Membership(s): Children's Book Council

**§American Historical Association**
Affiliate of Historians Film Committee
400 "A" St SE, Washington, DC 20003-3889
*Tel:* 202-544-2422 *Fax:* 202-544-8307
*E-mail:* aha@historians.org; awards@historians.org
*Web Site:* www.historians.org
*Key Personnel*
Exec Dir: Jim Grossman
Deputy Dir: Robert B Townsend *Tel:* 202-544-2422 ext 118 *E-mail:* rtownsend@historians.org
Founded: 1884
The umbrella organization for the history profession.
ISBN Prefix(es): 978-0-87229
Number of titles published annually: 15 Print; 3 Online
Total Titles: 120 Print; 11 Online

**American Hospital Association Press**, see AHA Press

**American Industrial Hygiene Association - AIHA**
3141 Fairview Park Dr, Suite 777, Falls Church, VA 22042
*Tel:* 703-849-8888 *Fax:* 703-207-3561
*E-mail:* infonet@aiha.org
*Web Site:* www.aiha.org
*Key Personnel*
Mgr, Prod Devt: Katie Robert *Tel:* 703-846-0738 *E-mail:* krobert@aiha.org
Mgr, Cust & Career & Employment Servs: Wanda Barbour *Tel:* 703-846-0782 *E-mail:* wbarbour@aiha.org
Founded: 1939
Serves the needs of occupational & environmental health professionals practicing industrial hygiene in industry, government, labor, academic institutions & independent organizations.
ISBN Prefix(es): 978-1-931504
Number of titles published annually: 15 Print; 1 CD-ROM; 1 Online
Total Titles: 100 Print; 3 CD-ROM

**§American Institute for Economic Research (AIER)**
250 Division St, Great Barrington, MA 01230
Mailing Address: PO Box 1000, Great Barrington, MA 01230-1000
*Tel:* 413-528-1216 *Toll Free Tel:* 888-528-0103; 888-528-1216 (orders) *Fax:* 413-528-0103
*E-mail:* info@aier.org
*Web Site:* www.aier.org
*Key Personnel*
CEO & Pres: Steven Adams
Dir, Mktg: John Sylbert *Tel:* 413-528-1216 ext 3153

Libn: Samantha Woodson *Tel:* 413-528-1216 ext 3116
Founded: 1933
Conducts independent, scientific, economic research to educate individuals, thereby advancing their personal interests & those of the nation.
ISBN Prefix(es): 978-0-913610
Number of titles published annually: 3 Print; 8 Online; 4 E-Book
Total Titles: 50 Print; 46 Online; 4 E-Book

**American Institute of Aeronautics & Astronautics**
1801 Alexander Bell Dr, Suite 500, Reston, VA 20191-4344
*Tel:* 703-264-7500 *Toll Free Tel:* 800-639-AIAA (639-2422) *Fax:* 703-264-7551
*E-mail:* custserv@aiaa.org
*Web Site:* www.aiaa.org
*Key Personnel*
Exec Dir: Dr Sandra Magnus
Dir & Team Leader, Cust Serv: Aida Davis
Ed-in-Chief, Aerospace America: Elaine Camhi
Prod Mgr, Printing & Circ: Craig Byl
Prod Mgr: Heather Brennan
Mktg Strategist & Publicist: Laura Sherman
Founded: 1963
Professional technical books; archival journals & technical meeting papers in the science & technology of aerospace engineering & systems, print CD-ROMs & online delivery.
ISBN Prefix(es): 978-0-915928; 978-0-930403; 978-1-56347
Number of titles published annually: 20 Print
Total Titles: 600 Print
Foreign Rep(s): D A Direct (Australia)
*Distribution Center:* Books International Inc, PO Box 960, Dulles, VA 20172 *Tel:* 703-682-2422 *Toll Free Tel:* 800-682-2422 *Fax:* 703-661-1501 *E-mail:* warehouse@aiaa.org

**American Institute of Certified Public Accountants**, see AICPA Professional Publications

**§American Institute of Chemical Engineers (AIChE)**
3 Park Ave, 19th fl, New York, NY 10016-5991
*Tel:* 203-702-7660 *Toll Free Tel:* 800-242-4363 *Fax:* 203-775-5177
*E-mail:* custserv@aiche.org
*Web Site:* www.aiche.org
*Key Personnel*
Pres: Phillip Westmoreland
Exec Dir: June C Wispelwey *Tel:* 646-495-1310 *E-mail:* junew@aiche.org
Dir, Meeting & Conference Programming: Kristine Chin *Tel:* 646-495-1366 *E-mail:* krisc@aiche.org
Pubns Dir: Stephen R Smith *Tel:* 646-495-1360 *E-mail:* steps@aiche.org
Mktg & Communs: Tim McCreight *Tel:* 646-495-1325 *E-mail:* timm@aiche.org
Founded: 1908
Chemical engineering books & journals, technical manuals, symposia proceedings, directories, software, CD-ROM.
ISBN Prefix(es): 978-0-8169
Number of titles published annually: 15 Print; 4 CD-ROM
Total Titles: 300 Print; 4 CD-ROM
Distributed by Dechema (selected titles)
Distributor for ASM International (selected titles); Dechema (selected titles); Engineering Foundation; IchemE (selected titles)
Foreign Rep(s): Ric Bessford (Europe, UK); Patrick Connolly (Belgium, France, Switzerland)
*Distribution Center:* Institution of Chemical Engineers, Davis Bldg, 165-189 Railway Terr, Rugby CV21 3HQ, United Kingdom

**American Institute of Physics**
2 Huntington Quadrangle, Suite 1NO1, Melville, NY 11747
*Tel:* 516-576-2200; 301-209-3165 (orders) *Toll Free Tel:* 800-777-4643 (hardcover books) *Fax:* 516-349-7669; 301-209-0882 (orders)
*E-mail:* aipinfo@aip.org
*Web Site:* www.aip.org
*Key Personnel*
VP, Publg: John Haynes *Tel:* 516-576-2253
Founded: 1931
Publisher of conference proceedings, professional journals, magazines & books.
ISBN Prefix(es): 978-0-88318; 978-1-56396; 978-0-7354
Number of titles published annually: 13 Print; 8 CD-ROM; 3 Online
Total Titles: 700 Print; 200 Online
Distributed by Springer-Verlag
Membership(s): AAP

**§American Law Institute**
4025 Chestnut St, Philadelphia, PA 19104-3099
SAN: 204-756X
*Tel:* 215-243-1600 *Toll Free Tel:* 800-253-6397 *Fax:* 215-243-1664; 215-243-1683
*Web Site:* www.ali.org
*Key Personnel*
Pres: Roberta Cooper Ramo
Treas: Carolyn Dineen King
Dir: Lance Liebman
Dir, Off of Mktg: Amy Shapiro
Lib Dir: Harry Kyriakodis *Tel:* 215-243-1654
Founded: 1923
Professional & scholarly legal books & treatises.
ISBN Prefix(es): 978-0-8318
Number of titles published annually: 10 Print
Total Titles: 13 CD-ROM; 13 Online

**The American Library Association (ALA)**
50 E Huron St, Chicago, IL 60611
*Tel:* 312-944-6780 *Toll Free Tel:* 800-545-2433 *Fax:* 312-280-5275
*E-mail:* editionsmarketing@ala.org
*Web Site:* www.alastore.ala.org
*Key Personnel*
Mktg Mgr: Jill Davis *Tel:* 800-545-2433 ext 5418 *E-mail:* jdavis@ala.org
Founded: 1876
Publisher of titles for librarians & educators; library & information science, professional books.
ISBN Prefix(es): 978-0-8389
Number of titles published annually: 36 Print; 1 CD-ROM; 1 Online
Total Titles: 400 Print; 2 CD-ROM; 1 Online
Foreign Rep(s): Eurospan (Africa, Europe, Israel, UK)
Foreign Rights: Canadian Library Association (Canada); Inbooks (James Bennett) (Australia)
*Orders to:* ALA, PO Box 932501, Atlanta, GA 31193-2501 *Toll Free Tel:* 866-746-7252 *Fax:* 770-280-4155 *E-mail:* ala-orders@pbd.com *Web Site:* www.alastore.ala.org
*Returns:* ALA Distribution Center, 1650 Bluegrass Lakes Pkwy, Alpharetta, GA 30004-7735 *Tel:* 770-280-4185 *Fax:* 770-280-4155 *E-mail:* ala-orders@pbd.com
*Distribution Center:* ALA Distribution Center, 1650 Bluegrass Lakes Pkwy, Alpharetta, GA 30004-7735 *Tel:* 770-280-4185 *Fax:* 770-280-4155 *E-mail:* ala-orders@pbd.com
*See separate listing for:*
**Association of College & Research Libraries (ACRL)**

**American Map Corp**
Subsidiary of Langenscheidt Publishers Group
36-36 33 St, 4th fl, Long Island City, NY 11106
SAN: 202-4624
*Tel:* 718-784-0055 *Toll Free Tel:* 888-774-7979 *Fax:* 718-784-0640 (admin); 718-784-1216 (sales & orders)
*E-mail:* sales@americanmap.com
*Web Site:* www.americanmap.com
*Key Personnel*
Pres: John Muchnicki
Chmn: Andreas Langenscheidt
Dir, Cartography: Jenny Nichols
Dir, Mktg: Christine Ramos
Founded: 1923
Maps & atlases; charts.
ISBN Prefix(es): 978-0-8416
Number of titles published annually: 30 Print
Total Titles: 1 CD-ROM
Imprints: Cleartype American Map Corp; Colorprint American Map Corp
Subsidiaries: ADC the Map People; Arrow Maps Inc; Creative Sales Corp; Hagstrom Map Co Inc; Hammond World Atlas Corp; Trakker Maps Inc
Distributed by Arrow Maps Inc; Creative Sales Corp
Distributor for De Lorme Atlas; Langenscheidt Publishers Group; RV Guides; Stubs Magazine
*Advertising Agency:* ATL/SD, 46-35 54 Rd, Maspeth, NY 11378, Contact: Sara Ascalon *Tel:* 718-784-0555 *Fax:* 718-784-0640 *E-mail:* sascalon@americanmap.com
*See separate listing for:*
**Hagstrom Map & Travel Center**

**§American Marketing Association**
Division of Health Services Marketing Division
311 S Wacker Dr, Suite 5800, Chicago, IL 60606
*Tel:* 312-542-9000 *Toll Free Tel:* 800-AMA-1150 (262-1150) *Fax:* 312-542-9001
*E-mail:* info@ama.org
*Web Site:* www.marketingpower.com
*Key Personnel*
CEO: Dennis Dunlap
Mng Ed: Christopher Bartone *Tel:* 312-543-9000 ext 9029 *E-mail:* cbartone@ama.org
Founded: 1937
One of the largest professional associations for marketers, has members worldwide in every area of marketing. For 7 decades the AMA has been an essential resource providing relevant marketing information that experienced marketers turn to every day. AMA produces forward-thinking journals catered to marketing professionals & academicians on a variety of topics.
ISBN Prefix(es): 978-0-87757
Number of titles published annually: 9 Print
Total Titles: 60 Print

**American Mathematical Society**
201 Charles St, Providence, RI 02904-2294
SAN: 201-1654
*Tel:* 401-455-4000 *Toll Free Tel:* 800-321-4267 *Fax:* 401-331-3842; 401-455-4046 (cust serv)
*E-mail:* ams@ams.org; cust-serv@ams.org
*Web Site:* www.ams.org
*Key Personnel*
Exec Dir: Dr Donald E McClure
Publr: Dr Sergei Gelfand
Assoc Exec Dir: Elizabeth A Huber
Assoc Exec Dir, Washington, DC: Samuel M Rankin, III
Exec Ed, Ann Arbor, MI: Dr Graeme Fairweather
Founded: 1888
Membership society & publisher of mathematics.
ISBN Prefix(es): 978-0-8218; 978-0-8284
Number of titles published annually: 100 Print
Total Titles: 3,400 Print; 2 CD-ROM; 28 Online
Imprints: Chelsea Publishing Co Inc
*Branch Office(s)*
1527 18 St NW, Washington, DC 20036-1358 (government relations, science policy) *Tel:* 202-588-1100 *Fax:* 202-588-1853 *E-mail:* amsdc@ams.org

Mathematical Reviews, 416 Fourth St, Ann Arbor, MI 48107-4820 (editorial) *Tel:* 734-996-5250 *Fax:* 734-996-2916 *E-mail:* mathrev@ams.org
Secretary of the AMS - Society Governance, Mathematics Dept, University of Tennessee, 237 Ayres Hall, Knoxville, TN 37996-1320 *Tel:* 865-974-6900 *Fax:* 865-974-2892 *E-mail:* secretary@ams.org
Distributor for Annales de la faculte des sciences de Toulouse mathematiques; Bar-Ilan University; Brown University; European Mathematical Society; Hindustan Book Agency; Independent University of Moscow; International Press; Mathematica Josephina; Mathematical Society of Japan; Narosa Publishing House; Ramanujan Mathematical Society; Science Press New York & Science Press Beijing; Societe Mathematique de France; Tata Institute of Fundamental Research; Theta Foundation of Bucharest; University Press; Vieweg Verlag Publications
Foreign Rep(s): Hindustan Book Agency (India); India Book House Ltd (India); Maruzen Co Ltd (Japan); Narosa Book Distributors (India); Neutrino Inc (Japan); Oxford University Press (Africa, Europe, Middle East)
*Warehouse:* Pawtucket Warehouse, 35 Monticello Place, Pawtucket, RI 02861, Contact: Tom A Freitas *Tel:* 401-729-1440 *Fax:* 401-728-3564 *E-mail:* taf@ams.org
*Distribution Center:* Pawtucket Warehouse, 35 Monticello Place, Pawtucket, RI 02861, Contact: Tom A Freitas *Tel:* 401-729-1440 *Fax:* 401-728-3564 *E-mail:* taf@ams.org

**American Medical Association**
515 N State St, Chicago, IL 60654
*Tel:* 312-464-5000 *Toll Free Tel:* 800-621-8335 *Fax:* 312-464-4184
*Web Site:* www.ama-assn.org
*Key Personnel*
CEO & EVP: Dr James Madara
VP, Busn Prods: Anthony J Frankos *Tel:* 312-464-5000 ext 5488
Founded: 1847
Medical profession.
ISBN Prefix(es): 978-1-57947
Number of titles published annually: 30 Print
Total Titles: 150 Print
*Advertising Agency:* GSP Marketing Services Inc
*Warehouse:* Catalog Resources Inc, 100 Enterprise Dr, Dover, DE 19901
Membership(s): AAP

**American Numismatic Society**
75 Varick St, 11th fl, New York, NY 10013
*Tel:* 212-571-4470 *Fax:* 212-571-4479
*E-mail:* ans@numismatics.org
*Web Site:* www.numismatics.org
*Key Personnel*
Exec Dir: Ute Wartenberg Kagan
Ad Ed: Joanne Isaac *Tel:* 212-571-4470 ext 112
Founded: 1858
Scholarly materials.
ISBN Prefix(es): 978-0-89722
Number of titles published annually: 5 Print
Total Titles: 100 Print

**American Occupational Therapy Association Inc**
4720 Montgomery Lane, Bethesda, MD 20824
Mailing Address: PO Box 31220, Bethesda, MD 20824-1220
*Tel:* 301-652-2682 *Toll Free Tel:* 800-377-8555 *Fax:* 301-652-7711
*Web Site:* www.aota.org
*Key Personnel*
Dir: Chris Davis
Founded: 1918
Single titles, newsletters, journals & magazines.
ISBN Prefix(es): 978-0-910317; 978-1-56900
Number of titles published annually: 25 Print
Total Titles: 150 Print

**American Oil Chemists' Society**, see AOCS Press

**American Philosophical Society**
104 S Fifth St, Philadelphia, PA 19106
SAN: 206-9016
*Tel:* 215-440-3425 *Fax:* 215-440-3450
*E-mail:* dianepub@comcast.net
*Web Site:* www.amphilsoc.org
*Key Personnel*
Pres: Clyde F Barker
Exec Offr: Keith Thomson
Ed: Mary McDonald *E-mail:* mmcdonald@amphilsoc.org
Founded: 1743
Nonprofit educational institution for promotion of useful knowledge in humanities & sciences.
ISBN Prefix(es): 978-0-87169; 978-1-60618
Number of titles published annually: 13 Print
Total Titles: 1,000 Print
Imprints: Lightning Rod Press; Memoirs; Proceedings; Transactions
Distributed by Diane Publishing Co
*Billing Address:* Diane Publishing Co, APS Fulfillment, 330 Pusey Ave, Unit 3 (rear), Collingdale, PA 19023 *Tel:* 610-461-6200 *Toll Free Tel:* 800-782-3833 *Fax:* 610-461-6130 *E-mail:* dianepublishing@gmail.com
*Orders to:* Diane Publishing Co, APS Fulfillment, 330 Pusey Ave, Unit 3 (rear), Collingdale, PA 19023 *Tel:* 610-461-6200 *Toll Free Tel:* 800-782-3833 *Fax:* 610-461-6130 *E-mail:* orders@dianepublishing.net
*Warehouse:* Diane Publishing Co, Contact: Curtis Fisher *Tel:* 610-461-6200 *Toll Free Tel:* 800-782-3833

**§American Phytopathological Society (APS)**
3340 Pilot Knob Rd, St Paul, MN 55121
*Tel:* 651-454-7250 *Toll Free Tel:* 800-328-7560 *Fax:* 651-454-0766
*E-mail:* aps@scisoc.org
*Web Site:* www.apsnet.org
*Key Personnel*
EVP: Steven Nelson *Tel:* 651-994-3832 *E-mail:* snelson@scisoc.org
Pubns Mktg Dir: Greg Grahek *Tel:* 651-994-3841 *E-mail:* ggrahek@scisoc.org
Founded: 1908
Scientific materials.
ISBN Prefix(es): 978-0-89054
Number of titles published annually: 10 Print; 2 CD-ROM; 4 Online
Total Titles: 330 Print; 40 CD-ROM; 2 Online
*See separate listing for:*
**APS PRESS**

**American Press**
Subsidiary of American Magazine
60 State St, Suite 700, Boston, MA 02109
SAN: 210-7007
*Tel:* 617-247-0022
*E-mail:* americanpress@flash.net
*Web Site:* www.americanpresspublishers.com
*Key Personnel*
Publr: R K Fox
Ed: Marci Taylor
Founded: 1911
College textbooks, study guides, lab manuals & handbooks.
ISBN Prefix(es): 978-0-89641
Number of titles published annually: 20 Print
Total Titles: 300 Print

**§American Printing House for the Blind Inc**
1839 Frankfort Ave, Louisville, KY 40206
SAN: 203-5235
Mailing Address: PO Box 6085, Louisville, KY 40206-0085
*Tel:* 502-895-2405 *Toll Free Tel:* 800-223-1839 (cust serv) *Fax:* 502-899-2274
*E-mail:* info@aph.org
*Web Site:* www.aph.org; shop.aph.org
*Key Personnel*
Pres: Tuck Tinsley, III *E-mail:* ttinsley@aph.org
VP, Pub Aff: Gary Mudd *E-mail:* gmudd@aph.org
PR Mgr: Roberta Williams *Tel:* 502-899-2357 *E-mail:* rwilliams@aph.org
Founded: 1858
Literature & aids for people who are visually impaired: braille text books, magazines & other items, large-type textbooks, talking books & magazines, educational & miscellaneous aids, talking PC hardware & software. Publisher of braille & reprints in braille.
ISBN Prefix(es): 978-1-61648
Number of titles published annually: 4,500 Print
Total Titles: 6,300 Print

**American Products Publishing Co**
Division of American Products Corp
8260 SW Nimbus Ave, Beaverton, OR 97008
*Tel:* 503-672-7502 *Toll Free Tel:* 800-668-8181 *Fax:* 503-672-7104
*E-mail:* info@american-products.com
*Web Site:* www.american-products.com
*Key Personnel*
Pres: Robert Shangle
VP: Barbara Shangle *E-mail:* barbara@american-products.com
Sales Mgr: David Mulder
Publisher of scenic books & wall calendars for the individual US states, American historic documents, books & prints.
ISBN Prefix(es): 978-1-58583; 978-1-884958; 978-1-55988
Number of titles published annually: 16 Print; 72 Online
Total Titles: 72 Print; 72 Online
*Distribution Center:* Book Wholesalers
Membership(s): ABA

**§American Psychiatric Publishing (APP)**
Division of American Psychiatric Association (APA)
1000 Wilson Blvd, Suite 1825, Arlington, VA 22209
SAN: 293-2288
*Tel:* 703-907-7322 *Toll Free Tel:* 800-368-5777 *Fax:* 703-907-1091
*E-mail:* appi@psych.org
*Web Site:* www.appi.org; www.psychiatryonline.org
*Key Personnel*
Publr: Rebecca D Rhinehart *E-mail:* rrinehart@psych.org
Dir, Fin & Busn Opers: Kathy Stein
Dir, Sales & Mktg: Patrick Hansard *E-mail:* phansard@psych.org
Edit Dir: John McDuffie *Tel:* 703-907-7871 *E-mail:* jmcduffie@psych.org
Edit Dir, American Journal of Psychiatry: Michael Roy
Ed-in-Chief, Books: Robert E Hales, MD
Mng Ed, Books: Greg Kuny
Opers Mgr: Debra Eubanks
Founded: 1981
Professional, reference & general trade books, college textbooks; behavioral & social sciences, psychiatry, medicine.
ISBN Prefix(es): 978-0-88048; 978-0-89042; 978-0-87318; 978-1-58562
Number of titles published annually: 30 Print; 40 Online; 30 E-Book
Total Titles: 715 Print; 3 CD-ROM; 300 Online; 300 E-Book; 1 Audio
Imprints: American Psychiatric Association (APA); American Psychiatric Publishing (APP)

Distributor for American Psychiatric Association (APA); Group for the Advancement of Psychiatry
Foreign Rep(s): Cranberry International (Latin America); Footprint Books Pty Ltd (Australia, New Zealand); iGroup (China, East Asia, India); International Publishers Representatives (Middle East); Login Brothers (Canada); Nankodo (Japan); NBN International (Europe, UK); Oxford University Press (Southern Africa)
Foreign Rights: John Scott Agency
*Warehouse:* Ware-Pak, 2427 Bond St, University Park, IL 60484-3170
Membership(s): AAP; American Association of University Presses

**American Psychological Association**
750 First St NE, Washington, DC 20002-4242
*Tel:* 202-336-5500 *Toll Free Tel:* 800-374-2721 *Fax:* 202-336-5620
*E-mail:* order@apa.org
*Web Site:* www.apa.org/books
*Key Personnel*
Publr & Exec Dir, Pubns & Databases: Gary R Vanden Bos, PhD *Tel:* 202-336-5795
Exec Dir, Sci Directorate: Steven J Breckler, PhD *Tel:* 202-336-5938
Exec Dir, Public & Memb Communs: Rhea K Farberman *Tel:* 202-336-5709
Founded: 1892
Publish scholarly & professional works including books, journals & related materials; the PsycINFO database & products derived from that database; the *APA Monitor*, a monthly magazine & a variety of other products including brochures & reports.
ISBN Prefix(es): 978-0-912704; 978-1-55798
Number of titles published annually: 65 Print
Total Titles: 700 Print
*Warehouse:* APA Order Dept, PO Box 92984, Washington, DC 20090-2984

**American Public Works Association**
2345 Grand Blvd, Suite 700, Kansas City, MO 64108-2625
*Tel:* 816-472-6100 *Toll Free Tel:* 800-848-2792 *Fax:* 816-472-1610
*Web Site:* www.apwa.net
*Key Personnel*
Ed, APWA Reporter: Kevin Clark *Tel:* 816-595-5230 *E-mail:* kclark@apwa.net
Founded: 1894
Public work, related publications, Public works magazine, *APWA Reporter*.
ISBN Prefix(es): 978-0-917084
Number of titles published annually: 12 Print
Total Titles: 12 Print
*Branch Office(s)*
1275 "K" St, Suite 750, Washington, DC 20005 *Tel:* 202-408-9541 *Fax:* 202-408-9542

**American Quilter's Society**
5801 Kentucky Dam Rd, Paducah, KY 42003-9323
Mailing Address: PO Box 3290, Paducah, KY 42002-3290
*Tel:* 270-898-7903 *Toll Free Tel:* 800-626-5420 (orders) *Fax:* 270-898-1173
*Web Site:* www.americanquilter.com
*Key Personnel*
Founder & Pres: Meredith Schroeder
Founded: 1983
Publish books & magazines, distributes books & operates quilting shows.
ISBN Prefix(es): 978-0-89145; 978-1-57432
Number of titles published annually: 20 Print; 10 CD-ROM; 4 E-Book
Total Titles: 300 Print; 20 CD-ROM; 7 E-Book
Imprints: AQS

**American Society for Information Science & Technology (ASIS&T)**, see Association for Information Science & Technology (ASIS&T)

**American Society for Nondestructive Testing**
1711 Arlingate Lane, Columbus, OH 43228-0518
Mailing Address: PO Box 28518, Columbus, OH 43228-0518
*Tel:* 614-274-6003 *Toll Free Tel:* 800-222-2768 *Fax:* 614-274-6899
*Web Site:* www.asnt.org
*Key Personnel*
Sr Mgr, Pubns: Tim Jones *Tel:* 614-274-6003 ext 204
Founded: 1941
Nonprofit association producing educational materials for members & nonmembers engaged in nondestructive testing.
ISBN Prefix(es): 978-0-931403
Number of titles published annually: 12 Print; 6 CD-ROM
Total Titles: 250 Print; 6 CD-ROM
Distributed by American Ceramic Society (ACerS); American Society for Mechanical Engineers (ASME); American Society for Metals (ASM); The American Welding Society (AWS); ASTM; Edison Welding Institute; Mean Free Path

**§American Society for Quality (ASQ)**
600 N Plankinton Ave, Milwaukee, WI 53203
Mailing Address: PO Box 3005, Milwaukee, WI 53201-3005
*Tel:* 414-272-8575 *Toll Free Tel:* 800-248-1946 (US & CN); 800-514-1564 (Mexico) *Fax:* 414-272-1734
*E-mail:* help@asq.org
*Web Site:* www.asq.org
*Key Personnel*
Acq Ed: Matt Meinholz
Proj Ed: Paul O'Mara
Communs Mgr: Michael Berry
Founded: 1983
Publisher of technical books: quality, statistical process control, ISO9000, six sigma, QS9000, ISO14000, statistics, reliability, auditing, sampling, standards' supplier quality & quality costs. Also management topics: total quality management, human resources & teamwork, health care, government, education & benchmarking, quality tools.
ISBN Prefix(es): 978-0-87389
Number of titles published annually: 25 Print; 5 E-Book
Total Titles: 300 Print; 5 CD-ROM; 15 E-Book
Distributed by GOAL/QPC; IEEE Computer Society Press; McGraw-Hill Professional Publishing; Productivity Press
*Distribution Center:* PBD, 905 Carlow Dr, Unit B, Bolingbrook, WI 60490

**American Society for Training & Development (ASTD)**
1640 King St, Box 1443, Alexandria, VA 22313-1443
SAN: 224-8972
*Tel:* 703-683-8100 *Toll Free Tel:* 800-628-2783 *Fax:* 703-683-8103
*E-mail:* publications@astd.org
*Web Site:* www.astd.org
*Key Personnel*
Sr Dir, Pubns: Holly Nogas *Tel:* 703-683-8173 *E-mail:* hnogas@astd.org
Dir, Prodn: Glenn Lisa Saltzman *Tel:* 703-683-8165 *E-mail:* gsaltzman@astd.org
Dir, Pubns: Cat Russo *Tel:* 703-683-8136 *Fax:* 703-683-9591 *E-mail:* crusso@astd.org
Founded: 1944
Internationally renowned source of insightful & practical information on workplace learning & performance topics, including training basics, evaluation & return-on investment, instructional systems development, e-learning, leadership & career development.
ISBN Prefix(es): 978-0-201; 978-0-7755; 978-1-56286
Number of titles published annually: 25 Print; 4 CD-ROM
Total Titles: 200 Print
Imprints: ASTD Press
Distributed by Cengage Learning Asia Pte Ltd (Asia); Eurospan Group (Europe, Middle East & the former Soviet Bloc); Knowledge Resources (South Africa); National Book Network (NBN) (US, CN, Australia & New Zealand)

**§American Society of Agricultural Engineers (ASABE)**
2950 Niles Rd, St Joseph, MI 49085-9659
*Tel:* 269-429-0300 *Fax:* 269-429-3852
*E-mail:* hq@asabe.org
*Web Site:* www.asabe.org
*Key Personnel*
Exec Dir: Darrin Drollinger *Tel:* 269-932-7007
Dir, Pubns: Donna Hull *Tel:* 269-932-7026
Book & Journal Ed: Peg McCann *Tel:* 269-932-7019
Journal Ed: Glenn Laing *Tel:* 269-932-7014
Pubns Asst: Sandy Rutter *Tel:* 269-932-7004 *E-mail:* rutter@asabe.org
Founded: 1907
Agricultural, biological & food systems, books & journals.
ISBN Prefix(es): 978-0-916150; 978-0-929355
Number of titles published annually: 4 Print
Total Titles: 150 Print; 2 CD-ROM

**American Society of Agronomy**
5585 Guilford Rd, Madison, WI 53711-1086
*Tel:* 608-273-8080 *Fax:* 608-273-2021
*E-mail:* headquarters@sciencesocieties.org
*Web Site:* www.agronomy.org
*Key Personnel*
CEO: Ellen Bergfeld *Tel:* 608-268-4979 *E-mail:* ebergfeld@sciencesocieties.org
Dir, Pubns: Mark Mandelbaum *Tel:* 608-268-4974 *E-mail:* mmandelbaum@sciencesocieties.org
Founded: 1907
Technical books for professionals in agronomy; crop science, soil science, environmental sciences & related fields.
ISBN Prefix(es): 978-0-89118
Number of titles published annually: 12 Print
Total Titles: 90 Print

**§American Society of Civil Engineers (ASCE)**
1801 Alexander Bell Dr, Reston, VA 20191-4400
SAN: 204-7594
*Tel:* 703-295-6300 *Toll Free Tel:* 800-548-2723 *Fax:* 703-295-6278
*E-mail:* marketing@asce.org
*Web Site:* www.asce.org
*Key Personnel*
Mng Dir, Pubns: Bruce Gossett *Tel:* 703-295-6311 *E-mail:* bgossett@asce.org
Dir, Prodn: Matt Boyle *Tel:* 703-295-6133
Dir, Mktg: William D Farnam *Tel:* 703-295-6252 *E-mail:* wfarnam@asce.org
Dir, Journals: Angela Cochran *Tel:* 703-295-6242
Rts & Perms: Xi Van Fleet *Tel:* 703-295-6032 *E-mail:* xvanfleet@asce.org
Cust Rel: Laurena Lamberty *Tel:* 703-295-6245
Founded: 1852
Books, newsletters, journals, CD-ROM journals, magazines & information products on civil engineering & related fields.
ISBN Prefix(es): 978-0-87262; 978-0-7844
Number of titles published annually: 50 Print
Total Titles: 1,394 Print; 27 CD-ROM
Imprints: ASCE Press
Foreign Rep(s): Apex Knowledge SDN BHD (Brunei, Malaysia); Book Marketing Services (India, Madras); Booknet Co LTD (Cambodia, Laos, Myanmar, Thailand, Vietnam); D A

Books (Australia, New Zealand, Papua New Guinea); Eurospan Group (Africa, Continental Europe, Middle East, UK); ICaves Ltd (Hong Kong); IG Knowledge Services Ltd (Taiwan); IGP Services PTE LTD (Indonesia, Singapore); IGROUP Asia Pacific Ltd (China); MegaTexts Phil Inc (Philippines); Shinwon Datanet Inc (Korea)

**American Society of Electroneurodiagnostic Technologists Inc**
402 E Bannister Rd, Suite A, Kansas City, KS 64131-3019
*Tel:* 816-931-1120 *Fax:* 816-931-1145
*E-mail:* info@aset.org
*Web Site:* www.aset.org
*Key Personnel*
Mktg & Communs Mgr: Sarah Ecker *Tel:* 816-931-1120 ext 3 *E-mail:* sarah@aset.org
Founded: 1959
Books on EEG, evoked potentials, nerve conduction & polysomnography technology.
ISBN Prefix(es): 978-1-57797
Number of titles published annually: 8 Print
Total Titles: 55 Print; 59 CD-ROM

**§American Society of Health-System Pharmacists**
7272 Wisconsin Ave, Bethesda, MD 20814
*Tel:* 301-657-3000; 301-664-8700
*Toll Free Tel:* 866-279-0681 (orders) *Fax:* 301-657-1251 (orders)
*E-mail:* custserv@ashp.org
*Web Site:* www.ashp.org
*Key Personnel*
VP, Sales & Mktg: Dean Menke
Founded: 1943
Medical scholarly books.
ISBN Prefix(es): 978-0-930530; 978-1-879907; 978-1-58528
Number of titles published annually: 20 Print
Total Titles: 115 Print
Foreign Rep(s): APAC (Asia); L Horvath (Eastern Europe); LPR (Middle East); LR International (Brazil); R Seshadri (India)
*Advertising Agency:* Cunningham Associates, 180 Old Tappan Rd, Old Tappan, NJ 07675, Contact: Jim Pattis *Tel:* 201-767-4170 *E-mail:* jpattis@cunnasso.com

**American Society of Mechanical Engineers (ASME)**
3 Park Ave, New York, NY 10016-5990
SAN: 201-1379
*Tel:* 212-591-7000 *Toll Free Tel:* 800-843-2763 (cust serv-US, CN & Mexico) *Fax:* 212-591-7674; 973-882-8113 (cust serv); 973-882-1717 (orders & inquiries)
*E-mail:* infocentral@asme.org
*Web Site:* www.asme.org
*Key Personnel*
Exec Dir: Thomas Loughlin
Dir, Worldwide Mktg: Peter Hess *Tel:* 212-591-7024 *Fax:* 212-591-7061 *E-mail:* hessp@asme.org
Mng Dir, Publg: Philip Di Vietro *Tel:* 212-591-7696 *E-mail:* divietrop@asme.org
Ad Promo Mgr: Anthony Asiaghi *Tel:* 212-591-7345 *E-mail:* asiaghia@asme.org
Fulfillment Quality Assurance Mgr: John Yelavich *Tel:* 973-244-2213 *Fax:* 973-882-8113 *E-mail:* yelavichj@asme.org
Spec Sales Coord: Craig Backhus *Tel:* 973-244-2241 *E-mail:* backhusc@asme.org
Cust Sales: Paul Francis *Tel:* 973-244-2304; Mary Ellen Galvin *Tel:* 973-244-2312
Founded: 1880
Publisher of codes & standards, journals, conference proceedings, professional references, *Mechanical Engineering* magazine, technical papers & reports.
ISBN Prefix(es): 978-0-87053; 978-0-7918
Number of titles published annually: 185 Print
Total Titles: 1,500 Print
Imprints: ASME Press
*Branch Office(s)*
1828 "L" St NW, Suite 906, Washington, DC 20036-5104 *Tel:* 202-785-3756 *Fax:* 202-429-9417 *E-mail:* grdept@asme.org
*Billing Address:* ASME Accounts Payable, 22 Law Dr, Fairfield, NJ 07007-2900 *Tel:* 973-882-1170 *Fax:* 973-882-5155
*Warehouse:* 22 Law Dr, Fairfield, NJ 07007-2900 *Tel:* 973-882-1170 *Fax:* 973-882-5155

**American Society of Plant Taxonomists**
University of Michigan Herbarium, 3600 Varsity Dr, Ann Arbor, MI 48108-2228
SAN: 282-969X
*Tel:* 734-647-2812 *Fax:* 734-998-0038
*Web Site:* www.aspt.net
*Key Personnel*
Ed-in-Chief: Christiane Anderson *E-mail:* chra@umich.edu
Founded: 1980
Botanical monographs.
ISBN Prefix(es): 978-0-912861
Number of titles published annually: 3 Print
Total Titles: 100 Print

**American Technical Publishers Inc**
10100 Orland Pkwy, Suite 200, Orland Park, IL 60467-5756
SAN: 206-8141
*Tel:* 708-957-1100 *Toll Free Tel:* 800-323-3471 *Fax:* 708-957-1101
*E-mail:* service@americantech.net
*Web Site:* www.go2atp.com
*Key Personnel*
Pres & Treas: Robert D Deisinger *E-mail:* rdd@americantech.net
SVP: J David Holloway *E-mail:* jdh@americantech.net
Ed-in-Chief & Acqs: Jonathan F Gosse *E-mail:* jfg@americantech.net
Mfg Mgr: Christopher Proctor *E-mail:* ctp@americantech.net
Founded: 1898
Technical, industrial & vocational textbooks, reference books & related materials.
ISBN Prefix(es): 978-0-8269
Number of titles published annually: 8 Print; 2 CD-ROM; 25 Online; 3 E-Book
Total Titles: 200 Print; 10 CD-ROM; 25 Online; 3 E-Book
Distributor for Craftsman Book Co
*Orders to:* Nelson Publishing, 1120 Birchmount Rd, Toronto, ON M1K 5G4, Canada (CN school orders) *Tel:* 416-752-9448 *Toll Free Tel:* 800-268-2222
*Returns:* 1155 W 175 St, Homewood, IL 60430, Contact: Gail Prohaska

**American Traveler Press**, see Golden West Cookbooks

**§American Water Works Association**
6666 W Quincy Ave, Denver, CO 80235
*Tel:* 303-794-7711 *Toll Free Tel:* 800-926-7337 *Fax:* 303-347-0804
*Web Site:* www.awwa.org
*Key Personnel*
Deputy Exec Dir: Paula MacIlwaine *Tel:* 303-347-6135 *E-mail:* pmacilwa@awwa.org
Dir, Publg: Liz Haigh *Tel:* 303-347-6268 *E-mail:* lhaigh@awwa.org
Founded: 1881
Water works technology & management.
ISBN Prefix(es): 978-0-89867; 978-1-58321
Number of titles published annually: 50 Print
Total Titles: 500 Print; 12 CD-ROM; 2 Online
Imprints: AWWA
Distributor for CRC Press; McGraw-Hill; John Wiley & Sons
Foreign Rep(s): Australian Water & Wastewater Association (Australia); Canadian Water & Wastewater Association (Canada)
Membership(s): Association Media & Publishing; Publishers Association of the West

**Amherst Media Inc**
175 Rano St, Suite 200, Buffalo, NY 14207
*Tel:* 716-874-4450 *Toll Free Tel:* 800-622-3278 *Fax:* 716-874-4508
*E-mail:* marketing@amherstmedia.com
*Web Site:* www.amherstmedia.com
*Key Personnel*
Pres & Publr: Craig Alesse
Sales Mgr: Kathryn Kingsbury Neaverth *E-mail:* kneaverth@amherstmedia.com
Founded: 1979
Publish how-to photography books.
ISBN Prefix(es): 978-0-936262; 978-1-58428
Number of titles published annually: 24 Print
Total Titles: 300 Print
Distributor for Firefly

**Amicus**
PO Box 1329, Mankato, MN 56002
*Tel:* 507-388-9357 *Fax:* 507-388-1779
*E-mail:* info@amicuspublishing.us; orders@amicuspublishing.us
*Web Site:* www.amicuspublishing.us
*Key Personnel*
Publr: Rebecca Glaser *E-mail:* rglaser@amicuspublishing.us
Sales Mgr: Jonathan Strickland
Opers Mgr: Cathy Stuve *E-mail:* cstuve@amicuspublishing.us
Prodn Mgr: Heather Dreisbach *E-mail:* hdreisbach@amicuspublishing.us
Founded: 2010
Promotes the wonder, diversity & challenges of the modern world. From our line for grades K-2 to career advice & healthy living for middle school & everything in between, you'll find library-bound books that not only inform but also move readers past passive reading into critical thinking & deeper understanding.
ISBN Prefix(es): 978-1-19350
Number of titles published annually: 150 Print
Total Titles: 450 Print

**AMMO Books LLC**
300 S Raymond Ave, Suite 3, Pasadena, CA 91105
*Tel:* 323-223-AMMO (223-2666)
*Toll Free Tel:* 888-642-AMMO (642-2666)
*Fax:* 323-978-4200
*Web Site:* www.ammobooks.com
*Key Personnel*
Pres: Paul Norton *E-mail:* paul@ammobooks.com
Contact: Steve Crist
Founded: 2006
Provocative, one-of-a-kind titles that highlight the best of the visual arts & pop culture.
ISBN Prefix(es): 978-0-978607; 978-1-934429
Number of titles published annually: 5 Print
Total Titles: 45 Print

**§Ampersand Inc/Professional Publishing Services**
1050 N State St, Chicago, IL 60610
*Tel:* 312-280-8905 *Fax:* 312-944-1582
*E-mail:* info@ampersandworks.com
*Web Site:* www.ampersandworks.com
*Key Personnel*
Pres & Publr: Suzanne T Isaacs
Founded: 1995 (began publishing books as well as consulting in Fall 2005)
Private publisher. Work is highly customized, tailored to the author's specific objectives & developed by professionals with over 30 years of publishing experience. Able to publish from ms to finished book in a matter of weeks, on time & on budget. Also supports marketing efforts, warehouse & distributes authors' books.

This publisher has indicated that 90% of their product line is author subsidized.
ISBN Prefix(es): 978-1-4507; 978-0-9818126; 978-0-9761235
Number of titles published annually: 10 Print; 5 E-Book
Total Titles: 31 Print; 10 E-Book
*Branch Office(s)*
203 Finland Place, New Orleans, LA 70131
Membership(s): The Association of Publishers for Special Sales

**AMS Press Inc**
Brooklyn Navy Yard, Unit 221, 63 Flushing Ave, Brooklyn, NY 11205-1005
SAN: 201-1743
*Tel:* 718-875-8100 *Fax:* 718-875-3800
*E-mail:* editorial@amspressinc.com
*Web Site:* www.amspressinc.com
*Key Personnel*
Pres: Gabriel Hornstein
Founded: 1962
Original publications & reprint editions of scholarly books & periodicals; reference works.
ISBN Prefix(es): 978-0-404
Number of titles published annually: 65 Print
Total Titles: 6,500 Print

**Amsco School Publications Inc**
315 Hudson St, New York, NY 10013-1085
SAN: 201-1751
*Tel:* 212-886-6500; 212-886-6565 *Toll Free Tel:* 800-969-8398 *Fax:* 212-675-7010
*E-mail:* info@amscopub.com
*Web Site:* www.amscopub.com
*Key Personnel*
CEO: Laurence Beller
Pres: Henry Brun
VP, Sales & Mktg: Irene Rubin *E-mail:* irubin@amscopub.com
Dir, Mfg & Prodn: Joseph Campanella
Mfg Mgr: Valerie Mackross
Founded: 1935
El-hi textbooks.
ISBN Prefix(es): 978-0-87720; 978-1-56765
Number of titles published annually: 100 Print
Total Titles: 500 Print

**Anaphora Literary Press**
5755 E River Rd, No 2201, Tucson, AZ 85750
*Tel:* 520-425-4266
*Web Site:* anaphoraliterary.com
*Key Personnel*
Dir: Dr Anna Faktorovich *E-mail:* director@anaphoraliterary.com
Founded: 2009
Publishes paperback & hardcover originals of creative poetry, short stories, novels & novellas & nonfiction books: critical, academic & business. Writers who are employed in the academia are especially encouraged to e-mail submissions. Offers a 50/50% split on profits, a 25-50% discount on the cover price to authors & a 55% discount to book stores & distributors. Please e-mail submissions only. Do not send submissions through the mail. Some marketing is provided, but assistance with marketing from writers is strongly encouraged. Submissions are primarily evaluated on writing quality.
ISBN Prefix(es): 978-1-937536
Number of titles published annually: 30 Print; 3 Online; 1 E-Book
Total Titles: 62 Print; 12 Online; 2 E-Book
Distributed by Coutts Information Services; Lightning Source
Membership(s): Council of Literary Magazines & Presses; Independent Book Publishing Professionals Group; MLA

**Anchor Group Publishing**
PO Box 551, Flushing, MI 48433
*E-mail:* anchorgrouppublishing@gmail.com
*Web Site:* anchorgrouppublishing.com
*Key Personnel*
Owner & CEO: Stacey Rourke *Tel:* 810-964-3767
Founded: 2011
Independently owned, traditional publisher of quality literary works meant to engage & inspire readers.
ISBN Prefix(es): 978-0-9852663; 978-0-9855385; 978-0-9886334
Number of titles published annually: 15 Print; 15 Online; 15 E-Book
Total Titles: 30 Print; 30 Online; 30 E-Book
Membership(s): IBPA, the Independent Book Publishers Association

**§Andrews McMeel Publishing LLC**
Division of Andrews McMeel Universal
1130 Walnut St, Kansas City, MO 64106-2109
*Toll Free Tel:* 800-851-8923; 800-943-9839 (cust serv) *Toll Free Fax:* 800-943-9831 (orders)
*Web Site:* www.andrewsmcmeel.com
*Key Personnel*
Chmn: John P McMeel
CEO & Pres: Hugh Andrews
Pres, Book Div: Kirsty Melville
SVP: Linda Jones
VP & Ed Dir, Calendar Div & Prod Devt Group: Michael Nonbello
VP, Content & Exec Prodr, Book Division: Andrea Colvin
VP, Mktg: Amy Worley
Founded: 1973
Publish calendars & humor.
ISBN Prefix(es): 978-88-7407
Number of titles published annually: 163 Print
Imprints: Accord Publishing; Udig (ebooks)
Distributor for Gooseberry Patch (North America); Signatures Network; Sporting News; Universe Publishing Calendars
Foreign Rights: Agenzia Letteraria Internazionale (Italy); Big Apple Agency Inc (China, Taiwan); The Book Publishers' Association of Israel, International Promotion & Literary Rights Department (Israel); DS Druck und Verlag (Eastern Europe); Europa Press (Scandinavia); Gamma Medya Agency (Turkey); Agence Hoffman (Germany); Japan UNI Agency Inc (Japan); JLM Literary Agents (Greece); Korea Copyright Center Inc (KCC) (Korea); Andrew Nurnberg Associates Ltd (Bulgaria); Abner Stein Agency (Australia, UK); Tuttle-Mori Agency Inc (Thailand); VVV Agency (France); Julio F Yanez, Agencia Literaria S L (Brazil, Latin America, Portugal, Spain)
*Orders to:* c/o Simon & Schuster Inc, 100 Front St, Riverside, NJ 08075
*Returns:* Simon & Schuster c/o Arnold Logistics, 4406 Industrial Park Rd, Bldg 7, Camp Hill, PA 17011
*Distribution Center:* Simon & Schuster, Inc, 100 Front St, Riverside, NJ 08075 *Toll Free Tel:* 800-268-3216

**Andrews University Press**
Division of Andrews University
Sutherland House, 8360 W Campus Circle Dr, Berrien Springs, MI 49104-1700
SAN: 241-0958
*Tel:* 269-471-6915; 269-471-6134 (orders) *Toll Free Tel:* 800-467-6369 (Visa, MC & American Express orders only) *Fax:* 269-471-6224
*E-mail:* aupo@andrews.edu
*Web Site:* www.universitypress.andrews.edu
*Key Personnel*
Dir: Ronald Knott
Selected areas of theology, education, philosophy, science, faith & learning.
ISBN Prefix(es): 978-0-943872; 978-1-883925
Number of titles published annually: 5 Print
Total Titles: 100 Print; 1 CD-ROM; 1 Online

**Angel City Press**
2118 Wilshire Blvd, Suite 880, Santa Monica, CA 90403
*Tel:* 310-395-9982 *Toll Free Tel:* 800-949-8039 *Fax:* 310-395-3353
*E-mail:* info@angelcitypress.com
*Web Site:* www.angelcitypress.com
*Key Personnel*
CEO & Publr: Paddy Calistro
Treas: Scott McAuley
Founded: 1992
Publish books on California & Southern California social & cultural history.
ISBN Prefix(es): 978-1-883318
Number of titles published annually: 8 Print
Total Titles: 70 Print
Distributor for Los Angeles Times Books
Foreign Rep(s): Turnaround Publishing Services (London)

**Angelus Press**
2915 Forest Ave, Kansas City, MO 64109
*Tel:* 816-753-3150 *Toll Free Tel:* 800-966-7337 *Fax:* 816-753-3557
*E-mail:* info@angeluspress.org
*Web Site:* www.angeluspress.org
*Key Personnel*
Ed: James Vogel
Founded: 1978
Monthly journal of Catholic Tradition; traditional Roman Catholic books.
ISBN Prefix(es): 978-0-935952; 978-1-892331
Number of titles published annually: 10 Print
Total Titles: 100 Print
Distributed by Catholic Treasures; Fatima Crusader

**Anhinga Press**
PO Box 3665, Tallahassee, FL 32315
*Tel:* 850-442-1408 *Fax:* 850-442-6323
*E-mail:* info@anhinga.org
*Web Site:* www.anhinga.org
*Key Personnel*
Dir & Intl Rts: Rick Campbell
Founded: 1972
ISBN Prefix(es): 978-0-938078
Number of titles published annually: 8 Print
Total Titles: 70 Print
*Distribution Center:* SPD/Small Press Distribution Inc, 1341 Seventh St, Berkeley, CA 94710-1409

**Ann Arbor Media Group**, see Spry Publishing

**Annual Reviews**
4139 El Camino Way, Palo Alto, CA 94306
SAN: 201-1816
Mailing Address: PO Box 10139, Palo Alto, CA 94303-0139
*Tel:* 650-493-4400 *Toll Free Tel:* 800-523-8635 *Fax:* 650-424-0910
*E-mail:* service@annualreviews.org
*Web Site:* www.annualreviews.org
*Key Personnel*
Pres & Ed-in-Chief: Samuel Gubins *E-mail:* sgubins@annualreviews.org
Mng Ed: Jennifer Jongsma *E-mail:* jjongsma@annualreviews.org
Mktg Mgr: Gabrielle Peterson *E-mail:* gpeterson@annualreviews.org
Mktg Specialist: Jenni Rankin *E-mail:* jrankin@annualreviews.org
Founded: 1932
Scientific review literature, in print & online, in the biomedical, life, physical & social sciences.
ISBN Prefix(es): 978-0-8243
Number of titles published annually: 40 Print; 40 Online
Foreign Rep(s): Gazelle Book Services Ltd (Africa, Continental Europe, Ireland, Middle East, UK); SARAS Books (Bangladesh, India, Pakistan, Sri Lanka)

*Returns:* National Distribution Services, 6118 Kingsport Hwy, Gray, TN 37615 (return authorization required)
Membership(s): ALA; International Federation of Library Associations & Institutions; Medical Library Association; National Federation of Advanced Information Services; SLA; Society for Scholarly Publishing; STM

**§ANR Publications University of California**
Division of Agriculture & Natural Resources, University of California
1301 S 46 St, Bldg 478 - MC 3580, Richmond, CA 94804
*Tel:* 510-665-2195 (cust serv) *Toll Free Tel:* 800-994-8849 *Fax:* 510-665-3427
*E-mail:* anrcatalog@ucdavis.edu
*Web Site:* anrcatalog.ucanr.edu
*Key Personnel*
Mktg Dir & Foreign Rts: Cynthia Kintigh *Tel:* 530-754-3911 *E-mail:* cckintigh@ucanr.edu
Mktg Coord: Marissa Palin *Tel:* 530-754-3934 *E-mail:* mpalin@ucanr.edu
Fulfillment Mgr: Jon Mercy *Tel:* 510-665-2161 *E-mail:* jrmercy@ucanr.edu
Cust Serv: Mary Allen-Crowley *Tel:* 510-665-2162
Peer reviewed publications on agriculture, gardening, integrated pest management, nutrition, childhood obesity & natural resources.
ISBN Prefix(es): 978-0-931876; 978-1-879906; 978-1-60107
Number of titles published annually: 16 Print; 2 CD-ROM; 30 Online; 5 E-Book
Total Titles: 850 Print; 15 CD-ROM; 500 Online; 5 E-Book
*Editorial Office(s):* 1850 Research Park Dr, Suite 200, Davis, CA 95618, Prodn Mgr: Ann Senuta *Tel:* 530-754-3908 *E-mail:* aesenuta@ucanr.edu
Membership(s): Publishers Association of the West

**§Antion & Associates**
PO Box 9558, Virginia Beach, VA 23450
*Tel:* 757-431-1366 *Toll Free Tel:* 800-448-6280 *Fax:* 757-431-2050
*E-mail:* orders@antion.com
*Web Site:* www.antion.com
*Key Personnel*
Owner: Thomas Antion
Founded: 1988
Electronic publishing only, query first.
ISBN Prefix(es): 978-0-926395
Number of titles published annually: 5 Print
Total Titles: 15 Print

**Antique Collectors Club Ltd**
Division of Antique Collectors Club Ltd (England)
116 Pleasant St, Suite 18, East Hampton, MA 01027
*Tel:* 413-529-0861 *Toll Free Tel:* 800-252-5231 *Fax:* 413-529-0862
*E-mail:* sales@antiquecc.com
*Web Site:* www.accdistribution.com
*Key Personnel*
Div Dir & Intl Rts: John Boncottie
Founded: 1966
Books on fine & decorative arts, gardening, architecture & antiques, multicultural.
ISBN Prefix(es): 978-1-85149; 978-0-907462; 978-0-902028; 978-0-906610; 978-0-9627359; 978-0-904017
Number of titles published annually: 300 Print
Total Titles: 1,500 Print
Imprints: ACC Editions; Garden Art Press
Divisions: ACC Distribution
*Foreign Office(s):* Sandy Lane, Old Martlesham, Woodbridge, Suffolk 1P12 4SD, United Kingdom *Tel:* (01394) 389950 *Fax:* (01394) 389999 *E-mail:* sales@antique-acc.com
Distributor for Acatos; Adler Planetarium & Astronomy; Umberto Allemandi; Architectura & Natura; Arnoldsche; Arsenale Editrice; Artprice.com; Bard Graduate Center; Barn Elms Publishing; Beagle Press; Chris Beetles Ltd; Benteli Verlag; Birmingham Museum of Art; Brioni Books; British Museum Press; Canal & Stamperia; Cartago; Colonial Williamsburg; Colophon; Colwood Press Ltd; The William G Congdon Foundation; Conran Octopus; Alain De Gourcuff Editeur; M H De Young Memorial Museum; Detroit Institute of Arts; Editoriale Jaca Book; Elvehjem Museum of Art; Grayson Publishing; Hachette Livre; Robert Hale; Han-Shan Tang Books; Alan Hartman; High Museum of Art; Images Publications; India Book House Ltd; Frances Lincoln; Loft Publications; Mapin; Marshall Editions; Merrick & Day; Museum of American Folk Art; National Galleries of Scotland; National Portrait Gallery; The National Trust; New Architecture Group Ltd; New Cavendish Books Ltd; Newark Museum; Packard Publishing; Peabody Essex Museum; Philadelphia Museum of Art; River Books Co Ltd; Gambero Rosso; Michael Russell; Scala Publishers; Superbrands Ltd; Third Millenium Publishing; Wadsworth Athenaeum; Wallace Collection; Watermark Press; Websters International Publishers; Philip Wilson Publishers
Foreign Rep(s): Jenny Gosling (Belgium, London, Luxembourg, Netherlands); Lilian Koe (Malaysia); Clive & Moira Malins (Northeast England, Scotland); Michael Morris (Middle East, Near East); Penny Padovani (Italy, Portugal, Spain); David Pearson (France); Ian Pringle (Brunei, Indonesia, Singapore, Thailand); Ed Summerson (China, Hong Kong, Philippines, South Korea, Taiwan); Ralph & Sheila Sumners (Japan); Robert Towers (Ireland, Northern Ireland)

**Antique Trader Books**
Imprint of Krause Publications Inc
c/o Krause Publications, 700 E State St, Iola, WI 54990-0001
*Tel:* 715-445-2214 *Toll Free Tel:* 888-457-2873 *Fax:* 715-445-4087
*Web Site:* www.krause.com
*Key Personnel*
Ed & Online Content Mgr: Eric Bradley
Founded: 1952
Collectibles, books, magazines, trades & crafts.
ISBN Prefix(es): 978-0-930625; 978-1-58221
Number of titles published annually: 20 Print
Total Titles: 200 Print

**Antrim House**
21 Goodrich Rd, Simsbury, CT 06070-1804
Mailing Address: PO Box 111, Tariffville, CT 06081
*Tel:* 860-217-0023 *Fax:* 860-217-0023
*E-mail:* eds@antrimhousebooks.com
*Web Site:* www.antrimhousebooks.com
*Key Personnel*
Ed: Robert McQuilkin
Founded: 1990
Publish cloth bound editions, perfect bound paperbacks & saddle stitched chapbooks by poets & memoirists. Also a limited number of art books. On occasion, issue CDs by these poets.
This publisher has indicated that 100% of their product line is author subsidized.
ISBN Prefix(es): 978-0-9662783; 978-0-9792226; 978-0-9770633; 978-0-9762091
Number of titles published annually: 16 Print; 2 Audio
Total Titles: 96 Print; 1 Audio
Membership(s): IBPA, the Independent Book Publishers Association

**AOCS Press**
Division of American Oil Chemists' Society
2710 S Boulder Dr, Urbana, IL 61802-6996
Mailing Address: PO Box 17190, Urbana, IL 61803-7190
*Tel:* 217-359-2344 *Fax:* 217-351-8091
*E-mail:* general@aocs.org
*Web Site:* www.aocs.org
*Key Personnel*
EVP: Pat Donnelly *Tel:* 217-359-2344 ext 147
Founded: 1909
Journals & monographs.
ISBN Prefix(es): 978-0-935315; 978-1-893997
Number of titles published annually: 10 Print; 5 CD-ROM
Total Titles: 100 Print; 21 CD-ROM; 2 Audio

**APA Planners Press**
Division of American Planning Association
205 N Michigan Ave, Suite 1200, Chicago, IL 60601
*Tel:* 312-431-9100 *Fax:* 312-786-6700
*E-mail:* customerservice@planning.org
*Web Site:* www.planning.org
*Key Personnel*
Dir, Pubns: Sylvia Lewis *Tel:* 312-786-6370 *E-mail:* slewis@planning.org
Sr Ed: Timothy Mennel *E-mail:* tmennel@planning.org
Founded: 1978
Books on planning.
ISBN Prefix(es): 978-0-918286; 978-1-884829; 978-1-932364
Number of titles published annually: 8 Print
Total Titles: 120 Print; 15 Audio
*Warehouse:* Ware-Pak, PO Box 2516, Cedar Rapids, IA 52406 *Tel:* 319-365-2518 *Fax:* 319-364-3426

**Aperture Books**
Division of Aperture Foundation Inc
547 W 27 St, 4th fl, New York, NY 10001
SAN: 201-1832
*Tel:* 212-505-5555 *Toll Free Tel:* 800-929-2323 *Fax:* 212-979-7759
*E-mail:* info@aperture.org
*Web Site:* www.aperture.org
*Key Personnel*
Exec Dir: Chris Boot
Publr: Lesley Martin
Intl Rts Contact: Kristian Orozco
Founded: 1952
Quarterly magazine; books on photography as fine art, history of photography, photojournalism, environment.
ISBN Prefix(es): 978-0-89381
Number of titles published annually: 25 Print
Total Titles: 250 Print
Imprints: Aperture Monographs; Masters of Photography; Writers & Artists on Photography Series
Distributed by Farrar, Straus & Giroux Inc
Foreign Rep(s): General Publishing (Canada); Robert Hale Ltd (UK); InterArt (France); Nilsson & Lamm (Belgium, Netherlands); Onslow Books Ltd (Western Europe); Penny Padavon (Greece, Italy, Portugal, Spain); Southern Publisher (New Zealand); Tower (Australia); Roger Ward (East Asia)
*Shipping Address:* Farrar, Straus & Giroux, c/o MPS 16365 James Madison Hwy, Gordonsville, VA 22942

**The Apex Press**
Imprint of Rowman & Littlefield Publishers Inc
4501 Forbes Blvd, Suite 200, Lanham, MD 20706
SAN: 281-8752
*Tel:* 301-459-3366 *Toll Free Tel:* 800-462-6420 *Toll Free Fax:* 800-388-4450
*E-mail:* customercare@rowman.com
*Key Personnel*
VP, Mktg & Sales: Linda May
HR Mgr: Jamie Goodman *Tel:* 301-459-3366 ext 5004 *E-mail:* jdgoodman@rowman.com

Publicity Mgr: Sam Caggiula *Tel:* 301-459-3366 ext 5628 *E-mail:* SCaggiula@rowman.com
Publicist & Ad Mgr: Lisa McAllister *Tel:* 301-459-3366 ext 5619 *E-mail:* LMcAllister@rowman.com
Founded: 1990
Specialize in books on education, economics, social & political issues, human rights, corporate power.
ISBN Prefix(es): 978-0-945257; 978-0-938960 (CITE); 978-1-891843
Number of titles published annually: 8 Print
Total Titles: 100 Print
Imprints: Policy Studies Associates (PSA)
Distributor for Bootstrap Press (US); The Other India Press (India)
*Billing Address:* PO Box 337, Croton-on-Hudson, NY 10520-0337
*Returns:* Whitehurst & Clark, c/o Apex Press, 1200 County Rd, Rte 523, Flemington, NJ 08822
*Shipping Address:* Whitehurst & Clark, c/o Apex Press, 1200 County Rd, Rte 523, Flemington, NJ 08822

**The Apocryphile Press**
1700 Shattuck Ave, Suite 81, Berkeley, CA 94709
*Tel:* 510-290-4349
*E-mail:* apocryphile@earthlink.net
*Web Site:* www.apocryphile.org
*Key Personnel*
Publr: John R Mabry
Founded: 1994
ISBN Prefix(es): 978-1-933993
Number of titles published annually: 12 Print
Total Titles: 140 Print

**Apogee Press**
2308 Sixth St, Berkeley, CA 94710
*E-mail:* editors.apogee@gmail.com
*Web Site:* www.apogeepress.com
*Key Personnel*
Ed: Alice Jones; Edward Smallfield *Tel:* 510-845-8800
Founded: 1998
Publishes innovative poetry with an emphasis on West Coast writers.
ISBN Prefix(es): 978-0-9669937; 978-0-9744687
Number of titles published annually: 3 Print
Total Titles: 29 Print
*Orders to:* Small Press Distribution, 1341 Seventh St, Berkeley, CA 94710-1409, Contact: Laura Moriarty *Toll Free Tel:* 800-869-7553 *Fax:* 510-524-1563 *E-mail:* spd@spdbooks.org
*Returns:* Small Press Distribution, 1341 Seventh St, Berkeley, CA 94710-1409, Contact: Laura Moriarty *Toll Free Tel:* 800-869-7553 *Fax:* 510-524-1563 *E-mail:* spd@spdbooks.org
*Shipping Address:* Small Press Distribution, 1341 Seventh St, Berkeley, CA 94710-1409, Contact: Laura Moriarty *Toll Free Tel:* 800-869-7553 *E-mail:* spd@spdbooks.org
*Warehouse:* Small Press Distribution, 1341 Seventh St, Berkeley, CA 94710-1409 *Toll Free Tel:* 800-869-7553 *E-mail:* spd@spdbooks.org
*Distribution Center:* Small Press Distribution, 1341 Seventh St, Berkeley, CA 94710-1409, Contact: Laura Moriarty *Toll Free Tel:* 800-869-7553 *Fax:* 510-524-1563
Membership(s): Council of Literary Magazines & Presses

**Apollo Managed Care Inc**
1651 Foothill Blvd, Santa Ana, CA 92705
*Tel:* 805-969-2606 *Fax:* 805-969-3749
*E-mail:* apollomanagedcare@cox.net
*Web Site:* www.apollomanagedcare.com
*Key Personnel*
CEO: Dr Margaret Bischel *E-mail:* mbischel@cox.net
Founded: 1987
Publish medical publications.
ISBN Prefix(es): 978-1-893826
Number of titles published annually: 5 Print; 1 CD-ROM; 5 Online
Total Titles: 40 Print; 1 CD-ROM; 40 Online
Distributed by Health Information Network; MarketResearch.com; Researchandmarkets.com

**APPA: The Association of Higher Education Facilities Officers**
1643 Prince St, Alexandria, VA 22314-2818
*Tel:* 703-684-1446 *Fax:* 703-549-2772
*Web Site:* www.appa.org
*Key Personnel*
Dir, Knowledge Mgmt: Steve Glazner *E-mail:* steve@appa.org
Pubn Mgr: Anita Dosik *E-mail:* anita@appa.org
Founded: 1914
All titles seek to enhance the development of leadership & professional management applicable to the planning, design, construction & operation of higher education facilities.
ISBN Prefix(es): 978-0-913359; 978-1-890956
Number of titles published annually: 5 Print
Total Titles: 60 Print
*Branch Office(s)*
APPA Publications, PO Box 1201, Alexandria, VA 22313-1201
*Distribution Center:* 13119 Pelfrey Lane, Fairfax, VA 22033

**Appalachian Mountain Club Books**
Division of Appalachian Mountain Club
5 Joy St, Boston, MA 02108
SAN: 203-4808
*Tel:* 617-523-0655 *Fax:* 617-523-0722
*Web Site:* www.outdoors.org
*Key Personnel*
Publr: Kevin Breunig *Tel:* 617-523-0655 ext 6573 *E-mail:* kbreunig@outdoors.org
Publr, AMC Books: Heather Stephenson *E-mail:* hstephenson@outdoors.org
Founded: 1897
Guidebooks, maps, outdoor recreation & conservation, mountain history, nature & travel for Northeast US.
ISBN Prefix(es): 978-0-910146; 978-1-878239; 978-1-929173
Number of titles published annually: 20 Print
Total Titles: 110 Print
Imprints: AMC Discover Series; AMC Nature Walks Series; AMC Quiet Water Guides; AMC River Guides; AMC Trail Guides
Distributed by The Globe Pequot Press
Foreign Rep(s): Canadian Manda Group (Canada); Windsor Books Ltd (Europe)
*Warehouse:* The Globe Pequot Press Inc, 246 Goose Lane, Guilford, CT 06437-0480 *Tel:* 203-455-4547 *Toll Free Tel:* 800-962-0973 *Fax:* 860-395-2855 *Web Site:* www.globe-pequot.com

**Appalachian Trail Conservancy**
799 Washington St, Harpers Ferry, WV 25425
Mailing Address: PO Box 807, Harpers Ferry, WV 25425-0807
*Tel:* 304-535-6331 *Toll Free Tel:* 888-287-8673 (orders only) *Fax:* 304-535-2667
*E-mail:* info@appalachiantrail.org
*Web Site:* www.appalachiantrail.org; www.atctrailstore.org
*Key Personnel*
Dir, Pub Aff: Brian B King
Founded: 1925
Books related to the Appalachian Trail.
ISBN Prefix(es): 978-0-917953; 978-1-889386
Number of titles published annually: 5 Print
Total Titles: 46 Print
*Distribution Center:* 179 E Burr Blvd, Unit N, Kearneysville, WV 25430

**Applause Theatre & Cinema Books**
Imprint of Hal Leonard Performing Arts Publishing Group
33 Plymouth St, Suite 302, Montclair, NJ 07042
*Tel:* 973-337-5034 *Toll Free Tel:* 800-637-2852 *Fax:* 973-337-5227
*E-mail:* info@applausepub.com
*Web Site:* www.applausepub.com
*Key Personnel*
Group Publr: John Cerullo *E-mail:* jcerullo@halleonard.com
Founded: 1983
Plays, theatre books, cinema books, entertainment, television; including DVDs.
ISBN Prefix(es): 978-0-936839; 978-1-55783
Number of titles published annually: 16 Print
Total Titles: 1,000 Print
*Sales Office(s):* 7777 W Bluemound Rd, Milwaukee, WI 53213
Distributed by Hal Leonard Corp
Distributor for The Working Arts Library; Glenn Young Books
*Billing Address:* 960 E Mark St, Winona, MN 55987
*Orders to:* 7777 W Blue Mound Rd, Milwaukee, WI 53213 *Toll Free Tel:* 800-554-0626
*Returns:* 960 E Mark St, Winona, MN 55987
*Warehouse:* 960 E Mark St, Winona, MN 55987 *Tel:* 507-454-2920 *Fax:* 507-454-8334

**Appletree Press Inc**
151 Good Counsel Dr, Suite 125, Mankato, MN 56001
*Tel:* 507-345-4848 *Toll Free Tel:* 800-322-5679 *Fax:* 507-345-3002
*E-mail:* eatwell@hickorytech.net
*Web Site:* www.appletreepress.com; www.appletree-press.com; www.letscookhealthymeals.com; www.appletree-press.us
*Key Personnel*
CEO & Publr: Linda Hachfeld *E-mail:* lindah@hickorytech.net
Founded: 1989
Independent health & nutrition publisher of cookbooks, food diaries, journaling tools & nutrition reference books. Focus on heart health, diabetes management, weight management, arthritis, vegetarian cooking, "how to" cookbooks for & by people with intellectual & developmental disabilities.
ISBN Prefix(es): 978-1-891011; 978-0-962047
Number of titles published annually: 3 Print
Total Titles: 20 Print
Imprints: On My Own (pictorial cookbooks for individuals with special needs; intellectual & developmental disabilities)
Membership(s): American Dietetic Association; The Association of Publishers for Special Sales; IBPA, the Independent Book Publishers Association; Midwest Independent Publishers Association

**Applewood Books Inc**
One River Rd, Carlisle, MA 01741
Mailing Address: PO Box 365, Bedford, MA 01730 SAN: 210-3419
*Tel:* 781-271-0055 *Fax:* 781-271-0056
*E-mail:* applewood@awb.com
*Web Site:* www.awb.com
*Key Personnel*
Pres & ISBN Contact: Phil Zuckerman *E-mail:* philz@awb.com
VP, Opers: Sue Cabezas *E-mail:* suec@awb.com
Founded: 1976
Americana reprints.
ISBN Prefix(es): 978-0-918222; 978-1-55709
Number of titles published annually: 500 Print
Total Titles: 4,000 Print
*Warehouse:* Ingram Publishers Services, 1280 Ingram Dr, Chambersburg, PA 17201
*See separate listing for:*
**Commonwealth Editions**

**Appraisal Institute**
200 W Madison, Suite 1500, Chicago, IL 60606
*Tel:* 312-335-4100 *Toll Free Tel:* 888-756-4624 *Fax:* 312-335-4400
*Web Site:* www.appraisalinstitute.org
*Key Personnel*
Sr Mgr, Pubns: Tep Shea-Joyce *E-mail:* tshea-joyce@appraisalinstitute.org
Founded: 1932
Professional real estate appraisal books, monographs, periodicals & videos.
ISBN Prefix(es): 978-0-911780; 978-0-922154
Number of titles published annually: 6 Print
Total Titles: 60 Print
Distributed by Dearborn Trade
Foreign Rep(s): Royal Institution of Chartered Surveyors (Africa, Caribbean, Commonwealth, Ethiopia, Europe, Far East)
*Distribution Center:* Appraisal Institute, c/o Grubb & Ellis, 55 Chastain Rd, Suite 107, Kennesaw, GA 30144 *Toll Free Tel:* 800-504-7440 *Fax:* 770-427-2254 *Web Site:* www.appraisalinstitute.org

**Apprentice Shop Books LLC**
18 Wentworth Dr, Bedford, NH 03110
Mailing Address: PO Box 375, Amherst, NH 03031
*Tel:* 603-472-8741 *Fax:* 603-472-2323
*E-mail:* info@apprenticeshopbooks.com
*Web Site:* www.apprenticeshopbooks.com
*Key Personnel*
Publr: Muriel Debois *E-mail:* mdubois@apprenticeshopbooks.com
Art Dir: Lisa Greenleaf *Tel:* 603-566-3104 *E-mail:* lgreenleaf@apprenticeshopbooks.com
Dir, Mktg: Darlene Mann *Tel:* 603-244-9263 *E-mail:* dmann@apprenticeshopbooks.com
Photo Researcher: Sheila Brown *Tel:* 603-494-0767 *E-mail:* sbrown@apprenticeshopbooks.com
ISBN Prefix(es): 978-0-9723410; 978-0-9842549; 978-0-9850144
Number of titles published annually: 3 Print
Total Titles: 12 Print; 12 Online
Membership(s): ABA; Children's Book Council; IBPA, the Independent Book Publishers Association; New England Independent Booksellers Association

**Apress Media LLC**
Subsidiary of Springer Science+Business Media LLC
233 Spring St, New York, NY 10013
*Tel:* 212-460-1500 *Fax:* 212-460-1575
*E-mail:* editorial@apress.com
*Web Site:* www.apress.com
*Key Personnel*
Pres & Publr: Paul Manning *E-mail:* paul.manning@apress.com
Edit Dir: Dominic Shakeshaft *E-mail:* dominic.shakeshaft@apress.com
Dir, Mktg & Opers: Jeff Stonefield *E-mail:* jeffstonefield@apress.com
Busn Devt: Jeff Pepper *E-mail:* jeffrey.pepper@apress.com
Technical publisher devoted to meeting the needs of IT professionals, software developers & programmers with books in print & electronic format.
ISBN Prefix(es): 978-1-893115; 978-1-59059; 978-1-4302

**§APS PRESS**
Imprint of American Phytopathological Society (APS)
3340 Pilot Knob Rd, St Paul, MN 55121
*Tel:* 651-454-7250 *Toll Free Tel:* 800-328-7560 *Fax:* 651-454-0766
*E-mail:* aps@scisoc.org
*Web Site:* www.shopapspress.org
*Key Personnel*
EVP: Steve Nelson *E-mail:* snelson@scisoc.org
Pubns Mktg Dir: Greg Grahek *Tel:* 651-454-7250 ext 141 *E-mail:* ggrahek@scisoc.org
Pubns Mktg Mgr: Ashley Armstrong *E-mail:* aarmstrong@scisoc.org
Founded: 1908
Publishers of key reference books, field guides, laboratory manuals & other scientific titles related to plant health.
ISBN Prefix(es): 978-0-89054; 978-84-7114; 978-84-8476
Number of titles published annually: 10 Print; 2 CD-ROM; 4 Online
Total Titles: 300 Print; 40 CD-ROM; 2 Online

**Aqua Quest Publications Inc**
486 Bayville Rd, Locust Valley, NY 11560-1209
Mailing Address: PO Box 700, Locust Valley, NY 11560-0700
*Tel:* 516-759-0476 *Toll Free Tel:* 800-933-8989 *Fax:* 516-759-4519
*E-mail:* info@aquaquest.com
*Web Site:* www.aquaquest.com
*Key Personnel*
Pres: Anthony A Bliss, Jr *E-mail:* tbliss@aquaquest.com
Opers Mgr: Josefina A Bliss *E-mail:* josiebliss@aquaquest.com
Founded: 1989
Publishes & distributes books on scuba diving, dive travel destinations, underwater photo/video, marine life, technical diving, marine related children's books, shipwrecks & dive related fiction.
ISBN Prefix(es): 978-0-9623389; 978-1-881652; 978-0-9752290
Number of titles published annually: 4 Print; 5 E-Book
Total Titles: 37 Print; 5 E-Book
Imprints: Watersport Books
*Distribution Center:* National Book Network, 15200 NBN Way, Blue Ridge Summit, PA 17214 *Tel:* 717-794-3800 *Toll Free Tel:* 800-462-6420 *Toll Free Fax:* 800-338-4550 *Web Site:* www.nbnbooks.com
Membership(s): IBPA, the Independent Book Publishers Association

**Arbutus Press**
2364 Pinehurst Trail, Traverse City, MI 49696
*Tel:* 231-946-7240
*E-mail:* info@arbutuspress.com
*Web Site:* www.arbutuspress.com
*Key Personnel*
Publr: Susan Bays
Founded: 1998
Midwest regional history & travel related.
ISBN Prefix(es): 978-0-9665316; 978-0-9766104; 978-1-933926
Number of titles published annually: 12 Print
Total Titles: 45 Print; 3 Audio
Membership(s): Great Lakes Independent Booksellers Association; IBPA, the Independent Book Publishers Association

**Arcade Publishing Inc**
Imprint of Skyhorse Publishing Inc
307 W 36 St, 11th fl, New York, NY 10018
*Tel:* 212-643-6816 *Fax:* 212-643-6819
*E-mail:* info@skyhorsepublishing.com (Subs & Foreign Rts)
*Web Site:* www.arcadepub.com
*Key Personnel*
Pres & Publr: Tony Lyons
Assoc Publr: Bill Wolfsthal *E-mail:* bwolfsthal@skyhorsepublishing.com
Founded: 1988
Trade fiction & nonfiction; adult & juvenile.
ISBN Prefix(es): 978-1-61145
Number of titles published annually: 100 Print; 100 E-Book
Total Titles: 700 Print
Distributed by W W Norton & Company Inc

**Arcadia Publishing Inc**
420 Wando Park Blvd, Mount Pleasant, SC 29464
SAN: 255-268X
*Tel.* 843-853-2070 *Toll Free Tel:* 888-313-2665 (orders only) *Fax:* 843-853-0044
*E-mail:* sales@arcadiapublishing.com
*Web Site:* www.arcadiapublishing.com
*Key Personnel*
Cont: Kristen Crawford
Sales Dir: Kate Everingham *E-mail:* keveringham@arcadiapublishing.com
Founded: 1992
Local history & vintage images.
ISBN Prefix(es): 978-0-7524; 978-0-7385
Number of titles published annually: 900 Print
Total Titles: 8,000 Print; 13,200 E-Book
*Warehouse:* Arcadia Distribution Ctr, Receiving Dock, Mount Pleasant, SC 29464 SAN: 255-2698

**Arcana Publishing**, see Lotus Press

**Arden Press Inc**
PO Box 418, Denver, CO 80201-0418
*Tel:* 303-697-6766 *Fax:* 303-697-3443
*E-mail:* ardenpress@msn.com
*Key Personnel*
Pres & Ed: Susan Conley
Founded: 1982
Nonfiction & primarily women's studies.
ISBN Prefix(es): 978-0-912869
Number of titles published annually: 3 Print
Total Titles: 14 Print
*Returns:* 20723 Seminole Rd, Indian Hills, CO 80454
*Shipping Address:* 20723 Seminole Rd, Indian Hills, CO 80454

**§Ardent Media Inc**
522 E 82 St, Suite 1, New York, NY 10028
*Tel:* 212-861-1501 *Fax:* 212-861-0998
*E-mail:* ivyboxer@aol.com; ardentmedia@hotmail.com
*Key Personnel*
Pres: Irving B Naiburg, Jr
Founded: 1998
Paperbacks, trade, textbooks, professional & reference books, Ardent Reprint Series (article reprints, formerly Bobbs-Merrill Reprint Series).
ISBN Prefix(es): 978-0-89197; 978-0-8422; 978-0-8290
Number of titles published annually: 10 Print
Total Titles: 4,500 Print
Distributor for Cyrco Press; Irvington Publishers; MSS Information Corp
Foreign Rep(s): Gazelle Book Services Ltd (Europe, Former USSR, Turkey, UK)

**ARE Press**
Division of The Association for Research & Enlightenment Inc (ARE)
215 67 St, Virginia Beach, VA 23451
*Tel:* 757-428-3588 *Toll Free Tel:* 800-333-4499 *Fax:* 757-491-0689
*Web Site:* www.edgarcayce.org
*Key Personnel*
Mktg Dir: Jennie Taylor Martin *Tel:* 757-457-7249 *E-mail:* jennie.taylor.martin@edgarcayce.org
Prodn, Rts & Trade Sales Mgr: Cassie McQuagge *Tel:* 757-457-7239 *E-mail:* cassie@edgarcayce.org
Founded: 1931
Holistic health & spiritual development, based on Edgar Cayce material.
ISBN Prefix(es): 978-0-87604
Number of titles published annually: 8 Print; 8 E-Book
Total Titles: 160 Print; 1 CD-ROM; 37 E-Book

Imprints: 4th Dimension Press
Divisions: Atlantic University; Edgar Cayce Foundation; Cayce-Reilly School of Massotherapy

**Ariadne Press**
270 Goins Ct, Riverside, CA 92507
*Tel:* 951-684-9202 *Fax:* 951-779-0449
*E-mail:* ariadnepress@aol.com
*Web Site:* www.ariadnebooks.com
*Key Personnel*
Partner: Jorun Johns
Founded: 1988
Studies in Austrian literature, culture & thought.
ISBN Prefix(es): 978-0-929497; 978-1-57241
Number of titles published annually: 12 Print
Total Titles: 205 Print
*Foreign Office(s):* Schaden, Sonnenfelsgasse 4, 1010 Vienna, Austria *Tel:* (01) 512-4856 *Fax:* (01) 512-6028 *E-mail:* buch.schaden@vienna.at
Foreign Rep(s): Schaden (Austria)
Foreign Rights: Gazelle (UK)

**Ariel Press**
Subsidiary of Light
88 N Gate Station Dr, Suite 106, Marble Hill, GA 30148
SAN: 652-1363
*Tel:* 770-894-4226 *Fax:* 706-579-1274
*E-mail:* lig201@lightariel.com
*Web Site:* www.lightariel.com
*Key Personnel*
Pres & Publr: Carl Japikse
Art Dir: Nancy Maxwell
Founded: 1975
Nonfiction hardcover & paperbound books; essays & subscription series on personal growth, creativity, holistic health & psychic phenomena; esoteric fiction; reprints.
ISBN Prefix(es): 978-0-89804
Number of titles published annually: 11 Print; 10 E-Book
Total Titles: 150 Print; 25 E-Book
Imprints: Enthea; Kudzu House
Distributor for Enthea; Kudzu House
Foreign Rep(s): Deep Books (England)

**§Ariel Starr Productions Inc**
PO Box 17, Demarest, NJ 07627-0017
*Tel:* 201-784-9148
*E-mail:* arielstarrprod@aol.com
*Key Personnel*
Pres: Cynthia Soroka
Founded: 1991
Publish any new & innovative projects.
ISBN Prefix(es): 978-1-889122
Number of titles published annually: 3 Print; 10 E-Book; 2 Audio
Total Titles: 20 Print; 1 Audio

**The Arion Press**
Division of Lyra Corp
The Presidio, 1802 Hays St, San Francisco, CA 94129
SAN: 203-1361
*Tel:* 415-668-2542 *Fax:* 415-668-2550
*E-mail:* arionpress@arionpress.com
*Web Site:* www.arionpress.com
*Key Personnel*
Publr: Andrew Hoyem
Dir, Mktg & Sales: Thomas Gladysz
Founded: 1974
Fine, limited edition illustrated books of fiction, literature & poetry.
ISBN Prefix(es): 978-0-910457
Number of titles published annually: 3 Print
Total Titles: 90 Print
Divisions: M & H Type

**Arkansas Research Inc**
PO Box 303, Conway, AR 72033
*Tel:* 501-470-1120
*E-mail:* sales@arkansasresearch.com
*Web Site:* www.arkansasresearch.com
*Key Personnel*
Owner & Lib Sales Dir: Ms Desmond Walls Allen
Founded: 1985
Genealogy & historical material.
ISBN Prefix(es): 978-1-56546; 978-0-941765
Number of titles published annually: 5 Print; 8 E-Book
Total Titles: 404 Print; 60 CD-ROM

**Arkham House Publishers Inc**
PO Box 546, Sauk City, WI 53583-0546
SAN: 206-9741
*Tel:* 608-643-4500 *Fax:* 608-643-5043
*E-mail:* sales@arkhamhouse.com
*Web Site:* www.arkhamhouse.com
*Key Personnel*
Pres: Danielle Jacobs
VP: Damon Derleth
Founded: 1939
Fantasy fiction; horror, macabre, science fiction.
ISBN Prefix(es): 978-0-87054
Number of titles published annually: 3 Print
Total Titles: 50 Print; 50 Online; 50 E-Book
Imprints: Mycroft & Moran

**ARO Publishing Co**
398 S 1100 W, Provo, UT 84601
*Tel:* 801-637-9115 *Fax:* 801-818-0616
*E-mail:* arobook@yahoo.com
*Web Site:* www.arobookpublishing.com
*Key Personnel*
Pres: Bob Reese
Founded: 1973 (sold 1985, repurchased 2006)
K-4 beginning to read.
ISBN Prefix(es): 978-0-89868
Number of titles published annually: 6 Print
Total Titles: 35 Print; 200 Online; 35 E-Book
Distributed by Barnes & Noble; Follett; Gumdrop Books

**Jason Aronson Inc**
Imprint of Rowman & Littlefield Publishing Group
4501 Forbes Blvd, Suite 200, Lanham, MD 20706
SAN: 201-0127
*Tel:* 301-459-3366 *Toll Free Tel:* 800-462-6420 (orders) *Fax:* 301-429-5748
*Web Site:* www.jasonaronson.com
*Key Personnel*
VP & Publr: Julie Kirsch *Tel:* 301-459-3366 ext 5309 *E-mail:* jkirsch@rowman.com
Mktg Dir: Dave Horvath
Rts & Perms: Patricia Zline *Tel:* 301-459-3366 ext 5420 *E-mail:* pzline@rowman.com
Acqs Ed, Psychotherapy/Psychoanalysis: Amy King *Tel:* 301-459-3366 ext 5305 *E-mail:* aking@rowman.com
Founded: 1965
Professional books in psychotherapy, psychoanalysis & psychology; academic, reference & trade Judaica books.
New titles to be released under the Rowman & Littlefield imprint.
ISBN Prefix(es): 978-0-87668; 978-1-56821; 978-0-7657
Number of titles published annually: 40 Print; 40 E-Book
Total Titles: 1,700 Print; 150 E-Book
Foreign Rep(s): Academic Marketing Services Pty Ltd (Botswana, Namibia, South Africa, Zimbabwe); APD Singapore Pte Ltd (Brunei, Cambodia, Indonesia, Laos, Malaysia, Singapore, Thailand, Vietnam); Asia Publishers Service Ltd (China, Hong Kong, Korea, Philippines, Taiwan); Avicenna Partnership Ltd (Afghanistan, Algeria, Armenia, Bahrain, Cyprus, Egypt, Iran, Iraq, Jordan, Kuwait, Lebanon, Libya, Morocco, Oman, Palestine, Qatar, Saudi Arabia, Sudan, Syria, Tunisia, United Arab Emirates, Yemen); Cranbury International LLC (Caribbean, Central America, Mexico, Pakistan, Puerto Rico, South America); DA Information Services Pty Td (Australia, New Zealand, Papua New Guinea); Durnell Marketing Ltd (Austria, Baltic States, Belgium, Czech Republic, Denmark, Finland, France, Germany, Greece, Hungary, Iceland, Italy, Malta, Netherlands, Norway, Poland, Portugal, Slovakia, Slovenia, Spain, Sweden, Switzerland); NBN International; Overleaf (Bangladesh, Bhutan, India, Nepal, Sri Lanka); United Publishers Service Ltd (Japan, South Korea)

**Art Image Publications**
Division of GB Publishing Inc
PO Box 160, Derby Line, VT 05830
*Toll Free Tel:* 800-361-2598 *Toll Free Fax:* 800-559-2598
*E-mail:* info@artimagepublications.com
*Web Site:* www.artimagepublications.com
*Key Personnel*
Pres: Yvan Boulerice
Educ Consultant: Rachel Ross *E-mail:* rachel.ross@artimagepublications.com
ISBN Prefix(es): 978-1-896876; 978-1-55292
Number of titles published annually: 12 Print
Total Titles: 52 Print

**The Art Institute of Chicago**
111 S Michigan Ave, Chicago, IL 60603-6404
SAN: 204-479X
*Tel:* 312-443-3600; 312-443-3540 (pubns) *Fax:* 312-443-1334 (pubns)
*Web Site:* www.artic.edu; www.artinstituteshop.org
*Key Personnel*
Pres & Dir: Douglas Druick *Tel:* 312-443-3632
Exec Dir, Pubns: Robert V Sharp *Tel:* 312-443-4962 *E-mail:* rsharp@artic.edu
Dir, Pubns: Sarah E Guernsey *Tel:* 312-443-3746 *E-mail:* sguernsey@artic.edu
Fin Mgr, Publns: Bryan Miller *Tel:* 312-857-7613 *E-mail:* bmiller@artic.edu
Ed: Maia M Rigas *Tel:* 312-443-4774 *E-mail:* mrigas@artic.edu
Photog Ed: Lauren Makholm *Tel:* 312-443-3539 *E-mail:* lmakholm@artic.edu
Asst Ed: Amy Peltz *Tel:* 312-443-4963 *E-mail:* apeltz@artic.edu
Prodn Coord: Joseph Mohan *Tel:* 312-443-4955 *E-mail:* jmohan@artic.edu
Founded: 1879
Exhibition catalogues, popular & scholarly art books on the museum's permanent collection: African art & Indian art of the Americas; American art; Ancient & Byzantine art; architecture & design; Asian art; contemporary art; European painting, sculpture & decorative arts; photography; prints & drawings; textiles.
ISBN Prefix(es): 978-0-86559
Number of titles published annually: 10 Print; 1 Online
Total Titles: 60 Print
Distributed by Yale University Press
*Warehouse:* TriLiteral, 100 Maple Ridge Rd, Cumberland, RI 02864

**Art of Living, PrimaMedia Inc**
1250 Bethlehem Pike, Suite 241, Hatfield, PA 19440
SAN: 299-8858
*Tel:* 215-660-5045 *Toll Free Tel:* 800-581-9020 *Fax:* 734-448-4125
*E-mail:* primamedia4@yahoo.com
*Key Personnel*
Publicity & Mktg: Sue Thomson *Tel:* 215-660-5045
Edit: Gia Carispat *E-mail:* primamedia12@yahoo.com

Billing: Joan Campo *E-mail:* primamedia40@gmail.com
Returns: Lisa Clarke
Contact: Katherine Rafter *Tel:* 215-660-5045
Number of titles published annually: 10 Print; 5 Online; 6 E-Book
Total Titles: 15 Online; 15 E-Book
Foreign Rep(s): Rebecca Ferrone (Australia, Canada, Europe)

**ArtAge Publications**
PO Box 19955, Portland, OR 97280
*Tel:* 503-246-3000 *Toll Free Tel:* 800-858-4998 *Fax:* 503-246-3006
*Web Site:* www.seniortheatre.com
*Key Personnel*
Pres: Bonnie L Vorenberg *E-mail:* bonniev@seniortheatre.com
Founded: 1997
The Senior Theatre Resource Center has the largest collection of plays, books & information for older performers. We help mature performers fulfill their theatrical dreams.
ISBN Prefix(es): 978-0-9669412
Number of titles published annually: 45 Print; 45 Online; 27 E-Book; 5 Audio
Total Titles: 350 Print; 300 Online; 200 E-Book; 11 Audio
Distributor for Heinemann; Hal Leonard
*Returns:* 7845 SW Capitol Hwy, Suite 12, Portland, OR 97219
Membership(s): IBPA, the Independent Book Publishers Association

**ARTAMO Press**
11 W Anapamu St, Santa Barbara, CA 93101
SAN: 851-7339
*Tel:* 805-568-1400 *Fax:* 805-568-1400
*E-mail:* admin@artamopress.com
*Web Site:* www.artamopress.com
*Key Personnel*
Publr: Dr Elvira Monika Laskowski-Caujolle
Dedicated to literature & the celebration of language. Our focus is on literary, non-mainstream fiction, contemporary poetry, essays, drama & nonfiction on writing.
ISBN Prefix(es): 978-0-9788475
Number of titles published annually: 5 Print
Total Titles: 15 Print
Membership(s): IBPA, the Independent Book Publishers Association; Small Publishers, Artists & Writers Network

**Arte Publico Press**
Affiliate of University of Houston
University of Houston, Bldg 19, Rm 10, 4902 Gulf Fwy, Houston, TX 77204-2004
*Tel:* 713-743-2998 (sales) *Toll Free Tel:* 800-633-2783 *Fax:* 713-743-2847 (sales)
*E-mail:* appinfo@uh.edu
*Web Site:* www.arte.uh.edu; artepublicopress.com
*Key Personnel*
Publr: Nicolas Kanellos
Busn Mgr: Nellie Gonzalez
Asst Dir: Marina Tristan
Intl Rts: Stefanie Gonzalez
Founded: 1979
Books by American Hispanic authors.
ISBN Prefix(es): 978-0-934770; 978-1-55885
Number of titles published annually: 30 Print
Total Titles: 400 Print
Imprints: Pinata Books
Subsidiaries: The Americas Review
Distributor for Bilingual Review Press; Latin American Review Press
Foreign Rights: The Asano Agency Inc (Japan); Eliane Benisti Literary Agency (France); Raquel de la Concha (Spain); Michael Meller Literary Agency GmbH (Germany)
Membership(s): AAP

**§Artech House Inc**
Subsidiary of Horizon House Publications Inc
685 Canton St, Norwood, MA 02062
SAN: 201-1441
*Tel:* 781-769-9750 *Toll Free Tel:* 800-225-9977 *Fax:* 781-769-6334
*E-mail:* artech@artechhouse.com
*Web Site:* www.artechhouse.com
*Key Personnel*
COO: Christopher Ernst *E-mail:* cernst@artechhouse.com
Pres & Publr: William M Bazzy
Edit & Prodn Dir: Darrell Judd
Dir, Sales, Mktg & Busn Devt: John W Stone *E-mail:* jwstone@artechhouse.com
Exec Ed: Judi Stone
Sr Acq Ed: Mark Walsh *E-mail:* mwalsh@artechhouse.com
Founded: 1970
Technical & engineering.
ISBN Prefix(es): 978-0-89006; 978-1-58053; 978-1-59693; 978-1-60807; 978-1-60783
Number of titles published annually: 30 Print; 40 E-Book
Total Titles: 500 Print; 250 E-Book
*Foreign Office(s):* 16 Sussex St, London SW1V 4RW, United Kingdom *Tel:* (020) 7596 8750 *Fax:* (020) 7630 0166 *E-mail:* artech-uk@artechhouse.com *Web Site:* www.artechhouse.com
Foreign Rep(s): Akateeminen (Finland); Anglo-American Book Co (Italy); Asian Books Pvt Ltd (India, Pakistan); C V Toko Buku Topen (Indonesia); Clarke Associates Ltd (Pacific Basin); Computer Press (Sweden); D A Book Pty Ltd (Australia, New Zealand); Dai-Iti Publications Trading Co Ltd (Japan); Diaz de Santos (Spain); Dietmar Dreier (Germany); DK Book House Co Ltd (Thailand); Freihofer AG (Switzerland); Kumi Trading Co Ltd (South Korea); Librairie Lavoisier (France); Login Brothers (Canada); Julio Logrado de Figueiredo Lda (Portugal); The Modern Book Co (UK); Pak Book Corp (Pakistan); Polyteknisk (Denmark); Sejong (Korea); Ta Tong Book Co Ltd (Taiwan); Tapir (Norway); Tecmedd (Brazil); UBS Library Services (Singapore); United Publishers Services Ltd (Japan, South Korea); L Wouters (Belgium)
Foreign Rights: ABE Marketing (Poland); BSB Distribution (Germany); Fleet Publications (Chile); Foyles (UK); Hoepli (Italy); Kuwkab (Mideast); Livraria Canuto (Brazil); Papsotiriou (Greece)
*Warehouse:* Publishers Storage & Shipping Corp (US only), 231 Industrial Park, 46 Development Rd, Fitchburg, MA 01420 *Tel:* 978-345-2121 *Fax:* 978-348-1233

**Artisan Books**
Division of Workman Publishing Co Inc
225 Varick St, New York, NY 10014-4381
*Tel:* 212-254-5900 *Toll Free Tel:* 800-722-7202 *Fax:* 212-254-8098
*E-mail:* artisaninfo@workman.com; artisaninfo@artisanbooks.com
*Web Site:* www.workman.com/artisanbooks/
*Key Personnel*
Publr: Ann Bramson
Dir, Mktg & Publicity: Allison McGeehon
Mng Ed: Trent Duffy
Exec Ed & Assoc Publr: Lia Ronnen
Sr Ed: Ingrid Abramovitch
Art Dir: Jan Derevjanik
Founded: 1993
Illustrated books & calendars to the trade.
ISBN Prefix(es): 978-1-885183; 978-1-57965
Number of titles published annually: 15 Print
Distributor for Greenwich Workshop Press
Foreign Rep(s): Thomas Allen & Son Ltd (Canada); Bookreps New Zealand (New Zealand); Hardie Grant Books (Australia); Melia Publishing Services (Ireland, UK)
Foreign Rights: Big Apple Agency Inc (China, Taiwan); Graal Literary Agency (Poland); Japan UNI Agency Inc (Japan); JLM Literary Agency (Greece); Katai & Bolza Literary Agents (Hungary); Alexander Korahenevski Agency (Russia); Korea Copyright Center Inc (KCC) (Korea); Kristin Olson Literary Agency SRO (Czech Republic); Mickey Pikarski (Israel); Caroline van Gelderen Literary Agency (Netherlands); Julio F Yanez Agencia Literaria S L (Latin America, Portugal, Spain)
*Shipping Address:* Banta Packaging & Fulfillment, N 9234 Lake Park Rd, Appleton, WI 54915

**§ASCD**
1703 N Beauregard St, Alexandria, VA 22311-1714
SAN: 201-1352
*Tel:* 703-578-9600 *Toll Free Tel:* 800-933-2723 *Fax:* 703-575-5400
*E-mail:* member@ascd.org
*Web Site:* www.ascd.org
*Key Personnel*
Publr: Richard Papale *Tel:* 703-575-5680 *E-mail:* richard.papale@ascd.org
Dir, Book Editing & Prodn: Julie Houtz *Tel:* 703-575-5706 *E-mail:* jhoutz@ascd.org
Dir, Mktg: James Mahoney *Tel:* 703-575-5631 *E-mail:* james.mahoney@ascd.org
Dir, Sales: Jean Pride *Tel:* 703-575-5634 *E-mail:* jpride@ascd.org
Acqs Ed: Genny Ostertag *Tel:* 703-575-5469 *E-mail:* gostertag@ascd.org
Intl Rts: Cat Russo *E-mail:* translations@ascd.org
Founded: 1943
Professional books for educators.
ISBN Prefix(es): 978-0-87120; 978-1-4166
Number of titles published annually: 30 Print; 20 E-Book
Total Titles: 350 Print; 319 E-Book

**Ascend Books**
10101 W 87 St, Suite 200, Overland Park, KS 66212
*Tel:* 913-948-5500; 913-948 7634 (ordering)
*Web Site:* www.ascendbooks.com
*Key Personnel*
CEO & Publr: Robert Snodgrass *E-mail:* bsnodgrass@ascendbooks.com
Founded: 2009
Publisher of books on sports & entertainment topics. Some childrens books.
ISBN Prefix(es): 978-0-9830619
Number of titles published annually: 12 Print; 10 E-Book
Total Titles: 35 Print; 14 E-Book
*Distribution Center:* Ingram Book Co, One Ingram Blvd, La Vergne, TN 37086 *Tel:* 615-793-5000 *Toll Free Tel:* 800-937-8200 *E-mail:* customer.service@ingrambook.com *Web Site:* www.ingrambook.com
Partners Books Distribution, 2325 Jarco Dr, Holt, MI 48842 *Tel:* 517-694-3205

**Ascension Press**
Member of Catholic Word
PO Box 1990, West Chester, PA 19380
*Tel:* 610-696-7795 *Toll Free Tel:* 800-376-0520 (sales & cust serv) *Fax:* 610-696-7796; 608-565-2025 (sales & cust serv)
*E-mail:* info@ascensionpress.com
*Web Site:* www.ascensionpress.com
*Key Personnel*
Mng Ed: Mike Flickinger *Tel:* 610-696-7795 ext 207
Dir of Mktg: Christopher Cope *E-mail:* ccope@ascensionpress.com
Dir of Sales: Lynn Klika
Dir, Theology of the Body: Steve Motyl
Dir of Community Rel: Corrinne Murphy
Religious educational publishers.

ISBN Prefix(es): 978-1-932645; 978-0-9742238; 978-0-9659228; 978-0-9744451; 978-1-5705848
Number of titles published annually: 15 Print
Total Titles: 250 Print; 200 Online; 40 Audio
*Sales Office(s):* W5180 Jefferson St, Necedah, WI 54646 *Tel:* 608-565-2020 *Toll Free Tel:* 800-376-0520 *Fax:* 608-565-5025
*Orders to:* W5180 Jefferson St, Necedah, WI 54646 *Tel:* 608-565-2020 *Toll Free Tel:* 800-376-0520 *Fax:* 608-565-2025
*Returns:* W5180 Jefferson St, Necedah, WI 54646 *Tel:* 608-565-2020 *Toll Free Tel:* 800-376-0520 *Fax:* 608-565-2025
*Warehouse:* W5180 Jefferson St, Necedah, WI 54646 *Tel:* 608-565-2020 *Toll Free Tel:* 800-376-0520 *Fax:* 608-565-2025
*Distribution Center:* W5180 Jefferson St, Necedah, WI 54646 *Tel:* 608-565-2020 *Toll Free Tel:* 800-376-0520 *Fax:* 608-565-2025

**ASCP Press**
Subsidiary of American Society for Clinical Pathology
33 W Monroe St, Suite 1600, Chicago, IL 60603
SAN: 207-9429
*Tel:* 312-541-4999 *Toll Free Tel:* 800-267-2727 *Fax:* 312-541-4998
*Web Site:* www.ascp.org
*Key Personnel*
Publr: Joshua R Weikersheimer *Tel:* 312-541-4866 *E-mail:* joshua.weikersheimer@ascp.org
Founded: 1959
Books, multimedia, slide sets, atlases, audiovisual seminars, videotapes, manuals, interactive software & videodiscs for lab professionals. Subjects include continuing education.
ISBN Prefix(es): 978-85-89189
Number of titles published annually: 15 Print; 13 CD-ROM; 7 Online
Total Titles: 212 Print; 31 CD-ROM; 80 Online

**ASCSA Publications**
American School of Classical Studies at Athens, 6-8 Charlton St, Princeton, NJ 08540-5232
*Tel:* 609-683-0800 *Fax:* 609-924-0578
*Web Site:* www.ascsa.edu.gr/publications
Founded: 1881
Publishing office for the American School of Classical Studies at Athens, an advanced research & teaching institution focused on the history & culture of Greece & the wider Greek world.
ISBN Prefix(es): 978-0-87661
Number of titles published annually: 12 Print; 1 Online
Total Titles: 300 Print; 1 Online
Imprints: American School of Classical Studies at Athens; Gennadeion Monographs; Hesperia
*Billing Address:* David Brown Book Co, PO Box 511, 28 Main St, Oakville, CT 06779, Contact: David Brown *Tel:* 860-945-9329 *Toll Free Tel:* 800-791-9354 *Fax:* 860-945-9468 *E-mail:* jim.drenning@dbbcdist.com *Web Site:* www.oxbowbooks.com
*Orders to:* David Brown Book Co, PO Box 511, 28 Main St, Oakville, CT 06779, Contact: David Brown *Tel:* 860-945-9329 *Toll Free Tel:* 800-791-9354 *Fax:* 860-945-9468 *E-mail:* jim.drenning@dbbcdist.com *Web Site:* www.oxbowbooks.com
*Returns:* David Brown Book Co, PO Box 511, 28 Main St, Oakville, CT 06779, Contact: David Brown *Tel:* 860-945-9329 *Toll Free Tel:* 800-791-9354 *Fax:* 860-945-9468 *E-mail:* jim.drenning@dbbcdist.com *Web Site:* www.oxbowbooks.com
*Shipping Address:* David Brown Book Co, PO Box 511, 28 Main St, Oakville, CT 06779, Contact: David Brown *Tel:* 860-945-9329 *Toll Free Tel:* 800-791-9354 *Fax:* 860-945-9468 *E-mail:* jim.drenning@dbbcdist.com *Web Site:* www.oxbowbooks.com
*Warehouse:* David Brown Book Co, PO Box 511, 28 Main St, Oakville, CT 06779, Contact: David Brown *Tel:* 860-945-9329 *Toll Free Tel:* 800-791-9354 *Fax:* 860-945-9468 *E-mail:* jim.drenning@dbbcdist.com *Web Site:* www.oxbowbooks.com
*Distribution Center:* David Brown Book Co, PO Box 511, 28 Main St, Oakville, CT 06779, Contact: David Brown *Tel:* 860-945-9329 *Toll Free Tel:* 800-791-9354 *Fax:* 860-945-9468 *E-mail:* jim.drenning@dbbcdist.com *Web Site:* www.oxbowbooks.com
Membership(s): AAP Professional/Scholarly Publishing Division; American Association of University Presses; Society for Scholarly Publishing

**Ash Tree Publishing**
PO Box 64, Woodstock, NY 12498
*Tel:* 845-246-8081 *Fax:* 845-246-8081
*E-mail:* info@ashtreepublishing.com
*Web Site:* www.ashtreepublishing.com
*Key Personnel*
Founder & Owner: Susun Weed
Orders: Michael Dattorre *E-mail:* wisewoman@herbshealing.com
ISBN Prefix(es): 978-1-888123; 978-0-9614620
Number of titles published annually: 3 Print; 1 CD-ROM; 1 Audio
Total Titles: 14 Print; 1 CD-ROM; 2 Audio
Distributed by Akasha Ltd; Ash Tree Publishing; Jocelyn Davies; Dempsey Your Distributor; New Leaf; Nutri-Books; Partners; The Tao of Books; VisionWorks

**Ashgate Publishing Co**
Subsidiary of Ashgate Publishing Ltd
101 Cherry St, Suite 420, Burlington, VT 05401-4405
SAN: 262-0308
*Tel:* 802-865-7641 *Toll Free Tel:* 800-535-9544 *Fax:* 802-865-7847
*E-mail:* info@ashgate.com
*Web Site:* www.ashgate.com
*Key Personnel*
Pres: Barbara J Church *Tel:* 802-865-7641 ext 310 *E-mail:* bchurch@ashgate.com
Fin Cont: Burta Kelly
Mktg Dir: Brandon De Coff
Founded: 1979
International publisher of scholarly studies in the humanities & social sciences. Covers a wide range of subject areas including law, professional, scholarly reference books, sociology, business management, philosophy, economics, art, music, literary studies, history & more.
ISBN Prefix(es): 978-0-566; 978-1-85742; 978-0-85967; 978-1-85628; 978-0-86078; 978-0-86127; 978-0-85331; 978-0-291; 978-0-7546; 978-1-85521; 978-1-85928; 978-1-84014; 978-0-85417; 978-1-4094
Number of titles published annually: 800 Print
Total Titles: 1,000 Print
Imprints: Ashgate; Gower; Lund Humphries
Distributor for Pickering & Chatto

**Ashland Creek Press**
2305 Ashland St, Suite C417, Ashland, OR 97520
*Tel:* 760-300-3620 *Fax:* 253-550-2019
*E-mail:* editors@ashlandcreekpress.com
*Web Site:* www.ashlandcreekpress.com
*Key Personnel*
Founder & Ed: Midge Raymond *E-mail:* midge@ashlandcreekpress.com; John Yunker *E-mail:* john@ashlandcreekpress.com
Founded: 2011
Small, independent publisher of books with a world view. From travel narratives to eco-literature, our mission is to publish a range of books that foster an appreciation for worlds outside our own, for nature & the animal kingdom & for the ways in which we all connect.
ISBN Prefix(es): 978-0-9796475
Number of titles published annually: 5 Print; 5 E-Book
Total Titles: 12 Print; 12 E-Book
Imprints: Ashland Creek Press; Byte Level Books
Membership(s): IBPA, the Independent Book Publishers Association

**Ashland Poetry Press**
Affiliate of Ashland University
Ashland University, 401 College Ave, Ashland, OH 44805
*Tel:* 419-289-5957 *Fax:* 419-289-5255
*E-mail:* app@ashland.edu
*Web Site:* www.ashland.edu/aupoetry
*Key Personnel*
Dir: Dr Stephen Haven *E-mail:* shaven@ashland.edu
Mng Ed: Sarah Wells *E-mail:* swells@ashland.edu
Ed: Dr Deborah Fleming *E-mail:* dfleming@ashland.edu
Founded: 1969
ISBN Prefix(es): 978-0-912592
Number of titles published annually: 10 Print
Total Titles: 60 Print
*Distribution Center:* Small Press Distribution, 1341 Seventh St, Berkeley, CA 94710-1409 *Web Site:* www.spdbooks.org
Membership(s): Council of Literary Magazines & Presses; IBPA, the Independent Book Publishers Association

**ASIS International**
1625 Prince St, Alexandria, VA 22314
*Tel:* 703-519-6200 *Fax:* 703-519-6299
*E-mail:* asis@asisonline.org
*Web Site:* www.asisonline.org
*Key Personnel*
Educ Publg Mgr: Evangeline A Pappas *E-mail:* epappas@asisonline.org
Founded: 1955
Organization for security professionals, with more than 33,000 members worldwide. Dedicated to increasing the effectiveness & productivy of security professionals by developing educational programs & materials that address broad security interests, such as the annual seminar & exhibits, as well as specific security topics. Also advocates the role & value of the security management profession to business, the media, government entities & the public.
ISBN Prefix(es): 978-1-887056
Number of titles published annually: 3 Print; 2 CD-ROM
Total Titles: 35 Print; 2 CD-ROM

**Aslan Publishing**
Division of Renaissance Book Services Corp
857 Post Rd, Suite 302, Fairfield, CT 06824
SAN: 242-6129
*Tel:* 203-372-0300 *Fax:* 203-374-4766
*E-mail:* information@aslanpublishing.com
*Web Site:* www.aslanpublishing.com
*Key Personnel*
Pres & Lib Sales Dir: Harold Levine *E-mail:* harold@aslanpublishing.com
Pubns Dir: Barbara Levine
Founded: 1984
Publish nonfiction books on personal growth, psychology & inspiration, parenting & education, health & cooking.
ISBN Prefix(es): 978-0-944031
Number of titles published annually: 3 Print
Total Titles: 32 Print
Foreign Rep(s): Central Book Services Pty Ltd (Australia)

**§ASM International**
9639 Kinsman Rd, Materials Park, OH 44073-0002
SAN: 204-7586
*Tel:* 440-338-5151 *Toll Free Tel:* 800-336-5152; 800-368-9800 (Europe) *Fax:* 440-338-4634
*E-mail:* memberservicecenter@asminternational.org
*Web Site:* asmcommunity.asminternational.org
*Key Personnel*
Mgr, E-document Prodn: Bonnie Sanders *Tel:* 440-338-5151 ext 5677
Founded: 1913
Technical & reference books.
ISBN Prefix(es): 978-0-87170
Number of titles published annually: 20 Print; 5 CD-ROM; 35 Online
Total Titles: 210 Print; 25 CD-ROM; 1,000 Online
Foreign Rep(s): ATP (Europe); B I Publications (India); Sejong Books Inc (Korea)
*Warehouse:* 14800 Munnberry Oval, Newbury, OH 44065

**§ASM Press**
Division of American Society for Microbiology
1752 "N" St NW, Washington, DC 20036-2904
*Tel:* 202-737-3600 *Toll Free Tel:* 800-546-2416 *Fax:* 202-942-9342
*E-mail:* books@asmusa.org
*Web Site:* estore.asm.org
*Key Personnel*
Exec Dir: Michael Goldberg *E-mail:* mgoldberg@asmusa.org
Dir, Books Div: Christine Charlip *E-mail:* ccharlip@asmusa.org
Dir, Journals Div: Barbara Goldman *E-mail:* bgoldman@asmusa.org
Mktg Mgr, Journals: Nichole Ridgeway *E-mail:* nridgeway@asmusa.org
Prod Mgr, Books Div: Kenneth April *E-mail:* kapril@asmusa.org
Mktg Coord: Elena Scalerbio *E-mail:* escalerbio@asmusa.org
Founded: 1899
Microbiology, cell biology, medicine, books, journals, proceedings & abstracts.
ISBN Prefix(es): 978-1-55581
Number of titles published annually: 25 Print; 1 CD-ROM; 15 Online
Total Titles: 250 Print; 3 CD-ROM; 25 Online
Foreign Rep(s): Cranbury International (Latin America); Information & Culture Korea (ICK) (South Korea); Donald MacIvor & Associates (Canada); Wiley-Blackwell (Africa, Europe, Middle East, UK)
Foreign Rights: Aditya Books Pvt Ltd (Bangladesh, India, Nepal, Pakistan, Sri Lanka); Apex Knowledge Sdn Bhd (Brunei, Malaysia); Booknet Co Ltd (Cambodia, Laos, Myanmar, Thailand, Vietnam); DA Information Services (Australia, Fiji, New Zealand, Papua New Guinea); iCaves Ltd (China, Hong Kong, Macau); IG Knowledge Services Ltd (Taiwan); MegaTEXTS Phil Inc (Philippines); United Publishers Services Ltd (Japan); John Wiley & Sons Ltd (Africa, Europe, Middle East); Woodslane (Australia, Fiji, New Zealand, Papua New Guinea, Solomon Islands)
*Orders to:* PO Box 605, Herndon, VA 20172 *Tel:* 703-661-1593 *Fax:* 703-661-1501 *E-mail:* asmmail@presswarehouse.com
*Returns:* 22883 Quicksilver Dr, Dulles, VA 20166

**§Aspatore Books**
Division of Thomson Reuters
35 Thomson Pl, Boston, MA 02210
*Toll Free Tel:* 866-ASPATORE (277-2867) *Fax:* 617-249-0219
*E-mail:* west.customer.service@thomsonreuters.com
*Web Site:* www.aspatore.com
*Key Personnel*
CEO & Publr: Jonathan R Aspatore
Founded: 1999
Publish only the biggest names in the business world, including C-level leaders (CEO, CTO, CFO, COO, CMO, Partner) from over half the world's 500 largest companies & other leading executives. By focusing on publishing only C-Level executives, we provide professionals of all levels with proven business intelligence from industry insiders, rather than relying on the knowledge of unknown authors & analysts.
ISBN Prefix(es): 978-1-58762; 978-1-59622
Number of titles published annually: 150 Print
Total Titles: 500 Print
Imprints: Aspatore Thought Leadership; Bigwig Briefs; Executive Reports; Inside the Minds; Line by Line

**Aspen Publishers Inc**, see Wolters Kluwer Law & Business

**Associated University Presses**
10 Schalks Crossing Rd, Suite 501-330, Plainsbury, NJ 08536
*Tel:* 609-269-8094 *Fax:* 609-269-8096
*E-mail:* aup440@aol.com
*Web Site:* www.aupresses.com
Founded: 1968
Book distributor.
ISBN Prefix(es): 978-0-8453
Number of titles published annually: 3 Print
Distributor for Susquehanna University Press

**§Association for Computing Machinery**
2 Penn Plaza, Suite 701, New York, NY 10121-0701
SAN: 267-7784
*Tel:* 212-626-0500 *Toll Free Tel:* 800-342-6626 *Fax:* 212-944-1318
*E-mail:* acmhelp@acm.org
*Web Site:* www.acm.org
*Key Personnel*
Pubns Dir: Bernard Rous *E-mail:* rous@acm.org
Founded: 1947
Computer science.
ISBN Prefix(es): 978-0-201; 978-85-89791; 978-1-58113
Number of titles published annually: 150 Print
Total Titles: 500 Print
Imprints: ACM Press
Membership(s): AAP

**Association for Information Science & Technology (ASIS&T)**
Formerly American Society for Information Science & Technology (ASIS&T)
1320 Fenwick Lane, Suite 510, Silver Spring, MD 20910
*Tel:* 301-495-0900 *Fax:* 301-495-0810
*E-mail:* asis@asis.org
*Web Site:* www.asis.org
*Key Personnel*
Exec Dir: Richard Hill *E-mail:* rhill@asis.org
Founded: 1937
Provides high-quality conference programs & publications for information systems developers, online professionals, information resource managers, librarians, records managers, academics & others who "bridge the gap".
ISBN Prefix(es): 978-0-87715
Number of titles published annually: 12 Print; 1 CD-ROM; 1 Online
Total Titles: 12 Print; 1 CD-ROM; 1 Online
Distributed by Information Today Inc; John Wiley & Sons Inc

**Association of College & Research Libraries (ACRL)**
Division of The American Library Association
50 E Huron St, Chicago, IL 60611
*Tel:* 312-280-2523 *Toll Free Tel:* 800-545-2433 (ext 2523) *Fax:* 312-280-2520
*E-mail:* acrl@ala.org
*Web Site:* www.ala.org/acrl
*Key Personnel*
Exec Dir: Mary Ellen K Davis *Tel:* 312-280-3248 *E-mail:* mdavis@ala.org
Founded: 1938
ISBN Prefix(es): 978-0-8389
Number of titles published annually: 8 Print
Total Titles: 60 Print

**Association of Research Libraries**
21 Dupont Circle NW, Suite 800, Washington, DC 20036
*Tel:* 202-296-2296 *Fax:* 202-872-0884
*E-mail:* arlhq@arl.org
*Web Site:* www.arl.org
*Key Personnel*
Pubns Prog Offr: Lee Anne George *E-mail:* leeanne@arl.org
Founded: 1932
Serial, occasional paper series & special topics of interest.
ISBN Prefix(es): 978-0-918006; 978-1-59407
Number of titles published annually: 10 Print; 14 Online
Total Titles: 600 Print; 90 Online
*Distribution Center:* ARL Publications Distribution Center, PO Box 531, Annapolis Junction, MD 20701-0531 *Tel:* 301-362-8196 *Fax:* 240-396-2479
Membership(s): AAP

**Association of School Business Officials International**
11401 N Shore Dr, Reston, VA 20190-4200
*Tel:* 703-478-0405 *Toll Free Tel:* 866-682-2729 *Fax:* 703-478-0205
*E-mail:* asboreq@asbointl.org; asbosba@asbointl.org
*Web Site:* www.asbointl.org
*Key Personnel*
Ed: Patricia George
Pubns Coord: Lauren Konopka *E-mail:* lkonopka@asbointl.org
Founded: 1910
Professional books.
ISBN Prefix(es): 978-0-910170; 978-0-810847; 978-1-1578860
Number of titles published annually: 8 Print
Total Titles: 40 Print

**Asta Publications LLC**
PO Box 1735, Stockbridge, GA 30281
*Tel:* 678-814-1320 *Toll Free Tel:* 800-482-4190 *Fax:* 678-814-1370
*E-mail:* info@astapublications.com
*Web Site:* www.astapublications.com
*Key Personnel*
Founder & CEO: Assuanta Howard *E-mail:* ahoward@astapublications.com
Founded: 2004
Helping authors bring their book concepts to life by delivering first-class products & services that are accurate & high quality.
This publisher has indicated that 30% of their product line is author subsidized.
ISBN Prefix(es): 978-0-9777060; 978-1-934947
Number of titles published annually: 50 Print
Total Titles: 100 Print
Membership(s): The Association of Publishers for Special Sales; PMA International

**§ASTM International**
100 Barr Harbor Dr, West Conshohocken, PA 19428
Mailing Address: PO Box C-700, West Conshohocken, PA 19428
*Tel:* 610-832-9500 *Fax:* 610-832-9555
*E-mail:* service@astm.org
*Web Site:* www.astm.org

*Key Personnel*
Pres: James A Thomas *Tel:* 610-832-9598
*Fax:* 610-832-9599 *E-mail:* jthomas@astm.org
VP, Pubns & Mktg: John Pace *Tel:* 610-832-9632
*Fax:* 610-832-9635 *E-mail:* jpace@astm.org
Sales Mgr: George Zajdel *Tel:* 610-832-9614
*Fax:* 610-832-9635 *E-mail:* gzajdel@astm.org
Founded: 1898
Standards, technical publications, data series manuals & journals on engineering, science, materials testing, safety, quality control.
ISBN Prefix(es): 978-0-8031
Number of titles published annually: 176 Print; 125 CD-ROM
Total Titles: 1,500 Print; 125 CD-ROM; 80 Online
*Foreign Office(s):* American Technical Publishers Ltd, 27-29 Knowl Piece, Wilbury Way, Hitchin, Herts SG4 OSX, United Kingdom *Tel:* (0462) 437933 *Fax:* (0462) 433678
Foreign Rep(s): American Technical Publishers Ltd (Europe)
Membership(s): AAP

**Astragal Press**
Imprint of Finney Company Inc
8075 215 St W, Lakeville, MN 55044
*Tel:* 952-469-6699 *Toll Free Tel:* 866-543-3045
*Fax:* 952-469-1968 *Toll Free Fax:* 800-330-6232
*E-mail:* info@astragalpress.com
*Web Site:* www.astragalpress.com
*Key Personnel*
Pres: Alan Krysan *E-mail:* akrysan@finneyco.com
Mktg Mgr: Krista Danilson
Founded: 1983
Early tools, trades & technology.
ISBN Prefix(es): 978-0-9618088; 978-1-879335; 978-1-931626
Number of titles published annually: 5 Print
Total Titles: 89 Print; 89 Online

**The Astronomical Society of the Pacific**
390 Ashton Ave, San Francisco, CA 94112
*Tel:* 415-337-1100 *Fax:* 415-337-5205
*Web Site:* www.astrosociety.org
*Key Personnel*
Exec Dir: James Manning
Founded: 1889
Books, booklets, tapes, slide sets, software & other educational materials about astronomy; Conference proceedings. Mercury Magazine. PASP (Publications of the Astronomical Society of the Pacific) Journal.
ISBN Prefix(es): 978-0-937707
Number of titles published annually: 20 Print; 1 CD-ROM; 20 E-Book; 1 Audio
Total Titles: 360 Print; 1 CD-ROM; 60 E-Book; 1 Audio

**Asylum Arts Press**, see Leaping Dog Press/Asylum Arts Press

**Atheneum Books for Young Readers**, see Simon & Schuster Children's Publishing

**Athletic Guide Publishing**
PO Box 1050, Flagler Beach, FL 32136
*Tel:* 386-439-2250 *Toll Free Tel:* 800-255-1050
*Fax:* 386-439-2249
*E-mail:* agp@flaglernet.com
*Web Site:* www.athleticguidepublishing.com
*Key Personnel*
Ed: Tom Keegan
Founded: 1990
Publish guides to various sports, especially hockey.
ISBN Prefix(es): 978-1-880941; 978-1-60179
Number of titles published annually: 35 Print
Total Titles: 120 Print

Imprints: American Sports Publishing; Old Kings Road Press
Membership(s): IBPA, the Independent Book Publishers Association

**Atlantic Law Book Co**
Division of Peter Kelsey Publishing Inc
22 Grassmere Ave, West Hartford, CT 06110-1215
*Tel:* 860-231-9300 *Fax:* 860-231-9242
*E-mail:* atlanticlawbooks@aol.com
*Web Site:* www.atlanticlawbooks.com
*Key Personnel*
VP: Richard Epstein
Founded: 1945
Law books for Connecticut legal practice. Marketed in Connecticut & other states & used by practitioners & judges in this state. The books are all written by law professors, lawyers or judges who are recognized experts in their respective fields. The material is updated regularly, usually by annual pocket supplements.
ISBN Prefix(es): 978-1-878698
Number of titles published annually: 12 Print; 2 CD-ROM
Total Titles: 12 Print; 2 CD-ROM

**Atlantic Publishing Group Inc**
1210 SW 23 Place, Ocala, FL 34471
*Tel:* 352-622-1825 *Toll Free Tel:* 800-814-1132
*Fax:* 352-622-1875
*E-mail:* sales@atlantic-pub.com
*Web Site:* www.atlantic-pub.com
*Key Personnel*
Publr: Doug Brown
General business, how-to, real estate, financial, education, nonprofit, restaurant management, hospitality training, videos & posters.
ISBN Prefix(es): 978-0-910627; 978-1-60138
Number of titles published annually: 100 Print; 25 CD-ROM
Total Titles: 500 Print; 150 CD-ROM
*Returns:* 315 E Washington St, Starke, FL 32091

**Atria Books**
Imprint of Atria Publishing Group
1230 Avenue of the Americas, New York, NY 10020
*Tel:* 212-698-7000 *Fax:* 212-698-7007
*Web Site:* www.simonandschuster.com
*Key Personnel*
Pres & Publr, Atria Publishing Group: Judith Curr *Tel:* 212-698-1260 *E-mail:* judith.curr@simonandschuster.com
SVP & Ed-in-Chief, Emily Bestler Books: Emily Bestler *Tel:* 212-698-7685 *E-mail:* emily.bestler@simonandschuster.com
VP & Edit Dir: Peter Borland *Tel:* 212-698-7569
*E-mail:* peter.borland@simonandschuster.com
VP & Sr Ed: Malaika Adero *Tel:* 212-698-1257
*E-mail:* malaika.adero@simonandschuster.com; Greer Kessel-Hendricks *Tel:* 212-698-7614
*E-mail:* greer.henrdicks@simonandschuster.com
VP & Dir, Subs Rts: Lisa Keim *Tel:* 212-698-7397 *E-mail:* lisa.keim@simonandschuster.com
VP & Sr Ed: Johanna Castillo *Tel:* 212-698-7339
*E-mail:* johanna.castillo@simonandschuster.com
VP, Publr, 37 Ink: Dawn Davis *Tel:* 212-698-2246
*E-mail:* dawn.davis@simonandschuster.com
Sr Dir, Art & Design: Jeanne Lee *Tel:* 212-698-7255 *E-mail:* jeanne.lee@simonandschuster.com
Sr Ed: Sarah Durand *Tel:* 212-698-1121
*E-mail:* sarah.durand@simonandschuster.com
Ed: Sarah Branham *Tel:* 212-698-7172
*E-mail:* sarah.branham@simonandschuster.com
Founded: 2002
ISBN Prefix(es): 978-0-671; 978-0-7434; 978-0-7432

Imprints: Atria Trade Paperback; Emily Bestler Books; Beyond Words; Strebor Books; Washington Square Press
Foreign Rights: Akcali Copyright Agency (Turkey); Antonella Antonelli Agenzia (Italy); Bardon-Chinese Media Agency (China, Thailand); The Book Publishers' Association of Israel, International Promotion & Literary Rights Department (Israel); Japan UNI Agency Inc (Japan); JLM Literary Agency (Greece); MOHRBOOKS AG, Literary Agency (Germany); La Nouvelle Agency; Andrew Nurnberg Associates Ltd (Bulgaria, Croatia, Estonia, Hungary, Latvia, Lithuania, Montenegro, Poland, Romania, Russia, Serbia, Slovakia, Slovenia); Sane Toregard Agency (Denmark, Finland, Norway, Sweden); Sebes & Van Gelderen Literary Agency; Tuttle-Mori Agency Inc (Thailand); Eric Yang Agency

**Atwood Publishing**
PO Box 3185, Madison, WI 53704-0185
*Tel:* 608-242-7101 *Toll Free Tel:* 888-242-7101
*Fax:* 608-242-7102
*E-mail:* customerservice@atwoodpublishing.com
*Web Site:* www.atwoodpublishing.com
*Key Personnel*
Publr: Linda Babler *E-mail:* lindab@atwoodpublishing.com
Founded: 1997
Book publishing for higher education market: teaching improvement, distance, education, student affairs, semiotics & administration.
ISBN Prefix(es): 978-1-891859
Number of titles published annually: 11 Print
Total Titles: 55 Print; 2 CD-ROM
*Returns:* 2095 Winnebago St, Suite B, Madison, WI 53704

**AudioGO**
Subsidiary of AudioGO Ltd
42 Whitecap Dr, North Kingstown, RI 02852
*Tel:* 401-295-3800 *Toll Free Tel:* 800-621-0182
*Fax:* 401-295-3899 *Toll Free Fax:* 877-492-0873
*E-mail:* info@audiogo.com
*Web Site:* www.audiogo.com
*Key Personnel*
COO: Mike Desrosiers *E-mail:* mike.desrosiers@audiogo.com
VP, Sales & Mktg: Michele Cobb
*E-mail:* michele.cobb@audiogo.com
Sr Acqs Ed: Robert Podrasky *E-mail:* bob.podrasky@audiogo.com
Acqs Ed: Risa Chubinsky; Vikki Warner
*E-mail:* vikki.warner@audiogo.com
Retail Sales Rep: Ed Slota *E-mail:* ed.slota@audiogo.com
Founded: 1976
Leading publisher of audiobooks from bestsellers to modern classics to award-winning dramatizations.
ISBN Prefix(es): 978-0-7927 (Sound Library & Multi-Voiced); 978-0-7451 (Sound Library); 978-1-57270 (BBC Audio); 978-1-932219 (Arkangel Shakespeare); 978-0-7450 (Sound Library); 978-1-60283 (BBC Audio & BBC Radio); 978-1-60998 (AudioGO)
Number of titles published annually: 72 Print; 100 E-Book; 600 Audio
Total Titles: 500 Print; 100 E-Book; 4,000 Audio
Imprints: Audio Bookshelf; BBC Audio; BBC Radio; Chivers Audio Books; Chivers Children's Audio Books; Gunsmoke Westerns; Sound Library Audiobooks
*Orders to:* Perseus Distribution, 1094 Flex Dr, Jackson, TN 38301 *Toll Free Tel:* 800-343-4499 *Toll Free Fax:* 800-351-5073
*E-mail:* orderentry@perseusbooks.com
*Distribution Center:* Perseus Distribution, 1094 Flex Dr, Jackson, TN 38301 *Toll Free*

*Tel:* 800-343-4499 *Toll Free Fax:* 800-351-5073
*E-mail:* orderentry@perseusbooks.com
Membership(s): Audio Publishers Association

**§Augsburg Fortress Publishers, Publishing House of the Evangelical Lutheran Church in America**
100 S Fifth St, Suite 600, Minneapolis, MN 55402
SAN: 169-4081
Mailing Address: PO Box 1209, Minneapolis, MN 55440-1209
*Tel:* 612-330-3300 *Toll Free Tel:* 800-426-0115 (ext 639, subns); 800-328-4648 (orders)
*E-mail:* info@augsburgfortress.org; copyright@augsburgfortress.org (reprint permission requests); customercare@augsburgfortress.org
*Web Site:* www.augsburgfortress.org
*Key Personnel*
CEO & Pres: Beth A Lewis *E-mail:* ceo@augsburgfortress.org
SVP: Tim Blevins *Tel:* 612-330-3300 ext 400 *E-mail:* tim.blevins@augsburgfortress.org
VP, HR: Sandy Middendorf
Publr & Mng Dir: Will Bergkamp *E-mail:* will.bergkamp@augsburgfortress.org
Publr, Worship & Music: Martin Seltz
Perms: Esther Diley *E-mail:* esther.dily@augsburgfortress.org
Founded: 1855
Publishing House of the Evangelical Lutheran Church in America.
ISBN Prefix(es): 978-0-8066; 978-0-8006
Number of titles published annually: 100 Print
Total Titles: 996 Print; 10 CD-ROM; 5 Audio
Imprints: Augsburg Books; Fortress Press
*Branch Office(s)*
Seminary Bookstore, Luther Seminary, 1568 Eustis St, St Paul, MN 55108-1445 *Tel:* 651-641-3440 *Toll Free Tel:* 800-541-4187 *Fax:* 651-641-3441 *E-mail:* bookstore@luthersem.edu
Wartburg Theological Seminary, 313 Wartburg Place, Dubuque, IA 52004 *Tel:* 563-588-0200
Union Theological Seminary, 3041 Broadway, New York, NY 10027 *Tel:* 212-662-7100
Trinity Lutheran Seminary Bookstore, 2199 E Main St, Columbus, OH 43209-2334 *Tel:* 614-236-4237 *Fax:* 614-236 8528
Seminary Bookstore, Lutheran Theological Seminary at Philadelphia, 7301 Germantown Ave, Philadelpia, PA 19119-1794 *Tel:* 215-286-4616
Lutheran Theological Southern Seminary Bookstore, 4201 N Main St, Columbia, SC 29203-5898 *Tel:* 808-691-1118
*Sales Office(s):* PO Box 1209, Minneapolis, MN 55440-1209
Foreign Rep(s): Alban Books Ltd (UK); Omega (New Zealand)
*Billing Address:* PO Box 1209, Minneapolis, MN 55440-1209
*Orders to:* PO Box 1209, Minneapolis, MN 55440-1209
*Returns:* 4001 Gantz Rd, Suite E, Grove City, OH 43123-1891
*Warehouse:* 4001 Gantz Rd, Suite E, Grove City, OH 43123-1891
*Distribution Center:* 4001 Gantz Rd, Suite E, Grove City, OH 43123-1891

**August House Inc**
3500 Piedmont Rd NE, Suite 310, Atlanta, GA 30305
*Tel:* 404-442-4420 *Toll Free Tel:* 800-284-8784 *Fax:* 404-442-4435
*E-mail:* ahinfo@augusthouse.com
*Web Site:* www.augusthouse.com
*Key Personnel*
CEO: Steve Floyd *E-mail:* steve@augusthouse.com
Creative Dir: Graham Anthony *E-mail:* graham@augusthouse.com
Dir, Devt: Rob Cleveland *E-mail:* rob@augusthouse.com
Founded: 1979
Folklore, multicultural folktales & storytelling.
ISBN Prefix(es): 978-0-87483
Number of titles published annually: 15 Print; 30 Online; 15 E-Book; 8 Audio
Total Titles: 350 Print; 300 Online; 15 E-Book; 71 Audio
Imprints: August House Audio; August House LittleFolk
Foreign Rights: The Fielding Agency (Whitney Lee)

**Aum Publications**
86-10 Parsons Blvd, Jamaica, NY 11432-3314
SAN: 201-128X
*Tel:* 347-744-3199
*Web Site:* www.srichinmoybooks.com/us/aum_publications
*Key Personnel*
Pres: Carl Brown
Sales Mgr: Ahuta Markman
Founded: 1973
Trade paperbacks; literature, Eastern philosophy, theology, occult, poetry, meditation; only books on or by Sri Chinmoy.
ISBN Prefix(es): 978-0-88497
Number of titles published annually: 5 Print
Total Titles: 53 Print; 2 CD-ROM
*Distribution Center:* Heart-Light Distributors, PO Box 85464, Seattle, WA 98145 *Toll Free Tel:* 800-739-2885 *Fax:* 206-523-5637

**AuthorHouse**
Division of Author Solutions Inc
1663 Liberty Dr, Bloomington, IN 47403
*Toll Free Tel:* 888-519-5121
*E-mail:* authorsupport@authorhouse.com
*Web Site:* www.authorhouse.com
*Key Personnel*
CEO: Andrew Phillips
CFO: Kevin G Gregory
CIO: Randy Davis
SVP, Sales: Don Seitz
SVP, Prodn Servs: Bill Becher
SVP, Mktg: Keith Ogorek
Founded: 1997
The leading provider of indie book publishing, marketing & bookselling services for authors around the globe. Committed to providing the highest level of customer service. Assign each author personal publishing & marketing consultants who provide guidance throughout the process. Released the 60,000th title in spring 2009.
This publisher has indicated that 100% of their product line is author subsidized.
ISBN Prefix(es): 978-1-58500; 978-0-9675669; 978-1-58721; 978-1-58820; 978-0-7596; 978-1-4033; 978-1-4107; 978-1-4140; 978-1-4184; 978-1-4208
Number of titles published annually: 7,500 Print
Total Titles: 80,000 Print
*Foreign Office(s):* AuthorHouse UK, 500 Avebury Blvd, Milton Keynes MK9 2BE, United Kingdom *Toll Free Tel:* 800-197-4150 *Toll Free Fax:* 800-197-4151
*Distribution Center:* Baker & Taylor Inc, 2550 W Tyvola Rd, Suite 300, Charlotte, CA 28217
Ingram Book Group, One Ingram Blvd, La Vergne, TN 37086-1986
Membership(s): ABA; Canadian Booksellers Association

**Authorlink Press**
Imprint of Authorlink®
755 Laguna, Irving, TX 75039-3218
*Tel:* 972-402-0101 *Toll Free Fax:* 866-381-1587
*Web Site:* www.authorlink.com
*Key Personnel*
CEO & Ed-in-Chief: Doris Booth *E-mail:* dbooth@authorlink.com
Founded: 1999
A traditional publisher specializing in true crime, books about the craft of writing, a few children's titles, books on women's issues & some self-help. Most of our titles are published as traditional runs & not as print on demand. We are an award-winning rights market-place where editors & agents buy & sell unpublished & published mss & screenplays. Provides the serious writer with access exposure to the broadest range of legitimate publishing professionals. Plus industry news, information & marketing services for publishers, literary agents, writers & readers.
ISBN Prefix(es): 978-1-928704
Number of titles published annually: 10 Print; 5 E-Book
Total Titles: 20 Print; 5 Online
*Orders to:* Lightning Source, 1246 Heil Quaker Blvd, La Vergne, TN 37086 *Tel:* 615-213-5815 *Fax:* 615-213-4426 *E-mail:* inquiry@lightningsource.com *Web Site:* www.lightningsource.com
*Distribution Center:* Lightning Source, 1246 Heil Quaker Blvd, La Vergne, TN 37086 *Tel:* 615-213-5815 *Fax:* 615-213-4426 *E-mail:* inquiry@lightningsource.com *Web Site:* www.lightningsource.com

**Autism Asperger Publishing Co**
15490 Quivira Rd, Overland Park, KS 66223
Mailing Address: PO Box 23173, Overland Park, KS 66223
*Tel:* 913-897-1004 *Toll Free Tel:* 877-277-8254 *Fax:* 913-681-9473
*E-mail:* aapcinfo@aapcpublishing.net
*Web Site:* www.aapcpublishing.net
Specialize in books & multimedia on autism spectrum disorders (ASD) & related exceptionalities for individuals on the spectrum, their parents, families, peers, educators & other professionals.
ISBN Prefix(es): 978-0-9672514; 978-1-931282; 978-1-937473; 978-1-934575

**Autumn House Press**
87 1/2 Westwood St, Pittsburgh, PA 15211
*Tel:* 412-381-4261
*Web Site:* www.autumnhouse.org
*Key Personnel*
Founder & Ed-in-Chief: Michael Simms *E-mail:* msimms@autumnhouse.org
Founded: 1998
Nonprofit corporation with the mission of publishing poetry, fiction & nonfiction. Submissions should be through one of the annual contests. Guidelines are posted on the web site.
ISBN Prefix(es): 978-0-9669419; 978-1-932870
Number of titles published annually: 10 Print; 1 Online; 10 E-Book; 1 Audio
Total Titles: 100 Print; 12 Online; 50 E-Book; 3 Audio

**Avalon Travel Publishing**
Member of The Perseus Books Group
1700 Fourth St, Berkeley, CA 94710-1711
*Tel:* 510-595-3664 *Fax:* 510-595-4228
*Web Site:* www.avalontravelbooks.com
*Key Personnel*
SVP & Publr: Bill Newlin
VP & Assoc Publr: Donna Galassi
VP, Prodn: Jane Musser
Edit Dir: Kevin McLain *Tel:* 510-595-3664 ext 3811
Founded: 1999
Avalon Travel Publishing, an imprint of Avalon Publishing Group, is the largest independent travel publisher in the United States. Major series include Rick Steves, Moon Handbooks, Moon Metro, Foghorn Outdoors, The Dog Lover's Companion, Living Abroad & Road Trip USA.

ISBN Prefix(es): 978-1-56261; 978-1-56691; 978-1-57354; 978-1-59880
Number of titles published annually: 211 Print
Total Titles: 700 Print
Distributed by Publishers Group West
*Orders to:* Publishers Group West/Perseus Books Group, 1094 Flex Dr, Jackson, TN 38301 *Toll Free Tel:* 800-788-3123 *Toll Free Fax:* 800-351-5073
*Distribution Center:* Publishers Group West/ Perseus Books Group, 1094 Flex Dr, Jackson, TN 38301 *Toll Free Tel:* 800-788-3123 *Toll Free Fax:* 800-351-5073

**Ave Maria Press**
PO Box 428, Notre Dame, IN 46556-0428
*Tel:* 574-287-2831 *Toll Free Tel:* 800-282-1865 *Fax:* 574-239-2904 *Toll Free Fax:* 800-282-5681
*E-mail:* avemariapress.1@nd.edu
*Web Site:* www.avemariapress.com
*Key Personnel*
CEO & Publr: Thomas Grady *Tel:* 574-287-2831 ext 212 *E-mail:* tgrady@nd.edu
Dir, Sales & Mktg: Karey Circosta *Tel:* 574-287-2831 ext 219 *E-mail:* kcircosta@nd.edu
Edit Dir: Robert Hamma *Tel:* 574-287-2831 ext 214 *E-mail:* robert.m.hamma.1@nd.edu
Design & Prodn Mgr: Kristen Bonelli *Tel:* 574-287-2831 ext 240 *E-mail:* hornyak.3@nd.edu
Inside Sales Mgr: Kay Luther *Tel:* 574-287-2831 ext 232 *E-mail:* k.luther.8@nd.edu
Founded: 1865
Adult paperback books of religious interest; prayer books & religious education materials, programs & textbooks.
ISBN Prefix(es): 978-0-87793 (Ave Maria Press); 978-0-939516 (Forest of Peace); 978-0-87061 (Christian Classics); 978-1-893732 (Sorin Books); 978-1-59471 (Ave Maria Press); 978-1-933495 (Sorin Books)
Number of titles published annually: 40 Print
Total Titles: 550 Print
Imprints: Christian Classics; Forest of Peace; Sorin Books
Foreign Rep(s): Alban Books Ltd (UK); John Garratt Publishing (Australia); Joseph's Inspirational (Canada); Pleroma Christian Supplies (New Zealand)
*Returns:* 19113 Douglas Rd, Notre Dame, IN 46556 SAN: 201-1255

**Avery**
Imprint of Penguin Group (USA) LLC
375 Hudson St, New York, NY 10014
SAN: 282-5074
*Tel:* 212-366-2000 *Fax:* 212-366-2643
*E-mail:* online@penguinputnam.com
*Web Site:* www.penguinputnam.com; us.penguingroup.com
*Key Personnel*
Pres & Publr, Gotham & Avery: William Shinker
VP, Assoc Publr, Gotham & Avery: Lisa Johnson
Exec Ed, Gotham: Charles Conrad
VP, Edit Dir: Megan Newman
Sr Ed: Lucia King
Assoc Dir, Publicity: Beth Parker
Asst Dir, Publicity: Lindsay Bezalel
Publicity Mgr: Anne Kosmoski
Founded: 1976 (acquired by Penguin Putnam Inc in the fall of 1999)
The imprint is dedicated to publishing books on health & nutrition with a complimentary, natural, or alternative focus.
ISBN Prefix(es): 978-0-89529; 978-1-58333
Number of titles published annually: 35 Print
Total Titles: 247 Print

**Avery Color Studios**
511 "D" Ave, Gwinn, MI 49841
*Tel:* 906-346-3908 *Toll Free Tel:* 800-722-9925 *Fax:* 906-346-3015
*E-mail:* averycolor@averycolorstudios.com
*Key Personnel*
Pres: Wells Chapin
Busn Mgr: Amy Chapin
Founded: 1956
Regional publisher specializing in nautical books.
ISBN Prefix(es): 978-0-932212; 978-1-892384
Number of titles published annually: 4 Print
Total Titles: 46 Print
Distributed by Partners Book Distributing

**Avisson Press Inc**
3007 Taliaferro Rd, Greensboro, NC 27408
Mailing Address: PO Box 38816, Greensboro, NC 27438-8816
*Tel:* 336-288-6989; 336-285-6763 *Fax:* 336-288-6989
*E-mail:* avisson4@aol.com
*Key Personnel*
Pres & Intl Rts Contact: Martin L Hester
Contact: Michael Blood
Founded: 1994
ISBN Prefix(es): 978-1-888105
Number of titles published annually: 4 Print
Total Titles: 67 Print
Membership(s): IBPA, the Independent Book Publishers Association; Society of Children's Book Writers & Illustrators

**AVKO Educational Research Foundation Inc**
3084 Willard Rd, Birch Run, MI 48415-9404
*Tel:* 810-686-9283 (orders & billing)
*Toll Free Tel:* 866-AVKO612 (285-6612)
*Fax:* 810-686-1101
*E-mail:* info@avko.org (gen inquiry)
*Web Site:* www.avko.org; www.avko.blogspot.org
*Key Personnel*
Res Dir: Don McCabe *Tel:* 810-686-9283 ext 203 *E-mail:* donmccabe@aol.com
Opers Mgr: Robert McCabe *Tel:* 810-686-9283 ext 202 *E-mail:* brian@avko.org
Accts Receivable & Accts Payable: Sue Johnson *Tel:* 810-686-9283 ext 201 *E-mail:* avkosueat@aol.com
Founded: 1974
Nonprofit organization devoted to providing free & low-cost materials for teaching language arts, keyboarding & reference. Our materials work great for dyslexics, homeschoolers & school teachers.
ISBN Prefix(es): 978-1-56400
Total Titles: 49 Print; 6 CD-ROM; 60 E-Book

**AVKO Foundation**, see AVKO Educational Research Foundation Inc

**Avotaynu Inc**
155 N Washington Ave, Bergenfield, NJ 07621
*Tel:* 201-387-7200 *Toll Free Tel:* 800-286-8296 *Fax:* 201-387-2855
*E-mail:* info@avotaynu.com
*Web Site:* www.avotaynu.com
*Key Personnel*
Publr: Gary Mokotoff *E-mail:* garymokotoff@avotaynu.com
Founded: 1984
Publisher of information & products of interest to persons researching their Jewish family history. This includes the journal & Avotaynu books. Offer books, maps, video tapes & CDs published by other companies through catalog.
ISBN Prefix(es): 978-0-9626373; 978-1-886223
Number of titles published annually: 2 Print
Total Titles: 62 Print

**§Awe-Struck Publishing**
Imprint of Mundania Press LLC
6457 Glenway Ave, Suite 109, Cincinnati, OH 45211-5222
*Toll Free Tel:* 888-232-0808 *Fax:* 513-598-9220
*E-mail:* inquiry@mundania.com; orders@mundania.com; submissions@awe-struck.net
*Web Site:* www.awe-struck.net; www.mundania.com
Founded: 1998
Full-service, royalty paying publisher of electronic books in the following formats: html, rocket, Palm, Visor, Pocket PC, Franklin, eBookman, Hiebook, pdf, MS Reader.
Subsidiary, Earthlink Press, publishes trade paperbacks; fiction (romance & science fiction) for disabled readers (Ennoble Line).
ISBN Prefix(es): 978-1-928670; 978-1-58749
Number of titles published annually: 12 Print; 42 Online; 42 E-Book
Total Titles: 104 Print; 200 Online; 200 E-Book
Subsidiaries: Earthling Press (trade quality print editions); HeatWave Romance (erotic romance/erotica)
*Distribution Center:* Palmdigital, 950 W Maude Ave, Sunnyvale, CA 94085 *Web Site:* www.ereader.com
ebookcorp.com, 121 Mount Vernon St, Boston, MA 02108 *Web Site:* ebookcorp.com
Fictionwise.com, 346 Main St, Chatham, NJ 07928 *Web Site:* www.fictionwise.com
Franklin E-books, Inc., One Franklin Plaza, Eight Terri Lane, Burlington, NJ 08016 *Web Site:* www.franklin.com
booksurge.com, 7290-B Investment Dr, Charleston, SC 29418 *Web Site:* www.booksurge.com
Lightning Source, 1246 Heil Quaker Blvd, Lavergne, TN 37086 *Web Site:* www.lightningsource.com
Amazon, 410 Terry Ave N, Seattle, WA 98109 *Web Site:* www.amazon.com
ebookad.com, 51 Remington Dr, Richmond Hill, ON L4S 1A1, Canada *Web Site:* www.ebookad.com
Mobipocket.com, 251 Bld Pereire, 75017 Paris, France *Web Site:* www.mobipocket.com
Membership(s): IBPA, the Independent Book Publishers Association

**AZ Books LLC**
245 Eighth Ave, Suite 180, New York, NY 10011
*Toll Free Tel:* 888-945-7723 *Toll Free Fax:* 888-945-7724
*Web Site:* www.azbooksusa.com
*Key Personnel*
VP: Robert Tod *Tel:* 888-945-7723 ext 10 *E-mail:* robert@azbooksusa.com
Natl Accts Mgr: Tom Jourdane *Tel:* 801-641-3184 *E-mail:* tom@azbooksusa.com
Edit: Kate Kmit *E-mail:* kate.kmit@az-books.com
Sales: Anastasia Lobynko *E-mail:* anastasia.lobynko@az-books.com
ISBN Prefix(es): 978-0-938045

**Azro Press**
1704 Llano St B, PMB 342, Santa Fe, NM 87505
*Tel:* 505-989-3272 *Fax:* 505-989-3832
*E-mail:* books@azropress.com
*Web Site:* www.azropress.com
*Key Personnel*
Pres: Gae Eisenhardt
Founded: 1997
Publish illustrated children's books with a Southwestern flavor.
ISBN Prefix(es): 978-1-929115
Number of titles published annually: 3 Print
Total Titles: 20 Print
Imprints: Green Knees

**Babalu Inc**
PO Box 23026, Santa Barbara, CA 93121
*Toll Free Tel:* 877-522-2258
*E-mail:* info@babaluinc.com
*Web Site:* www.babaluinc.com
*Key Personnel*
Pres: Blair Everett

Off Mgr: Jessica Riggleman
Founded: 1988
Children's books, toys & advent calendars.
ISBN Prefix(es): 978-1-56021
Number of titles published annually: 10 Print
Total Titles: 60 Print
Membership(s): ABA; Museum Store Association

**Babbage Press**
8939 Canby Ave, Northridge, CA 91325-2702
Mailing Address: PO Box 1819, Crestline, CA 91325-1819
*Tel:* 818-341-3161
*E-mail:* books@babbagepress.com
*Web Site:* www.babbagepress.com
*Key Personnel*
Owner: Arthur Byron Cover; Lydia C Marano
Founded: 1999
Specialty press publisher; science fiction, fantasy & horror.
ISBN Prefix(es): 978-1-930235
Number of titles published annually: 10 Print
Total Titles: 29 Print

**Baby Tattoo Books**
6045 Longridge Ave, Van Nuys, CA 91401
*Tel:* 818-416-5314
*E-mail:* info@babytattoo.com
*Web Site:* www.babytattoo.com
*Key Personnel*
Pres & Publr: Robert Self *E-mail:* bob@babytattoo.com
Founded: 2003
Publisher of art books by contemporary artists.
ISBN Prefix(es): 978-0-9729388; 978-0-9778949; 978-0-9793307; 978-0-9845210; 978-1-61404
Number of titles published annually: 4 Print
Total Titles: 30 Print
*Orders to:* SCB Distributors Inc, 15608 S New Century Dr, Gardena, CA 90248 *Toll Free Tel:* 800-729-6423
*Returns:* SCB Distributors Inc, 15608 S New Century Dr, Gardena, CA 90248 *Toll Free Tel:* 800-729-6423
*Shipping Address:* SCB Distributors Inc, 15608 S New Century Dr, Gardena, CA 90248 *Toll Free Tel:* 800-729-6423
*Warehouse:* SCB Distributors Inc, 15608 S New Century Dr, Gardena, CA 90248 *Toll Free Tel:* 800-729-6423
*Distribution Center:* SCB Distributors Inc, 15608 S New Century Dr, Gardena, CA 90248 *Toll Free Tel:* 800-729-6423

**Back to Eden Books**, see Lotus Press

**Backbeat Books**
Imprint of Hal Leonard Performing Arts Publishing Group
33 Plymouth St, Suite 302, Montclair, NJ 07042
*Tel:* 973-337-5034 *Toll Free Tel:* 800-637-2852 (Music Dispatch) *Fax:* 973-337-5227
*Web Site:* www.backbeatbooks.com
*Key Personnel*
Publr: John Cerullo
Founded: 1991
Books about popular music & musical instruments.
ISBN Prefix(es): 978-0-87930
Number of titles published annually: 30 Print
*Distribution Center:* Hal Leonard Performing Arts Publishing Group, 1210 Innovation Dr, Winona, MN 55987

**The Backwaters Press**
3502 N 52 St, Omaha, NE 68104-3506
*Tel:* 402-451-4052
*E-mail:* thebackwaterspress@gmail.com
*Web Site:* www.thebackwaterspress.org
*Key Personnel*
Publr & Ed: Greg Kosmicki
Assoc Ed: Rich Wyatt
Founded: 1997
Nonprofit 501(c)(3) literary press.
ISBN Prefix(es): 978-0-9677149; 978-0-9726187; 978-0-9765231; 978-0-9785782; 978-0-9793934; 978-0-9816936; 978-1-935218
Number of titles published annually: 10 Print
Total Titles: 70 Print
Membership(s): Association of Writers and Writing Programs; Council of Literary Magazines & Presses

**Baen Publishing Enterprises**
PO Box 1403, Riverdale, NY 10471-0605
*Tel:* 919-570-1640 *Fax:* 919-570-1644
*E-mail:* info@baen.com
*Web Site:* www.baen.com
*Key Personnel*
Publr: Toni Weisskopf *E-mail:* toni@baen.com
Founded: 1984
Only science fiction & fantasy.
ISBN Prefix(es): 978-0-671; 978-0-7434; 978-1-4165
Number of titles published annually: 70 Print; 50 Online; 40 E-Book
Total Titles: 700 Print; 250 Online; 200 E-Book
Distributed by Simon & Schuster
Foreign Rep(s): Lora Fountain (France); Alex Korzhenevshi (Russia); Kristin Olson (Czech Republic); Thomas Schlueck (Germany)

**§Bagwyn Books**
Imprint of Arizona Center for Medieval & Renaissance Studies (ACMRS)
975 S Myrtle Ave, Tempe, AZ 85281
Mailing Address: ACMRS/ASU, PO Box 874402, Tempe, AZ 85287-4402
*Tel:* 480-965-5900 *Fax:* 480-965-1681
*E-mail:* bagwynbooks@acmrs.org
*Web Site:* acmrs.org/publications/bagwyn
*Key Personnel*
Acqs Ed: Kendra TerBeek *Tel:* 480-965-8097 *E-mail:* kendra.terbeek@acmrs.org
Mng Ed: Roy Rukkila *Tel:* 480-727-6503 *E-mail:* roy.rukkila@acmrs.org
Founded: 2011
Publisher of historical fiction & fantasy from young adult to adult.
ISBN Prefix(es): 978-0-86698
Number of titles published annually: 4 Print; 4 E-Book
Total Titles: 1 Print
*Orders to:* Chicago Distribution Center, 11030 S Langley Ave, Chicago, IL 60628 *Tel:* 773-702-7000 *Toll Free Tel:* 800-621-2736 *Fax:* 773-702-7212 *Toll Free Fax:* 800-621-8476 *E-mail:* orders@press.uchicago.edu
*Returns:* Chicago Distribution Center, 11030 S Langley Ave, Chicago, IL 60628 *Tel:* 773-702-7000 *Toll Free Tel:* 800-621-2736 *Fax:* 773-702-7212 *Toll Free Fax:* 800-621-8476 *E-mail:* orders@press.uchicago.edu
*Shipping Address:* Chicago Distribution Center, 11030 S Langley Ave, Chicago, IL 60628 *Tel:* 773-702-7000 *Toll Free Tel:* 800-621-2736 *Fax:* 773-702-7212 *Toll Free Fax:* 800-621-8476 *E-mail:* orders@press.uchicago.edu
*Warehouse:* Chicago Distribution Center, 11030 S Langley Ave, Chicago, IL 60628 *Tel:* 773-702-7000 *Toll Free Tel:* 800-621-2736 *Fax:* 773-702-7212 *Toll Free Fax:* 800-621-8476 *E-mail:* orders@press.uchicago.edu
*Distribution Center:* Chicago Distribution Center, 11030 S Langley Ave, Chicago, IL 60628 *Tel:* 773-702-7000 *Toll Free Tel:* 800-621-2736 *Fax:* 773-702-7212 *Toll Free Fax:* 800-621-8476 *E-mail:* orders@press.uchicago.edu

**Baha'i Publishing**
Subsidiary of The National Spiritual Assembly of the Baha'is of the United States
415 Linden Ave, Wilmette, IL 60091
SAN: 213-7496
*Tel:* 847-425-7950 *Fax:* 847-425-7951
*E-mail:* bpt@usbnc.org
*Web Site:* books.bahai.us
*Key Personnel*
Gen Mgr & Rts & Perms: Tim Moore
Founded: 1902
Religion (Baha'i).
ISBN Prefix(es): 978-0-87743; 978-1-931847
Number of titles published annually: 15 Print
Total Titles: 2,000 Print; 250 Audio
*Shipping Address:* 2427 Bond St, University Park, IL 60466 *Toll Free Tel:* 800-705-4925 *Toll Free Fax:* 800-705-4923

**§Baker Books**
Division of Baker Publishing Group
6030 E Fulton Rd, Ada, MI 49301
Mailing Address: PO Box 6287, Grand Rapids, MI 49516-6287 SAN: 201-4041
*Tel:* 616-676-9185 *Toll Free Tel:* 800-877-2665; 800-679-1957 *Fax:* 616-676-9573 *Toll Free Fax:* 800-398-3111
*Web Site:* www.bakerpublishinggroup.com
*Key Personnel*
CEO & Chmn: Richard Baker
Pres: Dwight Baker
EVP & Publr: Jack Kuhatschek
EVP, Sales & Mktg: Dave Lewis
Art Dir: Cheryl Van Andel
Dist Mgr: Jack Boers
Prodn Mgr: Bob Bol
Rts & Perms: Marilyn Gordon
Exec Asst: Amanda Halash
Founded: 1939
Religion (Protestant).
ISBN Prefix(es): 978-0-8010
Number of titles published annually: 75 Print; 1 CD-ROM; 1 Audio
Total Titles: 1,200 Print; 4 CD-ROM; 2 Audio
Imprints: Hamewith; Hourglass
Foreign Rep(s): Christian Art (South Africa); Family Reading Publications (Australia); R Mitchell (Canada); Send The Light (Europe, UK); Soul Distributors (New Zealand)

**§The Baker Street Irregulars (BSI)**
7938 Mill Stream Circle, Indianapolis, IN 46278
*Tel:* 317-293-2212; 317-384-4728 (cell)
*Web Site:* bakerstreetjournal.com
*Key Personnel*
Wiggins, Chmn: Michael F Whelan
Founded: 1934
Literary society.
ISBN Prefix(es): 978-0-9648788; 978-0-9795550; 978-0-9846546
Number of titles published annually: 4 Print; 1 E-Book
Total Titles: 56 Print; 1 E-Book
*Returns:* DBI Distribution
*Shipping Address:* DBI Distribution
*Warehouse:* DBI Distribution
*Distribution Center:* DBI Distribution

**Baker's Plays**
Division of Samuel French Inc
45 W 25 St, New York, NY 10010
*Toll Free Tel:* 866-598-8449 *Fax:* 212-206-1429
*E-mail:* info@bakersplays.com
*Web Site:* www.bakersplays.com
*Key Personnel*
VP: Kenneth Dingledine *Tel:* 866-598-8449 ext 147
Founded: 1845
Publish exclusively plays & books on theatre.
ISBN Prefix(es): 978-0-87440
Number of titles published annually: 25 Print
Total Titles: 1,000 Print
*Distribution Center:* Samuel French Inc

**Balance Sports Publishing**
195 Lucero Way, Portola Valley, CA 94028

SAN: 857-3298
*Tel:* 650-561-9586 *Fax:* 650-391-9850
*E-mail:* info@balancesportspublishing.com
*Web Site:* www.balancesportspublishing.com
*Key Personnel*
Publr: Jim Lobdell *E-mail:* jlobdell@balancesportspublishing.com
Dir, Busn Opers: Colleen Anderson *E-mail:* canderson@balancesportspublishing.com
Dir, Prod Devt: Steve Seely *Tel:* 530-677-6728 *E-mail:* sseely@balancesportspublishing.com
Founded: 2008
Publishes high-quality youth sports books for youth sports coaches, parents, athletes & organization leaders. Our mission is to create titles that ensure every child has a positive youth sports experience & that every coach is inspired to help youngsters achieve their goals in sports while developing important life skills & character traits.
ISBN Prefix(es): 978-0-9821317
Number of titles published annually: 3 Print
Total Titles: 12 Print
*Returns:* 3623 Munster St, Suite B, Hayward, CA 94545, Contact: Bill Armor *Tel:* 510-732-6521 *Fax:* 510-732-6523 *E-mail:* orders@balancesportspublishing.com
*Shipping Address:* 3623 Munster St, Suite B, Hayward, CA 94545, Contact: Bill Armor *Tel:* 510-732-6521 *Fax:* 510-732-6523
*Warehouse:* 3623 Munster St, Suite B, Hayward, CA 94545, Contact: Bill Armor *Tel:* 510-732-6521 *Fax:* 510-732-6523
*Distribution Center:* 3623 Munster St, Suite B, Hayward, CA 94545, Contact: Bill Armor *Tel:* 510-732-6521 *Fax:* 510-732-6523
Membership(s): IBPA, the Independent Book Publishers Association

**Ball Publishing**, see Chicago Review Press

**Ball-Stick-Bird Publications Inc**
PO Box 429, Williamstown, MA 01267-0429
SAN: 222-5565
*Tel:* 413-664-0002 *Fax:* 413-664-0002
*E-mail:* info@ballstickbird.com
*Web Site:* www.ballstickbird.com
*Key Personnel*
Pres & Rts & Perms: Dr Renee Fuller, PhD
Founded: 1975
Children's reading series.
ISBN Prefix(es): 978-0-917740
Number of titles published annually: 13 Print
Total Titles: 13 Print; 13 Online

**Ballinger Publishing**
41 N Jefferson St, Suite 402, Pensacola, FL 32502
Mailing Address: PO Box 12665, Pensacola, FL 32591-2665
*Tel:* 850-433-1166 *Fax:* 850-435-9174
*E-mail:* info@ballingerpublishing.com
*Web Site:* www.ballingerpublishing.com
*Key Personnel*
Owner & Publr: Malcolm Ballinger *Tel:* 850-433-1166 ext 27 *E-mail:* malcolm@ballingerpublishing.com
Founded: 2001
Publishers of local & regional magazines.
ISBN Prefix(es): 978-0-9791103
Number of titles published annually: 80 Print
Distributed by Anderson Distribution; Media Solutions

**Bancroft Press**
3209 Bancroft Rd, Baltimore, MD 21215
Mailing Address: PO Box 65360, Baltimore, MD 21209-9945
*Tel:* 410-358-0658 *Fax:* 410-764-1967
*Web Site:* www.bancroftpress.com
*Key Personnel*
Design Dir: Andrew Bortz *E-mail:* abortz@bancroftpress.com
Ed, Fiction & Nonfiction: Bruce L Bortz *E-mail:* bruceb@bancroftpress.com
Founded: 1995
General interest trade book publisher; has received special recognition & ranks among the nation's top 100 independent presses. Worldwide rights & distribution.
ISBN Prefix(es): 978-1-890862
Number of titles published annually: 5 Print; 1 Audio
Total Titles: 60 Print; 1 Audio
Foreign Rights: Barbara Newman

**Bandanna Books**
1212 Punta Gorda St, No 13, Santa Barbara, CA 93103
SAN: 238-7956
*Tel:* 805-899-2145
*E-mail:* bandanna@cox.net
*Web Site:* www.bandannabooks.com; www.shakespeareplaybook.com; bookdoc.us
*Key Personnel*
Publr: Ms Sasha "Birdie" Newborn *E-mail:* birdie.newborn@gmail.com
Founded: 1981 (offshoot of Mudborn Press. Recent reprints still carry the Mudborn Press ISBN's)
Literary classics in translation or modernization, teacher supplements, language books; ebooks, web-based publications & audio podcasts. Also, Book Doc: MS critiquing & subsidy publishing.
ISBN Prefix(es): 978-0-942208; 978-0-930012
Number of titles published annually: 4 Print; 3 Online; 8 E-Book; 2 Audio
Total Titles: 52 Print; 28 E-Book
Imprints: College Editions (academic journals; critique & editing; subsidy publishing); Lovers (series of little dictionaries specific to a language & activity: Italian for Opera Lovers, French for Food Lovers); Mudborn Press (reprints, poetry, fiction, lit mag); Pussywillow (classics & older literature not often found on college reading lists); Shakespeare Playbooks (series of playbooks designed for directors to envision a play & to keep track of production details)

**B&H Publishing Group**
Division of LifeWay Christian Resources
One Lifeway Plaza, Nashville, TN 37234-0114
SAN: 201-937X
*Tel:* 615-251-2520 *Fax:* 615-251-5004
*Web Site:* www.bhpublishinggroup.com
*Key Personnel*
Pres & Publr: Tom Rainer
SVP, Mktg: John Thompson
VP, Sales: Craig Featherstone
Mktg Strategist, Christian Living, Leadership & Gift: Dave Schroeder
Founded: 1934
Religious trade publisher of nonfiction (Christian living, inspirational, devotional, contemporary issues); fiction; children's books; Bibles; Biblical reference; Biblical commentaries.
ISBN Prefix(es): 978-0-8054
Number of titles published annually: 95 Print
Total Titles: 700 Print; 5 Audio
Foreign Rights: Riggins International Rights Services (Worldwide exc USA)

**Banner of Truth**
63 E Louther St, Carlisle, PA 17013
Mailing Address: PO Box 621, Carlisle, PA 17013-0621
*Tel:* 717-249-5747 *Toll Free Tel:* 800-263-8085 (orders) *Fax:* 717-249-0604
*E-mail:* info@banneroftruth.org
*Web Site:* www.banneroftruth.co.uk; www.banneroftruth.org
*Key Personnel*
Mgr: Patrick Daly
Founded: 1957
Not for profit Evangelical Christian publisher.
ISBN Prefix(es): 978-0-85151
Number of titles published annually: 15 Print
Total Titles: 802 Print
*Foreign Office(s):* The Banner of Truth Trust, The Grey House, 3 Murrayfield Rd, Edinburgh EH12 6EL, United Kingdom *Tel:* (0131) 337 7310 *Fax:* (0131) 346 7484 *E-mail:* info@banneroftruth.co.uk
Membership(s): CBA: The Association for Christian Retail; Evangelical Christian Publishers Association

**Baptist Spanish Publishing House**, see Casa Bautista de Publicaciones

**Barbour Publishing Inc**
1810 Barbour Dr, Uhrichsville, OH 44683
*Tel:* 740-922-6045 *Fax:* 740-922-5948
*E-mail:* info@barbourbooks.com
*Web Site:* www.barbourbooks.com
*Key Personnel*
CEO & Pres: Tim H Martins *E-mail:* tmartins@barbourbooks.com
VP, Sales & Mktg: William Westfall *E-mail:* bwestfall@barbourbooks.com
Edit Dir: Kelly McIntosh *E-mail:* kmcintosh@barbourbooks.com
Founded: 1981
Christian books, Bibles, fiction, gift books, devotional journals, reference.
ISBN Prefix(es): 978-1-57748; 978-0-916441; 978-1-55748; 978-1-58660; 978-1-59310; 978-1-59789; 978-1-60260; 978-1-61626
Number of titles published annually: 244 Print
Total Titles: 793 Print
Imprints: Barbour Books
Foreign Rights: Christian Art Wholesale (South Africa); R G Mitchell; Nova Distributors (Canada, UK)

**Barcelona Publishers**
Pathway Book Service, 4 White Brook Rd, Gilsum, NH 03448
SAN: 298-6299
Mailing Address: 27602 Bogen Rd, New Braunfels, TX 78132-3873
*Tel:* 603-357-0236 *Fax:* 603-357-2073
*E-mail:* pbs@pathwaybook.com; barcelonapublishers@gvtc.com
*Web Site:* www.barcelonapublishers.com
*Key Personnel*
Prop: Kenneth E Bruscia *E-mail:* kbruscia@gvtc.com
Founded: 1991
Music therapy books & materials.
ISBN Prefix(es): 978-0-9624080; 978-1-891278
Number of titles published annually: 3 Print
Total Titles: 60 Print
Distributed by Pathway Books

**Barefoot Books**
2067 Massachusetts Ave, 5th fl, Cambridge, MA 02140
*Tel:* 617-576-0660 *Toll Free Tel:* 866-215-1756 (cust serv); 866-417-2369 (orders) *Fax:* 617-576-0049
*E-mail:* ussales@barefootbooks.com; help@barefootbooks.com
*Web Site:* www.barefootbooks.com
*Key Personnel*
CEO: Nancy Traversy *E-mail:* nancy.traversy@barefootbooks.com
Group Opers Dir: Karen Janson *E-mail:* karen.janson@barefootbooks.com
Ed-in-Chief (UK Off): Tessa Strickland *E-mail:* tessa.strickland@barefootbooks.co.uk

Founded: 1993
Publishes high quality picture books for children of all ages specializing in the work of authors & artists from many cultures, wrapping paper, artists prints & cards.
ISBN Prefix(es): 978-1-898000; 978-1-901223; 978-1-902283; 978-1-84148; 978-1-84686; 978-1-905236
Number of titles published annually: 30 Print; 12 Audio
Total Titles: 300 Print
*Foreign Office(s):* 294 Banbury Rd, Oxford Oxford OX2 7ED, United Kingdom, Contact: Elinor Brown *Tel:* (01865) 311100
*Returns:* RR Donnelley Packaging & Fulfillment, 655 Brighton Beach Rd, Menasha, WI 54952
*Warehouse:* RR Donnelley Packaging & Fulfillment, 655 Brighton Beach Rd, Menasha, WI 54952
Membership(s): ALA; Children's Book Council

**Barnhardt & Ashe Publishing**
444 Brickell Ave, Suite 51, PMB 432, Miami, FL 33131
*Toll Free Tel:* 800-283-6360 (orders)
*E-mail:* barnhardtashe@aol.com
*Web Site:* www.barnhardtashepublishing.com
Founded: 2001
ISBN Prefix(es): 978-0-9715402; 978-0-9801744
Number of titles published annually: 10 Print
Total Titles: 9 Print
Membership(s): AAP

**Barranca Press**
1450 Couse St, No 10, Taos, NM 87571
*Tel:* 575-613-1026
*E-mail:* editor@barrancapress.com
*Web Site:* www.barrancapress.com
*Key Personnel*
Editor: Lisa Noudehou *E-mail:* lisa@barrancapress.com
Founded: 2012
Booklist includes photojournalism, novels, literary collections, children's books & memoirs. Unsol mss accepted March-Aug annually. E-mail submissions preferred.
ISBN Prefix(es): 978-1-939604
Number of titles published annually: 5 Print; 5 E-Book
Total Titles: 5 Print

**Barricade Books Inc**
185 Bridge Plaza N, Suite 309, Fort Lee, NJ 07024
*Tel:* 201-944-7600 *Fax:* 201-917-4951
*E-mail:* customerservice@barricadebooks.com
*Web Site:* www.barricadebooks.com
*Key Personnel*
Pres & Treas: Carole Stuart *E-mail:* cstuart@barricadebooks.com
Prodn Mgr: Mark Morrell
Founded: 1992
ISBN Prefix(es): 978-0-942637; 978-0-9623032; 978-1-56980
Number of titles published annually: 30 Print
Total Titles: 200 Print
Imprints: Barricade Books
*Returns:* National Book Network, 4501 Forbes Blvd, Suite 200, Lanham, MD 20706 *Tel:* 301-459-3366 *Toll Free Tel:* 800-462-6420 *Fax:* 301-429-5746
*Warehouse:* National Book Network, 4501 Forbes Blvd, Suite 200, Lanham, MD 20706 *Tel:* 301-459-3366 *Toll Free Tel:* 800-462-6420 *Fax:* 301-429-5746
*Distribution Center:* National Book Network, 4501 Forbes Blvd, Suite 200, Lanham, MD 20706 *Tel:* 301-459-3366 *Toll Free Tel:* 800-462-6420 *Fax:* 301-429-5746
Membership(s): AAP

**Barringer Publishing**
Division of Schlesinger Advertising & Marketing
3259 Sundance Circle, Naples, FL 34109
*Tel:* 239-514-7364 *Fax:* 239-596-8135
*E-mail:* info@barringerpublishing.com
*Web Site:* www.barringerpublishing.com
*Key Personnel*
Owner: Jeff Schlesinger *E-mail:* js@barringerpublishing.com
Founded: 2009
Full service: cover & book design, editing, printing, marketing, advertising & public relations, web sites, graphics, displays & illustrations.
ISBN Prefix(es): 978-0-9825109
Number of titles published annually: 15 Print
Total Titles: 60 Print
Membership(s): IBPA, the Independent Book Publishers Association

**Barron's Educational Series Inc**
250 Wireless Blvd, Hauppauge, NY 11788
SAN: 201-453X
*Tel:* 631-434-3311 *Toll Free Tel:* 800-645-3476 *Fax:* 631-434-3723
*E-mail:* barrons@barronseduc.com
*Web Site:* www.barronseduc.com
*Key Personnel*
Chmn & CEO: Manuel H Barron
Pres & Publr: Ellen Sibley
VP, Sales & Mktg: Alex Holtz
Dir, Mktg: Lonny R Stein
Dir, School Sales & Lib Sales: Frederick Glasser
Intl Sales Mgr: Jackie Raab
Natl Sales Mgr: Jeff Goldman
Subs Rts Mgr & Intl Rts: Patricia Doyle
Acq Ed: Wayne Barr
Founded: 1941
El-hi & college education; guidance & test review.
ISBN Prefix(es): 978-0-8120; 978-0-7641
Number of titles published annually: 300 Print
Total Titles: 3,000 Print; 125 Audio
Foreign Rep(s): Book Marketing Services Inc (Canada)
Foreign Rights: Anthea Literary Agency (Bulgaria); Big Apple Agency Inc (China); Contacts/The Rights Agency (Canada); DRT International (Korea); Lora Fountain & Associates Literary Agency (France); International Editors' Co (Latin America, Portugal, Spain); Nurcihan Kesim Literary Agency Inc (Turkey); David Matlock Agency (Russia); Montreal Contacts/The Rights Agency (Canada (French-speaking)); OA Literary Agency (Greece); Tuttle-Mori Agency Inc (Japan)
*Advertising Agency:* Friedman, Harris & Partners

**Barrytown/Station Hill Press**
120 Station Hill Rd, Barrytown, NY 12507
SAN: 214-1485
*Tel:* 845-758-5293
*E-mail:* publishers@stationhill.org
*Web Site:* www.stationhill.org
*Key Personnel*
Pubns & Ed: George Quasha
Founded: 1977
General trade books, quality paperbacks & fine editions; poetry, fiction & discourse; visual arts; studies in literature & psychology, classics, translations, theater, creative nonfiction, health/New Age.
ISBN Prefix(es): 978-0-930794; 978-0-88268
Number of titles published annually: 6 Print
Total Titles: 300 Print
Foreign Rep(s): Lora Fountain (France); Gara Media (Germany); Japanville (Japan); Kerrigan (Spain); Living Weary (Italy)
*Distribution Center:* Midpoint Trade Books, 1263 Southwest Blvd, Kansas City, KS 66103 *Tel:* 913-362-7400 *Fax:* 913-362-7401 *E-mail:* info@midpointtradebooks.com *Web Site:* www.midpointtradebooks.com

**Bartleby Press**
Subsidiary of Jackson Westgate Inc
8600 Foundry St, Savage Mill Box 2043, Savage, MD 20763
SAN: 241-2098
*Tel:* 301-725-3906 *Toll Free Tel:* 800-953-9929 *Fax:* 301-725-0333
*E-mail:* inquiries@bartlebythepublisher.com
*Web Site:* www.bartlebythepublisher.com
*Key Personnel*
Publr: Jeremy Kay *E-mail:* publisher@bartlebythepublisher.com
Proj Ed: Greg Giroux
Founded: 1981
ISBN Prefix(es): 978-0-910155; 978-0-9625963; 978-0-935437
Number of titles published annually: 7 Print; 8 E-Book
Total Titles: 46 Print; 14 E-Book
Imprints: Elstreet Educational; Eshel Books; PS&E Publications
Distributor for BJE Press
Membership(s): IBPA, the Independent Book Publishers Association

**Basic Books**
Imprint of The Perseus Books Group
250 W 57 St, 15th fl, New York, NY 10107
*Tel:* 212-340-8164 *Fax:* 212-340-8135
*E-mail:* perseus.promos@perseusbooks.com
*Web Site:* www.basicbooks.com; perseusbooks.com
*Key Personnel*
Pres & CEO, Perseus Books Group: David Steinberger
VP, Assoc Publr & Mktg Dir: Clay Farr
Chief Mktg Offr: Matthew Goldberg
Group Publr: Susan Weinberg
Publr: Laura Heimert
Dir, Publicity: Michele Jacob
Asst Dir, Publicity: Betsy DeJesu
Publicist: Justin Hargett
Mng Ed: Chris Granville
Sr Exec Ed: Timothy Bartlett
Ed: Alex Littlefield; Tisse Takagi
Asst Ed: Kathy O'Donnell
Founded: 1952
Nonfiction only. Subjects include current affairs & memoirs.
ISBN Prefix(es): 978-0-465
Number of titles published annually: 100 Print
Total Titles: 1,000 Print
Imprints: Basic Civitas; Counterpoint
Distributed by CDS Distributors
Foreign Rep(s): James Benson (North Midlands, UK, Northern England, Staffordshire, UK); Jim Chalmers (Scotland); Kemper Conseil (Belgium, Luxembourg, Netherlands); Gilles Fauveau (Japan, Korea); Bernd Feldmann (Austria, Germany, Switzerland); Colin Flint Publishers Scandinavian Consultancy (Ben Greig) (Scandinavia); Charles Gibbes (Cyprus, Greece); Jaime C Gregorio (Guam, Philippines); Laszlo Horvath (Central Europe, Eastern Europe); Natalie Jones (London); Mark Latcham (Central London, UK, Southern Wales); Vivienne Lavery (Ireland); Mare Nostrum Publishing Consultants (David Pickering) (Italy); Mare Nostrum Publishing Consultants (Sabrina Cote) (France); Mare Nostrum Publishing Consultants (Cristina de Lara) (Portugal, Spain); Barbara Martin (Buckinghamshire, UK, East Midlands, UK, Gloucestershire, UK, West Midlands, UK); Miraida Morales (Caribbean, Latin America); Ray Potts (Middle East); Publisher's Group Worldwide (Africa, Asia, Central America, Middle East, South America); Scribe International (Camilla Dorsch) (Australia, New Zealand); David Smith (East Anglia, England, Southeast England); Wei Zhao (China, Hong Kong, Taiwan)
Foreign Rights: Bardon-Chinese Media Agency (China, Taiwan); Raquel de la Concha Agen-

cia Literaria (Raquel de la Concha) (Brazil, Latin America, Portugal, Spain); Agence Hoffman (Germany); Duran Kim Agency (Korea); Alexander Korzhenevski Agency (Russia); I Pikarski Agency (Israel); Santachiara Literary Agency (Roberto Santachiara) (Italy); Sebes & Van Gelderen Literary Agency (Netherlands); Tuttle-Mori Agency Inc (Japan)
*Warehouse:* CDS Distributors, 193 Edwards Dr, Jackson, TN 38301
*Distribution Center:* 1094 Flex Dr, Jackson, TN 38301 *Toll Free Tel:* 800-343-4499 *Toll Free Fax:* 800-351-5073

**Basic Health Publications Inc**
28812 Top of the World Dr, Laguna Beach, CA 92651
*Tel:* 949-715-7327 *Toll Free Tel:* 800-575-8890 (orders) *Fax:* 949-715-7328
*E-mail:* info@basichealthpub.com
*Web Site:* www.basichealthpub.com
*Key Personnel*
Pres & Publr: Norman Goldfind
Sales Dir: Ken Kaiman
Publicity: Courtney Dunham
Prodn: Boris M Lawer
Mng Ed: Cheryl Hirsch
Typesetter & Text Design: Gary Rosenberg
Ed: Susan Davis; Carol Rosenberg
Founded: 2001
ISBN Prefix(es): 978-1-59120
Number of titles published annually: 15 Print; 25 Online; 25 E-Book
Total Titles: 200 Print; 50 Online; 50 E-Book
Imprints: Basic Health Guides; Basic Health Publications; User's Guides
Foreign Rights: Athena Productions Inc (Worldwide)
*Returns:* Returns Dept, 885 Claycraft Rd, Columbus, OH 43230
*Warehouse:* 885 Claycraft Rd, Columbus, OH 43230, Cust Serv: Alice Heigel *Tel:* 614-863-3004 *Fax:* 614-863-9007 *E-mail:* aheigel@basicmediagroup.com

**Bay Tree Publishing LLC**
1400 Pinnacle Ct, Suite 406, Point Richmond, CA 94801-4178
*Tel:* 510-236-1475 *Toll Free Fax:* 866-552-7329
*Web Site:* www.baytreepublish.com
*Key Personnel*
Publr: David Cole *E-mail:* dcole@baytreepublish.com
Founded: 2002
ISBN Prefix(es): 978-0-9801758; 978-0-9720021; 978-0-9819577
Number of titles published annually: 5 Print; 5 E-Book
Total Titles: 20 Print; 8 E-Book
Imprints: Ardenwood Books
Foreign Rep(s): National Book Network (Les Petriw) (Australia, Canada, New Zealand, UK)
*Orders to:* National Book Network (NBN), 15200 NBN Way, Blue Ridge Summit, PA 17214 *Toll Free Tel:* 800-462-6420
*Returns:* National Book Network (NBN), 15200 NBN Way, Blue Ridge Summit, PA 17214
*Shipping Address:* National Book Network (NBN), 15200 NBN Way, Blue Ridge Summit, PA 17214
*Warehouse:* National Book Network (NBN), 15200 NBN Way, Blue Ridge Summit, PA 17214
*Distribution Center:* National Book Network (NBN), 15200 NBN Way, Blue Ridge Summit, PA 17214
Membership(s): Bay Area Independent Publishers Association; IBPA, the Independent Book Publishers Association; Northern California Book Publicity & Marketing Association

**Baylor University Press**
Baylor University, One Bear Place, Waco, TX 76798-7363
SAN: 685-317X
Mailing Address: PO Box 97363, Waco, TX 76798-7363
*Tel:* 254-710-3164 *Fax:* 254-710-3440
*Web Site:* www.baylorpress.com
*Key Personnel*
Dir: Dr Carey C Newman *E-mail:* carey_newman@baylor.edu
Prodn Mgr: Diane E Smith *E-mail:* diane_smith@baylor.edu
Founded: 1955
Scholarly books & monographs.
ISBN Prefix(es): 978-0-918954; 978-1-932792
Number of titles published annually: 30 Print
Total Titles: 110 Print
Distributed by Johns Hopkins University Press Fullfillment Service
*Distribution Center:* Johns Hopkins University Press Fullfillment Service, PO Box 50370, Baltimore, MD 21211-4370, Contact: Melinda Kelly *Tel:* 410-516-6956 *Fax:* 410-516-6998 *E-mail:* mrk@press.jhu.edu
Membership(s): American Political Science Association; Society of Bible Literature

**Baywood Publishing Co Inc**
26 Austin Ave, Amityville, NY 11701
SAN: 206-9326
Mailing Address: PO Box 337, Amityville, NY 11701-0337
*Tel:* 631-691-1270 *Toll Free Tel:* 800-638-7819 *Fax:* 631-691-1770
*E-mail:* baywood@baywood.com
*Web Site:* www.baywood.com
*Key Personnel*
Pres: Stuart Cohen
Electronic Content Mgr: Lorna Roher
Cust Rels: S Edwards
Rts & Perms & ISBN Contact: Julie Krempa
Founded: 1964
Professional journals & books: anthropology, archaeology, education, imagery, psychiatry & psychology, health services, health education, labor relations, sociology, mathematics, computers in education, thanatology, imagery, environment, technical communication, gerontology, fire science, employee rights.
ISBN Prefix(es): 978-0-89503
Number of titles published annually: 40 Print; 24 Online; 15 E-Book
Total Titles: 400 Print; 24 Online; 120 E-Book
Foreign Rep(s): Book Representation & Distribution Ltd (England, UK)

**BBC Audiobooks America**, see AudioGO

**BBS Publishing Corp**, see Bristol Park Books

**Beach Lane Books**, see Simon & Schuster Children's Publishing

**Beach Lloyd Publishers LLC**
40 Cabot Dr, Wayne, PA 19087-5619
SAN: 255-4992
Mailing Address: PO Box 2183, Southeastern, PA 19399-2183
*Tel:* 610-407-9107 *Toll Free Tel:* 866-218-3253 (pin 8668) *Fax:* 775-254-0633
*E-mail:* beachlloyd@erols.com
*Web Site:* www.beachlloyd.com
*Key Personnel*
Owner & Mgr: Joanne S Silver
Founded: 2002
Distribution Center: Baker & Taylor.
ISBN Prefix(es): 978-0-9743158; 978-0-9792778
Number of titles published annually: 3 Print; 1 Audio
Total Titles: 18 Print
*Sales Office(s):* PO Box 2183, Southeastern, PA 19399-2183
Distributed by Tralco (CN)
Distributor for Le Chambon-sur-Lignon; CIDEB (Italy); Deanne Scherlis Comer (DVDs); Ellipses (Paris); Fondation pour la Memoire de la Shoah (Paris); Kar-Ben Publishing; Kiron Editions du Felin (Paris); JP Lattes (Paris); Le Manuscrit (Paris); Oxford University Press (NYC)
*Billing Address:* PO Box 2183, Southeastern, PA 19399-2183
Membership(s): American Association of Teachers of French; IBPA, the Independent Book Publishers Association

**Beacon Hill Press of Kansas City**
Subsidiary of Nazarene Publishing House
PO Box 419527, Kansas City, MO 64141-6527
SAN: 202-9022
*Tel:* 816-931-1900 *Toll Free Tel:* 800-877-0700 (cust serv) *Fax:* 816-753-4071
*Web Site:* www.beaconhillbooks.com
*Key Personnel*
Dir: Bonnie Perry
Head, Mktg: Rachel McPherson
Mgr, Rts & Perms: Janet Stapleton
ISBN Contact: Richard Buckner
Founded: 1912
Religion (Nazarene), ministry resources, Christian care & spiritual growth.
ISBN Prefix(es): 978-0-83412
Number of titles published annually: 30 Print
Total Titles: 700 Print
Imprints: Lifestream; Lillenas Publishing Co (church music); Nazarene Publishing House
*Shipping Address:* 2923 Troost Ave, Kansas City, MO 64109

**Beacon Press**
25 Beacon St, Boston, MA 02108
SAN: 201-4483
*Tel:* 617-742-2110 *Fax:* 617-723-3097; 617-742-2290
*Web Site:* www.beacon.org
*Key Personnel*
Dir: Helene Atwan
Dir, Sales & Mktg & Assoc Publr: Tom Hallock
Prodn Dir: P J Tierney
Exec Ed: Amy Caldwell; Gayatri Patnaik
Founded: 1854
General nonfiction, religion & theology, current affairs, anthropology, women's studies, history, gay & lesbian studies, African-American studies, Latino studies, education, hardcover, paperback, ebook & audio.
ISBN Prefix(es): 978-0-8070
Number of titles published annually: 60 Print; 35 E-Book
Total Titles: 800 Print; 350 E-Book; 5 Audio
Imprints: Concord Library; The King Legacy (writings of Dr Martin Luther King Jr)
Distributed by Random House Publisher Services
Foreign Rep(s): New South Books (Australia, New Zealand); Publishers Group UK (UK)
Foreign Rights: Akcali Copyright Agency (Turkey); Eliane Benisti Literary Agency (France); Chinese Connection Agency (China); The Deborah Harris Agency (Israel); Agence Hoffman (Germany); International Editors' Co (Portugal, Spain); Agenzia Internazionale Literaria (Italy); Maxima Creative Agency (Indonesia); Paterson Marsh Ltd (UK); Prava I Prevodi Literary Agency (Eastern Europe exc Estonia, Latvia, Lituania & Russia, Greece); Agencia Riff (Brazil); Synopsis Literary Agency (Russia); Tuttle-Mori Agency Inc (Japan); Eric Yang Agency (Korea)
*Returns:* Random House Returns Dept, 1019 N State Rd 47, Crawfordsville, IN 47933
*Warehouse:* Random House Publishing Services, 400 Hahn Rd, Westminster, MD 21157 *Toll Free Tel:* 800-733-3000 *Toll Free*

*Fax:* 800-659-2436 *E-mail:* customerservice@randomhouse.com
Membership(s): American Association of University Presses; New England Independent Booksellers Association

**Bear & Co Inc**
Subsidiary of Inner Traditions International Ltd
One Park St, Rochester, VT 05767
Mailing Address: PO Box 388, Rochester, VT 05767-0388
*Tel:* 802-767-3174 *Toll Free Tel:* 800-932-3277 *Fax:* 802-767-3726
*E-mail:* customerservice@InnerTraditions.com
*Web Site:* InnerTraditions.com
*Key Personnel*
Pres: Ehud C Sperling *E-mail:* prez@InnerTraditions.com
VP & Mng Ed: Jeanie Levitan *E-mail:* jeaniel@InnerTraditions.com
VP, Opers: Diane Shepard *E-mail:* dianes@InnerTraditions.com
Dir, Content & Consumer Sales: Rob Meadows *E-mail:* robm@InnerTraditions.com
Dir, Sales & Mktg: John Hays *E-mail:* johnh@innertraditions.com
Print Mgr: Jon Desautels *E-mail:* jond@InnerTraditions.com
Acqs Ed: Jon Graham *E-mail:* jong@InnerTraditions.com
Sales & Mktg: Andrea Raymond *E-mail:* andyr@InnerTraditions.com
Spec Sales: Jessica Arsenault *E-mail:* jessa@InnerTraditions.com
Publicity & Foreign Rts & Perms: Cynthia Fowles *E-mail:* cynthiaf@InnerTraditions.com
Founded: 1980
Mysticism, philosophy, spirituality & medieval studies, contemporary prophecy, earth sciences, indigenous wisdom, new thought, alternative healing.
ISBN Prefix(es): 978-1-879181; 978-0-939680; 978-1-59143
Number of titles published annually: 13 Print
Total Titles: 240 Print
Imprints: Bear & Co; Bear Cub Books
Foreign Rep(s): Akasha Books Ltd (New Zealand); Brumby Books & Music (Australia); Michelle Morrow Curreri (all other territories, India); Deep Books (Europe, UK); India Book Distributors (India); Inner Traditions Canada (Canada); Real Books (South Africa); Zimpfer Books (Caribbean including Puerto Rico, Central America, Mexico, South America)
Foreign Rights: Agenzia Letteraria Internazionale (Italy); Akcali Copyright Agency (Turkey); Big Apple Agency Inc (China, Taiwan); The Book Publishers' Association of Israel, International Promotion & Literary Rights Department (Israel); Amina Marix Evans (Netherlands); Graal Literary Agency (Poland); Ilidio da Fonseca Matos (Portugal); International Editors' Co SL (Argentina, Spain); Simona Kessler International Copyright Agency Ltd (Romania); Alexander Korzhenevski Agency (Russia); Zvonimir Majdak (Croatia); Montreal-Contacts/The Rights Agency (Canada); Andrew Nurnberg Associates Ltd (Baltic States, Bulgaria, Czech Republic, Hungary); Read n Right Agency (Greece); Karin Schindler (Brazil); Thomas Schlueck GmbH (Germany); Agence Schweiger (France); Tuttle-Mori Agency Inc (Japan, Thailand); Eric Yang Agency (Korea)
*Warehouse:* Inner Traditions International, Airport Business Park, 364 Innovation Dr, North Clarendon, VT 05759, Contact: Jim Cassel *Tel:* 802-773-8930 *Fax:* 802-773-6993

**Beard Books Inc**
Member of Beard Group Inc
47 E South St, Suite 102, Frederick, MD 21701
Mailing Address: PO Box 4250, Frederick, MD 21705-4250
*Tel:* 240-629-3300 *Toll Free Tel:* 888-563-4573 (book orders) *Fax:* 240-629-3360
*E-mail:* info@beardbooks.com; order@beardbooks.com
*Web Site:* www.beardbooks.com; www.beardgroup.com
*Key Personnel*
Owner & Pres: Chris Beard
Founded: 1988
Publishers of softcover books & electronic newsletters for business & law.
ISBN Prefix(es): 978-1-893122; 978-1-58798
Number of titles published annually: 6 Print
Total Titles: 360 Print

**Bearport Publishing Co Inc**
45 W 21 St, Suite 3B, New York, NY 10010
*Tel:* 212-337-8577 *Toll Free Tel:* 877-337-8577 *Fax:* 212-337-8557 *Toll Free Fax:* 866-337-8557
*E-mail:* info@bearportpublishing.com
*Web Site:* www.bearportpublishing.com
*Key Personnel*
Pres & Publr: Kenn Goin
Assoc Publr, Mktg & Sales: Gabe Kaufman *E-mail:* gkaufman@bearportpublishing.com
VP, Design & Prodn: Spencer Brinker
Edit Dir: Adam Siegel
Sr Ed: Joyce Tavolacci
Natl Sales Mgr: Linda McGee
Founded: 2003
Curriculum-aligned, high-interest nonfiction for the library market.
ISBN Prefix(es): 978-1-59716; 978-1-936087; 978-1-61772
Number of titles published annually: 68 Print; 440 E-Book
Total Titles: 570 Print
*Returns:* Corporate Grapics, 2025 Lookout Dr, North Mankato, MN 56002 *Toll Free Tel:* 800-851-8767 *Fax:* 507-389-3399 *E-mail:* marketing@cgintl.com
*Shipping Address:* Corporate Grapics, 2025 Lookout Dr, North Mankato, MN 56002 *Toll Free Tel:* 800-851-8767 *Fax:* 507-389-3399
*Warehouse:* Corporate Grapics, 2025 Lookout Dr, North Mankato, MN 56002 *Toll Free Tel:* 800 851-8767 *Fax:* 507-389-3399
Membership(s): ALA; Children's Book Council

**§Beaufort Books**
27 W 20 St, Suite 1102, New York, NY 10011
*Tel:* 212-727-0222 *Fax:* 212-727-0195
*E-mail:* info@beaufortbooks.com
*Web Site:* www.beaufortbooks.com
*Key Personnel*
Pres: Eric M Kampmann
Mng Ed: Megan Trank *E-mail:* megan@beaufortbooks.com
ISBN Prefix(es): 978-1-59921
Number of titles published annually: 12 Print; 12 E-Book
Total Titles: 100 Print; 100 E-Book
Imprints: Moyer Bell; Papier-Mache Press
*Distribution Center:* Midpoint Trade Books, 27 W 20 St, Suite 1102, New York, NY 10011 *Tel:* 212-727-0190 *Fax:* 212-727-0195

**Beautiful America Publishing Co**
2600 Progress Way, Woodburn, OR 97071
Mailing Address: PO Box 244, Woodburn, OR 97071-0244
*Tel:* 503-982-4616 *Toll Free Tel:* 800-874-1233 *Fax:* 503-982-2825
*E-mail:* bapco@beautifulamericapub.com
*Web Site:* www.beautifulamericapub.com
*Key Personnel*
Pres: Beverly Paul
Founded: 1987
Nature & scenic regional books & calendars.
ISBN Prefix(es): 978-0-89802
Number of titles published annually: 5 Print
Total Titles: 28 Print
Imprints: Little America Publishing Co
Membership(s): Pacific Northwest Booksellers Association

**Beaver's Pond Press Inc**
7108 Ohms Lane, Edina, MN 55439-2129
*Tel:* 952-829-8818
*Web Site:* www.beaverspondpress.com
*Key Personnel*
CEO & Publr: Tom Kerber *Tel:* 952-641-5250 *E-mail:* tom@beaverspondpress.com
Publg Dir: Lily Coyle *Tel:* 952-641-5254 *E-mail:* lily@beaverspondpress.com
Mktg Mgr: Heather Kerber *Tel:* 952-641-5251 *E-mail:* heather@beaverspondpress.com
Founded: 1998
Mission is to mentor authors to publish the best book possible through strategic marketing & creative collaboration, with quality, commitment & connection as the three guiding principles.
ISBN Prefix(es): 978-1-59298
Number of titles published annually: 60 Print; 50 E-Book
Total Titles: 250 Print; 100 E-Book
*Branch Office(s)*
Book House Fulfillment, 5120 Cedar Lake Rd S, Minneapolis, MN 55416 *Web Site:* www.bookhousefulfillment.com
Membership(s): IBPA, the Independent Book Publishers Association; Midwest Independent Booksellers Association; Midwest Independent Publishers Association

**Beckett Media LLC**
22840 Savi Ranch Pkwy, Suite 200, Yorba Linda, CA 92887
SAN: 214-3313
*Tel:* 714-939-9991 *Toll Free Tel:* 800-332-3330 *Fax:* 714-939-9909 *Toll Free Fax:* 800-249-7761
*Web Site:* www.beckettmedia.com
*Key Personnel*
Acct Exec: Chris Crispell *Tel:* 714-200-1935 *E-mail:* ccrispell@beckett.com
Sales Mgr, Auto Group: Brandon Lillie *Tel:* 714-200-1931 *E-mail:* blillie@beckett.com
Ad Coord: Eric Gomez *Tel:* 714-200-1938 *E-mail:* egomez@beckett.com
Founded: 1973
Alternative health, paperbacks, periodicals & videos on martial arts, instructional & how-to.
ISBN Prefix(es): 978-0-86568
Number of titles published annually: 15 Print
Total Titles: 125 Print

**Bedford, Freeman & Worth Publishing Group, LLC**
Subsidiary of Macmillan
41 Madison Ave, 37th fl, New York, NY 10010
*Tel:* 212-576-9400 *Fax:* 212-689-2383
*Web Site:* www.macmillanhighered.com
*Key Personnel*
CEO: John Sargent
Pres, Macmillan Higher Ed: Joan Feinberg; Tom Scotty
Pres, W H Freeman & Worth: Elizabeth Widdicombe
Pres, Mac Labs Higher Ed: Nicholas Smith
Pres, New Ventures: Troy Williams
CTO: Alex Hottenstein
SVP, Fin & Admin, Macmillan Higher Ed: Jamie Demas
Founded: 1999
Bedford, Freeman & Worth Publishing Group, LLC is a group of 3 college & secondary school publishing companies: Bedford/St Martin's, W H Freeman & Co & Worth Publishers.
*See separate listing for:*
**Bedford/St Martin's**
**W H Freeman and Co**
**Worth Publishers**

**Bedford/St Martin's**
Division of Bedford, Freeman & Worth Publishing Group, LLC
75 Arlington St, Boston, MA 02116
*Tel:* 617-399-4000 *Toll Free Tel:* 800-779-7440 *Fax:* 617-426-8582
*Web Site:* www.bedfordstmartins.com
*Key Personnel*
Pres, Edit Dir: Denise Wydra
Ed-in-Chief, English: Karen Henry
Pubr, History: Mary Dougherty
Publr, Communs: Erika Gutierrez
Dir, Editing, Design & Prodn: Sue Brown
Dir, Mktg & Promo: Karen Soeltz
Ad & Promo Mgr: Shelby Disario
Founded: 1981
Humanities publisher specializing in English composition, literature, history, communication, college success & music.
ISBN Prefix(es): 978-0-312; 978-1-457
Number of titles published annually: 200 Print; 20 CD-ROM; 50 E-Book
*Branch Office(s)*
33 Irving Place, New York, NY 10003 *Tel:* 212-375-7000 *Toll Free Tel:* 800-223-1715
*Warehouse:* MPS Distribution Center, 16365 James Madison Hwy (US Rte 15), Gordonsville, VA 22942 *Toll Free Tel:* 888-330-8477 *Fax:* 540-672-7540 (cust serv) *Toll Free Fax:* 800-672-2054 (orders)
Membership(s): AAP

**Beekman Books Inc**
300 Old All Angels Hill Rd, Wappingers Falls, NY 12590
*Tel:* 845-297-2690 *Fax:* 845-297-1002
*E-mail:* manager@beekmanbooks.com
*Web Site:* www.beekmanbooks.com
*Key Personnel*
Pres: Michael Arthur
Founded: 1972
New titles, reprints & imported titles from England, Wales, India & Russia in all subject areas, particularly music, holistic healing, homeopathic medicine, business, medical & computer books.
ISBN Prefix(es): 978-0-8464
Number of titles published annually: 12 Print
Total Titles: 3,026 Print
Distributor for Chartered Institute for Personnel Development (CIPD); C W Daniel; Gomer Press; Music Sales Corp; Kogan Page

**Begell House Inc Publishers**
50 Cross Hwy, Redding, CT 06896
*Tel:* 203-938-1300 *Fax:* 203-938-1304
*E-mail:* orders@begellhouse.com
*Web Site:* www.begellhouse.com
*Key Personnel*
COO & VP: Vicky Lipowski *E-mail:* vicky@begellhouse.com
Pres: Yelena Shafeyeva *E-mail:* elena@begellhouse.com
Mktg Dir: Peter White *E-mail:* peterw@begellhouse.com
Founded: 1992
Science books & journals.
ISBN Prefix(es): 978-1-56700
Number of titles published annually: 5 Print
Total Titles: 200 Print
Subsidiaries: Begell-Atom LLC
*Foreign Office(s):* 3 Saint Peters St, Wallingford 0X14 1GU, United Kingdom, Contact: Mr Ray Johnson *Tel:* (01491) 834930 *Fax:* (01491) 834930 *E-mail:* ray@melbourne-house.demon.co.uk
Membership(s): AAP

**Behrman House Inc**
11 Edison Place, Springfield, NJ 07081
SAN: 201-4459
*Tel:* 973-379-7200 *Toll Free Tel:* 800-221-2755 *Fax:* 973-379-7280
*E-mail:* behrmanhouse@gmail.com; customersupport@behrmanhouse.com
*Web Site:* www.behrmanhouse.com
*Key Personnel*
CEO & Pres: David Behrman
VP & Dir: Terry Kaye
Sr Ed: Dena Neusner
Founded: 1921
Synagogue school textbooks & trade books (Jewish).
ISBN Prefix(es): 978-0-87441
Number of titles published annually: 212 Print
Total Titles: 500 Print; 3 CD-ROM
Distributor for Rossel Books

**Frederic C Beil Publisher Inc**
609 Whitaker St, Savannah, GA 31401
*Tel:* 912-233-2446
*E-mail:* books@beil.com
*Web Site:* www.beil.com
*Key Personnel*
Pres & Publr: Frederic C Beil *E-mail:* fcb@beil.com
Ed: Mary Ann Bowman *E-mail:* editor@beil.com
Founded: 1982
Biography, history & fiction.
ISBN Prefix(es): 978-0-913720; 978-1-929490
Number of titles published annually: 6 Print
Total Titles: 221 Print
Imprints: Hypermedia Inc; The Sandstone Press
Foreign Rep(s): Gazelle Ltd (Europe, UK)
*Warehouse:* 609 Howard St, Savannah, GA 31401
*Distribution Center:* 608 Howard St, Savannah, GA 31401 *E-mail:* orders@beil.com

**Bell Springs Publishing**
PO Box 1240, Willits, CA 95490-1240
SAN: 209-3138
*Tel:* 707-459-6372 *Toll Free Tel:* 800-515-8050 *Fax:* 707-459-6372
*E-mail:* publisher@bellsprings.com
*Web Site:* bellsprings.com; aboutpinball.com
*Key Personnel*
Publr: Sam Leandro *E-mail:* sam@bellsprings.com
Ed: Bernard Kamoroff *E-mail:* bk@bellsprings.com
Founded: 1976
Books, small business, pinball machines.
ISBN Prefix(es): 978-0-917510
Number of titles published annually: 10 Print; 10 Online; 10 E-Book
Total Titles: 20 Print; 10 Online; 10 E-Book
*Shipping Address:* 106 State St, Willits, CA 95490

**Bella Books**
PO Box 10543, Tallahassee, FL 32302
*Tel:* 850-576-2370 *Toll Free Tel:* 800-729-4992 *Fax:* 850-576-3498
*E-mail:* info@bellabooks.com; orders@bellabooks.com; ebooks@bellabooks.com
*Web Site:* www.bellabooks.com
*Key Personnel*
CEO & Publr: Linda Hill *E-mail:* linda@bellabooks.com
Founded: 1991
Publish books for, by & about women; fiction & nonfiction.
ISBN Prefix(es): 978-0-9628938; 978-1-883061
Number of titles published annually: 10 Print
Total Titles: 35 Print
Distributed by Banyan Tree; Turnaround (London)

**BelleBooks**
PO Box 300921, Memphis, TN 38130
*Tel:* 901-344-9024 *Fax:* 901-344-9068
*E-mail:* bellebooks@bellebooks.com
*Web Site:* www.bellebooks.com
*Key Personnel*
CEO & Pres: Debra Dixon
Dir, Mktg: Deborah Smith
Opers Mgr: Pamela Ireland
Sr Ed: Pat Van Wie
ISBN Prefix(es): 978-0-9768760
Number of titles published annually: 24 Print
Total Titles: 12 Print
Imprints: Bell Bridge Books
*Editorial Office(s):* 1092 Ridgeway Rd, Dahlonega, GA
Foreign Rep(s): Editio Dialog (France, Germany, Italy, Spain); Michael Wenzel (France, Germany, Italy, Spain)

**Bellerophon Books**
PO Box 21307, Santa Barbara, CA 93121-1307
SAN: 202-392X
*Tel:* 805-965-7034 *Toll Free Tel:* 800-253-9943 *Fax:* 805-965-8286
*E-mail:* sales@bellerophonbooks.com
*Web Site:* www.bellerophonbooks.com
*Key Personnel*
Pres: Ellen Knill
Founded: 1969
Children's art & history.
ISBN Prefix(es): 978-0-88388
Number of titles published annually: 6 Print
Total Titles: 142 Print

**§Belltown Media**
PO Box 980985, Houston, TX 77098
*Tel:* 713-344-1956 *Fax:* 713-583-7956
*E-mail:* subs@linuxjournal.com
*Web Site:* www.belltownmedia.com
*Key Personnel*
Publr: Carlie Fairchild *E-mail:* publisher@linuxjournal.com
Assoc Publr: Mark Irgang *E-mail:* mark@linuxjournal.com
Gen Mgr: Rebecca Cassity *E-mail:* rebecca@linuxjournal.com
Founded: 1968
Publish Linux Journal, a computer magazine.
ISBN Prefix(es): 978-0-916151; 978-1-57831
Number of titles published annually: 4 Print
Total Titles: 29 Print; 1 CD-ROM; 1 Online
Imprints: Linux Journal Press

**Ben Yehuda Press**
430 Kensington Rd, Teaneck, NJ 07666
*Tel:* 201-833-5145 *Toll Free Tel:* 800-809-3505 *Fax:* 201-917-1278
*E-mail:* orders@benyehudapress.com; yudel@benyehudapress.com
*Web Site:* www.benyehudapress.com
*Key Personnel*
Owner & Edit Dir: Larry Yudelson *E-mail:* larry@benyehudapress.com
Sr Ed: Eve Yudelson *E-mail:* eve@benyehudapress.com
Founded: 2005
Pluralistic Jewish publisher. We accept agented & unagented material. Prefer to see queries of a short synopsis (less than a page), the table of contents & the first 5 chapters if by mail or the complete ms by electronic submission.
ISBN Prefix(es): 978-0-9769862; 978-0-9789980
Number of titles published annually: 6 Print
Total Titles: 28 Print; 3 Online; 3 E-Book
Membership(s): IBPA, the Independent Book Publishers Association

**§BenBella Books Inc**
10300 N Central Expwy, Suite 400, Dallas, TX 75231
*Tel:* 214-750-3600 *Fax:* 214-750-3645
*E-mail:* feedback@benbellabooks.com
*Web Site:* www.benbellabooks.com; www.smartpopbooks.com

*Key Personnel*
Publr: Glenn Yeffeth *Tel:* 214-750-3628
*E-mail:* glenn@benbellabooks.com
Ed-in-Chief, General Nonfiction: Debbie Harmsen
Ed-in-Chief, Smart Pop: Leah Wilson
*E-mail:* leah@benbellabooks.com
Mktg Mgr: Jennifer Canzoneri *Tel:* 214-750-3600 ext 104 *E-mail:* jennifer@benbellabooks.com
Admin Mgr & Sales: Aida Herrera *Tel:* 214-361-7901 *E-mail:* aida@benbellabooks.com
Founded: 2001
The best of health & nutrition, pop culture & smart nonfiction.
ISBN Prefix(es): 978-1-932100; 978-1-933771
Number of titles published annually: 30 Print
Total Titles: 150 Print
Imprints: Smart Pop
*Orders to:* Perseus Distribution, Cust Serv, 1049 Flex Dr, Jackson, TN 38301 *Toll Free Tel:* 800-343-4499 *Toll Free Fax:* 800-351-5073 *E-mail:* orderentry@perseusbooks.com
*Returns:* Perseus Distribution, Returns Dept, 193 Edwards Dr, Jackson, TN 38301 *Tel:* 731-423-1973 *Fax:* 731-422-4044
*Shipping Address:* 193 Edwards Dr, Jackson, TN 38301 *Toll Free Tel:* 800-343-4499 *Toll Free Fax:* 800-351-5073
*Warehouse:* Perseus Distribution, 193 Edwards Dr, Jackson, TN 38301 *Toll Free Tel:* 800-343-4499 *Toll Free Fax:* 800-351-5073
*Distribution Center:* Perseus Distribution, 193 Edwards Dr, Jackson, TN 38301 *Toll Free Tel:* 800-343-4499 *Toll Free Fax:* 800-351-5073
Membership(s): IBPA, the Independent Book Publishers Association

**Matthew Bender & Co Inc**, see LexisNexis® Matthew Bender®

**R James Bender Publishing**
PO Box 23456, San Jose, CA 95153-3456
*Tel:* 408-225-5777 *Fax:* 408-225-4739
*E-mail:* order@bender-publishing.com
*Web Site:* www.bender-publishing.com
*Key Personnel*
Prop & Dir: Roger J Bender *E-mail:* rbender@bender-publishing.com
Founded: 1967
Military books & magazines.
ISBN Prefix(es): 978-0-912138
Number of titles published annually: 6 Print
Total Titles: 35 Print

**John Benjamins Publishing Co**
PO Box 27519, Philadelphia, PA 19118
SAN: 219-7677
*Tel:* 215-836-1200 *Toll Free Tel:* 800-562-5666 (orders) *Fax:* 215-836-1204
*E-mail:* service@benjamins.com
*Web Site:* www.benjamins.com
*Key Personnel*
Mgr: Paul Peranteau *E-mail:* paul@benjamins.com
Founded: 1981
Linguistics, language studies, English as a second language, terminology & art; translation studies; literacy; scientific study of consciousness & communication.
ISBN Prefix(es): 978-1-55619; 978-0-915027; 978-90-272; 978-1-58811
Number of titles published annually: 135 Print; 2 CD-ROM; 2 Online; 135 E-Book
Total Titles: 3,200 Print; 10 CD-ROM; 4 Online; 1,500 E-Book
Imprints: B R Gruener Publishing Co
Subsidiaries: John Benjamins North America Inc
*Foreign Office(s):* Box 36224, 1020 ME Amsterdam, Netherlands
*Orders to:* John Benjamins, PO Box 960, Herndon, VA 20172 *E-mail:* benjamins@presswarehouse.com
*Returns:* Books International, 22883 Quicksilver Dr, Dulles, VA 20166
*Shipping Address:* Books International, 22883 Quicksilver Dr, Dulles, VA 20166, Todd Riggelman *E-mail:* benjamins@presswarehouse.com
*Warehouse:* Books International, 22883 Quicksilver Dr, Dulles, VA 20166 *Fax:* 703-661-1501
*Distribution Center:* Books International, 22883 Quicksilver Dr, Dulles, VA 20166

**§Bentley Publishers**
Division of Robert Bentley Inc
1734 Massachusetts Ave, Cambridge, MA 02138-1804
SAN: 213-9839
*Tel:* 617-547-4170 *Toll Free Tel:* 800-423-4595 *Fax:* 617-876-9235
*E-mail:* sales@bentleypublishers.com
*Web Site:* www.bentleypublishers.com
*Key Personnel*
Chmn & Pres: Michael Bentley
Dir, Publg: Janet Barnes
Sr Ed: Charlie Burke
Sales & Mktg Mgr: Maurice Iglesias
Founded: 1949
Technical automotive reference, automotive repair manuals, automotive history, automotive performance driving & motorsports.
ISBN Prefix(es): 978-0-8376
Total Titles: 400 Print; 30 CD-ROM

**BePuzzled**
Division of University Games
2030 Harrison St, San Francisco, CA 94110
*Tel:* 415-503-1600 *Toll Free Tel:* 800-347-4818 *Fax:* 415-503-0085
*E-mail:* info@ugames.com
*Web Site:* www.ugames.com
*Key Personnel*
Pres: Bob Moog
Sr Prods Mgr: Connie Gee
Gen Mgr: Elise Gresch
Prod & Mktg Mgr: Melissa Fortunato
Puzzles with a plus-ages from preschool to adult.
ISBN Prefix(es): 978-1-57528; 978-1-57561
Number of titles published annually: 15 Print
Total Titles: 50 Print

**R J Berg Publisher**
79 Saint Paul St, Burlington, VT 05402-0369
Mailing Address: PO Box 30225, Indianapolis, IN 46230-0225
*Tel:* 802-557-0928
*E-mail:* rjbergpublisher@gmail.com; rjberg@americanparksandresorts.com
*Web Site:* www.americanparksandresorts.com
Founded: 1974
Publishers of American social & cultural history of food, art & travel.
ISBN Prefix(es): 978-0-89730
Number of titles published annually: 14 Print
Total Titles: 38 Print
Imprints: American Food History; College Days Press; Cruise Memories; InterAmerican Press Books; Memorable Meetings Press; News Books International; State Fair Books; Travel Memories Press

**Berghahn Books**
Affiliate of Berghahn Books Ltd (UK)
20 Jay St, Suite 512, Brooklyn, NY 11201
*Tel:* 212-233-6004 *Fax:* 212-233-6007
*E-mail:* info@berghahnbooks.com; salesus@berghahnbooks.com; editorial@journals.berghahnbooks.com
*Web Site:* www.berghahnbooks.com
*Key Personnel*
Publr & Ed-in-Chief: Dr Marion Berghahn
*E-mail:* publisher@berghahnbooks.com
Mng & Journals Edit Dir: Vivian Berghahn
Sales & Mktg Dir: Noreen Henson
Sr Ed: Ann DeVita
Prodn Mgr: Melissa Spinelli
Founded: 1994
Scholarly books & journals in humanities & social sciences.
ISBN Prefix(es): 978-1-57181; 978-1-84545
Number of titles published annually: 110 Print; 400 E-Book
Total Titles: 1,000 Print; 1,000 E-Book
Divisions: Berghahn Books Ltd (UK)
*Foreign Office(s):* 3 Newtec Place, Magdalen Rd, Oxford OX4 1RE, United Kingdom *Tel:* (01865) 250011 *Fax:* (01865) 250056
Distributor for Social Science Press; Yad Vashem
Foreign Rep(s): The African Moon Press (Chris Reinders) (South Africa); Avicenna (Middle East exc Israel); Cranbury Intl LLC (Ethan Atkin) (Caribbean, Central America, Latin America); Laszlo Horvarth (Central Europe, Eastern Europe); Iberian Book Services (Peter Prout) (Portugal, Spain); Inspirees International (China); K L Books Distributor (K L Lee) (Malaysia, Southeast Asia); Flavio Marcello (Italy); Missing Link (Germany); Reimmer Book Services (Ferdinan Reimmer) (West Africa); Sara Books Private Ltd (Ravindra Saxena) (India); David Towle Intl (David Towle) (Scandinavia); UBC Press (Canada); Unifacmanu Trading Co Ltd (Celine Li) (Taiwan); UPS (Japan); Woodslane P/L (Australia, New Zealand)
Foreign Rights: Afroditi Forti (Worldwide)
*Billing Address:* Books International Inc, PO Box 605, Herndon, VA 20172 *Tel:* 703-661-1500 *Toll Free Tel:* 800-540-8663 *Fax:* 703-661-1501
*Orders to:* Books International Inc, PO Box 605, Herndon, VA 20172 *Tel:* 703-661-1500 *Toll Free Tel:* 800-540-8663 *Fax:* 703-661-1501
*Returns:* Books International Inc, 22883 Quicksilver Dr, Sterling, VA 20166 *Tel:* 703-661-1500 *Toll Free Tel:* 800-540-8663 *Fax:* 703-661-1501
*Warehouse:* Books International Inc, PO Box 605, Herndon, VA 20172 *Tel:* 703-661-1500 *Toll Free Tel:* 800-540-8663 *Fax:* 703-661-1501

**Berkeley Slavic Specialties**
PO Box 3034, Oakland, CA 94609-0034
SAN: 212-7245
*Tel:* 510-653-8048 *Fax:* 510-653-6313
*E-mail:* 71034.456@compuserve.com
*Web Site:* www.berkslav.com
*Key Personnel*
Owner: Gareth K Perkins
Founded: 1971
Slavic culture, literature, language & history.
ISBN Prefix(es): 978-0-933884; 978-1-57201; 978-0-936041
Number of titles published annually: 3 Print
Total Titles: 120 Print
Imprints: Scythian Books
Subsidiaries: Barbary Coast Books

**Berkley Books**
Imprint of Penguin Group (USA) LLC
375 Hudson St, New York, NY 10014
SAN: 282-5074
*Tel:* 212-366-2000 *Fax:* 212-366-2666
*E-mail:* online@penguinputnam.com
*Web Site:* www.penguinputnam.com; us.penguingroup.com
*Key Personnel*
Pres & Publr: Leslie Gelbman
VP & Sr Exec Ed: Natalee Rosenstein
VP & Edit Dir, Berkley Publishing Group: Susan Allison
VP & Assoc Publr: Rick Nayer
VP & Exec Creative Dir: Rich Hasselberger
VP & Dir, Prodn: Patricia King
VP, Publicity Dir, Berkley Publishing Group/NAL/Riverhead/Perigee & Mktg Dir, Riverhead/Perigee: Craig Burke
VP & Exec Mktg Dir, Berkley Publishing Group/NAL/Riverhead Trade/Perigee: Rick Pascocello

Dir, Contracts: Robin Simon
Ed-in-Chief, Sci-Fi: Mary (Ginjer) Buchanan
VP, Exec Ed: Cindy Hwang
Exec Ed: Jacqueline Cantor; Tom Colgan; Denise Silvestro; Kathleen Seaver; Wendy McCurdy; Anne Sowards
Exec Mng Ed: Lara Robbins
Founded: 1955
ISBN Prefix(es): 978-0-425; 978-0-441; 978-0-515; 978-1-57297
Number of titles published annually: 677 Print
Total Titles: 4,433 Print
Imprints: Ace Books; Caliber; Jam; Jove; Prime Crime; Sensation
*Advertising Agency:* Spier NY

**Berkley Publishing Group**
Division of Penguin Group (USA) LLC
375 Hudson St, New York, NY 10014
SAN: 282-5074
*Tel:* 212-366-2000 *Fax:* 212-366-2385
*E-mail:* online@penguinputnam.com
*Web Site:* us.penguingroup.com
*Key Personnel*
Pres & Publr: Leslie Gelbman
VP & Sr Exec Ed: Natalee Rosenstein
VP & Edit Dir, Berkley Publishing Group: Susan Allison
VP, Assoc Publr & Exec Mng Ed: Rick Nayer
VP & Exec Creative Dir: Rich Hasselberger
VP & Dir, Prodn: Patricia King
VP & Publicity Dir, Berkley Publishing Group/NAL/Riverhead/Perigee & Mktg Dir, Riverhead/Perigee: Craig Burke
VP & Exec Mktg Dir, Berkley Publishing Group/NAL/Riverhead Trade/Perigee: Rick Pascocello
Dir, Contracts: Robin Simon
Ed-in-Chief, Sci-Fi: Mary (Ginjer) Buchanan
VP, Exec Ed: Cindy Hwang
Exec Ed: Tom Colgan; Denise Silvestro; Kathleen Seaver; Wendy McCurdy; Jacqueline Cantor; Anne Sowards
Exec Mng Ed: Lara Robbins
Founded: 1954
ISBN Prefix(es): 978-0-425; 978-0-515
Imprints: Ace Books; Berkley Books; Diamond Books; HPBooks; Jove; Perigee; Prentice Hall Press; Prime Crime; Riverhead Books (Paperback); Sensation
*Advertising Agency:* Spier NY

**Bernan**
Imprint of Rowman & Littlefield Publishing Group
4501 Forbes Blvd, Suite 200, Lanham, MD 20706
Mailing Address: PO Box 191, Blue Ridge Summit, PA 17214-0191
*Tel:* 301-459-7666 (cust serv & orders) *Fax:* 301-459-0056
*E-mail:* customercare@bernan.com
*Web Site:* www.bernan.com
*Key Personnel*
Dir: Bruce Samuelson *Tel:* 301-459-2255 ext 5711 *E-mail:* bsamuelson@bernan.com
Mktg Mgr: Veronica Dove *Tel:* 301-459-2255 ext 5716 *E-mail:* vdove@bernan.com
Publicist: Lisa McAllister *Tel:* 301-459-3366 ext 5619 *E-mail:* lmcallister@rowman.com
Founded: 1952
Publishes original government-related reference works & provides a wide range of services to help librarians build their government information collections.
ISBN Prefix(es): 978-1-59888
Number of titles published annually: 4 Print
Total Titles: 336 Print
*Distribution Center:* National Book Network, 15200 NBN Way, Blue Ridge Summit, PA 17214 *Tel:* 301-459-7666 *Toll Free Tel:* 800-865-3457 *Fax:* 301-459-6988 *Toll Free Fax:* 800-865-3450

**§Berrett-Koehler Publishers Inc**
235 Montgomery St, Suite 650, San Francisco, CA 94104
*Tel:* 415-288-0260 *Fax:* 415-362-2512
*E-mail:* bkpub@bkpub.com
*Web Site:* www.bkconnection.com
*Key Personnel*
Pres & Publr: Steven Piersanti
VP, Busn Devt: Johanna Vondeling
VP, Design & Prodn: Rick Wilson
VP, Edit & Digital: David Marshall
VP, Opers & Admin: Bob Liss
VP, Sales & Mktg: Kristen Frantz
Edit Dir: Neal Maillet
Dir, Subs & Intl Rts: Maria Jesus Aguilo
Online Mktg & Intl Sales Mgr: Zoe Mackey
Publicity Mgr: Katie Sheehan *Tel:* 415-743-6477 *E-mail:* ksheehan@bkpub.com
Sr Sales Mgr: Marina Cook *E-mail:* mcook@bkpub.com
Founded: 1992
Publications on business, work, stewardship, leadership, management, career development, human resources, entrepreneurship & global sustainability for the trade, scholarly, text & professional reference markets.
ISBN Prefix(es): 978-1-881052; 978-1-57675
Number of titles published annually: 40 Print
Total Titles: 320 Print
Foreign Rep(s): McGraw-Hill Asia (Southeast Asia); McGraw-Hill Book Co (Europe, Middle East, UK); Pearson Education (South Africa); Raincoast (Canada); Woodslane Pty Ltd (Australia, New Zealand)
*Warehouse:* AIDC, 82 Winter Sport Lane, Williston, VT 05495 *Toll Free Tel:* 800-929-2929 *Toll Free Fax:* 800-864-7626
*Distribution Center:* Ingram Publisher Services, One Ingram Blvd, La Vergne, TN 37086 *Toll Free Tel:* 800-509-4887 *Toll Free Fax:* 800-838-1149

**§Bess Press**
3565 Harding Ave, Honolulu, HI 96816
*Tel:* 808-734-7159; 808-734-7159 (ext 10, returns) *Toll Free Tel:* 800-910-2377 *Fax:* 808-732-3627
*E-mail:* sales@besspress.com
*Web Site:* www.besspress.com
*Key Personnel*
Owner & Publr: Benjamin E Bess *Tel:* 808-734-7159 ext 123
Exec Dir: David DeLuca *Tel:* 808-734-7159 ext 124 *E-mail:* deluca@besspress.com
Cust Sales Mgr: Desiree Kihano *Tel:* 808-734-7159 ext 110
Founded: 1979
Books about the Pacific Islands, with a special emphasis on Hawaii. Includes elementary & secondary level textbooks in Hawaiian & Pacific Island history, geography & environment, Hawaiian & Pacific bilingual language materials, popular regional trade paperbacks, cookbooks, anthologies, humor, Christmas, guides, how-to & children's books on Hawaii & Oceania.
ISBN Prefix(es): 978-0-935848; 978-1-880188; 978-1-57306
Number of titles published annually: 12 Print
Total Titles: 200 Print; 12 Audio
Distributed by The Islander Group (TIG) (Hawaii wholesaler/book dist)

**A M Best Co**
One Ambest Rd, Oldwick, NJ 08858
*Tel:* 908-439-2200 *Fax:* 908-439-3385
*E-mail:* customer_service@ambest.com; sales@ambest.com
*Web Site:* www.ambest.com
Founded: 1899
Insurance industry statistics & supporting material, rate & provide financial information about insurance companies.
ISBN Prefix(es): 978-0-89408
Number of titles published annually: 3 Print
Total Titles: 17 Print
*Foreign Office(s):* A M Best Asia-Pacific, Central Plaza, Suite 4004, 18 Harbour Rd, Hong Kong, Hong Kong *Tel:* 2827 3400 *Fax:* 2824 1833
A M Best Europe, 12 Arthur St, 6th fl, London EC4R 9AB, United Kingdom *Tel:* (020) 7626 6264

**Bethany House Publishers**
Division of Baker Publishing Group
11400 Hampshire Ave S, Bloomington, MN 55438
SAN: 201-4416
*Tel:* 952-829-2500 *Toll Free Tel:* 800-877-2665 (orders) *Fax:* 952-829-2568 *Toll Free Fax:* 800-398-3111 (orders)
*Web Site:* www.bethanyhouse.com; www.bakerpublishinggroup.com
*Key Personnel*
EVP & Dir: Jim Parrish
VP, Edit: David Horton *Fax:* 952-829-2568
VP, Mktg: Steve Oates
Natl Sales Mgr: Rob Teigen
Pres, Baker Publishing Group: Dwight Baker
EVP, Sales & Mktg, Baker Publishing Group: Dave Lewis
Founded: 1956
Religion (Evangelical).
ISBN Prefix(es): 978-0-87123; 978-1-55661; 978-0-7642; 978-0-76428
Number of titles published annually: 90 Print; 90 E-Book
Total Titles: 500 Print
Foreign Rep(s): Challenge Bookshops Enterprises of Ghana (Nigeria); Christian Literature Center (Hong Kong); Christian Literature Crusade (Japan); David C Cook (Canada); Filadelfiaforlaget A-S (Norway, Sweden); Glad Sounds (Malaysia); International Boekencentrum Pelgrim (Netherlands); Nova Distribution (UK); Omega Distributors Ltd (New Zealand); Salvation Book Center (Malaysia); Scripture Union (Singapore); Word of Life Press (Japan, Korea)
Foreign Rights: Winfried Bluth (Europe)

**Bethlehem Books**
Affiliate of Bethlehem Community
10194 Garfield St S, Bathgate, ND 58216
*Toll Free Tel:* 800-757-6831 *Fax:* 701-265-3716
*E-mail:* contact@bethlehembooks.com
*Web Site:* www.bethlehembooks.com
*Key Personnel*
Pres: Jim Rasmussen
Gen Mgr & Publr: Jack Sharpe *E-mail:* jsharpe@bethlehembooks.com
Founded: 1993
Children's & youth books.
ISBN Prefix(es): 978-1-883937; 978-1-932350
Number of titles published annually: 8 Print; 1 Audio
Total Titles: 49 Print; 2 Audio
Distributed by Ignatius Press
Foreign Rights: Canadian Home Education Resources (Canada); St Andrews Books (Canada); Saint Benedicts Book Centre (Australia); Salas Trading (Canada); Salt Books (New Zealand); Sunrise Marian Distributors (Canada)

**Betterway Books**
Imprint of F+W Media Inc
10151 Carver Rd, Suite 200, Blue Ash, OH 45242
*Tel:* 513-531-2690 *Toll Free Tel:* 800-666-0963 *Fax:* 513-891-7185 *Toll Free Fax:* 888-590-4082
*Web Site:* www.fwmedia.com
*Key Personnel*
Pres: Sara Domville
Founded: 1981
Instructional & self help books for creative people in the areas of home maintenance, repair,

woodworking, home-based business, sports & recreation, theater, arts, genealogy & gardening.
ISBN Prefix(es): 978-0-932620; 978-1-55870
Number of titles published annually: 10 Print
Total Titles: 130 Print
Imprints: Family Tree Books; Horticulture Books; Numismatics Books, Popular Woodworking Books; Sports Collectors Digest
*Returns:* F+W Media Inc, c/o Aero Fulfillment Services, 6023 Union Centre Blvd, West Chester, OH 45014
*Shipping Address:* F+W Media Inc, c/o Aero Fulfillment Services, 6023 Union Centre Blvd, West Chester, OH 45014

**Beyond Words Publishing Inc**
Affiliate of Simon & Schuster
20827 NW Cornell Rd, Suite 500, Hillsboro, OR 97124-9808
SAN: 666-4210
*Tel:* 503-531-8700 *Fax:* 503-531-8773
*Web Site:* www.beyondword.com
*Key Personnel*
Pres & Ed-in-Chief: Cynthia Black
Publr: Richard E Cohn
Mktg Mgr: George Lewis
Mng Ed: Lindsay Brown
Founded: 1983
Affiliate of Simon & Schuster through a co-publishing agreement with Atria Books, an imprint of Simon & Schuster.
ISBN Prefix(es): 978-0-941831; 978-1-885223; 978-1-58270
Number of titles published annually: 15 Print
Total Titles: 300 Print; 25 E-Book; 10 Audio
Imprints: The Earthsong Collection
Distributed by Simon & Schuster
Foreign Rights: Beyond Words Publishing

**§Bhaktivedanta Book Trust (BBT)**
9701 Venice Blvd, Suite 3, Los Angeles, CA 90034
Mailing Address: PO Box 341445, Los Angeles, CA 90034
*Tel:* 310-837-5283 *Toll Free Tel:* 800-927-4152 *Fax:* 310-837-1056
*E-mail:* store@krishna.com
*Web Site:* www.krishna.com
*Key Personnel*
Mktg & Dist Mgr: Stuart Kadetz *E-mail:* sura.acbsp@pamho.net
Warehouse Contact: Efren Gonzalez *Tel:* 310-523-4533 *Fax:* 310-523-4258
Founded: 1972
Books of Vedic culture & philosophy, vegetarianism, reincarnation & Karma.
ISBN Prefix(es): 978-0-89213; 978-91-7149; 978-0-912776
Number of titles published annually: 3 Print; 2 CD-ROM
Total Titles: 96 Print; 1 CD-ROM; 2 E-Book; 84 Audio
*Warehouse:* 705 E Gardena Blvd, Gardena, CA 90248

**BHB**, see BrickHouse Books Inc

**Bibliotheca Persica Press**
450 Riverside Dr, Suite 4, New York, NY 10027
*Tel:* 212-851-5723 *Fax:* 212-749-9524
*E-mail:* ey4@columbia.edu
*Key Personnel*
Publr: Prof Ehsan Yarshater
Multi-disciplinary humanities/Iranian studies.
ISBN Prefix(es): 978-0-933273
Number of titles published annually: 3 Print
Total Titles: 40 Print
*Sales Office(s):* Eisenbrauns Inc, PO Box 275, Winona Lake, IN 46590-0275 *Tel:* 574-269-2011 *Toll Free Tel:* 800-736-7921 (US only) *E-mail:* orders@eisenbrauns.com *Web Site:* www.eisenbrauns.com
*Billing Address:* Eisenbrauns Inc, PO Box 275, Winona Lake, IN 46590-0275 *Tel:* 574-269-2011 *Toll Free Fax:* 800-736-7921 (US only) *E-mail:* orders@eisenbrauns.com *Web Site:* www.eisenbrauns.com
*Returns:* Eisenbrauns Inc, PO Box 275, Winona Lake, IN 46590-0275 *Tel:* 574-269-2011 *Toll Free Fax:* 800-736-7921 (US only) *E-mail:* orders@eisenbrauns.com *Web Site:* www.eisenbrauns.com
*Shipping Address:* Eisenbrauns Inc, PO Box 275, Winona Lake, IN 46590-0275
*Distribution Center:* Eisenbrauns Inc, PO Box 275, Winona Lake, IN 46590-0275 *Tel:* 574-269-2011 *Toll Free Fax:* 800-736-7921 (US only) *E-mail:* orders@eisenbrauns.com *Web Site:* www.eisenbrauns.com

**Biblo-Moser**
PO Box 302, Cheshire, CT 06410-0302
*Tel:* 203-988-8100 *Fax:* 203-272-2308
*E-mail:* biblo.moser@snet.net
*Key Personnel*
Owner: Philip Moser
Founded: 1950
Do not accept unsol mss, publish reprint editions.
ISBN Prefix(es): 978-0-8196
Number of titles published annually: 3 Print
Total Titles: 250 Print
Imprints: Biblo; Biblo-Tannen; Moser

**Bick Publishing House**
16 Marion Rd, Branford, CT 06405
*Tel:* 203-208-5253 *Fax:* 203-208-5253
*E-mail:* bickpubhse@aol.com
*Web Site:* www.bickpubhouse.com
*Key Personnel*
Owner: Dale Carlson
EVP & Ed-in-Chief: Hannah Carlson
VP & Dir, Prodn & Mktg: Jennifer Payne
Founded: 1993
Adult & young adult professional information for general audience & teens on health & recovery, adult & teenage psychology, meditation, neuroscience, general science, special needs & wildlife rehabilitation.
ISBN Prefix(es): 978-1-884158
Number of titles published annually: 4 Print
Total Titles: 32 Print
Foreign Rep(s): Bob Erdmann (Worldwide)
Foreign Rights: Bob Erdmann (Worldwide)
*Distribution Center:* Bookmasters, 30 Amberwood Pkwy, Ashland, OH 44805, Acct Exec: Regina Hamner *Toll Free Tel:* 800-BOOKLOG (266-5564) *E-mail:* rhamner@bookmasters.com *Web Site:* www.bookmasters.com
Membership(s): IBPA, the Independent Book Publishers Association

**Big Apple Vision Publishing Inc**
Imprint of Big Apple Vision Books
PO Box 722, Stone Ridge, NY 12484-0722
*Tel:* 845-616-1346 *Fax:* 845-339-9928
*E-mail:* info@bigapplevision.com
*Web Site:* bigapplevision.com
*Key Personnel*
Contact: Michael Bennett *E-mail:* publicity@bigapplevision.com
Founded: 2002
This publisher has indicated that 80% of their product line is author subsidized.
ISBN Prefix(es): 978-0-9724327
Number of titles published annually: 10 Print
Total Titles: 14 Print
Foreign Rep(s): Louise Rosenzweig (Europe)
Foreign Rights: Louise Rosenzweig (Europe)
*Orders to:* Friesens Corp, 35 Sixth St SE, Altona, MB R0G 0B0, Canada
*Returns:* Friesens Corp, 35 Sixth St SE, Altona, MB R0G 0B0, Canada
*Shipping Address:* Friesens Corp, 35 Sixth St SE, Altona, MB R0G 0B0, Canada
*Warehouse:* Friesens Corp, 35 Sixth St SE, Altona, MB R0G 0B0, Canada
*Distribution Center:* Friesens Corp, 35 Sixth St SE, Altona, MB R0G 0B0, Canada

**Big Guy Books Inc**
1042 N El Camino Real, Suite B-231, Encinitas, CA 92024
SAN: 253-0392
*Tel:* 760-652-5360 *Toll Free Tel:* 800-536-3030 (booksellers' cust serv) *Fax:* 760-652-5362
*E-mail:* info@bigguybooks.com
*Web Site:* www.bigguybooks.com
*Key Personnel*
Pres: Robert Gould *E-mail:* robert@bigguybooks.com
Founded: 2000
Publishes high quality adventure stories for children. Combine cutting-edge graphics & old fashioned values to increase literacy as well as confidence & self respect in young readers.
ISBN Prefix(es): 978-1-929945
Number of titles published annually: 3 Print
Distributed by Arcturus Publishing Ltd (United Kingdom); Bookwise International (Australia); Independent Publishers Group (handles all Trade Distribution in the US); Scholastic New Zealand (New Zealand); Iwasaki Shoten (Japanese Translation)
Membership(s): ABA; ALA; IBPA, the Independent Book Publishers Association

**Bilingual Review Press/Editorial Bilingue**
Arizona State Univ, Hispanic Research Ctr, Tempe, AZ 85287-2702
SAN: 208-5526
Mailing Address: PO Box 875303, Tempe, AZ 85287-5303
*Tel:* 480-965-3867 *Toll Free Tel:* 866-965-3867 *Fax:* 480-965-0315
*E-mail:* brp@asu.edu
*Web Site:* www.asu.edu/brp
*Key Personnel*
Publr: Gary D Keller *Tel:* 480-965-3990 *E-mail:* gary.keller@asu.edu
Mng Ed, Bilingual: Karen Van Hooft *E-mail:* kvhbrp@asu.edu
Assoc Ed: Linda St George *E-mail:* linda.st.george@asu.edu
Founded: 1976
Publisher & distributor of US Hispanic creative literature, literary criticism & scholarship.
ISBN Prefix(es): 978-0-916950; 978-0-927534; 978-1-931010
Number of titles published annually: 8 Print
Total Titles: 154 Print; 2 CD-ROM
Distributor for Dos Pasos Editores; Lalo Press; Latin American Literary Review Press; Maize Press; Trinity University Press; Waterfront Press (selected titles from all)
*Shipping Address:* Administration Bldg, B Wing, Rm 255, Tempe, AZ 85281

**Biographical Publishing Co**
95 Sycamore Dr, Prospect, CT 06712-1493
*Tel:* 203-758-3661 *Fax:* 253-793-2618
*E-mail:* biopub@aol.com
*Web Site:* www.biopub.us
*Key Personnel*
Ed: John R Guevin
Founded: 1991
Pre-print, printing & marketing services.
ISBN Prefix(es): 978-0-9637240; 978-1-929882
Number of titles published annually: 15 Print; 10 E-Book
Total Titles: 85 Print; 98 Online; 30 E-Book
Distributor for Eagles Landing Publishing; Spyglass Books LLC
*Distribution Center:* Pathway Book Service, PO Box 89, Gilsum, NH 03448, VP: Judith Peter *Tel:* 603-357-0236 *Toll Free Tel:* 800-

345-6665 *Fax:* 603-357-2073 *E-mail:* judith.peter@pathwaybook.com *Web Site:* www.pathwaybook.com

**BioTechniques Books**
Division of Informa Business Information
52 Vanderbilt Ave, 7th fl, New York, NY 10017
*Tel:* 212-520-2777 *Fax:* 212-520-2705
*Web Site:* www.biotechniques.com
*Key Personnel*
Ed-in-Chief: Nathan S Blow, PhD *Tel:* 212-520-2738 *E-mail:* nathan.blow@informausa.com
Mktg Mgr: Damon Mastandrea *E-mail:* damon.mastandrea@informausa.com
Prodn Mgr: Yusef Ramelize *Tel:* 212-520-2715
Mng Ed: Tracy Peterson *Tel:* 212-520-2719
Founded: 1996
Research monographs, laboratory manuals & reference books in biotechnology, medicine & the life sciences.
ISBN Prefix(es): 978-1-881299
Number of titles published annually: 5 Print
Total Titles: 29 Print

**Birch Brook Press**
PO Box 81, Delhi, NY 13753-0081
*Tel:* 607-746-7453 (book sales & prodn) *Fax:* 607-746-7453
*E-mail:* birchbrook@copper.net
*Web Site:* www.birchbrookpress.info
*Key Personnel*
Publr & Ed: Tom Tolnay
Art Dir: Leigh Eckmair *E-mail:* birchbrook@copper.net
Sales Mgr: Tim Grain
Assoc Ed: Barbara de la Cuesta
Founded: 1982
Popular culture & literary books, printed letterpress on fine stock as well as offset trade editions. Books about books, fly fishing, the outdoors, baseball, fine poetry & theme-oriented anthologies. Limited editions club for signed/numbered letterpress editions.
ISBN Prefix(es): 978-0-913559; 978-0-978997
Number of titles published annually: 6 Print; 2 E-Book
Total Titles: 100 Print; 4 E-Book
Imprints: Birch Brook Press; Brief Books (miniature handcrafted books); Persephone Press (chapbooks, handcrafted, for outside organizations)
Subsidiaries: Birch Brook Impressions (designs, typesets & prints letterpress editions for outside publishers & organizations)
Distributor for Carpenter Gothic Press; Natural Heritage Press; Persephone Press
Foreign Rep(s): Gazelle Book Services (Europe, UK); Japan UNI Agency (Japan); Multicultural Books (Canada)
Foreign Rights: Chinese Connection (Hong Kong, Mainland China, Taiwan)
*Returns:* 2309 County Hwy 16, Delhi, NY 13753 (returns accepted eight months after purchase if in clean saleable condition for credit on new purchases), Billing & Returns Contact: Joyce Tolnay
*Warehouse:* 2309 County Hwy 16, Delhi, NY 13753
Membership(s): Academy of American Poets; IBPA, the Independent Book Publishers Association

**§George T Bisel Co Inc**
710 S Washington Sq, Philadelphia, PA 19106-3519
*Tel:* 215-922-5760 *Toll Free Tel:* 800-247-3526 *Fax:* 215-922-2235
*E-mail:* gbisel@bisel.com
*Web Site:* www.bisel.com
*Key Personnel*
Pres: Franklin Jon Zuch *E-mail:* fjzuch@bisel.com
VP: James L Betz *E-mail:* jbetz@bisel.com
Dir, Sales & Mktg: John Ahrens *E-mail:* jahrens@bisel.com
Ed-in-Chief: Tony Di Gioia *E-mail:* tonyd@bisel.com
Ed: Frank Coyne *E-mail:* fcoyne@bisel.com
Founded: 1876
Pennsylvania, New Jersey, Florida law practice subjects.
ISBN Prefix(es): 978-1-887024
Number of titles published annually: 8 Print
Total Titles: 75 Print; 10 CD-ROM; 1 Audio

**Bishop Museum Press**
1525 Bernice St, Honolulu, HI 96817
*Tel:* 808-847-3511; 808-847-8291 *Fax:* 808-848-4147
*E-mail:* press@bishopmuseum.org
*Web Site:* www.bishopmuseum.org/press
*Key Personnel*
CEO & Pres: Blaire D Collins
Founded: 1892
Hawaii's oldest publishing house specializing in trade & scholarly works on topics related to Hawaii & the Pacific.
This publisher has indicated that 50% of their product line is author subsidized.
Number of titles published annually: 10 Print
Total Titles: 90 Print

**§Bisk Education**
9417 Princess Palm Ave, Suite 400, Tampa, FL 33619
*Tel:* 813-621-6200 *Toll Free Tel:* 800-874-7877
*Web Site:* www.bisk.com
*Key Personnel*
Founder & Chmn: Nathan Bisk
COO & Pres: Andrew B Titen
Mktg Mgr: Andrea Daly
Founded: 1971
One of the leading providers of online, interactive continuing professional education, including continuing education for accountants, attorneys, physicians & nurses, CPA Exam preparation materials & web-based certificate, associate's bachelor's & master's degree programs from nationally known, regionally accredited universities, including Villanova University, Regis University, the University of South Florida, Saint Leo University & Jacksonville University.
ISBN Prefix(es): 978-1-57961
Number of titles published annually: 50 Print
Total Titles: 500 Print; 50 CD-ROM; 150 Online; 9 E-Book; 90 Audio
Imprints: Bisk CPA Review; Bisk CPE; Bisk-Totaltape; Regis External MBA Program
Distributed by Bisk Publishing Co

**§Bitingduck Press LLC**
1262 Sunnyoaks Cir, Altadena, CA 91001
*Tel:* 626-679-2494; 626-507-8033
*E-mail:* notifications@bitingduckpress.com
*Web Site:* bitingduckpress.com
*Key Personnel*
Ed-in-Chief: Jay Nadeau *E-mail:* jay@bitingduckpress.com
Creative Dir: Dena Eaton *E-mail:* dena@bitingduckpress.com
Technol Dir: Chris Lindensmith *E-mail:* chris@bitingduckpress.com
Ed: Susan Foster
Acqs Ed: Marie Nadeau *E-mail:* marie@bitingduckpress.com
Mktg/Contracts: Gretchen Lindensmith
Founded: 2012
Quality electronic publishing for a digital world.
ISBN Prefix(es): 978-1-938463
Number of titles published annually: 4 Print; 10 E-Book
Total Titles: 36 Print; 140 E-Book
Imprints: Boson Books
*Distribution Center:* Ingram Book Group, One Ingram Blvd, La Vergne, TN *Tel:* 615-793-5000
Membership(s): The Authors Guild; Independent Book Publishing Professionals Group
*See separate listing for:*
**Boson Books**

**BizBest Media Corp**
881 Alma Real Dr, Suite 220, Pacific Palisades, CA 90272
*E-mail:* info@bizbest.com
*Web Site:* www.bizbest.com
*Key Personnel*
CEO: Daniel Kehrer *E-mail:* dkehrer@bizbest.com
Publr: Roth Savage *E-mail:* savage@bizbest.com
Founded: 1999
The only integrated media company in America delivering independently researched & rated solution & resource publications for business owners & entrepreneurs across all regions & industries. BizBest books, publications & products meet the expanding information needs of small business owners, startups, consultants, advisors & educators. BizBest is non-commercial & accepts no advertising or sponsorships.
ISBN Prefix(es): 978-0-9719045
Number of titles published annually: 6 Print; 4 CD-ROM
Subsidiaries: BizBestLocal.com; BizBriefing.com; BizLaunchPad.com; BizOwnerOnly.com; Biz-Taxes.com; ManagingSmart.com; MyBiz-Daily.com; 140Main.com (social media smarts for local business); SalesSavvy.com; Small-Business.tv; SocialMyBusiness.com; Star-tupSmarts.com; YourBusinessMinute.com; Z140.com
Divisions: BizBest Media Features (syndicates small business-related content)

**§BJU Press**
Unit of Bob Jones University
1700 Wade Hampton Blvd, Greenville, SC 29614-0062
SAN: 223-7512
*Tel:* 864-242-5100 *Toll Free Tel:* 800-845-5731
*E-mail:* bjupinfo@bjupress.com
*Web Site:* www.bjupress.com
*Key Personnel*
Chief Pubn Offr, Bob Jones Univ: Bill Apelian
Dir, Mktg & Sales: Dawn L Watkins
Founded: 1974
El-hi textbooks & trade media.
ISBN Prefix(es): 978-0-89084; 978-1-57924; 978-1-59166
Total Titles: 2,500 Print
Imprints: JourneyForth Books; ShowForth Videos; SoundForth Music
Divisions: JourneyForth Books; ShowForth Videos; SoundForth Music
Distributed by Appalachian Bible Co Inc; Spring Arbor Distributors
*Warehouse:* 134 White Oak, Greenville, SC 29607-1218
Membership(s): CBA

**BkMk Press - University of Missouri-Kansas City**
5101 Rockhill Rd, Kansas City, MO 64110-2499
*Tel:* 816-235-2558 *Fax:* 816-235-2611
*E-mail:* bkmk@umkc.edu
*Web Site:* www.umkc.edu/bkmk
*Key Personnel*
Exec Ed: Robert Stewart *Tel:* 816-235-1120
Mng Ed: Ben Furnish
Assoc Ed: Michelle Boisseau *Tel:* 816-235-2561
Fine literature & essays.
ISBN Prefix(es): 978-0-933532; 978-1-886157
Number of titles published annually: 6 Print
Total Titles: 130 Print

*Distribution Center:* SPD (Small Press Distribution), 1341 Seventh St, Berkeley, CA 94710 (recent titles) *Toll Free Tel:* 800-869-7553
Membership(s): Association of Writers and Writing Programs; Council of Literary Magazines & Presses

**Black Classic Press**
3921 Vero Rd, Suite F, Baltimore, MD 21203-3414
SAN: 219-5836
Mailing Address: PO Box 13414, Baltimore, MD 21203-3414
*Tel:* 410-242-6954 *Toll Free Tel:* 800-476-8870 *Fax:* 410-242-6959
*E-mail:* email@blackclassicbooks.com; blackclassicpress@yahoo.com
*Web Site:* www.blackclassicbooks.com; www.bcpdigital.com
*Key Personnel*
Pres: W Paul Coates
Digital Print Consultant: Damani Coates
Founded: 1978
Publishing obscure & significant works by & about people of African descent.
ISBN Prefix(es): 978-0-933121; 978-1-57478
Number of titles published annually: 20 Print
Total Titles: 100 Print
Imprints: W M Duforcelf; Inprint Editions
Distributed by Publishers Group West
Membership(s): IBPA, the Independent Book Publishers Association

**Black Dog & Leventhal Publishers Inc**
Division of Workman Publishing Co Inc
151 W 19 St, New York, NY 10011
*Tel:* 212-647-9336 *Toll Free Tel:* 800-722-7202 *Fax:* 212-647-9332
*E-mail:* info@blackdogandleventhal.com; orders@workman.com
*Web Site:* www.blackdogandleventhal.com; blackdogonline.com
*Key Personnel*
Publr: J P Leventhal
Exec Ed: Becky Koh *E-mail:* becky@bdlev.com
Sales Dir: Maureen Winter *E-mail:* maureen@bdlev.com
Founded: 1993
Publish general interest fiction & nonfiction & illustrated books in hardcover & paperback; no unsol mss accepted, send query letter to editorial department.
ISBN Prefix(es): 978-0-9637056; 978-1-884822; 978-1-57912; 978-1-60376
Number of titles published annually: 40 Print
Total Titles: 260 Print
Imprints: Black Dog & Leventhal; Black Dog Paperbacks; Tess Press
Distributed by Workman Publishing Co Inc
Distributor for Play Bac Publishing
Foreign Rights: APD Singapore (Asia); Thomas Allen (Canada); Bookreps (New Zealand); Chris Lloyd (Ireland, UK); Alex Quaynor (Africa); Roli Books (India)
*Warehouse:* c/o Workman Publishing Banta Co, 677 Brighton Beach Rd, Menasha, WI 54952
*Distribution Center:* Perseus Distribution Services, 193 Edwards Dr, Jackson, TN 38301 (USA, CN & South America) *Toll Free Tel:* 800-343-4499 *Toll Free Fax:* 800-351-5073 *E-mail:* orderentry@perseusbooks.com
Peribo Pty Lyd, 58 Beaumont Rd, Mount Kuring-Gai, NSW 2080, Australia (Austrialia & New Zealand) *Tel:* (02) 9457 0011 *Fax:* (02) 9457 0022 *E-mail:* info@peribo.com.au
Critiques Livres Distribution, BP 93-24 rue Malmaison, 93172 Bagnolet, Cedex, France (France) *Tel:* (0143) 60 39 10 *Fax:* (0148) 97 37 06 *E-mail:* critiques.livres@wanadoo.fr
P S Publishers' Services, Ziegenhinerstr 169, 60433 Frankfort, Germany (Austria, Germany & German-speaking Switzerland, Frankfort, Germany)
Asia Publishers Services Ltd, Units B & D 17/F Gee Chang Hong Ctr 65, Wong Hang Rd, Aberdeen, Hong Kong (China, Hong Kong, Korea, Macau & Taiwan), Contact: Edward Summerson *Tel:* (0852) 2553 9289 *Fax:* (0852) 2554 2912 *E-mail:* aps_hk@asiapubs.com.hk
Maya Publishers Pvt Ltd, 4821, Parwana Bhawan, 3rd fl, 24, Ansari Rd, Daryaganj, New Delhi 110 002, India (India)
Infinite Book & Art Services, 2-28-12 Nishihara, Shibuya-ku, Tokyo 151-0066, Japan (Japan)
Van Ditmar Boekenimport BV, Joan Muyskenweg 6, 1069 CJ Amsterdam, Netherlands (Belgium & Netherlands), Contact: Gerdi Boor *Tel:* (0294) 494930 *Fax:* (0294) 494455 *E-mail:* g.boor@libridis-groep.com
APD Singapore Pte Ltd, Ruby Land Complex 1, 52 Genting Lane, No 06-05 349560, Singapore (South East Asia), Contact: Ian Pringle *Tel:* (065) 6749 3551 *Fax:* (065) 6749 3552 *E-mail:* ian@apdsing.com
Stephan Phillips Pty Ltd, PO Box 12246 Mill St, Cape Town 8010, South Africa (South Africa), Contact: George Thorne *Tel:* (021) 448 9839 *Fax:* (021) 447 9879 *E-mail:* info@stephanphillips.com
Padovani Books Ltd, 56 Rosebank, Holyport Rd, Fulham, London SW6 6LH, United Kingdom (Italy, Greece, Portugal & Spain)
Marston Book Services, PO Box 269, Abingdon Oxon OX14 4YN, United Kingdom (Africa, Australia, Europe, Middle East & UK) *Tel:* (01235) 465 500 *Fax:* (01235) 465 555 *E-mail:* direct.orders@marston.co.uk

**Black Dome Press Corp**
649 Delaware Ave, Delmar, NY 12054
*Tel:* 518-439-6512 *Toll Free Tel:* 800-513-9013 (orders) *Fax:* 518-439-1309
*E-mail:* blackdomep@aol.com
*Web Site:* www.blackdomepress.com
*Key Personnel*
Owner: Steve Hoare
Founded: 1990
Regional small press publishing New York State history & guide books.
ISBN Prefix(es): 978-1-883789; 978-0-9628523
Number of titles published annually: 5 Print
Total Titles: 80 Print
Membership(s): AAP

**Black Heron Press**
PO Box 13396, Mill Creek, WA 98082-1396
*Tel:* 425-355-4929 *Fax:* 425-355-4929
*Web Site:* blackheron.mav.net
*Key Personnel*
Publr & Lib Sales Dir: Jerry Gold *E-mail:* jgoldberon@aol.com
Founded: 1984
Literary fiction & nonfiction pertaining to independent publishing & the writing craft; literature, science fiction (not dungeons & dragons).
ISBN Prefix(es): 978-0-930773; 978-1-936364
Number of titles published annually: 4 Print
Total Titles: 70 Print
Foreign Rep(s): European-Latin American Literary Agency (Pina Von Prellwitz) (France, Italy, Latin America, Spain); International Titles (Loris Essay) (Asia, Austria, Eastern Europe, Germany, Northern Europe, Switzerland)
Foreign Rights: Europe-Latin America Literary Agency (Pina von Prellwitz) (France, Italy, Latin America, Portugal, Spain); International Titles (Loris Essay)
*Warehouse:* 620 112 St SE, Suite 355, Everett, WA 98208
*Distribution Center:* Midpoint Trade Books, 27 W 20 St, Suite 1102, New York, NY 10011 *Tel:* 212-727-0190 *Fax:* 212-727-0195

**§Black Mountain Press**
PO Box 9907, Asheville, NC 28815
*Tel:* 828-273-3332
*Web Site:* www.theblackmountainpress.com
*Key Personnel*
Publr: Jack Moe *E-mail:* jackmoe@theblackmountainpress.com
Sr Ed: Carlos Steward *E-mail:* carlos@theblackmountainpress.com
Ed: Joline Mechanic *Tel:* 828-254-2166 *E-mail:* jolene99@bellsouth.net
Founded: 1994
Literary press for emerging & established creative writers, with or without literary agents. Specialize in literary novels, short story collections, poetry & creative nonfiction.
ISBN Prefix(es): 978-0-9700165; 978-1-940605
Number of titles published annually: 10 Print; 10 E-Book
Total Titles: 25 Print; 10 E-Book

**Black Rabbit Books**
123 S Broad St, Mankato, MN 56001
Mailing Address: PO Box 3263, Mankato, MN 56002-3263
*Tel:* 507-388-1609 *Fax:* 507-388-1364
*E-mail:* info@blackrabbitbooks.com; orders@blackrabbitbooks.com
*Web Site:* www.blackrabbitbooks.com
*Key Personnel*
Natl Mktg Mgr: Ann Schwab
Assoc Publr: Jonathan Strickland
Founded: 2006
Founded on the principle that quality books produce quality readers. Our list of K-12 books has a wide variety of topics, innovative approaches & multiple reading levels to serve all facets of the school library market.
ISBN Prefix(es): 978-1-84234; 978-1-84193; 978-1-59920; 978-1-58340; 978-1-59771; 978-1-59566; 978-1-59604; 978-1-93288; 978-8-86098; 978-1-93383; 978-1-93279; 978-1-84837
Number of titles published annually: 375 Print
Total Titles: 2,000 Print
Imprints: Arcturus Publishing; Brown Bear Books; Cherrytree Books; Walter Foster Library; New Forest Press; QEB Publishing; Sea-to-Sea Publishing; Smart Apple Media; Stargazer Books; Zak Books
Foreign Rep(s): Saunders Book Co (Canada)

**The Blackburn Press**
PO Box 287, Caldwell, NJ 07006-0287
*Tel:* 973-228-7077 *Fax:* 973-228-7276
*Web Site:* www.blackburnpress.com
*Key Personnel*
Edit Dir & Publr: Frances Reed *E-mail:* freed@blackburnpress.com
Gen Mgr: Maryanne Kenny *E-mail:* mkenny@blackburnpress.com
Mktg & Cust Serv: Barbara R Chmiel *E-mail:* bchmiel@blackburnpress.com
Founded: 1999
Book titles, largely reprints, of classics in science & technology. Worldwide distributors.
ISBN Prefix(es): 978-1-930665; 978-1-932846
Number of titles published annually: 20 Print
Total Titles: 100 Print
*Distribution Center:* Baker & Taylor, 2550 W Tyrola Rd, Charlotte, NC *Toll Free Tel:* 800-775-1800 *Toll Free Fax:* 800-998-3316 *E-mail:* btinfo@baker-taylor.com *Web Site:* www.baker-tayor.com
Barnes & Noble, One Barnes & Noble Way, Monroe, NJ 08831 *Tel:* 732-656-7400
NACSCORP, 528 E Lorain St, Oberlin, OH 44074-1298, Dir, Merch Mktg: Joan Keehan *Tel:* 440-775-7777 *Toll Free Tel:* 800-321-3883 orders *E-mail:* service@nascorp.com *Web Site:* www.nascorp.com
Ingram, One Ingram Blvd, LaVergne, TN *Tel:* 615-793-5000 *Toll Free Tel:* 800-937-8200 *E-mail:* customer.service@ingrambook.com *Web Site:* www.ingrambook.com

Amazon.com, 440 Terry Ave N, Seattle, WA *E-mail:* amazonpublishing-pr@amazon.com *Web Site:* www.amazon.com
Adlibris.com, Box 3367, SE-103 59 Stockholm, Sweden
Mallry International Ltd, Aylesbeare Common Business Park, Exmouth Rd, Aylesbeare, Devon EX5 2DG, United Kingdom, Contact: Julian Hardinge *Tel:* (01395) 239199 *Fax:* (01395) 239168 *E-mail:* julian@malloryint.co.uk *Web Site:* www.malloryint.o.uk
Blackwell, Unipart House, Garsington Rd, Cowley, Oxford 0X4 2PG, United Kingdom *Tel:* (01865) 382 524 *Fax:* (01865) 382 790 *E-mail:* sales@blackwell.co.uk *Web Site:* bookshop.blackwell.co.uk
Gardners Books, One Whittle Dr, Eastbourne, East Sussex *Tel:* (01323) 521777 *Fax:* (01323) 521666 *E-mail:* custcare@gardners.com *Web Site:* www.gardners.com
Coutts & Co, 440 Stand, London WC2R 0QS, United Kingdom *Tel:* (020) 7753 1000 *Web Site:* www.coutts.com
Book Depository, PO Box 91, St Peter Port GY1 3EG, United Kingdom, Contact: Steve Potter *E-mail:* steve@bookdepository.co.uk
Aphrohead, 277-A Wennington Rd, Southport, Merseyside PR9 7TW, United Kingdom, Mng Dir: Paul Anderson *E-mail:* enquiries@aphrohead.com *Web Site:* aphrohead.com
Bertrams, Wakefield House, Pipers Way, Swindon, Wiltshire SN3 1RF, United Kingdom *Tel:* (0871) 803 6666 *Web Site:* www.bertrams.com

**John F Blair Publisher**
1406 Plaza Dr, Winston-Salem, NC 27103
SAN: 201-4319
*Tel:* 336-768-1374 *Toll Free Tel:* 800-222-9796 *Fax:* 336-768-9194
*Web Site:* www.blairpub.com
*Key Personnel*
Pres & Spec Projs Dir: Carolyn Sakowski *E-mail:* sakowski@blairpub.com
Dir, Design & Prodn: Debra Hampton *E-mail:* hampton@blairpub.com
Publicist: Trisina Dickerson *E-mail:* dickerson@blairpub.com
Founded: 1954
General trade.
ISBN Prefix(es): 978-0-910244; 978-0-89587
Number of titles published annually: 18 Print; 18 E-Book
Total Titles: 300 Print; 200 E-Book; 3 Audio
Distributor for Bandit Books; Bright Mountain Books; Canterbury House Publishing; Down Home Press; Eno Publishers; Hub City Press; Looking Glass Books; Lookout Books; New-South Books; Niche Publishing; Pennywell Press; Upper Ohio Valley Books; Walkabout Press; Willow Hill Press

**Bloch Publishing Co**
5875 Mining Terr, Suite 104, Jacksonville, FL 32257-3225
*Tel:* 904-880-7302 *Toll Free Tel:* 866-532-3977 *Fax:* 904-880-7307
*E-mail:* info@blochpub.com
*Web Site:* www.blochpub.com
*Key Personnel*
Pres: Mitchell Bloch
Founded: 1854
Judaica.
ISBN Prefix(es): 978-0-8197
Number of titles published annually: 8 Print
Total Titles: 100 Print
Distributor for Biblio; Menorah; Scarf Press; Sephardic House; Soncino

**Blood Moon Productions Ltd**
75 Saint Marks Place, Staten Island, NY 10301-1606
*Tel:* 718-556-9410
*E-mail:* editors@bloodmoonproductions.com
*Web Site:* bloodmoonproductions.com
*Key Personnel*
Pres & Publr:
Danforth Prince *E-mail:* danforthprince@bloodmoonproductions.com
Founded: 2004
A New York-based publishing enterprise dedicated to researching, salvaging & indexing the oral histories of America's entertainment industry.
ISBN Prefix(es): 978-0-9748118; 978-0-9786465; 978-1-936003
Number of titles published annually: 5 Print; 5 E-Book
Total Titles: 15 Print; 15 E-Book
Imprints: The Georgia Literary Association (earlier titles)
Distributed by National Book Network (North America, Australia, New Zealand); Turnaround (UK)
Membership(s): ABA; IBPA, the Independent Book Publishers Association; NAIBA; Southern Independent Booksellers Alliance

**Bloom's Literary Criticism**
Imprint of Infobase Learning
132 W 31 St, 17th fl, New York, NY 10001
*Toll Free Tel:* 800-322-8755 *Toll Free Fax:* 800-678-3633
*E-mail:* custserv@factsonfile.com
*Web Site:* www.infobasepublishing.com
*Key Personnel*
Chmn, Infobase Learning: Mark McDonnell
CFO, Infobase Publishing: Jim Housley
Edit Dir, Facts on File: Laurie Likoff
Dir, Licensing & Busn Devt, Infobase: Ben Jacobs *Tel:* 212-896-4268 *E-mail:* bjacobs@factsonfile.com
Dir, Mktg, Infobase Publishing: Zina Scarpulla
Dir, Opers, Infobase Publishing: Mark Zielinski
Offers hundreds of volumes of literary criticism edited by Harold Bloom, focusing on the writers & works most often studied in high schools & universities.
ISBN Prefix(es): 978-0-7910; 978-1-4381
Number of titles published annually: 67 Print; 67 E-Book
Total Titles: 453 Print; 525 E-Book
*Returns:* c/o Maple Press Distribution Ctr, 704 Legionaire Dr, Fredericksburg, PA 17026
*Warehouse:* c/o Maple Press Distribution Ctr, 704 Legionaire Dr, Fredericksburg, PA 17026
*Distribution Center:* c/o Maple Press Distribution Ctr, 704 Legionaire Dr, Fredericksburg, PA 17026

**Bloomsbury Academic**
80 Maiden Lane, Suite 704, New York, NY 10038
SAN: 213-8220
*Tel:* 212-953-5858 *Toll Free Tel:* 800-561-7704 *Fax:* 212-953-5944
*E-mail:* info@continuum-books.com
*Web Site:* www.continuumbooks.com
*Key Personnel*
Chmn & CEO: Oliver Gadsby *E-mail:* ogadsby@continuumbooks.com
Edit Dir: Dr David Barker *Tel:* 212-953-5858 ext 110 *E-mail:* david.barker@bloomsbury.com
Head, Sales - Americas: Derek Stordahl
Founded: 1999 (result of a merger between The Continuum Publishing Company of NY & the academic & religious publishing programs of Cassell plc in London)
Hardcover & paperbacks; scholary & professional & general interest; music, film, literature, media studies, the arts & popular culture; philosophy, religion, biblical studies, theology & spirituality, history, politics & contemporary issues, education; women studies & reference.
ISBN Prefix(es): 978-0-304; 978-0-7201; 978-0-8264; 978-1-56338; 978-0-7136; 978-0-86012; 978-0-225; 978-0-264; 978-0-7185; 978-0-86187; 978-1-85567; 978-0-7220; 978-0-567; 978-0-485; 978-1-84127; 978-1-85805; 978-1-84371; 978-0-8044; 978-0-223
Number of titles published annually: 150 Print
Total Titles: 6,000 Print
*Foreign Office(s):* The Tower Bldg, 11 York Rd, London SE1 7NX, United Kingdom *Tel:* (020) 7922 0880
Distributor for Paragon House; Spring Publications
Foreign Rep(s): Eliane Benisti (exclusive French); Liepman AG (exclusive German); Natoli Stefan & Olivia (exclusive Italian)
Foreign Rights: Allen & Unwin Pty Ltd (Australia); APD (Brunei, Indonesia, Malaysia, Singapore, Thailand, Vietnam); APS Ltd (China, Hong Kong, Philippines, South Korea, Taiwan); Robert Barnett (USA); BCR University Bookstore (Jamaica); Eliane Benisti Literary Agency (France); Bounty Press Ltd (Nigeria); Codasat Canada Ltd (Canada); Continuum (Africa exc North & South Africa, Caribbean, Germany, Israel, Netherlands, North America); Cranbury International LLC (Central America, Mexico, South America); Durnell Marketing Ltd (Europe); Horizon Books (Botswana, Lesotho, Namibia, South Africa, Swaziland); IPS (Middle East exc Israel, North Africa); Liepman AG (Switzerland); Richard Lyle (London); Maya Publishers Pvt Ltd (Bangladesh, India, Sri Lanka); Richard McNeace (USA); Natoli Stefan & Oliva Literary Agency (Italy); Novalis (Canada); Nick Pepper (Northern England, Scotland); Publishers Consultants & Representatives (Pakistan); Jonathan Rhodes (England, Midlands); Andrew Toal (England); United Publishers Services Ltd (Japan)

**Bloomsbury Publishing**
175 Fifth Ave, New York, NY 10010
*Tel:* 212-674-5151 *Toll Free Tel:* 800-221-7945 *Fax:* 212-780-0115; 212-982-2837
*E-mail:* marketingusa@bloomsbury.com; adultpublicityusa.@bloomsbury.com
*Web Site:* www.bloomsbury.com
*Key Personnel*
Founder & Chief Exec: Nigel Newton
Group Sales & Mktg Dir, UK & US: Kathleen Farrar
Sr Dir, Publicity & Communs: Marie Coolman
Group Fin Dir: Wendy Pallot
Mng Dir, Bloomsbury Children's & Educ Publg: Emma Hopkin
Publg Dir, Bloomsbury Children's: Cindy Loh
Publg Dir, Bloomsbury USA: George Gibson
Publg Dir, Education & Children's Nonfiction: Jayne Parsons
Publg Dir, Walker Children's: Emily Easton
Publr, Bloomsbury Press: Peter Ginna
Publicity Dir, Bloomsbury: Peter Miller
Publicity Dir, Bloomsbury Children's & Walker Childen's: Katy Hershberger
Assoc Dir, Publicity: Summer Smith
Exec Dir, US Mktg: Christina Gilbert
Dir: Richard Charkin
Dir, Adoption Sales-Bloomsbury Academic: Melanie Sankel
Dir, Mktg & Design: Alona Fryman
Dir, Trade & Digital Mktg: Laura Keefe
Mktg Dir, Children's: Kim Burns
Academic Opers Mgr: Ryan Tozzi
Prodn Mgr: Jiyeon Dew
Head, Sales - Americas: Derek Stordahl
Trade Sales Opers Mgr: Doug White
Sr Mng Ed: Melissa Kavonic
Exec Ed, Bloomsbury USA: Kathy Belden
Sr Ed, Bloomsbury Children's: Caroline Abbey; Mary Kate Castellani
Ed: Lea Beresford; Rachel Mannheimer
Assoc Ed & Asst to Dir: Lea Beresford

Assoc Ed, Bloomsbury Children's: Laura Whitaker; Brett Wright
Sr Publicist: Carrie Majer
Assoc Publicist: Laura Gianino; Jonathan Kroberger
Founded: 1998
No unsol mss.
ISBN Prefix(es): 978-1-58234
Number of titles published annually: 100 Print
Imprints: Bloomsbury Academic; Bloomsbury Kids; Bloomsbury Press (nonfiction); Bloomsbury USA (adult); Walker Books for Young Readers (children's); Walker & Company (adult & children's)
Distributed by Macmillan
*Orders to:* Macmillan Distribution Center, 16365 James Madison Hwy, Gordonsville, VA 22942-8501 *Toll Free Tel:* 888-330-8477 *Toll Free Fax:* 800-672-2054
*Returns:* Trafalgar Square Publishing, 814 N Franklin St, Chicago, IL 60610 *Tel:* 312-337-0747 *Fax:* 312-337-5985 *Web Site:* www.trafalgarsquarebooks.com; Macmillan Returns Center, 14301 Litchfield Rd, Orange, VA 22960
*Distribution Center:* Macmillan Distribution Center, 16365 James Madison Hwy, Gordonsville, VA 22942-8501 *Toll Free Tel:* 888-330-8477 *Toll Free Fax:* 800-672-2054

**Blue Apple Books**
515 Valley St, Suite 170, Maplewood, NJ 07040
*Tel:* 973-763-8191 *Toll Free Tel:* 800-722-6657; 800-733-3000 (orders) *Fax:* 973-763-5944
*E-mail:* info@blueapplebooks.com
*Web Site:* blueapplebooks.com
*Key Personnel*
Publr: Harriet M Ziefert
Assoc Publr: Elliot Kreloff
Dir, Opers: Kip Jacobson
Sales Dir: Rob Schaeffer
Exec Ed: Cecile Goyette
Founded: 2003
Publisher of innovative children's books. No unsol mass accepted at this time.
ISBN Prefix(es): 978-1-59354; 978-1-934706
Number of titles published annually: 60 Print
Total Titles: 300 Print
Distributed by Random House Inc
*Orders to:* Random House Children's Book Customer Service, 400 Hahn Rd, Westminster, MD 21157
*Returns:* Random House Inc, 1019 N State Rd 47, Crawfordsville, IN 47933

**Blue Book Publications Inc**
8009 34 Ave S, Suite 250, Minneapolis, MN 55425
*Tel:* 952-854-5229 *Toll Free Tel:* 800-877-4867 *Fax:* 925-853-1486
*E-mail:* support@bluebookinc.com
*Web Site:* www.bluebookofgunvalues.com; www.bluebookofguitarvalues.com
*Key Personnel*
Publr & Author: S P Fjestad *Tel:* 952-853-1486 ext 13 *E-mail:* stevef@bluebookinc.com
Exec Ed: Cassandra Faulkner *Tel:* 952-853-1486 ext 19 *E-mail:* cassandraf@bluebookinc.com
Busn Devt Offr: Adam Burt *Tel:* 952-853-1486 ext 20 *E-mail:* adam@bluebookinc.com
Founded: 1989
Industry leader in up-to-date & accurate values & information for firearms, airguns, modern black powder replicas, amplifiers & fretted instruments. Publisher of reference books, consumer pricing guides, encyclopedias & coffee table books. Online information provider/appraisals.
ISBN Prefix(es): 978-1-936120
Number of titles published annually: 13 Print; 4 CD-ROM; 8 Online
Total Titles: 29 Print; 4 CD-ROM; 8 Online
Membership(s): ABA; Midwest Independent Booksellers Association; Outdoor Writers Association of America

**Blue Crane Books**
PO Box 380291, Cambridge, MA 02238
*Tel:* 617-926-8989 *Fax:* 617-926-0982
*E-mail:* bluecrane@arrow1.com
*Key Personnel*
Publr: Mrs Alvart Badalian *Tel:* 617-926-8585 *E-mail:* alvart@arrow1.com
Art Dir: Mr Aramais Andonian
Ed: Ms Salpi H Ghazarian
Founded: 1991
Publish adult trade fiction & nonfiction, history, political & social sciences, culture & art. Special line of adult & children's books in Armenian & English translations of Armenian originals. No unsol mss.
ISBN Prefix(es): 978-0-9628715; 978-1-886434
Number of titles published annually: 3 Print
Total Titles: 20 Print

**§Blue Dolphin Publishing Inc**
13340-D Grass Valley Ave, Grass Valley, CA 95945
SAN: 223-2480
Mailing Address: PO Box 8, Nevada City, CA 95959-0008
*Tel:* 530-477-1503 *Toll Free Tel:* 800-643-0765 (orders) *Fax:* 530-477-8342
*E-mail:* bdolphin@bluedolphinpublishing.com
*Web Site:* www.bluedolphinpublishing.com
*Key Personnel*
Pres & Ed: Paul M Clemens *E-mail:* clemens@bluedolphinpublishing.com
Ed & Electronic Publg: Linda Maxwell
Mktg & Promo: Michael Clemens
Founded: 1985
Books, ebooks & audiotapes on health, psychology, self-help, comparative spiritual traditions, anthropology, education.
ISBN Prefix(es): 978-0-931892; 978-0-942444; 978-1-57733
Number of titles published annually: 20 Print; 20 Online; 20 E-Book; 3 Audio
Total Titles: 265 Print; 175 Online; 175 E-Book; 15 Audio
Imprints: Aura Imaging; Papillion Publishing (children's); Pelican Pond Publishing (fiction & poetry); Symposium Publishing (nonfiction)
Distributor for The Lotus Seed Press (China) (ISBN prefix: 962-8602)
Foreign Rep(s): Yorwerth Associates (Nigel Yorwerth) (Worldwide)
Foreign Rights: Editions Le Chaos (France); Agencia Riff (Brazil)

**§Blue Forge Press**
Formerly Orchard House Press
7419 Ebbert Dr SE, Port Orchard, WA 98367
SAN: 299-1330
*Tel:* 360-769-7174
*E-mail:* blueforgepress@gmail.com
*Key Personnel*
Owner & CEO: Jennifer DiMarco
Sr Ed: Ms Cris K A DiMarco
Founded: 1989
Historical fiction, science fiction, fantasy, erotica, children's books, games (CCG & RPG), mysteries, fiction, young adult & literary fiction. Writers must visit the web site for guidelines.
ISBN Prefix(es): 978-1-886383; 978-1-883573; 978-1-59092
Number of titles published annually: 150 Print; 10 CD-ROM; 200 E-Book; 20 Audio
Total Titles: 500 Print; 10 CD-ROM; 200 E-Book; 10 Audio

**Blue Mountain Arts Inc**
2905 Wilderness Place, Boulder, CO 80301
SAN: 169-0477
Mailing Address: PO Box 4549, Boulder, CO 80306-4549
*Tel:* 303-449-0536 *Toll Free Tel:* 800-525-0642 *Fax:* 303-417-6472 *Toll Free Fax:* 800-545-8573
*E-mail:* info@sps.com
*Web Site:* www.sps.com
*Key Personnel*
Pres: Robert Gall
Sales Admin: Vicki Cornelius
Founded: 1971
Publisher of trade books: inspirational, poetry, juvenile, young adult & gift books & sidelines.
ISBN Prefix(es): 978-0-88396; 978-1-58786; 978-1-59842
Number of titles published annually: 20 Print; 20 Online
Total Titles: 120 Print; 120 Online
Imprints: Artes Monte Azul; Blue Mountain Press®; Rabbit's Foot Press™
*Editorial Office(s):* PO Box 1007, Boulder, CO 80301, Contact: P Wayant
Foreign Rights: Christine Moritz (Worldwide)
*Returns:* 6455 Spine Rd, Boulder, CO 80301 SAN: 169-0477
*Shipping Address:* 6455 Spine Rd, Boulder, CO 80301, Contact: Wayne Ivers *Tel:* 303-449-0536 SAN: 169-0477
Membership(s): ABA; CBA; National Association of College Stores

**Blue Note Books**, see Blue Note Publications Inc

**Blue Note Publications Inc**
720 North Dr, Suite D, Melbourne, FL 32924
*Tel:* 321-799-2583 *Toll Free Tel:* 800-624-0401 (orders) *Fax:* 321-799-1942
*E-mail:* bluenotepress@gmail.com
*Web Site:* www.bluenotebooks.com
*Key Personnel*
Pres: Paul Maluccio
Publr: Carmen Abreu
Founded: 1988
Small press book publishing, production, printing, distribution, marketing.
ISBN Prefix(es): 978-1-878398
Number of titles published annually: 6 Print
Total Titles: 50 Print; 2 CD-ROM; 2 Audio
Imprints: Blue Note; Blue Note Books; Blue Note Music Manuscript Books
Membership(s): IBPA, the Independent Book Publishers Association

**§Blue Poppy Press**
Division of Blue Poppy Enterprises Inc
1990 57 Ct, Unit A, Boulder, CO 80301
*Tel:* 303-447-8372 *Toll Free Tel:* 800-487-9296 *Fax:* 303-245-8362
*E-mail:* info@bluepoppy.com
*Web Site:* www.bluepoppy.com
*Key Personnel*
Gen Mgr: Bruce Staff *E-mail:* bruce@bluepoppy.com
Mktg Dir: Honora Wolfe *E-mail:* honora@bluepoppy.com
Founded: 1982
Books on acupuncture & Chinese medicine.
ISBN Prefix(es): 978-0-936185; 978-1-891845
Number of titles published annually: 10 Print; 3 E-Book
Total Titles: 12 Print; 100 E-Book
Distributed by China Books; New Leaf Books; Partner's Book Distributing Inc; Partner's/West Book Distributing Inc; Redwing Book Co; Satas; Tools4Healing (Scott Mieras)

**Blue Rider Press**
Imprint of Penguin Group (USA) LLC
375 Hudson St, New York, NY 10014
*Tel:* 212-366-2000

*Key Personnel*
Pres & Publr: David Rosenthal
Assoc Publr: Aileen Boyle
Exec Ed: Sarah Hochman
Asst Publicity Dir: Brian Ulicky
Art Dir: Greg Kulick
Founded: 2011
Number of titles published annually: 28 Print
Total Titles: 32 Print

**BlueBridge**
Imprint of United Tribes Media Inc
PO Box 601, Katonah, NY 10536
*Tel:* 914-301-5901
*Web Site:* www.bluebridgebooks.com
*Key Personnel*
Founder & Publr: Jan-Erik Guerth
*E-mail:* janguerth@bluebridgebooks.com
Founded: 2004
Independent publisher of international nonfiction based near New York City. Subjects range from culture, history, biography, travel & current affairs to spirituality, self-help & inspiration. The BlueBridge Vision: Thoughtful Books for Mind & Spirit.
ISBN Prefix(es): 978-1-933346; 978-0-9742405
Number of titles published annually: 6 Print
Total Titles: 30 Print
*Distribution Center:* Independent Publishers Group (IPG), 814 N Franklin St, Chicago, IL 60610 (trade) *Tel:* 312-337-0747 (trade or publr inquiries) *Toll Free Tel:* 800-888-4741 (orders) *Fax:* 312-337-5985 *E-mail:* orders@ipgbook.com *Web Site:* www.ipgbook.com

**Bluestocking Press**
3045 Sacramento St, No 1014, Placerville, CA 95667-1014
SAN: 667-2981
Mailing Address: PO Box 1014, Placerville, CA 95667-1014
*Tel:* 530-622-8586 *Toll Free Tel:* 800-959-8586 *Fax:* 530-642-9222
*E-mail:* customerservice@bluestockingpress.com; orders@bluestockingpress.com
*Web Site:* www.bluestockingpress.com
*Key Personnel*
Owner & Pres: Jane A Williams *E-mail:* jane@bluestockingpress.com
Founded: 1987
Other subjects offered: free market economics, business, finance, justice, ancient Rome, World Wars, Mideast War. Sell on nonreturnable basis (except for books received damaged) to the reseller market.
ISBN Prefix(es): 978-0-942617
Number of titles published annually: 10 Print
Total Titles: 23 Print
*Sales Office(s):* PO Box 1014, Placerville, CA 95667-1014, Contact: Ann Marie *E-mail:* annmarie@bluestockingpress.com
*Billing Address:* PO Box 1014, Placerville, CA 95667-1014, Accts Payable: Jane Williams *E-mail:* jane@bluestockingpress.com
*Orders to:* PO Box 1014, Placerville, CA 95667-1014, Contact: Ann Marie *E-mail:* annmarie@bluestockingpress.com

**BNA Books**
Division of The Bureau of National Affairs Inc
1801 S Bell St, Arlington, VA 22202
SAN: 201-4262
Mailing Address: PO Box 7814, Edison, NJ 08818-7814
*Toll Free Tel:* 800-372-1033 *Fax:* 732-346-1624
*E-mail:* books@bna.com
*Web Site:* www.bnabooks.com
*Key Personnel*
Chmn: Paul Wojcik
Publr: Margret S Hullinger *Tel:* 703-341-5742 *E-mail:* mhullinger@bna.com
Dir Acqs & New Prod Devt: Timothy Darby *Tel:* 703-341-5762
Acqs Mgr: James Fattibene *Tel:* 703-341-5765
Mktg Mgr: Christine Chirichella *Tel:* 703-341-5761
Founded: 1929
Employment law: labor law, labor relations, employee benefits, labor arbitration, intellectual property law; health law: legal practice & reference.
ISBN Prefix(es): 978-0-87179; 978-1-57018
Number of titles published annually: 40 Print
Total Titles: 160 Print; 2 Online
*Orders to:* 30 Mayfield Ave, Edison, NJ 08837-3821; 9435 Key West Ave, Rockville, MD 20850 (loose-leaf pubns) *Toll Free Tel:* 800-253-0332 *Toll Free Fax:* 800-372-1033
*Returns:* 30 Mayfield Ave, Edison, NJ 08837-3821

**BNi Building News**
990 Park Center Dr, Suite E, Vista, CA 92081-8352
*Tel:* 760-734-1113 *Toll Free Tel:* 888-264-2665
*Web Site:* www.bnibooks.com
Founded: 1946
Construction & engineering.
ISBN Prefix(es): 978-1-55701; 978-1-878088
Number of titles published annually: 100 Print
Total Titles: 120 Print
*Branch Office(s)*
1612 S Clementine St, Anaheim, CA 92802-2901 *Tel:* 714-517-0971
Distributed by Macmillan

**BOA Editions Ltd**
250 N Goodman St, Suite 306, Rochester, NY 14607
*Tel:* 585-546-3410 *Fax:* 585-546-3913
*E-mail:* contact@boaeditions.org
*Web Site:* www.boaeditions.org
*Key Personnel*
Devt Dir: Melissa Hall *E-mail:* hall@boaeditions.org
Publr: Peter Conners *E-mail:* conners@boaeditions.org
Founded: 1976
Publication of books of poetry, poetry in translation & fiction.
ISBN Prefix(es): 978-0-918526; 978-1-880238; 978-1-929918; 978-1-934414
Number of titles published annually: 10 Print
Total Titles: 205 Print
*Orders to:* Consortium Book Sales & Distribution, The Keg House, Suite 101, 34 13 Ave NE, Minneapolis, MN 55413-1007 *Tel:* 612-746-2600 *Toll Free Tel:* 800-283-3572 (cust serv) *Fax:* 612-746-2606 *Web Site:* www.cbsd.com
*Shipping Address:* Perseus Ditribution, 193 Edwards Dr, Jackson, TN 38301 *Toll Free Tel:* 800-343-4499 *Toll Free Fax:* 800-351-5073 *Web Site:* www.perseusdistribution.com
*Warehouse:* Perseus Dsitribution, 1094 Flex Dr, Jackson, TN 38301 *Toll Free Tel:* 800-343-4499 *Toll Free Fax:* 800-351-5073 *Web Site:* www.perseusdistribution.com
*Distribution Center:* Consortium Book Sales & Distribution, The Keg House, Suite 101, 34 13 Ave NE, Minneapolis, MN 55413-1007 *Tel:* 612-746-2600 *Toll Free Tel:* 800-283-3572 (cust serv) *Fax:* 612-746-2606 *Web Site:* www.cbsd.com

**§BoardSource**
750 Ninth St NW, Suite 650, Washington, DC 20001-4793
*Tel:* 202-349-2500 *Toll Free Tel:* 877-892-6273 *Fax:* 202-349-2599
*E-mail:* members@boardsource.org
*Web Site:* www.boardsource.org
*Key Personnel*
CEO & Pres: Linda Crompton
Founded: 1988
Premier resource for practical information, tools & best practices, training & leadership development for board members of nonprofit organizations. Enables organizations to fulfill their missions by helping build effective nonprofit boards, offering credible support in solving tough problems.
ISBN Prefix(es): 978-0-925299; 978-1-58686
Number of titles published annually: 6 Print; 3 CD-ROM; 2 E-Book
Total Titles: 100 Print; 6 E-Book
Distributed by American Society of Association Executives

**§Bolchazy-Carducci Publishers Inc**
1570 Baskin Rd, Mundelein, IL 60060
SAN: 219-7685
*Tel:* 847-526-4344 *Toll Free Tel:* 800-392-6453 *Fax:* 847-526-2867
*E-mail:* info@bolchazy.com; orders@bolchazy.com
*Web Site:* www.bolchazy.com
*Key Personnel*
Owner & Pres: Dr Marie Carducci Bolchazy, PhD *E-mail:* marie@bolchazy.com
VP: Allan Bolchazy *E-mail:* abolchazy@bolchazy.com
Founded: 1978
Scholarly books, textbooks, language cassettes, CD-ROM Latin series, Latin music CDs & Slovak publications.
ISBN Prefix(es): 978-0-86516
Number of titles published annually: 15 Print; 3 CD-ROM; 5 Online; 10 E-Book; 5 Audio
Total Titles: 450 Print; 29 CD-ROM; 5 Online; 20 E-Book; 20 Audio
*Advertising Agency:* De Chant Hughes
*Returns:* 1576 Baskin Rd, Mundelein, IL 60060, Returns Coord: Betty Brendal *Tel:* 847-388-7144 *Fax:* 847-367-7684 *E-mail:* returns@bolchazy.com
*Warehouse:* 1576 Baskin Rd, Mundelein, IL 60060
*Distribution Center:* 1576 Baskin Rd, Mundelein, IL 60060 *Tel:* 847-388-7144 *Fax:* 847-367-7684

**§Bold Strokes Books Inc**
PO Box 249, Valley Falls, NY 12185
*Tel:* 518-677-5127 *Fax:* 518-677-5291
*E-mail:* bsb@boldstrokesbooks.com
*Web Site:* www.boldstrokesbooks.com
*Key Personnel*
Pres: Len Barot *E-mail:* publisher@boldstrokesbooks.com
Founded: 2004
Independent publishing company publishing works of gay, lesbian & feminist themed fiction in all genres, including general, genre & young adult fiction. Readership is international & all titles are released in print & multi-format ebook version. Employs conventional distribution channels to bring products to the customers.
ISBN Prefix(es): 978-1-9331100; 978-1-60282; 978-1-62639
Number of titles published annually: 90 Print; 110 Online; 90 E-Book; 25 Audio
Total Titles: 400 Print; 515 Online; 515 E-Book; 30 Audio
*Orders to:* Bella Distribution, 1041 Aenon Church Rd, Tallahassee, FL 32304
*Returns:* Bella Distribution, 1041 Aenon Church Rd, Tallahassee, FL 32304
*Shipping Address:* Bella Distribution, 1041 Aenon Church Rd, Tallahassee, FL 32304
*Warehouse:* Bella Distribution, 1041 Aenon Church Rd, Tallahassee, FL 32304
*Distribution Center:* Bella Distribution, 1041 Aenon Church Rd, Tallahassee, FL 32304,

Contact: Becky Arbogast *Toll Free Tel:* 800-533-1973 *Fax:* 850-576-3498 *E-mail:* info@belladistribution.com
Membership(s): IBPA, the Independent Book Publishers Association; Mystery Writers of America; Romance Writers of America; Science Fiction & Fantasy Writers of America

**Bonasa Press**
462 Chestnut St, Columbia, PA 17512-1230
*Tel:* 717-684-4215 *Fax:* 717-684-4215
*E-mail:* new@bonasapress.com (inquiries)
*Web Site:* www.bonasapress.com
*Key Personnel*
Publr & Ed: John D Taylor *E-mail:* jdt@bonasapress.com
Sales & Mktg: Nancy E Whiting *E-mail:* new@bonasapress.com
Founded: 2002
ISBN Prefix(es): 978-0-9725594; 978-0-9772778
Number of titles published annually: 4 Print
Total Titles: 14 Print
Membership(s): Outdoor Writers Association of America; Pennsylvania Outdoors Writers Association

**§Bondfire Books**
7680 Goddard St, Suite 220, Colorado Springs, CO 80920
*Tel:* 719-260-7080
*Web Site:* www.bondfirebooks.com
*Key Personnel*
Founder: Rick Christian
Exec Ed: Patton Dodd
ISBN Prefix(es): 978-1-939952
Number of titles published annually: 25 Print

**Book Marketing Works LLC**
50 Lovely St (Rte 177), Avon, CT 06001
Mailing Address: PO Box 715, Avon, CT 06001-0715
*Tel:* 860-675-1344
*Web Site:* www.bookmarketingworks.com
*Key Personnel*
Pres: Brian Jud *E-mail:* brianjud@bookmarketingworks.com
Founded: 1990
ISBN Prefix(es): 978-1-928782
Number of titles published annually: 10 Print
Total Titles: 26 Print
Imprints: Strong Books
Subsidiaries: Book Marketing Works

**Book Peddlers**
2950 W Dean Pkwy, No 1602, Minneapolis, MN 55416
*Tel:* 952-544-1154
*E-mail:* bookpeddlers@aol.com
*Web Site:* www.bookpeddlers.com; www.practicalparenting.com
*Key Personnel*
Owner & Publr: Vicki Lansky *E-mail:* vickilansky@aol.com
Mktg & PR: Diane Schwarze *E-mail:* diane@bookpeddlers.com
Founded: 1987
Nonfiction hardcover & audio tapes; gift-giving occasion books.
ISBN Prefix(es): 978-0-916773; 978-1-931863
Number of titles published annually: 1 Print; 2 E-Book
Total Titles: 20 Print; 3 CD-ROM; 15 E-Book
*Editorial Office(s):* 18330 Minnetonka Blvd, Deephaven, MN 55391, Contact: Vicki Lansky
*Distribution Center:* Publishers Group West (PGW)/Perseus, 1700 Fourth St, Berkeley, CA (book trade)

**Book Publishing Co**
415 Farm Rd, Summertown, TN 38483
Mailing Address: PO Box 99, Summertown, TN 38483-0099
*Tel:* 931-964-3571 *Fax:* 931-964-3518
*E-mail:* info@bookpubco.com
*Web Site:* www.bookpubco.com
*Key Personnel*
Pres: Robert Holzapfel
Ed: Cynthia Holzapfel
Mktg: Anna Pope *E-mail:* annap@bookpubco.com
Founded: 1974
Community-owned independent press committed to promoting books that educate, inspire & empower. Books on vegan & vegetarian cooking & nutrition, raw food lifestyle, natural health care & Native American culture.
ISBN Prefix(es): 978-0-913990; 978-1-57067; 978-1-55312
Number of titles published annually: 10 Print
Total Titles: 250 Print; 2 Audio
Imprints: Books Alive; Botanica Press; Healthy Living; Hippocrates Publications; Native Voices; Norwalk Press; 7th Generation
Distributor for Cherokee Publications; Crazy Crow; CRCS Publications; Critical Path; Gentle World; Magni Co; Sproutman Publications
Foreign Rep(s): Brumby Books (Australia); Faradawn (South Africa); Publishers Group UK (England)

**Book Sales Inc**
Division of The Quarto Group Inc
276 Fifth Ave, Suite 206, New York, NY 10001
SAN: 299-4062
*Tel:* 212-779-4972 *Toll Free Tel:* 866-483-5456 *Fax:* 212-779-6058
*E-mail:* sales@booksalesusa.com; customerservice@booksalesusa.com
*Web Site:* www.booksalesusa.com
*Key Personnel*
CEO & Pres: Melvin Shapiro
VP, Mktg & Acqs: Frank Oppel *Tel:* 212-779-4974 *E-mail:* frank@booksalesusa.com
Sales Dir: Steven Wilson *Tel:* 212-779-4973 *E-mail:* swilson@booksalesusa.com
Spec Sales: Daniel Rich *Tel:* 212-779-1816 *E-mail:* drich@booksalesusa.com
Exec Asst: Jennifer Yee *E-mail:* jyee@booksalesusa.com
Founded: 1952
Has been in the business of publishing & supplying books to wholesalers, mail order companies & retail stores for over 45 years. In addition to books we publish, we are one of the largest purchasers of other publishers' remainder &/or overstock titles for resale at significantly reduced prices. Categories include novels, cookbooks, history, juvenile, civil war, militaria, fine art, art instruction, how-to craft books, natural history, gardening & more.
ISBN Prefix(es): 978-0-89009; 978-1-55521; 978-0-7858
Number of titles published annually: 300 Print
Total Titles: 2,500 Print
Imprints: Alva Press; Blue & Grey; Castle Books; Chartwell Books; Knickerbocker Press; Wellfleet Press
*Billing Address:* 400 First Ave N, Suite 300, Minneapolis, MN 55401
*Returns:* 677 Brighton Rd, Menasha, WI 54952
*Warehouse:* c/o R R Donnelly, N9234 Lake Park Rd, Appleton, WI 54915 *Tel:* 612-344-8100 *Toll Free Tel:* 800-328-0590 *Fax:* 612-344-8691
Membership(s): ABA

**The Book Tree**
3316 Adams Ave, Suite A, San Diego, CA 92116
Mailing Address: PO Box 16476, San Diego, CA 92176
*Tel:* 619-280-1263 *Toll Free Tel:* 800-700-8733 (orders) *Fax:* 619-280-1285
*E-mail:* orders@thebooktree.com; titles@thebooktree.com
*Web Site:* thebooktree.com
*Key Personnel*
Owner: Paul Willey
Founded: 1992
Metaphysical, spiritual & controversial books; do not accept, respond to or return unsol mss.
ISBN Prefix(es): 978-1-885395, 978-1-58509
Number of titles published annually: 20 Print
Total Titles: 250 Print
Membership(s): IBPA, the Independent Book Publishers Association

**Bookhaven Press LLC**
302 Scenic Ct, Moon Township, PA 15108
SAN: 668-7075
*Tel:* 412-494-6926 *Toll Free Tel:* 800-782-7424 (orders only)
*E-mail:* info@bookhavenpress.com; orders@bookhavenpress.com
*Web Site:* bookhavenpress.com
*Key Personnel*
Pres & Publr: Dennis V Damp *E-mail:* ddamp@aol.com
Assoc Publr: Victor Richards *E-mail:* vrichards@bookhavenpress.com
Publicist: Dr Kate Bandos *Tel:* 800-304-3269 *E-mail:* kate@ksbpromotions.com
Off Mgr: Mary McGraw
Founded: 1985
Independent publishing house dedicated to producing award winning business, career & finance books & companion web sites. *The Book of U.S. Government Jobs* was awarded "Best Career Title" by the Benjamin Franklin Awards Committee. Our 4th edition of *Health Care Job Explosion* was nominated for Best Books 2006 (Business-Career) title by USA Book News. Bookhaven's titles have been reviewed & recommended by Library Journal, Booklist, the New York Times & Washington Post, Career Opportunities News & over 100 magazines, newspapers & journals. We also publish environmental compliance books & comprehensive web sites for our titles.
ISBN Prefix(es): 978-0-943641
Number of titles published annually: 3 Print; 2 E-Book
Total Titles: 6 Print; 3 E-Book
Membership(s): IBPA, the Independent Book Publishers Association

**§BookLogix**
1264 Old Alpharetta Rd, Alpharetta, GA 30005
SAN: 860-0376
*Tel:* 770-346-9979 *Toll Free Fax:* 888-564-7890
*E-mail:* sales@booklogix.com
*Web Site:* www.booklogix.com
*Key Personnel*
CEO & Pres: Ahmad Meradji *E-mail:* ahmad@booklogix.com
COO: Akash Mangru *E-mail:* kash@booklogix.com
Founded: 2009
This publisher has indicated that 80% of their product line is author subsidized.
ISBN Prefix(es): 978-1-61005
Number of titles published annually: 25 Print; 20 E-Book
Total Titles: 150 Print; 100 E-Book
*Distribution Center:* Baker & Taylor, 2550 W Tyvola Rd, Suite 300, Charlotte, NC 28217 *Tel:* 704-998-3100 *Toll Free Tel:* 800-775-1800 *Web Site:* www.btol.com

**Books In Motion**
Division of Classic Ventures Ltd
9922 E Montgomery, Suite 31, Spokane Valley, WA 99206
*Tel:* 509-922-1646 *Toll Free Tel:* 800-752-3199 *Fax:* 509-922-1445
*E-mail:* info@booksinmotion.com
*Web Site:* booksinmotion.biz

*Key Personnel*
Pres: Gary Challender
Founded: 1980
Produce fiction books on CD & MP3. Does not accept unsol mss. Criteria is exceptionally high for acceptance. There is no cost to the authors. Currently seeking subsidiary audio rights on previously print published titles.
ISBN Prefix(es): 978-1-55686; 978-1-58116; 978-1-59607; 978-1-60548
Number of titles published annually: 120 Audio
Total Titles: 2,000 Audio
Membership(s): Western Writers of America

**Books on Tape®**
Division of Random House Inc
c/o Sales Dept, 3070 Bristol St, Suite 650, Costa Mesa, CA 92626
*Toll Free Tel:* 800-733-3000 (cust serv)
*Toll Free Fax:* 800-940-7046
*Web Site:* www.booksontape.com
*Key Personnel*
VP, Lib & Academic Sales: Skip Dye
SVP & Publr, Random House Audio: Amanda D'Acierno
Mktg Dir: Cheryl Herman
Founded: 1975
For over 30 years Books on Tape® has offered the best in unabridged audio books. Our best selling & award-winning titles are produced in NY & LA studios & read by the finest narrators in the industry. Select from over 3,000 titles available, durable library packaging & delivered with a complement of services tailored to meet special needs of librarians & educators. Flexible standing order plans, featuring the freedom to choose your titles & free lifetime replacement guarantees. Books on Tape® is proud to exclusively have Listening Library®, the premier audio book publisher of children's & young adult literature, as its children's imprint.
Number of titles published annually: 300 Audio
Total Titles: 3,000 Audio
Imprints: Listening Library®
Divisions: Listening Library®
Distributor for Listening Library®
*Orders to:* Random House Inc, Library & School Services, 400 Hahn Rd, Westminster, MD 21157
*Returns:* Random House Inc, 1019 N SR 47, Crawfordville, NJ 47933
Membership(s): AASL; ALA; ALSC; California Library Association; National Council of Teachers of English; Public Library Association; YALSA

**Boom! Studios**
5670 Wilshire Blvd, Suite 450, Los Angeles, CA 90036
*Web Site:* www.boom-studios.com
*Key Personnel*
CEO: Ross Richie
VP, Publg & Mktg: Filip Sablik
Ed-in-Chief: Matt Gagnon
Founded: 2005
ISBN Prefix(es): 978-1-934506; 978-1-60886; 978-1-61398
Distributed by Simon & Schuster Sales & Marketing

**Borderline Publishing**
406 S Third St, Boise, ID 83702
*Tel:* 208-475-4950; 208-258-9544
*E-mail:* submissions@borderlinepublishing.com
*Web Site:* www.borderlinepublishing.com
*Key Personnel*
Contact: Kimberli Reynolds *Fax:* 208-258-9237 *E-mail:* submissions@borderlinepublishing.com
Founded: 2009
ISBN Prefix(es): 978-1-936408; 978-0-9841902; 978-1-937703; 978-0-9843669; 978-0-9845045
Number of titles published annually: 15 Print; 15 Online; 15 E-Book; 2 Audio
Total Titles: 40 Print; 40 Online; 40 E-Book
Imprints: Resilient Publishing LLC; Sevens Publishing
Distributor for Anderson Design; Brynwood Publishing
Membership(s): Idaho Writers Guild

**§Boson Books**
Imprint of Bitingduck Press
1262 Sunnyoaks Circle, Altadena, CA 91001
*Tel:* 626-507-8033
*Web Site:* www.bosonbooks.com
*Key Personnel*
Ed-in-Chief: Jay Nadeau *E-mail:* jay@bitingduckpress.com
Tech Dir: Chris Lindensmith *E-mail:* chris@bitingduckpress.com
Founded: 1994
Publish ebooks & selected print books. First commercial general ebook publisher.
ISBN Prefix(es): 978-1-886420; 978-0-917990; 978-1-932482
Number of titles published annually: 5 Print; 13 E-Book
Total Titles: 25 Print; 350 E-Book
Membership(s): The Authors Guild

**Bottom Dog Press**
c/o Firelands College of Bowling Green State Univ, PO Box 425, Huron, OH 44839-0425
SAN: 689-5492
*Tel:* 419-433-5560 (ext 20784) *Fax:* 419-616-3966
*Web Site:* smithdocs.net
*Key Personnel*
Dir & Publr: Larry Smith *E-mail:* lsmithdog@smithdocs.net
Assoc Ed: Allen Frost; Susanna Sharp Schwacke; Laura Smith
Founded: 1985
ISBN Prefix(es): 978-0-933087; 978-1-933064
Number of titles published annually: 5 Print; 2 Audio
Total Titles: 135 Print; 2 CD-ROM; 4 Audio
Imprints: Bird Dog Publishing; Bottom Dog Press
Distributor for The Firelands Writing Center (Heartlands Magazine)
*Returns:* c/o BGSU Firelands College, One University Dr, Huron, OH 44839
*Distribution Center:* Small Press Distribution, 1341 Seventh St, Berkeley, CA 94710-1409 *Tel:* 510-524-1668 *Toll Free Tel:* 800-869-7553 *Fax:* 510-524-0852 *E-mail:* spd@spdbooks.org *Web Site:* www.spdbooks.org
Baker & Taylor, 501 Gladiolus St, Momence, IL 60954
Membership(s): Council of Literary Magazines & Presses

**Thomas Bouregy & Co Inc**
160 Madison Ave, 5th fl, New York, NY 10016
SAN: 201-4173
*Tel:* 212-598-0222 *Fax:* 212-979-1862
*Key Personnel*
Publr: Ellen Bouregy-Mickelsen *E-mail:* emickelsen@avalonbooks.com
Founded: 1950
Fiction: mysteries, romances, westerns, historical romances.
ISBN Prefix(es): 978-0-8034
Number of titles published annually: 60 Print
Total Titles: 504 Print
*Warehouse:* Offset Paperback Distribution Center, One Passan Dr, Bldg 10, Laflin, PA 18702

**Eddie Bowers Publishing Co Inc**
PO Box 130, Peosta, IA 52068-0130
*Tel:* 563-582-8333 *Toll Free Tel:* 800-747-2411 *Fax:* 563-582-8555
*E-mail:* eddiebowerspub@aol.com
*Web Site:* www.eddiebowerspublishing.com
*Key Personnel*
Owner & Publr: Eddie Bowers
Founded: 1981
College textbooks.
ISBN Prefix(es): 978-0-912855; 978-0-945483; 978-0-57879
Number of titles published annually: 20 Print
Total Titles: 75 Print
Foreign Rep(s): Gazelle Book Services (England)

**R R Bowker LLC**
Subsidiary of ProQuest LLC
630 Central Ave, New Providence, NJ 07974
SAN: 214-1191
*Tel:* 908-286-1090 *Toll Free Tel:* 888-269-5372 (edit & cust serv, press 2 for returns) *Fax:* 908-219-0098; (020) 7832 1710 (UK for intl) *Toll Free Fax:* 877-337-7015 (domestic/US & CN)
*E-mail:* orders@proquest.com (domestic orders); customer_service@proquest.co.uk (intl)
*Web Site:* www.bowker.com
*Key Personnel*
VP & Gen Mgr: Sharon Lubrano
VP, Busn Devt: Angela D'Agostino
Founded: 1872
Leading provider of bibliographic information & management solutions designed to help publishers, booksellers & libraries better serve their customers. Creators of products & services that make books easier for people to discover, evaluate, order & experience, the company also generates research & resources for publishers, helping them understand & meet the interests of readers worldwide. Bowker, an affiliated business of ProQuest & the official ISBN Agency for Australia, United States & US territories, is headquartered in New Providence, NJ with additional operations in England & Australia.
ISBN Prefix(es): 978-0-8352
Number of titles published annually: 13 Print; 8 Online
Total Titles: 29 Print; 8 Online
*Foreign Office(s):* Thorpe - Bowker, Level One, 607 St Kilda Rd, Melbourne, Victoria 3004, Australia, Mng Dir: Gary Pengelly *Tel:* (03) 8517 8345 *Fax:* (03) 8517-8399 *E-mail:* yoursay@thorpe.com.au *Web Site:* www.thorpe.com.au
Bowker (UK) Ltd, St Andrew's House, 18-20 St Andrew St, London EC4A 3AG, United Kingdom, Mng Dir: Doug McMillan *Tel:* (020) 7832 1771 *Fax:* (020) 7832 1710 *E-mail:* sales@bowker.co.uk *Web Site:* www.bowker.co.uk
Membership(s): AAP; ALA; BISG; Canadian Booksellers Association; Evangelical Christian Publishers Association; National Association of College Stores

**BowTie Press®**
Division of BowTie Inc
3 Burroughs, Irvine, CA 92618
*Tel:* 949-855-8822 *Toll Free Tel:* 888-738-2665 *Fax:* 949-458-3856
*E-mail:* bowtiepress@bowtieinc.com
*Web Site:* www.bowtiepress.com
*Key Personnel*
Pres: Norman Ridker
Publr: Desiree Lynch
Mng Ed: April Balotro
Sales Mgr: Craig Horowitz
ISBN Prefix(es): 978-0-9629525; 978-1-889540; 978-1-931993
Number of titles published annually: 20 Print
Membership(s): AAP

**Boydell & Brewer Inc**
Affiliate of Boydell & Brewer Ltd (UK)
668 Mount Hope Ave, Rochester, NY 14620-2731

*Tel:* 585-275-0419 *Fax:* 585-271-8778
*E-mail:* boydell@boydellusa.net
*Web Site:* www.boydellandbrewer.com
*Key Personnel*
Mng Dir: Sue Smith *Tel:* 585-273-2817 *E-mail:* smith@boydellusa.net
Edit Dir: Suzanne Guiod *Tel:* 585-273-5778 *E-mail:* guiod@uofrochesterpress.net
Sales & Mktg Dir: Christine L Cody *Tel:* 585-273-5787 *E-mail:* cody@boydellusa.net
Accts Mgr: Eloise Puls *Tel:* 585-273-5777 *E-mail:* puls@boydellusa.net
Mktg Mgr: Anastasia Broikos *Tel:* 585-275-0391 *E-mail:* broikos@boydellusa.net
Founded: 1989
Publisher of scholarly books.
ISBN Prefix(es): 978-0-85115; 978-0-85991; 978-0-86193; 978-0-7293; 978-0-900411; 978-1-85566; 978-1-878822; 978-1-58046; 978-1-57113; 978-1-900639
Number of titles published annually: 200 Print
Total Titles: 3,100 Print
Imprints: Camden House; Canterbury & York Society; Companion Guides; James Curry Ltd; Early English Text Society; Lincoln Record Society; Plumbago Books; Royal Historical Society; Scholarly Digital Editions; Scottish Text Society; Suffolk Records Society; Tamesis; Toccata Press; University of Rochester Press; Victory History of the Counties of England; York Medieval Press
*Foreign Office(s):* Boydell & Brewer Ltd, Whitewell House, Saint Audrey's Park Rd, Melton, Woodbridge, Suffolk IP12 1SY, United Kingdom, Mng Ed: Peter Clifford *Tel:* (01394) 610600 *Fax:* (01394) 610316 *E-mail:* editorial@boydell.co.uk
*Orders to:* Boydell & Brewer Ltd, Whitewell House, Saint Audrey's Park Rd, Melton, Woodbridge, Suffolk IP12 1SY, United Kingdom, Mng Dir: Peter Clifford *E-mail:* editorial@boydell.co.uk
*Returns:* c/o PSSCMA, 46 Development Rd, Fitchburg, MA 01420-6019
*Warehouse:* c/o PSSCMA, 46 Development Rd, Fitchburg, MA 01420-6019 *Tel:* 978-345-2121 *Fax:* 978-348-1233
College Farm, Forward Green, Stawmarket, Suffolk IP14 5EH, United Kingdom

**Boyds Mills Press**
Subsidiary of Highlights for Children Inc
815 Church St, Honesdale, PA 18431
*Tel:* 570-253-1164 *Toll Free Tel:* 800-490-5111 *Fax:* 570-253-0179
*E-mail:* contact@boydsmillspress.com
*Web Site:* www.boydsmillspress.com
*Key Personnel*
VP: Mary-Alice Moore
Edit Dir, Book Publg: Elizabeth Van Doren *Tel:* 570-251-4570 *Fax:* 570-253-3110 *E-mail:* liz.vandoren@highlights.com
Sr Ed, Wordsong & Boyds: Rebecca Davis
Mktg & Perms Mgr: Kerry Mcmanus
Natl Accts Mgr: Mr Kreig Krumpe *Tel:* 614-324-7031 *Fax:* 614-324-7943 *E-mail:* kreig.krumpe@boydsmillspress.com
Asst Coordinating Ed: Sarah Lozo
Asst Ed: Sarah Zhang
Founded: 1990
Books for children of all ages.
ISBN Prefix(es): 978-1-56397; 978-1-878093; 978-1-59078
Number of titles published annually: 60 Print
Total Titles: 500 Print
Imprints: Calkins Creek (history); Front Street (children & young adult); Wordsong (poetry)
*See separate listing for:*
**Front Street**

**Boynton/Cook Publishers**
Imprint of Heinemann
361 Hanover St, Portsmouth, NH 03801-3912
SAN: 210-5829
Mailing Address: PO Box 6926, Portsmouth, NH 03802-6926
*Tel:* 603-431-7894 *Toll Free Tel:* 800-225-5800 *Fax:* 603-431-2214 *Toll Free Fax:* 877-231-6980
*E-mail:* custserv@heinemann.com
*Web Site:* www.boyntoncook.com
*Key Personnel*
Pres: Lesa Scott *E-mail:* lesa.scott@weinmann.com
Founded: 1981
College composition & rhetoric textbooks.
ISBN Prefix(es): 978-0-86709
Number of titles published annually: 25 Print
Total Titles: 250 Print
Distributed by Pearson Australia-Schools Division; Pearson Education Canada; Pearson New Zealand-Schools Division
*Orders to:* PO Box 6926, Portsmouth, NH 03802-6926
*Warehouse:* 465 S Lincoln Dr, Troy, MO 63376

**Boys Town Press**
Division of Boys Town
14100 Crawford St, Boys Town, NE 68010
*Tel:* 402-498-1320 *Toll Free Tel:* 800-282-6657 *Fax:* 402-498-1310
*E-mail:* btpress@boystown.org
*Web Site:* www.boystownpress.org
*Key Personnel*
Dir: Erin Green *Tel:* 402-498-1422 *E-mail:* erin.green@boystown.org
Sales Mgr: Patricia Martens *Tel:* 402-498-1334 *E-mail:* patricia.martens@boystown.org
Founded: 1992
Youth care & education books, parenting books, children's books, videos & audio, sign language products, inspirational titles.
ISBN Prefix(es): 978-0-938510; 978-1-889322; 978-1-934490
Number of titles published annually: 10 Print; 3 E-Book
Total Titles: 100 Print; 2 CD-ROM; 24 E-Book; 3 Audio
Distributed by Deep Books Ltd (Europe & UK); Footprint Books (Australia & New Zealand); Monarch Books of Canada Ltd (Canada)
Foreign Rights: Amer-Asia Books (Evelyn Lee) (China, Japan, Korea, Taiwan)
*Returns:* 250 Monsky Dr, Boys Town, NE 68010
*Warehouse:* 250 Monsky Dr, Boys Town, NE 68010
*Distribution Center:* Follett Library Resources, 2233 West St, River Grove, IL 60171-1895 *Tel:* 708-583-2000 *Toll Free Tel:* 888-511-5114 *Fax:* 708-621-4345 *Web Site:* www.follett.com
Baker & Taylor, 2550 W Tyvola Rd, Suite 300, Charlotte, NC 28217 *Tel:* 815-802-2479 *Toll Free Fax:* 800-411-8433 *Web Site:* www.baker-taylor.com
Ingram Book Co, One Ingram Blvd, Lavergne, TN 37086-3650
Membership(s): IBPA, the Independent Book Publishers Association

**§Bradford Publishing Co**
1743 Wazee St, Denver, CO 80202
*Tel:* 303-292-2590 *Toll Free Tel:* 800-446-2831 *Fax:* 303-298-5014
*E-mail:* marketing@bradfordpublishing.com; customerservice@bradfordpublishing.com
*Web Site:* www.bradfordpublishing.com
*Key Personnel*
Owner & Pres: Candace Boyle
Founded: 1881
Specialize in Colorado legal forms & law books.
ISBN Prefix(es): 978-1-883726
Number of titles published annually: 10 Print
Total Titles: 45 Print
Membership(s): IBPA, the Independent Book Publishers Association; Publishers Association of the West

**BradyGames**
Member of Penguin Group (USA) LLC
800 E 96 St, 3rd fl, Indianapolis, IN 46240
*Tel:* 317-428-3000 *Toll Free Tel:* 800-545-5912; 800-571-5840 (cust serv)
*E-mail:* bradyquestions@pearsoned.com
*Web Site:* www.bradygames.com
*Key Personnel*
VP & Publr: Mike Degler
Ed-in-Chief: H Leigh Davis
Natl Accts Mgr: Jennifer Coghlan
Licensing Mgr: Christian Sumner
Mktg Mgr: Katherine Hemlock
ISBN Prefix(es): 978-1-56686; 978-0-7440
Number of titles published annually: 25 Print
Total Titles: 103 Print

**Braille Co Inc**
65-B Town Hall Sq, Falmouth, MA 02540-2754
*Tel:* 508-540-0800 *Fax:* 508-548-6116
*E-mail:* braillinc@capecod.net
*Web Site:* home.capecod.net/~braillinc
*Key Personnel*
Pres: Josie P Little
VP: Deborah Shearer
Founded: 1971
Professional braille transcription & publishing of contemporary fiction & nonfiction. Publish braille textbooks & vocational materials, including mathematics, computer manuals, music & foreign language materials on order. Price list available in inkprint & braille.

**The Brainwaves® Center**, see Allen D Bragdon Publishers Inc

**Branden Books**
Subsidiary of Branden Publishing Co
PO Box 812094, Wellesley, MA 02482-0013
SAN: 201-4106
*Tel:* 781-235-3634
*E-mail:* branden@brandenbooks.com
*Web Site:* www.brandenbooks.com
*Key Personnel*
Pres: Margaret Starrett
VP: Robert Caso
Ed & Treas: Adolph Caso
Founded: 1909
Publisher of fiction & nonfiction books. Distribution center in Ypsilanti, MI.
ISBN Prefix(es): 978-0-8283
Number of titles published annually: 15 Print; 4 CD-ROM; 300 E-Book
Total Titles: 400 Print; 4 CD-ROM; 410 Online; 300 E-Book
Imprints: Art Treasures; Brashear Music Co; Four Seas; Bruce Humphries; International Pocket Library; Popular Technology
Distributor for Dante University of America Press Inc
Foreign Rep(s): Baker & Taylor (Worldwide); Gazelle (England); Ingram (Worldwide)
*Advertising Agency:* ADS-IPL
*Returns:* Publishers Storage & Shipping Corp, 660 S Mansfield, Ypsilanti, MI 48197
*Warehouse:* Publishers Storage & Shipping Corp, 660 S Mansfield, Ypsilanti, MI 48197

**Brandylane Publishers Inc**
5 S First St, Richmond, VA 23219
*Tel:* 804-644-3090 *Fax:* 804-644-3092
*Web Site:* www.brandylanepublishers.com
*Key Personnel*
Publr: Robert H Pruett *E-mail:* rhpruett@brandylanepublishers.com
Sr Ed: Mary A Tobey
Founded: 1985
Publisher & packager of books. Work with previously unpublished writers.
This publisher has indicated that 20% of their product line is author subsidized.

ISBN Prefix(es): 978-1-883911
Number of titles published annually: 15 Print; 15 Online; 15 E-Book
Total Titles: 60 Print; 40 Online; 7 E-Book
Imprints: Belle Isle Books
*Billing Address:* PO Box 274, Kilmarnock, VA 22482 *Tel:* 804-435-6900
Membership(s): IBPA, the Independent Book Publishers Association

**George Braziller Inc**
277 Broadway, Suite 708, New York, NY 10007
SAN: 201-9310
*Tel:* 212-260-9256 *Fax:* 212-267-3165
*E-mail:* georgebrazillerpr@gmail.com; editorial@georgebraziller.com
*Web Site:* www.georgebraziller.com
*Key Personnel*
Founder & Ed-at-Large: George Braziller
Pres & Ed: Michael Braziller *E-mail:* mbraziller@georgebraziller.com
Founded: 1955
Publishers of fine illustrated art books.
ISBN Prefix(es): 978-0-8076
Number of titles published annually: 4 Print
Total Titles: 300 Print
Distributed by Antique Collectors' Club Ltd
Foreign Rep(s): Antique Collectors' Club Ltd (Australia, England, Europe, India, New Zealand); United Publishers Services Ltd (Japan)
*Orders to:* W W Norton & Co Inc, 500 Fifth Ave, New York, NY 10110 *Toll Free Tel:* 800-233-4830 *Toll Free Fax:* 800-458-6515
*Warehouse:* National Book Co, 800 Keystone Industrial Park, Scranton, PA 18512 *Toll Free Tel:* 800-233-4830 *Toll Free Fax:* 800-458-6515
*Distribution Center:* W W Norton & Co Inc, 500 Fifth Ave, New York, NY 10110 *Toll Free Tel:* 800-233-4830 *Toll Free Fax:* 800-458-6515

**Breakaway Books**
PO Box 24, Halcottsville, NY 12438-0024
*Tel:* 607-326-4805 *Toll Free Tel:* 800-548-4348 (voicemail) *Fax:* 203-399-8073
*E-mail:* breakawaybooks@gmail.com
*Web Site:* www.breakawaybooks.com
*Key Personnel*
Publr: Garth Battista
Founded: 1994
Sports literature & books.
ISBN Prefix(es): 978-1-891369; 978-1-55821
Number of titles published annually: 10 Print
Total Titles: 100 Print; 1 E-Book
*Distribution Center:* Consortium, 34 13 Ave NE, Suite 101, Minneapolis, MN 55413-1007 *Toll Free Tel:* 800-283-3572 *Toll Free Fax:* 800-351-5073 *Web Site:* www.cbsd.com

**Breakthrough Publications Inc**
3 Iroquois St, Barn, Emmaus, PA 18049
*Tel:* 610-928-4061 (ext 12) *Toll Free Tel:* 800-824-5001 (ext 12) *Fax:* 610-928-4064
*E-mail:* dot@booksonhorses.com; ruth@booksonhorses.com
*Web Site:* www.booksonhorses.com
*Key Personnel*
Pres & Publr: Peter E Ognibene *Tel:* 914-928-4061 ext 12 *E-mail:* peterognibene@workkplace.com
Founded: 1980
Career & equestrian.
ISBN Prefix(es): 978-0-914327
Number of titles published annually: 30 Print
Total Titles: 50 Print
Imprints: Breakthrough Publications

**Nicholas Brealey Publishing**
20 Park Plaza, Suite 610, Boston, MA 02116
*Tel:* 617-523-3801 *Toll Free Tel:* 888-BREALEY (273-2539) *Fax:* 617-523-3708
*E-mail:* info@nicholasbrealey.com
*Web Site:* www.nicholasbrealey.com
*Key Personnel*
Publr & Foreign Rts: Nicholas Brealey *Tel:* (020) 7430 0224 *Fax:* (020) 7404 8311 *E-mail:* rights@nbrealey-books.com
Edit Dir: Erica Heilman
Mktg Dir: Nicole Le Blanc *E-mail:* nleblanc@nicholasbrealey.com
Sales & Mktg Mgr: Charles Dresner
Publg Coord: Bethany Sales
Founded: 1992
Professional/trade business book (hardcover & original paperback) publisher. Additional subjects include: international business & culture, training & human resources.
ISBN Prefix(es): 978-0-89106 (Davies-Black); 978-1-85788; 978-1-90483; 978-1-93193 (Intercultural Press); 978-1-87786 (Intercultural Press); 978-0-93366 (Intercultural Press)
Number of titles published annually: 200 Print
Total Titles: 270 Print
Imprints: Davies-Black Publishing
Divisions: Intercultural Press Inc
*Foreign Office(s):* 3-5 Spafield St, Clerkenwell, London EC1R 4QB, United Kingdom *Tel:* (020) 7239 0360 *Fax:* (020) 7239 0370 *E-mail:* sales@nicholasbrealey.com
*Orders to:* National Book Network, 15200 NBN Way, Blue Ridge Summit, PA 17214 *Toll Free Tel:* 800-462-6420 *Toll Free Fax:* 800-338-4550
*Returns:* National Book Network, 15200 NBN Way, Blue Ridge Summit, PA 17214 *Toll Free Tel:* 800-462-6420 *Toll Free Fax:* 800-338-4550
*Distribution Center:* National Book Network, 15200 NBN Way, Blue Ridge Summit, PA 17214 *Toll Free Tel:* 800-462-6420 *Toll Free Fax:* 800-338-4550
Membership(s): AAP; Independent Publisher's Guild; PA
*See separate listing for:*
**Davies-Black Publishing**
**Intercultural Press Inc**

**Brenner Information Group**
Division of Brenner Microcomputing Inc
PO Box 721000, San Diego, CA 92172-1000
SAN: 249-6496
*Tel:* 858-538-0093 *Toll Free Tel:* 800-811-4337 (orders)
*E-mail:* brenner@brennerbooks.com; sales@brennerbooks.com
*Web Site:* www.brennerbooks.com
*Key Personnel*
CFO: Carol Brenner
Publr: Robert Brenner
Founded: 1982 (began producing books 1987)
Collects, processes, packages & distributes information related to the pricing of desktop services.
ISBN Prefix(es): 978-0-929535; 978-1-930199
Number of titles published annually: 3 Print; 8 E-Book
Total Titles: 22 Print; 19 E-Book

**Brentwood Christian Press**
4000 Beallwood Ave, Columbus, GA 31904
Mailing Address: PO Box 4773, Columbus, GA 31914-4773
*Toll Free Tel:* 800-334-8861
*E-mail:* brentwood@aol.com
*Web Site:* www.brentwoodbooks.com
*Key Personnel*
Owner: U D Roberts
Founded: 1982
Publisher of Christian books.
ISBN Prefix(es): 978-1-55630
Number of titles published annually: 220 Print
Total Titles: 3,744 Print

**Brethren Press**
Division of Church of the Brethren General Board
1451 Dundee Ave, Elgin, IL 60120
SAN: 201-9329
*Tel:* 847-742-5100 *Toll Free Tel:* 800-323-8039 *Fax:* 847-742-6103 *Toll Free Fax:* 800-667-8188
*E-mail:* brethrenpress@brethren.org; cobweb@brethren.org
*Web Site:* www.brethrenpress.com
*Key Personnel*
Publr: Wendy McFadden *Tel:* 847-742-5100 ext 307 *E-mail:* wmcfadden@brethren.org
Dir, Mktg & Sales: Jeff Lennard *Tel:* 847-742-5100 ext 321 *E-mail:* jlennard@brethren.org
Founded: 1897
Trade books, church school curriculum, tracts & pamphlets & various media resources. Specialize in Bible study, theology, church history, practical discipleship, personal lifestyle issues, social concerns, peace & justice, devotional life & personal growth.
ISBN Prefix(es): 978-0-87178
Number of titles published annually: 6 Print
Total Titles: 100 Print
Imprints: faithQuest
Membership(s): Protestant Church-Owned Publishers Association

**Brewers Publications**
Division of Brewers Association
736 Pearl St, Boulder, CO 80302
Mailing Address: PO Box 1679, Boulder, CO 80306
*Tel:* 303-447-0816 *Toll Free Tel:* 888-822-6273 (CN & US) *Fax:* 303-447-2825
*E-mail:* info@brewersassociation.org
*Web Site:* www.brewersassociation.org
*Key Personnel*
Publr: Kristi Switzer *Tel:* 512-863-5227 *E-mail:* kristi@brewersassociation.org
Ed: Jill Redding *Tel:* 303-447-0816 ext 116
Founded: 1986
Not-for-profit educational publishing house & the foremost publisher of books on the art, science, history & culture of brewing for professional & amateur brewers & serious beer enthusiasts. Must know at least 10 brewers to query.
ISBN Prefix(es): 978-0-937381
Number of titles published annually: 3 Print
Total Titles: 50 Print
Distributed by National Book Network
Foreign Rep(s): Gazelle Book Services Ltd
Foreign Rights: Gazelle Book Services Ltd (Worldwide exc North America)
*Shipping Address:* National Book Network, 15200 NBN Way, Blue Ridge Summit, PA 17214 *Toll Free Tel:* 800-462-6420 *Toll Free Fax:* 800-338-4550 *E-mail:* custserv@nbnbooks.com
*Warehouse:* National Book Network, 15200 NBN Way, Blue Ridge Summit, PA 17214 *Tel:* 717-794-3800 *Toll Free Tel:* 800-462-6420 *Toll Free Fax:* 800-338-4550 *E-mail:* custserv@nbnbooks.com

**Brick Tower Press**
Imprint of J T Colby & Co Inc
1230 Park Ave, New York, NY 10128
*Tel:* 212-427-7139 *Toll Free Tel:* 800-68-BRICK (682-7425) *Fax:* 212-860-8852
*E-mail:* bricktower@aol.com
*Web Site:* www.bricktowerpress.com
*Key Personnel*
Publr: John T Colby, Jr
Founded: 1993
ISBN Prefix(es): 978-1-883283; 978-0-9531737; 978-1-899694
Number of titles published annually: 10 Print
Total Titles: 50 Print
Foreign Rep(s): Bookwise International (Australia, New Zealand); Gazelle Book Services (Europe, UK)
Foreign Rights: Bob Diforio (Worldwide); National Book Network (Canada, USA)

*Warehouse:* Brick Tower Press Distribution, 211 Denton Ave, Garden City Park, NY 11040
*Distribution Center:* Brick Tower Press Distribution, 211 Denton Ave, Garden City Park, NY 11040

**BrickHouse Books Inc**
306 Suffolk Rd, Baltimore, MD 21218
*Tel:* 410-235-7690 *Fax:* 410-235-7690
*Web Site:* www.towson.edu/clarindaharriss; www.brickhousebooks.edu; www.brickhousebooks.wordpress.com
*Key Personnel*
Dir & Ed-in-Chief: Clarinda Harriss *E-mail:* charriss@towson.edu
Founded: 1970
Poetry; mixed genres by gay & lesbian (Stonewall only); artistic prose, experimental prose.
ISBN Prefix(es): 978-0-932616; 978-1-935916; 978-1-938144
Number of titles published annually: 6 Print
Total Titles: 220 Print
Imprints: Chestnut Hills Press; New Poets Series; Stonewall
Subsidiaries: Chestnut Hills Press; New Poets Series; Side Street; Stonewall
Distributed by Itasca
Foreign Rep(s): Salmon Publishing (Ireland)

**Bridge-Logos Inc**
Bldg 200, Suite 220, 17750 NW 115 Ave, Alachua, FL 32615
*Tel:* 386-462-2525 *Toll Free Tel:* 800-631-5802 (orders) *Fax:* 386-462-2535 *Toll Free Fax:* 800-935-6467
*E-mail:* customerservice@bridgelogos.com; info@bridgelogos.com
*Web Site:* www.bridgelogos.com
*Key Personnel*
CEO & Publr: Lloyd Hildebrand *E-mail:* lhildebrand@bridgelogos.com
COO & Sales & Mktg Mgr: Mrs Shawn Myers *E-mail:* shawnmyers@bridgelogos.com
Founded: 1967
Bibles, Christian classics, spirit-filled life, Christian books; parenting, family, Eschatological, evangelism, revival, children's bibles.
ISBN Prefix(es): 978-0-88270; 978-0-61036
Number of titles published annually: 20 Print
Total Titles: 216 Print
Imprints: Bridge; Haven; Logos; Open Scroll; Synergy
Distributor for New Wine Press; RoperPenberthy Publishing Ltd; Sovereign World; Warboys LLC
Foreign Rep(s): Winfred Bluth (Germany)
Foreign Rights: W M Bluth (Germany)

**Bridge Publications Inc**
5600 E Olympic Blvd, Commerce City, CA 90022
SAN: 208-3884
*Tel:* 323-888-6200 *Toll Free Tel:* 800-722-1733 *Fax:* 323-888-6202
*E-mail:* info@bridgepub.com
*Web Site:* www.bridgepub.com
*Key Personnel*
Pres: Blake Silber
EVP: Ann Arnow *E-mail:* annarnow@bridgepub.com
VP, Pub Aff: Nicole Shell *E-mail:* nshell@bridgepub.com
Trade Sales Mgr: Don Arnow
Founded: 1981
Books on human potential development, self-improvement, education, management technology, children's literary works by L Ron Hubbard.
ISBN Prefix(es): 978-0-88404; 978-1-57318; 978-1-4031
Number of titles published annually: 1,100 Print; 100 CD-ROM; 8 Online; 1 Audio
Total Titles: 8,900 Print; 350 CD-ROM; 8 Online; 25 Audio
Imprints: BPI Records; Bridge Audio; Theta Books
*Branch Office(s)*
Bridge Publications Canada, 696 Yonge St, Toronto, ON M4Y-2A7, Canada, Contact: Emily Harris *Tel:* 416-964-8927 *Fax:* 416-964-3201
*Foreign Office(s):* Era Dinamica Editores, SA de CV, Pablo U Cello, No 16, Colonia de los Deportes CP 03710, Mexico, Contact: Irma Macias *Tel:* 525-598-4487 *Fax:* 525-598-4624
Foreign Rep(s): New Era Publications International (Copenhagen, Europe, Russia & former USSR)
Foreign Rights: New Era Publications International
*Advertising Agency:* Gildersleeve Inc, 3815 Shannon Rd, Los Angeles, CA, Contact: Jan Gildersleeve *Tel:* 323-663-8239 *Fax:* 323-661-8316
Membership(s): AIGA, the professional association for design; BISG; IBPA, the Independent Book Publishers Association; Printing Industries of America; Printing Industries of Southern California

**Bridge Works Publishing**
PO Box 1798, Bridgehampton, NY 11932-1798
*Tel:* 631-537-3418
*Web Site:* www.bridgeworksbooks.com
*Key Personnel*
Pres & Publr: Barbara Phillips *E-mail:* bap@hamptons.com
VP & Publr: Warren Phillips
Founded: 1992
Quality fiction & nonfiction, mostly hardcover. Reads agented mss only. Also carry e-books.
ISBN Prefix(es): 978-0-9816175
Number of titles published annually: 4 Print
Total Titles: 150 Print
Distributed by National Book Network
Foreign Rights: Writers House Inc (Worldwide)
*Distribution Center:* National Book Network, 15200 NBN Way, Blue Ridge Summit, PA 17214 *Toll Free Tel:* 800-462-6420 *Toll Free Fax:* 800-338-4550

**Brigantine Media**
211 North Ave, St Johnsbury, VT 05819
*Tel:* 802-751-8802 *Fax:* 802-751-8804
*Web Site:* brigantinemedia.com
*Key Personnel*
Acqs Ed: Neil Raphel *E-mail:* neil@brigantinemedia.com
Edit Chief: Janis Raye
Founded: 1990
ISBN Prefix(es): 978-0-9826644
Number of titles published annually: 12 Print; 2 Online; 12 E-Book
Total Titles: 25 Print; 2 Online; 18 E-Book
Imprints: Compass (educational materials for teachers); Voyage (fiction, primarily from VT & regional suthors)

**Bright Connections Media, A World Book Encyclopedia Company**
233 N Michigan Ave, Suite 2000, Chicago, IL 60601
*Tel:* 312-729-5800 *Fax:* 312-729-5610
*Web Site:* www.brightconnectionsmedia.com
*Key Personnel*
Pres: Donald Keller
VP, Mktg: Sean Klunder *E-mail:* sean.klunder@worldbook.com
Dir, Mktg: Jennifer Parello *E-mail:* jennifer.parello@worldbook.com
VP, Edit: Paul Kobasa *E-mail:* paul.kobasa@worldbook.com
VP, Intl: Richard Flower *E-mail:* richard.flower@worldbook.com
Founded: 2012
Nonfiction & playful educational material for young children through young adults.
ISBN Prefix(es): 978-1-62267
Number of titles published annually: 20 Print
Total Titles: 8 Print
*Sales Office(s):* Continental Sales Inc, 213 W Main St, Barrington, IL 60010 *Tel:* 847-381-6530 *Fax:* 847-382-0419 *E-mail:* bookreps@wybel.com *Web Site:* www.continentalsalesinc.com
*Orders to:* IPG, 814 N Franklin St, Chicago, IL 60610 *Toll Free Tel:* 866-289-2088 *Toll Free Fax:* 877-372-8892 *E-mail:* orders@innlog.net *Web Site:* www.innlog.net
*Distribution Center:* IPG, 814 N Franklin St, Chicago, IL 60610 *Tel:* 312-337-0747 *Toll Free Tel:* 800-888-4741 *Fax:* 312-337-5985 *Web Site:* www.ipgbook.com
Canadian Manda Group, 165 Dufferin St, Toronto, ON M6K 3H6, Canada *Tel:* 416-516-0911 *Fax:* 416-516-0917 *E-mail:* info@mandagroup.com *Web Site:* www.mandagroup.com

**Bright Mountain Books Inc**
206 Riva Ridge Dr, Fairview, NC 28730
SAN: 289-0674
*Tel:* 828-628-1768 *Toll Free Tel:* 800-437-3959 *Fax:* 828-628-1755
*E-mail:* booksbmb@charter.net
*Web Site:* brightmountainbooks.com
*Key Personnel*
VP, Prodn: Carol Bruckner *E-mail:* bmb-carolbruckner@charter.net
Sr Ed: Cynthia F Bright *E-mail:* bmb-cynthiabright@charter.net
Ed: Martha Fullington *E-mail:* bmb-marthafullington@charter.net
Founded: 1983
Nonfiction, regional.
ISBN Prefix(es): 978-0-914875
Number of titles published annually: 3 Print
Total Titles: 33 Print
Imprints: Historical Images; Ridgetop Books

**§Brill Inc**
Subsidiary of Koninklijke Brill N V
153 Milk St, 6th fl, Boston, MA 02109
*Tel:* 617-263-2323 *Toll Free Tel:* 800-962-4406 *Fax:* 617-263-2324
*E-mail:* cs@brillusa.com
*Web Site:* www.brill.com
*Key Personnel*
Pres, Sales & Mktg: Steve Dane
Off Mgr: Rose Luongo
Founded: 1683
Publishes high level, specialized, academic titles.
ISBN Prefix(es): 978-90-04
Number of titles published annually: 400 Print
Total Titles: 6,000 Print
*Orders to:* *Toll Free Tel:* 800-337-9255
*Returns:* Brill Academic Publishers Inc Returns Dept, 22883 Quicksilver Dr, Dulles, VA 20166
*Warehouse:* PO Box 605, Herndon, VA 20172 *Tel:* 703-661-1500 *Toll Free Tel:* 800-337-9255 *Fax:* 703-661-1501
*Distribution Center:* Book International

**Brilliance Audio**
Subsidiary of Amazon.com
1704 Eaton Dr, Grand Haven, MI 49417
*Tel:* 616-846-5256 *Toll Free Tel:* 800-648-2312 (orders only) *Fax:* 616-846-0630
*E-mail:* customerservice@brillianceaudio.com
*Web Site:* www.brillianceaudio.com
*Key Personnel*
VP & Assoc Publr: Eileen Hutton
Mng Dir: Mark Pereira *E-mail:* mpereira@brillianceaudio.com
Creative Dir: Colleen Rockey *Tel:* 616-846-5256 ext 709 *E-mail:* crockey@brillianceaudio.com
Fin Dir: Brad Dahl *Tel:* 616-846-5256 ext 750 *E-mail:* bdahl@brillianceaudio.com

Sales Dir: Steve Woessner *Tel:* 616-846-5256 ext 705 *E-mail:* swoessner@brillianceaudio.com
Acqs Ed: Sheryl Zajechowski *Tel:* 616-846-5256 ext 726 *E-mail:* szajechowski@brillianceaudio.com
Ed, Adult Nonfiction: Joe McNeely *Tel:* 616-846-5256 ext 755 *E-mail:* jmcneely@brillianceaudio.com
Acqs, Grand Harbor Press: Gary Krebs
Founded: 1984
Country's leading independent audiobook publisher.
ISBN Prefix(es): 978-0-930435; 978-1-56100; 978-1-56740; 978-1-58788; 978-1-59086; 978-1-59355; 978-1-59600; 978-1-59710; 978-1-59737; 978-1-4233; 978-1-4418; 978-1-61106; 978-1-4558
Number of titles published annually: 700 Audio
Total Titles: 2,300 Audio
Imprints: Grand Harbor Press
*Branch Office(s)*
Children's Division Office, 411 Theodore Fremd Ave, Rye, NY 10580 *Tel:* 914-925-3695
Membership(s): Audio Publishers Association

**Bristol Park Books**
Formerly BBS Publishing Corp
252 W 38 St, Suite 206, New York, NY 10018
*Tel:* 212-842-0700 *Fax:* 212-842-1771
*E-mail:* ralexander@bbspublishingcorp.com
Promotional hard cover reprints.
ISBN Prefix(es): 978-0-88365; 978-0-88486; 978-1-57866
Number of titles published annually: 50 Print
Total Titles: 100 Print

**Broden Books LLC**
3824 Sunset Dr, Spring Park, MN 55384
SAN: 920-0614
*Tel:* 952-471-1066
*E-mail:* media@brodenbooks.com
*Web Site:* www.brodenbooks.com
*Key Personnel*
CEO & Pres: Kathy La Pointe
Founded: 1999
Early childhood literacy resources for parents, schools & libraries. We are engaged in ongoing research into issues impacting literacy in the US. Our resources are sold worldwide through online & retail stores.
ISBN Prefix(es): 978-0-9832023
Number of titles published annually: 3 Print
Total Titles: 3 Print
Imprints: REAL Phonics™

**§Brookes Publishing Co Inc**
PO Box 10624, Baltimore, MD 21285-0624
SAN: 212-730X
*Tel:* 410-337-9580 (outside US & CN) *Toll Free Tel:* 800-638-3775 (US & CN) *Fax:* 410-337-8539
*E-mail:* custserv@brookespublishing.com
*Web Site:* www.brookespublishing.com
*Key Personnel*
Chmn of the Bd: Paul H Brookes
Pres: Jeffrey D Brookes *E-mail:* jbrookes@brookespublishing.com
EVP: Melissa A Behm *E-mail:* mbehm@brookespublishing.com
VP & Publr: George S Stamathis *E-mail:* gstamathis@brookespublishing.com
Edit Dir: Heather Shrestha *E-mail:* hshrestha@brookespublishing.com
Dir, HR & Oper: Erika Kinney *E-mail:* ekinney@brookespublishing.com
Dir, Mktg: Jessica Reighard *E-mail:* jreighard@brookespublishing.com
Sr Subs Rts & Contracts Mgr: Heather Lengyel *Tel:* 410-205-0466 *E-mail:* hlengyel@brookespublishing.com
Founded: 1978
Publishes professional books, textbooks, assessments, curricula & web-based products in the areas of: early childhood, early intervention, social-emotional development, literacy, learning disabilities, autism, behavior, special education, developmental disabilities, communication & language.
ISBN Prefix(es): 978-0-933716; 978-1-55766; 978-1-59857
Number of titles published annually: 65 Print; 5 CD-ROM; 5 Online; 50 E-Book
Total Titles: 600 Print; 20 CD-ROM; 10 Online; 50 E-Book
Subsidiaries: Health Professions Press (specialist publisher focused on the broad range of issues in gerontology, long-term care & health administration)
Distributed by The Eurospan Group (Africa, Europe & Middle East); Footprint Books Pty Ltd (Australia, Fiji, New Zealand & Papua New Guinea)
Foreign Rep(s): CRW Marketing Services for Publishers Inc (Guam, Philippines); Tahir Lodhi Publishers' Representatives (Pakistan); Sara Books Pvt Ltd (Bangladesh, India, Sri Lanka); STM Publishers Services (China, Hong Kong, Macau, Malaysia, Myanmar, Singapore, Thailand, Vietnam); Unifacmanu Trading Co Ltd (Taiwan)
*Returns:* Maple Logistics Solutions, 60 Grumbacher Rd, York, PA 17406
*Warehouse:* Maple Logistics Solutions, PO Box 15100, York, PA 17405 *Web Site:* www.maplelogisticssolutions.com
Membership(s): Association of Educational Publishers
*See separate listing for:*
**Health Professions Press**

**§Brookhaven Press**
PO Box 2287, La Crosse, WI 54602-2287
*Tel:* 608-781-0850 *Toll Free Tel:* 800-236-0850 *Fax:* 608-781-3883
*E-mail:* brookhaven@nmt.com
*Web Site:* www.brookhavenpress.com
*Key Personnel*
Mgr: Carol Berteotti *Tel:* 608-781-0850 ext 131 *E-mail:* carol.berteotti@nmt.com
Founded: 1973
Scan & reprint out-of-print county histories & genealogy books; also politics & performing arts.
ISBN Prefix(es): 978-1-58103; 978-1-4035
Number of titles published annually: 300 Print

**§The Brookings Institution Press**
Division of Brookings Institution
1775 Massachusetts Ave NW, Washington, DC 20036-2188
SAN: 201-9396
*Tel:* 202-536-3600 *Toll Free Tel:* 800-537-5487 *Fax:* 202-536-3623
*E-mail:* permissions@brookings.edu
*Web Site:* www.brookings.edu
*Key Personnel*
Pres: Strobe Talbott
VP & Dir: Robert L Faherty
Dir, Fin & Admin: Renuka Deonarain *Tel:* 202-536-3636 *E-mail:* rdeonarain@brookings.edu
Assoc Dir & Mktg Dir: Christopher Kelaher
Mng Ed: Janet Walker *E-mail:* jwalker@brookings.edu
Ed: Eileen Hughes
Dist Mgr: Terrence Melvin
Lib Mgr: Cyrus Behroozi
Founded: 1916
Economics, foreign policy & government affairs.
ISBN Prefix(es): 978-0-8157
Number of titles published annually: 50 Print; 50 E-Book
Total Titles: 1,205 Print; 1 CD-ROM; 1,031 E-Book
Distributor for American Chamber of Commerce to the European Union; Asia Pacific Research Center; Bertelsmann Foundation Publishers; Carnegie Endowment for International Peace; The Centre for Economic Policy Research; The Century Foundation; Economica; International Labor Offices; Japan Center for International Exchange; OECD; The Trilateral Commission; World Trade Organization
Foreign Rep(s): Julio E Emod (South America); Fred Hermans (Benelux, Denmark, Finland, France, Norway, Sweden); Ewa Ledochowicz (Eastern Europe); UWE Luedemann (Austria, Germany, Italy, Portugal, Spain, Switzerland); Mediamatics (India, Pakistan); NewSouth Books (Australia, New Zealand); Systematics Studies Ltd (Trinidad and Tobago); Taylor & Francis Asia Pacific (Brunei, China, Hong Kong, Korea, Malaysia, Philippines, Singapore, Taiwan); UBC Press, c/o Uni Presses (Canada); United Publishing Services Ltd (Japan); University Press Marketing (Cyprus, Greece, Ireland, Israel, Malta, UK)
Foreign Rights: Agency Literaria Internazionale (Italy); Tuttle-Mori Agency Inc (Japan)
Membership(s): AAP; American Association of University Presses

**Brookline Books**
8 Trumbull Rd, Suite B-001, Northampton, MA 01060
*Tel:* 603-669-7032 (orders); 413-584-0184 *Toll Free Tel:* 800-666-2665 (orders) *Fax:* 413-584-6184
*E-mail:* brbooks@yahoo.com
*Web Site:* www.brooklinebooks.com
Founded: 1985
Education, special needs, readings, general trade.
ISBN Prefix(es): 978-0-914797; 978-1-57129
Number of titles published annually: 5 Print
Total Titles: 125 Print
Imprints: Lumen

**Brooklyn Publishers LLC**
211 First Ave SE, Suite 200, Cedar Rapids, IA 52401
Mailing Address: PO Box 248, Cedar Rapids, IA 52406
*Tel:* 319-368-8012 *Toll Free Tel:* 888-473-8521 *Fax:* 319-368-8011
*E-mail:* customerservice@brookpub.com; editor@brookpub.com
*Web Site:* www.brookpub.com
*Key Personnel*
Sr Ed: David Burton
ISBN Prefix(es): 978-1-930961; 978-1-931000; 978-1-931805; 978-1-932404; 978-1-60003
Number of titles published annually: 100 Print
Total Titles: 600 Print

**Brooks/Cole**, see Wadsworth Publishing

**Brown Barn Books**
Division of Pictures of Record Inc
119 Kettle Creek Rd, Weston, CT 06883
*Tel:* 203-227-3387 *Fax:* 203-222-9673
*E-mail:* editorial@brownbarnbooks.com
*Web Site:* www.brownbarnbooks.com
*Key Personnel*
Pres & Ed: Nancy Hammerslough
Founded: 2003
Publisher of young adult fiction.
ISBN Prefix(es): 978-0-9746481; 978-0-9768126; 978-0-9798824
Number of titles published annually: 3 Print
Total Titles: 21 Print
Foreign Rep(s): Books Crossing Borders (Worldwide exc Canada & USA)
Membership(s): The Association of Publishers for Special Sales; IBPA, the Independent Book Publishers Association; NAIBA; NEBA

**Brown Books Publishing Group**
16250 Knoll Trail, Suite 205, Dallas, TX 75248
*Tel:* 972-381-0009 *Fax:* 972-248-4336
*E-mail:* publishing@brownbooks.com
*Web Site:* www.brownbooks.com
*Key Personnel*
CEO & Publr: Milli Brown
Prodn Mgr: Jessica Kinkel
Assoc Ed: Lucia R Retta
Founded: 1994
Full service independent publisher. Committed to producing high quality books of all genres for authors who choose to retain the rights to their intellectual property.
ISBN Prefix(es): 978-1-933285; 978-1-934812
Number of titles published annually: 150 Print
Total Titles: 1,000 Print
Divisions: Brown Books Agency; Brown Books Digital; Christian Press; The P3 Press; Personal Profiles
*Warehouse:* Cenveo, 3210 Miller Park Dr S, Suite 100, Garland, TX 75041 *Tel:* 972-271-0591
*Distribution Center:* Quality Books, 1003 W Pines Rd, Oregon, IL 61061
Follett Corp, 2233 West St, River Grove, IL 60171
Borders, 3140 Lohr Rd, Ann Arbor, MI 48108
Barnes & Noble, 122 Fifth Ave, New York, NY 10011
Baker & Taylor Inc, 2550 W Tyvola Rd, Suite 300, Charlotte, NC 28217
Ingram, One Ingram Blvd, La Vergne, TN 37086
Membership(s): IBPA, the Independent Book Publishers Association

**Karen Brown's Guides Inc**
16 E Third Ave, Suite 9, San Mateo, CA 94401
Mailing Address: PO Box 70, San Mateo, CA 94401-0070
*Tel:* 650-342-9117 *Fax:* 650-342-9153
*E-mail:* orders@karenbrown.com
*Web Site:* www.karenbrown.com
*Key Personnel*
Pres: Karen Brown Herbert *E-mail:* karen@karenbrown.com
Founded: 1977
General.
ISBN Prefix(es): 978-0-930328
Number of titles published annually: 17 Print
Total Titles: 17 Print
Foreign Rep(s): National Book Network (Australia, Europe, New Zealand)
*Distribution Center:* National Book Network, 4501 Forbes Blvd, Suite 200, Lanham, MD 20706, Pres: Jed Lyons *Tel:* 301 731-9538 *Toll Free Tel:* 800-462-6420 *Toll Free Fax:* 800-338-4550 *Web Site:* www.nbnbooks.com

**Bucknell University Press**
Affiliate of Associated University Presses
Taylor Hall, Bucknell University, Lewisburg, PA 17837
Mailing Address: c/o Associated University Presses, 2010 Eastpark Blvd, Cranbury, NJ 08512
*Tel:* 570-577-3674
*E-mail:* aup440@aol.com
*Web Site:* www.bucknell.edu/universitypress
*Key Personnel*
Dir: Greg Clingham *Tel:* 570-577-1552 *E-mail:* clingham@bucknell.edu
Edit Assoc: Pam Dailey *Tel:* 570-577-3674
Founded: 1968
ISBN Prefix(es): 978-0-8387
Number of titles published annually: 35 Print
Total Titles: 700 Print
Distributed by Rowman & Littlefield
Foreign Rep(s): Eurospan (Europe, UK); Scholarly Book Services (Canada); United Publishers Services (Japan)

**BuilderBooks.com**
Division of National Association of Home Builders (NAHB)
1201 15 St NW, Washington, DC 20005
SAN: 207-7035
*Tel:* 202-822-0200 *Toll Free Tel:* 800-223-2665 *Fax:* 202-266-8096 (edit)
*E-mail:* builderbooks@nahb.com
*Web Site:* www.builderbooks.com
*Key Personnel*
Staff VP: Lakisha Campbell *E-mail:* lcampbell@nahb.com
Mng Dir, Mktg: Patricia Potts
Mktg Mgr, NAHB: Jacqueline Barnes
Founded: 1943
Publish books about home construction & design, remodeling, land development, housing & construction management, sales & marketing of new homes, safety & seniors housing.
ISBN Prefix(es): 978-0-86718
Number of titles published annually: 7 Print
Total Titles: 150 Print
Distributor for National Association of Home Builders (NAHB)
*Orders to:* c/o Returns, National Association of Home Builders, 905 Carlow Dr, Unit B, Bolingbrook, IL 60490

**Bull Publishing Co**
PO Box 1377, Boulder, CO 80306
SAN: 208-5712
*Tel:* 303-545-6350 *Toll Free Tel:* 800-676-2855 *Fax:* 303-545-6354
*E-mail:* bullpublishing@msn.com
*Web Site:* www.bullpub.com
*Key Personnel*
Pres & Publr: James Bull
VP, Opers: Emily Sewell
Dir, Mktg: Claire Cameron
Founded: 1974
Self-care, nutrition & health care, physical fitness, weight loss, mental health, parenting & child care, psychology, self-help.
ISBN Prefix(es): 978-0-915950; 978-0-923521; 978-1-933503
Number of titles published annually: 6 Print; 1 Audio
Total Titles: 70 Print; 6 Audio
Foreign Rep(s): Gazelle (UK & the continent)
*Warehouse:* A & A Quality Shipping Services, 3623 Munster Ave, Unit B, Hayward, CA 94545
*Distribution Center:* Independent Publishers Group, 814 N Franklin St, Chicago, IL 60610 *Toll Free Tel:* 800-888-4741 *Web Site:* www.ipgbook.com

**Bunker Hill Publishing**
285 River Rd, Piermont, NH 03779
*Tel:* 603-272-9221 *Fax:* 603-283-7240
*E-mail:* mail@bunkerhillpublishing.com
*Web Site:* www.bunkerhillpublishing.com
*Key Personnel*
Publr: Ib Bellew *E-mail:* ibellew@bunkerhillpublishing.com
Mng Dir: Carole Kitchel Bellew *E-mail:* ckitchel@bunkerhillpublishing.com
Founded: 2001
Publishing & packaging.
ISBN Prefix(es): 978-1-59373
Number of titles published annually: 7 Print; 7 E-Book
Total Titles: 65 Print
*Distribution Center:* Midpoint Trade, 270 W 20 St, Suite 1102, New York, NY 10011 *Tel:* 212-727-0190 *Web Site:* www.midpointtradebooks.com

**§The Bureau For At-Risk Youth**
Subsidiary of The Guidance Group Inc
303 Crossways Park Dr, Woodbury, NY 11797
*Tel:* 516-496-4863 *Fax:* 516-496-4050
*Web Site:* www.at-risk.com; www.guidance-group.com
*Key Personnel*
Publr: Edward Werz
Founded: 1988
Educational materials on at-risk children's issues for educators, counselors, parents & children.
ISBN Prefix(es): 978-1-56688
Number of titles published annually: 10 Print
Total Titles: 210 Print
*Returns:* c/o Karol Media, 375 Stewart Rd, Wilkes-Barre, PA 18706-1246

**§Bureau of Economic Geology, University of Texas at Austin**
Division of University of Texas at Austin
10100 Burnet Rd, Bldg 130, Austin, TX 78758
Mailing Address: University Sta, Box X, Austin, TX 78713-8924
*Tel:* 512-471-1534
*E-mail:* pubsales@beg.utexas.edu
*Web Site:* www.beg.utexas.edu
*Key Personnel*
Dir: Scott W Tinker
Mgr, Pubn Sales: Amanda Masterson *E-mail:* amanda.masterson@beg.utexas.edu
Founded: 1909
Scientific & technical books in geosciences.
Number of titles published annually: 6 Print; 1 CD-ROM
Total Titles: 1,700 Print; 8 CD-ROM; 1,500 E-Book
Distributor for Gulf Coast Association of Geological Societies; Texas Memorial Museum (selected titles)
*Advertising Agency:* Gulf Coast Section-SEPM

**Burford Books**
101 E State St, No 301, Ithaca, NY 14850
*Tel:* 607-319-4373 *Fax:* 607-319-4373 *Toll Free Fax:* 866-212-7750
*E-mail:* info@burfordbooks.com
*Web Site:* www.burfordbooks.com
*Key Personnel*
Pres: Peter Burford
Founded: 1997
Publisher of books on the outdoors, sports, fitness, nature, travel, fishing, military, food & wine.
ISBN Prefix(es): 978-1-58080
Number of titles published annually: 6 Print; 6 E-Book
Total Titles: 97 Print; 25 E-Book
Foreign Rep(s): Gazelle Book Services Ltd (UK)
*Distribution Center:* National Book Network, 15200 NBN Way, Blue Ridge Summit, PA 17214 *Tel:* 717-794-3800

**Burns Archive Press**
Imprint of Burns Archive Photographic Distributors Ltd
140 E 38 St, New York, NY 10016
*Tel:* 212-889-1938 *Fax:* 212-481-9113
*Web Site:* www.burnsarchive.com
*Key Personnel*
CEO & Pres: Stanley B Burns, MD *E-mail:* burns@inch.com
Founded: 1979
Renowned for images of the darker side of life: death, disease, crime, racism, revolution & war. Provides a unique source of historic visual documentation containing over 700,000 vintage photographs. The Archive houses world-class holdings of African-American imagery & Judaica, as well as the foremost collection of early medical photography. More than a century of iconographic & historic photographs from the 1840s through the 1950s are available as stock photography. In addition, The Archive provides consultation, prepares exhibitions & publishes books on photographic history.

ISBN Prefix(es): 978-0-9612958; 978-0-9748688; 978-0-9748688; 978-0-9764495; 978-0-9764495; 978-1-934421; 978-1-936002
Number of titles published annually: 4 Print
Total Titles: 35 Print
Membership(s): American Book Producers Association

**§Business & Legal Reports Inc (BLR)**
100 Winners Circle, Suite 300, Brentwood, CT 37027
*Tel:* 860-510-0100 *Toll Free Tel:* 800-727-5257
*E-mail:* service@blr.com
*Web Site:* www.blr.com
*Key Personnel*
Founder: Robert L Brady
CEO: Dan Oswald
COO: Guy Crossley
Mng Ed: Celeste Blackburn
Ed: Catherine Leonard; Elaine Quayle
*E-mail:* equayle@blr.com
Founded: 1977
Business newsletters, books, booklets, films & CD-ROMs. Specialize in safety, human resource & environmental training & compliance.
ISBN Prefix(es): 978-1-55645
Total Titles: 380 Print; 113 CD-ROM; 4 Online; 4 E-Book
Membership(s): NEPA

**Business Expert Press**
Subsidiary of IGroup
222 E 46 St, New York, NY 10017-2906
*Tel:* 908-752-1257
*E-mail:* molly.hurford@businessexpertpress.com
*Web Site:* www.businessexpertpress.com
*Key Personnel*
Publr: David Parker *Tel:* 201-673-8784
*E-mail:* david.parker@businessexpertpress.com
Sales & Mktg Dir: Sheri Dean *Tel:* 919-803-0534
*E-mail:* sheri.dean@globalepress.com
Founded: 2008
Providing MBA level students with applied, concise textbooks that can be used in & out of the classroom.
ISBN Prefix(es): 978-1-60649
Number of titles published annually: 55 Print; 55 Online; 55 E-Book
Total Titles: 120 Print; 120 Online; 120 E-Book

**§Business Research Services Inc**
7720 Wisconsin Ave, Suite 213, Bethesda, MD 20814
SAN: 691-8522
*Tel:* 301-229-5561 *Toll Free Tel:* 800-845-8420
*Fax:* 301-229-6133
*E-mail:* brspubs@sba8a.com
*Web Site:* www.sba8a.com; www.setasidealert.com
*Key Personnel*
Pres & Publr: Thomas D Johnson
Founded: 1981
Directories of minority & women's businesses & marketing research firms; small business newsletters. No returns accepted.
ISBN Prefix(es): 978-0-933527
Number of titles published annually: 4 Print; 4 CD-ROM; 1 Online
Total Titles: 7 Print; 4 CD-ROM; 1 Online
Distributed by Basch; Book House; Coutts; Gale Research Inc; Midwest Library Service
Distributor for Riley & Johnson
Membership(s): National Directory Publishing Association; SLA

**Butte Publications Inc**
PO Box 1328, Hillsboro, OR 97123-1328
SAN: 299-8866
*Tel:* 503-648-9791 *Toll Free Tel:* 866-312-8883
*Fax:* 503-693-9526 *Toll Free Fax:* 866-412-8883 (orders only)
*E-mail:* service@buttepublications.com
*Web Site:* www.buttepublications.com
*Key Personnel*
Pres & Publr: Matthew H Brink
*E-mail:* mbrink@buttepublications.com
Founded: 1992
Resources serving the deaf community.
ISBN Prefix(es): 978-1-884362; 978-1-939349
Number of titles published annually: 5 Print; 1 CD-ROM
Total Titles: 50 Print; 5 CD-ROM
*Shipping Address:* 149 SE Third, Suite 450, Hillsboro, OR 97123

**By Design Press**, see Quite Specific Media Group Ltd

**Bywater Books**
PO Box 3671, Ann Arbor, MI 48106-3671
*Tel:* 734-662-8815
*Web Site:* bywaterbooks.com
*Key Personnel*
Publr & Ed-in-Chief: Kelly Smith
Publr: Michele Karlsberg; Marianne K Martin
*E-mail:* mkmbywater@aol.com; Val McDermid
Founded: 1992
Publish top quality lesbian fiction. Our Bloody Brits imprint publishes the finest mainstream British mysteries in the US.
ISBN Prefix(es): 978-1-932859
Number of titles published annually: 23 Print
Total Titles: 42 Print
Imprints: Amble Press; Bloody Brits Press

**§C & M Online Media Inc**
3905 Meadow Field Lane, Raleigh, NC 27606
*Tel:* 919-233-8164
*E-mail:* support@cmonline.com
*Web Site:* www.cmonline.com
*Key Personnel*
Pres: Nancy McAllister *E-mail:* nancy@cmonline.com
SVP & Dir, Tech Opers: David McAllister
*E-mail:* davidm@cmonline.com
Founded: 1994
Consultant to ebook publishers.
ISBN Prefix(es): 978-1-886420; 978-0-917990; 978-1-932482
Number of titles published annually: 1 Print; 1 Online; 1 E-Book
Total Titles: 4 Print; 2 Online
Imprints: The New South Co (20th century books for collectors)
Membership(s): The Authors Guild

**C & T Publishing Inc**
1651 Challenge Dr, Concord, CA 94520-5206
*Tel:* 925-677-0377 *Toll Free Tel:* 800-284-1114
*Fax:* 925-677-0373
*E-mail:* ctinfo@ctpub.com
*Web Site:* www.ctpub.com
*Key Personnel*
CEO: Todd Hensley
CFO: Tony Hensley
Edit Dir: Gailen Runge
Dir, Sales & Mktg: Sandy Balin *Tel:* 925-677-0377 ext 207 *E-mail:* sandyb@ctpub.com
Publr: Amy Marson
Founded: 1983
Specialize in fiber & paper craft books & products.
ISBN Prefix(es): 978-0-914881; 978-1-57120
Number of titles published annually: 60 Print; 2 CD-ROM
Total Titles: 300 Print; 5 CD-ROM; 10 Online
Distributed by Watson-Guptill Publications
Membership(s): Craft Hobby Association; IBPA, the Independent Book Publishers Association

**Caddo Gap Press**
3145 Geary Blvd, PMB 275, San Francisco, CA 94118
*Tel:* 415-666-3012 *Fax:* 415-666-3552
*E-mail:* info@caddogap.com
*Web Site:* www.caddogap.com
*Key Personnel*
Publr & Intl Rts: Alan H Jones
*E-mail:* alanhjones@caddogap.com
Assoc Publr: Heather L Hazuka
*E-mail:* hlhazuka@caddogap.com
Founded: 1989
Social foundations of education & teacher education & multicultural education.
ISBN Prefix(es): 978-0-9625945; 978-1-880192
Number of titles published annually: 4 Print
Total Titles: 50 Print

**Cadence Jazz Books**
Division of Cadnor Ltd
Cadence Bldg, Redwood, NY 13679
*Tel:* 315-287-2852 *Fax:* 315-287-2860
*E-mail:* cjb@cadencebuilding.com; cadence@cadencebuilding.com
*Web Site:* www.cadencebuilding.com
*Key Personnel*
Pres & Intl Rts: Robert D Rusch
Lib Sales Dir: M E Slim
Founded: 1992
Jazz, improvised music & biographies of jazz players.
ISBN Prefix(es): 978-1-881993
Number of titles published annually: 7 Print
Total Titles: 35 Print
Distributed by North Country Distributors

**Cadmus Editions**
PO Box 126, Belvedere-Tiburon, CA 94920-0126
SAN: 212-887X
*Tel:* 707-762-0510
*Web Site:* www.cadmuseditions.com
*Key Personnel*
Dir & Ed: Jeffrey Miller *E-mail:* jeffcadmus@aol.com
Founded: 1979
Fine editions & trade paperbacks; fiction, literature, poetry.
ISBN Prefix(es): 978-0-932274
Number of titles published annually: 3 Print
Total Titles: 32 Print; 1 Audio
*Sales Office(s):* Small Press Distribution, 1341 Seventh St, Berkeley, CA 94710-1409, Sales Mgr: Brent Cunningham *Tel:* 510-524-1668 *Toll Free Tel:* 800-869-7553 *Fax:* 510-524-0852 *E-mail:* spd@spdbooks.org *Web Site:* www.spdbooks.org
Foreign Rep(s): Artellus Ltd (UK, Western Europe)
Foreign Rights: Artellus Ltd (European Union, UK & Commonwealth)
*Orders to:* Small Press Distribution, 1341 Seventh St, Berkeley, CA 94710-1409, Sales Mgr: Brent Cunningham *Tel:* 510-524-1668 *Toll Free Tel:* 800-869-7553 *Fax:* 510-524-0852 *E-mail:* spd@spdbooks.org *Web Site:* www.spdbooks.org
*Returns:* Small Press Distribution, 1341 Seventh St, Berkeley, CA 94710-1409, Sales Mgr: Brent Cunningham *Tel:* 510-524-1668 *Toll Free Tel:* 800-869-7553 *Fax:* 510-524-0852 *E-mail:* spd@spdbooks.org *Web Site:* www.spdbooks.org
*Warehouse:* Small Press Distribution, 1341 Seventh St, Berkeley, CA 94710-1409, Sales Mgr: Brent Cunningham *Tel:* 510-524-1668 *Toll Free Tel:* 800-869-7553 *Fax:* 510-524-0852 *E-mail:* spd@spdbooks.org *Web Site:* www.spdbooks.org
*Distribution Center:* Small Press Distribution, 1341 Seventh St, Berkeley, CA 94710-1409, Sales Mgr: Brent Cunningham *Tel:* 510-524-1668 *Toll Free Tel:* 800-869-7553 *Fax:* 510-524-0852 *E-mail:* spd@spdbooks.org *Web Site:* www.spdbooks.org

**Caissa Editions**
Affiliate of Dale A Brandreth Books

PO Box 151, Yorklyn, DE 19736-0151
*Tel:* 302-239-4608
*Web Site:* www.chessbookstore.com
*Key Personnel*
Owner & Pres: Dale Brandreth
*E-mail:* dbrandreth3@comcast.net
Founded: 1971
Publisher of books that are primarily on chess.
ISBN Prefix(es): 978-0-939433
Number of titles published annually: 3 Print
Total Titles: 23 Print

**§Cambridge Educational**
Division of Infobase Learning
132 W 31 St, 17th fl, New York, NY 10001
*Toll Free Tel:* 800-322-8755 *Fax:* 609-671-0266
*Toll Free Fax:* 800-329-6687
*E-mail:* custserve@films.com
*Web Site:* cambridge.films.com
*Key Personnel*
CEO & Pres: Mark McDonald
Dir, Sales: Doug Humphrey
Founded: 1980
Produce & distribute educational materials & CD-ROMs. Specialize in crime & legal studies, family & consumer science, health & guidance, social studies & vocational/technical education & career education. Cambridge Educational is a trademark of Films Media Group.
ISBN Prefix(es): 978-0-927368; 978-1-56450
Number of titles published annually: 5 Print; 20 CD-ROM
Total Titles: 35 Print; 150 CD-ROM

**§Cambridge University Press**
Division of University of Cambridge
32 Avenue of the Americas, New York, NY 10013-2473
SAN: 200-206X
*Tel:* 212-924-3900; 212-337-5000
*Toll Free Tel:* 800-899-5222 *Fax:* 212-691-3239
*E-mail:* newyork@cambridge.org
*Web Site:* www.cambridge.org/us
*Key Personnel*
Mng Dir, Americas & Global Mng Dir, Eng Lang Teaching: Michael Peluse
Publg Dir, Humanities & Soc Sci: Dr Beatrice Rehl *E-mail:* brehl@cambridge.org
Press Dist Dir: Ian R Bradie
Dir, Sales & Mktg, Academic Books: Liza Murphy
Personnel Dir: Judith Grace
Academic Mktg Mgr: Michael Duncan
Mktg Mgr, ESL & Educ: Carine Mitchell
Journal Mkt Mgr: Susan Soule
Rts & Perms Mgr: Marc Anderson *Tel:* 212-691-3239 *E-mail:* manderson@cambridge.org
Journals Ed: Mark Zadrozny
Sr Ed, Engg: Peter Gordon
Sr Ed, Soc Sci: Lewis Bateman; Robert Dreesen
Sr Ed, Law: Dr John Berger
Sr Ed, Near Eastern & East Asian Studies: Marigold Acland *E-mail:* mackland@cambridge.org
Ed, Math & Computer Sci: Lauren Cowles
Founded: 1534
Scholarly & trade books, college textbooks & journals.
ISBN Prefix(es): 978-0-521
Number of titles published annually: 2,400 Print
Total Titles: 45,000 Print; 160 Online
*Foreign Office(s):* The Edinburgh Bldg, Shaftesbury Rd, Cambridge CB2 8BS, United Kingdom *Tel:* (01223) 358331
*Warehouse:* One Ingram Blvd, La Vergne, TN 17202
Membership(s): AAP; Association of American University Presses; BISG

**Camino Books Inc**
PO Box 59026, Philadelphia, PA 19102-9026
*Tel:* 215-413-1917 *Fax:* 215-413-3255
*E-mail:* camino@caminobooks.com
*Web Site:* www.caminobooks.com
*Key Personnel*
Pres & Publr: Edward J Jutkowitz
*E-mail:* ejutkowitz@caminobooks.com
Founded: 1987
Regional trade books for the Mid-Atlantic states.
ISBN Prefix(es): 978-0-940159; 978-1-933822
Number of titles published annually: 10 Print; 10 E-Book
Total Titles: 100 Print; 25 E-Book
*Warehouse:* Whitehurst & Clark Book Fulfillment Inc, 1200 County Rd, Rte 523, Flemington, NJ 08822 *Tel:* 908-782-2323

**Camino E E & Book Co**
PO Box 6400, Incline Village, NV 89450
*Tel:* 775-831-3078 *Fax:* 775-831-3078
*E-mail:* info@camino-books.com
*Web Site:* www.camino-books.com
*Key Personnel*
VP & Publr: Janae Pata
Founded: 1985
Dog breed reference books.
ISBN Prefix(es): 978-0-940808; 978-1-55893
Number of titles published annually: 24 Print
Total Titles: 363 Print

**Campfield & Campfield Publishing**
6521 Cutler St, Philadelphia, PA 19126
*Toll Free Tel:* 888-518-2440 *Fax:* 215-224-6696
*E-mail:* info@campfieldspublishing.com
*Web Site:* www.campfieldspublishing.com
*Key Personnel*
Publr: Charlene M Campfield; Leon V Campfield, Sr
Founded: 2009
Publisher of Christ-centered children's & young adult books.
ISBN Prefix(es): 978-0-9817025
Number of titles published annually: 6 Print; 6 Online
Total Titles: 4 Print; 5 Online
Membership(s): Christian Small Publishers Association

**Candlewick Press**
Subsidiary of Walker Books Ltd (London)
99 Dover St, Somerville, MA 02144-2825
*Tel:* 617-661-3330 *Fax:* 617-661-0565
*E-mail:* bigbear@candlewick.com
*Web Site:* www.candlewick.com
*Key Personnel*
Pres & Publr: Karen Lotz
SVP, Fin: Hilary Berkman
SVP, Sales & Digital Initiatives: John Mendelson
VP, Contracts & Royalties: Becky S Hemperly
Exec Dir, Mktg, Publicity & Events: Jennifer Roberts
Assoc Publr & Edit Dir: Liz Bicknell
Creative Dir & Assoc Publr: Chris Paul
US Ed, Nosy Crow: Joan Powers
Art Resource Coord: Anne Moore
Founded: 1991
Children's books.
ISBN Prefix(es): 978-1-56402; 978-0-7636
Number of titles published annually: 300 Print
Total Titles: 2,250 Print; 230 E-Book
Foreign Rights: Walker Books London
*Distribution Center:* Random House Publisher Services, 1745 Broadway, New York, NY 10019 *E-mail:* distribution@randomhouse.com *Web Site:* www.randomhouse.biz
Membership(s): Children's Book Council

**Canon Law Society of America**
Hecker Ctr, Suite 111, 3025 Fourth St NE, Washington, DC 20017-1102
SAN: 237-6296
*Tel:* 202-832-2350 *Fax:* 202-832-2331
*E-mail:* coordinator@clsa.org; info@clsa.org
*Web Site:* www.clsa.org
*Key Personnel*
Exec Coord: Sister Sharon Euart *E-mail:* seuart@clsa.org
Founded: 1939
Books on canon law & marriage.
ISBN Prefix(es): 978-0-943616
Number of titles published annually: 3 Print
Total Titles: 58 Print

**Cantos Para Todos**
2524 N Welgate Circle, Wichita, KS 67226
*Tel:* 316-239 6477
*Web Site:* www.cantos.org
*Key Personnel*
Publr: Roy Howard *E-mail:* 2rhoward@att.net
Artistic Dir: Carlene H Williams
Author: Mariana Murguia de Ferrer
Founded: 1989
Materials with multiworlds in mind. Multimedia, multicultural, multilingual materials for schools & homes.
This publisher has indicated that 100% of their product line is author subsidized.
ISBN Prefix(es): 978-0-9768650
Number of titles published annually: 2 Print; 20 CD-ROM; 5 E-Book
Total Titles: 30 Print; 75 CD-ROM; 5 E-Book
Foreign Rep(s): Mariana Murguia (Mexico)

**Capital Crime Press**
PO Box 272904, Fort Collins, CO 80527
*Tel:* 970-481-4894
*Web Site:* www.capitalcrimepress.com
*Key Personnel*
Pres & Sr Ed: Alex Cole *E-mail:* alexcole@capitalcrimepress.com
Founded: 2005
Independent publisher in the mystery/crime genre.
ISBN Prefix(es): 978-0-9776276
Number of titles published annually: 6 Print; 6 Audio
Total Titles: 9 Print
*Distribution Center:* SCB Distributors, 15608 S New Century Dr, Gardena, CA 90248, Gabriel T Wilmoth *Toll Free Tel:* 800-729-6423 *Web Site:* www.scbdistributors.com

**Capital Enquiry Inc**
1034 Emerald Bay Rd, No 435, South Lake Tahoe, CA 96150
*Tel:* 916-442-1434 *Toll Free Tel:* 800-922-7486
*Fax:* 916-244-2704
*E-mail:* info@capenq.com
*Web Site:* www.govbuddy.com
*Key Personnel*
Owner & Mktg Dir: Bruce Campbell
Founded: 1973
Legislative directories, information, maps (CA) zip code directory, diskette (CA) & US Congress Direct.
ISBN Prefix(es): 978-0-917982
Number of titles published annually: 7 Print
Total Titles: 15 Print
Distributor for Center for Investigative Reporting

**Capstone Publishers™**
1710 Roe Crest Dr, North Mankato, MN 56003
*Toll Free Tel:* 800-747-4992 (cust serv)
*Toll Free Fax:* 888-262-0705
*Web Site:* www.capstonepress.com
*Key Personnel*
Owner: Robert Coughlan
CEO: G Thomas Ahern
COO & CFO: William R Rouse
Chief Mktg Offr: Matthew A Keller
Edit Dir: Nick Healy
Gen Mgr: Ashley Andersen-Zantop
Founded: 1991
Provides new & struggling readers with a strong foundation on which to build reading success. Our broad range of nonfiction titles for grades PreK-8 easily blends a world of books with the world children experience every day.

ISBN Prefix(es): 978-1-56065; 978-0-7368
Number of titles published annually: 250 Print
Total Titles: 2,100 Print
Imprints: Capstone Press; Compass Point Books; Picture Window Books; Stone Arch Books
Divisions: Capstone Digital; Heinemann Raintree; Red Brick Learning
*Branch Office(s)*
7825 Telegraph Rd, Bloomington, MN 55438
*Billing Address:* PO Box 1150, MI 55, Minneapolis, MN 55480-1150
*Distribution Center:* 1905 Lookout Dr, North Mankato, MN 56003

**Captain Fiddle Music & Publications**
94 Wiswall Rd, Lee, NH 03824
*Tel:* 603-659-2658
*E-mail:* cfiddle@tiac.net
*Web Site:* captainfiddle.com
*Key Personnel*
Owner: Ryan J Thomson
Founded: 1985
ISBN Prefix(es): 978-0-931877
Number of titles published annually: 3 Print
Total Titles: 24 Print

**Aristide D Caratzas, Publisher**
Imprint of Melissa International Ltd
PO Box 344H, Scarsdale, NY 10583
*Tel:* 914-725-4847 *Fax:* 914-725-4847 (call first)
*E-mail:* contact@caratzas.com
*Web Site:* www.caratzas.com
*Key Personnel*
Publr: Aristide D Caratzas *E-mail:* aristide@caratzas.com
Founded: 1975
Scholarly & academic, textbooks, fine editions, reprints, paperbacks; regional, art, book trade, foreign language, history, literature, reference, religion.
ISBN Prefix(es): 978-0-89241
Number of titles published annually: 3 Print
Total Titles: 405 Print
Divisions: Melissa Media Associates Inc
*Editorial Office(s):* 11 Hypatias St, Plaka, 105 57 Athens, Greece, Mng Ed: Christiane Lange Caratzas *Tel:* 210-321-6475 *E-mail:* caratzasmelissabooks@gmail.com
*Foreign Office(s):* 11 Hypatias St, 105 57 Athens, Greece, Managing Editor: Christiane Lange Caratzas *Tel:* 210-321-6475
*Warehouse:* Conri Services Inc, 5 Skyline Dr, Hawthorne, NY 10532, Contact: Connie Levene *Tel:* 914-592-2300 *E-mail:* ninak@conriservices.com
Membership(s): American Historical Association

**Caravan Books**
Subsidiary of Academic Resources Corp
6946 E Stevens Rd, Cave Creek, AZ 85331-8677
SAN: 206-7323
*Tel:* 480-575-9945
*E-mail:* sfandr@msn.com
*Web Site:* www.scholarsbooklist.com
*Key Personnel*
Publr: Norman Mangouni
Founded: 1972
ISBN Prefix(es): 978-0-88206
Number of titles published annually: 10 Print
Total Titles: 130 Print

**§Cardiotext Publishing**
3405 W 44 St, Minneapolis, MN 55410
SAN: 852-2251
*Tel:* 612-925-2053 *Toll Free Tel:* 888-999-9174 *Fax:* 612-922-7556
*E-mail:* info@cardiotextpublishing.com
*Web Site:* www.cardiotextpublishing.com
*Key Personnel*
Pres: Mike Crouchet *Tel:* 612-746-3699 *E-mail:* mike.crouchet@cardiotext.com
Founded: 2007
Publish print & multimedia resources in the areas of cardiovascular medicine & imaging.
ISBN Prefix(es): 978-0-9790164; 978-1-935395
Number of titles published annually: 10 Print; 5 Online; 8 E-Book
Total Titles: 12 Print

**Cardoza Publishing**
5473 S Eastern Ave, Las Vegas, NV 89119
*Tel:* 702-870-7200 *Toll Free Tel:* 800-577-WINS (577-9467) *Fax:* 702-822-6500
*E-mail:* cardozabooks@aol.com; info@cardozabooks.com
*Web Site:* www.cardozabooks.com
*Key Personnel*
Publr & Author: Avery Cardoza
Founded: 1981
An independent publisher specializing in gaming, gambling, poker, backgammon & chess titles.
ISBN Prefix(es): 978-1-58042
Number of titles published annually: 15 Print
Total Titles: 200 Print
Distributor for Simon & Schuster
*Orders to:* Simon & Schuster, 100 Front St, Riverside, NJ 08075, Order Processing Dept *Toll Free Tel:* 800-223-2336 *Toll Free Fax:* 800-943-9831 *E-mail:* order_desk@distican.com

**§Cardweb.com Inc®**
999 Vanderbilt Beach Rd, 2nd fl, Naples, FL 34108
Mailing Address: PO Box 111687, Naples, FL 34108
*Tel:* 239-325-5300 *Toll Free Tel:* 800-874-8999 *Fax:* 239-236-0835 *Toll Free Fax:* 800-821-4627
*E-mail:* cardservices@cardweb.com; cardstaff@cardweb.com
*Web Site:* www.cardweb.com
*Key Personnel*
CEO: Robert B McKinley *E-mail:* rbmckinley@cardweb.com
Cust Serv Dir: Tirzah Callahan *E-mail:* tirzahc@cardweb.com
Founded: 1986
Research & publishing firm focused on the payment card industry.
ISBN Prefix(es): 978-0-943329
Number of titles published annually: 5 Print; 1 CD-ROM; 10 Online; 3 E-Book
Total Titles: 10 Print; 1 CD-ROM; 10 Online; 2,000 E-Book

**The Career Press Inc**
220 W Parkway, Unit 12, Pompton Plains, NJ 07444
*Tel:* 201-848-0310 *Toll Free Tel:* 800-CAREER-1 (227-3371) *Fax:* 201-848-1727
*Web Site:* www.careerpress.com
*Key Personnel*
Pres: Ronald W Fry
Dir, Sales & Publicity: Laurie Kelly-Pye *E-mail:* lkellypye@careerpress.com
Sr Acqs Ed: Michael Pye *E-mail:* mpye@careerpress.com
Edit Dir: Gina Hoogerhyde *E-mail:* ghoogerhyde@careerpress.com
Intl Rts: Allison Olson *E-mail:* allisoncareerpress@comcast.net
Founded: 1985
Reference books, careers, business & financial how-to, educational, New Age, weddings & motivational.
ISBN Prefix(es): 978-1-56414; 978-1-60163
Number of titles published annually: 75 Print
Total Titles: 400 Print
Imprints: New Page Books (www.newpagebooks.com)
Foreign Rep(s): Brumby Books (Australia, New Zealand); Deep Books Ltd (Europe, UK); McGraw-Hill Education (Asia); Phambili Agencies (South Africa); Ten Speed Press (Canada)
Foreign Rights: Allison Olson (Worldwide)

**§Caribe Betania Editores**
Division of Grupo Nelson Inc
PO Box 141000, Nashville, TN 37214-1000
*Tel:* 615-902-1893 *Toll Free Tel:* 800-322-7423 (ext 1893) *Fax:* 615-883-9376
*Web Site:* www.caribebetania.com
*Key Personnel*
Mktg: Claudia Duncan
Founded: 1949
Publisher of Spanish books & Bibles.
ISBN Prefix(es): 978-0-88113; 978-0-89922
Number of titles published annually: 50 Print
Total Titles: 480 Print

**Carlisle Press - Walnut Creek**
2673 Township Rd 421, Sugarcreek, OH 44681
*Tel:* 330-852-1900 *Toll Free Tel:* 800-852-4482 *Fax:* 330-852-3285
*Key Personnel*
Publr: Marvin Wengerd
Founded: 1992
Amish books & cookbooks, *Keeper's at Home* Magazine.
ISBN Prefix(es): 978-1-890050; 978-0-9642548; 978-1-933753
Number of titles published annually: 6 Print
Total Titles: 60 Print

**Carnegie Mellon University Press**
5032 Forbes Ave, Pittsburgh, PA 15289-1021
SAN: 211-2329
*Tel:* 412-268-2861 *Toll Free Tel:* 800-666-2211 *Fax:* 412-268-8706
*E-mail:* carnegiemellonuniversitypress@gmail.com
*Web Site:* www.cmu.edu/universitypress
*Key Personnel*
Dir: Gerald Costanzo
Sr Ed: Cynthia Lamb
Founded: 1974
ISBN Prefix(es): 978-0-915604; 978-0-88748
Number of titles published annually: 20 Print
Total Titles: 325 Print
*Billing Address:* PO Box 6525, Ithaca, NY 14851-6525
*Orders to:* Cornell University Press Services, PO Box 6525, 750 Cascadilla St, Ithaca, NY 14851
*Returns:* Cornell University Press Services, PO Box 6525, 750 Cascadilla St, Ithaca, NY 14851
*Warehouse:* Cornell University Press Services, PO Box 6525, 750 Cascadilla St, Ithaca, NY 14851, Contact: Ms Chris Jolluck *Toll Free Tel:* 800-666-2211 *Toll Free Fax:* 800-688-2877 *E-mail:* orderbook@cupserv.org *Web Site:* www.cupserv.org

**Carolina Academic Press**
700 Kent St, Durham, NC 27701
SAN: 210-7848
*Tel:* 919-489-7486 *Toll Free Tel:* 800-489-7486 *Fax:* 919-493-5668
*E-mail:* cap@cap-press.com
*Web Site:* www.cap-press.com; www.caplaw.com
*Key Personnel*
Publr: Keith R Sipe *Tel:* 919-489-7486 ext 120 *E-mail:* ksipe@cap-press.com
Sr Ed: Linda M Lacy *Tel:* 919-489-7486 ext 128 *E-mail:* linda@cap-press.com
Ed: Scott Sipe *Tel:* 919-489-7486 ext 129 *E-mail:* css@cap-press.com
Prodn & Design: Tim Colton *Tel:* 919-489-7486 ext 125 *E-mail:* tim@cap-press.com
Founded: 1974
Scholarly books & journals; anthropology, archaeology, criminal justice, economics, government, political science, history, reference, law, social science, african studies.
ISBN Prefix(es): 978-0-89089; 978-1-59460
Number of titles published annually: 100 Print

Total Titles: 600 Print
*Returns:* 101 Tobacco Rd, Oxford, NC 27565
*Warehouse:* 101 Tobacco Rd, Oxford, NC 27565

**Carolrhoda Books**
Division of Lerner Publishing Group Inc
241 First Ave N, Minneapolis, MN 55401
SAN: 201-9671
*Tel:* 612-332-3344 *Toll Free Tel:* 800-328-4929 *Fax:* 612-332-7615 *Toll Free Fax:* 800-332-1132
*E-mail:* info@lernerbooks.com
*Web Site:* www.lernerbooks.com
*Key Personnel*
Chmn: Harry J Lerner
CFO & EVP: Margaret Wunderlich
Pres & Publr: Adam Lerner
EVP, Sales: David Wexler
VP & Dir, Mktg & Digital Prods: Terri Soutor
VP, Prodn: Gary Hansen
Ed-in-Chief: Patricia M Stockland
Edit Dir: Andrew Karre
Rts Dir: Maria Kjoller
Dir, Prod Devt & Mkt Res: Lois Wallentine
Art Dir: Zach Marell
Dir, HR: Cyndi Radant
Founded: 1969
Juveniles: picture books & young adult fiction.
Number of titles published annually: 20 Print
Total Titles: 70 Print; 150 E-Book
Imprints: Carolrhoda Lab (young adult fiction)
Foreign Rep(s): INT Press Distribution (Australia); Monarch Books of Canada (Trade) (Canada); Phambili (Southern Africa); Publishers Marketing Services (Malaysia, Singapore); Saunders Book Co (Education) (Canada); South Pacific Books (New Zealand)
Foreign Rights: Japan Foreign Rights Centre (Japan); Korea Copyright Center (Korea); Michelle Lapautre Agence Junior (France); Literarische Agentur Silke Weniger (Germany); Rights People (UK & Commonwealth)
*Warehouse:* Lerning Publishing Group, 1251 Washington Ave N, Minneapolis, MN 55401

**Carolrhoda Lab™**
Imprint of Lerner Publishing Group Inc
241 First Ave N, Minneapolis, MN 55401
*Tel:* 612-332-3344 *Toll Free Tel:* 800-328-4929 *Fax:* 612-332-7615 *Toll Free Fax:* 800-332-1132 (US)
*E-mail:* info@lernerbooks.com
*Web Site:* www.lernerbooks.com
*Key Personnel*
Chmn: Harry J Lerner
Pres & Publr: Adam Lerner
CFO & EVP: Margaret Wunderlich
EVP, Sales: David Wexler
VP, Prodn: Gary Hansen
Ed-in-Chief: Patricia M Stockland
Edit Dir: Andrew Karre
Rts Dir: Maria Kjoller
VP & Dir, Mktg & Digital Prods: Terri Soutor
Dir, Prod Devt & Mktg Res: Lois Wallentine
Dir, Electronic Content: Dan Wallek
Creative Dir: Zach Marell
Founded: 2010 (imprint launched)
Dedicated to distinctive, provocative, boundary-pushing fiction for teens & their sympathizers.
Number of titles published annually: 10 Print
Total Titles: 22 E-Book
Foreign Rep(s): INT Books Distribution (Australia); Monarch Books of Canada (Canada); Phambili Agency (Southern Africa); Publishers Marketing Services (Malaysia, Singapore); Saunders Book Co/Education (Canada); South Pacific Books (New Zealand)
Foreign Rights: Japan Foreign-Rights Centre (Japan); Korea Copyright Center (Korea); Agence Michelle Lapautre (France); Rights People (UK & Commonwealth); Silke Weniger (Germany)
*Shipping Address:* Lerner Publishing Group Inc, 1251 Washington Ave N, Minneapolis, MN 55401, Contact: Ken Rued *Fax:* 612-204-9208
*Warehouse:* Lerner Publishing Group Inc, 1251 Washington Ave N, Minneapolis, MN 55401, Contact: Ken Rued *Fax:* 612-204-9208

**Carroll Publishing**
4701 Sangamore Rd, Suite S-155, Bethesda, MD 20816
SAN: 237-6334
*Tel:* 301-263-9800 *Toll Free Tel:* 800-336-4240 *Fax:* 301-263-9801
*E-mail:* info@carrollpub.com
*Web Site:* www.carrollpub.com
*Key Personnel*
Exec Acct Mgr: Shirley Paris *Tel:* 301-263-9800 ext 117 *E-mail:* smparis@carrollpub.com
Founded: 1973
Number of titles published annually: 21 Print; 4 Online
Total Titles: 21 Print; 4 Online
Membership(s): National Directory Publishing Association

**Carson-Dellosa Publishing LLC**
PO Box 35665, Greensboro, NC 27425-5665
*Tel:* 336-632-0084 *Toll Free Tel:* 800-321-0943 *Fax:* 336-808-3273 *Toll Free Fax:* 800-535-2669
*E-mail:* custsvc@carsondellosa.com
*Web Site:* www.carsondellosa.com
*Key Personnel*
CEO: Al Greco
Founded: 1976
Publishes supplementary educational materials, including activity books, resource guides, classroom materials & reproducibles, toddler-grade 8. Topics include reading, language arts, mathematics, science, the arts, social studies, English language learners, early childhood learning, Christian books & crafts.
ISBN Prefix(es): 978-0-513; 978-0-7424; 978-1-56822; 978-0-88012; 978-0-88724; 978-1-59441; 978-1-60022; 978-1-60418
Number of titles published annually: 80 Print; 10 E Book
Total Titles: 700 Print
Imprints: DJ Inkers; Rainbow Bridge Publishing; Wild Goose Co; Kelley Wingate Publications
*Branch Office(s)*
8720 Orion Place, Suite 200, Columbus, OH 43240, Cust Serv Mgr: Barbara Boggs *Toll Free Tel:* 800-228-6898
Distributor for Key Education; Mark Twain Media
Membership(s): Association of Educational Publishers

**Carstens Publications Inc**
108 Phil Hardin Rd, Newton, NJ 07860
*Tel:* 973-383-3355 *Toll Free Tel:* 888-526-5365 *Fax:* 973-383-4064
*E-mail:* carstens@carstens-publications.com
*Web Site:* www.carstens-publications.com
*Key Personnel*
Publr: Henry R Carstens *E-mail:* henry@carstens-publications.com
Ad Dir: John Earley
Founded: 1933
Books & magazines on railroads, railroad modeling & aeronautics.
ISBN Prefix(es): 978-0-911868; 978-1-59073
Number of titles published annually: 8 Print
Total Titles: 50 Print
Imprints: Carstens Hobby Books
*Advertising Agency:* High Point Media Inc
Membership(s): Better Business Bureau; Magazine Publishers of America

**CarTech Inc**
39966 Grand Ave, North Branch, MN 55056
*Tel:* 651-277-1200 *Toll Free Tel:* 800-551-4754 *Fax:* 651-277-1203
*E-mail:* info@cartechbooks.com
*Web Site:* www.cartechbooks.com
*Key Personnel*
Owner & Publr: David Arnold
Mktg & Sales Mgr: Molly Koecher *E-mail:* mollyk@cartechbooks.com
Founded: 1993
Automotive books.
ISBN Prefix(es): 978-1-884089; 978-1-932494
Number of titles published annually: 12 Print
Total Titles: 50 Print
Imprints: S-A Design Books
Distributed by MBI
Distributor for Brooklands Books Ltd; S-A Design
Foreign Rights: Brooklands Books Ltd (Australia, England)

**Amon Carter Museum**
3501 Camp Bowie Blvd, Fort Worth, TX 76107-2695
*Tel:* 817-738-1933; 817-738-5065 (PR) *Toll Free Tel:* 800-573-1933 *Fax:* 817-336-1123
*E-mail:* pr@cartermuseum.org
*Web Site:* www.cartermuseum.org
*Key Personnel*
Deputy Dir: Lori Eklund
Dir, Pubns: Will Gillham
Pubns Coord: Elizabeth Le Coney
Founded: 1961
Art & photography.
ISBN Prefix(es): 978-0-88360
Number of titles published annually: 5 Print
Total Titles: 19 Print
Distributed by Abrams & University of Washington Press
*Shipping Address:* 222 N University, Fort Worth, TX 76107

**Casa Bautista de Publicaciones**
Affiliate of Southern Baptist Convention
7000 Alabama Ave, El Paso, TX 79904
*Tel:* 915-566-9656 *Toll Free Tel:* 800-755-5958 (cust serv & orders) *Fax:* 915-562-6502; 915-565-9008 (orders)
*Web Site:* www.casabautista.org; www.editorialmh.org
*Key Personnel*
Gen Dir: Jorge E Diaz
Mktg & Sales Dir: Miryam Picott
Secy: Norma C Armengol *E-mail:* narmengol@casabautista.org
Founded: 1905
Religious publications in Spanish. Foreign distributors also located in all Latin.
ISBN Prefix(es): 978-0-311
Number of titles published annually: 16 Print
Total Titles: 895 Print; 895 E-Book; 40 Audio
Imprints: CBP/EMH
*Branch Office(s)*
Casa Bautista Miami, 12020 NW 40 St, Suite 103, Coral Springs, FL 33065, Contact: Allan Cardet *Tel:* 954-757-9800 *Toll Free Tel:* 800-985-9971 *Fax:* 954-757-9944 *E-mail:* cpbmiami@aol.com
*Foreign Office(s):* Casilla 2516, Santa Cruz, Bolivia *Tel:* (01) 343-0717 *Fax:* (01) 342-8193
Casilla 1253, Santiago, Chile, Contact: Emilio Zapata *Tel:* (02) 672-2114 *Fax:* (02) 695-7145
Apartado Aereo 55294, Bogota 2, DC, Colombia *Tel:* (01) 287-8602 *Fax:* (01) 287-8992
Apartado 285-2050, San Pedro Montes de Oca, San Jose, Costa Rica, Contact: Juan Brenes *Tel:* 2225-4565 *Fax:* 2224-3677
Apartado 880, Santo Domingo, Dominican Republic, Contact: Noraima Aquino *Tel:* 565-2282 *Fax:* 565-6944
Casilla 3236, Guayaquil, Ecuador *Tel:* (03) 445-5311 *Fax:* (03) 445-2610

Av Los Andes No J-14 Col Miramonte, San Salvador, El Salvador *Tel:* 260-8658 *Fax:* 260-1730
Apartado 1135, 01901 Guatemala, Guatemala *Tel:* 2253-0013 *Fax:* 2232-5225
Apartado 279, Tegucigalpa, Honduras, Contact: Oscar Herrera *Tel:* 2238-1481 *Fax:* 2237-9909
Independencia 36-B, Col Centro, 06050 Mexico DF, Mexico, Contact: Hortencia Vazquez *Tel:* (0155) 512-0206 *Fax:* (0155) 512-9475
Del Hospital Bautista 2-C, abajo5c. al sur casa No 1206, Managua, Nicaragua, Contact: Felix Ruix Rivera *Tel:* 222-2195 *Fax:* 278-4786
Ave Samuel Lewis No 9 (Ave 2 Sur) entre calles 53 y 54 Urb Obarrio, Panama 5, Panama *Tel:* 264-6469 *Fax:* 264-6736
Casilla 1415, Asuncion, Paraguay, Contact: Gail P Joule *Tel:* (021) 21-2952
Francisco Pizarro 388, Trujillo, Peru, Contact: Maria Elena Santos *Fax:* 424-5982
Calle San Alejandro 1825, Urb. San Ignacio, Rio Piedras, Puerto Rico *Tel:* 787-764-6175
Padre Mendez, No 142-B, 46900 Torrente, Valencia, Spain *Tel:* 961 563 578 *Fax:* 961 563 579
Distributed by LifeWay Christian Resources

**§Cascade Pass Inc**
4223 Glencoe Ave, Suite C-105, Marina Del Rey, CA 90292
*Tel:* 310-305-0210 *Toll Free Tel:* 888-837-0704 *Fax:* 310-305-7850
*Web Site:* www.cascadepass.com
*Key Personnel*
Pres: David Katz *E-mail:* dkatz@cascadepass.com
Proj Mgr: Judith Cohen *E-mail:* jlc@cascadepass.com
Founded: 1989
Science career books for children, environmental & sports.
ISBN Prefix(es): 978-1-880599
Number of titles published annually: 10 Print
Total Titles: 84 Print; 18 CD-ROM; 6 Audio

**Casemate Publishers & Book Distributors LLC**
908 Darby Rd, Havertown, PA 19083
*Tel:* 610-853-9131 *Fax:* 610-853-9146
*E-mail:* casemate@casematepublishing.com
*Web Site:* www.casematepublishing.com
*Key Personnel*
CEO & Pres: David Farnsworth
VP: Sarah Farnsworth
Founded: 2001
Publisher & distributor of military history, defense & travel books.
ISBN Prefix(es): 978-0-9711709; 978-1-932033
Number of titles published annually: 20 Print
Total Titles: 100 Print
Distributor for AF Editions; Airfile Publications; Amber Books (UK); Amberley Publishing (UK); Birlinn Publishing (UK); CAL Books; Casemate (USA); Casemate/Flashpoint; Compendium Films; Compendium Publishing (UK); D-Day Publishing (Belgium); Eagle Editions; Earthbound Publications; Formac Publishing (Canada); Foundry; Front Street Press (USA); Frontline Books; Greenhill Books; Grub Street (UK); Harpia Publishing; Heimdal; Helion & Co Ltd (UK); Histoire & Collections (France); Historical Archive Press; History Facts; Editions Charles Herissey (France); Historical Indexes (USA); Paul Holberton Publishing; Indo Editions (France); Ironclad Publishing (USA); De Krijger (Belgium); Lancer Publishers; Lorimer; Military Illustrated; MMP (UK/ Poland); OREP; Pen & Sword Books Ltd (UK); Pen & Sword Digital; Philedition; Riebel-Roque; RZM Publishing (USA); S I Publicaties BV; Savas Beatie (USA); Scarab Miniatures; Seaforth Publishing; Tattered Flag; 30 Degrees South Publishers; Vanwell-Looking Back Press; Vanwell Publishing (Canada); WAG Books; Warlord Games; Wharncliffe
Foreign Rep(s): Casemate UK (UK & Commonwealth)
*Returns:* c/o Casemate, 22883 Quicksilver Dr, Dulles, VA 20166
*Shipping Address:* c/o Casemate, 22883 Quicksilver Dr, Dulles, VA 20166
Membership(s): PMA International

**Castle Connolly Medical Ltd**
42 W 24 St, 2nd fl, New York, NY 10010
*Tel:* 212-367-8400 *Toll Free Tel:* 800-339-DOCS (339-3627) *Fax:* 212-367-0964
*Web Site:* www.castleconnolly.com
*Key Personnel*
Chmn: John K Castle
CEO & Pres: John J Connolly, EdD
VP, Chief Strategy & Opers Offr: William Liss-Levinson, PhD *E-mail:* bliss-levinson@castleconnolly.com
VP, Chief Med & Res Offr: Dr Jean Morgan
Mgr, Client Rel & Communs: Nicki Hughes *Tel:* 212-367-8400 ext 138 *E-mail:* nhughes@castleconnolly.com
Founded: 1991
Publishing company whose mission is to help consumers find the best healthcare with its "Top Doctors" guides.
ISBN Prefix(es): 978-1-883769; 978-1-935036; 978-0-984
Number of titles published annually: 3 Print
Total Titles: 10 Print
Membership(s): The Association of Publishers for Special Sales

**§Catholic Book Publishing Corp**
77 West End Rd, Totowa, NJ 07512
*Tel:* 973-890-2400 *Toll Free Tel:* 877-228-2665 *Fax:* 973-890-2410
*E-mail:* info@catholicbookpublishing.com
*Web Site:* www.catholicbookpublishing.com
Founded: 1911
For over 90 years, the leading publisher of quality Catholic resources—including Bibles, Missals, Prayer books, liturgical books, spirituality books, Spanish titles & children's books. The company's trademark St. Joseph Editions are distinctive for their large, easy-to-read typefaces; magnificent, full-color illustrations; & helpful & plentiful guides, summaries, notes, indices & photographs. Imprint Resurrection Press is noted for spirituality & personal growth titles. Imprint World Catholic Press complements the company's rich tradition of Bible publishing.
ISBN Prefix(es): 978-0-89942; 978-1-878718 (Resurrection Press); 978-0-529 (World Catholic Press); 978-1-933066 (Resurrection Press)
Number of titles published annually: 25 Print
Total Titles: 750 Print; 9 Audio
Imprints: Resurrection Press; World Catholic Press

**The Catholic Health Association of the United States**
4455 Woodson Rd, St Louis, MO 63134-3797
SAN: 201-968X
*Tel:* 314-427-2500 *Fax:* 314-253-0029
*E-mail:* servicecenter@chausa.org
*Web Site:* www.chausa.org
*Key Personnel*
VP, Communs & Mktg: Edward J Giganti *E-mail:* egiganti@chausa.org
Founded: 1915
Catholic health care resources, Catholic ministry, health, labor, medicine & nursing.
ISBN Prefix(es): 978-0-87125
Number of titles published annually: 3 Print; 1 CD-ROM; 2 Audio
Total Titles: 58 Print; 1 CD-ROM; 4 Audio

**The Catholic University of America Press**
240 Leahy Hall, 620 Michigan Ave NE, Washington, DC 20064
SAN: 203-6290
*Tel:* 202-319-5052 *Toll Free Tel:* 800-537-5487 (orders only) *Fax:* 202-319-4985
*E-mail:* cua-press@cua.edu
*Web Site:* cuapress.cua.edu
*Key Personnel*
Dir & Ed-in-Chief: Trevor C Lipscombe *E-mail:* lipscombe@cua.edu
Mng Ed: Teresa Walker *E-mail:* walkert@cua.edu
Acqs Ed: James Kruggel *E-mail:* kruggel@cua.edu
Mktg Mgr: Brian Roach *E-mail:* roach@cua.edu
Founded: 1939
ISBN Prefix(es): 978-0-8132
Number of titles published annually: 38 Print; 25 Online; 25 E-Book
Total Titles: 580 Print; 300 Online; 300 E-Book
Distributor for American Maritain Association; Institute for the Psychological Sciences Press (IPS); Sapientia Press
Foreign Rep(s): East West Export Books (Asia, Australia, New Zealand); Eurospan University Press Group (Africa, Europe, Middle East, UK); Scholarly Book Services (Canada)
*Orders to:* Hopkins Fulfillment Service, PO Box 50370, Baltimore, MD 21211-4370 *Toll Free Tel:* 800-537-5487 *Fax:* 410-516-6998 *E-mail:* hfscustserv@mail.press.jhu.edu
*Returns:* Hopkins Fulfillment Service, c/o Maple Press Co, Lebanon Distribution Ctr, PO Box 1287, Lebanon, PA 17042-1287
*Warehouse:* c/o Maple Press Co, Lebanon Distribution Ctr, 704 Legionaire Dr, Fredricksburg, PA 17042
Membership(s): Association of American University Presses

**Cato Institute**
1000 Massachusetts Ave NW, Washington, DC 20001-5403
*Tel:* 202-842-0200 *Toll Free Tel:* 800-767-1241 *Fax:* 202-842-3490
*E-mail:* catostore@cato.org
*Web Site:* www.cato.org
*Key Personnel*
Founder & Pres: Edward H Crane
Pubns Dir: David Lampo
Founded: 1977
Non-partisan, public-policy think tank.
ISBN Prefix(es): 978-0-932790; 978-1-882577; 978-1-930865; 978-1-933995
Number of titles published annually: 15 Print
Total Titles: 150 Print
Foreign Rights: Rights & Distribution Inc (Worldwide)
*Distribution Center:* National Book Network, 15200 NBN Way, Blue Ridge Summit, PA 17214, VP, Opers: Mike Cornell *Tel:* 717-794-3800 *Toll Free Tel:* 800-462-6420 *Fax:* 717-794-3828 *Web Site:* www.nbnbooks.com

**Caxton Press**
Division of The Caxton Printers Ltd
312 Main St, Caldwell, ID 83605-3299
SAN: 201-9698
*Tel:* 208-459-7421 *Toll Free Tel:* 800-657-6465 *Fax:* 208-459-7450
*E-mail:* publish@caxtonpress.com
*Web Site:* www.caxtonpress.com
*Key Personnel*
VP & Publr: Scott Gipson *E-mail:* sgipson@caxtonpress.com
Publg Asst/Website: Linsey Gonzales *E-mail:* lgonzales@caxtonpress.com
Founded: 1925 (J H Gipson; Still owned & managed by the Gipson family)
Hardcover & paperback.
ISBN Prefix(es): 978-0-87004
Number of titles published annually: 8 Print
Total Titles: 135 Print

Distributed by University of Nebraska Press
Distributor for Alpha Omega Publishing; Black Canyon Communications; Historic Idaho Series; Snake Country Publishing; University of Idaho Historical Manuscript Series; University of Idaho Press
*Orders to:* Longleaf Services Inc, 116 S Boundary St, Chapel Hill, SC 27514-3808 *Toll Free Tel:* 800-848-6224 *Toll Free Fax:* 800-272-6817 *E-mail:* customerservice@longleafservices.org
Membership(s): AAP

**§CCH, a Wolters Kluwer business**
2700 Lake Cook Rd, Riverwoods, IL 60015
SAN: 202-3504
*Tel:* 847-267-7000 *Toll Free Tel:* 800-525-3335 *Fax:* 773-866-3095
*Web Site:* www.cch.com
*Key Personnel*
CEO & Pres: Karen Abramson
Dir, Communs: Leslie Bonacum *Tel:* 847-267-7153 *E-mail:* mediahelp@cch.com
Founded: 1913
Current US International tax law, business, human resources, securities & health care law, tax, small business, home office human resources & health care.
ISBN Prefix(es): 978-0-8080
Number of titles published annually: 100 Print
Total Titles: 400 Print
Subsidiaries: CCH Peterson; CCH Riverwoods; CCH St Petersburg; CCH Tax Compliance; CCH Washington DC; LIS (Legal Information Services); Washington Service Bureau
*Foreign Office(s):* Wolters Kluwer nv, Apollolaan 153, PO Box 75248, 1070 AE Amsterdam, Netherlands *Tel:* (020) 60 70 400 *Fax:* (020) 60 70 490 *E-mail:* info@wolterskluwer.com *Web Site:* www.wolterskluwer.com
*Billing Address:* PO Box 4307, Carol Stream, IL 60197-4307
*Returns:* 7201 McKinney Circle, Frederick, MD 21704-8356
*Warehouse:* 4025 Peterson Ave, Chicago, IL 60646-6085

**CCL - Americas**, see Center for Creative Leadership LLC

**CDL Press**
PO Box 34454, Bethesda, MD 20827
*Tel:* 301-762-2066 *Fax:* 253-484-5542
*E-mail:* cdlpress@erols.com
*Web Site:* www.cdlpress.com
*Key Personnel*
Pres: Mark E Cohen
Founded: 1981
ISBN Prefix(es): 978-1-883053
Number of titles published annually: 6 Print
Total Titles: 63 Print
Imprints: CDL Press; University Press of Maryland
*Returns:* 11903 Reynolds Ave, Potomac, MD 20827

**Cedar Fort Inc**
2373 W 700 S, Springville, UT 84663
*Tel:* 801-489-4084 *Toll Free Tel:* 800-SKY-BOOK (759-2665) *Fax:* 801-489-1097 *Toll Free Fax:* 800-388-3727
*E-mail:* brycemortimer@cedarfort.com
*Web Site:* www.cedarfort.com
*Key Personnel*
Pres: Lyle Mortimer
Mktg: Josh Johnson *E-mail:* jjohnson@cedarfort.com
Billing: Cindy Bunce
Founded: 1986
Christian (primarily Latter-Day Saints), inspirational, motivational, LDS fiction & doctrinal.
ISBN Prefix(es): 978-1-55517
Number of titles published annually: 120 Print; 50 E-Book; 5 Audio
Total Titles: 500 Print

**Cedar Tree Books**
PO Box 4256, Wilmington, DE 19807
*Tel:* 302 998 4171 *Fax:* 302-998-4185
*E-mail:* books@ctpress.com
*Web Site:* www.cedartreebooks.com
Founded: 1925
This publisher has indicated that 30% of their product line is author subsidized.
ISBN Prefix(es): 978-1-892142
Number of titles published annually: 8 Print
Total Titles: 48 Print

**CEF Press**
Subsidiary of Child Evangelism Fellowship Inc
17482 State Hwy M, Warrenton, MO 63383-0348
Mailing Address: PO Box 348, Warrenton, MO 63383-0348
*Tel:* 636-456-4321 *Toll Free Tel:* 800-748-7710 (cust serv); 800-300-4033 (USA ministries) *Fax:* 636-456-9935
*E-mail:* cefexecutiveoffices@cefonline.com
*Web Site:* www.cefonline.com
Founded: 1939
Christian education curriculum.
ISBN Prefix(es): 978-1-55976
Number of titles published annually: 30 Print
Total Titles: 300 Print
Foreign Rep(s): CEFMARK (Australia)

**Celebra**
Imprint of Penguin Group (USA) LLC
375 Hudson St, New York, NY 10014
*Tel:* 212-366-2000 *Fax:* 212-366-2889
*Key Personnel*
Publr: Ray Garcia
Assoc Publr: Steve Meltzer
Number of titles published annually: 13 Print
Total Titles: 64 Print

**Celebrity Profiles Publishing**
Division of Edison & Kellogg
PO Box 344, Stony Brook, NY 11790
*Tel:* 631-862-8555 *Fax:* 631-862-0139
*E-mail:* celebpro4@aol.com
*Web Site:* www.richardgrudens.com
*Key Personnel*
Pres: James Snyder
Author: Richard Grudens
Founded: 1995
ISBN Prefix(es): 978-0-9763877
Number of titles published annually: 3 Print
Total Titles: 15 Print; 2 Audio
Membership(s): IBPA, the Independent Book Publishers Association

**Celestial Arts Publishing Co**
Imprint of Crown Publishing Group
2625 Alcatraz Ave, Suite 505, Berkeley, CA 94705-2702
*Tel:* 510-285-3000 *Toll Free Tel:* 800-841-2665; 800-733-3000 (orders & cust serv) *Fax:* 510-599-1629
*E-mail:* csorders@randomhouse.com
*Web Site:* www.tenspeed.com
Founded: 1963
ISBN Prefix(es): 978-0-912310; 978-0-89087; 978-1-58761
Number of titles published annually: 30 Print
*Editorial Office(s):* 1021 N State Rd 47, Crawfordsville, IN 47933
*Sales Office(s):* 1021 N State Rd 47, Crawfordsville, IN 47933
*Billing Address:* 1021 N State Rd 47, Crawfordsville, IN 47933
*Orders to:* Random House, 400 Hahn Rd, Westminster, MD 21157
*Returns:* 1021 N State Rd 47, Crawfordsville, IN 47933
*Warehouse:* Random House, 400 Hahn Rd, Westminster, MD 21157
*Distribution Center:* Random House, 400 Hahn Rd, Westminster, MD 21157

**§Cengage Learning**
200 First Stamford Place, Suite 400, Stamford, CT 06902
Mailing Address: PO Box 6904, Florence, KY 41022-6904
*Tel:* 203-965-8600 *Toll Free Tel:* 800-354-9706 *Fax:* 203-965-8599 *Toll Free Fax:* 800-487-8488
*E-mail:* esales@cengage.com
*Web Site:* www.cengage.com
*Key Personnel*
CEO: Michael Hansen
Exec Chmn: Ron Dunn
CFO: Dean Durbin
Chief Mktg Offr: Sandi Kirshner
Chief Mktg Offr, Acad & Prof Group: Cindy Cook
EVP & Chief Sales & Mktg Offr: Kevin Stone
EVP, Learning & Res Solutions: Manuel Guzman
EVP, New Media: William D Rieders
EVP, Sales: Rich Foley
SVP, HR: Mark Howe
Gen Coun: Ken Carson
Cengage Learning delivers highly-customized learning solutions for colleges, universities, instructors, students, libraries, government agencies, corporations & professionals around the world. These solutions are delivered through specialized content, applications & services that foster academic excellence & professional development, as well as provide measurable learning outcomes to its customers.
Number of titles published annually: 150 Print
Subsidiaries: Delmar Learning (www.delmarlearning.com); Gale (www.gale.com); Heinle (www.heinle.com); Wadsworth (www.wadsworth.com)
*Billing Address:* Cengage Learning Distribution Center, 10650 Toebben Dr, Independence, KY 41051 *Toll Free Tel:* 877-201-3962 *Toll Free Fax:* 800-248-4724
*Orders to:* Cengage Learning Distribution Center, 10650 Toebben Dr, Independence, KY 41051
*Returns:* Cengage Learning Distribution Center, 10650 Toebben Dr, Independence, KY 41051 *Tel:* 859-525-2230 *Toll Free Fax:* 800-248-4724
*Warehouse:* Cengage Learning Distribution Center, 10650 Toebben Dr, Independence, KY 41051
*Distribution Center:* Cengage Learning Distribution Center, 10650 Toebben Dr, Independence, KY 41051 *Tel:* 859-525-2230 *Toll Free Fax:* 800-248-4724 *E-mail:* esales@thomsonlearning.com
Membership(s): AAP
*See separate listing for:*
**Charles River Media**
**Chemical Education Resources Inc**
**Course Technology**
**Delmar**
**Gale**
**National Geographic Learning**
**Wadsworth Publishing**

**Center for Creative Leadership LLC**
Affiliate of Smith Richardson Foundation
One Leadership Place, Greensboro, NC 27410-9427
Mailing Address: PO Box 26300, Greensboro, NC 27438-6300
*Tel:* 336-545-2810; 336-288-7210 *Fax:* 336-282-3284
*E-mail:* info@ccl.org
*Web Site:* www.ccl.org/publications
*Key Personnel*
CEO & Pres: John R Ryan

CFO & EVP: Bradley E Shumaker
EVP, Res & Innovative Devt: David G Altman
Founded: 1970
Books on leadership & leadership development.
ISBN Prefix(es): 978-0-912879; 978-0-9638301; 978-1-882197
Number of titles published annually: 10 Print
Total Titles: 123 Print
*Foreign Office(s):* CCL-Europe, Rue Neerveld 101-103 Neerveldstr, 1200 Brussels, Belgium *Tel:* (02) 679 0910 *Fax:* (02) 673 6306 *E-mail:* ccl.emea@ccl.org
CCL-Asia, The Rutherford, Lobby B, No 03-07/08, Singapore Science Park Dr 1, Singapore 118261, Singapore *Tel:* 6854 6000 *Fax:* 6854 6001 *E-mail:* ccl.apac@ccl.org
Distributed by Jossey-Bass; John Wiley & Sons Inc
Distributor for Free Press; Harvard Business School Press; Jossey-Bass; Lominger Inc; John Wiley & Sons Inc

**Center for East Asian Studies (CEAS)**
Subsidiary of Western Washington University
Western Washington University, 516 High St, Bellingham, WA 98225-9057
*Tel:* 360-650-3339 *Fax:* 360-650-6110
*E-mail:* easpress@wwu.edu
*Web Site:* www.wwu.edu/eas
*Key Personnel*
Dir: Prof Edward Vajda *E-mail:* edward.vajda@wwu.edu
Mng Ed: Dr Scott Pearce *Tel:* 360-650-3897 *E-mail:* pearce@cc.wwu.edu
Founded: 1971
East Asia & Iran; Asia mainly monographs.
ISBN Prefix(es): 978-0-914584
Number of titles published annually: 3 Print
Total Titles: 30 Print

**§Center for Futures Education Inc**
345 Erie St, Grove City, PA 16127
Mailing Address: PO Box 309, Grove City, PA 16127-0309
*Tel:* 724-458-5860 *Fax:* 724-458-5962
*E-mail:* info@thectr.com
*Web Site:* www.thectr.com
*Key Personnel*
Treas: Lyn M Sennholz *E-mail:* lyn@thectr.com
Founded: 1981
Print & online books on commodity futures & securities.
ISBN Prefix(es): 978-0-915513
Number of titles published annually: 12 Print
Total Titles: 50 Print; 15 E-Book

**The Center for Learning**
29313 Clemens Rd, Suite 2-E, Westlake, OH 44145
*Tel:* 440-250-9341 *Fax:* 440-250-9715
*E-mail:* customerservice@centerforlearning.org
*Web Site:* www.centerforlearning.org
*Key Personnel*
CEO & Pres: Melanie Wall
Off Admin: Jo Ann Wagner *E-mail:* jwagner@centerforlearning.org
Founded: 1970
Founded to publish values based curriculum materials. All materials are written by master teachers who integrate academic objectives & ethical values. Nonprofit educational publisher of value based curriculum units with reproducible handouts for teachers of English/Language Arts, social studies, novel/dramas, biographies & religion. Specialize in advanced placement, genres; American, British & World novels & literature; skills, supplementary topics, writing; economics, social & global issues, US government & history, world history; Catholic teaching, ministry, retreats, adult faith resources, marriage & parenting, divorce & blended families, abstinence education & chastity; publish lesson plans for elementary & secondary grades.
ISBN Prefix(es): 978-1-56077
Number of titles published annually: 20 Print
Total Titles: 600 Print
*Orders to:* PO Box 910, Villa Maria, PA 16155 *Tel:* 724-964-8083 *Toll Free Tel:* 800-767-9090 *Fax:* 724-964-8992 *Toll Free Fax:* 888-767-8080
*Returns:* Returns Dept, Unit 10-H, 590 E Western Reserve Rd, Youngstown, OH 44514
*Distribution Center:* PO Box 910, Villa Maria, PA 16155, Cust Serv Mgr: Margaret Pugh *Tel:* 724-964-8083 *Toll Free Tel:* 800-767-9090 *Fax:* 724-964-8992 *Toll Free Fax:* 888-767 8080

**Center for Migration Studies of New York Inc (CMS)**
27 Carmine St, New York, NY 10014-4423
*Tel:* 212-337-3080 *Fax:* 646-998-4625
*E-mail:* cms@cmsny.org
*Web Site:* www.cmsny.org
*Key Personnel*
Exec Dir: Donald Kerwin
Dir, Res: Rachel Reyes *E-mail:* rreyes@cmsny.org
Founded: 1964
Journals & monographs on the sociodemographic, economic, political, historical & legal aspects of human migration & refugee movements.
ISBN Prefix(es): 978-0-913256; 978-0-934733; 978-1-57703
Number of titles published annually: 8 Print
Total Titles: 120 Print
*Foreign Office(s):* CEMLA, Avenida Independencia 20, C1099AAN Buenos Aires, Argentina
CMSS, Box 913, Darlinghurst, NSW 2010, Australia
CEPAM, Av Alberto Bins 1026-CP, 1658-90030 Porta Alegre, Brazil *Tel:* (0512) 258-246
CEM, Rua Dr Mario Vicente 1108-CP, 42756-04270 Sao Paulo, Brazil *Tel:* (011) 273-9031
CIEMI, 46 Rue de Montreuil, 75011 Paris, France *Tel:* 01 43 72 49 34
CSER, Via Dandolo 58, 00153 Rome RM, Italy *Tel:* (06) 580-9764; (06) 589-7664
SMC, PO Box 10541, Broadway Centre, Quezon City, Philippines
CSERPE, Oberwilerstr 112, 4054 Basel, Switzerland *Tel:* (061) 54-0661
CEPAM, Apdo 51480, Caracas 1050, Venezuela *Tel:* (0212) 924-463
Foreign Rep(s): CADEMS (Argentina); CCMS (Australia); Centro de Estudos Migratorios (Brazil); CIEM (France); CSER (Italy)

**The Center for Thanatology Research & Education Inc**
391 Atlantic Ave, Brooklyn, NY 11217-1701
*Tel:* 718-858-3026 *Fax:* 718-852-1846
*E-mail:* thanatology@pipeline.com
*Web Site:* www.thanatology.org
*Key Personnel*
Treas: Frank Colonnese
Dir: Roberta Halporn *E-mail:* rhalporn@pipeline.com
Media Dir: Constance Halporn
Founded: 1982
Deals exclusively with books on dying, death, bereavement & recovery from bereavement, as well as those on life-threatening illness, from the points of view of psychology & the arts. We also publish a line of materials on gravestone studies & cemeteries. We maintain a 2,500 book library on these subjects; open to the public.
ISBN Prefix(es): 978-0-930194
Number of titles published annually: 6 Print; 2 CD-ROM; 1 Online
Total Titles: 65 Print; 2 CD-ROM; 2 Online
Imprints: Center for Thanatology (books on cemetaries); Foundation Book & Periodical Division
Distributor for Association for Gravestone Studies; Calvary Hospital; Greenwood Cemetery
Membership(s): The Association of Publishers for Special Sales

**Center for Women Policy Studies**
1776 Massachusetts Ave NW, Suite 450, Washington, DC 20036
*Tel:* 202-872-1770 *Fax:* 202-296-8962
*E-mail:* cwps@centerwomenpolicy.org
*Web Site:* www.centerwomenpolicy.org
*Key Personnel*
Pres: Leslie R Wolfe, PhD *E-mail:* lwolfe@centerwomenpolicy.org
VP: Jennifer Tucker *E-mail:* jtucker@centerwomenpolicy.com
Founded: 1972
Violence against women, education, economic opportunity, work & family policy, workplace diversity, womens' health policy, women & AIDS, human trafficking of women & girls.
ISBN Prefix(es): 978-1-877966
Number of titles published annually: 12 Print
Total Titles: 65 Print

**Center Press**
PO Box 6936, Thousand Oaks, CA 91360-6936
*Tel:* 818-889-7071 *Fax:* 818-889-7072
*E-mail:* center@centerbooks.com
*Web Site:* centerbooks.com
*Key Personnel*
Publr & Author: Susan Artof *E-mail:* sartof@yahoo.com
Founded: 1990
ISBN Prefix(es): 978-1-889198; 978-0-9626888
Number of titles published annually: 3 Print
Total Titles: 15 Print
Imprints: Premier Novels (fiction)
Membership(s): IBPA, the Independent Book Publishers Association

**Center Street**
Division of Hachette Book Group
12 Cadillac Dr, Suite 480, Brentwood, TN 37027
*Tel:* 615-221-0996
*Web Site:* www.centerstreet.com
*Key Personnel*
SVP & Publr, Nashville Div: Rolf Zettersten
VP, Assoc Publr: Harry Helm
Sr Ed: Kate Hartson
Mktg Dir: Andrea Glickson
Ed: Christina Boys
Dir of Publicity: Shanon Stowe
Number of titles published annually: 25 Print
Total Titles: 195 Print
*Orders to:* Hachette Book Group, Order Dept, Three Center Plaza, Boston, MA 02108 (US orders) *Toll Free Tel:* 800-759-0190 *Toll Free Fax:* 800-286-9471
*Returns:* Hachette Book Group, Returns Dept, 322 S Enterprise Blvd, Lebanon, IN 46052

**Centering Corp**
7230 Maple St, Omaha, NE 68134
SAN: 298-1815
*Tel:* 402-553-1200 *Toll Free Tel:* 866-218-0101 *Fax:* 402-553-0507
*E-mail:* orders@centering.org
*Web Site:* www.centering.org
*Key Personnel*
Founder & Pres: Joy Johnson; Dr Marvin Johnson
Exec Dir: Janet Sieff *E-mail:* j1200@aol.com
Asst to Dir: Nick Sieff
Founded: 1977
Bereavement support; specializes in divorce, grief & loss. Nonprofit organization.
ISBN Prefix(es): 978-1-56123
Number of titles published annually: 10 Print
Total Titles: 150 Print

**Centerstream Publishing LLC**
PO Box 17878, Anaheim Hills, CA 92817-7878
SAN: 683-8022
*Tel:* 714-779-9390
*E-mail:* centerstrm@aol.com
*Web Site:* www.centerstream-usa.com
*Key Personnel*
Owner: Ron Middlebrook
Founded: 1971
Music history, bios, music instruction books, videos & DVDs: all instruments.
ISBN Prefix(es): 978-0-931759; 978-1-57424
Number of titles published annually: 20 Print; 10 CD-ROM
Total Titles: 250 Print; 30 CD-ROM
Subsidiaries: Centerbrook Publishing
Distributed by Booklines Hawaii; Hal Leonard Corp
Membership(s): IBPA, the Independent Book Publishers Association

**Central Conference of American Rabbis/CCAR Press**
355 Lexington Ave, 18th fl, New York, NY 10017
*Tel:* 212-972-3636 *Toll Free Tel:* 800-935-2227 *Fax:* 212-692-0819
*E-mail:* info@ccarnet.org
*Web Site:* www.ccarnet.org/ccar-press
*Key Personnel*
Pres: Jonathan Stein
Chief Exec: Steven A Fox *Tel:* 212-972-3636 ext 238 *E-mail:* sfox@ccarnet.org
Dir, Press: Hara Person *Tel:* 212-972-3636 ext 222 *E-mail:* hperson@ccarnet.org
Founded: 1889
Books on liturgy & Jewish practices from a liberal point of view.
ISBN Prefix(es): 978-0-88123; 978-0-916694
Number of titles published annually: 5 Print
Total Titles: 57 Print
*Shipping Address:* Mercedes Distribution Center, Brooklyn Navy Yard, Bldg 3, Brooklyn, NY 11205
*Warehouse:* Mercedes Distribution Center, Brooklyn Navy Yard, Bldg 3, Brooklyn, NY 11205

**Central European University Press**
224 W 57 St, 7th fl, New York, NY 10019
*Tel:* 212-547-6932 *Fax:* 646-557-2416
*Web Site:* www.ceupress.com
*Key Personnel*
Sales Mgr, US & CN: Martin Greenwald *E-mail:* martin.greenwald@opensocietyfoundations.org
Founded: 1993
Publish topics concerning past & present history & culture of the peoples living in Central & Eastern Europe & the former Soviet Union.
ISBN Prefix(es): 978-1-85866; 978-963-9116; 978-963-9241; 978-963-7326; 978-963-9776
Number of titles published annually: 20 Print
Total Titles: 240 Print; 10 E-Book
*Editorial Office(s):* Oktober 6 utca 14, Budapest 1051, Hungary, Dir: Krisztina Kos *Tel:* (01) 327 3844 *Fax:* (01) 327 3183 *E-mail:* kosk@ceu.hu
*Foreign Office(s):* Oktober 6, utca 14, Budapest 1051, Hungary, Sales & Mktg Mgr: Peter Inkei *Tel:* (01) 327-3181 *Fax:* (01) 327-3183 *E-mail:* inkeip@ceu.hu
Distributed by University of Toronto Press (Canada)
Distributor for International Debate Education Association; Local Government & Public Service Reform Initiative; Open Society Institute
Foreign Rep(s): Kubon & Sagner GmbH (Germany); NBN International (Australia, New Zealand, UK, Western Europe); Yushodo Co Ltd (Japan)
*Orders to:* Books International, PO Box 605, Herndon, VA 20172 *Tel:* 703-661-1500 *Fax:* 703-661-1501 *E-mail:* mgreenwald@sorosny.org *Web Site:* www.booksintl.com
*Returns:* Books International Inc, 22883 Quicksilver Dr, Dulles, VA 20166 *Tel:* 703-661-1500 *Fax:* 703-661-1501
*Shipping Address:* c/o Books International Inc, PO Box 605, Herndon, VA 20172 *Tel:* 703-661-1500 *Fax:* 703-661-1501
*Warehouse:* Books International Inc, 22883 Quicksilver Dr, Dulles, VA 20166 *Tel:* 703-661-1500 *Fax:* 703-661-1501

**Central Recovery Press (CRP)**
Unit of Central Recovery Treatment
3321 N Buffalo Dr, Suite 275, Las Vegas, NV 89129
*Tel:* 702-868-5830 *Fax:* 702-868-5831
*E-mail:* info@centralrecovery.com
*Web Site:* centralrecoverypress.com
*Key Personnel*
Exec Ed: Nancy Schenck *E-mail:* nschenck@centralrecovery.com
Publr: Bob Gray *E-mail:* bgray@centralrecovery.com
Sales & Mktg Mgr: Patrick Hughes *E-mail:* phughes@centralrecovery.com
Mng Ed: Nicole Thomas
Sr Ed: Helen O'Reilly
A progressive publishing company that sheds new light on an age-old problem: addiction. We hope to break the stigma of addiction by publishing quality books that holistically address the nature of this devastating disease. Offer a diverse selection of titles focused on recovery, addiction treatment & behavioral health topics. Our mission is to positively impact recovering individuals: their families, friends & allies, the behavioral health care field & the general public by creating, publishing & distributing a broad variety of unique & fresh publications that embrace best practices in addiction recovery & behavioral health care.
ISBN Prefix(es): 978-0-9799869
Number of titles published annually: 12 Print; 12 E-Book
Total Titles: 20 Print; 20 E-Book
Distributed by HCI Books Inc
Foreign Rep(s): HCI Books (Kelly Maragni)
Foreign Rights: HCI Books (Kelly Maragni)
*Orders to:* HCI Book Inc, 3201 SW 15 St, Deerfield Beach, FL 33442
*Returns:* HCI Book Inc, 3201 SW 15 St, Deerfield Beach, FL 33442
*Shipping Address:* HCI Book Inc, 3201 SW 15 St, Deerfield Beach, FL 33442, Natl Sales Mgr: Kelly Maragni
*Warehouse:* HCI Book Inc, 3201 SW 15 St, Deerfield Beach, FL 33442
*Distribution Center:* HCI Book Inc, 3201 SW 15 St, Deerfield Beach, FL 33442
Membership(s): IBPA, the Independent Book Publishers Association

**The Century Foundation**
Division of The Century Foundation Inc
41 E 70 St, New York, NY 10021
*Tel:* 212-535-4441; 212-879-9197 *Fax:* 212-879-9197
*E-mail:* info@tcf.org
*Web Site:* www.tcf.org
*Key Personnel*
Pres: Janice Nittoli
VP & Dir, Pubns: Jason Renker *Tel:* 212-452-7715 *Fax:* 212-535-9883 *E-mail:* renker@tcf.org
Cont: Philip Li
Mgr, Spec Events: Loretta Ahlrich *Tel:* 212-452-7722 *Fax:* 212-535-7534 *E-mail:* ahlrich@tcf.org
Founded: 1984
Reports of task forces, papers & books covering international & domestic policy issues.
ISBN Prefix(es): 978-0-87078
Number of titles published annually: 10 Print
Total Titles: 185 Print
*Branch Office(s)*
1333 "H" St NW, 10th fl, Washington, DC 20005 *Tel:* 202-387-0400 *Fax:* 202-483-9430
*Distribution Center:* The Brookings Institution, 1775 Massachusetts Ave NW, Washington, DC 20036 *Tel:* 410-516-6956 *Toll Free Tel:* 800-537-5487

**§Chain Store Guide (CSG)**
3922 Coconut Palm Dr, Tampa, FL 33619
*Tel:* 813-627-6957 *Toll Free Tel:* 800-927-9292 (orders) *Fax:* 813-627-6888
*E-mail:* info@csgis.com
*Web Site:* www.csgis.com
*Key Personnel*
Publr: Michael Jarvis
Dir, Prodn: Scott Mitchell
Founded: 1934
Directories of retail & wholesale companies.
ISBN Prefix(es): 978-0-86730
Number of titles published annually: 8 Print
Total Titles: 21 Print; 21 Online

**Chalice Press**
Division of Christian Board of Publications
483 E Lockwood Ave, Suite 100, St Louis, MO 63119
SAN: 201-4408
*Tel:* 314-231-8500 *Toll Free Tel:* 800-366-3383 *Fax:* 314-231-8524; 770-280-4039 (orders)
*E-mail:* customerservice@chalicepress.com
*Web Site:* www.chalicepress.com
*Key Personnel*
Pres & Publr: Brad Lyons *E-mail:* blyons@chalicepress.com
VP, Opers: Lynne Letchworth *E-mail:* lletchworth@chalicepress.com
Mgr, Sales & Mktg: Amber Moore *E-mail:* amoore@chalicepress.com
Founded: 1911
Religion (Protestant) & hymnals.
ISBN Prefix(es): 978-0-8272
Number of titles published annually: 25 Print
Total Titles: 400 Print
Distributed by Cokesbury
*Orders to:* PO Box 933119, Atlanta, GA 31193-3119
*Returns:* 3280 Summit Ridge Pkwy, Suite 100, Duluth, GA 30096 *Fax:* 770-280-4039
*Warehouse:* 3280 Summit Ridge Pkwy, Suite 100, Duluth, GA 30096 *Fax:* 770-280-4039
*Distribution Center:* Rainbow Book Agencies, 303 Arthur St, Fairfield, Victoria 3078, Australia *Tel:* 9481-6611 *Fax:* 9481-2371 *E-mail:* rba@rainbowbooks.com.au
Sperlings Church Supply, 85 Bathurst Dr, Waterloo, ON N2V 1Z4, Canada *Toll Free Tel:* 888-838-6626 *Fax:* 519-725-0668

**Champion Writers Inc**
5676 Ridge View Dr, Alexandria, VA 22310
*Tel:* 703-473-1392 *Fax:* 703-778-0294
*Web Site:* www.championwriters.com
*Key Personnel*
Dir: Andy Zhang *E-mail:* zhangqandy@gmail.com
Founded: 2007
Traditional technical publisher focused on computer books for IT professionals.
ISBN Prefix(es): 978-0-981
Number of titles published annually: 5 Print; 1 Online
Total Titles: 5 Print; 1 Online
Imprints: Aberdeen Bay
*Branch Office(s)*
9301 Maple St, Manassas, VA 20110, Contact: Acq Dir

Membership(s): Computer Technology Industry Association; IEEE; Microsoft Developer Network
*See separate listing for:*
**Aberdeen Bay**

**Channel Lake Inc**
238 E 30 St, No 1F, New York, NY 10016
Mailing Address: PO Box 1771, New York, NY 10156-1771
*Tel:* 347-329-5576 *Toll Free Tel:* 800-592-1566 (orders) *Toll Free Fax:* 866-794-5507
*E-mail:* info@channellake.com
*Web Site:* www.channellake.com; www.touristtown.com
*Key Personnel*
Exec Ed & Publr: Dirk Vanderwilt *E-mail:* dirk@channellake.com
Founded: 2005
Publishes travel guide books for America's most popular regional & national vacation destinations.
ISBN Prefix(es): 978-0-9767064; 978-0-9792043
Number of titles published annually: 4 Print
Total Titles: 4 Print
Imprints: Parkscape Press; Tourist Town Guides
*Distribution Center:* Midpoint Book Sales & Distribution, 27 W 20 St, Suite 1102, New York, NY 10011 *Tel:* 212-727-0190 *Fax:* 212-727-0195 *Web Site:* www.midpointtrade.com

**Channel Photographics**
980 Lincoln Ave, Suite 200-B, San Rafael, CA 94901
*Tel:* 415-456-2934 *Fax:* 415-456-4124
*Web Site:* www.channelphotographics.com
*Key Personnel*
Publr: Adrianne Casey *E-mail:* adrianne@channelphotographics.com; Steven Goff *E-mail:* steven@channelphotographics.com
ISBN Prefix(es): 978-0-9819942
*Branch Office(s)*
140 E 38 St, New York, NY 10016 *Tel:* 212-627-1400 ext 2 *Toll Free Fax:* 866-729-2725
16510 203 Place NE, Woodinville, WA 98077 *Tel:* 425-354-3690 *Toll Free Fax:* 866-729-2725
*Foreign Office(s):* 8 Commercial Tower, 30/F, Unit 06-07, 8 Sun Yip St, Chai Wan, Hong Kong
Via Meucci 24, 37036 San Martino Buon Albergo, Verona VR, Italy *Tel:* (045) 994855 *Fax:* (045) 994746

**Chaosium Inc**
22568 Mission Blvd, Suite 423, Hayward, CA 94541-5116
SAN: 692-6460
*Tel:* 510-583-1000 *Fax:* 510-583-1101
*Web Site:* www.chaosium.com
*Key Personnel*
Pres: Charlie Krank *Tel:* 510-583-1000 *Fax:* 510-583-1101
Founded: 1975
Publisher of horror anthologies & role playing games.
ISBN Prefix(es): 978-0-933635; 978-1-56882
Number of titles published annually: 18 Print; 12 E-Book
Total Titles: 226 Print; 60 E-Book
*Returns:* 728 "A" St, Hayward, CA 94541
*Warehouse:* 728 "A" St, Hayward, CA 94541

**Character Publishing**
23568 Montebella Rd, Pass Christian, MS 39571
*Tel:* 228-234-7651 *Fax:* 228-222-3321
*Web Site:* www.characterpublishing.org
*Key Personnel*
Owner: Jerusha Bosarge *E-mail:* jbosarge@characterpublishing.org
Founded: 2010
Specialize in books that nurture a particular character trait(s) in children, listed in a gold seal on the book cover to simplify book selection.
ISBN Prefix(es): 978-0-9839355; 978-0-9890797
Number of titles published annually: 10 Print; 6 E-Book
Total Titles: 6 Print
*Distribution Center:* Amazon.com *Tel:* 206-266-7180 *E-mail:* amazon-pr@amazon.com *Web Site:* www.amazon.com
Baker & Taylor, 2550 W Tyvola Rd, Suite 300, Charlotte, NC 28217 *Toll Free Tel:* 800-775-1800 *E-mail:* btinfo@baker-taylor.com *Web Site:* www.btol.com
Barnes & Noble, 76 Ninth Ave, New York, NY 10011 *Toll Free Tel:* 800-843-2665 *E-mail:* info@bn.com *Web Site:* www.barnesandnoble.com
Ingram, One Ingram Blvd, La Vergne, TN 37086, Contact: Stephen Merritt *Toll Free Tel:* 800-937-8222 ext 28309 *E-mail:* stephen.merritt@ingramcontent.com *Web Site:* www.ingrambook.com
NACSCORP, 528 E Lorain St, Oberlin, OH 44074-1298 *Toll Free Tel:* 800-321-3883 *E-mail:* service@nacscorp.com *Web Site:* www.nacscorp.com
Membership(s): The Association of Publishers for Special Sales; IBPA, the Independent Book Publishers Association

**Charisma Media**
600 Rinehart Rd, Lake Mary, FL 32746
*Tel:* 407-333-0600 (all imprints) *Toll Free Tel:* 800-283-8494 (Charisma Media, Siloam Press, Creation House); 800-665-1468 *Fax:* 407-333-7100 (all imprints)
*E-mail:* charisma@charismamedia.com
*Web Site:* www.charismamedia.com
*Key Personnel*
Owner & Pres: Stephen Strang
Ed: Marcus Yoars
Founded: 1975
Christianity.
ISBN Prefix(es): 978-0-88419
Number of titles published annually: 200 Print
Total Titles: 500 Print; 2 Audio
Imprints: Casa Creation (international publishing group); Creation House (co-publishing group); Siloam Press (health publishing group)
Membership(s): CBA: The Association for Christian Retail; Evangelical Christian Publishers Association

**CharismaLife Publishers**
600 Rinehart Rd, Lake Mary, FL 32746
*Tel:* 407-333-0600 *Toll Free Tel:* 800-451-4598 *Fax:* 407-333-7100
*E-mail:* charismalife@charismamedia.com
*Web Site:* www.charismamedia.com
*Key Personnel*
Owner & Pres: Stephen Strang *E-mail:* steve.strang@strang.com
Founded: 1990
Christian education materials such as: Sunday school curriculum, children's church programs, youth resources, training conferences.
ISBN Prefix(es): 978-1-57405
Number of titles published annually: 20 Print
Total Titles: 40 Print
Distributor for CharismaLife

**§The Charles Press, Publishers**
Subsidiary of The Oxbridge Corp
230 N 21 St, Suite 202, Philadelphia, PA 19103
*Tel:* 215-561-2786 *Fax:* 215-561-0191
*E-mail:* mailbox@charlespresspub.com
*Web Site:* www.charlespresspub.com
*Key Personnel*
Pres & Publr: Lauren Meltzer *E-mail:* lauren@charlespresspub.com
Prodn Mgr: Brad Fisher *E-mail:* brad@charlespresspub.com
Founded: 1983
Independent publishing house that specializes in scholarly, professional & trade books on the subjects of mental & physical health for professional (doctors, nurses, psychologists, etc), those involved in health care delivery & those receiving &/or in need of health care.
ISBN Prefix(es): 978-0-914783
Number of titles published annually: 10 Print; 1 CD-ROM; 1 Online
Total Titles: 125 Print; 1 CD-ROM; 1 Online
*Returns:* c/o Self-Service Storage, 2000 Hamilton St, No 2884, Philadelphia, PA 19130 (permission must be requested in advance of returns)

**Charles River Media**
Imprint of Cengage Learning
20 Channel Center St, Boston, MA 02210
*Toll Free Tel:* 800-354-9706 *Toll Free Fax:* 800-487-8488
*E-mail:* crminfo@cengage.com
*Web Site:* www.cengage.com; www.delmarlearning.com/charlesriver
Founded: 1994
Publishing computer books for web development, music technology, game development, graphic design & digital video.
ISBN Prefix(es): 978-1-886801; 978-1-58450
Number of titles published annually: 50 Print; 2 CD-ROM; 150 Online; 100 E-Book
Total Titles: 200 Print; 5 CD-ROM; 150 Online; 100 E-Book
Foreign Rep(s): IPR (Middle East); Login Brothers (Canada); Thomson Learning (Asia); Transatlantic (Europe); Woodslane (Australia)
Foreign Rights: David Pallai

**Charles Scribner's Sons®**
Imprint of Gale
27500 Drake Rd, Farmington Hills, MI 48331-3535
*Toll Free Tel:* 800-877-4253 *Toll Free Fax:* 800-414-5043
*E-mail:* gale.galeord@cengage.com
*Web Site:* www.gale.com/scribners
Founded: 1846
Publishes reference books in fields of history, science & literature for audiences ranging from high school students to professional researchers.

**Charlesbridge Publishing Inc**
85 Main St, Watertown, MA 02472
*Tel:* 617-926-0329 *Toll Free Tel:* 800-225-3214 *Fax:* 617-926-5720 *Toll Free Fax:* 800-926-5775
*E-mail:* books@charlesbridge.com
*Web Site:* www.charlesbridge.com
*Key Personnel*
Pres & Publr: Brent Farmer *E-mail:* bfarmer@charlesbridge.com
EVP & Assoc Publr: Mary Ann Sabia *E-mail:* masabia@charlesbridge.com
VP & Publr, Imagine Imprint: Charles Nurnberg
VP, Prodn: Brian Walker *E-mail:* bwalker@charlesbridge.com
VP, Sales: Jeremy Nurnberg *E-mail:* jnurnberg@charlesbridge.com
Art Dir: Susan Sherman *E-mail:* ssherman@charlesbridge.com
Edit Dir: Yolanda LeRoy *E-mail:* yolanda@charlesbridge.com
Founded: 1980
Children's illustrated picture books, board books, early readers, chapter books, middle grade fiction & nonfiction. Adult general trade, cookbooks, puzzle/game, humor & supplemental educational materials K-8.

ISBN Prefix(es): 978-0-88106; 978-1-57091; 978-1-56566; 978-0-934738; 978-1-890674; 978-1-879085; 978-1-58089; 978-1-936140 (Imagine)
Number of titles published annually: 50 Print; 40 E-Book
Total Titles: 600 Print; 436 E-Book
Imprints: Imagine Publishing
Distributor for American Express (travel & leisure, food & wine); EarlyLight Books
Foreign Rights: Thomas Allen & Son Ltd (Canada)
*Warehouse:* 117 Beaver St, Waltham, MA 02452
Membership(s): ABA; ALA; Association of Booksellers for Children; Bookbuilders of Boston; Children's Book Council; International Reading Association; MSA; NAIPR; National School Supply & Equipment Association; NCBA; NEBA; TLA

**Chelsea Green Publishing Co**
85 N Main St, Suite 120, White River Junction, VT 05001
SAN: 669-7631
*Tel:* 802-295-6300 *Toll Free Tel:* 800-639-4099 (cust serv, consumer & trade orders) *Fax:* 802-295-6444
*Web Site:* www.chelseagreen.com
*Key Personnel*
Pres & Publr: Margo Baldwin *E-mail:* mbaldwin@chelseagreen.com
Busn & Dist Dir: Sandi Eaton *E-mail:* seaton@chelseagreen.com
Communs Dir: Shay Totten *E-mail:* stotten@chelseagreen.com
Prodn Dir: Bill Bokermann *E-mail:* bbokermann@chelseagreen.com
Sr Ed & Subs Rts Mgr: Brianne Goodspeed *E-mail:* bgoodspeed@chelseagreen.com
Sr Ed: Makenna Goodman *E-mail:* mgoodman@chelseagreen.com; Joni Praded *E-mail:* jpraded@chelseagreen.com; Ben Watson *E-mail:* bwatson@chelseagreen.com
Author Events Mgr: Jenna Stewart *E-mail:* jstewart@chelseagreen.com
Spec & Corp Sales Mgr: Darrell Koerner *E-mail:* dkoerner@chelseagreen.com
Trade Sales Mgr: Michael Weaver *E-mail:* mweaver@chelseagreen.com
Founded: 1984
Books for sustainable living including: environment, building, nature, outdoors, sustainability, organic gardening, home, renewable energy, homesteading, politics & current events.
ISBN Prefix(es): 978-0-930031; 978-1-890132; 978-1-933392; 978-1-60358
Number of titles published annually: 35 Print; 35 E-Book
Total Titles: 300 Print; 250 E-Book
Distributor for AATEC Publications; American Council for an Energy Efficient Economy (ACEEE); Anomaly Press; Avalon House; Boye Knives Press; Cal-Earth; Earth Pledge; Eco Logic Books; Ecological Design Institute; Ecological Design Press; Empowerment Institute; Filaree Productions; Flower Press; Foundation for Deep Ecology; Fox Maple Press; Green Books; Green Building Press; Green Man Publishing; Groundworks; Hand Print Press; Holmgren Design Services; Jenkins Publishing; Knossus Project; Left To Write Press; Madison Area Community Supported Agriculture Coalition; Marion Institute; marketumbrella.org; Metamorphic Press; Moneta Publications; Ottographics; Peregrinzilla; Permanent Publications; Daniela Piazza Editore; Polyface; Rainsource Press; Raven Press; Anita Roddick Publications; Rural Science Institute; Seed Savers; Service Employees International Union; Slow Food Editore; Solar Design Association; Stonefield Publishing; Sun Plans Inc; Sustainability Press; Trailblazer Press; Trust for Public Land; Yes Books
Foreign Rep(s): Codasat: Hargreaves, Fuller, Paton (Canada)
*Warehouse:* c/o Claremont Ctr, 425 Washington St, No 185, Claremont, NH 03743, Warehouse Mgr: Dianna Hart *Tel:* 603-542-2312 *Fax:* 603-542-2806 *E-mail:* persephone@emlot.com

**Chelsea House Publishers**
Imprint of Infobase Learning
132 W 31 St, 17th fl, New York, NY 10001
SAN: 169-7331
*Tel:* 212-967-8800 *Toll Free Tel:* 800-322-8755 *Fax:* 917-339-0325; 917-339-0323 *Toll Free Fax:* 800-678-3633
*E-mail:* custserv@factsonfile.com
*Web Site:* www.infobasepublishing.com; www.infobaselearning.com
*Key Personnel*
Chmn: Mark McDonnell
CFO: Jim Housley
Dir, Publicity: Laurie Katz
Dir, Sales: Paul Conklin
Dir, Opers: Mark Zielinski
Creative Dir: Zina Scarpulla
Edit Dir: Laurie Likoff
Dir, Lib & Trade Sales: Coreena Schultz
Dir, Licensing & Intl Sales: Ben Jacobs
Founded: 1966
Offers timely & engaging young adult sets & series spanning a wide variety of subject areas. Chelsea Clubhouse, its elementary imprint, presents easy-to-read, full-color books for young readers in grades 2-6.
ISBN Prefix(es): 978-0-87754; 978-0-7910; 978-1-55546; 978-1-60413; 978-1-4381; 978-1-61753
Number of titles published annually: 230 Print; 230 E-Book
Total Titles: 1,866 Print; 1,680 E-Book
Imprints: Chelsea Clubhouse
Foreign Rep(s): CIS Educational; James Clarke & Co Ltd; EDH Reference (Canada); Macro Distributors; Maruzen Co Ltd; Premier Book Marketing; Southern Book Publishers
*Returns:* Chelsea House Publishers Returns Dept, c/o Maple Press Distribution Ctr, 704 Legionaire Dr, Fredericksburg, PA 17026
*Warehouse:* c/o Maple Press Distribution Ctr, 704 Legionaire Dr, Fredericksburg, PA 17026
*Distribution Center:* c/o Maple Press Distribution Ctr, 704 Legionaire Dr, Fredericksburg, PA 17026
Membership(s): AAP; ALA

**Chemical Education Resources Inc**
Division of Cengage Learning
10 Davis Dr, Belmont, CA 94002
SAN: 297-1909
*Toll Free Tel:* 800-543-0487 (ext 1308, orders); 800-355-9983 (cust serv) *Fax:* 215-243-3786 (edit) *Toll Free Fax:* 800-451-3661 (orders)
*Web Site:* www.cerlabs.com
Founded: 1984
Learning materials for college & university chemistry labs.
ISBN Prefix(es): 978-0-534
Total Titles: 350 Print

**§Cheng & Tsui Co Inc**
25 West St, 2nd fl, Boston, MA 02111-1213
*Tel:* 617-988-2400 *Toll Free Tel:* 800-554-1963 *Fax:* 617-426-3669; 617-556-8964
*E-mail:* service@cheng-tsui.com; orders@cheng-tsui.com
*Web Site:* www.cheng-tsui.com
*Key Personnel*
Pres: Jill Cheng
Founded: 1979
Publisher, importer & exporter of Asian books in English. Publish & distribute Asia related books & Chinese, Japanese & Korean language learning textbooks.
ISBN Prefix(es): 978-0-917056; 978-0-88727
Number of titles published annually: 30 Print
Total Titles: 640 Print; 75 CD-ROM; 4 Online; 4 E-Book
Distributor for Action Language Learning; aha! Chinese; Bider Technology; Cengage Learning Australia; China International Book Trading Co (Beijing, selected titles only); China Soft; China Sprout; Crabtree Publishing; Curriculum Corporation; Facets Video; Ilchokak Publishers; Italian School of East Asian Studies; JPT America Inc; Oxford University Press; Pan Asian Publications; Panmun Academic Services; Panpac Education; Paradigm Busters; Pearson Australia; Royal Asiatic Society (Korea Branch); SMC Publishing; Sogang University Institute; Stone Bridge Press; SUP Publishing Logistics; Tuttle Publishing; US International Publishing; White Rabbit Press; Yale University Press; Zeitgeist Films
*Warehouse:* Publishers Storage & Shipping Corp, 46 Development Rd, Fitchburg, MA 01420 *Tel:* 978-345-2121 ext 223 *Fax:* 978-348-1233 *Web Site:* www.pssc.com

**§Cherry Hill Publishing**
24344 Del Amo Rd, Ramona, CA 92065
SAN: 255-0075
*Tel:* 858-829-5550 *Toll Free Tel:* 800-407-1072 *Fax:* 760-203-1200
*E-mail:* operations@cherryhillpublishing.com; sales@cherryhillpublishing.com
*Web Site:* www.cherryhillpublishing.com
*Key Personnel*
Publr: Rick Roane *E-mail:* rick@cherryhillpublishing.com
Returns: Sharon Roane *Tel:* 858-735-5397 *E-mail:* sharon@cherryhillpublishing.com
Founded: 2002
Publisher of audiobook titles.
ISBN Prefix(es): 978-0-9843759; 978-9-723298; 978-0-9830086; 978-1-937028; 978-1-62079
Number of titles published annually: 15 CD-ROM; 20 Online; 5 E-Book; 15 Audio
Total Titles: 1 Print; 85 CD-ROM; 125 Online; 40 E-Book; 85 Audio
*Distribution Center:* Baker & Taylor, 2550 W Tyvola Rd, Suite 300, Charlotte, NC 28217 *Toll Free Tel:* 800-775-1800 *Fax:* 704-998-3100 *Web Site:* www.btol.com
Midwest Tape, 6950 Hall St, Holland, OH 43528 *Toll Free Tel:* 800-875-2785 *Toll Free Fax:* 800-444-6645 *E-mail:* info@midwesttapes.com *Web Site:* www.midwesttapes.com
Membership(s): Audio Publishers Association

**Cherry Lane Music Co**
315 Fifth Ave, Suite 801, New York, NY 10016
*Tel:* 646-470-3782 *Fax:* 212-251-0822
*Web Site:* www.cherrylaneprint.com
*Key Personnel*
CEO: Peter W Primont
SVP, Rts & Acqs: John Stix *E-mail:* jstix@cherrylaneprint.com
Founded: 1960
Pop & rock song books for guitar keyboard & other instruments.
ISBN Prefix(es): 978-0-89524; 978-1-57560
Number of titles published annually: 60 Print
Total Titles: 570 Print
Distributed by Hal Leonard Corp

**Chestnut Hills Press**, see BrickHouse Books Inc

**Chicago Review Press**
814 N Franklin St, Chicago, IL 60610
*Tel:* 312-337-0747 *Toll Free Tel:* 800-888-4741 *Fax:* 312-337-5110
*E-mail:* frontdesk@chicagoreviewpress.com
*Web Site:* www.chicagoreviewpress.com

*Key Personnel*
Publr: Cynthia Sherry
Mng Ed: Allison Felus
Mktg Mgr: Mary Kravenas
Sr Ed: Sue Bradanini Betz; Jerome Pohlen; Lisa Reardon; Yuval Taylor
Founded: 1973
ISBN Prefix(es): 978-1-56976; 978-1-55652; 978-1-88305 (Ball Publishing)
Number of titles published annually: 60 Print; 60 E-Book
Total Titles: 725 Print; 225 E-Book
Imprints: A Cappella Books; Ball Publishing; Lawrence Hill Books; Zephyr Press
Divisions: Independent Publishers Group
Foreign Rights: Independent Publishers Group (Susan Sewall) (Worldwide)

**Chicago Spectrum Press**
Imprint of Evanston Publishing Inc
12305 Westport Rd, Louisville, KY 40245
*Tel:* 502-899-1919 *Toll Free Tel:* 800-594-5190; 888-BOOKS-80 (266-5780) *Fax:* 502-896-0246
*E-mail:* request@evanstonpublishing.com; info@evanstonpublishing.com
*Web Site:* www.evanstonpublishing.com
*Key Personnel*
Pres & Sr Ed: Dorothy Kavka
Founded: 1986
Help authors & companies self-publish books. Also do packaging for publishers & maintain a catalog of their own publications.
ISBN Prefix(es): 978-1-886094; 978-1-58374
Number of titles published annually: 50 Print; 4 E-Book
Total Titles: 400 Print; 4 E-Book
Membership(s): Better Business Bureau; IBPA, the Independent Book Publishers Association; National Association of Women Business Owners

**Child Development Project**, see Developmental Studies Center

**Child Welfare League of America (CWLA)**
1726 "M" St, Suite 500, Washington, DC 20036
SAN: 201-9876
*Tel:* 202-688-4200 *Fax:* 202-833-1689
*Web Site:* www.cwla.org/pubs
*Key Personnel*
Dir, Mktg: Karen Dunn *E-mail:* kdunn@cwla.org
Founded: 1920
Provide relevant & timely publications that enable CWLA members & the child welfare field at large to improve services to children & their families.
ISBN Prefix(es): 978-0-87868; 978-1-58760
Number of titles published annually: 9 Print
Total Titles: 167 Print
Imprints: CWLA Press
*Billing Address:* CWLA, PO Box 345, Mount Morris, IL 61054-9834
*Orders to:* CWLA, PO Box 345, Mount Morris, IL 61054-9834 *Tel:* 770-280-4164 *Toll Free Tel:* 800-407-6273 *E-mail:* order@cwla.org
*Returns:* PBD Inc, c/o CWLA, 420 Eagleview Blvd, Exton, PA 19341
*Shipping Address:* PBD Inc, c/o CWLA, 420 Eagleview Blvd, Exton, PA 19341
*Warehouse:* PBD Inc, c/o CWLA, 420 Eagleview Blvd, Exton, PA 19341
*Distribution Center:* PBD Inc, c/o CWLA, 420 Eagleview Blvd, Exton, PA 19341

**Children's Book Press**
Imprint of Lee & Low Books
95 Madison Ave, Suite 1205, New York, NY 10016
*Tel:* 212-779-4400 *Fax:* 212-683-1894
*Web Site:* www.leeandlow.com
*Key Personnel*
Pres: Craig Low
Opers & Client Servs Mgr: John Man
Founded: 1975
Multicultural & bilingual picture books for children. Central American, African-American, Asian-American, Hispanic-American, Native American tales, folklore, contemporary fiction & nonfiction.
ISBN Prefix(es): 978-0-89239
Number of titles published annually: 6 Print
Total Titles: 30 Print
*Distribution Center:* Ingram Books, One Ingram Blvd, La Vergne, TN 37086 *Tel:* 615-793-5000 *Toll Free Tel:* 800-932-8200 *E-mail:* customerservice@ingrambook.com *Web Site:* www.ingrambook.com

**Children's Press®**, see Scholastic Consumer & Professional Publishing

**Child's Play®**
Affiliate of Child's Play (International) Ltd
250 Minot Ave, Auburn, ME 04210
*Toll Free Tel:* 800-472-0099; 800-639-6404 *Toll Free Fax:* 800-854-6989
*E-mail:* chpmaine@aol.com; cplay@earthlink.net
*Web Site:* www.childs-play.com/usa
*Key Personnel*
VP, Sales & Mktg: Joe Gardner
Gen Mgr: Laurie Reynolds
Founded: 1972
Children's books, games, toys & AV.
ISBN Prefix(es): 978-0-85953; 978-1-904550; 978-1-84643
Number of titles published annually: 30 Print
Total Titles: 450 Print; 8 Audio

**§The Child's World Inc**
1980 Lookout Dr, Mankato, MN 56003
*Tel:* 507-385-1044 *Toll Free Tel:* 800-599-READ (599-7323) *Toll Free Fax:* 888-320-2329
*E-mail:* sales@childsworld.com
*Web Site:* www.childsworld.com
*Key Personnel*
Pres: Mike Peterson
Off Mgr: Amy Dols
Founded: 1968
K-8 library books for childhood education; social studies.
ISBN Prefix(es): 978-0-89565; 978-1-56766
Number of titles published annually: 200 Print; 100 E-Book
Total Titles: 850 Print; 45 E-Book
Imprints: Tradition Books
Distributor for Tradition Books

**Childswork/Childsplay LLC**
Subsidiary of The Guidance Group Inc
303 Crossway Park Dr, Woodbury, NY 11797
*Toll Free Tel:* 800-962-1141 (cust serv) *Toll Free Fax:* 800-262-1886 (orders)
*E-mail:* info@childswork.com
*Web Site:* childswork.com
Founded: 1985
Psychological books, toys, games & counseling tools to assist counselors, therapists, teachers & parents help children cope with emotional & behavioral problems.
ISBN Prefix(es): 978-1-58815; 978-1-882732
Number of titles published annually: 85 Print
Total Titles: 76 Print
*Orders to:* PO Box 1246, Wilkes-Barre, PA 18703-1246
*Returns:* c/o Karol Media, 375 Stewart Rd, Wilkes-Barre, PA 18706-1458

**§China Books**
Division of Sino United Publishing (Holdings) Ltd
360 Swift Ave, Suite 48, South San Francisco, CA 94080
SAN: 169-0167
*Tel:* 650-872-7076 *Toll Free Tel:* 800-818-2017 (US only) *Fax:* 650-872-7808
*E-mail:* info@chinabooks.com
*Web Site:* www.chinabooks.com
*Key Personnel*
Mktg Dir: Kelly Feng *Tel:* 650-872-7076 ext 310 *E-mail:* kelly@chinabooks.com
Gen Mgr: Xin Wang
Founded: 1960
Fiction, trade, nonfiction, dictionaries, encyclopedias, maps, atlases, periodicals, sidelines, foreign language, secondary textbooks, juvenile & young adult, subscription & mail order, hardcover & paperback trade books; government, language arts, travel.
ISBN Prefix(es): 978-0-8351
Number of titles published annually: 10 Print
Total Titles: 750 Print; 20 Audio
Distributor for AsiaPac; CIBTC; Commercial Press; Foreign Languages Press; Joint Publishers; New World Press; Panda Books; Peace Books; Red Mansions Publishing

**Chosen Books**
Division of Baker Publishing Group
PO Box 6287, Grand Rapids, MI 49516-6287
SAN: 203-3801
*Tel:* 616-676-9185 *Toll Free Tel:* 800-877-2665 (orders only) *Fax:* 616-676-9573 *Toll Free Fax:* 800-398-3111 (orders only)
*Web Site:* www.bakerpublishinggroup.com
*Key Personnel*
Pres: Dwight Baker
Edit Dir: Chad Allen
Mktg Dir: Bobbie Jo Heyboer
Prodn & ISBN Contact: Robert Bol
Rts & Perms, Intl Rts: Marilyn Gordon
Founded: 1971
Religious.
ISBN Prefix(es): 978-0-8007
Number of titles published annually: 21 Print
Total Titles: 220 Print
Foreign Rep(s): Christian Art (South Africa); David C Cook Distribution (Canada); Family Reading Publications (Australia); Marston Book Services Ltd (Europe, UK); Soul Distributors Ltd (New Zealand)
*Shipping Address:* 6030 E Fulton Rd, Ada, MI 49301

**Christian Liberty Press**
502 W Euclid Ave, Arlington Heights, IL 60004
*Tel:* 847-259-4444 *Toll Free Tel:* 800-832-2741 (cust serv) *Fax:* 847-259-2941
*E-mail:* custserv@christianlibertypress.com
*Web Site:* www.shopchristianliberty.com
*Key Personnel*
Dir: Lars Johnson *E-mail:* larsj@christianlibertypress.com
Founded: 1985
Publisher of Christian education materials.
ISBN Prefix(es): 978-1-930092; 978-1-930367; 978-1-932971
Number of titles published annually: 6 Print; 3 CD-ROM; 4 Audio
Total Titles: 150 Print; 8 CD-ROM; 38 Audio
*Distribution Center:* STL Distribution, 100 Biblica Way, Elizabethton, TN 37643 *Toll Free Tel:* 800-289-2772 *Toll Free Fax:* 800-759-2779
Membership(s): CBA: The Association for Christian Retail

**Christian Light Publications Inc**
1050 Mount Clinton Pike, Harrisonburg, VA 22802
Mailing Address: PO Box 1212, Harrisonburg, VA 22803-1212
*Tel:* 540-434-1003 *Toll Free Tel:* 800-776-0478 *Fax:* 540-433-8896
*E-mail:* info@clp.org; orders@clp.org
*Web Site:* www.clp.org
*Key Personnel*
Gen Mgr: John Hartzler

Secy, Bd of Dirs: Merna B Shank
*E-mail:* mernas@clp.org
Founded: 1969
Books, booklets, tracts, Sunday school, vacation Bible school & Christian day school curriculum.
ISBN Prefix(es): 978-0-87813
Number of titles published annually: 12 Print
Total Titles: 160 Print

**Christian Schools International**
3350 E Paris Ave SE, Grand Rapids, MI 49512-3054
SAN: 204-1804
*Tel:* 616-957-1070 *Toll Free Tel:* 800-635-8288 *Fax:* 616-957-5022
*E-mail:* info@csionline.org
*Web Site:* www.csionline.org
*Key Personnel*
CEO & Pres: David Koetje *Tel:* 616-957-1070 ext 254 *E-mail:* dkoetje@csionline.org
Dir, Mktg: Lisa Tudor *Tel:* 616-957-1070 ext 235 *E-mail:* ltudor@csionline.org
Dir, Sales: Darryl Shelton *Tel:* 616-957-1070 ext 257 *E-mail:* dshelton@csionline.org
Founded: 1920
Classroom curriculum resources for students & teachers.
ISBN Prefix(es): 978-0-87463
Number of titles published annually: 18 Print; 2 CD-ROM
Total Titles: 172 Print; 11 CD-ROM
Imprints: CSI Publications

**§The Christian Science Publishing Society**
Division of The First Church of Christ, Scientist
210 Massachusettes Ave, Boston, MA 02115
*Tel:* 617-450-2000 *Toll Free Tel:* 800-288-7090 *Fax:* 617-450-7334
*Web Site:* www.spirituality.com
*Key Personnel*
Media Contact: Adam Scherr *Tel:* 617-450-3330 *E-mail:* scherra@christianscience.com
Founded: 1879
Books on healing, health & spirituality; major title: *Science & Health with Key to the Scriptures* by Mary Baker Eddy, available in 16 languages & English braille.
ISBN Prefix(es): 978-0-87952
Number of titles published annually: 17 Print
Total Titles: 17 Print

**Chronicle Books LLC**
680 Second St, San Francisco, CA 94107
SAN: 202-165X
*Tel:* 415-537-4200 *Toll Free Tel:* 800-759-0190 (cust serv) *Fax:* 415-537-4460 *Toll Free Fax:* 800-858-7787 (orders); 800-286-9471 (cust serv)
*E-mail:* frontdesk@chroniclebooks.com
*Web Site:* www.chroniclebooks.com
*Key Personnel*
Chmn & CEO: Nion McEvoy
COO: Tom Fernald
CIO: Paul Gore
Pres: Jack Jensen
VP, Sales & Mktg: Tyrrell Mahoney
Exec Dir, Busn Devt: Sarah Williams
Exec Dir, Dom Sales: Kimberly Anderson
Exec Dir, HR: Todd Presley
Exec Dir, Mktg & Publicity: Liza Algar
Exec Dir, Opers: John Carlson
Exec Edit Dir, Entertainment: Sarah Malarkey
Exec Publg Design Dir: Sara Schneider
Contracts Dir: Deirdre Merrill
Edit Dir, Formats: Christina Amini
HR Dir: Renee Banks *Tel:* 413-537-4200 ext 4259 *E-mail:* renee_banks@chroniclebooks.com
Publg Dir, Food & Drink/Lifestyle: Lorena Jones
Design Dir: Kristen Hewitt
Design Dir, Mktg Commun: Liz Rico
Dir, Sales, Spec & Mass Mkts: Suzanne Bass
Dir, Trade Sales: Rachel Geiger
Publr: Christine Carswell
Publg Dir, Children's: Ginee Seo
Assoc Dir, Mass Mkts: Lynda Zuber Sassi
Assoc Mktg Dir, Children's: Kim Lauber
Assoc Mktg Dir, Entertainment & Online: Albee Dalbotten
Assoc Mktg Dir, Food & Drink, Art/Design & Stationary: Peter Perez
Natl Acct Mgr: Kim Burns; Ryan Kelly
Natl Acct Mgr, Spec Sales Team: Julia Carvalho
Sr Mktg Mgr, Childrens: Kim Lauber
Sr Sales Mgr, Mass Mkts & Warehouse Clubs: Julie Hamilton
Sr Sales Mgr, Subs Rts: Johan Almqvist
Digital Sales & Dist Mgr: Kristina Jutzi
Assoc Design Mgr, New Format Devt: Amy Achaibou
Assoc Mgr, Mass Mkts: Erynn Im-Sato
Dist Acct Client Mgr: Candice Vallimont
Dist Client Coord: Graham Barry
Export Sales Coord: Mia Blankensop
Mktg Coord, Children's Div: Amber Morley
Sales Coord: Kelley Baker
Sales Material Coord: Julia Patrick
Sr Dist Coord, Opers: Mercury Ellis
Sr Ed: Kate Woodrow
Ed, Children's Group: Naomi Kirsten; Tamra Tuller
Ed, Lifestyle: Laura Lee Mattingly
Children's Book Designer: Tara Creehan; Ryan Hayes
Publicist, Stationary: Alyson Pullman
Distribution Analyst: Barrett Hooper
Asst Ed: Lisa Tauber
Asst Ed, Children's Group: Ariel Richardson
Digital Prodn Lead: Kesha Seeley
Founded: 1967
General nonfiction & fiction, cloth & paperbound: fine arts, gift, nature, outdoors, nationwide regional guidebooks, stationery, calendars & ancillary products.
ISBN Prefix(es): 978-0-87701; 978-0-8118
Number of titles published annually: 300 Print
Total Titles: 1,500 Print
Divisions: Adult Trade; Chronicle Books for Children; Chronicle Gift
Distributor for Blue Apple Books; Handprint Books; Laurence King Publishing; Moleskine; Princeton Architectural Press; SmartLab; SmartsCo
Foreign Rep(s): Bill Bailey Publishers Reps (Austria, Eastern Europe, Germany, Netherlands, Scandinavia, Switzerland); Bookport Associates (Italy, Southern Europe); Chronicle Books (Japan, Latin America, Puerto Rico); Critiques Livres (France); Michelle Curreri (Asia, Middle East); Hardie Grant Books (Australia); Publishers Group UK (Europe, UK); Raincoast Book (Canada); Real Books (South Africa); Southern Publishers Group (New Zealand)
Foreign Rights: Bettina Nibbe (Germany); Nordin Agency (Netherlands, Scandinavia); Frederique Porretta (France); Tao Media (China)
*See separate listing for:*
**Handprint Books Inc**

**§Chronicle Guidance Publications Inc**
66 Aurora St, Moravia, NY 13118-3569
SAN: 202-1641
*Tel:* 315-497-0330 *Toll Free Tel:* 800-622-7284 *Fax:* 315-497-0339
*E-mail:* customerservice@chronicleguidance.com
*Web Site:* www.chronicleguidance.com
*Key Personnel*
CEO & Pres: Cheryl L Fickeisen *E-mail:* cheryl@chronicleguidance.com
VP: Gary W Fickeisen
Asst VP: Christopher D Fickeisen
Founded: 1938
Education materials, kindergarten to higher education. Annual education-oriented directories & guides; career information briefs & reprint articles on occupations, interest inventories & life skills materials.
ISBN Prefix(es): 978-1-55631
Number of titles published annually: 2 Print; 3 CD-ROM; 2 Online
Total Titles: 15 Print; 1 CD-ROM; 2 Online
*Distribution Center:* Baker & Taylor, 2550 W Tyvola Rd, Charlotte, NC 28217 *Toll Free Tel:* 800-775-1800 *Fax:* 704-998-3100 *Web Site:* www.btol.com

**Cider Mill Press Book Publishers LLC**
12 Port Farm Rd, Kennebunkport, ME 04046
*Tel:* 207-967-8232 *Fax:* 207-967-8233
*Web Site:* www.cidermillpress.com
*Key Personnel*
Founder & Publr: John F Whalen, Jr *E-mail:* johnwhalen@cidermillpress.com
Founded: 2005
Publish creative, innovative, inspiring & visually stunning books & gift books.
ISBN Prefix(es): 978-1-933662; 978-1-60433
Number of titles published annually: 50 Print; 4 Audio
Total Titles: 135 Print; 2 Audio
Imprints: Applesauce Press; Cider Mill Press
Distributed by Simon & Schuster
Foreign Rights: Print Co Verlagsgesellschaft (Gabriella Scolik) (Europe)
Membership(s): ABA; BEA

**Cinco Puntos Press**
701 Texas Ave, El Paso, TX 79901
*Tel:* 915-838-1625 *Toll Free Tel:* 800-566-9072 *Fax:* 915-838-1635
*E-mail:* info@cincopuntos.com
*Web Site:* www.cincopuntos.com
*Key Personnel*
Owner & Publr: Bobby Byrd *E-mail:* bbyrd@cincopuntos.com; Lee Byrd *E-mail:* leebyrd@cincopuntos.com
Founded: 1985
Books of the Southwest US & bilingual children's literature.
ISBN Prefix(es): 978-0-938317
Number of titles published annually: 23 Print
Total Titles: 150 Print; 9 Audio
*Distribution Center:* Consortium Book Sales & Distribution, The Keg House, Suite 101, 34 13 Ave NE, Minneapolis, MN 55413-1007 *Tel:* 612-746-2600 *Toll Free Tel:* 800-283-3572 (cust serv) *Fax:* 612-746-2606 *E-mail:* info@cbsd.com *Web Site:* www.cbsd.com SAN: 631-760X

**§Circlet Press Inc**
39 Hurlbut St, Cambridge, MA 02138
*Tel:* 617-864-0492 *Toll Free Tel:* 800-729-6423 (orders)
*E-mail:* circletintern@gmail.com (edit queries); kjc@circlet.com (order fulfillment)
*Web Site:* www.circlet.com
*Key Personnel*
Founder & Publr: Cecilia Tan *E-mail:* ctan.circletpress@gmail.com
Publicist: Ava Perry
Founded: 1992
Anthologies of short stories of erotic science fiction/fantasy (a new subgenre) & cutting edge erotica.
ISBN Prefix(es): 978-0-9633970; 978-1-885865
Number of titles published annually: 2 Print; 2 Online; 25 E-Book; 5 Audio
Total Titles: 60 Print; 2 Online; 50 E-Book; 5 Audio
Imprints: Circumflex (nonfiction & how-to on sexuality); Luster Editions (alternative sexuality fiction & erotica); The Ultra Violet Library (gay & lesbian; science fiction not erotic)
Distributed by SCB Distributors

Foreign Rep(s): Bulldog Books (Australia); Turnaround Ltd (Europe, UK)
Foreign Rights: Lawrence Schimel (all other territories)

**Cistercian Publications Inc, Editorial Office**
Imprint of Liturgical Press
Saint John's Abbey, PO Box 7500, Collegeville, MN 56321
SAN: 202-1668
*Tel:* 320-363-2213 *Toll Free Tel:* 800-436-8431 *Fax:* 320-363-3299 *Toll Free Fax:* 800-445-5899
*E-mail:* editor@monks.org
*Web Site:* www.cistercianpublications.org
*Key Personnel*
Pres: Fr Brendan Freeman
Exec Ed: Fr Mark A Scott *Tel:* 502-549-4117 *E-mail:* editor@monks.org
Founded: 1969
Religion (Roman Catholic) & history.
ISBN Prefix(es): 978-0-87907
Number of titles published annually: 15 Print
Total Titles: 212 Print
Distributed by Liturgical Press
Distributor for Fairacres Press; Peregrina Press
*Returns:* Warepak, 2427 Bond St, University Park, IL 60466
*Shipping Address:* Warepak, 2427 Bond St, University Park, IL 60466

**Citadel Press**, see Kensington Publishing Corp

**City Lights Publishers**
261 Columbus Ave, San Francisco, CA 94133
SAN: 202-1684
*Tel:* 415-362-8193 *Fax:* 415-362-4921
*E-mail:* staff@citylights.com
*Web Site:* www.citylights.com
*Key Personnel*
Exec Dir & Publr: Elaine Katzenberger
PR & Mktg Dir: Stacey Lewis
Subs Rts Mgr: Robert Sharrard *E-mail:* sharrard@citylights.com
Open Media Series Founder & Ed: Greg Ruggiero
Publicity & Mktg Assoc: Jolene Torr
Founded: 1955
Publisher of progressive political nonfiction, innovative literature & poetry.
ISBN Prefix(es): 978-0-87286
Number of titles published annually: 12 Print
Total Titles: 200 Print
Foreign Rights: Agence Hoffman (France, Germany); Agenzia Letteraria Internazionale (Italy); Carmen Balcells Agencia Literaria SA (Spain)
*Distribution Center:* Consortium Book Sales & Distribution, The Keg House, Suite 101, 34 13 Ave NE, Minneapolis, MN 55413-1007 *Tel:* 612-746-2600 *Toll Free Tel:* 800-283-3572 (cust serv) *Fax:* 612-351-5073 *E-mail:* orderentry@perseusbooks.com *Web Site:* www.cbsd.com

**Clarion Books**
Imprint of Houghton Mifflin Harcourt
215 Park Ave S, New York, NY 10003
*Tel:* 212-420-5883 *Toll Free Tel:* 800-225-3362 (orders) *Fax:* 212-420-5855 *Toll Free Fax:* 800-634-7568 (orders)
*Web Site:* www.houghtonmifflinbooks.com
*Key Personnel*
Publr & Edit Dir: Dinah Stevenson
Sr Exec Ed: Anne Hoppe
Art Dir: Christine Kettner
Rts Mgr: Candace Finn
Assoc: Kate Green
Founded: 1965
Juvenile & young adult books, picture & chapter books, audiocassette packages.
ISBN Prefix(es): 978-0-89919; 978-0-395; 978-0-618
Number of titles published annually: 70 Print
Distributed by Houghton Mifflin Harcourt
*Returns:* 2700 N Richardt Ave, Indianapolis, IN 46219
Membership(s): Children's Book Council

**Clarity Press Inc**
3277 Roswell Rd NE, Suite 469, Atlanta, GA 30305
SAN: 688-9530
*Toll Free Tel:* 877-613-1495 (edit) *Toll Free Fax:* 877-613-7868
*E-mail:* claritypress@usa.net (foreign rts & perms)
*Web Site:* www.claritypress.com
*Key Personnel*
Edit Dir: Diana G Collier
Busn Mgr: Annette Gordon *Tel:* 404-647-6501 *E-mail:* businessmanager@claritypress.com
Founded: 1984
Scholarly works on contemporary justice & human rights issues.
ISBN Prefix(es): 978-0-932863
Number of titles published annually: 8 Print; 8 E-Book
Total Titles: 52 Print; 32 E-Book
Imprints: Clear Day Books (print-on-demand, rare books)
Foreign Rep(s): CIEL Book Distributors (Lebanon, Middle East); GB Gerakbudaya (Malaysia, Singapore); Marston Books (UK & the continent)
Foreign Rights: Luigi Celentano (Latin America, Spain); Chengdu Rightol Media (China)
*Distribution Center:* SCB Distributors, 15608 S New Century Dr, Gardena, CA 90248, Contact: Victor Duran *Tel:* 310-532-9400 *Toll Free Tel:* 800-729-6423 *Fax:* 310-532-7001 *E-mail:* victor@scbdistributors.com *Web Site:* www.scbdistributors.com
CIEL Book Co, Akef El Khoury Bldg, Dbayeh Hwy, Beirut, Lebanon (Middle East & North Africa) *Tel:* (04) 522149 ext 222 *Fax:* (04) 522144 *Web Site:* www.ciel.me
GB GerakBudaya Enterprise Sdn BhD, 11, Lorong 11/4E, 46200 Petaling Jaya, Selangor, Malaysia (Malaysia & Singapore) *Tel:* (03) 7957 8342 *Fax:* (03) 7954 9202 *E-mail:* gerakbudaya@pd.jaring.my
Marston Book Services Ltd, 160 Milton Park, Abingdon, Oxon OX14 4SD, United Kingdom (includes Europe) *Tel:* (01235) 465576 *Fax:* (01235) 465555 *E-mail:* trade.orders@marston.co.uk
Membership(s): AAP; Society for Scholarly Publishing

**Clarkson Potter Publishers**
Imprint of Crown Publishing Group
c/o Random House Inc, 1745 Broadway, New York, NY 10019
*Tel:* 212-782-9000 *Toll Free Tel:* 888-264-1745 *Fax:* 212-572-6181
*Web Site:* www.clarksonpotter.com; www.randomhouse.com/crown/clarksonpotter
*Key Personnel*
SVP & Publr, Clarkson Potter, Potter Craft, Potter Style, Watson-Guptill & Monacelli Press: Pam Krauss
VP & Assoc Publr: Doris Cooper
Creative Dir: Marysarah Quinn
Publicity Dir: Kate Tyler
Sr Publicist: Anna Mintz
Publicist: Sean Boyles
Sr Ed: Aliza Fogelson
Assoc Ed: Angelin Borsics; Ashley Phillips
Ed-at-Large: Francis Lam
Founded: 1959
Illustrated & non-illustrated books on style, design, architecture, cookery, gardening, crafts, fashion, health, house & home.
Random House Inc & its publishing entities are not accepting unsol submissions, proposals, mss or submission queries via e-mail at this time.
ISBN Prefix(es): 978-0-609; 978-0-307; 978-1-4000; 978-0-517
Number of titles published annually: 145 Print
Total Titles: 1,000 Print
Imprints: Clarkson Potter; Potter Craft; Potter Style
Distributed by Random House
*Advertising Agency:* Franklin Spier

**Classical Academic Press**
2151 Market St, Camp Hill, PA 17011
*Tel:* 717-730-0711 *Fax:* 717-730-0721
*E-mail:* info@classicalsubjects.com
*Web Site:* www.classicalacademicpress.com
*Key Personnel*
Publr: Christopher Perrin *E-mail:* cperrin@classicalsubjects.com
Founded: 2001
Kindergarten through 12th grade educational textbooks & media. Focus on classical education.
ISBN Prefix(es): 978-1-60051
Number of titles published annually: 5 Print; 2 Online; 12 E-Book; 3 Audio
Total Titles: 60 Print; 1 Online; 12 E-Book; 10 Audio
Imprints: Plum Tree Books
Foreign Rep(s): Baker & Taylor (New Zealand, UK)
*Shipping Address:* Baker & Taylor, 2550 W Tyvola Rd, Charlotte, NC 28217 *Tel:* 704-998-3100
Membership(s): IBPA, the Independent Book Publishers Association

**Classroom Connect**
Division of Houghton Mifflin Harcourt Learning Technology
222 Berkeley St, Boston, MA 02116
*Tel:* 617-351-5000 *Toll Free Tel:* 800-638-1639 (cust support)
*E-mail:* help@classroom.com
*Web Site:* corporate.classroom.com; www.hmhinnovation.com
*Key Personnel*
CEO & Pres: Jim Bowler
VP & Gen Mgr: Paul E Finer
VP, Sales: Melinda Cook
Founded: 1994
K-12 educator professional development & online classroom learning resources.
ISBN Prefix(es): 978-1-58282
*Orders to:* Houghton Mifflin Harcourt, 3800 Golf Rd, Suite 100, Rolling Meadows, IL 60008 *Toll Free Fax:* 800-567-2714
Membership(s): International Society for Technology in Education; Software & Information Industry Association

**CLC Ministries**
701 Pennsylvania Ave, Fort Washington, PA 19034
SAN: 169-7358
Mailing Address: PO Box 1449, Fort Washington, PA 19034
*Tel:* 215-542-1240 *Toll Free Tel:* 800-659-1240 *Fax:* 215-542-7580
*E-mail:* orders@clcpublications.com
*Web Site:* www.clcpublications.com
*Key Personnel*
Dir: David Almack *E-mail:* dalmack@clcusa.org
Dist: Charlie Hurd
Founded: 1941
Worldwide Christian mission organization.
ISBN Prefix(es): 978-0-87508
Number of titles published annually: 9 Print
Total Titles: 250 Print
Distributor for Christian Fellowship
Membership(s): EFMA

**Clear Light Publishers**
823 Don Diego Ave, Santa Fe, NM 87505
*Tel:* 505-989-9590 *Toll Free Tel:* 800-253-2747 (orders) *Fax:* 505-989-9519
*E-mail:* market@clearlightbooks.com
*Web Site:* www.clearlightbooks.com
*Key Personnel*
Publr: Harmon Houghton
Founded: 1981
ISBN Prefix(es): 978-0-940666; 978-1-57416
Number of titles published annually: 12 Print
Total Titles: 170 Print
Foreign Rights: Harmon Houghton Clear Light Books
Membership(s): ABA; ALA; Mountains & Plains Booksellers Association; New Mexico Book Association

**§Clearfield Co Inc**
Subsidiary of Genealogical Publishing Co
3600 Clipper Mill Rd, Suite 260, Baltimore, MD 21211
*Tel:* 410-837-8271 *Toll Free Tel:* 800-296-6687 (orders & cust serv) *Fax:* 410-752-8492
*E-mail:* sales@genealogical.com
*Web Site:* www.genealogical.com
*Key Personnel*
Mktg Dir: Joe Garonzik *E-mail:* jgaronzi@genealogical.com
Founded: 1989
Leading publisher of genealogy how-to books, reference books & CD-ROM publications in the US.
ISBN Prefix(es): 978-0-8063
Number of titles published annually: 100 Print; 4 CD-ROM
Total Titles: 1,000 Print
Membership(s): ABA; American Name Society; National Genealogical Society

**Cleis Press**
2246 Sixth St, Berkeley, CA 94710
*Tel:* 510-845-8000 *Toll Free Tel:* 800-780-2279 (US) *Fax:* 510-845-8001
*E-mail:* orders@cleispress.com
*Web Site:* www.cleispress.com; www.vivaeditions.com
*Key Personnel*
Publr: Frederique Delacoste *E-mail:* fdelacoste@cleispress.com
Publr, Cleis Press & Viva Editions: Brenda Knight *E-mail:* bknight@cleispress.com
Publr: Felice Newman *E-mail:* fnewman@cleispress.com
Founded: 1980
Outriders. Outwriters. Outliers. Cleis Press publishes works in the areas of fiction & LGBT studies, as well as romance, erotica, how-to sex guides, human rights, memoir & women's studies. Viva Editions are books that inform, entertain & enlighten. Books contain inspiration, self-help, women's issues, lifestyle, health, parenting, reference, gift & relationship advice.
ISBN Prefix(es): 978-0-939416; 978-1-57344
Number of titles published annually: 60 Print; 60 E-Book; 150 Audio
Total Titles: 600 Print; 400 E-Book
Imprints: Midnight Editions; Viva Editions
Foreign Rep(s): PGW - New South (Australia); Turnaround (Europe, UK)
Foreign Rights: Linda Biagi (Worldwide)
*Distribution Center:* Publishers Group West, 1700 Fourth St, Berkeley, CA 94710, Contact: Sarah Rosenberg *Toll Free Tel:* 800-788-3123 *Fax:* 510-520-3444 *Web Site:* www.pgw.com

**Clerisy Press**
Imprint of Keen Communications LLC
306 Greenup St, Covington, KY 41011
*Tel:* 513-861-4045 *Toll Free Tel:* 888-604-4537 *Fax:* 859-291-9111
*E-mail:* info@clerisypress.com
*Web Site:* www.clerisypress.com
*Key Personnel*
Pres: Richard Hunt *Tel:* 513-861-4045 ext 17 *E-mail:* richard@clerisypress.com
Mktg & Publicity Mgr: Ms Ronnie Kutys *Tel:* 513-861-4045 ext 14 *E-mail:* ronnie@clerisypress.com
Spec Sales Mgr: Kara Pelicano *Tel:* 513-861-4045 ext 22 *E-mail:* kara@clerisypress.com
Founded: 2006
Trade & custom publisher.
ISBN Prefix(es): 978-1-57860
Number of titles published annually: 10 Print; 10 E-Book
Total Titles: 100 Print; 100 E-Book
Imprints: Keen Custom Media
*Billing Address:* 2204 First Ave S, Suite 102, Birmingham, AL 35233, Contact: Marie Hillin *Tel:* 205-322-0439 *Fax:* 205-326-1012 *E-mail:* mhillin@menasharidge.com
*Distribution Center:* Publishers Group West, 1700 Fourth St, Berkeley, CA 94710
Membership(s): ABA; Great Lakes Independent Booksellers Association

**§Clinical Laboratory & Standards Institute (CLSI)**
950 W Valley Rd, Suite 2500, Wayne, PA 19087
*Tel:* 610-688-0100 *Toll Free Tel:* 877-447-1888 (orders) *Fax:* 610-688-0700
*E-mail:* customerservice@clsi.org
*Web Site:* www.clsi.org
*Key Personnel*
EVP: Glenn Fine
Sr Dir, Standards & Quality: Jennifer Adams *Tel:* 484-588-5941 *E-mail:* jadams@clsi.org
Dir, Mktg: Patrick McGinn *Tel:* 484-588-5933 *E-mail:* pmcginn@clsi.org
Dir, Memb Servs: Kristen Hodgson *Tel:* 610-688-0100 ext 1133 *E-mail:* kristenh@clsi.org
Edit Mgr: Megan Larrisey *Tel:* 610-688-0100 ext 1124 *E-mail:* meganl@clsi.org
Founded: 1968
Voluntary consensus standards & guidelines for medical testing & in vitro diagnostic products & healthcare services.
ISBN Prefix(es): 978-1-56238
Number of titles published annually: 30 Print
Total Titles: 200 Print

**Close Up Publishing**
Division of Close Up Foundation
1330 Braddock Place, Suite 400, Alexandria, VA 22314
*Tel:* 703-706-3300 *Toll Free Tel:* 800-CLOSE-UP (256-7387) *Fax:* 703-706-3564
*E-mail:* info@closeup.org
*Web Site:* www.closeup.org
*Key Personnel*
CEO & Pres, Close Up Foundation: Timothy S Davis, Esq
VP, Mktg & Prog Admin: Joe Geraghty
Founded: 1971
Publish supplemental texts, videos, teachers' guides & simulation activities for secondary school & college social studies, political science, government, economics, international relations & history courses & for general readership.
ISBN Prefix(es): 978-0-932765
Number of titles published annually: 1 Print; 3 Audio
Total Titles: 56 Print; 19 Audio

**Closson Press**
257 Delilah St, Apollo, PA 15613-1933
*Tel:* 724-337-4482 *Fax:* 724-337-9484
*E-mail:* clossonpress@comcast.net
*Web Site:* www.clossonpress.com
*Key Personnel*
Founder & Owner: Bob Closson; Marietta Closson
Founded: 1976
History & genealogy.
ISBN Prefix(es): 978-0-933227; 978-1-55856
Number of titles published annually: 40 Print
Total Titles: 800 Print
Distributed by Janaway Publishing; Masthof Press
Distributor for Hearthside Books; Darvin Martin CDs; Retrospect Publishing
Foreign Rep(s): Brian Mitchell (Ireland); Cornelia Schrader (France, Germany)

**Clovernook Printing House for the Blind & Visually Impaired**
Division of The Clovernook Center for the Blind & Visually Impaired
7000 Hamilton Ave, Cincinnati, OH 45231-5297
*Tel:* 513-522-3860 *Toll Free Tel:* 888-234-7156 *Fax:* 513-728-3946 (admin); 513-728-3950 (sales)
*E-mail:* customerservice@clovernook.org
*Web Site:* www.clovernook.org
*Key Personnel*
VP, Busn Opers: Christopher Faust
Mgr, Printing: Charlotte Begley *Tel:* 513-522-3860 ext 2244
Founded: 1914
Braille books & magazines; fiction & nonfiction.
Number of titles published annually: 155 Print
Total Titles: 170 Print
*Branch Office(s)*
346 Saint Paul Ave, Memphis, TN 38126 *Tel:* 901-523-9590

**CN Times Books**
Subsidiary of Beijing MediaTime Book Co Ltd
501 Fifth Ave, Suite 1708, New York, NY 10017
*Tel:* 212-867-8666
*Web Site:* cntimesbooks.com
*Key Personnel*
Pres: George Zhu
VP & Assoc Publr: Paul Harrington
Exec Mng Ed: Helen Song
Sales & Mktg Mgr: Sean Concannon
Founded: 2012
ISBN Prefix(es): 978-1-62774
Number of titles published annually: 60 Print; 60 E-Book
Total Titles: 20 Print; 20 E-Book
Membership(s): ABA

**Coaches Choice**
465 Reservation Rd, Marina, CA 93933
Mailing Address: PO Box 1828, Monterey, CA 93942-1828
*Toll Free Tel:* 888-229-5745 *Fax:* 831-372-6075
*E-mail:* info@coacheschoice.com
*Web Site:* www.coacheschoice.com
*Key Personnel*
Pres: James Peterson
Edit Mgr: Kristi Huelsing *E-mail:* kristih@coacheschoice.com
Founded: 1999
Instructional books & DVDs for coaches (football, basketball, baseball, softball, volleyball, soccer, track & field, etc); health, fitness & sports medicine professionals & camp professionals.
ISBN Prefix(es): 978-1-57167; 978-1-58518; 978-1-60679
Number of titles published annually: 40 Print

**§Coachlight Press LLC**
1704 Craig's Store Rd, Afton, VA 22920-2017
SAN: 254-2579
*Tel:* 434-823-1692
*E-mail:* sales@coachlightpress.com
*Web Site:* www.coachlightpress.com
*Key Personnel*
Mng Memb: Kim Murphy
Founded: 2001
ISBN Prefix(es): 978-0-9716790; 978-1-936785
Number of titles published annually: 1 Print; 1 CD-ROM; 2 E-Book

Total Titles: 7 Print; 4 CD-ROM; 7 E-Book
Membership(s): IBPA, the Independent Book Publishers Association

**Cobblestone Publishing**
Division of Carus Publishing Co
30 Grove St, Suite C, Peterborough, NH 03458
*Tel:* 603-924-7209 *Toll Free Tel:* 800-821-0115 *Fax:* 603-924-7380
*E-mail:* customerservice@caruspub.com
*Web Site:* www.cobblestonepub.com
*Key Personnel*
COO & Pres: Jason Patenaude *Tel:* 603-924-7209 ext 229
Edit Dir, Carus Publg Co: Lou Waryncia *Tel:* 603-924-7209 ext 219 *E-mail:* lwaryncia@caruspub.com
Founded: 1980
Children's magazines, occasional educational books & teacher's resources.
ISBN Prefix(es): 978-0-8126; 978-0-3824
Number of titles published annually: 60 Print
Total Titles: 900 Print
Distributed by PGW/Perseus
Membership(s): ALA; International Reading Association; National Middle School Association

**Codhill Press**
One Arden Lane, New Paltz, NY 12561
*Tel:* 845-255-4060 *Fax:* 845-255-6784
*E-mail:* codhillpress@aol.com
*Web Site:* www.codhill.com
*Key Personnel*
Ed: David Appelbaum *E-mail:* david@codhill.com
Founded: 1998
Literary small press.
ISBN Prefix(es): 978-1-930337
Number of titles published annually: 12 Print; 2 Online; 2 E-Book
Total Titles: 100 Print; 6 Online; 6 E-Book
Distributed by SUNY Press
*Orders to:* SUNY Press, PO Box 960, Herndon, VA 20172 *Tel:* 703-661-1575 *Toll Free Tel:* 877-204-6073 *Fax:* 703-996-1010 *Toll Free Fax:* 877-204-6074
*Warehouse:* Books International, 22883 Quicksilver Dr, Dulles, VA 20166 *Tel:* 703-661-1500
Membership(s): Council of Literary Magazines & Presses

**Coffee House Press**
79 13 Ave NE, Suite 110, Minneapolis, MN 55413
SAN: 206-3883
*Tel:* 612-338-0125 *Fax:* 612-338-4004
*Web Site:* www.coffeehousepress.org
*Key Personnel*
Publr: Christopher Fischbach *E-mail:* fish@coffeehousepress.org
Mktg & Publicity Dir: Tricia O'Reilly *E-mail:* tricia@coffeehousepress.org
Mktg & Sales Dir: Caroline Casey
Founded: 1984
Fine editions & trade books; contemporary poetry, short fiction, novels, literary essays & memoirs.
ISBN Prefix(es): 978-0-915124; 978-0-918273; 978-1-56689
Number of titles published annually: 14 Print
Total Titles: 250 Print
*Distribution Center:* Consortium Books Sales & Distribution, 34 13 Ave NE, Suite 101, St Paul, MN 55413 *Tel:* 612-746-2600 *Toll Free Tel:* 800-283-3572 *Fax:* 612-746-2606

**Cognizant Communication Corp**
18 Peekskill Hollow Rd, Putnam Valley, NY 10597-3213
Mailing Address: PO Box 37, Putnam Valley, NY 10579-0037
*Tel:* 845-603-6440; 845-603-6441 (warehouse & orders) *Fax:* 845-603-6442
*E-mail:* cogcomm@aol.com; sales@cognizantcommunication.com; inquiries@cognizantcommunication.com
*Web Site:* www.cognizantcommunication.com
*Key Personnel*
Chmn & Publr: Robert N Miranda
Pres: Lori Miranda
Founded: 1992
STM & social science books & journals. Subjects include: tourism research & leisure studies, medical research, engineering & psychology.
ISBN Prefix(es): 978-1-882345; 978-0-971587
Number of titles published annually: 11 Print
Total Titles: 51 Print; 1 CD-ROM; 1 Audio
Imprints: Innovation & Tourisms (INTO); Miranda Press Trade Division; Tourism Dynamic

**Cokesbury**, see Abingdon Press

**§Cold Spring Harbor Laboratory Press**
Division of Cold Spring Harbor Laboratory
500 Sunnyside Blvd, Woodbury, NY 11797-2924
SAN: 203-6185
*Tel:* 516-422-4100; 516-422-4101 *Toll Free Tel:* 800-843-4388 *Fax:* 516-422-4097; 516-422-4092 (submissions)
*E-mail:* cshpress@cshl.edu
*Web Site:* www.cshlpress.com
*Key Personnel*
Exec Dir: John Inglis *Tel:* 516-422-4005 *Fax:* 516-422-4092 *E-mail:* inglis@cshl.edu
Book Devt, Mktg & Sales Dir: Jan Argentine *E-mail:* argentine@cshl.edu
Book Prodn Mgr: Denise Weiss *Tel:* 516-422-4024 *Fax:* 516-422-4095 *E-mail:* weiss@cshl.edu
Head, Ad & Sponsorship Sales: Marcie Siconolfi *Tel:* 516-422-4010 *Fax:* 516-422-4092 *E-mail:* siconolf@cshl.edu
Dir, Serials Mktg & Sales: Wayne Manos *E-mail:* manos@cshl.edu
Mktg & Sales Acct Mgr: Elizabeth Powers *Tel:* 516-422-4101 *E-mail:* powerse@cshl.edu
Cust Serv, Warehousing & Dist Mgr: Geraldine Jaitin *E-mail:* jaitin@cshl.edu
Founded: 1933
Scholarly & scientific books; laboratory meeting results; protocols database; journals.
ISBN Prefix(es): 978-0-87969
Number of titles published annually: 20 Print
Total Titles: 220 Print; 1 CD-ROM; 15 E-Book; 2 Audio
Foreign Rep(s): Academic Books (Austria, Europe, France, Switzerland); Maruzen (Japan); NBN International (Europe, UK); Viva Books Pte Ltd (India)
*Warehouse:* Cold Spring Harbor Laboratory, Central Receiving & Distribution Ctr, 50 Gordon Dr, Syosset, NY 11791-4719, Warehouse Mgr: Sharon Story *Tel:* 516-422-4203 *E-mail:* story@cshl.edu
*Distribution Center:* Oxford University Press, 2001 Evans Rd, Cary, NC 27513

**College & University Professional Association for Human Resources (CUPA-HR)**
1811 Commons Point Dr, Knoxville, TN 37932
*Tel:* 865-637-7673 *Toll Free Tel:* 877-CUPA-HR4 (287-2474) *Fax:* 865-637-7674
*E-mail:* communications@cupahr.org
*Web Site:* www.cupahr.org
*Key Personnel*
Dir, Communs: Gayle Kiser *Tel:* 865-637-7673 ext 118 *E-mail:* gkiser@cupahr.org
Mng Ed: Missy Kline *Tel:* 865-637-7673 ext 118 *E-mail:* mkline@cupahr.org
Founded: 1946
Serves more than 11,000 higher education human resource professionals at nearly 1,700 colleges & universities.
ISBN Prefix(es): 978-0-910402
Number of titles published annually: 6 Print
Total Titles: 46 Print

**§The College Board**
45 Columbus Ave, New York, NY 10023-6917
SAN: 269-0829
*Tel:* 212-713-8000 *Fax:* 212-713-8063
*Web Site:* www.collegeboard.com
*Key Personnel*
Pres: Gaston Caperton
Founded: 1900
Educational & trade books in the fields of college admission, continuing education, guidance, curriculum, financial aid, educational research, college-level & advanced placement examinations & school reform.
ISBN Prefix(es): 978-0-87447
Number of titles published annually: 7 Print
Total Titles: 100 Print; 7 CD-ROM; 4 E-Book; 1 Audio
Distributed by Macmillan

**College Press Publishing Co**
2111 N Main St, Suite C, Joplin, MO 64801
SAN: 211-9951
Mailing Address: PO Box 1132, Joplin, MO 64802
*Tel:* 417-623-6280 *Toll Free Tel:* 800-289-3300 *Fax:* 417-623-1929
*E-mail:* books@collegepress.com
*Web Site:* www.collegepress.com/storefront
*Key Personnel*
Pres: Chris De Welt
Founded: 1959
Religion, theology, Bible study - Traditional Christian publishing house.
ISBN Prefix(es): 978-0-89900
Number of titles published annually: 15 Print; 2 CD-ROM
Total Titles: 100 Print; 1 Audio
Distributor for CBD; David C Cook Publishing
*Returns:* 850 N Grove Ave, Elgin, IL 60120-2892, Contact: David Cook

**College Publishing**
12309 Lynwood Dr, Glen Allen, VA 23059
*Tel:* 804-364-8410 *Toll Free Tel:* 800-827-0723 *Fax:* 804-364-8408
*E-mail:* collegepub@mindspring.com
*Web Site:* www.collegepublishing.us
*Key Personnel*
Publr: Stephen R Mosberg
Founded: 2001
Publish college textbooks in engineering, literature, linguistics & scholarly journals in engineering.
ISBN Prefix(es): 978-0-9679121; 978-1-932780
Number of titles published annually: 10 Print; 2 Online
Total Titles: 30 Print; 2 Online
*Orders to:* c/o Port City Fulfillment Services, 35 Ash Dr, Kimball, MI 48074 *Fax:* 810-388-9502
*Returns:* c/o Port City Fulfillment Services, 35 Ash Dr, Kimball, MI 48074

**The Colonial Williamsburg Foundation**
PO Box 1776, Williamsburg, VA 23187-1776
SAN: 203-297X
*Tel:* 757-229-1000 *Toll Free Tel:* 800-HISTORY (447-8679) *Fax:* 757-220-7325
*E-mail:* cwres@cwf.org; geninfo@cwf.org
*Web Site:* www.colonialwilliamsburg.org/publications
*Key Personnel*
Chmn of the Bd & Pres: Colin G Campbell *Tel:* 757-220-7200 *Fax:* 757-220-7727 *E-mail:* ccampbell@cwf.org
SVP, Fin & Admin: Robert Taylor *Tel:* 757-220-7410 *Fax:* 757-565-8891
VP, Prodns, Pubns & Learning Ventures: William White *Tel:* 757-220-7149 *Fax:* 757-220-8916 *E-mail:* wwhite@cwf.org

Dir & Mng Ed, Pubns & Rts/Perms: Paul Aron *Tel:* 757-220-7341 *E-mail:* paron@cwf.org
Founded: 1930
Trade & scholarly nonfiction, children's, young adult, juveniles & regional books specializing in aspects of eighteenth-century history in Virginia's colonial capital.
ISBN Prefix(es): 978-0-87935; 978-0-910412
Number of titles published annually: 6 Print
Total Titles: 100 Print; 28 Audio
Imprints: Colonial Williamsburg
Distributed by Harry N Abrams Inc; John F Blair Publisher; Clarkson Potter Publishers; Lexington Books; National Geographic; Ohio University Press; Quite Specific Media Group Ltd; Random House Children's Books; Rodale; Rowman & Littlefield; Scholastic Inc; Stackpole Books; Texas Tech University Press; The University of Virginia Press; University Press of New England; Yale University Press
*Shipping Address:* c/o Coastal Forms & Data Products, 141 Enterprise Dr, Newport News, VA 23603 *Tel:* 757-873-8806 *Toll Free Tel:* 800-241-4067 *Fax:* 757-873-7619
*Distribution Center:* 201 Fifth Ave, Williamsburg, VA 23185

**Colorado Geological Survey**
Division of Colorado Department of Natural Resources
Publications Section, 1313 Sherman St, Rm 715, Denver, CO 80203
*Tel:* 303-866-2611 *Fax:* 303-866-2461 (cust serv)
*E-mail:* pubscgs@state.co.us (cust serv)
*Web Site:* geosurvey.state.co.us
*Key Personnel*
Admin Asst, Pubns: Rachael Nickless *Tel:* 303-866-2611 ext 8321 *E-mail:* rachael.nickless@state.co.us
Founded: 1969
Publish books & maps on Colorado geology & resources.
ISBN Prefix(es): 978-1-884216
Number of titles published annually: 15 Print
Total Titles: 45 Print

**§Columbia Books & Information Services**
8120 Woodmont Ave, Suite 110, Bethesda, MD 20814
*Tel:* 202-464-1662 *Toll Free Tel:* 888-265-0600 (cust serv) *Fax:* 202-464-1775
*E-mail:* info@columbiabooks.com
*Web Site:* www.columbiabooks.com; www.lobbyists.info; www.associationexecs.com
*Key Personnel*
Edit & Tech: Matt Ouzounian *Tel:* 202-464-1662 ext 110 *E-mail:* mouzounian@columbiabooks.com
Dir of Mktg: Brittany Carter *Tel:* 202-464-1662 ext 109 *E-mail:* bcarter@columbiabooks.com
Sales: Tim Teehan *Tel:* 202-464-1662 ext 104 *E-mail:* tim@columbiabooks.com
Founded: 1966
Publish directories, reference books, newsletters & reports. Do not accept mss.
ISBN Prefix(es): 978-0-910416; 978-1-880873; 978-0-9715487
Number of titles published annually: 10 Print; 2 Online; 1 E-Book
Total Titles: 10 Print; 2 Online; 1 E-Book

**§Columbia University Press**
61 W 62 St, New York, NY 10023
SAN: 212-2472
*Tel:* 212-459-0600 *Toll Free Tel:* 800-944-8648 *Fax:* 212-459-3678
*E-mail:* cup_book@columbia.edu (orders & cust serv)
*Web Site:* cup.columbia.edu
*Key Personnel*
CFO: Richard Gehringer
Assoc Dir & Edit Dir: Jennifer Crewe
Publicity Dir & Asst Mktg Dir: Meredith Howard
Dir, Sales & Mktg: Brad Hebel
Publr, Fin & Economics: Myles Thompson
Publr, Life Sciences: Patrick Fitzgerald
Sr Exec Ed: Wendy Lochner
Exec Ed: Jennifer Perillo
Mng Ed: Anne McCoy
Ed: Anne Routon
Founded: 1893
Books of scholarly value, including nonfiction, general interest, scientific & technical books, textbooks in special fields at the university level & reference books.
ISBN Prefix(es): 978-0-231
Number of titles published annually: 4,200 Print; 120 E-Book
Total Titles: 7 CD-ROM; 4 Online; 350 E-Book
Imprints: Columbia Business School Publishing (business, finance & economics titles); Wallflower Press (film titles)
*Foreign Office(s):* John Wiley & Sons Ltd, One Oldlands Way, Bognor Regis, West Sussex PO22 9SA, United Kingdom *Tel:* (01243) 843 291 *Fax:* (01243) 843 296 *E-mail:* customer@wiley.com
Distributor for Auteur Books; Chinese University Press; East European Monographs; Edinburgh University Press; The European Consortium for Political Research; University of Tokyo Press
Foreign Rep(s): The African Moon Press (Chris Reinders) (Botswana, Lesotho, Namibia, South Africa, Swaziland, Zimbabwe); Apex Knowledge Sdn Bhd (Simon Tay) (Brunei, Malaysia); Aromix Books Co Ltd (Jane Lam) (Hong Kong); Aromix Books Co Ltd (Nick Woon); Avicenna Partnership Ltd (Claire de Gruchy) (Algeria, Cyprus, Jordan, Morocco, Palestine, Tunisia, Turkey); Avicenna Partnership Ltd (Bill Kennedy) (Bahrain, Egypt, Iran, Iraq, Kuwait, Lebanon, Libya, Oman, Qatar, Saudi Arabia, Syria, United Arab Emirates); Dominique Bartshukoff (Austria, Eastern Europe, Germany, Greece, Hungary, Portugal, Spain); Book Marketing Services (S Janakiraman) (India); Booknet Co Ltd (Suphaluck Sattabuz) (Thailand); Andrew Brewer (Europe, South Africa, UK); Everest International Publishing Services (Wei Zhao) (China); Footprints Books Pty Ltd (Kate O'Reilly) (Australia, New Zealand); HARBRA (Julio Emod) (South America); IGP Services Pte Ltd (Joseph Goh) (Cambodia, Indonesia, Laos, Myanmar, Singapore, Vietnam); Information & Culture Korea (Se-Yung Jun) (Korea); Peter Jacques (Belgium, Denmark, Finland, France, Italy, Norway, Poland, Sweden, Switzerland); Mega-TEXTS Phil Inc (Jean Lim) (Philippines); Ben Mitchell (South Coast of the UK); Elise Moser (Canada); Mical Moser (Canada); BK Norton (Chiafeng Peng) (Taiwan); BK Norton (Meilhua Sun) (Taiwan); Premium Educational Group (David R Rivera) (Caribbean, Puerto Rico); Publicaciones Educativas (Jose Rios) (Central America, Mexico); Rockbook (Akiko Iwamoto) (Japan); Rockbook (Gilles Fauveau) (Japan); United Publishers Services Ltd (Mark Gresham) (Japan); The University Press Group Ltd (Lois Edwards) (Europe, UK); Kelvin van Hasselt Publishing Services (Africa); World Press (Saleem A Malik) (Pakistan)
Foreign Rights: Agencia Literaria Raquel de la Concha (Spain); Akcali Copyright Agency (Turkey); Bardon-Chinese Media Agency (China); Best Literary & Rights Agency (Jeffrey Kim) (Korea); Bestun Korea (Ms Yumi Chun) (Korea); The English Agency (Japan) Ltd (Japan); Eulama Literary Agencies (Italy); Paul und Peter Fritz AG Literary Agency (Germany); Graal Literary Agency (Maria Starz-Kanska) (Poland); Korea Copyright Center (Ms Mi Sook Hong) (Korea); Andrew Nurnberg Associates Intl (Whitney Hsu & Jackie Huang) (China); Uli Rushby-Smith (Netherlands, UK); Eric Yang Agency (Korea)
*Advertising Agency:* Columbia Advertising Group
*Orders to:* Perseus Distribution, 1094 Flex Dr, Jackson, TN 38301 *Tel:* 731-988-4440 *Toll Free Tel:* 800-343-4499 *Toll Free Fax:* 800-351-5073
Membership(s): AAP; American Association of University Presses

**§Comex Systems Inc**
5 Cold Hill Rd, Suite 24, Mendham, NJ 07945
*Tel:* 973-543-2862 *Toll Free Tel:* 800-543-6959 *Fax:* 973-543-9644
*E-mail:* mail@comexsystems.com
*Web Site:* www.comexsystems.com
*Key Personnel*
VP: Doug Prybylowski *E-mail:* dpryb@comexsystems.com
Founded: 1973
Publish test preparation & other educational books.
ISBN Prefix(es): 978-1-56030
Number of titles published annually: 5 Print; 10 CD-ROM; 5 E-Book
Total Titles: 30 Print; 50 CD-ROM; 5 E-Book

**Common Courage Press**
One Red Barn Rd, Monroe, ME 04951
Mailing Address: PO Box 702, Monroe, ME 04951-0702
*Tel:* 207-525-0900 *Toll Free Tel:* 800-497-3207 *Fax:* 207-525-3068
*E-mail:* orders-info@commoncouragepress.com
*Web Site:* www.commoncouragepress.com
*Key Personnel*
Publr: Greg Bates *E-mail:* gbates@commoncouragepress.com
Founded: 1991
Books on race, feminism, gender issues, class, media, economics, ecology & foreign policy to help readers in the struggle for social justice. Accepting no new submissions.
ISBN Prefix(es): 978-0-9628838; 978-1-56751
Number of titles published annually: 20 Print
Total Titles: 90 Print
Distributor for Odonian Press; Real Story Series
Foreign Rights: James Bier (Worldwide exc USA)
*Distribution Center:* LPC Group, 1436 W Randolph St, Chicago, IL 60607 *Toll Free Tel:* 800-243-0138 *Toll Free Fax:* 800-334-3892

**Commonwealth Editions**
Imprint of Applewood Books Inc
One River Rd, Carlisle, MA 01741
*Tel:* 781-271-0055 *Toll Free Tel:* 800-277-5312 *Fax:* 781-271-0056
*E-mail:* customercare@awb.com
*Web Site:* www.awb.com
*Key Personnel*
Pres & Publr: Philip Zuckerman
Founded: 1988
Publisher of nonfiction books about New England & its historic places.
ISBN Prefix(es): 978-1-889833; 978-1-933212
Number of titles published annually: 12 Print
Total Titles: 125 Print
Membership(s): NEBA

**Communication Creativity**
4542 Melbourne Way, Highlands Ranch, CO 80130
*Tel:* 720-344-4388 *Toll Free Fax:* 866-685-0307
*Web Site:* www.selfpublishingresources.com (bookstore)
*Key Personnel*
Pres: Sue Collier *E-mail:* sue@selfpublishingresources.com
Sales & Ad Mgr: Doug Collier *E-mail:* doug@selfpublishingresources.com
Founded: 1977
Nonfiction & how-to.
ISBN Prefix(es): 978-0-918880
Number of titles published annually: 3 Print
Total Titles: 13 Print

Membership(s): The Association of Publishers for Special Sales; Colorado Independent Publishers Association; IBPA, the Independent Book Publishers Association; National Speakers Association; PMA International

**Community College Press**
Division of American Association of Community Colleges (AACC)
One Dupont Circle NW, Suite 410, Washington, DC 20036
*Tel:* 202-728-0200; 301-490-8116 (orders) *Toll Free Tel:* 800-250-6557 *Fax:* 202-223-9390 (edit); 301-604-0158 (orders); 202-833-2467
*E-mail:* aaccpub@ebrightkey.net
*Web Site:* www.aacc.nche.edu/bookstore
*Key Personnel*
SVP, Communs & Advancement: Norma G Kent *Tel:* 202-728-0200 ext 209 *E-mail:* nkent@aacc.nche.edu
Ed, Community College Press: Deanna D'Errico *E-mail:* dderrico@aacc.nche.edu
Founded: 1920
Paperback & hardcover.
ISBN Prefix(es): 978-0-87117
Number of titles published annually: 10 Print
Total Titles: 100 Print; 5 Audio
*Advertising Agency:* The Townsend Group, 2 Wisconsin Circle, Suite 900, Chevy Chase, MD 20815 *Tel:* 301-215-6710
*Orders to:* PO Box 311, Annapolis Junction, MD 20701
Membership(s): AAP

**Comprehensive Health Education Foundation (CHEF)**
159 S Jackson St, Suite 510, Seattle, WA 98104
SAN: 696-3668
*Tel:* 206-824-2907 *Toll Free Tel:* 800-323-2433 *Fax:* 206-824-3072
*E-mail:* info@chef.org
*Web Site:* www.chef.org
*Key Personnel*
Exec Dir: Melanie Gillespie
Cont: Michelle McCain
Founded: 1974
Health education curricula, books, videos & other mixed-media materials.
ISBN Prefix(es): 978-0-935529; 978-1-57021
Number of titles published annually: 4 Print
Total Titles: 20 Print

**Conciliar Press**
Division of Conciliar Media Ministries Inc
2747 Bond St, University Park, IL 60484
Mailing Address: PO Box 748, Chesterton, IN 46304
*Tel:* 219-728-2216 (outside US) *Toll Free Tel:* 800-967-7377 *Fax:* 708-534-7803 *Toll Free Fax:* 866-599-5208
*E-mail:* service@conciliarmedia.com
*Web Site:* www.conciliarpress.com
*Key Personnel*
CEO: John Maddex
Mktg Dir: Matthew Dorning *E-mail:* mdorning@consiliarmedia.com
Prodn Mgr & Ed: Carla Zell
Founded: 1978
Books, booklets, brochures, greeting cards, icons, liturgical & quarterly magazines.
ISBN Prefix(es): 978-0-9622713; 978-0-8821212
Number of titles published annually: 12 Print
Total Titles: 110 Print
Distributed by Light & Life; St Vladimir's
Distributor for Light & Life
Foreign Rights: Rainbow Books (Australia)

**Concordia Publishing House**
Subsidiary of The Luthern Church, Missouri Synod
3558 S Jefferson Ave, St Louis, MO 63118-3968
SAN: 202-1781
*Tel:* 314-268-1000 *Toll Free Tel:* 800-325-3040 (cust serv) *Toll Free Fax:* 800-490-9889 (cust serv)
*E-mail:* order@cph.org
*Web Site:* www.cph.org
*Key Personnel*
CEO & Pres: Dr Bruce G Kintz *Tel:* 314-268-1190 *E-mail:* bruce.kintz@cph.org
VP & Corp Coun: Jonathan D Schultz *E-mail:* jon.schultz@cph.org
Exec Dir, Edit & Publr: Rev Paul T McCain *E-mail:* paul.mccain@cph.org
Exec Dir, Fin: Peggy Anderson *E-mail:* peggy.anderson@cph.org
Exec Dir, Info Technologies: Steve Harris *E-mail:* steve.harris@cph.org
Exec Dir, Prodn Control & Quality Systems: Karen Capps *E-mail:* karen.capps@cph.org
Dir, Facilities: Tony Shimkus *E-mail:* tony.shimkus@cph.org
Dir, Graphic Design: Tim Agnew *E-mail:* tim.agnew@cph.org
Dir, Mktg: Brett Singleton *E-mail:* brett.singleton@cph.org
Dir, Opers: Bob Rothmeyer *E-mail:* bob.rothmeyer@cph.org
Dir, Sales: Paul Brunette *E-mail:* paul.brunette@cph.org
Founded: 1869
Theological works, sacred & family, devotional music, curriculum, computer software, bulletins, envelopes.
ISBN Prefix(es): 978-0-570; 978-0-7586
Number of titles published annually: 150 Print; 2 CD-ROM
Total Titles: 1,000 Print; 10 CD-ROM
Divisions: Concordia Academic Press; Editorial Concordia; Family Films
Membership(s): CBA: The Association for Christian Retail; Evangelical Christian Publishers Association; Protestant Church-Owned Publishers Association

**The Conference Board Inc**
845 Third Ave, New York, NY 10022-6679
SAN: 202-179X
*Tel:* 212-759-0900; 212-339-0345 (cust serv) *Fax:* 212-980-7014; 212-836-9740 (cust serv)
*E-mail:* info@conference-board.org
*Web Site:* www.conference-board.org
*Key Personnel*
CEO: Jon Spector
Rts & Perms: Chuck Mitchell
Founded: 1916
Periodic studies in management practices, economics & public affairs.
ISBN Prefix(es): 978-0-8237
Number of titles published annually: 25 Print; 25 Online
*Branch Office(s)*
20 N Wacker Dr, Suite 1840, Chicago, IL 60606 *Tel:* 312-609-1302 *Fax:* 312-609-0576
*Foreign Office(s):* Chaussee de La Hulpe 130, bte 11, 1000 Brussels, Belgium

**Connecticut Academy of Arts & Sciences**
PO Box 208211, New Haven, CT 06520-8211
*Tel:* 203-432-3113 *Fax:* 203-432-5712
*E-mail:* caas@yale.edu
*Web Site:* www.yale.edu/caas
*Key Personnel*
Pubns Chmn: Catherine Skinner *Tel:* 203-432-3787 *E-mail:* catherine.skinner@yale.edu
Founded: 1799
A learned society which holds a series of lectures; publisher of academic books.
ISBN Prefix(es): 978-1-878508
Number of titles published annually: 4 Print

**Consumer Press**
13326 SW 28 St, Suite 102, Fort Lauderdale, FL 33330-1102
SAN: 297-7888
*Tel:* 954-370-9153 *Fax:* 954-472-1008
*E-mail:* info@consumerpress.com
*Web Site:* consumerpress.com
*Key Personnel*
Pres: Diana Gonzalez
Edit Dir: Joseph J Pappas
Publicity Dir: Linda Muzzarelli
Founded: 1989
Consumer-oriented self-help & how-to titles. Specialize in nutrition, health & homeowner issues.
ISBN Prefix(es): 978-0-9628336; 978-1-891264; 978-0-9637641-7-1
Number of titles published annually: 9 Print
Total Titles: 12 Print
Imprints: Women's Publications
Membership(s): IBPA, the Independent Book Publishers Association

**Consumertronics**
Affiliate of Top Secret Consumertronics Global (TSC-Global)
8400 Menaul NE, Suite A-199, Albuquerque, NM 87112
Mailing Address: PO Box 23097, Albuquerque, NM 87192
*Tel:* 505-321-1034
*E-mail:* wizguru@consumertronics.net
*Web Site:* www.consumertronics.net
*Key Personnel*
Pres & CEO: John J Williams
VP: Laurencia Williams
Founded: 1971
Technical books, manuals & software.
ISBN Prefix(es): 978-0-934274
Number of titles published annually: 60 Print; 60 CD-ROM
Total Titles: 150 Print

**Contemporary Publishing Co of Raleigh Inc**
5849 Lease Lane, Raleigh, NC 27617
*Tel:* 919-851-8221 *Fax:* 919-851-6666
*E-mail:* questions@contemporarypublishing.com
*Web Site:* www.contemporarypublishing.com
*Key Personnel*
Publr: Charles E Grantham *E-mail:* chuck246cp@aol.com
Lib Sales Dir & Prodn Mgr: Erika Kessler *E-mail:* erikacpc@aol.com
Mktg Dir: Sherri Powell
Founded: 1977
Laboratory textbooks for college.
ISBN Prefix(es): 978-0-89892
Number of titles published annually: 10 Print
Total Titles: 90 Print; 1 CD-ROM

**Continental AfrikaPublishers**
Division of Afrikamawu Miracle Mission, AMI Inc
182 Stribling Circle, Spartanburg, SC 29301
*Tel:* 864-576-7992 *Fax:* 775-295-9699
*E-mail:* afrikalion@aol.com; afrikapharaoh@aol.com; afrikafiaga@aol.com; afrikadela@aol.com
*Web Site:* www.writers.net/writers/22249
*Key Personnel*
Publr: Prof Afrikadzata Deku, PhD
Founded: 1990
Afrikacentric books, booklets, cassettes & video documentaries, calendars, films on Continental Afrikan studies, Afrika Centricity, Pan-Continental Afrikanism, Continental Afrikan Government MIRACLE Project of the Century-its what, why, how & when.
ISBN Prefix(es): 978-1-56454
Number of titles published annually: 20 Print; 260 Online; 500 E-Book; 20 Audio
Total Titles: 260 Print; 260 Online; 638 E-Book; 20 Audio
*Foreign Office(s):* PO Box 209, Dansoman-Accra, Ghana, Chmn: Afrikanenyo Deku
Foreign Rep(s): Continental/Diaspora Afrikan (Worldwide)

**David C Cook**
4050 Lee Vance View, Colorado Springs, CO 80918
*Tel:* 719-536-0100 *Toll Free Tel:* 800-708-5550 *Fax:* 519-536-3269
*Web Site:* www.davidccook.com
*Key Personnel*
CEO & Pres: Chris Doornbos
SVP & Publr: Dan Rich
SVP, Sales & Mktg: C Ryan Dunham
Mng Dir: Greg Tombs
Specialize in portable & devotional books which inspire, encourage & motivate readers; gifts.
ISBN Prefix(es): 978-1-56292
Number of titles published annually: 50 Print
Total Titles: 2,500 Print

**Cooper Publishing Group LLC**
PO Box 1129, Traverse City, MI 49685
*Tel:* 231-933-9958 *Fax:* 231-933-9964
*E-mail:* jr4239@att.net
*Web Site:* www.cooperpublishinggroup.com
*Key Personnel*
Publr: I L Cooper *E-mail:* icooper100@aol.com
Founded: 1985
College textbooks; health & nutrition books; coaching education; biology; sports medicine, exercise physiology.
ISBN Prefix(es): 978-1-884125; 978-0-9769303
Number of titles published annually: 3 Print
Total Titles: 51 Print
Imprints: Biological Sciences Press
Foreign Rep(s): Japan Publications Trading Co Ltd (Japan)

**Cooper Square Press**
Imprint of Rowman & Littlefield Publishing Group
5360 Manhattan Circle, Suite 101, Boulder, CO 80303
*Tel:* 303-543-7835 *Fax:* 303-543-0043
*Web Site:* www.rlpgbooks.com; www.rlpgtrade.com
*Key Personnel*
Edit Dir: Rick Rinehart *Tel:* 303-543-7835 ext 318 *E-mail:* rrinehart@rowman.com
Founded: 1999
Hardcover & trade paperback publisher in history, the performing arts, biography & literature.
ISBN Prefix(es): 978-1-56833; 978-0-8154; 978-0-87833
Number of titles published annually: 12 Print
Total Titles: 300 Print
Imprints: Madison Books
*Branch Office(s)*
4501 Forbes Blvd, Lanham, MD 20706 *Tel:* 301-459-3366 *Fax:* 301-459-5748
Foreign Rep(s): Oxford Publicity Partnership (UK); Peribo (Australia)
*Orders to:* National Book Network, 15200 NBN Way, Blue Ridge Summit, PA 17214, Mgr, Cust Serv: Meg Phelps *Tel:* 717-794-3800 *Toll Free Tel:* 800-462-6420 *Fax:* 717-794-3803
*Returns:* National Book Network, 15200 NBN Way, Blue Ridge Summit, PA 17214, Mgr, Cust Serv: Meg Phelps *Toll Free Tel:* 800-462-6420 *Fax:* 717-794-3803
*Distribution Center:* National Book Network, 15200 NBN Way, Blue Ridge Summit, PA 17214, Mgr, Cust Serv: Meg Phelps *Toll Free Tel:* 800-462-6420 *Toll Free Fax:* 800-338-4550

**Copley Custom Textbooks**
Imprint of XanEdu Publishing Inc
530 Great Rd, Acton, MA 01720
*Tel:* 978-263-9090 *Toll Free Tel:* 800-562-2147 *Fax:* 978-263-9190
*E-mail:* publish@copleycustom.com; textbook@copleypublishing.com
*Web Site:* www.xanedu.com/copley
*Key Personnel*
CEO: Alar Elken
Founded: 1984
Custom publishing for the higher education market.
ISBN Prefix(es): 978-0-87411; 978-1-58152; 978-1-58390
Number of titles published annually: 85 Print; 5 CD-ROM; 10 E-Book
Total Titles: 400 Print
Imprints: Copley Editions; Copley Publishing Group

**Copper Canyon Press**
Fort Worden State Park, Bldg 33, Port Townsend, WA 98368
SAN: 206-488X
Mailing Address: PO Box 271, Port Townsend, WA 98368
*Tel:* 360-385-4925 *Toll Free Tel:* 877-501-1393 *Fax:* 360-385-4985
*E-mail:* poetry@coppercanyonpress.org
*Web Site:* www.coppercanyonpress.org
*Key Personnel*
Exec Ed: Michael Wiegers *Tel:* 360-385-4925 ext 102 *E-mail:* michael@coppercanyonpress.org
Mktg & Sales Dir: Joseph Bednarik *Tel:* 360-385-4925 ext 109 *Fax:* 360-385-4983 *E-mail:* joseph@coppercanyonpress.org
Devt Dir: George Knotek *Tel:* 360-385-4925 ext 103 *E-mail:* george@coppercanyonpress.org
Founded: 1972
Hardcover & paperback trade books of poetry.
ISBN Prefix(es): 978-0-914742; 978-1-55659
Number of titles published annually: 32 Print
Total Titles: 400 Print
Imprints: Ausable Press
Distributor for American Poetry Review/Honickman
*Shipping Address:* Fort Worden State Park, Bldg 313, Port Townsend, WA 98368
*Distribution Center:* Consortium Book Sales & Distribution, The Keg House, Suite 101, 34 13 Ave NE, Minneapolis, MN 55413-1007 *Tel:* 612-746-2600 *Toll Free Tel:* 800-283-3572 (cust serv) *Fax:* 612-746-2606 *Web Site:* www.cbsd.com

**§Copywriter's Council of America (CCA)**
Division of The Linick Group Inc
CCA Bldg, 7 Putter Lane, Middle Island, NY 11953-1920
Mailing Address: PO Box 102, Middle Island, NY 11953-0102
*Tel:* 631-924-3888 *Fax:* 631-924-8555
*E-mail:* cca4dmcopy@gmail.com
*Web Site:* www.AndrewLinickDirectMarketing.com/Copywriters-Council.html; www.NewWorldPressBooks.com
*Key Personnel*
Chmn, Consulting Group: Andrew S Linick, PhD *E-mail:* andrew@asklinick.com
VP: Roger Dextor
Lib Sales Dir: John Kelty
Founded: 1974
Article reprints, monographs; educational, professional & trade, fiction, nonfiction publications in direct response advertising, direct marketing, mail order, sales promotion, measurable response public relations, telemarketing, business-to-business marketing, desktop publishing, Internet marketing, e-commerce, e-books, consulting & management. Confidential reports, newsletters, little-known business secrets-library of super money makers you can use tomorrow. Also 300 e-books & e-reports available for licensing. Free 15 minute phone consultation for LMP readers - code LMP.
ISBN Prefix(es): 978-91-7098
Number of titles published annually: 36 Print; 25 E-Book
Total Titles: 350 Print; 50 E-Book
Imprints: CCA; National Association of Photo Sellers; New World Press; Publishers Trade Secrets Library
Distributor for ASL; Compu-Tek; National Association of Photo Sellers; PictureProfits® Tool Kit
*Advertising Agency:* LK Advertising Agency, 7 Putter Lane, Middle Island, NY 11953, VP: Roger Dextor *Tel:* 631-924-3888 *Web Site:* www.AndrewLinickDirectMarketing.com/LK-Advertising.html
Membership(s): ABA; American Association of Journalists & Authors; American Association of Magazine Photographers; American Book Producers Association; American Business Women's Association; American Marketing Association; American Medical Publishers Association; American Medical Writers Association; American Publishers Association; American Society of Magazine Editors; Association of Advertising & Marketing Professionals; Association of Directory Publishers; Direct Marketing Association; Direct Marketing Club of New York; International Food, Wine and Travel Writers Association

**Cornell Maritime Press Inc**
Imprint of Schiffer Publishing Ltd
4880 Lower Valley Rd, Atglen, PA 19310
SAN: 203-5901
*Tel:* 610-593-1777 *Fax:* 610-593-2002
*E-mail:* info@schifferbooks.com
*Web Site:* www.cmptp.com
*Key Personnel*
Pres: Pete Schiffer
EVP: Nancy Schiffer
Founded: 1938
Professional, technical books in maritime arts & sciences; boats & boat building; related hobbies & crafts.
ISBN Prefix(es): 978-0-87033
Number of titles published annually: 6 Print
Total Titles: 89 Print
Imprints: Tidewater Publishers
Distributor for Chesapeake Bay Maritime Museum; Independent Seaport Museum; Literary House Press; Maryland Historical Trust Press; Maryland Sea Grant Program
Membership(s): ABA; Mid-Atlantic Publishers Association

**Cornell University Press**
Division of Cornell University
Sage House, 512 E State St, Ithaca, NY 14850
SAN: 202-1862
*Tel:* 607-277-2338 *Fax:* 607-277-2374
*E-mail:* cupressinfo@cornell.edu; cupress-sales@cornell.edu
*Web Site:* www.cornellpress.cornell.edu
*Key Personnel*
CFO & Asst Dir: Roger A Hubbs *Tel:* 607-277-2696 ext 132 *E-mail:* rah9@cornell.edu
Dir: John G Ackerman *Tel:* 607-277-2338 ext 209 *E-mail:* jga4@cornell.edu
Ed-in-Chief: Peter Potter *Tel:* 607-277-2338 ext 241 *E-mail:* pjp33@cornell.edu
Edit Dir, ILR Press: Ms Frances Benson *E-mail:* fgb2@cornell.edu
Exec Ed: Roger Haydon *Tel:* 607-277-2338 ext 225 *E-mail:* rmh11@cornell.edu
Sci Acqs Ed: Heidi Steinmetz Lovette *Tel:* 607-277-2338 ext 234 *E-mail:* hsl22@cornell.edu
Acqs Ed: Michael J McGandy *E-mail:* mjm475@cornell.edu
Asst Dir & Mng Ed: Priscilla Hurdle *Tel:* 607-277-2338 ext 244 *E-mail:* plh9@cornell.edu
Design & Prod Mgr: Karen Kerr *Tel:* 607-277-2338 ext 235 *E-mail:* kg99@cornell.edu
Mktg Mgr: Mr Mahinder S Kingra *Tel:* 607-277-2338 ext 255 *E-mail:* msk55@cornell.edu
Sales Mgr: Nathan Gemignani *Tel:* 607-277-2338 ext 251 *E-mail:* ndg5@cornell.edu
Subs Rts Mgr: Tonya Cook *Tel:* 607-277-2397 *E-mail:* cup-subrights@cornell.edu
Asst to the Dir: Michael A Morris *Tel:* 607-277-2338 ext 210 *E-mail:* mam278@cornell.edu

Founded: 1869 (reconstituted in 1930)
General nonfiction, scholarly books & monographs; hardcover & paperbacks.
ISBN Prefix(es): 978-0-8014; 978-0-87546
Number of titles published annually: 150 Print
Total Titles: 2,200 Print
Imprints: Comstock Publishing Associates; ILR Press
Distributor for Cornell Southeast Asia Program (SEAP) Publications; Leuven University Press
Foreign Rep(s): Avicenna Partnership Ltd (Cyprus, Greece, Malta, Middle East, North Africa, Turkey); East-West Export Books (Asia); Footprint Books Pty Ltd (Australia, New Zealand, Oceania); Lexa Publishers' Representatives (Canada); Uwe Ludemann (Austria, Germany, Italy, Liechtenstein, Switzerland); University Presses Marketing (Benelux, France, Ireland, Israel, Portugal, Scandinavia, Spain, UK); US PubRep Inc (Latin America)
*Orders to:* Cup Services, 750 Cascadilla St, Ithaca, NY 14850 *Tel:* 607-277-2211 *Toll Free Tel:* 800-666-2211 *Toll Free Fax:* 800-688-2877 *E-mail:* orderbook@cupserv.org *Web Site:* cupserv.org
*Returns:* Cup Services, 750 Cascadilla St, Ithaca, NY 14850 *Tel:* 607-277-2211 *Toll Free Tel:* 800-666-2211 *Toll Free Fax:* 800-688-2877 *E-mail:* orderbook@cupserv.org *Web Site:* cupserv.org
*Shipping Address:* Cup Services, 750 Cascadilla St, Ithaca, NY 14850 *Tel:* 607-277-2211 *Toll Free Tel:* 800-666-2211 *Toll Free Fax:* 800-688-2877 *E-mail:* orderbook@cupserv.org *Web Site:* cupserv.org
*Warehouse:* Cup Services, 750 Cascadilla St, Ithaca, NY 14850 *Tel:* 607-277-2211 *Toll Free Tel:* 800-666-2211 *Toll Free Fax:* 800-688-2877 *E-mail:* orderbook@cupserv.org *Web Site:* cupserv.org
*Distribution Center:* Cup Services, 750 Cascadilla St, Ithaca, NY 14850 *Tel:* 607-277-2211 *Toll Free Tel:* 800-666-2211 *Toll Free Fax:* 800-688-2877 *E-mail:* orderbook@cupserv.org *Web Site:* cupserv.org
Membership(s): AAP; Association of American University Presses

**Cornell University Southeast Asia Program Publications**
Unit of Cornell University
213 Kahin Ctr, 640 Stewart Ave, Ithaca, NY 14850
*Tel:* 607-277-2211 *Toll Free Tel:* 800-666-2211 *Fax:* 607-277-6292 *Toll Free Fax:* 800-688-2877
*E-mail:* seap-pubs@cornell.edu
*Web Site:* www.einaudi.cornell.edu/southeastasia/publications
*Key Personnel*
Dist & Busn Mgr: Cindy Dickerson *Tel:* 607-255-8038 *Fax:* 607-255-7534
Mng Ed: Deborah Homsher *Tel:* 607-255-4359 *Fax:* 607-277-1904 *E-mail:* dlh10@cornell.edu
Pubns Asst: Fred Connor *E-mail:* flc2@cornell.edu
Founded: 1951
Publish books & one semiannual journal (Indonesia) on the history, politics, culture & languages of Southeast Asian countries.
ISBN Prefix(es): 978-0-87727; 978-0-87763
Number of titles published annually: 6 Print; 1 CD-ROM
Total Titles: 130 Print
Distributor for A U A Language Center
*Orders to:* SEAP Publications, Box 1004, Cornell University, Rm 241, 95 Brown Rd, Ithaca, NY 14850-2820, Dist Mgr: Denise Rice *Fax:* 607-255-7534 *Toll Free Fax:* 877-865-2432
*Shipping Address:* SEAP Publications, Box 1004, Cornell University, Rm 241, 95 Brown Rd, Ithaca, NY 14850-2820, Dist Mgr: Denise Rice *Fax:* 607-255-7534 *Toll Free Fax:* 877-865-2432
*Warehouse:* SEAP Publications, Box 1004, Cornell University, Rm 241, 95 Brown Rd, Ithaca, NY 14850-2820, Dist Mgr: Denise Rice *Fax:* 607-255-7534 *Toll Free Fax:* 877-865-2432
*Distribution Center:* SEAP Publications, Box 1004, Cornell University, Rm 241, 95 Brown Rd, Ithaca, NY 14850-2820 *Tel:* 607-255-8038 *Fax:* 607-255-7534 *Toll Free Fax:* 877-865-2432

**Cornerstone Book Publishers**
PO Box 24652, New Orleans, LA 70184
*E-mail:* info@cornerstonepublishers.com
*Web Site:* www.cornerstonepublishers.com
*Key Personnel*
Owner: Michael R Poll
ISBN Prefix(es): 978-1-887560
Number of titles published annually: 6 Print; 10 E-Book
Total Titles: 33 Print; 65 E-Book
Foreign Rep(s): Ingram (UK)

**Cortina Institute of Languages**
Division of Cortina Learning International Inc (CLI)
7 Hollyhock Rd, Wilton, CT 06897
*Tel:* 203-762-2510 *Toll Free Tel:* 800-245-2145 *Fax:* 203-762-2514
*Web Site:* www.cortina-languages.com
*Key Personnel*
Pres: Robert E Livesey *E-mail:* r.livesey@cortinalearning.com
Mng Ed: Magdalen B Livesey *E-mail:* m.livesey@cortinalearning.com
Gen Mgr: George Bollas *E-mail:* g.bollas@cortinalearning.com
Founded: 1958
Learning foreign languages for English speakers; English as a second language.
ISBN Prefix(es): 978-0-8489
Number of titles published annually: 15 Print
Total Titles: 277 Print
*Warehouse:* 15 Great Pasture Rd, Danbury, CT 06810 *Tel:* 203-778-9639 *Fax:* 203-778-4029

**Cortina Learning International Inc (CLI)**
7 Hollyhock Rd, Wilton, CT 06897-4414
*Tel:* 203-762-2510 *Toll Free Tel:* 800-245-2145 *Fax:* 203-762-2514
*E-mail:* info@cortinalearning.com
*Web Site:* www.cortinalearning.com
*Key Personnel*
Pres: Robert E Livesey *Tel:* 203-762-2510 ext 110 *E-mail:* r.livesey@cortinalearning.com
Mng Ed: Magdalen B Livesey *Tel:* 203-762-2510 ext 109 *E-mail:* m.livesey@cortinalearning.com
Gen Mgr: George Bollas *Tel:* 203-762-2510 ext 105 *E-mail:* g.bollas@cortinalearning.com
Founded: 1882
Foreign languages, English as second language, art instruction, writing instruction, fiction & nonfiction.
ISBN Prefix(es): 978-0-8327
Number of titles published annually: 5 Print
Total Titles: 50 Print
Divisions: Cortina Institute of Languages; Famous Artists School; Famous Writers School
*Warehouse:* 15 Great Pasture Rd, Danbury, CT 06810 *Tel:* 203-778-9639 *Fax:* 203-778-4029
*See separate listing for:*
**Cortina Institute of Languages**

**Corwin, a Sage Co**
2455 Teller Rd, Thousand Oaks, CA 91320
*Tel:* 805-499-9734 *Toll Free Tel:* 800-233-9936 *Fax:* 805-499-5323 *Toll Free Fax:* 800-417-2466
*E-mail:* info@corwin.com
*Web Site:* www.corwin.com
*Key Personnel*
VP & Edit Dir: Lisa Shaw
Exec, Mktg & Sales: Elena Nikitina
Sr Licensing Mgr & Foreign Rts Agent: Anna Termine *E-mail:* anna.termine@sagepub.com
Founded: 1990
Offers practical, research-based books, journals & multimedia resources specifically developed for principals, administrators, teachers, staff developers, curriculum developers, special & gifted educators & other PreK-12 education professionals.
ISBN Prefix(es): 978-0-7619; 978-0-8039; 978-1-4129; 978-1-8904; 978-1-5751; 978-1-5697; 978-0-9637
Number of titles published annually: 120 Print
Total Titles: 1,900 Print
Distributor for SAGE UK Resources for Educators
Foreign Rep(s): SAGE India (India); SAGE London (Europe, UK); SAGE Singapore (Asia-Pacific)

**§Cosimo Inc**
Old Chelsea Sta, PO Box 416, New York, NY 10011
*Tel:* 212-989-3616 *Fax:* 212-989-3662
*E-mail:* info@cosimobooks.com
*Web Site:* www.cosimobooks.com
Founded: 2005
Specialty publisher for independent authors, not-for-profit organizations & innovative businesses, dedicated to publishing books that inspire, inform & engage readers around the world. We offer authors & organizations full publishing support, while using the newest technologies to present their works in the most timely & effective way.
ISBN Prefix(es): 978-1-931044 (Paraview Print on Demand titles); 978-0-743497 (Paraview Pocket Books)
Number of titles published annually: 12 Print; 12 E-Book
Total Titles: 45 Print
Imprints: Cosimo Books; Cosimo Classics; Cosimo Reports; Paraview Pocket Books
Divisions: Paraview Press

**Costume + Fashion Press**, see Quite Specific Media Group Ltd

**Cotsen Institute of Archaeology Press**
308 Charles E Young Dr N, Fowler A163, Box 951510, Los Angeles, CA 90024
*Tel:* 310-206-9384 *Fax:* 310-206-4723
*E-mail:* ioapubs@ioa.ucla.edu
*Web Site:* www.ioa.ucla.edu
*Key Personnel*
Dir of Institute: Charles Stanish *Tel:* 310-267-5579 *E-mail:* stanish@anthro.ucla.edu
Pubns Mgr: Randi Danforth *E-mail:* cioapress@ioa.ucla.edu
Founded: 1974
Books, monographs & occasional papers in the field of archaeology.
ISBN Prefix(es): 978-0-917956
Number of titles published annually: 5 Print
Total Titles: 69 Print
*Distribution Center:* University of New Mexico Press, 1312 Basehart Rd SE, Albuquerque, NM *Tel:* 505-272-7777 *Toll Free Tel:* 800-249-7737 (ordering) *Toll Free Fax:* 800-622-8667 *E-mail:* unmpress@unm.edu *Web Site:* www.unmpress.com

**Cottonwood Press**
University of Kansas, Kansas Union, Rm 400, 1301 Jayhawk Blvd, Lawrence, KS 66045
*Tel:* 785-864-4520
*E-mail:* pwedge@ku.edu
*Web Site:* www.cottonwoodmagazine.org

*Key Personnel*
Ed: Tom Lorenz *Tel:* 785-864-2516 *E-mail:* tlorenz@ku.edu
Founded: 1965
Poetry & fiction.
ISBN Prefix(es): 978-1-878434
Number of titles published annually: 4 Print
Total Titles: 15 Print
Membership(s): Council of Literary Magazines & Presses

**Council for Exceptional Children (CEC)**
2900 Crystal Dr, Suite 1000, Arlington, VA 22201
*Toll Free Tel:* 888-232-7733 (memb servs); 866-509-0219 *Fax:* 703-264-9494
*E-mail:* service@cec.sped.org
*Web Site:* www.cec.sped.org
*Key Personnel*
Exec Dir: Bruce Ramirez *Tel:* 703-264-9415 *E-mail:* brucer@cec.sped.org
Founded: 1922
Mail order books & videos to improve the educational success of individuals with disabilities &/or gifts & talents.
ISBN Prefix(es): 978-0-86586
Number of titles published annually: 6 Print
Total Titles: 75 Print
*Branch Office(s)*
CEC Publications, PO Box 79026, Baltimore, MD 21279-0026
Distributed by Free Spirit Publishing Inc; LMD Inc (selected titles); Orchard House Inc
Distributor for Brooks (selected titles); Longman; Love Publishing; Pearson; Pro Ed; Sopris West

**Council for Research in Values & Philosophy (RVP)**
The Catholic University of America, Gibbons Hall, Rm B-12, 620 Michigan Ave NE, Washington, DC 20064
Mailing Address: PO Box 261, Cardinal Sta, Washington, DC 20064-0261
*Tel:* 202-319-6089 *Fax:* 202-319-6089
*E-mail:* cua-rvp@cua.edu
*Web Site:* www.crvp.org
*Key Personnel*
Gen Ed: George F McLean *E-mail:* mclean@cua.edu
Dir, Opers & Treas: Hu Yeping *E-mail:* huy@cua.edu
Founded: 1982
Works on philosophy, values, education, civil society, culture.
ISBN Prefix(es): 978-1-56518
Number of titles published annually: 25 Print; 25 Online
Total Titles: 220 Print; 215 Online
Imprints: The Council for Research in Values & Philosophy
*Orders to:* Oblate School of Theology (OST), 285 Oblate Dr, San Antonio, TX 78216

**Council Oak Books LLC**
2 W Sixth St, Suite 262, Tulsa, OK 74119
SAN: 689-5522
*Tel:* 918-743-BOOK (743-2665) *Toll Free Tel:* 800-247-8850 *Fax:* 918-743-4288
*E-mail:* publicity@counciloakbooks.com; order@counciloakbooks.com
*Web Site:* www.counciloakbooks.com
*Key Personnel*
Publr: Paulette Millichap *E-mail:* pmillichap@sbcglobal.net
Founded: 1984
Publisher of nonfiction titles that point the way to a richer life & a better world. Areas of special interest include world religions, Native American, Americana (especially Route 66), animals & nature.
ISBN Prefix(es): 978-0-933031 (Council Oak Books); 978-1-57178 (Council Oak Books); 978-1-879290 (Pagemill); 978-1-88517 (Wildcat Canyon Press)
Number of titles published annually: 10 Print
Total Titles: 300 Print
Imprints: Pagemill Press (Religious Studies); Wildcat Canyon Press (Women's relationships)
*Shipping Address:* Council Oak Fulfillment Center, 7601-A E 46 St, Tulsa, OK 74145, Prodn Mgr: Kelly Hauf *Tel:* 918-641-5565 *Fax:* 918-641-5569 *E-mail:* shipping@counciloakbooks.com *Web Site:* www.counciloakbooks.com

**Council of State Governments**
2760 Research Park Dr, Lexington, KY 40511
Mailing Address: PO Box 11910, Lexington, KY 40578-1910
*Tel:* 859-244-8000 *Toll Free Tel:* 800-800-1910 *Fax:* 859-244-8001
*E-mail:* sales@csg.org
*Web Site:* www.csg.org
*Key Personnel*
Exec Dir: David Adkins *E-mail:* dadkins@csg.org
Founded: 1933
Nonprofit association representing state government officials in all three branches. Publish reference guides, books, directories, journals, newsletters & conference proceedings & hold major regional & special topical conferences. Will contract or do grant-funded topic research. Specialize in corrections & public safety.
ISBN Prefix(es): 978-0-87292
Number of titles published annually: 10 Print
Total Titles: 72 Print
*Branch Office(s)*
1107 Ninth St, Suite 650, Sacramento, CA 95814, Exec Dir: Kent Briggs *Tel:* 916-553-4423 *Fax:* 916-446-5760 *E-mail:* csqw@csq.org
444 N Capitol St NW, Suite 401, Washington, DC 20001, Gen Coun & Off Mgr: Jim Brown *Tel:* 202-624-5460 *Fax:* 202-624-5452 *E-mail:* csqdc@csq.org
PO Box 98129, Decatur, GA 30359, Exec Dir: Colleen Cousineau *Tel:* 404-633-1866 *Fax:* 404-633-4896 *E-mail:* slc@csq.org
701 E 22 St, Suite 110, Lombard, IL 60148, Off Dir: Michael H McCabe *Tel:* 630-925-1922 *Fax:* 630-925-1930 *E-mail:* csqm@csq.org
100 Wall St, 20th fl, New York, NY 10005, Off Dir: Alan Sokolow *Tel:* 212-482-2320 *Fax:* 212-482-2344

**Council on Foreign Relations Press**
Division of Council on Foreign Relations
The Harold Pratt House, 58 E 68 St, New York, NY 10065
SAN: 201-7784
*Tel:* 212-434-9400 *Fax:* 212-434-9800
*E-mail:* publications@cfr.org
*Web Site:* www.cfr.org
*Key Personnel*
CIO & Publr: David Kellogg *E-mail:* dkellogg@cfr.org
Dir, Publg: Patricia Dorff *Tel:* 212-434-9514 *Fax:* 212-434-9859 *E-mail:* pdorff@cfr.org
Founded: 1922
Scholarly books on foreign policy, international economics, international affairs.
ISBN Prefix(es): 978-0-87609
Number of titles published annually: 10 Print
Total Titles: 228 Print
*Branch Office(s)*
1777 "F" St NW, Washington, DC 20006 *Tel:* 202-509-8400 *Fax:* 202-509-8490
Distributed by Brookings Institution Press
Membership(s): AAP

**Council on Social Work Education (CSWE)**
1701 Duke St, Suite 200, Alexandria, VA 22314-3457
*Tel:* 703-683-8080 *Fax:* 703-683-8493
*E-mail:* publications@cswe.org; info@cswe.org
*Web Site:* www.cswe.org
*Key Personnel*
Exec Dir: Julia M Watkins, PhD *Tel:* 703-519-2066 *E-mail:* jwatkins@cswe.org
Pubns Mgr: Elizabeth Simon *Tel:* 703-519-2076 *E-mail:* esimon@cswe.org
Founded: 1952 (Professional Association)
Professional books.
ISBN Prefix(es): 978-0-87293
Number of titles published annually: 6 Print
Total Titles: 75 Print
Membership(s): Association Media & Publishing

**Counterpath Press**
PO Box 18351, Denver, CO 80218
*E-mail:* editors@counterpathpress.org
*Web Site:* www.counterpathpress.org
*Key Personnel*
Publr: Julie Carr *E-mail:* jc@counterpathpress.org; Tim Roberts *E-mail:* tr@counterpathpress.org
Founded: 2006
Independent, nonprofit, literary publisher of poetry, fiction, drama, cross-genre work, literary & cultural theory & criticism, translations, reprints & high-quality internet material.
ISBN Prefix(es): 978-1-933996
Number of titles published annually: 6 Print
Total Titles: 15 Print
*Distribution Center:* Small Press Distribution, 1341 Seventh St, Berkeley, CA 94710-1409, Deputy Dir: Laura Moriarty *Tel:* 510-524-1668 *Fax:* 510-524-0852 *E-mail:* laura@spdbooks.org *Web Site:* www.spdbooks.org
Membership(s): Council of Literary Magazines & Presses

**Counterpoint Press LLC**
1919 Fifth St, Berkeley, CA 94710
*Tel:* 510-704-0230 *Fax:* 510-704-0268
*E-mail:* info@counterpointpress.com
*Web Site:* www.counterpointpress.com; www.sierraclub.org/books; www.softskull.com
*Key Personnel*
CEO, Publr & Exec Ed-at-Large: Charlie Winton
VP & Edit Dir: Jack Shoemaker
Publg Dir: Sharon Donovan
Publr, Counterpoint/Soft Skull: Rolph Blythe
Busn Mgr: Kelli Adams
Publicity Mgr: Earlita Chenault; Tiffany Lee
Ed-at-Large: Dan Smetanka
Founded: 1994
Publish literary work with an emphasis on fiction, natural history, philosophy & contemporary thought, history, art, poetry, narrative & nonfiction.
ISBN Prefix(es): 978-1-887178; 978-1-58243 (Counter Point); 978-1-59376 (Counter Point); 978-1-93336 (Soft Skull); 978-1-57805 (Serra Club Books); 978-0-97966 (Soft Skull); 978-1-93236 (Soft Skull)
Number of titles published annually: 60 Print
Total Titles: 60 Print
Imprints: Counterpoint; Sierra Club Books; Soft Skull Press
Distributed by Publishers Group West

**Country Music Foundation Press**
Division of Country Music Hall of Fame® & Museum
222 Fifth Ave S, Nashville, TN 37203
*Tel:* 615-416-2001 *Fax:* 615-255-2245
*E-mail:* info@countrymusichalloffame.com
*Web Site:* www.countrymusichalloffame.com
Founded: 1967
Publish books & calendars. Also author books for trade publications & co-publish with Vanderbilt University Press.
ISBN Prefix(es): 978-1-55859; 978-0-8265; 978-0-915608
Number of titles published annually: 4 Print

Total Titles: 40 Print
Distributed by Chronicle; Oxford University Press Inc; Providence Publishing; Universe; Vanderbilt University Press

**The Countryman Press**
Division of W W Norton & Co Inc
43 Lincoln Corners Way, Woodstock, VT 05091
SAN: 206-4901
Mailing Address: PO Box 748, Woodstock, VT 05091-0748
*Tel:* 802-457-4826 *Toll Free Tel:* 800-245-4151 *Fax:* 802-457-1678
*E-mail:* countrymanpress@wwnorton.com
*Web Site:* www.countrymanpress.com
*Key Personnel*
Chmn & Pres, W W Norton: W Drake McFeely
Edit Dir: Kermit Hummel *E-mail:* khummel@wwnorton.com
Sr Ed: Ann Treistman
Prod Mgr: Fred Lee *E-mail:* flee@wwnorton.com
Founded: 1973
ISBN Prefix(es): 978-1-58157; 978-0-88150; 978-0-942440; 978-0-912367
Number of titles published annually: 70 Print
Total Titles: 350 Print
Imprints: Backcountry Guides
Distributed by Penguin Books (CN only); W W Norton & Co Inc
Distributor for Mountain Pond Publishing Corp
Foreign Rep(s): W W Norton & Co Inc
*Advertising Agency:* Bennett Book Advertising
*Warehouse:* National Book Co Inc, 800 Keystone Industrial Park, Scranton, PA 18512-4601

**Course Technology**, see Wadsworth Publishing

**Course Technology**
Imprint of Cengage Learning
20 Channel Center St, Boston, MA 02210
*Tel:* 617-757-7900 *Toll Free Tel:* 800-354-9706 (cust serv) *Fax:* 617-757-7969
*E-mail:* reply@course.com
*Web Site:* www.cengage.com/coursetechnology; www.course.com
*Key Personnel*
CEO: Michael Hansen
Founded: 1989
Post-secondary educational materials featuring popular commercial software application packages.
ISBN Prefix(es): 978-0-534; 978-1-878748; 978-1-56527; 978-0-538; 978-0-7600; 978-0-7895; 978-1-929685; 978-1-931841; 978-0-9662889; 978-1-932094
Number of titles published annually: 850 Print
Total Titles: 930 Print
Distributed by South-Western Publishing
Foreign Rep(s): Nelson Canada (Canada); Professional Publications (Canada); Times Mirror (Canada)
*Advertising Agency:* Albuquerque Marketing
*Warehouse:* 10650 Tobben Rd, Independence, KY 41051

**§Covenant Communications Inc**
Division of Deseret Book Co
920 E State Rd, Suite F, American Fork, UT 84003-0416
Mailing Address: PO Box 416, American Fork, UT 84003-0416
*Tel:* 801-756-9966 *Toll Free Tel:* 800-662-9545 *Fax:* 801-756-1049
*E-mail:* info@covenant-lds.com
*Web Site:* www.covenant-lds.com
*Key Personnel*
VP, Mktg: Robby Nichols *Tel:* 801-756-1041 ext 106 *E-mail:* robbyn@covenant-lds.com
Mng Ed, Multimedia & Electronic Publg: Phil Reschke *Tel:* 801-756-1041 ext 114
Sales Mgr: Tammy Kolkman *Tel:* 801-756-1041 ext 122
Founded: 1958
Publish for the LDS (Mormon) market.
ISBN Prefix(es): 978-1-55503; 978-1-57734; 978-1-59156; 978-1-59811; 978-1-60681; 978-1-62108
Number of titles published annually: 60 Print; 60 E-Book; 50 Audio
Total Titles: 300 Print; 500 E-Book; 450 Audio

**Cowley Publications**
Imprint of Rowman & Littlefield Publishing Group
4501 Forbes Blvd, Suite 200, Lanham, MD 20706
SAN: 213-9987
*Tel:* 301-459-3366 *Toll Free Tel:* 800-462-6420 *Fax:* 301-429-5748 *Toll Free Fax:* 800-338-4550
*E-mail:* custserv@rowman.com
*Web Site:* rowman.com
*Key Personnel*
Dir, Sales: Sheila Burnett
Acqs Ed: Sarah Stanton
Founded: 1980
Contemporary spirituality, religion, cultural & social issues, history, theology.
ISBN Prefix(es): 978-0-936384; 978-1-56101
Number of titles published annually: 25 Print
Total Titles: 140 Print
Foreign Rep(s): Anglican Book Centre (Canada); Columba (Europe, Ireland, UK); John Garrett (Australia)
*Warehouse:* National Book Network (NBN), 15200 NBN Way, Blue Ridge Summit, PA 17214
*Distribution Center:* National Book Network (NBN), 15200 NBN Way, Blue Ridge Summit, PA 17214

**Coyote Press**
Affiliate of Archaeological Consulting
PO Box 3377, Salinas, CA 93912-3377
*Tel:* 831-422-4912 *Fax:* 831-422-4913
*E-mail:* orders@coyotepress.com
*Web Site:* www.coyotepress.com
*Key Personnel*
Owner & Ed: Gary Breschini, PhD
Founded: 1980
Archaeology, history, pre-history, ethnography, linguistics & rock art.
ISBN Prefix(es): 978-1-55567
Number of titles published annually: 50 Print
Total Titles: 3,000 Print

**CQ Press**
Division of SAGE Publications
2300 "N" St NW, Suite 800, Washington, DC 20037
*Tel:* 202-729-1900 *Toll Free Tel:* 866-4CQ-PRESS (427-7737) *Fax:* 202-729-1923 *Toll Free Fax:* 800-380-3810
*E-mail:* customerservice@cqpress.com
*Web Site:* www.cqpress.com
*Key Personnel*
Pres & Publr: John Jenkins
Mgr, Cust Serv & Opers: Judy L Plummer
Natl Sales Mgr: Ron Parisi
Founded: 1959
Publisher of books, directories, subscriptions & web products on American politics, federal & state government, American Institutions, campaigns & elections, current events & world affairs.
ISBN Prefix(es): 978-0-87289; 978-1-56802
Number of titles published annually: 50 Print
Total Titles: 300 Print; 4 CD-ROM; 1 Online; 3 E-Book
Foreign Rep(s): CQ Press (Lisa Larson); SAGE Publications (Amanda Fox); SAGE Publications (Sarah Broomhead); SAGE Publications Asia-Pacific Pte Ltd (Rosalia da Garcia)

**§Crabtree Publishing Co**
350 Fifth Ave, 59th fl, PMB 59051, New York, NY 10118
*Tel:* 212-496-5040 *Toll Free Tel:* 800-387-7650 *Toll Free Fax:* 800-355-7166
*E-mail:* custserv@crabtreebooks.com
*Web Site:* www.crabtreebooks.com
*Key Personnel*
Pres: Peter A Crabtree *Tel:* 212-496-5040 ext 225
Publr: Ms Bobbie Kalman
VP, Busn Devt & Foreign Rts Agent, North America: Sean Charlebois *Tel:* 212-496-5040 ext 240 *E-mail:* sean_c@crabtreebooks.com
Dir, Art & New Media: Robert MacGregor *Tel:* 212-496-5040 ext 231 *E-mail:* rob_m@crabtreebooks.com
Edit Dir: Kathy Middleton *Tel:* 212-496-5040 ext 226 *E-mail:* kathy_m@crabtreebooks.com
Mktg Dir: Lisa Maisonneuve *Tel:* 212-496-5040 ext 234 *E-mail:* lisa_m@crabtreebooks.com
Cont & Gen Mgr: John Siemens *Tel:* 212-496-5040 ext 229 *E-mail:* john_s@crabtreebooks.com
Cust Serv Mgr: Linda Wade *Tel:* 212-496-5040 ext 223 *E-mail:* linda_w@crabtreebooks.com
Sales & Mktg Mgr: Julie Alguire *Tel:* 212-496-5040 ext 235 *E-mail:* julie_a@crabtreebooks.com
Founded: 1978
Publisher of children's nonfiction & fiction; library binding & paperback for school & trade.
ISBN Prefix(es): 978-0-86505; 978-0-7787; 978-1-4271
Number of titles published annually: 201 Print; 634 E-Book; 48 Audio
Total Titles: 2,363 Print; 850 E-Book; 96 Audio
Subsidiaries: Crabtree Publishing Canada
Distributor for Bayard; Maren Green
Foreign Rep(s): BookSmart (China, Japan); INT Press (Australia, New Zealand); Roundhouse Group (European Union, UK); Titles (South Africa)
*Warehouse:* 255 Great Arrow Ave, Suite 1, Buffalo, NY 14207
Membership(s): ABA; ALA; American Alliance of Museums; Educational Book & Media Association; Museum Store Association; NAIPR; National Science Teachers Association

**§Craftsman Book Co**
6058 Corte Del Cedro, Carlsbad, CA 92011
SAN: 159-7000
Mailing Address: PO Box 6500, Carlsbad, CA 92018
*Tel:* 760-438-7828 *Toll Free Tel:* 800-829-8123 *Fax:* 760-438-0398
*Web Site:* www.craftsman-book.com
*Key Personnel*
Chmn & Intl Rts: Gary Moselle
EVP & Treas: Ben Moselle
Dir, Lib Sales & Mgr, Sales & Ad: Jennifer Johnson *Tel:* 760-438-7828 ext 105 *E-mail:* johnson@costbook.com
Edit Mgr & Rts & Perms: Laurence Jacobs *E-mail:* jacobs@costbook.com
Founded: 1952
Estimating software, trade & professional, state-specific contract-writing software, subscription, mail order & download, reference; construction industry.
ISBN Prefix(es): 978-0-934041; 978-0-910460; 978-1-57218
Number of titles published annually: 12 Print; 11 CD-ROM; 150 Online; 5 E-Book
Total Titles: 150 Print; 11 CD-ROM; 150 Online; 8 E-Book
Distributed by The Aberdeen Group; BNI Publications; Builders Book Inc; Quality Books
Distributor for BNI Publications; Builders Book Inc; Building News Inc; Home Builders Press
Foreign Rep(s): Gauge Publications (Canada)

**§CRC Press LLC**
Subsidiary of Taylor & Francis
6000 Broken Sound Pkwy NW, Suite 300, Boca Raton, FL 33487
*Tel:* 561-994-0555 *Toll Free Tel:* 800-272-7737 *Fax:* 561-998-9784; 561-997-7249 (edit); 561-361-6057 (tax dept); 561-989-9732 (orders) *Toll Free Fax:* 800-643-9428 (sales); 800-374-3401 (orders)
*E-mail:* orders@taylorandfrancis.com
*Web Site:* www.crcpress.com
*Key Personnel*
Pres: Emmett Dages
SVP, Publg & Online Prods: John Lavender *Tel:* 561-998-2579 *E-mail:* john.lavender@taylorandfrancis.com
SVP, Sales: Dennis Weiss *Tel:* 561-998-2510 *E-mail:* dennis.weiss@taylorandfrancis.com
Founded: 1913
ISBN Prefix(es): 978-0-8493; 978-0-87371; 978-1-56670
Number of titles published annually: 900 Print
Total Titles: 14,000 Print
Foreign Rights: CRC Press
*Warehouse:* Taylor & Francis, 7625 Empire Dr, Florence, KY 41042
*See separate listing for:*
**A K Peters Ltd**

**§Creating Crafts Group LLC**
741 Corporate Circle, Suite A, Golden, CO 80401
*Tel:* 303-215-5600
*E-mail:* editorial@creatingkeepsakes.com
*Web Site:* www.creatingkeepsakes.com
*Key Personnel*
Creative Dir: Erin Bayless
Ed-in-Chief: Jennafer Martin
Publishes books for creative people on photography, lettering, card-making, paper crafts & holidays, as well as on scrapbooking, quilting & sewing.
ISBN Prefix(es): 978-1-929180
Number of titles published annually: 6 Print; 2 CD-ROM
Total Titles: 15 Print; 2 CD-ROM
*Sales Office(s):* 14850 Pony Express Rd, Bluffdale, UT 84065 (sales to retail shops & distributors) *Toll Free Tel:* 800-815-3538 *Fax:* 801-816-8366 *E-mail:* sales@monsoonimages.com
*Billing Address:* 624 Maryland Ave NE, Suite 9, Washington, DC 20002
Membership(s): Publishers Association of the West

**The Creative Co**
123 S Broad St, Mankato, MN 56001
SAN: 202-201X
Mailing Address: PO Box 227, Mankato, MN 56002
*Tel:* 507-388-6273 *Toll Free Tel:* 800-445-6209 *Fax:* 507-388-2746
*E-mail:* info@thecreativecompany.us
*Web Site:* www.thecreativecompany.us
*Key Personnel*
Owner & Publr: Tom Peterson *Tel:* 507-388-6273 ext 225
VP, Retail Sales, Creative Editions & Creative Paperbacks: Anna Erikson
Founded: 1932
Gift books.
ISBN Prefix(es): 978-0-87191; 978-0-88682
Number of titles published annually: 110 Print
Total Titles: 3,500 Print
Imprints: Creative Editions; Creative Education; Creative Paperbacks
Foreign Rep(s): Saunders Book Co (Canada)
*Warehouse:* 2140 Howard Dr W, North Mankato, MN 56003

**Creative Homeowner**
Subsidiary of Courier Corp
24 Park Way, Upper Saddle River, NJ 07458-9960
SAN: 213-6627
Mailing Address: PO Box 38, Upper Saddle River, NJ 07458-0038
*Tel:* 201-934-7100 *Toll Free Tel:* 800-631-7795 (cust serv) *Fax:* 201-934-7541; 201-934-8971 (orders)
*E-mail:* info@creativehomeowner.com; customerservice@creativehomeowner.com
*Web Site:* www.creativehomeowner.com
*Key Personnel*
Publr: Timothy O Bakke *Tel:* 201-934-7100 ext 218
Sales Mgr: Judy Kessler
Sr Ed: Carol Endler Sterbenz
Founded: 1978
Quality trade paperbacks for home improvement, design, decorating, gardening, landscaping, home plans; home arts, hunting & fishing.
ISBN Prefix(es): 978-0-932944; 978-1-880029; 978-1-58011
Number of titles published annually: 20 Print
Total Titles: 220 Print
Foreign Rep(s): Thomas Allen & Son (Canada); J C C Inc (Latin America); Nationwide Book Dist; Nationwide Book Distributors (New Zealand); Parrot Reads Publishers (India); Phambili Agencies (South Africa); Publishers International Marketing (Southeast Asia); Steven Sussman (all other territories); Tasarim Publishing Group (Middle East)
Foreign Rights: Timothy O Bakke (all other territories)
Membership(s): BISG; IBPA, the Independent Book Publishers Association

**Cricket Books**
Division of Carus Publishing
70 E Lake St, Suite 300, Chicago, IL 60601
*Tel:* 603-924-7209 *Toll Free Tel:* 800-821-0115
*E-mail:* customerservice@caruspub.com
*Web Site:* www.cricketmag.com
*Key Personnel*
Edit Dir: Alice Letvin
Founded: 1973
ISBN Prefix(es): 978-0-8126
Number of titles published annually: 20 Print
Total Titles: 40 Print
*Distribution Center:* Publishers Group West, 1700 Fourth St, Berkeley, CA *Tel:* 510-809-3700 *Fax:* 510-809-3777 *Web Site:* www.pgw.com

**Crickhollow Books**
Imprint of Great Lakes Literary LLC
3147 S Pennsylvania Ave, Milwaukee, WI 53207
*Tel:* 414-294-4319
*E-mail:* info@crickhollowbooks.com
*Web Site:* www.crickhollowbooks.com
*Key Personnel*
Edit Dir: Philip Martin
Founded: 1993
Publish books on regional heritage, with a focus on books for children, fiction & chapter books with a regional slant.
ISBN Prefix(es): 978-1-883953
Number of titles published annually: 3 Print
Total Titles: 12 Print
Membership(s): IBPA, the Independent Book Publishers Association

**§Cross-Cultural Communications**
Division of Cross-Cultural Literary Editions Inc
239 Wynsum Ave, Merrick, NY 11566-4725
SAN: 208-6122
*Tel:* 516-868-5635 *Fax:* 516-379-1901
*E-mail:* info@cross-culturalcommunications.com; cccbarkan@optlonline.net; cccpoetry@aol.com
*Web Site:* www.cross-culturalcommunications.com
*Key Personnel*
Publr & Ed-in-Chief: Stanley H Barkan
Art Ed: Bebe Barkan
Asst Ed: Mia Barkan Clarke
Founded: 1971
Traditionally neglected languages & cultures in bilingual format, primarily poetry, some fiction, drama, music & art. Cross-cultural review series of world literature & art in sound, print & motion.
ISBN Prefix(es): 978-0-89304
Number of titles published annually: 20 Print; 1 CD-ROM; 100 Online; 1 Audio
Total Titles: 400 Print; 3 CD-ROM; 12 Audio
Imprints: ARC (Magazine & Press) (Israel); Chlen$kiy Publishing (US & Russia); Cross-Cultural Prototypes; Expressive Editions; Fact Publishers (Ukraine); Midrashic Editions; Nightingale Editions; Ostrich Editions; The Seventh Quarry (Wales, Seventh Quarry Chapbook Series); The Seventh Quarry Press
Subsidiaries: Bulgarian-American Cultural Society ALEKO (Chicago/Sofia, Bulgaria); Varlik (Turkey)
*Branch Office(s)*
3131 Mott Ave, Far Rockaway, NY 11691, Contact: Roy Cravzow *Tel:* 718-327-4714
6 Pfeiffer Ridge, Big Sur, CA 93920, Contact: Patricia Holt *Tel:* 831-667-2433 *E-mail:* surph8@yahoo.com
*Foreign Office(s):* Antigruppo Siciliano, Via Mogia 8, 90138 Palermo, Sicily PA, Italy, Contact: Nicolo D'Alessandro *Tel:* (091) 322030 *E-mail:* nicolodalessandro@virgilio.it
Distributed by Ad Infinitum Books; Hochelaga (Canada)
Distributor for Ad Infinitum Press; Arba Sicula (Magazine, US); Center of Emigrants from Serbia (Serbia); Decalogue Books (US); Greenfield Review Press (US); Hochelaga (Canada); Immagine&Poesia (Italy); Legas Publishers (CN); Lips (Magazine & Press) (US); Pholiota Press Inc (England); The Seventh Quarry Press (Wales); Shabdaguchha (Magazine & Press) (Bangladesh & US); Sicilia Parra (Magazine, US); Word & Quill Press (US)
Foreign Rep(s): Hassanal Abdullah (Bangladesh, USA); Karen Alkalay-Gut (Israel); Max Babi (India); Vahe Baladouni (Armenia, USA); Raymond Beauchemin (Canada); August Bover (Spain); Bohdan Boychuk (Ukraine), Gaetano Cipolla (Italy, USA); Nicolo D'Alessandro (Italy); Kristine Doll (Spain, USA); Christopher Fauske (Norway, USA); Isaac Goldemberg (Peru, USA); Theofil Halama (Czech Republic, USA); Talat S Halman (Turkey, USA); Luisa A Igloria (Philippines, USA); Vladimir Kandelaki (Georgia); Dovid Katz (UK); Naoshi Koriyama (Japan); Dariusz Thomasz Lebioda (Poland); Vladimir Levchev (Bulgaria, USA); Bijana D Obradovic (Montenegro, Serbia, USA); Ritva Poom (Estonia, Finland, USA); Kyung-Nyun "Kay" Kim Richards (South Korea, USA); Stephen A Sadow (Argentina, USA); Marco Scalabrino (Italy); Stoyan "Tchouki" Tchoukanov (Bulgaria); Peter Thabit Jones (UK); Tino Villanueva (Mexico, USA); Claire Nicolas White (Netherlands, USA); Sara Wolosker (Brazil)
Membership(s): ALTA

**Crossquarter Publishing Group**
1910 Sombra Ct, Santa Fe, NM 87505
Mailing Address: PO Box 23749, Santa Fe, NM 87502
*Tel:* 505-690-3923 *Fax:* 214-975-9715
*E-mail:* sales@crossquarter.com; info@crossquarter.com
*Web Site:* www.crossquarter.com
*Key Personnel*
CTO: Anthony Ravenscroft *E-mail:* aravenscroft@crossquarter.com
Exec Dir: Therese Francis
Founded: 1996

Small book press with some sidelines. Publishes books, e-books & information packages. No longer accept fiction queries.
ISBN Prefix(es): 978-1-890109
Number of titles published annually: 25 Print; 3 E-Book
Total Titles: 57 Print; 2 E-Book
Imprints: Crossquarter Breeze; CrossTIME; Fenris Brothers; Herbs & Spice; Xemplar
Membership(s): The Association of Publishers for Special Sales; IBPA, the Independent Book Publishers Association

**§The Crossroad Publishing Co**
831 Chestnut Ridge Rd, Chestnut Ridge, NY 10977
SAN: 287-0118
*Tel:* 845-517-0180 *Toll Free Tel:* 800-888-4741 (orders) *Fax:* 845-517-0181
*Web Site:* www.CrossroadPublishing.com
*Key Personnel*
CEO & Publr: Dr Gwendolin Herder
Edit Dir: Dr John Jones *E-mail:* jjones@crossroadpublishing.com
Off Admin: Grace Darmiento *E-mail:* administration@crossroadpublishing.com
Founded: 1980
Independent book publisher in religion, spirituality, theology, personal growth, leadership & parenting.
ISBN Prefix(es): 978-0-8245
Number of titles published annually: 30 Print; 1 CD-ROM; 1 Online; 4 E-Book; 1 Audio
Total Titles: 550 Print; 1 CD-ROM; 1 Online; 20 E-Book; 4 Audio
Imprints: Crossroad (trade secular & religious); Herder & Herder (Catholic parish & academic)
Foreign Rep(s): John Garratt (Australia); Novalis (Canada); Veritas (UK)
*Billing Address:* Independent Publishers Group, 814 N Franklin St, Chicago, IL 60610 *E-mail:* orders@ipgbook.com *Web Site:* www.ipgbook.com
Membership(s): Association of Catholic Publishers Inc

**Crossway**
Division of Good News Publishers
1300 Crescent St, Wheaton, IL 60187
SAN: 211-7991
*Tel:* 630-682-4300 *Toll Free Tel:* 800-635-7993 (orders); 800-543-1659 (cust serv) *Fax:* 630-682-4785
*E-mail:* info@crossway.org
*Web Site:* www.crossway.org
*Key Personnel*
Pres: Lane T Dennis
COO & EVP: Geoff Dennis
SVP, Book Div: Allan Fisher
SVP, Bible Prodn & SVP, Sales & Mktg: Randy Jahns
Natl Sales Mgr: Britt Edwards
Edit Administrator, Perms & ISBN Contact: Jill Carter *E-mail:* jcarter@crossway.org
Intl Rts: Patricia Slater
Founded: 1969
Books with an evangelical Christian perspective aimed at the religious market.
ISBN Prefix(es): 978-0-89107; 978-1-58134; 978-1-4335
Number of titles published annually: 80 Print
Total Titles: 354 Print; 9 Audio

**§Crown House Publishing Co LLC**
Division of Crown House Publishing Ltd (UK Co)
6 Trowbridge Dr, Bethel, CT 06801
SAN: 013-9270
*Tel:* 203-778-1300 *Toll Free Tel:* 877-925-1213 (cust serv); 866-272-8497 *Fax:* 203-778-9100
*E-mail:* info@chpus.com
*Web Site:* www.crownhousepublishing.com
*Key Personnel*
Pres: Mark Tracten *E-mail:* mtracten@chpus.com
Founded: 1996
Publisher of quality books in psychology & education.
ISBN Prefix(es): 978-1-89983; 978-1-90442; 978-1-84590; 978-0-98235
Number of titles published annually: 30 Print; 1 CD-ROM; 6 Audio
Total Titles: 330 Print; 2 CD-ROM; 30 Audio
Distributor for Developing Press Co; Human Alchemy Publications; Institute Press; Transforming Press
Foreign Rep(s): Footprint Books Pty Ltd (Australia, New Zealand)
Foreign Rights: Anglo-American Book Co Ltd (Europe, UK)
*Billing Address:* PO Box 2223, Williston, VT 05495
*Orders to:* PO Box 2223, Williston, VT 05495, Contact: Matt Drake *Fax:* 802-864-7626 *E-mail:* mdrake@aidcvt.com
*Returns:* 82 Wintersport Lane, Williston, VT 05496, Contact: Matt Drake *E-mail:* mdrake@aidcvt.com
*Shipping Address:* PO Box 2223, Williston, VT 05495, Contact: Laurie Kenyon *Tel:* 802-862-0095 ext 113 *Fax:* 802-864-7626 *E-mail:* info@chpus.com
*Warehouse:* PO Box 2223, Williston, VT 05495 *E-mail:* info@chpus.com
*Distribution Center:* 82 Wintersport Lane, Williston, VT 05496, Contact: Laurie Kenyon *Fax:* 802-864-7626 *E-mail:* lkenyon@aidcvt.com

**Crown Publishing Group**
Division of Random House Inc
c/o Random House Inc, 1745 Broadway, New York, NY 10019
*Tel:* 212-782-9000 *Toll Free Tel:* 888-264-1745 *Fax:* 212-940-7408
*Web Site:* www.randomhouse.com/crown
*Key Personnel*
Pres & Publr: Maya Mavjee
Pres & Publr, Waterbrook, Image & Convergent Books: Steve Cobb
EVP & Dir, Marketing: Donna Passanante
EVP & Dir, Publicity: Carisa Hays
SVP & Dir, Publg Opers: Jill Flaxman
SVP, Publg Opers: Pete Muller
SVP & Creative Dir: Whitney Cookman
SVP & Deputy Publr: David Drake
SVP & Publr, Clarkson Potter, Potter Craft & Potter Style: Lauren Shakely
SVP & Publr, Crown Archetype, Harmony Books, Crown Business & Crown Forum: Tina Constable
SVP & Publr, Crown Publishers, Broadway Books: Molly Stern
VP & Publr, Ten Speed Press: Aaron Wehner
VP & Publg Dir, Crown, Hogarth & Broadway Books: Jacob Lewis
VP & Assoc Publr, Ed-in-Chief, Doubleday Religion: Trace Murphy
VP & Assoc Publr, Trade Paperbacks: Catherine Pollock
VP & Exec Dir, Mktg, Waterbrook Multnomah: Carie Freimuth
VP & Dir, Sales, Mktg & Publicity, Ten Speed Press: Patricia Kelly
VP & Dir, Subs/Foreign Rts: Linda Kaplan
VP & Mng Ed: Amy Boorstein
Publr, Monacelli Press: Gianfranco Monacelli
Assoc Publr, Broadway Books & Hogart Paperbacks: Sheila O'Shea
Assoc Publr, Three Rivers Press & Crown Forum: Campbell Wharton
Creative Dir, Clarkson Potter & BOT: Marysarah Quinn
Dir, Community Devt: Kate Rados
Edit Dir, Crown Business: Roger Scholl
Edit Dir, Monacelli Press: Andrea Monfried
Mktg Dir, Crown Archetype, Harmony, Crown Business & Crown Forum: Meredith McGinnis
Mktg Dir, Crown Publishers & Broadway Books: Patty Berg
Mktg Dir, Ten Speed Press: Michele Crim
Deputy Mktg Dir, Crown Publishing Group & Mktg Dir, Clarkson Potter, Potter Craft, Potter Style & Monacelli Press: Donna Passannante
Sr Publicist: Megan Perritt
Publicist: Catherine Cullen; Rebecca Marsh
Publicity Dir, Clarkson Potter & Potter Style: Kate Tyler
Publicity Dir, Crown Archetype, Harmony Books, Crown Forum, Three Rivers: Tammy Blake
Publicity Dir, Crown Business: Tara Gilbride
Publicity Dir, Potter Craft, Watson-Guptill & Monacelli Press: Kim Small
Imprint Sales Dir: Candice Chaplin
Imprint Sales Dir, Publg Brands: Jacqueline Lebow
Publg Mgr, Crown Archetype, Harmony, Crown Business, Crown Forum: Mary Choteborsky
Publg Mgr, Three Rivers Press: Heather Lazare
Asst Mgr, Subs Rts: Nidhi Berry
Mktg Mgr, Hogarth, Crown & Broadway: Keyleigh George
Asst Mktg Mgr: Emily Davis
Exec Ed, Crown Archetype: Suzanne O'Neill
Exec Ed, Harmony Books: Sydny Miner
Mng Ed, Crown Trade, Broadway Books & Hogarth: Rachel Meier
Sr Ed, Crown Archetype: Talia Krohn
Sr Ed, Crown/Hogarth: Zack Wagman
Sr Ed, Nonfiction: Kevin Doughten
Ed, Broadway Books: Julian Pavia
Ed, Harmony Books: Leah Miller
Assoc Ed, Crown Archetype: Stephanie Knapp
Assoc Ed, Crown/Hogarth: Christine Kopprasch
Consulting Ed-at-Large, Harmony Books: Heather Jackson
Category Specialist: Allison Devlin
Founded: 1933
Nonfiction & fiction; illustrated books; business books.
Random House Inc & its publishing entities are not accepting unsol submissions, proposals, mss or submission queries via e-mail at this time.
ISBN Prefix(es): 978-0-609; 978-0-307; 978-0-8129; 978-1-4000; 978-0-517
Number of titles published annually: 400 Print
Imprints: Amphoto Books; Broadway Books; Clarkson Potter; Convergent Books; Crown Archetype; Crown Business; Crown Forum; Crown Publishers; Doubleday Religion; Harmony; Hogarth; The Monacelli Press; Potter Craft; Potter Style; Ten Speed Press; Three Rivers Press; Waterbrook Multnomah; Watson-Guptill
*See separate listing for:*
**Celestial Arts Publishing Co**
**Clarkson Potter Publishers**
**Ten Speed Press**
**Watson-Guptill Publications**

**Crumb Elbow Publishing**
PO Box 294, Rhododendron, OR 97049-0294
*Tel:* 503-622-4798
*Key Personnel*
Publr: Michael P Jones
Founded: 1979
Send an SASE for all mss, no exceptions.
ISBN Prefix(es): 978-0-89904
Number of titles published annually: 20 Print; 5 Audio
Total Titles: 500 Print
Imprints: Bear Meadows Research Group; Cascade Expeditions; Cascade Geographic Society; Ecosystem Research Group; Elbow Books; The Final Edition; Horse Latitudes Press; Lady Fern Press; Meadow Creek Press; Oregon Fever Books; Oregon River Watch; Read'n Run

Books; Research Centrex; Sealife Research Alliance; Silhouette Imprints; Timberline Productions; Trillium Mountain Productions; Tyee Press; Wildlife Research Group; Wild Mountain Press; Windflower Press

**§Crystal Clarity Publishers**
14618 Tyler Foote Rd, Nevada City, CA 95959
*Tel:* 530-478-7600 *Toll Free Tel:* 800-424-1055 *Fax:* 530-478-7610
*E-mail:* clarity@crystalclarity.com
*Web Site:* www.crystalclarity.com
*Key Personnel*
Pres & Publr: Skip Barrett *Tel:* 530-478-7600 ext 7606
Sales Mgr: Avital Miller *Tel:* 530-478-7600 ext 7605 *E-mail:* sales@crystalclarity.com
Founded: 1968
Self-help, psychology, philosophy, religion, business, books, tapes, videos, sidelines, metaphysical, health/healing.
ISBN Prefix(es): 978-0-916124; 978-1-878265; 978-1-56589
Number of titles published annually: 12 Print; 4 Audio
Total Titles: 104 Print; 15 Audio
Imprints: Clarity Sound & Light
Foreign Rep(s): Brumby Books (Australia); Deep Books Ltd (England, Europe); National Book Network (Canada, New Zealand); New Horizons (South Africa)
Foreign Rights: Alexandra McGilloway

**Crystal Productions**
1812 Johns Dr, Glenview, IL 60025
Mailing Address: PO Box 2159, Glenview, IL 60025-6159
*Tel:* 847-657-8144 *Toll Free Tel:* 800-255-8629 *Toll Free Fax:* 800-657-8149
*E-mail:* custserv@crystalproductions.com
*Web Site:* www.crystalproductions.com
*Key Personnel*
Chmn: Loretta Hubbard
Pres: Amy L Woodworth
VP: Douglas R Woodworth
Founded: 1979
Art education & earth science resources including books, CD-ROMs, DVDs, posters, prints, videos & timelines.
ISBN Prefix(es): 978-0-924509; 978-1-56290
Number of titles published annually: 3 Print; 3 CD-ROM
Total Titles: 8 Print

**Crystal Publishers Inc**
3460 Lost Hills Dr, Las Vegas, NV 89122
*Tel:* 702-434-3037 *Fax:* 702-434-3037
*Web Site:* www.crystalpub.com
*Key Personnel*
Pres: Frank Leanza *E-mail:* leanzaent@centurylink.net
Exec Dir: Inge Allen
Founded: 1985
Music books for schools & professionals.
ISBN Prefix(es): 978-0-934687
Number of titles published annually: 15 Print
Total Titles: 45 Print

**The CSIS Press**
Division of Center for Strategic & International Studies
1800 "K" St NW, Washington, DC 20006
*Tel:* 202-887-0200 *Fax:* 202-775-3199
*E-mail:* books@csis.org
*Web Site:* www.csis.org
*Key Personnel*
CEO & Pres: John J Hamre
Dir: James R Dunton *Tel:* 202-775-3160 *E-mail:* jdunton@csis.org
Mng Ed: Donna Spitler *Tel:* 202-775-3108 *E-mail:* dspitler@csis.org
Founded: 1962
Public policy research organization.
ISBN Prefix(es): 978-0-89206
Number of titles published annually: 65 Print; 65 Online; 25 E-Book
Total Titles: 250 Print; 100 Online; 200 E-Book
*Shipping Address:* Books International, 22883 Quicksilver Dr, Dulles, VA 20166 *Tel:* 703-661-1587 *Fax:* 703-661-1501 *E-mail:* bimail@presswarehouse.com
Membership(s): AAP

**§CSLI Publications**
Stanford University, Ventura Hall, 220 Panama St, Stanford, CA 94305-4115
*Tel:* 650-723-1839 *Fax:* 650-725-2166
*E-mail:* pubs@csli.stanford.edu
*Web Site:* cslipublications.stanford.edu
*Key Personnel*
Dir: Dikran Karagueuzian *Tel:* 650-723-1712 *E-mail:* dikran@csli.stanford.edu
Founded: 1985
Subjects include computer science, computational linguistics, linguistics & philosophy.
ISBN Prefix(es): 978-0-937073; 978-1-881526; 978-1-57586; 978-0-226
Number of titles published annually: 15 Print
Total Titles: 339 Print; 7 Online
Distributed by University of Chicago Press
*Advertising Agency:* University of Chicago Press, 1427 E 60 St, Chicago, IL 60637-2954 *Tel:* 773-568-1550 *Toll Free Tel:* 800-621-2736 *Fax:* 773-660-2235 *Toll Free Fax:* 800-621-8471

**CTB/McGraw-Hill**
Division of The McGraw-Hill Companies
20 Ryan Ranch Rd, Monterey, CA 93940-5703
*Tel:* 831-393-0700 *Toll Free Tel:* 800-538-9547 *Fax:* 831-393-7825
*Web Site:* www.ctb.com
*Key Personnel*
COO: Sandor Nagy *Tel:* 831-393-7070 *E-mail:* sandor_nagy@mcgraw-hill.com
Pres: Ellen Haley *Tel:* 831-393-7757 *Fax:* 831-393-7243 *E-mail:* ellen_haley@mcgraw-hill.com
VP, CTO: Bala Balachander *Tel:* 630-789-4168 *E-mail:* bala_balachander@mcgraw-hill.com
VP, Res, Prod Devt, Leadership: Richard Patz *Tel:* 831-334-0235 *E-mail:* richard_patz@mcgraw-hill.com
VP, Strategic Planning: Steven Paine *Tel:* 304-757-0093 *Fax:* 304-757-0094 *E-mail:* steven_paine@mcgraw-hill.com
Founded: 1926
Publishes nationally standardized tests, provides comprehensive scoring & reporting services & creates online solutions for managing & reporting test scores & student information to support sound accountability decisions.
ISBN Prefix(es): 978-0-9726382

**Cumberland House**
Imprint of Sourcebooks Inc
1935 Brookdale Rd, Suite 139, Naperville, IL 60563
*Tel:* 630-961-3900 *Toll Free Tel:* 800-43-BRIGHT (432-7444) *Fax:* 630-961-2168
*E-mail:* info@sourcebooks.com
*Web Site:* www.sourcebooks.com/products/cumberland.html
*Key Personnel*
CEO & Publr, Sourcebooks: Dominique Raccah
Founded: 1996
Nonfiction books & current subjects include cooking, regional topics, humor & lifestyle books.
ISBN Prefix(es): 978-1-888952; 978-1-58182
Number of titles published annually: 60 Print
Total Titles: 240 Print

Foreign Rep(s): Gazelle (UK); Jaguar Distribution (Canada)
Membership(s): ABA; IBPA, the Independent Book Publishers Association; Southern Independent Booksellers Alliance

**Cummings & Hathaway Publishers**
395 Atlantic Ave, East Rockaway, NY 11518
*Tel:* 516-593-3607 *Fax:* 516-593-1401
*Key Personnel*
Pres: William Burke
Founded: 1980
Publish paperback books only.
ISBN Prefix(es): 978-1-57981; 978-0-943025
Number of titles published annually: 5 Print
Total Titles: 48 Print

**CUNY Journalism Press**
Division of CUNY Graduate School of Journalism
219 W 40 St, New York, NY 10018
*Tel:* 646-758-7824 *Fax:* 646-758-7809
*Web Site:* www.journalism.cuny.edu; press.journalism.cuny.edu
Founded: 2012
Publish serious books about journalism & the news media - history, theory, criticism, craft, memoir & more.
ISBN Prefix(es): 978-1-939293
Number of titles published annually: 6 Print
Total Titles: 6 E-Book
Distributed by OR Books

**§Cup of Tea Books**
Imprint of PageSpring Publishing
2671 Bristol Rd, Columbus, OH 43221
Mailing Address: PO Box 21133, Columbus, OH 43221
*Tel:* 614-264-5588
*E-mail:* sales@pagespringpublishing.com
*Web Site:* www.cupofteabooks.com
*Key Personnel*
Ed: Rebecca Seum *Tel:* 614-283-9456 *E-mail:* rseum@pagespringpublishing.com
Sales & Mktg Dir: Lynn Bartels
Founded: 2012
Independent publisher. Specialize in quality women's fiction.
ISBN Prefix(es): 978-1-939403
Number of titles published annually: 6 Print; 6 E-Book
Total Titles: 2 Print; 2 E-Book

**Cupola Press®**
3280 Withers Ave, Lafayette, CA 94549
*Tel:* 925-285-7754 *Fax:* 925-256-6700
*Web Site:* www.cupolapress.com
*Key Personnel*
Owner: Gail Perry Johnston *Tel:* 925-256-4040 *E-mail:* gail@cupolapress.com
Founded: 2007
Produce unique books that inspire readers to see truth & celebrate. "Light Reading for International Living".
This publisher has indicated that 50% of their product line is author subsidized.
ISBN Prefix(es): 978-0-9793345
Number of titles published annually: 3 Print; 3 E-Book
Total Titles: 6 Print; 3 E-Book

**§Current Medicine Group (CMG)**
Division of Springer Healthcare Ltd
400 Market St, Suite 700, Philadelphia, PA 19106
*Tel:* 215-574-2266 *Toll Free Tel:* 800-427-1796 *Fax:* 215-574-2225
*E-mail:* info@currentmedicinegroup.com
*Web Site:* www.springerhealthcare.com
*Key Personnel*
Dir, Opers: Lori Holland *Tel:* 267-321-1705
Founded: 1986

Medical books & journals.
ISBN Prefix(es): 978-1-878132; 978-1-57340
Number of titles published annually: 30 Print
Total Titles: 101 Print; 40 CD-ROM
Imprints: Current Science Inc
*Branch Office(s)*
5 Marine View Plaza, Suite 218, Hoboken, NJ 07030 *Tel:* 201-222-8500 *Fax:* 201-222-1223
*Foreign Office(s):* 236 Gray's Inn Rd, London WC1X 8HL, United Kingdom *Tel:* (020) 7562 2930 *Fax:* (020) 3192 2011
Distributed by American Psychology Press; Appleton Lange; Blackwell Science; Butterworth-Heinemann; W B Saunders; Springer Verlag; Thieme; Williams & Wilkins

**Cycle Publishing**
1282 Seventh Ave, San Francisco, CA 94122-2526
*Tel:* 415-665-8214 *Toll Free Tel:* 877-353-1207 *Fax:* 415-753-8572
*E-mail:* contact@cyclepublishing.com
*Web Site:* www.cyclepublishing.com
*Key Personnel*
Principal & Publr: Rob van der Plas
Founded: 1985 (as Bicycle Books Inc)
Books on sports, fitness, home building & home buying; emphasis on cycling.
ISBN Prefix(es): 978-1-892495
Number of titles published annually: 6 Print
Total Titles: 30 Print
*Foreign Office(s):* Chris Lloyd, Stanley House, 3 Fleets Lane, Poole, Dorset BH15 3AJ, United Kingdom *Tel:* (01202) 649930
Distributed by Chris Lloyd
Foreign Rights: Orca Books (UK); Tower Books (Australia)
*Warehouse:* PCFS, 35 Ash Dr, Kimball, MI 48074
Membership(s): The Association of Publishers for Special Sales; IBPA, the Independent Book Publishers Association

**Cyclotour Guide Books**
160 Harvard St, Rochester, NY 14607
Mailing Address: PO Box 10585, Rochester, NY 14610-0585
*Tel:* 585-244-6157
*E-mail:* cyclotour@cyclotour.com
*Web Site:* www.cyclotour.com
*Key Personnel*
Publr & Author: Harvey Botzman
Founded: 1994
Books, bicycling related, bicycle (cycling) travel guides.
ISBN Prefix(es): 978-1-889602
Number of titles published annually: 4 Print
Total Titles: 7 Print

**Cypress House**
Imprint of Comp-Type Inc
155 Cypress St, Fort Bragg, CA 95437
*Tel:* 707-964-9520 *Toll Free Tel:* 800-773-7782 *Fax:* 707-964-7531
*E-mail:* cypresshouse@cypresshouse.com
*Web Site:* www.cypresshouse.com
*Key Personnel*
Pres: Cynthia Frank *E-mail:* cynthia@cypresshouse.com
Mng Ed: Joe Shaw *E-mail:* joeshaw@cypresshouse.com
Prodn Mgr: Michael Brechner *E-mail:* unclemike@cypresshouse.com
ISBN Prefix(es): 978-1-879384
Number of titles published annually: 10 Print
Total Titles: 1 Audio
Membership(s): ABA; IBPA, the Independent Book Publishers Association; Northern California Independent Booksellers Association; Pacific Northwest Booksellers Association

**Da Capo Press Inc & Lifelong Books**
Member of The Perseus Books Group
44 Farnsworth St, 3rd fl, Boston, MA 02210
SAN: 201-2944
*Tel:* 617-252-5200 *Toll Free Tel:* 800-343-4499 (orders) *Fax:* 617-252-5285
*Web Site:* www.perseusbooksgroup.com/dacapo
*Key Personnel*
Dir, Mktg: Kevin Hanover *Tel:* 617-252-5262
Sr Dir, Publicity: Lissa Warren *Tel:* 617-252-5212 *Fax:* 617-252-5265 *E-mail:* lissa.warren@perseusbooks.com
Sr Ed: Dan Ambrosio
Asst Ed: Christine Dore
Founded: 1964
Publishes a wide-ranging list of nonfiction titles, both hardcover & paperback, focusing on history, music, the performing arts, sports & popular culture. Lifelong Books is a health & wellness imprint founded in 2003 that publishes books on pregnancy, parenting, fitness, cooking, diabetes, psychology, personal growth & sexuality.
ISBN Prefix(es): 978-0-201; 978-0-7867; 978-0-306; 978-1-55561; 978-1-56858; 978-1-56924; 978-0-7382; 978-1-60094
Number of titles published annually: 90 Print
Total Titles: 5,000 Print
*Branch Office(s)*
387 Park Ave S, New York, NY 10016
Distributed by The Perseus Books Group
*Warehouse:* 1094 Flex Dr, Jackson, TN 38301

**Dalkey Archive Press**
University of Illinois, 1805 S Wright St, MC-011, Champaign, IL 61820
*Tel:* 217-244-5700 *Fax:* 217-244-9142
*E-mail:* contact@dalkeyarchive.com
*Web Site:* www.dalkeyarchive.com
*Key Personnel*
Dir: John O'Brien *E-mail:* obrien@dalkeyarchive.com
Publicity & Events Mgr: Martin Riker *E-mail:* riker@dalkeyarchive.com
Mgr: James Tennant
Founded: 1984
Literary fiction, translations & criticism. We keep works of literary value in print.
ISBN Prefix(es): 978-0-916583; 978-1-56478
Number of titles published annually: 112 Print
Total Titles: 550 Print
Distributed by W W Norton & Co
Foreign Rep(s): W W Norton & Co (Worldwide)
*Distribution Center:* W W Norton & Co Inc, c/o National Book Co, 800 Keystone Industrial Park, Scranton, PA 18512 *Toll Free Tel:* 800-245-4151 ext 1 *Toll Free Fax:* 800-458-6515

**Dalton Publishing**
PO Box 242, Austin, TX 78767
*Tel:* 512-567-4955 *Fax:* 512-879-6814
*E-mail:* dpquery@daltonpublishing.com
*Web Site:* www.daltonpublishing.com
*Key Personnel*
Publr: Deltina Hay *E-mail:* deltina@daltonpublishing.com
Sr Ed: Ric Williams *E-mail:* ric@austinchronicle.com
Founded: 2002
ISBN Prefix(es): 978-0-9844488; 978-0-9740703; 978-0-9817443
Number of titles published annually: 4 Print; 4 Online; 4 E-Book
Total Titles: 16 Print; 16 Online; 16 E-Book
Imprints: Wiggy Press
Foreign Rep(s): Midpoint Trade Books (Worldwide)
Foreign Rights: Midpoint Trade Books (Worldwide)
*Orders to:* Midpoint Trade Books, 1263 Southwest Blvd, Kansas City, KS 66103, Contact: Arlinda Moore *Tel:* 913-831-2233 *Fax:* 913-362-7401 *E-mail:* orders@midpt.com
*Returns:* Midpoint Trade Books, 1263 Southwest Blvd, Kansas City, KS 66103, Contact: Arlinda Moore *Tel:* 913-831-2233 *Fax:* 913-362-7401 *E-mail:* orders@midpt.com
*Shipping Address:* Midpoint Trade Books, 1263 Southwest Blvd, Kansas City, KS 66103, Contact: Arlinda Moore *Tel:* 913-831-2233 *Fax:* 913-362-7401 *E-mail:* orders@midpt.com
*Warehouse:* Midpoint Trade Books, 1263 Southwest Blvd, Kansas City, KS 66103, Contact: Arlinda Moore *Tel:* 913-831-2233 *Fax:* 913-362-7401 *E-mail:* orders@midpt.com
*Distribution Center:* Midpoint Trade Books, 27 W 20 St, Suite 1102, New York, NY 10011 (main office), Contact: Eric Kampmann *Tel:* 212-727-0190 *Fax:* 212-727-0195 *E-mail:* info@midpointtrade.com
Membership(s): The Association of Publishers for Special Sales; IBPA, the Independent Book Publishers Association

**Damron Co**
PO Box 422458, San Francisco, CA 94142-2458
*Tel:* 415-255-0404 *Toll Free Tel:* 800-462-6654 *Fax:* 415-703-9049
*E-mail:* info@damron.com
*Web Site:* www.damron.com
*Key Personnel*
Pres & Ed-in-Chief: Gina Gatta *E-mail:* gina@damron.com
Mng Ed: Erika O'Connor *E-mail:* erika@damron.com
Founded: 1964
Annual travel guides.
ISBN Prefix(es): 978-0-929435
Number of titles published annually: 3 Print
Total Titles: 4 Print; 1 Online
Distributed by SCB Distributors

**Dancing Dakini Press**
77 Morning Sun Dr, Sedona, AZ 86336
*Tel:* 928-852-0129
*E-mail:* editor@dancingdakinipress.com
*Web Site:* www.dancingdakinipress.com
*Key Personnel*
CEO: Robin Weeks *Tel:* 505-699-6044 *E-mail:* robin@dancingdakinipress.com
CFO: Ben Long *Tel:* 503-415-0229 *E-mail:* ben@benllong.com
Founded: 2012
Small publisher creating well-crafted books to inspire compassionate awareness, skillful means, authentic lives & a deep respect for all.
ISBN Prefix(es): 978-0-9836333
Number of titles published annually: 3 Print; 1 E-Book
Total Titles: 4 Print
*Orders to:* New Leaf Distribution Co, 401 Thornton Rd, Lithia Springs, GA 30122-1557, Contact: Lenora Whitmire *Tel:* 770-948-7845 *Fax:* 770-944-2313 *E-mail:* domestic@newleaf-dist.coom
*Returns:* New Leaf Distribution Co, 401 Thornton Rd, Lithia Springs, GA 30122-1557, Contact: Lenora Whitmire *Tel:* 770-948-7845 *Fax:* 770-944-2313 *E-mail:* lwhitmire@newleaf-dist.com
*Shipping Address:* New Leaf Distribution Co, 401 Thornton Rd, Lithia Springs, GA 30122-1557 *Tel:* 770-948-7845 *Fax:* 770-944-2313
*Warehouse:* New Leaf Distribution Co, 401 Thornton Rd, Lithia Springs, GA 30122-1557 *Tel:* 770-948-7845 *Fax:* 770-944-2313
*Distribution Center:* New Leaf Distribution Co, 401 Thornton Rd, Lithia Springs, GA 30122-1557, Contact: Lenora Whitmire *Tel:* 770-948-7845 *Fax:* 770-944-2313 *E-mail:* lwhitmire@newleaf-dist.com

**Dancing Lemur Press LLC**
PO Box 383, Pikeville, NC 27863-0383
*Tel:* 919-273-0939
*E-mail:* inquiries@dancinglemurpress.com
*Web Site:* www.dancinglemurpress.com

*Key Personnel*
Sr Ed: Lesley Wolfe
Founded: 2008
We strive to publish works that uplift & inspire, encouraging the reader to explore & discover while remaining morally grounded. At the heart of our young adult & science fiction lies positive relationship dynamics, optimistic attitudes & non-salacious material. Our nonfiction offers insightful information, uplifting ideas & real life opportunities. Our goal is to provide hope for readers.
ISBN Prefix(es): 978-0-9816210; 978-0-9827139; 978-1-9398440
Number of titles published annually: 5 Print; 4 E-Book
Total Titles: 7 Print; 7 E-Book
Membership(s): IBPA, the Independent Book Publishers Association

**John Daniel & Co**
Division of Daniel & Daniel Publishers Inc
PO Box 2790, McKinleyville, CA 95519-2790
SAN: 215-1995
*Tel:* 707-839-3495 *Toll Free Tel:* 800-662-8351 *Fax:* 707-839-3242
*E-mail:* dandd@danielpublishing.com
*Web Site:* www.danielpublishing.com
*Key Personnel*
Owner & Publr: John Daniel *E-mail:* john@danielpublishing.com
Owner & Sales Mgr: Susan Daniel *E-mail:* susan@danielpublishing.com
Founded: 1985
ISBN Prefix(es): 978-0-936784; 978-1-880284
Number of titles published annually: 4 Print
Total Titles: 200 Print
*Branch Office(s)*
2611 Kelly Ave, McKinleyville, CA 95519
Distributor for Fithian Press; Perseverance Press
*Returns:* 2611 Kelly Ave, McKinleyville, CA 95519
*Distribution Center:* SCB Distributors, 15608 S New Century Dr, Gardena, CA 90248, Contact: Aaron Silverman *Toll Free Tel:* 800-729-6423
Membership(s): IBPA, the Independent Book Publishers Association

**Dante University of America Press Inc**
PO Box 812158, Wellesley, MA 02482-0014
SAN: 220-150X
*Tel:* 781-235-3634 *Fax:* 781-790-1056
*E-mail:* danteu@danteuniversity.org
*Web Site:* www.danteuniversity.org
*Key Personnel*
Pres: Adolf Caso
Founded: 1980
Italian Americana.
ISBN Prefix(es): 978-0-937832
Number of titles published annually: 2 Print
Total Titles: 14 Print
Distributed by Branden Publishing Co
Foreign Rep(s): Baker & Taylor (Worldwide)
Foreign Rights: Gazelle (England)

**Dark Horse Comics**
Affiliate of Dark Horse Entertainment
10956 SE Main St, Milwaukie, OR 97222
*Tel:* 503-652-8815 *Fax:* 503-654-9440
*E-mail:* dhcomics@darkhorsecomics.com
*Web Site:* www.darkhorse.com
*Key Personnel*
Founder & Pres: Michael Richardson
Online Mktg Mgr: Matt Parkinson
Founded: 1986
Primary area is graphic novels; pop culture; limited edition hard covers, comics & popculture.
ISBN Prefix(es): 978-1-56971
Number of titles published annually: 200 Print
Total Titles: 600 Print
Imprints: Dark Horse Books; Dark Horse Comics
Distributed by LPC Group Inc
Foreign Rights: Anita Nelson

**§The Dartnell Corporation**
Subsidiary of Eli Research Inc
2222 Sedwick Dr, Durham, NC 27713
*Toll Free Tel:* 800-223-8720; 800-472-0148 (cust serv) *Fax:* 585-292-4392 *Toll Free Fax:* 800-508-2592
*E-mail:* customerservice@dartnellcorp.com
*Web Site:* www.dartnellcorp.com
Founded: 1916
Business information, training, motivation.
ISBN Prefix(es): 978-0-85013
Number of titles published annually: 20 Print
Total Titles: 300 Print

**The Darwin Press Inc**
PO Box 2202, Princeton, NJ 08543
SAN: 201-2987
*Tel:* 609-737-1349 *Toll Free Tel:* 866-772-9817 *Fax:* 609-737-0929
*E-mail:* books@darwinpress.com
*Web Site:* www.darwinpress.com
*Key Personnel*
Publr & Mng Dir: Ed Breisacher
Founded: 1970
Natural & behavioral sciences; Near Eastern studies; technical, scientific, reference.
ISBN Prefix(es): 978-0-87850
Number of titles published annually: 3 Print
Total Titles: 70 Print
Imprints: Darwin® Books
Foreign Rep(s): Gazelle (Europe)

**§Data Trace Publishing Co (DTP)**
110 West Rd, Suite 227, Towson, MD 21204-2316
Mailing Address: PO Box 1239, Brooklandville, MD 21022-1239
*Tel:* 410-494-4994 *Toll Free Tel:* 800-342-0454 (orders only) *Fax:* 410-494-0515
*E-mail:* info@datatrace.com; salesandmarketing@datatrace.com; editorial@datatrace.com; customerservice@datatrace.com
*Web Site:* www.datatrace.com
*Key Personnel*
VP, Edit & Acqs: Kimberly Collignon
Dir, Mktg: Cat Winders
Ad Mgr: Frank Tufariello
Founded: 1987
Full-service specialty publisher with interest in science, technical, law & medicine.
ISBN Prefix(es): 978-0-9637468; 978-1-57400
Number of titles published annually: 20 Print; 6 E-Book
Total Titles: 115 Print; 15 CD-ROM; 5 Online

**Daughters of St Paul**, see Pauline Books & Media

**May Davenport Publishers**
26313 Purissima Rd, Los Altos Hills, CA 94022
*Tel:* 650-947-1275 *Fax:* 650-947-1373
*E-mail:* mdbooks@earthlink.net
*Web Site:* www.maydavenportpublishers.com
*Key Personnel*
Ed & Publr: May Davenport
Founded: 1975
Create & distribute books for children/young adults (ages 15-18). With special grants, we print & distribute literary writings, which counselors at schools give to troubled teens. Books are written by teachers, writers, social workers, mental clinicians & counselors. We sell books by direct mail. Remainders are donated to schools in depressed areas who ask for free copies for their students to take home; to penal institutions who ask for our young adult books for their teenaged inmates & to literacy projects. The company originally created comic tales to read & for the child, 3-4 yrs old, to color the illustrations. Currently working on *Comic Tales Easy Reader Anthologies* for children/young adults.
ISBN Prefix(es): 978-0-9603118; 978-0-943864; 978-0-9794140
Number of titles published annually: 3 Print; 8 Online
Total Titles: 32 Print; 32 Online
Imprints: Md Books

**Davies-Black Publishing**
Imprint of Nicholas Brealey Publishing
20 Park Plaza, Suite 610, Boston, MA 02116
*Tel:* 617-523-3801 *Fax:* 617-523-3708
*E-mail:* info@nicholasbrealey.com
*Web Site:* www.nicholasbrealey.com
Founded: 1995
Book publishing in leadership & management, organization development, human resources & career management.
ISBN Prefix(es): 978-0-89106
Number of titles published annually: 12 Print
Total Titles: 120 Print
Foreign Rep(s): Bacchus Books CC (South Africa); Cengage Learning Asia (Asia-Pacific); Cengage Learning India (India); Eurospan Group (Europe, Middle East, North Africa, UK); NBN Canada (Canada); NBN/Central Book Services (Australia, New Zealand)
*Orders to:* National Book Network, 15200 NBN Way, Blue Ridge Summit, PA 17214 *Toll Free Tel:* 800-462-6420
*Warehouse:* 1150 Hamilton Ct, Menlo Park, CA 94025
*Distribution Center:* National Book Network, 15200 NBN Way, Blue Ridge Summit, PA 17214 *Toll Free Tel:* 800-462-6420
Membership(s): BISG; IBPA, the Independent Book Publishers Association

**The Davies Group Publishers**
PO Box 440140, Aurora, CO 80044-0140
*Tel:* 303-750-8374 *Fax:* 303-337-0952
*E-mail:* info@thedaviesgrouppublishers.com
*Web Site:* www.thedaviesgrouppublishers.com
*Key Personnel*
Publr: Elizabeth B Davies
Founded: 1991
Scholarly publisher; philosophy, humanities & social sciences.
ISBN Prefix(es): 978-1-888570; 978-0-9630076; 978-1-934542
Number of titles published annually: 3 Print; 10 E-Book
Total Titles: 85 Print; 85 E-Book

**§Davies Publishing Inc**
32 S Raymond Ave, Suites 4 & 5, Pasadena, CA 91105-1961
SAN: 217-3255
*Tel:* 626-792-3046 *Toll Free Tel:* 877-792-0005 *Fax:* 626-792-5308
*E-mail:* info@daviespublishing.com
*Web Site:* daviespublishing.com
*Key Personnel*
Pres & Publr: Michael Davies *E-mail:* mikedavies@daviespublishing.com
Corp Secy & Opers Mgr: Janet Heard *E-mail:* janetheard@daviespublishing.com
Digital Media Specialist: Dan Liota *E-mail:* danliota@daviespublishing.com
Prod Devt Specialist: Christian Jones *E-mail:* chrisjones@daviespublishing.com
Edit Assoc: Gina Caprari *E-mail:* ginacaprari@daviespublishing.com
Founded: 1981
Ultrasound education & test preparation: books, software, DVDs, mock examinations & flash-cards.
ISBN Prefix(es): 978-0-941022

Number of titles published annually: 8 Print; 2 CD-ROM
Total Titles: 48 Print; 6 CD-ROM
Imprints: Appleton Davies
Divisions: Davies Direct Booksellers
Membership(s): IBPA, the Independent Book Publishers Association

**§F A Davis Co**
1915 Arch St, Philadelphia, PA 19103
SAN: 200-2078
*Tel:* 215-568-2270 *Toll Free Tel:* 800-523-4049 *Fax:* 215-568-5065
*E-mail:* info@fadavis.com
*Web Site:* www.fadavis.com
*Key Personnel*
Chmn of the Bd: Robert H Craven, Sr
CFO & VP: Robert B Schenck
Pres: Robert H Craven, Jr
SVP: Judith Illov Neely
Exec Dir, Sales: Neil K Kelly
Dir, HR: Crystal Spraggins
Dir, Mktg: Virginia A Kelly
Publr: Lisa Biello; Joanne DaCunha; Lisa Deitch; Mary Gelbach; Robert Martone
Ed-in-Chief, Nursing: Jean Rodenberger
Founded: 1879
Publisher of nursing, medical & health profession texts, podcasts & clinical simulations.
ISBN Prefix(es): 978-0-8036
Number of titles published annually: 75 Print; 1 Online; 65 E-Book; 5 Audio
Total Titles: 399 Print; 150 E-Book; 10 Audio
*Distribution Center:* 404 N Second St, Philadelphia, PA 19123, Gen Mgr: John Lancaster *Tel:* 215-440-3001 *Toll Free Tel:* 800-323-3555 (orders, cust serv, returns) *Fax:* 215-440-3016

**DAW Books Inc**
375 Hudson St, 3rd fl, New York, NY 10014
SAN: 282-5074
*Tel:* 212-366-2096 *Fax:* 212-366-2090
*E-mail:* daw@us.penguingroup.com
*Web Site:* us.penguingroup.com; www.dawbooks.com
*Key Personnel*
Publr: Sheila E Gilbert; Elizabeth R Wollheim
Submission Ed: Peter Stampfel *E-mail:* submissions@us.penguingroup.com
Founded: 1971
Science fiction; fantasy; paperbound originals & reprints; hardcovers, trade paperbacks & ebook.
ISBN Prefix(es): 978-0-8099; 978-0-88677; 978-0-7564
Number of titles published annually: 60 Print; 40 E-Book
Total Titles: 325 Print
Imprints: DAW/Fantasy; DAW/Fiction; DAW/Science Fiction
Distributed by Penguin Group (USA) LLC
Foreign Rep(s): Agence Litteraire Hoffman (France); Graal Literary Agency (Czech Republic, Hungary, Poland, Slovakia); International Editors' Co (Argentina, Spain); Japan UNI Agency Inc (Japan); Nurcihan Kesim Literary Agency Inc (Turkey); Simona Kessler (Romania); Alexander Korzhenevski (Russia); Ilidio de Fonseca Matos (Portugal); Piergiorgio Nicolazzini Literary Agency (Italy); Andrew Nurnberg Associates Sofia Ltd (Bulgaria); O A Literary Agency (Greece); Ilana Pikarski (Israel); Karin Schindler (Brazil); Thomas Schlueck GmbH (Germany, Netherlands)

**The Dawn Horse Press**
Division of Avataric Pan-Communion of Adidam
10336 Loch Lomond Rd, No 305, Middletown, CA 95461
*Tel:* 707-928-6590 *Toll Free Tel:* 877-770-0772 *Fax:* 707-928-6590
*E-mail:* dhp@adidam.org
*Web Site:* www.dawnhorsepress.com
*Key Personnel*
Publr: Neil Panico *E-mail:* npanico@adidam.org
Founded: 1972
Produces & markets books, CDs & AV materials on every aspect of authentic spiritual life & human development based upon the wisdom & teaching of Avatar Adi Da Samraj.
ISBN Prefix(es): 978-0-913922; 978-0-918801; 978-0-918801; 978-1-57097; 978-0-929929
Number of titles published annually: 8 Print; 8 CD-ROM; 12 Online; 4 Audio
Total Titles: 49 Print; 19 CD-ROM; 65 Online; 1 E-Book; 33 Audio
*Shipping Address:* 12312 Hwy 175, Cobb Mountain, CA 95426, Contact: Patrick Forristal
*Distribution Center:* New Leaf Distributing Co, 401 Thorton Rd, Lithia Springs, GA 30122-1557 *Tel:* 770-948-7845 *Fax:* 770-944-2313 *E-mail:* newleaf@newleaf-dist.com *Web Site:* www.newleaf-dist.com
Membership(s): IBPA, the Independent Book Publishers Association

**Dawn Publications Inc**
12402 Bitney Springs Rd, Nevada City, CA 95959
*Tel:* 530-274-7775 *Toll Free Tel:* 800-545-7475 *Fax:* 530-274-7778
*E-mail:* nature@dawnpub.com; orders@dawnpub.com
*Web Site:* www.dawnpub.com
*Key Personnel*
Publr & Ed: Glenn Hovemann *E-mail:* glenn@dawnpub.com
Art Dir & Publr: Muffy Weaver *E-mail:* muffy@dawnpub.com
Mktg Dir: Sandy Philpott *E-mail:* sandy@dawnpub.com
Founded: 1979
Nature awareness nonfiction picture books for children, teachers, naturalists & parents; character value education; natural science.
ISBN Prefix(es): 978-0-916124; 978-1-883220; 978-1-58469
Number of titles published annually: 32 Print
Total Titles: 85 Print; 5 CD-ROM; 3 Audio
Foreign Rep(s): Deep Books Ltd (UK); Monarch Books of Canada (Canada); John Reed Book Distribution (Australia); SULA Book Distributors (South Africa)
Membership(s): ABA; APPL; IBPA, the Independent Book Publishers Association; Publishers Association of the West

**DawnSignPress**
6130 Nancy Ridge Dr, San Diego, CA 92121-3223
*Tel:* 858-625-0600 *Toll Free Tel:* 800-549-5350 *Fax:* 858-625-2336
*E-mail:* info@dawnsign.com
*Web Site:* www.dawnsign.com
*Key Personnel*
Founder & Pres: Joe Dannis
Mktg & Lib Sales Dir: Becky Ryan *E-mail:* beckyr@dawnsign.com
Founded: 1979
Specialty publisher of instructional sign language & educational deaf studies materials for both children & adults, deaf & hearing & interpreting.
ISBN Prefix(es): 978-0-915035; 978-1-58121
Number of titles published annually: 5 Print
Total Titles: 65 Print; 1 CD-ROM
Distributed by Gryphon House
Distributor for Gallaudet University Press; MIT Press; Random House Inc
Foreign Rights: Gloval Interprint (Hong Kong)

**Day Owl Press Corp**
PO Box 3574, Lantana, FL 33465
*Toll Free Tel:* 866-806-6981 *Toll Free Fax:* 866-854-4375
*E-mail:* info@dayowl.net
*Web Site:* www.dayowl.net; www.dayowlpresscorp.com
*Key Personnel*
Pres: Carolyn Clay
Founded: 2011
Independent publisher of offbeat unusual new works. Interested in books that are new, funny, intelligent, prophetical, unconventional, controversial, avant-garde, cutting edge, innovative, radical, revolutionary &/or otherwise atypical.
ISBN Prefix(es): 978-1-940401
Number of titles published annually: 30 Print; 30 Online; 30 E-Book; 5 Audio
Total Titles: 37 Print; 37 Online; 37 E-Book; 5 Audio
Membership(s): IBPA, the Independent Book Publishers Association

**dbS Productions**
PO Box 94, Charlottesville, VA 22902
*Tel:* 434-293-5502 *Toll Free Tel:* 800-745-1581 *Fax:* 434-293-5502
*E-mail:* info@dbs-sar.com
*Web Site:* www.dbs-sar.com
*Key Personnel*
CEO & Sr Scientist: Robert J Koester *E-mail:* robert@dbs-sar.com
Founded: 1989
Search & rescue.
ISBN Prefix(es): 978-1-879471
Number of titles published annually: 5 Print; 1 CD-ROM
Total Titles: 15 Print; 2 CD-ROM
Distributed by Oklahoma State University

**DC Entertainment**
Division of Warner Bros Entertainment Co
1700 Broadway, New York, NY 10019
*Tel:* 212-636-5400 *Toll Free Tel:* 800-887-6789 *Fax:* 212-636-5979
*E-mail:* dccomics@cambeywest.com
*Web Site:* www.dccomics.com; www.madmag.com; www.dcentertainment.com
*Key Personnel*
CEO: Diane Nelson
VP & Talent Rel & Servs: Terri Cunningham
VP, Book Trade Sales: Sue Pohja
VP, Mfg: Alison Gill
VP, Sales: Bob Wayne
Dir, Book Trade Mktg: Ailen Lujo
Publr: Dan Didio; Jim Lee
Founded: 1935
Innovative comics publishing in periodical & book formats. In addition to the world's most popular super-heroes - Superman, Batman & Wonder Woman - DC publishes cutting edge fantasy, horror, mystery, adventure, humor, nonfiction & general interest titles & maintains a 500+ title backlist in print. *MAD* Books is based on the classic magazine featuring Alfred E Neuman, Spy vs Spy & other icons. DC/MAD properties are also licensed for various publishing formats, as well as media, promotions & consumer products. DC Comics does not accept unsol mss. For more information, visit our web site at www.dcentertainment.com.
ISBN Prefix(es): 978-0-930289; 978-1-56389
Number of titles published annually: 1,050 Print
Total Titles: 500 Print
Imprints: DC Comics; DC Nation; 'MAD' Books; Vertigo; WildStorm Productions
Distributed by Random House Publisher Services (RHPS)

**§DC Press LLC**
750 Powderhorn Circle, Lake Mary, FL 32746
*Tel:* 407-688-1156
*Web Site:* www.dcpressbooks.com

*Key Personnel*
Pres & Publr: Dennis McClellan *E-mail:* dennis.dcpress@gmail.com
Founded: 2001
Independent niche publisher, producing books with emphasis on ethics, character, spirit, encouragement & volition in the area of self-help, business & careers & health care.
ISBN Prefix(es): 978-1-929902; 978-1-932021
Number of titles published annually: 6 Print; 6 E-Book
Total Titles: 80 Print; 3 CD-ROM; 40 E-Book
Foreign Rights: Russo Rights LLC (Worldwide)
*Distribution Center:* Midpoint Trade Books, 27 W 20 St, Suite 1002, New York, NY 10011, Contact: Eric Kampman *Tel:* 212-727-0190 *Fax:* 212-727-0195 *E-mail:* eric@midpointtrade.com *Web Site:* www.midpointtradebooks.com
Membership(s): The Association of Publishers for Special Sales; IBPA, the Independent Book Publishers Association

**§Walter De Gruyter Inc**
Subsidiary of Walter de Gruyter GmbH & Co KG
121 High St, 3rd fl, Boston, MA 02110
*Tel:* 857-284-7073 *Fax:* 857-284-7358
*E-mail:* USinfo@degruyter.com
*Web Site:* www.degruyter.com
*Key Personnel*
Mktg Mgr: Heather Anderson
Founded: 1749
Scholarly & scientific books, journals, paperbacks & hardcover reprints.
ISBN Prefix(es): 978-0-311; 978-0-3899
Number of titles published annually: 200 Print; 5 CD-ROM
Total Titles: 8,500 Print; 20 CD-ROM; 15 Online; 10 E-Book
Imprints: De Gruyter Mouton; De Gruyter Saur
*Foreign Office(s):* Walter de Gruyter GmbH & Co KG, Genthinerstr 13, 10785 Berlin, Germany *Tel:* (030) 260 05 0 *Fax:* (030) 260 05 251 *E-mail:* info@degruyter.com
Foreign Rep(s): Allied Publishers (India, Nepal, Sri Lanka); Book Club International (Bangladesh); Combined Representatives Worldwide Inc (Philippines), D A Books & Journals (Australia, New Zealand); Kumi Trading (South Korea); Kweilin Bookstore (Taiwan); Maruzen Co Ltd (Japan); Pak Book Corp (Pakistan); Parry's Book Center (Sendjrjan Berhad) (Brunei, Malaysia, Singapore); Swinden Book Co Ltd (Hong Kong); Verlags und Kommissionsbuchhandlung Dr Franz Hain (Austria); Walter de Gruyter Inc (Canada, Mexico, USA)
*Orders to:* Walter de Gruyter, PO Box 960, Herndon, VA 20172-0960 *Tel:* 703-661-1589 *Toll Free Tel:* 800-208-8144 *Fax:* 703-661-1501

**De Vorss & Co**
553 Constitution Ave, Camarillo, CA 93012-8510
SAN: 168-9886
Mailing Address: PO Box 1389, Camarillo, CA 93011-1389
*Tel:* 805-322-9010 *Toll Free Tel:* 800-843-5743 *Fax:* 805-322-9011
*E-mail:* service@devorss.com
*Web Site:* www.devorss.com
*Key Personnel*
Pres: Gary R Peattie *Tel:* 805-322-9010 ext 14 *E-mail:* gpeattie@devorss.com
VP: Melinda Grubbauer
Contact: Kathy Salyer *E-mail:* ksalyer@devorss.com
Founded: 1929
Publisher & distributor of metaphysical, spiritual, inspirational, self-help, body/mind/spirit & new thought books & sidelines since 1929.
ISBN Prefix(es): 978-0-87516
Number of titles published annually: 10 Print
Total Titles: 270 Print; 4 Audio
Distributor for Acropolis Books; Science of Mind Publications; White Eagle Publishing Trust (England)
Foreign Rep(s): Brumby Books (Australia); Deep Books (UK); Dempsey Canada (Canada)
*Billing Address:* PO Box 1389, Camarillo, CA 93011-1389

**Decent Hill Publishers LLC**
6100 Oak Tree Blvd, Suite 200, Cleveland, OH 44131
SAN: 858-2483
*Toll Free Tel:* 866-688-5325 *Toll Free Fax:* 866-688-5325
*E-mail:* support@decenthill.com
*Web Site:* www.decenthill.com
*Key Personnel*
Founder & CEO: Jude Odu
Book & music publisher.
ISBN Prefix(es): 978-1-936085
Total Titles: 25 Print; 25 Online; 25 E-Book
Imprints: Decent Hill; Felsen Press; The Lord's Press
Membership(s): American Society of Composers, Authors and Publishers; IBPA, the Independent Book Publishers Association

**Ivan R Dee Publisher**
Member of Rowman & Littlefield Publishing Group
4501 Forbes Blvd, Suite 200, Lanham, MD 20706
*Tel:* 301-459-3366 *Toll Free Tel:* 800-462-6420 (cust serv) *Fax:* 301-429-5748 *Toll Free Fax:* 800-338-4550 (orders)
*Web Site:* www.ivanrdee.com
*Key Personnel*
Publr: Ivan R Dee
Founded: 1988
Publish serious nonfiction for general readers.
ISBN Prefix(es): 978-0-929587; 978-1-56663; 978-1-879941; 978-1-56131
Number of titles published annually: 30 Print
Total Titles: 750 Print
Imprints: Elephant Paperbacks; New Amsterdam Books; J S Sanders & Co
Foreign Rep(s): Peter S Fritz (Germany); International Editors' Co (Spain); Oliva, Stefan & Oliva (Italy)
Foreign Rights: Peter S Fritz (Germany); International Editors' Co (Spain); Oliva Stefan & Oliva (Italy)
*Warehouse:* National Book Network, 15200 NBN Way, Blue Ridge Summit, PA 17214 *Toll Free Tel:* 800-462-6420 *Toll Free Fax:* 800-338-4550

**§Delmar**
Division of Cengage Learning
5 Maxwell Dr, Clifton Park, NY 12065-2919
SAN: 206-7544
Mailing Address: PO Box 8007, Clifton Park, NY 12065-8007
*Tel:* 518-348-2300 *Toll Free Tel:* 800-347-7707 (cust serv); 800-998-7498 *Fax:* 518-373-6200 *Toll Free Fax:* 800-487-8488 (cust serv)
*Web Site:* www.cengage.com/delmar; www.delmarlearning.com
*Key Personnel*
VP, Mktg: Jennifer Baker
Inside Acct Mgr: Todd Doherty *Tel:* 800-998-7498 ext 2565 *Fax:* 518-373-6465 *E-mail:* todd.doherty@cengage.com
Founded: 1945
Textbooks, software & supplementary, multimedia, professional reference & custom publishing & training materials for post-secondary & secondary schools in business, industry & government education, retail, education, electronics, technology, nursing & allied health, education & child care, agriculture, mathematics & vocational studies, automotive, travel & tourism & hospitality, cosmetology, engineering, paralegal, CAD, building trades, multimedia, graphic arts, distance education.
ISBN Prefix(es): 978-0-8273; 978-1-56253; 978-0-7668; 978-1-4018
Number of titles published annually: 300 Print
Total Titles: 9,000 Print; 595 CD-ROM; 5 Online; 8 E-Book; 1,681 Audio
Imprints: Autodesk Press; Chilton; Frontline; Milady; NetLearning; ONWord; PDR; Singular; Skidmore-Roth; West (Legal Studies)
Distributor for Aspire; Autodata; BOCA/ICC; CDX Global; Chilton; Haynes; Holt Enterprises; Scott Jones Publishing; LearningExpress; Meredith; NFPA; Prompt; Seloc; Truckload Carrier Assoc; Video Active Productions
Foreign Rep(s): Paraninfo (Portugal, Spain); Thomson Learning (Asia, Latin America, UK); Nelson Thomson Learning (Australia, Canada, New Zealand)
Foreign Rights: Paraninfo (Spain); Thomson Learning (Asia, Latin America, UK)
*Warehouse:* Thomson Distribution Center, 10650 Toebben Dr, Independence, KY 41051
*See separate listing for:*
**Milady**

**DeLorme Publishing Co Inc**
2 DeLorme Dr, Yarmouth, ME 04096
Mailing Address: PO Box 298, Yarmouth, ME 04096
*Tel:* 207-846-7000; 207-846-7111 (sales) *Toll Free Tel:* 800-561-5105; 800-511-2459 (cust serv) *Fax:* 207-846-7051 *Toll Free Fax:* 800-575-2244
*E-mail:* reseller@delorme.com
*Web Site:* www.delorme.com
*Key Personnel*
VP, Mktg: Kim Stiver *Tel:* 207-846-7018 *E-mail:* kim.stiver@delorme.com
Mktg Mgr: Charlie Conley *Tel:* 207-846-7022 *E-mail:* charlie.conley@delorme.com
Founded: 1976
Digital maps; software; posters.
ISBN Prefix(es): 978-0-89933
Number of titles published annually: 5 Print
Total Titles: 50 Print

**§Delphi Books**
PO Box 6435, Lee's Summit, MO 64064
*Toll Free Tel:* 800-431-1579 (orders)
*E-mail:* delphibks@yahoo.com
*Web Site:* www.delphibooks.us
*Key Personnel*
Publr: Fran Baker
Founded: 1998
ISBN Prefix(es): 978-0-9663397; 978-0-9765185; 978-0-9846015
Number of titles published annually: 10 Print; 5 E-Book
Total Titles: 18 Print
*Returns:* Ingram Book Co, One Ingram Blvd, La Vergne, TN 37086
*Shipping Address:* Ingram Book Co, One Ingram Blvd, La Vergne, TN 37086 *Tel:* 615-793-5000 *Toll Free Tel:* 800-937-8200 *E-mail:* customerservice@ingrambook.com *Web Site:* www.ingrambook.com
*Warehouse:* Ingram Book Co, One Ingram Blvd, La Vergne, TN 37086 *Tel:* 615-793-5000 *Toll Free Tel:* 800-937-8200 *E-mail:* customer.service@ingrambook.com *Web Site:* www.ingrambook.com
Membership(s): The Association of Publishers for Special Sales; The Authors Guild; The Authors Studio; Novelists Inc

**Delphinium Books**
PO Box 703, Harrison, NY 10528
*Tel:* 917-301-7496 (e-mail first)
*E-mail:* contactform@delphiniumbooks.com
*Web Site:* www.delphiniumbooks.com
Founded: 1986
ISBN Prefix(es): 978-1-883285

Number of titles published annually: 5 Print; 5 E-Book; 1 Audio
Total Titles: 45 Print; 30 E-Book; 1 Audio
Distributed by HarperCollins
Foreign Rights: David Marshall (Worldwide exc Canada)

**Delta Publishing Co**
Division of Delta Systems Co Inc
1400 Miller Pkwy, McHenry, IL 60050-7030
*Tel:* 815-363-3582 *Toll Free Tel:* 800-323-8270 (orders) *Fax:* 815-363-2948 *Toll Free Fax:* 800-909-9901
*E-mail:* custsvc@deltapublishing.com
*Web Site:* www.deltapublishing.com
*Key Personnel*
Pres: Richard R Patchin *E-mail:* d.patchin@deltapublishing.com
Founded: 1979
Publisher & distribution of English as a second language (ESL) & foreign language materials. Publisher of award-winning children's picture books in English-only, Spanish-only & bilingual formats. Returns within 90 days, no permission required for materials we distribute. Within 180 day for proprietary titles. All must be in perfect condition.
ISBN Prefix(es): 978-0-937354; 978-1-887744; 978-0-9720192; 978-0-9724973; 978-1-934960; 978-1-936299; 978-1-936402; 978-1-932748; 978-0-9794462; 978-0-9770906; 978-0-9795477
Number of titles published annually: 8 Print
Total Titles: 120 Print
Distributor for Alma Edizioni; Barron's; Cambridge University Press; Edilingual; Oxford University Press

**Demos Medical Publishing LLC**
Division of Mannheim Holdings LLC
11 W 42 St, New York, NY 10036
*Tel:* 212-683-0072 *Toll Free Tel:* 800-532-8663 *Fax:* 212-683-0118
*E-mail:* info@demosmedpub.com; orderdept@demosmedpub.com
*Web Site:* www.demosmedpub.com
*Key Personnel*
CEO: Theodore C Nardin *E-mail:* tnardin@demosmedpub.com
Publr: Beth Barry *E-mail:* bbarry@demosmedpub.com
Spec Sales & Foreign Rts: Reina Santana *E-mail:* rsantana@demospub.com
Exec Ed: Julia Pastore
Founded: 1985
Publish medical & nursing text & patient education titles in trade paperback.
ISBN Prefix(es): 978-0-937957; 978-1-888799
Number of titles published annually: 40 Print; 2 CD-ROM
Total Titles: 150 Print; 2 CD-ROM; 100 E-Book
Imprints: Demos Health
*Returns:* Publishers Storage & Shipping Corp, 46 Development Rd, Fitchburg, MA 01420, Contact: Peter Quick *Tel:* 978-345-2121 *Fax:* 978-348-1233
*Shipping Address:* Publishers Storage & Shipping Corp, 46 Development Rd, Fitchburg, MA 01420, Contact: Peter Quick *Tel:* 978-345-2121 *Fax:* 978-348-1233
*Warehouse:* Publishers Storage & Shipping Corp, 46 Development Rd, Fitchburg, MA 01420, Contact: Peter Quick *Tel:* 978-345-2121 *Fax:* 978-348-1233
*Distribution Center:* Publishers Storage & Shipping Corp, 46 Development Rd, Fitchburg, MA 01420, Contact: Peter Quick *Tel:* 978-345-2121 *Fax:* 978-348-1233
Membership(s): AAP

**§Deseret Book Co**
Subsidiary of Deseret Management Corp
57 W South Temple, Salt Lake City, UT 84101-1511
SAN: 201-3185
Mailing Address: PO Box 30178, Salt Lake City, UT 84130
*Tel:* 801-517-3372; 801-534-1515 *Toll Free Tel:* 800-453-4532 (orders); 888-846-7302 (orders) *Fax:* 801-517-3126
*E-mail:* dbol@deseretbook.com
*Web Site:* www.deseretbook.com
*Key Personnel*
CEO & Pres: Sheri L Dew
Publr: Lisa Mangum *E-mail:* lmangum@deseretbook.com
Founded: 1886
Juveniles & young adults, trade paperbacks; fiction, general nonfiction, religion (Mormon).
ISBN Prefix(es): 978-0-87747
Number of titles published annually: 150 Print
Total Titles: 1,100 Print; 1 CD-ROM; 120 Audio
Imprints: Bookcraft; Cinnamon Tree; Eagle Gate; Shadow Mountain
*Shipping Address:* 2240 W 1500 S, Salt Lake City, UT 84104 *Tel:* 801-517-3285 *Fax:* 801-972-4823
*See separate listing for:*
**Covenant Communications Inc**

**§DEStech Publications Inc**
439 N Duke St, Lancaster, PA 17602-4967
*Tel:* 717-290-1660 *Toll Free Tel:* 877-500-4337 *Fax:* 717-509-6100
*E-mail:* info@destechpub.com
*Web Site:* www.destechpub.com
*Key Personnel*
Pres: Anthony Deraco *E-mail:* aderaco@destechpub.com
Edit Dir: Dr Joseph Eckenrode *E-mail:* jeckenrode@destechpub.com
Prodn Dir: Stephen Spangler *E-mail:* sspangler@destechpub.com
Mktg Mgr: Michael T Hauck *E-mail:* mhauck@destechpub.com
Founded: 2001
Science, technical & medical publisher; proceedings publishing.
ISBN Prefix(es): 978-1-605950
Number of titles published annually: 12 Print; 5 CD-ROM; 2 Online
Total Titles: 115 Print; 22 CD-ROM; 3 Online
Foreign Rep(s): CRW Marketing Services for Publishers Inc (American Samoa, Guam, Philippines, Virgin Islands); DKG Info Systems (Hong Kong, India, Scandinavia, Western Europe); Tahir Lodhi Publisher's Representatives (Pakistan); LSR Libros Services (Latin America, Mexico); Transatlantic Publishers Group Ltd (Europe, Middle East, UK)

**Destiny Image Inc**
167 Walnut Bottom Rd, Shippensburg, PA 17257-0310
SAN: 253-4339
Mailing Address: PO Box 310, Shippensburg, PA 17257-0310
*Tel:* 717-532-3040 *Toll Free Tel:* 800-722-6774 (orders only) *Fax:* 717-532-9291
*E-mail:* sales@destinyimage.com
*Web Site:* www.destinyimage.com
*Key Personnel*
CEO & Pres: Don Nori, Jr
Dir, Sales & Mktg: Tom Ray
Founded: 1983
Publisher of Christian books.
ISBN Prefix(es): 978-0-914903; 978-1-56043; 978-0-938612; 978-0-7684
Number of titles published annually: 36 Print; 15 Audio
Total Titles: 300 Print; 5 Audio
Distributor for Mercy Place
Foreign Rep(s): Koorong (Australia); STL Ltd (UK); Word Alive (Canada)
Membership(s): ABA; CBA: The Association for Christian Retail; Evangelical Christian Publishers Association

**Development Concepts Inc**, see Impact Publications/Development Concepts Inc

**Developmental Studies Center**
2000 Embarcadero, Suite 305, Oakland, CA 94606-5300
*Tel:* 510-533-0213 *Toll Free Tel:* 800-666-7270 *Fax:* 510-464-3670
*E-mail:* pubs@devstu.org; info@devstu.org
*Web Site:* www.devstu.org
*Key Personnel*
Founder: Eric Schaps *Tel:* 510-533-0213 ext 240 *E-mail:* eric_schaps@devstu.org
Pres: Frank Snyder, PhD *Tel:* 510-533-0213 ext 237 *E-mail:* frank_snyder@devstu.org
Dir, Admin: Barbara Radcliffe
Dir, Dissemination & Mktg: Jan Berman *Tel:* 510-533-0213 ext 303 *E-mail:* jan_berman@devstu.org
Dir, Edit & Design: Lisa Kent Bandini *Tel:* 510-533-0213 ext 238 *E-mail:* lisa_kent_bandini@devstu.org
Dir, Fin & Opers: Rick Dinkle *Tel:* 510-533-0213 ext 242 *E-mail:* rick_dinkle@devstu.org
Dir, Info Technol: Mr Nazar Yousif *Tel:* 510-533-0213 ext 276 *E-mail:* nazar@devstu.org
Dir, Prog Devt: Lana Costantini MFA
Dir, Strategic Partnerships: Peter Brunn, MA *Tel:* 510-533-0213 ext 269 *E-mail:* peter_brunn@devstu.org
Founded: 1980
Books, teacher study packages, literature guides, in school & after school curricula in character education, reading & mathematics.
ISBN Prefix(es): 978-1-885603; 978-1-57621; 978-0-439
Number of titles published annually: 15 Print
Total Titles: 450 Print
*Advertising Agency:* DSC Direct

**§Dewey Publications Inc**
1840 Wilson Blvd, Suite 203, Arlington, VA 22201
SAN: 694-1451
*Tel:* 703-524-1355 *Fax:* 703-524-1463
*E-mail:* deweypublications@gmail.com
*Web Site:* www.deweypub.com
*Key Personnel*
Author: Peter Broida
Busn Mgr: Karen Troutman
Founded: 1984
ISBN Prefix(es): 978-1-878810; 978-1-932612
Number of titles published annually: 8 Print; 4 CD-ROM; 8 E-Book
Total Titles: 36 Print; 8 CD-ROM; 36 E-Book; 5 Audio

**Dharma Publishing**
35788 Hauser Bridge Rd, Cazadero, CA 95421
SAN: 201-2723
*Tel:* 707-847-3717 *Toll Free Tel:* 800-873-4276 *Fax:* 707-847-3380
*E-mail:* contact@dharmapublishing.com; customerservice@dharmapublishing.com
*Web Site:* www.dharmapublishing.com
*Key Personnel*
Mng Dir: Arnaud Maitland
Sales Dir: Rima Tamar *Tel:* 707-847-3717 ext 210 *E-mail:* rimat@dharmapublishing.com
Founded: 1971
Asian art, Eastern philosophy & psychology, Tibetan meditation & yoga, scholarly, history, biography, cosmology, juveniles, Asian culture.
ISBN Prefix(es): 978-0-913546; 978-0-89800
Number of titles published annually: 10 Print; 6 E-Book; 36 Audio

Total Titles: 120 Print; 12 E-Book; 48 Audio
*Sales Office(s):* 2210 Harold Way, Berkeley, CA 94704 *Tel:* 510-809-1540
Foreign Rep(s): Ka-Nying (India, Nepal); Nyingma Centrum Nederland (Netherlands); Nyingma Do Brazil (Brazil); Nyingma Gemeinschaft (Germany); Windhorse (Australia, UK); Wisdom Publications (UK)
Membership(s): AAP

**Dial Books for Young Readers**
Imprint of Penguin Group (USA) LLC
345 Hudson St, New York, NY 10014
SAN: 282-5074
*Tel:* 212-366-2000 *Fax:* 212-414-3396
*E-mail:* online@penguinputnam.com
*Web Site:* www.penguinputnam.com; us.penguingroup.com
*Key Personnel*
Pres & Publr, Dial: Lauri Hornik
Assoc Publr & Exec Mng Ed: Steve Meltzer
Assoc Publr & Exec Art Dir: Lily Malcolm
Exec Ed: Elizabeth Waniewski; Nancy Conescu
Sr Ed: Katherine Harrison; Lucia Monfried
Ed: Jessica Garrison
VP & Publr, Kathy Dawson Books: Kathy Dawson
Founded: 1961
ISBN Prefix(es): 978-0-8037
Number of titles published annually: 85 Print
Total Titles: 383 Print

**§Diamond Farm Book Publishers**
Division of Yesteryear Toys & Books Inc
Bailey Settlement Rd, Alexandria Bay, NY 13607
Mailing Address: PO Box 537, Alexandria Bay, NY 13607
*Tel:* 613-475-1771 *Toll Free Tel:* 800-481-1353 *Fax:* 613-475-3748 *Toll Free Fax:* 800-305-5138
*E-mail:* info@diamondfarm.com
*Web Site:* www.diamondfarm.com; www.yesteryeartoys.com
*Key Personnel*
Pres: Frank Van Meeuwen
Sales & Mktg: Shawn Van Meeuwen *E-mail:* shawn@diamondfarm.com
Founded: 1974
Agricultural textbooks & videos.
ISBN Prefix(es): 978-0-85236
Number of titles published annually: 4 Print
Total Titles: 12 Print; 1 CD-ROM; 1 Audio
*Branch Office(s)*
RR 3, Brighton, ON K0K 1H0, Canada
Distributor for Farming Press; Whittet

**Diane Publishing Co**
330 Pusey Ave, Suite 3 (rear), Collingdale, PA 19023-0617
Mailing Address: PO Box 617, Darby, PA 19023-0617
*Tel:* 610-461-6200 *Toll Free Tel:* 800-782-3833 *Fax:* 610-461-6130
*Web Site:* www.dianepublishing.net
*Key Personnel*
Pres & Publr: Herman Baron
VP, Edit: Dorothy Perkins
Mgr, Opers & Technol: Curtis Fisher *E-mail:* cfisher@dianepublishing.net
Founded: 1987
Publishes & repackages over 45,000 books, documents & reports in law enforcement, intelligence, security, military, education, biotechnology, medicine & health & high-technology. Most titles were originally prepared by US government agencies. Also distributes 9,000 nonfiction remainder books.
ISBN Prefix(es): 978-0-941375; 978-1-56806; 978-0-7881; 978-0-7567; 978-1-4223; 978-1-4289; 978-1-4379
Number of titles published annually: 1,800 Print
Total Titles: 47,000 Print; 14,000 E-Book

Distributor for Academy of Natural Sciences; American Philosophical Society; American Swedish Historical Museum; Augustinian Press; Chemical Heritage Foundation; Christ Church-Philadelphia; Friends of (Benjamin) Franklin; Geneological Society of Pennsylvania; Historical Society of Pennsylvania; Library Company of Philadelphia; University of Pennsylvania Libraries

**Direct Marketing Association (DMA)**
1120 Avenue of the Americas, New York, NY 10036-6700
SAN: 692-6487
*Tel:* 212-768-7277 *Fax:* 212-302-6714
*E-mail:* contenthub@the-dma.org; consumer@the-dma.org; customerservice@the-dma.org
*Web Site:* www.newdma.org
*Key Personnel*
CEO & Interim Pres: Linda A Woolley
Dir, Educ & Prof Devt: Michelle Tiletnick
Dir, Memb Communs & Sr Ed: Susan Taplinger
Founded: 1917
Directories, consumer guides, industry resource guides, statistical compilations, newsletter & council publications, quarterly magazine & electronic newsletter.
ISBN Prefix(es): 978-0-933641
Number of titles published annually: 5 Print
Total Titles: 5 Print
*Branch Office(s)*
1615 "L" St NW, Suite 1100, Washington, DC 20036

**Discipleship Publications International (DPI)**
5016 Spedale Ct, No 331, Spring Hill, TN 37174
*Tel:* 781-890-2489 (prodn & mktg); 419-281-1802 (orders outside US) *Toll Free Tel:* 888-DPI-BOOK (374-2665, orders only) *Fax:* 419-281-6883 (orders); 815-366-7465
*E-mail:* info@dpibooks.org
*Web Site:* www.dpibooks.org
*Key Personnel*
Mng Ed: Sheila Jones *E-mail:* sjones@dpibooks.org
Founded: 1993
Publishing books & audio on Biblical topics.
ISBN Prefix(es): 978-1-884553; 978-1-57782
Number of titles published annually: 6 Print; 1 CD-ROM; 5 E-Book; 1 Audio
Total Titles: 120 Print; 1 CD-ROM; 60 E-Book; 9 Audio
*Shipping Address:* Bookmasters, 30 Amberwood Pkwy, Ashland, OH 44805, Rep: Beth Boeh *Toll Free Tel:* 800-537-6727 *Fax:* 419-281-6883 *E-mail:* order@bookmasters.com *Web Site:* www.bookmasters.com
*Distribution Center:* Bookmasters, 30 Amberwood Pkwy, Ashland, OH 44805, Serv Rep: Vicki Maximovich *Tel:* 419-281-1802 *E-mail:* vmaximovich@bookmasters.com *Web Site:* www.bookmasters.com
Membership(s): IBPA, the Independent Book Publishers Association

**§Discovery House Publishers**
Division of RBC Ministries
3000 Kraft Ave SE, Grand Rapids, MI 49512
Mailing Address: PO Box 3566, Grand Rapids, MI 49501-3566
*Tel:* 616-942-2803 *Toll Free Tel:* 800-653-8333 (cust serv) *Fax:* 616-974-2224
*E-mail:* dhp@dhp.org; dhporders@dhp.org
*Web Site:* www.dhp.org
*Key Personnel*
Publr: Carol Holquist
Mng Ed: Judy Markham
Founded: 1987
Religious trade books; audio & video cassettes; recorded music.
ISBN Prefix(es): 978-0-929239; 978-1-57293

Number of titles published annually: 12 Print; 1 Audio
Total Titles: 200 Print; 3 CD-ROM; 150 Online; 1 Audio
Membership(s): CBA: The Association for Christian Retail; Evangelical Christian Publishers Association

**Disney-Hyperion Books**
Imprint of Disney Book Group
44 S Broadway, White Plains, NY 10601
*Tel:* 212-633-4400 *Fax:* 212-807-5880
*Web Site:* disney.go.com/books/index
*Key Personnel*
Exec Ed: Kevin Lewis
Mng Ed: Sara Liebling
Edit Dir: Stephanie Owens Lurie
Sr Ed: Catherine Onder
Ed: Abby Ranger
Founded: 1991
Publish high quality picture books, young adult fiction & nonfiction.
ISBN Prefix(es): 978-0-7868
Number of titles published annually: 250 Print
Total Titles: 2,200 Print
Imprints: Jump at the Sun; Michael di Capua Books; Volo
Foreign Rep(s): Little, Brown Canada Ltd; Little, Brown International
Foreign Rights: ACER Agencia Literaria (Spain); Agence Hoffman (Germany); Luigi Bernabo Associates SRL (Italy); Big Apple Agency Inc (China); BMSR Agencia Literaria (Brazil); The English Agency (Japan) Ltd (Japan); Harris/Elon Agency (Israel); Kooy & van Gelderen (Netherlands); Jacqueline Miller (France)
Membership(s): Children's Book Council
*See separate listing for:*
**Jump at the Sun**

**Disney Press**
Division of The Walt Disney Co
44 S Broadway, White Plains, NY 10601
*Tel:* 212-633-4400 *Fax:* 212-807-5432
*Web Site:* disney.go.com/index; disney.go.com/books/index
*Key Personnel*
Edit Dir: Wendy Lefkon
Dir, Subs Rts: Molly Kong
Mng Ed: Rodger Weinfeld
Founded: 1990
Publish fiction & fantasy.
ISBN Prefix(es): 978-1-56282; 978-0-7868
Number of titles published annually: 55 Print
Total Titles: 1,000 Print
Distributed by Hachette Book Group USA
Foreign Rep(s): Little, Brown Canada Ltd; Little, Brown International
Foreign Rights: A M Heath & Co Ltd (England); ACER Agencia Literaria (Spain); Agence Hoffman (Germany); Luigi Bernabo Associates SRL (Italy); Big Apple Agency Inc (China); BMSR Agencia Literaria (Brazil); The English Agency Ltd (Japan); Harris/Elon Agency (Israel); Monica Heyum Agency (Denmark, Finland, Iceland, Norway, Sweden); Kooy & van Gelderen (Netherlands); Michele Lapautre (France)
*Warehouse:* 3 Center Plaza, Boston, MA 02108-2003

**Disney Publishing Worldwide**
Subsidiary of The Walt Disney Co
44 S Broadway, 9th fl, White Plains, NY 10601-4411
*Tel:* 914-288-4100
*Web Site:* disney.go.com/books/index
*Key Personnel*
EVP: Andrew Sugerman
SVP & Gen Mgr, Global Magazines Div: Jeanne Mosure
SVP Fin, IT & Global Opers: Raj Murari

VP, Digital Media: Yves Saada
VP, Publg Opers: Terry Downes
Publicity Dir: Seale Ballenger
Mng Ed: Sara Liebling
Founded: 1930
Publisher of children's books, comics & magazines.
ISBN Prefix(es): 978-1-56115
Number of titles published annually: 275 Print
Total Titles: 1,000 Print
Imprints: Disney Editions; Disney Libri; Disney Press; Hyperion Books for Children; Jump at the Sun
Divisions: Disney Children's Book Group
*Branch Office(s)*
500 S Buena Vista St, Burbank, CA 91521
*Tel:* 914-288-4100

**Dissertation.com**
Imprint of Universal-Publishers Inc
23331 Water Circle, Boca Raton, FL 33486-8540
SAN: 299-3635
*Tel:* 561-750-4344 *Toll Free Tel:* 800-636-8329 *Fax:* 561-750-6797
*Web Site:* www.dissertation.com
*Key Personnel*
Publr: Jeffrey R Young
Prodn Ed: Christie Mayer
Founded: 1997
Academic books.
ISBN Prefix(es): 978-1-58112; 978-0-9658564; 978-1-59942; 978-1-61233; 978-1-62734
Number of titles published annually: 50 Print; 50 Online; 50 E-Book
Total Titles: 300 Print; 300 Online; 300 E-Book
Distributed by Bertrams UK

**Diversion Books**
80 Fifth Ave, Suite 1101, New York, NY 10011
*Tel:* 212-961-6390 (ext 7)
*E-mail:* info@diversionbooks.com
*Web Site:* www.diversionbooks.com
*Key Personnel*
Founder: Charles Platkin
Founder & CEO: Scott Waxman
Proj Mgr: Mary Cummings
Founded: 2010
ISBN Prefix(es): 978-0-9845151; 978-0-9829050; 978-0-9838395; 978-0-9839885; 978-0-9833371; 978-1-938120
Number of titles published annually: 10 Print; 50 E-Book
Total Titles: 52 E-Book

**DK**
Division of Penguin Group (USA) LLC
375 Hudson St, 2nd fl, New York, NY 10014-3672
*Tel:* 212-213-4800 *Toll Free Tel:* 877-342-5357 (cust serv) *Fax:* 212-213-5202
*Web Site:* us.dk.com
*Key Personnel*
SVP, Sales & Mktg: Therese Burke
Dir, Sales: Tom Korman
Dir, Spec Sales: Victoria Korlishin
VP, Dir, Fin & Opers: Simon Fraser
Dir, Mktg & Publicity: Rachel Kempster
Edit Dir, Children's: Nancy Ellwood
Dir, Opers: Sheila Phelan
Founded: 1974 (in UK)
Illustrated reference books on a wide range of topics for adults & children, including travel, health, history, sports, pets, atlases, dictionaries, music, art, decorating, astrology, sex & cooking.
ISBN Prefix(es): 978-1-879431; 978-1-56458; 978-0-7894; 978-0-7566
Number of titles published annually: 392 Print
Total Titles: 1,850 Print
Foreign Rep(s): Dorling Kindersley Ltd (UK)
*Advertising Agency:* Spier NY

*Warehouse:* Pearson Education, 135 S Mount Zion Rd, Lebanon, IN 46052
Membership(s): ABA; ALA; Children's Book Council; International Association of Culinary Professionals; International Reading Association; National Council of Teachers of English; National Science Teachers Association

**Do It Now Foundation**
PO Box 27568, Tempe, AZ 85285-7568
*Tel:* 480-736-0599 *Fax:* 480-736-0771
*Web Site:* www.doitnow.org
*Key Personnel*
Principal: Don Redifer
Pres & Exec Dir: Frank Peckous
Founded: 1968
Drugs, alcohol & health.
ISBN Prefix(es): 978-0-89230
Number of titles published annually: 50 Print
Total Titles: 150 Print

**Do-It-Yourself Legal Publishers**
Affiliate of Selfhelper Law Press of America
1588 Remsen Ave, Brooklyn, NY 11236
SAN: 214-1876
*Tel:* 718-684-4769 *Fax:* 718-684-4769
*E-mail:* ba07102@yahoo.com
*Key Personnel*
Sr Ed: Dan Benjamin
Founded: 1978
The simplest problems can be effectively handled by anyone with average common sense & a competent guidebook. Specialists in self-help, how-to law manuals & kits for the non-lawyer.
ISBN Prefix(es): 978-0-932704
Number of titles published annually: 7 Print
Total Titles: 30 Print
Imprints: The Selfhelper Law Press of America
Distributed by Brodart Co; Midwest Library Service; Quality Books; Unique Books
Foreign Rep(s): Yeh Yeh Book Gallery Ltd (Taiwan)

**§Dogwise Publishing**
Division of Direct Book Service Inc
403 S Mission St, Wenatchee, WA 98801
SAN: 132-9545
*Tel:* 509-663-9115 *Toll Free Tel:* 800-776-2665 *Fax:* 509-662-7233
*E-mail:* mail@dogwise.com
*Web Site:* www.dogwise.com
*Key Personnel*
Owner & Publr: Charlene Woodward
Owner: Larry Woodward
Founded: 2000
Publish how-to books on dog care, training, behavior, health & competition.
ISBN Prefix(es): 978-1-929242
Number of titles published annually: 10 Print
Total Titles: 90 Print; 260 E-Book
Membership(s): Book Publishers of the Northwest; Dogwise Association of America; IBPA, the Independent Book Publishers Association

**Tom Doherty Associates, LLC**
Subsidiary of Macmillan
175 Fifth Ave, 14th fl, New York, NY 10010
*Tel:* 646-307-5151 *Toll Free Tel:* 800-455-0340 *Fax:* 212-388-0191
*E-mail:* firstname.lastname@tor.com
*Web Site:* www.tor-forge.com
*Key Personnel*
Pres & Publr: Thomas Doherty
VP & Assoc Publr: Linda Quinton
Publicity Dir: Patty Garcia
Exec Dir of Mktg: Phyllis Azar
Mgr of Admin: Dana Giusio
Publr, Aerie Books: Kathleen Doherty
Art Dir: Irene Gallo
Art Dir, Mass Market/Forge Books: Seth Lerner
Exec Ed: Beth Meacham; Patrick Nielsen Hayden
Founded: 1980
Mass market & trade paperbacks; trade hardcover: fiction, horror, science fiction, fantasy, mystery, suspense, techno-thrillers, western fiction, American historicals, nonfiction, paranormal romance, true crime & biography.
ISBN Prefix(es): 978-0-8125; 978-0-7653
Number of titles published annually: 425 Print
Total Titles: 2,224 Print
Imprints: Aerie Books; Forge Books; Orb Books; Starscape; Tor; Tor Teen
Distributed by Macmillan
Foreign Rights: St Martin's Press
*Advertising Agency:* Slocum Advertising Agency
*Distribution Center:* MPS Distribution Center, 16365 James Madison Hwy, Gordonsville, VA 22942-8501 *Toll Free Tel:* 888-330-8477 *Fax:* 540-672-7540 (cust serv) *Toll Free Fax:* 800-672-2054 (orders) *E-mail:* firstinitial.lastname@mpsvirginia.com

**Dominie Press Inc**
Division of Pearson Learning Group
145 S Mount Zion Rd, Lebanon, IN 46052
Mailing Address: PO Box 2500, Lebanon, IN 46052
*Tel:* 765-483-6500 *Toll Free Tel:* 800-321-3106 (Pearson Cust Serv); 800-848-9500 *Toll Free Fax:* 877-260-2530
*Web Site:* www.pearsonschool.com; www.k12pearson.com
*Key Personnel*
Prod Specialist: Nancie Schenkel
Founded: 1987
Educational textbooks, children's books, Spanish books.
ISBN Prefix(es): 978-1-56270; 978-0-7685
Number of titles published annually: 240 Print
Total Titles: 2,500 Print
Distributor for Cambridge University Press (limited number of titles, adult GED)

**The Donning Company Publishers**
Subsidiary of Walsworth Publishing Co Inc
184 Business Park Dr, Suite 206, Virginia Beach, VA 23462
SAN: 211-6316
*Tel:* 757-497-1789 *Toll Free Tel:* 800-296-8572 *Fax:* 757-497-2542
*Web Site:* www.donning.com
*Key Personnel*
Gen Mgr: Steve Mull *Tel:* 800-369-2646 ext 3269 *E-mail:* steve.mull@donning.com
Sr Ed: Richard Horwege *E-mail:* richard.horwege@donning.com
Founded: 1974
Specialty book publisher of limited-edition commemorative volumes, pictorial histories & contemporary portraits.
ISBN Prefix(es): 978-0-915442; 978-0-89865
Number of titles published annually: 69 Print
Total Titles: 1,800 Print
Imprints: Portraits of America
*Branch Office(s)*
306 N Kansas Ave, Marceline, MO 64658, Mktg Specialist: Tonya Hannink *Tel:* 660-376-3543 ext 3278 *Toll Free Tel:* 800-369-2646 ext 3278 *Fax:* 660-258-7798 *E-mail:* tonya.hannink@donning.com
Foreign Rights: Writers House Inc

**Dordt College Press**
Affiliate of Dordt College
498 Fourth Ave NE, Sioux Center, IA 51250-1606
*Tel:* 712-722-6420 *Toll Free Tel:* 800-343-6738 *Fax:* 712-722-1198
*E-mail:* dordtpress@dordt.edu; bookstore@dordt.edu
*Web Site:* www.dordt.edu
*Key Personnel*
Mng Ed: John H Kok *Tel:* 712-722-6308 *E-mail:* jkok@dordt.edu

Founded: 1978
Publishes primarily academic books & monographs, plus a quarterly journal.
ISBN Prefix(es): 978-0-932914
Number of titles published annually: 6 Print
Total Titles: 45 Print

**Dorland Healthcare Information**
Division of Access Intelligence
4 Choke Cherry Rd, 2nd fl, Rockville, MD 20850
Mailing Address: PO Box 25128, Salt Lake City, UT 84121-0128
*Tel:* 301-354-2000 *Toll Free Tel:* 800-784-2332 *Fax:* 801-365-2300
*E-mail:* info@dorlandhealth.com
*Web Site:* www.dorlandhealth.com
*Key Personnel*
CEO & Pres, Access Intelligence: Don Pazour *Tel:* 215-875-1255
VP & Group Publr: Diane Schwartz *Tel:* 212-621-4964 *E-mail:* dschwartz@accessintel.com
Founded: 1950
Directories, market research, databases & mailing lists.
ISBN Prefix(es): 978-1-880874
Number of titles published annually: 6 Print; 1 CD-ROM; 4 Online
Total Titles: 6 Print; 1 CD-ROM; 4 Online
Imprints: Dorland Biomedical; Dorland Healthcare Information
Divisions: The Retention Solutions Group

**Dorrance Publishing Co Inc**
701 Smithfield St, Suite 301, Pittsburgh, PA 15222
*Toll Free Tel:* 800-695-9599; 800-788-7654 (gen cust orders); 888-840-8581 (bookstore orders & returns) *Fax:* 412-288-1786
*E-mail:* dorrinfo@dorrancepublishing.com
*Web Site:* www.dorrancepublishing.com
*Key Personnel*
Mng Dir: David Zeolla
Sr Mdsg Coord: Kathleen Haak *Tel:* 888-840-8581 *Fax:* 412-338-0427
Founded: 1920
Full service author services company.
This publisher has indicated that 100% of their product line is author subsidized.
ISBN Prefix(es): 978-0-8059; 978-1-4349; 978-1-4809
Number of titles published annually: 360 Print; 360 Online; 360 E-Book; 10 Audio
Total Titles: 2,500 Print; 2,200 Online; 2,200 E-Book; 5 Audio
Imprints: Red Lead Press; Rose Dog Books

**Dorset House Publishing Co Inc**
3143 Broadway, Suite 2-B, New York, NY 10027
SAN: 687-794X
*Tel:* 212-620-4053 *Toll Free Tel:* 800-DHBOOKS (342-6657, orders only) *Fax:* 212-727-1044
*E-mail:* info@dorsethouse.com
*Web Site:* www.dorsethouse.com
*Key Personnel*
Pres, Admin & Gen Mgr, Rts & Perms: Wendy Eakin
Founded: 1984
Professional books, management, business, consulting, geared to software engineering.
ISBN Prefix(es): 978-0-932633
Number of titles published annually: 5 Print; 5 E-Book
Total Titles: 54 Print; 5 E-Book
Foreign Rep(s): Alkem Co (S) Private Ltd (Brunei, Hong Kong, Indonesia, Japan, Korea, Malaysia, Myanmar, Philippines, Singapore, Taiwan, Thailand); Prism Books Pvt Ltd (Bangladesh, India, Nepal, Sri Lanka)
Foreign Rights: Chinese Connection (Hong Kong, Mainland China, Taiwan)
Membership(s): IBPA, the Independent Book Publishers Association

**Doubleday/Nan A Talese**
Imprint of Knopf Doubleday Publishing Group
c/o Random House Inc, 1745 Broadway, New York, NY 10019
*Tel:* 212-751-2600 *Toll Free Tel:* 800-638-6460 *Fax:* 212-572-2593
*Web Site:* www.knopfdoubleday.com
*Key Personnel*
Chmn: Sonny Mehta
Pres: Anthony Chirico
SVP, Publr & Ed-in-Chief: William Thomas
SVP, Publr, Pres & Edit Dir, Nan A Talese Books: Nan A Talese
SVP, Publg: Suzanne Herz
VP & Dir, Busn Opers: Justine LeCates
SVP & Dir, Intl Rts: Carol Brown Janeway
Dir, Dom Rts: Sean Yule
Mgr, Foreign Rts: Suzanne Smith
VP, Ad: Judy Jacoby
Exec Dir, Publicity: Alison Rich
Dir, Mktg: John Pitts
Group Sales Dir: Janet Cooke
Imprint Sales Dir: James Kimball
VP & Dir, Prodn/Design: Andrew W Hughes
VP & Dir, Interior Design & Desktop Publg: Peter Andersen
Dir, Art Jacket: John Fontana
VP & Mng Ed: Katherine Hourigan
Exec Ed: Alison Callahan; Gerry Howard; Jason Kaufman
Sr Ed: Kristine Puopolo; Jennifer Jackson
Ed: Melissa Ann Danaczko; Ronit Feldman
Founded: 1897
Random House Inc & its publishing entities are not accepting unsol submissions, proposals, mss or submission queries via e-mail at this time.
ISBN Prefix(es): 978-0-385; 978-0-7679
Foreign Rights: ALS-Agenzia Letteraria Santachiara (Roberto Santachiara) (Italy); Anthea Agency (Katalina Sabeva) (Bulgaria); Bardon-Chinese Media (Xu-Weiguang) (China); Bardon-Chinese Media Agency (Yu-Shiuan Chen) (Taiwan); The English Agency (Junzo Sawa) (Japan); Graal Literary Agency (Maria Strarz-Kanska) (Poland); The Deborah Harris Agency (Ilana Kurshan) (Israel); JLM Literary Agency (Nelly Moukakos) (Greece); Katai & Bolza Literary (Peter Bolza) (Croatia, Hungary); KCC (MiSook Hong) (Korea); Simona Kessler International (Simona Kessler) (Romania); Licht & Burr Literary Agency (Trine Licht) (Scandinavia); La Nouvelle Agence (Vanessa Kling) (France); Kristin Olson Literary Agency (Kristin Olson) (Czech Republic); Sebes & Van Gelderen Literary Agency (Paul Sebes) (Netherlands)

**§Dover Publications Inc**
31 E Second St, Mineola, NY 11501-3852
*Tel:* 516-294-7000 *Toll Free Tel:* 800-223-3130 (orders) *Fax:* 516-742-6953; 516-742-5049 (orders)
*Web Site:* store.doverdirect.com
*Key Personnel*
Pres: Frank Fontana
VP, Mktg: Ken Katzman *Tel:* 516-294-7000 ext 121 *E-mail:* kkatzman@doverpublications.com
Dir, Sales: Steven Sussman *Tel:* 516-294-7000 ext 122
Asst to Pres & Sr Reprint Ed: John Grafton
Founded: 1941
Trade, scientific, paperbound books; posters, language, literature & stationery items.
ISBN Prefix(es): 978-0-486
Number of titles published annually: 670 Print; 8 CD-ROM
Total Titles: 8,500 Print; 36 CD-ROM; 22 Audio
Foreign Rep(s): David & Charles (UK)
*Shipping Address:* 11 E Second St, Mineola, NY 11501

**Down East Books**
Imprint of Rowman & Littlefield Publishers Inc
680 Commercial St (US Rte 1), Rockport, ME 04856
Mailing Address: PO Box 679, Camden, ME 04843
*Tel:* 207-594-9544 *Toll Free Tel:* 800-685-7962 (US only orders); 800-766-1670 *Fax:* 207-594-7215
*E-mail:* submissions@downeast.com
*Web Site:* www.downeast.com
*Key Personnel*
Publr: John Viehman *E-mail:* jviehman@downeast.com
Ed-in-Chief: Paul Doiron
Assoc Ed: Michael Steere *Tel:* 207-594-9544 ext 406 *E-mail:* msteere@downeast.com
Founded: 1967
Tied directly to "Down East, The Magazine of Maine", the book publishing mission is to bring Maine's excess of literary & artistic talent to the book marketplace.
ISBN Prefix(es): 978-0-89272
Number of titles published annually: 25 Print; 16 E-Book
Total Titles: 350 Print; 50 E-Book
*Sales Office(s):* National Book Network, 15200 NBN Way, Blue Ridge Summit, PA 17214 *Toll Free Tel:* 800-462-6420
Distributor for Nimbus Publishing Ltd (selected titles, CN sales only)
*Distribution Center:* National Book Network, 15200 NBN Way, Blue Ridge Summit, PA 17214 *Tel:* 717-794-3800 *Toll Free Tel:* 800-462-6420 *Toll Free Fax:* 800-338-4550 *E-mail:* custserv@nbnbooks.com

**Down The Shore Publishing Corp**
638 Teal St, Cedar Run, NJ 08092
SAN: 661-082X
Mailing Address: PO Box 100, West Creek, NJ 08092
*Tel:* 609-978-1233 *Fax:* 609-597-0422
*E-mail:* dtsbooks@comcast.net; info@down-the-shore.com
*Web Site:* www.down-the-shore.com
*Key Personnel*
Founder & Pres: Raymond G Fisk *Tel:* 609-978-1233 ext 203
Founded: 1984
Regional books, local history; calendars; note cards.
ISBN Prefix(es): 978-0-9615208; 978-0-945582; 978-1-59322
Number of titles published annually: 6 Print
Total Titles: 70 Print
Imprints: Bufflehead Books; Cormorant Books; Cormorant Calendars; Terrapin Greetings
Membership(s): IBPA, the Independent Book Publishers Association

**§Dragon Door Publications**
5 E Country Rd B, Suite 3, Little Canada, MN 55117
*Tel:* 651-487-2180 *Toll Free Tel:* 800-899-5111 (orders & cust serv)
*E-mail:* support@dragondoor.com
*Web Site:* www.dragondoor.com
*Key Personnel*
Publr & Ed-in-Chief: John Du Cane
ISBN Prefix(es): 978-0-938045

**§Dragonfairy Press**
Imprint of Dragonfairy Press LLC
4355 Cobb Pkwy, Suite J116, Atlanta, GA 30339
*Tel:* 404-955-8150
*E-mail:* info@dragonfairypress.com
*Web Site:* www.dragonfairypress.com
*Key Personnel*
Sr Ed: Alicia Brewster; Kenya Wright
Founded: 2012
Independent publisher of adult & young adult speculative fiction, including fantasy, science

fiction, urban fantasy, paranormal romance, supernatural horror, dystopia & other subgenres.
ISBN Prefix(es): 978-0-9850230; 978-1-939452
Number of titles published annually: 8 Print; 8 E-Book
Total Titles: 10 Print; 8 E-Book
*Distribution Center:* Small Press United, Independent Publishers Group, 814 N Franklin St, Chicago, IL 60610 *Tel:* 312-337-0747 *Fax:* 312-337-5985 *E-mail:* frontdesk@ipgbook.com
Membership(s): IBPA, the Independent Book Publishers Association

**Drama Publishers**, see Quite Specific Media Group Ltd

**§Dramaline® Publications LLC**
36-851 Palm View Rd, Rancho Mirage, CA 92270-2417
SAN: 285-239X
*Tel:* 760-770-6076 *Fax:* 760-770-4507
*E-mail:* drama.line@verizon.net
*Key Personnel*
Owner: Roger Karshner
Gen Mgr & Intl Rts: Courtney Marsh
Founded: 1980
Scene-study books for actors.
ISBN Prefix(es): 978-0-9611792; 978-0-9409669
Number of titles published annually: 5 Print; 2 CD-ROM; 3 Online; 3 E-Book
Total Titles: 50 Print; 50 Online; 50 E-Book; 3 Audio
Imprints: Noble Porter Press
Foreign Rep(s): Gazelle Book Services (British Commonwealth); Tower Books (Australia)
*Returns:* Publishers Storage & Shipping Corp, 660 S Mansfield St, Ypsilanti, MI 48197
*Warehouse:* Publishers Storage & Shipping Corp, 660 S Mansfield St, Ypsilanti, MI 48197 *Tel:* 734-487-9720 *Fax:* 734-487-1890 *E-mail:* orders@psscmi.com
*Distribution Center:* Publishers Storage & Shipping Corp, 660 S Mansfield St, Ypsilanti, MI 48197

**Dramatic Publishing Co**
311 Washington St, Woodstock, IL 60098-3308
SAN: 201-5676
*Tel:* 815-338-7170 *Toll Free Tel:* 800-448-7469 *Fax:* 815-338-8981 *Toll Free Fax:* 800-334-5302
*E-mail:* plays@dramaticpublishing.com
*Web Site:* www.dramaticpublishing.com
*Key Personnel*
Pres: Christopher Sergel, III
VP: Gayle Sergel; Susan Sergel
Founded: 1885
Acting editions of plays & musicals & licensing productions of same.
ISBN Prefix(es): 978-0-87129; 978-1-58342
Number of titles published annually: 55 Print
Total Titles: 2,000 Print
Foreign Rep(s): DALRO Pty Ltd (Southern Africa); Origin Theatrical Pty Ltd (Australia); The Play Bureau NZ Ltd (New Zealand)

**Dramatists Play Service Inc**
440 Park Ave S, New York, NY 10016
*Tel:* 212-683-8960 *Fax:* 212-213-1539
*E-mail:* postmaster@dramatists.com
*Web Site:* www.dramatists.com
*Key Personnel*
Pres: Stephen Sultan *E-mail:* sultan@dramatists.com
VP, Pubns & IT: Michael Fellmeth *Tel:* 212-683-8960 ext 115 *E-mail:* fellmeth@dramatists.com
Founded: 1936
Publisher & licensor of plays & musicals.
ISBN Prefix(es): 978-0-8222
Number of titles published annually: 60 Print
Total Titles: 3,000 Print
Foreign Rights: DALRO (South Africa); Hal Leonard Australia Pty Ltd (Australia, New Zealand); Josef Weinberger (UK)

**Dream Catcher Publishing Inc**
PO Box 33883, Decatur, GA 30033
*Tel:* 404-486-7703 *Toll Free Tel:* 888-771-2800 *Toll Free Fax:* 888-771-2800
*E-mail:* dcp@dreamcatcherpublishing.org
*Web Site:* www.dreamcatcherpublishing.org
*Key Personnel*
Founder & Pres: Ms Dwan Hightower *E-mail:* ldh14@comcast.net
Founded: 2002
Small independent publisher, publishes first time authors. Fiction, nonfiction, children's books & poetry.
ISBN Prefix(es): 978-0-9720495; 978-0-9712189; 978-0-978120
Number of titles published annually: 6 Print; 50 Online
Total Titles: 50 Print
*Orders to:* Baker & Taylor Inc, 2550 W Tyvola Rd, Suite 300, Charlotte, NC 28217
Membership(s): IBPA, the Independent Book Publishers Association

**Dufour Editions Inc**
PO Box 7, Chester Springs, PA 19425
SAN: 201-341X
*Tel:* 610-458-5005 *Toll Free Tel:* 800-869-5677 *Fax:* 610-458-7103
*E-mail:* info@dufoureditions.com
*Web Site:* www.dufoureditions.com
*Key Personnel*
Pres & Publr: Christopher May
Publicity Dir: Larisa Werstler
Ed: Duncan May
Opers Mgr: Brad Elliott
Warehouse Mgr: Alishea Mock
Founded: 1949
Literary fiction, general nonfiction, literature, poetry, philosophy, history, drama & criticism.
ISBN Prefix(es): 978-0-8023
Number of titles published annually: 400 Print
Total Titles: 6,000 Print
Imprints: Dufour Editions' Distributed Presses
Distributor for Angel Books; Arcadia Books (London) (including Black Amber, Bliss, Eurocrime & Maia); Attic Press (including Atrium); Between the Lines; Black Amber Press; Blackstaff Press Ltd; Bliss; Bloodaxe Books Ltd; Brandon Books; Carysfort Press; Clo Iar-Chonnachta; Collins Press; Columba Books; Currach Press; Eland Books/Sickle Moon Books; Enitharmon Press; Eurocrime; Gill & Macmillan; Goblinshead; Hersilia; Liberties Press; The Liffey Press; Lilliput Press Ltd; Little Toller Books; Y Lolfa (including Alcemi); Maia Press; Mercier; New Island Books; Norvik Press; O'Brien Press; Orpen Press; Persephone Books; Portnoy Publishing; Route; Salmon Poetry; Colin Smythe Ltd; Stinging Fly Press; University College Dublin Press; Vagabond Voices; Veritas; The Waywiser Press
*Warehouse:* 124 Byers Rd, Chester Springs, PA 19425

**Duke University Press**
905 W Main St, Suite 18B, Durham, NC 27701
SAN: 201-3436
Mailing Address: PO Box 90660, Durham, NC 27708-0660
*Tel:* 919-688-5134 *Toll Free Tel:* 888-651-0122 *Fax:* 919-688-2615 *Toll Free Fax:* 888-651-0124
*E-mail:* orders@dukeupress.edu
*Web Site:* www.dukeupress.edu
*Key Personnel*
CFO: Norris Langley
Books Mktg Dir: Emily Young *E-mail:* bmktingmgr@dukeupress.edu
Edit Dir: Ken Wissoker *E-mail:* kwissoker@dukeupress.edu
Sr Ed: Valerie Millholland *E-mail:* vmillholland@dukeupress.edu
Acqs Ed, Journals: Erich Staib *Tel:* 919-687-3664
Sales Mgr: Michael McCullough *E-mail:* bsales@dukeupress.edu
Mktg Mgr, Journals Div: Cason Lynley *E-mail:* jrnl_mktg_mgr@dukeupress.edu
Assoc Mktg Mgr: H Lee Willoughby-Harris *Tel:* 919-687-3646 *E-mail:* textbooks@dukeupress.edu
Founded: 1921
Scholarly, trade & textbooks.
ISBN Prefix(es): 978-0-8223
Number of titles published annually: 120 Print
Total Titles: 1,300 Print; 1 E-Book
Distributor for Forest History Society
Foreign Rep(s): Combined Academic Publishers Ltd (Europe, Middle East, UK); East-West Export Books (Royden Muranaka) (Asia, The Pacific); Lexa Publishers Representatives (Mical Moser) (Canada)
Foreign Rights: Jos de Jong (Belgium, Luxembourg, Netherlands); Cristina de Lara Ruiz (Portugal, Spain); Bernd Feldmann (Austria, Germany, Switzerland); Colin Flint (Denmark, Finland, Iceland, Norway, Sweden); Charles Gibbes (Greece); Emma Hester (England, Scotland, Wales); Bill Kennedy (Middle East); Tony Moggach (Africa, Eastern Europe); David Pickering (France, Italy); Gabrielle Redmond (Ireland, Northern Ireland); Chris Reinders (South Africa)
*Advertising Agency:* Unabridged Advertising, Dafina Diabate *Tel:* 919-687-3649 *E-mail:* ddiabate@dukeupress.edu
*Warehouse:* 120 Golden Dr, Durham, NC 27705, Mgr: Don Griffin *Tel:* 919-384-0733 *Fax:* 919-384-9564
*Distribution Center:* Ubiquity Distributors, 607 Degraw St, Brooklyn, NY 11211 *Tel:* 718-875-5491 *Fax:* 718-875-8047

**Dumbarton Oaks**
1703 32 St NW, Washington, DC 20007
*Tel:* 202-339-6400 *Fax:* 202-339-6401; 202-298-8407
*E-mail:* doaksbooks@doaks.org
*Web Site:* www.doaks.org
*Key Personnel*
Pubns Asst: Lisa Wainwright
ISBN Prefix(es): 978-0-88402
Number of titles published annually: 8 Print
Total Titles: 260 Print
Distributed by Harvard University Press

**§Dun & Bradstreet**
103 JFK Pkwy, Short Hills, NJ 07078
*Tel:* 973-921-5500 *Toll Free Tel:* 800-526-0651; 800-234-3867 (cust serv)
*E-mail:* custserv@dnb.com
*Web Site:* www.dnb.com
*Key Personnel*
Chmn & CEO: Sara Mathew
Business & business reference; US & international coverage, country information.
ISBN Prefix(es): 978-1-56203
Total Titles: 31 Print; 20 CD-ROM

**Dunhill Publishing**
Division of Warwick Associates
18340 Sonoma Hwy, Sonoma, CA 95476
*Tel:* 707-939-0570 *Fax:* 707-938-3515
*E-mail:* dunhill@vom.com
*Web Site:* www.dunhillpublishing.com
*Key Personnel*
Pres: Simon Warwick-Smith *E-mail:* warwick@vom.com
Founded: 1985

Handles process of editing, prepress, design, printing, distribution, book reviews, book & author promotion, media contact, Internet sales & marketing, retail sales & marketing, fulfillment & shipping.
ISBN Prefix(es): 978-1-931501
Number of titles published annually: 10 Print
Total Titles: 10 Print

**Duquesne University Press**
600 Forbes Ave, Pittsburgh, PA 15282
*Tel:* 412-396-6610 *Fax:* 412-396-5984
*E-mail:* dupress@duq.edu
*Web Site:* www.dupress.duq.edu
*Key Personnel*
Dir: Susan Wadsworth-Booth
*E-mail:* wadsworth@duq.edu
Mktg & Busn Mgr: Lori R Crosby
*E-mail:* crosbyl@duq.edu
Prodn Ed: Kathleen Meyer *E-mail:* meyerk@duq.edu
Founded: 1927
Nonfiction: literary studies, ethics, philosophy, religion, philology, psychology, communication.
ISBN Prefix(es): 978-0-8207
Number of titles published annually: 10 Print
Total Titles: 120 Print
Foreign Rep(s): Gazelle (European Union)
*Warehouse:* CUP Services, 750 Cascadilla St, Ithaca, NY 14851-6525 *Toll Free Tel:* 800-666-2211 *Toll Free Fax:* 800-688-2877
*E-mail:* orderbook@cupserv.org
Membership(s): Association of American University Presses; Society for Scholarly Publishing

**§Dustbooks**
Affiliate of Associated Writing Programs
PO Box 100, Paradise, CA 95967-0100
SAN: 204-1871
*Tel:* 530-877-6110 *Toll Free Tel:* 800-477-6110
*Fax:* 530-877-0222
*E-mail:* publisher@dustbooks.com; info@dustbooks.com
*Web Site:* www.dustbooks.com
*Key Personnel*
Publr: Kathleen Glanville
Founded: 1964
Full service publishing company founded by Len Fulton.
ISBN Prefix(es): 978-0-913218; 978-0-916685
Number of titles published annually: 4 CD-ROM
Total Titles: 4 Print; 4 CD-ROM
Distributor for American Dust Publications

**Dutton**
Division of Penguin Group (USA) LLC
375 Hudson St, New York, NY 10014
SAN: 282-5074
*Tel:* 212-366-2000 *Fax:* 212-366-2262
*E-mail:* online@penguinputnam.com
*Web Site:* www.penguinputnam.com; us.penguingroup.com
*Key Personnel*
Pres & Publr: Brian Tart
VP, Ed-in-Chief: Ben Sevier
Exec Ed: Stephen Morrow; Jill Schwartzman
Sr Ed, Plume/Dutton: Denise Roy
VP, Assoc Publr & Dir, Publicity: Christine Ball
Mktg Dir: Carrie Swetonic
VP & Exec Creative Dir: Rich Hasselberger
VP, Prodn: Pat Lyons
Mng Ed: Susan Schwartz
ISBN Prefix(es): 978-0-525; 978-0-917657; 978-1-55611
Number of titles published annually: 40 Print
Total Titles: 130 Print
*Advertising Agency:* Spier NY

**Dutton Children's Books**
Imprint of Penguin Group (USA) LLC
345 Hudson St, New York, NY 10014
SAN: 282-5074
*Tel:* 212-366-2000
*E-mail:* online@penguinputnam.com
*Web Site:* www.penguinputnam.com; us.penguingroup.com
*Key Personnel*
VP & Publr: Julie Strauss-Gabel
Assoc Publr & Exec Mng Ed: Steven Meltzer
Founded: 1852 (as Dutton)
ISBN Prefix(es): 978-0-525
Number of titles published annually: 12 Print
Total Titles: 355 Print
Imprints: Dutton

**§DynaMinds Publishing**
6119 Nottingham Dr, Suite 1, Johnston, IA 50131
*Tel:* 515-270-5315 *Toll Free Tel:* 888-991-BOOK (991-2665)
*Web Site:* www.dynamindspublishing.com
*Key Personnel*
Publr: Charles Kuster *E-mail:* chuck@dynamindspublishing.com
Founded: 2002 (Parent company founded in 1980)
We are a niche publishing company that creates co-branded & custom products.
ISBN Prefix(es): 978-0-9712900
Number of titles published annually: 1 Print; 2 CD-ROM; 2 E-Book
Total Titles: 5 Print; 2 E-Book
*Orders to:* Box 106, Johnston, IA 50131
*Distribution Center:* Mackin Book Distribution
Membership(s): IBPA, the Independent Book Publishers Association; Midwest Independent Publishers Association

**E & E Publishing**
Division of The E & E Group LLC
1001 Bridgeway, Suite 227, Sausalito, CA 94965
*Tel:* 415-331-4025 *Fax:* 415-331-4023
*E-mail:* eandegroup@eandegroup.com
*Web Site:* www.eandegroup.com
*Key Personnel*
Deputy Dir: Eve Heidi Bine-Stock
Mng Dir: Edward Z Bine-Stock, Esq
Founded: 2000
Children's picture books & books for adults on how to write children's books.
ISBN Prefix(es): 978-0-9719898; 978-0-9748933; 978-0-9791606; 978-0-9831499
Number of titles published annually: 5 Print
Total Titles: 30 Print
*Distribution Center:* Baker & Taylor Inc, 2550 W Tyvola Rd, Suite 300, Charlotte, NC 28217
Ingram Book Group, One Ingram Blvd, La Vergne, TN 37086-1986 *Tel:* 615-213-8000
*Toll Free Tel:* 800-137-8000

**Eagan Press**
Imprint of AACC International
3340 Pilot Knob Rd, St Paul, MN 55121
*Tel:* 651-454-7250 *Toll Free Tel:* 800-328-7560
*Fax:* 651-454-0766
*E-mail:* aacc@scisoc.org
*Web Site:* www.aaccnet.org
*Key Personnel*
EVP: Steven C Nelson *E-mail:* snelson@scisoc.org
VP, Fin: Barbara Mock *E-mail:* bmock@scisoc.org
VP, Opers: Amy Hope *E-mail:* ahope@scisoc.org
Dir, Pubns: Greg Grahek *E-mail:* ggrahek@scisoc.org
Founded: 1995
Food science publishing.
ISBN Prefix(es): 978-1-891127
Number of titles published annually: 5 Print; 15 E-Book
Total Titles: 200 Print; 25 E-Book

**Eagle Publishing Inc**, see Regnery Publishing Inc

**Eagle's View Publishing**
Subsidiary of Westwind Inc
6756 North Fork Rd, Liberty, UT 84310
SAN: 240-6330
*Tel:* 801-393-4555, 801-745-0903 (edit)
*Toll Free Tel:* 800-547-3364 (orders over $100)
*Fax:* 801-745-0903 (edit); 801-393-4647
*E-mail:* sales@eaglefeathertrading.com
*Web Site:* www.eaglefeathertrading.com
*Key Personnel*
Pres & Publr: Monte Smith
Sales Mgr: Sue Smith *Tel:* 801-393-3991
Ed & Publicity: Denise Knight
Founded: 1982
Books on Indian arts, crafts & culture, mountain men & the early frontier, beading, historical clothing patterns, jewelry & how-to craft books in these areas.
ISBN Prefix(es): 978-0-943604
Number of titles published annually: 3 Print
Total Titles: 45 Print
*Orders to:* 168 W 12 St, Ogden, UT 84404
*Returns:* 168 W 12 St, Ogden, UT 84404
*Warehouse:* 168 W 12 St, Ogden, UT 84404

**Eakin Press**
Division of Sunbelt Media Inc
7005 Woodway Dr, Suite 114, Waco, TX 76712
Mailing Address: PO Box 21235, Waco, TX 76702
*Tel:* 254-235-6161 *Toll Free Tel:* 800-880-8642
*Fax:* 254-235-6230
*E-mail:* sales@eakinpress.com
*Web Site:* www.eakinpress.com
*Key Personnel*
Publr: Kris Gholson *E-mail:* kris@eakinpress.com
Founded: 1978
ISBN Prefix(es): 978-0-89015; 978-1-57168
Number of titles published annually: 50 Print
Total Titles: 490 Print; 220 E-Book; 1 Audio
Imprints: Nortex Press
Distributor for German Texan Heritage Society; San Antonio Express-News; Ellen Temple Publishing

**Earth Aware Editions**
10 Paul Dr, San Rafael, CA 94903
*Tel:* 415-526-1370 *Fax:* 415-526-1394
*E-mail:* info@earthawareeditions.com
*Key Personnel*
Pres: Raoul Goff *E-mail:* raoul@palacepress.com
Founded: 2004
Cutting-edge environmental & cultural topics that feature the unique voices & new concepts of leading thinkers, environmentalists, photojournalists, cultural commentators & artists.
ISBN Prefix(es): 978-1-932771
Number of titles published annually: 12 Print
Total Titles: 15 Print
*Shipping Address:* Publishers Group West, 40 Carl Kirkland Dr, Jackson, TN 38301
*Warehouse:* Publishers Group West, 40 Carl Kirkland Dr, Jackson, TN 38301
*Distribution Center:* Publishers Group West, 40 Carl Kirkland Dr, Jackson, TN 38301

**East Asian Legal Studies Program (EALSP)**
Division of University of Maryland School of Law
500 W Baltimore St, Suite 411, Baltimore, MD 21201-1786
*Tel:* 410-706-3870 *Fax:* 410-706-1516
*E-mail:* eastasia@law.umaryland.edu
*Web Site:* www.law.umaryland.edu/programs/international/eastasia
*Key Personnel*
Exec Ed & Assoc Ed-in-Chief: Chih-Yu T Wu
Gen Ed: Michael Van Altine
Founded: 1977
East Asian legal studies, political, economic & legal.
ISBN Prefix(es): 978-0-942182; 978-0-925153

Number of titles published annually: 4 Print
Total Titles: 218 Print

**East West Discovery Press**
PO Box 3585, Manhattan Beach, CA 90266
*Tel:* 310-545-3730 *Fax:* 310-545-3731
*E-mail:* info@eastwestdiscovery.com
*Web Site:* www.eastwestdiscovery.com
*Key Personnel*
Dir: Michael Smith
Publr & Ed: Icy Smith
Founded: 2000
Independent publisher & distributor of multicultural & bilingual books.
ISBN Prefix(es): 978-0-9701654; 978-0-9669437; 978-0-9799339; 978-0-9821675
Number of titles published annually: 10 Print
Total Titles: 30 Print
Membership(s): IBPA, the Independent Book Publishers Association

**EastBridge**
70 New Canaan Ave, Norwalk, CT 06850
*Tel:* 203-855-9125 *Fax:* 203-857-0730
*E-mail:* asia@eastbridgebooks.org
*Web Site:* www.eastbridgebooks.org
*Key Personnel*
Founding Dir & Mng Ed: J C West *E-mail:* west@eastbridgebooks.org
Dir & Sr Ed: A S Kaufmann *E-mail:* ask@eastbridgebooks.org
Ed, D'Asia Vu Reprint Lib: Chuck Hayford
Ed, The Missionary Enterprise in Asia: Kathleen Lodwick
Founded: 1997
Not for profit publisher in Asian Studies.
ISBN Prefix(es): 978-1-891936; 978-1-59988
Number of titles published annually: 20 Print
Total Titles: 75 Print
Imprints: D'Asia Vu Reprint Library (reprints of important classical works); The Missionary Enterprise in Asia (memoirs, autobiographies & biographies of missionaries in Asia); Signature Books (Asian literature, history & analysis); Voices of Asia (current books on Asia authoritatively translated from the original language)
Distributor for China Institute; John Helde; International Christian University Foundation; Nippon Foundation; Yosifumi Taguchi
Foreign Rep(s): Royal Asiatic Society, Korea Branch (Korea)
Membership(s): Association for Asian Studies

**Eastland Press**
1240 Activity Dr, Suite D, Vista, CA 92081
Mailing Address: PO Box 99749, Seattle, WA 98139
*Tel:* 206-217-0204 (edit); 760-598-9695 (orders) *Toll Free Tel:* 800-453-3278 (orders) *Fax:* 760-598-6083 (orders) *Toll Free Fax:* 800-241-3329 (orders)
*E-mail:* info@eastlandpress.com; orders@eastlandpress.com (orders-credit cards only)
*Web Site:* www.eastlandpress.com
*Key Personnel*
Gen Mgr: Patricia O'Connor
Mng Ed & Lib Sales Dir: John O'Connor
Author & Med Ed: Dan Bensky
Author & Prodn Mgr: Lilian Bensky
Founded: 1981
Chinese medicine, osteopathic & structural medicine, yoga. Use Seattle, WA address for submitting a ms or inquiring about a publication. Use Vista, CA address for ordering books.
ISBN Prefix(es): 978-0-939616
Number of titles published annually: 5 Print; 1 CD-ROM
Total Titles: 55 Print; 4 CD-ROM
Distributor for Journal of Chinese Medicine Publications
Membership(s): Publishers Association of the West

**Easy Money Press**
Subsidiary of Wolford & Associates
5419 87 St, Lubbock, TX 79424
*Tel:* 806-543-5215
*E-mail:* easymoneypress@yahoo.com
*Key Personnel*
Creative Dir: Henry Wolford *E-mail:* hcwolford@yahoo.com
Mktg Dir: Sheri Kephart
Prodn Dir: P J Max
Founded: 1996
ISBN Prefix(es): 978-0-9654563; 978-1-929714
Number of titles published annually: 3 Print; 3 E-Book
Total Titles: 22 Print; 12 E-Book
Imprints: Big Tree Books; EMP; Haase House

**Eaton Publishing**, see BioTechniques Books

**Eckankar**
PO Box 2000, Chanhassen, MN 55317-2000
*Tel:* 952-380-2200 *Toll Free Tel:* 800-275-2606 *Fax:* 952-380-2295 *Toll Free Fax:* 800-510-3650
*E-mail:* eckbooks@eckankar.org
*Web Site:* www.eckankar.org
*Key Personnel*
Pres: Peter Skelskey
Founded: 1965
Titles emphasize the value of personal experience as a vital & most natural basis for spiritual belief. Each title presents the Eckankar teachings as practical applications of ancient wisdom for today's world.
ISBN Prefix(es): 978-1-57043
Number of titles published annually: 5 Print; 4 Audio
Total Titles: 75 Print; 60 CD-ROM; 12 Audio
*Warehouse:* Eckankar, 1501 County Hospital Rd, Nashville, TN 37218 *E-mail:* sswift@apgbooks.com SAN: 630-818X
Membership(s): ABA; BISG; IBPA, the Independent Book Publishers Association; Midwest Independent Booksellers Association; Midwest Independent Publishers Association

**§Eclipse Press**
Subsidiary of Blood-Horse Publications Inc
3101 Beaumont Centre Circle, Lexington, KY 40513
*Tel:* 859-278-2361 *Toll Free Tel:* 800-866-2361 *Fax:* 859-276-6868
*E-mail:* editorial@eclipsepress.com; info@eclipsepress.com
*Web Site:* www.eclipsepress.com
*Key Personnel*
Pres & Publr: Marla Bickel
Ed: Jacqueline Duke *E-mail:* jduke@eclipsepress.com
Founded: 1916
Publications dedicated to the enjoyment, health & betterment of the equine industry.
ISBN Prefix(es): 978-0-939049; 978-1-58150
Number of titles published annually: 3 Print
Total Titles: 130 Print; 50 CD-ROM
Imprints: The Horse Health Care Library
Membership(s): IBPA, the Independent Book Publishers Association

**Ecopress**
Imprint of Finney Company Inc
8075 215 St W, Lakeville, MN 55044
*Tel:* 952-469-6699 *Toll Free Tel:* 800-846-7027 *Fax:* 952-469-1968 *Toll Free Fax:* 800-330-6232
*E-mail:* info@finneyco.com
*Web Site:* www.ecopress.com
*Key Personnel*
Pres: Alan E Krysan
Mktg Specialist: Krista Danielson
Founded: 1996
Produces books & art that enhance environmental awareness, offering high quality titles covering subjects such as rivers, hiking, plant & environmental guides.
ISBN Prefix(es): 978-1-89327; 978-0-96397
Number of titles published annually: 3 Print
Total Titles: 14 Print

**ECS**, see The Electrochemical Society (ECS)

**ECS Publishing Corp**
615 Concord St, Framingham, MA 01702
*Tel:* 508-620-7400 *Toll Free Tel:* 800-777-1919 *Fax:* 508-620-7401
*E-mail:* office@ecspub.com
*Web Site:* www.ecspublishing.com
*Key Personnel*
Owner & Pres: Robert Schuneman
Founded: 1993
Music publishing (sheet music).
ISBN Prefix(es): 978-0-911318
Number of titles published annually: 50 Print
Imprints: ARSIS Audio; Galaxy Music Corp; Highgate Press; Ione Press; E C Schirmer Music Co
Distributor for Randol Bass Music; Dunstan House; Edition Delrieu; Gaudia Music & Arts; Stainer & Bell Ltd; Vireo Press
*Orders to:* Canticle Distributing, 1727 Larkin Williams Rd, Fenton, MO 63026-2024 *Tel:* 636-305-0100 *Toll Free Tel:* 800-647-2117 (USA only) *Fax:* 636-305-0121 *E-mail:* morningstar@morningstarmusic.com
*Distribution Center:* Canticle Distributing, 1727 Larkin Williams Rd, Fenton, MO 63026-2024 *Tel:* 636-305-0100 *Toll Free Tel:* 800-647-2117 (USA only) *Fax:* 636-305-0121 *E-mail:* morningstar@morningstarmusic.com

**EDC Publishing**
Division of Educational Development Corp
10302 E 55 Place, Tulsa, OK 74146-6515
Mailing Address: PO Box 470663, Tulsa, OK 74147-0663
*Tel:* 918-622-4522 *Toll Free Tel:* 800-475-4522 *Fax:* 918-665-7919 *Toll Free Fax:* 800-743-5660
*E-mail:* edc@edcpub.com
*Web Site:* www.edcpub.com
*Key Personnel*
CEO & Pres: Randall White *E-mail:* rwhite@edcpub.com
VP, Publg: Ronald T McDaniel *E-mail:* rmcdaniel@edcpub.com
VP, InfoSystems: Craig M White
Cont & Corp Secy: Marilyn R Pinney
Founded: 1978
Children's books (fiction & nonfiction) & kid kits.
ISBN Prefix(es): 978-0-88110; 978-0-7460; 978-0-86020; 978-0-7945; 978-1-58086
Number of titles published annually: 200 Print
Total Titles: 1,800 Print; 22 CD-ROM
Imprints: Usborne Books
Distributor for Usborne Publishing

**Edgewise Press Inc**
24 Fifth Ave, Suite 224, New York, NY 10011
*Tel:* 212-982-4818 *Fax:* 212-982-1364
*E-mail:* epinc@mindspring.com
*Web Site:* www.edgewisepress.org
*Key Personnel*
CEO: Howard Johnson, Jr
Ed: Joy L Glass; Richard Milazzo
Founded: 1995
Publisher of serious art & literary books.
ISBN Prefix(es): 978-0-9646466; 978-1-893207
Number of titles published annually: 3 Print
Total Titles: 29 Print
Distributor for Editions d'Afrique du Nord; Sotoportego Editore Venice

**ediciones Lerner**
Division of Lerner Publishing Group Inc
241 First Ave N, Minneapolis, MN 55401
*Tel:* 612-332-3344 *Toll Free Tel:* 800-328-4929 *Fax:* 612-332-7615 *Toll Free Fax:* 800-332-1132
*E-mail:* info@lernerbooks.com
*Web Site:* www.lernerbooks.com
*Key Personnel*
Chmn: Harry J Lerner
Pres & Publr: Adam Lerner
CFO & EVP: Margaret Wunderlich
EVP, Sales: David Wexler
VP & Dir, Mktg & Digital Prods: Terri Soutor
Ed-in-Chief: Patricia M Stockland
VP, Prodn: Gary Hansen
Rts Dir: Maria Kjoller
Dir, Prod Devt & Mktg Res: Lois Wallentine
Dir, Electronic Content: Dan Wallek
Art Dir: Zach Marell
Dir, HR: Cyndi Radant
Publishes fiction & nonfiction books for PreK-4 in Spanish.
ISBN Prefix(es): 978-0-8225; 978-0-7613
Total Titles: 150 Print; 95 E-Book

**Ediciones Universal**
3090 SW Eighth St, Miami, FL 33135
SAN: 207-2203
Mailing Address: PO Box 450353, Miami, FL 33245-0353
*Tel:* 305-642-3234 *Fax:* 305-642-7978
*E-mail:* ediciones@ediciones.com
*Web Site:* www.ediciones.com
*Key Personnel*
Gen Mgr: Marta Salvat-Golik *E-mail:* marta@ediciones.com
Founded: 1965
Publish Spanish language books, specialize in Cuban topics.
ISBN Prefix(es): 978-0-89729; 978-1-59388
Number of titles published annually: 20 Print

**Editions Orphee Inc**
1240 Clubview Blvd N, Columbus, OH 43235-1226
*Tel:* 614-846-9517 *Fax:* 614-846-9794
*E-mail:* sales@editionsorphee.com
*Web Site:* www.editionsorphee.com
*Key Personnel*
Pres: Mr Matanya Orphee *E-mail:* m.orphee@orphee.com
Classical sheet music, books on music.
ISBN Prefix(es): 978-0-936186; 978-1-882612
Number of titles published annually: 12 Print
Total Titles: 20 Print
Distributed by Theodore Presser Co
Foreign Rep(s): Chanterelle Verlag (Germany)

**Editorial Bautista Independiente**
Division of Baptist Mid-Missions
3417 Kenilworth Blvd, Sebring, FL 33870-4469
*Tel:* 863-382-6350 *Toll Free Tel:* 800-398-7187 (US) *Fax:* 863-382-8650
*E-mail:* info@ebi-bmm.org; ebiweb@ebi-bmm.org
*Web Site:* www.ebi-bmm.org
*Key Personnel*
Gen Dir & Busn Mgr: Bruce Burkholder *Tel:* 336-922-6075
Founded: 1950
Sunday school materials, extension materials, Bible study-all in Spanish.
ISBN Prefix(es): 978-1-879892
Number of titles published annually: 5 Print
Total Titles: 170 Print
Distributor for Casa Bautista; CLIE; Portavoz

**Editorial Portavoz**
Division of Kregel Publications
733 Wealthy St SE, Grand Rapids, MI 49503-5553
SAN: 298-9115
Mailing Address: PO Box 2607, Grand Rapids, MI 49501-2607
*Toll Free Tel:* 877-733-2607 (ext 206) *Fax:* 616-493-1790
*E-mail:* portavoz@portavoz.com
*Web Site:* www.portavoz.com
*Key Personnel*
Pres: James R Kregel *E-mail:* president@kregel.com
Dir: Tito Mantilla
Founded: 1970
Christian products.
ISBN Prefix(es): 978-0-8254
Number of titles published annually: 30 Print
Total Titles: 600 Print
Membership(s): CBA: The Association for Christian Retail; Evangelical Christian Publishers Association; SEPA

**Editorial Unilit**
Division of Spanish House Inc
1360 NW 88 Ave, Miami, FL 33172
*Tel:* 305-592-6136 *Toll Free Tel:* 800-767-7726 *Fax:* 305-592-0087
*E-mail:* info@editorialunilit.com
*Web Site:* www.editorialunilit.com
*Key Personnel*
Pres: David Ecklebarger
Sales Mgr: Milton Reynosa *E-mail:* milton@editorialunilit.com
Founded: 1989
Publishing for the Spanish family.
ISBN Prefix(es): 978-1-56063; 978-0-7899
Number of titles published annually: 120 Print
Total Titles: 800 Print
Membership(s): CBA; Evangelical Christian Publishers Association; SEPA

**Educational Directories Inc (EDI)**
1025 W Wise Rd, Suite 101, Schaumburg, IL 60193
Mailing Address: PO Box 68097, Schaumburg, IL 60168-0097
*Tel:* 847-891-1250 *Toll Free Tel:* 800-357-6183 *Fax:* 847-891-0945
*E-mail:* info@ediusa.com
*Web Site:* www.ediusa.com
*Key Personnel*
Publr: Douglas Moody
Founded: 1904
Reference publications in education.
ISBN Prefix(es): 978-0-910536; 978-0-9821099; 978-0-9771602
Number of titles published annually: 3 Print
Total Titles: 3 Print; 1 CD-ROM

**Educational Impressions Inc**
350 Ramapo Valley Rd, Oakland, NJ 07436
*Tel:* 973-423-4666 *Toll Free Tel:* 800-451-7450 *Fax:* 973-423-5569
*Web Site:* www.edimpressions.com; www.awpeller.com
*Key Personnel*
Pres: Allan W Peller *E-mail:* awpeller@optonline.net
Dir, Sales & Mktg: Neil Peller
Founded: 1973
Supplemental textbooks, literature guides.
ISBN Prefix(es): 978-0-910857; 978-1-56644
Number of titles published annually: 30 Print
Total Titles: 450 Print
Distributed by Newbridge Communications Inc; Scholastic Inc; Scholastic-Tab Publications

**Educational Insights Inc**
Subsidiary of Learning Resources
152 W Walnut St, Suite 201, Gardena, CA 90248
SAN: 282-762X
*Toll Free Tel:* 800-933-3277 *Fax:* 847-281-2868 *Toll Free Fax:* 800-995-0506
*E-mail:* info@educationalinsights.com; cs@educationalinsights.com
*Web Site:* www.educationalinsights.com
*Key Personnel*
Pres & COO: Jim Whitney
Gen Mgr: Lisa Guili *Tel:* 847-968-3719
Press & Media: Maria Gonzalez *Tel:* 847-968-3722
Founded: 1962
El-hi instructional materials; teacher's aids, teaching machines & games.
ISBN Prefix(es): 978-0-88672; 978-1-56767
Number of titles published annually: 4 Print; 2 Audio
Total Titles: 92 Print
*Distribution Center:* Learning Resources, 380 N Fairway Dr, Vernon Hills, IL 60061

**Educator's International Press Inc**
18 Colleen Rd, Troy, NY 12180
*Tel:* 518-271-9886 *Fax:* 518-266-9422
*Web Site:* www.edint.com
*Key Personnel*
Publr: William Clockel
Founded: 1996
Educational foundations, teacher research, curriculum, special education.
ISBN Prefix(es): 978-0-9658339; 978-1-891928
Number of titles published annually: 6 Print
Total Titles: 35 Print

**Educators Progress Service Inc**
214 Center St, Randolph, WI 53956
SAN: 201-3649
*Tel:* 920-326-3126 *Toll Free Tel:* 888-951-4469 *Fax:* 920-326-3127
*E-mail:* epsinc@centurytel.net
*Web Site:* www.freeteachingaids.com
*Key Personnel*
Pres: Kathy Nehmer
Founded: 1934
Educator guides to free materials in various subject areas; video.
ISBN Prefix(es): 978-0-87708
Number of titles published annually: 16 Print
Total Titles: 16 Print

**Edupress Inc**
Imprint of Highsmith Publications
4810 Forrest Run Rd, Madison, WI 53704
*Tel:* 608-241-1201 *Toll Free Tel:* 800-694-5827 *Toll Free Fax:* 800-835-2329
*E-mail:* edupress@highsmith.com
*Web Site:* www.highsmith.com; www.edupressinc.com
*Key Personnel*
Dir: Matt Mulder *Tel:* 608-241-1201 ext 8573
Founded: 1956
Publisher of teacher resource materials.
ISBN Prefix(es): 978-1-56472
Number of titles published annually: 20 Print
Total Titles: 220 Print

**Wm B Eerdmans Publishing Co**
2140 Oak Industrial Dr NE, Grand Rapids, MI 49505
SAN: 220-0058
*Tel:* 616-459-4591 *Toll Free Tel:* 800-253-7521 *Fax:* 616-459-6540
*E-mail:* customerservice@eerdmans.com; sales@eerdmans.com
*Web Site:* www.eerdmans.com
*Key Personnel*
Pres: William B Eerdmans, Jr
VP & Ed-in-Chief: Jon Pott
VP & Treas: Claire Vander Kam
VP, Content & Technol: Klaas Wolterstorff *E-mail:* kwolter@eerdmans.com
VP, Mktg: Anita Eerdmans *E-mail:* aeerd@eerdmans.com
Sales Dir: Franklin Goldberg *E-mail:* fgoldberg@eerdmans.com

Ad Coord: Janice Myers *E-mail:* jmyers@eerdmans.com
Sales & Mktg Coord: Amy Kent *E-mail:* akent@eerdmans.com
Cust Serv & ISBN Contact: Karen Shippy *E-mail:* kshippy@eerdmans.com
Founded: 1915
Scholarly religious & religious reference, religion & social concerns, children's books.
ISBN Prefix(es): 978-0-8028
Number of titles published annually: 130 Print
Imprints: Eerdmans Books for Young Readers
Foreign Rep(s): Alban Books (Europe, UK); Asian Trading Corp (India); Bethesda Book Centre (Singapore); Christian Art Distributors (South Africa); Cru Asia Ltd (Singapore); Foundation Distributing Inc (Canada); KCBS (Korea); Koorong Books (Australia); Kyo Bun Kwan Inc (Japan); OM Books (India); Pustaka Sufes Sdn Bhd (Malaysia); SKS Books Warehouse (Singapore); Tien Dao (Hong Kong)

**Egmont USA**
Division of Egmont UK Inc
443 Park Ave S, Suite 806, New York, NY 10016
*Tel:* 212-685-0102
*E-mail:* egmontusa@egmont.com
*Web Site:* www.egmontusa.com
*Key Personnel*
Mng Dir & Publr: Andrea Cascardi
Sr Ed: Greg Ferguson
Assoc Ed: Alison Weiss
Ed-at-Large: Ruth Katcher
Sales & Mktg Dir: Margaret Coffee
Sales & Mktg Mgr: Katie Halata
Sales & Mktg Assoc: Robert Guzman
Founded: 2008
Publisher of high quality books for children & young adults. Tells stories through books, magazines, film, TV, music, games & mobile devices in more than thirty countries throughout the world.
ISBN Prefix(es): 978-1-60684
Number of titles published annually: 35 Print; 15 E-Book
Total Titles: 150 Print; 50 E-Book
*Foreign Office(s):* Egmont UK Ltd, 239 Kensington Hight St, London W86 SA, United Kingdom
Distributed by Random House Inc
Foreign Rep(s): Egmont UK Inc (Worldwide exc UK, Worldwide exc USA)
Foreign Rights: Rights People (UK & Commonwealth)
*Billing Address:* Random House Inc, c/o Cust Serv, 400 Hahn Rd, Westminster, MD 21157
*Orders to:* Random House Inc, c/o Cust Serv, 400 Hahn Rd, Westminster, MD 21157
*Returns:* 1019 N SR 47, Crowfordsville, IN 47933
*Warehouse:* 1019 N SR 47, Crowfordsville, IN 47933

**Eisenbrauns Inc**
PO Box 275, Winona Lake, IN 46590-0275
SAN: 200-7835
*Tel:* 574-269-2011 *Fax:* 574-269-6788
*E-mail:* customer_service@eisenbrauns.com; publisher@eisenbrauns.com
*Web Site:* www.eisenbrauns.com
*Key Personnel*
Pres & Publr: James E Eisenbraun *E-mail:* jeisenbraun@eisenbrauns.com
Ed: Beverly McCoy *E-mail:* bmccoy@eisenbrauns.com
Founded: 1975
Educational books, books on the Ancient Near East.
ISBN Prefix(es): 978-0-931464; 978-1-57506
Number of titles published annually: 24 Print; 2 CD-ROM; 10 E-Book
Total Titles: 350 Print; 10 CD-ROM; 29 E-Book

**§Elderberry Press Inc**
1393 Old Homestead Dr, Mezzanine, Oakland, OR 97462-9506
*Tel:* 541-459-6043
*Web Site:* www.elderberrypress.com
*Key Personnel*
Pres & Exec Ed: David W St John *E-mail:* editor@elderberrypress.com
Founded: 1997
Works closely with authors, from first reading of their ms to publishing & long after to ensure their book finds up to 50,000 or more readers.
ISBN Prefix(es): 978-0-9658407; 978-1-930859; 978-1-932762
Number of titles published annually: 12 Print; 12 Online; 12 E-Book
Total Titles: 300 Print; 120 Online; 100 E-Book; 1 Audio
Imprints: Poison Vine Books; Red Anvil Press
Distributor for Poison Vine Books; Red Anvil Press
Foreign Rep(s): Ingram Book Co (Worldwide)
Membership(s): IBPA, the Independent Book Publishers Association

**§The Electrochemical Society (ECS)**
65 S Main St, Bldg D, Pennington, NJ 08534-2839
*Tel:* 609-737-1902 *Fax:* 609-737-2743
*E-mail:* ecs@electrochem.org
*Web Site:* www.electrochem.org
*Key Personnel*
Deputy Exec Dir & Intl Rts: Mary E Yess *Tel:* 609-737-1902 ext 119 *E-mail:* mary.yess@electrochem.org
Exec Dir: Roque J Calvo *Tel:* 609-737-1902 ext 101 *E-mail:* roque.calvo@electrochem.org
Founded: 1902
Technical journals, members magazine, proceedings volumes, monographs, ECS Digital Library.
ISBN Prefix(es): 978-1-56677
Number of titles published annually: 30 Print; 1 CD-ROM; 4 Online
Total Titles: 300 Print; 1 CD-ROM; 4 Online
Distributed by American Institute of Physics (AIP) (journals); John Wiley & Sons (monographs)

**Edward Elgar Publishing Inc**
The William Pratt House, 9 Dewey Ct, Northampton, MA 01060-3815
SAN: 299-4615
*Tel:* 413-584-5551 *Toll Free Tel:* 800-390-3149 (orders) *Fax:* 413-584-9933
*E-mail:* info@e-elgar.com
*Web Site:* www.e-elgar.com
*Key Personnel*
Mktg Mgr: Melissa Davis
Founded: 1986
Books.
ISBN Prefix(es): 978-1-85898; 978-1-85278; 978-1-84064; 978-1-84376; 978-1-84542; 978-1-84720; 978-1-84844
Number of titles published annually: 300 Print; 250 E-Book
Total Titles: 4,000 Print; 1 CD-ROM; 700 E-Book
*Foreign Office(s):* Edward Elgar Publishing Ltd, the Lypiatts, 15 Lansdown Rd, Cheltenham, Glos GL50 2JA, United Kingdom *Tel:* (01242) 226934 *Fax:* (01242) 262111 *E-mail:* info@e-elgar.co.uk *Web Site:* www.e-elgar.co.uk
*Warehouse:* American International Distribution Corp, PO Box 574, Williston, VT 05495, Contact: Laurie Kenyon *Toll Free Tel:* 800-390-3149 *Fax:* 802-864-7626 *E-mail:* eep.orders@aidcvt.com

**Elite Books**
Division of Author's Publishing Cooperative (APC)
PO Box 442, Fulton, CA 95439
*Tel:* 707-525-9292 *Toll Free Fax:* 800-330-9798
*Web Site:* www.elitebooks.biz
*Key Personnel*
Ed-in-Chief: Dawson Church *E-mail:* dawson@authorspublishing.com
Media Mgr: Jeff Anderson *E-mail:* jeff@authorspublishing.com
Res Coord & Asst to Publr: Deb Tribbey *E-mail:* deb@authorspublishing.com
ISBN Prefix(es): 978-0-9720028; 978-0-9710888; 978-1-60070
Number of titles published annually: 12 Print
Distributed by Midpoint Trade
*Distribution Center:* Midpoint Trade, 27 W 20 St, Suite 1102, New York, NY 10010, Contact: Gail Kump *Tel:* 212-727-0190 *E-mail:* midpointny1@aol.com *Web Site:* www.midpointtrade.com
Membership(s): IBPA, the Independent Book Publishers Association

**Elliot's Books**
799 Forest Rd, Northford, CT 06472
*Tel:* 203-484-2184 *Fax:* 203-484-7644
*E-mail:* outofprintbooks1@mindspring.com
*Web Site:* www.elliotsbooks.com
*Key Personnel*
Publr & Owner: Elliot Ephraim
Founded: 1957
Academic.
ISBN Prefix(es): 978-0-686; 978-0-911830
Number of titles published annually: 100 Print
Total Titles: 1,150 Print

**Ellora's Cave**
Imprint of Ellora's Cave Publishing Inc
1056 Home Ave, Akron, OH 44310-3302
*Tel:* 330-253-3521
*E-mail:* service@ellorascave.com; comments@ellorascave.com
*Web Site:* www.ellorascave.com
*Key Personnel*
CEO: Patty Marks
EVP: Darrell King
Publr & Mng Ed: Raelene Gorlinsky
Ed-in-Chief: Kelli Collins
Founded: 2000
Publisher of erotic romances.
ISBN Prefix(es): 978-1-84360; 978-1-4199
Number of titles published annually: 120 Print
Total Titles: 500 Print
*Distribution Center:* Ingram Publisher Services, One Ingram Blvd, La Vergne, TN 37086-1986 *Toll Free Tel:* 800-400-5351 *E-mail:* customerservice@ingrampublisherservices.com *Web Site:* www.ingrampublisherservices.com

**Elsevier Engineering Information (Ei)**
Subsidiary of Elsevier Inc
360 Park Ave S, New York, NY 10010-1710
*Tel:* 212-989-5800 *Toll Free Tel:* 800-221-1044 *Fax:* 212-633-6380
*E-mail:* eicustomersupport@elsevier.com
*Web Site:* www.ei.org
*Key Personnel*
Dir, Scopus & EV Content Mgmt: Judy Salk
Founded: 1884
Provides online information, knowledge & support to engineering researchers. Flagship platform is Engineering Village & the primary database is Compendex.
ISBN Prefix(es): 978-0-87394
Number of titles published annually: 8 Online
Total Titles: 8 Online

**Elsevier, Health Sciences Division**
Division of Reed Elsevier Inc
1600 John F Kennedy Blvd, Suite 1800, Philadelphia, PA 19103-2899
*Tel:* 215-239-3900 *Toll Free Tel:* 800-523-1649 *Fax:* 215-239-3990

*Web Site:* www.elsevierhealth.com
*Key Personnel*
CFO, Health Sci Div: Bob Munro
SVP, US Global Medicine: Linda Belfus
VP, Sales: Jo Beth Griffin
VP, Book Prodn: Meeuwis Van Arkel
VP, Global Sales & Mktg: John Hope
Mng Dir, Nursing & Health Professions & Edit: Sally Schrefer
Founded: 1906
ISBN Prefix(es): 978-0-7506; 978-0-443; 978-0-444; 978-0-932883; 978-1-56053; 978-0-8016; 978-0-8151; 978-0-7216; 978-0-7020; 978-0-7234; 978-0-323; 978-0-7236; 978-1-4160; 978-1-55664; 978-0-920513; 978-1-898507; 978-1-932141; 978-1-4377; 978-1-4557
Number of titles published annually: 2,000 Print
Imprints: ASVP; B C Decker; Gower; Jems; Mosby; PSG; Saunders; Wolfe; Year Book
*Branch Office(s)*
6277 Sea Harbor Dr, Orlando, FL 32887-4800 *Tel:* 407-345-2000
3251 Riverport Lane, Maryland Heights, MO 63043 *Tel:* 314-872-8370 *Toll Free Tel:* 800-325-4177 *Fax:* 314-432-1380 SAN: 200-2280
360 Park Ave S, New York, NY 10010-1710 *Tel:* 212-989-5800 *Fax:* 212-633-3990
*Foreign Office(s):* 30-52 Smidmore St, Marrckville, NSW 2204, Australia
Beilstein Informationssysteme, Theodor-Heuss-Allee 108, 60486 Frankfurt, Germany
2F Higashi Azabu, One Chome Bldg, 1-9-15 Higashi Azabu, Minato-ku 106-0044, Japan
3 Killiney Rd 08-01, Winsland House I, Singapore 239519, Singapore
Linacre House, Jordan Hill, Oxford 0X2 8DP, United Kingdom
Distributor for G W Medical Publisher
Foreign Rights: John Scott & Co (Jake Scott)
*Shipping Address:* PO Box 437, Linn, MO 65051-0437
*Distribution Center:* Hwy 50 & Hwy CC, Linn, MO 65051

**§Elsevier Inc**
Subsidiary of Reed Elsevier
225 Wyman St, Waltham, MA 02144
*Tel:* 781-663-5200 *Fax:* 781-663-2262
*E-mail:* bookscustomerservice-usa@elsevier.com
*Web Site:* www.elsevier.com
*Key Personnel*
CEO, Reed Elsevier: Erik Engstrom
EVP, Opers: Adriaan Roosen *E-mail:* a.roosen@elsevier.com
Founded: 1880
Books for professionals, researchers & students in the sciences, technology, engineering, business & media. Also research monographs, major reference works & serials.
Number of titles published annually: 1,200 Print; 400 E-Book
Total Titles: 40,000 Print
*Branch Office(s)*
525 "B" St, Suite 1900, San Diego, CA 92101-4495 *Tel:* 619-231-0926
*Foreign Office(s):* Linacre House, Jordan Hill, Oxford OX2 8DP, United Kingdom, Contact: Duncan Enright *Tel:* (01865) 314563
Foreign Rep(s): Elsevier (UK) (Europe)
Foreign Rights: Elsevier; Linacre House (Europe)
Membership(s): AAP
*See separate listing for:*
**Elsevier Engineering Information (Ei)**
**Morgan Kaufmann**

**Elva Resa Publishing**
8362 Tamarack Village, Suite 119-106, St Paul, MN 55125
*Tel:* 651-357-8770 *Fax:* 501-641-0777
*E-mail:* staff@elvaresa.com
*Web Site:* www.elvaresa.com; www.almalittle.com
Founded: 1997
Books for & about military families.
ISBN Prefix(es): 978-1-934617; 978-0-9657483
Number of titles published annually: 4 Print
Total Titles: 22 Print
Imprints: Alma Little (children's books); Elva Resa; Juloya (inspirational works that help people celebrate life)
Membership(s): IBPA, the Independent Book Publishers Association; Midwest Independent Publishers Association

**§EMC Publishing**
Division of EMC Publishing LLC
875 Montreal Way, St Paul, MN 55102
SAN: 201-3800
*Tel:* 651-290-2800 (corp) *Toll Free Tel:* 800-328-1452 *Fax:* 651-290-2899 *Toll Free Fax:* 800-328-4564
*E-mail:* educate@emcp.com
*Web Site:* www.emcp.com
*Key Personnel*
CEO: Steve Van Thornout
CFO: Joy Hoppe
VP, Info Tech: Chuck Bratton
VP, Sales (Coll Div): Todd Larsen
VP, Sales: Gary Watkins
Mng Ed: Cheryl Drivdahl
Cust Care Mgr: Cheryl Monson
Mktg Mgr: Kerrie Goughnour
Founded: 1954
Paper & hardbound textbooks, audio, video, online Internet, CD-ROM, software microcomputer instructional materials in world language, business education, literature & language arts, social studies, medical, computer technology.
ISBN Prefix(es): 978-0-8219; 978-0-7638
Number of titles published annually: 100 Print; 75 CD-ROM; 20 Online; 100 E-Book; 80 Audio
Total Titles: 3,700 Print; 300 CD-ROM; 75 Online; 3,500 E-Book; 1,035 Audio
Subsidiaries: Paradigm Publishing Inc
Distributor for Sybex Inc
Foreign Rep(s): Wolfgang Kraft (Worldwide)
Foreign Rights: Wolfgang Kraft (Worldwide)
*See separate listing for:*
**JIST Publishing**

**Emerald Books**
Affiliate of YWAM Publishing
PO Box 55787, Seattle, WA 98155
*Tel:* 425-771-1153 *Toll Free Tel:* 800-922-2143 *Fax:* 425-775-2383
*E-mail:* books@ywampublishing.com
*Web Site:* www.ywampublishing.com
*Key Personnel*
Publr & Intl Rts: Warren Walsh
Mktg Dir: Wenke Warren
Ed: Ryan Davis
Founded: 1992
Christian theme.
ISBN Prefix(es): 978-1-883002; 978-1-932096
Number of titles published annually: 10 Print
Total Titles: 69 Print
Distributed by YWAM Publishing
*Shipping Address:* 7825 230 St SW, Edmonds, WA 98026 *Web Site:* ywampublishing.com

**Emmaus Road Publishing Inc**
Division of Catholics United for the Faith
827 N Fourth St, Steubenville, OH 43952
*Tel:* 740-283-2880 (outside US)
*Toll Free Tel:* 800-398-5470 (orders) *Fax:* 740-283-4011 (orders)
*E-mail:* questions@emmausroad.org
*Web Site:* www.emmausroad.org
*Key Personnel*
VP, Opers (CUF): Mrs Shannon M Minch-Hughes *Tel:* 740-283-2484 ext 115 *E-mail:* shughes@cuf.org
Order Processing: Michelle Olenick
Founded: 1998
Bible studies, biblically based apologetics & other materials faithful to the teaching of the Catholic church. Restocking fee of 20% for returns.
ISBN Prefix(es): 978-0-9663223; 978-1-931018
Number of titles published annually: 12 Print; 12 E-Book
Total Titles: 80 Print; 1 CD-ROM; 50 E-Book; 10 Audio

**Empire Press Media/Avant-Guide**
Unit of Empire Press Media Inc
244 Fifth Ave, Suite 2053, New York, NY 10001-7604
*Tel:* 917-512-3881 *Fax:* 212-202-7757
*E-mail:* info@avantguide.com; communications@avantguide.com; editor@avantguide.com
*Web Site:* www.avantguide.com
*Key Personnel*
Dir: Daniel Levine
Founded: 1999
Publishers of Avant-Guide travel books the only comprehensive travel guidebook series for adventurers who are too old for urban backpacking, but too young for hemetically-sealed tour buses. Avant-Guide books detail museums & neighborhoods as well as stylish hotels, chic shops & the best restaurants for every budget.
ISBN Prefix(es): 978-1-891603
Number of titles published annually: 8 Print; 10 Online; 10 E-Book
Total Titles: 24 Print; 20 Online; 20 E-Book
Imprints: Avant-Guide
Distributed by Publishers Group West
Foreign Rep(s): Hi Marketing (Europe, UK)
Foreign Rights: PGW (Canada)

**§Empire Publishing Service**
Division of The Empire (media group)
PO Box 1344, Studio City, CA 91614-0344
*Tel:* 818-784-8918
*E-mail:* empirepubsvc@att.net
*Web Site:* www.ppeps.com
*Key Personnel*
Dir, Opers: Joseph W Witt
Lib Sales Dir & Busn Mgr: David Cole
Founded: 1960
Publisher & distributor of entertainment books, plays & musicals, specialty books & printed music.
ISBN Prefix(es): 978-1-58690
Number of titles published annually: 70 Print; 5 CD-ROM
Total Titles: 4,365 Print; 15 CD-ROM; 22 Audio
Imprints: Arsis Press (music, worldwide); Classics With a Twist (world); Gaslight Publications (world); Paul Mould Publishing (world); Phantom Books & Music (world); Sisra Music Publishing (world); Spotlight Books (world); Jack Spratt Choral Music (world)
Subsidiaries: Best Books International
*Foreign Office(s):* EPS/Players Press Combined Trade, 20 Park Dr, Romford, Essex RM1 4LH, United Kingdom
Distributor for Arsis Press (world); Arte Publico Press (world); Ian Henry Publications (world); ISH Group (world exc Australia); Paul Mould Publishing (world)
*Advertising Agency:* Players Press Inc, PO Box 1132, Studio City, CA 91614-0132 *Tel:* 818-789-4980 *E-mail:* playerspress@att.net

**Enchanted Lion Books**
20 Jay St, Studio M-18, Brooklyn, NY 11231
*Tel:* 646-785-9272
*E-mail:* enchantedlion@gmail.com
*Web Site:* www.enchantedlionbooks.com
*Key Personnel*
Publr: Claudia Bedrick
Founded: 2002
Publish illustrated nonfiction picture books for children in the categories of art, biography &

history, science & nature, folktales & mythology.
ISBN Prefix(es): 978-1-59270
Number of titles published annually: 8 Print
Total Titles: 50 Print
Distributed by Consortium; Farrar, Straus & Giroux, LLC
*Orders to:* MPS Distribution Center, 16365 James Madison Hwy, Gordonsville, VA 22942 *Toll Free Tel:* 888-330-8477 ext 6540 *Toll Free Fax:* 800-672-2054 (orders)
*Returns:* Enchanted Lion Books, c/o MPS Distribution Center, 14301 Litchfield Rd, Orange, VA 22960
*Shipping Address:* MPS Distribution Center, 16365 James Madison Hwy, Gordonsville, VA 22942 *Toll Free Tel:* 888-330-8477 ext 6540 *Toll Free Fax:* 800-672-2054 (orders)
*Warehouse:* MPS Distribution Center, 16365 James Madison Hwy, Gordonsville, VA 22942 *Toll Free Tel:* 888-330-8477 ext 6540 *Toll Free Fax:* 800-672-2054 (orders)
*Distribution Center:* MPS Distribution Center, 16365 James Madison Hwy, Gordonsville, VA 22942 *Toll Free Tel:* 888-330-8477 ext 6540 *Toll Free Fax:* 800-672-2054 (orders)

**Encounter Books**
900 Broadway, Suite 601, New York, NY 10003
*Tel:* 212-871-6310 *Toll Free Tel:* 800-786-3839 *Fax:* 212-871-6311 *Toll Free Fax:* 877-811-1461
*E-mail:* read@encounterbooks.com
*Web Site:* www.encounterbooks.com
*Key Personnel*
Pres & Publr: Roger Kimball *E-mail:* kimball@encounterbooks.com
Exec Dir, Opers: Nola Tully *E-mail:* ntully@encounterbooks.com
Dir, Prodn: Heather Ohle *E-mail:* ohle@encounterbooks.com
Publicity Dir: Lauren Miklos *E-mail:* lmiklos@encounterbooks.com
Founded: 1998
Serious nonfiction books about history, culture, current events, religion, politics, social criticism & public policy.
ISBN Prefix(es): 978-1-893554; 978-1-59403
Number of titles published annually: 30 Print; 12 E-Book
Total Titles: 100 Print; 50 E-Book
*Returns:* PSSC-Returns, 660 S Mansfield, Ypsilanti, MI 48197
Membership(s): ABA; ALA; IBPA, the Independent Book Publishers Association

**§Encyclopaedia Britannica Inc**
331 N La Salle St, Chicago, IL 60654
*Tel:* 312-347-7159 (all other countries) *Toll Free Tel:* 800-323-1229 (US & CN) *Fax:* 312-294-2104
*E-mail:* editor@eb.com
*Web Site:* www.eb.com; www.britannica.com
*Key Personnel*
Pres: Jorge Cauz
EVP & Gen Coun: William J Bowe
SVP & Ed: Dale Hoiberg
SVP, Corp Devt: Michael Ross
VP, Fin: Richard Anderson
VP, Intl Opers: Leah Mansoor
Founded: 1768
Reference works, print & online for consumers & institutions.
ISBN Prefix(es): 978-0-85229
Subsidiaries: Merriam-Webster Inc
*Foreign Office(s):* Encyclopaedia Britannica Australia Ltd, Level 1, 90 Mount St, North Sydney, NSW 2060, Australia (Australia & Asia Pacific) *Tel:* (02) 9923 5600 *Fax:* (02) 9929 3753 *E-mail:* sales@britannica.com.au *Web Site:* www.britannica.com.au
Encyclopaedia Britannica France Ltd, 9 rue Antoine Chantin, 75685 Paris, France (France) *Tel:* 01 45 72 72 72 *Fax:* 01 45 72 03 43 *E-mail:* distributors@britannica.fr *Web Site:* www.britannica.fr
Encyclopaedia Britannica India Pvt Ltd, 140, Zamrudpur Shopping Complex, N-Block Rd, Greater Kailash-I, New Dehli 110048, India (Bahrain, Kuwait, Oman, Qatar, Saudi Arabia, United Arab Emirates, Yemen) *Tel:* (011) 4653-6450 *Fax:* (011) 2924-5116 *E-mail:* marketing@ebindia.com *Web Site:* www.britannicaindia.com
Britannica.com Israel Ltd, 16 Tozeret Ha'aretz St., Tel Aviv 67891, Israel (Israel) *Tel:* (03) 607 0400 *Fax:* (03) 607 0401 *Web Site:* www.britannicaindia.co.il
Britannica Japan Co Ltd, Da Vinci Nishi-Gotanda 2-F, 8-3-16 Nishi-Gotanda, Shinagawa-ku, Tokyo 141-0031, Japan (Japan) *Tel:* (03) 5436 1388 *Fax:* (03) 5436 1380 *E-mail:* info@britannica.co.jp *Web Site:* www.britannica.co.jp
Korea Britannica Corp, Jeilsangho B/D, 7th fl, 117 Jangchung-dong 1-ga, Jung-gu, Seoul 100-391, South Korea (Korea) *Tel:* (02) 1588 1768 *Fax:* (02) 2278 9983 *E-mail:* corporate@britannica.co.kr *Web Site:* www.britannica.co.kr
Britannica Asia Pacific Pty Ltd Taiwan Branch, Taiwan Branch, Room 402-F, 4-F, 10 Chungching S Rd, Sec 1, Taipei City 100, Taiwan (Taiwan) *Tel:* (02) 2311-2592 *Fax:* (02) 2311-2595
Encyclopaedia Britannica (UK) Ltd, Unity Wharf, 2nd fl, Mill St, London SE1 2BH, United Kingdom (Africa, Europe, Middle East) *Tel:* (020) 7500 7800 *Fax:* (020) 7500 7878 *E-mail:* enquiries@britannica.co.uk *Web Site:* www.britannica.co.uk
*See separate listing for:*
**Merriam-Webster Inc**

**Energy Information Administration (EIA)**
Imprint of US Government Printing Office
1000 Independence Ave SW, Washington, DC 20585
*Tel:* 202-586-8800 *Fax:* 202-586-0727
*E-mail:* infoctr@eia.doe.gov
*Web Site:* www.eia.doe.gov
*Key Personnel*
Dir: Gina Pearson *Tel:* 202-586-6537 *Fax:* 202-586-0114 *E-mail:* gina.pearson@eia.gov
Founded: 1977
Periodicals, analytical reports, energy statistics.
ISBN Prefix(es): 978-0-16
Number of titles published annually: 37 Print
Distributed by EPO; NTIS

**Energy Psychology Press**
Division of Soul Medicine Institute
1490 Mark West Springs Rd, Santa Rosa, CA 95404
Mailing Address: PO Box 442, Fulton, CA 95439
*Tel:* 707-237-6951 *Toll Free Fax:* 800-330-9798
*Web Site:* www.energypsychologypress.com
*Key Personnel*
Ed-in-Chief: Dawson Church *E-mail:* dawson@authorspublishing.com
Prodn Coord: Jeff Anderson *E-mail:* jeff@authorspublishing.com
Res Coord & Asst to Publr: Deb Tribbey *E-mail:* deb@authorspublishing.com
ISBN Prefix(es): 978-1-60415
Number of titles published annually: 6 Print
Distributed by Midpoint Trade
*Distribution Center:* Midpoint Trade, 27 W 20 St, Suite 1102, New York, NY 10010, Contact: Gail Kump *Tel:* 212-727-0190 *E-mail:* midpointny1@aol.com *Web Site:* www.midpointtrade.com
Membership(s): IBPA, the Independent Book Publishers Association

**§Enfield Publishing & Distribution Co**
234 May St, Enfield, NH 03748
Mailing Address: PO Box 699, Enfield, NH 03748
*Tel:* 603-632-7377 *Fax:* 603-632-5611
*E-mail:* info@enfieldbooks.com
*Web Site:* www.enfieldbooks.com
*Key Personnel*
Mng Dir: Linda Jones
Founded: 1996
Distribute foreign publishers.
ISBN Prefix(es): 978-0-9656184; 978-1-893598
Number of titles published annually: 5 Print
Total Titles: 11 Print
Distributor for AM Press; Beech River Books; Faculty Ridge Books; Green Lion Press; Hill Winds Press; Institution of Chemical Engineers; Kom Forlag; Letterland International Ltd; Lightning Up Press; Merion Books; Moose Country Press; Northern Forest Center; Portsmouth Marine Society; The Public Press; Secret Passage Press; Thistle Hill Publications; Trans Tech Publications; Treeline Press; Verlag Valentin Koerner; Vital Communities; Wageningen Academic Publishers; Wolf Legal Publishers

**Enigma Books**
360 E 116 St, New York, NY 10029
*Tel:* 212-933-1315
*E-mail:* editor@enigmabooks.com
*Web Site:* www.enigmabooks.com
Founded: 1999
ISBN Prefix(es): 978-1-929631; 978-0-9824911; 978-1-936274
Number of titles published annually: 12 Print; 15 E-Book
Total Titles: 200 Print; 100 E-Book
*Distribution Center:* Perseus Distribution, 387 Park Ave S, 12th fl, New York, NY 10016 *E-mail:* client.info@perseusbooks.com
Consortium, The Keg House, 34 13 Ave NE, Suite 101, Minneapolis, MN 55413

**Enslow Publishers Inc**
40 Industrial Rd, Dept F-61, Berkeley Heights, NJ 07922
SAN: 213-7518
Mailing Address: PO Box 398, Berkeley Heights, NJ 07922-0398
*Tel:* 908-771-9400 *Toll Free Tel:* 800-398-2504 *Fax:* 908-771-0925; 908-771-8400 (orders)
*E-mail:* customerservice@enslow.com; orders@enslow.com
*Web Site:* www.enslow.com; www.myreportlinks.com
*Key Personnel*
Pres & Mktg: Mark Enslow *E-mail:* marke@enslow.com
VP & Publr: Brian D Enslow *E-mail:* briane@enslow.com
Natl Sales Mgr: John C Martucci *E-mail:* johnm@enslow.com
Billing: Carmen Lester *E-mail:* carmenl@enslow.com
Founded: 1976
Juvenile & young adult educational nonfiction books.
ISBN Prefix(es): 978-0-89490; 978-0-7760; 978-1-59845
Number of titles published annually: 200 Print
Total Titles: 2,400 Print
Imprints: Enslow (middle & high school books); Enslow Elementary (pre-k through 5th grade); MyReportLinks.com Books (internet supported books)
Foreign Rep(s): Everybody's Books (Warren Halford) (South Africa); Read Pacific (New Zealand); Viking Books (Australia)
*Advertising Agency:* Crescent Place Advertising, PO Box 605, Short Hills, NJ 07078-0605
Membership(s): AASL; ALA; Educational Book & Media Association; TLA

**§Entangled Publishing**
2614 S Timberline Rd, Suite 109, Fort Collins, CO 80525
*Tel:* 724-208-7888 (sales)
*E-mail:* publisher@entangledpublishing.com
*Web Site:* www.entangledpublishing.com
*Key Personnel*
Publr & Edit Dir, Covet: Liz Pelletier
Exec Mktg Dir: Melissa Bourbon Ramirez
ISBN Prefix(es): 978-1-937044; 978-1-62266; 978-1-62061
Number of titles published annually: 48 Print; 312 E-Book
Imprints: Bliss; Brazen; Covet; Entangled Select; Entangled Suspense; Entangled Teen; Ever After; Flirt; Indulgence; Scandalous
Distributed by Macmillan

**EntertainmentPro**, see Quite Specific Media Group Ltd

**Entomological Society of America**
10001 Derekwood Lane, Suite 100, Lanham, MD 20706-4876
*Tel:* 301-731-4535 *Fax:* 301-731-4538
*E-mail:* esa@entsoc.org
*Web Site:* www.entsoc.org
*Key Personnel*
Interim Exec Dir: Ann Kenworthy *E-mail:* akenworthy@entsoc.org
Dir, Communs: Alan Kahan *Tel:* 301-731-4535 ext 3020 *E-mail:* akahan@entsoc.org
Subns Mgmt: Christopher Stelzig *E-mail:* chris@entsoc.org
Founded: 1889
Professional scientific society for entomologists. Publish research journals on all areas of entomology.
ISBN Prefix(es): 978-0-938522
Number of titles published annually: 3 Print; 1 CD-ROM; 5 Online
Total Titles: 55 Print; 1 CD-ROM; 5 Online

**§Environmental Law Institute**
2000 "L" St NW, Suite 620, Washington, DC 20036
*Tel:* 202-939-3800 *Fax:* 202-939-3868
*E-mail:* law@eli.org
*Web Site:* www.eli.org
*Key Personnel*
Chmn: Bill Eichbaum
Pres: Leslie Carothers *E-mail:* carothers@eli.org
VP, Pubns: Scott Schang *E-mail:* schang@eli.org
Dir, Mktg & Communs: Brett Kitchen *E-mail:* kitchen@eli.org
Ed, The Environmental Forum: Stephen Dujack *E-mail:* dujack@eli.org
Founded: 1969
Environmental studies, references, online database services, monographs, policy studies.
ISBN Prefix(es): 978-1-58576
Number of titles published annually: 6 Print; 30 Online
Total Titles: 53 Print; 1 CD-ROM; 200 Online
Distributed by Island Press

**Ephemera Bound Publishing**
Division of Equilibri-Yum Inc
719 Ninth St N, Fargo, ND 58102
SAN: 256-7644
*Toll Free Tel:* 888-642-3043 *Toll Free Fax:* 888-291-4052 (orders)
*E-mail:* publish@ephemera-bound.com; sales@ephemera-bound.com
*Web Site:* www.ephemera-bound.com
*Key Personnel*
Publr: Derek Dahlsad *E-mail:* derek@ephemera-bound.com
Contact: Deanna Dahlsad *E-mail:* deanna@ephemera-bound.com
Founded: 2005
Small publisher focusing on 'fringe' authors that may not receive the mainstream attention they deserve.
ISBN Prefix(es): 978-0-9771003; 978-0-9790067
Number of titles published annually: 12 Print
Total Titles: 13 Print
Imprints: Ephemera Bound; Gracie Passette Productions; Sex-Kitten.Net Books; Tit-Elation.com Books

**Epicenter Press Inc**
6524 NE 181 St, Suite 2, Kenmore, WA 98028
Mailing Address: PO Box 82368, Kenmore, WA 98028
*Tel:* 425-485-6822 (edit, mktg, busn off) *Toll Free Tel:* 800-950-6663 (orders) *Fax:* 425-481-8253
*E-mail:* info@epicenterpress.com
*Web Site:* www.epicenterpress.com
*Key Personnel*
Pres & Publr: Kent Sturgis *E-mail:* kent@epicenterpress.com
Dir, Spec Sales: Jennifer McCord *Tel:* 206-417-8545 *E-mail:* jenamccord@epicenterpress.com
Acq Ed: Lael Morgan *E-mail:* laelmorgan@cs.com
Fulfillment Mgr: Eydie Carlson *E-mail:* eydie@epicenterpress.com
Founded: 1988
Regional nonfiction trade publisher specializing in titles about Alaska & the Pacific Northwest. Trade distributor of titles by other publishers. Packager, print-broker & book publishing consultant.
ISBN Prefix(es): 978-0-945397; 978-0-9708493; 978-0-9724944; 978-0-9800825; 978-1-935347
Number of titles published annually: 7 Print; 10 E-Book
Total Titles: 100 Print; 60 E-Book
Divisions: Aftershocks Media (book packager, contract publishing services, consulting, book distribution)
Distributor for Appell Publishing; Coastal Publishing; Coffeetown Press; Delano Publishing; Documentary Media; Five Star Misadventures; Gold Fever Press; Arlene Lochridge; Raising Lucy Studios LLC; Saltry Press
Foreign Rights: Wales Literary Agency (Worldwide)
*Returns:* Pioneer Distribution Center, 18805 80 Place S, Kent, WA 98032, Contact: Lacie Parrino *Tel:* 425-251-0369 *Fax:* 425-251-3997 *E-mail:* lacie.parrino@p-h-s.com
*Warehouse:* Pioneer Distribution Center, 18805 80 Place S, Kent, WA 98032, Contact: Lacie Parrino *Tel:* 425-251-0369 *Fax:* 425-251-3997 *E-mail:* lacie.parrino@p-h-s.com
Membership(s): Book Publishers of the Northwest; IBPA, the Independent Book Publishers Association

**EPS/School Specialty Literacy & Intervention**
Division of School Specialty Inc
625 Mount Auburn St, 3rd fl, Cambridge, MA 02138-4555
SAN: 201-8225
Mailing Address: PO Box 9031, Cambridge, MA 02139-9031
*Tel:* 617-547-6706 *Toll Free Tel:* 800-225-5750 *Fax:* 617-547-0412 *Toll Free Fax:* 888-440-2665
*E-mail:* customerservice.eps@schoolspecialty.com
*Web Site:* eps.schoolspecialty.com
*Key Personnel*
Pres: Steven Korte
VP, Publg: Charles Heinle
VP, Mktg: Deborah Burns *E-mail:* deborah.burns@schoolspecialty.com
VP, Fin: Dave Ciommo
Founded: 1952
Technology & print educational materials for grades K-12, with particular emphasis on language arts, remedial reading skills, materials for the child with specific language disability, workbooks - elementary; workbooks - secondary, learning differences.
ISBN Prefix(es): 978-0-8388
Number of titles published annually: 25 Print
Total Titles: 800 Print
Imprints: Modern Learning Press
*Branch Office(s)*
Educators Publishing Service - Canada, PO Box 333, Sta A, Scarborough, ON M1K 5C1, Canada *Toll Free Tel:* 877-471-8123 *Toll Free Fax:* 877-635-0911
*Returns:* 80 Northwest Blvd, Nashua, NH 03063

**Ericson Books**
1614 Redbud St, Nacogdoches, TX 75965-2936
*Tel:* 936-564-3625 *Fax:* 936-552-8999
*E-mail:* kissinkuzzins@suddenlink.net
*Web Site:* www.ericsonbooks.com
*Key Personnel*
Owner & Publr: Carolyn Reeves Ericson
Exec Asst: Bonnie Ericson
Founded: 1975
Genealogical & East Texas history.
ISBN Prefix(es): 978-0-911317
Number of titles published annually: 5 Print
Total Titles: 60 Print
Distributed by Mountain Press; Byron Sistler
Distributor for Clearfield; Dietz Press; Southern Historical Press

**Ernst Publishing Co LLC**
Affiliate of Legal Publications LLC
99 Washington Ave, Suite 309, Albany, NY 12210
*Toll Free Tel:* 800-345-3822 *Toll Free Fax:* 800-252-0906
*E-mail:* clientservices@ernstpublishing.com
*Web Site:* www.ernstpublishing.com
*Key Personnel*
CEO & Pres: Gregory E Teal *Tel:* 800-345-3822 ext 101 *E-mail:* gregory.e.teal@ernstinfo.com
VP, Sales & Mktg: Jan Clark *Tel:* 800-345-3822 ext 201 *E-mail:* jan.clark@ernstinfo.com
Founded: 1992
ISBN Prefix(es): 978-1-881627
Number of titles published annually: 3 Print; 4 Online
Total Titles: 3 Print; 4 Online

**Eros Books**
463 Barlow Ave, Staten Island, NY 10308
*Tel:* 718-317-7484
*Web Site:* www.eros.thecraze.com
*Key Personnel*
Publr & Ed: Mary Nicholaou *E-mail:* marynicholaou@aol.com
Founded: 1997
Produce postmodern fiction & nonfiction artifacts, including qualitative literary research; newsletter & magazine; memoirs.
ISBN Prefix(es): 978-1-890812
Number of titles published annually: 3 Print; 3 Online; 3 E-Book
Total Titles: 18 Print; 10 Online; 9 E-Book
Distributed by Blue Dolphin; EBSCO; Magazine City; Magazine Line
Membership(s): The Association of Publishers for Special Sales; IBPA, the Independent Book Publishers Association

**ETC Publications**
1456 Rodeo Rd, Palm Springs, CA 92262
SAN: 201-4637
*Tel:* 760-316-9695 *Toll Free Tel:* 866-514-9969 *Fax:* 760-316-9681
*E-mail:* customer_service@etcpublications.com
*Web Site:* www.etcpublications.com
*Key Personnel*
Publr & Sr Ed: Evelyn Berry
Ed & Intl Rts: James Berry
Founded: 1972

Nonfiction & informational books.
ISBN Prefix(es): 978-0-88280
Number of titles published annually: 3 Print
Total Titles: 80 Print; 80 E-Book

**Etruscan Press**
Wilkes University, 84 W South St, Wilkes-Barre, PA 18766
*Tel:* 570-408-4546 *Fax:* 570-408-3333
*E-mail:* books@etruscanpress.org
*Web Site:* www.etruscanpress.org
*Key Personnel*
Exec Ed: Philip Brady
Sr Ed: Robert Mooney
Mng Ed: Starr Troup
Founded: 2001
Book of poems, novels, short stories, creative nonfiction, criticism & anthologies.
ISBN Prefix(es): 978-0-9745995
Number of titles published annually: 3 Print
Total Titles: 12 Print
*Distribution Center:* Consortium Book Sales & Distribution, The Keg House, 34 13 Ave NE, Suite 101, Minneapolis, MN 55413-1007 *Toll Free Tel:* 800-283-3572 *Web Site:* www.cbsd.com
Small Press Distribution, 1341 Seventh St, Berkeley, CA, Deputy Dir: Laura Moriarty *Tel:* 510-524-1668 *Toll Free Tel:* 800-869-7553 *Fax:* 510-524-0852 *Web Site:* www.spdbooks.org
Membership(s): Council of Literary Magazines & Presses; IBPA, the Independent Book Publishers Association

**Europa Editions**
Subsidiary of Edizioni E/O
214 W 29 St, Suite 1003, New York, NY 10001
*Tel:* 212-868-6844 *Fax:* 212-868-6845
*E-mail:* info@europaeditions.com
*Web Site:* www.europaeditions.com
*Key Personnel*
Publr: Kent Carroll
Publicist: Julia Haav
Ed-in-Chief: Michael Reynolds
Sales & Mktg Dir: Drew Schnoebelen
Founded: 2005
Publisher of international literary fiction in translation, domestic literary fiction, crime & narrative nonfiction.
ISBN Prefix(es): 978-1-933372
Number of titles published annually: 25 Print
Imprints: Tonga Books
*Distribution Center:* Penguin Group (USA) LLC, 405 Murray Hill Pkwy, East Rutherford, NJ 07073-2136 *Toll Free Tel:* 800-526-0275 *Toll Free Fax:* 800-227-9604 *E-mail:* orders@us.penguingroup.com

**European Masterpieces**
Imprint of LinguaText Ltd
103 Walker Way, Newark, DE 19711
SAN: 238-0307
*Tel:* 302-453-8695 *Fax:* 302-453-8601
*E-mail:* linguatext@juno.com
*Web Site:* www.europeanmasterpieces.com
*Key Personnel*
Owner & Publr: Michael Bolan *E-mail:* mike@linguatextltd.com
Founded: 2002
Publish classics of Spanish & French literature designed for the English-speaking college student. The complete text of the classic work is included in its native language with extensive English glosses & footnotes on every page, an English introduction & a glossary of Spanish or French to English.
ISBN Prefix(es): 978-1-58997
Number of titles published annually: 7 Print
Total Titles: 70 Print
Imprints: Cervantes & Co (Spanish Classics series); Juan De La Cuesta-Hispanic Monographs; Moliere & Co (French Classics series)
Distributor for Cervantes & Co (Spanish Classics series); Juan De La Cuesta-Hispanic Monographs; Moliere & Co (French Classics series)

**Evan-Moor Educational Publishers**
18 Lower Ragsdale Dr, Monterey, CA 93940-5746
*Tel:* 831-649-5901 *Toll Free Tel:* 800-714-0971 (cust serv); 800-777-4362 (orders) *Fax:* 831-649-6256 *Toll Free Fax:* 800-777-4332 (orders)
*E-mail:* sales@evan-moor.com; marketing@evan-moor.com
*Web Site:* www.evan-moor.com
*Key Personnel*
Founder & CEO: William Evans *E-mail:* bill@evan-moor.com
Founder & Publr: Joy Evans
Edit Dir: Lisa Vitarisi Mathews
Dir, Fin: David Miller
Dir, Mktg: Trisha Thomas
Dir, Publg: Andrea Weiss
Natl Sales Dir: Marcia K Wall
Founded: 1979
Supplemental educational materials in print & digital formats for parents & teachers of children ages 3-14. Subjects include reading, math, writing, science, social studies, arts & crafts & literature.
ISBN Prefix(es): 978-1-55799
Number of titles published annually: 25 Print; 60 Online; 25 E-Book
Total Titles: 450 Print; 450 Online; 450 E-Book
Membership(s): ABA; ALA; Association of Educational Publishers; National School Supply & Equipment Association

**Evangel Publishing House**
Division of Brethren in Christ Media Ministries Inc
2000 Evangel Way, Nappanee, IN 46550
SAN: 211-7940
Mailing Address: PO Box 189, Nappanee, IN 46550-0189
*Tel:* 574-773-3164 *Toll Free Tel:* 800-253-9315 (orders) *Fax:* 574-773-5934
*E-mail:* sales@evangelpublishing.com
*Web Site:* www.evangelpublishing.com; www.evangelpress.com
*Key Personnel*
VP, Busn: Darren Shaw *Tel:* 574-773-3164 ext 224 *E-mail:* dshaw@evangelpress.com
Founded: 1929
Religious books to serve the Brethren in Christ Church & Evangelical market.
ISBN Prefix(es): 978-0-934998 (Bethel Publishing); 978-0-916035; 978-1-928915; 978-1-891314 (Jordan Publishing)
Number of titles published annually: 5 Print; 1 E-Book
Total Titles: 185 Print; 1 E-Book; 1 Audio
Imprints: Francis Asbury Press; Bethel Publishing; Jordan Publishing
Distributor for Bethel Publishing
Foreign Rep(s): R G Mitchell Family Books (Canada)
*Returns:* 2673 E Market St, Nappanee, IN 46550

**M Evans & Co Inc**
Imprint of Rowman & Littlefield Publishing Group
4501 Forbes Blvd, Suite 200, Lanham, MD 20706
*Tel:* 301-459-3366 *Fax:* 301-429-5743
*Web Site:* www.rlpgtrade.com
*Key Personnel*
Dir: Ed Evans
Founded: 1963
Health, medical & business books.
ISBN Prefix(es): 978-0-87131; 978-1-59077
Number of titles published annually: 30 Print
Total Titles: 250 Print
Foreign Rights: Rights Unlimited
*Shipping Address:* National Book Network, 15200 NBN Way, Blue Ridge Summit, PA 17214 *Tel:* 717-794-3800 *Toll Free Tel:* 800-462-6420 *Fax:* 717-794-4801 *Toll Free Fax:* 800-338-4550
*Distribution Center:* National Book Network, 4720 Boston Way, Lanham, MD 20706

**Evanston Publishing Inc**
Division of Integrated Media Corp
12305 Westport Rd, Suite 4, Louisville, KY 40245-2712
*Tel:* 502-899-1919 *Toll Free Tel:* 888-BOOKS80 (266-5780) *Fax:* 502-565-2507
*E-mail:* info@evanstonpublishing.com
*Web Site:* www.evanstonpublishing.com
*Key Personnel*
Off Mgr: Sherry Welch
Founded: 1986
Production, prepress & printing for other publishers & individual authors. General trade, especially feminist, how-to, biography, history & poetry, consumer Q & A, consumer/legal guides & parenting.
ISBN Prefix(es): 978-1-879260; 978-1-58374
Number of titles published annually: 50 Print
Total Titles: 500 Print
Subsidiaries: Chicago Spectrum Press
Distributor for Chicago Spectrum Press
*See separate listing for:*
**Chicago Spectrum Press**

**Evergreen Pacific Publishing Ltd**
4204 Russell Rd, Suite M, Mukilteo, WA 98275-5424
*Tel:* 425-493-1451 *Fax:* 425-493-1453
*E-mail:* sales@evergreenpacific.com
*Web Site:* www.evergreenpacific.com
*Key Personnel*
Pres: Paul Hamstra
Founded: 1996
Books, charts & guides for water related recreations.
ISBN Prefix(es): 978-0-945265
Number of titles published annually: 4 Print
Total Titles: 15 Print
Imprints: Evergreen Pacific Publishing

**Excalibur Publications**
PO Box 89667, Tucson, AZ 85752-9667
*Tel:* 520-575-9057
*E-mail:* excaliburpublications@centurylink.net
*Key Personnel*
Ed-in-Chief: Alan M Petrillo
Founded: 1990
ISBN Prefix(es): 978-1-880677
Number of titles published annually: 4 Print
Total Titles: 20 Print
*Distribution Center:* Barnes & Noble, One Barnes & Noble Way, Suite B, Monroe, NJ 08831
Baker & Taylor, 2550 W Tyvola Rd, Suite 300, Charlotte, NC 28217
Amazon.com, 1200 12 Ave S, Suite 1200, Seattle, WA 98144-2734

**Excelsior Editions**
Imprint of State University of New York Press
22 Corporate Woods Blvd, 3rd fl, Albany, NY 12211-2504
SAN: 760-7261
*Tel:* 518-472-5000 *Toll Free Tel:* 877-204-6073 *Fax:* 518-472-5038 *Toll Free Fax:* 877-204-6074
*E-mail:* info@sunypress.edu
*Web Site:* www.sunypress.edu
*Key Personnel*
Co-Dir: James Peltz *Tel:* 518-641-0668 *E-mail:* james.peltz@sunypress.edu

Assoc Dir & Dir, Sales & Busn Devt: Daniel Flynn *Tel:* 518-641-0676 *E-mail:* daniel.flynn@sunypress.edu
Founded: 2008
Publish regional & trade books.
ISBN Prefix(es): 978-0-7914; 978-1-929373 (Hudson Valley region); 978-1-4384; 978-0-9722977 (Uncrowned Queens)
Number of titles published annually: 25 Print; 15 Audio
Total Titles: 174 Print; 95 E-Book; 1 Audio
Distributor for Albany Institute of History & Art; Uncrowned Queens
Foreign Rep(s): Apac Publishers Services Pte Ltd (China, Hong Kong, Indonesia, Malaysia, Singapore, Taiwan, Thailand, Vietnam); Eleanor Brasch Enterprises (Eleanor Brasch) (Australia, New Zealand); Cassidy & Associates Inc (Tom Cassidy) (China, Hong Kong, Taiwan); Lexa Publishers' Representatives (Elise & Mical Moser) (Canada); Mediamatics (Asoke K Ghosh) (India); NBN International (UK & the continent); United Publisher's Services Ltd (Japan); University Presses Marketing (Andrew Gilman) (Continental Europe, Ireland, Israel, UK); US PubRep Inc (Craig Falk) (Caribbean, Central America, Mexico, Puerto Rico, South America)
*Orders to:* SUNY Press, PO Box 960, Herndon, VA 20172-0960, Cust Serv *Tel:* 703-661-1575 *Fax:* 703-996-1010 *E-mail:* suny@presswarehouse.com
*Returns:* SUNY Press, Returns Dept, 22883 Quicksilver Dr, Herndon, VA 20166, Cust Serv *Tel:* 703-661-1575 *Fax:* 703-996-1010 *E-mail:* suny@presswarehouse.com
*Shipping Address:* SUNY Press, PO Box 960, Herndon, VA 20172-0960, Cust Serv *Tel:* 703-661-1575 *Fax:* 703-996-1010 *E-mail:* suny@presswarehouse.com
*Warehouse:* SUNY Press, PO Box 960, Herndon, VA 20172-0960, Cust Serv *Tel:* 703-661-1575 *Fax:* 703-996-1010 *E-mail:* suny@presswarehouse.com

**The Experiment**
260 Fifth Ave, Suite 3 South, New York, NY 10001-6425
*Tel:* 212-889-1659
*E-mail:* info@theexperimentpublishing.com
*Web Site:* www.theexperimentpublishing.com
*Key Personnel*
COO & CFO: Peter Burri
Pres & Publr: Matthew Lore
Assoc Publr: Daniel O'Connor
Sales Dir: Ani Chamichian
Digital Publg Mgr: Karen Giangreco
Publicity, Mktg & Sales Mgr: Jack Palmer
Publicity, Mktg & Sales Asst: Patrick Kelly
Asst Mng Ed: Molly Cavanaugh
Ed: Cara Bedick
Founded: 2008
ISBN Prefix(es): 978-1-61519
Number of titles published annually: 25 Print
Total Titles: 25 E-Book
*Sales Office(s):* Workman Publishing, 225 Varick St, New York, NY 10014-4381 SAN: 631-760X
Distributed by Workman Publishing
Foreign Rights: Maribeth Casey (Brazil, New Zealand, Worldwide exc Australia)
*Orders to:* Workman Publishing, 225 Varick St, New York, NY 10014-4381 *E-mail:* orders@workman.com
*Returns:* Workman Publishing Co Inc, c/o RR Donnelley, 677 Brighton Beach Rd, Menasha, WI 54952

**Eye in the Ear Children's Audio**
5 Crescent St, Portland, ME 04102
*Tel:* 207-780-1574 *Toll Free Tel:* 877-99-STORY (997-8679) *Fax:* 509-275-4252
*E-mail:* info@eyeintheear.com
*Web Site:* www.eyeintheear.com
*Key Personnel*
Owner: Frances Kelly *Tel:* 617-267-1396
Pres: Laurence A Kelly *E-mail:* lk@maine.rr.com
Founded: 1985
Production & distribution of quality classic children's audio stories.
ISBN Prefix(es): 978-0-944168
Number of titles published annually: 3 Audio
Total Titles: 31 Online; 31 Audio
*Editorial Office(s):* c/o MBC, 415 Congress St, Portland, ME 04101
*Sales Office(s):* 5 Crescent St, Portland, ME 04102
Distributed by Amazon.com; Audio Adventures; Chinaberry/Isabella; Christian Book Distributors; Landmark Audio Books
*Returns:* Fleetwood MultiMedia, 20 Wheeler St, Saint Lynn, MA 01910, Contact: Wayne Terminello *Toll Free Tel:* 800-353-1830 *Fax:* 781-599-2440 *E-mail:* wayne@fltwood.com
*Shipping Address:* Fleetwood MultiMedia, 20 Wheeler St, Saint Lynn, MA 01910, Contact: Wayne Terminello *Toll Free Tel:* 800-353-1830 *Fax:* 781-599-2440 *E-mail:* wayne@fltwood.com
*Warehouse:* Fleetwood MultiMedia, 20 Wheeler St, Saint Lynn, MA 01910, Contact: Wayne Terminello *Toll Free Tel:* 800-353-1830 *Fax:* 781-599-2440 *E-mail:* wayne@fltwood.com
*Distribution Center:* Fleetwood MultiMedia, 20 Wheeler St, Saint Lynn, MA 01910, Contact: Wayne Terminello *Toll Free Tel:* 800-353-1830 *Fax:* 781-599-2440 *E-mail:* wayne@fltwood.com

**Eye On Education**
6 Depot Way W, Larchmont, NY 10538
*Tel:* 914-833-0551 *Toll Free Tel:* 888-299-5350 *Fax:* 914-833-0761
*E-mail:* customer-service@eyeoneducation.com
*Web Site:* www.eyeoneducation.com
*Key Personnel*
Pres & Publr: Robert Sickles *E-mail:* sickles@eyeoneducation.com
Founded: 1992
Professional & reference books for educators.
ISBN Prefix(es): 978-1-883001; 978-1-930556; 978-1-59667
Number of titles published annually: 38 Print
Total Titles: 230 Print

**Faber & Faber Inc**
Affiliate of Farrar, Straus & Giroux, LLC
18 W 18 St, New York, NY 10011
SAN: 218-7256
*Tel:* 212-741-6900 *Fax:* 212-633-9385
*E-mail:* fsg.editorial@fsgbooks.com (edit inquiries)
*Web Site:* us.macmillan.com/faberandfaber.aspx
*Key Personnel*
SVP & Dir, Mktg & Publicity: Jeff Seroy *Tel:* 212-206-5323
Founded: 1976
Nonfiction for adults, plus film & theater; subjects include popular culture.
ISBN Prefix(es): 978-0-571; 978-0-86547
Number of titles published annually: 25 Print
Total Titles: 200 Print
Foreign Rep(s): Douglas & Marco D Vigevani (Australia, Canada)
*Shipping Address:* MPS Distribution Center, 16365 James Madison Hwy, Gordonsville, VA 22942
*Warehouse:* MPS Distribution Center, 16365 James Madison Hwy, Gordonsville, VA 22942

**§Facts On File**
Imprint of Infobase Learning
132 W 31 St, 17th fl, New York, NY 10001
SAN: 201-4696
*Tel:* 212-967-8800 *Toll Free Tel:* 800-322-8755 *Fax:* 917-339-0323 *Toll Free Fax:* 800-678-3633
*E-mail:* custserv@factsonfile.com
*Web Site:* infobasepublishing.com
*Key Personnel*
CEO & Pres: Mark McDonnell
CFO: Jim Housley
Dir, Opers: Mark Zielinski
Dir, Publicity: Laurie Katz
Edit Dir: Laurie Likoff
Dir, Licensing & Busn Devt: Ben Jacobs
Dir, Mktg: Zina Scarpulla
Founded: 1941
Award-winning publisher of authoritative curriculum-related print & online reference materials for schools & libraries.
ISBN Prefix(es): 978-0-8160; 978-1-60057; 978-1-4381; 978-1-57852
Number of titles published annually: 135 Print; 28 Online; 135 E-Book
Total Titles: 940 Print; 37 Online; 934 E-Book
*Returns:* Maple Logistics Solutions Distribution Center, 704 Legionaire Dr, Fredericksburg, PA 17026
*Warehouse:* Maple Logistics Solutions Distribution Center, 704 Legionaire Dr, Fredericksburg, PA 17026
*Distribution Center:* Maple Logistics Solutions Distribution Center, 704 Legionaire Dr, Fredericksburg, PA 17026

**Fair Winds Press**
Imprint of Quayside Publishing Group
100 Cummings Ctr, Suite 406-L, Beverly, MA 01915
*Tel:* 978-282-9590 *Toll Free Tel:* 800-328-0590 (sales) *Fax:* 978-283-2742
*E-mail:* customerservice@quaysidepub.com
*Web Site:* www.fairwindspress.com
*Key Personnel*
CEO & Pres, Quayside Publishing Group: Ken Fund *E-mail:* kfund@quaysidepub.com
Sr Acqs Ed: Jill Alexander
Founded: 2001
Offer nonfiction books in a range of practical categories, including nutrition & cookery, fitness, parenting, beauty, treating sickness, mental health & using new medicine.
ISBN Prefix(es): 978-1-59233
Number of titles published annually: 50 Print
Total Titles: 200 Print

**Fairchild Books**
Division of Bloomsbury Publishing Plc
1385 Broadway, New York, NY 10018
SAN: 201-470X
*Tel:* 212-419-5292 *Toll Free Tel:* 800-932-4724; 888-330-8477 (orders)
*E-mail:* orders@mpsvirginia.com
*Web Site:* www.fairchildbooks.com
*Key Personnel*
Publr: Priscilla McGeehon *Tel:* 212-419-5356 *E-mail:* priscilla.mcgeehon@bloomsbury.com
Dir, Sales: Melanie Sankel *Tel:* 212-419-5296 *E-mail:* melanie.sankel@bloomsbury.com
Sr Devt Ed: Joe Miranda *Tel:* 212-419-5367 *E-mail:* joseph.miranda@bloomsbury.com
Sr Prodn Ed: Elizabeth Marotta *Tel:* 212-419-5364 *E-mail:* elizabeth.marotta@bloomsbury.com
Sr Acct Mgr: Allison Jones *Tel:* 212-419-5346 *E-mail:* allison.jones@bloomsbury.com
Cust Serv Mgr: Sandra Washington *Tel:* 800-932-4724 (option 1) *E-mail:* sandra.washington@bloomsbury.com
Founded: 1910
Interior design, fashion, merchandising, marketing, management, retailing, careers market research art foundation, clothing, textiles. Other memberships include International Textiles Apparel Association (ITAA) & Interior Design Educators Council (IDEC).

ISBN Prefix(es): 978-0-87005; 978-1-56367; 978-1-60901
Number of titles published annually: 40 Print; 30 CD-ROM
Total Titles: 375 Print; 60 CD-ROM
*Orders to:* MPS Distribution Center, 16365 James Madison Hwy, Gordonsville, VA 22942-8501
*Returns:* MPS Distribution Center, 16365 James Madison Hwy, Gordonsville, VA 22942-8501
*Warehouse:* MPS Distribution Center, 16365 James Madison Hwy, Gordonsville, VA 22942-8501
*Distribution Center:* MPS Distribution Center, 16365 James Madison Hwy, Gordonsville, VA 22942-8501

**Fairleigh Dickinson University Press**
Affiliate of Rowman & Littlefield
M-GH2-01, 285 Madison Ave, Madison, NJ 07940
*Tel:* 973-443-8564 *Fax:* 974-443-8364
*E-mail:* fdupress@fdu.edu
*Web Site:* www.fdupress.org
*Key Personnel*
Dir: Harry Keyishian *E-mail:* fdupress@hotmail.com
Founded: 1967
Publish books in the humanities & social sciences, with special strengths in history & literature.
ISBN Prefix(es): 978-0-8386
Number of titles published annually: 40 Print
Total Titles: 1,500 Print
Distributed by Rowman & Littlefield
Foreign Rep(s): Eurospan (Europe, UK); Scholarly Book Services (Canada); United Publishers Services (Japan)

**The Fairmont Press Inc**
700 Indian Trail, Lilburn, GA 30047
SAN: 207-5946
*Tel:* 770-925-9388 *Fax:* 770-381-9865
*Web Site:* www.fairmontpress.com
*Key Personnel*
VP: Linda Hutchings *E-mail:* linda@fairmontpress.com
Circ Mgr: Beth Pearce
Mktg Mgr: Jackie Kurklis
Book Fulfillment Coord: Christine Maddox
Founded: 1973
Professional & reference books on energy, safety, environment, how-to & facility management.
ISBN Prefix(es): 978-0-915586; 978-0-88173
Number of titles published annually: 12 Print; 1 CD-ROM; 12 E-Book
Total Titles: 425 Print; 8 CD-ROM; 125 E-Book
Distributed by CRC Press; Taylor & Francis
Foreign Rep(s): CRC Press

**Faith Alive Christian Resources**
2850 Kalamazoo Ave SE, Grand Rapids, MI 49560
*Tel:* 616-224-0728 *Toll Free Tel:* 800-333-8300 *Fax:* 616-224-0834 *Toll Free Fax:* 888-642-8606
*E-mail:* info@faithaliveresources.org; sales@faithaliveresources.org; editors@faithaliveresources.org
*Web Site:* www.faithaliveresources.org
*Key Personnel*
Dir: Mark Rice
Mng Ed: Ruth Vanderhart *E-mail:* rvanderhart@crcna.org
Mktg Mgr: Elizabeth Waterfield
Founded: 1928
Publish materials for Sunday school & other children's ministries, youth ministry, adults & small groups, prayer & evangelism, church leadership, worship & disability ministry. Also publish the monthly magazine *The Banner* & the quarterly journal *Reformed Worship*.
ISBN Prefix(es): 978-0-933140; 978-0-930265; 978-1-56212; 978-1-59255
Number of titles published annually: 50 Print
Total Titles: 307 Print
Imprints: Faith Alive; Friendship Bible Studies; Libros Desafio; World Literature Ministries
*Distribution Center:* 3475 Mainway, PO Box 5070, CTN LCD-1, Burlington, ON L7R 3Y8, Canada
RCA Resources, 2 Sydney Ave, Mt Evelyn, Victoria 3796, Australia *Tel:* (3) 9736 2412 *Fax:* (3) 9736 2654 *E-mail:* resources@crca.org.au

**Faith & Fellowship Press**
Subsidiary of Church of the Lutheran Brethren
1020 W Alcott Ave, Fergus Falls, MN 56537
Mailing Address: PO Box 655, Fergus Falls, MN 56538-0655
*Tel:* 218-736-7357; 218-736-2200
*Toll Free Tel:* 800-332-9232
*E-mail:* ffbooks@clba.org; ffpublishing@clba.org
*Web Site:* www.faithandfellowship.org
*Key Personnel*
Dir: Tim Mathieson
Religious books, newsletters.
ISBN Prefix(es): 978-0-943167
Number of titles published annually: 8 Print
Total Titles: 59 Print

**Faith & Life Resources**
Division of Mennonite Publishing Network
1251 Virginia Ave, Harrisonburg, VA 22802-2434
*Toll Free Tel:* 800-245-7894 (orders & cust serv US); 800-631-6535 (orders & cust serv CN) *Toll Free Fax:* 877-271-0760
*E-mail:* mpcan@mpn.net
*Web Site:* www.faithandliferesources.org; www.mpn.net
*Key Personnel*
Edit Dir: Amy Gingerich *Tel:* 800-245-7894 ext 285 *E-mail:* agingerich@mpn.net
Founded: 1878
Small denominational publisher specializing in the production of innovative Christian education resources for children, youth, young adults, adults & intergenerational groups. Topics of interest include materials on peace & justice, evangelism, Christian service & radical Christian discipleship.
ISBN Prefix(es): 978-0-87303; 978-0-8361; 978-2-5008
Number of titles published annually: 10 Print
*Branch Office(s)*
718 Main St, Newton, KS 67114 *Tel:* 316-283-5155 *Fax:* 316-283-0454
490 Dutton Dr, Unit C-7, Waterloo, ON N2L 6H7, Canada *Tel:* 519-747-5722 *Fax:* 519-884-5824
Distributed by Herald Press

**§Faith Library Publications**
Subsidiary of RHEMA Bible Church
PO Box 50126, Tulsa, OK 74150-0126
*Tel:* 918-258-1588 (ext 2218) *Toll Free Tel:* 888-258-0999 (orders) *Fax:* 918-872-7710 (orders)
*E-mail:* flp@rhema.org
*Web Site:* www.rhema.org/store/wholesale
*Key Personnel*
Mgr: Brian Cumberland *Tel:* 918-258-1588 ext 2284
Founded: 1963
ISBN Prefix(es): 978-0-89276
Number of titles published annually: 4 Print; 15 CD-ROM
Total Titles: 185 Print; 93 CD-ROM; 50 E-Book
Distributed by Appalachian; Harrison House; Spring Arbor; Whitaker

**FaithWalk Publishing**
Imprint of CSS Publishing Co Inc
5450 N Dixie Hwy, Lima, OH 45807
*Tel:* 419-227-1818 *Toll Free Tel:* 800-537-1030 (orders: non-bookstore mkts) *Fax:* 419-224-9184
*Web Site:* www.faithwalkpub.com
*Key Personnel*
Pres & Prodn Mgr: David Runk *E-mail:* david@csspub.com
Ed: Missy Cotrell
Acctg: Patty Furr
Founded: 2002
ISBN Prefix(es): 978-0-9724196; 978-1-932902
Number of titles published annually: 10 Print
Total Titles: 31 Print
Membership(s): IBPA, the Independent Book Publishers Association

**FaithWords**
Division of Hachette Book Group
12 Cadillac Dr, Suite 480, Brentwood, TN 37027
*Tel:* 615-221-0996 *Fax:* 615-221-0962
*Web Site:* www.hachettebookgroup.com
*Key Personnel*
SVP & Publr, Nashville Div: Rolf Zettersten
VP, Assoc Publr, Mktg: Harry Helm
CBA Sales Dir: Robert Nealeigh
Publicity Dir, Nashville Div: Shanon Stowe
Art Dir: Jody Waldrup
Ed, Fiction: Christina Boys
Ed: Jana Burson
Founded: 2001
Publish books for the growing inspirational market. No unsol mss.
ISBN Prefix(es): 978-0-446
Number of titles published annually: 60 Print
Total Titles: 500 Print
*Orders to:* Hachette Book Group, 3 Center Plaza, Boston, MA 02108-2084 *Toll Free Tel:* 800-759-0190 *Toll Free Fax:* 800-286-9471
Membership(s): CBA; Evangelical Christian Publishers Association

**F+W Media Inc**
10151 Carver Rd, Suite 200, Blue Ash, OH 45242
*Tel:* 513-531-2690 *Toll Free Tel:* 800-289-0963 (trade accts); 800-258-0929 (orders)
*E-mail:* contact_us@fwmedia.com
*Web Site:* www.fwmedia.com
*Key Personnel*
Chmn & CEO: David Nussbaum
COO & CFO: Jim Ogle
Chief Digital Offr: Chad Phelps
Cont: Rich Werner
Pres: David Blansfield; Sara Domville
SVP, Opers: Phil Graham *E-mail:* phil.graham@fwmedia.com
VP, Communs: Stacie Berger *E-mail:* sberger@fwmedia.com
VP, E-Commerce: Lucas Hilbert
VP, HR & Talent Mgmt: Amy Meyer
Sales Dir: Joanne Widmer *E-mail:* joanne.widmer@fwmedia.com
Sales Dir, Adams Media: Karen Patterson
Edit Dir, Krause Publications: Paul Kennedy
Publr: Jamie Markle
Publr & Content Strategist: Phil Sexton
Publr & Content Strategist, Adams Media: Karen Cooper
Group Publr/Community Leader, Automotive/Outdoors: Jamie Wilkinson
Spec Sales Mgr, Adams Media: Lauren Rouleau
Digital Marketer: Bethany Carland-Adams
Exec Ed, Crimson Romance: Tara Gelsomino
Ed-in-Chief, Merit Press Books: Jacquelyn Mitchard
Sr Acqs Ed: Pamela Wissman
Busn Ed: Paul Dinas
Ebook Ed: India Amos
Founded: 1913
ISBN Prefix(es): 978-0-930625; 978-0-87349; 978-0-87341; 978-0-87069; 978-0-89689; 978-1-58221; 978-0-8019
Number of titles published annually: 200 Print

Total Titles: 860 Print
Imprints: Adams Media; Antique Trader Books; Crimson Romance (digital/POD); David & Charles; HOW Books; Interweave; Krause Publications; Merit Press Books (young adult); North Light Books; Prologue Books; Tyrus Books; Warman's; Writer's Digest Books
*Branch Office(s)*
10901 W 120 Ave, Suite 350, Broomfield, CO 80021 *Tel:* 303-442-0427
201 E Fourth St, Loveland, CO 80537 *Toll Free Tel:* 800-272-2193
38 E 29 St, 4th fl, New York, NY 10016 *Tel:* 212-447-1400 *Fax:* 212-447-5231
*Foreign Office(s):* Brunel House, Forde Close, Newton, Abbot, Devon TQ12 4PU, United Kingdom *Tel:* (01626) 323200 *Fax:* (01626) 323319
Foreign Rep(s): David Bateman (New Zealand); Capricorn Link (Australia); David & Charles (Europe, UK); F+W International (Europe, UK); IMA/Intermediaamericana (David Williams) (Caribbean, Latin America); IPR (Middle East); Manda Group (Canada); Penguin Books India (South Asia); Real Books (South Africa); Trinity Books (Southern Africa); The White Partnership (Andrew White) (East Asia, Southeast)
*Returns:* Aero Fulfillment Services, 6023 Union Centre Blvd, Fairfield, OH 45014; Fraser Direct, 100 Armstrong Ave, Georgetown, ON L7G 5S4, Canada
*See separate listing for:*
**Adams Media**
**Betterway Books**
**Krause Publications Inc**
**North Light Books**
**Writer's Digest Books**

**Farrar, Straus & Giroux Books for Young Readers**
Imprint of Macmillan Children's Publishing Group
175 Fifth Ave, New York, NY 10010
*Tel:* 212-741-6900; 646-307-5151
*Toll Free Tel:* 888-330-8477 (sales) *Fax:* 212-741-6973
*E-mail:* sales@fsgbooks.com; childrens.editorial@fsgbooks.com (edit inquiries)
*Web Site:* us.macmillan.com/fsgyoungreaders.aspx; us.macmillan.com
*Key Personnel*
VP & Edit Dir: Joy Peskin
Founded: 1953
Preschool through young adult fiction & nonfiction, hardcover & paperback.
Number of titles published annually: 80 Print
Total Titles: 700 Print
Imprints: Margaret Ferguson Books; Frances Foster Books; Sunburst Paperbacks
Membership(s): Children's Book Council

**Farrar, Straus & Giroux, LLC**
Subsidiary of Macmillan
18 W 18 St, New York, NY 10011
SAN: 206-782X
*Tel:* 212-741-6900 *Fax:* 212-633-9385
*E-mail:* fsg.publicity@fsgbooks.com
*Web Site:* us.macmillan.com/fsg.aspx
*Key Personnel*
Pres & Publr: Jonathan Galassi
EVP & Deputy Publr: Andrew Mandel *Tel:* 212-206-5354
SVP & Art Dir: Susan Mitchell
SVP & Dir, Mktg & Publicity: Jeff Seroy *Tel:* 212-206-5323
SVP, Opers: Joy Isenberg *Tel:* 212-206-5334
SVP & Sales Dir: Spenser Lee
VP & Cont, Rts & Perms: Erika Seidman
VP & Dir, Publicity: Sarita Varma *Tel:* 212-206-5327 *E-mail:* svarma@fsgbooks.com
VP & Ed-in-Chief: Eric Chinski
Exec Mng Ed: Debra Helfand
Exec Ed, Dir Digital & Paperback Publg & Publr, FSG Originals: Sean McDonald
Sr Ed: Alexander Star
Assoc Ed: Emily Bell
Ad Dir: Victoria Genna
Creative Dir: Rodrigo Corral
Design Dir: Abby Kagan
Sr Publicist: Brian Gittis; Steve Weil
Assoc Dir, Publicity: Lottchen Shivers
Asst Dir, Publicity: Kathy Daneman
Foreign Rts Mgr: Amber Hoover
Founded: 1946
General fiction, nonfiction, poetry & juveniles.
ISBN Prefix(es): 978-0-374
Number of titles published annually: 180 Print
Total Titles: 1,400 Print
Imprints: Sarah Crichton Books; Faber & Faber Inc; Farrar, Straus & Giroux Books for Young Readers; Hill & Wang; North Point Press; Scientific American
Distributor for Drawn & Quarterly; Gray Wolf Books
Foreign Rep(s): Pan Macmillan Ltd (UK); Raincoast Books (Canada); Marco Vigevani (Italy)
Foreign Rights: Agence Hoffman (Germany); Anoukh Foerg Literary Agency (Germany); Graal Literary Agency (Maria Starz-Kanska) (Poland); Harris/Elon Agency (Israel); International Copyright Agency (Simona Kessler) (Romania); International Editors' Co (Latin America, Spain); Katai & Bolza Literary Agents (Peter Bolza) (Hungary); Korea Copyright Center Inc (KCC) (Korea); Leonhardt & Hoier Literary Agency A/S (Scandinavia); MB Literary Agency (Monica Martin) (Portugal, Spain); Kristin Olson Literary Agency SRO (Czech Republic); Riff Agency (Jaoa Paulo) (Brazil); Riff Agency (Laura Paulo) (Brazil); Sebes & Van Gelderen Literary Agency (Netherlands); Tuttle-Mori Agency Inc (Asako Kawachi) (Japan); Marco Vigevani Literary Agency (Italy)
*Advertising Agency:* Verso Advertising
*Warehouse:* MPS Distribution Center, 16365 James Madison Highway, Gordonsville, VA 22942 *Toll Free Tel:* 888-330-8477
Membership(s): Children's Book Council
*See separate listing for:*
**Hill & Wang**
**North Point Press**

**§Father & Son Publishing Inc**
4909 N Monroe St, Tallahassee, FL 32303-7015
*Tel:* 850-562-2612 *Toll Free Tel:* 800-741-2712 (orders only) *Fax:* 850-562-0916
*Web Site:* www.fatherson.com
*Key Personnel*
Pres: Lance Coalson *E-mail:* lance@fatherson.com
Founded: 1982
Publishers of nonfiction, historical fiction, cookbooks, giftbooks & children's books.
ISBN Prefix(es): 978-0-942407; 978-1-935802
Number of titles published annually: 12 Print; 3 Audio
Total Titles: 125 Print; 15 Audio
Distributor for BADM Books
Membership(s): ABA; Florida Publishers Association Inc; National Association of Independent Publishers

**Favorable Impressions**
PO Box 69018, Pleasant Ridge, MI 48069
*Toll Free Tel:* 800-206-9513 *Fax:* 248-582-0912
*Web Site:* www.favimp.com
*Key Personnel*
Owner & SVP, Mktg & Opers: Dan R Harris *E-mail:* danh@favimp.com
Pres, Publr & Ed: Laurie Lanzen Harris *E-mail:* laurieh@favimp.com
Founded: 1995
Reference & nonfiction books for elementary school libraries & public libraries.
ISBN Prefix(es): 978-1-931360
Number of titles published annually: 5 Print
Total Titles: 40 Print
Membership(s): National Association of College Stores; TLA

**FC&A Publishing**
103 Clover Green, Peachtree City, GA 30269
*Tel:* 770-487-6307 *Toll Free Tel:* 800-226-8024 *Fax:* 770-631-4357
*E-mail:* customer_service@fca.com
*Web Site:* www.fca.com
*Key Personnel*
Mktg: Anne Kaufmann *Tel:* 770-487-6307 ext 2151 *E-mail:* anne_kaufmann@fca.com
Founded: 1969
ISBN Prefix(es): 978-0-915099; 978-1-890957; 978-1-932470
Number of titles published annually: 3 Print; 3 Online
Total Titles: 36 Print; 30 Online

**§Federal Bar Association**
1220 N Filmore St, Suite 444, Arlington, VA 22201
*Tel:* 571-481-9100 *Fax:* 571-481-9090
*E-mail:* fba@fedbar.org
*Web Site:* www.fedbar.org
*Key Personnel*
Exec Dir: Karen Silberman *E-mail:* ksilberman@fedbar.org
Deputy Exec Dir: Stacy King *E-mail:* sking@fedbar.org
Founded: 1920
Publish course materials, newsletters & The Federal Lawyer Magazine.
ISBN Prefix(es): 978-1-56986
Number of titles published annually: 15 Print; 1 CD-ROM
Total Titles: 350 Print; 1 CD-ROM; 2 Audio

**Federal Buyers Guide Inc**
324 Palm Ave, Santa Barbara, CA 93101
*Tel:* 805-963-6524 *Fax:* 805-963-7478
*E-mail:* info@gov-world.com; info@fbgglobal.com
*Web Site:* www.gov-world.com; www.federalbuyersguideinc.com; www.digitalsubs.com
*Key Personnel*
Founder & Publr: Stuart Miller
CEO: Afzal Hussein
Founded: 1985
Directories, reference books & monthly magazines.
Number of titles published annually: 3 Print
Total Titles: 5 Print

**Federal Street Press**
Division of Merriam-Webster Inc
25-13 Old Kings Hwy N, No 277, Darien, CT 06820
*Tel:* 203-852-1280 *Toll Free Tel:* 877-886-2830 *Fax:* 203-852-1389
*E-mail:* sales@federalstreetpress.com
*Web Site:* www.federalstreetpress.com
*Key Personnel*
Publr: Deborah Hastings *E-mail:* dhastings@federalstreetpress.com
Sales Mgr: Virginia Guilfoyle *E-mail:* vguilfoyle@federalstreetpress.com
Founded: 1998
Offers up-to-date, quality, value-priced language reference titles created in cooperation with the editors of Merriam-Webster Inc.
ISBN Prefix(es): 978-1-892859; 978-1-59695
Number of titles published annually: 5 Print
Total Titles: 45 Print

**Philipp Feldheim Inc**, see Feldheim Publishers (Philipp Feldheim Inc)

**Feldheim Publishers (Philipp Feldheim Inc)**
208 Airport Executive Park, Nanuet, NY 10954
SAN: 207-0545
*Tel:* 845-356-2282 *Toll Free Tel:* 800-237-7149 (orders) *Fax:* 845-425-1908
*E-mail:* sales@feldheim.com
*Web Site:* www.feldheim.com
*Key Personnel*
Pres: Yitzchak Feldheim
Mgr: Eli Hollander
Sales Mgr: Moshe Grossman
Founded: 1939
Translations from Hebrew of Jewish classical works & works of contemporary authors in the field of Orthodox Jewish thought & contemporary Jewish literature for ages three & up.
ISBN Prefix(es): 978-0-87306; 978-1-58330
Number of titles published annually: 100 Print
Total Titles: 800 Print
Imprints: Feldheim Publishers USA
*Foreign Office(s):* Yaakov Feldheim Publishers Ltd, Box 43163, 91431 Jerusalem, Israel
Distributor for Hamadia Publishing; Jerusalem Publications

**The Feminist Press at The City University of New York**
365 Fifth Ave, Suite 5406, New York, NY 10016
SAN: 213-6813
*Tel:* 212-817-7915 *Fax:* 212-817-1593
*E-mail:* info@feministpress.org
*Web Site:* www.feministpress.org
*Key Personnel*
Exec Dir/Publr: Jennifer Baumgardner *Tel:* 212-817-7916 *Fax:* 212-817-1593 *E-mail:* jbaumgardner@gc.cuny.edu
Edit Dir: Amy Scholder *E-mail:* amyscholder@earthlink.net
Prodn & Design Mgr: Drew Stevens *E-mail:* dstevens@gc.cuny.edu
Publicity & Events Mgr: Elizabeth Koke *E-mail:* ekoke@gc.cuny.edu
Mng Ed: Jeanann Pannasch
Devt Mgr: Nino Pesta *E-mail:* npesta@gc.cuny.edu
Founded: 1970
African studies, Asian American studies, international studies, history of feminism, women's studies, working class studies, current issues & women's literature from the Middle East, Africa, Asia & Latin America & US women writers.
ISBN Prefix(es): 978-0-912670; 978-0-935312; 978-1-55861
Number of titles published annually: 18 Print; 10 E-Book
Total Titles: 400 Print; 50 E-Book
Foreign Rights: Footprint Books (Australia, New Zealand); Roberta Oliva (Italy); Pontas Agency (Denmark, Finland, Latin America, Norway, Portugal, Spain, Sweden); Turnaround Publisher Services Ltd (Asia, Continental Europe, Middle East, UK); Literary Agent Silke Weniger (Germany)
*Orders to:* Consortium Book Sales & Distribution, 1094 Flex Dr, Jackson, TN 38301-5070 (a Perseus Distribution Services Co) *Toll Free Tel:* 800-283-3572 *E-mail:* info@cbsd.com *Web Site:* www.cbsd.com SAN: 631-760X
*Returns:* Consortium Book Sales & Distribution, 1094 Flex Dr, Jackson, TN 38301-5070 (a Perseus Distribution Services Co) *Toll Free Tel:* 800-283-3572 *E-mail:* info@cbsd.com *Web Site:* www.cbsd.com SAN: 631-760X
*Distribution Center:* Consortium Book Sales & Distribution, 1094 Flex Dr, Jackson, TN 38301-5070 (a Perseus Distribution Services Co) *Toll Free Tel:* 800-283-3572 *E-mail:* info@cbsd.com *Web Site:* www.cbsd.com SAN: 631-760X
Membership(s): AAP; Council of Literary Magazines & Presses; National Council for Research on Women (NCRW)

**Fence Books**
University at Albany, Science Library 320, 1400 Washington Ave, Albany, NY 12222
*Tel:* 518-591-8162
*E-mail:* fence.fencebooks@gmail.com
*Web Site:* www.fenceportal.org
*Key Personnel*
Publr & Ed: Rebecca Wolff *E-mail:* rebeccafence@gmail.com
Mng Ed: Rob Arnold *E-mail:* robfence@gmail.com
Founded: 2001
ISBN Prefix(es): 978-1-934200; 978-0-9771064; 978-0-9713189; 978-0-9663324; 978-0-9740909
Number of titles published annually: 6 Print
Total Titles: 60 Print

**Feral House**
1240 W Sims Way, Suite 124, Port Townsend, WA 98368
*Tel:* 323-666-3311 *Fax:* 323-297-4331
*E-mail:* info@feralhouse.com
*Web Site:* feralhouse.com
*Key Personnel*
Pres & Publr: Adam Parfrey
Founded: 1989
Pop culture, alternative, art, nonfiction, religion, sociology & social sciences.
ISBN Prefix(es): 978-0-922915; 978-1-932595
Number of titles published annually: 10 Print
Total Titles: 66 Print
Imprints: Process Media
*Distribution Center:* Consortium Book Sales & Distribution, The Keg House, 34 13 Ave NE, Suite 101, Minneapolis, MN 55413-1007 *Tel:* 612-746-2600 *Toll Free Tel:* 800-283-3572 (cust serv) *Fax:* 612-746-2606 *Web Site:* www.cbsd.com
Disticor Direct, 695 Westney Rd, Suite 14, Ajax, ON L1S 6M9, Canada *Tel:* 905-619-6565 *Toll Free Tel:* 800-668-7724 CN only *Fax:* 905-619-2903
Turnaround Publisher Services, Olympia Trading Estate, Unit 3, Coburg Rd, London N22 6TZ, United Kingdom *Tel:* (020) 8829-3000 *Fax:* (020) 8881-5088 *E-mail:* orders@turnaround-uk.com

**Ferguson Publishing**
Imprint of Infobase Learning
132 W 31 St, 17th fl, New York, NY 10001
*Tel:* 212-967-8800 *Toll Free Tel:* 800-322-8755 *Fax:* 917-339-0323 *Toll Free Fax:* 800-678-3633
*E-mail:* custserv@factsonfile.com
*Web Site:* infobasepublishing.com
*Key Personnel*
CEO & Pres: Mark McDonnell
CFO: Jim Housley
Edit Dir: Laurie Likoff
Dir, Licensing & Busn Devt: Ben Jacobs
Dir, Mktg: Zina Scarpulla
Dir, Opers: Mark Zielinski
Dir, Publicity: Laurie Katz
With its acclaimed career guidance & reference materials, Ferguson Publishing is known among librarians & guidance counselors as the premier publisher in the career education field.
ISBN Prefix(es): 978-0-8160; 978-0-87196; 978-0-89434; 978-1-60413; 978-1-4381
Number of titles published annually: 74 Print; 74 E-Book
Total Titles: 333 Print; 363 E-Book

**Howard Fertig, Publisher**
80 E 11 St, New York, NY 10003
SAN: 201-4777
*Tel:* 212-982-7922 *Fax:* 212-982-1099
*E-mail:* enquiries@hfertigbooks.com; orders@hfertigbooks.com
*Web Site:* www.hfertigbooks.com
*Key Personnel*
Pres & Ed-in-Chief: Howard Fertig
Founded: 1966
Scholarly reprints & originals in European history, literature & social sciences.
ISBN Prefix(es): 978-0-86527
Number of titles published annually: 12 Print
Total Titles: 160 Print

**Fiction Collective Two Inc (FC2)**
Imprint of University of Alabama Press
University Ctr, Suite 310, 3007 N Ben Wilson St, Victoria, TX 77901
*Tel:* 361-570-4200; 361-570-4207
*E-mail:* fc2cum@gmail.com
*Web Site:* www.fc2.org; www.uhv.edu
*Key Personnel*
Memb, Bd of Dirs: Daniel Waterman
Asst Ed: Carmen Edington *Tel:* 361-570-4118 *E-mail:* edingtonc@uhv.edu
Liason: Charles W Alcorn, PhD *Tel:* 361-570-4100 *E-mail:* alcornc@uhv.edu
Founded: 1973
Publish formally innovative fiction.
ISBN Prefix(es): 978-1-57366
Number of titles published annually: 6 Print
Total Titles: 200 Print
Distributed by University of Alabama Press
*Orders to:* University of Alabama Press, PO Box 870380, Tuskaloosa, AL 35487-0380 *Tel:* 773-702-7000 *Fax:* 773-702-7212 *Toll Free Fax:* 800-621-8476
*Returns:* University of Alabama Press, Chicago Distribution Ctr, 11030 S Langley Ave, Chicago, IL 60628 *Tel:* 773-702-7000 *Toll Free Tel:* 800-621-2736 *Fax:* 773-702-7212 *Toll Free Fax:* 800-621-8476
*Distribution Center:* University of Alabama Press, PO Box 870380, Tuskaloosa, AL 35487-0380 *Tel:* 773-702-7000 *Fax:* 773-702-7212 *Toll Free Fax:* 800-621-8476
Membership(s): Council of Literary Magazines & Presses

**Fifth Estate Publishing**
2795 County Hwy 57, Blounstville, AL 35031
SAN: 852-6419
*Toll Free Tel:* 855-299-2160
*E-mail:* admin@fifth-estate.net
*Web Site:* fifthestatepub.com
Founded: 2003
Publisher & distributor.
ISBN Prefix(es): 978-0-9746336; 978-0-9760992; 978-0-9768233; 978-1-933580; 978-1-936533
Number of titles published annually: 6 Print; 6 Online; 6 E-Book
Total Titles: 136 Print; 136 Online; 75 E-Book

**Film-Video Publications/Circus Source Publications**
7944 Capistrano Ave, West Hills, CA 91304
SAN: 211-1527
*Tel:* 818-340-0175 *Fax:* 818-340-6770
*E-mail:* circussource@aol.com
*Key Personnel*
Pres & Publr: Alan Gadney *Tel:* 818-340-6620
VP & Exec Ed: Carolyn Porter
Ed: Nancy Gadney
Founded: 1974
Reference books, directories & audio/video cassettes on film, video, photography, TV/radio broadcasting, writing, theater, business & finance, performing arts.
ISBN Prefix(es): 978-0-930828
Number of titles published annually: 20 Print; 10 Audio
Total Titles: 25 Print; 16 Audio
Foreign Rep(s): Australia & New Zealand Book Co (Australia); Fitzhenry & Whiteside (Canada); Reed Methuen Publishers (New Zealand)

*Advertising Agency:* Carolyn Chadwick Advertising
Membership(s): The Association of Publishers for Special Sales; Book Publicists of Southern California; IBPA, the Independent Book Publishers Association

**Filter Press LLC**
PO Box 95, Palmer Lake, CO 80133
SAN: 201-484X
*Tel:* 719-481-2420 *Toll Free Tel:* 888-570-2663 *Fax:* 719-481-2420
*E-mail:* info@filterpressbooks.com; orders@filterpressbooks.com
*Web Site:* filterpressbooks.com
*Key Personnel*
Pres: Doris Baker *E-mail:* doris@filterpressbooks.com
Founded: 1957
Publisher of books on the American West, Western expansion, Colorado history & biography.
ISBN Prefix(es): 978-0-910584; 978-0-86541
Number of titles published annually: 5 Print; 1 Audio
Total Titles: 62 Print; 11 E-Book; 2 Audio
*Returns:* 19980 Top O'Moor W, Monument, CO 80132
*Shipping Address:* 19980 Top O'Moor W, Monument, CO 80132
Membership(s): Colorado Association of Libraries; Colorado Independent Publishers Association; IBPA, the Independent Book Publishers Association; New Mexico Book Association; Women Writing the West

**Financial Executives Research Foundation Inc (FERF)**
Affiliate of Financial Executives International (FEI)
West Tower, 7th fl, 1250 Headquarters Plaza, Morristown, NJ 07960-6837
*Tel:* 973-765-1000 *Fax:* 973-765-1023
*Web Site:* www.financialexecutives.org
*Key Personnel*
Dir, Fin Servs & Devt: Lorna Raagas *Tel:* 973-765-1033 *E-mail:* lraagas@financialexecutives.org
Founded: 1944
Executive reports & full-length monographs of research related to financial topics. All publications available on PDF.
ISBN Prefix(es): 978-1-61509
Number of titles published annually: 20 Print
Total Titles: 120 Print; 120 Online

**Financial Times Press & Wharton School Publishing**
Imprint of Pearson
One Lake St, Upper Saddle River, NJ 07458
*Tel:* 201-236-7000 *Toll Free Tel:* 800-922-0579 (orders)
*Web Site:* www.ftpress.com
*Key Personnel*
VP & Exec Ed: Tim Moore *E-mail:* tim_moore@prenhall.com
Exec Ed: Jim Boyd *E-mail:* jim_boyd@prenhall.com
Publisher of business, management, investment & finance books for general consumers, professionals & students.
ISBN Prefix(es): 978-0-13
Number of titles published annually: 165 Print
Total Titles: 765 Print
Imprints: FT Press Delivers
*Foreign Office(s):* 128 Long Acre, London WC2E 9AN, United Kingdom *Tel:* (020) 7447 2000 *Fax:* (020) 7240 5771
*Orders to:* 200 Old Tappan Rd, Old Tappan, NJ 07675

**Fine Communications**
Division of Fine Creative Media Inc
322 Eighth Ave, 15th fl, New York, NY 10001
*Tel:* 212-595-3500 *Fax:* 212-595-3779
*Key Personnel*
Pres & Publr: Michael J Fine *E-mail:* mjf@mjfbooks.com
VP: Anton Fine; Kaethe Fine
Dir, Fin: Ian Teixeira
Dir, MJF Books: Scott Messina
Edit Dir: Jeffrey Broesche
Dir, Systems Admin & HR: Steve Fine
Dir, Prodn: Ben Lee
Art Dir: Lisa Chovnick
Dir, Acqs: Roz Siegel
Reprint Mgr: Colin Warnock
Ed: Camille Cauti
Assoc Ed: Jason Baker
Acqs Ed: Marlene Rosen-Fine
Sr Prodn Advisor: Stanley Last
Acqs Assoc: Elizabeth Brady; Josephine Fagan
Bookkeeper: Cindy Lew
Off Mgr: Sydney Friedman
Founded: 1991
Publish hardcover & paperback reprints of fiction & nonfiction; develop & produce Barnes & Noble Classics.
ISBN Prefix(es): 978-1-56731 (MJF Books); 978-1-59308 (Barnes & Noble Classics); 978-1-60671 (MJF Books)
Number of titles published annually: 100 Print
Total Titles: 1,000 Print
Imprints: Barnes & Noble Classics (produced & published in conjunction with Barnes & Noble Inc); MJF Books

**FineEdge.com**
14004 Biz Point Lane, Anacortes, WA 98221
*Tel:* 360-299-8500 *Fax:* 360-299-0535
*E-mail:* pub@fineedge.com
*Web Site:* www.fineedge.com
*Key Personnel*
Publr: Mark Bunzel
Founded: 1986
Publishing, wholesaling, outdoor guidebooks & maps; specializing in nautical books & mountain bicycling.
ISBN Prefix(es): 978-0-938665; 978-1-932310
Number of titles published annually: 3 Print
Total Titles: 50 Print; 1 CD-ROM; 2 Online
Imprints: Mountain Biking Press/FineEdge.com
Distributed by Heritage House; Sunbelt Publications Inc
Membership(s): IBPA, the Independent Book Publishers Association

**Finney Company Inc**
8075 215 St W, Lakeville, MN 55044
*Tel:* 952-469-6699 *Toll Free Tel:* 800-846-7027 *Fax:* 952-469-1968 *Toll Free Fax:* 800-330-6232
*E-mail:* info@finneyco.com
*Web Site:* www.finneyco.com
*Key Personnel*
Pres: Alan E Krysan
Mktg Specialist: Krista Danielson
Founded: 1946
Publish books with educational value; children's books, trade, travel guides & educational reference/textbooks.
ISBN Prefix(es): 978-0-9618088; 978-1-879335; 978-0-944280; 978-0-913163; 978-0-912486; 978-0-8134; 978-1-883477; 978-0-9627860; 978-0-9617767; 978-1-880654; 978-0-89317; 978-0-933855; 978-1-931626; 978-0-9616847; 978-0-911781; 978-0-9639705; 978-1-893272; 978-1-879535; 978-0-8200; 978-1-885258; 978-1-888025; 978-0-9662589
Number of titles published annually: 15 Print
Total Titles: 400 Print
Imprints: Anacus Press; Astragal Press; Bancroft-Sage Publishing; Ecopress; Great Outdoors Publishing Co; Lone Oak Press; Pogo Press; SkipJack Press; Windward Publishing
Divisions: Chester Book Co; Hobar Publications; The New Careers Center (Live Oak Publications is an imprint of The New Careers Center)
Distributor for Drache Publications; Images Unlimited Publishing; Pine Forest Publishing; Joyce Shellhart; Snaptail Press
Membership(s): National School Supply & Equipment Association
*See separate listing for:*
**Astragal Press**
**Ecopress**
**Hobar Publications**
**Pogo Press Inc**
**Windward Publishing**

**Fire Engineering Books & Videos**
Division of PennWell Publishing
1421 S Sheridan Rd, Tulsa, OK 74112
*Tel:* 918-831-9410 *Toll Free Tel:* 800-752-9764 *Fax:* 918-831-9555
*E-mail:* sales@pennwell.com
*Web Site:* www.pennwellbooks.com/fire.html
*Key Personnel*
Dir: Mary McGee *E-mail:* marym@pennwell.com
Mktg Mgr: Amanda Alvarez *E-mail:* amandab@pennwell.com
Founded: 1877
Fire science, suppression & protection, petroleum, electric power, water, hazardous materials books, videos & magazine.
ISBN Prefix(es): 978-1-57340; 978-0-912212; 978-0-87814
Number of titles published annually: 10 Print; 5 CD-ROM
Total Titles: 120 Print; 10 CD-ROM
Distributed by David Publishing; Fire Protection Publications
Distributor for Brady; Idea Bank; IFSTA; Mosby
Foreign Rep(s): Akademika AS (Scandinavia); Ish Dawar (India); Eurospan (Europe); Arturo Gutierrez Hernandez (Central America, Mexico); Terry Roberts (South America); Tapir (Scandinavia)

**First Avenue Editions**
Imprint of Lerner Publishing Group Inc
241 First Ave N, Minneapolis, MN 55401
*Tel:* 612-332-3344 *Toll Free Tel:* 800-328-4929 *Fax:* 612-332-7615 *Toll Free Fax:* 800-332-1132
*E-mail:* info@lernerbooks.com
*Web Site:* www.lernerbooks.com
*Key Personnel*
Chmn: Harry J Lerner
Pres & Publr: Adam Lerner
CFO & EVP: Margaret Wunderlich
EVP, Sales: David Wexler
VP & Dir, Mktg & Digital Prods: Terri Soutor
Ed-in-Chief: Patricia M Stockland
VP, Prodn: Gary Hansen
Rts Dir: Maria Kjoller
Dir, Prod Devt & Mkt Res: Lois Wallentine
Dir, Electronic Content: Dan Wallek
Art Dir: Zach Marell
Dir, HR: Cyndi Radant
Social studies, picture story books, art, multicultural issues, activity books & beginning readers.
Total Titles: 240 Print
Foreign Rep(s): INT Press Distribution (Australia); Monarch Books of Canada (Trade) (Canada); Phambili (Southern Africa); Publishers Marketing Services (Malaysia, Singapore); Saunders Book Co (Education) (Canada); South Pacific Books (New Zealand)
Foreign Rights: Japan Foreign-Rights Centre (Japan); Korea Copyright Center (Korea); Michelle Lapautre Agence Junior (France); Literarische Agentur Silke Weniger (Germany); Rights People (UK & Commonwealth)
*Warehouse:* 1251 Washington Ave N, Minneapolis, MN 55401

**Five Star Publications Inc**
4696 W Tyson St, Chandler, AZ 85226
Mailing Address: PO Box 6698, Dept LM, Chandler, AZ 85246-6698
*Tel:* 480-940-8182 *Toll Free Tel:* 866-471-0777 *Fax:* 480-940-8787
*E-mail:* info@fivestarpublications.com
*Web Site:* www.fivestarpublications.com
*Key Personnel*
Pres: Linda F Radke
Founded: 1985
Children's books & textbooks.
ISBN Prefix(es): 978-0-9619853; 978-1-877749; 978-1-58985
Number of titles published annually: 10 Print
Total Titles: 36 Print; 12 E-Book
Divisions: Publishers Support Services
Membership(s): Arizona Authors Association; Arizona Book Publishing Association; IBPA, the Independent Book Publishers Association; National Federation of Press Women; Publishers Association of the West

**FJH Music Co Inc**
2525 Davie Rd, Suite 360, Fort Lauderdale, FL 33317-7424
*Tel:* 954-382-6061 *Toll Free Tel:* 800-262-8744 *Fax:* 954-382-3073
*E-mail:* custserv@fjhmusic.com; sales@fjhmusic.com
*Web Site:* www.fjhmusic.com
*Key Personnel*
CEO & Pres: Frank J Hackinson
VP: Kyle Hackinson *E-mail:* kyleh@fjhmusic.com
Founded: 1988
Educational music publications.
ISBN Prefix(es): 978-0-929666; 978-1-56939
Number of titles published annually: 100 Print

**Flashlight Press**
527 Empire Blvd, Brooklyn, NY 11225
*Tel:* 718-288-8300 *Fax:* 718-972-6307
*E-mail:* editor@flashlightpress.com
*Web Site:* www.flashlightpress.com
*Key Personnel*
Publr: Harry Mauer *E-mail:* publisher@flashlightpress.com
Ed: Shari Dash Greenspan *E-mail:* editor@flashlightpress.com
Founded: 2004
Children's picture books that explore & illuminate.
ISBN Prefix(es): 978-0-9729225; 978-0-9799746
Number of titles published annually: 3 Print
Total Titles: 17 Print; 6 E-Book
*Returns:* Independent Publishers Group (IPG), c/o Returns Dept, 814 N Franklin St, Chicago, IL 60610 *Toll Free Tel:* 800-888-4741 *Fax:* 312-337-5985 *E-mail:* frontdesk@ipgbook.com
*Distribution Center:* Independent Publishers Group (IPG), 814 N Franklin St, Chicago, IL 60610 *Tel:* 312-337-0747 *Toll Free Tel:* 800-888-4741 *Fax:* 312-337-5985 *E-mail:* frontdesk@ipgbook.com *Web Site:* www.ipgbook.com

**§FleetSeek**
500 Lafayette Blvd, Suite 230, Fredericksburg, VA 22401
*Tel:* 540-899-9872 *Toll Free Tel:* 888-ONLY-TTS (665-9887) *Fax:* 540-899-1948
*E-mail:* fleetseek@fleetseek.com
*Web Site:* www.fleetseek.com
*Key Personnel*
Mng Dir: Ronald D Roth
Founded: 1980
Directories online relating to data in the trucking industry.
ISBN Prefix(es): 978-1-880701
Number of titles published annually: 4 Online
Total Titles: 1 CD-ROM; 4 Online

**Florida Academic Press**
Division of FAP Books Inc
PO Box 357425, Gainesville, FL 32635
SAN: 299-3643
*Tel:* 352-332-5104
*E-mail:* fapress@gmail.com
*Web Site:* www.floridaacademicpress.com
*Key Personnel*
Exec Ed: Dr Samuel Decalo
Founded: 1997
Please submit only complete mss, hard copy, with SASE &/or postage for return if needed. No query letters. 4-6 week assessment time if not interested; 5-10 weeks if interested. Best, fastest responses are by e-mail. If a contract is cut, ms must be returned to us as ready to print electronic PDF files. We can refer you to several moderately-priced graphic designers.
ISBN Prefix(es): 978-1-890357
Number of titles published annually: 8 Print; 2 E-Book
Total Titles: 44 Print; 6 E-Book
Imprints: New Voices (primarily fiction)
Distributor for Publisher's Stone Publications

**Florida Funding Publications Inc**
Division of John L Adams & Co Inc
PO Box 561565, Miami, FL 33256
*Tel:* 305-251-2203 *Fax:* 305-251-2773
*E-mail:* info@floridafunding.com
*Key Personnel*
Pres: John Adams
Founded: 1985
Grant & funding reference materials.
ISBN Prefix(es): 978-1-879543
Number of titles published annually: 3 Print; 1 CD-ROM; 1 Online
Total Titles: 1 CD-ROM; 1 Online

**Flying Pen Press LLC**
1660 Niagara St, Denver, CO 80220
*Tel:* 303-375-0499 *Fax:* 303-375-0499
*E-mail:* generalinquiries@flyingpenpress.com; bookorders@flyingpenpress.com; returns@flyingpenpress.com; info@flyingpenpress.com
*Web Site:* www.flyingpenpress.com
*Key Personnel*
Publr: David A Rozansky *E-mail:* publisher@flyingpenpress.com
Founded: 2007
Publisher of fiction & nonfiction.
ISBN Prefix(es): 978-0-9795889
Number of titles published annually: 10 Print; 10 E-Book
Total Titles: 12 Print; 1 E-Book
Imprints: Carpe Diem Professional Calendars; Flying Pen Press Colorado; Flying Pen Press Park Trek; Flying Pen Press Rocky Mountain West; Flying Pen Press Science Fiction; Flying Pen Press Southwest; Flying Pen Press Travel Guides; Flying Piggybank Press; The Press for Humanitarian Causes; Traveling Pen Press
*Distribution Center:* Lightning Source Inc, 1246 Heil Quaker Blvd, La Vergne, TN 37086
Membership(s): IBPA, the Independent Book Publishers Association; Mountains & Plains Independent Publishers Association

**Focus on the Family**
8605 Explorer Dr, Colorado Springs, CO 80920-1051
*Tel:* 719-531-5181 *Toll Free Tel:* 800-A-FAMILY (232-6459) *Fax:* 719-531-3424
*Web Site:* focusonthefamily.com
Founded: 1986
Casebound & soft cover (adult & children) dealing with family relationships & emphasizing the importance of values & Christian principles in people's lives.
ISBN Prefix(es): 978-0-929608; 978-1-56179; 978-1-58997; 978-1-60482; 978-1-62405; 978-1-62471
Number of titles published annually: 60 Print
Total Titles: 200 Print; 4 CD-ROM; 60 Audio
Imprints: Adventures in Odyssey; Brio Girls; Focus on the Family; Heritage Builders; Life on the Edge; Radio Theatre; Renewing the Heart; Ribbits; That the World May Know
Distributed by Baker Books; Cook Communications; Harvest House; Moody Press; Tommy Nelson; Standard Publishing Co; Tyndale House Publishers; Zondervan

**Focus Publishing/R Pullins Co Inc**
Subsidiary of R Pullins Co
PO Box 369, Newburyport, MA 01950
*Tel:* 978-462-7288 (edit) *Toll Free Tel:* 800-848-7236 (orders) *Fax:* 978-462-9035 (edit)
*E-mail:* orders@pullins.com
*Web Site:* www.pullins.com
*Key Personnel*
Publr: Ron Pullins
Cust Rels & Accts Mgr: Kerri Wetherbee
Founded: 1985
Classical & modern languages.
ISBN Prefix(es): 978-0-941051; 978-1-58510
Number of titles published annually: 30 Print; 1 CD-ROM; 3 E-Book; 2 Audio
Total Titles: 200 Print; 5 CD-ROM; 1 E-Book; 2 Audio
Imprints: Focus Classical Library; Focus Philosophical Library; Focus Texts
Distributor for Domus Latina Publishing
Foreign Rep(s): Accademia Vivarium Novum (Italy); Antike Zum Begreifen (Austria, Germany); Clovis (France); Cultura Clasica SL (Spain); DA Direct (Australia, New Zealand); NBN International (Durnell Marketing) (Ireland, UK)
*Returns:* PSSC, 231 Industrial Park, 46 Development Rd, Fitchburg, MA 01420
*Shipping Address:* PSSC, 231 Industrial Park, 46 Development Rd, Fitchburg, MA 01420
*Warehouse:* PSSC, 231 Industrial Park, 46 Development Rd, Fitchburg, MA 01420
*Distribution Center:* PSSC, 231 Industrial Park, 46 Development Rd, Fitchburg, MA 01420
Membership(s): AAP

**Fodor's Travel Publications**
Division of Random House Inc
c/o Random House Inc, 1745 Broadway, New York, NY 10019
SAN: 204-1073
*Tel:* 212-829-6714 *Toll Free Tel:* 800-733-3000 *Fax:* 212-572-2248
*Web Site:* www.fodors.com
*Key Personnel*
SVP & Publr: Amanda D'Acierno
Exec Dir, Edit & Content Strategy: Arabella Bowen
VP, Creative Dir: Fabrizio La Rocca
Mng Ed: Linda Schmidt
Edit Dir: Linda Cabasin
Dir, Subs/Foreign Rts: Linda Kaplan *Tel:* 212-572-2060 *E-mail:* lkaplan@randomhouse.com
Founded: 1936
Travel guides, foreign & domestic.
Random House Inc & its publishing entities are not accepting unsol submissions, proposals, mss, or submission queries via e-mail at this time.
ISBN Prefix(es): 978-0-679; 978-0-307; 978-0-676; 978-1-4000
Number of titles published annually: 100 Print
Total Titles: 640 Print; 30 E-Book
Imprints: Compass American Guides; Fodor's
*Branch Office(s)*
2775 Matheson Blvd E, Mississauga, ON L4W 4P7, Canada
*Foreign Office(s):* 20 Vauxhall Bridge Rd, London SW1V 2SA, United Kingdom
*Warehouse:* Random House, 400 Hahn Rd, Westminster, MD 21157

**Fons Vitae**
49 Mockingbird Valley Dr, Louisville, KY 40207-1366
*Tel:* 502-897-3641 *Fax:* 502-893-7373
*E-mail:* fonsvitaeky@aol.com
*Web Site:* www.fonsvitae.com
*Key Personnel*
Dir: Gray Henry *E-mail:* grayh101@aol.com
Proj Dir: Elena Lloyd-Sidle
Busn Mgr: Lucy Langman
Mktg & Multimedia: Paul T Carney
Founded: 1997
Fons Vitae is both an academic charity with 501c(3) charitable status & a refereed publishing house which ensures the highest scholarly standards for its publications. Authentic text, impeccably translated & exquisitely produced, make these volumes useful for both the university classroom & for those interested in the eternal verities with no compromise to a recent soft focus on spirituality.
ISBN Prefix(es): 978-1-887752
Number of titles published annually: 10 Print; 5 CD-ROM
Total Titles: 97 Print; 5 CD-ROM
Distributor for African American Islamic Institute; Anqa Press (UK); Aperture (NY); Archetype (UK); Broadstone Books; Dar Nun; Golganooza Press (UK); Islamic Texts Society (UK); Matheson Trust; Parabola; Paragon; Parvardigar Press; Pir Press (NY); Qiblah Books; Quilliam Press (UK); Sandala Productions; Sophia Perennis; Sri Lanka Institute of Traditional Studies; Thesaurus Islamicus Foundation; Tradigital; White Thread Press (US); Wisdom Foundation; World Wisdom (US); Zaytuna Institute Press (US)
Foreign Rep(s): Airlift (UK); American University Cairo Press (AUC) (Middle East)
*Distribution Center:* Independent Publishers Group (IPG)

**Fordham University Press**
2546 Belmont Ave, University Box L, Bronx, NY 10458
SAN: 201-6516
*Tel:* 718-817-4795 *Fax:* 718-817-4785
*Web Site:* www.fordhampress.com
*Key Personnel*
Dir: Fredric Nachbaur *E-mail:* fnachbaur@fordham.edu
Edit Dir: Helen Tartar *Tel:* 718-817-4787 *E-mail:* tartar@fordham.edu
Mktg Dir: Kathleen O'Brien-Nicholson *E-mail:* bkaobrien@fordham.edu
Busn Mgr: Margaret Noonan *E-mail:* mnoonan@fordham.edu
Asst Busn Mgr: Marie Hall *E-mail:* mhall21@fordham.edu
Prodn & Design Mgr: Loomis Mayer *Tel:* 718-817-4788 *E-mail:* lmayer@fordham.edu
Asst Mktg Mgr: Katie Sweeney *E-mail:* kasweeney@fordham.edu
Mng Ed: Eric Newman *Tel:* 718-817-4786 *E-mail:* ernewman@fordham.edu
Edit Assoc & Asst to Dir: Will Cerbone *E-mail:* wcerbone@fordham.edu
Asst Ed: Tom Lay *E-mail:* tlay@fordham.edu
Founded: 1907
Scholarly books & journals, New York regional books, general trade books & videos.
ISBN Prefix(es): 978-0-8232
Number of titles published annually: 42 Print
Total Titles: 450 Print
Imprints: Rose Hill Books
*Sales Office(s):* Oxford University Press, 2001 Evans Rd, Cary, NC 27513 *Toll Free Tel:* 800-445-9714 *Fax:* 919-677-1303 *E-mail:* custserv.us@oup.com SAN: 658-1293
Distributed by Oxford University Press (US & CN)
Distributor for Creighton University Press; Institute for Advanced Study in the Theatre Arts (IASTA); Little Room Press; The Reconstructionist Press; Rockhurst University Press; St Bede's Publications; University of San Francisco Press
Foreign Rep(s): Combine Academic Publishers Ltd (Africa, Europe, Middle East); Cranbury International LLC (Ethan Atkin) (India, Latin America); East West Export Books (EWEB) c/o University of Hawaii (Royden Muranaka) (Asia, The Pacific)
*Orders to:* Oxford University Press, 2001 Evans Rd, Cary, NC 27513 *Toll Free Tel:* 800-445-9714 *Fax:* 919-677-1303 *E-mail:* custserv.us@oup.com SAN: 658-1293
*Returns:* Maple Press Distribution Center, 704 Legionnaire Dr, Fredricksburg, PA 17026
Membership(s): AAP; Association of American University Presses; Association of Jesuit University Presses

**Fort Ross Inc Russian-American Publishing Projects**
Division of Fort Ross Inc
26 Arthur Place, Yonkers, NY 10701
*Tel:* 914-375-6448 *Fax:* 718-775-8340
*E-mail:* fortross@optonline.net
*Web Site:* www.fortrossinc.com
*Key Personnel*
Pres & Exec Dir: Dr Vladimir Kartsev *E-mail:* vkartsev2000@yahoo.com
Founded: 1992
Books in Russian. Russia-related books in English, co-publishing of books of American authors in Russia. Big scale Russian/American publishing projects (joint ventures, etc).
ISBN Prefix(es): 978-1-57480
Number of titles published annually: 10 Print
Total Titles: 60 Print
Foreign Rep(s): Nova Littera (Baltic States, Belarus, Eastern Europe, Russia, Ukraine)

**Fortress Press**, see Augsburg Fortress Publishers, Publishing House of the Evangelical Lutheran Church in America

**Forum Press Inc**, see Harlan Davidson Inc/Forum Press Inc

**The Forum Press Inc**
3100 W Warner Ave, Suite 7, Santa Ana, CA 92704
*Tel:* 714-545-3114 *Fax:* 714-545-3116
*E-mail:* theforumpress@cs.com
*Web Site:* www.theforumpress.com
*Key Personnel*
Publr: Kira Fulks
Founded: 2009
Publisher & distributer of books.
ISBN Prefix(es): 978-0-9842752
Number of titles published annually: 10 Print
Total Titles: 4 Print

**§Forum Publishing Co**
383 E Main St, Centerport, NY 11721
*Tel:* 631-754-5000 *Toll Free Tel:* 800-635-7654 *Fax:* 631-754-0630
*E-mail:* forumpublishing@aol.com
*Web Site:* www.forum123.com
*Key Personnel*
CEO & Publr: Martin Stevens
Founded: 1981
Business magazines & books.
ISBN Prefix(es): 978-0-9626141
Number of titles published annually: 5 Print
Total Titles: 15 Print; 6 CD-ROM

**Forward Movement Publications**
Affiliate of The Episcopal Church
412 Sycamore St, Cincinnati, OH 45202-4110
*Tel:* 513-721-6659 *Toll Free Tel:* 800-543-1813 *Fax:* 513-721-0729 (orders)
*E-mail:* orders@forwardmovement.org (orders & cust serv)
*Web Site:* www.forwardmovement.org
*Key Personnel*
Mng Ed: Richelle Thompson *E-mail:* rthompson@forwardmovement.org
Dir, Busn Opers: D Jane Paraskevopoulos *E-mail:* jparaskevo@forwardmovement.org
Founded: 1934
Founded to help reinvigorate the life of the Episcopal church.
ISBN Prefix(es): 978-0-88028
Number of titles published annually: 2 Print
Total Titles: 50 Print; 1 Audio
Imprints: FMP
Distributor for Anglican Book Centre
*Warehouse:* 10001 Alliance Rd, Cincinnati, OH 45242

**Walter Foster Publishing Inc**
Subsidiary of The Quarto Group Inc
3 Wrigley, Suite A, Irvine, CA 92618
SAN: 249-051X
*Tel:* 949-380-7510 *Toll Free Tel:* 800-426-0099; 800-826-6600 (orders) *Fax:* 949-380-7575
*E-mail:* info@walterfoster.com
*Web Site:* www.walterfoster.com
*Key Personnel*
CEO & Pres: Ross Sarracino
VP, Sales-Arts/Crafts: Dan Widner
Sales Coord: Elizabeth Gilbert
Founded: 1922
Instructional art books, specialty art & creative products.
ISBN Prefix(es): 978-0-929261; 978-1-56010
Number of titles published annually: 30 Print
Total Titles: 275 Print
Foreign Rep(s): Apple Press
*Orders to:* c/o MBI Publishing Co, 400 First St N, Suite 300, Minneapolis, MN 55401 *Tel:* 612-344-8691 *E-mail:* walterfoster@quaysidepub.com

**§The Foundation Center**
79 Fifth Ave, New York, NY 10003-3076
SAN: 207-5687
*Tel:* 212-620-4230 *Toll Free Tel:* 800-424-9836 *Fax:* 212-807-3677
*E-mail:* order@foundationcenter.org
*Web Site:* www.fdncenter.org; foundationcenter.org
*Key Personnel*
Pres: Bradford K Smith *Tel:* 212-807-3602 *E-mail:* bks@foundationcenter.org
Fulfillment Mgr: Laura Cascio *Tel:* 212-807-2426
Founded: 1956
Reference books on US foundations, corporations & their grant-making activities & books about philanthropy & nonprofit management.
ISBN Prefix(es): 978-0-87954; 978-1-931923; 978-1-59542
Number of titles published annually: 12 Print; 3 Online
Total Titles: 292 Print; 3 Online; 25 E-Book
*Branch Office(s)*
312 Sutter St, Suite 606, San Francisco, CA 94108-4314 *Tel:* 415-397-0902
1627 "K" St NW, 3rd fl, Washington, DC 20006-1708 *Tel:* 202-331-1400
50 Hurt Plaza, Suite 150, Atlanta, GA 30303-2914 *Tel:* 404-880-0094
1422 Euclid Ave, Suite 1600, Cleveland, OH 44115-2001 *Tel:* 216-861-1933

**The Foundation for Economic Education Inc**
30 S Broadway, Irvington-on-Hudson, NY 10533
*Tel:* 914-591-7230 *Toll Free Tel:* 800-960-4FEE (960-4333) *Fax:* 914-591-8910
*E-mail:* freeman@fee.org (query/submit: attention Sheldon Richman, all others: attention Michael Nolan)
*Web Site:* www.thefreemanonline.org; www.fee.org

*Key Personnel*
Mng Ed: Michael Nolan *Tel:* 914-591-7230 ext 122 *E-mail:* mnolan@fee.org
Ed: Sheldon Richman *E-mail:* srichman@fee.org
Founded: 1946
"The Freeman" magazine, also economics/personal freedom books.
ISBN Prefix(es): 978-1-57246; 978-0-910614
Number of titles published annually: 5 Print
Total Titles: 87 Print

**Foundation Press Inc**
395 Hudson St, New York, NY 10014
SAN: 281-7225
Mailing Address: c/o West Education, 610 Opperman Dr, Eagan, MN 66123
*Tel:* 212-367-6790 *Toll Free Tel:* 877-888-1330 *Fax:* 212-367-6799
*E-mail:* foundation-press@thomsonreuters.com
*Web Site:* www.foundation-press.com
*Key Personnel*
Publr: John Bloomquist
Founded: 1931
Law, business, political science, criminal justice, curriculum books, graduate & undergraduate primarily in law.
ISBN Prefix(es): 978-0-88277; 978-1-56662; 978-1-58778
Number of titles published annually: 120 Print
Total Titles: 500 Print
*Warehouse:* Eagan Distribution Center, 525 Wescott Rd, Eagan, MN 55123

**Foundation Publications**
900 S Euclid St, La Habra, CA 90631
Mailing Address: PO Box 6439, Anaheim, CA 92816
*Tel:* 714-879-2286 *Toll Free Tel:* 800-257-6272 *Fax:* 714-535-2164
*E-mail:* info@foundationpublications.com
*Web Site:* www.foundationpublications.com
*Key Personnel*
EVP: Pike Lambeth *E-mail:* pike@foundationpublications.com
Founded: 1971
Publish New American Standard Bible, La Biblia de Las Americas & Nueva Biblia Latinoamericana de Hoy.
ISBN Prefix(es): 978-0-910618; 978-1-58135; 978-1-885217
Number of titles published annually: 5 Print
Total Titles: 8 Print; 1 CD-ROM
*Distribution Center:* Anchor Distributors, 1030 Hunt Valley Circle, New Kensington, PA 15068 *Toll Free Fax:* 800-444-4484
STL Distribution, 100 Biblica Way, Elizabethton, TN 37643 *Toll Free Tel:* 800-289-2772
Membership(s): Evangelical Christian Publishers Association; SEPA

**Fox Chapel Publishing Co Inc**
1970 Broad St, East Petersburg, PA 17520
*Tel:* 717-560-4703 *Toll Free Tel:* 800-457-9112 *Fax:* 717-560-4702
*E-mail:* customerservice@foxchapelpublishing.com
*Web Site:* www.foxchapelpublishing.com
*Key Personnel*
Pres & Intl Rts Contact: Alan Giagnocavo *E-mail:* alan@foxchapelpublishing.com
Prodn: Troy Thorne
Founded: 1991
Books & magazines for woodworkers, woodcarvers & other hobby enthusiasts.
ISBN Prefix(es): 978-1-56523
Number of titles published annually: 35 Print
Total Titles: 260 Print
Imprints: Scroll Saw Woodworking & Crafts; Woodcarving Illustrated Magazine
Distributed by Ingram Publisher Services
Distributor for Reader's Digest; Taunton Sterling Dover

**Fox Run Press LLC**
7840 Bullet Rd, Peyton, OH 80831
Mailing Address: PO Box 64380, Colorado Springs, CO 80962
*Tel:* 719-482-4035 *Fax:* 719-623-0254
*E-mail:* info@foxrunpress.com
*Web Site:* www.foxrunpress.com
*Key Personnel*
Ed: Ron Hardman *E-mail:* ron@foxrunpress.com
Sales: Shelly Johnson
Acctg: Kevin Cronk
Founded: 2008
Publish books, eBooks & online content for children's fiction & historical fiction titles.
ISBN Prefix(es): 978-0-9819607
Number of titles published annually: 5 Print; 5 E-Book
Total Titles: 3 Print
*Distribution Center:* Ingram Publisher Services, One Ingram Blvd, La Vergne, TN 37086 *Tel:* 615-793-5000 *E-mail:* orders@ingrambook.com
Membership(s): The Association of Publishers for Special Sales; IBPA, the Independent Book Publishers Association

**FPMI Solutions Inc**
245 Business Park Rd, Suite A, Madison, AL 35758
*Tel:* 256-539-1850 *Toll Free Tel:* 888-644-3764 *Fax:* 256-539-0911
*E-mail:* info@fpmi.com
*Web Site:* www.fpmisolutions.com; www.fpmi.com
*Key Personnel*
Pres: Stephen A Moffett
EVP, Opers: Clyde B Blandford, Jr
Founded: 1985
Government publications.
ISBN Prefix(es): 978-0-936295; 978-1-930542
Number of titles published annually: 4 Print
Total Titles: 20 Print
*Branch Office(s)*
1033 N Fairfax St, Alexandria, VA 22314 *Tel:* 703-690-7000 *Fax:* 703-690-7009

**§Franciscan Media**
Formerly St Anthony Messenger Press
28 W Liberty St, Cincinnati, OH 45202
SAN: 204-6237
*Tel:* 513-241-5615 *Toll Free Tel:* 800-488-0488 *Fax:* 513-241-0399
*E-mail:* books@americancatholic.org
*Web Site:* www.americancatholic.org
*Key Personnel*
Pres: Rev Jeff Scheeler, OFM
CEO & Publr: Rev Dan Kroger, OFM *Tel:* 513-241-5615 ext 127 *E-mail:* dank@americancatholic.org
Dir, Mktg, Sales & Internet: Barbara Baker *Tel:* 513-241-5615 ext 101 *E-mail:* bkbaker@americancatholic.org
Prodn Dir: Br Robert A Lucero, OFM *Tel:* 513-241-5615 ext 150 *E-mail:* robertl@americancatholic.org
Art Dir: Jeanne Kortekamp *Tel:* 513-241-5615 ext 113 *E-mail:* jeannek@americancatholic.org
Ad Mgr: Fred Limke *Tel:* 513-241-5615 ext 117 *E-mail:* flimke@americancatholic.org
Rts & Perms Mgr: Katie Carroll *Tel:* 513-241-5615 ext 141 *E-mail:* katiec@americancatholic.org
Founded: 1970
Religion (Catholic); inspirational resources for parishes, schools & individuals; books, videos, audio books, e-books, weekly & Sunday homily programs; monthly subscription newsletters, monthly magazine; American Catholic (web site).
ISBN Prefix(es): 978-0-912228; 978-0-86716; 978-1-61636
Number of titles published annually: 35 Print; 35 E-Book; 25 Audio
Total Titles: 480 Print; 100 E-Book; 200 Audio
Imprints: Fischer Productions; Franciscan Communications; Ikonographics; Servant Books
Distributor for Franciscan Communications (books & videos); Ikonographics (videos)
Foreign Rep(s): Pleroma Christian Supplies (New Zealand); Rainbow/Word of Life (Australia); Redemptorist Publications Book Service (UK)
Membership(s): Association of Catholic Publishers Inc; Canadian Booksellers Association; Catholic Press Association; Society of Professional Journalists

**Franklin, Beedle & Associates Inc**
22462 SW Washington St, Sherwood, OR 97140
*Tel:* 503-625-4445 *Toll Free Tel:* 800-322-2665 *Fax:* 503-625-4434
*E-mail:* orderpro@fbeedle.com
*Web Site:* www.fbeedle.com
*Key Personnel*
Pres & Publr: James F Leisy, Jr *E-mail:* jimleisy@fbeedle.com
Ed: Tom Sumner *E-mail:* tsumner@fbeedle.com
Founded: 1985
College textbooks in computer science, information systems & computers in education, educational software, computer engineering, computer information systems, information technology.
ISBN Prefix(es): 978-0-938661; 978-1-887902; 978-1-59028
Number of titles published annually: 10 Print; 5 E-Book
Total Titles: 50 Print; 5 E-Book
Imprints: William, James & Co (humanities publr); Xpat Fiction
Distributor for Blue Sky Gallery; Photolucida Book
Foreign Rep(s): Transatlantic Publishers (Europe, Middle East, UK)
Membership(s): Association for Computing Machinery

**Franklin Watts®**, see Scholastic Consumer & Professional Publishing

**Frederick Fell Publishers Inc**
2131 Hollywood Blvd, Suite 305, Hollywood, FL 33020
SAN: 208-2365
*Tel:* 954-925-5242
*E-mail:* fellpub@aol.com (admin only)
*Web Site:* www.fellpub.com
*Key Personnel*
Pres & Publr: Donald L Lessne *E-mail:* donlessne@aol.com
Ed-in-Chief: Ms Barbara Newman *E-mail:* felleditor@aol.com
Founded: 1943
An award-winning publisher of general trade books. The series we publish include the Know-it-All Guides, the Top 100 series & Heroes & Heroines series & So You Want To Be series.
ISBN Prefix(es): 978-0-88391
Number of titles published annually: 24 Print; 50 E-Book
Total Titles: 150 Print; 150 E-Book
Foreign Rep(s): Gazelle Book Services (UK & the continent); Jarir Bookstore (Tony Herold) (Worldwide); Monarch Books of Canada (Canada); Parrot Reads Publishers (Indian subcontinent); Trinity Books (South Africa); Zimpfer Books (Caribbean, Central America, Mexico, South America)
Foreign Rights: AgenciaLiteraria S L (Montse Yanez) (Latin America, Mexico, Spanish & Portuguese); Big Apple Agency (Mathilde-Wang) (Taiwan); Big Apple Agency (Maggie Han) (China); Book Publishers Association of Israel (Shoshi Grajower) (Israel); Daniel Doglioli (Italy); Graal Literary Agency (Magda

Cabajewksa) (Poland); Imprima Korea Agency (Joseph Lee) (Korea); International Copyright Agency Ltd (Simona Kessler) (Romania); Christiane Janssen (Germany); Japan UNI Agency Inc (Japan); Jarir Bookstore (Tony Herold) (Saudi Arabia); JS Literary & Media Agency (Somjai Raksasee) (Thailand); Nurcihan Kesim Literary Agency (Filiz Karaman) (Turkey); LEX Copyright Office (Norbert Uzseka) (Hungary); Maxima Creative Agency (Santo Manurung) (Indonesia); Nova Littera S L (Konstantin Paltchikov) (Russia); Andrew Nurnberg Associates Ltd (Tatjana Zoldnere) (Latvia, Lithuania, Ukraine); Andrew Nurnberg Associates Prague (Petra Tobiskova) (Czech Republic); Andrew Nurnberg Associates Sofia (Anna Droumeva) (Bulgaria); OA Literary Agency (Greece); Parrot Reads Publishers (Rajiv Jha) (India); Plima Literary Agency (Mila Perisic) (Croatia, Serbia, Slovenia); Karin Schindler (Brazil); Tuttle-Mori Agency Inc (Japan)

*Distribution Center:* Bookmasters, 30 Amberwood Pkwy, Ashland, OH 44805, Contact: Tony Pro *Tel:* 419-281-0200 *Toll Free Tel:* 800-537-6727 *Fax:* 419-281-0200 *E-mail:* tproe@bookmasters.com

Monarch Books of Canada, 5000 Dufferin St, Downsview, ON M3H 5T5, Canada, Contact: Ron Gurfinkel *Tel:* 416-663-8231 *E-mail:* ron@monarchbooks.ca

Trinity Books, PO Box 242, Randburg 2125, South Africa *Tel:* (011) 787-4010 *Fax:* (011) 781-1501 *E-mail:* trinity@iafrica.com

Gazelle Book Services Ltd, White Cross Mills, Hightown, Lancaster LA1 4XS, United Kingdom *Tel:* (01524) 68765 *Fax:* (01524) 63232 *E-mail:* sales@gazellebooks.co.uk

**§Free Spirit Publishing Inc**
217 Fifth Ave N, Suite 200, Minneapolis, MN 55401-1260
*Tel:* 612-338-2068 *Toll Free Tel:* 800-735-7323 *Fax:* 612-337-5050 *Toll Free Fax:* 866-419-5199
*E-mail:* help4kids@freespirit.com
*Web Site:* www.freespirit.com
*Key Personnel*
Pres & Publr: Judy Galbraith
Intl Rts Mgr: Sara Hartman-Seeskin
Founded: 1983
SELF-HELP FOR KIDS® & SELF-HELP FOR TEENS®, offer books & learning materials for parents, educators, children & teens. Topics include: self-esteem, stress management, school success, creativity, relationships with friends & family, social action, special needs (i.e. children with LD/learning differences, gifted & talented & at-risk youth), bullying & conflict resolution.
ISBN Prefix(es): 978-0-915793; 978-1-57542; 978-0-9665988
Number of titles published annually: 25 Print; 1 CD-ROM
Total Titles: 170 Print; 2 CD-ROM; 3 Audio
Foreign Rep(s): Educational Distributors (New Zealand); Incentive Plus (UK); Monarch Books (Canada); Willow Connection (Australia)

**§W H Freeman and Co**
Member of Bedford, Freeman & Worth Publishing Group, LLC
41 Madison Ave, 37th fl, New York, NY 10010
*Tel:* 212-576-9400 *Fax:* 212-689-2383
*Web Site:* www.whfreeman.com
*Key Personnel*
Pres: Elizabeth Widdicombe
Publr: Ruth Baruth; Kate Parker; Peter Marshall
VP, Dir of Prodn: Ellen Cash
Mng Ed: Philip McCaffrey
Dir, Custom & Digital Progs: Susan Brennan
Dir, Mktg & Promo: John Britch
Dir, Mktg Devt: Steven Rigolosi
Dir, Fin & Admin: Linda Glover
Intl Rts Dir: Ilene Ellenbogen
Founded: 1946
Science & mathematics texts for the higher education market & high school advanced courses.
ISBN Prefix(es): 978-0-312; 978-1-57259; 978-1-4292
Number of titles published annually: 25 Print; 20 Online; 20 E-Book
Total Titles: 500 Print
Foreign Rep(s): Macmillan East Asia (China, Hong Kong, Indonesia, Korea, Philippines, Singapore, Thailand, Vietnam); Macmillan Publishers (Taiwan); Palgrave Macmillan (Australia, New Zealand); Palgrave Macmillan UK (Africa, Caribbean, Europe, India, Japan, Latin America, Middle East, Pakistan, UK); UBSD Distribution SDN BHD (Malaysia)
*Warehouse:* MPS Distribution Center, 16365 James Madison Hwy (US Rte 15), Gordonsville, VA 22942 *Toll Free Tel:* 888-330-8477 *Fax:* 540-672-7540 (cust serv) *Toll Free Fax:* 800-672-2054 (orders)

**Samuel French Inc**
45 W 25 St, New York, NY 10010-2751
*Tel:* 212-206-8990 *Toll Free Tel:* 866-598-8449 *Fax:* 212-206-1429
*E-mail:* info@samuelfrench.com
*Web Site:* www.samuelfrench.com
*Key Personnel*
Pres: Nate Collins *E-mail:* ncollins@samuelfrench.com
Dir, Opers: Kenneth Dingledine *E-mail:* kdingledine@samuelfrench.com
Literary Mgr: Amy Rose Marsh *E-mail:* amarsh@samuelfrench.com
Founded: 1830
Plays.
ISBN Prefix(es): 978-0-573
Number of titles published annually: 130 Print
Total Titles: 5,000 Print
Divisions: Baker's Play; Baker's Play
*Branch Office(s)*
Samuel French Bookshop, 7623 Sunset Blvd, Hollywood, CA 90046
*Foreign Office(s):* Samuel French Ltd, 52 Fitzroy St, London W1T 5JR, United Kingdom, Opers Dir: David Webster *Tel:* (020) 7387 9373 *Fax:* (020) 7387 2161 *E-mail:* theatre@samuelfrench-london.co.uk *Web Site:* www.samuelfrench-london.co.uk
Distributed by Baker's Plays; Samuel French Ltd (UK)
Distributor for Baker's Plays; Samuel French Ltd (UK)
Foreign Rights: DALRO (Botswana, Lesotho, Namibia, South Africa, Swaziland); Drama League of Ireland (Ireland); Origin Theatrical (New Zealand)
*See separate listing for:*
**Baker's Plays**

**Fresh Air Books**
Imprint of Upper Room Books
1908 Grand Ave, Nashville, TN 37212
Mailing Address: PO Box 340004, Nashville, TN 37203-0004
*Toll Free Tel:* 800-972-0433 (orders) *Fax:* 615-340-7266
*E-mail:* freshairbooks@me.com
*Web Site:* www.bookstore.upperroom.org (orders)
*Key Personnel*
Edit Asst: Joanna Bradley *Tel:* 615-340-7256 *E-mail:* jbradley@gbod.org
Founded: 2009
Nonprofit publisher of religious materials.
ISBN Prefix(es): 978-1-935205
Number of titles published annually: 4 Print
Total Titles: 7 Print; 2 E-Book
*Returns:* PBD Worldwide Fulfillment Services, Discipleship Resources, Upper Rm, Return Door 16, 1650 Bluegrass Lakes Pkwy, Alpharetta, GA 30004
*Warehouse:* PBD Worldwide Fulfillment Services, 1650 Bluegrass Lakes Pkwy, Alpharetta, GA 30004 *Tel:* 770-442-8633 *Fax:* 770-442-9742
*Distribution Center:* PBD Worldwide Fulfillment Services, 1650 Bluegrass Lakes Pkwy, Alpharetta, GA 30004

**Friends United Press**
Subsidiary of Friends United Meeting
101 Quaker Hill Dr, Richmond, IN 47374
SAN: 201-5803
*Tel:* 765-962-7573 *Toll Free Tel:* 800-537-8839 *Fax:* 765-966-1293
*E-mail:* friendspress@fum.org
*Web Site:* www.fum.org/shop
*Key Personnel*
Communs Ed: Katie Terrell Wonsik *E-mail:* katiet@fum.org
Founded: 1969
Paperbound books; religion (Society of Friends-Friends United Meeting).
ISBN Prefix(es): 978-0-913408; 978-0-944350
Number of titles published annually: 2 Print; 2 Online
Total Titles: 81 Print; 67 Online
Membership(s): IBPA, the Independent Book Publishers Association; Protestant Church-Owned Publishers Association; Quakers Uniting in Publications

**Frog Books**
Imprint of North Atlantic Books
2526 Martin Luther King Jr Way, Berkeley, CA 94704
Mailing Address: PO Box 12327, Berkeley, CA 94712
*Tel:* 510-549-4270 *Toll Free Tel:* 800-733-3000 (book orders only) *Fax:* 510-549-4276 *Toll Free Fax:* 800-659-2436 (orders)
*E-mail:* orders@northatlanticbooks.com
*Web Site:* www.northatlanticbooks.com
*Key Personnel*
CEO & Publr: Richard Grossinger *E-mail:* chard@lmi.net
Assoc Publr & Mng Dir: Doug Reil *Tel:* 510-549-4270 ext 29
Art Dir: Paula Morrison
Gen Mgr & Accts Payable: Ed Angel
Dist & Mktg Lead: Drew Cavenaugh *Tel:* 510-549-4270 ext 18 *E-mail:* dcavenaugh@northatlanticbooks.com
Foreign Rts Mgr: Sarah Serafimidis *Tel:* 510-549-4270 ext 16 *E-mail:* sserafimidis@northatlanticbooks.com
Founded: 1993
Internal martial arts, alternative medicine, somatic psychology, sports, science, women's topics, psychology, political/current affairs, Buddhism, gay & lesbian, environmental, art books (if bought direct), sustainable development, ecology, parenting, popular culture, body work, literary nonfiction, memoir, biography & children's picture books.
ISBN Prefix(es): 978-1-883319; 978-1-58394
Number of titles published annually: 33 Print
Total Titles: 200 Print; 7 E-Book
Distributed by North Atlantic Books
Foreign Rep(s): Airlift Books (Europe, UK); PGW (Canada); John Reed (Australia); Tuttle-Mori Agency (Japan)
Foreign Rights: Eliane Benisti (France); Hagenbach & Bender (Germany); Karin Schindler (Brazil)
*Orders to:* Publishers Group West, 1170 Trademark Dr, Reno, NV 89511
*Returns:* Publishers Group West, 7326 Winton Dr, Indianapolis, IN 46268 *Toll Free Tel:* 800-788-3123 *Fax:* 775-850-2501 *E-mail:* cole.mclachlan@pgw.com; Publishers Group West, 1170 Trademark Dr, Reno, NV 89511

*Shipping Address:* Publisher's Group West, Distribution Ctr, 5045 W 79 St, Indianapolis, IN 46268
*Distribution Center:* Publishers Group West, 1170 Trademark Dr, Reno, NV 89511
Membership(s): Northern California Book Publicity & Marketing Association

**Front Street**
Imprint of Boyds Mills Press
815 Church St, Honesdale, PA 18431
*Tel:* 570-253-1164 *Toll Free Tel:* 800-490-5111
*E-mail:* contact@boydsmillspress.com
*Web Site:* www.frontstreetbooks.com
*Key Personnel*
VP & Edit Dir, Boyds Mills Press: Mary-Alice Moore
Founded: 1994
ISBN Prefix(es): 978-1-886910; 978-1-932425; 978-1-59078
Number of titles published annually: 15 Print
Total Titles: 80 Print
Distributed by Boyds Mills Press
Foreign Rights: Ombretta Borgia Presenza (Italy); Laura Cecil Literary Agency (England); Japan UNI Agency Inc (Japan); Korea Copyright Center Inc (KCC) (Korea)
Membership(s): ALA; Children's Book Council

**Fugue State Press**
PO Box 80, Cooper Sta, New York, NY 10276
*E-mail:* info@fuguestatepress.com
*Web Site:* www.fuguestatepress.com
Founded: 1992
Ambitious innovative novels of a high literary quality.
ISBN Prefix(es): 978-1-879193
Number of titles published annually: 3 Print
Total Titles: 23 Print
Distributed by Small Press Distribution (SPD)

**Fulcrum Publishing Inc**
4690 Table Mountain Dr, Suite 100, Golden, CO 80403
SAN: 200-2825
*Tel:* 303-277-1623 *Toll Free Tel:* 800-992-2908 *Fax:* 303-279-7111 *Toll Free Fax:* 800-726-7112
*E-mail:* info@fulcrumbooks.com; orders@fulcrumbooks.com
*Web Site:* www.fulcrumbooks.com
*Key Personnel*
Publr: Sam Scinta
Ed & Prodn Mgr: Haley Berry
Ed: Carolyn Sobczak
Founded: 1984
Nonfiction trade: Western culture & history, Native American culture & history, environment & nature, popular culture, lifestyle, outdoor recreation, public policy & gardening.
ISBN Prefix(es): 978-1-55591; 978-0-9725776 (Speck Press); 978-1-933108 (Speck Press)
Number of titles published annually: 40 Print
Total Titles: 450 Print; 250 E-Book; 5 Audio
Imprints: Speaker's Corner (public policy series)
*Distribution Center:* Consortium Book Sales & Distribution, The Keg House, 34 13 Ave NE, Suite 101, Minneapolis, MN 55413-1007, Contact: Jim Nichols *Tel:* 612-746-2600 *Fax:* 612-746-2606 *E-mail:* info@cbsd.com *Web Site:* www.cbsd.com
Membership(s): AAP; ABA; Midwest Independent Booksellers Association; Mountains & Plains Independent Booksellers Association; Pacific Northwest Booksellers Association; Publishers Association of the West

**FurnitureCore**
1385 Peachtree St NE, Suite 310, Atlanta, GA 30309
*Tel:* 404-961-3764 *Fax:* 404-961-3749
*E-mail:* info@furniturecore.com
*Web Site:* www.furniturecore.com
*Key Personnel*
Owner & Pres: Bob George
Founded: 1985 (acquired in 2008)
Specializes in business, industry & statistical reports.
ISBN Prefix(es): 978-0-921577; 978-1-894330; 978-1-894960
Number of titles published annually: 12 Print; 10 Online
Total Titles: 56 Print; 30 Online
Distributor for AMA Research; Business & Research Associates

**§Future Horizons Inc**
721 W Abram St, Arlington, TX 76013
*Tel:* 817-277-0727 *Toll Free Tel:* 800-489-0727 *Fax:* 817-277-2270
*E-mail:* info@fhautism.com
*Web Site:* www.fhautism.com
*Key Personnel*
Pres: R Wayne Gilpin
Founded: 1996
Resources on Autism/Asperger's Syndrome, including books, video tapes, DVDs, magazines & conferences.
ISBN Prefix(es): 978-1-885477; 978-1-932565; 978-1-935274
Number of titles published annually: 6 Print
Total Titles: 10 Print

**Gagosian Gallery**
980 Madison Ave, New York, NY 10075
*Tel:* 212-744-2313 *Fax:* 212-772-7962
*E-mail:* newyork@gagosian.com
*Web Site:* www.gagosian.com
Founded: 1989
Publish fine editions & illustrated books on contemporary & modern art.
ISBN Prefix(es): 978-1-880154
Number of titles published annually: 10 Print
Total Titles: 40 Print
*Branch Office(s)*
456 N Camden Dr, Beverly Hills, CA 90210 *Tel:* 310-271-9400 *Fax:* 310-271-9420

**Galaxy Press**
7051 Hollywood Blvd, Suite 200, Hollywood, CA 90028
SAN: 254-6906
*Tel:* 323-466-7815 *Toll Free Tel:* 877-8GALAXY (842-5299)
*E-mail:* customers@galaxypress.com
*Web Site:* www.galaxypress.com
*Key Personnel*
Pres & Publr: John Goodwin *Tel:* 323-466-7812 *E-mail:* jgoodwin@galaxypress.com
SVP, Opers: Kim Catalano *Tel:* 323-466-7815 ext 145 *E-mail:* kcatalano@galaxypress.com
Founded: 2002
Publisher of the fiction works of L Ron Hubbard.
ISBN Prefix(es): 978-1-59212
Number of titles published annually: 13 Print; 14 E-Book; 14 Audio
Total Titles: 60 Print; 50 E-Book; 40 Audio
Imprints: Galaxy Audio; Galaxy Music
*Returns:* 6121 Malburg Way, Vernon, CA 90058 *Tel:* 323-588-8777
*Warehouse:* 6121 Malburg Way, Vernon, CA 90058 *Tel:* 323-588-8777
*Distribution Center:* 6121 Malburg Way, Vernon, CA 90058 *Tel:* 323-588-8777

**Galde Press Inc**
PO Box 460, Lakeville, MN 55044
*Tel:* 952-891-5991 *Toll Free Tel:* 800-777-3454 *Fax:* 952-891-6091
*Web Site:* www.galdepress.com
*Key Personnel*
Owner & Publr: Phyllis Galde *E-mail:* phyllis@galdepress.com
Founded: 1991
Independent publisher of books on a variety of subjects & have over 100 titles in print.
ISBN Prefix(es): 978-1-880090; 978-1-931942
Number of titles published annually: 11 Print
Total Titles: 108 Print

**§Gale**
Unit of Cengage Learning
27500 Drake Rd, Farmington Hills, MI 48331-3535
SAN: 213-4373
*Tel:* 248-699-4253 *Toll Free Tel:* 800-877-4253 *Fax:* 248-699-8049 *Toll Free Fax:* 800-414-5043 (orders)
*E-mail:* gale.salesassistance@cengage.com
*Web Site:* www.gale.cengage.com
*Key Personnel*
EVP & Publr: Frank Menchaca
SVP, Mktg: Mr Nader Qaimari
Founded: 1954
Gale, part of Cengage Learning, serves the world's information & education needs through its vast & dynamic content pools, which are used by students & consumers in their libraries, schools & on the Internet. It is best known for the accuracy, breadth & convenience of its data, addressing all types of information needs – from homework help to health questions to business profiles – in a variety of formats.
ISBN Prefix(es): 978-0-8103; 978-0-7876; 978-3-598; 978-0-02-865; 978-0-684-806
Number of titles published annually: 50 Print
Imprints: Christian Large Print; Five Star™; Greenhaven Press®; KidHaven Press™; Large Print Press™; Lucent Books®; Macmillan Reference USA™; Primary Source Media™; St James Press®; Schirmer Reference™; Scholarly Resources Inc; Charles Scribner's Sons®; The TAFT Group®; Thorndike Press®; Twayne Publishers™; U X L™; Wheeler Publishing™
*Branch Office(s)*
10 Davis Dr, Belmont, CA 94002 *Tel:* 650-595-2350
*Distribution Center:* 10650 Toebben Dr, Independence, KY 41051
*See separate listing for:*
**Charles Scribner's Sons®**
**Greenhaven Press®**
**Lucent Books®**
**Macmillan Reference USA™**
**St James Press®**
**Thorndike Press®**
**Twayne Publishers™**

**§Galen Press Ltd**
PO Box 64400, Tucson, AZ 85728-4400
*Tel:* 520-577-8363 *Fax:* 520-529-6459
*E-mail:* sales@galenpress.com
*Web Site:* www.galenpress.com
*Key Personnel*
Owner & Publr: Mary Lou Iserson
VP, Mktg & Spec Sales: Mary Lou Sherk *E-mail:* ml@galenpress.com
Ed-in-Chief: Jennifer G Gilbert *E-mail:* jennifer@galenpress.com
Founded: 1993
Publish non-clinical health related books in medical education, death & dying & bioethics.
ISBN Prefix(es): 978-1-883620
Number of titles published annually: 2 Print; 1 CD-ROM; 3 E-Book
Total Titles: 32 Print; 1 CD-ROM; 6 E-Book
Membership(s): The Association of Publishers for Special Sales

**§Gallaudet University Press**
800 Florida Ave NE, Washington, DC 20002-3695
SAN: 205-261X
*Tel:* 202-651-5488 *Fax:* 202-651-5489
*E-mail:* gupress@gallaudet.edu
*Web Site:* gupress.gallaudet.edu

*Key Personnel*
Exec Dir: Gary Aller
Edit Dir: Ivey P Wallace
Asst Dir: Dan Wallace
Founded: 1980
Reference books, scholarly, educational & general interest books on deaf studies, deaf culture & issues, sign language textbooks.
ISBN Prefix(es): 978-0-913580; 978-0-930323; 978-1-56368
Number of titles published annually: 16 Print
Total Titles: 300 Print; 4 CD-ROM
Distributor for Signum Verlag
*Warehouse:* Chicago Distribution Ctr, 11030 S Langley Ave, Chicago, IL 60628, Karen Hyzy *Toll Free Tel:* 800-621-2736; 800-630-9347 *Fax:* 773-702-7212 *Toll Free Fax:* 800-621-8476
Membership(s): American Association of University Presses

**Gallery Books**
Imprint of Gallery Publishing Group
1230 Avenue of the Americas, New York, NY 10020
*Toll Free Tel:* 800-456-6798 *Fax:* 212-698-7284
*E-mail:* consumer.customerservice@simonandschuster.com
*Web Site:* www.simonsays.com
*Key Personnel*
Pres: Louise Burke
VP & Publr, Gallery Books: Jennifer Bergstrom
VP & Assoc Publr: Michele Martin
Ed-at-Large, Gallery Books: Tricia Boczkowski
VP & Sr Ed, Pocket Books, Gallery Books & Threshold Editions: Mitchell Ivers
VP & Dir, Publicity, Pocket Books, Gallery Books & Threshold Editions: Jennifer Robinson
VP & Dir, Rts, Pocket Books & Gallery Books: Paul O'Halloran
Exec Ed, Pocket Books & Gallery Books, Ed Dir, Pocket Star: Lauren McKenna
Exec Ed, Pocket Books & Gallery Books: Karen Kosztolnyik
Sr Ed, Pocket Books & Gallery Books: Micki Nuding
Sr Ed, Gallery Books: Jeremie Ruby-Strauss
Sr Ed, Media, Pocket Books & Gallery Books: Edward Schlesinger
Sr Ed, Pocket Books, Gallery Books & Threshold Editions: Abby Zidle
Ed, Pocket Books & Gallery Books: Adam Wilson
Mng Ed, Pocket Books, Gallery Books & Threshold Editions: Kevin McCahill
Publg Mgr, Pocket Books, Gallery Books & Threshold Editions: Brigitte Smith
Dir, Publicity, Pocket Books, Gallery Books & Threshold Editions: Jean Anne Rose
Deputy Dir, Rts, Threshold Editions: Marie Florio
Sr Art Dir, Pocket Books, Gallery Books & Threshold Editions: Lisa Litwack
Dir, Mktg: Elizabeth Psaltis
Mktg Mgr, Gallery Books & Threshold Editions: Natalie Ebel
Online Mktg Mgr, Gallery Books: Ellen Chan
Founded: 1939
Trade paperbacks & hardcovers; mass market, reprints & originals.
ISBN Prefix(es): 978-0-671; 978-0-7434; 978-1-4165
Imprints: Downtown Press; G-unit; Karen Hunter Publishing; MTV Books; Pocket Star; Pocket Books Trade Paperback; Star Trek®; Threshold Editions; VH-1; World Wrestling Entertainment
Foreign Rights: Antonella Antonelli Agenzia (Italy); Arts & Licensing International (Mainland China, Taiwan); Book Publishers Association of Israel (Israel); Japan UNI Agency (Japan); JLM Literary Agency (Greece); Nurcihan Kesim Literary Agency Inc (Turkey); Mohrbooks Literary Agency (Germany); La Nouvelle Agence (France); Andrew Nurnberg Associates (Bulgaria, Croatia, Czech Republic, Estonia, Hungary, Latvia, Lithuania, Montenegro, Poland, Romania, Russia, Serbia, Slovakia, Slovenia); Sane Toregard Agency (Denmark, Finland, Iceland, Norway, Sweden); Sebes & Van Gelderen Literary Agency (Netherlands); Tuttle-Mori Agency Inc (Thailand); Eric Yang Agency (Korea)

**§Gallopade International Inc**
611 Hwy 74 S, Suite 2000, Peachtree City, GA 30269
SAN: 213-8441
Mailing Address: PO Box 2779, Peachtree City, GA 30269
*Tel:* 770-631-4222 *Toll Free Tel:* 800-536-2GET (536-2438) *Fax:* 770-631-4810 *Toll Free Fax:* 800-871-2979
*E-mail:* customerservice@gallopade.com
*Web Site:* www.gallopade.com
*Key Personnel*
CEO: Carole Marsh *E-mail:* carole@gallopade.com
Pres & Intl Rts: Michele Yother *E-mail:* michele@gallopade.com
VP: Michael Longmeyer *E-mail:* michael@gallopade.com
Founded: 1979
"State stuff" for all 50 states including activity books, games, maps, posters, stickies, etc. Subjects include travel, regional, school travel supply, home school, juvenile mysteries, human sex education, multicultural, preschool through adult.
ISBN Prefix(es): 978-0-935326; 978-1-55609; 978-0-7933; 978-0-635
Number of titles published annually: 500 Print; 50 CD-ROM; 200 Online; 200 E-Book
Total Titles: 15,000 Print; 200 CD-ROM; 10,050 Online; 10,050 E-Book; 13 Audio
Imprints: American Milestones; A Bio To Grow On; Black Jazz Pizzazz & Razzmatazz; The Day That Was Different; Here & Now; Heroes & Helpers; Carole Marsh Books; Carole Marsh Mysteries; New Traditions; 1000 Readers; Smart Sex Stuff for Kids; State Experience; State Stuff
Subsidiaries: Six House; The World's Largest Publishing Co
Membership(s): National School Supply & Equipment Association

**Gareth Stevens Publishing**
111 E 14 St, Suite 349, New York, NY 10003
Mailing Address: PO Box 29088, New York, NY 10087-9088
*Toll Free Tel:* 800-542-2595 *Toll Free Fax:* 877-542-2596 (cust serv)
*E-mail:* customerservice@gspub.com
*Web Site:* www.garethstevens.com
Founded: 1983
ISBN Prefix(es): 978-0-918831; 978-1-55532; 978-0-8368
Number of titles published annually: 400 Print
Total Titles: 1,500 Print
Divisions: AmericanKids Preview; American Library Preview; Books & Libros; Library One Direct; World Reference Resources; Young Adult Resources
*Returns:* c/o Maple Press Distribution Ctr, 60 Grumbacher Rd, York, PA 17406

**§Garland Science Publishing**
Member of The Taylor & Francis Group
711 Third Ave, 8th fl, New York, NY 10017
*Tel:* 212-216-7800 *Fax:* 212-281-4487
*E-mail:* science@garland.com
*Web Site:* www.garlandscience.com
*Key Personnel*
Pres, Taylor & Francis US: Emmett Dages
VP, Sales, Taylor & Francis US: Dennis Weiss
VP, Garland Science: Denise Schanck *E-mail:* denise.schanck@taylorandfrancis.com
Founded: 1969
Textbooks & professional books in biology & chemistry.
ISBN Prefix(es): 978-0-8153; 978-1-5603
Number of titles published annually: 50 Print; 4 CD-ROM; 30 E-Book
Total Titles: 50 Print; 4 CD-ROM; 30 E-Book
*Branch Office(s)*
4133 Whitney Ave, Hamden, CT 06578 *Tel:* 203-281-4487 *Toll Free Tel:* 800-627-6273 *Fax:* 203-230-1186
*Warehouse:* Taylor & Francis/Garland, 7625 Empire Dr, Florence, KY 41042 *Toll Free Tel:* 800-634-7064 *Toll Free Fax:* 800-248-4724
*Web Site:* www.garlandscience.com

**§Garrett Publishing Inc**
800 Fairway Dr, Suite 340, Deerfield Beach, FL 33441
*Tel:* 561-953-1322 *Fax:* 561-953-1940
*Key Personnel*
Pres: Hillel Presser
Exec Admin Asst: Katie Erenati
Founded: 1990
Business & finance books for the lay person & professional.
ISBN Prefix(es): 978-1-880539
Number of titles published annually: 5 Print; 2 E-Book
Total Titles: 40 Print
Foreign Rights: Singer Media Corp

**Gateways Books & Tapes**
Division of Institute for the Development of the Harmonious Human Being Inc
PO Box 370, Nevada City, CA 95959-0370
SAN: 211-3635
*Tel:* 530-271-2239 *Toll Free Tel:* 800-869-0658 *Fax:* 530-272-0184
*E-mail:* info@gatewaysbooksandtapes.com
*Web Site:* www.gatewaysbooksandtapes.com; www.retrosf.com (Retro Science Fiction Imprint)
*Key Personnel*
Sr Ed & Intl Rts: Iven Lourie *E-mail:* ilourie@oro.net
Founded: 1971
Trade & fine art book publisher. Categories include psychology, spirituality, metaphysics, Judaica, science fiction & limited editions.
ISBN Prefix(es): 978-0-89556
Number of titles published annually: 6 Print; 4 CD-ROM; 4 Audio
Total Titles: 35 Print; 8 CD-ROM; 300 Audio
Imprints: Artemis Books (2 titles); Consciousness Classics; Retro Science Fiction
Distributor for Cloister Recordings (audio & video tapes)

**Gault Millau Inc/Gayot Publications**
4311 Wilshire Blvd, Suite 405, Los Angeles, CA 90010
*Tel:* 323-965-3529 *Fax:* 323-936-2883
*E-mail:* info@gayot.com
*Web Site:* www.gayot.com
*Key Personnel*
Pres: Andre Gayot
Publr & Ed-in-Chief: Alain Gayot
Founded: 1986
Publish travel guides to world destinations with a rating system to the best hotels, restaurants & shops.
ISBN Prefix(es): 978-1-881066
Number of titles published annually: 12 Print
Total Titles: 16 Print; 5 E-Book
Imprints: Gault Millau; GAYOT
Subsidiaries: Tastes Newsletter
Divisions: The Food Paper
Distributed by Publishers Group West

**Gauthier Publications Inc**
PO Box 806241, St Clair Shores, MI 48080
SAN: 857-2119
*Tel:* 313-458-7141 *Fax:* 586-279-1515
*E-mail:* info@gauthierpublications.com
*Web Site:* www.gauthierpublications.com
*Key Personnel*
CEO: Daniel J Gauthier *E-mail:* daniel@gauthierpublications.com
Creative Dir: Elizabeth Gauthier *E-mail:* elizabeth@gauthierpublications.com
Founded: 2008
Devoted to printing high quality literary work. Our mission is simple, to introduce reading early & help promote a lifetime love for the written word by putting out captivating & unique titles that are tailored to their audience. We are proud to say all of our books are printed & bound in the USA & our Hungry Goat Press line is made with 100% post consumer recycled paper because we think a good book means more than an exciting plot-line. Distribution also by Amazon & BWI.
ISBN Prefix(es): 978-0-9820812; 978-0-9833593
Number of titles published annually: 8 Print
Total Titles: 10 Print
Imprints: DragonFish Comics (graphic novels); Frog Legs Ink (children's books); Hungry Goat Press (young adult books)
*Distribution Center:* Follett, 1340 Ridgeview Dr, McHenry, IL 60050 SAN: 169-1902
Diamond, 1966 Greenspring Dr, Suite 300, Timonium, MD 21093 *Toll Free Tel:* 800-452-6642
Membership(s): ABA

**Gefen Books**
11 Edison Place, Springfield, NJ 07081
*Tel:* 516-593-1234 *Toll Free Tel:* 800-477-5257 *Fax:* 516-295-2739
*E-mail:* info@gefenpublishing.com; gefenny@gefenpublishing.com
*Web Site:* www.israelbooks.com
*Key Personnel*
Publr: Ilan Greenfield *Tel:* (02) 538-0247 *Fax:* (02) 538-8423 *E-mail:* ilan@gefenpublishing.com
Sales Mgr: Maury Storch
Founded: 1981
General interest, mainly books from Israel. Specialize in Judaic interest, Israel, art, Holocaust & Jewish history. Can supply any books published in Israel &/or in the Hebrew language.
ISBN Prefix(es): 978-965-229
Number of titles published annually: 25 Print
Total Titles: 425 Print; 400 Online; 400 E-Book
Imprints: Gefen Publishing Ltd
Subsidiaries: IsraBook
Divisions: Medical Publishing (Gefen)
*Foreign Office(s):* Gefen Publishing House Ltd, 6 Hatzvi St, 94386 Jerusalem, Israel
Distributor for Bar Ilan; Magnes Press

**Gem Guides Book Co**
1275 W Ninth St, Upland, CA 91786
*Tel:* 626-855-1611 *Toll Free Tel:* 800-824-5118 (orders) *Fax:* 626-855-1610
*E-mail:* info@gemguidesbooks.com
*Web Site:* www.gemguidesbooks.com
*Key Personnel*
Mgr, Opers & Ed: Greg Warner
Off Mgr: Nannette Becerra
Sales: Michael Moran
Edit Asst: Nancy Fox
Founded: 1965
Publisher & distributor of regional & specialty trade books; rocks, minerals, crystals, Old West, western & southwestern region & local interests.
ISBN Prefix(es): 978-0-935182; 978-1-889786
Number of titles published annually: 7 Print
Total Titles: 80 Print
Imprints: Gembooks
Distributed by Nevada Publications
Distributor for Borden Publishing; Brynmorgen Press; Clear Creek Publishing; Earth Love Publishing; Editions du Signe; Gemstone Press; Golden West Books; Grand Canyon Association; Heaven & Earth Press; Hexagon Press; International Jewelry Publications; George R Jezek Photography; Cy Johnson & Son; KC Publications Inc; Many Moons Press; Naturegraph; Nevada Publications; Out of This World Press; Pinyon Publishing; Primer Publications; Ram Publishing; Recreation Sales; Shortfuse Press; Sierra Press; Delos Toole; Trees Co; Tri-Star Boze Books; Weseanne Publications
Membership(s): ABA; IBPA, the Independent Book Publishers Association; Northern California Independent Booksellers Association

**GemStone Press**
Division of Longhill Partners Inc
Sunset Farm Offices, Rte 4, Woodstock, VT 05091
SAN: 134-5621
Mailing Address: PO Box 237, Woodstock, VT 05091
*Tel:* 802-457-4000 *Toll Free Tel:* 800-962-4544 *Fax:* 802-457-4004
*E-mail:* sales@gemstonepress.com
*Web Site:* www.gemstonepress.com
*Key Personnel*
Pres & Publr: Stuart M Matlins
SVP, Fin & Admin: Amy Wilson
VP, Edit & Prodn: Emily Wichland *Fax:* 802-457-5032
Dir, Sales & Mktg Admin: Barbara Heise
Founded: 1987
Books on buying, enjoying, identifying & selling jewelry & gems for the consumer, collector, hobbyist, investor & jewelry trade.
ISBN Prefix(es): 978-0-943763
Number of titles published annually: 4 Print
Total Titles: 15 Print
Distributed by Bayard/Novalis (Canada); Gazelle (UK); Rainbow Book Agencies (Australia)
Foreign Rep(s): Gazelle (Europe, UK)
Foreign Rights: Andreas Brunner (Germany); The Deborah Harris Agency (Israel); International Editors' Co (Spain); A Korzhenevski (Russia); Andrew Nurnberg Associates Ltd (Hungary); Katia Schumer (Brazil); L Strakova Nurnberg Associates (Czech Republic); Susanna Zevi Agenzia Letteraria (Italy)
*Returns:* 28 River St, Windsor, VT 05089

**§Genealogical Publishing Co**
Subsidiary of Genealogical.com
3600 Clipper Mill Rd, Suite 260, Baltimore, MD 21211
*Tel:* 410-837-8271 *Toll Free Tel:* 800-296-6687 *Fax:* 410-752-8492
*Web Site:* www.genealogical.com
*Key Personnel*
VP & Ed-in-Chief: Michael Tepper *E-mail:* mtepper@genealogical.com
Mktg Dir: Joe Garonzik *E-mail:* jgaronzi@genealogical.com
Mgr, Book Dept: Roger Sherr *E-mail:* rsherr@genealogical.com
Founded: 1959
Genealogy, local history, immigration history & source records. Products are non-returnable, unless mis-shiped or damaged in shipment.
ISBN Prefix(es): 978-0-8063
Number of titles published annually: 50 Print; 5 CD-ROM
Total Titles: 352 Print; 84 CD-ROM
Subsidiaries: Clearfield Co Inc
*See separate listing for:*
**Clearfield Co Inc**

**Genesis Press Inc**
PO Box 101, Columbus, MS 39701
*Toll Free Tel:* 888-463-4461 (orders only)
*Web Site:* www.genesis-press.com
*Key Personnel*
Owner & Pres: Wilbur O Colom
Off Mgr: Diane Blair
Founded: 1993
Privately owned African-American book publisher.
ISBN Prefix(es): 978-1-885478; 978-1-58571
Number of titles published annually: 26 Print
Total Titles: 160 Print
Imprints: Black Coral; INDIGO; Indigo Love Spectrum; Indigo Vibe; Mt Blue; Obsidian; Sage Books
Membership(s): AAP

**Geological Society of America (GSA)**
3300 Penrose Place, Boulder, CO 80301-1806
SAN: 201-5978
Mailing Address: PO Box 9140, Boulder, CO 80301-9140
*Tel:* 303-357-1000 *Fax:* 303-357-1070
*E-mail:* pubs@geosociety.org (prodn); editing@geosociety.org (edit)
*Web Site:* www.geosociety.org
*Key Personnel*
Exec Dir: John W Hess *Tel:* 303-357-1039 *E-mail:* jhess@geosociety.org
Ad Mgr: Ann H Crawford *Tel:* 303-357-1053 *E-mail:* acrawford@geosociety.org
Founded: 1888
General earth sciences, cover such areas as geology, economic geology, engineering geology, geochemistry, geomorphology, marine geology, mineralogy, paleontology, petrology, seismology, solid earth geophysics, structural geology, tectonics & environmental geology.
ISBN Prefix(es): 978-0-8137
Number of titles published annually: 9 Print
Total Titles: 200 Print
*Branch Office(s)*
1200 New York Ave NW, Suite 400, Washington, DC 20005, Dir, Geoscience Policy: Kasey White *Tel:* 202-669-0466 *E-mail:* kwhite@geosociety.org
Foreign Rep(s): Geological Society of London (UK)

**§Geolytics Inc**
28 Brunswick Wood Dr, East Brunswick, NJ 08816
Mailing Address: PO Box 10, East Brunswick, NJ 08816
*Tel:* 732-651-2000 *Toll Free Tel:* 800-577-6717 *Fax:* 732-651-2721
*E-mail:* support@geolytics.com; questions@geolytics.com
*Web Site:* www.geolytics.com
*Key Personnel*
Mktg Dir: Katia Segre Cohen
Founded: 1987
Provider of census, demographic & geographic data for academic & business researchers.
ISBN Prefix(es): 978-1-892445
Number of titles published annually: 4 Print; 4 CD-ROM
Total Titles: 22 Print; 22 CD-ROM

**Georgetown University Press**
3240 Prospect St NW, Suite 250, Washington, DC 20007
*Tel:* 202-687-5889 (busn) *Toll Free Tel:* 800-537-5487 *Fax:* 202-687-6340 (edit)
*E-mail:* gupress@georgetown.edu
*Web Site:* press.georgetown.edu
*Key Personnel*
Dir & Acqs: Richard Brown, PhD *Tel:* 202-687-5912 *E-mail:* reb7@georgetown.edu
Mktg & Sales Dir: John W Warren
Busn Mgr: Ioan Suciu *Tel:* 202-687-5641 *E-mail:* suciui@georgetown.edu
Edit & Prodn Mgr: Deborah Weiner *Tel:* 202-687-6251 *E-mail:* weinerd@georgetown.edu

Languages, Linguistics Acqs & Dir, Georgetown Languages: Hope LeGro *Tel:* 202-687-4704 *E-mail:* hjs6@georgetown.edu
Intl Aff, Public Policy & Public Mgmt Acqs Ed: Donald Jacobs *Tel:* 202-687-5218 *E-mail:* dpj5@georgetown.edu
Intellectual Property Mgr: Laura Leichum *Tel:* 202-687-7687 *E-mail:* lal75@georgetown.edu
Founded: 1966
Bioethics; international affairs & human rights; languages & linguistics; political science, public policy & public management; religion & ethics.
ISBN Prefix(es): 978-0-87840; 978-1-58901
Number of titles published annually: 40 Print; 2 Audio
Total Titles: 500 Print; 9 Audio
*Orders to:* Hopkins Fulfillment Service, PO Box 50370, Baltimore, MD 21211-4370 *Toll Free Tel:* 800-537-5487 *Fax:* 410-516-6998 *E-mail:* hfscustserv@press.jhu.edu
*Returns:* Hopkins Fulfillment Service, c/o Maple Press, Lebanon Distribution Ctr, 704 Legionaire Dr, Fredericksburg, PA 17026
*Warehouse:* c/o Maple Press Co, Lebanon Distribution Ctr, 704 Legionaire Dr, Fredericksburg, PA 17026

**Gestalt Journal Press**
PO Box 278, Gouldsboro, ME 04607-0278
*Tel:* 207-963-7064 *Toll Free Fax:* 866-460-8795
*E-mail:* press@gestalt.org
*Web Site:* www.gestaltjournalpress.com
Founded: 1977
Mental health, gestalt therapy specifically.
ISBN Prefix(es): 978-0-939266
Number of titles published annually: 3 Print; 10 E-Book
Total Titles: 41 Print; 2 CD-ROM; 20 E-Book; 4 Audio

**§Getty Publications**
1200 Getty Center Dr, Suite 500, Los Angeles, CA 90049-1682
SAN: 208-2276
*Tel:* 310-440-7365 *Toll Free Tel:* 800-223-3431 (orders) *Fax:* 310-440-7758
*E-mail:* pubsinfo@getty.edu
*Web Site:* www.getty.edu/publications
*Key Personnel*
Publr: Kara Kirk *Tel:* 310-440-6066 *E-mail:* kkirk@getty.edu
Gen Mgr: Carolyn Simmons *Tel:* 310-440-7130 *E-mail:* csimmons@getty.edu
Rts Mgr: Leslie Rollins *Tel:* 310-440-7102 *E-mail:* lrollins@getty.edu
Ed-in-Chief: Robert T Flynn *Tel:* 310-440-6486 *E-mail:* rflynn@getty.edu
Founded: 1982
Produces a wide variety of books in the fields of art, photography, archaeology, architecture, conservation & the humanities for both general & specialized audiences. These award-winning publications complement & often result from the work of the J Paul Getty Museum, the Getty Conservation Institute & the Getty Research Institute. Publications include illustrated exhibition catalogues, illustrated works on single artists & art history, works on cultural history, scholarly monographs, critical editions of translated works, comprehensive studies of the Getty's collections, educational books to interest children of all ages in art & gift books.
ISBN Prefix(es): 978-0-89236; 978-1-60606
Number of titles published annually: 50 Print; 1 Online
Total Titles: 434 Print; 3 CD-ROM; 1 Online
Distributed by University of Chicago Press (US only)
Foreign Rep(s): Canadian Manda Group (Canada); EWEB (Asia, Pacific Rim); Roundhouse Group (Europe, UK)
Membership(s): AAP; Association of American University Presses; CAA; International Association of Museum Publishers; International Association of Scholarly Publishers; International Group of Publishing Libraries; Society for Scholarly Publishing

**GIA Publications Inc**
7404 S Mason Ave, Chicago, IL 60638
*Tel:* 708-496-3800 *Toll Free Tel:* 800-GIA-1358 (442-1358) *Fax:* 708-496-3828
*E-mail:* custserv@giamusic.com
*Web Site:* www.giamusic.com
*Key Personnel*
COO & Pres: Alec Harris *E-mail:* alech@giamusic.com
Founded: 1941
Publish sacred choral music, hymnals, books & recordings. Also publish music education materials.
ISBN Prefix(es): 978-0-941050; 978-1-57999
Number of titles published annually: 200 Print
Total Titles: 6,000 Print; 250 Audio

**Gibbs Smith Publisher**
1877 E Gentile St, Layton, UT 84041
Mailing Address: PO Box 667, Layton, UT 84041-0667 SAN: 201-9906
*Tel:* 801-544-9800 *Toll Free Tel:* 800-748-5439; 800-835-4993 (orders) *Fax:* 801-544-5582 *Toll Free Fax:* 800-213-3023 (orders only)
*E-mail:* info@gibbs-smith.com
*Web Site:* www.gibbs-smith.com
*Key Personnel*
Dir, Mktg & PR: Dan Moench *Tel:* 801-544-9800 ext 156 *E-mail:* dan.moench@gibbs-smith.com
Founded: 1969
ISBN Prefix(es): 978-0-87905; 978-1-58685
Number of titles published annually: 50 Print; 50 Online
Total Titles: 350 Print; 200 Online
Imprints: Ancient City Press; Wyrick & Co
Foreign Rep(s): Peribo (Australia, New Zealand); Publishers Group (Worldwide); Rain Coast (Canada)
*Returns:* 570 N Sportsplex Dr, Kaysville, UT 84037
*Shipping Address:* 570 N Sportsplex Dr, Kaysville, UT 84037
Membership(s): AAP

**Gifted Education Press**
10201 Yuma Ct, Manassas, VA 20109
Mailing Address: PO Box 1586, Manassas, VA 20109-1586
*Tel:* 703-369-5017
*Web Site:* www.giftededpress.com
*Key Personnel*
Publr & Dir: Maurice D Fisher *E-mail:* mfisher345@comcast.net
Founded: 1981
Books, quarterly newsletter, bimonthly newsletter, teaching guides & supplemental materials for students. Education of gifted children.
ISBN Prefix(es): 978-0-910609
Number of titles published annually: 10 Print
Total Titles: 80 Print

**Gival Press**
Imprint of Gival Press LLC
5200 N First St, Arlington, VA 22203
SAN: 852-0787
Mailing Address: PO Box 3812, Arlington, VA 22203 SAN: 852-0787
*Tel:* 703-351-0079 *Fax:* 703-351-0079
*E-mail:* givalpress@yahoo.com
*Web Site:* www.givalpress.com
*Key Personnel*
Publr & Ed: Robert L Giron
Founded: 1998
Small, independent literary press.
ISBN Prefix(es): 978-1-928589
Number of titles published annually: 5 Print; 1 E-Book
Total Titles: 56 Print; 15 E-Book
*Distribution Center:* Bookmasters, 30 Amberwood Pkwy, Ashland, OH 44805 *Tel:* 419-281-1802
Membership(s): AAP; The Association of Publishers for Special Sales; Council of Literary Magazines & Presses; IBPA, the Independent Book Publishers Association; Publishing Triangle

**Glenbridge Publishing Ltd**
19923 E Long Ave, Centennial, CO 80016-1969
SAN: 243-5403
*Tel:* 720-870-8381 *Toll Free Tel:* 800-986-4135 (orders) *Fax:* 720-230-1209
*E-mail:* glenbridge@qwestoffice.net
*Web Site:* www.glenbridgepublishing.com
*Key Personnel*
Pres & Intl Rts: Mary B Keene
VP & Ed: James A Keene
Founded: 1986
Publish nonfiction, hardcover originals, reprints & paperback originals.
ISBN Prefix(es): 978-0-944435
Number of titles published annually: 5 Print
Total Titles: 60 Print

**Peter Glenn Publications**
Division of Blount Communications
306 NE Second St, 2nd fl, Delray Beach, FL 33483
*Tel:* 561-404-4290 *Toll Free Tel:* 888-332-6700 *Fax:* 561-892-5786
*Web Site:* www.pgdirect.com
*Key Personnel*
CEO & Publr: Gregory James Blount *E-mail:* gjames@pgdirect.com
Dir: L Chip Brill; Umberto Guido, III
Ed: Todd Heustess
Founded: 1956
Directories for the world of advertising, TV & film publicity; directories & how-to books for performing arts, fashion & modeling industry.
ISBN Prefix(es): 978-0-87314
Number of titles published annually: 9 Print
Total Titles: 9 Print; 6 E-Book

**Glimmer Train Press Inc**
PO Box 80430, Portland, OR 97280
*Tel:* 503-221-0836 *Fax:* 503-221-0837
*E-mail:* editors@glimmertrain.org
*Web Site:* www.glimmertrain.org
*Key Personnel*
Co-Ed: Susan Burmeister-Brown *E-mail:* susan@glimmertrain.org; Linda Swanson-Davies *E-mail:* linda@glimmertrain.org
Founded: 1990
In addition to books, also publishes quarterly short story paperback.
ISBN Prefix(es): 978-1-880966; 978-1-59553
Number of titles published annually: 4 Print
Total Titles: 81 Print
Distributor for Glimmer Train Stories
Membership(s): Council of Literary Magazines & Presses

**Glitterati Inc**
322 W 57 St, No 19T, New York, NY 10019
*Tel:* 212-362-9119 *Fax:* 646-607-4433
*E-mail:* info@glitteratiincorporated.com
*Web Site:* glitteratiincorporated.com
*Key Personnel*
CEO & Pres: Martha Hallett *E-mail:* mhallett@glitteratiincorporated.com
Assoc Publr: Jessica Guerrero *E-mail:* jguerrero@glitteratiincorporated.com
Publicity Mgr: Mi Mi Chloe Park *E-mail:* mcpark@glitteratiincorporated.com
Foreign Rts: Peter Garlid *E-mail:* peter@glitteratiincorporated.com

Independent producer & publisher of distinctive in-on-paper products for domestic & international markets.
ISBN Prefix(es): 978-0-9721152; 978-0-9765851; 978-0-9777531; 978-0-9793384; 978-0-9801557; 978-0-9822669; 978-0-9823412; 978-0-9823799; 978-0-9832702
Number of titles published annually: 9 Print
Total Titles: 58 Print; 1 Audio

### Global Authors Publications (GAP)
38 Bluegrass, Middleberg, FL 32068
*Tel:* 904-425-1608
*E-mail:* gapbook@yahoo.com
*Key Personnel*
Publr: Kathleen Walls
Book Ed: Barbara Sachs Sloan
Founded: 2003
Offer complete subsidy publishing services & consider any genre except pornography or text books. Books must be at least 48 pages & not more than 700. We have set a literary standard with all the books we have published already & we do not plan to change our reputation. We won't publish everything that is offered us. Provide an affordable alternative to traditional publishing.
This publisher has indicated that 100% of their product line is author subsidized.
ISBN Prefix(es): 978-0-97
Number of titles published annually: 6 Print
Total Titles: 30 Print
Imprints: Flaming Magnolia

### Global Publishing, Sales & Distribution
980 Lincoln Ave, Suite 200-B, San Rafael, CA 94901
*Tel:* 415-456-2934 *Fax:* 415-456-4124
*Web Site:* www.globalpsd.com
*Key Personnel*
Publr: Adrianne Casey *E-mail:* adrianne@globalpsd.com; Steven Goff *E-mail:* steven@globalpsd.com
ISBN Prefix(es): 978-0-9819942
*Branch Office(s)*
140 E 38 St, New York, NY 10116 *Tel:* 212-627-1400 ext 2 *Toll Free Fax:* 866-729-2725
16510 203 Place NE, Woodinville, WA 98077 *Tel:* 425-354-3690 *Toll Free Fax:* 866-729-2725
*Foreign Office(s):* 8 Commercial Tower, 30/F, Unit 06-07, 8 Sun Yip St, Chai Wan, Hong Kong
Via Meucci 24, 37036 San Martino Buon Albergo, Verona, Italy *Tel:* (045) 994855 *Fax:* (045) 994746

### Global Training Center Inc
PO Box 221977, El Paso, TX 79913-4977
*Tel:* 915-534-7900 *Toll Free Tel:* 800-860-5030 *Fax:* 915-534-7903
*E-mail:* contact@globaltrainingcenter.com
*Web Site:* www.globaltrainingcenter.com
*Key Personnel*
Pres: Elsa Solorzano
Founded: 1992
Training seminar/workshops covering International Documentation, NAFTA, Importing, etc.
ISBN Prefix(es): 978-1-891249
Number of titles published annually: 23 Print
Total Titles: 23 Print

### The Globe Pequot Press
Division of Morris Book Publishing LLC
246 Goose Lane, Guilford, CT 06437
SAN: 201-9892
Mailing Address: PO Box 480, Guilford, CT 06437-0480
*Tel:* 203-458-4500 *Toll Free Tel:* 800-243-0495 (orders only); 888-249-7586 (cust serv) *Fax:* 203-458-4601 *Toll Free Fax:* 800-820-2329 (orders & cust serv)
*E-mail:* info@globepequot.com
*Web Site:* www.globepequot.com
*Key Personnel*
Pres & Publr: Jim Joseph
VP, Sales: Chris Grimm *Tel:* 203-458-4536 *E-mail:* chris.grimm@globepequot.com
Exec Dir, Edit: Janice Goldklang
Dir, Prodn: Kevin Lynch *Tel:* 203-458-4507 *E-mail:* kevin.lynch@globepequot.com
Dir, Subs Rts: Gail Blackhall *Tel:* 203-458-4540 *E-mail:* gail.blackhall@globepequot.com
Dir, Skirt!: Mary Norris *Tel:* 203-458-4520 *E-mail:* mary.norris@globepequot.com
Edit Dir: Steve Culpepper *Tel:* 203-458-4544 *E-mail:* steve.culpepper@globepequot.com
Mgr, Dist Busn: Andrea Jacobs *Tel:* 203-458-4552 *E-mail:* andrea.jacobs@globepequot.com
Exec Ed: Erin Turner *Tel:* 406-442-6597 *E-mail:* erin.turner@globepequot.com
Ed, Lyons Press: James Jayo
Founded: 1947
Travel guidebooks, regional books, sports, how-to, outdoor recreation, personal finance, self-help, sports, cooking, entertaining, military history, fishing, hunting, gift books.
ISBN Prefix(es): 978-0-937959; 978-1-56044; 978-1-57380; 978-1-57540; 978-1-882997; 978-0-87842; 978-0-87106; 978-0-7627; 978-0-89933; 978-1-898323 (Bradt); 978-0-934641; 978-1-56440; 978-1-84162 (Bradt); 978-0-912367; 978-0-933469; 978-0-934802; 978-0-934318; 978-1-57034; 978-1-58592; 978-1-901970 (Sawday)
Number of titles published annually: 500 Print; 500 E-Book
Total Titles: 2,800 Print; 1,000 E-Book
Imprints: Bradt Travel Guides; Thomas Cook Publishing; Falcon®; FalconGuides®; Footprint Guides; Fun with the Family; GPP® Life; Hoop Tales®; Insiders' Guides®; Knack™; The Lyons Press; Off The Beaten Path®; On My Mind Series; Outside America; PopOut®; Pro Tactics™; Recommended Country Inns®; Skirt!®; Stadium Stories; Three Forks®; TwoDot®
Distributor for Appalachian Mountain Club; Boone & Crockett Club; Bradt Travel Guides; Thomas Cook Publishing; D & B Publishing; Day Hikes Books Inc; Earthbound Sports; Everyman Chess; Explorer Publishing; Montana Historical Society Press; New Holland Publishers Ltd (London, UK); Alastair Sawday Publishing (co-publr); Stoecklein Publishing; Trailblazer Publications; Visit Britain; Waterford Press; Western Horseman; Woodall Publications
Foreign Rep(s): Canadian Manda Group (Canada); Windsor Publications International (UK); Woodslane NZ Ltd (New Zealand); Woodslane Party Ltd (Australia)
*Returns:* Globe Pequot Press Distribution Center, 128 Pinnacle Dr, Springfield, TN 37172, Dist Ctr Mgr: Mark Love *Tel:* 615-382-3983 *Toll Free Tel:* 800-955-3983 *Fax:* 615-382-6952 *E-mail:* mark.love@globepequot.com
*Distribution Center:* Globe Pequot Press Distribution Center, 128 Pinnacle Dr, Springfield, TN 37172, Dist Ctr Mgr: Mark Love *Tel:* 615-382-3983 *Toll Free Tel:* 800-955-3983 *Fax:* 615-382-6952 *E-mail:* mark.love@globepequot.com
Membership(s): AAP; ABA; BISG; NEBA
*See separate listing for:*
**The Lyons Press**

### David R Godine Publisher Inc
15 Court Sq, Suite 320, Boston, MA 02108-4715
SAN: 213-4381
*Tel:* 617-451-9600 *Fax:* 617-350-0250
*E-mail:* pub@godine.com
*Web Site:* www.godine.com
*Key Personnel*
Pres & Publr: David R Godine
Mktg & Subs Rts Dir: Sue Berger Ramin *E-mail:* sue@godine.com
Black Sparrow Publr: Susan Barba
Prodn Mgr: Jennifer Delaney
Founded: 1969
Fiction & nonfiction, history, biography, typography, art & photography, poetry, horticulture, Americana, cooking, regional, mysteries, juveniles.
ISBN Prefix(es): 978-0-87923; 978-1-56792; 978-0-87685; 978-1-57423
Number of titles published annually: 40 Print
Total Titles: 500 Print
Imprints: Black Sparrow; Imago Mundi; Nonpareil Books; Pocket Paragon; Verba Mundi
*Sales Office(s):* 426 Nutting Rd, PO Box 450, Jaffrey, NH 03452
Foreign Rep(s): Big Apple Agency Inc (Kelly Chang) (Taiwan); Mercedes Casanovas Agencia (Maria Lynch) (Spain); The English Agency (Hamish Macaskill) (Japan); Paul & Peter Fritz Agency (Peter Fritz) (Switzerland); Graal Literary Agency (Magda Koceba) (Poland); KM Agency (Klassje Mul) (UK); Korea Copyright Center (Jae-Yeon Ryu) (Korea); Sheila Land Associates (Ben Mason) (UK); Michelle Lapautre Agence (Michelle Lapautre) (France); Natoli Stefan & Oliva Agenzia (Roberta Oliva) (Italy); Agencia Literara SUN (Crina Chitan) (Romania)
Foreign Rights: Mercedes Casanovas (Spain); The English Agency (Japan); Paul & Peter Fritz (Germany); Korea Copyright Center (Korea); Sheila Land Associates (UK); Catherine Lapautre (France); Michelle Lapautre (France); Natoli, Stefan & Oliva (Italy)
*Orders to:* 426 Nutting Rd, PO Box 450, Jaffrey, NH 03452
*Warehouse:* 426 Nutting Rd, PO Box 450, Jaffrey, NH 03452 *Tel:* 603-532-4100 *Toll Free Tel:* 800-344-4771 *Fax:* 603-532-5940 *Toll Free Fax:* 800-226-0934 *E-mail:* order@godine.com
Membership(s): AAP

### Golden West Cookbooks
Division of American Traveler Press
5738 N Central Ave, Phoenix, AZ 85012-1316
*Tel:* 602-234-1574 *Toll Free Tel:* 800-521-9221 *Fax:* 602-234-3062
*E-mail:* info@americantravelerpress.com
*Web Site:* www.americantravelerpress.com
*Key Personnel*
Gen Mgr: Bill Fessler
Founded: 1973
Cookbooks & books on Southwest nonfiction.
ISBN Prefix(es): 978-0-914846; 978-1-885590
Number of titles published annually: 5 Print
Total Titles: 150 Print
Membership(s): Publishers Association of the West

### Gollehon Press Inc
3655 Glenn Dr SE, Grand Rapids, MI 49546
*Tel:* 616-949-3515 *Fax:* 616-949-8674
*Web Site:* www.gollehonbooks.com
*Key Personnel*
Pres: John T Gollehon *E-mail:* john@gollehonbooks.com
Publr: Kathy Gollehon
Ed: Becky Anderson
Sales Mgr: Jerome K Smith
Founded: 1983
Books related to Christian religions, young adult, health, how-to, reference, collectibles & current affairs; no unsol mss. Brief book proposals are reviewed. Simultaneous submissions are encouraged.
ISBN Prefix(es): 978-0-914839
Number of titles published annually: 15 Print
Total Titles: 97 Print
Imprints: Gollehon Books; GPC/Gollehon
*Warehouse:* Offset/Gollehon Distribution Ctr, 10 Passan Dr, Bldg 10, Laflin, PA 18702

**Good Books**
Subsidiary of Good Enterprises Ltd
3518 Old Philadelphia Pike, Intercourse, PA 17534
SAN: 693-9597
Mailing Address: PO Box 419, Intercourse, PA 17534
*Tel:* 717-768-7171 *Toll Free Tel:* 800-762-7171 *Fax:* 717-768-3433 *Toll Free Fax:* 888-768-3433
*E-mail:* custserv@goodbks.com
*Web Site:* www.goodbooks.com
*Key Personnel*
Publr & Mktg Mgr: Merle Good
Sr Ed: Phyllis Good
Founded: 1979
Trade hardcover & paperback books: cookbooks, crafts, general nonfiction, children's, how-to, family/parenting, fiction, poetry, inspirational & books about the Amish & Mennonites.
ISBN Prefix(es): 978-0-934672; 978-1-56148
Number of titles published annually: 20 Print
Total Titles: 280 Print
Distributed by Simon & Schuster
Foreign Rights: Merle Good
*Advertising Agency:* Good Advertising

**Good Parent Inc**
One Regency Plaza, Suite 1001, Providence, RI 02903
SAN: 860-1917
*Tel:* 401-316-1322 *Toll Free Fax:* 866-718-0344
*Web Site:* www.goodparentinc.com
*Key Personnel*
Mng Ed: Robert Jackson *E-mail:* robertjackson@goodparentinc.com
PR: Alyssa Sullivan *Tel:* 617-899-8631
Sr Ed: Sarah Jacque
Founded: 2010
Publish parenting self-help books in the field of psychology.
ISBN Prefix(es): 978-0-9832183
Number of titles published annually: 4 Print
Total Titles: 4 Print
Imprints: GoodParentGoodChild
Membership(s): AAP

**Goodheart-Willcox Publisher**
18604 W Creek Dr, Tinley Park, IL 60477-6243
SAN: 203-4387
*Tel:* 708-687-5000 *Toll Free Tel:* 800-323-0440 *Fax:* 708-687-0315 *Toll Free Fax:* 888-409-3900
*E-mail:* custserv@g-w.com
*Web Site:* www.g-w.com
*Key Personnel*
CEO & Pres: John F Flanagan
VP, Admin & Treas: Robert Kelly
VP, Sales: Todd Scheffers
Ad Coord: Zak Semens *Tel:* 708-623-1826 *E-mail:* zsemens@g-w.com
Founded: 1921
Industrial technical; family & consumer sciences & career textbooks.
ISBN Prefix(es): 978-0-87006; 978-1-56637; 978-1-59070; 978-1-60525
Number of titles published annually: 25 Print
Total Titles: 150 Print; 100 CD-ROM; 150 Online
Foreign Rep(s): Baker & Taylor International (Europe); Oxford University Press (Canada)

**Goodluck Guides**
134 W Canyonview Dr, Longview, WA 98632
*Tel:* 360-575-1236 *Fax:* 360-885-1872
*Key Personnel*
Owner: Gail Folgedalen
Lib Sales Dir & Mktg Mgr: Lee Folgedalen
Founded: 1982
Publish regional events guides.
ISBN Prefix(es): 978-1-881005
Number of titles published annually: 3 Print
Total Titles: 4 Print
Imprints: Holiday Bazaar Guide-OR; Holiday Bazaar Guide-WA; Oregon Events Guide; Washington Events Guide
Distributed by The News Group; Partners West
*Shipping Address:* The News Group, 3400 D Industry Dr E, Fife, WA 98424 *Tel:* 253-922-8011 *Toll Free Tel:* 800-843-2995

**Goosebottom Books**
Imprint of Goosebottom Books LLC
710 Portofino Lane, Foster City, CA 94404
SAN: 859-8029
*Tel:* 650-204-4076 *Toll Free Fax:* 888-407-5286
*E-mail:* info@goosebottombooks.com
*Web Site:* goosebottombooks.com
*Key Personnel*
Publr: Shirin Yim Bridges *E-mail:* shirin.bridges@goosebottombooks.com
Founded: 2010
A small press dedicated to stealth education through fun nonfiction.
ISBN Prefix(es): 978-0-9845098 (Real Princesses); 978-0-9834256 (Dastardly Dames); 978-1-937463 (Augmented Reality)
Number of titles published annually: 6 Print; 6 E-Book
Total Titles: 15 Print
*Orders to:* Independent Publishers Group (IPG), 814 N Franklin St, Chicago, IL 60610 *Toll Free Tel:* 800-888-4741 *E-mail:* orders@ipgbook.com *Web Site:* www.ipgbook.com
*Distribution Center:* Independent Publishers Group (IPG), 814 N Franklin St, Chicago, IL 60610 *Toll Free Tel:* 800-888-4741 *E-mail:* orders@ipgbook.com *Web Site:* www.ipgbook.com
Membership(s): Bay Area Independent Publishers Association; IBPA, the Independent Book Publishers Association; Northern California Independent Booksellers Association

**Gordian Press**
37 Crescent Ave, Staten Island, NY 10301
SAN: 201-6389
*Tel:* 718-273-8291
*Key Personnel*
Pres & Ed: Roger Texier *E-mail:* roger.texier@verizon.net
Founded: 1964
Reprints & original titles.
ISBN Prefix(es): 978-0-87752; 978-0-87753
Number of titles published annually: 5 Print
Total Titles: 275 Print
Imprints: Phaeton Press
Distributor for Phaeton Press

**Gorgias Press LLC**
954 River Rd, Piscataway, NJ 08854
*Tel:* 732-885-8900 *Fax:* 732-885-8908
*E-mail:* helpdesk@gorgiaspress.com
*Web Site:* www.gorgiaspress.com
*Key Personnel*
Pres: George Anton Kiraz, PhD
VP: Christine Altinis-Kiraz, PhD
Founded: 2001
Academic publishers of specialty books; provides for author/small publisher's digitization & publishing services needs.
ISBN Prefix(es): 978-1-59333; 978-0-9713097; 978-0-9715986; 978-1-931956; 978-1-60724
Number of titles published annually: 70 Print
Total Titles: 320 Print
Imprints: Euphrates; Harp of the Gazelle; Tigris
Distributed by Oxbow (UK)
Distributor for Yeshiva University Museum Press
Membership(s): IBPA, the Independent Book Publishers Association

**Gospel Publishing House (GPH)**
Division of General Council of the Assemblies of God
1445 Boonville Ave, Springfield, MO 65802
SAN: 206-8826
*Tel:* 417-862-2781 *Toll Free Tel:* 800-641-4310 *Fax:* 417-863-1874; 417-862-5881 *Toll Free Fax:* 800-328-0294
*E-mail:* custsrvreps@ag.org
*Web Site:* www.gospelpublishing.com
*Key Personnel*
Special Asst to Exec Leadership Team & Gen Mgr: Sol Arledge, Jr
Founded: 1914
Religion (Assemblies of God); sign-language textbooks & curricular materials.
ISBN Prefix(es): 978-0-88243
Number of titles published annually: 6 Print
Total Titles: 250 Print
Imprints: Logion Press; Radiant Books; Radiant Life Curricular
*Distribution Center:* Bookmasters, 30 Amberwood Pkwy, Ashland, OH 44805 *Tel:* 419-281-5000 *Toll Free Tel:* 800-537-6727 *Fax:* 419-280-0200 *E-mail:* info@bookmasters.com *Web Site:* www.bookmasters.com
Spring Arbor Distributors Inic, One Ingram Blvd, La Vergne, TN 37086-1986 *Toll Free Tel:* 800-395-4340 *Toll Free Fax:* 800-876-0186 *E-mail:* customerservice@ingramcontent.com *Web Site:* www.ingramcontent.com

**Gotham Books**
Imprint of Penguin Group (USA) LLC
375 Hudson St, New York, NY 10014
*Key Personnel*
Pres & Publr, Gotham & Avery: William Shinker
VP, Edit Dir: Lauren Marino
Exec Ed: Charles Conrad
VP, Assoc Publr, Gotham Books & Avery: Lisa Johnson
Publicity Mgr: Lindsay Bezalel
Founded: 2001
Specialize in business, current affairs, consumer reference, food writing, golf, health & fitness, history, memoirs, personal finance, popular culture, self-help, spirituality, sports, pets, travel narrative & narrative nonfiction.
ISBN Prefix(es): 978-1-59240
Number of titles published annually: 62 Print
Total Titles: 285 Print

**Government Institutes (GI)**
Imprint of The Rowman & Littlefield Publishing Group
4501 Forbes Blvd, Suite 200, Lanham, MD 20706
SAN: 214-3801
*Tel:* 301-459-3366 (ext 5622) *Toll Free Tel:* 800-462-6420 *Fax:* 301-429-5748 *Toll Free Fax:* 800-338-4550
*Web Site:* www.govinstpress.com
*Key Personnel*
Publr & Edit Dir: Marcus Boggs *Tel:* 301-459-3366 ext 5418 *E-mail:* mboggs@rowman.com
Mktg Mgr: Veronica M Dove *E-mail:* vdove@bernan.com
Publicist & Ad Mgr: Lisa McAllister *E-mail:* lmcallister@rowman.com
Founded: 1973
Law, regulatory & technical books & environmental safety, code of federal regulations, quality, risk, industrial hygiene.
ISBN Prefix(es): 978-0-86587; 978-1-59191; 978-1-60590
Number of titles published annually: 30 Print
Total Titles: 305 Print

**Grade Finders Inc**
PO Box 944, Exton, PA 19341-0908
*Tel:* 610-269-7070 *Toll Free Tel:* 877-524-7080 *Fax:* 610-269-7077
*E-mail:* info@gradefinders.com
*Web Site:* www.gradefinders.com

*Key Personnel*
CEO: William A Subers *E-mail:* bill@gradefinders.com
Pres: Mark Subers
Prodn Mgr: P J Subers
Founded: 1967
Producer of paper buyers guides (USA & Europe); publish two business directories on paper grades on the Internet.
ISBN Prefix(es): 978-0-929502
Number of titles published annually: 3 Print; 2 Online
Total Titles: 3 Print; 3 Online
Distributed by Graphic Arts Association; National Paper Trade Association; North American Publishing; Printing Industries of America

**The Graduate Group/Booksellers**
86 Norwood Rd, West Hartford, CT 06117-2236
Mailing Address: PO Box 370351, West Hartford, CT 06137-0351
*Tel:* 860-233-2330 *Toll Free Tel:* 800-484-7280 ext 3579 *Fax:* 860-233-2330
*E-mail:* graduategroup@hotmail.com
*Web Site:* www.graduategroup.com
*Key Personnel*
Partner: Mara Whitman
Lib Sales Dir: Robert Whitman *Tel:* 860-232-3100
Founded: 1964
Publish career oriented reference books & self-help books for libraries, career & placement offices in the US & abroad, law enforcement, career series, exam preparation.
ISBN Prefix(es): 978-0-938609
Number of titles published annually: 20 Print; 1 Online
Total Titles: 100 Print; 2 Online

**Grafco Productions**
971 E Callaway Rd, Marietta, GA 30060
*Tel:* 770-436-1500 *Toll Free Tel:* 800-381-9169 *Fax:* 770-435-3793
*Web Site:* www.jackwboone.com
*Key Personnel*
Owner & Publr: Jack W Boone *E-mail:* jabo@jackwboone.com
Founded: 1964
General trade.
ISBN Prefix(es): 978-1-880719
Number of titles published annually: 5 Print
Total Titles: 21 Print
Imprints: Grafco Rock Books

**Grand Central Publishing**
Division of Hachette Book Group
237 Park Ave, New York, NY 10017
SAN: 282-5368
*Tel:* 212-364-1100
*Web Site:* www.hachettebookgroup.com
*Key Personnel*
EVP, Hachette Book Group & Publr, Grand Central Publishing: Jamie Raab
VP & Ed-in-Chief, Hardcovers: Deb Futter
VP, Edit Dir, Life & Style: Karen Murgolo
VP, Ed-in-Chief, Paperbacks: Beth de Guzman
VP, Assoc Publr: Emi Battaglia
VP, Exec Ed, Grand Central Publishing, Publr & Ed-in-Chief, Business Plus: Rick Wolff
Exec Ed, Forever: Amy Pierpont
VP, Exec Dir of Publicity: Jennifer Romanello
Dir of Hachette Book Group Multicultural Publicity: Linda Duggins
VP, Creative Dir: Anne Twomey
VP, Subs Rts: Nancy Wiese
Founded: 1961
Hardcover, trade paperback & mass market paperback, reprint & original, fiction & nonfiction, audio books. Unsol/unagented mss not accepted.
ISBN Prefix(es): 978-0-445; 978-0-446; 978-0-89296
Number of titles published annually: 260 Print
Total Titles: 3,860 Print
Imprints: Business Plus; Forever; Forever Yours; Grand Central Life/Style; Twelve; Vision
Foreign Rights: Antonella Antonelli Agenzia (Italy); Bardon Far Eastern Agents (Taiwan); Graal Literary Agency (Poland); Imprima Korea Agency (Korea); Katai & Bolza Literary Agents (Hungary); Simona Kessler International Copyright Agency Ltd (Romania); La Nouvelle Agence (France); Andrew Nurnberg Associates Ltd (Baltic States, Bulgaria, Mainland China, Russia); OA Literary Agency (Greece); Kristin Olson Literary Agency SRO (Czech Republic, Slovakia); Pikarski Agency (Israel); Prava I Prevodi International Literary Agency (Croatia, Slovenia); RDC Agencia Literaria (Brazil, Latin America, Spain); Sane Toregard Agency (Denmark, Finland, Iceland, Norway, Sweden); Thomas Schlueck GmbH (Germany)
*Advertising Agency:* Publishers Advertising
*Shipping Address:* Hachette Book Group Distribution Center, 121 N Enterprise Blvd, Lebanon, IN 46052 *Tel:* 765-483-9900 *Fax:* 765-483-0706
Membership(s): AAP; BISG

**Donald M Grant Publisher Inc**
PO Box 187, Hampton Falls, NH 03844-0187
*Tel:* 603-778-7191 *Fax:* 603-778-7191
*Web Site:* www.grantbooks.com
*Key Personnel*
Pres: Robert K Wiener *E-mail:* robert@grantbooks.com
VP: Paul Wiener
Dir, Opers: Karen French *E-mail:* karenf@grantbooks.com
Founded: 1964
Horror, science fiction, art & fantasy illustrated books.
ISBN Prefix(es): 978-0-937986; 978-1-880418
Number of titles published annually: 4 Print
Total Titles: 55 Print
Distributor for Archival; Oswald Train

**Graphic Arts Books**
Unit of Ingram Content Group Inc
7820 NE Holman St, Suite B-9, Portland, OR 97218
Mailing Address: PO Box 56118, Portland, OR 97236-6618
*Tel:* 503-254-5591 *Fax:* 503-254-5609
*E-mail:* info-ga@graphicartsbooks.com
*Web Site:* www.graphicartsbooks.com
*Key Personnel*
Publg Dir: Douglas Pfeiffer
Ed: Kathy Howard
Founded: 1967
ISBN Prefix(es): 978-0-88240
Number of titles published annually: 35 Print; 30 E-Book
Total Titles: 250 Print; 75 E-Book
Imprints: Alaska Northwest Books®; WestWinds Press®
*Distribution Center:* Ingram Publisher Services, One Ingram Blvd, La Vergne, TN *Toll Free Tel:* 866-400-5351 *Toll Free Fax:* 800-838-1149
Membership(s): Publishers Association of the West

**Graphic Universe™**
Division of Lerner Publishing Group Inc
241 First Ave N, Minneapolis, MN 55401
Mailing Address: Empire State Bldg, Suite 7206, 350 Fifth Ave, New York, NY 10118
*Tel:* 612-332-3344 *Toll Free Tel:* 800-328-4929 *Fax:* 612-332-7615 *Toll Free Fax:* 800-332-1132
*E-mail:* info@lernerbooks.com
*Web Site:* www.lernerbooks.com
*Key Personnel*
Chmn: Harry J Lerner
CFO & EVP: Margaret Wunderlich
Pres & Publr: Adam Lerner
EVP, Sales: David Wexler
VP & Dir, Mktg & Digital Prods: Terri Soutor
Ed-in-Chief: Patricia M Stockland
VP, Prodn: Gary Hansen
Rts Dir: Maria Kjoller
Dir, Prod Devt & Mktg Res: Lois Wallentine
Dir, Electronic Content: Dan Wallek
Art Dir: Zach Marell
Dir, HR: Cyndi Radant
Founded: 2006
Publish graphic novel fiction & nonfiction books for children & young adults.
Total Titles: 150 Print; 145 E-Book
Foreign Rep(s): INT Press Distribution (Australia); Phambili (Southern Africa); Publishers Marketing Service (Brunei, Malaysia, Singapore); South Pacific Books (New Zealand)
Foreign Rights: Sandra Bruna Agencia Literaria (Spain); Japan Foreign-Rights Centre (JFC) (Japan); Korea Copyright Center Inc (KCC) (Korea); Agence Michelle Lapautre (France); Rights People (UK & Commonwealth)
*Distribution Center:* Lerner Publishing Group, 1251 Washington Ave N, Minneapolis, MN 55401

**Gray & Company Publishers**
1588 E 40 St, Suite 3-A, Cleveland, OH 44103
*Tel:* 216-431-2665 *Toll Free Tel:* 800-915-3609
*E-mail:* sales@grayco.com
*Web Site:* www.grayco.com
*Key Personnel*
Pres: David Gray
Mktg: Chris Andrikanich *E-mail:* promotions@grayco.com
Founded: 1991
Books about Cleveland & Northeast Ohio & Ohio.
ISBN Prefix(es): 978-1-886228; 978-1-59851
Number of titles published annually: 7 Print
Total Titles: 75 Print

**Graywolf Press**
250 Third Ave N, Suite 600, Minneapolis, MN 55401
*Tel:* 651-641-0077 *Fax:* 651-641-0036
*E-mail:* wolves@graywolfpress.org
*Web Site:* www.graywolfpress.org
*Key Personnel*
Dir & Publr: Fiona McCrae
Edit Dir: Katie Dublinski
Publicity Dir: Erin Kottke
Devt Dir: Kit Briem
Mktg Dir: Michael Taeckens
Sr Ed: Jeffrey Shotts
Sales & Busn Mgr: Leslie Koppenhaver
Mktg & Admin Asst: Marisa Atkinson
Ed Asst: Steve Woodward
Contrib Ed: Brigid Hughes
Founded: 1974
Poetry, fiction, nonfiction.
ISBN Prefix(es): 978-1-55597
Number of titles published annually: 30 Print
Total Titles: 200 Print; 30 E-Book
Foreign Rights: Agence Michelle Lapautre (France); Michael Meller Literary Agency GmbH (Germany)
*Billing Address:* MPS Distribution Center, 16365 James Madison Hwy, Gordonsville, VA 22942
*Warehouse:* MPS Distribution Center, 16365 James Madison Hwy, Gordonsville, VA 22942
*Distribution Center:* MPS Distribution Center, 16365 James Madison Hwy, Gordonsville, VA 22942 *Tel:* 212-206-5311 *Toll Free Tel:* 888-330-8477 *Fax:* 540-672-7540

**Great Potential Press Inc**
Division of Anodyne Inc

7025 E First Ave, Suite 5, Scottsdale, AZ 85251
*Tel:* 602-954-4200 *Toll Free Tel:* 877-954-4200
*Fax:* 602-954-0185
*Web Site:* www.greatpotentialpress.com
*Key Personnel*
Pres & Publr: James T Webb
VP, Acq Ed, Devt Ed: Janet Gore *E-mail:* janet@greatpotentialpress.com
Founded: 1982
Books relating to social/emotional needs & other characteristics of gifted children. Types of Publications: Educational Guide Books & books for parents & adults.
ISBN Prefix(es): 978-0-910707
Number of titles published annually: 5 Print
Total Titles: 58 Print; 4 CD-ROM; 1 Audio
Imprints: Gifted Psychology Press
Foreign Rights: Amer-Asia Book (Evelyn Lee) (Asia)
*Returns:* 5223 N 41 Place, Phoenix, AZ 85018
*Distribution Center:* Ingram Book Co, One Ingram Blvd, La Vergne, TN 37086
Membership(s): Arizona Book Publishing Association; IBPA, the Independent Book Publishers Association

**Great Quotations Inc**
8102 S Lemont Rd, Suite 300, Woodridge, IL 60517
*Tel:* 630-985-2628 *Toll Free Tel:* 800-830-3020
*Fax:* 630-985-2610
*E-mail:* info@greatquotationsinc.com
*Web Site:* greatquotationsinc.com
*Key Personnel*
Pres: Ringo Suek
Founded: 1984
Motivation, inspiration & humor titles, also gifts.
ISBN Prefix(es): 978-1-56245; 978-0-931089
Number of titles published annually: 30 Print
Total Titles: 500 Print
Imprints: G Q Publishing

**Great Source Education Group**
Subsidiary of Houghton Mifflin Harcourt Publishing Company
181 Ballardvale St, Wilmington, MA 01887
Mailing Address: PO Box 7050, Wilmington, MA 01887-7050
*Tel:* 978-661-1471 *Toll Free Tel:* 800-289-4490
*Toll Free Fax:* 800-289-3994
*Web Site:* www.greatsource.com
*Key Personnel*
Pres: Steve Zukowski *E-mail:* steve.zukowski@hmhpub.com
Founded: 1996
Supplemental school instructional materials.

**Green Dragon Books**
12 S Dixie Hwy, Suite 202, Lake Worth, FL 33460
*Tel:* 561-533-6231 *Toll Free Tel:* 800-874-8844
*Fax:* 561-533-6233 *Toll Free Fax:* 888-874-8844
*E-mail:* info@greendragonbooks.com
*Key Personnel*
Chmn & Publr: Gary Wilson
Founded: 1969
ISBN Prefix(es): 978-1-63006; 978-1-62386
Number of titles published annually: 12 Print; 12 Online; 12 E-Book
Total Titles: 400 Print; 400 Online; 400 E-Book
Foreign Rights: Montreal-Contacts/The Rights Agency (Worldwide)

**Green Eagle Press**
PO Box 20329, New York, NY 10025
*Tel:* 212-663-2167 *Fax:* 212-316-7650
~~*E-mail:* mail@greeneagle.org~~
LOD *Web Site:* www.greeneagle.org
*Key Personnel*
Edit Dir: Cy A Adler
Founded: 1974
ISBN Prefix(es): 978-0-914018
Number of titles published annually: 3 Print; 1 CD-ROM; 1 E-Book
Total Titles: 1 CD-ROM
*Editorial Office(s):* 241 W 97 St Suite 14-N, New York, NY 10025
*Sales Office(s):* 241 W 97 St Suite 14-N, New York, NY 10025
*Billing Address:* 241 W 97 St Suite 14-N, New York, NY 10025

**Green Integer**
6022 Wilshire Blvd, Suite 202-C, Los Angeles, CA 90036
SAN: 216-3063
*Tel:* 323-857-1115 *Fax:* 323-857-0143
*E-mail:* info@greeninteger.com
*Web Site:* www.greeninteger.com
*Key Personnel*
Publr: Douglas Messerli *E-mail:* douglas.messerli@gmail.com
Founded: 1978
Contemporary fiction, criticism, drama & poetry.
ISBN Prefix(es): 978-0-940650; 978-1-55713
Number of titles published annually: 25 Print
Total Titles: 300 Print
Imprints: New American Fiction Series; New American Poetry Series; Sun & Moon Classics
Foreign Rights: Elaine Benesti Literary Agency (France); Bookbank SA (Spain); Paul & Peter Fritz AG Literary Agency (Germany, Switzerland); Japan UNI Agency Inc (Japan); Leonhardt Literary Agency (Scandinavia); Natoli, Stefan & Oliva Literary Agency (Italy); Rogan Pikarski Literary Agency (Israel)
*Distribution Center:* Consortium Book Sales & Distribution, 1045 Westgate Dr, Suite 90, St Paul, MN 55114-1065 *Tel:* 651-221-9035 *Toll Free Tel:* 800-283-3572 (cust serv) *Fax:* 612-746-2606 *E-mail:* info@cbsd.com *Web Site:* www.cbsd.com

**§Green King Press**
4211 Fenwick Village Dr, Savannah, GA 31419
*Tel:* 843-325-6821
*Key Personnel*
Publr: Kevin Fulton *E-mail:* kvnfltn@msn.com
Founded: 2011
Print & digital publishing.
ISBN Prefix(es): 978-0-615; 978-0-578
Number of titles published annually: 1,000 Print; 1,000 Online; 1,000 E-Book
Total Titles: 600 Print; 600 Online; 600 E-Book

**Green Sugar Press**
2200 E Devon Ave, Suite 340, Des Plaines, IL 60018-4503
*Tel:* 773-580-7780; 615-254-2402 (orders); 615-254-2488 (returns) *Fax:* 615-254-2405 (orders); 615-254-2405 (returns) *Toll Free Fax:* 866-270-4100
*E-mail:* order@greensugarpress.com
*Web Site:* www.greensugarpress.com
*Key Personnel*
Publr & Author: Tim "Sugar" Magner *E-mail:* sugar@greensugarpress.com
Ed: Ryan Newhouse *Tel:* 406-546-5280 *E-mail:* ryan_newhouse@hotmail.com
Regl Sales: Cammy Hines *Tel:* 847-977-2723 *Fax:* 847-699-1401 *E-mail:* cammy@greensugarpress.com
Illus: Lindsay Knapp *Tel:* 865-679-3838 *E-mail:* lindsaykn@gmail.com
Founded: 2007
Publish books to engage, enlighten & entertain children with the wonders of nature.
ISBN Prefix(es): 978-0-9820417
Number of titles published annually: 6 Print
Total Titles: 3 Print
Distributed by Associated Publishers Group; Follett Library Resources
Foreign Rep(s): Follett Library Resources Canada (Canada)
*Shipping Address:* Associated Publishers Group, 7344 Cockrill Bend Blvd, Nashville, TN 37209, Contact: Richard Cox *Tel:* 615-254-2425 *Fax:* 615-254-2408 *E-mail:* rcox@apgbooks.com
*Warehouse:* Associated Publishers Group, 7344 Cockrill Bend Blvd, Nashville, TN 37209, Contact: Richard Cox *Tel:* 615-254-2425 *Fax:* 615-254-2408 *E-mail:* rcox@apgbooks.com

**Greenhaven Press®**
Imprint of Gale
27500 Drake Rd, Farmington Hills, MI 48331
*Toll Free Tel:* 800-877-4253 (cust serv & orders) *Fax:* 248-699-8051 (cust serv)
*Toll Free Fax:* 800-414-5043 (orders only)
*E-mail:* gale.customerservice@cengage.com; gale.galeord@thomson.com (orders)
*Web Site:* www.gale.cengage.com/greenhaven
*Key Personnel*
Mng Ed: Elizabeth Deschenes
Admin Coord: Kristine Burns *Tel:* 248-699-8661 *E-mail:* kristine.burns@cengage.com
Founded: 1970
High school, college & secondary nonfiction social studies & debate books for classrooms & libraries: social studies reference series; library & paper bound books in area studies, criminal justice, the environment, health, Literary Companion & American History series & AT Issues series.
ISBN Prefix(es): 978-0-89908; 978-1-56510; 978-0-7377
Number of titles published annually: 200 Print
Total Titles: 3,500 Print

**Greenleaf Book Group LLC**
4005 Banister Lane, Suite B, Austin, TX 78704
Mailing Address: PO Box 91869, Austin, TX 78709
*Tel:* 512-891-6100 *Toll Free Tel:* 800-932-5420
*Fax:* 512-891-6150
*E-mail:* contact@greenleafbookgroup.com
*Web Site:* www.greenleafbookgroup.com
*Key Personnel*
Chmn & CEO: Clint Greenleaf
COO: Tanya Hall
Mng Ed: Kris Pauls
HR & Sr Proj Mgr: Alan Grimes
Founded: 1997
Publisher & distributor specializing in the development of independent authors & the growth of small presses. Our publishing model was designed to support independent authors & allow writers to retain the rights to their work & still compete with major publishing houses. We also distribute select titles from small & independent publishers to major trade outlets, including bookstores, libraries & airport retailers. We serve the small & independent publishing community by offering industry guidance, business development, production, distribution & marketing services.
ISBN Prefix(es): 978-0-9665319; 978-1-929774
Number of titles published annually: 100 Print
Total Titles: 350 Print
Imprints: Emerald Book Co; 500/5000 Press Inc; Greenleaf Book Group Press; Live Oak; Olive Tree Book Co
*Returns:* Archway, 20770 Westwood Dr, Strongsville, OH 44149
Membership(s): AAP; The Association of Publishers for Special Sales; BookSense Publisher Partner; IBPA, the Independent Book Publishers Association; Midwest Publishing Association; National Speakers Association; Society of Children's Book Writers & Illustrators

**Greenleaf Book Group Press**, see Greenleaf Book Group LLC

**§Greenwoman Publishing LLC**
1823 W Pikes Peak Ave, Colorado Springs, CO 80904-3844
Mailing Address: PO Box 6587, Colorado Springs, CO 80934-6587
*Tel:* 719-473-9237 *Fax:* 719-473-9237
*Web Site:* www.greenwomanpublishing.com
*Key Personnel*
Owner, Publr & Ed: Sandra Knauf
*E-mail:* sandra@greenwomanmagazine.com
Assoc Publr & Deputy Ed: Zora Knauf
Founded: 2011
Publisher of *Greenwoman Magazine*, a biannual literary garden writing magazine in print & electronic. Publish books on subjects related to gardening, sustainability & biography. Also published its first fiction book, a young adult environmental fantasy, in 2013.
ISBN Prefix(es): 978-0-9897056
Number of titles published annually: 6 Print; 6 E-Book
Total Titles: 1 Print; 3 E-Book

**§Greenwood Research Books & Software**
Division of Greenwood Research
PO Box 12102, Wichita, KS 67277-2102
*Tel:* 316-214-5103
*Web Site:* greenray4ever.com (ordering)
*Key Personnel*
Lib Sales Dir & Gen Mgr: James A Green
*E-mail:* jimgreenhimself@gmail.com
Founded: 1990 (in Clearwater, FL & relocated to Wichita, KS in 1991)
Science & engineering emphasis: Medical Image Processing.
ISBN Prefix(es): 978-1-890121
Number of titles published annually: 6 Print
Total Titles: 15 Print
*Distribution Center:* Midwest Library Service, 11443 St Charles Rock Rd, Bridgeton, MO 63044-2789 *Tel:* 314-739-3100 *Toll Free Tel:* 800-325-8833 *Fax:* 314-739-1326 *Toll Free Fax:* 800-962-1009 *E-mail:* mail@midwestls.com *Web Site:* midwestls.com
Membership(s): IBPA, the Independent Book Publishers Association

**Grey House Publishing Inc™**
4919 Rte 22, Amenia, NY 12501
Mailing Address: PO Box 56, Amenia, NY 12501-0056
*Tel:* 518-789-8700 *Toll Free Tel:* 800-562-2139 *Fax:* 518-789-0556
*E-mail:* books@greyhouse.com
*Web Site:* www.greyhouse.com
*Key Personnel*
Pres: Richard Gottlieb *Fax:* 518-789-0544 *E-mail:* rhg@greyhouse.com
Edit Dir: Laura Mars-Proietti *E-mail:* lmars@greyhouse.com
VP, Mktg: Jessica Moody *Tel:* 518-789-8700 ext 101 *E-mail:* jmoody@greyhouse.com
Publr: Leslie Mackenzie *E-mail:* lmackenzie@greyhouse.com
Founded: 1979
Directories, reference books & encyclopedias in history, business, economics, health & demographic areas.
ISBN Prefix(es): 978-1-930956; 978-1-891482; 978-0-939300; 978-1-59237; 978-1-61925
Number of titles published annually: 48 Print
Total Titles: 60 Print; 25 Online; 26 E-Book
Imprints: Grey House; Sedgwick Press; Universal Reference
Divisions: Grey House Publishing Canada
Membership(s): ALA

**Griffin Publishing LLC**
PO Box 28627, Santa Ana, CA 92799-8627
*Tel:* 714-556-7067 *Toll Free Tel:* 800-472-9741 *Fax:* 714-556-7067
*E-mail:* info@griffinpublishing.com
*Web Site:* www.griffinpublishing.com
*Key Personnel*
Pres: Bob Howland
Dir, Opers: Robin Howland
Proj Mgr: Bryan Howland
ISBN Prefix(es): 978-1-882180; 978-1-58000
Number of titles published annually: 30 Print
Total Titles: 112 Print
Foreign Rep(s): Gazelle (Europe)

**Grolier Online®**, see Scholastic Consumer & Professional Publishing

**Grosset & Dunlap**
Imprint of Penguin Group (USA) LLC
345 Hudson St, New York, NY 10014
*Tel:* 212-366-2000
*E-mail:* online@penguinputnam.com
*Web Site:* www.penguinputnam.com; us.penguingroup.com
*Key Personnel*
Pres & Publr, Grosset & Dunlap/Price Stern Sloan: Francesco Sedita
Ed-in-Chief, Early Readers & Assoc Publr, Warne: Bonnie Bader
Ed-in-Chief, Series & Licenses: Sarah Fabiny
VP & Ed-at-Large: Jane O'Connor
Sr Ed: Rob Valois
Art Dir: Giuseppe Castellano
Licensing Mgr: Robyn Bissette
Founded: 1898
ISBN Prefix(es): 978-0-448; 978-1-58184
Number of titles published annually: 133 Print
Total Titles: 1,098 Print
Imprints: PSS; Somerville House USA

**§Group Publishing Inc**
1515 Cascade Ave, Loveland, CO 80538
Mailing Address: PO Box 481, Loveland, CO 80539-0481
*Tel:* 970-669-3836 *Toll Free Tel:* 800-447-1070 *Fax:* 970-292-4373
*E-mail:* info@group.com
*Web Site:* www.group.com
*Key Personnel*
Founder & Chmn: Thom Schultz
Database Mktg Mgr: Eric Dowdy
Ed & Copyright Coord: Kerri Loesche
*E-mail:* kloesche@group.com
Founded: 1974
Books, magazines, video & audio tapes, computer online service, curriculum.
ISBN Prefix(es): 978-1-55945; 978-0-7644; 978-0-931529
Number of titles published annually: 40 Print
Total Titles: 400 Print; 2 CD-ROM; 15 Audio
Imprints: Faith Weaver Bible Curriculum™; FW Friends™; Group Workcamps™; Group's Hands-On Bible Curriculum™; Kids Own Worship™
Foreign Rights: Canaanland (Malaysia); Group Canada (Canada); KCBS Inc (Korea); Koorung Books Pty Ltd (Australia)
*Returns:* 1615 Cascade Ave, Loveland, CO 80538
*Shipping Address:* 1615 Cascade Ave, Loveland, CO 80538
Membership(s): CBA; Evangelical Christian Publishers Association

**Grove/Atlantic Inc**
841 Broadway, 4th fl, New York, NY 10003-4793
SAN: 201-4890
*Tel:* 212-614-7850 *Toll Free Tel:* 800-521-0178 *Fax:* 212-614-7886
*E-mail:* info@groveatlantic.com
*Web Site:* www.groveatlantic.com
*Key Personnel*
Pres & Publr: Morgan Entrekin
*E-mail:* mentrekin@groveatlantic.com
Fin Cont: Bill Weinberg *E-mail:* bweinberg@groveatlantic.com
Exec Ed: Joan Bingham *E-mail:* jbingham@groveatlantic.com; Elisabeth Schmitz *E-mail:* eschmitz@groveatlantic.com
Prodn Dir: Sue Cole *E-mail:* scole@groveatlantic.com
Dir, Publicity: Deb Seager *E-mail:* dseager@groveatlantic.com
Art Dir: Charles Woods *E-mail:* cwoods@groveatlantic.com
Dir, Subs Rts & Ed: Amy Hundley
*E-mail:* ahundley@groveatlantic.com
Sr Mktg Mgr: Jason Pinter
Sr Publicist: John Mark Boling; Stephanie Giraldi
Mng Ed: Michael Hornburg *E-mail:* mhornburg@groveatlantic.com
Sr Ed: Corinna Barsan; Jamison Stoltz
*E-mail:* jamison.stoltz@groveatlantic.com
Assoc Publr: Judy Hottensen
Asst Ed: Peter Blackstock
Founded: 1917
General fiction & nonfiction, hardcover & paperbound.
ISBN Prefix(es): 978-0-8021; 978-0-87113; 978-1-84195; 978-1-84767
Number of titles published annually: 120 Print; 30 E-Book
Total Titles: 1,200 Print; 250 E-Book
Imprints: Atlantic Books Ltd; Atlantic Monthly Press; Black Cat; Granta; Grove Press; The Mysterious Press; Open City
*Sales Office(s):* Publishers Group West/Perseus Distribution Co, 1700 Fourth St, Berkeley, CA 94710 *Tel:* 510-528-1444
Distributed by Publishers Group West/Perseus Distribution Co
Distributor for Granta Magazine; Open City Books
Foreign Rep(s): Publishers Group Canada (Canada); Publishers Group International
Foreign Rights: AnatoliaLit Agency (Amy Spangler) (Turkey); Antonella Antonelli Agenzia Letteraria (Italy); Carmen Balcells Agencia Literaria SA (Anna Bofill) (Portugal); Carmen Balcells Agency Literaria SA (Maribel Luque) (Latin America, Spain); Beijing Representative Office (Jackie Huang) (China); Eliane Benisti Agency (France); Graal Literary Agency (Kamila Kanafa) (Poland); International Copyright Agency (Ms Simona Kessler) (Romania); Japan Uni Agency Inc (Kenny Okayama) (Japan); Katai & Bolza (Peter Bolza) (Hungary); Korea Copyright Center Inc (Ms Gayoung Kim) (Korea); Andrew Nurnberg Associates (Ms Tatjana Zoldnere) (Estonia, Latvia, Lithuania); Kristin Olson Literary Agency (Kristin Olson) (Czech Republic); Owl's Agency (Mr Seiichiro Shimono) (Japan); Riff Agency (Brazil); Synopsis Literary Agency (Natalia Sanina) (Russia); Taiwan Representative Office (Whitney Hsu) (Taiwan); ULF Toregard Agency (Ulf Toregard) (Netherlands, Scandinavia)
*Billing Address:* Publishers Group West/Perseus Distribution Co, 1700 Fourth St, Berkeley, CA 94710 *Tel:* 510-528-1444
*Orders to:* Perseus Books Group, 1094 Flex Dr, Jackson, TN 38301 *Toll Free Tel:* 800-343-4499 *E-mail:* orderentry@perseusbook.com; Publishers Group Canada, 559 College St, Suite 402, Toronto, ON M6G 1A9, Canada *E-mail:* info@pgcbooks.ca
*Returns:* Perseus Distribution, 193 Edwards Dr, Jackson, TN 38301 *Toll Free Tel:* 800-343-4499; Raincoast Books, 9050 Shaughnessy St, Vancouver, BC V6P 6E5, Canada *Toll Free Tel:* 800-663-5714 *E-mail:* customerservice@raincoast.com
*Shipping Address:* Perseus Distribution, 193 Edwards Dr, Jackson, TN 38301 *Tel:* 510-528-1444 *Toll Free Tel:* 800-788-3123 *Fax:* 510-528-3444 *Web Site:* www.pgw.com
*Warehouse:* Perseus Distribution, 193 Edwards Dr, Jackson, TN 38301

*Distribution Center:* Perseus Distribution, 193 Edwards Dr, Jackson, TN 38301
Membership(s): AAP

**Gryphon Books**
PO Box 209, Brooklyn, NY 11228-0209
*E-mail:* gryphonbooks@att.net
*Web Site:* www.gryphonbooks.com
*Key Personnel*
Owner & Pres: Gary Lovisi
Founded: 1983
Book Shows, NY Collectible PB & Pulp Fiction Expo (annual trade show & exhibit). No mss accepted, only query letters with SASE.
ISBN Prefix(es): 978-0-936071
Number of titles published annually: 20 Print
Total Titles: 150 Print
Imprints: Gryphon Crime Series; Gryphon Doubles; Gryphon SF Rediscovery Series; Paperback Parade Collector Specials
Distributor for PPC; Zeon

**Gryphon Editions**
PO Box 34461, Bethesda, MD 20827
*Tel:* 301-983-4171 *Toll Free Tel:* 800-633-8911 *Fax:* 301-983-8734
*E-mail:* gryphonedn@gmail.com
*Web Site:* www.gryphoneditions.com
*Key Personnel*
Pres & Publr: Richard G Ritter
Founded: 1977
Reprints: medicine, law, political philosophy, science; fine editions.
Number of titles published annually: 25 Print
Total Titles: 750 Print
*Editorial Office(s):* 22 Cherbourg Ct, Potomac, MD 20854
*Distribution Center:* Bindtech Distribution, 428 Harding Industrial Blvd, Nashville, TN 37211

**Gryphon House Inc**
Subsidiary of Kaplan Early Learning Co
10770 Columbia Pike, Suite 201, Silver Spring, MD 20901
*Tel:* 301-595-9500 *Toll Free Tel:* 800-638-0928 *Fax:* 301-595-0051 *Toll Free Fax:* 877-638-7576
*E-mail:* info@ghbooks.com
*Web Site:* www.gryphonhouse.com
*Key Personnel*
Publr: Clarissa Willis *E-mail:* clarissa@ghbooks.com
Ed-in-Chief: Kathleen Charner *E-mail:* kathy@ghbooks.com
Mktg Dir: Jennifer Lewis *E-mail:* jennifer@ghbooks.com
Sales Dir: Pat Conte *E-mail:* pat@ghbooks.com
Mktg Mgr: TaKisha Adams *E-mail:* takisha@ghbooks.com
Founded: 1971
Publishes & distributes books for teachers & parents of young children.
ISBN Prefix(es): 978-0-87659
Number of titles published annually: 20 Print; 5 E-Book
Total Titles: 200 Print; 20 E-Book
Distributor for Aha Communications; Book Peddlers; Deya Brashears; Bright Ring Publishing; Building Blocks; Center for the Child Care Workforce; Chatterbox Press; Chicago Review Press; Children's Resources International; Circle Time Publishers; Sydney Gurewitz Clemens; Conari Press; Council Oak Books; Dawn Sign Press; Delmar Publishers Inc; Early Educator's Press; Educators for Social Responsibility; Family Center of Nova University; Jean Feldman; Floris Books; Hawthorne Press; Highscope; Hunter House Publishers; Kaplan Press; Loving Guidance Inc; Miss Jackie Inc; Monjeu Press; National Center Early Childhood Workforce; New England AEYC; New Horizons; Nova Southeastern University; Pademelon Press; Partner Press; Pollyanna Productions; Robins Lane Press; School Renaissance; Southern Early Childhood Association; Steam Press; Syracuse University Press; Teaching Strategies; Telshare Publishing
Foreign Rep(s): Monarch Books (Canada); Pademelon Press (Australia)
*Shipping Address:* Independent Publishers Group (IPG), 814 N Franklin St, Chicago, IL 60610 *Toll Free Tel:* 800-888-4741 *Web Site:* www.ipgbook.com
*Distribution Center:* Independent Publishers Group (IPG), 814 N Franklin St, Chicago, IL 60610 *Toll Free Tel:* 800-888-4741 *Web Site:* www.ipgbook.com
Membership(s): BEA; NACCRRA; National School Supply & Equipment Association

**Guernica Editions Inc**
2250 Military Rd, Tonawanda, NY 14150-6000
Mailing Address: PO Box 117, Sta P, Toronto, ON M5S 2S6, Canada
*Tel:* 416-576-9403 *Fax:* 716-693-2667; 716-692-7479 *Toll Free Fax:* 800-221-9985 (orders)
*E-mail:* guernicaeditions@cs.com
*Web Site:* www.guernicaeditions.com
*Key Personnel*
CEO & Publr: Connie McParland *E-mail:* conniemcparland@guernicaeditions.com
Publr & Ed-in-Chief: Michael Mirolla *E-mail:* michaelmirolla@guernicaeditions.com
Founded: 1978
Translation into English.
ISBN Prefix(es): 978-0-919349; 978-0-920717; 978-2-89135; 978-1-55071
Number of titles published annually: 28 Print
Total Titles: 320 Print; 1 Audio
Foreign Rights: Independent Publishers Group (USA); Paul & Company
*Distribution Center:* Gazelle Book Services (UK), White Cross Mills, High Town, Lancaster LA1 1XS, United Kingdom *Tel:* (0152) 468765 *Fax:* (0152) 463232

**Guideposts Book & Inspirational Media**
16 E 34 St, 12th fl, New York, NY 10016
*Tel:* 212-251-8100 *Toll Free Tel:* 800-431-2344 (cust serv) *Fax:* 212-684-0689
*Web Site:* guideposts.org
*Key Personnel*
VP & Ed-in-Chief: David Morris
Founded: 1948
Inspirational books & videos.
ISBN Prefix(es): 978-0-9661766
Number of titles published annually: 30 Print

**§The Guilford Press**
72 Spring St, 4th fl, New York, NY 10012
SAN: 212-9442
*Tel:* 212-431-9800 *Toll Free Tel:* 800-365-7006 (ext 1, orders) *Fax:* 212-966-6708
*E-mail:* orders@guilford.com; info@guilford.com
*Web Site:* www.guilford.com
*Key Personnel*
Pres & Gen Mgr: Robert Matloff *E-mail:* bob.matloff@guilford.com
Ed-in-Chief: Seymour Weingarten *E-mail:* seymour.weingarten@guilford.com
Busn Mgr: David Mitchell *E-mail:* david.mitchell@guilford.com
Mng Ed: Judith Grauman *E-mail:* judith.grauman@guilford.com
Mktg Dir: Marian Robinson *E-mail:* marian.robinson@guilford.com
Lib Sales Dir & Sales Mgr: Anne Patota *Tel:* 212-431-9800 ext 217 *E-mail:* anne.patota@guilford.com
Prodn Mgr: Katya Edwards *E-mail:* katya.edwards@guilford.com
Asst Sales Mgr: Ms Indre "Indy" Melynis *Tel:* 212-431-9800 ext 229 *E-mail:* indre.melynis@guilford.com
Credit Mgr: Vernita Hurston *Tel:* 212-431-9800 ext 230 *E-mail:* vernita.hurston@guilford.com
Fulfillment Mgr: William McEvoy *E-mail:* william.mcevoy@guilford.com
Intl Rts, Perms & ISBN Contact: Kathy Kuehl *E-mail:* kathy.kuehl@guilford.com
Founded: 1978
Professional & reference books, videos, journals & software in psychology, psychiatry & the behavioral sciences, neuroscience, research methods, education & literacy & geography.
ISBN Prefix(es): 978-0-89862; 978-1-57230; 978-1-59385; 978-1-60623; 978-1-60918; 978-1-4625
Number of titles published annually: 90 Print; 90 E-Book
Total Titles: 1,250 Print; 2 CD-ROM; 450 E-Book; 16 Audio
*Foreign Office(s):* Taylor & Francis Informa UK, 27 Church Rd, Hove, East Sussex BN3 2FA, United Kingdom *Web Site:* www.taylorandfrancis.com
Foreign Rep(s): Cranbury International (Caribbean, Pakistan, South America); Disvan Enterprises (India); Footprint Books (Australia, New Zealand); Horizon Books (South Africa); International Publisher Representatives (Middle East); Taylor & Francis Asia Pacific (Asia, China); Taylor & Francis Informa UK (Europe, UK); Unifacmanu (Taiwan); United Publishers Services (Japan)
*Returns:* c/o Maple Press Distribution Ctr, I-83 Industrial Park, 60 Grumbacher Rd, York, PA 17406
*Warehouse:* c/o Maple Press Distribution Ctr, I-83 Industrial Park, 60 Grumbacher Rd, York, PA 17406

**§Gulf Publishing Co**
2 Greenway Plaza, Suite 1020, Houston, TX 77046
Mailing Address: PO Box 2608, Houston, TX 77252
*Tel:* 713-529-4301 *Fax:* 713-520-4433
*E-mail:* books@gulfpub.com
*Web Site:* www.gulfpub.com
*Key Personnel*
CEO & Pres: John T Royall
Publr, World Oil Magazine: Ron Higgins
Publr, Hydrocarbon Processing: Bill Wageneck
Founded: 1916
Communications company dedicated to the petrochemical industry & related industries.
ISBN Prefix(es): 978-1-933762; 978-0-9765113
Number of titles published annually: 10 Print; 3 CD-ROM
Total Titles: 20 Print; 30 CD-ROM
Distributor for Editions Technip; Elsevier; Pennwell; Simon & Schuster; Wiley

**Hachai Publishing**
527 Empire Blvd, Brooklyn, NY 11225
SAN: 251-3749
*Tel:* 718-633-0100 *Fax:* 718-633-0103
*E-mail:* info@hachai.com
*Web Site:* www.hachai.com
*Key Personnel*
Pres: Yerachmiel Binyominson
Publr & Sales: Yossi Leverton *E-mail:* yossi@hachai.com
Ed: Dina Rosenfeld *E-mail:* dlr@hachai.com
Founded: 1988
Full color children's Judaica books.
ISBN Prefix(es): 978-0-922613; 978-1-929628
Number of titles published annually: 5 Print
Total Titles: 90 Print
Distributor for Attara; Kerem
Membership(s): Association of Jewish Book Publishers; Association of Jewish Libraries; IBPA, the Independent Book Publishers Association

**Hachette Book Group**
Subsidiary of Hachette Livre
237 Park Ave, New York, NY 10017
*Tel:* 212-364-1100 *Toll Free Tel:* 800-759-0190 (cust serv) *Fax:* 212-364-0933 (intl orders) *Toll Free Fax:* 800-286-9471 (cust serv)
*Web Site:* www.HachetteBookGroup.com
*Key Personnel*
Chmn & CEO: David Young
EVP, COO: Ken Michaels
EVP, HBG & CFO: Thomas Maciag
EVP, Chief Mktg/Sales Offr: Evan Schnittman
VP, Distr, Sales & Servs: Todd McGarity
EVP, HBG & Busn Aff & Gen Coun: Carol Ross
EVP, HBG & Publr, Grand Central Publishing: Jamie Raab
EVP, HBG & Publr, Little, Brown and Company: Michael Pietsch
SVP, HBG & Publr, Little, Brown Books for Young Readers: Megan Tingley
SVP, HBG & Publr, Orbit: Tim Holman
SVP, HBG & Publr, Nashville Div: Rolf Zettersten
VP & Communs Dir: Sophie Cottrell
VP, HR: Andrea Weinzimer
SVP, Ad & Promo: Martha Otis
VP, Fulfillment (Boston): Richard Coe
VP, Contracts: Andrea Shallcross
VP, Subs Rts: Nancy Wiese
SVP, CIO: Ralph Munsen
VP, Intl Sales: Bob Michel
Hachette Book Group (HBG) is a leading trade publisher based in New York & a division of Hachette Livre, the second-largest publisher in the world. HBG publishes under the divisions of Little, Brown and Company, Little Brown Books for Young Readers, Grand Central Publishing, Hachette Nashville, Orbit & Hachette Digital.
Divisions: Grand Central Publishing; Hachette Digital; Little, Brown and Company; Little, Brown Books for Young Readers; Nashville Division; Orbit
Distributor for Harry N Abrams Inc; Amazing People Club; Chronicle Books; Disney Book Group; Filipacchi Publishing; Gildan Media; Hachette UK; innovativeKids®; Kensington; Marvel; Microsoft Learning; Octopus Books; Oxmoor House; Phaidon Press; Time Inc Home Entertainment
*Orders to:* Order Dept, Three Center Plaza, Boston, MA 02108 (United States) *Toll Free Tel:* 800-759-0190 *Toll Free Fax:* 800-286-9471 *Web Site:* www.hachettebookgroup.com
*Returns:* Returns Dept, 322 S Enterprise Blvd, Lebanon, IN 46052
*Shipping Address:* Hachette Book Group Distribution Center, 121 N Enterprise Blvd, Lebanon, IN 46052 *Tel:* 765-483-9900 *Fax:* 765-483-0706
*See separate listing for:*
**Center Street**
**FaithWords**
**Grand Central Publishing**
**Hachette Digital**
**Little, Brown and Company**
**Little, Brown Books for Young Readers**
**Orbit**

**Hachette Digital**
Division of Hachette Book Group
237 Park Ave, New York, NY 10017
*Tel:* 212-364-0600
*Key Personnel*
Publr Dir: Anthony Goff
Exec Dir: Neil DeYoung
Dir of Digital Audio Opers: Kim Sayle
Sr Mgr, Digital Accts: Siobhan Padgett
Sr Mktg & Publicity Mgr: Megan Fitzpatrick
Digital Mng Ed: Liz Kessler
Number of titles published annually: 126 Print

**Hackett Publishing Co Inc**
3333 Massachusetts Ave, Indianapolis, IN 46218
SAN: 201-6044
Mailing Address: PO Box 44937, Indianapolis, IN 46244-0937
*Tel:* 317-635-9250 (orders & cust serv) *Fax:* 317-635-9292 *Toll Free Fax:* 800-783-9213
*E-mail:* customer@hackettpublishing.com
*Web Site:* www.hackettpublishing.com
*Key Personnel*
Chair & Publr: James Hullett
VP & Mktg Dir: John Pershing *Tel:* 617-234-0371 *E-mail:* johnp@hackettpublishing.com
Secy & Treas: Cheri Brown
Edit Asst & Off Mgr: Christina Kowalewski *Tel:* 617-234-0375 *E-mail:* christinak@hackettpublishing.com
Founded: 1972
College textbooks & scholarly books; emphasis on philosophy, political theory, political science, classics, history & literature.
ISBN Prefix(es): 978-0-915144; 978-0-915145; 978-0-87220; 978-1-60384
Number of titles published annually: 30 Print; 30 E-Book
Total Titles: 545 Print; 175 E-Book
*Editorial Office(s):* Hackett Publishing Co Inc, PO Box 390007, Cambridge, MA 02139 *Tel:* 617-497-6303 *Fax:* 617-661-8703 *E-mail:* editorial@hackettpublishing.com
*Sales Office(s):* Hackett Publishing Co Inc, PO Box 390007, Cambridge, MA 02139
Distributor for Bryn Mawr Commentaries
Foreign Rep(s): Combined Representatives Worldwide (Asia, The Pacific); Gazelle Book Services Ltd (Europe, UK); UNIREPS (Australia, New Zealand)
Foreign Rights: Eulama
*Orders to:* PO Box 44937, Indianapolis, IN 46244-0937

**Hadronic Press Inc**
35246 US 19 N, No 115, Palm Harbor, FL 34684
*Tel:* 727-934-9593 *Fax:* 727-934-9275
*E-mail:* hadronic@tampabay.rr.com
*Web Site:* www.hadronicpress.com
*Key Personnel*
Pres: Carla G Gandiglio
Founded: 1978
Mathematics & physics; theoretical biology & chemistry.
ISBN Prefix(es): 978-1-57485
Number of titles published annually: 10 Print
Total Titles: 92 Print

**§Hagstrom Map & Travel Center**
Subsidiary of American Map Corp
51 W 43 St, New York, NY 10036
SAN: 203-543X
*Toll Free Tel:* 800-432-MAPS (432-6277) *Fax:* 212-398-9856
*Web Site:* www.americanmap.com
*Key Personnel*
Chmn: Andreas Langenscheidt
Pres: Marc Jennings *Fax:* 718-784-3294
Dir, Cartography: Vera Lorenz
Founded: 1916
Maps, atlases, guides.
ISBN Prefix(es): 978-0-88097
Total Titles: 1 CD-ROM
Distributor for ADC The Map People; American Map Corp; Arrow Maps Inc; Creative Sales Corp; De Lorme Atlas; Hammond World Atlas Corp; Langenscheidt; RV International Maps & Atlases; Stubs Guides; Trakker Maps Inc
*Advertising Agency:* ATL/SD, Contact: Sara Ascalon *E-mail:* sascalon@americanmap.com

**§Haights Cross Communications Inc**
136 Madison Ave, 8th fl, New York, NY 10016
*Tel:* 212-209-0500 *Fax:* 212-209-0501
*E-mail:* info@haightscross.com
*Web Site:* www.haightscross.com
*Key Personnel*
CEO & Pres: Ronald Schlosser *Tel:* 914-289-9420 *Fax:* 914-289-9421
CFO: Paul J Crecca *E-mail:* pjcrecca@haightscross.com
SVP, Fin & Planning & Treas: Melissa L Linsky
SVP, Mkt Res: Julie Latzer *Tel:* 914-289-9400 ext 452 *E-mail:* jlatzer@haightscross.com
CEO & Pres, Triumph Learning: Kevin McAliley *Tel:* 212-652-0222 *E-mail:* kmcaliley@triumphlearning.com
CEO & Pres, Recorded Books: R Scott Williams
CEO & Pres, Options Publishing: Gunnar Voltz *E-mail:* gvoltz@optionspublishing.com
Pres, Buckle Down Publishing: Thomas Emerick *E-mail:* temerick@buckledown.com
Founded: 1996
Educational & professional publishing group that creates books, instructional materials, audio products, periodicals, software & online services, serving the following markets: K-12 supplemental education, public & school library publishing, audio books & medical publishing.
Number of titles published annually: 856 Print; 10 CD-ROM; 50 Online; 10 E-Book; 787 Audio
Total Titles: 6,200 Print; 20 CD-ROM; 50 Online; 10 E-Book; 5,808 Audio
Subsidiaries: Buckle Down Publishing (www.buckledown.com); Oakstone Medical Publishing; Options Publishing; Recorded Books; Sundance/Newbridge Publishing; Triumph Learning
*Foreign Office(s):* Recorded Books/W F Howes, Rearsby Business Park, Unit 3, Gaddesby Lane, Rearsby, Leics LE7 4YH, United Kingdom, Mng Dir: Sean Sibley *Tel:* (011) 0016-230-1144 *Fax:* (011) 0016-230-1155
Membership(s): AAP; ALA; Audio Publishers Association; International Reading Association; Specialized Information Publishers Association
*See separate listing for:*
**Triumph Learning**

**§Hal Leonard Books**
Imprint of Hal Leonard Performing Arts Publishing Group
33 Plymouth St, Suite 302, Montclair, NJ 07042
*Tel:* 973-337-5034 *Fax:* 973-337-5227
*Key Personnel*
Publr: John Cerullo
Founded: 1984
Publisher of books on the music business, audio technology, instrument history & more.
ISBN Prefix(es): 978-1-4234
Number of titles published annually: 30 Print
Total Titles: 1,000 Print; 300 E-Book
Imprints: Amadeus Press (classical music & opera); Applause Theatre & Cinema Books; Backbeat Books (music trade books); Limelight Editions (instruction, ref & how-to titles)
*Sales Office(s):* 7777 W Bluemound Rd, Milwaukee, WI 53213, Contact: Doug Lady *Tel:* 414-774-3630
*Returns:* Hal Leonard, 1210 Innovation Dr, Winona, MN 55987, Contact: Kim Jereczek *E-mail:* kjereczek@halleonard.com
*Warehouse:* Hal Leonard, 1210 Innovation Dr, Winona, MN 55987, Contact: Tony Prodzinski *E-mail:* tprodzinski@halleonard.com

**§Hal Leonard Corp**
7777 W Bluemound Rd, Milwaukee, WI 53213
Mailing Address: PO Box 13819, Milwaukee, WI 53213-0819
*Tel:* 414-774-3630 *Toll Free Tel:* 800-524-4425 *Fax:* 414-774-3259
*E-mail:* sales@halleonard.com
*Web Site:* www.halleonard.com; twitter.com/#!/HalleonardBooks
*Key Personnel*
Chmn & CEO: Keith Mardak

Pres: Larry Morton
Publicity Mgr: Lori Hagopian *Tel:* 414-479-8406
*E-mail:* lhagopian@halleonard.com
Sales Mgr, Book Trade: Mike Hansen
*E-mail:* mhansen@halleonard.com
Consumer Prods Accts Mgr: David Cywinski
*E-mail:* dcywinski@halleonard.com
Founded: 1947
The world's largest music print publisher, with an incomparable selection of sheet music, songbooks, music related books, self-instruction books, CD packs & videos, music reference & special interest titles, music biographies, children's music products; CD-ROMs, DVDs, performance videos & more. Additional offices in New York, Nashville, Australia, Belgium, France, Germany, Holland, Italy, Switzerland & the UK.
ISBN Prefix(es): 978-1-57424; 978-1-57560; 978-0-88188; 978-0-7935; 978-0-634; 978-1-14234
Number of titles published annually: 2,000 Print
Total Titles: 200,000 Print; 15 CD-ROM
Imprints: Berklee Press; Centerstream Publications; Cherry Lane Music Co; Ashley Mark Publishing Co; Musicians Institute Press; G Shirmer; Vintage Guitar
Distributor for Amadeus Press; Applause Theatre & Cinema Books; Artistpro; Ashley Music; Backbeat Books; Beacon Music; Berklee Press; Fred Bock Music Company; Boosey & Hawkes; Centerstream Publications; Cherry Lane Music Co; Cinema Books; Community Music Videos; Creative Concepts; DC Publications; Devine Entertainment Corp; Editions Durand; Editions Max Eschig; Editions Salabert; EM Books; EMI Christian; Faber Music Ltd; Guitar One; Guitar World; Home Recording; Homespun Tapes; Houston Publications; Hudson Music; iSong CD-ROMs; Jawbone Press; Kenyon Publications; Limelight Editions; Ashley Mark Publishing Co; Edward B Marks Music; Meredith Music; Modern Drummer Publications; Music Sales America; Musicians Institute Press; Musikverlage Han Sikorski; Christopher Parkening; Reader's Digest; Record Research; Ricordi; Lee Roberts Publications; Rubank Publications; G Schirmer Inc (Associated Music Publishers); Second Floor Music; Sing Out Corp; Star Licks Videos; Bernard Stein Music Co; String Letter Press; Tara Publications; Transcontinental Music; 21st Century Publications; Vintage Guitar; Word Music; Writer's Digest
*Shipping Address:* 1210 Innovation Dr, Winona, MN 55987 *Tel:* 507-454-2920 *Fax:* 507-454-4042
*Warehouse:* 960 E Mark St, Winona, MN 55987
*Distribution Center:* 1210 Innovation Dr, Winona, MN 55987

**Halcyon Press Ltd**
2206 N Gordon St, Suite D, Alvin, TX 77511
Mailing Address: PO Box 260, Pearland, TX 77588
*Tel:* 281-585-9559 *Toll Free Tel:* 866-774-5786
*E-mail:* info@halcyon-press.com; editor@halcyonpress.com
*Web Site:* www.halcyonpress.com
*Key Personnel*
Ed: David Raley *Fax:* 713-774-5788
*E-mail:* david.raley@gmail.com
Founded: 2000
Commercial book publisher.
ISBN Prefix(es): 978-0-9706054; 978-1-931823
Number of titles published annually: 3 Print
Total Titles: 100 Print; 220 E-Book
Imprints: Kingsley Literary Services
Distributor for Plato Publishing

**Half Halt Press Inc**
20042 Benevola Church Rd, Boonsboro, MD 21713
Mailing Address: PO Box 67, Boonsboro, MD 21713-0067
*Tel:* 301-733-7119 *Toll Free Tel:* 800-822-9635 (orders) *Fax:* 301-733-7408
*E-mail:* mail@halfhaltpress.com
*Key Personnel*
Publr: Elizabeth Rowland *E-mail:* elizabeth@halfhaltpress.com
Founded: 1985
Publish own equestrian titles exclusively & distribute for British equestrian publisher. Horses & horsemanship & equestrian related topics.
ISBN Prefix(es): 978-0-939481; 978-1-872082; 978-1-872119
Number of titles published annually: 6 Print
Total Titles: 175 Print
Distributor for The Kenilworth Press Ltd; Quiller Publishing

**Hamilton Books**
Member of Rowman & Littlefield Publishing Group
4501 Forbes Blvd, Suite 200, Lanham, MD 20706
*Tel:* 301-459-3366 *Toll Free Tel:* 800-462-6420 (cust serv) *Fax:* 301-429-5748
*Toll Free Fax:* 800-388-4550 (cust serv)
*Web Site:* www.hamilton-books.com
*Key Personnel*
VP: Julie Kirsch *Tel:* 301-459-3366 ext 5309
*E-mail:* jkirsch@rowman.com
Founded: 2002
Serious nonfiction: memoirs, biographies, autobiographies, religious perspectives.
ISBN Prefix(es): 978-0-7618
Number of titles published annually: 40 Print; 40 E-Book
Total Titles: 150 Print; 80 E-Book
Membership(s): AAP

**§Hamilton Stone Editions**
PO Box 43, Maplewood, NJ 07040
*Tel:* 973-378-8361
*E-mail:* hstone@hamiltonstone.org
*Web Site:* www.hamiltonstone.org
*Key Personnel*
Edit Dir: Meredith Sue Willis
*E-mail:* meredithsuewillis@gmail.com
Artistic Dir: Lynda Schor *E-mail:* lynda.schor@gmail.com
Dir: Halvard Johnson *E-mail:* halvard@gmail.com; Edith Konecky *E-mail:* erkonecky@verizon.net; Nathan Leslie *E-mail:* nleslie@nvcc.edu; Carole Rosenthal
*E-mail:* crlrosenthal@gmail.com
Founded: 2003
Independent press for independent literary writing. Dedicated to vivid writing that probes the hidden realities of the everyday, valuing most highly the kind of writing that displays a multifaced vision. Interested in keeping new books in print & bringing forgotten, excellent old books back into print.
ISBN Prefix(es): 978-0-9654043; 978-0-9714873
Number of titles published annually: 4 Print; 3 E-Book
Total Titles: 30 Print; 10 E-Book
*Shipping Address:* 311 Prospect St, South Orange, NJ 07079

**Hampton Press Inc**
307 Seventh Ave, Suite 506, New York, NY 10001
*Tel:* 646-638-3800 *Toll Free Tel:* 800-894-8955
*Fax:* 646-638-3802
*E-mail:* hamptonpr1@aol.com
*Web Site:* www.hamptonpress.com
*Key Personnel*
Pres: Barbara Bernstein
Founded: 1992
ISBN Prefix(es): 978-1-881303; 978-1-57273; 978-1-61289
Number of titles published annually: 35 Print
Total Titles: 650 Print
Foreign Rep(s): Eurospan Group (Asia, Australia, Europe, UK)

**Hampton Roads Publishing Co Inc**
211 E High St, Charlottesville, VA 22902
*Tel:* 978-465-0504 *Toll Free Tel:* 800-423-7087 (orders) *Fax:* 978-465-0243
*E-mail:* hrpub@rwwbooks.com
*Web Site:* www.hamptonroadspub.com
*Key Personnel*
CEO & Pres: Randy Davila
Sales & Mktg Dir: Greg Brandenburgh
Founded: 1989
Trade publishing, specialize in metaphysics, self-help, integrative medicine, visionary fiction, paranormal phenomena.
ISBN Prefix(es): 978-1-878901; 978-1-57174
Number of titles published annually: 30 Print
Total Titles: 350 Print; 2 Audio
Distributed by Red Wheel/Weiser LLC
Foreign Rights: Linda Biagi (Worldwide)
*Warehouse:* Hampton Roads Publishing Co Inc, c/o Books International, 22883 Quicksilver Dr, Dulles, VA 20166

**§Hancock House Publishers**
1431 Harrison Ave, Blaine, WA 98230-5005
*Tel:* 604-538-1114 *Toll Free Tel:* 800-938-1114
*Fax:* 604-538-2262 *Toll Free Fax:* 800-983-2262
*E-mail:* sales@hancockhouse.com
*Web Site:* www.hancockhouse.com
*Key Personnel*
Publr & Intl Rts: David Hancock
Founded: 1975
Specialize in natural history (world) & regional northwest history.
ISBN Prefix(es): 978-0-88839
Number of titles published annually: 15 Print
Total Titles: 240 Print
*Branch Office(s)*
19313 Zero Ave, Surrey, BC V3S 9R9, Canada

**Handprint Books Inc**
Imprint of Chronicle Books LLC
413 Sixth Ave, Brooklyn, NY 11215-3310
*Tel:* 718-768-3696 *Toll Free Tel:* 800-722-6657 (orders) *Fax:* 718-369-0844 *Toll Free Fax:* 800-858-7787 (orders)
*E-mail:* info@handprintbooks.com
*Web Site:* www.handprintbooks.com
*Key Personnel*
Pres & Publr: Christopher Franceschelli
*E-mail:* cmf@handprintbooks.com
Exec Ed: Ann Tobias *Tel:* 718-768-1414
*E-mail:* anntobias@handprintbooks.com
Founded: 2000
Publisher of high-quality books for children.
ISBN Prefix(es): 978-1-929766; 978-1-59354
Number of titles published annually: 12 Print
Distributed by Chronicle Books
*Returns:* Chronicle Books, c/o Genco Fullfillment, 1585 Linda Way, Door 1, Sparks, NV 89431

**Hanging Loose Press**
231 Wyckoff St, Brooklyn, NY 11217
SAN: 206-4960
*Tel:* 347-529-4738 *Fax:* 347-227-8215
*E-mail:* print225@aol.com
*Web Site:* www.hangingloosepress.com
*Key Personnel*
Ed & Intl Rts: Robert Hershon
Ed: Dick Lourie; Mark Pawlak
Founded: 1966
Poetry & short fiction.
ISBN Prefix(es): 978-0-914610; 978-1-882413; 978-1-931236
Number of titles published annually: 8 Print
Total Titles: 200 Print
Membership(s): Council of Literary Magazines & Presses

**Hanley-Wood LLC**
Division of Hanley-Wood Inc
One Thomas Circle NW, Suite 600, Washington, DC 20005
*Tel:* 202-452-0800 *Fax:* 202-785-1974
*Web Site:* www.hanleywood.com
*Key Personnel*
CEO: Frank Anton *E-mail:* fanton@handleywood.com
Ed-at-Large: Richard Yelton *Tel:* 630-605-7203 *E-mail:* ryelton@hanleywood.com
Founded: 1956
Books & trade magazines on concrete construction, masonry construction & concrete production.
ISBN Prefix(es): 978-0-924659
Number of titles published annually: 10 Print
Total Titles: 40 Print; 1 CD-ROM

**Hannacroix Creek Books Inc**
1127 High Ridge Rd, No 110-B, Stamford, CT 06905-1203
SAN: 299-9560
*Tel:* 203-968-8098 *Fax:* 203-968-0193
*E-mail:* hannacroix@aol.com
*Web Site:* www.hannacroixcreekbooks.com
*Key Personnel*
CEO & Pres: Dr Jan Yager
Founded: 1996
Trade publisher of quality & innovative fiction & nonfiction books & journals that entertain, educate & inform.
ISBN Prefix(es): 978-1-889262
Number of titles published annually: 5 Print; 3 E-Book; 2 Audio
Total Titles: 28 Print; 3 E-Book; 2 Audio
Foreign Rep(s): International Editors' Co (Flavia Sala) (Brazil)
Foreign Rights: Bookman (Scandinavia); Lora Fountain & Associates Literary Agency (France); Antonia Kerrigan Literary Agency (Latin America, Spain)
Membership(s): AAP; IBPA, the Independent Book Publishers Association; Women's Media Group

**§Hanser Publications LLC**
Subsidiary of Carl Hanser Verlag GmbH & Co KG
6915 Valley Ave, Cincinnati, OH 45244-3029
*Tel:* 513-527-8977 *Toll Free Tel:* 800-950-8977; 877-751-5052 (orders) *Fax:* 513-534-7803 *Toll Free Fax:* 800-527-8801
*E-mail:* info@hanserpublications.com
*Web Site:* www.hanserpublications.com
*Key Personnel*
Mktg Mgr: Valerie Lauer *E-mail:* valerie.lauer@hanserpublications.com
Founded: 1993
Technical & reference books & related products in manufacturing, metalworking & products finishing. Hanser Publishers: technical, engineering & science reference books, monographs, textbooks & journals in plastics technology, polymer & materials science.
ISBN Prefix(es): 978-1-56990
Number of titles published annually: 17 Print
Total Titles: 312 Print; 250 Online
*Foreign Office(s):* Carl Hanser Verlag, Kolbergerstr 22, 81679 Munich, Germany, Contact: Wolfgang Beisler *Tel:* (089) 99 93 00 *Fax:* (089) 98 48 09
Distributor for Gardner Publications Inc; Hanser Gardner Publications (imprint also); Hanser Publishers (call Hanser Verlag)
Foreign Rep(s): Allied Publishers Pvt (India, Nepal, Sri Lanka); D A Book Depot Pty (Australia, New Zealand, Papua New Guinea); Eastern Book Services (Japan); Michael Goh (Singapore)
*Warehouse:* 6925 Valley Ave, Cincinnati, OH 45244
*Distribution Center:* Ware-Pak LLC, 2427 Bond St, University Heights, IL 60484 *Tel:* 708-587-4124 *Toll Free Tel:* 877-751-5052 *E-mail:* hanser@ware-pak.com

**§Harcourt Achieve**
Division of Houghton Mifflin Harcourt
6277 Sea Harbor Dr, Orlando, FL 32887
*Tel:* 407-345-2000 *Toll Free Tel:* 800-531-5015 (cust serv/orders) *Toll Free Fax:* 800-699-9459 (cust serv/orders)
*Web Site:* www.harcourtachieve.com
*Key Personnel*
CEO & Pres: Linda K Zecher
CFO & COO: Eric Shuman
COO, HMH Pub Co: Joel Zucker
EVP: William Bayers
VP, Communs: Joe Blumenfeld *Tel:* 617-351-5000 *E-mail:* joe.blumenfeld@hmhco.com
Founded: 2001
Educational materials for PreK, elementary, secondary, test preparation, ESL & professional development for educators.
ISBN Prefix(es): 978-0-8172; 978-0-8114; 978-0-7312; 978-0-7327; 978-0-7901; 978-0-7578; 978-0-7635; 978-1-4189; 978-0-7398; 978-1-4190; 978-1-5574; 978-0-4350; 978-0-9473
Total Titles: 8,000 Print; 8,000 Online
*See separate listing for:*
**Rigby**

**§Harcourt Inc**
Division of Houghton Mifflin Harcourt
6277 Sea Harbor Dr, Orlando, FL 32887
SAN: 200-2736
*Tel:* 407-345-2000 *Toll Free Tel:* 800-225-5425 (cust serv/orders) *Toll Free Fax:* 800-269-5232 (cust serv/orders)
*Web Site:* www.hmhco.com
*Key Personnel*
CEO & Pres: Linda K Zecher
CFO & COO: Eric Shuman
COO, HMH Pub Co: Joel Zucker
EVP: William Bayers
VP, Communs: Joe Blumenfeld *Tel:* 617-351-5000 *E-mail:* joe.blumenfeld@hmhco.com
Founded: 1919
ISBN Prefix(es): 978-0-15
Total Titles: 8,000 Print; 8,000 Online
Imprints: Great Source; Harcourt Achieve; Rigby; Saxon; Steck Vaughn
Membership(s): AAP; BISG; Children's Book Council; Software & Information Industry Association
*See separate listing for:*
**Harcourt Mifflin School Publishers**

**Harcourt Inc**, see Houghton Mifflin Harcourt

**§Harcourt Mifflin School Publishers**
Division of Harcourt Inc
6277 Sea Harbor Dr, Orlando, FL 32887
*Tel:* 407-345-2000 *Toll Free Tel:* 800-225-5425 (cust serv) *Fax:* 407-345-3016 (cust serv) *Toll Free Fax:* 800-874-6418; 800-269-5232 (cust serv)
*Web Site:* www.harcourtschool.com
*Key Personnel*
SVP, Sales & Mktg: Katie Crowe-Lile
SVP, Mktg: Margaret deBoer
VP & Ed-in-Chief, Math: Patricia Brill
VP & Ed-in-Chief, Science & Health: Peggy Smith Herbst
Founded: 1919
ISBN Prefix(es): 978-0-15
Number of titles published annually: 500 Print
Total Titles: 20,000 Print; 43 CD-ROM; 3,500 E-Book; 466 Audio
*Sales Office(s):* 5513 N Cumberland Ave, Chicago, IL 60656 *Tel:* 773-594-5110 *Toll Free Fax:* 800-787-8707
1175 N Stemmons Fwy, Lewisville, TX 75067 *Toll Free Tel:* 800-426-6577 *E-mail:* hsplewis@harcourtschool.com
*Warehouse:* Interstate Industrial Park, 151 Heller & Benigno Blvd, Bellmawr, NJ 08031-2515
1175 N Stemmons Fwy, Lewisville, TX 75067

**§Hard Shell Word Factory**
Imprint of Mundania Press LLC
6457 Glenway Ave, No 109, Cincinnati, OH 45211
*Toll Free Tel:* 888-232-0808 *Toll Free Fax:* 888-460-4752
*E-mail:* books@hardshell.com
*Web Site:* www.hardshell.com
Founded: 1996
Royalty publisher of fiction & nonfiction books, e-books & trade paperback.
ISBN Prefix(es): 978-1-58200; 978-0-7599
Number of titles published annually: 50 Print; 60 E-Book
Total Titles: 325 Print; 450 E-Book
Imprints: HSWF
Distributed by All-Romance Ebooks; Amazon Kindle; Apple iBookStore; B&N.com; Fictionwise; Lightning Source/Ingram; Mobipocket; Smashwords
Membership(s): Electronically Published Internet Connection; IBPA, the Independent Book Publishers Association

**Harlan Davidson Inc/Forum Press Inc**
773 Glenn Ave, Wheeling, IL 60090-6900
SAN: 201-2375
*Tel:* 847-541-9720 *Fax:* 847-541-9830
*E-mail:* harlandavidson@harlandavidson.com
*Web Site:* www.harlandavidson.com
*Key Personnel*
Chmn of the Bd & Pres: Angela E Davidson
VP & Cont: Dorothy Kopf
VP & Ed: Andrew J Davidson
Prodn Mgr: Linda Gaio
Founded: 1972
College & secondary textbooks, classics.
ISBN Prefix(es): 978-0-88295; 978-0-88273
Number of titles published annually: 5 Print
Total Titles: 240 Print
Imprints: American History Series; Crofts Classics Series
Foreign Rep(s): Gazelle Book Services (Europe, Near East)
Membership(s): National Association of College Stores

**Harlequin Enterprises Ltd**
Subsidiary of Torstar Corp
233 Broadway, Suite 1001, New York, NY 10279
SAN: 200-2450
*Tel:* 212-553-4200 *Fax:* 212-227-8969
*E-mail:* CustomerService@harlequin.com
*Web Site:* www.harlequin.com
*Key Personnel*
Edit Dir: Margaret Marbury
Sr Exec Ed: Tara Gavin; Glenda Howard
Exec Ed: Joan Marlow Golan; Mary-Theresa Hussey
Exec Ed, MIRA: Tara Parsons
Mng Ed: Kathleen Reed
Mng Edit Coord, NY/Toronto: Beth Attwood
Sr Ed: Gail Chasan; Tina James; Patience Bloom; Ann Leslie Tuttle; Denise Zaza
Sr Ed, Mira Books: Erika Imranyi
Sr Ed, Silhouette Desire: Stacy Boyd
Ed: Rebecca Hunt
Ed, Carina Press: Kerri Buckley
Assoc Ed, HQN & LUNA: Kate Dresser
Ed-at-Large: Leslie Wainger
Publicity Mgr, Fiction: Emer Flounders
Assoc Publicist: Lauren Jackson; Jessica Rosenberg
Founded: 1980

Adult contemporary, historical romance novels & women's fiction.
ISBN Prefix(es): 978-0-373
Number of titles published annually: 1,400 Print
Imprints: Carina Press; Harlequin; HQN Books; Kimani; Luna Books; MIRA Books; Red Dress Ink; Silhouette; Steeple Hill
Distributed by Simon & Schuster Mass Merchandise Sales Co
*Distribution Center:* 3010 Walden Ave, Depew, NY 14043
Membership(s): AAP; Association of Canadian Publishers; BISG

**§Harmonie Park Press**
Liberty Professional Ctr, 35675 Mound Rd, Sterling Heights, MI 48310-4727
SAN: 206-7641
*Tel:* 586-979-2077; 586-979-1844 (cust serv)
*Toll Free Tel:* 800-422-4880 *Fax:* 586-979-1786; 586-979-1863 (cust serv)
*E-mail:* info@harmonieparkpress.com
*Web Site:* harmonieparkpress.com
*Key Personnel*
Pres, Busn Mgr, Rts & Perms: Elaine Gorzelski *E-mail:* egorzelski@harmonieparkpress.com
VP: David Gorzelski
Data Proc Mgr: Darlene Brown
Mng Ed: Karen Simmons; Samuel Wiersma
Ed: Jennifer Burke; Patricia O'Connor; Claire Ann Selestow; Randi Vincent; Barbara Williams
Founded: 1948
Music reference works, original monographs in musicology.
ISBN Prefix(es): 978-0-911772; 978-0-89990
Number of titles published annually: 10 Print; 1 Online
Total Titles: 100 Print; 1 CD-ROM; 1 Online
Membership(s): Music Library Association

**HarperCollins Children's Books**
Division of HarperCollins Publishers
10 E 53 St, New York, NY 10022
SAN: 202-5760
*Tel:* 212-207-7000
*Web Site:* www.harpercollinschildrens.com
*Key Personnel*
Pres & Publr: Susan Katz *E-mail:* Susan.Katz@harpercollins.com
SVP, Assoc Publr & Ed-in-Chief: Kate Jackson *E-mail:* Kate.Jackson@harpercollins.com
SVP, Children's Sales: Andrea Pappenheimer *E-mail:* Andrea.Pappenheimer@harpercollins.com
VP, Children's Mktg: Diane Naughton *E-mail:* Diane.Naughton@harpercollins.com
VP, Fin: Randy Rosema *E-mail:* Randy.Rosema@harpercollins.com
VP, Prodn & Creative Opers: Tracey Menzies
Exec Art Dir: Alison Donalty; Amy Ryan
Edit Dir: Rosemary Brosnan; Nancy Inteli
Dir, Children's Inventory: Sheryl Moore-Anderson
Dir, Integrated Mktg: Lauren Flower
Dir, Intellectual Property Devt: Dan Ehrenhaft
Exec Ed: Alexandra Cooper; Kristen Pettit
Exec Ed, Katherine Tegen Books: Claudia Gabel; Anica Rissi
Sr Ed: Sarah Landis; Abby Ranger
Assoc Ed, Balzer & Bray: Sara Sargent
Ed: Karen Chaplin; Jocelyn Davies; Andrew Harwell; Molly O'Neill
Publicity Mgr: Caroline Sun
Picture books, juvenile fiction & nonfiction, young adult novels.
ISBN Prefix(es): 978-0-06; 978-0-688; 978-0-380; 978-0-694; 978-0-690
Imprints: Amistad; Balzer & Bray; Collins; Greenwillow Books; HarperCollins Children's Audio; HarperCollins Children's Books; HarperCollins e-books; HarperFestival; HarperTeen; HarperTrophy; Rayo; Katherine Tegen Books; TOKYOPOP; Walden Pond Press
Membership(s): Children's Book Council

**HarperCollins General Books Group**
Division of HarperCollins Publishers
10 E 53 St, New York, NY 10022
*Tel:* 212-207-7000 *Fax:* 212-207-7633
*Web Site:* www.harpercollins.com
*Key Personnel*
Pres & Publr: Michael Morrison
SVP: Claudia Boutote
SVP & Publr, It Books & Deputy Publr, Morrow/Voyager/Avon: Lynn Grady
SVP & Publr, Perennial: Jonathan Burnham
SVP & Publr, William Morrow/Eos/Avon/Harper Paperbacks: Liate Stehlik
SVP & Dir, Dom & Foreign Rts: Brenda Segel *E-mail:* Brenda.Segel@harpercollins.com
SVP & Exec Ed, Harper Div & Edit Dir, Harper Perennial & Harper Paperbacks: Cal Morgan
SVP & Exec Ed: Karen Rinaldi
SVP, Fin & Publg: Len Marshall *E-mail:* Len.Marshall@harpercollins.com
SVP, Publicity: Tina Andreadis
Pres & Publr, Ecco: Daniel Halpern
Pres & Publr, HarperCollins' General Books Group: Michael Morrison
VP: Gideon Weil
VP & Publr, Harper Busn: Hollis Heimbouch
VP & Publr, Harper Design: Marta Schooler
VP & Exec Ed, William Morrow: Dan Mallory
VP & Assoc Publr, Ecco & Amistad: Craig Young
VP, Deputy Gen Counsel: Beth Silfin
VP, Mktg: Carrie Bloxson
VP, Prodn & Creative Opers: Tracey Menzies
Publr, Amistad & Exec Ed, Ecco: Dawn Davis
Exec Dir, Digital Prod Devt: Adrianna Dufay; Brian Perrin
Assoc Publr, Harper Perennial & Harper Paperbacks: Amy Baker
Assoc Publr, It Books: Kevin Callahan
Chief Mktg Offr: Angela Tribelli
Sr Dir, Mktg, Harper/Harper Business/Broadside Books: Leah Wasielewski
Sr Dir, Mktg, HarperOne: Laina Adler
Sr Dir, Publicity/Harper One: Suzanne Wickham
Sr Dir, Publicity, Morrow/Avon: Ben Bruton; Pamela Spengler-Jaffee
Sr Mktg Dir, William Morrow: Tavia Kowalchuk
Edit Dir, Amistad: Tracy Sherrod
Edit Dir, Broadside Books: Adam Bellow
Edit Dir, William Morrow/Avon: Erika Tsang
Dir, Audience Devt: Jim Hanas
Dir, Prodn Edit, Harper, Harper Business & Collins Reference: John Jusino
Dir, Brand Devt, William Morrow: Kathryn Gordon
Dir, Publicity: Brianne Halverson
Publg Opers Dir, Willian Morrow & Ecco: Catherine Felgar
Publicity Dir, Harper One: Darcy Cohan; Melinda Mullen
Publicity Dir, William Morrow & Avon: Shelby Meizlik
Assoc Dir, Mktg: Brianne Halverson; Katie O'Callaghan
Assoc Dir, Mktg, It Books & Harper Design: Michael Barrs
Assoc Dir, Publicity, Harper One: Julie Burton
Assoc Dir, Publicity, It Books: Heidi Metcalfe
Assoc Dir, Publicity, Morrow/Avon: Danielle Bartlett
Publicity Mgr, Ecco: Ashley Garland
Sr Mktg Mgr: Stephanie Selah
Sr Mgr, Digital Mktg: Dana Trombley
Exec Ed: Julie Will
Exec Ed, Creative Devt: Matt Harper
Exec Ed, Ecco: Hilary Redmon
Exec Ed, Harper Children's: Erica Sussman
Exec Ed, HarperOne: Roger Freet
Exec Ed, It Books: Mark Chait; Esther Margolis; Carrie Thornton
Exec Ed, William Morrow: Peter Hubbard; Rachel Kahan; Adam Korn
Sr Ed: May Chen; Katherine Nintzel; Denise Oswald
Sr Ed, HarperOne: Genoveva Llosa; Jeanette Perez
Ed: Maya Ziv
Ed, Ecco: Libby Edelson
Ed, William Morrow/Avon: Amanda Bergeron; Emily Krump; Tessa Woodward
ISBN Prefix(es): 978-0-06
Imprints: Amistad; Avon; Avon Impulse (digital only); Avon Inspire; Avon Red; Bourbon Street Books; Broadside Books; Caedmon; Collins; Ecco; Harper; Harper Business; Harper Design; Harper Paperbacks; Harper Perennial; Harper Voyager; Harper Wave; HarperAudio; HarperBibles; HarperCollins; HarperCollins e-Books; HarperLuxe (large print); HarperOne; Infinitum Nihil; It Books; Dennis Lehane Books; William Morrow; William Morrow Trade Paperbacks; Newmarket Press for It Books; Rayo

**§HarperCollins Publishers**
Subsidiary of News Corporation
10 E 53 St, New York, NY 10022
SAN: 200-2086
*Tel:* 212-207-7000 *Fax:* 212-207-7145
*Web Site:* www.harpercollins.com
*Key Personnel*
CEO: Brian Murray *E-mail:* Brian.Murray@harpercollins.com
EVP, Opers & Technol: Larry Nevins
Chief Digital Offr: Chantal Restivo-Alessi
CFO: Janet Gervasio *E-mail:* Janet.Gervasio@harpercollins.com
CIO: Rick Schwartz *E-mail:* Rick.Schwartz@harpercollins.com
SVP & Gen Coun: Chris Goff
SVP, Consumer Insight: David Boyle
SVP, HR: Diane Bailey
SVP, Mkt Insight & Sales Opers: Frank Albanese
Pres, Sales: Josh Marwell *E-mail:* Josh.Marwell@harpercollins.com
SVP, Sales Analytics: Dan Lubart
SVP, Dist Opers: Joe Franceschelli
VP, Corp Communs: Erin Crum
VP, Assoc Gen Coun: Kyran Cassidy
VP & Dir, Foreign Rts: Juliette Shapland
VP, Prodn & Creative Opers: Tracey Menzies
Affiliate Publr, Harper Collins 360: Jean Marie Kelly
Asst Mgr, Corp Communs: Katie Levine
Founded: 1817
HarperCollins is one of the leading English-language publishers in the world & is a subsidiary of News Corp (NYSE: NWS, NWS.A; ASX: NCP, NCPDP). Headquartered in New York, the company has publishing groups in the US, Canada, Australasia & the UK. Its publishing groups (US) include the HarperCollins General Books Group, HarperCollins Children's Books Group, Zondervan; outside the US: HarperCollins Australia, HarperCollins Canada, HarperCollins India, HarperCollins New Zealand & HarperCollins UK.
ISBN Prefix(es): 978-0-06; 978-0-688; 978-0-380; 978-0-694
Number of titles published annually: 1,700 Print
Imprints: Beech Tree Books; Greenwillow Books; HarperCollins; Hearst Books; It Books; Lothrop, Lee & Shepard Books; Morrow Junior Books; Mulberry Books; Quill Trade Paperbacks
Distributed by Cynthia Publishing Co; Ingram Publisher Services/Spring Arbor (Christian market)
Distributor for Perseus (Addison Wesley Trade); Basic Books; Civitas; Counterpoint; Delphinium Books; GT Publishing; Public Affairs; TV Books

Foreign Rep(s): Publishers International Marketing Services
Foreign Rights: Kezban Akcali Agency (Turkey); Antonella Antonelli Agenzia (Italy); Bardon Far Eastern Agents (China, Taiwan); Eliane Benisti Literary Agency (France); Mercedes Casanovas (Spain); Lynn Franklin (Russia); June Hall Literary Agency; Kooy & Van Gerderen Agency (Netherlands); Licht & Licht Agency (Denmark, Finland, Norway, Sweden); Rogan Pikarski Literary Agency (Israel); Gerd Plessl Agency (Czech Republic, Greece, Hungary, Montenegro, Poland, Serbia); Tuttle-Mori Agency Inc (Japan)
*Advertising Agency:* Franklin Spier Inc
Membership(s): AAP; BISG
*See separate listing for:*
**HarperCollins Children's Books**
**HarperCollins General Books Group**
**Zondervan, A HarperCollins Company**

**HarperCollins Publishers Sales**
10 E 53 St, New York, NY 10022
*Fax:* 212-207-7000
*Web Site:* www.harpercollins.com
*Key Personnel*
Pres, Sales: Josh Marwell *E-mail:* Josh.Marwell@harpercollins.com
SVP, Children's Sales: Andrea Pappenheimer *E-mail:* Andrea.Pappenheimer@harpercollins.com
SVP, Group Sales Dir, Gen Books: Doug Jones
SVP, Mkt Insight & Sales Opers: Frank Albanese
SVP, Sales Analytics & Pricing: Dan Lubart
VP & Deputy Dir, Sales: Mary Beth Thomas
VP & Deputy Dir, Sales, Children's: Kerry Moynagh
Dir, Sales & Retail Mktg: Kristine Macrides
Natl Acct Mgr: Rachel Levenberg
Mgr, Sales Opers: Eric Lovaas
Asst Mgr, Sales & Retail Mktg: Lillie Walsh
Founded: 1817
Group members include: HarperCollins Trade, HarperPerennial, HarperCollins Children's Books, HarperPaperbacks, HarperPrism, HarperHorizon, HarperSanFrancisco; Harper Reference & HarperBusiness.
Imprints: Access; Amistad; Avon Books; Cademon; Ecco; Eos; Fourth Estate; HarperAudio; HarperBusiness; HarperCollins; HarperDesign; HarperEntertainment; HarperLarge Print; HarperResource; HarperSanFrancisco; HarperTorch; William Morrow; William Morrow Cookbooks; Perennial; Perennial Currents; Perennial Dark Alley; PerfectBound; Rayo; Regan Books

**Harper's Magazine Foundation**
Division of Franklin Square Press
666 Broadway, 11th fl, New York, NY 10012
*Tel:* 212-420-5720 *Toll Free Tel:* 800-444-4653 *Fax:* 212-228-5889
*E-mail:* harpers@harpers.org
*Web Site:* www.harpers.org
*Key Personnel*
VP & Gen Mgr: Lynn Carlson *E-mail:* lynn@harpers.org
Deputy Ed: James Marcus
Ed: Ellen Rosenbush
Founded: 1850
General trade.
ISBN Prefix(es): 978-1-879957
Number of titles published annually: 12 Print
Total Titles: 30 Print

**§Harrison House Publishers**
7498 E 46 Place, Tulsa, OK 74145
SAN: 208-676X
Mailing Address: PO Box 35035, Tulsa, OK 74153-1035
*Tel:* 918-523-5700 *Toll Free Tel:* 800-888-4126 *Toll Free Fax:* 800-830-5688
*Web Site:* www.harrisonhouse.com
Founded: 1975
Charismatic/Christian publishing house.
ISBN Prefix(es): 978-1-57794; 978-0-89274
Number of titles published annually: 50 Print
Total Titles: 400 Online

**Hartman Publishing Inc**
8529-A Indian School Rd NE, Albuquerque, NM 87112
*Tel:* 505-291-1274 *Toll Free Tel:* 800-999-9534 *Fax:* 505-291-1284 *Toll Free Fax:* 800-474-6106
*E-mail:* orders@hartmanonline.com; help@hartmanonline.com
*Web Site:* www.hartmanonline.com
*Key Personnel*
Publr: Mark Hartman
Mng Ed: Susan Alvare
Founded: 1994
Publish a variety of in-service training materials & textbooks for certified nursing assistants & home health aides. Subjects include Alzheimer's disease, infection control, body mechanics, abuse & neglect, AIDS/HIV & communication skills.
ISBN Prefix(es): 978-1-888343
Number of titles published annually: 12 Print; 1 CD-ROM; 1 Audio
Total Titles: 40 Print; 1 CD-ROM; 1 Audio
Imprints: Care Spring
Distributor for Beverly Foundation
Membership(s): New Mexico Book Association

**Harvard Art Museums**
32 Quincy St, Cambridge, MA 02138
*Tel:* 617-495-1440; 617-496-6529 (edit) *Fax:* 617-495-9985
*E-mail:* am_shop@harvard.edu
*Web Site:* www.harvardartmuseums.org
*Key Personnel*
Dir, Communs: Daron Manoogian
Founded: 1901
Art history.
ISBN Prefix(es): 978-0-916724; 978-1-891771
Number of titles published annually: 5 Print
Total Titles: 70 Print
Distributed by Yale University Press

**Harvard Business Press**
Division of Harvard Business Publishing
300 N Beacon St, Watertown, MA 02472
SAN: 202-277X
*Tel:* 617-783-7400 *Fax:* 617-783-7489
*E-mail:* custserv@hbsp.harvard.edu
*Web Site:* www.harvardbusiness.org
*Key Personnel*
Ed-in-Chief: Adi Ignatius
Rts Mgr: Audra Longert
Publicity Mgr: Julie De Voll
Assoc Ed: Ania Wieckowski
Founded: 1984
Trade & professional books for the business management & academic audiences: 1. strategy, 2. leadership, 3. innovation, 4. organizational behavior/human resource management, finance management, marketing, production & operations management. Harvard Business Review & Reference books & Internet.
ISBN Prefix(es): 978-0-87584; 978-1-57851; 978-1-4221; 978-1-59139
Number of titles published annually: 70 Print
Total Titles: 550 Print
Imprints: Harvard Business Reference
Distributed by Client Distribution Services
Foreign Rep(s): McGraw-Hill Education (Africa, Asia, Australia, Canada, Europe, Middle East, New Zealand); United Publishers Services Ltd (Japan)

**The Harvard Common Press**
535 Albany St, Boston, MA 02118
SAN: 208-6778
*Tel:* 617-423-5803 *Toll Free Tel:* 888-657-3755 *Fax:* 617-695-9794
*E-mail:* orders@harvardcommonpress.com; info@harvardcommonpress.com
*Web Site:* www.harvardcommonpress.com
*Key Personnel*
Pres & Publr: Bruce P Shaw
Assoc Publr: Adam Salome
Spec Sales Dir: Megan Weireter
Exec Ed: Valerie Cimino
Founded: 1976
General nonfiction: cookbooks, small business guides, travel guides, child care & parenting.
ISBN Prefix(es): 978-0-916782; 978-0-87645; 978-1-55832
Number of titles published annually: 15 Print
Total Titles: 150 Print
Imprints: Gambit Books
Distributed by Houghton Mifflin Harcourt
Foreign Rep(s): Gazelle; Southern Publishing Group
Foreign Rights: Dan Bial

**Harvard Education Publishing Group**
Division of Harvard University
8 Story St, 1st fl, Cambridge, MA 02138
*Tel:* 617-495-3432 *Toll Free Tel:* 800-513-0763 (subns); 888-437-1437 (orders) *Fax:* 617-496-3584; 978-348-1233 (orders)
*E-mail:* hepg@harvard.edu
*Web Site:* www.hepg.org
*Key Personnel*
Dir: Douglas Clayton *E-mail:* douglas_clayton@gse.harvard.edu
Asst Dir & Ed-in-Chief: Caroline Chauncey *E-mail:* caroline_chauncey@gse.harvard.edu
Publisher of books & journals on education practice, research & policy.
ISBN Prefix(es): 978-1-891792; 978-1-883433; 978-0-916690
Number of titles published annually: 8 Print
Total Titles: 60 Print
Imprints: Harvard Education Letter; Harvard Education Press; Harvard Educational Review Reprint Series

**Harvard Square Editions**
2152 Beachwood Terr, Hollywood, CA 90068
*Tel:* 323-469-8932 *Fax:* 323-469-8932
*Web Site:* harvardsquareeditions.org
*Key Personnel*
Ed-in-Chief: David Landau
Outreach Dir: Simone Weingarten *E-mail:* sw@harvardsquareeditions.org
Founded: 2000
Publishing house run by Harvard alumni. Author pays 25% of cost of galley proofs.
ISBN Prefix(es): 978-0-9833216
Number of titles published annually: 5 Print; 5 E-Book
Total Titles: 12 Print; 12 E-Book

**Harvard Ukrainian Research Institute**
Subsidiary of Harvard University
34 Kirkland St, Cambridge, MA 02138
SAN: 208-967X
*Tel:* 617-495-4053 *Fax:* 617-495-8097
*E-mail:* huri@fas.harvard.edu
*Web Site:* www.huri.harvard.edu
*Key Personnel*
Mgr, Pubns: Marika Whaley *E-mail:* mwhaley@fas.harvard.edu
Founded: 1973
ISBN Prefix(es): 978-0-916458; 978-1-932650
Number of titles published annually: 5 Print; 3 Online
Total Titles: 85 Print; 6 Online
Distributed by Harvard University Press

**Harvard University Press**
79 Garden St, Cambridge, MA 02138-1499
SAN: 200-2043

*Tel:* 617-495-2600; 401-531-2800 (intl orders) *Toll Free Tel:* 800-405-1619 (orders) *Fax:* 617-495-5898 (general); 617-496-4677 (edit & rts); 401-531-2801 (intl orders) *Toll Free Fax:* 800-406-9145 (orders)
*E-mail:* contact_hup@harvard.edu
*Web Site:* www.hup.harvard.edu
*Key Personnel*
Asst Dir & CFO: Timothy Doyle *E-mail:* timothy_doyle@harvard.edu
Dir: William P Sisler *E-mail:* william_sisler@harvard.edu
Dir, Design & Prodn: Tim Jones *E-mail:* tim_jones@harvard.edu
Dir, Intellectual Property & Subs Rts: Stephanie Vyce *E-mail:* stephanie_vyce@harvard.edu
Promo & Ad Dir: Sheila Barrett *E-mail:* sheila_barrett@harvard.edu
Asst Dir, Sales & Mktg: Susan Donnelly *E-mail:* susan_donnelly@harvard.edu
Asst Dir, Univ Rel & Exec Ed, Sci & Med: Michael G Fisher *E-mail:* michael_fisher@harvard.edu
Ed-in-Chief: Susan Boehmer *E-mail:* susan_boehmer@harvard.edu
Mng Ed: Mary Ann Lane *E-mail:* mary_lane@harvard.edu
Sr Exec Ed, History & Contemporary Aff: Joyce Seltzer *E-mail:* joyce_seltzer@harvard.edu
Exec Ed, Humanities: Lindsay Waters *E-mail:* lindsay_waters@harvard.edu
Exec Ed, Soc Sci: Michael A Aronson *E-mail:* michael_aronson@harvard.edu
Exec Ed-at-Large: Elizabeth Knoll *E-mail:* elizabeth_knoll@harvard.edu; Sharmila Sen *E-mail:* sharmila_sen@harvard.edu
Exec Ed-at-Large, History: Kathleen McDermott *E-mail:* kathleen_mcdermott@harvard.edu
Publicity Mgr: Phoebe Kosman *E-mail:* phoebe_kosman@harvard.edu
Sales Mgr & Digital Content Mgr: Vanessa Vinarub *E-mail:* vanessa_vinarub@harvard.edu
HR: Judy Wilburn *Tel:* 617-495-2602 *E-mail:* judy_wilburn@harvard.edu
Founded: 1913
General scholarly, medical, scientific.
ISBN Prefix(es): 978-0-674
Number of titles published annually: 200 Print
Total Titles: 4,700 Print
Imprints: Belknap Press
*Foreign Office(s):* Vernon House, 23 Sicilian Ave, London WC1A 2QS, United Kingdom *Tel:* (020) 3463 2350 *Fax:* (020) 7831 9261 *E-mail:* info@harvardup.co.uk
Distributor for Harvard Center for Middle Eastern Studies; Harvard Center for Population Studies; Harvard Center for the Study of World Religions; Harvard College Library (including Houghton Library Judaica division); Harvard Department of the Classics; Harvard Department of Sanskrit & Indian Studies; Harvard Ukrainian Research Institute; Harvard University Asia Center; Harvard University David Rockefeller Center for Latin American Studies; Harvard-Yenching Institute; Peabody Museum of Archaeology & Ethnology
Foreign Rep(s): Academic Book Promotions (Benelux, France, Scandinavia); Aromix Books (Hong Kong); Avicenna Ltd (Bill Kennedy) (Bahrain, Egypt, Iraq, Kuwait, Lebanon, Libya, Oman, Qatar, Saudi Arabia, Syria, United Arab Emirates, Yemen); Avicenna Ltd (Claire de Gruchy) (Cyprus, Jordan, Malta, Morocco, Tunisia, Turkey); John Eklund (Canada exc British Columbia); Everest International Publishing Services (Wei Zhao) (China); Harvard University Press London (Greece, India, Ireland, UK); IMA (Tony Moggach) (Africa); InBooks/James Bennett Pty Ltd (Australia, New Zealand); Information & Culture, Korea (South Korea); Jahan Adib Co (Iran); Ewa Ledochiwicz (Albania, Bosnia and Herzegovina, Croatia, Czech Republic, Estonia, Hungary, Latvia, Lithuania, Montenegro, Poland, Romania, Russia, Serbia, Slovakia, Slovenia); Uwe Ludemann (Austria, Germany, Italy, Portugal, Spain, Switzerland); Patricia Nelson (British Columbia); B K Norton (Taiwan); Palgrave (Cory Voigt) (Southern Africa); Rockbook Inc (Japan); World Press (Pakistan); Yuha Associates (Malaysia); Zimpfer Global Services (Caribbean, Central America)
Foreign Rights: Akcali Agency (Turkey); L'Autre Agence (France); Bardon-Chinese Media Agency (China, Hong Kong, Taiwan); Bookman Literary Agency (Denmark, Finland, Iceland, Norway, Sweden); The English Agency (Japan); Graal Literary Agency (Bulgaria, Croatia, Czech Republic, Macedonia, Poland, Romania, Serbia, Slovakia); The Deborah Harris Agency (Israel); International Editors' Co (Central America, Latin America, South America, Spain); Alexander Korzhenevski Agency (Russia); Liepman Agency Ag (Germany, Switzerland); OA Literary Agency (Greece); Suzanna Zevi Agenzia Letteraria (Italy)
*Shipping Address:* Triliteral LLC, 100 Maple Ridge Dr, Cumberland, RI 02864-1769
Membership(s): AAP; BISG

**Harvest Hill Press**
PO Box 55, Salisbury Cove, ME 04672-0055
*Tel:* 207-288-8900 *Toll Free Tel:* 888-288-8900 *Fax:* 207-288-3611
*E-mail:* shop@harvesthillpress.com
*Web Site:* www.harvesthillpress.com
*Key Personnel*
Pres: Sherri Eldridge
Founded: 1994
Cookbooks & printed kitchen stationery for gift, children's & book markets.
ISBN Prefix(es): 978-1-886862
Number of titles published annually: 3 Print
Total Titles: 40 Print
Imprints: Coastal New England Publications
Distributed by University Press of New England
Membership(s): IBPA, the Independent Book Publishers Association

**Harvest House Publishers Inc**
990 Owen Loop N, Eugene, OR 97402-9173
SAN: 207-4745
*Tel:* 541-343-0123 *Toll Free Tel:* 888-501-6991 *Fax:* 541-342-6410
*E-mail:* admin@harvesthousepublishers.com
*Web Site:* www.harvesthousepublishers.com
*Key Personnel*
Pres: Bob Hawkins, Jr
Intl Rts: Sharon Burke
Sr Ed & Ms Coord: Nick Harrison
Founded: 1974
Evangelical Christian books; no unsol mss.
ISBN Prefix(es): 978-0-89081; 978-1-56507; 978-0-7369
Number of titles published annually: 160 Print; 6 Audio
Total Titles: 800 Print; 6 Audio
Membership(s): BISG

**§Hatherleigh Press**
Subsidiary of Hatherleigh Co Ltd
522 46 Ave, Suite 200, Long Island City, NY 11101
*Tel:* 718-786-5338 *Toll Free Tel:* 800-367-2550 *Fax:* 718-706-6087 *Toll Free Fax:* 800-733-3000 (orders)
*E-mail:* info@hatherleigh.com
*Web Site:* www.hatherleighpress.com; www.hatherleigh.com
*Key Personnel*
Pres: Andrew Flach
Edit: June Eding
Assoc Publr: Ryan Tumambing *E-mail:* publicity@hatherleighpress.com
Founded: 1995
Paper & hardbound books, audio, e-books, CE courses in mental health, psychology, psychiatry, health & fitness.
ISBN Prefix(es): 978-1-886330; 978-1-57826
Number of titles published annually: 30 Print; 1 E-Book; 1 Audio
Total Titles: 240 Print; 1 E-Book; 4 Audio
Imprints: getfitnow.com Books, Healthy Living Books
Distributed by Random House Distribution Services
Foreign Rep(s): Random House

**§Hay House Inc**
2776 Loker Ave W, Carlsbad, CA 92010
SAN: 630-477X
Mailing Address: PO Box 5100, Carlsbad, CA 92018-5100
*Tel:* 760-431-7695 (ext 2, intl) *Toll Free Tel:* 800-654-5126 (ext 2, US) *Toll Free Fax:* 800-650-5115
*E-mail:* info@hayhouse.com; editorial@hayhouse.com
*Web Site:* www.hayhouse.com
*Key Personnel*
Founder & Chmn: Louise L Hay
CEO & Pres: Reid Tracy
COO: Margarete Nielsen
Founded: 1984
Self-help/New Age, health, philosophy, spiritual growth & awareness, mental & environmental harmony books; also self-healing; biography, producers & distributors of recordings & video pertaining to health of mind, body & spirit. Accept agented submissions only; SASE required.
ISBN Prefix(es): 978-0-937611; 978-1-56170; 978-1-4019
Number of titles published annually: 50 Print; 50 Audio
Total Titles: 300 Print; 350 Audio
Imprints: New Beginnings Press; Smiley Books
Divisions: Balboa Press
*Branch Office(s)*
250 Park Ave S, Suite 201, New York, NY 10003 *Tel:* 646-484-4950 *Fax:* 646-484-4956
*Foreign Office(s):* Hayhouse Australia Pty Ltd, 18/36 Ralph St, Alexandria, NSW 2015, Australia *Tel:* (02) 9669 4299 *Fax:* (02) 9669 4144 *Web Site:* www.hayhouse.com.au
Hayhouse Publishers India, Muskaan Complex, Plot No 3, B-2, Vasant Kunj, New Delhi 110070, India *Tel:* (011) 4176 1620 *Fax:* (011) 4176 1630 *Web Site:* www.hayhouse.co.in
Hayhouse SA Pty Ltd, PO Box 990, Witkoppen 2068, South Africa *Web Site:* www.hayhouse.co.za
Hayhouse UK Ltd, 292-B Kensal Rd, London W10 5BE, United Kingdom *Tel:* (020) 8962 1230 *Fax:* (020) 8962 1239 *Web Site:* www.hayhouse.co.uk
Distributed by Dempsey-Your Distributor Inc; Raincoast
*Returns:* 995 Joshua Way, Suite B, Vista, CA 92081 *Toll Free Tel:* 800-654-5126
*Warehouse:* 2750 Progress St, Suite B, Vista, CA 92081-8449 *Tel:* 760-431-7695 *Fax:* 760-431-6948

**Haynes Manuals Inc**
Division of The Haynes Publishing Group
861 Lawrence Dr, Newbury Park, CA 91320
*Tel:* 805-498-6703 *Toll Free Tel:* 800-4-HAYNES (442-9637) *Fax:* 805-498-2867
*E-mail:* cstn@haynes.com
*Web Site:* www.haynes.com
*Key Personnel*
Chmn: John H Haynes
Pres: Eric Oakley
Mktg Dir: George Brueggeman
Founded: 1960
Publisher & importer of books on domestic & foreign autos & motorcycles & historical & technical motoring.

ISBN Prefix(es): 978-0-946609; 978-1-56392
Number of titles published annually: 13 Print
Total Titles: 690 Print
Distributed by Motorbooks International
Distributor for G T Foulis; Haynes Owners Workshop Manuals; Oxford Illustrated Press
*Warehouse:* Eastern Warehouse, 1299 Bridgestone Pkwy, La Vergne, TN 37086 *Fax:* 615-793-5325

**§Hazelden Publishing**
Division of Hazelden Foundation
15251 Pleasant Valley Rd, Center City, MN 55012-0011
SAN: 125-1953
Mailing Address: PO Box 176, Center City, MN 55012-0176
*Tel:* 651-213-4200 *Toll Free Tel:* 800-257-7810 *Fax:* 651-213-4590
*E-mail:* info@hazelden.org
*Web Site:* www.hazelden.org
*Key Personnel*
SVP & COO, Publg: Nick Motu
Exec Dir: Kristine Van Hoof-Haines
Founded: 1954
Adult trade hardcover & paperbacks; curriculum, workbooks, giftbooks, video & audio; self-help, addiction & recovery, personal & spiritual growth; computer based products, wellness products, young adult nonfiction.
ISBN Prefix(es): 978-0-89486; 978-1-56838; 978-0-89638; 978-0-942421; 978-0-935908; 978-1-56246; 978-0-934125
Number of titles published annually: 12 Print
Total Titles: 500 Print; 500 E-Book; 10 Audio
Imprints: Hazelden/Johnson Institute; Hazelden/Keep Coming Back; Hazelden-Pittman Archives Press
Distributed by Health Communications Inc (trade)
Distributor for Obsessive Anonymous
Foreign Rep(s): Eurospan (Europe, Ireland, UK); RecoverOz (Australia, New Zealand)

**§HCPro Inc**
200 Hoods Lane, Marblehead, MA 01945
Mailing Address: PO Box 1168, Marblehead, MA 01945
*Tel:* 781-639-1872 *Toll Free Tel:* 800-650-6787 *Toll Free Fax:* 800-639-8511
*E-mail:* customerservice@hcpro.com
*Web Site:* www.hcpro.com
*Key Personnel*
CEO: Brian K Bussey
COO & Pres: Rob Stuart
CFO & SVP: Kevin F Collins
VP, Sales & Mktg: John Hope
Founded: 1986
Healthcare administration & management. Specialize medicine, nursing, newsletters.
ISBN Prefix(es): 978-1-885829
Number of titles published annually: 110 Print; 4 CD-ROM; 30 Online; 5 E-Book; 60 Audio
Total Titles: 125 Print; 5 CD-ROM; 40 Online; 25 E-Book; 75 Audio
Imprints: Opus Communications
Subsidiaries: The Greeley Co
*Orders to:* 100 Hoods Lane, Marblehead, MA 01945
*Warehouse:* 100 Hoods Lane, Marblehead, MA 01945
*Distribution Center:* 100 Hoods Lane, Marblehead, MA 01945
Membership(s): NEPA

**Health Administration Press**
Division of Foundation of the American College of Healthcare Executives
One N Franklin St, Suite 1700, Chicago, IL 60606-3491
SAN: 207-0464
*Tel:* 312-424-2800 *Fax:* 312-424-0014
*E-mail:* hap1@ache.org
*Web Site:* www.ache.org; www.ache.org/hap.cfm (orders)
*Key Personnel*
VP: Maureen Glass *Tel:* 312-424-9450 *E-mail:* mglass@ache.org
Mktg Mgr: Kaye Muench *Tel:* 312-424-9470 *E-mail:* kmuench@ache.org
Acqs: Janet Davis *Tel:* 312-424-9460 *E-mail:* jdavis@ache.org
Asst Dir, Editing: Ed Avis *Tel:* 312-424-9481 *E-mail:* eavis@ache.org
Founded: 1972
Health administration, health care, law & medicine, medical care organization; books & journals.
ISBN Prefix(es): 978-0-910701; 978-1-56793
Number of titles published annually: 20 Print
Total Titles: 150 Print; 1 E-Book
Imprints: American College of Healthcare Executives Management Series; AUPHA Press/Health Administration Press; Executive Essentials
*Branch Office(s)*
PO Box 75145, Baltimore, MD 21275, Contact: Melissa Lawson *Tel:* 301-362-6905 *Fax:* 301-206-9789
Foreign Rep(s): iGroup (Asia); Login Bros (Canada)
*Billing Address:* 9050 Junction Dr, Annapolis Junction, MD 20701
*Orders to:* 9050 Junction Dr, Annapolis Junction, MD 20701
*Returns:* 9050 Junction Dr, Annapolis Junction, MD 20701
*Shipping Address:* 9050 Junction Dr, Annapolis Junction, MD 20701
*Warehouse:* 9050 Junction Dr, Annapolis Junction, MD 20701, Contact: Melissa Lawson *Tel:* 301-362-6905 *Fax:* 301-206-9789
*Distribution Center:* 9050 Junction Dr, Annapolis Junction, MD 20701

**Health Communications Inc**
3201 SW 15 St, Deerfield Beach, FL 33442-8190
SAN: 212-100X
*Tel:* 954-360-0909 *Toll Free Tel:* 800-441-5569 (cust serv) *Fax:* 954-360-0034
*Web Site:* www.hcibooks.com; hci-online.com
*Key Personnel*
Pres & Publr: Peter Vegso
EVP: Christian Blonshine
Edit Dir: Allison Janse Collins; Candace Johnson
Mktg Dir: Kelly Maragni
Art Dir: Larissa Henoch
Publicity & Media Contact: Kim Weiss
Foreign Rts & Distribution: Lori Golden
Foreign Rts Agent: Luc Jutras
Founded: 1977
Publishers of nonfiction paperbacks & hardcover books on self-help, personal growth, diet, fitness, inspiration, health, parenting, women's issues, teens, religion, psychology, addiction & recovery.
ISBN Prefix(es): 978-0-932194; 978-1-55874; 978-0-75730
Number of titles published annually: 50 Print
Total Titles: 500 Print; 36 Audio
Imprints: HCI Books; HCI Teens; Vows
*See separate listing for:*
**Simcha Press**

**§Health Forum Inc**
Subsidiary of American Hospital Association
155 N Wacker Dr, Suite 400, Chicago, IL 60606
SAN: 216-5872
*Tel:* 312-893-6884 *Toll Free Tel:* 800-242-2626 *Fax:* 312-422-4600
*E-mail:* hfcustsvc@healthforum.com
*Web Site:* www.ahaonlinestore.com; www.healthforum.com
*Key Personnel*
Mktg Dir, Publg: Mr Pat Foy *E-mail:* pfoy@healthforum.com
Edit Dir, Books: Rick Hill *Tel:* 312-893-6863 *E-mail:* rhill@healthforum.com
Founded: 1936
Publisher of professional books & textbooks for health care professionals. Specialize in books that help hospital executives & department heads manage their business better & achieve improved patient satisfaction. We also provide ICD-10-CM/PCS & data information from the AHA Central Office & the American Hospital Association annual survey of hospitals.
ISBN Prefix(es): 978-1-55648; 978-0-87258
Number of titles published annually: 10 Print; 2 CD-ROM; 2 E-Book
Total Titles: 16 Print; 2 CD-ROM; 3 E-Book
Imprints: AHA (American Hospital Association); AHA Press
*Billing Address:* AHA Services Inc, 155 N Wacker Dr, Suite 400, Chicago, IL 60606, Contact: Dick Riccetti *Tel:* 312-422-3227 *Fax:* 312-422-4597 *E-mail:* rriccetti@aha.org
*Orders to:* AHA Services Inc, PO Box 933283, Atlanta, GA 31193-3283 *Toll Free Fax:* 866-516-5817 *E-mail:* aha-orders@pbd.com
*Returns:* AHA Services Inc, Cust Returns, 3280 Summit Ridge Pkwy, Duluth, GA 30096
*Warehouse:* AHA Services Inc, 3280 Summit Ridge Pkwy, Duluth, GA 30096 (AHA order services) *Toll Free Fax:* 866-516-5817 *E-mail:* aha-orders@pbd.com
*Distribution Center:* Rittenhouse Book Distributors, 511 Feheley Dr, King of Prussia, PA 19406, Contact: Nicole Gallo *Toll Free Tel:* 800-345-6425 *Fax:* 610-277-0390 *E-mail:* n.gallo@rittenhouse.com *Web Site:* www.rittenhouse.com
Majors Education Solutions, 500 E Corporate Dr, Suite 600, Lewisville, TX 75057, Contact: Martha Yeahquo *Tel:* 972-353-1100 *Toll Free Tel:* 800-633-1851 *Fax:* 972-353-1300 *E-mail:* customerservice@majors.com *Web Site:* www.majors.com
Membership(s): American Hospital Association; IBPA, the Independent Book Publishers Association
*See separate listing for:*
**AHA Press**

**Health InfoNet Inc**
231 Market Place, No 331, San Ramon, CA 94583
*Tel:* 925-358-4370 *Toll Free Tel:* 800-446-1121 *Fax:* 925-358-4377
*E-mail:* hinbooks@aol.com
*Web Site:* hinbooks.com
*Key Personnel*
VP: Lois Kamoroff *E-mail:* logo47@sbcglobal.net
Founded: 1993
Medical patient information materials (including booklets & web).
ISBN Prefix(es): 978-1-885274
Number of titles published annually: 3 Print
Total Titles: 50 Print; 50 Online; 50 E-Book

**Health Information Network HIN**, see Health InfoNet Inc

**§Health Press NA Inc**
2920 Carlisle Blvd NE, Suite 111, Albuquerque, NM 87110
*Tel:* 505-888-1394 *Toll Free Tel:* 877-411-0707 *Fax:* 505-888-1521
*E-mail:* goodbooks@healthpress.com
*Web Site:* www.healthpress.com
*Key Personnel*
Publr & Pres: Kathleen Frazier
Founded: 1988
Health & patient education books for the whole family.
ISBN Prefix(es): 978-0-929173
Number of titles published annually: 4 Print
Total Titles: 35 Print

**§Health Professions Press**
Division of Paul H Brookes Publishing Co Inc
409 Washington Ave, Suite 500, Towson, MD 21204
SAN: 297-7338
Mailing Address: PO Box 10624, Baltimore, MD 21285-0624
*Tel:* 410-337-9585 *Toll Free Tel:* 888-337-8808 *Fax:* 410-337-8539
*E-mail:* custserv@healthpropress.com
*Web Site:* www.healthpropress.com
*Key Personnel*
Pres: Melissa A Behm
Dir, Pubns: Mary H Magnus *E-mail:* mmagnus@healthpropress.com
Mktg Coord: Kaitlin Konecke
Founded: 1989
Hardcover, paperback & digital professional resources & textbooks in aging, Alzheimer's disease, long-term care & health administration.
ISBN Prefix(es): 978-1-878812; 978-1-932529; 978-1-938870
Number of titles published annually: 10 Print; 2 CD-ROM
Total Titles: 100 Print; 10 CD-ROM
Distributed by The Eurospan Group (Africa, Europe & Middle East); Footprint Books Pty Ltd (Australia, Fiji, New Zealand & Papua New Guinea); Login Brothers (Canada); Unifacmanu Trading Co Ltd (Taiwan)
Foreign Rep(s): CRW Marketing Services for Publishers Inc (Guam, Philippines); Tahir Lodhi Publishers' Representatives (Pakistan); Sara Books Pvt Ltd (Bangladesh, India, Sri Lanka); STM Publishers Services Pte Ltd (China, Hong Kong, Malaysia, Myanmar, Singapore, Thailand, Vietnam)
*Warehouse:* Maple Logistics Solutions, 60 Grumbacher Rd I-83 Industrial Park, PO Box 15100, York, PA 17406
Membership(s): IBPA, the Independent Book Publishers Association

**Health Research Books**
62 Seventh St, Pomeroy, WA 99347
Mailing Address: PO Box 850, Pomeroy, WA 99347
*Tel:* 509-843-2385 *Toll Free Tel:* 888-844-2386 *Fax:* 509-843-2387
*E-mail:* publish@pomeroy-wa.com
*Web Site:* www.healthresearchbooks.com
*Key Personnel*
Owner: Benjamin C Roberts; Nikki Jones Roberts
Founded: 1952
Publish reprints of rare, hard to find, out-of-print books. Subjects include mysticism, Egyptology, divination, UFOs, hypnotism, mental & spiritual healing, acupuncture, metaphysical, palmistry & many, many more.
ISBN Prefix(es): 978-0-7873
Number of titles published annually: 300 Print
Total Titles: 1,400 Print

**Healthy Learning**, see Coaches Choice

**§HeartMath LLC**
14700 W Park Ave, Boulder Creek, CA 95006
*Tel:* 831-338-8700 *Toll Free Tel:* 800-450-9111 *Fax:* 831-338-9861
*E-mail:* inquiry@heartmath.com
*Web Site:* www.heartmath.com
*Key Personnel*
Global Dir: Bruce Cryer
EVP, Strategic Devt: Howard Martin
SVP, Sales & Mktg: Catherine Calarco
VP, Fin/COO: Chris Jacob
Founded: 1998
Publishers of The HeartMath System.
ISBN Prefix(es): 978-1-879052
Number of titles published annually: 16 Print
Total Titles: 2 CD-ROM; 7 Audio

**Hearts & Tummies Cookbook Co**
Division of Quixote Press
3544 Blakslee St, Wever, IA 52658
*Tel:* 319-372-7480 *Toll Free Tel:* 800-571-2665 *Fax:* 319-372-7485
*E-mail:* quixotepress@gmail.com; heartsntummies@gmail.com
*Web Site:* www.heartsntummies.com
*Key Personnel*
Pres & Intl Rts: Bruce Carlson
Founded: 1982
Cookbooks.
ISBN Prefix(es): 978-1-878488; 978-1-57166
Number of titles published annually: 28 Print
Total Titles: 300 Print
Imprints: Black Iron Cooking Co; Hearts 'n Tummies Cookbook Co; Kid Help Publishing Co; PYO (Publish Your Own Co); Quixote Press

**Hebrew Union College Press**
Division of Hebrew Union College
3101 Clifton Ave, Cincinnati, OH 45220
*Tel:* 513-221-1875 *Fax:* 513-221-0321
*E-mail:* hucpress@huc.edu
*Web Site:* huc.edu
*Key Personnel*
Chmn Pubns Comm: Michael A Meyer
Founded: 1921
Scholarly Jewish books.
ISBN Prefix(es): 978-0-87820
Number of titles published annually: 3 Print
Total Titles: 100 Print
Distributed by Wayne State University Press

**Heian International Inc**
Imprint of Stone Bridge Press Inc
PO Box 8208, Berkeley, CA 94707
SAN: 213-2036
*Tel:* 510-524-8732 *Toll Free Tel:* 800-947-7271 *Fax:* 510-524-8711 *Toll Free Fax:* 888-411-8527
*E-mail:* sbp@stonebridge.com (gen & orders)
*Web Site:* www.stonebridge.com
*Key Personnel*
Publr: Peter Goodman
Founded: 1973
General trade, juvenile; languages, dictionaries & literature, Oriental culture, customs, philosophy & religion; classic Japanese art calendars & books.
ISBN Prefix(es): 978-0-89346
Number of titles published annually: 4 Print
Total Titles: 40 Print

**Heimburger House Publishing Co**
7236 W Madison St, Forest Park, IL 60130
*Tel:* 708-366-1973 *Fax:* 708-366-1973
*E-mail:* info@heimburgerhouse.com
*Web Site:* www.heimburgerhouse.com
*Key Personnel*
Publr: Donald J Heimburger
Founded: 1962
Publish books & magazines on railroad & other transportation subjects; list includes more than 300 book titles.
ISBN Prefix(es): 978-0-911581
Number of titles published annually: 5 Print
Total Titles: 75 Print
Distributor for Black Dog & Leventhal; Book Sales Inc; Boyds Mills Press; Canadian Caboose Press; Carstens; Child's Play International; Evergreen Press; Firefly Books Ltd; Fitzhenry & Whiteside Ltd; Fordham University Press; Globe Pequot Press; Golden Hill Press; Harbour Publishing; HarperCollins; Johns Hopkins University Press; Hot Box Press; Houghton Mifflin Harcourt; Howling at the Moon Press; Iconografix; Indiana University Press; Kalmbach Publishing; Krause Publications; Motorbooks International; National Book Network; New York University Press; W W Norton & Co; Penquin Putnam Inc; Pictorial Histories Publishing Co; Sono Nis Press; Steam Passages Publishing; Sterling Publishing; Sugar Cane Press; Syracuse University Press; Thunder Bay Press; University of Minnesota Press; University of Scranton; Westcliffe Publishing; John Wiley & Sons

**§William S Hein & Co Inc**
2350 N Forest Rd, Getzville, NY 14068
*Tel:* 716-882-2600 *Toll Free Tel:* 800-828-7571 *Fax:* 716-883-8100
*E-mail:* mail@wshein.com; marketing@wshein.com
*Web Site:* www.wshein.com
*Key Personnel*
Chmn of the Bd: William S Hein, Jr *E-mail:* whein@wshein.com
Pres: Kevin M Marmion *Tel:* 716-882-2600 ext 115 *E-mail:* kmarmion@wshein.com
SVP: Daniel Rosati *E-mail:* drosati@wshein.com
Founded: 1961
Publish & reprint law & related materials, hard copy, micro, CDs & online products.
ISBN Prefix(es): 978-0-8377; 978-0-89941; 978-1-57588
Number of titles published annually: 30 Print; 2 CD-ROM; 1 Online
Total Titles: 5,000 Print; 5 CD-ROM; 2 Online
Imprints: Fred B Rothman Publications
Distributor for Ashgate; Aspen; Butterworths; Sweet & Maxwell; John Wiley & Sons Inc
*Returns:* 24 E Ferry St, Buffalo, NY 14209 *E-mail:* returns@wshein.com
Membership(s): American Association of Law Libraries; Canadian Association of Law Libraries; Library Binding Institute

**§Heinemann**
Division of Houghton Mifflin Harcourt
361 Hanover St, Portsmouth, NH 03801-3912
SAN: 210-5829
Mailing Address: PO Box 6926, Portsmouth, NH 03802-6926
*Tel:* 603-431-7894 *Toll Free Tel:* 800-225-5800 (US) *Fax:* 603-431-2214 *Toll Free Fax:* 877-231-6980 (US)
*E-mail:* custserv@heinemann.com
*Web Site:* www.heinemann.com
*Key Personnel*
Pres: Lesa Scott
VP, Edit: Leigh Peake
Founded: 1978
Education - professional books for teachers K-college. literacy, math, social studies, drama, art & English teaching. Hardcover & paperbound. Trade - drama, world literature, education, African studies. Hardcover & paperbound class.
ISBN Prefix(es): 978-0-86709; 978-1-4050; 978-0-325
Number of titles published annually: 115 Print
Total Titles: 1,500 Print
Imprints: African Writers Series; Boynton/Cook; Caribbean Writers Series; Firsthand
*See separate listing for:*
**Boynton/Cook Publishers**

**Heinle**, see Wadsworth Publishing

**§Hellgate Press**
Imprint of L & R Publishing
PO Box 3531, Ashland, OR 97520
*Tel:* 541-973-5154 *Toll Free Tel:* 800-795-4059
*E-mail:* info@hellgatepress.com
*Web Site:* www.hellgatepress.com
*Key Personnel*
Owner: Harley B Patrick *E-mail:* harley@hellgatepress.com
Founded: 1975
Military history; adventure travel, veteran memoirs, historical & adventure fiction.
ISBN Prefix(es): 978-1-55571
Number of titles published annually: 10 Print

Total Titles: 70 Print
Distributed by Midpoint Trade Books
Foreign Rep(s): Midpoint Trade Books
*Shipping Address:* Midpoint Trade Books, 1263 Southwest Blvd, Kansas City, KS 66103, Contact: James Fisher *Tel:* 913-362-7400

**§Helm Publishing**
PO Box 9691, Treasure Island, FL 33740
SAN: 254-7562
*Tel:* 727-623-5014
*Web Site:* www.publishersdrive.com
*Key Personnel*
CEO: Dianne Helm *E-mail:* dianne@publishersdrive.com
Founded: 1994
Specialize in new & emerging authors in fiction/nonfiction genres.
This publisher has indicated that 50% of their product line is author subsidized.
ISBN Prefix(es): 978-0-9723011; 978-0-9760919; 978-0-9769193; 978-0-0930109; 978-0-9850488; 978-0-9841397; 978-0-9820605; 978-0-9801780; 978-0-9792328; 978-0-9778205
Number of titles published annually: 8 Print; 1 CD-ROM; 15 E-Book
Total Titles: 120 Print; 1 CD-ROM; 75 E-Book
Membership(s): ABA

**Hemingway Western Studies Center**
Boise State University, 1910 University Dr, Boise, ID 83725-1135
*Tel:* 208-426-1999; 208-426-1514 *Fax:* 208-426-4373
*E-mail:* books@booksboisestate.com
*Web Site:* www.booksboisestate.com
*Key Personnel*
Interim Dir: Tara Penry
Founded: 1986
Specialize in artists' books on Rocky Mountain issues & regional popular scholarship; no return policy.
ISBN Prefix(es): 978-0-932129
Number of titles published annually: 3 Print
Total Titles: 12 Print
*Shipping Address:* BSU Publications Office *Tel:* 208-426-1514 *E-mail:* books@boisestate.edu *Web Site:* www.booksboisestate.com

**Hendrick-Long Publishing Co**
10635 Tower Oaks, Suite D, Houston, TX 77070
*Tel:* 832-912-READ (912-7323) *Fax:* 832-912-7353
*E-mail:* hendrick-long@worldnet.att.net
*Web Site:* www.hendricklongpublishing.com
*Key Personnel*
VP & Ed: Vilma Long
Publr: Michael Long
Founded: 1969
Texas & southwest material for juveniles & young adults.
ISBN Prefix(es): 978-0-937460; 978-1-885777
Number of titles published annually: 6 Print
Total Titles: 113 Print
Distributor for NES, The Official Tasp Study Guide
Membership(s): Publishers Association of the West

**Hendrickson Publishers Inc**
PO Box 3473, Peabody, MA 01961-3473
*Tel:* 978-532-6546 *Toll Free Tel:* 800-358-3111 *Fax:* 978-573-8111
*E-mail:* orders@hendrickson.com
*Web Site:* www.hendrickson.com
*Key Personnel*
VP: Dave Townsley
Sales: Bobby Koduvalil
Contact: Kris Orlando
Founded: 1978
Religious reference, language, history & theology.
ISBN Prefix(es): 978-0-913573; 978-0-943575; 978-0-917006; 978-1-56563
Number of titles published annually: 40 Print; 3 CD-ROM
Total Titles: 450 Print
Imprints: Prince Press
Foreign Rep(s): Alban Books (Europe, UK)
Foreign Rights: KCBS (Korea)
*Orders to:* David C Cook Distribution Canada, 55 Woodslee Ave, Paris, ON N3L 3E5, Canada (CN) *Toll Free Tel:* 800-263-2664 *Toll Free Fax:* 800-461-8575 *E-mail:* custserv@davidccook.ca *Web Site:* www.davidccook.ca; Alban Books Ltd, 14 Belford Rd, Edinburgh, Scotland EH4 3BL, United Kingdom *Tel:* (0131) 226 2217 *Fax:* (0131) 225 5999 *Web Site:* www.albanbooks.com
*Warehouse:* 140 Summit St, Peabody, MA 01960
*Distribution Center:* Anchor Distributors, 1030 Hunt Valley Circle, New Kensington, PA 15068 *Tel:* 724-334-7000 *Toll Free Tel:* 800-444-4484 *Fax:* 724-334-1200 *Toll Free Fax:* 800-765-1960 *Web Site:* www.anchordistributors.com
Appalachian/STL Distribution, 522 Princeton Rd, Johnson City, TN 37601 *Toll Free Tel:* 800-289-2772 *Toll Free Fax:* 800-759-2779 *Web Site:* www.stl-distribution.com

**Hensley Publishing**
6116 E 32 St, Tulsa, OK 74135
*Tel:* 918-664-8520 *Toll Free Tel:* 800-288-8520 (orders only) *Fax:* 918-664-8562
*E-mail:* customerservice@hensleypublishing.com
*Web Site:* www.hensleypublishing.com
*Key Personnel*
Pres: Neal Hensley
Dir, Publg: Terri Kalfas
Founded: 1965
Bible studies.
ISBN Prefix(es): 978-1-56322
Number of titles published annually: 5 Print
Total Titles: 27 Print
Membership(s): CBA

**Her Own Words LLC**
PO Box 5264, Madison, WI 53705-0264
*Tel:* 608-271-7083 *Fax:* 608-271-0209
*Web Site:* www.herownwords.com; www.nontraditionalcareers.com
*Key Personnel*
Mgr: Jocelyn Riley *E-mail:* jocelynriley@herownwords.com
Founded: 1986
Women's history, literature, arts & women in non-traditional careers.
ISBN Prefix(es): 978-1-60118
Number of titles published annually: 6 Print; 6 Audio
Total Titles: 36 Print; 36 Audio
Imprints: Women In Nontraditional Careers

**Herald Press**
Imprint of MennoMedia
1251 Virginia Ave, Harrisonburg, VA 22802-2434
SAN: 202-2915
*Toll Free Tel:* 800-245-7894 (orders-US); 800-999-3534; 800-631-6535 (orders-CN) *Toll Free Fax:* 877-271-0760
*E-mail:* info@MennoMedia.org
*Web Site:* www.heraldpress.com; store.mennomedia.org
*Key Personnel*
Exec Dir, MennoMedia: Russ Eanes *E-mail:* russ@mennomedia.org
Edit Dir: Amy Gingerich *E-mail:* agingerich@mpn.net
Mktg & Sales Dir, MennoMedia: Steve Shenk
Acqs: Dorothy Hartman *E-mail:* dorothyh@thirdwaymedia.org
Perms: Joshua Byler *E-mail:* jbyler@mpn.net
Proofreader & Off Asst: Michelle Cannillo *Tel:* 800-245-7894 ext 333 *E-mail:* michellec@mpn.net
Founded: 1908
General Christian trade books, family, devotional, cookbooks, juveniles, adult fiction, Bible study, theology, peace & social concerns, missions, Amish & Mennonite history & culture, songbooks.
ISBN Prefix(es): 978-0-8361
Number of titles published annually: 20 Print
Total Titles: 400 Print
*Branch Office(s)*
718 N Main St, Newton, KS 67114 *Tel:* 316-281-4412 *Toll Free Tel:* 800-245-7894 ext 220 *Fax:* 316-283-0454
490 Dutton Dr, Unit C-8, Waterloo, ON N2L 6H7, Canada, Cust Serv: Kathy Shantz *Tel:* 519-747-5722 *Fax:* 519-747-5721-orders *E-mail:* hpcan@mpn.net
Membership(s): Canadian Booksellers Association; CBA: The Association for Christian Retail; Evangelical Christian Publishers Association

**Herald Publishing House**
Division of Community of Christ
1001 W Walnut St, Independence, MO 64051
SAN: 202-2907
Mailing Address: PO Box 390, Independence, MO 64051-0390
*Tel:* 816-521-3015 *Toll Free Tel:* 800-767-8181 *Fax:* 816-521-3066
*E-mail:* sales@heraldhouse.org
*Web Site:* www.heraldhouse.org
*Key Personnel*
Fiscal Servs Specialist: Suzan Hudson
Edit Dir: Linda Booth *E-mail:* lbooth@cofchrist.org
Busn: Carina Wilson
Founded: 1860
Religion (Community of Christ).
ISBN Prefix(es): 978-0-8309
Number of titles published annually: 12 Print
Total Titles: 360 Print
Imprints: Graceland Press; Independence Press
Foreign Rep(s): Steve Weber (Canada)

**Heritage Books Inc**
100 Railroad Ave, Suite 104, Westminster, MD 21157-4826
*Tel:* 410-876-6101 *Toll Free Tel:* 800-876-6103 *Fax:* 410-558-6574
*E-mail:* info@heritagebooks.com; orders@heritagebooks.com
*Web Site:* www.heritagebooks.com
*Key Personnel*
CEO & Pres: Craig R Scott *E-mail:* crscott@heritagebooks.com
Founded: 1978
Books on local history, genealogy & Americana.
ISBN Prefix(es): 978-0-917890; 978-1-55613; 978-0-7884; 978-1-58549; 978-0-940907; 978-1-888265
Number of titles published annually: 600 Print; 150 CD-ROM
Total Titles: 4,007 Print; 1,000 CD-ROM
Imprints: Eagle Editions; Fireside Fiction; Heritage Books; Willow Bend Books
Distributor for Carroll County Genealogical Society; Fairfax Genealogical Society; National Genealogical Society; Virginia Genealogical Society

**§The Heritage Foundation**
214 Massachusetts Ave NE, Washington, DC 20002-4999
*Tel:* 202-546-4400 *Toll Free Tel:* 800-544-4843 *Fax:* 202-546-8328
*E-mail:* info@heritage.org
*Web Site:* www.heritage.org

*Key Personnel*
Pres: Jim DeMint
EVP: Phil N Truluck
Creative Dir: Melissa Bluey
Founded: 1973
Domestic policy, foreign policy & defense.
ISBN Prefix(es): 978-0-89195
Number of titles published annually: 7 Print; 2 CD-ROM
Total Titles: 19 Print; 2 CD-ROM; 8 E-Book

**Heryin Books Inc**
1033 E Main St, Suite 202, Alhambra, CA 91801
*Tel:* 626-289-2238 *Fax:* 626-289-3865
*E-mail:* editor@heryin.com
*Web Site:* www.heryin.com
*Key Personnel*
Pres & Ed-in-Chief: Yih-Fen Chou *E-mail:* yihfen@heryin.com
Founded: 2004
Publish children's picture books for readers of all ages. At the heart of each book is humanity & sympathy.
ISBN Prefix(es): 978-0-9762056
Number of titles published annually: 5 Print
Total Titles: 13 Print
*Distribution Center:* IPG Books, 814 Franklin St, Chicago, IL 60610 *Toll Free Tel:* 800-888-4741 *E-mail:* frontdesk@ipgbook.com *Web Site:* www.ipgbook.com

**Herzl Press**
Subsidiary of World Zionist Organization
633 Third Ave, 21st fl, New York, NY 10017
*Tel:* 212-339-6020 *Fax:* 212-318-6176
*E-mail:* midstreamthf@aol.com
*Web Site:* www.midstreamthf.com
*Key Personnel*
Chmn, Theodore Herzl Foundation: Kalman Sultanik
Busn Mgr: Sam Bloch
Ed: Leo Haber
Founded: 1954
Dictionaries, encyclopedias, fine editions, paperbacks, journals, translations.
ISBN Prefix(es): 978-0-930830
Number of titles published annually: 2 Print
Total Titles: 30 Print
Distributed by Associated University Presses; Cornwal Books

**Heuer Publishing LLC**
211 First Ave SE, Suite 200, Cedar Rapids, IA 52401
Mailing Address: PO Box 248, Cedar Rapids, IA 52406
*Tel:* 319-368-8008 *Toll Free Tel:* 800-950-7529 *Fax:* 319-368-8011
*E-mail:* editor@hitplays.com
*Web Site:* www.hitplays.com
*Key Personnel*
Publr: Steven S Michalicek
Ed: Ms Geri Albrecht
Founded: 1928
Play & musical publisher; Publishes plays, musicals, operas/opperettas & guides (choreography, costume, production/staging) for amateur & professional markets including junior & senior high schools, college/university & community theatres. Focus includes comedy, drama, fantasy, mystery & holiday with special interest focus in multicultural, historic, classic literature, Shakespearian theatre, interactive, teen issues & biographies. Pays by percentage royalty or outright purchase.
ISBN Prefix(es): 978-1-61588
Number of titles published annually: 7 Print
Total Titles: 150 Print

**Hewitt Homeschooling Resources**
Division of Hewitt Research Foundation
2103 Main St, Washougal, WA 98671
Mailing Address: PO Box 9, Washougal, WA 98671
*Tel:* 360-835-8708 *Toll Free Tel:* 800-348-1750 *Fax:* 360-835-8697
*E-mail:* info@hewitthomeschooling.com
*Web Site:* hewitthomeschooling.com
*Key Personnel*
Pres: April Purtell
Founded: 1964
Homeschooling, curriculum.
ISBN Prefix(es): 978-0-913717; 978-1-57896
Number of titles published annually: 6 Print
Total Titles: 150 Print

**Heyday Books**
1633 University Ave, Berkeley, CA 94703
SAN: 207-2351
Mailing Address: PO Box 9145, Berkeley, CA 94709-0145
*Tel:* 510-549-3564 *Fax:* 510-549-1889
*E-mail:* heyday@heydaybooks.com; orders@heydaybooks.com
*Web Site:* www.heydaybooks.com
*Key Personnel*
Exec Dir: Malcolm Margolin *E-mail:* malcolm@heydaybooks.com
Mng Ed: Margaret Dubin
Founded: 1974
Nonprofit company that specializes in California Indians, California history & literature, regional conservation & ecology; women of California; literary anthologies; Asian-American; art & photography.
ISBN Prefix(es): 978-0-930588; 978-1-890771; 978-0-9666691; 978-1-59714
Number of titles published annually: 25 Print
Total Titles: 110 Print
Imprints: Bay Tree Books; California Historical Society; California Legacy Books (reprints); Essential Series; Great Valley Books (books by Central Valley authors); Inlandia Institute; Yosemite Association
*Returns:* Heyday Books, c/o Fulfillco, 2801 Merced St, San Leadro, CA 94577
*Warehouse:* Heyday Books, c/o Fulfillco, 2801 Merced St, San Leadro, CA 94577

**Hi Willow Research & Publishing**
PO Box 131266, Spring, TX 77393
*Toll Free Tel:* 800-873-3043 *Fax:* 936-271-4560
*E-mail:* lmcsourcesales@gmail.com
*Web Site:* www.lmcsource.com
*Key Personnel*
Owner: David V Loertscher
Founded: 1978
Books for schools & libraries.
ISBN Prefix(es): 978-0-931510; 978-1-933170
Number of titles published annually: 8 Print
Total Titles: 35 Print
Distributed by LMC Source

**Higginson Book Co**
148 Washington St, Salem, MA 01970
*Tel:* 978-745-7170 *Fax:* 978-745-8025
*E-mail:* orders@higginsonbooks.com
*Web Site:* www.higginsonbooks.com
*Key Personnel*
Mgr: Robert Murphy *E-mail:* r.a.murphy@verizon.net
Founded: 1970
Reprints & new material.
ISBN Prefix(es): 978-0-8328; 978-0-7404
Number of titles published annually: 200 Print
Total Titles: 15,000 Print
Distributor for Genealogical Publishing Co

**High Plains Press**
403 Cassa Rd, Glendo, WY 82213
Mailing Address: PO Box 123, Glendo, WY 82213
*Tel:* 307-735-4370 *Toll Free Tel:* 800-552-7819 *Fax:* 307-735-4590
*E-mail:* editor@highplainspress.com
*Web Site:* highplainspress.com
*Key Personnel*
Founder & Publr: Nancy Curtis *E-mail:* nancy@highplainspress.com
Founded: 1984
Books about Wyoming & the American West.
ISBN Prefix(es): 978-0-931271
Number of titles published annually: 5 Print
Total Titles: 56 Print
Membership(s): IBPA, the Independent Book Publishers Association; Publishers Association of the West

**High Tide Press**
Subsidiary of The Trinity Foundation
1805 Ferro Rd, New Lenox, IL 60451
*Web Site:* www.hightidepress.com
*Key Personnel*
Dir: Anne C Ward *Tel:* 800-235-6009 *E-mail:* award@hightidepress.com
Founded: 1995
Full-service publisher of hardcover & paperback books & one quarterly magazine for the book trade & professional niche markets. Specializes in the fields of developmental & intellectual disabilities, behavioral health, non-profit management, social enterprise, leadership.
ISBN Prefix(es): 978-0-9653744; 978-1-892696
Number of titles published annually: 2 Print; 1 Online
Total Titles: 46 Print
Imprints: High Tide Monograph Series (Focused on high quality management practices in behavioral health & developmental disability services.); Midewin Series (focused on the prevention of abuse & neglect of persons with disabilities)
*Orders to:* Cherry Hill Bookstore, 2505 E Washington St, Joliet, IL 60433 (part of Trinity Foundation), Cust Serv: Molly Garbrecht *Tel:* 815-722-0166 *Toll Free Tel:* 800-469-9461 *Fax:* 815-722-2726 *E-mail:* molly@cherryhillbooks.com *Web Site:* www.cherryhillbooks.com
Membership(s): IBPA, the Independent Book Publishers Association

**Highlights for Children**
1800 Watermark Dr, Columbus, OH 43215-1060
Mailing Address: PO Box 269, Columbus, OH 43216-0269
*Tel:* 614-486-0631 *Toll Free Tel:* 800-962-3661 (Highlights Club cust serv); 800-255-9517 (Highlights Magazine cust serv)
*Web Site:* www.highlights.com
*Key Personnel*
CEO: Kent S Johnson
Edit Dir, Book Publg: Liz Van Doren
Ed-in-Chief (PA off): Christine French Cully
Sr Ed: Mary Colgan
Dir, Sales: Dave Bolen
ISBN Prefix(es): 978-0-87534
Number of titles published annually: 150 Print
*Editorial Office(s):* 803 Church St, Honesdale, PA 18431 *Tel:* 570-253-1080 *Fax:* 570-251-7847
*See separate listing for:*
**Stenhouse Publishers**

**Hill & Wang**
Division of Farrar, Straus & Giroux, LLC
18 W 18 St, New York, NY 10011
SAN: 201-9299
*Tel:* 212-741-6900 *Fax:* 212-633-9385
*E-mail:* fsg.publicity@fsgbooks.com; fsg.editorial@fsgbooks.com
*Web Site:* us.macmillan.com/hillandwang.aspx
*Key Personnel*
SVP, Mktg & Publicity, FSG: Jeff Seroy *E-mail:* jeff.seroy@fsgbooks.com
Dir, Ad & Promos, FSG: Vicki Genna *Tel:* 212-206-5314 *E-mail:* victoria.genna@fsgbooks.com

VP & Contracts Dir, FSG: Erika Seidman
*E-mail:* erika.seidman@fsgbooks.com
Founded: 1956
General nonfiction, history & drama.
ISBN Prefix(es): 978-0-8090
Number of titles published annually: 10 Print
*Warehouse:* MPS Distribution Ctr, 16365 James Madison Hwy, Gordonsville, VA 22942 *Toll Free Tel:* 888-330-8477

**Lawrence Hill Books**, see Chicago Review Press

**Hillsdale College Press**
Division of Hillsdale College
33 E College St, Hillsdale, MI 49242
*Tel:* 517-437-7341 *Toll Free Tel:* 800-437-2268 *Fax:* 517-517-3923
*E-mail:* news@hillsdale.edu
*Web Site:* www.hillsdale.edu
*Key Personnel*
Ed & VP, External Aff: Douglas A Jeffrey *Tel:* 517-607-2538 *E-mail:* douglas.jeffrey@hillsdale.edu
Founded: 1974
Single author books & collected essays of historical, political & economic interest.
ISBN Prefix(es): 978-0-916308

**Hillsdale Educational Publishers Inc**
39 North St, Hillsdale, MI 49242
SAN: 159-8759
*Tel:* 517-437-3179 *Fax:* 517-437-0531
*E-mail:* davestory@aol.com
*Web Site:* www.hillsdalepublishers.com; michbooks.com
*Key Personnel*
Pres & Author: David B McConnell
Founded: 1965
Publish & distribute regional titles for schools & libraries.
ISBN Prefix(es): 978-0-910726; 978-1-931466
Number of titles published annually: 4 Print; 1 CD-ROM; 1 Audio
Total Titles: 18 Print; 1 CD-ROM; 1 Audio

**§Hilton Publishing**
1630 45 St, Suite B101, Munster, IN 46321
*Tel:* 219-922-4868 *Fax:* 219-922-6407
*E-mail:* orders@hiltonpub.com
*Web Site:* www.hiltonpub.com
*Key Personnel*
Publr: Jena Rausch *Tel:* 317-229-6650 ext 6001
Founded: 1996
Publish books in health & wellness, minority health, religion (health-related). Consistent themes of publications include living with & preventing various disease states, illustrating & promoting components of healthy living, embracing & illuminating cultural diversity related to health & wellbeing & fostering health in the Christian community. Books are peer reviewed by experts in the appropriate fields to insure we have included the most current, accurate & relevant information. We publish informative & educational books for the general public as well as books aimed at the medical community.
ISBN Prefix(es): 978-0-9654553; 978-0-9675258; 978-0-9716067; 978-0-9743144; 978-0-9764443; 978-0-9773160; 978-0-9777779; 978-0-9800649; 978-0-9815381; 978-0-9841447; 978-0-9847566
Number of titles published annually: 12 Print; 3 CD-ROM; 4 Online; 7 E-Book; 3 Audio
Total Titles: 30 Print; 3 CD-ROM; 4 Online; 7 E-Book; 3 Audio
Foreign Rep(s): Gabriel Wilmoth (Canada, Germany, USA)
Foreign Rights: Nigel Yorwerth (Worldwide)
Membership(s): Indiana Minority Supplier Development Council; National Minority Supplier Development Council; North Carolina Ministry Supplier Development Council

**Himalayan Institute Press**
Division of Himalayan International Institute of Yoga Science and Philosophy
952 Bethany Tpke, Honesdale, PA 18431-9706
*Tel:* 570-253-5551 *Toll Free Tel:* 800-822-4547 *Fax:* 570-253-4500
*E-mail:* info@himalayaninstitute.org
*Web Site:* www.himalayaninstitute.org
*Key Personnel*
Chmn & Spiritual Head: Pandit Rajmani Tigunait, PhD
Dir, Mktg: Todd Wolfenberg *Tel:* 570-647-1440 *E-mail:* twolfenberg@himalayaninstitute.org
Founded: 1971
Publish audio, video & books on yoga, meditation, holistic health, philosophy, psychology & stress management.
ISBN Prefix(es): 978-0-89389
Number of titles published annually: 4 Print; 3 E-Book; 2 Audio
Total Titles: 60 Print; 10 Audio
Imprints: Yoga International (bimonthly mag)
Foreign Rights: Hagenbach & Bender GmbH (Worldwide)

**Hippocrene Books Inc**
171 Madison Ave, New York, NY 10016
*Tel:* 212-685-4373; 212-685-4375 *Fax:* 212-779-9338
*E-mail:* info@hippocrenebooks.com; orderdept@hippocrenebooks.com (orders); contact@hippocrenebooks.com
*Web Site:* www.hippocrenebooks.com
*Key Personnel*
Founder & Pres: George Blagowidow
Edit Dir: Priti Chitnis Gress
Founded: 1971
Foreign language dictionaries & studies, international cookbooks, international literary classics, love poetry, concise illustrated histories of countries.
ISBN Prefix(es): 978-0-87052; 978-0-7818
Number of titles published annually: 30 Print
Total Titles: 600 Print; 25 Audio
Foreign Rights: A B E Marketing (Poland); Gazelle Book Services (England); E A Milley Enterprises (Canada)
*Shipping Address:* W A Book Service Inc, 26 Ranick Rd, Hauppauge, NY 11788

**The Historic New Orleans Collection**
533 Royal St, New Orleans, LA 70130
*Tel:* 504-523-4662 *Fax:* 504-598-7104
*E-mail:* wrc@hnoc.org
*Web Site:* www.hnoc.org
*Key Personnel*
Exec Dir: Priscilla Lawrence *E-mail:* priscill@hnoc.org
Dir, Pubns: Dr Jessica Dorman *Tel:* 504-598-7174 *E-mail:* jessicad@hnoc.org
Founded: 1966
Publications related to Louisiana history & to the holdings of The Historic New Orleans Collection; preservation manuals for family papers, photographs, etc.
ISBN Prefix(es): 978-0-917860
Number of titles published annually: 3 Print
Total Titles: 52 Print

**History Publishing Co LLC**
173 Rte 9W, Palisades, NY 10964
SAN: 850-5942
Mailing Address: PO Box 700, Palisades, NY 10964
*Tel:* 845-398-8161 *Fax:* 845-231-6167
*E-mail:* historypublish@aol.com; info@historypublishingco.com
*Web Site:* www.historypublishingco.com
*Key Personnel*
Publr: Don Bracken *Tel:* 845-359-1765 *E-mail:* djb@historypublishingco.com
Assoc Publr: Carolyn Doyle Winter *Tel:* 845-548-2784 *E-mail:* cdw@historypublishingco.com
Edit Dir: Alexis Starke *E-mail:* alex@historypublishingco.com
Sales Mgr: Thomas Ryan
Founded: 2007
Trade book publisher dealing in 18th-20th century history. Strong focus on history told from the first person perspective by people who participated in the making of history or were ongoing witness to the making of history.
ISBN Prefix(es): 978-19339-09
Number of titles published annually: 10 Print; 12 Online; 10 E-Book
Total Titles: 20 Print; 19 Online; 19 E-Book
Imprints: Chronology Books; Today's Books
*Returns:* Midpoint Trade Books, 5701 Ranch Dr, Little Rock, AR 72223, Dir: Julie Hardison *Tel:* 913-362-1120 *Fax:* 913-632-7401 *E-mail:* julie@midpointtrade.com *Web Site:* midpointtrade.com
*Warehouse:* Midpoint Trade Books, 5701 Ranch Dr, Little Rock, AR 72223, Dir: Julie Hardison *Tel:* 913-362-1120 *Fax:* 913-362-7401 *E-mail:* julie@midpointtrade.com *Web Site:* midpointtrade.com
*Distribution Center:* INscribe Digital, 444 Spear St, Suite 213, San Francisco, CA 94105
Midpoint Trade Books, 5701 Ranch Dr, Little Rock, AR 72223, Dir: Julie Hardison *Tel:* 913-362-1120 *Fax:* 913-362-7401 *E-mail:* julie@midpointtrade.com *Web Site:* midpointtrade.com
Membership(s): IBPA, the Independent Book Publishers Association

**W D Hoard & Sons Co**
28 W Milwaukee Ave, Fort Atkinson, WI 53538-2018
Mailing Address: PO Box 801, Fort Atkinson, WI 53538-0801
*Tel:* 920-563-5551 *Fax:* 920-563-7298
*E-mail:* hoards@hoards.com
*Web Site:* www.hoards.com; www.hoardprinting.com
*Key Personnel*
Book Ed: Elvira Kau *E-mail:* hdbooks@hoards.com
Founded: 1870
Dairy oriented & some agricultural, regional publications, catalogs & specialty projects.
ISBN Prefix(es): 978-0-932147
Number of titles published annually: 3 Print
Total Titles: 22 Print
Imprints: Hoard's Dairyman Magazine

**Hobar Publications**
Division of Finney Company Inc
8075 215 St W, Lakeville, MN 55044
*Tel:* 952-469-6699 *Toll Free Tel:* 800-846-7027 *Fax:* 952-469-1968 *Toll Free Fax:* 800-330-6232
*E-mail:* info@finneyco.com
*Web Site:* www.finney-hobar.com
*Key Personnel*
Pres: Alan E Krysan
Mktg Specialist: Krista Danielson
Founded: 1964
Produces educational materials for grades 7-12 in the areas of agriculture, career exploration & guidance & technical education.
ISBN Prefix(es): 978-0-913163; 978-0-9616847
Number of titles published annually: 4 Print
Total Titles: 45 Print
Imprints: Agronomy Publications; K A Publishing
Divisions: National Farm Book Co
Distributor for Drache Publications
Membership(s): National Association of Agriculture Educators

**§Hobbes End Publishing LLC**
Subsidiary of Hobbes End Entertainment LLC
PO Box 193, Aubrey, TX 76227

*Tel:* 940-365-2230
*E-mail:* publisher@hobbesendpublishing.com
*Web Site:* www.hobbesendpublishing.com
*Key Personnel*
Pres: Jairus Reddy
Founded: 2004
Primarily a fiction publishing company who specializes in adult fiction, fantasy, children's fiction, fantasy, science fiction & horror. Services include business to business publications as well as services to other companies in the literary industry.
ISBN Prefix(es): 978-0-9763510
Number of titles published annually: 5 Print
Total Titles: 15 Print

**Hobblebush Books**
17-A Old Milford Rd, Brookline, NH 03033
*Tel:* 603-672-4317 *Fax:* 603-672-4317
*E-mail:* hobblebush@charter.net
*Web Site:* www.hobblebush.com
*Key Personnel*
Owner & Pres: Mr Sidney Hall, Jr *E-mail:* sidhall@charter.net
Mktg Dir: Amy Wood *E-mail:* amy.hobblebush@charter.net
Founded: 1993
Independent publisher of both literary & nonliterary titles. Book editing, design, typesetting & printing services.
ISBN Prefix(es): 978-0-9636413; 978-0-9760896; 978-0-9801672
Number of titles published annually: 6 Print
Total Titles: 37 Print; 1 E-Book
Distributor for Abelard Press; Oyster River Press; Plaidswede Publishing
*Orders to:* Small Press Distributors, 1341 Seventh St, Berkeley, CA 94710-1409 (bookstores & libs) *Toll Free Tel:* 800-869-7553 *Fax:* 510-524-0852 *Web Site:* www.spdbooks.org; Quality Books Inc, 1003 W Pines Rd, Oregon, IL 61061 *Toll Free Tel:* 800-323-4241 *Fax:* 815-732-4499 *Web Site:* www.quality-books.com; The Distributors, 702 S Michigan, South Bend, IN 46601 (trade) *Tel:* 574-232-8500 *Fax:* 312-803-0887 *E-mail:* schools@thedistributors.com *Web Site:* www.thedistributors.com; Baker & Taylor, 2550 W Tyvola Rd, Suite 300, Charlotte, NC 28217 (trade) *Tel:* 704-998-3100 *Toll Free Tel:* 800-775-1800 *E-mail:* btinfo@btol.com *Web Site:* www.btol.com
*Distribution Center:* Small Press Distributors, 1341 Seventh St, Berkeley, CA 94710-1409 (bookstores & libs) *Toll Free Tel:* 800-869-7553 *Fax:* 510-524-0852 *Web Site:* www.spdbooks.org
Quality Books Inc, 1003 W Pines Rd, Oregon, IL 61061 *Toll Free Tel:* 800-323-4241 *Fax:* 815-732-4499 *Web Site:* www.quality-books.com
The Distributors, 702 S Michigan, South Bend, IN 46601 (trade) *Tel:* 574-232-8500 *Fax:* 312-803-0887 *E-mail:* schools@thedistributors.com *Web Site:* www.thedistributors.com
Baker & Taylor, 2550 W Tyvola Rd, Suite 300, Charlotte, NC 28217 (trade) *Tel:* 704-998-3100 *Toll Free Tel:* 800-775-1800 *Web Site:* www.btol.com
Membership(s): Council of Literary Magazines & Presses; Independent Publishers of New England; New Hampshire Writers Project

**Hogrefe Publishing**
38 Chauncy St, Suite 1002, Boston, MA 02111
SAN: 293-2792
*Toll Free Tel:* 866-823-4726 *Fax:* 617-354-6875
*E-mail:* publishing@hogrefe.com
*Web Site:* www.hogrefe.com
*Key Personnel*
Publg Mgr: Robert Dimbleby *E-mail:* robert.dimbleby@hogrefe.com
Founded: 1978
Books & journals in the fields of medicine, neurosciences, psychiatry, psychology.
ISBN Prefix(es): 978-0-88937; 978-0-920887; 978-1-61676 (ebooks); 978-1-61334 (EPUB)
Number of titles published annually: 15 Print
*Foreign Office(s):* Hogrefe Verlag, Merkelstr 3, 37085 Goettingen, Germany *Tel:* (0551) 99950 420 *Fax:* (0551) 99950 425
Distributor for Verlag Hans Huber Hogrefe AG (Switzerland); Hogrefe Verlag (Germany)
*Orders to:* Bookmasters, 30 Amberwood Pkwy, Ashland, OH 44805, Dist Servs Mgr: Cheryl Householder *Tel:* 419-281-1802 *Toll Free Tel:* 800-228-3749 *Fax:* 419-281-6883
*Returns:* Bookmasters, 30 Amberwood Pkwy, Ashland, OH 44805, Dist Servs Mgr: Cheryl Householder *Tel:* 419-281-1802 *Toll Free Tel:* 800-228-3749 *Fax:* 419-281-6883
*Distribution Center:* Bookmasters, 30 Amberwood Pkwy, Ashland, OH 44805, Dist Servs Mgr: Cheryl Householder *Tel:* 419-281-1802 *Toll Free Tel:* 800-228-3749 *Fax:* 419-281-6883

**Hohm Press**
Subsidiary of HSM LLC
PO Box 4410, Chino Valley, AZ 86323
*Tel:* 928-636-3331 *Toll Free Tel:* 800-381-2700 *Fax:* 928-636-7519
*E-mail:* hppublisher@cableone.net; hohmpresseditor@gmail.com
*Web Site:* www.hohmpress.com
*Key Personnel*
Gen Mgr & Sales Dir: Dasya Anthony Zuccarello
Mng Ed: Regina Sara Ryan
Prodn: Joe Bala Zuccarello
Founded: 1975
Independent publisher of books on spirituality & consciousness studies.
ISBN Prefix(es): 978-0-934252; 978-1-890772
Number of titles published annually: 6 Print; 6 E-Book
Total Titles: 180 Print; 30 E-Book; 6 Audio
Imprints: Kalindi Press (books on natural health & nutrition, children's & family health)
Foreign Rep(s): Gazelle (Europe)
Foreign Rights: Hagenbach & Bender GmbH (Worldwide exc USA)
*Shipping Address:* 860 Staley Lane, Chino Valley, AZ 86323
*Warehouse:* 860 Staley Lane, Chino Valley, AZ 86323
*Distribution Center:* SCB Distributors, 15608 S New Century Dr, Gardena, CA 90248 (US & CN)

**Holiday House Inc**
425 Madison Ave, New York, NY 10017
SAN: 202-3008
*Tel:* 212-688-0085 *Fax:* 212-421-6134
*E-mail:* holiday@holidayhouse.com
*Web Site:* www.holidayhouse.com
*Key Personnel*
Pres: John Briggs
VP & Ed-in-Chief: Mary Cash
VP, Sales: Barbara A Walsh
VP, Mktg: Theresa M Borzumato
VP, Rts, Perms & Digital Publg: Julia Gallagher
Dir, Art & Design: Claire Counihan
Dir, Prodn: Lisa Lee
Exec Ed: Grace Maccarone
Cont: Judith Ang
Dir, Opers: Lisa Morales
Publicist: Hayley Gonnason
Mktg Assoc: Mariana Cruz-Munoz
Asst Ed: Kelly Laughman
Edit Asst: Sally Morgridge
Cust Serv: Kathryn Hoban
Founded: 1935
Juvenile & young adult books.
ISBN Prefix(es): 978-0-8234
Number of titles published annually: 80 Print
Total Titles: 800 Print
Foreign Rep(s): Thomas Allen & Son Ltd (Canada)
Foreign Rights: Big Apple Agency Inc (China, Taiwan); Lora Fountain (Belgium, France, Italy, Netherlands, Spanish & Portuguese); Caroline Hill-Trevor (Greece, Scandinavia, Turkey, UK Commonwealth); KCC International (Korea); Tuttle-Mori Agency Inc (Japan); Literarische Agentur Silke Weniger (Austria, Germany)
*Shipping Address:* Maple-Vail Distribution Center, 1000 Strickler Rd, Mount Joy, PA 17552
Membership(s): Children's Book Council

**Hollym International Corp**
18 Donald Place, Elizabeth, NJ 07208
SAN: 211-0172
*Tel:* 908-353-1655 *Fax:* 908-353-0255
*E-mail:* contact@hollym.com
*Web Site:* www.hollym.com
*Key Personnel*
Pres: Gene S Rhie
Founded: 1977
Korea related books.
ISBN Prefix(es): 978-0-930878; 978-1-56591
Number of titles published annually: 10 Print
Total Titles: 155 Print
*Foreign Office(s):* Hollym Corp, 13-13 Gwancheol-dong, Jongno-gu, 110-111 Seoul, South Korea, Contact: Kim-Man Ham *Tel:* (02) 735-7551 *Fax:* (02) 730-5149 *E-mail:* info@hollym.co.kr *Web Site:* www.hollym.co.kr

**Hollywood Film Archive**
8391 Beverly Blvd, PMB 321, Los Angeles, CA 90048
*Tel:* 323-655-4968
*Web Site:* hfarchive.com
*Key Personnel*
Dir: D Richard Baer
Dir, Admin: Howard Schiller
Founded: 1972
Publication, sales & distribution of comprehensive movie, video & TV reference books.
ISBN Prefix(es): 978-0-913616
Number of titles published annually: 3 Print
Total Titles: 34 Print
Subsidiaries: Cinema Book Society
Distributor for R R Bowker
*Advertising Agency:* Tartan Advertising

**Holmes & Meier Publishers Inc**
PO Box 943, Teaneck, NJ 07666
SAN: 201-9280
*Tel:* 201-833-2270 *Fax:* 201-833-2272
*E-mail:* info@holmesandmeier.com
*Web Site:* www.holmesandmeier.com
*Key Personnel*
Publr: Miriam H Holmes
Founded: 1969
Scholarly & trade hardcover & paperbacks; general nonfiction & fiction, reference, biography, autobiography & history. Jewish studies, cultural studies, ethnic & immigration studies, area studies, international affairs, women's studies, art, architecture, costume & theatre.
ISBN Prefix(es): 978-0-8419
Number of titles published annually: 8 Print
Total Titles: 600 Print
Subsidiaries: Africana Publishing Co
*Orders to:* Gazelle Book Services, White Cross Mills, High Town, Lancaster LA1 4KS, United Kingdom (Europe, UK) *Tel:* (0152) 468765 *Fax:* (0152) 463232 *E-mail:* sales@gazellebooks.co.uk
*Returns:* GMI Distribution, 60 Clyde Rd, Somerset, NJ 08873
*Warehouse:* GMI Distribution, 60 Clyde Rd, Somerset, NJ 08873
Membership(s): IBPA, the Independent Book Publishers Association

**Holmes Publishing Group LLC**
PO Box 2370, Sequim, WA 98382
*Tel:* 360-681-2900 *Fax:* 360-351-9909

*E-mail:* holmespub@fastmail.fm
*Web Site:* jdholmes.com
*Key Personnel*
CEO & Pres: Teddy Holmes
Founded: 1971
Religions of the world, New Age, occult, orientalia, metaphysical, philosophy, astrology & theology. No returns accepted.
ISBN Prefix(es): 978-1-55818; 978-0-916411
Number of titles published annually: 16 Print
Total Titles: 389 Print
Imprints: Alchemical Press; Alexandrian Press; Contra/Thought; Near Eastern Press; Sure Fire Press
Distributor for Capall-Bann (UK); Fulgur Ltd; Jerusalem Press; Starfire Publishing; Three Hands Press; Xoanon Publishing
Foreign Rep(s): Mandrake Press Ltd (UK)
*Distribution Center:* New Leaf Distributing Co, 401 Thornton Rd, Lithia Springs, GA 30122-1557 *Tel:* 770-948-7845 *Fax:* 770-944-2313 *Web Site:* www.newleaf-dist.com

**Henry Holt and Company, LLC**
Division of Macmillan
175 Fifth Ave, New York, NY 10010
SAN: 200-2108
*Tel:* 646-307-5151 *Toll Free Tel:* 888-330-8477 (orders) *Fax:* 646-307-5285
*E-mail:* firstname.lastname@hholt.com
LOD *Web Site:* www.henryholt.com
*Key Personnel*
Pres & Publr: Stephen Rubin
Deputy Publr, VP, Sales & Mktg: Maggie Richards
VP, Dir of Publicity: Patricia Eisemann
Dir, Perms & Copyright: Mimi Ross
Art Dir: Richard Pracher
Exec Mng Ed, Adult Trade: Kenn Russell
Ed-in-Chief, NY: Gillian Blake
Publr, Metropolitan Books: Sara Bershtel
Sr Ed, Metropolitan Books: Riva Hocherman
Edit Dir, Times Books: Paul Golob
Founded: 1866
ISBN Prefix(es): 978-0-8050 (Holt)
Number of titles published annually: 100 Print
Total Titles: 3,000 Print
Imprints: Henry Holt; Holt Paperbacks; John Macrae Books; Metropolitan Books; Times Books
Foreign Rep(s): Raincoast (Canada)
Foreign Rights: Agencia Riff (Brazil); Anthea Agency (Bulgaria); Author Rights Agency Ltd (Russia); Bardon-Chinese Media Agency (Mainland China, Taiwan); Eliane Benisti Literary Agency (France); The English Agency (Japan) Ltd (Japan); Graal Literary Agency (Maria Strarz-Kanska) (Poland); The Deborah Harris Agency (Israel); Internationaal Literatuur Bureau BV (Netherlands); International Copyright Agency Ltd (Simona Kessler) (Romania); Asli Karasuil Telif Haklari (Asli Karasuil Ermis) (Turkey); Katai & Bolza Literary Agents (Hungary); Korea Copyright Center Inc (KCC) (Korea); Leonhardt & Hoier (Scandinavia); Liepman Agency (Eva Koralnik & Ronit Zafran) (Germany); Literarni Aventura sro (Czech Republic, Slovakia); MB Agencia Literaria (Portugal, Spain); Plima Literary Agency (Croatia, Serbia, Slovenia); Marco Vigevani Agenzia Letteraria (Italy)
*Advertising Agency:* Verso Advertising, 50 W 17 St, New York, NY 10010 *Tel:* 212-292-2990 *Web Site:* www.versoadvertising.com
*Warehouse:* MPS, 16365 James Madison Hwy, Gordonsville, VA 22942, SVP, Opers: Michael Shareck *Tel:* 540-672-7698 SAN: 631-5011
Membership(s): AAP

**§Holt McDougal**
Division of Houghton Mifflin Harcourt
1900 S Batavia Ave, Geneva, IL 60134
*Tel:* 630-232-2550 *Toll Free Tel:* 800-462-6595 *Toll Free Fax:* 888-872-8380
*E-mail:* k12orders@hmco.com
*Web Site:* holtmcdougal.hmhco.com/hm/home.htm
Founded: 1866
Textbooks & related learning materials in language arts, math, science, social studies & world languages for grades 6-12.
ISBN Prefix(es): 978-0-03
Total Titles: 1,408 Print; 1,511 CD-ROM; 159 Online; 135 E-Book; 66 Audio
*Warehouse:* 1175 N Stemmons Fwy, Lewisville, TX 75067

**Holy Cow! Press**
PO Box 3170, Mount Royal Sta, Duluth, MN 55803
*Tel:* 218-724-1653 *Fax:* 218-724-1653
*E-mail:* holycow@holycowpress.org
*Web Site:* www.holycowpress.org
*Key Personnel*
Publr & Ed: Jim Perlman
Founded: 1977
ISBN Prefix(es): 978-0-930100; 978-0-9779458
Number of titles published annually: 6 Print
Total Titles: 56 Print
*Distribution Center:* Consortium Book Sales & Distribution, 1045 Westgate Dr, Saint Paul, MN 55413-1004 (www.cbsd.com) *Toll Free Tel:* 800-283-3572 (cust serv) *Fax:* 651-221-0124

**Holy Cross Orthodox Press**
Division of Hellenic College Inc
50 Goddard Ave, Brookline, MA 02445
*Tel:* 617-731-3500 *Fax:* 617-850-1460
*E-mail:* press@hchc.edu
*Web Site:* www.hchc.edu
*Key Personnel*
Dir: Dr Anton Vrame
Mng Ed, Greek Orthodox Theological Revie: Herald Gjura
Founded: 1974
Books on Orthodox Christian religion.
ISBN Prefix(es): 978-0-917651; 978-1-885652; 978-2-825415
Number of titles published annually: 10 Print
Total Titles: 120 Print

**Homa & Sekey Books**
140 E Ridgewood Ave, Paramus, NJ 07652
*Tel:* 201-261-8810 *Toll Free Tel:* 800-870-HOMA (870-4662 orders) *Fax:* 201-261-8890
*E-mail:* info@homabooks.com
*Web Site:* www.homabooks.com
*Key Personnel*
Publr: Shawn Ye
Founded: 1997
Publisher & distributor of books on Asia.
ISBN Prefix(es): 978-1-931907; 978-0-966542
Number of titles published annually: 15 Print
Distributor for China Encyclopedia Publishing House; China Intercontinental Press; China Zhejiang Publishing United Group
Foreign Rights: Eric Yang Agency (Korea)
Membership(s): IBPA, the Independent Book Publishers Association

**Home Planners LLC**
Subsidiary of Hanley-Wood Inc
3275 W Ina Rd, Suite 260, Tucson, AZ 85741
SAN: 201-5382
*Tel:* 520-297-8200 *Toll Free Tel:* 800-521-6797 *Fax:* 520-297-6219 *Toll Free Fax:* 800-224-6699
*E-mail:* customerservice@eplans.com
*Web Site:* www.eplans.com
Founded: 1946
Designer of home & landscape plans, publisher of home plans & books, landscape, interior design books & magazines & construction blueprints.
ISBN Prefix(es): 978-0-918894; 978-1-881955; 978-1-931131
Number of titles published annually: 10 Print
Total Titles: 60 Print
Distributed by Creative Homeowner Press; H B Fenn & Co
*Advertising Agency:* Home Plans Advertising
*Distribution Center:* Home Planners Distribution Ctr, 29333 Lorie Lane, Wixom, MI 48393

**Homestead Publishing**
Affiliate of Book Design Ltd
Box 193, Moose, WY 83012-0193
*Tel:* 307-733-6248 *Fax:* 307-733-6248
*E-mail:* orders@homesteadpublishing.net
*Web Site:* www.homesteadpublishing.net
*Key Personnel*
Publr: Carl Schreier *Tel:* 415-621-5039
Contact: Diane Henderson
Founded: 1980
Also publish guide books.
ISBN Prefix(es): 978-0-943972
Number of titles published annually: 8 Print; 2,000 Online; 6 E-Book
Total Titles: 268 Print; 4,500 Online; 16 E-Book
*Branch Office(s)*
4388 17 St, San Francisco, CA 94114 *Tel:* 415-621-5039 *Fax:* 415-621-5039
*Warehouse:* 4030 W Lake Creek Dr, Wilson, WY 83014

**Hoover Institution Press**
Subsidiary of Hoover Institution on War, Revolution & Peace
Stanford University, 434 Galvez Mall, Stanford, CA 94305-6010
SAN: 202-3024
*Tel:* 650-725-7146; 650-723-3373 *Toll Free Tel:* 800-935-2882 *Fax:* 650-723-8626
*E-mail:* hooverpress@stanford.edu
*Web Site:* www.hoover.org; www.hooverpress.org
*Key Personnel*
Mng Ed, Hoover Digest: Charles Lindsey *Tel:* 650-723-1471 *E-mail:* digesteditor@stanford.edu
Mng Ed, Education Next: Carol Peterson *E-mail:* cpeterso@latte.harvard.edu
Mng Ed, Policy Review: Liam Julian *E-mail:* polrev@hoover.stanford.edu
Book Prodn Mgr: Marshall Blanchard *Tel:* 650-725-3460
Founded: 1962
Studies on domestic & international policy, studies of nationalities in Central & Eastern Europe, history & political science; bibliographies & surveys of Hoover Institution's resources.
ISBN Prefix(es): 978-0-8179
Number of titles published annually: 27 Print
Total Titles: 675 Print; 75 Online
Foreign Rep(s): East-West Export Books (Asia, Hawaii, The Pacific)
*Orders to:* Chicago Distribution Center, 11030 S Langley Ave, Chicago, IL 60628 *Tel:* 773-702-7000 *Toll Free Tel:* 800-621-2736 *Toll Free Fax:* 800-621-8476 *E-mail:* orders@press.uchicago.edu
*Returns:* Chicago Distribution Center, 11030 S Langley Ave, Chicago, IL 60628 *Tel:* 773-702-7000 *Toll Free Tel:* 800-621-2736 *Toll Free Fax:* 800-621-8476 *E-mail:* orders@press.uchicago.edu

**Hoover's, Inc**
5800 Airport Blvd, Austin, TX 78752
*Tel:* 512-374-4500 *Toll Free Tel:* 866-307-3812 *Fax:* 512-374-4501
*E-mail:* info@hoovers.com
*Web Site:* www.hoovers.com
*Key Personnel*
Pres: Ms Hyune Hand
VP, Technol: Mamie Jones
VP, Busn: Jeff Cross

VP, Mktg: James Rogers
VP, Prod Devt: Greg Stern
Founded: 1990
Business reference books & online services.
ISBN Prefix(es): 978-1-878753; 978-1-57311
Number of titles published annually: 7 Print
Total Titles: 7 Print; 3 Online
Imprints: Hoover's Business Press; Hoover's Handbooks
*Foreign Office(s):* William Snyder Publishing Assoc, 5 Five Mile Dr, Oxford 0X2 8HT, United Kingdom
Foreign Rep(s): William Snyder Publishing Associates (England)

**Hope Publishing Co**
380 S Main Place, Carol Stream, IL 60188
*Tel:* 630-665-3200 *Toll Free Tel:* 800-323-1049 *Fax:* 630-665-2552
*E-mail:* hope@hopepublishing.com
*Web Site:* www.hopepublishing.com
*Key Personnel*
Pres: John Shorney *E-mail:* john@hopepublishing.com
VP: Scott Shorney *E-mail:* scott@hopepublishing.com; Steve Shorney *E-mail:* steve@hopepublishing.com
Founded: 1892
Choir music, hymnals, instrumental music books & hand bell music.
ISBN Prefix(es): 978-0-916642
Number of titles published annually: 3 Print
Total Titles: 15 Print
Divisions: Agape; Providence Press; Somerset Press; Tabernacle Publishing
*Advertising Agency:* Lamplighter Agency

**Horizon Publishers & Distributors Inc**
191 N 650 E, Bountiful, UT 84010-3628
*Tel:* 801-292-7102
*E-mail:* ldshorizonpublishers@gmail.com
*Web Site:* www.ldshorizonpublishers.com
*Key Personnel*
Owner & Pres: Duane S Crowther
Owner & VP: Jean D Crowther
Founded: 1971
Christian (primarily Latter-day Saints), inspirational, health foods, self sufficient living, music, marriage & family, children's activities, needlework, nonfiction, biography paperbacks & hardbound.
ISBN Prefix(es): 978-0-88290
Number of titles published annually: 30 Print
Total Titles: 521 Print; 35 CD-ROM; 40 Audio
Distributed by Cedar Fort Inc

**Hospital & Healthcare Compensation Service**
Subsidiary of John R Zabka Associates Inc
3 Post Rd FL, Suite 3, Oakland, NJ 07436
Mailing Address: PO Box 376, Oakland, NJ 07436-0376
*Tel:* 201-405-0075 *Fax:* 201-405-2110
*E-mail:* allinfo@hhcsinc.com
*Web Site:* www.hhcsinc.com
*Key Personnel*
Dir, Client Servs: Sharah Wallace *Tel:* 201-405-0075 ext 14 *E-mail:* swallace@hhcsinc.com
Dir, Reports: Rosanne Zabka *Tel:* 201-405-0075 ext 11 *E-mail:* rzabka@hhcsinc.com
Founded: 1971
Publisher of salary & benefits reports for hospital, nursing home, assisted living, CCRC, home care, hospice & rehabilitation employees.
ISBN Prefix(es): 978-0-939326; 978-1-934847
Number of titles published annually: 11 Print; 11 CD-ROM
Total Titles: 10 Print; 11 CD-ROM

**Host Publications**
1000 E Seventh St, Suite 201, Austin, TX 78702
*Tel:* 512-236-1290 *Fax:* 512-236-1208
*Web Site:* www.hostpublications.com
*Key Personnel*
Pres: Joe W Bratcher, III *E-mail:* jbratcher@hostpublications.com
Dir, Fulfillment: Susan Lesak *E-mail:* slesak@hostpublications.com
Founded: 1987
ISBN Prefix(es): 978-0-924047
Number of titles published annually: 6 Print
Total Titles: 50 Print
*Distribution Center:* Small Press Distribution, 1341 17 St, Berkeley, CA 94710-1409, Sales & Mktg Mgr: Dr Brent Cunningham *Tel:* 510-524-1668 *Toll Free Tel:* 800-869-7553 *E-mail:* spd@spdbooks.org *Web Site:* www.spdbooks.org
Membership(s): IBPA, the Independent Book Publishers Association

**Houghton Mifflin Company**, see Houghton Mifflin Harcourt

**§Houghton Mifflin Harcourt**
222 Berkeley St, Boston, MA 02116-3764
*Tel:* 617-351-5000 *Toll Free Tel:* 800-225-5425 (Pre-K-8); 800-462-6595 (6–12; Advanced & Electives); 800-289-4490 (Specialized Curriculum: Great Source, Rigby, Saxon, Steck-Vaughn; Homeschool; Adult Ed); 800-323-9540 (Assessment: Riverside Publishing); 888-391-3245 (SkillsTutor); 888-242-6747 option 2 (Destination Series; Classroom Connect; Earobics; Edmark; Learning Village; Riverdeep); 800-225-3362 (Houghton Mifflin Harcourt Trade & Reference Publishers); 800-225-5800 (Heinemann) *Fax:* 617-351-1125
*Web Site:* www.hmhco.com
*Key Personnel*
~~CEO & Pres: Linda K Zecher~~
Chief Content Offr & EVP, Corp Aff: Mary Cullinane
CIO: Brook Colangelo
EVP & Gen Coun: William Bayers
EVP, Emerging Mkts: Chip Greene
EVP & Gen Mgr, Innovation & New Ventures Group: Fiona O'Carroll
SVP, Consumer Prods & Mktg: Wendy Bronfin
SVP, Head of Intl Mkts: Mark Short
Pres, Trade & Reference Publishers: Gary Gentel
Pres, The Learning Co: Tony Bordon
EVP & COO, Education Group: Eric Shuman
SVP, HR: Joanne Karimi
EVP, Comprehensive Curriculum, Education Group: Rita Schaefer
EVP & Gen Mgr, Specialized Solutions: Scott Bowker
SVP & Gen Mgr, Enterprise Solutions: Russ Carlson
EVP, Intl Mkts, Education Group: Terry Nealon
EVP, Global Prod & Content Devt, Education Group: Bethlam Forsa
SVP & CIO: Paul Wilcox
VP & Exec Mng Ed: Ann-Marie Pucillo
Exec Dir, Mass Mkt & Specialty Retail Channels: Colleen Murphy
Head, Strategy & Alliances: Tim Cannon
Sr Designer: Patrick Barry; Brian Moore
Sr Mktg Mgr: Katrina Kruse
Sr Natl Accts Mgr: Peter Cohen
Natl Acct Mgr: James Phirmam
Sr Publicist: Stephanie Kim
Sr Publicity Assoc: Simmi Aujla
Mktg Specialist, Culinary Team: Jessica Gilo
Founded: 1832
With education products & services used by 57 million students throughout all 50 U.S. states & 120 countries, Houghton Mifflin Harcourt is a global education & learning company. The world's largest provider of materials for Pre-K-12 learning, HMH is leading the way with innovative solutions & approaches to the challenges facing education today. Through curricula excellence coupled with technology innovations & professional services, HMH collaborates with school districts, administrators, teachers, parents & students, providing interactive, results-driven learning solutions. Its Educational Consulting Services group works to increase student achievement in underperforming schools by developing, implementing & supporting education transformation through sustained district partnerships. With origins dating back to 1832, the company also publishes an extensive line of reference works & award-winning literature for adults & young readers. For more information, visit www.hmhco.com.
ISBN Prefix(es): 978-0-395 (Houghton Mifflin/Mariner); 978-0-618 (Houghton Mifflin/Mariner/Clarion); 978-0-151 (Harcourt); 978-0-547 (Mariner); 978-0-753 (Kingfisher)
Imprints: HMH Education Group; HMH Trade and Reference Publishers; The Learning Company; SkillsTutor
Distributor for Chambers; Harrap; Larousse Bilingual; Larousse Mexico; The Old Farmer's Almanac
Membership(s): AAP; ABA; ALA; American Bar Association; Association of Booksellers for Children; Association of Catholic Publishers Inc; Association of Educational Publishers; Association of Test Publishers; Children's Book Council; Dictionary Society of North America; National Catholic Education Association; Society of Printers; Software & Information Industry Association
*See separate listing for:*
**Clarion Books**
**Great Source Education Group**
**Harcourt Achieve**
**Harcourt Inc**
**Holt McDougal**
**Houghton Mifflin Harcourt K-12 Publishers**
**Houghton Mifflin Harcourt Trade & Reference Division**
**Riverside Publishing**
**Saxon Publishers**

**Houghton Mifflin Harcourt K-12 Publishers**
Division of Houghton Mifflin Harcourt
222 Berkeley St, Boston, MA 02116-3764
*Tel:* 617-351-5000 *Toll Free Tel:* 800-225-5425 (cust serv)
*Web Site:* www.hmhco.com; www.hmheducation.com
*Key Personnel*
~~Pres: Donna Lucki~~
SVP, Open Territory Sales: Edward Bonessi *Tel:* 800-284-0819 *E-mail:* ed.bonessi@hmhpub.com
SVP, K-12 Mktg: Margaret deBoer
SVP & Publr: Alice Sullo
VP & Edit Dir, Reading/Language Arts & Bilingual Educ: Jim Chapman
Dir, School & Lib Mktg: Lisa Di Sarro
E-Mktg & Publicity Specialist: Roshan Nozari
Elementary school textbooks, educational materials & services.
*Sales Office(s):* 637 Cypress Hills Dr, Encinitas, CA 92024, Regl VP: John Sipe *Tel:* 858-535-3901
8400 E Prentice Ave, Denver, CO 80232-2550, VP & Regl Mgr: Deborah Lehman
5555 Triangle Pkwy, Suite 150, Norcross, GA 30092, VP & Regl Mgr: Deborah Sanders *Tel:* 404-449-5881
1900 S Batavia Ave, Geneva, IL 60134 *Tel:* 630-232-2550
307 Fellowship Rd, Suite 104, Mount Laurel, NJ 08054, VP & Regl Mgr: Gwen Durden-Simmons *Tel:* 609-452-0200
13400 Midway Rd, Dallas, TX 75244, VP & Regl Mgr: Mary Lytle *Tel:* 972-980-1100

**Houghton Mifflin Harcourt Trade & Reference Division**
Division of Houghton Mifflin Harcourt Publishing Company

222 Berkeley St, Boston, MA 02116-3764
SAN: 200-2388
*Tel:* 617-351-5000 *Toll Free Tel:* 800-225-3362
*Web Site:* www.houghtonmifflinbooks.com
*Key Personnel*
Pres: Gary Gentel
SVP, Busn Planning & Strategy: Cheryl Cramer Toto
SVP, Prodn & Creative Servs: Sandy Grebenar
SVP, Sales & Mktg: Laurie Brown
SVP & Publr, Adult Trade & Ref: Bruce Nichols
SVP & Publr, Children's Books: Betsy Groban
VP, Digital Mktg Strategy: Sanj Kharbanda
VP, Prodn: Jill Lazer
VP, Trade Pbks, Edit Dir, Mariner & CliffsNotes & Dir, Tolkien Projects: Ken Carpenter
VP, Trade Sales & Children's Mktg: Maire Gorman
VP, Publr & Edit Dir, Clarion Div: Dinah Stevenson
VP & Exec Mng Dir, Trade: Rebecca Saikia-Wilson
VP & Exec Dir, Publicity: Lori Glazer
VP & Creative Dir: Michaela Sullivan
VP & Dir, Subs Rts: Deborah Engel
VP & Dir, Cust Serv & Opers: Marilyn Harris
VP & Dir, Digital Busn Devt: David J Langevin *Tel:* 617-351-3325 *E-mail:* david.langevin@hmhpub.com
VP & Dir, Electronic Devt: David Jost
VP & Ed-in-Chief, Children's: Mary Wilcox
Exec Dir, Children's Publicity: Karen Walsh
Natl Accts Dir: Josh Harwood
Dir, Culinary Mktg: Brad Parsons
Dir, Field Sales & Dist: Beth Ineson
Digital Edit Dir, Ebook Publg: Daniel Nayeri
Edit Dir, Children's: Jeannette Larson
Edit Dir, Rux Martin Books: Rux Martin
Assoc Dir, Publicity: Taryn Roeder
Mng Ed: Mary Huot
Mng Ed, Children's: Ann-Marie Pucillo
Mng Ed, Cookbooks: Marina Padakis
Mng Ed, Digital Cookbooks: Rebecca Springer
Sr Exec Ed: Susan Canavan; Deanne Urmy
Sr Exec Ed, Children's: Margaret Raymo
Exec Ed, CliffsNotes: Greg Tubach
Sr Ed: Lauren Wein; Courtney Young
Assoc Ed, Children's: Adah Nuchi
Assoc Ed, Culinary: Stephanie Fletcher
Assoc Prodn Ed, Adult Trade: Sarah Iani
Head, Culinary Prog: Natalie Chapman
Sr Designer: Patrick Barry; Brian Moore
Sr Mktg Mgr: Katrina Krause
Sr Publicist: Michelle Bonanno
Sr Publicity Assoc: Simmi Aujla
Publicist, Culinary Group: Brittany Edwards
General literature, fiction, nonfiction, biography, autobiography, history, poetry & juvenile publications, dictionary, reference books, cookbooks & guidebooks.
ISBN Prefix(es): 978-0-89919; 978-0-395; 978-1-85697; 978-0-7534; 978-0-618; 978-1-88152
Number of titles published annually: 400 Print; 1 CD-ROM; 1 Online; 14 Audio
Total Titles: 3,300 Print; 2 CD-ROM; 2 Online; 110 Audio
Imprints: American Heritage Dictionary; Betty Crocker®; Clarion Books; CliffNotes™; Eamon Dolan Books; Graphia; Harcourt Children's; HMH Franchise; Houghton Mifflin Books for Children; Houghton Mifflin Harcourt; Mariner Books; Rux Martin Books; New Harvest; Sandpiper
*Editorial Office(s):* 215 Park Ave S, New York, NY 10003 *Tel:* 212-420-5800
Distributed by Hachette Book Group
Distributor for Harvard Common Press; Larausse; Old Farmers Almanac
*Orders to:* Houghton Mifflin Harcourt Trade Customer Service, 181 Ballardvale St, PO Box 705, Wilmington, MA 01887 *Toll Free Tel:* 800-225-3362 *Toll Free Fax:* 800-634-7568
*Returns:* Houghton Mifflin Harcourt Publishing Company, Trade Returns Department, 2700 N Richard Ave, Indianapolis, IN 46219

**House of Collectibles**
Imprint of Random House Information Group
1745 Broadway, New York, NY 10019
*Tel:* 212-782-9000 *Fax:* 212-572-4997
*Web Site:* www.houseofcollectibles.randomhouse.com; www.randomhouse.com
Publisher that collectors, dealers & investors around the world turn to for detailed reference information & current market values on all antiques & collectibles-whether they want to know the history of Gustav Stickley furniture, buy a Chinese vase, sell their grandmother's depression glass or evaluate the worth of their Star Wars memorabilia. The House of Collectibles books are compiled by experts, renowned for accuracy & completeness & profusely illustrated, many with full color. Accept unsol proposals & mss from authors who are experts in the antiques & collectibles areas, also accept mss & proposals from agents.
ISBN Prefix(es): 978-0-307; 978-0-676; 978-1-4000; 978-0-87637
Total Titles: 4 Print

**House to House Publications**
Division of DOVE Christian Fellowship International
11 Toll Gate Rd, Lititz, PA 17543
*Tel:* 717-627-1996 *Toll Free Tel:* 800-848-5892 *Fax:* 717-627-4004
*E-mail:* h2hp@dcfi.org
*Web Site:* www.h2hp.com; www.dcfi.org
*Key Personnel*
Pubns Ed: Nancy Barnett
Receptionist & Orders: Jayne Althouse
Founded: 1997
Provide resources for the body of Christ worldwide.
ISBN Prefix(es): 978-1-886973
Number of titles published annually: 3 Print
Total Titles: 37 Print; 18 Audio
Divisions: Partnership Publications

**Housing Assistance Council**
1025 Vermont Ave NW, Suite 606, Washington, DC 20005
*Tel:* 202-842-8600 *Fax:* 202-347-3441
*E-mail:* hac@ruralhome.org
*Web Site:* www.ruralhome.org
*Key Personnel*
Sr Policy Analyst: Leslie R Strauss *E-mail:* leslie@ruralhome.org
Founded: 1971
Provides technical housing services, loans, program & policy assistance, training, research & information. Specializes in research reports, technical manuals & information pieces, all exclusively about low-income rural housing in the US.
ISBN Prefix(es): 978-1-58064
Number of titles published annually: 15 Print; 15 Online
Total Titles: 80 Print; 50 Online
*Branch Office(s)*
717 "K" St, Suite 404, Sacramento, CA 95814 *Tel:* 916-706-1836 *Fax:* 916-706-1849 *E-mail:* western@ruralhome.org
600 W Peachtree St NW, Suite 1500, Atlanta, GA 30308 *Tel:* 404-892-4824 *Fax:* 404-892-1204 *E-mail:* southeast@ruralhome.org
10100 NW Ambassador Dr, Suite 310, Kansas City, MO 64153-1362 *Tel:* 816-880-0400 *Fax:* 816-880-0500 *E-mail:* midwest@ruralhome.org
3939 San Pedro NE, Suite C-6, Albuquerque, NM 87110 *Tel:* 505-883-1003 *Fax:* 505-883-1005 *E-mail:* southwest@ruralhome.org

**Howard Books**
Imprint of Atria Publishing Group
216 Centerview Dr, Suite 303, Brentwood, TN 37027
SAN: 298-7597
*Tel:* 615-873-2080 *Fax:* 615-370-3834
*E-mail:* howardbooks@simonandschuster.com (info)
*Web Site:* www.howardpublishing.com
*Key Personnel*
VP, Publr: Jonathan Merkh
VP & Ed-in-Chief: Becky Nesbitt
VP, Dir, Subs Rts (domestic): Lisa Keim
VP, Assoc Publr: Rob Birkhead
Sr Ed: Philis Boultinghouse; Beth Adams
Art Dir: Bruce Gore
Mng Ed: Karen Longino
Imprint Mktg Mgr: Brandi Lewis
Sr Ed: Jessica Wong
Dir of Publicity: Jennifer Smith
Publicist: Bonnie MacIssac
Admin Coord: Katie Sandell
Assoc Ed: Amanda Demastus
Founded: 1969
Inspirational books.
ISBN Prefix(es): 978-1-4165; 978-1-58229; 978-1-4391
Number of titles published annually: 50 Print
Foreign Rights: Akcali Copyright Agency (Turkey); Antonella Antonelli Agenzia; Book Publishers' Association of Israel, International Promotion & Literary Rights Dept (Israel); International Editors' Company (Latin America, Portugal, Spain); Japan UNI Agency Inc (Japan); JLM Literary Agency (Greece); Korea Copyright Center Inc (KCC) (Korea); Mohrbooks AG, Literary Agency; La Nouvelle Agence; Andrew Nurnberg Associates Ltd (Bulgaria, China, Croatia, Czech Republic, Estonia, Hungary, Latvia, Lithuania, Montenegro, Poland, Romania, Russia, Serbia, Slovakia, Slovenia, Taiwan); Sane Toregard Agency (Denmark, Finland, Norway, Sweden); Karin Schindler (Brazil); Sebes & Van Gelderen Literary Agency (Netherlands); Tuttle-Mori Agency Inc (Thailand)
Membership(s): CBA: The Association for Christian Retail; Evangelical Christian Publishers Association

**Howard University Press**
2225 Georgia Ave NW, Suite 718, Washington, DC 20059
SAN: 202-3067
*Tel:* 202-238-2570 *Fax:* 202-588-9849
*E-mail:* howardupress@howard.edu
*Web Site:* www.hupress.howard.edu
Founded: 1972
Dedicated to publishing noteworthy new scholarship that addresses the contributions, conditions & concerns of African Americans, other people of African descent & people of color around the world in a broad array of disciplines.
ISBN Prefix(es): 978-0-88258
Number of titles published annually: 3 Print
Total Titles: 130 Print
Foreign Rights: The Permissions Co
*Billing Address:* PO Box 50283, Hampden Sta, Baltimore, MD 21211
*Orders to:* PO Box 50283, Hampden Sta, Baltimore, MD 21211 *Tel:* 410-516-6947 *Toll Free Tel:* 800-537-5487
*Returns:* c/o Maple Press Co, Lebanon Distribution Ctr, 704 Legionaire Dr, Frederick, PA 17026
*Warehouse:* c/o Maple Press Co, Lebanon Distribution Ctr, 704 Legionaire Dr, Frederick, PA 17026 *Tel:* 410-516-6965 *Toll Free Tel:* 800-537-5487 *Fax:* 410-516-6998
Membership(s): AAP; American Association of University Presses

**HPBooks**
Imprint of Penguin Group (USA) LLC
375 Hudson St, New York, NY 10014
SAN: 282-5074
*Tel:* 212-366-2000
*E-mail:* online@penguinputnam.com
*Web Site:* www.penguinputnam.com; us.penguingroup.com
*Key Personnel*
VP, Publr: John Duff
Sales Rep: Hal Holding
Founded: 1964
Automotive book publisher. High performance, restoration & racing how-to books for automotive enthusiasts. Cover domestic & foreign vehicles. Also publishes cookbooks.
ISBN Prefix(es): 978-0-89586; 978-0-912656; 978-1-55788
Total Titles: 104 Print; 72 E-Book
*Advertising Agency:* Spier NY

**§HRD Press**
22 Amherst Rd, Amherst, MA 01002-9709
SAN: 201-9213
*Tel:* 413-253-3488 *Toll Free Tel:* 800-822-2801 *Fax:* 413-253-3490
*E-mail:* info@hrdpress.com; customerservice@hrdpress.com
*Web Site:* www.hrdpress.com
*Key Personnel*
CEO & Publr: Robert W Carkhuff *E-mail:* rwc@hrdpress.com
Cust Rel Mgr: Donna Long
Founded: 1972
Textbooks & off-the-shelf workshops on human resource development, management & training. Packaged training materials & assessments.
ISBN Prefix(es): 978-0-914234; 978-0-87425
Number of titles published annually: 25 Print
Total Titles: 600 Print; 20 E-Book
Distributed by Ane Books (India); Centre for Customer Care (CCC) (Malaysia); Eurospan Ltd (Europe); HRD Central (Australia); IBS Buku SDN BHD (Malaysia); Knowledge Resources (South Africa); Management Learning Resources (United Kingdom); Multimedia HRD Pvt Ltd (India); PSI Consulting Inc (Korea); RV Crest International Inc/FDIX (Philippines); Trainee (South Africa); Training & Development Materials of Canada (Canada)
*Returns:* c/o ViaTech Publishing Solutions Inc, 8857 Alexander Rd, Batavia, NY 14020

**Hudson Hills Press LLC**
3556 Main St, Manchester, VT 05254
Mailing Address: PO Box 205, Manchester, VT 05254
*Tel:* 802-362-6450 *Fax:* 802-362-6459
*E-mail:* artbooks@hudsonhills.com; editorial@hudsonhills.com (submissions)
*Web Site:* www.hudsonhills.com
*Key Personnel*
Sales & Internet Mktg Mgr: Kristen van Breen
Founded: 1978
Renowned titles on fine art, photography, decorative arts & architecture.
ISBN Prefix(es): 978-0-933920; 978-1-55595
Number of titles published annually: 20 Print
Total Titles: 150 Print
Distributed by National Book Network
Foreign Rights: Peribo (Australia); Windsor Books International (Europe, UK)

**Hudson Institute**
1015 15 St NW, 6th fl, Washington, DC 20005
*Tel:* 202-974-2400 *Toll Free Tel:* 888-554-1325 (bookstore inquiries) *Fax:* 202-974-2410
*E-mail:* info@hudson.org
*Web Site:* www.hudson.org
*Key Personnel*
Communs & Web Mgr: James Bologna *Tel:* 202-974-6456 *E-mail:* jbologna@hudson.org
Founded: 1961
Books, monographs, briefing papers, newsletters.
ISBN Prefix(es): 978-1-55813
Number of titles published annually: 10 Print
Total Titles: 60 Print
*Branch Office(s)*
90 Broad St, 20th fl, New York, NY 10004, Pres: Herb London *Tel:* 212 232-8720 *Fax:* 212-232-8725

**Hudson Park Press**
232 Madison Ave, Rm 1400, New York, NY 10016
*Tel:* 212-929-8898 *Fax:* 212-208-0946
*Key Personnel*
Pres: Gilman Park *E-mail:* gpark@hudsonpark.com
Mktg Dir & Intl Rts: C B Sayre
Edit Dir: Adele Ursone *E-mail:* ajursone@aol.com
Spec Sales Mgr: Martha Moran *E-mail:* mmoran@hudsonpark.com
Founded: 1995
Publishing & custom packaging of art & photography books, calendars, record books, social stationery, related sidelines.
ISBN Prefix(es): 978-1-57461
Number of titles published annually: 10 Print
Total Titles: 80 Print
Distributed by Publishers Group West

**§Human Kinetics Inc**
1607 N Market St, Champaign, IL 61820
Mailing Address: PO Box 5076, Champaign, IL 61825-5076 SAN: 211-7088
*Tel:* 217-351-5076 *Toll Free Tel:* 800-747-4457 *Fax:* 217-351-1549 (orders/cust serv)
*E-mail:* info@hkusa.com
*Web Site:* www.humankinetics.com
*Key Personnel*
Founder & Pres: Rainer Martens
CEO: Brian Holding
EVP: Julie S Martens
VP, Fin: Tina Rothery
VP, Prod Devt: Holly Gilly
VP, Sales & Mktg: Steve Ruhlig *E-mail:* stever@hkusa.com
VP, Acqs: Ted Miller
Founded: 1974
Scholarly books, college textbooks & trade books in physical education, sports medicine & science, coaching, sport technique & fitness, courses, CDs & DVDs.
ISBN Prefix(es): 978-0-931250; 978-0-87322; 978-0-88011; 978-0-918438; 978-0-7360; 978-0-912781; 978-1-4504
Total Titles: 1,693 Print; 174 CD-ROM; 387 Online
*Branch Office(s)*
Human Kinetics Canada, 475 Devonshire Rd, Unit 100, Windsor, ON N8Y 2L5, Canada *Tel:* 519-971-9500 *Toll Free Tel:* 800-465-7301 (CN) *Fax:* 519-971-9797 *E-mail:* info@hkcanada.com
*Foreign Office(s):* Human Kinetics Australia, PO Box 80, Torrens Park 5062, Australia *Tel:* (08) 8372-0999 *Fax:* (08) 8372 0998 *E-mail:* info@hkaustralia.com
Human Kinetics Europe, 107 Bradford Rd, Stanningly, Leeds LS28 6AT, United Kingdom *Tel:* (0113) 255 5665 *Fax:* (0113) 255 5885 *E-mail:* custserv@hkeurope.com
Foreign Rep(s): Alkem Co (Bangladesh, Brunei, Indonesia, Laos, Malaysia, Philippines, Singapore, Thailand); Comprajato (Brazil); CRW Marketing Services for Publishers Inc (Philippines); Dasansogo Co Ltd (Korea); Disvan Enterprises (India); Eureka Press (Japan); Laszlo Horvath (Hungary, Romania, Russia, Slovakia); Icon Books (Malaysia, Singapore, Vietnam); InterMedia Americana (Caribbean); Kemper Conseil (Belgium, France, Germany); Kinemed Technologies (Chile); KinesWorld (China, Hong Kong); Libreria Medica (Colombia); David Towle International (Norway); Unifacmanu Trading Co Ltd (Taiwan)

**§Human Rights Watch**
350 Fifth Ave, 34th fl, New York, NY 10118-3299
*Tel:* 212-290-4700 *Fax:* 212-736-1300
*E-mail:* hrwnyc@hrw.org
*Web Site:* www.hrw.org
*Key Personnel*
Pubns Dir: Grace Choi
Communs Dir: Emma Daly *Tel:* 212-216-1835
Founded: 1978
Nonprofit human rights organization publishing books & newsletters on human rights practices in more than 80 countries worldwide; documents arbitrary imprisonment, censorship, disappearances, due process of law, murder, prison conditions, torture, violations of laws of war & other abuses of internationally recognized human rights.
ISBN Prefix(es): 978-0-938579; 978-0-929692; 978-1-56432
Number of titles published annually: 67 Print
Total Titles: 1,000 Print; 60 E-Book
Imprints: Human Rights Watch Books

**Humanics Publishing Group**, see Green Dragon Books

**§Humanix Books LLC**
Division of NewsMaxx
PO Box 20989, West Palm Beach, FL 33416
*Tel:* 561-459-5997 *Toll Free Tel:* 855-371-7810 *Fax:* 561-241-6448 *Toll Free Fax:* 855-371-7809
*E-mail:* info@humanixbooks.com
*Web Site:* www.humanixbooks.com
*Key Personnel*
Dir of Publg: Andy Brown
Mng Dir: Jennifer Wilson
Sales Mgr: Gina Sinnett
Exec Ed: Pam Pantelo
Founded: 2012
Trade paperbacks, hard cover & ebooks in the following areas: finance, investing, health, wellness, lifestyle, business, leadership, management, politics, current events, success, motivation, history & military.
ISBN Prefix(es): 978-1-63006
Number of titles published annually: 6 Print; 2 E-Book
Total Titles: 6 Print; 2 E-Book
*Orders to:* Ingram Book Co, One Ingram Blvd, La Vergne, TN 37086
*Distribution Center:* Ingram Book Co, One Ingram Blvd, La Vergne, TN 37086 *Tel:* 615-793-5000 *Web Site:* www.ingrambookcontent.com

**Hungry? City Guides**
714 W Olympic Blvd, Suite 934, Los Angeles, CA 90015
*Fax:* 213-749-2080
*Web Site:* www.hungryguides.com
*Key Personnel*
Founder & COO: Mari Florence *Tel:* 213-749-2060 *E-mail:* mari@hungrycityguides.com
CEO & Pres: Adam Guild
Contact: Whitney Welsh
Founded: 2004
Dining guides.
ISBN Prefix(es): 978-1-893329
Number of titles published annually: 10 Print; 52 Online
Total Titles: 27 Print

**Hunter House Publishers**
1515 1/2 Park St, Alameda, CA 94501
Mailing Address: PO Box 2914, Alameda, CA 94501-0914 SAN: 281-7969

*Tel:* 510-865-5282 *Toll Free Tel:* 800-266-5592 *Fax:* 510-865-4295
*E-mail:* ordering@hunterhouse.com
*Web Site:* www.hunterhouse.com
*Key Personnel*
Mng Ed: Alexandra Mummery *E-mail:* editorial@hunterhouse.com
Cust Serv Mgr & Orders Contact: Christina Sverdrup *E-mail:* ordering@hunterhouse.com
Founded: 1978
Self-help health, fitness, sexuality, personal growth, relationships, violence prevention & intervention, life skills, specialized teaching & counseling resources.
ISBN Prefix(es): 978-0-89793
Number of titles published annually: 12 Print
Total Titles: 250 Print
Foreign Rep(s): Alternative Books (South Africa); Astam Books (Australia); Deep Books (Europe, UK); PGW (Canada)
*Warehouse:* 2324 Times Way, Alameda, CA 94501
Membership(s): IBPA, the Independent Book Publishers Association

**§Hunter Publishing Inc**
222 Clematis St, West Palm Beach, FL 33401
SAN: 695-3425
*Tel:* 561-835-2022
*Web Site:* www.amazingadventures.net
*Key Personnel*
Founder & Pres: Michael Hunter *E-mail:* michael@hunterpublishing.com
Founded: 1985
Books for travelers.
ISBN Prefix(es): 978-0-935161; 978-1-55650; 978-0-85039; 978-0-681; 978-0-929756; 978-0-85285; 978-3-259; 978-3-88989; 978-1-85691; 978-2-89464; 978-1-84306; 978-1-58843
Number of titles published annually: 50 E-Book
Total Titles: 550 E-Book
Imprints: Adventure Guides; Alive Guides; State & National Parks Guides

**Huntington Library Press**
Division of Huntington Library, Art Collections & Botanical Gardens
1151 Oxford Rd, San Marino, CA 91108
SAN: 202-313X
*Tel:* 626-405-2172 *Fax:* 626-585-0794
*E-mail:* booksales@huntington.org
*Web Site:* www.huntington.org
*Key Personnel*
Dir: Susan Green *E-mail:* sgreen@huntington.org
Mng Ed: Jean Patterson *E-mail:* jpatterson@huntington.org
Founded: 1920
Scholarly nonfiction in English & American history, literature & art.
ISBN Prefix(es): 978-0-87328
Number of titles published annually: 6 Print
Total Titles: 77 Print
Distributed by University of California Press

**Huntington Press Publishing**
3665 Procyon St, Las Vegas, NV 89103-1907
*Tel:* 702-252-0655 *Toll Free Tel:* 800-244-2224 *Fax:* 702-252-0675
*E-mail:* sales@huntingtonpress.com
*Web Site:* www.huntingtonpress.com
*Key Personnel*
Publr: Anthony Curtis *E-mail:* publisher@huntingtonpress.com
Founded: 1983
Books relating to gambling & Las Vegas.
ISBN Prefix(es): 978-0-929712; 978-1-935396
Number of titles published annually: 10 Print
Total Titles: 81 Print; 75 Online; 75 E-Book
Imprints: Vegas Lit

**Hutton Electronic Publishing**
160 N Compo Rd, Westport, CT 06880-2102
*Tel:* 203-226-2588 *Fax:* 230-226-2588
*E-mail:* huttonbooks@hotmail.com
*Key Personnel*
Ed-in-Chief: Caroline DuBois Hutton
Founded: 2005
Digital publishing for Kindle, Nook, etc; print-on-demand. All books received personal attention & are professionally designed & listed for distribution in the Ingram Catalog, available through Amazon, B&N Online & local bookstores. Promotion notes available for all Huttonelectronicpublishing.com authors. All royalties are split 50-50, author & publisher. Some books paid 100% by authors, others, by special arrangement with the publisher, at varying percentages subsidized by the publisher. Please inquire by e-mail for further information. Prize-winning illustrators available as needed.
ISBN Prefix(es): 978-0-9742894; 978-0-9785171
Number of titles published annually: 10 Print; 10 E-Book
Total Titles: 20 Print; 20 E-Book
*Distribution Center:* Lightning Source Inc, 1246 Heil Quaker Blvd, La Vergne, TN 37086

**Hyperion**
1500 Broadway, 3rd fl, New York, NY 10036
*Tel:* 212-536-6500
*Web Site:* hyperionbooks.com
*Key Personnel*
Pres & Publr: Ellen Archer
VP, Mktg & Digital Media: Mindy Stockfield
Exec Dir, Opers: Sharon Kitter
Exec Dir, Pre-Prodn/Prodn: Linda Prather
Exec Dir, Subs Rts: Jill Sansone
Exec Fin Dir: Terri Lombardi
Art Dir: Georgia A Morrissey
Contracts Dir: Jean Marie Pierson
Dir, Communs: Christine Ragasa
Edit Dir, Franchise Publg: Laura Hopper
Sales Dir: Maha Khalil
Ed-in-Chief: Elisabeth Dyssegaard
Mng Ed: Navorn Johnson
Sr Ed: Ruth Pomerance
Ed: Matt Inman; Samantha (Sam) O'Brien
Sr Mgr, Digital Publg & Emerging Technol: Andrew Elliott
Founded: 1990
General trade books in hardcover & trade paperback, nonfiction, mass market.
ISBN Prefix(es): 978-1-56282; 978-0-7868; 978-1-4013
Imprints: Hyperion Audio; Hyperion eBooks
Distributed by Hachette Book Group
Foreign Rights: Luigi Bernabo Associates SRL (Italy); Big Apple Agency Inc (Taiwan); The English Agency (Japan) Inc (Japan); Agence Hoffman (Germany); La Nouvelle Agence (France); Sebes & Van Gelderen Literary Agency (Netherlands)
*Orders to:* Hachette Book Group, 3 Center Plaza, Boston, MA 02108, Attn: Order Dept *Toll Free Tel:* 800-759-0190 *Toll Free Fax:* 800-331-1664
*Returns:* Hachette Book Group, 322 S Enterprise Blvd, Lebanon, IN 46052, Attn: Returns Dept; Hachette Book Group, 326 S Enterprise Blvd, Lebanon, IN 46052, Attn: Stripped Cover Returns
*Distribution Center:* Hachette Book Group, 3 Center Plaza, Boston, MA 02108 *Toll Free Tel:* 800-759-0190 *Toll Free Fax:* 800-331-1664
Membership(s): AAP

**Ibex Publishers**
PO Box 30087, Bethesda, MD 20824
SAN: 696-866X
*Tel:* 301-718-8188 *Toll Free Tel:* 888-718-8188 *Fax:* 301-907-8707
*E-mail:* info@ibexpub.com
*Web Site:* www.ibexpublishers.com
*Key Personnel*
Publr: Mr Farhad Shirzad *E-mail:* fs@ibex.net
Founded: 1979
English & Persian language books about Iran.
ISBN Prefix(es): 978-0-936347; 978-1-58814
Number of titles published annually: 15 Print
Total Titles: 330 Print; 3 CD-ROM; 5 Audio
Imprints: IBEX Press; Iranbooks Press
Distributor for Farhang Moaser

**IBFD North America Inc (International Bureau of Fiscal Documentation)**
Division of IBFD Foundation
8100 Boone Blvd, Suite 210, Vienna, VA 22182
*Tel:* 703-442-7757 *Fax:* 703-442-7758
*E-mail:* americas@ibfd.org
*Web Site:* www.ibfd.org
*Key Personnel*
Mgr, Americas: Steven Stroschein
Founded: 1938
International taxation & investment & tax law.
Number of titles published annually: 30 Print
Total Titles: 30 Print; 1 CD-ROM; 42 Online
*Foreign Office(s):* HJE Wenckebachweg 210, 1096 AS Amsterdam, Netherlands *Tel:* (020) 554 0100 *E-mail:* info@ibfd.org

**ICMA**, see International City/County Management Association (ICMA)

**Iconografix Inc**
1830-A Hanley Rd, Hudson, WI 54016
Mailing Address: PO Box 446, Hudson, WI 54016
*Tel:* 715-381-9755 *Toll Free Tel:* 800-289-3504 (orders only) *Fax:* 715-381-9756
*E-mail:* info@iconografixinc.com
*Web Site:* www.iconografixinc.com
*Key Personnel*
Edit Dir: Dylan Frautschi
Founded: 1992
Publish special historical interest photographic books.
ISBN Prefix(es): 978-1-882256; 978-1-58388
Number of titles published annually: 24 Print
Total Titles: 300 Print
Divisions: Enthusiast Books; The Transportation Book Service
Distributed by Motorbooks International
*Shipping Address:* Motorbooks International, 729 Prospect Ave, Osceola, WI 54020

**Idaho Center for the Book**
Affiliate of Library of Congress
Boise State University, 1910 University Dr, Boise, ID 83725
*Tel:* 208-426-1000 *Toll Free Tel:* 800-992-8398 (outside ID) *Fax:* 208-426-1243
*Web Site:* www.lili.org/icb; www.boisestatebooks.com (orders)
*Key Personnel*
Dir: Stephanie Bacon *E-mail:* sbacon@boisestate.edu
Founded: 1993
Idaho book history & culture.
ISBN Prefix(es): 978-0-932129
Number of titles published annually: 6 Print
Total Titles: 25 Print; 1 CD-ROM
*Editorial Office(s):* ICB, MS 1525 BSU, Boise, ID 83725

**Ideals Publications, a Guideposts Co**
2630 Elm Hill Pike, Suite 100, Nashville, TN 37214
SAN: 213-4403
*Toll Free Tel:* 800-586-2572 (cust serv) *Fax:* 615-781-1447
*Web Site:* www.idealsbooks.com
*Key Personnel*
VP, Sales & Group Publr: Marty Flanagan
Publr: Peggy Schaefer *E-mail:* pschaefer@guideposts.org
Founded: 1944
Publisher of *IDEALS* magazine, children's books & boardbooks.

ISBN Prefix(es): 978-0-8249; 978-0-89542
Number of titles published annually: 45 Print
Total Titles: 200 Print
Imprints: CandyCane Press; Ideals; Ideals Children's Books; Williamson Books
Distributor for Hinkler Books; Rourke Publishing; Smart Ink; Smart Kidz; Someday Baby

**Idyll Arbor Inc**
39129 264 Ave SE, Enumclaw, WA 98022
*Tel:* 360-825-7797 *Fax:* 360-825-5670
*E-mail:* sales@idyllarbor.com
*Web Site:* www.idyllarbor.com
*Key Personnel*
Pres & Intl Rts: Tom Blaschko *E-mail:* tom@idyllarbor.com
Founded: 1984
Publish health care books, information for recreational therapists & activity directors & books on social issues.
ISBN Prefix(es): 978-1-882883; 978-0-937663; 978-1-930461; 978-1-61158
Number of titles published annually: 8 Print; 8 E-Book
Total Titles: 100 Print; 50 E-Book; 1 Audio
Imprints: Issues Press (covering important social issues such as addictions & health care for returning military personnel); Pine Winds Press (discussions of the life force, including spiritual reality, bigfoot, fairies & other strange phenomena)
Foreign Rights: Columbine Communications (Worldwide exc Canada & USA)
Membership(s): Book Publishers of the Northwest; IBPA, the Independent Book Publishers Association; Pacific Northwest Booksellers Association

**§IEEE Computer Society**
2001 "L" St NW, Suite 700, Washington, DC 20036-4928
SAN: 264-620X
*Tel:* 202-371-0101 *Toll Free Tel:* 800-272-6657 (memb info) *Fax:* 202-728-9614
*E-mail:* help@computer.org
*Web Site:* www.computer.org
*Key Personnel*
Exec Dir: Angela R Burgess *E-mail:* aburgess@computer.org
Busn Analytics Mgr: John Reimer *E-mail:* jreimer@computer.org
Dir, Sales & Mktg: Chris Jensen *E-mail:* cjensen@computer.org
Founded: 1980
Tutorials, reports, reprint collections, conference proceedings, textbooks & CD-ROMs.
ISBN Prefix(es): 978-0-8186; 978-0-7695
Number of titles published annually: 155 Print
Total Titles: 808 Print; 5 CD-ROM
*Branch Office(s)*
106662 Los Vaqueros Circle, Los Alamitos, CA 90720-1314 *Tel:* 714-821-8380 *Fax:* 714-821-4010
*Foreign Office(s):* KFK Bldg, 2-14-14 Minami-Aoyama, Minato-ku, Tokyo 107-0062, Japan *Tel:* (03) 3408 3118 *Fax:* (03) 3408 3553 *E-mail:* tokyo.ofc@computer.org

**§IEEE Press**
Division of Institute of Electrical & Electronics Engineers Inc (IEEE)
445 Hoes Lane, Piscataway, NJ 08854
*Tel:* 732-562-3418 *Fax:* 732-562-1746
*E-mail:* pressbooks@ieee.org (proposals & info)
*Web Site:* www.ieee.org/press
*Key Personnel*
Dir, Books & Info Servs: Kenneth Moore *E-mail:* k.moore@ieee.org
Founded: 1971
Professional books & texts in electrical & computer engineering, computer science, electrotechnology, general engineering, applied mathematics. Tutorials in technical subjects.
ISBN Prefix(es): 978-0-87942; 978-0-7803; 978-0-471
Number of titles published annually: 40 Print
Total Titles: 450 Print; 425 E-Book
Imprints: Wiley-IEEE Press
Distributed by John Wiley & Sons Inc
Foreign Rep(s): John Wiley & Sons Inc
Foreign Rights: John Wiley & Sons Inc
Membership(s): AAP

**IET**
c/o Inspec Inc, 379 Thornall St, Edison, NJ 08837-2225
*Tel:* 732-321-5575; 732-321-5579 *Fax:* 732-321-5702
*E-mail:* iee@inspecinc.com
*Web Site:* www.theiet.org/inspec
*Key Personnel*
VP, Sales: Michael Ornstein
Electronic Journals Exec: Neil Dennis
Mktg Mgr: Lisa White *Tel:* 732-321-5579 ext 205
Founded: 1871
Professional books, journals, magazines & conference proceedings in many areas of electrical & electronic engineering, including telecommunications, computing, power, control, radar, circuits, materials & more.
ISBN Prefix(es): 978-0-85296; 978-0-906048; 978-0-86341
Number of titles published annually: 30 Print
Total Titles: 500 Print; 300 E-Book
Imprints: IEE; Inspec; Peter Peregrinus Ltd
*Foreign Office(s):* Michael Faraday House, 6 Hills Way, Stevenage, Herts SG1 2AY, United Kingdom (journal & magazine sales) *Tel:* (01438) 313 311 *Fax:* (01438) 765 526 *E-mail:* postmaster@iee.org
Foreign Rep(s): Cranbury International (Latin America, Mexico, South America)
*Orders to:* c/o Books International Inc, PO Box 605, Herndon, VA 20172 *Tel:* 703-661-1573 *Toll Free Tel:* 800-230-7286 (US & CN) *Fax:* 703-661-1501 *E-mail:* ieemail@presswarehouse.com
*Distribution Center:* c/o Books International Inc, PO Box 605, Herndon, VA 20172 *Tel:* 703-661-1500 *Fax:* 703-661-1501
Membership(s): Association of Learned & Professional Society Publishers; STM

**IFPRI**, see International Food Policy Research Institute

**Ignatius Press**
Division of Guadalupe Associates Inc
1348 Tenth Ave, San Francisco, CA 94122-2304
SAN: 214-3887
*Tel:* 415-387-2324 *Toll Free Tel:* 800-651-1531 (orders) *Fax:* 415-387-0896
*E-mail:* info@ignatius.com
*Web Site:* www.ignatius.com
*Key Personnel*
Pres: Mark Brumley *E-mail:* mark@ignatius.com
Ed: Fr Joseph Fessio SJ
Prodn Ed: Carolyn Lemon
Mktg Dir: Anthony J Ryan
Art Dir: Roxanne Lum
Mktg Mgr: Eva Mutean *E-mail:* eva@ignatius.com
Foreign Rts: Penelope Boldrick
Founded: 1978
Religion (Catholic).
ISBN Prefix(es): 978-0-89870; 978-1-58617
Number of titles published annually: 30 Print
Total Titles: 510 Print; 55 Audio
Imprints: Ignatius
Subsidiaries: Catholic Dossier; Catholic Faith; The Catholic World Report; Homiletic & Pastoral Review
Distributor for Bethlehem Books; Veritas
Foreign Rep(s): Asian Trading Corp (India); B Broughton Co; Catholic Supplies Ltd (New Zealand); Veritas (Ireland); Words Ink (England, Scotland)
*Orders to:* PO Box 1339, Fort Collins, CO 80522-1339, Contact: Neil McCaffrey *Toll Free Tel:* 800 651 1531
*Warehouse:* McCaffrey Enterprises, 1331 Red Cedar Circle, Fort Collins, CO 80522

**§IHS Jane's**
Subsidiary of IHS Inc
110 N Royal St, Suite 200, Alexandria, VA 22314-1651
SAN: 286-357X
*Tel:* 703-683-3700 *Toll Free Tel:* 800-824-0768 (sales) *Fax:* 703-836-0297 *Toll Free Fax:* 800-836-0297
*E-mail:* customercare@ihs.com
*Web Site:* www.ihs.com
*Key Personnel*
America's Mktg Mgr: Jim Scanlon
Founded: 1897
Hard copy, online services, magazines, CD-ROM, electronic databases on defense aerospace, transportation & terrorism subjects.
ISBN Prefix(es): 978-0-7106; 978-0-354; 978-0-356
Number of titles published annually: 110 Print
Total Titles: 180 Print
*Foreign Office(s):* Cera51 Bldg, 1-21-8 Ebisu, Shibuya-ku, Tokyo 150-0013, Japan (Japan) *Tel:* (03) 579 19663 *Fax:* (03) 542 06402 *E-mail:* japan@janes.com
78 Shenton Way, No 10-02 079120, Singapore (Asia) *Tel:* 6576 0866 *Fax:* 6226 1185 *E-mail:* asiapacific@janes.com
PO Box 502138, Dubai, United Arab Emirates (Middle East) *Tel:* (04) 390 2335 *Fax:* (04) 390 8848 *E-mail:* mideast@janes.com
163 Brighton Rd, Coulsdon, Surrey CR5 2YH, United Kingdom (Africa & Europe) *Tel:* (020) 8700 3700 *Fax:* (020) 8763 1006 *E-mail:* info.uk@janes.com
*Warehouse:* ITP Distribution Center, 7625 Empire Dr, Florence, KY 41042

**IHS Press**
222 W 21 St, Suite F-122, Norfolk, VA 23517
*Toll Free Tel:* 877-447-7737 *Toll Free Fax:* 877-447-7737
*E-mail:* info@ihspress.com; tradesales@ihspress.com (wholesale sales); order@ihspress.com
*Web Site:* www.ihspress.com
Founded: 2001
ISBN Prefix(es): 978-0-9714894; 978-0-9718286; 978-1-932528; 978-1-60570
Number of titles published annually: 12 Print; 12 E-Book
Total Titles: 42 Print; 42 E-Book
*Distribution Center:* Intrepid Group, 1331 Red Cedar Circle, Fort Collins, CO 80524

**§Illinois State Museum Society**
Affiliate of Illinois State Museum
502 S Spring St, Springfield, IL 62706-5000
*Tel:* 217-782-7386 *Fax:* 217-782-1254
*E-mail:* editor@museum.state.il.us
*Web Site:* www.museum.state.il.us
*Key Personnel*
Museum Dir: Bonnie Styles *Tel:* 217-782-7011 *E-mail:* bwstyles@museum.state.il.us
Assoc Museum Dir: Karen Witter *E-mail:* kwitter@museum.state.il.us
Museum Ed: Andy Hanson *Tel:* 217-782-6700 *E-mail:* ahanson@museum.state.il.us
Founded: 1877
Softcover texts, quarterly magazines, quarterly newsletters, quarterly calendars of events & activities brochures, educational posters & CD-ROM.
ISBN Prefix(es): 978-0-89792

Number of titles published annually: 5 Print
Total Titles: 1 CD-ROM

**§Illuminating Engineering Society of North America (IES)**
120 Wall St, 17th fl, New York, NY 10005-4001
*Tel:* 212-248-5000 *Fax:* 212-248-5017; 212-248-5018
*E-mail:* ies@ies.org
*Web Site:* www.ies.org
*Key Personnel*
Mktg Mgr: Clayton Gordon *Tel:* 212-248-5000 ext 110 *E-mail:* cgordon@ies.org
Founded: 1906
ISBN Prefix(es): 978-0-87995
Number of titles published annually: 10 Print; 1 E-Book
Total Titles: 90 Print; 1 E-Book
Distributor for McGraw-Hill; Taylor & Francis; John Wiley & Sons Inc

**Illumination Arts Publishing**
808 Sixth St S, Suite 200, Kirkland, WA 98033
Mailing Address: PO Box 1865, Bellevue, WA 98009-1865
*Tel:* 425-968-5097 *Fax:* 425-968-5634
*E-mail:* liteinfo@illumin.com
*Web Site:* www.illumin.com
*Key Personnel*
Pres: John Thompson
Founded: 1987
Publishing of uplifting/inspiring children's picture books.
ISBN Prefix(es): 978-0-935699; 978-0-9740190; 978-0-9701907
Number of titles published annually: 4 Print

**Imagination Publishing Group**
PO Box 1304, Dunedin, FL 34697
*Toll Free Tel:* 888-701-6481 *Fax:* 727-736-1791
*E-mail:* info@dannythedragon.com
*Web Site:* www.dannythedragon.com
*Key Personnel*
Pres: Alan Wayne
Asst: Kuryn Mitchell
Founded: 2008
Publisher of fine quality printed products.
ISBN Prefix(es): 978-0-9800
Number of titles published annually: 5 Print; 2 Audio
Total Titles: 3 Print; 1 Audio
Membership(s): ABA; Association of Booksellers for Children; Florida Association for Media in Education; Florida Association for Partners in Education; Florida Publishers Association Inc; Society of Children's Book Writers & Illustrators; Southern Independent Booksellers for Children

**§Imago Press**
3710 E Edison St, Tucson, AZ 85716
*Tel:* 520-327-0540
*Web Site:* www.oasisjournal.org
*Key Personnel*
Publr: Leila Joiner *E-mail:* ljoiner@dakotacom.net
Founded: 2002
Provide a place for older authors to present their work to appreciative audiences. Our flagship offering is the *OASIS Journal*, an annual anthology of short fiction, short nonfiction & poetry by writers over fifty, produced in conjunction with the OASIS Institute, a national nonprofit organization that promotes ongoing education for seniors.
ISBN Prefix(es): 978-0-9725303; 978-0-9799341; 978-1-935437
Number of titles published annually: 5 Print; 5 E-Book
Total Titles: 41 Print; 30 E-Book
Membership(s): IBPA, the Independent Book Publishers Association

**§ImaJinn Books Inc**
PO Box 74274, Phoenix, AZ 85087-4274
*Toll Free Tel:* 877-625-3592
*E-mail:* orders@imajinnbooks.com
*Web Site:* www.imajinnbooks.com
*Key Personnel*
CEO & Pres: Linda Kichline *Tel:* 623-236-3361 *E-mail:* linda@imajinnbooks.com
Founded: 1998
Specialize in publishing & selling paranormal romance, urban fantasy, regency romance & erotica.
ISBN Prefix(es): 978-1-893896; 978-0-9759653; 978-1-933417; 978-1-61026
Number of titles published annually: 24 Print
Total Titles: 100 Print
Imprints: Forever Regency (regency line); ImaJinn Books (paranormal & urban fantasy line); Silk & Magic (erotica line)
Membership(s): The Association of Publishers for Special Sales; IBPA, the Independent Book Publishers Association

**Immedium**
Imprint of Immedium Inc
535 Rockdale Dr, San Francisco, CA 94127
Mailing Address: PO Box 31846, San Francisco, CA 94131
*Tel:* 415-452-8546 *Fax:* 360-937-6272
*E-mail:* orders@immedium.com; sales@immedium.com
*Web Site:* www.immedium.com
*Key Personnel*
Publr: Oliver Chin *E-mail:* o.chin@comcast.net
Ed: Don Menn
Acqs Ed: Amy Ma
Graphic Design: Elaine Chu
Founded: 2005
Publish wonderfully illustrated children's picture books, Asian American topics & contemporary arts & culture.
ISBN Prefix(es): 978-1-59702
Number of titles published annually: 4 Print; 4 Online; 4 E-Book
Total Titles: 25 Print; 20 Online; 20 E-Book
Foreign Rep(s): John Reed Book Distribution (Australia, New Zealand)
Foreign Rights: HarperCollins UK (UK & Commonwealth)
*Orders to:* Consortium, 1045 Westgate Dr, Suite 90, Saint Paul, MN 55114-1065 *Tel:* 651-621-9035 *Toll Free Tel:* 800-283-3572 (cust serv) *Fax:* 651-221-0124 *E-mail:* info@cbsd.com *Web Site:* www.cbsd.com
*Returns:* Consortium, 1045 Westgate Dr, Suite 90, Saint Paul, MN 55114-1065 *Tel:* 651-621-9035 *Toll Free Tel:* 800-283-3572 (cust serv) *Fax:* 651-221-0124 *E-mail:* info@cbsd.com *Web Site:* www.cbsd.com
*Shipping Address:* Consortium, 1045 Westgate Dr, Suite 90, Saint Paul, MN 55114-1065 *Tel:* 651-621-9035 *Toll Free Tel:* 800-283-3572 (cust serv) *Fax:* 651-221-0124 *E-mail:* info@cbsd.com *Web Site:* www.cbsd.com
*Warehouse:* Consortium, 1045 Westgate Dr, Suite 90, Saint Paul, MN 55114-1065 *Tel:* 651-621-9035 *Toll Free Tel:* 800-283-3572 (cust serv) *Fax:* 651-221-0124 *E-mail:* info@cbsd.com *Web Site:* www.dbsd.com
*Distribution Center:* Consortium, 1045 Westgate Dr, Suite 90, Saint Paul, MN 55114-1065 *Tel:* 561-621-9035 *Toll Free Tel:* 800-283-3572 (cust serv) *Fax:* 651-221-0124 *E-mail:* info@cbsd.com *Web Site:* www.cbsd.com

**§Impact Publications/Development Concepts Inc**
9104 Manassas Dr, Suite N, Manassas Park, VA 20111-5211
*Tel:* 703-361-7300 *Toll Free Tel:* 800-361-1055 (cust serv) *Fax:* 703-335-9486
*E-mail:* query@impactpublications.com
*Web Site:* www.impactpublications.com; www.ishoparoundtheworld.com; www.veteransworld.com; www.middleeasttravellover.com
*Key Personnel*
Pres: Ronald Krannich, PhD
Founded: 1982
Career & travel publications.
ISBN Prefix(es): 978-1-57023
Number of titles published annually: 18 Print
Total Titles: 167 Print
Distributed by National Book Network

**Impact Publishers Inc**
PO Box 6016, Atascadero, CA 93423-6016
SAN: 202-6864
*Tel:* 805-466-5917 (opers & admin offs) *Toll Free Tel:* 800-246-7228 (orders) *Fax:* 805-466-5919 (opers & admin offs)
*E-mail:* info@impactpublishers.com
*Web Site:* www.impactpublishers.com; www.bibliotherapy.com
*Key Personnel*
Pres & Ed: Robert E Alberti
Publr: Melissa Froehner
Cust Serv Mgr: Cheyenne Ladd
Intl Rts: Jean Trumbull
Founded: 1970
Self-help, relationships, divorce recovery, health, families & parenting, juvenile nonfiction & systematic training for effective parenting.
ISBN Prefix(es): 978-0-915166; 978-1-886230
Number of titles published annually: 10 Print; 1 CD-ROM; 1 Audio
Total Titles: 40 Print; 1 CD-ROM; 3 Audio
Imprints: Little Imp Books; The Practical Therapist Series; Rebuilding Books
Distributor for STEP Publishers (Systematic Training for Effective Parenting)
Foreign Rep(s): Footprint Books (Australia, New Zealand); Publishers Group UK (UK)
Foreign Rights: Bardon Agency (China, Taiwan); Bookbank SL (Latin America, Spain); Japan UNI Agency (Japan); Kayi Literary Agency (Turkey); Montreal Contacts (Canada, France); O A Literary Agency (Greece); The Riff Agency (Portugal); Agentia Literara Sun (Romania)
*Advertising Agency:* IMP Advertising
Membership(s): AAP; IBPA, the Independent Book Publishers Association

**Imprint Publications Inc**
207 E Ohio St, Suite 377, Chicago, IL 60611
*Tel:* 773-288-0782 *Fax:* 773-288-0792
*E-mail:* imppub@aol.com
*Web Site:* www.imprint-chicago.com
*Key Personnel*
Pres & Ed-in-Chief: Anthony Cheung
Founded: 1990
Scholarly & trade books. Subject specialties: social sciences & humanities.
ISBN Prefix(es): 978-1-879176
Number of titles published annually: 8 Print
Total Titles: 30 Print

**Incentive Publications Inc**
2400 Crestmoor Rd, Suite 211, Nashville, TN 37215
SAN: 203-8005
*Tel:* 615-385-2934 *Toll Free Tel:* 800-421-2830 *Fax:* 615-385-2967
*E-mail:* comments@incentivepublications.com
*Web Site:* www.incentivepublications.com
*Key Personnel*
CEO: Ron Chase
Pres: J Blake Parker
Dir, Devt & Prodn: Jill S Norris
Founded: 1968
Preschool through high school supplementary educational materials for students, parents & teachers.
ISBN Prefix(es): 978-0-913916; 978-0-86530
Number of titles published annually: 25 Print

Total Titles: 425 Print; 1 CD-ROM
Imprints: A-To-Z Series; Basic/Not Boring K-8 Grades; Integrating Instruction Series; Kids' Stuff; Language Literacy Lessons; Learning Fun; Ready to Learn; Table Top Series
Foreign Rights: Hawker Brownlow (Australia)
*Warehouse:* 811 Cowan St, Nashville, TN 37207

**Independent Information Publications**
Division of Computing!
3357 21 St, San Francisco, CA 94110
*Tel:* 415-643-8600
*E-mail:* linda@movedoc.com
*Web Site:* www.movedoc.com
Founded: 1982
ISBN Prefix(es): 978-0-913733
Number of titles published annually: 4 Print; 1 CD-ROM; 6 Online; 2 E-Book
Total Titles: 5 Print; 1 CD-ROM; 4 Online; 2 E-Book
Imprints: IIP Consumers Series
*Branch Office(s)*
IIP, 500 Kentucky Ave, Savannah, GA 31404, Contact: Cima Star *Tel:* 912-233-8873
Distributed by Pathway Book Service
*Shipping Address:* Pathway Book Service, PO Box 89, Gilsum, NH 03448 *Tel:* 603-357-0236 *E-mail:* pbs@pathwaybook.com *Web Site:* www.pathwaybook.com
Membership(s): IBPA, the Independent Book Publishers Association

**§Independent Institute**
100 Swan Way, Oakland, CA 94621-1428
*Tel:* 510-632-1366 *Toll Free Tel:* 800-927-8733 *Fax:* 510-568-6040
*E-mail:* orders@independent.org
*Web Site:* www.independent.org
*Key Personnel*
Founder & CEO: David J Theroux *E-mail:* dtheroux@independent.org
Acqs Dir: Roy M Carlisle *Tel:* 510-632-1366 ext 112 *E-mail:* rcarlisle@independent.org
Communs Dir: Lindsay Boyd *Tel:* 202-725-7722 *E-mail:* lboyd@independent.org
Research Dir: Alex Tabarrok *E-mail:* atabarro@gmu.edu
Founded: 1986
Non-profit research & publication. Branch office in Washington, DC.
ISBN Prefix(es): 978-0-945999; 978-1-59813
Number of titles published annually: 10 Print; 1 CD-ROM; 2 Online; 6 E-Book; 1 Audio
Total Titles: 79 Print; 21 E-Book
*Distribution Center:* Independent Publishers Group, 814 N Franklin St, Chicago, IL 60610 *Toll Free Tel:* 800-888-4741 *Web Site:* www.ipgbook.com
Membership(s): IBPA, the Independent Book Publishers Association; Independent Publishers Group

**Indiana Historical Society Press (IHS Press)**
450 W Ohio St, Indianapolis, IN 46202-3269
SAN: 201-5234
*Tel:* 317-232-1882; 317-234-0026 (orders); 317-234-2716 (edit) *Toll Free Tel:* 800-447-1830 (orders) *Fax:* 317-234-0562 (orders); 317-233-0857 (edit)
*E-mail:* ihspress@indianahistory.org; orders@indianahistory.org (orders)
*Web Site:* www.indianahistory.org; shop.indianahistory.org (orders)
*Key Personnel*
CEO & Pres: John Herbst *E-mail:* jherbst@indianahistory.org
Natl Sales Coord: Becke Bolinger *Tel:* 317-234-3683 *E-mail:* bbolinger@indianahistory.org
Buyer/Mgr, Retail Opers: Phil Janes *E-mail:* pjanes@indianahistory.org
Sr Ed: Ray Boomhower *E-mail:* rboomhower@indianahistory.og
Founded: 1886
Books, journals & newsletters on Indiana history, including an illustrated history magazine & a family history magazine. Also offers videos, recordings, prints, note cards & other gift items.
ISBN Prefix(es): 978-0-87195
Number of titles published annually: 2 Print; 1 Online
Total Titles: 90 Print; 1 Online; 3 Audio

**Indiana University African Studies Program**
Indiana University, 221 Woodburn Hall, Bloomington, IN 47405
*Tel:* 812-855-8284 *Fax:* 812-855-6734
*E-mail:* afrist@indiana.edu
*Web Site:* www.indiana.edu/~afrist
*Key Personnel*
Dir: Samuel Obeng *E-mail:* sobeng@indiana.edu
Assoc Dir: Maria Grosz-Ngate *Tel:* 812-855-5081 *E-mail:* mgrosz@indiana.edu
Admin Mgr: Helen Harrell *E-mail:* hharrell@indiana.edu
Founded: 1965
Monograph & working papers, humanities, interdisciplinary study of Africa.
ISBN Prefix(es): 978-0-941934
Number of titles published annually: 50 Print
Total Titles: 52 Print

**§Indiana University Press**
601 N Morton St, Bloomington, IN 47404-3797
SAN: 202-5647
*Tel:* 812-855-8817 *Toll Free Tel:* 800-842-6796 (orders only) *Fax:* 812-855-7931; 812-855-8507
*E-mail:* iupress@indiana.edu; iuporder@indiana.edu (orders)
*Web Site:* www.iupress.indiana.edu
*Key Personnel*
Dir: Janet Rabinowitch *Tel:* 812-855-4773 *E-mail:* jrabinow@indiana.edu
Dir, Prodn: Bernadette Zoss *Tel:* 812-855-5563 *E-mail:* bzoss@indiana.edu
Dir, Opers: Dan Nichols *Tel:* 812-855-4901 *E-mail:* nichodan@indiana.edu
Dir, Electronic & Serials Publg: Kathryn Caras *Tel:* 812-855-3830 *E-mail:* kcaras@indiana.edu
Edit Dir: Robert Sloan *Tel:* 812-855-7561 *E-mail:* rjsloan@indiana.edu
Exec Dir, Office of Scholarly Publg: Carolyn Walters
Dir, Sales & Mktg: Dave Hulsey *Tel:* 812-855-6553 *E-mail:* hulseyd@indiana.edu
Sales Mgr: Mary Beth Haas *Tel:* 812-855-9440 *E-mail:* mbhaas@indiana.edu
Mng Ed: Angela Burton *Tel:* 812-855-9686 *E-mail:* burtonan@indiana.edu
Sr Sponsoring Ed: Dee Mortensen *Tel:* 812-855-0268 *E-mail:* mortense@indiana.edu
Sponsoring Ed: Linda Oblack *Tel:* 812-855-2175 *E-mail:* loblack@indiana.edu; Rebecca Tolen *Tel:* 812-855-2756 *E-mail:* retolen@indiana.edu
Mgr, Accts Receivable: Kimberly B Childers *Tel:* 812-855-4134 *E-mail:* kchilder@indiana.edu
Rts & Perms Mgr & Asst to Dir: Peter Froehlich *Tel:* 812-855-6314 *E-mail:* pfroehli@indiana.edu
Ms Ed: Marvin Keenan *Tel:* 812-855-5064 *E-mail:* mwkeenan@indiana.edu
Founded: 1950
Trade & scholarly nonfiction; film & media studies, literature & music, African studies, backlist, classical studies, contemporary issues, cultural studies, folklore, international studies, Jewish studies, journals, Middle East studies, paleontology, philanthropy, politics/political science, railroads & transportation, Russian studies.
ISBN Prefix(es): 978-0-253
Number of titles published annually: 170 Print; 2 CD-ROM; 5 Audio
Total Titles: 2,500 Print; 8 CD-ROM
Imprints: Quarry Books (regional imprint for Midwest)
Foreign Rep(s): Agenzia Letteraria Internazionale (Italy); Carmen Balcells Agencia (Spain); Paul & Peter Fritz Ag (Germany); Balcells Mello e Souza Riff Agencia Literaria (Brazil); La Nouvelle Agence (France)
*Shipping Address:* 802 E 13 St, Bloomington, IN 47408-2101 *Tel:* 812-855-4362 *Fax:* 812-855-8507
*Warehouse:* 802 E 13 St, Bloomington, IN 47408-2101, Contact: Mark Kelly *Tel:* 812-855-4362 *Fax:* 812-855-8507 *E-mail:* markkell@indiana.edu

**§Industrial Press Inc**
989 Avenue of the Americas, 19th fl, New York, NY 10018
SAN: 202-6945
*Tel:* 212-889-6330 *Toll Free Tel:* 888-528-7852 *Fax:* 212-545-8327
*E-mail:* info@industrialpress.com
*Web Site:* www.industrialpress.com
*Key Personnel*
Owner & Pres: Alex Luchars
Cont: Peter Burri
Edit Dir: John F Carleo *Tel:* 212-889-6330 ext 19 *E-mail:* jcarleo@industrialpress.com
Prodn & Art Dir: Janet Romano
Founded: 1883
Scientific & technical handbooks, professional & reference books.
ISBN Prefix(es): 978-0-8311
Number of titles published annually: 28 Print; 10 CD-ROM; 10 E-Book
Total Titles: 320 Print; 40 CD-ROM; 40 E-Book
Foreign Rep(s): APAC (Southeast Asia); Asia Publishers Group (Far East exc Japan); Elsevier Pty Ltd (Australia); Techbooks Wholesale (New Zealand); Thompson Nelson (Canada); Transatlantic Publishers Group (Europe, Middle East, UK)
*Advertising Agency:* Flamm Advertising Inc
*Returns:* Ware-Pak, 2427 Bond St, University Park, IL 60466, Contact: Tammy Cote *Tel:* 708-587-4124 *Fax:* 708-587-4167
*Warehouse:* Ware-Pak, 2427 Bond St, University Park, IL 60466, Contact: Tammy Cote *Tel:* 708-587-4124 *Fax:* 708-587-4167
Membership(s): AAP

**Information Age Publishing Inc**
PO Box 79049, Charlotte, NC 28271-7047
*Tel:* 704-752-9125 *Fax:* 704-752-9113
*E-mail:* infoage@infoagepub.com
*Web Site:* www.infoagepub.com
*Key Personnel*
Pres & Pubr: George F Johnson *E-mail:* george@infoagepub.com
Founded: 1999
Social science publisher of academic & scholarly book series & journals.
ISBN Prefix(es): 978-1-930608; 978-1-931576; 978-1-59311
Number of titles published annually: 120 Print; 9 Online; 120 E-Book
Total Titles: 2,000 Print; 800 E-Book
Foreign Rep(s): James Bennett Pty Ltd (Australia); Sara Book (India); Capital Book (India); Cranberry International (Latin America); DA Information Services (Australia, New Zealand); The Eurospan Group; Information Age Publishing (Europe); Logan Brothers (Canada); Taylor & Francis Asia Pacific (Singapore); United Publisher Services (Japan)

**§Information Gatekeepers Inc**
1340 Soldiers Field Rd, Suite 2, Boston, MA 02135
*Tel:* 617-782-5033 *Toll Free Tel:* 800-323-1088 *Fax:* 617-782-5735

*E-mail:* info@igigroup.com
*Web Site:* www.igigroup.com
*Key Personnel*
CEO & Pres: Paul Polishuk, PhD
Fulfillment Mgr: Jaime Perez *E-mail:* fulfill@igigroup.com
Founded: 1977
Fiber optics, optical networks, wireless, ATM, XDSL & telecommunications, trade shows, conferences, newsletters, market studies & consulting.
ISBN Prefix(es): 978-0-918435; 978-1-56851
Number of titles published annually: 35 Print
Total Titles: 542 Print
*Foreign Office(s):* IPI Services Pty Ltd, 128 Chalmers St, Surry Hills, NSW 2010, Australia *Tel:* (02) 9319 7933 *Fax:* (02) 9319-3408 *E-mail:* ipi@ipi.com
Global Informaton Inc, A Sahi Bank Bldg, 4th fl, 151 Kamiasao, A Sno-ku, Kawasaki 215, Japan *Tel:* (044) 952 0102 *Fax:* (044) 952 0109 *E-mail:* k.endo@gii.co.jp
OIC, Sam Hwam Bldg 38-1, 3rd fl, Wonhyoru 1-9a, Yongsan-Ku, Seoul, South Korea *Tel:* (027) 49 86 40 *Fax:* (027) 49 86 41
c/o CMS, 122 High St, Chesham, Berks HP5 1EB, United Kingdom *Tel:* (01494) 771 734 *Fax:* (01494) 779 994
Foreign Rep(s): Chiltern Magazine Services (England); Chongno Book Center Co Ltd (Korea); Global Information Inc (Japan); Investment Publications Information Service (Australia); Overseas Information Services (Korea)
Membership(s): IEEE; The Optical Society; Plastic Optical Fiber Trade Organization

**Information Publications Inc**
2995 Woodside Rd, Suite 400-182, Woodside, CA 94062
*Tel:* 650-568-6170 *Toll Free Tel:* 877-544-4636 *Fax:* 650-568-6150 *Toll Free Fax:* 877-544-4635
*E-mail:* info@informationpublications.com
*Web Site:* www.informationpublications.com
*Key Personnel*
Pres & Publr: Eric J Weiner *Tel:* 650-568-6170 ext 201 *E-mail:* eric@informationpublications.com
Founded: 1980
Statistical reference books; statistical profiles of cities & states; Asian, Black & Hispanic populations; energy, transportation & the environment.
ISBN Prefix(es): 978-0-931845; 978-0-911273; 978-0-941391; 978-0-929960
Number of titles published annually: 12 Print; 6 CD-ROM; 6 E-Book
Total Titles: 12 Print; 6 CD-ROM; 6 E-Book
Membership(s): ALA; IBPA, the Independent Book Publishers Association

**§Information Today, Inc**
143 Old Marlton Pike, Medford, NJ 08055-8750
*Tel:* 609-654-6266 *Toll Free Tel:* 800-300-9868 (cust serv) *Fax:* 609-654-4309
*E-mail:* custserv@infotoday.com
*Web Site:* www.infotoday.com
*Key Personnel*
Pres & CEO: Thomas H Hogan, Sr
VP, Admin: John Yersak
VP, Content: Richard T Kaser *E-mail:* kaser@infotoday.com
VP, Mktg & Busn Devt: Thomas Hogan, Jr
VP, IT: Bill Spence *E-mail:* spence@infotoday.com
VP, Graphics & Prodn: M Heide Dengler *E-mail:* hdengler@infotoday.com
Ed-in-Chief & Publr, Book Publg Div: John B Bryans *E-mail:* jbryans@infotoday.com
Ad Sales Mgr: David Panara *E-mail:* dpanara@infotoday.com
Book Mktg & Exhibits: Robert Colding *E-mail:* rcolding@infotoday.com
Founded: 1980
Publisher specializing in: Books, directories, newspapers, journals, newsletters, conferences & information services for users & producers of digital information content & technologies, including professionals in the library, publishing, online information, K-12 education, business research & IT, knowledge management, customer relationship management, speech technology & streaming media industries. ITI's book publishing division comprises 1 trade & 3 professional imprints. ITI's reference division is the publisher of *LMP, ILMP, American Book Trade Directory, Library and Book Trade Almanac* & other professional reference titles.
ISBN Prefix(es): 978-0-938734; 978-0-904933; 978-1-57387; 978-0-910965
Number of titles published annually: 28 Print; 15 E-Book
Total Titles: 430 Print; 200 E-Book
Imprints: ASI Books (books for indexing professionals from the American Society for Indexing); ASIS&T Monograph Series (scholarly monographs from the American Society for Information Science & Technology); CyberAge Books (books for tech-savvy consumers & business information users; nationally distributed to the book trade by IPG); Information Today Books (practical books for library & information professionals)
Membership(s): ALA; American Society for Indexing; Association for Independent Information Professionals; Association for Information Science & Technology; Independent Publishers Group; SLA

**§Infosential Press**
1162 Dominion Dr W, Mobile, AL 36695
*Tel:* 251-776-5656; 251-716-8178
*Key Personnel*
Pres: Dr Richard J Wood *E-mail:* rwood1947@gmail.com
Founded: 1997
Publisher of nonfiction & reference electronic books.
ISBN Prefix(es): 978-1-930852
Number of titles published annually: 1 Print; 1 Online; 1 E-Book
Total Titles: 1 Print; 8 CD-ROM; 7 Online; 8 E-Book
Distributed by EBL; netLibrary

**Infosources Publishing**
140 Norma Rd, Teaneck, NJ 07666
*Tel:* 201-836-7072
*Web Site:* www.infosourcespub.com
*Key Personnel*
Publr & Ed: Arlene L Eis
Founded: 1981
Legal reference books; newsletters; online databases. Publisher of The Informed Librarian Online.
ISBN Prefix(es): 978-0-939486
Number of titles published annually: 5 Print; 4 Online
Total Titles: 4 Print

**Ingalls Publishing Group Inc (IPG)**
PO Box 2500, Banner Elk, NC 28604
*Tel:* 828-297-6884 *Fax:* 828-297-6880
*E-mail:* sales@ingallspublishinggroup.com
*Web Site:* www.ingallspublishinggroup.com
*Key Personnel*
Publr: Robert Ingalls
Exec Ed: Barbara Ingalls *E-mail:* barbingalls@aol.com
Sr Ed: Albert A Bell; Judy Geary *E-mail:* editor@ingallspublishinggroup.com
Sales & Opers Mgr: Rebecca Owen
Founded: 2001
Small publishing company focusing on fiction, historical fiction & memoir. Dedicated to discovering the truly excellent mss overlooked by other houses due to changing literary fashion or a narrowly focused target audience.
ISBN Prefix(es): 978-0-9713045; 978-1-932158
Number of titles published annually: 6 Print
Total Titles: 40 Print
Imprints: Almont Books; Ingalls Publishing
Distributor for Southlore Press
*Shipping Address:* Ingram Book Group, One Ingram Blvd, La Vergne, TN 37086 *Tel:* 615-793-5000 *Web Site:* www.ingrambook.com
*Warehouse:* Ingram Book Group, One Ingram Blvd, La Vergne, TN 37086 *Tel:* 615-793-5000 *Web Site:* www.ingrambook.com
*Distribution Center:* Ingram Book Group, One Ingram Blvd, La Vergne, TN 37086 *Tel:* 615-793-5000 *Web Site:* www.ingrambook.com
Membership(s): IBPA, the Independent Book Publishers Association; NAIBA; Southern Independent Booksellers Alliance

**Inkwater Press**
Imprint of Firstbooks.com Inc
6750 SW Franklin St, Suite A, Portland, OR 97223
*Tel:* 503-968-6777 *Fax:* 503-968-6779
*E-mail:* orders@inkwaterbooks.com
*Web Site:* www.inkwaterpress.com
*Key Personnel*
Pres: Jeremy Solomon *E-mail:* jeremy@inkwaterpress.com
Founded: 2002
Publishing services to individuals & corporations as well as author-subsidized publishing.
This publisher has indicated that 95% of their product line is author subsidized.
ISBN Prefix(es): 978-0-9719414; 978-1-59299
Number of titles published annually: 70 Print; 70 E-Book
Total Titles: 430 Print; 115 E-Book; 2 Audio
Imprints: Franklin Street Books; Inkwater Press

**Inner Traditions International Ltd**
One Park St, Rochester, VT 05767
SAN: 208-6948
Mailing Address: PO Box 388, Rochester, VT 05767
*Tel:* 802-767-3174 *Toll Free Tel:* 800-246-8648 *Fax:* 802-767-3726
*E-mail:* customerservice@InnerTraditions.com
*Web Site:* www.InnerTraditions.com
*Key Personnel*
Pres: Ehud C Sperling *E-mail:* prez@InnerTraditions.com
VP & Mng Ed: Jeanie Levitan *E-mail:* jeaniel@InnerTraditions.com
VP, Opers: Diane Shepard *E-mail:* dianes@InnerTraditions.com
Dir, Sales & Mktg: John Hays *E-mail:* johnh@InnerTraditions.com
Print Mgr: Jon Desautels *E-mail:* jond@InnerTraditions.com
Acqs Ed: Jon Graham *E-mail:* jong@InnerTraditions.com
Sales & Mktg: Andrea Raymond *E-mail:* andyr@InnerTraditions.com
Spec Sales: Jessica Arsenault *E-mail:* jessa@InnerTraditions.com
Publicity & Foreign Rts & Perms: Cynthia Fowles *E-mail:* cynthiaf@InnerTraditions.com
Founded: 1975

Nonfiction cloth & quality trade paperbacks; audio cassettes & CDs (ethnic music & meditation aids).
ISBN Prefix(es): 978-0-89281; 978-1-59477
Number of titles published annually: 66 Print; 240 E-Book
Total Titles: 1,347 Print; 590 E-Book; 17 Audio
Imprints: Bear & Co; Bear Cub Books; Bindu Books; Destiny Books; Destiny Recordings; Healing Arts Press; Inner Traditions; Inner Traditions en espanol; Inner Traditions India; Park Street Press
Foreign Rep(s): Akasha Books Ltd (New Zealand); Brumby Books & Music (Australia); Michelle Morrow Curreri (all other territories, India); Deep Books (Europe, UK); India Book Distributors (India); Inner Traditions Canada (Canada); Real Books (South Africa); Zimpfer Books (Caribbean including Puerto Rico, Central America, Mexico, South America)
Foreign Rights: Akcali Copyright Agency (Turkey); Big Apple Agency Inc (China, Taiwan); The Book Publishers' Association of Israel, International Promotion & Literary Rights Dept (Israel); Amina Marix Evans (Netherlands); Graal Literary Agency (Poland); Ilidio da Fonseca Matos (Portugal); International Editors' Co SL (Argentina, Spain); Simona Kessler International Copyright Agency Ltd (Romania); Alexander Korzhenevski Agency (Russia); Agenzia Letteraria Internazionale (Italy); Zvonimir Majdak (Croatia); Montreal Contacts/The Rights Agency (Canada); Andrew Nurnberg Associates Ltd (Baltic States, Bulgaria, Czech Republic, Hungary); Read n Right Agency (Greece); Karin Schindler (Brazil); Thomas Schlueck GmbH (Germany); Agence Schweiger (France); Tuttle-Mori Agency Inc (Japan, Thailand); Eric Yang Agency (Korea)
*Warehouse:* Inner Traditions International - Bear & Co, Airport Business Park, 364 Innovation Dr, North Clarendon, VT 05759, Contact: Jim Cassel *Tel:* 802-773-8930 *Fax:* 802-773-6993
*See separate listing for:*
**Bear & Co Inc**

**innovativeKids®**
Division of Innovative USA® Inc
50 Washington St, Suite 201, Norwalk, CT 06854
*Tel:* 203-838-6400
*E-mail:* info@innovativekids.com
*Web Site:* www.innovativekids.com
*Key Personnel*
CEO: Michael S Levins *E-mail:* mlevins@innovativekids.com
Pres & Publr: Shari Kaufman *Tel:* 203-838-6400 ext 305 *E-mail:* skaufman@innovativekids.com
Founded: 1989
Publishing interactive, tactile books for preschool through elementary school age children - unusual formats that foster the growth of essential learning skills.
ISBN Prefix(es): 978-1-58476
Number of titles published annually: 50 Print
Total Titles: 150 Print
Membership(s): ABA; American Book Producers Association; ASTRA; IBPA, the Independent Book Publishers Association; National School Supply & Equipment Association; Toy International Association

**Insight Editions**
Imprint of Palace Press International
10 Paul Dr, San Rafael, CA 94903
*Tel:* 415-526-1370 *Toll Free Tel:* 800-809-3792
*E-mail:* info@insighteditions.com
*Web Site:* www.insighteditions.com
*Key Personnel*
Pres & Publr: Raoul Goff *E-mail:* raoul@palacepress.com
Acqs Ed: Jake Gerli *Tel:* 415-526-1376 *E-mail:* jake@palacepress.com
Intl Rts & Mktg Mgr: Charles Gerli
Sr Ed: Roxanna Aliaga
Founded: 2000
Renowned for creating beautiful, innovative books that excel in the marketplace. Insight Editions brings the vision & style of high-end illustrated books to the realm of the arts & entertainment.
ISBN Prefix(es): 978-1-933784
Number of titles published annually: 15 Print
Total Titles: 20 Print
Distributed by Welcome Books
*Shipping Address:* Publishers Group West, 1700 Fourth St, Berkeley, CA 94710 *Toll Free Tel:* 800-788-3123 *Web Site:* www.pgw.com
*See separate listing for:*
**Mandala Publishing**

**§Institute of Continuing Legal Education**
1020 Greene St, Ann Arbor, MI 48109-1444
*Tel:* 734-764-0533 *Toll Free Tel:* 877-229-4350 *Fax:* 734-763-2412 *Toll Free Fax:* 877-229-4351
*E-mail:* icle@umich.edu
*Web Site:* www.icle.org
*Key Personnel*
Dir: Lynn P Chard *E-mail:* lchard@umich.edu
Admin Dir: Karen R Brown
Pubns & Online Prods Dir: Mary Hiniker
Specialty Progs Dir: Sheldon Stark
Educ Dir: Jeffrey E Kirkley
Founded: 1959
Books, supplements, disk products, audio, web site.
ISBN Prefix(es): 978-0-88288
Number of titles published annually: 5 Print
Total Titles: 55 Print
Imprints: ICLE

**§Institute of Environmental Sciences and Technology - IEST**
2340 S Arlington Heights Rd, Suite 100, Arlington Heights, IL 60005-4516
*Tel:* 847-981-0100 *Fax:* 847-981-4130
*E-mail:* information@iest.org
*Web Site:* www.iest.org
*Key Personnel*
Exec Dir: Roberta Burrows *Tel:* 847-981-0100 ext 11 *E-mail:* executive@iest.org
Dir, Communs & Progs: Diana Granitto *Tel:* 847-981-0100 ext 19 *E-mail:* director@iest.org
Tech Ed: Heidi Parsons *Tel:* 847-981-0100 ext 16 *E-mail:* editorial@iest.org
Memb & Acctg Coord: Mara Douvris *Tel:* 847-981-0100 ext 25 *E-mail:* membershipdept@iest.org
Mktg & Meeting Coord: Heather Woodin *Tel:* 847-981-0100 ext 20 *E-mail:* marketing@iest.org
A multidisciplinary, international society whose members are recognized worldwide for their contributions to the environmental sciences in the area of contamination control in electronics manufacturing & pharmaceutical processes; design, test & evaluation of commercial & military equipment; product reliability issues associated with commercial & military systems.
ISBN Prefix(es): 978-0-915414; 978-1-877862; 978-0-9747313; 978-0-9787868
Number of titles published annually: 3 Print
Total Titles: 26 CD-ROM; 48 Online

**Institute of Governmental Studies**
Subsidiary of University of California, Berkeley
109 Moses Hall, Suite 2370, Berkeley, CA 94720-2370
*Tel:* 510-642-1428 *Fax:* 510-642-3020; 510-642-5537 (orders)
*E-mail:* igspress@berkeley.edu
*Web Site:* www.igs.berkeley.edu
*Key Personnel*
Dir, Pubns: Ethan Rarick *E-mail:* erarick@berkeley.edu
Pubns Ed: Maria Wolf *E-mail:* mariaw@berkeley.edu
Public policy issues.
ISBN Prefix(es): 978-0-87772
Number of titles published annually: 6 Print
Total Titles: 54 Print

**§Institute of Jesuit Sources (IJS)**
3601 Lindell Blvd, St Louis, MO 63108
*Tel:* 314-633-4622 *Fax:* 314-633-4623
*E-mail:* ijs@jesuitsources.com
*Web Site:* www.jesuitsources.com
*Key Personnel*
Dir: Fr John W Padberg *Tel:* 314-633-4400
Assoc Ed: John Montag
Founded: 1961
Books on history & spirituality of the society of Jesus (Jesuits) translated from non-English sources & originally in English.
ISBN Prefix(es): 978-0-912422; 978-1-880810
Number of titles published annually: 8 Print
Total Titles: 103 Print; 1 CD-ROM

**§Institute of Mathematical Geography**
Division of Arlinghaus Enterprises LLC
1964 Boulder Dr, Ann Arbor, MI 48104
*Tel:* 734-975-0246
*E-mail:* image@imagenet.org
*Web Site:* www.imagenet.com
*Key Personnel*
Founding Dir: Sandra Lach Arlinghaus *E-mail:* sandy@almalach.com
Founded: 1986
Publish scholarly books & college text books; also publish electronic journal books.
ISBN Prefix(es): 978-1-877751
Number of titles published annually: 3 Print
Total Titles: 39 Print; 13 E-Book

**§Institute of Police Technology & Management**
Division of University of North Florida
University Ctr, 12000 Alumni Dr, Jacksonville, FL 32224-2678
*Tel:* 904-620-4786 *Fax:* 904-620-2453
*E-mail:* info@iptm.org; orders@iptm.org
*Web Site:* www.iptm.org
*Key Personnel*
Dir: Leonard R Jacob *E-mail:* ljacob@unf.edu
Founded: 1980
In-service training for law enforcement, civilian personnel; marketing of publications, templates & videos. Specialize in traffic crash investigation & reconstruction; law enforcement management & supervision; criminal investigation; DUI & drug law enforcement; radar/laser speed enforcement; law enforcement computer training; gangs & other specialized subjects.
ISBN Prefix(es): 978-1-884566
Number of titles published annually: 7 Print; 2 CD-ROM
Total Titles: 65 Print; 6 CD-ROM
Foreign Rep(s): Paul Feenan (Australia, South Pacific)
Foreign Rights: Pacific Traffic Education Ctr (Canada)

**The Institutes™**
720 Providence Rd, Suite 100, Malvern, PA 19355-3433
*Tel:* 610-644-2100 *Toll Free Tel:* 800-644-2101 *Fax:* 610-640-9576
*E-mail:* customerservice@theinstitutes.org
*Web Site:* www.theinstitutes.org
*Key Personnel*
Pres/CEO: Peter Miller
Dir, Edit Servs: Jason Scarpello
Property-casualty continuing insurance education.
ISBN Prefix(es): 978-0-89463; 978-0-89462
Number of titles published annually: 12 Print
Total Titles: 120 Print

**The Institution of Engineering & Technology**, see IET

**Inter-American Development Bank**
Division of Multilateral Development Bank
1300 New York Ave NW, Washington, DC 20577
*Tel:* 202-623-1000 *Fax:* 202-623-3096
*E-mail:* pic@iadb.org
*Web Site:* www.iadb.org/pub
*Key Personnel*
Pres: Luis Alberto Moreno
EVP: Julie T Katzman
Founded: 1959
Economic development, in Latin America & the Caribbean.
ISBN Prefix(es): 978-0-940602; 978-1-886938; 978-1-931003
Number of titles published annually: 30 Print
Total Titles: 120 Print
Distributed by Johns Hopkins University Press

**§Inter-University Consortium for Political & Social Research (ICPSR)**
Affiliate of University of Michigan Institute for Social Research
330 Packard St, Ann Arbor, MI 48104
Mailing Address: PO Box 1248, Ann Arbor, MI 48106-1248
*Tel:* 734-647-5000 *Fax:* 734-647-8200
*E-mail:* netmail@icpsr.umich.edu
*Web Site:* www.icpsr.umich.edu
*Key Personnel*
Dir: George Alter *Tel:* 734-615-7652 *E-mail:* altergc@umich.edu
Dir, Summer Prog in Quantitative Methods of Social Res: William Jacoby *Tel:* 734-763-6281 *E-mail:* wgjacoby@umich.edu
Asst Dir: Mary Vardigan *Tel:* 734-615-7908 *E-mail:* vardigan@umich.edu
Ed: Dan Meisler
Founded: 1962
Provides access to social science data collections & documentation. Additional subjects include: demography & aging/gerontology.
ISBN Prefix(es): 978-0-89138
Number of titles published annually: 300 Online
Total Titles: 7,500 Online

**Intercultural Development Research Association (IDRA)**
5815 Callaghan Rd, Suite 101, San Antonio, TX 78228
*Tel:* 210-444-1710 *Fax:* 210-444-1714
*E-mail:* contact@idra.org
*Web Site:* www.idra.org
*Key Personnel*
CEO & Pres: Dr Maria "Cuca" Robledo Montecel
Communs Mgr: Christie Goodman
Founded: 1973
Independent & private, nonprofit organization dedicated to creating schools that work for all children; works with people to create & apply cutting-edge educational policies & practices that value & empower all children, families & communities. Conducts research & development activities, creates, implements & administers innovative education programs & provides teacher, administrator, parent training & technical assistance.
ISBN Prefix(es): 978-1-878550
Number of titles published annually: 10 Print
Total Titles: 34 Print

**Intercultural Press Inc**
Division of Nicholas Brealey Publishing
20 Park Plaza, Suite 610, Boston, MA 02116
SAN: 212-6699
*Tel:* 617-523-3801 *Toll Free Tel:* 888-273-2539 *Fax:* 617-523-3708
*E-mail:* info@interculturalpress.com
*Web Site:* www.interculturalpress.com
*Key Personnel*
Dir: Jennifer Delaney
Founded: 1980
Books, training & educational materials on intercultural, cross-cultural & diversity subjects, including reference books, bibliographies, manuals, handbooks, nonfiction.
ISBN Prefix(es): 978-0-933662; 978-1-877864; 978-1-931930
Number of titles published annually: 12 Print
Total Titles: 94 Print
Distributed by NBN

**Interlink Publishing Group Inc**
46 Crosby St, Northampton, MA 01060
SAN: 664-8908
*Tel:* 413-582-7054 *Toll Free Tel:* 800-238-LINK (238-5465) *Fax:* 413-582-7057
*E-mail:* info@interlinkbooks.com
*Web Site:* www.interlinkbooks.com
*Key Personnel*
Publr & Edit Dir: Michel Moushabeck *Tel:* 413-582-7054 ext 204 *E-mail:* michel@interlinkbooks.com
Lib Sales Dir: Brenda Eaton
Publicity Dir: Moira Megargee
Founded: 1987
World travel, world literature, world history, politics & ethnic cooking.
ISBN Prefix(es): 978-0-940793; 978-1-56656
Number of titles published annually: 60 Print; 40 E-Book
Total Titles: 950 Print; 500 E-Book
Imprints: Clockroot Books; Codagen Guides USA; Crocodile Books; Interlink Books; Olive Branch Press
Distributed by Publishers Group West (digital dist servs via Constellation)
Distributor for Black & White Publishing (UK); Camerapix Publishers International; Georgina Campbell Guides (Ireland); Macmillan Caribbean (UK); Quartet Books (UK); Rucksack Readers (UK); Serif Publishing Ltd (UK); Sheldrake Press (UK); Signal Books (UK); Waverley Books (UK); Neil Wilson Publishing (UK)
Foreign Rep(s): Codasat Canada Ltd (Canada); Electra Media Group (Southeast Asia); Network Book Distribution Ltd (Europe, UK); Palgrave Macmillan (Australia, New Zealand); Peter Ward Book Exports (Middle East)

**International Book Centre Inc**
2391 Auburn Rd, Shelby Township, MI 48317
SAN: 208-7022
Mailing Address: PO Box 295, Troy, MI 48085
*Tel:* 586-254-7230 *Fax:* 586-254-7230
*E-mail:* ibc@ibcbooks.com
*Web Site:* www.ibcbooks.com
*Key Personnel*
Owner: Doris Mukalla
Founded: 1974
Publisher of foreign language books. Specialize in the language & culture of the Middle East.
ISBN Prefix(es): 978-0-86685
Number of titles published annually: 2 Print; 2 Audio
Total Titles: 28 Print; 5 Audio
Distributor for Library du Liban (Lebanon); Stacey Intl Ltd (London); University of Michigan

**§International City/County Management Association (ICMA)**
777 N Capitol St NE, Suite 500, Washington, DC 20002-4201
*Tel:* 202-289-4262 *Toll Free Tel:* 800-745-8780 *Fax:* 202-962-3500
*E-mail:* customerservice@icma.org
*Web Site:* icma.org
*Key Personnel*
Exec Dir: Robert J O'Neill, Jr *E-mail:* roneill@icma.org
Dir, Pubns: Ann Mahoney *Tel:* 202-962-3643
Founded: 1914
Local government leadership & management organization that provides member support; publications, data & information; peer & results-oriented assistance; training & professional development to more than 8,200 city, town & county experts throughout the world.
ISBN Prefix(es): 978-0-87326
Number of titles published annually: 10 Print; 2 CD-ROM; 25 Online
Total Titles: 200 Print; 7 CD-ROM; 85 Online
*Warehouse:* PBD, 1650 Bluegrass Lakes Pkwy, Alpharetta, GA 30004 *Tel:* 770-442-8633
*Distribution Center:* PBD, 1650 Bluegrass Lakes Pkwy, Alpharetta, GA 30004 *Tel:* 770-442-8633

**International Code Council Inc**
5360 Workman Mill Rd, Whittier, CA 90601-2256
*Tel:* 562-699-0541 *Toll Free Tel:* 888-422-7233 *Fax:* 562-908-5524; 562-699-8031
*E-mail:* es@icc-es.org
*Web Site:* www.iccsafe.org
*Key Personnel*
SVP, Busn & Prod Devt: Mark Johnson *Tel:* 562-699-0541 ext 3248 *E-mail:* mjohnson@icc-es.org
Founded: 1922
Publisher of construction codes & regulations used in US & abroad.
ISBN Prefix(es): 978-1-58001; 978-1-884590; 978-1-892395
Number of titles published annually: 60 Print; 10 CD-ROM
Total Titles: 200 Print; 20 CD-ROM

**International Council of Shopping Centers (ICSC)**
1221 Avenue of the Americas, 41st fl, New York, NY 10020-1099
*Tel:* 646-728-3800 *Fax:* 732-694-1755
*E-mail:* icsc@icsc.org
*Web Site:* www.icsc.org
*Key Personnel*
Dir, Pubns: Patricia Montagni *Tel:* 646-728-3494 *Fax:* 732-694-1767 *E-mail:* pmontagni@icsc.org
Founded: 1957
Books & ebooks.
ISBN Prefix(es): 978-0-927547; 978-0-913598; 978-1-58268
Number of titles published annually: 15 Print; 5 E-Book
Total Titles: 75 Print; 5 E-Book
*Foreign Office(s):* 29 Queen Anne's Gate, London SW1H 9BU, United Kingdom *Tel:* (020) 7976 3102 *Fax:* (020) 7976 3101 *E-mail:* info.europe@icsc.org
*Warehouse:* BrightKey, 9050 Junction Dr, Annapolis Junction, MD 20701 *Tel:* 301-362-6900
*Distribution Center:* BrightKey, 9050 Junction Dr, Annapolis Junction, MD 20701 *Tel:* 301-362-6900

**§International Evangelism Crusades Inc**
9101 Topanga Canyon Blvd, Unit 209, Chatsworth, CA 91311-5763
*Tel:* 818-882-0039 *Fax:* 818-998-6712
*Key Personnel*
Pres: Dr Julie Ann Stranges, PhD *E-mail:* jules4vets@yahoo.com
EVP: Rev Tiffany James Hardy
Founded: 1959
Religion, space & science.
ISBN Prefix(es): 978-0-933470
Number of titles published annually: 3 Print
Total Titles: 26 Print; 15 CD-ROM; 26 Audio

**International Food Policy Research Institute**
Member of Consultative Group on International Agricultural Research (CGIAR)
2033 "K" St NW, Washington, DC 20006-1002

*Tel:* 202-862-5600 *Fax:* 202-467-4439
*E-mail:* ifpri@cgiar.org
*Web Site:* www.ifpri.org
*Key Personnel*
Dir Gen: Shenggen Fan
Communs Dir: Klaus von Grebner *E-mail:* k. vongrebner@cgiar.org
Founded: 1975
Research reports, occasional papers & newsletter series, books, briefs, abstracts.
ISBN Prefix(es): 978-0-89629
Number of titles published annually: 270 Print; 2 CD-ROM; 270 Online
Total Titles: 3,980 Print; 21 CD-ROM; 3,634 Online
Distributed by Johns Hopkins University Press

**International Foundation of Employee Benefit Plans**
18700 W Bluemound Rd, Brookfield, WI 53045
Mailing Address: PO Box 69, Brookfield, WI 53008-0069
*Tel:* 262-786-6700 *Toll Free Tel:* 888-334-3327 *Fax:* 262-786-8780
*E-mail:* editor@ifebp.org
*Web Site:* www.ifebp.org
*Key Personnel*
Sr Dir, Info Svcs & Pubns: Dee Birschel *E-mail:* deeb@ifebp.org
Assoc Dir, Book Pubns: Pat Bonner *E-mail:* patb@ifebp.org
Founded: 1954
Books, periodicals.
ISBN Prefix(es): 978-0-89154
Number of titles published annually: 5 Print; 5 CD-ROM; 3 E-Book
Total Titles: 30 Print; 15 CD-ROM; 15 E-Book
Membership(s): Association Media & Publishing; IBPA, the Independent Book Publishers Association

**The International Institute of Islamic Thought**
500 Grove St, Suite 200, Herndon, VA 20170
*Tel:* 703-471-1133 *Fax:* 703-471-3922
*E-mail:* iiit@iiit.org
*Web Site:* www.iiit.org
*Key Personnel*
Pres: Abusolayman Abdulhamid
Dir, Pubns: Dr Jamal Barzinji
Mgr, Pubns: Riyad Al-Yemany
Founded: 1981
Books, books on tape, video cassettes.
ISBN Prefix(es): 978-0-912463; 978-1-56564
Number of titles published annually: 40 Print
Total Titles: 350 Print

**§International Linguistics Corp**
Learnables, 12220 Blue Ridge Blvd, Suite G, Grandview, MO 64030
*Tel:* 816-765-8855 *Toll Free Tel:* 800-237-1830 (orders) *Fax:* 816-765-2855
*E-mail:* learnables@sbcglobal.net
*Web Site:* www.learnables.com
*Key Personnel*
Gen Mgr: Jennifer Elliott
Founded: 1976
Foreign & English language materials, language teaching materials.
ISBN Prefix(es): 978-0-939990; 978-1-887371
Number of titles published annually: 5 Print; 3 CD-ROM; 1 Online; 3 Audio
Total Titles: 52 Print; 10 CD-ROM; 1 Online; 50 Audio
*Orders to:* Learnables, 12220 Blue Ridge Blvd, Suite G, Grandview, MO 64030

**§International Monetary Fund (IMF) Editorial & Publications Division**
Division of International Org (IGO)
700 19 St NW, HQ1-7-124, Washington, DC 20431
SAN: 203-8188
*Tel:* 202-623-7430 *Fax:* 202-623-7201
*E-mail:* publications@imf.org
*Web Site:* www.imfbookstore.org
*Key Personnel*
Publr: Jeremy Clift
Assoc Publr: Sean Culhane
Founded: 1946
Publishes books, periodicals & electronic products covering international finance, monetary issues, statistics & exchange rates, which are sold worldwide by distributors, bookstores & direct mail.
ISBN Prefix(es): 978-0-939934; 978-1-55775; 978-1-58906; 978-1-61635
Number of titles published annually: 120 Print; 12 CD-ROM; 200 E-Book
Total Titles: 750 Print
*Orders to:* IMF Publications, PO Box 92780, Washington, DC 20090
Membership(s): AAP; Association of American University Presses; Association of Learned & Professional Society Publishers; CrossRef

**§International Press of Boston Inc**
387 Somerville Ave, Somerville, MA 02143
Mailing Address: PO Box 43502, Somerville, MA 02143
*Tel:* 617-623-3016 *Fax:* 617-623-3101
*E-mail:* ipb-info@intlpress.com; ipb-orders@intlpress.com
*Web Site:* www.intlpress.com
*Key Personnel*
Gen Mgr: Brian Bianchini *Tel:* 617-623-3855 *E-mail:* ipb-mgmt@intlpress.com
Founded: 1992
Publish books, monographs, conference proceedings in advanced mathematics.
ISBN Prefix(es): 978-1-57146
Number of titles published annually: 13 Print
Total Titles: 89 Print; 3 CD-ROM
Distributed by AMS

**International Publishers Co Inc**
235 W 23 St, New York, NY 10011
SAN: 202-5655
*Tel:* 212-366-9816 *Fax:* 212-366-9820
*E-mail:* service@intpubnyc.com
*Web Site:* www.intpubnyc.com
*Key Personnel*
Pres & Ed: Betty Smith
Founded: 1924
Short discount titles & Marxist classics. Trade in cloth & paperback, general nonfiction, social sciences, classic & contemporary Marxism-Leninism, literature, poetry & biography, labor, women's studies.
ISBN Prefix(es): 978-0-7178
Number of titles published annually: 4 Print
Total Titles: 160 Print
Imprints: New World Paperbacks
Foreign Rep(s): Global Book Marketing (London, UK)
*Warehouse:* WC Books, 1200 County Rd, Rte 523, Flemington, NJ 08822, Contact: Brad Searles *Tel:* 908-782-2323 *Fax:* 908-237-2407
Membership(s): ABA; The Association of Publishers for Special Sales; IBPA, the Independent Book Publishers Association; National Association of College Stores

**International Reading Association**
800 Barksdale Rd, Newark, DE 19711-3204
Mailing Address: PO Box 8139, Newark, DE 19714-8139
*Tel:* 302-731-1600 *Toll Free Tel:* 800-336-7323 (US & CN) *Fax:* 302-731-1057
*E-mail:* customerservice@reading.org
*Web Site:* www.reading.org
*Key Personnel*
Exec Ed, Pubns: Shannon Fortner *Tel:* 302-731-6978 *Fax:* 302-368-2449 *E-mail:* sfortner@reading.org
Developmental Ed: Tori Bachman *Tel:* 302-731-1600 ext 452 *Fax:* 302-368-2449 *E-mail:* tbachman@reading.org
Founded: 1956
Books & journals related to reading instruction & literary education.
ISBN Prefix(es): 978-0-87207
Number of titles published annually: 10 Print; 5 E-Book
Total Titles: 150 Print; 15 E-Book
*Branch Office(s)*
444 N Capitol St NW, Suite 524, Washington, DC 20001 *Tel:* 202-624-8800 *Fax:* 202-624-8826
Foreign Rights: Academics Plus (Andrea Permel) (UK); Eurospan Group (Catherine Lawn) (Trinidad and Tobago)

**International Research Center for Energy & Economic Development**
850 Willowbrook Rd, Boulder, CO 80302
*Tel:* 303-442-4014 *Fax:* 303-442-5042
*E-mail:* info@iceed.org
*Web Site:* www.iceed.org
*Key Personnel*
Dir: Dorothea H El Mallakh
Lib Sales Dir: Helen El Mallakh
Founded: 1974
Monographs & hardcover; public policy; journal.
ISBN Prefix(es): 978-0-918714
Number of titles published annually: 3 Print
Total Titles: 80 Print
*Warehouse:* William S Hein & Co Inc, 1285 Main St, Buffalo, NY 14209 (for back orders of earlier volumes)

**§International Risk Management Institute Inc**
12222 Merit Dr, Suite 1450, Dallas, TX 75251-2276
*Tel:* 972-960-7693 *Fax:* 972-371-5120
*E-mail:* info27@irmi.com
*Web Site:* www.irmi.com
*Key Personnel*
Pres: Jack Gibson
VP, Fin & Admin: Cathy Roberts
Founded: 1978
Publish both print & online books on commercial & personal lines of insurance.
ISBN Prefix(es): 978-1-886813
Number of titles published annually: 36 Print
Total Titles: 34 Print; 1 CD-ROM

**International Society for Technology in Education**
180 W Eighth Ave, Suite 300, Eugene, OR 97401-2916
*Tel:* 541-302-3777 (intl) *Toll Free Tel:* 800-336-5191 (US & CN) *Fax:* 541-302-3778
*E-mail:* iste@iste.org
*Web Site:* www.iste.org; www.iste.org/bookstore (orders)
*Key Personnel*
CEO: Don Knezek *Tel:* 541-302-3777 ext 126
Deputy CEO: Leslie Conery *Tel:* 541-302-3776
Dir, Publg: Courtney Burkholder *Tel:* 541-434-8922 *E-mail:* cburkholder@iste.org
Dir, Mktg: Tracee Aliotti *Tel:* 541-681-3805
Founded: 1979
Work with experienced educators to develop & produce practical resources for classroom teachers, teacher educators & technology leaders. Home of the National Educational Technology Standards (NETS), ISTE is the trusted source for educational technology books & courseware.
ISBN Prefix(es): 978-1-56484
Number of titles published annually: 12 Print
Total Titles: 60 Print

**§International Society of Automation (ISA)**
67 T W Alexander Dr, Research Triangle Park, NC 27709-0185

Mailing Address: PO Box 12277, Research Triangle Park, NC 27709-2277
*Tel:* 919-549-8411 *Fax:* 919-549-8288
*E-mail:* info@isa.org
*Web Site:* www.isa.org
*Key Personnel*
Exec Dir: Patrick Gouhin
Dir, Publg, Mktg & Sales: Tim Feldman
Founded: 1945
Technical books, references, journals, video-based training programs, directories, software, standards, proceedings, CD-ROM, electronic references.
ISBN Prefix(es): 978-1-55617
Number of titles published annually: 20 Print
Total Titles: 139 Print; 10 CD-ROM; 20 E-Book
Foreign Rep(s): Eurospan (Europe)

**§International Wealth Success Inc**
PO Box 186, Merrick, NY 11566-0186
*Tel:* 516-766-5850 *Toll Free Tel:* 800-323-0548 *Fax:* 516-766-5919
*E-mail:* admin@iwsmoney.com
*Web Site:* www.iwsmoney.com
*Key Personnel*
Pres & Ed: Tyler G Hicks *E-mail:* tyghicks@aol.com
Founded: 1966
Publish a variety of business & financial titles in the fields of small business, real estate, mail order, import-export & financing.
ISBN Prefix(es): 978-0-934311; 978-0-914306; 978-1-56150
Number of titles published annually: 6 Print; 3 CD-ROM; 4 Online; 6 E-Book; 4 Audio
Total Titles: 120 Print; 4 CD-ROM; 12 Online; 12 E-Book; 1 Audio

**InterVarsity Press**
Division of InterVarsity Christian Fellowship/USA
430 Plaza Dr, Westmont, IL 60559-1234
SAN: 202-7089
Mailing Address: PO Box 1400, Downers Grove, IL 60515
*Tel:* 630-734-4000 *Toll Free Tel:* 800-843-9487 *Fax:* 630-734-4200
*E-mail:* email@ivpress.com
*Web Site:* www.ivpress.com
*Key Personnel*
Publr: Robert A Fryling *Tel:* 630-734-4001 *E-mail:* bfryling@ivpress.com
Edit Dir: Andrew T Le Peau *Tel:* 630-734-4036 *E-mail:* alepeau@ivpress.com
Assoc Edit Dir: Cindy Bunch *Tel:* 630-734-4078 *E-mail:* cbunch@ivpress.com
Sr Ed: Daniel Reid *Tel:* 360-379-2599 *E-mail:* dgreid@ivpress.com
Art Dir: Cindy Kiple *Tel:* 630-734-4024 *E-mail:* ckiple@ivpress.com
Dir, Busn & Fin: James Hagen *Tel:* 630-734-4005 *E-mail:* jhagen@ivpress.com
Dir, Prodn & Fulfillment: Anne Gerth *Tel:* 630-734-4027 *E-mail:* agerth@ivprss.com
Dir, Sales & Mktg: Jeff Crosby *Tel:* 630-734-4017 *E-mail:* jcrosby@ivpress.com
Rts & Perms: Ellen Hsu *Tel:* 630-734-4034 *E-mail:* ehsu@ivpress.com
Founded: 1947
Religion (interdenominational); textbooks.
ISBN Prefix(es): 978-0-87784; 978-0-8308
Number of titles published annually: 100 Print; 70 E-Book; 1 Audio
Total Titles: 1,800 Print; 5 CD-ROM; 850 E-Book; 6 Audio
Imprints: Formatio (books that follow the rich tradition of the church in the journey of spiritual formation); IVP Academic (publishing to facilitate broader conversations in the academy & the church); IVP Books (thoughtful books on church, culture & mission); IVP Connect (resources for Bible study & small groups); LifeGuide Bible Studies (guides on books of the Bible & key Biblical topics)
*Branch Office(s)*
Port Townsend, WA 98368, Sr Ed: Dr Dan Reid *E-mail:* dgreid@ix.netcom.com
*Foreign Office(s):* IVP Book Centre, Norton St, Nottingham NG7 3HR, United Kingdom, Fin & Opers Mgr: George Russell *Tel:* (0115) 978 1054 *Fax:* (0115) 942 2694 *E-mail:* sales@ivpbooks.com *Web Site:* www.ivpbooks.com
Foreign Rep(s): Inter-Varsity Press - UK (Africa, Asia, Europe)
Membership(s): Evangelical Christian Publishers Association

**Interweave Press LLC**
Unit of Aspire Media LLC
201 E Fourth St, Loveland, CO 80537
*Tel:* 970-669-7672 *Toll Free Tel:* 800-272-2193 *Fax:* 970-667-8317
*E-mail:* interweaveservice@interweave.com
*Web Site:* www.interweave.com
*Key Personnel*
SVP & Publr: John Bolton
Founder & Creative Dir: Linda Ligon
VP, Mktg & Sales & Book Publr: Stephen Koenig
Mktg & Sales Dir: Elisabeth Malzahn
Edit Dir: Susanne Woods
Proj Mgr: Mary KinCannon
Sr Designer: Julia Boyles
Acqs Ed, Book Div: Allison Korleski
Ed: Erica Smith
Founded: 1975
ISBN Prefix(es): 978-0-934026; 978-1-883010; 978-1-931499; 978-0-9796073
Number of titles published annually: 28 Print
Total Titles: 210 Print
Distributed by Keith Ainsworth Pty Ltd, Australia; David Bateman Ltd, New Zealand; Search Press, UK
Membership(s): Publishers Association of the West

**The Intrepid Traveler**
152 Saltonstall Pkwy, Rear Entrance, East Haven, CT 06512
Mailing Address: PO Box 531, Branford, CT 06405-0531
*Tel:* 203-469-0214 *Fax:* 203-469-0430
*E-mail:* admin@intrepidtraveler.com
*Web Site:* www.intrepidtraveler.com
*Key Personnel*
Publr: Kelly Monaghan
Assoc Publr: Sally Scanlon *E-mail:* sscanlon@intrepidtraveler.com
Founded: 1990
Publish travel how-to & guidebooks titles.
ISBN Prefix(es): 978-0-9627892; 978-1-887140
Number of titles published annually: 4 Print
Total Titles: 24 Print
Distributed by National Book Network Inc (NBN)
Membership(s): IBPA, the Independent Book Publishers Association; Travel Publishers Association

**Iron Gate Publishing**
PO Box 999, Niwot, CO 80544
*Tel:* 303-530-2551 *Fax:* 303-530-5273
*E-mail:* editor@irongate.com; booknews@reunionsolutions.com
*Web Site:* www.irongate.com; www.reunionsolutions.com
*Key Personnel*
Publr & Ed: Dina C Carson *E-mail:* editor@irongate.com
Founded: 1990
Genealogy, self-publishing, reference, reunion planning how-to.
ISBN Prefix(es): 978-1-879579; 978-0-9724975
Number of titles published annually: 6 Print; 6 CD-ROM; 25 Online; 25 E-Book
Total Titles: 31 Print; 6 CD-ROM; 17 Online; 25 E-Book
Imprints: KinderMed Press; Reunion Solutions Press
Membership(s): The Association of Publishers for Special Sales; Colorado Independent Publishers Association; IBPA, the Independent Book Publishers Association; Publishers Association of the West

**Irvington Publishers Inc**, see Ardent Media Inc

**ISI Books**
Imprint of Intercollegiate Studies Institute Inc
3901 Centerville Rd, Wilmington, DE 19807-1938
*Tel:* 302-652-4600 *Toll Free Tel:* 800-526-7022 *Fax:* 302-652-1760
*E-mail:* info@isi.org; isibooks@isi.org
*Web Site:* www.isibooks.org
*Key Personnel*
Pres: Christopher G Long
EVP: Jeffrey O Nelson
VP & Ed-in-Chief: Jed Donahue *E-mail:* jdonahue@isi.org
Founded: 1993
ISI Books is a publisher of serious, but accessible interdisciplinary books & journals, focused on the liberal arts.
ISBN Prefix(es): 978-1-882926; 978-1-932236
Number of titles published annually: 20 Print
Total Titles: 130 Print

**Island Press**
1718 Connecticut Ave NW, Suite 300, Washington, DC 20009
SAN: 212-5129
*Tel:* 202-232-7933 *Toll Free Tel:* 800-828-1302 *Fax:* 202-234-1328
*E-mail:* info@islandpress.org
*Web Site:* www.islandpress.org
*Key Personnel*
Pres: Charles C Savitt
EVP & Publr: David Miller
VP, Sales & Mktg: Brian Weese
Exec Ed: Barbara Dean
Founded: 1984
Books about the environment for professionals, students & general readers, autobiography-scientific; land use planning; environmental economics; nature essays; "green" architecture.
ISBN Prefix(es): 978-0-933280; 978-1-55963; 978-1-59726; 978-1-61091
Number of titles published annually: 40 Print; 40 E-Book
Total Titles: 800 Print; 175 E-Book
Imprints: Shearwater Books
Distributor for Environmental Law Institute (ELI); IUCN; Techne Press
Foreign Rights: Angela Osborn
*Shipping Address:* University of Chicago Distribution Center, 11030 S Langley Ave, Chicago, IL 60628 *Tel:* 773-702-7000 *Toll Free Tel:* 800-621-2736 *Fax:* 773-702-7212 *Toll Free Fax:* 800-621-8476 *E-mail:* custserv@press.uchicago.edu
Membership(s): American Association of University Presses; BISG

**ISTE**, see International Society for Technology in Education

**§Italica Press**
595 Main St, Suite 605, New York, NY 10044
SAN: 695-1805
*Tel:* 917-371-0563 *Fax:* 212-838-7812
*E-mail:* info@italicapress.com
*Web Site:* www.italicapress.com
*Key Personnel*
Pres & Publr, Electronic Publg: Eileen Gardiner *E-mail:* egardiner@italicapress.com

Secy & Publr, Electronic Publg: Ronald G Musto
*E-mail:* rgmusto@italicapress.com
Founded: 1985
English translations of Latin & Italian works from the Middle Ages to the present.
ISBN Prefix(es): 978-0-934977; 978-1-59910
Number of titles published annually: 7 Print; 20 E-Book
Total Titles: 200 Print; 60 E-Book

**iUniverse**
Division of Author Solutions Inc
1663 Liberty Dr, Bloomington, IN 47403
*Toll Free Tel:* 800-AUTHORS (288-4677)
*Fax:* 812-355-4085
*Web Site:* www.iuniverse.com
*Key Personnel*
CEO: Andrew Phillips
CFO: Kevin G Gregory
SVP, Worldwide Sales: Don Seitz
SVP, Prodn Servs: Bill Becher
VP, Mktg: Keith Ogorek
Founded: 1999
iUniverse is the industry's leading book marketing, editorial services & supported self-publishing company. The iUniverse management team has extensive editorial & managerial experience with traditional publishers such as Random House, Wiley, Macmillan, Chronicle Books & Addison-Wesley. iUniverse maintains a strategic alliance with Chapters Indigo in Canada & titles accepted into the iUniverse Rising Star program are featured in a special collection on BarnesandNoble.com.
This publisher has indicated that 100% of their product line is author subsidized.
ISBN Prefix(es): 978-0-9665514; 978-1-58348; 978-0-9668591; 978-1-893652; 978-0-595
Number of titles published annually: 4,500 Print
Total Titles: 30,000 Print
*Distribution Center:* Baker & Taylor Inc
Ingram Book Group
Membership(s): AAP; Canadian Booksellers Association

**Jade Rabbit**, see Quite Specific Media Group Ltd

**§Jain Publishing Co**
PO Box 3523, Fremont, CA 94539
SAN: 213-6503
*Tel:* 510-659-8272 *Fax:* 510-659-0501
*E-mail:* mail@jainpub.com
*Web Site:* www.jainpub.com
*Key Personnel*
Pres & Publr: Mukesh Jain
Founded: 1989
College textbooks & supplements, professional & scholarly references, ebooks & elearning products & services.
ISBN Prefix(es): 978-0-89581; 978-0-87573
Number of titles published annually: 10 Print; 1 CD-ROM; 2 Online; 2 E-Book
Total Titles: 200 Print; 1 CD-ROM; 2 Online; 4 E-Book
Imprints: Asian Humanities Press

**JayJo Books LLC**
Subsidiary of The Guidance Group
303 Crossways Park Dr, Woodbury, NY 11797
*Tel:* 516-496-8492 *Toll Free Tel:* 800-999-6884
*Fax:* 516-496-4050 *Toll Free Fax:* 800-262-1886
*E-mail:* jayjobooks@guidance-group.com
*Web Site:* www.guidance-group.com; www.jayjo.com
*Key Personnel*
Publr: Ed Werz
Founded: 1992
Educational books to help parents, teachers & children cope with chronic illness, special needs & health education.
ISBN Prefix(es): 978-0-9639449; 978-1-891383
Number of titles published annually: 4 Print
Total Titles: 26 Print

**Jewish Lights Publishing**
Division of Longhill Partners Inc
Sunset Farm Offices, Rte 4, Woodstock, VT 05091
SAN: 134-5621
Mailing Address: PO Box 237, Woodstock, VT 05091
*Tel:* 802-457-4000 *Toll Free Tel:* 800-962-4544 (orders only) *Fax:* 802-457-4004
*E-mail:* sales@jewishlights.com
*Web Site:* www.jewishlights.com
*Key Personnel*
Publr & Ed-in-Chief: Stuart M Matlins
VP, Edit & Prodn: Emily Wichland
PR: Jennifer Rataj
Founded: 1990
General trade adult & children's books on spirituality, theology, philosophy, mysticism, women's studies, recovery/self-help/healing & history for people of all faiths & backgrounds.
ISBN Prefix(es): 978-1-879045; 978-1-58023
Number of titles published annually: 40 Print; 40 E-Book
Total Titles: 500 Print; 450 E-Book
Foreign Rep(s): Bayard-Novalis (Canada); Deep Books (Europe, UK); Disticor Direct (Canada); Pleroma Christian Supplies (Shirley Duthie) (New Zealand); Rainbow Books (Australia, New Zealand); Brian Scheiffer Agencies (South Africa)
Foreign Rights: The Deborah Harris Agency (Israel); Alexander Korzhenevski Agency (Russia); Andrew Nurnberg Associated Ltd (Hungary); Katia Schumer (Brazil); Christian Schweiger Agency (France, Germany); Susanna Zevi Agenzia Letteraria (Italy)
*Returns:* 28 River St, Windsor, VT 05089
*Distribution Center:* Baker & Taylor, 2550 W Tyvola Rd, Suite 300, Charlotte, NC 28217 *Tel:* 704-998-3100 *Web Site:* www.btol.com
Ingram Book Co, One Ingram Blvd, La Vergne, TN 37086 *Tel:* 615-793-5000 *Web Site:* www.ingrambook.com
New Leaf Distributing Co, 401 Thornton Rd, Lithia Springs, GA 30122-1577 *Tel:* 770-948-7845 *Fax:* 770-944-2313 *Web Site:* www.newleaf-dist.com

**Jewish Publication Society**
2100 Arch St, 2nd fl, Philadelphia, PA 19103
SAN: 201-0240
*Tel:* 215-832-0600 *Toll Free Tel:* 800-234-3151
*Fax:* 215-568-2017
*E-mail:* jewishbook@jps.org
*Web Site:* www.jps.org
*Key Personnel*
CEO & Ed: Barry L Schwartz
*E-mail:* bschwartz@jps.org
Mng Ed: Carol Hupping *E-mail:* chupping@jps.org
Bookkeeper: Trisha Lubrant
Founded: 1888
Books of Jewish interest.
ISBN Prefix(es): 978-0-8276
Number of titles published annually: 15 Print; 20 E-Book
Total Titles: 250 Print; 60 E-Book; 1 Audio
*Distribution Center:* Longleaf Services Inc, 116 S Boundary St, Chapel, NC 27514-3808 *Tel:* 919-966-7449 *Fax:* 919-962-2704
*E-mail:* customerservice@longleafservices.org
*Web Site:* www.longleafservices.org
Membership(s): Association of American University Presses

**§Jhpiego**
Affiliate of The Johns Hopkins University
1615 Thames St, Baltimore, MD 21231-3492
*Tel:* 410-537-1800 *Fax:* 410-537-1473
*E-mail:* info@jhpiego.net; orders@jhpiego.net
*Web Site:* www.jhpiego.org
*Key Personnel*
CEO & Pres: Leslie D Mancuso, PhD
COO: Edwin J Judd
CIO: Glenn R Strachan
VP, External Affs & Communs: Melody McCoy
Founded: 1973
Reproductive health, medical texts, family planning, maternal health, HIV/AIDS & cervical cancer prevention & treatment, infection prevention.
ISBN Prefix(es): 978-0-929817
Number of titles published annually: 5 Print
Total Titles: 80 Print; 4 CD-ROM

**The Jim Henson Co**
1416 N La Brea Ave, Hollywood, CA 90028
*Tel:* 323-802-1500 *Fax:* 323-802-1825
*Web Site:* www.henson.com
*Key Personnel*
Chmn: Brian Henson
CEO: Lisa Henson, Esq
COO & Pres: Peter Schube
CFO & EVP: Laurie Don
EVP, Busn & Legal Aff: Dan Scharf
EVP, Children's Entertainment: Halle Stanford
EVP, Global Dist: Richard Goldsmith
SVP, Admin: Joe Henderson
SVP, Global Consumer Prods: Melissa Segal
SVP, Mktg & PR: Nicole Goldman
VP, New Media: Allyson Smith
VP, Prodn Fin & Physical Prodn: Brittan Brown
Creative Supvr, JHCS: Peter Brooke
Founded: 1955
Humor, craft, coffee table, children's concept & storybooks, comic books, novelty books, activity & coloring books, children's book clubs, movie & TV tie-ins.
Number of titles published annually: 25 Print; 1 Audio
Total Titles: 400 Print
*Branch Office(s)*
37-18 Northern Blvd, Suite 400, Long Island City, NY 11101 *Tel:* 212-794-2400 *Fax:* 212-439-7452
Distributed by At a Glance; Walter Foster; Golden Books Family Entertainment; Grolier; KidsBooks; Penguin Group (USA) LLC; PK; Random House; Reader's Digest Children's Books; Running Press; Simon & Schuster
Foreign Rep(s): Bi Plano (Spain); Design Rights Intl (UK); Gaffney (Australia); Publishing Partner (Germany)

**§JIST Publishing**
Division of EMC Publishing
875 Montreal Way, St Paul, MN 55102
SAN: 240-2351
*Tel:* 317-613-4200 *Toll Free Tel:* 800-328-1452
*Toll Free Fax:* 800-328-4564
*E-mail:* educate@emcp.com
*Web Site:* jist.emcpublishingllc.com
*Key Personnel*
CEO & Pres: Steve Van Thornout
CFO: Joy Hoppe
Sr Acct Mgr: Bob Grilliot
Inside Sales Mgr: Athena Wampler
Trade Sales Mgr: Tom Doherty
*E-mail:* tdoherty@cardinalpub.com
Founded: 1981
Job search (resumes, cover letters, interviewing), career planning, job retention, occupational reference, assessment, self-help, career exploration, occupational information, character education, life skills, CD-ROMs & reference books, videos & software.
ISBN Prefix(es): 978-0-94278; 978-1-56370; 978-1-57112; 978-1-930780; 978-1-55864; 978-1-59357
Number of titles published annually: 50 Print; 2 CD-ROM; 20 E-Book; 1 Audio

Total Titles: 350 Print; 6 CD-ROM; 60 E-Book; 1 Audio
Imprints: JIST Life; JIST Works
Membership(s): IBPA, the Independent Book Publishers Association

**John Deere Publishing**
Division of Deere & Co
5440 Corporate Park Dr, Davenport, IA 52807
*Tel:* 309-765-4951 *Toll Free Tel:* 800-522-7448 (orders) *Fax:* 563-355-3690; 309-748-4083
*E-mail:* johndeerepublishing@johndeere.com
*Web Site:* www.deere.com
*Key Personnel*
Publr & IT Analyst: Shirley Parchert
*E-mail:* parchertshirley@johndeere.com
Founded: 1967
ISBN Prefix(es): 978-0-86691
Number of titles published annually: 8 Print
Total Titles: 27 Print
*Warehouse:* Quad City Consolidation, 2900 Research Pkwy, Davenport, IA 52806

**§The Johns Hopkins University Press**
Affiliate of The Johns Hopkins University
2715 N Charles St, Baltimore, MD 21218-4363
SAN: 202-7348
*Tel:* 410-516-6900; 410-516-6987 (journals outside US & CN) *Toll Free Tel:* 800-537-5487 (book orders & cust serv); 800-548-1784 (journal orders) *Fax:* 410-516-6968; 410-516-3866 (journal orders)
*E-mail:* hfscustserv@press.jhu.edu (cust serv); jrnlcirc@press.jhu.edu (journal orders)
*Web Site:* www.press.jhu.edu; muse.jhu.edu/about/subscriptions/index.html (Project Muse subns)
*Key Personnel*
Dir: Kathleen Keane *E-mail:* kk@press.jhu.edu
Dir, Devt: Jack Holmes *E-mail:* jmh@press.jhu.edu
Edit Dir: Greg Britton *E-mail:* gb@press.jhu.edu
Dir, Fin & Admin: Erik Smist *E-mail:* eas@press.jhu.edu
Dir, Mktg & Online Book Publg: Becky Brasington Clark *E-mail:* rbc@press.jhu.edu
Sales Dir: Tom Lovett *E-mail:* tjl@press.jhu.edu
Journals Publr: William M Breichner
*E-mail:* wmb@press.jhu.edu
Exec Ed: Vincent J Burke *E-mail:* vjb@press.jhu.edu; Jacqueline C Wehmueller
*E-mail:* jcwmueller@press.jhu.edu
Ed: Matthew McAdam *E-mail:* mxm@press.jhu.edu
Mng Ed: Juliana M McCarthy *E-mail:* jmm@press.jhu.edu
Sr Acqs Ed: Robert J Brugger *E-mail:* rbrugger@press.jhu.edu
Assoc Ed: Suzanne Flinchbaugh *E-mail:* skf@press.jhu.edu
Asst Ed: Greg Nicholl *E-mail:* gan@press.jhu.edu
Design & Prodn Mgr: John Cronin *E-mail:* jgc@press.jhu.edu
Fulfillment Opers Mgr: David Breier
*E-mail:* dgb@press.jhu.edu
Mgr, Info Systems: Stacey L Armstead
*E-mail:* sla@press.jhu.edu
Journals Mktg Mgr: Lisa Klose *E-mail:* llk@press.jhu.edu
Journals Subn Mgr: Alta H Anthony
*E-mail:* aha@press.jhu.edua
Publicity Mgr: Kathy Alexander *E-mail:* ka@press.jhu.edu
Rts Mgr: Kelly Rogers *E-mail:* klr@press.jhu.edu
Mktg & Sales Coord: Catherine Bergeron
*E-mail:* cab@press.jhu.edu
Journals Prodn Supvr: Carol Hamblen
*E-mail:* crh@press.jhu.edu
Trade Publicist: Christina Cheakalos
Ad: Karen L Willmes *E-mail:* klw@press.jhu.edu
Founded: 1878
Scholarly books, nonfiction of general interest, paperbacks, scholarly journals.
ISBN Prefix(es): 978-0-8018
Number of titles published annually: 200 Print
Total Titles: 3,200 Print; 5 Online; 795 E-Book
*Sales Office(s):* Collins-Terry Associates, 2031 N Craig St, Altadena, CA 91001, Contact: Alan Read *Fax:* 626-356-4630 *E-mail:* alanread@earthlink.net
Collins-Terry Associates, 247 Fourth St, Loft 402, Oakland, CA, Contact: David Terry
*Tel:* 510-813-9854 *Fax:* 510-465-7668
*E-mail:* dmterry@aol.com
Miller Trade Book Marketing, 363 W Erie St, Suite 7-E, Chicago, IL 60654, Contact: Bruce Miller *Tel:* 312-423-7880 *Fax:* 312-276-8109
*E-mail:* orders@millertrade.com
Book Traveler, Box 193, 1289 N Fordham Blvd, Chapel Hill, NC 27514, Contact: Roger Sauls *Tel:* 919-490-5656 *Fax:* 919-490-0297
*E-mail:* roger_165@msn.com
Collins-Terry Associates, 19216 SE 46 Place, Issaquah, WA 98027, Contact: Ted H Terry
*Tel:* 425-747-3411 *Fax:* 425-747-0366
*E-mail:* colterryassoc@aol.com
Distributor for Baylor University Press; The Brookings Institution Press; Catholic University of America Press; Center for Talented Youth; Georgetown University Press; Johns Hopkins Aids Service; Howard University Press; Maryland Historical Society; Resources for the Future; University of Massachusetts Press; University of Pennsylvania Museum; University of Pennsylvania Press; University of Washington Press; The University Press of Kentucky; Urban Institute Press; The Woodrow Wilson Center Press; World Resources Institute
Foreign Rep(s): Academic Book Promotions (Fred Hermans) (Benelux, Denmark, France, Iceland, Scandinavia); Apex Knowledge Sdn Bhd (Simon Tay) (Brunei, Malaysia); Aromix Books Co Ltd (Jane Lam) (Hong Kong); Avicenna Partnership Ltd (Bill Kennedy) (Bahrain, Egypt, Iran, Iraq, Kuwait, Lebanon, Libya, Oman, Qatar, Saudi Arabia, Sudan, Syria, United Arab Emirates, Yemen); Avicenna Partnership Ltd (Claire de Gruchy) (Algeria, Cyprus, Greece, Jordan, Malta, Morocco, Palestine, Tunisia, Turkey); CRW Books (Tony Sagun) (Philippines); Everest International Publishing Services (Wei Zhao) (China); Footprint Books Pty Ltd (Kate O'Reilly) (Australia, Fiji, New Zealand, Papua New Guinea); Peter Hodgkiss (North UK, Scotland); Josh Houston (Southern Wales, Southwest England); ICK Information Services (Mr Se-Yung Jun) (Korea); IGP Services Pte Ltd (Joseph Goh) (Cambodia, Indonesia, Laos, Myanmar, Singapore, Vietnam); Ewa Ledochowicz (Eastern Europe); Lexa Publishers' Representatives (Mical Moser) (Canada); Uwe Luedemann (Austria, Germany, Italy, Portugal, Spain, Switzerland); B K Norton (Ms Meihua Sun) (Taiwan); Provider of Contents & Information (Mr P C Tham) (Singapore); Rave Media (Rahul Srivastava) (India); Rockbook Inc (Japan); Sally Sharp (Northwest England); Robert Towers (Ireland, Northern Ireland); World Press (Saleem Malik) (Pakistan); Matthew Wright (London, Midlands); Yale Representation Ltd (UK); Zimpfer Books Latin America & the Caribbean (Cynthia Zimpfer) (Caribbean, Latin America, Mexico, South America)
Foreign Rights: Agenzia Letteraria (Italy); The Chinese Connection Agency (China); Du Ran Kim Agency (Korea); The English Agency (Japan); GRAL sp zoo (Poland); The Deborah Harris Agency (Israel); International Editors' Co (Spain); Japan Uni Agency (Japan); The Kalem Literary Agency (Turkey); La Nouvelle Agence (France); Tuttle-Mori Agency (Japan)
*Advertising Agency:* Welch, Mirabile & Co Inc
*Orders to:* PO Box 19966, Baltimore, MD 21211-0966
*Returns:* Hopkins Fulfillment Service, c/o Maple Press Co, Lebanon Distribution Ctr, PO Box 50370, Baltimore, MD 21211-4370
*Warehouse:* Lebanon Distribution Center, 704 Legionaire Dr, Fredricksburg, PA 17026
*Distribution Center:* Footprint Books Pty Ltd, 1/6-A Prosperity Parade, Warriewood, NSW 2102, Australia, Contact: Kate O'Reilly
*Tel:* (02) 9997 3973 *Fax:* (02) 9997 3185
*E-mail:* sales@footprint.com.au *Web Site:* www.footprint.com.au
United Publishers Services Ltd, 1-32-5 Higashi-Shinagawa, Shinagawa-Ku, Tokyo 140-0002, Japan *Tel:* (03) 5479 7251 *Fax:* (03) 5479 7307
*E-mail:* info@ups.co.jp
John Wiley & Sons Ltd, Distribution Ctr, One Oldlands Way, Bognor Regis, West Sussex PO22 9SA, United Kingdom *Tel:* (01243) 843294 *Fax:* (01243) 843296 *E-mail:* cs-books@wiley.co.uk
Membership(s): AAP; BISG

**Johnson Books**
Division of Big Earth Publishing
3005 Center Green Dr, Suite 225, Boulder, CO 80301
SAN: 201-0313
*Tel:* 303-443-9766 *Toll Free Tel:* 800-258-5830 *Fax:* 303-443-9687
*E-mail:* books@bigearthpublishing.com
*Web Site:* www.bigearthpublishing.com; www.johnsonbooks.com
*Key Personnel*
Publr & Mng Ed: Mira Perrizo *Tel:* 303-541-1511
*E-mail:* mperrizo@bigearthpublishing.com
Mktg Dir: Linda Doyle *Tel:* 303-541-1506
*E-mail:* ldoyle@bigearthpublishing.com
Founded: 1978
Hardcover & paperbound originals & reprints: nonfiction history, nature, archaeology, guidebooks, outdoors, travel, astronomy, American West, environment, Native American.
ISBN Prefix(es): 978-0-933472; 978-1-55566
Number of titles published annually: 20 Print
Total Titles: 160 Print
*Shipping Address:* 2650 S Juni St, Englewood, CO 80110
*Warehouse:* 2650 S Juni St, Englewood, CO 80110

**Jonathan David Publishers Inc**
68-22 Eliot Ave, Middle Village, NY 11379
SAN: 169-5274
*Tel:* 718-456-8611 *Fax:* 718-894-2818
*E-mail:* info@jdbooks.com; customerservice@jdbooks.com
*Web Site:* www.jdbooks.com
*Key Personnel*
Cont: Carol A Zelezny
Treas: Thelma R Kolatch
Pres & Ed-in-Chief: Alfred J Kolatch
VP, Sales & Mktg: Marvin Sekler
Edit Dir: David Kolatch
Admin Asst: Barbara Burke
Founded: 1948
Judaica reference & general.
ISBN Prefix(es): 978-0-8246
Number of titles published annually: 3 Print
Total Titles: 160 Print
Imprints: PenQuill Press
Distributor for American-Israeli Cooperative; Emet Publishers; Feldheim; IBS; JKAP Publications; Purity Press; Seraphic Press

**§Jones & Bartlett Learning LLC**
Division of Ascend Learning
5 Wall St, Burlington, MA 01803
*Tel:* 978-443-5000 *Toll Free Tel:* 800-832-0034 *Fax:* 978-443-8000
*E-mail:* info@jblearning.com
*Web Site:* www.jblearning.com
*Key Personnel*
Chmn of the Bd: Clayton E Jones
CEO: Ty Field
COO: Donald W Jones, Jr *E-mail:* djones@jbpub.com

Pres: James Homer
SVP & Chief Mktg Offr: Alison Pendergast
Founded: 1983
Seventh largest academic publisher.
ISBN Prefix(es): 978-0-86720; 978-0-7637
Number of titles published annually: 300 Print
Total Titles: 2,500 Print; 100 CD-ROM
*Foreign Office(s):* Jones & Bartlett Learning Intl, Express Park, Bristol Rd, Bridgewater, Somerset TA6 4RR, United Kingdom *Tel:* (01278) 427800 *Fax:* (01278) 421077 *E-mail:* jbeurope@jblearning.com
Foreign Rep(s): Academic Marketing Services Ltd (Michael Brightmore) (South Africa); Advanced Marketing Associates (Kevin Fong) (Malaysia, Singapore); BNC Publishers Services Inc (Nanette Beramo) (Guam, Philippines); Cengage Learning Asia Pte Ltd (Cambodia, Hong Kong, Indonesia, Laos, Vietnam); Merry Chang (Taiwan); Cranbury International LLC (Caribbean, South America); Elsevier Australia (Australia, Fiji, New Zealand); Benjamin Ho (China, Thailand); Impact Korea (ChongHo Ra) (South Korea); IPR (International Publishers Representatives) (Middle East); Jones & Bartlett India Pvt Ltd (Vinod Vasishtha) (Bangladesh, India, Sri Lanka); The White Partnership (Andrew White) (Japan); World Press (Saleem Malik) (Pakistan)
*Returns:* 905 Carlow Dr, Unit 5, Bolingbrook, IL 60490
*Warehouse:* 905 Carlow Dr, Unit B, Bollingbrook, IL 60490

**Jones McClure Publishing**
3131 Eastside St, Suite 300, Houston, TX 77098
Mailing Address: PO Box 3348, Houston, TX 77253-3348
*Tel:* 713-335-8200 *Toll Free Tel:* 800-626-6667 *Fax:* 713-335-8201
*E-mail:* comments@jonesmcclure.com
*Web Site:* www.jonesmcclure.com
*Key Personnel*
Pres: Baird Craft
Founded: 1992
Provides a comprehensive desk reference to the trial lawyer, through codes, commentaries & form covering several areas of Texas law & federal litigation, written in an easy to follow, plain English format.
ISBN Prefix(es): 978-1-884554
Number of titles published annually: 22 Print
Total Titles: 22 Print; 3 CD-ROM

**§Joshua Tree Publishing**
1016 W Jackson Blvd, Suite 500, Chicago, IL 60607
*Tel:* 312-893-7525
*E-mail:* info@joshuatreepublishing.com
*Web Site:* www.joshuatreepublishing.com; www.centaurbooks.com (imprint); www.chiralhouse.com (imprint)
*Key Personnel*
Pres & Publr: John Paul Owles *E-mail:* jpo@joshuatreepublishing.com
Founded: 1977
Believe in authors & dedicated to making the dream of being a published author a reality. Specialize in works that uplift the human spirit, inspire people to reach for higher goals & touch the hearts of readers.
ISBN Prefix(es): 978-0-9710954; 978-0-9778311; 978-0-9768677; 978-0-9845904; 978-0-982370; 978-0-9823703; 978-0-9829803
Number of titles published annually: 18 Print; 18 E-Book
Total Titles: 70 Print; 30 E-Book
Imprints: Centaur Books; Chiral House; Heroides Publishing; Joshua Tree Publishing
Membership(s): Book Publicists of Southern California; IBPA, the Independent Book Publishers Association

**Jossey-Bass**
Imprint of John Wiley & Sons Inc
One Montgomery St, Suite 1200, San Francisco, CA 94104
*Tel:* 415-433-1740 *Toll Free Tel:* 800-956-7739 *Fax:* 415-433-0499 (edit/mktg)
*Web Site:* www.josseybass.com; www.pfeiffer.com
*Key Personnel*
Dir, HR: Susan Call
Founded: 1966
General education, higher & adult education, management & business, human resources, training, health & health administration, social & behavioral sciences, psychology, conflict resolution, mediation & negotiation, religion, nonprofit & public management.
ISBN Prefix(es): 978-1-55542; 978-0-87589; 978-0-7879; 978-0-88390; 978-0-89384
Total Titles: 5,000 Print
Imprints: Pfeiffer
*Orders to:* John Wiley & Sons Inc, Customer Service, One Wiley Dr, Somerset, NJ 08875-1272 *Tel:* 732-469-4400 *Toll Free Tel:* 800-225-5945 *Fax:* 732-302-2300 *E-mail:* customer@wiley.com
*Returns:* John Wiley & Sons Inc, Customer Service, One Wiley Dr, Somerset, NJ 08875-1272 *Tel:* 732-469-4400 *Toll Free Tel:* 800-225-5945 *Fax:* 732-302-2300 *E-mail:* customer@wiley.com

**Journal of Roman Archaeology LLC**
95 Peleg Rd, Portsmouth, RI 02871
*Tel:* 401-683-1955 *Fax:* 401-683-1975
*E-mail:* jra@journalofromanarch.com
*Web Site:* www.journalofromanarch.com
*Key Personnel*
Publr & Gen Ed: John H Humphrey
Founded: 1988
Annual journal & supplementary series.
ISBN Prefix(es): 978-1-887829
Number of titles published annually: 6 Print
Total Titles: 96 Print

**§Joy Publishing Co**
Division of California Clock Co
PO Box 9901, Fountain Valley, CA 92708
SAN: 663-3544
*Tel:* 714-545-4321 *Toll Free Tel:* 800-454-8228 *Fax:* 714-708-2099
*Web Site:* www.joypublishing.com; www.kit-cat.com
*Key Personnel*
Pres: Woody Young *E-mail:* woody@joypublishing.com
Founded: 1986
Publish spiritual books.
ISBN Prefix(es): 978-0-939513
Number of titles published annually: 10 Print
Total Titles: 70 Print; 3 CD-ROM; 3 Online; 3 Audio
*Shipping Address:* 16060 Abajo Circle, Fountain Valley, CA 92708

**Joyce Media Inc**
3413 Soledad Canyon Rd, Acton, CA 93510-1974
Mailing Address: PO Box 57, Acton, CA 93510-0057
*Tel:* 661-269-1169 *Fax:* 661-269-2139
*E-mail:* help@joycemediainc.com
*Web Site:* www.joycemediainc.com
*Key Personnel*
Pres: John Joyce
Founded: 1968
General interest publications; specialize in sign language & newspapers.
ISBN Prefix(es): 978-0-913072
Number of titles published annually: 40 Print; 3 CD-ROM
Total Titles: 35 CD-ROM; 2 Online; 2 E-Book; 2 Audio

**Judaica Press Inc**
123 Ditmas Ave, Brooklyn, NY 11218
SAN: 204-9856
*Tel:* 718-972-6200 *Toll Free Tel:* 800-972-6201 *Fax:* 718-972-6204
*E-mail:* info@judaicapress.com; orders@judaicapress.com
*Web Site:* www.judaicapress.com
*Key Personnel*
Pres: Gloria Goldman
Mng Ed: Norman Shapiro *E-mail:* nshapiro@judaicapress.com
Founded: 1963
Classic & contemporary Jewish literature in Hebrew & English.
ISBN Prefix(es): 978-0-910818; 978-1-880582; 978-1-932443; 978-1-60763
Number of titles published annually: 25 Print; 6 E-Book
Total Titles: 400 Print; 12 E-Book
Imprints: Zahava Publications
Foreign Rep(s): Lehmanns (Europe, UK); Shanky's (Israel)

**Judson Press**
Division of American Baptist Churches in the USA
588 N Gulph Rd, King of Prussia, PA 19406
Mailing Address: PO Box 851, Valley Forge, PA 19482-0851 SAN: 201-0348
*Toll Free Tel:* 800-458-3766 *Fax:* 610-768-2107
*Web Site:* www.judsonpress.com
*Key Personnel*
Publr: Laura Alden *E-mail:* laura.alden@abhms.org
Mktg Dir: Linda Johnson-LeBlanc *Tel:* 610-768-2458 *E-mail:* linda.johnson-leblanc@abhms.org
Busn Mgr: Ronald Freeland
Ed: Rebecca Irwin-Diehl *Tel:* 610-768-2109 *E-mail:* rebecca.irwin-diehl@abhms.org
Founded: 1824
Religion (Baptist & nondenominational Christian), African American, women & multicultural; cloth & paperback.
ISBN Prefix(es): 978-0-8170
Number of titles published annually: 12 Print; 2 Audio
Total Titles: 350 Print; 1 CD-ROM; 2 Audio

**Jump at the Sun**
Imprint of Disney-Hyperion Books
114 Fifth Ave, New York, NY 10011
*Tel:* 212-633-4400 *Fax:* 212-633-4809
*Web Site:* disney.go.com
Founded: 1998
Books celebrating the African-American experience & culture.
ISBN Prefix(es): 978-0-7868
Number of titles published annually: 2 Print; 2 E-Book
Total Titles: 100 Print; 100 E-Book

**Jungle Wagon Press**
5116 Didier Ave, Rockford, IL 61101
SAN: 920-6426
*Tel:* 815-988-9048
*E-mail:* junglewagonpress@gmail.com
*Web Site:* www.junglewagonpress.com
*Key Personnel*
Owner: Angela Malavolti
Founded: 2011
Provides publishing services including editing, professional illustrations, design, ISBN, copyright, printing & marketing. Specialize in high quality children's picture books, often with an educational element.
This publisher has indicated that 80% of their product line is author subsidized.
ISBN Prefix(es): 978-0-9834092
Number of titles published annually: 3 Print
Total Titles: 5 Print

**JustUs & Associates**
1420 NW Gilman Blvd, Suite 2154, Issaquah, WA 98027-7001
*Tel:* 425-392-0897
*E-mail:* sales@horary.com
*Web Site:* www.horary.com
*Key Personnel*
Pres: Carol A Wiggers
Founded: 1983
Periodicals & journals on astrology.
ISBN Prefix(es): 978-1-878935
Number of titles published annually: 50 Print
Total Titles: 150 Print

**§Kabbalah Publishing**
1100 S Robertson Blvd, Los Angeles, CA 90035
*Tel:* 310-601-1039; 310-657-7957
*E-mail:* kcla@kabbalah.com; customerservice@kabbalahpublishing.com
*Web Site:* www.kabbalah.com; www.kabbalahpublishing.com
*Key Personnel*
Busn Devt Mgr: Melissa Knight *Tel:* 310-601-1006 *E-mail:* melissa.knight@kabbalah.com
Founded: 2002
Dedicated to bringing the world's oldest & deepest treasury of spiritual wisdom.
ISBN Prefix(es): 978-157-189; 978-0-943-688; 978-0-924-457
Number of titles published annually: 15 Print; 2 CD-ROM; 2 Online; 2 E-Book; 2 Audio
Total Titles: 35 Print; 3 CD-ROM; 2 Online; 4 E-Book; 4 Audio
Foreign Rights: Kabbalah Agency (Worldwide)

**Kaeden Corp**
PO Box 16190, Rocky River, OH 44116-0190
*Tel:* 440-617-1400 *Toll Free Tel:* 800-890-7323 *Fax:* 440-617-1403
*E-mail:* info@kaeden.com
*Web Site:* www.kaeden.com
*Key Personnel*
Pres: Craig Urmston *E-mail:* curmston@kaeden.com
Ed: Lisa Stenger *E-mail:* lstenger@kaeden.com
Founded: 1986
Books for emergent, early & fluent readers, grades K, 1, 2 & 3, reading recovery & guided reading programs.
ISBN Prefix(es): 978-1-879835; 978-1-57874
Number of titles published annually: 16 Print
Total Titles: 300 Print; 7 CD-ROM; 72 E-Book; 7 Audio
Imprints: Kaeden Books
Membership(s): AAP; American Educational Publishers; International Reading Association; National Council of Teachers of English; Reading Recovery Council of North America

**Kamehameha Publishing**
Division of Kamehameha Schools
567 S King St, Suite 118, Honolulu, HI 96813
*Toll Free Tel:* 800-523-6200 *Fax:* 808-541-5305
*E-mail:* publishing@ksbe.edu
*Web Site:* kamehamehapublishing.org
*Key Personnel*
Dir: Kehaunani Abad, PhD
Mng Ed: Matthew Corry *Tel:* 808-523-6267
Founded: 1933
Book, journal & poster publishing in the areas of Hawaiian history, Hawaiian studies, Hawaiian language & Hawaiian culture.
ISBN Prefix(es): 978-0-87336
Number of titles published annually: 12 Print
Total Titles: 100 Print
Imprints: Kamehameha Publishing; Kamehameha Schools Press
Distributed by Islander Group
Membership(s): The Association of Publishers for Special Sales; Hawaii Book Publishers Association; IBPA, the Independent Book Publishers Association

**Kane Miller Books**
Division of Educational Development Corp
4901 Morena Blvd, Suite 213, San Diego, CA 92117
SAN: 295-8945
*E-mail:* info@kanemiller.com
*Web Site:* www.kanemiller.com
*Key Personnel*
Publr: Kira Lynn
Mktg: Lynn Kelley
Founded: 1984
Juvenile picture books & middle grade fiction from around the world.
ISBN Prefix(es): 978-0-916291; 978-1-929132; 978-1-933605; 978-1-61067
Number of titles published annually: 60 Print
Total Titles: 250 Print
*Warehouse:* Educational Development Corp, 10302 E 55 Place, Tulsa, OK 74146
*Distribution Center:* Ingram Book Co (Canada)
Membership(s): ABA; ALA; Association of Booksellers for Children; United States Board on Books for Young People

**Kane Press Inc**
350 Fifth Ave, Suite 7206, New York, NY 10118-7200
*Tel:* 212-268-1435
*E-mail:* info@kanepress.com
*Web Site:* www.kanepress.com
*Key Personnel*
Publr: Joanne E Kane *E-mail:* jkane@kanepress.com
Sr Ed: Juliana Hanford *E-mail:* project4@kanepress.com
Cust Serv Mgr: Nadia Di Mattia *E-mail:* ndimattia@kanepress.com
Founded: 1996
Publishes books for children ages 3 to 11, including picture books & first chapter books.
ISBN Prefix(es): 978-1-57565
Number of titles published annually: 12 Print; 12 E-Book; 15 Audio
Total Titles: 186 Print; 124 E-Book; 41 Audio
*Sales Office(s):* Lerner Publishing Group, 241 First Ave N, Minneapolis, MN 55401-1607, VP & Dir, Sales: David Wexler *Toll Free Tel:* 800-328-4929 *Toll Free Fax:* 800-332-1132 *Web Site:* www.lernerbooks.com
Distributed by Lerner Publishing Group
*Orders to:* Lerner Publishing Group, 1251 Washington Ave N, Minneapolis, MN 55401-1036 *Toll Free Tel:* 800-328-4929 *Toll Free Fax:* 800-332-1132 *Web Site:* www.lernerbooks.com
*Returns:* Lerner Publishing Group, 1251 Washington Ave N, Minneapolis, MN 55401-1036 *Toll Free Tel:* 800-328-4929 *Toll Free Fax:* 800-332-1132 *Web Site:* www.lernerbooks.com
*Warehouse:* Lerner Publishing, 1251 Washington Ave N, Minneapolis, MN 55401 *Toll Free Tel:* 800-328-4929 *Toll Free Fax:* 800-332-1132 *Web Site:* www.lernerbooks.com
*Distribution Center:* Lerner Publishing Group, 1251 Washington Ave N, Minneapolis, MN 55401-1036 *Toll Free Tel:* 800-328-4929 *Toll Free Fax:* 800-332-1132 *Web Site:* www.lernerbooks.com
Membership(s): Educational Book & Media Association; International Reading Association; NAIPR; National Council for the Social Studies; National Council of Teachers of Mathematics; National Science Teachers Association

**Kaplan Publishing**
Unit of Kaplan Inc
395 Hudson St, 4th fl, New York, NY 10014
*Tel:* 212-618-2400 *Toll Free Tel:* 888-KAPLAN8 (527-5268) *Fax:* 917-344-2499 *Toll Free Fax:* 877-712-5487
*E-mail:* book.support@kaplan.com
*Web Site:* www.kaplanpublishing.com
*Key Personnel*
Chmn & CEO: Andrew S Rosen
Pres & Publr: Maureen McMahon
SVP, Mktg: Melissa Mack
VP, Learning Serv: Allison Risko
Assoc Dir, Digital Opers: Shayna Webb
Info Architect: Edwina Lui
Publisher of academic & professional development resources. Produce more than 150 new titles annually in the areas of medical, nursing, legal & education interest, test preparation, college & graduate school admissions, academic & professional development. Additional subjects are medical & legal history. Provides test prep materials for a variety of standard tests, including GRE, GMAT, LSAT, SAT, MCAT, TOEFL & more.
ISBN Prefix(es): 978-0-7931; 978-0-684; 978-0-7432; 978-1-57410; 978-0-936894; 978-1-4195; 978-1-4277; 978-0-9727; 978-1-60373
Number of titles published annually: 430 Print; 325 E-Book
Total Titles: 550 Print; 4 CD-ROM; 60 Online; 325 E-Book
Distributed by Simon & Schuster (S&S standard freight, credit, payment & returns policies apply)
Foreign Rep(s): Simon & Schuster (Asia exc Philippines, Canada, Central Europe, Eastern Europe, India, Ireland, Middle East, Scandinavia, UK)
*Warehouse:* Simon & Schuster, 100 Front St, Riverside, NJ 08075 *Toll Free Tel:* 800-223-2336 (cust serv)

**Kapp Books LLC**
3602 Rocky Meadow Ct, Fairfax, VA 22033
*Tel:* 703-261-9171 *Fax:* 703-621-7162
*E-mail:* info@kappbooks.com
*Web Site:* www.kappbooks.com
*Key Personnel*
Mng Dir: Parveen Ahuja
Founded: 2006
ISBN Prefix(es): 978-1-60346
Number of titles published annually: 100 Print
Total Titles: 350 Print; 10 CD-ROM
Membership(s): IBPA, the Independent Book Publishers Association

**Kar-Ben Publishing**
Division of Lerner Publishing Group Inc
241 First Ave N, Minneapolis, MN 55401
*Tel:* 612-332-3344 *Toll Free Tel:* 800-4-KARBEN (452-7236) *Fax:* 612-332-7615 *Toll Free Fax:* 800-332-1132
*Web Site:* www.karben.com
*Key Personnel*
Chmn: Harry J Lerner
Pres: Adam Lerner
Publr: Joni Sussman *E-mail:* jsussman@karben.com
Rts Dir: Maria Kjoller
Founded: 1976
Jewish books, calendars & cassettes; preschool & primary, activity books, holiday books, folktales, services.
ISBN Prefix(es): 978-1-58013
Total Titles: 240 Print; 175 E-Book
Foreign Rep(s): Bravo (UK); Mazeltov Books (Australia)
*Warehouse:* Lerner Publishing Group, 1251 Washington Ave N, Minneapolis, MN 55401

**Kazi Publications Inc**
3023 W Belmont Ave, Chicago, IL 60618
*Tel:* 773-267-7001 *Fax:* 773-267-7002
*E-mail:* info@kazi.org
*Web Site:* www.kazi.org
*Key Personnel*
Pres: Liaquat Ali
Mktg Dir: Mary Bakhtiar
Founded: 1972

Nonprofit organization; print, publish & distribute; Islamic books in Arabic, English & Urdu language.
ISBN Prefix(es): 978-0-935782; 978-1-56744; 978-0-933511; 978-1-871031
Number of titles published annually: 30 Print; 6 E-Book
Total Titles: 401 Print
Imprints: ABC Intl Group Inc; Abjad Books; Library of Islam
Distributor for Foundation for Traditional Studies; Great Books of the Islamic World; Islamic Foundation

**§J J Keller & Associates, Inc**
3003 Breezewood Lane, Neenah, WI 54957
Mailing Address: PO Box 368, Neenah, WI 54957-0368
*Tel:* 920-722-2848 *Toll Free Tel:* 877-564-2333 *Toll Free Fax:* 800-727-7516
*E-mail:* sales@jjkeller.com
*Web Site:* www.jjkeller.com/jjk
*Key Personnel*
Chmn: Robert L Keller
CEO & Pres: Jim Keller
VP, Strategy & Busn Planning: Marne Keller-Krikava
Promos Mgr: Tom Hines
Founded: 1953
Publish regulatory compliance, "best practices" & training products dealing with occupational safety, job safety, environment & industry & motor-carrier (trucking) operations. On demand, print, CD-ROM, intranet & Internet formats.
ISBN Prefix(es): 978-1-57943; 978-0-934674; 978-1-877798
Number of titles published annually: 4 Print
Total Titles: 300 Print; 100 CD-ROM
*Branch Office(s)*
7273 State Rd 76, Neenah, WI 54956-9614
*Sales Office(s):* 1315 Gillingham Rd, Neenah, WI 54956-4503
600 S Nicolet Rd, Appleton, WI 54914-8285
700 N Lynndale Dr, Appleton, WI 54914-3019
Distributed by AMACOM Books
Distributor for Chilton Book Co; International Air Transport Association; National Archives & Records Administration; National Institute of Occupational Safety & Health; Office of the Federal Register; Research & Special Programs Administration of the US Department of Transportation; John Wiley & Sons Inc

**Kelsey Street Press**
2824 Kelsey St, Berkeley, CA 94705
*Tel:* 510-845-2260 *Fax:* 510-548-9185
*E-mail:* info@kelseyst.com
*Web Site:* www.kelseyst.com
*Key Personnel*
Founding Ed: Patricia Dienstfrey; Rena Rosenwasser
Off Mgr: Ramsay Breslin
Founded: 1974
Nonprofit press, publish experimental poetry & short fiction by women & collaborations between poets & artists.
ISBN Prefix(es): 978-0-932716
Number of titles published annually: 3 Print
Total Titles: 45 Print
*Orders to:* Small Press Distribution, 1341 Seventh St, Berkeley, CA 94710 (contact Small Press Distribution for large orders) *Tel:* 510-524-1668 *Toll Free Tel:* 800-869-7553 *E-mail:* orders@spdbooks.org *Web Site:* www.spdbooks.org
Membership(s): Council of Literary Magazines & Presses

**Kendall/Hunt Publishing Co**
4050 Westmark Dr, Dubuque, IA 52002-2624
SAN: 203-9184
Mailing Address: PO Box 1840, Dubuque, IA 52004-1840
*Tel:* 563-589-1000 *Toll Free Tel:* 800-228-0810 (orders) *Fax:* 563-589-1046 *Toll Free Fax:* 800-772-9165
*E-mail:* orders@kendallhunt.com
*Web Site:* www.kendallhunt.com
*Key Personnel*
Chmn & CEO: Mark C Falb
COO & Pres: Chad M Chandlee
VP, Opers: Tim Beitzel
VP, Higher Educ Div: David Tart
VP, K-12 Div: Charles Cook
Founded: 1969
Higher education custom publishing, K-12 math & science.
ISBN Prefix(es): 978-0-8403; 978-0-7872; 978-0-7575
Number of titles published annually: 1,500 Print; 200 Online
Total Titles: 6,500 Print; 10 CD-ROM; 5,500 Online; 6,500 E-Book
*Warehouse:* 7200 Chavenelle Dr, Dubuque, IA 52002
Membership(s): ASCD; International Reading Association; National Council of Supervisors of Mathematics; National Council of Teachers of Mathematics; National Science Teachers Association

**Kennedy Information Inc**
Division of Bureau of National Affairs (BNA)
One Phoenix Mill Lane, 3rd fl, Peterborough, NH 03458
*Tel:* 603-924-0900; 603-924-1006 *Toll Free Tel:* 800-531-0007 *Fax:* 603-924-4460
*E-mail:* bookstore@kennedyinfo.com; customerservice@kennedyinfo.com
*Web Site:* www.kennedyinfo.com
*Key Personnel*
COO: Daniel Houder *Tel:* 603-924-0900 ext 673 *E-mail:* dhouder@kennedyinfo.com
Founded: 1970
Newsletters, special reports, books, directories of management consultants, executive recruiters & outplacement consultants.
ISBN Prefix(es): 978-0-916654; 978-1-885922
Number of titles published annually: 20 Print; 1 CD-ROM; 3 Online
Total Titles: 50 Print; 1 CD-ROM
Imprints: Consultants News; Consulting Magazine; Executive Recruiter News; Management Consultant International; Recruiting Trends
Foreign Rights: Consultants News; Consulting Magazine; Executive Recruiter News; Management Consultant International; Recruiting Trends

**Kensington Publishing Corp**
119 W 40 St, New York, NY 10018
SAN: 207-9860
*Tel:* 212-407-1500 *Toll Free Tel:* 800-221-2647 *Fax:* 212-935-0699
*Web Site:* www.kensingtonbooks.com
*Key Personnel*
CEO & Pres: Steven Zacharius
CFO: Michael Rosamilia
VP & Publr: Laurie Parkin
Edit Dir: Audrey La Fehr
Edit Dir, Brava Books: Alicia Condon
Ed-in-Chief, Citadel Press: Michaela Hamilton
Ed-in-Chief, Kensington: John Scognamiglio
Exec Ed: Gary Goldstein; Selena James
Sr Ed: Esi Sogah
Assoc Ed: Peter Senftleben
Asst Ed: Martin Biro
Creative Dir: Janice Rossi
Digital Mktg Dir: Alex Nicolajsen
Dir, Mktg: Lesleigh Irish-Underwood
Dir, Publicity & PR: Karen Auerbach
Info Technol Dir: Jonathan Cohen
Prodn Dir: Joyce Kaplan
Subs Rts Dir: Meryl Earl
Assoc Dir, Sales: Darla Freeman
Asst Dir, Publicity: Vida Engstrand
Foreign Rts Mgr: Jackie Dinas
Gen Coun: Barbara Bennett
Cust Serv: Guy Chapman
Founded: 1975
Mass market paperback originals including thillers & men's adventure.
ISBN Prefix(es): 978-0-89083; 978-0-8217
Number of titles published annually: 500 Print
Total Titles: 9,000 Print
Imprints: Aphrodisia; Brava; Citadel; Dafina; Kensington Books; KTeen; Pinnacle Books; Zebra Books
Distributed by Hachette Book Group USA; Penguin Group (USA) LLC
Distributor for Genesis Press; Marimba Books; New Horizon Press; Urban Books; Vibe Books
Foreign Rights: Agenzia Letteraria Internazionale (Italy); Big Apple Agency Inc (China); The Book Publishers' Association of Israel, International Promotion & Literary Rights Dept (Israel); Graal Literary Agency (Poland); International Editors' Co (Latin America, Mexico); International Literatuur Bureau (ILB) (Netherlands); Maxima Creative Agency (Santo Manurung) (Indonesia); La Nouvelle Agence (France); Andrew Nurnberg Associates (Tatjana Zoldnere) (Baltic States); Andrew Nurnberg Associates (Judit Hermann) (Croatia, Hungary); Andrew Nurnberg Literary Agency (Ludmilla Sushkova) (Russia); Kristin Olson Literary Agency SRO (Czech Republic, Slovakia); ONK Agency Ltd (Turkey); Read n Right Agency (Greece); Lennart Sane Agency AB (Scandinavia); Karin Schindler (Brazil); Thomas Schlueck GmbH (Germany); Shin Won Agency Co (Korea); Tuttle-Mori Agency Inc (Japan, Thailand)
*Warehouse:* Penguin Group (USA) LLC, Pittston, PA
*Distribution Center:* Pearson Canada Distribution Centre, 195 Henry Walker Pkwy, Newmarket, ON L3Y 74B, Canada *Tel:* 905-858-7888 *Fax:* 905-853-7865 *Web Site:* www.pearsoned.ca

**Kent State University Press**
1118 University Library Bldg, 1125 Risman Dr, Kent, OH 44242
SAN: 201-0437
Mailing Address: PO Box 5190, Kent, OH 44242-0001
*Tel:* 330-672-7913; 419-281-1802 *Fax:* 330-672-3104
*E-mail:* ksupress@kent.edu
*Web Site:* www.kentstateuniversitypress.com
*Key Personnel*
Dir & Rts & Perms: Will Underwood *E-mail:* wunderwo@kent.edu
Journals Mgr: Carol Heller *Tel:* 330-672-8090 *E-mail:* cheller1@kent.edu
Mktg Mgr: Susan L Cash *Tel:* 330-672-8097 *E-mail:* scash@kent.edu
Acquiring Ed: Joyce Harrison *Tel:* 330-672-8099 *E-mail:* jharri18@kent.edu
Founded: 1965
Scholarly nonfiction, with emphasis on Civil War, military history, literary studies, archaeology, biography & Midwest regional.
ISBN Prefix(es): 978-0-87338; 978-1-60635
Number of titles published annually: 35 Print; 35 E-Book
Total Titles: 700 Print; 150 E-Book
Imprints: Black Squirrel Books
Foreign Rep(s): East-West Export Books (Asia, Australia, The Pacific); Eurospan Ltd (Africa, Europe, Middle East, UK); Scholarly Book Services (Canada)
*Orders to:* Bookmasters, 30 Amberwood Pkwy, Ashland, OH 44805, Contact: Elaine Lattanzi *Tel:* 419-281-1802 *Toll Free Tel:* 800-247-6553 *Fax:* 419-281-6883

*Returns:* Bookmasters, 30 Amberwood Pkwy, Ashland, OH 44805, Contact: Elaine Lattanzi *Tel:* 419-281-1802 *Toll Free Tel:* 800-247-6553 *Fax:* 419-281-6883
*Warehouse:* Bookmasters, 30 Amberwood Pkwy, Ashland, OH 44805, Contact: Elaine Lattanzi *Tel:* 419-281-1802 *Toll Free Tel:* 800-247-6553 *Fax:* 419-281-6883
*Distribution Center:* Bookmasters, 30 Amberwood Pkwy, Ashland, OH 44805, Contact: Elaine Lattanzi *Tel:* 419-281-1802 *Toll Free Tel:* 800-247-6553 *Fax:* 419-281-6883
Membership(s): ABA; American Association of University Presses

**Kessinger Publishing LLC**
PO Box 1404, Whitefish, MT 59937
*E-mail:* books@kessingerpub.com
*Web Site:* www.kessinger.net
*Key Personnel*
Pres: Roger A Kessinger
Founded: 1988
Alchemy, free masonry, ancient civilization, astrology, Bible study, comparative religion, Egyptology, esotericism, gnosticism, health, hermetics, magic, metaphysical, mysticism, Rosicrucian.
ISBN Prefix(es): 978-0-922802; 978-1-56459; 978-0-7661; 978-1-4192; 978-1-4191
Number of titles published annually: 5,000 Print; 5,000 E-Book
Imprints: Kessinger Publishing®

**§Key Curriculum, A McGraw-Hill Education Company**
1150 65 St, Emeryville, CA 94608
*Tel:* 510-595-7000 *Toll Free Tel:* 800-995-6284 *Fax:* 510-595-7040 (orders) *Toll Free Fax:* 800-541-2442
*Web Site:* www.keycurriculum.com
*Key Personnel*
CEO: Karen Coe *Tel:* 510-595-7000 ext 152
VP, Fin & Acctg: Joel Gingold
Publr: Steven Rasmussen *Tel:* 510-595-7000 ext 132
Founded: 1971 (as Key Curriculum Project)
High school & middle school, math & science textbooks, software, supplementals & manipulatives.
ISBN Prefix(es): 978-0-913684; 978-1-55953
Number of titles published annually: 125 Print; 20 CD-ROM
Total Titles: 550 Print; 20 CD-ROM; 6 Online
Subsidiaries: KCP Technologies Inc
Foreign Rep(s): Business Advantage Development (Denmark, Finland, Norway, Sweden); Chartwell-Yorke Mathematics Software & Books (England, Northern Ireland, Scotland); Creative Learning Systems (South Africa); Michael deVilliers (South Africa); Dreyfous & Association (Dominican Republic, Puerto Rico); EdSoft (Australia, New Zealand); Grupo Editorial Iberoamerica (Latin America); Instituto Tecnologico de Costa Rico (ITCR) (Costa Rica); Learning Interactive Pte Ltd (Brunei, Indonesia, Malaysia, Singapore, Thailand); McGraw-Hill Ryerson Limited (Canada); Media Direct (Italy); QED Books (England, Northern Ireland, Scotland); Rhombus (Belgium); Sigma Communications Ltd (West Indies); Spectrum Educational Supplies Ltd (Canada); Springer-Verlag GmbH & Co (Europe exc UK, India, Middle East); Springer-Verlag H K Ltd (Brunei, China, Indonesia, Malaysia, Philippines, South Korea, Thailand, Vietnam); Springer-Verlag Iberia SA (Portugal, Spain); Springer-Verlag Tokyo/Eastern Book Service (Japan); Tec-Quest SA (Mexico); Virtual Image (Australia, New Zealand); W&G Australia Pty Ltd
Foreign Rights: Centre for Educational Technology (Israel); Cheneliere/McGraw-Hill (Canada (French-speaking)); Institute of New Technologies in Education (Russia); JasonTech Inc (Korea); L&R Uddannelse (Denmark); Mathlove (Korea); People's Education Press (China); Pliroforiki Technognosia (Greece); Yano Electric Co Ltd (Japan)
Membership(s): National Council of Teachers of Mathematics

**Kidsbooks LLC**
312 Stuart St, Boston, MA 02116
SAN: 666-3729
*Tel:* 617-425-0300 *Fax:* 617-425-0232
*E-mail:* sales@kidsbooks.com; customerservice@kidsbooks.com
*Web Site:* www.kidsbooks.com
*Key Personnel*
CEO & Foreign Rts Agent: Dan Blau
Founded: 1987
Juvenile & young adult trade & mass market paperback & hardcover & Search & Find Board Books, novelty books. Branch office in Boston, MA.
ISBN Prefix(es): 978-0-942025; 978-1-56156; 978-1-58865
Number of titles published annually: 100 Print
Total Titles: 3,000 Print
Imprints: KidsBooks; Learning Challenge; Masterwork Books
Foreign Rep(s): Trish Pugsley (Western Europe)
Foreign Rights: Dan Blau; Mauricio Placencia (Mexico, South America)

**Jessica Kingsley Publishers Inc**
400 Market St, Suite 400, Philadelphia, PA 19106
SAN: 256-2391
*Tel:* 215-922-1161 *Toll Free Tel:* 866-416-1078 (cust serv) *Fax:* 215-922-1474
*E-mail:* orders@jkp.com
*Web Site:* www.jkp.com
*Key Personnel*
VP, Sales & Mktg: Laurie Schesinger
Mktg Mgr: Tony Schiavo *E-mail:* tony.schiavo@jkp.com
Founded: 2004
Publish books for the consumer on Autism Spectrum Disorders & related developmental disorders; books for professionals in expressive arts therapies: art, music, drama & dance & social work; books on Tai Chi & Quigong.
ISBN Prefix(es): 978-1-85302; 978-1-84310
Number of titles published annually: 150 Print
Total Titles: 1,800 Print
Imprints: Singing Dragon
*Foreign Office(s):* 116 Pentonville Rd, London N1 9JB, United Kingdom, Contact: Dee Brigham *Tel:* (020) 7833 2307 *Fax:* (020) 7837 2917 *E-mail:* post@jkp.com
Foreign Rep(s): Asia Publishers Services (China, Korea, Philippines, Taiwan); Book Promotions (South Africa); Footprint Book (Australia, New Zealand); Publishers Marketing Services (Indonesia, Malaysia, Singapore); STM Pte Ltd (Thailand); UBC (Canada); United Publishers Services (Japan); Viva Marketing (India)

**Kinship Books**
781 Rte 308, Rhinebeck, NY 12572
*Tel:* 845-876-5840 (orders)
*E-mail:* kinshipbooks@cs.com
*Web Site:* www.kinshipny.com
*Key Personnel*
Owner: Susan Kelly Fitzgerald
Founded: 1967
Books of genealogical source information, histories, directory & journals.
ISBN Prefix(es): 978-1-56012
Number of titles published annually: 5 Print
Total Titles: 240 Print

**Kirk House Publishers**
PO Box 390759, Minneapolis, MN 55439
*Tel:* 952-835-1828 *Toll Free Tel:* 888-696-1828 *Fax:* 952-835-2613
*E-mail:* publisher@kirkhouse.com
*Web Site:* www.kirkhouse.com
*Key Personnel*
Publr: Leonard Flachman
Founded: 1994
ISBN Prefix(es): 978-1-886513; 978-1-932688; 978-1-933794
Number of titles published annually: 15 Print; 3 E-Book
Total Titles: 300 Print; 30 E-Book; 4 Audio
Imprints: Lutheran University Press; Quill House Publishers
Membership(s): IBPA, the Independent Book Publishers Association; Midwest Independent Publishers Association

**§Kirkbride Bible Co Inc**
1102 Deloss St, Indianapolis, IN 46203
Mailing Address: PO Box 606, Indianapolis, IN 46206-0606
*Tel:* 317-633-1900 *Toll Free Tel:* 800-428-4385 *Fax:* 317-633-1444
*E-mail:* sales@kirkbride.com; info@kirkbride.com
*Web Site:* www.kirkbride.com
*Key Personnel*
Pres: Michael Gage
Founded: 1915
Bible publisher, also children's Bible.
ISBN Prefix(es): 978-0-88707
Number of titles published annually: 5 Print
Total Titles: 7 Print; 3 CD-ROM
*Advertising Agency:* Canal Advertising

**Kiva Publishing Inc**
10 Bella Loma, Santa Fe, NM 87506
*Tel:* 909-896-0518
*E-mail:* kivapub@aol.com
*Web Site:* www.kivapub.com
*Key Personnel*
Publr: Stephen W Hill
Founded: 1993
Publish Native American & Southwest regional books & cards.
ISBN Prefix(es): 978-1-885772
Number of titles published annually: 3 Print
Total Titles: 40 Print
Membership(s): The Association of Publishers for Special Sales; IBPA, the Independent Book Publishers Association; New Mexico Publishers Association; Publishers Association of the West

**Klutz**
Division of Scholastic Corp
450 Lambert Ave, Palo Alto, CA 94306
*Tel:* 650-857-0888 *Toll Free Tel:* 800-737-4123 *Fax:* 650-857-9110
*E-mail:* thefolks@klutz.com
*Web Site:* www.klutz.com
*Key Personnel*
Founder: John Cassidy
Mktg Asst: Leslie Kostka *E-mail:* leslie_kostka@klutz.com
Founded: 1977
Creator of innovative activity products for kids that stimulate growth through creativity. Klutz products combine clear instructions with everything you need to give kids a hands-on experience ranging from the artistic to the scientific & beyond.
ISBN Prefix(es): 978-0-932592; 978-1-57054; 978-1-878257; 978-1-59174
Number of titles published annually: 14 Print
Total Titles: 150 Print
Foreign Rep(s): Catapulta Children's Entertainment SA (South America); Novelty Corp (Central America); Scholastic (Australia, Canada, Hong Kong, New Zealand, UK)
*Warehouse:* 2931 E McCarty St, Jefferson City, MO 65111

**Kluwer Law International (KLI)**, see Wolters Kluwer Law & Business

**§Wolters Kluwer Law & Business**
Formerly Aspen Publishers Inc
Subsidiary of Wolters Kluwer
76 Ninth Ave, 7th fl, New York, NY 10011-5201
SAN: 203-4999
*Tel:* 212-771-0600 *Toll Free Tel:* 800-234-1660 (cust serv); 800-638-8437 (orders); 800-317-3113 (bookstore sales) *Toll Free Fax:* 800-901-9075 (cust serv); 800-561-4845 (bookstore sales)
*Web Site:* www.aspenpublishers.com
*Key Personnel*
CEO & Pres: Robert Lemmond
Chief Mktg Offr: Alan Scott
VP, Busn Devt: Aaron Yaverski
VP, Corp & Govt: Paul Gibson
VP, Fin: Susan Pikitch
VP, Legal Mkts: Bob Lemmond
VP, Opers & IT: Gustavo Dobles
Founded: 1959
Publisher of legal, business & health care titles for professionals. Publishes more than 500 journals, newsletters, electronic products & loose-leaf manuals & has more than 1000 active professional & textbook titles.
ISBN Prefix(es): 978-0-89443; 978-0-912862; 978-0-912654; 978-0-8342; 978-1-56706; 978-0-87094; 978-0-87189; 978-0-471; 978-0-316
Number of titles published annually: 100 Print; 16 CD-ROM; 55 Online
Total Titles: 1,500 Print; 107 CD-ROM; 55 Online; 1 Audio
Foreign Rep(s): David Bartolone
*Distribution Center:* 7201 McKinney Circle, Frederick, MD 21704 *Tel:* 301-698-7100 *Fax:* 301-695-7931

**Allen A Knoll Publishers**
200 W Victoria St, 2nd fl, Suite A, Santa Barbara, CA 93101-3627
SAN: 299-0539
*Tel:* 805-564-3377 *Toll Free Tel:* 800-777-7623 *Fax:* 805-966-6657
*E-mail:* bookinfo@knollpublishers.com
*Web Site:* www.knollpublishers.com
*Key Personnel*
Lib Sales & Mktg Dir: Abby Schott
Shipping & Receiving Mgr: Lisa Carroll
Accts: Elizabeth Hanning-Yu *E-mail:* elizabeth@knollpublishers.com
Accts Receivable & Accts Payable: Solera Hurley
Founded: 1991
Books for intelligent people who read for fun. No unsol mss.
ISBN Prefix(es): 978-0-9627297; 978-1-888310
Number of titles published annually: 5 Print
Total Titles: 45 Print
Membership(s): Independent Publishers Association

**Alfred A Knopf/Everyman's Library**
Imprint of Knopf Doubleday Publishing Group
c/o Random House Inc, 1745 Broadway, New York, NY 10019
*Tel:* 212-751-2600 *Toll Free Tel:* 800-638-6460 *Fax:* 212-572-2593
*Web Site:* www.knopfdoubleday.com
*Key Personnel*
Chmn: Sonny Mehta
Pres: Anthony Chirico
EVP & Publr, Everyman's Library: Anne Messitte
EVP & Exec Dir, Publicity, Promo & Media Rel: Paul Bogaards
SVP & Assoc Publr: Christine Gillespie
SVP & Edit Dir, Everyman's Library: LuAnn Walther
SVP & Dir, Intl Rts: Carol Brown Janeway
VP & Dir, Art Jacket: Carol Carson
VP & Dir, Busn Opers: Justine LeCates
VP & Dir, Creative Mktg: Anne-Lise Spitzer
VP & Dir, Interior Design & Desktop Publg: Peter Andersen
VP & Dir, Prodn/Design: Andrew W Hughes
VP & Dir, Promo & Serial Rts: Gabrielle Brooks
VP & Dir, Publicity: Nicholas Latimer
VP & Edit Dir: Robin Desser
VP & Exec Ed: Jordan Pavlin
VP & Mng Ed: Katherine Hourigan
VP & Sr Ed: Victoria Wilson; Jonathan Segal; George Andreou
VP & Ed-at-Large: Gary Fisketjon
Sr Ed: Ann Close; Jennifer Jackson; Andrew Miller
Sr Ed, Poetry: Deborah Garrison
Ed: Diana Coglianese
Ed-at-Large: Carole Baron
Dir, Ad: Stephanie Kloss
Dir, Dom Rts: Sean Yule
Dir, Mktg, Everyman's Library: Roz Parr
Group Sales Dir: Janet Cooke
Imprint Sales Dir: James Kimball
Assoc Dir, Publicity: Kathryn Zuckerman
Publicity Mgr: Josie Kals
Publicist: Erica Hinsley; Elizabeth Lindsay
Assoc Publicist: Erinn McGrath
Asst, Publicity: Madeline Caldwell
Mktg Mgr: Sara Eagle
Asst Mktg Mgr: Danielle Plafsky
Mgr, Foreign Rts: Suzanne Smith
Founded: 1915
Random House Inc & its publishing entities are not accepting unsol submissions, proposals, mss, or submission queries via e-mail at this time.
ISBN Prefix(es): 978-0-679; 978-0-7679; 978-1-4000; 978-0-394
Foreign Rights: ALS-Agenzia Letteraria Santachiara (Roberto Santachiara) (Italy); Anthea Agency (Katalina Sabeva) (Bulgaria); Bardon-Chinese Media (Xu Weiguang) (China); Bardon-Chinese Media Agency (Yu-Shiuan Chen) (Taiwan); The English Agency (Junzo Sawa) (Japan); Graal Literary Agency (Maria Strarz-Kanska) (Poland); The Deborah Harris Agency (Ilana Kurshan) (Israel); JLM Literary Agency (Nelly Moukakos) (Greece); Katai & Bolza Literary (Peter Bolza) (Croatia, Hungary); KCC (MiSook Hong) (Korea); Simona Kessler International (Simona Kessler) (Romania); Licht & Burr Literary Agency (Trine Licht) (Scandinavia); La Nouvelle Agence (Vanessa Kling) (France); Kristin Olson Literary Agency (Kristin Olson) (Czech Republic); Sebes & Van Gelderen Literary Agency (Paul Sebes) (Netherlands)

**Kodansha USA Inc**
Subsidiary of Kodansha Ltd (Japan)
451 Park Ave S, 7th fl, New York, NY 10016
SAN: 201-0526
*Tel:* 917-322-6200 *Fax:* 212-935-6929
*E-mail:* info@kodansha-usa.com
*Web Site:* www.kodansha-intl.com
*Key Personnel*
CEO: Takashi Sakuda
Founded: 2008
Publishes hardcover & paperback books in English on Japanese cultures, history, art, architecture, design, craft, gardening, literature, material arts, language, cookbooks, travel & memoir.
ISBN Prefix(es): 978-0-87011; 978-0-87040; 978-1-56836; 978-4-7700; 978-4-88996; 978-4-81709
Number of titles published annually: 50 Print
Total Titles: 500 Print
Imprints: Kodansha America; Kodansha Globe; Kodansha International
Distributed by Oxford University Press
Distributor for Japan Publications Inc; Japan Publications Trading Co Inc
Foreign Rep(s): Fitzhenry & Whiteside (Canada); Kodansha Europe Ltd (Europe)
*Warehouse:* Oxford University Press, 2001 Evans Rd, Cary, NC 27513 *Toll Free Tel:* 800-451-7556 *Fax:* 919-677-1303

**§Kogan Page Publishers**
1518 Walnut St, Suite 1100, Philadelphia, PA 19102
*Tel:* 215-928-9112 *Fax:* 215-928-9113
*E-mail:* info@koganpage.com
*Web Site:* www.koganpageusa.com
*Key Personnel*
Mng Dir: Helen Kogan
Dir: Keith Ashfield
Founded: 1967
Publish books & e-versions of them.
ISBN Prefix(es): 978-0-7494
Number of titles published annually: 30 Print; 20 Online; 40 E-Book
Total Titles: 400 Print; 40 Online; 300 E-Book
*Foreign Office(s):* 120 Pentonville Rd, London N1 9JN, United Kingdom *Tel:* 0207-278-0433 *Web Site:* www.koganpage.com
Distributor for Stanford University Press (distribute outside the Americas)
Foreign Rep(s): Kogan Page London (Worldwide exc USA)
Foreign Rights: Kogan Page London (Worldwide exc USA)
*Billing Address:* IPS, One Ingram Blvd, La Vergne, TN 37086
*Orders to:* IPS, One Ingram Blvd, La Vergne, TN 37086 *Toll Free Tel:* 800-961-2026 *Toll Free Fax:* 800-838-1149 *E-mail:* customer.service@ingrampublisherservices.com *Web Site:* www.ingrampublisherservices.com/PDF/HowToOrder.pdf
*Returns:* IPS, 1210 Ingram Dr, Chambersburg, PA 17201
*Distribution Center:* IPS, One Ingram Blvd, La Vergne, TN 37086

**§Koho Pono LLC**
15024 SE Pinegrove Loop, Clackamas, OR 97015
*Tel:* 503-723-7392 *Toll Free Tel:* 800-937-8000 (orders) *Toll Free Fax:* 800-876-0186 (orders)
*E-mail:* info@kohopono.com; orders@ingrambook.com
*Web Site:* kohopono.com
*Key Personnel*
Publr: Scott Burr *Tel:* 408-689-0888; Dayna Hubenthal
Founded: 2010
Multimedia publishing company that is passionate about growth & improvement for all aspects of life: business, career, relationships & personal. Specialize in innovation, awareness, process improvement, change management & strengthening relationships for business & individuals. Support the evolution of consciousness, self exploration & the pursuit of increasing relevance in life.
ISBN Prefix(es): 978-0-984554
Number of titles published annually: 3 Print; 3 Online; 3 E-Book; 3 Audio
Total Titles: 6 Print; 6 Online; 2 E-Book; 3 Audio
*Shipping Address:* Lightning Source Inc, 1246 Heil Quaker Blvd, La Vergne, TN 37086, Contact: Amy Waugh *Tel:* 615-213-5815 *Fax:* 615-213-4725 *E-mail:* inquiry@lightningsource.com
*Warehouse:* Lightning Source Inc, 1246 Heil Quaker Blvd, La Vergne, TN 37086, Contact: Amy Waugh *Tel:* 615-213-5815 *Fax:* 615-213-4725 *E-mail:* inquiry@lightningsource.com
*Distribution Center:* Ingram Book Co, One Ingram Blvd, La Vergne, TN 37086 *Tel:* 615-793-5000 *Toll Free Tel:* 800-937-8200 *E-mail:* customer.service@ingrambook.com
Lightning Source Inc, 1246 Heil Quaker Blvd, La Vergne, TN 37086, Contact: Amy Waugh

*Tel:* 615-213-5815 *Fax:* 615-213-4725
*E-mail:* inquiry@lightningsource.com
Membership(s): Northwest Association of Book Publishers

**Konecky & Konecky LLC**
72 Ayers Point Rd, Old Saybrook, CT 06475
*Tel:* 860-388-0878 *Fax:* 860-388-0273
*Web Site:* www.koneckyandkonecky.com
*Key Personnel*
Publr: Sean Konecky *E-mail:* seankon@comcast.net
Founded: 1982
Hardcover art books & Civil War history, military history, biography, religion & spirituality.
ISBN Prefix(es): 978-1-56852; 978-0-914427
Number of titles published annually: 35 Print
Total Titles: 150 Print
Imprints: Konecky & Konecky (K&K); Tabard Press
Distributor for Octavo Editions

**KotaPress**
135 Pony Soldier Rd, Sedona, AZ 86336-4613
*Tel:* 928-225-5416
*E-mail:* info@kotapress.com
*Web Site:* kotapress.com
*Key Personnel*
Ed: Kara L C Jones *E-mail:* editor@kotapress.com
Creative Dir: Hawk Jones *E-mail:* hawk@kotapress.com
Founded: 1999
Expressive arts, small press, organization supporting authors exploring grief & healing thru poetry, prose, art, nonfiction & memoir.
ISBN Prefix(es): 978-1-929359
Number of titles published annually: 4 Print; 12 Online; 6 E-Book
Total Titles: 25 Print; 4 Online; 20 E-Book

**H J Kramer Inc**
Affiliate of New World Library
PO Box 1082, Tiburon, CA 94920
*Tel:* 415-884-2100 (ext 10) *Toll Free Tel:* 800-972-6657 *Fax:* 415-435-5364
*E-mail:* hjkramer@jps.net
*Web Site:* www.hjkramer.com; www.newworldlibrary.com
*Key Personnel*
Pres: Linda Kramer
Intl Rts: Suezen Stone *Tel:* 415-499-1622 *E-mail:* Suezenstone@msn.com
Mktg & Publicity: Monique Muhlenkamp *E-mail:* monique@newworldlibrary.com
Founded: 1984
Personal growth, self-help, spiritual growth, trade paperbacks & hardcovers. Any correspondence regarding mss must be accompanied by an appropriately sized SASE.
ISBN Prefix(es): 978-0-915811; 978-1-932073
Number of titles published annually: 3 Print
Total Titles: 70 Print
Foreign Rep(s): Airlift Books (UK); Akasha Books Ltd (New Zealand); Brumby Books/Gemcraft (Australia); Publishers Group Canada (Canada); Real Books (South Africa)
*Orders to:* Publisher Group West, 1700 Fourth St, Berkeley, CA 94710 *Toll Free Tel:* 800-788-3123 *Fax:* 510-528-3444

**Krause Publications Inc**
Subsidiary of F+W Media Inc
700 E State St, Iola, WI 54990
SAN: 202-6554
*Tel:* 715-445-2214 *Toll Free Tel:* 800-258-0929 (cust serv); 888-457-2873 (orders) *Fax:* 715-445-4087
*E-mail:* bookorders@krause.com
*Web Site:* www.krausebooks.com
*Key Personnel*
Founder: Chester L Krause
CFO: Jim Ogle
Pres: David Blansfield
Publr, Books: Sara Domville
Publr, Log House & Metal Roofing: Hugh McAloon
Dir, Libr Sales: Mary Roco
Mktg: Corinne Zielke
Prodn: Marilyn McGrane
Intl Rts Contact: Laurie Smith
ISBN Prefix(es): 978-0-87349; 978-0-87341; 978-0-87069; 978-0-89689; 978-0-8019
Number of titles published annually: 150 Print
Total Titles: 1,000 Print
Imprints: Antique Trader Books; Books Americana; DBI Books; Gun Digest® Books; Warman's
Distributor for Country Bumpkin; David & Charles; Colin Gower; Quarto Books
Foreign Rep(s): David Bateman Ltd (New Zealand); Canadian Manda Group (Canada); Capricorn Link (Australia); David & Charles (Europe, UK); Real Books (Southern Africa); Marta Schooler (Asia, Latin America, Middle East)
*See separate listing for:*
**Antique Trader Books**

**Kregel Publications**
Division of Kregel Inc
733 Wealthy St SE, Grand Rapids, MI 49503-5553
SAN: 298-9115
Mailing Address: PO Box 2607, Grand Rapids, MI 49501-2607
*Tel:* 616-451-4775 *Toll Free Tel:* 800-733-2607 *Fax:* 616-451-9330
*E-mail:* kregelbooks@kregel.com
*Web Site:* www.kregel.com
*Key Personnel*
Pres: James R Kregel *E-mail:* president@kregel.com
VP, Publg: Jerold W Kregel
Exec Dir, Sales & Mktg: David Hill *Tel:* 616-451-4775 ext 235 *E-mail:* dave@kregel.com
Publr & Rts & Perms: Dennis Hillman
Founded: 1949
Evangelical Christian publications including devotionals, Bible study & reference.
ISBN Prefix(es): 978-0-8254
Number of titles published annually: 75 Print
Total Titles: 800 Print
Imprints: Editorial Portavoz; Kregel Academic & Professional; Kregel Classics; Kregel Kidzone; Kregel Publications
Distributor for Candle Books; Monarch Books
Foreign Rep(s): Christian Art Wholesale (South Africa); Christian Literature Crusade (Japan); David C Cook (Canada); Omega Distribution (New Zealand); STL Distribution (UK); Word of Life Press (Korea)
Membership(s): Evangelical Christian Publishers Association
*See separate listing for:*
**Editorial Portavoz**

**Krieger Publishing Co**
1725 Krieger Dr, Malabar, FL 32950
SAN: 202-6562
*Tel:* 321-724-9542 *Toll Free Tel:* 800-724-0025 *Fax:* 321-951-3671
*E-mail:* info@krieger-publishing.com
*Web Site:* www.krieger-publishing.com
*Key Personnel*
CEO: Robert E Krieger
Pres: Donald E Krieger
VP: Maxine D Krieger
Ad Mgr: Cheryl Stanton
Cust Serv: Dianne Struckman
Founded: 1969
A scientific-technical publisher serving the college textbook market. Reprints & new titles: technical, science, psychology, geology, humanities, ecology, history, social sciences, engineering, mathematics, chemistry, adult educational, herpetology, space science.
ISBN Prefix(es): 978-0-88275; 978-0-89464; 978-0-89874; 978-1-57524
Number of titles published annually: 11 Print
Total Titles: 1,000 Print; 2 CD-ROM
Imprints: Anvil Series; Exploring Community History Series; Orbit Series; Professional Practices; Public History
Foreign Rep(s): Eurospan (Middle East, UK)
*Advertising Agency:* Krieger Enterprises Inc

**KTAV Publishing House Inc**
888 Newark Ave, Jersey City, NJ 07306
*Tel:* 201-963-9524 *Fax:* 201-963-0102
*E-mail:* orders@ktav.com
*Web Site:* www.ktav.com
*Key Personnel*
Pres: Bernard Scharfstein *E-mail:* bernie@ktav.com
Founded: 1924
Books of Jewish interest; juvenile, textbooks; scholarly Judaica & interfaith issues.
ISBN Prefix(es): 978-0-87068; 978-0-88125; 978-1-60280
Number of titles published annually: 20 Print
Total Titles: 840 Print
Distributor for Yeshiva University Press

**Kumarian Press**
Division of Lynne Rienner Publishers Inc
1800 30 St, Suite 314, Boulder, CO 80301
*Tel:* 303-444-6684 *Toll Free Tel:* 800-232-0223 (orders only) *Fax:* 303-444-0824
*E-mail:* questions@rienner.com
*Web Site:* www.kpbooks.com
*Key Personnel*
Ed & Assoc Publr: Jim Lance
Founded: 1977
Academic, professional books, college textbooks in social sciences: international development, international relations, political science, political economy, economics, globalization, women & gender studies, conflict resolution, environment, sustainability, civil society & NGO's.
ISBN Prefix(es): 978-0-931816; 978-1-56549; 978-1-887208
Number of titles published annually: 18 Print; 10 E-Book
Total Titles: 300 Print; 100 E-Book
Foreign Rep(s): Alkem Co (Brunei, Indonesia, Malaysia, Philippines, Singapore, Taiwan, Vietnam); Eurospan (Europe, Middle East, North Africa, UK); Everest Media International Services (Nepal); Njigua Books (Eastern Africa, Ethiopia, Kenya, Sudan, Tanzania, Uganda); Sara Books Pvt Ltd (Bangladesh, India, Indian subcontinent, Pakistan, Sri Lanka)
Membership(s): The Association of Publishers for Special Sales; IBPA, the Independent Book Publishers Association

**Kumon Publishing North America**
300 Frank Burr Blvd, Suite 6, Teaneck, NJ 07666
*Tel:* 201-836-2105 *Fax:* 201-836-1559
*E-mail:* books@kumon.com
*Web Site:* www.kumonbooks.com
*Key Personnel*
SVP: Brian Klingborg
Founded: 2004
Publisher of children's educational books & toys.
ISBN Prefix(es): 978-4-7743; 978-1-93241
Number of titles published annually: 20 Print
Total Titles: 105 Print

**George Kurian Reference Books**
PO Box 519, Baldwin Place, NY 10505-0519
*Tel:* 914-962-3287 *Fax:* 914-962-3287
*Key Personnel*
Pres: George Kurian *E-mail:* gtkurian@aol.com
Founded: 1972
Reference books for libraries, schools, colleges.
ISBN Prefix(es): 978-0-914746

Number of titles published annually: 7 Print
Total Titles: 102 Print
Imprints: Foreign Affairs Information Service
Foreign Rights: Gazelle Book Services (UK)
*Shipping Address:* 3689 Campbell Ct, Yorktown Heights, NY 10598

**§L & L Dreamspell**
376 W Quarry Rd, London, TX 76854
*Tel:* 281-703-2405
*E-mail:* publishing@lldreamspell.com
*Web Site:* www.lldreamspell.com
*Key Personnel*
Publr & Owner: Linda Houle *E-mail:* linda@lldreamspell.com; Lisa Rene Smith *E-mail:* lisa@lldreamspell.com
Founded: 2006
ISBN Prefix(es): 978-0-9787723; 978-1-60318
Number of titles published annually: 36 Print
Total Titles: 200 Print; 115 E-Book

**L & R Publishing**, see Hellgate Press

**§LaChance Publishing LLC**
120 Bond St, Brooklyn, NY 11217
*Tel:* 917-855-7537 *Fax:* 646-390-1326
*E-mail:* info@lachancepublishing.com
*Web Site:* www.lachancepublishing.com
*Key Personnel*
Pres: Victor Starsia *E-mail:* victor@lachancepublishing.com
Sr Ed: Richard Gore *Tel:* 201-232-9229 *E-mail:* richard@lachancepublishing.com
Founded: 2005
Health related titles for a general audience.
ISBN Prefix(es): 978-1-9341840
Number of titles published annually: 3 Print; 5 E-Book
Total Titles: 11 Print; 11 E-Book
Distributed by Independent Publishers Group
Membership(s): IBPA, the Independent Book Publishers Association

**LadybugPress**
Division of NewVoices Inc
16964 Columbia River Dr, Sonora, CA 95370
SAN: 299-0377
*Tel:* 209-694-8340 *Toll Free Tel:* 888-892-5000 *Fax:* 209-694-8916
*E-mail:* ladybugpress@ladybugbooks.com
*Web Site:* www.ladybugbooks.com
*Key Personnel*
Publr: Georgia Jones
Founded: 1996
Books & audio books of particular interest to women.
This publisher has indicated that 40% of their product line (primarily fiction & poetry) is author-subsidized.
ISBN Prefix(es): 978-1-889409
Number of titles published annually: 8 Print; 2 CD-ROM; 1 Audio
Total Titles: 27 Print; 15 CD-ROM; 9 Audio
Membership(s): IBPA, the Independent Book Publishers Association

**Lake Claremont Press**
Imprint of Everything Goes Media LLC
1026 W Van Buren St, 2nd fl, Chicago, IL 60607
Mailing Address: PO Box 1524, Milwaukee, WI 53201
*Tel:* 312-226-8400 *Fax:* 312-226-8420
*E-mail:* lcp@lakeclaremont.com
*Web Site:* www.lakeclaremont.com
*Key Personnel*
Owner & Publr: Sharon Woodhouse *E-mail:* sharon@lakeclaremont.com
Founded: 1994
Histories & guidebooks on the Chicago area by local authors with a passion & organizations with a mission.

ISBN Prefix(es): 978-1-893121; 978-0-9642426
Number of titles published annually: 3 Print; 6 E-Book
Total Titles: 50 Print
*Distribution Center:* IPG, 814 N Franklin St, Chicago, IL 60610

**Lake Superior Port Cities Inc**
310 E Superior St, Suite 125, Duluth, MN 55802
Mailing Address: PO Box 16417, Duluth, MN 55816-0417
*Tel:* 218-722-5002 *Toll Free Tel:* 888-BIG-LAKE (244-5253) *Fax:* 218-722-4096
*E-mail:* reader@lakesuperior.com
*Web Site:* www.lakesuperior.com
*Key Personnel*
Pres & Publr: Cynthia Hayden *E-mail:* cmh@lakesuperior.com
Publr: Paul L Hayden *E-mail:* plh@lakesuperior.com
Ed: Konnie Le May *E-mail:* kon@lakesuperior.com
Founded: 1979
Began as regional magazine publisher & expanded services to include books, travel guides, calendars, maps & merchandise.
ISBN Prefix(es): 978-0-942235
Number of titles published annually: 3 Print
Total Titles: 25 Print
Membership(s): International Regional Magazine Association; Midwest Independent Booksellers Association; Midwest Independent Publishers Association; Minnesota Magazine & Publications Association

**LAMA Books**
2381 Sleepy Hollow Ave, Hayward, CA 94545-3429
*Tel:* 510-785-1091 *Toll Free Tel:* 888-452-6244 *Fax:* 510-785-1099
*Web Site:* www.lamabooks.com
*Key Personnel*
Pres: Steve Meyer *E-mail:* steve@lamabooks.com
Sales & Mktg Dir: Barbara Ragusa
Founded: 1970
Develop & publish books for HVAC; occupational trades, reading development, teacher preparation; directories-occupational programs in California community colleges.
ISBN Prefix(es): 978-0-88069
Number of titles published annually: 5 Print
Total Titles: 50 Print

**Lanahan Publishers Inc**
324 Hawthorne Rd, Baltimore, MD 21210-2303
*Tel:* 410-366-2434 *Toll Free Tel:* 866-345-1949 *Fax:* 410-366-8798 *Toll Free Fax:* 888-345-7257
*E-mail:* info@lanahanpublishers.com
*Web Site:* www.lanahanpublishers.com
*Key Personnel*
Pres: Donald W Fusting
Founded: 1995
College textbook publisher.
ISBN Prefix(es): 978-0-9652687; 978-1-930398
Number of titles published annually: 4 Print
Total Titles: 20 Print

**Landauer Corp**
3100 101 St, Suite A, Urbandale, IA 50322
*Tel:* 515-287-2144 *Toll Free Tel:* 800-557-2144 *Fax:* 515-276-5102
*E-mail:* info@landauercorp.com
*Web Site:* www.landauercorp.com
*Key Personnel*
Pres & Publr: Jeramy Landauer
VP, Sales & Admin: Kathryn Jacobson
Founded: 1991
Publishing & licensing for the home arts working with leading designers & artists.

ISBN Prefix(es): 978-1-890621; 978-0-9646870; 978-0-9793711; 978-9-9770166; 978-1-935726; 978-0-9825586; 978-0-9818040
Number of titles published annually: 12 Print
Total Titles: 114 Print
Foreign Rep(s): A Great Notion (Canada); Alba Patchwork (Spain); N Jefferson (Canada); Quilt Source (Canada); John Reed Book Distribution (Australia); RJR Fabrics (Europe); Roundhouse Group (England); Stallion Press (Singapore); Virka (Iceland)
Membership(s): ABA; IBPA, the Independent Book Publishers Association

**Landes Bioscience**
1806 Rio Grande St, Austin, TX 78701
*Tel:* 512-637-6050 *Toll Free Tel:* 800-736-9948 *Fax:* 512-637-6079
*E-mail:* info@landesbioscience.com
*Web Site:* www.landesbioscience.com
*Key Personnel*
Pres: Ronald Landes
Sales: Cynthia Conomos *E-mail:* cynthia@landesbioscience.com
Founded: 1990
Bioscience & medical books for researchers, clinicians & students.
ISBN Prefix(es): 978-1-57059
Number of titles published annually: 70 Print
Total Titles: 700 Print
Imprints: Vademecum
Foreign Rights: John Scott & Co

**§Peter Lang Publishing Inc**
Subsidiary of Verlag Peter Lang AG (Switzerland)
29 Broadway, 18th fl, New York, NY 10006-3223
SAN: 241-5534
*Tel:* 212-647-7706 *Toll Free Tel:* 800-770-5264 (cust serv) *Fax:* 212-647-7707
*Web Site:* www.peterlang.com
*Key Personnel*
SVP & Mng Dir: Christopher S Myers *E-mail:* chrism@plang.com
Sales & Mktg Dir: Patricia Mulrane Clayton
Lead Ed: Heidi Burns
Mktg Coord: Michael McFadden
Founded: 1982
Scholarly monographs & textbooks in the humanities, social sciences, media studies, Festschriften & conference proceedings.
ISBN Prefix(es): 978-0-8204; 978-1-4331
Number of titles published annually: 240 Print
Total Titles: 2,500 Print
*Foreign Office(s):* Verlag Peter Lang GmbH, Eschborner-Landstr 42-50, 60489 Frankfurt/Main, Germany, Mgr: Jurgen-Matthias Springer *Tel:* (069) 78 07 05 0 *Fax:* (069) 78 07 05 50
Verlag Peter Lang AG, Hochfeldstr 32, 3012 Bern, Switzerland *Tel:* (031) 306 1717 *Fax:* (031) 306 1727
Foreign Rep(s): Verlag Peter Lang GmbH (Germany)

**LangMarc Publishing**
PO Box 90488, Austin, TX 78709-0488
SAN: 297-519X
*Tel:* 512-394-0989 *Toll Free Tel:* 800-864-1648 (orders) *Fax:* 512-394-0829
*E-mail:* langmarc@booksails.com
*Web Site:* www.langmarc.com
*Key Personnel*
Pres & Lib Sales Dir: Lois Qualben
VP: Susan Reue
Prodn Mgr: Michael Qualben
Founded: 1991
Publisher of inspirational titles.
ISBN Prefix(es): 978-1-880292
Number of titles published annually: 3 Print; 20 E-Book
Total Titles: 75 Print

Imprints: Harbor Lights
*Shipping Address:* 7500 Shadowridge Run, No 28, Austin, TX 78749, Pres: Lois Qualben SAN: 297-519X

**Lantern Books**
Division of Booklight Inc
128 Second Place, Garden Suite, Brooklyn, NY 11231
*Tel:* 212-414-2275
*E-mail:* editorial@lanternbooks.com; info@lanternmedia.net
*Web Site:* www.lanternbooks.com
*Key Personnel*
Pres: Gene Gollogly *E-mail:* gene@lanternbooks.com
Mng Dir: Kara Davis *E-mail:* kara@lanternbooks.com
Dir, Publg: Martin Rowe
ISBN Prefix(es): 978-1-59056; 978-1-930051; 978-1-57582; 978-1-929297
Number of titles published annually: 15 Print
Total Titles: 150 Print
Foreign Rep(s): Ceres Books (New Zealand); Deep Books (Europe, UK)
Foreign Rights: Sabine Weeke
*Billing Address:* Steiner Books, Quicksilver Dr, Sterling, VA 20166 *E-mail:* anthroposophicmail@presswarehouse.com
*Orders to:* PO Box 960, Herndon, VA 20172-0960 *Tel:* 703-661-1594 *Toll Free Tel:* 800-856-8664 *Fax:* 703-661-1501 *E-mail:* anthroposophicmail@presswarehouse.com
*Returns:* Steiner Books, Quicksilver Dr, Sterling, VA 20166 *E-mail:* anthroposophicmail@presswarehouse.com
*Shipping Address:* Steiner Books, Quicksilver Dr, Sterling, VA 20166 *Tel:* 703-661-1500 *E-mail:* anthroposophicmail@presswarehouse.com
*Warehouse:* Steiner Books, Quicksilver Dr, Sterling, VA 20166 *Tel:* 703-661-1500 *E-mail:* anthroposophicmail@presswarehouse.com
*Distribution Center:* Steiner Books, Quicksilver Dr, Sterling, VA 20166 *Tel:* 703-661-1500 *E-mail:* anthroposophicmail@presswarehouse.com
Membership(s): ABA

**Laredo Publishing Co Inc**
465 Westview Ave, Englewood, NJ 07631
*Tel:* 201-408-4048 *Fax:* 201-408-5011
*E-mail:* info@laredopublishing.com
*Web Site:* www.laredopublishing.com
*Key Personnel*
Pres: Sam Laredo *E-mail:* laredo@laredopublishing.com
Edit Dir: Raquel Benatar *E-mail:* raquel@renaissancehouse.net
ISBN Prefix(es): 978-1-56492
Number of titles published annually: 25 Print
Total Titles: 150 Print
Imprints: Renaissance House
*See separate listing for:*
**Renaissance House**

**Lark Crafts**
Imprint of Sterling Publishing Co Inc
67 Broadway, Asheville, NC 28801
*Tel:* 828-253-0467 *Fax:* 828-253-7952
*E-mail:* info@larkbooks.com
*Web Site:* www.larkcrafts.com; www.larkbooks.com
*Key Personnel*
Content Team Leader: Nicole McConville *E-mail:* nicole@sterlingpublishing.com
Social Media & Digitial Mktg Coord: Beth Sweet *E-mail:* beth@sterlingbooks.com
Founded: 1979
How-to books in crafts & photography.
ISBN Prefix(es): 978-0-937274; 978-1-887374; 978-1-57990; 978-1-60059
Number of titles published annually: 120 Print
Total Titles: 400 Print
Foreign Rights: Sterling Publishing Co Inc
*Shipping Address:* Sterling Publishing Co Inc, 40 Saw Mill Pond Rd, Edison, NJ 08837 *Toll Free Tel:* 800-367-9692 *Toll Free Fax:* 800-542-7567

**Larson Publications**
4936 State Rte 414, Burdett, NY 14818
*Tel:* 607-546-9342 *Toll Free Tel:* 800-828-2197 *Fax:* 607-546-9344
*E-mail:* custserv@larsonpublications.com
*Web Site:* www.larsonpublications.com
*Key Personnel*
Mktg Dir & Publr: Amy Opperman Cash *E-mail:* amy@larsonpublications.com
Founded: 1982
Resources for spiritual independence & social relevance.
ISBN Prefix(es): 978-0-943914; 978-1-936012
Number of titles published annually: 6 Print; 1 CD-ROM; 1 Online; 5 E-Book
Total Titles: 88 Print; 1 CD-ROM; 25 E-Book; 3 Audio
Foreign Rep(s): Gazelle Bookservices Ltd (Europe, UK); Bokforlaget Robert Larson (Scandinavia)
Foreign Rights: Literaryventuresfund (Mary Bisbee-Beek)
*Distribution Center:* New Leaf Distributing Co, 401 Thornton Rd, Lithia Springs, GA 30122-1557 *Tel:* 770-948-7845 *Toll Free Tel:* 800-326-2665 *Fax:* 770-944-2313 *E-mail:* newleaf@newleaf-dist.com *Web Site:* www.newleaf-dist.com
National Book Network, 15200 NBN Way, Blue Ridge Summit, PA 17214 *Toll Free Tel:* 800-462-6420 *Toll Free Fax:* 800-338-4550 *E-mail:* custserv@nbnbooks.com *Web Site:* www.nbnbooks.com

**§Lasaria Creative Publishing**
4094 Majestic Lane, Suite 352, Fairfax, VA 22033
*E-mail:* submissions@lasariacreative.com
*Web Site:* www.lasariacreative.com
*Key Personnel*
Publg Analyst: Adam Lee *E-mail:* adamlee@lasariacreative.com
Founded: 2008
Author-owned independent publishing company looking for nonfiction, general fiction, short stories & juvenile fiction books. We encourage first time authors & are willing to help get your work into mainstream distribution channels. Also offer editing services for new authors.
ISBN Prefix(es): 978-0-9818367
Number of titles published annually: 10 Print; 10 Online; 10 E-Book
Total Titles: 12 Print; 12 Online; 12 E-Book

**Latin American Literary Review Press**
PO Box 17660, Pittsburgh, PA 15235-0860
*Tel:* 412-824-7903 *Fax:* 412-824-7909
*E-mail:* lalrp.editor@gmail.com
*Web Site:* www.lalrp.org
*Key Personnel*
Founding Ed & Pres: Dr Yvette E Miller
Founded: 1980
Publish Latin American literature in English translation. Publish Latin American Literary Review, a semiannual journal of scholarly essays & book reviews on the literatures of Spanish America & Brazil, which also distributes Spanish books on social sciences, history & art.
ISBN Prefix(es): 978-0-935480; 978-1-891270
Number of titles published annually: 4 Print
Total Titles: 146 Print
*Orders to:* Independent Publishers Group, 814 N Franklin St, Chicago, IL 60610 *Toll Free Tel:* 800-888-4741 *E-mail:* orders@ipgbook.com *Web Site:* www.ipgbooks.com
Membership(s): Council of Literary Magazines & Presses

**Laughing Elephant**
3645 Interlake N, Seattle, WA 98103
*Tel:* 206-447-9229 *Toll Free Tel:* 800-354-0400 *Fax:* 206-447-9189
*E-mail:* support@laughingelephant.com
*Web Site:* www.laughingelephant.com
*Key Personnel*
Pres & Publr: Harold Darling
Ed-in-Chief: Abigail Darling
Ed: Christina Darling
Founded: 1986
Publish books, cards & printed gifts with an emphasis on imagery, especially from antique children's books, self-generating content.
ISBN Prefix(es): 978-1-883211; 978-0-9621131; 978-1-59583
Number of titles published annually: 8 Print
Total Titles: 80 Print
Imprints: Darling & Co; Green Tiger Press

**§Law School Admission Council**
662 Penn St, Newtown, PA 18940
Mailing Address: PO Box 40, Newtown, PA 18940
*Tel:* 215-968-1101
*E-mail:* lsacinfo@lsac.org
*Web Site:* www.lsac.org
*Key Personnel*
Dir, Communs: Wendy Margolis *Tel:* 215-968-1219 *E-mail:* wmargolis@lsac.org
Founded: 1947
Standardized testing, legal education & law school admission activities, law school admission test preparation.
ISBN Prefix(es): 978-0-9846360
Number of titles published annually: 4 Print; 2 Online
Total Titles: 30 Print; 2 Online
*Distribution Center:* Ingram Publisher Services, 14 Ingram Blvd, La Vergne, TN 37086 *Toll Free Tel:* 866-400-5351 *Toll Free Fax:* 800-838-1149 *E-mail:* customer.service@ingrampublisherservices.com *Web Site:* ipage.ingrambook.com SAN: 631-8630

**Law Tribune Books**
Division of American Lawyer Media
201 Ann Uccello St, 4th fl, Hartford, CT 06103
*Tel:* 860-527-7900 *Fax:* 860-527-7433
*E-mail:* lawtribune@alm.com
*Web Site:* www.ctlawtribune.com
*Key Personnel*
Publr: Jeffrey L Forte *Tel:* 860-757-6650 *E-mail:* jforte@alm.com
Ed-in-Chief: Paul Sussman *Tel:* 860-757-6640 *E-mail:* psussman@alm.com
Mng Ed: Jay Stapleton *Tel:* 860-757-6642 *E-mail:* jstapleton@alm.com
Busn Mgr: Heather Granger *Tel:* 860-757-6612 *E-mail:* hgranger@alm.com
Founded: 1974
Publisher of books, newspapers & other materials for the legal community & the public.
ISBN Prefix(es): 978-0-910051
Number of titles published annually: 20 Print
Total Titles: 20 Print; 3 E-Book
Imprints: The Connecticut Law Tribune

**The Lawbook Exchange Ltd**
33 Terminal Ave, Clark, NJ 07066-1321
*Tel:* 732-382-1800 *Toll Free Tel:* 800-422-6686 *Fax:* 732-382-1887
*E-mail:* law@lawbookexchange.com
*Web Site:* www.lawbookexchange.com

*Key Personnel*
Pres: Greg Talbot
Mng Ed, Pubns: Valerie Horowitz
Mgr, Antiquarian Books Dept: Michael von der Linn, PhD
Founded: 1983
Publisher of books on legal history. Also reprints of legal classics.
ISBN Prefix(es): 978-1-886363; 978-1-58477; 978-0-9630106
Number of titles published annually: 100 Print
Total Titles: 1,000 Print
Membership(s): Antiquarian Booksellers Association of America; International League of Antiquarian Booksellers

**Merloyd Lawrence Inc**
102 Chestnut St, Boston, MA 02108
*Tel:* 617-523-5895 *Fax:* 617-252-5285
*Key Personnel*
Pres & Ed: Merloyd Ludington Lawrence *E-mail:* merloyd.lawrence@perseusbooks.com
Intl Rts, The Perseus Books Group: Carolyn Savarese
Founded: 1982
Co-publisher with The Perseus Books Group.
Number of titles published annually: 6 Print; 6 E-Book
Total Titles: 77 Print; 33 E-Book
Distributed by The Perseus Books Group

**§Lawyers & Judges Publishing Co Inc**
917 N Swan Rd, Suite 300, Tucson, AZ 85711
Mailing Address: PO Box 30040, Tucson, AZ 85751-0040
*Tel:* 520-323-1500 *Toll Free Tel:* 800-209-7109 *Fax:* 520-323-0055 *Toll Free Fax:* 800-330-8795
*E-mail:* sales@lawyersandjudges.com
*Web Site:* www.lawyersandjudges.com
*Key Personnel*
Pres & Publr: Steve Weintraub *E-mail:* steve@lawyersandjudges.com
Founded: 1963
Professional, text & reference materials in law, accident reconstruction, legal economics & taxation, forensics, medicine.
ISBN Prefix(es): 978-0-88450; 978-0-913875; 978-1-930056
Number of titles published annually: 25 Print; 8 CD-ROM
Total Titles: 103 Print; 16 CD-ROM
*Advertising Agency:* Global Sales Network
*Warehouse:* GENCO, 545 Coney Island Dr, Sparks, NV 89431

**Leadership Directories**
104 Fifth Ave, 3rd fl, New York, NY 10011
*Tel:* 212-627-4140 *Fax:* 212-645-0931
*E-mail:* info@leadershipdirectories.com
*Web Site:* www.leadershipdirectories.com
*Key Personnel*
CEO & Pres: Gretchen Teichgraeber
VP, Prod Mktg: Sue Healy *E-mail:* shealy@leadershipdirectories.com
VP, Sales & Mktg: Adam Bernacki *E-mail:* abernacki@leadershipdirectories.com
Sr Relationship Mgr: Jim Marcus *Tel:* 212-433-1408 *E-mail:* jmarcus@leadershipdirectories.com
Founded: 1969
Provider of premium contact solutions, covering the public & private sectors. Leadership Directories maintains a database of biographical & contact information on nearly 600,000 leaders & executives from 30,000-40,000 organizations. Content is available online, as datafeeds & preselected lists, or in print.
Number of titles published annually: 14 Print
Total Titles: 14 Print; 11 Online
Imprints: Yellow Books

*Branch Office(s)*
1667 "K" St NW, Suite 801, Washington, DC 20006, VP, Brand Devt: Imogene Akins Hutchinson *Tel:* 202-347-7757 *Fax:* 202-628-3430

**Leadership Ministries Worldwide/OBR**
3755 Pilot Point, Chattanooga, TN 37416
Mailing Address: PO Box 21310, Chattanooga, TN 37424-0310
*Tel:* 423-855-2181 *Toll Free Tel:* 800-987-8790 *Fax:* 423-855-8616
*E-mail:* info@outlinebible.org
*Web Site:* www.outlinebible.org
*Key Personnel*
Pres: John Willoughby
Commentaries.
ISBN Prefix(es): 978-1-57407; 978-0-945863
Number of titles published annually: 12 Print
Total Titles: 275 Print
Membership(s): Evangelical Christian Publishers Association

**§Leaping Dog Press/Asylum Arts Press**
PO Box 90473, Raleigh, NC 27675-0473
*Tel:* 919-809-9045
*E-mail:* sales@leapingdogpress.com
*Web Site:* www.leapingdogpress.com
*Key Personnel*
Ed & Publr: Mr Jordan D Jones *E-mail:* editor@leapingdogpress.com
Founded: 1985
Publishers of contemporary literature; online only.
ISBN Prefix(es): 978-1-58775; 978-1-878580
Number of titles published annually: 4 Online
Total Titles: 4 Online
Imprints: Asylum Arts Press
*Distribution Center:* Bookmasters, 30 Amberwood Pkwy, Ashland, OH 44805 *Toll Free Tel:* 877-312-3520
Membership(s): Council of Literary Magazines & Presses; IBPA, the Independent Book Publishers Association; Northern California Independent Booksellers Association

**Learnables Foreign Language Courses**, see International Linguistics Corp

**§THE Learning Connection®**
4100 Silverstar Rd, Suite D, Orlando, FL 32808
*Tel:* 407-292-2125 *Toll Free Tel:* 800-218-8489 *Fax:* 407-292-2123
*E-mail:* tlc@tlconnection.com
*Web Site:* www.tlconnection.com
*Key Personnel*
Gen Mgr: Ryan Handberg *E-mail:* ryan@tlconnection.com
Founded: 1991
Thematic Literacy Centers & teacher's guides for early childhood & middle school; parent involvement & family literacy; bilingual, math, science, multicultural, manipulatives, technology.
ISBN Prefix(es): 978-1-56831
Number of titles published annually: 15 Print; 15 CD-ROM; 5 Audio
Total Titles: 1,000 Print; 15 CD-ROM; 50 Audio
Imprints: Computer Connections; PAKS-Parents & Kids
*Branch Office(s)*
300 E 93 St, Suite 29C, New York, NY 10128, VP, NJ Accts: Timothy Sasman
Membership(s): International Reading Association

**Learning Links Inc**
PO Box 326, Cranbury, NJ 08512
SAN: 175-081X
*Tel:* 516-437-9071 *Toll Free Tel:* 800-724-2616 *Fax:* 516-437-5392
*E-mail:* info@learninglinks.com
*Web Site:* www.learninglinks.com
*Key Personnel*
Owner: Linda Bradley
Founded: 1976
Publish study guides for novels for school use, grades 1-12. Distribute paperback books, audios, videos, craft kits & book-related toys.
ISBN Prefix(es): 978-0-88122; 978-1-56982; 978-0-7675
Number of titles published annually: 25 Print
Total Titles: 850 Print
Imprints: Novel-Ties Study Guides
Divisions: Swan Books
Distributor for Harcourt; HarperCollins; Houghton Mifflin Harcourt Publishing Company; Little, Brown & Company; Penguin Group (USA) LLC; Random House Inc; Scholastic; Simon & Schuster
Membership(s): International Reading Association

**LearningExpress LLC**
2 Rector St, 26th fl, New York, NY 10006
*Tel:* 212-995-2566 *Toll Free Tel:* 800-295-9556 (ext 2) *Fax:* 212-995-5512
*E-mail:* customerservice@learningexpressllc.com (cust serv)
*Web Site:* www.learningexpressllc.com
*Key Personnel*
CEO & Pres: Barry Lippman
COO & CFO: Kheil McIntyre
CTO: Tammy Cunningham
VP, Busn Devt: Helen Sileno
Dir, Cust Serv: Shana Ashwood
Dir, Sales, Lib & Educ Solutions: Tom Burnosky
Founded: 1995
Publishes print & online test-preparation resources, skill building tools, study guides & career guidance materials for the trade, library, school & consumer markets.
ISBN Prefix(es): 978-1-57685
Number of titles published annually: 40 Print; 4 CD-ROM; 30 Online; 40 E-Book
Total Titles: 200 Print; 12 CD-ROM; 300 Online; 150 E-Book
Imprints: LearningExpress
*Sales Office(s):* National Book Network, 4501 Forbes Blvd, Suite 200, Lanham, MD 20706
Distributed by National Book Network
*Orders to:* National Book Network, 15200 NBN Way, Blue Ridge Summit, PA 17214 *Tel:* 717-794-3800 *Toll Free Tel:* 800-462-6420 *Toll Free Fax:* 800-338-4550 *E-mail:* customercare@nbnbooks.com
*Returns:* National Book Network, 15200 NBN Way, Blue Ridge Summit, PA 17214 *Tel:* 717-794-3800 *Toll Free Tel:* 800-462-6420 *Toll Free Fax:* 800-338-4550 *E-mail:* customercare@nbnbooks.com
*Warehouse:* National Book Network, 15200 NBN Way, Blue Ridge Summit, PA 17214

**Lectorum Publications Inc**
Subsidiary of Scholastic Inc
205 Chubb Ave, Lyndhurst, NJ 07071
*Toll Free Tel:* 800-345-5946 *Fax:* 201-559-2201 *Toll Free Fax:* 877-532-8676
*E-mail:* lectorum@lectorum.com
*Web Site:* www.lectorum.com
*Key Personnel*
CEO & Pres: Alex Correa *E-mail:* acorrea@lectorum.com
Opers Mgr: Fernando Febus *E-mail:* ffebus@lectorum.com
Sales Mgr, Trade: Laura Bejarano *E-mail:* lbejarano@lectorum.com
Website Mgr: Marjorie Samper
Founded: 1960
Distribute children & adult books in Spanish, with over 25,000 titles from more than 500 domestic & foreign publishers. Serves schools & libraries, as well as the trade & various specialized markets, with children's books in Spanish, including works originally written in Spanish, translations from other languages & the

Spanish-language editions of many popular children's books.
ISBN Prefix(es): 978-1-880507; 978-1-930332
Number of titles published annually: 10 Print

**Lederer Books**
Division of Messianic Jewish Publishers
6120 Day Long Lane, Clarksville, MD 21029
*Tel:* 410-531-6644 *Toll Free Tel:* 800-410-7367 (orders) *Fax:* 717-761-7273
*E-mail:* lederer@messianicjewish.net; customerservice@messianicjewish.net
*Web Site:* www.messianicjewish.net
*Key Personnel*
Pres: Barry Rubin *E-mail:* president@messianicjewish.net
Founded: 1949
Publish & distribute Messianic Jewish books & other products.
ISBN Prefix(es): 978-1-880226
Number of titles published annually: 12 Print
Total Titles: 60 Print
Distributor for Chosen People Ministries; First Fruits of Zion; Jewish New Testament Publications
Foreign Rep(s): Winfried Bluth (Europe)
Foreign Rights: Winfried Bluth (Europe)
Membership(s): CBA: The Association for Christian Retail; Evangelical Christian Publishers Association

**Lee & Low Books Inc**
95 Madison Ave, New York, NY 10016
*Tel:* 212-779-4400 *Toll Free Tel:* 888-320-3190 (ext 28, orders only) *Fax:* 212-683-1894 (orders only); 212-532-6035
*E-mail:* general@leeandlow.com
*Web Site:* www.leeandlow.com
*Key Personnel*
Pres: Craig Low *E-mail:* clow@leeandlow.com
VP & Edit Dir: Louise May
Publr: Jason Low *E-mail:* jlow@leeandlow.com
Founded: 1991
Publisher of high quality multicultural children's books. We provide for the school, library & bookstore market.
ISBN Prefix(es): 978-1-880000; 978-1-58430; 978-1-600
Number of titles published annually: 15 Print; 15 E-Book
Total Titles: 650 Print; 50 E-Book; 50 Audio
Imprints: Bebop Books; Children's Book Press; Tu Books
*See separate listing for:*
**Children's Book Press**

**Left Coast Press Inc**
1630 N Main St, Suite 400, Walnut Creek, CA 94596
*Tel:* 925-935-3380 *Fax:* 925-935-2916
*E-mail:* explore@lcoastpress.com
*Web Site:* www.lcoastpress.com
*Key Personnel*
Founder & Publr: Mitch Allen
Founded: 2005
Publisher of scholarly books & journals on social sciences & humanities.
ISBN Prefix(es): 978-1-59874; 978-1-61132
Number of titles published annually: 40 Print; 35 E-Book
Total Titles: 300 Print; 250 E-Book
Distributor for Intervention Press (Denmark); UCL Institute of Archaeology (UK)
Foreign Rep(s): Eurospan (Africa, Europe, Middle East); Footpoint Books (Australia, New Zealand)
*Distribution Center:* University Chicago Press, 1427 E 60 St, Chicago, IL 60637-2954

**Legacy Press**, see Rainbow Publishers

**Lehigh University Press**
Affiliate of Rowman & Littlefield Publishing Group (RLPG)
B-040 Christmas-Saucon Hall, 14 E Packer Ave, Bethlehem, PA 18015
*Tel:* 610-758-3933 *Fax:* 610-758-6331
*E-mail:* inlup@lehigh.edu
*Web Site:* inpress.sites.lehigh.edu
Founded: 1985
18th century American studies, East Asian studies, literary theory & criticism, history & technology, science, sociology, biography & the Arts. Submissions welcome on any topic that is intellectually substantive.
ISBN Prefix(es): 978-1-61146
Number of titles published annually: 10 Print
Total Titles: 149 Print
Distributed by Rowman & Littlefield

**Leilah Publications**
PO Box 1863, Tempe, AZ 85280-1863
*Tel:* 480-241-4120
*E-mail:* leilah@leilahpublications.com
*Web Site:* leilahpublications.com
*Key Personnel*
Dir: Joshua Seraphim
Mgmt Consultant: Amany El-Ameera Daghesty
Founded: 2006
Brings a global vision of art & writing for the 21st century, publishing & investing in avante-garde artists, lyricists, writers, actors, actresses & poets.
ISBN Prefix(es): 978-0-9829992
Number of titles published annually: 3 Print; 3 Online; 3 E-Book; 1 Audio
Total Titles: 16 Print; 16 Online; 3 E-Book; 1 Audio
Subsidiaries: Brigids Books
*Warehouse:* Ingram/Lightning Source, 1246 Neil Quaker Blvd, La Vergne, TN 37086
*Distribution Center:* Ingram/Lightning Source, 1246 Neil Quaker Blvd, La Vergne, TN 37086
Membership(s): American Academy of Religion

**Leisure Arts Inc**
Division of Liberty Media
5701 Ranch Dr, Little Rock, AR 72223
SAN: 666-9565
*Tel:* 501-868-8800 *Toll Free Tel:* 800-643-8030 *Fax:* 501-868-8748
*Web Site:* www.leisurearts.com
*Key Personnel*
CEO: Rick Barton
Sales: Mike Behar
Founded: 1971
Hard & soft cover books featuring instructions for needlework, crafts, cooking & gardening.
ISBN Prefix(es): 978-0-942237; 978-1-57486; 978-1-60140
Number of titles published annually: 200 Print
Total Titles: 2,000 Print

**The Lentz Leadership Institute**
Imprint of The Refractive Thinker Press
9065 Big Plantation Ave, Las Vegas, NV 89143
SAN: 857-7994
*Tel:* 702-719-9214 *Toll Free Fax:* 877-298-5172
*E-mail:* orders@lentzleadership.com
*Web Site:* www.lentzleadership.com; www.refractivethinker.com
*Key Personnel*
Chief Refractive Thinker: Dr Cheryl Lentz *Tel:* 702-421-6294 *E-mail:* drcheryllentz@gmail.com
Founded: 2008
Publishes scholarly materials as part of The Anthology series: The Refractive Thinker Series, to include the educational seminar series for public speaking. Individual books & individual doctoral or graduate level publications by participating authors are also published. Offer APA doctoral & graduate editing services.

ISBN Prefix(es): 978-0-9823036; 978-0-9828740
Number of titles published annually: 4 Print; 4 Online; 4 E-Book
Total Titles: 13 Print; 6 Online; 6 E-Book
Imprints: Pensiero Press
Distributed by BCH Fulfillment & Distribution; Lightning Source
Membership(s): IBPA, the Independent Book Publishers Association

**Hal Leonard Performing Arts Publishing Group**, see Amadeus Press/Hal Leonard Performing Arts Publishing Group

**Lerner Publications**
Division of Lerner Publishing Group Inc
241 First Ave N, Minneapolis, MN 55401
SAN: 201-0828
*Tel:* 612-332-3344 *Toll Free Tel:* 800-328-4929 *Fax:* 612-332-7615 *Toll Free Fax:* 800-332-1132
*E-mail:* info@lernerbooks.com
*Web Site:* www.lernerbooks.com
*Key Personnel*
Chmn: Harry J Lerner
Pres & Publr: Adam Lerner
EVP, Sales: David Wexler
VP & Dir, Mktg & Digital Prods: Terri Soutor
Ed-in-Chief: Patricia M Stockland
CFO & EVP: Margaret Wunderlich
VP, Prodn: Gary Hansen
Rts Dir: Maria Kjoller
Dir, Prod Devt & Mkt Res: Lois Wallentine
Dir, Electronic Content: Dan Wallek
Art Dir: Zach Marell
Dir, HR: Cyndi Radant
Founded: 1959
Juveniles: science, history, sports, fiction, art, geography, aviation, environment, ethnic, multicultural issues & activity books.
Total Titles: 1,025 Print; 665 E-Book
Foreign Rep(s): INT Press Distribution (Australia); Monarch Books of Canada (Trade) (Canada); Phambili (Southern Africa); Publishers Marketing Service (Malaysia, Singapore); Saunders Book Co (Education) (Canada); South Pacific Books (New Zealand)
Foreign Rights: Japan Foreign-Rights Centre (Japan); Korea Copyright Center (KCC) (Korea); Michelle Lapautre Agence Junior (France); Literarische Agentur Silke Weniger (Germany); Rights People (UK & Commonwealth)
*Warehouse:* Lerner Publishing Group, 1251 Washington Ave N, Minneapolis, MN 55401

**Lerner Publishing Group Inc**
241 First Ave N, Minneapolis, MN 55401
SAN: 201-0828
*Tel:* 612-332-3344 *Toll Free Tel:* 800-328-4929 *Fax:* 612-332-7615 *Toll Free Fax:* 800-332-1132
*E-mail:* info@lernerbooks.com
*Web Site:* www.lernerbooks.com
*Key Personnel*
Chmn: Harry J Lerner
CFO & EVP: Margaret Wunderlich
Pres & Publr: Adam Lerner
EVP, Sales: David Wexler
VP & Dir, Mktg & Digital Prods: Terri Soutor
VP, Prodn: Gary Hansen
Ed-in-Chief: Patricia M Stockland
Rts Dir: Maria Kjoller
Art Dir: Zach Marell
Dir, Electronic Content: Dan Wallek
Dir, Prod Devt & Market Res: Lois Wallentine
Dir, HR: Cyndi Radant
School & Lib Sales Mgr: Brad Richason
Founded: 1959
ISBN Prefix(es): 978-0-87614; 978-1-58013; 978-0-8225; 978-0-7613; 978-1-57505; 978-0-92937; 978-0-93049; 978-1-58196

Number of titles published annually: 450 Print
Total Titles: 4,800 Print; 2,000 E-Book
Imprints: Carolrhoda Books Inc; Carolrhoda Lab™; Darby Creek Publishing; ediciones Lerner; First Avenue Editions; Graphic Universe™; Lerner Publications; LernerClassroom; Millbrook Press; Twenty-First Century Books
Divisions: Kar-Ben Publishing; Lerner Books UK; Lerner Publisher Services
Distributor for Andersen Press USA; Columbus Zoo; Gecko Press; Inside Pocket Publishing; JR Comics; The Kane Press; MVP Books; Red Chair Press; Stoke Books; We Do Listen
Foreign Rep(s): Bravo (Kar-Ben) (UK & the continent); Int Books (Australia); J Appleseed, A Division of Saunders (Canada); Mazeltov Books (Kar-Ben) (Australia); Monarch Books of Canada/Trade (Canada); Phambili Agencies (Botswana, Lesotho, Namibia, South Africa, Swaziland, Zimbabwe); Publishers Marketing Services (Brunei, Malaysia, Singapore); Saunders Book Co/Education (Canada); South Pacific Books (New Zealand)
Foreign Rights: Japan Foreign-Rights Center (Japan); Korea Copyright Center (KCC) (Korea); Michelle Lapautre Agence Junior (France); Literarische Agentur Silke Weniger (Germany); Rights People (UK & Commonwealth)
*Warehouse:* 1251 Washington Ave N, Minneapolis, MN 55401
*See separate listing for:*
**Carolrhoda Books**
**Carolrhoda Lab™**
**ediciones Lerner**
**First Avenue Editions**
**Graphic Universe™**
**Kar-Ben Publishing**
**Lerner Publications**
**LernerClassroom**
**Millbrook Press**
**Twenty-First Century Books**

**LernerClassroom**
Division of Lerner Publishing Group Inc
241 First Ave N, Minneapolis, MN 55401
*Tel:* 612-332-3344 *Toll Free Tel:* 800-328-4929 *Fax:* 612-332-7615 *Toll Free Fax:* 800-332-1132
*E-mail:* info@lernerbooks.com
*Web Site:* www.lernerbooks.com
*Key Personnel*
Chmn: Harry J Lerner
CFO & EVP: Margaret Wunderlich
Pres & Publr: Adam Lerner
EVP, Sales: David Wexler
VP & Dir, Mktg & Digital Prods: Terri Soutor
Ed-in-Chief: Patricia M Stockland
VP, Prodn: Gary Hansen
Rts Dir: Maria Kjoller
Dir, Prod Devt & Mkt Res: Lois Wallentine
Dir, Electronic Content: Dan Wallek
Art Dir: Zach Marell
Dir, HR: Cyndi Radant
Nonfiction children's publications with teaching guides.
Total Titles: 860 Print; 35 E-Book
Foreign Rep(s): INT Books (Australia); Monarch Books of Canada (Canada); Phambili (Southern Africa); Publishers Marketing Services (Brunei, Malaysia, Singapore); South Pacific Books (New Zealand)
Foreign Rights: Japan Foreign-Rights Centre (Japan); Korea Copyright Center (Korea); Michelle Lapautre Agence Junior (France); Literarische Agentur Silke Weniger (Germany); Rights People (UK & Commonwealth)
*Warehouse:* Lerner Publishing Group, 1251 Washington Ave N, Minneapolis, MN 55401

**Lessiter Publications**
225 Regency Ct, Suite 200, Brookfield, WI 53045
Mailing Address: PO Box 624, Brookfield, WI 53008-0624
*Tel:* 262-782-4480 *Toll Free Tel:* 800-645-8455 *Fax:* 262-782-1252
*E-mail:* info@lesspub.com
*Web Site:* www.lesspub.com
*Key Personnel*
Chmn & Edit Dir: Frank Lessiter
Pres: Mike Lessiter
Founded: 1981
Animals, farm equipment, business, sports, veterinary science (equine hoof care).
ISBN Prefix(es): 978-0-944079
Number of titles published annually: 6 Print
Total Titles: 35 Print

**Letterbox/Papyrus of London Publishers USA**
10501 Broom Hill Dr, Suite 1-F, Las Vegas, NV 89134-7339
*Tel:* 702-256-3838
*E-mail:* lb27383@cox.net
*Key Personnel*
Mng Dir: Anthony Wade
Ed-in-Chief: Geoffrey Hutchison-Cleaves, MA
Fin Offr: Josef Kase *Tel:* 702-256-3838 ext 2 *E-mail:* jfkase2@cox.net
Spec Orders Mgr: Erica Neubauer
Rts & Perms: Mrs H Neubauer *Tel:* 702-256-3838 ext 8
Founded: 1946 (at Penley Court, 173 Strand, London EC4)
No submissions accepted through Dec 31, 2013.
Also distributor.
ISBN Prefix(es): 978-0-943698
Number of titles published annually: 3 Print
Total Titles: 131 Print
Imprints: Challenges of Aging Instruction Booklets; Difficult Subjects Made Easy Instruction Booklets
*Advertising Agency:* ShowKase Advertising & Public Relations, 3250 S Fort Apache Rd, Suite 217, Las Vegas, NV 89117, Acct Exec: Ms Robin Lindsay
*Distribution Center:* Baker & Taylor Books, PO Box 8888, Momence, IL 60954 *Tel:* 908-541-7459

**Letterbox Service**, see Letterbox/Papyrus of London Publishers USA

**Level 4 Press Inc**
13518 Jamul Dr, Jamul, CA 91935-1635
*Fax:* 619-374-7311
*E-mail:* sales@level4press.com
*Web Site:* www.level4press.com
*Key Personnel*
Founder & CEO: William Roetzheim
Founded: 2006
ISBN Prefix(es): 978-0-9768001; 978-1-933769
Number of titles published annually: 1 Print; 6 Audio
Total Titles: 35 Print; 15 Audio

**Lexington Books**
Imprint of Rowman & Littlefield Publishing Group
4501 Forbes Blvd, Suite 200, Lanham, MD 20706
*Tel:* 301-459-3366 *Fax:* 301-429-5749
*Web Site:* www.lexingtonbooks.com
*Key Personnel*
VP & Publr: Julie Kirsch *Tel:* 301-459-3366 ext 5309 *E-mail:* jkirsch@rowman.com
Mktg Mgr: Dave Horvath *E-mail:* dhorvath@rowman.com
Premier publisher of scholarly monographs & textbooks. Subjects include classics, political science, political theory, philosophy, history, international relations, literary studies, public policy, sociology, anthropology, religion, communications, cultural studies, education & area studies.
ISBN Prefix(es): 978-0-7391
Number of titles published annually: 350 Print; 300 E-Book
Total Titles: 3,000 Print; 1,500 E-Book
Foreign Rep(s): Academic Marketing Services Pty Ltd (Botswana, Namibia, South Africa, Zimbabwe); APD Singapore Pte Ltd (Brunei, Cambodia, Indonesia, Laos, Malaysia, Singapore, Thailand, Vietnam); Asia Publishers Service Ltd (China, Hong Kong, Korea, Philippines, Taiwan); Avicenna Partnership Ltd (Afghanistan, Algeria, Armenia, Bahrain, Cyprus, Egypt, Iran, Iraq, Jordan, Kuwait, Lebanon, Libya, Morocco, Oman, Palestine, Qatar, Saudi Arabia, Sudan, Syria, Tunisia, United Arab Emirates, Yemen); Cranbury International LLC (Caribbean, Central America, Mexico, Pakistan, Puerto Rico, South America); DA Information Services Pty Ltd (Australia, New Zealand, Papua New Guinea); Durnell Marketing Ltd (Austria, Baltic States, Belgium, Czech Republic, Denmark, Finland, France, Germany, Greece, Hungary, Iceland, Italy, Malta, Netherlands, Norway, Poland, Portugal, Slovakia, Slovenia, Spain, Sweden, Switzerland); Overleaf (Bangladesh, India, Nepal); United Publishers Service Ltd (Japan, South Korea)
Foreign Rights: Clare Cox (Worldwide)
*Orders to:* Rowman & Littlefield Publishing Group, 15200 NBN Way, Blue Ridge Summit, PA 17214 *Tel:* 717-794-3800 *Toll Free Tel:* 800-462-6420 *Fax:* 717-794-3803 *E-mail:* custserv@rowman.com
Membership(s): AAP

**§LexisNexis®**
Division of Reed Elsevier Inc
701 E Water St, Charlottesville, VA 22902
SAN: 202-6317
*Tel:* 434-972-7600 *Toll Free Tel:* 800-446-3410 *Fax:* 434-961-5576
*E-mail:* customer.support@lexisnexis.com
*Web Site:* www.lexisnexis.com
*Key Personnel*
CEO, US Legal Mkts: Mike Walsh
Founded: 1897
Multivolume legal reference works, state codes & single-volume legal texts, treatises & casebooks. Most material also in online versions.
ISBN Prefix(es): 978-0-8205; 978-0-3271; 978-0-8806
Imprints: Michie
*Shipping Address:* Broome Corp Park, 136 Carlin Rd, Conklin, NY 13748 *Tel:* 607-772-2600 *Toll Free Tel:* 800-323-9608

**§LexisNexis/Martindale-Hubbell**
Member of The Reed Elsevier Group
121 Chanlon Rd, New Providence, NJ 07974
SAN: 205-8863
Mailing Address: PO Box 1001, Summit, NJ 07902-1001
*Tel:* 908-464-6800 *Toll Free Tel:* 800-526-4902 *Fax:* 908-464-3553
*E-mail:* info@martindale.com
*Web Site:* www.martindale.com
*Key Personnel*
Sr Dir, Entity Management Group: Mark Van Orman
Founded: 1868
Publisher of the *Martindale-Hubbell Law Directory* in hardcopy, on CD-ROM & available through LexisNexis & on the Internet; containing listings of over 1 million lawyers & law firms worldwide. Other publications include *Law Digest*, a summary of laws from each of the 50 states & over 60 countries; *Martindale-Hubbell Law Directory International Edition*, designed for the international legal community & *Martindale-Hubbell Bar Register of Preeminent Lawyers*, listing of 10,000 law practices

designated as outstanding by members of the legal community.
ISBN Prefix(es): 978-1-56160
Number of titles published annually: 5 Print; 1 CD-ROM; 1 Online
Total Titles: 5 Print; 1 CD-ROM; 1 Online

**§LexisNexis® Matthew Bender®**
Member of The LexisNexis Group
1275 Broadway, Albany, NY 12204
*Tel:* 518-487-3000 *Toll Free Tel:* 800-424-4200 *Fax:* 518-487-3083
*Web Site:* bender.lexisnexis.com
Founded: 1887
Treatises, text & form books, newsletters, periodicals & manuals for the legal, accounting, insurance, banking & related professions, selected libraries on CD-ROM.
Branch locations also in New York City & Dayton, OH.
ISBN Prefix(es): 978-0-8205; 978-1-4224
Total Titles: 577 Print; 277 CD-ROM; 27 Online; 277 E-Book
*Branch Office(s)*
Immaculata Hall, 32 S Ewing St, Helena, MT 59601 *Toll Free Tel:* 800-227-9597
121 Chanlon Rd, New Providence, NJ 07974 *Tel:* 908-464-6800 *Toll Free Tel:* 800-526-4902
701 E Water St, Charlottesville, VA 22902 *Tel:* 434-972-7600 *Toll Free Tel:* 800-446-3410

**Liberty Fund Inc**
8335 Allison Pointe Trail, Suite 300, Indianapolis, IN 46250-1684
SAN: 202-6740
*Tel:* 317-842-0880 *Toll Free Tel:* 800-955-8335; 800-866-3520; 800-368-7897 ext 6069 (cust serv) *Fax:* 317-577-9067; 317-579-6060 (cust serv); 708-534-7803
*E-mail:* books@libertyfund.org; info@libertyfund.org
*Web Site:* www.libertyfund.org
*Key Personnel*
VP, Publg: Patricia Gallagher
Mktg & Fulfillment Dir: Kristen Beach *Tel:* 317-842-0880 ext 6050 *E-mail:* kbeach@libertyfund.org
Mng Ed: Dan Kirklin
Founded: 1960
A publisher of print & electronic scholarly resources including new editions of classic works in American constitutional history, European history, natural law, law, modern political thought, economics & education.
ISBN Prefix(es): 978-0-913966; 978-0-86597
Number of titles published annually: 20 Print; 100 Online
Total Titles: 360 Print; 1,450 Online; 1 Audio
Foreign Rep(s): Academic Sales & Marketing (Andrew Jones) (Midlands, Northern England); Jim Biaho (Italy); Mara Cheli (Italy); Peter Couzens (Asia); Everybodys Book's (Warren Halford) (Southern Africa); Export Sales Agency (Ted Dougherty) (Austria, Germany, Switzerland); Four Corners Sales Agency (Charlotte Kelly) (Ireland, London, Scotland, Southern England, Wales); Gazelle Academic (Mark Trotter) (London); Charles Gibbes (Cyprus, Greece); Iberian Book Services (Charlotte Prout) (Gibraltar, Portugal, Spain); Iberian Book Services (Peter Prout); Marketing Solutions LLP (Andrew Wallace) (Central London, UK, East Anglia, England); Maya Publishers Pvt Ltd (India); Tony Moggach (Eastern Europe); David Towle (Baltic States, Northern Europe, Scandinavia)
*Distribution Center:* Scholarly Book Services, 289 Ridgeland Ave, Unit 105, Toronto, ON M6A 1Z6, Canada *Toll Free Tel:* 800-847-9736
Membership(s): AAP; ALA

**Libraries Unlimited**
Imprint of ABC-CLIO
130 Cremona Dr, Santa Barbara, CA 93117
Mailing Address: PO Box 1911, Santa Barbara, CA 93116-1911
*Tel:* 805-968-1911 *Toll Free Tel:* 800-368-6868 *Fax:* 805-685-9685 *Toll Free Fax:* 866-270-3856
*E-mail:* customerservice@abc-clio.com
*Web Site:* www.abc-clio.com; www.abc-clio.com
Founded: 1964
Library science textbooks, annotated bibliographies, reference books, professional books for school media specialists as well as resource & activity books for librarians & teachers; storytelling resources & collections.
ISBN Prefix(es): 978-0-87287; 978-1-56308
Number of titles published annually: 80 Print
Total Titles: 600 Print; 5 Audio
Imprints: Linworth Publishing
*See separate listing for:*
**Linworth Publishing**

**The Library of America**
14 E 60 St, New York, NY 10022-1006
SAN: 286-9918
*Tel:* 212-308-3360 *Fax:* 212-750-8352
*E-mail:* info@loa.org
*Web Site:* www.loa.org
*Key Personnel*
CEO & Pres: Cheryl Hurley
CFO & VP: Daniel W Baker
VP & Publr: Max Rudin
Assoc Publr: Brian McCarthy *Tel:* 212-308-3360 ext 227 *E-mail:* bmccarthy@loa.org
Ed-in-Chief: Geoffrey O'Brien
Dir, Mktg: David Cloyce Smith
Prodn Ed: Trish Hoard
Cust Serv Mgr: Laura Gazlay
Founded: 1979
Collected editions of classic American authors; literature, history, philosophy, drama, poetry & journalism.
ISBN Prefix(es): 978-0-940450; 978-1-883011; 978-1-931082; 978-1-59853
Number of titles published annually: 14 Print
Total Titles: 300 Print
Distributed by Penguin Group (USA) LLC
Foreign Rep(s): Penguin Canada (Canada); United Publishers Service (Japan)
*Warehouse:* Penguin Group (USA) LLC, One Grosset Dr, Kirkwood, NY 13795

**Library of Virginia**
800 E Broad St, Richmond, VA 23219-8000
*Tel:* 804-692-3999; 804-692-3500 *Fax:* 804-692-3736
*Web Site:* www.lva.virginia.gov
*Key Personnel*
Dir, Pubns & Educ Servs: Gregg Kimball *Tel:* 804-692-3722 *E-mail:* gregg.kimball@lva.virginia.gov
Founded: 1823
Monographs & reference works on Virginia history.
ISBN Prefix(es): 978-0-88490
Number of titles published annually: 4 Print
Total Titles: 75 Print

**Libros Para Ninos**, see Simon & Schuster Children's Publishing

**Mary Ann Liebert Inc**
140 Huguenot St, 3rd fl, New Rochelle, NY 10801-5215
*Tel:* 914-740-2100 *Toll Free Tel:* 800-654-3237 *Fax:* 914-740-2101
*E-mail:* info@liebertpub.com
*Web Site:* www.liebertonline.com
*Key Personnel*
SVP: Harriet I Matysko *Tel:* 914-740-2182 *E-mail:* hmatysko@liebertpub.com
Dir, Ad Prodn-Genetic Engg & Biotechnology News: Anne B Chin Aleong *Tel:* 914-740-2178 *E-mail:* achin@genengnews.com
Ad Prodn Mgr: Kathleen De Souza *Tel:* 914-740-2295 *E-mail:* kdesouza@liebertpub.com
Supvr, Ad Prodn-GEN Print & Online & MAL Journals: Sherine Morris *Tel:* 914-740-2174 *E-mail:* smorris@liebertpub.com
Ad Prodn: Wanda Sanchez *Tel:* 914-740-2178 *E-mail:* wsanchez@liebertpub.com
Founded: 1980
Medical & sci-tech journals, books & newspapers. Additional subjects include: biomedical research, integrative medicine (CAM), public policy, public health/policy, gender & population studies, regenerative medicine, clinical medicine, biotechnology, environmental studies, humanities, life sciences, allied health & surgery.
ISBN Prefix(es): 978-0-913113
Number of titles published annually: 3 Print; 3 Online
Total Titles: 65 Print; 70 Online
Divisions: Genetic Engineering & Biotechnology News
*Foreign Office(s):* Impress Media, Carrington Kirk, Carrington, Midlothian EH23 4LR, United Kingdom, Contact: Hilary Turnbull *Tel:* (01875) 825700 *Fax:* (01875) 825701 *E-mail:* hturnbull@genengnews.com

**Life Cycle Books**
Division of Life Cycle Books Ltd (Canada)
PO Box 799, Fort Collins, CO 80522
SAN: 692-7173
*Toll Free Tel:* 800-214-5849 *Toll Free Fax:* 888-690-8532
*E-mail:* orders@lifecyclebooks.com; support@lifecyclebooks.com
*Web Site:* www.lifecyclebooks.com
*Key Personnel*
Founder & Pres: Paul Broughton *E-mail:* paulb@lifecyclebooks.com
Founded: 1973
Books, pamphlets, brochures & audiovisuals on human life issues.
ISBN Prefix(es): 978-0-919225
Number of titles published annually: 6 Print
Total Titles: 41 Print

**Light-Beams Publishing**
10 Toon Lane, Lee, NH 03861
*Tel:* 603-659-1300 *Toll Free Tel:* 800-397-7641
*E-mail:* info@light-beams.com
*Web Site:* www.light-beams.com
*Key Personnel*
Mktg Mgr: Mark Forman *E-mail:* mforman@light-beams.com
Founded: 2000
Specialize in & publishes award-winning children's books & videos for children ages 3 & up.
ISBN Prefix(es): 978-0-9708104; 978-0-9766289
Number of titles published annually: 10 Print
*Distribution Center:* Independent Publishers Group, 814 N Franklin St, Chicago, IL 60610 (exclusive distributor to the book trade) *Toll Free Tel:* 800-888-4741 *Web Site:* www.ipgbook.com

**Light Technology Publishing**
4030 E Huntington Dr, Flagstaff, AZ 86004
Mailing Address: PO Box 3540, Flagstaff, AZ 86003-3540
*Tel:* 928-526-1345 *Toll Free Tel:* 800-450-0985 *Fax:* 928-714-1132
*E-mail:* publishing@lighttechnology.net
*Web Site:* www.lighttechnology.com
*Key Personnel*
Owner & Publr: O'Ryin Swanson
Sidona Journal, metaphysical publications, mostly channelled.

ISBN Prefix(es): 978-1-891824; 978-1-929385
Number of titles published annually: 15 Print
Total Titles: 150 Print
Foreign Rights: Hagenbach & Bender GmbH (Worldwide exc USA)
Membership(s): AAP

**Lighthouse Publishing of the Carolinas**
2333 Barton Oaks Dr, Raleigh, NC 27614-7940
*E-mail:* lighthousepublishingcarolinas@gmail.com
*Web Site:* lighthousepublishingofthecarolinas.com
*Key Personnel*
Acqs Ed: Eddie Jones
Assoc Ed: Loree Lough
ISBN Prefix(es): 978-0-9833196; 978-0-9822065; 978-0-9847655; 978-1-938499
Number of titles published annually: 12 Print
Total Titles: 22 Print; 12 E-Book
Membership(s): IBPA, the Independent Book Publishers Association

**Liguori Publications**
One Liguori Dr, Liguori, MO 63057-1000
*Tel:* 636-464-2500 *Toll Free Tel:* 866-848-2492; 800-325-9521 *Fax:* 636-464-8449
*Web Site:* www.liguori.org
*Key Personnel*
Pres & Publr: Fr Mathew Kessler
Dir, Fin & Busn Opers: Suann Fields
Mng Ed, Libros Liguori: Jose Antonio Medina
Rts & Perms & Intl Rts: Christopher Miller
Founded: 1947
Academic & trade books on religion (Catholic) & spirituality, inspirational & educational resources for parishes & schools, devotional music, bulletins, pamphlets, Liguorian magazine.
ISBN Prefix(es): 978-0-89243; 978-0-7648
Number of titles published annually: 30 Print
Total Titles: 600 Print; 14 CD-ROM
Imprints: Libros Liguori; Liguori/Triumph
Distributor for Redemptorist Publications
Foreign Rep(s): Redemptorist Publications Book Services (England)

**Limelight Editions**
Imprint of Hal Leonard Performing Arts Publishing Group
33 Plymouth St, Suite 302, Montclair, NJ 07042
*Tel:* 973-337-5034 *Fax:* 973-337-5227
*Web Site:* limelighteditions.com
*Key Personnel*
Group Publr: John Cerullo
Full service trade publisher that produces books, book/CDs & DVDs on the performing arts including cinema, dance & theater.
ISBN Prefix(es): 978-0-87910
Number of titles published annually: 10 Print; 2 Audio
Total Titles: 300 Print; 5 Audio
*Sales Office(s):* 7777 W Bluemound Rd, Milwaukee, WI 53213 *Toll Free Tel:* 800-554-0626
Distributed by Hal Leonard Corp
*Billing Address:* 960 E Mark St, Winona, MN 55987 *Tel:* 507-454-2920 *Fax:* 507-454-9334
*Orders to:* 7777 W Bluemound Rd, Milwaukee, WI 53213 *Toll Free Tel:* 800-554-0626
*Returns:* 1210 Innovation Dr, Winona, MN 55987 *Tel:* 507-454-2920 *Fax:* 507-454-8334
*Warehouse:* 1210 Innovation Dr, Winona, MN 55987 *Tel:* 507-454-2920 *Fax:* 507-454-8334
*Distribution Center:* 960 E Mark St, Winona, MN 55987 *Tel:* 507-454-2920 *Fax:* 507-454-8334

**Linden Publishing Co Inc**
2006 S Mary St, Fresno, CA 93721
*Tel:* 559-233-6633 *Toll Free Tel:* 800-345-4447 (orders) *Fax:* 559-233-6933
*Web Site:* lindenpub.com
*Key Personnel*
Pres & Publr: Richard Sorsky *E-mail:* richard@lindenpub.com
Founded: 1977
ISBN Prefix(es): 978-0-941936; 978-1-933502; 978-1-884956; 978-1-884995
Number of titles published annually: 12 Print
Total Titles: 180 Print
Imprints: Craven Street Books; Quill Driver Books; Word Dancer Press
Distributed by IPG
Foreign Rights: Books Crossing Borders (Worldwide)
Membership(s): ABA; IBPA, the Independent Book Publishers Association

**Lindisfarne Books**
Imprint of SteinerBooks
610 Main St, Great Barrington, MA 01230
Mailing Address: PO Box 749, Great Barrington, MA 01230
*Tel:* 413-528-8233 *Fax:* 413-528-8826
*E-mail:* service@lindisfarne.org
*Web Site:* www.lindisfarne.org
*Key Personnel*
CEO & Pres: Eugene Gollogly *E-mail:* gene@steinerbooks.org
Ed-in-Chief: Christopher Bamford
Founded: 1979
Fine quality books in the areas of philosophy, psychology, new sciences, comparative theology, art & literature, emphasizing the synthesis of science, religion & art.
ISBN Prefix(es): 978-0-940262; 978-1-58420; 978-0-9701097
Number of titles published annually: 5 Print
Total Titles: 103 Print
Distributed by Floris Books
Foreign Rep(s): Floris Books (UK)
*Orders to:* PO Box 960, Herndon, VA 20172 *Tel:* 703-661-1594 *Toll Free Tel:* 800-856-8664 *Fax:* 703-661-1501
*Warehouse:* PO Box 960, Herndon, VA 20172 *Tel:* 703-661-1594

**LinguaText Ltd**
103 Walker Way, Newark, DE 19711
SAN: 238-0307
*Tel:* 302-453-8695 *Fax:* 302-453-8695 *Toll Free Fax:* 800-784-4935
*E-mail:* linguatextext@juno.com
*Web Site:* www.linguatextltd.com
*Key Personnel*
Publr: Michael Bolan *Fax:* 302-453-8601
Ed, Juan de la Cuesta Hispanic Monographs: Michael McGrath *Tel:* 912-478-0115 *Fax:* 912-478-0652 *E-mail:* mmcgrath@georgiasouthern.edu
Founded: 1974
Publish foreign language textbooks (Portuguese), scholarly monographs on Spanish literature from medieval to modern & student editions of Spanish & French classic literature designed for English speakers.
60% subvented by institution.
ISBN Prefix(es): 978-0-936388; 978-0-942566; 978-1-58871; 978-1-58977
Number of titles published annually: 20 Print
Total Titles: 290 Print
Imprints: Juan de la Cuesta—Hispanic Monographs; European Masterpieces
Distributor for Juan de la Cuesta—Hispanic Monographs; European Masterpieces
Membership(s): CSA; Text & Academic Authors
*See separate listing for:*
**European Masterpieces**

**LinguiSystems Inc**
3100 Fourth Ave, East Moline, IL 61244
*Tel:* 309-755-2300 *Toll Free Tel:* 800-776-4332 *Fax:* 309-755-2377 *Toll Free Fax:* 800-577-4555
*E-mail:* service@linguisystems.com
*Web Site:* www.linguisystems.com
*Key Personnel*
Owner: Linda Bowers; Rosemary Huisingh
Acqs Coord: Paul Johnson
Founded: 1977
Acquisition, editing, manufacturing, marketing & fulfillment; educational books, tapes & games for speech therapy, special education & regular education.
ISBN Prefix(es): 978-1-55999; 978-0-7606
Number of titles published annually: 50 Print
Total Titles: 137 Print

**§The Linick Group Inc**
Linick Bldg, 7 Putter Lane, Middle Island, NY 11953
Mailing Address: PO Box 102, Middle Island, NY 11953-0102
*Tel:* 631-924-3888; 631-924-8555 *Fax:* 631-924-8555
*E-mail:* linickgroup@gmail.com; andrew@AskLinick.com
*Web Site:* www.AndrewLinickDirectMarketing.com/Publishers-Advice.html; www.NewWorldPressBooks.com
*Key Personnel*
Lib Sales Dir: Jill Reynolds
Founded: 1968
Specialized health titles, health care, weight loss, exercise, fitness, martial arts/self-defense, wine & spirits, mature market, multicultural & bilingual picture; multi-media, workbooks & instructional material, public relations, restaurants & travel & tourism; confidential reports, foreign countries, newsletters, business & direct response advertising & marketing, communications, subscription & mail order, photography, psychology, e-commerce, e-books, e-publishing, Internet interactive campaigns, targeted e-public relations on a guaranteed placement basis.
ISBN Prefix(es): 978-0-917098
Number of titles published annually: 25 Print; 10 CD-ROM; 450 Online; 50 E-Book
Total Titles: 125 Print; 120 CD-ROM; 950 Online; 350 E-Book
Imprints: CCA; Isshin-Ryu Productions; LKA Inc; National Association of Photo Sellers™; New World Press (NWP)
Distributed by New World Press Books; Okinawan Kobujutsu Kyokai Association (OKKA)
Distributor for Linick International; LKA Inc; National Association of Photo Sellers™
*Advertising Agency:* LK Advertising Agency, 7 Putter Lane, PO Box 102, Middle Island, NY 11953-0102, EVP: Roger Dextor *Tel:* 631-924-3888; 631-924-8555 *Fax:* 631-924-8555 *E-mail:* printmedia4less@gmail.com *Web Site:* www.newworldpressbooks.com
*Distribution Center:* Bookmasters, 30 Amberwood Pkwy, Ashland, OH 44805
*See separate listing for:*
**Copywriter's Council of America (CCA)**

**Linworth Publishing**
Imprint of Libraries Unlimited
130 Cremona Dr, Santa Barbara, CA 93117
Mailing Address: PO Box 1911, Santa Barbara, CA 93116-1911
*Tel:* 805-968-1911 *Toll Free Tel:* 800-368-6868 *Fax:* 805-685-9685 *Toll Free Fax:* 866-270-3856
*E-mail:* customerservice@abc-clio.com
*Web Site:* www.abc-clio.com
*Key Personnel*
Pres & Publr: Marlene Woo-Lun
Founded: 1982
Professional book & magazine publishing for school library media specialists.
ISBN Prefix(es): 978-0-938865; 978-1-58683
Number of titles published annually: 20 Print
Total Titles: 100 Print
Imprints: Linworth Learning

**LionHearted Publishing Inc**
PO Box 618, Zephyr Cove, NV 89448-0618

*Tel:* 775-853-3221 *Toll Free Tel:* 888-546-6478 *Toll Free Fax:* 888-546-6478
*E-mail:* admin@lionhearted.com
*Web Site:* www.lionhearted.com
*Key Personnel*
Founder & CEO: Kim A Heathman *E-mail:* kimheathman@mac.com
Founded: 1994
Publisher of single title romance novels. Check web site to see if open for submissions, then submit the Release Form posted online.
ISBN Prefix(es): 978-1-57343
Number of titles published annually: 3 Print; 3 Online; 3 E-Book
Total Titles: 30 Print; 35 Online; 35 E-Book

**Lipper Marketplace**
Division of Thomson Reuters
195 Broadway, 5th fl, New York, NY 10007
*Tel:* 646-822-3450; 646-223-4000 (sales) *Toll Free Tel:* 800-782-5555 (orders)
*E-mail:* general.info@thomsonreuters.com
*Web Site:* www.lippermarketplace.com
Founded: 1974
Publish directories/databases of institutional investment market.
ISBN Prefix(es): 978-0-922460; 978-1-891851
Number of titles published annually: 6 Print
Total Titles: 5 Print

**§Lippincott Williams & Wilkins**
Unit of Wolters Kluwer Health
530 Walnut St, Philadelphia, PA 19106-3621
SAN: 201-0933
*Tel:* 215-521-8300 *Toll Free Tel:* 800-638-3030 (orders & cust serv)
*E-mail:* orders@lww.com
*Web Site:* www.lww.com
*Key Personnel*
VP, Communs: Robert Dekker *Tel:* 215-521-8928 *E-mail:* robert.dekker@wolterskluwer.com
Dir, Mktg & Communs: Connie Hughes *Tel:* 646-674-6348 *E-mail:* connie.hughes@wolterskluwer.com
Sr Mktg Mgr, Journals: Laurie Hee *Tel:* 215-521-8322 *E-mail:* laurie.hee@wolterskluwer.com
Founded: 1792
Medicine, dentistry life sciences, nursing, allied health, veterinary medicine books, journals, textbooks, looseleaf, newsletters & media.
ISBN Prefix(es): 978-0-397; 978-0-316; 978-0-87434; 978-1-58255; 978-0-683; 978-0-7817; 978-1-5877
Total Titles: 4,000 E-Book
*Branch Office(s)*
2 Commerce Sq, 2001 Market St, Philadelphia, PA 19103
323 Norristown Rd, Suite 200, Ambler, PA 19002-2758 *Tel:* 215-646-8700 *Fax:* 215-654-1328
William Kluwer Health, 2700 Lake Cook Rd, Riverwoods, IL 60015 *Tel:* 847-580-5000
351 W Camden St, Baltimore, MD 21201 *Tel:* 410-528-4000
Healthcare Group, 333 Seventh Ave, 19th & 20th fl, New York, NY 10001 *Toll Free Tel:* 800-933-6525
*Foreign Office(s):* Lippincott Williams & Wilkins Pty Ltd, 9 Hunter St, Level 18, Suite 1801, Sydney, NSW 2000, Australia *Tel:* (02) 9276-6600 *Fax:* (02) 9231-1255
Lippincott Williams & Wilkins Asia Ltd, Harbor City, Wharf T & T Ctr, Suite 908-910, 7 Canton Rd, Tsim Sha Tsui, Kowloon, Hong Kong *Tel:* 2610-2339 *Fax:* 2421-1123
250 Waterloo Rd, London SE1 8RD, United Kingdom *Tel:* (020) 7981 0600 *Fax:* (020) 7981 0601

*Warehouse:* 16522 Hunters Green Pkwy, Hagerstown, MD 21740 *Tel:* 301-223-2300 *Fax:* 301-223-2398
*Distribution Center:* 16522 Hunters Green Pkwy, Hagerstown, MD 21740 *Tel:* 301-223-2300 *Fax:* 301-223-2398

**Listen & Live Audio Inc**
PO Box 817, Roseland, NJ 07068-0817
*Tel:* 201-558-9000 *Toll Free Tel:* 800-653-9400 (orders) *Fax:* 201-558-9800
*Web Site:* www.listenandlive.com
*Key Personnel*
Pres: Alfred C Martino *E-mail:* alfred@listenandlive.com
Publr: Alisa Weberman *E-mail:* alisa@listenandlive.com
Founded: 1995
Strictly audio books, self-help, fiction, motivational & men's adventure.
ISBN Prefix(es): 978-1-885408; 978-1-931953; 978-1-59316
Number of titles published annually: 10 Audio
Total Titles: 500 Audio
Membership(s): Audio Publishers Association; IBPA, the Independent Book Publishers Association

**Little, Brown and Company**
Division of Hachette Book Group
237 Park Ave, New York, NY 10017
*Tel:* 212-364-1100 *Fax:* 212-364-0952
*E-mail:* firstname.lastname@hbgusa.com
*Web Site:* www.HachetteBookGroup.com
*Key Personnel*
EVP, Hachette Book Group & Publr, Little, Brown and Company: Michael Pietsch
VP, Edit Dir: Geoff Shandler
VP, Ed-in-Chief: Judy Clain
VP, Edit Dir, Reagan Arthur Books: Reagan Arthur
VP, Publr, Digital & Pbk: Terry Adams
Edit Dir, Mulholland Books: Josh Kendall
VP, Creative Dir: Mario Pulice
VP, Mktg Dir: Heather Fain
Exec Dir of Publicity: Nicole Dewey
VP, Subs Rts, Hachette Book Group: Nancy Wiese
Dir, Intl Rts: Tracy Williams
Founded: 1837
Little, Brown and Company, the adult trade division of Hachette Book Group, is one of the country's oldest & most distinguished publishing houses. Unsol/unagented mss not accepted.
ISBN Prefix(es): 978-0-316
Number of titles published annually: 142 Print
Imprints: Back Bay Books; Mulholland Books
*Sales Office(s):* Hachette Book Group, 237 Park Ave, New York, NY 10017 (spec mkts) *Toll Free Tel:* 800-222-6747 *Toll Free Fax:* 800-477-5925
Foreign Rights: Agencia Literaria Balcells (Portugal, Spain); Bardon Chinese Media (China, Taiwan); Luigi Bernabo Associates SRL (Italy); BMSR Ag Literaria (Brazil); JLM Literary Agency (Greece); Nurcihan Kesim Literary Agency Inc (Turkey); The KM Agency (Netherlands); Agence Michelle Lapautre (France); Mohrbooks Agency (Germany); Andrew Nurnberg Associates LTD (Baltic States, Bulgaria, Croatia, Czech Republic, Hungary, Poland, Romania, Russia & former USSR); I Pitarski Ltd Literary Agency (Israel); Sane Toregard Agency (Scandinavia); Tuttle-Mori Agency Inc (Japan); Eric Yang Agency (Korea)
*Orders to:* Hachette Book Group, 3 Center Plaza, Boston, MA 02108-2084 *Toll Free Tel:* 800-759-0190 *Toll Free Fax:* 800-286-9471
*Returns:* Hachette Book Group, 322 S Enterprise Blvd, Lebanon, IN 46052
*Shipping Address:* Hachette Book Group, 121 N Enterprise Blvd, Lebanon, IN 46052

**Little, Brown Books for Young Readers**
Division of Hachette Book Group
237 Park Ave, New York, NY 10017
SAN: 200-2205
*Tel:* 212-364-1100 *Toll Free Tel:* 800-759-0190 (cust serv)
*Web Site:* www.HachetteBookGroup.com
*Key Personnel*
SVP, Hachette Book Group & Publr, Little, Brown Books for Young Readers: Megan Tingley
VP, Deputy Publr: Andrew Smith
Creative Dir: David Caplan
Edit Dir: Alvina Ling
Sr Exec Ed, Franchise & Licensed Book Prog: Erin Stein
VP, Exec Dir, Publicity & Communs: Melanie Chang
Sr Ed, Poppy Imprint: Elizabeth Bewley
Sr Exec Ed: Andrea Spooner
Ed-in-Chief: Liza Baker
Dir, Subs Rts: Amy Habayeb
Dir, School & Lib Mktg: Victoria Stapleton
Assoc Dir, Publicty: Lisa Moraleda
Founded: 1837
Specializes in board books, novelty items, picture books, middle reader, young adult fiction & nonfiction & selected media tie-ins.
ISBN Prefix(es): 978-0-316
Number of titles published annually: 198 Print
Imprints: LBKids; Poppy; Megan Tingley Books
*Orders to:* Hachette Book Group, 3 Center Plaza, Boston, MA 02108-2084 *Toll Free Tel:* 800-759-0190 *Toll Free Fax:* 800-286-9471
*Shipping Address:* Hachette Book Group Distribution Center, 121 N Enterprise Blvd, Lebanon, IN 46052 *Tel:* 765-483-9900 *Fax:* 765-483-0706
Membership(s): AAP; ALA; Children's Book Council; Women's National Book Association

**The Little Entrepreneur**
Imprint of Harper Arrington Publishing
c/o Harper-Arrington, 18701 Grand River, Suite 105, Detroit, MI 48223
*Toll Free Tel:* 888-435-9234 *Fax:* 248-281-0373
*E-mail:* info@harperarringtonmedia.com
*Web Site:* www.thelittlee.com; www.harperarringtonmedia.com
*Key Personnel*
Founder & Publr: Jay Arrington; Michael Harper
Media Rels: John Thomas
Media Contact: Lance Smith
Founded: 2004
ISBN Prefix(es): 978-0-9764161
Number of titles published annually: 3 Print; 1 CD-ROM
Total Titles: 4 Print; 2 CD-ROM; 1 Online
*Branch Office(s)*
8033 Sunset Blvd, Suite 1074, Los Angeles, CA 90046
One Penn Plaza, Suite 6232, New York, NY 10119
Distributed by Harper Arrington Publishing

**Little Simon**, see Simon & Schuster Children's Publishing

**Little Simon Inspirations**, see Simon & Schuster Children's Publishing

**§Liturgical Press**
Division of The Order of St Benedict Inc
PO Box 7500, St John's Abbey, Collegeville, MN 56321-7500
SAN: 202-2494
*Tel:* 320-363-2213 *Toll Free Tel:* 800-858-5450 *Fax:* 320-363-3299 *Toll Free Fax:* 800-445-5899
*E-mail:* sales@litpress.org
*Web Site:* www.litpress.org

*Key Personnel*
Dir: Peter Dwyer *Tel:* 320-363-2533 *E-mail:* pdwyer@osb.org
Assoc Publr, Parish Mkt: Michelle Verkuilen *Tel:* 320-363-2227 *E-mail:* mverkuilen@osb.org
Fin Dir: Sandra Eiynck *Tel:* 320-363-2225 *E-mail:* seiynck@csbsju.edu
Sales & Mktg Mgr: Brian Woods *Tel:* 320-363-3953 *E-mail:* bwoods@csbsju.edu
Founded: 1926
Began publishing for the Church in 1926 & continues to sustain the original mission of proclaiming the Good News of Jesus Christ. Liturgical Press is a trusted publisher of liturgy, scripture, theology & spirituality evolving to serve the changing needs of the Church.
ISBN Prefix(es): 978-0-87907; 978-0-8146
Number of titles published annually: 90 Print; 50 E-Book
Total Titles: 1,500 Print; 10 CD-ROM; 50 E-Book; 20 Audio
Imprints: Cistercian Publications; Michael Glazier Books; Liturgical Press Books; Pueblo Books
Foreign Rep(s): B Broughton Co Ltd (Canada); The Catholic Bookshop (South Africa); Claretian Publications (Philippines); Columba Book Service (European Union, Ireland, UK); John Garratt Publishing (Australia); Katong Catholic Book Centre Pte Ltd (Malaysia, Singapore); Pleroma Christian Supplies (New Zealand); Spring Arbor/Ingram (Tennessee)
*Advertising Agency:* Liturgical Advertising Agency
*See separate listing for:*
**Cistercian Publications Inc, Editorial Office**

**Liturgy Training Publications**
Subsidiary of Archdiocese of Chicago
3949 S Racine Ave, Chicago, IL 60609-2523
SAN: 670-9052
*Tel:* 773-579-4900 *Toll Free Tel:* 800-933-1800 (US & CN only orders) *Fax:* 773-486-7094 *Toll Free Fax:* 800-933-7094 (US & CN only orders)
*E-mail:* orders@ltp.org
*Web Site:* www.ltp.org
*Key Personnel*
Dir: John A Thomas *Tel:* 773-579-4900 ext 3557 *E-mail:* jthomas@ltp.org
Assoc Dir: Theresa Pincich *Tel:* 773-579-4900 ext 3537 *E-mail:* tpincich@ltp.org
Busn Mgr: Maureen Como *Tel:* 773-579-4900 ext 3553 *E-mail:* mcomo@ltp.org
Mktg, Sales & Fulfillment Mgr: Kathleen Sommers *Tel:* 773-579-4900 ext 3570 *E-mail:* ksommers@ltp.org
Trade Accts Rep: Irene Sanchez *Tel:* 773-579-4900 ext 3566 *E-mail:* isanchez@ltp.org
Founded: 1964
Books & periodicals on Roman Catholic liturgy, worship & prayer in the home & church.
ISBN Prefix(es): 978-0-929650; 978-1-56854; 978-1-59525
Number of titles published annually: 30 Print; 2 CD-ROM; 20 E-Book; 2 Audio
Total Titles: 500 Print; 6 CD-ROM; 80 E-Book; 7 Audio
Imprints: Catechesis of the Good Shepherd Publications; Hillenbrand Books
Distributor for United States Catholic Conference Publications
Foreign Rep(s): The Catholic Bookshop (South Africa); Katong Catholic Book Centre (Malaysia); McCrimmons Bookstore/Publisher (UK exc Ireland); Pleroma Christian Supplies (New Zealand); Word of Life Distributors (Australia)
Membership(s): Association of Catholic Publishers Inc

**The Live Oak Press LLC**
PO Box 60036, Palo Alto, CA 94306-0036
*Tel:* 650-853-0197 *Fax:* 815-366-8205
*E-mail:* info@liveoakpress.com
*Web Site:* www.liveoakpress.com
*Key Personnel*
Founder & Pres: David M Hamilton
Founded: 1982
Publishes California literary history.
ISBN Prefix(es): 978-0-931095; 978-0-931378
Number of titles published annually: 3 Print
Total Titles: 14 Print
Membership(s): ALA; Association of College & Research Libraries; The Authors Guild; IBPA, the Independent Book Publishers Association; PINC; Publishing Professionals Network; Society for Scholarly Publishing

**Living Language**
Imprint of Random House Audio Publishing Group
c/o Random House Inc, 1745 Broadway, New York, NY 10019
*Tel:* 212-782-9000 *Toll Free Tel:* 800-733-3000 (orders) *Toll Free Fax:* 800-659-2436
*E-mail:* livinglanguage@randomhouse.com
*Web Site:* www.livinglanguage.com
*Key Personnel*
SVP & Publr: Amanda D'Acierno
Assoc Dir, Mng Edit: Alison Skrabek
Publg Dir: Christopher Warnasch
Dir, Subs/Foreign Rts: Linda Kaplan
Creative Mktg Mgr: Heather Dalton
Mgr, Subs/Foreign Rts: Maren Monitello
Founded: 1946
Self-study foreign language & ESL. Online courses, apps & digital content; Sign Language & dictionaries.
Random House Inc & its publishing entities are not accepting unsol submissions, proposals, mss, or submission queries via e-mail at this time.
ISBN Prefix(es): 978-0-609; 978-0-307
Number of titles published annually: 12 Print
Total Titles: 22 Print; 122 Audio

**§Living Stream Ministry (LSM)**
2431 W La Palma Ave, Anaheim, CA 92801
*Tel:* 714-991-4681 *Fax:* 714-236-6005
*E-mail:* books@lsm.org
*Web Site:* www.lsm.org
*Key Personnel*
Intl Rts Contact: Yorke Warden
Lib Sales Dir: John Pester
Founded: 1963
Religious publications.
ISBN Prefix(es): 978-0-87083; 978-1-57593; 978-0-7363
Number of titles published annually: 50 Print
Total Titles: 1,500 Print

**Livingston Press**
Division of University of West Alabama
University of West Alabama, Sta 22, Livingston, AL 35470
SAN: 851-917X
*Tel:* 205-652-3470 *Fax:* 205-652-3717
*Web Site:* www.livingstonpress.uwa.edu
*Key Personnel*
Dir: Joe Taylor *E-mail:* jwt@uwa.edu
Founded: 1984
ISBN Prefix(es): 978-0-942979; 978-0-930501; 978-1-931982; 978-1-60489
Number of titles published annually: 11 Print; 10 E-Book; 2 Audio
Total Titles: 120 Print; 60 E-Book; 1 Audio
Imprints: Swallow's Tale Press
Distributor for Swallow's Tale Press
*Distribution Center:* Small Press Distribution (SPD), 1341 Seventh St, Berkeley, CA 94710-1409 *Tel:* 510-524-1668 *Toll Free Tel:* 800-869-7553 *E-mail:* spd@spdbooks.org *Web Site:* www.spdbooks.org
Membership(s): Council of Literary Magazines & Presses; IBPA, the Independent Book Publishers Association

**Llewellyn Publications**
Division of Llewellyn Worldwide Ltd
2143 Wooddale Dr, Woodbury, MN 55125
SAN: 201-100X
*Tel:* 651-291-1970 *Toll Free Tel:* 800-843-6666 *Fax:* 651-291-1908
*E-mail:* publicity@llewellyn.com
*Web Site:* www.llewellyn.com
*Key Personnel*
Pres: Carl L Weschcke
Publr: Bill Krause
Dir, Publicity: Steven Pomije
Dir, Sales: Rhonda Ogren
ISBN Contact: Todd Pazdera
Founded: 1901
Body, mind, spirit. Trade publisher.
ISBN Prefix(es): 978-0-87542; 978-1-56718; 978-0-7387
Number of titles published annually: 110 Print; 10 CD-ROM
Total Titles: 900 Print
Imprints: Flux (teen, fiction, children's literature, paperback); Midnight Ink (mystery, trade, fiction, paperback)
Distributor for Lo Scarabeo
Foreign Rep(s): Airlift (UK)
Foreign Rights: Oxana Schroeder

**The Local History Co**
112 N Woodland Rd, Pittsburgh, PA 15232-2849
*Tel:* 412-362-2294 *Toll Free Tel:* 866-362-0789 (orders) *Fax:* 412-362-8192
*E-mail:* info@thelocalhistorycompany.com; sales@thelocalhistorycomany.com
*Web Site:* www.thelocalhistorycompany.com
*Key Personnel*
Chief Content Offr: Cheryl R Towers *Tel:* 412-362-1844 *E-mail:* editor@thelocalhistorycompany.com
Founded: 2001
Publishers of history & heritage.
ISBN Prefix(es): 978-0-9711835; 978-0-9744715; 978-0-9770429
Number of titles published annually: 10 Print
Total Titles: 25 Print
Imprints: Towers Maguire Publishing
Membership(s): IBPA, the Independent Book Publishers Association

**Locks Art Publications/Locks Gallery**
Division of Locks Gallery
600 Washington Sq S, Philadelphia, PA 19106
*Tel:* 215-629-1000
*E-mail:* info@locksgallery.com
*Web Site:* www.locksgallery.com
*Key Personnel*
Dir: Sueyun Locks
Founded: 1968
Exhibition catalogue, monographs on contemporary art.
ISBN Prefix(es): 978-1-879173; 978-0-9623799
Number of titles published annually: 8 Print
Total Titles: 45 Print

**Loft Press Inc**
9293 Fort Valley Rd, Fort Valley, VA 22652
*Tel:* 540-933-6210 *Fax:* 540-933-6523
*E-mail:* books@loftpress.com
*Key Personnel*
Pres & Publr: Stephen R Hunter
Ed-in-Chief: Ann A Hunter
Founded: 1987
ISBN Prefix(es): 978-0-9630797; 978-1-893846
Number of titles published annually: 4 Print; 2 CD-ROM
Total Titles: 128 Print; 2 CD-ROM
Imprints: Eschat Press; Far Muse Press; Merry Muse Press; Punch Press
*Advertising Agency:* AAH Advertising *Tel:* 540-933-6211
Membership(s): Washington Book Publishers

**§Logos Bible Software**
1313 Commercial St, Bellingham, WA 98225-4307
*Tel:* 360-527-1700 *Toll Free Tel:* 800-875-6467 *Fax:* 360-527-1707
*E-mail:* sales@logos.com
*Web Site:* www.logos.com
Founded: 1991
Electronic & e-book publisher & technology provider.
ISBN Prefix(es): 978-1-57799
Number of titles published annually: 30 CD-ROM; 200 E-Book
Total Titles: 200 CD-ROM; 4,000 E-Book
Membership(s): CBA; Evangelical Christian Publishers Association; Society of Bible Literature

**Logos Press**
Imprint of thinkBiotech LLC
3909 Witmer Rd, Suite 416, Niagara Falls, NY 14305
*Fax:* 815-346-3514
*E-mail:* info@logos-press.com
*Web Site:* www.logos-press.com
*Key Personnel*
Ed: Yali Friedman
Founded: 2003
Specializes in reference & text books addressing the use of knowledge to make intelligent strategic decisions. Target audiences include college & advanced courses, business managers, directors & C-level executives. The objective is to help advanced students & decision makers implement their ideas based on solid fundamentals.
ISBN Prefix(es): 978-0-9734676; 978-1-934899
Number of titles published annually: 4 Print; 4 Online
Total Titles: 12 Print; 4 Online

**Lonely Planet**
150 Linden St, Oakland, CA 94607
*Tel:* 510-893-8555 *Toll Free Tel:* 800-275-8555 (orders) *Fax:* 510-893-8563
*E-mail:* info@lonelyplanet.com
*Web Site:* www.lonelyplanet.com
*Key Personnel*
CEO: Daniel Houghton
VP, Mktg & Client Solutions: Lainey Franks
VP, Publg & Publr, Americas: Brice Gosnell
VP, Sales: Gary Todoroff
Dir, Trade Channel Mktg & Natl Accts: Leslie Davisson
Natl Accts Mgr: Avi Martin
Sr Mgr, Consumer Mktg & Communs: Rana Freedman
Sr Design Mgr: Gerilyn Attebery
Prodn Lead, US-Based Client Solutions: Jennifer Pentes
Content Prodr: Rachel Berg
UI Designer: Clare Chadwick
Founded: 1973
Create & deliver the most compelling & comprehensive travel content in the world, giving travellers trustworthy information, engaging opinions, powerful images & informed perspectives on destinations around the globe. While known primarily for its 600+ travel guidebooks, we also offer an award-winning web site, photographic image library, television production, distribution & digital travel content licensing.
ISBN Prefix(es): 978-0-908086; 978-0-86442
Number of titles published annually: 100 Print
Total Titles: 600 Print
*Foreign Office(s):* 90 Maribyrnong St, Footscray, Victoria 3011, Australia
72-82 Rosebery Ave, London EC1R 4RW, United Kingdom
Foreign Rep(s): A B E Marketing (Poland); Altair (Spain); Asia Books Co Ltd (Thailand); Asia Publishers' Services Ltd (China, Hong Kong, Taiwan); David Bateman Ltd (New Zealand); The Book Centre (Pakistan); Booktraders Ltd (Cyprus, Czech Republic, Greece, Israel, Malta, Middle East, Turkey); Brettschneider (Germany); CDE (sales: English & French editions) (France); Centralivros (Portugal); TB Clarke (Overseas Pty Ltd) (Fiji); CLB Marketing Services (Croatia, Hungary, Montenegro, Romania, Serbia, Slovenia); CV Java Books (Indonesia); Dinternal (Russia); Electra Media Group Pty Ltd (Guam, Micronesia, Philippines); Eleftheroudakis SA (Greece); Faradawn (South Africa); Freytag & Berndt U Artaria KG (Austria); Geocentre ILH (Germany); Geographical Tours Ltd (Israel); IMA Distribution (East Asia); India Book Distributors (Bombay) Ltd (India, Nepal); Intercontinental Marketing Corp (Japan); International Educational Library (Greece); Kartbutiken (Sweden); Lannoo Publishers (Belgium); Logos Art Srl (Italy); MPH Distributors (Malaysia, Singapore); Nilsson & Lamm Bv (Netherlands); Olf SA (Switzerland); Raincoast Books (Canada); Cav Giovanni Russano SAS (Italy); Scanvik Books Aps (Denmark, Finland, Iceland, Norway); Jana Seta (Latvia); Shoestring International (Korea); Sklep Podroznika (Poland); SODIS (distribution) (France); Text Book Centre Ltd (Kenya); Trak Trade Centre (Estonia); The Travel Bookshop (Switzerland); Vijitha Yapa Bookshop (Pvt) Ltd (Sri Lanka); Westland Sundries Ltd (Kenya); Yab Yay Yayimcilik Sanayi (Turkey)

**§Long River Press**
360 Swift Ave, Suite 48, South San Francisco, CA 94080
*Tel:* 650-872-7718 (ext 312) *Fax:* 650-872-7808
*E-mail:* info@longriverpress.com
*Web Site:* www.chinabooks.com
*Key Personnel*
Edit & Mng Dir: Mr Chris Robyn *E-mail:* chris@sinomediausa.com
Founded: 2002
Trade & academic titles related to China studies. Print & e-book publisher & distributor.
ISBN Prefix(es): 978-1-59265 (Long River Press)
Number of titles published annually: 10 Print; 5 E-Book
Total Titles: 100 Print; 10 E-Book
*Distribution Center:* Perseus Distribution Services, 1094 Flex Dr, Jackson, TN 38301-5070 *Toll Free Tel:* 800-343-4499
Membership(s): Association for Asian Studies

**Looseleaf Law Publications Inc**
Division of Warodean Corp
43-08 162 St, Flushing, NY 11358
Mailing Address: PO Box 650042, Fresh Meadows, NY 11365-0042
*Tel:* 718-359-5559 *Toll Free Tel:* 800-647-5547 *Fax:* 718-539-0941
*E-mail:* info@looseleaf.com
*Web Site:* www.looseleaflaw.com
*Key Personnel*
Owner: Michael L Loughrey
VP & Edit: Mary Loughrey
Sales Dir: Hilary McKeon
Founded: 1967
Law books; study aids for law enforcement, students, attorneys & court personnel.
ISBN Prefix(es): 978-0-930137; 978-1-889031; 978-1-932777
Number of titles published annually: 11 Print
Total Titles: 160 Print; 25 CD-ROM

**§Lorenz Educational Press**
Division of The Lorenz Corp
501 E Third St, Dayton, OH 45402
Mailing Address: PO Box 802, Dayton, OH 45401-0802
*Tel:* 937-228-6118 *Toll Free Tel:* 800-444-1144 *Fax:* 937-223-2042
*E-mail:* lep@lorenz.com
*Web Site:* www.lorenzeducationalpress.com
*Key Personnel*
VP: Debra Kaiser *E-mail:* debk@lorenz.com
Founded: 2008
Educational publishing division includes visual resources, instructional guides & reproducibles, elementary supplementals.
ISBN Prefix(es): 978-1-42911
Number of titles published annually: 10 Print
Total Titles: 75 Print; 75 E-Book; 7 Audio
Membership(s): National School Supply & Equipment Association

**Lost Classics Book Company LLC**
411 N Wales Dr, Lake Wales, FL 33853-3881
*Tel:* 863-678-3149 (edit off) *Fax:* 863-678-0802
*E-mail:* mgeditor@lostclassicsbooks.com
*Web Site:* www.lostclassicsbooks.com
*Key Personnel*
Owner: Michael Alan Fitterling
Founded: 1996
Republish late 19th & early 20th century literature & textbooks to aid parents & teachers in educating children.
ISBN Prefix(es): 978-0-9652735; 978-1-890623
Number of titles published annually: 8 Print
Total Titles: 43 Print
Imprints: Road Dog Publications (motorcycling books)
*Distribution Center:* National Book Network, 15200 NBN Way, Blue Ridge Summit, PA 17214 *Tel:* 717-794-3800 *Fax:* 717-794-3828
Membership(s): IBPA, the Independent Book Publishers Association

**Lost Horse Press**
Subsidiary of The Academy of Northwest Writers & Publishers
105 Lost Horse Lane, Sandpoint, ID 83864
*Tel:* 208-255-4410
*E-mail:* losthorsepress@mindspring.com
*Web Site:* www.losthorsepress.org
*Key Personnel*
Publr: Christine Holbert
Founded: 1998
Nonprofit independent press that publishes poetry titles of high literary merit & makes available fine contemporary literature through cultural, educational & publishing programs & activities.
ISBN Prefix(es): 978-0-9668612; 978-0-9717265; 978-0-9762114; 978-0-9800289
Number of titles published annually: 10 Print; 1 CD-ROM; 1 Audio
Total Titles: 70 Print; 2 CD-ROM; 1 Audio
Distributed by University of Washington Press
*Distribution Center:* University of Washington Press, 4333 Brooklyn Ave NE, Seattle, WA 98195 *Tel:* 410-516-6956 *Toll Free Tel:* 800-537-5487 *Fax:* 410-516-6998 *E-mail:* hfscustserv@press.jhu.edu *Web Site:* www.washington.edu/uwpress
Membership(s): Council of Literary Magazines & Presses

**Lotus Light Publications**, see Lotus Press

**Lotus Press**
Division of Lotus Brands Inc
PO Box 325, Twin Lakes, WI 53181-0325
*Tel:* 262-889-8561 *Toll Free Tel:* 800-824-6396 (orders) *Fax:* 262-889-2461
*E-mail:* lotuspress@lotuspress.com
*Web Site:* www.lotuspress.com
*Key Personnel*
Pres: Santosh Krinsky *E-mail:* santosh@lotuspress.com
Founded: 1981
Health, yoga, Native American & New Age metaphysics, Vedic astrology.
ISBN Prefix(es): 978-0-941524; 978-0-910261; 978-0-914955; 978-0-940985; 978-0-940676; 978-0-930736

Number of titles published annually: 6 Print; 2 CD-ROM; 2 Online; 15 E-Book; 3 Audio
Total Titles: 325 Print; 5 CD-ROM; 10 Online; 175 E-Book; 42 Audio
Imprints: Arcana Publishing; DIPTI; Shangri-La; Specialized Software
Distributor for Back to Eden Books; Dipti; East West Cultural Center; Les Editions E T C, Inner Worlds Music; November Moon; S A B D A; Sadhana Publications; Samata Books; Sri Aurobindo Ashram; Star Sounds
*Warehouse:* 1100 Lotus Dr, Bldg 3, Silver Lake, WI 53170
Membership(s): Network of Alternatives for Publishers, Retailers & Artists Inc

**Louisiana State University Press**
3990 W Lakeshore Dr, Baton Rouge, LA 70808
SAN: 202-6597
*Tel:* 225-578-6666 *Fax:* 225-578-6461
*E-mail:* lsupress@lsu.edu
*Web Site:* lsupress.org
*Key Personnel*
Dir: MaryKatherine Callaway *E-mail:* mkc@lsu.edu
Asst Dir & Design & Prodn Mgr: Laura Gleason *Tel:* 225-578-6469 *E-mail:* lgleasn@lsu.edu
Mktg Mgr: Erin Rolfs *Tel:* 225-578-8282 *E-mail:* erolfs@lsu.edu
Mng Ed: Lee Campbell Sioles *Tel:* 225-578-6467 *E-mail:* lsioles@lsu.edu
Fulfillment Opers Mgr: Becky Brown *Tel:* 225-578-6415 *E-mail:* rbrown@lsu.edu
Founded: 1935
Scholarly, regional, general; humanities & social sciences; southern history & literature; poetry; government & political science; music; paperbacks; fiction.
ISBN Prefix(es): 978-0-8071
Number of titles published annually: 85 Print
Total Titles: 1,000 Print; 4 CD-ROM
Subsidiaries: McIntosh & Otis
Foreign Rep(s): East-West Export Books (Asia, Australia, Japan, New Zealand, The Pacific); Scholarly Book Services (Canada)
*Orders to:* Longleaf Services, PO Box 8895, Chapel Hill, NC 27515 *Toll Free Tel:* 800-848-6224 *Toll Free Fax:* 800-272-6817
*Returns:* Longleaf Services Inc, c/o Maple Press Co, Lebanon Distribution Ctr, 704 Legionaire Dr, Fredericksburg, PA 17026
*Warehouse:* Longleaf Services Inc, c/o Maple Press Co, Lebanon Distribution Ctr, 704 Legionaire Dr, Fredericksburg, PA 17026
Membership(s): AAP; American Association of University Presses

**Love Inspired Books**
Imprint of Harlequin Enterprises Ltd
233 Broadway, Suite 1001, New York, NY 10279
SAN: 200-2450
*Tel:* 212-553-4200 *Fax:* 212-227-8969
*E-mail:* customer_service@harlequin.ca
*Web Site:* www.loveinspiredbooks.com
*Key Personnel*
Pres & Publr: Donna Hayes
EVP, Global Publg & Strategy: Loriana Sacilotto
Exec Ed: Joan Marlow Golan *Tel:* 212-553-4240 *E-mail:* joanmarlow_golan@harlequin.ca
Ed, Love Inspired: Emily Rodmell
Founded: 1997
Inspirational romance novels, romantic suspense & women's fiction.
ISBN Prefix(es): 978-0-373
Number of titles published annually: 192 Print
Imprints: Love Inspired; Love Inspired Historical; Love Inspired Suspense
*Distribution Center:* 3010 Walden Ave, Depew, NY 14043

**Love Publishing Co**
9101 E Kenyon Ave, Suite 2200, Denver, CO 80237
SAN: 205-2482
*Tel:* 303-221-7333 *Toll Free Tel:* 877-240-6396 *Fax:* 303-221-7444
*E-mail:* lpc@lovepublishing.com
*Web Site:* www.lovepublishing.com
*Key Personnel*
Pres & Publr: Stanley F Love
Mktg Coord: Laura Brindle *E-mail:* laura@lovepublishing.com
Founded: 1968
College textbooks, journals & professional books in counseling, social work & special needs education.
ISBN Prefix(es): 978-0-89108
Number of titles published annually: 8 Print; 1 E-Book
Total Titles: 125 Print; 1 E-Book
Foreign Rep(s): Eurospan (Europe, UK); Publishers Marketing Service (Malaysia, Singapore)
Membership(s): AAP

**Loving Healing Press Inc**
5145 Pontiac Trail, Ann Arbor, MI 48105
SAN: 255-7770
*Tel:* 734-417-4266 *Toll Free Tel:* 888-761-6268 (US & CN) *Fax:* 734-663-6861
*E-mail:* info@lovinghealing.com
*Web Site:* www.lovinghealing.com; www.modernhistorypress.com (imprint)
*Key Personnel*
Pres: Victor R Volkman
Founded: 2003
Dedicated to producing books about innovative & rapid therapies to empower authors in redefining what is possible for healing the mind & spirit.
ISBN Prefix(es): 978-1-932690
Number of titles published annually: 15 Print; 15 E-Book; 2 Audio
Total Titles: 120 Print; 140 E-Book; 6 Audio
Imprints: Modern History Press (memoirs of people who have lived through significant events); Victorian Heritage Press (showcasing the best of 19th century contemporary histories)
Foreign Rep(s): Lightning Source UK (Europe)
Membership(s): IBPA, the Independent Book Publishers Association

**Loyola Press**
3441 N Ashland Ave, Chicago, IL 60657
SAN: 211-6537
*Tel:* 773-281-1818 *Toll Free Tel:* 800-621-1008 *Fax:* 773-281-0555 (cust serv); 773-281-4129 (edit)
*E-mail:* customerservice@loyolapress.com
*Web Site:* www.loyolapress.com; www.spiritedtalk.org
*Key Personnel*
Pres: Terry Locke
Exec Ed & Acqs: Joseph Durepos *E-mail:* durepos@loyolapress.com
Digital Rts Mgr & Foreign Rep: Andrew Yankech
Founded: 1912
Catholic publisher of books for elementary schools, parishes & the general trade.
ISBN Prefix(es): 978-0-8294
Number of titles published annually: 20 Print; 5 Audio
Total Titles: 350 Print
Distributor for Jesuit Consortium

**LPD Press**
925 Salamanca NW, Los Ranchos de Albuquerque, NM 87107-5647
*Tel:* 505-344-9382 *Fax:* 505-345-5129
*E-mail:* info@nmsantos.com
*Web Site:* nmsantos.com
*Key Personnel*
Sr Partner: Barbe Awalt; Paul Rhetts
Founded: 1984
Publisher of books on the American Southwest & a quarterly magazine on the art & culture of the American Southwest.
ISBN Prefix(es): 978-0-9641542; 978-1-890689
Number of titles published annually: 18 Print
Total Titles: 125 Print; 1 CD-ROM; 1 E-Book
Imprints: Rio Grande Books
Membership(s): IBPA, the Independent Book Publishers Association; New Mexico Book Association; New Mexico Book Co-op

**§LRP Publications**
360 Hiatt Dr, Palm Beach Gardens, FL 33418
*Tel:* 561-622-6520 *Toll Free Tel:* 800-341-7874 *Fax:* 561-622-0757
*E-mail:* custserve@lrp.com
*Web Site:* www.lrp.com
*Key Personnel*
Pres: Kenneth F Kahn
Founded: 1977
Legal & general nonfiction in the areas of education, bankruptcy, employment, disability, workers compensation, personal injury & human resources.
ISBN Prefix(es): 978-0-934753
Number of titles published annually: 500 Print; 10 CD-ROM; 95 Online; 5 Audio
Total Titles: 9,000 Print; 10 CD-ROM; 95 Online; 8 Audio
Subsidiaries: LRP Magazine Group
Divisions: Jury Verdict Research; LRP Magazine Group

**LRS**
Division of Library Reproduction Service
14214 S Figueroa St, Los Angeles, CA 90061-1034
*Tel:* 310-354-2610 *Toll Free Tel:* 800-255-5002 *Fax:* 310-354-2601
*E-mail:* largeprintsb@aol.com
*Web Site:* lrs-largeprint.com
*Key Personnel*
Pres: Peter Jones
Founded: 1946
Large print books for adults & children including classics & fiction.
ISBN Prefix(es): 978-1-58118
Number of titles published annually: 16 Print
Total Titles: 150 Print

**Lucent Books®**
Imprint of Gale
27500 Drake Rd, Farmington Hills, MI 48331
*Tel:* 248-699-4253 *Fax:* 248-699-8004
*E-mail:* gale.customerservice@cengage.com
*Web Site:* www.gale.com/greenhaven
*Key Personnel*
Mgr, Prodn: Ellen McGeagh *Tel:* 248-699-8397 ext 1726 *E-mail:* ellen.mcgeagh@cengage.com
Founded: 1988
Curriculum-related nonfiction books aimed at the junior high level that explore current issues, historical topics, health, science/technology & biography. Active series include: *Diseases & Disorders, Hot Topics, People in the News, Technology 360 & World History.*
ISBN Prefix(es): 978-1-56006; 978-1-59018
Number of titles published annually: 85 Print; 60 E-Book
Distributed by Greenhaven Imprints
Distributor for Greenhaven Press; Kidhaven Press

**§Lucky Marble Books**
Imprint of PageSpring Publishing
2671 Bristol Rd, Columbus, OH 43221
Mailing Address: PO Box 21133, Columbus, OH 43221
*Tel:* 614-264-5588
*E-mail:* sales@pagespringpublishing.com
*Web Site:* www.luckymarblebooks.com

*Key Personnel*
Ed: Katherine Matthews *Tel:* 614-327-3676
*E-mail:* yaeditor@pagespringpublishing.com
Sales & Mktg Dir: Lynn Bartels
Founded: 2012
Independent publisher. Specialize in high quality fiction for young adult & middle grade readers.
ISBN Prefix(es): 978-1-939403
Number of titles published annually: 4 Print; 4 E-Book

**Luminis Books Inc**
13245 Blacktern Way, Carmel, IN 46033
Mailing Address: 1950 E Greyhound Pass, Suite 18, PMB 280, Carmel, IN 46033-7400
*Tel:* 317-840-5838
*E-mail:* editor@luminisbooks.com
*Web Site:* www.luminisbooks.com
*Key Personnel*
Pres: Tracy Richardson
Founded: 2008
Publish young adult, middle grade & literary fiction.
ISBN Prefix(es): 978-1-935462
Number of titles published annually: 7 Print; 7 E-Book
Total Titles: 10 Print; 10 E-Book
*Advertising Agency:* RTC Publicity
*Orders to:* Midpoint Trade Books, 27 W 20 St, Suite 1102, New York, NY 10011
*Returns:* Midpoint Trade Books, 27 W 20 St, Suite 1102, New York, NY 10011
*Distribution Center:* Midpoint Trade Books, 27 W 20 St, Suite 1102, New York, NY 10011
Membership(s): IBPA, the Independent Book Publishers Association; Society of Children's Book Writers & Illustrators

**Luna Bisonte Prods**
137 Leland Ave, Columbus, OH 43214
*Tel:* 614-846-4126
*Web Site:* www.johnmbennett.net; www.lulu.com/spotlight/lunabisonteprods
*Key Personnel*
Head & Intl Rts: John M Bennett
*E-mail:* bennettjohnm@gmail.com
Founded: 1974
Avant-garde to experimental literature & poetry.
ISBN Prefix(es): 978-0-935350; 978-1-892280
Number of titles published annually: 25 Print; 2 Audio
Total Titles: 350 Print; 50 Audio

**Lutheran Braille Workers Inc**
13471 California St, Yucaipa, CA 92399
Mailing Address: PO Box 5000, Yucaipa, CA 92399-1450
*Tel:* 909-795-8977 *Fax:* 909-795-8970
*E-mail:* lbw@lbwinc.org
*Web Site:* www.lbwinc.org
*Key Personnel*
Pres: Rev Dr Phillip Pledger
Founded: 1943
Produce & distribute free braille & large print biblical & Christian literature in more than 30 languages for the blind & visually impaired in over 120 countries.
Number of titles published annually: 5 Print
Total Titles: 200 Print

**Lyceum Books Inc**
5758 S Blackstone Ave, Chicago, IL 60637
*Tel:* 773-643-1902 *Fax:* 773-643-1903
*E-mail:* lyceum@lyceumbooks.com
*Web Site:* www.lyceumbooks.com
*Key Personnel*
Pres & Publr: David C Follmer
Edit Coord: Catherine Dixon *E-mail:* catherine@lyceumbooks.com
Founded: 1988
Books for social service practitioners & social service students.
ISBN Prefix(es): 978-0-925065; 978-1-933478
Number of titles published annually: 14 Print
Total Titles: 90 Print; 2 E-Book
*Returns:* 2427 Bond St, University Park, IL 60466
*Warehouse:* 2427 Bond St, University Park, IL 60466

**Lyndon B Johnson School of Public Affairs**
University of Texas at Austin, 2315 Red River St, Austin, TX 78712-1536
Mailing Address: University of Texas at Austin, PO Box Y, Austin, TX 78713-8925
*Tel:* 512-471-3200 *Fax:* 512-471-4697
*E-mail:* pubsinfo@uts.cc.utexas.edu; lbjdeansoffice@austin.utexas.edu
*Web Site:* www.utexas.edu/lbj
*Key Personnel*
Asst to Dean: Lilana Merubia *E-mail:* lmerubia@mail.utexas.edu
Founded: 1972
Working papers; public service monographs; policy research projects; conference proceedings.
Return policy: No refunds; replace damaged books only. All sales are final. Prepayment usually required.
ISBN Prefix(es): 978-0-89940
Number of titles published annually: 5 Print
Total Titles: 300 Print

**Lynx House Press**
420 W 24 St, Spokane, WA 99203
*Tel:* 509-624-4894
*Web Site:* www.lynxhousepress.org
*Key Personnel*
Dir & Ed-in-Chief: Christopher Howell
*E-mail:* cnhowell@ewu.edu
Prodn Mgr: Barbara Anderson
Dist Coord: David Luckert
Intl Rts: John Orr
Founded: 1972
Fiction & poetry.
ISBN Prefix(es): 978-0-89924
Number of titles published annually: 3 Print
Total Titles: 134 Print
Distributed by University of Washington Press
*Distribution Center:* Hopkins Fulfillment Service, 704 Legionaire Dr, Fredericksburg, PA 17026
*Tel:* 410-516-6956

**The Lyons Press**
Imprint of The Globe Pequot Press
246 Goose Lane, Guilford, CT 06437
Mailing Address: PO Box 480, Guilford, CT 06437
*Tel:* 203-458-4500 *Fax:* 203-458-4668
*E-mail:* info@globepequot.com
*Web Site:* www.lyonspress.com; www.globepequot.com
*Key Personnel*
HR Dir: Valerie Brown *Tel:* 203-458-4544
*Fax:* 203-458-4601
Founded: 1978
Outdoors, natural history, sports, fitness, cooking, military history, fishing, hunting, equine, nonfiction, fiction, practical, Americana, outdoor skills, pets, nautical, survival & adventure.
ISBN Prefix(es): 978-1-55821; 978-0-8329; 978-1-58574; 978-1-59228; 978-0-936644; 978-0-941130
Number of titles published annually: 180 Print
Total Titles: 1,500 Print
Foreign Rep(s): Windsor Publications International (UK)
Foreign Rights: Gail Blackhall
*Warehouse:* The Globe Pequot Press Distribution Center, 128 Pinnacle Dr, Springfield, TN 37172

**M U Press**, see Marquette University Press

**Pat MacKay Projects**, see Quite Specific Media Group Ltd

**Macmillan**
Subsidiary of Verlagsgruppe Georg von Holtzbrinck GmbH
175 Fifth Ave, New York, NY 10010
*Tel:* 646-307-5151 *Fax:* 212-420-9314
*E-mail:* firstname.lastname@macmillan.com
*Web Site:* www.macmillan.com
*Key Personnel*
CEO: John Sargent
COO: Peter Garabedian
Pres, Macmillan Children's Publishing Group: Jonathan Yaged
SVP & Publg Dir, Macmillan Children's Publishing Group: Simon Boughton; Jean Feiwel
Div VP & Publr, Audio: Mary Beth Roche
Pres & Publr, Farrar, Straus & Giroux: Jonathan Galassi
Pres & Publr, Henry Holt & Company: Stephen Rubin
SVP & Publr, St Martin's Press: Sally Richardson
EVP & Publr, St Martin's Press: Matthew Shear
Pres & Publr, Tom Doherty Associates: Thomas Doherty
Editor-at-Large: John Sterling
Pres of Sales: Alison Lazarus
SVP of Opers, MPS: Michael Shareck
SVP, Fin: Edward Garrett
VP, Fin Planning & Admin: Cathy Goodfriend
VP, Treas & Tax Dir: Michael Ross
VP, Fin & Admin: Allan Meese
EVP, Digital Publg & Strategic Technol: Fritz Foy
SVP & CIO: Chris Kohn
VP, Academic Mktg: Peter Janssen
VP, Supply Chain & Sales Opers: Tom Stouras
VP, Busn Devt: Kenneth Eng
VP, Macmillan Speakers Bureau: Mariann Donato
SVP, Gen Coun: Paul Sleven
VP, Dir of HR: Helaine Ohl
Founded: 1986
Macmillan is the administrative, sales, distribution & information technology arm of the Macmillan group in the United States, which includes Bedford, Freeman & Worth Publishing Group, LLC (W H Freeman, Worth Publishers & Bedford/St Martin's); Tom Doherty Associates, LLC (Tor & Forge Books); Faber and Faber Inc; Farrar, Straus and Giroux, LLC; Feiwel and Friends; First Second; Hayden McNeil; Henry Holt and Company, LLC; Macmillan Audio; Nature America Inc; Palgrave Macmillan; Picador; Roaring Brook Press; St Martin's Press, LLC; Scientific American Inc; Square Fish.
*Distribution Center:* MPS Distribution Center, 16365 James Madison Hwy, Gordonsville, VA 22942-8501 *Toll Free Tel:* 888-330-8477 *Fax:* 540-672-7540 (cust serv)
*Toll Free Fax:* 800-672-2054 (orders)
*E-mail:* firstinitiallastname@mpsvirginia.com
*See separate listing for:*
**Bedford, Freeman & Worth Publishing Group, LLC**
**Tom Doherty Associates, LLC**
**Farrar, Straus & Giroux, LLC**
**Henry Holt and Company, LLC**
**Picador**
**St Martin's Press, LLC**

**Macmillan Audio**
Division of Macmillan
175 Fifth Ave, New York, NY 10010
*Tel:* 646-307-5151 *Toll Free Tel:* 888-330-8477 (cust serv) *Fax:* 917-534-0980
*E-mail:* firstname.lastname@macmillan.com
*Web Site:* www.macmillanaudio.com
*Key Personnel*
Div VP & Publr: Mary Beth Roche
Dir of Mktg: Brant Janeway
Dir of Prodn: Laura Wilson
Sr Art Dir: Margo Goody
Edit Dir: Robert Allen

Founded: 1987
ISBN Prefix(es): 978-1-55927; 978-0-7927; 978-0-940687; 978-1-59397; 978-1-4272
Number of titles published annually: 100 Audio
Distributed by BBC Audiobooks America (library editions)
Distributor for HighRoads Media
*Orders to:* MPS Order Dept, 16365 James Madison Hwy, Gordonsville, VA 22942-8501 *Toll Free Tel:* 888-330-8477 *Fax:* 540-672-7540 *Toll Free Fax:* 800-672-2054
Membership(s): Audio Publishers Association; Publishers' Publicity Association

**§Macmillan Reference USA™**
Imprint of Gale
12 Lunar Dr, Woodbridge, CT 06525
*Tel:* 203-397-2600 *Toll Free Tel:* 800-444-0799 *Fax:* 203-397-8296
*Web Site:* www.gale.cengage.com/macmillan/
*Key Personnel*
EVP & Publr: Frank Menchaca
Total Titles: 47 CD-ROM

**Madavor Media**
21027 Crossroads Circle, Waukesha, WI 53187-1612
Mailing Address: PO Box 1612, Waukesha, WI 53187-1612
*Tel:* 262-796-8776 *Toll Free Tel:* 800-533-6644 (cust serv & orders) *Fax:* 262-796-1615 (sales & cust serv); 262-798-6468 (edit)
*Web Site:* www.kalmbach.com
*Key Personnel*
Pres: Charles R Croft *E-mail:* ccroft@kalmbach.com
VP, Mktg: Dan Lance
Books Publr: Diane Bacha *E-mail:* dbacha@kalmbach.com
Books Ed-in-Chief: Diane Wheeler *E-mail:* dwheeler@kalmbach.com
Circ Mgr: Michael Barbee
Founded: 1934
Special interest books, calendars & magazines in the astronomy, jewelry making, crafts, hobby & collectibles market.
ISBN Prefix(es): 978-0-89024; 978-0-913135; 978-0-89778; 978-0-87116
Number of titles published annually: 35 Print
Total Titles: 135 Print
Imprints: Greenberg Books; Kalmbach Books
Distributed by Publishers Group West (PGW)

**Madison House Publishers**
Member of Rowman & Littlefield Publishing Group Inc
4501 Forbes Blvd, Lanham, MD 20706
SAN: 247-4433
*Tel:* 301-459-3366 *Toll Free Tel:* 800-462-6420 *Fax:* 301-306-0941
*Web Site:* rlpgbooks.com
*Key Personnel*
Pres: Jed Lyons
Founded: 1988
American history & culture.
ISBN Prefix(es): 978-0-945612; 978-0-7425
Number of titles published annually: 5 Print
Total Titles: 60 Print
Distributor for Center for Study of American Constitution

**Mage Publishers Inc**
1032 29 St NW, Washington, DC 20007
*Tel:* 202-342-1642 *Toll Free Tel:* 800-962-0922 *Fax:* 202-342-9269
*Web Site:* www.mage.com
*Key Personnel*
Art Dir: Najmieh Batmanglij *E-mail:* nb@mage.com
Publr & Ed: Mohammad Batmanglij *E-mail:* mb@mage.com
Asst to Publr & Rts Contact: Amin Sepehri *E-mail:* as@mage.com
Founded: 1985
Persian literature, art & culture in English; poetry, fiction, art & history.
ISBN Prefix(es): 978-0-934211; 978-1-933823
Number of titles published annually: 4 Print
Total Titles: 75 Print
Imprints: Jefferson Editions
Distributed by University of Toronto Press
*Returns:* Tasco, Mage Returns, 9 Jay Gould Ct, Waldorf, MD 20602
*Warehouse:* Tasco, 9 Jay Gould Ct, Waldorf, MD 20602
Membership(s): AAP

**The Magni Co**
Subsidiary of The Magni Group Inc
7106 Wellington Point Rd, McKinney, TX 75070
*Tel:* 972-540-2050 *Fax:* 972-540-1057
*E-mail:* sales@magnico.com; info@magnico.com
*Web Site:* www.magnico.com
*Key Personnel*
Pres: Evan B Reynolds
EVP: Darlene Reynolds
Founded: 1982
Health & beauty books, weight loss books, informative books, organizer books.
ISBN Prefix(es): 978-1-882330
Number of titles published annually: 5 Print; 1 CD-ROM; 3 Online; 50 E-Book; 2 Audio
Total Titles: 61 Print; 2 CD-ROM; 50 Online; 50 E-Book; 9 Audio
Imprints: MAGNI
Membership(s): ABA

**Maharishi University of Management Press**
Subsidiary of Maharishi University of Management
1000 N Fourth St, Dept 1155, Fairfield, IA 52557-1155
*Tel:* 641-472-1101 *Toll Free Tel:* 800-831-6523 *Fax:* 641-472-1122
*E-mail:* mumpress@mum.edu
*Web Site:* www.mumpress.com
*Key Personnel*
Dir: Harry Bright
Founded: 1974
Specialize in books about transcendental meditation.
ISBN Prefix(es): 978-0-9616944; 978-0-923569
Number of titles published annually: 5 Print
Total Titles: 50 Print; 4 Audio
Distributed by Fairfield Press; Penguin Group (USA) LLC

**Maisonneuve Press**
Division of Institute for Advanced Cultural Studies
6423 Adelphi Rd, Hyattsville, MD 20782
Mailing Address: PO Box 426, College Park, MD 20741-0241
*Tel:* 301-277-7505 *Fax:* 301-277-2467
*Web Site:* www.maisonneuvepress.com
*Key Personnel*
Dir & Ed: Robert Merrill *E-mail:* rm@maisonnuevepress.com
Assoc Ed: Dennis Crow; Thomas Wilkinson
Founded: 1988
Publish books for academic market. Not currently accepting new mss.
ISBN Prefix(es): 978-0-944624
Number of titles published annually: 8 Print
Total Titles: 32 Print
Distributed by Merlin Press (London, England)
Membership(s): IBPA, the Independent Book Publishers Association

**Management Advisory Services & Publications (MASP)**
PO Box 81151, Wellesley Hills, MA 02481-0001
SAN: 203-8692
*Tel:* 781-235-2895 *Fax:* 781-235-5446
*E-mail:* info@masp.com
*Web Site:* www.masp.com
*Key Personnel*
Principal & Ed: Jay Kuong *E-mail:* jaykmasp@aol.com
Founded: 1972
A well established publications & advisory & training services company with a concentration in enterprise governance, internal controls, information technology security, auditing & contingency planning & business continuity fields. This includes reference books, journals & practitioners' manuals. Under the enterprise governance field, MASP publishes books on Sarbanes-Oxley compliance. Additionally, as part of the diversification efforts, we publish a few literary fiction books.
ISBN Prefix(es): 978-0-940706
Number of titles published annually: 10 Print
Total Titles: 75 Print
*Foreign Office(s):* Santa Fe Ave, Buenos Aires, Argentina, Contact: D Ramos *E-mail:* dramos@satlink.com

**§Management Concepts Inc**
8230 Leesburg Pike, Suite 800, Vienna, VA 22182
*Tel:* 703-790-9595 *Toll Free Tel:* 800 506-4450 *Fax:* 703-790-1371
*E-mail:* publications@managementconcepts.com
*Web Site:* www.managementconcepts.com
*Key Personnel*
Pres: Tom Dungan, III
Edit Dir: Myra Strauss
Mktg Dir: David Taylor
Publr & Foreign Rts Agent, Worldwide: Mary Cowell
Sales: Chae Kim
Founded: 1981
Books, newsletters, looseleafs & electronic products serving the information needs of project management, acquisition & federal financial management professionals.
ISBN Prefix(es): 978-1-56726
Number of titles published annually: 20 Print; 5 CD-ROM
Foreign Rep(s): NBN (Europe)
*Warehouse:* Brightkey, 1780 Crossroads Dr, Odenton, MD 21113, Contact: Sandi Hessie *Tel:* 301-604-3305 ext 1406 *Web Site:* www.managementconcepts.com

**§Management Sciences for Health**
784 Memorial Dr, Cambridge, MA 02139
*Tel:* 617-250-9500 *Fax:* 617-250-9090
*E-mail:* bookstore@msh.org
*Web Site:* www.msh.org
*Key Personnel*
Deputy Dir, Pubns: Barbara K Timmons *Tel:* 617-250-9291 *E-mail:* btimmons@msh.org
Founded: 1971
Established to "assist, promote, evaluate, manage & perform research on the delivery of health care," establish "methods & procedures leading to the improvement of health & social services" & conduct education & publishing in these areas. MSH's publications unit develops & distributes books & a quarterly periodical to further MSH's mission, which is to help close the gap between knowledge about public health problems & action to solve them.
MSH currently stocks about three dozen products, most of which are books (including monographs, manuals & handbooks, some of which are available on CD-ROM). Many are available in languages other than English. Major products are The Manager continuing education quarterly; Managing Drug Supply (first published in 1981); instructional manuals (CORE, MOST, HOSPICAL, FIMAT); the Lessons from MSH & Stubbs monograph series; the series of "success stories" (20-page color book-

lets that present the highlights of successful programs) & books ranging from textbooks to syntheses of research.
MHS has offices in Afghanistan, Angola, Guinea, Haiti, Indonesia, Malawi, the Philippines & Senegal.
ISBN Prefix(es): 978-0-913723
Number of titles published annually: 2 Print; 1 CD-ROM
Total Titles: 39 Print; 4 CD-ROM
*Branch Office(s)*
4301 N Fairfax Dr, Suite 400, Arlington, VA 22203-1627, Contact: Keith Johnson *Tel:* 703-248-6575 *Fax:* 703-524-7898 *E-mail:* kjohnson@msh.org
*Foreign Office(s):* MSH Europe, 13, Chemin du Levant, 01210 Ferney-Voltaire, France, Contact: Elise Pacquetet *Tel:* 04 50 40 22 75 *Fax:* 04 50 42 98 74 *E-mail:* epacquetet@msh.org
Distributed by Kumarian Press
Foreign Rep(s): Last-First Networks (Asia-Pacific); Teaching Aids at Low Cost (TALC) (Worldwide)
*Warehouse:* The Field Companies, Watertown Warehouse, 650 Pleasant St (rear), Watertown, MA 02472, Contact: David O Wilson *Tel:* 617-923-0444 *Fax:* 617-923-6039 *E-mail:* davew@fieldcompanies.com
*Distribution Center:* The Field Companies, Watertown Warehouse, 650 Pleasant St (rear), Watertown, MA 02472, Contact: David O Wilson *Tel:* 617-923-0444 *Fax:* 617-923-6039 *E-mail:* davew@fieldcompanies.com
Membership(s): IBPA, the Independent Book Publishers Association

**Mandala Publishing**
Imprint of Insight Editions
10 Paul Dr, San Rafael, CA 94903
*Tel:* 415-526-1370 *Fax:* 415-526-1394 *Toll Free Fax:* 866-509-0515
*E-mail:* info@insighteditions.com
*Web Site:* www.mandalapublishing.com
*Key Personnel*
CEO & Publr: Raoul Goff *E-mail:* raoul@insighteditions.com
Founded: 1987
Full color coffee table books & minibooks, as well as decks, calendars, journals, greeting cards, art prints & incense. Topics include: environmental issues, women's studies, Asian art, music, philosophy, cross-cultural issues & Hinduism.
ISBN Prefix(es): 978-1-886069; 978-1-932771; 978-1-60109; 978-0-945475
Number of titles published annually: 40 Print; 2 Audio
Total Titles: 300 Print; 200 Online; 10 Audio
*Shipping Address:* Publishers Group West, 40 Carl Kirkland Dr, Jackson, TN 38301
*Warehouse:* Publishers Group West, 40 Carl Kirkland Dr, Jackson, TN 38301
*Distribution Center:* Publishers Group West, 40 Carl Kirkland Dr, Jackson, TN 38301

**Manhattan Publishing Co**
Division of US & Europe Books Inc
670 White Plains Rd, Scarsdale, NY 10583
*Tel:* 914-472-4650 *Fax:* 914-472-4316
*E-mail:* coe@manhattanpublishing.com
*Web Site:* www.manhattanpublishing.com
*Key Personnel*
Pres: Kenneth Polin
Lib Sales Dir: Cathy Polin
Founded: 1938
Import sales for Council of Europe, European Court of Human Rights.
Number of titles published annually: 200 Print
Total Titles: 3,000 Print; 20 CD-ROM
Distributor for Council of Europe; European Court of Human Rights

**Manic D Press Inc**
250 Banks St, San Francisco, CA 94110
Mailing Address: PO Box 410804, San Francisco, CA 94141
*Tel:* 415-648-8288 *Fax:* 415-648-8288
*E-mail:* info@manicdpress.com
*Web Site:* www.manicdpress.com
*Key Personnel*
Publr & Intl Rts: Jennifer Joseph
Founded: 1984
Poetry & unusual fiction & alternative travel books, emphasis on innovative, new & established styles, writers & artists, paperbacks, general adult books.
ISBN Prefix(es): 978-0-916397; 978-1-933149
Number of titles published annually: 8 Print
Total Titles: 120 Print
Foreign Rep(s): Publishers Group Canada (Canada); Turnaround Distribution (England, Europe)
*Distribution Center:* Consortium Book Sales & Distribution, The Keg House, 34 13 Ave NE, Suite 101, Minneapolis, MN 55413-1007 *Tel:* 612-746-2600 *Toll Free Tel:* 800-283-3572 (cust serv) *Fax:* 612-746-2606 *Web Site:* www.cbsd.com
Membership(s): Council of Literary Magazines & Presses; Northern California Book Publicity & Marketing Association

**Manning Publications Co**
20 Baldwin Rd, Shelter Island, NY 11964
Mailing Address: 178 S Hill Dr, Westampton, NJ 08060
*Toll Free Tel:* 800-294-4747 (orders)
*E-mail:* orders@manning.com
*Web Site:* www.manning.com
*Key Personnel*
Publr: Marjan Bace *Fax:* 203-629-8535 *E-mail:* maba@manning.com
Assoc Publr: Michael Stephens
Dir, Prodn: Mary Piergies
Busn Mgr: Kimberly Dickinson *Tel:* 856-375-2597 *E-mail:* kidi@manning.com
Founded: 1990
Full-scale company whose titles are distributed in the US, Europe & Asia.
ISBN Prefix(es): 978-1-884777; 978-1-930110; 978-1-932394; 978-1-933988; 978-1-61729; 978-1-935182
Number of titles published annually: 25 Print; 10 E-Book
Total Titles: 300 Print; 20 CD-ROM; 200 E-Book
Distributed by IPG; Pearson Education; Prentice Hall; TransQuest Publishers Pte Ltd
*Distribution Center:* O'Reilly Media Inc, 1005 Granvenstein Hwy N, Sebastopol, CA 95472 (US & CN) *Tel:* 707-829-1515 *Toll Free Tel:* 800-998-9939 *Toll Free Fax:* 800-997-9901 *E-mail:* retailics@oreilly.com *Web Site:* www.oreilly.com
Woodslane Pty Lane, Unit 7/5 Vuko Place, Warriewood, NSW 2102, Australia (Australia, New Zealand, Pacific Islands) *Tel:* 02 9970 5111 *Fax:* 02 9970 5002 *E-mail:* info@woodslane.com.au *Web Site:* www.woodslane.com.au
Pansing Distribution Pte Ltd, 438 Ang Mo Kio Industrial Park 1, Off Ang Mo Kio Ave 10, Singapore, Singapore (Hong Kong, Malaysia, Singapore, South Korea, Taiwan, Thailand) *Tel:* 6319 9939 *Fax:* 6459 4931 *E-mail:* infobooks@pansing.com
Pearson Education, Edinburgh Gate, Harlow, Essex CM20 2JE, United Kingdom (Africa, Europe, UK) *Tel:* (01279) 623928 *Fax:* (01279) 414130 *E-mail:* enq.orders@pearsoned-ema.com *Web Site:* www.pearson-books.com

**MapEasy Inc**
PO Box 80, Wainscott, NY 11975-0080
*Tel:* 631-537-6213 *Toll Free Tel:* 888-627-3279 *Fax:* 631-537-4541
*E-mail:* info@mapeasy.com
*Web Site:* www.mapeasy.com
*Key Personnel*
Owner: Gary Bradhering *Tel:* 631-537-6213 ext 160; Chris Harris *Tel:* 631-537-6213 ext 150 *E-mail:* charris@mapeasy.com
Founded: 1989
Guidemaps & location guides to cities in North America, Western Europe & Asia.
ISBN Prefix(es): 978-1-878979
Number of titles published annually: 4 Print
Total Titles: 72 Print

**MAR*CO Products Inc**
1443 Old York Rd, Warminster, PA 18974
*Tel:* 215-956-0313 *Toll Free Tel:* 800-448-2197 *Fax:* 215-956-9041
*E-mail:* help@marcoproducts.com
*Web Site:* www.marcoproducts.com
*Key Personnel*
Opers Mgr: Kathy Crocco
Founded: 1977
Educational guidance materials for elementary & secondary counselors, psychologists & social workers.
ISBN Prefix(es): 978-1-884063; 978-1-57543
Number of titles published annually: 12 Print; 20 Online; 25 E-Book
Total Titles: 300 Print; 400 Online
Distributed by ASCA; Boulden Publishing; Burnell Books; Calloway House; Career Kids FYI; CFKR Career; Character Development; Community Intervention; Courage to Change; Cress Productions Co; EDU Reference; Educational Media Corp; Incentive Plus; Jist; Mental Health Resources; National Professional Resources; National Resource Center Youth Services; NIMCO Bookstore; Paperbacks for Educators; School Speciality; SourceResource; STARS-National Center for Youths; WRS Group; YouthLight Inc
Distributor for Boulden; Center for Youth Issues/STARS; Educational Media; HarperCollins

**Marathon Press**
1500 Square Turn Blvd, Norfolk, NE 68701
Mailing Address: PO Box 407, Norfolk, NE 68702-0407
*Tel:* 402-371-5040 *Toll Free Tel:* 800-228-0629 *Fax:* 402-371-9382
*Web Site:* www.marathonpress.com
*Key Personnel*
Owner: Rex Alewel
Pres: Bruce Price
Founded: 1974
Books on professional photography.
ISBN Prefix(es): 978-0-934420
Number of titles published annually: 5 Print
Total Titles: 30 Print

**Maren Green Publishing Inc**
5630 Memorial Ave N, Suite 3, Oak Park Heights, MN 55082
*Tel:* 651-439-4500 *Toll Free Tel:* 800-287-1512 *Fax:* 651-439-4532
*E-mail:* info@marengreen.com
*Web Site:* www.marengreen.com
*Key Personnel*
Owner & Pres: Todd Snow *E-mail:* toddsnow@marengreen.com
Founded: 2006
Fiction & nonfiction books for children newborn to age 9.
This publisher has indicated that 100% of their product line is author subsidized.
ISBN Prefix(es): 978-1-934277
Number of titles published annually: 5 Print
Total Titles: 19 Print
Imprints: Books Good For Young Children™
Distributed by Crabtree Publishing Inc
Foreign Rights: Sylvia Hayse Literary Agency (Worldwide)
Membership(s): ABA; IBPA, the Independent Book Publishers Association

**Margaret K McElderry**, see Simon & Schuster Children's Publishing

**Marick Press**
PO Box 36253, Grosse Pointe Farms, MI 48236
*Tel:* 313-407-9236
*E-mail:* orders@marickpress.com
*Web Site:* www.marickpress.com
*Key Personnel*
Publr: Mariela Griffor
Mng Ed: Sandra Kuizenga *Tel:* 989-671-0403
Poetry Ed: Peter Stern
A not-for-profit literary publisher founded to preserve the best work by poets around the world including many under published women poets. We seek out & publish the best new work from an eclectic range of aesthets - work that is technically accomplished, distinctive in style & thematically fresh.
ISBN Prefix(es): 978-0-9779703; 978-1-934851
Number of titles published annually: 6 Print
Total Titles: 45 Print

**Marine Education Textbooks Inc**
124 N Van Ave, Houma, LA 70363-5895
SAN: 215-9651
*Tel:* 985-879-3866 *Fax:* 985-879-3911
*E-mail:* email@marineeducationtextbooks.com
*Web Site:* www.marineeducationtextbooks.com
*Key Personnel*
Pres: Gwen M Block
VP: Richard A Block
Founded: 1970
Training & educational books for preparation of USCG Exams. Marine safety signs, nautical charts.
ISBN Prefix(es): 978-0-934114; 978-1-879778
Number of titles published annually: 6 Print
Total Titles: 40 Print
Imprints: Marine Survey Press

**Marine Techniques Publishing**
126 Western Ave, Suite 266, Augusta, ME 04330-7249
SAN: 298-7805
*Tel:* 207-622-7984
*E-mail:* info@marinetechpublishing.com; sales@marinetechpublishing.com
*Web Site:* marinetechpublishing.com; www.groups.yahoo.com/group/marinetechniquespublishing
*Key Personnel*
Owner & Pres: James L Pelletier
Founded: 1983
Industry specific directories; maritime/worldwide merchant marine; naval architecture; marine biology, chemistry, geology; civil, marine engineering; electrical, electronic marine engineering; energy, oil & gas offshore; mechanical marine engineering; transportation, marine. Commercial merchant marine - worldwide directories, *Mariner's Employment Guide* & maritime autobiographies (true maritime stories).
This publisher has indicated that 100% of their product line is author subsidized.
ISBN Prefix(es): 978-0-9644915; 978-0-9798008
Number of titles published annually: 5 Print; 276 Online; 2 E-Book; 2 Audio
Total Titles: 100 Print; 20 CD-ROM; 276 Online; 2 E-Book; 2 Audio
Distributed by Armchair Sailor Books & Charts; Baker, Lyman & Co; Bluewater Books & Charts; The Book House Inc; BooksXYZ.com; Brodart Books Co; Captain's Nautical Supplies; Coutts Library Services Inc; Elsevier Science, Technology & Business Books; Emery-Pratt Co; Follett Library Resources Inc; Landfall Navigation; Marine Education Textbooks Inc; MaritimeEmployment.com; Pilothouse Nautical Books & Charts; Seabreeze Books & Charts; Washington Book Distributors
Distributor for Academic Press; Best Publishing Co; Butterworth-Heinemann; Clarkson Research Services Ltd; Elsevier, Science & Technology Books; Focal Press; Gulf Professional Publishers; PennWell Business & Industrial Division; W B Saunders Co; Waterfront Soundings Productions; Witherby Seamanship International Ltd
Foreign Rep(s): Chapters Inc (Canada, Ontario); W H Everett & Sons Ltd (England, London, UK); Lavoisier (France)
Membership(s): American Maritime Association; American Society of Naval Engineers; Association of Marine Engineers; The Association of Publishers for Special Sales; IBPA, the Independent Book Publishers Association; Independent Publishers of New England; Lloyd's Maritime Information Register; Women's Maritime Association

**Marion Street Press Inc**
4207 SE Woodstock Blvd, No 168, Portland, OR 97206
*Tel:* 503-888-4624 *Toll Free Fax:* 866-571-8359
*E-mail:* marionstreetpress@gmail.com
*Web Site:* www.marionstreetpress.com
*Key Personnel*
Publr: Kel Winter
Founded: 1993
Books for writers & journalists.
ISBN Prefix(es): 978-0-9665176; 978-0-9729937; 978-1-933338
Number of titles published annually: 12 Print
Total Titles: 60 Print
Foreign Rep(s): IPG (Canada)
Membership(s): The Association of Publishers for Special Sales; IBPA, the Independent Book Publishers Association; National Association of Independent Publishers

**Marketscope Group Books LLC**
PO Box 3118, Huntington Beach, CA 92605-3118
*Tel:* 562-343-5414 *Fax:* 562-343-5417
*E-mail:* info@marketscopegroup.com; fxtv@msn.com
*Key Personnel*
Publr: Ronnie Kovach
Opers Mgr: Kathy Desthieux
Founded: 1985
Books on recreational fishing.
ISBN Prefix(es): 978-0-934061
Number of titles published annually: 6 Print
Total Titles: 6 Print

**Markowski International Publishers**
One Oakglade Circle, Hummelstown, PA 17036-9525
*Tel:* 717-566-0468
*E-mail:* info@possibilitypress.com
*Web Site:* www.possibilitypress.com; www.aeronauticalpublishers.com
*Key Personnel*
Publr: Mike Markowski
Founded: 1981
Books on personal development, business, success, motivation, aviation & model aviation.
ISBN Prefix(es): 978-0-938716
Number of titles published annually: 6 Print
Total Titles: 40 Print
Imprints: Aeronautical Publishers; Possibility Press
Distributed by Executive Books; Moborbooks
Membership(s): IBPA, the Independent Book Publishers Association

**Marquette Books**
3107 E 62 Ave, Spokane, WA 99223
SAN: 251-5261
*Tel:* 509-290-9240 *Fax:* 509-448-2191
*E-mail:* books@marquettebooks.com
*Web Site:* www.marquettebooks.com
*Key Personnel*
Owner & Publr: Theresa Stimson
Copy Ed: Dr David Demers
Founded: 2001
ISBN Prefix(es): 978-0-922993; 978-0-9816018; 978-0-9826597
Number of titles published annually: 3 Print
Total Titles: 92 Print

**Marquette University Press**
1415 W Wisconsin Ave, Milwaukee, WI 53233
Mailing Address: PO Box 3141, Milwaukee, WI 53201-3141
*Tel:* 414-288-1564 *Toll Free Tel:* 800-247-6553 (cust serv) *Fax:* 414-288-7813
*Web Site:* www.marquette.edu/mupress
*Key Personnel*
Dir: Dr Andrew Tallon *Tel:* 414-288-7298 *E-mail:* andrew.tallon@marquette.edu
Mgr: Maureen Kondrick *E-mail:* maureen.kondrick@marquette.edu
Founded: 1916
Publications in the humanities by scholars of international reputation. Specializing in philosophy, theology, humanities & history.
ISBN Prefix(es): 978-0-87462
Number of titles published annually: 18 Print; 1 CD-ROM; 15 E-Book
Total Titles: 400 Print; 3 CD-ROM; 75 E-Book
Foreign Rep(s): Scholarly Book Services (Canada)
*Orders to:* Bookmasters, 30 Amberwood Pkwy, Ashland, OH 44805 *Toll Free Tel:* 800-247-6553 *Fax:* 419-281-6883 *E-mail:* orders@atlasbooks.com *Web Site:* www.atlasbooksdistribution.com
*Returns:* Bookmasters, 30 Amberwood Pkwy, Ashland, OH 44805 *Fax:* 419-281-6883 *E-mail:* orders@atlasbooks.com *Web Site:* www.atlasbooksdistribution.com
*Distribution Center:* Bookmasters, 30 Amberwood Pkwy, Ashland, OH 44805, Contact: Beth Boeh *Tel:* 419-281-1802 ext 1408 *Fax:* 419-281-6883 *E-mail:* orders@atlasbooks.com *Web Site:* www.atlasbooksdistribution.com
Membership(s): American Association of University Presses; Association of Jesuit University Presses

**Marquis Who's Who LLC**
300 Connell Dr, Suite 2000, Berkeley Heights, NJ 07922
SAN: 202-6120
*Tel:* 908-673-1000 *Toll Free Tel:* 800-473-7020 *Fax:* 908-673-1189
*E-mail:* customerservice@marquiswhoswho.com (cust serv, sales)
*Web Site:* www.marquiswhoswho.com
*Key Personnel*
CEO: Fred Marks *Tel:* 908-673-1010 *E-mail:* fred.marks@marquiswhoswho.com
Founded: 1898
Publisher of comprehensive biographical references available in print, online & mailing list. Major Marquis Who's Who publications include *Who's Who in America, Who's Who in the World* & *Who's Who of American Women.*
ISBN Prefix(es): 978-0-8379
Number of titles published annually: 15 Print
Total Titles: 20 Online
*See separate listing for:*
**National Register Publishing**

**Marriage Transformation LLC**
2409 Hamill Rd, Hixson, TN 37343-4034
*Tel:* 423-599-0153
*E-mail:* staff@marriagetransformation.com
*Web Site:* www.marriagetransformation.com
*Key Personnel*
Pres: Susanne M Alexander *E-mail:* susanne@marriagetransformation.com
Relationship & marriage education.

This publisher has indicated that 90% of their product line is author subsidized.
ISBN Prefix(es): 978-0-9726893
Number of titles published annually: 3 Print; 6 E-Book
Total Titles: 10 Print
Distributed by Barringer; Longman
Membership(s): American Society of Journalists & Authors

**Marshall & Swift**
777 S Fiqueroa St, 12th fl, Los Angeles, CA 90017
*Tel:* 213-683-9000 *Toll Free Tel:* 800-544-2678 *Fax:* 213-683-9043
*E-mail:* csinquiry@marshallswift.com
*Web Site:* www.marshallswift.com
*Key Personnel*
Pres: Peter Wells
Res Supvr: Gary Miller
Founded: 1932
Building cost databases for the construction market & insurance industry.
ISBN Prefix(es): 978-1-56842
Number of titles published annually: 10 Print
Total Titles: 21 Print
Imprints: Valuation Press
Distributed by McGraw-Hill Book Co
*Warehouse:* 1625 W Temple, Los Angeles, CA 90026

**Marshall Cavendish Corp**
Member of Times International Publishing Group
99 White Plains Rd, Tarrytown, NY 10591-9001
*Tel:* 914-332-8888 *Toll Free Tel:* 800-821-9881 *Fax:* 914-332-8102
*E-mail:* customerservice@marshallcavendish.com; mcc@marshallcavendish.com
*Web Site:* marshallcavendish.us; marshallcavendishdigital.com; marshallcavendishebooks.com
*Key Personnel*
CEO: Eng Leok Chng
Sales & Mktg Dir: Craig Dunn
Sr Accountant: Richard Moore
Accts Payable Assoc: Imelda Guarin
Mktg Asst: Bridget A Schultz
Mktg Coord: Mark Tancredi
Educ Consultant: Barbara Schneer
Sr Educ Consultant: Diana Kyle
Sr Mgr, e-Learning Solutions-MCE: Rahim Ghani
Sales Consultant-MCE: Leander Moore
Sr Educ Consultant: Jackelyn Classen
Tech & Sales Support Engr: Courtney Noe
Sr Educ Consultant: Christopher Coyne
Accts Receivable Mgr: Robin Costello
IT Mgr: Stephen Dolled
Sr Cust Serv: Norma Palazzo
Admin Asst: Servando Rosario
Founded: 1970
International publisher of books, directories, magazines & digital platforms. Products reach across the globe in 13 languages & our publishing network spans Asia & the US. Dedicated to the promotion of lifelong learning & self-development as we stride into the 21st century.
ISBN Prefix(es): 978-1-85435; 978-0-7614
Number of titles published annually: 320 Print; 10 Online; 300 E-Book
Total Titles: 1,200 Print; 57 Online; 590 E-Book
Imprints: Marshall Cavendish Adult Trade; Marshall Cavendish Benchmark; Marshall Cavendish Digital; Marshall Cavendish Education; Marshall Cavendish Reference
Distributed by Marshall Cavendish Ltd (UK)
Foreign Rep(s): Peter Pal Library Suppliers (Australia)
*Warehouse:* Swan Packaging, 415 Hamburg Tpke, Wayne, NJ 07470
Membership(s): ALA; Children's Book Council

**Martindale-Hubbell**, see LexisNexis/Martindale-Hubbell

**Martingale®**
19021 120 Ave NE, Suite 102, Bothell, WA 98011
*Tel:* 425-483-3313 *Toll Free Tel:* 800-426-3126 *Fax:* 425-486-7596
*E-mail:* info@martingale-pub.com
*Web Site:* www.martingale-pub.com
*Key Personnel*
CEO & Pres: Tom Wierzbicki
CFO: Keith Brants
Design Dir: Paula Schlosser
Edit Dir: Mary Green
Mktg Mgr: Karen Johnson *Tel:* 425-483-3313 ext 1387
Mgr, Trade Sales: Shelley Santa
Founded: 1976
Quilting, knitting & crafting.
ISBN Prefix(es): 978-1-56477
Number of titles published annually: 55 Print; 55 E-Book
Total Titles: 250 Print; 120 E-Book
Imprints: That Patchwork Place

**Maryland Historical Society**
201 W Monument St, Baltimore, MD 21201
*Tel:* 410-685-3750 *Fax:* 410-385-2105
*Web Site:* www.mdhs.org
*Key Personnel*
Dir, Pubns & Library Servs: Patricia Anderson, PhD *Tel:* 410-685-3750 ext 317 *E-mail:* panderson@mdhs.org
Founded: 1844
Publish historical books.
ISBN Prefix(es): 978-0-938420
Number of titles published annually: 5 Print
Total Titles: 45 Print
Distributed by Alan C Hood & Co Inc
*Orders to:* Alan C Hood & Co Inc, PO Box 775, Chambersburg, PA 17201, Contact: Alan Hood *Tel:* 717-267-0867 *Fax:* 717-267-0572
*Returns:* Maple Press Distribution Ctr, I-83 Industrial Park, York, PA 17405
*Shipping Address:* Maple Press Distribution Ctr, I-83 Industrial Park, York, PA 17405, Contact: Alan C Hood *Tel:* 717-267-0867 *Fax:* 717-267-0572
*Warehouse:* Maple Press Distribution Ctr, I-83 Industrial Park, York, PA 17405
*Distribution Center:* Maple Press Distribution Ctr, I-83 Industrial Park, York, PA 17405

**Maryland History Press**
PO Box 206, Fruitland, MD 21826-0206
*Tel:* 410-742-2682 *Toll Free Tel:* 877-742-2682 *Fax:* 410-505-4555
*E-mail:* sales@marylandhistorypress.com
*Web Site:* www.marylandhistorypress.com
*Key Personnel*
Pres: Elaine Patterson
Founded: 1999
Provide quality books on various topics & by various authors to help celebrate America's uniqueness...people, events, culture & environs. Services provided are publishing services, author-subsidy program, consignments, distribution services via national company, book searches & web site exposure through major online booksellers.
The publisher has indicated that 85% of their product line is author subsidized.
ISBN Prefix(es): 978-0-9703802
Number of titles published annually: 3 Print
Total Titles: 10 Print; 10 Online
Distributor for Dogwood Ridge Books; Tapestry Press Ltd
*Warehouse:* 109 Clyde Ave, Fruitland, MD 21826
*Distribution Center:* Follett Library Resources Inc, 1349 Ridgeview Dr, McHenry, IL 60050, Contact: Gail Wieczorek *Tel:* 815-759-1700 *E-mail:* gail.wieczorek@flr.follett.com *Web Site:* www.follett.com
Baker & Taylor, PO Box 8888, Momemce, IL 60954
Membership(s): The Association of Publishers for Special Sales

**Marymark Press**
45-08 Old Millstone Dr, East Windsor, NJ 08520
*Tel:* 609-443-0646
*Key Personnel*
Publr & Ed: Mark Sonnenfeld
Founded: 1994
Independent small press publishing vehicle; various size chapbooks, broadsides, writing samplers, give-out sheets, single sheets, audio sound collages. Experimental writing. Prefer automatic writing/avant-garde genre.
ISBN Prefix(es): 978-0-9632820; 978-1-887379; 978-0-9844182; 978-0-9798819
Number of titles published annually: 10 Print; 3 Audio
Total Titles: 400 Print; 35 Audio

**Mason Crest Publishers**
370 Reed Rd, Suite 302, Broomall, PA 19008
*Tel:* 610-543-6200 *Toll Free Tel:* 866-MCP-BOOK (627-2665) *Fax:* 610-543-3878
*Web Site:* www.masoncrest.com
*Key Personnel*
Pres: Daniel Hilferty *E-mail:* dhilferty@masoncrest.com
Principal & Creative Dir: Louis Cohen *Tel:* 917-763-7760
CEO: Philip Cohen *E-mail:* pcohen@masoncrest.com
Cont: Diana Daniels *E-mail:* ddaniels@masoncrest.com
Opers Mgr: Lee Wark *Tel:* 610-583-0211 *Fax:* 610-583-0212 *E-mail:* lwark@masoncrest.com
Cust Serv: Grace Baffa *Tel:* 610-543-6200 ext 113 *E-mail:* gbaffa@masoncrest.com
Founded: 2001
Mason Crest Publishers is committed to publishing the finest nonfiction school, library & curriculum products available today. Our titles are full-color & include a glossary, index, further reading section, Internet resources & are library bound. Subjects include reality shows.
ISBN Prefix(es): 978-1-59084; 978-1-4222
Number of titles published annually: 300 Print; 300 E-Book
Total Titles: 2,000 Print; 1,600 E-Book
*Returns:* 701 Ashland Ave, Bays 1 & 2, Folcroft, PA 19032, Opers Mgr: Lee Wark *Tel:* 610-583-0211 *Fax:* 610-583-0212 *E-mail:* lee6250@aol.com
*Shipping Address:* 701 Ashland Ave, Bays 1 & 2, Folcroft, PA 19032, Opers Mgr: Lee Wark *Tel:* 610-583-0211 *Fax:* 610-583-0212 *E-mail:* lee6250@aol.com
*Warehouse:* 701 Ashland Ave, Bays 1 & 2, Folcroft, PA 19032, Opers Mgr: Lee Wark *Tel:* 610-583-0211 *Fax:* 610-583-0212 *E-mail:* lee6250@aol.com
*Distribution Center:* 701 Ashland Ave, Bays 1 & 2, Folcroft, PA 19032, Opers Mgr: Lee Wark *Tel:* 610-583-0211 *Fax:* 610-583-0212 *E-mail:* lee6250@aol.com
Membership(s): Friends of Libraries of USA; IBPA, the Independent Book Publishers Association

**The Massachusetts Historical Society**
1154 Boylston St, Boston, MA 02215-3695
*Tel:* 617-536-1608 *Fax:* 617-859-0074
*E-mail:* publications@masshist.org
*Web Site:* www.masshist.org
*Key Personnel*
Dir, Pubns: Ondine E Le Blanc *Tel:* 617-646-0524 *E-mail:* oleblanc@masshist.org

Founded: 1792
Scholarly historical regional publications.
ISBN Prefix(es): 978-0-934909; 978-0-9652584
Number of titles published annually: 4 Print
Total Titles: 80 Print
Distributed by University of Virginia Press

**Massachusetts Institute of Technology Libraries**
77 Massachusetts Ave, Bldg 14-S, Rm 0551, Cambridge, MA 02139-4307
*Tel:* 617-253-5651 *Fax:* 617-253-8894
*Web Site:* libraries.mit.edu/docs
*Key Personnel*
Dir, Libs: Ann Wolpert *Tel:* 617-253-5297 *E-mail:* awolpert@mit.edu
Assoc Dir, Admin: Keith Glavash *Tel:* 617-253-7059 *E-mail:* kglavash@mit.edu
Communs Offr: Heather Denny *Tel:* 617-253-5686 *E-mail:* hdenny@mit.edu
Founded: 1863
MIT theses, dissertations, technical reports & working papers.
ISBN Prefix(es): 978-0-911379
Number of titles published annually: 2,000 Print
Total Titles: 15,000 Print

**§Master Books**
Subsidiary of New Leaf Publishing Group
PO Box 726, Green Forest, AR 72638-0726
*Tel:* 870-438-5288 *Fax:* 870-438-5120
*E-mail:* nlp@newleafpress.net
*Web Site:* www.nlpg.com
*Key Personnel*
Edit Asst: Craig Froman
Founded: 1975
Publish Biblically-based, scientifically sound creation materials & curriculum.
ISBN Prefix(es): 978-0-89051
Number of titles published annually: 25 Print; 20 E-Book
Total Titles: 395 Print; 3 CD-ROM; 70 E-Book; 2 Audio
*Shipping Address:* 3142 Hwy 103 N, Green Forest, AR 72638

**Materials Research Society**
506 Keystone Dr, Warrendale, PA 15086-7537
SAN: 686-0125
*Tel:* 724-779-3003 *Fax:* 724-779-8313
*E-mail:* info@mrs.org
*Web Site:* www.mrs.org
*Key Personnel*
Dir, Pubns & Mktg: Eileen Kiley Novak *Tel:* 724-779-2742 *E-mail:* enovak@mrs.org
Founded: 1973
Scientific reports on leading edge topics in materials research.
ISBN Prefix(es): 978-0-931837; 978-1-55899
Number of titles published annually: 30 Print
Total Titles: 900 Print

**Math Solutions®**
Unit of Scholastic Education
150 Gate 5 Rd, Suite 101, Sausalito, CA 94965
*Tel:* 415-332-4181 *Toll Free Tel:* 800-868-9092 *Fax:* 415-331-1931 *Toll Free Fax:* 877-942-8837
*E-mail:* info@mathsolutions.com; orders@mathsolutions.com
*Web Site:* www.mathsolutions.com
*Key Personnel*
Founder & Math Educ Consultant: Marilyn Burns
CEO & Pres: Christine Willig
Dir, Sales & Client Rels: Jane Manning Hyatt *E-mail:* jmhyatt@mathsolutions.com
Edit Mgr: Jamie Cross
Founded: 1994
Dedicated to improving the teaching of mathematics by providing professional development of the highest quality to teachers & administrators.
ISBN Prefix(es): 978-0-941355
Number of titles published annually: 10 Print
Total Titles: 80 Print
*Shipping Address:* 1805 S McDowell Blvd, Petaluma, CA 94954, Contact: Taber Auren *Tel:* 707-769-0722
*Warehouse:* 1805 S McDowell Blvd, Petaluma, CA 94954, Contact: Taber Auren *Tel:* 707-769-0722
Membership(s): ASCD; National Council of Teachers of Mathematics

**Math Teachers Press Inc**
4850 Park Glen Rd, Minneapolis, MN 55416
*Tel:* 952-545-6535 *Toll Free Tel:* 800-852-2435 *Fax:* 952-546-7502
*E-mail:* info@movingwithmath.com
*Web Site:* www.movingwithmath.com
*Key Personnel*
Founder & Pres: Caryl K Pierson *E-mail:* cpierson@movingwithmath.com
Founded: 1985
Pre K-12 manipulative-based math curriculum.
ISBN Prefix(es): 978-0-933383; 978-1-891192; 978-1-931106; 978-1-59167
Number of titles published annually: 3 Print
Total Titles: 70 Print

**The Mathematical Association of America**
1529 18 St NW, Washington, DC 20036-1358
SAN: 203-9737
*Tel:* 202-387-5200 *Toll Free Tel:* 800-741-9415 *Fax:* 202-265-2384
*E-mail:* maahq@maa.org
*Web Site:* www.maa.org
*Key Personnel*
Pres: Paul Manthey Zorn
CFO: Sharon Tryon *E-mail:* stryon@maa.org
Treas: James Daniel
Secy: Barbara Faires *E-mail:* faires@westminster.edu
Assoc Secy: Gerard Venema
Exec Dir: Michael Pearson
Assoc Dir, Pubns: Carol Baxter *E-mail:* cbaxter@maa.org
Dir, Info Technol: John Wyatt *E-mail:* jwyatt@maa.org
Dir, Membership & Mktg: Stephen Coolbaugh
Dir, Pubns & Communs: Ivars Peterson
Founded: 1915
Mathematical books & journals.
ISBN Prefix(es): 978-0-88385
Number of titles published annually: 15 Print; 2 CD-ROM
Total Titles: 200 Print; 2 CD-ROM
Distributed by Cambridge University Press
Foreign Rep(s): Cambridge University Press (Africa, Europe, Middle East)
*Orders to:* MAA Service Center, PO Box 91112, Washington, DC 20090-1112 *Tel:* 301-607-7800 *Toll Free Tel:* 800-331-1622 *Fax:* 301-206-9789 *E-mail:* maaservice@maa.org

**§Maupin House Publishing**
2300 NW 71 Place, Gainesville, FL 32653
SAN: 250-7676
Mailing Address: PO Box 90148, Gainesville, FL 32607-0148 SAN: 250-7684
*Tel:* 352-373-5588 *Toll Free Tel:* 800-524-0634 *Fax:* 352-373-5546
*E-mail:* info@maupinhouse.com
*Web Site:* www.maupinhouse.com
*Key Personnel*
Pres & Publr: Julia Graddy *E-mail:* publisher@maupinhouse.com
VP & House Coun: Robert Graddy *E-mail:* rgraddy@maupinhouse.com
Ed & Prodn Mgr: Emily Raij *E-mail:* eraij@maupinhouse.com
Edit & Mktg Asst: Tiffany Morgan *E-mail:* tmorgan@maupinhouse.com
Founded: 1989
Publish professional resources for preK-12 teachers for writing education, reading & general language arts. K-8 writing curriculum. Staff development training in writing workshop.
ISBN Prefix(es): 978-0-929895
Number of titles published annually: 12 Print; 4 E-Book; 2 Audio
Total Titles: 85 Print; 1 Audio
Membership(s): ASCD; Association of Educational Publishers; IBPA, the Independent Book Publishers Association; International Reading Association; National Council of Teachers of English

**Mazda Publishers Inc**
One Park Plaza, Suite 600, Irvine, CA 92614
SAN: 658-120X
Mailing Address: PO Box 2603, Costa Mesa, CA 92628
*Tel:* 714-751-5252 *Fax:* 714-751-4805
*E-mail:* mazdapub@aol.com
*Web Site:* www.mazdapub.com
*Key Personnel*
Founder & Pres: Dr Ahmad Jabbari
Ed-at-Large: Ann West
Founded: 1980
Publishes scholarly books dealing with the Middle East, Central Asia & North Africa; critical reviews of poetry; Central Asia including art & architecture.
ISBN Prefix(es): 978-1-56859
Number of titles published annually: 20 Print
Total Titles: 250 Print

**MBI Publishing Co**
Division of Keyside Publishing Group
400 First Ave N, Suite 300, Minneapolis, MN 55401
*Toll Free Tel:* 800-328-0590 *Fax:* 612-344-8691
*E-mail:* trade@mbipublishing.com (US trade orders & sales)
*Web Site:* www.qbookshop.com
*Key Personnel*
VP, Opers: Joe Cella
Founded: 1965
Book publisher & distributor.
ISBN Prefix(es): 978-0-87938; 978-0-7603; 978-0-89658
Number of titles published annually: 600 Print
Total Titles: 7,000 Print
Imprints: Motorbooks; Voyageur Press; Zenith Press

**McBooks Press Inc**
ID Booth Bldg, 520 N Meadow St, Ithaca, NY 14850
*Tel:* 607-272-2114 *Fax:* 607-273-6068
*E-mail:* mcbooks@mcbooks.com
*Web Site:* www.mcbooks.com
*Key Personnel*
Publr & Intl Rts Contact: Alexander Skutt *E-mail:* alex@mcbooks.com
Art Dir: Panda Musgrove *E-mail:* panda@mcbooks.com
Founded: 1979
Trade books; specialize in historical fiction, vegetarianism, NYS regional books, period nautical, military fiction, sports including boxing.
ISBN Prefix(es): 978-1-59013
Number of titles published annually: 10 Print; 10 E-Book
Total Titles: 175 Print; 134 E-Book
Foreign Rep(s): Gazelle Book Services Ltd (Europe, UK)
*Orders to:* Independent Publishers Group, 814 N Franklin St, Chicago, IL 60610 *Tel:* 312-337-0747 *Toll Free Tel:* 800-888-4741 *Fax:* 312-337-5985 *Toll Free Fax:* 800-338-4550 *E-mail:* orders@ipgbook.com *Web Site:* www.ipgbook.com
*Distribution Center:* Independent Publishers Group, 814 N Franklin St, Chicago, IL 60610 *Tel:* 312-337-0747 *Toll Free Tel:* 800-888-

4741 *Fax:* 312-337-5985 *Toll Free Fax:* 800-338-4550 *E-mail:* orders@ipgbook.com *Web Site:* www.ipgbook.com

**McClanahan Publishing House Inc**
88 Cedar St, Kuttawa, KY 42055-0100
Mailing Address: PO Box 100, Kuttawa, KY 42055
*Tel:* 270-388-9388 *Toll Free Tel:* 800-544-6959 *Fax:* 270-388-6186
*E-mail:* books@kybooks.com
*Web Site:* www.kybooks.com
*Key Personnel*
Pres & Exec Ed: Michelle Stone *E-mail:* mstone@kybooks.com
Mktg Dir: Karlee Alexander *E-mail:* kalexander@kybooks.com
Art Dir: James Asher
Busn Mgr: Jo Doty *E-mail:* jdoty@kybooks.com
Founded: 1983
Full service publisher offering art services & artist illustration, jacket design, book design & layout. Self-publishing division provides these services as well for authors who want to retain control of their work.
ISBN Prefix(es): 978-0-913383; 978-0-9758788
Number of titles published annually: 15 Print
Total Titles: 140 Print
Imprints: Four Rivers Press

**McCutchan Publishing Corp**
3220 Blume Dr, Suite 197, Richmond, CA 94806
SAN: 203-9486
*Tel:* 510-758-5510 *Toll Free Tel:* 800-227-1540 *Fax:* 510-758-6078
*E-mail:* mccutchanpublish@sbcglobal.net
*Web Site:* www.mccutchanpublishing.com
*Key Personnel*
Pres & Publr: Nancy Runyon
ISBN Contact & Rts & Perms: Kim Sharrar
Founded: 1963
College textbooks & professional books in education, hotel & restaurant management & law enforcement education.
ISBN Prefix(es): 978-0-8211
Number of titles published annually: 3 Print
Total Titles: 100 Print

**The McDonald & Woodward Publishing Co**
431 E College St, Granville, OH 43023
*Tel:* 740-321-1140 *Toll Free Tel:* 800-233-8787 *Fax:* 740-321-1141
*E-mail:* mwpubco@mwpubco.com
*Web Site:* www.mwpubco.com
*Key Personnel*
Publr & Intl Rts Mgr: Jerry N McDonald *E-mail:* jmcd@mwpubco.com
Mktg Mgr: Trish Newcomb *E-mail:* tnewcomb@mwpubco.com
Founded: 1986
Books (primarily adult) in natural history & cultural history; co-publish with educational & governmental entities.
ISBN Prefix(es): 978-0-939923
Number of titles published annually: 8 Print
Total Titles: 50 Print

**§McFarland**
960 NC Hwy 88 W, Jefferson, NC 28640
Mailing Address: PO Box 611, Jefferson, NC 28640-0611
*Tel:* 336-246-4460 *Toll Free Tel:* 800-253-2187 (orders) *Fax:* 336-246-5018; 336-246-4403 (orders)
*E-mail:* info@mcfarlandpub.com
*Web Site:* www.mcfarlandpub.com
*Key Personnel*
Pres: Robert Franklin *E-mail:* rfranklin@mcfarlandpub.com
EVP: Rhonda Herman *E-mail:* rherman@mcfarlandpub.com
Edit Dir: Steve Wilson *E-mail:* swilson@mcfarlandpub.com
Dir, Fin & Admin: Margie Turnmire *E-mail:* mturnmire@mcfarlandpub.com
Dir, Sales & Mktg: Karl-Heinz Roseman *E-mail:* kroseman@mcfarlandpub.com
Subs & Intl Rights: Beth Cox *E-mail:* bcox@mcfarlandpub.com
Sr Acqs Ed: Gary Mitchem *E-mail:* gmitchem@mcfarlandpub.com
Acqs Ed: Charles Perdue *E-mail:* cperdue@mcfarlandpub.com
Founded: 1979
A leading independent publisher of academic & nonfiction books, known for covering popular topics in a serious fashion & for manufacturing books to meet high library standards.
ISBN Prefix(es): 978-0-89950; 978-0-7864
Number of titles published annually: 400 Print; 350 E-Book
Total Titles: 5,000 Print; 2,000 E-Book
Subsidiaries: McFarland & Co Ltd, Publishers (London, UK)
Foreign Rep(s): DA Information Services (Australia, New Zealand, Papua New Guinea); Eurospan (Europe, Middle East, North Africa, UK)
*Returns:* 961 NC Hwy 88 W, Jefferson, NC 28640
*Shipping Address:* 961 NC Hwy 88 W, Jefferson, NC 28640

**§McGraw-Hill Career Education**
Division of McGraw-Hill Higher Education
1333 Burr Ridge Pkwy, Burr Ridge, IL 60527
*Tel:* 630-789-4000 *Toll Free Tel:* 800-338-3987 (cust serv) *Fax:* 630-789-5523; 614-755-5645 (cust serv)
*Web Site:* www.mhhe.com
*Key Personnel*
VP, Learning Solutions: Tom Malek *Tel:* 314-446-9572 *E-mail:* tom.malek@mheducation.com
Mng Dir: Scott Davidson *Tel:* 314-439-6862 *E-mail:* scott.davidson@mheducation.com
Dir, Sales: Micaela Haidle *E-mail:* micaela.haidle@mheducation.com
Founded: 2001
Provides textbooks & educational materials to post-secondary, trade & career schools.
ISBN Prefix(es): 978-0-697; 978-0-256; 978-0-07
Number of titles published annually: 100 Print; 7 CD-ROM; 50 Online; 75 E-Book
Total Titles: 2,315 Print; 250 Online; 350 E-Book
*Branch Office(s)*
McGraw-Hill Learning Solutions, 8900 Keystone at the Crossing, Suite 950, Indianapolis, IN 46240
*Returns:* 860 Taylor Station Rd, Blacklick, OH 43004-0539
*Distribution Center:* 860 Taylor Station Rd, Blacklick, OH 43004-0539

**The McGraw-Hill Companies Inc**, see McGraw-Hill Financial

**McGraw-Hill Contemporary Learning Series**
Division of McGraw-Hill Higher Education
501 Bell St, Dubuque, IA 52001
SAN: 201-3460
*Toll Free Tel:* 800-243-6532
*Web Site:* www.mhcls.com
*Key Personnel*
Pres, Science, Engg & Mathematics: Kurt Strand *Tel:* 563-584-6633 *Fax:* 563-584-6600 *E-mail:* kurt_strand@mcgraw-hill.com
SVP, Sales MHHE: Doug Hughes *Tel:* 630-789-5121 *Fax:* 630-789-6944 *E-mail:* doug_hughes@mcgraw-hill.com
Founded: 1971
Thought-provoking series of supplements & online web sites appropriate for college-level courses or for library purchase. Materials span over 20 disciplines & cover compelling, current topics & issues. The publications include annual discipline readers, debate style readers, online readers, geographic/atlas readers & college textbooks.
ISBN Prefix(es): 978-0-07; 978-0-697; 978-0-87967; 978-1-56134; 978-0-7024; 978-0-7235; 978-1-25
Number of titles published annually: 50 Print; 50 Online; 125 E-Book
Total Titles: 350 Print; 350 Online; 246 E-Book

**McGraw-Hill Create**
Division of McGraw-Hill Higher Education
501 Bell St, Dubuque, IA 52001
*Tel:* 563-584-6000 *Fax:* 563-584-6600
*E-mail:* first_last@mcgraw-hill.com
*Web Site:* www.mhhe.com
*Key Personnel*
Dir, Print Solutions: Beth Kundert *Tel:* 563-584-6302 *Fax:* 563-584-6301 *E-mail:* beth_kundert@mcgraw-hill.com
Sr Opers Mgr: Pat Koch *Tel:* 609-426-5721 *Fax:* 609-426-5900 *E-mail:* pat_koch@mcgraw-hill.com
Mgr, Custom Publg Reps: Shirley Grall *Tel:* 563-584-6303 *Fax:* 563-584-6300 *E-mail:* shirley_grall@mcgraw-hill.com
Sr Mgr, Create Mktg Servs: Dudley Land *Tel:* 530-621-3976 *Fax:* 775-255-9197 *E-mail:* dudley_land@mcgraw-hill.com
Dir, Opers & Content Mgmt: Cat Mattura *Tel:* 212-904-3559 *Fax:* 212-904-2340 *E-mail:* cat_mattura@mcgraw-hill.com
VP: Chris Perlee *Tel:* 732-275-1251 *E-mail:* christian_perlee@mcgraw-hill.com
Order Fulfullment Mgr: Kathy Kilburg *Tel:* 563-584-6282 *E-mail:* kathyj_kilburg@mcgraw-hill.com
Mktg Mgr: Rachel Egan *Tel:* 614-532-5589 *E-mail:* rachel_egan@mcgraw-hill.com
Custom products derived from McGraw-Hill copyrighted material; college textbook & electronic book adaptations; supplemental materials.
ISBN Prefix(es): 978-0-07
*Branch Office(s)*
148 Princeton-Hightstown Rd, Hightstown, NJ 08520
2 Penn Plaza, 12th fl, New York, NY 10121-2298
*Distribution Center:* The McGraw-Hill Companies, Distribution Center, 860 Taylor Station Rd, Blacklick, OH 43004

**McGraw-Hill/Dushkin**, see McGraw-Hill Contemporary Learning Series

**§McGraw-Hill Education**
2 Penn Plaza, New York, NY 10121-2298
*Tel:* 212-904-2000
*E-mail:* customer.service@mcgraw-hill.com
*Web Site:* www.mheducation.com; www.mheducation.com/custserv.html
*Key Personnel*
CEO & Pres: Lloyd Waterhouse
Pres, McGraw-Hill Education International: Mark Dorman
Pres, CTB/McGraw-Hill: Ellen Haley *Tel:* 831-393-7757 *Fax:* 831-393-7243 *E-mail:* ellen_haley@mcgraw-hill.com
Chief Digital & Info Offr: Bruce D Marcus *Tel:* 212-904-3416 *Fax:* 212-904-3391 *E-mail:* bruce_marcus@mcgraw-hill.com
EVP: William F Oldsey *Tel:* 212-904-4298 *Fax:* 212-904-4299 *E-mail:* william_oldsey@mcgraw-hill.com
SVP, Fin & Opers: Joseph Micallef *Tel:* 212-904-2485 *Fax:* 212-904-4745 *E-mail:* joseph_micallef@mcgraw-hill.com
SVP, Pub & Govt Aff: Rosemarie Cappabianca *Tel:* 212-904-4563 *Fax:* 212-904-6664 *E-mail:* rosemarie_cappabianca@mcgraw-hill.com

SVP, R&D: Charlotte Frank *Tel:* 212-512-6512 *Fax:* 212-512-4769 *E-mail:* charlotte_frank@mcgraw-hill.com
SVP, HR: Maryellen Valaitis *Tel:* 212-904-3621 *Fax:* 212-904-3661 *E-mail:* maryellen_valaitis@mcgraw-hill.com
VP, Learning Ecosystems: Vineet Madan *Tel:* 212-904-3941 *E-mail:* vineet_madan@mcgraw-hill.com
VP, Communs & Mktg: Mary Skafidas *Tel:* 212-904-2078 *Fax:* 212-904-6287 *E-mail:* mary_skafidas@mcgraw-hill.com
Sr Dir, Busn Devt: Derek Wessler *Tel:* 212-904-4311 *E-mail:* derek_wessler@mcgraw-hill.com
Founded: 1989
McGraw-Hill Education, a division of The McGraw-Hill Companies (NYSE: MHP), is a leading global provider of instructional, assessment & reference solutions that empower professionals & students of all ages. McGraw-Hill Education has offices in numerous countries & publishes in more than 40 languages. Additional information is available at mheducation.com.
ISBN Prefix(es): 978-0-07
Imprints: CTB/McGraw-Hill; Glencoe/McGraw-Hill; The Grow Network/McGraw-Hill; Macmillan/McGraw-Hill; McGraw-Hill Contemporary; McGraw-Hill Create; McGraw-Hill Education Australia, New Zealand & South Africa; McGraw-Hill Education Europe, Middle East and Africa; McGraw-Hill Education Latin America; McGraw-Hill Education - Mexico; McGraw-Hill Education - Spain; McGraw-Hill Humanities, Social Sciences, Languages; McGraw-Hill/Irwin; McGraw-Hill Professional; McGraw-Hill Professional Development; McGraw-Hill Ryerson; McGraw-Hill Science, Engineering, Mathematics; SRA/McGraw-Hill; Tata/McGraw-Hill; The Wright Group/McGraw-Hill
*Distribution Center:* McGraw-Hill Education Distribution Center: Norcross, 26510 Jimmy Carter Blvd, Norcross, GA 30071 *Tel:* 404-442-3347
McGraw-Hill Education Distribution Center: Gahanna, 860 Taylor Station Rd, Blacklick, OH 43004 *Tel:* 614-755-4151
McGraw-Hill Education Distribution Center: DeSoto, 220 E Danieldale Rd, DeSoto, TX 75115-2490 *Tel:* 214-224-1111
Membership(s): AAP
*See separate listing for:*
**CTB/McGraw-Hill**
**McGraw-Hill International Publishing Group**
**McGraw-Hill Professional**
**McGraw-Hill School Education Group**

**§McGraw-Hill Financial**
Formerly The McGraw-Hill Companies Inc
1221 Avenue of the Americas, 50th fl, New York, NY 10020
SAN: 200-2248
*Tel:* 212-512-2000
*Web Site:* www.mhfi.com
*Key Personnel*
Chmn, Pres & CEO: Harold W (Terry) McGraw, III
Pres, McGraw-Hill Education: Robert Bahash
Pres, Standard & Poors: Deven Sharma
Pres, Info & Media Servs: Glenn S Goldberg
CFO: Jack Callahan
EVP, HR: John Berisford *Tel:* 212-512-6544 *Fax:* 212-512-3481 *E-mail:* john_berisford@mhfi.com
SVP, Corp Aff & Exec Asst to the Chmn: Edward Smith *Tel:* 212-512-3915 *E-mail:* ted_smyth@mhfi.com
SVP, Investor Rels: Donald S Rubin
EVP, Global Strategy: Charles Teschner, Jr
Founded: 1888
A global information services provider for the financial services, education & business information markets.
ISBN Prefix(es): 978-0-8385; 978-0-07; 978-0-83
Divisions: Information & Media Services; McGraw-Hill Education; Standard & Poor's
Membership(s): AAP; American Business Media; Association of Test Publishers; Better Business Bureau; Brookings Institution; Business Roundtable; Conference Board; Copyright Clearance Center; Council for the Americas; Council of Foreign Relations; Direct Marketing Association; Emergency Committee for American Trade; Entertainment Software Rating Board; European Institute; Magazine Publishers of America; National Association of Broadcasters; National Governor's Association; Private Sector Council; Software & Information Industry Association; United States Chamber of Commerce; United States Council for International Business; US-ASEAN Business Council; US-China Business Council

**§McGraw-Hill Higher Education**
1333 Burr Ridge Pkwy, Burr Ridge, IL 60527
*Tel:* 630-789-4000 *Toll Free Tel:* 800-338-3987 (cust serv) *Fax:* 614-755-5645 (cust serv)
*Web Site:* www.mhhe.com
*Key Personnel*
Pres: Brian Kibby *Tel:* 630-789-5076 *Fax:* 630-789-6942 *E-mail:* brian.kibby@mheducation.com
SVP, MHHE Fin: Mona Leung *E-mail:* mona.leung@mheducation.com
SVP, Prods & Mkts: Kurt Strand *Tel:* 563-584-6633 *Fax:* 563-584-6600 *E-mail:* kurt.strand@mheducation.com
SVP, Sales: Doug Hughes *Tel:* 630-789-5121 *E-mail:* doug.hughes@mheducation.com
VP, Content Prodn & Tech Servs: Kim David *Tel:* 563-584-6650 *Fax:* 563-584-6701 *E-mail:* kim.david@mheducation.com
VP, MHHE Global Publg: Michael Hays *Tel:* 212-904-5979 *Fax:* 212-904-5974 *E-mail:* michael.hays@mheducation.com
Founded: 1996
College texts.
ISBN Prefix(es): 978-0-07; 978-0-697; 978-0-256; 978-0-87; 978-1-25
Number of titles published annually: 1,100 Print; 50 CD-ROM; 750 Online; 800 E-Book; 5 Audio
Total Titles: 12,000 Print; 1,600 CD-ROM; 6,000 Online; 6,000 E-Book; 120 Audio
Imprints: McGraw-Hill Contemporary Learning Series; McGraw-Hill Create; McGraw-Hill Humanities, Social Sciences, Languages; McGraw-Hill/Irwin; McGraw-Hill Learning Solutions; McGraw-Hill Science, Engineering, Mathematics
*Branch Office(s)*
McGraw-Hill Science, Engineering, Mathematics, 501 Bell St, Dubuque, IA 52001 *Tel:* 563-584-6000 *Fax:* 563-584-6600
McGraw-Hill Humanities, Social Sciences, Languages, 2 Penn Plaza, 20th fl, New York, NY 10121 *Tel:* 212-904-2000
*Orders to:* The McGraw-Hill Companies, Distribution Center, 860 Taylor Station Rd, Blacklick, OH 43004-0539 *Toll Free Tel:* 800-338-3987 *Fax:* 614-755-5654
*Returns:* The McGraw-Hill Companies, Distribution Center, 860 Taylor Station Rd, Blacklick, OH 43004-0539 *Toll Free Tel:* 800-338-3987 *Fax:* 614-755-5654
*Shipping Address:* The McGraw-Hill Companies, Distribution Center, 860 Taylor Station Rd, Blacklick, OH 43004-0539 *Toll Free Tel:* 800-338-3987 *Fax:* 614-755-5654
*Warehouse:* The McGraw-Hill Companies, Distribution Center, 860 Taylor Station Rd, Blacklick, OH 43004-0539 *Toll Free Tel:* 800-338-3987 *Fax:* 614-755-5654
*Distribution Center:* The McGraw-Hill Companies, Distribution Center, 860 Taylor Station Rd, Blacklick, OH 43004-0539 *Toll Free Tel:* 800-338-3987 *Fax:* 614-755-5654
*See separate listing for:*
**McGraw-Hill Career Education**
**McGraw-Hill Contemporary Learning Series**
**McGraw-Hill Create**
**McGraw-Hill Humanities, Social Sciences, Languages**
**McGraw-Hill/Irwin**
**McGraw-Hill Science, Engineering, Mathematics**

**McGraw-Hill Humanities, Social Sciences, Languages**
Division of McGraw-Hill Higher Education
2 Penn Plaza, 20th fl, New York, NY 10121
*Tel:* 212-904-2000 *Toll Free Tel:* 800-338-3987 (cust serv) *Fax:* 614-755-5645 (cust serv)
*Web Site:* www.mhhe.com
*Key Personnel*
SVP, Prods & Mkts: Kurt Strand *Tel:* 563-584-6633 *Fax:* 563-584-6600 *E-mail:* kurt.strand@mheducation.com
SVP, Sales: Doug Hughes *Tel:* 630-789-5121 *Fax:* 630-789-6944 *E-mail:* doug.hughes@mheducation.com
VP & Ed-in-Chief: Mike Ryan *Tel:* 212-904-3044 *Fax:* 212-904-3813 *E-mail:* michael.ryan@mheducation.com
VP, Content Prodn & Tech Servs: Kim David *Tel:* 563-584-6650 *Fax:* 563-584-6701 *E-mail:* kim.david@mheducation.com
Founded: 1944
Publishes college textbooks & numerous e-books.
ISBN Prefix(es): 978-0-07; 978-0-697; 978-0-87; 978-1-25
Number of titles published annually: 300 Print; 11 CD-ROM; 225 Online; 225 E-Book; 15 Audio
Total Titles: 3,500 Print; 150 CD-ROM; 1,800 Online; 1,800 E-Book; 225 Audio
*Returns:* 860 Taylor Station Rd, Blacklick, OH 43004-0539
*Distribution Center:* 860 Taylor Station Rd, Blacklick, OH 43004-0539

**McGraw-Hill International Publishing Group**
Division of McGraw-Hill Education
2 Penn Plaza, New York, NY 10121
*Tel:* 212-904-2000
*Web Site:* www.mcgraw-hill.com
*Key Personnel*
Pres, McGraw-Hill Education International: Mark Dorman
VP, Latin America (Mexico): Javier Nerya *Tel:* (55) 1473-5008 *E-mail:* andres_rodriguez@mcgraw-hill.com
SVP, IPG Canada: David Swail *Tel:* 905-430-5006 *Fax:* 905-430-5020 *E-mail:* david_swail@mcgraw-hill.com
EVP & CFO, Ryerson (Ontario, CN): Gordon Dyer *Tel:* 905-430-5032 *Fax:* 905-430-5020
VP, IBG Opers (UK): Raymond Yager *Tel:* (01628) 502962 *Fax:* (01628) 502963
VP, Fin, LHPG (Mexico): Juan Ortega *Tel:* (55) 5081-4471 *E-mail:* fernando_urresta@mcgraw-hill.com
VP & Mng Dir, India: Ajay Shukla *Tel:* (011) 204-383410 *E-mail:* ajay_shuka@mcgraw-hill.com
Mng Dir, Europe: John Donovan *Tel:* (01628) 502971 *E-mail:* john_donovan@mcgraw-hill.com
ISBN Prefix(es): 978-0-07

**§McGraw-Hill/Irwin**
Division of McGraw-Hill Higher Education
1333 Burr Ridge Pkwy, Burr Ridge, IL 60527
*Tel:* 630-789-4000 *Toll Free Tel:* 800-338-3987 (cust serv) *Fax:* 630-789-6942; 614-755-5645 (cust serv)
*Web Site:* www.mhhe.com

*Key Personnel*
VP & Chief Mktg Offr: Sharon Loeb *Tel:* 212-904-3731 *E-mail:* sharon_loeb@mcgraw-hill.com
VP & Natl Sales Mgr: Doug Hughes *Tel:* 630-789-5121 *E-mail:* doug_hughes@mcgraw-hill.com
VP, Content Prodn & Tech Servs: Kim David *Tel:* 563-584-6650 *E-mail:* kim_david@mcgraw-hill.com
Founded: 1933
College textbooks & numerous ebook titles.
ISBN Prefix(es): 978-0-07; 978-0-697; 978-0-256
Number of titles published annually: 230 Print; 57 CD-ROM; 203 Online; 183 E-Book
Total Titles: 1,929 Print; 630 CD-ROM; 2,046 Online; 1,945 E-Book; 1 Audio
*Returns:* 860 Taylor Station Rd, Blacklick, OH 43004-0539
*Distribution Center:* 860 Taylor Station Rd, Blacklick, OH 43004-0539

**§McGraw-Hill Professional**
Division of McGraw-Hill Education
1221 Avenue of the Americas, New York, NY 10020
*Tel:* 212-512-2000
*Web Site:* www.mhprofessional.com
*Key Personnel*
Pres: Philip R Ruppel
VP, Sales: Lynda Luppino
VP, Publr - Med: Scott Grillo
Dir, STM Rts: Mary Murray
Exec Ed: Donya Dickerson; Tom Miller
Publishes "need-to-know" books & other products for a broad range of professional, technical & consumer/reference markets. Key subject areas include business, computing, medicine, technical & consumer reference including foreign languages, dictionaries & self-help. The company also provides online information services to the medical & other markets.
ISBN Prefix(es): 978-0-07
Number of titles published annually: 1,100 Print; 5 Online; 500 E-Book
Total Titles: 12,500 Print; 43 Online; 2,000 E-Book
Imprints: Certification Press; International Marine Publishing; Irwin Professional; Lange Medical Books; NTC Contemporary Books; Oracle Press; Ragged Mountain Press; Schaum
*Branch Office(s)*
McGraw-Hill Medical, 1333 Burr Ridge Pkwy, Burr Ridge, IL 60527, Ed-in-Chief: James Shanahan *Tel:* 630-789-4000
McGraw-Hill Professional, One Prudential Plaza, Suite 900, 130 E Randolph St, 9th fl, Chicago, IL 60601, Publr: Christopher Brown *Tel:* 312-233-7611
*Shipping Address:* 7500 Chavenelle Rd, Dubuque, IA 52002
*Warehouse:* 7500 Chavenelle Rd, Dubuque, IA 52002
*Distribution Center:* 7500 Chavenelle Rd, Dubuque, IA 52002
Membership(s): AAP; American Medical Publishers Association; International Association of Scientific, Technical & Medical Publishers

**McGraw-Hill School Education Group**
Division of McGraw-Hill Education
8787 Orion Place, Columbus, OH 43240
*Tel:* 614-430-4000 *Toll Free Tel:* 800-848-1567
*Web Site:* www.mheducation.com
*Key Personnel*
Pres: Peter Cohen
SVP, Sales: Thomas O Bruce *E-mail:* thomas_bruce@mcgraw-hill.com
Founded: 1971
Educational materials for elementary, middle school & high school.
ISBN Prefix(es): 978-0-02; 978-0-07; 978-0-31; 978-0-39; 978-0-53; 978-0-65; 978-0-67; 978-0-80; 978-0-84; 978-0-89; 978-0-93; 978-0-96; 978-1-57; 978-1-58; 978-1-88
Imprints: Glencoe (grades 6-12); Macmillan (grades PreK-5)
*Branch Office(s)*
One Prudential Plaza, 130 E Randolph St, Suite 900, Chicago, IL 60601 *Tel:* 312-233-6500
2 Penn Plaza, New York, NY 10121 *Tel:* 212-904-2000
Foreign Rep(s): The McGraw-Hill Companies (Worldwide); McGraw-Hill Ryerson Limited (Canada)
*Orders to:* 860 Taylor Station Rd, Blacklick, OH 43004-0543, SVP, Cust Opers: Gerald A Salters *Tel:* 614-759-3825 ext 3825 *Toll Free Tel:* 800-334-7344 *Fax:* 614-759-3670 *E-mail:* gary_salters@mcgraw-hill.com
*Returns:* 6405 Commerce Ct, Groveport, OH 43125
*Shipping Address:* 6405 Commerce Ct, Groveport, OH 43125, Sr Dir, Dist: Richard Sestrich *Tel:* 614-835-2302 *Fax:* 614-835-2303
*Warehouse:* DeSoto Distribution Center, 220 E Danieldale Rd, DeSoto, TX 75115-9915 *Toll Free Tel:* 800-442-9685 *Fax:* 972-224-5444
*Distribution Center:* 6405 Commerce Ct, Groveport, OH 43125 *Toll Free Tel:* 800-334-7344
*See separate listing for:*
**SRA/McGraw-Hill**
**Wright Group/McGraw-Hill**

**§McGraw-Hill Science, Engineering, Mathematics**
Division of McGraw-Hill Higher Education
501 Bell St, Dubuque, IA 52001
*Tel:* 563-584-6000 *Toll Free Tel:* 800-338-3987 (cust serv) *Fax:* 614-755-5645 (cust serv)
*Web Site:* www.mhhe.com
*Key Personnel*
SVP, Prods & Mkts: Kurt Strand *Tel:* 563-584-6633 *Fax:* 563-584-6600 *E-mail:* kurt.strand@mheducation.com
SVP, Sales: Doug Hughes *Tel:* 630-789-5121 *Fax:* 630-789-6944 *E-mail:* doug.hughes@mheducation.com
VP & Gen Mgr: Marty Lange *Tel:* 563-584-6648 *Fax:* 563-584-6601 *E-mail:* marty.lange@mheducation.com
VP, Content Prodn & Tech Servs: Kim David *Tel:* 563-584-6650 *Fax:* 563-584-6701 *E-mail:* kim.david@mheducation.com
Founded: 1944
College textbook publisher.
ISBN Prefix(es): 978-0-07; 978-0-697; 978-1-25
Number of titles published annually: 260 Print; 8 CD-ROM; 176 Online; 152 E-Book
Total Titles: 1,790 Print; 337 CD-ROM; 1,609 Online; 1,262 E-Book
Imprints: McGraw-Hill
*Branch Office(s)*
1333 Burr Ridge Pkwy, Burr Ridge, IL 60527 *Tel:* 630-789-4000 *Fax:* 630-789-5030
*Returns:* 860 Taylor Station Rd, Blacklick, OH 43004-0539
*Distribution Center:* 860 Taylor Station Rd, Blacklick, OH 43004-0539

**McKenna Publishing Group**
425 POA Place, San Luis Obispo, CA 93405
*Tel:* 805-550-1667
*Web Site:* www.mckennapubgrp.com
*Key Personnel*
Publr: Eric Bollinger *E-mail:* ric@mckennapubgrp.com
Art Dir: Leslie Parker
Founded: 2001
ISBN Prefix(es): 978-0-9713659; 978-1-932172
Number of titles published annually: 8 Print
Total Titles: 46 Print

**McPherson & Co**
148 Smith Ave, Kingston, NY 12401
SAN: 203-0632
Mailing Address: PO Box 1126, Kingston, NY 12402-1126
*Tel:* 845-331-5807 *Toll Free Tel:* 800-613-8219 *Fax:* 845-331-5807 *Toll Free Fax:* 800-613-8219
*E-mail:* bmcphersonco@gmail.com
*Web Site:* www.mcphersonco.com
*Key Personnel*
Publr & Ed-in-Chief: Bruce R McPherson *E-mail:* bmcpher@verizon.net
Founded: 1973
Fiction, anthropology, belles lettres & avant-garde art.
ISBN Prefix(es): 978-0-914232; 978-0-929701; 978-1-878352 (Saroff Books); 978-1-62054
Number of titles published annually: 6 Print; 10 E-Book
Total Titles: 130 Print; 5 E-Book
Imprints: Documentext; McPherson & Co; Recovered Classics; Saroff Editions; Treacle Press
Foreign Rights: Agnese Incisa Agenzia Literaria (Italy); Kerigan-Moro Literary (Portugal, Spain); La Nouvelle Agence (France); Prava i Prevodi (Bulgaria, Czech Republic, Hungary, Poland, Serbia, Slovenia); Literarische Agentur Simon (Germany)
*Orders to:* PO Box 1126, Kingston, NY 12402-1126
*Distribution Center:* Central Books, 99 Wallis Rd, London E9 5LN, United Kingdom
Membership(s): Council of Literary Magazines & Presses

**McSweeney's Publishing**
849 Valencia St, San Francisco, CA 94110
*Tel:* 415-642-5609 (cust serv)
*Web Site:* www.mcsweeneys.net
*Key Personnel*
Publr: Laura Howard
Edit Dir: Ethan Nosowsky
Publicity Dir: Isaac Fitzgerald
Assoc Publr: Adam Krefman
Founded: 1998
ISBN Prefix(es): 978-1-936365
Number of titles published annually: 25 Print
Total Titles: 150 Print
Foreign Rights: The Wylie Agency (Worldwide)
*Distribution Center:* Publishers Group West, 1700 Fourth St, Berkeley, CA 94710 *Tel:* 510-809-3700 *Fax:* 510-809-3777 *E-mail:* info@pgw.com *Web Site:* www.pgw.com

**MDR, A D & B Co**
6 Armstrong Rd, Suite 301, Shelton, CT 06484
*Tel:* 203-926-4800 *Toll Free Tel:* 800-333-8802
*E-mail:* mdrinfo@dnb.com
*Web Site:* www.schooldata.com
*Key Personnel*
VP, Opers: Mike Subrizi
VP, Mktg: Moira McArdle *Tel:* 203-225-4743
Founded: 1969
First choice for marketing information & services for the K-12, higher education, library, early childhood & related education markets. Powered by the most complete, current & accurate education databases available in the industry, MDR provides e-mail contacts & deployment, direct mail lists, sales contact & lead solutions, along with web & social media marketing services.
ISBN Prefix(es): 978-1-57953
Number of titles published annually: 51 Print
*Branch Office(s)*
1050 17 St, Suite 1100, Denver, CO 80265, Pres, MDR Prof Servs: Andy Lacy *Tel:* 303-209-9400 *Fax:* 303-209-9401
20 S Clark St, Suite 2100, Chicago, IL 60603 *Tel:* 312-263-4169 *Fax:* 312-345-4360
Membership(s): Association of Educational Publishers

**Meadowbrook Press**
6110 Blue Circle Dr, Suite 237, Minnetonka, MN 55343
SAN: 207-3404
*Toll Free Tel:* 800-338-2232 *Fax:* 952-930-1940
*E-mail:* info@meadowbrookpress.com
*Web Site:* www.meadowbrookpress.com
*Key Personnel*
Pres & Publr: Bruce Lansky
VP, Fin & Admin: Molly Brutger
Prodn Mgr: Pam Peterson
Founded: 1975
Trade paperbacks; baby & child care, parenting, health, children's activities, humor, parties & games, children's poetry, adult light verse & business travel.
ISBN Prefix(es): 978-0-88166 (Meadowbrook Press); 978-0-684 (book trade); 978-0-416 (book trade); 978-0-7432 (book trade); 978-0-689 (book trade); 978-0-671 (book trade)
Number of titles published annually: 15 Print
Total Titles: 120 Print
Distributed by Simon & Schuster
Foreign Rep(s): Chris Lloyd Sales & Marketing Services (UK); Monarch Books of Canada (Canada)
Foreign Rights: AM-USA (Seiko Uyeda) (Japan); Arrowsmith Agency (Nina Arrowsmith) (Germany); Big Apple Agency Inc (Wendy King) (China, Taiwan); The Book Publishers Association of Israel (Shoshi Grajower) (Israel); Bridge Communications Co (Pat Akkarasawrt) (Thailand); Iris Literary Agency (Catherine Fragou) (Greece); Alexander Korzhenevski Agency (Alexander Korzhenevski) (Russia); Maxima Creative Agency (Santo Manurung) (Indonesia); Montreal Contacts/The Rights Agency (Luc Jutras) (Canada); Montreal Contacts/The Rights Agency (Anne Confuron) (Canada (French-speaking), France); Kristin Olson Literary Agency (Kristin Olson) (Czech Republic); Publishing & Data Services (Sue Francis) (Australia); RDC Agencia Literaria (Beatriz Coll) (Latin America, Portugal, Spain); Margit Schaleck Literary Agency (Margit Schaleck) (Denmark); Tuttle-Mori Agency Inc (Thailand); WNET (H Katia Schumer) (Brazil); Eric Yang Agency (Henry Shin) (Korea)

**me+mi publishing inc**
400 S Knoll St, Suite B, Wheaton, IL 60187
*Tel:* 630-752-9951 *Toll Free Tel:* 888-251-1444 *Fax:* 630-588-9804
*E-mail:* rw@rosawesley.com
*Web Site:* www.memima.com
*Key Personnel*
Principal & Publr: Gladys Rosa-Mendoza; Mark Wesley
Founded: 2002
Independent publisher dedicated to creating the highest quality books available in two or more languages for infants & toddlers.
ISBN Prefix(es): 978-0-9679748; 978-1-931398
Number of titles published annually: 7 Print
Total Titles: 22 Print
Imprints: The English Spanish Foundation Series
Membership(s): Association of Educational Publishers; IBPA, the Independent Book Publishers Association

**§R S Means, a Reed Construction Data Co**
Subsidiary of Reed Construction Data
700 Longwater Dr, Norwell, MA 02061
*Tel:* 781-422-5000 *Toll Free Tel:* 800-334-3509 *Fax:* 781-585-8814 *Toll Free Fax:* 800-632-6701
*Web Site:* rsmeans.reedconstructiondata.com
*Key Personnel*
VP, Sales: John Shea
Prod Mgr, RS Means Books: Andrea Sillah
Founded: 1942
Books, electronic data: construction cost data, engineering, how-to.
ISBN Prefix(es): 978-0-911950; 978-0-87629
Number of titles published annually: 25 Print
Total Titles: 150 Print
Divisions: Cost Annuals
Distributed by John Wiley & Sons Inc
*Advertising Agency:* The Stancliff Agency

**Medals of America**
114 Southchase Blvd, Fountain Inn, SC 29644
*Toll Free Tel:* 800-605-4001 *Toll Free Fax:* 800-407-8640
*E-mail:* jholt@usmedals.com
*Key Personnel*
Publr: Frank Foster *Fax:* 864-601-1108
*E-mail:* ffoster@usmedals.com
Founded: 1992
Offer complete illustrated guides to United States military medals, decorations & insignia of the Army, Navy, Marines, Air Force, Coast Guard & Merchant Marines, United Nations & Vietnam.
ISBN Prefix(es): 978-1-884452
Number of titles published annually: 7 Print; 1 Audio
Total Titles: 13 Print; 15 Online; 2 Audio
Foreign Rep(s): Greenhill Books (UK)
Membership(s): IBPA, the Independent Book Publishers Association

**MedBooks**
Division of Professional Education Workshops & Seminars
101 W Buckingham Rd, Richardson, TX 75081-4802
*Tel:* 972-643-1809 *Toll Free Tel:* 800-443-7397 *Fax:* 972-994-0215
*E-mail:* medbooks@medbooks.com
*Web Site:* www.medbooks.com
*Key Personnel*
Owner & Pres: Patrice Morin-Spatz
Founded: 1985
Specialize in books on health insurance coding & processing for medical offices, insurance companies & other health professions.
ISBN Prefix(es): 978-0-976269
Number of titles published annually: 5 Print
Total Titles: 25 Print
Distributed by JA Majors
Membership(s): American Health Information Management Association; IBPA, the Independent Book Publishers Association

**Medical Group Management Association (MGMA)**
104 Inverness Terr E, Englewood, CO 80112-5306
*Tel:* 303-799-1111; 303-799-1111 (ext 1244, billing & returns); 303-799-1111 (ext 1295, dist ctr); 303-799-1111 (ext 1268, edit off); 303-799-1111 (ext 1888, book orders); 303-799-1111 (ext 1874, ad rates); 303-799-1111 (ext 1295, shipping & warehouse) *Toll Free Tel:* 877-275-6462 *Fax:* 303-784-6110
*E-mail:* support@mgma.com
*Web Site:* www.mgma.com
Founded: 1926
Specialize in medical practice management.
ISBN Prefix(es): 978-1-56829
Number of titles published annually: 8 Print; 4 CD-ROM; 1 E-Book
Total Titles: 150 Print; 15 CD-ROM; 1 E-Book; 2 Audio
*Branch Office(s)*
Government Affairs, 1717 Pennsylvania Ave NW, No 600, Washington, DC 20006, Contact: Anders Gilberg *Tel:* 202-293-3450 *Fax:* 202-293-2787
Distributor for American Medical Association; Aspen Publishers; Greenbranch; HAP (Health Adminstration Press); Jones & Bartlett Learning; J Wiley & Sons

**Medical Physics Publishing Corp (MPP)**
4513 Vernon Blvd, Madison, WI 53705-4964
*Tel:* 608-262-4021 *Toll Free Tel:* 800-442-5778 (cust serv) *Fax:* 608-265-2121
*E-mail:* mpp@medicalphysics.org
*Web Site:* www.medicalphysics.org
*Key Personnel*
Gen Mgr & Intl Rts: Ms Bobbett Shaub
*E-mail:* bobbett@medicalphysics.org
Ed: Todd Hanson *E-mail:* todd@medicalphysics.org
Founded: 1985
Publish & distribute books & CD-ROMs in medical physics & related fields.
ISBN Prefix(es): 978-0-944838; 978-1-930524
Number of titles published annually: 6 Print
Total Titles: 62 Print; 3 CD-ROM
Imprints: Cogito Books

**Medieval & Renaissance Texts & Studies**, see MRTS

**Medieval Institute Publications**
Division of Medieval Institute of Western Michigan University
WMU East Campus, 100-E Walwood Hall, Kalamazoo, MI 49008
Mailing Address: 1903 W Michigan Ave, Kalamazoo, MI 49008-5432
*Tel:* 269-387-8755 (orders) *Fax:* 269-387-8750
*Web Site:* www.wmich.edu/medieval/mip
*Key Personnel*
Mng Ed: Patricia Hollahan *Tel:* 269-387-8754
*E-mail:* patricia.hollahan@wmich.edu
Publish 110 book titles, 3 journals.
ISBN Prefix(es): 978-1-918720; 978-1-879288; 978-1-58044
Number of titles published annually: 14 Print
Total Titles: 140 Print

**MedMaster Inc**
3337 Hollywood Oaks Dr, Fort Lauderdale, FL 33312
Mailing Address: PO Box 640028, Miami, FL 33164-0028
*Tel:* 954-962-8414 *Toll Free Tel:* 800-335-3480 *Fax:* 954-962-4508
*E-mail:* mmbks@aol.com
*Web Site:* www.medmaster.net
*Key Personnel*
Founder & Pres: Stephen Goldberg
*E-mail:* stgoldberg@aol.com
VP & Secy: Harriet Goldberg
Founded: 1979
Medical book & software publishers; medical subjects for education of medical students & other health professionals.
ISBN Prefix(es): 978-0-940780
Number of titles published annually: 6 Print; 3 CD-ROM; 1 E-Book
Total Titles: 50 Print; 8 CD-ROM
*Returns:* 360 NE 191 St, Miami, FL 33179
*Warehouse:* 360 NE 191 St, Miami, FL 33179

**The Russell Meerdink Co Ltd**
1555 S Park Ave, Neenah, WI 54956
SAN: 249-1680
*Tel:* 920-725-0955 *Toll Free Tel:* 800-635-6499 *Fax:* 920-725-0709
*E-mail:* questions@horseinfo.com
*Web Site:* www.horseinfo.com
*Key Personnel*
Mng Dir & Intl Rts Contact: Jan Meerdink
*E-mail:* jmeerdink@horseinfo.com
Founded: 1980
Equine titles & thoroughbred data services. Distribution & mail order sales of equine titles.
ISBN Prefix(es): 978-0-929346
Number of titles published annually: 8 Print; 2 CD-ROM
Total Titles: 33 Print; 4 CD-ROM

**Mehring Books Inc**
PO Box 48377, Oak Park, MI 48237-5977
*Tel:* 248-967-2924 *Fax:* 248-967-3023
*E-mail:* sales@mehring.com
*Web Site:* www.mehring.com
*Key Personnel*
Pres: Helen Halyard
Sales Rep: Heather Jowsey
Founded: 1998
Books & journals on contemporary events, history, political economy, Trotsky's writings.
ISBN Prefix(es): 978-0-929087; 978-1-893638
Number of titles published annually: 3 Print
Total Titles: 56 Print
Foreign Rep(s): Arbeiterpresse Verlag (Germany); Mehring Books (Australia, England)

**Mel Bay Publications Inc**
4 Industrial Dr, Pacific, MO 63069-0066
*Tel:* 636-257-3970 *Toll Free Tel:* 800-863-5229 *Fax:* 636-257-5062 *Toll Free Fax:* 800-660-9818
*E-mail:* email@melbay.com
*Web Site:* www.melbay.com
*Key Personnel*
Pres: Bryndon Bay *E-mail:* bryndon@melbay.com
VP, Web/IT: Tony Cornejo *E-mail:* tcornejo@melbay.com
Cust Serv Mgr: Connie Hartmann *E-mail:* connie@melbay.com
Info Systems Supv: Sharon Feldmann *E-mail:* sharon@melbay.com
Founded: 1947
Innovative instructional & performance material for most instruments.
ISBN Prefix(es): 978-0-7866; 978-0-87166; 978-1-56222; 978-8-83206
Number of titles published annually: 500 Print
Total Titles: 4,500 Print
Imprints: Building Excellence; Cathedral Music Press; Editions Classicae; Creative Keyboard; First Lessons; Getting Into; Gig Savers; Qwikguide; School of the Blues; You Can Teach Yourself
Divisions: Cathedral Music Press; Creative Keyboard Publications
*Foreign Office(s):* Mel Bay Music Ltd, Fortis House, Office 512, 160 London Rd, Barking, Essex IG11 8BB, United Kingdom (sales agent for Europe), Mng Dir: Chris Statham *Tel:* (020) 8214 1222 *Fax:* (020) 8214 1328 *E-mail:* salesuk@melbay.com *Web Site:* www.melbay.com
Distributor for AcuTab Publications Inc; AMA; Chanterelle; Stefan Grossman's Guitar Workshop; Hardie Press; Learn Roots Music; Maggies Music; Malley's; Registry of Guitar Tutors (RGT); RGB Arte Visual; Scott's Highland Services; Voggenreiter Publishers; Walton's; SR Wheat
Foreign Rep(s): ATN Inc (Japan); Chorus Productions (Finland); Mel Bay Music Ltd (Belgium, Central Germany, Croatia, Czech Republic, Denmark, Eastern Africa, Eastern Europe exc Estonia, Latvia, Lituania & Russia); Music Sales (Australia, New Zealand); People's Music Publishing House (China)
*Advertising Agency:* Mel Bay Licensing, Industrial Dr, No 4, Pacific, MO 63069, Dir, Music Licensing: Julie Price *Tel:* 678-772-0021 *E-mail:* licensing@melbay.com *Web Site:* www.licensing.melbay.com
Membership(s): ABA

**The Mellen Poetry Press**
240 Portage Rd, Lewiston, NY 14092
SAN: 207-110X
Mailing Address: PO Box 450, Lewiston, NY 14092-0450
*Tel:* 716-754-2266; 716-754-1400 (mktg); 716-754-2788 (order fulfillment) *Fax:* 716-754-4056; 716-754-1860 (fulfillment)
*E-mail:* cservice@mellenpress.com
*Web Site:* www.mellenpress.com
*Key Personnel*
Founder & CEO: Herbert Richardson
Publr: Ruth Koheil
Dir & Acqs: Dr John Rupnow *Tel:* 716-754-2266 *E-mail:* jrupnow@mellenpress.com
Fulfillment Dir: Irene Miller *E-mail:* imiller@mellenpress.com
Mktg Dir: Bradley Kaye *E-mail:* editor@mellenpress.com
Prodn Mgr & Perms Ed: Patricia Schultz *E-mail:* pschultz@mellenpress.com
Founded: 1974
Poetry & poetic theory.
ISBN Prefix(es): 978-0-88946; 978-0-7734
Number of titles published annually: 40 Print
Total Titles: 600 Print
*Branch Office(s)*
Box 67, Queenston, ON, Canada
*Foreign Office(s):* The Edwin Mellen Press Ltd UK, Mellen House, 16 College St, Lampeter, Ceredigion SA48 7DY, United Kingdom, Mgr, Wales/UK Off: Mrs Iona Williams *Tel:* (01570) 423 356 *Fax:* (01570) 423 775 *E-mail:* emp@mellenpress.co.uk
*Advertising Agency:* Lewiston Business Services

**Menasha Ridge Press Inc**
Division of Keen Communications
2204 First Ave S, Suite 102, Birmingham, AL 35233
*Tel:* 205-322-0439 *Toll Free Tel:* 888-604-4537 *Fax:* 205-326-1012
*E-mail:* info@menasharidge.com
*Web Site:* www.menasharidge.com
*Key Personnel*
Pres: Molly B Merkle *Tel:* 205-443-7993 *E-mail:* mmerkle@menasharidge.com
Publr: Robert W Sehlinger *Tel:* 205-443-7989 *E-mail:* bsehlinger@menasharidge.com
Mktg & Publicity Specialist: Pat LaFleur *Tel:* 859-815-7207 *E-mail:* pat@menasharidge.com
Founded: 1982
Outdoor recreation, travel, nature & reference guides.
ISBN Prefix(es): 978-0-89732
Number of titles published annually: 35 Print; 35 E-Book
Total Titles: 140 Print; 100 E-Book
*Orders to:* Publishers Group West, 1700 Fourth St, Berkeley, CA 94710 *Toll Free Tel:* 800-788-3123 *Toll Free Fax:* 800-351-5073 *Web Site:* www.pgw.com
*Returns:* Perseus Distribution Returns Dept, 193 Edwards Dr, Jackson, TN 38301 *Toll Free Tel:* 800-788-3123
Membership(s): ABA; Southern Independent Booksellers Alliance

**Mercer University Press**
368 Orange St, Macon, GA 31201
Mailing Address: 1400 Coleman Ave, Macon, GA 31207 SAN: 220-0716
*Tel:* 478-301-2880 *Toll Free Tel:* 866-895-1472 *Fax:* 478-301-2585
*E-mail:* mupressorders@mercer.edu
*Web Site:* www.mupress.org
*Key Personnel*
Dir: Marc Jolley *Tel:* 478-301-2880 *E-mail:* jolley_ma@mercer.edu
Publg Asst: Marsha Luttrell *Tel:* 478-301-4266 *E-mail:* luttrell_mm@mercer.edu
Mktg Dir: Mary Beth Kosowski *Tel:* 478-301-4262 *E-mail:* kosowski_mb@mercer.edu
Cust Serv Assoc: Candice E Morris *Tel:* 478-301-4261 *E-mail:* morris_ce@mercer.edu
Busn Off: Jenny Toole *Tel:* 478-301-4267 *E-mail:* toole_rw@mercer.edu
Founded: 1979
History, philosophy, religion, Southern studies, Southern literature, literary studies, regional interest.
ISBN Prefix(es): 978-0-86554; 978-0-88146
Number of titles published annually: 40 Print
Total Titles: 1,200 Print
Foreign Rep(s): East-West Export Books (Royden Muranaka) (Asia, Australia, New Zealand); The Eurospan Group (Africa, Central Asia, Europe, Middle East, UK)
*Warehouse:* 1701 Seventh St, Macon, GA 31206
Membership(s): American Association of University Presses

**Merit Publishing International Inc**
6839 Villas Dr S, Boca Raton, FL 33433
*Tel:* 561-350-0329; 561-697-1116 (orders)
*E-mail:* merituk@aol.com; meritpi@aol.com
*Web Site:* www.meritpublishing.com
*Key Personnel*
Owner & Pres: Gene Evans
Owner & VP: Dr Marta Garrido
Founded: 1986 (Founded in UK 1986, US 1992)
Medical publishing & marketing in all clinical areas. Questions & answers series, visual diagnosis self-tests series, customized books, slide kits, newsletters, proceedings & monographs, new perspectives series, guides to families & children series.
ISBN Prefix(es): 978-1-873413
Number of titles published annually: 13 Print; 3 CD-ROM
Total Titles: 65 Print; 3 CD-ROM; 3 Online
*Foreign Office(s):* 30 Wey Barton, Byfleet, Surrey KT14 7EF, United Kingdom, Mrs Gene Evans *Tel:* (01932) 844526 *Fax:* (01932) 820419
Foreign Rep(s): Gazelle (UK); Momento Medico (Italy)
Foreign Rights: J & C Ediciones Medicas (Latin America, Spain)
*Orders to:* Midpoint Trade Books, 27 W 20 St, Suite 1102, New York, NY 10011; Baker & Taylor, 2550 W Tyrola Rd, Suite 300, Charlotte, NC 28217 (wholesale) *Tel:* 704-998-3100 *Toll Free Tel:* 800-775-1800 *Web Site:* www.btol.com; Ingram Book Co, One Ingram Blvd, Lavergne, TN 37086 *Tel:* 615-793-5000 *Toll Free Tel:* 800-937-8200 *E-mail:* customer.service@ingrambook.com *Web Site:* www.ingrambook.com
*Distribution Center:* Midpoint Trade Books, 27 W 20 St, Suite 1102, New York, NY 10011 *Tel:* 212-727-0190 *Fax:* 212-727-0195 *Web Site:* www.midpointtradebooks.com
Membership(s): IBPA, the Independent Book Publishers Association

**Meriwether Publishing Ltd/Contemporary Drama Service**
885 Elkton Dr, Colorado Springs, CO 80907-3522
SAN: 208-4716
Mailing Address: PO Box 7710, Colorado Springs, CO 80933-7710
*Tel:* 719-594-4422 *Toll Free Tel:* 800-937-5297 *Fax:* 719-594-9916 *Toll Free Fax:* 888-594-4436
*E-mail:* customerservice@meriwether.com
*Web Site:* www.meriwether.com
*Key Personnel*
Pres & Intl Rts: A Mark Zapel *Tel:* 719-594-4422 ext 127 *E-mail:* mzapel@meriwether.com
Assoc Ed: Ted Zapel *E-mail:* tzapel@meriwether.com
Edit Asst: Nicole Rutledge *Tel:* 719-594-4422 ext 124 *E-mail:* editor@meriwether.com
Founded: 1967
Books on theater, drama, performing arts, costuming, stagecraft, theatre games, play anthologies, plays, musicals, theatre arts DVDs, Christian drama resources, theatre/drama education.
ISBN Prefix(es): 978-0-916260; 978-1-56608
Number of titles published annually: 35 Print
Total Titles: 998 Print
Subsidiaries: Contemporary Drama Service

Foreign Rep(s): Fitzhenry & Whiteside (Canada); Gazelle Book Service (Europe, UK); Hanbury Plays (UK); Mentone Educational Centre (Australia)
Membership(s): Publishers Association of the West

**§Merriam Press**
133 Elm St, Suite 3R, Bennington, VT 05201-2250
*Tel:* 802-447-0313
*Web Site:* www.merriam-press.com
*Key Personnel*
Owner & Intl Rts: Ray Merriam *E-mail:* ray@merriam-press.com
Founded: 1988
Primarily WWII/military history, memoirs & some fiction; also some non-military history, fiction, memoirs, poetry.
This publisher has indicated that 90% of their product line is author subsidized.
ISBN Prefix(es): 978-1-57638
Number of titles published annually: 30 Print; 20 CD-ROM; 20 E-Book
Total Titles: 190 Print; 150 CD-ROM; 20 E-Book

**§Merriam-Webster Inc**
Subsidiary of Encyclopaedia Britannica Inc
47 Federal St, Springfield, MA 01102
Mailing Address: PO Box 281, Springfield, MA 01102-0281
*Tel:* 413-734-3134 *Toll Free Tel:* 800-828-1880 (orders & cust serv) *Fax:* 413-731-5979 (sales)
*E-mail:* support@merriam-webster.com
*Web Site:* www.merriam-webster.com
*Key Personnel*
Pres & Publr: John M Morse
CFO: Caryl Schivley
VP & Assoc Publr: James W Withgott
VP & Dir, Sales: Jed Santoro *E-mail:* jsantoro@m-w.com
Art Dir: Lynn Stowe Tomb
Dir, Eng Lang Learning Publg: Jane Mairs
Dir, Mktg: Meghan Lieberwirth *E-mail:* mlieberwirth@merriam-webster.com
Busn Devt Mgr: Matthew Dube
Founded: 1831
Dictionaries & language reference products.
ISBN Prefix(es): 978-0-87779
Number of titles published annually: 4 Print
Total Titles: 104 Print; 7 CD-ROM; 2 Online; 2 E-Book
Imprints: Federal Street Press
Divisions: Federal Street Press
*See separate listing for:*
**Federal Street Press**

**Mesorah Publications Ltd**
4401 Second Ave, Brooklyn, NY 11232
SAN: 213-1269
*Tel:* 718-921-9000 *Toll Free Tel:* 800-637-6724 *Fax:* 718-680-1875
*E-mail:* artscroll@mesorah.com
*Web Site:* www.artscroll.com; www.mesorah.com
*Key Personnel*
Pres & Intl Rts Contact: Meir Zlotowitz
EVP & Ed-in-Chief: Nosson Scherman
VP & Prodn Mgr: Jacob Brander *E-mail:* jacob@mesorah.com
Founded: 1976
Judaica, Bible study, liturgical materials, juvenile, history, Holocaust, Talmud, novels.
ISBN Prefix(es): 978-0-89906; 978-1-57819
Number of titles published annually: 50 Print
Total Titles: 850 Print
Imprints: Art Scroll Series; Shaar Press; Tamar Books
Distributor for NCSY Publications
Foreign Rep(s): Stephen Blitz (Israel)
*Returns:* 222 44 St, Brooklyn, NY 11232

**Messianic Jewish Publishers**
Division of Messianic Jewish Communications
6120 Day Long Lane, Clarksville, MD 21029
*Tel:* 410-531-6644 *Toll Free Tel:* 800-410-7367 (orders) *Fax:* 410-531-9440 (no orders)
*E-mail:* lederer@messianicjewish.net; rightsandpermissions@messianicjewish.net (rights & perms)
*Web Site:* messianicjewish.net
*Key Personnel*
Pres: Barry Rubin *E-mail:* president@messianicjewish.net
Mng Ed: Lisa Rubin
Founded: 1949
Publish & distribute Messianic Jewish books & other products.
ISBN Prefix(es): 978-1-880226
Number of titles published annually: 12 Print; 6 E-Book
Total Titles: 82 Print; 40 E-Book
Distributor for Chosen People Ministries; First Fruits of Zion; Jewish New Testament Publications
Foreign Rep(s): Winfried Bluth (Europe)
Foreign Rights: Winfried Bluth (Europe)
Membership(s): CBA: The Association for Christian Retail; Evangelical Christian Publishers Association
*See separate listing for:*
**Lederer Books**

**§The Metropolitan Museum of Art**
1000 Fifth Ave, New York, NY 10028
SAN: 202-6279
*Tel:* 212-879-5500; 212-570-3725 *Fax:* 212-396-5062
*E-mail:* editorial@metmuseum.org
*Web Site:* www.metmuseum.org
*Key Personnel*
CEO & Dir: Thomas P Campbell
Pres: Emily K Rafferty
Publr & Ed-in-Chief: Mark Polizzotti
Assoc Publr & Gen Mgr, Pubns: Gwen Roginsky
Chief Prodn Mgr: Peter Antony
Mgr, Spec Pubns: Robie Rogge
Founded: 1870
Art books, exhibition catalogs, quarterly bulletin, annual journal.
ISBN Prefix(es): 978-0-87099; 978-1-58839
Number of titles published annually: 30 Print
Total Titles: 250 Print; 5 CD-ROM
Distributed by Yale University Press
Foreign Rep(s): Yale University Press
*Warehouse:* Middle Village, Queens, NY 11381-0001

**MFA Publications**
Imprint of Museum of Fine Arts Boston
465 Huntington Ave, Boston, MA 02115
*Tel:* 617-369-4233 *Fax:* 617-369-3459
*Web Site:* www.mfa.org/publications
*Key Personnel*
Publr: Emiko Usui *Tel:* 617-369-4231 *E-mail:* eusui@mfa.org
Prod Mgr: Terry McAweeney
Sales & Mktg: Chris Di Pietro *E-mail:* cdipietro@mfa.org
Founded: 1877
Exhibition & collection catalogues; general interest & trade arts publications, children's books. No returns accepted.
ISBN Prefix(es): 978-0-87846
Number of titles published annually: 12 Print
Total Titles: 80 Print
Imprints: ArtWorks
Distributed by Art Books/D A P
*Warehouse:* c/o PSSC, 46 Development Rd, Fitchburg, MA 01420

**MGI Management Institute Inc**
Subsidiary of SmartPros Ltd
12 Skyline Dr, Hawthorne, NY 10532
*Tel:* 914-428-6500 *Toll Free Tel:* 800-932-0191 *Fax:* 914-428-0773
*E-mail:* mgiusa@aol.com
*Web Site:* www.mgi.org
*Key Personnel*
Mgr: Sandra Wacht
Founded: 1968
Home study guides.
Number of titles published annually: 60 Print
Total Titles: 60 Print; 5 Online; 5 E-Book

**Michelin Maps & Guides**
Division of Michelin North America Inc
One Parkway S, Greenville, SC 29615-5022
*Tel:* 864-458-5565 *Fax:* 864-458-5665 *Toll Free Fax:* 866-297-0914; 888-773-7979
*E-mail:* orders@americanmap.com (orders)
*Web Site:* www.michelintravel.com; www.michelinguide.com
*Key Personnel*
Dir, B&B Sales & Mktg: Christopher Aufmuth
Cust Serv Mgr: Steve Hunt
Gen Mgr: Hellan Mitchell *E-mail:* hellan.mitchell@us.michelin.com
Founded: 1900
Specialize in travel publications; hotel & restaurant guides.
ISBN Prefix(es): 978-2-06; 978-1-90
Number of titles published annually: 50 Print
Total Titles: 175 Print
Distributed by Editions du Renouveau Pedagogique (French titles in Canada); Langenscheidt Publishing Group; MAPART Publishing (CN only); NBN (guides for North America); Penguin Canada (English titles in Canada)
*Orders to:* PO Box 19001, Greenville, SC 29615 *Toll Free Tel:* 800-423-0485 *Toll Free Fax:* 800-378-7471

**Michigan Municipal League**
Affiliate of National League of Cities
1675 Green Rd, Ann Arbor, MI 48105
Mailing Address: PO Box 1487, Ann Arbor, MI 48106-1487
*Tel:* 734-662-3246 *Toll Free Tel:* 800-653-2483 *Fax:* 734-663-4496
*Web Site:* www.mml.org
*Key Personnel*
Ed: Kim Cekola *Tel:* 734-669-6321 *E-mail:* kcekola@mml.org
Founded: 1899
Municipal topics & newsletters, services & publications for local governments in Michigan.
ISBN Prefix(es): 978-1-929923
Number of titles published annually: 6 Print
Distributor for Crisp Books

**§Michigan State University Press (MSU Press)**
Division of Michigan State University
1405 S Harrison Rd, Suite 25, East Lansing, MI 48823
SAN: 202-6295
*Tel:* 517-355-9543 *Fax:* 517-432-2611 *Toll Free Fax:* 800-678-2120
*E-mail:* msupress@msu.edu
*Web Site:* www.msupress.msu.edu
*Key Personnel*
Dir: Gabriel Dotto *Tel:* 517-884-6900
Asst Dir & Ed-in-Chief: Julie L Loehr *Tel:* 517-884-6905 *E-mail:* loehr@msu.edu
Mng Ed: Kristine M Blakeslee *Tel:* 517-884-6912
Prodn Mgr: Annette K Tanner *Tel:* 517-884-6910
Busn & Fin Offr: Julie Wrzesinski *Tel:* 517-884-6922
Mktg & Sales: Julie K Reaume *Tel:* 517-884-6920
Founded: 1947
Scholarly works & general nonfiction trade books.
ISBN Prefix(es): 978-1-882997; 978-0-916418; 978-0-944311; 978-0-88406; 978-0-937191; 978-1-55238; 978-0-87013

Number of titles published annually: 40 Print; 2 CD-ROM; 10 E-Book
Total Titles: 650 Print; 4 CD-ROM; 59 E-Book
Distributed by UBC Press, Canada
Distributor for Mackinac Historic Parks; MSU Museum; University of Alberta Press; University of Calgary Press; University of Manitoba Press
Foreign Rep(s): Eurospan (Europe); Raincoast Books-University of British Columbia Press (Canada)
*Orders to:* Chicago Distribution Center, 11030 S Langley Ave, Chicago, IL 60628 *Toll Free Tel:* 800-621-2736 *Toll Free Fax:* 800-621-8476 *Web Site:* www.press.uchicago.edu
*Returns:* Chicago Distribution Center, 11030 S Langley Ave, Chicago, IL 60628 *Toll Free Tel:* 800-621-2736 *Toll Free Fax:* 800-621-8476 *Web Site:* www.press.uchicago.edu
*Distribution Center:* Chicago Distribution Center, 11030 S Langley Ave, Chicago, IL 60628 *Toll Free Tel:* 800-621-2736 *Toll Free Fax:* 800-621-8476 *Web Site:* www.press.uchicago.edu
Membership(s): American Association of University Presses; Society for Scholarly Publishing

**§Microsoft Press**
Division of Microsoft Corp
One Microsoft Way, Redmond, WA 98052-6399
SAN: 264-9969
*Tel:* 425-882-8080 *Toll Free Tel:* 800-677-7377 *Fax:* 425-936-7329
*Web Site:* www.microsoft.com/learning/books
*Key Personnel*
Assoc Publr & Developer: Al Valvano
Founded: 1983
Computing, technical, professional & chess.
ISBN Prefix(es): 978-1-55615; 978-1-57231; 978-0-7356
Number of titles published annually: 160 Print
Total Titles: 400 Print; 20 CD-ROM; 100 Online; 1 E-Book
Subsidiaries: Microsoft Press France; Microsoft Press Germany
Distributed by O'Reilly Media (Asia, Australia, Europe, New Zealand, North America, UK); Shroff Publishers & Distributors (India)
Foreign Rep(s): ITP Nelson
*Warehouse:* 121 N Enterprise Blvd, Lebanon, IN 46052
*Distribution Center:* John Wiley & Sons, 111 River St, Hoboken, NJ 07030-5774 *Tel:* 201-748-6000 *Fax:* 201-748-6088 *E-mail:* info@wiley.com *Web Site:* www.wiley.com

**Mid-List Press**
6524 Brownlee Dr, Nashville, TN 37205-3038
*Tel:* 615-822-3777 *Fax:* 612-823-8387
*E-mail:* guide@midlist.org
*Web Site:* www.midlist.org
*Key Personnel*
Bd Pres: Dan Verdick
Exec Dir: Marianne Leslie Nora
Publr: Lane Stiles
Founded: 1989
Fiction, creative nonfiction & poetry.
ISBN Prefix(es): 978-0-922811
Number of titles published annually: 2 Print; 5 E-Book
Total Titles: 60 Print; 7 E-Book

**Midmarch Arts Press**
300 Riverside Dr, New York, NY 10025-5239
SAN: 200-8882
*Tel:* 212-666-6990
*Web Site:* midmarchartspress.org
*Key Personnel*
Dir: Cynthia Navaretta
Mgr: Lynda Hulkower
Ed: Sylvia Moore; Judy Seigel
Founded: 1975
Books.
ISBN Prefix(es): 978-1-877675
Number of titles published annually: 3 Print
Total Titles: 118 Print
*Returns:* 19 Deep Six Dr, East Hampton, NY 11937
*Warehouse:* 19 Deep Six Dr, East Hampton, NY 11937
Membership(s): College Art Association; International Association of Art Critics

**Midnight Marquee Press Inc**
9721 Britinay Lane, Baltimore, MD 21234
*Tel:* 410-665-1198
*E-mail:* mmarquee@aol.com
*Web Site:* www.midmar.com
*Key Personnel*
Pres: Gary Svehla
VP & Lib Sales Dir: Susan Svehla
Founded: 1995
Publisher of books, two magazines, graphic novels—main focus on film history, biographies & mysteries.
ISBN Prefix(es): 978-1-887664
Number of titles published annually: 6 Print
Total Titles: 150 Print

**§MidWest Plan Service (MWPS)**
Affiliate of Iowa State University-Information Technology Services
Iowa State University, 122 Davidson Hall, Ames, IA 50011-3080
*Tel:* 515-294-4337 *Toll Free Tel:* 800-562-3618 *Fax:* 515-294-9589
*E-mail:* mwps@iastate.edu
*Web Site:* www.mwps.org
*Key Personnel*
Graphics & Pubns: Kathy Walker *E-mail:* kjwalker@iastate.edu
Liaison: Jay Harmon *E-mail:* jharmon@iastate.edu
Founded: 1932
Educational publishing consortium located at Iowa State University that provides science-based low cost & free information & building plans to persons in agriculture & related businesses as well as to acreage & home owners.
ISBN Prefix(es): 978-0-89373
Number of titles published annually: 3 Print; 1 CD-ROM; 2 Online; 1 E-Book
Total Titles: 77 Print; 6 CD-ROM; 19 Online; 2 E-Book
Distributed by Natural Resource Agriculture & Engineering Service
Distributor for Natural Resource Agriculture & Engineering Service

**Mike Murach & Associates Inc**
4340 N Knoll Ave, Fresno, CA 93722
SAN: 264-2255
*Tel:* 559-440-9071 *Toll Free Tel:* 800-221-5528 *Fax:* 559-440-0963
*E-mail:* murachbooks@murach.com
*Web Site:* www.murach.com
*Key Personnel*
Pres: Ben Murach
Mktg: Cynthia Vasquez *Tel:* 559-440-9071 ext 18 *E-mail:* cyndi@murach.com
Founded: 1974
Computer books.
ISBN Prefix(es): 978-0-911625; 978-1-890774
Number of titles published annually: 5 Print
Total Titles: 50 Print
Distributed by Shroff Publishers (reprints)
Foreign Rep(s): BPB Publications Ltd (India); Gazelle Book Services Ltd (Continental Europe, UK); Woodslane Pty Ltd (Australia, New Zealand)

**§Milady**
Division of Cengage Learning
Executive Woods, 5 Maxwell Dr, Clifton Park, NY 12065-2919
*Tel:* 518-348-2300 *Toll Free Tel:* 800-998-7498 *Fax:* 518-373-6309
*Web Site:* milady.cengage.com
*Key Personnel*
Pres: Dawn Gerrain *Tel:* 518-348-2300 ext 2409 *E-mail:* dawn.gerrain@cengage.com
Dir, Indust Rels: Sandra Bruce *Tel:* 518-348-2300 ext 2378
Founded: 1928
Textbooks, workbooks, exam reviews, AV materials & instructional software, newsletters, cosmetology & beauty education.
ISBN Prefix(es): 978-1-56253; 978-0-87350; 978-1-4018; 978-1-4180
Number of titles published annually: 220 Print
Total Titles: 288 Print
*Foreign Office(s):* Cengage Learning-Australia, 80 Dorcas St, Level 7, South Melbourne, Victoria 3205, Australia *Tel:* (03) 9685 4111 *Fax:* (03) 9685 4199
Cengage Learning-Latin America, Av Santa Fe 505 piso 12, Col Cruz Manca Sante Fe, Cuajimalpa CP, 05349 Mexico, DF, Mexico *Tel:* 55 1500 6000
Cengage Learning-EMEA, Cheriton House, North Way, Andover, Hampshire SP10 5BE, United Kingdom *Tel:* (01264) 332424 *Fax:* (01264) 342763
*Distribution Center:* 10650 Toebben Dr, Independence, KY 41051

**Military Info Publishing**
PO Box 41211, Plymouth, MN 55442
*Tel:* 763-533-8627 *Fax:* 763-533-8627
*E-mail:* publisher@military-info.com
*Web Site:* www.military-info.com
*Key Personnel*
Publr: Bruce A Hanesalo
Founded: 1987
Reprint historical military technology, including 34 books, 11,000 photocopies & 400 other items.
ISBN Prefix(es): 978-1-886848
Number of titles published annually: 4 Print
Total Titles: 34 Print

**Military Living Publications**
Division of Military Marketing Services Inc
333 Maple Ave E, Suite 3130, Vienna, VA 22180-4717
*Tel:* 703-237-0203 (ext 1) *Toll Free Tel:* 877-363-4677 (ext 1) *Fax:* 703-997-8861
*E-mail:* customerservice@militaryliving.com
*Web Site:* www.militaryliving.com
*Key Personnel*
CEO: William R Crawford, Sr
Founded: 1969
Publisher of military travel atlases, maps & directories; for military only.
ISBN Prefix(es): 978-0-914862; 978-1-931424
Number of titles published annually: 8 Print
Total Titles: 12 Print
Foreign Rep(s): US Forces Exchanges

**Milkweed Editions**
1011 Washington Ave S, Suite 300, Minneapolis, MN 55415-1246
*Tel:* 612-332-3192 *Toll Free Tel:* 800-520-6455 *Fax:* 612-215-2550
*Web Site:* www.milkweed.org
*Key Personnel*
CEO & Publr: Daniel Slager
Sales & Mktg Dir: Sue Ostfield
Content Mgr: Anna Weggel
Devt Mgr: Kate Strickland
Ed & Prog Mgr: Patrick Thomas *E-mail:* patrick_thomas@milkweed.org
Assoc Ed: Allison Wigen
Publicist: Meredith Kessler
Admin Asst: Tracy Mumford
Founded: 1980
Literary, nonprofit, independent press.
ISBN Prefix(es): 978-0-915943; 978-1-57131

Number of titles published annually: 18 Print; 18 E-Book; 1 Audio
Total Titles: 250 Print; 10 E-Book; 5 Audio
Foreign Rights: Ben Barnhart (Worldwide)
*Distribution Center:* Publishers Group West, 1700 Fourth St, Berkeley, CA 94710 *Tel:* 510-809-3700 *Toll Free Tel:* 800-788-3123 *Fax:* 510-528-3444
Membership(s): ABA; Children's Book Council; Council of Literary Magazines & Presses; IBPA, the Independent Book Publishers Association; Midwest Independent Booksellers Association; Southern Independent Booksellers Alliance

**Millbrook Press**
Division of Lerner Publishing Group Inc
241 First Ave N, Minneapolis, MN 55401
*Tel:* 612-332-3344 *Toll Free Tel:* 800-328-4929 (US only) *Fax:* 612-332-7615 *Toll Free Fax:* 800-332-1132
*Key Personnel*
Chmn: Harry J Lerner
CFO & EVP: Margaret Wunderlich
Pres & Publr: Adam Lerner
EVP, Sales: David Wexler
VP & Dir, Mktg & Digital Prods: Terri Soutor
Ed-in-Chief: Patricia M Stockland
Edit Dir: Carol Hinz
VP, Prodn: Gary Hansen
Rts Dir: Maria Kjoller
Dir, Prod Devt & Mktg Res: Lois Wallentine
Dir, Electronic Content: Dan Wallek
Art Dir: Zach Marell
Dir, HR: Cyndi Radant
Founded: 1989
ISBN Prefix(es): 978-1-56294; 978-1-878841; 978-0-7613; 978-1-878137
Total Titles: 630 Print; 560 E-Book
Foreign Rep(s): INT Press Distribution (Australia); Monarch (Canada); Phambili (Southern Africa); Publishers Marketing Services (Brunei, Malaysia, Singapore); Saunders (Canada); South Pacific Books (New Zealand)
Foreign Rights: Japan Foreign-Rights Centre (Japan); Korea Copyright Center (Korea); Michelle Lapautre Agence Junior (France); Literarische Agentur Silke Weniger (Germany); Rights People (UK & Commonwealth)
*Warehouse:* Lerner Publishing Group, 1251 Washington Ave N, Minneapolis, MN 55401

**Richard K Miller Associates**
4132 Atlanta Hwy, Suite 110, Loganville, GA 30052
*Tel:* 770-466-9709 *Toll Free Tel:* 888-928-RKMA (928-7562) *Fax:* 770-466-6879 *Toll Free Fax:* 877-928-RKMA (928-7562)
*Web Site:* rkma.com
*Key Personnel*
Pres: Richard K Miller
Founded: 1972
Market research reference handbooks for college & corporate libraries. Subjects include consumer behavior, marketing, retail, travel, healthcare, entertainment & restaurants.
ISBN Prefix(es): 978-1-57783
Number of titles published annually: 10 Print; 10 Online
Total Titles: 10 Print; 10 Online

**Robert Miller Gallery**
524 W 26 St, New York, NY 10001
*Tel:* 212-366-4774 *Fax:* 212-366-4454
*E-mail:* rmg@robertmillergallery.com
*Web Site:* www.robertmillergallery.com
*Key Personnel*
Dir: Betsy Miller
Founded: 1977
Art books on artwork by represented artists.
ISBN Prefix(es): 978-0-944680
Number of titles published annually: 3 Print
Total Titles: 30 Print

**§Milliken Publishing Co**
Division of The Lorenz Corp
501 E Third St, Dayton, OH 45402
Mailing Address: PO Box 802, Dayton, OH 45401-0802
*Tel:* 937-228-6118 *Toll Free Tel:* 800-444-1144 *Fax:* 937-223-2042
*E-mail:* order@lorenz.com
*Web Site:* www.lorenz.educationalpress.com
*Key Personnel*
VP, Mktg: Debra Kaiser *E-mail:* debk@lorenz.com
Founded: 1960
Educational publishing division includes visual resources, instructional guides & reproducibles; elementary supplementals.
ISBN Prefix(es): 978-0-88335; 978-1-55863; 978-1-42911
Number of titles published annually: 20 Print
Total Titles: 400 Print; 20 CD-ROM; 200 E-Book; 6 Audio
Membership(s): National School Supply & Equipment Association

**§The Minerals, Metals & Materials Society (TMS)**
Affiliate of AIME
184 Thorn Hill Rd, Warrendale, PA 15086
*Tel:* 724-776-9000 *Toll Free Tel:* 800-759-4867 *Fax:* 724-776-3770
*E-mail:* publications@tms.org (orders)
*Web Site:* www.tms.org (orders)
*Key Personnel*
Exec Dir: James J Robinson *E-mail:* robinson@tms.org
Content Specialist: Matt Baker *E-mail:* mbaker@tms.org
Founded: 1871
Leading professional society dedicated to the development & dissemination of scientific & engineering knowledge for materials-centered technology. The society is the only professional organization that encompasses the entire spectrum of materials & engineering, from minerals processing through the advanced applications of materials.
ISBN Prefix(es): 978-0-87339
Number of titles published annually: 25 Print

**Minnesota Historical Society Press**
Division of Minnesota Historical Society
345 Kellogg Blvd W, St Paul, MN 55102-1906
SAN: 202-6384
*Tel:* 651-259-3205; 651-259-3000 *Toll Free Tel:* 800-621-2736 (warehouse) *Fax:* 651-297-1345 *Toll Free Fax:* 800-621-8476 (warehouse)
*E-mail:* info-mhspress@mnhs.org
*Web Site:* www.mhspress.org
*Key Personnel*
Dir & Intl Rts: Pamela McClanahan *Tel:* 651-259-3210 *E-mail:* pamela.mcclanahan@mnhs.org
Ed-in-Chief: Ann Regan *Tel:* 651-259-3206 *E-mail:* ann.regan@mnhs.org
Mktg & Sales Mgr: Mary Poggione *Tel:* 651-259-3204 *E-mail:* mary.poggione@mnhs.org
Mng Ed: Shannon M Pennefeather *Tel:* 651-259-3212 *E-mail:* shannnon.pennefeather@mnhs.org
Founded: 1849
Scholarly & trade books on Upper Midwest history & prehistory.
ISBN Prefix(es): 978-0-87351
Number of titles published annually: 20 Print; 100 E-Book
Total Titles: 350 Print; 6 Audio
Imprints: Borealis Books
Foreign Rep(s): Gazelle Books Services Ltd (Europe, UK)
*Warehouse:* Chicago Distribution Center, 11030 S Langley Ave, Chicago, IL 60628 *Toll Free Tel:* 800-621-2736 (orders) *Toll Free Fax:* 800-621-8476 (orders)
Membership(s): American Association of University Presses

**MIT List Visual Arts Center**
MIT E 15-109, 20 Ames St, Cambridge, MA 02139
*Tel:* 617-253-4400; 617-253-4680 *Fax:* 617-258-7265
*E-mail:* mlinga@mit.edu
*Web Site:* listart.mit.edu
*Key Personnel*
Dir: Paul C Ha
Asst Dir: David Freilach *Tel:* 617-253-5076 *E-mail:* freilach@mit.edu
Admin Asst: Barbra Pine *Tel:* 617-253-9479 *E-mail:* barbra@media.mit.edu
Founded: 1966
Contemporary art.
ISBN Prefix(es): 978-0-938437
Number of titles published annually: 6 Print
Distributed by DAP Distributed Art Publishers

**§The MIT Press**
55 Hayward St, Cambridge, MA 02142
SAN: 202-6414
*Tel:* 617-253-5255 *Toll Free Tel:* 800-207-8354 (orders) *Fax:* 617-258-6779; 617-577-1545 (orders)
*Web Site:* mitpress.mit.edu
*Key Personnel*
Cont: Charles Hale *Tel:* 617-258-0577 *E-mail:* chale@mit.edu
Dir: Ellen W Faran *Tel:* 617-253-4078 *E-mail:* ewfaran@mit.edu
Dir, Fin & Opers & Assoc Dir: Rebecca Schrader *Tel:* 617-253-5250 *E-mail:* recs@mit.edu
Dir, Journals: Nick Lindsay *Tel:* 617-258-0594 *E-mail:* nlindsay@mit.edu
Mktg Dir: Katie Hope *Tel:* 617-258-0603 *E-mail:* khope@mit.edu
Dir, Sales: Anne Bunn *Tel:* 617-253-8838 *E-mail:* annebunn@mit.edu
Dir, Technol: Bill Trippe *Tel:* 617-452-3747 *E-mail:* trippe@mit.edu
Edit Dir: Gita Manaktala *Tel:* 617-253-3172 *E-mail:* manak@mit.edu
Mng Ed: Michael Sims *Tel:* 617-253-2080 *E-mail:* msims@mit.edu
Exec Ed: Roger L Conover *Tel:* 617-253-1677 *E-mail:* conover@mit.edu; Robert Prior *Tel:* 617-253-1584 *E-mail:* prior@mit.edu
Sr Acqs Ed: John S Covell *Tel:* 617-253-3757 *E-mail:* jcovell@mit.edu; James S De Wolf *Tel:* 617-253-1558 *E-mail:* jdewolf@mit.edu; Phil Laughlin *Tel:* 617-252-1636 *E-mail:* laughlin@mit.edu; Clay Morgan *Tel:* 617-253-4113 *E-mail:* claym@mit.edu; Douglas Sery *Tel:* 617-253-5187 *E-mail:* dsery@mit.edu
Acqs Ed: Marguerite Avery *Tel:* 617-253-1653 *E-mail:* mavery@mit.edu; Jane MacDonald *Tel:* 617-253-1605 *E-mail:* janem@mit.edu
Ad Mgr: Anar Badalov *Tel:* 617-253-3516 *E-mail:* badalov@mit.edu
Design Mgr: Yasuyo Iguchi *Tel:* 617-253-8034 *E-mail:* iguchi@mit.edu
Digital Publg Mgr: Jake Furbush *Tel:* 617-258-0583 *E-mail:* jfurbush@mit.edu
Exhibits Mgr: John Costello *Tel:* 617-258-5764 *E-mail:* jcostell@mit.edu
Prodn Mgr: Janet Rossi *Tel:* 617-253-2882 *E-mail:* janett@mit.edu
Promos & Direct Mail Mgr: Astrid Baehrecke *Tel:* 617-253-7297 *E-mail:* baehreck@mit.edu
Publicity Mgr: Colleen Lanick *Tel:* 617-253-2874 *E-mail:* colleenl@mit.edu
Subs Rts Mgr: Cristina Sanmartin *Tel:* 617-253-0629 *E-mail:* csan@mit.edu

Textbook Promos Mgr: Michelle Pullano
*Tel:* 617-253-3620 *E-mail:* mpullano@mit.edu
Asst Journals Mgr & Journals Busn Mgr: June McCaull *Tel:* 617-258-0593 *E-mail:* jmccaull@mit.edu
Bookstore Mgr: John Jenkins *Tel:* 617-253-5249 *E-mail:* jjenkins@mit.edu
Founded: 1962
Scholarly & professional books, advanced textbooks, nonfiction trade books & reference books; architecture & design, cognitive sciences & linguistics, computer science & artificial intelligence, economics & management sciences, environmental studies; philosophy, neuroscience; technology studies; new media; paperbacks, journals.
ISBN Prefix(es): 978-0-262
Number of titles published annually: 250 Print
Total Titles: 3,400 Print; 5 CD-ROM; 2 Online; 1 E-Book
Imprints: Bradford Books
*Foreign Office(s):* The MIT Press Ltd, One Duchess St, Suite 2, London W1W 6AN, United Kingdom *Tel:* (020) 7306 0603 *Fax:* (020) 7306 0604 *E-mail:* info@mitpress.org.uk
Distributor for AAAI Press; Canadian Centre for Architecture; Zone Books
Foreign Rep(s): Academic Book Promotions (France, Scandinavia); American University Press Group (Hong Kong, Japan, Korea, Taiwan); Apac Publishers Services Pte Ltd; Cassidy & Associates (China); Rodney Franklin Agency (Israel); Christopher Humphrys; Humphrys Roberts Associates (Latin America); Uwe Ludemann (Austria, Germany, Italy, Switzerland); Mediamatics (India); MIT Press Ltd (Greece, Ireland, UK); David Stimpson (Australia, Canada, New Zealand); Cory Voigt Associates (South Africa)
Foreign Rights: Agencia Litterana Carmen Balcells (Maribel Luque) (Spain); Bardon-Chinese Media (Joanne Yang) (Taiwan); The Berlin Agency (Frauke Jung-Lindemann) (Germany); The English Agency (Tsutomu Yawata) (Japan); Graal Literary Agency (Lukasz Wrobel) (Poland); The Deborah Harris Agency (Ilana Kurshan) (Israel); Agence Hoffman (Christine Scholz) (France); The Kayi Agency (Dilek Kayi) (Turkey); KCC (Sageun Lee) (Korea); Alexander Korzheneveski Agency (Alexander Korzheneveski) (Russia); OA Literary Agency (Michael Avramides) (Greece); Reiser Literary Agency (Roberto Gilodi) (Italy); Agencia Riff (Joao Riff) (Brazil)
*Warehouse:* Triliteral LLC, 100 Maple Ridge Dr, Cumberland, RI 02864 *Tel:* 401-658-4226 *Fax:* 401-658-4193 *Toll Free Fax:* 800-406-9145 *E-mail:* orders@triliteral.org
Membership(s): AAP; Association of American University Presses

**Mitchell Lane Publishers Inc**
PO Box 196, Hockessin, DE 19707
SAN: 858-3749
*Tel:* 302-234-9426 *Toll Free Tel:* 800-814-5484 *Fax:* 302-234-4742 *Toll Free Fax:* 866-834-4164
*E-mail:* orders@mitchelllane.com
*Web Site:* www.mitchelllane.com
*Key Personnel*
Pres & Publr: Barbara J Mitchell *E-mail:* barbaramitchell@mitchelllane.com
VP, Sales & Mktg: Robert P Mitchell *Tel:* 302-731-9750 *E-mail:* robertmitchell@mitchelllane.com
Founded: 1993
Nonfiction for children & young adults.
ISBN Prefix(es): 978-1-883845; 978-1-58415; 978-1-61228
Number of titles published annually: 80 Print; 80 E-Book
Total Titles: 1,200 Print; 300 E-Book

*Editorial Office(s):* 1104 Kelly Dr, Newark, DE 19711
Foreign Rep(s): Edu-Reference (Canada); David Hall (Africa, Australia, Continental Europe, Ireland)
*Warehouse:* 20 Shea Way, Suite 205, Newark, DE 19713
Membership(s): Educational Book & Media Association

**Mobility International USA**
132 E Broadway, Suite 343, Eugene, OR 97401
*Tel:* 541-343-1284 *Fax:* 541-343-6812
*E-mail:* info@miusa.org
*Web Site:* www.miusa.org
*Key Personnel*
CEO & Exec Dir: Susan Sygall
Founded: 1981
The mission of Mobility International USA (MIUSA) is to empower people with disabilities through international exchange & international development to achieve their human rights.
MIUSA manages the National Clearinghouse on Disability & Exchange (NCDE), a project sponsored by the bureau of Educational & Cultural Affairs of the US Department of State.
ISBN Prefix(es): 978-1-880034
Number of titles published annually: 4 Print
Total Titles: 6 Print

**§Modern Language Association of America (MLA)**
26 Broadway, 3rd fl, New York, NY 10004-1789
SAN: 202-6422
*Tel:* 646-576-5000 *Fax:* 646-458-0030
*E-mail:* info@mla.org
*Web Site:* www.mla.org
*Key Personnel*
Pres: Michael Berube *E-mail:* mberube@mla.org
Exec Dir: Rosemary G Feal *Tel:* 646-576-5102 *E-mail:* execdirector@mla.org
Mktg & Sales Dir: Kathleen Hansen *Tel:* 646-576-5018 *E-mail:* khansen@mla.org
Opers Dir: Amilde Hadde *E-mail:* ahadde@mla.org
Dir of Convention Progs: Maribeth T Kraus *E-mail:* mkraus@mla.org
Dir, Print & Electronic Prodn: Judith Altreuter *E-mail:* judith@mla.org
Assoc Exec Dir & Dir, Public Opers: Judy Goulding *E-mail:* judy@mla.org
Founded: 1883
Research & teaching tools in languages & literature; professional publications for college teachers.
ISBN Prefix(es): 978-0-87352
Number of titles published annually: 12 Print
Total Titles: 300 Print; 1 CD-ROM; 1 Online
*Shipping Address:* 81 New St, 3rd fl, New York, NY 10004

**Modern Memoirs**
34 Main St, No 9, Amherst, MA 01002-2367
*Tel:* 413-253-2353
*Web Site:* www.modernmemoirs.com
*Key Personnel*
Founder & Pres: Kitty Axelson-Berry *E-mail:* kitty@modernmemoirs.com
Assoc Publr: Ali de Groot *E-mail:* ali@modernmemoirs.com
Founded: 1994
Private publishing services for discerning clients.
This publisher has indicated that 100% of their product line is author subsidized.
ISBN Prefix(es): 978-0-9662602
Number of titles published annually: 12 Print
Total Titles: 135 Print
Imprints: White Poppy Press
Membership(s): Association of Personal Historians; The Association of Publishers for Special Sales; IBPA, the Independent Book Publishers Association

**Modern Publishing**
Division of Unisystems Inc
155 E 55 St, New York, NY 10022
*Tel:* 212-826-0850 *Fax:* 212-759-9069
*Web Site:* www.modernpublishing.com
*Key Personnel*
Pres: Andrew Steinberg *E-mail:* asteinberg@modernpublishing.com
Founded: 1969
Juvenile, reference books; general nonfiction, humor, puzzle books.
ISBN Prefix(es): 978-0-7666
Number of titles published annually: 180 Print
Total Titles: 357 Print
Imprints: Block Board Books; Bubble Books; Detect-A-Word; Early Learners; Flip N Fun; Honey Bear Books; I Love You; Look at Me; Ready Reader Storybooks
*Warehouse:* Lehigh Valley Industrial Park, 2410 Brodhead Rd, Bethlehem, PA 18020

**The Monacelli Press**
236 W 27 St, 4th fl, New York, NY 10001
*Tel:* 212-229-9925
*E-mail:* contact@monacellipress.com
*Web Site:* www.monacellipress.com
*Key Personnel*
Publr: Gianfranco Monacelli
Mng Ed & Prodn Dir: Elizabeth White
Publicity Dir: Andrea Monfried *E-mail:* amonfried@monacellipress.com
Founded: 1994
High-quality, illustrated, hardcover & paperback books on art, architecture, decorative arts, interior design, fashion, photography, landscape, urbanism & graphic design.
ISBN Prefix(es): 978-1-58093; 978-1-885254

**Mondial**
203 W 107 St, Suite 6-C, New York, NY 10025
*Tel:* 646-807-8031 *Fax:* 208-361-2863
*E-mail:* contact@mondialbooks.com
*Web Site:* www.mondialbooks.com
*Key Personnel*
Owner: Uday K Dhar
Publr: Ulrich Becker
Founded: 2004
Specialize in fiction & nonfiction translated into English from other languages or originally written in English or German. All kinds of publications (fiction & nonfiction) in the international language Esperanto.
ISBN Prefix(es): 978-1-59569
Number of titles published annually: 15 Print; 10 E-Book
Total Titles: 160 Print; 1 CD-ROM; 30 E-Book

**Mondo Publishing**
200 Sherwood Ave, Farmingdale, NY 11735
*Tel:* 212-268-3560 *Toll Free Tel:* 888-88-MONDO (886-6636) *Toll Free Fax:* 888-532-4492
*E-mail:* info@mondopub.com
*Web Site:* www.mondopub.com
*Key Personnel*
Pres: Mark Vineis
Edit Dir: Susan Eddy
Mktg: Jackie Greenspan
Founded: 1986
K-5 literacy materials & professional development services.
ISBN Prefix(es): 978-1-879531; 978-1-57255; 978-1-58653; 978-1-59034; 978-1-59366; 978-1-60201
Number of titles published annually: 200 Print
Total Titles: 500 Print
Imprints: Mondo
*Warehouse:* 113 Amfesco Dr, Plainview, NY 11803
Membership(s): Children's Book Council

**Money Market Directories**
Unit of Standard & Poor's
401 E Market St, Charlottesville, VA 22902
Mailing Address: PO Box 1608, Charlottesville, VA 22902-1608
*Tel:* 434-977-1450 *Toll Free Tel:* 800-446-2810 *Fax:* 434-979-9962
*Web Site:* www.mmdwebaccess.com
*Key Personnel*
Dir: Jay Zacter
Mng Ed: Jehu Martin
Direct Mktg Specialist: Misty Combs *E-mail:* misty_combs@standardandpoors.com
Founded: 1970
Financial information regarding pension funds, nonprofits & service providers plus investment managers & consultants. Publications available as e-directories & online.
ISBN Prefix(es): 978-0-939712
Number of titles published annually: 3 Print; 2 CD-ROM; 1 Online; 4 E-Book
Total Titles: 3 Print; 2 CD-ROM; 1 Online; 4 E-Book

**The Mongolia Society Inc**
Indiana University, 322 Goodbody Hall, 1011 E Third St, Bloomington, IN 47405-7005
*Tel:* 812-855-4078 *Fax:* 812-855-4078
*E-mail:* monsoc@indiana.edu
*Web Site:* www.mongoliasociety.org
*Key Personnel*
Pres: Dr Alicia Campi
VP: Dr Christopher Atwood
Exec Dir: Susie Drost
Mng Ed: David Bade
Secy: Dr Peter Marsh
Treas: Tristra Newyear Yeager
Founded: 1961
Interests, culture & language of Mongolia.
ISBN Prefix(es): 978-0-910980
Number of titles published annually: 4 Print
Total Titles: 60 Print

**Monkfish Book Publishing Co**
22 E Market St, Suite 304, Rhinebeck, NY 12572
*Tel:* 845-876-4861
*E-mail:* monkfish@monkfishpublishing.com
*Web Site:* www.monkfishpublishing.com
*Key Personnel*
Publr: Paul Cohen *E-mail:* bookcohen@aol.com
Founded: 2002
Publisher of spirituality & religion titles. Also operates a self-publishing company.
ISBN Prefix(es): 978-0-9823246; 978-0-9766843; 978-0-9726357; 978-0-9798828; 978-0-9749359
Number of titles published annually: 4 Print; 4 Online; 4 E-Book
Total Titles: 40 Print; 32 Online; 32 E-Book
Divisions: Epigraph Publishing Service (subsidy publishers)
*Orders to:* Consortium Book Sales & Distribution, 3413 13 Ave NE, Suite 101, Minneapolis, MN 55413-1007 *Toll Free Tel:* 800-283-3572
*Distribution Center:* Consortium Book Sales & Distribution, 3413 13 Ave NE, Suite 101, Minneapolis, MN 55413-1007 *Tel:* 612-746-2600 *Toll Free Tel:* 800-283-3572 *Fax:* 612-746-2606

**The Montana Council for Indian Education**
1240 Burlington Ave, Billings, MT 59102-4224
SAN: 202-2117
*Tel:* 406-652-7598 (AM); 406-248-3465 (PM) *Fax:* 406-248-1297
*E-mail:* cie@cie-mt.org
*Web Site:* www.cie-mt.org
*Key Personnel*
Pres & Ed: Hap Gilliland *E-mail:* hapg@q.com
Busn Mgr & Lib Sales Dir: Sue A Clague
Founded: 1968
Publish only books giving a true picture of American Indian life & culture; for use in schools. Full refund available for undamaged books.
ISBN Prefix(es): 978-0-89992
Number of titles published annually: 3 Print
Total Titles: 130 Print; 2 Online
Imprints: Indian Culture Series

**Montana Historical Society Press**
Capitol Complex, 225 N Roberts St, Helena, MT 59620
Mailing Address: PO Box 201201, Helena, MT 59620-1201
*Tel:* 406-444-0090 (edit); 406-444-2890 (ordering/mktg); 406-444-2694 *Toll Free Tel:* 800-243-9900 *Fax:* 406-444-2696 (ordering/mktg)
*Web Site:* www.montanahistoricalsociety.org
*Key Personnel*
Ed & Dir, Publns: Molly Holz *E-mail:* mholz@mt.gov
Membership Coord: Rebecca Baumann *Tel:* 406-444-2918 *E-mail:* mhsmembership@mt.gov
Founded: 1891
ISBN Prefix(es): 978-0-917298; 978-0-9721522; 978-0-9759196; 978-0-9801292
Number of titles published annually: 4 Print
Total Titles: 45 Print; 1 Online; 1 Audio
Distributed by Globe Pequot Press

**Montemayor Press**
663 Hyland Hill Rd, Washington, VT 05675
Mailing Address: PO Box 1551, Montpelier, VT 05601
*Tel:* 802-883-5081
*E-mail:* montepress@aol.com
*Web Site:* www.montemayorpress.com
*Key Personnel*
Publr: Edward Myers
Exec Ed: Edith Poor
Founded: 1999
Independent publisher whose mission is to print & distribute quality fiction & nonfiction to adult, young adult & juvenile audiences.
ISBN Prefix(es): 978-0-9674477; 978-1-932727
Number of titles published annually: 1 Print; 2 E-Book
Total Titles: 20 Print; 2 E-Book
Membership(s): Council of Literary Magazines & Presses; IBPA, the Independent Book Publishers Association

**Monthly Review Press**
Division of Monthly Review Foundation Inc
146 W 29 St, Suite 6W, New York, NY 10001
SAN: 202-6481
*Tel:* 212-691-2555 *Toll Free Tel:* 800-670-9499 *Fax:* 212-727-3676
*E-mail:* mreview@igc.org
*Web Site:* www.MonthlyReview.org
*Key Personnel*
Mng Dir: Martin Paddio
Mktg Publicity Mgr: Scott Borchert
Founded: 1949
Economics, politics, history, sociology & world affairs.
ISBN Prefix(es): 978-0-85345; 978-1-58367
Number of titles published annually: 15 Print
Total Titles: 550 Print
Distributed by New York University Press
*Billing Address:* New York University Press, 838 Broadway, 3rd fl, New York, NY 10003
*Orders to:* New York University Press, 838 Broadway, 3rd fl, New York, NY 10003 *Toll Free Tel:* 800-996-6987 *Fax:* 212-995-4798
*Returns:* Maple Press Distribution Ctr Lebanon, 704 Legionaire Dr, Fredericksburg, PA 17026
*Warehouse:* Maple Press Distribution Ctr Lebanon, 704 Legionaire Dr, Fredericksburg, PA 17026

**Moody Publishers**
Affiliate of Ministry of Moody Bible Institute
820 N La Salle Blvd, Chicago, IL 60610
SAN: 202-5604
*Tel:* 312-329-4000 *Toll Free Tel:* 800-678-8812 (cust serv) *Fax:* 312-329-2019
*Web Site:* www.moodypublishers.com
*Key Personnel*
VP & Publr: Greg Thornton
VP: Wade Koenig
Edit Dir: Dave De Wit
Dir, Mktg: John Hinkley
Publicist: Janis Backing
Founded: 1894
Religion (interdenominational).
ISBN Prefix(es): 978-0-8024; 978-1-881273 (Northfield Publishing)
Number of titles published annually: 75 Print
Total Titles: 1,000 Print; 10 Audio
Imprints: Lift Every Voice; Northfield Publishing; River North
Foreign Rep(s): Biblicum AS (Norway); Bookhouse Australia Ltd (Australia); Challenge Bookshops (Nigeria); Christian Art Wholesale (South Africa); Christian Literature Crusade (Hong Kong); David C Cook Distribution (Canada); Editeurs de Litterature Biblique (Germany); Euro-Outreach Ministries (East Africa, Kenya, Nairobi); Hong Kong Tien Dao Publishing House Ltd (Belgium); Kesho Publications (Zimbabwe); Matopo Book Room (Philippines); Overseas Missionary Fellowship (Canada); Rhema Boekimport (Singapore); S & U Book Centre (New Zealand); S-U Wholesale; Send the Light (England)
*Shipping Address:* 215 W Locust St, Chicago, IL 60610

**Morehouse Publishing**
Imprint of Church Publishing Inc
4775 Linglestown Rd, Harrisburg, PA 17112
SAN: 202-6511
*Tel:* 717-541-8130 *Toll Free Tel:* 800-877-0012 (orders only); 800-242-1918 (cust serv) *Fax:* 717-541-8136; 717-541-8128 (orders only)
*Web Site:* www.morehousepublishing.com
*Key Personnel*
VP, Prodn: Loraine Simonello
Founded: 1884
Spirituality, religious, lay ministry, liturgy, church supplies, music cassettes & CDs, all from an Episcopal/Anglican perspective. No illustrated children's books.
ISBN Prefix(es): 978-0-8192
Number of titles published annually: 40 Print
Total Titles: 462 Print
Distributor for Gracewing (UK)
Foreign Rep(s): Novalis (Canada)
Foreign Rights: The Continuum International Publishing Group (Worldwide exc USA)
*Warehouse:* Morehouse Distribution Center, 3101 N Seventh St, Harrisburg, PA 17110

**Morgan James Publishing**
5 Penn Plaza, 23rd fl, New York, NY 10001
*Tel:* 212-655-5470 *Toll Free Tel:* 800-485-4943 *Fax:* 516-908-4496
*E-mail:* csauer@morganjamespublishing.com
*Web Site:* www.morganjamespublishing.com
*Key Personnel*
Founder: David L Hancock *E-mail:* david@morganjamespublishing.com
Founded: 2003
Provides entrepreneurs with the vital information, inspiration & guidance they need to be successful.
ISBN Prefix(es): 978-0-9746133; 978-0-9758570; 978-0-9760901; 978-0-9768491; 978-1-933596; 978-1-60037; 978-0-9815058; 978-0-9817906; 978-0-9820750; 978-0-9823793
Number of titles published annually: 130 Print; 90 E-Book
Total Titles: 415 Print

*Returns:* IPS Warehouse, 1280 Ingram Dr, Chambersburg, PA 17201
Membership(s): AAP

**Morgan Kaufmann**
Imprint of Elsevier Inc
225 Wyman St, Waltham, MA 02451
*Toll Free Tel:* 866-607-1417 *Fax:* 619-699-6310
*Web Site:* www.mkp.com
*Key Personnel*
Publr: Steve Elliot
Mktg Mgr: Brent de la Cruz
Intl Rts: Edna Lopez-Franco
Lib Sales: Tom Rosenthal *Tel:* 619-699-6806
Natl Acct Sales: Peg O'Malley *Tel:* 415-647-7867
Founded: 1984
Computer science book publishers including database, networking, architecture, engineering, graphics & artificial intelligence.
ISBN Prefix(es): 978-1-55860
Number of titles published annually: 65 Print
Total Titles: 1,600 Print
*Orders to:* 3251 Riverport Lane, Maryland Heights, MO 63040
*Returns:* 3251 Riverport Lane, Maryland Heights, MO 63040
*Warehouse:* 3251 Riverport Lane, Maryland Heights, MO 63040

**Morgan Reynolds Publishing**
620 S Elm St, Suite 387, Greensboro, NC 27406
*Tel:* 336-275-1311 *Toll Free Tel:* 800-535-1504 *Fax:* 336-275-1152 *Toll Free Fax:* 800-535-5725
*E-mail:* editorial@morganreynolds.com
*Web Site:* www.morganreynolds.com
*Key Personnel*
Founder & Publr: John Riley
Mktg Dir: Anita Richardson *E-mail:* anita@morganreynolds.com
Mng & Acqs Ed: Sharon F Doorasamy *E-mail:* sharon@morganreynolds.com
Founded: 1993
Hardcover trade & library-bound editions.
ISBN Prefix(es): 978-1-883846; 978-1-931798; 978-1-59935
Number of titles published annually: 100 Print
Total Titles: 300 Print

**Morning Sun Books Inc**
PO Box 326, Kutztown, PA 19530-0326
*Tel:* 610-683-8566 *Fax:* 610-683-3287
*Web Site:* www.morningsunbooks.com
*Key Personnel*
Pres: Robert J Yanosey
Founded: 1986
Color photography of railroads during 1940-1970 period.
ISBN Prefix(es): 978-1-878887; 978-1-58248
Number of titles published annually: 24 Print
Total Titles: 350 Print

**William Morrow & Co Inc**, see HarperCollins Publishers

**Morton Publishing Co**
925 W Kenyon Ave, Unit 12, Englewood, CO 80110
SAN: 210-9174
*Tel:* 303-761-4805 *Fax:* 303-762-9923
*E-mail:* contact@morton-pub.com
*Web Site:* www.morton-pub.com
*Key Personnel*
Pres & Intl Rts: Douglas Morton *E-mail:* mortond@morton-pub.com
Busn & Off Mgr: Chrissy De Mier *E-mail:* chrissyd@morton-pub.com
Sales Mgr: Carter Fenton *E-mail:* carterf@morton-pub.com
Biology Ed: David Ferguson *E-mail:* davidf@morton-pub.com
Returns: Jo Ann Sutton *E-mail:* joanns@morton-pub.com
Founded: 1977
Allied health, biology, pharmacy, computer information technology, speech & educational.
ISBN Prefix(es): 978-0-89582; 978-1-61731
Number of titles published annually: 10 Print
Total Titles: 50 Print
Foreign Rep(s): Northrose Associates (Canada)

**Mosaic Press**
4500 Witmer Industrial Estates, PMB 145, Niagara Falls, NY 14305-1386
Mailing Address: 1252 Speers Rd, Units 1 & 2, Oakville, ON L6L 5N9, Canada
*Tel:* 905-825-2130 *Fax:* 905-825-2130
*E-mail:* info@mosaic-press.com
*Web Site:* www.mosaic-press.com
*Key Personnel*
Publr: Howard Aster *E-mail:* mosaicpress@on.aibn.com
Founded: 1974
Literary scholarly books. No unsol mss.
ISBN Prefix(es): 978-0-88962
Number of titles published annually: 19 Print
Total Titles: 502 Print
*Warehouse:* 1252 Speers Rd, Units 1 & 2, Oakville, ON L6L 5N9, Canada
*Distribution Center:* Gazelle Book Services Ltd, White Cross Mills, Hightown LA1 4XS, United Kingdom
Midpoint, 5701 Ranch Dr, Little Rock, AR 72223-9633 (US) *Toll Free Tel:* 800-643-8030 *Fax:* 501-868-6321
Publishers Group of Canada, 300-76 Stafford St, Toronto, ON M6J 2S1, Canada (CN) *Tel:* 416-934-9900 *Fax:* 416-934-1410 *E-mail:* info@pgcbooks.ca

**Mount Olive College Press**
Affiliate of Mount Olive College
634 Henderson St, Mount Olive, NC 28365
*Tel:* 252-286-6851 *Fax:* 919-658-7180
*Web Site:* www.mountolivecollege.edu
*Key Personnel*
Edit Dir: Dr Pepper Worthington
Founded: 1990
Poetry, drama, biography, devotional, travel, essay, novel, cookbook, photography, children's books, literary criticism.
ISBN Prefix(es): 978-0-9627087; 978-1-880994
Number of titles published annually: 5 Print
Total Titles: 75 Print

**Mountain n' Air Books**
2947-A Honolulu Ave, La Crescenta, CA 91214
Mailing Address: PO Box 12540, La Crescenta, CA 91224-5540
*Tel:* 818-248-9345 *Toll Free Tel:* 800-446-9696 *Fax:* 818-248-6516 *Toll Free Fax:* 800-303-5578
*Web Site:* www.mountain-n-air.com
*Key Personnel*
Pres: Gilberto d'Urso *E-mail:* gilberto@mountain-n-air.com
Publr & Ed: Mary K d'Urso
Founded: 1985
Outdoor guides, nonfiction, cookbooks & travel adventures, maps.
ISBN Prefix(es): 978-1-879415
Number of titles published annually: 10 Print
Total Titles: 94 Print
Imprints: Mountain Air Books
Distributor for Tom Harrison Cartography

**Mountain Press Publishing Co**
1301 S Third W, Missoula, MT 59801
SAN: 202-8832
Mailing Address: PO Box 2399, Missoula, MT 59806-2399
*Tel:* 406-728-1900 *Toll Free Tel:* 800-234-5308 *Fax:* 406-728-1635
*E-mail:* info@mtnpress.com
*Web Site:* www.mountain-press.com
*Key Personnel*
History Ed: Gwen McKenna
Natural History & Roadside Geology Series Ed: Jennifer Carey
Busn Mgr: Rob Williams
Gen Mgr: John Rimel *E-mail:* johnargyle@aol.com
Mktg Mgr: Anne Iverson *Tel:* 406-728-1900 ext 131 *E-mail:* anne@mtnpress.com
Graphic Design: Jeannie Painter
Founded: 1948
ISBN Prefix(es): 978-0-87842; 978-0-9632562; 978-0-9626999; 978-1-886370; 978-1-889921; 978-1-892784; 978-0-9676747; 978-0-9717748; 978-0-9724827
Number of titles published annually: 20 Print
Total Titles: 150 Print
Imprints: Geology Underfoot Series; Mountain Sports Press Series; Roadside Geology Series; Roadside History Series; Tumbleweed Series
Distributor for Bucking Horse Books; Clark City Press; Companion Press; Cottonwood Publishing; Hops Press; Npustin Publishing; Western Edge Press

**The Mountaineers Books**
Division of The Mountaineers Club
1001 SW Klickitat Way, Suite 201, Seattle, WA 98134
*Tel:* 206-223-6303 *Toll Free Tel:* 800-553-4453 *Fax:* 206-223-6306 *Toll Free Fax:* 800-568-7604
*E-mail:* mbooks@mountaineersbooks.org
*Web Site:* www.mountaineersbooks.org
*Key Personnel*
Publr: Helen Cherullo *Tel:* 206-223-6303 ext 122
Ed-in-Chief: Kate Rogers *Tel:* 206-223-6303 ext 109
Mng Ed: Margaret Sullivan *Tel:* 206-223-6303 ext 133 *E-mail:* margarets@mountaineersbooks.org
Sr Ed: Mary Metz *Tel:* 206-223-6303 ext 119 *E-mail:* marym@mountaineersbooks.org
Dir, Sales & Mktg: Doug Canfield *Tel:* 206-223-6303 ext 114
Digital Media Mgr: Ashley Knecht *E-mail:* ashleyk@mountaineersbooks.org
Publicist: Emily White *Tel:* 206-223-6303 ext 138
Founded: 1961
Mountaineering, backpacking, hiking, cross-country skiing, bicycling, canoeing, kayaking, trekking, nature, conservation, green living & sustainability; outdoor how-to, guidebooks & maps; nonfiction adventure-travel accounts; biographies of outdoor people; reprint editions of mountaineering classics; adventure narratives.
ISBN Prefix(es): 978-0-89886; 978-0-916890
Number of titles published annually: 20 Print
Total Titles: 550 Print
Imprints: Braided River; Skipstone
Distributor for The American Alpine Club Press; Colorado Mountain Club Press
Foreign Rep(s): Cordee Publishing (UK)

**§De Gruyter Mouton**
Imprint of Walter de Gruyter GmbH & Co KG
121 High St, 3rd fl, Boston, MA 02110
*Tel:* 857-284-7073 *Fax:* 857-284-7358
*E-mail:* degruytermail@presswarehouse.com (orders & claims)
*Web Site:* www.degruyter.com
*Key Personnel*
Mktg Mgr: Heather Anderson *Tel:* 857-284-7073 ext 106 *E-mail:* heather.anderson@degruyter.com
Founded: 1956
Scholarly books & journals.
ISBN Prefix(es): 978-0-311; 978-90-279
Number of titles published annually: 75 Print; 2 Online
Total Titles: 2,500 Print; 3 CD-ROM; 10 Online

*Foreign Office(s):* Walter de Gruyter GmbH & Co KG, Genthinerstr 13, 10785 Berlin, Germany *Tel:* (030) 260 05-0 *Fax:* (030) 260 05-251 *E-mail:* info@degruyter.com
Distributed by Walter de Gruyter Inc
Foreign Rep(s): Allied Publishers Ltd (India, Nepal, Sri Lanka); Book Club International (Bangladesh); Combined Representatives Worldwide Inc (Philippines); D A Books & Journals (Australia, New Zealand); Walter de Gruyter Inc (Canada, Mexico); Verlags und Kommissionsbuchhandlung Dr Franz Hain (Austria); Kumi Trading (South Korea); Kweilin Bookstore (Taiwan); Maruzen Co Ltd (Japan); Pak Book Corp (Pakistan); Parry's Book Center (Sendjrjan Berhad) (Brunei, Malaysia, Singapore); Swinden Book Co Ltd (Hong Kong)
*Orders to:* Walter de Gruyter, PO Box 960, Herndon, VA 20172-0960 *Tel:* 703-661-1589 *Toll Free Tel:* 800-208-8144 *Fax:* 703-661-1501
*Shipping Address:* 22803 Quicksilver Dr, Dulles, VA 20166-2019

**Moznaim Publishing Corp**
4304 12 Ave, Brooklyn, NY 11219
SAN: 214-4123
*Tel:* 718-438-7680 *Fax:* 718-438-1305
*E-mail:* sales@moznaim.com
*Key Personnel*
Pres: Menachem Wagshal
VP: Moshe Sternlicht
Founded: 1981
Judaica books in Hebrew, English & Spanish.
ISBN Prefix(es): 978-0-940118; 978-1-885220
Number of titles published annually: 7 Print
Total Titles: 200 Print
*Foreign Office(s):* 10 Telmie Yosef St, Mishor Adumim, Israel *Tel:* (02) 5333441 *Fax:* (02) 5354345
Distributor for Avamra Institute; Breslov Research Institute; Red Wheel-Weiser Inc

**MRTS**
Imprint of Arizona Center for Medieval & Renaissance Studies (ACMRS)
PO Box 874402, Tempe, AZ 85287-4402
*Tel:* 480-727-6503 *Toll Free Tel:* 800-621-2736 (orders) *Fax:* 480-965-1681 *Toll Free Fax:* 800-621-8476 (orders)
*E-mail:* mrts@asu.edu
*Web Site:* www.acmrs.org/pubs
*Key Personnel*
Mng Ed: Roy Rukkila *E-mail:* roy.rukkila@asu.edu
Scholarly/academic press. Specialize in medieval & Renaissance texts & studies.
ISBN Prefix(es): 978-0-86698
Number of titles published annually: 24 Print
Total Titles: 440 Print
*Sales Office(s):* Chicago Distribution Center, 11030 S Langley Ave, Chicago, IL 60628 *Tel:* 773-702-7000 *Toll Free Tel:* 800-621-2736 *Fax:* 773-702-7212 *Toll Free Fax:* 800-621-8476 *E-mail:* orders@press.uchicago.edu *Web Site:* www.press.uchicago.edu
*Billing Address:* Chicago Distribution Center, 11030 S Langley Ave, Chicago, IL 60628 *Tel:* 773-702-7000 *Toll Free Tel:* 800-621-2736 *Fax:* 773-702-7212 *Toll Free Fax:* 800-621-8476 *E-mail:* orders@press.uchicago.edu *Web Site:* www.press.uchicago.edu
*Orders to:* Chicago Distribution Center, 11030 S Langley Ave, Chicago, IL 60628 *Tel:* 773-702-7000 *Toll Free Tel:* 800-621-2736 *Fax:* 773-702-7212 *Toll Free Fax:* 800-621-8476 *E-mail:* orders@press.uchicago.edu *Web Site:* www.press.uchicago.edu
*Returns:* Chicago Distribution Center, 11030 S Langley Ave, Chicago, IL 60628 *Tel:* 773-702-7000 *Toll Free Tel:* 800-621-2736 *Fax:* 773-702-7212 *Toll Free Fax:* 800-621-8476 *E-mail:* orders@press.uchicago.edu *Web Site:* www.press.uchicago.edu
*Distribution Center:* Chicago Distribution Center, 11030 S Langley Ave, Chicago, IL 60628 *Tel:* 773-702-7000 *Toll Free Tel:* 800-621-2736 *Fax:* 773-702-7212 *Toll Free Fax:* 800-621-8476 *E-mail:* orders@press.uchicago.edu *Web Site:* www.press.uchicago.edu

**§Multicultural Publications Inc**
Subsidiary of Making Education Reform Imperative Today Inc (MERIT)
936 Slosson St, Akron, OH 44320
Mailing Address: PO Box 8001, Akron, OH 44320-0001
*Tel:* 330-865-9578 *Fax:* 330-865-9578
*E-mail:* multiculturalpub@prodigy.net
*Key Personnel*
CEO & Pres: Bobby L Jackson
Dir, Mktg & Promos & Intl Rts: James Lynell
Lib Sales Dir: Rae Neal
Founded: 1992
Books, greeting cards, dolls & stuffed toys, multimedia.
ISBN Prefix(es): 978-0-9634932; 978-1-884242
Number of titles published annually: 1 Print; 1 CD-ROM; 1 Online
Total Titles: 28 Print; 2 CD-ROM; 28 Online; 4 Audio
*Branch Office(s)*
1907 Massillon Rd, Akron, OH 44312
*Returns:* 1907 Massillon Rd, Akron, OH 44312
*Shipping Address:* 1907 Massillon Rd, Akron, OH 44312

**Multimedia Larga**
900 S Boardman Dr, No G72, Gallup, NM 87301
*Tel:* 505-726-1720
*Key Personnel*
Dir & Publr: Minh L Perez *E-mail:* m_l_perez@yahoo.com
Ed: Jo Anne McGray
Intl Rts Contact & Lib Sales Dir: J Castillo
Founded: 1990
Publishers of books, journals, e-books & e-journals.
ISBN Prefix(es): 978-1-879585; 978-1-931233
Number of titles published annually: 15 Print; 10 Online; 40 E-Book
Total Titles: 90 Print; 40 Online; 68 E-Book
Foreign Rep(s): W B Vasantha Kandasami; M Monu
*Distribution Center:* ProQuest Inc

**§Mundania Press LLC**
6457 Glenway Ave, Suite 109, Cincinnati, OH 45211-5222
SAN: 255-013X
*Tel:* 513-490-2822 *Fax:* 513-598-9220 *Toll Free Fax:* 888-460-4752
*E-mail:* books@mundania.com; inquiry@mundania.com
*Web Site:* www.mundania.com
*Key Personnel*
COO & Sr Ed: Skyla Dawn Cameron
Pres & Mktg Dir: Bob Sanders *Tel:* 513-404-7357 *E-mail:* bob@mundania.com
Art Dir: Niki Browning
Founded: 2002
Provides authors with publishing & distribution worldwide. Submissions are currently open & actively look for any fiction with exception being poetry. All other specifics are listed on the web site.
ISBN Prefix(es): 978-0-9723670; 978-1-59426
Number of titles published annually: 500 Print; 100 CD-ROM; 500 Online; 900 E-Book; 5 Audio
Total Titles: 700 Print; 200 CD-ROM; 700 Online; 900 E-Book; 1 Audio
Imprints: Awe-Struck; Hard Shell; Phaze Books
Foreign Rep(s): Lightning Source (UK, USA)
Membership(s): Electronically Published Internet Connection; IBPA, the Independent Book Publishers Association

**Municipal Analysis Services Inc**
PO Box 13453, Austin, TX 78711-3453
*Tel:* 512-327-3328 *Fax:* 413-740-1294
*E-mail:* munilysis@hotmail.com
*Key Personnel*
Pres: Greg Michels
Founded: 1983
Government of Your State annual series database.
ISBN Prefix(es): 978-1-55507; 978-0-31738
Number of titles published annually: 82 Print; 40 CD-ROM; 80 E-Book
Total Titles: 2,200 Print; 200 CD-ROM; 240 E-Book

**The Museum of Modern Art**
11 W 53 St, New York, NY 10019
SAN: 202-5809
*Tel:* 212-708-9443 *Fax:* 212-333-6575
*E-mail:* moma_publications@moma.org
*Web Site:* www.moma.org
*Key Personnel*
Prodn Dir: Marc Sapir
Publr: Christopher Hudson
Assoc Publr: Charles R Kim
Edit Dir: David Frankel
Founded: 1929
Art, architecture, design, photography, film.
ISBN Prefix(es): 978-0-87070
Number of titles published annually: 18 Print
Total Titles: 1,250 Print
Distributed by Distributed Art Publishers (DAP) (US & Canada only)
Foreign Rep(s): Thames & Hudson Ltd (Worldwide exc Canada & USA)
*Warehouse:* South River Distribution, South River, NJ 08882
Membership(s): American Alliance of Museums; American Association of University Presses; CAA

**§Museum of New Mexico Press**
Unit of New Mexico State Department of Cultural Affairs
725 Camino Lejo, Suite C, Santa Fe, NM 87505
SAN: 202-2575
Mailing Address: PO Box 2087, Santa Fe, NM 87504-2087
*Tel:* 505-476-1155; 505-272-7777 (orders) *Toll Free Tel:* 800-249-7737 (orders) *Fax:* 505-476-1156 *Toll Free Fax:* 800-622-8667 (orders)
*Web Site:* www.mnmpress.org
*Key Personnel*
Dir: Anna Gallegos *Tel:* 505-476-1154 *E-mail:* anna.gallegos@state.nm.us
Art Dir & Prodn Mgr: David Skolkin *Tel:* 505-476-1159 *E-mail:* david.skolkin@state.nm.us
Edit Dir: Mary Wachs *Tel:* 505-476-1161 *E-mail:* mary.wachs@state.nm.us
Mktg & Sales Dir: Renee Tambeau *E-mail:* renee.tambeau@state.nm.us
Design Assoc: Jason Valdez
Founded: 1951
Publications related to Native America, Hispanic Southwest, 20th century art, photography, folk art & folklore, nature & gardening, architecture & the Americas.
ISBN Prefix(es): 978-0-89013
Number of titles published annually: 15 Print
Total Titles: 140 Print
Distributed by University of New Mexico Press
Foreign Rep(s): Codasat Canada Ltd (Canada); East-West Export Books (Asia-Pacific); Gazelle Book Services (Europe); US PubRep (Caribbean, Latin America, Mexico, Puerto Rico)
*Warehouse:* University of New Mexico Press

**Mutual Publishing**
1215 Center St, Suite 210, Honolulu, HI 96816
*Tel:* 808-732-1709 *Fax:* 808-734-4094
*E-mail:* info@mutualpublishing.com
*Web Site:* www.mutualpublishing.com
*Key Personnel*
Dir, Sales & Mktg: Gay Wong
*E-mail:* gaywong@mutualpublishing.com
Founded: 1974
Publishing, print brokering & packaging. Editorial & design services; trade, mass market paperback, coffee table & souvenir books.
ISBN Prefix(es): 978-1-56647
Number of titles published annually: 50 Print
Total Titles: 330 Print

**Mystic Seaport Museum Inc**
PO Box 6000, Mystic, CT 06355-0990
SAN: 213-7550
*Tel:* 860-572-5302; 860-572-0711 (visitor serv) *Toll Free Tel:* 800-248-1066 (wholesale orders only); 800-331-2665 (retail orders only) *Fax:* 860-572-5321
*E-mail:* info@mysticseaport.org
*Web Site:* www.mysticseaport.org
*Key Personnel*
Pres: Stephen C White *E-mail:* administration@mysticseaport.com
EVP: Susan Funk; Marcy Withington
Dir, Busn Devt: Mary Anne Stets
Founded: 1929
Scholarly & trade books on American maritime history & art.
ISBN Prefix(es): 978-0-913372; 978-0-939510
Number of titles published annually: 3 Print
Total Titles: 84 Print
Imprints: American Maritime Library
Distributor for Glencannon; Ten Pound Island Books
Foreign Rep(s): Nimbus (Canada); Dalton Young Assoc (UK)

**NACE International**
1440 S Creek Dr, Houston, TX 77084-4906
*Tel:* 281-228-6200 *Toll Free Tel:* 800-797-NACE (797-6223) *Fax:* 281-228-6300
*E-mail:* firstservice@nace.org
*Web Site:* www.nace.org
*Key Personnel*
Exec Dir: Bob Chalker *Tel:* 281-228-6250
Dir, Pubns: Gretchen Jacobson *Tel:* 281-228-6207 *E-mail:* gretchen.jacobson@nace.org
Founded: 1943
Publishes technical books on corrosion control & prevention & materials selection, design & degradation issues. Books are developed by individual authors/editors utilizing corrosion experts to contribute text. Compilations of technical papers from NACE conferences & symposia are also issued on an annual basis.
ISBN Prefix(es): 978-1-877914; 978-0-915567; 978-1-57590
Number of titles published annually: 50 Print
Total Titles: 425 Print; 30 CD-ROM; 4 Online; 80 Audio
*Foreign Office(s):* Menara Hap Seng, Level 16, Suite 812, Jalan P Ramlee, 50250 Kuala Lumpur, Malaysia *Tel:* (03) 9236 7333 *Fax:* (03) 9236 7410 *E-mail:* astley.pung@nace.org
Distributed by Australasian Corrosion Association
Distributor for ASM International; ASTM; AWS; Butterworth-Heinemann; Cambridge University Press; CASTI Publishing; Compass Publications; CRC Press; Marcel Dekker Inc; E&FN Spon; Elsevier Science Publishers; Gulf Publishing; Industrial Press; Institute of Materials; ISO; McGraw-Hill; MTI; Prentice Hall; Professional Publications; SSPC; Swedish Corrosion Institute; John Wiley & Sons Inc
Foreign Rep(s): ABI (India); ATP (Europe); BI Publications (Asia); IBS (India)

**NACE Press**, see NACE International

**NAL**
Division of Penguin Group (USA) LLC
375 Hudson St, New York, NY 10014
SAN: 282-5074
*Tel:* 212-366-2000
*E-mail:* online@penguinputnam.com
*Web Site:* www.penguinputnam.com; us.penguingroup.com
*Key Personnel*
VP & Publr: Kara Welsh
VP, Prodn: Pat Lyons
VP & Exec Creative Dir: Rich Hasselberger
VP, Sr Art Dir: Anthony Ramondo
VP & Publicity Dir: Craig Burke
VP & Exec Mktg Dir, Berkley Publishing Group, NAL & Riverhead Trade, Perigee: Rick Pascocello
VP & Assoc Publr: Rick Nayer
VP, Edit Dir: Claire Zion
Exec Ed: Tracy Bernstein; Danielle Perez; Ellen Edwards
Exec Mng Ed: Frank Walgren
Sr Ed: Kerry Janiszewski; Brent Howard; Sandra Harding; Laurien Wade; Jennifer Schuster
Founded: 1948
ISBN Prefix(es): 978-0-451
Number of titles published annually: 415 Print
Total Titles: 2,630 Print
Imprints: New American Library; Onyx; Roc; Signet; Signet Classics; Topaz
*Advertising Agency:* Spier NY

**The Narrative Press**
2041 E "A" St, Torrington, WY 82240
*Tel:* 307-532-3495 *Fax:* 307-532-3495
*E-mail:* service@narrativepress.com
*Web Site:* www.narrativepress.com
*Key Personnel*
Ed: Vickie Zimmer
Founded: 2001
Publishes true first person accounts of historical adventure & exploration.
ISBN Prefix(es): 978-1-58976
Number of titles published annually: 4 Print; 20 E-Book
Total Titles: 104 Print; 78 E-Book

**NASW Press**
Division of National Association of Social Workers (NASW)
750 First St NE, Suite 700, Washington, DC 20002
SAN: 202-893X
*Tel:* 202-408-8600 *Fax:* 203-336-8312
*E-mail:* press@naswdc.org
*Web Site:* www.naswpress.org
*Key Personnel*
Publr: Cheryl Bradley *E-mail:* cbradley@naswdc.org
Mktg Mgr: Sharon Fletcher *E-mail:* sfletcher@naswdc.org
Mng Ed & ISBN Contact: John Cassels *E-mail:* jcassels@naswdc.org
Mng Ed: Kristina Campbell *E-mail:* kcampbell@naswdc.org
Founded: 1955
Professional & scholarly books & journals in the social sciences.
ISBN Prefix(es): 978-0-87101
Number of titles published annually: 10 Print; 2 CD-ROM
Total Titles: 100 Print; 2 CD-ROM; 5 Online; 6 Audio
*Orders to:* PBD Worldwide Fulfillment Services, 1650 Bluegrass Lakes Pkwy, Alpharetta, GA 30004 *Tel:* 770-238-0450 *Toll Free Tel:* 800-227-3590 *Fax:* 770-238-0453 *Toll Free Fax:* 866-494-1499 *E-mail:* nasw@pbd.com *Web Site:* www.pbd.com
*Returns:* PBD Worldwide Fulfillment Services, 1650 Bluegrass Lakes Pkwy, Alpharetta, GA 30004 *Tel:* 770-238-0450 *Toll Free Tel:* 800-227-3590 *Fax:* 770-238-0453 *Toll Free Fax:* 866-494-1499 *E-mail:* nasw@pbd.com *Web Site:* www.pbd.com
*Shipping Address:* PBD Worldwide Fulfillment Services, 1650 Bluegrass Lakes Pkwy, Alpharetta, GA 30004 *Tel:* 770-238-0450 *Toll Free Tel:* 800-227-3590 *Fax:* 770-238-0453 *Toll Free Fax:* 866-494-1499 *E-mail:* nasw@pbd.com *Web Site:* www.pbd.com
*Warehouse:* PBD Worldwide Fulfillment Services, 1650 Bluegrass Lakes Pkwy, Alpharetta, GA 30004 *Tel:* 770-238-0450 *Toll Free Tel:* 800-227-3590 *Fax:* 770-238-0453 *Toll Free Fax:* 866-494-1499 *E-mail:* nasw@pbd.com *Web Site:* www.pbd.com
*Distribution Center:* PBD Worldwide Fulfillment Services, 1650 Bluegrass Lakes Pkwy, Alpharetta, GA 30004 *Tel:* 770-238-0450 *Toll Free Tel:* 800-227-3590 *Fax:* 770-238-0453 *Toll Free Fax:* 866-494-1499 *E-mail:* nasw@pbd.com *Web Site:* www.pbd.com
Membership(s): Association Media & Publishing

**Nataraj Books**
7967 Twist Lane, Springfield, VA 22153
*Tel:* 703-455-4996 *Fax:* 703-455-4001
*E-mail:* nataraj@erols.com; orders@natarajbooks.com
*Web Site:* www.natarajbooks.com
*Key Personnel*
Pres: Vinod Mahajan
Founded: 1986
Books from South Asia.
ISBN Prefix(es): 978-1-881338
Number of titles published annually: 7 Print
Total Titles: 70 Print
*Orders to:* 7073 Brookfield Plaza, Springfield, VA 22150 *Fax:* 703-912-9052

**Nation Books**
Imprint of The Nation Institute
116 E 16 St, 8th fl, New York, NY 10003
SAN: 216-4663
*Tel:* 212-822-0264 *Fax:* 212-253-5356
*E-mail:* submissions@nationbooks.org
*Web Site:* www.nationbooks.org
*Key Personnel*
Group Publr: Susan Weinberg
Edit Dir: Carl Bromley
Dir, Devt & Public Programming: Ruth Baldwin *Tel:* 212-822-0250 ext 266 *E-mail:* ruth@nationbooks.org
Founded: 2000
Specializes in publishing books from a progressive social & political viewpoint with independent & critical thoughts on current issues of the day.
ISBN Prefix(es): 978-1-56025
Number of titles published annually: 30 Print
Total Titles: 175 Print
Foreign Rep(s): Chistra Bopardikar
Foreign Rights: Yulia Borodyanskaya
*Orders to:* Publishers Group West, 1700 Fourth St, Berkley, CA 94710 *Tel:* 510-528-1444 *Toll Free Tel:* 800-788-3123
*Distribution Center:* Publishers Group West, c/o Advanced Marketing Services, 5045 W 79 St, Indianapolis, IN 46268

**§National Academies Press (NAP)**
Division of National Academies
Lockbox 285, 500 Fifth St NW, Washington, DC 20001
SAN: 202-8891
Mailing Address: PO Box 741500, Atlanta, GA 30374-1500
*Tel:* 202-334-3313 *Toll Free Tel:* 888-624-8373 (cust serv) *Fax:* 202-334-2451 (cust serv); 202-334-2793 (mktg dept)

*E-mail:* customer_service@nap.edu
*Web Site:* www.nap.edu
*Key Personnel*
Dir: Barbara Kline Pope *Tel:* 202-334-3328 *E-mail:* bkline@nas.edu
Deputy Exec Dir, Communs: Ann Merchant *Tel:* 202-334-3117 *E-mail:* amerchan@nas.edu
Exec Ed: Stephen Mautner *Tel:* 202-334-3336 *E-mail:* smautner@nas.edu
Dir, Publg Servs: Dottie Lewis *Tel:* 202-334-2409 *E-mail:* dlewis@nas.edu
Art Dir: Francesca Moghari *Tel:* 202-334-3323 *E-mail:* fmoghari@nas.edu
Founded: 1863
Science, technology & health, scholarly & trade books.
ISBN Prefix(es): 978-0-309
Number of titles published annually: 200 Print
Total Titles: 3,500 Print; 1,000 E-Book
Imprints: Joseph Henry Press
*Foreign Office(s):* Cumnor Hill, 12 Hid's Copse Rd, Oxford 0X2 9JJ, United Kingdom
Foreign Rep(s): Durnell Marketing Ltd (Europe, Ireland); Footprint Books Pty Ltd (Australia, New Zealand); Kinokuniya (Japan); Maruzen Co Ltd (Japan); US PubRep Inc (Caribbean including Puerto Rico, Central America, Mexico, South America); Viva Group (India); World Scientific Publishing Co Pte Ltd (Brunei, China, Hong Kong, India, Indonesia, Korea, Malaysia, Philippines, Singapore, Taiwan, Thailand)
*Orders to:* Marston Book Service Ltd, PO Box 269, Abingdon, Oxon OX14 4YN, United Kingdom (for UK & Europe) *Tel:* (01235) 465500 *Fax:* (01235) 465555 *Web Site:* www.marston.co.uk
*Returns:* 22883 Quicksilver Dr, Dulles, VA 20166
Membership(s): AAP

**The National Alliance Research Academy**
Division of The National Alliance for Insurance Education & Research
3630 N Hills Dr, Austin, TX 78755
Mailing Address: PO Box 27027, Austin, TX 78755-2027
*Tel:* 512-345-7932 *Toll Free Tel:* 800-633-2165 *Fax:* 512-349-6194
*E-mail:* alliance@scic.com
*Web Site:* www.scis.com/academy
*Key Personnel*
CEO & Pres, National Alliance for Insurance Education & Research: William T Hold, PhD
Assoc Dir: William J Hold
Founded: 1983
Insurance research & education.
ISBN Prefix(es): 978-1-878204
Number of titles published annually: 4 Print
Total Titles: 15 Print; 1 CD-ROM; 1 Audio

**National Association for Music Education**
1806 Robert Fulton Dr, Reston, VA 20191
*Tel:* 703-860-4000 *Toll Free Tel:* 800-462-6420 (orders & returns); 800-336-3768 *Fax:* 703-860-1531
*Web Site:* www.menc.org; www.nafme.org
*Key Personnel*
Collegiate Mgr: Becky Spray
Founded: 1907
Books on all phases of music education in schools & communities; professional philosophy & practical techniques, the arts & art education as a whole; current issues in music teaching & learning; music education advocacy.
ISBN Prefix(es): 978-0-940796; 978-1-56545
Number of titles published annually: 15 Print; 3 Online
Total Titles: 151 Print; 3 Online
*Editorial Office(s):* Rowman & Littlefield Publishing Group Inc, 4501 Forbes Blvd, Lanham, MD 20706
Distributed by Rowman & Littlefield Education
*Orders to:* Rowman & Littlefield Publishing Group Inc, 15200 NBN Way, Blue Ridge Summit, PA 17214 *Tel:* 717-794-3800 *Toll Free Tel:* 800-462-6420 *Fax:* 717-794-3803 *Toll Free Fax:* 800-338-4550 *E-mail:* orders@rowman.com
*Distribution Center:* National Book Network *Web Site:* www.nbnbooks.com

**National Association of Broadcasters (NAB)**
1771 "N" St NW, Washington, DC 20036-2891
*Tel:* 202-429-5300 *Fax:* 202-429-4199
*E-mail:* nab@nab.org
*Web Site:* www.nab.org
*Key Personnel*
COO & CFO: Janet McGregor *Tel:* 202-429-5304
EVP, Mktg & Communs: Michelle Lehman *Tel:* 202-429-5444 *E-mail:* mlehman@nab.org
EVP, Conventions & Busn Opers: Mr Chris Brown
Trade association representing radio & television stations & companies that serve the broadcasting industry.
ISBN Prefix(es): 978-0-89324
Number of titles published annually: 15 Print
Total Titles: 71 Print
Distributed by Allyn & Bacon; Lawrence Erlbaum Assoc; Focal Press; Macmillan Publishing Co; Tab Books; Wadsworth Inc

**§National Association of Insurance Commissioners**
2301 McGee St, Suite 800, Kansas City, MO 64108-2662
*Tel:* 816-842-3600; 816-783-8300 (cust serv) *Fax:* 816-783-8175; 816-460-7593 (cust serv)
*E-mail:* prodserv@naic.org
*Web Site:* www.naic.org
*Key Personnel*
Mgr II, PRISM: Renee Jensen *Tel:* 816-783-8305 *Fax:* 816-460-7452 *E-mail:* rjensen@naic.org
Sr Prod Devt/Prodn Mgr: William Maher *Tel:* 813-783-8301 *Fax:* 813-460-7670 *E-mail:* wmaher@naic.org
Founded: 1871
ISBN Prefix(es): 978-0-89382; 978-1-59917
Number of titles published annually: 110 Print
Total Titles: 356 Print; 110 Online; 110 E-Book
*Branch Office(s)*
NAIC Government Relations, Hall of the States, Suite 701, 4444 N Capitol St NW, Washington, DC 20001-1509, Dir: Ethan Sonnichsen *Tel:* 202-471-3990
Capital Markets & Investment Analysis Office, 48 Wall St, 6th fl, New York, NY 10005-2906, Dir: Chris Evangel *Tel:* 212-398-9000 *Fax:* 212-382-4207

**National Association of Secondary School Principals (NASSP)**
1904 Association Dr, Reston, VA 20191-1537
*Tel:* 703-860-0200 *Toll Free Tel:* 800-253-7746 *Fax:* 703-476-5432
*E-mail:* membership@principals.org; sales@principals.org; publications2@nassp.org (communs & devt)
*Web Site:* www.principals.org
*Key Personnel*
Sr Dir, Communs & Devt: Bob Farrace *Tel:* 703-860-7257 *E-mail:* farraceb@principals.org
Founded: 1916
Journals, magazines, monographs, newsletters, videos & software.
ISBN Prefix(es): 978-0-88210
Number of titles published annually: 6 Print
Total Titles: 74 Print
Imprints: NASSP
*Advertising Agency:* Publishers Associates

**National Book Co**
Division of Educational Research Associates
PO Box 8795, Portland, OR 97207-8795
SAN: 212-4661
*Tel:* 503-228-6345 *Fax:* 810-885-5811
*E-mail:* info@eralearning.com
*Web Site:* www.eralearning.com
*Key Personnel*
VP, SE Reg: Richard R Gallagher
Dir, Spec Materials: Mark R Salser
Prodn Mgr: Ward J Stroud
Founded: 1960
Individualized mastery learning programs for elementary, secondary & college levels, consisting of multimedia materials in business education, home economics, language skills, mathematics, science, shorthand skills, social studies, general & vocational education; special trade publications, particularly in subjects relating to education. Computer software; reference books; Black/Afro-American history; English as a second language.
ISBN Prefix(es): 978-0-89420
Number of titles published annually: 25 Print
Total Titles: 175 Print; 100 Audio
Imprints: Halcyon House

**National Braille Press**
88 Saint Stephen St, Boston, MA 02115-4302
*Tel:* 617-266-6160 *Toll Free Tel:* 800-548-7323 (cust serv); 888-965-8965 *Fax:* 617-437-0456
*E-mail:* orders@nbp.org
*Web Site:* www.nbp.org
*Key Personnel*
Pres: Brian A MacDonald *E-mail:* bmacdonald@nbp.org
VP, Publg & Prod Devt: Diane Croft *E-mail:* dcroft@nbp.org
VP, Braille Pubns: Tony Grima *Tel:* 617-266-6160 ext 29 *E-mail:* agrima@nbp.org
VP, Natl Mktg & Community Rel: Kimberly Ballard *E-mail:* kballard@nbp.org
Founded: 1929
Braille books & magazines.
ISBN Prefix(es): 978-0-939173
Number of titles published annually: 30 Print; 15 E-Book
Total Titles: 50 Print; 1 CD-ROM; 14 E-Book

**National Catholic Educational Association**
1005 N Glebe Rd, Suite 525, Arlington, VA 22201
*Tel:* 571-257-0010 *Toll Free Tel:* 800-711-6232 *Fax:* 703-243-0025
*E-mail:* nceaadmin@ncea.org
*Web Site:* www.ncea.org
*Key Personnel*
Pres: Karen M Ristau, PhD *E-mail:* president@ncea.org
Nonfiction: educational trends, methodology, innovative programs, teacher education & in-service, research, technology, financial & public relations programs, management systems all applicable to nonpublic education.
ISBN Prefix(es): 978-1-55833
Number of titles published annually: 25 Print
Total Titles: 225 Print

**§National Center for Children in Poverty**
Division of Mailman School of Public Health at Columbia University
215 W 125 St, 3rd fl, New York, NY 10027
*Tel:* 646-284-9600 *Fax:* 646-284-9623
*E-mail:* info@nccp.org
*Web Site:* www.nccp.org
*Key Personnel*
Dir, External Aff: Morris Ardoin *Tel:* 646-284-9616 *E-mail:* ardoin@nccp.org
Founded: 1989
Nonprofit publisher of monographs, reports, statistical updates, working papers & issue briefs concerning children under six who live in poverty in the US. Topics cover impact of poverty on child health & development; statistical profiles of poor children & their families;

research programs on the effects of poverty; research on policies that could reduce the young child poverty rate; integrated social & human services (private & public) for low-income families. Welfare reform & children, research forum on children, families & the new federalism.
ISBN Prefix(es): 978-0-926582
Number of titles published annually: 24 Print
Total Titles: 40 Print; 20 E-Book

**National Center For Employee Ownership (NCEO)**
1736 Franklin St, 8th fl, Oakland, CA 94612-3445
*Tel:* 510-208-1300 *Fax:* 510-272-9510
*E-mail:* customerservice@nceo.org
*Web Site:* www.nceo.org
*Key Personnel*
Exec Dir: Loren Rodgers *Tel:* 510-208-1307 *E-mail:* lrodgers@nceo.org
Dir, Publg & Info Technol: Scott Rodrick *Tel:* 510-208-1315 *E-mail:* srodrick@nceo.org
Founded: 1981
Employee ownership books, pamphlets & newsletter.
ISBN Prefix(es): 978-0-926902
Number of titles published annually: 4 Print; 5 E-Book
Total Titles: 50 Print

**National Conference of State Legislatures (NCSL)**
7700 E First Place, Denver, CO 80230
*Tel:* 303-364-7700 *Fax:* 303-364-7800
*E-mail:* books@ncsl.org
*Web Site:* www.ncsl.org
*Key Personnel*
Exec Dir: William T Pound
Ed: Karen Hansen
Meeting Mgr: Stacy Householder *Tel:* 303-364-7700 ext 1352 *E-mail:* stacy.householder@ncsl.org
Founded: 1975
Books, magazines, series of papers & issue briefs on state public policy issues.
ISBN Prefix(es): 978-1-55516; 978-1-58024
Number of titles published annually: 100 Print
Total Titles: 200 Print
*Branch Office(s)*
444 N Capitol St NW, Suite 515, Washington, DC 20001 *Tel:* 202-624-5400 *Fax:* 202-737-1069

**National Council of Teachers of English (NCTE)**
1111 W Kenyon Rd, Urbana, IL 61801-1096
*Tel:* 217-328-3870 *Toll Free Tel:* 877-369-6283 (cust serv) *Fax:* 217-328-9645
*E-mail:* orders@ncte.org
*Web Site:* www.ncte.org
*Key Personnel*
Exec Dir: Kent Williamson *Tel:* 217-278-3601
Pubns Dir: Kurt Austin *Tel:* 217-278-3619
Sr Ed: Bonny Graham *Tel:* 217-278-3618
Dir, Cust Serv: Sheri Ellenberger *Tel:* 217-278-3697
Purch & Prodn Mgr: Charles Hartman *Tel:* 217-278-3664
Perms Coord: Shellie Elson *Tel:* 217-278-3638 *Fax:* 217-328-0977 *E-mail:* permissions@ncte.org
Books Prog Asst: Kim Black
Founded: 1911
Nonprofit professional association of educators in English studies, literacy & language arts. Specialize in the teaching of English & the language arts at all grade levels; research reports; guidelines & position statements; journals.
ISBN Prefix(es): 978-0-8141
Number of titles published annually: 10 Print
Total Titles: 240 Print; 2 CD-ROM
Imprints: Principles in Practice

**§National Council of Teachers of Mathematics (NCTM)**
1906 Association Dr, Reston, VA 20191-1502
SAN: 202-9057
*Tel:* 703-620-9840 *Toll Free Tel:* 800-235-7566 *Fax:* 703-476-2970
*E-mail:* nctm@nctm.org
*Web Site:* www.nctm.org
*Key Personnel*
Pres: Linda M Gojak
Exec Dir: Kichoon Yang
Assoc Exec Dir, Communs: Kenneth Krehbiel *E-mail:* kkrehbiel@nctm.org
Dir, Pubns: Joanne Hodges *Tel:* 703-620-9840 ext 2129
Founded: 1920
Professional publications, including books (printed & online), monographs & yearbooks. Members include individuals, institutions, students, teachers & educators. Multiyear plans available to individual & institutional members.
ISBN Prefix(es): 978-0-87353
Number of titles published annually: 15 Print
Total Titles: 175 Print
Distributed by Eric Armin Inc Education Ctr; Delta Education; Didax Educational Resources; Educators Outlet; ETA Cuisenaire; Lakeshore Learning Materials; NASCO; Spectrum

**National Council on Radiation Protection & Measurements (NCRP)**
7910 Woodmont Ave, Suite 400, Bethesda, MD 20814-3095
*Tel:* 301-657-2652 *Toll Free Tel:* 800-229-2652 *Fax:* 301-907-8768
*E-mail:* ncrppubs@ncrponline.org
*Web Site:* www.ncrponline.org; www.ncrppublications.org
*Key Personnel*
Pres: Thomas Tenforde, PhD *E-mail:* tenforde@ncrponline.org
Exec Dir: David A Schauer *E-mail:* schauer@ncrponline.org
Mng Ed: Cindy L O'Brien *E-mail:* obrien@ncrponline.org
Sr Word Processor: Luvenia J Hawkins
Edit Asst: Bonnie G Walker
Founded: 1928
NCRP reports, statements, proceedings, commentaries, news; Taylor lectures.
ISBN Prefix(es): 978-0-913392; 978-0-929600
Number of titles published annually: 4 Print
Total Titles: 150 Print

**National Crime Prevention Council**
2001 Jefferson Davis Hwy, Suite 901, Arlington, VA 22202
*Tel:* 202-466-6272 *Fax:* 202-296-1356
*E-mail:* ncpc@fulfills.org (orders)
*Web Site:* www.ncpc.org
*Key Personnel*
CEO & Pres: Ann M Harkins
Mng Dir, Progs, Training & Multimedia Servs: Judy Kirby *E-mail:* kirby@ncpc.org
Founded: 1982
Crime prevention publications, training & technical assistance; McGruff public service advertising campaign, conferences & on-site training & technical assistance.
ISBN Prefix(es): 978-0-934513; 978-1-929888; 978-1-59686
Number of titles published annually: 5 Print
Total Titles: 90 Print
*Shipping Address:* NCPC Fulfillment Center, 49 Elk St, Amsterdam, NY 12010 *Toll Free Tel:* 800-627-2911

**National Education Association (NEA)**
1201 16 St NW, Washington, DC 20036-3290
*Tel:* 202-833-4000 *Fax:* 202-822-7974
*Web Site:* www.nea.org
*Key Personnel*
Secy/Treas: Rebecca "Becky" Pringle
Pres: Dennis Van Roekel
VP: Lily Eskelsen
Exec Dir: John C Stocks
Dir, PR: Andy Linebaugh *Tel:* 202-822-7218 *E-mail:* alinebaugh@nea.org
Founded: 1857
Professional development publications for K-12 & higher education & AV materials for educators. Web site with resources & general information for educators & the general public.
ISBN Prefix(es): 978-0-8106
Number of titles published annually: 7 Print; 2 CD-ROM; 2 Online
Total Titles: 189 Print; 2 CD-ROM; 9 Online
Imprints: NEA Professional Library

**§National Gallery of Art**
Fourth St & Pennsylvania Ave NW, Washington, DC 20565
Mailing Address: 2000 S Club Dr, Landover, MD 20785
*Tel:* 202-737-4215; 202-842-6480 *Fax:* 202-842-6733
*E-mail:* casva@nga.gov
*Web Site:* www.nga.gov
*Key Personnel*
Deputy Publr & Prodn Mgr: Chris Vogel
Ed-in-Chief: Judy Metro
Founded: 1941
Exhibition catalogues, catalogues of the collection & scholarly monographs.
ISBN Prefix(es): 978-0-89468
Number of titles published annually: 12 Print
Total Titles: 112 Print; 2 CD-ROM; 1 Online
Distributed by Abrams; Bulfinch/Little; Cambridge University Press; Hudson Hills; Lund Humphries/Ashgate; OAP; Princeton University Press; Thames & Hudson; Yale University Press

**National Geographic Books**
Division of National Geographic Society
1145 17 St NW, Washington, DC 20036-4688
*Tel:* 202-857-7000 *Fax:* 202-857-7670
*Web Site:* www.nationalgeographic.com
*Key Personnel*
Pres, Book Publg Group & EVP, NGS: Declan Moore
SVP & Gen Mgr, Book Publg Group: Hector Sierra *E-mail:* hsierra@ngs.org
EVP, Children's Publg: Melinda Gerosa Bellows
SVP & Edit Dir: Anne Alexander
VP & Ed-in-Chief, Children's Books: Nancy Laties Feresten *E-mail:* nfereste@ngs.org
VP, Retail & Dir, Dist: Linda Howey *E-mail:* lhowey@ngs.org
VP, Sales & Mktg, Direct to Consumer: Heidi Vincent *E-mail:* hvincent@ngs.org
Dir, Mng Edit: Jennifer Thornton
Dir, Photog: Susan Blair
Ed-in-Chief: Barbara Brownell
Founded: 1888
Nonfiction general illustrated reference, travel, photography, history, science. Children's nonfiction with emphasis on school & library markets.
ISBN Prefix(es): 978-0-7922; 978-0-87044
Number of titles published annually: 180 Print
Total Titles: 700 Print; 15 E-Book
Imprints: National Geographic Adventure Classics; National Geographic Adventure Press; National Geographic Books; National Geographic Children's Books; National Geographic Directions
Distributed by PGUK / Hi Marketing (United Kingdom); Random House (Worldwide exc UK)

Foreign Rights: Maeyee Lee (Worldwide); Rachel Love (Worldwide); Mary Jo Slazak (USA)
Membership(s): AAP

**National Geographic Learning**
Unit of Cengage Learning
One Lower Ragsdale Dr, Bldg 1, Suite 200, Monterey, CA 93940
*Tel:* 831-625-3666
*Web Site:* www.ngl.cengage.com
Founded: 1980
Publisher of K-12 language & literary educational materials; Spanish & English.
ISBN Prefix(es): 978-0-917837; 978-1-56334
Number of titles published annually: 10 CD-ROM; 10 Online
Membership(s): AAP

**National Geographic Society**
1145 17 St NW, Washington, DC 20036-4688
SAN: 202-8956
*Tel:* 202-857-7000 *Fax:* 202-429-5727
*Web Site:* www.nationalgeographic.com
*Key Personnel*
Pres, Books & Publg Group & EVP: Declan Moore
Pres, Magazines & Publg Admin: John Griffin
Pres, Global Media Group: Timothy T Kelly
Ed-in-Chief, Adult Books: Barbara Brownell
Founded: 1888
Books for adults; nonfiction.
ISBN Prefix(es): 978-0-87044
Number of titles published annually: 75 Print
Total Titles: 450 Print
Distributed by Random House
Membership(s): AAP; Children's Book Council
*See separate listing for:*
**National Geographic Books**

**§National Golf Foundation**
1150 S US Hwy One, Suite 401, Jupiter, FL 33477
*Tel:* 561-744-6006 *Toll Free Tel:* 888-275-4643 *Fax:* 561-744-6107
*E-mail:* general@ngf.org
*Web Site:* www.ngf.org
*Key Personnel*
CEO & Pres: Dr Joseph Beditz
Founded: 1936
Premier publisher of research & information for the business of golf. Over 200 publications are offered on golf consumer research, industry & market trends, golf facility development & operations, golf range development, instruction & player development.
ISBN Prefix(es): 978-0-9638647; 978-1-57701
Number of titles published annually: 4 Print
Total Titles: 100 Print; 1 CD-ROM; 2 Online; 1 Audio

**National Information Standards Organization**
One N Charles St, Suite 1905, Baltimore, MD 21201
*Tel:* 301-654-2512 *Toll Free Tel:* 866-957-1593 *Fax:* 410-685-5278
*E-mail:* nisohq@niso.org
*Web Site:* www.niso.org
*Key Personnel*
Mng Dir: Todd Carpenter *E-mail:* tcarpenter@niso.org
Busn Devt & Opers Mgr: Victoria Kinnear *E-mail:* vkinnear@niso.org
Maintain & develop technical standards for libraries, publishers & information services.
ISBN Prefix(es): 978-1-880124
Number of titles published annually: 6 Print; 6 E-Book
Total Titles: 60 Print; 3 Online; 60 E-Book
Distributor for Niso Press

**National Institute for Trial Advocacy (NITA)**
1685 38 St, Suite 200, Boulder, CO 80301-2735
*Tel:* 720-890-4860 *Toll Free Tel:* 877-648-2632; 800-225-6482 (orders & returns) *Fax:* 720-890-7069
*E-mail:* info@nita.org
*Web Site:* www.nita.org
*Key Personnel*
Exec Dir: John Baker *E-mail:* jbaker@nita.org
Dir, Sales & Mktg: Daniel McHugh *E-mail:* dmchugh@nita.org
Publr: Wendy Velez *E-mail:* wvelez@nita.org
Mng Ed: Eric H Sorensen *Tel:* 303-953-6823 *E-mail:* esorensen@nita.org
Founded: 1970
Legal & litigation training.
ISBN Prefix(es): 978-1-55681
Number of titles published annually: 20 Print; 1 CD-ROM
Total Titles: 350 Print; 2 CD-ROM; 12 Audio

**National League of Cities**
1301 Pennsylvania Ave NW, Washington, DC 20004-1763
*Tel:* 202-626-3100 *Fax:* 202-626-3043
*E-mail:* info@nlc.org
*Web Site:* www.nlc.org
*Key Personnel*
Dir, Ctr for Pub Aff & Memb Rel: Amy Elsbree *E-mail:* elsbree@nlc.org
Memb Rel Rep: Mae Davis *E-mail:* mdavis@nlc.org
Founded: 1924
ISBN Prefix(es): 978-0-933729; 978-1-886152
Number of titles published annually: 5 Print
Total Titles: 50 Print; 1 CD-ROM

**National Learning Corp**
212 Michael Dr, Syosset, NY 11791
*Tel:* 516-921-8888 *Toll Free Tel:* 800-632-8888 *Fax:* 516-921-8743
*E-mail:* info@passbooks.com
*Web Site:* www.passbooks.com
*Key Personnel*
Pres: Michael P Rudman
Founded: 1967
Basic competency tests for college, high school & occupations; functional literacy; career, general, vocational & technical, adult & continuing, special, cooperative & community education; professional licensure; test preparation books for civil service, postal service, government careers, armed forces, high school & college equivalency; college, graduate & professional school enhancement; certification & licensing in engineering & technical careers, teaching, law, dentistry, medicine & allied health professions.
ISBN Prefix(es): 978-0-8373
Number of titles published annually: 3 Print
Total Titles: 5,000 Print
Imprints: ACT Proficiency Examination Program; Admission Test Series; Career Examination Series; Certified Nurse Series (CN); College Level Examination Series; College Proficiency Examination Series; Dante Series; Graduate Record Examination Series; National Teacher Examination Series; Occupational Competency Examination Series; Passbooks; Regents External Degree Series; Teachers License Examination Series; Test Your Knowledge Books; Undergraduate Program Field Test Series; What Do You Know About Books
Subsidiaries: Delaney Books Inc; Frank Merriwell Inc
Membership(s): AAP

**National Notary Association (NNA)**
9350 De Soto Ave, Chatsworth, CA 91311
Mailing Address: PO Box 541032, Los Angeles, CA 90054-1032
*Tel:* 818-739-4000 *Toll Free Tel:* 800-876-6827 *Toll Free Fax:* 800-833-1211
*E-mail:* nna@nationalnotary.org
*Web Site:* www.nationalnotary.org
*Key Personnel*
CEO: Marc A Reiser
CFO & EVP: Jane Eagle
Pres: Milton G Valera
EVP: Debora M Thaw
SVP, Systems & Opers: Ronald Johnson
Dir, Mktg: Thomas K Hayden
Founded: 1957
Publish books, periodical, videos, seminars.
ISBN Prefix(es): 978-0-9600158; 978-0-933134; 978-1-891133
Number of titles published annually: 15 Print
Total Titles: 40 Print

**National Park Service Media Services**
Subsidiary of US Department of the Interior
67 Mather Place, Harpers Ferry, WV 25425
Mailing Address: PO Box 50, Harpers Ferry, WV 25425-0050
*Tel:* 304-535-5050 *Fax:* 304-535-6176
*Web Site:* www.nps.gov/hfc
*Key Personnel*
Dir: Don Kodak *Tel:* 304-535-6104
Ed: Diane Liggett
Pubns Supv: Melissa Cronyn
Founded: 1965
Official National Park Service handbooks, maps & brochures.
ISBN Prefix(es): 978-0-912627
Number of titles published annually: 3 Print
Total Titles: 43 Print
*Warehouse:* US Govt Printing Office, Superintendent of Documents, Washington, DC 20402

**National Publishing Co**
Subsidiary of Courier Corp
11311 Roosevelt Blvd, Philadelphia, PA 19154-2105
Mailing Address: PO Box 16234, Philadelphia, PA 19114-0234
*Tel:* 215-676-1863 *Toll Free Tel:* 888-333-1863 *Fax:* 215-673-8069
*Web Site:* www.courier.com
*Key Personnel*
VP, Sales: Michael LoRusso *E-mail:* mlorusso@courier.com
VP, Mfg: Robert Chilton *E-mail:* rchilton@courier.com
Founded: 1863
Publish Bibles & Testaments (King James Version); foreign language scriptures.
ISBN Prefix(es): 978-0-8340
Number of titles published annually: 3 Print
Total Titles: 65 Print
Imprints: Keystone; NPC
Distributed by Oxford University Press
Membership(s): AAP; BISG; BMI; CBA: The Association for Christian Retail; Evangelical Christian Publishers Association; National Bible Association

**National Register Publishing**
Division of Marquis Who's Who LLC
300 Connell Dr, Suite 2000, Berkeley Heights, NJ 07922
*Toll Free Tel:* 800-473-7020 *Fax:* 908-673-1189
*E-mail:* NRPsales@marquiswhoswho.com (sales); NRPeditorial@marquiswhoswho.com (edit)
*Web Site:* www.nationalregisterpublishing.com
Founded: 1915
Publisher of business information directories available in print, online & mailing list for commercial & reference use.
ISBN Prefix(es): 978-0-87217
Number of titles published annually: 5 Print
Total Titles: 1 Online

**National Resource Center for Youth Services (NRCYS)**
Division of University of Oklahoma-Outreach
Schusterman Ctr, Bldg 4W, 4502 E 41 St, Tulsa, OK 74135-2512

*Tel:* 918-660-3700 *Toll Free Tel:* 800-274-2687 *Fax:* 918-660-3737
*Web Site:* www.nrcys.ou.edu
*Key Personnel*
Dir: Peter R Correia, III *E-mail:* pcorreia@ou.edu
Assoc Dir: Kristi Charles *E-mail:* klcharles@ou.edu
Asst Prog Dir: TeRessa Kaemmerling *E-mail:* tkaemmerling@ou.edu
Founded: 1985
Curricula & resource manuals for professionals & volunteers who work with foster care & at-risk teenagers.
ISBN Prefix(es): 978-1-878848
Number of titles published annually: 3 Print
Total Titles: 20 Print

**National Science Teachers Association (NSTA)**
1840 Wilson Blvd, Arlington, VA 22201-3000
*Tel:* 703-312-9205 *Toll Free Tel:* 800-722-NSTA; 800-277-5300 (orders) *Fax:* 703-526-9754 *Toll Free Fax:* 888-433-0526 (orders)
*Web Site:* www.nsta.org/store
*Key Personnel*
Assoc Exec Dir & Publr: David Beacom *Tel:* 703-312-9207 *Fax:* 703-526-9754 *E-mail:* dbeacom@nsta.org
Founded: 1944
Books & periodicals.
ISBN Prefix(es): 978-0-87355; 978-1-93353; 978-1-936137
Number of titles published annually: 25 Print; 25 E-Book
Total Titles: 200 Print; 127 E-Book
Distributor for AAAS; BSCS; Corwin; Heinemann; IRA
Foreign Rep(s): Alkem (Southeast Asia)
Membership(s): AAP; American Society of Association Executives; Association Media & Publishing; Association of Educational Publishers

**The National Underwriter Co**
Division of Summit Business Media
5081 Olympic Blvd, Erlanger, KY 41018-3164
*Tel:* 859-692-2100 *Toll Free Tel:* 800-543-0874 *Fax:* 859-692-2289
*E-mail:* customerservice@nuco.com
*Web Site:* www.nationalunderwriter.com
*Key Personnel*
Interim CFO & COO: Thomas M Flynn
CIO: David MacDonald
Founded: 1897
ISBN Prefix(es): 978-0-87218
Number of titles published annually: 3 Print
Total Titles: 15 Print

**The Nautical & Aviation Publishing Co of America Inc**
845-A Lowcountry Blvd, Mount Pleasant, SC 29464
SAN: 213-3431
*Tel:* 843-856-0561 *Fax:* 843-856-3164
*Web Site:* www.nauticalandaviation.com
*Key Personnel*
Pres: Jan W Snouck-Hurgronje
Founded: 1979
Military history & aviation.
ISBN Prefix(es): 978-1-877853; 978-0-933852
Number of titles published annually: 4 Print; 2 Audio
Total Titles: 47 Print; 2 Audio
Imprints: N & A
*Warehouse:* REO Distribution, One Solutions Way, Waynesboro, VA 22980

**§Naval Institute Press**
Division of US Naval Institute
291 Wood Rd, Annapolis, MD 21402-5034
SAN: 202-9006
*Tel:* 410-268-6110 *Toll Free Tel:* 800-233-8764 *Fax:* 410-295-1084; 410-571-1703 (cust serv)
*E-mail:* webmaster@navalinstitute.org; customer@navalinstitute.org (cust serv); trade@usni.org
*Web Site:* www.nip.org; www.usni.org
*Key Personnel*
CEO: Peter H Daly *E-mail:* trade@usni.org
Mktg Dir: George Keating *Tel:* 410-295-1025 *E-mail:* gkeating@usni.org
Press Dir: Rick Russell *E-mail:* rrussell@usni.org
Publicist: Judy Heise *Tel:* 410-295-1028 *E-mail:* jheise@usni.org
Mktg Mgr: Claire Noble *Tel:* 410-295-1039 *E-mail:* cnoble@usni.org
Mng Ed: Susan Corrado *Tel:* 410-295-1032 *E-mail:* scorrado@usni.org
Sr Acqs Ed: Thomas Cutler *E-mail:* tcutler@usni.org
Subs Rts Ed: Susan Todd Brook *E-mail:* sbrook@usni.org
Cust Serv: Jaemellah Kemp
Founded: 1873
Naval & maritime subjects: professional, biography, science, history, ship & aviation references, US Naval Institute magazines; literature.
ISBN Prefix(es): 978-0-87021; 978-1-55750; 978-1-59114
Number of titles published annually: 65 Print
Total Titles: 800 Print
Distributed by Publishers Group West (digital only)
Foreign Rep(s): Eurospan Group (Africa, Asia, Australia, Europe, India, Middle East, Oceania, UK); Scholarly Book Services (Canada)
*Warehouse:* US Naval Institute, 2427 Bond St, University Park, IL 60466 *Toll Free Tel:* 800-233-8764
Membership(s): Association of American University Presses

**NavPress Publishing Group**
Division of The Navigators
3820 N 30 St, Colorado Springs, CO 80904
SAN: 211-5352
Mailing Address: PO Box 35002, Colorado Springs, CO 80935
*Tel:* 719-548-9222 *Toll Free Tel:* 800-366-7788 *Toll Free Fax:* 800-343-3902
*E-mail:* customerservice@navpress.com
*Web Site:* www.navpress.com
*Key Personnel*
Interim CEO: Charlie Dokmo
Sales & Trade Mktg Dir: Eric Helus
Founded: 1975
Paperbacks, mass market & trade, hardcovers, periodicals; religious (Protestant) materials.
ISBN Prefix(es): 978-0-89109; 978-1-57683
Number of titles published annually: 123 Print
Total Titles: 380 Print; 2 Audio
Imprints: NavPress; Think

**NBM Publishing Inc**
40 Exchange Place, Suite 1308, New York, NY 10005
SAN: 210-0835
*Tel:* 212-643-5407 *Toll Free Tel:* 800-886-1223 *Fax:* 212-643-1545
*E-mail:* admin@nbmpub.com
*Web Site:* www.nbmpub.com
*Key Personnel*
Pres & Publr: Terry Nantier
Off Mgr: Martha Samuel
Founded: 1976
Graphic novels.
ISBN Prefix(es): 978-0-918348; 978-1-56163
Number of titles published annually: 20 Print; 20 E-Book
Total Titles: 200 Print; 20 E-Book
Imprints: Amerotica (erotic graphic novels from North American authors); ComicsLit (best fiction in graphic novels from around the world); Eurotica (erotic graphic novels from European authors); Forever Nuts (reprints of classic comic strips)
Distributed by IPG
Foreign Rep(s): IPG (Canada); Turnaround (Europe, UK)
*Returns:* IPG, 600 N Pulaski Rd, Chicago, IL 60624
*Warehouse:* IPG Distribution Center, 600 N Pulaski Rd, Chicago, IL 60624
Membership(s): Children's Book Council; IBPA, the Independent Book Publishers Association

**NCRP**, see National Council on Radiation Protection & Measurements (NCRP)

**§Neal-Schuman Publishers Inc**
100 William St, Suite 2004, New York, NY 10038
SAN: 210-2455
*Tel:* 212-925-8650 *Toll Free Tel:* 866-NS-BOOKS (672-6657) *Fax:* 212-219-8916 *Toll Free Fax:* 877-231-6980
*E-mail:* info@neal-schuman.com
*Web Site:* www.neal-schuman.com
*Key Personnel*
Pres: Patricia Glass Schuman
EVP: John Vincent Neal
VP, Fin & New Busn Devt: Kathryn Suarez *E-mail:* suarez.kathryn@neal-schuman.com
Founded: 1976
How-to manuals, technology, library & information science texts.
ISBN Prefix(es): 978-0-918212; 978-1-55570
Number of titles published annually: 32 Print; 5 CD-ROM
Total Titles: 320 Print; 25 CD-ROM
*Foreign Office(s):* 3 Henrietta St, London WC2E 8LU, United Kingdom
Distributor for Chandos; Facet
Foreign Rep(s): James Bennett (Australia, New Zealand); Eurospan (Europe, UK); I-Group (Asia Pacific) (Asia); Ontario Library Association (Canada)
*Warehouse:* 1200 County Rd, Rte 523, Flemington, NJ 08822
Membership(s): ALA; Ontario Library Association

**NeDeo Press**
PO Box 668, Robbins, NC 27325
*Web Site:* www.nedeopress.com
*Key Personnel*
Dir: Barbara S Bane *E-mail:* bbane@nedeopress.com
Founded: 2005
Publish quality fiction & nonfiction books to entertain & inform for both regional & national markets.
ISBN Prefix(es): 978-0-9763874
Number of titles published annually: 3 Print
Total Titles: 7 Print
Membership(s): IBPA, the Independent Book Publishers Association; Independent Publishers Association

**Neibauer Press & Church Supplier**
Division of Louis Neibauer Co Inc
20 Industrial Dr, Warminster, PA 18974
*Tel:* 215-322-6200 *Toll Free Tel:* 800-322-6203 *Fax:* 215-322-2495
*E-mail:* sales@neibauer.com; sales@churchsupplier.com
*Web Site:* www.churchsupplier.com
*Key Personnel*
Pres: Nathan Neibauer *E-mail:* nathan@neibauer.com
Founded: 1967
ISBN Prefix(es): 978-1-878259
Number of titles published annually: 5 Print
Total Titles: 30 Print
Membership(s): CBA: The Association for Christian Retail

**Nevraumont Publishing Co**
259 E 134 St, 2nd fl loft, Bronx, NY 10454-4405

*Tel:* 718-993-6192
*E-mail:* info@nevraumontpublishing.com
*Web Site:* nevraumontpublishing.com
*Key Personnel*
Owner & Publr: Peter N Nevraumont
*E-mail:* peter@nevraumontpublishing.com
Founded: 1989
Natural history.
ISBN Prefix(es): 978-0-945223
Number of titles published annually: 5 Print
Total Titles: 30 Print
Distributed by Harry N Abrams Inc; Basic Books; Copernicus Press; Crown Publishing; W H Freeman; Harper Collins; Henry Holt; Alfred A Knopf; Pantheon Books; Penguin Putnam; Pi Press; Princeton University Press; Rizzoli International; Simon & Schuster; Texas A & M University Press; University of California Press; Westview Press; John Wiley & Sons; Yale University Press
Foreign Rights: Birkhauser Verlag (Switzerland); Dinalivro (Portugal); Julio Einaudi (Italy); Hainan (China); Edicions Proa (Spain); Sejong (Korea); Selica Shobo (Japan); Shidosha (Japan); Spektrum (Germany); TusQuets (Spain); Weidenfeld & Nicolson (UK); Witwatersrand University Press (England); Jorge Zahar Ediciones (Brazil)

**New American Library**, see NAL

**New Amsterdam Books**, see Ivan R Dee Publisher

**New Canaan Publishing Co LLC**
2384 N Hwy 341, Rossville, GA 30741
*Tel:* 423-285-8672
*E-mail:* djm@newcanaanpublishing.com
*Web Site:* www.newcanaanpublishing.com
*Key Personnel*
Pres: David J Mittelstadt
Founded: 1995
Publisher of children's books, selected Christian works for all ages & humor books confronting current trends & issues.
ISBN Prefix(es): 978-1-889658
Number of titles published annually: 4 Print
Total Titles: 23 Print
*Distribution Center:* Advocate Distribution Services™, 100 Biblica Way, Elizabethton, TN 37643 *Web Site:* www.advocatedistribution.com
Membership(s): IBPA, the Independent Book Publishers Association

**§New City Press**
Division of Focolare Movement
202 Comforter Blvd, Hyde Park, NY 12538
SAN: 203-7335
*Tel:* 845-229-0335 *Toll Free Tel:* 800-462-5980 (orders only) *Fax:* 845-229-0351
*E-mail:* info@newcitypress.com
*Web Site:* www.newcitypress.com
*Key Personnel*
Publr & Gen Mgr: Gary Brandl
*E-mail:* garybrandl@newcitypress.com
Accts Payable: Ms Soki Stanczyk
*E-mail:* accountant@newcitypress.com
Cust Serv: Nick Cianfarani *E-mail:* orders@newcitypress.com
Founded: 1964
Publishes spiritual works of all Christian eras, including the Church Fathers, the spiritual masters of the middle-ages, as well as publications of contemporary spirituality & theology.
ISBN Prefix(es): 978-0-911782; 978-1-56548
Number of titles published annually: 25 Print
Total Titles: 215 Print
Imprints: NCP
Distributor for Ciudad Nueva (Spain/Argentina); New City (Great Britain)
Foreign Rep(s): Enderle Book Co (Japan); John Garratt Publishing (Australia); Jerome's Specialist Booksellers (New Zealand); Joseph's Inspirational (Canada); New City (China, England, Ireland, Philippines); Preca Bookshop (Malta)

**§New Concepts Publishing**
106-A W Hill Ave, Valdosta, GA 31636
*E-mail:* service@newconceptspublishing.com; submissions@newconceptspublishing.com
*Web Site:* www.newconceptspublishing.com
*Key Personnel*
Pres: Madris De Pasture *E-mail:* madris@newconceptspublishing.com
Ed-in-Chief: Andrea De Pasture *E-mail:* andrea@newconceptspublishing.com
Founded: 1996
ISBN Prefix(es): 978-1-58608
Number of titles published annually: 50 Print; 192 Online; 144 E-Book
Total Titles: 200 Print; 700 Online; 700 E-Book

**New Dimensions Publishing**
11248 N 11 St, Phoenix, AZ 85020
*Tel:* 602-861-2631 *Toll Free Tel:* 800-736-7367 *Fax:* 602-944-1235
*E-mail:* info@thedream.com
*Web Site:* www.thedream.com
*Key Personnel*
Pres: Keith Varnum *E-mail:* keith@thedream.com
Founded: 1989
Book & audio tape publisher.
ISBN Prefix(es): 978-0-9722699
Number of titles published annually: 3 Print; 5 Audio
Total Titles: 6 Print; 5 Audio
Membership(s): The Association of Publishers for Special Sales; IBPA, the Independent Book Publishers Association

**New Directions Publishing Corp**
80 Eighth Ave, New York, NY 10011
SAN: 202-9081
*Tel:* 212-255-0230 *Fax:* 212-255-0231
*E-mail:* newdirections@ndbooks.com; editorial@ndbooks.com
*Web Site:* ndbooks.com
*Key Personnel*
Pres & Publr: Barbara Epler *E-mail:* bepler@ndbooks.com
EVP: Laurie Callahan *E-mail:* lcallahan@ndbooks.com
Art Dir & Prodn Mgr: Erik Rieselbach
*E-mail:* erieselbach@ndbooks.com
Founded: 1936
Modern literature, poetry, criticism & belles lettres.
ISBN Prefix(es): 978-0-8112
Number of titles published annually: 30 Print
Total Titles: 930 Print
Distributed by W W Norton Co
Foreign Rep(s): Australia Pansing Distribution (Malaysia, Singapore); Everest International Publishing Services (China); Hardy Bigfoss International Co Ltd (Cambodia, Laos, Myanmar, Thailand, Vietnam); MK International Ltd (Japan); B K Norton Ltd (Korea, Taiwan); W W Norton & Co Ltd (Africa, Europe, Ireland, Middle East, UK); Penguin Books Canada Ltd (Canada); Penguin Group New Zealand (New Zealand); Transglobal Publishers Services Ltd (Hong Kong, Macau); US Pub Rep Inc (Caribbean, Central America, Mexico, South America); John Wiley & Son (Australia)
Foreign Rights: Agenzia Letteraria Internazionale (Italy); Carmen Balcells Agencia Literaria (Spain); Agence Hoffman (France, Germany); Orion Literary Agency (Japan); Laurence Pollinger Ltd (British Commonwealth)
*Warehouse:* National Book Co, 800 Keystone Industrial Park, Scranton, PA 18512 *Tel:* 212-790-9453 *Toll Free Tel:* 800-233-4830 *Toll Free Fax:* 800-458-6515
*Distribution Center:* W W Norton Co, 500 Fifth Ave, New York, NY 10110

**§New Forums Press Inc**
1018 S Lewis St, Stillwater, OK 74074
Mailing Address: PO Box 876, Stillwater, OK 74076-0876
*Tel:* 405-372-6158 *Toll Free Tel:* 800-606-3766 *Fax:* 405-377-2237
*E-mail:* submissions@newforums.com
*Web Site:* www.newforums.com
*Key Personnel*
Pres: Douglas Dollar *E-mail:* ddollar@newforums.com
Founded: 1981
Practical & innovative academic journals, newsletters & books for educators in two & four year colleges & universities. Textbooks are also a primary interest.
ISBN Prefix(es): 978-0-913507; 978-1-58107
Number of titles published annually: 25 Print; 2 Online; 2 E-Book
Total Titles: 198 Print; 2 Online; 3 E-Book
*Advertising Agency:* Copy & Art, 219 E Greenvale Ct, Stillwater, OK 74075 *Tel:* 405-377-8224
Membership(s): The Association of Publishers for Special Sales

**New Harbinger Publications Inc**
5674 Shattuck Ave, Oakland, CA 94609
*Tel:* 510-652-0215 *Toll Free Tel:* 800-748-6273 (orders only) *Fax:* 510-652-5472 *Toll Free Fax:* 800-652-1613
*E-mail:* nhhelp@newharbinger.com; customerservice@newharbinger.com
*Web Site:* www.newharbinger.com
*Key Personnel*
Acq Ed: Catherine Sutker *E-mail:* catherine@newharbinger.com
Gen Mgr: Matt McKay, PhD *E-mail:* matt@newharbinger.com
Intl Rts: Dorothy Smyk *E-mail:* dorothy@newharbinger.com
Prodn Mgr: Michele Waters *E-mail:* michele@newharbinger.com
Founded: 1973
We offer the best in self-help psychology & health publications for tackling real problems.
ISBN Prefix(es): 978-1-57224
Number of titles published annually: 50 Print; 1 E-Book; 1 Audio
Total Titles: 250 Print; 1 E-Book; 46 Audio
Imprints: Context Press; Instant Help; Noetic Books
Foreign Rights: Raincoast Books (UK); Real Books (South Africa); John Reed Book Distributors (Australia); Southern Publishers Group (New Zealand)
*Returns:* 660 S Mansfield St, Ypsilant, MI 48197

**New Horizon Press**
PO Box 669, Far Hills, NJ 07931-0669
SAN: 677-119X
*Tel:* 908-604-6311 *Toll Free Tel:* 800-533-7978 (orders only) *Fax:* 908-604-6330
*E-mail:* nhp@newhorizonpressbooks.com
*Web Site:* www.newhorizonpressbooks.com
*Key Personnel*
VP, Fin & Mktg: Jo Anne Thomas *E-mail:* jct@newhorizonpressbooks.com
Publr & Ed-in-Chief: Dr Joan S Dunphy
Founded: 1982
True stories of uncommon heroes, true crime, social issues, behavioral, political science & psychologically-oriented nonfiction, trade paper, children's self-help, helping children deal with crisis.
ISBN Prefix(es): 978-0-88282; 978-1-933893

Number of titles published annually: 12 Print; 12 E-Book
Total Titles: 185 Print; 25 Online
Imprints: Small Horizons
Foreign Rights: Books Crossing Borders Inc (Betty Ann Crawford) (Worldwide)
*Orders to:* Publishers Group West (Perseus Distribution), 1700 Fourth St, Berkeley, CA 94710 *Toll Free Tel:* 800-788-3123 *Fax:* 510-528-3614 *Toll Free Fax:* 800-351-5073 *Web Site:* www.pgw.com
*Returns:* Perseus Distribution Returns Dept, 1700 Fourth St, Berkeley, CA 94710 *Toll Free Tel:* 800-788-3123 *Toll Free Fax:* 800-351-5073
*Distribution Center:* Publishers Group West (Perseus Distribution), 1700 Fourth St, Berkeley, CA 94710 *Tel:* 510-809-3700 *Toll Free Tel:* 800-788-3123 *Fax:* 510-809-3777 *Toll Free Fax:* 800-351-5073 *E-mail:* info@pgw.com *Web Site:* www.pgw.com

**New Issues Poetry & Prose**
Affiliate of Western Michigan University
Western Michigan University, 1903 W Michigan Ave, Kalamazoo, MI 49008-5463
*Tel:* 269-387-8185 *Fax:* 269-387-2562
*E-mail:* new-issues@wmich.edu
*Web Site:* www.wmich.edu/newissues
*Key Personnel*
Mng Ed: Kimberly Kolbe
Ed: William Olsen
Founded: 1996
ISBN Prefix(es): 978-1-930974
Number of titles published annually: 8 Print
Total Titles: 130 Print
*Distribution Center:* Small Press Distribution, 1341 Seventh St, Berkeley, CA 94710-1409 *Toll Free Tel:* 800-869-7553 *Web Site:* www.spdbooks.corg
Partners, 2325 Jarco Dr, Holt, MI 48842 *Toll Free Tel:* 800-336-3137 *Fax:* 517-694-0617

**New Leaf Press Inc**
Division of New Leaf Publishing Group
3142 Hwy 103 N, Green Forest, AR 72638-2233
Mailing Address: PO Box 726, Green Forest, AR 72638-0726
*Tel:* 870-438-5288 *Toll Free Tel:* 800-999-3777 *Fax:* 870-438-5120
*E-mail:* nlp@newleafpress.net
*Web Site:* www.newleafpress.net
*Key Personnel*
Asst Ed: Craig Froman
Founded: 1975
Christian living & creation books; evangelical, devotionals.
ISBN Prefix(es): 978-0-89221
Number of titles published annually: 35 Print; 25 E-Book
Total Titles: 390 Print; 70 E-Book

**New Poets Series**, see BrickHouse Books Inc

**The New Press**
38 Greene St, 4th fl, New York, NY 10013
*Tel:* 212-629-8802 *Toll Free Tel:* 800-343-4489 (orders) *Fax:* 212-629-8617 *Toll Free Fax:* 800-351-5073 (orders)
*E-mail:* newpress@thenewpress.com
*Web Site:* www.thenewpress.com
*Key Personnel*
Founder & Ed-at-Large: Andre Schiffrin
Exec Dir: Diane Wachtell
Prodn Dir: Fran Forte
Fin Dir: Carline Yup
Publr: Ellen Adler
Sr Mng Ed: Maury Botton
Edit Dir: Marc Favreau
Founded: 1990
Nonprofit publisher in the public interest; politics, education, current affairs, history, biography, economics, international fiction in translation.
ISBN Prefix(es): 978-1-56584
Number of titles published annually: 50 Print
Total Titles: 800 Print; 200 E-Book
Foreign Rep(s): MK International Ltd (Japan); W W Norton & Co Ltd (USA); I B Taurus & Co Ltd (Worldwide); University of Toronto Press (Canada)
Foreign Rights: Carmen Balcells (Spain); Ursula Bender (Germany); Ann Christine Danielsson (Scandinavia); Cristina de Mello e Souza; Beth Elon (Israel); Mary Kling (France); William Miller (Japan); Susanna Zevi (Italy)

**New Readers Press**
Division of ProLiteracy
1320 Jamesville Ave, Syracuse, NY 13210
SAN: 202-1064
*Tel:* 315-422-9121 *Toll Free Tel:* 800-448-8878 *Fax:* 315-422-6369 *Toll Free Fax:* 866-894-2100
*E-mail:* nrp@proliteracy.org
*Web Site:* www.newreaderspress.com
*Key Personnel*
Busn Dir: Susan Willey *Tel:* 315-422-9121 ext 260
ISBN Contact: Mike Shaffer
Founded: 1965
Books & periodical for adults & young adult reading at a 0-8 reading level, basic reading & writing materials, English as a second language, mathematics & GED prep.
ISBN Prefix(es): 978-0-88336; 978-1-56420; 978-1-56853; 978-0-929631
Number of titles published annually: 20 Print
Total Titles: 550 Print; 41 Audio
Foreign Rep(s): Frontier Books (Canada)
Foreign Rights: Frontier BookStore (Canada); Laubach Literacy Ontario (Canada)

**New Rivers Press**
c/o Minnesota State University Moorhead, 1104 Seventh Ave S, Moorhead, MN 56563
*Tel:* 218-477-5870 *Fax:* 218-477-2236
*E-mail:* nrp@mnstate.edu
*Web Site:* www.newriverspress.com; www.mnstate.edu/newriverspress
*Key Personnel*
Mng Ed: Dr Suzzanne Kelley *E-mail:* kelleysu@mnstate.edu
Sr Ed: Dr Alan Davis *Tel:* 218-477-4681 *E-mail:* davisa@mnstate.edu
Founded: 1968
Books of poetry, short stories & novellas, creative nonfiction, memoir.
ISBN Prefix(es): 978-0-912284; 978-0-89823
Number of titles published annually: 6 Print; 6 E-Book
Total Titles: 340 Print
*Distribution Center:* Consortium Books Sales & Distribution, The Keg House, Suite 101, 34 13 Ave NE, Minneapolis, MN 55413-1007 *Tel:* 612-746-2600 *Toll Free Tel:* 800-283-3572 (cust serv) *Fax:* 612-746-2606 *Web Site:* www.cbsd.com
Membership(s): Association of Writers and Writing Programs; Council of Literary Magazines & Presses

**New Strategist Publications Inc**
120 W State St, 4th fl, Ithaca, NY 14850
Mailing Address: PO Box 242, Ithaca, NY 14851-0242
*Tel:* 607-273-0913 *Toll Free Tel:* 800-848-0842 *Fax:* 607-277-5009
*E-mail:* demographics@newstrategist.com
*Web Site:* newstrategist.com
*Key Personnel*
Pres & Publr: Penelope Wickham
Ed-in-Chief: Cheryl Russell
Founded: 1990
Publish reference books; demographics & consumer spending.
ISBN Prefix(es): 978-1-885070; 978-1-933588; 978-1-935775
Number of titles published annually: 20 Print; 20 Online
Total Titles: 32 Print; 32 Online

**New Victoria Publishers**
PO Box 13173, Chicago, IL 60613-0173
*Tel:* 773-793-2244 *Toll Free Tel:* 888-530-4588
*E-mail:* newvictoriapub@att.net
*Web Site:* www.newvictoria.com
*Key Personnel*
CEO & Pres: P Feuerhaken
Founded: 1976
Lesbian feminist fiction & nonfiction books.
ISBN Prefix(es): 978-0-934678; 978-1-892281
Number of titles published annually: 4 Print; 4 E-Book
Total Titles: 91 Print; 80 E-Book
*Distribution Center:* ASP Wholesale, 3623 Munster Ave, Hayward, CA 87016, Contact: Bert Herrman
Bella Distribution, 1041 Aenon Church Rd, Tallahasse, FL 32304 *Toll Free Tel:* 800-533-1973 *Web Site:* belladistribution.com
Women & Children First Books, 5233 N Clark St, Chicago, IL 60640 *Tel:* 773-769-9299 *E-mail:* wcfbooks@aol.com *Web Site:* www.womenandchildrenfirst.com

**New Win Publishing**
Division of Academic Learning Co LLC
9682 Telstar Ave, Suite 110, El Monte, CA 91731
SAN: 217-1201
*Tel:* 626-448-3448 *Fax:* 626-602-3817
*E-mail:* info@academiclearningcompany.com
*Web Site:* www.newwinpublishing.com; www.wbusinessbooks.com/
*Key Personnel*
Publr: Arthur Chou
Founded: 1988
General nonfiction: business books for sales, marketing & entrepreneurship, crafts, reference, health & nutrition, healthy gourmet cooking, career development, outdoor sports, hunting, shooting, fishing, decoys & dogs.
ISBN Prefix(es): 978-0-8329
Number of titles published annually: 25 Print
Total Titles: 70 Print
Imprints: WBusiness Books; Winchester Press; ZHealth Books

**New World Library**
Division of Whatever Publishing Inc
14 Pamaron Way, Novato, CA 94949
SAN: 211-8777
*Tel:* 415-884-2100 *Toll Free Tel:* 800-227-3900 (ext 52, retail orders); 800-972-6657 *Fax:* 415-884-2199
*E-mail:* escort@newworldlibrary.com
*Web Site:* www.newworldlibrary.com
*Key Personnel*
Pres: Marc Allen *E-mail:* marc@newworldlibrary.com
Edit Dir: Georgia Hughes *E-mail:* georgia@newworldlibrary.com
Mktg Dir & Assoc Publr: Munro Magruder *E-mail:* munro@newworldlibrary.com
Prodn Dir: Tona Pearce- Meyers *E-mail:* tona@newworldlibrary.com
Publicity Dir: Monique Muhlenkamp *E-mail:* monique@newworldlibrary.com
Sr Ed: Jason Gardner *E-mail:* jason@newworldlibrary.com
Submissions Ed: Jonathan Wichmann *E-mail:* jonathan@newworldlibrary.com
Foreign Rts Mgr: Danielle Galat *E-mail:* danielle@newworldlibrary.com
Soc Media Mgr & Sr Publicist: Kim Corbin *E-mail:* kim@newworldlibrary.com
Spec Sales Mgr: Ami Parkerson *E-mail:* ami@newworldlibrary.com
Founded: 1977

Publisher of books on self-improvement, personal growth & spirituality, health & wellness, pets & animals, psychology & women's interest.
ISBN Prefix(es): 978-0-915811; 978-0-931432; 978-1-880032; 978-0-945934; 978-1-57731; 978-1-882591; 978-1-930722; 978-1-932073
Number of titles published annually: 35 Print; 35 E-Book; 2 Audio
Total Titles: 525 Print; 450 E-Book; 35 Audio
Imprints: Amber-Allen Publishing; Nataraj
Divisions: H J Kramer
Foreign Rep(s): Akasha Books (New Zealand); Brumby Books (Australia); Dempsey-Your Distributor (Canada); Publishers Group Canada (Canada); Publishers Group International (Continental Europe, India, Japan, Korea, Latin America, Middle East, Philippines, South America, Southeast Asia, Taiwan); Publishers Group UK (UK); Real Books (South Africa)
*Distribution Center:* Publishers Group West, 193 Edwards Dr, Jackson, TN 38301-7795 *Toll Free Tel:* 800-788-3123 *Web Site:* www.pgw.com
Membership(s): AAP Professional/Scholarly Publishing Division; BEA; Northern California Independent Booksellers Association; Publishers Association of the West

**New York Academy of Sciences**
7 World Trade, 40th fl, 250 Greenwich St, New York, NY 10007-2157
SAN: 203-753X
*Tel:* 212-298-8600 *Toll Free Tel:* 800-843-6927 *Fax:* 212-298-3644
*E-mail:* nyas@nyas.org; publications@nyas.org
*Web Site:* www.nyas.org
*Key Personnel*
CEO & Pres: Ellis Rubenstein *Tel:* 212-298-8686 *E-mail:* erubenstein@nyas.org
COO: Richard Baum *Tel:* 212-298-8695 *E-mail:* rbaum@nyas.org
VP, HR: Wendy Caruso Schneider *Tel:* 212-298-8680 *E-mail:* wschneider@nyas.org
Dir, Scientific Pubns & Ed-in-Chief, ANNALS of the NYAS: Douglas Braaten, PhD *Tel:* 212-298-8634 *E-mail:* dbraaten@nyas.org
Founded: 1817
Annals & transactions of the New York Academy of Sciences, also publish *Update Magazine*.
ISBN Prefix(es): 978-0-89072; 978-0-89766; 978-1-57331
Number of titles published annually: 32 Print
Total Titles: 333 Print
Distributed by Wiley Blackwell Publishers
Membership(s): AAP

**The New York Botanical Garden Press**
Division of The New York Botanical Garden
2900 Southern Blvd, Bronx, NY 10458-5126
*Tel:* 718-817-8721 *Fax:* 718-817-8842
*E-mail:* nybgpress@nybg.org
*Web Site:* www.nybgpress.org
*Key Personnel*
Mng Ed, NYBG Press: Joy Runyon *Tel:* 718-817-8574
Cust Serv: Diedra Howson *Tel:* 718-817-8918 *E-mail:* dhowson@nybg.org
Founded: 1896
Dissemination of information on the scientific study of plants.
ISBN Prefix(es): 978-0-89327
Number of titles published annually: 15 Print
Total Titles: 244 Print
*Warehouse:* Maple-Vail Distribution Center, PO Box 15100, York, PA 17405
*Distribution Center:* Maple-Vail Distribution Center, PO Box 15100, York, PA 17405
Membership(s): AAP

**New York Public Library**
Publications Office, 2nd fl, 188 Madison Ave, New York, NY 10016-4314
*Tel:* 917-275-6975
*Web Site:* www.nypl.org
*Key Personnel*
Dir, PR: Angela Montefinise
Founded: 1895
Reference books, exhibition catalogs, literature & humanities; hardcover & softcover.
ISBN Prefix(es): 978-0-87104
Number of titles published annually: 5 Print
Total Titles: 60 Print

**New York State Bar Association**
One Elk St, Albany, NY 12207
SAN: 226-1952
*Tel:* 518-463-3200 *Toll Free Tel:* 800-582-2452 *Fax:* 518-487-5517
*Web Site:* www.nysba.org
*Key Personnel*
CLE (Continuing Legal Educ) Pubns Dir: Daniel J McMahon *Tel:* 518-487-5582 *E-mail:* dmcmahon@nysba.org
Founded: 1985
Legal publications, including hardbound, looseleaf, softbound & diskettes.
ISBN Prefix(es): 978-0-942954
Number of titles published annually: 110 Print; 6 CD-ROM
Total Titles: 600 Print; 500 Online

**New York University Press**
838 Broadway, 3rd fl, New York, NY 10003-4812
SAN: 658-1293
*Tel:* 212-998-2575 (edit) *Toll Free Tel:* 800-996-6987 (orders) *Fax:* 212-995-3833 (orders)
*E-mail:* information@nyupress.org; customerservice@nyupress.org; orders@nyupress.org
*Web Site:* www.nyupress.org
*Key Personnel*
Dir: Steve Maikowski
Mktg & Sales Dir: Mary Beth Jarrad
Asst Dir & Ed-in-Chief: Eric Zinner
Prodn Mgr: Charles Hames
Exec Ed: Ilene Kalish
Mng Ed: Despina P Gimbel
Sr Ed: Deborah Gershenowitz
Ed: Jennifer Hammer
Publicist: Betsy Steve
Order Fulfillment & Spec Sales Supv: Kevin Cooper
Founded: 1916
Publish a wide array of provocative & compelling titles, as well as works of lasting scholarly & reference value.
ISBN Prefix(es): 978-0-8147
Number of titles published annually: 100 Print
Total Titles: 2,000 Print
Distributor for Combined Academic Publishers Ltd; Footprint Books; Monthly Review Press
*Returns:* c/o Maple Press Distribution Center, Lebanon Distribution Ctr, 704 Legionaire Dr, Fredricksburg, PA 17026
*Warehouse:* c/o Maple Press Distribution Ctr, Legionnaire Dr, Lebanon, PA 17042 *Tel:* 717-865-7600 *Fax:* 717-865-7800
Membership(s): AAP; Association of American University Presses

**Newbury Street Press**
Imprint of New England Historic Genealogical Society
101 Newbury St, Boston, MA 02116
*Tel:* 617-536-5740 *Toll Free Tel:* 888-296-3447 (NEHGS membership) *Fax:* 617-536-7307
*E-mail:* sales@nehgs.org
*Web Site:* www.newenglandancestors.org
*Key Personnel*
CEO & Pres: D Brenton Simons
Dir, Pubns: Scott C Steward *Tel:* 617-226-1208 *E-mail:* ssteward@nehgs.org
Dir, Devt: Ted MacMahon *Tel:* 617-226-1218 *E-mail:* tmacmahon@nehgs.org
Sales Coord: Rick Park *Tel:* 617-226-1212 *E-mail:* rpark@nehgs.org
Founded: 1996
A special publications division of The New England Historic Genealogical Society which publishes scholarly books & compiled genealogies.
ISBN Prefix(es): 978-0-88082
Number of titles published annually: 10 Print
Total Titles: 67 Print

**NewSouth Books**
Imprint of NewSouth Inc
105 S Court St, Montgomery, AL 36104
*Tel:* 334-834-3556 *Fax:* 334-834-3557
*E-mail:* info@newsouthbooks.com
*Web Site:* www.newsouthbooks.com
*Key Personnel*
Owner & Publr: Suzanne La Rosa
Owner & Ed-in-Chief: Randall Williams
Mng Ed: Brian Seidman *E-mail:* brian@newsouthbooks.com
Founded: 2000
Independent book publisher, publishing 15-20 titles per year, including literary fiction & nonfiction, with a special emphasis on books about the history & culture of the South.
ISBN Prefix(es): 978-1-58838; 978-1-60306
Number of titles published annually: 20 Print; 10 Online; 10 E-Book
Total Titles: 175 Print; 30 Online; 30 E-Book
Imprints: Junebug Books; NewSouth Books; NewSouth Classics
Distributed by John F Blair Publisher
*Billing Address:* 1406 Plaza Dr, Winston-Salem, NC 27103
*Returns:* 1406 Plaza Dr, Winston-Salem, NC 27103
*Shipping Address:* 1406 Plaza Dr, Winston-Salem, NC 27103
*Warehouse:* 1406 Plaza Dr, Winston-Salem, NC 27103
*Distribution Center:* 1406 Plaza Dr, Winston-Salem, NC 27103
Membership(s): Southern Independent Booksellers Alliance

**§Nightingale-Conant**
6245 W Howard St, Niles, IL 60714
*Tel:* 847-647-0306 *Toll Free Tel:* 800-572-2770; 800-557-1660 (sales); 800-560-6081 (cust serv) *Fax:* 847-647-7145; 847-647-9143 (sales)
*E-mail:* distributordivision@nightingale.com (orders)
*Web Site:* www.nightingale.com
*Key Personnel*
Chmn of the Bd: Vic Conant
CEO & Pres: Gary Chappell *E-mail:* garyc@nightingale.com
Founded: 1960
Audio, video books & CD-ROMs in the areas of sales, skills, wealth building, spiritual growth, foreign language & personal development.
ISBN Prefix(es): 978-1-55525
Number of titles published annually: 3 Print; 1 CD-ROM; 12 Audio
Total Titles: 190 Print; 5 CD-ROM; 400 Audio
Subsidiaries: Nightingale-Conant (UK)
Distributed by William Morrow; Simon & Schuster

**§Nilgiri Press**
Division of Blue Mountain Center of Meditation
3600 Tomales Rd, Tomales, CA 94971
*Tel:* 707-878-2369
*E-mail:* info@easwaran.org
*Web Site:* www.easwaran.org
*Key Personnel*
Mktg & Prodn: Debbie McMurray *E-mail:* debbie.mcmurray@nilgiripress.org
Intl Rts: Jennifer Jones *E-mail:* jennifer.jones@nilgiripress.org
Founded: 1972

Timeless wisdom for daily living books, video & audio.
ISBN Prefix(es): 978-0-915132; 978-1-888314; 978-1-58638
Number of titles published annually: 3 Print; 10 E-Book; 10 Audio
Total Titles: 28 Print
Foreign Rep(s): Publishers Group West
Foreign Rights: Publishers Group West (Canada)

**NK Publications Inc**
Affiliate of Loukoumi Books
PO Box 1735, Radio City Sta, New York, NY 10101-1735
*E-mail:* info@nkpublications.com
*Web Site:* www.nkpublications.com
*Key Personnel*
Pres: Nick Katsoris
Founded: 2002
ISBN Prefix(es): 978-0-9705100; 978-0-9841610
Number of titles published annually: 10 Print

**No Frills Buffalo**
119 Dorchester Rd, Buffalo, NY 14213
*Tel:* 716-510-0520
*E-mail:* contact@nofrillsbuffalo.com
*Web Site:* www.nofrillsbuffalo.com
*Key Personnel*
Founder: Mark Pogodzinski
Founded: 2009
Publishing new & engaging authors. Provides editorial services, interior & cover design, publicity & a chance to succeed.
ISBN Prefix(es): 978-0-615; 978-0-578
Number of titles published annually: 4 Print; 4 E-Book
Total Titles: 12 Print; 4 E-Book
Distributed by Aardvark
Membership(s): Independent Publishers Association

**No Starch Press Inc**
38 Ringold St, San Francisco, CA 94103
*Tel:* 415-863-9900 *Toll Free Tel:* 800-420-7240 *Fax:* 415-863-9950
*E-mail:* info@nostarch.com
*Web Site:* www.nostarch.com
*Key Personnel*
Pres: William Pollock
Busn Mgr: Leigh Poehler *E-mail:* leigh@nostarch.com
Founded: 1994
General computer trade; Linux.
ISBN Prefix(es): 978-1-886411; 978-1-593270
Number of titles published annually: 24 Print; 24 E-Book
Total Titles: 120 Print; 120 E-Book
Imprints: Linux Journal Press
Distributed by O'Reilly Media
Membership(s): IBPA, the Independent Book Publishers Association

**§NOLO**
Subsidiary of Internet Brands Inc
950 Parker St, Berkeley, CA 94710
SAN: 206-7935
*Web Site:* www.nolo.com
Founded: 1972
A leading provider of plain-English legal information & products for consumers & businesses. Most efforts are focused on a network of web sites featuring extensive free content, do-it-yourself products including forms, software & ebooks, as well as a consumer-friendly lawyer directory. Pioneered the self-help law movement in 1972 when two legal aid attorneys set out to demystify the law for people who couldn't afford lawyers.
This publisher has indicated that 100% of their product line is author subsidized.
ISBN Prefix(es): 978-0-87337; 978-1-41330
Number of titles published annually: 60 Print; 200 Online; 200 E-Book; 7 Audio
Total Titles: 200 Print; 200 Online; 200 E-Book; 7 Audio
*Distribution Center:* Ingram Publisher Services, One Ingram Blvd, La Vergne, TN 37086 *Toll Free Tel:* 855-802-8230 *Toll Free Fax:* 800-838-1149 *E-mail:* customerservice@ingrampublisherservices.com *Web Site:* www.ingrampublisherservices.com
Membership(s): ALA

**The Noontide Press**
Imprint of Legion for the Survival of Freedom
PO Box 2719, Newport Beach, CA 92659-1319
*Tel:* 714-593-9725 *Fax:* 714-593-9731
*E-mail:* orders@noontidepress.com
*Web Site:* www.noontidepress.com
*Key Personnel*
Pres: Mark Weber
Founded: 1968
Publisher & mail-order distributor of books, disks & tapes.
ISBN Prefix(es): 978-0-939482
Number of titles published annually: 3 Print; 3 Audio
Total Titles: 3 Print; 2 CD-ROM; 50 Audio

**Norilana Books**
PO Box 209, Highgate Center, VT 05459-0209
SAN: 851-8556
*E-mail:* service@norilana.com
*Web Site:* www.norilana.com
*Key Personnel*
Owner & Publr: Vera Nazarian
Founded: 2006
Beautifully produced & packaged editions, primarily classics of world literature & quality originals.
ISBN Prefix(es): 978-1-934169; 978-1-934648; 978-1-60762
Number of titles published annually: 100 Print
Total Titles: 300 Print
Imprints: Curiosities; Leda; Spirit; The Sword of Norilana; Taleka; YA Angst

**North Atlantic Books**
Division of Society for the Study of Native Arts & Sciences
2526 Martin Luther King Jr Way, Berkeley, CA 94704
SAN: 203-1655
Mailing Address: PO Box 12327, Berkeley, CA 94712-3327
*Tel:* 510-549-4270 *Fax:* 510-549-4276
*Web Site:* www.northatlanticbooks.com
*Key Personnel*
Publr: Richard Grossinger
Assoc Publr & Mng Dir: Doug Reil *Tel:* 510-549-4270 ext 29 *E-mail:* dreil@northatlanticbooks.com
Dir, Sales & Dist: Janet Levin *Tel:* 510-549-4270 ext 35 *E-mail:* jlevin@northatlanticbooks.com
Dir, Publg: Roslyn Bullas *Tel:* 510-549-4270 ext 30 *E-mail:* rbullas@northatlanticbooks.com
Art Dir: Paula Morrison
Contracts Mgr: Susan Bumps *Tel:* 510-549-4270 ext 13 *E-mail:* sbumps@northatlanticbooks.com
Foreign Rts & Perms Mgr: Sarah Serafimidis *Tel:* 510-549-4270 ext 16 *E-mail:* sserafimidis@northatlanticbooks.com
Founded: 1974
North Atlantic Books has been located in Berkeley, California since 1977. Over this period, North Atlantic has become a leading publisher of alternative health, nutrition, bodywork, martial arts & spiritual titles.
ISBN Prefix(es): 978-1-883319; 978-0-913028; 978-0-938190; 978-1-55643; 978-1-58394 (Frog Ltd Books)
Number of titles published annually: 65 Print; 100 E-Book
Total Titles: 1,000 Print; 100 E-Book
Imprints: Blue Snake Books; Evolver Editions; Frog Books
Distributor for DharmaCafe; Energy Arts; Ergos Institute; Heaven & Earth Publications; New Pacific Press; Rangjung Yeshe Publications; Sunfood Living
Foreign Rep(s): Publishers Group UK (UK); Random House Inc International Sales Div (Africa, Asia, Australia, Caribbean, Europe, Latin America, Middle East, New Zealand, South Africa); Random House of Canada Limited (Canada)
*Orders to:* Random House Distribution Services, 400 Hahn Rd, Westminister, MD 21157 (bookstore orders) *Toll Free Tel:* 800-733-3000 *Toll Free Fax:* 800-659-2436 *E-mail:* csorders@randomhouse.com *Web Site:* www.randomhouse.com
*Returns:* Random House Returns Department, 1019 N State Road 47, Crawfordsville, IN 47933
*Distribution Center:* Random House Distribution Services, 400 Hahn Rd, Westminister, MD 21157
Membership(s): Northern California Book Publicity & Marketing Association
*See separate listing for:*
**Frog Books**

**North Carolina Office of Archives & History**
Historical Publications Section, 4622 Mail Service Ctr, Raleigh, NC 27699-4622
*Tel:* 919-733-7442 (ext 225) *Fax:* 919-733-1439
*Web Site:* www.ncpublications.com; nc-historical-publications.stores.yahoo.net (online store)
*Key Personnel*
Administrator: Donna E Kelly *Tel:* 919-733-7442 ext 223 *E-mail:* donna.kelly@ncdcr.gov
Mktg Mgr: William A Owens, Jr *E-mail:* bill.owens@ncdcr.gov
Sales Mgr: Trudy Rayfield *Tel:* 919-733-7442 ext 221 *E-mail:* trudy.rayfield@ncdcr.gov
Founded: 1903
State government agency that publishes nonfiction hardcover & trade paperback books relating to North Carolina; publishes maps, posters, facsimile documents & the *North Carolina Historical Review*, a scholarly journal of history.
ISBN Prefix(es): 978-0-86526
Number of titles published annually: 4 Print
Total Titles: 160 Print

**North Country Books Inc**
220 Lafayette St, Utica, NY 13502-4312
*Tel:* 315-735-4877 *Toll Free Tel:* 800-342-7409 (orders) *Fax:* 315-738-4342
*E-mail:* ncbooks@verizon.net
*Web Site:* www.northcountrybooks.com
*Key Personnel*
Owner & Pres: Robert B Igoe, Jr *E-mail:* rbigoe@verizon.net
Gen Mgr: Zach Steffen
Founded: 1965
Book publisher & distributor of New York state regional titles to bookstores, schools & libraries, booksellers & non-traditional outlets.
ISBN Prefix(es): 978-0-932052; 978-0-925168; 978-0-9629159; 978-0-8478; 978-0-9760640
Number of titles published annually: 9 Print
Total Titles: 140 Print
Imprints: North Country Books; North Country Classics

**North Country Press**
126 Main St, Unity, ME 04988
SAN: 247-9680
Mailing Address: PO Box 501, Unity, ME 04988
*Tel:* 207-948-2208 *Fax:* 207-948-9000
*E-mail:* info@northcountrypress.com
*Web Site:* www.northcountrypress.com

*Key Personnel*
Publr: Patricia Newell
Founded: 1977
Regional press dealing with New England (specializing in Maine) subjects. Three lines: outdoor (hunting, fishing, etc); humor, lore; literature (mysteries, essays, poetry).
ISBN Prefix(es): 978-0-945980
Number of titles published annually: 5 Print
Total Titles: 42 Print

**North Light Books**
Division of F+W Media Inc
10151 Carver Rd, Suite 200, Blue Ash, OH 45242
*Tel:* 513-531-2690 *Toll Free Tel:* 800-666-0963 *Fax:* 513-891-7185 *Toll Free Fax:* 888-590-4082
*E-mail:* contact_us@fwmedia.com
*Web Site:* www.fwmedia.com
*Key Personnel*
Pres, Book Div: Sara Domville
SVP, Opers: Phil Graham
Dir, Trade Sales: Shawn Metts *E-mail:* shawn.metts@fwmedia.com
Communs Dir: Stacie Berger *E-mail:* stacie@fwmedia.com
Sales Admin: Mark Hoopler *Tel:* 513-531-2690 ext 11477 *E-mail:* mark.hoopler@fwmedia.com
Founded: 1958
Top-quality instructional books to help fine artists & graphic designers find personal satisfaction & professional success.
ISBN Prefix(es): 978-0-89134; 978-1-58180; 978-1-60061
Number of titles published annually: 600 Print
Total Titles: 6,000 Print
Imprints: HOW Books; Impact Books
*Returns:* F+W Media Inc, c/o Aero Fulfillment Services, 6023 Union Centre Blvd, West Chester, OH 45014
*Shipping Address:* F+W Media Inc, c/o Aero Fulfillment Services, 6023 Union Centre Blvd, West Chester, OH 45014

**North Point Press**
Imprint of Farrar, Straus & Giroux, LLC
18 W 18 St, 8th fl, New York, NY 10011
*Tel:* 212-741-6900 *Toll Free Tel:* 888-330-8477 *Fax:* 212-633-9385
*Web Site:* www.fsgbooks.com
*Key Personnel*
SVP, Mktg & Publicity: Jeff Seroy *Tel:* 212-741-6900 ext 6323
Dir, Publicity & Promo: Sarita Varma
VP, Contracts & Perms: Erika Seidman
Founded: 1981
Nonfiction, environment, nature, design, food, spirituality.
ISBN Prefix(es): 978-0-86547
Number of titles published annually: 10 Print
Foreign Rep(s): HarperCollins Publishers (Canada); Jacaranda Wiley Ltd (Australia); Orion Ltd (Worldwide)
Foreign Rights: Agence Hoffman (Ursula Bender) (Germany); Graal Literary Agency (Maria Strarz-Kanska) (Poland); The Deborah Harris Agency (Efrat Lev) (Israel); International Copyright Agency (Simona Kessler) (Romania); International Editors' Co (Isabel Monteagudo) (Argentina, Portugal, Spain); Katai & Bolza (Peter Bolza) (Hungary); KCC (MiSook Hong) (Korea); Leonhardt & Hoier (Anneli Hoier) (Denmark, Scandinavia); Literami Agentura (Kristin Olson) (Czech Republic); Riff Agency (Laura Paulo) (Brazil); Sebes & Van Gelderen Literary Agency (Mariska Kleinhoonte van Os) (Netherlands); Tuttle-Mori Agency Inc (Asako Kawachi) (Japan); Marco Vigevani Agenzia Letteraria (Marco Vigevani) (Italy)

**North River Press Publishing Corp**
27 Rosseter St, Great Barrington, MA 01230
SAN: 202-1048
Mailing Address: PO Box 567, Great Barrington, MA 01230-0567
*Tel:* 413-528-0034 *Toll Free Tel:* 800-486-2665 *Fax:* 413-528-3163 *Toll Free Fax:* 800-BOOK-FAX (266-5329)
*E-mail:* info@northriverpress.com
*Web Site:* www.northriverpress.com
*Key Personnel*
Pres: Laurence Gadd
VP: Amy Gallagher
Founded: 1971
General nonfiction, business books, hardcovers & paperback.
ISBN Prefix(es): 978-0-88427
Number of titles published annually: 6 Print
Total Titles: 40 Print; 1 Audio

**North Star Press of Saint Cloud Inc**
PO Box 451, St Cloud, MN 56302-0451
*Tel:* 320-558-9062 *Toll Free Tel:* 888-820-1636 *Fax:* 320-558-9063
*E-mail:* info@northstarpress.com
*Web Site:* www.northstarpress.com
*Key Personnel*
Publr: Corinne A Dwyer
Busn Mgr: Cecelia Dwyer
Ed: Brandon Paumen
Founded: 1969
Regional, women's issues, Minnesota history & fiction, Finnish ethnic, nature.
ISBN Prefix(es): 978-0-87839
Number of titles published annually: 50 Print; 40 E-Book
Total Titles: 500 Print; 55 E-Book
*Shipping Address:* 19485 Estes Rd, Clearwater, MN 55320
Membership(s): IBPA, the Independent Book Publishers Association; Midwest Independent Booksellers Association; Midwest Independent Publishers Association; Minnesota Library Association

**Northeast-Midwest Institute**
50 "F" St NW, Suite 950, Washington, DC 20001
*Tel:* 202-544-5200 *Fax:* 202-544-0043
*E-mail:* info@nemw.org
*Web Site:* www.nemw.org
*Key Personnel*
Pres: Allegra Cangelosi *Tel:* 202-464-4014 *E-mail:* acangel@nemw.org
Dir, Admin & Fin: Amy Brooks *Tel:* 202-464-4012 *E-mail:* abrooks@nemw.org
Founded: 1976
Energy, environment, economic development, human resources.
ISBN Prefix(es): 978-1-882061
Number of titles published annually: 3 Print
Total Titles: 50 Print

**Northern Illinois University Press**
2280 Bethany Rd, DeKalb, IL 60115
SAN: 202-8875
*Tel:* 815-753-1826; 815-753-1075 *Fax:* 815-753-1845
*Web Site:* www.niupress.niu.edu
*Key Personnel*
Dir: J Alex Schwartz *Tel:* 815-753-1075 *E-mail:* aschwartz@niu.edu
Mng Ed: Susan Bean *Tel:* 815-753-9908 *E-mail:* sbean@niu.edu
Ed: Amy Farranto *Tel:* 815-753-9946 *E-mail:* afarranto@niu.edu; Sara Hoerdeman *Tel:* 815-753-9907 *E-mail:* shoerdeman@niu.edu
Prodn & Design Mgr: Julia Fauci *Tel:* 815-753-9904 *E-mail:* jfauci@niu.edu
Founded: 1965
Publishes nonfiction on a variety of topics in the humanities, arts & social sciences. With more than 400 books in print, each year it brings out about twenty new books on aspects of history, politics, anthropology & literature. In fulfilling its broadly educational mission, the Press publishes books for inquiring general readers as well as for specialists.
ISBN Prefix(es): 978-0-87580
Number of titles published annually: 32 Print
Total Titles: 450 Print
Imprints: Switchgrass Books (literary fiction)
Foreign Rep(s): Eurospan (Europe, Middle East, UK); United Publishers Service Ltd (Japan, South Korea)
*Distribution Center:* Chicago Distribution Center, 11030 S Langley Ave, Chicago, IL 60628 *Toll Free Fax:* 800-621-8476 *E-mail:* orders@press.uchicago.edu
Membership(s): American Association for the Advancement of Slavic Studies; American Association of University Presses; American Historical Association; Organization of American Historians

**Northwestern University Press**
629 Noyes St, Evanston, IL 60208-4210
SAN: 202-5787
*Tel:* 847-491-2046 *Toll Free Tel:* 800-621-2736 (orders only) *Fax:* 847-491-8150
*E-mail:* nupress@northwestern.edu
*Web Site:* www.nupress.northwestern.edu
*Key Personnel*
Dir: Jane Bunker
Sr Ed & Asst Dir: Henry Carrigan *Tel:* 847-491-8112 *E-mail:* h-carrigan@northwestern.edu
Prodn Mgr: A C Racette *Tel:* 847-491-8113 *E-mail:* a-racette@northwestern.edu
Sales & Subs Rts Mgr: Parneshia Jones *Tel:* 847-471-7420 *E-mail:* p-jones3@northwestern.edu
Mktg & Publicity Mgr: Rudy Faust *Tel:* 847-467-0319 *E-mail:* r-faust@northwestern.edu
Founded: 1958
Scholarly books, with emphasis on literature & language, philosophy, works in translation, theatre.
ISBN Prefix(es): 978-0-8101
Number of titles published annually: 60 Print
Imprints: Curbstone Press, The Marlboro Press; TriQuarterly Books
Distributor for Lake Forrest College Press; Third World Press; Tia Chucha Press
*Distribution Center:* Chicago Distribution Center, 11030 S Langley, Chicago, IL 60628 *Toll Free Fax:* 800-621-8476
Membership(s): Association of American University Presses
*See separate listing for:*
**TriQuarterly Books**

**§W W Norton & Company Inc**
500 Fifth Ave, New York, NY 10110-0017
SAN: 202-5795
*Tel:* 212-354-5500 *Toll Free Tel:* 800-233-4830 (orders & cust serv) *Fax:* 212-869-0856 *Toll Free Fax:* 800-458-6515
*Web Site:* www.wwnorton.com
*Key Personnel*
Chair & Pres: W Drake McFeely
CFO & VP: Stephen King
VChair & VP, Coll Dept: Roby Harrington
VChair & VP, Trade Dept: Jeannie Luciano
EVP, National Book Co: Raymond E Worrell
VP & Edit Dir, Coll Dept: Julia Reidhead
VP & Dir, Sales & Mktg, Coll Dept: Stephen P Dunn
VP & Mgr, Intl Sales: Dorothy M Cook
VP & Mng Ed, Trade Dept: Nancy K Palmquist
VP & Dir, Prodn Dept: Tim McGuire
VP & Dir, Trade Prodn: Julia Druskin
VP & Art Dir, Trade Hardcover: Ingsu Liu
VP & Corp Art Dir: Debra Morton Hoyt
VP & Foreign Rts Mgr: Elisabeth Kerr
Assoc Dir, Subs Rts: Felice Mello
Cust Serv Mgr: Flossie Hallett

Perms Mgr: Elizabeth Clementson
Perms & Copyright Mgr: Claire Reinertsen
Contracts Mgr: Jessie Hughes
VP & Ed, Coll Dept: Carol Stiles Bemis; Jon Durbin; Stephen A Forman; Marilyn Moller; Maribeth Payne; Jack Repcheck; Peter J Simon
Assoc Dir, Electronic Media, Coll Dept: April Lange
Natl Sales Mgr, Coll Dept: Michael Wright
Busn Mgr, Coll Dept: Emily Turner
VP & Exec Ed: Alane Mason
VP & Exec Ed, Trade Dept: Jill Bialosky
VP & Ed, Trade Dept: Amy Cherry; Maria Guarnaschelli; Angela von der Lippe
VP & Dir, Natl Accts: Deirdre F Dolan
VP & Dir, Lib Sales & Mktg: Dosier D Hammond
VP & Dir, Sales & Mktg, Trade Dept: William F Rusin
VP & Exec Dir, Publicity & PR: Louise Brockett
Dir, Digital Mktg & Strategy: Peter Kay
Natl Field Sales Mgr, Trade Dept: Rick Raeber
Publicity Dir, Trade Dept: Elizabeth Riley
VP, Assoc Publg Dir: Nomi Victor
Publr & Ed-in-Chief, Liveright & Co: Robert Weil
Sales & Mktg Dir, Dist Servs: Eugenia Pakalik
Internet Acct Mgr: John Di Bello
Edit Dir, Prof Books Dept: Deborah A Malmud
Sr Ed, Prof Books in Architecture & Design: Nancy N Green
Assoc Mng Ed, Prof Books Dept: Andrea Costella
Mktg Mgr, Prof Books Dept: Kevin Olsen
VP & Dir, Opers: Jorie Krumpfer
Ed-in-Chief, Trade Dept: John Glusman
Sr Ed, Trade Dept: Brendan Curry; Tom Mayer
Sr Ed: Matt Weiland
CIO & VP: Ray Worrell
VP & Ed, Coll Dept: Karl Bakeman
Ed, Coll Dept: Erik Fahlgren; Aaron Javsicas; Ann Shin; Sheri Snavely; Betsy Twitchell
Dir, Electronic Media: Cliff Landesman *E-mail:* c.landesman@wwnorton.com
Assoc Dir, Electronic Media: Steve Hoge
Ed, Liveright & Co: Katie Henderson Adams
Cont: Katarzyna Kulikowski
HR: Jamie Finkelman
Founded: 1923
General nonfiction & fiction; trade paperbacks; college texts, professional books, architecture & interior design.
No unsol mss accepted.
ISBN Prefix(es): 978-0-393; 978-0-87140
Number of titles published annually: 400 Print; 110 E-Book
Total Titles: 4,800 Print; 75 CD-ROM; 600 E-Book
Imprints: Backcountry Publications; Countryman Press; Liveright & Co
*Foreign Office(s):* Castle House, 75/76 Wells St, London W1T 3QT, United Kingdom, Mng Dir & VP: Edward Crutchley *Tel:* (020) 7323 1579 *Fax:* (020) 7436 4553
Distributor for Airphoto International Ltd/ Odyssey Publications; Albatross Publishing House; Atlas & Co; Blue Guides Ltd; George Braziller Inc; Chess Information & Research Center; Dalkey Archive Press; Fantagraphics Books; Kales Press; New Directions Publishing Corp; Ontario Review Press; Peace Hill Press; Pegasus Books; Persea Books Inc; Pushcart Press; Quantuck Lane Press; Skyhorse Publishing; Thames & Hudson
Foreign Rep(s): APAC Publishers Services (Indonesia, Malaysia, Singapore); Everest International Publishing Services (China); Hardy Bigfoss International Co Ltd (Cambodia, Laos, Myanmar, Thailand, Vietnam); M K International Ltd (Japan); B K Norton Ltd (Korea, Taiwan); W W Norton & Company Ltd (UK) (Africa, Bangladesh, Europe, India, Ireland, Middle East, Pakistan, UK); Pansing Distribution Ptd Ltd (Malaysia, Singapore); Pearson Education (New Zealand); Penguin Books Canada Ltd (Canada); Transglobal Publishers Services Ltd (Hong Kong, Macau); US Pub Rep Inc (Caribbean, Central America, Mexico, South America); John Wiley & Sons Australia Ltd (Australia)
Foreign Rights: Akcali Copyright Agency (Turkey); L'Autre Agence (France); Carmen Balcells Agencia Literaria (Portugal, Spain); Bardon Chinese Media Agency (China, Taiwan); Graal Literary Agency (Poland); The Deborah Harris Agency (Israel); International Copyright Agency (Romania); Japan UNI Agency (Japan); Katai & Bolza (Hungary); Duran Kim Agency (Korea); Mohrbooks (Germany); Nordin Agency (Scandinavia); Andrew Nurnberg Associates (Baltic States, Bulgaria, Russia); Olson Literary Agents (Czech Republic); The Riff Agency (Brazil); Roberto Santachiara Literary Agency (Italy); Marianne Schonbach Literary Agency (Netherlands)
*Advertising Agency:* Verso Advertising
*Shipping Address:* National Book Co Inc, Keystone Industrial Park, Scranton, PA 18512
*See separate listing for:*
**The Countryman Press**

**Norwood House Press**
PO Box 316598, Chicago, IL 60631
*Tel:* 773-467-0837 *Toll Free Tel:* 866-565-2900 *Fax:* 773-467-9686 *Toll Free Fax:* 866-565-2901
*E-mail:* customerservice@norwoodhousepress.com
*Web Site:* www.norwoodhousepress.com
Founded: 2005
Publisher specializing in children's books for the school & library.
ISBN Prefix(es): 978-1-59953
Number of titles published annually: 75 Print; 50 E-Book
Total Titles: 163 Print; 50 E-Book

**Nova Press**
9058 Lloyd Place, West Hollywood, CA 90069
*Tel:* 310-275-3513 *Toll Free Tel:* 800-949-6175 *Fax:* 310-281-5629
*E-mail:* novapress@aol.com
*Web Site:* www.novapress.net
*Key Personnel*
Pres & Electronic Publg: Jeff Kolby
Founded: 1993
Publishes test prep books, software, phone apps & online courses for the SAT, GRE, LSAT, GMAT, MCAT & TOEFL.
ISBN Prefix(es): 978-1-889057
Total Titles: 24 Print; 6 CD-ROM; 22 Online; 24 E-Book

**Nova Publishing Co**
1103 W College St, Carbondale, IL 62901
SAN: 695-8117
*Tel:* 618-457-3521 *Toll Free Tel:* 800-748-1175 (cust serv) *Fax:* 618-457-2552
*E-mail:* info@novapublishing.com
*Web Site:* www.novapublishing.com
*Key Personnel*
CFO: Janet Sitarz
Mgr: Melanie Bray *E-mail:* melanie@novapublishing.com
Founded: 1986
Publisher of small business & consumer legal books & software.
ISBN Prefix(es): 978-0-935755; 978-1-892949
Number of titles published annually: 6 Print
Total Titles: 35 Print
Imprints: Earthpress
*Shipping Address:* National Book Network, 15200 NBN Way, Blue Ridge Summit, PA 17214 *Tel:* 717-394-3800 *Toll Free Tel:* 800-462-6420 *Toll Free Fax:* 800-338-4550 *Web Site:* www.nbnbooks.com
Membership(s): IBPA, the Independent Book Publishers Association

**Nova Science Publishers Inc**
400 Oser Ave, Suite 1600, Hauppauge, NY 11788-3619
*Tel:* 631-231-7269 *Fax:* 631-231-8175
*E-mail:* main@novapublishers.com
*Web Site:* www.novapublishers.com
*Key Personnel*
Pres: Nadia Columbus
Founded: 1985
Scientific, technical, medical & social sciences publishing; trade books - hardcover & softcover.
ISBN Prefix(es): 978-0-941743
Number of titles published annually: 2,000 Print; 10 CD-ROM
Total Titles: 20,000 Print
Imprints: Noel Press; Nova Biomedical Press; Nova Global Affairs Press; Nova History Press; Nova Music; Nova Science Books; Novinka Books; Snova Books; Troitsa Books

**NPS**, see BrickHouse Books Inc

**NRP®**, see National Register Publishing

**nursesbooks.org, The Publishing Program of ANA**
Division of American Nurses Association
8515 Georgia Ave, Suite 400, Silver Spring, MD 20910-3492
*Tel:* 301-628-5000 *Toll Free Tel:* 800-924-9053; 800-637-0323 (orders) *Fax:* 301-628-5001
*E-mail:* anp@ana.org
*Web Site:* www.nursesbooks.org; www.nursingworld.org
*Key Personnel*
Publr: Rosanne Roe
Ed & Proj Mgr: Eric Wurzbacher *E-mail:* eric.wurzbacher@ana.org
Health care & nursing.
ISBN Prefix(es): 978-1-55810
Number of titles published annually: 8 Print
Total Titles: 45 Print

**NYBG Press**, see The New York Botanical Garden Press

**§Nystrom Herff Jones Education Division**
4719 W 62 St, Indianapolis, IN 46268-2593
SAN: 203-5529
*Tel:* 317-612-3901 *Toll Free Tel:* 800-621-8086 (cust serv) *Fax:* 317-329-3305
*E-mail:* info@nystromnet.com
*Web Site:* www.nystromnet.com
*Key Personnel*
Pres: Joe Slaughter
Dir, Mktg: Don Rescigno *E-mail:* dprescigno@herffjones.com
Founded: 1903
Social studies, history & geography programs, maps, globes, atlases & multimedia.
ISBN Prefix(es): 978-0-7825; 978-0-88463
Number of titles published annually: 3 Print
Total Titles: 50 Print; 5 CD-ROM; 1 E-Book

**§OAG Worldwide**
3025 Highland Pkwy, Suite 200, Downers Grove, IL 60515-5561
*Tel:* 630-515-5300 *Toll Free Tel:* 800-342-5624 (cust serv) *Fax:* 630-515-3251
*E-mail:* contactus@oag.com
*Web Site:* www.oag.com
Founded: 1929
Supplier of independent travel info.
ISBN Prefix(es): 978-0-9776295

Number of titles published annually: 11 Print; 5 CD-ROM; 5 Online
Total Titles: 11 Print; 5 CD-ROM; 5 Online
*Foreign Office(s):* 18F, Caroline Centre, Lee Gardens Two, 28 Yun Ping Rd, Causeway Bay, Hong Kong *Tel:* 2965 1700 *Fax:* 2965 1777 *E-mail:* custsvcaspac@oag.com
Toranomon, 40 MT Bldg 9F, 5-13-1 Toranomon, Minato ku, Tokyo 105-0001, Japan *Tel:* 36402 7301 *Fax:* 36402 7302 *E-mail:* acustsvcjpn@oag.com
3 Lim Teck Kim Rd, No 10-01, Singapore Technologies Bldg, Singapore 088934, Singapore *Tel:* 6395-5868 *Fax:* 6293-6566 *E-mail:* custsvcsaspac@oag.com
Church St, Dunstable, Bedfordshire LU5 4HB, United Kingdom (headquarters) *Tel:* (01582) 600111 *Fax:* (01582) 695230 *E-mail:* customers@oag.com

**Oak Knoll Press**
310 Delaware St, New Castle, DE 19720
*Tel:* 302-328-7232 *Toll Free Tel:* 800-996-2556 *Fax:* 302-328-7274
*E-mail:* oakknoll@oakknoll.com
*Web Site:* www.oakknoll.com
*Key Personnel*
Pres: Robert D Fleck *E-mail:* bob@oakknoll.com
Publg Dir: Laura Williams *E-mail:* laura@oakknoll.com
Antiquarian & Lib Sales: Robert Fleck, III *E-mail:* rob@oakknoll.com
Founded: 1976
Publish scholarly books (books about books), bibliographies, book arts & book history.
ISBN Prefix(es): 978-1-884718; 978-1-58456
Number of titles published annually: 25 Print
Total Titles: 1,100 Print; 1 CD-ROM
Distributor for American Antiquarian Society; Bibliographical Society of America; Bibliographical Society of University of Virginia; The Bibliographical Society (UK); Block Museum; Boston College; John Carter Brown Library; Bryn Mawr College; Catalpa Press; Caxton Club; Center for Book Arts; Chapin Library; Fondation Custodia; The Grolier Club; Hes & De Graaf; Historic New Orleans Collection; Library of Congress-Center for the Book; The Manuscript Society; New England Bibliographies; Providence Athenaeum; Rivendale Press; Tate Galleries; Texas State Historical Association; Typophiles; Winterthur Museum; Yushodo Press
Membership(s): AAP; Antiquarian Booksellers Association of America; International League of Antiquarian Booksellers

**Oak Tree Press**
140 E Palmer St, Taylorville, IL 62568
*Tel:* 217-824-6500
*E-mail:* publisher@oaktreebooks.com; info@oaktreebooks.com; query@oaktreebooks.com; pressdept@oaktreebooks.com; bookorders@oaktreebooks.com
*Web Site:* www.oaktreebooks.com; www.otpblog.blogspot.com
*Key Personnel*
Publr: Ms Billie Johnson
PR Mgr: Jeana Thompson *Tel:* 217-825-4489
Acqs Ed: Ms Sunny Frazier
Ed: Marilyn Olsen *E-mail:* coptaleseditor@oaktreebooks.com
Off Mgr: Suzanne Yazell *E-mail:* officemanager@oaktreebooks.com
Founded: 1998
Independent press that publishes fiction & nonfiction. Emphasis on mysteries & romances with series potential, business books, self help & how-to.
ISBN Prefix(es): 978-1-892343; 978-1-61009
Number of titles published annually: 50 Print; 50 E-Book
Total Titles: 200 Print; 200 E-Book
Imprints: Acorn (children's books); Coptales (stories by & about law enforcement professionals...cops, medical examiners, criminal defense attorneys, DAs); Dark Oak Mysteries (all mystery genres, from amateur sleuths to hard-boiled detectives); Mystic Oaks (paranormal mysteries & romances); Oak Tree Books (mainstream fiction, how-to, memoir, self-help); Timeless Love (all romance genres, from sweet to steamy); Wild Oak (western)
Membership(s): Sisters in Crime

**Oaklea Press**
Unit of Oaklea Press Inc
41 Old Mill Rd, Richmond, VA 23226-3111
*Tel:* 804-308-3906 *Fax:* 804-980-7057
*Web Site:* oakleapress.com
*Key Personnel*
Publr: Stephen H Martin *E-mail:* shmartin@oakleapress.com
Founded: 1995
Tradebook publisher.
ISBN Prefix(es): 978-1-892538; 978-0-9646601; 978-0-9664098
Number of titles published annually: 6 Print; 8 E-Book; 6 Audio
Total Titles: 45 Print; 8 E-Book; 6 Audio
Imprints: New Marketplace; Oaklea Press
*Sales Office(s):* Delphi Distribution, 1263 Southwest Blvd, Kansas City, KS 66103, Contact: Amanda Garcia *Toll Free Tel:* 866-463-8541 *E-mail:* agarcia@delphidistribution.com *Web Site:* www.delphidistribution.com
*Distribution Center:* Delphi Distribution, 1263 Southwest Blvd, Kansas City, KS 66103, Contact: Amanda Garcia *Toll Free Tel:* 866-463-8541 *E-mail:* agarcia@delphidistribution.com *Web Site:* www.delphidistribution.com
Membership(s): IBPA, the Independent Book Publishers Association

**§Oakstone Publishing LLC**
Division of Boston Ventures
100 Corporate Pkwy, Suite 600, Birmingham, AL 35242
*Toll Free Tel:* 800-633-4743 *Fax:* 205 995-1926
*E-mail:* service@oakstonemedical.com
*Web Site:* www.oakstonepublishing.com; www.cmeonly.com; www.cdeonly.com
*Key Personnel*
CEO & Pres: Diane Munson
CFO & EVP: Donnie Parkerson
SVP, Opers & HR: Connie Fleming *Tel:* 205-437-3015
VP & Publr: Marianne Kerr
VP, Corp Devt: H Montgomery Rains
Founded: 1975
Produce board review programs for medical specialties.
Number of titles published annually: 20 CD-ROM; 4 Online; 5 Audio
Total Titles: 46 CD-ROM; 12 Online; 42 Audio
Imprints: Clinical Advances; Inservice Reviews; Journalbytes.com; MKSAP® Audio Companion; MultiMedia Reviews®; Practical Reviews®; QuickScan Reviews®; Select; SESAP Audio Companion; Topic Series
Membership(s): Specialized Information Publishers Association

**Oberlin College Press**
Subsidiary of Oberlin College
50 N Professor St, Oberlin, OH 44074-1091
SAN: 212-1883
*Tel:* 440-775-8408 *Fax:* 440-775-8124
*E-mail:* oc.press@oberlin.edu
*Web Site:* www.oberlin.edu/ocpress
*Key Personnel*
Mng Ed & Intl Rts Contact: Marco Wilkinson
First Ed: David Young
Ed: David Walker
Assoc Ed: Pamela Alexander; Kazim Ali; DeSales Harrison
Ed-at-Large: Martha Collins
Founded: 1969
Poetry in translation; contemporary American poetry.
ISBN Prefix(es): 978 0 932440
Number of titles published annually: 3 Print
Total Titles: 55 Print
Distributed by University Press of New England (UPNE)
*Orders to:* University Press of New England (UPNE), One Court St, Suite 250, Lebanon, NH 03766 *Toll Free Tel:* 800-421-1561 *Fax:* 603-448-9429 *Web Site:* www.upne.com
*Returns:* University Press of New England (UPNE), c/o Maple Logistics Solutions, Lebanon Distribution Ctr, 704 Legionaire Dr, Fredericksburg, PA 17026 *Tel:* 603-448-1533 ext 503 *Fax:* 603-448-9429
Membership(s): Council of Literary Magazines & Presses

**Ocean Press**
511 Avenue of the Americas, Suite 96, New York, NY 10011-8436
*Tel:* 212-260-3690
*E-mail:* info@oceanbooks.com.au; orders@oceanbooks.com.au (orders only)
*Web Site:* www.oceanbooks.com.au
*Key Personnel*
Dir & Publr: Deborah Shnookal
Founded: 1990
ISBN Prefix(es): 978-1-875284; 978-1-876175; 978-1-920888; 978-1-921235
Number of titles published annually: 30 Print
Total Titles: 260 Print
*Foreign Office(s):* PO Box 1015, North Melbourne, Victoria 3051, Australia *Tel:* (03) 9326 4280 *Fax:* (03) 9329 5040
Immobiliaria Jardines de 5ta, Avenida 5ta y 114, Apartamento 135, Playa, Havana, Cuba *Tel:* (07) 204-1324
Distributed by Consortium Book Sales & Distribution

**Ocean Publishing**
Division of The Gromling Group Inc
PO Box 1080, Flagler Beach, FL 32136-1080
SAN: 254-8755
*Tel:* 386-517-1600
*E-mail:* publisher@oceanpublishing.org
*Web Site:* www.oceanpublishing.org
*Key Personnel*
Publr: Frank Gromling
Founded: 2002
Traditional publisher of quality nonfiction books about nature, marine life, environment & conservation.
ISBN Prefix(es): 978-0-9717; 978-0-9767
Number of titles published annually: 4 Print
Total Titles: 26 Print; 10 E-Book
Foreign Rights: Independent Publishers Group (Worldwide)
*Distribution Center:* Independent Publishers Group, 814 N Franklin St, Chicago, IL 60610 *Tel:* 312-337-0747 *Fax:* 312-337-5985
Membership(s): Florida Publishers Association Inc; IBPA, the Independent Book Publishers Association

**Ocean Tree Books**
1325 Cerro Gordo Rd, Santa Fe, NM 87501
Mailing Address: PO Box 1295, Santa Fe, NM 87504 SAN: 241-0478
*Tel:* 505-983-1412 *Fax:* 505-983-0899
*Web Site:* www.oceantree.com
*Key Personnel*
Dir: Richard Polese *E-mail:* richard@oceantree.com
Publicity & Mktg: Hudson White
Off Mgr: Martin Burch

Founded: 1983
General trade with emphasis on Southwestern & Southern travel, faith & spirit & peacemaking. Distribution Centers: Baker & Taylor, Books West LLC & New Leaf Distributing Co.
ISBN Prefix(es): 978-0-943734; 978-0-9712548
Number of titles published annually: 5 Print
Total Titles: 60 Print
Imprints: Adventure Roads Travel; OTB Legacy Editions; Peacewatch Editions
Distributed by Treasure Chest Books
Foreign Rep(s): Blessingway Author Services (Worldwide)
Foreign Rights: Blessingway Author Services
Membership(s): IBPA, the Independent Book Publishers Association; New Mexico Book Association; Publishers Association of the West

**Oceana®**
Division of Oxford University Press USA
Law Division, 13th fl, 198 Madison Ave, New York, NY 10016-4314
SAN: 202-5744
*Tel:* 212-726-6000 *Toll Free Tel:* 800-451-7556 (orders only) *Fax:* 212-726-6457 (edit)
*E-mail:* oxfordonline@oup.com; custserv.us@oup.com
*Web Site:* www.oup.com/us
*Key Personnel*
VP & Publr: Peter Berkery, Jr *E-mail:* peter.berkery@oup.com
Founded: 1946
Legal publisher of international business & trade; investments & banking; arbitration & litigation; intellectual property; comparative law; constitutional law; environmental law; legal research & reference tools, legal history, law for the layperson, treaties, white collar crime; looseleaf & online services; monographs & multi-volume reference sets.
ISBN Prefix(es): 978-0-379; 978-0-19
Number of titles published annually: 45 Print; 2 Online
Total Titles: 100 Print; 10 Online; 1 E-Book

**Oceanview Publishing**
CEO Center at Mediterranean Plaza, Suite 120-G, 595 Bay Isles Rd, Longboat Key, FL 34228
*Tel:* 941-387-8500 *Fax:* 941 387-0039
*Web Site:* www.oceanviewpub.com
Founded: 2006
ISBN Prefix(es): 978-1-933515; 978-1-60809
Number of titles published annually: 12 Print
Total Titles: 52 Print
*Billing Address:* Midpoint Trade Books, c/o Leisure Arts, 5701 Ranch Dr, Little Rock, AR 72223 *Tel:* 501-868-8800 ext 259 *Fax:* 501-877-5603 *E-mail:* customerorders@leisurearts.com
*Distribution Center:* Midpoint Trade Books, c/o Leisure Arts, 5701 Ranch Dr, Little Rock, AR 72223 *Tel:* 501-868-8800 ext 259 *Fax:* 501-877-5603 *E-mail:* customerorders@leisurearts.com
Membership(s): International Thriller Writers Inc; Mystery Writers of America

**§OCP**
5536 NE Hassalo St, Portland, OR 97213
*Tel:* 503-281-1191 *Toll Free Tel:* 800-548-8749 *Fax:* 503-282-3486 *Toll Free Fax:* 800-843-8181
*E-mail:* liturgy@ocp.org
*Web Site:* www.ocp.org
*Key Personnel*
Publr: John Limb *E-mail:* jlimb@ocp.org
Mktg Mgr: Monica Rada *E-mail:* mrada@ocp.org
Cust Serv Mgr: Tim Dooley *Tel:* 503-460-5489 *E-mail:* tdooley@ocp.org
Founded: 1922
Books of music & liturgy.
ISBN Prefix(es): 978-0-915531
Number of titles published annually: 25 Print; 25 Audio
Total Titles: 500 Print; 1 CD-ROM; 1 Online; 2,500 Audio
Imprints: Pastoral Press
Foreign Rights: Decani Music; Rainbow Book Agencies (Australia); Universal Songs (England, Europe, Ireland, UK)
Membership(s): CBA; CMPA

**Octane Press**
808 Kinney Ave, Austin, TX 78704
*Tel:* 512-334-9441 *Fax:* 512-852-4737
*E-mail:* info@octanepress.com
*Web Site:* www.octanepress.com
*Key Personnel*
Publr: Lee Klancher *E-mail:* lee@octanepress.com
Ed: Tobias Gros *E-mail:* tobias@octanepress.com
Designer: Tom Heffron *E-mail:* tom@octanepress.com
Print Buyer: Joe Sita *E-mail:* joe@octanepress.com
Founded: 2010
Niche book publisher.
ISBN Prefix(es): 978-0-9821733; 978-0-9829131; 978-1-937747
Number of titles published annually: 10 Print; 5 E-Book
Total Titles: 18 Print; 10 E-Book
Foreign Rep(s): Star Book Sales (Europe)
Membership(s): IBPA, the Independent Book Publishers Association; Motorsports Press Guild

**Odyssey Books**
Division of The Ciletti Publishing Group Inc
2421 Redwood Ct, Longmont, CO 80503-8155
*Tel:* 720-494-1473 *Fax:* 720-494-1471
*E-mail:* books@odysseybooks.net
*Web Site:* cilettipublishinggroup.com
*Key Personnel*
Pres & Publr: Barbara Ciletti *E-mail:* barbaraj@odysseybooks.net
Promo: Erin Jones
Founded: 1995
Provides fiction & nonfiction for the retail trade, library, education & consumer markets.
ISBN Prefix(es): 978-0-9768655
Number of titles published annually: 20 Print
Membership(s): ABA; ALA; CMN; IBPA, the Independent Book Publishers Association; International Reading Association; National Council of Teachers of English; National Science Teachers Association

**OECD Washington Center**, see Organization for Economic Cooperation & Development

**Ohio Genealogical Society**
611 State Rte 97 W, Bellville, OH 44813-8813
*Tel:* 419-886-1903 *Fax:* 419-886-0092
*E-mail:* ogs@ogs.org
*Web Site:* www.ogs.org
*Key Personnel*
Pres: Funda Peters
Lib Dir: Thomas Stephen Neel
Founded: 1959
Family history library & society.
ISBN Prefix(es): 978-0-935057
Number of titles published annually: 3 Print
Total Titles: 25 Print

**Ohio State University Foreign Language Publications**
Division of Foreign Language Center
198 Hagerty Hall, 1775 College Rd, Columbus, OH 43210-1340
*Tel:* 614-292-3838 *Toll Free Tel:* 800-678-6999 *Fax:* 614-688-3355
*E-mail:* flpubs@osu.edu
*Web Site:* www.flpubs.osu.edu
*Key Personnel*
Pubns Mgr: Lauren Barrett
Founded: 1972
Foreign language individualized instruction materials for less commonly taught languages.
ISBN Prefix(es): 978-0-87415
Number of titles published annually: 5 Print
Total Titles: 280 Print

**Ohio State University Press**
180 Pressey Hall, 1070 Carmack Rd, Columbus, OH 43210-1002
*Tel:* 614-292-6930 *Fax:* 614-292-2065 *Toll Free Fax:* 800-621-8476
*E-mail:* info@osupress.org
*Web Site:* ohiostatepress.org
*Key Personnel*
Dir: Malcolm Litchfield *Tel:* 614-292-7818 *E-mail:* ml@osupress.org
Mng Ed: Eugene O'Connor, PhD *Tel:* 614-292-3667 *E-mail:* eugene@osupress.org
Mktg Dir: Laurie Avery *Tel:* 614-292-1462 *E-mail:* laurie.avery@osupress.org
Asst Dir: Kathy Edwards *Tel:* 614-292-3692 *E-mail:* edwards@osupress.org
Founded: 1957
General scholarly & trade nonfiction & fiction; classics.
ISBN Prefix(es): 978-0-8142
Number of titles published annually: 30 Print
Total Titles: 270 Print
Foreign Rep(s): East-West Export Books
*Distribution Center:* University of Chicago Distribution Center, 11030 S Langley Ave, Chicago, IL 60628 *Tel:* 773-568-1550 *Toll Free Tel:* 800-621-2736 *Fax:* 773-702-7212

**Ohio University Press**
215 Columbus Rd, Suite 101, Athens, OH 45701-2979
*Tel:* 740-593-1154 *Fax:* 740-593-4536
*Web Site:* www.ohioswallow.com
*Key Personnel*
Exec Ed: Kevin Haworth
Sr Ed: Gillian Berchowitz *Tel:* 740-593-1159 *E-mail:* gillianberchowitz@ohio.edu
Mng Ed: Nancy Basmajian *E-mail:* nbasmajia1@ohio.edu
Busn Mgr & Foreign Rts: Kristi Goldsberry *E-mail:* goldsbek@ohio.edu
Mktg Mgr: Sarah Welsch
Perms Spec: Sally Welch
Founded: 1964
Publisher of scholarly & trade books.
ISBN Prefix(es): 978-0-8214; 978-0-8040; 978-0-89680; 978-0-940717
Number of titles published annually: 50 Print
Total Titles: 600 Print
Imprints: Swallow Press
Foreign Rep(s): East-West Export Books (Asia, Australia, New Zealand, Pacific Region); Eurospan (Africa, Continental Europe, Middle East, UK)
*Orders to:* Chicago Distribution Center, 11030 S Langley Ave, Chicago, IL 60628 *Tel:* 773-702-7000 *Toll Free Tel:* 800-621-2736 *Fax:* 773-702-7212 *Toll Free Fax:* 800-621-8476
*Warehouse:* Chicago Distribution Center, 11030 S Langley Ave, Chicago, IL 60628 *Toll Free Tel:* 800-621-2736 *Toll Free Fax:* 800-621-8476
Membership(s): American Association of University Presses
*See separate listing for:*
**Swallow Press**

**Old Barn Enterprises Inc**
600 Kelly Rd, Carthage, NC 28327
*Tel:* 910-947-2587 *Fax:* 480-287-9017
*E-mail:* jeffandpam@nynphotoschool.com
*Web Site:* www.nynphotoschool.com

*Key Personnel*
Pres: Jeff Farr
Founded: 1992
Publish, professional books, home study courses, photography & marketing.
ISBN Prefix(es): 978-1-879009
Number of titles published annually: 3 Print
Total Titles: 8 Print
Imprints: Old Barn Publishing, Scots Plaid Press

**§Olde & Oppenheim Publishers**
3219 N Margate Place, Chandler, AZ 85224
*E-mail:* olde_oppenheim@hotmail.com
*Web Site:* oldeandoppenheimpublishers.com
*Key Personnel*
Dir, Mktg: Mike Gratz
Animation, satire, slice-of-life.
ISBN Prefix(es): 978-0-944861
Number of titles published annually: 3 Print; 2 CD-ROM; 2 Online; 2 E-Book
Total Titles: 13 Print

**The Oliver Press Inc**
Charlotte Sq, 5707 W 36 St, Minneapolis, MN 55416-2510
*Tel:* 952-926-8981 *Toll Free Tel:* 800-8-OLIVER (865-4837) *Fax:* 952-926-8965
*E-mail:* orders@oliverpress.com
*Web Site:* www.oliverpress.com
*Key Personnel*
Publr & Ed: Mark Lerner *E-mail:* mark@oliverpress.com
Admin: Charles Helgesen *E-mail:* charles@oliverpress.com
Founded: 1991
Nonfiction children's books.
ISBN Prefix(es): 978-1-881508
Number of titles published annually: 10 Print
Total Titles: 100 Print
Imprints: Clara House Books
Foreign Rights: John Reed Book Distribution (Australia)

**OMNI Publishers Inc**
29131 Bulverde Rd, San Antonio, TX 78260
Mailing Address: PO Box 408, Bulverde, TX 78163
*Tel:* 210-778-4437 *Fax:* 830-438-4645
*Web Site:* www.omnipublishers.com; www.educatorethicsseries.com
*Key Personnel*
Owner: Ruth Lansing
Gen Mgr: Jim Lansing *E-mail:* jim@omnipublishers.com
Founded: 1989
Books on law & real estate, national education products, Texas law.
ISBN Prefix(es): 978-1-891172
Number of titles published annually: 25 Print
Total Titles: 65 Print

**Omnibus Press**
Division of Music Sales Ltd
257 Park Ave S, 20th fl, New York, NY 10010
*Tel:* 212-254-2100 *Toll Free Tel:* 800-431-7187 *Fax:* 212-254-2013 *Toll Free Fax:* 800-345-6842
*E-mail:* info-us@omnibuspress.com
*Web Site:* www.musicsales.com; omnibuspressusa.com
*Key Personnel*
Pres: Barrie Edwards
VP, Admin & Opers: Denise Maurin
Founded: 1976
Pop culture, music & film books.
ISBN Prefix(es): 978-0-8256; 978-0-7119; 978-0-86001; 978-1-84449
Number of titles published annually: 30 Print
Total Titles: 500 Print
Distributor for Big Meteor; Gramophone
*Distribution Center:* Music Sales Distribution Center, 445 Bellvale Rd, Chester, NY 10918
*Tel:* 845-469-4699 *Toll Free Tel:* 800-431-7187 *Fax:* 845-469-7544 *Toll Free Fax:* 800-345-6842 *E-mail:* info@musicsales.com *Web Site:* www.musicsales.com

**Omnidawn Publishing**
1632 Elm Ave, Richmond, CA 94805-1614
SAN: 299-3236
*Tel:* 510-237-5472 *Toll Free Tel:* 800-792-4957 *Fax:* 510-232-8525
*E-mail:* manager@omnidawn.com
*Web Site:* www.omnidawn.com
*Key Personnel*
Founder & Publr: Kenneth Keegan *E-mail:* kkeegan@omnidawn.com; Rusty Morrison *E-mail:* rusty@omnidawn.com
Asst Ed: Rebecca Stoddard *E-mail:* rstoddard@omnidawn.com
Founded: 1996
Publishers of poetry & fabulist & new wave fabulist fiction.
ISBN Prefix(es): 978-1-890650
Number of titles published annually: 7 Print
Total Titles: 21 Print
*Distribution Center:* Independent Publishers Group (IPG), 814 N Franklin St, Chicago, IL 60610 *Tel:* 312-337-0747 *Toll Free Tel:* 800-888-4741 *Fax:* 312-337-5985 *E-mail:* frontdesk@ipgbook.com *Web Site:* www.ipgbook.com

**Omnigraphics Inc**
155 W Congress, Suite 200, Detroit, MI 48226
SAN: 249-2520
*Tel:* 313-961-1340 *Toll Free Tel:* 800-234-1340 (cust serv) *Fax:* 313-961-1383 *Toll Free Fax:* 800-875-1340 (cust serv)
*E-mail:* info@omnigraphics.com
*Web Site:* www.omnigraphics.com
*Key Personnel*
Founder & Chmn: Frederick G Ruffner, Jr
Founder & Publr: Peter E Ruffner *E-mail:* peter@omnigraphics.com
SVP: Matthew Barbour *E-mail:* matt@omnigraphics.com
Opers Mgr: Kevin Hayes
Founded: 1985
Reference books, periodicals & journals for libraries & schools, directories.
ISBN Prefix(es): 978-1-55888; 978-0-7808
Number of titles published annually: 40 Print; 1 Online
Total Titles: 400 Print; 1 Online
*Advertising Agency:* Marley & Cratchit
*Orders to:* PO Box 625, Holmes, PA 19043
*Returns:* 2050 Elmwood Ave, Sharon Hill, PA 19079

**Omohundro Institute of Early American History & Culture**
Swem Library, Ground fl, 400 Landrum Dr, Williamsburg, VA 23185
Mailing Address: PO Box 8781, Williamsburg, VA 23187-8781 SAN: 201-5161
*Tel:* 757-221-1110 *Fax:* 757-221-1047
*E-mail:* ieahc1@wm.edu
*Web Site:* oieahc.wm.edu
*Key Personnel*
Dir: Karin A Wulf *Tel:* 757-221-1133
Ed, Pubns: Fredrika J Teute *Tel:* 757-221-1118 *E-mail:* fjteut@wm.edu
Founded: 1943
Scholarly books on early American history culture & literature 1500-1815. Founded & still sponsored jointly by the College of William & Mary & the Colonial Williamsburg Foundation.
ISBN Prefix(es): 978-0-910776
Number of titles published annually: 4 Print
Total Titles: 205 Print
Distributed by The University of North Carolina Press

**§OneSource**
Division of Infogroup
300 Baker Ave, Concord, MA 01742
*Tel:* 978-318-4300 *Toll Free Tel:* 866-354-6936 *Fax:* 978-318-4690
*E-mail:* sales@onesource.com
*Web Site:* www.onesource.com
*Key Personnel*
Pres: Philip Garlick
SVP, Global Sales & Serv: Colleen Honan
Founded: 1984
Database of approximately 50,000 US technicians manufacturers, developers & services.
ISBN Prefix(es): 978-1-57114
Number of titles published annually: 5 Online
Total Titles: 5 CD-ROM; 5 Online
*Foreign Office(s):* Citigroup Ctr, Level 39, 2 Park St, Sydney, NSW 2000, Australia *Tel:* (02) 9004 7868 *Fax:* (02) 9004 7070
Global Business Park, MG Rd, Gurgaon 122002, India *Tel:* 987 1046415
208-A Telok Ayer St, Singapore 068642, Singapore *Tel:* 6221 7920 *Fax:* 6221 7929
55 Old Broad St, 3rd fl, London EC2M 1RX, United Kingdom *Tel:* (0207) 382 8800 *Fax:* (0207) 382 8801

**Online Training Solutions Inc (OTSI)**
2217 152 Ave NE, Redmond, WA 98052
Mailing Address: PO Box 951, Bellevue, WA 98009-0951
*Toll Free Tel:* 888-308-6874 *Toll Free Fax:* 888-308-6875
*Web Site:* www.otsi.com
*Key Personnel*
Pres: Joan Lambert
Founded: 1987
Educational & professional book publisher.
ISBN Prefix(es): 978-1-879399; 978-1-58278
Number of titles published annually: 12 Print
Total Titles: 60 Print
*Returns:* 602 Bellevue Way SE, Bellevue, WA 98004
Membership(s): Women's Business Enterprise National Council

**§Ooligan Press**
Portland State University, 369 Neuberger Hall, 724 SW Harrison St, Portland, OR 97201
*Tel:* 503-725-9748 *Fax:* 503-725-3561
*E-mail:* ooligan@ooliganpress.pdx.edu
*Web Site:* ooligan.pdx.edu
*Key Personnel*
Prog Dir: Dennis Stovall *E-mail:* stovall@pdx.edu
Founded: 2001
ISBN Prefix(es): 978-1-932010
Number of titles published annually: 6 Print; 6 E-Book
Total Titles: 30 Print
*Orders to:* Ingram Publisher Services, One Ingram Blvd, La Vergne, TN 37086-1986 *Toll Free Tel:* 866-400-5351
Membership(s): Association of Writers and Writing Programs; Publishers Association of the West

**Open Court**
Division of Carus Publishing Co
70 E Lake St, Suite 300, Chicago, IL 60601
*Tel:* 312-701-1720 *Toll Free Tel:* 800-815-2280 (orders only) *Fax:* 312-701-1728
*E-mail:* opencourt@caruspub.com
*Web Site:* www.opencourtbooks.com
*Key Personnel*
Edit Dir: David Ramsay Steele
Ed: Kerri Mommer
Founded: 1887
Academic philosophy, popular culture & philosophy.
ISBN Prefix(es): 978-0-87548; 978-0-912050; 978-0-89688; 978-0-8126
Number of titles published annually: 20 Print

Total Titles: 350 Print
*Orders to:* 30 Grove St, Suite C, Peterborough, NH 03458 *Fax:* 603-924-7380

**Open Horizons Publishing Co**
PO Box 2887, Taos, NM 87571
*Tel:* 575-751-3398 *Fax:* 575-751-3100
*E-mail:* info@bookmarket.com
*Web Site:* www.bookmarket.com
*Key Personnel*
Owner & Publr: John Kremer
*E-mail:* johnkremer@bookmarket.com
Assoc Publr & Lib Sales Dir: Gail Berry
Mktg Dir: Bob Sanny
Founded: 1982
Books for publishers & direct marketers.
ISBN Prefix(es): 978-0-912411
Number of titles published annually: 3 Print; 3 CD-ROM; 3 Online; 40 E-Book; 3 Audio
Total Titles: 21 Print; 16 CD-ROM; 6 Online; 43 E-Book; 12 Audio
Distributed by National Book Network
Membership(s): The Association of Publishers for Special Sales; IBPA, the Independent Book Publishers Association

**Open Road Publishing**
PO Box 284, Cold Spring Harbor, NY 11724-0284
*Tel:* 631-692-7172
*E-mail:* jopenroad@aol.com
*Web Site:* www.openroadguides.com
*Key Personnel*
Publr: Jonathan Stein
Founded: 1993
Travel, domestic & foreign, how-to, biographies, current events, sports, fantasy & commentary.
ISBN Prefix(es): 978-1-892975; 978-1-59360
Number of titles published annually: 22 Print
Total Titles: 62 Print
Imprints: Cold Spring Press
Distributed by Simon & Schuster
Foreign Rep(s): Roundhouse (UK)

**§OPIS/STALSBY Directories & Databases**
Division of United Communications Group
3349 Hwy 138, Bldg D, Suite D, Wall, NJ 07719
*Tel:* 732-901-8800 *Toll Free Tel:* 800-275-0950 *Toll Free Fax:* 800-450-5864
*E-mail:* opisstalsbylistings@opisnet.com
*Web Site:* www.opisnet.com
*Key Personnel*
Dir, Prodn: Renee Ortner *E-mail:* rortner@opisnet.com
Supervising Ed: Bonnie Walling *Tel:* 732-730-2536 *E-mail:* bwalling@opisnet.com
Founded: 1980
ISBN Prefix(es): 978-0-911299
Number of titles published annually: 4 Print
Total Titles: 4 Print; 4 CD-ROM

**Optometric Extension Program Foundation**
1921 E Carnegie Ave, Suite 3-L, Santa Ana, CA 92705-5510
*Tel:* 949-250-8070 *Fax:* 949-250-8157
*E-mail:* oep@oep.org
*Web Site:* www.oepf.org
*Key Personnel*
Exec Dir: Robert A Williams *E-mail:* rwilliams@oep.org
Dir, Pubns: Sally Marshall Corngold
*E-mail:* smcorngold@oep.org
Cust Serv Specialist: Kathleen Patterson
*E-mail:* kpatterson@oep.org
Founded: 1928
Books, journals, pamphlets, catalogs & directories.
ISBN Prefix(es): 978-0-943599; 978-0-929780
Number of titles published annually: 10 Print; 1 CD-ROM
Total Titles: 150 Print; 3 CD-ROM

**§OptumInsight™**
12125 Technology Dr, Eden Prairie, MN 55334
*Tel:* 952-833-7100 *Toll Free Tel:* 888-445-8745; 800-765-6713 *Fax:* 952-833-7201
*E-mail:* insight@optum.com
*Web Site:* www.optuminsight.com
*Key Personnel*
CEO: Andrew Slavitt
Chief Strategy Offr: John Nackel
Founded: 1983
Books & software for health-care professionals.
ISBN Prefix(es): 978-1-56337; 978-1-56329
Number of titles published annually: 90 Print; 5 Online
Total Titles: 90 Print; 8 CD-ROM; 5 Online
*Branch Office(s)*
1755 Telstar Dr, Suite 400, Colorado Springs, CO 80920 *Tel:* 719-277-7545 *Toll Free Tel:* 800-341-6141 *Fax:* 719-277-0254
400 Capital Blvd, Rocky Hill, CT 06067 *Tel:* 860-221-0054 *Toll Free Tel:* 800-367-2427 *Fax:* 860-221-0209
8345 Lenexa Dr, Suite 300, Lenexa, KS 66214 *Tel:* 913-904-0515 *Toll Free Tel:* 800-457-4697 *Fax:* 913-904-0505
301 N Hurstibourne Pkwy, Suite 200, Louisville, KY 40222 *Tel:* 502-326-8900 *Toll Free Tel:* 888-452-5000 *Fax:* 502-326-5376
70 Royal Little Dr, Providence, RI 02904 *Tel:* 401-331-5300 *Fax:* 401-331-5301
2525 Lake Park Blvd, Salt Lake City, UT 84120 *Tel:* 801-982-3000 *Toll Free Tel:* 800-464-3649 *Fax:* 801-982-4000
12018 Sunrise Valley Dr, Suite 400, Reston, VA 20191 *Tel:* 571-521-7661 *Toll Free Tel:* 800-464-3649 *Fax:* 571-521-7237
10701 W Research Dr, Wauwatosa, WI 53226-3452 *Toll Free Tel:* 800-651-8313 *Fax:* 414-443-4331
Distributed by American Medical Association; Mosby
Distributor for American Medical Association; Medical Economics; Mosby
*Warehouse:* 3687 W Great Lake Dr, Suite C, Salt Lake City, UT 84120

**Orange Frazer Press Inc**
37 1/2 W Main St, Wilmington, OH 45177
Mailing Address: PO Box 214, Wilmington, OH 45177-0214
*Tel:* 937-382-3196 *Toll Free Tel:* 800-852-9332 (orders) *Fax:* 937-383-3159
*E-mail:* ofrazer@erinet.com
*Web Site:* www.orangefrazer.com
*Key Personnel*
Publr: Marcy Hawley
Ed: John Baskin
Tech & Design: Tim Fauley
Off Mgr: Sarah Hawley
Founded: 1987
Regional book publisher specializing in Ohio nonfiction (reference, sports, commentary, travel, nature, etc). Production & design is considered "high-end". Recent winner of the Ohioana 2000 Citation Award for Excellence in Publishing.
ISBN Prefix(es): 978-1-882203; 978-0-9619637; 978-1-933197
Number of titles published annually: 16 Print
Total Titles: 60 Print
Membership(s): The Association of Publishers for Special Sales; IBPA, the Independent Book Publishers Association

**Orbis Books**
Division of Maryknoll Fathers & Brothers
Price Bldg, 85 Ryder Rd, Ossining, NY 10562
Mailing Address: PO Box 302, Maryknoll, NY 10545-0302 SAN: 202-828X
*Tel:* 914-941-7636 *Toll Free Tel:* 800-258-5838 (orders) *Fax:* 914-941-7005
*E-mail:* orbisbooks@maryknoll.org
*Web Site:* www.orbisbooks.com
*Key Personnel*
Publr & Ed-in-Chief: Robert Ellsberg
*E-mail:* rellsberg@maryknoll.org
Assoc Publr & Mktg Mgr: Bernadette B Price
*E-mail:* bprice@maryknoll.org
Busn Mgr: William Medeot *E-mail:* bmedeot@maryknoll.org
Sales Mgr: Michael Lawrence
*E-mail:* mlawrence@maryknoll.org
Ed-at-Large: Michael Leach *E-mail:* mleach@maryknoll.org
Rts & Perms & Asst to Publr: Doris Goodnough
*E-mail:* dgoodnough@maryknoll.org
Founded: 1970
Publisher of a wide range of books on prayer, spirituality, Catholic life, theology, mission & current affairs.
ISBN Prefix(es): 978-0-88344; 978-1-57075; 978-1-60833; 978-1-62698
Number of titles published annually: 50 Print; 50 E-Book
Total Titles: 743 Print; 160 E-Book
Foreign Rep(s): Alban Books (Europe, UK); Bayard/Novalis Distribution (Canada); Catholic Book Shop (South Africa); Rainbow Book Agencies (Australia)
*Advertising Agency:* Roth Advertising, PO Box 96, Sea Cliff, NY 11579-0096, Contact: Charles Roth *Tel:* 516-674-8603 *Fax:* 516-674-8606
*Warehouse:* Maryknoll Center Warehouse, 79 Ryder Rd, Ossining, NY 10562, Warehouse Mgr: Jim Matthieu *Tel:* 914-941-7636 ext 2613
Membership(s): Association of Catholic Publishers Inc

**Orbit**
Division of Hachette Book Group
237 Park Ave, New York, NY 10017
*Tel:* 212-364-1100 *Toll Free Tel:* 800-759-0190
*Web Site:* www.orbitbooks.net
*Key Personnel*
SVP, Hachette Book Group & Publr, Orbit: Tim Holman
Publg Dir, Yen Press: Kurt Hassler
Creative Dir: Lauren Panepinto
Sr Ed: Devi Pillai
Ed: Tom Bouman
Founded: 2008
Orbit is a leading publisher of science fiction & fantasy with imprints in the UK, US & Australia. We publish across the spectrum of science fiction & fantasy—from action-packed urban fantasy to widescreen space opera; from sweeping epic adventures to near-future thrillers.
Number of titles published annually: 200 Print
Imprints: Yen Press
*Orders to:* Hachette Book Group, 3 Center Plaza, Boston, MA 02108-9471 *Toll Free Tel:* 800-759-0190 *Toll Free Fax:* 800-286-9471
*Shipping Address:* Hachette Book Group Distribution Center, 121 N Enterprise Blvd, Lebanon, IN 46052 *Tel:* 765-483-9900 *Fax:* 765-483-0706

**Orca Book Publishers**
PO Box 468, Custer, WA 98240-0468
*Tel:* 250-380-1229 *Toll Free Tel:* 800-210-5277 *Fax:* 250-380-1892 *Toll Free Fax:* 877-408-1551
*E-mail:* orca@orcabook.com
*Web Site:* www.orcabook.com
*Key Personnel*
Publr: Andrew Wooldridge *E-mail:* andrew.wooldridge@orcabook.com
Edit Dir: Robert Tyrrell *E-mail:* tyrrell@orcabook.com
Founded: 1982
Children & young adult literature.
ISBN Prefix(es): 978-1-55143; 978-0-920501
Number of titles published annually: 60 Print
Total Titles: 350 Print

*Branch Office(s)*
PO Box 5626, Victoria, BC V8R 6S4, Canada
Distributor for The Book Publishing Co; Coteau Books; Creative Book Publishing; Formac Publishing; Lobster Press; James Lorimer & Co; Nimbus Publishing; Polestar Calendars; Second Story Press; 7th Generation; Sono Nis Pres; Sumach Press; Tradewind Books; Tuckamore Books; Tudor House
Foreign Rights: Transatlantic Literary Agency (Samantha Haywood) (Worldwide exc North America)
*Warehouse:* 7056 Portal Way, Bldg E, Ferndale, WA 98248
Membership(s): ABA; ALA; Association of Book Publishers of British Columbia; Association of Canadian Publishers; Canadian Booksellers Association; Canadian Library Association; Educational Book & Media Association

**Orchard House Press**, see Blue Forge Press

**§Orchard Publications**
39510 Paseo Padre Pkwy, Suite 315, Fremont, CA 94538
SAN: 254-1645
*Tel:* 510-792-6077 *Fax:* 510-792-6097
*E-mail:* info@orchardpublications.com; orchard@orchardpublications.com
*Web Site:* www.orchardpublications.com
*Key Personnel*
Pres: Steven T Karris
Founded: 1992
Publisher of applied math & engineering textbooks.
This publisher has indicated that 100% of their product line is author subsidized.
ISBN Prefix(es): 978-0-9709511; 978-0-9744239; 978-1-934404
Number of titles published annually: 2 Print; 2 Online; 2 E-Book
Total Titles: 11 Print; 11 Online; 11 E-Book
Membership(s): The Association of Publishers for Special Sales; IBPA, the Independent Book Publishers Association

**Orchises Press**
PO Box 320533, Alexandria, VA 22320-4533
*Tel:* 703-683-1243
*Web Site:* mason.gmu.edu/~lathbury/
*Key Personnel*
Pres & Ed-in-Chief: Roger Lathbury
*E-mail:* lathbury@gmu.edu
Founded: 1983
Small press.
ISBN Prefix(es): 978-0-914061; 978-1-932535
Number of titles published annually: 3 Print
Total Titles: 130 Print

**Oregon Catholic Press**, see OCP

**Oregon State University Press**
121 The Valley Library, Corvallis, OR 97331-4501
SAN: 202-8328
*Tel:* 541-737-3166 *Toll Free Tel:* 800-621-2736 (orders) *Fax:* 541-737-3170 *Toll Free Fax:* 800-426-3797 (orders)
*E-mail:* osu.press@oregonstate.edu
*Web Site:* oregonstate.edu/dept/press; osupress.oregonstate.edu
*Key Personnel*
Dir: Fay Chadwell *E-mail:* fay.chadwell@oregonstate.edu
Assoc Dir: Tom Booth *Tel:* 503-796-0547 *E-mail:* thomas.booth@oregonstate.edu
Acqs Ed: Mary Elizabeth Braun *E-mail:* mary.braun@oregonstate.edu
Mng Ed: Jo Alexander *E-mail:* jo.alexander@oregonstate.edu
Edit & Prodn Asst: Judy Radovsky *E-mail:* judy.ravosky@oregonstate.edu
Founded: 1961
ISBN Prefix(es): 978-0-87071
Number of titles published annually: 15 Print
Total Titles: 225 Print
Foreign Rights: East-West Export Books (Royden Muranaka) (Asia-Pacific); Eurospan Group (Africa, Europe, Middle East); US PubRep Inc (Craig Falk) (Latin America); UTP Distribution (Canada)
*Distribution Center:* Chicago Distribution Center, 11030 S Langley Ave, Chicago, IL 60628 *Toll Free Tel:* 800-621-2736 *Toll Free Fax:* 800-621-8476

**O'Reilly Media Inc**
1005 Gravenstein Hwy N, Sebastopol, CA 95472
*Tel:* 707-827-7000; 707-827-7019
*Toll Free Tel:* 800-998-9938; 800-889-8969
*Fax:* 707-829-0104; 707-824-8268
*E-mail:* orders@oreilly.com
*Web Site:* www.oreilly.com
*Key Personnel*
Founder & CEO: Tim O'Reilly
VP: Sara Winge *Tel:* 707-827-7109
*E-mail:* sara@oreilly.com
Dir, Sales: Mike Leonard *Tel:* 707-827-7078
*E-mail:* mleonard@oreilly.com
Founded: 1978
Technical computer book publisher, conference provider.
ISBN Prefix(es): 978-0-937175; 978-1-56592; 978-0-596
Number of titles published annually: 140 Print; 65 E-Book
Total Titles: 800 Print
*Branch Office(s)*
O'Reilly AlphaTech Ventures (OATV), One Lombard St, Suite 303, San Francisco, CA 94111 *Tel:* 415-693-0200 *Web Site:* www.oatv.com
10 Fawcett St, Cambridge, MA 02138 *Tel:* 617-354-5800 *Toll Free Tel:* 800-775-7731 *Fax:* 617-661-1116
*Foreign Office(s):* O'Reilly Beijing, Cheng Ming Mansion, Bldg C, Suite 807, No 2 Xizhimen South St, Xicheng District, Beijing 100035, China, Contact: Michelle Chen *Tel:* (010) 88097475 *Fax:* (010) 88097463 *E-mail:* orb@oreilly.com *Web Site:* www.oreilly.com.cn
O'Reilly Verlag, Balthasarstr 81, 50670 Cologne, Germany, Contact: Anke Wallbrecher *Tel:* (0221) 9731600 *Fax:* (0221) 973160-8 *E-mail:* anfragen@oreilly.de *Web Site:* www.oreilly.de
Intelligent Plaza, Bldg 1-F, 26 Banchi 27, Sakamachi, Shinjuku-ku, Tokyo 160-0002, Japan, Contact: Kenji Watari *Tel:* (03) 3356 5227 *Fax:* (03) 3356 5261 *E-mail:* kenji@oreilly.com *Web Site:* www.oreilly.co.jp
Gostrey House, Union Rd, Farnham, Surrey GU9 7PT, United Kingdom *Tel:* (01252) 721284 *Fax:* (01252) 722337 *E-mail:* information@oreilly.co.uk *Web Site:* www.oreilly.uk
Distributor for Microsoft Press (North America)
Foreign Rep(s): WoodsLane (Australia, New Zealand)
*Distribution Center:* Les Editions Flammarion Itee, 375 Ave Laurier Ouest, Montreal, QC H2V 2K3, Canada (The Americas) *Tel:* 514-277-8807 *Fax:* 514-278-2085 *E-mail:* info@flammarion.qc.ca
WoodsLane Pty Ltd, 7/5 Vuko Place, Warriewood, NSW 2102, Australia (Australia & New Zealand) *Tel:* (02) 9970 5111 *Toll Free Tel:* 800-006-723 *Fax:* (02) 9970 5002 *Toll Free Fax:* 800-006-715 *E-mail:* info@woodslane.com.au *Web Site:* www.woodslane.com.au
SODIS, 128 av du Mal de Lattre de Tassigny, 77403 Lagny Cedex, France (Austria, Germany, Liechtenstein, Luxembourg & Switzerland) *Tel:* 01 60 07 82 99 *Fax:* 01 64 30 32 27
STP Distributors Pte Ltd (TQ), 10/F, Block C, Seaview Estate, 2-8 Watson Rd, North Point, Hong Kong (Hong Kong), Contact: Ray Chan *Tel:* 2992 0878 *Fax:* 2992 0983 *E-mail:* ray@tplhk.com.hk
Shroff Publishers & Distributors Pvt Ltd, C-103, TTC Industrial Area, MIDC, Pawane, Navi Mumbai 400 701, India (India) *Tel:* (022) 2763 4290 *Fax:* (022) 2768 3337 *E-mail:* spdorders@shroffpublishers.com *Web Site:* www.shroffpublishers.com
Eastern Book Service Inc, 3-13 Hongo 3-chome, Bunkyo-ku, Tokyo 160-8480, Japan (Japan) *Tel:* (03) 3818 0861 *Fax:* (03) 3818 0864 *E-mail:* orders@svt-ebs.co.jp *Web Site:* www.svt-ebs.co.jp
Hanbit Media Inc, Chungmu Bldg 301, Yonnamdong 568-33, Mapo-gu, Seoul, South Korea (Korea) *Tel:* (02) 325-0397 *Fax:* (02) 325-9697 *E-mail:* thkim@hanbitbook.co.kr *Web Site:* www.hanbitbook.co.kr
Pansing Distribution Sdn Bhd, Lot 557 A & B, Jalan Subang 3, Subang Jaya Industrial Estate, 47610 Subang Jaya, Selangor, Darul Ehsan, Malaysia (Malaysia), Sales Mgr: Ms Kavitajit Kaur *Tel:* (03) 56310794 *Fax:* (03) 56384337 *E-mail:* kavitajit@my.pansing.com
Pansing Distribution Pte Ltd, Times Ctr, One New Industrial Rd 536196, Singapore (Singapore & Indonesia), Prod Specialist: Benjamin Xu *Tel:* 6319 9939 *Fax:* 6459 4930 *E-mail:* benjaminxu@pansing.com
Tenlong Computer Book Co Ltd, No 107 Chong Ching S Rd, Sec 1, Taipei, Taiwan (Taiwan) *Tel:* (02) 2371-7725 *Fax:* (02) 2331-1905 *E-mail:* service@tenlong.com.tw *Web Site:* www.tenlong.com.tw
Far East Publications Ltd, 253 Asoke, 12th fl, Sukhumit 21, Klongteoy Nua, Wattana District, Bangkok 10110, Thailand (Thailand), Contact: Puripat Pakavaleetorn *Tel:* (02) 2611908 *Fax:* (02) 2611912 *E-mail:* puripat@pansing.com
Wiley Distribution Services Ltd, One Oldlands Way, Bonor Regis, West Sussex P022 9SA, United Kingdom (Africa, Europe (excluding Austria, Germany, Liechtenstein, Luxembourg & Switzerland), Middle East & UK) *Tel:* (01243) 843242 *Toll Free Tel:* 800-243407 *Fax:* (01243) 843302 *E-mail:* cs-books@wiley.co.uk

**§Organization for Economic Cooperation & Development**
Division of Organization for Economic Cooperation & Development (France)
2001 "L" St NW, Suite 650, Washington, DC 20036-4922
*Tel:* 202-785-6323 *Toll Free Tel:* 800-456-6323 (dist ctr/pubns orders) *Fax:* 202-785-0350
*E-mail:* washington.contact@oecd.org
*Web Site:* www.oecdwash.org; www.oecd.org
*Key Personnel*
Deputy Head & Sales Mgr: Kathleen Deboer *Tel:* 202-822-3870 *E-mail:* kathleen.deboer@oecd.org
Founded: 1961
Periodicals, books, magnetic tapes, diskettes & microfiche, CD-ROM, online services.
ISBN Prefix(es): 978-92-64; 978-92-821
Number of titles published annually: 300 Print; 50 CD-ROM; 300 Online; 200 E-Book
Total Titles: 3,500 Print; 50 CD-ROM; 6,500 Online; 1,200 E-Book
*Foreign Office(s):* 2 rue Andre-Pascal, 75775 Paris Cedex 16, France *Tel:* (01) 45 24 82 00 *Fax:* (01) 45 24 85 00
Distributor for International Energy Agency (Imprint); International Transportation Forum; Nuclear Energy Agency (Imprint)
*Orders to:* Turpin Distribution Services Ltd, The Bleachery, 143 West St, New Milford, CT 06776 *Toll Free Tel:* 800-456-6323 *Fax:* 781-829-9052

*Distribution Center:* Turpin Distribution Services Ltd, The Bleachery, 143 West St, New Milford, CT 06776 *Toll Free Tel:* 800-456-6323 *Fax:* 860-350-0039

**Oriental Institute Publications**
Division of University of Chicago
1155 E 58 St, Chicago, IL 60637
*Tel:* 773-702-5967 *Fax:* 773-702-9853
*E-mail:* oi-publications@uchicago.edu; oi-museum@uchicago.edu; oi-administration@uchicago.edu
*Web Site:* oi.uchicago.edu
*Key Personnel*
Mng Ed, Pubns: Thomas Urban *E-mail:* t-urban@uchicago.edu
Ed, Pubns Off: Leslie Schramer *E-mail:* leslie@uchicago.edu
Founded: 1919
Academic publications.
ISBN Prefix(es): 978-0-918986; 978-1-885923
Number of titles published annually: 10 Print; 10 Online
Total Titles: 250 Print; 250 Online
*Orders to:* The David Brown Book Co, PO Box 511, Oakville, CT 06779 *Tel:* 860-945-9329 *Toll Free Tel:* 800-791-9354 *Fax:* 860-945-9468
*Distribution Center:* The David Brown Book Co, PO Box 511, Oakville, CT 06779 *Tel:* 860-945-9329 *Toll Free Tel:* 800-791-9354 *Fax:* 860-945-9468

**The Original Falcon Press**
1753 E Broadway Rd, No 101-277, Tempe, AZ 85282
*Tel:* 602-708-1409
*E-mail:* info@originalfalcon.com
*Web Site:* www.originalfalcon.com
*Key Personnel*
Pres: Nicholas Tharcher *E-mail:* nick@originalfalcon.com
Founded: 1982
Books, audio tapes, video tapes.
ISBN Prefix(es): 978-1-935150; 978-1-61869
Number of titles published annually: 10 Print; 10 E-Book; 10 Audio
Total Titles: 50 Print; 40 E-Book; 30 Audio
Imprints: Falcon Press; Golden Dawn Publications; New Falcon Publications
*Distribution Center:* New Leaf Distributing Co, 401 Thornton Rd, Lithia Springs, GA 30122-1557 *Tel:* 770-948-7845 *Fax:* 770-944-2313 *E-mail:* newleaf@newleaf-dist.com *Web Site:* www.newleaf-dist.com
Quanta Distribution, 3251 Kennedy Rd, Unit 20, Toronto, ON M1V 2J9, Canada *Tel:* 416-410-9411 *Toll Free Tel:* 888-436-7962 *Fax:* 416-291-8764 *E-mail:* quantamail@quanta.ca *Web Site:* www.quanta.ca
John Reed Book Distribution, 2/11 Yandala St, Tea Garden, NSW 2324, Australia, Dir: John Reed *Tel:* (02) 4997 2936 *Fax:* (02) 4997 2937 *E-mail:* sales@johnreedbooks.com.au *Web Site:* www.johnreedbooks.com.au
Gazelle Book Services Ltd, White Cross Mills, High Town, Lancaster LA1 4XS, United Kingdom *Tel:* (0152) 468765 *Web Site:* www.gazellebookservices.co.uk

**Original Publications**
PO Box 236, Old Beth Page, NY 11804
SAN: 133-0225
*Tel:* 516-605-0547 *Toll Free Tel:* 888-622-8581 *Fax:* 516-605-0549
*E-mail:* originalpub@aol.com
*Web Site:* www.occult1.com
*Key Personnel*
Publr & Dist: Mark Benezra
Founded: 1962
African religion, New Age, spirituality, Santeria & occult books; Distribution Ctrs: Azure Green & New Leaf Distribution Co.
ISBN Prefix(es): 978-0-942272
Number of titles published annually: 40 Print
Total Titles: 50 Print
*Distribution Center:* Azure Green
New Leaf Distributing Co

**ORO editions**
31 Commercial Blvd, Suite F, Novato, CA 94949
*Tel:* 415-883-3300 *Fax:* 415-883-3309
*E-mail:* info@oroeditions.com
*Web Site:* www.oroeditions.com
*Key Personnel*
Contact: Gordon Goff *E-mail:* gordon@oroeditions.com
Founded: 2003
ISBN Prefix(es): 978-0-9746800; 978-0-9774672; 978-0-9793801; 978-0-9795395; 978-0-9814628; 978-0-9820607; 978-0-9819857; 978-0-9826226; 978-0-935935
Number of titles published annually: 25 Print; 8 E-Book

**OSA, The Optical Society**
2010 Massachusetts Ave NW, Washington, DC 20036-1023
*Tel:* 202-223-8130 *Toll Free Tel:* 800-766-4672
*E-mail:* custserv@osa.org
*Web Site:* www.osa.org
*Key Personnel*
Chief Publg Offr: Elizabeth Nolan *Tel:* 202-416-1949 *E-mail:* enolan@osa.org
Sr Dir, IT: Sean Bagshaw *Tel:* 202-416-1905 *E-mail:* sbagsh@osa.org
Deputy Sr Dir, Pubns: Keith Allen *Tel:* 202-416-1906 *E-mail:* kallen@osa.org
Mss Dir: Kelly Cohen *Tel:* 202-416-1917 *Fax:* 202-416-6129 *E-mail:* kcohen@osa.org
Dir, Sales & Publg: Alan N Tourtlotte *Tel:* 202-416-1908 *Fax:* 202-416-1408 *E-mail:* atourt@osa.org
Rts & Perms: Hannah Bembia *Tel:* 202-416-1920 *Fax:* 202-416-6129 *E-mail:* hbembi@osa.org
Founded: 1916
Journal publishing, meetings & technical membership.
ISBN Prefix(es): 978-1-55752
Number of titles published annually: 20 Online
Total Titles: 230 Online
Foreign Rep(s): David Charles e-Licensing (Europe); Globe Publication Pvt Ltd (India); iGroup (Asia exc India & Japan, Australia, New Zealand); Kinokuniya (Japan)
*Orders to:* Optical Society of America, PO Box 55480, Boston, MA 02205-9923 *Tel:* 202-416-1908
Membership(s): American Institute of Physics

**Osprey Publishing Inc**
Subsidiary of Osprey Publishing Ltd
4301 21 St, Suite 220B, Long Island City, NY 11101
*Tel:* 718-433-4402 *Fax:* 718-433-4497
*E-mail:* ospreyusa@ospreypublishing.com
*Web Site:* www.ospreypublishing.com
Founded: 1969
Series publishing in history, military nonfiction, local interest, genre fiction: science fiction/fantasy, young adult & mysteries.
ISBN Prefix(es): 978-1-85532; 978-0-85045; 978-1-84176; 978-1-84603 (Osprey); 978-1-84908 (Osprey); 978-0-85766 (Angry Robot)
Number of titles published annually: 120 Print
Total Titles: 2,500 Print
Imprints: Aircraft of the Aces; Angry Robot; Aviation Elite Units; Battle Orders; Campaign; Combat Aircraft; Command; Duel; Elite; Essential Histories; Exhibit A (crime & mystery fiction); Field of Glory; Force on Force; Fortress; General Aviation; General Military; Graphic History; Men at Arms; Modelling Manuals; Modelling Masterclass; New Vanguard; Old House; Osprey; Osprey Modelling; Raid; Shire (local history); Strange Chemistry (young adult & science fiction, fantasy); Wargaming; Warrior; Weapon
*Foreign Office(s):* Osprey Publishing Ltd, Midland House, West Way, Botley, Oxon OX2 0PH, United Kingdom, Off Mgr: Diane Hobbs *Tel:* (01865) 727022 *Fax:* (01865) 242009 *E-mail:* diane.hobbs@ospreypublishing.com
Distributed by Random House (US & CN)
*Distribution Center:* TBS (The Book Service), Colchester Rd, Frating Green, Colchester, Essex CO7 7DW, United Kingdom (Worldwide)

**Other Press LLC**
2 Park Ave, 24th fl, New York, NY 10016
*Tel:* 212-414-0054 *Toll Free Tel:* 877-843-6843 *Fax:* 212-414-0939
*E-mail:* editor@otherpress.com; rights@otherpress.com
*Web Site:* www.otherpress.com
*Key Personnel*
Publr: Judith Feher-Gurewich
Assoc Publr: Paul Kozlowski
CFO: Bill Foo
Dir, Publicity: Sarah Reidy
Dir, Subs Rts: Lauren Shekari
Mgr, Online Publicity & Social Media: Terrie Akers
Sr Publicist: Jessica Greer
Publicist: Megan Feulner
Publicity & Mktg Coord: Sophia Sherry
Ed: Sulay Hernandez
Asst Ed: Marjorie De Witt
Founded: 1998
Publish literary fiction, literature in translation, trade nonfiction, memoir, cultural studies, biographies & other subjects.
ISBN Prefix(es): 978-1-892746; 978-1-59051
Number of titles published annually: 25 Print; 25 E-Book
Distributed by Random House Inc
Foreign Rep(s): Eurospan (professional titles outside of North America); Random House International Sales; Random House of Canada Limited (Canada)
Membership(s): ABA; Council of Literary Magazines & Presses; IBPA, the Independent Book Publishers Association

**OTTN Publishing**
16 Risler St, Stockton, NJ 08559
*Tel:* 609-397-4005 *Toll Free Tel:* 866-356-6886 *Fax:* 609-397-4007
*E-mail:* inquiries@ottnpublishing.com
*Web Site:* www.ottnpublishing.com
*Key Personnel*
Publr: Jim Gallagher *E-mail:* jgallagher@ottnpublishing.com
Founded: 1998
Provide a full range of editorial services from developing book or series ideas to providing a finished product all at a reasonable price.
ISBN Prefix(es): 978-1-59556
Number of titles published annually: 5 Print
Total Titles: 17 Print
Membership(s): IBPA, the Independent Book Publishers Association

**§Our Sunday Visitor Publishing**
Division of Our Sunday Visitor Inc
200 Noll Plaza, Huntington, IN 46750
SAN: 202-8344
*Tel:* 260-356-8400 *Toll Free Tel:* 800-348-2440 (orders) *Fax:* 260-356-8472 *Toll Free Fax:* 800-498-6709
*E-mail:* osvbooks@osv.com (book orders)
*Web Site:* www.osv.com
*Key Personnel*
Chmn of the Bd: Bishop Kevin C Rhoades
Pres & Publr: Greg Erlandson *E-mail:* gerlandson@osv.com
Assoc Publr & Ed: Owen Campion *E-mail:* ocampion@osv.com

Exec Asst: Michelle Hogan *E-mail:* mhogan@osv.com
Founded: 1912
Religious books: trade, adult & juvenile general interest & reference, hardcover & paperback early childhood school; religious magazines & newspapers, audiocassettes, videocassettes & CD-ROM.
ISBN Prefix(es): 978-0-87973; 978-1-931709; 978-0-9707756
Number of titles published annually: 60 Print
Total Titles: 600 Print; 6 CD-ROM; 8 Audio
Foreign Rep(s): Baker & Taylor (Worldwide exc Canada, France, Malta, New Zealand, South Africa & UK); B Broughton (Canada); Catholic Supplies (New Zealand); Preca (Malta); Veritas (UK); Veritas Co Ltd (Ireland); Grace Wing (Canada, UK, Worldwide exc Australia); Word of Life (Australia)

**OUT OF YOUR MIND...AND INTO THE MARKETPLACE™**
13381 White Sand Dr, Tustin, CA 92780-4565
*Tel:* 714-544-0248 *Toll Free Tel:* 800-419-1513 *Fax:* 714-730-1414
*Web Site:* www.business-plan.com
*Key Personnel*
Owner & Publr: Linda Pinson *E-mail:* lpinson@business-plan.com
Asst Publr: Julie Filppi *E-mail:* jfilppi@aol.com
Mktg Dir: Ndaba Mdhlongwa *E-mail:* ndaba@business-plan.com
Founded: 1986
Publisher of entrepreneurial books & business plan software.
This publisher has indicated that 80% of their product line is author subsidized.
ISBN Prefix(es): 978-0-944205
Number of titles published annually: 2 Print; 1 CD-ROM; 6 E-Book
Total Titles: 3 Print; 1 CD-ROM; 6 E-Book
*Distribution Center:* Independent Publishers Group (IPG), 814 N Franklin St, Chicago, IL 60610, Title Devt Mgr: Mary Rowles *Toll Free Tel:* 800-888-4741 *E-mail:* mrowles@ipgbook.com *Web Site:* ipg.com
Membership(s): IBPA, the Independent Book Publishers Association

**The Overlook Press**
Subsidiary of Peter Mayer Publishers Inc
141 Wooster St, Suite 4-B, New York, NY 10012
SAN: 202-8360
*Tel:* 212-673-2210; 845-679-6838 (orders & dist) *Fax:* 212-673-2296
*E-mail:* sales@overlookny.com (orders)
*Web Site:* www.overlookpress.com
*Key Personnel*
Pres & Publr: Peter Mayer
Dir, Publicity: Jack Lamplough
Mgr, Contract & Subs Rts & Assoc Ed: Liese Mayer
Sales Mgr: Jill Lichtenstadter
Ed: Dan Crissman
Assoc Ed: Mark Krotov
Assoc Publicist: Theresa Collier; Michael Goldsmith
Founded: 1971
Fiction, general nonfiction, theatre, biography, art, architecture, history, design, film, popular culture, hardcover reprints & trade paperbacks.
ISBN Prefix(es): 978-0-87951; 978-1-58567; 978-1-59020
Number of titles published annually: 90 Print
Total Titles: 1,000 Print
Imprints: Ardis Russian Literature; Elephant's Eye; Tusk Ivory; Tusk Paperbacks
Distributed by Penguin Group (USA) LLC
Foreign Rights: Agencia Literaria Carmen Balcells (Portugal, South America, Spain); The Deborah Harris Agency (Israel); Asli Karasuil (Turkey); Agence Michelle Lapautre (Belgium, France); Agenzia Letteraria (Italy); Licht & Burr Literary Agency APS (Scandinavia); Dr Ruth Liepman Agency (Germany, Switzerland); Andrew Nurnberg Associates (Bulgaria, China, Croatia, Czech Republic, Estonia, Hungary, Latvia, Lithuania, Montenegro, Poland, Romania, Russia, Serbia, Taiwan); Agencia Riff (Lucia Riff) (Brazil); Sebes & Van Gelderen Literary Agency (Netherlands); Tuttle-Mori Agency Inc (Japan)
Membership(s): AAP; National Book Foundation

**The Overmountain Press**
Division of Sabre Industries Inc
PO Box 1261, Johnson City, TN 37605-1261
SAN: 687-6641
*Tel:* 423-926-2691 *Toll Free Tel:* 800-992-2691 (orders) *Fax:* 423-232-1252
*E-mail:* orders@overmtn.com
*Web Site:* www.overmtn.com
*Key Personnel*
Publr: Elizabeth L Wright *E-mail:* beth@overmtn.com
Mng Ed: Daniel Lewis *E-mail:* daniel@overmtn.com
Sr Ed: Sherry Lewis *E-mail:* sherry@overmtn.com
Mktg: Karin O'Brien *E-mail:* karino@overmtn.com
Founded: 1970
Exhibit at trade shows, festivals, conventions. Subjects include Southern Appalachian nonfiction, history & children.
ISBN Prefix(es): 978-0-932807; 978-1-57072
Number of titles published annually: 10 Print
Total Titles: 300 Print
Imprints: Silver Dagger Mysteries

**Richard C Owen Publishers Inc**
PO Box 585, Katonah, NY 10536-0585
*Tel:* 914-232-3903 *Toll Free Tel:* 800-336-5588 *Fax:* 914-232-3977
*E-mail:* rcostaff@rcowen.com
*Web Site:* www.rcowen.com
*Key Personnel*
Pres & Publr: Richard C Owen *E-mail:* richardowen@rcowen.com
Founded: 1982
Education, language arts & literacy.
ISBN Prefix(es): 978-0-913461; 978-1-878450; 978-1-57274
Number of titles published annually: 5 Print
Total Titles: 378 Print
*Warehouse:* 245 Rte 100, Somers, NY 10589

**Owl About Books Publisher Inc**
1632 Royalwood Circle, Joshua, TX 76058
Mailing Address: PO Box 867, Joshua, TX 76058
*Tel:* 682-553-9078 *Fax:* 817-558-8983
*E-mail:* owlaboutbooks@gmail.com
*Web Site:* www.owlaboutbooks.com
*Key Personnel*
Pres: Dorota Harrington
Founded: 2011
Privately owned & devoted to publishing literature for children. Educational series philosophy is best described by the company's motto "Children's learning has no limits." Specialize in beautifully illustrated reading resources for parents & children with special needs. Well-placed fun facts accompany most of the stories & provide educational benefit.
ISBN Prefix(es): 978-1-937752
Number of titles published annually: 7 Print; 7 Online
Total Titles: 14 Print; 11 Online
Membership(s): IBPA, the Independent Book Publishers Association

**§Oxbridge® Communications Inc**
39 W 29 St, Suite 301, New York, NY 10001
*Tel:* 212-741-0231 *Toll Free Tel:* 800-955-0231 *Fax:* 212-633-2938
*E-mail:* info@oxbridge.com
*Web Site:* www.oxbridge.com
*Key Personnel*
CEO: Louis Hagood
Pres: Patricia Hagood
Founded: 1964
Over the last 40 years, Oxbridge has built the largest database of information on US & Canadian periodicals & catalogs with a total of 72,000 titles. Data is available online, on CD & in print. Oxbridge publishes the *Standard Periodical Directory, the National Directory of Magazines, the National Directory of Catalogs & the Oxbridge Directory of Newsletters.*
ISBN Prefix(es): 978-1-891783
Number of titles published annually: 4 Print; 1 CD-ROM; 1 Online
Total Titles: 4 Print; 1 CD-ROM; 1 Online

**§Oxford University Press USA**
Division of University of Oxford
198 Madison Ave, New York, NY 10016
SAN: 202-5892
*Tel:* 212-726-6000 *Toll Free Tel:* 800-451-7556 (orders); 800-445-9714 (cust serv) *Fax:* 919-677-1303
*E-mail:* custserv.us@oup.com
*Web Site:* www.oup.com/us
*Key Personnel*
CEO: Nigel Portwood
CFO: Kevin Allison
Pres, OUP USA & Publr, Academic & Trade: Nido Pfund
VP & Publr, Clinical Medicine: Catherine Barnes
VP & Publr, Higher Educ: John Challice
VP & Dir, Dist, Cary, NC: Tom Shannon
VP & Dir, HR: Marilyn Okrent
VP, Global Mktg: Colleen Scollans
VP, Publr Rel: Casper Grathwohl
Head, Academic Publg Div: Tim Barton
Head, Design, Global Academic Busn: Linda Secondari
Head, US Content Opers: Deborah Shor
Head, US Dictionaries: Katherine Martin
Head, US Stock Planning & Pubns: Bill Haydis
Dir, Academic/Trade Mkt: Kim Craven
Edit Dir, Higher Educ: Patrick Lynch
Edit Dir, Ref Acqs: Damon Zucca
Ed-in-Chief, Acad/Trade Edit: Suzanne Ryan
Ed-in-Chief, Social Sciences: David McBride
Cust Serv Dir: Cheryl Ammons-Longtin
Dir, Direct Mktg: Rose Pintaudi-Jones
Dir, Fin: Dottie Warlick
Dir, Fin & Opers: Jim Jordan
Dir, Global Busn Devt: Nancy Roberson
Dir, Global Online Mktg: Sarah Ultsch
Dir, Higher Educ Mkt & Sales: Frank Mortimer
Dir, HR, Cary, NC: Cherlynn Hoover
Dir, Info Systems: Raju Gadiraju
Dir, Instl Sales: Rebecca Seger
Dir, Inventory Planning: Ken Guerin
Dir, Mktg & Dist: Kurt Hettler
Dir, Med Sales & Mktg: Greg Bussy
Dir, Publicity: C Purdy
Divisional Systems Mgr: James Martin
Facilities/Off Servs Mgr, NY: Terese Dickerson
Facilities Mgr, Cary, NC: Chris Vidourek
Mgr, Brand & Communs: Caite Panzer
Mgr, ebook Global Supply Chain: Margaret Harrison
Mgr, Mkt Res: Karen Langsam
Mgr, Off Strategy Mgt: Laurea Salvatore
Publicity Mgr: Tara Kennedy
Reprints & Mfg Supplier Mgr: Chris Critelli
Stock Planning Project Mgr: Nancy Wu
Warehouse Mgr: Todd Hayes
General Coun: Barbara Cohen
Training & Devt: David Mintzer
Founded: 1896 (1478 in UK)
Scholarly, professional & reference books in the humanities, science, medicine & social studies; nonfiction trade, Bibles, college textbooks, music, English as a second language, paperbacks, children's books, journals, online reference &

online scholarly. Prospective authors should consult the Oxford University Press web site for submission guidelines & proposal submission policy.
ISBN Prefix(es): 978-0-19
Number of titles published annually: 3,000 Print; 6 CD-ROM; 50 Online; 400 E-Book; 23 Audio
Total Titles: 26,000 Print; 27 CD-ROM; 100 Online; 400 E-Book; 220 Audio
Imprints: Clarendon Press
*Foreign Office(s):* Great Clarendon St, Oxford OX2 6DP, United Kingdom (worldwide headquarters) *Tel:* (018165) 556-767
Distributor for The American Chemical Society; American University in Cairo; Arnold Clarendon; Cold Spring Harbor Laboratory Press; Engineering Press; Fordham University Press; Getty; Greenwich Medical Media; Grove Dictionaries; Hurst; IRL; Kodansha; Roxbury Publishing; Saunders; Thomson Publishing
Foreign Rights: Gersh Agency
*Returns:* 2001 Evans Rd, Cary, NC 27513 *Toll Free Tel:* 800-451-7556 *Web Site:* www.oup.com/us
*Warehouse:* 2001 Evans Rd, Cary, NC 27513 *Toll Free Tel:* 800-451-7556 *Web Site:* www.oup.com/us
*Distribution Center:* 2001 Evans Rd, Cary, NC 27513 *Toll Free Tel:* 800-451-7556 *Web Site:* www.oup.com/us
Membership(s): AAP; American Association of University Presses; BISG
*See separate listing for:*
**Oceana®**
**Roxbury Publishing Co**

**Oxmoor House Inc**
Division of Time Home Entertainment Inc
2100 Lakeshore Dr, Birmingham, AL 35209
SAN: 205-3462
*Tel:* 205-445-6000 *Toll Free Tel:* 800-366-4712; 888-891-8935 (cust serv); 800-765-6400 (orders)
*Web Site:* www.oxmoorhouse.com
Founded: 1968
General interest books; cooking, gardening, decorating, home improvement, travel, entertaining, health, motion film companions, custom products, celebrity how-to, crafts, art, hobbies; book & binder programs.
ISBN Prefix(es): 978-0-8487
Number of titles published annually: 250 Print
Total Titles: 329 Print
Imprints: Coastal Living Books; Cooking Light Books; Health Books; Southern Living Books; Sunset Books
Distributed by H B Fenn (Canada); Leisure Arts Inc
Foreign Rep(s): Beckett Sterling (New Zealand); General Publishing Co (Canada); Little, Brown & Co, UK (Europe, UK); Struik Book Distributers (South Africa); Transworld Publishers (Australia)

**Ozark Mountain Publishing Inc**
PO Box 754, Huntsville, AR 72740-0754
*Tel:* 479-738-2348 *Toll Free Tel:* 800-935-0045 *Fax:* 479-738-2448
*E-mail:* info@ozarkmt.com
*Web Site:* www.ozarkmt.com
*Key Personnel*
Founder & Pres: Dolores Cannon *E-mail:* decannon@msn.com
Off Mgr: Julia Degan *E-mail:* julia@ozarkmt.com
Edit Asst: Joy Newman *E-mail:* joy@ozarkmt.com
Founded: 1992
Publish nonfiction New Age/metaphysical & spiritual type books.
ISBN Prefix(es): 978-0-9632776; 978-1-886940
Number of titles published annually: 10 Print
Total Titles: 50 Print

Foreign Rights: Ajatus Publishing Co (Finland); Gazelle Books Distributor (England, Europe); Gill & Macmillan (Ireland); Helfa A W (Poland); Jaico (India); Luciernaga Oceano (Spain); Lyubka Mihailova (Bulgaria); Quanta Distribution Inc (Canada); Schriwer Forlag (Norway); Stigmarion (Russia)

**Ozark Publishing Inc**
PO Box 228, Prairie Grove, AR 72753-0228
*Tel:* 479-595-9522 *Toll Free Tel:* 800-321-5671 *Fax:* 479-846-2843
*E-mail:* srg304@yahoo.com
*Web Site:* www.ozarkpublishing.us
*Key Personnel*
Mng Ed: Dave Sargent
Mgr: Dave Sargent, Jr
Founded: 1988
Children & young adult books. All books have a moral; the children's books include both fact & fiction.
ISBN Prefix(es): 978-1-56763
Number of titles published annually: 60 Print
Total Titles: 700 Print; 80 Audio
Distributed by Amazon.com; Apple; Barnes & Noble; Econoclad; Follett; Gumdrop; Perma-Bound; Stay Bound
*Shipping Address:* 13062 Butler, Prairie Grove, AR 72753

**P & R Publishing Co**
1102 Marble Hill Rd, Phillipsburg, NJ 08865
SAN: 205-3918
Mailing Address: PO Box 817, Phillipsburg, NJ 08865
*Tel:* 908-454-0505 *Toll Free Tel:* 800-631-0094 *Fax:* 908-859-2390
*E-mail:* sales@prpbooks.com; generalinfo@prpbooks.com
*Web Site:* prpbooks.com
*Key Personnel*
Pres: Bryce H Craig *E-mail:* bryce@prpbooks.com
VP, Edit: Marvin Padgett *E-mail:* mpadgett@prpbooks.com
Sr Proj Mgr: Aaron Gottier *E-mail:* aarong@prpbooks.com
Founded: 1930
Books on religion (Protestant) & philosophy.
ISBN Prefix(es): 978-0-87552; 978-1-59638
Number of titles published annually: 40 Print; 40 E-Book
Total Titles: 580 Print; 1 CD-ROM; 340 Online; 100 E-Book
Foreign Rights: Fred Rudy (Worldwide)
Membership(s): Evangelical Christian Publishers Association

**P R B Productions**
963 Peralta Ave, Albany, CA 94706-2144
*Tel:* 510-526-0722 *Fax:* 510-527-4763
*E-mail:* prbprdns@aol.com
*Web Site:* www.prbmusic.com
*Key Personnel*
Prop & Publr: Peter R Ballinger; Leslie J Gold
Founded: 1989
Jobbing music engraving; performing editions.
ISBN Prefix(es): 978-1-56571
Number of titles published annually: 10 Print
Total Titles: 300 Print

**P S M J Resources Inc**
10 Midland Ave, Newton, MA 02458
*Tel:* 617-965-0055 *Toll Free Tel:* 800-537-7765 *Fax:* 617-965-5152
*E-mail:* info@psmj.com
*Web Site:* www.psmj.com
Founded: 1980
Books, survey reports & audio cassette programs for architects, engineers, interior designers, urban designers, planners, landscape architects on business & financial management; marketing; time & personnel management; legal topics; project management; human resources; newsletters; consulting & educational seminars.
ISBN Prefix(es): 978-1-55538
Number of titles published annually: 12 Print
Total Titles: 100 Print
*Branch Office(s)*
2746 Rangewood Rd, Atlanta, GA 30345 *Tel:* 770-723-9651 *Fax:* 815-461-7478 *E-mail:* dbustein@psmj.com
*Foreign Office(s):* PO Box 773, Artarmon, NSW 2064, Australia *Tel:* (02) 9411 4819 *Fax:* (02) 9419 6044 *E-mail:* egoullet@psmj.com
242 Dorcas St, South Melbourne, Victoria 3205, Australia *Tel:* (03) 9686-3846 *Fax:* (03) 9682-5169 *E-mail:* cnelson@psmj.com

**Pace University Press**
Unit of Pace University
Dept of Publishing, Rm 805-E, 551 Fifth Ave, New York, NY 10176
*Tel:* 212-346-1417 *Fax:* 212-346-1165
*Web Site:* www.pace.edu/press
*Key Personnel*
Dir: Sherman Raskin *E-mail:* sraskin@pace.edu
Chmn, Edit Comm: Mark Hussey *E-mail:* mhussey@pace.edu
Founded: 1988
Academic books in the humanities.
ISBN Prefix(es): 978-0-944473
Number of titles published annually: 6 Print
Total Titles: 52 Print

**Pacific Press Publishing Association**
Division of Seventh-Day Adventist Church
1350 N Kings Rd, Nampa, ID 83687-3193
Mailing Address: PO Box 5353, Nampa, ID 83653-5353
*Tel:* 208-465-2500 *Toll Free Tel:* 800-447-7377 *Fax:* 208-465-2531
*Web Site:* www.pacificpress.com
*Key Personnel*
CIO: Ed Bahr *Tel:* 208-465-2630 *E-mail:* edubah@pacificpress.com
Pres & Gen Mgr: Dale Galusha *Tel:* 208-465-2501 *E-mail:* dalgal@pacificpress.com
VP, Fin: Don Upson *Tel:* 208-465-2536 *E-mail:* don.upson.sr@pacificpress.com
VP, Mktg & Sales: Doug Church *Tel:* 208-465-2505 *E-mail:* douchu@pacificpress.com
VP, Prodn: Chuck Bobst *Tel:* 208-465-2611 *E-mail:* chubob@pacificpress.com
VP, Prod Devt: Jerry Thomas *E-mail:* jertho@pacificpress.com
Magazine Sr Ed: Marvin Moore *Tel:* 208-465-2577 *E-mail:* marmoo@pacificpress.com
Magazine Juv Ed: A Sox *Tel:* 208-465-2580 *E-mail:* ailsox@pacificpress.com
Ad: Bonnie Laing *Tel:* 208-465-2524 *E-mail:* bonlai@pacificpress.com
Sales: Dave Gatten *Tel:* 208-465-2618 *E-mail:* davgat@pacificpress.com
Libn: Bonnie Tyson-Flyn *Tel:* 208-465-2582 *E-mail:* bontys@pacificpress.com
Intl Rts: Carolyn Curtis *Tel:* 208-465-2511 *E-mail:* carcur@pacificpress.com
Trade Mktg Dir: Beverly Logan *Tel:* 208-465-2550 *E-mail:* bevlog@pacificpress.com
Founded: 1874
Religion (Seventh-day Adventist).
ISBN Prefix(es): 978-0-8163
Number of titles published annually: 39 Print
Total Titles: 350 Print; 2 CD-ROM; 675 Online; 2 Audio

**Paintbox Press**
275 Madison Ave, Suite 600, New York, NY 10016
*Tel:* 212-878-6610 *Fax:* 212-202-6157
*E-mail:* info@paintboxpress.com
*Web Site:* www.paintboxpress.com

*Key Personnel*
Owner: Pamela Pease
PR: Kelly Smith
Founded: 1998
Pop-ups & books on art & design.
ISBN Prefix(es): 978-0-966943; 978-0-977790
Number of titles published annually: 4 Print
Total Titles: 10 Print
Membership(s): AIGA, the professional association for design; Children's Book Council; Society of Illustrators

**§Painted Pony Inc**
Subsidiary of Wind River Development Fund
3 Ethete Rd, Fort Washakie, WY 82514
Mailing Address: PO Box 661, Fort Washakie, WY 82514-0661
*Tel:* 307-335-7330 *Toll Free Tel:* 877-253-3824 *Fax:* 307-335-7332
*E-mail:* ppi@wrdf.org
*Web Site:* www.paintedponyinc.com
*Key Personnel*
Pres: Scott Ratliff
Publg Mgr: Jon Cox *Tel:* 307-857-6643 *Fax:* 307-857-7050 *E-mail:* jonc@proformtech.com
Founded: 2004
ISBN Prefix(es): 978-0-9759806
Number of titles published annually: 5 Print; 3 Audio
Total Titles: 5 Print; 3 Audio

**Paladin Press**
Division of Paladin Enterprises Inc
Gunbarrel Tech Ctr, 7077 Winchester Circle, Boulder, CO 80301
SAN: 212-0305
*Tel:* 303-443-7250 *Toll Free Tel:* 800-392-2400 *Fax:* 303-442-8741
*E-mail:* service@paladin-press.com
*Web Site:* www.paladin-press.com
*Key Personnel*
Pres & Publr: Peder C Lund
Edit Dir & Sr Ed: Donna Duvall *E-mail:* donnad@paladin-press.com
Art Dir: Barbara Beasley
Sales & Mktg Mgr: Brad Efting
Cust Rel, Trade & Mail Order Sales: Jeanne Vaughan
Founded: 1970
New titles & reprints on military science & history, weaponry, martial arts & self-defense, survival, police science, terrorism & general interest.
ISBN Prefix(es): 978-0-87364; 978-1-58160
Number of titles published annually: 60 Print
Total Titles: 800 Print
Imprints: C E P Inc; Flying Machines Press; Sycamore Island Books
Distributed by Amazon.com; Barnes & Noble; Borders
*Advertising Agency:* J S O Advertising Inc
Membership(s): IBPA, the Independent Book Publishers Association

**Palgrave Macmillan**
Division of St Martin's Press, LLC
175 Fifth Ave, Suite 200, New York, NY 10010
*Tel:* 646-307-5151 *Fax:* 212-777-6359
*E-mail:* firstname.lastname@palgrave-usa.com
*Web Site:* us.macmillan.com/Palgrave.aspx
*Key Personnel*
Mng Dir: Dominic Knight
Edit Dir: Farideh Koohi-Kamali; Karen Wolny
Exec Ed: Laurie Harting
Prodn & Opers Dir: Alan Bradshaw
Assoc Dir, Mktg & Publicity: Michelle Fitzgerald
Assoc Dir, Mktg: Denise de la Rosa
Sales & Commercial Dir, Scholarly: Lorraine Keelan
Assoc Dir, Online Sales: Roohana Khan
Assoc Dir, Channel Sales: Marit Vagstad
Dir, Creative Servs: Carol St Thomasino
Busn Systems Mgr: Anne Carter
Founded: 1952
Scholarly & trade publisher - cross market publisher.
ISBN Prefix(es): 978-0-312; 978-0-333; 978-1-4039; 978-0-230
Number of titles published annually: 3,200 Print; 2 Online; 850 E-Book
Total Titles: 28,000 Print
Distributor for Berg Publishers; British Film Institute; Manchester University Press; Pluto Press; I B Tauris & Co Ltd; Zed Books
Membership(s): AAP Professional/Scholarly Publishing Division

**Palindrome Press**
PO Box 4151, Fairfax, VA 22124-8151
*Tel:* 703-242-1734 *Fax:* 703-242-1734
*E-mail:* palindromepress@yahoo.com
*Key Personnel*
Publr: Patrick G Finegan, Jr
Founded: 1990
Subject specialties include finance, film scripts & screenplays.
ISBN Prefix(es): 978-1-878905
Number of titles published annually: 6 Print
Total Titles: 12 Print

**Palladium Books Inc**
39074 Webb Ct, Westland, MI 48185
SAN: 294-9504
*Tel:* 734-721-2903 (orders) *Fax:* 734-721-1238
*Web Site:* www.palladiumbooks.com
*Key Personnel*
Pres: Kevin Siembieda *E-mail:* ksiembieda@palladiumbooks.com
Sr Ed: Alex Marciniszyn *E-mail:* alex@palladiumbooks.com
Founded: 1981
Role-playing game books & supplements.
ISBN Prefix(es): 978-0-916211; 978-1-57457
Number of titles published annually: 15 Print
Total Titles: 190 Print

**§Palm Island Press**
411 Truman Ave, Key West, FL 33040
SAN: 298-4024
*Tel:* 305-296-3102
*E-mail:* pipress2@gmail.com
*Key Personnel*
Gen Mgr: Donald Langille
Founded: 1994
ISBN Prefix(es): 978-0-9643434; 978-0-9743524
Number of titles published annually: 3 Print; 2 E-Book
Total Titles: 15 Print; 2 E-Book
Membership(s): Florida Publishers Association Inc; IBPA, the Independent Book Publishers Association

**Palm Kids™**
Formerly Soundprints
Division of Palm Publishing LLC
50 Washington St, 12th fl, Norwalk, CT 06854
*Toll Free Tel:* 800-409-2457
*E-mail:* customercare@palmkids.com; sales@palmkids.com
*Web Site:* www.palmkids.com
*Key Personnel*
Pres: Claire Fennessey
Publr: Mark Ciechon
VP, Sales: Bill Hermes
Sr Art Dir: E J Klopper
Founded: 1988
Board books, picture books, treasuries, early reading chapter books, nature, environment & children's classics. Age group: pre-school, ages 5-10. Soundprints produces realistic storybooks, audiobooks & toys authenticated by the Smithsonian Institution & other education & conservation programs. Subjects include natural history, science & social studies for ages 3-10. Little Soundprints imprint produces wildlife stories, nursery rhymes & children's classics. Most titles available with audio & toys.
ISBN Prefix(es): 978-0-924483; 978-1-56899; 978-1-931465; 978-1-59249; 978-1-60727
Number of titles published annually: 30 Print; 20 Audio
Total Titles: 140 Print; 120 Audio
Subsidiaries: Studio Mouse
Distributor for Musical Kidz LLC
Foreign Rep(s): J C Carrillo (Caribbean, Latin America); Curreri World Services (Asia, Middle East); H B Fenn (Canada); Sonja Merz International (Asia, Middle East)
Foreign Rights: Jacqueline Miller (France, Germany)
*Returns:* PO Box 8020, Ashton, PA 19014-9910
Membership(s): ABA; IBPA, the Independent Book Publishers Association; Museum Store Association; National School Supply & Equipment Association; Toy International Association

**Palmetto Bug Books**
121 N Hibiscus Dr, Miami Beach, FL 33139
*Tel:* 305-531-9813 *Fax:* 305-604-1516
*E-mail:* palmettobugbooks@gmail.com
*Key Personnel*
Pres: Reginald Roach
Founded: 1992
Small publisher of fiction with a slant toward south Florida.
ISBN Prefix(es): 978-0-9634499
Number of titles published annually: 4 Print; 1 Online; 1 E-Book
Total Titles: 4 Print; 4 Online; 4 E-Book

**Pangaea Publications**
226 Wheeler St S, St Paul, MN 55105-1927
*Tel:* 651-226-2032 *Fax:* 651-226-2032
*E-mail:* info@pangaea.org
*Web Site:* pangaea.org
*Key Personnel*
Pres: Bonnie Hayskar *E-mail:* bonzi@pangaea.org
Founded: 1991
Publisher for nature & peoples of the earth.
ISBN Prefix(es): 978-0-9630180; 978-1-929165
Number of titles published annually: 4 Print
Total Titles: 32 Print
Membership(s): AAP; SATW

**§Panoptic Enterprises**
PO Box 11220, Burke, VA 22009-1220
SAN: 265-3141
*Tel:* 703-451-5953 *Toll Free Tel:* 800-594-4766 *Fax:* 703-451-5953
*E-mail:* panoptic@fedgovcontracts.com
*Web Site:* www.fedgovcontracts.com
*Key Personnel*
Pres & Intl Rts: Vivina H McVay
VP: Barry McVay
Founded: 1982
Books on how-to obtain & administer federal contracts.
ISBN Prefix(es): 978-0-912481
Number of titles published annually: 6 Print
Total Titles: 12 Print
*Returns:* 6055 Ridge Ford Dr, Burke, VA 22015
*Shipping Address:* 6055 Ridge Ford Dr, Burke, VA 22015
*Warehouse:* 6055 Ridge Ford Dr, Burke, VA 22015
Membership(s): IBPA, the Independent Book Publishers Association; Washington Book Publishers

**Pantheon Books/Schocken Books**
Imprint of Knopf Doubleday Publishing Group
c/o Random House Inc, 1745 Broadway, New York, NY 10019
SAN: 202-862X
*Tel:* 212-751-2600 *Toll Free Tel:* 800-638-6460 *Fax:* 212-572-6030

*Key Personnel*
EVP & Publg Dir: Patricia Johnson
VP & Dir, Edit: Daniel Frank
VP & Exec Ed: Erroll McDonald
VP & Dir, Prodn: Andy Hughes
VP & Assoc Publr: Christine Gillespie
Mng Ed & Dir, Edit, Schocken Books: Altie Karper
Sr Ed, Pantheon Books: Shelley Wanger
Sr Ed: Deborah Garrison
Ed: Diana Coglianese
Dir, Busn Opers: Justine LeCates
Dir, Dom Rts (Reprint Rts): Sean Yule
Dir, Publicity: Michiko Clark
Assoc Dir, Publicity: Michelle Somers
Asst Mgr, Dom Rts (Book Club, Serial & Performance): Thomas Dobrowolski
Asst Mgr, Foreign Rts: Suzanne Smith
Founded: 1942
Fiction & nonfiction.
Random House Inc & its publishing entities are not accepting proposals, mss or submission queries via e-mail at this time.
ISBN Prefix(es): 978-0-679; 978-0-8052; 978-0-375
Imprints: Schocken Books
Foreign Rep(s): Century Hutchinson Group (South America); Colt Associates (Africa exc South Africa); Steve Franklin (Israel); India Book Distributors (India); International Publishers Representatives (Middle East exc Israel); Pandemic Ltd (Continental Europe exc Scandinavia); Periodical Management Group Inc (Mexico); Random Century (Australia); Random House New Zealand Ltd (New Zealand); Random House of Canada Limited (Canada); Random House UK Ltd (UK); Saga Books ApS (Scandinavia); Sonrisa Book Service (Latin America exc Mexico); Yohan (Japan)
Foreign Rights: Agencia Literaria BMSR (Brazil); Arts & Licensing International (China); Carmen Balcells Agencia (Spain); DRT International (Korea); The English Agency (Japan); Graal Literary Agency (Poland); JLM Literary Agency (Greece); Katai & Bolza (Hungary); Agence Michelle Lapautre (France); Licht & Licht Agency (Scandinavia); Literarni Agentura (Czech Republic); Roberto Santachiara (Italy); Sebes & Van Gelderen Literary Agency (Netherlands)

**Pants On Fire Press**
2062 Harbor Cove Way, Winter Garden, FL 34787
*Tel:* 863-546-0760
*E-mail:* submission@pantsonfirepress.com
*Web Site:* www.pantsonfirepress.com
*Key Personnel*
Publr: David Powers *E-mail:* david@pantsonfirepress.com
Dir, Mktg: Cris Francet *E-mail:* cris@pantsonfirepress.com
Founded: 2007
Publish popular genre fiction for children, teens & discerning adults. Select nonfiction health & technical books.
ISBN Prefix(es): 978-0-9827271
Number of titles published annually: 12 Print; 12 E-Book; 1 Audio
Total Titles: 9 Print; 9 E-Book; 1 Audio
Foreign Rights: Joe Veltre (Worldwide)
*Distribution Center:* Publishers Group West, 1700 Fourth St, Berkeley, CA 94710 *E-mail:* info@pgw.com *Web Site:* www.pgw.com
Membership(s): IBPA, the Independent Book Publishers Association

**Paper Thoughts Publishing**
PO Box 13003, Coyote, CA 95013
*Tel:* 408-782-4407
*E-mail:* paperthougthspub@aol.com
*Web Site:* paperthoughtspublishing.com
*Key Personnel*
Owner: Michelle Martin
Founded: 2011
Publisher of most genres, fiction & nonfiction.
ISBN Prefix(es): 978-0-9857355
Number of titles published annually: 4 Print; 4 Online; 4 E-Book; 1 Audio
Total Titles: 3 Print

**Papercutz**
40 Exchange Place, Suite 1308, New York, NY 10005
*Tel:* 212-643-5407 *Toll Free Tel:* 800-886-1223 *Fax:* 212-643-1545
*E-mail:* papercutz@papercutz.com
*Web Site:* www.papercutz.com
*Key Personnel*
CEO & Pres: Terry Nantier
Ed-in-Chief: Jim Salicup
Founded: 2005
Graphic novels for ages 7-14.
ISBN Prefix(es): 978-1-59707
Number of titles published annually: 40 Print; 12 Online
Total Titles: 150 Print
Distributed by Macmillan
*Orders to:* MPS Distribution Center, 16365 James Madison Hwy, Gordonsville, VA 22942 *Toll Free Tel:* 888-330-8477 *Toll Free Fax:* 800-672-2054
*Warehouse:* MPS Distribution Center, 16365 James Madison Hwy, Gordonsville, VA 22942 *Toll Free Tel:* 888-330-8477 *Toll Free Fax:* 800-672-2054
*Distribution Center:* MPS Distribution Center, 16365 James Madison Hwy, Gordonsville, VA 22942 *Toll Free Tel:* 888-330-8477 *Toll Free Fax:* 800-672-2054

**Papyrus Publishers**, see Letterbox/Papyrus of London Publishers USA

**§Para Publishing LLC**
PO Box 8206-240, Santa Barbara, CA 93118-8206
SAN: 215-8981
*Tel:* 805-968-7277 *Toll Free Tel:* 800-727-2782 *Fax:* 805-968-1379
*Web Site:* www.parapublishing.com
*Key Personnel*
Owner & Publr: Dan Poynter *E-mail:* danpoynter@parapublishing.com
Off Mgr: Becky Carbone *E-mail:* becky@parapublishing.com
Founded: 1969
Illustrated nonfiction trade books; parachutes, skydiving & aspects of book publishing; book marketing, promotion & distribution.
ISBN Prefix(es): 978-1-56860
Number of titles published annually: 6 Print; 1 CD-ROM; 6 Online; 6 E-Book; 1 Audio
Total Titles: 33 Print; 3 CD-ROM; 15 Online; 15 E-Book; 3 Audio
Imprints: Parachuting Publications
Divisions: Global eBook Awards; Paralists; Para Publishing Seminars; Poynter Consulting; Publishing Poynters Newsletter
Distributed by NBN
Foreign Rep(s): NBN (Australia, Canada, UK)
Foreign Rights: Bob Erdmann
*Advertising Agency:* Chadwick Advertising
*Shipping Address:* 530 Ellwood Ridge, Santa Barbara, CA 93117-1407
Membership(s): IBPA, the Independent Book Publishers Association

**Parabola Books**
Subsidiary of Society for the Study of Myth & Tradition
20 W 20 St, 2nd fl, New York, NY 10011
*Tel:* 212-822-8806 *Toll Free Tel:* 800-592-2521 (subns) *Fax:* 212-822-8823
*E-mail:* info@parabola.org
*Web Site:* www.parabola.org
*Key Personnel*
Publr & Ed-in-Chief: Jeff Zaleski
Exec Ed: Tracy Cochran
Mng Ed: Dale Fuller
Founded: 1976
Classic & contemporary works exploring the human search for meaning through story, art, psychology, science, etc. Subject specialties include essays, literary analysis, interviews, mythology & multiculturalism.
ISBN Prefix(es): 978-0-930407
Number of titles published annually: 4 Print
Total Titles: 130 Print

**Parachute Publishing LLC**
Division of Parachute Properties LLC
322 Eighth Ave, Suite 702, New York, NY 10001
*Tel:* 212-691-1422 *Fax:* 212-645-8769
*E-mail:* tlabreglia@parachutepublishing.com
*Web Site:* www.parachutepublishing.com
*Key Personnel*
CEO & Chmn: Joan Waricha *E-mail:* jwaricha@parachutepublishing.com
Chair: Jane Stine *Tel:* 212-691-1421 *E-mail:* jstine@parachutepublishing.com
Founded: 1983
Children's & adult fiction & nonfiction: original books & series, books from licensed properties.
ISBN Prefix(es): 978-0-938753
Number of titles published annually: 100 Print; 2 E-Book
Total Titles: 1,000 Print
Distributed by Bantam; Bendon; Berkley; Grosset; Harcourt; HarperCollins; Harper Entertainment; Kensington; Dorling Kindersley; Little, Brown; Pocket; Random House; Running Press; Scholastic; Simon & Schuster
Membership(s): American Book Producers Association; Children's Book Council

**Paraclete Press Inc**
36 Southern Eagle Cartway, Brewster, MA 02631
SAN: 282-1508
Mailing Address: PO Box 1568, Orleans, MA 02653-1568
*Tel:* 508-255-4685 *Toll Free Tel:* 800-451-5006 *Fax:* 508-255-5705
*E-mail:* mail@paracletepress.com
*Web Site:* www.paracletepress.com
*Key Personnel*
CEO & Pres: Pamela Jordan
Ed-in-Chief & Assoc Publr: Jon Sweeney
Founded: 1981
Spirituality, personal testimonies, devotionals, literary fiction, new editions of classics & CDs.
ISBN Prefix(es): 978-1-55725; 978-0-941478
Number of titles published annually: 38 Print
Total Titles: 145 Print; 3 Audio
Distributor for Abbey of Saint Peter of Solesmes; Gloriae Dei Cantores
Membership(s): CBA; Evangelical Christian Publishers Association

**§Paradigm Publications**
Division of Redwing Book Co
202 Bendix Dr, Taos, NM 87571
*Tel:* 575-758-7758 *Toll Free Tel:* 800-873-3946 (US); 888-873-3947 (CN) *Fax:* 575-758-7768
*Web Site:* www.paradigm-pubs.com; www.redwingbooks.com
*Key Personnel*
Publr: Robert L Felt *E-mail:* bob@paradigm-pubs.com
Founded: 1980
Scholarly books on traditional Chinese medicine & acupuncture.
ISBN Prefix(es): 978-0-912111
Number of titles published annually: 2 Print
Total Titles: 60 Print; 12 E-Book; 1 Audio

**§Paradigm Publishers**
5589 Arapahoe Ave, Suite 206A, Boulder, CO 80303
*Tel:* 303-245-9054
*Web Site:* www.paradigmpublishers.com
*Key Personnel*
Pres & Publr: Dean Birkencamp
VP & Assoc Publr: Jennifer Knerr
Dir, Edit Prodn: Laura Esterman
Dir, Sales & Mktg: Pete Hammond
Busn Mgr & Data Opers Mgr: Maggie Faber
Foreign Rts & Journals Mgr: Jason Barry
Founded: 2003
ISBN Prefix(es): 978-1-59451; 978-1-61205
Total Titles: 500 Print
Foreign Rep(s): Brookside Publishing Services (Ireland, Northern Ireland); Compass Academic Ltd (UK exc Northern Ireland); Durnell Marketing (Europe exc Ireland); Footprint Books Pty Ltd (Australia, New Zealand); IMA (Tony Moggach) (Africa exc South Africa); Jacana Media Pty Ltd (Botswana, Lesotho, Namibia, South Africa, Swaziland); Maya Publishers Pvt Ltd (Surit Mitra) (India); Missing Link Versandbuchhandlung (Germany); Taylor & Francis Asia Pacific (Far East exc Japan); United Publishers Services Ltd (Japan); University of BC Press (Canada)
Foreign Rights: Brookside Publishing Services (Northern Ireland); Compass Academic Ltd (UK exc Ireland); Durnell Marketing (Europe exc Ireland & UK); Footprint Books Pty Ltd (Australia, New Zealand); IMA (Tony Moggach) (Africa exc South Africa); Jacana Media (Pty) Ltd (Botswana, Lesotho, Namibia, South Africa, Swaziland); Maya Publishers Pvt Ltd (Surit Mitra) (India); Missing Link Versandbuchhandlung (Germany); Taylor & Francis Asia Pacific (Far East exc Japan); United Publishers Service (Japan)
*Orders to:* PO Box 605, Herndon, VA 20172-0605 *Toll Free Tel:* 800-887-1591 *Fax:* 703-661-1501 *E-mail:* paradigmmail@presswarehouse.com; University of Toronto Press, 5201 Dufferin St, Toronto, ON M3H 5T8, Canada *Tel:* 416-667-7791 *Toll Free Tel:* 800-565-9523 *Fax:* 416-667-7832 *Toll Free Fax:* 800-221-9985 *E-mail:* utpbooks@utpress.utoronto.ca; Pluto Press/Marston Book Services, 345 Archway Rd, London N6 5AA, United Kingdom (UK & Europe) *Tel:* (020) 8348 2724 *Fax:* (020) 8348 9133 *E-mail:* pluto@plutobooks.com *Web Site:* www.plutobooks.com
*Returns:* 22883 Quicksilver Dr, Dulles, VA 20166

**Paradise Cay Publications Inc**
550 S "G" St, Suite 1, Arcata, CA 95521
Mailing Address: PO Box 29, Arcata, CA 95518-0029
*Tel:* 707-822-9063 *Toll Free Tel:* 800-736-4509 *Fax:* 707-822-9163
*E-mail:* info@paracay.com
*Web Site:* www.paracay.com
*Key Personnel*
Owner & Dir: Jim Morehouse *E-mail:* jim@paracay.com
Publr: Matt Morehouse *E-mail:* matt@paracay.com
Founded: 1977
Nautical books, videos, art prints, cruising guides & software.
ISBN Prefix(es): 978-0-939837; 978-0-9646036
Number of titles published annually: 6 Print
Total Titles: 82 Print; 4 Audio
Imprints: Pardey Publications
Foreign Rep(s): Boat Books (Australia); Islamorado Internacional (Panama); The Nautical Mind (Canada); Transpacific Marine (New Zealand)

**Paragon House**
1925 Oakcrest Ave, Suite 7, St Paul, MN 55113-2619
*Tel:* 651-644-3087 *Toll Free Tel:* 800-447-3709 *Fax:* 651-644-0997
*E-mail:* paragon@paragonhouse.com
*Web Site:* www.paragonhouse.com
*Key Personnel*
Pres: Gordon L Anderson
Acqs Mgr & Opers Coord: Rosemary Yokoi
Founded: 1982
Nonfiction; reference, academic/scholarly monographs, trade & college paperbacks. History, religion, philosophy, New Age & Jewish interest, reference.
ISBN Prefix(es): 978-1-55778; 978-0-913729; 978-0-913757; 978-0-89226; 978-0-943852; 978-0-88702; 978-1-885118
Number of titles published annually: 10 Print
Total Titles: 400 Print
Imprints: IRF Books; Life Wisdom; PWPA Books
Distributed by Continuum International Publishing USA
Distributor for International Conferences on the Unity of the Sciences; Professors World Peace Academy
Foreign Rep(s): Roundhouse Publishing (Europe, UK)
Foreign Rights: Paragon House (Worldwide)
*Shipping Address:* National Book Network, 15200 NBN Way, Blue Ridge Summit, PA 17214 *Tel:* 717-794-3800 *Toll Free Tel:* 800-561-7704 *Fax:* 717-794-3803 *E-mail:* orders@continuumbooks.com

**§Parallax Press**
Division of Unified Buddhist Church
2236-B Sixth St, Berkeley, CA 94710
Mailing Address: PO Box 7355, Berkeley, CA 94707-0355 SAN: 663-4494
*Tel:* 510-525-0101 *Toll Free Tel:* 800-863-5290 (orders) *Fax:* 510-525-7129
*E-mail:* info@parallax.org
*Web Site:* www.parallax.org
*Key Personnel*
Publr: Travis Masch *Tel:* 510-525-0101 ext 104 *E-mail:* travism@parallax.org
Sr Ed: Rachel Neumann *Tel:* 510-525-0101 ext 113 *E-mail:* rachel@parallax.org
Founded: 1986
Trade paperbacks; audio cassettes; subscription & mail-order books.
ISBN Prefix(es): 978-0-938077; 978-1-888375
Number of titles published annually: 15 Print
Total Titles: 7 Audio
Imprints: Plum Blossom Books (mindfulness books for children)
Foreign Rights: Cecile Barendsma (all other territories); Brother Phap Kham (Vietnam); Literaturmanufaktur (Ursula Richard) (Germany); Plum Village Foundation (Thailand); Shantum Seth (India)
*Distribution Center:* Publishers Group West, 1094 Flex Dr, Jackson, TN 38301 *Toll Free Tel:* 800-788-3123 *Toll Free Fax:* 800-351-5073 *E-mail:* orderentry@perseusbooks.com *Web Site:* www.pgw.com
Publishers Group Canada, 559 College St, Suite 402, Vancouver, BC M6G 1A9, Canada *Tel:* 604-323-7106 *Toll Free Tel:* 800-663-5714 *Fax:* 604-323-2600 *Toll Free Fax:* 800-565-3770 *E-mail:* customerservice@raincoast.com *Web Site:* www.pgcbooks.ca
Publishers Group UK, 8 The Arena, Mollison Ave, Enfield, Middlesex EN3 7NJ, United Kingdom *Tel:* (020) 8804 0400 *Fax:* (020) 8804 0044 *E-mail:* info@pguk.co.uk

**Paramount Market Publishing Inc**
950 Danby Rd, Suite 136, Ithaca, NY 14850
*Tel:* 607-275-8100 *Toll Free Tel:* 888-787-8100 *Fax:* 607-275-8101
*E-mail:* editors@paramountbooks.com
*Web Site:* www.paramountbooks.com
Founded: 1999
Marketing, market research, market segments & brand management.
ISBN Prefix(es): 978-0-9571439; 978-0-9725290; 978-0-9766973; 978-0-9786602; 978-0-9801745; 978-0-9819869; 978-0-9830436
Number of titles published annually: 6 Print; 6 E-Book
Total Titles: 85 Print; 60 E-Book
Imprints: PMP

**Parenting Press Inc**
11065 Fifth Ave NE, Suite F, Seattle, WA 98125
SAN: 215-6938
Mailing Address: PO Box 75267, Seattle, WA 98175-0267
*Tel:* 206-364-2900 *Toll Free Tel:* 800-99-BOOKS (992-6657) *Fax:* 206-364-0702
*E-mail:* office@parentingpress.com; marketing@parentingpress.com
*Web Site:* www.parentingpress.com
*Key Personnel*
Pres: Elizabeth Crary
Opers Mgr: Homer Henderson *Tel:* 206-364-2900 ext 101
Acqs: Carolyn Threadgill *Tel:* 206-364-2900 ext 107 *E-mail:* cthreadgill@parentingpress.com
Mktg: Linda Carlson *Tel:* 206-364-2900 ext 105
Founded: 1979
Parenting, social skill building, personal safety for children, discipline, feelings, temperament, development, boundaries, problem solving, social relations.
ISBN Prefix(es): 978-0-943990; 978-0-9602862 (Co-published with Raefield-Roberts); 978-1-884734; 978-1-936903
Number of titles published annually: 6 Print; 26 Online; 2 E-Book
Total Titles: 113 Print; 5 Online; 11 E-Book
Distributor for Raefield-Roberts, Publishers
*Distribution Center:* IPG, 814 N Franklin St, Chicago, IL 60610 *Tel:* 312-337-0747 *Toll Free Tel:* 800-888-4741 *Fax:* 312-337-5985 *Web Site:* www.ipgbook.com
Membership(s): Book Publishers of the Northwest; IBPA, the Independent Book Publishers Association; Publishers Association of the West

**Park Genealogical Books**
PO Box 130968, Roseville, MN 55113-0968
*Tel:* 651-488-4416 *Fax:* 651-488-2653
*Web Site:* www.parkbooks.com
*Key Personnel*
Owner: Mary Hawker Bakeman *E-mail:* mbakeman@parkbooks.com
Founded: 1974
Minnesota genelogy.
ISBN Prefix(es): 978-0-915709; 978-1-932212
Number of titles published annually: 5 Print
Total Titles: 140 Print

**Park Place Publications**
591 Lighthouse Ave, Suite 10, Pacific Grove, CA 93950
SAN: 297-5238
Mailing Address: PO Box 829, Pacific Grove, CA 92950-0829
*Tel:* 831-649-6640 *Toll Free Tel:* 888-702-4500
*E-mail:* publishingbiz@sbcglobal.net
*Web Site:* www.parkplacepublications.com
*Key Personnel*
Owner & Publr: Patricia Hamilton
Founded: 1991
Provides book publishing, graphic design & prepress services. Founded on the premise that "Books make a world of difference" (the company slogan).
This publisher has indicated that 90% of their product line is author subsidized.
ISBN Prefix(es): 978-1-877809
Number of titles published annually: 15 Print
Total Titles: 50 Print; 14 Online

Imprints: Alamos Press (American & Mexican culture & bilingual); At Home on the Road (travel)
Membership(s): The Association of Publishers for Special Sales; IBPA, the Independent Book Publishers Association; Small Publishers, Artists & Writers Network

**Parlay Press**
301 Central Ave, No 311, Hilton Head, SC 29926
*Toll Free Fax:* 888-301-3116
*E-mail:* mail@parlaypress.com
*Web Site:* www.parlaypress.com
*Key Personnel*
Publr: Peyton Parker
Founded: 1988
Publishes textbooks on language & writing.
ISBN Prefix(es): 978-0-9644636; 978-0-9767180
Number of titles published annually: 4 Print

**§Parmenides Publishing**
3753 Howard Hughes Pkwy, Suite 200, Las Vegas, NV 89169
SAN: 254-4342
*Tel:* 702-892-3934 *Fax:* 702-892-3939
*E-mail:* info@parmenides.com
*Web Site:* www.parmenides.com
*Key Personnel*
CEO & Publr: Sara Hermann *E-mail:* sherman@parmenides.com
VP & Sales Dir: Gale Carr *E-mail:* gcarr@parmenides.com
Founded: 2000
Independent publishing house. Specialize in literature on philosophy, especially ancient Greek philosophy for the academic & trade markets.
ISBN Prefix(es): 978-1-930972
Number of titles published annually: 10 Print; 10 Online; 4 Audio
Total Titles: 28 Print; 15 Online; 4 Audio
Divisions: ParmenidesAudio™; ParmenidesFiction™
Foreign Rep(s): APAC (Tom Cassidy) (Brunei, Cambodia, China, Hong Kong, Indonesia, Malaysia, Myanmar, Singapore, Taiwan, Thailand, Vietnam)
*Orders to:* The University of Chicago Press Distribution Center, 1427 E 60 St, Chicago, IL 60637 *Toll Free Tel:* 800-621-2736 *Fax:* 773-702-9756 *E-mail:* orders@press.uchicago.edu
*Returns:* The University of Chicago Press Distribution Center, 11030 S Langley, Chicago, IL 60628 *Tel:* 773-702-7700 *Fax:* 773-702-9756 *Toll Free Fax:* 800-621-8476 *E-mail:* orders@press.uchicago.edu
*Shipping Address:* The University of Chicago Press Distribution Center, 11030 S Langley, Chicago, IL 60628 *Tel:* 773-702-7700 *Fax:* 773-702-9756 *Toll Free Fax:* 800-621-8476 *E-mail:* orders@press.uchicago.edu
*Warehouse:* The University of Chicago Press Distribution Center, 11030 S Langley, Chicago, IL 60628 *Tel:* 773-702-7700 *Fax:* 773-702-9756 *Toll Free Fax:* 800-621-8476 *E-mail:* orders@press.uchicago.edu
*Distribution Center:* The University of Chicago Press Distribution Center, 11030 S Langley, Chicago, IL 60628 *Tel:* 773-702-7700 *Toll Free Tel:* 800-621-8476 (orders) *Fax:* 773-702-9756 *Toll Free Fax:* 800-621-8476 *E-mail:* orders@press.uchicago.edu
Membership(s): AAP

**§Pastoral Press**
Imprint of OCP Publications Inc
5536 NE Hassalo, Portland, OR 97213-3638
*Tel:* 503-281-1191 *Toll Free Tel:* 800-548-8749 *Fax:* 503-282-3486 *Toll Free Fax:* 800-462-7329
*E-mail:* liturgy@ocp.org
*Web Site:* www.ocp.org
*Key Personnel*
Publr: John Limb
Ed: Bari Columbari
Mktg: Kelsey Markham
Founded: 1985
Association presses, professional books & scholarly books, books on religion & theology.
ISBN Prefix(es): 978-0-915531; 978-0-9602378; 978-0-912405; 978-1-56929
Number of titles published annually: 8 Print
Total Titles: 190 Print
Foreign Rep(s): Decani Music Ltd (UK); Rainbow Book Agencies (Australia)

**Path Press Inc**
1229 Emerson St, Evanston, IL 60201
SAN: 630-2041
*Tel:* 847-492-0177
*E-mail:* pathpressinc@aol.com
*Key Personnel*
Pres: Bennett J Johnson
Founded: 1962
Books for African-American & Third World people.
ISBN Prefix(es): 978-0-910671
Number of titles published annually: 3 Print
Total Titles: 43 Print
Subsidiaries: African-American Book Distributors Inc
*Advertising Agency:* R J Dale Advertising Inc, 211 E Ontario St, Chicago, IL 60611 *Tel:* 312-644-2316

**Pathfinder Publishing Inc**
120 S Houghton Rd, Suite 138, Tucson, AZ 85748
SAN: 694-2571
*Tel:* 520-647-0158 *Toll Free Tel:* 800-977-2282 *Fax:* 520-647-0160
*Web Site:* www.pathfinderpublishing.com
*Key Personnel*
CEO & Pres: Bill Mosbrook *E-mail:* bill@pathfinderpublishing.com
Treas: Evelyn Mosbrook *E-mail:* evelyn@pathfinderpublishing.com
Founded: 1985
Books & audiotape books. Specialize in music, psychology & military.
ISBN Prefix(es): 978-0-934793
Number of titles published annually: 3 Print; 1 Audio
Total Titles: 50 Print; 3 Audio
Membership(s): IBPA, the Independent Book Publishers Association

**Patria Press Inc**
PO Box 752, Carmel, IN 46082
*Tel:* 317-577-1321 *Fax:* 413-215-8030
*E-mail:* moreinfo@patriapress.com
*Web Site:* www.patriapress.com; www.facebook.com/YoungPatriotsBooks; twitter.com/#!/kidsbios
*Key Personnel*
Pres & Publr: Florrie Binford Kichler
Founded: 1999
Publisher of the Young Patriots Series of children's historical fiction.
ISBN Prefix(es): 978-1-882859
Number of titles published annually: 2 Print; 2 E-Book
Total Titles: 14 Print; 14 E-Book
Imprints: Young Patriots Series
*Sales Office(s):* Independent Publishers Group (IPG), 814 N Franklin St, Chicago, IL 60610 SAN: 153-7504
*Billing Address:* Independent Publishers Group (IPG), 814 N Franklin St, Chicago, IL 60610 SAN: 153-7504
*Orders to:* Independent Publishers Group (IPG), 814 N Franklin St, Chicago, IL 60610 *Tel:* 312-337-0747 *Toll Free Tel:* 800-888-4741 *Fax:* 312-337-5985 *E-mail:* orders@ipgbook.com *Web Site:* www.ipgbook.com SAN: 153-7504
*Returns:* Independent Publishers Group (IPG), 814 N Franklin St, Chicago, IL 60610 SAN: 153-7504
*Shipping Address:* Independent Publishers Group (IPG), 814 N Franklin St, Chicago, IL 60610 *Tel:* 312-337-0747 *Toll Free Tel:* 800-888-4741 *Fax:* 312-337-5985 *E-mail:* orders@ipgbook.com *Web Site:* www.ipgbook.com SAN: 153-7504
*Warehouse:* Independent Publishers Group (IPG), 814 N Franklin St, Chicago, IL 60610 SAN: 153-7504
Membership(s): BISG; Children's Book Council; IBPA, the Independent Book Publishers Association; Women's National Book Association

**Paul Dry Books**
1616 Walnut St, Suite 808, Philadelphia, PA 19103
*Tel:* 215-231-9939 *Fax:* 215-231-9942
*E-mail:* editor@pauldrybooks.com
*Web Site:* www.pauldrybooks.com
*Key Personnel*
Owner & Publr: Paul Dry *E-mail:* pdry@pauldrybooks.com
Mng Ed: John Corenswet *E-mail:* jcorenswet@pauldrybooks.com
Assoc Ed: William Schofield
Literary publications: fiction, history & essays.
ISBN Prefix(es): 978-0-9664913; 978-0-9679675; 978-1-58988
Number of titles published annually: 6 Print
Total Titles: 6 Print

**Paula Wiseman Books**, see Simon & Schuster Children's Publishing

**Pauline Books & Media**
Division of Daughters of St Paul
50 Saint Paul's Ave, Boston, MA 02130
SAN: 203-8900
*Tel:* 617-522-8911 *Toll Free Tel:* 800-876-4463 (orders); 800-836-9723 (cust serv) *Fax:* 617-541-9805
*E-mail:* orderentry@pauline.org (cust serv); editorial@paulinemedia.com (ms submissions)
*Web Site:* www.pauline.org
*Key Personnel*
Publr & Edit Dir: Sr Mary Mark Wickenhiser
Promo Mgr: Sr Denise Cecilia Benjamin
Acqs Ed: Sr Sean Marie David Mayer; Sr Christina Wegendt
Children's & Teen Ed: Sr Marlyn Evangelina Monge; Jaymie Stuart Wolfe
Intl Rts: Brad McCracken
Book Center Acqs: Anthony Ruggiero
Edit Asst, Acqs: Brittany Schlorff *E-mail:* editorial@paulinemedia.com
Founded: 1932
Spirituality, prayer books, teachers' resources for religious education, liturgical books, church documents, adult religious instruction, saints lives, faith & culture, music & music CDs.
ISBN Prefix(es): 978-0-8198
Number of titles published annually: 75 Print; 1 Audio
Total Titles: 600 Print; 72 Audio
Imprints: Catholic Approach Series; Encounter the Saints Series; Faith & Culture; Pauline Comics Series; The Saints Series; Theology of the Body Series; Cardinal Van Thuan Series

**§Paulist Press**
997 MacArthur Blvd, Mahwah, NJ 07430-9990
SAN: 202-5159
*Tel:* 201-825-7300 *Toll Free Tel:* 800-218-1903 *Fax:* 201-825-8345 *Toll Free Fax:* 800-836-3161
*E-mail:* info@paulistpress.com
*Web Site:* www.paulistpress.com

*Key Personnel*
VP & Gen Mgr: Kevin Maguire
Dir, Sales: Bob Byrns *Tel:* 201-825-7300 ext 231 *E-mail:* bbyrns@paulistpress.com
Dir, Mktg: Gloria A Capik *E-mail:* gcapik@paulistpress.com
Publr & Edit Dir: Mark-David Janus, CSP *E-mail:* mdjanus@paulistpress.com
Mng Ed: Donna Crilly *E-mail:* dcrilly@paulistpress.com
Prodn Dir: Kimberly Bernard *E-mail:* aekroth@paulistpress.com
Rts & Intl Rts: Angela Ekroth
Academic Ed: Nancy de Flon
Ed-at-Large: Christopher Bellitto
Ed: Enrique Aguilar; James Quigley
Publicity: Mary Ann Carey *E-mail:* mcarey@paulistpress.com
Founded: 1866
Resources with emphasis on biblical studies, Christian, Catholic & ecumenical formation & education, ethics & social issues, pastoral ministry, personal growth, spirituality, philosophy, theology.
ISBN Prefix(es): 978-0-8091
Number of titles published annually: 90 Print
Total Titles: 1,600 Print
Imprints: HiddenSpring; E T Nedder Publishing; The Newman Press; Stimulus Books
Foreign Rep(s): Columba Book Service (Europe); Katong Catholic Book Centre Pte Ltd (Singapore); KCBS Inc (Korea); Novalis (Canada); Pleroma Christian Supplies (New Zealand); PRECA Bookshop (Malta); Rainbow Book Agencies/Word of Life (Australia); St Paul's India (India); St Paul's Liberia (Liberia)
*Warehouse:* 39 Ramapo Valley Rd, Mahwah, NJ 07430

**Peabody Museum Press**
Unit of Peabody Museum of Archaeology & Ethnology, Harvard University
11 Divinity Ave, Cambridge, MA 02138
*Tel:* 617-495-4255 *Fax:* 617-495-7535
*E-mail:* peapub@fas.harvard.edu
*Web Site:* www.peabody.harvard.edu/publications
*Key Personnel*
Exec Ed: Joan O'Donnell *E-mail:* jkodonn@fas.harvard.edu
Proj Mgr: Donna Dickerson *E-mail:* ddickers@fas.harvard.edu
Founded: 1888
ISBN Prefix(es): 978-0-87365
Number of titles published annually: 9 Print
Total Titles: 140 Print
*Distribution Center:* Harvard University Press

**Peace Hill Press**
18021 The Glebe Lane, Charles City, VA 23030
*Tel:* 804-829-5043 *Toll Free Tel:* 877-322-3445 (orders) *Fax:* 804-829-5704
*E-mail:* info@peacehillpress.com
*Web Site:* www.peacehillpress.com
*Key Personnel*
CEO: Jay Wise
Ed-in-Chief: Susan Wise Bauer
Exec Administrator: Kim Norton
Founded: 2001
Publish educational books for home school families & schools & books for the well-trained mind.
ISBN Prefix(es): 978-0-9714129; 978-1-933339
Number of titles published annually: 5 Print
Total Titles: 12 Print
Distributed by W W Norton & Co
Foreign Rights: Richard Henshaw (Central America, South America)

**Peachpit Press**
Division of Pearson Education
1249 Eighth St, Berkeley, CA 94710
*Tel:* 510-524-2178 *Toll Free Tel:* 800-283-9444 *Fax:* 510-524-2221
*E-mail:* info@peachpit.com
*Web Site:* www.peachpit.com
*Key Personnel*
VP & Publr: Nancy Ruenzel *Tel:* 510-524-2178 ext 124 *Fax:* 510-524-2385 *E-mail:* nancy.ruenzel@peachpit.com
Assoc Publr: Hannah Onstad-Latham
Exec Ed: Clifford Colby
Ed-in-Chief: Nancy Davis
Dir, Mktg: Scott Cowlin *E-mail:* scott.cowlin@peachpit.com
Busn Mgr: Keasley Jones
Founded: 1986
ISBN Prefix(es): 978-0-201; 978-1-56609; 978-0-938151
Number of titles published annually: 180 Print
Total Titles: 400 Print

**Peachtree Publishers**
1700 Chattahoochee Ave, Atlanta, GA 30318-2112
SAN: 212-1999
*Tel:* 404-876-8761 *Toll Free Tel:* 800-241-0113 *Fax:* 404-875-2578 *Toll Free Fax:* 800-875-8909
*E-mail:* hello@peachtree-online.com
*Web Site:* www.peachtree-online.com
*Key Personnel*
Subs Rts: Kathy Landwehr
Sales: Laura Palermo *Tel:* 404-876-8761 ext 114
Founded: 1977
Children's fiction & nonfiction, self-help & health/parenting & regional guides.
ISBN Prefix(es): 978-0-931948; 978-0-934601; 978-1-56145
Number of titles published annually: 40 Print
Total Titles: 300 Print
Imprints: Freestone; Peachtree Jr
Foreign Rep(s): Fitzhenry & Whiteside Publishers (Canada); Jacqueline Miller Agency (France)
Foreign Rights: Kathy Landwehr (Worldwide)

**Peanut Butter & Jelly Press LLC**
PO Box 590239, Newton, MA 02459-0002
SAN: 299-7444
*Tel:* 617-630-0945 *Fax:* 617-630-0945 (call first)
*E-mail:* info@pbjpress.com
*Web Site:* www.publishinggame.com; www.pbjpress.com
*Key Personnel*
Owner: Elizabeth Harris
Off Mgr: Alyza Harris *E-mail:* alyza@publishinggame.com
Founded: 1998
General Trade Books - hardcover & softcover, including our best selling *The Infertility Diet: Get Pregnant and Prevent Miscarriage* now in it's 12th printing; BookSense selection: *Terrorism & Kids: Comforting Your Child* & *The Publishing Game* 3 in the series.
ISBN Prefix(es): 978-1-893290
Number of titles published annually: 5 Print
Total Titles: 11 Print
Membership(s): ABA; The Association of Publishers for Special Sales; Great Lakes Independent Booksellers Association; IBPA, the Independent Book Publishers Association; International Association of Writers; NEBA; Pacific Northwest Booksellers Association; Southern Independent Booksellers Alliance

**Pearson Arts & Sciences**
Division of Pearson Education
51 Madison Ave, New York, NY 10010
*Tel:* 917-981-2200
*Web Site:* www.pearsonhighered.com
*Key Personnel*
Pres, ECP: Roth Wilkofsky *Tel:* 917-981-2300 *Fax:* 917-981-2210 *E-mail:* roth.wilkofsky@pearson.com
Number of titles published annually: 200 Print

**Pearson Benjamin Cummings**
Imprint of Pearson Higher Education
1301 Sansome St, San Francisco, CA 94111-1122
*Tel:* 415-402-2500 *Toll Free Tel:* 800-922-0579 (orders) *Fax:* 415-402-2590
*E-mail:* question@aol.com
*Web Site:* www.pearsonhighered.com
*Key Personnel*
Pres: Linda Baron Davis
VP & Dir, Mktg: Stacy Treco
Other subjects include: anatomy, physiology & microbiology.
ISBN Prefix(es): 978-0-201; 978-0-582; 978-0-8053; 978-0-321; 978-0-8465
*Orders to:* 75 Arlington St, Suite 300, Boston, MA 02116-3988 *Tel:* 617-848-7500

**Pearson Business Publishing**
Unit of Pearson Higher Education Division
One Lake St, Upper Saddle River, NJ 07458
*Tel:* 201-236-7000
*Web Site:* www.pearsonhighered.com
*Key Personnel*
Pres: Jerome Grant

**Pearson Career, Health, Education & Technology**
Division of Pearson Education
One Lake St, Upper Saddle River, NJ 07458
*Tel:* 201-236-7000 *Fax:* 201-236-7755

**Pearson Education**
One Lake St, Upper Saddle River, NJ 07458
*Tel:* 201-236-7000 *Fax:* 201-236-6549
*E-mail:* communications@pearsoned.com
*Web Site:* www.pearsoned.com
ISBN Prefix(es): 978-0-582
*Orders to:* 200 Old Tappan Rd, Old Tappan, NJ 07675
*See separate listing for:*
**Pearson Arts & Sciences**
**Pearson Career, Health, Education & Technology**
**Pearson Education/ELT**
**Pearson Higher Education**
**Pearson School**

**Pearson Education**
1900 E Lake Ave, Glenview, IL 60025
*Tel:* 847-729-3000 *Toll Free Tel:* 800-535-4391 (Midwest) *Fax:* 847-729-8910
*Key Personnel*
COO & EVP: George McGuirk
Pres, Digital: Bob Roliardi
EVP, Lit, Math, Sci & Humanities: Emily Swenson
VP, HR: Stuart G Cohn *E-mail:* stuart.cohn@pearsoned.com
Total Titles: 100 Print

**Pearson Education/ELT**
Division of Pearson Education
10 Bank St, 9th fl, White Plains, NY 10606-1951
*Tel:* 914-287-8000
*Web Site:* www.pearsonelt.com
*Key Personnel*
VP & Dir, Publg-Coll ELT: Pietro Alongi
VP & Dir, Publg-School ELT: Ed Lamprich
VP, Design & Prodn: Rhea Banker
VP, Mktg: Kate McLoughlin
Mktg Dir: Oliva Fernandez
Prodn Ed: Christopher Leonowicz
Number of titles published annually: 100 Print
*Foreign Office(s):* Harlow Office, Edinburgh Gate, Harlow, Essex CM20 2JE, United Kingdom *Tel:* (01279) 623623 *Fax:* (01279) 431059

**§Pearson Education International Group**
One Lake St, Upper Saddle River, NJ 07458
*Tel:* 201-236-7000
*Key Personnel*
EVP & COO: John LaVacca
Number of titles published annually: 6 Print

**Pearson Higher Education**
Division of Pearson Education
One Lake St, Upper Saddle River, NJ 07458
*Tel:* 201-236-7000 *Fax:* 201-236-3381
*Web Site:* www.pearsonhighered.com
*Key Personnel*
CEO: Tim Bozik
COO: George Werner
SVP, Systems & Technol: Jack Reilly
SVP & Dir, Publg Servs: Logan Campbell
ISBN Prefix(es): 978-0-13; 978-0-205; 978-0-8428; 978-0-87618; 978-0-87619; 978-0-87628; 978-0-89303
Imprints: Pearson Addison Wesley; Pearson Allyn & Bacon; Pearson Benjamin Cummings; Pearson Longman; Pearson Prentice Hall
*See separate listing for:*
**Allyn & Bacon**
**Pearson Benjamin Cummings**
**Pearson Business Publishing**
**Pearson Humanities & Social Sciences**
**Pearson Learning Solutions**

**Pearson Humanities & Social Sciences**
Unit of Pearson Higher Education Division
One Lake St, Upper Saddle River, NJ 07458
*Tel:* 201-236-7000 *Fax:* 201-236-3400
*Key Personnel*
Pres: Yolanda de Rooy
VP & Busn Mgr: Robert Santini
Asst VP & Dir, Prodn: Barbara Kittle
EIC & Edit Dir, Humanities & Eng: Charlyce Jones Owen
EIC, Soc Sci & Psychology: Nancy Roberts
EIC, Devt: Susanna Lesan
EIC, Modern Langs: Rosemary Bradley
Total Titles: 250 Print

**Pearson Learning Solutions**
Unit of Pearson Higher Education
501 Boyleston St, Suite 900, Boston, MA 02116
SAN: 214-0225
*Tel:* 617-848-6300 *Toll Free Tel:* 800-428-4466 (orders) *Fax:* 617-848-6358
*E-mail:* pcp@pearsoncustom.com
*Web Site:* www.pearsoned.com
*Key Personnel*
CEO: Donald Kilburn *Tel:* 617-671-3300
ISBN Prefix(es): 978-0-8087; 978-0-536
*Branch Office(s)*
Pearson Custom Publishing, 7110 Ohms Lane, Edina, MN 55439-2143 *Tel:* 952-831-1881 *Toll Free Tel:* 800-922-2579 *Fax:* 952-831-3167

**Pearson School**
Unit of Pearson Education
One Lake St, Upper Saddle River, NJ 07458
*Tel:* 201-236-7000
*Web Site:* www.pearsonschool.com
*Key Personnel*
EVP, Sales: Rick Culp
EVP, Prod Devt & Solutions: Jeffrey Ikler
ISBN Prefix(es): 978-0-13; 978-0-205; 978-0-556; 978-0-8224

**T H Peek Publisher**
Division of Clearweave Corp
PO Box 7406, Ann Arbor, MI 48107
SAN: 693-9708
*Tel:* 734-222-8205 *Fax:* 734-661-0136
*E-mail:* info@thpeekpublisher.com
*Web Site:* www.thpeekpublisher.com
*Key Personnel*
Owner: Colin D O'Brien
Founded: 1966
Ms acquisition, editorial, art, design, distribution, advertising & promotion.
ISBN Prefix(es): 978-0-917962; 978-1-935770
Number of titles published annually: 3 Print
Total Titles: 6 Print
Imprints: Alice Greene & Co

**Peel Productions Inc**
9415 NE Woodridge St, Vancouver, WA 98664
*Toll Free Tel:* 800-345-6665
*E-mail:* contact@drawbooks.com
*Web Site:* www.peelbooks.com
*Key Personnel*
Publr & Mktg Dir: Douglas C DuBosque
Ed: Susan Joyce DuBosque
Founded: 1985
ISBN Prefix(es): 978-0-939217
Number of titles published annually: 6 Print
Total Titles: 45 Print
Membership(s): Children's Book Council

**Pelican Publishing Co**
1000 Burmaster St, Gretna, LA 70053-2246
SAN: 212-0623
*Tel:* 504-368-1175 *Toll Free Tel:* 800-843-1724 *Fax:* 504-368-1195
*E-mail:* sales@pelicanpub.com (sales); office@pelicanpub.com (permission); promo@pelicanpub.com (publicity)
*Web Site:* www.pelicanpub.com
*Key Personnel*
Pres & Publr: Kathleen Calhoun Nettleton *Tel:* 504-368-1175 ext 312
Promo Dir: Antoinette de Alteriis
Dir, Sales: Joseph Billingsley
Ed & ISBN Contact: Nina Kooij *E-mail:* editorial@pelicanpub.com
Rts & Perms: Sally Boitnott *Tel:* 504-368-1175 ext 310
Founded: 1926
General, motivational, inspirational, nostalgia, note cards, almanacs, business & children's.
ISBN Prefix(es): 978-0-911116; 978-0-88289; 978-1-56554; 978-1-58980
Number of titles published annually: 70 Print; 1 E-Book; 10 Audio
Total Titles: 2,600 Print; 1 CD-ROM; 1 E-Book; 35 Audio
Imprints: Robert L Crager & Co; Dixie Press; Dove Inspirational Press; Jackson Square Press; Louisiana Book Distributors
Subsidiaries: Pelican International Corp
Distributor for Hope Publishing House; Marmac Publishing Co; SelfHelp Success Books
Foreign Rights: Fitzhenry & Whiteside Publishers (Canada); Roundhouse Group (Europe, Ireland, UK)
*Advertising Agency:* Bayou Advertising
Membership(s): AAP; Children's Book Council; Great Lakes Independent Booksellers Association; Jewish Book Publishers Association; Mid-South Booksellers Association; Midwest Independent Booksellers Association; Museum Store Association; Publishers Association of the West; Southern Independent Booksellers Alliance

**Pendragon Press**
Subsidiary of Camelot Publishing Co Inc
52 White Hill Lane, Hillsdale, NY 12529-5839
Mailing Address: PO Box 190, Hillsdale, NY 12529
*Tel:* 518-325-6100 *Toll Free Tel:* 877-656-6381 (orders) *Fax:* 518-325-6102
*E-mail:* editor@pendragonpress.com
*Web Site:* www.pendragonpress.com
*Key Personnel*
Mng Ed: Robert J Kessler
Founded: 1972
Reference works on books & musicology including music/aesthetics, biographies, music theory, organ, harpsichord, historic brass, 20th century music, French opera, music & religion.
ISBN Prefix(es): 978-0-918728; 978-0-945193; 978-1-57647
Number of titles published annually: 15 Print
Total Titles: 266 Print
Distributed by LIM Editrice SRL (Italy); G Ricordi (Italy)
Distributor for Croatian Musicological Society
Foreign Rep(s): Eurospan Ltd (Europe)

**Penfield Books**
215 Brown St, Iowa City, IA 52245
SAN: 221-6671
*Tel:* 319-337-9998 *Toll Free Tel:* 800-728-9998 *Fax:* 319-351-6846
*E-mail:* penfield@penfieldbooks.com
*Web Site:* www.penfieldbooks.com
*Key Personnel*
Publr: Joan Liffring-Zug Bourret
Returns Assoc: John Johnson *Tel:* 319-337-0570
Founded: 1979 (also known as Penfield Press in the past)
Ethnic (Czech, Danish, Dutch, Finnish, French, German, Irish, Italian, Mexican, Norwegian, Polish, Scandinavian, Scottish, Slovak, Swedish & Ukrainian); cookbooks; crafts & folk art; history; ethnic cultural cookbooks, cookbooks of the states. No unsol mss.
ISBN Prefix(es): 978-0-941016; 978-1-932043; 978-1-57216
Number of titles published annually: 6 Print; 6 CD-ROM; 15 E-Book
Total Titles: 168 Print; 268 Online; 70 E-Book
*Distribution Center:* Amazon.ca (CN)
Amazon.com
Bergquist
Book Marketing Plus
Createspace.com
Kindle
Partners

**Penguin Audiobooks**
Imprint of Penguin Group (USA) LLC
375 Hudson St, New York, NY 10014
SAN: 282-5074
*Tel:* 212-366-2000
*E-mail:* online@penguinputnam.com
*Web Site:* www.penguinputnam.com; us.penguingroup.com
*Key Personnel*
Exec Prodr: Patti Pirooz *Tel:* 212-366-2402 *E-mail:* patti.pirooz@us.penguingroup.com
Founded: 1990
Abridged, unabridged formats; simultaneous release with hardcover.
ISBN Prefix(es): 978-0-14; 978-0-453; 978-0-942110; 978-1-56511
Total Titles: 1 Print
Imprints: Penguin*HighBridge Audio
Distributor for Arkangel Complete Shakespeare; Highbridge Audio
*Advertising Agency:* Spier NY
*Warehouse:* Penguin Group (USA) LLC, One Grosset Dr, Kirkwood, NY 13795 *Tel:* 607-775-5586
Membership(s): Audio Publishers Association

**Penguin Books**
Imprint of Penguin Group (USA) LLC
375 Hudson St, New York, NY 10014
SAN: 282-5074
*Tel:* 212-366-2000
*E-mail:* online@penguinputnam.com
*Web Site:* www.penguinputnam.com; www.penguinclassics.com; us.penguingroup.com
*Key Personnel*
Pres & Publr, Penguin Books, Publr, Plume & VP, Penguin Group (USA) LLC: Kathryn Court
VP, Ed-in-Chief, Assoc Publr: Patrick Nolan
Sr Ed: Paul Slovak

Assoc Publr & Edit Dir, Penguin Classics: Elda Rotor
Sr Ed, Penguin Classics: John Siciliano
Exec Mng Ed: Matt Giarratano
VP & Exec Creative Dir: Paul Buckley
VP Dir, Mktg, Penguin Plume/Exec Dir, Academic Sales & Mktg: John Fagan
VP, Publicity: Maureen Donnelly
Dir, Ad & Promo: Dennis Swaim
Founded: 1935
ISBN Prefix(es): 978-0-14
Number of titles published annually: 244 Print
Total Titles: 4,425 Print
Imprints: Penguin; Penguin Classics; Penguin Compass; Penguin 20th Century Classics
Distributor for Pearson Technology Group Canada
*Advertising Agency:* Spier NY

**Penguin Group (USA) LLC**
Subsidiary of Pearson plc
375 Hudson St, New York, NY 10014
SAN: 282-5074
*Tel:* 212-366-2000 *Toll Free Tel:* 800-847-5515 (inside sales); 800-631-8571 (cust serv) *Fax:* 212-366-2666; 607-775-4829 (inside sales)
*E-mail:* online@us.penguingroup.com
*Web Site:* www.penguin.com; us.penguingroup.com
*Key Personnel*
Pres, G P Putnam's Sons: Ivan Held
Pres, Penguin Books for Young Readers: Don Weisberg
Pres, Mass Market Pbks: Leslie Gelbman
Pres & Publr, Penguin & Publr, Plume: Kathryn Court
Pres & Publr, Penguin Press: Ann Godoff
Pres, Viking Plume: Clare Ferraro
Pres & Publr Dutton: Brian Tart
Pres & Publr, Gotham & Avery Books: William Shinker
Pres & Publr, Portfolio & Sentinel Books: Adrian Zackheim
Pres & Publr, Blue Rider: David Rosenthal
Ed-In-Chief, Hudson Street Press: Caroline Sutton
Edit Dir, Plume: Philip Budnick
EVP, Busn Opers: Doug Whiteman
SVP, Penguin Group (USA) LLC & Pres, Sales, Adult Hardcover/Young Readers: Dick Heffernan
SVP, Penguin Group (USA) LLC & Pres, Sales, Pbk: Norman Lidofsky
SVP & Dir, Sales for Penguin Young Readers Group: Felicia Frazier
SVP & Dir, Subs Rts: Leigh Butler
SVP, Legal Aff & Corp Coun: Alex Gigante
SVP, Dist: James C Clark
SVP & Corp Dir, Busn Aff: John Schline
VP, Secy & Gen Coun: Karen Mayer
VP & Dir, Opers: Yvette Dano
VP Order Fulfillment: Linda Bay
VP & Dir, Corp Transportation: Andrew Orlando
VP & Corp Dir, HR: Carol Peterson
VP & Dir, Bldg Admin: Heidi Kagan
VP, HR: Paige McInerney
VP & Print Prodn Dir: Vincenzo Ruggiero
Dir, Mfg Procurement: Mike Gallagher
Dir, Intellectual Property Group: Peter Harris
Media Rel Mgr: Erica Glass
Founded: 1996
Publisher of consumer books in both hardcover & paperback for adults & children. Also produces maps, calendars, audio books & mass merchandise products.
Adult: hardcover, trade paperbacks & mass market paperbacks (originals & reprints)
Children: hardcover picture books, paperback picture books, board & novelty books
Young Adult: hardcover & trade paperback
Mass merchandise products.
ISBN Prefix(es): 978-0-201; 978-0-89529; 978-0-425; 978-0-441; 978-0-515; 978-1-57297; 978-0-14; 978-0-8037; 978-0-525; 978-0-452; 978-0-917657; 978-1-55611; 978-0-7232; 978-0-399; 978-0-698; 978-0-448; 978-1-58184; 978-0-89586; 978-0-912656; 978-1-55788; 978-0-87477; 978-0-451; 978-0-453; 978-0-670; 978-0-7860; 978-0-8431; 978-1-57395; 978-1-55773; 978-1-57322; 978-1-58333
Imprints: Ace (paperback); Ace/Putnam (hardcover); Alpha Books, Avery; Berkley Books (Paperback); Blue Rider (hardcover); DAW (hardcover & paperback); Dial Books for Young Readers (children's); Pam Dorman Books; Dutton (hardcover); Dutton Children's Books (children's); Gotham; Grosset & Dunlap (children's); Grosset/Putnam (hardcover); HPBooks (paperback); Hudson Street Press; InterMix; Jove (paperback); Minedition; Onyx (paperback); PaperStar (children's); Penguin (paperback); Penguin Classics (paperback); The Penguin Press; Perigee (paperback); Philomel Books (children's); Plume (paperback); Portfolio; Price Stern Sloan Inc (hardcover, paperback & children's); Puffin (children's); Putnam (hardcover); Razorbill; Riverhead Books (hardcover & paperback); ROC (paperback); Sentinel; Signet (paperback); Signet Classics (paperback); Studio; Jeremy P Tarcher (hardcover & paperback); Topaz (paperback); Viking (hardcover); Viking Children's Books (children's); Viking Compass (hardcover); Frederick Warne (children's); Wee Sing (children's)
Subsidiaries: Frederick Warne; Grosset & Dunlap
Distributor for Arkangel; Bibli O'Phile; Consumer Guide/PIL; DAW Books Inc; Dream Works; Granta; HighBridge Audio; Kensington Publishing Corp; The Library of America; The Monacelli Press; The Overlook Press; Reader's Digest
Foreign Rights: Penguin (Australia, Canada, India, New Zealand, South Africa, UK); Penguin Putnam International Sales
*Advertising Agency:* Mesa Group; Spier NY
*Distribution Center:* One Grosset Dr, Kirkwood, NY 13795 (hardcover, juvenile & audio imprints) *Tel:* 607-775-1740 *Fax:* 607-775-5586
One Commerce Rd, Pittston Township, PA 18640 (mass market & trade paperback imprints) *Tel:* 570-655-5965 *Fax:* 570-655-3907
Membership(s): AAP
*See separate listing for:*
**Alpha**
**Avery**
**Berkley Books**
**Berkley Publishing Group**
**Blue Rider Press**
**BradyGames**
**Celebra**
**DAW Books Inc**
**Dial Books for Young Readers**
**DK**
**Dutton**
**Dutton Children's Books**
**Gotham Books**
**Grosset & Dunlap**
**HPBooks**
**NAL**
**Penguin Audiobooks**
**Penguin Books**
**The Penguin Press**
**Penguin Young Readers Group**
**Perigee Books**
**Philomel**
**Plume**
**Portfolio**
**Prentice Hall Press**
**Price Stern Sloan**
**Puffin Books**
**Putnam Berkley Audio**
**The Putnam Publishing Group**
**GP Putnam's Sons (Hardcover)**
**Razorbill**
**Riverhead Books (Hardcover)**
**Riverhead Books (Trade Paperback)**
**Jeremy P Tarcher**
**Viking**
**Viking Children's Books**
**Viking Studio**
**Frederick Warne**

**Penguin Group (USA) LLC Sales**
375 Hudson St, New York, NY 10014
SAN: 282-5074
*Tel:* 212-366-2000
*E-mail:* online@penguinputnam.com
*Web Site:* us.penguingroup.com
*Key Personnel*
Pres & Dir, Sales, Adult Hardcover/YR: Dick Heffernan
Pres, Pbk Sales: Norman Lidofsky
SVP & Dir, Sales for Penguin Young Readers Group: Felicia Frazier
VP & Dir, Dist Sales: Ken Kaye
VP & Dir, Natl Accts, Adult Div: John Lawton
VP, Online Sales & Mktg, Trade Div: Timothy McCall
VP & Dir, Adult Hardcover, Field Sales: Katya Shannon
VP & Dir, Field Sales, Pbk: Patricia Weyenberg
VP, Dir, Field Sales & Mass Mkt Sales/Dir, Sales Busn Devt: Jackie Engel Steinberg
VP, Dir, Sales, Mass Mkt Mdse/Wholesale: Mary McGrath
VP, Intl Sales, Latin America, Caribbean & Mexico: Carlos Azula
VP & Dir, Premium Sales: Lisa Vitelli
VP, Dir, Spec Mkts: Jennifer Schwabinger
VP & Dir, Custom & Proprietary Sales: Sandra Dear
VP, Sr Dir, Academic Mktg & Sales: Alan Walker
Exec Dir, Natl Accts Pbk Sales: Don Redpath
Sr Dir, Intl Sales & Mktg: Devin Kirk
Dir, Trade Pbk Sales: Hank Cochrane
Dir, Natl Accts, Children's Div: Kimberly Highland
Dir, Dist Client Sales: Kristen Feehan
Dir, Spec Mkts: Laura Koch
Dir, Digital Busn: Caroline Riordan
Dir, Online Sales & Mktg: Kent Anderson
Dir, Digital Sales, Children's Div: Stephanie Sabol
Natl Accts Mgr, Adult Div: Fred Huber; Paul Deykerhoff; Glenn Timony; Mark McDiarmid; Christine Mosley
Natl Accts Mgr, Children's Div: Albert Winebarger; Alexis Lunsford
Natl Accts Mgr, Mass Mdse, Children's Div: Andrea Mai; Elissa Baillie
Natl Accts Mgr, Pbk: Carla Clifford; Sharon Gamboa
Educ Sales Mgr: Mary Raymond
Natl Accts Mgr & Publg Coord, Religious Mkt: William Bauers
Natl Accts Wholesale Mgr: Christina Stout
Natl Accts Mgr: Vance Lee, Jr
Natl Accts Mgr, Online Sales & Mktg: Kevin Che
Natl Accts Mgr, Apple: Lisa Pannek

**The Penguin Press**
Imprint of Penguin Group (USA) LLC
375 Hudson St, New York, NY 10014
*Key Personnel*
Pres & Ed-in-Chief: Ann Godoff
VP & Publr: Scott Moyers
VP, Exec Ed: Colin Dickerman
VP, Assoc Publr: Tracy Locke
VP, Art Dir: Darren Haggar
Publicity Dir: Sarah Hutson
Sr Ed: Andrea Walker; Virginia Smith
Ed: Lindsay Whalen
Founded: 2003
Publishers of literary fiction & select nonfiction.
ISBN Prefix(es): 978-1-59420
Number of titles published annually: 38 Print
Total Titles: 127 Print

**Penguin Young Readers Group**
Division of Penguin Group (USA) LLC

345 Hudson St, New York, NY 10014
*Tel:* 212-366-2000
*E-mail:* online@penguinputnam.com
*Web Site:* www.penguinputnam.com; us.penguingroup.com
*Key Personnel*
Pres, Penguin Young Readers Div: Don Weisberg
VP, Assoc Publr: Jennifer Haller
SVP & Dir, Sales for Penguin Young Readers Group: Felicia Frazier
VP & Dir, Subs Rts (Penguin Children's): Helen Boomer
VP & Dir, Mfg: Ginny Anson-Turturro
VP & Dir, Contracts & Busn Aff: George Schumacher
VP, Mktg & Mktg Design Servs: Emily Romero
VP, Digital Content Devt: Adam Royce
Exec Dir, Brand Mgmt: Jocelyn Schmidt
Exec Dir, Licensing: Lori Burke
Exec Dir, Trade Mktg: Erin Berger
Dir, Pre-School & YR Mktg: Jed Bennett
Dir, School Book Fair Sales: Tanni Tytel
Dir of Publicity: Shanta Newlin
Dir, School & Lib: Scottie Bowditch
Founded: 1997
Children's hardcover picture books; fiction & nonfiction; trade paperbacks; picture book paperbacks; board & novelty books; calendars.
ISBN Prefix(es): 978-0-201; 978-0-14; 978-0-8037; 978-0-525; 978-0-7232; 978-0-399; 978-0-698; 978-0-448; 978-1-58184; 978-0-670; 978-0-8431
Imprints: Kathy Dawson Books; Dial Books for Young Readers; Dutton Children's Books; Dutton Interactive; Grosset & Dunlap; Paperstar; Philomel; Price Stern Sloan; PSS; Puffin Books; G P Putnam's Sons; Viking Children's Books; Frederick Warne
*Distribution Center:* Penguin Group (USA) Juvenile Imprints, One Grosset Dr, Kirkwood, NY 13795 *Tel:* 607-775-1740 *Fax:* 607-775-5586
*See separate listing for:*
**GP Putnam's Sons (Children's)**

**Peninsula Publishing**
26666 Birch Hill Way, Los Altos Hills, CA 94022
*Tel:* 650-948-2511 *Fax:* 650-948-5004
*E-mail:* sales@peninsulapublishing.com
*Web Site:* www.peninsulapublishing.com
*Key Personnel*
Publr: Charles Wiseman *E-mail:* cwiseman@peninsulapublishing.com
Off Mgr: Hannah Wiseman
Founded: 1978
Publish new titles & reprints in the field of acoustics & sound.
ISBN Prefix(es): 978-0-932146
Number of titles published annually: 3 Print
Total Titles: 30 Print
Distributed by Scitech Publishing Inc
Membership(s): ABA; Acoustical Society of America; American Institute of Physics

**Pennsylvania Historical & Museum Commission**
Subsidiary of The Commonwealth of Pennsylvania
Commonwealth Keystone Bldg, 400 North St, Harrisburg, PA 17120-0053
SAN: 282-1532
*Tel:* 717-783-2618 *Toll Free Tel:* 800-747-7790 *Fax:* 717-787-8312
*E-mail:* ra-pabookstore@state.pa.us
*Web Site:* www.pabookstore.com; www.phmc.state.pa.us
*Key Personnel*
Chief, Pubns: Jean Cutler *E-mail:* jecutler@state.pa.us
Sales Mgr: Susan Lindeman *E-mail:* slindeman@state.pa.us
Founded: 1913
Books, booklets & references on Pennsylvania prehistory, history, culture & natural history, both scholarly & popular.
ISBN Prefix(es): 978-0-911124; 978-0-89271
Number of titles published annually: 5 Print
Total Titles: 145 Print

**§Pennsylvania State Data Center**
Subsidiary of Institute of State & Regional Affairs
Penn State Harrisburg, 777 W Harrisburg Pike, Middletown, PA 17057-4898
*Tel:* 717-948-6336 *Fax:* 717-948-6754
*E-mail:* pasdc@psu.edu
*Web Site:* pasdc.hbg.psu.edu
*Key Personnel*
Dir: Susan Copella *Tel:* 717-948-6427 *E-mail:* sdc3@psu.edu
Founded: 1981
Policy, demographical analytical reports, hard copy & computer discs.
ISBN Prefix(es): 978-0-939667; 978-1-58036
Number of titles published annually: 5 Print; 5 CD-ROM
Total Titles: 130 Print; 130 CD-ROM; 1 E-Book

**The Pennsylvania State University Press**
Division of The Pennsylvania State University
University Support Bldg 1, Suite C, 820 N University Dr, University Park, PA 16802-1003
SAN: 213-5760
*Tel:* 814-865-1327 *Toll Free Tel:* 800-326-9180 *Fax:* 814-863-1408 *Toll Free Fax:* 877-778-2665
*E-mail:* info@psupress.org
*Web Site:* www.psupress.org
*Key Personnel*
Dir, Press: Patrick Alexander *Tel:* 814-867-2209 *E-mail:* pha3@psu.edu
Asst Press Dir, Design & Prodn Mgr: Jennifer Norton *Tel:* 814-863-8061 *E-mail:* jsn4@psu.edu
Asst Press Dir, Mktg & Sales Dir: Tony Sanfilippo *Tel:* 814-863-5994 *E-mail:* ajs23@psu.edu
Busn Mgr: Tina Laychur *Tel:* 814-863-5993 *E-mail:* cgw3@psu.edu
Info Systems Mgr: Ed Spicer *E-mail:* res122@psu.edu
Publicity Mgr: Danny Bellet *Tel:* 814-863-0524 *E-mail:* hms7@psu.edu
Mng Ed: Laura Reed-Morrisson *Tel:* 814-865-1606 *E-mail:* lxr168@psu.edu
Exec Ed: Eleanor Goodman *Tel:* 814-867-2212 *E-mail:* ehg11@psu.edu
Prodn Coord, Books & Journals: Patricia Mitchell *Tel:* 814-867-2216 *E-mail:* pam18@psu.edu
Chief Designer: Steven Kress *Tel:* 814-867-2215 *E-mail:* srk5@psu.edu
Founded: 1956
Scholarly books & journals; art & architectural history; literature & literary criticism, philosophy, religion, social sciences, law, history, Latin American studies, regional books on mid-Atlantic area; Special Series: Literature & Philosophy; Penn State Series in the History of the Book; Re-Reading the Canon; Keystone Books (regional); American & European Philosophy; Magic in History; Rural Studies; Refiguring Modernism; Buildings, Landscapes & Societies.
ISBN Prefix(es): 978-0-271
Number of titles published annually: 60 Print
Total Titles: 1,300 Print; 3 CD-ROM; 12 Online; 100 E-Book
Imprints: Keystone Books
Foreign Rep(s): European University Press Group (Africa, Central America, Europe, Middle East, South America, UK); United Publishers Services (China); University of Toronto Press (Canada)
Membership(s): AAP; Association of American University Presses

**PennWell Books**
Division of PennWell
1421 S Sheridan Rd, Tulsa, OK 74112
Mailing Address: PO Box 21288, Tulsa, OK 74121-1288
*Tel:* 918-831-9410 *Toll Free Tel:* 800-752-9764 *Fax:* 918-831-9555
*E-mail:* sales@pennwell.com
*Web Site:* www.pennwellbooks.com
*Key Personnel*
CEO & Pres: Bob Biolchini
Dir: Mary McGee *E-mail:* marym@pennwell.com
Prodn Mgr: Sheila Brock
Mktg Coord: Jane Green
Cust Serv: Holly Fournier
Founded: 1973
Publish both technical & nontechnical books. Written by selected industry experts, our books will help you broaden your expertise in your current field, understand other related disciplines & provide quick-glance references as a topic arrives in your daily routine. Our products make excellent classroom, seminar & in-house training texts.
ISBN Prefix(es): 978-0-912212; 978-0-87814; 978-1-59370
Number of titles published annually: 20 Print
Total Titles: 400 Print; 5 Audio
Foreign Rep(s): Cranbury Intl LLC (Ethan Atkin) (Central America, South America); Ish Dawar (India); Eurospan Group Ltd (Europe, UK); Intercontinental Marketing (Japan, South Korea); Dar Kriedieh (Brazil); STM Publishers Rep (Tony Poh) (Southeast Asia)

**§Pentecostal Publishing House**
Subsidiary of United Pentecostal Church International
8855 Dunn Rd, Hazelwood, MO 63042
SAN: 219-3817
*Tel:* 314-837-7300 *Fax:* 314-336-1803
*E-mail:* pphordersdept@upci.org (orders)
*Web Site:* www.pentecostalpublishing.com
*Key Personnel*
Administrator: Billy Babb
Purch: Terri Miller
Edit: Robin Johnson
Founded: 1945
Trade paperbacks, periodicals, bibliographies; religion (Protestant), Bibles, foreign languages, crafts, self-help.
ISBN Prefix(es): 978-0-912315; 978-0-932581; 978-1-56722; 978-0-7577
Number of titles published annually: 10 Print; 10 CD-ROM
Total Titles: 400 Print; 35 CD-ROM
Imprints: Word Aflame Press
Subsidiaries: Word Aflame Press
Distributed by Anchor Distributors; Christian Network International; Innovative Marketing; Spring Arbor

**Penton Media**
9800 Metcalf Ave, Overland Park, KS 66212
SAN: 204-3416
Mailing Address: PO Box 12901, Overland Park, KS 66282-2901
*Tel:* 913-967-1719 *Toll Free Tel:* 800-262-1954 (cust serv) *Fax:* 913-967-1901 *Toll Free Fax:* 800-633-6219
*E-mail:* bookorders@penton.com
*Web Site:* www.buypenton.com
*Key Personnel*
Sales Mgr: Matt Tusken
Publisher of repair manuals for motorcycles, ATV, PWC, boats, outdoor power equipment, snowmobiles & tractors, as well as valuation guides.
ISBN Prefix(es): 978-0-89287; 978-0-87288; 978-0-1599
Number of titles published annually: 25 Print
Total Titles: 532 Print
Imprints: Ac-u-Kwik; Clymer ProSeries; Clymer Publications; EC&M Books; Electrical Whole-

saling; The Electronics Source Book; Equipment Watch; I&T Shop Service; Penton-Price Digests
*Shipping Address:* Smart Warehousing, 1869 N Topping Ave, Kansas City, MO 64120

**Peoples Education Inc**
Subsidiary of Peoples Educational Holdings Inc
299 Market St, Suite 240, Saddle Brook, NJ 07663
Mailing Address: PO Box 513, Saddle Brook, NJ 07663-0513
*Tel:* 201-712-0090 *Toll Free Tel:* 800-822-1080 *Fax:* 201-712-0045; 201-712-1016
*Web Site:* www.peopleseducation.com; www.peoplescollegeprep.com; www.measuringuplive.com; www.brightpointliteracy.com
*Key Personnel*
CEO & Pres: Brian Beckwith *E-mail:* brianbeckwith@peoplesed.com
Chief Creative Offr & EVP: Diane M Miller *E-mail:* dmiller@peoplesed.com
CFO & EVP: Michael DeMarco *E-mail:* mdemarco@peoplesed.com
Founded: 1990
Publisher & marketer of print & electronic educational materials for the K-12 school market. We focus our efforts in three market areas: test preparation, assessment & instruction, literacy & college preparation.
ISBN Prefix(es): 978-1-61526; 978-1-61527; 978-1-936025; 978-1-936027; 978-1-936028; 978-1-936029; 978-1-936030; 978-1-61602; 978-1-61734; 978-1-60979; 978-1-936026; 978-1-936031; 978-1-56256; 978-1-58984; 978-1-4138
Number of titles published annually: 50 Print
Total Titles: 2,000 Print
Imprints: Asante®; BrightPoint Literacy; Measuring Up®
Distributor for Learning Media; Nelson Canada; New Path Learning; W W Norton; Rubicon; John Wiley & Sons
Membership(s): American Educational Publishers

**Per Annum Inc**
555 Eighth Ave, Suite 203, New York, NY 10018
SAN: 289-3673
*Tel:* 212-647-8700 *Toll Free Tel:* 800-548-1108 *Fax:* 212-647-8716
*E-mail:* info@perannum.com
*Web Site:* www.perannum.com
*Key Personnel*
Pres: Alicia B Settle
Acct Exec: Liz Smith *Tel:* 212-647-8700 ext 202
Founded: 1979
Guide books, agendas.
ISBN Prefix(es): 978-1-57499
Number of titles published annually: 16 Print
Total Titles: 16 Print
Distributor for New Yorker Desk Diary

**Peradam Press**
Subsidiary of The Center for Cultural & Naturalist Studies
PO Box 6, North San Juan, CA 95960-0006
*Tel:* 530-292-4266 *Fax:* 530-292-4266
*E-mail:* peradam@earthlink.net
*Key Personnel*
Pres & Sr Ed: Linda Birkholz
Exec Ed: Dan Cronin
Ed: Patricia Hicks
Founded: 1993
General trade books hardcover & paperbacks.
ISBN Prefix(es): 978-1-885420
Number of titles published annually: 8 Print
Total Titles: 60 Print
*Shipping Address:* 19074 Oak Tree Rd, Nevada City, CA 95959

**Perfection Learning Corp**
2680 Berkshire Pkwy, Clive, IA 50325
*Tel:* 515-278-0133 *Toll Free Tel:* 800-762-2999 *Fax:* 515-278-2980
*Web Site:* perfectionlearning.com
*Key Personnel*
Design Dir: Randy Messer *E-mail:* rmesser@plconline.com
Edit Dir (Elem): Sue Thies *E-mail:* sthies@plconline.com
Mktg Opers Dir: Mark Hagenberg *E-mail:* mhagenberg@plconline.com
Founded: 1926
Elementary & secondary product line covers such content areas as reading, literature, math, test preparation, writing, vocabulary, handwriting, spelling & more.
ISBN Prefix(es): 978-0-89598
Number of titles published annually: 30 Print
Total Titles: 500 Print
Imprints: Cover Craft; Cover-to-Cover; Literature & Thought; Passages; Retold Classics; Summit Books; Tale Blazers
Distributor for Abrams; Ace Books; Airmont; Annick Press; Archway; Atheneum; Baker Books; Ballantine; Bantam; Barrons; Berkley; Blake Books; Candlewick Press; Charlesbridge Press; Chelsea House; Children's Press; Chronicle Books; Crabtree Publishing; Crown; Disney Press; Distri Books; DK; Doubleday; Dutton; F+W Media Inc; Farrar, Straus & Giroux Inc; Fawcett; Firefly; First Avenue; Free Spirit; Fulcrum; Golden Books; Greenhaven Press Inc; Hammond Pub; Harcourt Inc; Hayes; Gareth Stevens; Frederick Warne
Foreign Rep(s): Ron Grant, School Book Fairs Ltd (Canada)
*Warehouse:* 1000 N Second Ave, PO Box 500, Logan, IA 51546-0500 *Toll Free Tel:* 800-831-4190 *Fax:* 712-644-2392 *E-mail:* orders@perfectionlearning.com

**Perigee Books**
Imprint of Penguin Group (USA) LLC
375 Hudson St, New York, NY 10014
SAN: 282-5074
*Tel:* 212-366-2000 *Fax:* 212-366-2365
*E-mail:* perigeebooks@us.penguingroup.com
*Web Site:* www.penguin.com
*Key Personnel*
Publr: John Duff
Ed-in-Chief: Marian Lizzi
Exec Ed: Meg Leder
Founded: 1980
Focus on prescriptive nonfiction.
ISBN Prefix(es): 978-0-399
Number of titles published annually: 73 Print
Total Titles: 517 Print
*Advertising Agency:* Spier NY

**The Permanent Press**
4170 Noyac Rd, Sag Harbor, NY 11963
*Tel:* 631-725-1101 *Fax:* 631-725-8215
*E-mail:* info@thepermanentpress.com
*Web Site:* www.thepermanentpress.com
*Key Personnel*
Co-Publr: Judith Shepard *E-mail:* judith@thepermanentpress.com; Martin Shepard *E-mail:* shepard@thepermanentpress.com
Mng Ed: Cathy Suter *E-mail:* cathy@thepermanentpress.com
ISBN Prefix(es): 978-1-877946; 978-0-932966; 978-1-57962
Imprints: Second Chance Press
*See separate listing for:*
**Second Chance Press**

**Persea Books**
277 Broadway, Suite 708, New York, NY 10007
SAN: 212-8233
*Tel:* 212-260-9256 *Fax:* 212-267-3165
*E-mail:* info@perseabooks.com
*Web Site:* www.perseabooks.com
*Key Personnel*
Pres & Publr: Michael Braziller
VP & Edit Dir: Karen Braziller
Ed & Perms: Gabriel Fried
Founded: 1975
Literature, poetry, biography, multicultural fiction & nonfiction, women's studies, fiction, memoir, contemporary affairs, young adult & adult anthologies for schools & colleges.
ISBN Prefix(es): 978-0-89255
Number of titles published annually: 12 Print
Total Titles: 500 Print
Imprints: Karen & Michael Braziller Books
Distributed by W W Norton & Co
Distributor for Ontario Review Press
*Distribution Center:* W W Norton c/o National Book Co, Keystone Industrial Park, Scranton, PA 18512 *Toll Free Fax:* 800-233-4830

**The Perseus Books Group**
387 Park Ave S, 12th fl, New York, NY 10016
*Tel:* 212-340-8100 *Toll Free Tel:* 800-343-4499 (cust serv) *Fax:* 212-340-8105
*Web Site:* www.perseusbooksgroup.com
*Key Personnel*
CEO & Pres: David Steinberger
COO: Joe Mangan
CFO: Charles Gallagher
Pres, Dist Client Servs: Sabrina McCarthy
VP: Anjali V Jolly; J T Mauk
VP, Legal Aff: Teresa Young Bernstein
VP, Prog Off: Patrick Kirk
VP, Supply Chain & Sales Opers: Greg Anastas
Sr Mng Dir: John C Fox; Sheryl Schwartz; Kenneth M Socha
Mng Dir: John M Glazer
Dir, Constellation Global Mktg & Communs: Agustina Casal
Dir, Corp Strategy & Busn Devt: Scott Edinburgh
Dir, HR: Lindsey Pullen *E-mail:* lindsey.pullen@perseusbooks.com
Publicity Dir, Weinstein Books: Kathleen Schmidt
Head, Sales: Matty Goldberg
Founded: 1997
Perseus Books, LLC does not accept unsol mss or proposals.
ISBN Prefix(es): 978-0-938289; 978-1-58097; 978-0-7382; 978-1-882810; 978-1-60286
Number of titles published annually: 50 Print
Total Titles: 530 Print
Imprints: Avalon Travel; Basic Books; Basic Civitas Books; Courage Books; Da Capo Lifelong Books; Da Capo Press; Nation Books; PublicAffairs; Running Press; Running Press-Kids; Running Press-Miniature Editions; Seal Press; Weinstein Books; Westview Press
Distributed by NOW; Perseus Distribution Services
*Orders to:* 1094 Flex Dr, Jackson, TN 38301 *Toll Free Tel:* 800-343-4499 *Toll Free Fax:* 800-351-5073
*Distribution Center:* 1094 Flex Dr, Jackson, TN 38301 *Toll Free Tel:* 800-343-4499 *Toll Free Fax:* 800-351-5073
*See separate listing for:*
**Avalon Travel Publishing**
**Basic Books**
**Da Capo Press Inc & Lifelong Books**
**PublicAffairs**
**Running Press Book Publishers**
**Westview Press**

**Peter Pauper Press, Inc**
202 Mamaroneck Ave, White Plains, NY 10601-5376
SAN: 204-9449
*Tel:* 914-681-0144 *Fax:* 914-681-0389
*E-mail:* customerservice@peterpauper.com; orders@peterpauper.com
*Web Site:* www.peterpauper.com
*Key Personnel*
CEO: Laurence Beilenson *E-mail:* lbeilenson@peterpauper.com

VP: John Hartley *E-mail:* jhartley@peterpauper.com
Edit Dir: Barbara Paulding *E-mail:* bpaulding@peterpauper.com
Art Dir: Heather Zschock *E-mail:* hzschock@peterpauper.com
Publr: Evelyn L Beilenson *E-mail:* ebeilenson@peterpauper.com
Sr Ed: Lois Kaufman *E-mail:* lkaufman@peterpauper.com
Founded: 1928
Decorated hardcover gift, inspirational; quotations, miniatures, journals, photo albums, children's picture books, children's activity books, travel guides.
ISBN Prefix(es): 978-0-88088; 978-1-59359; 978-1-44130
Number of titles published annually: 60 Print; 15 E-Book
Total Titles: 500 Print; 270 E-Book
Imprints: Inspire Books
Foreign Rep(s): For Arts Sake (Australia, New Zealand); Alejandra Garza (Mexico); Saskia Knobbe (Netherlands); Bara Kristinsdottir (Iceland); Peter Pauper Press UK (UK); Phambili (Southern Africa); Israel Ring (Brazil); Sunstate Books (Australia, New Zealand)
*Shipping Address:* Conri Services Inc, 5 Skyline Dr, Hawthorne, NY 10532, Contact: Connie Levene *Tel:* 914-592-2300 *Fax:* 914-592-2174
*Warehouse:* Conri Services Inc, 5 Skyline Dr, Hawthorne, NY 10532, Contact: Connie Levene *Tel:* 914-592-2300 *Fax:* 914-592-2174

**§Peterson Institute for International Economics**
1750 Massachusetts Ave NW, Washington, DC 20036-1903
SAN: 293-2865
*Tel:* 202-328-9000 *Toll Free Tel:* 800-522-9139 (orders) *Fax:* 202-328-5432; 202-659-3225
*E-mail:* orders@petersoninstitute.org
*Web Site:* www.petersoninstitute.org
*Key Personnel*
Dir: C Fred Bergsten
Dir, Pubns & Mktg: Ed Tureen *E-mail:* etureen@piie.com
Edit Dir & Public Policy Fellow: Steven R Weisman *Tel:* 202-454-1331 *E-mail:* media@piie.com
Founded: 1981
Trade & textbooks on key economic, monetary, trade & investment issues.
ISBN Prefix(es): 978-0-88132
Number of titles published annually: 15 Print; 14 Online
Total Titles: 300 Print; 200 Online; 35 E-Book
Distributed by DA Information Services (Australia, New Zealand & Papua New Guinea); East West Export Books (Cambodia, China, Indonesia, Japan, Philippines, Singapore, Taiwan, Thailand & Vietnam); The Eurospan Group (Africa, Eastern & Western Europe, Iran, Israel, Russia & Turkey); Renouf Bookstore (Canada); United Publishers Services Ltd (Japan & Republic of Korea); Viva Books PVT (Bangladesh, India, Nepal & Sri Lanka)
Distributor for Center for Global Development
*Orders to:* Peterson Institute for International Economics, PO Box 960, Herndon, VA 20172 *Toll Free Tel:* 800-522-9139 *Fax:* 703-661-1501 *E-mail:* petersonmail@presswarehouse.com *Web Site:* bookstore.petersoninstitute.org
*Returns:* Peterson Institute for International Economics, 22883 Quicksilver Dr, Dulles, VA 20166
Membership(s): AAP; Society for Scholarly Publishing; Washington Book Publishers

**§Peterson's, a Nelnet Company**
Princeton Pike Corporate Ctr, 2000 Lenox Dr, Lawrenceville, NJ 08648
*Tel:* 609-896-1800
*E-mail:* sales@petersons.com
*Web Site:* www.petersons.com
*Key Personnel*
Mng Dir, Digital Publg: Stephen Clemente
Founded: 1966
Education, career books, software & CD-ROM, data licensing, test preparation, financial aid & adult education, online lead generation.
ISBN Prefix(es): 978-1-56079; 978-0-7689
Number of titles published annually: 50 Print; 2 E-Book
Total Titles: 120 Print; 2 E-Book
Imprints: Peterson's/Pacesetter Books
Foreign Rights: Ann-Christine Daniellsson Agency (Scandinavia); International Editors' Co (Latin America, Spain); Frederique Parretta Agency (Canada (French-speaking), France); Pikarski (Israel); Tuttle-Mori Agency Inc (Japan, Thailand)
Membership(s): BISG

**Petroleum Extension Service (PETEX)**
Division of University of Texas
University of Texas at Austin-PETEX, One University Sta, R8100, Austin, TX 78712-1100
*Tel:* 512-471-5940 *Toll Free Tel:* 800-687-4132 *Fax:* 512-471-9410 *Toll Free Fax:* 800-687-7839
*E-mail:* plach@www.utex.edu; petex@www.utexas.edu
*Web Site:* www.utexas.edu/ce/petex
*Key Personnel*
Sr Mgr, Publg & Communs: Debbie Denehy *E-mail:* ddenehy@austin.utexas.edu
Founded: 1944
Training reference materials for oil field personnel including ebook titles.
ISBN Prefix(es): 978-0-88698
Number of titles published annually: 10 Print
Total Titles: 400 Print
*Branch Office(s)*
PETEX, 2700-W W Thorne Dr, Houston, TX 77073-3410
*Shipping Address:* 10100 Burnet Rd, Austin, TX 78758-4445

**§Pflaum Publishing Group**
Division of Peter Li Inc
2621 Dryden Rd, Suite 300, Dayton, OH 45439
*Tel:* 937-293-1415 *Toll Free Tel:* 800-543-4383; 800-523-4625 (sales) *Fax:* 937-293-1310 *Toll Free Fax:* 800-370-4450
*E-mail:* service@pflaum.com
*Web Site:* pflaum.com
*Key Personnel*
VP & Dir, Sales: Michael Raffio *E-mail:* mraffio@peterli.com
VP, Mktg: Mr Terry Perkins *Tel:* 212-818-0700 *Fax:* 212-818-0708 *E-mail:* tperkins@peterli.com
Ed-in-Chief: Michael Donald Thomas *Tel:* 937-293-1415 ext 1118 *E-mail:* mthomas@peterli.com
Founded: 1885
Weekly liturgical magazines for PreK-8. Sacramental preparation for children & teens, catechetical resources for PreK-12, religious educators & youth ministers. Branch offices in Phoenix, AZ & New York, NY.
ISBN Prefix(es): 978-0-937997; 978-0-89837; 978-1-933178; 978-1-935042
Number of titles published annually: 20 Print
Total Titles: 75 Print; 15 CD-ROM; 15 Online; 10 E-Book
Membership(s): Association of Catholic Publishers Inc; National Catholic Education Association; National Catholic Educational Exhibitors

**Phaidon Press Inc**
Subsidiary of Phaidon Press Ltd
180 Varick St, 14th fl, New York, NY 10014
*Tel:* 212-652-5400 *Toll Free Tel:* 800-759-0190 (cust serv) *Fax:* 212-652-5410 *Toll Free Fax:* 800-286-9471 (cust serv)
*E-mail:* ussales@phaidon.com
*Web Site:* www.phaidon.com
*Key Personnel*
VP: Mary Albi
Publicity & Mktg Dir: Liz Thompson *Tel:* 212-652-5217 *E-mail:* lthompson@phaidon.com
Sales Dir: James Whittaker *Tel:* 905-338-6480 *E-mail:* jwhittaker@phaidon.com
Publicist: Peter Tittiger
Sales Rep, Northeast: Richard Gregg *Tel:* 617-964-5669 *E-mail:* rgregg@phaidon.com
Founded: 1923
Illustrated books on fine art, architecture, design, photography, decorative arts, film & music.
ISBN Prefix(es): 978-0-7148
Number of titles published annually: 70 Print
Total Titles: 525 Print
*Foreign Office(s):* Phaidon Sarl, 65 rue Montmartre, Paris 75002, France *Tel:* 01 55 28 38 38 *Fax:* 01 55 28 38 39
Phaidon Verlag, Grunbergerstr 81, 10245 Berlin, Germany *Tel:* (030) 28 88 64 14 *Fax:* (030) 28 04 48 79
Phaidon Srl, Corso Sempione 33, 20145 Milan MI, Italy *Tel:* (024) 399-0450 *Fax:* (024) 399-0450
Phaidon KK, AD Homes 104, 3-28-18 Yushima, Bunkyo-ku, Tokyo 113-0034, Japan *Tel:* (03) 5812 6839
Phaidon Press, C/ Buenos Aires, 54 3º 3, Barcelona 08036, Spain *Tel:* 934193833 *Fax:* 934193833
Phaidon Press Ltd, 18 Regents Wharf, All Saints St, London N1 9PA, United Kingdom *Tel:* (020) 7843 1000 *Fax:* (020) 7843 1010 *E-mail:* enquiries@phaidon.com *Web Site:* www.phaidon.com
Distributor for Mitchell Beazley; Electa

**Phi Delta Kappa International®**
320 W Eighth St, Suite 216, Bloomington, IN 47405
Mailing Address: PO Box 7888, Bloomington, IN 47407-7888
*Tel:* 812-339-1156 *Toll Free Tel:* 800-766-1156 *Fax:* 812-339-0018
*E-mail:* customerservice@pdkintl.org
*Web Site:* www.pdkintl.org
*Key Personnel*
Exec Dir: Bill Bushaw *Tel:* 703-988-4036 *E-mail:* bbushaw@pdkintl.org
Dir, Mktg & Communs: Asley McDonald Kinkaid *Tel:* 703-988-4037 *E-mail:* akinkaid@pdkintl.org
Founded: 1906
International professional association of educators.
ISBN Prefix(es): 978-0-87367
Number of titles published annually: 30 Print
Total Titles: 220 Print; 1 CD-ROM
*Branch Office(s)*
Phi Delta Kappa Educational Foundation, 408 N Union St, Bloomington, IN 47405-3800, Contact: Lynn Lewis *Toll Free Tel:* 800-776-1156 ext 2222 *E-mail:* llewis@pdkintl.org
Foreign Rep(s): Unifacmann Trading Co (Taiwan)

**Philadelphia Museum of Art**
2525 Pennsylvania Ave, Philadelphia, PA 19130
*Tel:* 215-684-7250 *Fax:* 215-235-8715
*Web Site:* www.philamuseum.org
*Key Personnel*
Dir, Publg: Sherry Babbitt *Tel:* 215-684-7242 *E-mail:* sbabbitt@philamuseum.org
Prodn Mgr: Rich Bonk
Ed: Kathleen Krattenmaker
Assoc Ed: Mary Cason; David Updike
Founded: 1901
Illustrated scholarly works on the permanent collection & exhibitions at the museum.

ISBN Prefix(es): 978-0-87633
Number of titles published annually: 7 Print
Total Titles: 80 Print
Distributed by Yale University Press

**Philomel**
Imprint of Penguin Group (USA) LLC
345 Hudson St, New York, NY 10014
*Tel:* 212-366-2000
*Key Personnel*
Pres & Publr: Michael Green
Exec Ed: Jill Santopolo
Assoc Publr/Exec Mng Ed: David Briggs
Art Dir: Semadar Megged
Founded: 1980
Number of titles published annually: 41 Print
Total Titles: 367 Print

**Philosophical Library Inc**
PO Box 251, New York, NY 10024
*Tel:* 212-886-1873; 212-873-6070 *Fax:* 212-873-6070
*E-mail:* editors@philosophicallibrary.com
*Web Site:* philosophicallibrary.com
*Key Personnel*
Mgr: Regeen Runes Najar *E-mail:* editors@philosophicallibrary.com
Founded: 1941
Comprehensive collection of mid-level reference books. A consistent source for serious readers, libraries, academic institutions & booksellers worldwide. Also have a program for Print On Demand.
ISBN Prefix(es): 978-0-8022
Number of titles published annually: 70 Print; 70 E-Book
Total Titles: 500 Print; 200 E-Book
Distributed by Kensington Publishing Corp (subs rts: Meryl Earl); OpenRoadMedia.com
Foreign Rights: Kensington Publishing Corp (Meryl Earl) (Worldwide)

**Philosophy Documentation Center**
PO Box 7147, Charlottesville, VA 22906-7147
*Tel:* 434-220-3300 *Toll Free Tel:* 800-444-2419 *Fax:* 434-220-3301
*E-mail:* order@pdcnet.org
*Web Site:* www.pdcnet.org
*Key Personnel*
Dir: George Leaman *E-mail:* leaman@pdcnet.org
Assoc Dir: Pamela K Swope *E-mail:* pkswope@pdcnet.org
Electronic Publg & Mktg: Susanne Mueller-Grote *E-mail:* smg@pdcnet.org
Founded: 1966
ISBN Prefix(es): 978-0-912632; 978-1-889680
Number of titles published annually: 30 Print; 15 Online
Total Titles: 80 Print; 120 Online
Distributor for Imprint Academic

**Phoenix Society for Burn Survivors**
1835 R W Berends Dr SW, Grand Rapids, MI 49519
*Tel:* 616-458-2773 *Toll Free Tel:* 800-888-BURN (888-2876) *Fax:* 616-458-2831
*E-mail:* info@phoenix-society.org
*Web Site:* www.phoenix-society.org
*Key Personnel*
Exec Dir: Amy Acton *E-mail:* amy@phoenix-society.org
Founded: 1977
Books regarding burns.
Number of titles published annually: 3 Print
Total Titles: 35 Print; 35 E-Book

**Piano Press**
1425 Ocean Ave, Suite 17, Del Mar, CA 92014
Mailing Address: PO Box 85, Del Mar, CA 92014-0085
*Tel:* 619-884-1401 *Fax:* 858-755-1104
*E-mail:* pianopress@pianopress.com
*Web Site:* www.pianopress.com
*Key Personnel*
Owner & Ed: Elizabeth C Axford *E-mail:* lizaxford@pianopress.com
Music Typesetter: David Murray; Mark So
Audio Engr: John Dawes; Denny Martin; Matthew Dela Pola; Peter Sprague; Kris Stone
Webmaster & Mktg: Frank Tranfaglia
Edit Asst: Kathy Alward; Carol Buckley; Katie Cook; Dee Rome; Gay Salo
Founded: 1998
Publishes songbooks & CDs as well as music-related coloring books & poetry for the educational & family markets.
ISBN Prefix(es): 978-0-9673325; 978-1-931844
Number of titles published annually: 6 Print; 1 Audio
Total Titles: 100 Print
Membership(s): American Society of Composers, Authors and Publishers; The Recording Academy; Society of Children's Book Writers & Illustrators

**Picador**
Subsidiary of Macmillan
175 Fifth Ave, 19th fl, New York, NY 10010
*Tel:* 646-307-5151 *Fax:* 212-253-9627
*E-mail:* firstname.lastname@picadorusa.com
*Web Site:* www.picadorusa.com
*Key Personnel*
VP & Publr: Stephen Morrison
VP, Sales & Mktg: Darin Keesler
Exec Dir, Publicity: James Meader
Sr Publicist: Gabrielle Gantz
Sr Ed: Anna deVries; David Rogers
Creative Dir: Henry Yee
Sr Designer: LeeAnn Falciani
Founded: 1995
ISBN Prefix(es): 978-0-312
Number of titles published annually: 90 Print
Total Titles: 7,000 Print
*Distribution Center:* MPS Distribution Center, 16365 James Madison Hwy, Gordonsville, VA 22942-8501 *Toll Free Tel:* 888-330-8477 *Fax:* 540-672-7540 (cust serv) *Toll Free Fax:* 800-672-2054 (orders) *E-mail:* firstinitiallastname@mpsvirginia.com

**Picasso Project**
Division of Alan Wofsy Fine Arts
1109 Geary Blvd, San Francisco, CA 94109
*Tel:* 415-292-6500 *Fax:* 415-292-6594
*E-mail:* editeur@earthlink.net (editorial); picasso@art-books.com (orders)
*Web Site:* www.art-books.com
*Key Personnel*
Mgr: Adios Butler
Ed: Alan Hyman
Founded: 1990
Publish & distribute comprehensive catalogues on the works of Pablo Picasso. Distribution center located in Ashland, OH.
ISBN Prefix(es): 978-1-55660
Number of titles published annually: 6 Print; 4 CD-ROM
Total Titles: 22 Print; 12 CD-ROM
Distributed by Alan Wofsy Fine Arts
Distributor for Cramer (Switzerland); Kornfeld (Switzerland); Ramie (France)
*Billing Address:* PO Box 2210, San Francisco, CA 94126-2110
*Distribution Center:* Ashland, OH 44805
Membership(s): AAP

**Piccadilly Books Ltd**
PO Box 25203, Colorado Springs, CO 80936-5203
SAN: 665-9969
*Tel:* 719-550-9887
*E-mail:* orders@piccadillybooks.com
*Web Site:* www.piccadillybooks.com
*Key Personnel*
Publr: Bruce Fife *E-mail:* bruce@piccadillybooks.com
Founded: 1985
Health & nutrition, entertainment, performing arts, humorous skits & sketches, writing.
ISBN Prefix(es): 978-0-941599; 978-1-936709
Number of titles published annually: 3 Print
Total Titles: 70 Print; 10 E-Book; 2 Audio
Foreign Rep(s): Gazelle Books (Europe)
Membership(s): IBPA, the Independent Book Publishers Association

**§Picton Press**
814 E Elkcam Circle, Marco Island, FL 34145-2558
Mailing Address: 1637 Briarwood Ct, Marco Island, FL 34145-4007
*Tel:* 239-970-2442
*E-mail:* sales@pictonpress.com (orders)
*Web Site:* www.pictonpress.com
*Key Personnel*
Pres: Lewis Bunker Rohrbach *E-mail:* lewisrohrbach@hotmail.com
Founded: 1973
Genealogical & historical books.
ISBN Prefix(es): 978-0-89725
Number of titles published annually: 15 Print; 25 CD-ROM
Total Titles: 1,000 Print; 1,000 CD-ROM; 1 E-Book
Imprints: New England History Press; Penobscot Press; Picton Press

**Pictorial Histories Publishing Co**
521 Bickford St, Missoula, MT 59801
Mailing Address: 713 S Third St, Missoula, MT 59801
*Tel:* 406-549-8488 *Toll Free Tel:* 888-763-8350 *Fax:* 406-728-9280
*E-mail:* phpc@montana.com
*Web Site:* www.pictorialhistoriespublishing.com
*Key Personnel*
Pres & Publr: Stan Cohen
Founded: 1976
History books.
ISBN Prefix(es): 978-0-933126; 978-0-929521; 978-1-57510
Number of titles published annually: 4 Print
Total Titles: 180 Print

**Pie in the Sky Publishing LLC**
8031 E Phillips Circle, Centennial, CO 80112
*Tel:* 303-773-0851 *Fax:* 303-773-0851
*E-mail:* pieintheskypublishing@msn.com
*Web Site:* www.pieintheskypublishing.com
*Key Personnel*
Pres: Ann Simmons
Publr: Nancy L Mills *Tel:* 303-221-1551
Founded: 1998
Publishers of high quality, brightly illustrated children's picture books. Most stories are written for both the reader & listener.
ISBN Prefix(es): 978-1-893815
Number of titles published annually: 5 Print; 1 Audio
Total Titles: 9 Print; 1 Audio
*Distribution Center:* Book West

**Pieces of Learning**
Division of Creative Learning Consultants Inc
1990 Market Rd, Marion, IL 62959-8976
SAN: 298-461X
*Tel:* 618-964-9426 *Toll Free Tel:* 800-729-5137 *Toll Free Fax:* 800-844-0455
*E-mail:* piecesoflearning@verizon.net
*Web Site:* www.piecesoflearning.com
*Key Personnel*
Pres: Kathy Balsamo
Busn Mgr: Stan Balsamo
Founded: 1989
Teacher supplementary educational books; mail order.

ISBN Prefix(es): 978-1-880505; 978-0-9623835; 978-0-945799; 978-0-913839; 978-1-931334
Number of titles published annually: 16 Print
Total Titles: 350 Print; 50 E-Book
Distributed by ALPS Publishing; A W Peller & Associates; Professional Associate Publishing; Prufrock Press Inc
Membership(s): National School Supply & Equipment Association

**The Pilgrim Press/United Church Press**
700 Prospect Ave, Cleveland, OH 44115-1100
*Toll Free Tel:* 800-537-3394 (cust serv-indivs); 800-654-5129 (cust serv-commercial accts) *Fax:* 216-736-2206 (orders)
*E-mail:* proposals@thepilgrimpress.com
*Web Site:* www.thepilgrimpress.com; www.unitedchurchpress.com
*Key Personnel*
Dir: Ann Poston *Tel:* 216-736-3755 *E-mail:* stavetet@ucc.org
Edit Dir: Kim Martin Sadler *Tel:* 216-736-3756 *E-mail:* sadlerk@ucc.org
Dir, Prodn: Janice W Brown *Tel:* 216-736-3763 *E-mail:* brownj@ucc.org
Dir, Dist Servs: Marie Tyson *Tel:* 216-736-3777 *E-mail:* tysonm@ucc.org
Graphic Designer: Robyn Nordstrom *Tel:* 216-736-3758 *E-mail:* nordstrr@ucc.org
Mktg Communs Assoc: Aimee Jannsohn *Tel:* 216-736-3761 *E-mail:* jannsoha@ucc.org
Mktg Communs: Tiffany French
Mktg: Darlene Grant
Mktg Asst: Juliet Dombos *Tel:* 216-736-3766 *E-mail:* dombosj@ucc.org
Founded: 1608
Alternative spiritualities; peace & justice; world religions; contemporary ministry.
ISBN Prefix(es): 978-0-8298
Number of titles published annually: 20 Print
Total Titles: 485 Print

**Pilgrim Publications**
PO Box 66, Pasadena, TX 77501-0066
*Tel:* 713-477-4261 *Fax:* 713-477-7561
*E-mail:* pilgrimpub@aol.com
*Web Site:* members.aol.com/pilgrimpub/; www.pilgrimpublications.com
*Key Personnel*
Dir: Bob Ross
Founded: 1969
The works & sermons of Charles H Spurgeon (1834-1892).
ISBN Prefix(es): 978-1-56186
Number of titles published annually: 4 Print
Total Titles: 200 Print
Distributor for Christian Focus; Fox River Press; Hess Publications
*Warehouse:* 1609 Preston, Pasadena, TX 77503
Membership(s): CBA: The Association for Christian Retail

**Pine Forge Press**
Subsidiary of SAGE Publications Inc
2455 Teller Rd, Thousand Oaks, CA 91320
*Tel:* 805-499-4224; 805-499-9774 (orders) *Fax:* 805-499-0871 (orders)
*E-mail:* info@sagepub.com
*Web Site:* www.sagepub.com; www.pineforge.com
*Key Personnel*
Pres & CEO, SAGE Pubns: Blaise Simqu
Founded: 1991
Texts & software for use in graduate & undergraduate social & behavioral science courses.
ISBN Prefix(es): 978-0-8039
Number of titles published annually: 25 Print
Total Titles: 150 Print

**Pineapple Press Inc**
PO Box 3889, Sarasota, FL 34230-3889
SAN: 631-8630
*Tel:* 941-706-2507 *Toll Free Tel:* 866-766-3850 (orders) *Fax:* 941-706-2509 *Toll Free Fax:* 800-838-1149 (orders)
*E-mail:* info@pineapplepress.com; customer.service@ingrampublisherservices.com
*Web Site:* www.pineapplepress.com
*Key Personnel*
Pres: David M Cussen *E-mail:* david@pineapplepress.com
Exec Ed: June Cussen *E-mail:* june@pineapplepress.com
Founded: 1982
ISBN Prefix(es): 978-0-910923; 978-1-56164
Number of titles published annually: 25 Print
Total Titles: 300 Print
*Warehouse:* Ingram Publisher Services, 1210 Ingram Dr, Chambersburg, PA 17202

**Pinnacle Books**, see Kensington Publishing Corp

**Pioneer Publishing Co**
Hwy 82 E, Carrolton, MS 38917
Mailing Address: PO Box 408, Carrolton, MS 38917-0408
*Tel:* 662-237-6010
*E-mail:* pioneerse@tecinfo.com
*Web Site:* www.pioneersoutheast.com
*Key Personnel*
Owner: Betty C Wiltshire
ISBN Prefix(es): 978-1-885480
Number of titles published annually: 6 Print
Total Titles: 100 Print

**Pippin Press**
229 E 85 St, New York, NY 10028
Mailing Address: PO Box 1347, Gracie Sta, New York, NY 10028
*Tel:* 212-288-4920 *Fax:* 908-237-2407
*Key Personnel*
Pres, Publr & Ed-in-Chief: Barbara Francis
Mng Ed & Rts Dir: Gregory Filling
Sr Ed: Joyce Segal
Sales Mgr & Lib Sales Dir: Alan Frese
Founded: 1987
Small chapter books for ages 7-10, humorous fiction for all ages, novels for ages 8-12 & unusual nonfiction for ages 6-12.
ISBN Prefix(es): 978-0-945912
Number of titles published annually: 4 Print
Total Titles: 55 Print
Foreign Rep(s): Baker & Taylor Books (Canada); Baker & Taylor International (Worldwide exc Canada)
*Orders to:* Whitehurst & Clark Book Fulfillment Inc, 1200 County Rd, Rte 523, Flemington, NJ 08822 *Tel:* 908-782-2323 *Toll Free Tel:* 800-488-8040
*Returns:* Whitehurst & Clark Book Fulfillment Inc, 1200 County Rd, Rte 523, Flemington, NJ 08822 *Tel:* 908-782-2323 *Toll Free Tel:* 800-488-8040
*Shipping Address:* Whitehurst & Clark Book Fulfillment Inc, 1200 County Rd, Rte 523, Flemington, NJ 08822 *Tel:* 908-782-2323 *Toll Free Tel:* 800-488-8040
*Warehouse:* Whitehurst & Clark Book Fulfillment Inc, 1200 County Rd, Rte 523, Flemington, NJ 08822 *Tel:* 908-782-2323 *Toll Free Tel:* 800-488-8040
*Distribution Center:* Whitehurst & Clark Book Fulfillment Inc, 1200 County Rd, Rte 523, Flemington, NJ 08822 *Tel:* 908-782-2323 *Toll Free Tel:* 800-488-8040
Membership(s): ALA

**PJD Publications Ltd**
PO Box 966, Westbury, NY 11590-0966
SAN: 202-0068
*Tel:* 516-626-0650 *Fax:* 516-626-4456
*Web Site:* www.pjdonline.com
*Key Personnel*
CEO & Pres: Siva Sankar *E-mail:* sankar@pjdonline.com
Tech: Barbara Kelly
Founded: 1968
Biomedical & educational books, philosophy, scholarly, science & social sciences, books & journals.
ISBN Prefix(es): 978-0-9600290; 978-0-915340
Number of titles published annually: 6 Print
Total Titles: 15 Print
Divisions: Institute for Research Information; Office & Print Technologies; PJD Electronic Publishing

**Platinum Press LLC**
37 Rte 80, Killingworth, CT 06419
*Tel:* 860-663-3882 *Fax:* 718-875-5065
*Key Personnel*
Pres: Herbert J Cohen *E-mail:* herbertjcohen@aol.com
Founded: 1990
Publish nonfiction; book producer & packager; appointment books, diaries, date books, journals, blankbooks & joke books.
ISBN Prefix(es): 978-1-879582
Number of titles published annually: 8 Print
Total Titles: 105 Print; 2 E-Book

**Platypus Media LLC**
725 Eighth St SE, Washington, DC 20003
*Tel:* 202-546-1674 *Toll Free Tel:* 877-PLATYPS (752-8977) *Fax:* 202-546-2356
*E-mail:* info@platypusmedia.com
*Web Site:* www.platypusmedia.com
*Key Personnel*
Pres: Dia L Michels
Founded: 2000
An independent publisher creating books for families, teachers & parenting professionals.
ISBN Prefix(es): 978-1-930775
Number of titles published annually: 4 Print; 2 Audio
Total Titles: 16 Print; 2 Audio
*Warehouse:* Border Mail Services, Champlain, NY
*Distribution Center:* National Book Network, 4501 Forbes Blvd, Lanham, MD 20706 *Tel:* 301-459-3366 *Toll Free Tel:* 800-787-6859 *Fax:* 301-459-5746 *Web Site:* www.nbnbooks.com
Membership(s): The Association of Publishers for Special Sales; Children's Book Council; IBPA, the Independent Book Publishers Association; Washington Book Publishers; Women's National Book Association
*See separate listing for:*
**Science, Naturally!™**

**§Players Press Inc**
PO Box 1132, Studio City, CA 91614-0132
*Tel:* 818-789-4980
*E-mail:* playerspress@att.net
*Web Site:* www.ppeps.com
*Key Personnel*
CEO & Pres: Robert Gordon
VP, Ed: David Wainright
VP, Opers: Chris Cordero
Busn Mgr: David Cole
Sales Mgr: M Cohen
Founded: 1965
Publisher of plays, musicals & performing arts textbooks & Sherlock Holmes. Represents world rights for other publishers of performing arts books (film, theater, television). Distributes English Speaking World for other publishers of entertainment books & Sherlockian. Publishes costume books in English & German.
ISBN Prefix(es): 978-0-88734; 978-1-85729
Number of titles published annually: 60 Print; 5 CD-ROM
Total Titles: 2,085 Print; 62 CD-ROM; 4 Audio

Imprints: Healthwatch; Players Press; Showcase
Divisions: Players Press (Canada); Player Press A/Z Ltd; Player Press Ltd (UK)
*Foreign Office(s):* 20 Park Dr, Romford, Essex RM1 4LH, United Kingdom
Distributor for Camelion Plays; Garland-Clark Editors; Macmillan Education (UK); Preston Editions
Foreign Rep(s): Players Press Germany GMBH; Players Press UK Ltd (UK)
Foreign Rights: Players Press International (Europe)
*Advertising Agency:* Empire Enterprises, PO Box 1344, Studio City, CA 91614-0344 *Tel:* 818-784-8918
Membership(s): ABA

**Playhouse Publishing**
PO Box 1962, Cleveland, OH 44106
*Tel:* 330-926-1313 *Fax:* 330-475-8579
*E-mail:* info@picturemepress.com
*Web Site:* www.picturemepress.com
*Key Personnel*
Pres: Deborah D'Andrea
Spec Sales Dir: Noelle Pangle *Tel:* 216-375-3544 *E-mail:* n.pangle@picturemepress.com
Founded: 1989
Children's book publisher of interactive titles.
ISBN Prefix(es): 978-1-878338; 978-1-57151
Number of titles published annually: 15 Print
Total Titles: 130 Print
Imprints: Little Lucy & Friends™; Look & Learn™; Nibble Me Books™; Picture Me Books™; Picture, Play & Tote™; Pretend & Play™; Sparkle Shapes
Membership(s): ABA; IBPA, the Independent Book Publishers Association

**Pleasure Boat Studio: A Literary Press**
201 W 89 St, New York, NY 10024
*Toll Free Tel:* 888-810-5308 *Toll Free Fax:* 888-810-5308
*E-mail:* pleasboat@nyc.rr.com
*Web Site:* www.pleasureboatstudio.com
*Key Personnel*
Publr: Jack Estes
Founded: 1996
Fiction, nonfiction & poetry.
ISBN Prefix(es): 978-0-9651413; 978-1-929355; 978-0-912887
Number of titles published annually: 4 Print
Total Titles: 48 Print
Imprints: Aequitas Books (nonfiction only); Caravel Books (mysteries only)
Divisions: Empty Bowl Press
Distributed by Partners/West; Small Press Distribution
Distributor for Empty Bowl Press
Foreign Rights: Books Crossing Borders (Worldwide)
*Returns:* 721 Mount Pleasant Rd, Port Angeles, WA 98362, Contact: Jo Anne Hughes *Tel:* 360-457-5541
*Shipping Address:* 721 Mount Pleasant Rd, Port Angeles, WA 98362, Contact: Jo Anne Hughes *Tel:* 360-457-5541
Membership(s): Council of Literary Magazines & Presses; IBPA, the Independent Book Publishers Association

**§Plexus Publishing, Inc**
Affiliate of Information Today, Inc
143 Old Marlton Pike, Medford, NJ 08055
*Tel:* 609-654-6500 *Fax:* 609-654-4309
*E-mail:* info@plexuspublishing.com
*Web Site:* www.plexuspublishing.com
*Key Personnel*
Pres & CEO: Thomas H Hogan, Sr
Ed-in-Chief & Publr, Book Publg Div: John B Bryans *E-mail:* jbryans@plexuspublishing.com
Mng Ed, Book Publg Div: Amy M Reeve *Tel:* 609-654-6500 ext 116 *E-mail:* areeve@plexuspublishing.com
VP, Mktg & Busn Devt: Thomas Hogan, Jr
Book Mktg & Exhibits: Robert Colding *Tel:* 609-654-6500 ext 330 *E-mail:* rcolding@plexuspublishing.com
Admin & Cust Serv: Deb Kranz *Tel:* 609-654-6500 ext 117 *E-mail:* dkranz@plexuspublishing.com
HR Dir: Mary S Hogan *E-mail:* shogan@plexuspublishing.com
Founded: 1977
Regional book publisher specializing in nature, history & fiction for readers interested in the NJ Pinelands, Atlantic City/Jersey shore, Philadelphia & surrounds. No children's books, poetry, religion, or calendars.
ISBN Prefix(es): 978-0-937548; 978-0-9666748
Number of titles published annually: 3 Print
Total Titles: 47 Print
Imprints: Medford Press (trade book titles, nationally dist by IPG); Plexus Books (regional titles/NJ topics especially Southern NJ history, nature/Pinelands, fiction)
*Distribution Center:* Independent Publishers Group (IPG) (Medford Press imprint only)

**§The Plough Publishing House**
Imprint of Church Communities Foundation
PO Box 903, Rifton, NY 12471-0903
SAN: 202-0092
*E-mail:* info@plough.com
*Web Site:* www.plough.com
*Key Personnel*
Mgr: Chris Meier
Founded: 1920
Religion (Anabaptist), church history, children's education, Christian communal living; music; social justice, radical Christianity; social issues.
ISBN Prefix(es): 978-0-87486
Number of titles published annually: 3 Print; 5 Online; 5 E-Book
Total Titles: 45 Print; 42 Online; 42 E-Book
*Foreign Office(s):* Darvell Community Plough UK, Robertsbridge, East Sussex TN32 5DR, United Kingdom
Foreign Rep(s): Darvell Community

**Ploughshares**
Subsidiary of Ploughshares Inc
Emerson College, 120 Boylston St, Boston, MA 02116
*Tel:* 617-824-3757
*E-mail:* pshares@pshares.org
*Web Site:* www.pshares.org
*Key Personnel*
Dir & Ed: Ladette Randolph
Founded: 1971
Journal publishing.
ISBN Prefix(es): 978-0-933277; 978-1-933058
Number of titles published annually: 3 Print
Total Titles: 118 Print; 9 E-Book
Membership(s): Combined Book Exhibit

**§Plowshare Media**
405 Vincente Way, La Jolla, CA 92037
SAN: 857-2933
Mailing Address: PO Box 278, La Jolla, CA 92038
*E-mail:* sales@plowsharemedia.com
*Web Site:* plowsharemedia.com
*Key Personnel*
Mng Partner: Maryann Callery *E-mail:* mc@plowsharemedia.com; Thomas P Tweed *E-mail:* tt@plowsharemedia.com
Founded: 2008
Handle all aspects of book publishing including acquisition, editing, typesetting, cover design, printing, marketing & promotion.
ISBN Prefix(es): 978-9-821145
Number of titles published annually: 3 Print; 3 E-Book
Total Titles: 7 Print; 2 E-Book
Imprints: Plowshare Media; RELS Press (nonprofit)
Membership(s): IBPA, the Independent Book Publishers Association

**§Plum Tree Books**
Imprint of Classical Academic Press LLC
2151 Market St, Camp Hill, PA 17011
*Tel:* 717-730-0711 *Fax:* 717-730-0721
*E-mail:* info@classicalsubjects.com
*Web Site:* www.plumtreebooks.com
*Key Personnel*
Publr: Christopher Perrin *E-mail:* cperrin@classicalsubjects.com
Founded: 2012
Old Virtues, New Stories™ - children's stories presented entirely through digital formats.
ISBN Prefix(es): 978-1-60051

**Plume**
Division of Penguin Group (USA) LLC
375 Hudson St, New York, NY 10014
SAN: 282-5074
*Tel:* 212-366-2000 *Fax:* 212-366-2666
*E-mail:* online@penguinputnam.com
*Web Site:* www.penguinputnam.com; us.penguingroup.com
*Key Personnel*
Pres: Clare Ferraro
Publr: Kathryn Court
Edit Dir: Philip Budnick
Sr Ed: Becky Cole
Sr Ed, Plume/Dutton: Denise Roy
VP, Prodn: Pat Lyons
Exec Dir, Publicity: Elizabeth Keenan
Dir, Art: Jaya Miceli
ISBN Prefix(es): 978-0-452
Number of titles published annually: 83 Print
Total Titles: 947 Print

**§Plunkett Research Ltd**
PO Drawer 541737, Houston, TX 77254-1737
*Tel:* 713-932-0000 *Fax:* 713-932-7080
*E-mail:* customersupport@plunkettresearch.com
*Web Site:* www.plunkettresearch.com
*Key Personnel*
CEO & Publr: Jack W Plunkett *E-mail:* jack_plunkett@plunkettresearch.com
Founded: 1985
Provider of business & industry information to corporate, library, academic & government markets. Plunkett's unique reference books are the only complete sources written in lay language for readers of all types. In many cases, these valuable resources are the only comprehensive guides covering the specific industries involved. Publish in print & electronic formats.
ISBN Prefix(es): 978-0-9638268; 978-1-891775
Number of titles published annually: 27 Print; 29 CD-ROM; 30 Online; 30 E-Book
Total Titles: 27 Print; 30 CD-ROM; 30 Online; 30 E-Book

**Pocket Books**, see Gallery Books

**Pocket Press Inc**
PO Box 25124, Portland, OR 97298-0124
*Toll Free Tel:* 888-237-2110 *Toll Free Fax:* 877-643-3732
*E-mail:* sales@pocketpressinc.com
*Web Site:* www.pocketpressinc.com
*Key Personnel*
Pres: Bruce Coorpender
Sales & Mktg: Bob Born
Founded: 1992
Reference books for law enforcement.
ISBN Prefix(es): 978-1-884493; 978-1-61371

Number of titles published annually: 40 Print
Total Titles: 40 Print

**Pocket Star**, see Gallery Books

**Pocol Press**
6023 Pocol Dr, Clifton, VA 20124-1333
SAN: 253-6021
*Tel:* 703-830-5862
*E-mail:* chrisandtom@erols.com
*Web Site:* www.pocolpress.com
*Key Personnel*
Owner & Publr: J Thomas Hetrick
Founded: 1999
Leaders in short fiction & baseball history from first-time non-agented authors. Several books used as college textbooks. All titles also ebooks available from Amazon for Kindle.
ISBN Prefix(es): 978-1-929763
Number of titles published annually: 4 Print; 4 E-Book
Total Titles: 53 Print; 53 E-Book
Membership(s): The Association of Publishers for Special Sales

**Pogo Press Inc**
Imprint of Finney Company Inc
8075 215 St W, Lakeville, MN 55044
SAN: 665-2107
*Tel:* 952-469-6699 *Toll Free Tel:* 800-846-7027 *Fax:* 952-469-1968 *Toll Free Fax:* 800-330-6232
*E-mail:* info@finneyco.com
*Web Site:* www.pogopress.com
*Key Personnel*
Pres: Alan Krysan
Mktg Specialist: Krista Danielson
Founded: 1986
Popular culture.
ISBN Prefix(es): 978-0-9617767; 978-1-880654
Number of titles published annually: 3 Print
Total Titles: 41 Print
*Distribution Center:* SCB Distributors, 15608 S New Century Dr, Gardena, CA 90248 *Tel:* 310-532-9400 *Toll Free Tel:* 800-729-6423 *Fax:* 310-532-7001 *E-mail:* info@scbdistributors.com

**Pointed Leaf Press**
136 Baxter St, New York, NY 10013
*Tel:* 212-941-1800 *Fax:* 212-941-1822
*E-mail:* info@pointedleafpress.com
*Web Site:* www.pointedleafpress.com
*Key Personnel*
Publg Dir: Suzanne Slesin
Founded: 2002
ISBN Prefix(es): 978-0-9727661; 978-0-9777875; 978-0-9823585; 978-0-9833889; 978-1-938461

**Poisoned Pen Press Inc**
6962 E First Ave, Suite 103, Scottsdale, AZ 85251
*Tel:* 480-945-3375 *Toll Free Tel:* 1-800-421-3976 *Fax:* 480-949-1707
*E-mail:* info@poisonedpenpress.com
*Web Site:* www.poisonedpenpress.com
*Key Personnel*
Pres: Robert Rosenwald *E-mail:* robert@perfectniche.com
Publr: Jessica Tribble *E-mail:* jessica@poisonedpenpress.com
Ed-in-Chief: Barbara Peters *E-mail:* barbara@poisonedpenpress.com
Acqs Ed: Annette Rogers *E-mail:* annette@poisonedpenpress.com
Prodn Mgr: Nan Beams *E-mail:* nan@poisonedpenpress.com
Founded: 1997
Publishing high quality works in the field of mystery. Interested in publishing books that we think booksellers everywhere & especially independent mystery booksellers would want to have available to sell. Electronic submissions only. Visit www.poisonedpenpress.com, click on Publishing Information, then on Manuscript Submission Guidelines for submission information.
ISBN Prefix(es): 978-1-890208; 978-1-59058
Number of titles published annually: 40 Print
Total Titles: 300 Print
Foreign Rep(s): Baror International (Worldwide)
Foreign Rights: Danny Baror (Worldwide)
Membership(s): Arizona Book Publishing Association; IBPA, the Independent Book Publishers Association; Publishers Association of the West

**Polar Bear & Co**
8 Brook St, Solon, ME 04979
Mailing Address: PO Box 311, Solon, ME 04979-0311
*Tel:* 207-643-2795
*Web Site:* www.polarbearandco.com
*Key Personnel*
Publr & Consultant: Paul Cornell du Houx
Founded: 1991
Rebuilding our cultural heritage with words & art, we are publishers of high quality fiction & nonfiction who provide consultancy services for writers, artists & photographers who wish to bring out that spark in us all. We produce books highlighting social & environmental issues, works that grow with the readership in time.
ISBN Prefix(es): 978-1-882190
Number of titles published annually: 6 Print
Total Titles: 40 Print; 3 Audio
*Foreign Office(s):* 22-12 Miyamotocho Itabashiku, T174 Tokyo, Japan, Contact: Takafumi Suzuki
*Distribution Center:* Baker & Taylor, 2550 Tyvola Rd, Suite 300, Charlotte, NC 28217 *Tel:* 704-998-3100 *Toll Free Tel:* 800-775-1800 *Web Site:* www.btol.com

**Police Executive Research Forum**
1120 Connecticut Ave NW, Suite 930, Washington, DC 20036
*Tel:* 202-466-7820 *Fax:* 202-466-7826
*E-mail:* perf@policeforum.org
*Web Site:* www.policeforum.org
*Key Personnel*
Dir, Communs: Craig Fischer *Tel:* 202-454-8332
Opers Admin: Rebecca Neuburger *Tel:* 202-454-8300 *E-mail:* rneuburger@policeforum.org
Chief of Staff: Andrea Luna *Tel:* 202-454-8346
Receptionist/Staff Asst: Alicia Armstrong
Founded: 1977
Community policing, POP, police research & management, police & criminal justice.
ISBN Prefix(es): 978-1-878734
Number of titles published annually: 5 Print
Total Titles: 70 Print
*Distribution Center:* Whitehurst & Clark, 1200 Rte 523, Flemington, NJ 08822, Contact: Brad Searles *Toll Free Tel:* 888-202-4563 *Fax:* 908-237-2407 *E-mail:* wcbooks@aol.com

**Pomegranate Communications Inc**
19018 NE Portal Way, Portland, OR 97230
*Tel:* 503-328-6500 *Toll Free Tel:* 800-227-1428 *Fax:* 503-328-9330 *Toll Free Fax:* 800-848-4376
*E-mail:* info@pomegranate.com
*Web Site:* www.pomegranate.com
*Key Personnel*
Pres & Intl Rts: Thomas F Burke
Publr: Katie Burke
Asst Publr: Becky Holtzman
Intl Sales Dir: Josh Rifkin
Founded: 1968
Fine arts publisher of books, calendars, posters, notecards, postcards & journals.
ISBN Prefix(es): 978-0-87654; 978-1-56640; 978-0-7649
Number of titles published annually: 12 Print
Total Titles: 152 Print
Imprints: PomegranateKids
Foreign Rep(s): Ashton International (Far East, Middle East); Canadian Manda (Canada); Hardie Grant Books (Australia, New Zealand); Pomegranate Europe Ltd (Europe, UK); Pomegranate International Sales (Africa, Latin America)
Membership(s): Publishers Association of the West

**Portfolio**
Subsidiary of Penguin Group (USA) LLC
375 Hudson St, New York, NY 10014
*Key Personnel*
Pres & Publr: Adrian Zackheim
VP, Assoc Publr & Mktg Dir: William Weisser
Sr Ed: Niki Papadopoulos; Maria Gagliano
Dir, Publicity: Allison McLean
Art Dir: Christopher Sergio
Founded: 2001
Specialize in management, leadership, marketing, business narrative, investing, personal finance, economics & career advice.
ISBN Prefix(es): 978-1-59184
Number of titles published annually: 78 Print
Total Titles: 286 Print

**Posterity Press Inc**
4948 Saint Elmo Ave, 3rd fl, Bethesda, MD 20814
Mailing Address: PO Box 71081, Chevy Chase, MD 20813
*Tel:* 301-652-2384 *Fax:* 301-652-2543
*Web Site:* www.posteritypress.com
*Key Personnel*
Publr & Chief Edit Offr: Philip Kopper *E-mail:* publisher@posteritypress.com
Founded: 1995
Aside from conventional (trade) publishing, we offer & advocate venture publishing in which a sponsor, author & or other third party shares the risk financially.
This publisher has indicated that 50% of their product line is author subsidized.
ISBN Prefix(es): 978-1-889274
Number of titles published annually: 4 Print
Total Titles: 40 Print
Membership(s): AAP

**Potomac Books Inc**
Imprint of University of Nebraska Press
22841 Quicksilver Dr, Dulles, VA 20166
*Tel:* 703-661-1548 *Fax:* 703-661-1547
*E-mail:* pbimail@presswarehouse.com
*Web Site:* www.potomacbooksinc.com
*Key Personnel*
Publr: Samuel R Dorrance *Tel:* 703-996-1028 *E-mail:* sam@booksintl.com
Prodn Ed: Katherine Owens
Mktg: Laura Briggs
Founded: 1984 (prior to 2005, Brassey's Inc)
ISBN Prefix(es): 978-1-57488; 978-1-59797
Number of titles published annually: 80 Print; 50 E-Book
Total Titles: 550 Print; 400 E-Book
Foreign Rep(s): International Publishers Representatives (IPR) (Middle East); Login Brothers Canada (Canada); Orca Book Services (Europe, Ireland, UK); Peribo (Australia, New Zealand); Transatlantic Publishers Group Ltd (UK)
Foreign Rights: The Asano Agency Inc (Japan); CA-LINK International LLC (China); Graal Literary Agency (Eastern Europe, Poland); Natoli, Stefan & Oliva (Italy); La Nouvelle Agence (France); Julio F Yanez Agencia Literaria SL (Spanish languages)
*Distribution Center:* Books International, 22883 Quicksilver Dr, Dulles, VA 20166 *Tel:* 703-661-1500 *Fax:* 703-661-1501
Membership(s): NAIPR

**powerHouse Books**
Division of powerHouse Cultural Entertainment Inc
37 Main St, Brooklyn, NY 11201
*Tel:* 212-604-9074 *Fax:* 212-366-5247
*E-mail:* info@powerhousebooks.com
*Web Site:* www.powerhousebooks.com
*Key Personnel*
Publr: Daniel Power
Mng Ed: Craig Cohen *E-mail:* press@powerhousebooks.com
Founded: 1995
Contemporary art, photography & image-based cultural books.
ISBN Prefix(es): 978-1-57687
Number of titles published annually: 45 Print; 1 E-Book
Total Titles: 350 Print; 3 E-Book; 1 Audio
Imprints: Miss Rosen Edition
Distributed by Random House Publisher Services
Distributor for Antinous Press; Juno Books; MTV Press; Throckmorton Press; VH1 Press; Vice Books
Foreign Rep(s): Bookwise International Pty Ltd (Australia); Critiques Livres (France); Peter Hyde Associates (South Africa); Perseus Books Group (Canada); Shimada (Japan); Turnaround (Austria, Eastern Europe, Germany, Ireland, Mediterranean, Scandinavia, Switzerland, UK)
Foreign Rights: Bookwise International Pty Ltd (Australia); Critiques Livres (France); Turnaround (UK)
*Warehouse:* Random House

**Practice Management Information Corp (PMIC)**
4727 Wilshire Blvd, Suite 300, Los Angeles, CA 90010
SAN: 139-438X
*Tel:* 323-954-0224 *Fax:* 323-954-0253
*Toll Free Fax:* 800-633-6556 (orders)
*E-mail:* orders@medicalbookstore.com; customer.service@pmiconline.com
*Web Site:* www.pmiconline.com
*Key Personnel*
Publr & Pres: James B Davis
Founded: 1986
Books & software for physicians, hospitals, insurance companies & other healthcare professionals on medical coding, reimbursement, practice management, financial management & medical risk management.
ISBN Prefix(es): 978-1-878487 (Health Info); 978-1-57066
Number of titles published annually: 35 Print
Total Titles: 35 Print
Imprints: Health Information Press (HIP)
*Branch Office(s)*
PMIC Sales Office, 2001 Butterfield Rd, Suite 850, Downers Grove, IL 60515 *Tel:* 630-964-7800 *Toll Free Tel:* 800-MEDSHOP *Fax:* 630-964-8873

**§Practising Law Institute**
810 Seventh Ave, New York, NY 10019
SAN: 203-0136
*Tel:* 212-824-5700 *Toll Free Tel:* 800-260-4PLI (260-4754 cust serv) *Fax:* 212-265-4742 (intl) *Toll Free Fax:* 800-321-0093 (local)
*E-mail:* info@pli.edu
*Web Site:* www.pli.edu
*Key Personnel*
CFO & Treas: Frank De Vivo *Tel:* 212-824-5709 *E-mail:* fdevivo@pli.edu
CIO: Kenneth Moskowitz *Tel:* 212-824-5766 *E-mail:* kmoskowitz@pli.edu
Pres: Victor J Rubino *Tel:* 212-824-5701 *E-mail:* vrubino@pli.edu
EVP: Sandra R Geller *Tel:* 212-824-5796 *E-mail:* sgeller@pli.edu
VP: William Cubberley *Tel:* 212-824-5761 *E-mail:* wcubberley@pli.edu
VP, Cust Rel: Kevin Kelly *Tel:* 212-824-8839 *E-mail:* kkelly@pli.edu
VP, Progs: Anita C Shapiro *Tel:* 212-824-5760 *E-mail:* ashapiro@pli.edu
Founded: 1933
Professional books for lawyers; CDs, DVDs, CD-ROMs, programs.
ISBN Prefix(es): 978-0-87224; 978-1-4024
Number of titles published annually: 181 Print
Total Titles: 233 Print; 4 CD-ROM; 206 Online; 308 Audio
Imprints: PLI
*Branch Office(s)*
Monadnock Bldg, 1st fl, 685 Market St, San Francisco, CA 94105-4200 *Tel:* 415-498-2800
Distributed by PLI
*Shipping Address:* PMDS, 1780A Crossroads Dr, Odenton, MD 21113 *Tel:* 301-604-3305

**Prayer Book Press Inc**
Subsidiary of Media Judaica Inc
1363 Fairfield Ave, Bridgeport, CT 06605
SAN: 282-1796
*Tel:* 203-384-2284 *Fax:* 203-579-9109
*Key Personnel*
Pres & Ed: Jonathan D Levine
VP & Prodn Mgr: Andrew Amsel
VP & Sales & Dist Mgr: Walter B Stern
Compt: Sharon Dworkin
Founded: 1933
Religion (Jewish); prayer books, textbooks, gift editions & reference.
ISBN Prefix(es): 978-0-87677
Number of titles published annually: 5 Print; 1 Audio
Total Titles: 50 Print; 5 Audio
Imprints: Center for Contemporary Judaica

**Prentice Hall Press**
Division of Penguin Group (USA) LLC
375 Hudson St, New York, NY 10014
*Tel:* 212-366-2000 *Fax:* 212-366-2666
*Key Personnel*
Publr, Busn, Self-Help & Health: John Duff
Ed: Jeanette Shaw
Founded: 1913
Number of titles published annually: 7 Print
Total Titles: 134 Print

**PREP Publishing**
Subsidiary of PREP Inc
1110 1/2 Hay St, Suite C, Fayetteville, NC 28305
*Tel:* 910-483-6611 *Toll Free Tel:* 800-533-2814
*E-mail:* preppub@aol.com
*Web Site:* www.prep-pub.com
*Key Personnel*
Publr: Anne McKinney
Lib Sales Dir: Frances Sweeney
Founded: 1994
Books designed to enrich people's lives & help optimize the human experience. Publisher of general trade books, fiction & nonfiction, especially books related to careers, job hunting, government jobs & business planning, marketing & entrepreneurship. Fiction titles include mysteries, Christian fiction & romance.
ISBN Prefix(es): 978-1-885288
Number of titles published annually: 8 Print
Total Titles: 52 Print
Imprints: Business Success Series; Government Jobs Series; Judeo Christian Ethics Series; Anne McKinney Career Series
*Advertising Agency:* McKinney Communications, PO Box 66, Fayetteville, NC 28302-0066, Contact: Pat Mack
*Warehouse:* 435 W Russell St, Fayetteville, NC 28301
Membership(s): Council of Literary Magazines & Presses; IBPA, the Independent Book Publishers Association; Southern Independent Booksellers Alliance

**Presbyterian Publishing Corp**
100 Witherspoon St, Louisville, KY 40202
*Tel:* 502-569-5000 *Toll Free Tel:* 800-523-1631 (US only) *Fax:* 502-569-5113
*E-mail:* ppcmail@presbypub.com
*Web Site:* www.wjkbooks.com
*Key Personnel*
COO: Monty Anderson *E-mail:* manderson@wjkbooks.com
Pres & Publr: Marc Lewis *E-mail:* mlewis@wjkbooks.com
Exec Dir, Publg & Edit: David Dobson *Tel:* 502-569-5394 *E-mail:* ddobson@wjkbooks.com
Exec Dir, Sales & Mktg: Gavin Stephens *E-mail:* gstephens@wjkbooks.com
Founded: 1838
Biblical studies, academic & scholarly textbooks, general trade religious books.
ISBN Prefix(es): 978-0-664; 978-0-8042
Number of titles published annually: 80 Print; 2 CD-ROM
Total Titles: 1,700 Print; 5 CD-ROM
Imprints: Geneva Press
Divisions: Westminster John Knox Press
Distributed by Spring Arbor Distributors
Distributor for Epworth; SCM
Foreign Rep(s): Alban Books Ltd (Europe, UK)
*See separate listing for:*
**Westminster John Knox Press**

**The Press at California State University, Fresno**
Unit of California State University, Fresno
2380 E Keats, M/S MB 99, Fresno, CA 93740-8024
*Tel:* 559-278-3056 *Fax:* 559-278-6758
*E-mail:* press@csufresno.edu
*Web Site:* shop.thepressatcsufresno.com; thepressatcsufresno.com
*Key Personnel*
Gen Mgr: Carla Millar
Founded: 1982
Art, architecture, drama, music, film & the media, New Age politics, business, autobiography, Armenian history, Fresno history & Literary magazine. Peer reviewed multi-disciplinary victimology journal.
ISBN Prefix(es): 978-0-912201
Number of titles published annually: 4 Print; 1 Online
Total Titles: 30 Print

**Prestel Publishing**
900 Broadway, Suite 603, New York, NY 10003
*Tel:* 212-995-2720 *Toll Free Tel:* 888-463-6110 (cust serv) *Fax:* 212-995-2733
*E-mail:* sales@prestel-usa.com
*Web Site:* www.prestel.com
*Key Personnel*
VP: Stephen Hulburt *Tel:* 212-995-2720 ext 22 *E-mail:* shulburt@prestel-usa.com
Sales & Mktg Mgr: Raya Thoma *E-mail:* rthoma@prestel-usa.com
Publicist: Samantha Waller *E-mail:* swaller@prestel-usa.com
Founded: 1999
ISBN Prefix(es): 978-3-7913
Number of titles published annually: 75 Print
Total Titles: 450 Print
Distributor for Die Gestalten Verlag (DGV); Loft; Lars Muller; Periscope; Schirmer/Mosel
*Warehouse:* Innovative Logistics, 575 Prospect St, Lakewood, NJ 08701 *Tel:* 732-363-5679 *Fax:* 732-363-0338 *Toll Free Fax:* 877-372-8892

**Price Stern Sloan**
Imprint of Penguin Group (USA) LLC
345 Hudson St, New York, NY 10014
SAN: 282-5074
*Tel:* 212-366-2000
*E-mail:* online@penguinputnam.com

*Web Site:* www.penguinputnam.com; us.penguingroup.com
*Key Personnel*
VP & Publr: Francesco Sedita
Founded: 1963
ISBN Prefix(es): 978-0-201; 978-0-8431
Number of titles published annually: 29 Print
Total Titles: 319 Print
Imprints: Crazy Games; Doodle Art; Serendipity; Troubador Press; Wee Sing

**§Price World Publishing LLC**
1300 W Belmont Ave, Suite 20-G, Chicago, IL 60657
*Toll Free Tel:* 888-234-6896 *Fax:* 216-803-0350
*E-mail:* publishing@priceworldpublishing.com; info@priceworldpublishing.com
*Web Site:* www.priceworldpublishing.com
*Key Personnel*
Pres & Exec Ed: Robert Price, Esq *Tel:* 888-234-6896 ext 713 *E-mail:* rprice@priceworldpublishing.com
Acqs Ed: Bob Grant *Tel:* 888-234-6896 ext 710
Founded: 2001
Bringing books & ebooks to global markets.
ISBN Prefix(es): 978-1-932549; 978-0-9724102; 978-1-61984; 978-1-93691
Number of titles published annually: 25 Print; 1 CD-ROM; 150 E-Book
Total Titles: 127 Print; 2 CD-ROM; 357 E-Book
Distributed by David Bateman Ltd (New Zealand); Cardinal Publisher's Group (US); Fortytwo Bookz Galaxy (India); Gazelle Book Services (UK); Monarch Books of Canada (CN); John Reed Books (Australia)
Foreign Rep(s): Rights & Distribution Inc (Brunei, Hong Kong, Malaysia, New Zealand, Philippines, Singapore, South Africa, Thailand)
Foreign Rights: Rights & Distribution Inc
*Orders to:* Cardinal Publishers Group, 2402 Shadeland Ave, Suite A, Indianapolis, IN 46219, Pres: Tom Doherty *Tel:* 317-352-8200 *Fax:* 317-352-8202 *E-mail:* tdoherty@cardinalpub.com *Web Site:* www.cardinalpub.com
Membership(s): American Bar Association; IBPA, the Independent Book Publishers Association

**Prima Games**
Imprint of Random House Information Group
3000 Lava Ridge Ct, Roseville, CA 95661
SAN: 289-5609
*Tel:* 916-787-7000 *Fax:* 916-787-7001
*Web Site:* www.primagames.com
*Key Personnel*
Pres: Debra Kempker
Founded: 1984
Computer & video game guides.
Random House Inc & its publishing entities are not accepting unsol submissions, proposals, mss, or submission queries via e-mail at this time.
ISBN Prefix(es): 978-0-7615
Number of titles published annually: 150 Print
Total Titles: 1,100 Print

**Primary Research Group Inc**
2753 Broadway, Suite 156, New York, NY 10025
*Tel:* 212-736-2316 *Fax:* 212-412-9097
*E-mail:* primaryresearchgroup@gmail.com
*Web Site:* www.primaryresearch.com
*Key Personnel*
Pres: James Moses
Founded: 1989
Monographs, books, surveys & research reports on library science industry, economics, publishing (book, electronic & magazine), telecommunication, entertainment & higher education.
ISBN Prefix(es): 978-1-57440
Number of titles published annually: 35 Print
Total Titles: 175 Print
Distributed by Academic Book Center; Ambassador Books; The Book House; Coutts Library Service; Croft House Books; Eastern Book Company; MarketResearch.com; Midwest Library Service; OPAMP Technical Books; Emory Pratt; Research & Markets; Rittenhouse Book Distributors; Total Information; Yankee Book Peddler

**Princeton Architectural Press**
37 E Seventh St, New York, NY 10003
*Tel:* 212-995-9620 *Toll Free Tel:* 800-722-6657 (dist); 800-759-0190 (sales) *Fax:* 212-995-9454
*E-mail:* sales@papress.com
*Web Site:* www.papress.com
*Key Personnel*
Publr: Kevin C Lippert *Tel:* 212-995-9620 ext 203 *E-mail:* lippert@papress.com
Dir, Sales, Publicity & Mktg: Katharine Myers *Tel:* 212-995-9620 ext 216 *E-mail:* katharine@papress.com
Sr Ed: Linda Lee *Tel:* 212-995-9620 ext 226 *E-mail:* linda@papress.com
Publicist: Diane Levinson
Founded: 1981
Publisher of high quality books in architecture, graphic design & visual culture.
ISBN Prefix(es): 978-0-910413; 978-1-878271; 978-1-56898
Number of titles published annually: 100 Print
Total Titles: 700 Print
Distributed by Chronicle Books
Distributor for Balcony Press; Hyphen Press
Foreign Rep(s): Abrams UK (David Gooding) (Europe, Ireland, UK); Chronicle Books (Central America, South America, USA); JCC Enterprises Inc (Bermuda, Caribbean, Latin America); Raincoast Books (Canada)
*Distribution Center:* Chronicle Books, 680 Second St, San Francisco, CA 94107 *Toll Free Tel:* 800-759-0190 *Toll Free Fax:* 800-286-9471 *E-mail:* order.desk@hbgusa.com *Web Site:* www.chroniclebooks.com

**§Princeton Book Co Publishers**
614 Rte 130, Hightstown, NJ 08520
*Tel:* 609-426-0602 *Toll Free Tel:* 800-220-7149 *Fax:* 609-426-1344
*E-mail:* pbc@dancehorizons.com; elysian@princetonbookcompany.com
*Web Site:* www.dancehorizons.com
*Key Personnel*
Pres & Rts & Perms: Charles Woodford
Dir: Connie Woodford
Ad & Internet: John McMenamin
Cust Serv: Marcia Sylvester
Founded: 1975
Specialize in dance.
ISBN Prefix(es): 978-0-916622; 978-0-87127; 978-0-903102; 978-0-85418; 978-0-932582; 978-0-7121; 978-0-8463; 978-0-340
Number of titles published annually: 6 Print; 3 E-Book
Total Titles: 150 Print; 14 E-Book
Imprints: Dance Horizons; Dance Horizons Video; Elysian Editions (adult nonfiction)
Distributed by Dance Books Ltd
Distributor for Dance Books Ltd; Dance Notation Bureau
Foreign Rep(s): Dance Books Ltd (UK); Footprint Books (Australia, New Zealand)
*Shipping Address:* Whitehurst & Clark, 1200 County Rd, Rte 523, Flemington, NJ 08822
*Warehouse:* Whitehurst & Clark, 1200 County Rd, Rte 523, Flemington, NJ 08822

**§The Princeton Review**
Imprint of Random House Information Group
c/o Random House Inc, 1745 Broadway, New York, NY 10019
*Toll Free Tel:* 800-733-3000 *Fax:* 212-782-9682
*E-mail:* princetonreview@randomhouse.com
*Web Site:* www.princetonreview.com
*Key Personnel*
VP & Publr: Tom Russell
Mng Ed: Alison Stoltzfus
Test preparation, college & graduate school guides, career guides & general study aids.
Random House Inc & its publishing entities are not accepting unsol submissions, proposals, mss, or submission queries via e-mail at this time.
Number of titles published annually: 75 Print; 12 CD-ROM
Total Titles: 230 Print; 15 CD-ROM

**Princeton University Press**
41 William St, Princeton, NJ 08540-5237
*Tel:* 609-258-4900 *Toll Free Tel:* 800-777-4726 (orders) *Fax:* 609-258-6305 *Toll Free Fax:* 800-999-1958
*E-mail:* orders@cpfsinc.com
*Web Site:* press.princeton.edu
*Key Personnel*
Exec Ed: Seth Ditchik *Tel:* 609-258-9428; Robert Tempio *Tel:* 609-258-0843
Publr, Field Guides & Exec Ed: Robert Kirk *Tel:* 609-258-4884
Dir: Peter Dougherty *Tel:* 609-258-6778 *E-mail:* peter_dougherty@press.princeton.edu
Sales Dir: Timothy Wilkins *Tel:* 609-258-4877
Publicity Dir: Andrew DeSio *Tel:* 609-258-5165
Asst Press Dir & Mktg Dir: Adam Fortgang *Tel:* 609-258-4896 *E-mail:* adam_fortgang@press.princeton.edu
Asst Dir, Ed-in-Chief & Exec Ed: Brigitta van Rheinberg *Tel:* 609-258-4935 *E-mail:* brigitta_vanrheinberg@press.princeton.edu
Assoc Dir & Cont: Patrick Carroll *Tel:* 609-258-2486 *E-mail:* patrick_carroll@press.princeton.edu
Exhibits Mgr: Melissa Burton *Tel:* 609-258-4915 *E-mail:* melissa_burton@press.princeton.edu
Exec Ed (anthropology, music, religion): Fred Appel *Tel:* 609-258-2484
Sr Ed (biology & earth sciences): Alison Kalett *Tel:* 609-258-9232
Sr Ed (political science, American history): Eric Crahan *Tel:* 609-258-4922
Sr Ed (literature, art): Alison MacKeen *Tel:* 609-258-4569
Exec Ed & Ref & Backlist Ed: Anne Savarese *Tel:* 609-258-4937
Founded: 1905
Scholarly, scientific & trade books on all subjects.
ISBN Prefix(es): 978-0-691
Number of titles published annually: 250 Print; 100 E-Book
Total Titles: 4,000 Print; 800 E-Book
Imprints: Bollingen Series
*Foreign Office(s):* 6 Oxford St, Woodstock, Oxfordshire 0X20 1TW, United Kingdom, Publg Dir, Europe: Caroline Priday *Tel:* (01993) 814500 *Fax:* (01993) 814504 *E-mail:* cpriday@pupress.co.uk
c/o John Wiley & Sons Distribution Center, One Oldlands Way, Bognor Regis, West Sussex P022 9NQ, United Kingdom
Foreign Rep(s): African Moon Press (Chris Reinders) (South Africa); APD (Singapore); Aromix Books Co Ltd (Hong Kong); Avicenna Partnership Ltd (Claire de Gruchy) (Algeria, Cyprus, Jordan, Libya, Malta, Morocco, Palestine, Tunisia); Book Promotions Ltd (South Africa); Everest International Publishing Services (Wei Zhao) (China); ICK (Information & Culture) (Korea); S Janakiraman, Book Marketing Services (Bangladesh, Sri Lanka); B K Norton (Taiwan); Rockbook (Japan); University Press Group (Africa, Europe, India, Israel, Middle East, Pakistan, UK); Kelvin van Hasselt Publishing Services (Africa exc North & South Africa); World Press (Saleem Malik) (Pakistan)

Foreign Rights: APD (Malaysia, Thailand); Mega Texts (Philippines)
*Advertising Agency:* Caslon
*Orders to:* California/Princeton Fulfillment Services Inc, 1445 Lower Ferry Rd, Ewing, NJ 08618 *Tel:* 609-883-1759 *Toll Free Tel:* 800-777-4726 *Fax:* 609-883-7413 *Toll Free Fax:* 800-999-1958 *E-mail:* orders@cpfsinc.com; University Press Group Ltd, New Era Estate, Oldlands Way, Bognor Regis, West Sussex P022 9NQ, United Kingdom (UK & Europe), Contact: Lous Edwards *Tel:* (01243) 842165 *Fax:* (01243) 842167 *E-mail:* sales@upguk.com
*Warehouse:* California/Princeton Fulfillment Services Inc, 1445 Lower Ferry Rd, Ewing, NJ 08618 *Tel:* 609-883-1759 *Fax:* 609-883-7413 *E-mail:* orders@cpfsinc.com
Membership(s): AAP; American Association of University Presses; BISG

**§Printing Industries of America**
200 Deer Run Rd, Sewickley, PA 15143-2600
*Tel:* 412-741-6860; 412-259-1770
*E-mail:* membercentral@printing.org (orders)
*Web Site:* www.printing.org
*Key Personnel*
Dir: Amy Woodall
Mng Ed: Deanna Gentile
Ed: Joe Deemer
Founded: 1924
Textbooks & reference books on graphic communications techniques & technology.
ISBN Prefix(es): 978-0-88362
Number of titles published annually: 10 Print; 5 E-Book
Total Titles: 250 Print; 10 E-Book

**Printing Industries Press**, see Printing Industries of America

**Privacy Journal**
PO Box 28577, Providence, RI 02908
*Tel:* 401-274-7861 *Fax:* 401-274-4747
*E-mail:* orders@privacyjournal.net
*Web Site:* www.privacyjournal.net
*Key Personnel*
Publr: Robert Ellis Smith
Founded: 1974
Monthly newsletter.
ISBN Prefix(es): 978-0-930072
Number of titles published annually: 1 Print; 1 CD-ROM; 1 E-Book
Total Titles: 12 Print; 1 CD-ROM; 5 E-Book
Membership(s): The Association of Publishers for Special Sales; The Authors Guild; IBPA, the Independent Book Publishers Association; Independent Publishers of New England

**PRO-ED Inc**
8700 Shoal Creek Blvd, Austin, TX 78757-6897
SAN: 222-1349
*Tel:* 512-451-3246 *Toll Free Tel:* 800-897-3202 *Fax:* 512-451-8542 *Toll Free Fax:* 800-397-7633
*E-mail:* general@proedinc.com
*Web Site:* www.proedinc.com
*Key Personnel*
COO & Gen Coun: Robert Lum *Tel:* 512-451-3246 ext 664
Founded: 1977
College & professional reference books, tests, student materials, journals in education & psychology.
ISBN Prefix(es): 978-0-936104; 978-0-89079
Number of titles published annually: 50 Print
Total Titles: 1,500 Print

**Pro Lingua Associates Inc**
74 Cotton Mill Hill, Suite A-315, Brattleboro, VT 05301
Mailing Address: PO Box 1348, Brattleboro, VT 05302-1348 SAN: 216-0579
*Tel:* 802-257-7779 *Toll Free Tel:* 800-366-4775 *Fax:* 802-257-5117
*E-mail:* info@prolinguaassociates.com
*Web Site:* www.prolinguaassociates.com
*Key Personnel*
Pres & Publr: Arthur A Burrows *E-mail:* andy@prolinguaassociates.com
Treas & Lib Sales Dir: Elise C Burrows
VP & Ed: Raymond C Clark
Secy: Patrick R Moran
Founded: 1980
Teacher resource handbooks, language teacher training handbooks, English language & foreign language texts.
ISBN Prefix(es): 978-0-86647
Number of titles published annually: 7 Print
Total Titles: 114 Print; 8 Online; 11 Audio
Foreign Rep(s): Attica La Librarie des Langues (France); Baja Ediciones SA (BESA) (Mexico); Bookman Books (Taiwan); English Language Bookshop (England); Foreign Language Bookshop (Australia); Foreign Language Ltd (Korea); Independent Publishers International (Japan); Nellie's Group Ltd (Japan); B K Norton (Taiwan); The Resource Centre (Canada)
Membership(s): Children's Book Council; Teachers of English to Speakers of Other Languages

**§Productivity Press**
Division of Taylor & Francis Group
c/o Routledge, 711 Third Ave, New York, NY 10017
SAN: 290-036X
*Tel:* 212-216-7800 *Toll Free Tel:* 800-634-7064 (orders) *Fax:* 212-563-2269 *Toll Free Fax:* 800-248-4724 (orders)
*E-mail:* info@productivitypress.com; orders@taylorandfrancis.com
*Web Site:* www.productivitypress.com
*Key Personnel*
Sr Acqs Ed: Michael Sinocchi *Tel:* 212-216-7867 *E-mail:* michael.sinocchi@taylorandfrancis.com
Mgr, Mktg: Christopher Manion *Tel:* 800-272-7737 ext 2508 *E-mail:* chris.manion@taylorandfrancis.com
Founded: 1983
Books & AV programs. Publishes & distributes materials on productivity, quality improvement, product development, corporate management, profit management & employee involvement for business & industry. Many products are direct source materials from Japan that have been translated into English for the first time.
ISBN Prefix(es): 978-0-915299; 978-1-56327; 978-0-915801
Number of titles published annually: 12 Print
Total Titles: 200 Print; 4 CD-ROM
Imprints: Healthcare Performance Press; Productivity Press Spanish Imprint
Foreign Rep(s): Asia Pacific Research Center (Singapore); Books Aplenty (South Africa); Learning & Productivity (Australia); OCAPT Inc (Canada); Prism Books Private Ltd (India); Productivity Editorial Consultores SPD CV (Mexico)

**Professional Communications Inc**
20968 State Rd 22, Caddo, OK 74729
Mailing Address: PO Box 10, Caddo, OK 74729-0010
*Tel:* 580-367-9838 *Toll Free Tel:* 800-337-9838 *Fax:* 580-367-9989
*E-mail:* info@pcibooks.com
*Web Site:* www.pcibooks.com
*Key Personnel*
Pres & Publr: J Malcolm Beasley *Tel:* 631-661-2852 *Fax:* 631-661-2167 *E-mail:* jmbpci@earthlink.net
VP: Phyllis Jones Freeny
Founded: 1992
Medicine.
ISBN Prefix(es): 978-1-884735; 978-0-932610
Number of titles published annually: 5 Print
Total Titles: 41 Print
*Branch Office(s)*
Bulk Sales only, 400 Center Bay Dr, West Islip, NY 11795

**§The Professional Education Group Inc (PEG)**
Subsidiary of CredibleLaw
12401 Minnetonka Blvd, Suite 200, Minnetonka, MN 55305-3994
*Tel:* 952-933-9990 *Toll Free Tel:* 800-229-2531 *Fax:* 952-933-7784
*E-mail:* orders@proedgroup.com
*Web Site:* www.proedgroup.com
*Key Personnel*
Pres: Paul A Fogelberg *E-mail:* paul@proedgroup.com
SVP: Henry Lake *E-mail:* henry@proedgroup.com
Founded: 1981
Continuing legal education materials; audio & video programs & books.
ISBN Prefix(es): 978-0-943380; 978-1-932831
Number of titles published annually: 6 Print; 1 CD-ROM; 6 Online; 5 Audio
Total Titles: 43 Print; 40 CD-ROM; 40 Online; 43 Audio
Distributed by ALI-ABA; American Bar Association
Distributor for ALI-ABA; American Bar Association; ASPEN
Membership(s): Association for Continuing Legal Education

**§Professional Publications Inc (PPI)**
1250 Fifth Ave, Belmont, CA 94002
SAN: 264-6315
*Tel:* 650-593-9119 *Toll Free Tel:* 800-426-1178 (orders) *Fax:* 650-592-4519
*E-mail:* info@ppi2pass.com
*Web Site:* www.ppi2pass.com
*Key Personnel*
Pres: Michael Lindeburg
Dir, New Prod Devt: Sarah Hubbard *Tel:* 650-593-9119 ext 128 *E-mail:* shubbard@ppi2pass.com
Dir, Prodn: Cathy Schrott *E-mail:* cschrott@ppi2pass.com
Dir, Mktg: Greg Monteforte *E-mail:* gmonteforte@ppi2pass.com
Founded: 1975
Provider of exam review books, online products, DVDs & live class in the fields of engineering, land surveying, LEED, architecture, interior design & landscape architecture. Specialty engineering areas include civil, structural, seismic, mechanical, electrical, environmental, chemical, nuclear, geotechnical & industrial engineering fields.
ISBN Prefix(es): 978-0-932276; 978-0-912045; 978-1-888577; 978-1-59126
Number of titles published annually: 10 Print; 1 CD-ROM; 2 Online
Total Titles: 120 Print; 1 CD-ROM; 2 Online
Distributor for American Association of State Highway & Transportation Officials; American Wood Council (American Forest & Paper Association) (National Design Specification for Wood Construction (NDS) & others); International Code Council; McGraw-Hill Professional (green building, design & construction titles, LEED titles); National Council of Examiners for Engineering & Surveying; Reg Review Inc (ASBOG geology exam review); SmartPros; Transportation Research Board Code; US Green Building Council (LEED reference guides)
Membership(s): American Society of Civil Engineers; American Society of Engineering Educators; American Society of Mechanical Engineers; National Society of Professional Engineers; US Green Building Council

**Professional Resource Press**
Imprint of Professional Resource Exchange Inc
1891 Apex Rd, Sarasota, FL 34240-9386
SAN: 240-1223
Mailing Address: PO Box 3197, Sarasota, FL 34230-3197
*Tel:* 941-343-9601 *Toll Free Tel:* 800-443-3364 *Fax:* 941-343-9201 *Toll Free Fax:* 866-804-4843 (orders)
*E-mail:* orders@prpress.com
*Web Site:* www.prpress.com
*Key Personnel*
Pres: Lawrence G Ritt
VP: Judith W Ritt
Mktg & Lib Sales Dir: Jude Warinner
Mng Ed: Laurie Girsch *Tel:* 941-343-9403
Founded: 1979
Books (clinical & forensic psychology), audio & video cassettes, CD-ROM, continuing education programs & texts for mental health & health care professionals. Includes medicine & nursing.
ISBN Prefix(es): 978-0-943158; 978-1-56887
Number of titles published annually: 15 Print; 5 CD-ROM; 4 E-Book; 3 Audio
Total Titles: 230 Print; 10 CD-ROM; 4 E-Book; 17 Audio
*Advertising Agency:* Ashley Ball Group, 630 Venice Lane, Sarasota, FL 34242 *Tel:* 941-350-7790
Membership(s): The Association of Publishers for Special Sales

**Progressive Press**
6200 Juniper Rd (entrance on Sunny Vista), Joshua Tree, CA 92252-4144
SAN: 222-5395
Mailing Address: PO Box 126, Joshua Tree, CA 92252
*Tel:* 760-366-3695 *Fax:* 760-366-3695
*E-mail:* info@progressivepress.com
*Web Site:* www.progressivepress.com
*Key Personnel*
Owner: John-Paul Leonard
Founded: 1973
Small publisher of political trade paperbacks. Also provides distribution for one Canadian publisher & several self-published authors. Front list: politics, backlist: New Age.
ISBN Prefix(es): 978-0-930852; 978-1-61577
Number of titles published annually: 6 Print
Total Titles: 30 Print
Imprints: Arthritis Research; Banned Books; Collections Livrier; Leaves of Healing; Prensa Pensar; Progressive Press; Tree of Life Books
Distributor for Global Research
Foreign Rep(s): Central Books (UK); Disticor (Canada); Gazelle (UK); New Horizons (South Africa); Woodslane (Australia)
Foreign Rights: Ota Ryu (Japan); Beniamino Soressi (Italy); Thinkers Library (Malaysia); Gerhard Wisnewski (Germany)
Membership(s): IBPA, the Independent Book Publishers Association; PMA International

**Prometheus Books**
59 John Glenn Dr, Amherst, NY 14228-2119
SAN: 202-0289
*Tel:* 716-691-0133 *Toll Free Tel:* 800-421-0351 *Fax:* 716-691-0137
*E-mail:* marketing@prometheusbooks.com; editorial@prometheusbooks.com
*Web Site:* www.Prometheusbooks.com
*Key Personnel*
Chmn: Paul Kurtz
Pres: Jonathan Kurtz
VP, Busn & Admin Dir: Lynette Nisbet
Pyr Edit Dir: Lou Anders *E-mail:* landers@prometheusbooks.com
Dir, Rts: Gretchen Kurtz *E-mail:* rights@prometheusmail.com
Dir, Publicity: Jill Maxick *Tel:* 800-853-7545 *E-mail:* jmaxick@prometheusbooks.com
Ed-in-Chief: Steven L Mitchell *E-mail:* smitchell@prometheusbooks.com
Mgr, Print-on-Demand Div: Patrick Martin
Publicist: Meghan Quinn
Founded: 1969
Philosophy, social sciences/current events, popular science, religion & politics.
ISBN Prefix(es): 978-0-87975; 978-1-57392; 978-1-59102; 978-1-61614
Number of titles published annually: 120 Print; 100 E-Book
Total Titles: 2,300 Print; 1,500 E-Book
Imprints: Humanity Books (scholarly/academic); Pyr (science fiction/fantasy)
Foreign Rep(s): Random House Publisher Services (Worldwide)
*Advertising Agency:* University Advertising, PO Box 924, Amhurst, NY 14226

**ProQuest LLC**
Subsidiary of Cambridge Information Group Inc
789 E Eisenhower Pkwy, Ann Arbor, MI 48108-3218
Mailing Address: PO Box 1346, Ann Arbor, MI 48106-1346
*Tel:* 734-761-4700 *Toll Free Tel:* 800-521-0600 *Fax:* 734-975-6486 *Toll Free Fax:* 800-864-0019
*E-mail:* info@proquest.com
*Web Site:* www.proquest.com
*Key Personnel*
CEO: Kurt Sanford
CFO: Philip Evans
SVP, Global Sales: Simon Beale
SVP, HR & Busn Servs: Elliot Forsyth
SVP, Mktg & Cust Care: Lynda James-Gilboe
SVP, Publg & Global Content Alliances: Rod Gauvin
SVP, Res Solutions: Boe Horton
VP, Content Opers: Vince Price
VP, Technol & Gen Mgr, Cambridge Opers: John Taylor
Gen Coun & Global Content Alliances: Kevin Norris
Interim Dialog Gen Mgr: Julie Janusz
Publisher, distributor & aggregator of value-added information to libraries, government, universities & schools in over 160 countries. Access to information in periodicals, newspapers, doctoral dissertations & out-of-print books (retrospective scholarly works). Produce & publish Dissertation Abstracts International.
ISBN Prefix(es): 978-0-8357; 978-0-608; 978-0-7837; 978-0-591; 978-0-9702937; 978-0-599; 978-1-931694; 978-1-59399; 978-0-496; 978-0-542; 978-1-4247; 978-0-9778091; 978-1-4345; 978-0-549
Number of titles published annually: 56 Print
Total Titles: 56 Print
*Branch Office(s)*
Micromedia Proquest, 20 Victoria St, Toronto, ON M5C 2N8, Canada
*Foreign Office(s):* The Quorum, Barnwell Rd, Cambridge CB5 8SW, United Kingdom
*See separate listing for:*
**R R Bowker LLC**

**ProStar Publications Inc**
3 Church Circle, Suite 109, Annapolis, MD 21401
SAN: 210-525X
Mailing Address: 8643 Hayden Place, Culver City, CA 90232
*Tel:* 310-280-1010 *Toll Free Tel:* 800-481-6277 *Fax:* 310-280-1025 *Toll Free Fax:* 800-487-6277
*E-mail:* editor@prostarpublications.com
*Web Site:* www.prostarpublications.com
*Key Personnel*
Pres & Publr: Peter L Griffes *E-mail:* peter@prostarpublications.com
Founded: 1965
Books about boating: regional guides, planning, navigation data, nautical charts, marine fauna, how-to, travel, technical, general fiction & music.
ISBN Prefix(es): 978-0-930030; 978-1-57785
Number of titles published annually: 145 Print
Total Titles: 440 Print; 30 CD-ROM
Imprints: Atlantic Boating Almanac; Lighthouse Press; Pacific Boating Almanac; US Coast Pilot

**§The PRS Group Inc**
6320 Fly Rd, Suite 102, East Syracuse, NY 13057-9358
*Tel:* 315-431-0511 *Fax:* 315-431-0200
*E-mail:* custserv@prsgroup.com
*Web Site:* www.prsgroup.com
*Key Personnel*
Pres: Mary Lou Walsh
Circ Mgr: Patti Davis
Asst to Pres: Dianna Spinner *E-mail:* dspinner@prsgroup.com
Founded: 1979
Over 100 reports, newsletters, journals & volumes per year for international business. No returns without prior approval.
ISBN Prefix(es): 978-1-933539
Number of titles published annually: 3 Print
Total Titles: 20 Print; 100 CD-ROM; 100 Online; 100 E-Book
Imprints: International Country Risk Guide; Political Risk Services

**Prufrock Press**
PO Box 8813, Waco, TX 76714-8813
SAN: 851-9188
*Tel:* 254-756-3337 *Toll Free Tel:* 800-998-2208 *Fax:* 254-756-3339 *Toll Free Fax:* 800-240-0333
*E-mail:* info@prufrock.com
*Web Site:* www.prufrock.com
*Key Personnel*
Publr & Mktg Dir: Joel McIntosh *Tel:* 254-756-3337 ext 203 *E-mail:* jmcintosh@prufrock.com
Sr Ed & Perms Coord: Jennifer Robins *E-mail:* jrobins@prufrock.com
Founded: 1977
Publish supplementary text books & teacher guides for grades K-12, including gifted educational materials.
ISBN Prefix(es): 978-1-883055; 978-0-931724
Number of titles published annually: 20 Print
Total Titles: 200 Print
Membership(s): IBPA, the Independent Book Publishers Association

**§Psychological Assessment Resources Inc (PAR)**
16204 N Florida Ave, Lutz, FL 33549
*Tel:* 813-968-3003; 813-449-4065 *Toll Free Tel:* 800-331-8378 *Fax:* 813-968-2598; 813-961-2196 *Toll Free Fax:* 800-727-9329
*E-mail:* custsup@parinc.com
*Web Site:* www4.parinc.com
*Key Personnel*
Chmn & CEO: R Bob Smith, III *E-mail:* bsmith@parinc.com
COO & EVP: Kay Cunningham *E-mail:* kcunningham@parinc.com
VP, Cust Serv: Cynthia Lumpee *E-mail:* clumpee@parinc.com
VP, Mktg & Sales: Jim Gyurke *E-mail:* jgyurke@parinc.com
VP, R&D: Travis White *E-mail:* twhite@parinc.com
Exec Asst to CEO: Vicki King
Founded: 1978
Career, psychological, neuropsychology, educational & clinical assessments products; software.
ISBN Prefix(es): 978-0-911907
Number of titles published annually: 10 Print; 2 CD-ROM; 1 Online

Total Titles: 150 Print; 20 CD-ROM; 3 Online; 5 Audio
Distributed by ACER; Pro-Ed; The Psychological Corp; Riverside Publishing; Western Psychological Service
Distributor for American Guidance Service; Pro-Ed; The Psychological Corp; Riverside Publishing; Rorschach Workshops
Foreign Rep(s): ACER (Australia); Tea Ediciones (Spain); Testzentrale (Germany)
*Returns:* 16130 N Florida Ave, Lutz, FL 33549 *E-mail:* gpresson@parinc.com
*Warehouse:* 16130 N Florida Ave, Lutz, FL 33549 *E-mail:* gpresson@parinc.com

**Psychology Press**
Imprint of Taylor & Francis Group
711 Third Ave, 8th fl, New York, NY 10017
*Tel:* 212-216-7800 *Toll Free Tel:* 800-634-7064 *Fax:* 212-563-2269
*Web Site:* www.psypress.com
*Key Personnel*
Publr: Paul Dukes *Tel:* 917-351-7103 *E-mail:* paul.dukes@taylorandfrancis.com
Founded: 1983
Created to serve the needs of researchers, students & professionals concerned with the science of human & animal behavior, Psychology Press publishes academic psychology at all levels, including student texts, handbooks, monographs, professional books & scientific journals. Key areas include cognitive psychology, cognitive neuroscience, developmental psychology & family studies, industrial & organizational psychology, neuropsychology & language disorders, research methods & statistics, social psychology.
ISBN Prefix(es): 978-0-8058; 978-0-86377; 978-1-84169; 978-1-84872
Number of titles published annually: 102 Print; 4 CD-ROM; 90 E-Book
Total Titles: 6,000 Print; 6 CD-ROM
*Sales Office(s):* CRC Press/Taylor & Francis, 6000 Broken Sound Pkwy NW, Suite 300, Boca Raton, FL 33487 *Toll Free Tel:* 800-272-7737 *Toll Free Fax:* 800-374-3401 *E-mail:* orders@crcpress.com
*Foreign Office(s):* 27 Church Rd, Hove BN3 2FA, United Kingdom, Mng Dir: Michael Forster *Tel:* (020) 7017 6000 *Fax:* (020) 7017 6717 *E-mail:* info@psypress.co.uk
Foreign Rep(s): Ethan Atkin (Latin America)
Foreign Rights: Taylor & Francis (Worldwide)
*Distribution Center:* Taylor & Francis, 7625 Empire Dr, Florence, KY 41042 *Toll Free Tel:* 800-634-7064 *Toll Free Fax:* 800-248-4724 *E-mail:* orders@taylorandfrancis.com

**Public Citizen**
1600 20 St NW, Washington, DC 20009
*Tel:* 202-588-1000 *Fax:* 202-588-7798
*E-mail:* public_citizen@citizen.org
*Web Site:* www.citizen.org
*Key Personnel*
CFO: Joe Stoshak
Pres: Robert Weissman
Founded: 1971
Books & reports; consumer advocacy organization.
ISBN Prefix(es): 978-0-937188; 978-1-58231
Number of titles published annually: 47 Print
Total Titles: 48 Print
Divisions: Congress Watch; Critical Mass Energy Project; Global Trade Watch; Health Research GP Buyers UP; Litigation GP
*Branch Office(s)*
215 Pennsylvania Ave SE, Washington, DC 20003 *Tel:* 202-546-4996
1303 San Antonio St, Austin, TX 78701 *Tel:* 512-477-1155
Distributed by Addison Wesley; Simon & Schuster Pocket Books
Foreign Rights: Random House-Pantheon

**PublicAffairs**
Member of The Perseus Books Group
250 W 57 St, Suite 1321, New York, NY 10107
*Tel:* 212-397-6666 *Toll Free Tel:* 800-343-4499 (orders) *Fax:* 212-397-4277
*E-mail:* publicaffairs@perseusbooks.com
*Web Site:* www.publicaffairsbooks.com
*Key Personnel*
Founder & Ed-at-Large: Peter Osnos
Publr: Clive Priddle
Dir, Publicity: Jaime Leifer
Mktg Dir & Sr Ed: Lisa Kaufman
Group Publr: Susan Weinberg
Publicity Mgr: Tessa Shanks
Mng Ed: Melissa Raymond
Sr Ed: Ben Adams; Clara Platter
Ed: Brandon Proia
Contributing Ed: John Mahaney
Off Administrator: Darrell Jonas *E-mail:* darrell.jonas@publicaffairsbooks.com
Founded: 1997
Current affairs, history, biography, journalism & social criticism.
ISBN Prefix(es): 978-1-891620; 978-1-58648
Number of titles published annually: 60 Print
Total Titles: 300 Print
*Orders to:* Perseus Distribution Service, 1094 Flex Dr, Jackson, TN 38301 *Toll Free Fax:* 800-351-5073
*Warehouse:* Perseus Distribution Service, 1094 Flex Dr, Jackson, TN 38301 *Toll Free Fax:* 800-351-5073
*Distribution Center:* Perseus Distribution Service, 1094 Flex Dr, Jackson, TN 38301 *Toll Free Fax:* 800-351-5073

**§Publication Consultants**
8370 Eleusis Dr, Anchorage, AK 99502
*Tel:* 907-349-2424 *Fax:* 907-349-2426
*E-mail:* books@publicationconsultants.com
*Web Site:* www.publicationconsultants.com
*Key Personnel*
Owner & Publr: Evan Swensen *E-mail:* evan@publicationconsultants.com
Founded: 1978
This publisher has indicated that 40% of their product line is author subsidized.
ISBN Prefix(es): 978-0-9644809; 978-1-888125; 978-1-59433
Number of titles published annually: 30 Print; 30 E-Book
Total Titles: 307 Print; 154 E-Book
Membership(s): Alaska Writers Guild; Better Business Bureau

**Publications International Ltd**
7373 N Cicero Ave, Lincolnwood, IL 60712
*Tel:* 847-676-3470 *Fax:* 847-676-3671
*Web Site:* www.pilbooks.com
*Key Personnel*
CEO: Louis Weber
Founded: 1967
ISBN Prefix(es): 978-0-7853; 978-0-88176; 978-1-56173; 978-1-4127; 978-1-60553; 978-1-4508

**Pudding House Publications**
Affiliate of Pudding House Innovative Writers Programs
81 Shadymere Lane, Columbus, OH 43213
*Tel:* 614-986-1881
*Web Site:* www.puddinghousepublications.com
*Key Personnel*
Pres & Dir: Jennifer Bosveld
Founded: 1979
Literary journal, chapbooks, anthologies, educational books on the writing process, literature/poetry publishing, workshops, seminars, retreats, web site, posters, broadsides, magazines.
ISBN Prefix(es): 978-0-944754; 978-1-930755; 978-1-58998
Number of titles published annually: 150 Print; 1 Online
Total Titles: 1,200 Print; 1 Online

**Puffin Books**
Imprint of Penguin Group (USA) LLC
345 Hudson St, New York, NY 10014
SAN: 282-5074
*Tel:* 212-366-2000
*E-mail:* online@penguinputnam.com
*Web Site:* www.penguinputnam.com; us.penguingroup.com
*Key Personnel*
Pres & Publr: Eileen Kreit
Mng Ed, Assoc Publr: Gerard Mancini
Edit Dir: Kristin Gilson
VP & Exec Art Dir, Penguin Young Readers Design Group: Deborah Kaplan
Exec Ed: Jennifer Bonnell
Founded: 1935
ISBN Prefix(es): 978-0-14
Number of titles published annually: 87 Print
Total Titles: 1,724 Print
Membership(s): Children's Book Council

**Purdue University Press**
Stewart Ctr 370, 504 W State St, West Lafayette, IN 47907-2058
SAN: 203-4026
*Tel:* 765-494-2038 *Fax:* 765-496-2442
*E-mail:* pupress@purdue.edu
*Web Site:* www.thepress.purdue.edu
*Key Personnel*
Ed: Katherine Purple
Prodn Mgr: Bryan Shaffer
Intl Rts: Anu Hansen
Founded: 1960
Publisher of scholarly titles with emphasis on business, veterinary medicine, health issues & the humanities.
ISBN Prefix(es): 978-0-911198; 978-1-55753
Number of titles published annually: 25 Print; 3 E-Book
Total Titles: 350 Print; 10 E-Book
Imprints: Ichor Business Books; Nota Bell Books; PUP Books
Foreign Rep(s): APAC Publishers Services Pty Ltd (Asia, China, Hawaii, Pacific Islands, Singapore, Taiwan, Thailand); Cranbury International (Africa, India, Latin America, South America); The Eurospan Group (Continental Europe, Israel, Middle East, UK); Footprint Books Pty Ltd (Australia, New Zealand); Scholarly Book Services Inc (Canada); United Publishers Services Ltd (Japan)
Foreign Rights: Atmarr Agency Services; Global Rights Agent; Anu Hansen
*Orders to:* Bookmasters, 30 Amberwood Pkwy, Ashland, OH 44805 *Toll Free Tel:* 800-247-6553 *Fax:* 419-281-6883 *Web Site:* www.bookmasters.com/purduepress
*Returns:* Bookmasters, 30 Amberwood Pkwy, Ashland, OH 44805 *Toll Free Tel:* 800-247-6553 *Fax:* 419-281-6883 *Web Site:* www.bookmasters.com/purduepress
*Warehouse:* Bookmasters, 30 Amberwood Pkwy, Ashland, OH 44805 *Toll Free Tel:* 800-247-6553 *Fax:* 419-281-6883 *Web Site:* www.bookmasters.com/purduepress
*Distribution Center:* Bookmasters, 30 Amberwood Pkwy, Ashland, OH 44805 *Toll Free Tel:* 800-247-6553 *Fax:* 419-281-6883 *Web Site:* www.bookmasters.com/purduepress
Membership(s): American Association of University Presses

**§Pureplay Press**
195 26 Ave, No 2, San Francisco, CA 94121
*Tel:* 310-597-0328
*E-mail:* info@pureplaypress.com
*Web Site:* www.pureplaypress.com

*Key Personnel*
Publr & Ed: David Landau *E-mail:* editor@pureplaypress.com
Assoc Publr: Wakeford Gong *E-mail:* wclr@ix.netcom.com
Founded: 2001
Publish books in English & Spanish about history & culture or containing those things (as in literature).
ISBN Prefix(es): 978-0-9714366; 978-0-9765096
Number of titles published annually: 3 Print
Foreign Rights: IMC Literary Agency (all other territories)
Membership(s): IBPA, the Independent Book Publishers Association; PEN Center USA

**Purple House Press**
Imprint of Purple House Inc
8100 US Hwy 62 E, Cynthiana, KY 41031
Mailing Address: PO Box 787, Cynthiana, KY 41031
*Tel:* 859-235-9970
*Web Site:* www.purplehousepress.com
*Key Personnel*
Publr: Jill Morgan *E-mail:* jill@purplehousepress.com
Dir, Cust Fulfillment, Managed Info Servs: Ray Sanders *E-mail:* ray@purplehousepress.com
Founded: 2000
Reissue of children's classics from the 1920s-1990s.
ISBN Prefix(es): 978-1-930900
Number of titles published annually: 8 Print; 3 E-Book
Total Titles: 50 Print; 10 E-Book
*Warehouse:* Purple House Inc, c/o Avi's Warehouse, 974-B US Hwy 62 E, Cynthiana, KY 41031

**Purple Mountain Press Ltd**
1060 Main St, Fleischmanns, NY 12430
Mailing Address: PO Box 309, Fleischmanns, NY 12430-0309 SAN: 222-3716
*Tel:* 845-254-4062 *Toll Free Tel:* 800-325-2665 (orders) *Fax:* 845-254-4476
*E-mail:* purple@catskill.net
*Web Site:* www.catskill.net/purple
*Key Personnel*
Pres & Publr: Wray Rominger
Founded: 1973
Publish adult nonfiction books about colonial history & New York State; history, natural history, folklore, the arts, outdoor recreation, a few regional mysteries, also maritime books.
ISBN Prefix(es): 978-0-935796; 978-0-916346; 978-1-930098
Number of titles published annually: 6 Print
Total Titles: 150 Print
Divisions: Harbor Hill Books
Distributor for Carmania Press London (North America only)

**Purple People Inc**
2301 W Hwy 89A, Suite 102, Sedona, AZ 86336
Mailing Address: PO Box 3194, Sedona, AZ 86340-3194
*Tel:* 928-204-6400 *Fax:* 928-282-2603
*E-mail:* info@purplepeople.com
*Web Site:* www.purplepeople.com; www.bulliedtosilence.com
*Key Personnel*
Founder: Susan Faith
VP, Prodn: Tami Pivnick *E-mail:* grfx@purplepeople.com
Prodr, Writer - DEH Productions: Susan Broude
Dir, Ed - DEH Productions: Tami Pivnick *E-mail:* tami@purplepeople.com
Founded: 1997
Promote equality among all humans & respect for all living creatures. Our primary focus is on publishing books to inspire children which are consistent with our purpose. Specialize in books that present challenging topics in a thought-provoking, creative way that spurs conversation between adult & child. Part of the proceeds of the books will be donated to charities that benefit children, animals & the environment. Services: provide inspirational speakers for events, author signings & publishing consultation.
ISBN Prefix(es): 978-0-9707793
Number of titles published annually: 5 Print; 2 CD-ROM; 3 Audio
Total Titles: 2 Print
Subsidiaries: Dog Eats Hat Productions

**Purple Pomegranate Productions**
Division of Jews for Jesus
60 Haight St, San Francisco, CA 94102
*Tel:* 415-864-2600 *Fax:* 415-552-8325
*E-mail:* sf@jewsforjesus.org
*Web Site:* www.jewsforjesus.org
*Key Personnel*
Mdse Mgr: Shannon Fischer
Jewish evangelism, books, pamphlets, music.
ISBN Prefix(es): 978-0-9616148; 978-1-881022
Number of titles published annually: 3 Print
Total Titles: 45 Print; 5 E-Book; 19 Audio

**Pushcart Press**
PO Box 380, Wainscott, NY 11975-0380
SAN: 202-9871
*Tel:* 631-324-9300
*Key Personnel*
Pres: Bill Henderson
Founded: 1972
Trade books, literary anthologies.
ISBN Prefix(es): 978-0-916366; 978-1-888889
Number of titles published annually: 6 Print
Total Titles: 65 Print
Distributed by W W Norton & Co Inc
*Distribution Center:* 500 Fifth Ave, New York, NY 10110

**Putnam Berkley Audio**
Imprint of Penguin Group (USA) LLC
375 Hudson St, New York, NY 10014
SAN: 282-5074
*Tel:* 212-366-2000 *Fax:* 212-366-2666
*E-mail:* online@penguinputnam.com
*Web Site:* www.penguinputnam.com; us.penguingroup.com
*Key Personnel*
Assoc Publr, Dir & Exec Prodr: Patti Pirooz *Tel:* 212-366-2402 *Fax:* 212-366-2643 *E-mail:* patti.pirooz@us.penguingroup.com
Founded: 1996
Abridged, unabridged formats; simultaneous release with hardcover.
Total Titles: 21 Audio
Distributor for Arkangel
*Orders to:* Penguin Group (USA) LLC, 405 Murray Hill Pkwy, East Rutherford, NJ 07073 *Toll Free Tel:* 800-788-6262
*Returns:* Penguin Group (USA) LLC, 405 Murray Hill Pkwy, East Rutherford, NJ 07073
*Warehouse:* Penguin Group (USA) LLC, One Grosset Dr, Kirkwood, NY 13795 *Fax:* 607-775-5586

**The Putnam Publishing Group**
Division of Penguin Group (USA) LLC
375 Hudson St, New York, NY 10014
SAN: 282-5074
*Tel:* 212-366-2000 *Toll Free Tel:* 800-631-8571 *Fax:* 212-366-2643
*E-mail:* online@penguinputnam.com
*Web Site:* www.penguinputnam.com; us.penguingroup.com
Imprints: Avery; Putnam Adult; Putnam Berkley Audio; Putnam Juvenile; Riverhead Books; Jeremy P Tarcher; Tarcher/Penguin
*Advertising Agency:* Mesa Group

**GP Putnam's Sons (Children's)**
Member of Penguin Young Readers Group
345 Hudson St, New York, NY 10014
SAN: 282-5074
*Tel:* 212-366-2000 *Fax:* 212-414-3393
*E-mail:* online@penguinputnam.com
*Web Site:* us.penguingroup.com
*Key Personnel*
VP & Publr, Putnam Books for Young Readers: Jennifer Besser
VP & Art Dir: Cecilia Yung
Assoc Edit Dir: Susan Kochan
Exec Ed: Arianne Lewin
Ed: Stacey Barney
Assoc Publr & Exec Mng Ed: David Briggs
Pres & Publr, Nancy Paulsen Books: Nancy Paulsen
Founded: 1838
ISBN Prefix(es): 978-0-399; 978-0-698
Number of titles published annually: 51 Print
Total Titles: 386 Print
Imprints: PaperStar
Membership(s): Children's Book Council

**GP Putnam's Sons (Hardcover)**
Imprint of Penguin Group (USA) LLC
375 Hudson St, New York, NY 10014
SAN: 282-5074
*Tel:* 212-366-2000
*E-mail:* online@penguinputnam.com
*Web Site:* us.penguingroup.com
*Key Personnel*
Pres: Ivan Held
SVP & Publr: Neil Nyren
VP & Assoc Publr: Catharine Lynch
VP & Exec Ed: Christine Pepe
VP & Publr, Amy Einhorn Books: Amy Einhorn
VP & Ed: Marian Wood
Exec Ed: Kerri Kolen; Nita Taublib; Leslie Gelbman
Sr Ed: John Duff
Dir, Religious Pubns: Joel Fotinos
VP, Dir of Mktg, Assoc Publr Putnam/Riverhead: Kate Stark
Dir, Publicity: Alexis Welby
VP & Prodn Dir: William Peabody
VP, Exec Creative Dir: Rich Hasselberger
Dir, Copy Ed: Linda Rosenberg
Dir, Art Interiors: Claire Vaccaro
Dir, Contracts & Copyrights: Jennifer Uram
Founded: 1838
Fiction & general nonfiction.
ISBN Prefix(es): 978-0-399
Number of titles published annually: 65 Print
Total Titles: 208 Print
Imprints: Ace/Putnam; Grosset/Putnam; Amy Einhorn Books; Putnam; Putnam Berkley Audio; Marian Wood Books
*Advertising Agency:* Mesa Group

**Pyncheon House**
6 University Dr, Suite 105, Amherst, MA 01002
SAN: 297-6269
*Key Personnel*
Ed-in-Chief: David R Rhodes
Founded: 1991
Fine editions & trade books; contemporary poetry, short fiction, novels & essays; member of Library of Congress CIP Program.
ISBN Prefix(es): 978-1-881119
Number of titles published annually: 4 Print
Total Titles: 16 Print

**§QED Press**
Imprint of Comp-Type Inc
155 Cypress St, Fort Bragg, CA 95437
SAN: 248-966X
*Tel:* 707-964-9520 *Toll Free Tel:* 800-773-7782 *Fax:* 707-964-7531
*E-mail:* qedpress@mcn.org
*Web Site:* www.cypresshouse.com

*Key Personnel*
Pres: Cynthia Frank *E-mail:* cynthia@cypresshouse.com
Mng Ed: Joe Shaw *E-mail:* joeshaw@cypresshouse.com
Sr Ed: John Fremont *E-mail:* john@cypresshouse.com
Off Mgr: Stephanie Rosencrans *E-mail:* stephanie@cypresshouse.com
Founded: 1986
Award-winning publishing company whose vision is to publish books that inspire. Specialize in health & healing titles, paper airplane books, first fiction & emotional intelligence books.
ISBN Prefix(es): 978-0-936609; 978-1-879384; 978-1-882897; 978-1-935448
Number of titles published annually: 3 Print
Total Titles: 100 Print
Membership(s): ABA; Bay Area Independent Publishers Association; IBPA, the Independent Book Publishers Association; Northern California Independent Booksellers Association; Pacific Northwest Booksellers Association

**Quackenworth Publishing**
PO Box 4747, Culver City, CA 90231-4747
*Tel:* 310-945-5634 *Toll Free Tel:* 888-701-4991 *Fax:* 310-945-5709 *Toll Free Fax:* 888-892-6339
*E-mail:* info@quackenworth.com
*Web Site:* www.quackenworth.com; www.wittybittybunch.com
*Key Personnel*
Pres: David Hollaway
Dir, Sales & Mktg: Damien Harvey *E-mail:* damien@quackenworth.com
Dir, Online Strategy: Anthony Green *E-mail:* anthony@quackenworth.com
Founded: 2003
Publisher & distributor of children's books & educational materials.
ISBN Prefix(es): 978-1-933211
Number of titles published annually: 10 Print
Total Titles: 60 Print; 12 CD-ROM; 8 E-Book
Distributed by BWI
*Returns:* 20223 Campaign Dr, Carson, CA 90746
*Warehouse:* 5855 Centinela Ave, Los Angeles, CA 90045

**Quail Ridge Press**
101 Brooks Dr, Brandon, MS 39042
Mailing Address: PO Box 123, Brandon, MS 39043 SAN: 214-2201
*Tel:* 601-825-2063 *Toll Free Tel:* 800-343-1583 *Fax:* 601-825-3091 *Toll Free Fax:* 800-864-1082
*E-mail:* info@quailridge.com
*Web Site:* quailridge.com
*Key Personnel*
COO: Terresa Ray *E-mail:* tray@quailridge.com
Publr: Barney McKee *E-mail:* bmckee@quailridge.com
Ed-in-Chief: Gwen McKee *E-mail:* gmckee@quailridge.com
Founded: 1978
Cookbooks, general interest, regional, health.
ISBN Prefix(es): 978-0-937552
Number of titles published annually: 4 Print
Total Titles: 132 Print

**§Quality Medical Publishing Inc**
2248 Welsch Industrial Ct, St Louis, MO 63146-4222
*Tel:* 314-878-7808 *Toll Free Tel:* 800-348-7808 *Fax:* 314-878-9937
*E-mail:* qmp@qmp.com
*Web Site:* www.qmp.com
*Key Personnel*
Pres: Karen Berger *E-mail:* kberger@qmp.com
Founded: 1987
Medical books (especially surgery); plastic, neurological, spine & orthopaedics.
ISBN Prefix(es): 978-0-942219; 978-1-57626
Number of titles published annually: 16 Print
Total Titles: 145 Print; 2 CD-ROM
Imprints: QMP

**Quayside Publishing Group**
Subsidiary of The Quarto Group Inc (London, UK)
400 First Ave N, Suite 300, Minneapolis, MN 55401
SAN: 289-7148
*Tel:* 612-344-8100 *Toll Free Tel:* 800-328-0590 (sales); 800-458-0454 *Fax:* 612-344-8691
*E-mail:* sales@creativepub.com
*Web Site:* www.qbookshop.com
*Key Personnel*
CEO & Pres: Ken Fund
CFO: George Maspeller
Publr, Home Improvement: Bryan Trandem
Dir, Quayside Dist Servs: John Groton
Represents a dynamic group of imprints dedicated to providing quality & excellence to its readers. Each imprint embodies the breadth & scope of its specialty topics.
ISBN Prefix(es): 978-0-86573; 978-1-58923; 978-1-61673; 978-1-61058; 978-1-61059; 978-1-61060; 978-1-62788
Number of titles published annually: 300 Print
Total Titles: 4,000 Print
Imprints: Book Sales Inc; Cool Springs Press; Creative Publishing International; Fair Winds Press; Walter Foster Publishing; Motorbooks; MVP Books; Quarry Books; Quiver; Rockport Publishers; Voyageur Press; Zenith Press
Distributed by Hachette US
Distributor for Aurum Press; Walter Foster Publishing; Frances Lincoln (adult trade list); Roto-Vision; Jacqui Small
*See separate listing for:*
**Fair Winds Press**

**Quicksilver Productions**
PO Box 340, Ashland, OR 97520-0012
*Tel:* 541-482-5343 *Fax:* 508-590-0099
*E-mail:* celestialcalendars@email.com
*Web Site:* www.quicksilverproductions.com
*Key Personnel*
Prop: Jim Maynard
Off Mgr: Lisa Devalin
Founded: 1972
Publisher of calendars & cookbooks.
ISBN Prefix(es): 978-0-930356 (cookbooks); 978-1-935482 (astrological calendars)
Number of titles published annually: 4 Print
Total Titles: 8 Print

**Quincannon Publishing Group**
PO Box 8100, Glen Ridge, NJ 07028-8100
*Tel:* 973-380-9942
*E-mail:* editors@quincannongroup.com
*Web Site:* www.quincannongroup.com
*Key Personnel*
Ed-in-Chief: Alan Quincannon
Ed: Holly Benedict
Consulting Ed: Jeanne Wilcox
Lib Sales Dir & Admin Asst: Patricia Drury
Publicity: Loretta Bolger
Intl Rts: Loris Essary
Founded: 1990
Regional mystery novels made unique by involving some element of a region's history (i.e. the story's setting & time frame or the mystery's origin); custom tailored books for local & regional museums.
ISBN Prefix(es): 978-1-878452
Number of titles published annually: 3 Print
Total Titles: 18 Print; 17 Online
Imprints: Compass Point Mysteries; Jersey Yarns; Learning & Coloring Books; Rune-Tales; Tory Corner Editions
Foreign Rep(s): International Titles

**§Quintessence Publishing Co Inc**
4350 Chandler Dr, Hanover Park, IL 60133
SAN: 215-9783
*Tel:* 630-736-3600 *Toll Free Tel:* 800-621-0387 *Fax:* 630-736-3633
*E-mail:* contact@quintbook.com; service@quintbook.com
*Web Site:* www.quintpub.com
*Key Personnel*
Pres: H W Haase
VP, Opers & Dir, Lib Sales: William Hartman *Tel:* 630-736-3600 ext 413 *E-mail:* whartman@quintbook.com
Founded: 1950
Professional & scholarly books, journals, medicine, dentistry, health & nutrition, medical history.
ISBN Prefix(es): 978-0-931386; 978-0-86715
Number of titles published annually: 20 Print; 2 CD-ROM
Total Titles: 410 Print; 80 CD-ROM; 250 Audio
Imprints: Quintessence Books; Quintessence of Dental Technology; Quintessence Pockets
*Foreign Office(s):* 2-4 Ifenpfad, 12107 Berlin, Germany *Tel:* (030) 761-805 *Fax:* (030) 761-80693 *E-mail:* info@quintessenz.de *Web Site:* www.quintessenz.de
Quint House Bldg, 326 Hongo, Bunkyo-ku Tokyo, Japan *Tel:* (03) 5842-2270 *Fax:* (03) 5800-7598 *E-mail:* info@quint-j.co.jp *Web Site:* www.quint-j.co.jp
2 Graston Rd, New Malden, Surrey KT3 3AB, United Kingdom *Tel:* (020) 8949-6087 *Fax:* (020) 8336-1484 *E-mail:* info@quintpub.co.uk *Web Site:* www.quintpub.co.uk
Distributor for Quintessence Publishing Co Ltd (Japan); Quintessence Publishing Ltd (London); Quintessence Verlags GmbH
*Advertising Agency:* QPC Advertising Inc

**Quirk Books**
215 Church St, Philadelphia, PA 19106
*Tel:* 215-627-3581 *Fax:* 215-627-5220
*E-mail:* general@quirkbooks.com
*Web Site:* www.quirkbooks.com
*Key Personnel*
Owner & CEO, Quirk Productions: David Borgenicht
Pres: Brett Cohen
Publr: Jason Rekulak
Assoc Dir, Publicity & Mktg: Melissa Monachello
Dir, Digital & Print Prodn: John McGurk
Mng Ed: Mary Ellen Wilson
Sr Ed: Jennifer Adams
Publicity Mgr: Nicole de Jackmo
Mktg & Soc Media Coord: Eric Smith
Edit Asst: Margaret McGuire; Jane Morley
Founded: 2002
Publishing list focuses on irreverent pop-culture, humor, gift, self-help & "impractical" reference books. The actual subject matter of our books is quite diverse. Publish everything from childcare tips & magic tricks to advice on stain removal. All of our books have a distinct sense of style, a refreshing sense of humor & innovative production values.
ISBN Prefix(es): 978-1-931686; 978-1-59474
Number of titles published annually: 25 Print
Total Titles: 150 Print
Distributed by Random House Publisher Services

**Quite Specific Media Group Ltd**
7373 Pyramid Place, Hollywood, CA 90046
*Tel:* 323-851-5797 *Fax:* 323-851-5798
*E-mail:* info@quitespecificmedia.com
*Web Site:* www.quitespecificmedia.com
*Key Personnel*
Publr: Ralph Pine *E-mail:* rpine@quitespecificmedia.com
Founded: 1967

Publish original books as well as co-publish with foreign publishers. Specialize in costumes, fashion & theatre.
ISBN Prefix(es): 978-0-89676
Number of titles published annually: 8 Print
Total Titles: 80 Print
Imprints: By Design Press; Costume & Fashion Press; Drama Publishers; EntertainmentPro; Jade Rabbit; Pat MacKay Projects
Foreign Rep(s): Nick Hern Books (UK)
*Warehouse:* Publishers Storage & Shipping Corp, 660 S Mansfield, Ypsilanti, MI 48197, VP, Opers: Donna Moore *Tel:* 734-487-9720 ext 130

**Quixote Press**
3544 Black St, Wever, IA 52658
*Tel:* 319-372-7480 *Toll Free Tel:* 800-571-2665 *Fax:* 319-372-7485
*E-mail:* heartsntummies@gmail.com; potpress@gmail.com
*Key Personnel*
Pres: Bruce Carlson
Founded: 1985
Regional paperback books of humor or folklore & cookbooks. Consulting work for self-publishers.
ISBN Prefix(es): 978-1-878488; 978-1-57166
Number of titles published annually: 35 Print
Total Titles: 350 Print
Imprints: Black Iron Cookin' Co; Hearts & Tummies Cookbook Co; Raise the Dough in 30 Days Co
Divisions: Quixote Press
*See separate listing for:*
**Hearts & Tummies Cookbook Co**

**Rada Press Inc**
1277 Fairmount Ave, St Paul, MN 55105
*Tel:* 651-645-3304
*E-mail:* info@radapress.com
*Web Site:* www.radapress.com
*Key Personnel*
Publr & Ed: Irving Fang *Tel:* 651-645-3304 *E-mail:* fangx001@umn.edu
Prodn Head: Ron-Michael Pellant *E-mail:* rm@radapress.com
Mktg Dir: Daisy Pellant *E-mail:* daisy@radapress.com
Founded: 1975
ISBN Prefix(es): 978-0-9604212; 978-1-933011
Number of titles published annually: 2 Print; 1 E-Book
Total Titles: 13 Print; 1 E-Book
Imprints: Tree Frog Publications

**§Radix Press**
Subsidiary of UGF/OR
11715 Bandlon Dr, Houston, TX 77072
*Tel:* 281-879-5688
*Web Site:* www.specialforcesbooks.com
*Key Personnel*
Dir: Stephen Sherman *E-mail:* sherman1@flash.net
Founded: 1983
Directories, reference books. All unsol mss sent will be discarded.
ISBN Prefix(es): 978-0-9624009; 978-0-9623992; 978-1-929932
Number of titles published annually: 3 Print; 2 CD-ROM
Total Titles: 40 Print; 12 CD-ROM
Imprints: Electric Strawberry Press

**Rainbow Books Inc**
PO Box 430, Highland City, FL 33846
SAN: 221-9859
*Tel:* 863-648-4420 *Fax:* 863-647-5951
*E-mail:* info@rainbowbooksinc.com
*Web Site:* www.rainbowbooksinc.com
*Key Personnel*
Pres & Edit Dir: Betsy Lampe
Publr: Betty Wright *E-mail:* blfallot@aol.com
Opers Dir: C Marzen Lampe
Prodn Mgr: Marilyn Ratzlaff
Founded: 1979
How-to both for the adult layman & the juvenile markets, self-help, reference, resource & general books; parenting; nonfiction; also package books for other publishers & act as consultants, mystery & mainstream fiction at 50,000 or 75,000 words.
ISBN Prefix(es): 978-0-935834; 978-1-56825
Number of titles published annually: 20 Print
Total Titles: 141 Print
Foreign Rep(s): Hagenbach & Bender (Worldwide exc USA)
Foreign Rights: Hagenbach & Bender (Worldwide exc USA)
*Warehouse:* Publishers Storage & Shipping Corp, 660 S Mansfield St, Ypsilanti, MI 48197-5167, Contact: Donna Moore *Tel:* 734-487-9720 *Fax:* 734-487-1890 *E-mail:* dmoore@psscmi.com *Web Site:* www.pssc.com
Membership(s): AAP; Florida Publishers Association Inc; National Association of Independent Publishers

**Rainbow Publishers**
PO Box 261129, San Diego, CA 92196
*Tel:* 858-277-1167 *Toll Free Tel:* 800-323-7337 *Toll Free Fax:* 800-331-0297
*E-mail:* info@rainbowpublishers.com; editor@rainbowpublishers.com (edit dept)
*Web Site:* www.rainbowpublishers.com
*Key Personnel*
Publr: Daniel Miley
Founded: 1951
Christian education books.
ISBN Prefix(es): 978-0-937282; 978-1-885358; 978-1-58411
Number of titles published annually: 12 Print
Total Titles: 250 Print
Imprints: Legacy Press; Rainbow Publishers

**Ram Publishing Co**
Subsidiary of Garrett Electronics
1881 W State St, Garland, TX 75042
*Tel:* 972-494-6151 *Toll Free Tel:* 800-527-4011 *Fax:* 972-494-1881
*E-mail:* sales@garrett.com
*Web Site:* www.garrett.com
*Key Personnel*
Ed: Steve Moore
Founded: 1967
Nonfiction on treasure hunting with a metal detector & metal detector security.
ISBN Prefix(es): 978-0-915920
Number of titles published annually: 3 Print
Total Titles: 15 Print

**§RAND Corp**
1776 Main St, Santa Monica, CA 90407-2138
Mailing Address: PO Box 2138, Santa Monica, CA 90407-2138
*Tel:* 310-393-0411 *Fax:* 310-393-4818
*Web Site:* www.rand.org
*Key Personnel*
Dir, Opers: Jane Ryan *Tel:* 310-393-0411 ext 7260 *E-mail:* ryan@rand.org
Dir, Strategic Communs: Peg Schumacher *E-mail:* pege@rand.org
Mng Ed: Steve Kistler
Mgr, Design, Prodn & Dist: Paul Murphy
Print & Dist Mgr: Tim Erickson
Cust Serv Supv: Amy Majczyk *Tel:* 412-683-2300 ext 4604
Founded: 1948
Public policy research.
ISBN Prefix(es): 978-0-8330
Number of titles published annually: 140 Print; 100 Online; 50 E-Book
Total Titles: 20,000 Print; 11,000 Online; 1,250 E-Book
Divisions: Office of External Affairs
Foreign Rep(s): Aditya Books Pvt Ltd (India); Booknet Co Ltd (Cambodia, Laos, Myanmar, Thailand, Vietnam); ChoiceTEXTS Ltd (Indonesia, Singapore); iCaves Ltd (Hong Kong); IG Knowledge Services Ltd (Taiwan); iGroup (Brunei, China, Hong Kong, India, Indonesia, Malaysia, Philippines, Singapore, Taiwan); iGroup Press Co Ltd (China); Inbooks (Australia); Information Development Consultancy (IDC) (Korea); MegaTEXTS Phil Inc (Philippines); NBN Canada (Canada); NBN/DA Trade (Australia, New Zealand); NBN International (Europe, Middle East, UK)
*Orders to:* RAND Distribution Services, 4570 Fifth Ave, Pittsburgh, PA 15213, Cust Serv Mgr: Amy Majczyk *Tel:* 412-683-2300 *Toll Free Tel:* 877-584-8642 *Fax:* 412-802-4981 *E-mail:* order@rand.org
*Distribution Center:* National Book Network, 4720 Boston Way, Blue Ridge Summit, PA 17214 *Tel:* 717-794-3800 *Toll Free Tel:* 800-462-6420 *Toll Free Fax:* 800-338-4550 *E-mail:* mcozy@nbnbooks.com *Web Site:* www.nbnbooks.com
Membership(s): AAP; AIGA, the professional association for design; American Association of University Presses; Public Relations Society of America; Society for Scholarly Publishing; Washington Book Publishers

**§Rand McNally**
9855 Woods Dr, Skokie, IL 60077
SAN: 203-3917
Mailing Address: PO Box 7600, Chicago, IL 60680-7600
*Tel:* 847-329-8100 *Toll Free Tel:* 800-678-7263 *Fax:* 847-329-6139
*E-mail:* ctsales@randmcnally.com; mediarelations@randmcnally.com
*Web Site:* www.randmcnally.com
*Key Personnel*
CEO & Pres: David Muscatel
VP, Mktg: Kendra Ensor
Founded: 1856
Road atlases & maps; world atlases; mileage & routing publications & software; educational maps, atlases; children's atlases, maps, books; electronic multimedia products; retail & online stores; online travel services, travel software.
Publisher of the *Thomas Guide* atlas series.
ISBN Prefix(es): 978-0-528
Number of titles published annually: 20 Print
Total Titles: 100 Print; 5 CD-ROM
Imprints: Rand McNally for Kids
Subsidiaries: Allmaps
*Warehouse:* 106 Hi-Lane, Richmond, KY 40475

**Random House Audio Publishing Group**
Subsidiary of Random House Inc
1745 Broadway, New York, NY 10019
*E-mail:* audio@randomhouse.com
*Web Site:* www.randomhouse.com/audio
*Key Personnel*
VP & Publr: Amanda D'Acierno
VP, Opers: Sue Daulton
Dir, Mktg: Heather Dalton
Random House Inc & its publishing entities are not accepting unsol submissions, proposals, mss, or submission queries via e-mail at this time.
ISBN Prefix(es): 978-0-7393; 978-0-375
Number of titles published annually: 500 Print; 300 Audio
Total Titles: 2,000 Print; 894 Audio
*See separate listing for:*
**Living Language**

**Random House Children's Books**
Division of Random House Inc
1745 Broadway, New York, NY 10019
*Tel:* 212-782-9000 *Toll Free Tel:* 800-200-3552 *Fax:* 212-782-9452

*Web Site:* randomhousekids.com

*Key Personnel*

Pres & Publr: Barbara Marcus

EVP, Publg Opers: Rich Romano

SVP & Assoc Publr: Judith Haut

SVP & Dir, Sales: Joan DeMayo

SVP, Mktg: John Adamo

VP, Subs Rts Mkts: Pam White

VP & Publr, Bantam Delacorte Dell: Beverly Horowitz

VP & Publr, Crown Books for Young Readers: Phoebe Yeh

VP & Publg Dir, Wendy Lamb Books: Wendy Lamb

VP, Assoc Publr & Art Dir, Random House/ Golden Books Young Readers Group: Cathy Goldsmith

VP, Publg Dir, Knopf/Crown: Nancy Hinkel

VP, Exec Mng Ed: Denise DeGennaro

VP & Ed-in-Chief, Random House Books for Young Readers & Publg Dir, Golden Group: Mallory Loehr

Exec Dir, Mktg & Design Opers: Mary Beth Kilkelly

Exec Dir, Art & Design, Knopf Delacorte Dell Young Readers Group: Isabel Warren-Lynch

Dir, School & Lib Mktg: Adrienne Waintraub

VP, Dir, Brand/Category Mgmt: Enid Chaban

Assoc Publg Dir, Random House/Golden Books Group: Michelle Nagler

Assoc Publg Dir & Exec Ed, Knopf/Crown: Nancy Siscoe

Publicity Dir: Noreen Herits

VP, Prodn Dir: Linda Palladino

Art Dir, Random House Books for Young Readers: Jan Gerardi

Art Dir, Mass Mkt, Random House/Golden Books Young Readers Group: Tracy Tyler

Art Dir, KDD Art Group: Alison Impey

Assoc Art Dir, KDD Art Group: Stephanie Moss

Exec Ed, Doubleday: Francoise Bui

Exec Ed, Media & Series, Bantam Delacorte Dell: Wendy Loggia

Edit Dir, Picture Books: Maria Modugno

Publicity Mgr & Online Media Specialist: Dominique Cimina

Publicist & Online Media Specialist: Meg O'Brien

Publicist: Casey Lloyd, Emily Pourclau; Elizabeth Zajac

Assoc Dir, Subs Rts: Kim Wrubel

Edit Dir, Sesame Workshop, Random House Books for Young Readers: Naomi Kleinberg

Ed-in-Chief & Exec Dir, Licensed Publg, Golden Books: Chris Angelilli

Exec Ed: Erin Clarke

Exec Ed, Disney Books for Young Readers: Andrea Posner-Sanchez

Exec Ed, Random House Books for Young Readers: Heidi Kilgras

Edit Dir, Novelty, Random House/Golden Books Young Readers Group: Dennis Shealy

Dir, Mktg, New Media: Linda Leonard

VP & Publg Dir, Schwartz & Wade Books: Anne Schwartz; Lee Wade

Assoc Art Dir: Sarah Hokanson

Assoc Publ Dir, Knopf Children's: Melanie Cecka

Sr Ed, Knopf Books for Young Readers: Michele Burke

Ed: Frank Berrios

Ed, Knopf Books for Young Readers: Allison Worchte

Asst Ed: Courtney Carbone

Mktg Coord: Melissa Zar

Jr Designer: Jinna Shin

Prodn Assoc: Alice Rahaeuser

Publg Consultant: Robin Corey

Random House Inc & its publishing entities are not accepting unsol submissions, proposals, mss, or submission queries via e-mail at this time.

ISBN Prefix(es): 978-0-679; 978-0-307; 978-0-676; 978-0-375; 978-1-4000; 978-1-58836

Imprints: Beginner Books; Robin Corey Books; Crown Books for Young Readers; Delacorte Books for Young Readers; Doubleday Books for Young Readers; Dragonfly; Golden Books; Alfred A Knopf Books for Young Readers; Laurel-Leaf; Random House Books for Young Readers; Schwartz and Wade Books; Wendy Lamb Books; Yearling

Divisions: Knopf Delacorte Dell Young Readers Group; Random House/Golden Books Young Readers Group

*Warehouse:* Crawfordsville Distribution Center, 1019 N State Rd 47, Crawfordsville, IN 47933

*Distribution Center:* Crawfordsville Distribution Center, 1019 N State Rd 47, Crawfordsville, IN 47933

Membership(s): Association of Booksellers for Children; Children's Book Council

**§Random House Inc**

Division of Bertelsmann AG

1745 Broadway, New York, NY 10019

SAN: 202-5507

*Tel:* 212-782-9000 *Toll Free Tel:* 800-726-0600

*Web Site:* www.randomhouse.com

*Key Personnel*

Chmn: John Makinson

CEO: Markus Dohle

COO & Pres, Sales, Opers & Digital: Madeline McIntosh

Chief HR Offr: Frank Steinert

Chmn, Knopf: Sonny Mehta

Pres & Publr, Crown Publishing Group: Maya Mavjee

Pres & Publr, Random House Children's Books: Barbara Marcus

Pres & Publr, Random House Publishing Group: Gina Centrello

Pres, Knopf Publishing Group: Tony Chirico

Pres, RH Films & VP, Ed-at-Large: Peter Gethers

EVP, Communs: Stuart Applebaum

EVP & Gen Coun: Katherine Trager

SVP & Assoc Gen Coun: Matthew Martin; Anke Steinecke

SVP, Publr Digital Content: Scott Shannon

VP, Corp Projs: Brendan Cahill

VP, Digital Publg Dir: Allison Dobson

VP, Dir Digital Strategy: Matt Schwartz

VP & Dir, Intl Mktg & British Commonwealth Sales: Christopher Dufault

VP & Publr, Crown Books for Young Readers: Phoebe Yeh

Assoc Publr & Edit Strategy: Gina Wachtel

Sr Dir, Content Mktg: Kristen Fritz

Assoc Ed, Alibi: Randall Klein

Assoc Ed, Hydra: Sarah Peed

Ed-at-Large, Flirt & Loveswept: Sue Grimshaw

Random House Inc & its publishing entities are not accepting unsol submissions, proposals, mss, or submission queries via e-mail at this time.

ISBN Prefix(es): 978-0-307; 978-0-679; 978-0-553; 978-0-676; 978-0-375; 978-0-87665; 978-0-805

Imprints: Alibi (mystery, thriller, suspense); Anchor Bible Commentary; Anchor Bible Dictionary; Anchor Bible Reference Library; Anchor Books; AtRandom.com; Ballantine Books; Ballantine Wellspring; Bantam Books; Bantam Hardcover; Bantam Mass Market; Bantam Skylark; Bantam Starfire; Bantam Trade Paperback; BDD Audio Publishing; Bell Tower; Children's Classics; Children's Media; Clarkson Potter; Crescent Books; Crimeline; Crown Books for Young Readers; Crown Publishers Inc; CTW Publishing; Currency; David Fickling Books; Del Rey; Delacorte Books for Young Readers; Delacorte Press; Dell; Dell Laurel Leaf; Dell Yearling; Delta; Derrydale; The Dial Press; Discovery Books; Disney Books for Young Readers; Domain; Doubleday; Doubleday Bible Commentary; Doubleday Books for Young Readers; Doubleday/Galilee; Doubleday/Image; Dragonfly Books; DTP; Everyman's Library; Fanfare; Fawcett; First Choice Chapter Books; Flirt (new adult); Fodor's; Golden Books; Gramercy Books; Harmony Books; House of Collectibles; Hydra (science fiction & fantasy); Island; Ivy; Alfred A Knopf; Knopf Books for Young Readers; Knopf Guides; Laurel Leaf Books; Library of Contemporary Thought; Living Language; Loveswept (digital only romance); Main Street Books; Modern Library; The Monacelli Press; The New Jerusalem Bible; One World; Pantheon Books; Picture Yearling; The Princeton Review; Random House; Random House Books for Young Readers; Random House Children's Publishing; Random House Digital; Random House Large Print Publishing; Random House Reference & Information Publishing; Schocken Books; Schwartz & Wade Books; Shaye Areheart Books; Sierra Club Adult Books; Skylark; Spectra; Nan A Talese; Testament Books; Three Rivers Press; Times Books; Villard Books; Vintage Books; Wendy Lamb Books; Wings Books; Yearling

*Branch Office(s)*

WaterBrook Press, 5446 N Academy, Suite 200, Colorado Springs, CO 80918 *Tel:* 719-590-4999 *Fax:* 719-590-8977

Random House of Canada Limited, 2775 Matheson Blvd E, Mississauga, ON L4W 4P7, Canada *Tel:* 905-624-0672 *Toll Free Tel:* 888-523-9292 (orders) *Fax:* 905-624-6217 *Web Site:* www.randomhouse.ca

Bantam Books Canada Inc, One Toronto St, Suite 300, Toronto, ON M5C 2V6, Canada *Tel:* 416-364-4449 *Fax:* 416-364-6863

Doubleday Canada, One Toronto St, Suite 300, Toronto, ON M5C 2V6, Canada *Tel:* 416-364-4449 *Fax:* 416-364-6863

*Editorial Office(s):* One Toronto St, Suite 300, Toronto, ON M5C 2V6, Canada *Tel:* 416-777-9477 *Fax:* 416-777-9470

*Foreign Office(s):* Random House Australia Pty Ltd, 16 Dalmore Dr, Scoresby, Victoria 3153, Australia *Tel:* (03) 9753-4511 *Fax:* (03) 9753-3944

Random House Australia Pty Ltd, 20 Alfred St, Milsons Point, Sydney, NSW 2061, Australia *Tel:* (02) 9954-9966 *Fax:* (02) 9954-4562

Random House New Zealand Ltd, 18 Poland Rd, Glenfield, Auckland 0627, New Zealand *Tel:* (09) 444-7197 *Fax:* (09) 444-7524

Random House South Africa Pty Ltd, Endulini, East Wing, 5A Jubilee Rd, Parktown, Sandton 2193, South Africa *Tel:* (011) 484-3538 *Fax:* (011) 484-6180

Tiptree Book Services, Colchester Rd, Frating Green, Colchester, Essex C07 7DW, United Kingdom *Tel:* (01206) 256000 *Fax:* (01206) 255916

Grantham Book Services, Alma Park Industrial Estate, Isaac Newton Way, Grantham, Lincs NG31 9SD, United Kingdom *Tel:* (01476) 541000 *Fax:* (01476) 590223

Doubleday London, 61-63 Uxbridge Rd, Ealing, London W5 5SA, United Kingdom *Tel:* (020) 8231 6717 *Fax:* (020) 8231 6718

Random House UK Ltd, 20 Vauxhall Bridge Rd, London SW1V 2SA, United Kingdom *Tel:* (020) 7840 8400 *Fax:* (020) 7233 8791

Transworld Publishers Ltd, 61-63 Uxbridge Rd, Ealing, London W5 5SA, United Kingdom *Tel:* (020) 8579-2652 *Fax:* (020) 8579-5479

Transworld Publishers Ltd, Sanders Rd, Finedon Rd Industrial Estate, Wellingborough, Northamptonshire NN8 4BU, United Kingdom (dist ctr) *Tel:* (0193) 322-5761 *Fax:* (0193) 327-1235

Distributor for Karen Brown's Guides; Mondadori Spanish Language; National Geographic; Princeton Review; Rizzoli; Rugged Land; Shambhala; Smithsonian Books; Soho Press; Steerforth Press; The Taunton Press; Ten Speed Press; Wizards of the Coast

*Shipping Address:* Westminster Distribution Center, 400 Hahn Rd, Westminster, MD 21157
*Tel:* 410-848-1900 *Fax:* 410-386-7013
Membership(s): AAP; BISG
*See separate listing for:*
**Books on Tape®**
**Crown Publishing Group**
**Fodor's Travel Publications**
**Random House Audio Publishing Group**
**Random House Children's Books**
**Random House Large Print**
**Random House Publishing Group**
**Random House Reference/Random House Puzzles & Games/House of Collectibles**
**WaterBrook Multnomah Publishing Group**

**Random House Large Print**
Division of Random House Inc
1745 Broadway, New York, NY 10019
*Tel:* 212-782-9000 *Fax:* 212-782-9484
*Key Personnel*
Edit Dir: Amy Metsch
Founded: 1990
Acquires & publishes general interest fiction & nonfiction in large print editions.
Random House Inc & its publishing entities are not accepting unsol submissions, proposals, mss, or submission queries via e-mail at this time.
ISBN Prefix(es): 978-0-679
Number of titles published annually: 40 Print
Total Titles: 300 Print

**Random House Publishing Group**
Division of Random House Inc
1745 Broadway, New York, NY 10019
SAN: 214-1175
*Toll Free Tel:* 800-200-3552
*Web Site:* atrandom.com
*Key Personnel*
Pres & Publr: Gina Centrello
Publr, Random House & Dial Press: Susan Kamil
Publr, Spiegel & Grau: Julie Grau; Cindy Spiegel
Deputy Publr, Nonfiction & Publr, Modern Library: Thomas Perry
Assoc Publr & Edit Strategy: Gina Wachtel
Assoc Publr, Del Rey Manga: Dallas Middaugh
Assoc Publr, Nonfiction, Ballantine Bantam Dell: Richard Callison
Assoc Publr, Spiegel & Grau & Dir, Mktg, Random House, Spiegel & Grau, Dial Press & Modern Library: Leigh Merchant
Group EVP & Dir, Publg: Bill Takes
Group SVP & Creative Dir: Paolo Pepe
Group SVP & Mktg Dir: Sanyu Dillon
EVP, Assoc Publr & Exec Edit Dir: Kate Medina
SVP & Dir, Publg Opers: Lisa Feuer
SVP & Dir, Intl Sales & East Asian Busn Devt: Cyrus Kheradi
SVP & Publr, Ballantine Bantam Dell: Libby McGuire
SVP: Amanda Close; Nihar Malaviya; Nina von Moltke
SVP, Ed-in-Chief, Ballantine Bantam Dell: Jennifer Hershey
SVP & Edit Dir, Ballantine: Linda Marrow
SVP, Corp Communs: Claire von Schilling
SVP & Dir, Publicity: Theresa Zoro
SVP & Publr, Digital Content: Scott Shannon
VP & Dir, Corp Devt & Strategy: Milena Alberti
VP & Dir, Digital Strategy: Matt Schwartz
VP & Dir, Publicity, Random House: Sally Marvin
VP & Dir, Subs Rts: Denise Cronin
VP & Edit Dir, Bantam Books/Delacorte Press: Kate Miciak
VP & Edit Dir, Nonfiction: Andy Ward
VP & Edit Dir, Nonfiction, Ballantine Bantam Dell: Jennifer Tung
VP & Exec Ed: David Ebershoff
VP, Assoc Publr, Ballantine Bantam Dell: Kim Hovey
VP, Assoc Publr, Random House & Dial Press: Avideh Bashirrad
VP, Digital Publg Dir: Allison Dobson
Edit Dir, Fiction, Ballantine Bantam Dell: Mark Tavani
Edit Dir, Nonfiction, Ballantine Bantam Dell: Luke Dempsey
Exec Dir, Art/Design: Robbin Schiff
Sr Dir, Art/Design: Beck Stvan
Sr Art Dir: Joe Perez
Exec Ed, Ballantine: Pamela Cannon; Marnie Cochran; Susanna Porter
Exec Ed, Random House: Susan Mercandetti; Will Murphy
Dir, Ad & Promo: Stacey Witcraft
Dir, Dom Rts: Rachel Bernstein
Dir, Interior Design: Carole Lowenstein
Dir, Partnerships & Busn Devt: Melissa Milsten
Group Sales Dir: Cynthia Lasky
Imprint Sales Dir: Allyson Pearl
Deputy Dir, Publicity: London King
Asst Dir, Publicity: Maria Braeckel
Assoc Dir, Foreign Rts: Rachel Kind
Sr Mng Ed, Random House & Copy Chief: Benjamin Dreyer
Sr Mgr, Ad & Promos: Elizabeth Fabian
Publicity Mgr: Greg Kubie; Alison Masciovecchio
Sr Publicist: Michelle Jasmine
Assoc Publicist: Steve Boriack; Ella Maslin
Sr Ed, Ballantine Bantam Dell: Ryan Doherty
Ed: Caitlin Alexander; Keith Clayton; Kate Collins; Tracy Devine; Noah Eaker; Anne Groell; Kendra Harpster; Dana Isaacson; Christopher Jackson; Jonathan Jao; Tricia Pasternak; Jennifer Smith; Shauna Summers; Paul Taunton
Ed, Spiegel & Grau: Jessica Sindler
Assoc Ed: Kaela Myers; Sam Nicholson; Anna Pitoniak
Assoc Ed, Alibi: Randall Klein
Assoc Ed, Hydra: Sarah Reed
Assoc Ed, Spiegel & Grau: Laura Van der Veer
Ed-at-Large, Del Rey/Ballantine: Shelly Shapiro
Ed-at-Large, Flirt & Loveswept: Sue Grimshaw
Founded: 1925
General fiction & nonfiction hardcover, trade & mass market paperbacks.
Random House Inc & its publishing entities are not accepting unsol submissions, proposals, mss, or submission queries via e-mail at this time.
ISBN Prefix(es): 978-0-307; 978-0-679; 978-0-89141; 978-0-345; 978-0-449; 978-0-8129; 978-0-375; 978-1-4000; 978-1-58836; 978-0-8041
Number of titles published annually: 700 Print; 150 E-Book
Total Titles: 5,900 Print; 1,100 E-Book
Imprints: Alibi (mystery, thriller, suspense); Ballantine Books; Bantam Books; Del Rey; Dell; The Dial Press; Flirt (new adult); Hydra (science fiction & fantasy); Loveswept (digital only romance); Modern Library; One World; Presidio Press; Random House; Spiegel & Grau; Triumph Books; Villard; Zinc Ink
*Warehouse:* 400 Hahn Rd, Westminster, MD 21157

**Random House Reference/Random House Puzzles & Games/House of Collectibles**
Imprint of Random House Audio Publishing Group
1745 Broadway, New York, NY 10019
*Toll Free Tel:* 800-733-3000 *Toll Free Fax:* 800-659-2436
*E-mail:* words@random.com; puzzles@random.com
*Key Personnel*
SVP & Publr: Amanda D'Acierno
Assoc Dir, Mng Edit: Alison Skrabek
Dir, Subs/Foreign Rts: Linda Kaplan
Publishes reference, crossword puzzle books & chess books & price guides for collectibles.
Random House Inc & its publishing entities are not accepting unsol submissions, proposals, mss, or submission queries via e-mail at this time.
ISBN Prefix(es): 978-0-8129; 978-0-375
Total Titles: 215 Print
Imprints: Boston Globe Puzzle Books; Chicago Tribune Crosswords; House of Collectibles; Los Angeles Times Crosswords; McKay Chess Library; Random House Websters; Washington Post Crosswords

**§Rattapallax Press**
217 Thompson St, Suite 353, New York, NY 10012
*E-mail:* info@rattapallax.com
*Web Site:* www.rattapallax.com
*Key Personnel*
Pres & Publr: Ram Devineni
Founded: 2000
ISBN Prefix(es): 978-1-892494
Number of titles published annually: 4 Print; 1 CD-ROM; 15 Online; 15 E-Book; 15 Audio
Total Titles: 15 Print; 1 CD-ROM; 15 Online; 15 E-Book; 15 Audio
*Distribution Center:* Small Press Distribution, 1341 Seventh St, Berkeley, CA 94710-1409
*Tel:* 510-524-1668 *Toll Free Tel:* 800-869-7553
*E-mail:* spd@spdbooks.org *Web Site:* www.spdbooks.org
Membership(s): Council of Literary Magazines & Presses

**Raven Productions Inc**
PO Box 188, Ely, MN 55731
*Tel:* 218-365-3375 *Fax:* 678-306-3375
*E-mail:* raven@ravenwords.com; order@ravenwords.com
*Web Site:* www.ravenwords.com
Founded: 1999
ISBN Prefix(es): 978-0-9677057; 978-0-9766264; 978-0-9794202; 978-0-9801045; 978-0-9819307; 978-0-9883508; 978-0-9835189
Number of titles published annually: 3 Print
Total Titles: 20 Print
Imprints: Rosebud Books
Distributed by Adventure Publications
*Warehouse:* R & R, 420 N 15 Ave E, Ely, MN 55731
Membership(s): IBPA, the Independent Book Publishers Association; Midwest Independent Publishers Association

**Raven Publishing Inc**
125 Cherry Creek Rd, Norris, MT 59745
SAN: 254-5861
Mailing Address: PO Box 2866, Norris, MT 59745
*Tel:* 406-685-3545 *Toll Free Tel:* 866-685-3545
*Fax:* 406-685-3599
*E-mail:* info@ravenpublishing.net
*Web Site:* www.ravenpublishing.net
*Key Personnel*
Founder & Pres: Janet Muirhead Hill
*E-mail:* janet@ravenpublishing.net
Founded: 2001
ISBN Prefix(es): 978-0-9714161; 978-0-9772525
Number of titles published annually: 4 Print; 3 Online
Total Titles: 17 Print; 17 Online
*Billing Address:* PO Box 2866, Norris, MT 59745
Membership(s): IBPA, the Independent Book Publishers Association

**Raven Tree Press**
Division of Delta Publishing
1400 Miller Pkwy, McHenry, IL 60050-7030
SAN: 253-6005
*Tel:* 815-363-3582 *Toll Free Tel:* 800-323-8270
*Fax:* 815-363-2948 *Toll Free Fax:* 800-909-9901
*E-mail:* raven@raventreepress.com
*Web Site:* www.raventreepress.com

*Key Personnel*
Mktg Dir: Diane Bergeron *E-mail:* d.bergeron@deltapublishing.com
Founded: 2000
Children's bilingual (English-Spanish) picture books. Check web site for submission details.
ISBN Prefix(es): 978-0-9701107; 978-0-9720192; 978-0-9724973
Number of titles published annually: 20 Print; 10 Online
Total Titles: 50 Print; 136 Online
Membership(s): Children's Book Council; IBPA, the Independent Book Publishers Association; Society of Children's Book Writers & Illustrators

**§Ravenhawk™ Books**
Division of The 6DOF Group
7739 E Broadway Blvd, No 95, Tucson, AZ 85710
*Tel:* 520-296-4491 *Fax:* 520-296-4491
*E-mail:* ravenhawk6dof@yahoo.com
*Web Site:* 6dofsolutions.com
*Key Personnel*
Publr: Karl Lasky
Founded: 1998
Royalty publisher specializing in general trade, hard/softcover, fiction, nonfiction, self-help, teaching texts for professionals, crime, mystery & suspense fiction. E-books, CD/DVD audio books. Ms submissions are by invitation only through acknowledged literary agents.
ISBN Prefix(es): 978-1-893660
Number of titles published annually: 6 Print; 4 CD-ROM; 4 Online; 8 E-Book; 4 Audio
Total Titles: 32 Print; 1 Online; 2 E-Book
*Advertising Agency:* GERACI Promotions, 7739 E Broadway Blvd, No 95, Tucson, AZ 85710 *Tel:* 480-427-2183 *E-mail:* info@6dofsolutions.com
*Distribution Center:* Baker & Taylor
Ingram
Membership(s): Interactive Creative Artists Network; National Writers Association; Society of Southwestern Authors

**Rayve Productions Inc**
PO Box 726, Windsor, CA 95492
SAN: 248-4250
*Tel:* 707-838-6200 *Toll Free Tel:* 800-852-4890 *Fax:* 707-838-2220
*E-mail:* rayvepro@aol.com
*Web Site:* www.rayveproductions.com; www.foodandwinebooks.com
*Key Personnel*
Pres: Norm Ray
VP & Ed-in-Chief: Barbara F Ray
Founded: 1989
Business guidebooks, illustrated children's books, history books, counseling, parenting, caregiving & cookbooks.
ISBN Prefix(es): 978-1-877810; 978-1-893718; 978-0-9629927
Number of titles published annually: 5 Print
Total Titles: 35 Print; 1 CD-ROM; 1 Audio
Imprints: LifeTimes; Toucan Tales
Membership(s): IBPA, the Independent Book Publishers Association

**Razorbill**
Imprint of Penguin Group (USA) LLC
345 Hudson St, New York, NY 10014
*Tel:* 212-366-2000
*Key Personnel*
Pres & Publr: Ben Schrank
Assoc Publr: Erin Berger
Ed: Caroline Donofrio
Founded: 2004
ISBN Prefix(es): 978-1-59514
Number of titles published annually: 42 Print
Total Titles: 159 Print

**The Reader's Digest Association Inc**
750 Third Ave, New York, NY 10017
SAN: 212-4416
*Tel:* 914-238-1000; 646-293-6284 *Toll Free Tel:* 800-310-6261 (cust serv) *Fax:* 914-238-4559
*Web Site:* www.rd.com; www.rda.com
*Key Personnel*
Chmn: Randall Curran
CEO & Pres: Robert E Guth
CFO & EVP: Paul Tomkins *E-mail:* paul_tomkins@rda.com
Global CIO & SVP: Joe Held
EVP, Busn Opers: Albert L Peruzza
SVP, Gen Coun/Secy: Andrea Newborn
VP & Treas: William H Magill
VP, Global Communs: Susan Fraysse Russ *E-mail:* susan_russ@rda.com
VP & Assoc Publr: Rosanne McManus
Mng Dir & Publr, Children's Brand: Neil Wertheimer
Membership(s): AAP
*See separate listing for:*
**Reader's Digest Children's Books**
**Reader's Digest General Books**
**Reader's Digest Trade Books**
**Reader's Digest USA Select Editions**

**Reader's Digest Children's Books**
Subsidiary of The Reader's Digest Association Inc
44 S Broadway, White Plains, NY 10601
SAN: 283-2143
*Tel:* 914-238-1000 *Toll Free Tel:* 800-934-0977
*Web Site:* www.rdtradepublishing.com
*Key Personnel*
Pres & Publr: Harold Clarke *E-mail:* Harold_Clarke@rd.com
VP, Assoc Publr: Rosanne McManus *E-mail:* Rosanne_McManus@rd.com
Creative Dir: Julia Sabbagh *E-mail:* Julia_Sabbagh@rd.com
VP, Sales & Mktg Dir: Stacey Ashton *E-mail:* Stacey_Ashton@rd.com
Dir, Custom Publg: Debra Polansky *E-mail:* Debra_Polansky@rd.com
Founded: 1994
Publishers of children's interactive books, including major world class brands.
ISBN Prefix(es): 978-0-7944
Number of titles published annually: 150 Print
Total Titles: 400 Print
Foreign Rep(s): Jennifer Fifield (Worldwide exc USA)

**Reader's Digest General Books**
Division of The Reader's Digest Association Inc
Reader's Digest Rd, Pleasantville, NY 10570-7000
SAN: 240-9720
*Tel:* 914-238-1000 *Toll Free Tel:* 800-304-2807 (cust serv) *Fax:* 914-244-7436
*Key Personnel*
Pres & CEO: Mary Berner
SVP & Gen Coun: Michael A Brizel
SVP & Pres, Intl: Thomas D Gardner
SVP & CFO: Michael S Geltzeiler
SVP & Pres, North America & Global Ed-in-Chief: Eric Schrier
VP & Circ Dir: Dawn Zier
VP & Treas: William H Magill
VP, Global Communs: William K Adler
Mgr, Rts & Perms: Lisa Garrett Smith
Founded: 1961
Direct marketed reference books on home maintenance & repair, health & fitness, crafts & hobbies, history, cooking, travel, geography, religion, nature, law, medicine, gardening, English usage & vocabulary.
ISBN Prefix(es): 978-0-89577
Number of titles published annually: 10 Print

**Reader's Digest Trade Books**
Division of Reader's Digest Association Inc
44 S Broadway, White Plains, NY 10601
SAN: 240-9720
*Tel:* 914-244-7503 *Fax:* 914-244-4841
*Web Site:* www.rd.com
*Key Personnel*
Pres & Publr: Harold Clarke
VP & Assoc Publr: Rosanne McManus
Exec Ed: Dolores York
VP & Dir, Sales & Mktg: Stacy Ashton
Creative Dir: Julia Sabbagh
Dir, Prodn & Prod Devt: Debbie Gagnon
Founded: 1971
Illustrated trade (retail) reference books on home maintenance & repair, gardening, home decorating, crafts, art instruction, cooking, health & fitness, pet care, photography, family reference, religion & inspiration, science & nature, travel & atlases, humor.
ISBN Prefix(es): 978-0-7621
Number of titles published annually: 100 Print
Total Titles: 350 Print
Distributed by Penguin Group (USA) LLC

**Reader's Digest USA Select Editions**
Division of The Reader's Digest Association Inc
44 S Broadway, 7th fl, White Plains, NY 10601
*Tel:* 914-238-1000 *Toll Free Tel:* 800-304-2807 (cust serv) *Fax:* 914-831-1560
*Web Site:* www.rda.com/readers-digest-select-editions
*Key Personnel*
Pres & Publr, Books & Music: Harold Clarke *E-mail:* harold_clarke@rd.com
Exec Ed: Jim Menick *E-mail:* jim_menick@rd.com
Founded: 1950
Publishers of current fiction & general nonfiction in condensed form. Selections are licensed from original publisher.
ISBN Prefix(es): 978-0-89577

**Recorded Books LLC**
Division of Haights Cross Communications LLC
270 Skipjack Rd, Prince Frederick, MD 20678
SAN: 677-8887
*Tel:* 410-535-5590 *Toll Free Tel:* 800-638-1304; 877-732-2898 *Fax:* 410-535-5499
*E-mail:* customerservice@recordedbooks.com
*Web Site:* www.recordedbooks.com
*Key Personnel*
CEO & Pres: Rich Freese
COO: Edward Longo *E-mail:* elongo@recordedbooks.com
CFO: Neil Tress *E-mail:* ntress@recordedbooks.com
VP, Sales & Mktg: Matthew Walker *E-mail:* mwalker@recordedbooks.com
Dir, Acqs: Brian Sweany
Founded: 1979
Independent publisher of unabridged audiobooks & distributor of films & other media content delivered in CD & downloadable formats, to consumers, libraries & schools.
ISBN Prefix(es): 978-0-7887; 978-1-4025
Number of titles published annually: 700 Print; 250 CD-ROM; 100 Online; 50 E-Book; 787 Audio
Total Titles: 8,000 Print; 1,000 CD-ROM; 100 Online; 50 E-Book; 5,808 Audio
Imprints: Classic Library; Clipper Audio (UK); Griot Audio; Lone Star Audio; Pimlseur Language Programs; Recorded Books Audiolibros; Recorded Books Evergreen; Recorded Books Inspirational; Romantic Sounds Audio; Sci-Fi Audio; Southern Voices Audio; Your Coach in a Box
*Branch Office(s)*
Audio Adventures, 200 Skipjack Rd, Prince Frederick, MD 20678, Contact: Scott Williams *Toll Free Tel:* 800-580-2989 *Web Site:* www.landmarkaudio.com

*Foreign Office(s):* WF Howes, Unit 4, Rearsby Business Park, Gaddesby Lane, Rearsby, Leics LE7 4YH, United Kingdom (recorded books), Mng Dir: Sean Sibley *Tel:* (011) 0016-230-1144 *Fax:* (011) 0016-230-1155
Distributor for Buena Vista DVDs; The Film Movement DVDs
*Distribution Center:* Audio Adventures, 200 Skipjack Rd, Prince Frederick, MD 20678, Contact: Scott Williams *Toll Free Tel:* 800-580-2989 *Web Site:* www.landmarkaudio.com
Membership(s): Audio Publishers Association

**Red Chair Press**
PO Box 333, South Egremont, MA 01258-0333
*Toll Free Tel:* 888-327-2141 (ext 110) *Toll Free Fax:* 888-533-4037
*E-mail:* info@redchairpress.com
*Web Site:* www.redchairpress.com
*Key Personnel*
Pres & Publr: Keith Garton *E-mail:* keith@redchairpress.com
Creative Dir: Jeff Dinardo
Founded: 2009
Fiction & nonfiction books & ebook apps; social & emotional learning. Books about good decision making for children ages 4-8.
ISBN Prefix(es): 978-1-936163; 978-1-937529
Number of titles published annually: 20 Print; 12 CD-ROM; 20 E-Book
Total Titles: 54 Print; 32 CD-ROM; 54 E-Book
Distributed by Lerner Publishing
Foreign Rep(s): Lerner Publishing (Maria Kjoller)
Membership(s): Association of Educational Publishers; The Association of Publishers for Special Sales; IBPA, the Independent Book Publishers Association; Society of Children's Book Writers & Illustrators

**Red Dust Inc**
1148 Fifth Ave, New York, NY 10128
SAN: 203-3860
*Tel:* 212-348-4388
*Web Site:* www.reddustbooks.com
*Key Personnel*
Pres & Publr: Joanna Gunderson *E-mail:* reddustjg@aol.com
Founded: 1961
Works by new writers; fiction, poetry, nonsequential texts.
ISBN Prefix(es): 978-0-87376
Number of titles published annually: 3 Print
Total Titles: 84 Print
*Editorial Office(s):* 845 Hancock St, Brooklyn, NY 11233, Mng Ed: Donald Breckenridge *Tel:* 347-721-7790 *E-mail:* dpbreckenridge@yahoo.com

**Red Hen Press**
PO Box 40820, Pasadena, CA 91114
*Tel:* 626-356-4760 *Fax:* 626-356-9974
*Web Site:* www.redhen.org
*Key Personnel*
Pres & Publr: Mark E Cull *E-mail:* mark@redhen.org
Mng Ed: Kate Gale *E-mail:* kategale@verizon.net
Founded: 1994
Publish perfect bound collections of poetry, short stories & books of a literary nature. Also sponsor several literary awards, along with the literary journal *The Los Angeles Review.*
ISBN Prefix(es): 978-0-9639528; 978-1-888996; 978-1-59709
Number of titles published annually: 20 Print
Total Titles: 350 Print
Imprints: Arktoi Books; Boreal Books; Xeno Books
*Distribution Center:* Chicago Distribution Center, 11030 S Langley, Chicago, IL 60628 *Toll Free Tel:* 800-621-2736 *Toll Free Fax:* 800-621-8476 *E-mail:* orders@press.uchicago.edu
Membership(s): Association of Writers and Writing Programs; Council of Literary Magazines & Presses

**Red Moon Press**
PO Box 2461, Winchester, VA 22604-1661
*Tel:* 540-722-2156
*E-mail:* redmoon@shentel.net
*Web Site:* www.redmoonpress.com
Founded: 1993
Largest & most prestigious publisher of English-language haiku & related forms in the world.
ISBN Prefix(es): 978-1-9657818; 978-1-893959
Number of titles published annually: 10 Print
Total Titles: 110 Print
Imprints: Pond Frog Editions; Soffietto Editions

**Red Rock Press**
331 W 57 St, Suite 175, New York, NY 10019
*Tel:* 212-362-8304 *Fax:* 212-362-6216
*E-mail:* info@redrockpress.com
*Web Site:* www.redrockpress.com
*Key Personnel*
Creative Dir: Ilene Barth
Sales Dir: Richard Barth *E-mail:* richard@redrockpress.com
Founded: 1998
Gift books.
ISBN Prefix(es): 978-0-97143; 978-1-93317
Number of titles published annually: 3 Print
Total Titles: 50 Print

**Red Sea Press Inc**
541 W Ingham Ave, Suite B, Trenton, NJ 08638
*Tel:* 609-695-3200 *Fax:* 609-695-6466
*E-mail:* customerservice@africaworldpressbooks.com
*Web Site:* www.africaworldpressbooks.com
*Key Personnel*
Pres & Publr: Kassahun Checole
Opers Mgr: Senait Kassahun
Founded: 1985
Publisher of books on the Horn of Africa, Latin America; distributor of books on the Third World.
ISBN Prefix(es): 978-0-932415; 978-1-56902
Number of titles published annually: 100 Print
Total Titles: 1,200 Print
Imprints: Karnak House
Foreign Rights: Turnaround Publisher Services (Europe, London)

**Red Wheel/Weiser/Conari**
65 Parker St, Suite 7, Newburyport, MA 01950
*Tel:* 978-465-0504 *Toll Free Tel:* 800-423-7087 (orders) *Fax:* 978-465-0243
*E-mail:* info@rwwbooks.com
*Web Site:* www.redwheelweiser.com
*Key Personnel*
CEO & Pres: Michael Kerber *Tel:* 978-465-0504 ext 1115 *E-mail:* mkerber@rwwbooks.com
Publr: Jan Johnson *Tel:* 415-978-2665 ext 102
Publicity Dir: Bonni Hamilton
Publicist: Kat Salazar
Assoc Prodn Dir: Jordan Overby
Ed: Amber Guetebier
Publg Admin Asst: Kimberly Ehart
Founded: 1956
Self-help, new consciousness, spirituality, inspiration, women's interest & esoteric subjects from many traditions.
ISBN Prefix(es): 978-0-943233 (Conari); 978-0-87728 (Weiser); 978-1-57863 (Weiser); 978-1-59003 (Red Wheel); 978-1-57324 (Conari)
Number of titles published annually: 50 Print
Total Titles: 1,000 Print
Imprints: Hampton Roads Publishing
*Editorial Office(s):* 665 Third Street, Suite 400, San Francisco, CA 94107
Distributor for Nicolas Hays Inc
Foreign Rep(s): Brumby Books (Australia); Deep Books (UK); ITI-Canada (Canada)
Foreign Rights: Linda Biagi (Worldwide)
*Warehouse:* Books International Inc, 22883 Quicksilver Dr, Dulles, VA 20166
Membership(s): ABA

**RedBone Press**
PO Box 15571, Washington, DC 20003
*Tel:* 202-667-0392 *Fax:* 301-588-0588
*E-mail:* info@redbonepress.com
*Web Site:* www.redbonepress.com
*Key Personnel*
Publr: Lisa C Moore
Founded: 1997
Publishes black, gay & lesbian literature.
ISBN Prefix(es): 978-0-9656659; 978-0-9786251
Number of titles published annually: 3 Print
Total Titles: 20 Print; 1 Audio
*Distribution Center:* Small Press Distribution, 1341 Seventh St, Berkeley, CA 94710-1409 *Tel:* 510-524-1668 *Toll Free Tel:* 800-869-7553 *E-mail:* spd@spdbooks.org *Web Site:* www.spdbooks.org
Membership(s): Council of Literary Magazines & Presses

**Redleaf Press**
Division of Think Small
10 Yorkton Ct, St Paul, MN 55117
SAN: 212-8691
*Tel:* 651-641-0508 *Toll Free Tel:* 800-423-8309 *Toll Free Fax:* 800-641-0115
*Web Site:* www.redleafpress.org
*Key Personnel*
Co-Dir: Paul Bloomer *E-mail:* pbloomer@redleafpress.org; David Heath *E-mail:* dheath@redleafpress.org
Mng Ed: Doug Schmitz *E-mail:* dschmitz@redleafpress.org
Mktg Mgr: Eric Johnson *E-mail:* ejohnson@redleafpress.org
Sales Mgr: Inga Weberg *E-mail:* iweberg@redleafpress.org
Founded: 1973
Resources for early childhood professionals including. early childhood curriculum, professional development, family child care business, record keeping & parenting.
ISBN Prefix(es): 978-0-934140; 978-1-884834; 978-1-929610; 978-1-933653; 978-1-60554
Number of titles published annually: 32 Print; 3 CD-ROM; 50 E-Book
Total Titles: 270 Print; 15 CD-ROM; 5 Online; 50 E-Book
Distributed by護Pademelon Press Pty Ltd (Australia)
Foreign Rights: Perseus (Worldwide)
*Distribution Center:* Consortium Book Sales & Distribution, The Keg House, Suite 101, 34 13th Ave NE, Minneapolis, MN 55413 (US book trade & libs) *Tel:* 612-746-2600 *Toll Free Tel:* 800-283-3572 (cust serv) *Fax:* 612-746-2606 *Web Site:* www.cbsd.com
Monarch Books of Canada, 5000 Dufferin St, Downsview, ON M3H 5T5, Canada
Pademelon Press Pty Ltd, Unit 7/3 Packard Ave, Castle Hill, NSW 2154, Australia *Tel:* (02) 9634 4655 *Fax:* (02) 9680 4634
Eurospan Group, 3 Henrietta St, London WC2E 8LU, United Kingdom (UK, Continental Europe, Africa, Asia & Middle East) *Tel:* (01767) 604972 *Fax:* (01767) 601640 *E-mail:* eurospan@turpin-distribution.com
Membership(s): National School Supply & Equipment Association

**Robert D Reed Publishers**
PO Box 1992, Bandon, OR 97411-1192
*Tel:* 541-347-9882 *Fax:* 541-347-9883
*E-mail:* 4bobreed@msn.com
*Web Site:* www.rdrpublishers.com

*Key Personnel*
Publr: Robert D Reed
Founded: 1977
All types of publications for trade, educational institutions, individuals & corporations.
ISBN Prefix(es): 978-1-889710; 978-1-885003; 978-1-931741
Number of titles published annually: 25 Print
Total Titles: 225 Print
Foreign Rep(s): Sylvia Hayse Literary Agency

**Reedswain Inc**
88 Wells Rd, Spring City, PA 19475
*Tel:* 610-495-9578 *Toll Free Tel:* 800-331-5191 *Fax:* 610-495-6632
*E-mail:* orders@reedswain.com
*Web Site:* www.reedswain.com
*Key Personnel*
Pres & Foreign Rts: Richard Kentwell
Founded: 1987
Soccer coaching books.
ISBN Prefix(es): 978-1-8809; 978-1-59164
Number of titles published annually: 10 Print
Total Titles: 190 Print

**The Re-evaluation Counseling Communities**
719 Second Ave N, Seattle, WA 98109
Mailing Address: Main Office Sta, PO Box 2081, Seattle, WA 98111-2081
*Tel:* 206-284-0311 *Fax:* 206-284-8429
*E-mail:* ircc@rc.org
*Web Site:* www.rc.org
*Key Personnel*
Ed: Katie Kauffman
Founded: 1954
Articles about Re-evaluation Counseling (Co-Counseling) - the theory, the practice, the applications & implications.
ISBN Prefix(es): 978-0-911214; 978-0-913937; 978-1-885357; 978-1-58429
Number of titles published annually: 6 Print
Total Titles: 263 Print

**Referee Books**
Imprint of Referee Enterprises Inc
2017 Lathrop Ave, Racine, WI 53405
*Tel:* 262-632-8855 *Toll Free Tel:* 800-733-6100 *Fax:* 262-632-5460
*E-mail:* questions@referee.com
*Web Site:* www.referee.com
*Key Personnel*
Pres: Barry Mano *E-mail:* bmano@naso.org
Founded: 1976
Publish sports officiating publications; magazines, books, manuals & booklets on officiating, umpiring, baseball, basketball, football, soccer, softball & athletics referee books.
ISBN Prefix(es): 978-1-58208; 978-0-9660209
Number of titles published annually: 25 Print
Total Titles: 75 Print

**Reference Publications Inc**
218 Saint Clair River Dr, Algonac, MI 48001
SAN: 208-4392
Mailing Address: PO Box 344, Algonac, MI 48001-0344
*Tel:* 810-794-5722 *Fax:* 810-794-7463
*E-mail:* referencepub@sbcglobal.net
*Key Personnel*
Pres & Ed: Marie Aline Irvine
Dir, Mktg: Dominique Irvine
Legal Coun: John Somers
Founded: 1975
Mail order & reference books. Specialize in botanical & medicinal plants, Americana, Amerindian & African reference books & botanical works.
ISBN Prefix(es): 978-0-917256
Number of titles published annually: 2 Print
Total Titles: 24 Print
Imprints: Encyclopaedia Africana
*Sales Office(s):* PO Box 344, Algonac, MI 48001-0344

**§Reference Service Press**
5000 Windplay Dr, Suite 4, El Dorado Hills, CA 95762-9319
*Tel:* 916-939-9620 *Fax:* 916-939-9626
*E-mail:* info@rspfunding.com
*Web Site:* www.rspfunding.com
*Key Personnel*
Pres: Gail Schlachter, PhD
*E-mail:* gailschlachter@rspfunding.com
Founded: 1975
Online financial aid databases, financial aid directories & resources.
ISBN Prefix(es): 978-1-58841
Number of titles published annually: 15 Print; 56 Online; 10 E-Book
Total Titles: 25 Print; 3 CD-ROM; 56 Online; 15 E-Book
Membership(s): American Indian Library Association; California Library Association; IBPA, the Independent Book Publishers Association

**ReferencePoint Press Inc**
17150 Via del Campo, Suite 205, San Diego, CA 92127
Mailing Address: PO Box 27779, San Diego, CA 92198
*Tel:* 858-618-1314 *Toll Free Tel:* 888-479-6436 *Fax:* 858-618-1730
*E-mail:* orders@referencepointpress.com
*Web Site:* www.referencepointpress.com
*Key Personnel*
Pres & Publr: Dan Leone *Tel:* 858-618-1314 ext 102 *E-mail:* dan@referencepointpress.com
Founded: 2006
Publish series nonfiction for young adults: current issues, health, science & paranormal.
ISBN Prefix(es): 978-1-60152
Number of titles published annually: 75 Print; 75 E-Book
Total Titles: 300 Print; 300 E-Book
Foreign Rep(s): Saunders Book Co (Canada)
*Returns:* Bang Fulfillment, 217 Etak Dr, Brainerd, MN 56401
*Warehouse:* Bang Fulfillment, 217 Etak Dr, Brainerd, MN 56401, Contact: Perry Gienger *Toll Free Tel:* 800-328-0450 *Fax:* 218-829-7145 *E-mail:* perryg@bangprinting.com

**Reformation Heritage Books**
2965 Leonard St NE, Grand Rapids, MI 49525
*Tel:* 616-977-0889 *Fax:* 616-285-3246
*E-mail:* orders@heritagebooks.org
*Web Site:* www.heritagebooks.org
*Key Personnel*
Chmn: Joel R Beeke
Contact: Jonathan Engelsma
Founded: 1993
Sell new & used religious books with emphasis on experiential religion. Also republish out-of-print Puritan works.
ISBN Prefix(es): 978-1-892777
Number of titles published annually: 40 Print
Total Titles: 250 Print; 70 E-Book

**§Regal Books**
Division of Gospel Light
1957 Eastman Ave, Ventura, CA 93003
SAN: 203-3852
*Tel:* 805-644-9721 *Toll Free Tel:* 800-446-7735 (orders)
*Web Site:* www.regalbooks.com; www.gospellight.com
*Key Personnel*
CFO: Todd White
Pres: Bill T Greig, III
Publg Dir: Stan Jantz *E-mail:* stan.jantz@regalbooks.com
Founded: 1933
Faith books. Christian publisher of books & DVDs, with topics ranging from worship to women's needs & from prayer to praise. No unsol mss.
ISBN Prefix(es): 978-0-8307
Number of titles published annually: 50 Print
Total Titles: 500 Print
Foreign Rep(s): Christian Art Distributors (South Africa); CRU Singapore (Singapore); Glad Sounds Sdn Bhd (Malaysia); KI Entertainment (Australia); Kingsway Communications (Ireland, UK); Koorong Books (Australia); OMF Literature Inc (Philippines); Soul Distributors (New Zealand); Trust Media (Ireland, UK)
*Advertising Agency:* Gospel Light Worldwide, Contact: Elaine Montefu *Toll Free Tel:* 800-737-6071 *Fax:* 805-477-4987 *Web Site:* www.glww.org

**§Regal Crest Enterprises LLC**
229 Sheridan Loop, Belton, TX 76513
*Tel:* 409-527-1188 *Toll Free Fax:* 866-294-9628
*E-mail:* info@regalcrestbooks.biz
*Web Site:* www.regalcrest.biz
*Key Personnel*
Owner: Cathy Bryerose
Founded: 2003 (originally in 1999 as Renaissance Alliance Publishing Inc)
Traditional royalty publisher using innovative print technology.
ISBN Prefix(es): 978-1-932300; 978-1-935053
Number of titles published annually: 24 Print; 24 E-Book
Total Titles: 148 Print; 20 E-Book
Imprints: Blue Beacon Books (nonfiction); Mystic Books (paranormal); Quest Books (action, adventure, mystery, police procedure, detective); RCE (drama & general fiction); Silver Dragon Books (science fiction/fantasy); Troubadour Books (poetry, short story, anthology); YA Books (young adult); Yellow Rose Books (romance)
Foreign Rep(s): Bella Distribution Inc (Worldwide); Ingram (Worldwide)
*Distribution Center:* Bella Distribution Inc, 1041 Aenon Church Rd, Tallahassee, FL 32302 *Toll Free Tel:* 800-533-1973
Ingram, One Ingram Blvd, La Vergne, TN 17202

**Regnery Publishing Inc**
Subsidiary of Eagle Publishing Inc
One Massachusetts Ave NW, Washington, DC 20001
*Tel:* 202-216-0600 *Toll Free Tel:* 888-219-4747 *Fax:* 202-216-0612
*Web Site:* www.regnery.com
*Key Personnel*
Pres & Publr: Marjory G Ross
Pres, Eagle Publishing Inc: Jeffrey J Carneal
Dir, Publicity: Alberto Rojas *E-mail:* arojas@eaglepub.com
Dir, Sales: Mark Bloomfield
Exec Ed: Harry W Crocker, III
Foreign Rts: Alex Novak *E-mail:* anovak@eaglepub.com
Perms: Maria Ruhl *E-mail:* mruhl@eaglepub.com
Founded: 1947
Trade book publisher.
ISBN Prefix(es): 978-0-89526; 978-1-59698; 978-1-62157
Number of titles published annually: 35 Print
Total Titles: 400 Print
Imprints: Gateway; Little Patriot Press; Regnery; Regnery History
*Distribution Center:* Perseus Distribution Services, 193 Edwards Dr, Jackson, TN 38301

**Regular Baptist Press**
Division of General Association of Regular Baptist Churches
1300 N Meacham Rd, Schaumburg, IL 60173-4806

*Tel:* 847-843-1600 *Toll Free Tel:* 800-727-4440 (orders only); 888-588-1600 *Fax:* 847-843-3757
*E-mail:* rbp@garbc.org
*Web Site:* www.regularbaptistpress.org
*Key Personnel*
Book Ed & Intl Rts Contact: Norman A Olson *E-mail:* nolson@garbc.org
Founded: 1952
Curriculum & Christian books.
ISBN Prefix(es): 978-0-87227; 978-1-59402
Number of titles published annually: 6 Print

**Renaissance House**
Imprint of Laredo Publishing Co Inc
465 Westview Ave, Englewood, NJ 07631
*Tel:* 201-408-4048 *Fax:* 201-408-5011
*E-mail:* info@renaissancehouse.net
*Web Site:* www.renaissancehouse.net
*Key Personnel*
Pres: Sam Laredo *E-mail:* laredo@renaissancehouse.net
Edit Dir: Raquel Benatar *E-mail:* raquel@renaissancehouse.net
Founded: 1991
Book developer & publisher of high quality illustrated children's books. Specialize in Spanish bilingual market. Works with more than 60 illustrators. Offers editorial services, project development & management.
ISBN Prefix(es): 978-1-56492
Number of titles published annually: 30 Print
Total Titles: 150 Print
Distributed by SRA/McGraw-Hill

**Research & Education Association (REA)**
61 Ethel Rd W, Piscataway, NJ 08854
*Tel:* 732-819-8880 *Fax:* 732-819-8808 (orders)
*E-mail:* info@rea.com
*Web Site:* www.rea.com
*Key Personnel*
Pres: Rich Weisman *E-mail:* rweisman@rea.com
VP, Sales: Roger Romano *E-mail:* rromano@rea.com
VP, Publg: Pamela Weston *E-mail:* pweston@rea.com
Cust Serv Mgr: Rosemarie Hannigan *E-mail:* rhannigan@rea.com
Founded: 1959
Professional books, secondary & college study guides & test preparation books, biology, business, engineering, mathematics, general science, history, social sciences, accounting & computer science.
ISBN Prefix(es): 978-0-87891; 978-0-7386
Number of titles published annually: 50 Print; 10 CD-ROM; 5 Audio
Total Titles: 1,200 Print; 26 CD-ROM; 7 Audio

**Research Press**
2612 N Mattis Ave, Champaign, IL 61822
SAN: 203-381X
Mailing Address: PO Box 9177, Dept 11-W, Champaign, IL 61826-9177
*Tel:* 217-352-3273 *Toll Free Tel:* 800-519-2707 *Fax:* 217-352-1221
*E-mail:* rp@researchpress.com; orders@researchpress.com
*Web Site:* www.researchpress.com
*Key Personnel*
Chmn of the Bd: Cynthia Parkinson Martin
Pres: Judy Parkinson *E-mail:* jparkinson@researchpress.com
Mng Ed & Rts & Perms: Karen Steiner
Prodn Mgr: Jeff Helgesen
Secy: Deborah Wilcoxon
Founded: 1968
ISBN Prefix(es): 978-0-87822
Number of titles published annually: 4 Print
Total Titles: 200 Print; 2 Audio

Foreign Rep(s): Footprint Books (Australia); Incentive Plus (UK)
Foreign Rights: Books Crossing Borders

**§Resource Publications Inc**
160 E Virginia St, Suite 170, San Jose, CA 95112-5876
SAN: 209-3081
*Tel:* 408-286-8505 *Fax:* 408-287-8748
*E-mail:* orders@rpinet.com
*Web Site:* www.rpinet.com
*Key Personnel*
Pres & Publr: William Burns *E-mail:* billb@rpinet.com
Busn Mgr: Mary J Dent *E-mail:* maryd@rpinet.com
Mktg Mgr: Joshua P Burns *E-mail:* joshb@rpinet.com
Founded: 1973
Hardcover & paperback, reference, religious trade & general trade books, textbooks & periodicals with emphasis on peer counseling, applied storytelling, recovery & personal growth & on imagination & creative resources for leaders & artists. Resources primarily for worship & ministry.
ISBN Prefix(es): 978-0-89390
Number of titles published annually: 4 Print; 2 CD-ROM; 3 Online; 2 E-Book
Total Titles: 245 Print; 2 CD-ROM; 3 Online; 12 E-Book; 10 Audio
Foreign Rep(s): Columba Book Service (Europe); Pleroma Catholic Supplies (New Zealand); Rainbow Books (Australia, New Zealand); St Pauls India (India)

**§Fleming H Revell**
Division of Baker Book House Co
PO Box 6287, Grand Rapids, MI 49516-6287
SAN: 203-3801
*Tel:* 616-676-9185 *Toll Free Tel:* 800-877-2665; 800-679-1957 *Fax:* 616-676-9573
*Web Site:* www.revellbooks.com
*Key Personnel*
Pres: Dwight Baker
Mktg Dir: Twila Bennett
Mng Ed: Mary Wenger
Ed: Jennifer Leep
Prodn & ISBN Contact: Robert Bol
Rts & Perms & Intl Rts: Marilyn Gordon
Founded: 1870
Religious.
ISBN Prefix(es): 978-0-8007
Number of titles published annually: 100 Print
Total Titles: 5 Audio
Imprints: Spire Books
Foreign Rep(s): Christian Art (South Africa); David C Cook Distribution (Canada); Marston Book Services Ltd (Europe, UK); Soul Distributors Ltd (New Zealand)
*Shipping Address:* 6030 E Fulton Rd, Ada, MI 49301

**§Review & Herald Publishing Association**
55 W Oak Ridge Dr, Hagerstown, MD 21740
*Tel:* 301-393-3000 *Toll Free Tel:* 800-234-7630 *Fax:* 301-393-4055 (edit); 301-393-3222 (book div)
*E-mail:* editorial@rhpa.org
*Web Site:* www.reviewandherald.com
*Key Personnel*
Pres: Mark B Thomas
Founded: 1849
Religion (Seventh-day Adventist), health, nutrition & education.
ISBN Prefix(es): 978-0-8280
Number of titles published annually: 43 Print
Total Titles: 1,600 Print; 2 CD-ROM; 10 Audio
Foreign Rep(s): Stanborough Press Ltd (England)

**Rhemalda Publishing**
PO Box 1790, Moses Lake, WA 98837
*E-mail:* editor@rhemalda.com; customer_service@rhemalda.com
*Web Site:* rhemalda.com
*Key Personnel*
Pres & Publr: Rhett Hoffmeister
VP: Emmaline Hoffmeister
Founded: 2009
ISBN Prefix(es): 978-0-615-32885-0; 978-0-9827434; 978-1-936850
Number of titles published annually: 15 Print; 12 Online; 12 E-Book
Total Titles: 45 Print; 45 Online; 45 E-Book

**Lynne Rienner Publishers Inc**
1800 30 St, Suite 314, Boulder, CO 80301
SAN: 683-1869
*Tel:* 303-444-6684 *Fax:* 303-444-0824
*E-mail:* questions@rienner.com; cservice@rienner.com
*Web Site:* www.rienner.com
*Key Personnel*
CEO & Pres: Lynne C Rienner
Dir, Mktg & Sales: Sally Glover *E-mail:* sglover@rienner.com
Mgr, Cust Serv: Nancy Spohn
Rts & Perms: Alessandra Downey
Founded: 1984
Scholarly & reference books & journals, college textbooks; comparative politics, US politics, international relations, sociology, Third World literature & literary criticism.
ISBN Prefix(es): 978-0-931477; 978-1-55587; 978-1-56000; 978-1-57454; 978-0-89410; 978-1-58826; 978-1-935049 (FirstForumPress)
Number of titles published annually: 70 Print
Total Titles: 1,050 Print
Divisions: FirstForumPress (scholarly monographs); Kumarian Press
Distributor for Center for US-Mexican Studies; Ayebia Clarke Publishing Ltd (African lit); St Andrews Center for Syrian Studies
Foreign Rep(s): Apac (Asia, The Pacific); Cranbury International LLC (Latin America); Far Eastern Booksellers (Japan); Kinokuniya Co Ltd (Japan); Maruzen Co Ltd (Japan); Palgrave Macmillan (Australia); Turpin Distribution (Europe); Viva (India)
*Warehouse:* 22883 Quicksilver Dr, Dulles, VA 20166, Contact: Vartan Ajamian
Membership(s): AAP
*See separate listing for:*
**Kumarian Press**

**§Rigby**
Imprint of Harcourt Achieve
9205 Southpark Center Loop, Orlando, FL 32819
*Toll Free Tel:* 800-531-5015; 800-289-4490 *Toll Free Fax:* 800-289-3994
*Web Site:* rigby.hmhco.com/en/rigby.htm
*Key Personnel*
Interim CEO: Michael Muldowney
CFO: Martijn Tel
SVP, Sales: Joe McHale
VP, Prod Devt: Lynelle Morgenthaler
VP, Mktg: Carol Wolf
Founded: 1987
Educational materials for PreK, elementary, secondary, adult GED, test preparation, ESL & professional development for educators.
Total Titles: 4,000 Print

**Rio Nuevo Publishers**
451 N Bonita Ave, Tucson, AZ 85745
Mailing Address: PO Box 5250, Tucson, AZ 85703
*Tel:* 520-623-9558 *Toll Free Tel:* 800-969-9558 *Fax:* 520-624-5888 *Toll Free Fax:* 800-715-5888
*E-mail:* info@rionuevo.com (cust serv)
*Web Site:* www.rionuevo.com
*Key Personnel*
Dir, Sales: Suzan Glosser

Founded: 1975
Publisher of fine regional southwestern photographic, cooking & historical books & quality Native American books.
ISBN Prefix(es): 978-1-887896; 978-1-933855
Number of titles published annually: 12 Print
Total Titles: 125 Print
Imprints: Rio Chico (educ & children's books)
Membership(s): Society of Children's Book Writers & Illustrators

**Rising Sun Publishing**
PO Box 70906, Marietta, GA 30007-0906
*Tel:* 770-518-0369 *Toll Free Tel:* 800-524-2813 *Fax:* 770-587-0862
*E-mail:* info@rspublishing.com
*Web Site:* www.rspublishing.com
*Key Personnel*
CFO: Mychal Wynn
Founded: 1982
Primary focus is educational training & materials.
ISBN Prefix(es): 978-1-880463
Number of titles published annually: 5 Print
Total Titles: 32 Print; 4 Audio

**River City Publishing LLC**
1719 Mulberry St, Montgomery, AL 36106
*Tel:* 334-265-6753 *Fax:* 334-265-8880
*E-mail:* sales@rivercitypublishing.com
*Web Site:* www.rivercitypublishing.com
*Key Personnel*
Publr: Carolyn Newman *E-mail:* cjnewman_seacrest@rivercitypublishing.com
Ed: Fran Norris *E-mail:* fnorris@rivercitypublishing.com
Sales Mgr: William Hicks *E-mail:* whicks@rivercitypublishing.com
Founded: 1989
Acquisition, editing, design, composition, marketing & sales of new books. Regional fiction & narrative nonfiction, especially books about the South, civil rights, folk art, contemporary fiction, regionally related travel history.
ISBN Prefix(es): 978-1-881320; 978-0-9622815; 978-1-57966; 978-0-913515
Number of titles published annually: 4 Print; 4 E-Book
Total Titles: 200 Print
Imprints: Elliott & Clark Publishing; River City Kids; Starrhill Press
Membership(s): Southern Independent Booksellers Alliance

**§Riverdale Avenue Books (RAB)**
5676 Riverdale Ave, Bronx, NY 10471
*Tel:* 212-279-6418
*Web Site:* www.riverdaleavebooks.com
*Key Personnel*
Publr: Lori Perkins
Edit Dir: Donald Weise
Founded: 2012
Hybrid publisher of fiction & nonfiction, e-pub, print & audio.
ISBN Prefix(es): 978-1-936833 (Magnus); 978-1-62601 (RAB)
Number of titles published annually: 60 Print; 60 Online; 60 E-Book; 10 Audio
Total Titles: 43 Print; 60 Online; 60 E-Book; 5 Audio
Imprints: RAB Desire (erotica & romance); RAB HSF (horror, science fiction & fantasy); RAB Pop (pop culture); RAB Truth (erotic memoir line); Riverdale Ave Books/Magnus Books (LGBT titles)
Foreign Rights: L Perkins Agency (Emily Keyes)

**Riverhead Books (Hardcover)**
Imprint of Penguin Group (USA) LLC
375 Hudson St, New York, NY 10014
SAN: 282-5074
*Tel:* 212-366-2000
*E-mail:* online@penguinputnam.com
*Web Site:* www.penguinputnam.com; us.penguingroup.com
*Key Personnel*
Pres: Susan Petersen Kennedy
VP & Publr: Geoffrey Kloske
VP, Edit Dir: Rebecca Saletan
VP & Exec Ed: Sarah McGrath
Exec Ed: Jake Morrissey
Sr Ed: Megan Lynch
Dir, Publicity: Jynne Martin
VP, Dir of Mktg (HC), Assoc Publr: Kate Stark
Art Dir: Helen Yentus
Assoc Dir, Publicity: Katharine Freeman
Publicity Mgr: Claire McGinnis
Sr Publicist: Liz Hohenadel
Publicist: Glory Plata
Founded: 1995
ISBN Prefix(es): 978-1-57322
Number of titles published annually: 40 Print
Total Titles: 115 Print
*Advertising Agency:* Mesa Group

**Riverhead Books (Trade Paperback)**
Imprint of Penguin Group (USA) LLC
375 Hudson St, New York, NY 10014
SAN: 282-5074
*Tel:* 212-366-2000
*E-mail:* online@penguinputnam.com
*Web Site:* www.penguinputnam.com; us.penguingroup.com
*Key Personnel*
VP, Mktg Dir (Trade Pbk): Rick Pascocello
Art Dir: Helen Yentus
Founded: 1995
ISBN Prefix(es): 978-1-57322
Number of titles published annually: 37 Print
Total Titles: 400 Print
*Advertising Agency:* Spier NY

**Riverside Publishing**
Subsidiary of Houghton Mifflin Harcourt Publishing Co
3800 Golf Rd, Suite 200, Rolling Meadows, IL 60008
SAN: 213-554X
*Tel:* 630 467-7000 *Toll Free Tel:* 800-323-9540 *Fax:* 630-467-7192 (cust serv)
*E-mail:* rpc_customer_service@hmhpub.com (cust serv)
*Web Site:* www.riversidepublishing.com
*Key Personnel*
Pres: Jim Nicholson
VP, Sales & Mktg: Don Back
Regl VP, Sales (Northern Region): Jeff Squires
Regl VP, Sales (Southern Region): Ellis Tesh
Regl VP, Sales (Western Region): Darlene Hart
VP, Sales Opers: Mort Cohen
Dir, Mktg & Sales Opers: Kim Ross
Natl Dir, Prod Specialization Group: Van Mabie
Founded: 1852 (as Riverside Press)
Develops & sells print & digital assessment tools for the education & clinical markets.
ISBN Prefix(es): 978-0-8292
Number of titles published annually: 20 Print
Imprints: Wintergreen/Orchard House Inc
Foreign Rep(s): ACER (Australia); Artsberg (Hong Kong); Camera-Mundi (Puerto Rico); Nelson Canada (Canada); NFER-Nelson (UK); NZCER (New Zealand); Psicologiay Material-Tecnico (Spain); Taskmaster (UK)

**Rizzoli International Publications Inc**
Subsidiary of RCS Rizzoli Corp New York
300 Park Ave S, 4th fl, New York, NY 10010-5399
*Tel:* 212-387-3400 *Toll Free Tel:* 800-522-6657 (orders only) *Fax:* 212-387-3535
*E-mail:* publicity@rizzoliusa.com
*Web Site:* www.rizzoliusa.com
*Key Personnel*
CFO: Alan Rutsky
VP & Publr: Charles Miers
VP & Dir, Mktg & Sales: Jennifer Pierson
Exec Publicity Dir: Pam Sommers
Dir, Prodn: Maria Pia Gramaglia
Dir, Spec Sales: Tracey Petitt
Assoc Dir, Publicity: Jessica Napp
Mktg Mgr, Creative Servs & Social/New Media: Linda Pricci
Intl Sales Mgr: Susan Masry
Sales Mgr: John Dean
Sr Ed, Architecture: David Morton
Sr Ed, Ex Libris: Alessandra Lusardi
Dist Coord: Jerry Hoffnagle
Founded: 1976
Fine arts, architecture, photography, decorative arts, cookbooks, gardening & landscape design, fashion & sports.
ISBN Prefix(es): 978-0-8478
Number of titles published annually: 100 Print
Imprints: Ex Libris; Flammarion; Marsilio; Pie Books; RCS Libri; Rizzoli First; Rizzoli, New York; SkiraRizzoli Publishing; Universe
Distributed by Random House
Distributor for Editions Flammarion; Skira Editore
*Advertising Agency:* Rizzoli Graphic Studios
*Returns:* Random House, 1019 N State Rd 47, Crawfordsville, IN 47933; Random House of Canada Ltd, 2775 Mattheson Blvd E, Mississauga, ON L4W 4P7, Canada *Toll Free Tel:* 800-733-3000 *Toll Free Fax:* 800-659-2436
*See separate listing for:*
**Universe Publishing**

**The RoadRunner Press**
122 NW 32 St, Oklahoma City, OK 73118
Mailing Address: PO Box 2564, Oklahoma City, OK 73101
*Tel:* 405-524-6205 *Fax:* 405-524-6312
*E-mail:* info@theroadrunnerpress.com; orders@theroadrunnerpress.com
*Web Site:* www.theroadrunnerpress.com
*Key Personnel*
Publr & Ed: Jeanne Devlin *E-mail:* jeanne@theroadrunnerpress.com
Dir, Sales & Mktg: Gaylene Murphy *Tel:* 405-340-7035
Founded: 2010
A small indie publishing house specializing in quality young adult fiction & regional nonfiction as well as select nonfiction & literary fiction.
ISBN Prefix(es): 978-1-937054
Number of titles published annually: 10 Print; 6 E-Book
Total Titles: 10 Print; 3 E-Book
*Returns:* Aero Corp, 1377 Tefft Ct, Saline, MI 48176
*Warehouse:* Aero Corp, 1377 Tefft Ct, Saline, MI 48176
Membership(s): ALA; IBPA, the Independent Book Publishers Association; Midwest Independent Publishers Association; Mountains & Plains Independent Publishers Association; Publishers Association of the West

**Roaring Brook Press**
Member of Macmillan Children's Publishing Group
175 Fifth Ave, New York, NY 10010
*Tel:* 646-307-5151
*Web Site:* us.macmillan.com/roaringbrookpressaspx
*Key Personnel*
Publr: Simon Boughton
Sr Ed, First Second Books: Calista Brill *Tel:* 646-307-5386
Founded: 2002
ISBN Prefix(es): 978-0-7613; 978-1-59643
Number of titles published annually: 50 Print
Imprints: First Second Books

**Roaring Forties Press**
1053 Santa Fe Ave, Berkeley, CA 94706
*Tel:* 510-527-5461
*E-mail:* info@roaringfortiespress.com
*Web Site:* www.roaringfortiespress.com
*Key Personnel*
Founder & Publr: Deirdre Greene *E-mail:* dmg@roaringfortiespress.com
Founder: Nigel Quinney *E-mail:* nq@roaringfortiespress.com
Publisher of travel books & literary fiction.
ISBN Prefix(es): 978-0-9766706; 978-0-9777429; 978-0-9823410; 978-1-938901; 978-0-9843165
Number of titles published annually: 3 Print; 15 E-Book
Total Titles: 17 Print; 35 E-Book
*Distribution Center:* Independent Publishers Group, 814 N Franklin St, Chicago, IL 60610 *Tel:* 312-337-0747 (trade or publr inquiries) *Toll Free Tel:* 800-888-4741 (orders) *Fax:* 312-337-5985 *Web Site:* www.ipgbook.com
Turnaround Publisher Services Ltd, Olympia Trading Estate, Unit 3, Coburg Rd, Wooden Green, London N22 6TZ, United Kingdom *Tel:* (020) 8829 3000 *Web Site:* www.turnaround-uk.com
Membership(s): IBPA, the Independent Book Publishers Association

**James A Rock & Co Publishers**
900 S Irby St, Suite 508, Florence, SC 29501
*Toll Free Tel:* 800-411-2230 *Fax:* 843-395-5975
*E-mail:* jrock@rockpublishing.com
*Web Site:* rockpublishing.com
*Key Personnel*
Publr: James A Rock
Founded: 1977
ISBN Prefix(es): 978-0-918736; 978-1-59663
Number of titles published annually: 20 Print
Total Titles: 76 Print
Imprints: Aonian Press (contemporary, historical & suspense romance); Castle Keep Books (children & young adult); Seaboard Press (nonfiction); Sense of Wonder Press (science fiction, fantasy, horror); Yellowback Mysteries (mystery, detective)
Membership(s): AAP

**RockBench Publishing Corp**
6101 Stillmeadow Dr, Nashville, TN 37211-6518
SAN: 855-5559
*Tel:* 615-831-2277 *Fax:* 615-831-2212
*E-mail:* info@rockbench.com
*Web Site:* www.rockbench.com
*Key Personnel*
Acqs Ed: David C Baker *E-mail:* david@rockbench.com
Circ Mgr: Jane Lawrence *E-mail:* jane@recourses.com
Royalties: Julie Warren *E-mail:* info@recourses.com
Founded: 2008
Publish courageous thought leadership content for the business community.
ISBN Prefix(es): 978-1-60544
Number of titles published annually: 7 Print; 5 E-Book; 2 Audio
Total Titles: 14 Print; 5 E-Book
*Advertising Agency:* faceoutstudio, 520 SW Powerhouse Dr, Suite 628, Bend, OR 97702-1295, Pres: Mr Torrey Sharp *Tel:* 541-323-3220 *Fax:* 541-323-3221 *E-mail:* torrey@faceoutstudio.com *Web Site:* www.faceoutstudio.com
Membership(s): The Association of Publishers for Special Sales; IBPA, the Independent Book Publishers Association

**The Rockefeller University Press**
Unit of Rockefeller University
1114 First Ave, 3rd fl, New York, NY 10065-8325
*Tel:* 212-327-7938 *Fax:* 212-327-8587
*E-mail:* rupress@rockefeller.edu
*Web Site:* www.rupress.org
*Key Personnel*
Fin Dir: Ray Fastiggi *Tel:* 212-327-8567 *E-mail:* fastigg@rockefeller.edu
Prodn Dir: Rob O'Donnell *Tel:* 212-327-8545 *E-mail:* odonner@rockefeller.edu
Mktg Assoc: Laraine Karl *E-mail:* lkarl@rockefeller.edu
Founded: 1906
Currently publishes biomedical journals & books.
ISBN Prefix(es): 978-0-87470
Number of titles published annually: 1 Print
Total Titles: 8 Print; 3 Online; 6 Audio
Foreign Rep(s): Charlesworth (China); iGroup Asia Pacific Ltd (Asia-Pacific)
Membership(s): AAP Professional/Scholarly Publishing Division; Association of American University Presses; Association of Learned & Professional Society Publishers; Society for Scholarly Publishing

**Rocky Mountain Mineral Law Foundation**
9191 Sheridan Blvd, Suite 203, Westminister, CO 80031
*Tel:* 303-321-8100 *Fax:* 303-321-7657
*E-mail:* info@rmmlf.org
*Web Site:* www.rmmlf.org
*Key Personnel*
Exec Dir: Stevia Walther *Tel:* 303-321-8100 ext 101
Assoc Dir: Frances Hartogh *Tel:* 303-321-8100 ext 118; Mark Holland *Tel:* 303-321-8100 ext 106 *E-mail:* mholland@rmmlf.org
Founded: 1955
Natural resources & legal education.
ISBN Prefix(es): 978-0-929047; 978-0-882047
Number of titles published annually: 5 Print
Total Titles: 81 Print; 1 CD-ROM

**Rocky River Publishers LLC**
PO Box 1679, Shepherdstown, WV 25443-1679
*Tel:* 304-876-1868 *Fax:* 304-263-2949
*E-mail:* rockyriverpublishers@citlink.net
*Web Site:* www.rockyriver.com
*Key Personnel*
Pres: Miriam J Wilson
Founded: 1987
High quality books & materials with creative approaches to help children deal with problems & needs they may have from infancy to adulthood.
ISBN Prefix(es): 978-0-944576
Number of titles published annually: 3 Print
Total Titles: 20 Print
Distributed by Follett Library Resources; C E Mendez Foundation Inc

**Rod & Staff Publishers Inc**
Hwy 172, Crockett, KY 41413
Mailing Address: PO Box 3, Crockett, KY 41413-0003
*Tel:* 606-522-4348 *Fax:* 606-522-4896
*Toll Free Fax:* 800-643-1244 (ordering in US)
*Key Personnel*
Busn Mgr: John Martin
Founded: 1958
Religious-story books; church, Sunday & Christian school materials & tracts.
ISBN Prefix(es): 978-0-7399
Number of titles published annually: 20 Print
Total Titles: 700 Print

**Rodale Books**
Imprint of Rodale Inc
400 S Tenth St, Emmaus, PA 18098
SAN: 200-2477
*Tel:* 610-967-5171 *Toll Free Tel:* 800-848-4735 (cust serv)
*E-mail:* customerservice@rodale.com
*Web Site:* www.rodaleinc.com
*Key Personnel*
Chmn & CEO: Maria Rodale *Tel:* 610-967-8550
VP & Publr: Mary Ann Naples
VP, Brand & Digital Communs: Allison Hobson Falkenberry
Exec Ed: Mark Weinstein
Founded: 1930 (by J I Rodale)
Adult trade titles in health & fitness, gardening, cooking, spirituality & pet care.
ISBN Prefix(es): 978-0-87857; 978-1-57954; 978-0-87596; 978-1-4050; 978-1-59486; 978-1-60529; 978-1-60961; 978-1-62336
Number of titles published annually: 100 Print
*Branch Office(s)*
733 Third Ave, 8th fl, New York, NY 10017-3204
Distributed by Macmillan
Foreign Rights: Pan Macmillan (Marei Pittner) (Worldwide exc Canada & USA)
*Distribution Center:* MPS Distribution Center, 16365 James Madison Hwy, Gordonsville, VA 22942-8501 *Toll Free Tel:* 888-330-8477 *Toll Free Fax:* 800-672-2054 *E-mail:* orders@mpsvirginia.com

**Roman Catholic Books**
Division of Catholic Media Apostolate Inc
PO Box 2286, Fort Collins, CO 80522-2286
*Tel:* 970-490-2735 *Fax:* 904-212-1287
*Web Site:* www.booksforcatholics.com
*Key Personnel*
Pres: Roger A McCaffrey *E-mail:* cxpeditor@gmail.com
VP, Mktg: Maureen Williamson *E-mail:* maureen@intrepidgroup.com
Founded: 1981
Traditional Catholic books.
ISBN Prefix(es): 978-0-912141; 978-1-929291; 978-0-9793540; 978-1-934888
Number of titles published annually: 10 Print
Total Titles: 270 Print

**Roncorp Music**
Division of Northeastern Music Publications
PO Box 517, Glenmoore, PA 19343
*Tel:* 610-942-2370 *Fax:* 610-942-0660
*E-mail:* info@nemusicpub.com
*Web Site:* www.nemusicpub.com
*Key Personnel*
Pres: Randy Navarre
Founded: 1978
Music & music texts.
ISBN Prefix(es): 978-0-939103
Number of titles published annually: 15 Print
Total Titles: 300 Print

**Ronin Publishing Inc**
PO Box 22900, Oakland, CA 94609
*Tel:* 510-420-3669 *Fax:* 510-420-3672
*E-mail:* ronin@roninpub.com
*Web Site:* www.roninpub.com
*Key Personnel*
Publr: Beverly Potter *E-mail:* beverly@roninpub.com
Founded: 1983
Small, independent publisher in San Francisco Bay Area.
ISBN Prefix(es): 978-0-914171; 978-1-57951
Number of titles published annually: 6 Print; 8 E-Book
Total Titles: 110 Print; 80 E-Book; 2 Audio
Imprints: And/Or Books; Books for Independent Minds
Foreign Rep(s): Airlift (UK); PGW (Canada)
Foreign Rights: Interlicense (Worldwide)
*Distribution Center:* Publishers Group West, 1700 Fourth St, Berkeley, CA 94710 *Tel:* 510-809-3700 *Fax:* 510-809-3777 *E-mail:* info@pgw.com *Web Site:* www.pgw.com
New Leaf Distributing Co, 401 Thornton Rd, Lithia Springs, GA 30122 *Tel:* 770-948-7845 *Fax:* 770-944-2313 *Web Site:* www.newleaf-dist.com

Membership(s): ABA; The Association of Publishers for Special Sales; IBPA, the Independent Book Publishers Association; Northern California Book Publicity & Marketing Association

**The Rosen Publishing Group Inc**
29 E 21 St, New York, NY 10010
SAN: 203-3720
*Tel:* 212-777-3017 *Toll Free Tel:* 800-237-9932 *Toll Free Fax:* 888-436-4643
*E-mail:* info@rosenpub.com
*Web Site:* www.rosenpublishing.com
*Key Personnel*
Pres: Roger Rosen
Founded: 1950
Hardcover, library editions, vocational guidance; personal guidance; music & art catalogs; drug abuse prevention, self-esteem development, values & ethics, new international writing, multicultural, African heritage, graphic nonfiction, curriculum related nonfiction. Grades PreK-12.
ISBN Prefix(es): 978-0-8239; 978-1-4042
Number of titles published annually: 200 Print
Total Titles: 2,000 Print
Imprints: Power Kids Press
Divisions: Rosen Classroom Books & Materials
*Warehouse:* Maple Press Distribution, 60 Grumbacher Rd, York, PA 17405

**§Ross Books**
PO Box 4340, Berkeley, CA 94704-0340
*Tel:* 510-841-2474 *Fax:* 510-295-2531
*E-mail:* sales@rossbooks.com
*Web Site:* www.rossbooks.com
*Key Personnel*
Owner & Pres: Franz H Ross
Sales: Benny Juarez
Founded: 1977
General trade books & e-Books.
ISBN Prefix(es): 978-0-89496
Number of titles published annually: 4 Print; 1 CD-ROM; 3 E-Book; 1 Audio
Total Titles: 26 Print; 2 CD-ROM; 2 Online; 6 E-Book; 2 Audio
Imprints: Baldar
Membership(s): Northern California Book Publicity & Marketing Association

**Ross Publishing LLC**
392 Central Park W, Suite 20-C, New York, NY 10025-5878
SAN: 201-8969
*Tel:* 212-765-8200
*E-mail:* info@rosspub.com
*Web Site:* www.rosspub.com
*Key Personnel*
Chmn of the Bd & Pres: Norman A Ross *E-mail:* norman@rosspub.com
Founded: 1972
Publisher of reference books (US Census reprints); Slavica, microfilms on Central America, Black Panthers, etc. Request permission for all returns.
ISBN Prefix(es): 978-0-88354
Number of titles published annually: 3 Print
Total Titles: 400 Print; 30 Audio
*Warehouse:* Publishers Storage & Shipping Corp, 46 Development Rd, Fitchburg, MA 01420 *Tel:* 978-345-2121 *Fax:* 978-348-1233

**§Rothstein Associates Inc**
4 Arapaho Rd, Brookfield, CT 06804-3104
*Tel:* 203-740-7400 *Toll Free Tel:* 888-768-4783 *Fax:* 203-740-7401
*E-mail:* info@rothstein.com
*Web Site:* www.rothstein.com
*Key Personnel*
Pres: Philip Jan Rothstein *E-mail:* pjr@rothstein.com
Edit Dir: Kristen Noakes-Fry *Tel:* 727-258-8389 *E-mail:* knfwriter@rothstein.com
Mktg Dir: Terri Mitchem *Tel:* 352-596-1192 *E-mail:* mtmitchem@rothstein.com
Creative Mktg: Kathryn Kavicky *Tel:* 203-388-8641 *E-mail:* kathryn@rothstein.com
Founded: 1985
Publish books & software for business.
ISBN Prefix(es): 978-0-9641648; 978-1-931332
Number of titles published annually: 20 Print; 6 CD-ROM; 12 E-Book
Total Titles: 80 Print; 36 CD-ROM; 25 E-Book

**Rough Guides**
Subsidiary of Pearson PLC
375 Hudson St, New York, NY 10014
SAN: 282-5074
*Toll Free Tel:* 800-631-8571
*E-mail:* mail@roughguides.com
*Web Site:* www.roughguides.com
*Key Personnel*
Mng Ed (US): Andrew Rosenberg
Dir, New Media (US): Jennifer Gold
Sr Mktg Mgr (US): Megan Kennedy
Prodn Dir (UK): Aimee Hampson
Publr (UK): Mark Ellingham
Travel Publr (UK): Martin Dunford
Founded: 1982
Travel guides; phrasebooks, music & film reference; pop culture; city & country maps; world & Internet reference.
ISBN Prefix(es): 978-1-85828; 978-1-84353
Number of titles published annually: 60 Print; 10 E-Book
Total Titles: 425 Print; 40 E-Book
*Foreign Office(s):* 80 Strand, London WC2R 0RL, United Kingdom *Tel:* (020) 7010-3700 *Fax:* (020) 7010-6767
Distributed by Penguin Group (USA) LLC
*Orders to:* 405 Murray Hill Pkwy, East Rutherford, NJ 07073 *Toll Free Tel:* 800-526-0275 *Toll Free Fax:* 800-227-9604
*Returns:* 199 Pearson Pkwy, Lebanon, IN 46052

**§The Rough Notes Co Inc**
Subsidiary of Insurance Publishing Plus Corp
11690 Technology Dr, Carmel, IN 46032-5600
*Tel:* 317-582-1600 *Toll Free Tel:* 800-428-4384 (cust serv) *Fax:* 317-816-1000 *Toll Free Fax:* 800-321-1909
*E-mail:* rnc@roughnotes.com
*Web Site:* www.roughnotes.com
*Key Personnel*
VP & Natl Sales Dir: Eric Hall *E-mail:* ehall@roughnotes.com
Opers Mgr: Sam Berman
Founded: 1878
Technical/educational reference material specific to the property/casualty insurance industry.
ISBN Prefix(es): 978-1-56461
Number of titles published annually: 10 Print
Total Titles: 40 Print; 4 Online
*Advertising Agency:* AdCom Group

**Routledge**, see Psychology Press

**Routledge/Taylor & Francis**
Member of Taylor & Francis Group
711 Third Ave, 8th fl, New York, NY 10017
SAN: 213-196X
*Tel:* 212-216-7800 *Toll Free Tel:* 800-634-7064 (orders) *Fax:* 212-564-7854
*Web Site:* www.routledge.com
Founded: 1836
Academic books in the humanities, social & behavioral sciences. Academic reference. Professional titles in architecture, education & the behavioral sciences.
ISBN Prefix(es): 978-0-915202 (formerly Accelerated Development); 978-1-55959 (formerly Accelerated Development); 978-0-87630 (formerly Brunner-Routledge); 978-1-57958 (formerly Fitzroy Dearborn); 978-0-8240 (formerly Garland); 978-0-8153 (formerly Garland); 978-0-415 (Routledge); 978-0-87830 (Theatre Arts); 978-1-85000 (formerly RoutledgeFalmer); 978-0-7007 (formerly Routledge Curzon); 978-0-419 (formerly Spon); 978-0-946653 (formerly Europa); 978-1-85743 (formerly Europa); 978-0-7494 (formerly Kogan Page); 978-90-5701 (formerly Gordon & Breach); 978-1-58391 (formerly BrunnerRoutledge); 978-1-88496 (formerly Fitzroy Dearborn); 978-90-5702 (formerly Harwood Academic); 978-3-7186 (formerly Harwood Academic); 978-90-5823 (formerly Harwood Academic); 978-0-19713 (formerly Routledge Curzon); 978-0-72860 (formerly Routledge Curzon); 978-0-75070 (formerly RoutledgeFalmer)
Number of titles published annually: 2,000 Print; 2,000 Online; 2,000 E-Book
Total Titles: 33,000 Print; 21,000 Online; 21,000 E-Book
Imprints: CRC Press; Garland Science; Psychology Press; Routledge
*Sales Office(s):* Taylor & Francis, 6000 Broken Sound Pkwy, Suite 300, Boca Raton, FL 33487, VP, Sales: Dennis Weiss *Tel:* 561-994-0555 *Toll Free Tel:* 800-272-7737 *Fax:* 561-989-8732 *Toll Free Fax:* 800-374-3401
*Foreign Office(s):* 2 Park Sq, Milton Park, Abingdon Oxon OX14 4RN, United Kingdom, Group Sales Dir: Christoph Chesher *Tel:* (020) 7017 6000 *Fax:* (020) 7017 6699 *E-mail:* book.orders@tandf.co.uk
Distributor for David Fulton
Foreign Rights: Jennifer Strong (Worldwide)
*Warehouse:* Taylor & Francis, 7625 Empire Dr, Florence, KY 41042-2919 *Toll Free Tel:* 800-634-7064 *Toll Free Fax:* 800-248-4724 *E-mail:* orders@taylorandfrancis.com

**Rowman & Littlefield Publishers Inc**
4501 Forbes Blvd, Suite 200, Lanham, MD 20706
SAN: 208-5143
*Tel:* 301-459-3366 *Toll Free Tel:* 800-462-6420 (cust serv) *Fax:* 301-429-5748
*Web Site:* www.rowmanlittlefield.com
*Key Personnel*
Group CFO & Pres: Jed Lyons
CFO: George Franzak
EVP, Fin & Opers: Robert Marsh
SVP & Exec Ed: Jonathan Sisk *E-mail:* jsisk@rowmanlittlefield.com
Rts & Perms Dir: Clare Cox *Tel:* 301-459-3366 ext 308 *E-mail:* ccox@rowman.com
Sales Dir: Sheila Burnett *Tel:* 301-459-3366 ext 5606 *E-mail:* sburnett@rowmanlittlefield.com
Exec Ed: Charles Harmon
Founded: 1949
Policy studies; supplemental books & monographs, academic publisher.
ISBN Prefix(es): 978-0-8476; 978-0-7425
Number of titles published annually: 350 Print
Total Titles: 2,000 Print
*Foreign Office(s):* 10 Thornbury Rd, Plymouth, Devon PL6 7PP, United Kingdom, Contact: Suzanne Wheatley *Tel:* (05602) 698234 *Fax:* (05602) 698234 *E-mail:* swheatley@rowman.com
Foreign Rep(s): Academic Marketing Services Pty Ltd (Botswana, Namibia, South Africa, Zimbabwe); APD Singapore Pte Ltd (Brunei, Cambodia, Indonesia, Laos, Malaysia, Singapore, Thailand, Vietnam); Aristotle House (Simons Watts) (Cameroon, Ethiopia, The Gambia, Ghana, Kenya, Malawi, Mauritius, Nigeria, Tanzania, Uganda); Asia Publishers Service Ltd (China, Hong Kong, Korea, Philippines); Avicenna Partnership Ltd (Middle East); Cranbury International LLC (Caribbean, Central America, Mexico, Puerto Rico, South America); Durnell Marketing Ltd (Europe); Inbooks (Australia, New Zealand, Papua New Guinea); Overleaf (Bangladesh, Bhutan, India, Nepal, Sri Lanka); Publishers Representatives (Pakistan); Quantum

Publishing Solutions Ltd (UK); United Publishers Services Ltd (Japan)
*Warehouse:* 15200 NBN Way, Warehouse C, Blue Ridge Summit, PA 17214 *Tel:* 717-794-3800 *Fax:* 717-794-3803

**Roxbury Publishing Co**
Imprint of Oxford University Press
2001 Evans Rd, Cary, NC 27513
SAN: 213-6422
*Toll Free Tel:* 800-280-0280; 800-451-7556 (orders); 800-455-9714 *Fax:* 919-677-8877; 919-677-1303
*E-mail:* highered.us@oup.com; custserv.us@oup.com
*Web Site:* www.us.oup.com/us/catalog/he/; www.roxbury.net
Founded: 1981
College textbooks & supplements, criminal justice, corrections, family studies.
ISBN Prefix(es): 978-0-935732; 978-1-931719; 978-1-891487; 978-1-933220
Number of titles published annually: 20 Print
Total Titles: 125 Print

**Royal Fireworks Press**
First Ave, Unionville, NY 10988
Mailing Address: PO Box 399, Unionville, NY 10988
*Tel:* 845-726-4444 *Fax:* 845-726-3824
*E-mail:* mail@rfwp.com
*Web Site:* www.rfwp.com
*Key Personnel*
Pres: Dr Tom M Kemnitz *E-mail:* tmk@rfwp.com
Dir, Order Dept & Cust Rel: Margaret Foley
Founded: 1977
Educational materials for gifted children, their parents & teachers; reading materials; adult literacy/education materials; fiction series for middle school: mystery & adventure; novels of growing up; young adult science fiction; youth against violence early childhood program (K-3).
ISBN Prefix(es): 978-0-89824; 978-0-88092
Number of titles published annually: 60 Print; 10 CD-ROM; 10 Audio
Total Titles: 997 Print; 10 CD-ROM; 12 Audio
Distributor for KAV Books; Silk Label Books; Trillium Press

**§Running Press Book Publishers**
Member of The Perseus Books Group
2300 Chestnut St, Philadelphia, PA 19103-4399
SAN: 204-5702
*Tel:* 215-567-5080 *Toll Free Tel:* 800-343-4499 (cust serv & orders) *Fax:* 215-568-2919 *Toll Free Fax:* 800-453-2884 (cust serv & orders)
*E-mail:* perseus.promos@perseusbooks.com
*Web Site:* www.runningpress.com
*Key Personnel*
Div Publr: Christopher Navratil
VP, Mktg Dir: Allison Devlin
VP, Sales: Matty Goldberg
Design Dir: Frances Soo Ping Chow
Edit Dir: Jennifer Kasius
Edit Dir, Running Press Miniature Editions: Jennifer Leczkowski
Sr Ed: Kristen Wiewora
Ed: Cindy de la Hoz; Jordana Tusman
Ed, Running Press Children's: Lisa Cheng
Publicity Mgr: Seta Zink
Sr Publicist: Gigi Lamm
Digital Mktg Assoc: Stephanie Dennis
Founded: 1972
Hardcover & paperback trade books; art, craft/how-to, general nonfiction, children's books, promotional books, notebooks, journals & Miniature Editions™, cookbooks, books & products.
ISBN Prefix(es): 978-1-56138; 978-0-7624
Number of titles published annually: 150 Print
Total Titles: 2,000 Print; 6 CD-ROM
Imprints: Courage Books (illustrated gift books, promotional titles); Running Press; Running Press Kids; Running Press Miniature Editions
Distributor for Wine Enthusiast
Foreign Rep(s): Book Promotions (Nicky Stubbs) (South Africa); Gilles Fauveau (Japan, Korea); Jaime Gregorio (Philippines); Sharad Mohan (Bangladesh, India, Maldives, Nepal, Pakistan, Sri Lanka); New South Books (Australia, New Zealand); Perseus Books Group UK (Europe, Ireland, UK); Perseus International (Suk Lee) (Middle East); Perseus International (all other territories, Caribbean, Latin America); June Poonpanich (Cambodia, Indonesia, Laos, Thailand, Vietnam); Wei Zhao (China, Hong Kong, Taiwan)
Foreign Rights: Anthea Agency (Katalina Sabeva) (Bulgaria); Bardon-Chinese Media Agency (David Tsai) (China, Taiwan); Raquel de la Concha Agencia Literaria (Raquel de la Concha & Marilu Casquero) (Brazil, Latin America, Portugal, Spain); Duran Kim Agency (Duran Kim & Joe Moon) (Korea); Paul & Peter Fritz Agency (Peter Fritz, Christian Dittus & Antonia Fritz) (Germany); Deborah Harris Agency (Efrat Lev) (Israel); Anna Jarota Agency (Anna Jarota) (France); Nurcihan Kesim Literary Agency (Turkey); Alexander Korzhenevski Agency (Alexander & Tania Korzhenevski) (Russia); Livia Stoia Agency (Livia Stoia & Mirela Calota) (Albania, Bosnia and Herzegovina, Croatia, Macedonia, Montenegro, Romania, Serbia, Slovenia); Maxima Creative Agency (Santo Manurung) (Indonesia); Kristin Olson Literary Agency (Kristin Olson) (Czech Republic, Slovakia); Oxford Literary & Rights Agency (Hana Whitton) (Ukraine); Read n' Right Agency (Nike Davarinou) (Greece); Lennart Sane Agency (Philip Sane) (Scandinavia); Santachiara Literary Agency (Roberto Santachiara) (Italy); Sebes & Van Gelderen Literary Agency (Paul Sebes & Mariska Kleinhoonte van Os) (Netherlands); Torus-Books Literary & Scouting Agency Ltd (Gynn Kalman) (Hungary); Tuttle-Mori Agency (Mr Thananchai Pandey) (Thailand, Vietnam); Tuttle-Mori Agency Inc (Manami Tamaoki & Asako Kawachi) (Japan)
*Orders to:* Raincoast Books, 2440 Viking Way, Richmond, BC V6V 1N2, Canada *Toll Free Tel:* 800-663-5714 *Toll Free Fax:* 800-565-3770 *E-mail:* orders@raincoastbooks.com; Grantham Book Services, Trent Rd, Grantham NG31 7XQ, United Kingdom (UK, Europe & Ireland) *Tel:* (0147) 654 1080 *Fax:* (0147) 654 1061 *E-mail:* orders@gbs.tbs-ltd.co.uk
*Distribution Center:* 210 American Dr, Jackson, TN 38301 *Toll Free Tel:* 800-343-4499 *Toll Free Fax:* 800-351-5073

**Russell Sage Foundation**
112 E 64 St, New York, NY 10065
SAN: 201-4521
*Tel:* 212-750-6000 *Toll Free Tel:* 800-524-6401 *Fax:* 212-371-4761
*E-mail:* info@rsage.org
*Web Site:* www.russellsage.org
*Key Personnel*
Pres: Eric Wanner
Dir, Pubns: Suzanne Nichols
Dir, Communs: David Haproff
Founded: 1907
Sociology, economics, political science.
ISBN Prefix(es): 978-0-87154
Number of titles published annually: 25 Print
Total Titles: 1,000 Print
Foreign Rep(s): University Presses Marketing (Continental Europe, Ireland, Israel, UK)
*Advertising Agency:* Verso Book Advertising Inc
*Shipping Address:* CUP Services, 750 Cascadilla St, Ithaca, NY 14851

**Russian Information Service Inc**
PO Box 567, Montpelier, VT 05601
*Tel:* 802-223-4955
*E-mail:* editors@russianlife.com
*Web Site:* www.russianlife.com
*Key Personnel*
Pres & Publr: Paul E Richardson *E-mail:* paulr@russianlife.com
Founded: 1990
Publish magazines, books, info, maps for business & independent travel to Russia.
ISBN Prefix(es): 978-1-880100
Number of titles published annually: 3 Print; 3 E-Book
Total Titles: 20 Print; 20 E-Book
Imprints: Edward & Dee

**Russian Life Magazine**, see Russian Information Service Inc

**Rutgers University Press**
Division of Rutgers, The State University
106 Somerset St, 3rd fl, New Brunswick, NJ 08901
SAN: 203-364X
*Tel:* 858-445-7784 (edit); 848-445-7788 *Toll Free Tel:* 800-848-6224 (orders only) *Fax:* 732-745-4935 (acqs, edit, mktg, perms & prodn) *Toll Free Fax:* 800-272-6817 (fulfillment)
*Web Site:* rutgerspress.rutgers.edu
*Key Personnel*
Dir: Marlie Wasserman *E-mail:* marlie@rutgers.edu
Assoc Dir & Ed-in-Chief: Leslie Mitchner *E-mail:* lmitch@rutgers.edu
Mktg & Sales Dir: Elizabeth Scarpelli *E-mail:* escarpel@rutgers.edu
Pre-Press Dir: Marilyn A Campbell *E-mail:* marilync@rutgers.edu
E-Mktg Mgr & Webmaster: Brice Hammack *E-mail:* bhammack@rutgers.edu
Publicity Mgr: Lisa Fortunato *E-mail:* jwi@rutgers.edu
Rts Mgr & Asst to Dir: Allyson Fields *E-mail:* amfields@rutgers.edu
Exec Ed, Clinical Health & Medicine: Dana Dreibelbis *Tel:* 848-445-7792 *E-mail:* dana.dreibelbis@rutgers.edu
Ed: Katie Keeran *Tel:* 848-445-7786 *E-mail:* ckeeran@rutgers.edu
Acq Ed: Peter Mickulas *E-mail:* mickulas@rutgers.edu
Edit Prodn Coord: Ann Hegeman *E-mail:* hegeman@rutgers.edu
Edit Asst: Katie Keeran
Founded: 1936
Scholarly, but accessible mss in the social sciences, sciences, humanities & regional books.
ISBN Prefix(es): 978-0-8135
Number of titles published annually: 90 Print; 80 E-Book
Total Titles: 3,000 Print; 700 Online; 780 E-Book
Foreign Rep(s): East-West Export Books (Australia, Far East, New Zealand); Eurospan (Europe); Rutgers University Press (Africa, Latin America, Mideast); Scholarly Book Services Inc (Canada)
*Returns:* Maple Vail Distribution, 704 Legionaire Dr, Fredericksburg, PA 17026
*Warehouse:* Maple Vail Distribution, 704 Legionaire Dr, Fredericksburg, PA 17026
Membership(s): American Association of University Presses

**§Saddleback Educational Publishing**
3120-A Pullman St, Costa Mesa, CA 92626
SAN: 860-0902
*Tel:* 714-640-5200 *Toll Free Tel:* 888-SDLBACK (735-2225); 800-637-8715 *Fax:* 714-640-5297 *Toll Free Fax:* 888-734-4010
*E-mail:* contact@sdlback.com
*Web Site:* www.sdlback.com

*Key Personnel*
Pres: Arianne McHugh
Founded: 1982
Publish high-interest, low-readabilty material for middle school & high school. Solutions for struggling learners.
ISBN Prefix(es): 978-1-56254; 978-1-59905; 978-1-6165
Number of titles published annually: 200 Print; 10 CD-ROM; 20 E-Book; 10 Audio
Total Titles: 2,000 Print; 150 CD-ROM; 400 E-Book; 150 Audio
Distributed by Children's Plus; Delaney; Follett
Membership(s): American Educational Publishers; Educational Book & Media Association; National School Supply & Equipment Association

**§William H Sadlier Inc**
9 Pine St, New York, NY 10005
SAN: 204-0948
*Tel:* 212-227-2120 *Toll Free Tel:* 800-221-5175 (cust serv) *Fax:* 212-312-6080
*Web Site:* www.sadlier.com
*Key Personnel*
Chmn of the Bd: Frank S Dinger
Treas: Raymond Sagan
Pres: William S Dinger
EVP & Publr, Sadlier: Rosemary Calicchio
VP & Dir, Mktg: Alexandra Rivas-Smith
VP & Natl Field Sales Mgr: John Bonenberger
VP & Natl Sales Administrator: Kevin O'Donnell
Creative Dir: Vincent Gallo
Gen Coun: Angela Dinger
Cust Serv: Melissa Gibbons
Founded: 1832
Pre-school, elementary & secondary textbooks on catechetics, sacraments, reading/language arts, mathematics; adult catechetical programs.
ISBN Prefix(es): 978-0-8215
Number of titles published annually: 4 Print
Divisions: Sadlier; Sadlier-Oxford

**§SAE (Society of Automotive Engineers International)**
400 Commonwealth Dr, Warrendale, PA 15096-0001
SAN: 216-0811
*Tel:* 724-776-4841; 724-776-4970 (outside US & CN) *Toll Free Tel:* 877-606-7323 (cust serv) *Fax:* 724-776-0790 (cust serv)
*E-mail:* publications@sae.org; customerservice@sae.org
*Web Site:* www.sae.org
*Key Personnel*
CEO: David L Schutt
Pres: Donald Hillebrand
Treas: Ronald Rath
Founded: 1905
Scientific & technical publications.
ISBN Prefix(es): 978-0-89883; 978-1-56091; 978-0-7680
Number of titles published annually: 150 Print
Total Titles: 650 Print; 23 CD-ROM; 1 Online; 15 E-Book; 1 Audio
*Branch Office(s)*
1200 "G" St NW, Suite 800, Washington, DC 20005 *Tel:* 202-463-7318
Automotive Headquarters, 755 W Big Beaver Rd, Suite 1600, Troy, MI 48084 *Tel:* 248-273-2455 *Fax:* 248-273-2494
5 Research Dr, Greenville, SC 29607 *Tel:* 724-776-4841
*Foreign Office(s):* SAE International China Office, Rm 3037, 3F, Silver Ct, No 85 Taoyuan Rd, Huangpu District, Shanghai 200021, China
Aerospace Standards Europe Office, One York St, London W1U 6PA, United Kingdom *Tel:* (020) 70341250
Distributor for Coordinating Research Council Inc
Foreign Rep(s): Aeromarine Vehicles (Singapore); Allied Publishers Pvt Ltd (India); Booknet Co Ltd (Thailand); China National Publications (China); China Publishers Marketing (China); EBSCO Korea (Korea); Eurospan (Marc Bedwell) (Asia-Pacific exc China); Eurospan Group (Africa, Australasia, Brazil, Europe, Oceania); Eurospan India (India); GDI Co Ltd (Korea); Kinokuniya Co Ltd (Japan); Maruzen Co Book Division (Japan); Normdocs (Russia); PB for Books (Pathumthani) Co Ltd (Thailand); SAE Australasia (Australasia, Oceania); SAE Brasil (Brazil); SAE International China Office (China); SAE of Japan (Japan); Ta Tong Book Co Ltd (Taiwan); UBS Library Services Pte Ltd (Singapore); UBSD Distrubution Sdn Bhd (Malaysia); YPJ Publications & Distributors Sdn Bhd (Malaysia)

**Safari Press**
15621 Chemical Lane, Bldg B, Huntington Beach, CA 92649
*Tel:* 714-894-9080 *Toll Free Tel:* 800-451-4788 *Fax:* 714-894-4949
*E-mail:* info@safaripress.com
*Web Site:* www.safaripress.com
*Key Personnel*
CEO: Ludo J Wurfbain
Chief Ed: J Neufeld
Founded: 1984
Specialize in big-game hunting, firearms, wingshooting, Africana & sporting; hardcover trade & limited editions.
ISBN Prefix(es): 978-0-924357; 978-0-940143; 978-1-57157
Number of titles published annually: 10 Print
Total Titles: 250 Print
Distributor for Quiller

**Safer Society Foundation Inc**
29 Union St, Brandon, VT 05733
Mailing Address: PO Box 340, Brandon, VT 05733-0340
*Tel:* 802-247-3132 *Fax:* 802-247-4233
*E-mail:* info@safersociety.org
*Web Site:* www.safersociety.org
Founded: 1985
Specialize in titles relating to the prevention & treatment of sexual abuse.
ISBN Prefix(es): 978-1-884444
Number of titles published annually: 4 Print
Total Titles: 80 Print
Imprints: Safer Society Press
Foreign Rep(s): Open Leaves Books (Australia); Visions Book Store Ltd (Canada)
Membership(s): IBPA, the Independent Book Publishers Association

**Sagamore Publishing LLC**
1807 Federal Dr, Urbana, IL 61801
SAN: 292-5788
*Tel:* 217-359-5940 *Toll Free Tel:* 800-327-5557 (orders) *Fax:* 217-359-5975
*E-mail:* books@sagamorepub.com
*Web Site:* www.sagamorepub.com
*Key Personnel*
CEO & Publr: Dr Joseph J Bannon, Sr
Pres & Intl Rts: Peter L Bannon
Dir, Mktg & Sales: William Anderson
Founded: 1974
ISBN Prefix(es): 978-0-915611; 978-1-57167
Number of titles published annually: 15 Print
Total Titles: 210 Print; 6 Online
Distributor for American Academy for Park & Recreation Administration
Foreign Rep(s): Gazelle Book Services Ltd (Continental Europe, Ireland, UK); HM Leisure Planning (Australia, New Zealand)

**SAGE Publications**
2455 Teller Rd, Thousand Oaks, CA 91320
*Toll Free Tel:* 800-818-7243 *Toll Free Fax:* 800-583-2665
*E-mail:* info@sagepub.com
*Web Site:* www.sagepub.com
*Key Personnel*
Founder, Chmn & Publr: Sara Miller McCune
CEO & Pres: Blaise R Simqu
Founded: 1965
Professional & reference books, supplementary texts, journals, papers & newsletters in the social & behavioral sciences.
ISBN Prefix(es): 978-0-8039
Number of titles published annually: 275 Print
Total Titles: 5,731 Print
Imprints: Corwin Press; CQ Press; Learning Matters; Adam Matthew; Pine Forge Press
Subsidiaries: Corwin Press Inc
Divisions: Scolari
*Foreign Office(s):* Sage Publications India Pvt Ltd, B1/I-1 Mohan Cooperative Indus Area, Mathura Rd, New Delhi 110 044, India *Tel:* (011) 4053 9222 *Fax:* (011) 4053 9234
SAGE Publications Asia-Pacific Pte Ltd, 3 Church St, Samsung Hub, Unit 10-04, Singapore 049483, Singapore *Tel:* 6220-1800 *Fax:* 6438-1008 *E-mail:* apac-librarysales@sagepub.co.uk
Sage Publications Ltd, One Oliver's Yard, 55 City Rd, London EC1Y 1SP, United Kingdom *Tel:* (020) 7324 8500 *Fax:* (020) 7324 8600
Foreign Rep(s): Astam Books Pty Ltd (Australia, New Zealand); Sage Publications India Pvt Ltd (India, South Asia); Sage Publications Ltd (Africa, Asia-Pacific, Europe, Middle East, UK); United Publishers Services Ltd (Japan, Korea)
*See separate listing for:*
**CQ Press**

**Saint Andrews College Press**
Subsidiary of Saint Andrews Presbyterian College
1700 Dogwood Mile, Laurinburg, NC 28352-5598
*Tel:* 910-277-5310 *Fax:* 910-277-5020
*E-mail:* press@sapc.edu
*Web Site:* www.sapc.edu/sapress
*Key Personnel*
Ed: Cate Johnson
Founded: 1969
ISBN Prefix(es): 978-0-932662; 978-1-879934
Number of titles published annually: 5 Print
Total Titles: 100 Print

**St Anthony Messenger Press**, see Franciscan Media

**St Augustine's Press Inc**
PO Box 2285, South Bend, IN 46680-2285
*Tel:* 574-291-3500 *Toll Free Tel:* 888-997-4994 *Fax:* 574-291-3700
*Web Site:* www.staugustine.net
*Key Personnel*
Pres & Publr: Bruce Fingerhut *E-mail:* bruce@staugustine.net
Prodn: Benjamin Fingerhut *Tel:* 773-983-8471 *E-mail:* benjaminfingerhut@yahoo.com
Founded: 1996
Scholarly & trade publishing in humanities; Ad Agency, Design Promotion.
ISBN Prefix(es): 978-1-890318; 978-1-883357; 978-1-58731
Number of titles published annually: 30 Print
Total Titles: 450 Print
Imprints: Carthage Reprints; William of Moerbeke Translation (literal translations of major works in philosopy, theology & cultural history)
*Editorial Office(s):* 17917 Killington Way, South Bend, IN 46614-9773
*Sales Office(s):* University of Chicago Press, Sales Dept, 1429 E 60 St, Chicago, IL 60637-2954, Sales Dir: John Kessler *Tel:* 773-702-7248 *Fax:* 773-702-9756 *E-mail:* jkessler@press.uchicago.edu
Distributed by University of Chicago Press

Distributor for Dumb Ox Books (publishes the Aristotelian Commentaries of Thomas Aquinas & like works); Fidelity Press (culture, history & politics from a Catholic viewpoint); Hardwood Press (trade books, mostly in sports & regional works)
Foreign Rights: Jeremy Beer (Worldwide exc USA)
*Billing Address:* Chicago Distribution Center, 11030 S Langley Ave, Chicago, IL 60628-3893, Sue Tranchita *Tel:* 773-702-7014 *Fax:* 773-702-7002 *E-mail:* st@press.uchicago.edu
*Orders to:* Chicago Distribution Center, 11030 S Langley Ave, Chicago, IL 60628-3893, Karen Hyzy *Tel:* 773-702-7000 *Toll Free Tel:* 800-621-2736 *Fax:* 773-702-7212 *Toll Free Fax:* 800-621-8476 *E-mail:* kh@press.uchicago.edu
*Returns:* Chicago Distribution Center, 11030 S Langley Ave, Chicago, IL 60628-3893, Sue Tranchita *Tel:* 773-702-7014 *Fax:* 773-702-7002 *E-mail:* st@press.uchicago.edu
*Shipping Address:* Chicago Distribution Center, 11030 S Langley Ave, Chicago, IL 60628-3893, Karen Hyzy *Tel:* 773-702-7000 *Toll Free Tel:* 800-621-2736 *Fax:* 773-702-7212 *Toll Free Fax:* 800-621-8476 *E-mail:* kh@press.uchicago.edu
*Warehouse:* Chicago Distribution Center, 11030 S Langley Ave, Chicago, IL 60628-3893, Sue Tranchita *Tel:* 773-702-7014 *Fax:* 773-702-7002 *E-mail:* st@press.uchicago.edu
*Distribution Center:* Chicago Distribution Center, 11030 S Langley Ave, Chicago, IL 60628-3893 *Toll Free Tel:* 800-621-8471 *Toll Free Fax:* 800-621-8471 *E-mail:* kh@press.uchicago.edu

**St Herman Press**
Subsidiary of Brotherhood of St Herman of Alaska
10 Beegum Gorge Rd, Platina, CA 96076
SAN: 661-583X
Mailing Address: PO Box 70, Platina, CA 96076-0070
*Tel:* 530-352-4430 *Fax:* 530-352-4432
*E-mail:* stherman@stherman.com
*Web Site:* www.stherman.com
*Key Personnel*
CFO: Nicholas Liebmann
Pres: Abbott Hilarian
Secy: Paisius Bjerke
Founded: 1963
Publisher of books about the Orthodox Christian faith & Orthodox monasticism. Special emphasis on recent saints & spirituality, curriculum & textbooks.
ISBN Prefix(es): 978-0-938635; 978-1-887904
Number of titles published annually: 3 Print
Total Titles: 70 Print
Imprints: Brotherhood of St Herman of Alaska; Fr Seraphim Rose Foundation; St Herman Press; St Paisius Abbey; St Paisius Missionary School; St Xenia Skete; Valaam Society of America
*Foreign Office(s):* V Ivlenkov, Box 1854 Q, Melbourne, Victoria 3001, Australia
Orthodox Christian Books Ltd, Townhouse Farm, Studio 7, Alsager Rd, Audley, Staffordshire ST7 8JQ, United Kingdom, CEO: Nicholas Chapman *Fax:* (011)178-272-3930 *E-mail:* 101600.262@compuserve.com
Distributed by Light & Life Publishing Co
Foreign Rep(s): Vladimir Ivlenkov (Australia); Orthodox Christian Books Ltd (Nicholas Chapman) (England)
*Shipping Address:* 4430 Hwy 36 W, Platina, CA 96076

**St James Press®**
Imprint of Gale
27500 Drake Rd, Farmington Hills, MI 48331-3535
*Tel:* 248-699-4253 *Toll Free Tel:* 800-877-4253 (orders) *Fax:* 248-699-8035 *Toll Free Fax:* 800-414-5043 (orders)
*E-mail:* gale.galeord@cengage.com
*Web Site:* www.gale.cengage.com
Founded: 1968
ISBN Prefix(es): 978-1-55862; 978-0-912289
Total Titles: 303 Print

**St Johann Press**
315 Schraalenburgh Rd, Haworth, NJ 07641
*Tel:* 201-387-1529 *Fax:* 201-501-0698
*Web Site:* www.stjohannpress.com
*Key Personnel*
Pres: David Biesel *E-mail:* d.biesel@verizon.net
VP: Diane Biesel
Dir, Sales & Promos: Deborah Brugger
Mgr, Acctg: Barbara Stinnett
Founded: 1990
Started as a book packager & consultant. Began publishing in 1998.
ISBN Prefix(es): 978-1-878282; 978-1-937943
Number of titles published annually: 9 Print
Total Titles: 95 Print
Distributor for MerwinAsia
Membership(s): ALA

**St Joseph's University Press**
5600 City Ave, Philadelphia, PA 19131-1395
SAN: 240-8368
*Tel:* 610-660-3402 *Fax:* 610-660-3412
*E-mail:* sjupress@sju.edu
*Web Site:* www.sjupress.com
*Key Personnel*
Dir: Mr Carmen R Croce *E-mail:* ccroce@sju.edu
Edit Dir of the Press: Rev Joseph F Chorpenning *Tel:* 610-660-1214 *E-mail:* jchorpen@sju.edu
Founded: 1971
Scholarly books on early modern Catholicism & the visual arts, regional studies (Philadelphia & environments), Jesuit studies (history, visual arts).
ISBN Prefix(es): 978-0-916101
Number of titles published annually: 5 Print
Total Titles: 60 Print
Membership(s): American Association of University Presses; Association of Jesuit University Presses

**St Martin's Press, LLC**
Subsidiary of Macmillan
175 Fifth Ave, New York, NY 10010
SAN: 200-2132
*Tel:* 646-307-5151 *Fax:* 212-420-9314
*E-mail:* firstname.lastname@macmillan.com
*Web Site:* www.stmartins.com
*Key Personnel*
EVP & COO, Macmillan Trade Publg: Steve Cohen
SVP & Pres, SMP Trade/MM Publg: Sally Richardson
EVP & Publr: Matthew Shear
EVP, Mktg & Digital Media Strategy: Jeff Dodes
VP & Assoc Publr: Matthew Baldacci
VP, Dir of Fin: Thomas Cronin
VP, Fin & Acctg: John Cusack
VP, Exec Ed & Publr: Thomas Dunne
VP, Publr of Minotaur: Andrew Martin
Div VP, Publg Opers: Sidney Conde
VP & Assoc Publr, MM/Griffin: Jennifer Enderlin
VP, Assoc Publr, Pbk/Ref Group: Anne Marie Tallberg
Div VP & Assoc Publr, Pbk/Ref Group: Lisa Senz
VP, Dir of Prodn/Mfg: Karen Gillis
Div VP, Dir of Publicity: John Murphy
Assoc Publicity Dir, Pbk/Ref Group: John Karle
Deputy Dir of Publicity: Dori Weintraub
Dir of Subs Rts: Kerry Nordling
Div VP, Creative Dir, Trade: Stephen Snider
VP, Creative Dir, Pbks: Michael Storrings
Exec Art Dir, SMP/Minotaur: David Rotstein
Assoc Publr/Exec Ed, Thomas Dunne Books: Peter Wolverton
Div VP, Ed-in-Chief, Trade: George Witte
Exec Mng Ed, Pbk/Ref Group: John Rounds
Sr Exec Mng Ed, Trade: Amelie Littell
Exec Ed, Pbk/Ref Group: Marc Resnick
Edit Dir, Minotaur Books: Kelley Ragland
Exec Ed: Elizabeth Beier; Brenda Copeland; Hope Dellon; Michael Flamini; Kathryn Huck; Keith Kahla; Monique Patterson; Charles Spicer
Exec Ed, Mgr of Concept Devt: Jennifer Weis
Dir, Quick & Dirty Tips: Kathy Doyle
Founded: 1952
General nonfiction, fiction, reference, scholarly, mass market, travel, children's books.
For information on ordering & returns, visit www.macmillan.com.
ISBN Prefix(es): 978-0-312
Number of titles published annually: 1,000 Print
Imprints: Thomas Dunne Books; Griffin; Minotaur; Weight Watchers
Distributor for Berg Publishers; Bloomsbury USA; College Board; Manchester University Press; Palgrave Macmillan; Papercutz; Rodale; I B Tauris; Walker and Company; Zed Books
Foreign Rep(s): H B Fenn & Co Ltd (Canada); Macmillan India (India); Macmillan New Zealand (New Zealand); Melia UK (Ireland, UK); Pan Macmillan Australia (Australia); Pan Macmillan-Hong Kong (Asia, Middle East); Pan Macmillan South Africa (South Africa); Pan Macmillan UK (Caribbean, Latin America); Pan Macmillan UK (Europe, Israel)
Foreign Rights: Big Apple Agency Inc (China, Taiwan); The Book Publishers Association of Israel (Israel); Eliane Benisti (France); International Editors' Co (Portugal, South America, Spain); Nurcihan Kesim Literary Agency Inc (Turkey); Lex Copyright Office (Hungary); Literary Services (Italy); Prava I Prevodi (Eastern Europe, Greece); Sane Toregard Agency (Denmark, Finland, Iceland, Norway, Sweden); Thomas Schlueck GmbH (Germany); Tuttle-Mori Agency Inc (Thailand)
*Distribution Center:* MPS Distribution Center, 16365 James Madison Hwy, Gordonsville, VA 22942-8501 *Toll Free Tel:* 888-330-8477 *Fax:* 540-672-7540 (cust serv) *Toll Free Fax:* 800-672-2054 (orders)
Membership(s): AAP
*See separate listing for:*
**Palgrave Macmillan**

**Saint Mary's Press**
Subsidiary of Christian Brothers Publications
702 Terrace Heights, Winona, MN 55987-1318
SAN: 203-073X
*Tel:* 507-457-7900 *Toll Free Tel:* 800-533-8095 *Fax:* 507-457-7990 *Toll Free Fax:* 800-344-9225
*E-mail:* smpress@smp.org
*Web Site:* www.smp.org
*Key Personnel*
CEO & Pres: John M Vitek
Exec Dir, Delivery: Caren Yang
Libn & ISBN Contact: Connie Jensen
Founded: 1943
High School curriculum, paperbound & digital; religion (Catholic); Bibles, youth ministry resources.
ISBN Prefix(es): 978-0-88489
Number of titles published annually: 25 Print
Total Titles: 483 Print
Distributor for Group Publishing
Foreign Rep(s): The Bible Society (New Zealand); B Broughton Ltd (Canada); Catholic News, Books & Media (Singapore); John Garratt Publishing (Australia); Herald Publications SDN BHD (Malaysia); Pleroma Christian Supplies (New Zealand); Redemptorist Publications (UK)

**Saint Nectarios Press**
10300 Ashworth Ave N, Seattle, WA 98133-9410
SAN: 159-0170
*Tel:* 206-522-4471 *Toll Free Tel:* 800-643-4233 *Fax:* 206-523-0550
*E-mail:* orders@stnectariospress.com
*Web Site:* www.stnectariospress.com
*Key Personnel*
Dir: Neketas S Palassis *E-mail:* frneketas@gmail.com
Busn Mgr: Nina S Seco *E-mail:* seco@orthodoxpress.org
Founded: 1977
Traditional Eastern Orthodox books.
ISBN Prefix(es): 978-0-913026
Number of titles published annually: 3 Print
Total Titles: 50 Print

**St Pauls/Alba House**
Division of The Society of St Paul
2187 Victory Blvd, Staten Island, NY 10314-6603
SAN: 201-2405
*Tel:* 718-761-0047 (edit & prodn); 718-698-2759 (mktg & billing) *Toll Free Tel:* 800-343-2522 *Fax:* 718-761-0057
*E-mail:* sales@stpauls.us; marketing@stpauls.us
*Web Site:* www.stpauls.us; www.albahouse.org
*Key Personnel*
Ed-in-Chief & Contact, ISBN & Rts & Perms: Fr Edmund C Lane *E-mail:* edmund_lane@juno.com
Copy Ed: Br Frank Sadowski
Prodn Mgr & Art Dir: Br Edward Donaher *E-mail:* edonaher@aol.com
Treas: Br Richard C Brunner
Mktg: Fr Matthew Roehrig *Tel:* 718-698-2759 *E-mail:* marketing@stpauls.us
Founded: 1961
Religion (Catholic), bible, education, pastoral care, prayer books, biography, spirituality, psychology, philosophy, theology, Spanish titles (Roman Catholic), bereavement, church, ethics, homilies, liturgy, marriage & family life, prayer, religious education, saints lives, scripture, cassettes & videos.
ISBN Prefix(es): 978-0-8189
Number of titles published annually: 24 Print; 10 CD-ROM; 20 Online; 20 E-Book
Total Titles: 425 Print; 85 CD-ROM; 33 Online; 33 E-Book
*Foreign Office(s):* Edizioni Paoline, Piazza Soncino, 5 20092 Cinisello Balsamo (MI), Italy
Foreign Rep(s): St Paul Publications (Australia, Canada, India, Ireland, Italy, Philippines, South Africa, UK)

**Sts Judes imPress**
5537 Waterman Blvd, Suite 2-W, St Louis, MO 63112
*Tel:* 314-454-0064
*E-mail:* stjudes1@att.net
*Key Personnel*
Publr: Lawrence A Murray
Founded: 1989
Historical novels, socio-economic studies, religious history & science.
ISBN Prefix(es): 978-0-9722149; 978-0-9766599; 978-0-9801289
Number of titles published annually: 3 Print; 2 CD-ROM; 12 Online
Total Titles: 38 Print; 12 CD-ROM; 12 Online

**Salem Press Inc**
Division of EBSCO Publishing
2 University Plaza, Suite 310, Hackensack, NJ 07601
SAN: 208-838X
*Tel:* 201-968-0500 *Toll Free Tel:* 800-221-1592; 866-550-8122 *Fax:* 201-968-0511
*E-mail:* csr@salempress.com
*Web Site:* salempress.com
*Key Personnel*
Territory Sales Mgr: Pamela Brunke *E-mail:* pbrunke@salempress.com
Founded: 1949
Reference books & online products for middle school, secondary school, colleges & public libraries.
ISBN Prefix(es): 978-0-89356; 978-1-58765
Number of titles published annually: 25 Print; 10 Online; 15 E-Book
Total Titles: 150 Print; 35 Online; 60 E-Book
Imprints: Magill's Choice
Foreign Rep(s): Aditya Books Pvt Ltd (Bangladesh, India, Nepal, Pakistan, Sri Lanka); Alkem Co (S) Pte Ltd (Brunei, Hong Kong, Indonesia, Korea, Malaysia, Philippines, Singapore, Taiwan, Thailand, Vietnam); Eurospan Ltd (Africa, Europe, Middle East, UK); Grey House Publishing Canada (Canada); Somohano Express SA de CV (Mexico); Warner Books Pty Ltd (Australia, New Zealand); Yushodo Co Ltd (Japan)

**Salina Bookshelf Inc**
3120 N Caden Ct, Suite 4, Flagstaff, AZ 86004
SAN: 253-0503
*Toll Free Tel:* 877-527-0070 *Fax:* 928-526-0386
*Web Site:* www.salinabookshelf.com
*Key Personnel*
Pres: Eric Lockard *Tel:* 928-527-0700 ext 425 *E-mail:* elockard@salinabookshelf.com
Art Dir: Baje Whitethorne, Jr *Tel:* 928-527-0700 ext 202
Founded: 1994
Publisher of multicultural books with a strong focus on the stories of the Navajo people. Our textbooks, children's picture books & electronic media in Navajo & English are resources for the home, library & classroom. We recognize the importance of portraying traditional language & culture & of making this knowledge accessible to a broad spectrum of curious minds.
ISBN Prefix(es): 978-1-893354; 978-0-9644189
Number of titles published annually: 10 Print; 3 Audio
Total Titles: 65 Print; 1 CD-ROM; 6 Audio
Membership(s): American Indian Library Association; Children's Book Council; IBPA, the Independent Book Publishers Association; Publishers Association of the West

**§Samhain Publishing Ltd**
11821 Mason Montgomery Rd, Suite 4-B, Cincinnati, OH 45249
*Tel:* 513-453-4688 *Toll Free Tel:* 800-509-4158 (orders) *Fax:* 513-583-0191
*E-mail:* support@samhainpublishing.com
*Web Site:* www.samhainpublishing.com
*Key Personnel*
Pres: Christina M Brashear *E-mail:* cbrashear@samhainpublishing.com
Publr: Lindsey Faber
Edit Dir: Heather Osborn
Exec Ed, Horror: Don D'Auria
Founded: 2005
Publish all genres & heat levels of romance, erotica & fantasy, urban fantasy & science fiction with strong romantic elements, ebooks & trade papers.
ISBN Prefix(es): 978-1-59998
Number of titles published annually: 1,000 Print; 300 Online; 300 E-Book
Total Titles: 1,000 Online; 1,000 E-Book
Imprints: RetroRomance™ (classic romance novels published between the 1970s & early 2000s)
*Returns:* Ingram Book Co, One Ingram Blvd, La Vergne, TN 37086 *Tel:* 615-793-5000 *Toll Free Tel:* 800-937-8200 *E-mail:* customer.service@ingrambook.com *Web Site:* www.ingrambook.com
*Shipping Address:* Ingram Book Co, One Ingram Blvd, La Vergne, TN 37086 *Tel:* 615-793-5000 *Toll Free Tel:* 800-937-8200 *E-mail:* customer.service@ingrambook.com *Web Site:* www.ingrambook.com
*Warehouse:* Ingram Book Co, One Ingram Blvd, La Vergne, TN 37086 *Tel:* 615-793-5000 *Toll Free Tel:* 800-937-8200 *E-mail:* customer.service@ingrambook.com *Web Site:* www.ingrambook.com

**Sams Technical Publishing LLC**
Division of AGS Capital LLC
Imprint of Quickfact®
9850 E 30 St, Indianapolis, IN 46229
*Tel:* 317-396-5336 *Toll Free Tel:* 800-428-7267 *Fax:* 317-489-3406 *Toll Free Fax:* 800-552-3910
*E-mail:* customercare@samswebsite.com
*Web Site:* www.samswebsite.com
*Key Personnel*
COO: Lou Hurrle *E-mail:* lhurrle@samswebsite.com
Founded: 1946
Publisher of Photofact repair manuals.
ISBN Prefix(es): 978-0-7906
Number of titles published annually: 100 Print
Total Titles: 400 Print
Imprints: Indy-Tech Publishing; Photofact®
*Orders to:* Cardinal Publishers Group, 2222 Hillside Ave, Indianapolis, IN 46218, Tom Doherty *Tel:* 317-879-0871 *Fax:* 317-879-0872 *E-mail:* tdoherty@cardinalpub.com
*Returns:* Cardinal Publishers Group, 2222 Hillside Ave, Indianapolis, IN 46218, Tom Doherty *Tel:* 317-879-0871 *Fax:* 317-879-0872 *E-mail:* tdoherty@cardinalpub.com
*Shipping Address:* Cardinal Publishers Group, 2222 Hillside Ave, Indianapolis, IN 46218, Tom Doherty *Tel:* 317-879-0871 *Fax:* 317-879-0872 *E-mail:* tdoherty@cardinalpub.com
*Warehouse:* Cardinal Publishers Group, 2222 Hillside Ave, Indianapolis, IN 46218, Tom Doherty *Tel:* 317-879-0871 *Fax:* 317-879-0872 *E-mail:* tdoherty@cardinalpub.com
*Distribution Center:* Cardinal Publishers Group, 2222 Hillside Ave, Indianapolis, IN 46218, Tom Doherty *Tel:* 317-879-0871 *Fax:* 317-879-0872 *E-mail:* tdoherty@cardinalpub.com

**San Diego State University Press**
Division of San Diego State University Foundation
Arts & Letters 283, 5500 Campanile Dr, San Diego, CA 92182-6020
*Tel:* 619-594-6220 (orders)
*Web Site:* sdsupress.sdsu.edu
*Key Personnel*
Dir: Prof Harry Polkinhorn *E-mail:* hpolkinh@mail.sdsu.edu
Edit Bd: Dr Bill Nericcio *Tel:* 619-594-1524
Founded: 1959
Scholarly & trade, monographs.
ISBN Prefix(es): 978-0-916304; 978-1-879691
Number of titles published annually: 2 Print; 2 Online
Imprints: Binational Press; Hyperbole
Distributor for Institute for Regional Studies of the Californias

**J S Sanders & Co Inc**, see Ivan R Dee Publisher

**Sandlapper Publishing Inc**
1281 Amelia St NE, Orangeburg, SC 29115-5475
SAN: 203-2678
Mailing Address: PO Box 730, Orangeburg, SC 29116-0730
*Tel:* 803-531-1658 *Toll Free Tel:* 800-849-7263 (orders only) *Fax:* 803-534-5223 *Toll Free Fax:* 800-337-9420
*E-mail:* sales@sandlapperpublishing.com
*Web Site:* www.sandlapperpublishing.com

*Key Personnel*
Owner & Pres: Amanda Gallman
*E-mail:* agallman@sandlapperpublishing.com
Founded: 1982
Nonfiction material about South Carolina only. Submit query letter.
ISBN Prefix(es): 978-0-87844
Number of titles published annually: 10 Print
Total Titles: 100 Print

**§Santa Monica Press LLC**
215 S Hwy 101, Suite 110, Solana Beach, CA 92075
SAN: 298-1459
Mailing Address: PO Box 850, Solana Beach, CA 92075
*Tel:* 858-793-1890 *Toll Free Tel:* 800-784-9553 *Fax:* 858-777-0444
*E-mail:* books@santamonicapress.com
*Web Site:* www.santamonicapress.com
*Key Personnel*
Publr: Jeffrey Goldman *E-mail:* jgoldman@santamonicapress.com
Founded: 1994
Publish an eclectic line of books. Our critically acclaimed titles are sold in retail outlets around the world. Our authors are recognized experts who receive coverage both nationally & internationally. We're not afraid to cast a wide editorial net. Our list of lively & modern nonfiction titles includes books in such categories as popular culture, film history, photography, humor, biography, travel & reference.
ISBN Prefix(es): 978-0-9639946; 978-1-891661; 978-1-59580
Number of titles published annually: 12 Print; 12 E-Book
Total Titles: 125 Print; 75 E-Book
Foreign Rep(s): Turnaround Publisher Services Ltd (Africa, Asia, Europe, UK); Woodslane (Australia, New Zealand)
Foreign Rights: IPG (Susan Sewall)
*Orders to:* Independent Publishers Group, 814 N Franklin St, Chicago, IL 60610 *Tel:* 312-337-0747 *Toll Free Tel:* 800-888-4741 *Fax:* 312-337-5985 *E-mail:* orders@ipgbook.com *Web Site:* www.ipgbook.com
*Returns:* IPG Warehouse, 600 N Pulaski Rd, Chicago, IL 60624, Contact: Mark Noble *Tel:* 312-337-0747 *Fax:* 312-337-5985 *Web Site:* www.ipgbook.com
*Warehouse:* IPG Warehouse, 600 N Pulaski Rd, Chicago, IL 60624, Contact: Mark Noble *Tel:* 312-337-0747 *Fax:* 312-337-5985 *Web Site:* www.ipgbook.com
*Distribution Center:* Independent Publishers Group, 814 N Franklin St, Chicago, IL 60610 *Tel:* 312-337-0747 *Toll Free Tel:* 800-888-4741 *Fax:* 312-337-5985 *E-mail:* orders@jpgbook.com *Web Site:* www.ipgbook.com

**Santillana USA Publishing Co Inc**
Division of The Richmond Publishing Co Inc
2023 NW 84 Ave, Doral, FL 33122
SAN: 205-1133
*Tel:* 305-591-9522 *Toll Free Tel:* 800-245-8584 *Fax:* 305-591-9145 *Toll Free Fax:* 888-248-9518
*E-mail:* customerservice@santillanausa.com
*Web Site:* www.santillanausa.com; www.alfaguara.net
*Key Personnel*
CEO & Pres: Miguel Tapia *E-mail:* mtapia@santillanausa.com
Mktg Dir: Kathy Jimenez *E-mail:* kjimenez@santillanausa.com
Dir, Children's Lit & Trade Div: Silvia Matute *E-mail:* smatute@santillanausa.com
Founded: 1972
Educational & Spanish language trade books; English as a second language & bilingual textbooks; Spanish as a foreign language.
ISBN Prefix(es): 978-0-88272; 978-1-56014; 978-1-58105; 978-1-58986; 978-1-59437
Number of titles published annually: 50 Print; 3 CD-ROM; 5 Audio
Total Titles: 1,200 Print; 3 CD-ROM; 15 Audio
Imprints: Aguilar; Alfaguara; Santillana; Taurus
Membership(s): AAP

**SAR Press**, see School for Advanced Research Press

**Sarabande Books Inc**
2234 Dundee Rd, Suite 200, Louisville, KY 40205
*Tel:* 502-458-4028 *Fax:* 502-458-4065
*E-mail:* info@sarabandebooks.org
*Web Site:* www.sarabandebooks.org
*Key Personnel*
Pres & Ed-in-Chief: Sarah Gorham
Mng Ed: Kirby Gann
Founded: 1994
Short fiction, poetry & literary nonfiction collections.
ISBN Prefix(es): 978-1-889330; 978-1-932511
Number of titles published annually: 10 Print; 1 E-Book
Total Titles: 160 Print; 1 E-Book
Membership(s): ABA; Academy of American Poets; Association of Writers and Writing Programs; Council of Literary Magazines & Presses; PEN Center USA

**SAS Publishing**
Imprint of SAS Institute Inc
100 SAS Campus Dr, Cary, NC 27513-2414
*Tel:* 919-677-8000 *Fax:* 919-677-4444
*E-mail:* saspress@sas.com
*Web Site:* www.sas.com/publishing
*Key Personnel*
Ed-in-Chief: Julie M Platt *E-mail:* julie.platt@sas.com
Founded: 1976
Books about SAS or JMP software.
ISBN Prefix(es): 978-1-55544; 978-0-917382
Number of titles published annually: 50 Print
Distributed by John Wiley & Sons Inc
Distributor for AMACOM Books; Breakfast Communications; CRC Press; Duxbury; Harcourt; Harvard Business School Press; McGraw-Hill; Oxford; Prentice-Hall; Springer; John Wiley & Sons Inc

**Sasquatch Books**
1904 S Main St, Suite 710, Seattle, WA 98101
SAN: 289-0208
*Tel:* 206-467-4300 *Toll Free Tel:* 800-775-0817 *Fax:* 206-467-4301
*E-mail:* custserv@sasquatchbooks.com
*Web Site:* www.sasquatchbooks.com
*Key Personnel*
Publr & Edit Dir: Gary Luke *Tel:* 206-826-4304 *E-mail:* gluke@sasquatchbooks.com
Sales & Mktg Dir: Sarah Hanson *Tel:* 206-826-4303 *E-mail:* shanson@sasquatchbooks.com
Founded: 1986
Nonfiction of & from the West Coast.
ISBN Prefix(es): 978-0-934007; 978-0-912365; 978-1-57061
Number of titles published annually: 40 Print
Total Titles: 390 Print; 3 Audio
Imprints: Best Places® Guidebooks Series; Paws IV
Foreign Rep(s): Publishers Group Canada (Canada)
*Distribution Center:* Random House Publisher Services, 1700 Fourth St, Berkeley, CA 94710 *Toll Free Tel:* 800-788-3123 *Fax:* 510-528-3444

**§Satya House Publications**
22 Turkey St, Hardwick, MA 01037
Mailing Address: PO Box 122, Hardwick, MA 01037
*Tel:* 413-477-8743
*E-mail:* info@satyahouse.com; orders@satyahouse.com
*Web Site:* www.satyahouse.com
*Key Personnel*
Publr: Julie Murkette *E-mail:* julie@satyahouse.com
Founded: 2003
Independent publishing company.
This publisher has indicated that 25% of their product line is author subsidized.
ISBN Prefix(es): 978-0-9729191; 978-0-9818720; 978-1-9358740
Number of titles published annually: 4 Print; 4 E-Book
Total Titles: 16 Print; 1 CD-ROM; 9 E-Book
Foreign Rep(s): Gazelle (UK)
Foreign Rights: Sylvia Hayse Literary Agency LLC (Worldwide exc USA)
*Distribution Center:* Midpoint Trade Books, 27 W 20 St, Suite 1102, New York, NY 10011 *Tel:* 212-727-0190 *Web Site:* www.midpointtrade.com
Membership(s): IBPA, the Independent Book Publishers Association; Independent Publishers of New England

**Savant Books & Publications LLC**
2630 Kapiolani Blvd, Suite 1601, Honolulu, HI 96826
*Tel:* 808-941-3927 *Fax:* 808-941-3927
*E-mail:* savantbooks@gmail.com
*Web Site:* www.savantbooksandpublications.com
*Key Personnel*
Owner: Daniel S Janik
Dir, Mktg & Dist: Setsuko Tsuchiya
Founded: 2007
Publishes unpublished, post-modern works of enduring value "with a twist" for English readers throughout the world. Special interest areas include: fiction (novels - all genres), nonfiction (transformative education, memoirs, academic theses & dissertations of note, singe-author textbooks & workbooks).
ISBN Prefix(es): 978-0-9841175; 978-0-9845552; 978-0-9829987; 978-0-9832861
Number of titles published annually: 15 Print
Total Titles: 70 Print

**Saxon Publishers**
Imprint of Houghton Mifflin Harcourt Publishing Company
9205 Southpark Center Loop, Orlando, FL 32819
*Toll Free Tel:* 800-289-4490 *Toll Free Fax:* 800-289-3994
*E-mail:* greatservice@hmhpub.com
*Web Site:* saxonpublishers.hmhco.com
Founded: 1981
Educational materials for K-12.
Number of titles published annually: 78 Print

**SBPRA**, see Strategic Book Publishing & Rights Agency (SBPRA)

**Scarecrow Press Inc**
Imprint of Rowman & Littlefield Publishing Group
4501 Forbes Blvd, Suite 200, Lanham, MD 20706
*Tel:* 301-459-3366 *Fax:* 301-429-5748
*Web Site:* www.scarecrowpress.com
*Key Personnel*
CEO & Pres: Jed Lyons *E-mail:* jlyons@rowman.com
Publr & Edit Dir: Marcus Boggs
VP, Mktg & Sales: Linda May
Rts & Perms Dir: Clare Cox
Sales Dir: Sheila Burnett
Exec Ed: Charles Harmon
Founded: 1950

Reference books & texts in music, film, information technology, theater, performing arts, history, religion & cultural studies. Professional & reference books in library & information sciences & government regulatory areas. Co-publishing with Rutgers Jazz Institute, Music Library Association, American Theological Library Association & Children's Literature Association.
New titles to be released under the Rowman & Littlefield imprint.
ISBN Prefix(es): 978-0-8108; 978-1-57886
Number of titles published annually: 175 Print; 2 CD-ROM; 10 Online; 5 E-Book
Total Titles: 5,000 Print; 6 CD-ROM; 100 Online; 30 E-Book
*Distribution Center:* 15200 NBN Way, PO Box 191, Blue Ridge Summit, PA 17214 *Toll Free Tel:* 800-462-6420 *Toll Free Fax:* 800-338-4550

**§Scarletta**
10 S Fifth St, Suite 1105, Minneapolis, MN 55402
*Tel:* 612-455-0252 *Fax:* 612-338-4817
*E-mail:* info@scarlettapress.com
*Web Site:* www.scarlettapress.com
*Key Personnel*
Publr & Creative Dir: Nancy Tuminelly *E-mail:* nancy@mightymedia.com
Publicity Dir: Desiree Bussiere *E-mail:* desiree@scarlettapress.com
Mng Ed: Nora Evans *E-mail:* nora@scarlettapress.com
Founded: 2005
Independently publishes works with quality editorial & design for children & adults. Innovation, passion & attention to detail defines the approach to every title published.
This publisher has indicated that 50% of their product line is author subsidized.
ISBN Prefix(es): 978-0-9765201; 978-0-9798249; 978-0-9824584; 978-0-9830219; 978-1-938063
Number of titles published annually: 12 Print; 12 E-Book
Total Titles: 26 Print; 22 E-Book
Imprints: Scarletta Junior Readers (middlegrade literature); Scarletta Kids (picture books & first reader/beginner books); Scarletta Press (adult titles); Red Portal Press
Foreign Rights: Letter Soup Rights Agency (Allison Olson) (Worldwide)
*Returns:* Perseus Distribution, Returns Dept, 193 Edwards Dr, Jackson, TN
*Distribution Center:* Publishers Group West, 1700 Fourth St, Berkeley, CA 94710 *Tel:* 510-809-3700 *Toll Free Tel:* 800-788-3123
Membership(s): ABA; ABC; Children's Book Council; Midwest Independent Booksellers Association; Midwest Independent Publishers Association; Minnesota Book Publishers Roundtable; Society of Children's Book Writers & Illustrators

**Scepter Publishers**
PO Box 1391, New York, NY 10802
*Tel:* 212-354-0670 *Toll Free Tel:* 800-322-8773 *Fax:* 212-354-0736
*Web Site:* www.scepterpublishers.org
*Key Personnel*
Pres & Publr: Nathan Davis *Tel:* 646-205-1508 *E-mail:* nathan@scepterpublishers.org
Orders & Cust Serv: Kevin Lay *E-mail:* kevin@scepterpublishers.org
Founded: 1954
Catholic Book Publishing including doctrinal works, theology & liturgy.
ISBN Prefix(es): 978-0-933932; 978-0-1889334; 978-1-594170
Number of titles published annually: 10 Print
Total Titles: 150 Print
*Distribution Center:* Maple-Vail Distribution, 1000 Strickler Rd, Mount Joy, PA 17552

**Schaffner Press**
PO Box 41567, Tucson, AZ 85717
*E-mail:* tim@schaffnerpress.com
*Web Site:* www.schaffnerpress.com
Founded: 2001
Independent publisher of books of social relevance for the discerning reader.
ISBN Prefix(es): 978-0-9710598; 978-0-9801394; 978-0-9824332; 978-1-936182
Number of titles published annually: 6 Print; 4 E-Book
Total Titles: 16 Print; 10 E-Book

**§Schiel & Denver Book Publishers**
10685-B Hazelhurst Dr, Suite 8575, Houston, TX 77043
*Tel:* 832-699-0264 *Toll Free Tel:* 888-629-4449 *Toll Free Fax:* 888-224-2721
*E-mail:* enquiries@schieldenver.com
*Web Site:* www.schieldenver.com
*Key Personnel*
Sr Mgr: Simon Hornby *E-mail:* simon.hornby@schieldenver.com
Acqs Mgr: Ken Hudson *E-mail:* ken.hudson@schieldenver.com
Author Servs Mgr: Hannah Bell *E-mail:* hannah.bell@schieldenver.com
Founded: 2008
Independent book publishers offering professional ISBN book publishing, editing & book marketing services to first time & veteran authors with the support of an expert book publishing team.
This publisher has indicated that 50% of their product line is author subsidized.
ISBN Prefix(es): 978-1-84903
Number of titles published annually: 90 Print
Total Titles: 100 Print; 100 Online; 50 E-Book
Imprints: Heirloom Children's Book Publishers
*Foreign Office(s):* Schiel & Denver Publishing Ltd, The Meridian, 4 Copthall House, Station Sq, Coventry CV1 2FL, United Kingdom *Tel:* (0844) 54 99 191 *Fax:* (0844) 507 0985 *E-mail:* enquiries@schieldenver.co.uk
*Distribution Center:* Baker & Taylor
Ingram
Membership(s): AAP; ATA

**Schiffer Publishing Ltd**
4880 Lower Valley Rd, Atglen, PA 19310
SAN: 208-8428
*Tel:* 610-593-1777 *Fax:* 610-593-2002
*E-mail:* schifferbk@aol.com
*Web Site:* www.schifferbooks.com
*Key Personnel*
Pres & Ed-in-Chief: Pete Schiffer
EVP: Nancy Schiffer
Spec Sales: Joe Langman
Founded: 1974
Collecting, art books, antiques, architecture, toys, woodcarving, hobbies, weaving, color, metaphysics, aviation, military books, automotive books, design & fashion.
ISBN Prefix(es): 978-0-916838; 978-0-88740; 978-0-7643
Number of titles published annually: 300 Print
Total Titles: 5,000 Print
Imprints: Canal Press; Cornell Maritime Press; Geared Up Publications; Kaiser-Barlow; LW Books; Para Research; Schiffer; Schiffer Fashion Press; Schiffer LTD; Schiffer Military History; Tidewater Publishers; Whitford Press
Distributor for The Donning Co
Foreign Rights: Bushwood Books (Europe)
*See separate listing for:*
**Cornell Maritime Press Inc**

**Schirmer**, see Wadsworth Publishing

**Schirmer Trade Books**
Imprint of Music Sales Corp
180 Madison Ave, 24th fl, New York, NY 10016
*Tel:* 212-254-2100 *Toll Free Tel:* 800-431-7187 (orders) *Fax:* 212-254-2013
*Web Site:* www.musicsales.com
*Key Personnel*
Pres: Barrie Edwards *E-mail:* be@musicsales.com
Dir, Digital Publg: Tomas Wise
Founded: 1935
Committed to intelligent, educational & entertaining books about all aspects of music, especially the recording arts, music business, genre histories & musician biographies.
ISBN Prefix(es): 978-0-8256; 978-0-7119
Number of titles published annually: 25 Print
Total Titles: 300 Print
*Sales Office(s):* 445 Bellvale Rd, Chester, NY 10918-0572, Contact: Steve Wilson *Toll Free Tel:* 800-431-7187 *Toll Free Fax:* 800-345-6842 *E-mail:* sw@musicsales.com
*Foreign Office(s):* 8/9 Frith St, London W1D 3JB, United Kingdom *Tel:* (0207) 434-0066 *Fax:* (0207) 734-2246
Distributor for Big Meteor Publishing; Independent Music Press
*Billing Address:* 445 Bellvale Rd, Chester, NY 10918-0572 *Toll Free Tel:* 800-431-7187 *Toll Free Fax:* 800-345-6842 *E-mail:* info@musicsales.com
*Orders to:* 445 Bellvale Rd, Chester, NY 10918-0572 *Toll Free Tel:* 800-431-7187 *Toll Free Fax:* 800-345-6842 *E-mail:* info@musicsales.com
*Returns:* 445 Bellvale Rd, Chester, NY 10918-0572 *Toll Free Tel:* 800-431-7187 *Toll Free Fax:* 800-345-6842 *E-mail:* info@musicsales.com
*Shipping Address:* 445 Bellvale Rd, Chester, NY 10918-0572 *Toll Free Tel:* 800-431-7187 *Toll Free Fax:* 800-345-6842 *E-mail:* info@musicsales.com
*Warehouse:* 445 Bellvale Rd, Chester, NY 10918-0572 *Toll Free Tel:* 800-431-7187 *Toll Free Fax:* 800-345-6842 *E-mail:* info@musicsales.com
*Distribution Center:* 445 Bellvale Rd, Chester, NY 10918-0572 *Toll Free Tel:* 800-431-7187 *Toll Free Fax:* 800-345-6842 *E-mail:* info@musicsales.com
Membership(s): ADA; American Society of Journalists & Authors; IBPA, the Independent Book Publishers Association; Women's National Book Association

**§Schlager Group Inc**
2501 Oak Lawn Ave, Suite 440, Dallas, TX 75219
*Toll Free Tel:* 888-416-5727 *Fax:* 214-347-9469
*E-mail:* info@schlagergroup.com
*Web Site:* www.schlagergroup.com
*Key Personnel*
Pres: Neil Schlager *Tel:* 888-416-5727 ext 801 *E-mail:* neil@schlagergroup.com
Mng Ed: Marcia Merryman-Means *Tel:* 888-416-5727 ext 803 *E-mail:* marcia@schlagergroup.com; Benjamin Painter *Tel:* 888-416-5727 ext 802 *E-mail:* benjamin@schlagergroup.com
Founded: 1997
Publisher of books & Internet materials for history instructors & students. Foreign Reps in Africa, Australia, Bangladesh, Canada, Europe, India, Japan, Mexico, Middle East, Nepal, New Guinea, New Zealand, Pakistan, Southeast Asia, Sri Lanka & UK, all via Salem Press Inc distributors & representatives.
ISBN Prefix(es): 978-9-797758; 978-9-35306
Number of titles published annually: 2 Print; 1 Online; 2 E-Book
Total Titles: 5 Print; 1 Online; 5 E-Book
Divisions: Milestone Documents
Distributed by Salem Press (ref books only)
*Orders to:* Salem Press, 2 University Plaza, Suite 121, Hackensack, NJ 07601 (ref books only)
*Returns:* Salem Press, 2 University Plaza, Suite 121, Hackensack, NJ 07601 (ref books only)

*Shipping Address:* Salem Press, 2 University Plaza, Suite 121, Hackensack, NJ 07601 (ref books only) *Toll Free Tel:* 800-221-1592 *Fax:* 201-968-1411 *E-mail:* csr@salempress.com *Web Site:* www.salempress.com
Membership(s): American Historical Association; Organization of American Historians

**Scholars' Facsimiles & Reprints**
Subsidiary of Academic Resources Corp
6946 E Stevens Rd, Cave Creek, AZ 85331-8677
SAN: 203-2627
*Tel:* 480-575-9945
*E-mail:* sfandr@msn.com
*Web Site:* www.scholarsbooklist.com
*Key Personnel*
Publr: Norman Mangouni
Founded: 1936
Facsimile reprints of rare books of scholarly interest, microforms, occasional originals.
ISBN Prefix(es): 978-0-8201
Number of titles published annually: 5 Print
Total Titles: 575 Print

**Scholastic Classroom & Community Group**
Division of Scholastic Inc
524 Broadway, New York, NY 10012
*Tel:* 212-343-6100
*Web Site:* www.scholastic.com
*Key Personnel*
Pres: Greg Worrell
VP & Gen Mgr: Karine Apollon; Allison Feldman
SVP & Publr: Patrick Daley
The Scholastic Classroom & Community Group includes Classroom Books, Literacy Initiatives, Teaching Resources & Family & Community Engagement. The division provides education materials that reach more than 25 million students in 65 percent of U.S. schools & supports programs & partnerships that promote & build literacy in communities across the country.
ISBN Prefix(es): 978-0-531; 978-0-545

**Scholastic Consumer & Professional Publishing**
Division of Scholastic Inc
557 Broadway, New York, NY 10012
*Tel:* 212-343-6100 *Toll Free Tel:* 800-621-1115 *Fax:* 800-621-1115
*Web Site:* www.scholastic.com
*Key Personnel*
Pres: Hugh Roome
VP, Sales & Marketing: Pam Sader
VP, Lib & After School Mkts: Evan St Lifer
Scholastic Consumer & Professional Publishing is a leading print & digital publisher of children's nonfiction magazine & reference materials for schools & public libraries, which include digital brands such as BookFlix & TrueFlix & the prestigious imprints Children's Press®, Franklin Watts® & Grolier Online®. Also publisher of magazines including Scholastic News & Junior Scholastic. In addition, the division sells Scholastic Trade books to the school library market & publishes Scholastic Instructor & Adminstr@tor Magazines.
ISBN Prefix(es): 978-0-516; 978-0-531; 978-0-7172
Imprints: Children's Press®; Franklin Watts®; Grolier Online®
*Warehouse:* 2931 E McCarty St, Jefferson City, MO 65101 (Free shipping)

**Scholastic Education**
Division of Scholastic Inc
524 Broadway, New York, NY 10012
*Tel:* 212-343-6100 *Fax:* 212-343-6189
*Web Site:* www.scholastic.com
*Key Personnel*
EVP, Scholastic Inc & Pres, Scholastic Education: Margery Mayer
COO, Scholastic Educ: Beth Polcari
SVP, Prod Devt: Rosamund Else-Mitchell
Chief Academic Offr & SVP: Francie Alexander
SVP, Natl Sales: Joe Welty
SVP, Scholastic Achievement Partners: Duncan Young
VP, Res & Validation: Kristin DeVivo
VP, Educ Technol: Midian Kurland
VP, Strategic Publg: Linda Shuster
Grounded in the most current scientific research, Scholastic Education develops technology products & services that include intervention, instruction, assessment & data management & professional development. READ 180®, the nation's leading adolescent literacy program for struggling readers, serves more than one million students every day.
ISBN Prefix(es): 978-0-516; 978-0-590; 978-0-439; 978-0-926891; 978-1-55998; 978-1-57809; 978-1-59009
Divisions: Assessment; Curriculum Solutions; Early Childhood Education; Intervention; Professional Development; Publishing Services; Research; Sales & Marketing; Technology
*See separate listing for:*
**Math Solutions®**

**§Scholastic Inc**
557 Broadway, New York, NY 10012
*Tel:* 212-343-6100 *Toll Free Tel:* 800-scholastic
*Web Site:* www.scholastic.com
*Key Personnel*
Chmn, Pres & CEO: Richard Robinson
EVP, Chief Admin Offr & CFO: Maureen O'Connell
EVP, Gen Coun: Andrew Hedden
Pres, Trade Publg: Ellie Berger
EVP, Pres, Reading Club & E-Commerce: Judith A Newman
EVP & Pres, Scholastic Educ: Margery Mayer
Pres, Scholastic Book Fairs: Alan Boyko
EVP & Pres, Consumer & Prof Publg: Hugh Roome
Pres, Scholastic Classroom & Community Group: Greg Worrell
EVP & Pres, Scholastic Media: Deborah A Forte
EVP & Pres, Intl Growth Mkts: Shane Armstrong
SVP, Corp Communs & Media Rel: Kyle Good
Founded: 1920
Scholastic Corporation (NASDAQ: SCHL) is the world's largest publisher & distributor of children's books & a leader in educational technology & related services & children's media. Scholastic creates quality books & ebooks, print & technology-based learning materials & programs, magazines, multi-media & other products that help children learn both at school & at home. The company distributes its products & services worldwide through a variety of channels, including school-based book clubs & book fairs, retail stores, schools, libraries, on-air & online at www.scholastic.com.
ISBN Prefix(es): 978-0-590; 978-0-439
*Distribution Center:* 2931 E McCarty St, Jefferson City, MO 65101
100 Plaza Drive W, Secaucus, NJ 07094
Membership(s): AAP; ALA; Children's Book Council
*See separate listing for:*
**Lectorum Publications Inc**
**Scholastic Consumer & Professional Publishing**
**Scholastic Education**
**Scholastic International**
**Scholastic Media**
**Scholastic Trade Division**

**§Scholastic International**
Division of Scholastic Inc
557 Broadway, New York, NY 10012
*Tel:* 212-343-6100; 646-330-5288 (intl cust serv) *Toll Free Tel:* 800-SCHOLASTIC (800-724-6527) *Fax:* 646-837-7878
*E-mail:* international@scholastic.com
*Key Personnel*
EVP & Pres, Intl: Shane Armstrong
Fin Dir: Joe Macca
VP, Export Sales & Mktg: Anne Boynton-Trigg
VP, Global Prod Devt: Edie Perkins
VP, New Busn Devt: Carol Sakoian
Scholastic International includes the publication & distribution of products & services outside the US by the company's international operations & its exports businesses. Scholastic has operations in Canada, the UK, Australia, New Zealand, Asia & Puerto Rico.
ISBN Prefix(es): 978-0-590; 978-0-439; 978-0-545
Subsidiaries: Caribe Grolier Inc; Grolier International Inc Philippines; Grolier International Inc Singapore; Grolier International Inc Thailand; Grolier (Malaysia) Sdn Bhd; Scholastic Argentina SA; Scholastic Australia Pty Ltd; Scholastic Canada Ltd; Scholastic Education Information Consulting (Shanghai) Co, Ltd; Scholastic Education International (Singapore) Pvt Ltd; Scholastic Grolier International Inc Indonesia; Scholastic Hong Kong Ltd; Scholastic India Private Ltd; Scholastic Ireland Ltd; Scholastic Ltd UK; Scholastic Mexico SA; Scholastic New Zealand Ltd

**Scholastic Media**
Division of Scholastic Inc
524 Broadway, 5th fl, New York, NY 10012
*Tel:* 212-389-3900 *Fax:* 212-389-3886
*Key Personnel*
EVP, Scholastic Inc & Pres, Scholastic Media: Deborah Forte
SVP, Mktg & Consumer Prods: Leslye Schaefer
VP, Fin: Ken Yamamoto
VP, Consumer Prods: Gary Hymowitz
VP, Mktg & Brand Mgmt: Daisy Kline
VP, Prodn & Digital Prods: Caroline Fraser
Dir, Global Prog Sales & Mdsg: Anthony Kosiewska
Scholastic Media, the entertainment & media division of Scholastic, is a leading producer of quality, family-oriented content across multiple platforms, including consumer products, feature film, television, video, interactive, mobile, audio & apps & is a major developer & marketer of children's brands worldwide. Scholastic Media's award-winning brand portfolio includes Clifford The Big Red Dog, I SPY, The Magic School Bus, WordGirl, The 39 Clues, Goosebumps, Animorphs, Maya & Miguel, Turbo Dogs, Fly Guy & Dragon.
ISBN Prefix(es): 978-0-439

**Scholastic Trade Division**
Division of Scholastic Inc
557 Broadway, New York, NY 10012
*Tel:* 212-343-6100; 212-343-4685 (export sales) *Fax:* 212-343-4714 (export sales)
*Web Site:* www.scholastic.com
*Key Personnel*
Pres, Trade Publg: Ellie Berger
VP, Group Publr: Lori Benton
VP & Publr, Arthur A Levine Books: Arthur A Levine
VP, Publr & Edit Dir, Scholastic Press: David Levithan
VP, Publr: Debra Dorfman
VP & Edit Dir, The Blue Sky Press: Bonnie Verburg
Publr, Michael di Capua Books: Michael di Capua
VP, Ed-at-Large: Andrea Pinkney
VP, Creative Dir & Edit Dir, Graphix: David Saylor
VP, Trade Sales: Alan Smagler
VP, Trade Fin: David Ascher
VP, Edit Dir, Orchard Books, Scholastic Press Picture Books & Cartwheel Books: Ken Geist
Exec Ed & Mgr, Scholastic en espanol: Maria Dominguez

Exec Ed, Scholastic Press: Dianne Hess
VP, Mktg: Stacy Lellos
VP, Publicity: Tracy van Straaten
Exec Dir, Creative Servs & Mktg/Sales Opers: Leslie Garych
Dir, Brand Mgmt: Julie Amitie
Exec Mng Ed/Dir of Prodn: Karyn Browne
Pres, Klutz: Jeff Pinsker
Scholastic Trade Books is an award-winning publisher of original children's books. Scholastic publishes more than 600 new hardcover, paperback & novelty books each year.
ISBN Prefix(es): 978-0-590; 978-0-439; 978-0-545
Number of titles published annually: 600 Print
Total Titles: 6,000 Print
Imprints: Arthur A Levine Books; The Blue Sky Press; Cartwheel Books; Chicken House; Graphix; Klutz; Little Shepherd; Michael di Capua Books; Orchard Books; Point; PUSH; Scholastic en Español; Scholastic Nonfiction; Scholastic Paperbacks; Scholastic Press; Scholastic Reference
*Distribution Center:* 2931 E McCarty St, Jefferson City, MO 65102 *Tel:* 573-635-5881

**§Scholium International Inc**
151 Cow Neck Rd, Port Washington, NY 11050
*Tel:* 516-767-7171
*E-mail:* info@scholium.com
*Web Site:* www.scholium.com
*Key Personnel*
Pres: Arthur Candido
EVP & Juv Ed: Elena M Candido
Founded: 1973
Science, medicine & technology.
ISBN Prefix(es): 978-0-87936
Number of titles published annually: 10 Print; 1 CD-ROM
Total Titles: 300 Print; 5 CD-ROM
Distributor for Dechema Series; Macmillan (UK); Micelle Press; Royal Society of London; Zuckschwerdt Verlag (Munich, Germany)

**Schonfeld & Associates Inc**
1931 Lynn Circle, Libertyville, IL 60048
SAN: 255-2361
*Tel:* 847-816-4870 *Toll Free Tel:* 800-205-0030 *Fax:* 847-816-4872
*E-mail:* saiinfo@saibooks.com
*Web Site:* www.saibooks.com
*Key Personnel*
Pres: Carol Greenhut *E-mail:* cgreenhut@saibooks.com
Founded: 1977
Author statistical reference works.
ISBN Prefix(es): 978-1-878339; 978-1-932024; 978-0-989055
Number of titles published annually: 9 Print; 12 CD-ROM; 12 E-Book
Total Titles: 10 Print; 12 CD-ROM; 12 E-Book

**School for Advanced Research Press**
660 Garcia St, Santa Fe, NM 87505
Mailing Address: PO Box 2188, Santa Fe, NM 87504-2188
*Tel:* 505-954-7206 *Toll Free Tel:* 888-390-6070 *Fax:* 505-954-7241
*E-mail:* press@sarsf.org
*Web Site:* sarpress.sarweb.org
*Key Personnel*
Dir: Lynn Thompson Baca *Tel:* 505-954-7260 *E-mail:* baca@sarsf.org
Founded: 1907
Scholarly & general-interest books on anthropology, archaeology, Native American art & the American Southwest.
ISBN Prefix(es): 978-1-930618; 978-0-933452
Number of titles published annually: 12 Print
Total Titles: 142 Print
Foreign Rep(s): Eurospan Ltd (Africa, Asia, Australasia, Europe, Middle East, UK); Scholarly Book Services (Canada)

**School Guide Publications**
210 North Ave, New Rochelle, NY 10801
*Tel:* 914-632-1220 *Toll Free Tel:* 800-433-7771 *Fax:* 914-632-3412
*E-mail:* info@religiousministries.com
*Web Site:* www.graduateguide.com; www.schoolguides.com; www.religiousministries.com
*Key Personnel*
Pres & Publr: Myles Ridder *E-mail:* mridder@schoolguides.com
Founded: 1886
Directories for colleges, institutions & religious communities.
Number of titles published annually: 5 Print; 3 Online
Total Titles: 15 Print; 3 Online
Membership(s): Copywriter's Council of America; National Association of College Admission Counseling

**School of Government**
Division of The University of NC Chapel Hill
University of North Carolina, CB 3330, Chapel Hill, NC 27599-3330
*Tel:* 919-966-4119 *Fax:* 919-962-2707
*Web Site:* www.sog.unc.edu
*Key Personnel*
Mktg & Sales Mgr: Katrina W Hunt *E-mail:* khunt@sog.unc.edu
Founded: 1931
Textbooks, casebooks, manuals & guidebooks, monographs, reports, e-books & bulletins.
ISBN Prefix(es): 978-1-56011
Number of titles published annually: 20 Print; 1 CD-ROM; 5 Online; 1 E-Book
Total Titles: 250 Print; 5 CD-ROM; 400 Online; 70 E-Book

**§School Zone Publishing Co**
1819 Industrial Dr, Grand Haven, MI 49417
*Tel:* 616-846-5030 *Toll Free Tel:* 800-253-0564 *Fax:* 616-846-6181 *Toll Free Fax:* 800-550-4618 (orders only)
*Web Site:* www.schoolzone.com
*Key Personnel*
Pres: Joan Hoffman
VP, Retail Sales: Sharon Winningham *Tel:* 616-846-5030 ext 217 *E-mail:* sharonw@schoolzone.com
Founded: 1979
Instructional materials for early childhood, pre-K to 6th grade; educational workbooks, flashcards & software.
ISBN Prefix(es): 978-0-88743; 978-0-938256; 978-1-58947
Number of titles published annually: 12 Print; 12 CD-ROM
Total Titles: 300 Print; 50 CD-ROM

**Schreiber Publishing Inc**
PO Box 4193, Rockville, MD 20849
SAN: 203-2465
*Tel:* 301-725-3906 *Toll Free Tel:* 800-296-1961 (sales) *Fax:* 301-725-0333 (orders)
*E-mail:* schreiberpublishing@comcast.net
*Web Site:* schreiberlanguage.com; shengold.com
*Key Personnel*
Pres: Jeremy Kay
Ed & Off Asst: Greg Giroux
Founded: 1954 (as Shengold Publishers)
Books on language & translation, Judaica history, Holocaust memoirs, juveniles, reference books, fiction, art books.
ISBN Prefix(es): 978-0-88400; 978-1-887563
Number of titles published annually: 12 Print; 7 E-Book; 1 Audio
Total Titles: 145 Print; 32 E-Book; 1 Audio
Imprints: Shengold Books
Foreign Rights: Bet Alim (Israel); Gazelle (Europe, UK); Importadora Agrimen (Latin America)

*Shipping Address:* National Book Network, 15200 NBN Way, Blue Ridge Summit, PA 17214, Contact: Christine Wolf *Tel:* 717-794-3800 *Fax:* 717-794-3804
*Warehouse:* National Book Network, 15200 NBN Way, Blue Ridge Summit, PA 17214, Contact: Christine Wolf *Tel:* 717-794-3800 *Fax:* 717-794-3804
*Distribution Center:* National Book Network, 4720 Boston Way, Lanham, MD 20706, Contact: Eileen Judd *Tel:* 301-459-3366 *Toll Free Tel:* 800-462-6420 *Fax:* 301-459-1705

**§Science & Humanities Press**
Subsidiary of Banis & Associates
56 Summit Point, St Charles, MO 62201
*Tel:* 636-394-4950
*Web Site:* sciencehumanitiespress.com; beachhousebooks.com; macroprintbooks.com; earlyeditionsbooks.com; heuristicsbooks.com
*Key Personnel*
CEO & Publr: Robert J Banis *E-mail:* banis@sciencehumanitiespress.com
Founded: 1994
Publish books with a mission. Titles include adapting to living with a disability, computer capabilities, education & specialized medical/wellness topics. Most interested in books that have enduring human value, promoting the kind of world we all want to live in. Prefer inquiries by e-mail. No unsol mss; author guidelines on web site (sciencehumanitiespress.com).
ISBN Prefix(es): 978-1-888725; 978-1-59630
Number of titles published annually: 20 Print; 20 E-Book; 1 Audio
Total Titles: 110 Print; 10 Online; 60 E-Book; 4 Audio
Imprints: BeachHouse Books; Early Editions Books; Heuristic Books; MacroPrintBooks
Membership(s): IBPA, the Independent Book Publishers Association; St Louis Publishers Association

**Science, Naturally!™**
Affiliate of Platypus Media
725 Eighth St SE, Washington, DC 20003
*Tel:* 202-465-4798 *Toll Free Tel:* 866-724-9876 *Fax:* 202-558-2132
*E-mail:* info@sciencenaturally.com
*Web Site:* www.sciencenaturally.com
*Key Personnel*
Pres: Dia L Michels *E-mail:* dia@sciencenaturally.com
Founded: 2001
Committed to increasing science literacy by exploring & demystifying key science topics.
ISBN Prefix(es): 978-0-9678020
Number of titles published annually: 5 Print; 5 E-Book
Total Titles: 7 Print; 7 E-Book
*Warehouse:* Ware Pak Inc, 2427 Bond St, University Park, IL 60466 *Tel:* 708-534-2600 *Fax:* 708-534-7803 *Web Site:* www.ware-pak.com
*Distribution Center:* National Book Network, 4501 Forbes Blvd, Lanham, MD 20706 *Tel:* 301-459-3366 *Fax:* 301-429-5746 *E-mail:* custserv@nbnbooks.com

**Science Publishers Inc**
Imprint of Edenbridge Ltd
PO Box 699, Enfield, NH 03748-0699
*Tel:* 603-632-7377 *Fax:* 603-632-5611
*E-mail:* info@scipub.net
*Web Site:* www.scipub.net
*Key Personnel*
Pres & Intl Rts: Vijay Primlani
Sales Exec & Lib Sales Dir: Linda Jones
Founded: 1992
Publish scholarly & scientific books.
ISBN Prefix(es): 978-1-886106; 978-1-57808; 978-1-881570

Number of titles published annually: 50 Print; 1 CD-ROM
Total Titles: 800 Print
*Foreign Office(s):* c/o Plymbridge Distributors Ltd, Estover Rd, Plymouth PL6 7PY, United Kingdom *E-mail:* orders@plymbridge.com
Distributed by CRC Press
Foreign Rep(s): Academic Marketing Services Pty Ltd (South Africa); James Benson (Ireland, UK); Paulo Ceschi (Brazil); Jim Chalmers (Ireland, UK); D A Information Services (Australia); MICHAEL GOH (Southeast Asia); IMA (North Africa); International Publishers Representatives Ltd (Middle East, North Africa); Ben Kato (Japan); Kemper Conseil Publishing (Benelux, Switzerland); Mark Latcham (Ireland, UK); Livraria Polytechnica Ltda (Brazil); Marcello s.a.s (France, Italy, Portugal, Spain); Minimax SAS (Italy); P B Foreign Book Centre LP (Cambodia, Thailand, Vietnam); P F Books (Indonesia); SHS Publishers' Consultants & Representatives (Austria, Germany, Switzerland); David Towle (Scandinavia)

**Scobre Press Corp**
2255 Calle Clara, La Jolla, CA 92037
*Toll Free Tel:* 877-726-2734 *Fax:* 858-551-1232
*E-mail:* info@scobre.com
*Web Site:* www.scobre.com
*Key Personnel*
Owner & Pres: Scott Blumenthal
Owner: Brett Hodus
Founded: 1999
ISBN Prefix(es): 978-0-9741692; 978-1-933423
Number of titles published annually: 6 Print
Total Titles: 12 Print

**§Scott Publishing Co**
Division of AMOS Publishing Co
911 S Vandemark Rd, Sidney, OH 45365
Mailing Address: PO Box 828, Sidney, OH 45365-0828
*Tel:* 937-498-0802 *Toll Free Tel:* 800-572-6885 (cust serv) *Fax:* 937-498-0807 *Toll Free Fax:* 800-488-5349
*E-mail:* cuserv@amospress.com
*Web Site:* www.amosadvantage.com
*Key Personnel*
Ed: Charles Snee
Dealers Sales Rep: Joellen Walter
Founded: 1863
Stamp collecting catalogs, reference books & stamp collecting accessories.
ISBN Prefix(es): 978-0-89487
Number of titles published annually: 8 Print
Total Titles: 8 Print

**Scribner**
Imprint of Scribner Publishing Group
1230 Avenue of the Americas, New York, NY 10020
*Key Personnel*
Pres: Susan Moldow
SVP & Publr: Nan Graham
VP, Assoc Publr: Rosalind Lippel
VP & Ed-in-Chief: Colin Harrison
Dir, Subs Rts & Mgr, Mktg: Paul O'Halloran
Art Dir: Tal Goretsky
Dir, Prodn: Olga Leonardo
Mgr, Mktg: Kara Watson
VP/Dir, Publicity: Brian Belfiglio
Deputy Dir of Publicity: Katie Monaghan
Sr Ed: Brant Rumble; Shannon Welch
Ed: Whitney Frick; Paul Whitlatch
Asst Ed: Daniel Burgess
Edit Asst: Katrina Diaz; John Glynn
Publg Asst: Seema Mahanian
ISBN Prefix(es): 978-0-684; 978-0-7432
Number of titles published annually: 70 Print
Imprints: Scribner Classics; Scribner Poetry

**Scripta Humanistica Publishing International**
Subsidiary of Brumar Communications
1383 Kersey Lane, Potomac, MD 20854
*Tel:* 301-294-7949 *Fax:* 301-424-9584
*E-mail:* info@scriptahumanistica.com
*Web Site:* www.scriptahumanistica.com
*Key Personnel*
Chmn of the Bd & Publr: Prof Bruno M Damiani *Tel:* 301-340-1095 *E-mail:* damiani@cua.edu
Founded: 1984
Publish reference books in the Humanities.
ISBN Prefix(es): 978-0-916379
Number of titles published annually: 5 Print
Total Titles: 171 Print; 171 Online
*Editorial Office(s):* Dept of Romance Languages, 512 Williams Hall, Philadelphia, PA 19104-6305, Gen Ed: Jose M Regueiro *Tel:* 215-898-5124 *Fax:* 215-898-0933 *E-mail:* jrequeir@sas.upenn.edu
Foreign Rep(s): Grant & Cutler Ltd (Northern Europe, UK); Leader Books SA (Greece, Middle East); Portico (Africa, Southern Europe, Spain); Scripta Humanistica (Caribbean, Latin America); Spain Shobo Co Inc (Asia, Australia, New Zealand)
*Distribution Center:* Baker & Taylor, 501 S Gladiolus Ave, Momence, IL 60954-1799 *Tel:* 815-472-2444
Yankee Book Peddler Inc, 999 Maple St, Contoocook, NH 03229-3374 *Tel:* 603-746-3102 *Fax:* 603-746-5628
Coutts Library Service, Dept A916379, 1823 Maryland Ave, Niagara Falls, NY 14302 *Tel:* 716-282-8627 *Fax:* 716-282-3831
Grant & Cutler Ltd, 55-57 Great Marlborough St, London W1V 1DD, United Kingdom *Tel:* (01) 734-2012
Leader Books SA, 62 Koniaristr, Ampelokipi GR11521, Greece *Tel:* (01) 64-52-825 *Fax:* (01) 64-49-924
Spain Shobo Co Ltd, Yamoto, PO Box 12, Miyagui 981-0503, Japan *Tel:* (0225) 84-1280 *Fax:* (0225) 84-1283 *E-mail:* info@spainshobo.co.jp
Scripta Humanistica, Calle Union 657, Miramar 00907, Puerto Rico *Tel:* 809-723-2445
Portico Librerias SA, Calle Munoz Seca 6, 50005 Zaragoza, Spain *Tel:* (976) 55 70 39 *Fax:* (976) 35 32 26 *E-mail:* jalcrudo@porticolibrerias.es

**The Scriptural Research & Publishing Co Inc**
344 E Johnson Ave, Cheshire, CT 06410
Mailing Address: PO Box 725, New Britain, CT 06050-0725
*Tel:* 203-272-1780 *Fax:* 203-272-2296
*E-mail:* src1@srpublish.org
*Web Site:* www.scripturalresearch.com
*Key Personnel*
Administrator: Joseph R Poulin
Founded: 1995
Religious & scripturally-based books.
ISBN Prefix(es): 978-1-57277
Number of titles published annually: 2 Print; 1 E-Book
Total Titles: 50 Print; 1 Audio

**Scurlock Publishing Co Inc**
1293 Myrtle Springs Rd, Texarkana, TX 75503
*Tel:* 903-832-4726 *Toll Free Tel:* 800-228-6389 (US & CN) *Fax:* 903-831-3177
*E-mail:* custserv@scurlockpublishing.com
*Web Site:* muzzleloadermag.com; www.scurlockpublishing.com
*Key Personnel*
Publr & Ed-in-Chief: Bill Scurlock
Mng Ed: Linda Scurlock
Founded: 1974
Historical nonfiction, early American nonfiction, hunting nonfiction, muzzleloading arms & shooting.
ISBN Prefix(es): 978-0-9605666; 978-1-880655
Number of titles published annually: 1 Print
Total Titles: 16 Print

**Seal Press**
Member of Perseus Books Group
1700 Fourth St, Berkeley, CA 94710
SAN: 215-3416
*Tel:* 510-595-3664 *Fax:* 510-595-4228
*E-mail:* seal.press@perseusbooks.com
*Web Site:* www.sealpress.com
*Key Personnel*
VP & Publr: Krista Lyons
VP, Prodn: Jane Musser
Exec Ed: Laura Mazer
Publicist: Eva Zimmerman
Founded: 1976
Publish books on a broad range of subjects by & for women.
ISBN Prefix(es): 978-0-931188; 978-1-878067; 978-1-58005
Number of titles published annually: 25 Print
Total Titles: 232 Print
*Orders to:* Publishers Group West, 1094 Flex Dr, Jackson, TN 38301 *Toll Free Tel:* 800-788-3123 *Toll Free Fax:* 800-351-5073
*Distribution Center:* Publishers Group West, 1094 Flex Dr, Jackson, TN 38301 *Toll Free Tel:* 800-788-3123 *Toll Free Fax:* 800-351-5073

**Search Institute Press®**
Division of Search Institute
The Banks Bldg, Suite 125, 615 First Ave NE, Minneapolis, MN 55413
*Tel:* 612-376-8955 *Toll Free Tel:* 800-888-7828 *Fax:* 612-692-5553
*E-mail:* si@search-institute.org
*Web Site:* www.search-institute.org
*Key Personnel*
Dir, Serv & Content Devt: Rebecca Post *E-mail:* beckyp@search-institute.org
Provide practical, hope-filled books to create a world in which young people are valued & thrive. Content is based on Search Institute's 50 years of research & focuses on the 40 Developmental Assets®, a framework of qualities, experiences & relationships youth need to succeed. Publishe resources for adults & youth that help strengthen communities by nurturing parents, concerned & caring adults, young people, educators & youth- family- & community-service professionals.
ISBN Prefix(es): 978-1-57482
Number of titles published annually: 4 Print; 4 E-Book
Total Titles: 110 Print; 50 E-Book
*Distribution Center:* Independent Publishers Group (IPG), 814 N Franklin St, Chicago, IL 60610 *Tel:* 312-337-0747 *Toll Free Tel:* 800-888-4741 (orders) *Fax:* 312-337-5985 *E-mail:* orders@ipgbook.com *Web Site:* www.ipgbook.com
Membership(s): ABC

**Second Chance Press**
Imprint of The Permanent Press
4170 Noyac Rd, Sag Harbor, NY 11963
SAN: 213-1633
*Tel:* 631-725-1101
*E-mail:* info@thepermanentpress.com
*Web Site:* www.thepermanentpress.com
*Key Personnel*
Co-Publr: Judith Shepard *E-mail:* judith@thepermanentpress.com; Martin Shepard *E-mail:* shepard@thepermanentpress.com
Mng Ed: Cathy Suter *E-mail:* cathy@thepermanentpress.com
Typesetting, Design & Prodn: Susan Ahlquist *E-mail:* susan@thepermanentpress.com
Founded: 1977
Originals & reprints of literary works in hardcover & paperback.
ISBN Prefix(es): 978-0-933256
Number of titles published annually: 16 Print
Total Titles: 450 Print
Foreign Rights: Nike Davarinou (Greece); Kira Dominguez (Australia); Lora Fountain Agency

(France); Jill Hughes (Eastern Europe); Intl Editors (Jennifer Houge) (Portugal, Spain); Jane Judd (UK); Andrew Nurnberg Associates (China); ONK Agency Ltd (Turkey); Thomas Schlueck (Germany); Rita Vivian (Italy); Eric Yang (Korea)

**§See-More's Workshop**
325 West End Ave, Suite 12-B, New York, NY 10023
*Tel:* 212-724-0677 *Fax:* 212-724-0767
*E-mail:* sbt@shadowboxtheatre.org
*Web Site:* www.shadowboxtheatre.org
*Key Personnel*
Administrator: Elaine Brand *E-mail:* ebrand@shadowboxtheatre.org
Founded: 1992
Publishing arm of the The Shadow Box Theatre, New York's musical puppet theatre for children. Publishes children's books, audio tapes & CDs & videos based on the shows.
ISBN Prefix(es): 978-1-882601
Number of titles published annually: 3 Print; 1 Audio
Total Titles: 10 Print; 10 Online; 10 Audio
*Distribution Center:* Amazon.com, 1200 12th Ave, Suite 1200, Seattle, WA 98144-2734 *Toll Free Tel:* 866-216-1074 *Web Site:* www.amazon.com
Brodart Co, 500 Arch St, Williamsport, PA 17701 *Tel:* 570-326-2461 *Toll Free Tel:* 800-233-8467 *Fax:* 570-326-1479 *E-mail:* support@brodart.com *Web Site:* www.brodart.com
Follett Library Resources, 1340 Ridgeview Dr, McHenry, IL 60050 *Tel:* 815-759-1700 *Toll Free Tel:* 888-511-5114 *Fax:* 815-759-9831 *Toll Free Fax:* 800-852-5458 *E-mail:* customerservice@flr.follett.com *Web Site:* www.titlewave.com

**See Sharp Press**
PO Box 1731, Tucson, AZ 85702-1731
*Tel:* 520-338-2151
*E-mail:* info@seesharppress.com
*Web Site:* www.seesharppress.com
*Key Personnel*
Founder, Publr & Sr Ed: Charles Bufe
Founded: 1984
Iconoclastic trade paperbacks & pamphlets on a wide variety of nonfiction topics.
ISBN Prefix(es): 978-1-884365
Number of titles published annually: 6 Print; 1 CD-ROM
Total Titles: 45 Print; 2 CD-ROM
Foreign Rights: Independent Publishers Group (Worldwide)
*Distribution Center:* Independent Publishers Group, 814 N Franklin, Chicago, IL 60610 *Tel:* 312-337-0747 *Toll Free Tel:* 800-888-4741 orders *Fax:* 312-337-5985 *Web Site:* www.ipgbook.com
Membership(s): IBPA, the Independent Book Publishers Association

**Seedling Publications Inc**
Imprint of Continental Press
520 E Bainbridge St, Elizabethtown, PA 17022
*Toll Free Tel:* 800-233-0759 *Toll Free Fax:* 888-834-1303
*E-mail:* info@continentalpress.com
*Web Site:* www.continentalpress.com
*Key Personnel*
Pres: Eric Beck *E-mail:* ebeck@continentalpress.com
Founded: 1992
Books for beginning readers in 8-16 page format; leveled readers-parental involvement materials.
ISBN Prefix(es): 978-0-8454
Number of titles published annually: 15 Print
Total Titles: 275 Print
Distributed by Kendall Hunt Publishing
Foreign Rep(s): PSI

**SelectBooks Inc**
One Union Sq W, Suite 909, New York, NY 10003
*Tel:* 212-206-1997 *Fax:* 212-206-3815
*E-mail:* info@selectbooks.com
*Web Site:* www.selectbooks.com
*Key Personnel*
Founder & Publr: Kenzi Sugihara *E-mail:* kenzi@selectbooks.com
Publicity Mgr: Kenichi Sugihara *E-mail:* kenichi@selectbooks.com
Founded: 2001
Book publisher.
ISBN Prefix(es): 978-1-59079
Number of titles published annually: 10 Print; 5 E-Book; 2 Audio
Total Titles: 50 Print; 5 E-Book; 3 Audio
*Sales Office(s):* Midpoint Trade Books, 27 W 20 St, Suite 1102, New York, NY 10011 *Tel:* 212-727-0190 *Fax:* 212-727-0195 *E-mail:* midpointny1@aol.com
Foreign Rights: Waterside Productions (Worldwide)
*Orders to:* Midpoint Trade Books, 27 W 20 St, Suite 1102, New York, NY 10011 *Tel:* 212-727-0190 *Fax:* 212-727-0195 *E-mail:* orders@midpt.com *Web Site:* www.midpointtrade.com
*Returns:* Midpoint Trade Books, 27 W 20 St, Suite 1102, New York, NY 10011 *Tel:* 212-727-0190 *Fax:* 212-727-0195 *E-mail:* orders@midpt.com *Web Site:* www.midpointtrade.com
*Distribution Center:* Midpoint Trade Books, 27 W 20 St, Suite 1102, New York, NY 10011 *Tel:* 212-727-0190 *Fax:* 212-727-0195 *Web Site:* www.midpointtrade.com
Baker & Taylor, 2550 W Tyvola Rd, Suite 300, Charlotte, NC 28217 *Tel:* 704-998-3100 *Toll Free Tel:* 800-775-1800 *Web Site:* www.btol.com
Ingram Content Group Inc, One Ingram Blvd, La Vergne, TN 37086 *Tel:* 615-793-5000 *E-mail:* inquiry@ingramcontent.com *Web Site:* www.ingramcontent.com
Membership(s): IBPA, the Independent Book Publishers Association

**§Self-Counsel Press Ltd**
4152 Meridian St, Suite 105-471, Bellingham, WA 98226
SAN: 240-9925
*Toll Free Tel:* 800-663-3007
*E-mail:* orders@self-counsel.com
*Web Site:* www.self-counsel.com
*Key Personnel*
Pres: Diana R Douglas *E-mail:* drdouglas@self-counsel.com
Mng Ed: Richard Day *E-mail:* rday@self-counsel.com
Mktg Mgr: Tyler Douglas *Tel:* 604-986-3366 ext 215
Founded: 1971
Legal, business & reference books.
ISBN Prefix(es): 978-1-55180; 978-1-77040
Number of titles published annually: 15 Print; 5 CD-ROM
Total Titles: 230 Print; 100 CD-ROM
*Branch Office(s)*
1481 Charlotte Rd, North Vancouver, BC V7J 1H1, Canada *Tel:* 604-986-3366 *Fax:* 604-986-3947 SAN: 115-0545
Membership(s): ALA

**Self-Realization Fellowship Publishers**
3208 Humboldt St, Los Angeles, CA 90031
SAN: 204-5788
*Tel:* 323-276-6002 *Toll Free Tel:* 888-773-8680 *Fax:* 323-927-1624
*Web Site:* www.srfpublishers.org
*Key Personnel*
Sales Mgr: Phil Gray *E-mail:* philg@srfpublishers.org
Mktg: Mike Baake *E-mail:* mikeb@srfpublishers.org
Founded: 1920 (by Paramahansa Yogananda)
Publisher for the complete works of Paramahansa Yogananda.
ISBN Prefix(es): 978-0-87612
Number of titles published annually: 10 Print; 7 Audio
*Returns:* 3233 N San Fernando Rd, Unit 2, Los Angeles, CA 90065, Mark Russell *Tel:* 323-276-6000 *E-mail:* markr@yogananda-srf.org SAN: 204-5688
Membership(s): IBPA, the Independent Book Publishers Association

**Sentient Publications LLC**
1113 Spruce St, Boulder, CO 80302
*Tel:* 303-443-2188 *Fax:* 303-381-2538
*E-mail:* contact@sentientpublications.com
*Web Site:* www.sentientpublications.com
*Key Personnel*
Publr: Connie Shaw *E-mail:* cshaw@sentientpublications.com
Founded: 2001
Ecology, education, health, science, spirituality. Publish quality nonfiction books that arise from the spirit of inquiry & the richness of the inherent dialogue between writer & reader.
ISBN Prefix(es): 978-0-9710786; 978-1-59181
Number of titles published annually: 5 Print; 5 E-Book
Total Titles: 105 Print; 105 E-Book; 10 Audio
Foreign Rights: ANA Sofia Ltd (Bulgaria, Romania); Asli Karasuil Telif Haklari Ajansi (Turkey); Book Publishers Association of Israel (Israel); Giro di Parole (Italy); The English Agency (Japan); International Editors' Co (Spain); JLM Literary Agency (Greece); Michelle Lapautre Literary Agency (France); Maxima Creative Agency (Indonesia); Andrew Nurnberg (China); Piper & Poppenhusen (Germany); H Katia Schumer (Brazil); Silkroad Publishers Agency (Thailand)
*Orders to:* National Book Network, 4720 Boston Way, Lanham, MD 20706 *Tel:* 301-459-3366 *Toll Free Tel:* 800-462-6420 *Fax:* 301-459-1705 *Web Site:* www.nbnbooks.com
*Shipping Address:* National Book Network, 4720 Boston Way, Lanham, MD 20706 *Tel:* 301-459-3366 *Toll Free Tel:* 800-462-6420 *Fax:* 301-459-1705 *Web Site:* www.nbnbooks.com
*Distribution Center:* National Book Network, 4720 Boston Way, Lanham, MD 20706 *Tel:* 301-459-3366 *Toll Free Tel:* 800-462-6420 *Fax:* 301-459-1705 *Web Site:* www.nbnbooks.com
Membership(s): Publishers Association of the West

**Serindia Publications**
PO Box 10335, Chicago, IL 60610-0335
*Tel:* 312-664-5531 *Fax:* 312-664-4389
*E-mail:* info@serindia.com
*Web Site:* www.serindia.com
*Key Personnel*
Publr: Shane Suvikapakornkul
Founded: 1976 (established in London)
ISBN Prefix(es): 978-1-932476
Number of titles published annually: 11 Print
Total Titles: 60 Print
Distributed by Art Media Resources Inc (US & CN)
Foreign Rep(s): Kodansha Europe (Europe, UK); Paragon Asia Co Ltd (Singapore, Southeast Asia, Thailand); United Century Book Service (Hong Kong, Mainland China); The Variety Book Depot (Bhutan, India, Nepal, South Asia)

**Seven Footer Kids**
Imprint of Seven Footer Press
247 W 30 St, 11th fl, New York, NY 10001-2824
*Tel:* 212-710-9340 *Fax:* 212-710-9344
*E-mail:* info@sevenfooter.com
*Web Site:* www.sevenfooterpress.com

*Key Personnel*
Pres & Publr: David Gomberg
Chief Creative Offr: Justin Heimberg
Founded: 2009
Dedicated to publishing books that, together, children & parents can learn from & enjoy.
ISBN Prefix(es): 978-0-9740439; 978-0-9788178; 978-4-93734
Number of titles published annually: 12 Print
Total Titles: 20 Print
*Distribution Center:* Publishers Group West, 1094 Flex Dr, Jackson, TN 38301 *Toll Free Tel:* 800-788-2123 *Toll Free Fax:* 800-351-5073 *Web Site:* www.pgw.com

**Seven Footer Press**
Subsidiary of Seven Footer Entertainment LLC
247 W 30 St, 2nd fl, New York, NY 10001-2824
*Tel:* 212-710-9340 *Fax:* 212-710-9344
*E-mail:* info@sevenfooter.com
*Web Site:* www.sevenfooterpress.com
*Key Personnel*
Pres & Publr: David Gomberg
Chief Creative Offr: Justin Heimberg
Founded: 2004
Publishes cutting-edge nonfiction: innovative humor, puzzle, gift & high-concept books including the enormously successful *Would You Rather . . .?* series.
ISBN Prefix(es): 978-0-9740439; 978-0-9788178; 978-1-934734
Number of titles published annually: 20 Print; 5 E-Book
Total Titles: 51 Print; 4 E-Book
Imprints: Seven Footer Kids
*Distribution Center:* Publishers Group West, 1094 Flex Dr, Jackson, TN 38301 *Toll Free Tel:* 800-788-2123 *Toll Free Fax:* 800-351-5073 *Web Site:* www.pgw.com
*See separate listing for:*
**Seven Footer Kids**

**Seven Locks Press**
3100 W Warner Ave, Suite 8, Santa Ana, CA 97204
Mailing Address: PO Box 25689, Santa Ana, CA 92799
*E-mail:* sevenlocks@aol.com
*Web Site:* www.sevenlockspublishing.com
*Key Personnel*
Publr: James C Riordan
Founded: 1973
Publishes a variety of hardcover & trade paperback books; foreign rights agents worldwide; foreign representatives in UK, European Union & South Africa.
This publisher has indicated that 30% of their product line is author subsidized.
ISBN Prefix(es): 978-0-9801270; 978-1-931643; 978-0-929
Number of titles published annually: 25 Print
Total Titles: 500 Print
Membership(s): AAP; Northern California Independent Booksellers Association; Pacific Northwest Booksellers Association; Southern California Independent Booksellers Association

**Seven Stories Press**
140 Watts St, New York, NY 10013
*Tel:* 212-226-8760 *Fax:* 212-226-1411
*E-mail:* info@sevenstories.com
*Web Site:* www.sevenstories.com
*Key Personnel*
Publr: Daniel Simon *E-mail:* dan@sevenstories.com
Assoc Publr & Exec Ed: Amber Qureshi
Opers Dir: Jon Gilbert *E-mail:* jon@sevenstories.com
Dir, Mktg & Publicity, Triangle Square Books: Ruth Weiner *E-mail:* ruth@sevenstories.com
Mng Ed: Elizabeth DeLong
Founded: 1995
Publish original hardcover & paperback books for the general reader in the area of literature, literature in translation, popular culture, politics, media studies, health & nutrition & sports. No unsol mss.
ISBN Prefix(es): 978-1-58322; 978-1-888363
Number of titles published annually: 50 Print; 15 E-Book; 2 Audio
Total Titles: 380 Print; 36 E-Book; 2 Audio
Imprints: Siete Cuentos Editorial
Foreign Rep(s): Turnaround Distribution (European Union, UK)
Foreign Rights: Anatoliat Agency (Turkey); Big Apple Agency (China, Taiwan); Paul & Peter Fritz Agency (Germany); Deborah Harris Agency (Israel); Japan Uni Agency Inc (Japan); Katai & Bolza Literary Agents (Hungary); Duran Kim Agency (Korea); MB Agencia Literaria (Spain); Piergiorgio Nicolazzini Literary Agency (Italy); Andrew Nurnberg Associates (Russia); Sandorf Literary Agency (Bosnia and Herzegovina, Croatia, Kosovo, Macedonia, Montenegro, Serbia, Slovenia); Tonnheim Literary Agency (Scandinavia); Villas-Boas & Moss (Luciana Villas-Bous) (Brazil)
*Distribution Center:* Random House, 400 Hahn Rd, Westminster, MD 21157 *Tel:* 410-848-1900 *Toll Free Tel:* 800-933-3000 *Web Site:* www.randomhouse.com

**§Shadow Mountain**
PO Box 30178, Salt Lake City, UT 84130
*Tel:* 801-534-1515 *Fax:* 801-517-3474
*E-mail:* submissions@shadowmountain.com
*Web Site:* shadowmountain.com
*Key Personnel*
Acq Ed: Allison Mathews
Founded: 1985
US-based publisher committed to providing books (print, electronic & audio) that offer value-based messages for readers of all ages. Publish quality children's fantasy & numerous bestsellers in the inspiration, fiction, history & business genres.
ISBN Prefix(es): 978-0-88494; 978-1-59038; 978-1-57345; 978-1-57008; 978-0-87579; 978-1-60908
Number of titles published annually: 25 Print; 2 Online; 25 E-Book; 10 Audio
Total Titles: 200 Print; 2 Online; 70 E-Book; 80 Audio
Imprints: Proper Romance
*Distribution Center:* Baker & Taylor, 2550 W Tyvola Rd, Suite 300, Charlotte, NC 28217 *Tel:* 704-998-3100 *Web Site:* www.btol.com
Ingram Content Group, One Ingram Blvd, La Vergne, TN 37086 *Tel:* 615-793-5000 *Web Site:* www.ingramcontent.com
Membership(s): ABC; BEA; Children's Book Council; IBPA, the Independent Book Publishers Association; Mountains & Plains Independent Publishers Association; Romance Writers of America

**§Shambhala Publications Inc**
Horticultural Hall, 300 Massachusetts Ave, Boston, MA 02115
SAN: 203-2481
*Tel:* 617-424-0030 *Toll Free Tel:* 866-424-0030 (off); 888-424-2329 (cust serv) *Fax:* 617-236-1563
*E-mail:* customercare@shambhala.com
*Web Site:* www.shambhala.com
*Key Personnel*
Founder & Ed-in-Chief: Samuel Bercholz
Owner & EVP: Sara Bercholz
Owner & Ed: Ivan Bercholz
Pres: Nikko Odiseos
Publr: Julie Saidenberg
Sr Ed: David O'Neal
Mng Ed: Liz Shaw
Ed, Roost Books: Rochelle Bourgault
Ed: Beth Frankl
Acquiring Ed & Ed, Roost Books: Jennifer Urban-Brown
Ed-at-Large: Susan Piver
Sr Designer: Jim Zaccaria
Founded: 1969
Trade books; art, literature, comparative religion, philosophy, science, psychology & related subjects.
ISBN Prefix(es): 978-0-307; 978-0-87773; 978-1-56957; 978-1-57062; 978-1-59030
Number of titles published annually: 85 Print; 50 Online
Total Titles: 600 Print; 50 Online
Imprints: Roost Books; Snow Lion
Distributed by Random House Inc
Foreign Rep(s): Airlift Books (UK); Random House Australia Ltd (Australia); Random House of Canada Ltd (Canada); Random House of New Zealand (New Zealand)
Foreign Rights: ACER (Spain); The English Agency (Japan); Anoukh Foerg (Germany); La Nouvelle Agence (Vanessa Kling) (France); Karen Schindler (Brazil)
*Advertising Agency:* Vermillion Graphics, Boulder, CO 80302
*Returns:* Random House Returns Dept, 400 Bennett Dr, Westminster, MD 21157
*Shipping Address:* Random House Distribution Center, 400 Hahn Rd, Westminster, MD 21157
*See separate listing for:*
**Snow Lion Publications Inc**

**§M E Sharpe Inc**
80 Business Park Dr, Suite 202, Armonk, NY 10504
SAN: 202-7100
*Tel:* 914-273-1800 *Toll Free Tel:* 800-541-6563 *Fax:* 914-273-2106
*E-mail:* info@mesharpe.com
*Web Site:* www.mesharpe.com
*Key Personnel*
Pres: Myron E Sharpe
VP & Dir, New Prod Devt: Donna Sanzone *E-mail:* dsanzone@mesharpe.com
VP & Dir, Mktg & Sales: Diana McDermott *E-mail:* dmcdermott@mesharpe.com
VP & Edit Dir: Patricia A Kolb *E-mail:* pkolb@mesharpe.com
Exec Ed, Mgmt: Harry Briggs *E-mail:* briggs.harry@gmail.com
Founded: 1958
Scholarly books in social sciences, international relations, area studies, management. College texts, reference, trade, business & professional books. Scholarly & professional journals.
ISBN Prefix(es): 978-0-87332; 978-1-56324; 978-0-7656
Number of titles published annually: 80 Print; 6 Online; 35 E-Book
Total Titles: 1,200 Print; 3 CD-ROM; 9 Online; 200 E-Book
Imprints: East Gate Books; North Castle Books; Sharpe Focus; Sharpe Online Reference; Sharpe Reference
Foreign Rep(s): APAC Publishers Services Pte Ltd (American Samoa, Brunei, Cambodia, Guam, Indonesia, Korea, Laos, Malaysia, Micronesia, Papua New Guinea, Philippines, Singapore, Solomon Islands, Thailand, Vietnam); Applied Media (India); J Coutts Library Services Ltd (Canada); DA Information Services (Australia, New Zealand, Pacific Basin); The Eurospan Group (Algeria, Bahrain, Egypt, Europe, Iran, Iraq, Israel, Jordan, Lebanon, Libya, Morocco, Oman, Palestine, Qatar, Saudi Arabia, Sudan, Tunisia, Turkey, United Arab Emirates, UK, Yemen); ITA Beijing (China, Hong Kong, Taiwan); Kinokuniya Co Ltd (Japan); PAK Book Corp (Pakistan); United Publishers Services Ltd (Japan)
*Warehouse:* Maple Press Distribution Center, 1000 Strickler Rd, Mount Joy, PA 17552

*Distribution Center:* Maple Press Distribution Center, 1000 Strickler Rd, Mount Joy, PA 17552
Membership(s): ALA; Society for Scholarly Publishing

**Sheffield Publishing Co**
Subsidiary of Waveland Press Inc
9009 Antioch Rd, Salem, WI 53168
Mailing Address: PO Box 359, Salem, WI 53168-0359
*Tel:* 262-843-2281 *Fax:* 262-843-3683
*E-mail:* info@spcbooks.com
*Web Site:* www.spcbooks.com
*Key Personnel*
Mng Ed: Stephen R Nelson
Busn Mgr: Jodi R Jacobsen *E-mail:* jodi@spcbooks.com
Founded: 1984
Publisher of college texts & supplements.
ISBN Prefix(es): 978-0-88133; 978-1-879215
Number of titles published annually: 10 Print
Total Titles: 17 Print

**Shenanigan Books**
84 River Rd, Summit, NJ 07901
*Tel:* 908-219-4275 *Fax:* 908-219-4485
*E-mail:* info@shenaniganbooks.com
*Web Site:* www.shenaniganbooks.com
*Key Personnel*
Creative Dir: Mary Watson
Children's Literature: craft/picture/board books.
ISBN Prefix(es): 978-0-9726614; 978-1-934860
Number of titles published annually: 6 Print
Membership(s): ALA; Children's Book Council; IBPA, the Independent Book Publishers Association

**Shengold Publishers Inc**, see Schreiber Publishing Inc

**Shen's Books**
1547 Palos Verdes Mall, Unit 291, Walnut Creek, CA 94597
SAN: 138-2926
*Tel:* 925-262-8108 *Toll Free Tel:* 800-456-6660 *Fax:* 925-415-6136 *Toll Free Fax:* 888-269-9092
*E-mail:* info@shens.com
*Web Site:* www.shens.com
*Key Personnel*
Owner & Pres: Renee Ting *E-mail:* renee@shens.com
Founded: 1985
Children's books.
ISBN Prefix(es): 978-1-885008
Number of titles published annually: 3 Print
Total Titles: 25 Print
Membership(s): ABA; IBPA, the Independent Book Publishers Association

**Shepard Publications**
PO Box 280, Friday Harbor, WA 98250
*Web Site:* www.shepardpub.com
*Key Personnel*
Owner & Pres: Aaron Shepard
ISBN Prefix(es): 978-0-938497; 978-1-62035; 978-0-9849616
Number of titles published annually: 4 Print; 4 E-Book
Total Titles: 30 Print; 15 E-Book
Imprints: Islander Press; Shepard & Piper (literary fiction & nonfiction); Shepard Publications (practical nonfiction, alternative viewpoints & professional resources); Simple Productions (nonviolence, lifestyle alternatives, music); Skyhook Press (children's)
*Distribution Center:* Lightning Source Inc, 1246 Heil Quaker Blvd, La Vergne, TN 37086 *Tel:* 615-213-5815 *Fax:* 615-213-4725
Lightning Source UK Ltd, Chapter House, Pittfield, Kiln Farm, Milton Keynes MK11 3LW, United Kingdom *Tel:* (0845) 121 4567 *Fax:* (0845) 121 4594 *E-mail:* enquiries@lightningsource.co.uk

**Sherman Asher Publishing**
126 Candelario St, Santa Fe, NM 87501
*Tel:* 505-988-7214
*E-mail:* westernedge@santa-fe.net
*Web Site:* www.shermanasher.com; www.westernedgepress.com
*Key Personnel*
Owner & Publr: James Mafchir
Founded: 1995
Literary books that include Spanish, English & bilingual memoirs & Judaica.
ISBN Prefix(es): 978-0-9644196; 978-1-890932
Number of titles published annually: 3 Print
Total Titles: 29 Print
Imprints: Western Edge Press (titles: 3)
*Distribution Center:* SCB Distributors, 15608 S New Century Dr, Gardena, CA 90248 *Tel:* 310-532-9400 *Toll Free Tel:* 800-729-6423 *Fax:* 310-532-7001

**Sheron Enterprises Inc**
1035 S Carley Ct, North Bellmore, NY 11710
*Tel:* 516-783-5885
*E-mail:* contact@longislandbookpublisher.com
*Web Site:* www.longislandbookpublisher.com
*Key Personnel*
Owner & Pres: Sheryl Perry
Secy: Ronald Perry
Founded: 1996
Publish college textbooks, lab manuals & study aids for college professors with small & large print runs as well as helping unknown authors get published: poetry.
ISBN Prefix(es): 978-1-891877
Number of titles published annually: 5 Print
Total Titles: 26 Print

**Shields Publications**
PO Box 669, Eagle River, WI 54521-0669
*Tel:* 715-479-4810 *Fax:* 715-479-3905
*E-mail:* wormbooks@wormbooks.com
*Web Site:* www.wormbooks.com
*Key Personnel*
Owner: Lynda Bolte
Founded: 1951
Publisher of books about earthworms, vermiculture, vermicomposting, commercial worm production.
ISBN Prefix(es): 978-0-914116
Number of titles published annually: 22 Print
Total Titles: 22 Print; 1 CD-ROM

**Show What You Know® Publishing, A Lorenz Company**
501 E Third St, Dayton, OH 45402
*Tel:* 614-764-1211; 937-228-6118 *Toll Free Tel:* 877-PASSING (727-7464) *Fax:* 937-233-2042
*E-mail:* info@swykonline.com
*Web Site:* www.swykonline.com; www.lorenzeducationalpress.com
*Key Personnel*
Pres: Geoff Lorenz
Educational publisher of K-12 supplemental test-preparation books & other materials.
ISBN Prefix(es): 978-1-884183; 978-1-59230
Number of titles published annually: 90 Print
Total Titles: 275 Print
Membership(s): IBPA, the Independent Book Publishers Association

**SIAM**, see Society for Industrial & Applied Mathematics

**Side Street**, see BrickHouse Books Inc

**Sierra Club Books**
85 Second St, 2nd fl, San Francisco, CA 94105
SAN: 203-2406
*Tel:* 415-977-5500 *Fax:* 415-977-5794
*E-mail:* books.publishing@sierraclub.org
*Web Site:* www.sierraclubbooks.org
*Key Personnel*
Publr: Helen Sweetland *E-mail:* helen.sweetland@sierraclub.org
Calendar Prog Coord: Mollie Eldemir *E-mail:* mollie.eldemir@sierraclub.org
Founded: 1892
Publisher of books on nature & the environment, including children's books & calendars.
ISBN Prefix(es): 978-0-87156; 978-1-57805
Number of titles published annually: 10 Print
Total Titles: 125 Print
Divisions: Sierra Club Books for Children; Sierra Club Calendars
Distributed by Chronicle Books (Sierra Club Calendars); Gibbs Smith (Sierra Club Books for Children)
Distributor for Counterpoint Press
*Distribution Center:* Publishers Group West, 1700 Fourth St, Berkeley, CA 94710 *Tel:* 510-809-3700 *Fax:* 510-809-3777 *E-mail:* info@pgw.com *Web Site:* www.pgw.com

**Siglio**
2432 Medlow Ave, Los Angeles, CA 90041
*Tel:* 310-857-6935 *Fax:* 310-728-6844
*E-mail:* publisher@sigliopress.com
*Web Site:* sigliopress.com
*Key Personnel*
Publr: Lisa Pearson
Founded: 2008
ISBN Prefix(es): 978-0-9799562; 978-1-938221

**Signalman Publishing**
3700 Commerce Blvd, Kissimmee, FL 34741
*Tel:* 407-504-4103 *Toll Free Tel:* 888-907-4423
*E-mail:* info@signalmanpublishing.com
*Web Site:* www.signalmanpublishing.com
*Key Personnel*
Pres: John McClure *E-mail:* john@signalmanpublishing.com
Ed: Urmila McClure *E-mail:* urmila@signalmanpublishing.com
Founded: 2008
Specialize in bringing nonfiction works to the Kindle format. Have also branched out into trade paper with both nonfiction & fiction works.
This publisher has indicated that 45% of their product line is author subsidized.
ISBN Prefix(es): 978-0-9840614; 978-1-935991
Number of titles published annually: 12 Print; 14 E-Book
Total Titles: 56 Print; 76 E-Book
*Orders to:* Lightning Source, 1246 Heil Quaker Blvd, La Vergne, TN 37086, Contact: Pam Dover *Tel:* 615-213-4690 *Fax:* 615-213-4725 *E-mail:* pam.dover@lightningsource.com
*Shipping Address:* Lightning Source, 1246 Heil Quaker Blvd, La Vergne, TN 37086, Contact: Pam Dover *Tel:* 615-213-4690 *Fax:* 615-213-4725 *E-mail:* pam.dover@lightningsource.com
Membership(s): The Association of Publishers for Special Sales; Christian Small Publishers Association

**Signature Books Publishing LLC**
564 W 400 N, Salt Lake City, UT 84116-3411
SAN: 217-4391
*Tel:* 801-531-1483 *Toll Free Tel:* 800-356-5687 (orders) *Fax:* 801-531-1488
*E-mail:* people@signaturebooks.com
*Web Site:* www.signaturebooks.com; www.signaturebookslibrary.org
*Key Personnel*
Pres: George D Smith
Mng Dir: Ronald L Priddis

Busn Mgr: Keiko Jones *Tel:* 801-531-1483 ext 102 *E-mail:* keiko@signaturebooks.com
Shipping Mgr: Greg Jones
Mktg: Tom Kimball
Prodn & Design: Connie Disney
Off Mgr: Jani Fleet
Founded: 1980
Western Americana.
ISBN Prefix(es): 978-0-941214; 978-1-56085
Number of titles published annually: 10 Print
Total Titles: 173 Print; 1 CD-ROM
Imprints: Smith-Pettit Foundation; Smith Research Associates
Distributor for Charles Redd Center; Tanner Trust Fund

**§SIL International**
7500 W Camp Wisdom Rd, Dallas, TX 75236-5629
*Tel:* 972-708-7400 *Fax:* 972-708-7350
*E-mail:* publications_intl@sil.org
*Web Site:* www.ethnologue.com; www.sil.org
*Key Personnel*
Asst Mgr: Darryl Johnson
Founded: 1942
Books.
ISBN Prefix(es): 978-0-88312; 978-1-55671
Number of titles published annually: 6 Print
Total Titles: 160 Print; 2 CD-ROM; 3 Online; 3 E-Book

**Silicon Press**
25 Beverly Rd, Summit, NJ 07901
*Tel:* 908-273-8919 *Fax:* 908-273-6149
*E-mail:* info@silicon-press.com
*Web Site:* www.silicon-press.com
*Key Personnel*
CEO: Indu Gehani
Founded: 1987
Books about computers & technology/fiction.
ISBN Prefix(es): 978-0-929306
Number of titles published annually: 10 Print; 4 Audio
Total Titles: 45 Print

**Silman-James Press**
3624 Shannon Rd, Los Angeles, CA 90027
*Tel:* 323-661-9922 *Toll Free Tel:* 877-SJP-BOOK (757-2665) *Fax:* 323-661-9933
*E-mail:* info@silmanjamespress.com
*Web Site:* www.silmanjamespress.com
*Key Personnel*
Publr: Gwen Feldman *E-mail:* gwen@silmanjamespress.com; Jim Fox *E-mail:* jim@silmanjamespress.com
Founded: 1990
Publishers of books on film, filmmaking, the motion picture industry & the performing arts.
ISBN Prefix(es): 978-1-879505
Number of titles published annually: 3 Print
Total Titles: 75 Print
Divisions: Siles Press (chess & nonfiction titles)
Distributed by Codasat Canada Ltd
Foreign Rep(s): Gazelle Book Services (Continental Europe, UK)
*Returns:* 660 S Mansfield, Ypsilanti, MI 48197

**Silver Leaf Books LLC**
13 Temi Rd, Holliston, MA 01746
Mailing Address: PO Box 6460, Holliston, MA 01746
*E-mail:* sales@silverleafbooks.com; editor@silverleafbooks.com; customerservice@silverleafbooks.com
*Web Site:* www.silverleafbooks.com
*Key Personnel*
Mng Dir: Clifford B Bowyer *E-mail:* cbbowyer@silverleafbooks.com
Edit Mgr: Brett Fried *E-mail:* bfried@silverleafbooks.com
Sales Mgr: Marilyn Fried *E-mail:* mfried@silverleafbooks.com
Founded: 2003
ISBN Prefix(es): 978-0-9744354; 978-0-9787782; 978-1-60975
Number of titles published annually: 6 Print; 8 E-Book
Total Titles: 26 Print; 25 E-Book

**Silver Moon Press**
400 E 85 St, New York, NY 10028
*Toll Free Tel:* 800-874-3320 *Fax:* 212-988-8112
*E-mail:* mail@silvermoonpress.com
*Web Site:* www.silvermoonpress.com
*Key Personnel*
Publr: David Katz
Founded: 1992
Publish curriculum workbooks in mathematics, English language arts & social studies for the K-8 market.
ISBN Prefix(es): 978-1-881889; 978-1-893110
Number of titles published annually: 4 Print
Total Titles: 110 Print
*Returns:* c/o The Oliver Press, 5707 W 36 St, Minneapolis, MN 55416
*Warehouse:* c/o Metro-Pack Inc, 37 Jeanne Dr, Newburgh, NY 12550 *Tel:* 845-564-5275 *Fax:* 845-564-5305

**SilverHouse Books**
555 NE 15 St, Suite 2-i, Miami, FL 33132
*Tel:* 305-747-1258
*E-mail:* info@silverhousebooks.com
*Web Site:* www.silverhousebooks.com
*Key Personnel*
VP: Rebeca Del'Isola
Founded: 2010
Small publisher of children's & young adult books.
ISBN Prefix(es): 978-0-9829312; 978-0-9831038; 978-0-9847909
Number of titles published annually: 6 Print; 6 Online; 6 E-Book
Total Titles: 6 Print; 6 Online; 6 E-Book
Membership(s): IBPA, the Independent Book Publishers Association

**Simba Information**
Division of Market Research Group
60 Long Ridge Rd, Suite 300, Stamford, CT 06902
SAN: 210-2021
*Tel:* 203-325-8193 *Toll Free Tel:* 888-297-4622 (cust serv) *Fax:* 203-325-8975
*E-mail:* customerservice@simbainformation.com
*Web Site:* www.simbainformation.com
*Key Personnel*
Mng Ed/Analyst: Kathy Mickey
Founded: 1989
Newsletters & research reports for information companies. Subject specialties: publishing & media.
ISBN Prefix(es): 978-0-918110
Number of titles published annually: 15 Print; 15 Online
Total Titles: 75 Print; 75 Online
Membership(s): AAP; BISG

**Simcha Press**
Imprint of Health Communications Inc
3201 SW 15 St, Deerfield Beach, FL 33442-8190
*Tel:* 954-360-0909 ext 212 *Toll Free Tel:* 800-851-9100 ext 212 *Toll Free Fax:* 800-424-7652
*E-mail:* simchapress@hcibooks.com
*Web Site:* www.hcibooks.com
*Key Personnel*
Dir, Communs & Mgr: Kim Weiss *E-mail:* kimw@hcibooks.com
Founded: 1999
Nonfiction titles for those on the path of Jewish enrichment. Jewish interest, spirituality, inspirational, mysticism & recovery.
ISBN Prefix(es): 978-1-55874; 978-0-7573
Number of titles published annually: 4 Print; 4 Online; 4 E-Book
Total Titles: 13 Print; 13 Online; 8 E-Book
Foreign Rights: Claude Choquette

**Simon & Schuster**
Imprint of Simon & Schuster Publishing Group
1230 Avenue of the Americas, New York, NY 10020
*Tel:* 212-698-7000 *Toll Free Tel:* 800-223-2348 (cust serv); 800-223-2336 (orders) *Toll Free Fax:* 800-943-9831 (orders)
*Web Site:* www.simonandschuster.com
*Key Personnel*
Pres & Publr: Jonathan Karp
VP & Edit Dir: Alice E Mayhew
VP & Ed-in-Chief: Marysue Rucci
VP & Exec Ed: Priscilla Painton; Trish Todd
VP & Sr Ed: Robert Bender; Thomas LeBien
VP & Assoc Publr: Richard Rhorer; Suzanne Donahue
VP & Exec Mng Ed: Irene Kheradi
VP & Dir, Subs Rts: Lance Fitzgerald
VP & Dir, Publicity, Sr Ed: Cary Goldstein
VP & Exec Art Dir, Trade Art: Jackie Seow
Sr Ed: Jofie Ferrari-Adler; Ben Loehnen; Sarah Knight; Millicent Bennett; Karyn Marcus
Ed: Michael Szczerban
Assoc Ed: Johanna Li; Sydney Tanigawa; Molly Lindley; Nick Greene; Emily Graff
Asst Ed: Jonathan Cox
Edit Asst: Sarah Nalle; Brit Hvide
Assoc Dir, Subs Rts: Marie Florio
Deputy Dir, Publicity: Julia Prosser
Assoc Dir, Publicity: Larry Hughes
Publicity Mgr: Anne Tate; Meg Cassidy; Jennifer Garza
Sr Publicist: Maureen Cole; Kate Gales; Jessica Lawrence
Publicist: Leah Johanson
Assoc Publicist: Erin Reback
Publicity Asst: Maggie Higby; Elizabeth Gay; Meg Miller; Alicia Samuel
Art Dir, Trade Art: Michael Accordino
Sr Mktg Mgr: Nina Pajak
Online Mktg Mgr: Elina Vaysbeyn
Mktg Mgr: Marie Kent; Stephen Bedford
Assoc Mktg Mgr: Andrea DeWerd
Publg Assoc: Laura Tatham
ISBN Prefix(es): 978-0-684
Number of titles published annually: 125 Print
Imprints: Folgers Shakespeare Library; Free Press
Foreign Rights: Akali Copyright Agency (Turkey); Antonella Antonelli Agenzia (Italy); Book Publishers Association of Israel (Israel); Japan UNI Agency (Japan); JLM Literary Agency (Greece); KCC (Korea Copyright Center) (Korea); Mohrbooks Literary Agency (Germany); La Nouvelle Agence (France); Andrew Nurnberg Associates (Bulgaria, Croatia, Czech Republic, Estonia, Hungary, Latvia, Lithuania, Montenegro, Poland, Romania, Serbia, Slovakia, Slovenia); Sane Toregard Agency (Denmark, Finland, Iceland, Norway); Sebes & Van Gelderen Literary Agency (Netherlands); Tuttle-Mori Agency Inc (Thailand)

**Simon & Schuster Audio**
Division of Simon & Schuster, Inc
1230 Avenue of the Americas, New York, NY 10020
*Web Site:* audio.simonandschuster.com
*Key Personnel*
Pres & Publr: Chris Lynch
VP, Audio Prodn: Elisa Shokoff
VP, Audio Sales: Ken Oxenreider
VP & Edit Dir: Tom Spain
Dir, Pimsleur Lang Prog: Robert Riger
Dir, Mktg: Sarah Lieberman
Publicity Mgr: Lauren Pires
Audiobooks & Pimsleur Language Programs.
ISBN Prefix(es): 978-0-684; 978-0-7435; 978-0-671; 978-1-4423

Number of titles published annually: 100 Audio
Imprints: Audioworks; Beyond Words; Encore; Pimsleur; Sound Ideas
Distributor for Monostereo
*Shipping Address:* Total Warehouse Services, 2207 Radcliffe St, Bristol, PA 19007

**Simon & Schuster Books for Young Readers**, see Simon & Schuster Children's Publishing

**Simon & Schuster Children's Publishing**
Division of Simon & Schuster, Inc
1230 Avenue of the Americas, New York, NY 10020
*Tel:* 212-698-7000
*Web Site:* KIDS.SimonandSchuster.com; TEEN.SimonandSchuster.com; simonandschuster.net; simonandschuster.biz
*Key Personnel*
Pres & Publr: Jon Anderson
VP & Publr, Simon Pulse, Aladdin: Bethany Buck
VP & Publr, Licensed & Novelty Publr, Simon Spotlight, Libros Para Ninos, Little Simon, Little Simon Inspirations: Valerie Garfield
VP & Publr, S&S Books for Young Readers, Atheneum, McElderry Books: Justin Chanda
VP & Publr, Paula Wiseman Books: Paula Wiseman
VP & Publr, Beach Lane Books: Allyn Johnston
VP & Deputy Publr, S&S Books for Young Readers, Atheneum, McElderry Books, Paula Wiseman Books, Beach Lane Books: Anne Zafian
VP & Deputy Publr, Aladdin, Simon Pulse, Little Simon, Simon Spotlight: Mara Anastas
VP & Creative Dir: Dan Potash
VP & Exec Mng Ed: Lisa Donovan
VP, Subs Rts: Stephanie Voros
VP, Dir of Children's Sales: Mary Marotta
VP & Edit Dir, S&S Books for Young Readers: David Gale
VP & Edit Dir, Atheneum: Caitlyn Dlouhy
VP, Dir of Mktg: Lucille Rettino
VP, Dir of Publicity: Paul Crichton
VP, Edit Dir, McElderry Books: Karen Wojtyla
Edit Dir, Simon Pulse: Patrick Price
Edit Dir, Aladdin: Fiona Simpson
Edit Dir, Simon Spotlight: Karen Sargent
Edit Dir, Little Simon, Little Simon Inspirations: Sonali Fry
Exec Art Dir, Simon Pulse, Aladdin: Russell Gordon
Exec Art Dir, Atheneum, McElderry, Beach Lane Books: Ann Bobco
Exec Art Dir, Little Simon, Simon Spotlight: Channi Yammer
Exec Art Dir, S&S Books for Young Readers, Paula Wiseman Books: Lizzy Bromley
Dir, Educ & Lib: Michelle Fadlalla
Exec Ed, S&S Books for Young Readers: Zareen Jaffrey
Exec Ed, Aladdin: Karen Nagel
Exec Ed, Atheneum: Namrata Tripathi
Exec Ed, Simon Pulse: Liesa Abrams
Sr Ed, Simon Spotlight: Siobhan Ciminera
Sr Ed, Beach Lane Books: Andrea Welch
Sr Ed, S&S Books for Young Readers: Christian Trimmer
Sr Mktg Mgr, Aladdin, Simon Pulse: Carolyn Swerdloff
Assoc Mktg Mgr, Trade Imprints: Chrissy Noh
Assoc Mktg Mgr, Licensed & Novelty Publg: Julie Christopher
Ed, Aladdin: Annette Pollert
Ed, Simon Spotlight: Lisa Rao
Preschool through young adult, hardcover & paperback fiction, nonfiction, trade, library, mass market titles & novelty books.
ISBN Prefix(es): 978-0-02; 978-0-609; 978-0-689; 978-0-7434; 978-1-4169
Number of titles published annually: 750 Print
Total Titles: 4,329 Print
Imprints: Aladdin Paperbacks; Atheneum Books for Young Readers; Beach Lane Books; Libros Para Ninos; Little Simon; Little Simon Inspirations; Margaret K McElderry Books; Simon & Schuster Books for Young Readers; Simon Pulse; Simon Spotlight; Paula Wiseman Books

**Simon & Schuster Digital**
Division of Simon & Schuster, Inc
1230 Avenue of the Americas, New York, NY 10020
*Tel:* 212-698-7547
*Web Site:* www.simonandschuster.com; kids.simonandschuster.com; www.simonandschuster.ca; www.simonandschuster.co.uk; www.simonandschuster.net; www.simonandschuster.biz; www.tipsoncareerandmoney.com; www.tipsonhealthyliving.com; www.tipsonhomeandstyle.com; www.tipsonlifeandlove.com
*Key Personnel*
EVP & Chief Digital Offr: Ellie Hirschhorn *Tel:* 212-698-2144 *E-mail:* ellie.hirschhorn@simonandschuster.com
VP, Mktg & New Prods: Adrian Norman *Tel:* 212-698-2349 *E-mail:* adrian.norman@simonandschuster.com
VP, Engg: Ken Judy *Tel:* 212-698-7135 *E-mail:* ken.judy@simonandschuster.com
VP, Prod Devt: David Krivda *Tel:* 212-698-1273 *E-mail:* david.krivda@simonandschuster.com
VP & Exec Dir of Content & Programming: Sue Fleming *Tel:* 212-698-7641 *E-mail:* sue.fleming@simonandschuster.com
Founded: 1996
Manages company web site (www.simonandschuster.com) & all digital content production, marketing & distribution.
Number of titles published annually: 1,500 E-Book
Imprints: www.simonandschuster.com

**§Simon & Schuster, Inc**
Division of CBS Corporation
1230 Avenue of the Americas, New York, NY 10020
SAN: 200-2450
*Tel:* 212-698-7000 *Fax:* 212-698-7007
*E-mail:* firstname.lastname@simonandschuster.com
*Web Site:* www.simonandschuster.com
*Key Personnel*
Pres & CEO: Carolyn K Reidy
EVP, Opers & CFO: Dennis Eulau
EVP, Sales & Mktg: Michael Selleck
EVP & Chief Digital Offr: Ellie Hirschhorn
Pres & Publr, Simon & Schuster Audio: Chris Lynch
Pres & Publr, Children's Publishing Div: Jon Anderson
Pres & Publr, Simon & Schuster Publishing Group: Jonathan Karp
Pres & Publr, Scribner Publishing Group: Susan Moldow
Pres & Publr, Gallery Publishing Group: Louise Burke
Pres & Publr, Atria Publishing Group: Judith Curr
Pres & Publr, Simon & Schuster Canada: Kevin Hanson
VP & Publr, Howard Books: Jonathan Merkh
VP & Publr, Touchstone: Stacy Creamer
Chief Exec & Publr, Simon & Schuster UK: Ian Chapman
Mng Dir, Simon & Schuster Australia: Lou Johnson
EVP, Gen Coun: David Hillman
SVP, Mktg: Liz Perl
VP, HR: Carolyn Connolly
SVP, Corp Communs: Adam Rothberg
VP, Fin & Strategic Planning: David Byrnes
SVP, Group Cont: Dave Upchurch
VP, Busn Opers: Frank Nunez
VP, Gen Mgr, Adult, Children's & Audio: Craig Mandeville
VP, Client Publr Servs: Stephen Black
VP, Busn Devt: Joe Bulger
VP, Global eBook Mkt Devt & Strategy: Doug Stambaugh
VP, Dir of Prodn & Mfg: Karen Romano
Dir, Digital Content Devt: Samantha Cohen
VP, Dist & Fulfillment: Dave Schaeffer
VP, Facilities: Lee Kartsaklis
Dir, Order Mgmt: Francine Leinheiser
VP, Contracts: Jeff Wilson
Mgr, Perms: Agnes Fisher
VP, Dir, Ad & Promo: Mark Speer
Founded: 1924
ISBN Prefix(es): 978-0-02; 978-0-941831; 978-1-885223; 978-0-7867; 978-0-13; 978-1-878990; 978-0-07; 978-0-7318; 978-0-669; 978-0-8095; 978-1-56025; 978-0-88708; 978-0-7434; 978-1-58270; 978-0-7435; 978-1-4169; 978-1-4165; 978-0-89256; 978-0-9674601; 978-0-9711953; 978-1-58229; 978-1-59309; 978-1-84737; 978-1-84738; 978-1-84739; 978-0-684; 978-0-7432; 978-0-689; 978-0-671; 978-1-4391; 978-1-903650; 978-1-928998; 978-1-4423; 978-1-4424; 978-1-4516; 978-1-84983; 978-0-9870685; 978-0-85720; 978-0-85707; 978-1-62266; 978-1-4711; 978-1-4767; 978-1-4814; 978-1-921997; 978-1-922052; 978-1-925030
*Branch Office(s)*
Beach Lane Books, 5666 La Jolla Blvd, No 154, La Jolla, CA 92037 *Tel:* 858-551-0860 *Fax:* 858-551-0492
Pimsleur, 30 Monument Sq, Concord, MA 01742 *Tel:* 978-369-7525
1639 Rte 10 E, Parsippany, NJ 07054 (royalties, accts payable, fin) *Tel:* 973-656-6000 *Fax:* 973-656-6070
Howard Books, 216 Centerview Dr, Suite 303, Brentwood, TN 37027 *Tel:* 615-873-2080 *Fax:* 615-370-3834
Simon & Schuster Canada, 116 King St E, Suite 300, Toronto, ON M5A 1J3, Canada *Tel:* 647-427-8882 *Fax:* 647-430-9446
*Foreign Office(s):* Simon & Schuster Australia Pty Ltd, 450 Miller St, Suite 19a, Level 1, Bldg C, Cammeray, NSW 2062, Australia *Tel:* (02) 9983 6600 *Fax:* (02) 9988 4232 (sales & mktg) *E-mail:* cservice@simonandschuster.com.au *Web Site:* www.simonandschuster.com.au/
Simon & Schuster Publishers India Pvt Ltd, 2316, Tower–A, The Corenthum A -41, Sector -62, Noida, Uttar Pradesh 201301, India
Simon & Schuster UK Ltd, 222 Gray's Inn Rd, 1st fl, London WC1X 8HB, United Kingdom *Tel:* (020) 7316-1900 *Fax:* (020) 7316-0333 *E-mail:* enquiries@simonandschuster.co.uk *Web Site:* www.simonandschuster.co.uk
Distributor for Andrews McMeel Publishing LLC; Avatar Press; Backlist LLC (div of Chicken Soup for the Soul Publishing); Baen Books; Baseball America; BL Publishing (div of Games Workshop); Boom! Studios; Cardoza Publishing; Chicken Soup for the Soul Publishing; Cider Mill Press Book Publishers; Downtown Bookworks; Good Books; Harlequin Enterprises Ltd (billing only); Hooked on Phonics (Sandviks HOP Inc/Sandvik Publishing); Inner Traditions/Bear & Company; Kaplan Publishing; Kinfolk; Manhattan GMAT; Meadowbrook Press; Merck Publishing; Open Road Publishing; Pikachu Press (Pokemon Company International); Reader's Digest Children's Publishing; Rebellion Publishing; Ripley Entertainment Inc (Ripley's Believe it or Not); Tuttle Publishing; VIZ Media; Weldon Owen; World Almanac (div of Facts on File)
*Returns:* Simon & Schuster, c/o Jacobson Companies, 4406 Industrial Park Rd, Bldg 7, Camp Hill, PA 17011 (by appt; to schedule call 717-730-5212 ext 5316)
*Shipping Address:* Riverside Distribution Center, 100 Front St, Riverside, NJ 08075 (trade,

children's, audio, mass-market & dist clients) *Tel:* 856-461-6500 *Fax:* 856-824-2402; Bristol Distribution Center, 2207 Radcliffe St, Bristol, PA 19007 *Tel:* 215-785-0531 *Fax:* 215-826-3002
Membership(s): AAP; BISG
*See separate listing for:*
**Simon & Schuster Audio**
**Simon & Schuster Children's Publishing**
**Simon & Schuster Digital**
**Simon & Schuster Sales & Marketing**

**Simon & Schuster Sales & Marketing**
Division of Simon & Schuster, Inc
1230 Avenue of the Americas, New York, NY 10020
*Tel:* 212-698-7000
*Key Personnel*
EVP, Sales & Mktg: Michael Selleck *Tel:* 212-698-7420 *E-mail:* michael.selleck@simonandschuster.com
SVP, Mktg: Liz Perl *Tel:* 212-698-1204 *E-mail:* liz.perl@simonandschuster.com
VP & Dir, Dist Sales & Retail Mktg: Gary Urda *Tel:* 212-698-7389 *E-mail:* gary.urda@simonandschuster.com
VP & Dir, Children's Sales: Mary Marotta *Tel:* 212-698-2855 *E-mail:* mary.marotta@simonandschuster.com
VP & Dir, Retail Sales: Paula Amendolara *Tel:* 212-698-7069 *E-mail:* paula.amendolara@simonandschuster.com
VP & Dir, Digital Sales: Colin Shields *Tel:* 212-698-7536 *E-mail:* colin.shields@simonandschuster.com
VP & Dir, Intl Sales: Mr Seth Russo *Tel:* 212-698-7422 *E-mail:* seth.russo@simonandschuster.com
VP & Dir, Sales & Client Communs: Eileen Gentillo *Tel:* 212-698-7470 *E-mail:* eileen.gentillo@simonandschuster.com
VP, Dir of Ad & Promo: Mark Speer *E-mail:* mark.speer@simonandschuster.com
Dir, Spec Mkts: Sumya Ojakli *Tel:* 212-698-7202 *E-mail:* sumya.ojakli@simonandschuster.com
Dir, Dist Client Publrs: Michael Perlman *Tel:* 212-698-7061 *E-mail:* michael.perlman@simonandschuster.com
Dir of Mktg, Children's Books: Lucille Rettino *E-mail:* lucille.rettino@simonandschuster.com
Dir of Mktg, Adult Trade: Wendy Sheanin *E-mail:* wendy.sheanin@simonandschuster.com
Dir of Educ & Lib Mktg: Michelle Fadlalla *E-mail:* michelle.fadlalla@simonandschuster.com
Distributor for Andrews McMeel Publishing LLC; Applesauce Press (children's); Avatar Press; Baen Books; Baseball America; Boom! Studios; Cardoza; Chicken Soup for the Soul; Cider Mill Press Book Publishers; Downtown Bookworks; Games Workshop; Harlequin (billing only); Kaplan Publishing; Manhattan Prep; Meadowbrook Press; Merck; Open Road; Reader's Digest Children's Books; Rebellion; Ripley Entertainment; VIZ Media; Weldon Owen; World Almanac (children's)

**Simon Pulse**, see Simon & Schuster Children's Publishing

**Simon Spotlight**, see Simon & Schuster Children's Publishing

**§Sinauer Associates Inc**
23 Plumtree Rd, Sunderland, MA 01375
SAN: 203-2392
Mailing Address: PO Box 407, Sunderland, MA 01375-0407 SAN: 203-2392
*Tel:* 413-549-4300 *Fax:* 413-549-1118
*E-mail:* publish@sinauer.com; orders@sinauer.com
*Web Site:* www.sinauer.com
*Key Personnel*
Pres & Biology Ed: Andrew D Sinauer
VP & Dir, Mktg & Dist: Dean Scudder
Mng Ed: Carol J Wigg
Biology Ed: C Azelie Fortier
Psychology Ed: Sydney Carroll
Busn Mgr: Penny Grant
Prodn Mgr: Christopher Small
Mktg Coord: Marie Scavotto *E-mail:* scavotto@sinauer.com
Rts & Perms: Sherri Ellsworth
Founded: 1969
College textbooks & reference works in the biological & behavioral sciences.
ISBN Prefix(es): 978-0-87893, 978-1-60535
Number of titles published annually: 10 Print
Total Titles: 97 Print; 23 CD-ROM; 4 Online; 37 E-Book
Foreign Rep(s): Alkem (Bangladesh, Brunei, Cambodia, Hong Kong, Indonesia, Laos, Malaysia, Myanmar, Philippines, Singapore, Taiwan, Thailand); FUNPEC-Editora (Brazil); Macmillan Publishers New Zealand Ltd (New Zealand); Palgrave Macmillan (Africa, Australia, Brazil, Caribbean, China, Europe, Japan, Korea, Latin America, Middle East, Nepal, Pakistan, Russia, Sri Lanka, UK); Shinil Books Co Ltd (Korea); World Science Publishing Co (Korea)
*Warehouse:* Publishers Storage & Shipping Corp, 46 Development Rd, Fitchburg, MA 01420 *Tel:* 978-345-2121 *Fax:* 978-348-1233

**Six Gallery Press**
PO Box 90145, Pittsburgh, PA 15224-0545
*Web Site:* www.sixgallerypress.com
*Key Personnel*
Publr & Ed: Che Elias *E-mail:* rocketsconstrue@yahoo.com; Michael Hafftka *E-mail:* michael@sixgallerypress.com
Founded: 2000
Independent press producing & marketing experimental literature. We promote these books through reviews in journals, online & through author readings as well as special events including bookfairs.
ISBN Prefix(es): 978-0-9703840; 978-0-9726301; 978-0-9810091; 978-0-9782962
Number of titles published annually: 10 Print
Total Titles: 50 Print
Imprints: Convergence
*Distribution Center:* Small Press Distribution, 1341 Seventh St, Berkeley, CA 94710-1409

**Skandisk Inc**
6667 W Old Shakapee Rd, Suite 109, Bloomington, MN 55438-2622
*Tel:* 952-829-8998 *Toll Free Tel:* 800-468-2424 *Fax:* 952-829-8992
*E-mail:* tomten@skandisk.com
*Web Site:* www.skandisk.com
*Key Personnel*
Pres: Mike Sevig *E-mail:* mike@skandisk.com
Prodn Mgr: Lisa Hamnes *E-mail:* lhamnes@skandisk.com
Founded: 1975
Publisher & distributor of books with a particularly strong selection of titles of Scandinavian interest, including children's books, mythology, historical fiction, Scandinavian culture & Scandinavian humor.
ISBN Prefix(es): 978-0-9615394; 978-1-57534
Number of titles published annually: 3 Print
Total Titles: 25 Print; 1 CD-ROM
Membership(s): ABA

**§SkillPath Publications**
Division of The Graceland University Center for Professional Development & Lifelong Learning Inc
PO Box 2768, Mission, KS 66201-2768
*Tel:* 913-362-3900 *Toll Free Tel:* 800-873-7545 *Fax:* 913-362-4241
*E-mail:* customercare@skillpath.net; products@skillpath.net
*Web Site:* www.skillpath.com
*Key Personnel*
Acct Rep: Casey Smith
Founded: 1989
Books, audio programs, computer based training.
ISBN Prefix(es): 978-1-878542; 978-1-57294; 978-1-929874; 978-1-934589
Number of titles published annually: 10 Print
Total Titles: 50 Print; 4 Audio
Divisions: CompuMaster
*Branch Office(s)*
100 Armstrong Ave, Georgetown, ON L7G 5S4, Canada *Fax:* 913-362-4241
*Foreign Office(s):* GPO Box 1747, Melbourne, Victoria 3001, Australia *Tel:* (0800) 145 231 *Fax:* (0800) 145 244 *Web Site:* www.skillpath.com.au
FreePost 105776, PO Box 742, Wellington 6140, New Zealand *Tel:* (0800) 447 301 *Fax:* (0800) 447 304 *Web Site:* www.skillpath.co.nz
PO Box 203, Chessington KT9 9BZ, United Kingdom *Tel:* (0800) 328 1140 *Fax:* (0800) 892972 *Web Site:* www.skillpath.co.uk
Distributor for Franklin Covey; Pearson Technology; Thomson Publishing; John Wiley

**Skinner House Books**
Imprint of Unitarian Universalist Association
25 Beacon St, Boston, MA 02108-2800
*Tel:* 617-742-2100 *Fax:* 617-742-7025
*E-mail:* skinnerhouse@uua.org
*Web Site:* www.skinnerhouse.org
*Key Personnel*
Edit Dir: Mary Benard
Edit Asst: Betsy Martin *Tel:* 617-948-4644 *E-mail:* betsymartin@uua.org
Founded: 1975
Specialize in spirituality, inspirational literature, books on church resources for religious liberals.
ISBN Prefix(es): 978-0-933840; 978-1-55896
Number of titles published annually: 15 Print
Total Titles: 265 Print
*Sales Office(s):* Red Wheel/Weiser/Conari, 65 Parker St, Suite 7, Newburyport, MA 01950 *Tel:* 978-465-0504 *Toll Free Tel:* 800-423-7087 *Fax:* 978-465-0243 *E-mail:* orders@redwheelweiser.com *Web Site:* redwheelweiser.com
*Returns:* Red Wheel/Weiser/Conari, 65 Parker St, Suite 7, Newburyport, MA 01950 *Tel:* 978-465-0504 *Toll Free Tel:* 800-423-7087 *Fax:* 978-465-0243 *E-mail:* orders@redwheelweiser.com *Web Site:* redwheelweiser.com
*Distribution Center:* Red Wheel/Weiser/Conari, 65 Parker St, Suite 7, Newburyport, MA 01950 *Tel:* 978-465-0504 *Toll Free Tel:* 800-423-7087 *Fax:* 978-465-0243 *E-mail:* info@redwheelweiser.com *Web Site:* redwheelweiser.com

**Sky Oaks Productions Inc**
19544 Sky Oaks Way, Los Gatos, CA 95030
Mailing Address: PO Box 1102, Los Gatos, CA 95031
*Tel:* 408-395-7600 *Fax:* 408-395-8440
*E-mail:* tprworld@aol.com
*Web Site:* www.tpr-world.com
*Key Personnel*
Pres: Virginia Lee Asher
Founded: 1973
ISBN Prefix(es): 978-0-940296; 978-1-56018
Number of titles published annually: 4 Print
Total Titles: 300 Print; 40 Online; 40 E-Book; 7 Audio

**Sky Publishing**
90 Sherman St, Cambridge, MA 02140

*Tel:* 617-864-7360 *Toll Free Tel:* 866-644-1377 *Fax:* 617-864-6117
*E-mail:* info@skyandtelescope.com
*Web Site:* www.skyandtelescope.com
*Key Personnel*
VP & Publg Dir: Joel Toner
Ed-in-Chief: Robert Naeye
Sr Ed: Dennis di Cicco; Alan M MacRobert
Assoc Ed: Tony Flanders
Founded: 1941
Astronomy books & software, maps, posters, globes, sidelines.
ISBN Prefix(es): 978-0-933346
Number of titles published annually: 15 Print
Total Titles: 20 Print

**SkyLight Paths Publishing**
Division of LongHill Partners Inc
Sunset Farm Offices, Rte 4, Woodstock, VT 05091
SAN: 134-5621
Mailing Address: PO Box 237, Woodstock, VT 05091-0237
*Tel:* 802-457-4000 *Toll Free Tel:* 800-962-4544 *Fax:* 802-457-4004
*E-mail:* sales@skylightpaths.com
*Web Site:* www.skylightpaths.com
*Key Personnel*
Pres & Publr: Stuart M Matlins
SVP, Admin & Fin: Amy M Wilson *E-mail:* awilson@longhillpartners.com
VP, Edit & Prodn: Emily Wichland *E-mail:* ewichland@longhillpartners.com
Founded: 1999
General trade books for seekers & believers of all faith traditions. Subject areas include spirituality, children's, self-help, crafts, interfaith, spiritual living, eastern & western religion.
ISBN Prefix(es): 978-1-893361; 978-1-59473
Number of titles published annually: 20 Print
Total Titles: 200 Print
Foreign Rep(s): Bayard/Novalis (Canada); Deep Books (Europe, UK); Director Direct (Canada); Rainbow Book Agencies (Australia, New Zealand); Brian Scheiffer Agencies (South Africa)
Foreign Rights: Andreas Brunner Literature Agentur (Germany); Deborah Harris Agency (Israel); International Editors' Co (IECO) (Isabel Monteagudo) (Spain); A Korzhenevski (Russia); Nurnberg Associates (Judit Hermann) (Hungary); Nurnberg Associates (L Strakova) (Czech Republic); H Katia Schumer (Brazil); Susanna Zevi (Italy)
*Returns:* 28 River St, Windsor, VT 05089

**§Slack Incorporated**
6900 Grove Rd, Thorofare, NJ 08086-9447
SAN: 201-8632
*Tel:* 856-848-1000 *Toll Free Tel:* 800-257-8290 *Fax:* 856-848-6091
*E-mail:* sales@slackinc.com
*Web Site:* www.slackbooks.com
*Key Personnel*
SVP, Books & Journals: John H Bond *E-mail:* jbond@slackinc.com
Mktg Communs Dir: Michelle Gatt *E-mail:* mgatt@slackinc.com
Founded: 1960
Academic textbooks & professional reference books: medicine, occupational therapy, physical therapy, ophthalmology, gastroenterology, orthopedics, athletic training, pediatrics, nursing & other areas.
ISBN Prefix(es): 978-1-55642
Number of titles published annually: 35 Print; 2 CD-ROM; 10 E-Book
Total Titles: 250 Print; 15 CD-ROM; 25 E-Book
Divisions: Journal Publishing; Professional Book Publishing; Trade Book Publishing
Foreign Rep(s): DA Information Services (Australia); EuroSpan (Europe); Login Brothers (Canada); McGraw-Hill (Asia)
Foreign Rights: John Scott Co
*Advertising Agency:* Alcyon Advertising
*Distribution Center:* 200 Richardson Ave, Bldg B, Swedesboro, NJ 08085

**Sleeping Bear Press™**
315 Eisenhower Pkwy, Suite 200, Ann Arbor, MI 48108
*Toll Free Tel:* 800-487-2323 *Fax:* 734-794-0004
*E-mail:* sleepingbearpress@cengage.com
*Web Site:* www.sleepingbearpress.com
*Key Personnel*
Publr: Heather Hughes
Publicity: Audrey Mitnick
Founded: 1998
Publisher of children's books infants to young adults.
ISBN Prefix(es): 978-1-886947; 978-1-58536
Number of titles published annually: 32 Print
Total Titles: 451 Print
Membership(s): ALA; Association of Children's Booksellers; International Reading Association

**§Slipdown Mountain Publications LLC**
28151 Quarry Lake Rd, Lake Linden, MI 49945
*Tel:* 906-523-4118 *Toll Free Tel:* 866-341-3705 *Toll Free Fax:* 866-341-3705
*E-mail:* books@jacobsvillebooks.com
*Web Site:* www.jacobsvillebooks.com
*Key Personnel*
Publr: Walt Shiel *E-mail:* walt@jacobsvillebooks.com
Staff Libn: Lisa Shiel *E-mail:* lisa@jacobsvillebooks.com
Founded: 2003
Independent micro-publisher of fiction & nonfiction books. All new books published through Jacobsville Books imprint. Publish historical & speculative fiction, military history, alternative views of science, cryptozoology & paranormal subjects. All books are available in print & most are available in popular ebook formats (Kindle/mobi, EPUB, PDF).
ISBN Prefix(es): 978-0-9746553; 978-1-934631
Number of titles published annually: 5 Print; 6 E-Book
Total Titles: 14 Print; 27 E-Book
Imprints: Jacobsville Books
Subsidiaries: Five Rainbows Services for Authors & Publishers (publishing services)
Membership(s): The Association of Publishers for Special Sales

**Small Business Advisors Inc**
11 Franklin Ave, Hewlett, NY 11557
Mailing Address: PO Box 758, Armonk, NY 10504-0758
*Tel:* 516-374-1387; 914-260-1027 *Fax:* 516-374-1175; 720-294-3202
*E-mail:* info@smallbusinessadvice.com
*Web Site:* www.smallbusinessadvice.com
*Key Personnel*
Contact: Eric Gelb *E-mail:* eric@smallbusinessadvice.com; Joe Gelb *E-mail:* joe@smallbusinessadvice.com
Founded: 1991
Publisher of books, e-books & blogs on small business, finance & marketing/copyrighting.
ISBN Prefix(es): 978-1-890158
Number of titles published annually: 4 Print
Total Titles: 15 Print; 1 Audio
Membership(s): IBPA, the Independent Book Publishers Association

**Smith & Kraus Publishers Inc**
40 Walch Dr, Portland, ME 04103
Mailing Address: PO Box 127, Lyme, NH 03768-0127
*Tel:* 207-523-2585 *Toll Free Tel:* 877-668-8680 *Fax:* 207-699-3698
*E-mail:* editor@smithandkraus.com
*Web Site:* www.smithandkraus.com
*Key Personnel*
Pres & Publr: Marisa Smith Kraus
Founded: 1990
Drama books, monologues, books of interest to our theatrical community, play anthologies. Smith & Kraus Global: religious/political.
ISBN Prefix(es): 978-0-9622722; 978-1-880399; 978-1-57525
Number of titles published annually: 35 Print
Total Titles: 500 Print
Imprints: Smith & Kraus Books For Kids (young adult fiction)
Subsidiaries: Smith & Kraus Global (world affairs)
Foreign Rep(s): Agnes Krup Literary Agency

**§M Lee Smith Publishers LLC**
5201 Virginia Way, Brentwood, TN 37027
Mailing Address: PO Box 5094, Brentwood, TN 37024-5094
*Tel:* 615-373-7517 *Toll Free Tel:* 800-274-6774 *Fax:* 615-373-5183
*E-mail:* custserv@mleesmith.com
*Web Site:* www.mleesmith.com
*Key Personnel*
Chmn: M Lee Smith
CFO: Lawton Miller
Pres: Dan Oswald
VP, Mktg: Guy Crossley
VP, Content: Brad Forrister
Dir, Cust Serv & Circulation: Kim Mesecher
Founded: 1975
Legal newsletters/legal book related titles.
ISBN Prefix(es): 978-0-925773; 978-1-60029; 978-0-9605796
Number of titles published annually: 130 Print
Total Titles: 2 CD-ROM; 60 Online

**Steve Smith Autosports**
PO Box 11631, Santa Ana, CA 92711-1631
*Tel:* 714-639-7681 *Fax:* 714-639-9741
*Web Site:* www.stevesmithautosports.com
*Key Personnel*
Pres & Publr: Steve Smith *E-mail:* steve@ssapubl.com
Founded: 1971
Specialize in auto racing technical books.
ISBN Prefix(es): 978-0-936834
Number of titles published annually: 5 Print
Total Titles: 200 Print

**Smithsonian Scholarly Press**
Division of Smithsonian Institution
Aerospace Bldg, 704-A, MRC 957, Washington, DC 20013
Mailing Address: PO Box 37012, Washington DC, DC 20013-7012
*Tel:* 202-633-3017 *Fax:* 202-633-6877
*E-mail:* schol_press@si.edu
*Web Site:* www.scholarlypress.si.edu
Founded: 1966
General trade & adult nonfiction.
ISBN Prefix(es): 978-0-87474; 978-1-56098; 978-1-58834
Number of titles published annually: 70 Print
Total Titles: 800 Print
Distributed by Rowman & Littlefield Publishers Inc
Distributor for Biological Diversity Handbook Series; Handbook of North American Indians; Smithsonian Library of the Solar System; Smithsonian Series in Archaeological Inquiry; Smithsonian Series in Comparative Evolutionary Biology; Smithsonian Series in Ethnographic Inquiry
*Distribution Center:* WW Norton

**§Smyth & Helwys Publishing Inc**
6316 Peake Rd, Macon, GA 31210-3960
*Tel:* 478-757-0564 *Toll Free Tel:* 800-747-3016 (orders only); 800-568-1248 (orders only) *Fax:* 478-757-1305
*E-mail:* information@helwys.com

*Web Site:* www.helwys.com
*Key Personnel*
Pres & CEO: Cecil P Staton, Jr
Publr & EVP: Keith Gammons *E-mail:* keith@helwys.com
Founded: 1990
Christian books, literature, Sunday School books (curriculum).
ISBN Prefix(es): 978-1-880837; 978-0-9628455; 978-1-57312
Number of titles published annually: 30 Print
Total Titles: 330 Print
Foreign Rep(s): Grace Wing Publishers (England)

**Snow Lion Publications Inc**
Imprint of Shambhala Publications
300 Massachusetts Ave, Boston, MA 02115
*Tel:* 617-236-0030 *Fax:* 617-236-1563
*E-mail:* customercare@shambhala.com
*Web Site:* www.shambhala.com/snowlion
*Key Personnel*
VP, Sales: Julie Saidenberg
Founded: 1980
Trade & scholarly books on Tibetan Buddhism & Tibet & books by the Dalai Lama.
ISBN Prefix(es): 978-0-937938; 978-1-55939
Number of titles published annually: 18 Print; 20 E-Book
Total Titles: 300 Print; 220 E-Book; 1 Audio

**Society for Human Resource Management (SHRM)**
1800 Duke St, Alexandria, VA 22314
*Tel:* 703-548-3440 *Toll Free Tel:* 800-444-5006 (orders) *Fax:* 703-535-6490
*E-mail:* shrm@shrm.org; shrmstore@shrm.org
*Web Site:* www.shrm.org
Trade organization of human resource professional with over 170,000 members.
ISBN Prefix(es): 978-0-939900; 978-1-58644; 978-1-932132
Number of titles published annually: 14 Print
Total Titles: 100 Print

**§Society for Industrial & Applied Mathematics**
3600 Market St, 6th fl, Philadelphia, PA 19104-2688
*Tel:* 215-382-9800 *Toll Free Tel:* 800-447-7426 *Fax:* 215-386-7999
*E-mail:* siambooks@siam.org
*Web Site:* www.siam.org
*Key Personnel*
Exec Dir: James M Crowley *E-mail:* jcrowley@siam.org
Publr: David K Marshall *E-mail:* marshall@siam.org
Mng Ed: Kelly Thomas *E-mail:* thomas@siam.org
Cont: Lauren Steidel *E-mail:* steidel@siam.org
Dir, Mktg & Sales: Michelle Montgomery *Tel:* 215-382-9800 ext 368 *E-mail:* montgomery@siam.org
Pubns Mgr: Mitchell Chernoff *E-mail:* chernoff@siam.org
Sr Acqs Ed: Elizabeth Greenspan *E-mail:* greenspan@siam.org
Cust Serv Mgr: Arlette Liberatore *E-mail:* liberatore@siam.org
Membership Mgr: Susan Whitehouse *E-mail:* whitehouse@siam.org
Founded: 1952
Journals, books, conferences & reprints in mathematics/computer science/statistics/physical science.
ISBN Prefix(es): 978-0-89871
Number of titles published annually: 16 Print
Total Titles: 325 Print; 35 CD-ROM; 2 E-Book

**§Society for Mining, Metallurgy & Exploration**
12999 E Adam Aircraft Circle, Englewood, CO 80112
*Tel:* 303-948-4200 *Toll Free Tel:* 800-763-3132 *Fax:* 303-973-3845
*E-mail:* cs@smenet.org
*Web Site:* www.smenet.org
*Key Personnel*
Exec Dr: Dave Kanagy
Sr Ed: Bill Gleason; Georgene Renner
Pubn Ed: Steve Kral *E-mail:* kral@smenet.org
Founded: 1871
Also publishes monthly magazine, quarterly journal, trade books, hardbound & paperback. Everything is mining related.
ISBN Prefix(es): 978-0-87335
Number of titles published annually: 5 Print
Total Titles: 80 Print; 15 CD-ROM
Foreign Rep(s): Affiliated East-West Press (India); Australian Mineral Foundation (Australia)

**Society of American Archivists**
17 N State St, Suite 1425, Chicago, IL 60602-4061
SAN: 211-7614
*Tel:* 312-606-0722 *Toll Free Tel:* 866-722-7858 *Fax:* 312-606-0728
*E-mail:* info@archivists.org
*Web Site:* www.archivists.org
*Key Personnel*
Exec Dir: Nancy Beaumont *E-mail:* nbeaumont@archivists.org
Dir, Publg: Teresa Brinati *E-mail:* tbrinati@archivists.org
Founded: 1936
Archival literature; preservation.
ISBN Prefix(es): 978-0-931828; 978-1-931666
Number of titles published annually: 5 Print
Total Titles: 72 Print

**Society of Automotive Engineers International**, see SAE (Society of Automotive Engineers International)

**Society of Biblical Literature**
The Luce Ctr, Suite 350, 825 Houston Mill Rd, Atlanta, GA 30329
*Tel:* 404-727-3100 *Fax:* 404-727-3101 (corp)
*E-mail:* sbl@sbl-site.org
*Web Site:* www.sbl-site.org
*Key Personnel*
Exec Dir: John F Kutsko *E-mail:* john.kutsko@sbl_site.org
Dir, Pubns: Bob Buller *E-mail:* bob.buller@sbl_site.org
Mktg Mgr: Kathie Klein *Tel:* 404-727-2325 *E-mail:* kathie.klein@sbl-site.org
Founded: 1880
A learned society whose purpose is to stimulate the critical investigation of Biblical literature.
ISBN Prefix(es): 978-0-89130; 978-0-7885; 978-0-88414; 978-1-58983
Number of titles published annually: 35 Print; 20 E-Book
Total Titles: 640 Print; 99 E-Book
Distributor for Brown Judaic Studies; Sheffield Phoenix Press
*Orders to:* PO Box 2243, Williston, VT 05495-2243 *Tel:* 802-864-6185 *Toll Free Tel:* 877-725-3334 *Fax:* 802-864-7626
*Warehouse:* 82 Winter Sport Lane, Williston, VT 05495 *Tel:* 802-864-6185 *Toll Free Tel:* 877-725-3334 *Fax:* 802-864-7626

**Society of Environmental Toxicology & Chemistry**
229 S Baylen St, 2nd fl, Pensacola, FL 32502
*Tel:* 850-469-1500 *Fax:* 850-469-9778
*E-mail:* setac@setac.org
*Web Site:* www.setac.org
*Key Personnel*
Sr Publg Mgr: Mimi Meredith *Tel:* 850-469-1500 ext 113 *E-mail:* mimi.meredith@setac.org
Founded: 1979
Supports publications of scientific value relating to environmental topics. Proceedings of technical workshops that explore current & prospective environmental issues are published as peer-reviewed technical documents. Publications are used by scientists, engineers & managers because of their technical basis & comprehensive, state-of-the-science reviews; association press; nonprofit, professional society.
ISBN Prefix(es): 978-1-880611
Number of titles published annually: 8 Print; 1 CD-ROM
Total Titles: 105 Print; 5 CD-ROM
Imprints: SETAC Press

**§Society of Exploration Geophysicists**
8801 S Yale Ave, Tulsa, OK 74137
Mailing Address: PO Box 702740, Tulsa, OK 74170-2740
*Tel:* 918-497-5500 *Fax:* 918-497-5557
*E-mail:* web@seg.org
*Web Site:* www.seg.org
*Key Personnel*
Dir, Pubns: Ted Bakamjian *Tel:* 918-497-5506 *E-mail:* tbakamjian@seg.org
Manuscript Tracking Specialist: Merrily Sanzalone *Tel:* 918-497-5507 *E-mail:* msanzalone@seg.org
Founded: 1930
Types of publications: textbooks; videos; technical journals & web site.
ISBN Prefix(es): 978-1-56080; 978-0-931839
Number of titles published annually: 3 Print
Total Titles: 100 Print; 9 CD-ROM

**§Society of Manufacturing Engineers**
One SME Dr, Dearborn, MI 48121
SAN: 203-2376
*Tel:* 313-425-3000 *Toll Free Tel:* 800-733-4763 (cust serv) *Fax:* 313-425-3400
*E-mail:* publications@sme.org
*Web Site:* www.sme.org
*Key Personnel*
CEO & Exec Dir: Mark Tomlinson *Tel:* 313-425-3100 *E-mail:* mtomlinson@sme.org
Dir, Prof Devt: Jeannine Kunz
SME Resource Ctr: Carol Selleck
E-Libn: Carol Tower *Tel:* 313-425-3288 *E-mail:* ctower@sme.org
Founded: 1932
Professional engineering association.
ISBN Prefix(es): 978-0-87263
Number of titles published annually: 5 Print
Total Titles: 150 Print; 21 CD-ROM
Distributed by American Technical Publishers Inc; McGraw-Hill; Productivity Press
Distributor for Free Press Division of MacMillan; Industrial Press; McGraw-Hill; Prentice Hall; John Wiley & Sons Inc
Foreign Rights: American Technical Publishers (UK); DA Book Pty Ltd (Australia); Elsevier Science Publishers (Netherlands)

**The Society of Naval Architects & Marine Engineers**
601 Pavonia Ave, Jersey City, NJ 07306-2907
SAN: 202-0572
*Tel:* 201-798-4800 *Toll Free Tel:* 800-798-2188 *Fax:* 201-798-4975
*Web Site:* www.sname.org
*Key Personnel*
Pubns Dir: Susan Evans Grove *E-mail:* sevans@sname.org
Reference books, directories, periodicals, technical research reports & bulletins on naval architecture, marine engineering & ocean engineering.
ISBN Prefix(es): 978-0-87033; 978-0-9603048; 978-0-939773; 978-0-7698
Number of titles published annually: 6 Print
Total Titles: 29 Print

**Soho Press Inc**
853 Broadway, New York, NY 10003
SAN: 202-5531
*Tel:* 212-260-1900 *Fax:* 212-260-1902
*E-mail:* soho@sohopress.com; publicity@sohopress.com
*Web Site:* www.sohopress.com
*Key Personnel*
Publr: Bronwen Hruska *E-mail:* bhruska@sohopress.com
Mng Ed: Mark Doten *E-mail:* mdoten@sohopress.com
Sr Ed: Juliet Grames
Publicity & Mktg: Paul Oliver *E-mail:* poliver@sohopress.com
Founded: 1986 (Soho Press was incorporated in 1986 & published its first books in 1987)
Hard & softcover trade books: fiction, mysteries, general nonfiction, history & social history.
ISBN Prefix(es): 978-0-939149; 978-1-56947; 978-1-61695
Number of titles published annually: 70 Print; 68 E-Book
Total Titles: 350 Print
Imprints: Soho Constable; Soho Crime; Soho Teen
Distributed by Random House
Foreign Rights: ACER Agencia Literaria (Latin America, Portugal, Spain); AnatoliaLit Agency (Turkey); Biagi Rights Management (UK); English Agency (Juzzo Sawa) (Japan); Grayhawk Agency (Taiwan); Deborah Harris Agency (Israel); Agence Hoffman (France); International Editors Co (Flavia Sala) (Brazil); Leonardt & Hoier Literary Agency (Scandinavia); Meller Literary Agency (Germany); Jan Michael (Belgium, Netherlands); Daniela Micura Literary Services (Italy); PLS (Publishing Language Service) (Korea); Prava i Prevodi (Bulgaria, Croatia, Czech Republic, Hungary, Montenegro, Poland, Romania, Russia, Serbia, Slovakia, Slovenia); Read N' Right Agency (Nike Davarinou) (Greece)
*Orders to:* Random House Customer Service, 400 Hahn Rd, Westminster, MD 21157 *Toll Free Tel:* 800-733-3000; 800-669-1536 (electronic orders) *Toll Free Fax:* 800-659-2436 *Web Site:* www.randomhouse.com/backyard/order.html SAN: 631-760X; Random House of Canada Ltd, 2775 Matheson Blvd E, Mississauga, ON L4W 4P7, Canada *Toll Free Tel:* 888-523-9292; 800-258-4233 (electronic orders) *Toll Free Fax:* 888-562-9924
*Distribution Center:* Random House Customer Service, 400 Hahn Rd, Westminster, MD 21157 *Toll Free Tel:* 800-733-3000; 800-669-1536 (electronic orders) *Toll Free Fax:* 800-659-2436 *Web Site:* www.randomhouse.com/backyard/order.html SAN: 631-760X
Random House of Canada Ltd, 2775 Matheson Blvd E, Mississauga, ON L4W 4P7, Canada *Toll Free Tel:* 888-523-9292; 800-258-4233 (electronic orders) *Toll Free Fax:* 888-562-9924

**Soil Science Society of America**
5585 Guilford Rd, Madison, WI 53711-5801
*Tel:* 608-273-8080 *Fax:* 608-273-2021
*E-mail:* headquarters@soils.org
*Web Site:* www.soils.org
*Key Personnel*
CEO: Ellen Bergfeld *E-mail:* ebergfeld@sciencesocieties.org
Founded: 1936
Technical books for professionals in soil science.
ISBN Prefix(es): 978-0-89118
Number of titles published annually: 5 Print
Total Titles: 90 Print

**Solano Press Books**
PO Box 773, Point Arena, CA 95468
*Tel:* 707-884-4508 *Toll Free Tel:* 800-931-9373 *Fax:* 707-884-4109
*E-mail:* spbooks@solano.com
*Web Site:* www.solano.com
*Key Personnel*
Publr: Ling-Yen Jones
Acqs Ed: Natalie Macris
Asst to Publr: Nancy McLaughlin
Founded: 1984
Professional books: law, public administration, real estate, land use, environment, urban planning, environmental analysis & management.
ISBN Prefix(es): 978-0-9614657; 978-0-923956
Number of titles published annually: 4 Print
Total Titles: 22 Print

**Solution Tree**
555 N Morton St, Bloomington, IN 47404
*Tel:* 812-336-7700 *Toll Free Tel:* 800-733-6786 *Fax:* 812-336-7790
*E-mail:* info@solution-tree.com
*Web Site:* www.solution-tree.com
*Key Personnel*
Dist Rel: Cindy Johnson *E-mail:* cindy.johnson@solution-tree.com
Founded: 1987
Provides tested & proven resources that help those who work with youth create safe & caring schools, agencies & communities where all children succeed.
ISBN Prefix(es): 978-1-879639; 978-1-932127
Number of titles published annually: 20 Print
Total Titles: 200 Print; 2 Audio

**SOM Publishing**
Subsidiary of School of Metaphysics
163 Moon Valley Rd, Windyville, MO 65783
SAN: 159-5423
*Tel:* 417-345-8411 *Fax:* 417-345-6668
*E-mail:* som@som.org; dreamschool@dreamschool.org
*Web Site:* www.som.org; www.dreamschool.org
*Key Personnel*
CEO: Dr Barbara Condron
Pres: Dr Laurel Clark
Founded: 1973
Publish books in the fields of dream interpretation, Kundalini, holistic health, visualization, interfaith studies, meditation, Religious-Christian, past life recall & spiritual enlightenment.
ISBN Prefix(es): 978-0-944386
Number of titles published annually: 3 Print
Total Titles: 30 Print
*Distribution Center:* New Leaf Distributing Co, 401 Thornton Rd, Lithia Springs, GA 30122-1557 *Tel:* 770-948-7845 *Fax:* 770-944-2313 *E-mail:* newleaf@newleaf-dist.com *Web Site:* www.newleaf-dist.com

**Somerset Hall Press**
416 Commonwealth Ave, Suite 612, Boston, MA 02215
*Tel:* 617-236-5126
*E-mail:* info@somersethallpress.com
*Web Site:* www.somersethallpress.com
*Key Personnel*
Publr: Dean Papademetriou
Founded: 2003
Independent press specializing in literary & scholarly titles with a special interest in Greek studies.
ISBN Prefix(es): 978-0-9724661; 978-0-9774610; 978-1-935244
Number of titles published annually: 3 Print
Total Titles: 20 Print

**Soncino Press Ltd**
123 Ditmas Ave, Brooklyn, NY 11218
*Tel:* 718-972-6200 *Toll Free Tel:* 800-972-6201 *Fax:* 718-972-6204
*E-mail:* info@soncino.com
*Web Site:* www.soncino.com
*Key Personnel*
Pres: Gloria Goldman
Mng Ed: Norman Shapiro *E-mail:* nshapiro@soncino.com
Bible, Talmud & Judaism.
ISBN Prefix(es): 978-1-871055; 978-0-900689
Total Titles: 75 Print

**Sophia Institute Press®**
522 Donald St, Unit 3, Bedford, NH 03110
Mailing Address: PO Box 5284, Manchester, NH 03108 SAN: 657-7172
*Tel:* 603-836-5505 *Toll Free Tel:* 800-888-9344 *Fax:* 603-641-8108 *Toll Free Fax:* 888-288-2259
*E-mail:* orders@sophiainstitute.com
*Web Site:* www.sophiainstitute.com
*Key Personnel*
Pres: Charlie McKinney
Prodn Mgr: Sheila M Perry *E-mail:* production@sophiainstitute.com
Founded: 1983
Books on religion (Roman Catholicism).
ISBN Prefix(es): 978-0-918477; 978-1-928832; 978-1-933184
Number of titles published annually: 24 Print
Total Titles: 110 Print
Foreign Rep(s): Family Life International (New Zealand); Family Publications (UK); John XXIII Fellowship (Australia); Redemptorist Publications Alphonsus House (UK); St Andrews Church Supply (Canada); St Joseph's Workshops (Canada); Southwell Books (UK); Sunrise Marion Center (Canada)

**§Sopris West Educational Services**
Imprint of Cambium Learning Inc
17855 Dallas Pkwy, Suite 400, Dallas, TX 75287
*Tel:* 303-651-2829 *Toll Free Tel:* 800-547-6747 *Fax:* 303-776-5934 *Toll Free Fax:* 888-819-7767
*E-mail:* customerservice@sopriswest.com
*Web Site:* www.sopriswest.com
Founded: 1978
Training, development materials for educators.
ISBN Prefix(es): 978-0-944584; 978-1-57035; 978-1-59318
Number of titles published annually: 100 Print
Total Titles: 350 Print

**§Soul Mate Publishing**
PO Box 24, Macedon, NY 14502
*Tel:* 585-598-4791
*E-mail:* submissions@soulmatepublishing.com
*Web Site:* www.soulmatepublishing.com
*Key Personnel*
Ed-in-Chief: Deborah Gilbert
Founded: 2010
ISBN Prefix(es): 978-1-61935
Number of titles published annually: 100 E-Book
Total Titles: 15 Print; 120 E-Book
Membership(s): Romance Writers of America

**§Sound Feelings Publishing**
18375 Ventura Blvd, No 8000, Tarzana, CA 91356
*Tel:* 818-757-0600
*E-mail:* information@soundfeelings.com
*Web Site:* www.soundfeelings.com
*Key Personnel*
Founder & Pres: Howard Richman
This publisher has indicated that 80% of their product line is author subsidized.
ISBN Prefix(es): 978-0-9615963; 978-1-882060
Number of titles published annually: 1 Print; 3 E-Book; 2 Audio
Total Titles: 7 Print; 10 E-Book; 11 Audio
Foreign Rep(s): Gazelle (Europe)

**Soundprints**, see Palm Kids™

**Sounds True Inc**
413 S Arthur Ave, Louisville, CO 80027
*Tel:* 303-665-3151 *Toll Free Tel:* 800-333-9185

*E-mail:* customerservice@soundstrue.com
*Web Site:* www.soundstrue.com
*Key Personnel*
Founder & Publr: Tami Simon
Founded: 1985
ISBN Prefix(es): 978-1-56455; 978-1-59179; 978-1-60407; 978-1-62203

**§Sourcebooks Inc**
1935 Brookdale Rd, Suite 139, Naperville, IL 60563
SAN: 666-7864
Mailing Address: PO Box 4410, Naperville, IL 60567-4410
*Tel:* 630-961-3900 *Toll Free Tel:* 800-432-7444 *Fax:* 630-961-2168
*E-mail:* info@sourcebooks.com; customersupport@sourcebooks.com
*Web Site:* www.sourcebooks.com
*Key Personnel*
CEO & Publr: Dominique Raccah
COO & SVP: Barbara Briel
SVP & Dir, Technol & Content Delivery: Lynn Dilger
VP & Edit Dir: Todd Stocke *Tel:* 630-536-0543 *E-mail:* todd.stocke@sourcebooks.com
Art Servs Mgr: Helen Nam
Busn Devt Mgr, Put Me In The Story: Lyron Bennett *Tel:* 630-536-0540 *E-mail:* lyron.bennett@sourcebooks.com
Edit Mgr, Sourcebooks EDU: Suzanna Bainbridge *Tel:* 630-961-3900 ext 248
Edit Mgr, Sourcebooks Casablanca: Deb Werksman *Tel:* 203-876-9790 *E-mail:* deb.werksman@sourcebooks.com
Edit Mgr, Sourcebooks Jabberwocky: Steve Geck *Tel:* 212-414-1701 ext 2226 *E-mail:* steve.geck@sourcebooks.com
Edit Mgr, Sourcebooks Landmark: Shana Drehs *Tel:* 630-536-0535 *E-mail:* shana.drehs@sourcebooks.com
Edit Mgr, Fire & Sr Ed, Casablanca: Leah Hultenschmidt *Tel:* 212-414-1701 ext 2229 *E-mail:* leah.hultenschmidt@sourcebooks.com
Assoc Ed, Jabberwocky & Fire: Aubrey Poole
Ed: Stephanie Bowen *Tel:* 630-536-0588
Asst Ed, Trade Div: Jenna Skwarek
Mktg Mgr, Retail & Libr: Valerie Pierce *Tel:* 630-961-3900 ext 233 *E-mail:* valerie.pierce@sourcebooks.com
Mktg Assoc, Digital Initiatives: Sarah Henry
Publicity Mgr: Heather Moore *Tel:* 630-536-0553 *E-mail:* heather.moore@sourcebooks.com
Publicity Mgr, Children's & Young Adult: Derry Wilkins *Tel:* 212-414-1701 ext 2227 *E-mail:* derry.wilkins@sourcebooks.com
Sr Publicist, NY Off: Nicole Villeneuve
Sr Publicist, Sourcebooks Casablanca: Danielle Jackson
Ebook Prodn Coord: Jessica Zulli
Founded: 1987
Nonfiction, fiction, romance novels, children's books, young adult, gift books & calendars.
ISBN Prefix(es): 978-0-942061; 978-1-57071; 978-1-57248; 978-0-913825; 978-1-883518; 978-0-9629162; 978-1-887166; 978-1-4022
Number of titles published annually: 300 Print; 270 E-Book
Total Titles: 1,800 Print; 1,200 E-Book
Imprints: Cumberland House (nonfiction gift, history & cooking); Sourcebooks Casablanca (romance novels & nonfiction relationships, sex & weddings titles); Sourcebooks Fire (young adult); Sourcebooks Jabberwocky; Sourcebooks Landmark (fiction); Sourcebooks MediaFusion (multimedia books); Sphinx Publishing (self-help law, real estate & law)
*Branch Office(s)*
18 Cherry St, Suite 1W, Milford, CT 06460 *Tel:* 203-876-9790
Sourcebooks New York, 232 Madison Ave, Suite 1100, New York, NY 10018 *Tel:* 212-414-1701
Distributed by Raincoast Books
Distributor for Prufrock Press
Foreign Rep(s): Eliane Benisti (France); The Deborah Harris Agency (Israel); Inter-Ko (Korea); Nurcihan Kesim Literary Agency Inc (Turkey); Maxima Creative Agency (Indonesia); Piergiorgio Nicolazzini (Italy); Nova Littera Ltd (Russia); Prava I Prevodi (Eastern Block, Slovakia); Karen Schindler (Brazil); Tuttle-Mori Agency Inc (Japan, Thailand); Yanez Agencia Literaria (Spain)
*Returns:* RR Donnelley, 677 Brighton Beach Rd, Menasha, WI 54952
*Warehouse:* RR Donnelley, N9234 Lake Park Rd, Appleton, WI 54915 *Tel:* 920-969-6400 *Fax:* 920-969-6441
*See separate listing for:*
**Cumberland House**
**Sphinx Publishing**

**Sourced Media Books**
29 Via Regalo, San Clemente, CA 92673
*Tel:* 949-813-0182
*E-mail:* info@sourcemediabooks.com
*Web Site:* sourcedmediabooks.com
*Key Personnel*
Publr: Amy Cook, PhD
Sr Ed: Alden Weight, PhD
Founded: 2009
ISBN Prefix(es): 978-0-9841068; 978-1-937458
Number of titles published annually: 15 Print; 15 Online; 15 E-Book
Total Titles: 18 Print; 18 Online; 18 E-Book
Distributed by Gibbs-Smith; Many Hats Media
*Distribution Center:* Brigham Distributing, 110 S 800 W, Brigham City, UT 84302

**South Carolina Bar**
Continuing Legal Education Div, 950 Taylor St, Columbia, SC 29201
Mailing Address: PO Box 608, Columbia, SC 29202-0608
*Tel:* 803-799-6653 *Toll Free Tel:* 800-768-7787 *Fax:* 803-799-4118
*E-mail:* scbar-info@scbar.org
*Web Site:* www.scbar.org
*Key Personnel*
Pubns Dir: Alicia Hutto *E-mail:* ahutto@scbar.org
Continuing Legal Educ Dir: Terry Burnett *Tel:* 803-799-6653 ext 152 *E-mail:* tburnett@scbar.org
Founded: 1979
Law materials, legal treatises, manuals & software.
ISBN Prefix(es): 978-0-943856
Number of titles published annually: 10 Print
Total Titles: 80 Print

**South End Press**
Affiliate of Institute for Social & Cultural Change
PO Box 382132, Cambridge, MA 02238
SAN: 211-979X
*Tel:* 718-874-0089 *Toll Free Fax:* 800-960-0078
*E-mail:* southend@southendpress.org; info@southendpress.org
*Web Site:* www.southendpress.org
*Key Personnel*
Publr & Ed: Jocelyn Burrell; Asha Tall
Founded: 1977
Collectively managed nonprofit publisher of original trade paperbacks offering nonfiction analyses of politics, culture, ecology & feminism, race & sexuality from a radical perspective.
ISBN Prefix(es): 978-0-89608
Number of titles published annually: 10 Print
Total Titles: 260 Print
Foreign Rep(s): Consortium Book Sales & Distribution (Canada)
*Distribution Center:* Consortium Book Sales & Distribution, The Keg House, 34 13 Ave NE, Suite 101, Minneapolis, MN 55413-1007 *Tel:* 612-746-2600 *Toll Free Tel:* 800-283-3572 (cust serv) *Fax:* 612-746-2606 *E-mail:* consortium@cbsd.com *Web Site:* www.cbsd.com SAN: 200-6049

**South Platte Press**
PO Box 163, David City, NE 68632-0163
*Tel:* 402-367-3554
*E-mail:* railroads@windstream.net
*Web Site:* www.southplattepress.net
*Key Personnel*
Publr: James J Reisdorff
Founded: 1982
Railroad related titles.
ISBN Prefix(es): 978-0-942035
Number of titles published annually: 5 Print
Total Titles: 20 Print

**Southern Historical Press Inc**
375 W Broad St, Greenville, SC 29601
Mailing Address: PO Box 1267, Greenville, SC 29602-1267
*Tel:* 864-233-2346 *Toll Free Tel:* 800-233-0152 *Fax:* 864-233-2349
*Key Personnel*
Pres: LaBruce M S Lucas
Founded: 1967
Historical & genealogical.
ISBN Prefix(es): 978-0-89308
Number of titles published annually: 20 Print
Total Titles: 370 Print

**Southern Illinois University Press**
Division of Southern Illinois University
1915 University Press Dr, SIUC Mail Code 6806, Carbondale, IL 62901-4323
SAN: 203-3623
*Tel:* 618-453-2281 *Fax:* 618-453-1221
*E-mail:* custserv@press.uchicago.edu; rights@siu.edu
*Web Site:* www.siupress.com
*Key Personnel*
Ed-in-Chief: Karl Kageff *Tel:* 618-453-6629 *E-mail:* kageff@siu.edu
Edit Design & Prodn Mgr: Barbara Martin *Tel:* 618-453-6614 *E-mail:* bbmartin@siu.edu
Mktg & Sales Mgr: Amy Etcheson *Tel:* 618-453-6623 *E-mail:* aetcheson@siu.edu
Publicity Mgr: Bridgett Brown *Tel:* 618-453-6633 *E-mail:* bcbrown@siu.edu
Rts & Perms Mgr: Angela Moore-Swafford *Tel:* 618-453-6619 *E-mail:* angmoore@siu.edu
Founded: 1956
Scholarly nonfiction, educational material, rhetoric & composition, aviation, history, film & theatre, speech communication, regional history, media studies & poetry.
ISBN Prefix(es): 978-0-8093
Number of titles published annually: 54 Print
Total Titles: 1,200 Print; 2 CD-ROM; 17 Audio
Foreign Rep(s): East West Export Books (Royden Muranaka) (Asia, Australia, Pacific Rim); Eurospan (Andrew Wong) (Europe, Middle East); Scholarly Book Services Inc (Laura Rust) (Canada)
*Distribution Center:* Chicago Distribution Center, 11030 S Langley Ave, Chicago, IL 60628-3830 *Toll Free Tel:* 800-621-2736 *Toll Free Fax:* 800-621-8476
Membership(s): Association of American University Presses

**South-Western**, see Wadsworth Publishing

**Soyinfo Center**
PO Box 234, Lafayette, CA 94549-0234
SAN: 212-8411
*Tel:* 925-283-2991
*E-mail:* info@soyinfocenter.com
*Web Site:* www.soyinfocenter.com
*Key Personnel*
Pres & Ed-in-Chief: William Shurtleff

Founded: 1976
Books & bibliographies on all aspects of soybeans & soyfoods; industry & marketing studies. All books since 2008 published in PDF format on the web free of charge.
ISBN Prefix(es): 978-0-933332; 978-1-928914
Number of titles published annually: 3 Print; 12 Online
Total Titles: 62 Print; 15 Online
*Shipping Address:* 1021 Dolores Dr, Lafayette, CA 94549

**Sphinx Publishing**
Division of Sourcebooks Inc
1935 Brookdale Rd, Suite 139, Naperville, IL 60563
Mailing Address: PO Box 4410, Naperville, IL 60567-4410
*Tel:* 630-961-3900 *Toll Free Tel:* 800-43-bright (432-7448) *Fax:* 630-961-2168
*E-mail:* info@sourcebooks.com
*Web Site:* www.sourcebooks.com
*Key Personnel*
VP & Edit Dir: Todd Stocke *Tel:* 630-961-3900 ext 243 *E-mail:* todd.stocke@sourcebooks.com
Self-help law books (trade).
ISBN Prefix(es): 978-1-57071; 978-1-57248; 978-0-913825
Number of titles published annually: 5 Print; 5 E-Book
Total Titles: 300 Print; 100 E-Book
*Warehouse:* R R Donnelley, N-9234 Lake Park Rd, Appleton, WI 54915 *Tel:* 920-969-6400 *Fax:* 920-969-6441

**§SPIE**
1000 20 St, Bellingham, WA 98225-6705
Mailing Address: PO Box 10, Bellingham, WA 98227-0010
*Tel:* 360-676-3290 *Toll Free Tel:* 888-504-8171 *Fax:* 360-647-1445
*E-mail:* spie@spie.org
*Web Site:* www.spie.org
*Key Personnel*
Dir, Pubns & Intl Rts Contact: Eric Pepper
Founded: 1955
Scientific, technical books & journals, proceedings of symposia.
ISBN Prefix(es): 978-0-8194
Number of titles published annually: 380 Print; 30 CD-ROM
Total Titles: 7,075 Print; 450 CD-ROM
Imprints: SPIE Press

**Spinsters Ink**
Division of Spinsters Ink Publishing Co
PO Box 242, Midway, FL 32343
*E-mail:* info@spinstersink.com; editorialdirector@spinstersink.com
*Web Site:* www.spinstersink.com
*Key Personnel*
Publr: Linda Hill *E-mail:* linda@spinstersink.com
Founded: 1978
Novels & nonfiction by women about women, including social justice.
ISBN Prefix(es): 978-1-935226; 978-1-883523
Number of titles published annually: 8 Print; 12 E-Book
Total Titles: 100 Print; 24 E-Book
Imprints: Grave Issues
*Sales Office(s):* Bella Distribution, PO Box 10543, Tallahassee, FL 32302, Linda Hill *Toll Free Tel:* 800-729-4992
Foreign Rep(s): Airlift Book Co (Europe); Bulldog Distribution (Australia)
*Distribution Center:* Bella Distribution, PO Box 10543, Tallahassee, FL 32302 *Toll Free Tel:* 800-729-4992

**Spizzirri Publishing Inc**
PO Box 9397, Rapid City, SD 57709-9397
*Tel:* 605-348-2749 *Toll Free Tel:* 800-325-9819 *Fax:* 605-348-6251 *Toll Free Fax:* 800-322-9819
*E-mail:* spizzpub@aol.com
*Web Site:* www.spizzirri.com
*Key Personnel*
Pres: Linda Spizzirri
Founded: 1978
Educational coloring books, book-cassette packages, activity books, work books & 'how-to-draw books. Ages, pre-school thru 5th grade featuring realistic illustrations & museum curator approved texts on topics, including everything from dinosaurs to space.
ISBN Prefix(es): 978-0-86545
Number of titles published annually: 3 Print
Total Titles: 200 Print

**§Springer**
Subsidiary of Springer Science+Business Media
233 Spring St, New York, NY 10013-1578
*Tel:* 212-460-1500 *Toll Free Tel:* 800-SPRINGER (777-4643) *Fax:* 212-460-1575
*E-mail:* service-ny@springer.com
*Web Site:* www.springer.com
*Key Personnel*
Pres, Springer Science+Business Media LLC & EVP, Medicine, Biomedicine & Life Sci, Springer: William F Curtis, PhD
Pres, STM Sales, Global Academic & Govt, Springer: Syed Hasan
Pres, Apress & EVP, Computer Sci: Paul Manning
CFO, Springer Americas: Christian Staral
CFO, Springer US: Ned Woods
VP, Cust Serv & Fulfillment-Secaucus: Richard Sabol
VP, HR: Eileen Purelis
VP, Prodn: Henry Krell
Dir, Edit Opers-Clinical Medicine: Lori Holland
Edit Dir, Biomed & Life Sci: Carolyn Honour
Edit Dir, Busn Law, Statistics: Nicholas Phillipson
Edit Dir, Clinical Medicine: Antoinette Cimino; Richard Lansing
Edit Dir, Computer Sci: Jennifer Evans
Edit Dir, Engg: Alexander Greene
Edit Dir, Human Sci: Dieter Merkle
Edit Dir, Mathematics: Mark Strauss
Edit Dir, Physics: Harry Blom
Dir, Lib Mktg & Acct Devt: Jason Marcakis
Founded: 1842 (1964 NY office)
Scientific, medical, technical, research, reference books & periodicals.
ISBN Prefix(es): 978-0-387
Number of titles published annually: 6,500 Print; 6,000 E-Book
Total Titles: 70,000 Print; 36,000 Online; 38,000 E-Book
Imprints: Apress; BioMed Central; Birkhauser Science; Copernicus; Current Medicine Group; Humana Press; Springer; Springer Healthcare
*Foreign Office(s):* Heidelberger Platz 3, 14197 Berlin, Germany
Tiergartenstr 17, 69121 Heidelberg, Germany
Van Godewijckstr 30, 3311 GX Dordrecht, Netherlands
Membership(s): International Association of Scientific, Technical & Medical Publishers

**§Springer Publishing Co LLC**
11 W 42 St, 15th fl, New York, NY 10036-8002
SAN: 203-2236
*Tel:* 212-431-4370 *Toll Free Tel:* 877-687-7476 *Fax:* 212-941-7842
*E-mail:* marketing@springerpub.com; cs@springerpub.com (orders); editorial@springerpub.com
*Web Site:* www.springerpub.com
*Key Personnel*
CEO & Pres: Theodore C Nardin *E-mail:* tnardin@springerpub.com
VP, Sales & Mktg: Jason Roth *E-mail:* jroth@springerpub.com
Edit Dir: Nancy Hale *E-mail:* nhale@springerpub.com
Dir, Journal Pubns: James C Costello *E-mail:* jcostello@springerpub.com
Dir, Spec Sales & Rts: Annette Imperati *E-mail:* aimperati@springerpub.com
Sr Sales Dir: Matt Conmy *E-mail:* mconmy@springerpub.com
Nursing Publr: Margaret Zuccarini *E-mail:* mzuccarini@springerpub.com
Exec Ed: Sheri W Sussman *E-mail:* swsussman@springerpub.com
Exec Ed, Nursing: Elizabeth Nieginski *E-mail:* enieginski@springerpub.com
Sr Acqs Ed: Joseph Morita *E-mail:* jmorita@springerpub.com
Acqs Ed: Stephanie Drew *E-mail:* sdrew@springerpub.com
Founded: 1950 (Feb 2004, acquired by Mannheim Holdings, LLC, subsidiary of Mannheim Trust)
Professional books, encyclopedias, college textbooks & journals; nursing, psychology, gerontology/geriatrics, medical education, public health, rehabilitation, social work & scholarly health sciences.
ISBN Prefix(es): 978-0-8261
Number of titles published annually: 100 Print
Total Titles: 700 Print
Foreign Rep(s): Cranbury International LLC (Argentina, Brazil, Chile, Colombia, Costa Rica, Ecuador, El Salvador, Guatemala, Guyana, Jamaica, Mexico, Panama, Paraguay, Peru, Puerto Rico, Trinidad and Tobago, Venezuela, Virgin Islands); Elsevier-Australia (Australia, New Zealand); The Eurospan Group (Europe, Middle East); Login Brothers Canada (Canada); Taylor & Francis Asia Pacific (China, Hong Kong, Indonesia, Korea, Malaysia, Singapore, Taiwan, Thailand, Vietnam); Taylor & Francis Books India Pvt Ltd (Bangladesh, India, Pakistan, Sri Lanka)
*Shipping Address:* Ingram Publishers Services, One Ingram Blvd, La Vergne, TN 37006 *Tel:* 978-345-2121 *Toll Free Tel:* 877-687-7476 *Fax:* 978-348-1233 *Web Site:* www.ingrampublisherservices.com
*Warehouse:* Ingram Publishers Services, One Ingram Blvd, La Vergne, TN 37006 *Tel:* 978-345-2121 *Toll Free Tel:* 877-687-7476 *Fax:* 978-348-1233 *Web Site:* www.ingrampublisherservices.com
Membership(s): AAP; American Medical Publishers Association; STM

**Spry Publishing**
Formerly Ann Arbor Media Group
2500 S State St, Ann Arbor, MI 48104
*Tel:* 734-913-1700 *Toll Free Tel:* 877-722-2264 *Fax:* 734-913-1249
*E-mail:* info@sprypub.com
*Web Site:* www.sprypub.com
*Key Personnel*
Prod Serv Mgmt: Lynne Johnson *E-mail:* ljohnson@aaeditions.com
Sales & Mktg: James Edwards *E-mail:* jedwards@aaeditions.com
Founded: 1999
ISBN Prefix(es): 978-1-58726
Number of titles published annually: 20 Print
Total Titles: 120 Print
Imprints: Mitten Press
Membership(s): Great Lakes Independent Booksellers Association; IBPA, the Independent Book Publishers Association; Midatlantic Book Publishers Association

**Square One Publishers Inc**
115 Herricks Rd, Garden City Park, NY 11040
*Tel:* 516-535-2010 *Toll Free Tel:* 877-900-BOOK (900-2665) *Fax:* 516-535-2014
*E-mail:* sq1publish@aol.com

*Web Site:* www.squareonepublishers.com
*Key Personnel*
Pres & Publr: Rudy Shur
Sales Dir: Ken Kaiman
Dir, Publicity & Mktg: Anthony Pomes
Art Dir: Jeannie Tudor
Mgr, Opers: Robert Love
Exec Ed: Joanne Abrams
Sr Ed: Marie Caratozzolo
Founded: 2000
Specialize in adult nonfiction books. Topics covered include collectibles, cooking, general interest, history, how-to, parenting, self-help & health.
ISBN Prefix(es): 978-0-7570
Number of titles published annually: 25 Print
Total Titles: 400 Print; 1 Audio
Distributed by Thomas Allen & Son
Distributor for InnoVision Health Media; Rainbow Ridge Books
Foreign Rep(s): Thomas Allen & Son (Canada); Brumby Books (Australia, New Zealand); J C Carrillo Inc (Caribbean, Latin America); Cassidy & Associates (China); Deep Books (Europe, UK); Pen International (Singapore); R & S Summers (Southeast Asia); Trinity Books (South Africa); Yasmy International Marketing (Japan)
Membership(s): ABA; ALA; The Association of Publishers for Special Sales; IBPA, the Independent Book Publishers Association

**§SRA/McGraw-Hill**
Division of McGraw-Hill School Education Group
8787 Orion Place, Columbus, OH 43240
*Tel:* 614-430-4000 *Fax:* 614-430-4303
*E-mail:* sra@mcgraw-hill.com
*Web Site:* www.sraonline.com
Founded: 1938
Supplemental & curriculum materials for kindergarten through high school & direct instruction programs. Online instruction & assessment.
ISBN Prefix(es): 978-0-307; 978-0-8126; 978-0-383
Number of titles published annually: 2,000 Print; 100 CD-ROM; 100 Online; 200 Audio
Total Titles: 18,000 Print; 500 CD-ROM; 500 Online; 10,000 Audio
Membership(s): AAP; Association of Educational Publishers; International Reading Association; National Council of Supervisors of Mathematics; National Council of Teachers of Mathematics

**SSPC: The Society for Protective Coatings**
40 24 St, 6th fl, Pittsburgh, PA 15222-4656
*Tel:* 412-281-2331 *Toll Free Tel:* 877-281-7772 (US only) *Fax:* 412-281-9992
*E-mail:* info@sspc.org
*Web Site:* www.sspc.org
*Key Personnel*
Exec Dir: William Shoup *Tel:* 412-281-2331 ext 2230 *E-mail:* shoup@sspc.org
Pubns Fulfillment Coord: Jeannine Bodack *Tel:* 412-281-2331 ext 2204 *E-mail:* bodack@sspc.org
Founded: 1950
Technical publications; CD-ROMs, standards for industry.
ISBN Prefix(es): 978-0-938477; 978-1-889060
Number of titles published annually: 12 Print
Total Titles: 80 Print
Distributed by Technical Publishing Co

**§ST Media Group Book Division**
Division of ST Media Group Intl
11262 Cornell Park Dr, Cincinnati, OH 45242
SAN: 204-5974
*Tel:* 513-421-2050 *Toll Free Tel:* 866-265-0954 *Fax:* 513-421-5144
*E-mail:* books@stmediagroup.com
*Web Site:* www.stmediagroup.com
*Key Personnel*
Dir: Mark Kissling *Tel:* 800-925-1110 ext 399 *E-mail:* mark.kissling@stmediagroup.com
Founded: 1906
Books, magazines, buyers' guides: sign, screen printing, visual merchandising & store design industries, large format digital printing & package design.
ISBN Prefix(es): 978-0-911380; 978-0-944094
Number of titles published annually: 6 Print
Total Titles: 44 Print

**§Stackpole Books**
5067 Ritter Rd, Mechanicsburg, PA 17055
SAN: 202-5396
*Tel:* 717-796-0411 *Toll Free Tel:* 800-732-3669 *Fax:* 717-796-0412
*Web Site:* www.stackpolebooks.com
*Key Personnel*
Pres: David Detweiler
VP & Dir, Creative Servs & Prodn: Tracy Patterson
VP & Publr: Judith Schnell *E-mail:* jschnell@stackpolebooks.com
Ed: Mark Allison; Kyle Weaver
Rts: Mark Allison *Tel:* 717-796-0411 ext 153
Founded: 1933
Trade book publisher with a proud, 80 plus year history of publishing titles in the categories of outdoor sports, nature, crafts, history, military, military reference & regional. Strong in fly fishing, nature guides, military history & military reference, we publish deep in our niche areas. Presently expanding into the fast-growing world of e-books while continuing to produce alternative, high-quality hardcovers, trade paperbacks & e-books.
ISBN Prefix(es): 978-0-8117
Number of titles published annually: 100 Print; 5 CD-ROM
Total Titles: 1,500 Print; 5 CD-ROM
Distributor for The Army War College Foundation Press; Barclay Creek Press; Headwater Books; Historical Society of Western Pennsylvania; Homespun Video; Northwest Fly Fishing; Quiller Press Ltd; Ryton Publications; The Sausage Maker; Stackpole Magazines; Swan Hill
Foreign Rights: Bardon Chinese Media Agency (Phillip Chen) (China); Alex Korzheneuski (Russia); Hana Whitton (Eastern Europe)

**Standard International Media Holdings**
568 Ninth St S, Suite 201, Naples, FL 34102-7336
*Tel:* 239-649-7077 *Fax:* 239-649-5832
*E-mail:* sales@standardinternationalmedia.com
*Web Site:* www.standardinternationalmedia.com
*Key Personnel*
CFO: Connie Miller *Tel:* 239-649-7077 ext 2224 *E-mail:* connie@standardinternationalmedia.com
Pres: Simon Bailey *E-mail:* simon@standardinternationalmedia.com
Intl Sales Dir: Elaine Evans *Tel:* 239-649-7077 ext 2223 *E-mail:* elaine@standardinternationalmedia.com
Founded: 1994
Book publisher & distributor.
ISBN Prefix(es): 978-1-888777; 978-1-58279; 978-1-86091
Total Titles: 200 Print
Imprints: Chef Express; Chef Success; Trident Reference
Foreign Rights: Elaine Evans (Worldwide)
*Warehouse:* 14560 Global Pkwy, Fort Myers, FL 33913

**Standard Publications Inc**
PO Box 2226, Champaign, IL 61825-2226
SAN: 912-9251
*Tel:* 217-898-7825 *Fax:* 630-214-0564
*E-mail:* spi@standardpublications.com
*Web Site:* standardpublications.com
Founded: 2001
ISBN Prefix(es): 978-0-9709788; 978-0-9722691; 978-1-59462; 978-1-60424; 978-1-60597; 978-1-4385; 978-1-61742
Number of titles published annually: 3 Print
Total Titles: 10,000 Print

**Standard Publishing**
8805 Governors Hill Dr, Suite 400, Cincinnati, OH 45249
SAN: 110-5515
*Tel:* 513-931-4050 *Toll Free Tel:* 800-543-1353 *Fax:* 513-931-0950 *Toll Free Fax:* 877-867-5751
*E-mail:* customerservice@standardpub.com
*Web Site:* www.standardpub.com
*Key Personnel*
VP, Prod Devt: Matt Lockhart
Dir, Adult & Teen: Lindsay Black
Dir, Sales: Ken Lorenz
Mng Ed: James Nieman
Sr Ed: Jon Underwood
Ed: Shawn McMullen; Ron Nickelson; Margie Redford; Margaret K Williams
Ed, Children's: Karen Cain
Ed, Christian Standard: Mark Taylor
Asst Ed, The Lookout: Sheryl Overstreet
Magazine Prodn Coord, Christian Standard: Diane Jones
Rts Coord: Joann VanMeter
Sr Designer: Andrew Quach; Sandy Wimmer
Book Designer: Steve Clark
Graphic Designer: Bob Korth
Graphic Designer & Prodn Technician: Dale Meyers
Founded: 1866
Religious children's books, Sunday school literature & supplies, helps for Sunday school teachers, youth & adult trade books.
ISBN Prefix(es): 978-0-87239; 978-0-87403; 978-0-7847
Number of titles published annually: 75 Print
Total Titles: 700 Print; 30 CD-ROM
Imprints: Happy Day Books
Foreign Rights: Foundation Distributing Inc (Canada); Omega (New Zealand); Salvation Book Centre (Malaysia); Scripture Press Foundation Ltd (UK)

**§Standard Publishing Corp**
155 Federal St, 13th fl, Boston, MA 02110
*Tel:* 617-457-0600 *Toll Free Tel:* 800-682-5759 *Fax:* 617-457-0608
*Web Site:* www.spcpub.com
*Key Personnel*
Pres & Publr: John C Cross, Esq
Prodn Mgr & Classified Ad Mgr: Nakeesha Warner
Mktg Mgr: Susanne Edes Dillman *Tel:* 617-457-0600 ext 229 *E-mail:* s.dillman@spcpub.com
Circ Mgr & Cust Serv: Kelly Cotter
Ad Sales Mgr: Barbara Crockett
Founded: 1865
Insurance.
ISBN Prefix(es): 978-0-923240
Number of titles published annually: 10 Print
Total Titles: 10 Print; 3 CD-ROM
Subsidiaries: John Liner Organization
*Branch Office(s)*
Insurance Record, 9601 White Rock Trail, Suite 213, Dallas, TX 75238
Distributed by LexisNexis; Silverplume, a Vertafore Co

**Stanford University Press**
1450 Page Mill Rd, Palo Alto, CA 94304-1124
SAN: 203-3526
*Tel:* 650-723-9434 *Fax:* 650-725-3457
*E-mail:* info@sup.org
*Web Site:* www.sup.org

*Key Personnel*
Publr: Michael Keller
Publg Dir & Ed-in-Chief: Kate Wahl *E-mail:* kwahl@stanford.edu
Dir: Dr Alan Harvey *E-mail:* aharvey@stanford.edu
Dir, Edit, Design & Prodn: Patricia Myers *E-mail:* pmyers@stanford.edu
Dir, Fin & Opers: Jean H Kim *E-mail:* plcmnkim@stanford.edu
Dir, Sales & Mktg: David B Jackson *E-mail:* david.jackson@stanford.edu
Art Dir: Robert Ehle *E-mail:* ehle@stanford.edu
Exec Ed: Dr Geoffrey R H Burn *E-mail:* grhburn@stanford.edu
Sr Ed, Busn Economics & Organizational Studies: Margo Beth Fleming *E-mail:* mbfleming@stanford.edu
Sr Ed, History, Jewish & Asian Studies: Stacy Wagner *E-mail:* swagner@stanford.edu
Sr Ed, Literature, Philosophy & Religion: Dr Emily-Jane Cohen
Acqs Ed, Anthropology, Asian Studies & Law: Michelle Lipinski *E-mail:* mlipinski@stanford.edu
Contracts & Rts Mgr: Ariane de Pree-Kajfez
Prodn Mgr: Harold Moorehead *E-mail:* hmoorehead@stanford.edu
Exhibits Mgr: Christie Cochrell *E-mail:* cochrell@stanford.edu
Founded: 1925
ISBN Prefix(es): 978-0-8047
Number of titles published annually: 150 Print; 40 E-Book
Total Titles: 2,500 Print; 400 E-Book
Imprints: Stanford Business Books; Stanford Security Studies; Stanford Law Books; Stanford General Books; Stanford University Press
Foreign Rep(s): East-West Export Books (Asia, Australia, Hawaii, New Zealand, The Pacific); Eurospan Group (Africa, Central Asia, Europe, Middle East, UK)
*Returns:* Chicago Distribution Center, 11030 S Langley Ave, Chicago, IL 60628 *Tel:* 773-568-1550 *Toll Free Tel:* 800-621-2736 *Fax:* 773-660-2235 *Toll Free Fax:* 800-621-8471 *E-mail:* custserv@press.uchicago.edu
*Warehouse:* Chicago Distribution Center, 11030 S Langley Ave, Chicago, IL 60628 *Tel:* 773-568-1550 *Toll Free Tel:* 800-621-2736 *Fax:* 773-660-2235 *Toll Free Fax:* 800-621-8471 *E-mail:* custserv@press.uchicago.edu
*Distribution Center:* Chicago Distribution Center, 11030 S Langley Ave, Chicago, IL 60628 *Tel:* 773-568-1550 *Toll Free Tel:* 800-621-2736 *Fax:* 773-660-2235 *Toll Free Fax:* 800-621-8471 *E-mail:* custserv@press.uchicago.edu
Membership(s): AAP; Association of American University Presses

**Star Bright Books Inc**
13 Landsdowne St, Cambridge, MA 02139
*Tel:* 617-354-1300 *Fax:* 617-354-1399
*E-mail:* info@starbrightbooks.com; orders@starbrightbooks.com
*Web Site:* www.starbrightbooks.com
*Key Personnel*
Publr: Deborah Shine
Founded: 1995
Independent children's book publisher.
ISBN Prefix(es): 978-1-887734; 978-1-932065; 978-1-59572
Number of titles published annually: 16 Print
Total Titles: 400 Print
Membership(s): ABA; ALA; IBPA, the Independent Book Publishers Association

**Star Publishing Co Inc**
650 El Camino Real, Redwood City, CA 94063
SAN: 212-6958
*Tel:* 650-591-3505 *Fax:* 650-591-3898
*E-mail:* mail@starpublishing.com
*Web Site:* www.starpublishing.com
*Key Personnel*
Publr: Stuart A Hoffman *E-mail:* stuart@starpublishing.com
Founded: 1978
College/university textbooks, laboratory manuals; reference books; professional books; California history/local history.
ISBN Prefix(es): 978-0-89863
Number of titles published annually: 14 Print
Total Titles: 205 Print
Imprints: Encore Editions

**STARbooks Press**
Affiliate of Florida Literary Foundation (FLF)
PO Box 711612, Herndon, VA 20171
*E-mail:* contact@starbookspress.com
*Web Site:* www.starbookspress.com
*Key Personnel*
Sr Edit Dir: Eric Summers
Founded: 1980
ISBN Prefix(es): 978-1-877978; 978-1-891855
Number of titles published annually: 8 Print
Total Titles: 30 Print; 1 Audio
Imprints: Florida Literary Foundation (FLF) Press; Starbooks

**§Starcrafts LLC**
334-A Calef Hwy, Epping, NH 03042
SAN: 208-5380
*Tel:* 603-734-4300 *Toll Free Tel:* 866-953-8458 (24 hr message ctr) *Fax:* 603-734-4311
*E-mail:* astrosales@astrocom.com; starcrafts@comcast.net
*Web Site:* www.astrocom.com; starcraftspublishing.com; acspublications.com
*Key Personnel*
Owner & Publr: Maria K Simms *E-mail:* maria@starcraftpublishing.com
Cust Serv: Thomas Canfield *E-mail:* tom@starcraftpublishing.com
Founded: 1973
Astrology: ephemerides, chart interpretation.
ISBN Prefix(es): 978-0-935127; 978-0-917086; 978-0-9762422; 978-1-934976
Number of titles published annually: 8 Print; 1 CD-ROM
Total Titles: 60 Print; 5 CD-ROM; 1 Audio
Imprints: ACS Publications; Starcrafts LLC
Foreign Rep(s): The Rights Agency (Canada)
*Distribution Center:* New Leaf Distributing Co, 401 Thornton Rd, Lithia Springs, GA 30122-1557 *Tel:* 770-948-7845 *Fax:* 770-944-2313 *E-mail:* newleaf@newleaf-dist.com *Web Site:* www.newleaf-dist.com

**Stargazer Publishing Co**
958 Stanislaus Dr, Corona, CA 92881
Mailing Address: PO Box 77002, Corona, CA 92877-0100
*Tel:* 951-898-4619 *Toll Free Tel:* 800-606-7895 (orders) *Fax:* 951-898-4633
*E-mail:* stargazer@stargazerpub.com; orders@stargazerpub.com
*Web Site:* www.stargazerpub.com
Founded: 1995
ISBN Prefix(es): 978-0-9643853; 978-1-933277; 978-0-9713756
Number of titles published annually: 10 Print; 5 CD-ROM; 5 E-Book
Total Titles: 22 Print; 5 CD-ROM; 5 E-Book
*Warehouse:* Publishers Storage & Shipping Corp, 660 S Mansfield, Ypsilante, MI 48197
Membership(s): California Readers; IBPA, the Independent Book Publishers Association; National Association of College Stores; Publishers Association of Los Angeles; Society of Children's Book Writers & Illustrators

**StarGroup International Inc**
1194 Old Dixie Hwy, Suite 201, West Palm Beach, FL 33413
*Tel:* 561-547-0667 *Fax:* 561-843-8530
*E-mail:* info@stargroupinternational.com
*Web Site:* www.stargroupinternational.com
*Key Personnel*
CEO & Pres: Brenda Star *E-mail:* brenda@stargroupinternational.com
Creative Dir: Mel Abfier
Head Writer & Film/Video Prodr: Shawn McAllister
Media Specialist: Sam Smyth
Founded: 1983
Create books to be used as marketing & media tools. For over two decades have maintained access to the best researchers, writers, editors, proofreaders, designers & printers in the industry, while offering public relations & marketing services. StarGroup's speciality is creating books for clients to enhance their credibility & position them as experts in their field.
This publisher has indicated that 75% of their product line is author subsidized.
ISBN Prefix(es): 978-1-884886
Number of titles published annually: 25 Print
Total Titles: 100 Print
Membership(s): Florida Publishers Association Inc; IBPA, the Independent Book Publishers Association

**State University of New York Press**
22 Corporate Woods Blvd, 3rd fl, Albany, NY 12211-2504
SAN: 760-7261
*Tel:* 518-472-5000 *Toll Free Tel:* 877-204-6073 (orders) *Fax:* 518-472-5038 *Toll Free Fax:* 877-204-6074 (orders)
*E-mail:* suny@presswarehouse.com (orders); info@sunypress.edu (edit off)
*Web Site:* www.sunypress.edu
*Key Personnel*
Co-Dir: Donna Dixon *Tel:* 518-641-0651 *E-mail:* donna.dixon@sunypress.edu; James Peltz *Tel:* 518-641-0668 *E-mail:* james.peltz@sunypress.edu
Assoc Dir & Dir, Sales & Busn Devt: Daniel Flynn *Tel:* 518-641-0676 *E-mail:* daniel.flynn@sunypress.edu
Dir, Mktg & Publicity: Fran Keneston *Tel:* 518-641-0660 *E-mail:* fran.keneston@sunypress.edu
Rts & Perms: Sharla Clute *Tel:* 518-641-0653 *E-mail:* sharla.clute@sunypress.edu
Founded: 1966
Scholarly nonfiction, especially works in philosophy, psychology, African American studies, gender/sexuality studies, American Indian studies, museum/archival science, Asian Studies & religious studies.
ISBN Prefix(es): 978-0-87395; 978-0-88706; 978-0-7914; 978-1-4384
Number of titles published annually: 150 Print; 140 Online; 140 E-Book; 2 Audio
Total Titles: 5,210 Print; 3,500 Online; 3,500 E-Book; 2 Audio
Imprints: Excelsior Editions
Distributor for Albany Institute of History & Art; Codhill Press; Samuel Dorsky Museum of Art; Mount Ida Press; New Netherland Institute; Rockefeller Institute Press; Uncrowned Queens
Foreign Rep(s): Apac Publishers Services Pte Ltd (China, Hong Kong, Indonesia, Malaysia, Singapore, Taiwan, Thailand, Vietnam); Eleanor Brasch Enterprises (Australia, New Zealand); Cassidy & Associates Inc (China, Hong Kong, Taiwan); Lexa Publishers' Representatives (Canada); Mediamatics (India); United Publishers Services Ltd (Japan); University Presses Marketing (Continental Europe, Ireland, Israel, UK); US Pub Rep Inc (Caribbean, Central America, Mexico, Puerto Rico, South America)
*Billing Address:* PO Box 960, Herndon, VA 20172-0960 *Tel:* 703-661-1575 *Fax:* 703-996-1010
*Orders to:* PO Box 960, Herndon, VA 20172-0960 *Tel:* 703-661-1575 *Fax:* 703-996-1010
*Returns:* 22883 Quicksilver Dr, Dulles, VA 20166 *Tel:* 703-661-1575 *Fax:* 703-996-1010

*Shipping Address:* PO Box 960, Herndon, VA 20172-0960 *Tel:* 703-661-1575 *Fax:* 703-996-1010
*Warehouse:* PO Box 960, Herndon, VA 20172-0960 *Tel:* 703-661-1575 *Fax:* 703-996-1010
*Distribution Center:* NBN International, Estover Rd, Plymouth PL6 7PY, United Kingdom *Tel:* (01752) 202-301 *Fax:* (01752) 202-233 *E-mail:* orders@nbninternational.com
Membership(s): ABA; Association of American University Presses; National Association of Independent Publishers
*See separate listing for:*
**Excelsior Editions**

**Steerforth Press**
45 Lyme Rd, Suite 208, Hanover, NH 03755-1222
*Tel:* 603-643-4787 *Fax:* 603-643-4788
*E-mail:* info@steerforth.com
*Web Site:* www.steerforth.com
*Key Personnel*
Publr: Chip Fleischer *E-mail:* chip@steerforth.com
Sr Ed: Alan Lelchuk; Michael Moore; Thomas Powers
Fiction Ed: Roland Pease *E-mail:* roland@steerforth.com
Publg Opers & Foreign Rts: Helga Schmidt *E-mail:* helga@steerforth.com
Founded: 1993
ISBN Prefix(es): 978-1-883642; 978-0-944072; 978-1-58195; 978-1-58642
Number of titles published annually: 18 Print
Total Titles: 200 Print
Imprints: Zoland Books
Foreign Rights: Agence Bookman (Scandinavia); Big Apple Agency Inc (Taiwan); The English Agency (Japan); Anouk H Foerg; Harris-Elon Agency (Israel); International Editors' Co SA (Argentina, Brazil, Latin America, Portugal, Spain); Katai & Bolza (Hungary); David Marshall; Daniela Micura Literary Services (Italy); Onk Agency (Turkey)
*Distribution Center:* Random House Distribution Center, 400 Hahn Rd, Westminster, MD 21157 *Toll Free Tel:* 800-733-3000 *Toll Free Fax:* 800-659-2436
Membership(s): ABA; IBPA, the Independent Book Publishers Association; New England Independent Booksellers Association

**§SteinerBooks**
610 Main St, Great Barrington, MA 01230
*Tel:* 413-528-8233 *Fax:* 413-528-8826
*E-mail:* friends@steinerbooks.org
*Web Site:* www.steinerbooks.org
*Key Personnel*
CEO & Pres: Gene Gollogly *Tel:* 212-414-2275 ext 11 *Fax:* 212-414-2412 *E-mail:* gene@steinerbooks.org
Edit & Art Dir: Mary Giddens
Ed-in-Chief: Christopher Bamford
Founded: 1928
American & English editions of works by Rudolf Steiner & related authors.
ISBN Prefix(es): 978-0-910142; 978-0-88010
Number of titles published annually: 29 Print
Total Titles: 451 Print
Imprints: Bell Pond Books; Lindisfarne Books
Distributed by Rudolf Steiner Press UK
Distributor for Chiron Publications; Clairview Books; Floris Books; Hawthorn Press; Lantern Books; Rudolph Steiner Press; Temple Lodge Publishing
Foreign Rep(s): Ceres (New Zealand); Peter Hyde & Associates (South Africa); Rudolf Steiner Press (UK)
*Orders to:* PO Box 960, Herndon, VA 20172-0960 *Tel:* 703-661-1594 *Fax:* 703-661-1501 *E-mail:* service@steinerbooks.org SAN: 201-1824
*See separate listing for:*
**Lindisfarne Books**

**Steller Publishing**
2114 S Live Oak Pkwy, Wilmington, NC 28403
SAN: 860-2298
*Tel:* 910-269-7444
*E-mail:* info@stellar-publishing.com
*Web Site:* www.stellar-publishing.com
*Key Personnel*
Publr: Winifred Jones *E-mail:* publisher@stellar-publishing.com
Founded: 2000
This publisher has indicated that 50% of their product line is author subsidized.
ISBN Prefix(es): 978-0-970341
Number of titles published annually: 3 Print
Total Titles: 9 Print

**Stemmer House Publishers Inc**
Division of Pathway Book Service
4 White Brook Rd, Gilsum, NH 03448
SAN: 207-9623
Mailing Address: PO Box 89, Gilsum, NH 03448
*Tel:* 603-357-0236 *Toll Free Tel:* 800-345-6665 *Fax:* 603-357-2073
*E-mail:* info@stemmer.com
*Web Site:* www.stemmer.com
*Key Personnel*
Pres & Publr: Judith Peter
Founded: 1975
Books in the arts & crafts, audiocassettes, illustrated books, multicultural studies & children's books on the environment.
ISBN Prefix(es): 978-0-916144; 978-0-88045
Number of titles published annually: 10 Print
Total Titles: 150 Print; 5 Audio
Imprints: Great Architectural Replica Series; International Design Library®; NaturEncyclopedia Series
Foreign Rep(s): Gazelle Ltd (Europe, UK); John Reed Books (Australia, New Zealand)
*Returns:* Pathway Book Service, 4 White Brook Rd, Gilsum, NH 03448
*Shipping Address:* Pathway Book Service, 4 White Brook Rd, Gilsum, NH 03448
*Warehouse:* Pathway Book Service, 4 White Brook Rd, Gilsum, NH 03448
*Distribution Center:* Pathway Book Service, 4 White Brook Rd, Gilsum, NH 03448

**§Stenhouse Publishers**
Division of Highlights for Children
480 Congress St, Portland, ME 04101-3451
*Tel:* 207-253-1600 *Toll Free Tel:* 888-363-0566 *Fax:* 207-253-5121 *Toll Free Fax:* 800-833-9164
*E-mail:* customerservice@stenhouse.com
*Web Site:* www.stenhouse.com
*Key Personnel*
Edit Dir: Philippa Stratton *E-mail:* philippa@stenhouse.com
Founded: 1993
Professional books for teachers.
ISBN Prefix(es): 978-1-57110
Number of titles published annually: 20 Print; 3 Online; 15 E-Book
Total Titles: 300 Print; 200 E-Book; 3 Audio
Distributor for Pembroke Publishers
Foreign Rep(s): Curriculum Corp (Australia, New Zealand); EUROSPAN (Africa, Central America, China, Europe, Hong Kong, India, Japan, Korea, South America, Taiwan, UK); Pembroke Publishers (Canada); Publishers Marketing Services (Southeast Asia)
*Billing Address:* PO Box 11020, Portland, ME 04104-7020, Opers Mgr: Elaine Cyr *E-mail:* ecyr@stenhouse.com
*Warehouse:* 4200 Parkway Ct, Hilliard, OH 43026, Contact: Jane Cavarozzi *Tel:* 614-487-2883 *Fax:* 614-529-0670

**Stephens Press™**
Subsidiary of Stephens Media LLC
1111 W Bonanza Rd, Las Vegas, NV 89106
Mailing Address: PO Box 70, Las Vegas, NV 89125-0070
*Tel:* 702-387-5260 *Toll Free Tel:* 888-951-2665 *Fax:* 702-387-2997
*E-mail:* info@stephenspress.com
*Web Site:* www.stephenspress.com
*Key Personnel*
Pres: Carolyn Hayes Uber *Tel:* 702-383-0486 *E-mail:* cuber@stephenspress.com
Publg Coord: Stacey Stonum Fott *E-mail:* sfott@stephenspress.com
Bookkeeper: Serena Smith *Tel:* 702-383-0253 *E-mail:* ssmith@stephenspress.com
Founded: 2003
Book division of Las Vegas Review-Journal & 40 other US newspapers.
ISBN Prefix(es): 978-932-173; 978-935-043
Number of titles published annually: 15 Print
Total Titles: 140 Print; 4 E-Book
Imprints: CityLife Books
*Sales Office(s):* Midpoint Trade Books, 27 W 20th St, Suite 1102, New York, NY 10011 *Tel:* 212-727-0190 *Fax:* 212-727-0195 *Web Site:* midpointtradebooks.com
*Shipping Address:* Midpoint Trade Books, 1263 Southwest Blvd, Kansas City, KS 66103 *Tel:* 913-362-7400 *Fax:* 913-362-7401 *E-mail:* info@midpointtradebooks.com *Web Site:* www.midpointtradebooks.com
*Warehouse:* Midpoint Trade Books, 1263 Southwest Blvd, Kansas City, KS 66103 *Tel:* 913-362-7400 *Fax:* 913-362-7401 *E-mail:* info@midpointtradebooks.com *Web Site:* www.midpointtradebooks.com
*Distribution Center:* Midpoint Trade Books, 1263 Southwest Blvd, Kansas City, KS 66103 *Tel:* 913-362-7400 *Fax:* 913-362-7401 *E-mail:* info@midpointtradebooks.com *Web Site:* www.midpointtradebooks.com
Membership(s): IBPA, the Independent Book Publishers Association

**Sterling Publishing Co Inc**
387 Park Ave S, 11th fl, New York, NY 10016-8810
SAN: 211-6324
*Tel:* 212-532-7160 *Toll Free Tel:* 800-367-9692 *Fax:* 212-213-2495
*Web Site:* www.sterlingpub.com
*Key Personnel*
Compt: Tom Allen
EVP: Theresa Thompson
VP & Edit Dir: Carlo DeVito; Michael Fragnito
VP, Sales Opers: Adria Dougherty *Tel:* 646-688-2444 *E-mail:* adougherty@sterlingpub.com
Dir, HR: Kerri Cuocci
Dir, Special Sales: Nicole Vines Verlin
Dir, Subs Rts & Export: Marilyn Kretzer
Sr Mgr, Natl Accts Trade Sales: Josh Mrvos
Founded: 1949
Publisher of quality nonfiction & fiction books for adults & children. Subject categories include art & photography, cookbooks, wine, self-improvement, mind/body/spirit, business, history, reference, science & nature, home reference, gardening, music, sports, lifestyle & design, hobbies, crafts, classics, study guides, puzzles & games, children's nonfiction, picture, board & humor books.
ISBN Prefix(es): 978-0-7607; 978-0-945352; 978-0-304; 978-0-87192; 978-0-937274; 978-1-887374; 978-1-57990; 978-0-8069; 978-1-86351; 978-1-895569; 978-0-233; 978-0-85177; 978-0-297; 978-1-85375; 978-1-57389; 978-1-85585; 978-1-84188; 978-0-7528; 978-1-85648; 978-1-4027; 978-1-58816; 978-1-84212; 978-1-84340; 978-1-889538; 978-1-931543; 978-1-58663; 978-1-59308; 978-1-84442; 978-1-84486; 978-1-84483; 978-1-60059; 978-0-7134; 978-0-7538; 978-1-4091; 978-1-4114;

978-1-4440; 978-0-9786968; 978-0-9799433; 978-1-84293; 978-1-84732; 978-1-877080; 978-1-905417; 978-1-905857; 978-1-906250; 978-1-906388; 978-1-906787; 978-1-931559; 978-1-933027; 978-1-934618; 978-88-544; 978-1-4351; 978-1-4547; 978-1-4549; 978-1-60736; 978-1-61837; 978-1-78097; 978-1-84994; 978-1 84796; 978-1-86200; 978-1-907152; 978-1-907554; 978-1-907967; 978-1-908449; 978-1-936096
Number of titles published annually: 1,500 Print
Total Titles: 6,000 Print
Imprints: Hearst Books; Lark Books; Puzzlewright Press; Sterling; Sterling Epicure; Sterling Ethos; Sterling Innovation; Sterling/Tamos; Sterling/Zambezi; Union Square Press
Distributor for Duncan Baird; Batsford (selected titles); Boxer Books; Brooklyn Botanic Garden (selected titles); Carlton Books; Cassell (selected titles); Collins & Brown (selected titles); Conway; Davis Publications (selected titles); Sally Milner (selected titles); Orion (selected titles); Phoenix Press (selected titles); Silver Oak; Sixth & Spring (selected titles); Sky Publishing; Watkins; Weidenfeld & Nicolson (selected titles); White Star Publishers
Foreign Rep(s): Angell Eurosales (Scandinavia); Ariel Balatbat (Guam, Philippines); David Bateman Ltd (New Zealand); Capricorn Link Ltd (Australia); Guild of Master Craftsman (UK); Hardy Bigfoss International Co Ltd (Cambodia, Laos, Thailand, Vietnam); BK Norton (Taiwan); Penguin Books Malaysia (Malaysia); Penguin Books SA (Portugal, Spain); Penguin Books Singapore (Singapore); Penguin India (Bangladesh, India, Nepal, Sri Lanka); Penguin Italia SRL (Italy); Phambili Agencies (adult titles only) (South Africa); Publishers International Marketing (Malta, Middle East); Grazyna Soszynska (Central Europe, Eastern Europe)
Foreign Rights: Agence Litteraire Lora Fountain (France); Graal Literary Agency (Poland); Katai & Bolza Literary Agents; Ute Korner Literary Agent (Spain); Alexander Korzhenevski (Russia); Kristin Olson Literary Agency (Czech Republic); Literarische Agentur Silke Weniger
*Warehouse:* Sterling Warehouse, 40 Saw Mill Pond Rd, Edison, NJ 08817 *Tel:* 732-248-6563 *Toll Free Fax:* 800-775-8736
*See separate listing for:*
**Lark Crafts**

**Stewart, Tabori & Chang**
Imprint of Harry N Abrams Inc
115 W 18 St, 6th fl, New York, NY 10011
SAN: 239-0361
*Tel:* 212-519-1200 *Fax:* 212-519-1210
*Web Site:* www.abramsbooks.com
*Key Personnel*
CEO & Pres: Michael Jacobs
SVP & Publr: Leslie Stoker
Exec Dir, Publicity: Katrina Weidknecht
Sr Ed: Liana Allday; Natalie Kaire
Founded: 1981
Art, illustrated gift books, gardening, cookbooks, African American history, interior design, New Age, photography, popular culture, humor, weddings.
ISBN Prefix(es): 978-1-55670; 978-0-941434; 978-1-58479
Number of titles published annually: 80 Print
Total Titles: 250 Print
Foreign Rep(s): Ralph & Sheila Summers (Southeast Asia); Paul Walton (South Africa); David Williams (South America)
Foreign Rights: General Publishing (Canada); Hi Marketing UK (Europe, UK); Korea Copyright Center (Korea); New Holland (Australia); Onslow Books Ltd (Europe); Sigma Literary Agency (Korea); Southern Publishers Group (New Zealand); Tuttle-Mori Agency Inc (Japan); David Williams (South America)

**§Stipes Publishing LLC**
204 W University, Champaign, IL 61820
Mailing Address: PO Box 526, Champaign, IL 61824-0526
*Tel:* 217-356-8391 *Fax:* 217-356-5753
*E-mail:* stipes01@sbcglobal.net
*Web Site:* www.stipes.com
*Key Personnel*
Partner & Electronic Publg: Benjamin Watts
Partner: J L Hecker
Founded: 1927
Primarily educational, some overlap trade publishing in music & horticulture.
ISBN Prefix(es): 978-0-87563; 978-1-58874
Number of titles published annually: 15 Print
Total Titles: 550 Print; 2 CD-ROM; 1 Online; 1 E-Book; 2 Audio

**STM Learning Inc**
8045 Big Bend Blvd, Suite 202, St Louis, MO 63119-2714
*Tel:* 314-993-2728 *Toll Free Tel:* 800-600-0330 *Fax:* 314-993-2281
*E-mail:* info@stmlearning.com; orders@stmlearning.com
*Web Site:* www.stmlearning.com
*Key Personnel*
Pres: Marianne Whaley *E-mail:* marianne@stmlearning.com
VP: Glenn Whaley *E-mail:* glenn@stmlearning.com
Founded: 1993
Medical & legal, nursing & allied health texts & references; medical consumer books; child care & development, clinical & forensic medical references.
ISBN Prefix(es): 978-1-878060; 978-1-936590
Number of titles published annually: 4 Print; 3 CD-ROM
Total Titles: 24 Print; 7 CD-ROM
*Advertising Agency:* GW Graphics & Publishing
*Distribution Center:* Amazon.com
Barnes & Noble
Rittenhouse

**STOCKCERO Inc**
3785 NW 82 Ave, Suite 302, Doral, FL 33166
*Tel:* 305-722-7628 *Fax:* 305-477-5794
*E-mail:* sales@stockcero.com
*Web Site:* www.stockcero.com
*Key Personnel*
CEO: Pablo Agrest Berge *E-mail:* pagrest@stockcero.com
Founded: 2000
Committed to building an every expanding collection of significant books, comprising Spanish literature, both Peninsular & Latin American. Our editions are conceived with modern non-native Spanish speaking readers & students in mind, so they include updated & sharply focused footnotes, prefaces & bibliographies written by scholarly literary editors.
ISBN Prefix(es): 978-987-1136; 978-1-934768
Number of titles published annually: 14 Print
Total Titles: 114 Print

**Stone & Scott Publishers**
PO Box 56419, Sherman Oaks, CA 91413-1419
SAN: 297-3030
*Tel:* 818-904-9088 *Fax:* 818-787-1431
*E-mail:* friday@stoneandscott.com
*Web Site:* stoneandscott.com
*Key Personnel*
Owner: Les Boston *E-mail:* bostonlespaul@roadrunner.com
Founded: 1990
ISBN Prefix(es): 978-0-9627031; 978-1-891135
Number of titles published annually: 2 Print; 16 Online
Total Titles: 18 Print; 12 Online
Distributor for New Wind Press; Lois Rose Rose
Membership(s): Book Publicists of Southern California; IBPA, the Independent Book Publishers Association; Publishers Association of Los Angeles

**Stone Bridge Press Inc**
1393 Solano Ave, Suite C, Albany, CA 94706
Mailing Address: PO Box 8208, Berkeley, CA 94706
*Tel:* 510-524-8732 *Toll Free Tel:* 800-947-7271 (orders) *Fax:* 510-524-8711
*E-mail:* sbp@stonebridge.com; sbpedit@stonebridge.com
*Web Site:* www.stonebridge.com
*Key Personnel*
Founder & Publr: Peter Goodman
Founded: 1989
Books on Japan & Asia.
ISBN Prefix(es): 978-0-89346; 978-1-880656; 978-0-9628137; 978-4-89684; 978-4-925080; 978-1-933330
Number of titles published annually: 12 Print; 10 Online; 10 E-Book
Total Titles: 150 Print; 15 Online; 15 E-Book
Imprints: Heian International (children's & crafts); Impromptu Journaling Books; Michi Japanese Arts and Ways (Japanese arts); The Rock Spring Collection of Japanese Literature; Stone Bridge Classics; Stone Bridge Fiction
Distributed by Consortium Book Sales & Distribution Inc (US & CN); Sonja Merz International (China, Japan, Korea & Southeast Asia); Publishers Group UK (Europe & UK)
Distributor for IBC Publishing
Foreign Rep(s): Brumby (Australia); PSD (South Africa); Publishers Group UK (UK)
Foreign Rights: IE Illustrata
Membership(s): Bay Area Independent Publishers Association; IBPA, the Independent Book Publishers Association
*See separate listing for:*
**Heian International Inc**

**Stonewall**, see BrickHouse Books Inc

**Stoneydale Press Publishing Co**
523 Main St, Stevensville, MT 59870-2839
Mailing Address: PO Box 188, Stevensville, MT 59870-0188
*Tel:* 406-777-2729 *Toll Free Tel:* 800-735-7006 *Fax:* 406-777-2521
*Web Site:* www.stoneydale.com
*Key Personnel*
Publr: Dale A Burk
Founded: 1976
Outdoor recreation, regional history & reminisces of Northern Rockies region.
ISBN Prefix(es): 978-0-912299; 978-1-931291
Number of titles published annually: 8 Print
Total Titles: 120 Print
Membership(s): Mountains & Plains Booksellers Association; Pacific Northwest Booksellers Association

**Storey Publishing LLC**
210 MASS MoCA Way, North Adams, MA 01247
SAN: 203-4158
*Tel:* 413-346-2100 *Toll Free Tel:* 800-441-5700 (orders); 800-793-9396 (edit) *Fax:* 413-346-2199; 413-346-2196 (edit)
*E-mail:* sales@storey.com
*Web Site:* www.storey.com
*Key Personnel*
CEO & Pres: Dan Reynolds *E-mail:* dan.reynolds@storey.com
Publr: Deborah Balmuth *E-mail:* deborah.balmuth@storey.com

Dir, Publicity: Amy Greeman *E-mail:* amy.greeman@storey.com
Rts Dir: Maribeth Casey *Tel:* 413-346-2135 *E-mail:* maribeth.casey@storey.com
HR & Opers Mgr: Marci Saunders *E-mail:* marci.saunders@storey.com
Trade & Gift Sales Mgr: Adrienne Franceschi
Founded: 1983
How-to books on country living, gardening, cooking, natural health, home building, country business, crafts, small-scale livestock, pets, beer & wine, children's nonfiction.
ISBN Prefix(es): 978-0-945352; 978-0-88266; 978-1-58017
Number of titles published annually: 50 Print
Total Titles: 500 Print
Distributed by Workman Publishing Co Inc
Foreign Rep(s): Thomas Allen & Sons Ltd (Canada); Bill Bailey Publishers' Representatives (Europe); Bookreps NZ Ltd (Susan Holmes) (New Zealand); Capricorn Link Australia Pty Ltd (Australia); Michelle Morrow Curreri (Asia, Middle East); IMA/Intermediaamericana Ltd (David Williams) (Caribbean, Latin America); Melia Publishing Services (UK); Trinity Books CC (South Africa)

**§The Story Plant**
Division of Studio Digital CT LLC
PO Box 4331, Stamford, CT 06907
*Tel:* 203-722-7920
*E-mail:* thestoryplant@thestoryplant.com
*Web Site:* www.thestoryplant.com
*Key Personnel*
Publr: Lou Aronica *E-mail:* lou.aronica@thestoryplant.com
Assoc Publr: Mitchell Maxwell *E-mail:* mitchell.maxwell@thestoryplant.com
Founded: 2008
Independent publisher of commercial fiction. The focus is on author development & building publishing programs for each author. Currently a digital-first publisher, which means that books are launched simultaneously in ebook & short-print-run paperback.
ISBN Prefix(es): 978-1-61188
Number of titles published annually: 18 Print; 18 E-Book
Total Titles: 32 Print; 32 E-Book
*Distribution Center:* Perseus Distribution, 250 W 57 St, New York, NY 10107, Contact: Jessica Schmidt *Toll Free Tel:* 800-343-4499 *E-mail:* jessica.schmidt@perseusbooks.com

**Strata Publishing Inc**
PO Box 1303, State College, PA 16804
SAN: 298-9794
*Tel:* 814-234-8545 *Fax:* 814-238-7222
*E-mail:* stratapub@stratapub.com
*Web Site:* www.stratapub.com
*Key Personnel*
Publr: Kathleen Domenig
Gen Mgr: Brian Henry
Founded: 1990
Books in communication & journalism for mid-level & advanced college courses, scholars & professionals. Return authorization required.
ISBN Prefix(es): 978-0-9634489; 978-1-891136
Number of titles published annually: 3 Print
Total Titles: 16 Print

**Strategic Book Publishing & Rights Agency (SBPRA)**
12620 FM 1960, Suite A-43 507, Houston, TX 77065
*Tel:* 703-637-6370 *Toll Free Tel:* 888-808-6190
*Web Site:* www.sbpra.com
*Key Personnel*
CEO: Robert Fletcher
Founded: 2007
Provides book publishing, marketing & ebook services to over 10,000 writers around the world, employing 150 people who live throughout the US & work virtually through telecommunication. We are experiencing over 30% growth per year, having published approximately 3000 authors with almost 100 new releases per month. Our books are available through Ingram, the largest book distributor in the world, as well distributors as well as in bookstores such as Barnes & Noble & all online channels. Strategic Book Group attends & exhibits at the major book expositions in London, New York, China & Germany each year.
ISBN Prefix(es): 978-1-61204
Number of titles published annually: 475 Print; 85 E-Book
Total Titles: 2,786 Print; 3,062 Online; 336 E-Book
Imprints: Eloquent/Strategic

**§Stress Free Kids®**
2561 Chimney Springs Dr, Marietta, GA 30062
*Toll Free Tel:* 800-841-4204 *Toll Free Fax:* 866-302-2759
*E-mail:* media@stressfreekids.com
*Web Site:* www.stressfreekids.com
*Key Personnel*
Founder: Lori Lite; Rick Lite
Founded: 1996
Books, CDs (physical & digital formats), lesson plans to help children & teens manage stress, lower anxiety & decrease anger, while improving self-esteem.
ISBN Prefix(es): 978-0-9708633; 978-0-9787781; 978-0-9800328
Number of titles published annually: 2 Print; 5 Online; 4 E-Book; 4 Audio
Total Titles: 35 Print; 12 Audio

**The Jesse Stuart Foundation (JSF)**
1645 Winchester Ave, Ashland, KY 41101
SAN: 245-8837
Mailing Address: PO Box 669, Ashland, KY 41105-0669
*Tel:* 606-326-1667 *Fax:* 606-325-2519
*E-mail:* jsf@jsfbooks.com
*Web Site:* www.jsfbooks.com
*Key Personnel*
CEO & Sr Ed: James M Gifford
Founded: 1979
Publisher of Appalachia-Kentuckiana. Not accepting unsol mss at this time.
ISBN Prefix(es): 978-0-945084
Number of titles published annually: 8 Print
Total Titles: 75 Print

**Stylus Publishing LLC**
22883 Quicksilver Dr, Sterling, VA 20166-2012
SAN: 299-1853
Mailing Address: PO Box 605, Herndon, VA 20172-0605
*Tel:* 703-661-1504 (edit & sales) *Toll Free Tel:* 800-232-0223 (orders & cust serv) *Fax:* 703-661-1547
*E-mail:* stylusmail@presswarehouse.com (orders & cust serv); stylusinfo@styluspub.com
*Web Site:* www.styluspub.com
*Key Personnel*
Pres & Publr: John von Knorring *E-mail:* jvk@styluspub.com
VP, Mktg & Busn Devt: Andrea Ciecierski *Tel:* 703-996-1036 *E-mail:* andrea@styluspub.com
Mktg & Publicity Mgr: Shaqunia Clark *E-mail:* shaqunia@styluspub.com
Opers: Robin von Knorring *E-mail:* robin@styluspub.com
Founded: 1996
Publish books for faculty & administrators in higher education. Distributes books in the areas of art, business, training, psychology & psychotherapy as well as educational & scholarly titles & books on Third World development & the environment. Subsidiary imprint Kumarian Press publishes in international development.
ISBN Prefix(es): 978-1-57922
Number of titles published annually: 30 Print
Total Titles: 400 Print; 2 CD-ROM
Subsidiaries: The Institution of Engineering & Technology (IET)
Distributor for Aeon Books; American Association for Higher Education; Cabi Books; Commonwealth Scientific & Industrial Research Organization (CSIRO); The Commonwealth Secretariat; Cork University Press; Global Professional Publishing; IDRC; Institute of Education; Karnac Books; KIT Publishers; The Institution of Engineering & Technology (IET); Nordic Africa Institute; Oxfam Publishing; Practical Action; Thorogood Publishing; Trentham Books Ltd; Women, Law & Development International (WLDI); World Health Organization (WHO)
Foreign Rep(s): Eurospan (Kumarian Press) (Europe, Middle East, UK)
*Distribution Center:* Books International Inc, 22883 Quicksilver Dr, Dulles, VA 20166

**Success Advertising & Publishing**
Division of The Success Group
3419 Dunham Rd, Warsaw, NY 14569
SAN: 678-9501
*Tel:* 585-786-5663
*Key Personnel*
Pres & Publr: Allan H Smith *E-mail:* allan33001@aol.com
VP: Ginger B Smith
Book Ed: Robin Garretson
Founded: 1978
How-to, self-help, crafts, business, home-based business.
ISBN Prefix(es): 978-0-931113
Number of titles published annually: 7 Print
Total Titles: 58 Print
Divisions: Academy of Continuing Education; National Doll Society of America; Success Advertising

**Summa Publications**
PO Box 660725, Birmingham, AL 35266-0725
*Tel:* 205-822-0463 *Fax:* 205-822-0463
*Web Site:* summapub2.googlepages.com
*Key Personnel*
Owner & Publr: Thomas M Hines *E-mail:* tmhines@samford.edu
Founded: 1983
Critical works, scholarly publications in French & Francophone; no fiction.
ISBN Prefix(es): 978-0-917786; 978-1-883479
Number of titles published annually: 6 Print
Total Titles: 119 Print

**Summer Institute of Linguistics Inc**, see SIL International

**§Summit University Press**
63 Summit Way, Gardiner, MT 59030-9314
*Tel:* 406-848-9742; 406-848-9500 *Toll Free Tel:* 800-245-5445 (retail orders) *Fax:* 406-848-9650 *Toll Free Fax:* 800-221-8307
*E-mail:* info@summituniversitypress.com
*Web Site:* www.summituniversitypress.com
*Key Personnel*
Dir: Norman N Millman *Tel:* 406-848-9743 *E-mail:* director@summituniversitypress.com
Prodn Dir: Christopher Allen *E-mail:* production@summituniversitypress.com
Founded: 1975
Global publisher of fine books & audiotapes on spirituality. Very active foreign rights sales. Also specializes in New Age & mind, body & spirit.
ISBN Prefix(es): 978-0-916766; 978-0-922729
Number of titles published annually: 5 Print; 45 Online; 45 E-Book

Total Titles: 100 Print; 14 CD-ROM; 45 Online; 47 E-Book; 70 Audio
*Distribution Center:* National Book Network, 4501 Forbes Blvd, Suite 200, Lanham, MD 20706 *Tel:* 301-459-3366 *Fax:* 301-429-5746 *E-mail:* custserv@nbnbooks.com *Web Site:* www.nbnbooks.com
NBN Canada/Rowman & Littlefield Publishing Group, 67 Mowat Ave, Suite 241, Toronto, ON M6K 3E3, Canada *Tel:* 416-534-1660 *Toll Free Tel:* 877-626-2665 *Fax:* 416-534-3699 *Web Site:* www.nbnbooks.com
NBN International, Plymbridge House, Estover Rd, Plymouth, Devon PL6 7PY, United Kingdom *Tel:* (01752) 202300 *Fax:* (01752) 202330 *E-mail:* enquiries@nbninternational.com
Membership(s): IBPA, the Independent Book Publishers Association

**Summy-Birchard Inc**
Subsidiary of Warner/Chappell Music
10585 Santa Monica Blvd, Los Angeles, CA 90025
*Tel:* 310-441-8600 *Fax:* 310-441-8780
*Web Site:* www.warnerchappell.com
*Key Personnel*
VP, Admin: Jeremy Blietz *E-mail:* jeremy.blietz@warnerchappell.com
Founded: 1872
Educational music books.
ISBN Prefix(es): 978-0-87487; 978-1-58951
Number of titles published annually: 25 Print; 8 Audio
Total Titles: 500 Print; 120 Audio
Divisions: Suzuki Method International
Distributed by Alfred Publications
Distributor for Carisch SPA; IMP
Foreign Rep(s): Warner/Chappell

**Sun Books - Sun Publishing Co**
Division of The Sun Companies
PO Box 5588, Santa Fe, NM 87502-5588
SAN: 206-1325
*Tel:* 505-471-5177; 505-473-4161
*Toll Free Tel:* 877-849-0051 *Fax:* 505-473-4458
*E-mail:* info@sunbooks.com
*Web Site:* www.sunbooks.com
*Key Personnel*
Pres & Rts & Perms: Skip Whitson
Lib Sales Dir: Robyn Covelli-Hunt
Founded: 1973
Motivational, success, business, recovery, inspirational, history, self-help, new thought, philosophy, western mysticism, scholarly; oriental philosophy & studies. No unsol mss. Query first by e-mail.
ISBN Prefix(es): 978-0-89540
Number of titles published annually: 12 Print
Total Titles: 400 Print
Imprints: Far West Publishing; Sun Books
Subsidiaries: Far West Publishing Co
Divisions: Sun Books
Distributor for Far West Publishing Co; Sun Books
Foreign Rights: Skip Whitson
*Advertising Agency:* Sun Agency

**Sun Publishing**, see Sun Books - Sun Publishing Co

**Sunbelt Publications Inc**
1256 Fayette St, El Cajon, CA 92020-1511
SAN: 630-0790
Mailing Address: PO Box 191126, San Diego, CA 92159
*Tel:* 619-258-4911 *Toll Free Tel:* 800-626-6579 (cust serv) *Fax:* 619-258-4916
*E-mail:* service@sunbeltpub.com; info@sunbeltpub.com
*Web Site:* www.sunbeltbooks.com
*Key Personnel*
CEO: Lowell Lindsay *Tel:* 619-258-4911 ext 111 *E-mail:* llindsay@sunbeltpub.com
Pres: Diana Lindsay *Tel:* 619-258-4905 ext 104 *E-mail:* dlindsay@sunbeltpub.com
Acctg & Opers Mgr: Terry Cochran *Tel:* 619-258-4905 ext 110 *E-mail:* tcochran@sunbeltpub.com
Pubns Mgr: Debi Young *Tel:* 619-258-4905 ext 103 *E-mail:* dyoung@sunbeltpub.com
Founded: 1984
Publisher & distributor of natural history, science, pictorial & travel specializing in Alta & Baja, California.
ISBN Prefix(es): 978-0-932653; 978-0-916251
Number of titles published annually: 10 Print
Total Titles: 75 Print
Imprints: First Choice
Distributor for Abbott Publishing; Alti Corp; Amaroma Ediciones (architectural & design publisher in Mexico); Amigos de Bolsa Chica; Anza-Borrego Foundation; W H Berger; Best Guides LLC; Bobolink Media; Joan Brady; California Sea Grant; Paul Douglas Campbell; Daddy's Heroes Inc; Dawsons Book Shop; Leland Fetzer; Flying Diamond; Fun Places Publishing; Jeffrey Garcia; Maureen Gilmer; Glove Pequot; Green Grass Press; Healey Publishing; hikingcamping.com; Huckleberry House LLC; Intellect Publishing; Island Paradise Publishing; Jaguar Tales; Scott G Kyle; Lawtech Publishing; Little Oak Press; Loretta T Marra; Mission San Juan Capistrano Women's Guild; Newtona LLC; Northcross Books; Nelson Papucci; Bette L Pegas; Linda Pequegnat; Picaro Publishing; Planeta Peninsula (Publisher from Mexico); Phil R Pryde; Quick Reference Publishing; R & B Food & Culture Production; Random House; Renegade Enterprises; Rincon Publishing Co; San Diego Architecture Foundation; San Diego Association of Geologists; San Diego City Works Press; San Diego Natural History Museum; San Diego Police Historical Association; San Dieguit River Park Joint Powers Authority; Save Our Heritage Organization; The Sektor Co; Spark Avenue; Surf Angel Publications; Trail Wisdom; Herbert B Turner; University of California Press; Armand Vallee; En Ville; Wigton Publishing; Wilderness Press; Wolf Water Press
Membership(s): Association of Earth Science Editors; IBPA, the Independent Book Publishers Association; Outdoor Writers Association of America; Publishers Association of the West

**Sunburst Digital Inc**
3150 W Higgins Rd, Suite 140, Hoffman Estates, IL 60169
*Toll Free Tel:* 800-321-7511 *Toll Free Fax:* 888-800-3028
*E-mail:* service@sunburst.com; sales@sunburst.com
*Web Site:* sunburst.com; edresources.com
*Key Personnel*
Dir, Sales: Dan Sladek
Founded: 1972
Developer & publisher of multimedia educational software, videos & printed supplements for use in schools. Publish school products for grades K-12 under the Sunburst brand & distribute Knowledge Adventure® brand school products.
ISBN Prefix(es): 978-0-395; 978-0-89466
Number of titles published annually: 3 Print

**Sundance/Newbridge Publishing**
Division of Rowman & Littlefield Publishing Group
33 Boston Post Rd W, Suite 440, Marlborough, MA 01752
*Toll Free Tel:* 888-200-2720; 800-343-8204 (Sundance cust serv & orders); 800-867-0307 (Newbridge cust serv & orders)
*Toll Free Fax:* 800-456-2419 (orders)
*E-mail:* info@sundancepub.com; info@newbridgeonline.com
*Web Site:* www.sundancepub.com; www.newbridgeonline.com
*Key Personnel*
Pres: Paul Konowitch *E-mail:* pkonowitch@sundancepub.com
SVP, Sales: John Atkocaitis *E-mail:* jatkocaitis@sundancepub.com
Founded: 1981
Supplemental educational publisher for PreK-8 that creates standards-based classroom materials for reading in the content areas.
ISBN Prefix(es): 978-1-56784; 978-1-58273; 978-1-4007
Number of titles published annually: 150 Print; 36 Audio
Total Titles: 680 Print; 118 Audio
Imprints: Early Math; Early Science; Early Social Studies; GoFacts Guided Writing; Kids Corner; Newbridge Discovery Links; Ranger Rick Science Program; Thinking Like a Scientist
Foreign Rep(s): Schmelzer PSI
Membership(s): AAP; International Reading Association; National Science Teachers Association

**§Sunrise River Press**
Affiliate of Cartech Books/Specialty Press
39966 Grand Ave, North Branch, MN 55056
*Tel:* 651-277-1400 *Toll Free Tel:* 800-895-4585 *Fax:* 651-277-1203
*E-mail:* info@sunriseriverpress.com; sales@sunriseriverpress.com
*Web Site:* www.sunriseriverpress.com
Publisher of consumer books & books for the professional healthcare market with an emphasis on self-help, weight loss, nutrition, diet, food & recipes with additional focus on family health, fitness & specific diseases such as cancer, anorexia, Alzheimer's, autism & depression.
ISBN Prefix(es): 978-0-9624814; 978-1-934716
Number of titles published annually: 10 Print

**Sunstone Press**
PO Box 2321, Santa Fe, NM 87504-2321
SAN: 214-2090
*Tel:* 505-988-4418 *Toll Free Tel:* 800-243-5644 *Fax:* 505-988-1025 (orders only)
*Web Site:* www.sunstonepress.com
*Key Personnel*
Pres & Treas: James Clois Smith, Jr
Dir, Opers & Sales: Carl Daniel Condit
Founded: 1971
Mainstream & Southwestern US titles, general nonfiction, fiction & how-to craft books.
ISBN Prefix(es): 978-0-913270 (print editions); 978-0-86534 (print editions); 978-1-61139 (eBooks)
Number of titles published annually: 100 Print; 125 E-Book
Total Titles: 1,000 Print; 1,000 E-Book
Imprints: Sundial Books
Foreign Rights: Daniel Bial Literary Agency
Membership(s): New Mexico Book Association

**SUNY Press**, see State University of New York Press

**Superintendent of Documents**, see US Government Printing Office

**Surrey Books**
Imprint of Agate Publishing
1328 Greenleaf St, Evanston, IL 60202
SAN: 275-8857
*Tel:* 847-475-4457 *Toll Free Tel:* 800-326-4430
*Web Site:* agatepublishing.com/surrey
*Key Personnel*
Pres & Publr: Doug Seibold *E-mail:* seibold@agatepublishing.com
Founded: 1982

Trade books. Specialize in nonfiction: cooking, health & lifestyle.
ISBN Prefix(es): 978-0-940625; 978-1-57284
Number of titles published annually: 20 Print
Total Titles: 120 Print
Distributed by Publishers Group West
Membership(s): International Association of Culinary Professionals

**Susquehanna University Press**
Affiliate of Associated University Presses
514 University Ave, Selinsgrove, PA 17870
*Tel:* 570-372-4175 *Fax:* 570-372-4021
*E-mail:* supress@susqu.edu
*Web Site:* www.susqu.edu/su_press
*Key Personnel*
Dir: Dr Rachana Sachdev *Tel:* 570-372-4200 *E-mail:* rsachdev@susqu.edu
Mng Ed: Sarah Bailey
Founded: 1944
Publish books that participate in recent ongoing conversations about scholarly issues, & that offer new insights on traditional materials.
ISBN Prefix(es): 978-0-941664; 978-0-945636; 978-1-57591
Number of titles published annually: 15 Print
Total Titles: 250 Print
Distributed by Associated University Presses
Foreign Rep(s): The Eurospan Group (Africa, Europe, Middle East, UK); Scholarly Book Services (Canada)
*Orders to:* Associated University Presses, 10 Schalks Crossing Rd, Suite 501-330, Plainsboro, NJ 08536 *Tel:* 609-269-8094 *Fax:* 609-269-8096 *E-mail:* aup440@aol.com; Scholarly Book Services Inc, 473 Adelaide St W, 4th fl, Toronto, ON M5A 1T1, Canada *Toll Free Tel:* 800-847-9736 *Toll Free Fax:* 800-220-9895 *E-mail:* orders@sbookscan.com; The Eurospan Group (EDS), Covent Garden, 3 Henrietta St, London WC2E 8LU, United Kingdom *Tel:* (020) 7240 0856 *Fax:* (020) 7379 0609 *E-mail:* orders@edspubs.co.uk

**Swallow Press**
Imprint of Ohio University Press
215 Columbus Rd, Suite 101, Athens, OH 45701
*Tel:* 740-593-1158 (Jeff Kallet) *Fax:* 740-593-4536
*Web Site:* www.ohioswallow.com
*Key Personnel*
Dir: Gillian Berchowitz *Tel:* 740-593-1159 *E-mail:* berchowitz@ohio.edu
Sales & Mktg Dir: Sarah Welsch *Tel:* 740-593-1160 *E-mail:* welsh@ohio.edu
Mng Ed: Nancy Basmajian *Tel:* 740-593-1161 *E-mail:* basmajia@ohio.edu
Busn Mgr: Kristi Goldsberry *Tel:* 740-593-1156 *E-mail:* goldsbek@ohio.edu
Founded: 1940
Publisher of scholarly & trade books.
ISBN Prefix(es): 978-0-8040
Number of titles published annually: 10 Print
Total Titles: 600 Print
Foreign Rep(s): Combined Academic Publishers (Europe); EWEB (Pacific Rim)
*Orders to:* Chicago Distribution Center, 11030 S Langley Ave, Chicago, IL 60628 *Toll Free Tel:* 800-621-2736 *Toll Free Fax:* 800-621-8476
*Warehouse:* Chicago Distribution Center, 11030 S Langley Ave, Chicago, IL 60628 *Toll Free Tel:* 800-621-2736 *Toll Free Fax:* 800-621-8476

**Swan Isle Press**
11030 S Langley Ave, Chicago, IL 60628
Mailing Address: PO Box 408790, Chicago, IL 60640-8790
*Tel:* 773-728-3780 (edit); 773-702-7000 (cust serv) *Toll Free Tel:* 800-621-2736 (cust serv) *Fax:* 773-702-7212 (cust serv) *Toll Free Fax:* 800-621-8476 (cust serv)
*E-mail:* info@swanislepress.com
*Web Site:* www.swanislepress.com
*Key Personnel*
Founder, Dir & Ed: David Rade
Founded: 1999
Not-for-profit literary publisher, dedicated to publishing poetry, fiction & nonfiction that inspire & educate while advancing the knowledge & appreciation of literature, art & culture.
ISBN Prefix(es): 978-0-9678808; 978-0-9748881
Number of titles published annually: 4 Print; 2 E-Book
Total Titles: 1 E-Book
*Editorial Office(s):* PO Box 408790, Chicago, IL 60640-8790
Distributed by University of Chicago Press
Foreign Rep(s): University of Chicago Press (Worldwide)
*Orders to:* Baker & Taylor, 2550 W Tyvola Rd, Suite 300, Charlotte, NC 28217 *Tel:* 704-998-3100 *Toll Free Tel:* 800-775-1800 *E-mail:* btinfo@baker-taylor.com *Web Site:* www.btol.com; Ingram Book Co, One Ingram Blvd, La Vergne, TN 37086 *Tel:* 615-793-5000 *Toll Free Tel:* 800-937-8200 *E-mail:* customer.service@ingrambook.com *Web Site:* www.ingrambook.com
Membership(s): AAP

**Swedenborg Foundation Press**
320 N Church St, West Chester, PA 19380
SAN: 202-5280
*Tel:* 610-430-3222 *Toll Free Tel:* 800-355-3222 (cust serv) *Fax:* 610-430-7982
*E-mail:* info@swedenborg.com
*Web Site:* www.swedenborg.com
*Key Personnel*
Opers Mgr: Morgan Beard *Tel:* 610-430-3222 ext 12 *E-mail:* mbeard@swedenborg.com
Founded: 1849
Books & DVDs by, or relating to, the theological works & spiritual insights of Emanuel Swedenborg & related literature.
ISBN Prefix(es): 978-0-87785
Number of titles published annually: 10 Print
Total Titles: 200 Print
*Orders to:* Continental Sales Inc (CSI), 213 W Main St, Barrington, IL 60010 *Tel:* 847-381-6530 *Fax:* 847-382-0419 *E-mail:* bookreps@wybel.com; Wybel Marketing Group Inc, 213 W Main St, Barrington, IL 60010 *Tel:* 847-382-0384 *Fax:* 847-382-0385 *E-mail:* bookreps@wybel.com; Melman-Moster Associates Inc, 43 Yawpo Ave, Suite 6, Oakland, NJ 07436 *Tel:* 201-651-9400 *Fax:* 201-651-9440 *E-mail:* books@melman-moster.com; Faherty & Associates, 6665 SW Hampton St, Suite 100, Portland, OR 97223 *Tel:* 503-639-3113 *Fax:* 503-598-9850 *E-mail:* faherty@fahertybooks.com; Southern Territory Associates, 4508 64 St, Lubbock, TX 79414 *Tel:* 806-799-9997 *Fax:* 806-799-9777 *E-mail:* sta77@suddenlink.net; Rainbow Book Agencies, 303 Arthur St, Fairfield 3078, Australia *Tel:* (0613) 9481 6611 *Fax:* (0613) 9481 2371 *E-mail:* rba@rainbowbooks.com.au *Web Site:* www.rainbowbooks.com.au
*Returns:* University of Chicago Press/The Chicago Distribution Center, 11030 S Langley Ave, Chicago, IL 60628
*Distribution Center:* University of Chicago Press/The Chicago Distribution Center, 11030 S Langley Ave, Chicago, IL 60628

**§SYBEX Inc**
Division of John Wiley & Sons Inc
111 River St, Hoboken, NJ 07030-5774
SAN: 211-1667
*Tel:* 201-748-6000 *Fax:* 201-748-6088
*E-mail:* info@wiley.com
*Web Site:* www.sybex.com; www.wiley.com
Founded: 1976
For beginning, intermediate & advanced users of all types of software & hardware, including how-to books on various networking, word processing, database, graphics & spreadsheet software, certification, as well as computer games & Internet books, graphics & programming.
ISBN Prefix(es): 978-0-89588; 978-0-7821; 978-0-47028
Number of titles published annually: 150 Print
Total Titles: 601 Print; 2 CD-ROM
Foreign Rep(s): Robert Blake (Central America, Mexico); Phillip Bowie (Caribbean); Cynthia Chiang (China); Rolando De Vera (Philippines); Tadashi Hase (Japan); Hee-Jeong Ihn (South Korea); Steven Loo (Malaysia); Natalie Lord (Europe, UK); Ledy Martinez (Brazil, South America); Roger Ming (Taiwan); Glenn Allen Smith (Hong Kong); Kriangsak Subsinburana (Thailand); Retno Sugiarti (Indonesia); Joyce Yang (China); Angela Yeo (Singapore)

**§Sylvan Dell Publishing**
612 Johnnie Dodds Blvd, Suite A-2, Mount Pleasant, SC 29464
SAN: 256-6109
*Tel:* 843-971-6722 *Toll Free Tel:* 877-243-3457 *Fax:* 843-216-3804
*E-mail:* customerservice@sylvandellpublishing.com; info@sylvandellpublishing.com
*Web Site:* www.sylvandellpublishing.com
*Key Personnel*
Publr: Lee German *E-mail:* leegerman@sylvandellpublishing.com
Ed: Donna German *E-mail:* donnagerman@sylvandellpublishing.com
PR: Heather Williams *E-mail:* heatherwilliams@sylvandellpublishing.com
Bookstore & Gift Shop Sales: Justin Pressley *E-mail:* justinpressley@sylvandellpublishing.com
School & Lib Sales: Emily Gooch *E-mail:* emilygooch@sylvandellpublishing.com
Off Mgr: Kelly McGinty *Tel:* 877-958-2600 *E-mail:* kellymcginty@sylvandellpublishing.com
Founded: 2004
Young company on a mission to create picture books that will excite children's imagination, are artistically spectacular & have educational value. Most of our stories are fictional but relate to a nonfictional theme of science, nature or animals. Each book is seriously vetted for scientific accuracy before publication. We reserve 3-5 pages in the back of each book to add our "Creative Minds" section, loaded with fun facts, crafts & games to supplement the educational thread of the book. Ebooks with auto read, auto flip & selectible English & Spanish text in audio.
ISBN Prefix(es): 978-0-9764943; 978-0-9768823; 978-0-9777423; 978-1-934359
Number of titles published annually: 14 Print; 14 Online; 14 E-Book
Total Titles: 83 Print; 83 Online; 83 E-Book
Distributed by Mariposa Press (France); MV Mojica & Associates Co (Philippines); Saunders Book Co (Canada)
Foreign Rights: Sylvia Hayes Literary Agency
*Distribution Center:* The R L Bryan Co, 301 Greystone Blvd, Columbia, SC 29210 *Tel:* 803-343-6700 *Toll Free Tel:* 800-476-1844 *Fax:* 803-343-6838 *Web Site:* www.rlbryan.com
The Reading Warehouse, PO Box 41328, North Charleston, SC 29423 *E-mail:* customerservice@thereadingwarehouse.com *Web Site:* www.thereadingwarehouse.com
Bound to Stay Bound, 1880 W Morton Ave, Jacksonville, IL 62650 *Toll Free Tel:* 800-637-6586 *Toll Free Fax:* 800-747-2872 *E-mail:* btsb@btsb.com *Web Site:* www.btsb.com
Perma-Bound, 617 E Vandalia Rd, Jacksonville, IL 62650 *Tel:* 217-243-5451 *Toll Free Tel:* 800-637-9581 *Fax:* 217-243-7505 *Toll Free Fax:* 800-551-1169 *E-mail:* books@perma-bound.com *Web Site:* www.perma-bound.com

BWI, 1340 Ridgeview Dr, McHenry, IL 60050 *Tel:* 815-578-4592 *Toll Free Tel:* 800-888-4478 *Fax:* 815-578-4680 *Toll Free Fax:* 800-888-6319 *E-mail:* support@titletales.com *Web Site:* www.bwibooks.com
Quality Books Inc, 1003 W Pines Rd, Oregon, IL 61061 *Toll Free Tel:* 800-323-4241 *Fax:* 815-732-4499 *E-mail:* info@quality books.com *Web Site:* www.quality-books.com
Follett, 2233 Wes St, River Grove, IL 60171-1895 *Tel:* 708-583-2000 *Toll Free Tel:* 800-621-4345 *Fax:* 708-452-9347 *E-mail:* customerservice@flr.follett.com *Web Site:* www.flr.follett.com
Mackin Educational Resources, 3505 County Rd 42 W, Burnsville, MN 55306 *Tel:* 952-895-9540 *Toll Free Tel:* 800-245-9540 *Fax:* 952-894-8806 *Toll Free Fax:* 800-369-5490 *E-mail:* customerservice@mackin.com *Web Site:* www.mackin.com
Unique Books, 5010 Kemper Ave, St Louis, MO 63139 *Toll Free Tel:* 800-533-5446 *Web Site:* www.uniquebooksinc.com
The Regent Book Co, 101 E Main St, Bldg 5, Little Falls, NJ 07424 *Tel:* 937-574-7600 *Toll Free Tel:* 800-999-9554 *Fax:* 937-944-5073 *Toll Free Fax:* 888-597-3661 *E-mail:* info@regentbook.com *Web Site:* www.regentbook.com
Baker & Taylor, 2550 W Tyvola Rd, Suite 300, Charlotte, NC 28217 *Toll Free Tel:* 800-775-1800 *Fax:* 704-998-3100 *E-mail:* btinfo@baker-taylor.com *Web Site:* www.btol.com
Brodart, 500 Arch St, Williamsport, PA 17701 *Tel:* 570-326-2461 *Toll Free Tel:* 800-233-8487 *Fax:* 570-326-1479 *E-mail:* support@brodart.com *Web Site:* www.brodart.com
Davidson Titles, PO Box 3538, Jackson, TN 38303-3538 *Toll Free Tel:* 800-433-3903 *Toll Free Fax:* 800-787-7935 *E-mail:* info@davidsontitles.com *Web Site:* www.davidsontitles.com
Ingram, One Ingram Blvd, La Vergne, TN 37086 *Tel:* 615-793-5000 *Toll Free Tel:* 800-937-8200 *E-mail:* customer.service@ingrambook.com *Web Site:* www.ingrambook.com
Penworthy, 219 N Milwaukee St, Milwaukee, WI 53202 *Tel:* 414-287-4600 *Toll Free Tel:* 800-262-2665 *Fax:* 414-287-4602 *E-mail:* info@penworthy.com *Web Site:* www.penworthy.com
Membership(s): ABA; ABC; BookSense Publisher Partner; Children's Book Council; Florida Publishers Association Inc; IBPA, the Independent Book Publishers Association; International Reading Association; MSA; NAIPR; National Association for Bilingual Education; North American Bookdealers Exchange; Northern California Independent Booksellers Association; Southern Independent Booksellers Alliance

**§Synapse Information Resources Inc**
1247 Taft Ave, Endicott, NY 13760
*Tel:* 607-748-4145 *Toll Free Tel:* 888-SYN-CHEM (796-2436) *Fax:* 607-786-3966
*E-mail:* salesinfo@synapseinfo.com
*Web Site:* www.synapseinfo.com
*Key Personnel*
Owner & Pres: Irene Ash *E-mail:* iash@synapseinfo.com
Owner: Michael Ash
Founded: 1981
Chemical database references for industry. Publish both books & CD-ROMs in industrial chemistry. Reference books & software serving the industrial chemical market.
ISBN Prefix(es): 978-1-890595
Number of titles published annually: 3 Print; 3 CD-ROM
Total Titles: 20 Print; 23 CD-ROM

**§SynergEbooks**
948 New Hwy 7, Columbia, TN 38401
SAN: 254-4962
*Tel:* 931-223-5990
*E-mail:* synergebooks@aol.com
*Web Site:* www.synergebooks.com
*Key Personnel*
Publr & Exec Ed: Debra Staples
Founded: 1999
Electronic publishing house & bookstore that also include CD-ROMs, audio books & trade paperbacks. Genres include fiction, nonfiction, romance, young adults fantasy, science fiction, poetry, humor, mystery/suspense, inspiration, cookbooks, self-help/reference, business, true crime, New Age, Native American & a children's section.
ISBN Prefix(es): 978-0-9702; 978-0-7443; 978-1-931540
Number of titles published annually: 8 Print; 50 E-Book; 3 Audio
Total Titles: 54 Print; 425 CD-ROM; 425 Online; 425 E-Book; 3 Audio
Membership(s): Electronically Published Internet Connection; IBPA, the Independent Book Publishers Association

**Syracuse University Press**
621 Skytop Rd, Suite 110, Syracuse, NY 13244-5290
SAN: 206-9776
*Tel:* 315-443-5534 *Toll Free Tel:* 800-365-8929 (cust serv) *Fax:* 315-443-5545
*E-mail:* supress@syr.edu
*Web Site:* syracuseuniversitypress.syr.edu
*Key Personnel*
Dir: Alice Randal Pfeiffer *Tel:* 315-443-5535 *E-mail:* arpfeiff@syr.edu
Sr Busn Mgr: Karen Lockwood *Tel:* 315-443-5536 *E-mail:* kflockwo@syr.edu
Acqs Ed: Deanna McCay *Tel:* 315-443-5543 *E-mail:* dhmccay@syr.edu
Order Supv: Lori Lazipone *Tel:* 315-443-2597
Design Specialist: Lynn Wilcox *Tel:* 315-443-1975 *E-mail:* lphoppel@syr.edu
Mktg Coord: Lisa Kuerbis *Tel:* 315-443-5546 *E-mail:* lkuerbis@syr.edu
Founded: 1943
Scholarly, general & regional nonfiction; Middle East; Irish studies; medieval; women studies; Iroquois studies; television; religion & politics; geography; sports & leisure; space, place & society; literature; Jewish studies (fiction & nonfiction).
ISBN Prefix(es): 978-0-8156
Number of titles published annually: 60 Print
Total Titles: 1,800 Print
Imprints: Adirondack Museum
Distributed by Alen House; Dedelas Press
Foreign Rep(s): Victoria Davies (Western USA); Eurospan University Press Group Ltd (Africa, Continental Europe, Middle East, UK); EWEB (Royden Muranaka) (Asia, Australia, Far East, Hawaii, India, New Zealand, Pakistan); Miller Trade Book Marketing (Midwestern States); Scholarly Book Services Inc (Canada); Nancy Suib & Associates (Western USA); UMG Publishers Representatives (David K Brown) (Eastern States); UMG Publishers Representatives (Jay Bruff) (Eastern States)
*Orders to:* Long Leaf Services, 116 S Boundary St, Chapel Hill, NC 27514-3808 *Toll Free Tel:* 800-848-6224 *Toll Free Fax:* 800-272-6817 *E-mail:* customerservice@longleafservices.org *Web Site:* www.longleafservices.org
*Returns:* Long Leaf Services, 116 S Boundary St, Chapel Hill, NC 27514-3808 *Toll Free Tel:* 800-848-6224 *Toll Free Fax:* 800-272-6817 *E-mail:* customerservice@longleafservices.org *Web Site:* www.longleafservices.org
*Distribution Center:* Long Leaf Services, 116 S Boundary St, Chapel Hill, NC 27514-3808 *Toll Free Tel:* 800-848-6224 *Toll Free Fax:* 800-272-6817 *E-mail:* customerservice@longleafservices.org *Web Site:* www.longleafservices.org

**Tachyon Publications**
1459 18 St, Suite 139, San Francisco, CA 94107
*Tel:* 415-285-5615
*E-mail:* tachyon@tachyonpublications.com
*Web Site:* www.tachyonpublications.com
*Key Personnel*
Publr & Ed: Jacob Weisman
Mng Ed: Jill Roberts
Lead Designer: Elizabeth Story
Founded: 1997
Science fiction & fantasy publishing.
This publisher has indicated that 100% of their product line is author subsidized.
ISBN Prefix(es): 978-0-9648320; 978-1-892391; 978-1-61696
Number of titles published annually: 10 Print; 4 E-Book
Total Titles: 108 Print; 33 E-Book
Foreign Rights: Linn Prentiss (Worldwide)
*Shipping Address:* Independent Publishers Group, 814 N Franklin St, Chicago, IL 60610
*Distribution Center:* Independent Publishers Group, 814 N Franklin St, Chicago, IL 60610
Membership(s): Science Fiction & Fantasy Writers of America

**§Tahrike Tarsile Qur'an Inc**
80-08 51 Ave, Elmhurst, NY 11373
*Tel:* 718-446-6472 *Fax:* 718-446-4370
*E-mail:* read@koranusa.org
*Web Site:* www.koranusa.org
*Key Personnel*
Pres: Aun Ali Khalfan
Publishers & distributors of the Holy Quran & other Islamic books, videos & CDs.
ISBN Prefix(es): 978-0-940368; 978-1-879402
Number of titles published annually: 5 Print
Total Titles: 50 Print

**TAN Books**
Imprint of Saint Benedict Press LLC
PO Box 410487, Charlotte, NC 28241
*Toll Free Tel:* 800-437-5876 *Fax:* 815-226-7770
*E-mail:* customerservice@tanbooks.com
*Web Site:* tanbooks.benedictpress.com; benedictpress.com
*Key Personnel*
Publr: Robert Gallagher
Founded: 1967
Publish traditional Catholic books, especially reprint classic works.
ISBN Prefix(es): 978-0-89555
Number of titles published annually: 15 Print
Total Titles: 550 Print

**T&T Clark International**
Imprint of Bloomsbury Publishing PLC
1385 Broadway, 5th fl, New York, NY 10018
*Tel:* 212-953-5858 *Toll Free Tel:* 800-561-7704 (orders) *Fax:* 212-953-5944
*Web Site:* www.continuumbooks.com
*Key Personnel*
Assoc Publr, Theology: Anna Turton
Sr Ed, Biblical Studies: Dominic Mattos
Mktg Mgr: Kara Zavada *E-mail:* kara.zavada@bloomsbury.com
Founded: 1821
Biblical studies, theology & church history.
ISBN Prefix(es): 978-0-8264; 978-1-56338; 978-0-334; 978-0-7162; 978-0-567
Number of titles published annually: 100 Print
Total Titles: 2,200 Print
Foreign Rep(s): Codasat (Canada)

**Tanglewood Press**
PO Box 3009, Terre Haute, IN 47803
*Tel:* 812-877-9488; 412-741-1579 (orders) *Toll Free Tel:* 800-836-4994 (orders) *Fax:* 412-741-0609 (orders)
*Web Site:* www.tanglewoodbooks.com

*Key Personnel*
Publr: Peggy Tierney *E-mail:* ptierney@tanglewoodbooks.com
Acqs Ed: Kairi Hamlin
Founded: 2003
Ms submissions accepted, see web site for guidelines. Send picture book mss or query letter with sample chapters for middle reader or young adult novels to Kairi Hamlin, Acqs Ed with SASE.
ISBN Prefix(es): 978-0-9749303; 978-1-933718
Number of titles published annually: 5 Print; 1 Audio
Total Titles: 35 Print; 2 Audio
*Distribution Center:* Publishers Group West (PGW), 1700 Fourth St, Berkeley, CA 94710 *Tel:* 510-809-3700 *Toll Free Tel:* 800-788-3123 *Fax:* 510-809-3777 *E-mail:* info@pgw.com *Web Site:* www.pgw.com

**§Tantor Media Inc**
2 Business Park, Old Saybrook, CT 06475
*Toll Free Tel:* 877-782-6867 *Toll Free Fax:* 888-782-7821
*Web Site:* www.tantor.com
*Key Personnel*
VP, Sales: John Molish *Tel:* 877-782-6867 ext 34 *E-mail:* jmolish@tantor.com
Dir, Acqs: Ron Formica *Tel:* 877-782-6867 ext 31 *E-mail:* ron@tantor.com
Mktg Mgr: Allan Hoving *Tel:* 877-782-6867 ext 76 *E-mail:* ahoving@tantor.com
Founded: 2001
Independent publisher & producer of audiobooks, ebooks, trade & paperback books. Publish fiction & nonfiction titles across all genres & categories.
Number of titles published annually: 12 Print; 750 Online; 15 E-Book; 700 Audio
Total Titles: 10 Print; 3,600 Online; 45 E-Book; 3,500 Audio
Imprints: Tantor Audio; Tantor Media
Foreign Rep(s): IPS (Worldwide)
Membership(s): ALA; Audio Publishers Association; Public Library Association

**Tapestry Press Ltd**
19 Nashoba Rd, Littleton, MA 01460
*Tel:* 978-486-0200 *Toll Free Tel:* 800-535-2007 *Fax:* 978-486-0244
*E-mail:* publish@tapestrypress.com
*Web Site:* www.tapestrypress.com
*Key Personnel*
Pres: Michael J Miskin
Publr: Elizabeth A Larsen
VP & Ed-in-Chief: Sara E Hofeldt
Founded: 1988
College textbooks & journals; custom textbooks & anthologies.
ISBN Prefix(es): 978-0-924234; 978-1-56888; 978-1-59830
Number of titles published annually: 100 Print
Total Titles: 175 Print

**Taplinger Publishing Co Inc**
PO Box 175, Marlboro, NJ 07746-0175
SAN: 213-6821
*Tel:* 305-256-7880 *Fax:* 305-256-7816
*E-mail:* taplingerpub@yahoo.com (rts & perms, edit, corp only)
*Key Personnel*
Pres: Louis Strick
VP & Treas: Theodore D Rosenfeld
Founded: 1955
General nonfiction, including art, biography, calligraphy, graphic arts, history, music.
ISBN Prefix(es): 978-0-8008
Number of titles published annually: 4 Print
Total Titles: 100 Print
Imprints: Crescendo
Foreign Rep(s): Baker & Taylor International (Africa, Asia, Europe, South Africa, South America)
*Orders to:* Parkwest Publications LLC, PO Box 310251, Miami, FL 33231-0251, Contact: Brian Squire *Tel:* 305-256-7880 *E-mail:* mail@parkwestpubs.com *Web Site:* www.parkwestpubs.com
*Returns:* Parkwest Publications LLC, 14332 SW 142 Ave, Miami, FL 33186, Contact: Brian Squire *Tel:* 305-256-7880
*Warehouse:* Parkwest Publications LLC, 14332 SW 142 Ave, Miami, FL 33186, Contact: Brian Squire *Tel:* 305-256-7880
*Distribution Center:* Parkwest Publications LLC, PO Box 310251, Miami, FL 33231-0251, Contact: Brian Squire *Tel:* 305-256-7880 *E-mail:* mail@parkwestpubs.com *Web Site:* www.parkwestpubs.com

**Jeremy P Tarcher**
Imprint of Penguin Group (USA) LLC
375 Hudson St, New York, NY 10014
SAN: 282-5074
*Tel:* 212-366-2000
*E-mail:* online@penguinputnam.com
*Web Site:* www.penguinputnam.com; us.penguingroup.com
*Key Personnel*
VP & Publr: Joel Fotinos
VP, Ed-in-Chief & Exec Ed: Mitchell Horowitz
Publicity & Mktg Dir: Brianna Yamashita
Exec Ed: Sara Carder
Founded: 1965
Nonfiction: cookbooks, crafts, humor, music & dance, health, nutrition, psychology, self-help, social sciences & sociology, biography, child care & development, behavioral sciences, business, human relations, education.
ISBN Prefix(es): 978-0-87477
Number of titles published annually: 51 Print
Total Titles: 566 Print

**Taschen America**
6671 Sunset Blvd, Suite 1508, Los Angeles, CA 90028
*Tel:* 323-463-4441 *Toll Free Tel:* 888-TASCHEN (827-2436) *Fax:* 323-463-4442
*E-mail:* contact-us@taschen.com
*Web Site:* www.taschen.com
*Key Personnel*
Busn Mgr: Meghan Clarke *E-mail:* m.clarke@taschen.com
Founded: 1996
Publishers of high-quality, reasonably priced illustrated books on the subjects of art, architecture, design, photography, erotica, gay interest & popular culture.
ISBN Prefix(es): 978-3-8228; 978-3-8365
Number of titles published annually: 80 Print
Total Titles: 500 Print
Imprints: Taschen GmbH
*Distribution Center:* Ingram, One Ingram Blvd, Lavergne, TN 37086 *Toll Free Tel:* 888-558-2624

**§The Taunton Press Inc**
63 S Main St, Newtown, CT 06470
SAN: 210-5144
Mailing Address: PO Box 5506, Newtown, CT 06470-5506
*Tel:* 203-426-8171 *Toll Free Tel:* 800-477-8727 (cust serv); 800-888-8286 (orders) *Fax:* 203-426-3434
*E-mail:* booksales@taunton.com
*Web Site:* www.taunton.com
*Key Personnel*
Pres: Tim Rahr
VP, Trade Sales: Jay Annis
Founded: 1975
Woodworking, home building, fiber arts, cooking & gardening books, magazines, DVDs & web sites.
ISBN Prefix(es): 978-0-918804; 978-0-942391; 978-1-56158; 978-1-60085
Number of titles published annually: 50 Print; 10 CD-ROM; 60 E-Book; 1 Audio
Total Titles: 525 Print; 100 CD-ROM; 10 Online; 300 E-Book; 1 Audio
Distributor for Academia Barilla
Foreign Rep(s): Capricorn Books (Australia); Guild of Master Craftsman (Europe); Random House Canada (Canada); Stanson Yeung (Asia); Zimpfer Books (Caribbean, Latin America)
Foreign Rights: Librisource Inc (Worldwide)
*Warehouse:* 141 Sheridan Dr, Naugatuck, CT 06770
*Distribution Center:* Ingram Publisher Services, One Ingram Blvd, La Vergne, TN 37086 *Tel:* 615-793-5000

**Taylor & Francis Inc**
325 Chestnut St, Suite 800, Philadelphia, PA 20036-1802
*Tel:* 215-625-8900 *Toll Free Tel:* 800-354-1420 *Fax:* 215-625-2940
*E-mail:* customer.service@taylorandfrancis.com
*Web Site:* www.taylorandfrancis.com
*Key Personnel*
Pres: Kevin J Bradley
VP, Prodn: Ed Cilurso *E-mail:* ed.cilurso@taylorandfrancis.com
Journals Mktg Dir: Deborah Lovell *E-mail:* deborah.lovell@taylorandfrancis.com
Journals Sales Dir: Margaret Walker *Tel:* 215-625-8900 ext 14346 *E-mail:* margaret.walker@taylorandfrancis.com
Founded: 1974
Journals in engineering, physical science, psychology, sociology, physics, chemistry, mathematics, environmental science, business, public health, marketing, arts, anthropology, political science, library science & LGBT studies.
ISBN Prefix(es): 978-1-56032; 978-0-87630; 978-0-86377; 978-0-8448; 978-0-85066; 978-0-85109; 978-0-905273; 978-1-85000
Number of titles published annually: 585 Print
Total Titles: 1,500 Print
Imprints: CRC Press; Garland Science; Psychology Press; Routledge; Taylor & Francis Asia Pacific; Taylor & Francis Books
*Foreign Office(s):* Taylor & Francis Group, Milton Park, 2 & 4 Park Sq, Abingdon, Oxford OX14 4RN, United Kingdom *Tel:* (0204) 017 4258 *Fax:* (0207) 017 6336
*Orders to:* 7625 Empire Dr, Florence, KY 41042-2929 *Toll Free Tel:* 800-634-7064 *Toll Free Fax:* 800-248-4724 *E-mail:* orders@taylorandfrancis.com; Bookpoint, 130 Milton Park, Abingdon, Oxon OX14 4SB, United Kingdom (Africa, Asia, Australia, Europe) *Tel:* (01235) 400 400 *Fax:* (01235) 400 401 *E-mail:* book.orders@tandf.co.uk
*Distribution Center:* 7625 Empire Dr, Florence, KY 41042 *Toll Free Tel:* 800-634-7064 *Toll Free Fax:* 800-248-4724 *E-mail:* orders@taylorandfrancis.com

**Taylor-Dth Publishing**
108 Caribe Isle, Novato, CA 94949
*Tel:* 415-299-1087
*Web Site:* www.taylor-dth.com
*Key Personnel*
Owner: Harold Miller *E-mail:* hmiller@taylor-dth.com
Founded: 2001
Limited book publisher.
ISBN Prefix(es): 978-0-9747532; 978-0-9727583; 978-0-9774431
Number of titles published annually: 4 Print
Total Titles: 40 Print

**TCU Press**, see Texas Christian University Press

**Teach Me Tapes Inc**
6016 Blue Circle Dr, Minnetonka, MN 55343
*Tel:* 952-933-8086 *Toll Free Tel:* 800-456-4656 *Fax:* 952-933-0512
*E-mail:* marie@teachmetapes.com
*Web Site:* www.teachmetapes.com
*Key Personnel*
Owner & Pres: Judy Mahoney *E-mail:* judy@teachmetapes.com
Founded: 1985
ISBN Prefix(es): 978-0-934633; 978-1-59972
Number of titles published annually: 3 Print
Total Titles: 100 Print; 37 Audio
*Distribution Center:* Amazon.com
Follett/BWI

**Teacher Created Resources Inc**
6421 Industry Way, Westminster, CA 92683
*Tel:* 714-891-7895 *Toll Free Tel:* 800-662-4321; 888-343-4335 *Fax:* 714-892-0283 *Toll Free Fax:* 800-525-1254
*E-mail:* custserv@teachercreated.com
*Web Site:* www.teachercreated.com
*Key Personnel*
Founder & Pres: Mary Dupuy Smith
Founded: 1982
Publishes PreK-12 curriculum programs, supplemental resource materials & technology products. Also, provides professional staff development for teachers.
ISBN Prefix(es): 978-1-55734
Number of titles published annually: 250 Print
Total Titles: 1,500 Print

**§Teachers College Press**
Affiliate of Teachers College, Columbia University
1234 Amsterdam Ave, New York, NY 10027
SAN: 213-263X
Mailing Address: PO Box 20, Williston, VT 05495-0020
*Tel:* 212-678-3929 *Toll Free Tel:* 800-575-6566 *Fax:* 212-678-4149; 802-864-7626
*E-mail:* tcpress@tc.columbia.edu; tcp.orders@aidcvt.com (orders)
*Web Site:* www.teacherscollegepress.com
*Key Personnel*
Dir: Carole Saltz
Exec Acqs Ed: Brian Ellerbeck *E-mail:* ellerbeck@tc.edu
Sr Acqs Ed: Marie Ellen Larcada *E-mail:* larcada@tc.edu
Acqs Ed: Meg Lemke *E-mail:* lemke@tc.edu
Prod Mgr: Peter Sieger
Subs Rts Mgr & Spec Sale Coord: Libby Powell *E-mail:* lpowell@tc.edu
Founded: 1904
Professional books & textbooks in education; tests, classroom materials & reference works.
ISBN Prefix(es): 978-0-8077
Number of titles published annually: 60 Print; 1 CD-ROM
Total Titles: 1,123 Print; 1 CD-ROM
Foreign Rep(s): Baker & Taylor International (Africa, Asia, Australia, Latin America, Middle East, Orient, South America); Eurospan Ltd (Europe, UK); Guidance Center (Canada)
*Orders to:* Baker & Taylor International, PO Box 6885, Bridgewater, NJ 08807-0885 *Tel:* 908-541-7305 *Fax:* 908-541-7853 *E-mail:* btinfo@btol.com *Web Site:* www.btol.com; University of Toronto Press-Guidance Centre, 5201 Dufferin St, Toronto, ON M3H 5T8, Canada (CN) *Toll Free Tel:* 800-565-9523 *Toll Free Fax:* 800-221-9958 *E-mail:* utpbooks@utpress.utoronto.ca *Web Site:* www.utpress.utoronto.ca; Pademelon Press Pty Ltd, PO Box 6500, Baulkham Hills, NSW 2153, Australia (Australia & New Zealand) *Tel:* (02) 9634 4655 *Fax:* (02) 9680 4634 *E-mail:* enquiry@pademelonpress.com.au; Kinokuniya Co Ltd, Book Import Dept, 3-7-10 Shimo-Meguro, Meguro-Ku, 153-8504 Tokyo, Japan (Japan) *Tel:* (03) 6910-0531 *Fax:* (03) 6420-1362 *E-mail:* info@kinokuniya.co.jp *Web Site:* www.kinokuniya.co.jp/english/index.html; Publishers Marketing Services Pte Ltd, Unit 509, Block E, Phileo Damansara 1, Jalan 16/11, Off Jalan Damansara, 46350 Petaling Jaya, Selangor, Malaysia (Brunei & Malaysia), Contact: Karen Lim *Tel:* (0603) 7955 3588 *Fax:* (0603) 7955 3017 *E-mail:* karenlim@pms.com.sg *Web Site:* www.pms.com.sg; CRW Marketing Services for Publishers Inc, 4 Topaz Rd, Greenheights, Taytay, 1920 Rizal, Philippines (Guam & Philippines), Contact: Tony Sagun *Tel:* (0632) 660 8430 *Fax:* (0632) 660 0342 *E-mail:* lwwagent@pldtdsl.net; Publishers Marketing Services Pte Ltd, 10C Jalan Ampas, No 07-01, Ho Seng Lee Flatted Warehouse, Singapore 329513, Singapore (Singapore), Contact: Raymond Lim *Tel:* (065) 6256 5166 *Fax:* (065) 6253 0008 *E-mail:* raymondlim@pms.com.sg *Web Site:* www.pms.com.sh; Everybody's Books, PO Box 301321, Durban North 4016, South Africa (South Africa) *Tel:* (031) 569 2229 *Fax:* (031) 569 2234 *E-mail:* warren@ebboks.co.za; Unifacmanu Trading Co Ltd, 4F, 91, Ho-Ping E Rd, Sec 1, Taipei 10609, Taiwan (Taiwan) *Tel:* (02) 2391-4280 *Fax:* (02) 2394-3103 *E-mail:* unifacmu@ms34@hinet.net *Web Site:* www.unifacmanu.com.tw/unifhome3.htm; Eurospan, c/o Turpin Distribution, Stratton Business Park, Pegasus Dr, Biggleswade, Bedfordshire SG18 8TQ, United Kingdom (Africa, Continental Europe, Middle East & UK) *Tel:* (01767) 604972 *Fax:* (01767) 601640 *E-mail:* eurospan@turpin-distribution.com *Web Site:* www.eurospanbookstore.com/tcp
*Returns:* Returns Dept, 82 Wintersport Lane, Williston, VT 05495
Membership(s): AAP; American Association of University Presses; BISG

**§Teacher's Discovery**
Division of American Eagle Co Inc
2741 Paldan Dr, Auburn Hills, MI 48326
*Toll Free Tel:* 800-832-2437 *Toll Free Fax:* 800-287-4509
*E-mail:* foreignlanguage@teachersdiscovery.com; worldlanguage@teachersdiscovery.com
*Web Site:* www.teachersdiscovery.com
*Key Personnel*
Owner: Skip McWilliams
Mktg Mgr: Steve Giroux *Tel:* 248-276-4918
Founded: 1969
Distribute several proprietary items we create; also publish several works written by authors other than those employed by Teachers Discovery; social studies, English, science & teachers of Spanish, French & German.
Number of titles published annually: 200 Print
*Branch Office(s)*
2676 Paldan Dr, Auburn Hills, MI 48326 *Toll Free Tel:* 800-583-6454 *Toll Free Fax:* 888-395-6686 *E-mail:* english@teachersdiscovery.com

**Teachers of English to Speakers of Other Languages Inc (TESOL)**
1925 Ballenger Ave, Alexandria, VA 22314-6820
*Tel:* 703-836-0774 *Toll Free Tel:* 888-547-3369 *Fax:* 703-836-7864
*E-mail:* info@tesol.org
*Web Site:* www.tesol.org
*Key Personnel*
Exec Dir: Rosa Aronson *Tel:* 703-836-0774 ext 505 *E-mail:* raronson@tesol.org
Publg Mgr: Carol Edwards *Tel:* 703-836-0774 ext 525 *E-mail:* cedwards@tesol.org
Founded: 1966
Professional educator association & publisher of professional education related books.
ISBN Prefix(es): 978-0-939791; 978-1-1931
Number of titles published annually: 6 Print
Total Titles: 90 Print; 1 CD-ROM
Distributed by Alta Book Ctr; Delta Systems Inc; New Readers Press; Saddleback Educational
*Orders to:* PO Box 79283, Baltimore, MD 21279 *Tel:* 240-646-7037 *Toll Free Tel:* 888-891-0041 *Fax:* 301-206-9789 *E-mail:* tesolpubs@brightkey@brightkey.net
*Distribution Center:* Tesol Publications At Tasco, PO Box 753, Waldorf, MD 20604 *E-mail:* tesolpubs@brightkey.com

**§Teaching & Learning Co**
501 E Third St, Dayton, OH 45402
Mailing Address: PO Box 802, Dayton, OH 45401-0802
*Tel:* 937-228-6118 *Toll Free Tel:* 800-444-1144 *Fax:* 937-223-2042
*E-mail:* info@lorenz.com
*Key Personnel*
VP, Mktg: Debra Kaiser *E-mail:* debk@lorenz.com
Founded: 1994
Educational publishing division includes visual resources, instructional guides & reproducibles, elementary supplementals.
ISBN Prefix(es): 978-1-57310
Number of titles published annually: 35 Print
Total Titles: 400 Print; 325 E-Book; 10 Audio
Membership(s): National School Supply & Equipment Association

**§Teaching Strategies**
7101 Wisconsin Ave, Suite 700, Bethesda, MD 20814
*Tel:* 301-634-0818 *Toll Free Tel:* 800-637-3652 *Fax:* 301-657-0250
*E-mail:* customerrelations@teachingstrategies.com
*Web Site:* www.teachingstrategies.com
*Key Personnel*
COO: Andrea Valentine *E-mail:* andreav@teachingstrategies.com
Founded: 1988
Curriculum, assessment & training materials for early childhood education (birth-age 8) & parent's guides; web subscription service.
ISBN Prefix(es): 978-1-879537; 978-0-9602892; 978-1-60617
Number of titles published annually: 5 Print
Total Titles: 66 Print
Distributor for Gryphon House
*Orders to:* PO Box 42243, Washington, DC 20015
*Returns:* Teaching Strategies Inc, c/o RRD P & F, 1077 Prospect Lane, Kaukauna, WI 54130

**§Temple University Press**
Division of Temple University of the Commonwealth System of Higher Education
1852 N Tenth St, Philadelphia, PA 19122-6099
SAN: 202-7666
*Tel:* 215-926-2140 *Toll Free Tel:* 800-621-2736 *Fax:* 215-926-2141
*E-mail:* tempress@temple.edu
*Web Site:* www.temple.edu/tempress
*Key Personnel*
Dir: Alex Holzman *E-mail:* aholzman@temple.edu
Dir, Prodn & Electronic Publg: Charles Ault *E-mail:* charles.ault@temple.edu
Mktg Dir & Asst Dir: Ann-Marie Anderson *E-mail:* anderson@temple.edu
Exec Ed: Micah Kleit *E-mail:* micah.kleit@temple.edu
Ad & Promo Mgr: Irene Imperio Kull *E-mail:* irene.imperio@temple.edu
Busn Mgr: Barry Adams *E-mail:* barry.adams@temple.edu
Cust Serv Mgr: Karen Baker *E-mail:* karen.baker@temple.edu
Publicity Mgr: Gary Kramer *E-mail:* gkramer@temple.edu

Rts & Perms & Intl Rts: Sara Cohen *E-mail:* sara.cohen@temple.edu
Founded: 1969
Scholarly books; all regional interests.
ISBN Prefix(es): 978-0-87722; 978-1-56639; 978-1-59213; 978-1-4399
Number of titles published annually: 45 Print
Total Titles: 1,450 Print
Foreign Rep(s): Baker & Taylor Ltd (Asia, The Pacific, Worldwide exc Canada); Combined Academic Publishing (CAP) (Europe); East-West Export Books (Royden Muranaka) (Asia, The Pacific); Lynn McClory (Canada)
*Returns:* Temple University Press Chicago Distribution Center, 11030 S Langley, Chicago, IL 60628 *Tel:* 773-702-7000 *Fax:* 773-702-7000 *Toll Free Fax:* 800-621-8476
*Warehouse:* Temple University Press Chicago Distribution Center, 11030 S Langley, Chicago, IL 60628, Contact: Sue Tranchita *Tel:* 773-702-7000 *Fax:* 773-702-7000 *Toll Free Fax:* 800-621-8476
Membership(s): Association of American University Presses; Society for Scholarly Publishing

**Templegate Publishers**
302 E Adams St, Springfield, IL 62701
SAN: 123-0115
Mailing Address: PO Box 5152, Springfield, IL 62705-5152
*Tel:* 217-522-3353 (edit & sales); 217-522-3354 (billing) *Toll Free Tel:* 800-367-4844 (orders only) *Fax:* 217-522-3362
*E-mail:* wisdom@templegate.com; orders@templegate.com (sales)
*Web Site:* www.templegate.com
*Key Personnel*
Dir & Owner: Thomas M Garvey *E-mail:* tmg@templegate.com
Exec Ed, Rts & Perms & Publicity: John Fisher
Sales & Ad Mgr, ISBN & Lib Sales Dir: Elaine Garvey
Founded: 1947
Nonfiction.
ISBN Prefix(es): 978-0-87243
Number of titles published annually: 4 Print
Total Titles: 225 Print
Imprints: Octavo Press
Foreign Rep(s): Gracewing (Europe); Rainbow Book Agencies (Australia)

**Templeton Press**
Subsidiary of John Templeton Foundation
300 Conshohocken State Rd, Suite 550, West Conshohocken, PA 19428
*Tel:* 484-531-8380 *Fax:* 484-531-8382
*E-mail:* tpinfo@templetonpress.org
*Web Site:* www.templetonpress.org
*Key Personnel*
Ed-In-Chief: Susan Arellano *E-mail:* sarellano@templetonpress.org
Mktg Mgr: Matt Smiley *E-mail:* msmiley@templetonpress.org
Founded: 1987
Focus on science & religion, spirituality & health, character development & business.
ISBN Prefix(es): 978-1-890151; 978-1-932031; 978-1-59947
Number of titles published annually: 20 Print; 20 E-Book
Total Titles: 167 Print; 100 E-Book; 20 Audio
Foreign Rights: Rainbow Book Agencies (Australia)
*Billing Address:* Chicago Distribution Center, 11030 S Langley Ave, Chicago, IL 60628 *Tel:* 773-702-7000 *Toll Free Tel:* 800-621-2736 *Fax:* 773-702-7212 *Toll Free Fax:* 800-621-8476 *Web Site:* www.chicagodistributioncenter.org
*Orders to:* Chicago Distribution Center, 11030 S Langley Ave, Chicago, IL 60628 *Tel:* 773-702-7000 *Toll Free Tel:* 800-621-2736 *Fax:* 773-702-7212 *Toll Free Fax:* 800-621-8476 *Web Site:* www.chicagodistributioncenter.org
*Returns:* Chicago Distribution Center, 11030 S Langley Ave, Chicago, IL 60628 *Tel:* 773-702-7000 *Toll Free Tel:* 800-621-2736 *Fax:* 773-702-7212 *Toll Free Fax:* 800-621-8476 *Web Site:* www.chicagodistributioncenter.org
*Shipping Address:* Chicago Distribution Center, 11030 S Langley Ave, Chicago, IL 60628 *Tel:* 773-702-7000 *Toll Free Tel:* 800-621-2736 *Fax:* 773-702-7212 *Toll Free Fax:* 800-621-8476 *Web Site:* www.chicagodistributioncenter.org
*Warehouse:* Chicago Distribution Center, 11030 S Langley Ave, Chicago, IL 60628 *Tel:* 773-702-7000 *Toll Free Tel:* 800-621-2736 *Fax:* 773-702-7212 *Toll Free Fax:* 800-621-8476 *Web Site:* www.chicagodistributioncenter.org
*Distribution Center:* Chicago Distribution Center, 11030 S Langley Ave, Chicago, IL 60628 *Tel:* 773-702-7000 *Toll Free Tel:* 800-621-2736 *Fax:* 773-702-7212 *Toll Free Fax:* 800-621-8476 *Web Site:* www.chicagodistributioncenter.org
Membership(s): IBPA, the Independent Book Publishers Association; Network of Alternatives for Publishers, Retailers & Artists Inc

**Temporal Mechanical Press**
Division of Enos Mills Cabin Museum & Gallery
6760 Hwy 7, Estes Park, CO 80517-6404
*Tel:* 970-586-4706
*E-mail:* enosmillscbn@earthlink.net
*Web Site:* www.enosmills.com
*Key Personnel*
Owner: Elizabeth M Mills; Eryn Mills
ISBN Prefix(es): 978-1-928878
Number of titles published annually: 3 Print
Total Titles: 32 Print

**Ten Speed Press**
Imprint of Crown Publishing Group
2625 Alcatraz Ave, Unit 505, Berkeley, CA 94705
SAN: 202-7674
*Tel:* 510-285-3000 *Toll Free Tel:* 800-841-BOOK (841-2665)
*E-mail:* csorders@randomhouse.com
*Web Site:* crownpublishing.com/imprint/ten-speed-press
*Key Personnel*
Publr: Aaron Wehner
VP & Assoc Publr: Hannah Rahill
Edit Dir: Julie Bennett
Mktg Dir: Michele Crim
Mng Art Dir: Elizabeth Stromberg
Publicity Dir, Cookbooks: Kristin Casemore
Assoc Mgr, Publicity & Mktg: Kelly Snowden
Sr Ed: Lisa Westmoreland
Ed: Sara Golski
Assoc Ed: Emily Timberlake
Sr Designer: Katy Brown
Designer: Sarah Pulver
Sr Publicist: Kara Van de Water
Mktg Asst: Ashley Matuszak
Founded: 1971
Trade, paperbound, fine editions: Americana & regional, art, book trade, business, history, social sciences, cooking, gardening, hobbies, recreation, health, meditation, philosophy, education, humor, animal/pet, self-help, how-to, travel, reference.
ISBN Prefix(es): 978-1-58761; 978-1-58091; 978-1-58008; 978-1-60774
Number of titles published annually: 100 Print
Total Titles: 587 Print
Foreign Rep(s): Random House (Worldwide)

**Teora USA LLC**
505 Hampton Park Blvd, Unit G, Capitol Heights, MD 20743
SAN: 256-1220
*Tel:* 301-986-6990 *Toll Free Tel:* 800-974-2105 *Fax:* 301-350-5480 *Toll Free Fax:* 800-358-3754
*E-mail:* 2010@teora.com
*Web Site:* www.teora.com
*Key Personnel*
Busn Mgr: Teodor Raducanu
Contact: Maria Nedelcu
Founded: 2003
ISBN Prefix(es): 978-1-59496
Number of titles published annually: 6 Print
Total Titles: 60 Print
Imprints: Teora
*Distribution Center:* Fitzhenry & Whiteside, 195 Allstate Pkwy, Markham, ON L3R 4T8, Canada *Tel:* 904-477-9700 *Toll Free Fax:* 800-260-9777
Membership(s): IBPA, the Independent Book Publishers Association

**TESOL**, see Teachers of English to Speakers of Other Languages Inc (TESOL)

**Teton NewMedia**
90 E Simpson, Suite 110, Jackson, WY 83001
Mailing Address: PO Box 4833, Jackson, WY 83001
*Tel:* 307-732-0028 *Toll Free Tel:* 877-306-9793 *Fax:* 307-734-0841
*E-mail:* sales@tetonnm.com
*Web Site:* www.tetonnm.com
*Key Personnel*
Mktg Mgr: Sara Scartz-Montesano *Tel:* 307-732-0028 ext 101 *E-mail:* sara@tetonnm.com
Founded: 1999 (By John Sphar & Carroll Cann)
Health science publisher that focuses on producing high quality, affordable veterinary text & reference books.
ISBN Prefix(es): 978-1-893441; 978-1-59161
Number of titles published annually: 6 Print; 2 CD-ROM
Total Titles: 25 Print; 18 CD-ROM
Distributed by Blackwells; LifeLearn; Logan Brothers; Rittenhouse; Yankee
Distributor for LifeLearn

**Tetra Press**
Division of Pfizer Inc
3001 Commerce St, Blacksburg, VA 24060
*Tel:* 540-951-5400 *Toll Free Tel:* 800-526-0650 *Fax:* 540-951-5415
*E-mail:* consumer@tetra-fish.com
*Web Site:* www.tetra-fish.com
*Key Personnel*
Prod Mgr: Wayne Marton
Fish, reptiles, amphibians & ponds.
ISBN Prefix(es): 978-1-56465
Number of titles published annually: 3 Print
Total Titles: 114 Print
*Branch Office(s)*
Speciality Book Marketing Inc, 443 Park Ave S, New York, NY 10016, Contact: William Corsa
Distributed by Voyageur Press

**Texas A&M University Press**
Division of Texas A&M University
John H Lindsey Bldg, Lewis St, 4354 TAMU, College Station, TX 77843-4354
SAN: 207-5237
*Tel:* 979-845-1436 *Toll Free Tel:* 800-826-8911 (orders) *Fax:* 979-847-8752 *Toll Free Fax:* 888-617-2421 (orders)
*E-mail:* upress@tamu.edu
*Web Site:* www.tamupress.com
*Key Personnel*
Dir: Dr Charles Backus *Tel:* 979-458-3980 *E-mail:* charles.backus@tamu.edu
Lib Sales Dir & Mktg Mgr: Gayla Christiansen *Tel:* 979-845-0148 *E-mail:* gayla-c@tamu.edu
Ed-in-Chief & Mng Ed: Shannon Davies *Tel:* 979-845-0759 *E-mail:* sdavies@tamu.edu
Mgr, Cust Rel: Sharon Mills *Tel:* 979-458-3994 *E-mail:* sharon-mills@tamu.edu

Design Mgr: Mary Ann Jacob *Tel:* 979-845-3694 *E-mail:* m-jacob@tamu.edu
Fin Mgr: Dianna Sells *Tel:* 979-845-0146 *E-mail:* d-sells@tamu.edu
Publicity & Ad Mgr: Holli Estridge *Tel:* 979-458-3982 *E-mail:* holli.stridge@tamu.edu
Trade Sales: David Neel *Tel:* 979-458-3981 *E-mail:* d-neel@tamu.edu
Founded: 1974
Scholarly nonfiction, regional studies, economics, history, natural history, presidential studies, anthropology, US-Mexican borderlands studies, women's studies, nautical archaeology, military studies, agriculture, Texas history & archaeology.
ISBN Prefix(es): 978-0-89096; 978-1-58544; 978-1-60344; 978-1-60344
Number of titles published annually: 60 Print; 1 CD-ROM
Total Titles: 1,400 Print; 2 CD-ROM; 900 E-Book; 4 Audio
Distributor for Stephen F Austin State University Press; McWhiney Foundation Press/State House Press; Southern Methodist University Press; Texas Christian University Press; Texas Review Press; Texas State Historical Association; University of North Texas Press
Foreign Rep(s): Eurospan Group (Europe, UK); EWEB (Asia, Australia, Middle East, New Zealand, Pacific Islands); Scholarly Book Services (Laura Rust) (Canada); Texas A&M University Press (USA); US PubRep Inc (Craig Falk) (Latin America)
Foreign Rights: Tamu Press
Membership(s): Association of American University Presses

**Texas Christian University Press**
3000 Sandage Ave, Fort Worth, TX 76109
Mailing Address: PO Box 298300, Fort Worth, TX 76129
*Tel:* 817-257-7822 *Toll Free Tel:* 800-826-8911 *Fax:* 817-257-5075
*Web Site:* www.prs.tcu.edu
*Key Personnel*
Dir: Dan Williams *Tel:* 817-257-5907 *E-mail:* d.e.williams@tcu.edu
Prodn Mgr: Melinda Esco *Tel:* 817 257 6874 *E-mail:* m.esco@tcu.edu
Mktg Coord: Rebecca Allen *Tel:* 817-257-6872 *E-mail:* rebecca.a.allen@tcu.edu
Ed: Kathy S Walton *Tel:* 817-257-5074 *E-mail:* k.s.walton@tcu.edu
Founded: 1966
History & literature of Texas & the American West.
ISBN Prefix(es): 978-0-912646; 978-0-87565
Number of titles published annually: 15 Print; 20 Online
Total Titles: 440 Print; 20 Online; 50 E-Book; 1 Audio
Distributed by Texas A&M University Press
Foreign Rep(s): Texas A&M University Press
*Shipping Address:* Texas A&M University Press, Tamus 4354, College Station, TX 77843-4354, Contact: Sharon Mills
*Warehouse:* Texas A&M University Press, Tamus 4354, College Station, TX 77843-4354, Contact: Sharon Mills
Membership(s): Association of American University Presses

**Texas State Historical Association**
Stovall Hall 175, 1400 W Highland St, Denton, TX 76203
Mailing Address: 1155 Union Circle, Suite 311580, Denton, TX 76203-5017
*Tel:* 940-369-5200 *Fax:* 940-369-5248
*Web Site:* www.tshaonline.org
*Key Personnel*
Dir: Kent Calder
Assoc Ed: Ryan Schumacher *E-mail:* ryanschumacher@tshaonline.org
Founded: 1897
Books & articles related to Texas history.
ISBN Prefix(es): 978-0-87611
Number of titles published annually: 4 Print
Total Titles: 125 Print; 3 Online
Distributed by Texas A&M University Press

**Texas Tech University Press**
2903 Fourth St, Suite 201, Lubbock, TX 79409
Mailing Address: Box 41037, Lubbock, TX 79409-1037
*Tel:* 806-742-2982 *Toll Free Tel:* 800-832-4042 *Fax:* 806-742-2979
*E-mail:* ttup@ttu.edu
*Web Site:* www.ttupress.org
*Key Personnel*
Dir: Robert Mandel *E-mail:* robert.mandel@ttu.edu
Exhibits & Publicity Mgr: John Brock *E-mail:* john.brock@ttu.edu
Off Mgr: Isabel Williams *E-mail:* isabel.williams@ttu.edu
Ed-in-Chief: Judith Keeling *E-mail:* judith.keeling@ttu.edu
Mng Ed: Joanna Conrad *E-mail:* joanna.conrad@ttu.edu
Prodn: Kasey McBeath *E-mail:* kasey.mcbeath@ttu.edu
Cust Service Rep: LaTisha Roberts *E-mail:* latisha.roberts@ttu.edu
Asst to Dir: Jada Rankin *E-mail:* jada.rankin@ttu.edu
Founded: 1971
Scholarly books & journals: biological sciences, literary criticism, museum-related sciences, specialized regional, poetry, history, fiction. Also costume history.
ISBN Prefix(es): 978-0-89672
Number of titles published annually: 25 Print
Total Titles: 364 Print
Distributor for National Ranching Heritage Center
*Distribution Center:* Chicago Distribution Center, 11030 S Langley Ave, Chicago, IL 60628 SAN: 202-5280
Membership(s): Association of American University Presses; Publishers Association of the West

**§University of Texas Press**
Division of University of Texas
2100 Comal St, Austin, TX 78722
SAN: 212-9876
Mailing Address: PO Box 7819, Austin, TX 78713-7819
*Tel:* 512-471-7233 *Fax:* 512-232-7178
*E-mail:* utpress@uts.cc.utexas.edu
*Web Site:* www.utexaspress.com
*Key Personnel*
CFO: Joyce Lewandoski
Dir, Press: Dave Hamrick
Ed-in-Chief: Theresa May
Acq Ed: Jim Burr
Mgr & Intl Rts Contact: Laura Bost
Asst Mktg Mgr: Nancy Bryan
Sales Mgr: Gianna La Norte
Credit Mgr & Cust Serv: Brenda Jo Hoggutt
Prodn Mgr: Ellen McKie
Ad, Exhibits Mgr: Chris Farmer
Founded: 1950
General scholarly nonfiction, Latin America, Middle Eastern studies, Southwest regional, social sciences, humanities & science, linguistics, architecture, classics, natural history, Latin American literature in translation.
ISBN Prefix(es): 978-0-292
Number of titles published annually: 100 Print
Total Titles: 2,200 Print; 1 CD-ROM; 1 Online
Distributor for Bat Conservation International; Institute for Mesoamerican Studies; Menil Foundation; Rothko Chapel; Texas Parks & Wildlife Department
Foreign Rep(s): East-West Export Books (Australia, New Zealand); Nicholas Esson (Europe, UK); Hargraves, Fuller & Paton (Canada); Marketing Dept, University of Texas (Caribbean)
Membership(s): AAP; Association of American University Presses

**Texas Western Press**
Affiliate of University of Texas at El Paso
c/o University of Texas at El Paso, 500 W University Ave, El Paso, TX 79968-0633
SAN: 202-7712
*Tel:* 915-747-5688 *Toll Free Tel:* 800-488-3798 (orders only) *Fax:* 915-747-7515
*E-mail:* twpress@utep.edu
*Web Site:* twp.utep.edu
*Key Personnel*
Dir: Robert Stakes
Founded: 1952
Scholarly books on the history, art, photography & culture of the American Southwest.
ISBN Prefix(es): 978-0-87404
Number of titles published annually: 3 Print
Total Titles: 63 Print; 1 Audio
Imprints: Southwestern Studies
Distributed by University of Texas Press
Membership(s): American Association of University Presses

**TFH Publications Inc**
Subsidiary of Central Garden & Pet Corp
One TFH Plaza, Third & Union Aves, Neptune City, NJ 07753
SAN: 202-7720
*Tel:* 732-988-8400 *Toll Free Tel:* 800-631-2188 *Fax:* 732-776-8763
*E-mail:* info@tfh.com
*Web Site:* www.tfh.com
*Key Personnel*
CEO & Pres: Glen Axelrod
Publr: Christopher T Reggio *E-mail:* creggio@tfh.com
Founded: 1952
Pet care reference books & specialty magazines.
ISBN Prefix(es): 978-0-87666; 978-0-86622; 978-0-7938; 978-1-890087 (Microcosm Books); 978-0-9820262 (Microcosm Books)
Number of titles published annually: 40 Print; 40 E-Book
Total Titles: 1,200 Print; 200 E-Book
Imprints: Microcosm Books
Divisions: Nylabone Products
Foreign Rep(s): Brooklands Aquarium Ltd (New Zealand); Fitzhenry & Whiteside (Canada); Rolf C Hagen Ltd (Canada); Interpet Publishing (England); TFH Pty Ltd (Australia); Trinity Books (South Africa)
Foreign Rights: Richard Gay (all other territories)
*Warehouse:* 50 TFH Way, Neptune City, NJ 07753

**Thames & Hudson**
500 Fifth Ave, New York, NY 10110
SAN: 202-5795
*Tel:* 212-354-3763 *Toll Free Tel:* 800-233-4830 *Fax:* 212-398-1252
*E-mail:* bookinfo@thames.wwnorton.com
*Web Site:* www.thamesandhudsonusa.com
*Key Personnel*
Pres & Publr: Will Balliett
Edit Dir: Christopher Sweet
Assoc Mktg Dir: Lauren Miller
Publicity: Tiffany McKenna
Founded: 1977
Nonfiction trade, quality paperbacks & college texts on art, archaeology, architecture, crafts, history & photography.
ISBN Prefix(es): 978-0-500
Number of titles published annually: 150 Print
Total Titles: 1,000 Print
Distributed by W W Norton & Co Inc
*Advertising Agency:* Verso

*Shipping Address:* National Book Co Inc, Keystone Industrial Park, Scranton, PA 18512
Membership(s): AAP

**Theatre Communications Group**
520 Eighth Ave, 24th fl, New York, NY 10018-4156
*Tel:* 212-609-5900 *Fax:* 212-609-5901
*E-mail:* tcg@tcg.org
*Web Site:* www.tcg.org
*Key Personnel*
Publr: Terence Nemeth *E-mail:* tnemeth@tcg.org
Edit Dir & Ed: Kathy Sova
Founded: 1961
Performing arts, dramatic literature.
ISBN Prefix(es): 978-0-930452; 978-1-55936
Number of titles published annually: 20 Print
Total Titles: 250 Print
Distributor for Absolute Classics; Aurora Metro Publications; Nick Hern Books; Oberon Books; Padua Playwrights Press; PAJ Publications; Playwrights Canada Press; Martin E Segal Theatre Center Publications; Ubu Repertory Theatre Publications
Foreign Rep(s): Nick Hern Books (UK); Playwrights Canada Press (Canada)
*Distribution Center:* Consortium Book Sales & Distribution, The Keg House, 34 13 Ave NE, Suite 101, Minneapolis, MN 55413-1007 *Tel:* 612-746-2600 *Toll Free Tel:* 800-283-3572 (cust serv) *Fax:* 612-746-2606 *Web Site:* www.cbsd.com

**Theosophical Publishing House/Quest Books**
Division of The Theosophical Society in America
306 W Geneva Rd, Wheaton, IL 60187
SAN: 202-5698
Mailing Address: PO Box 270, Wheaton, IL 60189-0270
*Tel:* 630-665-0130 (ext 347) *Toll Free Tel:* 800-669-9425 (ext 347) *Fax:* 630-665-8791
*E-mail:* customerservice@questbooks.net
*Web Site:* www.questbooks.net
*Key Personnel*
Publg Mgr: Sharron Dorr *E-mail:* sdorr@questbooks.net
Opers Mgr: Pat Griebeler *Tel:* 630-665-0130 ext 354 *E-mail:* operations@questbooks.net
Mktg Mgr: Nicole Smoley *E-mail:* marketing@questbooks.net
Rts & Perms: Laly Diaz *E-mail:* permissions@questbooks.net
Intl Rts: DeLacy Sarantos *E-mail:* foreignrights@questbooks.net
Ed: Richard Smoley *E-mail:* editor@questbooks.net
Founded: 1965
Publish books of intelligence, readability & insight for the contemporary spiritual seeker. Our books explore ancient wisdom, modern science, world religions, philosophy, the arts & the inner meaning of life to provide dynamic tools for spiritual healing & self-transformation.
ISBN Prefix(es): 978-0-8356
Number of titles published annually: 10 Print
Total Titles: 400 Print; 50 Audio
Imprints: Quest Books
Foreign Rep(s): Airlift Book Co (Europe, UK); Alternative Books (South Africa); Aquamarin Verlag (Germany); Brumby Books (Australia); Theosofische Vereniging in Nederland (Netherlands); Theosophical Publishing House (India); Theosophical Publishing House Manila (Philippines); Theosophical Society in New Zealand (New Zealand)
*Distribution Center:* National Book Network, 15200 NBN Way, Blue Ridge Summit, PA 17214
Membership(s): ABA; ALA; IBPA, the Independent Book Publishers Association

**§Theosophical University Press**
Affiliate of Theosophical Society (Pasadena)
PO Box C, Pasadena, CA 91109-7107
SAN: 205-4299
*Tel:* 626-798-3378 *Fax:* 626-798-4749
*E-mail:* tupress@theosociety.org
*Web Site:* www.theosociety.org
*Key Personnel*
Dir: Randell C Grubb
Mgr & Intl Rts: Will Thackara
Cust Serv: Ina Belderis
Founded: 1886
Quality theosophical literature.
ISBN Prefix(es): 978-0-911500; 978-1-55700
Number of titles published annually: 3 Print; 5 Online
Total Titles: 86 Print; 1 CD-ROM; 132 Online; 5 Audio
Imprints: Sunrise Library
*Foreign Office(s):* Theosophical University Press Agency, 664 Glenhuntly Rd, South Caulfield, Melbourne, Victoria 3162, Australia, Contact: Andrew Rooke *Tel:* (03) 9528 1011 *Fax:* (03) 9528 3907 *E-mail:* andrewrooke@hotmail.com *Web Site:* theosophydownunder.org
Theosophischer Verlag GmbH, Brunnenstr 11, 56414 Hundsangen, Germany, Contact: Jochen Hannappel *Tel:* (06432) 3001240 *Fax:* (06432) 96053 *E-mail:* kontakt@theosophischer-verlag.de *Web Site:* www.theosophischer-verlag.de
Theosophical University Press Agency, Daal en Bergselaan 68, 2565 AG The Hague, Netherlands, Contact: Coen Vonk *Tel:* (070) 323 1776 *Fax:* (070) 325 7275 *E-mail:* tupa@theosofie.net *Web Site:* www.theosofie.net
Theosophical University Press South African Agency, PO Box 504, Constantia 7848, South Africa, Contact: Dewald Bester *Tel:* (021) 4342281 *E-mail:* besterdewald@gmail.com
Teosofiska Bokforlaget, Barnhusgatan 13, 411 11 Gothenburg, Sweden *E-mail:* teobok@glocalnet.net *Web Site:* hem.fyristorg.com/teosofi/TeosofiskaBokforlaget/index.htm
The Theosophical Society, PO Box 48, Penrhyndeudraeth, Gwynedd LL49 0AQ, United Kingdom *E-mail:* ts-uk@talktalk.net *Web Site:* www.theosophical.org.uk
*Warehouse:* 2416 N Lake Ave, Altadena, CA 91001

**§Thieme Medical Publishers Inc**
Subsidiary of Georg Thieme Verlag KG
333 Seventh Ave, 18th fl, New York, NY 10001
SAN: 202-7399
*Tel:* 212-760-0888 *Toll Free Tel:* 800-782-3488 *Fax:* 212-947-1112
*E-mail:* customerservice@thieme.com
*Web Site:* www.thieme.com
*Key Personnel*
Pres: Brian Scanlan *Tel:* 212-584-4707 *E-mail:* bscanlan@thieme.com
Sales Dir: Mike Rossman *Tel:* 631-365-4625 *E-mail:* mike.roseman@thieme.com
Founded: 1979
Electronic products, apps, books, journals, textbooks in clinical medicine, dentistry, speech & hearing, allied health, audiology, organic chemistry plus electronic products, medical education & databases.
ISBN Prefix(es): 978-0-913258; 978-0-86577; 978-1-58890; 978-1-60406
Number of titles published annually: 50 Print; 3 CD-ROM; 50 Online
Total Titles: 605 Print; 50 Online; 605 E-Book
*Foreign Office(s):* Georg Thieme Verlag, PO Box 30 11 20, 70451 Stuttgart, Germany *Tel:* (0711) 89310 *Fax:* (0711) 8931410 *E-mail:* customerservice@thieme.de *Web Site:* www.thieme.de
Foreign Rep(s): Login Canada (Canada); Woodslane (Australia)
Foreign Rights: Barbara Pfeifer (Worldwide)
*Warehouse:* Mount Joy Distribution Center, 1000 Strickler Rd, Mount Joy, PA 17552
Membership(s): AAP; Independent Publishers Association; STM

**Thinkers' Press Inc**
1524 Le Claire St, Davenport, IA 52803
SAN: 176-4632
*Tel:* 563-271-6657
*E-mail:* info@chessbutler.com
*Web Site:* www.thinkerspressinc.com
*Key Personnel*
Pres & Busn Mgr: Bob Long
Founded: 1971
Mainly publish books on chess & other related areas; software, online titles, videos, etc. having to do with the game of chess.
ISBN Prefix(es): 978-0-938650; 978-1-888710
Number of titles published annually: 8 Print
Total Titles: 170 Print

**Third World Press**
7822 S Dobson Ave, Chicago, IL 60619
Mailing Address: PO Box 19730, Chicago, IL 60619
*Tel:* 773-651-0700 *Fax:* 773-651-7286
*E-mail:* twpress3@aol.com
*Web Site:* www.twpbooks.com
*Key Personnel*
Publr: Haki R Madhubuti
Ed: Gwendolyn Mitchell
Founded: 1967
Publishers of quality Black fiction, nonfiction, poetry, drama, young adult & children literature; primarily adult literature.
ISBN Prefix(es): 978-0-88378
Number of titles published annually: 10 Print
Total Titles: 100 Print
Distributed by IPG

**Charles C Thomas Publisher Ltd**
2600 S First St, Springfield, IL 62704
SAN: 201-9485
*Tel:* 217-789-8980 *Toll Free Tel:* 800-258-8980 *Fax:* 217-789-9130
*E-mail:* books@ccthomas.com
*Web Site:* www.ccthomas.com
*Key Personnel*
Pres: Michael Payne Thomas
Cont: Cheryl Steelman
Founded: 1927
Medicine, allied health sciences, science, technology, education, public administration, law enforcement, behavioral & social sciences, special education.
ISBN Prefix(es): 978-0-398
Number of titles published annually: 60 Print
Total Titles: 905 Print
*Advertising Agency:* Thomas Advertising Agency
*Returns:* PO Box 19265, Springfield, IL 62794-6265

**Thomas Geale Publications Inc**
PO Box 370540, Montara, CA 94037-0540
*Tel:* 650-728-5219 *Toll Free Tel:* 800-554-5457 *Fax:* 650-728-0918
*E-mail:* justthink@comcast.net
*Key Personnel*
Pres: Sydney Tyler-Parker
Secy: Nancy L Geale
Founded: 1982
Curriculum for schools, preschool through grade 8; general educational materials, reading & thinking.
Number of titles published annually: 20 Print
Total Titles: 30 Print
Imprints: Just Think®; Stretch Think®; Thing Quest®; Young Think®
Foreign Rights: Nederlands Corp (Japan)
*Shipping Address:* 583 Sixth St, Montara, CA 94037

**§Thomas Nelson Inc**
Subsidiary of Faith Media
501 Nelson Place, Nashville, TN 37214

SAN: 209-3820
Mailing Address: PO Box 141000, Nashville, TN 37214-1000
*Tel:* 615-889-9000 *Toll Free Tel:* 800-251-4000 *Fax:* 615-902-1548
*E-mail:* publicity@thomasnelson.com
*Web Site:* www.thomasnelson.com
*Key Personnel*
Chmn: Michael Hyatt
CEO & Pres, Christian Publg Div: Mark Schoenwald
EVP & Chief Live Events Offr: Mary Graham
SVP, Book Publg: David Moberg
SVP & Chief Serv Offr: Vance Lawson
SVP, Specialty Publg: Laura Minchew
VP, Independent Christian Retail Sales: Russ Schwartz
VP, Marketing, Live Events: Patrick Koors
VP & Publr, Fiction Div: Daisy Hutton
Sr Dir, Mktg: Chad Cannon
Dir, Corp Communs: Casey Francis
Founded: 1798
Bibles & Testaments, trade, Christian & inspirational books, gift books, children's books & videos.
ISBN Prefix(es): 978-0-8407; 978-1-4047
Number of titles published annually: 600 Print
Total Titles: 3,500 Print; 6 CD-ROM; 30 Audio
Imprints: Max Lucado Books
Divisions: Grupo Nelson
Distributed by Winston-Derek
Distributor for Discovery House; Oliver-Nelson (Atlanta, GA)
Foreign Rep(s): Angela Gottlieb; Yvette Lopez; Harley Rollins; Snapdragon Productions; Lew Ullian
Foreign Rights: Winford Bluth
*Advertising Agency:* The Admasters
*Shipping Address:* 506 Nelson Place, Nashville, TN 37214
*See separate listing for:*
**Thomas Nelson Publishers**
**Tommy Nelson**

**Thomas Nelson Publishers**
Division of Thomas Nelson Inc
PO Box 141000, Nashville, TN 37214-1000
*Tel:* 615-889-9000 *Toll Free Tel:* 800-251-4000 *Fax:* 615-902-2129
*Web Site:* www.thomasnelson.com
*Key Personnel*
VP & Publr, Fiction Div: Daisy Hutton
Founded: 1951
Editing, marketing & distribution of Christian books, audio & video, Bibles.
ISBN Prefix(es): 978-0-8499
Number of titles published annually: 600 Print

**Thomas Publications**
3245 Fairfield Rd, Gettysburg, PA 17325
Mailing Address: PO Box 3031, Gettysburg, PA 17325
*Tel:* 717-642-6600 *Toll Free Tel:* 800-840-6782 *Fax:* 717-642-5555
*E-mail:* info@thomaspublications.com
*Web Site:* www.thomaspublications.com
*Key Personnel*
Owner: Dean S Thomas
Founded: 1986
Civil War, U Boats, historical, all nonfiction.
ISBN Prefix(es): 978-0-939631; 978-1-57747
Number of titles published annually: 5 Print
Total Titles: 200 Print

**Thomson Reuters Westlaw™**
610 Opperman Dr, Eagan, MN 55123
*Tel:* 651-687-7000 *Toll Free Tel:* 800-328-9352 (sales); 800-328-4880 (cust serv) *Fax:* 651-687-7302
*Web Site:* store.westlaw.com
*Key Personnel*
Pres, Legal Div: Mike Suchsland
Founded: 1804
Publisher of state statutes, attorney general opinions & practice manuals for the US & international.
ISBN Prefix(es): 978-0-8322; 978-0-7620; 978-0-8366; 978-0-87632
Number of titles published annually: 4 Print
*Branch Office(s)*
Aqueduct Bldg, Rochester, NY 14694 *Tel:* 585-546-5530 *Toll Free Tel:* 800-527-0430 *Fax:* 585-327-6269
Distributor for Law Library Microform Consortium
*Returns:* 545 Wescott Rd, Eagan, MN 55123

**Thorndike Press®**
Imprint of Gale
10 Water St, Suite 310, Waterville, ME 04901
*Toll Free Tel:* 800-233-1244 (ext 4, cust serv/orders); 800-877-4253 (cust serv) *Toll Free Fax:* 877-363-4253 (cust serv); 800-558-4676 (orders)
*E-mail:* gale.printorders@cengage.com; international@cengage.com (orders for customers outside US & CN)
*Web Site:* thorndike.gale.com
*Key Personnel*
Publr: Jamie Knobloch *E-mail:* jamie.knobloch@cengage.com
Edit Dir: Mary P Smith
Promos Assoc: Barb Littlefield
Founded: 1980
Large print titles for the public library market. Standard print original works in Western & mystery genres.
ISBN Prefix(es): 978-0-7862; 978-1-4104; 978-1-58724; 978-1-59414; 978-1-59413; 978-1-59415
Number of titles published annually: 1,500 Print
Total Titles: 4,000 Print
Imprints: Christian Large Print; Five Star; Kennebec Large Print; Large Print Press; Thorndike Large Print; Wheeler Publishing
Distributed by S & B Books Ltd (Canada)
Distributor for Grand Central/Hachette Large Print; HarperLuxe; Mills & Boon Large Print; Random House Large Print

**Threshold Editions**, see Gallery Books

**Tide-mark Press**
176 Broad St, Windsor, CT 06095
Mailing Address: PO Box 20, Windsor, CT 06095-0020
*Tel:* 860-683-4499 *Toll Free Tel:* 888-461-4619 *Fax:* 860-683-4055
*E-mail:* customerservice@tide-mark.com
*Web Site:* www.tidemarkpress.com
*Key Personnel*
Publr: Scott Kaeser *Tel:* 860-683-4499 ext 108 *E-mail:* scott@tide-mark.com
ISBN Prefix(es): 978-1-55949; 978-1-59490
Number of titles published annually: 4 Print
Total Titles: 24 Print
Foreign Rep(s): Gazelle (Europe)

**Tiger Tales**
5 River Rd, Suite 128, Wilton, CT 06897
SAN: 253-6382
*Tel:* 920-387-2333 *Fax:* 920-387-9994
*Web Site:* www.tigertalesbooks.com
*Key Personnel*
Dir, Sales: Barb Knight *E-mail:* barbknight@netwurx.net
Founded: 2000
Publish imaginative, entertaining hardcover & paperback picture books as well as board & novelty books for children ages 2-7. Committed to publishing children's books that will capture the imagination of children & adults alike.
ISBN Prefix(es): 978-1-58925
Number of titles published annually: 65 Print
Total Titles: 280 Print
*Sales Office(s):* PO Box 70, Iron Ridge, WI 53035
*Orders to:* PO Box 411037, Kansas City, MO 64141-1037, Contact: Vanessa Ottens *Tel:* 913-362-7400 *Fax:* 913-362-7401 *E-mail:* vanessa@midpt.com
*Returns:* 1263 Southwest Blvd, Kansas City, KS 66103 *Tel:* 913-362-7400 *Fax:* 913-362-7401 *E-mail:* warehouse@midpt.com
*Shipping Address:* 1263 Southwest Blvd, Kansas City, KS 66103, Contact: Linda Reeder *Tel:* 913-362-7400 *Fax:* 913-362-7401 *E-mail:* linda@midpt.com
*Warehouse:* 1263 Southwest Blvd, Kansas City, KS 66103, Contact: Linda Reeder *Tel:* 913-362-7400 *Fax:* 913-362-7401 *E-mail:* linda@midpt.com

**Tilbury House Publishers**
Imprint of WordSplice Studio LLC
103 Brunswick Ave, Gardiner, ME 04345
*Tel:* 207-582-1899 *Toll Free Tel:* 800-582-1899 (orders) *Fax:* 207-582-8227
*E-mail:* tilbury@tilburyhouse.com
*Web Site:* www.tilburyhouse.com
*Key Personnel*
Publr: Jennifer Bunting *Fax:* 207-582-8227
Sales Mgr: Donna Gerardo
Children's Book Ed: Audrey Maynard
Founded: 1990
ISBN Prefix(es): 978-0-88448
Number of titles published annually: 10 Print
Total Titles: 100 Print
Membership(s): ABA; IBPA, the Independent Book Publishers Association

**Timber Press Inc**
Subsidiary of Workman Publishing Co
133 SW Second Ave, Suite 450, Portland, OR 97204
SAN: 216-082X
*Tel:* 503-227-2878 *Toll Free Tel:* 800-327-5680 *Fax:* 503-227-3070
*E-mail:* info@timberpress.com
*Web Site:* www.timberpress.com
*Key Personnel*
Assoc Publr: Andrew Beckman
Ed-in-Chief: Tom Fischer
Trade & Gift Sales Mgr: Adrienne Franceschi
Founded: 1976
Gardening, horticulture, botany, natural history, Pacific Northwest regional.
ISBN Prefix(es): 978-0-88192
Number of titles published annually: 50 Print
Total Titles: 300 Print
Imprints: Timber Press
*Foreign Office(s):* 6a Lonsdale Rd, London NW6 6RD, United Kingdom, Contact: Anna Mumford *Tel:* (020) 7372 4601 *Fax:* (020) 7372 4601 *E-mail:* info@timberpress.co.uk
Distributed by Thomas Allen & Son

**§Time Being Books**
Imprint of Time Being Press
10411 Clayton Rd, Suites 201-203, St Louis, MO 63131
*Tel:* 314-432-1771 *Fax:* 314-432-7939
*E-mail:* tbbooks@sbcglobal.net
*Web Site:* www.timebeing.com
*Key Personnel*
Mng Ed: Jerry Call *E-mail:* tbbookseditor@sbcglobal.net
Off Mgr & Asst Ed: Trilogy Mattson
Founded: 1988
No authorization required for returns - books must be returned within one year of invoice date.
ISBN Prefix(es): 978-1-877770; 978-1-56809
Number of titles published annually: 6 Print; 6 Online; 8 E-Book
Total Titles: 113 Print; 113 Online; 14 E-Book; 11 Audio

*Distribution Center:* Amazon.com, 440 Terry Ave N, Seattle, WA 98901
BarnesandNoble.com
Follett Library Resources, 1340 Ridgeview Dr, McHenry, IL 60050 *Toll Free Tel:* 888-511-5114 *E-mail:* customerservice@flr.follett.com
Small Press Distribution, 1341 Seventh St, Berkely, CA 94710-1409

**TLC**, see THE Learning Connection®

**The Toby Press LLC**
2 Great Pasture Rd, Danbury, CT 06810
Mailing Address: PO Box 8531, New Milford, CT 06776-8531 SAN: 253-9985
*Tel:* 203-830-8508 *Fax:* 203-830-8512
*E-mail:* toby@tobypress.com
*Web Site:* www.tobypress.com; www.korenpub.com
*Key Personnel*
Publr: Matthew Miller
Sales Dir: Daniel Mishkin
Founded: 1999
Publish fiction, essays & literature.
ISBN Prefix(es): 978-1-902881; 978-1-59264
Number of titles published annually: 37 Print
Total Titles: 800 Print
Imprints: Koren; Maggid; Steinsaltz
*Shipping Address:* Focus Mailing, 2 Great Pasture Rd, Danbury, CT 06810 *Tel:* 203-830-8500 *Fax:* 203-830-2516
*Warehouse:* Focus Mailing, 2 Great Pasture Rd, Danbury, CT 06810 *Tel:* 203-830-8500 *Fax:* 203-830-2516
*Distribution Center:* Focus Mailing, 2 Great Pasture Rd, Danbury, CT 06810 *Tel:* 203-830-8500 *Fax:* 203-830-2516
Baker & Taylor, 2550 W Tyvola Rd, Suite 300, Charlotte, NC 28217 *Tel:* 714-998-3100 *Toll Free Tel:* 800-775-1800 *Fax:* 704-998-3319
Brodart, 500 Arch St, Williamsport, PA 17701 *Tel:* 570-326-2461 *Toll Free Tel:* 800-999-6799 *Fax:* 570-326-1479
Ingram, One Ingram Blvd, La Vergne, TN 37086 *Toll Free Tel:* 800-400-5351

**§Todd Publications**
3500 NE Sixth Dr, Boca Raton, FL 33431
SAN: 207-0804
*Tel:* 561-910-0440 *Fax:* 561-910-0440
*E-mail:* toddpub@aol.com
*Key Personnel*
Owner & Publr: Barry Klein
Founded: 1973
Directories & reference books to the trade. Returns accepted within 30 days when in resalable condition.
ISBN Prefix(es): 978-0-87340; 978-0-915344
Number of titles published annually: 10 Print; 2 CD-ROM
Total Titles: 15 Print; 2 CD-ROM

**Tommy Nelson**
Division of Thomas Nelson Inc
501 Nelson Place, Nashville, TN 37214
Mailing Address: PO Box 141000, Nashville, TN 37214-1000
*Tel:* 615-889-9000 *Toll Free Tel:* 800-251-4000 *Fax:* 615-391-5225
*Web Site:* www.tommynelson.com
*Key Personnel*
Chmn of the Bd: Michael Hyatt
CEO: Mark Schoenwald
Founded: 1984
Inspirational children's books for evangelical & secular marketplace & other products.
ISBN Prefix(es): 978-0-8499; 978-1-4003
Number of titles published annually: 75 Print; 10 Audio
Total Titles: 200 Print; 8 E-Book; 50 Audio

**§Top of the Mountain Publishing**
Division of Powell Productions
PO Box 2244, Pinellas Park, FL 33780-2244
SAN: 287-590X
*Tel:* 727-391-3958
*E-mail:* tag@abcinfo.com; info@abcinfo.com
*Web Site:* abcinfo.com; www.topofthemountain.com
*Key Personnel*
Dir: Judith Powell *E-mail:* judi@abcinfo.com; Tag Powell
Intl Rts & Lib Sales Dir: Sharon Boulder
PR: Lance Wilson
Founded: 1979
Exhibits at international, national bookfairs, BFA, Frankfurt Book Fairs; no unsol mss.
ISBN Prefix(es): 978-0-914295; 978-1-56087
Number of titles published annually: 6 Print; 100 Audio
Total Titles: 23 Print; 12 CD-ROM
*Advertising Agency:* Powell Productions
*Shipping Address:* 4837 62 St N, Kenneth City, FL 33709
*Distribution Center:* Ingram Book Co
New Leaf Distributing Co

**§Top Publications Ltd**
12221 Merit Dr, Suite 950, Dallas, TX 75251
*Tel:* 972-628-6414 *Fax:* 972-233-0713
*E-mail:* info@toppub.com
*Web Site:* toppub.com
*Key Personnel*
Mgr: Bill Manchee
Founded: 1999
Number of titles published annually: 3 Print; 2 CD-ROM; 3 E-Book; 2 Audio
Total Titles: 55 Print; 19 CD-ROM; 55 E-Book; 19 Audio
Imprints: TOP
*Orders to:* Ingram Book Co, One Ingram Blvd, Lavergne, TN 37086-3650 *Web Site:* ipage.ingrambook.com
*Warehouse:* 2427 Bond St, University Park, IL 60950
Membership(s): IBPA, the Independent Book Publishers Association

**Tor Books**, see Tom Doherty Associates, LLC

**Torah Aura Productions**
4423 Fruitland Ave, Los Angeles, CA 90058
*Tel:* 323-585-7312 *Toll Free Tel:* 800-238-6724 *Fax:* 323-585-0327
*E-mail:* misrad@torahaura.com; orders@torahaura.com
*Web Site:* www.torahaura.com
*Key Personnel*
Pres: Alan Rowe *E-mail:* alan@torahaura.com
Founded: 1981
Textbooks, Judaica.
ISBN Prefix(es): 978-0-933873; 978-0-943527
Number of titles published annually: 30 Print
Total Titles: 500 Print
Distributor for Free Spirit (selected titles)

**Torah Umesorah Publications**
Division of Torah Umesorah-National Society for Hebrew Day Schools
620 Foster Ave, Brooklyn, NY 11230
*Tel:* 718-259-1223 *Fax:* 718-259-1795
*E-mail:* publications@torah-umesorah.org
*Key Personnel*
Dir, Pubns: Shmuel Yaakov Klein
Founded: 1946
Text teaching aids & visual aids for Yeshiva-day schools & Hebrew schools, students & teachers; posters & workbooks.
ISBN Prefix(es): 978-0-914131
Number of titles published annually: 5 Print
Total Titles: 82 Print
Foreign Rep(s): Chaim Turkel Volume Distributors (UK)

**Tortuga Press**
2777 Yulupa Ave, PMB 181, Santa Rosa, CA 95405
SAN: 299-1756
*Tel:* 707-544-4720 *Toll Free Tel:* 866-4TORTUGA (486-7884) *Fax:* 707-544-5609
*E-mail:* info@tortugapress.com
*Web Site:* www.tortugapress.com
*Key Personnel*
Publr: Matthew Gollub *E-mail:* mg@tortugapress.com
Off Mgr: Simone Peters
Founded: 1997
Creator of award-winning children's literature & multi-media products to delight & open young people's minds.
ISBN Prefix(es): 978-1-889910
Number of titles published annually: 4 Print; 2 Audio
Total Titles: 16 Print; 7 Audio
*Warehouse:* Anchor Mini Storage, 220 Business Park Dr, Rohnert Park, CA 94928 *Tel:* 707-588-1919 *Fax:* 707-588-9330
Membership(s): California Association of Bilingual Education; California School Library Association; IBPA, the Independent Book Publishers Association; TLA

**§TotalRecall Publications Inc**
1103 Middlecreek, Friendswood, TX 77546
*Tel:* 281-992-3131
*E-mail:* sales@totalrecallpress.com
*Web Site:* www.totalrecallpress.com
*Key Personnel*
Pres: Bruce Moran *E-mail:* bruce@totalrecallpress.com
Gen Mgr: Corby Tate *E-mail:* corby@totalrecallpress.com
Mktg Dir: Terri Mitchem *Tel:* 352-596-1192 *E-mail:* mtmitchem@aol.com
Founded: 1999
Publish nonfiction books in a variety of professional fields, including computer & financial certification exam preparation & library education with many titles adopted as college texts. The exam preparation study guides offer free downloads of a proprietary interactive test engine that generates randomized mock exams designed to identify a candidate's strengths & weaknesses & determine where to allocate study time. These titles are also distributed electronically to libraries, corporations & government agencies via NetLibrary, ebrary & Books24x7.com. The company is now expanding into fiction, especially mystery/thrillers & launched three mystery series in 2008-2009 with several more series currently in development. Other areas of expansion include self-help, travel & religion.
ISBN Prefix(es): 978-1-59095
Number of titles published annually: 20 Print; 10 Online; 20 E-Book
Total Titles: 250 Print; 120 Online; 250 E-Book
Membership(s): International Thriller Writers Inc; Mystery Writers of America

**Touchstone**
Imprint of Scribner Publishing Group
1230 Avenue of the Americas, New York, NY 10020
*Key Personnel*
Pres: Susan Moldow
VP & Publr: Stacy Creamer
Assoc Publr: David Falk
VP & Dir, Subs Rts: Paul O'Halloran
Art Dir: Cherlynne Li
Mktg Mgr: Meredith Vilarello
Online Mktg Mgr: Ana Paula De Lima
Asst Dir, Subs Rts: Marie Florio
Edit Dir: Sally Kim
Sr Ed: Michelle Howry; Matthew Benjamin
Ed: Lauren Spiegel

Edit Asst: Miya Kumangai; Brendan Culliton; Melissa Vipperman Cohen
Publr's Asst: Emily Cavedon
ISBN Prefix(es): 978-0-684
Number of titles published annually: 60 Print
Imprints: Libros en Espanol; Touchstone
Foreign Rights: Akcali Copyright Agency (Turkey); Antonella Antonelli Agenzia (Italy); Book Publishers Association of Israel (Israel); Japan UNI Agency (Japan); JLM Literary Agency (Greece); KCC (Korea Copyright Center); Mohrbooks Literary Agency (Germany); La Nouvelle Agence; Andrew Nurnberg Associates (Bulgaria, Croatia, Czech Republic, Estonia, Hungary, Latvia, Lithuania, Montenegro, Poland, Romania, Russia, Serbia, Slovakia, Slovenia); Sane Toregard Agency (Denmark, Finland, Iceland, Norway, Sweden); Sebes & Van Gelderen Literary Agency (Netherlands); Tuttle-Mori Agency Inc (Thailand)

**§Tower Publishing Co**
588 Saco Rd, Standish, ME 04084
*Tel:* 207-642-5400 *Toll Free Tel:* 800-969-8693 *Fax:* 207-264-3870
*E-mail:* info@towerpub.com
*Web Site:* www.towerpub.com
*Key Personnel*
Publr: Michael Lyons
Mng Ed: Mary Anne Hildreth
Business & manufacturing directories, law publications, business databases.
ISBN Prefix(es): 978-0-89442
Number of titles published annually: 20 Print

**Tracks Publishing**
140 Brightwood Ave, Chula Vista, CA 91910
*Tel:* 619-476-7125 *Toll Free Tel:* 800-443-3570 *Fax:* 619-476-8173
*E-mail:* tracks@cox.net
*Web Site:* www.startupsports.com
Founded: 1993
ISBN Prefix(es): 978-1-884654; 978-1-935937
Number of titles published annually: 2 Print; 6 E-Book
Total Titles: 35 Print; 105 E-Book
*Distribution Center:* IPG, 814 N Franklin St, Chicago, IL 60610 *Tel:* 312-337-0747 *Fax:* 312-337-5985
Membership(s): IBPA, the Independent Book Publishers Association

**Trafalgar Square Books**
388 Howe Hill Rd, North Pomfret, VT 05053
SAN: 213-8859
Mailing Address: PO Box 257, North Pomfret, VT 05053-0257
*Tel:* 802-457-1911 *Toll Free Tel:* 800-423-4525 *Fax:* 802-457-1913
*E-mail:* tsquare@sover.net; info@trafalgarbooks.com
*Web Site:* www.trafalgarbooks.com; www.horseandriderbooks.com
*Key Personnel*
Pres & Publr: Caroline Robbins
Mng Dir: Martha Cook *E-mail:* mcook@sover.net
Dir, Mktg & Promo: Kim Cook *E-mail:* kimcook@sover.net
Sr Ed: Rebecca Didier *E-mail:* rdidier@sover.net
Founded: 1972
ISBN Prefix(es): 978-0-943955; 978-1-57076
Number of titles published annually: 25 Print
Total Titles: 300 Print
Distributed by IPG
Distributor for J A Allen; Atlantic Books; Beautiful Books; Bene Factum Publishing; Elliott & Thompson; Peter Owen Publishers; Pitch Publishing

**Trafford**
Division of Author Solutions Inc
1663 Liberty Dr, Bloomington, IN 47403
*Toll Free Tel:* 888-232-4444
*E-mail:* customersupport@trafford.com
*Web Site:* www.trafford.com
*Key Personnel*
CEO & Pres: Andrew Phillips
SVP, Mktg: Keith Ogorek
SVP, Prodn Servs & Output Opers: Bill Becher
SVP, Worldwide Sales: Don Seitz
Media Mgr: Kevin Gray *Tel:* 812-339-6000 *E-mail:* kgray@authorsolutions.com
Founded: 1995
The first company in the world to offer an "on-demand publishing service" & led the independent publishing revolution since its establishment. One of the earliest publishers to utilize the Internet for selling books. More than 10,000 authors from over 120 countries have utilized Trafford's experience for self-publishing their books.
This publisher has indicated that 100% of their product line is author subsidized.
ISBN Prefix(es): 978-1-55369; 978-1-55212; 978-1-55395; 978-1-4120; 978-1-4122; 978-1-4251
Number of titles published annually: 800 Print
Total Titles: 2,243 Print
*Distribution Center:* Baker & Taylor Inc, 2550 W Tyvola Rd, Suite 300, Charlotte, NC 28217 *Tel:* 704-998-3100 *Toll Free Tel:* 800-775-1800 *E-mail:* btinfo@baker-taylor.com *Web Site:* www.btol.com
Ingram Book Group, One Ingram Blvd, La Vergne, TN 37086 *Tel:* 615-793-5000 *Toll Free Tel:* 800-937-8200 *E-mail:* customer.service@ingrambook.com *Web Site:* www.ingrambook.com
Membership(s): ABA; Canadian Booksellers Association

**Trails Books**
Division of Big Earth Publishing
3005 Center Green Dr, Suite 225, Boulder, CO 80301
*Tel:* 303-541-1506 *Toll Free Tel:* 800-258-5830
*E-mail:* books@bigearthpublishing.com
*Web Site:* www.trailsbooks.com
*Key Personnel*
Publr: Linda Doyle
Founded: 1970
Regional trade books-Wisconsin & Upper Great Lakes, travel guide books.
ISBN Prefix(es): 978-1-879483; 978-1-931599; 978-0-915024
Number of titles published annually: 20 Print
Total Titles: 120 Print
Imprints: Acorn Guides; Prairie Classics; Prairie Oak Press; Quiz Master Books (pop culture trivia); Trails Books Guide
Membership(s): Midwest Independent Booksellers Association

**Training Resource Network Inc (TRN)**
PO Box 439, St Augustine, FL 32085-0439
SAN: 299-2647
*Tel:* 904-823-9800 (cust serv) *Toll Free Tel:* 800-280-7010 (orders) *Fax:* 904-823-3554
*E-mail:* customerservice@trninc.com
*Web Site:* www.trn-store.com
*Key Personnel*
Sr Ed: Dawn Langton *E-mail:* dawnl@trninc.com
Founded: 1990
Publisher & distributor.
ISBN Prefix(es): 978-1-883302
Number of titles published annually: 4 Print
Total Titles: 20 Print
*Returns:* 316 Saint George St, St Augustine, FL 32084
Membership(s): Public Relations Society of America

**Tralco-Lingo Fun**
3909 Witmer Rd, Suite 856, Niagara Falls, NY 14305
*Tel:* 905-575-5717 *Toll Free Tel:* 888-487-2526 *Fax:* 905-575-1783 *Toll Free Fax:* 866-487-2527
*E-mail:* contact@tralco.com
*Web Site:* www.tralco.com
*Key Personnel*
Owner & Pres: Karen Traynor *E-mail:* karen@tralco.com
Founded: 1982
Publisher & distributor of second language educational materials.
ISBN Prefix(es): 978-0-921376
Number of titles published annually: 10 Print; 12 CD-ROM
Total Titles: 300 Print
*Branch Office(s)*
1030 Upper James St, Suite 101, Hamilton, ON L9C 6X6, Canada
Distributor for Languages for Kids
Membership(s): National School Supply & Equipment Association

**Trans-Atlantic Publications Inc**
311 Bainbridge St, Philadelphia, PA 19147
SAN: 694-0234
*Tel:* 215-925-5083 *Fax:* 215-925-1912
*Web Site:* www.transatlanticpub.com; www.businesstitles.com
*Key Personnel*
Pres & Intl Rts: Ronald Smolin
Mgr: Jeff Goldstein *E-mail:* jeffgolds@comcast.net
Founded: 1984
Popular culture.
ISBN Prefix(es): 978-0-13; 978-0-340 (Hodder Education); 978-0-330; 978-0-333; 978-0-283; 978-0-7487; 978-0-85950; 978-1-85776; 978-1-87403; 978-1-85486; 978-0-7522; 978-1-891696; 978-0-273; 978-0-174; 978-0-85242; 978-1-4441
Number of titles published annually: 200 Print
Total Titles: 2,500 Print
Imprints: BainBridgeBooks
Distributor for Book Guild; Book House; Financial Times Publishing; Hodder Education; Instituto Monsa de Ediciones SA (art books from Spain); Longman; Midwest Library Service; Nexus Special Interests; Pearson Education; Nelson Thornes

**Trans Tech Publications**
c/o Enfield Distribution Co, 234 May St, Enfield, NH 03748
Mailing Address: PO Box 699, Enfield, NH 03748-0699
*Tel:* 603-632-7377 *Fax:* 603-632-5611
*E-mail:* usa-ttp@ttp.net; info@enfieldbooks.com
*Web Site:* www.ttp.net
*Key Personnel*
Owner & VP: Thomas Woehlbier *E-mail:* t.woehlbier@ttp.net
Intl Rts: Fred Woehlbier *E-mail:* f.woehlbier@ttp.net
Dir, US Dist: Linda Jones
Founded: 1967
Materials sciences & engineering.
ISBN Prefix(es): 978-0-87849; 978-3-908450
Number of titles published annually: 150 Print
Total Titles: 900 Print
Imprints: Scitec Publications
*Foreign Office(s):* Kreuzstr 10, 8635 Durnten-Zurich, Switzerland *Tel:* (041) 44922 1033 *E-mail:* info@ttp.net
Distributed by Curran Associates Inc; Yankee Book Peddler
Distributor for Enfield Publishers

**Transaction Publishers Inc**
10 Corporate Place S, 35 Berrue Circle, Piscataway, NJ 08854
*Tel:* 732-445-2280; 732-445-1245 (orders) *Toll Free Tel:* 888-999-6778 (dist ctr) *Fax:* 732-445-3138

*E-mail:* trans@transactionpub.com; orders@transactionpub.om
*Web Site:* www.transactionpub.com
*Key Personnel*
Chmn of the Bd: Irving Louis Horowitz
*E-mail:* ihorowitz@transactionpub.com
Pres: Mary E Curtis *E-mail:* mcurtis@transactionpub.com
Mktg Mgr: Mindy Waizer *E-mail:* mwaizer@transactionpub.com
Order Dept Mgr: Nancy Conine
IT Mgr: Jeffrey Stetz
Rts & Perms Mgr: Maureen Feldman
Founded: 1962
Independent publisher of books & serials in all disciplines of the social sciences & related areas.
ISBN Prefix(es): 978-0-202 (Aldine Transaction); 978-1-56000; 978-0-87855; 978-0-88738; 978-0-7658; 978-1-4128
Number of titles published annually: 200 Print; 100 E-Book
Total Titles: 6,200 Print
Imprints: Aldine Transaction; Center for Urban Policy Research; Transaction Large Print
Distributor for Bridge 21; International Communication Organization (ICO); IWGIA; The Netherlands Institute for Social Research; Ontos Verlag; Editions Scholasticae; Studien Verlag; Witwatersrand University Press
Foreign Rights: The Azano Agency (Mr Kiyoshi Azano) (Japan); Eliane Benisti Agent Litteraire (Eliane Benisti) (France); Big-Apple Tuttle-Mori Agency (Vinelle Pan) (Taiwan); Big-Apple Tuttle-Mori Agency (Lily Chen) (China); International Editors' Co (Isabel Monteagudo) (Spain); International Editors' Co (Flavia Sala) (Brazil); International Editors' Co (Nicolas Costa) (Argentina, Latin America); Korea Copyright Center Inc (Korea); Prava i Prevodi Literary Agency (Mr Predrog Milenkovic) (Bulgaria, Greece, Poland, Romania, Russia, Serbia)
*Advertising Agency:* Paine-Whitman Agency
*Warehouse:* Raritan Ctr, 300 McGaw Dr, Edison, NJ 08837

**Transcontinental Music Publications**
Division of Union for Reform Judaism
633 Third Ave, New York, NY 10017
*Tel:* 212-650-4101; 212-650-4120
*Toll Free Tel:* 888-489-8242 (orders) *Fax:* 212-650-4119
*E-mail:* tmp@urj.org; press@urj.org
*Web Site:* www.transcontinentalmusic.com
*Key Personnel*
Music Ed: Jayson Rodovsky
Music Libn/Edit Asst: Rachel Wetstein
Founded: 1938
Publishers of Jewish music.
ISBN Prefix(es): 978-1-8074
Number of titles published annually: 50 Print; 5 Audio
Total Titles: 1,000 Print; 75 Audio
Imprints: Cantors Assembly; Hazamir; Sacred Music Press; Theophilis
Membership(s): Magazine Publishers of America; National Music Publishers' Association

**§Transportation Research Board**
Division of The National Academies
500 Fifth St NW, Washington, DC 20001
Mailing Address: Lock Box 289, Washington, DC 20055
*Tel:* 202-334-2934; 202-334-3213 (orders); 202-334-3072 (subns) *Fax:* 202-334-2519
*E-mail:* trbsales@nas.edu
*Web Site:* trb.org
*Key Personnel*
Mgr, Pubn Sales & Affilliate Servs: Andrea Kisiner *Tel:* 202-334-3214
Founded: 1920
Research results, TRR (online journal), bibliographies & abstracts on books pertaining to civil engineering, public transit, aviation, freight, transportation administration & economics & transportation law.
ISBN Prefix(es): 978-0-309
Number of titles published annually: 150 Print; 5 CD-ROM; 100 Online
Total Titles: 2,300 Print; 40 CD-ROM; 1,000 Online
Imprints: National Cooperative Highway Research Program; Transit Cooperative Research Program

**Travel Keys**
PO Box 160691, Sacramento, CA 95816-0691
SAN: 682-2452
Mailing Address: PO Box 162266, Sacramento, CA 95816-2266
*Tel:* 916-452-5200 *Fax:* 916-452-5200
*Key Personnel*
Publr & Ed: Peter B Manston
Ed: Robert C Bynum
Founded: 1984
How-to travel books & antique guides; travel books worldwide; newsletter about travel books.
ISBN Prefix(es): 978-0-931367
Number of titles published annually: 6 Print
Total Titles: 19 Print
*Advertising Agency:* Travel Key Media, 2510 "S" St, Sacramento, CA 95816-7307 *Tel:* 916-452-5200
*Shipping Address:* Travel Key Media, 2510 "S" St, Sacramento, CA 95816-7307 *Tel:* 916-452-5200

**Travelers' Tales**
Subsidiary of Solas House Inc
2320 Bowdoin St, Palo Alto, CA 94306
*Tel:* 650-462-2110 *Fax:* 650-462-6305
*E-mail:* ttales@travelerstales.com
*Web Site:* www.travelerstales.com
*Key Personnel*
Publr: James O'Reilly
Exec Ed: Larry Habegger
Ed-at-Large: Sean O'Reilly
Founded: 1992
Sponsors annual Solas Awards for Best Travel Writing. For more information see www.besttravelwriting.com.
ISBN Prefix(es): 978-1-885211; 978-1-932361
Number of titles published annually: 8 Print; 10 E-Book
Total Titles: 135 Print
*Sales Office(s):* Publishers Group West, 1700 Fourth St, Berkeley, CA 94710 *Tel:* 510-528-1444 *Fax:* 510-528-3444
*Billing Address:* Publishers Group West, 1700 Fourth St, Berkeley, CA 94710 *Tel:* 510-528-1444 *Fax:* 510-528-3444
*Orders to:* Publishers Group West, 1700 Fourth St, Berkeley, CA 94710 *Tel:* 510-528-1444 *Fax:* 510-528-3444
*Shipping Address:* Perseus PGW, 193 Edwards Dr, Jackson, TN 38301 *Toll Free Tel:* 800-343-4499
*Warehouse:* Publishers Group West, 1700 Fourth St, Berkeley, CA 94710 *Tel:* 510-528-1444 *Fax:* 510-528-3444
*Distribution Center:* Publishers Group West, 1700 Fourth St, Berkeley, CA 94710 *Tel:* 510-528-1444 *Fax:* 510-528-3444

**Treasure Bay Inc**
PO Box 119, Novato, CA 94948
*Tel:* 415-884-2888 *Fax:* 415-884-2840
*E-mail:* webothread@comcast.net
*Web Site:* www.webothread.com
*Key Personnel*
Pres: Don Panec
Founded: 1997
Publish educational children's books, that specialize in books for parent involvement in reading.
ISBN Prefix(es): 978-1-891327; 978-1-60115
Number of titles published annually: 12 Print
Total Titles: 100 Print

**Treehaus Communications Inc**
906 W Loveland Ave, Loveland, OH 45140
Mailing Address: PO Box 249, Loveland, OH 45140-0249
*Tel:* 513-683-5716 *Toll Free Tel:* 800-638-4287 (orders) *Fax:* 513-683-2882 (orders)
*E-mail:* treehaus@treehaus1.com
*Web Site:* www.treehaus1.com
*Key Personnel*
Pres: Gerard A Pottebaum
Founded: 1973
Children's books, liturgical & catechetical material for children & adults.
ISBN Prefix(es): 978-0-929496; 978-1-886510
Number of titles published annually: 6 Print
Total Titles: 55 Print

**Triad Publishing Co**
Imprint of Triad Communications Ltd
PO Box 13355, Gainesville, FL 32604
*Tel:* 352-373-5800 *Fax:* 352-373-1488
*Toll Free Fax:* 800-854-4947
*E-mail:* orders@triadpublishing.com
*Web Site:* www.triadpublishing.com
*Key Personnel*
Chmn of the Bd & Publr: Lorna Rubin
*E-mail:* lorna@triadpublishing.com
Treas: Melvin L Rubin
Order Dept & Cust Rel: Donna L Hamon
*E-mail:* donna@triadpublishing.com
Founded: 1978
Consumer health & medical education for professionals.
ISBN Prefix(es): 978-0-937404
Number of titles published annually: 3 Print; 1 CD-ROM
Total Titles: 25 Print; 2 CD-ROM
*Returns:* IFM Services, 2302 Kanawha Terr, St Albans, WV 25177-3212
*Shipping Address:* IFM Services, 2302 Kanawha Terr, St Albans, WV 25177-3212
Membership(s): The Association of Publishers for Special Sales; IBPA, the Independent Book Publishers Association; National Association of Science Writers

**Trident Inc**
885 Pierce Butler Rte, St Paul, MN 55104
*Tel:* 651-638-0077 *Fax:* 651-638-0084
*E-mail:* info@atlas-games.com
*Web Site:* www.atlas-games.com
*Key Personnel*
Pres & Intl Rts: John Nephew
Founded: 1990
Role-playing games, card games.
ISBN Prefix(es): 978-1-887801
Number of titles published annually: 20 Print
Total Titles: 120 Print
Imprints: Atlas Games

**Trigram Music Inc**, see Wimbledon Music Inc & Trigram Music Inc

**The Trinity Foundation**
PO Box 68, Unicoi, TN 37692-0068
*Tel:* 423-743-0199 *Fax:* 423-743-2005
*Web Site:* www.trinityfoundation.org
*Key Personnel*
Pres & Dir: Thomas W Juodaitis
*E-mail:* tjtrinityfound@aol.com
Founded: 1977
Scholarly Christian books.
ISBN Prefix(es): 978-0-940931; 978-1-891777
Number of titles published annually: 5 Print; 3 E-Book
Total Titles: 67 Print; 1 CD-ROM; 3 E-Book

**Trinity University Press**
Unit of Trinity University
One Trinity Place, San Antonio, TX 78212-7200
*Tel:* 210-999-8884 *Fax:* 210-999-8838
*E-mail:* books@trinity.edu
*Web Site:* www.tupress.org
*Key Personnel*
Dir: Barbara Ras
Mng Ed: Sarah Nawrocki
Assoc Dir, Sales & Mktg: Thomas Payton
Busn Mgr: Lee Ann Sparks
Mktg Mgr: Ms Burgin Streetman
Founded: 2002 (after 14 years of inoperation)
Publish titles for the general trade & academic markets.
ISBN Prefix(es): 978-1-59534; 978-0-911536
Number of titles published annually: 12 Print; 12 E-Book
Total Titles: 80 Print; 80 E-Book
*Distribution Center:* Publishers Group West, 1700 Fourth St, Berkeley, CA 94710 (booksellers & libraries) *Toll Free Tel:* 800-788-3123 *Fax:* 510-528-3614

**TripBuilder Media Inc**
15 Oak St, Westport, CT 06880-2027
SAN: 297-7893
*Tel:* 203-227-1255 *Toll Free Tel:* 800-525-9745 *Fax:* 203-227-1257
*E-mail:* info@tripbuilder.com
*Web Site:* www.tripbuilder.com
*Key Personnel*
Pres: Nancy Judson *E-mail:* njudson@tripbuilder.com
EVP: Steven Tanzer
Founded: 1989
Travel guides.
ISBN Prefix(es): 978-1-56621
Number of titles published annually: 20 Print

**TriQuarterly Books**
Imprint of Northwestern University Press
629 Noyes St, Evanston, IL 60201
*Toll Free Tel:* 800-621-2736 (orders only) *Fax:* 847-467-2096
*E-mail:* nupress@northwestern.edu
*Web Site:* www.nupress.northwestern.edu
*Key Personnel*
Dir: Jane Bunker *Tel:* 847-491-8111 *E-mail:* j-bunker@northwestern.edu
Founded: 1989
Special attention to new writing talent, the non-commercial work of established writers & writing in translation. Special emphasis on poetry.
ISBN Prefix(es): 978-0-8101
Number of titles published annually: 6 Print
Total Titles: 75 Print

**TriQuarterly Books**, see Northwestern University Press

**TRISTAN Publishing**
2355 Louisiana Ave, Minneapolis, MN 55427
*Tel:* 763-545-1383 *Toll Free Tel:* 866-545-1383 *Fax:* 763-545-1387
*E-mail:* info@tristanpublishing.com
*Web Site:* www.tristanpublishing.com
*Key Personnel*
Owner & Publr: Brett Waldman *E-mail:* bwaldman@tristanpublishing.com
Owner & VP Sales, Mktg & Relationships: Sheila Waldman *E-mail:* swaldman@tristanpublishing.com
Cont: Roger Challman *E-mail:* rchallman@tristanpublishing.com
Founded: 2002
Exquisite gift books that inspire, uplift & touch lives.
ISBN Prefix(es): 978-0-931674
Number of titles published annually: 6 Print
Total Titles: 40 Print; 2 Audio
Imprints: TRISTAN OUTDOORS; Waldman House Press

**Triumph Books**
814 N Franklin St, Chicago, IL 60610
*Toll Free Tel:* 800-888-4741 (orders only) *Fax:* 312-663-3557
*Web Site:* www.triumphbooks.com
*Key Personnel*
Publr: Mitch Rogatz
Edit Dir: Tom Bast
Dir, Sales: Phil Springstead
Mktg Mgr: Tom Galvin
Founded: 1989
Leading publisher of sports titles & official rule books of NFL, NHL, MLB, NCAA, among others.
ISBN Prefix(es): 978-0-9624436; 978-1-880141; 978-1-57243; 978-1-892049 (Benchmark Press); 978-1-60078; 978-1-62368; 978-1-61749
Number of titles published annually: 95 Print; 75 E-Book
Total Titles: 600 Print; 100 E-Book
Imprints: Benchmark Press; Triumph Entertainment
Foreign Rep(s): Monarch Books of Canada (Canada); Peribo Pty Ltd (Australia, New Zealand)
Foreign Rights: RoundHouse Publishing Ltd (Europe, UK)
*Distribution Center:* Independent Publishers Group (IPG), 814 N Franklin St, Chicago, IL 60610 *Web Site:* www.ipgbook.com
Membership(s): ABA

**§Triumph Learning**
Division of Haights Cross Communications Inc
136 Madison Ave, 7th fl, New York, NY 10016
*Tel:* 212-652-0200 *Toll Free Tel:* 800-221-9372 (cust serv) *Toll Free Fax:* 866-805-5723
*E-mail:* info@triumphlearning.com; customerservice@triumphlearning.com
*Web Site:* www.triumphlearning.com
*Key Personnel*
Pres: Kevin McAliley *Tel:* 212-652-0222 *E-mail:* kmcaliley@triumphlearning.com
CFO & COO: Brian Gurley *Tel:* 212-652-0252 *E-mail:* bgurley@triumphlearning.com
EVP, Sales & Mktg: Ken Butkus *Tel:* 212-652-0234 *E-mail:* kbutkus@triumphlearning.com
EVP, Prod Devt: Linda Sanford *Tel:* 212-652-0279 *E-mail:* lsanford@triumphlearning.com
SVP, Prodn & Technol: Karen Emerson *Tel:* 212-652-0212
SVP, Sales: Marc Keller *E-mail:* mkeller@triumphlearning.com
Founded: 1964
K-12 supplementary publisher that creates standards-based skill building & test prep products, which are highly aligned to state & national assessments.
ISBN Prefix(es): 978-0-87694; 978-1-58620; 978-1-59823
Number of titles published annually: 150 Print; 40 CD-ROM
Total Titles: 1,000 Print; 40 CD-ROM
Imprints: Coach; Jumpstart; Ladders; Workout
*Warehouse:* One Beeman Rd, Northborough, MA 01532
Membership(s): AAP

**Truman State University Press**
Unit of Truman State University
100 E Normal Ave, Kirksville, MO 63501-4221
*Tel:* 660-785-7336 *Toll Free Tel:* 800-916-6802 *Fax:* 660-785-4480
*E-mail:* tsup@truman.edu
*Web Site:* tsup.truman.edu
*Key Personnel*
Dir & Ed-in-Chief: Nancy Rediger *E-mail:* nancyr@truman.edu
Founded: 1986
University Press, scholarly, early modern studies, American studies, regional & general titles, contemporary nonfiction & poetry.
ISBN Prefix(es): 978-0-940474; 978-0-943549; 978-1-931112; 978-1-935503
Number of titles published annually: 12 Print; 15 E-Book
Total Titles: 175 Print; 50 E-Book
Foreign Rep(s): Gazelle Book Services (Europe); Scholarly Book Services (Canada)
Membership(s): PMA International

**TSG Foundation**, see TSG Publishing Foundation Inc

**§TSG Publishing Foundation Inc**
28641 N 63 Place, Cave Creek, AZ 85331
SAN: 250-6726
Mailing Address: PO Box 7068, Cave Creek, AZ 85237-7068
*Tel:* 480-502-1909 *Fax:* 480-502-0713
*E-mail:* info@tsgfoundation.org
*Web Site:* www.tsgfoundation.org
*Key Personnel*
Pres & Intl Rts: Gita Saraydarian
Founded: 1987
Publish & sell books by Torkom Saraydarian, spiritual training center.
ISBN Prefix(es): 978-0-929874; 978-0-911794; 978-0-9656203
Number of titles published annually: 3 Print
Total Titles: 120 Print; 1 CD-ROM
Foreign Rep(s): TSG (UK) Ltd (Europe, UK)

**Tudor Publishers Inc**
3109 Shady Lawn Dr, Greensboro, NC 27408
*Tel:* 336-288-5395
*E-mail:* tudorpublishers@triad.rr.com
*Key Personnel*
Pres: Eugene E Pfaff, Jr
Sr Publr: Pamela Cocks
Assoc Ed: Nancy Strange
Founded: 1985
ISBN Prefix(es): 978-0-936389
Number of titles published annually: 12 Print
Total Titles: 80 Print
Imprints: Cornwallis Press; Parker/Thomas Press

**Tughra Books**
345 Clifton Ave, Clifton, NJ 07011
*Tel:* 973-777-2704 *Fax:* 973-457-7334
*E-mail:* info@tughrabooks.com
*Web Site:* www.tughrabooks.com
*Key Personnel*
Dir, Pubns: Huseyin Senturk *E-mail:* senturk@tughrabooks.com
Dir, Mktg: Ahmet Idil *E-mail:* agi@tughrabooks.com
Sr Ed: Yusuf Alan *E-mail:* alan@tughrabooks.com
Founded: 2001
Publishing, design & printing.
ISBN Prefix(es): 978-975-7388; 978-0-9704370; 978-1-932099 (Blue Dome); 978-1-59784
Number of titles published annually: 15 Print
Total Titles: 185 Print
Imprints: The Fountain; The Light
Distributor for Kaynak; Nile Publishing; Zambak
Foreign Rep(s): Gazelle (Europe, UK)
Foreign Rights: Kaynak Licensing (Africa, Asia, Australia, Europe, Middle East)
*Distribution Center:* National Book Network (NBN), 4501 Forbes Blvd, Suite 200, Lanham, MD 20706 *Tel:* 301-459-3366 *Fax:* 301-429-5746 *Web Site:* www.nbnbooks.com
Membership(s): AAP; ABA; IBPA, the Independent Book Publishers Association

**Tupelo Press Inc**
PO Box 1767, North Adams, MA 01247
SAN: 254-3281
*Tel:* 413-664-9611 *Fax:* 413-664-9711
*E-mail:* info@tupelopress.org
*Web Site:* www.tupelopress.org
*Key Personnel*
Publr & Ed-in-Chief: Jeffrey Levine
*E-mail:* publisher@tupelopress.org
Mng Ed: Jim Schley
Founded: 1999
Independent, nonprofit literary press.
ISBN Prefix(es): 978-1-932195
Number of titles published annually: 10 Print
Total Titles: 60 Print
Membership(s): Association of Writers and Writing Programs; Council of Literary Magazines & Presses

**Turner Publishing Co**
200 Fourth Ave N, Suite 950, Nashville, TN 37219
*Tel:* 615-255-BOOK (255-2665) *Fax:* 615-255-5081
*E-mail:* marketing@turnerpublishing.com; submissions@turnerpublishing.com
*Web Site:* www.turnerpublishing.com
*Key Personnel*
Pres & Publr: Todd Bottorff
Exec Ed: Diane Gedymin
Acctg Mgr: Angie Lithgow
Founded: 1984
Trade publisher.
ISBN Prefix(es): 978-1-56311
Number of titles published annually: 36 Print
Total Titles: 2,100 Print
Imprints: Ancestry; Fieldstone Alliance; Iroquois Press (fiction); Ramsey & Todd; Turner; Wiley
*Branch Office(s)*
445 Park Ave, 9th fl, New York, NY 10022
*Tel:* 646-291-8961 *Fax:* 646-291-8962
*Warehouse:* c/o IPS, 1210 Ingram Dr, Chambersburg, PA 17202
Membership(s): AAP; ABA; IBPA, the Independent Book Publishers Association

**Turtle Point Press**
233 Broadway, Rm 946, New York, NY 10279
*Tel:* 212-945-6622
*E-mail:* countomega@aol.com
*Web Site:* www.turtlepointpress.com
*Key Personnel*
Pres & Intl Rts Contact: Jonathan D Rabinowitz
Founded: 1990
Lost literary fiction, contemporary fiction, art history, art criticism, poetry, biography.
ISBN Prefix(es): 978-0-9627987; 978-1-885983; 978-1-885583; 978-1-933527
Number of titles published annually: 4 Print
Total Titles: 100 Print
Imprints: Books & Co/Turtle Point; Helen Marx/Turtle Point; Turtle Point
Foreign Rep(s): Turnaround (UK)
*Distribution Center:* Consortium Book Sales & Distribution, 1094 Flex Dr, Jackson, TN 38301-5070 *Tel:* 612-746-2600 *Toll Free Tel:* 800-283-3572 (cust serv) *Toll Free Fax:* 800-351-5073 *E-mail:* info@cbsd.com *Web Site:* www.cbsd.com

**Tuttle Publishing**
Member of Periplus Publishing Group
Airport Business Park, 364 Innovation Dr, North Clarendon, VT 05759-9436
SAN: 213-2621
*Tel:* 802-773-8930 *Toll Free Tel:* 800-526-2778 *Fax:* 802-773-6993 *Toll Free Fax:* 800-FAX-TUTL
*E-mail:* info@tuttlepublishing.com
*Web Site:* www.tuttlepublishing.com
*Key Personnel*
CEO & Pres: Eric Oey
Mng Dir: Michael Sargent
Publg Dir: Ed Walters
Sales & Mktg Dir: Christopher Johns
*E-mail:* cjohns@tuttlepublishing.com
Founded: 1948
Founded by Charles E Tuttle in Tokyo, Tuttle Publishing publishes books to span the East & West, publisher of high quality books & book kits on a wide range of topics including Asian culture, cooking, martial arts, spirituality, philosophy, travel, language, art, architecture & design.
ISBN Prefix(es): 978-0-8048; 978-4-333 (Kosei Publishing Co); 978-1-85391 (Merehurst Ltd); 978-0-460 (Everyman Paperbacks); 978-4-07 (Shufunotomo Co); 978-4-900737; 978-962-593 (Periplus Editions); 978-0-945971 (Periplus Editions); 978-0-935621 (Healing Tao Books); 978-0-933756 (Paperweight Press); 978-0-7946 (Periplus Editions); 978-0-970171 (Kotan); 978-1-840590 (Milet); 978-4-8053
Number of titles published annually: 200 Print
Total Titles: 2,000 Print; 20 Audio
Imprints: Everyman's Classic Library in Paperback; Kosei Publishing Co; Kotan Publishing Inc; Merehurst Ltd; Milet Publishing Ltd; Periplus Editions
*Foreign Office(s):* 5-4-12 Osaki Shinagawa-ku, 141-0032 Tokyo, Japan *Tel:* (03) 5437 0171 *Fax:* (03) 5437 0755 *E-mail:* tuttle-sales@gol.com
Periplus Publishing Group, Olivine Bldg No 06-01/03, 130 Joo Seng Rd, Singapore 368357, Singapore *Tel:* 6280 3320 *Fax:* 6280 6290 *E-mail:* inquiries@periplus.com.sg *Web Site:* www.periplus.com
Distributed by Publishers Group West (digital only)
Distributor for Healing Tao Books; Kosei Publishing Co; Kotan Publishing Inc; Milet Publishing Ltd; Paperweight Press; Periplus Editions; Shanghai Press; Shufunotomo Co; Tai Chi Foundation
Foreign Rep(s): Airlift Book Co (UK); Bill Bailey Publishers Representatives (Europe); Berkeley Books Pte Ltd (Southeast Asia); Humphrys Roberts Associates (Caribbean, Central America, Mexico, South America); Nilsson & Lamm (Netherlands); Ray Potts (Middle East); Ten Speed (Canada); Trinity Books (South Africa); Tuttle Publishing (Japan)

**Tuxedo Press**
546 E Springville Rd, Carlisle, PA 17015
*Tel:* 717-258-9733 *Fax:* 717-243-0074
*E-mail:* info@tuxedo-press.com
*Web Site:* tuxedo-press.com
*Key Personnel*
Publr: Thomas R Benjey *E-mail:* tom@tuxedo-press.com
Assoc Ed: Ann Fitch *E-mail:* ann@tuxedo-press.com
Founded: 2005
Small press of nonfiction books. Titles released to date have been historical in nature. Future releases may also include political topics. New releases are offset print; reprints are POD. Considering expansion to audiobooks. Titles are of US interest only.
ISBN Prefix(es): 978-0-9774486; 978-1-936161
Number of titles published annually: 5 Print
Total Titles: 15 Print; 3 E-Book
*Advertising Agency:* Anne Dozier & Associates, 313 E 84 St, Suite 1-B, New York, NY 10028, Contact: Anne Dozier *Tel:* 212-717-0276 *E-mail:* annedozier@aol.com
*Orders to:* Ingram Book Co, 14 Ingram Blvd, La Vergne, TN 37086 *Tel:* 615-213-5335 *Fax:* 615-213-5430
*Distribution Center:* Ingram Book Co, 14 Ingram Blvd, La Vergne, TN 37086 *Tel:* 615-213-5335 *Fax:* 615-213-5430
Membership(s): IBPA, the Independent Book Publishers Association

**§Twayne Publishers™**
Imprint of Gale
27500 Drake Rd, Farmington Hills, MI 48331-3535
Mailing Address: PO Box 9187, Farmington Hills, MI 48333-9187
*Tel:* 248-699-4253 *Toll Free Tel:* 800-877-4253; 800-363-4253 *Toll Free Fax:* 800-414-5043
*E-mail:* gale.galeord@cengage.com
*Web Site:* www.gale.com
Founded: 1949
Critical biographies & studies on literature authors from around the world.
ISBN Prefix(es): 978-0-8057
Number of titles published annually: 6 E-Book
*Returns:* Cengage Learning, 10650 Toebben Dr, Independence, KY 41051-5100

**Twenty-First Century Books**
Division of Lerner Publishing Group Inc
241 First Ave N, Minneapolis, MN 55401
*Tel:* 612-332-3344 *Toll Free Tel:* 800-328-4929 *Fax:* 612-332-7615 *Toll Free Fax:* 800-332-1132
*E-mail:* info@lernerbooks.com
*Web Site:* www.lernerbooks.com
*Key Personnel*
Chmn: Harry J Lerner
CFO & EVP: Margaret Wunderlich
Pres & Publr: Adam Lerner
EVP, Sales: David Wexler
VP & Dir, Mktg & Digital Prods: Terri Soutor
Ed-in-Chief: Patricia M Stockland
Edit Dir: Domenica Di Piazza
VP, Prodn: Gary Hansen
Rts Dir: Maria Kjoller
Dir, Prod Devt & Mktg Res: Lois Wallentine
Dir, Electronic Content: Dan Wallek
Art Dir: Zach Marell
Dir, HR: Cyndi Radant
Publisher of nonfiction books for the upper grades & young adults.
ISBN Prefix(es): 978-0-8050; 978-1-56294; 978-0-7613; 978-0-941477
Total Titles: 480 Print; 240 E-Book
Foreign Rep(s): INT Press Distribution (Australia); Phambili (Southern Africa); Publishers Marketing Service (Brunei, Malaysia, Singapore); South Pacific Books (New Zealand)
Foreign Rights: Sandra Bruna Agencia Literaria (Spain); Japan Foreign-Rights Centre (Japan); Korea Copyright Center (Korea); Michelle Lapautre Agence Junior (France); Rights People (UK & Commonwealth)
*Warehouse:* Lerner Publishing Group, 1251 Washington Ave N, Minneapolis, MN 55401

**§Twenty-Third Publications**
Division of Bayard Inc
One Montauk Ave, Suite 200, New London, CT 06320
*Tel:* 860-437-3012 *Toll Free Tel:* 800-321-0411 (orders) *Toll Free Fax:* 800-572-0788
*E-mail:* 23ppweb@bayard-inc.com
*Web Site:* www.twentythirdpublications.com
*Key Personnel*
Publr: Therese Ratliff
Edit Dir: Dan Connors
Mktg Dir: Dan Smart
Compt: Leslie Williams
Prodn Mgr: Paul Borque
Rts & Perms: Kerry Moriarty
Founded: 1967
ISBN Prefix(es): 978-0-89622; 978-1-58595
Number of titles published annually: 45 Print; 6 CD-ROM
Total Titles: 450 Print; 24 CD-ROM
Distributed by Columba (UK); John Garrett (Australia); Novalis (Canada)
Distributor for Novalis (Canada)

Foreign Rights: Bayard Presse International (Asia, Central Europe, Eastern Europe)
Membership(s): Association of Catholic Publishers Inc; Catholic Press Association

**§Twilight Times Books**
PO Box 3340, Kingsport, TN 37664-0340
*Tel:* 423-323-0183 *Fax:* 423-323-0183
*E-mail:* publisher@twilighttimes.com
*Web Site:* www.twilighttimesbooks.com
*Key Personnel*
Publr: Lida E Quillen
Mng Ed: Ardy M Scott
Ed: Eric Olsen
Tech Support: Michael D Bobbitt
Founded: 1999
Royalty paying small press trade publisher of speculative fiction. Our mission is to promote excellence in writing & great literature. Currently publishing limited edition hardcover, first edition trade paperback books & electronic books as downloads in various formats.
ISBN Prefix(es): 978-1-931201; 978-1-933353; 978-1-60619
Number of titles published annually: 14 Print; 20 E-Book
Total Titles: 105 Print; 130 E-Book
Imprints: Paladin Timeless Books; Twilight Visions
Distributed by Brodart Co; BWI Books
Foreign Rep(s): Editura Eminescu (Romania)
*Distribution Center:* Twilight Trade Books, Kingsport, TN
Membership(s): The Association of Publishers for Special Sales; Electronically Published Internet Connection; IBPA, the Independent Book Publishers Association; Small Publishers, Artists & Writers Network; Speculative Literature Foundation

**Twin Peaks Press**
PO Box 8, Vancouver, WA 98666-0008
SAN: 692-4034
*Tel:* 360-694-2462 *Toll Free Tel:* 800-637-2256
*E-mail:* twinpeaks@pacifier.com
*Web Site:* www.twinpeakspress.com
*Key Personnel*
Pres: Helen Hecker
Founded: 1982
ISBN Prefix(es): 978-0-933261
Number of titles published annually: 8 Print
Total Titles: 10 Print

**Two Thousand Three Associates**
4180 Saxon Dr, New Smyrna Beach, FL 32169
*Tel:* 386-690-2503
*E-mail:* ttta1@att.net
*Web Site:* www.twothousandthree.com
*Key Personnel*
Intl Rts & Lib Sales Dir: Frederick B Smith
Mktg Dir: Hank Hankshaw
Publicity Dir: Barbara Brent
Asst to Pres: Geoffery Crawford Tell
Founded: 1995
Nonfiction including memoirs, humor, sports & travel.
ISBN Prefix(es): 978-0-9639905; 978-1-892285
Number of titles published annually: 4 Print
Total Titles: 16 Print
Membership(s): Independent Publishers Association; Independent Publishers Group

**§Tyndale House Publishers Inc**
351 Executive Dr, Carol Stream, IL 60188
SAN: 206-7749
*Tel:* 630-668-8300 *Toll Free Tel:* 800-323-9400
*Web Site:* www.tyndale.com
*Key Personnel*
CEO & Pres: Mark Taylor
COO: Jeff Johnson
VP, Group Publr: Ron Beers; Doug Knox; Jim Kraus
VP, Publg Servs: CJ Van Wagner
Intl Accts Mgr: James Elwell
Natl Accts Mgr: Mark Di Cicco
Foreign & Domestic Rts & Perms: Jade Doyel
Spec Sales: Charlie Swaney
E-Books: Alan Huizenga
Cust Serv: Lori Walling
Founded: 1962
Religion: hardcover & paperback originals & reprints, ebooks, Bibles, reference, DVDs, audio CDs & software.
ISBN Prefix(es): 978-0-8423; 978-1-4143
Number of titles published annually: 125 Print; 1 CD-ROM; 73 Online; 75 E-Book; 25 Audio
Total Titles: 1,000 Print; 5 CD-ROM; 300 E-Book; 225 Audio
Imprints: BarnaBooks (George Barna titles); Living Books (mass paperback); Resurgence (Mars Hill Church); SaltRiver (deeper Christian thought); Tyndale Audio (adult audio books); Tyndale Entertainment (kids' audio/video products); Tyndale Kids (children's); Tyndale Momentum; Tyndale Ninos (Spanish children's)
Distributor for Focus on the Family
*Advertising Agency:* Design Promotion
Membership(s): Evangelical Christian Publishers Association

**§Type & Archetype Press**
Imprint of Type & Temperament Inc
846 Dupont Rd, Suite-C, Charleston, SC 29407
Mailing Address: PO Box 14285, Charleston, SC 29422-4285
*Tel:* 843-406-9113 *Toll Free Tel:* 800-447-8973 *Fax:* 843-406-9118
*E-mail:* info@typetemperament.com
*Web Site:* www.typetemperament.com; typenewsletter.com
*Key Personnel*
Pres: William D G Murray *E-mail:* wdgmurray@aol.com
Founded: 1974
Books, materials, seminar kits, audio & video tapes for people interested in personality styles & practical applications of psychological type & archetypes, the Myers Briggs Type Indicator & the Pearson-Marr Archetype Indicator.
ISBN Prefix(es): 978-1-878287
Number of titles published annually: 3 Print
Total Titles: 23 Print; 7 CD-ROM; 24 Audio

**UBM Global Trade**
Subsidiary of United Business Media Ltd
2 Penn Plaza, 12th fl, Newark, NJ 07105-2251
*Tel:* 203-523-7034 *Toll Free Tel:* 800-221-5488 (ext 7841)
*E-mail:* joc@halldata.com
*Web Site:* www.ubmglobaltrade.com
Founded: 2000
Provider of proprietary data, news, business intelligence & analytical content supporting commercial maritime, rail, trucking, warehousing & logistics industries worldwide.
ISBN Prefix(es): 978-0-9649630; 978-1-891131
Number of titles published annually: 63 Print; 1 CD-ROM; 1 E-Book
Total Titles: 50 Print; 4 CD-ROM; 3 E-Book
*Branch Office(s)*
400 Windsor Corporation Park, 50 Millstone Rd, Suite 200, East Windsor, NJ 08520
30 Two Bridges Rd, Suite 227, Fairfield, NJ 07004
300 Bldg, 100-300 American Metro Blvd, Hamilton, NJ 08619
213 Carnegie Ctr, Suite 203, Princeton, NJ 08540
300 W Grand Ave, Suite 205, Escondido, CA 92025 *Tel:* 760-294-5563
Bixby Executive Ctr, 4401 Atlantic Ave, Long Beach, CA 90802
GRE Shoreline Sq, 301 E Ocean Ave, Suite 275, Long Beach, CA 90802
Press Bldg, 529 14 St, Washington, DC 20045
1800 Eller Dr, Fort Lauderdale, FL 33316
2831 Talleyrand Ave, Jacksonville, FL 32206
Miami Springs Plaza, 4471 NW 36 St, Suite 247, Miami Springs, FL 33166
3400 Lakeside Dr, Suite 515, Miramar, FL 33027 *Toll Free Tel:* 800-991-9994
2 E Bryan St, Suite 402, Savannah, GA 31401
938 Lafayette St, Suite 413, New Orleans, LA 70113
400 Northampton St, Suite 704, Easton, MA 18042
MAI Ctr, 2000 Kennedy Ave, Suite 202-D, San Juan, PR 00920
BDA Lluberas 368 KM 12.6, Yauco, PR 00698
7141 Office City Dr, Suite 219, Houston, TX 77087
7 S Nevada St, Suite 200, Seattle, WA 98134
2202 Port of Tacoma Rd, Tacoma, WA 98421
1155 Rene-Levesque Blvd W, Suite 3310, Montreal, QC H3B 2J6, Canada

**UCLA Fowler Museum of Cultural History**
308 Charles E Young Dr N, Los Angeles, CA 90095
Mailing Address: PO Box 951549, Los Angeles, CA 90095-1549
*Tel:* 310-825-4361 *Fax:* 310-206-7007
*Web Site:* www.fmch.ucla.edu
*Key Personnel*
Mng Ed & Intl Rts Contact: Lynne Kostman *Tel:* 310-794-9582 *E-mail:* lkostman@arts.ucla.edu
Founded: 1963
Active publisher of African, Southeast Asian & Latin American arts publications.
ISBN Prefix(es): 978-0-930741; 978-0-9748729
Number of titles published annually: 5 Print
Total Titles: 71 Print
Distributed by University of Washington Press
*Shipping Address:* 308 Charles Young Dr N, Los Angeles, CA 90095-1549

**UCLA Latin American Center Publications**
UCLA Latin American Institute, 10343 Bunche Hall, Los Angeles, CA 90095
Mailing Address: PO Box 951447, Los Angeles, CA 90095-1447
*Tel:* 310-825-4571 *Fax:* 310-206-6859
*E-mail:* latinamctr@international.ucla.edu
*Web Site:* www.international.ucla.edu/lai
*Key Personnel*
Interim Dir: Kevin Terraciano *E-mail:* terraciano@international.ucla.edu
Exec Dir: David Arriaza
Dir, Pubns: Orchid Mazurkiewicz
Founded: 1959
Scholarly books & journals in Latin American studies.
ISBN Prefix(es): 978-0-87903
Number of titles published annually: 6 Print; 1 CD-ROM; 1 Online
Total Titles: 124 Print; 1 CD-ROM; 1 Online

**Ugly Duckling Presse**
The Old American Can Factory, 232 Third St, Suite E002, Brooklyn, NY 11215
*Tel:* 347-948-5170
*E-mail:* udp_mailbox@yahoo.com; info@uglyducklingpresse.org
*Web Site:* www.uglyducklingpresse.org
*Key Personnel*
Pres: Matvei Yankelevich
Mng Ed: Anna Moschovakis
Ed: Gregory L Ford; Ryan Haley
Artist Book Ed: Ellie Ga
Founded: 1993
A nonprofit arts & publishing collective.
ISBN Prefix(es): 978-0-9727684
Number of titles published annually: 8 Print; 2 Audio
Total Titles: 20 Print
Imprints: Emergency Gazette; Knock-off Books; New York Nights; 6 x 6 Magazine

Distributor for United Artists
Membership(s): Council of Literary Magazines & Presses

**ULI-The Urban Land Institute**
1025 Thomas Jefferson St NW, Suite 500-W, Washington, DC 20007-5201
*Tel:* 202-624-7000; 410-626-7505 (cust serv outside US) *Toll Free Tel:* 800-321-5011 (cust serv) *Fax:* 202-624-7140; 410-626-7147 (orders only) *Toll Free Fax:* 800-248-4585
*E-mail:* bookstore@uli.org; customerservice@uli.org
*Web Site:* www.uli.org
*Key Personnel*
SVP & Publr: Gayle Berens *E-mail:* gayle.berens@uli.org
Founded: 1936
Books related to land use & development; real estate.
ISBN Prefix(es): 978-0-87420
Number of titles published annually: 10 Print; 10 E-Book
Total Titles: 100 Print; 26 Online; 10 E-Book
Foreign Rights: Joanne Wang
*Orders to:* Independent Publishers Group, 814 N Franklin St, Chicago, IL 60610 *Toll Free Tel:* 800-888-4741 *E-mail:* orders@ipgbook.com
*Warehouse:* 810 Cromwell Park Dr, Suite D, Glen Burnie, MD 21061
*Distribution Center:* Independent Publishers Group, 814 N Franklin St, Chicago, IL 60610, VP: Paul Murphy *Tel:* 312-337-0747 *Toll Free Tel:* 800-888-4741 *Fax:* 312-337-5985 *E-mail:* frontdesk@ipgbook.com *Web Site:* ipgbook.com

**Ultramarine Publishing Co Inc**
12 Washington Ave, Hastings-on-Hudson, NY 10706
*Tel:* 914-478-1339
*Key Personnel*
Sales Mgr: Christopher P Stephens *E-mail:* csteph01@sprynet.com
Founded: 1970
ISBN Prefix(es): 978-0-89366
Number of titles published annually: 5 Print
Total Titles: 250 Print

**Ulysses Press**
PO Box 3440, Berkeley, CA 94703-0440
*Tel:* 510-601-8301 *Toll Free Tel:* 800-377-2542 *Fax:* 510-601-8307
*E-mail:* ulysses@ulyssespress.com
*Web Site:* www.ulyssespress.com
*Key Personnel*
Publr: Ray Riegert *E-mail:* rayriegert@ulyssespress.com
EVP: Bryce Willett *E-mail:* brycewillett@ulyssespress.com
Founded: 1983
Travel guides, health books, mind, body & spirit, lifestyle & sexuality titles.
ISBN Prefix(es): 978-0-915233; 978-1-56975
Number of titles published annually: 50 Print
Total Titles: 150 Print
Imprints: Hidden Travel Series; Seastone
Distributed by Publishers Group West
Foreign Rep(s): Hi Marketing (Central America, Continental Europe, Far East, South Africa, South America, UK); Raincoast Book Distribution Ltd (Canada)
Foreign Rights: InterLicense
*Shipping Address:* 3286 Adeline St, Suite 1, Berkeley, CA 94703 *Toll Free Tel:* 800-377-2542
Membership(s): IBPA, the Independent Book Publishers Association; SATW

**Unarius Academy of Science Publications**
Division of Unarius Educational Foundation
145 S Magnolia Ave, El Cajon, CA 92020-4522
SAN: 168-9614
*Tel:* 619-444-7062 *Toll Free Tel:* 800-475-7062 *Fax:* 619-444-9637
*E-mail:* uriel@unarius.org
*Web Site:* www.unarius.org
*Key Personnel*
Ed: Celeste Appel
Founded: 1954
Books, CDs & DVDs describing a new science of life, past-life therapy, extraterrestrial civilizations, the prehistory of earth, the psychology of consciousness: a course in self mastery. Unarius provides the foundation for personal growth that will lead to the development of self-mastery & the clairvoyant aptitudes of the mind. Alternate formats offered in addition to DVDs: Mp3, CD & videos in Mp4. Classes in past-life therapy are webcast on Sunday 7pm Pacific time.
ISBN Prefix(es): 978-0-932642; 978-0-935097
Number of titles published annually: 4 Print
Total Titles: 90 Print; 70 Audio
Divisions: Audio Books; Greeting Cards; Inspirational Art; Public Access Broadcasting; Unarius Video Productions

**Unicor Medical Inc**
4160 Carmichael Rd, Montgomery, AL 36106
*Tel:* 334-260-8150 *Toll Free Tel:* 800-825-7421 *Toll Free Fax:* 800-305-8030
*E-mail:* sales@unicormed.com
*Web Site:* www.unicormed.com
*Key Personnel*
CEO: Rex Stanley
CFO: Wanda K Hamm *E-mail:* whamm@unicormed.com
VP, Pubns: Nikki Vrocher
VP, Busn Devt: Stuart Newsome *E-mail:* snewsome@unicormed.com
Medical books, medical ICD-9 coding books & coding software.
ISBN Prefix(es): 978-1-56781
Number of titles published annually: 14 Print
Total Titles: 14 Print

**The United Educators Inc**
900 N Shore Dr, Suite 279, Lake Bluff, IL 60044-2210
SAN: 204-8795
*Tel:* 847-234-3700 *Toll Free Tel:* 800-323-5875 *Fax:* 847-234-8705
*E-mail:* unitededucators@yahoo.com
*Web Site:* www.theunitededucatorsinc.com
*Key Personnel*
Pres: Remo D Piazzi
Secy: Diane W Jones
Treas: Peter Ewing
Founded: 1993
Encyclopedias & subscription books.
ISBN Prefix(es): 978-0-87566
Subsidiaries: Standard Educational Corp

**§United Nations Publications**
2 United Nations Plaza, Rm DC2-0853, New York, NY 10017
SAN: 206-6718
*Tel:* 212-963-8302 *Toll Free Tel:* 800-253-9646 *Fax:* 212-963-3489
*E-mail:* publications@un.org
*Web Site:* unp.un.org
*Key Personnel*
Chief, UN Pubns: Christopher Woodthorpe
Deputy Chief & Ad Rep: Vlad Vitkovski *E-mail:* vitkovskiv@un.org
Chief of Unit, Geneva, Europe, Middle East & Africa: Nicolas Bovay
Sales & Mktg Offr: Irina Lumelsky
Trade Sales: Andrea Goncalves
Founded: 1946
Trade & textbooks published by United Nations, International Court of Justice, UNEP, INSTRAW, UNIDO, UNDP, UNU & UNITAR on world & national economy, international trade, disarmament, social questions, human rights, international law, questions of international importance.
ISBN Prefix(es): 978-92-1
Number of titles published annually: 700 Print; 60 Online
Total Titles: 4,800 Print; 35 CD-ROM; 900 E-Book
*Foreign Office(s):* Section des Ventes et Commercialisation, Bureau E-4, 1211 Geneva 10, Switzerland, Contact: Nicolas Bovay
Distributor for ICJ; INSTRAW; IOM; UNCITRAL; UNDP; UNFPA; UNICEF; UNICRI; UNIDIR; UNIDO; UNITAR; UNU
*Shipping Address:* United Nations, NL-210, New York, NY 10017 *Tel:* 212-963-8065

**§United States Holocaust Memorial Museum**
100 Raoul Wallenberg Place SW, Washington, DC 20024-2126
*Tel:* 202-314-7837; 202-488-6144 (orders) *Toll Free Tel:* 800-259-9998 (orders) *Fax:* 202-479-9726; 202-488-0438 (orders)
*E-mail:* cahs_publications@ushmm.org
*Web Site:* www.ushmm.org
*Key Personnel*
Dir, Academic Pubns, Center for Advanced Holocaust Studies: Benton M Arnovitz *Tel:* 202-488-6117 *E-mail:* barnovitz@ushmm.org
Dir, Museum Bookstore & Holocaust Lib Sales Opers: Jerry Rehm
Acting Dir, Creative Servs (Prodn): Amy Donovan
Exhibitions Projs: Ted Phillips
Perms: Karen Coe
Pubns Offr, Ctr Fellows Projs: Steven Feldman
Pubns Offr, Ctr Staff Applied Res Projs: Mel Hecker
Founded: 1993
Co-publish original monographs, translations, classic reprints, testimonial materials & a scholarly journal; publish memoirs & related titles of Holocaust Publications' Holocaust Library imprint (assets acquired in 1993), as well as occasional papers, exhibition catalogues & related works.
ISBN Prefix(es): 978-0-89604
Number of titles published annually: 12 Print
Total Titles: 130 Print
Imprints: Holocaust Library
Foreign Rights: Goldfarb & Associates (selected titles)

**United States Institute of Peace Press**
2301 Constitution Ave NW, Washington, DC 20037
*Tel:* 202-457-1700 (edit); 703-661-1590 (cust serv) *Toll Free Tel:* 800-868-8064 (cust serv) *Fax:* 202-429-6063; 703-661-1501 (cust serv)
*Web Site:* bookstore.usip.org
*Key Personnel*
Dir, Pubns: Valerie Norville *Tel:* 202-429-4147 *E-mail:* vnorville@usip.org
Prodn Mgr: Marie Marr Jackson
Sales, Mktg & Rts Mgr, Pubns Off: Kay Hechler *Tel:* 202-429-3816 *E-mail:* khechler@usip.org
Mng Ed: Michelle Slavin
Founded: 1989
Area of international peacebuilding, policy analysis & conflict resolution. Primarily publish research results from grants, fellowship & commissioned research.
ISBN Prefix(es): 978-1-878379; 978-1-929223; 978-1-601270
Number of titles published annually: 10 Print
Total Titles: 160 Print
Foreign Rep(s): University Presses Marketing (Europe, Greece, India, Ireland, Israel, Scandinavia, UK)
*Orders to:* PO Box 605, Herndon, VA 20172-0605 (sales & returns/bookseller, wholesaler &

instl) *E-mail:* usipmail@presswarehouse.com
SAN: 254-6965
*Shipping Address:* 22883 Quicksilver Dr, Dulles, VA 20166 (indiv returns)

**United States Pharmacopeia**
12601 Twinbrook Pkwy, Rockville, MD 20852-1790
*Tel:* 301-881-0666 *Toll Free Tel:* 800-227-8772 *Fax:* 301-816-8237 (mktg)
*E-mail:* marketing@usp.org
*Web Site:* www.usp.org
*Key Personnel*
CEO: Dr Roger L Williams, MD *Tel:* 301-881-0666 ext 8300
Founded: 1820
Reference books & directories; Databases in print & electronic formats.
ISBN Prefix(es): 978-0-913595
Number of titles published annually: 5 Print
Total Titles: 25 Print; 2 CD-ROM
Distributed by Consumer Reports; Login Brothers Book Co; Login Publishing Consortium
Foreign Rep(s): Deutscher Apotheker Verlag (Austria, Germany, Switzerland); Login Brothers Canada (Canada); Maruzen Co Ltd (Japan); Pharmaceutical Society of Australia (Australia); Pharmasystems (Canada); Ernesto Reichmann Distribuidora de Livros Ltda (Brazil)
*Distribution Center:* Matthews Book Co, 11559 Rock Island Ct, Maryland Heights, MO 63043 *Tel:* 314-432-1400 *Toll Free Fax:* 800-421-8816
National Technical Information Service, 5285 Port Royal Rd, Springfield, VA 22161 *Tel:* 703-487-4825 *Fax:* 703-487-4098
Promachem LLC, PO Box 1126, 2931 Soldier Springs Rd, Laramie, WY 82070 *Tel:* 307-742-6343 *Fax:* 307-745-7936
Rittenhouse Book Distributors, Inc, 522 Feheley Dr, King of Prussia, PA 19406 *Toll Free Tel:* 800-345-6425 *Toll Free Fax:* 800-223-7488

**United States Tennis Association**
70 W Red Oak Lane, White Plains, NY 10604
*Tel:* 914-696-7000 *Fax:* 914-696-7027
*Web Site:* www.usta.com
*Key Personnel*
Dir, Publg: Richard S Rennert *E-mail:* rennert@usta.com
Edit Dir: Mark Preston *E-mail:* preston@usta.com
Founded: 1881
Tennis materials; books, magazines & souvenir programs.
ISBN Prefix(es): 978-0-938822
Number of titles published annually: 5 Print
Total Titles: 25 Print
Distributed by Triumph Books; Universe Publishing; H O Zimman Inc

**United Synagogue Book Service**
Division of United Synagogue of Conservative Judaism
820 Second Ave, New York, NY 10017
SAN: 203-0551
*Tel:* 212-533-7800 *Toll Free Tel:* 800-594-5617 (warehouse only) *Fax:* 212-253-5422
*E-mail:* booksvc@uscj.org
*Web Site:* secure.uscj.org/bookservice
*Key Personnel*
Admin Asst: Robert Clurman
Founded: 1913
Religion (Jewish); textbooks, juveniles; history, music, Hebrew language instruction, AV materials, liturgical, adult books & prayer books.
ISBN Prefix(es): 978-0-8381
Number of titles published annually: 5 Print
Total Titles: 230 Print
Imprints: Burning Bush Press; National Academy for Adult Jewish Studies; United Synagogue Commission on Jewish Education; United Synagogue of Conservative Judaism
Distributor for Rabbinical Assembly of America
*Shipping Address:* Mercedes Book Distributors, Brooklyn Navy Yard, Bldg 3, Brooklyn, NY 11205

**Unity Books**
Division of Unity School of Christianity
1901 NW Blue Pkwy, Unity Village, MO 64065-0001
*Tel:* 816-524-3550 (ext 3300); 816-251-3571 (sales) *Fax:* 816-251-3557
*Web Site:* www.unity.org
*Key Personnel*
Publg Specialist: Sharon Sartin *Fax:* 816-607-0516 *E-mail:* sartinsm@unityonline.org
Founded: 1889
Books, CDs, pamphlets.
ISBN Prefix(es): 978-0-87159
Number of titles published annually: 9 Print; 9 E-Book
Total Titles: 100 Print; 27 E-Book; 10 Audio
Distributed by De Vorss & Co
*Distribution Center:* Ingram, One Ingram Blvd, La Vergne, AL 37086
Membership(s): IBPA, the Independent Book Publishers Association; Network of Alternatives for Publishers, Retailers & Artists Inc

**Univelt Inc**
Affiliate of American Astronautical Society
740 Metcalf St, No 13 & 15, Escondido, CA 92025
Mailing Address: PO Box 28130, San Diego, CA 92198-0130
*Tel:* 760-746-4005 *Fax:* 760-746-3139
*E-mail:* sales@univelt.com
*Web Site:* www.univelt.com; www.astronautical.org
*Key Personnel*
Pres & Publr: Robert H Jacobs
Founded: 1970
Publisher for American Astronautical Society, International Academy of Astronautics, Lunar & Planetary Society, National Space Society. Specialize in astronautics & aerospace engineering.
ISBN Prefix(es): 978-0-912183; 978-0-87703
Number of titles published annually: 10 Print; 6 CD-ROM
Total Titles: 363 Print
Distributor for Astronautical Society of Western Australia; US Space Foundation

**Universal-Publishers Inc**
23331 Water Circle, Boca Raton, FL 33486-8540
SAN: 299-3635
*Tel:* 561-750-4344 *Toll Free Tel:* 800-636-8329 *Fax:* 561-750-6797
*Web Site:* www.universal-publishers.com
*Key Personnel*
Publr: Jeffrey R Young
Founded: 1997
Dictionaries, encyclopedias, textbooks-all, university presses. Scholarly books, reprints, professional books, paperbacks, directories & reference books.
ISBN Prefix(es): 978-1-58112; 978-1-59942; 978-1-61233; 978-1-62734
Number of titles published annually: 60 Print; 50 E-Book
Total Titles: 1,500 Print; 1,000 E-Book
Imprints: Brown Walker Press; Dissertation.com
*Distribution Center:* Ingram Book Group, One Ingram Blvd, La Vergne, TN 37086 *Tel:* 615-793-5000 *Web Site:* www.ingramcontent.com
Bertrams, One Broadland Business Park, Norwich NR7 0WF, United Kingdom *E-mail:* books@bertrams.com *Web Site:* www.bertrams.com
*See separate listing for:*
**Dissertation.com**

**Universe Publishing**
Division of Rizzoli International Publications Inc
300 Park Ave S, 4th fl, New York, NY 10010
*Tel:* 212-387-3400 *Fax:* 212-387-3535
*Web Site:* www.rizzoliusa.com
Founded: 1956
Architecture, fine art, photography, illustrated gift books, fashion, culinary, popular culture, children's, design, style & calendars.
ISBN Prefix(es): 978-0-87663; 978-1-55550; 978-0-7893
Number of titles published annually: 60 Print
Imprints: Universe; Universe Calendars
Distributed by Random House
Foreign Rep(s): Bill Bailey (Central Europe); Bookport Associates (Southern Europe); Michelle Curreri (Asia); Hi Marketing (UK); IMA (Eastern Europe); IPR (Middle East); Marston Book Services Ltd (Europe, UK); Random House (Canada); Murray Sutton (Scandinavia); Cynthia Zimpfer (Latin America)

**University Council for Educational Administration**
The University of Texas at Austin, Dept of Educ Admin, Coll of Educ, One University Sta, D-5400, Austin, TX 78712-0374
*Tel:* 512-475-8592 *Fax:* 512-471-5974
*E-mail:* ucea.org@gmail.com
*Web Site:* www.ucea.org
*Key Personnel*
Exec Dir: Michelle D Young *E-mail:* mdy8n@eservices.virginia.edu
Founded: 1934
Books, journals, monographs, newsletters.
ISBN Prefix(es): 978-1-55996
Number of titles published annually: 5 Print
Total Titles: 23 Print
*Shipping Address:* The University of Texas at Austin, Dept of Educ Admin, Sanchez Bldg, Rm 310N, 1900 Speedway, Austin, TX 78705

**The University of Akron Press**
120 E Mill St, Suite 415, Akron, OH 44308
*Tel:* 330-972-6953 *Toll Free Tel:* 800-247-6553 (orders) *Fax:* 330-972-8364
*E-mail:* uapress@uakron.edu
*Web Site:* www.uakron.edu/uapress
Founded: 1988
Publish books on technology & the environment, poetry, Ohio history & culture, Ohio politics, law, psychology.
ISBN Prefix(es): 978-1-884836; 978-1-931968; 978-1-935603; 978-0-962262; 978-1-937378
Number of titles published annually: 12 Print; 5 E-Book
Total Titles: 170 Print; 30 E-Book
Imprints: Buchtel Books; Ringtaw Books
Distributor for Principia Press
*Orders to:* 30 Amberwood Pkwy, Ashland, OH 44805 *Tel:* 419-281-1802 *Fax:* 419-281-6883 *E-mail:* orders@atlasbooks.com
*Returns:* 30 Amberwood Pkwy, Ashland, OH 44805 *Tel:* 419-281-1802

**University of Alabama Press**
200 Hackberry Lane, 2nd fl, Tuscaloosa, AL 35487
*Tel:* 205-348-5180 *Fax:* 205-348-9201
*Web Site:* www.uapress.ua.edu
*Key Personnel*
Dir: Curtis L Clark *Tel:* 205-348-1560 *E-mail:* cclark@uapress.ua.edu
Dir, Sales & Mktg: J D Wilson
Busn Mgr: Rosalyn Carr *Tel:* 205-348-1567 *E-mail:* rcarr@uapress.ua.edu
Mktg & Sales Mgr: Shana R Rivers *Tel:* 205-348-9534 *E-mail:* srrivers@uapress.ua.edu
Prodn Mgr: W Richard Cook *Tel:* 205-348-1571 *E-mail:* rcook@uapress.ua.edu
Mng Ed: Crissie Johnson *Tel:* 205-348-9708 *E-mail:* cjohnson@uapress.ua.edu

Rts & Perms: Claire Lewis Evans *Tel:* 205-348-1561 *E-mail:* levans@uapress.ua.edu
Founded: 1945
American & Latin American history & culture, religious & ethnohistory, rhetoric & communications, African American & Native American studies, Judaic studies, Southern regional studies, theatre & regional trade titles.
ISBN Prefix(es): 978-0-8173; 978-0-914590; 978-0-932511; 978-1-57366
Number of titles published annually: 70 Print; 25 E-Book
Total Titles: 1,200 Print; 100 E-Book
Imprints: Fiction Collective 2 (FC2); Fire Ant Books
Foreign Rep(s): East-West Export Books (Asia); Eurospan (Europe); Scholarly Book Services (Canada)
*Distribution Center:* Chicago Distribution Center, 11030 S Langley, Chicago, IL 60628 (orders) *Tel:* 773-702-7000 (orders) *Toll Free Tel:* 800-621-2736 (orders) *Fax:* 773-702-7212
SAN: 630-6047
*See separate listing for:*
**Fiction Collective Two Inc (FC2)**

**§University of Alaska Press**
794 University Ave, Suite 220, Fairbanks, AK 99709
SAN: 203-3011
Mailing Address: PO Box 756240, Fairbanks, AK 99775-6240
*Tel:* 907-474-5831 *Toll Free Tel:* 888-252-6657 (US only) *Fax:* 907-474-5502
*E-mail:* fypress@uaf.edu
*Web Site:* www.uaf.edu/uapress
*Key Personnel*
Dir: Joan Braddock, PhD *E-mail:* jfbraddock@alaska.edu
Acqs Ed & Mng Ed: James Engelhardt *E-mail:* james.engelhardt@alaska.edu
Prodn Mgr: Sue Mitchell *E-mail:* sue.mitchell@alaska.edu
Sales & Dist Coord: Laura Walker *E-mail:* laura.walker@alaska.edu
Asst to Dir: Amy Simpson *E-mail:* amy.simpson@alaska.edu
Founded: 1967
Emphasis on scholarly & nonfiction works related to Alaska, the circumpolar regions & the North Pacific rim.
ISBN Prefix(es): 978-0-912006; 978-1-889963; 978-1-60223
Number of titles published annually: 24 Print
Total Titles: 220 Print
Imprints: Alaska Writer Laureate Series; Classic Reprint Series; Geology and Geography of Alaska Series; Great Explorer Series; Lantern-Light Library; Literary Reprint Series; Oral Biography Series; Rasmuson Library Historical Translation Series; Snowy Owl Books
Distributor for Alaska Native Language Center; Alaska Quarterly Review; Alaska Sea Grant; Alutiiq Museum; Anchorage Museum Association; Anchorage Museum of Art History; Arctic Studies Center of the Smithsonian Museum; Far to the North Press; Geophysical Institute; Limestone Press; Spirit Mountain Press; UA Museum; Vanessapress
*Distribution Center:* Chicago Distribution Center, 11030 S Langley Ave, Chicago, IL 60628 (for orders outside Alaska) *Toll Free Tel:* 800-621-2736 *Toll Free Fax:* 800-621-8476
Membership(s): Alaska History Association; Alaska Library Association; Association of American University Presses; IBPA, the Independent Book Publishers Association; Pacific Northwest Booksellers Association

**The University of Arizona Press**
355 S Euclid Ave, Suite 103, Tucson, AZ 85719-6654
SAN: 205-468X
*Tel:* 520-621-1441 *Toll Free Tel:* 800-426-3797 (orders) *Fax:* 520-621-8899 *Toll Free Fax:* 800-426-3797
*E-mail:* uap@uapress.arizona.edu
*Web Site:* www.uapress.arizona.edu
*Key Personnel*
Interim Dir & Sales & Mktg Mgr: Kathryn Conrad *E-mail:* kconrad@uapress.arizona.edu
Ed-in-Chief: Dr Allyson Carter *E-mail:* allysonc@uapress.arizona.edu
Acquiring Ed: Kristen Buckles *E-mail:* kbuckles@uapress.arizona.edu
Busn Mgr: Shay Cameron *E-mail:* scameron@uapress.arizona.edu
Publicity Mgr: Holly Schaffer *Tel:* 520-621-3920 *E-mail:* hollys@uapress.arizona.edu
Editing & Prodn Mgr: Lisa Stallings *E-mail:* lstallings@uapress.arizona.edu
Founded: 1959
Scholarly & regional nonfiction about Arizona, the American West & Mexico, Latino Studies, Latin American Studies, Native American studies, anthropology & environmental studies.
ISBN Prefix(es): 978-0-8165
Number of titles published annually: 55 Print
Total Titles: 783 Print
Distributor for Ironwood Press; OSU Press
Foreign Rep(s): East-West Export Books (Asia, The Pacific); William Gills (Africa, Europe, Middle East); University of British Columbia Press (Canada)
*Shipping Address:* 330 S Toole Ave, Tucson, AZ 85701
Membership(s): American Association of University Presses; Arizona Book Publishing Association; Publishers Association of the West

**The University of Arkansas Press**
Division of The University of Arkansas
McIlroy House, 105 N McIlroy Ave, Fayetteville, AR 72701
*Tel:* 479-575-3246 *Toll Free Tel:* 800-626-0090 *Fax:* 479-575-6044
*E-mail:* uapress@uark.edu
*Web Site:* www.uapress.com
*Key Personnel*
Dir: Lawrence Malley *Tel:* 479-575-3096 *E-mail:* lmalley@uark.edu
Dir, Editing, Design & Prodn: Brian King *Tel:* 479-575-6780 *E-mail:* brking@uark.edu
Busn Mgr: Mike Bieker *Tel:* 479-575-3859 *E-mail:* mbieker@uark.edu
Founded: 1980
General humanities: popular culture, Middle East studies, Civil War & civil rights studies.
ISBN Prefix(es): 978-0-938626; 978-1-55728; 978-0-912456
Number of titles published annually: 20 Print
Total Titles: 560 Print; 150 E-Book
Distributor for Butler Center for Arkansas Studies; Hearne Fine Art; Moon City Press; Ozark Society; Phoenix International
Foreign Rights: Eurospan (Africa, Europe, Middle East, UK)
*Advertising Agency:* Ad Lib *Fax:* 479-575-6044
*Orders to:* 1580 W Mitchell St, Fayetteville, AR 72701
*Returns:* 1580 W Mitchell St, Fayetteville, AR 72701
*Warehouse:* 1580 W Mitchell St, Fayetteville, AR 72701
*Distribution Center:* 1580 W Mitchell St, Fayetteville, AR 72701
Membership(s): American Association of University Presses

**University of California, ANR Publications**, see ANR Publications University of California

**§University of California Institute on Global Conflict & Cooperation**
Subsidiary of University of California
9500 Gilman Dr, MC 0518, La Jolla, CA 92093-0518
*Tel:* 858-534-3352 *Fax:* 858-534-7655
*E-mail:* igcc-cp@ucsd.edu
*Web Site:* www-igcc.ucsd.edu
*Key Personnel*
Sr Ed: Lynne Bush *Tel:* 858-534-1979 *E-mail:* lbush@ucsd.edu
Founded: 1983
IGCC NEWSWired (policy briefs & newsletters), IGCC Review (policy papers) & books authored by members of the University of California faculty & other participants in sponsored research programs.
ISBN Prefix(es): 978-0-934637
Number of titles published annually: 6 Print
Total Titles: 74 Print; 60 E-Book
Distributed by Brookings Institution Press; Columbia International Affairs Online (CIAO); Cornell University Press; Garland Publishers; Lynn-Reinner Publishing; Penn State University Press; Princeton University Press; Transaction Publishers; University of Michigan Press; Westview Press

**§University of California Press**
2120 Berkeley Way, Berkeley, CA 94704-1012
*Tel:* 510-642-4247 *Fax:* 510-643-7127
*E-mail:* askucp@ucpress.edu (books); customerservice@ucpressjournals.com (journals)
*Web Site:* www.ucpress.edu
*Key Personnel*
CFO & Asst Dir: Anna Weidman
Mng Dir, UK & Europe: Andrew Brewer
Dir: Alison Mudditt
Dir, Design & Prodn: Anthony Crouch
Dir, Digital Content Devt & Acqs Ed: Laura Cerruti
Edit Dir & Asst Dir: Denise Penrose
Dir, Mktg & Sales: Julie Christianson *E-mail:* julie.christianson@ucpress.edu
Assoc Dir, Sales: Amy-Lynn Fischer
Assoc Dir, UC Press & Dir, Journals & Digital Publg Div: Rebecca Simon
Exec Ed: Chuck Crumly
Regl Ed: Kim Robinson
Mng Ed: Marilyn Schwartz
Poetry Ed: Rachel Berchten
Acqs Ed: Kari Dahlgren; Blake Edgar; Mary C Francis; Niels Hooper; Hannah Love; Reed Malcolm; Kate Marshall; Eric A Schmidt; Naomi Schneider
ISBN Contact: Sierra Filucci
Founded: 1893
Trade nonfiction, scholarly & scientific nonfiction, translations & journals; paperbacks, limited fiction (reprints).
ISBN Prefix(es): 978-0-520
Number of titles published annually: 260 Print; 10 Online; 10 E-Book
Total Titles: 4,200 Print; 60 Online; 60 E-Book
Imprints: The Ahmanson Foundation Humanities Endowment Fund; Ahmanson-Murphy (fine arts); The Atkinson Family Imprint (higher educ); Authors; The Stephen Bechtel Fund (ecology & the environment); The George Gund Foundation (African American studies); The Fletcher Jones Foundation (humanities); Philip E Lilienthal (Asian studies); Joan Palevsky (classical lit); Roth Family Foundation (music in America); A Naomi Schneider Book; Simpson (humanities); The S Mark Taper Foundation (Jewish studies)
*Branch Office(s)*
Journals & Digital Publishing, 2000 Center St, Suite 303, Berkeley, CA 94704-1223 *Tel:* 510-643-7154 *Fax:* 510-642-9917
*Foreign Office(s):* University Presses of California, Columbia & Princeton Ltd, One Oldlands Way, Bognor Regis, West Sussex P022 9SA, United Kingdom *Tel:* 01243-843291 *Fax:* 01243-820250 *E-mail:* sales@upccp.demon.co.uk

Distributor for art-SITES; British Film Institute; Huntington Library; Sierra Club Books (adult trade)
Foreign Rep(s): Thomas V Cassidy (China); Adrian Greenwood (Europe, UK); Andrew & Atsuko Ishigami (Japan); David Stimpson (Australia, Canada)
*Advertising Agency:* Fiat Lux
*Orders to:* California-Princeton Fulfillment Services Inc, 1445 Lower Ferry Rd, Ewing, NJ 08618 *Tel:* 609-883-1759 *Toll Free Tel:* 800-777-4726 *Fax:* 609-883-7413 *Toll Free Fax:* 800-999-1958 *E-mail:* orders@cpfsinc.com
*Warehouse:* California-Princeton Fulfillment Services Inc, 1445 Lower Ferry Rd, Ewing, NJ 08618 *Tel:* 609-883-1759 *Toll Free Tel:* 800-777-4726 *Fax:* 609-883-7413 *Toll Free Fax:* 800-999-1958 *E-mail:* orders@cpfsinc.com
Membership(s): AAP

**University of Chicago Press**
1427 E 60 St, Chicago, IL 60637-2954
SAN: 202-5280
*Tel:* 773-702-7700; 773-702-7600 *Toll Free Tel:* 800-621-2736 (orders) *Fax:* 773-702-9756; 773-660-2235 (orders); 773-702-2708
*E-mail:* custserv@press.uchicago.edu; marketing@press.uchicago.edu
*Web Site:* www.press.uchicago.edu
*Key Personnel*
Dir: Garrett P Kiely *Tel:* 773-702-8878 *E-mail:* gkiely@press.uchicago.edu; Donald Linn *Tel:* 773-702-7020 *E-mail:* dlinn@press.uchicago.edu
Deputy Dir: Christopher Heiser *Tel:* 773-702-2998
Exec Dir, IT: Patti O'Shea *Tel:* 773-702-8521
Journals Dir: Michael Magoulias *Tel:* 773-753-2669 *E-mail:* mmagoulias@press.uchicago.edu
Exec Ed: Susan Bielstein *Tel:* 773-702-7633 *E-mail:* sbielstein@press.uchicago.edu; T David Brent *Tel:* 773-702-7642 *E-mail:* dbrent@press.uchicago.edu; Douglas C Mitchell *Tel:* 773-702-0427 *E-mail:* dmitchell@press.uchicago.edu; John Tryneski *Tel:* 773-702-7648 *E-mail:* jtryneski@press.uchicago.edu
Edit Dir, Humanities & Sci: Alan G Thomas *Tel:* 773-702-7644 *E-mail:* athomas@press.uchicago.edu
Edit Dir, Ref: Paul Schellinger *Tel:* 773-702-2376 *E-mail:* pschellinger@press.uchicago.edu
Edit Dir, Sci & Soc Sci: Christie Henry *Tel:* 773-702-0468 *E-mail:* chenry@press.uchicago.edu
Sr Ed: Karen Merikangas Darling *Tel:* 773-702-7641 *E-mail:* kdarling@press.uchicago.edu; Joe Jackson *Tel:* 773-702-7769 *E-mail:* jjackson@press.uchicago.edu; Timothy Mennel *Tel:* 773-702-0158 *E-mail:* tmennel@press.uchicago.edu
Sr Proj Ed: Mary Laur *E-mail:* mlaur@press.uchicago.edu
Ed: Christopher Rhodes *Tel:* 773-702-4517 *E-mail:* crhodes@press.uchicago.edu; Marta Tonegutti *Tel:* 773-702-0427 *E-mail:* mtonegutti@press.uchicago.edu
Pbk Ed: Maggie Hivnor *Tel:* 773-702-7649 *E-mail:* mhivnor@press.uchicago.edu
Asst Ed: Christopher Chung *E-mail:* cdchung@press.uchicago.edu; Amy Collier *Tel:* 773-702-1227 *E-mail:* acollier@press.uchicago.edu; Randolph Petilos *Tel:* 773-702-7647
UK Ed-at-Large: James Attlee
Pubns Mgr, Journals Div: Tess Mullen *Tel:* 773-702-7442; Gordon Rudy
Asst to Dir: Ellen Zalewski *Tel:* 773-702-8879 *E-mail:* emz@press.uchicago.edu
Founded: 1891
Scholarly, nonfiction, advanced texts, monographs, clothbound & paperback, scholarly & professional journals, reference books & atlases.
ISBN Prefix(es): 978-0-226
Number of titles published annually: 250 Print
Total Titles: 5,400 Print; 1 E-Book
Distributor for Canadian Museum of Nature; Conservation International; National Bureau of Economic Research; National Gallery of Canada; National Society for the Study of Education; Oriental Institute
Foreign Rep(s): Academic Book Promotions (Benelux, France, Scandinavia); The American University Press Group (Hong Kong, Japan, Korea, Taiwan); Thomas Cassidy (China); Ewa Ledochowicz (Eastern Europe); Uwe Ludemann (Austria, Germany, Italy, Switzerland); Mediamatics (India); Publishers Marketing & Research Associates (Caribbean, Latin America); Arie Ruitenbeek (Portugal, Spain); The University Press Group (Australia, Canada, New Zealand); University Presses Marketing (Greece, Ireland, Israel, UK)
*Distribution Center:* 11030 S Langley Ave, Chicago, IL 60628 *Toll Free Fax:* 800-621-8476 (US & CN)
Membership(s): AAP; American Association of University Presses

**University of Delaware Press**
200A Morris Library, 181 S College Ave, Newark, DE 19717-5267
*Tel:* 302-831-1149 *Fax:* 302-831-6549
*E-mail:* ud-press@udel.edu
*Web Site:* www2.lib.udel.edu/udpress
*Key Personnel*
Chmn, Bd of Eds: Dr Donald C Mell *E-mail:* dmell@udel.edu
Mng Ed: Karen G Druliner *E-mail:* druliner@udel.edu
Founded: 1922
Literary studies, especially Shakespeare, Renaissance & Early Modern literature; Eighteenth-Century Studies, French literature, art history & history & cultural studies of Delaware & the Eastern Shore.
ISBN Prefix(es): 978-0-87413; 978-1-61149
Number of titles published annually: 37 Print
Total Titles: 1,053 Print
Distributed by Rowman & Littlefield
*Distribution Center:* Rowman & Littlefield, 15200 NBN Way, Blue Ridge Summit, PA 17214 *Toll Free Tel:* 800-462-6420 *Toll Free Fax:* 800-338-4550 *Web Site:* rowmanlittlefield.com
Quantum Publishing Solutions Ltd, 2 Cheviot Rd, Paisley PA2 8AN, United Kingdom *Tel:* (07702) 831967
Durnell Marketing Ltd, 2 Linden Close, Tunbridge Wells TN4 8HH, United Kingdom (Europe including Ireland) *Tel:* (01892) 544272 *Fax:* (01892) 511152 *E-mail:* orders@durnell.co.uk

**University of Georgia Press**
Main Library, 3rd fl, 320 S Jackson St, Athens, GA 30602
*Tel:* 706-369-6130 *Fax:* 706-369-6131; 706-369-6162
*E-mail:* books@ugapress.uga.edu (orders)
*Web Site:* www.ugapress.org
*Key Personnel*
Dir: Lisa Bayer *Tel:* 706-542-0027 *E-mail:* lbayer@ugapress.uga.edu
Ed-in-Chief: Mick Gusinde-Duffy *Tel:* 706-542-9907 *E-mail:* mgd@ugapress.uga.edu
Sales & Mktg Dir: David Des Jardines *Tel:* 706-542-9758 *E-mail:* ddesjard@ugapress.uga.edu
Asst Dir, Design & Prodn: Kathi Morgan *Tel:* 706-542-2491 *E-mail:* kdmorgan@ugapress.uga.edu
Founded: 1938
Publisher of scholarly works, creative & literary works, regional works & digital projects.
ISBN Prefix(es): 978-0-8203
Number of titles published annually: 80 Print; 60 E-Book
Total Titles: 1,800 Print; 450 E-Book
Distributor for Golden Coast Publishing Co; Telfair Museums
Foreign Rep(s): East-West Export Books (Asia, Far East); Eurospan Group (Africa, Europe, Middle East); Scholarly Book Services Inc (Canada)
*Orders to:* 4435 Atlanta Hwy, West Dock, Athens, GA 30602 *Toll Free Tel:* 800-266-5842 *Fax:* 706-425-3061
Membership(s): Association of American University Presses

**University of Hawaii Press**
2840 Kolowalu St, Honolulu, HI 96822
SAN: 202-5353
*Tel:* 808-956-8255 *Toll Free Tel:* 888-UHPRESS (847-7377) *Fax:* 808-988-6052 *Toll Free Fax:* 800-650-7811
*E-mail:* uhpbooks@hawaii.edu
*Web Site:* www.uhpress.hawaii.edu
*Key Personnel*
CFO: Joel Cosseboom *E-mail:* cosseboo@hawaii.edu
Dir & Intl Rts: William Hamilton *Tel:* 808-956-6218 *E-mail:* hamilton@hawaii.edu
Mktg Dir: Colins Kawai *Tel:* 808-956-6417 *E-mail:* ckawai@hawaii.edu
Exec Ed: Patricia Crosby *Tel:* 808-956-8694 *E-mail:* pcrosby@hawaii.edu
Acq Ed: Masako Ikeda *Tel:* 808-956-8696 *E-mail:* masakoi@hawaii.edu; Pamela Kelley *Tel:* 808-956-6207 *E-mail:* pkelley@hawaii.edu; Keith Leber *Tel:* 808-956-6208 *E-mail:* kleber@hawaii.edu
eMktg Mgr & Copywriter: Stephanie Chun *Tel:* 808-956-6426 *E-mail:* chuns@hawaii.edu
Journals Mgr: Joel Bradshaw *Tel:* 808-956-6790 *E-mail:* bradshaw@hawaii.edu
Prod Mgr, Asian Studies: Steve Hirashima *Tel:* 808-956-8698 *E-mail:* stevehir@hawaii.edu
Promo Mgr, Hawaii & Pacific Studies: Carol Abe *Tel:* 808-956-8697 *E-mail:* abec@hawaii.edu
Sales Mgr: Royden Muranaka *Tel:* 808-956-6214 *E-mail:* royden@hawaii.edu
Computer Specialist: Wanda C China *Tel:* 808-956-6227 *E-mail:* wchina@hawaii.edu
Founded: 1947
Scholarly & general books & monographs, particularly those dealing with the Pacific & Asia; regional books; journals.
ISBN Prefix(es): 978-0-8248; 978-0-87022
Number of titles published annually: 100 Print
Total Titles: 1,300 Print
Imprints: Kolowalu Books; Latitude 20
Subsidiaries: East-West Export Books
Distributor for Ateneo De Manila University Press; Global Oriental; Huia Publishers; Nordic Insititute of Asian Studies; The Numata Center; Pandanus Books; Pasifika Press; Singapore University Press; University of the Phillipines Press
Foreign Rep(s): East-West Export Books (Asia, Australia, New Zealand); The Eurospan Group (Africa, Continental Europe, Middle East, UK); Scholarly Book Services (Canada)
*Advertising Agency:* Manini Promotions
*Warehouse:* 99-1422 Koaha Place, Aiea, HI 96701
Membership(s): American Association of University Presses

**University of Illinois Press**
Unit of University of Illinois
1325 S Oak St, MC-566, Champaign, IL 61820-6903
SAN: 202-5310
*Tel:* 217-333-0950 *Fax:* 217-244-8082
*E-mail:* uipress@uillinois.edu; journals@uillinois.edu
*Web Site:* www.press.uillinois.edu

*Key Personnel*
Dir: Willis G Regier *Tel:* 217-244-0728 *E-mail:* wregier@uillinois.edu
Art Dir: Dustin Hubbart *Tel:* 217-333-9227 *E-mail:* dhubbert@uillinois.edu
Ed-in-Chief: Laurie Matheson *Tel:* 217-244-4685 *E-mail:* lmatheso@uillinois.edu
Direct Mktg & Ad Mgr: Denise Peeler *Tel:* 217-244-4690 *E-mail:* dpeeler@uillinois.edu
Edit Design & Prodn Mgr: Jennifer Reichlin *Tel:* 217-244-3279 *E-mail:* reichlin@uillinois.edu
Exhibits Mgr: Margo Chaney *Tel:* 217-244-6491 *E-mail:* mehaney@uillinois.edu
Journals Mgr: Clydette Wantland *Tel:* 217-244-6496 *E-mail:* cwantland@uillinois.edu
Prodn Mgr: Kristine Ding *Tel:* 217-244-4701 *E-mail:* kding@uillinois.edu
Publicity Mgr: Michael Roux *Tel:* 217-244-4689 *E-mail:* mroux@uillinois.edu
Sales Mgr: Lynda Schuh *Tel:* 217-333-9071 *E-mail:* lschuh@uillinois.edu
Founded: 1918
Working-class & ethnic studies, religion, architecture, film studies, political science, folklore, Chicago, food studies, immigration studies, American history, women's history, music history, regional history.
ISBN Prefix(es): 978-0-252
Number of titles published annually: 100 Print
Total Titles: 1,700 Print; 10 Online
Foreign Rep(s): Combined Academic Publishers Ltd (Africa, Europe, Middle East, UK); B K Norton (China, Hong Kong, Korea, Taiwan); Scholarly Book Services Inc (Canada); United Publishers Services Ltd (Japan)
*Orders to:* c/o Chicago Distribution Center, 11030 S Langley Ave, Chicago, IL 60628 *Tel:* 773-702-7000 *Toll Free Tel:* 800-621-2736 *Fax:* 773-702-7212 *Toll Free Fax:* 800-621-8476 *E-mail:* orders@press.uchicago.edu
*Returns:* c/o Chicago Distribution Center, 11030 S Langley Ave, Chicago, IL 60628 *Tel:* 773-702-7000 *Toll Free Tel:* 800-621-2736 *Fax:* 773-702-7212 *Toll Free Fax:* 800-621-8476 *E-mail:* orders@press.uchicago.edu
*Warehouse:* c/o Chicago Distribution Center, 11030 S Langley Ave, Chicago, IL 60628 *Tel:* 773-702-7000 *Toll Free Tel:* 800-621-2736 *Fax:* 773-702-7212 *Toll Free Fax:* 800-621-8476 *E-mail:* orders@press.uchicago.edu
Membership(s): AAP; Association of American University Presses

**University of Iowa Press**
119 W Park Rd, 100 Kuhl House, Iowa City, IA 52242-1000
SAN: 282-4868
*Tel:* 319-335-2000 *Toll Free Tel:* 800-621-2736 (orders only) *Fax:* 319-335-2055 *Toll Free Fax:* 800-621-8476 (orders only)
*E-mail:* uipress@uiowa.edu
*Web Site:* www.uiowapress.org
*Key Personnel*
Dir: James McCoy *Tel:* 319-335-2013 *E-mail:* james-mccoy@uiowa.edu
Ed: Holly Carver *E-mail:* holly-carver@uiowa.edu
Assoc Dir & Design & Prodn Mgr: Karen Copp *Tel:* 319-335-2014 *E-mail:* karen-copp@uiowa.edu
Founded: 1969
Creative fiction, nonfiction, poetry, regional studies, theatre history & literary criticism.
ISBN Prefix(es): 978-0-87745; 978-1-58729
Number of titles published annually: 35 Print
Total Titles: 400 Print
Foreign Rep(s): Eurospan (Europe, UK); EWEB (Asia, Australia, New Zealand, The Pacific)
*Orders to:* Chicago Distribution Center, 11030 S Langley Ave, Chicago, IL 60628 *E-mail:* orders@press.uchicago.edu
*Returns:* Chicago Distribution Center, 11030 S Langley Ave, Chicago, IL 60628 *E-mail:* orders@press.uchicago.edu
*Distribution Center:* Chicago Distribution Center, 11030 S Langley Ave, Chicago, IL 60628 *Toll Free Tel:* 800-621-2736 *Toll Free Fax:* 800-621-8476 *E-mail:* orders@press.uchicago.edu
Membership(s): American Association of University Presses

**University of Louisiana at Lafayette Press**
PO Box 40831, UL, Lafayette, LA 70504-0831
*Tel:* 337-482-6027 *Fax:* 337-482-6028
*E-mail:* cls@louisiana.edu
*Web Site:* www.ulpress.org
*Key Personnel*
Dir: Michael Martin
Asst Dir: James Wilson
Sales & Mktg Dir: Melissa Teutsch
Founded: 1973
Publish titles on Louisiana culture & history.
ISBN Prefix(es): 978-0-940984; 978-1-887366; 978-1-935754
Number of titles published annually: 10 Print
Total Titles: 150 Print
*Shipping Address:* 302 E Saint Mary Blvd, Lafayette, LA 70504

**University of Massachusetts Press**
East Experiment Sta, 671 N Pleasant St, Amherst, MA 01003
*Tel:* 413-545-2217 *Fax:* 413-545-1226
*E-mail:* info@umpress.umass.edu
*Web Site:* www.umass.edu/umpress
*Key Personnel*
Dir: Bruce Wilcox *Tel:* 413-545-4990 *E-mail:* wilcox@umpress.umass.edu
Busn Mgr: Yvonne Crevier *Tel:* 413-545-4994 *E-mail:* ycrevier@umpress.umass.edu
Design & Prodn Mgr: Jack Harrison *Tel:* 413-545-4998 *E-mail:* harrison@umpress.umass.edu
Promo Mgr: Karen Fisk *Tel:* 413-545-4987 *E-mail:* kfisk@umpress.umass.edu
Assoc Prodn Mgr & Design: Sally Nichols *Tel:* 413-545-4997 *E-mail:* snichols@umpress.umass.edu
Mng Ed: Carol Betsch *Tel:* 413-545-4991 *Fax:* 413-545-2216 *E-mail:* betsch@umpress.umass.edu
Sr Ed: Clark Dougan *Tel:* 413-545-4989 *E-mail:* cdougan@umpress.umass.edu
Ed: Brian Halley *Tel:* 617-287-6510 *Fax:* 617-287-5616 *E-mail:* brian.halley@umb.edu
Founded: 1963
Scholarly works & serious nonfiction, including African American studies, American history, American studies, architecture & landscape design, disability studies, environmental studies, gender studies, history of the book, journalism & media studies, literary & cultural studies, Native American studies, technology studies, urban studies & books of regional interest.
ISBN Prefix(es): 978-0-87023; 978-1-55849; 978-1-62534
Number of titles published annually: 40 Print; 35 E-Book
Total Titles: 1,000 Print; 400 E-Book
*Sales Office(s):* Columbia Consortium, Sales Consortium Mgr: Catherine Hobbs *Tel:* 804-690-8529 *E-mail:* catherinehobbs@earthlink.net
Foreign Rep(s): East-West Export Books (Asia, Australia); Eurospan (Africa, Europe, Middle East); Scholarly Book Services (Canada)
*Orders to:* Hopkins Fulfillment Services, PO Box 50370, Baltimore, MD 21211-4370 *Tel:* 410-516-6965 *Toll Free Tel:* 800-537-5487 *Fax:* 410-516-6998 *E-mail:* hfcustserv@mail.press.jhu.edu
*Shipping Address:* Hopkins Fulfillment Services, PO Box 50370, Baltimore, MD 21211-4370 *Tel:* 410-516-6965 *Toll Free Tel:* 800-537-5487 *Fax:* 410-516-6998 *E-mail:* hfcustserv@mail.press.jhu.edu
*Distribution Center:* INscribe Digital, 444 Spear St, Suite 213, San Francisco, CA 94105
Membership(s): Association of American University Presses

**University of Michigan Center for Japanese Studies**
Unit of University of Michigan
1007 E Huron St, Ann Arbor, MI 48104-1690
*Tel:* 734-647-8885 *Fax:* 734-647-8886
*E-mail:* ii.cjspubs@umich.edu
*Web Site:* www.cjspubs.lsa.umich.edu
*Key Personnel*
Exec Ed: Bruce E Willoughby *E-mail:* bew@umich.edu
Founded: 1947
This publisher has indicated that 50% of their product line is author subsidized.
ISBN Prefix(es): 978-0-939512; 978-1-929280
Number of titles published annually: 4 Print
Total Titles: 130 Print

**University of Michigan Press**
Unit of University of Michigan
839 Greene St, Ann Arbor, MI 48104-3209
SAN: 202-5329
*Tel:* 734-764-4388 *Fax:* 734-615-1540
*E-mail:* esladmin@umich.edu
*Web Site:* www.press.umich.edu
*Key Personnel*
Interim Dir & Digital Mgr: Karen Hill *Tel:* 734-763-4134 *E-mail:* kahi@umich.edu
Sales & Mktg Dir & Foreign Sales Mgr: Michael Kehoe *Tel:* 734-936-0388 *E-mail:* mkehoe@umich.edu
HR Mgr: Christina Milton *Tel:* 734-764-4390 *E-mail:* cmilton@umich.edu
Prodn Mgr: John Grucelski *Tel:* 734-764-4391 *E-mail:* jgrucel@umich.edu
ESL Mgr & ESL Foreign Rts Mgr: Kelly Sippell *Tel:* 734-764-4447 *E-mail:* ksippell@umich.edu
Founded: 1930
Aims for diversity in its books & in its audiences.
ISBN Prefix(es): 978-0-472
Number of titles published annually: 110 Print; 100 E-Book
Total Titles: 3,000 Print; 700 E-Book; 24 Audio
Imprints: Ann Arbor Paperbacks; digitalculture
Distributed by Eurospan (territory restricted to Europe, Africa & UK)
Distributor for Center for Chinese Studies, University of Michigan; Center for South & Southeast Asian Studies, University of Michigan
Foreign Rep(s): APAC Publishers Services (Asia, The Pacific); EUROSPAN (Europe); United Publishers Services Ltd (Japan)
*Returns:* Client Distribution Services, 193 Edwards Dr, Jackson, TN 38301 *Toll Free Tel:* 800-343-4499 *Toll Free Fax:* 800-351-5073 *E-mail:* orderentry@perseusbooks.com
*Distribution Center:* Client Distribution Services, 193 Edwards Dr, Jackson, TN 38301 *Toll Free Tel:* 800-343-4499 *Toll Free Fax:* 800-351-5073 *E-mail:* orderentry@perseusbooks.com

**University of Minnesota Press**
111 Third Ave S, Suite 290, Minneapolis, MN 55401-2520
SAN: 213-2648
*Tel:* 612-627-1970 *Fax:* 612-627-1980
*E-mail:* ump@umn.edu
*Web Site:* www.upress.umn.edu
*Key Personnel*
Dir: Doug Armato
Mktg Dir: Emily Hamilton
Mgr, MMPI: Beverly Kaemmer
Prodn Mgr: Daniel Ochsner
Opers Mgr: Susan Doerr
Copyediting Mgr: Laura Westlund
Exec Ed: Richard Morrison
Sr Acqs Ed: Todd Orjala
Publicist: Heather Skinner

Sales Coord: Erik Anderson
Intl Rts Contact: Jeff Moen
Direct Mail: Maggie Sattler
Founded: 1925
University press, scholarly, professional, reference, textbooks; regional nonfiction; cultural theory, media studies, literary theory, gay & lesbian studies, sociology, art, political science, geography, anthropology.
ISBN Prefix(es): 978-0-8166
Number of titles published annually: 110 Print; 110 E-Book
Total Titles: 1,800 Print; 1,600 E-Book
Foreign Rep(s): Harry Howell (Australia, New Zealand); Lexa Publishers (Canada); United Publishers Services Ltd (Japan); University Presses Marketing (Israel, UK); Wolfgang Wingerter (Europe)
*Returns:* Chicago Distribution Center, 11030 S Langley Ave, Chicago, IL 60628
*Shipping Address:* Chicago Distribution Center, 11030 S Langley Ave, Chicago, IL 60628 *Tel:* 773-568-1550 *Toll Free Tel:* 800-621-2736 (orders only) *Toll Free Fax:* 800-621-8476 (orders only)
Membership(s): Association of American University Presses

**University of Missouri Press**
2910 Le Mone Blvd, Columbia, MO 65201
SAN: 203-3143
*Tel:* 573-882-7641 *Toll Free Tel:* 800-621-2736 (orders) *Fax:* 573-884-4498
*Web Site:* press.umsystem.edu
*Key Personnel*
Interim Dir: Dwight Browne
Interim Mktg Mgr: Beth Chandler
Publicity Mgr: Lyn Smith *E-mail:* smithls@missouri.edu
Ed-in-Chief & Assoc Dir: Clair Willcox
Rts: Steve Hammer
Founded: 1958
Scholarly books, general trade, art, regional, intellectual thought, history, literary criticism, African-American, journalism, political science, sports & women's studies.
ISBN Prefix(es): 978-0-8262
Number of titles published annually: 30 Print
Total Titles: 900 Print
Distributor for Missouri History Museum; St Louis Mercantile Library
Foreign Rep(s): East-West Export Books (Asia, New Zealand, Pacific Islands); Eurospan (Africa, Continental Europe, Middle East, UK); Scholarly Book Services (Canada)

**University of Nebraska at Omaha Center for Public Affairs Research**
CPACS Bldg, Rm 108, 6001 Dodge St, Omaha, NE 68182
SAN: 665-4339
*Tel:* 402-554-2134
*Web Site:* www.unomaha.edu/cpar
*Key Personnel*
Dir & Sr Res Assoc: Jerry Deichert
*E-mail:* jdeicher@unomaha.edu
Professional books.
ISBN Prefix(es): 978-1-55719
Number of titles published annually: 6 Print
Total Titles: 130 Print

**University of Nebraska Press**
Division of University of Nebraska at Lincoln
1111 Lincoln Mall, Lincoln, NE 68588-0630
*Tel:* 402-472-3581; 919-966-7449 (cust serv & foreign orders) *Toll Free Tel:* 800-848-6224 (cust serv & US orders) *Fax:* 402-472-6214; 919-962-2704 (cust serv & foreign orders) *Toll Free Fax:* 800-526-2617 (cust serv & US orders)
*E-mail:* pressmail@unl.edu
*Web Site:* www.nebraskapress.unl.edu
*Key Personnel*
Dir: Donna Shear *Tel:* 402-472-2861
*E-mail:* dshear2@unl.edu
Ed-in-Chief: Derek Krissoff
Mktg Mgr: Martyn Beeny
Rts & Perms, Intl Rts: Leif Milliken *Tel:* 402-472-7702 *E-mail:* lmilliken2@unl.edu
Publicity Mgr: Cara Pesek *Tel:* 402-472-7710
*E-mail:* cpesek2@unl.edu
Humanities Ed: Kristen Elias-Rowley *Tel:* 402-472-5949 *E-mail:* keliasrowley2@unl.edu
Founded: 1941
General scholarly nonfiction, including agriculture & natural resources, anthropology, history, literature & criticism, musicology, philosophy, psychology, wildlife & reference works; emphasis on literature & the history of the Trans-Mississippi West. Trade paperbacks, including fiction & science fiction.
ISBN Prefix(es): 978-0-8032
Total Titles: 3,200 Print; 2 CD-ROM
Imprints: Bison Books; Potomac Books
Distributor for Buros Institute; Caxton Press; Creighton University Press; Society for American Baseball Research
Foreign Rep(s): Codasat Canada (Canada); Combined Academic Publishers Ltd (Europe); East-West Export Books (EWEB) (Asia, Australia, New Zealand, The Pacific)
*Advertising Agency:* Scholarly Press Advertising Services
*Warehouse:* Maple Press Co, Lebanon Distribution Ctr, 704 Legionaire Dr, Fredericksburg, PA 17026
Membership(s): American Association of University Presses
*See separate listing for:*
**Potomac Books Inc**

**University of Nevada Press**
University of Nevada, M/S 0166, Reno, NV 89557-0166
SAN: 203-316X
*Tel:* 775-784-6573 *Fax:* 775-784-6200
*Web Site:* www.unpress.nevada.edu
*Key Personnel*
Dir: Joanne O'Hare *Tel:* 775-682-7389
*E-mail:* johare@unpress.nevada.edu
Busn Mgr: Jo Anne Banducci *Tel:* 775-682-7387
*E-mail:* jbanducci@unpress.nevada.edu
Design & Prodn Mgr: Kathleen Szawiola
*Tel:* 775-682-7391 *E-mail:* szawiola@unpress.nevada.edu
Founded: 1961
ISBN Prefix(es): 978-0-87417
Number of titles published annually: 20 Print; 20 E-Book
Total Titles: 400 Print
Foreign Rep(s): East-West Books (Asia-Pacific); Eurospan University Press Group (Africa, Central America, Europe, Middle East, South America, UK); Scholarly Book Service (Canada)
*Orders to:* Chicago Distribution Center, 11030 S Langley Ave, Chicago, IL 60628 (Pubnet@202.5280) *Toll Free Tel:* 800-621-2736 *Toll Free Fax:* 800-621-8476
*E-mail:* custserv@press.uchicago.edu
*Warehouse:* Chicago Distribution Center, 11030 S Langley Ave, Chicago, IL 60628 (Pubnet@202.5280) *Toll Free Tel:* 800-621-2736 *Toll Free Fax:* 800-621-8476
*E-mail:* custserv@press.uchicago.edu
Membership(s): American Association of University Presses; Publishers Association of the West

**University of New Mexico**
University of New Mexico, Humanities Dept, Rm 253, Albuquerque, NM 87131-0001
SAN: 213-9588
Mailing Address: MSC05 3185, One Univ of New Mexico, Albuquerque, NM 87131-0001
*Tel:* 505-277-2346; 505-272-7777 (cust serv) *Toll Free Tel:* 800-249-7737 (orders only) *Fax:* 505-277-3343; 505-272-7778 (cust serv) *Toll Free Fax:* 800-622-8667 (orders only)
*E-mail:* unmpress@unm.edu; custserv@upress.unm.edu (order dept)
*Web Site:* unmpress.com
*Key Personnel*
Dir: John W Byram *Tel:* 505-277-3495
*E-mail:* jbyram@upress.unm.edu
Assoc Dir, Busn Opers: Richard Schuetz
*Tel:* 505-277-3284 *E-mail:* rschuetz@upress.unm.edu
Rts & Perms Coord: Briony Jones
*E-mail:* briony@unm.edu
Book Designer: Catherine Leonardo *Tel:* 505-277-3299
Founded: 1929
General, young adult, scholarly & regional books.
ISBN Prefix(es): 978-0-8263
Number of titles published annually: 90 Print
Total Titles: 1,750 Print
Distributor for Avanyu Publishing; Fresco Fine Art Publications LLC; La Frontera Publishing; West End Press
Foreign Rep(s): Codasat (Canada); Eurospan Ltd (Africa, Europe, Middle East, UK); EWEB (Asia, Australia); US PubRep (Craig Falk) (Caribbean including Puerto Rico, Central America, Latin America, Mexico)
*Shipping Address:* 1312 Basehart Rd SE, Albuquerque, NM 87106-4363
Membership(s): Association of American University Presses

**§The University of North Carolina Press**
116 S Boundary St, Chapel Hill, NC 27514-3808
SAN: 203-3151
*Tel:* 919-966-3561 *Fax:* 919-966-3829
*E-mail:* uncpress@unc.edu
*Web Site:* www.uncpress.unc.edu
*Key Personnel*
Sr Dir, Mktg & Digital Busn Devt: Dino Battista
*Tel:* 919-962-0579 *E-mail:* dino_battista@unc.edu
Dir: John Sherer
Dir, Contracts & Subs Rts: Vicky Wells *Tel:* 919-962-0369 *E-mail:* vicki_wells@unc.edu
Dir, Publicity & ISBN Contact: Gina M Mahalek
*Tel:* 919-962-0581 *E-mail:* gina_mahalek@unc.edu
Edit Dir: Mark Simpson-Vos *Tel:* 919-962-0535
Sales Dir: Michael Donatelli *Tel:* 919-962-0475
*E-mail:* michael_donatelli@unc.edu
Asst Dir & Sr Ed: Charles Grench *Tel:* 919-962-0481 *E-mail:* charles_grench@unc.edu
Asst Dir & Mng Ed: Ron Maner *Tel:* 919-962-0540 *E-mail:* ron_maner@unc.edu
Acqs Ed: Brandon Proia
Founded: 1922
General, scholarly, regional.
ISBN Prefix(es): 978-0-8078
Number of titles published annually: 100 Print
Total Titles: 776 E-Book
Distributor for Museum of Early Southern Decorative Arts; North Carolina Museum of Art; Southeastern Center for Contemporary Art; Valentine Museum
Foreign Rep(s): East-West Export Books (Asia, Australia, New Zealand, The Pacific); EDIREP (Caribbean, Central America, Mexico, South America); Eurospan University Press Group (Africa, Continental Europe, Middle East, UK); Scholarly Book Services (Canada)
*Advertising Agency:* Brimley Agency
*Orders to:* Long Leaf Services Inc, PO Box 8895, Chapel Hill, NC 27515-8895 *Toll Free Tel:* 800-848-6224 *Toll Free Fax:* 800-272-6817
*E-mail:* customerservice@longleafservices.org
*Returns:* Longleaf Returns, c/o Maple Press Co, Lebanon Distribution Center, 704 Legionaire Dr, Fredericksburg, PA 17026
Membership(s): AAP; BISG

**University of North Texas Press**
Stovall Hall, Suite 174, 1400 Highland St, Denton, TX 76201
SAN: 249-4280
Mailing Address: 1155 Union Circle, No 311336, Denton, TX 76203-5017
*Tel:* 940-565-2142 *Fax:* 940-565-4590
*Web Site:* www.unt.edu/untpress
*Key Personnel*
Dir: Ronald Chrisman *E-mail:* ronald.chrisman@unt.edu
Asst Dir: Karen De Vinney *E-mail:* karen.devinney@unt.edu
Founded: 1987
ISBN Prefix(es): 978-0-929398; 978-1-57441
Number of titles published annually: 16 Print; 5 Online
Total Titles: 300 Print; 75 Online
Distributed by Texas A&M University Press
Foreign Rep(s): East-West Export Books (Asia, Australia, Hawaii, New Zealand, Pacific Islands); Eurospan Group (Europe); Scholarly Book Services (Canada); US Pub Rep Inc (Latin America)
*Distribution Center:* University Consortium, John H Lindsey Bldg, Lewis St, 4354 Tamu, College Station, TX 77843-4354 *Toll Free Tel:* 800-826-8911 *Toll Free Fax:* 888-617-2421
Membership(s): American Association of University Presses

**University of Notre Dame Press**
310 Flanner Hall, Notre Dame, IN 46556
SAN: 203-3178
*Tel:* 574-631-6346 *Fax:* 574-631-8148
*E-mail:* undpress@nd.edu
*Web Site:* www.undpress.nd.edu
*Key Personnel*
Interim Mng Dir: Harv Humphrey *Tel:* 574-631-3265 *E-mail:* hjhumphrey@nd.edu
Mng Ed: Rebecca De Boer *Tel:* 574-631-4908 *E-mail:* rdeboer@nd.edu
Busn Mgr: Diane Schaut *Tel:* 574-631-4904 *E-mail:* dschaut@nd.edu
Prodn & Design Mgr: Wendy McMillen *Tel:* 574-631-4907 *E-mail:* wmcmill@nd.edu
Coord, Off Servs: Gina Bixler *Tel:* 574-631-4915 *E-mail:* gbixler@nd.edu
Founded: 1949
Academic books, hardcover & paperback; philosophy, Irish studies, literature, theology, international relations, sociology & general interest.
ISBN Prefix(es): 978-0-268
Number of titles published annually: 50 Print
Total Titles: 800 Print
Foreign Rep(s): Eurospan; EWEB
*Returns:* Chicago Distribution Center, 11030 S Langley, Chicago, IL 60628 *Tel:* 773-702-7000 (rest of world) *Toll Free Tel:* 800-621-2736 (US & CN) *Fax:* 773-702-7212 (rest of world) *Toll Free Fax:* 800-621-8476 (US & CN)
*Distribution Center:* Chicago Distribution Center, 11030 S Langley Ave, Chicago, IL 60628 *Tel:* 773-702-7000 (rest of world) *Toll Free Tel:* 800-621-2736 (US & CN) *Fax:* 773-702-7212 (rest of world) *Toll Free Fax:* 800-621-8476 (US & CN)
Membership(s): Association of American University Presses

**University of Oklahoma Press**
2800 Venture Dr, Norman, OK 73069-8216
SAN: 203-3194
*Tel:* 405-325-2000 *Toll Free Tel:* 800-627-7377 (orders) *Fax:* 405-364-5798 (orders) *Toll Free Fax:* 800-735-0476 (orders)
*E-mail:* presscs@ou.edu
*Web Site:* www.oupress.com
*Key Personnel*
CFO & Rts & Perms: Diane Cotts *Tel:* 405-325-3276 *E-mail:* dcotts@ou.edu
Dir: B Byron Price *Tel:* 405-325-5666 *E-mail:* b_byron_price@ou.edu
Dir, Sales & Mktg: Dale Bennie *Tel:* 405-325-3207 *E-mail:* dbennie@ou.edu
Ed-in-Chief: Charles Rankin *Tel:* 405-325-2873 *E-mail:* cerankin@ou.edu
Mng Ed: Steven Baker *Tel:* 405-325-1325 *E-mail:* steven.b.baker@ou.edu
Fulfillment Mgr: Diane Cotts *Tel:* 405-325-3276 *E-mail:* dcotts@ou.edu
Prodn Mgr: Emmy Ezzell *Tel:* 405-325-3186 *E-mail:* eezzell@ou.edu
Publicity Mgr: Sandy See *Tel:* 405-325-3200 *E-mail:* ssee@ou.edu
Founded: 1928
Scholarly & general interest books on Americana, Native American studies, Western history, regional interest, natural history, anthropology, archaeology, military history, literature, classical studies, women's studies & political science.
ISBN Prefix(es): 978-0-8061; 978-0-87062 (Arthur H Clark Co)
Number of titles published annually: 90 Print; 80 E-Book
Total Titles: 1,680 Print; 5 CD-ROM; 1,280 E-Book
Imprints: Arthur H Clark Co
Distributor for Cherokee National Press; Chickasaw Press; Dakota Institute; Denver Art Museum; Gilcrease Museum; Vanderbilt University Press
Membership(s): American Association of University Presses

**§University of Pennsylvania Museum of Archaeology & Anthropology**
Division of University of Pennsylvania
3260 South St, Philadelphia, PA 19104-6324
*Tel:* 215-898-5723 *Fax:* 215-573-2497
*E-mail:* info@pennmuseum.org; publications@pennmuseum.org
*Web Site:* www.penn.museum
*Key Personnel*
Dir, Pubns: James R Mathieu
Admin Coord: Maureen Goldsmith
Founded: 1887
ISBN Prefix(es): 978-0-686; 978-0-934718; 978-0-924171; 978-1-873415; 978-1-931707
Number of titles published annually: 14 Print
Total Titles: 210 Print; 6 CD-ROM
*Billing Address:* Hopkins Fulfillment Service, PO Box 50370, Baltimore, MD 21211-4370 *Toll Free Tel:* 800-537-5487 *Fax:* 410-516-6998 *E-mail:* hfscustserv@press.jhu.edu
*Orders to:* Hopkins Fulfillment Service, PO Box 50370, Baltimore, MD 21211-4370 *Toll Free Tel:* 800-537-5487 *Fax:* 410-516-6998 *E-mail:* hfscustserv@press.jhu.edu
*Returns:* Hopkins Fulfillment Service, PO Box 50370, Baltimore, MD 21211-4370 *Toll Free Tel:* 800-537-5487 *Fax:* 410-516-6998 *E-mail:* hfscustserv@press.jhu.edu
*Shipping Address:* Hopkins Fulfillment Service, PO Box 50370, Baltimore, MD 21211-4370 *Toll Free Tel:* 800-537-5487 *Fax:* 410-516-6998 *E-mail:* hfscustserv@press.jhu.edu

**University of Pennsylvania Press**
3905 Spruce St, Philadelphia, PA 19104
SAN: 202-5345
*Tel:* 215-898-6261 *Fax:* 215-898-0404
*E-mail:* custserv@pobox.upenn.edu
*Web Site:* www.pennpress.org
*Key Personnel*
Dir: Eric Halpern *Tel:* 215-898-6263 *E-mail:* ehalpern@upenn.edu
Mktg Dir: Laura Waldron *Tel:* 215-898-1673 *E-mail:* lwaldron@upenn.edu
Busn Mgr: Joseph Guttman *Tel:* 215-898-1670 *E-mail:* josephgg@upenn.edu
Editing & Prodn Mgr: Elizabeth Glover *Tel:* 215-898-1675 *E-mail:* gloverel@upenn.edu
Publicity & PR Mgr: Saunders Robinson *Tel:* 215-898-1674 *E-mail:* jorobin@upenn.edu
Ed-in-Chief: Peter A Agree *Tel:* 215-573-3816 *E-mail:* agree@upenn.edu
Mng Ed: Alison Anderson *Tel:* 215-898-1678 *E-mail:* anderaa@upenn.edu
History Ed: Robert Lockhart *Tel:* 215-898-1677 *E-mail:* rlochhar@upenn.edu
Humanities Ed: Jerome E Singerman *Tel:* 215-898-1681 *E-mail:* singerma@upenn.edu
Politics & Policy Ed: Bill Finan *Tel:* 215-573-7129 *E-mail:* wfinan@upenn.edu
Founded: 1890
Scholarly & semipopular nonfiction, especially in architecture, history, literature & criticism, social sciences, & human rights.
ISBN Prefix(es): 978-0-8122
Number of titles published annually: 120 Print; 120 Online
Total Titles: 1,200 Print; 800 E-Book
Imprints: Pine Street Books
Foreign Rep(s): University Presses Marketing (Europe, UK)
Foreign Rights: East-West Export Books Inc (Southeast Asia); Scholarly Book Services (Canada); University Presses Marketing (Europe, Middle East, UK)
*Orders to:* Penn Press, c/o Hopkins Fulfillment Services, Hampden Sta, Box 50370, Baltimore, MD 21211 *Toll Free Tel:* 800-537-5487 *Fax:* 410-516-6998 *E-mail:* hfscustserv@press.jhu.edu
*Returns:* Penn Press, c/o Maple Press Co, Lebanon Distribution Center, 704 Legionaire Dr, Fredericksburg, PA 17026
*Warehouse:* Maple Press Distribution Ctr, PO Box 1287, 704 Legionaire Dr, Lebanon, PA 17042 *Tel:* 717-865-7600 *Web Site:* www.maple-vail.com
Membership(s): American Association of University Presses

**University of Pittsburgh Press**
Eureka Bldg, 5th fl, 3400 Forbes Ave, Pittsburgh, PA 15260
*Tel:* 412-383-2456 *Fax:* 412-383-2466
*E-mail:* info@upress.pitt.edu
*Web Site:* www.upress.pitt.edu
*Key Personnel*
Dir: Cynthia Miller *E-mail:* cymiller@pitt.edu
Edit Dir & Dir, Electronic Publg: Peter Kracht *E-mail:* pek6@pitt.edu
Mktg Dir: Lowell Britson *E-mail:* lbritson@pitt.edu
Mng Ed: Alexander Wolfe *E-mail:* apw20@pitt.edu
Busn Mgr: Cindy Wessels *E-mail:* caw1@pitt.edu
Rts & Perms: Margie K Bachman *Tel:* 412-383-2544 *E-mail:* mkbachma@pitt.edu
Publicist: Maria Sticco *E-mail:* mes5@pitt.edu
Founded: 1936
Scholarly nonfiction; poetry, regional books, short fiction; Russian & East European studies; composition & rhetoric, Latin American studies, environmental history, urban studies, philosophy of science, political science.
ISBN Prefix(es): 978-0-8229
Number of titles published annually: 65 Print
Total Titles: 1,012 Print; 65 E-Book
Imprints: Golden Triangle Books (historical fiction for young readers)
*Sales Office(s):* Chicago Distribution Center, 11030 S Langley Ave, Chicago, IL 60628
Distributed by University of Chicago Press Distribution Center
Foreign Rep(s): East-West Export Books (Asia, The Pacific); Eurospan (Africa, Europe, Middle East, UK); Scholarly Book Services (Canada)
*Billing Address:* Chicago Distribution Center, 11030 S Langley Ave, Chicago, IL 60628
*Returns:* Chicago Distribution Center, 11030 S Langley Ave, Chicago, IL 60628
*Warehouse:* Chicago Distribution Center, 11030 S Langley Ave, Chicago, IL 60628 *Tel:* 773-702-7000 *Toll Free Tel:* 800-621-2736 *Fax:* 773-702-7212 *Toll Free Fax:* 800-621-8471

*Distribution Center:* Chicago Distribution Center, 11030 S Langley Ave, Chicago, IL 60628
Membership(s): Association of American University Presses

**University of Puerto Rico Press**
(La Editorial, Universidad de Puerto Rico)
Subsidiary of University of Puerto Rico
Edificio La Editorial (level 2), Carr No 1, KM 12.0, Jardin Botanico Norte, San Juan, PR 00927
Mailing Address: PO Box 23322, Rio Piedras, PR 00931-3322 SAN: 208-1245
*Tel:* 787-250-0435; 787-250-0550
*Toll Free Tel:* 877-338-7788 *Fax:* 787-753-9116
*E-mail:* info@laeditorialupr.com
*Web Site:* www.laeditorialupr.com
Founded: 1947
General fiction & nonfiction, reference books, college texts; Latin America.
ISBN Prefix(es): 978-0-8477
Number of titles published annually: 50 Print
Total Titles: 1,047 Print
Imprints: Coleccion Antologia Personal; Coleccion Aqui y Ahora; Coleccion Caribena; Coleccion Ciencias Naturales; Coleccion Clasicos No Tan Clasicos; Coleccion Cuadernos La Torre; Coleccion Cuentos de un Mundo Perdido; Coleccion Cultura Basica; Coleccion Dos Lenguas; Coleccion Mujeres de Palabra; Coleccion Nueve Pececitos; Coleccion Obras Completas Eugenio Maria de Hostos (edicion critica); Coleccion Puertorriquena; Coleccion San Pedrito
Foreign Rep(s): Baker & Taylor/Libros Sin Fronteras (USA); DESA (Latin America); Lectorum Publications (USA); Libreria La Trinitaria (Dominican Republic)
Membership(s): American Association of University Presses

**University of Rochester Press**
Affiliate of Boydell & Brewer Inc
668 Mount Hope Ave, Rochester, NY 14620-2731
*Tel:* 585-275-0419 *Fax:* 585-271-8778
*E-mail:* boydell@boydellusa.net
*Web Site:* www.urpress.com
*Key Personnel*
Edit Dir: Suzanne Guiod *E-mail:* suzanne.guiod@rochester.edu
Prodn Dir: Sue Smith *E-mail:* smith@boydellusa.net
Dir, Sales & Mktg: Michael Richards
Accts Mgr: Eloise Puls *Tel:* 585-273-5777 *E-mail:* puls@boydellusa.net
Founded: 1989
Philosophy, music & African studies titles.
ISBN Prefix(es): 978-1-878822; 978-1-58046
Number of titles published annually: 25 Print
Total Titles: 132 Print
*Foreign Office(s):* PO Box 9, Woodbridge Suffolk IP12 3DF, United Kingdom
Foreign Rep(s): Boydell & Brewer (Europe, Japan)
*Warehouse:* Publishers Storage & Shipping Corp, 231 Industrial Park, 46 Development Rd, Fitchburg, MA 01420-6019, Contact: John Salvey *Tel:* 978-345-2121 *Fax:* 978-348-1233

**University of Scranton Press**
Division of University of Scranton
445 Madison Ave, Scranton, PA 18510
*Tel:* 570-941-4228 *Fax:* 570-941-7085
*E-mail:* salesoffice@scranton.edu
*Web Site:* academic.scranton.edu/organization/upress
*Key Personnel*
Prodn Mgr: Patricia Mecadon *E-mail:* mecadonp1@scranton.edu
Founded: 1988
Specialize in religious studies & philosophy of religion & culture of Northeast PA.
ISBN Prefix(es): 978-0-940866; 978-1-58966
Number of titles published annually: 10 Print; 5 Online; 5 E-Book
Total Titles: 80 Print; 38 Online; 26 E-Book
Imprints: Ridge Row Books
Subsidiaries: Ridge Row Press
*Advertising Agency:* Trinka Ravaioli Pettinato Grapevine Design, 1641 Sanderson Ave, Scranton, PA 18509 *Tel:* 570-558-0203 *Fax:* 570-558-0204 *E-mail:* grapevine_design@yahoo.com
*Distribution Center:* Offset Paperback, 101 Memorial Hwy, Dallas, PA 18612 *Tel:* 570-675-5261 *Fax:* 570-675-8714 *Web Site:* www.bvg-opm-books.com
Membership(s): American Association of University Presses; Association of Jesuit University Presses

**§University of South Carolina Press**
Affiliate of University of South Carolina
1600 Hampton St, Suite 544, Columbia, SC 29208
SAN: 203-3224
*Tel:* 803-777-5245 *Toll Free Tel:* 800-768-2500 (orders) *Fax:* 803-777-0160 *Toll Free Fax:* 800-868-0740 (orders)
*Web Site:* www.sc.edu/uscpress
*Key Personnel*
Dir: Jonathan Haupt *Tel:* 800-777-2243 *E-mail:* jhaupt@mailbox.sc.edu
Asst Dir, Opers: Linda Haines Fogle *Tel:* 803-777-4848 *E-mail:* lfogle@mailbox.sc.edu
Busn Mgr: Vicki Sewell *Tel:* 803-777-7754 *E-mail:* sewellvc@mailbox.sc.edu
Design & Prodn Mgr: Pat Callahan *Tel:* 803-777-2449 *E-mail:* mpcallah@mailbox.sc.edu
Mng Ed: William Adams *Tel:* 803-777-5075 *E-mail:* adamswb@mailbox.sc.edu
Asst to Dir: Vicki Bates *Tel:* 803-777-5245 *E-mail:* batesvc@mailbox.sc.edu
Founded: 1944
American history/studies, Southern studies, military history, maritime history, literary studies including contemporary American & British literature & modern world literature, religious studies, speech/communication, social work.
ISBN Prefix(es): 978-0-87249; 978-1-57003
Number of titles published annually: 50 Print
Total Titles: 700 Print; 2 CD-ROM; 2 Audio
Distributor for McKissick Museum; Saraland Press; South Carolina Bar Association; South Carolina Historical Society
Foreign Rep(s): East-West Export Books (Asia, The Pacific); Eurospan University Press Group (Europe, UK); Scholarly Book Services (Canada)
*Warehouse:* 718 Devine St, Columbia, SC 29208, Contact: Libby Mack *Tel:* 803-777-1108 *Fax:* 803-777-0026
Membership(s): American Association of University Presses; Southern Independent Booksellers Alliance

**University of Tennessee Press**
110 Conference Center Bldg, 600 Henley St, Knoxville, TN 37996-4108
SAN: 212-9930
*Tel:* 865-974-3321 *Toll Free Tel:* 800-621-2736 (orders) *Fax:* 865-974-3724 *Toll Free Fax:* 800-621-8476 (orders)
*E-mail:* custserv@utpress.org
*Web Site:* www.utpress.org
*Key Personnel*
Dir: Scott Danforth *E-mail:* danforth@utk.edu
Mng Ed: Stan Ivester *E-mail:* ivester@utk.edu
Acqs Ed: Kerry Webb *E-mail:* webbke@utk.edu
Mktg Mgr: Cheryl Carson *E-mail:* ccarson3@utk.edu
Publicist: Tom Post *Tel:* 865-974-5466 *E-mail:* tpost@utk.edu
Busn Mgr: Lisa Davis *E-mail:* ldavis49@utk.edu
Founded: 1940
Scholarly & regional nonfiction.
ISBN Prefix(es): 978-0-87049; 978-1-57233
Number of titles published annually: 40 Print
Total Titles: 650 Print; 1 Online
Foreign Rep(s): East-West Export Books Inc (Asia, The Pacific)
*Distribution Center:* Chicago Distribution Center, 11030 S Langley, Chicago, IL 60628
Membership(s): AAP; Association of American University Presses

**University of Texas at Arlington School of Urban & Public Affairs**
511 University Hall, 5th fl, 601 S Nedderman Dr, Arlington, TX 76010
Mailing Address: PO Box 19588, Arlington, TX 76019
*Tel:* 817-272-3071 *Fax:* 817-272-3415
*E-mail:* supa@uta.edu
*Web Site:* www.uta.edu/supa
*Key Personnel*
Dir, Communs: Joanne Lovito-Nelson *E-mail:* nelsonjm@uta.edu
Contact: Prof Richard L Cole *E-mail:* cole@uta.edu
Newsletter, working papers, books, reports on community revitalization, population projection, charter school evaluation, strategic planning, land use planning, transportation planning, social welfare policy, urban politics, social planning, urban public finance, consensus, building & dispute resolution, group facilitation, urban management, environmental planning & analysis.
ISBN Prefix(es): 978-0-936440
Number of titles published annually: 15 Print
Total Titles: 40 Print

**§The University of Utah Press**
Subsidiary of University of Utah
J Willard Marriott Library, Suite 5400, 295 S 1500 E, Salt Lake City, UT 84112-0860
SAN: 220-0023
*Tel:* 801-581-6771 *Toll Free Tel:* 800-621-2736 (orders) *Fax:* 801-581-3365 *Toll Free Fax:* 800-621-8471
*E-mail:* info@upress.utah.edu
*Web Site:* www.uofupress.com
*Key Personnel*
Dir & Mng Ed: Glenda Cottter *E-mail:* glenda.cotter@utah.edu
Busn Mgr & Perms: Sharon Day *E-mail:* sharon.day@utah.edu
Mktg & Sales Mgr: Linda Manning *E-mail:* linda.manning@utah.edu
Prodn Mgr: Jessica Booth *E-mail:* jessica.booth@utah.edu
Founded: 1949
Scholarly books, regional studies, anthropology, archaeology, linguistics, Mesoamerican studies, natural history, western history, outdoor recreation.
ISBN Prefix(es): 978-0-87480; 978-1-60781
Number of titles published annually: 30 Print
Total Titles: 375 Print; 1 CD-ROM
Imprints: Bonneville Books (trade)
Distributor for BYU Museum of Peoples & Cultures; BYU Studies; KUED (Utah PBS affiliate); Canyonlands Natural History Association; Western Epics Publications
Foreign Rep(s): East-West Export Books (Asia, Australia, Hawaii, New Zealand, Oceania); Scholarly Book Services Inc (Canada)
*Orders to:* The Chicago Distribution Center, 11030 S Langley Ave, Chicago, IL 60628 *Tel:* 773-702-7000 *Toll Free Tel:* 800-621-2736 *Fax:* 773-702-7212 *Toll Free Fax:* 800-621-8741 *Web Site:* www.uofupress.com
*Returns:* The Chicago Distribution Center, 11030 S Langley Ave, Chicago, IL 60628

**The University of Virginia Press**
Affiliate of University of Virginia

PO Box 400318, Charlottesville, VA 22904-4318
*Tel:* 434-924-3468 (cust serv); 434-924-3469 (cust serv) *Toll Free Tel:* 800-831-3406 (orders) *Fax:* 434-982-2655 *Toll Free Fax:* 877-288-6400
*E-mail:* vapress@virginia.edu
*Web Site:* www.upress.virginia.edu
*Key Personnel*
Dir: Penelope J Kaiserlian *Tel:* 434-924-3361 *E-mail:* pkaiserlian@virginia.edu
Dir, Mktg: Mark Saunders *Tel:* 434-924-6064 *E-mail:* mhs5u@virginia.edu
Database Mgr: Mary MacNeil *E-mail:* mmm5w@virginia.edu
Mgr, Design & Prodn: Martha Farlow *Tel:* 434-924-3585 *E-mail:* mfarlow@virginia.edu
Mktg & Publicity Mgr: Emily Grandstaff *Tel:* 434-982-2932 *E-mail:* ekg4a@virginia.edu
Acqs Ed, Architecture & Environmental: Boyd Zenner
Acqs Ed, Humanities: Cathie Brettschneider *Tel:* 434-982-3033 *E-mail:* cib8b@virginia.edu
Acqs Ed, Soc Sci & History: Richard Holway *Tel:* 434-924-7301 *E-mail:* rkh2a@virginia.edu
Cust Serv: Brenda Fitzgerald
Founded: 1963
General scholarly nonfiction with emphasis on history, literature & regional books.
ISBN Prefix(es): 978-0-8139; 978-978-0
Number of titles published annually: 60 Print; 40 E-Book
Total Titles: 1,250 Print
Distributor for Colonial Society of Massachusetts; Mount Vernon Ladies Association
Foreign Rep(s): East-West Export Books (The Pacific); Eurospan (Europe)
*Shipping Address:* 500 Edgemont, Charlottesville, VA 22903
Membership(s): American Association of University Presses

**§University of Washington Press**
433 Brooklyn Ave NE, Seattle, WA 98195-9570
SAN: 212-2502
Mailing Address: PO Box 50096, Seattle, WA 98145-5096
*Tel:* 206-543-4050 *Toll Free Tel:* 800-537-5487 (orders) *Fax:* 206-543-3932; 410-516-6998 (orders)
*E-mail:* uwpress@u.washington.edu
*Web Site:* www.washington.edu/uwpress/
*Key Personnel*
Dir: Nicole Mitchell
Assoc Dir & Gen Mgr: Mary Anderson *E-mail:* maryande@u.washington.edu
Exec Ed: Lorri Hagman *E-mail:* lhagman@u.washington.edu
Mng Ed: Marilyn Trueblood *E-mail:* marilynt@u.washington.edu
Asst Mng Ed: Mary Ribesky *E-mail:* ribesky@u.washington.edu
Mktg Mgr: Alice Herbig *Tel:* 206-221-4994 *E-mail:* aherbig@u.washington.edu
Prodn Mgr: Pam Canell *Tel:* 206-221-5893
Sales Mgr: Rachael Levay *Tel:* 617-871-0295 *Fax:* 617-945-0137 *E-mail:* remann@u.washington.edu
Subs Rts Mgr & Asst to Dir: Denise Clark *Tel:* 206-543-4057 *E-mail:* ddclark@u.washington.edu
Sr Designer: Tom Eykemans *Tel:* 206-221-7004
Founded: 1920
General scholarly nonfiction, reprints, imports.
ISBN Prefix(es): 978-0-295
Number of titles published annually: 68 Print
Total Titles: 1,500 Print; 1 CD-ROM
Foreign Rep(s): Combined Academic Publisher Ltd (UK); Douglas & McIntyre (Canada); University of British Columbia Press (Canada)

**University of Wisconsin Press**
1930 Monroe St, 3rd fl, Madison, WI 53711-2059
SAN: 501-0039
*Tel:* 608-263-0668 *Toll Free Tel:* 800-621-2736 (orders) *Fax:* 608-263-1173 *Toll Free Fax:* 800-621-2736 (orders)
*E-mail:* uwiscpress@uwpress.wisc.edu (main off)
*Web Site:* www.wisc.edu/wisconsinpress
*Key Personnel*
Press Dir: Sheila M Leary *Tel:* 608-263-1101 *E-mail:* smleary@wisc.edu
Journals Mgr: Jason Gray *Tel:* 608-263-0667 *E-mail:* jmgray5@wisc.edu
Mktg & Sales Mgr: Andrea Christofferson *Tel:* 608-263-0814 *E-mail:* aschrist@wisc.edu
Prodn Mgr & ISBN Contact: Terry Emmrich *Tel:* 608-263-0731 *E-mail:* temmrich@wisc.edu
Sr Acqs Ed: Raphael Kadushin *Tel:* 608-263-1062 *E-mail:* kadushin@wisc.edu
Founded: 1937
Academic Press, including regional Midwest titles & trade titles.
ISBN Prefix(es): 978-0-87972; 978-0-299; 978-1-928755; 978-0-87020; 978-0-9671787; 978-1-931; 978-8-158; 978-0-9682722; 978-0-924119; 978-0-9655464; 978-0-9718963; 978-0-9624369; 978-0-932900; 978-1-931569
Number of titles published annually: 80 Print; 1 CD-ROM; 1 Audio
Total Titles: 1,385 Print; 8 CD-ROM; 3 Audio
Imprints: Popular Press; Terrace Books
Distributor for The Center for the Study of Upper Midwestern Culture; Dryad Press; Elvehjem Museum of Art; International Brecht Society; Max Kade Institute for German-American Studies; Spring Freshet Press; Wisconsin Academy of Sciences, Arts & Letters; Wisconsin Historical Society Press; Wisconsin Veterans Museum
Foreign Rights: East-West Export Books Inc (Asia, Australia, New Zealand, The Pacific); Eurospan Ltd (Africa, Continental Europe, Iceland, Ireland, Middle East, UK)
*Advertising Agency:* Ad Vantage, Anne Herger
*Orders to:* Chicago Distribution Center, 11030 S Langley Ave, Chicago, IL 60628-3892 SAN: 202-5280
*Returns:* Chicago Distribution Center, 11030 S Langley Ave, Chicago, IL 60628-3892 SAN: 202-5280
*Shipping Address:* Chicago Distribution Center, 11030 S Langley Ave, Chicago, IL 60628-3892 SAN: 202-5280
*Warehouse:* Chicago Distribution Center, 11030 S Langley Ave, Chicago, IL 60628-3892 SAN: 202-5280
*Distribution Center:* East-West Export Books, c/o University of Hawaii Press, 2840 Kolowalu St, Honolulu, HI 96822 (Asia, the Pacific, Australia & New Zealand) *Tel:* 808-956-8830 *Fax:* 808-988-6052 *E-mail:* eweb@hawaii.edu
Chicago Distribution Center, 11030 S Langley Ave, Chicago, IL 60628-3892 *Tel:* 773-568-1550 *Toll Free Tel:* 800-621-2736 *Fax:* 773-660-2235 *Toll Free Fax:* 800-621-8476 SAN: 202-5280
Eurospan Group, c/o Turpin Distribution, Stratton Business Park, Pegasus Dr, Biggleswade, Beds SG18 8TQ, United Kingdom (Africa, Europe, Middle East, UK & Russia) *Tel:* (01767) 604972 *Fax:* (01767) 601640 *E-mail:* eurospan@turpin-distribution.com
Membership(s): Association of American University Presses; Midwest Independent Booksellers Association; Wisconsin Library Association

**University of Wisconsin-School of Architecture & Urban Planning**
2131 E Hartford Ave, Rm 225, Milwaukee, WI 53211
Mailing Address: PO Box 413, Milwaukee, WI 53201-0413
*Tel:* 414-229-4014 *Fax:* 414-229-6976
*E-mail:* sarupead@uwm.edu
*Web Site:* www.uwm.edu/SARUP
*Key Personnel*
Dir & Administrator: Carolyn Esswein
Architecture, design & urban planning.
ISBN Prefix(es): 978-0-938744
Total Titles: 50 Online

**University Press of America Inc**
Member of Rowman & Littlefield Publishing Group
4501 Forbes Blvd, Suite 200, Lanham, MD 20706
SAN: 200-2256
*Tel:* 301-459-3366 *Toll Free Tel:* 800-462-6420 *Fax:* 301-429-5748 *Toll Free Fax:* 800-338-4550
*Web Site:* www.univpress.com
*Key Personnel*
Chmn: Stanley D Plotnick
CEO & Pres: James E Lyons
CFO: George Franzak
VP, Mfg & Prod: Stephen Driver
Dir, Mktg: Dave Horvath *E-mail:* dhorvath@rowman.com
Mgr, Rts & Perms & Intl Rts Contact: Clare Cox *E-mail:* ccox@rowman.com
Acqs Ed: Laura Espinoza *E-mail:* lespinoza@univpress.com; Lindsay MacDonald *E-mail:* lmacdonald@univpress.com
Founded: 1975
Scholarly monographs, college texts, conference proceedings, professional books & reprints in the social sciences & the humanities.
ISBN Prefix(es): 978-0-8191; 978-0-7618
Number of titles published annually: 150 Print; 100 E-Book
Total Titles: 10,000 Print; 600 E-Book
Imprints: Hamilton Books
*Branch Office(s)*
67 Mowat Ave, Suite 241, Toronto, ON M6K 3E3, Canada, Contact: Les Petriw *Tel:* 416-534-1660 *Toll Free Tel:* 877-626-2665 *Fax:* 416-534-3699 *E-mail:* kstinson@rowmanlittlefield.com
Distributor for Atlantic Council; Center for National Policy Press; Harvard Center for International Affairs; International Law Institute; Joint Center for Political & Economic Studies Press; Society of the Cincinnati; White Burkett Miller Center
Foreign Rep(s): NBN Plymbridge (Europe, UK); United Publishers Services
Foreign Rights: United Publishers Service (Japan)
*Shipping Address:* 15200 NBN Way, Blue Ridge Summit, PA 17214-0191 *Toll Free Tel:* 800-462-6420 *Fax:* 717-794-3812 *Toll Free Fax:* 800-338-4550
Membership(s): AAP

**University Press of Colorado**
5589 Arapahoe Ave, Suite 206-C, Boulder, CO 80303
SAN: 202-1749
*Tel:* 720-406-8849 *Toll Free Tel:* 800-621-2736 (orders) *Fax:* 720-406-3443
*Web Site:* www.upcolorado.com
*Key Personnel*
Dir & Ed: Darrin Pratt *E-mail:* darrin@upcolorado.com
Mng Ed: Laura Furney *E-mail:* laura@upcolorardo.com
Founded: 1965
Scholarly & regional nonfiction.
ISBN Prefix(es): 978-0-87081
Number of titles published annually: 20 Print; 10 E-Book
Total Titles: 340 Print; 3 CD-ROM; 334 E-Book
Distributor for Center for Literary Publishing; Colorado Historical Society
Foreign Rep(s): Codasat Canada Ltd (Canada); East-West Export Books Inc (Asia, Middle East, Near East, The Pacific); Gazelle Book Services (Europe, Ireland, UK)

*Returns:* Chicago Distribution Center, Returns Processing Ctr, 11030 S Langley, Chicago, IL 60628 *Toll Free Tel:* 800-621-2736
*Distribution Center:* Chicago Distribution Center, 11030 S Langley, Chicago, IL 60628 *Toll Free Tel:* 800-624-2736
Membership(s): Association of American University Presses

**University Press of Florida**
Affiliate of State University System of Florida
15 NW 15 St, Gainesville, FL 32603-2079
SAN: 207-9275
*Tel:* 352-392-1351 *Toll Free Tel:* 800-226-3822 (orders only) *Fax:* 352-392-0590 *Toll Free Fax:* 800-680-1955 (orders only)
*E-mail:* info@upf.com
*Web Site:* www.upf.com
*Key Personnel*
Dir: Meredith Morris-Babb *E-mail:* mb@upf.com
Assoc Dir & Prepress Mgr: Lynn Werts *E-mail:* lw@upf.com
Asst Dir & Mng Ed: Michele Fiyak-Burkley *E-mail:* mf@upf.com
Assoc Dir, Sales & Mktg: Dennis Lloyd *E-mail:* dl@upf.com
Ed-in-Chief: Amy Gorelick *E-mail:* ag@upf.com
Busn Mgr: Kim Lake *E-mail:* kl@upf.com
Founded: 1945
Scholarly & regional nonfiction.
ISBN Prefix(es): 978-0-8130
Number of titles published annually: 100 Print; 100 E-Book
Total Titles: 2,830 Print; 1,850 E-Book
Imprints: Orange Grove Textbooks
Membership(s): American Association of University Presses

**University Press of Kansas**
2502 Westbrooke Circle, Lawrence, KS 66045-4444
SAN: 203-3267
*Tel:* 785-864-4154; 785-864-4155 (orders) *Fax:* 785-864-4586
*E-mail:* upress@ku.edu; upkorders@ku.edu (orders)
*Web Site:* www.kansaspress.ku.edu
*Key Personnel*
Dir: Fred M Woodward *Tel:* 785-864-4667 *E-mail:* fwoodward@ku.edu
Assoc Dir & Sr Ed: Charles T Myers *Tel:* 785-864-9160 *E-mail:* ctmyers@ku.edu
Art Dir & Ad Mgr: Karl Janssen *Tel:* 785-864-9164 *E-mail:* kjanssen@ku.edu
Ed-in-Chief: Michael Briggs *Tel:* 785-864-9162 *E-mail:* mbriggs@ku.edu
Busn Mgr: Conrad Roberts *Tel:* 785-864-9158 *E-mail:* ceroberts@ku.edu
Exhibits & Direct Mail Mgr: Debra Diehl *Tel:* 785-864-9166 *E-mail:* ddiehl@ku.edu
Publicity Mgr: Rebecca Murray Schuler *Tel:* 785-864-9170 *E-mail:* rmschuler@ku.edu
Founded: 1946
General scholarly nonfiction: American & western history, government & political science, military history, legal history, regional, women's studies, cultural studies, presidential studies.
ISBN Prefix(es): 978-978-07006
Number of titles published annually: 50 Print
Total Titles: 1,200 Print; 1 CD-ROM
Foreign Rep(s): East-West Export Books (Asia, The Pacific); Eurospan Ltd (Africa, Europe, Middle East, UK); Scholarly Book Services Inc (Canada)
*Returns:* University Press of Kansas Warehouse, 2445 Westbrooke Circle, Lawrence, KS 66045-4440
*Warehouse:* University Press of Kansas Warehouse, 2445 Westbrooke Circle, Lawrence, KS 66045-4440
Membership(s): Association of American University Presses

**The University Press of Kentucky**
663 S Limestone St, Lexington, KY 40508-4008
SAN: 203-3275
*Tel:* 859-257-8400 *Fax:* 859-257-8481
*Web Site:* www.kentuckypress.com
*Key Personnel*
Dir: Stephen M Wrinn *Tel:* 859-257-8432 *E-mail:* smwrin2@uky.edu
Dir, Fin & Admin: Craig Wilkie *Tel:* 859-257-8436 *E-mail:* crwilk00@uky.edu
Dir, Mktg & Sales: John P Hussey *Tel:* 859-257-4249 *Fax:* 859-323-4981 *E-mail:* jphuss2@uky.edu
Acting Dir, Editing, Design & Prodn: David Cobb *Tel:* 859-257-4252 *Fax:* 859-257-2984 *E-mail:* dlcobb2@uky.edu
Asst Dir, Fin & Admin: Teresa Wells Collins *Tel:* 859-257-8405 *E-mail:* twell1@uky.edu
Acqs Ed: Anne Dean Watkins *Tel:* 859-257-8434 *Fax:* 859-257-2984 *E-mail:* adwatk0@uky.edu
Founded: 1943
ISBN Prefix(es): 978-0-8131
Number of titles published annually: 70 Print; 70 E-Book
Total Titles: 1,200 Print; 550 E-Book
Distributor for Kentucky Historical Society
Foreign Rep(s): Eurospan (UK & the continent); Scholarly Book Services (Canada)
*Orders to:* Hopkins Fulfillment Services, PO Box 50370, Baltimore, MD 21211-4370 *Tel:* 410-516-6956 *Toll Free Tel:* 800-537-5487 *Fax:* 410-516-6998 *E-mail:* hfscustserv@press.jhu.edu
*Returns:* Hopkins Fulfillment Services, c/o Maple Press Co, Lebanon Dist Ctr, 704 Legionaire Dr, Fredericksburg, PA 17026 *Toll Free Tel:* 800-537-5487 *Fax:* 410-516-6998 *E-mail:* hfscustserv@press.jhu.edu
Membership(s): AAP; Association of American University Presses

**University Press of Mississippi**
3825 Ridgewood Rd, Jackson, MS 39211-6492
SAN: 203-1914
*Tel:* 601-432-6205 *Toll Free Tel:* 800-737-7788 (orders & cust serv) *Fax:* 601-432-6217
*E-mail:* press@mississippi.edu
*Web Site:* www.upress.state.ms.us
*Key Personnel*
Dir: Leila W Salisbury *E-mail:* lsalisbury@mississippi.edu
Asst Dir/Ed-in-Chief: Craig Gill *E-mail:* cgill@mississippi.edu
Asst Dir/Art Dir: John Langston *E-mail:* jlangston@mississippi.edu
Asst Dir/Mktg Dir: Steve Yates *E-mail:* syates@mississippi.edu
Asst Dir/Busn Mgr: Isabel Metz *E-mail:* imetz@mississippi.edu
Data Servs & Course Adoptions Mgr: Kathy Burgess *E-mail:* kburgess@mississippi.edu
Ad & Publicity Mgr: Clint Kimberling *E-mail:* ckimberling@mississippi.edu
Mng Ed: Anne Stascavage *E-mail:* astascavage@mississippi.edu
Acquiring Ed: Walter Biggins *E-mail:* wbiggins@mississippi.edu
Sr Prodn Ed: Mrs Shane Gong Stewart *E-mail:* sgong@mississippi.edu
Asst Prodn Mgr/Designer/Electronic Projs Mgr: Todd Lape *E-mail:* tlape@mississippi.edu
Cust Serv & Order Supv: Ms Sandy Alexander *Tel:* 601-432-6704 *Fax:* 601-432-6217 *E-mail:* salexander@mississippi.edu
Admin Asst/Rts & Perms Mgr: Cynthia Foster *Tel:* 601-432-6205 *Fax:* 601-432-6217 *E-mail:* cfoster@mississippi.edu
Designer: Pete Halverson *E-mail:* phalverson@mississippi.edu
Edit Assoc: Valerie Jones *E-mail:* vjones@mississippi.edu
Electronic & Direct-to-Consumer Mktg Specialist: Kristin Kirkpatrick *E-mail:* kkirkpatrick@mississippi.edu
Edit Asst: Katie Keene *E-mail:* kkeene@mississippi.edu
Mktg Asst: Courtney McCreary *E-mail:* cmccreary@mississippi.edu
Founded: 1970
Publisher of trade & scholarly books, nonfiction, fiction & regional.
ISBN Prefix(es): 978-0-87805; 978-1-57806; 978-1-934110; 978-1-60473; 978-1-61703; 978-1-62103
Number of titles published annually: 80 Print; 80 E-Book
Total Titles: 1,100 Print; 760 E-Book
Foreign Rep(s): Bill Bailey Publishers' Representatives (Europe); East-West Export Books (Asia, Australia, Hawaii, The Pacific); Roundhouse Group (Africa, India, Ireland, Middle East, UK); Scholarly Book Services Inc (Canada)
*Advertising Agency:* PM Productions, 203 Summer Hill Rd, Madison, MS 39110, Designer: Patti Mitchell *E-mail:* pattipmpro@aol.com
*Returns:* Maple Logistics Solutions, Lebanon Distribution Ctr, 704 Legionnaire Dr, Fredericksburg, PA 17026 (non-USPS deliveries); Maple Logistics Solutions, Lebanon Distribution Ctr, PO Box 1287, Lebanon, PA 17042 (all USPS deliveries)
*Warehouse:* Maple Logistics Solutions, Lebanon Distribution Ctr, 704 Legionnaire Dr, Fredericksburg, PA 17026
Membership(s): American Association of University Presses

**University Press of New England**
One Court St, Suite 250, Lebanon, NH 03766
SAN: 203-3283
*Tel:* 603-448-1533 *Toll Free Tel:* 800-421-1561 (orders only) *Fax:* 603-448-7006; 603-643-1540
*E-mail:* university.press@dartmouth.edu
*Web Site:* www.upne.com
*Key Personnel*
Dir: Michael Burton
Assoc Dir, Opers: Thomas Johnson
Acqs Ed-in-Chief: Phyllis Deutsch
Acqs Ed: Stephen Hull; Richard Pult
Publicity & Rts Mgr: Barbara Briggs
Sales & Trade Exhibits Mgr: Sherri Strickland
Founded: 1970
Scholarly, nonfiction, regional, New England fiction.
ISBN Prefix(es): 978-0-87451; 978-1-58465
Number of titles published annually: 70 Print
Total Titles: 825 Print; 300 E-Book
Imprints: Brandeis University Press; Dartmouth College Press; Hardscrabble Books; Northeastern University Press; Tufts University Press; University of New Hampshire Press; University of Vermont Press
Distributor for Beinecke Rare Book & Manuscript Library; Bibliopola Press; CavanKerry Press; Chipstone Foundation; Fence Books; Four Way Books; Isabella Stewart Gardner Museum; Harvest Hill Press; National Poetry Foundation; New England College; Nicolin Fields Publishing; Peter E Randall Publisher; The Sheep Meadow Press; Vermont Folklife Center; Wesleyan University Press; Winterthur Museum Garden & Library
Foreign Rep(s): East-West Export Books (Australia, New Zealand, The Pacific); Eurospan University Press Group (Europe, Middle East, UK); University of British Columbia Press (Canada)
*Advertising Agency:* New England Imprints, One Court St, Lebanon, NH 03766, Contact: Sara J Carpenter *Tel:* 603-448-1533 ext 231 *Fax:* 603-448-7006

*Returns:* UPNE Fulfillment, c/o Maple Press Co, Lebanon Distribution Ctr, PO Box 1287, Lebanon, PA 17026 *Tel:* 603-448-1533 ext 503 *Fax:* 603-448-9429
*Warehouse:* UPNE Fulfillment, c/o Maple Press Co, Lebanon Distribution Ctr, PO Box 1287, Lebanon, PA 17026 *Tel:* 603-448-1553 ext 503 *Fax:* 603-448-9429
Membership(s): Association of American University Presses; NEBA

**University Publishing Group**
219 W Washington St, Hagerstown, MD 21740
*Tel:* 240-420-0036 *Toll Free Tel:* 800-654-8188 *Fax:* 240-718-7100
*E-mail:* editorial@upgbooks.com; orders@upgbooks.com; sales@upgbooks.com
*Web Site:* www.upgbooks.com
*Key Personnel*
Owner & Treas: Norman Quist
Pres: Leslie Le Blanc *E-mail:* leblanc@upgbooks.com
Cust Serv Mgr: Mary Gesford
Founded: 1985
Publish books in medicine, social sciences, philosophy & law.
ISBN Prefix(es): 978-1-55572
Number of titles published annually: 6 Print
Total Titles: 35 Print

**University Publishing House**
PO Box 1664, Mannford, OK 74044
*Tel:* 918-865-4726
*E-mail:* upub3@juno.com
*Web Site:* www.universitypublishinghouse.net
*Key Personnel*
Owner & Pres: Randell Nyborg
Founded: 1987
Industrial & automotive, classic fiction reprints, mail order books & industrial processes.
ISBN Prefix(es): 978-1-877767; 978-1-57002
Number of titles published annually: 5 Print
Total Titles: 140 Print

**University Science Books**
20 Edgeshill Rd, Mill Valley, CA 94941
SAN: 213-8085
*Tel:* 415-332-5390 *Fax:* 415-383-3167
*E-mail:* univscibks@igc.org
*Web Site:* www.uscibooks.com
*Key Personnel*
Pres: Bruce Armbruster
VP & Intl Rts Contact: Kathy Armbruster
Assoc Publr/Edit: Jane Ellis *Tel:* 973-378-3900 *Fax:* 973-378-3925 *E-mail:* bjellis@igc.org
Founded: 1978
Intermediate level college textbooks & monographs in astronomy, chemistry, biochemistry & physics, environmental science, technical writing, biology, reference books, children's books.
ISBN Prefix(es): 978-0-935702; 978-1-891389
Number of titles published annually: 8 Print
Total Titles: 200 Print
Divisions: University Science Books
Foreign Rep(s): W H Freeman (Europe)
Foreign Rights: Alfaomega Grupo Editor (Mexico); Eastern Book Service Inc (Japan); Palgrave/Macmillan's Global Academic Publishing (Europe, India)
*Orders to:* Books International Inc, PO Box 605, Herndon, VA 20172, Contact: Todd Riggleman *Tel:* 703-661-1572 *Fax:* 703-661-1501
*Returns:* Books International Inc, 22883 Quicksilver Dr, Dulles, VA 20166 (15% restocking fee, damaged books not accepted) *Tel:* 703-661-1572 *Fax:* 703-661-1501
*Distribution Center:* Books International Inc, 22883 Quicksilver Dr, Dulles, VA 20166 (10% discount on all web orders) *Tel:* 703-661-1572 *Fax:* 703-661-1501 *E-mail:* todd@booksintl.com

**UnKnownTruths.com Publishing Co**
8815 Conroy Windermere Rd, Suite 190, Orlando, FL 32835
SAN: 255-6375
*Tel:* 407-929-9207 *Fax:* 407-876-3933
*E-mail:* info@unknowntruths.com
*Web Site:* unknowntruths.com
*Key Personnel*
CFO: Lynda Cassidy *Tel:* 407-876-7737
Pres: Walter Parks *E-mail:* wparks@unknowntruths.com
PR: Cherie Carter *E-mail:* cherie@unknowntruths.com
Founded: 2002
Formed to publish true stories of the unusual or of the previously unexplained. Stories typically provide radically different views from those that have shaped the understandings of our natural world, our religions, our science, our history & even the foundations of our civilizations. Also include stories of the very important life-entending medical breakthroughs: stem cell therapies, genetic therapies, cloning & other emerging findings that promise to change the very meaning of life.
ISBN Prefix(es): 978-0-9745393
Number of titles published annually: 12 Print; 4 Online
*Advertising Agency:* James Brooke & Associates, 2660 Second St, Suite 1, Santa Monica, CA 90405, PR: Cherie Carter *Tel:* 310-396-8070 *Fax:* 310-396-8071 *E-mail:* cherie@unknowntruths.com
*Distribution Center:* New Leaf Distributing Co, 401 Thornton Rd, Lithia Springs, GA 30122 *Tel:* 770-948-7845 *Fax:* 770-944-2313
Quality Books Inc, 1003 W Pines Rd, Oregon, IL 61061 *Toll Free Tel:* 800-323-4241 *Fax:* 815-732-4499
Membership(s): The Association of Publishers for Special Sales; IBPA, the Independent Book Publishers Association

**§Unlimited Publishing LLC**
Box 99, Nashville, IN 47448
*Tel:* 206-666-5484
*E-mail:* info@unlimitedpublishing.com; publish@unlimitedpublishing.com
*Web Site:* www.unlimitedpublishing.com
Founded: 2000
Bringing back out-of-print books & new nonfiction by professional writers. See web site for submission guidelines before sending a proposal. No simultaneous submissions; e-mail queries preferred, unsol mss sent by post will not be returned.
ISBN Prefix(es): 978-1-58832
Number of titles published annually: 50 Print; 25 Online; 25 E-Book
Total Titles: 300 Print
Membership(s): The Association of Publishers for Special Sales; IBPA, the Independent Book Publishers Association

**UNO Press**
Division of University of New Orleans
University of New Orleans Metro College, Educ Bldg, Suite 210, 2000 Lakeshore Dr, New Orleans, LA 70148
*Tel:* 504-280-7457 *Fax:* 504-280-7317
*E-mail:* unopress@uno.edu
*Web Site:* unopress.org
Founded: 2000
University Publishing House.
ISBN Prefix(es): 978-0-9728143; 978-0-9706190; 978-1-60801
Number of titles published annually: 9 Print; 3 E-Book
Total Titles: 12 Print; 3 E-Book
Distributed by Biblio
Membership(s): IBPA, the Independent Book Publishers Association

**Unveiled Media LLC**
PO Box 930463, Verona, WI 53593
*Tel:* 707-986-8345
*Web Site:* www.unveiledmedia.com
*Key Personnel*
Publr: Michael Seelen *E-mail:* mseelen@unveiledmedia.com
Founded: 2012
Boutique publisher. Specialize in photography, works of fiction & children's books.
ISBN Prefix(es): 978-0-9776385
Number of titles published annually: 3 Print; 3 E-Book
Total Titles: 3 Print; 3 E-Book
Imprints: Cotton Candy Press; Iron Icon Books
*Distribution Center:* Create Space
Lightning Source
Membership(s): IBPA, the Independent Book Publishers Association

**W E Upjohn Institute for Employment Research**
300 S Westnedge Ave, Kalamazoo, MI 49007-4686
*Tel:* 269-343-5541; 269-343-4330 (pubns) *Toll Free Tel:* 888-227-8569 *Fax:* 269-343-7310
*E-mail:* publications@upjohninstitute.org
*Web Site:* www.upjohn.org
*Key Personnel*
Mgr, Publns: Richard Wyrwa *E-mail:* wyrwa@upjohninstitute.org
Founded: 1959
Labor economics & industrial relations.
ISBN Prefix(es): 978-0-88099; 978-0-911558
Number of titles published annually: 12 Print; 8 E-Book
Total Titles: 160 Print; 80 E-Book
Membership(s): Association of American University Presses

**Upper Access Inc**
87 Upper Access Rd, Hinesburg, VT 05461
SAN: 667-1195
*Tel:* 802-482-2988 *Toll Free Tel:* 800-310-8320 *Fax:* 802-304-1005
*E-mail:* info@upperaccess.com
*Web Site:* www.upperaccess.com
*Key Personnel*
VP & Publr: Stephen T Carlson *E-mail:* steve@upperaccess.com
Assoc Publr: Thomas Gray
Devt Dir: Ron Lawrence *Tel:* 802-899-2276 *Fax:* 802-899-1291 *E-mail:* ron@pubassist.com
Sales Dir: Kristen Lewis
Founded: 1986
Publisher of nonfiction books to improve the quality of life. Also publish business software.
ISBN Prefix(es): 978-0-942679
Number of titles published annually: 3 Print; 2 E-Book
Total Titles: 49 Print; 4 E-Book
Imprints: Upper Access Books
*Orders to:* Midpoint National, 1263 Southwest Blvd, Kansas City, KS 66103 (for trade sales & returns) *Tel:* 913-362-7400 *E-mail:* info@midpt.com *Web Site:* www.midpt.com
*Returns:* Midpoint National, 1263 Southwest Blvd, Kansas City, KS 66103 (for trade sales & returns) *Tel:* 913-362-7400 *E-mail:* info@midpt.com *Web Site:* www.midpt.com
*Shipping Address:* Midpoint National, 1263 Southwest Blvd, Kansas City, KS 66103 (for trade sales & returns) *Tel:* 913-362-7400 *E-mail:* info@midpt.com *Web Site:* www.midpt.com
*Warehouse:* Midpoint National, 1263 Southwest Blvd, Kansas City, KS 66103 (for trade sales & returns) *Tel:* 913-362-7400 *E-mail:* info@midpt.com *Web Site:* www.midpt.com
*Distribution Center:* Midpoint National, 1263 Southwest Blvd, Kansas City, KS 66103 (for trade sales & returns) *Tel:* 913-362-7400

*E-mail:* info@midpt.com *Web Site:* www.midpt.com
Membership(s): The Association of Publishers for Special Sales; IBPA, the Independent Book Publishers Association; Independent Publishers of New England

**§Upper Room Books**
Division of The Upper Room
1908 Grand Ave, Nashville, TN 37212
SAN: 203-3364
Mailing Address: PO Box 340004, Nashville, TN 37203-0004
*Tel:* 615-340-7200 *Toll Free Tel:* 800-972-0433 *Fax:* 615-340-7266
*E-mail:* urbooks@upperroom.org
*Web Site:* www.upperroom.org
*Key Personnel*
Edit Dir: Jeannie Crawford-Lee
Dir, Prodn & Scheduling: Debbie Gregory *Tel:* 615-340-7224
Edit Asst: Joanna Bradley *E-mail:* jbradley@gbod.org
Founded: 1935
Prayer & devotional life publications. No fiction or poetry accepted.
ISBN Prefix(es): 978-0-8358
Number of titles published annually: 20 Print
Imprints: Fresh Air Books
Foreign Rights: Riggins International Rights (Worldwide exc North America)
*Warehouse:* PBD Inc, 1650 Bluegrass Pkwy, Alpharetta, GA 30201
Membership(s): ABA; CBA: The Association for Christian Retail; Evangelical Christian Publishers Association
*See separate listing for:*
**Fresh Air Books**

**Upstart Books™**
Imprint of Highsmith Inc
4810 Forest Run Rd, Madison, WI 53704
Mailing Address: PO Box 14410, Madison, WI 53708
*Tel:* 608-241-1201 *Toll Free Tel:* 800-448-4887 (orders) *Toll Free Fax:* 800-448-5828
*E-mail:* custsvc@upstartpromotions.com
*Web Site:* www.upstartbooks.com
*Key Personnel*
Dir, Pubns: Matt Mulder *E-mail:* mmulder@highsmith.com
Mng Ed: Michelle McCardell *E-mail:* mmcardell@highsmith.com
Founded: 1990
Reading activities & library skills for teachers & children's librarians; storytelling activity books & Internet resources.
ISBN Prefix(es): 978-0-917846; 978-0-913853; 978-1-57950; 978-1-932146
Number of titles published annually: 12 Print
Total Titles: 100 Print

**§The Urban Institute Press**
2100 "M" St NW, Washington, DC 20037
SAN: 203-3380
*Tel:* 202-261-5885; 410-516-6956 (orders) *Toll Free Tel:* 877-UIPRESS (847-7377); 800-537-5487 (orders) *Fax:* 202-467-5775
*E-mail:* dinscoe@urban.org; hfscustserv@press.jhu.edu
*Web Site:* www.uipress.org
*Key Personnel*
Dir: Kathleen Courrier *E-mail:* kcourrie@ui.urban.org
Prodn Mgr: Scott Forrey *Tel:* 202-261-5647
Prodn Ed: Devlan O'Connor *Tel:* 202-261-5752 *E-mail:* doconnor@urban.org
Founded: 1968
Public policy, economics, government, social sciences.
ISBN Prefix(es): 978-0-87766
Number of titles published annually: 10 Print
Membership(s): American Association of University Presses

**§Urban Land Institute**
1025 Thomas Jefferson St NW, Suite 500-W, Washington, DC 20007
*Tel:* 202-624-7000 *Toll Free Tel:* 800-321-5011 (cust serv) *Fax:* 410-626-7140
*E-mail:* bookstore@uli.org; customerservice@uli.org
*Web Site:* www.uli.org/books
*Key Personnel*
VP, Mktg: Lori Hatcher *E-mail:* lori.hatcher@uli.org
Sr Accts Payable Coord: Ben Abraham *Tel:* 202-624-7156 *E-mail:* babraham@uli.org
Founded: 1936
International nonprofit research & education institute concentrating on best practices in real estate development & responsible use of land.
ISBN Prefix(es): 978-0-87420
Number of titles published annually: 15 Print; 1 CD-ROM
Total Titles: 78 Print; 4 CD-ROM
Imprints: ULI
Foreign Rep(s): Joanne Wang (China)

**Urim Publications**
Division of Lambda Publishers Inc
c/o Lambda Publications Inc, 527 Empire Blvd, Brooklyn, NY 11225-3121
*Tel:* 718-972-5449 *Fax:* 718-972-6307
*E-mail:* publisher@urimpublications.com
*Web Site:* urimpublications.com
*Key Personnel*
Pres & Publr: Tzvi Mauer
Children's Book Ed: Shari Dash Greenspan *E-mail:* children@urimpublications.com
Founded: 1997
Publisher & worldwide distributor of new & classic books with Jewish content.
ISBN Prefix(es): 978-965-7108
Number of titles published annually: 8 Print
Total Titles: 35 Print
Subsidiaries: Flashlight Press
*Editorial Office(s):* PO Box 52287, Jerusalem 91521, Israel *Tel:* (02) 679-7633 *Fax:* (02) 679-7634 *Web Site:* www.urimpublications.com

**§URJ Books & Music**
Division of Union for Reform Judaism
633 Third Ave, New York, NY 10017-6778
SAN: 203-3291
*Tel:* 212-650-4120 *Fax:* 212-650-4119
*E-mail:* press@urj.org
*Web Site:* www.ujrbooksandmusic.com
*Key Personnel*
Mktg Dir: Stephen Becker
Ed-in-Chief: Michael H Goldberg
Founded: 1873
Religion (Jewish), Reform Judaism; textbooks, juveniles & adult trade books, audiovisual materials, social action, history, biography, ceremonies.
ISBN Prefix(es): 978-0-8074
Number of titles published annually: 25 Print
Total Titles: 250 Print; 1 CD-ROM; 200 Audio
*Distribution Center:* Mercedes Distribution Center, Brooklyn Navy Yard, Bldg 3, Brooklyn, NY 11205
Membership(s): AAP

**US Conference of Catholic Bishops**
USCCB Publishing, 3211 Fourth St NE, Washington, DC 20017
*Tel:* 202-541-3090 *Toll Free Tel:* 800-235-8722 (orders only) *Fax:* 202-722-8709
*E-mail:* css@usccb.org; publications@usccb.org
*Web Site:* www.usccbpublishing.org
*Key Personnel*
Dir & Publr: Paul Henderson
Founded: 1938
The official publisher for the United States Catholic Bishop & Vatican documents; English & Spanish.
ISBN Prefix(es): 978-1-55586; 978-1-57455
Number of titles published annually: 20 Print
Total Titles: 820 Print
*Returns:* USCCB Returns, 3570 Blatensburg Rd, Brentwood, MD 20722
Membership(s): Association of Catholic Publishers Inc

**US Games Systems Inc**
179 Ludlow St, Stamford, CT 06902
SAN: 206-1368
*Tel:* 203-353-8400 *Toll Free Tel:* 800-54-GAMES (544-2637) *Fax:* 203-353-8431
*E-mail:* info@usgamesinc.com
*Web Site:* www.usgamesinc.com
*Key Personnel*
Founder & Chmn: Stuart R Kaplan
VP, Export Sales: Barbara Bensaid
Treas: Ricky Cruz
Art Dir: Paula Palmer
Founded: 1968
Popular & scholarly works in the field of tarot, educational games & the history of symbolism of playing cards; reprints of historical tarot decks & playing cards from the past five centuries.
ISBN Prefix(es): 978-0-913866; 978-0-88079; 978-1-57281
Number of titles published annually: 10 Print
Total Titles: 400 Print
Imprints: Cove Press
Distributor for A G Muller & Cie
Foreign Rep(s): Airlift Book Company (UK); Koppenhol Agenturen (Netherlands); Lion Playing Card Co (Israel); A G Muller & Cie (Switzerland); David Westnedge Ltd (UK)

**§US Government Printing Office**
Division of US Government
Superintendent of Documents, 732 N Capitol St NW, Washington, DC 20401
*Tel:* 202-512-1800 *Toll Free Tel:* 866-512-1800 (orders) *Fax:* 202-512-2104
*E-mail:* contactcenter@gpo.gov
*Web Site:* bookstore.gpo.gov (sales)
*Key Personnel*
Dir, Sales & Mktg: Jeffrey Turner *Tel:* 202-512-1055
Founded: 1861
Distributor & printer of federal government publications & public documents in various formats including ebooks; military, space exploration, political science.
ISBN Prefix(es): 978-0-16
Number of titles published annually: 250 Print; 15 Online
Total Titles: 2,500 Print; 140 CD-ROM
Imprints: Energy Information Administration (EIA)
*Orders to:* PO Box 979050, Saint Louis, MO 63197-9000
*See separate listing for:*
**Energy Information Administration (EIA)**

**Utah Geological Survey**
Division of Utah Dept of Natural Resources
1594 W North Temple, Suite 3110, Salt Lake City, UT 84116-3154
Mailing Address: PO Box 146100, Salt Lake City, UT 84114-6100
*Tel:* 801-537-3300 *Toll Free Tel:* 888-UTAH-MAP (882-4627 bookstore) *Fax:* 801-537-3400
*E-mail:* geostore@utah.gov
*Web Site:* geology.utah.gov
*Key Personnel*
Geological Pubns Ed: Vicky Clarke *Tel:* 801-537-3330 *E-mail:* vickyclarke@utah.gov
Founded: 1935
ISBN Prefix(es): 978-1-55791

Number of titles published annually: 5 Print; 35 CD-ROM; 5 Online
Total Titles: 750 Print; 70 CD-ROM; 38 Online

**Utah State University Press**
Division of Utah State University
3078 Old Main Hill, Logan, UT 84322-3078
*Tel:* 435-797-1362 *Fax:* 435-797-0313
*Web Site:* www.usupress.org
*Key Personnel*
Dir: Michael Spooner *E-mail:* michael.spooner@usu.edu
Mktg Mgr: Dan Miller *E-mail:* d.miller@usu.edu
Founded: 1969
ISBN Prefix(es): 978-0-87421
Number of titles published annually: 18 Print
Total Titles: 120 Print
Imprints: University Press of Colorado
Membership(s): Association of American University Presses

**VanDam Inc**
11 W 20 St, 4th fl, New York, NY 10011-3704
*Tel:* 212-929-0416 *Toll Free Tel:* 800-UNFOLDS (863-6537) *Fax:* 212-929-0426
*E-mail:* info@vandam.com
*Web Site:* www.vandam.com
*Key Personnel*
Principal & Pres: Stephan C VanDam *Tel:* 212-929-0416 ext 10 *E-mail:* stephan@vandam.com
VP, Sales: Bob Troast *Tel:* 212-929-0416 ext 12 *E-mail:* bob@vandam.com
Founded: 1984
Publisher of UNFOLDS® maps; licensor of patented folding technology used to produce UNFOLDS® products.
ISBN Prefix(es): 978-0-931141; 978-1-932527; 978-1-934395
Number of titles published annually: 25 Print
Total Titles: 100 Print
Imprints: Eurostar; Smartmaps®; That VanDam Book; UNFOLDS®; @tlas®
Divisions: VanDam Advertising; VanDam Licensing; VanDam Publishing
Foreign Rep(s): LAC (Italy); RV Verlag (Germany)
*Advertising Agency:* Streetsmart®; Travelsmart®; VanDam Advertising

**Vandamere Press**
3580 Morris St N, St Petersburg, FL 33713
SAN: 657-3088
Mailing Address: PO Box 149, St Petersburg, FL 33731
*Tel:* 727-556-0950 *Toll Free Tel:* 800-551-7776 *Fax:* 727-556-2560
*E-mail:* orders@vandamere.com
*Web Site:* www.vandamere.com
*Key Personnel*
Publr & Ed-in-Chief: Arthur Brown *E-mail:* abrown@vandamere.com
Dir, Spec Sales: Stephanie Brown
Sr Book Ed: Pat Berger
Acq Ed: Jerry Frank
Wholesale Sales: John Cabin
Founded: 1984
Tradebook.
ISBN Prefix(es): 978-0-918339
Number of titles published annually: 8 Print
Total Titles: 70 Print
Distributor for ABI Professional Publications (non-exclusive); JMC Press (exclusive to trade); NRH Press (non-exclusive); Quodlibetal Features

**Vanderbilt University Press**
Division of Vanderbilt University
2014 Broadway, Suite 320, Nashville, TN 37203
SAN: 202-9308
Mailing Address: VU Sta B, No 351813, Nashville, TN 37235-1813
*Tel:* 615-322-3585 *Toll Free Tel:* 800-627-7377 (orders only) *Fax:* 615-343-8823 *Toll Free Fax:* 800-735-0476 (orders only)
*E-mail:* vupress@vanderbilt.edu
*Web Site:* www.vanderbiltuniversitypress.com
*Key Personnel*
Dir: Michael Ames
Mng Ed: Joell Smith Borne
Design & Prodn Mgr: Dariel Mayer *E-mail:* dariel.mayer@vanderbilt.edu
Busn Mgr & Rts & Perms: Bethany Graham
Sales & Mktg Mgr: Sue Havlish
Mktg & New Media Assoc: Betsy Phillips *E-mail:* betsy.phillips@vanderbilt.edu
Founded: 1940
Scholarly nonfiction, humanities, social sciences, literary criticism, history, regional studies, applied mathematics, philosophy.
ISBN Prefix(es): 978-0-8265
Number of titles published annually: 25 Print
Total Titles: 250 Print; 2 CD-ROM; 1 E-Book
Imprints: Country Music Foundation Press; Vanderbilt Library of American Philosophy
Distributed by University of Oklahoma Press
Distributor for Country Music Foundation Press
Foreign Rep(s): Royden Muranaka (Australia, China, Hong Kong, India, Japan, Korea, New Zealand, Pacific Islands, Pakistan, Philippines, Southeast Asia, Taiwan)

**Vault.com Inc**
75 Varick St, 8th fl, New York, NY 10013
*Tel:* 212-366-4212 *Fax:* 212-366-6117
*E-mail:* feedback@staff.vault.com
*Web Site:* www.vault.com
*Key Personnel*
Prodr: Phil Stott
Founded: 1997
"Insider" career development for professionals.
ISBN Prefix(es): 978-1-58131
Number of titles published annually: 4 Print; 10 Online
Total Titles: 61 Print; 124 Online
*Distribution Center:* Client Distribution Services Inc, 193 Edwards Dr, Jackson, TN 38301, Pres: Gilbert Perlman *Toll Free Tel:* 800-343-4499 *Toll Free Fax:* 800-351-5073 *E-mail:* orderentry@cdsbooks.com SAN: 631-760X

**Vedanta Press**
Subsidiary of Vedanta Society of Southern California
1946 Vedanta Place, Hollywood, CA 90068
*Tel:* 323-960-1736 *Toll Free Tel:* 800-816-2242
*E-mail:* info@vedanta.com
*Web Site:* www.vedanta.com
*Key Personnel*
Mgr: Robert Adjemian *E-mail:* bob@vendanta.org
Founded: 1945
ISBN Prefix(es): 978-81-85301 (Advaita Ashrama); 978-0-87481; 978-81-8172 (Ramakrishna Math)
Number of titles published annually: 13 CD-ROM; 13 Online; 14 Audio
Total Titles: 13 CD-ROM; 13 Online; 14 Audio
Distributor for Advaita Ashrama; Ananda Ashrama; Ramakrishna Math
Membership(s): IBPA, the Independent Book Publishers Association

**Velazquez Press**
Division of Academic Learning Co LLC
9682 Telstar Ave, Suite 110, El Monte, CA 91731
*Tel:* 626-448-3448 *Fax:* 626-602-3817
*E-mail:* info@academiclearningcompany.com
*Web Site:* www.velazquezpress.com
*Key Personnel*
Sales Mgr: Jonathan Ruiz *E-mail:* jruiz@academiclearningcompany.com
Founded: 2003
Publisher of bilingual dictionaries.
ISBN Prefix(es): 978-1-59495
Number of titles published annually: 4 Print
Total Titles: 10 Print

**The Vendome Press**
1334 York Ave, 3rd fl, New York, NY 10021
*Tel:* 212-737-5297 *Fax:* 212-737-5340
*E-mail:* info@vendomepress.com
*Web Site:* www.vendomepress.com
*Key Personnel*
Founder & Chmn: Alexis Gregory
Pres: Mark Magowan
Prodn Ed: Alecia Reddick
Ed: Jackuelen Decter
Founded: 1981
Illustrated art, architecture & lifestyle books.
ISBN Prefix(es): 978-0-86565
Number of titles published annually: 15 Print
Total Titles: 85 Print
Distributed by Harry N Abrams Inc

**Venture Publishing Inc**
1999 Cato Ave, State College, PA 16801
SAN: 240-897X
*Tel:* 814-234-4561 *Fax:* 814-234-1651
*E-mail:* vpublish@venturepublish.com
*Web Site:* www.venturepublish.com
*Key Personnel*
Off Mgr: Kay Whiteside *E-mail:* cawhiteside@venturepublish.com
Prodn: George Lauer *E-mail:* glauer@venturepublish.com; Richard Yocum *E-mail:* vpublish@venturepublish.com
Founded: 1979
Parks & recreation, social sciences & sociology, leisure studies, long term care, therapeutic recreation.
ISBN Prefix(es): 978-0-910251; 978-1-892132
Number of titles published annually: 8 Print
Total Titles: 86 Print
Foreign Rep(s): Creative & More Inc (Taiwan); HM Leisure Planning Pty Ltd (Australia, Canada, New Zealand)

**Verso**
20 Jay St, Suite 1010, Brooklyn, NY 11201
*Tel:* 718-246-8160 *Fax:* 718-246-8165
*E-mail:* verso@versobooks.com
*Web Site:* www.versobooks.com
*Key Personnel*
Mng Dir: Jacob Stevens
Founded: 1970
Nonfiction, progressive studies on politics, history, society & culture.
ISBN Prefix(es): 978-0-86091; 978-0-85984; 978-0-84467
Number of titles published annually: 80 Print
Total Titles: 2,000 Print
*Foreign Office(s):* 6 Meard St, London W1F OE6, United Kingdom
Distributed by Penguin (Canada); W W Norton (USA)
Foreign Rep(s): Verso (England)
Foreign Rights: Verso (Worldwide)
*Shipping Address:* Marston Book Services, Kemp Hall Bindery, Osney Mead, Oxford, United Kingdom
*Warehouse:* National Book Co Inc, 800 Keystone Industrial Park, Scranton, PA 18512

**Victory in Grace Printing**
Division of Victory in Grace Ministries
60 Quentin Rd, Lake Zurich, IL 60047
*Tel:* 847-438-4494 *Toll Free Tel:* 800-78-GRACE (784-7223) *Fax:* 847-438-4232
*Web Site:* www.victoryingrace.org
*Key Personnel*
Dir: Jim Boyce
Founded: 2000
Publish conservative evangelical books, audio series, magazines & tracts.
ISBN Prefix(es): 978-0-9679145; 978-0-9719262

Number of titles published annually: 3 Print; 4 E-Book; 3 Audio
Total Titles: 9 Print; 4 E-Book; 15 Audio

**Viking**
Imprint of Penguin Group (USA) LLC
375 Hudson St, New York, NY 10014
SAN: 282-5074
*Tel:* 212-366-2000
*E-mail:* online@penguinputnam.com
*Web Site:* www.penguinputnam.com; us.penguingroup.com
*Key Personnel*
Pres: Clare Ferraro
VP, Publr (Viking): Paul Slovak
VP & Dir, Mktg: Nancy Sheppard
VP & Dir, Publicity: Carolyn Coleburn
VP & Ed-at-Large: Carole DeSanti
VP & Publr, Pam Dorman Books/Viking: Pamela Dorman
VP & Exec Creative Dir: Paul Buckley
Dir, Ad & Promo: Dennis Swaim
VP, Assoc Publr & Edit Dir (Nonfiction): Wendy Wolf
Exec Ed: Carolyn Carlson
VP, Exec Dir of Copyediting: Tory Klose
Exec Mng Ed: Tricia Conley
Exec Ed: Rick Kot; Joy de Menil
Founded: 1925
ISBN Prefix(es): 978-0-670
Number of titles published annually: 80 Print
Total Titles: 250 Print
Imprints: Viking Compass
*Advertising Agency:* Spier NY

**Viking Children's Books**
Imprint of Penguin Group (USA) LLC
345 Hudson St, New York, NY 10014
*Tel:* 212-366-2000
*E-mail:* online@penguinputnam.com
*Web Site:* www.penguinputnam.com; us.penguingroup.com
*Key Personnel*
VP & Publr: Ken Wright
Assoc Publr & Mng Ed: Gerard Mancini
VP & Art Dir: Denise Cronin
Edit Dir, Picture Books: Tracy Gates
Sr Ed: Sharyn November
Editor-at-Large: Regina Hayes
Founded: 1925
ISBN Prefix(es): 978-0-670
Number of titles published annually: 55 Print
Total Titles: 557 Print
Membership(s): Children's Book Council

**Viking Studio**
Imprint of Penguin Group (USA) LLC
375 Hudson St, New York, NY 10014
SAN: 282-5074
*Tel:* 212-366-2000
*E-mail:* online@penguinputnam.com
*Web Site:* www.penguinputnam.com; us.penguingroup.com
*Key Personnel*
Pres, Viking/Plume Studio Books: Clare Ferraro
Founded: 1988
ISBN Prefix(es): 978-0-14; 978-0-670
Number of titles published annually: 4 Print
Total Titles: 40 Print
*Advertising Agency:* Spier NY

**Carl Vinson Institute of Government**
University of Georgia, 201 N Milledge Ave, Athens, GA 30602
*Tel:* 706-542-2736 *Fax:* 706-542-9301
*Web Site:* www.cviog.uga.edu
*Key Personnel*
Dir: Laura Meadows *Tel:* 706-542-6192
Communs Coord: Courtney Yarbrough *Tel:* 706-542-6221
Founded: 1927
Instruction, technical assistance, research & publications for state & local governments & communities.
ISBN Prefix(es): 978-0-89854
Number of titles published annually: 10 Print; 2 CD-ROM
Total Titles: 70 Print; 3 CD-ROM

**Vintage & Anchor Books**
Imprint of Knopf Doubleday Publishing Group
c/o Random House Inc, 1745 Broadway, New York, NY 10019
*Tel:* 212-572-2420
*E-mail:* vintageanchorpublicity@randomhouse.com
*Web Site:* vintage-anchor.knopfdoubleday.com
*Key Personnel*
EVP & Publr: Anne Messitte
SVP & Exec Edit Dir: Luann Walther
VP & Assoc Publr: Beth Lamb
VP & Exec Ed: Edward Kastenmeier
VP & Dir, Publicity: Russell Perreault
Dir, Academic Mktg: Keith Goldsmith
Dir, Ad & Promos: Irena Vukov-Kendes
Dir, Digital Devt: Laura Crisp
Dir, Online Mktg: Paige Smith
Dir, Spanish Lang Publg: Jaime de Pablos
Mng Ed: Stephen McNabb
Mgr, Backlist: Barbara Richard
Sr Ed: Lexy Bloom; Tim O'Connell
Sr Publicist: Angie Venezia
Founded: 1952
Random House Inc & its publishing entities are not accepting unsol submissions, queries via e-mail at this time.
ISBN Prefix(es): 978-0-307; 978-0-679 (Vintage); 978-0-385 (Anchor Books); 978-0-7679 (Anchor Books); 978-0-375 (Vintage); 978-1-4000; 978-0-394 (Vintage)
Number of titles published annually: 350 Print; 380 E-Book
Total Titles: 5,300 Print; 3,500 E-Book
Imprints: Anchor Books
Foreign Rights: Anthea Agency (Katalina Sabeva) (Bulgaria); Bardon-Chinese Media Agency (Xu Weiguang) (China); Bardon-Chinese Media Agency (Yu Shiuan Chen) (Taiwan); Bardon-Chinese Media Agency (David Tsai) (Taiwan); The English Agency (Hamish Macaskill) (Japan); The English Agency (Junzo Sawa) (Japan); Graal Literary Agency (Maria Strarz-Kanska) (Poland); The Deborah Harris Agency (Ilana Kurshan) (Israel); JLM Literary Agency (Nelly Moukakou) (Greece); Katai & Bolza Literary (Peter Bolza) (Croatia, Hungary, Serbia); Simona Kessler Agency (Simona Kessler) (Romania); Korea Copyright Center (MiSook Hong) (Korea); Licht & Burr Literary Agency (Trine Licht) (Scandinavia); La Nouvelle Agence (Vanessa Kling) (France); Kristin Olson Literary Agency (Kristin Olson) (Czech Republic); Agenzia Letteraria Santachiara (Roberto Santachiara) (Italy); Sebes & Van Gelderen Literary Agency (Holland)

**Visible Ink Press®**
43311 Joy Rd, Suite 414, Canton, MI 48187-2075
*Tel:* 734-667-3211 *Fax:* 734-667-4311
*E-mail:* info@visibleink.com
*Web Site:* www.visibleink.com
*Key Personnel*
Owner: Roger Janecke
Founded: 1990
Popular reference publisher specializing in handy answer books, spiritual phenomena & encyclopedias.
ISBN Prefix(es): 978-0-8103; 978-0-7876; 978-1-57859
Number of titles published annually: 10 Print; 10 E-Book
Total Titles: 50 Print; 50 E-Book
*Distribution Center:* Independent Publishers Group, 814 N Franklin St, Chicago, IL 60610 *Tel:* 312-337-0747 *Toll Free Tel:* 800-888-4741 (orders) *Fax:* 312-337-5985

**§Visual Profile Books Inc**
302 Fifth Ave, New York, NY 10001
SAN: 213-1552
*Tel:* 212-279-7000 *Fax:* 212-279-7014
*Web Site:* www.visualreference.com
*Key Personnel*
Group Publr: Larry Fuersich *Tel:* 212-279-7000 ext 314 *E-mail:* larry@visualreference.com
Founded: 1931
Architecture, interior & graphic design.
ISBN Prefix(es): 978-0-9825989
Number of titles published annually: 15 Print
Total Titles: 115 Print; 75 Online
Distributed by Innovative Logistics (US & CN)
Foreign Rep(s): HarperCollins International (Worldwide exc Canada & USA)
Foreign Rights: Larry Fuersich

**Viva Editions**, see Cleis Press

**Volcano Press**
21496 National St, Volcano, CA 95689
Mailing Address: PO Box 270, Volcano, CA 95689-0270 SAN: 220-0015
*Tel:* 209-296-7989 *Toll Free Tel:* 800-879-9636 *Fax:* 209-296-4515
*E-mail:* sales@volcanopress.com
*Web Site:* www.volcanopress.com
*Key Personnel*
Publr: Adam Gottstein *E-mail:* adam@volcanopress.com
Publr Emerita & Edit Consultant: Ruth Gottstein
Founded: 1969
General trade, professional books, Spanish language books; medicine, health & nutrition, psychology, social sciences, women's studies, domestic violence.
ISBN Prefix(es): 978-0-912078; 978-1-884244
Number of titles published annually: 3 Print; 3 E-Book
Total Titles: 50 Print; 1 Audio
Imprints: Glide Publications; Kazan Media
*Sales Office(s):* PO Box 270, Volcano, CA 95689-0270 SAN: 220-0015
*Billing Address:* PO Box 270, Volcano, CA 95689-0270 SAN: 220-0015

**Ludwig von Mises Institute**
518 W Magnolia Ave, Auburn, AL 36832
*Tel:* 334-321-2100 *Fax:* 334-321-2119
*E-mail:* info@mises.org
*Web Site:* www.mises.org
*Key Personnel*
CEO: Lew Rockwell
Bookstore Mgr: Brandon Hill *E-mail:* brandon@mises.org
Founded: 1982
Nonprofit educational organization devoted to the Austrian School of Economics.
ISBN Prefix(es): 978-0-945466; 978-1-933550
Number of titles published annually: 7 Print; 8 Audio
Total Titles: 54 Print

**W for Wine**, see The Wine Appreciation Guild Ltd

**Wadsworth**, see Wadsworth Publishing

**§Wadsworth Publishing**
Division of Cengage Learning™
20 Davis Dr, Belmont, CA 94002
SAN: 200-2213
*Tel:* 650-595-2350 *Fax:* 650-592-3022 *Toll Free Fax:* 800-522-4923
*Web Site:* www.cengage.com

*Key Personnel*
CEO & Pres: Ronald Dunn
CFO: Dean Durbin
Pres, Soc Sci & Humanities Publg: Sean Wakely
Pres, Mathematics & Sci Publg: Michael Johnson
Pres, Busn & Prof Publg: Ed Mousa
SVP, Mktg: Jonathan Hulbert
SVP & CTO: Pat Call
VP, HR: Paula Sari
Dir, Corp Communs: Lindsay Brown
Founded: 1956
A leading provider of higher education textbooks, software & Internet materials for the humanities, social sciences, behavioral sciences, mathematics, science, statistics, business & professional.
ISBN Prefix(es): 978-0-314; 978-0-312; 978-0-534; 978-0-8222; 978-0-8384; 978-0-89582; 978-0-8304; 978-1-56593; 978-0-8125; 978-1-57259; 978-0-324; 978-0-922914; 978-0-028; 978-0-030; 978-0-126; 978-0-155; 978-0-759; 978-0-766; 978-0-769; 978-0-827; 978-0-829; 978-0-8783; 978-0-882; 978-1-87910; 978-0-9997
Number of titles published annually: 700 Print
Total Titles: 5,000 Print; 125 CD-ROM; 170 E-Book; 325 Audio
Imprints: Brooks/Cole; Course Technology; Delmar; Heinle; Schirmer; South-Western; Wadsworth
Distributed by Cengage Learning™
Foreign Rep(s): Nelson Thomson Learning (Canada); Thomas Nelson Australia-Thomson Learning (Australia, New Zealand); Thomson Learning Editories (Caribbean, Latin America); Thomson Learning International (Asia, Europe, France, Germany, Japan, Middle East, South Africa)
Foreign Rights: Thomson Learning, Foreign Rights Division (Worldwide)
*Distribution Center:* Cengage Learning Distribution Center, 10650 Toebben Dr, Independence, KY 41051 *Toll Free Tel:* 800-544-0550 *Fax:* 859-647-4599 *E-mail:* claimscs@cengage.com
Membership(s): AAP

**Wake Forest University Press**
A5 Tribble Hall, Wake Forest University, Winston-Salem, NC 27109
Mailing Address: PO Box 7333, Winston-Salem, NC 27109-7333
*Tel:* 336-758-5448 *Fax:* 336-758-5636
*E-mail:* wfupress@wfu.edu
*Web Site:* www.wfu.edu/wfupress
*Key Personnel*
Founder & Advising Ed: Dillon Johnston
Dir & Ed: Jefferson Holdridge
Mgr & Asst Dir: Candide Jones
*E-mail:* jonescm@wfu.edu
Founded: 1975
Contemporary Irish poetry.
ISBN Prefix(es): 978-0-916390; 978-1-930630
Number of titles published annually: 5 Print
Total Titles: 85 Print

**Walch Education**
40 Walch Dr, Portland, ME 04103-1286
SAN: 203-0268
*Tel:* 207-772-2846 *Toll Free Tel:* 800-558-2846 *Fax:* 207-772-3105 *Toll Free Fax:* 888-991-5755
*E-mail:* customerservice@walch.com
*Web Site:* www.walch.com
*Key Personnel*
Chmn of the Bd: Peter S Walch
CFO: James R Walker, Jr *E-mail:* jwalker@walch.com
Pres: Al Noyes *E-mail:* anoyes@walch.com
VP, Educ: Jill Rosenblum *E-mail:* jrosenblum@walch.com
Sales Mgr: Amy Kayne *E-mail:* akayne@walch.com
Founded: 1927
Educational books & supplementary materials for middle school through adult.
ISBN Prefix(es): 978-0-8251
Number of titles published annually: 100 Print; 75 Online
Total Titles: 1,700 Print; 850 Online
Membership(s): ASCD; International Reading Association; National Council for the Social Studies; National Council of Teachers of English; National Council of Teachers of Mathematics; National Science Teachers Association

**Walch Publishing**, see Walch Education

**Walker & Co**
Division of Bloomsbury USA
175 Fifth Ave, 3rd fl, New York, NY 10010-7728
SAN: 202-5213
*Web Site:* www.walkerbooks.com
*Key Personnel*
Publr: George L Gibson *Tel:* 646-438-6075
*E-mail:* george.gibson@bloomsburyusa.com
Publg Dir, Walker Children's: Emily Easton
*E-mail:* emily.easton@bloomsburyusa.com
Mktg & Assoc Sales Mgr, Books for Young Readers: Beth Eller *Tel:* 646-438-6076
Ed, Nonfiction: Jacqueline Johnson
*E-mail:* jacqueline.johnson@bloomsburyusa.com
Founded: 1959
Adult & juvenile fiction & nonfiction, paper & hardcover.
ISBN Prefix(es): 978-0-8027
Number of titles published annually: 70 Print
Total Titles: 1,200 Print
Foreign Rep(s): Penguin (Canada)
Foreign Rights: Omiros Ausamides (Greece); Erica Berla (Italy); Beatriz Coll (Portugal, Spain); Ann-Christine Danielsson (Scandinavia); Simonia Kessler (Romania); Efrat Lev (Israel); Frederique Porretta (France); Natalia Sanina (Russia); Thomas Schlueck (Germany); Sebes & Van Gelderen Literary Agency (Netherlands); Anke Vogel (Hungary); Eric Yang (Korea)
*Warehouse:* MPS, 16365 James Madison Hwy, Gordonsville, VA 22942
Membership(s): Children's Book Council

**Frederick Warne**
Imprint of Penguin Group (USA) LLC
345 Hudson St, New York, NY 10014
SAN: 282-5074
*Tel:* 212-366-2000
*E-mail:* online@penguinputnam.com
*Web Site:* www.penguinputnam.com; us.penguingroup.com
Founded: 1865
ISBN Prefix(es): 978-0-7232
Number of titles published annually: 22 Print
Total Titles: 201 Print
Foreign Rep(s): Agenzia Letteraria Internazionale (Italy); Bardon-Chinese (China); DRT International (Korea); I Pikarski Ltd Literary Agency (Israel); ICBS (Netherlands, Scandinavia); International Press Agency (South Africa); Japan UNI (Japan); Literari Agentura (Czech Republic); Mohrbooks (Germany); La Nouvelle Agence (France)

**Warren Communications News Inc**
2115 Ward Ct NW, Washington, DC 20037
*Tel:* 202-872-9200 *Toll Free Tel:* 800-771-9202 *Fax:* 202-293-3435; 202-318-8350
*E-mail:* info@warren-news.com; newsroom@warren-news.com
*Web Site:* www.warren-news.com
*Key Personnel*
Chmn & Publr: Paul Warren
Pres & Ed: Daniel Warren *E-mail:* dwarren@warren-news.com
Exec Ed Emeritus: Dawson B Nail
Exec Ed: R Michael Feazel
Sr Ed: Jeff Berman
Assoc Mng Ed: Gaye Nail
NY Bureau Chief: Paul Gluckman
Founded: 1945
Newsletters & directories.
ISBN Prefix(es): 978-0-911486
Number of titles published annually: 10 Print
Total Titles: 10 Print
*Branch Office(s)*
276 Fifth Ave, Suite 1111, New York, NY 10001
*Toll Free Tel:* 800-771-5410

**Washington State University Press**
Division of Washington State University
Cooper Publications Bldg, Grimes Way, Pullman, WA 99164
SAN: 206-6688
Mailing Address: PO Box 645910, Pullman, WA 99164-5910
*Tel:* 509-335-3518; 509-335-7880 (order fulfillment) *Toll Free Tel:* 800-354-7360 *Fax:* 509-335-8568
*E-mail:* wsupress@wsu.edu
*Web Site:* wsupress.wsu.edu
*Key Personnel*
Dir: Mary Read *E-mail:* read@wsu.edu
Prodn Ed & Fulfillment/Sales Coord: Nancy Grunewald *Tel:* 509-335-5817
*E-mail:* grunewan@wsu.edu
Mktg Mgr & Acqs: Caryn Lawton *Tel:* 509-335-7877 *E-mail:* lawton@wsu.edu
Founded: 1928
Trade & scholarly books focusing on the history, natural history, military history, culture & politics of the greater Pacific Northwest region (Washington, Idaho, Oregon, Western Montana, British Columbia & Alaska). Refer to web site for submission guidelines.
ISBN Prefix(es): 978-0-87422
Number of titles published annually: 4 Print
Total Titles: 182 Print
*Sales Office(s):* Hand Associates, 408 30 Ave, Seattle, WA 98122, Sales Rep: David Diehl *Tel:* 206-328-0295 *E-mail:* david_diehl@mindspring.com
Wholesale Solutions, 1959 NW Dock Place, Suite 3002, Seattle, WA 98107, Contact: Neal Warnick *Tel:* 206-310-9207 *E-mail:* neal@wholesale-solutions.net
Hand Associates, 16 Nelson Ave, Mill Valley, CA 94941-2120, Sales Rep: Jock Hayward *Tel:* 415-383-3883 *E-mail:* handhayward@earthlink.net
Hand Associates, 3851 Daisy Circle, Seal Beach, CA 90740-2901, Sales Rep: Pam Sheppard *Tel:* 562-431-0771 *E-mail:* hand.pams@gmail.com
Distributor for The Hutton Settlement (single title); Oregon Writers Colony (single title); Pacific Institute (single title); Washington State Historical Society (single title); WSU Museum of Art
*Distribution Center:* Partners Book Distributing West Inc, 1901 Raymond Ave SW, Suite C, Renton, WA 98055 *Tel:* 425-227-8486 *Fax:* 425-204-1448
Baker & Taylor Books, PO Box 8888, Momence, IL 60954 (US & Canada) *Toll Free Tel:* 800-775-1100 *Toll Free Fax:* 800-775-7480
Ingram Book Co, One Ingram Blvd, LaVergne, TN 37086 (US & Canada) *Toll Free Tel:* 800-937-8000
Membership(s): Association of American University Presses; Pacific Northwest Booksellers Association

**Water Environment Federation**
601 Wythe St, Alexandria, VA 22314-1994
*Tel:* 703-684-2400 *Toll Free Tel:* 800-666-0206 *Fax:* 703-684-2492
*E-mail:* csc@wef.org (cust serv)
*Web Site:* www.wef.org

*Key Personnel*
Association Devt: Jack Benson *Tel:* 703-684-2493 *E-mail:* jbenson@wef.org
Founded: 1928
Scientific publisher of environmental titles. Seeks authors of sound, state-of-the-art environmental material.
ISBN Prefix(es): 978-0-943244; 978-1-881369
Number of titles published annually: 15 Print
Total Titles: 220 Print

**§Water Resources Publications LLC**
PO Box 630026, Highlands Ranch, CO 80163-0026
SAN: 209-9136
*Tel:* 720-873-0171 *Toll Free Tel:* 800-736-2405 *Fax:* 720-873-0173 *Toll Free Fax:* 800-616-1971
*E-mail:* info@wrpllc.com
*Web Site:* www.wrpllc.com
*Key Personnel*
Busn Mgr: Jennie Campbell
Founded: 1971
Publish & distribute books & computer programs on water resources & related fields.
ISBN Prefix(es): 978-0-918334; 978-1-887201
Number of titles published annually: 10 Print
Total Titles: 450 Print; 35 CD-ROM
Distributor for ASAE; ASCE
*Shipping Address:* 10607 Flatiron Rd, Littleton, CO 80124
*Warehouse:* 10607 Flatiron Rd, Littleton, CO 80124

**Water Row Press**
Subsidiary of Water Row Books
PO Box 438, Sudbury, MA 01776
*Tel:* 508-485-8515 *Fax:* 508-229-0885
*E-mail:* contact@waterrowbooks.com
*Web Site:* www.waterrowbooks.com
*Key Personnel*
Publr: Jeffrey H Weinberg
Ed: Cisco Harland
Prodn Mgr: Betsy Kirschbaum
Founded: 1985
Publishers of modern literature, poetry, graphic novels; specialize in books by & about "Beat" writers; comic art.
ISBN Prefix(es): 978-0-934953
Number of titles published annually: 12 Print
Total Titles: 29 Print
Distributed by Water Row Books
Distributor for Water Row Books; Weinberg Books

**WaterBrook Multnomah Publishing Group**
Imprint of Random House Inc
12265 Oracle Blvd, Suite 200, Colorado Springs, CO 80921
*Tel:* 719-590-4999 *Toll Free Tel:* 800-603-7051 (orders) *Fax:* 719-590-8977 *Toll Free Fax:* 800-294-5686 (orders)
*E-mail:* info@waterbrookmultnomah.com
*Web Site:* waterbrookmultnomah.com
*Key Personnel*
Pres & Publr, WaterBrook Multnomah & Image Books: Steve Cobb
Dir, Sales: Lori Addicott
Dir, Publg Opers: Debbie Mitchell
Sr Ed: Ron Lee
Sr Ed, Fiction: Shannon Hill Marchese
Founded: 1996
Offer a broad range of Christian nonfiction & fiction titles in hardcover & trade paperback for adult & young readers, as well as children's books.
Random House Inc & its publishing entities are not accepting unsol submissions, proposals, mss, or submission queries via e-mail at this time.
ISBN Prefix(es): 978-0-87788; 978-1-57856; 978-1-4000
Number of titles published annually: 80 Print; 1 CD-ROM; 1 Audio
Total Titles: 1,000 Print; 4 CD-ROM; 6 E-Book; 15 Audio
Imprints: Shaw Books (fisherman)
Membership(s): Evangelical Christian Publishers Association

**Watermark Publishing**
1088 Bishop St, Suite 310, Honolulu, HI 96813
*Tel:* 808-587-7766 *Toll Free Tel:* 866-900-BOOK (900-2665) *Fax:* 808-521-3461
*E-mail:* info@bookshawaii.net
*Web Site:* www.bookshawaii.net
*Key Personnel*
Dir, Sales & Mktg: Dawn Sakamoto *Tel:* 808-534-7170 *E-mail:* dawn@bookshawaii.net
ISBN Prefix(es): 978-0-9720932; 978-0-9705787; 978-0-9631154; 978-0-9753740; 978-0-9779143; 978-0-9790647; 978-0-9796769; 978-0-9815086
Number of titles published annually: 15 Print
Total Titles: 55 Print

**Watson-Guptill Publications**
Imprint of Crown Publishing Group
c/o Random House Inc, 1745 Broadway, New York, NY 10019
*Tel:* 212-782-9000 *Fax:* 212-940-7381
*E-mail:* crownbiz@randomhouse.com
*Web Site:* www.randomhouse.com/crown/watsonguptill
*Key Personnel*
Art Dir: Jess Morphew *E-mail:* jmorphew@randomhouse.com
Prodn Dir: Alyn Evans *E-mail:* alevans@randomhouse.com
Publicity Dir: Kim Small *E-mail:* ksmall@randomhouse.com
Deputy Mktg Dir: Donna Passannante *E-mail:* dpassannante@randomhouse.com
Exec Ed, Art: Candace Raney
Sr Ed, Potter Craft: Betty Wong *E-mail:* bwong@randomhouse.com
Sr Acqs Ed, Amphoto Books: Julie Mazur *E-mail:* jmazur@randomhouse.com
Ed: Patrick Barb *E-mail:* pbarb@randomhouse.com
Founded: 1937
Art instruction, graphic design, fine arts, comics & cartooning, video game art, photography, crafts (jewelry, fiber arts, paper crafts), fashion, film & pop culture.
ISBN Prefix(es): 978-0-8230; 978-0-8174; 978-1-58065
Number of titles published annually: 60 Print
Total Titles: 800 Print
Foreign Rep(s): Bookwise International (Australia, New Zealand); The Guild of Master Craftsmen (UK); Peter Hyde Associates (South Africa)
*Orders to:* Specialty Retail Div, Random House Inc, 1745 Broadway, MD 6-3, New York, NY 10019 *Toll Free Tel:* 800-729-2960 *Toll Free Fax:* 800-292-9071 *E-mail:* specialmarkets@randomhouse.com

**Watson Publishing International LLC**
PO Box 1240, Sagamore Beach, MA 02562-1240
*Tel:* 508-888-9113 *Fax:* 508-888-3733
*E-mail:* orders@watsonpublishing.com; orders@shpusa.com
*Web Site:* www.shpusa.com; www.watsonpublishing.com
*Key Personnel*
CEO & Pres: Neale W Watson, Esq *E-mail:* nww@shpusa.com
Founded: 1971
Scholarly books on the history, philosophy & sociology of science, technology & medicine.
ISBN Prefix(es): 978-0-88135
Number of titles published annually: 5 Print
Total Titles: 120 Print
Imprints: Prodist; Science History Publications USA; Neale Watson Academic Publications
*Shipping Address:* Publishers Storage & Shipping Corp, 46 Development Rd, Fitchburg, MA 01420-6020, Publr Rep: Donna Machonis *Tel:* 978-345-2121 ext 380

**Waveland Press Inc**
4180 IL Rte 83, Suite 101, Long Grove, IL 60047-9580
SAN: 209-0961
*Tel:* 847-634-0081 *Fax:* 847-634-9501
*E-mail:* info@waveland.com
*Web Site:* www.waveland.com
*Key Personnel*
Pres & Publr: Neil Rowe
Ed: Carol Rowe
Mktg Mgr: Thomas Curtin
Prodn Mgr & Intl Rts: Don Rosso
Off Mgr: Jennena Jackolin
Founded: 1975
College textbooks & supplements.
ISBN Prefix(es): 978-0-88133; 978-0-917974; 978-1-57766
Number of titles published annually: 40 Print
Total Titles: 700 Print
Subsidiaries: Sheffield Publishing Co
*See separate listing for:*
**Sheffield Publishing Co**

**Wayne State University Press**
Leonard N Simons Bldg, 4809 Woodward Ave, Detroit, MI 48201-1309
SAN: 202-5221
*Tel:* 313-577-6120 *Toll Free Tel:* 800-978-7323 *Fax:* 313-577-6131
*Web Site:* www.wsupress.wayne.edu
*Key Personnel*
Chmn, Edit Bd: Jerry Herron
Dir: Jane Hoehner
Mgr, Sales & Mktg: Emily Nowak
Acqs Mgr: Kathryn Wildfong
Busn Mgr: Andrew Kaufman
Edit Design & Prodn: Kristin Harpster Lawrence
Order Fulfillment: Theresa Martinelli
Founded: 1941
Scholarly & trade books in African American studies, film & television, women's studies, Jewish studies, poetry, speech & language pathology, fairy tales & folklore, regional studies & urban studies.
ISBN Prefix(es): 978-0-8143
Number of titles published annually: 40 Print
Total Titles: 2,500 Print; 2 CD-ROM
Imprints: Great Lakes Books; Painted Turtle Books (general-interest trade imprint)
Distributor for Cranbrook Institute of Science; Detroit Institute of Arts; Hebrew Union College Press; Marick Press
Foreign Rep(s): Eurospan (Africa, Europe, Middle East, UK); EWEB (Far East); Scholarly Book Services (Canada)
*Warehouse:* 40 W Hancock St, Detroit, MI 48201
Membership(s): Association of American University Presses

**Wayside Publishing**
11 Jan Sebastian Dr, Suite 5, Sandwich, MA 02563
*Tel:* 508-833-5096 *Toll Free Tel:* 888-302-2519 *Fax:* 508-833-6284
*E-mail:* wayside@sprintmail.com
*Web Site:* www.waysidepublishing.com
*Key Personnel*
Owner & Publr: Greg Greuel
Assoc: Lee Ann Carstanjen
Founded: 1988
Humanities, English & foreign language textbooks & history.
ISBN Prefix(es): 978-1-877653
Number of titles published annually: 5 Print
Total Titles: 54 Print

**Welcome Books®**
Imprint of Welcome Enterprises
6 W 18 St, Unit 4B, New York, NY 10011
*Tel:* 212-989-3200 *Fax:* 212-989-3205
*E-mail:* info@welcomebooks.com
*Web Site:* www.welcomebooks.com
*Key Personnel*
Pres: Clark Wakabayashi *E-mail:* clark@welcomebooks.com
Publr: Lena Tabori *E-mail:* lena@welcomebooks.com
Assoc Publr: Katrina Fried *E-mail:* katrina@welcomebooks.com
Proj Dir: Alice Wong *E-mail:* alice@welcomebooks.com
Art Dir: Greg Wakabayashi *E-mail:* greg@welcomebooks.com
Mng Ed: Natasha Tabori Fried *E-mail:* natasha@welcomebooks.com
Founded: 1980
Illustrated books for adult trade & gift market.
ISBN Prefix(es): 978-0-941807
Number of titles published annually: 8 Print
Total Titles: 100 Print
Distributed by Random House
Distributor for AAP; Cerf & Peterson; Music Sales; Zeke Holdings Ltd
*Distribution Center:* Random House, 400 Hahn Rd, Westminster, MD 21157 *Toll Free Tel:* 800-733-3000 *Toll Free Fax:* 800-659-2436
Membership(s): American Book Producers Association

**Welcome Rain Publishers LLC**
217 Thompson St, Suite 473, New York, NY 10012
*Tel:* 212-686-1909
*Web Site:* welcomerain.com
*Key Personnel*
Publr: John Weber
Founded: 1997
General trade publisher.
ISBN Prefix(es): 978-1-56649
Number of titles published annually: 21 Print
Total Titles: 95 Print
Distributed by National Book Network

**Wellington Press**
Division of BooksUPrint.com Inc
9601-30 Miccosukee Rd, Tallahassee, FL 32309
*Tel:* 850-878-6500
*E-mail:* peacegames@aol.com
*Web Site:* www.peacegames.com
*Key Personnel*
Pres & Intl Rts: David W Felder, PhD
Founded: 1982
Publish philosophy books, including texts, & role play peacegames that examine conflicts of all types.
ISBN Prefix(es): 978-0-910959; 978-1-57501
Number of titles published annually: 10 Print; 10 E-Book
Total Titles: 85 Print; 90 Online; 100 E-Book

**Wellness Institute/Self Help Books LLC**
515 W North St, Pass Christian, MS 39571-2605
*Tel:* 228-452-0770 *Fax:* 228-452-0775
*Web Site:* selfhelpbooks.com
*Key Personnel*
Dir: Harold Dawley, Jr *E-mail:* hdawley@bellsouth.net
Founded: 1974
Exclusively publisher of self-help books.
ISBN Prefix(es): 978-1-58741
Number of titles published annually: 30 Print; 30 E-Book
Total Titles: 100 Print; 70 E-Book
Imprints: Selfhelpbooks.com

**Eliot Werner Publications Inc**
31 Willow Lane, Clinton Corners, NY 12514
Mailing Address: PO Box 268, Clinton Corners, NY 12514
*Tel:* 845-266-4241 *Fax:* 845-266-3317
*E-mail:* eliotwerner@optonline.net
*Web Site:* www.eliotwerner.com
Founded: 2001
Academic & scholarly books in anthropology, archaeology, psychology, sociology & related fields; writing, editing & contract publishing.
ISBN Prefix(es): 978-0-9712427; 978-0-9719587; 978-0-9752738; 978-0-9797731
Number of titles published annually: 6 Print
Total Titles: 45 Print
Imprints: Percheron Press

**Wescott Cove Publishing Co**
Imprint of Far Horizons Media Co
1227 S Florida Ave, Rockledge, FL 32955
Mailing Address: PO Box 560989, Rockledge, FL 32956
*Tel:* 321-690-2224 *Fax:* 321-690-0853
*E-mail:* customerservice@farhorizonsmedia.com
*Web Site:* www.farhorizonsmedia.com
*Key Personnel*
Publr: Will Standley
Books on boating, cruising, yachting & the adventurous life.
ISBN Prefix(es): 978-0-918752
Number of titles published annually: 16 Print; 4 E-Book
Total Titles: 16 Online; 16 E-Book
*Distribution Center:* Ingram Book Co, One Ingram Blvd, La Vergne, TN 37086 *Tel:* 615-793-5000 *Toll Free Tel:* 800-937-8200 *E-mail:* customer.service@ingrambook.com *Web Site:* www.ingrambook.com
Membership(s): The Association of Publishers for Special Sales

**Wesleyan Publishing House**
Division of Wesleyan Church Corp
13300 Olio Rd, Fishers, IN 46037
Mailing Address: PO Box 50434, Indianapolis, IN 46250-0434
*Tel:* 317-774-3853 *Toll Free Tel:* 800-493-7539 *Fax:* 317-774-3865 *Toll Free Fax:* 800-788-3535
*E-mail:* wph@wesleyan.org
*Web Site:* www.wesleyan.org/wph
*Key Personnel*
CEO: Craig A Dunn
Gen Publr: Donald Cady
Founded: 1968
ISBN Prefix(es): 978-0-89827
Number of titles published annually: 11 Print
Total Titles: 60 Print
*Returns:* Innovative Inc, 4280 Piedmont Pkwy, Suite 105, Greensboro, NC 27410 (Attn: Cust Serv)
Membership(s): CBA: The Association for Christian Retail; Christian Holiness Partnership; Evangelical Christian Publishers Association; Holiness Publisher's Association; Protestant Church-Owned Publishers Association

**Wesleyan University Press**
215 Long Lane, Middletown, CT 06459-0433
*Tel:* 860-685-7711 *Fax:* 860-685-7712
*Web Site:* www.wesleyan.edu/wespress
*Key Personnel*
Dir & Ed-in-Chief: Suzanna L Tamminen *Tel:* 860-685-7727 *E-mail:* stamminen@wesleyan.edu
Asst Dir & Mktg Mgr: Leslie Starr *Tel:* 860-685-7725 *E-mail:* lstarr@wesleyan.edu
Acqs Ed: Parker Smathers *Tel:* 860-685-7730 *E-mail:* psmathers@wesleyan.edu
Publicist: Stephanie Elliott *Tel:* 860-685-7723 *E-mail:* selliott@wesleyan.edu
Founded: 1957
Editorial program which has been awarded six Pulitzer Prizes; distinguished history of publishing scholarly & trade books that have influenced American poetry & critical thought over the last four decades.
ISBN Prefix(es): 978-0-8195
Number of titles published annually: 25 Print
Total Titles: 425 Print
Imprints: Music/Culture; Early Classics of Science Fiction; Wesleyan Poetry
Foreign Rep(s): East-West Export Books (Asia, Australia, New Zealand, The Pacific); Eurospan University Press Group (Europe, Middle East, UK); University of British Columbia Press (Canada)
*Shipping Address:* UPNE, One Court St, Suite 250, Lebanon, NH 03766-1358 *Tel:* 603-448-1533 *Toll Free Tel:* 800-421-1561 *Fax:* 603-448-9429 *E-mail:* university.press@dartmouth.edu
*Distribution Center:* University Press of New England, One Court St, Suite 250, Lebanon, NH 03766 *Tel:* 603-448-1533 *Fax:* 603-643-1540 *E-mail:* university.press@dartmouth.edu
Membership(s): AAP; Association of American University Presses; NEBA

**§West Academic Publishing**
610 Opperman Dr, Eagan, MN 55123
*Tel:* 651-687-7000 *Toll Free Tel:* 800-328-2209 (bookstore orders); 800-313-WEST (313-9378) *Toll Free Fax:* 800-213-2323 (bookstore orders)
*E-mail:* westacademic@thomsonreuters.com
*Web Site:* www.westacademic.com
*Key Personnel*
Mng Ed, Study Aides: Staci Herr *E-mail:* staci.herr@thomsonreuters.com
Founded: 1953
Law school casebook, statute, study aid & career success publisher.
ISBN Prefix(es): 978-0-1590; 978-0-3141
Number of titles published annually: 50 Print; 2 CD-ROM
Total Titles: 375 Print; 10 CD-ROM; 60 Audio

**West Virginia University Press**
West Virginia University, PO Box 6295, Morgantown, WV 26506-6295
*Tel:* 304-293-8400 *Toll Free Tel:* 866-WVU-PRES (988-7737) *Fax:* 304-293-6585
*E-mail:* press@wvu.edu
*Web Site:* www.wvupress.com
*Key Personnel*
Dir & Ed-in-Chief: Carrie Mullen *Tel:* 304-293-8400 ext 2 *E-mail:* carrie.mullen@mail.wvu.edu
Journals Mgr: Hilary Attfield *Tel:* 304-293-8400 ext 5 *E-mail:* hilary.attfield@mail.wvu.edu
Mktg Mgr: Abby Freeland *Tel:* 304-293-8400 ext 6 *E-mail:* abby.freeland@mail.wvu.edu
Prodn & Design Mgr: Than Saffel *Tel:* 304-293-8400 ext 4 *E-mail:* than.saffel@mail.wvu.edu
Off Mgr: Floann Downey *Tel:* 304-293-8400 ext 1 *E-mail:* fdowney2@mail.wvu.edu
Edit & Prodn Asst: Rachel King *Tel:* 304-293-8400 ext 3 *E-mail:* rachel.king@mail.wvu.edu
Founded: 1965
ISBN Prefix(es): 978-1-933202; 978-0-937058
Number of titles published annually: 12 Print; 1 CD-ROM; 1 Audio
Total Titles: 75 Print; 8 CD-ROM; 2 Audio
Imprints: Vandalia Press
*Orders to:* Chicago Distribution Center, 11030 S Langley Ave, Chicago, IL 60628 *Toll Free Tel:* 800-621-2736 *Toll Free Fax:* 800-621-8476 *E-mail:* orders@press.chicago.edu
*Distribution Center:* Chicago Distribution Center, 11030 S Langley Ave, Chicago, IL 60628 *Tel:* 773-702-7000 (Intl) *Toll Free Tel:* 800-621-2736 *Fax:* 773-702-7212 (Intl) *Toll Free Fax:* 800-621-8476
Membership(s): Association of American University Presses

**Westcliffe Publishers Inc**
Imprint of Big Earth Publishing
3360 Mitchell Lane, Suite E, Boulder, CO 80301
SAN: 239-7528
*Toll Free Tel:* 800-258-5830 *Fax:* 303-443-9687
*E-mail:* books@bigearthpublishing.com
*Web Site:* www.bigearthpublishing.com/westcliffe-publishers
*Key Personnel*
CEO & Pres: John Fielder
Founded: 1979
Photographic publisher; specialize in landscape, nature & scenic subjects, trail guides.
ISBN Prefix(es): 978-0-942394; 978-0-929969; 978-1-56579
Number of titles published annually: 18 Print; 16 Online
Total Titles: 125 Print; 125 Online

**Western Pennsylvania Genealogical Society**
4400 Forbes Ave, Pittsburgh, PA 15213-4080
*Tel:* 412-687-6811 (answering machine)
*E-mail:* info@wpgs.org
*Web Site:* www.wpgs.org
*Key Personnel*
Pubns Chair: Irene Dinning *E-mail:* publicity@wpgs.org
Committee Chair: Suzanne M Johnston
Pres: Debbie Kapp *E-mail:* president@wpgs.org
Pres Elect: Marilyn Cocchiola Holt
Founded: 1974
ISBN Prefix(es): 978-0-9745162
Number of titles published annually: 10 Print; 1 CD-ROM; 40 Online
Total Titles: 40 Print; 1 CD-ROM; 1 Online; 1 E-Book
Distributed by Mechling Associates
Membership(s): National Genealogical Society

**Western Reflections Publishing Co**
951 N Hwy 149, Lake City, CO 81235
Mailing Address: PO Box 1149, Lake City, CO 81235-1149
*Tel:* 970-944-0110 *Toll Free Tel:* 800-993-4490 *Fax:* 970-944-0273
*E-mail:* publisher@westernreflectionspublishing.com
*Web Site:* www.westernreflectionspublishing.com
*Key Personnel*
Pres: P David Smith
Founded: 1996
History & culture of the western US with an emphasis on Colorado.
ISBN Prefix(es): 978-1-890437; 978-1-932738
Number of titles published annually: 6 Print
Total Titles: 170 Print

**Westernlore Press**
PO Box 35305, Tucson, AZ 85740-5305
SAN: 202-9650
*Tel:* 520-297-5491 *Fax:* 520-297-1722
*Key Personnel*
Pres & Ed: Lynn R Bailey
Treas & ISBN Contact: Anne G Bailey
Founded: 1941
History & biography, anthropology, historic archaeology & historic sites & ethnohistory pertaining to the greater American West.
ISBN Prefix(es): 978-0-87026
Number of titles published annually: 6 Print
Total Titles: 65 Print

**§Westminster John Knox Press**
Imprint of Presbyterian Publishing Corp
100 Witherspoon St, Louisville, KY 40202-1396
SAN: 202-9669
*Tel:* 502-569-5052 *Toll Free Tel:* 800-227-2872 (US only) *Fax:* 502-569-8308 *Toll Free Fax:* 800-541-5113 (US & CN)
*E-mail:* wjk@wjkbooks.com; customer_service@wjkbooks.com
*Web Site:* www.wjkbooks.com
*Key Personnel*
COO: Monty Anderson *E-mail:* manderson@wjkbooks.com
Pres & Publr: Marc Lewis *E-mail:* mlewis@wjkbooks.com
Exec Dir, Publg & Edit Dir: David Dobson *E-mail:* ddobson@wjkbooks.com
Exec Dir, Sales & Mktg: Gavin Stephens *E-mail:* gstephens@presbypub.com
Mktg Mgr: Emily Kiefer *E-mail:* ekeifer@wjkbooks.com
Acqs Ed: Jana Riess *E-mail:* jreiss@wjkbooks.com
Rts & Perms: Michele Blum *E-mail:* mblum@wjkbooks.com
Founded: 1838
With a publishing heritage that dates back more than 160 years, WJK Press publishes religious & theological books & resources for scholars, clergy, laity & general readers. The publisher employs the motto "Challenging the Mind, Nourishing the Soul".
ISBN Prefix(es): 978-0-664; 978-0-8042
Number of titles published annually: 150 Print
Total Titles: 1,100 Print; 2 CD-ROM; 2 Audio
*Foreign Office(s):* 13 Hellesdon Park Rd, Norwich Norfolk NR6 5DR, United Kingdom *Tel:* (01603) 612 914 *E-mail:* orders@norwichbooksandmusic.co.uk
Distributor for SCM
Foreign Rep(s): Academic Books for Seminaries (Rocky C L Chen) (Taiwan); Africa Christian Textbooks (Nigeria); Canaanland Distributors Sdn Bhd (Malaysia); Christian Book Discounters (South Africa); Claretian Communications Inc (Philippines); Cross Communications Ltd (Alexander Y C Lee) (Hong Kong); Import-Export & Wholesale Center (India); Korea Christian Book Service Inc (South Korea); Methodist Publishing House (South Africa); Omega Distributors Ltd (New Zealand); SKS Books Warehouse (Lek Eng Khiang) (Singapore)
*Distribution Center:* Presbyterian Publishing Corp, 341 Great Circle Rd, Nashville, TN 37228 *Toll Free Tel:* 800-227-2872 *Toll Free Fax:* 800-541-5113 *Web Site:* www.ppcpub.com

**Westview Press**
Member of The Perseus Books Group
2465 Central Ave, Boulder, CO 80301
SAN: 219-970X
*Tel:* 303-444-3541 *Fax:* 720-406-7336
*E-mail:* westview.orders@perseusbooks.com
*Web Site:* www.perseusbooksgroup.com; www.westviewpress.com
*Key Personnel*
CEO & Pres: David Steinberger
COO & VP: Joe Mangan
Publr: Cathleen Tetro
Exec Dir & Edit Dir, History & Area Studies: Priscilla McGeehon
Exec Ed: Karl Yambert *E-mail:* karly@perseusbooks.com
Founded: 1975
Quality nonfiction, general audience trade books & college textbooks in the following areas: history, political science, international relations, military history, sociology, current affairs, criminology, women's studies, gender studies, journalism, anthropology, archaeology, art & art history, philosphy, religion, physics, mathematics, earth, planetary & space sciences.
ISBN Prefix(es): 978-0-8133
Number of titles published annually: 100 Print
Total Titles: 2,000 Print
*Sales Office(s):* The Perseus Books Group, 387 Park Ave S, 12th fl, New York City, NY 10016 *Tel:* 212-340-8100 *Toll Free Tel:* 800-343-4499 *Fax:* 212-340-8125 *Toll Free Fax:* 800-351-5073 *Web Site:* www.perseusbooksgroup.com
*Foreign Office(s):* Perseus Running Press UK, 69-70 Temple Chambers, 3-7 Temple Ave, London EC4Y 0HP, United Kingdom *Tel:* (0207) 353 7771 *Fax:* (0207) 353 7786 *E-mail:* enquiries@perseusbooks.co.uk
Foreign Rep(s): Sabrina Cote (France); Bernd Feldman (Austria, Germany, Switzerland); Charles Gibbes (Greece); Ben Greig (Scandinavia), Lazlo Horvath (Central Europe, Eastern Europe); Kemper Conseil (Belgium, Luxembourg, Netherlands); Mare Nostrum Publishing Consultants (David Pickering) (Italy); Mare Nostrum Publishing Consultants (Cristina De Lara) (Portugal, Spain); Perseus Running Press UK (Europe, UK); Publishers Scandinavian Consultancy (Ben Greig); Publishers Scandinavian Consultancy (Colin Flint) (Scandinavia); Zytek Publishing (South Africa)
Foreign Rights: Anthea Agency (Katalina Sabeva) (Bulgaria); Bardon-Chinese Media Agency (David Tsai) (China, Taiwan); Raquel de la Concha Agencia Literaria (Raquel de la Concha) (Brazil, Latin America, Portugal, Spain); Paul & Peter Fritz Agency (Peter Fritz, Christian Dittus & Antonia Fritz) (Germany); Deborah Harris Agency (Efrat Lev) (Israel); Anna Jarota Agency (Anna Jarota) (France); Nurcihan Kesim Literary Agency Inc (Filiz Karaman) (Turkey); Duran Kim Agency (Duran Kim & Joe Moon) (Korea); Alexander Korzhenevski Agency (Alexander Korzhenevski & Tania Korzhenevski) (Russia); Maxima Creative Agency (Santo Manurung) (Indonesia); Kristin Olson Literary Agency (Kristin Olson) (Czech Republic, Slovakia); Oxford Literary & Rights Agency (Hana Whitton) (Ukraine); Read n' Right Agency (Nike Davarinou) (Greece); Lennart Sane Agency (Phillip Sane) (Scandinavia); Santachiara Literary Agency (Roberto Santachiara) (Italy); Sebes & Van Gelderen Literary Agency (Paul Sebes) (Netherlands); Livia Stoia Agency (Livia Stoia & Cristiana Lazareanu) (Albania, Bosnia and Herzegovina, Croatia, Macedonia, Montenegro, Romania, Serbia, Slovenia); Torus-Books Literary & Scouting Agency Ltd (Gynn Kalman) (Hungary); Tuttle-Mori Agency Inc (Manami Tamaoki) (Japan); Tuttle-Mori Agency Inc (Mr Thananchai Pandey) (Thailand, Vietnam)
*Advertising Agency:* Bennett Books
*Orders to:* The Perseus Books Group, 1094 Flex Dr, Jackson, TN 38301 *Toll Free Tel:* 800-343-4499 *Toll Free Fax:* 800-351-5073
*Distribution Center:* Consortium Book Sales & Distribution, The Keg House, Suite 101, 34 13 Ave NE, Minneapolis, MN 55413-1007 *Tel:* 612-746-2600 *Toll Free Tel:* 800-283-3572 *Fax:* 612-746-2606 *Web Site:* www.cbsd.com
The Perseus Books Group, 1094 Flex Dr, Jackson, TN 38301 *Toll Free Tel:* 800-343-4499 *Toll Free Fax:* 800-351-5073
Publishers Group West, 1700 Fourth St, Berkeley, CA 97410 *Tel:* 510-809-3700 *Fax:* 510-809-3777 *E-mail:* info@pgw.com *Web Site:* www.publishersgroupwest.com
Membership(s): AAP

**WH&O International**
Division of Meristem Systems Corp
892 Worcester St, Suite 130, Wellesley, MA 02482
Mailing Address: PO Box 812785, Wellesley, MA 02482-0025
*Tel:* 508-525-5370 *Fax:* 508-525-5370
*E-mail:* whobooks@hotmail.com
*Web Site:* www.whobooks.com
*Key Personnel*
Pres: Dennis Hamilton
Founded: 1989
Technical books.
ISBN Prefix(es): 978-1-878960
Number of titles published annually: 6 Print
Total Titles: 12 Print
Foreign Rep(s): Generation Systems of UK

**Wharton School Publishing**, see Financial Times Press & Wharton School Publishing

**Wheatherstone Press**
Subsidiary of Dickinson Consulting Group
PO Box 257, Portland, OR 97207-0257
*Tel:* 503-244-8929 *Fax:* 503-244-9795
*E-mail:* relocntr@nwlink.com
*Web Site:* www.wheatherstonepress.com
*Key Personnel*
CEO & Pres: Jan Dickinson
Founded: 1983
Publishes handbooks & step-by-step guides covering all phases of relocation, including internationally.
ISBN Prefix(es): 978-0-9613011
Number of titles published annually: 3 Print
Total Titles: 49 Print
Foreign Rep(s): 111

**§Whitaker House**
1030 Hunt Valley Circle, New Kensington, PA 15068
*Tel:* 724-334-7000 *Toll Free Tel:* 877-793-9800 *Fax:* 724-334-1200 *Toll Free Fax:* 800-765-1960
*E-mail:* publisher@whitakerhouse.com
*Web Site:* whitakerhouse.com
*Key Personnel*
Mng Dir: Tom Cox
Foreign Rts Mgr: Saralinda Newbury
Author Liaison: Christine Whitaker
Founded: 1970
ISBN Prefix(es): 978-0-88368; 978-1-60374
Number of titles published annually: 40 Print; 8 CD-ROM; 40 E-Book; 8 Audio
Total Titles: 500 Print; 20 CD-ROM; 100 E-Book; 40 Audio
Foreign Rep(s): Donna Rowley
Membership(s): BEA; CBA; National Religious Broadcasters

**White Cloud Press**
300 E Hersey St, Suite 11, Ashland, OR 97520
Mailing Address: PO Box 3400, Ashland, OR 97520
*Tel:* 541-488-6415 *Toll Free Tel:* 800-380-8286 *Fax:* 541-482-7708
*E-mail:* info@whitecloudpress.com
*Web Site:* www.whitecloudpress.com
*Key Personnel*
Publr: Steve Scholl *E-mail:* scholl@whitecloudpress.com
Prodn Mgr: Christy Collins *E-mail:* christy@whitecloudpress.com
Admin Asst & Intl Rts & Perms: Ezra Penalba *E-mail:* ezra@whitecloudpress.com
Founded: 1993
General trade, emphasis on religion & fiction.
ISBN Prefix(es): 978-1-883991; 978-0-9745245
Number of titles published annually: 6 Print
Total Titles: 60 Print; 40 E-Book; 4 Audio
Imprints: Caveat Press; Confluence Books; RiverWood Books
Subsidiaries: Confluence Book Services
Foreign Rights: Danny Baror; Nigel Yorwerth
*Distribution Center:* Publishers Group West, 1700 Fourth St, Berkley, CA 94710 *Toll Free Tel:* 800-788-3123 *Toll Free Fax:* 800-351-5073 *Web Site:* www.pgw.com
Membership(s): IBPA, the Independent Book Publishers Association

**White Pine Press**
PO Box 236, Buffalo, NY 14201
*Tel:* 716-627-4665 *Fax:* 716-627-4665
*E-mail:* wpine@whitepine.org
*Web Site:* www.whitepine.org
*Key Personnel*
Mng Dir: Elaine La Mattina
Publr & Ed: Dennis Maloney *E-mail:* dennismaloney@yahoo.com
Founded: 1973
Specialize in poetry, essays, fiction, literature in translation.
ISBN Prefix(es): 978-0-934834; 978-1-877727; 978-1-877800; 978-1-893996
Number of titles published annually: 10 Print
Total Titles: 160 Print
Subsidiaries: Springhouse Editions
Distributor for Springhouse Editions
*Distribution Center:* Consortium Book Sales & Distribution, The Keg House, Suite 101, 34 13 Ave NE, Minneapolis, MN 55413-1007 *Tel:* 612-746-2600 *Toll Free Tel:* 800-283-3572 (cust serv) *Fax:* 612-746-2606 *Web Site:* www.cbsd.com

**White Wolf Publishing Inc**
Division of CCP North America
250 Ponce de Leon Ave, Suite 700, Decatur, GA 30030
*Tel:* 404-292-1819 *Toll Free Tel:* 800-454-9653
*E-mail:* questions@white-wolf.com
*Web Site:* www.white-wolf.com
*Key Personnel*
Mktg Dir: Philippe Boulle
Founded: 1991
Fiction & game books.
ISBN Prefix(es): 978-1-56504; 978-1-58846
Number of titles published annually: 60 Print
Total Titles: 280 Print
Imprints: Borealis; Exalted; Sword & Sorcery; Two Wolf Press; World of Darkness

**Whitehorse Press**
107 E Conway Rd, Center Conway, NH 03813-4012
*Tel:* 603-356-6556 *Toll Free Tel:* 800-531-1133 *Fax:* 603-356-6590
*E-mail:* customerservice@whitehorsepress.com
*Web Site:* www.whitehorsebooks.com
*Key Personnel*
Owner & Publr: Daniel W Kennedy
Owner & Mktg Mgr: Judith M Kennedy *E-mail:* judy@whitehorsepress.com
Founded: 1989
Travel Guides & how-to books: motorcycle touring, care & maintenance, restoration.
ISBN Prefix(es): 978-0-9621834; 978-1-884313
Number of titles published annually: 6 Print
Total Titles: 50 Print
Foreign Rep(s): Gazelle Books Ltd (UK); Woodslane (Australia)
*Distribution Center:* Quayside Distribution, 100 Cummings Ctr, Suite 406-L, Beverly, MA 01915 *Tel:* 978-282-3500

**Whitman, Albert & Co**, see Albert Whitman & Co

**§Whittier Publications Inc**
3115 Long Beach Rd, Oceanside, NY 11572
*Tel:* 516-432-8120 *Toll Free Tel:* 800-897-TEXT (897-8398) *Fax:* 516-889-0341
*E-mail:* info@whitbooks.com
*Key Personnel*
Pres: Judith Etra
Founded: 1990
Textbooks, trade, self-help, biology, history, mathematics, chemistry, sociology.
ISBN Prefix(es): 978-1-878045; 978-1-57604
Number of titles published annually: 200 Print
Imprints: Obelisk Books
*Branch Office(s)*
6429 Warren Dr, Norcross, GA 30093

**§Whole Person Associates Inc**
210 W Michigan St, Duluth, MN 55802-1908
*Tel:* 218-727-0500 *Toll Free Tel:* 800-247-6789 *Fax:* 218-727-0505
*E-mail:* books@wholeperson.com
*Web Site:* www.wholeperson.com
*Key Personnel*
Owner & Publr: Carlene Sippola
Founded: 1980
Stress management & wellness promotion.
ISBN Prefix(es): 978-0-938586; 978-1-57025
Number of titles published annually: 8 Print; 5 Audio
Total Titles: 160 Print; 29 CD-ROM; 38 Audio
Imprints: Whole Person Associates

**§Wide World of Maps Inc**
2626 W Indian School Rd, Phoenix, AZ 85017
*Tel:* 602-279-2324 *Toll Free Tel:* 800-279-7654 *Fax:* 602-279-2350
*E-mail:* sales@maps4u.com
*Web Site:* www.maps4u.com
*Key Personnel*
Pres: James L Willinger *Tel:* 602-433-0616 *Fax:* 602-433-0695 *E-mail:* james@maps4u.com
Founded: 1976
Atlases, charts, guide books, maps, map software, map accessories & more.
ISBN Prefix(es): 978-0-938448; 978-1-887749
Number of titles published annually: 6 Print; 2 CD-ROM
Total Titles: 20 Print; 2 CD-ROM
Imprints: Yellow 1
Divisions: Desert Charts; Metro Maps; Phoenix Mapping Service
Distributed by Rand McNally
Distributor for Benchmark Maps; Big Sky Maps; Franko Maps; MacVan Maps (Colorado Springs); Metro Maps; Rand McNally

**Wide World Publishing**
PO Box 476, San Carlos, CA 94070-0476
SAN: 211-1462
*Tel:* 650-593-2839 *Fax:* 650-595-0802
*E-mail:* wwpbl@aol.com
*Web Site:* wideworldpublishing.com
*Key Personnel*
Partner & Intl Rts: Elvira Monroe
Founded: 1976
Trade paperbacks, cookbooks, mathematics, calendars, travel books & guides, math books.
ISBN Prefix(es): 978-0-933174; 978-1-884550
Number of titles published annually: 6 Print
Total Titles: 35 Print
Imprints: Math Products Plus; Wide World Publishing; Wide World Publishing/Tetra
Distributed by The Islander Group Inc; Perseus Books Group; Publishers Group West
Foreign Rep(s): Publishers Group West (Asia, Canada, Europe)

**Markus Wiener Publishers Inc**
231 Nassau St, Princeton, NJ 08542
SAN: 282-5465
*Tel:* 609-921-1141 *Fax:* 609-921-1140
*E-mail:* publisher@markuswiener.com
*Web Site:* www.markuswiener.com
*Key Personnel*
Pres: M Markus Wiener
VP & Ed: Shelley Frisch
Ed: Janet Stern
Mktg & Ad: Stacey Garstein *E-mail:* stacey@markuswiener.com
Prodn: Cheryl Mirkin
Founded: 1981
Books & journals in Middle Eastern, Latin American, African & Caribbean studies, world history & religion. Textbooks, artificial intelligence. Returns: write for permission.
ISBN Prefix(es): 978-0-910129; 978-0-945179; 978-1-55876
Number of titles published annually: 25 Print
Total Titles: 300 Print
Imprints: Rutgers Series in Accounting Research; Topics in World History

Foreign Rep(s): Eurospan (Africa, Asia, Asia-Pacific, Australia, Europe)
Foreign Rights: Verlagsburo Wetterstein Munich (Africa, Asia, Europe, Germany, Latin America, Middle East)

**Michael Wiese Productions**
12400 Ventura Blvd, No 1111, Studio City, CA 91604
*Tel:* 818-379-8799 *Toll Free Tel:* 800-833-5738 (orders) *Fax:* 818-986-3408
*E-mail:* mwpsales@mwp.com; fulfillment@portcity.com
*Web Site:* www.mwp.com
*Key Personnel*
Founder & Publr: Michael Wiese
VP: Ken Lee *Tel:* 206-283-2948 *E-mail:* kenlee@mwp.com
Spec Sales: Michele Chong *Tel:* 818-841-4123
Founded: 1981
Publisher of books on screenwriting & filmmaking.
ISBN Prefix(es): 978-0-941188
Number of titles published annually: 15 Print
Total Titles: 170 Print
*Distribution Center:* Ingram Publisher Services, One Ingram Blvd, La Vergne, TN 37086 *Toll Free Tel:* 866-400-5351 *E-mail:* customerservice@ingrampublisherservices.com *Web Site:* www.ingrampublisherservices.com

**Wilderness Adventures Press Inc**
45 Buckskin Rd, Belgrade, MT 59714
*Tel:* 406-388-0112 *Toll Free Tel:* 866-400-2012
*E-mail:* books@wildadvpress.com
*Web Site:* store.wildadvpress.com
*Key Personnel*
Pres & Prodn Ed: Chuck Johnson *Tel:* 406-388-0112 ext 12 *Fax:* 406-388-0120 *E-mail:* chuckj@wildadvpress.com
Secy & Treas: Blanche Johnson *Tel:* 406-388-0112 ext 14 *Fax:* 406-388-0120 *E-mail:* blanche@wildadvpress.com
Founded: 1994
Outdoor guidebooks, sporting books & cookbooks, fly fishing, dog training & big game hunting, plus maps.
ISBN Prefix(es): 978-1-885106; 978-1-932098
Number of titles published annually: 6 Print
Total Titles: 82 Print
Distributed by Angler's Book Supply; Books West; Inter Sports; Partners Book Distributor; Partners West; Raymond C Rumpf & Son Inc
*Distribution Center:* Baker & Taylor, 2550 W Tyvola Rd, Suite 300, Charlotte, NC 28217 *Tel:* 704-998-3100 *Toll Free Tel:* 800-775-1800 *Web Site:* www.btol.com
Ingram Publisher Services, One Ingram Blvd, La Vergne, TN 37086 *Toll Free Tel:* 866-400-5351 *E-mail:* customerservice@ingrampublisherservices.com *Web Site:* www.ingrampublisherservices.com

**Wildflower Press**
Affiliate of Oakbrook Press
Oakbrook Press, 3301 S Valley Dr, Rapid City, SD 57703
Mailing Address: PO Box 3362, Rapid City, SD 57709
*Tel:* 605-381-6385 *Fax:* 605-343-8733
*E-mail:* info@wildflowerpress.org; bookorder@wildflowerpress.org
*Web Site:* www.wildflowerpress.org
*Key Personnel*
Pres: L J Bryant *E-mail:* wildflowerpress@live.com
Publicity Dir: Robert E Fuchs *E-mail:* pr@wildflowerpress.org
Literary Agent: Charlene Caulfield
Sales: Jordan Dadah
Edit: Leisette Fox
Publicity Asst: William Everett
Billing: Christina MacLachlan
Founded: 2010
Small press specializing in publishing works of fiction with a significant message. Not a vanity press; no funds required to publish.
ISBN Prefix(es): 978-0-9835332
Number of titles published annually: 5 Print; 5 E-Book
Total Titles: 1 Print
Membership(s): IBPA, the Independent Book Publishers Association

**Wildlife Education Ltd**
2418 Noyes St, Evanston, IL 60201
*Toll Free Tel:* 800-477-5034
*E-mail:* owls5@zoobooks.com; helpdesk@zoobooks.com
*Web Site:* www.zoobooks.com; wildlife-ed.com
*Key Personnel*
CEO & Pres: Robert W Harper
COO & VP: John O Toraason
Publr: Ed Shadek
Edit Dir: Renee C Burch; Marjorie Shaw
Sales Mgr: Kurt Von Hertsenberg *E-mail:* kurt@zoobooks.com
Founded: 1980
Books on wildlife & animals. Also publishes Zoobooks Magazine.
ISBN Prefix(es): 978-0-937934; 978-1-888153
Number of titles published annually: 12 Print
Total Titles: 200 Print
Membership(s): Association of Educational Publishers

**Wildside Press**
414 Hungerford Dr, Suite 234, Rockville, MD 20850
Mailing Address: 9710 Traville Gateway Dr, Suite 234, Rockville, MD 20850
*Tel:* 301-762-1305 *Fax:* 301-762-1306
*E-mail:* wildside@wildsidepress.com
*Web Site:* www.wildsidebooks.com
*Key Personnel*
Publr: John Betancourt
Dir, Publg Opers: Carla Coupe
Founded: 1989
Reprints of classic science fiction, fantasy, mystery, reference & mainstream.
ISBN Prefix(es): 978-1-880448; 978-1-58715; 978-1-59224
Number of titles published annually: 1,000 Print; 400 E-Book; 100 Audio
Total Titles: 10,000 Print; 1,100 E-Book; 800 Audio
Imprints: Borgo Press; Owlswick Press; Point Blank
Foreign Rights: Donald Maass Agency (Worldwide exc USA)

**§Wiley-Blackwell**
Commerce Place, 350 Main St, Malden, MA 02148
*Tel:* 781-388-8200 *Fax:* 781-388-8210
*E-mail:* info@wiley.com
*Web Site:* www.wiley.com
*Key Personnel*
Publr: Alison Labbate *E-mail:* alabbate@wiley.com
Founded: 1984
General, scholarly, reference & college texts, with an emphasis on the humanities, social sciences & business. Also medical allied health, veterinary, earth & life sciences, environment & engineering.
ISBN Prefix(es): 978-0-631; 978-0-85520; 978-0-86216; 978-1-55786; 978-1-57718
Number of titles published annually: 500 Print
Total Titles: 4,500 Print

**§John Wiley & Sons Inc**
111 River St, Hoboken, NJ 07030-5774
SAN: 202-5183
*Tel:* 201-748-6000 *Toll Free Tel:* 800-225-5945 (cust serv) *Fax:* 201-748-6088
*E-mail:* info@wiley.com
*Web Site:* www.wiley.com
*Key Personnel*
Chmn of the Bd: Peter B Wiley
Corp Secy: Michael L Preston
CEO & Pres: Stephen M Smith
CFO & EVP: John Kritzmacher
EVP: Ellis E Cousens
Chief Acctg Offr & VP: Edward J Melando
SVP, HR: William J Arlington
SVP & Gen Coun: Gary M Rinck
SVP & Gen Mgr, Global Educ: Joseph Sheridan Heider
SVP, STMS Div: Steve Miron
VP & Treas: Vincent Marzano
VP & Dir, Open Access: Rachel Burley
Dir, Corp Media Rel: Linda Dunbar
Founded: 1807
Global publisher of print & electronic products specializing in professional & consumer books & subscription services; scientific, technical, medical books & journals; textbooks & educational materials for undergraduate & graduate students as well as lifelong learners. Wiley has publishing, marketing & distribution centers in the United States, Canada, Europe, Asia & Australia.
ISBN Prefix(es): 978-0-470; 978-0-471; 978-0-442; 978-0-8436; 978-0-87055
Number of titles published annually: 1,500 Print
Total Titles: 15,000 Print
Imprints: Audel™; Capstone; Ernst & Sohn; For Dummies®; Frommer's™; Halsted Press; Howell Book House; Jossey-Bass; Pfeiffer; Scripta-Technica; Valusource; Visual™; Wiley; Wiley-Heyden; Wiley Interscience®; John Wiley & Sons; Wiley-Liss; Wiley-VCH; Wrox™
*Orders to:* 1045 Crosspoint Blvd, Indianapolis, IN 46256 *Toll Free Tel:* 877-762-2974 *Toll Free Fax:* 800-597-3299
*Returns:* Heller Park Ctr, 360 Mill Rd, Edison, NJ 08817 *Tel:* 732-650-4600 *Fax:* 732-650-4619
*Shipping Address:* One Wiley Dr, Somerset, NJ 08875-1272 *Tel:* 732-469-4400 *Toll Free Tel:* 800-225-5945 *Fax:* 732-302-2300
Membership(s): AAP
*See separate listing for:*
**Jossey-Bass**
**John Wiley & Sons Inc Higher Education**
**John Wiley & Sons Inc Professional/Trade Group**
**John Wiley & Sons Inc Scientific, Technical, Medical & Scholarly (STMS)**

**John Wiley & Sons Inc Higher Education**
Division of John Wiley & Sons Inc
111 River St, Hoboken, NJ 07030-5774
*Tel:* 201-748-6000 *Toll Free Tel:* 800-225-5945 (cust serv) *Fax:* 201-748-6008
*E-mail:* info@wiley.com
*Web Site:* www.wiley.com
*Key Personnel*
Exec Publr: Kaye Pace
VP & Natl Sales Mgr: Patty Stark
VP, Prodn & Mfg, High School: Ann Berlin
VP, Prod & E-Busn Devt: Joe Heider
VP & Dir, Mktg: Susan Elbe
VP, Sales & Mktg: M J O'Leary
VP, Strategic Devt: Bruce Spatz
Mktg & Sales Coord: Kathi Zhang
Total Titles: 615 Print

**John Wiley & Sons Inc Professional/Trade Group**
Division of John Wiley & Sons Inc
111 River St, Hoboken, NJ 07030
*Tel:* 201-748-6000 *Toll Free Tel:* 800-225-5945 (cust serv) *Fax:* 201-748-6088
*E-mail:* info@wiley.com

*Web Site:* www.wiley.com
*Key Personnel*
VP, Trade Sales: Dean Karrel
VP, Prodn & Mfg: Elizabeth Doble
VP & Dir, Sales: George Stanley
VP, Mktg & Opers: Margie Schustack
VP, Mktg: Larry Olson
Dir, Digital Publg: David Goehring

**John Wiley & Sons Inc Scientific, Technical, Medical & Scholarly (STMS)**
Division of John Wiley & Sons Inc
111 River St, Hoboken, NJ 07030
*Tel:* 201-748-6000 *Toll Free Tel:* 800-225-5945 (cust serv) *Fax:* 201-748-6088
*E-mail:* info@wiley.com
*Web Site:* www.wiley.com
*Key Personnel*
SVP: Steve Miron
VP, Global Content Mgmt: Craig Van Dyck
VP, Global Sales: Reed Elfenbein

**William Carey Library Publishers**
Division of US Center for World Mission
1605 E Elizabeth St, Pasadena, CA 91104
*Tel:* 626-720-8210 *Toll Free Tel:* 866-732-6657 (orders & cust serv)
*E-mail:* assistant@wclbooks.com
*Web Site:* www.missionbooks.org
*Key Personnel*
Gen Mgr: Jeff Minard *E-mail:* manager@wclbooks.com
Founded: 1969
Cross-cultural Christian mission work & experiences in frontier countries.
ISBN Prefix(es): 978-0-87808
Number of titles published annually: 15 Print
Total Titles: 250 Print; 3 CD-ROM
Imprints: Mandate Press
*Orders to:* STL Distribution, 100 Biblica Way, Elizabethton, TN 37643 *Toll Free Tel:* 800-647-7466
Membership(s): Evangelical Christian Publishers Association; IBPA, the Independent Book Publishers Association

**§William K Bradford Publishing Co Inc**
31 Main St, Maynard, MA 01754
SAN: 250-4456
*Toll Free Tel:* 800-421-2009 *Fax:* 978-897-1806
*E-mail:* wkb@wkbradford.com
*Web Site:* www.wkbradford.com
*Key Personnel*
Pres & VP, Sales: Thomas M Haver
VP, Design & Prodn: Jessica Holland
Founded: 1988
Educational software & copymasters supplementary material, K-12 mathematics, testing & guide books (classmaster).
ISBN Prefix(es): 978-1-55930; 978-0-7898
Number of titles published annually: 12 Print; 15 CD-ROM
Total Titles: 80 Print; 130 CD-ROM
Membership(s): AAP

**§Williams & Company Book Publishers**
1317 Pine Ridge Dr, Savannah, GA 31406
*Tel:* 912-352-0404
*E-mail:* bookpub@comcast.net
*Web Site:* www.pubmart.com
*Key Personnel*
Publr & Ed-in-Chief: Thomas A Williams, PhD
Founded: 1989
How-to books, literary fiction.
ISBN Prefix(es): 978-1-878853
Number of titles published annually: 10 Print
Total Titles: 15 Print; 20 E-Book
Imprints: Venture Press; Williams & Co Publishers
Distributed by Syracuse University Press

*Warehouse:* Juliana Group, 1110 Staley Ave, Savanah, GA 31405
Membership(s): Independent Publishers Association

**Willow Creek Press**
9931 Hwy 70 W, Minocqua, WI 54548
Mailing Address: PO Box 147, Minocqua, WI 54548
*Tel:* 715-358-7010 *Toll Free Tel:* 800-850-9453 *Fax:* 715-358-2807
*E-mail:* info@willowcreekpress.com
*Web Site:* www.willowcreekpress.com
*Key Personnel*
Publr: Tom Petrie
VP, Sales: Jeremy Petrie *E-mail:* jpetrie@willowcreekpress.com
Mng Dir: Donny Ruebel
Founded: 1986
Willow Creek Press specializes in publishing high quality books most specifically related to nature, animals, wildlife, hunting, fishing & gardening. The company also offers a unique line of cookbooks & has established a niche in the pet book market. The company also publishes high quality nature, wild life, fishing, pet & sporting calendars.
ISBN Prefix(es): 978-1-57223
Number of titles published annually: 24 Print
Total Titles: 130 Print; 3 Audio
Membership(s): AAM; AAP

**Wilshire Book Co**
9731 Variel Ave, Chatsworth, CA 91311-4315
SAN: 205-5368
*Tel:* 818-700-1522 *Fax:* 818-700-1527
*Web Site:* www.mpowers.com
*Key Personnel*
Pres & Rts & Perms: Melvin Powers *E-mail:* mpowers@mpowers.com
Founded: 1947
Mail order; advertising, psychological self-help books, sports & gambling; originals & reprints, fables for adults; computer business book on Internet, horse books, joke books.
ISBN Prefix(es): 978-0-87980
Number of titles published annually: 25 Print
Total Titles: 400 Print; 400 Online
Foreign Rep(s): Baker & Taylor International (Worldwide exc Canada)

**H W Wilson**
Imprint of EBSCO Publishing
10 Estes St, Ipswich, MA 01938
*Tel:* 978-356-6500 *Toll Free Tel:* 800-653-2726 (US & CN) *Fax:* 978-356-6565
*E-mail:* information@ebscohost.com
*Web Site:* www.ebscohost.com
*Key Personnel*
CEO & Pres: Harold Regan
VP, Sales & Mktg: Deborah V Loeding
VP, Cont: James F Phelan
VP, Info Systems: Lucian A Parziale
VP, Off of Personnel: John O'Connor
VP, Cataloging & Gen Ref Servs: Joseph Miller, MLS, PhD
VP, Indexing & Edit Servs: Mark Gauthier
Dir, Mktg: Frank W Daly
US Sales Mgr: Nancy Kolady
Founded: 1898
An icon in the library community for more than 100 years, H W Wilson is dedicated to providing the highest-quality references in the world. Via the WilsonWeb Internet Service, on WilsonDisc CD-ROM & in print, more than 50 H W Wilson reference databases meet the research needs of customers around the globe. Wilson periodicals databases bring users full-text, page images, abstracts & indexing of thousands of leading magazines & journals. Acclaimed Wilson specialty library catalogs support collection development in children's, school & public libraries & Wilson print references consistently earn reviewers' praise. For more on H W Wilson visit www.hwwilson.com. Types of publications: reference databases (biography databases, periodicals databases: full text articles, abstracts, indexing) & reference books.
ISBN Prefix(es): 978-0-8242
Number of titles published annually: 13 Print
Total Titles: 200 Print; 50 CD-ROM; 80 Online

**Wimbledon Music Inc & Trigram Music Inc**
1801 Century Park E, Suite 2400, Los Angeles, CA 90067
*Tel:* 310-556 9683 *Fax:* 310-277-1278
*E-mail:* irishmex127@gmail.com
*Web Site:* www.wimbtri.net
*Key Personnel*
Dir, Pubns: Peter Dorfman
Founded: 1978
ISBN Prefix(es): 978-0-938170
Number of titles published annually: 35 Print

**Wimmer Cookbooks**
Division of Mercury Printing
4650 Shelby Air Dr, Memphis, TN 38118
*Tel:* 901-362-8900 *Toll Free Tel:* 800-363-1771
*E-mail:* wimmer@wimmerco.com
*Web Site:* www.wimmerco.com
*Key Personnel*
Pres: Danny Bailey
VP: Doug McNeill *E-mail:* dmcneill@wimmerco.com
Dir, Dist: Robyn Hite *E-mail:* rhite@wimmerco.com
Founded: 1946
Development, publishing, manufacturing, marketing & distribution of community & self-published cookbooks.
ISBN Prefix(es): 978-1-879958
Number of titles published annually: 50 Print
Total Titles: 250 Print
Imprints: Tradery House

**§Wind Canyon Books**
PO Box 7035, Stockton, CA 95267
*Tel:* 209-956-1600 *Toll Free Tel:* 800-952-7007 *Fax:* 209-956-9424 *Toll Free Fax:* 888-289-7086
*E-mail:* books@windcanyonbooks.com
*Web Site:* www.windcanyonbooks.com
*Key Personnel*
Owner: George Jaquith
Founded: 1996
ISBN Prefix(es): 978-0-943691; 978-1-891118
Number of titles published annually: 5 Print
Total Titles: 70 Print

**Windsor Books**
Division of Windsor Marketing Corp
260 Montauk Hwy, Suite 5, Bayshore, NY 11706
SAN: 203-2945
Mailing Address: PO Box 280, Brightwaters, NY 11718
*Tel:* 631-665-6688 *Toll Free Tel:* 800-321-5934
*E-mail:* windsor.books@att.net
*Web Site:* www.windsorpublishing.com
*Key Personnel*
Founder: Alfred Schmidt
Mng Ed: Jeff Schmidt
Founded: 1968
Business, economics & investment.
ISBN Prefix(es): 978-0-930233
Number of titles published annually: 5 Print
*Advertising Agency:* A Schmidt Agency

**Windward Publishing**
Imprint of Finney Company Inc
8075 215 St W, Lakeville, MN 55044
*Tel:* 952-469-6699 *Toll Free Tel:* 800-846-7027 *Fax:* 952-469-1968 *Toll Free Fax:* 800-330-6232

*E-mail:* info@finneyco.com
*Web Site:* www.finneyco.com
*Key Personnel*
Pres: Alan E Krysan
Mktg Mgr: Krista Danielson
Founded: 1973
Publishes books with educational value; children's books & trade books. Topics covered are natural history/science, nature & outdoor recreation.
ISBN Prefix(es): 978-0-89317
Number of titles published annually: 5 Print
Total Titles: 42 Print

**§The Wine Appreciation Guild Ltd**
Formerly W for Wine
360 Swift Ave, Suites 30 & 34, South San Francisco, CA 94080
SAN: 201-9515
*Tel:* 650-866-3020 *Toll Free Tel:* 800-231-9463 *Fax:* 650-866-3513
*E-mail:* info@wineappreciation.com
*Web Site:* www.wineappreciation.com
*Key Personnel*
Pres: Donna Bottrell
Ed: Maurice Sullivan
Intl Rts: Elliott Mackey
Lib Sales Dir: Bryan Imelli *Tel:* 650-866-3020 ext 22 *E-mail:* bryan@wineappreciation.com
Founded: 1974
Publisher of books on the subject of wine.
ISBN Prefix(es): 978-0-932664; 978-1-891267
Number of titles published annually: 7 Print; 1 CD-ROM; 7 E-Book; 4 Audio
Total Titles: 112 Print; 3 CD-ROM; 16 Audio
Imprints: Forrest Hill Press; Vintage Image; Wine Advisory Board
Foreign Rep(s): Books for Europe (Continental Europe, Middle East); Eos Libros (Latin America); Horizon Books (Malaysia, Singapore); McArthur & Co (Canada); Peribo Books (Australia); Stephen Phillips Pty Ltd (South Africa); Vine House Distribution (UK)
*Advertising Agency:* Vintage Image, 360 Swift Ave, Suite 34, South San Francisco, CA 94080 *Toll Free Tel:* 800-231-9463 *Fax:* 650-866-3513 *E-mail:* info@wineappreciation.com *Web Site:* www.wineappreciation.com

**WinePress Publishing**
1730 Railroad St, Enumclaw, WA 98022
*Tel:* 360-802-9758 *Toll Free Tel:* 800-326-4674 *Fax:* 360-802-9992
*Web Site:* www.winepresspublishing.com
*Key Personnel*
Exec Offr: Malcolm Fraser
Founded: 1991
Custom publishing.
This publisher has indicated that 98% of their product line is author subsidized.
ISBN Prefix(es): 978-1-57921; 978-1-4141
Number of titles published annually: 280 Print; 3 Audio
Total Titles: 1,582 Print; 5 Audio
Imprints: Annotation Press; UpWrite Books; Wine Press
*Orders to:* PO Box 428, Enumclaw, WA 98022 *Toll Free Tel:* 877-421-7323
*Returns:* PO Box 428, Enumclaw, WA 98022 *Toll Free Tel:* 877-421-7323
*Warehouse:* 2551 Cole St, Suite H, Enumclaw, WA 98022, Contact: Larry Filato *Tel:* 360-802-2907 *Fax:* 360-802-2908
*Distribution Center:* 2551 Cole St, Suite H, Enumclaw, WA 98022, Contact: Larry Filato *Tel:* 360-802-2907 *Fax:* 360-802-2908
Membership(s): Canadian Booksellers Association; Evangelical Christian Publishers Association

**§Wings Press**
627 E Guenther, San Antonio, TX 78210-1134
*Tel:* 210-271-7805 *Fax:* 210-271-7805
*E-mail:* press@wingspress.com
*Web Site:* www.wingspress.com
*Key Personnel*
Publr & Ed: Bryce Milligan *E-mail:* milligan@wingspress.com
Founded: 1975
Literary book publishing.
ISBN Prefix(es): 978-0-916727; 978-0-930324
Number of titles published annually: 15 Print; 20 Online; 20 E-Book; 1 Audio
Total Titles: 113 Print; 1 CD-ROM; 4 Audio
Foreign Rights: Independent Publisher's Group (Susan M Sewall)
*Orders to:* Independent Publisher's Group (IPG), 814 N Franklin St, Chicago, IL 60624, Contact: Tito Garcia *Tel:* 312-337-0747 *Fax:* 312-337-5985 *E-mail:* tgarcia@ipgbook.com
*Returns:* Independent Publisher's Group Distribution Center, 600 N Pulaski Rd, Chicago, IL 60624, Contact: Tito Garcia *Tel:* 312-337-0747 *Fax:* 312-337-5985 *E-mail:* tgarcia@ipgbook.com
*Shipping Address:* Independent Publisher's Group Distribution Center, 600 N Pulaski Rd, Chicago, IL 60624, Contact: Tito Garcia *Tel:* 312-337-0747 *Fax:* 312-337-5985 *E-mail:* tgarcia@ipgbook.com
*Warehouse:* Independent Publisher's Group Distribution Center, 600 N Pulaski Rd, Chicago, IL 60624, Contact: Tito Garcia *Tel:* 312-337-0747 *Fax:* 312-337-5985 *E-mail:* tgarcia@ipgbook.com
*Distribution Center:* Independent Publisher's Group Distribution Center, 600 N Pulaski Rd, Chicago, IL 60624, Contact: Tito Garcia *Tel:* 312-337-0747 *Fax:* 312-337-5985 *E-mail:* tgarcia@ipgbook.com

**WingSpread Publishers**
Division of Zur Ltd
2020 State Rd, Camp Hill, PA 17011
*Tel:* 717-761-7044 *Toll Free Tel:* 800-884-4571 *Fax:* 717-761-7273
*E-mail:* customerservice@echurchdepot.com
*Web Site:* wingspreadpublishers.com
*Key Personnel*
Pres: Ken Paton
Publr: Doug Waardenburg *Tel:* 717-761-7044 ext 302
Publicist: Pam Vossman
Trade Sales Dir & Intl Rts: Drew Park *E-mail:* dpark@christianpublications.com
Founded: 1883
ISBN Prefix(es): 978-0-87509; 978-0-88965; 978-1-60066
Number of titles published annually: 10 Print
Total Titles: 80 Print

**Winters Publishing**
705 E Washington St, Greensburg, IN 47240
SAN: 298-1645
Mailing Address: PO Box 501, Greensburg, IN 47240
*Tel:* 812-663-4948 *Toll Free Tel:* 800-457-3230 *Fax:* 812-663-4948 *Toll Free Fax:* 800-457-3230
*E-mail:* winterspublishing@gmail.com
*Web Site:* www.winterspublishing.com
*Key Personnel*
Owner & Publr: Mr Tracy Winters
Founded: 1988
Publish Christian books, Bed & Breakfast cookbooks, directories, other nonfiction & children's books.
ISBN Prefix(es): 978-0-9625329; 978-1-883651
Number of titles published annually: 12 Print
Total Titles: 50 Print
Imprints: Faith Press
Distributor for Anchors Away
*Distribution Center:* Partners Book Distributors, 2325 Jarco Dr, Holt, MI 48842 *Tel:* 517-694-3205
STL Distribution, 100 Biblica Way, Elizabethton, TN 37643 *Toll Free Tel:* 800-289-2772
Ingram Book Co, One Ingram Blvd, La Vergne, TN 37086 *Tel:* 615-793-5000
Partners West Book Distributors, 1901 Raymond Ave SW, Renton, WA 98057 *Tel:* 425-227-8486

**Winterthur Museum & Country Estate**
5105 Kennett Pike, Wilmington, DE 19735
*Tel:* 302-888-4663 *Toll Free Tel:* 800-448-3883 *Fax:* 302-888-4950
*Web Site:* www.winterthur.org
ISBN Prefix(es): 978-0-912724
Number of titles published annually: 4 Print
Total Titles: 40 Print
Distributed by Abrams; Acanthus; W W Norton & Company Inc; Schiffer; University Press of New England
Membership(s): ABA; American Alliance of Museums; Art Libraries Society

**§Wisconsin Dept of Public Instruction**
125 S Webster St, Madison, WI 53703
Mailing Address: PO Box 7841, Madison, WI 53707-7841
*Tel:* 608-266-2188 *Toll Free Tel:* 800-441-4563 *Fax:* 608-267-9110
*E-mail:* pubsales@dpi.state.wi.us
*Web Site:* www.dpi.wi.gov/pubsales
*Key Personnel*
Communs Dir: John Johnson *Tel:* 608-266-1771 *E-mail:* john.johnson@dpi.state.wi.us
State Superintendent of Public Instruction: Tony Evers, PhD
Specialize in English, math, science & social studies, character education, driver education & traffic safety, career & technical education, world languages & teaching strategies.
ISBN Prefix(es): 978-1-57337
Number of titles published annually: 8 Print; 4 CD-ROM
Total Titles: 120 Print; 10 CD-ROM
*Sales Office(s):* Drawer 179, Milwaukee, WI 53293-0179, Dir: John Johnson *Tel:* 608-266-2188 *Toll Free Tel:* 800-243-8782 *Fax:* 608-267-9110 *E-mail:* john.johnson@dpi.state.wi.us *Web Site:* dpi.wi.gov/pubsales

**Wisdom Publications Inc**
199 Elm St, Somerville, MA 02144
*Tel:* 617-776-7416 *Toll Free Tel:* 800-272-4050 (orders) *Fax:* 617-776-7841
*E-mail:* info@wisdompubs.org
*Web Site:* www.wisdompubs.org
*Key Personnel*
Publr: Timothy McNeill *Tel:* 617-776-7416 ext 22
Promo: Lydia Anderson *E-mail:* promo@wisdompubs.org
Acqs Ed: Josh Bartok *Tel:* 617-776-7416 ext 26
Founded: 1976
Books on Buddhism published in various series encompassing theory & practice, biography, history, art & culture.
ISBN Prefix(es): 978-0-86171
Number of titles published annually: 20 Print
Total Titles: 158 Print
Imprints: Pali Text Society
Divisions: Wisdom Archive
Foreign Rep(s): Wisdom Books (Europe)
Foreign Rights: ACER (Spain); Eliane Benisti (France); Chinese Connection Agency (China); Fritz Literary Agency (Germany); Eric Yang Agency (Korea)
*Orders to:* Publishers Group West (PGW), 1700 Fourth St, Berkeley, CA 94710 *Tel:* 510-809-3700 *Fax:* 510-809-3777

**Wish Publishing**
PO Box 10337, Terre Haute, IN 47801-0337
*Web Site:* www.wishpublishing.com

*Key Personnel*
Publr: Holly Kondras *E-mail:* holly@wishpublishing.com
Founded: 1999
Trade publishing focused exclusively on women's sports, health & fitness.
ISBN Prefix(es): 978-1-930546
Number of titles published annually: 3 E-Book
Total Titles: 50 Print; 5 E-Book
Imprints: Equilibrium Books
Distributed by Cardinal Publishers Group
Membership(s): IBPA, the Independent Book Publishers Association

**Wittenborn Art Books**
Division of Alan Wofsy Fine Arts
1109 Geary Blvd, San Francisco, CA 94109
*Tel:* 415-292-6500 *Toll Free Tel:* 800-660-6403 *Fax:* 415-292-6594
*E-mail:* wittenborn@art-books.com
*Web Site:* www.art-books.com
*Key Personnel*
Ed: Alan Hyman *E-mail:* editeur@earthlink.net
Opers Mgr: J Thrombly
Acqs: Lancelot Andrewes *E-mail:* beauxarts@earthlink.net
Rts: Mark Hyman *Tel:* 510-666-1150 *E-mail:* art-books.com@jps.net
Prodn: Duke Mantee *Tel:* 510-482-3677
Founded: 1939
Publish deluxe edition art reference books & artist books. Subject specialties include art, bibliography & decorative arts. Warehouse located in Ashland, OH.
ISBN Prefix(es): 978-0-8150
Number of titles published annually: 9 Print; 4 CD-ROM
Total Titles: 180 Print; 30 CD-ROM
Imprints: Documents of Modern Art; George Wittenborn
Distributor for Ides et Calendes SA; Menil Foundation; UCLA/Hammer Museum
*Billing Address:* PO Box 2210, San Francisco, CA 94126
*Warehouse:* Ashland, OH 44805
Membership(s): AAP

**Wizards of the Coast LLC**
Subsidiary of Hasbro Inc
1600 Lind Ave SW, Renton, WA 98057-3305
Mailing Address: PO Box 707, Renton, WA 98057-0707
*Tel:* 425-226-6500
*Web Site:* www.wizards.com/dnd/novels.aspx
Founded: 1975 (as TSR Inc)
Publisher of fantasy, science fiction & horror novels. Young adult game material; role-playing games, trading card games, board games & books, makers of Dungeons & Dragons. Not seeking proposals for our shared world lines at this time. Guidelines are available on our web site by clicking on Writers Guidelines under Novels Links.
ISBN Prefix(es): 978-0-88038; 978-1-56076; 978-0-7869
Number of titles published annually: 50 Print; 60 E-Book
Total Titles: 300 Print
Distributed by Random House

**Alan Wofsy Fine Arts**
1109 Geary Blvd, San Francisco, CA 94109
SAN: 207-6438
Mailing Address: PO Box 2210, San Francisco, CA 94126-2210
*Tel:* 415-292-6500 *Toll Free Tel:* 800-660-6403 *Fax:* 415-292-6594 (off & cust serv); 415-512-0130 (acctg)
*E-mail:* order@art-books.com (orders); editeur@earthlink.net (edit); beauxarts@earthlink.net (cust serv)
*Web Site:* www.art-books.com
*Key Personnel*
Chmn of the Bd: Lord Cohen
CEO: Alan Wofsy
Art Dir: Zeke Greenberg
Ed, French Books: Charles DuPont
Ed, German Books: Willi Rahm
PR Mgr: Milton J Goldbaum
Website Mgr: Steven Barich
Website & Imaging: Matt Novack
Mktg: Andy Redkin
Libn: Adios Butler
Coun: Judith Mazia
Rts: Elizabeth Regina Snowden
Founded: 1969
Art reference books, bibliographies, art books, iconographies, prints, posters & notecards. Distribution center & warehouse located in Ashland, OH.
ISBN Prefix(es): 978-0-915346; 978-1-55660
Number of titles published annually: 20 Print; 5 CD-ROM; 60 Online
Total Titles: 350 Print; 10 CD-ROM; 500 Online
Imprints: Beauxarts; Collegium Graphicum; The Picasso Project
*Branch Office(s)*
401 China Basin St, San Francisco, CA 94158-2133 (sales & cust serv)
Distributor for Bora; Brusberg (Berlin); Cramer (Geneva); Huber; Ides et Calendes; Kornfeld & Co; Welz; Wittenborn Art Books
*Warehouse:* Ashland, OH 44805
*Distribution Center:* Ashland, OH 44805
Membership(s): AAP
*See separate listing for:*
**Picasso Project**
**Wittenborn Art Books**

**Wolters Kluwer US Corp**
Subsidiary of Wolters Kluwer NV (The Netherlands)
2700 Lake Cook Rd, Riverwoods, IL 60015
*Tel:* 847-267-7000 *Fax:* 847-580-5192
*Web Site:* www.wolterskluwer.com
*Key Personnel*
Chmn: Nancy McKinstry
Medical books & journals, law books, business & tax publications.
Total Titles: 5,000 Print
Imprints: Adis International; Aspen Publishers Incorporated; CCH INCORPORATED; CT Corporation; Lippincott, Williams & Wilkins
*Foreign Office(s):* Zuidpoolsingel 2, PO Box 1030, 2400 BA Alphen aan den Rijn, Netherlands (headquarters) *Tel:* (0172) 641 400 *Fax:* (0172) 474 889 *E-mail:* info@wolterskluwer.com

**Woodbine House**
6510 Bells Mill Rd, Bethesda, MD 20817
SAN: 692-3445
*Tel:* 301-897-3570 *Toll Free Tel:* 800-843-7323 *Fax:* 301-897-5838
*E-mail:* info@woodbinehouse.com
*Web Site:* www.woodbinehouse.com
*Key Personnel*
Publr: Fran Marinaccio
Prodn Mgr: Brenda A Ruby *E-mail:* bruby@woodbinehouse.com
Acqs Ed & Perms: Nancy Gray Paul *E-mail:* ngpaul@woodbinehouse.com
Mktg Mgr & Intl Rts: Fran M Marinaccio *E-mail:* fmarinaccio@woodbinehouse.com
Sales: Sarah A Strickler *E-mail:* sstrickler@woodbinehouse.com
Ed: Susan S Stokes *E-mail:* sstokes@woodbinehouse.com
Founded: 1985
Trade nonfiction, hardcover & paperback.
ISBN Prefix(es): 978-0-933149; 978-1-890627; 978-1-60613
Number of titles published annually: 10 Print
Total Titles: 70 Print
Foreign Rep(s): Gazelle Book Service (Europe); Monarch Books (Canada); Silvereye Education Publications (Australia, Pacific Rim)
Foreign Rights: Writer's House
*Returns:* IFC, 3570 Bladensburg Rd, Brentwood, MD 20722 *Tel:* 301-779-4660
*Warehouse:* Woodbine House, c/o IFC, 3570 Bladensburg Rd, Brentwood, MD 20722

**Woodland Publishing Inc**
515 S 700 E, Suite 2D, Salt Lake City, UT 84102
SAN: 219-3531
*Toll Free Tel:* 800-277-3243 *Fax:* 801-334-1913
*E-mail:* info@woodlandpublishing.com
*Web Site:* www.woodlandpublishing.com
*Key Personnel*
Mng Ed: Michelle Billeter
Founded: 1975
General trade & paperbacks, professional books; health & nutrition.
ISBN Prefix(es): 978-0-89557; 978-1-58054
Number of titles published annually: 15 Print
Total Titles: 200 Print
Distributed by Summit Beacon
*Warehouse:* 500 N 1030 W, Lindon, UT 84042 *Toll Free Tel:* 800-777-2665 *Fax:* 801-785-8511
*Distribution Center:* New Leaf Distributing Co, 401 Thornton Rd, Lithia Springs, GA 30122-1557 *Tel:* 770-948-7845 *Toll Free Tel:* 800-326-2665 *Fax:* 770-944-2313 *Web Site:* www.newleaf-dist.com
Nutri-Books, 790 W Tennessee Ave, Denver, CO 80217 *Toll Free Tel:* 800-279-2048

**The Woodrow Wilson Center Press**
Division of The Woodrow Wilson International Center for Scholars
One Woodrow Wilson Plaza, 1300 Pennsylvania Ave NW, Washington, DC 20004-3027
*Tel:* 202-691-4000 *Fax:* 202-691-4001
*E-mail:* press@wilsoncenter.org
*Web Site:* wilsoncenter.org
*Key Personnel*
Dir: Joseph F Brinley, Jr *Tel:* 202-691-4042 *E-mail:* joe.brinley@wilsoncenter.org
Founded: 1988
Humanities & social sciences; policy studies.
ISBN Prefix(es): 978-0-943875; 978-1-930365
Number of titles published annually: 12 Print
Total Titles: 200 Print
Imprints: Wilson Center Press; Woodrow Wilson Center Press/Johns Hopkins University Press; Woodrow Wilson Center Press/Stanford University Press
Distributed by Columbia University Press; The Johns Hopkins University Press; Stanford University Press; University of California Press

**WoodstockArts**
PO Box 1342, Woodstock, NY 12498
*Tel:* 845-679-8111
*E-mail:* info@woodstockarts.com
*Web Site:* www.woodstockarts.com
*Key Personnel*
Founder: Julia Blelock; Weston Blelock
Founded: 1999
ISBN Prefix(es): 978-0-9679268
Number of titles published annually: 3 Print
Membership(s): IBPA, the Independent Book Publishers Association

**Workers Compensation Research Institute**
955 Massachusetts Ave, Cambridge, MA 02139
*Tel:* 617-661-9274 *Fax:* 617-661-9284
*E-mail:* wcri@wcrinet.org
*Web Site:* www.wcrinet.org
Founded: 1983
Workers compensation public policy research.
ISBN Prefix(es): 978-0-935149
Number of titles published annually: 14 Print
Total Titles: 100 Print

**§Workman Publishing Co Inc**
225 Varick St, 9th fl, New York, NY 10014-4381
SAN: 203-2821
*Tel:* 212-254-5900 *Toll Free Tel:* 800-722-7202
*Fax:* 212-254-8098
*E-mail:* info@workman.com
*Web Site:* www.workman.com
*Key Personnel*
COO: Walter Weintz *Tel:* 212-614-7593 *E-mail:* walter@workman.com
Cont: Richard Petry *Tel:* 212-614-7552 *E-mail:* richardp@workman.com
Chief Admin Offr: Glenn D'Agnes *Tel:* 212-614-7798 *E-mail:* glenn@workman.com
Gen Mgr: Jill Dulber *Tel:* 212-614-7532 *E-mail:* jill@workman.com
Acting Publr: Susan Bolotin *Tel:* 212-614-7514 *E-mail:* susan@workman.com
Assoc Publr: Page Edmunds *Tel:* 212-614-7528 *E-mail:* page@workman.com
Exec Dir, Publicity: Selina Meere *E-mail:* selina@workman.com
Assoc Dir, Publicity: Courtney Greenhalgh
Creative Dir: Vaughn Andrews
Dir, Children's Publg: Raquel Jaramillo *Tel:* 212-614-7573 *E-mail:* raquel@workman.com
Dir, Digital Publg: Andrea Flick-Nisbit *Tel:* 212-614-7579 *E-mail:* andrea@workman.com
Dir, Gift & Mass Merchant Sales: Jodi Weiss *Tel:* 212-614-7529 *E-mail:* jodiw@workman.com
Dir, Gift Field Sales: Marilyn Barnett *Tel:* 212-614-7737 *E-mail:* marilyn@workman.com
Dir, Intl Sales & Licensing: Kristina Peterson *Tel:* 212-614-5617 *E-mail:* kristina@workman.com
Dir, Premium & Spec Sales: Jenny Mandel *Tel:* 212-614-7508 *E-mail:* jenny@workman.com
Licensing Dir: Pat Upton *Tel:* 212-614-7588 *E-mail:* pat@workman.com
Sales Mgr, Retail: Steven Pace *Tel:* 212-614-7780 *E-mail:* steven@workman.com
Exec Ed: Suzanne Rafer *Tel:* 212-614-7516 *E-mail:* suzanne@workman.com
Sr Ed: Mary Ellen O'Neill; Bruce Tracy
Prodn Mgr: Doug Wolff *Tel:* 212-614-7595 *E-mail:* doug@workman.com
Mgr, Cust Serv: Shirley Ortiz *Tel:* 212-614-7583 *E-mail:* shirley@workman.com
Asst Mgr, Cust Serv: Natalya Pilguy *Tel:* 212-614-7555 *E-mail:* natalya@workman.com
Publicist: Anwesha Basu; John Duggan; Maggie Gleason
Founded: 1967
General nonfiction, calendars.
ISBN Prefix(es): 978-0-89480; 978-1-56305; 978-0-7611
Number of titles published annually: 345 Print
Divisions: Algonquin Books of Chapel Hill; Artisan; Highbridge Audio; Storey Publishing; Timber Press; Workman Speakers Bureau
Distributor for Black Dog & Leventhal; The Experiment; Greenwich Workshop Press Fearless Critic Media
Foreign Rep(s): Thomas Allen & Son Ltd (Canada); Bookreps New Zealand (New Zealand); Hardie Grant Books (Australia); Melia Publishing Services (Ireland, UK)
Foreign Rights: Big Apple Agency Inc (China, Taiwan); Graal Literary Agency (Poland); Japan UNI Agency (Japan); JLM Literary Agency (Greece); Katai & Bolza Literary Agency (Hungary); KCC (Korea); Alexander Korahenevski Agency (Russia); Kristin Olson Literary Agency (Czech Republic); Mickey Pikarski (Israel); Sebes & Van Gelderen Literary Agency (Netherlands); Julio F Yanez Agencia Literaria (Latin America, Portugal, Spain)
*Returns:* RR Donnelley Fulfillment, 655 Brighton Beach Rd, Menasha, WI 54952
*Warehouse:* RR Donnelley Fulfillment, N9234 Lake Park Rd, Appleton, WI 54915, Mgr, Cust Serv: Kim Rose *Tel:* 920-969-6411 *Fax:* 920-969-6441 *E-mail:* kim.m.rose@rrd.com
Membership(s): AAP
*See separate listing for:*
**Black Dog & Leventhal Publishers Inc**
**Timber Press Inc**

**World Almanac®**
Imprint of Infobase Learning
132 W 31 St, New York, NY 10001
SAN: 211-6944
*Toll Free Tel:* 800-322-8755
*E-mail:* almanac@factsonfile.com
*Web Site:* www.worldalmanac.com
*Key Personnel*
Sr Ed: Sarah Janssen *E-mail:* sjanssen@factsonfile.com
Rts & Licensing: Ben Jacobs *E-mail:* bjacobs@factsonfile.com
Founded: 1868
Annual juvenile & adult reference books.
ISBN Prefix(es): 978-1-60057
Number of titles published annually: 3 Print
Total Titles: 3 Print
Foreign Rep(s): Adnkronos Libri SRL (Italy)

**§World Bank Publications**
Member of The World Bank Group
Office of the Publisher, 1818 "H" St NW, U-11-1104, Washington, DC 20433
*Tel:* 202-458-4497 *Toll Free Tel:* 800-645-7247 (cust serv) *Fax:* 202-522-2631; 202-614-1237
*E-mail:* books@worldbank.org; pubrights@worldbank.org (foreign rts)
*Web Site:* www.worldbank.org/publications; publications.worldbank.org
*Key Personnel*
Publr: H Dirk Koehler
Foreign Rts Mgr: Valentina Kalk *E-mail:* pubrights@worldbank.org
Sales Mgr: Jose de Buerba *Tel:* 202-473-0393 *E-mail:* jdebuerba@worldbank.org
Founded: 1944
Publish over 200 new titles annually in support of the World Bank's mission to fight poverty & distributes them globally in both print & electronic formats; electronic online subscription database; international affairs.
ISBN Prefix(es): 978-0-8213
Number of titles published annually: 200 Print; 10 CD-ROM; 3 Online; 30 E-Book
Total Titles: 2,000 Print; 50 CD-ROM; 3 Online; 50 E-Book
Imprints: World Bank
Foreign Rep(s): International Publishing Services (Middle East, North Africa)
*Billing Address:* Books International Inc, PO Box 959, Herndon, VA 20172-0960
*Orders to:* Books International Inc, PO Box 959, Herndon, VA 20172-0960
*Returns:* Books International Inc Returns Depts, 22883 Quicksilver Dr, Dulles, VA 20166
*Shipping Address:* Books International Inc Returns Depts, 22883 Quicksilver Dr, Dulles, VA 20166
*Warehouse:* Books International Inc, PO Box 959, Herndon, VA 20172-0960
*Distribution Center:* Books International Inc, PO Box 959, Herndon, VA 20172-0960
Membership(s): AAP

**§World Book Inc**
Subsidiary of The Scott Fetzer Co
233 N Michigan, Suite 2000, Chicago, IL 60601
SAN: 201-4815
*Tel:* 312-729-5800 *Toll Free Tel:* 800-967-5325 (consumer sales, US); 800-463-8845 (consumer sales, CN); 800-975-3250 (school & lib sales, US); 800-837-5365 (school & lib sales, CN); 866-866-5200 (web sales) *Fax:* 312-729-5600; 312-729-5606 *Toll Free Fax:* 800-433-9330 (school & lib sales, US); 888-690-4002 (school lib sales, CN)
*Web Site:* www.worldbook.com
*Key Personnel*
Pres: Donald D Keller
VP, Edit & Ed-in-Chief: Paul A Kobasa
VP, Licensing Busn Devt: Richard Flower
Founded: 1917
Publisher of high-quality, award-winning, educational reference & nonfiction publications for the school & library market & home market, in print, CD-ROM & online formats.
ISBN Prefix(es): 978-0-7166
Number of titles published annually: 40 Print; 6 CD-ROM
Total Titles: 320 Print; 91 CD-ROM; 10 Online

**World Citizens**
Affiliate of Cinema Investments Co Inc
PO Box 131, Mill Valley, CA 94942-0131
*Tel:* 415-380-8020 *Toll Free Tel:* 800-247-6553 (orders only)
*Key Personnel*
Ed-in-Chief: Joan Ellen
Ed: John Ballard
Assoc Ed: Jack Henry
Sales Mgr & Intl Rts: Steve Ames
Founded: 1984
Cross cultural & multi-cultural novels & texts. Adult, educational, trade & young adult divisions.
ISBN Prefix(es): 978-0-932279
Number of titles published annually: 6 Print; 4 CD-ROM; 6 E-Book; 4 Audio
Total Titles: 18 Print; 2 CD-ROM; 10 Online; 10 E-Book; 8 Audio
Imprints: Classroom Classics; New Horizons Book Publishing Co; Skateman Publications
Distributed by Inland
*Returns:* Bookmasters, PO Box 388, Ashland, OH 44805-0388 *Fax:* 401-201-6883
*Distribution Center:* Bookmasters, PO Box 388, Ashland, OH 44805-0388 *Fax:* 419-201-6883

**§World Resources Institute**
10 "G" St NE, Suite 800, Washington, DC 20002
*Tel:* 202-729-7600 *Fax:* 202-729-7610
*Web Site:* www.wri.org
*Key Personnel*
Dir, Pubns: Hyacinth Billings *Tel:* 202-729-7712
Founded: 1982
Professional, scholarly & general interest publications, including energy, the environment, agriculture, forestry, natural resources, economics, geography, climate, biotechnology & development. Some titles co-published with university presses & commercial publishers.
ISBN Prefix(es): 978-0-915825; 978-1-56973
Number of titles published annually: 10 Print
Total Titles: 420 Print; 2 CD-ROM

**§World Scientific Publishing Co Inc**
27 Warren St, Suite 401-402, Hackensack, NJ 07601
*Tel:* 201-487-9655 *Toll Free Tel:* 800-227-7562 *Fax:* 201-487-9656 *Toll Free Fax:* 888-977-2665
*E-mail:* wspc@wspc.com
*Web Site:* www.wspc.com
*Key Personnel*
Publr: K K Phuna
Contact: Calandra Braswell *Tel:* 201-487-9655 ext 309
Founded: 1981
Number of titles published annually: 400 Print
Total Titles: 5,000 Print
Subsidiaries: Imperial College Press
*Warehouse:* 46 Development Rd, Fitchburg, MA 01420

**§World Trade Press**
800 Lindberg Lane, Suite 190, Petaluma, CA 94952
*Tel:* 707-778-1124 *Toll Free Tel:* 800-833-8586 *Fax:* 707-778-1329
*Web Site:* www.worldtradepress.com
*Key Personnel*
CEO & Publr: Edward G Hinkelman *Tel:* 707-778-1124 ext 204 *E-mail:* egh@worldtradepress.com
Founded: 1990
Professional books for international trade & business travel.
ISBN Prefix(es): 978-0-9631864; 978-1-885073
Number of titles published annually: 8 Print; 240 Online; 26 E-Book
Total Titles: 118 Print; 2,260 Online; 88 E-Book
Distributed by Reference Press

**World Vision Resources**
Subsidiary of World Vision International
800 W Chestnut Ave, Monrovia, CA 91016-3198
*Tel:* 626-303-8811; 909-463-2998 (intl orders) *Toll Free Tel:* 800-777-7752 (US only) *Fax:* 909-463-2999
*E-mail:* wvresources@worldvision.org
*Web Site:* www.worldvisionresources.com
*Key Personnel*
Exec Ed: Jojo Palmer *Tel:* 626-303-8811 ext 7720
Founded: 1968
Books & other products promoting strategies for the mission activities of the Christian churches.
ISBN Prefix(es): 978-0-912552; 978-1-887983
Number of titles published annually: 20 Print

**WorldTariff**
Division of FedEx Corp
220 Montgomery St, Suite 448, San Francisco, CA 94104-3410
*Tel:* 415-391-7501; 415-591-6666 *Toll Free Tel:* 800-556-9334 *Fax:* 415-391-7537 (Fax/Modem)
*Web Site:* www.worldtariff.com; ftn.fedex.com/wtonline
*Key Personnel*
Acct Exec & Contact: Ray Brown
Founded: 1961
Publish customs duty & tax information.
ISBN Prefix(es): 978-1-56745
Number of titles published annually: 100 Print
Total Titles: 22 Online
*Foreign Office(s):* Eurotariff, National House, 60-66 Wardour St, 6th fl, London W1V 3HP, United Kingdom

**§Worth Publishers**
Member of Bedford, Freeman & Worth Publishing Group, LLC
41 Madison Ave, 37th fl, New York, NY 10010
*Tel:* 212-576-9400 *Fax:* 212-561-8281
*Web Site:* www.worthpub.com
*Key Personnel*
Pres: Elizabeth Widdicombe
Sr Publr: Catherine Woods
Dir, Fin & Admin: Linda Glover
VP, Dir of Prodn: Ellen Cash
Mng Ed: Philip McCaffrey
Dir, Mktg & Promo: John Britch
Dir, Mkt Devt: Steven Rigolosi
Intl Rts Dir: Ilene Ellenbogen
Founded: 1966
Social science texts for the higher education market & advanced high school courses.
ISBN Prefix(es): 978-1-57259; 978-1-4292; 978-0-7167
Number of titles published annually: 10 E-Book
Total Titles: 300 Print
Foreign Rep(s): Macmillan East Asia (China, Hong Kong, Indonesia, Korea, Philippines, Singapore, Thailand, Vietnam); Macmillan Publishers (Taiwan); Palgrave Macmillan (Australia, New Zealand); Palgrave Macmillan UK (Africa, Caribbean, Europe, India, Japan, Latin America, Middle East, Pakistan, UK); USBD Distribution SDN BHD (Malaysia)
*Warehouse:* MPS Distribution Center, 16365 James Madison Hwy (US Rte 15), Gordonsville, VA 22942 *Toll Free Tel:* 888-330-8477 *Fax:* 540-672-7540 (cust serv) *Toll Free Fax:* 800-672-2054 (orders)

**§Wright Group/McGraw-Hill**
Division of McGraw-Hill School Education Group
8787 Orion Place, Columbus, OH 43240
*Tel:* 614-430-4000 *Toll Free Tel:* 800-537-4740
*Web Site:* www.wrightgroup.com
Founded: 1975
Publish a wide array of instructional materials for PreK-adult education. Specialize in reading, language arts, mathematics, ELL & intervention programs for small group & whole group instruction. Offerings include substantial teacher materials, including detailed lesson plans, teacher guides & professional resources & staff development opportunities.
ISBN Prefix(es): 978-0-02; 978-0-940156; 978-0-07; 978-0-7802; 978-0-7327; 978-1-57039; 978-0-658; 978-0-322; 978-0-7622; 978-0-7699; 978-1-4045; 978-1-58210; 978-1-55624; 978-1-55911; 978-1-57257; 978-0-8092; 978-0-8442; 978-0-88488; 978-1-56107; 978-1-57699; 978-1-876842
Number of titles published annually: 2,000 Print; 100 CD-ROM; 100 Online; 200 Audio
Total Titles: 18,000 Print; 500 CD-ROM; 500 Online; 10,000 Audio
Imprints: Breakthrough to Literacy; Contemporary; Creative Publications; DLM; Everyday Mathematics
Membership(s): AAP; American Educational Publishers; Association of Educational Publishers

**Write Bloody Publishing**
2306 E Cesar Chavez, Suite 103, Austin, TX 78706
*E-mail:* writebloody@gmail.com
*Web Site:* writebloody.com
*Key Personnel*
Pres: Derrick Brown
Founded: 2004
Poetry publisher.
ISBN Prefix(es): 978-0-9789989; 978-0-9815213; 978-0-9821488; 978-0-9842515; 978-0-9845031; 978-1-935904
Number of titles published annually: 14 Print; 6 E-Book; 6 Audio
Total Titles: 90 Print; 40 E-Book; 6 Audio
Imprints: Write Fuzzy
*Sales Office(s):* SCB Distributing, 15608 S New Century Dr, Gardena, CA 90248, Contact: Gabriel Wilmoth *Toll Free Tel:* 800-729-6423 *E-mail:* gabriel@scbdistributors.com
Foreign Rep(s): Gabriel Wilmoth (Canada, Germany, USA)
*Advertising Agency:* Public Eye, Dir: Kevin Finley
*Orders to:* SCB Distributing, 15608 S New Century Dr, Gardena, CA 90248, Contact: Gabriel Wilmoth *Toll Free Tel:* 800-729-6423 *E-mail:* gabriel@scbdistributors.com
*Shipping Address:* SCB Distributing, 15608 S New Century Dr, Gardena, CA 90248, Contact: Gabriel Wilmoth *Toll Free Tel:* 800-729-6423 *E-mail:* gabriel@scbdistributors.com
*Distribution Center:* SCB Distributing, 15608 S New Century Dr, Gardena, CA 90248, Contact: Gabriel Wilmoth *Toll Free Tel:* 800-729-6423 *E-mail:* gabriel@scbdistributors.com

**Write Stuff Enterprises Inc**
1001 S Andrew Ave, Suite 120, Fort Lauderdale, FL 33316
*Tel:* 954-462-6657 *Toll Free Tel:* 800-900-2665 *Fax:* 954-462-6023
*E-mail:* legends@writestuffbooks.com
*Web Site:* www.writestuffbooks.com
*Key Personnel*
CEO & Pres: Jeffrey L Rodengen
Leading publisher of historical works focusing on industry & technology.
ISBN Prefix(es): 978-0-945903
Number of titles published annually: 4 Print; 4 E-Book
Imprints: Write Stuff®
Membership(s): ABA; IBPA, the Independent Book Publishers Association; National Business Aviation Association

**Writer's AudioShop**
1316 Overland Stage Rd, Dripping Springs, TX 78620
*Tel:* 512-264-7067 *Fax:* 512-264-7067
*E-mail:* wrtaudshop@aol.com
*Web Site:* www.writersaudio.com
*Key Personnel*
Publr: Elaine Davenport
Founded: 1985
Audio publisher.
ISBN Prefix(es): 978-1-880717
Number of titles published annually: 4 Audio
Total Titles: 35 Audio
Membership(s): Audio Publishers Association

**Writer's Digest Books**
Imprint of F+W Media Inc
10151 Carver Rd, Suite 200, Blue Ash, OH 45242
*Tel:* 513-531-2690 *Toll Free Tel:* 800-289-0963 *Fax:* 513-531-7185
*E-mail:* writersdigest@fwmedia.com (edit)
*Web Site:* www.writersdigest.com
*Key Personnel*
CEO: David Nuwsbaum
Pres: Sara Domville
Prodn Dir: Phil Graham *E-mail:* phil.graham@fwpubs.com
Publr: Phil Sexton *E-mail:* phil.sexton@fwmedia.com
Rts & Perms: Laura Smith *E-mail:* laura.smith@fwpubs.com
Top-quality instructional & reference books to help creative people find personal satisfaction & professional success. Topics covered include writing, photography, songwriting & poetry.
ISBN Prefix(es): 978-0-89879; 978-1-58297
Number of titles published annually: 160 Print
Total Titles: 150 Print; 1 CD-ROM
Imprints: Abbott Press
Foreign Rep(s): David Bateman Ltd (New Zealand); BookMovers Group (Canada); Capricorn Link (Australia); David & Charles Ltd (UK); Real Books (South Africa); Marta Schooler (Asia, Central America, Mexico, Middle East, South America)
*Returns:* Aero Fulfillment Services, 2800 Henkle Dr, Lebanon, OH 45036

**Writers of the Round Table Press**
990 Bob-O-Link Rd, Highland Park, IL 60035
Mailing Address: PO Box 511, Highland Park, IL 60035-0511
*Tel:* 949-375-1006 *Fax:* 815-346-2398
*E-mail:* mike@writersoftheroundtable.com
*Web Site:* www.roundtablecompanies.com
*Key Personnel*
CEO & Pres: Corey Michael Blake *Tel:* 847-682-3493 *E-mail:* corey@roundtablecompanies.com
VP: David Cohen *Tel:* 904-233-3383 *E-mail:* david@roundtablecompanies.com
Directoress of Happiness: Erin Cohen *Tel:* 815-346-2398 *E-mail:* erin@roundtablecompanies.com
Organizational Off Architect: Mike Winicour *E-mail:* mike@roundtablecompanies.com

Founded: 1996
Produce stories that inform, educate, entertain & inspire with a personalized approach to every project. Bestselling authors as well as first time authors & entrepreneurs, our clients are thought leaders & heart-centered businesses eager to engage in a collaborative creative process to amplify their message & emotionally connect with their audiences. A percentage of business is in repurposing nonfiction content in the illustrated form of graphic novels that we capture & then repurpose across creative mediums.
ISBN Prefix(es): 978-0-61066; 978-0-9814545; 978-0-9822206
Imprints: Round Table Comics
*Branch Office(s)*
8826 Goodbys Executive Dr, Suite A, Jacksonville, FL 32210, Billing: Kelly Umbelina *Tel:* 904-619-0533
*Editorial Office(s):* PO Box 511, Highland Park, IL 60035-0511
*Sales Office(s):* PO Box 511, Highland Park, IL 60035-0511
Foreign Rights: Graal Literary Agency (Albania, Bulgaria, Croatia, Czech Republic, Estonia, Hungary, Latvia, Lithuania, Poland, Romania, Serbia, Slovakia, Slovenia); Grayhawk Agency (China, Indonesia, Taiwan, Thailand, Vietnam); Dany Hong Agency (Korea); International Editors' Co (Argentina, Brazil, Portugal, Spain); Tuttle-Mori Agency Inc (Japan)
*Advertising Agency:* Alison & Partners, 8880 Rio San Diego Dr, Suite 1090, San Diego, CA 92108, Contact: Amy Toosley *Tel:* 619-533-7976 *Fax:* 619-543-0030 *E-mail:* amy@allisonpr.com
*Returns:* 15200 NBN Way, Blue Ridge Summit, PA 17214, Contact: Vicki Funk *Tel:* 717-794-3800 ext 3538 *E-mail:* vfunk@nbnbooks.com
*Shipping Address:* 15200 NBN Way, Blue Ridge Summit, PA 17214, Contact: Karen Mattscheck *Tel:* 717-794-3800 ext 3513 *E-mail:* kmattscheck@nbnbooks.com
*Distribution Center:* 15200 NBN Way, Blue Ridge Summit, PA 17214, Contact: Karen Mattscheck *Tel:* 717-794-3800 ext 3513 *E-mail:* kmattscheck@nbnbooks.com
Membership(s): BEA; IBPA, the Independent Book Publishers Association

**Wyndham Hall Press**
5050 Kerr Rd, Lima, OH 45806
SAN: 686-6743
*Tel:* 419-648-9124 *Toll Free Tel:* 866-895-0977 *Fax:* 419-648-9124; 413-208-2409
*E-mail:* whpbooks@wyndhamhallbooks.com; orders@wyndhamhallbooks.com
*Web Site:* www.wyndhamhallpress.com
*Key Personnel*
Mng Ed: Mark S McCullough *E-mail:* mark@wyndhamhallpress.com
Founded: 1981
Scholarly monographs & textbooks.
ISBN Prefix(es): 978-1-55605; 978-0-932269
Number of titles published annually: 8 Print
Total Titles: 242 Print

**XanEdu Publishing Inc**, see Copley Custom Textbooks

**§Xist Publishing**
16604 Sonora St, Tustin, CA 92782
Mailing Address: PO Box 61593, Tustin, CA 92602
*Tel:* 949-478-2568
*E-mail:* info@xistpublishing.com
*Web Site:* www.xistpublishing.com
*Key Personnel*
Pres: Calee Lee
COO: Jacob Lee
Founded: 2010
Digital-first publisher. Specialize in children's ebooks for every major device.
ISBN Prefix(es): 978-1-62395
Number of titles published annually: 30 Print; 50 E-Book
Total Titles: 107 Print; 170 E-Book
Membership(s): Society of Children's Book Writers & Illustrators

**Xlibris Corp**
Division of Author Solutions Inc
1663 Liberty Dr, Suite 200, Bloomington, IN 47403
*Toll Free Tel:* 888-795-4274 *Fax:* 610-915-0294
*E-mail:* info@xlibris.com
*Web Site:* www.xlibris.com
*Key Personnel*
CEO: Andrew Phillips
CFO: Kevin G Gregory
CIO: James Stanley
SVP, Prodn Servs: Bill Becher
SVP, Sales: Mr Terry Dwyer
VP, HR: Christopher Schrader
VP, Mktg: Keith Ogorek
VP, Prodn & Edit Servs: Ms Robin Lasek
Founded: 1997
One of the leading publishing services providers for authors, Xlibris provides authors with a broad set of publishing options including hardcover, trade paperback, custom leather bound & full-color formats. In addition, Xlibris offers its authors the widest selection of professional, marketing & bookselling services. Since its founding, Xlibris has published more than 25,000 titles.
This publisher has indicated that 100% of its product line is author subsidized.
ISBN Prefix(es): 978-0-7388; 978-0-9663501; 978-1-4010; 978-1-4134; 978-1-59926; 978-1-4257; 978-1-4363; 978-1-4415
Number of titles published annually: 5,100 Print
Total Titles: 25,000 Print
*Distribution Center:* Baker & Taylor Inc
Ingram Book Group
Membership(s): ABA; Canadian Booksellers Association

**§XML Press**
Subsidiary of R L Hamilton & Associates LLC
24310 Moulton Pkwy, Suite O-175, Laguna Hills, CA 92637
*Tel:* 970-231-3624
*E-mail:* publisher@xmlpress.net
*Web Site:* xmlpress.net
*Key Personnel*
Publr: Richard Hamilton *E-mail:* hamilton@xmlpress.net
CFO: Mei-li Lu *E-mail:* meili@xmlpress.net
Founded: 2008
Specialize in publications for technical communicators, content strategists, managers & marketers, with an emphasis on XML technology, social media & management. Also provides publication services to corporations that want to make their technical documentation available in print form through retail channels.
ISBN Prefix(es): 978-0-9822191; 978-1-937434
Number of titles published annually: 12 Print; 5 E-Book
Total Titles: 20 Print
*Distribution Center:* Ingram, One Ingram Blvd, La Vergne, TN 37086
Membership(s): Organization of Advancement of Structured Information Standards; Society for Technical Communication

**Yale Center for British Art**
1080 Chapel St, New Haven, CT 06510-2302
Mailing Address: PO Box 208280, New Haven, CT 06520-8280
*Tel:* 203-432-2800 *Toll Free Tel:* 877-274-8278 *Fax:* 203-432-9628
*E-mail:* ycba.info@yale.edu
*Web Site:* www.yale.edu/ycba; britishart.yale.edu
*Key Personnel*
Dir: Amy Meyers
Founded: 1977
Exhibition catalogues.
ISBN Prefix(es): 978-0-930606
Number of titles published annually: 4 Print
Total Titles: 61 Print
*Foreign Office(s):* Premier Book Marketing, One Gower St, London WC1E 6HA, United Kingdom
Foreign Rep(s): Premier Book Marketing (UK)

**§Yale University Press**
Division of Yale University
302 Temple St, New Haven, CT 06511-8909
SAN: 203-2740
Mailing Address: PO Box 209040, New Haven, CT 06520-9040
*Tel:* 401-531-2800 (cust serv); 203-432-0960 *Toll Free Tel:* 800-405-1619 (cust serv) *Fax:* 203-432-0948; 401-531-2801 (cust serv) *Toll Free Fax:* 800-406-9145 (cust serv)
*E-mail:* customer.care@trilateral.org (cust serv); language.yalepress@yale.edu
*Web Site:* www.yalebooks.com
*Key Personnel*
Chmn of the Bd: Peter Workman
COO: Kate Brown
CFO: John D Rollins
Dir: John Donatich
Art Dir: Nancy Ovedovitz
Dir, Digital Publg: David Schiffman
Edit Dir: Chris Rogers
Dir, Mktg & Promo: Heather D'Auria
Prodn Dir: Christina Coffin
Promo Dir: Sarah F Clark
Publicity Dir: Brenda King
Sales Dir: Jay Cosgrove
Sr Sales Mgr, Art & Digital Publg: Stephen Cebik
Ad Mgr: Peter Sims
Asst Promo Dir: Debra Bozzi
Publr, Art & Architecture: Patricia Fidler
Online Mktg Mgr: Ivan Lett
Sr Publicist: Jennifer Doerr
Publicist: Alden Ferro; Julia Haav
Exec Ed, Economics: William Frucht
Exec Ed, Sci & Medicine: Jean E Thomson-Black
Exec Ed-at-Large: Steve Wasserman
Sr Ed: Eric Brandt
Sr Ed, Humanities: Eric Brandt
Ed, Art & Architecture: Michelle Komie
Ed, Courcebooks: Sarah Miller
Ed, Sci: Joseph Calamia
Ed, World Lang: Tim Shea *E-mail:* tim.shea@yale.edu
Assoc Ed, History: Laura Davulis
Assoc Ed: Vadim Staklo
Asst Ed, Politics & Intl Rel: Jaya Aninda Chatterjee
Admin Asst: Erica Dorpalen
Founded: 1908
Scholarly.
ISBN Prefix(es): 978-0-300
Number of titles published annually: 350 Print
Total Titles: 5,000 Print
*Foreign Office(s):* 47 Bedford Sq, London WC1B 3DP, United Kingdom
Distributor for Addison Gallery of American Art, Phillips Academy; The Art Institute of Chicago; The Bard Graduate Center; Dallas Museum of Art; Harvard University Art Museums; Japan Society; The Jewish Museum; Kimbell Art Museum; Paul Mellon Centre; The Menil Collection; The Metropolitan Museum of Art; National Gallery, London; National Gallery of Art (Washington, DC); Philadelphia Museum of Art; Princeton University Art Museum; Sterling & Francine Clark Art Institute; Whitney Museum of American Art; Yale Center for British Art; Yale University Art Gallery

Foreign Rep(s): Rockbook (Japan, South Korea, Taiwan); David Stimpson (Australia, Canada, New Zealand)
Foreign Rights: Ann Bihan (England); Craig Falk (Latin America, Mexico, South America)
*Shipping Address:* TriLiteral, 100 Maple Ridge Dr, Cumberland, RI 02864-1769 *Tel:* 401-658-4226
Membership(s): AAP; Association of American University Presses

**Yard Dog Press**
710 W Redbud Lane, Alma, AR 72921-7247
*Tel:* 479-632-4693 *Fax:* 479-632-4693
*Web Site:* www.yarddogpress.com
*Key Personnel*
Ed-in-Chief: Selina Rosen *E-mail:* selinarosen@cox.net
Tech Ed & Orders Contact: Lynn Stranathan *E-mail:* lynnstran@cox.net
Founded: 1995
Micro press specializing in science fiction, fantasy & horror.
ISBN Prefix(es): 978-1-893687; 978-0-9824704; 978-1-937105
Number of titles published annually: 5 Print
Total Titles: 120 Print
Imprints: Double Dog (flip books - two short novels); Just Cause (non-genre books)
Membership(s): Science Fiction & Fantasy Writers of America

**YBK Publishers Inc**
39 Crosby St, New York, NY 10013
*Tel:* 212-219-0135 *Fax:* 212-219-0136
*E-mail:* info@ybkpublishers.com
*Key Personnel*
Pres: Otto Barz *E-mail:* obarz@ybkpublishers.com
Founded: 2001
Print-on-demand; general trade & nonfiction.
ISBN Prefix(es): 978-0-9703923; 978-0-9764359; 978-1-936411
Number of titles published annually: 7 Print
Total Titles: 55 Print
*Distribution Center:* Lightning Source, 1246 Heil Quaker Blvd, La Vergne, TN 37086 *Tel:* 615-213-5815 *Fax:* 615-213-4426 *E-mail:* inquiry@ybkpublishers.com
Membership(s): IBPA, the Independent Book Publishers Association

**Yeshiva University Press**
500 W 185 St, New York, NY 10033-3201
Mailing Address: KTAV Publishing House Inc, 2540 Amerstam Ave, New York, NY 10033
*Tel:* 212-960-5400 *Fax:* 212-960-0043
*Web Site:* www.yu.edu
*Key Personnel*
Pres: Richard Joel *Tel:* 212-960-5300 *E-mail:* president@yu.edu
ISBN Prefix(es): 978-0-87068; 978-0-88125; 978-1-60280
Total Titles: 71 Print
Distributed by KTAV Publishing House Inc

**YMAA Publication Center**
PO Box 480, Wolfeboro, NH 03894
SAN: 665-2077
*Tel:* 603-569-7988 *Toll Free Tel:* 800-669-8892 *Fax:* 603-569-1889
*E-mail:* ymaa@aol.com
*Web Site:* www.ymaa.com
*Key Personnel*
Publr: David Ripianzi *E-mail:* davidr@ymaa.com
Prodn Mgr: Tim Comrie *E-mail:* tcomrie@ymaa.com
Sales Rep: David Silver *E-mail:* dsilver@ymaa.com
Founded: 1984
Publisher of in-depth books, videos & DVDs on martial arts, meditation, traditional Chinese medicine & alternative health therapies.
ISBN Prefix(es): 978-0-940871; 978-1-886969; 978-1-59439
Number of titles published annually: 10 Print; 10 E-Book
Total Titles: 80 Print; 50 E-Book; 4 Audio
Distributor for Wind Records (Chinese healing music)
Foreign Rep(s): Agencia Literarie SL (Montse F Yanez) (Mexico, Spain); Big Apple Agency (Maggie Han) (China); Big Apple Agency (China, Taiwan); The Book Publishers Association of Israel (Shoshi Grajower) (Israel); Daniel Doglioli (Italy); Graal Literary Agency (Madga Cabajewska) (Poland); Imprima Korea Agency (Joseph Lee) (Korea); International Copyright Agency (Simona Kessler) (Romania); Christiane Janssen (Germany); Japan Uni Agency (Taeko Nagatsuka) (Japan); JS Literary & Media Agency (Somjai Raksasee) (Thailand); Nurcihan Kesim Literary Agency Inc (Filiz Karaman) (Turkey); Maxima Creative Agency (Santo Manurung) (Indonesia); Nova Littera SL (Konstantin Paltchikov) (Russia); Andrew Nurnberg Associates (Tatjana Zoldnere) (Latvia, Lithuania, Ukraine); Andrew Nurnberg Associates (Petra Tobiskova) (Czech Republic); Andrew Nurberg Associates (Anna Droumeva) (Bulgaria); OA Literary Agency (Michael Avramides) (Greece); Plima Literary Agency (Mila Perisic) (Croatia, Serbia, Slovenia); Karin Schindler Rights Rep (Suely Pedro Dos Santos) (Brazil); Karin Schindler Rights Rep (Karin Schindler) (Brazil); Ralph & Sheila Summers (Hong Kong, Korea, Malaysia, Philippines, Singapore, Taiwan, Thailand); Tuttle Mori Agency Inc (Fumi Nishijima) (Japan)
Foreign Rights: Agencia Literaria (Brazil, Portugal); Big Apple Agency Inc (China, Taiwan); Bookman (Denmark, Finland, Iceland, Norway, Sweden); Imprima Korea Agency (Korea); Jarir Bookstore (Egypt, Middle East, Saudi Arabia); JS Literary & Media Agency (Thailand); Maxima Creative (Indonesia); La Nouvelle Agency (Belgium, Switzerland); Nova Littera Ltd (Russia); Andrew Nurnberg Associates (Baltic States); Andrew Nurnberg Associates Sofia (Bulgaria); OA Literary Agency (Greece); Permissions & Rights (Albania, Croatia, Montenegro, Serbia, Slovenia); Tuttle-Mori Agency Inc (Japan); Julio F Yanez Agencia Leteraria (Mexico, Spain, Spanish languages, Spanish Latin America)
*Orders to:* Baker & Taylor, 2550 W Tyvola Rd, Charlotte, NC *Toll Free Tel:* 800-775-1800 *Fax:* 704-998-3100 *Web Site:* www.btol.com; Ingram Book Co, One Ingram Blvd, La Vergne, TN *Tel:* (615) 793-5000 *Toll Free Tel:* 800-937-8200 *Web Site:* www.ingrambook.com; National Book Network, 15200 NBN Way, Blue Ridge Summit, PA 17214 *Tel:* 717-794-3800 *Toll Free Tel:* 800-462-6420 *Toll Free Fax:* 800-338-4550 *E-mail:* custserv@nbnbooks.com *Web Site:* www.nbnbooks.com; New Leaf Distributing Co, 401 Thornton Rd, Lithia Springs, GA 30122-1557 *Tel:* 770-948-7845 *Toll Free Tel:* 800-944-2313 *Fax:* 770-994-2313 *E-mail:* newleaf@newleaf-dist.com *Web Site:* www.newleaf-dist.com
*Distribution Center:* National Book Network, 15200 NBN Way, Blue Ridge Summit, PA 07214 *Tel:* 717-794-3800 *Toll Free Tel:* 800-338-4550 *Toll Free Fax:* 800-338-4550 *E-mail:* custserv@nbnbooks.com *Web Site:* www.nbnbooks.com
Membership(s): ABA; IBPA, the Independent Book Publishers Association

**§Yotzeret Publishing**
PO Box 18662, St Paul, MN 55118-0662
*Tel:* 651-470-3853 *Fax:* 651-224-7447
*E-mail:* info@yotzeretpublishing.com; orders@yotzeretpublishing.com
*Web Site:* yotzeretpublishing.com
*Key Personnel*
Publr: Sheyna Galyan
Founded: 2002
Adult & children's books & ebooks from a Jewish perspective.
ISBN Prefix(es): 978-1-59287
Number of titles published annually: 2 Print; 2 E-Book; 1 Audio
Total Titles: 7 Print; 7 E-Book
*Orders to:* Partners Publishers Group (PPG), 2325 Jarco Dr, Holt, MI 48842 (distributes to Ingram, Baker & Taylor & others) *Tel:* 517-694-3205 *Fax:* 517-694-0617 *E-mail:* info@partnerspublishersgroup.com *Web Site:* www.partnerspublishersgroup.com
*Distribution Center:* Partners Publishers Group (PPG), 2325 Jarco Dr, Holt, MI 48842 *Tel:* 517-694-3205 *Fax:* 517-694-0617 *E-mail:* info@partnerspublishersgroup.com *Web Site:* www.partnerspublishersgroup.com
Membership(s): IBPA, the Independent Book Publishers Association; Midwest Independent Publishers Association; Minnesota Book Publishers Roundtable

**Young People's Press Inc (YPPI)**
814 Morena Blvd, Suite 102, San Diego, CA 92110
*Tel:* 619-296-1297 (orders) *Toll Free Tel:* 800-231-9774
*E-mail:* admin@youngpeoplespress.com
*Web Site:* www.youngpeoplespress.com
*Key Personnel*
Pres: Robert J Saielli *Tel:* 619-296-1070 *E-mail:* rjs@youngpeoplespress.com
Founded: 1994
Elementary curriculum in math, pre-school, home schooling, social skills & character building, language arts, literature & social sciences.
ISBN Prefix(es): 978-1-885658; 978-1-57279
Number of titles published annually: 10 Print; 5 E-Book
Total Titles: 245 Print; 15 E-Book; 16 Audio
Imprints: Kens Math
*Returns:* 411 Main St, Mosinee, WI 54455, Contact: Tim Kennedy *Tel:* 715-693-4682 *Fax:* 715-693-4682 *E-mail:* forms@mtc.net
*Warehouse:* 411 Main St, Mosinee, WI 54455, Contact: Patty Pflum *Tel:* 619-296-1070 *Fax:* 619-296-1297 *E-mail:* ppflum@youngpeoplespress.com

**Your Culture Gifts**
12801 Old Columbia Pike, Apt 218, Silver Spring, MD 20904
SAN: 854-3208
Mailing Address: PO Box 1245, Ellicott City, MD 21041
*Tel:* 410-900-0184 *Fax:* 410-461-2415
*E-mail:* info@yourculturegifts.com
*Web Site:* www.yourculturegifts.com
*Key Personnel*
Pres: Frank Sauri
Mgr: Trudy Sauri
Founded: 2002
Publishes cultural stories presented in a combination of historical fiction & nonfiction genres for the purpose of introducing children to the richness of world cultures, social geography, world history, language, food & tradition.
ISBN Prefix(es): 978-0-9797637
Number of titles published annually: 5 Print
Total Titles: 4 Print
Membership(s): IBPA, the Independent Book Publishers Association

**YPPI**, see Young People's Press Inc (YPPI)

**YWAM Publishing**
Division of Youth with a Mission
PO Box 55787, Seattle, WA 98155-0787
*Tel:* 425-771-1153 *Toll Free Tel:* 800-922-2143 *Fax:* 425-775-2383
*E-mail:* books@ywampublishing.com
*Web Site:* www.ywampublishing.com
*Key Personnel*
Mktg Dir: Wenche Warren *E-mail:* marketing@ywampublishing.com
Founded: 1960
Books on missions, evangelism & discipleship & also religious classics.
ISBN Prefix(es): 978-0-927545
Number of titles published annually: 10 Print; 2 CD-ROM
Total Titles: 260 Print; 15 CD-ROM; 10 Audio
Distributor for Emerald Books
*Shipping Address:* 7825 230 St SW, Edmonds, WA 98026
*Warehouse:* 7825 230 St SW, Edmonds, WA 98026

**§Zagat Survey LLC**
76 Ninth Ave, 4th fl, New York, NY 10011
SAN: 289-4777
*Tel:* 212-977-6000 *Toll Free Tel:* 866-817-9947 (orders); 800-540-9609 *Fax:* 212-977-9760; 802-864-9846 (order related)
*E-mail:* corpsales@zagat.com; shop@zagat.com
*Web Site:* www.zagat.com
*Key Personnel*
Founder & Chair: Nina S Zagat *E-mail:* nina@zagat.com; Tim Zagat
Founded: 1979
Provider of consumer survey-based information on where to eat, drink, stay & play worldwide.
ISBN Prefix(es): 978-1-57006
Number of titles published annually: 40 Print
Total Titles: 40 Print
Foreign Rep(s): Prentice-Hall (Canada)

**Zaner-Bloser Inc**
Subsidiary of Highlights for Children Inc
1201 Dublin Rd, Columbus, OH 43215-1026
*Tel:* 614-486-0221 *Toll Free Tel:* 800-421-3018 (cust serv) *Toll Free Fax:* 800-992-6087 (orders)
*E-mail:* zbcsd@zaner-bloser.com; international@zaner-bloser.com
*Web Site:* www.zaner-bloser.com
*Key Personnel*
Pres: Robert Page
Founded: 1888
Elementary textbooks for critical thinking, whole language, substance abuse prevention, spelling & handwriting; modality (learning styles) kit, professional education books, storytelling kits & early childhood education.
ISBN Prefix(es): 978-0-88309; 978-0-88085
Number of titles published annually: 200 Print
Foreign Rep(s): Childrens Press
*Advertising Agency:* EDPUB
*Orders to:* PO Box 16764, Columbus, OH 43216-6764
*Warehouse:* 4200 Parkway Ct, Hilliard, OH 43026

**Zarahemla Books**
869 E 2680 N, Provo, UT 84604
*Tel:* 801-368-7374 *Fax:* 801-418-2081
*E-mail:* info@zarahemlabooks.com
*Web Site:* zarahemlabooks.com
*Key Personnel*
Publr: Christopher Bigelow *E-mail:* chris@zarahemlabooks.com
Founded: 2006
Alternative Mormon-themed fiction & memoir.
ISBN Prefix(es): 978-0-9787971; 978-0-9843603
Number of titles published annually: 3 Print
Total Titles: 18 Print

**Zebra Books**, see Kensington Publishing Corp

**Zeig, Tucker & Theisen Inc**
3614 N 24 St, Phoenix, AZ 85016
*Tel:* 480-389-4342 *Toll Free Tel:* 800-666-2211 (orders) *Fax:* 602-944-8118
*E-mail:* marketing@zeigtucker.com
*Web Site:* www.zeigtucker.com
*Key Personnel*
Pres: Jeffrey K Zeig *Tel:* 602-944-6529 *Fax:* 602-944-8118 *E-mail:* jeff@zeigtucker.com
Busn Mgr: Stacey Moore *E-mail:* stacey@zeigtucker.com
Mng Ed: Chuck Lakin *E-mail:* chuck@zeigtucker.com
Founded: 1998
ISBN Prefix(es): 978-1-891944; 978-1-932462
Number of titles published annually: 10 Print
Total Titles: 45 Print; 8 Audio
*Editorial Office(s):* 3606 N 24 St, Phoenix, AZ 86015 *Tel:* 480-389-4342 *Fax:* 602-944-8118
*Billing Address:* Cornell University Press Services, PO Box 6525, Ithaca, NY 14851-6525
*Orders to:* Cornell University Press Services, PO Box 6525, Ithaca, NY 14851-6525 *Tel:* 607-277-2211 *Toll Free Tel:* 800-666-2211 *E-mail:* orderbook@cupserv.org
*Returns:* Cornell University Press Services, PO Box 6525, Ithaca, NY 14851-6525 *Tel:* 607-277-2211 *Toll Free Tel:* 800-666-2211 *E-mail:* orderbook@cupserv.org
*Shipping Address:* Cornell University Press Services, PO Box 6525, Ithaca, NY 14851-6525
*Warehouse:* Cornell University Press Services, PO Box 6525, Ithaca, NY 14851-6525 *Toll Free Tel:* 800-666-2211
*Distribution Center:* Cornell University Press Services, PO Box 6525, Ithaca, NY 14851-6525

**Zephyr Press**, see Chicago Review Press

**Zest Books**
35 Stillman St, Suite 121, San Francisco, CA 94107
*Tel:* 415-777-8654 *Fax:* 415-777-8653
*E-mail:* info@zestbooks.net; publicity@zestbooks.net
*Web Site:* zestbooks.net
*Key Personnel*
Publr: Hallie Warshaw *E-mail:* hallie@zestbooks.net
Edit Dir: Daniel Harmon
Mktg & Publicity Mgr: Jo Beaton
ISBN Prefix(es): 978-0-9772660
Number of titles published annually: 14 Print; 14 E-Book
Total Titles: 60 Print
Distributed by Houghton Mifflin Harcourt
*Distribution Center:* Houghton Mifflin Harcourt, Trade & Ref Cust Serv, 9205 Southpark Center Loop, 3rd fl, Orlando, FL 32819 *Toll Free Tel:* 800-225-3362 *Toll Free Fax:* 800-634-7568 *E-mail:* customercare@hmhco.com

**§Zondervan, A HarperCollins Company**
5300 Patterson Ave SE, Grand Rapids, MI 49530
SAN: 203-2694
*Tel:* 616-698-6900 *Toll Free Tel:* 800-226-1122; 800-727-1309 (retail orders) *Fax:* 616-698-3350 *Toll Free Fax:* 800-698-3256 (retail orders)
*E-mail:* zinfo@zondervan.com
*Web Site:* www.zondervan.com
*Key Personnel*
CFO & EVP: Gary Wicker *Tel:* 616-698-3269
EVP & Ed-in-Chief: Stan Gundry
EVP, Sales: Verne Kenney *Tel:* 616-698-3548
Pres, Youth Specialties: Mark Oestreicher *Tel:* 619-440-2333 *E-mail:* marko@youthspecialties.com
EVP, Support Opers & HR: Allen R Kerkstra *Tel:* 616-698-3409 *E-mail:* al.kerkstra@zondervan.com
SVP, Busn Technol Servs: Sue J Boylan *Tel:* 616-698-3361 *E-mail:* sue-anne.boylan@zondervan.com
VP, PR & Communs: Jason Vines *E-mail:* jason.vines@zondervan.com
VP & Publr, Fiction Div: Daisy Hutton
Dir, Intl Sales: Jennifer Dibble *E-mail:* jennifer.dibble@zondervan.com
Founded: 1931
A world leader in Christian communications & the leading Christian publishing brand. For more than 75 years, Zondervan has delivered transformational Christian experiences through general & academic resources authored by influential leaders & emerging voices & been honored with more Christian Book Awards than any other publisher. Headquartered in Grand Rapids, Mich., with offices in San Diego & Miami, Zondervan conducts events & publishes its bestselling Bibles, books, audio, video, curriculum, software & digital products through its Zondervan, eZondervan, Zonderkidz, Youth Specialties, Editorial Vida & National Pastors Convention brands. Zondervan resources are sold worldwide through retail stores, online & by Zondervan ChurchSource & are translated into nearly 200 languages in more than 60 countries.
ISBN Prefix(es): 978-0-310
Number of titles published annually: 200 Print; 4 CD-ROM; 30 Online; 50 E-Book; 50 Audio
Total Titles: 5,000 Print; 30 CD-ROM; 300 Online; 300 E-Book; 400 Audio
Divisions: Editorial Vida; Youth Specialties; Zonderkidz
*Foreign Office(s):* Zondervan, Shrewsbury, United Kingdom, Sales & Mktg Mgr: Ian Matthews *E-mail:* ian.matthews@zondervan.com *Web Site:* www.zondervan.com/world
Membership(s): AAP; ABA; Audio Publishers Association; Better Business Bureau; BISAC; BISG; CBA; Chamber of Commerce; Evangelical Christian Publishers Association; Evangelical Press Association; Society of Bible Literature; Society of Children's Book Writers & Illustrators; Software & Information Industry Association

**Zone Books dba Urzone Inc**
1226 Prospect Ave, Brooklyn, NY 11218
*Tel:* 718-686-0048 *Toll Free Tel:* 800-405-1619 (orders & cust serv) *Fax:* 718-686-9045 *Toll Free Fax:* 800-406-9145 (orders)
*E-mail:* orders@triliteral.org
*Web Site:* www.zonebooks.org
*Key Personnel*
Gen Mgr & Intl Rts: Gus Kiley *E-mail:* gkiley@zonebooks.org
Mng Ed: Meighan Gale *E-mail:* mgale@zonebooks.org
Ed: Jonathan Crary; Michel Feher; Hal Foster; Ramona Naddaff
Founded: 1985
Publish books in the arts & humanities & social sciences.
ISBN Prefix(es): 978-0-942299; 978-1-890951
Number of titles published annually: 6 Print
Total Titles: 59 Print
Imprints: Swerve Editions
Distributed by The MIT Press
Foreign Rights: Carmen Balcells (Spain); English Agency (Japan); Paul & Peter Fritz (Germany); Graal Literary Agency (Eastern Block); Agnese Incisa (Italy)
*Warehouse:* The MIT Press c/o Triliteral LLC, 100 Maple Ridge Dr, Cumberland, RI 02864-1769
*Distribution Center:* The MIT Press, 55 Hayward St, Cambridge, MA 02142 *E-mail:* mitpress-orders@mit.edu

John Wiley & Sons, Southern Cross Trading Estate, One Oldlands Way, Bognor Regis, West Sussex P022 9SA, United Kingdom (UK & the Continent) *Tel:* (01243) 779777 *Fax:* (01243) 820250 *E-mail:* cs-books@wiley.co.uk

**ZOVA Books**
PO Box 21833, Long Beach, CA 90801
*Tel:* 805-426-9682 *Fax:* 562-394-9568
*Web Site:* www.zovabooks.com
*Key Personnel*
CEO: Matthew Pizzo
Publr: Molly Lewis *E-mail:* molly@zovabooks.com
Ed-in-Chief: Daniel Silva
Founded: 2010
A boutique publishing company specializing in unique fiction for young & old. Catalog is built on partnerships with local authors & screenwriters, creating a collection of cinematic fiction suitable for multimedia developement.
ISBN Prefix(es): 978-0-9827880; 978-0-9840350
Number of titles published annually: 10 Print; 10 E-Book
Total Titles: 14 Print; 14 E-Book
*Distribution Center:* Baker & Taylor, 2550 W Tyvola Rd, Suite 300, Charlotte, NC 28217 *Tel:* 704-998-3100 *Fax:* 704-998-3319

**Zumaya Publications LLC**
3209 S IH 35, Suite 1086, Austin, TX 78741
*Tel:* 512-402-5298 *Fax:* 253-660-2009
*E-mail:* acquisitions@zumayapublications.com
*Web Site:* www.zumayapublications.com
*Key Personnel*
Exec Ed/Publr: Liz Burton
Partner: Joyanne Moul
CFO: Marianne Moul
Acqs Ed: Rie Sheridan Rose
Founded: 2001
Trade paperback & ebook formats offering full-length works of fiction & nonfiction.
ISBN Prefix(es): 978-1-93413; 978-1-93484
Number of titles published annually: 30 Print; 30 E-Book
Total Titles: 200 Print; 200 E-Book
Imprints: Arcane (mysteries of the spirit); Boundless; Embraces; Enigma; Otherworlds (speculative fiction, science fiction, fantasy & paranormal suspense); Thresholds (imagination); Yesterdays (journeys into the past - both real & imaginary)
Membership(s): IBPA, the Independent Book Publishers Association

# U.S. Publishers — Geographic Index

## COLORADO



## CONNECTICUT



## DELAWARE



## DISTRICT OF COLUMBIA

## FLORIDA



## GEORGIA



## HAWAII



## IDAHO



## ILLINOIS

## INDIANA



## IOWA



## KANSAS



## KENTUCKY



## LOUISIANA



## MAINE



## MARYLAND

## MASSACHUSETTS



## MICHIGAN



## MINNESOTA

## MISSISSIPPI



## MISSOURI



## MONTANA



## NEBRASKA



## NEVADA



## NEW HAMPSHIRE



## NEW JERSEY



## NEW MEXICO

## NEW YORK

## NORTH CAROLINA

## NORTH DAKOTA



## OHIO



## OKLAHOMA



## OREGON



## PENNSYLVANIA



## RHODE ISLAND

## SOUTH CAROLINA



## SOUTH DAKOTA



## TENNESSEE



## TEXAS



## UTAH



## VERMONT



## VIRGINIA

## WASHINGTON



## WEST VIRGINIA



## WISCONSIN



## WYOMING



## PUERTO RICO

# U.S. Publishers — Type of Publication Index

## ASSOCIATION PRESSES



## AUDIOBOOKS

## AV MATERIALS



## BELLES LETTRES



## BIBLES

## BIBLIOGRAPHIES



## BRAILLE BOOKS



## CD-ROM, EBOOKS

## CHILDREN'S BOOKS

## COMPUTER SOFTWARE



## DATABASES

## DICTIONARIES, ENCYCLOPEDIAS



## DIRECTORIES, REFERENCE BOOKS

## FINE EDITIONS, ILLUSTRATED BOOKS

## FOREIGN LANGUAGE & BILINGUAL BOOKS

## GENERAL TRADE BOOKS - HARDCOVER

## JUVENILE & YOUNG ADULT BOOKS

## LARGE PRINT BOOKS



## MAPS, ATLASES



## PAPERBACK BOOKS - MASS MARKET

## PAPERBACK BOOKS - TRADE

## PERIODICALS, JOURNALS

## PROFESSIONAL BOOKS

## REPRINTS

## SCHOLARLY BOOKS

## SIDELINES



## SUBSCRIPTION & MAIL ORDER BOOKS

## TEXTBOOKS - ELEMENTARY



## TEXTBOOKS - SECONDARY

## TEXTBOOKS - COLLEGE

## TRANSLATIONS



## UNIVERSITY PRESSES

## VIDEOS, DVDS

# U.S. Publishers — Subject Index

## ACCOUNTING



## ADVERTISING



## AERONAUTICS, AVIATION



## AFRICAN AMERICAN STUDIES

## AGRICULTURE



## ALTERNATIVE



## AMERICANA, REGIONAL

## ANIMALS, PETS

## ANTHROPOLOGY



## ANTIQUES



## ARCHAEOLOGY

## ARCHITECTURE & INTERIOR DESIGN



## ART

## ASIAN STUDIES



## ASTROLOGY, OCCULT



## ASTRONOMY

## AUTOMOTIVE



## BEHAVIORAL SCIENCES



## BIBLICAL STUDIES

## BIOGRAPHY, MEMOIRS

## BIOLOGICAL SCIENCES



## BUSINESS

## CAREER DEVELOPMENT

## CHEMISTRY, CHEMICAL ENGINEERING



## CHILD CARE & DEVELOPMENT

## CIVIL ENGINEERING



## COMMUNICATIONS



## COMPUTER SCIENCE

## COMPUTERS



## COOKERY

## CRAFTS, GAMES, HOBBIES



## CRIMINOLOGY

## DEVELOPING COUNTRIES



## DISABILITY, SPECIAL NEEDS



## DRAMA, THEATER

## EARTH SCIENCES



## ECONOMICS

## EDUCATION

## ELECTRONICS, ELECTRICAL ENGINEERING



## ENERGY



## ENGINEERING (GENERAL)

## ENGLISH AS A SECOND LANGUAGE



## ENVIRONMENTAL STUDIES

## EROTICA



## ETHNICITY

## FASHION



## FICTION

## FILM, VIDEO

## FINANCE



## FOREIGN COUNTRIES

## GARDENING, PLANTS



## GAY & LESBIAN



## GENEALOGY

## GEOGRAPHY, GEOLOGY



## GOVERNMENT, POLITICAL SCIENCE

## HEALTH, NUTRITION

## HISTORY

## HOUSE & HOME



## HOW-TO

## HUMAN RELATIONS

## HUMOR



## INSPIRATIONAL, SPIRITUALITY

## JOURNALISM



## LABOR, INDUSTRIAL RELATIONS



## LANGUAGE ARTS, LINGUISTICS

## LAW

## LIBRARY & INFORMATION SCIENCES



## LITERATURE, LITERARY CRITICISM, ESSAYS

## MANAGEMENT

## MARITIME



## MARKETING

## MATHEMATICS



## MECHANICAL ENGINEERING



## MEDICINE, NURSING, DENTISTRY

## MILITARY SCIENCE



## MUSIC, DANCE

## MYSTERIES, SUSPENSE



## NATIVE AMERICAN STUDIES

## NATURAL HISTORY

## NONFICTION (GENERAL)

## OUTDOOR RECREATION



## PARAPSYCHOLOGY

## PHILOSOPHY



## PHOTOGRAPHY

## PHYSICAL SCIENCES



## PHYSICS

## POETRY

## POP CULTURE



## PSYCHOLOGY, PSYCHIATRY

## PUBLIC ADMINISTRATION



## PUBLISHING & BOOK TRADE REFERENCE



## RADIO, TV



## REAL ESTATE

## REGIONAL INTERESTS



## RELIGION - BUDDHIST



## RELIGION - CATHOLIC

## RELIGION - HINDU



## RELIGION - ISLAMIC



## RELIGION - JEWISH

## RELIGION - PROTESTANT



## RELIGION - OTHER

## ROMANCE

## SCIENCE (GENERAL)

## SCIENCE FICTION, FANTASY



## SECURITIES



## SELF-HELP

## SOCIAL SCIENCES, SOCIOLOGY

## SPORTS, ATHLETICS



## TECHNOLOGY

## THEOLOGY

## TRANSPORTATION



## TRAVEL & TOURISM

## VETERINARY SCIENCE



## WESTERN FICTION



## WINE & SPIRITS



## WOMEN'S STUDIES

# Imprints, Subsidiaries & Distributors

A Cappella Books, *imprint of* Chicago Review Press

A G Fiction™, *imprint of* American Girl Publishing

A K Peters Ltd, *division of* CRC Press LLC

A-R Editions Inc, *distributor for* AIM (American Institute of Musicology)

A-To-Z Series, *imprint of* Incentive Publications Inc

A U A Language Center, *distributed by* Cornell University Southeast Asia Program Publications

AAAI Press, *imprint of* Association for the Advancement of Artificial Intelligence, *distributed by* The MIT Press

AAAS, *distributed by* National Science Teachers Association (NSTA)

A&D Xtreme, *imprint of* ABDO Publishing Group

AAP, *distributed by* Welcome Books®

AAPG (American Association of Petroleum Geologists), *distributor for* Geological Society of London, *distributed by* Affiliated East - West Press Private Ltd, Canadian Society of Petroleum Geologists, Geological Society of London

Aardvark, *distributor for* No Frills Buffalo

AATEC Publications, *distributed by* Chelsea Green Publishing Co

Abaris Books, *division of* Opal Publishing Corp

Abbeville Kids, *imprint of* Abbeville Publishing Group

Abbeville Press, *imprint of* Abbeville Publishing Group

Abbey of Saint Peter of Solesmes, *distributed by* Paraclete Press Inc

Abbott Press, *imprint of* Writer's Digest Books

Abbott Publishing, *distributed by* Sunbelt Publications Inc

ABC-CLIO Ltd, *subsidiary of* ABC-CLIO

ABC Intl Group Inc, *imprint of* Kazi Publications Inc

Abdo & Daughters Publishing, *imprint of* ABDO Publishing Group

ABDO Publishing Group, *subsidiary of* Abdo Consulting Group Inc (ACGI), Abdo Consulting Group Inc (ACGI), *distributed by* Rockbottom Book Co

Abelard Press, *distributed by* Hobblebush Books

Aberdeen Bay, *imprint of* Champion Writers Inc, *distributed by* Champion Writers Inc

The Aberdeen Group, *distributor for* Craftsman Book Co

ABI Professional Publications, *distributed by* Vandamere Press

Abingdon Press, *imprint of* The United Methodist Publishing House, *distributor for* Church Publishing Inc, Judson Press, Upper Room Books

Abjad Books, *imprint of* Kazi Publications Inc

Abrams, *distributor for* National Gallery of Art, Winterthur Museum & Country Estate, *distributed by* Perfection Learning Corp

Abrams & University of Washington Press, *distributor for* Amon Carter Museum

Abrams Appleseed, *imprint of* Harry N Abrams Inc

Abrams Books, *imprint of* Harry N Abrams Inc

Abrams Books for Young Readers, *imprint of* Harry N Abrams Inc

Abrams ComicArts, *imprint of* Harry N Abrams Inc

Harry N Abrams Inc, *distributed by* Hachette Book Group

Harry N Abrams Inc, *subsidiary of* La Martiniere Groupe, *distributor for* American Federation of Arts, Booth-Clibborn Editions, The Colonial Williamsburg Foundation, 5 Continents Editions, Nevraumont Publishing Co, Royal Academy Publications, Tate Publishing, V&A Publishing, The Vendome Press, *distributed by* Editions Alain

Abrams Image, *imprint of* Harry N Abrams Inc

Abrams Learning Trends, *subsidiary of* Learning Trends LLC, *distributor for* General Education Services (New Zealand)

The ABS Group, *distributed by* American Academy of Environmental Engineers

Absolute Classics, *distributed by* Theatre Communications Group

ACA, *imprint of* American Counseling Association

Academia Barilla, *distributed by* The Taunton Press Inc

Academic Book Center, *distributor for* Primary Research Group Inc

Academic Press, *imprint of* Elsevier, *distributed by* Marine Techniques Publishing

Academy Chicago Publishers, *distributor for* Wicker Park Press

Academy of Continuing Education, *division of* Success Advertising & Publishing

Academy of Natural Sciences, *distributed by* Diane Publishing Co

Academy of Nutrition & Dietetics, *distributed by* Small Press United (Eat Right Press)

Acanthus, *distributor for* Winterthur Museum & Country Estate

Acanthus Publishing, *division of* The Ictus Group LLC

Acatos, *distributed by* Antique Collectors Club Ltd

ACC Distribution, *division of* Antique Collectors Club Ltd

ACC Editions, *imprint of* Antique Collectors Club Ltd

Accent Publications, *subsidiary of* Cook Communications Ministries

Access, *imprint of* HarperCollins Publishers Sales

Accord Publishing, *imprint of* Andrews McMeel Publishing LLC

Ace, *imprint of* Penguin Group (USA) LLC

Ace Books, *imprint of* Berkley Books, Berkley Publishing Group, *distributed by* Perfection Learning Corp

ACE/Oryx, *imprint of* American Council on Education

Ace/Putnam, *imprint of* Penguin Group (USA) LLC, GP Putnam's Sons (Hardcover)

ACER, *distributor for* Psychological Assessment Resources Inc (PAR)

ACM Press, *imprint of* Association for Computing Machinery

Acorn, *imprint of* Oak Tree Press

Acorn Guides, *imprint of* Trails Books

Acres USA, *division of* Acres USA Inc, Acres USA Inc

Acropolis Books, *distributed by* De Vorss & Co

ACS Publications, *imprint of* Starcrafts LLC

ACT Proficiency Examination Program, *imprint of* National Learning Corp

ACTA Publications, *distributor for* Grief Watch, Veritas

Action Language Learning, *distributed by* Cheng & Tsui Co Inc

ACU Press, *affiliate of* Abilene Christian University

Ac-u-Kwik, *imprint of* Penton Media

AcuTab Publications Inc, *distributed by* Mel Bay Publications Inc

Ad Infinitum Books, *distributor for* Cross-Cultural Communications

Ad Infinitum Press, *distributed by* Cross-Cultural Communications

Adam Hill Publications, *division of* Adam Hill Advertising Corp

Adams Business, *imprint of* Adams Media

Adams Media, *imprint of* F+W Media Inc, F+W Media Inc

ADASI Publishing Co, *distributor for* Wall & Thompson

ADC the Map People, *subsidiary of* American Map Corp, *distributed by* Hagstrom Map & Travel Center

ADD Warehouse, *distributor for* Bantam, Guilford Press, Plenum, Simon & Schuster, Slossen, Woodbine House, *distributed by* Boys Town Press, Child Play, MHS

Addison Gallery of American Art, Phillips Academy, *distributed by* Yale University Press

Addison Wesley, *distributor for* Public Citizen

Adirondack Museum, *imprint of* Syracuse University Press

Adis International, *imprint of* Wolters Kluwer US Corp

Adler Planetarium & Astronomy, *distributed by* Antique Collectors Club Ltd

Admission Test Series, *imprint of* National Learning Corp

Adult Trade, *division of* Chronicle Books LLC

Advaita Ashrama, *distributed by* Vedanta Press

Adventure Guides, *imprint of* Hunter Publishing Inc

Adventure Publications, *distributor for* Blacklock Nature Photography, Kollath-Stensaas, Nodin Press, Pocket Guides Publishing, Raven Productions Inc

Adventure Roads Travel, *imprint of* Ocean Tree Books

Adventures in Odyssey, *imprint of* Focus on the Family

Adventures Unlimited Press, *distributor for* Eagle Wing Books, EDFU Books, Yelsraek Publishing

Advocate House, *imprint of* A Cappela Publishing

The AEI Press, *division of* American Enterprise Institute, *distributed by* MIT (selected titles)

Aeon Books, *distributed by* Stylus Publishing LLC

Aequitas Books, *imprint of* Pleasure Boat Studio: A Literary Press

Aerie Books, *imprint of* Tom Doherty Associates, LLC

Aeronautical Publishers, *imprint of* Markowski International Publishers

AF Editions, *distributed by* Casemate Publishers & Book Distributors LLC

Affiliated East - West Press Private Ltd, *distributor for* AAPG (American Association of Petroleum Geologists)

African-American Book Distributors Inc, *subsidiary of* Path Press Inc

African American Islamic Institute, *distributed by* Fons Vitae

African Writers Series, *imprint of* Heinemann

Africana Publishing Co, *subsidiary of* Holmes & Meier Publishers Inc

Aftershocks Media, *division of* Epicenter Press Inc

Agape, *division of* Hope Publishing Co

Agathon Press, *imprint of* Algora Publishing

Agronomy Publications, *imprint of* Hobar Publications

Aguilar, *imprint of* Santillana USA Publishing Co Inc

AHA (American Hospital Association), *imprint of* Health Forum Inc

aha! Chinese, *distributed by* Cheng & Tsui Co Inc

Aha Communications, *distributed by* Gryphon House Inc

AHA Press, *subsidiary of* Health Forum Inc, *imprint of* Health Forum Inc

AHLP Books, *imprint of* Africana Homestead Legacy Publishers Inc

AHLP Communications, *imprint of* Africana Homestead Legacy Publishers Inc

The Ahmanson Foundation Humanities Endowment Fund, *imprint of* University of California Press

Ahmanson-Murphy, *imprint of* University of California Press

Ahsahta Press, *distributed by* Small Press Distribution

AICPA Professional Publications, *subsidiary of* American Institute of Certified Public Accountants, *distributor for* Wiley, *distributed by* CCH, Practitioners Publishing Co, Thomson Reuters

AIM (American Institute of Musicology), *distributed by* A-R Editions Inc

Keith Ainsworth Pty Ltd, Australia, *distributor for* Interweave Press LLC

Aircraft of the Aces, *imprint of* Osprey Publishing Inc

Airfile Publications, *distributed by* Casemate Publishers & Book Distributors LLC

Airmont, *distributed by* Perfection Learning Corp

Airphoto International Ltd/Odyssey Publications, *distributed by* W W Norton & Company Inc

AK Press, *distributed by* AK Press Distribution

AK Press Distribution, *subsidiary of* AK Press Inc, AK Press Inc, *distributor for* AK Press, Crimethinc, Freedom Press, Payback Press, Phoenix Press, Rebel Inc, Rebel Press

Akasha Ltd, *distributor for* Ash Tree Publishing

Aladdin Paperbacks, *imprint of* Simon & Schuster Children's Publishing

Editions Alain, *distributor for* Harry N Abrams Inc

Alamos Press, *imprint of* Park Place Publications

Alan Wofsy Fine Arts, *distributor for* Bora, Brusberg (Berlin), Cramer (Geneva), Huber, Ides et Calendes, Kornfeld & Co, Picasso Project, Welz, Wittenborn Art Books

Alaska Native Language Center, *division of* University of Alaska Fairbanks, *distributed by* University of Alaska Press

Alaska Northwest Books®, *imprint of* Graphic Arts Books

Alaska Quarterly Review, *distributed by* University of Alaska Press

Alaska Sea Grant, *distributed by* University of Alaska Press

Alaska Writer Laureate Series, *imprint of* University of Alaska Press

Alban Publishing, *division of* The Alban Institute Inc

Albany Institute of History & Art, *distributed by* Excelsior Editions, State University of New York Press

Albatross Publishing House, *distributed by* W W Norton & Company Inc

Albert Whitman & Co, *distributed by* Open Road

Alchemical Press, *imprint of* Holmes Publishing Group LLC

Aldine Transaction, *imprint of* Transaction Publishers Inc

Alen House, *distributor for* Syracuse University Press

Alexandrian Press, *imprint of* Holmes Publishing Group LLC

Alfaguara, *imprint of* Santillana USA Publishing Co Inc

Alfred Publications, *distributor for* Summy-Birchard Inc

Alfred Publishing Company Inc, *distributor for* Dover, Faber Music, Myklas Music Press, National Guitar Workshop

Algonquin Books of Chapel Hill, *division of* Workman Publishing Co Inc, *distributor for* Black Dog & Lenventhal, Fearless Critic Media, Greenwich Workshop Press, *distributed by* Workman Publishing Co Inc

Algonquin Young Readers, *imprint of* Algonquin Books of Chapel Hill

ALI-ABA, *distributor for* The Professional Education Group Inc (PEG), *distributed by* The Professional Education Group Inc (PEG)

ALI-ABA Continuing Professional Education, *affiliate of* American Bar Association & American Law Institute

Alibi, *imprint of* Random House Inc, Random House Publishing Group

Alice James Books, *division of* Alice James Poetry Cooperative Inc

Alive Guides, *imprint of* Hunter Publishing Inc

All-Romance Ebooks, *distributor for* Hard Shell Word Factory

Umberto Allemandi, *distributed by* Antique Collectors Club Ltd

J A Allen, *distributed by* Trafalgar Square Books

Thomas Allen & Son, *distributor for* Square One Publishers Inc, Timber Press Inc

Allmaps, *subsidiary of* Rand McNally

Alloy Entertainment, *division of* Alloy Online, *distributed by* Avon Books, HarperCollins, Hyperion, Little, Brown & Co, Penguin Group (USA) LLC, Random House Inc, Scholastic Books, Simon & Schuster

Allworth Press, *imprint of* Skyhorse Publishing Inc, *distributed by* W W Norton

Allyn & Bacon, *imprint of* Pearson Higher Education, *distributor for* National Association of Broadcasters (NAB)

Alma Edizioni, *distributed by* Delta Publishing Co

Alma Little, *imprint of* Elva Resa Publishing

Almont Books, *imprint of* Ingalls Publishing Group Inc (IPG)

Alpha, *imprint of* Penguin Group (USA) LLC

Alpha Books, *imprint of* Penguin Group (USA) LLC

Alpha Omega Publishing, *distributed by* Caxton Press

ALPHA Publications of America Inc, *affiliate of* Alpha Legal Forms & More

ALPS Publishing, *distributor for* Pieces of Learning

Alta Book Ctr, *distributor for* Teachers of English to Speakers of Other Languages Inc (TESOL)

AltaMira Press, *imprint of* Rowman & Littlefield Publishing Group, *distributor for* American Association for State & Local History

Alti Corp, *distributed by* Sunbelt Publications Inc

Alutiiq Museum, *distributed by* University of Alaska Press

Alva Press, *imprint of* Book Sales Inc

AM Press, *distributed by* Enfield Publishing & Distribution Co

AMA, *distributed by* Mel Bay Publications Inc

AMA Research, *distributed by* FurnitureCore

AMACOM Books, *division of* American Management Association, *distributor for* J J Keller & Associates, Inc, *distributed by* McGraw-Hill International, SAS Publishing

Amadeus Press, *imprint of* Hal Leonard Books, *distributed by* Hal Leonard Corp

Amadeus Press/Hal Leonard Performing Arts Publishing Group, *imprint of* Hal Leonard Performing Arts Publishing Group, Hal Leonard Performing Arts Publishing Group

Amaroma Ediciones, *distributed by* Sunbelt Publications Inc

Frank Amato Publications Inc, *distributed by* Angler's Book Supply

Amazing People Club, *distributed by* Hachette Book Group

Amazon.com, *distributor for* Eye in the Ear Children's Audio, Ozark Publishing Inc, Paladin Press

Amazon Kindle, *distributor for* Hard Shell Word Factory

Ambassador Books, *distributor for* Primary Research Group Inc

Amber-Allen Publishing, *imprint of* New World Library

Amber Allure, *imprint of* Amber Quill Press LLC

Amber Books, *distributed by* Casemate Publishers & Book Distributors LLC

Amber Heat, *imprint of* Amber Quill Press LLC

Amberley Publishing, *distributed by* Casemate Publishers & Book Distributors LLC

Amble Press, *imprint of* Bywater Books

AMC Discover Series, *imprint of* Appalachian Mountain Club Books

AMC Nature Walks Series, *imprint of* Appalachian Mountain Club Books

AMC Quiet Water Guides, *imprint of* Appalachian Mountain Club Books

AMC River Guides, *imprint of* Appalachian Mountain Club Books

AMC Trail Guides, *imprint of* Appalachian Mountain Club Books

America West Publishers, *subsidiary of* Global Insights Inc

American Academy for Park & Recreation Administration, *distributed by* Sagamore Publishing LLC

American Academy of Environmental Engineers, *distributor for* The ABS Group, CRC Press, McGraw-Hill, Pearson Education, Prentice Hall, John Wiley & Sons Inc

American Academy of Orthopaedic Surgeons, *distributed by* Jones & Bartlett Publishers

The American Alpine Club Press, *division of* The American Alpine Club, *distributed by* Mountaineers Books, The Mountaineers Books

American Anthropological Association (AAA), *distributed by* Wiley-Blackwell

American Antiquarian Society, *distributed by* Oak Knoll Press

American Association for Higher Education, *distributed by* Stylus Publishing LLC

American Association for State & Local History, *distributed by* AltaMira Press

American Association for Vocational Instructional Materials, *distributor for* Southeastern Cooperative Wildlife Disease Study

American Association of Blood Banks, *distributed by* Karger

American Association of State Highway & Transportation Officials, *distributed by* Professional Publications Inc (PPI)

American Bar Association, *distributor for* The Professional Education Group Inc (PEG), *distributed by* The Professional Education Group Inc (PEG)

American Biographical Institute, *division of* Historical Preservations of America Inc, Historical Preservations of America Inc

American Book Business Press, *imprint of* American Book Publishing

American Book Classics, *imprint of* American Book Publishing

American Carriage House Publishing, *distributed by* Faith Works Books

American Ceramic Society (ACerS), *distributor for* American Society for Nondestructive Testing

American Chamber of Commerce to the European Union, *distributed by* The Brookings Institution Press

The American Chemical Society, *distributor for* Royal Society of Chemistry, *distributed by* Oxford University Press, Oxford University Press USA

American College of Healthcare Executives Management Series, *imprint of* Health Administration Press

American College of Surgeons, *distributed by* Cine-Med Inc, Scientific American Medicine

American Council for an Energy Efficient Economy (ACEEE), *distributed by* Chelsea Green Publishing Co

American Council on Education, *distributed by* Rowman & Littlefield

American Counseling Association, *distributor for* Association for Assessment in Counseling & Education, Association for Counselor Education & Supervision, *distributed by* Counseling Outfitters, Mental Health Resources, Paperbacks for Educators, ProEd, Self-Esteem Shop, Social Sciences School Services

American Diabetes Association, *distributed by* Publishers Group West

American Dust Publications, *distributed by* Dustbooks

American Express, *distributed by* Charlesbridge Publishing Inc

American Federation of Arts, *distributed by* Harry N Abrams Inc, Distributed Art Publishers, Hudson Hills Press Inc, Scala Publishers, University of Washington Press, Yale University Press

American Food History, *imprint of* R J Berg Publisher

American Geological Institute (AGI), *distributed by* W H Freeman, It's About Time Inc, Prentice Hall

American Girl Library®, *imprint of* American Girl Publishing

American Girl Publishing, *subsidiary of* Mattel

The American Girls Collection®, *imprint of* American Girl Publishing

American Guidance Service, *distributed by* Psychological Assessment Resources Inc (PAR)

American Heritage Dictionary, *imprint of* Houghton Mifflin Harcourt Trade & Reference Division

American Historical Association, *affiliate of* Historians Film Committee

American History Series, *imprint of* Harlan Davidson Inc/Forum Press Inc

American Institute of Chemical Engineers (AIChE), *distributor for* ASM International (selected titles), Dechema (selected titles), Engineering Foundation, IchemE (selected titles), *distributed by* Dechema (selected titles)

American Institute of Physics, *distributed by* Springer-Verlag

American Institute of Physics (AIP), *distributor for* The Electrochemical Society (ECS)

American-Israeli Cooperative, *distributed by* Jonathan David Publishers Inc

American Library Preview, *division of* Gareth Stevens Publishing

American Map Corp, *subsidiary of* Langenscheidt Publishers Group, *distributor for* De Lorme Atlas, Langenscheidt Publishers Group, RV Guides, Stubs Magazine, *distributed by* Arrow Maps Inc, Creative Sales Corp, Hagstrom Map & Travel Center

American Maritain Association, *distributed by* The Catholic University of America Press

American Maritime Library, *imprint of* Mystic Seaport Museum Inc

American Marketing Association, *division of* Health Services Marketing Division

American Mathematical Society, *distributor for* Annales de la faculte des sciences de Toulouse mathematiques, Bar-Ilan University, Brown University, European Mathematical Society, Hindustan Book Agency, Independent University of Moscow, International Press, Mathematica Josephina, Mathematical Society of Japan, Narosa Publishing House, Ramanujan Mathematical Society, Science Press New York & Science Press Beijing, Societe Mathematique de France, Tata Institute of Fundamental Research, Theta Foundation of Bucharest, University Press, Vieweg Verlag Publications

American Medical Association, *distributor for* OptumInsight™, *distributed by* Medical Group Management Association (MGMA), OptumInsight™

American Milestones, *imprint of* Gallopade International Inc

American Philosophical Society, *distributed by* Diane Publishing Co

American Poetry Review/Honickman, *distributed by* Copper Canyon Press

American Press, *subsidiary of* American Magazine

American Products Publishing Co, *division of* American Products Corp

American Psychiatric Association (APA), *imprint of* American Psychiatric Publishing (APP), *distributed by* American Psychiatric Publishing (APP)

American Psychiatric Publishing (APP), *division of* American Psychiatric Association (APA), *imprint of* American Psychiatric Publishing (APP), *distributor for* American Psychiatric Association (APA), Group for the Advancement of Psychiatry

American Psychology Press, *distributor for* Current Medicine Group (CMG)

American School of Classical Studies at Athens, *imprint of* ASCSA Publications

American Society for Mechanical Engineers (ASME), *distributor for* American Society for Nondestructive Testing

American Society for Metals (ASM), *distributor for* American Society for Nondestructive Testing

American Society for Nondestructive Testing, *distributed by* American Ceramic Society (ACerS), American Society for Mechanical Engineers (ASME), American Society for Metals (ASM), The American Welding Society (AWS), ASTM, Edison Welding Institute, Mean Free Path

American Society for Quality (ASQ), *distributed by* GOAL/QPC, IEEE Computer Society Press, McGraw-Hill Professional Publishing, Productivity Press

American Society for Training & Development (ASTD), *distributed by* Cengage Learning Asia Pte Ltd (Asia), Eurospan Group (Europe, Middle East & the former Soviet Bloc), Knowledge Resources (South Africa), National Book Network (NBN) (US, CN, Australia & New Zealand)

American Society of Association Executives, *distributor for* BoardSource

American Sports Publishing, *imprint of* Athletic Guide Publishing

American Swedish Historical Museum, *distributed by* Diane Publishing Co

American Technical Publishers Inc, *distributor for* Craftsman Book Co, Society of Manufacturing Engineers

American University & Colleges Press, *imprint of* American Book Publishing

American University in Cairo, *distributed by* Oxford University Press USA

American Water Works Association, *distributor for* CRC Press, McGraw-Hill, John Wiley & Sons

The American Welding Society (AWS), *distributor for* American Society for Nondestructive Testing

American Wood Council (American Forest & Paper Association), *distributed by* Professional Publications Inc (PPI)

AmericanKids Preview, *division of* Gareth Stevens Publishing

The Americas Review, *subsidiary of* Arte Publico Press

Amerotica, *imprint of* NBM Publishing Inc

Amherst Media Inc, *distributor for* Firefly

Amigos de Bolsa Chica, *distributed by* Sunbelt Publications Inc

Amistad, *imprint of* HarperCollins Children's Books, HarperCollins General Books Group, HarperCollins Publishers Sales

Amphoto Books, *imprint of* Crown Publishing Group

AMS, *distributor for* International Press of Boston Inc

Amulet Books, *imprint of* Harry N Abrams Inc

Anacus Press, *imprint of* Finney Company Inc

Ananda Ashrama, *distributed by* Vedanta Press

Anaphora Literary Press, *distributed by* Coutts Information Services, Lightning Source

Ancestry, *imprint of* Turner Publishing Co

Anchor Bible Commentary, *imprint of* Random House Inc

Anchor Bible Dictionary, *imprint of* Random House Inc

Anchor Bible Reference Library, *imprint of* Random House Inc

Anchor Books, *imprint of* Random House Inc, Vintage & Anchor Books

Anchor Distributors, *distributor for* Pentecostal Publishing House

Anchorage Museum Association, *distributed by* University of Alaska Press

Anchorage Museum of Art History, *distributed by* University of Alaska Press

Anchors Away, *distributed by* Winters Publishing

Ancient City Press, *imprint of* Gibbs Smith Publisher

And/Or Books, *imprint of* Ronin Publishing Inc

Andersen Press USA, *distributed by* Lerner Publishing Group Inc

Anderson Design, *distributed by* Borderline Publishing

Anderson Distribution, *distributor for* Ballinger Publishing

Andrews McMeel Publishing LLC, *division of* Andrews McMeel Universal, *distributor for* Gooseberry Patch (North America), Signatures Network, Sporting News, Universe Publishing Calendars, *distributed by* Simon & Schuster, Inc, Simon & Schuster Sales & Marketing

Andrews University Press, *division of* Andrews University

Ane Books, *distributor for* HRD Press

Angel Books, *distributed by* Dufour Editions Inc

Angel City Press, *distributor for* Los Angeles Times Books

Angelus Press, *distributed by* Catholic Treasures, Fatima Crusader

Angler's Book Supply, *distributor for* Frank Amato Publications Inc, Wilderness Adventures Press Inc

Anglican Book Centre, *distributed by* Forward Movement Publications

Angry Robot, *imprint of* Osprey Publishing Inc

Ann Arbor Paperbacks, *imprint of* University of Michigan Press

Annales de la faculte des sciences de Toulouse mathematiques, *distributed by* American Mathematical Society

Annick Press, *distributed by* Perfection Learning Corp

Annotation Press, *imprint of* WinePress Publishing

Anomaly Press, *distributed by* Chelsea Green Publishing Co

Another Great Achiever Series, *imprint of* Advance Publishing Inc

Anqa Press, *distributed by* Fons Vitae

ANR Publications University of California, *division of* Agriculture & Natural Resources, University of California

Antinous Press, *distributed by* powerHouse Books

Antique Collectors Club Ltd, *division of* Antique Collectors Club Ltd (England), Antique Collectors Club Ltd (England), *distributor for* Acatos, Adler Planetarium & Astronomy, Umberto Allemandi, Architectura & Natura, Arnoldsche, Arsenale Editrice, Artprice.com, Bard Graduate Center, Barn Elms Publishing, Beagle Press, Chris Beetles Ltd, Benteli Verlag, Birmingham Museum of Art, Brioni Books, British Museum Press, Canal & Stamperia, Cartago, Colonial Williamsburg, Colophon, Colwood Press Ltd, The William G Congdon Foundation, Conran Octopus, Alain De Gourcuff Editeur, M H De Young Memorial Museum, Detroit Institute of Arts, Editoriale Jaca Book, Elvehjem Museum of Art, Gambero Rosso, Grayson Publishing, Hachette Livre, Robert Hale, Han-Shan Tang Books, Alan Hartman, High Museum of Art, Images Publications, India Book House Ltd, Frances Lincoln, Loft Publications, Mapin, Marshall Editions, Merrick & Day, Museum of American Folk Art, National Galleries of Scotland, National Portrait Gallery, The National Trust, New Architecture Group Ltd, New Cavendish Books Ltd, Newark Museum, Packard Publishing, Peabody Essex Museum, Philadelphia Museum of Art, River Books Co Ltd, Michael Russell, Scala Publishers, Superbrands Ltd, Third Millenium Publishing, Wadsworth Athenaeum, Wallace Collection, Watermark Press, Websters International Publishers, Philip Wilson Publishers

Antique Collectors' Club Ltd, *distributor for* George Braziller Inc

Antique Trader Books, *imprint of* F+W Media Inc, Krause Publications Inc

Coleccion Antologia Personal, *imprint of* University of Puerto Rico Press

Anvil Series, *imprint of* Krieger Publishing Co

Anza-Borrego Foundation, *distributed by* Sunbelt Publications Inc

AOCS Press, *division of* American Oil Chemists' Society

Aonian Press, *imprint of* James A Rock & Co Publishers

APA Planners Press, *division of* American Planning Association

Aperture, *distributed by* Fons Vitae

Aperture Books, *division of* Aperture Foundation Inc, *distributed by* Farrar, Straus & Giroux Inc

Aperture Monographs, *imprint of* Aperture Books

The Apex Press, *imprint of* Rowman & Littlefield Publishers Inc, Rowman & Littlefield Publishing Group, *distributor for* Bootstrap Press (US), The Other India Press (India)

Aphrodisia, *imprint of* Kensington Publishing Corp

Apollo Managed Care Inc, *distributed by* Health Information Network, MarketResearch.com, Researchandmarkets.com

Appalachian, *distributor for* Faith Library Publications

Appalachian Bible Co Inc, *distributor for* BJU Press

Appalachian Mountain Club, *distributed by* The Globe Pequot Press

Appalachian Mountain Club Books, *division of* Appalachian Mountain Club, *distributed by* The Globe Pequot Press

Appell Publishing, *distributed by* Epicenter Press Inc

Applause Theatre & Cinema Books, *imprint of* Hal Leonard Books, Hal Leonard Performing Arts Publishing Group, Hal Leonard Performing Arts Publishing Group, *distributor for* The Working Arts Library, Glenn Young Books, *distributed by* Hal Leonard Corp, Hal Leonard Corp

Apple, *distributor for* Ozark Publishing Inc

Apple iBookStore, *distributor for* Hard Shell Word Factory

Applesauce Press, *imprint of* Cider Mill Press Book Publishers LLC, *distributed by* Simon & Schuster Sales & Marketing

Appleton Davies, *imprint of* Davies Publishing Inc

Appleton Lange, *distributor for* Current Medicine Group (CMG)

Appraisal Institute, *distributed by* Dearborn Trade

Apress, *imprint of* Springer

Apress Media LLC, *subsidiary of* Springer Science+Business Media, Springer Science+Business Media LLC

APS PRESS, *imprint of* American Phytopathological Society (APS)

AQS, *imprint of* American Quilter's Society

Coleccion Aqui y Ahora, *imprint of* University of Puerto Rico Press

Arba Sicula, *distributed by* Cross-Cultural Communications

ARC (Magazine & Press), *imprint of* Cross-Cultural Communications

Arcade Publishing Inc, *imprint of* Skyhorse Publishing Inc, *distributed by* W W Norton & Company Inc

Arcadia Books (London), *distributed by* Dufour Editions Inc

Arcadia Publishing Inc, *imprint of* Tempus Publishing Group

Arcana Publishing, *imprint of* Lotus Press

Arcane, *imprint of* Zumaya Publications LLC

Archetype, *distributed by* Fons Vitae

Architectura & Natura, *distributed by* Antique Collectors Club Ltd

Archival, *distributed by* Donald M Grant Publisher Inc

Archway, *distributed by* Perfection Learning Corp

Arctic Studies Center of the Smithsonian Museum, *distributed by* University of Alaska Press

Arcturus Publishing, *imprint of* Black Rabbit Books

Arcturus Publishing Ltd, *distributor for* Big Guy Books Inc

Ardent Media Inc, *distributor for* Cyrco Press, Irvington Publishers, MSS Information Corp

Ardenwood Books, *imprint of* Bay Tree Publishing LLC

Ardis Russian Literature, *imprint of* The Overlook Press

ARE Press, *division of* The Association for Research & Enlightenment Inc (ARE), The Association for Research & Enlightenment Inc (ARE)

Ariel Press, *subsidiary of* Light, *distributor for* Enthea, Kudzu House

The Arion Press, *division of* Lyra Corp

Arkangel, *distributed by* Penguin Group (USA) LLC, Putnam Berkley Audio

Arkangel Complete Shakespeare, *distributed by* Penguin Audiobooks

Arktoi Books, *imprint of* Red Hen Press

Armchair Sailor Books & Charts, *distributor for* Marine Techniques Publishing

Eric Armin Inc Education Ctr, *distributor for* National Council of Teachers of Mathematics (NCTM)

The Army War College Foundation Press, *distributed by* Stackpole Books

Arnoldsche, *distributed by* Antique Collectors Club Ltd

ARO Publishing Co, *distributed by* Barnes & Noble, Follett, Gumdrop Books

Jason Aronson Inc, *imprint of* Rowman & Littlefield Publishing Group

Arrow Maps Inc, *subsidiary of* American Map Corp, *distributor for* American Map Corp, *distributed by* Hagstrom Map & Travel Center

Arsenale Editrice, *distributed by* Antique Collectors Club Ltd

ARSIS Audio, *imprint of* ECS Publishing Corp

Arsis Press, *imprint of* Empire Publishing Service, *distributed by* Empire Publishing Service

Art Books/D A P, *distributor for* MFA Publications

Art Image Publications, *division of* GB Publishing Inc

The Art Institute of Chicago, *distributed by* Yale University Press

Art Media Resources Inc, *distributor for* Serindia Publications

Art Scroll Series, *imprint of* Mesorah Publications Ltd

art-SITES, *distributed by* University of California Press

Art Treasures, *imprint of* Branden Books

Artabras, *imprint of* Abbeville Publishing Group

ArtAge Publications, *distributor for* Heinemann, Hal Leonard

Arte Publico Press, *affiliate of* University of Houston, *distributor for* Bilingual Review Press, Latin American Review Press, *distributed by* Empire Publishing Service

Artech House Inc, *subsidiary of* Horizon House Publications Inc, Horizon House Publications Inc

Artemis Books, *imprint of* Gateways Books & Tapes

Arthritis Research, *imprint of* Progressive Press

Arthur A Levine Books, *imprint of* Scholastic Trade Division

Artisan, *division of* Workman Publishing Co Inc, *imprint of* Algonquin Books of Chapel Hill

Artisan Books, *division of* Workman Publishing Co Inc, *distributor for* Greenwich Workshop Press

Artistpro, *distributed by* Hal Leonard Corp

Artprice.com, *distributed by* Antique Collectors Club Ltd

ArtWorks, *imprint of* MFA Publications

ASAE, *distributed by* Water Resources Publications LLC

Asante®, *imprint of* Peoples Education Inc

Francis Asbury Press, *imprint of* Evangel Publishing House

ASCA, *distributor for* MAR*CO Products Inc

ASCE, *distributed by* Water Resources Publications LLC

ASCE Press, *imprint of* American Society of Civil Engineers (ASCE)

Ascension Press, *member of* Catholic Word

ASCP Press, *subsidiary of* American Society for Clinical Pathology

Ash Tree Publishing, *distributor for* Ash Tree Publishing, *distributed by* Akasha Ltd, Ash Tree Publishing, Jocelyn Davies, Dempsey Your Distributor, New Leaf, Nutri-Books, Partners, The Tao of Books, VisionWorks

Ashgate, *imprint of* Ashgate Publishing Co, *distributed by* William S Hein & Co Inc

Ashgate Publishing Co, *subsidiary of* Ashgate Publishing Ltd, *distributor for* Pickering & Chatto

Ashland Creek Press, *imprint of* Ashland Creek Press

Ashland Poetry Press, *affiliate of* Ashland University

Ashley Music, *distributed by* Hal Leonard Corp

ASI Books, *imprint of* Information Today, Inc

Asia Pacific Research Center, *distributed by* The Brookings Institution Press

Asian Humanities Press, *imprint of* Jain Publishing Co

AsiaPac, *distributed by* China Books

ASIS&T Monograph Series, *imprint of* Information Today, Inc

ASL, *distributed by* Copywriter's Council of America (CCA)

Aslan Publishing, *division of* Renaissance Book Services Corp

ASM International, *distributed by* American Institute of Chemical Engineers (AIChE), NACE International

ASM Press, *division of* American Society for Microbiology

ASME Press, *imprint of* American Society of Mechanical Engineers (ASME)

Aspatore Books, *division of* Thomson Reuters

Aspatore Thought Leadership, *imprint of* Aspatore Books

ASPEN, *distributed by* William S Hein & Co Inc, The Professional Education Group Inc (PEG)

Aspen Publishers, *distributed by* Medical Group Management Association (MGMA)

Aspen Publishers Incorporated, *imprint of* Wolters Kluwer US Corp

Aspire, *distributed by* Delmar

Assessment, *division of* Scholastic Education

Associated Publishers Group, *distributor for* Green Sugar Press

Associated University Presses, *distributor for* Herzl Press, Susquehanna University Press

Association for Assessment in Counseling & Education, *distributed by* American Counseling Association

Association for Counselor Education & Supervision, *distributed by* American Counseling Association

Association for Gravestone Studies, *distributed by* The Center for Thanatology Research & Education Inc

Association for Information Science & Technology (ASIS&T), *distributed by* Information Today Inc, John Wiley & Sons Inc

Association of College & Research Libraries (ACRL), *division of* The American Library Association, The American Library Association (ALA)

ASTD Press, *imprint of* American Society for Training & Development (ASTD)

ASTM, *distributor for* American Society for Nondestructive Testing, *distributed by* NACE International

Astragal Press, *imprint of* Finney Company Inc

Astronautical Society of Western Australia, *distributed by* Univelt Inc

ASVP, *imprint of* Elsevier, Health Sciences Division

Asylum Arts Press, *imprint of* Leaping Dog Press/Asylum Arts Press

At a Glance, *distributor for* The Jim Henson Co

At Home on the Road, *imprint of* Park Place Publications

Ateneo De Manila University Press, *distributed by* University of Hawaii Press

Atheneum, *distributed by* Perfection Learning Corp

Atheneum Books for Young Readers, *imprint of* Simon & Schuster Children's Publishing

The Atkinson Family Imprint, *imprint of* University of California Press

Atlantic Boating Almanac, *imprint of* ProStar Publications Inc

Atlantic Books, *distributed by* Trafalgar Square Books

Atlantic Books Ltd, *imprint of* Grove/Atlantic Inc

Atlantic Council, *distributed by* University Press of America Inc

Atlantic Law Book Co, *division of* Peter Kelsey Publishing Inc, Peter Kelsey Publishing Inc

Atlantic Monthly Press, *imprint of* Grove/Atlantic Inc

Atlantic University, *division of* ARE Press

Atlas & Co, *distributed by* W W Norton & Company Inc

Atlas Games, *imprint of* Trident Inc

AtRandom.com, *imprint of* Random House Inc

Atria Books, *imprint of* Atria Publishing Group

Atria Trade Paperback, *imprint of* Atria Books

Attara, *distributed by* Hachai Publishing

Attic Press, *distributed by* Dufour Editions Inc

@tlas®, *imprint of* VanDam Inc

Audel™, *imprint of* John Wiley & Sons Inc

Audio Adventures, *distributor for* Eye in the Ear Children's Audio

Audio Books, *division of* Unarius Academy of Science Publications

Audio Bookshelf, *imprint of* AudioGO

AudioGO, *subsidiary of* AudioGO Ltd

Audioworks, *imprint of* Simon & Schuster Audio

Augsburg Books, *imprint of* Augsburg Fortress Publishers, Publishing House of the Evangelical Lutheran Church in America

August House Audio, *imprint of* August House Inc

August House LittleFolk, *imprint of* August House Inc

Augustinian Press, *distributed by* Diane Publishing Co

AUPHA Press/Health Administration Press, *imprint of* Health Administration Press

Aura Imaging, *imprint of* Blue Dolphin Publishing Inc

Aurora Metro Publications, *distributed by* Theatre Communications Group

Aurum Press, *distributed by* Quayside Publishing Group

Ausable Press, *imprint of* Copper Canyon Press

Stephen F Austin State University Press, *distributed by* Texas A&M University Press

Australasian Corrosion Association, *distributor for* NACE International

Auteur Books, *distributed by* Columbia University Press

AuthorHouse, *division of* Author Solutions Inc

Authorlink Press, *imprint of* Authorlink®

Authors, *imprint of* University of California Press

Autodata, *distributed by* Delmar

Autodesk Press, *imprint of* Delmar

Avalon House, *distributed by* Chelsea Green Publishing Co

Avalon Travel, *imprint of* The Perseus Books Group

Avalon Travel Publishing, *member of* The Perseus Books Group, *distributed by* Publishers Group West

Avamra Institute, *distributed by* Moznaim Publishing Corp

Avant-Guide, *imprint of* Empire Press Media/Avant-Guide

Avanyu Publishing, *distributed by* University of New Mexico

Avatar Press, *distributed by* Simon & Schuster, Inc, Simon & Schuster Sales & Marketing

Avery, *imprint of* Penguin Group (USA) LLC, Penguin Group (USA) LLC, The Putnam Publishing Group

Avery Color Studios, *distributed by* Partners Book Distributing

Aviation Elite Units, *imprint of* Osprey Publishing Inc

AVKO Educational Research Foundation Inc, *division of* AVKO Foundation

Avon, *imprint of* HarperCollins General Books Group

Avon Books, *imprint of* HarperCollins Publishers Sales, *distributor for* Alloy Entertainment

Avon Impulse, *imprint of* HarperCollins General Books Group

Avon Inspire, *imprint of* HarperCollins General Books Group

Avon Red, *imprint of* HarperCollins General Books Group

Awe-Struck, *imprint of* Mundania Press LLC

Awe-Struck Publishing, *imprint of* Mundania Press LLC

AWS, *distributed by* NACE International

AWWA, *imprint of* American Water Works Association

Artes Monte Azul, *imprint of* Blue Mountain Arts Inc

Back Bay Books, *imprint of* Little, Brown and Company

Back to Eden Books, *distributed by* Lotus Press

Backbeat Books, *imprint of* Hal Leonard Books, Hal Leonard Performing Arts Publishing Group, *distributed by* Hal Leonard Corp

Backcountry Guides, *imprint of* The Countryman Press

Backcountry Publications, *imprint of* W W Norton & Company Inc

Backlist LLC, *distributed by* Simon & Schuster, Inc

BADM Books, *distributed by* Father & Son Publishing Inc

Baen Books, *distributed by* Simon & Schuster, Inc, Simon & Schuster Sales & Marketing

Baen Publishing Enterprises, *distributed by* Simon & Schuster

Bagwyn Books, *imprint of* Arizona Center for Medieval & Renaissance Studies (ACMRS)

Baha'i Publishing, *subsidiary of* The National Spiritual Assembly of the Baha'is of the United States, The National Spiritual Assembly of the Baha'is of the United States

BainBridgeBooks, *imprint of* Trans-Atlantic Publications Inc

Duncan Baird, *distributed by* Sterling Publishing Co Inc

Baker Books, *division of* Baker Publishing Group, *distributor for* Focus on the Family, *distributed by* Perfection Learning Corp

Baker, Lyman & Co, *distributor for* Marine Techniques Publishing

Baker's Play, *division of* Samuel French Inc

Baker's Plays, *division of* Samuel French Inc, *distributor for* Samuel French Inc, *distributed by* Samuel French Inc

Balboa Press, *division of* Hay House Inc

Balcony Press, *distributed by* Princeton Architectural Press

Baldar, *imprint of* Ross Books

Ball Publishing, *imprint of* Chicago Review Press

Ballantine, *distributed by* Perfection Learning Corp

Ballantine Books, *imprint of* Random House Inc, Random House Publishing Group

Ballantine Wellspring, *imprint of* Random House Inc

Ballinger Publishing, *distributed by* Anderson Distribution, Media Solutions

Balzer & Bray, *imprint of* HarperCollins Children's Books

Bancroft-Sage Publishing, *imprint of* Finney Company Inc

B&H Publishing Group, *division of* LifeWay Christian Resources

Bandit Books, *distributed by* John F Blair Publisher

B&N.com, *distributor for* Hard Shell Word Factory

Banned Books, *imprint of* Progressive Press

Bantam, *distributor for* Parachute Publishing LLC, *distributed by* ADD Warehouse, Perfection Learning Corp

Bantam Books, *imprint of* Random House Inc, Random House Publishing Group

Bantam Hardcover, *imprint of* Random House Inc

Bantam Mass Market, *imprint of* Random House Inc

Bantam Skylark, *imprint of* Random House Inc

Bantam Starfire, *imprint of* Random House Inc

Bantam Trade Paperback, *imprint of* Random House Inc

Banyan Tree, *distributor for* Bella Books

Bar Ilan, *distributed by* Gefen Books

Bar-Ilan University, *distributed by* American Mathematical Society

Barbary Coast Books, *subsidiary of* Berkeley Slavic Specialties

Barbour Books, *imprint of* Barbour Publishing Inc

Barcelona Publishers, *distributed by* Pathway Books

Barclay Creek Press, *distributed by* Stackpole Books

Bard Graduate Center, *distributed by* Antique Collectors Club Ltd

The Bard Graduate Center, *distributed by* Yale University Press

Barn Elms Publishing, *distributed by* Antique Collectors Club Ltd

BarnaBooks, *imprint of* Tyndale House Publishers Inc

Barnes & Noble, *distributor for* ARO Publishing Co, Ozark Publishing Inc, Paladin Press

Barnes & Noble Classics, *imprint of* Fine Communications

Barricade Books, *imprint of* Barricade Books Inc

Barringer, *distributor for* Marriage Transformation LLC

Barringer Publishing, *division of* Schlesinger Advertising & Marketing

Barron's, *distributed by* Delta Publishing Co

Barrons, *distributed by* Perfection Learning Corp

Bartleby Press, *subsidiary of* Jackson Westgate Inc, *distributor for* BJE Press

Basch, *distributor for* Business Research Services Inc

Baseball America, *distributed by* Simon & Schuster, Inc, Simon & Schuster Sales & Marketing

Basic Books, *imprint of* The Perseus Books Group, *distributor for* Nevraumont Publishing Co, *distributed by* CDS Distributors, HarperCollins Publishers

Basic Civitas, *imprint of* Basic Books

Basic Civitas Books, *imprint of* The Perseus Books Group

Basic Health Guides, *imprint of* Basic Health Publications Inc

Basic Health Publications, *imprint of* Basic Health Publications Inc

Basic/Not Boring K-8 Grades, *imprint of* Incentive Publications Inc

Randol Bass Music, *distributed by* ECS Publishing Corp

Bat Conservation International, *distributed by* University of Texas Press

David Bateman Ltd, *distributor for* Price World Publishing LLC

David Bateman Ltd, New Zealand, *distributor for* Interweave Press LLC

Batsford, *distributed by* Sterling Publishing Co Inc

Battle Orders, *imprint of* Osprey Publishing Inc

Bay Tree Books, *imprint of* Heyday Books

Bayard, *distributed by* Crabtree Publishing Co

Bayard/Novalis, *distributor for* GemStone Press

Baylor University Press, *distributed by* The Johns Hopkins University Press, Johns Hopkins University Press Fullfillment Service

BBC Audio, *imprint of* AudioGO

BBC Audiobooks America, *distributor for* Macmillan Audio

BBC Radio, *imprint of* AudioGO

BCH Fulfillment & Distribution, *distributor for* The Lentz Leadership Institute

BDD Audio Publishing, *imprint of* Random House Inc

Beach Lane Books, *imprint of* Simon & Schuster Children's Publishing

Beach Lloyd Publishers LLC, *distributor for* Le Chambon-sur-Lignon, CIDEB (Italy), Deanne Scherlis Comer (DVDs), Ellipses (Paris), Fondation pour la Memoire de la Shoah (Paris), Kar-Ben Publishing, Kiron Editions du Felin (Paris), JP Lattes (Paris), Le Manuscrit (Paris), Oxford University Press (NYC), *distributed by* Tralco (CN)

BeachHouse Books, *imprint of* Science & Humanities Press

Beacon Hill Press of Kansas City, *subsidiary of* Nazarene Publishing House

Beacon Music, *distributed by* Hal Leonard Corp

Beacon Press, *distributed by* Random House Publisher Services

Beagle Press, *distributed by* Antique Collectors Club Ltd

Bear & Co, *imprint of* Bear & Co Inc, Inner Traditions International Ltd

Bear & Co Inc, *subsidiary of* Inner Traditions International Ltd

Bear Cub Books, *imprint of* Bear & Co Inc, Inner Traditions International Ltd

Bear Meadows Research Group, *imprint of* Crumb Elbow Publishing

Beard Books Inc, *member of* Beard Group Inc

Beautiful Books, *distributed by* Trafalgar Square Books

Beauxarts, *imprint of* Alan Wofsy Fine Arts

Mitchell Beazley, *distributed by* Phaidon Press Inc

Bebop Books, *imprint of* Lee & Low Books Inc

The Stephen Bechtel Fund, *imprint of* University of California Press

Bedford, Freeman & Worth Publishing Group, LLC, *subsidiary of* Macmillan

Bedford/St Martin's, *division of* Bedford, Freeman & Worth Publishing Group, LLC, *member of* Bedford, Freeman & Worth Publishing Group, LLC

Bedside Books, *imprint of* American Book Publishing

Beech River Books, *distributed by* Enfield Publishing & Distribution Co

Beech Tree Books, *imprint of* HarperCollins Publishers

Beekman Books Inc, *distributor for* Chartered Institute for Personnel Development (CIPD), C W Daniel, Gomer Press, Music Sales Corp, Kogan Page

Chris Beetles Ltd, *distributed by* Antique Collectors Club Ltd

Begell-Atom LLC, *subsidiary of* Begell House Inc Publishers

Beginner Books, *imprint of* Random House Children's Books

Behrman House Inc, *distributor for* Rossel Books

Beinecke Rare Book & Manuscript Library, *distributed by* University Press of New England

Belknap Press, *imprint of* Harvard University Press

Bell Bridge Books, *imprint of* BelleBooks

Bell Pond Books, *imprint of* SteinerBooks

Bell Tower, *imprint of* Random House Inc

Bella Books, *distributed by* Banyan Tree, Turnaround (London)

Belle Isle Books, *imprint of* Brandylane Publishers Inc

Benchmark Maps, *distributed by* Wide World of Maps Inc

Benchmark Press, *imprint of* Triumph Books

Bendon, *distributor for* Parachute Publishing LLC

Bene Factum Publishing, *distributed by* Trafalgar Square Books

John Benjamins North America Inc, *subsidiary of* John Benjamins Publishing Co

Benteli Verlag, *distributed by* Antique Collectors Club Ltd

Bentley Publishers, *division of* Robert Bentley Inc, Robert Bentley Inc

BePuzzled, *division of* University Games

Berg Publishers, *distributed by* Palgrave Macmillan, St Martin's Press, LLC

W H Berger, *distributed by* Sunbelt Publications Inc

Berghahn Books, *affiliate of* Berghahn Books Ltd (UK), *distributor for* Social Science Press, Yad Vashem

Berghahn Books Ltd (UK), *division of* Berghahn Books

Berklee Press, *imprint of* Hal Leonard Corp, *distributed by* Hal Leonard Corp

Berkley, *distributor for* Parachute Publishing LLC, *distributed by* Perfection Learning Corp

Berkley Books, *imprint of* Berkley Publishing Group, Penguin Group (USA) LLC, Penguin Group (USA) LLC

Berkley Publishing Group, *division of* Penguin Group (USA) LLC

Bernan, *imprint of* Rowman & Littlefield Publishing Group

Bertelsmann Foundation Publishers, *distributed by* The Brookings Institution Press

Bertrams UK, *distributor for* Dissertation.com

Bess Press, *distributed by* The Islander Group (TIG) (Hawaii wholesaler/book dist)

Best Books International, *subsidiary of* Empire Publishing Service

Best Guides LLC, *distributed by* Sunbelt Publications Inc

Best Places® Guidebooks Series, *imprint of* Sasquatch Books

Best Publishing Co, *distributed by* Marine Techniques Publishing

Emily Bestler Books, *imprint of* Atria Books

Bethany House Publishers, *division of* Baker Publishing Group

Bethel Publishing, *imprint of* Evangel Publishing House, *distributed by* Evangel Publishing House

Bethlehem Books, *affiliate of* Bethlehem Community, *distributed by* Ignatius Press

Betterway Books, *imprint of* F+W Media Inc, F+W Media Inc

Betty Crocker®, *imprint of* Houghton Mifflin Harcourt Trade & Reference Division

Between the Lines, *distributed by* Dufour Editions Inc

Beverly Foundation, *distributed by* Hartman Publishing Inc

Beyond Words, *imprint of* Atria Books, Simon & Schuster Audio

Beyond Words Publishing Inc, *affiliate of* Simon & Schuster, *distributed by* Simon & Schuster

Bibli O'Phile, *distributed by* Penguin Group (USA) LLC

Biblio, *distributor for* UNO Press, *distributed by* Bloch Publishing Co

Bibliographical Society of America, *distributed by* Oak Knoll Press

Bibliographical Society of University of Virginia, *distributed by* Oak Knoll Press

The Bibliographical Society (UK), *distributed by* Oak Knoll Press

Bibliopola Press, *distributed by* University Press of New England

Biblo, *imprint of* Biblo-Moser

Biblo-Tannen, *imprint of* Biblo-Moser

Bider Technology, *distributed by* Cheng & Tsui Co Inc

Big Apple Vision Publishing Inc, *imprint of* Big Apple Vision Books

Big Buddy Books, *imprint of* ABDO Publishing Group

Big Guy Books Inc, *distributed by* Arcturus Publishing Ltd (United Kingdom), Bookwise International (Australia), Independent Publishers Group (handles all Trade Distribution in the US), Scholastic New Zealand (New Zealand), Iwasaki Shoten (Japanese Translation)

Big Meteor, *distributed by* Omnibus Press

Big Meteor Publishing, *distributed by* Schirmer Trade Books

Big Sky Maps, *distributed by* Wide World of Maps Inc

Big Tree Books, *imprint of* Easy Money Press

Bigwig Briefs, *imprint of* Aspatore Books

Bilingual Review Press, *distributed by* Arte Publico Press

Bilingual Review Press/Editorial Bilingue, *distributor for* Dos Pasos Editores, Lalo Press, Latin American Literary Review Press, Maize Press, Trinity University Press, Waterfront Press (selected titles from all)

Binational Press, *imprint of* San Diego State University Press

Bindu Books, *imprint of* Inner Traditions International Ltd

A Bio To Grow On, *imprint of* Gallopade International Inc

Biographical Publishing Co, *distributor for* Eagles Landing Publishing, Spyglass Books LLC

Biological Diversity Handbook Series, *distributed by* Smithsonian Scholarly Press

Biological Sciences Press, *imprint of* Cooper Publishing Group LLC

BioMed Central, *imprint of* Springer

BioTechniques Books, *division of* Informa Business Information

Birch Brook Impressions, *subsidiary of* Birch Brook Press

Birch Brook Press, *imprint of* Birch Brook Press, *distributor for* Carpenter Gothic Press, Natural Heritage Press, Persephone Press

Bird Dog Publishing, *imprint of* Bottom Dog Press

Birkhauser Science, *imprint of* Springer

Birlinn Publishing, *distributed by* Casemate Publishers & Book Distributors LLC

Birmingham Museum of Art, *distributed by* Antique Collectors Club Ltd

Bisk CPA Review, *imprint of* Bisk Education

Bisk CPE, *imprint of* Bisk Education

Bisk Education, *distributed by* Bisk Publishing Co

Bisk Publishing Co, *distributor for* Bisk Education

Bisk-Totaltape, *imprint of* Bisk Education

Bison Books, *imprint of* University of Nebraska Press

BizBest Media Features, *division of* BizBest Media Corp

BizBestLocal.com, *subsidiary of* BizBest Media Corp

BizBriefing.com, *subsidiary of* BizBest Media Corp

BizLaunchPad.com, *subsidiary of* BizBest Media Corp

BizOwnerOnly.com, *subsidiary of* BizBest Media Corp

BizTaxes.com, *subsidiary of* BizBest Media Corp

BJE Press, *distributed by* Bartleby Press

BJU Press, *unit of* Bob Jones University, *distributed by* Appalachian Bible Co Inc, Spring Arbor Distributors

BL Publishing, *distributed by* Simon & Schuster, Inc

Black Amber Press, *distributed by* Dufour Editions Inc

Black & White Publishing (UK), *distributed by* Interlink Publishing Group Inc

Black Canyon Communications, *distributed by* Caxton Press

Black Cat, *imprint of* Grove/Atlantic Inc

Black Classic Press, *distributed by* Publishers Group West

Black Coral, *imprint of* Genesis Press Inc

Black Dog & Lenventhal, *distributed by* Algonquin Books of Chapel Hill

Black Dog & Leventhal, *imprint of* Black Dog & Leventhal Publishers Inc, *distributed by* Heimburger House Publishing Co, Workman Publishing Co Inc

Black Dog & Leventhal Publishers Inc, *division of* Workman Publishing Co Inc, *distributor for* Play Bac Publishing, *distributed by* Workman Publishing Co Inc

Black Dog Paperbacks, *imprint of* Black Dog & Leventhal Publishers Inc

Black Iron Cookin' Co, *imprint of* Quixote Press

Black Iron Cooking Co, *imprint of* Hearts & Tummies Cookbook Co

Black Jazz Pizzazz & Razzmatazz, *imprint of* Gallopade International Inc

Black Sparrow, *imprint of* David R Godine Publisher Inc

Black Squirrel Books, *imprint of* Kent State University Press

Blacklock Nature Photography, *distributed by* Adventure Publications

Blackstaff Press Ltd, *distributed by* Dufour Editions Inc

Blackwell Science, *distributor for* Current Medicine Group (CMG)

Blackwells, *distributor for* Teton NewMedia

John F Blair Publisher, *distributor for* Bandit Books, Bright Mountain Books, Canterbury House Publishing, The Colonial Williamsburg Foundation, Down Home Press, Eno Publishers, Hub City Press, Looking Glass Books, Lookout Books, NewSouth Books, Niche Publishing, Pennywell Press, Upper Ohio Valley Books, Walkabout Press, Willow Hill Press

Blake Books, *distributed by* Perfection Learning Corp

Bliss, *imprint of* Entangled Publishing, *distributed by* Dufour Editions Inc

Bloch Publishing Co, *distributor for* Biblio, Menorah, Scarf Press, Sephardic House, Soncino

Block Board Books, *imprint of* Modern Publishing

Block Museum, *distributed by* Oak Knoll Press

Blood Moon Productions Ltd, *distributed by* National Book Network (North America, Australia, New Zealand), Turnaround (UK)

Bloodaxe Books Ltd, *distributed by* Dufour Editions Inc

Bloody Brits Press, *imprint of* Bywater Books

Bloom's Literary Criticism, *imprint of* Infobase Learning

Bloomsbury Academic, *imprint of* Bloomsbury Publishing, *distributor for* Paragon House, Spring Publications

Bloomsbury Kids, *imprint of* Bloomsbury Publishing

Bloomsbury Press, *imprint of* Bloomsbury Publishing

Bloomsbury Publishing, *distributed by* Macmillan

Bloomsbury USA, *imprint of* Bloomsbury Publishing, *distributed by* St Martin's Press, LLC

Blue & Grey, *imprint of* Book Sales Inc

Blue Apple Books, *distributed by* Chronicle Books LLC, Random House Inc

Blue Beacon Books, *imprint of* Regal Crest Enterprises LLC

Blue Dolphin, *distributor for* Eros Books

Blue Dolphin Publishing Inc, *distributor for* The Lotus Seed Press (China) (ISBN prefix: 962-8602)

Blue Guides Ltd, *distributed by* W W Norton & Company Inc

Blue Mountain Press®, *imprint of* Blue Mountain Arts Inc

Blue Note, *imprint of* Blue Note Publications Inc

Blue Note Books, *imprint of* Blue Note Publications Inc

Blue Note Music Manuscript Books, *imprint of* Blue Note Publications Inc

Blue Poppy Press, *division of* Blue Poppy Enterprises Inc, *distributed by* China Books, New Leaf Books, Partner's Book Distributing Inc, Partner's/West Book Distributing Inc, Redwing Book Co, Satas, Tools4Healing (Scott Mieras)

Blue Rider, *imprint of* Penguin Group (USA) LLC

Blue Rider Press, *imprint of* Penguin Group (USA) LLC

Blue Sky Gallery, *distributed by* Franklin, Beedle & Associates Inc

The Blue Sky Press, *imprint of* Scholastic Trade Division

Blue Snake Books, *imprint of* North Atlantic Books

BlueBridge, *imprint of* United Tribes Media Inc

Bluestar, *imprint of* Amber Lotus Publishing

Bluewater Books & Charts, *distributor for* Marine Techniques Publishing

BNA Books, *division of* The Bureau of National Affairs Inc, The Bureau of National Affairs Inc

BNi Building News, *distributed by* Macmillan

BNI Publications, *distributor for* Craftsman Book Co, *distributed by* Craftsman Book Co

BoardSource, *distributed by* American Society of Association Executives

Bobolink Media, *distributed by* Sunbelt Publications Inc

BOCA/ICC, *distributed by* Delmar

Fred Bock Music Company, *distributed by* Hal Leonard Corp

Bollingen Series, *imprint of* Princeton University Press

Bonneville Books, *imprint of* The University of Utah Press

Book Guild, *distributed by* Trans-Atlantic Publications Inc

Book House, *distributor for* Business Research Services Inc, *distributed by* Trans-Atlantic Publications Inc

The Book House, *distributor for* Primary Research Group Inc

The Book House Inc, *distributor for* Marine Techniques Publishing

Book Marketing Works, *subsidiary of* Book Marketing Works LLC

Book Peddlers, *distributed by* Gryphon House Inc

Book Publishing Co, *distributor for* Cherokee Publications, Crazy Crow, CRCS Publications, Critical Path, Gentle World, Magni Co, Sproutman Publications

The Book Publishing Co, *distributed by* Orca Book Publishers

Book Sales Inc, *division of* The Quarto Group Inc, *imprint of* Quayside Publishing Group, *distributed by* Heimburger House Publishing Co

Bookcraft, *imprint of* Deseret Book Co

Booklines Hawaii, *distributor for* Centerstream Publishing LLC

Books Alive, *imprint of* Book Publishing Co

Books Americana, *imprint of* Krause Publications Inc

Books & Co/Turtle Point, *imprint of* Turtle Point Press

Books & Libros, *division of* Gareth Stevens Publishing

Books for Independent Minds, *imprint of* Ronin Publishing Inc

Books Good For Young Children™, *imprint of* Maren Green Publishing Inc

Books In Motion, *division of* Classic Ventures Ltd, Classic Ventures Ltd

Books on Tape®, *division of* Random House Inc, *distributor for* Listening Library®

Books West, *distributor for* Wilderness Adventures Press Inc

BooksXYZ.com, *distributor for* Marine Techniques Publishing

Bookwise International, *distributor for* Big Guy Books Inc

Boom! Studios, *distributed by* Simon & Schuster, Inc, Simon & Schuster Sales & Marketing

Boone & Crockett Club, *distributed by* The Globe Pequot Press

Boosey & Hawkes, *distributed by* Hal Leonard Corp

Booth-Clibborn Editions, *distributed by* Harry N Abrams Inc

Bootstrap Press (US), *distributed by* The Apex Press

Bora, *distributed by* Alan Wofsy Fine Arts

Borden Publishing, *distributed by* Gem Guides Book Co

Borderline Publishing, *distributor for* Anderson Design, Brynwood Publishing

Borders, *distributor for* Paladin Press

Boreal Books, *imprint of* Red Hen Press

Borealis, *imprint of* White Wolf Publishing Inc

Borealis Books, *imprint of* Minnesota Historical Society Press

Borgo Press, *imprint of* Wildside Press

Boson Books, *imprint of* Bitingduck Press, Bitingduck Press LLC

Boston College, *distributed by* Oak Knoll Press

Boston Globe Puzzle Books, *imprint of* Random House Reference/Random House Puzzles & Games/House of Collectibles

Botanica Press, *imprint of* Book Publishing Co

Bottom Dog Press, *imprint of* Bottom Dog Press, *distributor for* The Firelands Writing Center (Heartlands Magazine)

Boulden, *distributed by* MAR*CO Products Inc

Boulden Publishing, *distributor for* MAR*CO Products Inc

Boundless, *imprint of* Zumaya Publications LLC

Bourbon Street Books, *imprint of* HarperCollins General Books Group

R R Bowker, *distributed by* Hollywood Film Archive

R R Bowker LLC, *subsidiary of* ProQuest LLC

BowTie Press®, *division of* BowTie Inc

Boxer Books, *distributed by* Sterling Publishing Co Inc

Boydell & Brewer Inc, *affiliate of* Boydell & Brewer Ltd (UK)

Boyds Mills Press, *subsidiary of* Highlights for Children Inc, *distributor for* Front Street, *distributed by* Heimburger House Publishing Co

Boye Knives Press, *distributed by* Chelsea Green Publishing Co

Boynton/Cook, *imprint of* Heinemann

Boynton/Cook Publishers, *imprint of* Heinemann, *distributed by* Pearson Australia-Schools Division, Pearson Education Canada, Pearson New Zealand-Schools Division

Boys Town Press, *division of* Boys Town, *distributor for* ADD Warehouse, *distributed by* Deep Books Ltd (Europe & UK), Footprint Books (Australia & New Zealand), Monarch Books of Canada Ltd (Canada)

BPI Records, *imprint of* Bridge Publications Inc

Bradford Books, *imprint of* The MIT Press

Bradt Travel Guides, *imprint of* The Globe Pequot Press, *distributed by* The Globe Pequot Press

Brady, *distributed by* Fire Engineering Books & Videos

Joan Brady, *distributed by* Sunbelt Publications Inc

BradyGames, *member of* Penguin Group (USA) LLC

Braided River, *imprint of* The Mountaineers Books

Brandeis University Press, *imprint of* University Press of New England

Branden Books, *subsidiary of* Branden Publishing Co, *distributor for* Dante University of America Press Inc

Branden Publishing Co, *distributor for* Dante University of America Press Inc

Brandon Books, *distributed by* Dufour Editions Inc

Brashear Music Co, *imprint of* Branden Books

Deya Brashears, *distributed by* Gryphon House Inc

Brava, *imprint of* Kensington Publishing Corp

Brazen, *imprint of* Entangled Publishing

George Braziller Inc, *distributed by* Antique Collectors' Club Ltd, W W Norton & Company Inc

Karen & Michael Braziller Books, *imprint of* Persea Books

Breakfast Communications, *distributed by* SAS Publishing

Breakthrough Publications, *imprint of* Breakthrough Publications Inc

Breakthrough to Literacy, *imprint of* Wright Group/McGraw-Hill

Brenner Information Group, *division of* Brenner Microcomputing Inc

Breslov Research Institute, *distributed by* Moznaim Publishing Corp

Brethren Press, *division of* Church of the Brethren General Board

Brewers Publications, *division of* Brewers Association, *distributed by* National Book Network

Brick Tower Press, *imprint of* J T Colby & Co Inc

BrickHouse Books Inc, *distributed by* Itasca

Bridge, *imprint of* Bridge-Logos Inc

Bridge Audio, *imprint of* Bridge Publications Inc

Bridge-Logos Inc, *distributor for* New Wine Press, RoperPenberthy Publishing Ltd, Sovereign World, Warboys LLC

Bridge 21, *distributed by* Transaction Publishers Inc

Bridge Works Publishing, *distributed by* National Book Network

Brief Books, *imprint of* Birch Brook Press

Bright Mountain Books, *distributed by* John F Blair Publisher

Bright Ring Publishing, *distributed by* Gryphon House Inc

BrightPoint Literacy, *imprint of* Peoples Education Inc

Brigids Books, *subsidiary of* Leilah Publications

Brill Inc, *subsidiary of* Koninklijke Brill N V

Brilliance Audio, *subsidiary of* Amazon.com, Amazon.com Inc

Brio Girls, *imprint of* Focus on the Family

Brioni Books, *distributed by* Antique Collectors Club Ltd

British Film Institute, *distributed by* Palgrave Macmillan, University of California Press

British Museum Press, *distributed by* Antique Collectors Club Ltd

Broadside Books, *imprint of* HarperCollins General Books Group

Broadstone Books, *distributed by* Fons Vitae

Broadway Books, *imprint of* Crown Publishing Group

Brodart Books Co, *distributor for* Marine Techniques Publishing

Brodart Co, *distributor for* Do-It-Yourself Legal Publishers, Twilight Times Books

Brookes Publishing Co Inc, *distributed by* The Eurospan Group (Africa, Europe & Middle East), Footprint Books Pty Ltd (Australia, Fiji, New Zealand & Papua New Guinea)

Brookings Institution Press, *distributor for* Council on Foreign Relations Press, University of California Institute on Global Conflict & Cooperation

The Brookings Institution Press, *division of* Brookings Institution, *distributor for* American Chamber of Commerce to the European Union, Asia Pacific Research Center, Bertelsmann Foundation Publishers, Carnegie Endowment for International Peace, The Centre for Economic Policy Research, The Century Foundation, Economica, International Labor Offices, Japan Center for International Exchange, OECD, The Trilateral Commission, World Trade Organization, *distributed by* The Johns Hopkins University Press

Brooklands Books Ltd, *distributed by* CarTech Inc

Brooklyn Botanic Garden, *distributed by* Sterling Publishing Co Inc

Brooks, *distributed by* Council for Exceptional Children (CEC)

Brooks/Cole, *imprint of* Wadsworth Publishing

Brotherhood of St Herman of Alaska, *imprint of* St Herman Press

Gustav Broukal Press, *imprint of* American Atheist Press

Brown Barn Books, *division of* Pictures of Record Inc

Brown Bear Books, *imprint of* Black Rabbit Books

Brown Books Agency, *division of* Brown Books Publishing Group

Brown Books Digital, *division of* Brown Books Publishing Group

John Carter Brown Library, *distributed by* Oak Knoll Press

Brown Judaic Studies, *distributed by* Society of Biblical Literature

Brown University, *distributed by* American Mathematical Society

Brown Walker Press, *imprint of* Universal-Publishers Inc

Karen Brown's Guides, *distributed by* Random House Inc

Brusberg (Berlin), *distributed by* Alan Wofsy Fine Arts

Bryn Mawr College, *distributed by* Oak Knoll Press

Bryn Mawr Commentaries, *distributed by* Hackett Publishing Co Inc

Brynmorgen Press, *distributed by* Gem Guides Book Co

Brynwood Publishing, *distributed by* Borderline Publishing

BSCS, *distributed by* National Science Teachers Association (NSTA)

Bubble Books, *imprint of* Modern Publishing

Buchtel Books, *imprint of* The University of Akron Press

Bucking Horse Books, *distributed by* Mountain Press Publishing Co

Buckle Down Publishing, *subsidiary of* Haights Cross Communications Inc

Bucknell University Press, *affiliate of* Associated University Presses, *distributed by* Rowman & Littlefield

Buddy Books, *imprint of* ABDO Publishing Group

Buena Vista DVDs, *distributed by* Recorded Books LLC

Bufflehead Books, *imprint of* Down The Shore Publishing Corp

BuilderBooks.com, *division of* National Association of Home Builders (NAHB), *distributor for* National Association of Home Builders (NAHB)

Builders Book Inc, *distributor for* Craftsman Book Co, *distributed by* Craftsman Book Co

Building Blocks, *distributed by* Gryphon House Inc

Building Excellence, *imprint of* Mel Bay Publications Inc

Building News Inc, *distributed by* Craftsman Book Co

Bulfinch/Little, *distributor for* National Gallery of Art

Bulgarian-American Cultural Society ALEKO, *subsidiary of* Cross-Cultural Communications

The Bureau For At-Risk Youth, *subsidiary of* The Guidance Group Inc

Bureau of Economic Geology, University of Texas at Austin, *division of* University of Texas at Austin, *distributor for* Gulf Coast Association of Geological Societies, Texas Memorial Museum (selected titles)

Burnell Books, *distributor for* MAR*CO Products Inc

Burning Bush Press, *imprint of* United Synagogue Book Service

Burns Archive Press, *imprint of* Burns Archive Photographic Distributors Ltd

Buros Institute, *distributed by* University of Nebraska Press

Business & Research Associates, *distributed by* FurnitureCore

Business Expert Press, *subsidiary of* IGroup

Business Plus, *imprint of* Grand Central Publishing

Business Research Services Inc, *distributor for* Riley & Johnson, *distributed by* Basch, Book House, Coutts, Gale Research Inc, Midwest Library Service

Business Success Series, *imprint of* PREP Publishing

Butler Center for Arkansas Studies, *distributed by* The University of Arkansas Press

Butterworth-Heinemann, *distributor for* Current Medicine Group (CMG), *distributed by* Marine Techniques Publishing, NACE International

Butterworths, *distributed by* William S Hein & Co Inc

BWI, *distributor for* Quackenworth Publishing

BWI Books, *distributor for* Twilight Times Books

By Design Press, *imprint of* Quite Specific Media Group Ltd

Byte Level Books, *imprint of* Ashland Creek Press

BYU Museum of Peoples & Cultures, *distributed by* The University of Utah Press

BYU Studies, *distributed by* The University of Utah Press

C & T Publishing Inc, *distributed by* Watson-Guptill Publications

C E P Inc, *imprint of* Paladin Press

Cabi Books, *distributed by* Stylus Publishing LLC

Cademon, *imprint of* HarperCollins Publishers Sales

Cadence Jazz Books, *division of* Cadnor Ltd, Cadnor Ltd, *distributed by* North Country Distributors

Caedmon, *imprint of* HarperCollins General Books Group

Caissa Editions, *affiliate of* Dale A Brandreth Books

CAL Books, *distributed by* Casemate Publishers & Book Distributors LLC

Cal-Earth, *distributed by* Chelsea Green Publishing Co

Caliber, *imprint of* Berkley Books

California Historical Society, *imprint of* Heyday Books

California Legacy Books, *imprint of* Heyday Books

California Sea Grant, *distributed by* Sunbelt Publications Inc

Calkins Creek, *imprint of* Boyds Mills Press

Calloway House, *distributor for* MAR*CO Products Inc

Calvary Hospital, *distributed by* The Center for Thanatology Research & Education Inc

Cambridge Educational, *division of* Infobase Learning

Cambridge University Press, *division of* University of Cambridge, *distributor for* The Mathematical Association of America, National Gallery of Art, *distributed by* Delta Publishing Co, Dominie Press Inc, NACE International

Camden House, *imprint of* Boydell & Brewer Inc

Camelion Plays, *distributed by* Players Press Inc

Camerapix Publishers International, *distributed by* Interlink Publishing Group Inc

Campaign, *imprint of* Osprey Publishing Inc

Georgina Campbell Guides (Ireland), *distributed by* Interlink Publishing Group Inc

Paul Douglas Campbell, *distributed by* Sunbelt Publications Inc

Canadian Caboose Press, *distributed by* Heimburger House Publishing Co

Canadian Centre for Architecture, *distributed by* The MIT Press

Canadian Museum of Nature, *distributed by* University of Chicago Press

Canadian Society of Petroleum Geologists, *distributor for* AAPG (American Association of Petroleum Geologists)

Canal & Stamperia, *distributed by* Antique Collectors Club Ltd

Canal Press, *imprint of* Schiffer Publishing Ltd

Candle Books, *distributed by* Kregel Publications

Candlewick Press, *subsidiary of* Walker Books Ltd (London), *distributed by* Perfection Learning Corp

CandyCane Press, *imprint of* Ideals Publications, a Guideposts Co

Canterbury & York Society, *imprint of* Boydell & Brewer Inc

Canterbury House Publishing, *distributed by* John F Blair Publisher

Gloriae Dei Cantores, *distributed by* Paraclete Press Inc

Cantors Assembly, *imprint of* Transcontinental Music Publications

Canyonlands Natural History Association, *distributed by* The University of Utah Press

Capall-Bann (UK), *distributed by* Holmes Publishing Group LLC

Capital Enquiry Inc, *distributor for* Center for Investigative Reporting

Capstone, *imprint of* John Wiley & Sons Inc

Capstone Digital, *division of* Capstone Publishers™

Capstone Press, *imprint of* Capstone Publishers™

Captain's Nautical Supplies, *distributor for* Marine Techniques Publishing

Aristide D Caratzas, Publisher, *imprint of* Melissa International Ltd, Melissa International Ltd

Caravan Books, *subsidiary of* Academic Resources Corp, Academic Resources Corp

Caravel Books, *imprint of* Pleasure Boat Studio: A Literary Press

Cardinal Publisher's Group, *distributor for* Price World Publishing LLC

Cardinal Publishers Group, *distributor for* Wish Publishing

Cardoza, *distributed by* Simon & Schuster Sales & Marketing

Cardoza Publishing, *distributor for* Simon & Schuster, *distributed by* Simon & Schuster, Inc

Care Spring, *imprint of* Hartman Publishing Inc

Career Examination Series, *imprint of* National Learning Corp

Career Kids FYI, *distributor for* MAR*CO Products Inc

Caribbean Writers Series, *imprint of* Heinemann

Caribe Betania Editores, *division of* Grupo Nelson Inc

Caribe Grolier Inc, *subsidiary of* Scholastic International

Coleccion Caribena, *imprint of* University of Puerto Rico Press

Carina Press, *imprint of* Harlequin Enterprises Ltd

Carisch SPA, *distributed by* Summy-Birchard Inc

Carlton Books, *distributed by* Sterling Publishing Co Inc

Carmania Press London, *distributed by* Purple Mountain Press Ltd

Carnegie Endowment for International Peace, *distributed by* The Brookings Institution Press

Carolrhoda Books, *division of* Lerner Publishing Group Inc

Carolrhoda Books Inc, *imprint of* Lerner Publishing Group Inc

Carolrhoda Lab, *imprint of* Carolrhoda Books

Carolrhoda Lab™, *imprint of* Lerner Publishing Group Inc

Carpe Diem Professional Calendars, *imprint of* Flying Pen Press LLC

Carpenter Gothic Press, *distributed by* Birch Brook Press

Carroll County Genealogical Society, *distributed by* Heritage Books Inc

Carson-Dellosa Publishing LLC, *distributor for* Key Education, Mark Twain Media

Carstens, *distributed by* Heimburger House Publishing Co

Carstens Hobby Books, *imprint of* Carstens Publications Inc

Cartago, *distributed by* Antique Collectors Club Ltd

CarTech Inc, *distributor for* Brooklands Books Ltd, S-A Design, *distributed by* MBI

Amon Carter Museum, *distributed by* Abrams & University of Washington Press

Carthage Reprints, *imprint of* St Augustine's Press Inc

Cartwheel Books, *imprint of* Scholastic Trade Division

Carysfort Press, *distributed by* Dufour Editions Inc

Casa Bautista, *distributed by* Editorial Bautista Independiente

Casa Bautista de Publicaciones, *affiliate of* Southern Baptist Convention, *distributed by* LifeWay Christian Resources

Casa Creation, *imprint of* Charisma Media

Cascade Expeditions, *imprint of* Crumb Elbow Publishing

Cascade Geographic Society, *imprint of* Crumb Elbow Publishing

Casemate, *distributed by* Casemate Publishers & Book Distributors LLC

Casemate/Flashpoint, *distributed by* Casemate Publishers & Book Distributors LLC

Casemate Publishers & Book Distributors LLC, *distributor for* AF Editions, Airfile Publications, Amber Books (UK), Amberley Publishing (UK), Birlinn Publishing (UK), CAL Books, Casemate (USA), Casemate/Flashpoint, Compendium Films, Compendium Publishing (UK), D-Day Publishing (Belgium), Eagle Editions, Earthbound Publications, Formac Publishing (Canada), Foundry, Front Street Press (USA), Frontline Books, Greenhill Books, Grub Street (UK), Harpia Publishing, Heimdal, Helion & Co Ltd (UK), Editions Charles Herissey (France), Histoire & Collections (France), Historical Archive Press, Historical Indexes (USA), History Facts, Paul Holberton Publishing, Indo Editions (France), Ironclad Publishing (USA), De Krijger (Belgium), Lancer Publishers, Lorimer, Military Illustrated, MMP (UK/ Poland), OREP, Pen & Sword Books Ltd (UK), Pen & Sword Digital, Philedition, Riebel-Roque, RZM Publishing (USA), S I Publicaties BV, Savas Beatie (USA), Scarab Miniatures, Seaforth Publishing, Tattered Flag, 30 Degrees South Publishers, Vanwell-Looking Back Press, Vanwell Publishing (Canada), WAG Books, Warlord Games, Wharncliffe

Cassell, *distributed by* Sterling Publishing Co Inc

CASTI Publishing, *distributed by* NACE International

Castle Books, *imprint of* Book Sales Inc

Castle Keep Books, *imprint of* James A Rock & Co Publishers

Catalpa Press, *distributed by* Oak Knoll Press

Catechesis of the Good Shepherd Publications, *imprint of* Liturgy Training Publications

Cathedral Music Press, *division of* Mel Bay Publications Inc, *imprint of* Mel Bay Publications Inc

Catholic Approach Series, *imprint of* Pauline Books & Media

Catholic Dossier, *subsidiary of* Ignatius Press

Catholic Faith, *subsidiary of* Ignatius Press

Catholic Treasures, *distributor for* Angelus Press

Catholic University of America Press, *distributed by* The Johns Hopkins University Press

The Catholic University of America Press, *distributor for* American Maritain Association, Institute for the Psychological Sciences Press (IPS), Sapientia Press

The Catholic World Report, *subsidiary of* Ignatius Press

CavanKerry Press, *distributed by* University Press of New England

Caveat Press, *imprint of* White Cloud Press

Caxton Club, *distributed by* Oak Knoll Press

Caxton Press, *division of* The Caxton Printers Ltd, The Caxton Printers Ltd, *distributor for* Alpha Omega Publishing, Black Canyon Communications, Historic Idaho Series, Snake Country Publishing, University of Idaho Historical Manuscript Series, University of Idaho Press, *distributed by* University of Nebraska Press

Edgar Cayce Foundation, *division of* ARE Press

Cayce-Reilly School of Massotherapy, *division of* ARE Press

CBD, *distributed by* College Press Publishing Co

CBP/EMH, *imprint of* Casa Bautista de Publicaciones

CCA, *imprint of* Copywriter's Council of America (CCA), The Linick Group Inc

CCH, *distributor for* AICPA Professional Publications

CCH, a Wolters Kluwer business, *subsidiary of* Wolters Kluwer

CCH INCORPORATED, *imprint of* Wolters Kluwer US Corp

CCH Peterson, *subsidiary of* CCH, a Wolters Kluwer business

CCH Riverwoods, *subsidiary of* CCH, a Wolters Kluwer business

CCH St Petersburg, *subsidiary of* CCH, a Wolters Kluwer business

CCH Tax Compliance, *subsidiary of* CCH, a Wolters Kluwer business

CCH Washington DC, *subsidiary of* CCH, a Wolters Kluwer business

CDL Press, *imprint of* CDL Press

CDS Distributors, *distributor for* Basic Books

CDX Global, *distributed by* Delmar

Cedar Fort Inc, *distributor for* Horizon Publishers & Distributors Inc

CEF Press, *subsidiary of* Child Evangelism Fellowship Inc, Child Evangelism Fellowship Inc

Celebra, *imprint of* Penguin Group (USA) LLC

Celebrity Profiles Publishing, *division of* Edison & Kellogg

Celestial Arts Publishing Co, *imprint of* Crown Publishing Group, Crown Publishing Group

Cengage Learning™, *distributor for* Wadsworth Publishing

Cengage Learning Asia Pte Ltd, *distributor for* American Society for Training & Development (ASTD)

Cengage Learning Australia, *distributed by* Cheng & Tsui Co Inc

Centaur Books, *imprint of* Joshua Tree Publishing

Center for Book Arts, *distributed by* Oak Knoll Press

Center for Chinese Studies, University of Michigan, *distributed by* University of Michigan Press

Center for Contemporary Judaica, *imprint of* Prayer Book Press Inc

Center for Creative Leadership LLC, *affiliate of* Smith Richardson Foundation, *distributor for* Free Press, Harvard Business School Press, Jossey-Bass, Lominger Inc, John Wiley & Sons Inc, *distributed by* Jossey-Bass, John Wiley & Sons Inc

Center for East Asian Studies (CEAS), *subsidiary of* Western Washington University

Center for Global Development, *distributed by* Peterson Institute for International Economics

Center for Investigative Reporting, *distributed by* Capital Enquiry Inc

Center for Literary Publishing, *distributed by* University Press of Colorado

Center for National Policy Press, *distributed by* University Press of America Inc

Center for South & Southeast Asian Studies, University of Michigan, *distributed by* University of Michigan Press

Center for Study of American Constitution, *distributed by* Madison House Publishers

Center for Talented Youth, *distributed by* The Johns Hopkins University Press

Center for Thanatology, *imprint of* The Center for Thanatology Research & Education Inc

The Center for Thanatology Research & Education Inc, *distributor for* Association for Gravestone Studies, Calvary Hospital, Greenwood Cemetery

Center for the Child Care Workforce, *distributed by* Gryphon House Inc

The Center for the Study of Upper Midwestern Culture, *distributed by* University of Wisconsin Press

Center for US-Mexican Studies, *distributed by* Lynne Rienner Publishers Inc

Center for Urban Policy Research, *imprint of* Transaction Publishers Inc

Center for Youth Issues/STARS, *distributed by* MAR*CO Products Inc

Center of Emigrants from Serbia, *distributed by* Cross-Cultural Communications

Center Street, *division of* Hachette Book Group

Centerbrook Publishing, *subsidiary of* Centerstream Publishing LLC

Centerstream Publications, *imprint of* Hal Leonard Corp, *distributed by* Hal Leonard Corp

Centerstream Publishing LLC, *distributed by* Booklines Hawaii, Hal Leonard Corp

Central European University Press, *distributor for* International Debate Education Association, Local Government & Public Service Reform Initiative, Open Society Institute, *distributed by* University of Toronto Press (Canada)

Central Recovery Press (CRP), *unit of* Central Recovery Treatment, *distributed by* HCI Books Inc

Centre for Customer Care (CCC), *distributor for* HRD Press

The Centre for Economic Policy Research, *distributed by* The Brookings Institution Press

The Century Foundation, *division of* The Century Foundation Inc, The Century Foundation Inc, *distributed by* The Brookings Institution Press

Cerf & Peterson, *distributed by* Welcome Books®

Certification Press, *imprint of* McGraw-Hill Professional

Certified Nurse Series (CN), *imprint of* National Learning Corp

Cervantes & Co, *imprint of* European Masterpieces, *distributed by* European Masterpieces

CFKR Career, *distributor for* MAR*CO Products Inc

Chalice Press, *division of* Christian Board of Publications, *distributed by* Cokesbury

Challenges of Aging Instruction Booklets, *imprint of* Letterbox/Papyrus of London Publishers USA

Chambers, *distributed by* Houghton Mifflin Harcourt

Le Chambon-sur-Lignon, *distributed by* Beach Lloyd Publishers LLC

Champion Writers Inc, *distributor for* Aberdeen Bay

Chandos, *distributed by* Neal-Schuman Publishers Inc

Chanterelle, *distributed by* Mel Bay Publications Inc

Chapin Library, *distributed by* Oak Knoll Press

Character Development, *distributor for* MAR*CO Products Inc

CharismaLife, *distributed by* CharismaLife Publishers

CharismaLife Publishers, *distributor for* CharismaLife

The Charles Press, Publishers, *subsidiary of* Oxbridge Corp, The Oxbridge Corp

Charles River Media, *imprint of* Cengage Learning

Charles Scribner's Sons®, *imprint of* Gale

Charlesbridge Press, *distributed by* Perfection Learning Corp

Charlesbridge Publishing Inc, *distributor for* American Express (travel & leisure, food & wine), EarlyLight Books

Chartered Institute for Personnel Development (CIPD), *distributed by* Beekman Books Inc

Chartwell Books, *imprint of* Book Sales Inc

Chatterbox Press, *distributed by* Gryphon House Inc

The Checkerboard Library, *imprint of* ABDO Publishing Group

Chef Express, *imprint of* Standard International Media Holdings

Chef Success, *imprint of* Standard International Media Holdings

Chelsea Clubhouse, *imprint of* Chelsea House Publishers

Chelsea Green Publishing Co, *distributor for* AATEC Publications, American Council for an Energy Efficient Economy (ACEEE), Anomaly Press, Avalon House, Boye Knives Press, Cal-Earth, Earth Pledge, Eco Logic Books, Ecological Design Institute, Ecological Design Press, Empowerment Institute, Filaree Productions, Flower Press, Foundation for Deep Ecology, Fox Maple Press, Green Books, Green Building Press, Green Man Publishing, Groundworks, Hand Print Press, Holmgren Design Services, Jenkins Publishing, Knossus Project, Left To Write Press, Madison Area Community Supported Agriculture Coalition, Marion Institute, marketumbrella.org, Metamorphic Press, Moneta Publications, Ottographics, Peregrinzilla, Permanent Publications, Daniela Piazza Editore, Polyface, Rainsource Press, Raven Press, Anita Roddick Publications, Rural Science Institute, Seed Savers, Service Employees International Union, Slow Food Editore, Solar Design Association, Stonefield Publishing, Sun Plans Inc, Sustainability Press, Trailblazer Press, Trust for Public Land, Yes Books

Chelsea House, *distributed by* Perfection Learning Corp

Chelsea House Publishers, *imprint of* Infobase Learning

Chelsea Publishing Co Inc, *imprint of* American Mathematical Society

Chemical Education Resources Inc, *division of* Cengage Learning

Chemical Heritage Foundation, *distributed by* Diane Publishing Co

Cheng & Tsui Co Inc, *distributor for* Action Language Learning, aha! Chinese, Bider Technology, Cengage Learning Australia, China International Book Trading Co (Beijing, selected titles only), China Soft, China Sprout, Crabtree Publishing, Curriculum Corporation, Facets Video, Ilchokak Publishers, Italian School of East Asian Studies, JPT America Inc, Oxford University Press, Pan Asian Publications, Panmun Academic Services, Panpac Education, Paradigm Busters, Pearson Australia, Royal Asiatic Society (Korea Branch), SMC Publishing, Sogang University Institute, Stone Bridge Press, SUP Publishing Logistics, Tuttle Publishing, US International Publishing, White Rabbit Press, Yale University Press, Zeitgeist Films

Cherokee National Press, *distributed by* University of Oklahoma Press

Cherokee Publications, *distributed by* Book Publishing Co

Cherry Lane Music Co, *imprint of* Hal Leonard Corp, *distributed by* Hal Leonard Corp, Hal Leonard Corp

Cherrytree Books, *imprint of* Black Rabbit Books

Chesapeake Bay Maritime Museum, *distributed by* Cornell Maritime Press Inc

Chess Information & Research Center, *distributed by* W W Norton & Company Inc

Chester Book Co, *division of* Finney Company Inc

Chestnut Hills Press, *subsidiary of* BrickHouse Books Inc, *imprint of* BrickHouse Books Inc

Chicago Review Press, *distributed by* Gryphon House Inc

Chicago Spectrum Press, *subsidiary of* Evanston Publishing Inc, *imprint of* Evanston Publishing Inc, *distributed by* Evanston Publishing Inc

Chicago Tribune Crosswords, *imprint of* Random House Reference/Random House Puzzles & Games/House of Collectibles

Chickasaw Press, *distributed by* University of Oklahoma Press

Chicken House, *imprint of* Scholastic Trade Division

Chicken Soup for the Soul, *distributed by* Simon & Schuster Sales & Marketing

Chicken Soup for the Soul Publishing, *distributed by* Simon & Schuster, Inc

Child Play, *distributor for* ADD Warehouse

Children's Book Press, *imprint of* Lee & Low Books, Lee & Low Books Inc

Children's Classics, *imprint of* Random House Inc

Children's Media, *imprint of* Random House Inc

Children's Plus, *distributor for* Saddleback Educational Publishing

Children's Press, *distributed by* Perfection Learning Corp

Children's Press®, *imprint of* Scholastic Consumer & Professional Publishing

Children's Resources International, *distributed by* Gryphon House Inc

Child's Play®, *affiliate of* Child's Play (International) Ltd

Child's Play International, *distributed by* Heimburger House Publishing Co

The Child's World Inc, *distributor for* Tradition Books

Childswork/Childsplay LLC, *subsidiary of* The Guidance Group Inc

Chilton, *imprint of* Delmar, *distributed by* Delmar

Chilton Book Co, *distributed by* J J Keller & Associates, Inc

China Books, *division of* Sino United Publishing (Holdings) Ltd, *distributor for* AsiaPac, Blue Poppy Press, CIBTC, Commercial Press, Foreign Languages Press, Joint Publishers, New World Press, Panda Books, Peace Books, Red Mansions Publishing

China Encyclopedia Publishing House, *distributed by* Homa & Sekey Books

China Institute, *distributed by* EastBridge

China Intercontinental Press, *distributed by* Homa & Sekey Books

China International Book Trading Co, *distributed by* Cheng & Tsui Co Inc

China Soft, *distributed by* Cheng & Tsui Co Inc

China Sprout, *distributed by* Cheng & Tsui Co Inc

China Zhejiang Publishing United Group, *distributed by* Homa & Sekey Books

Chinaberry/Isabella, *distributor for* Eye in the Ear Children's Audio

Chinese University Press, *distributed by* Columbia University Press

Chipstone Foundation, *distributed by* University Press of New England

Chiral House, *imprint of* Joshua Tree Publishing

Chiron Publications, *distributed by* SteinerBooks

Chivers Audio Books, *imprint of* AudioGO

Chivers Children's Audio Books, *imprint of* AudioGO

Chlen$kiy Publishing, *imprint of* Cross-Cultural Communications

Chosen Books, *division of* Baker Publishing Group

Chosen People Ministries, *distributed by* Lederer Books, Messianic Jewish Publishers

Christ Church-Philadelphia, *distributed by* Diane Publishing Co

Christian Book Distributors, *distributor for* Eye in the Ear Children's Audio

Christian Classics, *imprint of* Ave Maria Press

Christian Fellowship, *distributed by* CLC Ministries

Christian Focus, *distributed by* Pilgrim Publications

Christian Large Print, *imprint of* Gale, Thorndike Press®

Christian Network International, *distributor for* Pentecostal Publishing House

Christian Press, *division of* Brown Books Publishing Group

The Christian Science Publishing Society, *division of* First Church of Christ, Scientist, The First Church of Christ, Scientist

Chronicle, *distributor for* Country Music Foundation Press

Chronicle Books, *distributor for* Handprint Books Inc, Princeton Architectural Press, Sierra Club Books, *distributed by* Hachette Book Group, Perfection Learning Corp

Chronicle Books for Children, *division of* Chronicle Books LLC

Chronicle Books LLC, *distributor for* Blue Apple Books, Handprint Books, Laurence King Publishing, Moleskine, Princeton Architectural Press, SmartLab, SmartsCo

Chronicle Gift, *division of* Chronicle Books LLC

Chronology Books, *imprint of* History Publishing Co LLC

Church Publishing Inc, *distributed by* Abingdon Press

CIBTC, *distributed by* China Books

CIDEB, *distributed by* Beach Lloyd Publishers LLC

Cider Mill Press, *imprint of* Cider Mill Press Book Publishers LLC

Cider Mill Press Book Publishers, *distributed by* Simon & Schuster, Inc, Simon & Schuster Sales & Marketing

Cider Mill Press Book Publishers LLC, *distributed by* Simon & Schuster

Coleccion Ciencias Naturales, *imprint of* University of Puerto Rico Press

Cine-Med Inc, *distributor for* American College of Surgeons

Cinema Book Society, *subsidiary of* Hollywood Film Archive

Cinema Books, *distributed by* Hal Leonard Corp

Cinnamon Tree, *imprint of* Deseret Book Co

Circle Time Publishers, *distributed by* Gryphon House Inc

Circlet Press Inc, *distributed by* SCB Distributors

Circumflex, *imprint of* Circlet Press Inc

Cistercian Publications, *imprint of* Liturgical Press

Cistercian Publications Inc, Editorial Office, *imprint of* Liturgical Press, *distributor for* Fairacres Press, Peregrina Press, *distributed by* Liturgical Press

Citadel, *imprint of* Kensington Publishing Corp

CityLife Books, *imprint of* Stephens Press™

Ciudad Nueva (Spain/Argentina), *distributed by* New City Press

Civitas, *distributed by* HarperCollins Publishers

Clairview Books, *distributed by* SteinerBooks

Clara House Books, *imprint of* The Oliver Press Inc

Arnold Clarendon, *distributed by* Oxford University Press USA

Clarendon Press, *imprint of* Oxford University Press USA

Clarion Books, *imprint of* Houghton Mifflin Harcourt, Houghton Mifflin Harcourt Trade & Reference Division, *distributed by* Houghton Mifflin Harcourt

Clarity Sound & Light, *imprint of* Crystal Clarity Publishers

Arthur H Clark Co, *imprint of* University of Oklahoma Press

Clark City Press, *distributed by* Mountain Press Publishing Co

Ayebia Clarke Publishing Ltd, *distributed by* Lynne Rienner Publishers Inc

Clarkson Potter, *imprint of* Clarkson Potter Publishers, Crown Publishing Group, Random House Inc

Clarkson Potter Publishers, *imprint of* Crown Publishing Group, *distributor for* The Colonial Williamsburg Foundation, *distributed by* Random House

Clarkson Research Services Ltd, *distributed by* Marine Techniques Publishing

Classic Library, *imprint of* Recorded Books LLC

Classic Reprint Series, *imprint of* University of Alaska Press

Editions Classicae, *imprint of* Mel Bay Publications Inc

Classics With a Twist, *imprint of* Empire Publishing Service

Classroom Classics, *imprint of* World Citizens

Classroom Connect, *division of* Houghton Mifflin Harcourt Learning Technology

CLC Ministries, *distributor for* Christian Fellowship

Clear Creek Publishing, *distributed by* Gem Guides Book Co

Clear Day Books, *imprint of* Clarity Press Inc

Clearfield, *distributed by* Ericson Books

Clearfield Co Inc, *subsidiary of* Genealogical Publishing Co

Cleartype American Map Corp, *imprint of* American Map Corp

Sydney Gurewitz Clemens, *distributed by* Gryphon House Inc

Clerisy Press, *imprint of* Keen Communications LLC

CLIE, *distributed by* Editorial Bautista Independiente

Client Distribution Services, *distributor for* Harvard Business Press

CliffNotes™, *imprint of* Houghton Mifflin Harcourt Trade & Reference Division

Clinical Advances, *imprint of* Oakstone Publishing LLC

Clipper Audio (UK), *imprint of* Recorded Books LLC

Clo Iar-Chonnachta, *distributed by* Dufour Editions Inc

Clockroot Books, *imprint of* Interlink Publishing Group Inc

Cloister Recordings, *distributed by* Gateways Books & Tapes

Close Up Publishing, *division of* Close Up Foundation

Closson Press, *distributor for* Hearthside Books, Darvin Martin CDs, Retrospect Publishing, *distributed by* Janaway Publishing, Masthof Press

Clovernook Printing House for the Blind & Visually Impaired, *division of* The Clovernook Center for the Blind & Visually Impaired

Clymer ProSeries, *imprint of* Penton Media

Clymer Publications, *imprint of* Penton Media

CN Times Books, *subsidiary of* Beijing Media-Time Book Co Ltd

Coach, *imprint of* Triumph Learning

Coastal Living Books, *imprint of* Oxmoor House Inc

Coastal New England Publications, *imprint of* Harvest Hill Press

Coastal Publishing, *distributed by* Epicenter Press Inc

Cobblestone Publishing, *division of* Carus Publishing Co, *distributed by* PGW/Perseus

Codagen Guides USA, *imprint of* Interlink Publishing Group Inc

Codasat Canada Ltd, *distributor for* Silman-James Press

Codhill Press, *distributed by* State University of New York Press, SUNY Press

Coffeetown Press, *distributed by* Epicenter Press Inc

Cogito Books, *imprint of* Medical Physics Publishing Corp (MPP)

Cokesbury, *distributor for* Chalice Press

Cold Spring Harbor Laboratory Press, *division of* Cold Spring Harbor Laboratory, *distributed by* Oxford University Press USA

Cold Spring Press, *imprint of* Open Road Publishing

Collections Livrier, *imprint of* Progressive Press

College Board, *distributed by* St Martin's Press, LLC

The College Board, *distributed by* Macmillan

College Days Press, *imprint of* R J Berg Publisher

College Editions, *imprint of* Bandanna Books

College Level Examination Series, *imprint of* National Learning Corp

College Press Publishing Co, *distributor for* CBD, David C Cook Publishing

College Proficiency Examination Series, *imprint of* National Learning Corp

Collegium Graphicum, *imprint of* Alan Wofsy Fine Arts

Collins, *imprint of* HarperCollins Children's Books, HarperCollins General Books Group

Collins & Brown, *distributed by* Sterling Publishing Co Inc

Collins Press, *distributed by* Dufour Editions Inc

Colonial Society of Massachusetts, *distributed by* The University of Virginia Press

Colonial Williamsburg, *imprint of* The Colonial Williamsburg Foundation, *distributed by* Antique Collectors Club Ltd

The Colonial Williamsburg Foundation, *distributed by* Harry N Abrams Inc, John F Blair Publisher, Clarkson Potter Publishers, Lexington Books, National Geographic, Ohio University Press, Quite Specific Media Group Ltd, Random House Children's Books, Rodale, Rowman & Littlefield, Scholastic Inc, Stackpole Books, Texas Tech University Press, The University of Virginia Press, University Press of New England, Yale University Press

Colophon, *distributed by* Antique Collectors Club Ltd

Colorado Geological Survey, *division of* Colorado Department of Natural Resources

Colorado Historical Society, *distributed by* University Press of Colorado

Colorado Mountain Club Press, *distributed by* The Mountaineers Books

Colorprint American Map Corp, *imprint of* American Map Corp

Columba, *distributor for* Twenty-Third Publications

Columba Books, *distributed by* Dufour Editions Inc

Columbia Business School Publishing, *imprint of* Columbia University Press

Columbia International Affairs Online (CIAO), *distributor for* University of California Institute on Global Conflict & Cooperation

Columbia University Press, *distributor for* Auteur Books, Chinese University Press, East European Monographs, Edinburgh University Press, The European Consortium for Political Research, University of Tokyo Press, The Woodrow Wilson Center Press

Columbus Zoo, *distributed by* Lerner Publishing Group Inc

Colwood Press Ltd, *distributed by* Antique Collectors Club Ltd

Combat Aircraft, *imprint of* Osprey Publishing Inc

Combined Academic Publishers Ltd, *distributed by* New York University Press

Deanne Scherlis Comer, *distributed by* Beach Lloyd Publishers LLC

ComicsLit, *imprint of* NBM Publishing Inc

Command, *imprint of* Osprey Publishing Inc

Commercial Press, *distributed by* China Books

Common Courage Press, *distributor for* Odonian Press, Real Story Series

Commonwealth Editions, *imprint of* Applewood Books Inc

Commonwealth Scientific & Industrial Research Organization (CSIRO), *distributed by* Stylus Publishing LLC

The Commonwealth Secretariat, *distributed by* Stylus Publishing LLC

Community College Press, *division of* American Association of Community Colleges (AACC)

Community Intervention, *distributor for* MAR*CO Products Inc

Community Music Videos, *distributed by* Hal Leonard Corp

Companion Guides, *imprint of* Boydell & Brewer Inc

Companion Press, *distributed by* Mountain Press Publishing Co

Compass, *imprint of* Brigantine Media

Compass American Guides, *imprint of* Fodor's Travel Publications

Compass Point Books, *imprint of* Capstone Publishers™

Compass Point Mysteries, *imprint of* Quincannon Publishing Group

Compass Publications, *distributed by* NACE International

Compendium Films, *distributed by* Casemate Publishers & Book Distributors LLC

Compendium Publishing, *distributed by* Casemate Publishers & Book Distributors LLC

Compu-Tek, *distributed by* Copywriter's Council of America (CCA)

CompuMaster, *division of* SkillPath Publications

Computer Connections, *imprint of* THE Learning Connection®

Comstock Publishing Associates, *imprint of* Cornell University Press

Conari Press, *distributed by* Gryphon House Inc

Conciliar Press, *division of* Conciliar Media Ministries Inc, *distributor for* Light & Life, *distributed by* Light & Life, St Vladimir's

Concord Library, *imprint of* Beacon Press

Concordia Academic Press, *division of* Concordia Publishing House

Concordia Publishing House, *subsidiary of* The Lutheran Church, Missouri Synod, The Luthern Church, Missouri Synod

Confluence Book Services, *subsidiary of* White Cloud Press

Confluence Books, *imprint of* White Cloud Press

The William G Congdon Foundation, *distributed by* Antique Collectors Club Ltd

Congress Watch, *division of* Public Citizen

The Connecticut Law Tribune, *imprint of* Law Tribune Books

Conran Octopus, *distributed by* Antique Collectors Club Ltd

Consciousness Classics, *imprint of* Gateways Books & Tapes

Conservation International, *distributed by* University of Chicago Press

Consortium, *distributor for* Enchanted Lion Books

Consortium Book Sales & Distribution, *distributor for* Ocean Press

Consortium Book Sales & Distribution Inc, *distributor for* Stone Bridge Press Inc

Consultants News, *imprint of* Kennedy Information Inc

Consulting Magazine, *imprint of* Kennedy Information Inc

Consumer Guide/PIL, *distributed by* Penguin Group (USA) LLC

Consumer Reports, *distributor for* United States Pharmacopeia

Consumertronics, *affiliate of* Top Secret Consumertronics Global (TSC-Global)

Contemporary, *imprint of* Wright Group/McGraw-Hill

Contemporary Drama Service, *subsidiary of* Meriwether Publishing Ltd/Contemporary Drama Service

Context Press, *imprint of* New Harbinger Publications Inc

Continental AfrikaPublishers, *division of* Afrikamawu Miracle Mission, AMI Inc

Continuum International Publishing USA, *distributor for* Paragon House

Contra/Thought, *imprint of* Holmes Publishing Group LLC

Convergence, *imprint of* Six Gallery Press

Convergent Books, *imprint of* Crown Publishing Group

Conway, *distributed by* Sterling Publishing Co Inc

Cook Communications, *distributor for* Focus on the Family

David C Cook Publishing, *distributed by* College Press Publishing Co

Thomas Cook Publishing, *imprint of* The Globe Pequot Press, *distributed by* The Globe Pequot Press

Cooking Light Books, *imprint of* Oxmoor House Inc

Cool Springs Press, *imprint of* Quayside Publishing Group

Cool Trash to Treasure, *imprint of* ABDO Publishing Group

Cooper Square Press, *imprint of* Rowman & Littlefield Publishing Group

Coordinating Research Council Inc, *distributed by* SAE (Society of Automotive Engineers International)

Copernicus, *imprint of* Springer

Copernicus Press, *distributor for* Nevraumont Publishing Co

Copley Custom Textbooks, *imprint of* XanEdu Publishing Inc

Copley Editions, *imprint of* Copley Custom Textbooks

Copley Publishing Group, *imprint of* Copley Custom Textbooks

Copper Canyon Press, *distributor for* American Poetry Review/Honickman

Coptales, *imprint of* Oak Tree Press

Copywriter's Council of America (CCA), *division of* The Linick Group Inc, *distributor for* ASL, Compu-Tek, National Association of Photo Sellers, PictureProfits® Tool Kit

Core Library, *imprint of* ABDO Publishing Group

Robin Corey Books, *imprint of* Random House Children's Books

Cork University Press, *distributed by* Stylus Publishing LLC

Cormorant Books, *imprint of* Down The Shore Publishing Corp

Cormorant Calendars, *imprint of* Down The Shore Publishing Corp

Cornell Maritime Press, *imprint of* Schiffer Publishing Ltd

Cornell Maritime Press Inc, *imprint of* Schiffer Publishing Ltd, *distributor for* Chesapeake Bay Maritime Museum, Independent Seaport Museum, Literary House Press, Maryland Historical Trust Press, Maryland Sea Grant Program

Cornell Southeast Asia Program (SEAP) Publications, *distributed by* Cornell University Press

Cornell University Press, *division of* Cornell University, *distributor for* Cornell Southeast Asia Program (SEAP) Publications, Leuven University Press, University of California Institute on Global Conflict & Cooperation

Cornell University Southeast Asia Program Publications, *unit of* Cornell University, *distributor for* A U A Language Center

Cornwal Books, *distributor for* Herzl Press

Cornwallis Press, *imprint of* Tudor Publishers Inc

Cortina Institute of Languages, *division of* Cortina Learning International Inc (CLI)

Corwin, *distributed by* National Science Teachers Association (NSTA)

Corwin, a Sage Co, *distributor for* SAGE UK Resources for Educators

Corwin Press, *imprint of* SAGE Publications

Corwin Press Inc, *subsidiary of* SAGE Publications

Cosimo Books, *imprint of* Cosimo Inc

Cosimo Classics, *imprint of* Cosimo Inc

Cosimo Reports, *imprint of* Cosimo Inc

Cost Annuals, *division of* R S Means, a Reed Construction Data Co

Costume & Fashion Press, *imprint of* Quite Specific Media Group Ltd

Coteau Books, *distributed by* Orca Book Publishers

Cotton Candy Press, *imprint of* Unveiled Media LLC

Cottonwood Publishing, *distributed by* Mountain Press Publishing Co

Council for Exceptional Children (CEC), *distributor for* Brooks (selected titles), Longman, Love Publishing, Pearson, Pro Ed, Sopris West, *distributed by* Free Spirit Publishing Inc, LMD Inc (selected titles), Orchard House Inc

The Council for Research in Values & Philosophy, *imprint of* Council for Research in Values & Philosophy (RVP)

Council Oak Books, *distributed by* Gryphon House Inc

Council of Europe, *distributed by* Manhattan Publishing Co

Council on Foreign Relations Press, *division of* Council on Foreign Relations, *distributed by* Brookings Institution Press

Counseling Outfitters, *distributor for* American Counseling Association

Counterpoint, *imprint of* Basic Books, Counterpoint Press LLC, *distributed by* HarperCollins Publishers

Counterpoint Press, *distributed by* Sierra Club Books

Counterpoint Press LLC, *distributed by* Publishers Group West

Country Bumpkin, *distributed by* Krause Publications Inc

Country Music Foundation Press, *division of* Country Music Hall of Fame® & Museum, *imprint of* Vanderbilt University Press, *distributed by* Chronicle, Oxford University Press Inc, Providence Publishing, Universe, Vanderbilt University Press

Countryman Press, *imprint of* W W Norton & Company Inc

The Countryman Press, *division of* W W Norton & Co Inc, W W Norton & Company Inc, *distributor for* Mountain Pond Publishing Corp, *distributed by* W W Norton & Co Inc, Penguin Books (CN only)

Courage Books, *imprint of* The Perseus Books Group, Running Press Book Publishers

Courage to Change, *distributor for* MAR*CO Products Inc

Course Technology, *imprint of* Cengage Learning, Wadsworth Publishing, *distributed by* South-Western Publishing

Coutts, *distributor for* Business Research Services Inc

Coutts Information Services, *distributor for* Anaphora Literary Press

Coutts Library Service, *distributor for* Primary Research Group Inc

Coutts Library Services Inc, *distributor for* Marine Techniques Publishing

Cove Press, *imprint of* US Games Systems Inc

Covenant Communications Inc, *division of* Deseret Book Co

Cover Craft, *imprint of* Perfection Learning Corp

Cover-to-Cover, *imprint of* Perfection Learning Corp

Covet, *imprint of* Entangled Publishing

Franklin Covey, *distributed by* SkillPath Publications

Cowley Publications, *imprint of* Rowman & Littlefield Publishing Group

Coyote Press, *affiliate of* Archaeological Consulting

CQ Press, *division of* SAGE Publications, *imprint of* SAGE Publications

Crabtree Publishing, *distributed by* Cheng & Tsui Co Inc, Perfection Learning Corp

Crabtree Publishing Canada, *subsidiary of* Crabtree Publishing Co

Crabtree Publishing Co, *distributor for* Bayard, Maren Green

Crabtree Publishing Inc, *distributor for* Maren Green Publishing Inc

Craftsman Book Co, *distributor for* BNI Publications, Builders Book Inc, Building News Inc, Home Builders Press, *distributed by* The Aberdeen Group, American Technical Publishers Inc, BNI Publications, Builders Book Inc, Quality Books

Robert L Crager & Co, *imprint of* Pelican Publishing Co

Cramer (Geneva), *distributed by* Alan Wofsy Fine Arts

Cramer (Switzerland), *distributed by* Picasso Project

Cranbrook Institute of Science, *distributed by* Wayne State University Press

Craven Street Books, *imprint of* Linden Publishing Co Inc

Crazy Crow, *distributed by* Book Publishing Co

Crazy Games, *imprint of* Price Stern Sloan

CRC Press, *imprint of* Routledge/Taylor & Francis, Taylor & Francis Inc, *distributor for* The Fairmont Press Inc, Science Publishers Inc, *distributed by* American Academy of Environmental Engineers, American Water Works Association, NACE International, SAS Publishing

CRC Press LLC, *subsidiary of* Taylor & Francis

CRCS Publications, *distributed by* Book Publishing Co

Creation House, *imprint of* Charisma Media

Creative Book Publishing, *distributed by* Orca Book Publishers

Creative Concepts, *distributed by* Hal Leonard Corp

Creative Editions, *imprint of* The Creative Co

Creative Education, *imprint of* The Creative Co

Creative Homeowner, *subsidiary of* Courier Corp

Creative Homeowner Press, *distributor for* Home Planners LLC

Creative Keyboard, *imprint of* Mel Bay Publications Inc

Creative Keyboard Publications, *division of* Mel Bay Publications Inc

Creative Paperbacks, *imprint of* The Creative Co

Creative Publications, *imprint of* Wright Group/McGraw-Hill

Creative Publishing International, *imprint of* Quayside Publishing Group

Creative Sales Corp, *subsidiary of* American Map Corp, *distributor for* American Map Corp, *distributed by* Hagstrom Map & Travel Center

Creighton University Press, *distributed by* Fordham University Press, University of Nebraska Press

Crescendo, *imprint of* Taplinger Publishing Co Inc

Crescent Books, *imprint of* Random House Inc

Cress Productions Co, *distributor for* MAR*CO Products Inc

Sarah Crichton Books, *imprint of* Farrar, Straus & Giroux, LLC

Cricket Books, *division of* Carus Publishing, Carus Publishing Co

Crickhollow Books, *imprint of* Great Lakes Literary LLC

Crimeline, *imprint of* Random House Inc

Crimethinc, *distributed by* AK Press Distribution

Crimson Romance, *imprint of* F+W Media Inc

Crisp Books, *distributed by* Michigan Municipal League

Critical Mass Energy Project, *division of* Public Citizen

Critical Path, *distributed by* Book Publishing Co

Croatian Musicological Society, *distributed by* Pendragon Press

Crocodile Books, *imprint of* Interlink Publishing Group Inc

Croft House Books, *distributor for* Primary Research Group Inc

Crofts Classics Series, *imprint of* Harlan Davidson Inc/Forum Press Inc

Cross-Cultural Communications, *division of* Cross-Cultural Literary Editions Inc, *distributor for* Ad Infinitum Press, Arba Sicula (Magazine, US), Center of Emigrants from Serbia (Serbia), Decalogue Books (US), Greenfield Review Press (US), Hochelaga (Canada), Immagine&Poesia (Italy), Legas Publishers (CN), Lips (Magazine & Press) (US), Pholiota Press Inc (England), The Seventh Quarry Press (Wales), Shabdaguchha (Magazine & Press) (Bangladesh & US), Sicilia Parra (Magazine, US), Word & Quill Press (US), *distributed by* Ad Infinitum Books, Hochelaga (Canada)

Cross-Cultural Prototypes, *imprint of* Cross-Cultural Communications

Crossquarter Breeze, *imprint of* Crossquarter Publishing Group

Crossroad, *imprint of* The Crossroad Publishing Co

CrossTIME, *imprint of* Crossquarter Publishing Group

Crossway, *division of* Good News Publishers

Crown, *distributed by* Perfection Learning Corp

Crown Archetype, *imprint of* Crown Publishing Group

Crown Books for Young Readers, *imprint of* Random House Children's Books, Random House Inc

Crown Business, *imprint of* Crown Publishing Group

Crown Forum, *imprint of* Crown Publishing Group

Crown House Publishing Co LLC, *division of* Crown House Publishing Ltd, Crown House Publishing Ltd (UK Co), *distributor for* Developing Press Co, Human Alchemy Publications, Institute Press, Transforming Press

Crown Publishers, *imprint of* Crown Publishing Group

Crown Publishers Inc, *imprint of* Random House Inc

Crown Publishing, *distributor for* Nevraumont Publishing Co

Crown Publishing Group, *division of* Random House Inc

Cruise Memories, *imprint of* R J Berg Publisher

CSI Publications, *imprint of* Christian Schools International

The CSIS Press, *division of* Center for Strategic & International Studies

CSLI Publications, *distributed by* University of Chicago Press

CT Corporation, *imprint of* Wolters Kluwer US Corp

CTB/McGraw-Hill, *division of* McGraw-Hill Education, The McGraw-Hill Companies, *imprint of* McGraw-Hill Education

CTW Publishing, *imprint of* Random House Inc

Coleccion Cuadernos La Torre, *imprint of* University of Puerto Rico Press

Coleccion Cuentos de un Mundo Perdido, *imprint of* University of Puerto Rico Press

Juan de la Cuesta—Hispanic Monographs, *imprint of* LinguaText Ltd, *distributed by* LinguaText Ltd

Coleccion Cultura Basica, *imprint of* University of Puerto Rico Press

Cumberland House, *imprint of* Sourcebooks Inc

CUNY Journalism Press, *division of* CUNY Graduate School of Journalism, *distributed by* OR Books

Cup of Tea Books, *imprint of* PageSpring Publishing

Curbstone Press, *imprint of* Northwestern University Press

Curiosities, *imprint of* Norilana Books

Currach Press, *distributed by* Dufour Editions Inc

Curran Associates Inc, *distributor for* Trans Tech Publications

Currency, *imprint of* Random House Inc

Current Medicine Group, *imprint of* Springer

Current Medicine Group (CMG), *division of* Springer Healthcare Ltd, *distributed by* American Psychology Press, Appleton Lange, Blackwell Science, Butterworth-Heinemann, W B Saunders, Springer Verlag, Thieme, Williams & Wilkins

Current Science Inc, *imprint of* Current Medicine Group (CMG)

Curriculum Corporation, *distributed by* Cheng & Tsui Co Inc

Curriculum Solutions, *division of* Scholastic Education

James Curry Ltd, *imprint of* Boydell & Brewer Inc

Fondation Custodia, *distributed by* Oak Knoll Press

CWLA Press, *imprint of* Child Welfare League of America (CWLA)

CyberAge Books, *imprint of* Information Today, Inc

Cycle Publishing, *distributed by* Chris Lloyd

Cynthia Publishing Co, *distributor for* HarperCollins Publishers

Cypress House, *imprint of* Comp-Type Inc

Cyrco Press, *distributed by* Ardent Media Inc

D & B Publishing, *distributed by* The Globe Pequot Press

D'Asia Vu Reprint Library, *imprint of* EastBridge

D-Day Publishing, *distributed by* Casemate Publishers & Book Distributors LLC

Da Capo Lifelong Books, *imprint of* The Perseus Books Group

Da Capo Press, *imprint of* The Perseus Books Group

Da Capo Press Inc & Lifelong Books, *member of* The Perseus Books Group, *distributed by* The Perseus Books Group

DA Information Services, *distributor for* Peterson Institute for International Economics

Daddy's Heroes Inc, *distributed by* Sunbelt Publications Inc

Dafina, *imprint of* Kensington Publishing Corp

Dakota Institute, *distributed by* University of Oklahoma Press

Dalkey Archive Press, *distributed by* W W Norton & Co, W W Norton & Company Inc

Dallas Museum of Art, *distributed by* Yale University Press

Damron Co, *distributed by* SCB Distributors

Dance Books Ltd, *distributor for* Princeton Book Co Publishers, *distributed by* Princeton Book Co Publishers

Dance Horizons, *imprint of* Princeton Book Co Publishers

Dance Horizons Video, *imprint of* Princeton Book Co Publishers

Dance Notation Bureau, *distributed by* Princeton Book Co Publishers

C W Daniel, *distributed by* Beekman Books Inc

John Daniel & Co, *division of* Daniel & Daniel Publishers Inc, *imprint of* Daniel & Daniel Publishers Inc, *distributor for* Fithian Press, Perseverance Press

Dante Series, *imprint of* National Learning Corp

Dante University of America Press Inc, *distributed by* Branden Books, Branden Publishing Co

DAP Distributed Art Publishers, *distributor for* MIT List Visual Arts Center

Dar Nun, *distributed by* Fons Vitae

Darby Creek Publishing, *imprint of* Lerner Publishing Group Inc

Dark Horse Books, *imprint of* Dark Horse Comics

Dark Horse Comics, *imprint of* Dark Horse Comics, *affiliate of* Dark Horse Entertainment, *distributed by* LPC Group Inc

Dark Oak Mysteries, *imprint of* Oak Tree Press

Darling & Co, *imprint of* Laughing Elephant

Dartmouth College Press, *imprint of* University Press of New England

The Dartnell Corporation, *subsidiary of* Eli Research Inc

Darwin® Books, *imprint of* The Darwin Press Inc

The Darwin Press Inc, *imprint of* Darwin® Books

David & Charles, *imprint of* F+W Media Inc, *distributed by* Krause Publications Inc

David Fickling Books, *imprint of* Random House Inc

David Publishing, *distributor for* Fire Engineering Books & Videos

Davies-Black Publishing, *imprint of* Nicholas Brealey Publishing

Davies Direct Booksellers, *division of* Davies Publishing Inc

Jocelyn Davies, *distributor for* Ash Tree Publishing

Davies-Black Publishing, *imprint of* Nicholas Brealey Publishing

Davis Publications, *distributed by* Sterling Publishing Co Inc

DAW, *imprint of* Penguin Group (USA) LLC

DAW Books Inc, *affiliate of* Penguin Group (USA) LLC, *distributed by* Penguin Group (USA) LLC

DAW/Fantasy, *imprint of* DAW Books Inc

DAW/Fiction, *imprint of* DAW Books Inc

DAW/Science Fiction, *imprint of* DAW Books Inc

The Dawn Horse Press, *division of* Avataric Pan-Communion of Adidam

Dawn Sign Press, *distributed by* Gryphon House Inc

DawnSignPress, *distributor for* Gallaudet University Press, MIT Press, Random House Inc, *distributed by* Gryphon House

Kathy Dawson Books, *imprint of* Penguin Young Readers Group

Dawsons Book Shop, *distributed by* Sunbelt Publications Inc

Day Hikes Books Inc, *distributed by* The Globe Pequot Press

The Day That Was Different, *imprint of* Gallopade International Inc

DBI Books, *imprint of* Krause Publications Inc

dbS Productions, *distributed by* Oklahoma State University

DC Comics, *imprint of* DC Entertainment

DC Entertainment, *division of* Warner Bros Entertainment, Warner Bros Entertainment Co, *distributed by* Random House Publisher Services (RHPS)

DC Nation, *imprint of* DC Entertainment

DC Publications, *distributed by* Hal Leonard Corp

Alain De Gourcuff Editeur, *distributed by* Antique Collectors Club Ltd

De Gruyter Mouton, *imprint of* Walter de Gruyter GmbH & Co KG, Walter De Gruyter Inc, *distributed by* Walter de Gruyter Inc

De Gruyter Saur, *imprint of* Walter De Gruyter Inc

Walter De Gruyter Inc, *division of* Walter de Gruyter GmbH & Co KG, *subsidiary of* Walter de Gruyter GmbH & Co KG, *distributor for* De Gruyter Mouton

Juan De La Cuesta-Hispanic Monographs, *imprint of* European Masterpieces, *distributed by* European Masterpieces

De Lorme Atlas, *distributed by* American Map Corp, Hagstrom Map & Travel Center

De Vorss & Co, *distributor for* Acropolis Books, Science of Mind Publications, Unity Books, White Eagle Publishing Trust (England)

M H De Young Memorial Museum, *distributed by* Antique Collectors Club Ltd

Dearborn Trade, *distributor for* Appraisal Institute

Decalogue Books, *distributed by* Cross-Cultural Communications

Decent Hill, *imprint of* Decent Hill Publishers LLC

Dechema, *distributor for* American Institute of Chemical Engineers (AIChE), *distributed by* American Institute of Chemical Engineers (AIChE)

Dechema Series, *distributed by* Scholium International Inc

B C Decker, *imprint of* Elsevier, Health Sciences Division

Dedelas Press, *distributor for* Syracuse University Press

Ivan R Dee Publisher, *member of* Rowman & Littlefield Publishing Group

Deep Books Ltd, *distributor for* Boys Town Press

Marcel Dekker Inc, *distributed by* NACE International

Del Rey, *imprint of* Random House Inc, Random House Publishing Group

Delacorte Books for Young Readers, *imprint of* Random House Children's Books, Random House Inc

Delacorte Press, *imprint of* Random House Inc

Delaney, *distributor for* Saddleback Educational Publishing

Delaney Books Inc, *subsidiary of* National Learning Corp

Delano Publishing, *distributed by* Epicenter Press Inc

Dell, *imprint of* Random House Inc, Random House Publishing Group

Dell Laurel Leaf, *imprint of* Random House Inc

Dell Yearling, *imprint of* Random House Inc

Delmar, *division of* Cengage Learning, *imprint of* Wadsworth Publishing, *distributor for* Aspire, Autodata, BOCA/ICC, CDX Global, Chilton, Haynes, Holt Enterprises, Scott Jones Publishing, LearningExpress, Meredith, NFPA, Prompt, Seloc, Truckload Carrier Assoc, Video Active Productions

Delmar Learning, *subsidiary of* Cengage Learning

Delmar Publishers Inc, *distributed by* Gryphon House Inc

Delphinium Books, *distributed by* HarperCollins, HarperCollins Publishers

Delta, *imprint of* Random House Inc

Delta Education, *distributor for* National Council of Teachers of Mathematics (NCTM)

Delta Publishing Co, *division of* Delta Systems Co Inc, *distributor for* Alma Edizioni, Barron's, Cambridge University Press, Edilingual, Oxford University Press

Delta Systems Inc, *distributor for* Teachers of English to Speakers of Other Languages Inc (TESOL)

Demos Health, *imprint of* Demos Medical Publishing LLC

Demos Medical Publishing LLC, *division of* Mannheim Holdings LLC

Dempsey Your Distributor, *distributor for* Ash Tree Publishing

Dempsey-Your Distributor Inc, *distributor for* Hay House Inc

Denver Art Museum, *distributed by* University of Oklahoma Press

Derrydale, *imprint of* Random House Inc

Deseret Book Co, *subsidiary of* Deseret Management Corp, Deseret Management Corp

Desert Charts, *division of* Wide World of Maps Inc

Destiny Books, *imprint of* Inner Traditions International Ltd

Destiny Image Inc, *distributor for* Mercy Place

Destiny Recordings, *imprint of* Inner Traditions International Ltd

Detect-A-Word, *imprint of* Modern Publishing

Detroit Institute of Arts, *distributed by* Antique Collectors Club Ltd, Wayne State University Press

Developing Press Co, *distributed by* Crown House Publishing Co LLC

Devine Entertainment Corp, *distributed by* Hal Leonard Corp

DharmaCafe, *distributed by* North Atlantic Books

Dial Books for Young Readers, *imprint of* Penguin Group (USA) LLC, Penguin Group (USA) LLC, Penguin Young Readers Group

The Dial Press, *imprint of* Random House Inc, Random House Publishing Group

Diamond Books, *imprint of* Berkley Publishing Group

Diamond Farm Book Publishers, *division of* Yesteryear Toys & Books Inc, *distributor for* Farming Press, Whittet

Diane Publishing Co, *distributor for* Academy of Natural Sciences, American Philosophical Society, American Swedish Historical Museum, Augustinian Press, Chemical Heritage Foundation, Christ Church-Philadelphia, Friends of (Benjamin) Franklin, Geneological Society of Pennsylvania, Historical Society of Pennsylvania, Library Company of Philadelphia, University of Pennsylvania Libraries

Didax Educational Resources, *distributor for* National Council of Teachers of Mathematics (NCTM)

Die Gestalten Verlag (DGV), *distributed by* Prestel Publishing

Dietz Press, *distributed by* Ericson Books

Difficult Subjects Made Easy Instruction Booklets, *imprint of* Letterbox/Papyrus of London Publishers USA

digitalculture, *imprint of* University of Michigan Press

Dipti, *imprint of* Lotus Press, *distributed by* Lotus Press

Discovery Books, *imprint of* Random House Inc

Discovery House, *distributed by* Thomas Nelson Inc

Discovery House Publishers, *division of* RBC Ministries

Disney Book Group, *distributed by* Hachette Book Group

Disney Books for Young Readers, *imprint of* Random House Inc

Disney Children's Book Group, *division of* Disney Publishing Worldwide

Disney Editions, *imprint of* Disney Publishing Worldwide

Disney-Hyperion Books, *imprint of* Disney Book Group

Disney Libri, *imprint of* Disney Publishing Worldwide

Disney Press, *division of* The Walt Disney Co, The Walt Disney Co, *imprint of* Disney Publishing Worldwide, *distributed by* Hachette Book Group USA, Perfection Learning Corp

Disney Publishing Worldwide, *subsidiary of* The Walt Disney Co

Dissertation.com, *imprint of* Universal-Publishers Inc, *distributed by* Bertrams UK

Distri Books, *distributed by* Perfection Learning Corp

Distributed Art Publishers, *distributor for* American Federation of Arts

Distributed Art Publishers (DAP), *distributor for* The Museum of Modern Art

Dixie Press, *imprint of* Pelican Publishing Co

DJ Inkers, *imprint of* Carson-Dellosa Publishing LLC

DK, *division of* Penguin Group (USA) LLC, *distributed by* Perfection Learning Corp

DLM, *imprint of* Wright Group/McGraw-Hill

Do-It-Yourself Legal Publishers, *affiliate of* Selfhelper Law Press of America, *distributed by* Brodart Co, Midwest Library Service, Quality Books, Unique Books

Documentary Media, *distributed by* Epicenter Press Inc

Documentext, *imprint of* McPherson & Co

Documents of Modern Art, *imprint of* Wittenborn Art Books

Dog Eats Hat Productions, *subsidiary of* Purple People Inc

Dogwise Publishing, *division of* Direct Book Service Inc

Dogwood Ridge Books, *distributed by* Maryland History Press

Tom Doherty Associates, LLC, *subsidiary of* Macmillan, *distributed by* Macmillan

Domain, *imprint of* Random House Inc

Dominie Press Inc, *division of* Pearson Learning Group, *distributor for* Cambridge University Press (limited number of titles, adult GED)

Domus Latina Publishing, *distributed by* Focus Publishing/R Pullins Co Inc

The Donning Co, *distributed by* Schiffer Publishing Ltd

The Donning Company Publishers, *subsidiary of* Walsworth Publishing Co Inc

Doodle Art, *imprint of* Price Stern Sloan

Dordt College Press, *affiliate of* Dordt College

Dorland Biomedical, *imprint of* Dorland Healthcare Information

Dorland Healthcare Information, *division of* Access Intelligence, *imprint of* Dorland Healthcare Information

Pam Dorman Books, *imprint of* Penguin Group (USA) LLC

Samuel Dorsky Museum of Art, *distributed by* State University of New York Press

Coleccion Dos Lenguas, *imprint of* University of Puerto Rico Press

Dos Pasos Editores, *distributed by* Bilingual Review Press/Editorial Bilingue

Double Dog, *imprint of* Yard Dog Press

Doubleday, *imprint of* Random House Inc, *distributed by* Perfection Learning Corp

Doubleday Bible Commentary, *imprint of* Random House Inc

Doubleday Books for Young Readers, *imprint of* Random House Children's Books, Random House Inc

Doubleday/Galilee, *imprint of* Random House Inc

Doubleday/Image, *imprint of* Random House Inc

Doubleday/Nan A Talese, *imprint of* Knopf Doubleday Publishing Group

Doubleday Religion, *imprint of* Crown Publishing Group

Dove Inspirational Press, *imprint of* Pelican Publishing Co

Dover, *distributed by* Alfred Publishing Company Inc

Down East Books, *imprint of* Rowman & Littlefield Publishers Inc, Rowman & Littlefield Publishing Group, *distributor for* Nimbus Publishing Ltd (selected titles, CN sales only)

Down Home Press, *distributed by* John F Blair Publisher

Downtown Bookworks, *distributed by* Simon & Schuster, Inc, Simon & Schuster Sales & Marketing

Downtown Press, *imprint of* Gallery Books

Drache Publications, *distributed by* Finney Company Inc, Hobar Publications

Dragonfairy Press, *imprint of* Dragonfairy Press LLC

DragonFish Comics, *imprint of* Gauthier Publications Inc

Dragonfly, *imprint of* Random House Children's Books

Dragonfly Books, *imprint of* Random House Inc

Drama Publishers, *imprint of* Quite Specific Media Group Ltd

Drawn & Quarterly, *distributed by* Farrar, Straus & Giroux, LLC

Dream Works, *distributed by* Penguin Group (USA) LLC

Dryad Press, *distributed by* University of Wisconsin Press

DTP, *imprint of* Random House Inc

Duel, *imprint of* Osprey Publishing Inc

W M Duforcelf, *imprint of* Black Classic Press

Dufour Editions' Distributed Presses, *imprint of* Dufour Editions Inc

Dufour Editions Inc, *distributor for* Angel Books, Arcadia Books (London) (including Black Amber, Bliss, Eurocrime & Maia), Attic Press (including Atrium), Between the Lines, Black Amber Press, Blackstaff Press Ltd, Bliss, Bloodaxe Books Ltd, Brandon Books, Carysfort Press, Clo Iar-Chonnachta, Collins Press, Columba Books, Currach Press, Eland Books/Sickle Moon Books, Enitharmon Press, Eurocrime, Gill & Macmillan, Goblinshead, Hersilia, Liberties Press, The Liffey Press, Lilliput Press Ltd, Little Toller Books, Y Lolfa (including Alcemi), Maia Press, Mercier, New Island Books, Norvik Press, O'Brien Press, Orpen Press, Persephone Books, Portnoy Publishing, Route, Salmon Poetry, Colin Smythe Ltd, Stinging Fly Press, University College Dublin Press, Vagabond Voices, Veritas, The Waywiser Press

Duke University Press, *distributor for* Forest History Society

Dumb Ox Books, *distributed by* St Augustine's Press Inc

Dumbarton Oaks, *distributed by* Harvard University Press

Dunhill Publishing, *division of* Warwick Associates

Thomas Dunne Books, *imprint of* St Martin's Press, LLC

Dunstan House, *distributed by* ECS Publishing Corp

Dustbooks, *affiliate of* Associated Writing Programs, *distributor for* American Dust Publications

Dutton, *division of* Penguin Group (USA) LLC, *imprint of* Dutton Children's Books, Penguin Group (USA) LLC, *distributed by* Perfection Learning Corp

Dutton Children's Books, *imprint of* Penguin Group (USA) LLC, Penguin Young Readers Group

Dutton Interactive, *imprint of* Penguin Young Readers Group

Duxbury, *distributed by* SAS Publishing

E & E Publishing, *division of* The E & E Group LLC

Eagan Press, *imprint of* AACC International

Eagle Editions, *imprint of* Heritage Books Inc, *distributed by* Casemate Publishers & Book Distributors LLC

Eagle Gate, *imprint of* Deseret Book Co

Eagle Wing Books, *distributed by* Adventures Unlimited Press

Eagles Landing Publishing, *distributed by* Biographical Publishing Co

Eagle's View Publishing, *subsidiary of* Westwind Inc, Westwind Inc

Eakin Press, *division of* Sunbelt Media Inc, *distributor for* German Texan Heritage Society, San Antonio Express-News, Ellen Temple Publishing

Eamon Dolan Books, *imprint of* Houghton Mifflin Harcourt Trade & Reference Division

E&FN Spon, *distributed by* NACE International

Early Childhood Education, *division of* Scholastic Education

Early Classics of Science Fiction, *imprint of* Wesleyan University Press

Early Editions Books, *imprint of* Science & Humanities Press

Early Educator's Press, *distributed by* Gryphon House Inc

Early English Text Society, *imprint of* Boydell & Brewer Inc

Early Learners, *imprint of* Modern Publishing

Early Math, *imprint of* Sundance/Newbridge Publishing

Early Science, *imprint of* Sundance/Newbridge Publishing

Early Social Studies, *imprint of* Sundance/Newbridge Publishing

EarlyLight Books, *distributed by* Charlesbridge Publishing Inc

Earth Love Publishing, *distributed by* Gem Guides Book Co

Earth Pledge, *distributed by* Chelsea Green Publishing Co

Earthbound Publications, *distributed by* Casemate Publishers & Book Distributors LLC

Earthbound Sports, *distributed by* The Globe Pequot Press

Earthling Press, *subsidiary of* Awe-Struck Publishing

Earthpress, *imprint of* Nova Publishing Co

The Earthsong Collection, *imprint of* Beyond Words Publishing Inc

East Asian Legal Studies Program (EALSP), *division of* University of Maryland School of Law

East European Monographs, *distributed by* Columbia University Press

East Gate Books, *imprint of* M E Sharpe Inc

East West Cultural Center, *distributed by* Lotus Press

East West Export Books, *distributor for* Peterson Institute for International Economics

East-West Export Books, *subsidiary of* University of Hawaii Press

EastBridge, *distributor for* China Institute, John Helde, International Christian University Foundation, Nippon Foundation, Yosifumi Taguchi

Eastern Book Company, *distributor for* Primary Research Group Inc

Eastland Press, *imprint of* Terence Dalton Ltd, *distributor for* Journal of Chinese Medicine Publications

Easy Money Press, *subsidiary of* Wolford & Associates

EBL, *distributor for* Infosential Press

EBSCO, *distributor for* Eros Books

EC&M Books, *imprint of* Penton Media

Ecco, *imprint of* HarperCollins General Books Group, HarperCollins Publishers Sales

Eclipse Press, *subsidiary of* Blood-Horse Publications Inc

Eco Logic Books, *distributed by* Chelsea Green Publishing Co

Ecological Design Institute, *distributed by* Chelsea Green Publishing Co

Ecological Design Press, *distributed by* Chelsea Green Publishing Co

Econoclad, *distributor for* Ozark Publishing Inc

Economica, *distributed by* The Brookings Institution Press

Ecopress, *imprint of* Finney Company Inc

Ecosystem Research Group, *imprint of* Crumb Elbow Publishing

ECS Publishing Corp, *distributor for* Randol Bass Music, Dunstan House, Edition Delrieu, Gaudia Music & Arts, Stainer & Bell Ltd, Vireo Press

EDC Publishing, *division of* Educational Development Corp, Educational Development Corp, *distributor for* Usborne Publishing

EDFU Books, *distributed by* Adventures Unlimited Press

Edgewise Press Inc, *distributor for* Editions d'Afrique du Nord, Sotoportego Editore Venice

ediciones Lerner, *division of* Lerner Publishing Group Inc, *imprint of* Lerner Publishing Group Inc

Edilingual, *distributed by* Delta Publishing Co

Edinburgh University Press, *distributed by* Columbia University Press

Edison Welding Institute, *distributor for* American Society for Nondestructive Testing

Edition Delrieu, *distributed by* ECS Publishing Corp

Editions d'Afrique du Nord, *distributed by* Edgewise Press Inc

Editions du Signe, *distributed by* Gem Guides Book Co

Editions Durand, *distributed by* Hal Leonard Corp

Les Editions E T C, *distributed by* Lotus Press

Editions Max Eschig, *distributed by* Hal Leonard Corp

Editions Orphee Inc, *distributed by* Theodore Presser Co

Editions Salabert, *distributed by* Hal Leonard Corp

Editions Technip, *distributed by* Gulf Publishing Co

Editorial Bautista Independiente, *division of* Baptist Mid-Missions, *distributor for* Casa Bautista, CLIE, Portavoz

Editorial Concordia, *division of* Concordia Publishing House

Editorial Portavoz, *division of* Kregel Publications, *imprint of* Kregel Publications

Editorial Unilit, *division of* Spanish House Inc

Editoriale Jaca Book, *distributed by* Antique Collectors Club Ltd

EDU Reference, *distributor for* MAR*CO Products Inc

Educational Impressions Inc, *distributed by* Newbridge Communications Inc, Scholastic Inc, Scholastic-Tab Publications

Educational Insights Inc, *subsidiary of* Learning Resources

Educational Media, *distributed by* MAR*CO Products Inc

Educational Media Corp, *distributor for* MAR*CO Products Inc

Educators for Social Responsibility, *distributed by* Gryphon House Inc

Educators Outlet, *distributor for* National Council of Teachers of Mathematics (NCTM)

Edupress Inc, *imprint of* Highsmith Publications

Edward & Dee, *imprint of* Russian Information Service Inc

Eerdmans Books for Young Readers, *imprint of* Wm B Eerdmans Publishing Co

Egmont USA, *division of* Egmont UK Inc, Egmont UK Ltd, *distributed by* Random House Inc

Amy Einhorn Books, *imprint of* GP Putnam's Sons (Hardcover)

Eland Books/Sickle Moon Books, *distributed by* Dufour Editions Inc

Elbow Books, *imprint of* Crumb Elbow Publishing

Elderberry Press Inc, *distributor for* Poison Vine Books, Red Anvil Press

Electa, *distributed by* Phaidon Press Inc

Electric Strawberry Press, *imprint of* Radix Press

Electrical Wholesaling, *imprint of* Penton Media

The Electrochemical Society (ECS), *distributed by* American Institute of Physics (AIP) (journals), John Wiley & Sons (monographs)

The Electronics Source Book, *imprint of* Penton Media

Elephant Paperbacks, *imprint of* Ivan R Dee Publisher

Elephant's Eye, *imprint of* The Overlook Press

Elite, *imprint of* Osprey Publishing Inc

Elite Books, *division of* Author's Publishing Cooperative (APC), *distributed by* Midpoint Trade

Elliott & Clark Publishing, *imprint of* River City Publishing LLC

Elliott & Thompson, *distributed by* Trafalgar Square Books

Ellipses, *distributed by* Beach Lloyd Publishers LLC

Ellora's Cave, *imprint of* Ellora's Cave Publishing Inc

Eloquent/Strategic, *imprint of* Strategic Book Publishing & Rights Agency (SBPRA)

Elsevier, *distributed by* Gulf Publishing Co

Elsevier Engineering Information (Ei), *subsidiary of* Elsevier Inc

Elsevier, Health Sciences Division, *division of* Reed Elsevier Inc, *distributor for* G W Medical Publisher

Elsevier Inc, *subsidiary of* Reed Elsevier, Reed Elsevier Inc

Elsevier, Science & Technology Books, *distributed by* Marine Techniques Publishing

Elsevier Science Publishers, *distributed by* NACE International

Elsevier Science, Technology & Business Books, *distributor for* Marine Techniques Publishing

Elstreet Educational, *imprint of* Bartleby Press

Elva Resa, *imprint of* Elva Resa Publishing

Elvehjem Museum of Art, *distributed by* Antique Collectors Club Ltd, University of Wisconsin Press

Elysian Editions, *imprint of* Princeton Book Co Publishers

EM Books, *distributed by* Hal Leonard Corp

Embraces, *imprint of* Zumaya Publications LLC

EMC Publishing, *division of* EMC Corp, EMC Publishing LLC, *distributor for* Sybex Inc

Emerald Book Co, *imprint of* Greenleaf Book Group LLC

Emerald Books, *affiliate of* YWAM Publishing, *distributed by* YWAM Publishing

Emergency Gazette, *imprint of* Ugly Duckling Presse

Emery-Pratt Co, *distributor for* Marine Techniques Publishing

Emet Publishers, *distributed by* Jonathan David Publishers Inc

EMI Christian, *distributed by* Hal Leonard Corp

Emmaus Road Publishing Inc, *division of* Catholics United for the Faith

EMP, *imprint of* Easy Money Press

Empire Press Media/Avant-Guide, *unit of* Empire Press Media Inc, *distributed by* Publishers Group West

Empire Publishing Service, *division of* The Empire, The Empire (media group), *distributor for* Arsis Press (world), Arte Publico Press (world), Ian Henry Publications (world), ISH Group (world exc Australia), Paul Mould Publishing (world)

Empowerment Institute, *distributed by* Chelsea Green Publishing Co

Empty Bowl Press, *division of* Pleasure Boat Studio: A Literary Press, *distributed by* Pleasure Boat Studio: A Literary Press

Enchanted Lion Books, *distributed by* Consortium, Farrar, Straus & Giroux, LLC

Encore, *imprint of* Simon & Schuster Audio

Encore Editions, *imprint of* Star Publishing Co Inc

Encounter the Saints Series, *imprint of* Pauline Books & Media

Encyclopaedia Africana, *imprint of* Reference Publications Inc

Energy Arts, *distributed by* North Atlantic Books

Energy Information Administration (EIA), *imprint of* US Government Printing Office, *distributed by* EPO, NTIS

Energy Psychology Press, *division of* Soul Medicine Institute, *distributed by* Midpoint Trade

Enfield Publishers, *distributed by* Trans Tech Publications

Enfield Publishing & Distribution Co, *distributor for* AM Press, Beech River Books, Faculty Ridge Books, Green Lion Press, Hill Winds Press, Institution of Chemical Engineers, Kom Forlag, Letterland International Ltd, Lightning Up Press, Merion Books, Moose Country Press, Northern Forest Center, Portsmouth Marine Society, The Public Press, Secret Passage Press, Thistle Hill Publications, Trans Tech Publications, Treeline Press, Verlag Valentin Koerner, Vital Communities, Wageningen Academic Publishers, Wolf Legal Publishers

Engineering Foundation, *distributed by* American Institute of Chemical Engineers (AIChE)

Engineering Press, *distributed by* Oxford University Press USA

The English Spanish Foundation Series, *imprint of* me+mi publishing inc

Enigma, *imprint of* Zumaya Publications LLC

Enitharmon Press, *distributed by* Dufour Editions Inc

Eno Publishers, *distributed by* John F Blair Publisher

Enslow, *imprint of* Enslow Publishers Inc

Enslow Elementary, *imprint of* Enslow Publishers Inc

Entangled Publishing, *distributed by* Macmillan

Entangled Select, *imprint of* Entangled Publishing

Entangled Suspense, *imprint of* Entangled Publishing

Entangled Teen, *imprint of* Entangled Publishing

EntertainmentPro, *imprint of* Quite Specific Media Group Ltd

Enthea, *imprint of* Ariel Press, *distributed by* Ariel Press

Enthusiast Books, *division of* Iconografix Inc

Environmental Law Institute, *distributed by* Island Press

Environmental Law Institute (ELI), *distributed by* Island Press

Eos, *imprint of* HarperCollins Publishers Sales

Ephemera Bound, *imprint of* Ephemera Bound Publishing

Ephemera Bound Publishing, *division of* Equilibri-Yum Inc

Epicenter Press Inc, *distributor for* Appell Publishing, Coastal Publishing, Coffeetown Press, Delano Publishing, Documentary Media, Five Star Misadventures, Gold Fever Press, Arlene Lochridge, Raising Lucy Studios LLC, Saltry Press

Epigraph Publishing Service, *division of* Monkfish Book Publishing Co

EPO, *distributor for* Energy Information Administration (EIA)

EPS/School Specialty Literacy & Intervention, *division of* School Specialty Inc

Epworth, *distributed by* Presbyterian Publishing Corp

Equilibrium Books, *imprint of* Wish Publishing

Equipment Watch, *imprint of* Penton Media

Ergos Institute, *distributed by* North Atlantic Books

Ericson Books, *distributor for* Clearfield, Dietz Press, Southern Historical Press, *distributed by* Mountain Press, Byron Sistler

Lawrence Erlbaum Assoc, *distributor for* National Association of Broadcasters (NAB)

Ernst & Sohn, *imprint of* John Wiley & Sons Inc

Ernst Publishing Co LLC, *affiliate of* Legal Publications LLC

Eros Books, *distributed by* Blue Dolphin, EBSCO, Magazine City, Magazine Line

Eschat Press, *imprint of* Loft Press Inc

Eshel Books, *imprint of* Bartleby Press

Essential Histories, *imprint of* Osprey Publishing Inc

Essential Library, *imprint of* ABDO Publishing Group

Essential Series, *imprint of* Heyday Books

ETA Cuisenaire, *distributor for* National Council of Teachers of Mathematics (NCTM)

Euphrates, *imprint of* Gorgias Press LLC

Eurocrime, *distributed by* Dufour Editions Inc

Europa Editions, *subsidiary of* Edizioni E/O

The European Consortium for Political Research, *distributed by* Columbia University Press

European Court of Human Rights, *distributed by* Manhattan Publishing Co

European Masterpieces, *imprint of* LinguaText Ltd, *distributor for* Cervantes & Co (Spanish Classics series), Juan De La Cuesta-Hispanic Monographs, Moliere & Co (French Classics series), *distributed by* LinguaText Ltd

European Mathematical Society, *distributed by* American Mathematical Society

Eurospan, *distributor for* University of Michigan Press

Eurospan Group, *distributor for* American Society for Training & Development (ASTD)

The Eurospan Group, *distributor for* Brookes Publishing Co Inc, Health Professions Press, Peterson Institute for International Economics

Eurospan Ltd, *distributor for* HRD Press

Eurostar, *imprint of* VanDam Inc

Eurotica, *imprint of* NBM Publishing Inc

Evangel Publishing House, *division of* Brethren in Christ Media Ministries Inc, *distributor for* Bethel Publishing

M Evans & Co Inc, *imprint of* Rowman & Littlefield Publishing Group

Evanston Publishing Inc, *division of* Integrated Media Corp, *distributor for* Chicago Spectrum Press

Ever After, *imprint of* Entangled Publishing

Evergreen Pacific Publishing, *imprint of* Evergreen Pacific Publishing Ltd

Evergreen Press, *distributed by* Heimburger House Publishing Co

Everyday Mathematics, *imprint of* Wright Group/McGraw-Hill

Everyman Chess, *distributed by* The Globe Pequot Press

Everyman's Classic Library in Paperback, *imprint of* Tuttle Publishing

Everyman's Library, *imprint of* Random House Inc

Everything, *imprint of* Adams Media

Evolver Editions, *imprint of* North Atlantic Books

Ex Libris, *imprint of* Rizzoli International Publications Inc

Exalted, *imprint of* White Wolf Publishing Inc

Excelsior Editions, *imprint of* State University of New York Press, *distributor for* Albany Institute of History & Art, Uncrowned Queens

Executive Books, *distributor for* Markowski International Publishers

Executive Essentials, *imprint of* Health Administration Press

Executive Recruiter News, *imprint of* Kennedy Information Inc

Executive Reports, *imprint of* Aspatore Books

Exhibit A, *imprint of* Osprey Publishing Inc

The Experiment, *distributed by* Workman Publishing, Workman Publishing Co Inc

Explorer Publishing, *distributed by* The Globe Pequot Press

Exploring Community History Series, *imprint of* Krieger Publishing Co

Expressive Editions, *imprint of* Cross-Cultural Communications

Eye in the Ear Children's Audio, *distributed by* Amazon.com, Audio Adventures, Chinaberry/Isabella, Christian Book Distributors, Landmark Audio Books

F+W Media Business Now, *imprint of* Adams Media

F+W Media Inc, *distributed by* Perfection Learning Corp

Faber & Faber Inc, *imprint of* Farrar, Straus & Giroux, LLC, *affiliate of* Farrar, Straus & Giroux, LLC

Faber Music, *distributed by* Alfred Publishing Company Inc

Faber Music Ltd, *distributed by* Hal Leonard Corp

Facet, *distributed by* Neal-Schuman Publishers Inc

Facets Video, *distributed by* Cheng & Tsui Co Inc

Fact Publishers, *imprint of* Cross-Cultural Communications

Facts On File, *imprint of* Infobase Learning

Faculty Ridge Books, *distributed by* Enfield Publishing & Distribution Co

Fair Winds Press, *imprint of* Quayside Publishing Group

Fairacres Press, *distributed by* Cistercian Publications Inc, Editorial Office

Fairchild Books, *division of* Bloomsbury Publishing Plc

Fairfax Genealogical Society, *distributed by* Heritage Books Inc

Fairfield Press, *distributor for* Maharishi University of Management Press

Fairleigh Dickinson University Press, *affiliate of* Rowman & Littlefield, *distributed by* Rowman & Littlefield

The Fairmont Press Inc, *distributed by* CRC Press, Taylor & Francis

Faith Alive, *imprint of* Faith Alive Christian Resources

Faith & Culture, *imprint of* Pauline Books & Media

Faith & Fellowship Press, *subsidiary of* Church of the Lutheran Brethren

Faith & Life Resources, *division of* Mennonite Publishing Network, *distributed by* Herald Press

Faith Library Publications, *subsidiary of* RHEMA Bible Church, *distributed by* Appalachian, Harrison House, Spring Arbor, Whitaker

Faith Press, *imprint of* Winters Publishing

Faith Weaver Bible Curriculum™, *imprint of* Group Publishing Inc

Faith Works Books, *distributor for* American Carriage House Publishing

faithQuest, *imprint of* Brethren Press

FaithWalk Publishing, *imprint of* CSS Publishing Co Inc

FaithWords, *division of* Hachette Book Group

Falcon®, *imprint of* The Globe Pequot Press

Falcon Press, *imprint of* The Original Falcon Press

FalconGuides®, *imprint of* The Globe Pequot Press

Family Center of Nova University, *distributed by* Gryphon House Inc

Family Films, *division of* Concordia Publishing House

Family Tree Books, *imprint of* Betterway Books

Famous Artists School, *division of* Cortina Learning International Inc (CLI)

Famous Writers School, *division of* Cortina Learning International Inc (CLI)

Fanfare, *imprint of* Random House Inc

Fantagraphics Books, *distributed by* W W Norton & Company Inc

Far Muse Press, *imprint of* Loft Press Inc

Far to the North Press, *distributed by* University of Alaska Press

Far West Publishing, *imprint of* Sun Books - Sun Publishing Co

Far West Publishing Co, *subsidiary of* Sun Books - Sun Publishing Co, *distributed by* Sun Books - Sun Publishing Co

Farming Press, *distributed by* Diamond Farm Book Publishers

Farrar, Straus & Giroux Books for Young Readers, *imprint of* Farrar, Straus & Giroux, LLC, Macmillan Children's Publishing Group

Farrar, Straus & Giroux Inc, *distributor for* Aperture Books, *distributed by* Perfection Learning Corp

Farrar, Straus & Giroux, LLC, *subsidiary of* Macmillan, *distributor for* Drawn & Quarterly, Enchanted Lion Books, Gray Wolf Books

Father & Son Publishing Inc, *distributor for* BADM Books

Fatima Crusader, *distributor for* Angelus Press

Fawcett, *imprint of* Random House Inc, *distributed by* Perfection Learning Corp

Fearless Critic Media, *distributed by* Algonquin Books of Chapel Hill

Federal Street Press, *division of* Merriam-Webster Inc, *imprint of* Merriam-Webster Inc

Feldheim, *distributed by* Jonathan David Publishers Inc

Feldheim Publishers (Philipp Feldheim Inc), *distributor for* Hamadia Publishing, Jerusalem Publications

Feldheim Publishers USA, *imprint of* Feldheim Publishers (Philipp Feldheim Inc)

Jean Feldman, *distributed by* Gryphon House Inc

Felsen Press, *imprint of* Decent Hill Publishers LLC

Fence Books, *distributed by* University Press of New England

H B Fenn, *distributor for* Oxmoor House Inc

H B Fenn & Co, *distributor for* Home Planners LLC

Fenris Brothers, *imprint of* Crossquarter Publishing Group

Margaret Ferguson Books, *imprint of* Farrar, Straus & Giroux Books for Young Readers

Ferguson Publishing, *imprint of* Infobase Learning

Leland Fetzer, *distributed by* Sunbelt Publications Inc

Fiction Collective 2 (FC2), *imprint of* University of Alabama Press

Fiction Collective Two Inc (FC2), *imprint of* University of Alabama Press, *distributed by* University of Alabama Press

Fictionwise, *distributor for* Hard Shell Word Factory

Fidelity Press, *distributed by* St Augustine's Press Inc

Field of Glory, *imprint of* Osprey Publishing Inc

Fieldstone Alliance, *imprint of* Turner Publishing Co

Filaree Productions, *distributed by* Chelsea Green Publishing Co

Filipacchi Publishing, *distributed by* Hachette Book Group

The Film Movement DVDs, *distributed by* Recorded Books LLC

The Final Edition, *imprint of* Crumb Elbow Publishing

Financial Executives Research Foundation Inc (FERF), *affiliate of* Financial Executives International (FEI)

Financial Times Press & Wharton School Publishing, *imprint of* Pearson

Financial Times Publishing, *distributed by* Trans-Atlantic Publications Inc

Fine Communications, *division of* Fine Creative Media Inc, Fine Creative Media Inc

FineEdge.com, *distributed by* Heritage House, Sunbelt Publications Inc

Finney Company Inc, *distributor for* Drache Publications, Images Unlimited Publishing, Pine Forest Publishing, Joyce Shellhart, Snaptail Press

Fire Ant Books, *imprint of* University of Alabama Press

Fire Engineering Books & Videos, *division of* PennWell Corp, PennWell Publishing, *distributor for* Brady, Idea Bank, IFSTA, Mosby, *distributed by* David Publishing, Fire Protection Publications

Fire Protection Publications, *distributor for* Fire Engineering Books & Videos

Firefly, *distributed by* Amherst Media Inc, Perfection Learning Corp

Firefly Books Ltd, *distributed by* Heimburger House Publishing Co

The Firelands Writing Center (Heartlands Magazine), *distributed by* Bottom Dog Press

Fireside Fiction, *imprint of* Heritage Books Inc

First Avenue, *distributed by* Perfection Learning Corp

First Avenue Editions, *imprint of* Lerner Publishing Group Inc

First Choice, *imprint of* Sunbelt Publications Inc

First Choice Chapter Books, *imprint of* Random House Inc

First Fruits of Zion, *distributed by* Lederer Books, Messianic Jewish Publishers

First Lessons, *imprint of* Mel Bay Publications Inc

First Second Books, *imprint of* Roaring Brook Press

FirstForumPress, *division of* Lynne Rienner Publishers Inc

Firsthand, *imprint of* Heinemann

Fischer Productions, *imprint of* Franciscan Media

Fithian Press, *distributed by* John Daniel & Co

Fitzhenry & Whiteside Ltd, *distributed by* Heimburger House Publishing Co

5 Continents Editions, *distributed by* Harry N Abrams Inc

500/5000 Press Inc, *imprint of* Greenleaf Book Group LLC

Five Rainbows Services for Authors & Publishers, *subsidiary of* Slipdown Mountain Publications LLC

Five Star, *imprint of* Thorndike Press®

Five Star™, *imprint of* Gale

Five Star Misadventures, *distributed by* Epicenter Press Inc

Flaming Magnolia, *imprint of* Global Authors Publications (GAP)

Flammarion, *imprint of* Rizzoli International Publications Inc

Editions Flammarion, *distributed by* Rizzoli International Publications Inc

Flashlight Press, *subsidiary of* Urim Publications

Flip N Fun, *imprint of* Modern Publishing

Flirt, *imprint of* Entangled Publishing, Random House Inc, Random House Publishing Group

Florida Academic Press, *division of* FAP Books Inc, *distributor for* Publisher's Stone Publications

Florida Funding Publications Inc, *division of* John L Adams & Co Inc, John L Adams & Co Inc

Florida Literary Foundation (FLF) Press, *imprint of* STARbooks Press

Floris Books, *distributor for* Lindisfarne Books, *distributed by* Gryphon House Inc, Steiner-Books

Flower Press, *distributed by* Chelsea Green Publishing Co

Flux, *imprint of* Llewellyn Publications

Flying Diamond, *distributed by* Sunbelt Publications Inc

Flying Machines Press, *imprint of* Paladin Press

Flying Pen Press Colorado, *imprint of* Flying Pen Press LLC

Flying Pen Press Park Trek, *imprint of* Flying Pen Press LLC

Flying Pen Press Rocky Mountain West, *imprint of* Flying Pen Press LLC

Flying Pen Press Science Fiction, *imprint of* Flying Pen Press LLC

Flying Pen Press Southwest, *imprint of* Flying Pen Press LLC

Flying Pen Press Travel Guides, *imprint of* Flying Pen Press LLC

Flying Piggybank Press, *imprint of* Flying Pen Press LLC

FMP, *imprint of* Forward Movement Publications

Focal Press, *distributor for* National Association of Broadcasters (NAB), *distributed by* Marine Techniques Publishing

Focus Classical Library, *imprint of* Focus Publishing/R Pullins Co Inc

Focus on the Family, *imprint of* Focus on the Family, *distributed by* Baker Books, Cook Communications, Harvest House, Moody Press, Tommy Nelson, Standard Publishing Co, Tyndale House Publishers, Tyndale House Publishers Inc, Zondervan

Focus Philosophical Library, *imprint of* Focus Publishing/R Pullins Co Inc

Focus Publishing/R Pullins Co Inc, *subsidiary of* R Pullins Co, R Pullins Co, *distributor for* Domus Latina Publishing

Focus Texts, *imprint of* Focus Publishing/R Pullins Co Inc

Fodor's, *imprint of* Fodor's Travel Publications, Random House Inc

Fodor's Travel Publications, *division of* Random House Inc, *subsidiary of* Random House Inc

Folgers Shakespeare Library, *imprint of* Simon & Schuster

Follett, *distributor for* ARO Publishing Co, Ozark Publishing Inc, Saddleback Educational Publishing

Follett Library Resources, *distributor for* Green Sugar Press, Rocky River Publishers LLC

Follett Library Resources Inc, *distributor for* Marine Techniques Publishing

Fondation pour la Memoire de la Shoah, *distributed by* Beach Lloyd Publishers LLC

Fons Vitae, *distributor for* African American Islamic Institute, Anqa Press (UK), Aperture (NY), Archetype (UK), Broadstone Books, Dar Nun, Golganooza Press (UK), Islamic Texts Society (UK), Matheson Trust, Parabola, Paragon, Parvardigar Press, Sophia Perennis, Pir Press (NY), Qiblah Books, Quilliam Press (UK), Sandala Productions, Sri Lanka Institute of Traditional Studies, Thesaurus Islamicus Foundation, Tradigital, White Thread Press (US), Wisdom Foundation, World Wisdom (US), Zaytuna Institute Press (US)

The Food Paper, *division of* Gault Millau Inc/ Gayot Publications

Footprint Books, *distributor for* Boys Town Press, *distributed by* New York University Press

Footprint Books Pty Ltd, *distributor for* Brookes Publishing Co Inc, Health Professions Press

Footprint Guides, *imprint of* The Globe Pequot Press

For Dummies®, *imprint of* John Wiley & Sons Inc

Force on Force, *imprint of* Osprey Publishing Inc

Fordham University Press, *distributor for* Creighton University Press, Institute for Advanced Study in the Theatre Arts (IASTA), Little Room Press, The Reconstructionist Press, Rockhurst University Press, St Bede's Publications, University of San Francisco Press, *distributed by* Heimburger House Publishing Co, Oxford University Press (US & CN), Oxford University Press USA

Foreign Affairs Information Service, *imprint of* George Kurian Reference Books

Foreign Languages Press, *distributed by* China Books

Forest History Society, *distributed by* Duke University Press

Forest of Peace, *imprint of* Ave Maria Press

Forever, *imprint of* Grand Central Publishing

Forever Nuts, *imprint of* NBM Publishing Inc

Forever Regency, *imprint of* ImaJinn Books Inc

Forever Yours, *imprint of* Grand Central Publishing

Forge Books, *imprint of* Tom Doherty Associates, LLC

Formac Publishing, *distributed by* Casemate Publishers & Book Distributors LLC, Orca Book Publishers

Formatio, *imprint of* InterVarsity Press

Forrest Hill Press, *imprint of* The Wine Appreciation Guild Ltd

Fort Ross Inc Russian-American Publishing Projects, *division of* Fort Ross Inc

Fortress, *imprint of* Osprey Publishing Inc

Fortress Press, *imprint of* Augsburg Fortress Publishers, Publishing House of the Evangelical Lutheran Church in America

Fortytwo Bookz Galaxy, *distributor for* Price World Publishing LLC

Forward Movement Publications, *affiliate of* The Episcopal Church, *distributor for* Anglican Book Centre

Frances Foster Books, *imprint of* Farrar, Straus & Giroux Books for Young Readers

Walter Foster, *distributor for* The Jim Henson Co

Walter Foster Library, *imprint of* Black Rabbit Books

Walter Foster Publishing, *imprint of* Quayside Publishing Group, *distributed by* Quayside Publishing Group

Walter Foster Publishing Inc, *subsidiary of* The Quarto Group Inc

G T Foulis, *distributed by* Haynes Manuals Inc

Foundation Book & Periodical Division, *imprint of* The Center for Thanatology Research & Education Inc

Foundation for Deep Ecology, *distributed by* Chelsea Green Publishing Co

Foundation for Traditional Studies, *distributed by* Kazi Publications Inc

Foundry, *distributed by* Casemate Publishers & Book Distributors LLC

The Fountain, *imprint of* Tughra Books

Four Rivers Press, *imprint of* McClanahan Publishing House Inc

Four Seas, *imprint of* Branden Books

Four Way Books, *distributed by* University Press of New England

4th Dimension Press, *imprint of* ARE Press

Fourth Estate, *imprint of* HarperCollins Publishers Sales

Fox Chapel Publishing Co Inc, *distributor for* Reader's Digest, Taunton Sterling Dover, *distributed by* Ingram Publisher Services

Fox Maple Press, *distributed by* Chelsea Green Publishing Co

Fox River Press, *distributed by* Pilgrim Publications

Franciscan Communications, *imprint of* Franciscan Media, *distributed by* Franciscan Media

Franciscan Media, *distributor for* Franciscan Communications (books & videos), Ikonographics (videos)

Franklin, Beedle & Associates Inc, *distributor for* Blue Sky Gallery, Photolucida Book

Franklin Street Books, *imprint of* Inkwater Press

Franklin Watts®, *imprint of* Scholastic Consumer & Professional Publishing

Franko Maps, *distributed by* Wide World of Maps Inc

Free Press, *imprint of* Simon & Schuster, *distributed by* Center for Creative Leadership LLC

Free Press Division of MacMillan, *distributed by* Society of Manufacturing Engineers

Free Spirit, *distributed by* Perfection Learning Corp, Torah Aura Productions

Free Spirit Publishing Inc, *distributor for* Council for Exceptional Children (CEC)

Freedom Press, *distributed by* AK Press Distribution

W H Freeman, *distributor for* American Geological Institute (AGI), Nevraumont Publishing Co

W H Freeman and Co, *member of* Bedford, Freeman & Worth Publishing Group, LLC

Freestone, *imprint of* Peachtree Publishers

Samuel French Inc, *distributor for* Baker's Plays, Samuel French Ltd (UK), *distributed by* Baker's Plays, Samuel French Ltd (UK)

Samuel French Ltd, *distributor for* Samuel French Inc, *distributed by* Samuel French Inc

Fresco Fine Art Publications LLC, *distributed by* University of New Mexico

Fresh Air Books, *imprint of* Upper Room Books

Friends of (Benjamin) Franklin, *distributed by* Diane Publishing Co

Friends United Press, *subsidiary of* Friends United Meeting

Friendship Bible Studies, *imprint of* Faith Alive Christian Resources

Frog Books, *imprint of* North Atlantic Books, *distributed by* North Atlantic Books

Frog Legs Ink, *imprint of* Gauthier Publications Inc

Frommer's™, *imprint of* John Wiley & Sons Inc

Front Street, *imprint of* Boyds Mills Press, *distributed by* Boyds Mills Press

Front Street Press, *distributed by* Casemate Publishers & Book Distributors LLC

La Frontera Publishing, *distributed by* University of New Mexico

Frontline, *imprint of* Delmar

Frontline Books, *distributed by* Casemate Publishers & Book Distributors LLC

FT Press Delivers, *imprint of* Financial Times Press & Wharton School Publishing

Fugue State Press, *distributed by* Small Press Distribution (SPD)

Fulcrum, *distributed by* Perfection Learning Corp

Fulgur Ltd, *distributed by* Holmes Publishing Group LLC

David Fulton, *distributed by* Routledge/Taylor & Francis

Fun Places Publishing, *distributed by* Sunbelt Publications Inc

Fun with the Family, *imprint of* The Globe Pequot Press

FurnitureCore, *distributor for* AMA Research, Business & Research Associates

FW Friends™, *imprint of* Group Publishing Inc

G Q Publishing, *imprint of* Great Quotations Inc

G-unit, *imprint of* Gallery Books

G W Medical Publisher, *distributed by* Elsevier, Health Sciences Division

Galaxy Audio, *imprint of* Galaxy Press

Galaxy Music, *imprint of* Galaxy Press

Galaxy Music Corp, *imprint of* ECS Publishing Corp

Gale, *division of* Cengage Learning, *unit of* Cengage Learning, *subsidiary of* Cengage Learning

Gale Research Inc, *distributor for* Business Research Services Inc

Gallaudet University Press, *distributor for* Signum Verlag, *distributed by* DawnSignPress

Gallery Books, *imprint of* Gallery Publishing Group

Gambero Rosso, *distributed by* Antique Collectors Club Ltd

Gambit Books, *imprint of* The Harvard Common Press

Games Workshop, *distributed by* Simon & Schuster Sales & Marketing

Jeffrey Garcia, *distributed by* Sunbelt Publications Inc

Garden Art Press, *imprint of* Antique Collectors Club Ltd

Isabella Stewart Gardner Museum, *distributed by* University Press of New England

Gardner Publications Inc, *distributed by* Hanser Publications LLC

Garland-Clark Editors, *distributed by* Players Press Inc

Garland Publishers, *distributor for* University of California Institute on Global Conflict & Cooperation

Garland Science, *imprint of* Routledge/Taylor & Francis, Taylor & Francis Inc

Garland Science Publishing, *member of* Taylor & Francis Group, The Taylor & Francis Group

John Garrett, *distributor for* Twenty-Third Publications

Gaslight Publications, *imprint of* Empire Publishing Service

Gateway, *imprint of* Regnery Publishing Inc

Gateways Books & Tapes, *division of* Institute for the Development of the Harmonious Human Being Inc, Institute for the Development of the Harmonious Human Being Inc, *distributor for* Cloister Recordings (audio & video tapes)

Gaudia Music & Arts, *distributed by* ECS Publishing Corp

Gault Millau, *imprint of* Gault Millau Inc/Gayot Publications

Gault Millau Inc/Gayot Publications, *distributed by* Publishers Group West

GAYOT, *imprint of* Gault Millau Inc/Gayot Publications

Gazelle, *distributor for* GemStone Press

Gazelle Book Services, *distributor for* Price World Publishing LLC

Geared Up Publications, *imprint of* Schiffer Publishing Ltd

Gecko Press, *distributed by* Lerner Publishing Group Inc

Gefen Books, *distributor for* Bar Ilan, Magnes Press

Gefen Publishing Ltd, *imprint of* Gefen Books

Gem Guides Book Co, *distributor for* Borden Publishing, Brynmorgen Press, Clear Creek Publishing, Earth Love Publishing, Editions du Signe, Gemstone Press, Golden West Books, Grand Canyon Association, Heaven & Earth Press, Hexagon Press, International Jewelry Publications, George R Jezek Photography, Cy Johnson & Son, KC Publications Inc, Many Moons Press, Naturegraph, Nevada Publications, Out of This World Press, Pinyon Publishing, Primer Publications, Ram Publishing, Recreation Sales, Shortfuse Press, Sierra Press, Delos Toole, Trees Co, Tri-Star Boze Books, Weseanne Publications, *distributed by* Nevada Publications

Gembooks, *imprint of* Gem Guides Book Co

Gemstone Press, *division of* Longhill Partners Inc, Longhill Partners Inc, *distributed by* Bayard/Novalis (Canada), Gazelle (UK), Gem Guides Book Co, Rainbow Book Agencies (Australia)

Genealogical Publishing Co, *subsidiary of* Genealogical.com, *distributed by* Higginson Book Co

Geneological Society of Pennsylvania, *distributed by* Diane Publishing Co

General Aviation, *imprint of* Osprey Publishing Inc

General Education Services (New Zealand), *distributed by* Abrams Learning Trends

General Military, *imprint of* Osprey Publishing Inc

Genesis Press, *distributed by* Kensington Publishing Corp

Genetic Engineering & Biotechnology News, *division of* Mary Ann Liebert Inc

Geneva Press, *imprint of* Presbyterian Publishing Corp

Gennadeion Monographs, *imprint of* ASCSA Publications

Gentle World, *distributed by* Book Publishing Co

Geological Society of London, *distributor for* AAPG (American Association of Petroleum Geologists), *distributed by* AAPG (American Association of Petroleum Geologists)

Geology and Geography of Alaska Series, *imprint of* University of Alaska Press

Geology Underfoot Series, *imprint of* Mountain Press Publishing Co

Geophysical Institute, *distributed by* University of Alaska Press

Georgetown University Press, *distributed by* The Johns Hopkins University Press

The Georgia Literary Association, *imprint of* Blood Moon Productions Ltd

German Texan Heritage Society, *distributed by* Eakin Press

getfitnow.com Books, *imprint of* Hatherleigh Press

Getting Into, *imprint of* Mel Bay Publications Inc

Getty, *distributed by* Oxford University Press USA

Getty Publications, *distributed by* University of Chicago Press (US only)

Gibbs Smith, *distributor for* Sierra Club Books

Gibbs-Smith, *distributor for* Sourced Media Books

Gifted Psychology Press, *imprint of* Great Potential Press Inc

Gig Savers, *imprint of* Mel Bay Publications Inc

Gilcrease Museum, *distributed by* University of Oklahoma Press

Gildan Media, *distributed by* Hachette Book Group

Gill & Macmillan, *distributed by* Dufour Editions Inc

Maureen Gilmer, *distributed by* Sunbelt Publications Inc

Gival Press, *imprint of* Gival Press LLC

Michael Glazier Books, *imprint of* Liturgical Press

Glencannon, *distributed by* Mystic Seaport Museum Inc

Glencoe, *imprint of* McGraw-Hill School Education Group

Glencoe/McGraw-Hill, *imprint of* McGraw-Hill Education

Peter Glenn Publications, *division of* Blount Communications

Glide Publications, *imprint of* Volcano Press

Glimmer Train Press Inc, *distributor for* Glimmer Train Stories

Glimmer Train Stories, *distributed by* Glimmer Train Press Inc

Global eBook Awards, *division of* Para Publishing LLC

Global Oriental, *distributed by* University of Hawaii Press

Global Professional Publishing, *distributed by* Stylus Publishing LLC

Global Research, *distributed by* Progressive Press

Global Trade Watch, *division of* Public Citizen

Globe Pequot Press, *distributor for* Montana Historical Society Press, *distributed by* Heimburger House Publishing Co

The Globe Pequot Press, *division of* Morris Book Publishing LLC, *distributor for* Appalachian Mountain Club, Appalachian Mountain Club Books, Boone & Crockett Club, Bradt Travel Guides, Thomas Cook Publishing, D & B Publishing, Day Hikes Books Inc, Earthbound Sports, Everyman Chess, Explorer Publishing, Montana Historical Society Press, New Holland Publishers Ltd (London, UK), Alastair Sawday Publishing (co-publr), Stoecklein Publishing, Trailblazer Publications, Visit Britain, Waterford Press, Western Horseman, Woodall Publications

Glove Pequot, *distributed by* Sunbelt Publications Inc

GOAL/QPC, *distributor for* American Society for Quality (ASQ)

Goblinshead, *distributed by* Dufour Editions Inc

GoFacts Guided Writing, *imprint of* Sundance/Newbridge Publishing

Gold Fever Press, *distributed by* Epicenter Press Inc

Golden Books, *imprint of* Random House Children's Books, Random House Inc, *distributed by* Perfection Learning Corp

Golden Books Family Entertainment, *distributor for* The Jim Henson Co

Golden Coast Publishing Co, *distributed by* University of Georgia Press

Golden Dawn Publications, *imprint of* The Original Falcon Press

Golden Hill Press, *distributed by* Heimburger House Publishing Co

Golden Triangle Books, *imprint of* University of Pittsburgh Press

Golden West Books, *distributed by* Gem Guides Book Co

Golden West Cookbooks, *division of* American Traveler Press

Golganooza Press, *distributed by* Fons Vitae

Gollehon Books, *imprint of* Gollehon Press Inc

Gomer Press, *distributed by* Beekman Books Inc

Good Books, *subsidiary of* Good Enterprises Ltd, Good Enterprises Ltd, *distributed by* Simon & Schuster, Simon & Schuster, Inc

Goodluck Guides, *distributed by* The News Group, Partners West

GoodParentGoodChild, *imprint of* Good Parent Inc

Gooseberry Patch, *distributed by* Andrews McMeel Publishing LLC

Goosebottom Books, *imprint of* Goosebottom Books LLC

Gordian Press, *distributor for* Phaeton Press

Gorgias Press LLC, *distributor for* Yeshiva University Museum Press, *distributed by* Oxbow (UK)

Gospel Publishing House (GPH), *division of* General Council of the Assemblies of God

Gotham, *imprint of* Penguin Group (USA) LLC

Gotham Books, *imprint of* Penguin Group (USA) LLC

Government Institutes (GI), *imprint of* Rowman & Littlefield Publishing Group, The Rowman & Littlefield Publishing Group

Government Jobs Series, *imprint of* PREP Publishing

Gower, *imprint of* Ashgate Publishing Co, Elsevier, Health Sciences Division

Colin Gower, *distributed by* Krause Publications Inc

GPC/Gollehon, *imprint of* Gollehon Press Inc

GPP® Life, *imprint of* The Globe Pequot Press

Graceland Press, *imprint of* Herald Publishing House

Gracewing (UK), *distributed by* Morehouse Publishing

Grade Finders Inc, *distributed by* Graphic Arts Association, National Paper Trade Association, North American Publishing, Printing Industries of America

Graduate Record Examination Series, *imprint of* National Learning Corp

Grafco Rock Books, *imprint of* Grafco Productions

Gramercy Books, *imprint of* Random House Inc

Gramophone, *distributed by* Omnibus Press

Grand Canyon Association, *distributed by* Gem Guides Book Co

Grand Central/Hachette Large Print, *distributed by* Thorndike Press®

Grand Central Life/Style, *imprint of* Grand Central Publishing

Grand Central Publishing, *division of* Hachette Book Group

Grand Harbor Press, *imprint of* Brilliance Audio

Donald M Grant Publisher Inc, *distributor for* Archival, Oswald Train

Granta, *imprint of* Grove/Atlantic Inc, *distributed by* Penguin Group (USA) LLC

Granta Magazine, *distributed by* Grove/Atlantic Inc

Graphia, *imprint of* Houghton Mifflin Harcourt Trade & Reference Division

Graphic Arts Association, *distributor for* Grade Finders Inc

Graphic Arts Books, *unit of* Ingram Content Group Inc

Graphic History, *imprint of* Osprey Publishing Inc

Graphic Universe™, *imprint of* Lerner Publishing Group Inc

Graphic Universe™, *division of* Lerner Publishing Group Inc

Graphix, *imprint of* Scholastic Trade Division

Grave Issues, *imprint of* Spinsters Ink

Gray Wolf Books, *distributed by* Farrar, Straus & Giroux, LLC

Grayson Publishing, *distributed by* Antique Collectors Club Ltd

Great Architectural Replica Series, *imprint of* Stemmer House Publishers Inc

Great Books of the Islamic World, *distributed by* Kazi Publications Inc

Great Explorer Series, *imprint of* University of Alaska Press

Great Lakes Books, *imprint of* Wayne State University Press

Great Outdoors Publishing Co, *imprint of* Finney Company Inc

Great Potential Press Inc, *division of* Anodyne Inc, Anodyne Inc

Great Source, *imprint of* Harcourt Inc

Great Source Education Group, *subsidiary of* Houghton Mifflin Harcourt, Houghton Mifflin Harcourt Publishing Company

Great Valley Books, *imprint of* Heyday Books

The Greeley Co, *subsidiary of* HCPro Inc

Green Books, *distributed by* Chelsea Green Publishing Co

Green Building Press, *distributed by* Chelsea Green Publishing Co

Green Grass Press, *distributed by* Sunbelt Publications Inc

Green Knees, *imprint of* Azro Press

Green Lion Press, *distributed by* Enfield Publishing & Distribution Co

Green Man Publishing, *distributed by* Chelsea Green Publishing Co

Green Sugar Press, *distributed by* Associated Publishers Group, Follett Library Resources

Green Tiger Press, *imprint of* Laughing Elephant

Greenberg Books, *imprint of* Madavor Media

Greenbranch, *distributed by* Medical Group Management Association (MGMA)

Alice Greene & Co, *imprint of* T H Peek Publisher

Greenfield Review Press, *distributed by* Cross-Cultural Communications

Greenhaven Imprints, *distributor for* Lucent Books®

Greenhaven Press, *distributed by* Lucent Books®

Greenhaven Press®, *imprint of* Gale

Greenhaven Press Inc, *distributed by* Perfection Learning Corp

Greenhill Books, *distributed by* Casemate Publishers & Book Distributors LLC

Greenleaf Book Group Press, *imprint of* Greenleaf Book Group LLC

Greenwich Medical Media, *distributed by* Oxford University Press USA

Greenwich Workshop Press, *distributed by* Algonquin Books of Chapel Hill, Artisan Books

Greenwich Workshop Press Fearless Critic Media, *distributed by* Workman Publishing Co Inc

Greenwillow Books, *imprint of* HarperCollins Children's Books, HarperCollins Publishers

Greenwood Cemetery, *distributed by* The Center for Thanatology Research & Education Inc

Greenwood Press, *imprint of* ABC-CLIO

Greenwood Research Books & Software, *division of* Greenwood Research

Greeting Cards, *division of* Unarius Academy of Science Publications

Grey House, *imprint of* Grey House Publishing Inc™

Grey House Publishing Canada, *division of* Grey House Publishing Inc™

Grief Watch, *distributed by* ACTA Publications

Griffin, *imprint of* St Martin's Press, LLC

Griot Audio, *imprint of* Recorded Books LLC

Grolier, *distributor for* The Jim Henson Co

The Grolier Club, *distributed by* Oak Knoll Press

Grolier International Inc Philippines, *subsidiary of* Scholastic International

Grolier International Inc Singapore, *subsidiary of* Scholastic International

Grolier International Inc Thailand, *subsidiary of* Scholastic International

Grolier (Malaysia) Sdn Bhd, *subsidiary of* Scholastic International

Grolier Online®, *imprint of* Scholastic Consumer & Professional Publishing

Grosset, *distributor for* Parachute Publishing LLC

Grosset & Dunlap, *subsidiary of* Penguin Group (USA) LLC, *imprint of* Penguin Group (USA) LLC, Penguin Young Readers Group

Grosset/Putnam, *imprint of* Penguin Group (USA) LLC, GP Putnam's Sons (Hardcover)

Stefan Grossman's Guitar Workshop, *distributed by* Mel Bay Publications Inc

Groundworks, *distributed by* Chelsea Green Publishing Co

Group for the Advancement of Psychiatry, *distributed by* American Psychiatric Publishing (APP)

Group Publishing, *distributed by* Saint Mary's Press

Group Workcamps™, *imprint of* Group Publishing Inc

Group's Hands-On Bible Curriculum™, *imprint of* Group Publishing Inc

Grove/Atlantic Inc, *distributor for* Granta Magazine, Open City Books, *distributed by* Publishers Group West/Perseus Distribution Co

Grove Dictionaries, *distributed by* Oxford University Press USA

Grove Press, *imprint of* Grove/Atlantic Inc

The Grow Network/McGraw-Hill, *imprint of* McGraw-Hill Education

Grub Street, *distributed by* Casemate Publishers & Book Distributors LLC

B R Gruener Publishing Co, *imprint of* John Benjamins Publishing Co

Gryphon Books, *distributor for* PPC, Zeon

Gryphon Crime Series, *imprint of* Gryphon Books

Gryphon Doubles, *imprint of* Gryphon Books

Gryphon House, *distributor for* DawnSignPress, *distributed by* Teaching Strategies

Gryphon House Inc, *subsidiary of* Kaplan Early Learning Co, *distributor for* Aha Communications, Book Peddlers, Deya Brashears, Bright Ring Publishing, Building Blocks, Center for the Child Care Workforce, Chatterbox Press, Chicago Review Press, Children's Resources International, Circle Time Publishers, Sydney Gurewitz Clemens, Conari Press, Council Oak Books, Dawn Sign Press, Delmar Publishers Inc, Early Educator's Press, Educators for Social Responsibility, Family Center of Nova University, Jean Feldman, Floris Books, Hawthorne Press, Highscope, Hunter House Publishers, Kaplan Press, Loving Guidance Inc, Miss Jackie Inc, Monjeu Press, National Center Early Childhood Workforce, New England AEYC, New Horizons, Nova Southeastern University, Pademelon Press, Partner Press, Pollyanna Productions, Robins Lane Press, School Renaissance, Southern Early Childhood Association, Steam Press, Syracuse University Press, Teaching Strategies, Telshare Publishing

Gryphon SF Rediscovery Series, *imprint of* Gryphon Books

GT Publishing, *distributed by* HarperCollins Publishers

Guilford Press, *distributed by* ADD Warehouse

The Guilford Press, *division of* Guilford Publications Inc

Guitar One, *distributed by* Hal Leonard Corp

Guitar World, *distributed by* Hal Leonard Corp

Gulf Coast Association of Geological Societies, *distributed by* Bureau of Economic Geology, University of Texas at Austin

Gulf Professional Publishers, *distributed by* Marine Techniques Publishing

Gulf Publishing, *distributed by* NACE International

Gulf Publishing Co, *distributor for* Editions Technip, Elsevier, Pennwell, Simon & Schuster, Wiley

Gumdrop, *distributor for* Ozark Publishing Inc

Gumdrop Books, *distributor for* ARO Publishing Co

Gun Digest® Books, *imprint of* Krause Publications Inc

The George Gund Foundation, *imprint of* University of California Press

Gunsmoke Westerns, *imprint of* AudioGO

Haase House, *imprint of* Easy Money Press

Hachai Publishing, *distributor for* Attara, Kerem

Hachette Book Group, *subsidiary of* Hachette Livre, *distributor for* Harry N Abrams Inc, Amazing People Club, Chronicle Books, Disney Book Group, Filipacchi Publishing, Gildan Media, Hachette UK, Houghton Mifflin Harcourt Trade & Reference Division, Hyperion, innovativeKids®, Kensington, Marvel, Microsoft Learning, Octopus Books, Oxmoor House, Phaidon Press, Time Inc Home Entertainment

Hachette Book Group USA, *distributor for* Disney Press, Kensington Publishing Corp

Hachette Digital, *division of* Hachette Book Group

Hachette Livre, *distributed by* Antique Collectors Club Ltd

Hachette UK, *distributed by* Hachette Book Group

Hachette US, *distributor for* Quayside Publishing Group

Hackett Publishing Co Inc, *distributor for* Bryn Mawr Commentaries

Hagstrom Map & Travel Center, *subsidiary of* American Map Corp, *distributor for* ADC The Map People, American Map Corp, Arrow Maps Inc, Creative Sales Corp, De Lorme Atlas, Hammond World Atlas Corp, Langenscheidt, RV International Maps & Atlases, Stubs Guides, Trakker Maps Inc

Hagstrom Map Co Inc, *subsidiary of* American Map Corp

Hal Leonard Books, *imprint of* Hal Leonard Performing Arts Publishing Group

Hal Leonard Corp, *distributor for* Amadeus Press, Applause Theatre & Cinema Books, Artistpro, Ashley Music, Backbeat Books, Beacon Music, Berklee Press, Fred Bock Music Company, Boosey & Hawkes, Centerstream Publications, Centerstream Publishing LLC, Cherry Lane Music Co, Cinema Books, Community Music Videos, Creative Concepts, DC Publications, Devine Entertainment Corp, Editions Durand, Editions Max Eschig, Editions Salabert, EM Books, EMI Christian, Faber Music Ltd, Guitar One, Guitar World, Home Recording, Homespun Tapes, Houston Publications, Hudson Music, iSong CD-ROMs, Jawbone Press, Kenyon Publications, Limelight Editions, Ashley Mark Publishing Co, Edward B Marks Music, Meredith Music, Modern Drummer Publications, Music Sales America, Musicians Institute Press, Musikverlage Han Sikorski, Christopher Parkening, Reader's Digest, Record Research, Ricordi, Lee Roberts Publications, Rubank Publications, G Schirmer Inc (Associated Music Publishers), Second Floor Music, Sing Out Corp, Star Licks Videos, Bernard Stein Music Co, String Letter Press, Tara Publications, Transcontinental Music, 21st Century Publications, Vintage Guitar, Word Music, Writer's Digest

Halcyon House, *imprint of* National Book Co

Halcyon House Publishers, *imprint of* Acres USA

Halcyon Press Ltd, *distributor for* Plato Publishing

Robert Hale, *distributed by* Antique Collectors Club Ltd

Half Halt Press Inc, *distributor for* The Kenilworth Press Ltd, Quiller Publishing

Halsted Press, *imprint of* John Wiley & Sons Inc

Hamadia Publishing, *distributed by* Feldheim Publishers (Philipp Feldheim Inc)

Hamewith, *imprint of* Baker Books

Hamilton Books, *member of* Rowman & Littlefield Publishing Group, *imprint of* University Press of America Inc

Hammond Pub, *distributed by* Perfection Learning Corp

Hammond World Atlas Corp, *subsidiary of* American Map Corp, *distributed by* Hagstrom Map & Travel Center

Hampton Roads Publishing, *imprint of* Red Wheel/Weiser/Conari

Hampton Roads Publishing Co Inc, *distributed by* Red Wheel/Weiser LLC

Han-Shan Tang Books, *distributed by* Antique Collectors Club Ltd

Hand Print Press, *distributed by* Chelsea Green Publishing Co

Handbook of North American Indians, *distributed by* Smithsonian Scholarly Press

Handprint Books, *distributed by* Chronicle Books LLC

Handprint Books Inc, *imprint of* Chronicle Books LLC, *distributed by* Chronicle Books

Hanley-Wood LLC, *division of* Hanley-Wood Inc, Hanley-Wood Inc

Hanser Gardner Publications, *distributed by* Hanser Publications LLC

Hanser Publications LLC, *subsidiary of* Carl Hanser Verlag GmbH & Co KG, Carl Hanser Verlag GmbH & Co KG, *distributor for* Gardner Publications Inc, Hanser Gardner Publications (imprint also), Hanser Publishers (call Hanser Verlag)

Hanser Publishers, *distributed by* Hanser Publications LLC

HAP (Health Adminstration Press), *distributed by* Medical Group Management Association (MGMA)

Happy Day Books, *imprint of* Standard Publishing

Harbor Hill Books, *division of* Purple Mountain Press Ltd

Harbor Lights, *imprint of* LangMarc Publishing

Harbour Publishing, *distributed by* Heimburger House Publishing Co

Harcourt, *distributor for* Parachute Publishing LLC, *distributed by* Learning Links Inc, SAS Publishing

Harcourt Achieve, *division of* Houghton Mifflin Harcourt, *imprint of* Harcourt Inc

Harcourt Children's, *imprint of* Houghton Mifflin Harcourt Trade & Reference Division

Harcourt Inc, *division of* Houghton Mifflin Harcourt, *distributed by* Perfection Learning Corp

Harcourt Mifflin School Publishers, *division of* Harcourt Inc

Hard Shell, *imprint of* Mundania Press LLC

Hard Shell Word Factory, *imprint of* Mundania Press LLC, *distributed by* All-Romance Ebooks, Amazon Kindle, Apple iBookStore, B&N.com, Fictionwise, Lightning Source/Ingram, Mobipocket, Smashwords

Hardie Press, *distributed by* Mel Bay Publications Inc

Hardscrabble Books, *imprint of* University Press of New England

Hardwood Press, *distributed by* St Augustine's Press Inc

Harlequin, *imprint of* Harlequin Enterprises Ltd, *distributed by* Simon & Schuster Sales & Marketing

Harlequin Enterprises Ltd, *subsidiary of* Torstar Corp, *distributed by* Simon & Schuster, Inc, Simon & Schuster Mass Merchandise Sales Co

Harmony, *imprint of* Crown Publishing Group

Harmony Books, *imprint of* Random House Inc

Harp of the Gazelle, *imprint of* Gorgias Press LLC

Harper, *imprint of* HarperCollins General Books Group

Harper Arrington Publishing, *distributor for* The Little Entrepreneur

Harper Business, *imprint of* HarperCollins General Books Group

Harper Collins, *distributor for* Nevraumont Publishing Co

Harper Design, *imprint of* HarperCollins General Books Group

Harper Entertainment, *distributor for* Parachute Publishing LLC

Harper Paperbacks, *imprint of* HarperCollins General Books Group

Harper Perennial, *imprint of* HarperCollins General Books Group

Harper Voyager, *imprint of* HarperCollins General Books Group

Harper Wave, *imprint of* HarperCollins General Books Group

HarperAudio, *imprint of* HarperCollins General Books Group, HarperCollins Publishers Sales

HarperBibles, *imprint of* HarperCollins General Books Group

HarperBusiness, *imprint of* HarperCollins Publishers Sales

HarperCollins, *imprint of* HarperCollins General Books Group, HarperCollins Publishers, HarperCollins Publishers Sales, *distributor for* Alloy Entertainment, Delphinium Books, Parachute Publishing LLC, *distributed by* Heimburger House Publishing Co, Learning Links Inc, MAR*CO Products Inc

HarperCollins Children's Audio, *imprint of* HarperCollins Children's Books

HarperCollins Children's Books, *division of* HarperCollins Publishers, *imprint of* HarperCollins Children's Books

HarperCollins e-books, *imprint of* HarperCollins Children's Books, HarperCollins General Books Group

HarperCollins General Books Group, *division of* HarperCollins Publishers

HarperCollins Publishers, *subsidiary of* News Corporation, *distributor for* Basic Books, Civitas, Counterpoint, Delphinium Books, GT Publishing, Perseus (Addison Wesley Trade), Public Affairs, TV Books, *distributed by* Cynthia Publishing Co, Ingram Publisher Services/Spring Arbor (Christian market)

HarperDesign, *imprint of* HarperCollins Publishers Sales

HarperEntertainment, *imprint of* HarperCollins Publishers Sales

HarperFestival, *imprint of* HarperCollins Children's Books

HarperLarge Print, *imprint of* HarperCollins Publishers Sales

HarperLuxe, *imprint of* HarperCollins General Books Group, *distributed by* Thorndike Press®

HarperOne, *imprint of* HarperCollins General Books Group

HarperResource, *imprint of* HarperCollins Publishers Sales

Harper's Magazine Foundation, *division of* Franklin Square Press

HarperSanFrancisco, *imprint of* HarperCollins Publishers Sales

HarperTeen, *imprint of* HarperCollins Children's Books

HarperTorch, *imprint of* HarperCollins Publishers Sales

HarperTrophy, *imprint of* HarperCollins Children's Books

Harpia Publishing, *distributed by* Casemate Publishers & Book Distributors LLC

Harrap, *distributed by* Houghton Mifflin Harcourt

Harrison House, *distributor for* Faith Library Publications

Tom Harrison Cartography, *distributed by* Mountain n' Air Books

Alan Hartman, *distributed by* Antique Collectors Club Ltd

Hartman Publishing Inc, *distributor for* Beverly Foundation

Harvard Art Museums, *distributed by* Yale University Press

Harvard Business Press, *division of* Harvard Business Publishing, *distributed by* Client Distribution Services

Harvard Business Reference, *imprint of* Harvard Business Press

Harvard Business School Press, *distributed by* Center for Creative Leadership LLC, SAS Publishing

Harvard Center for International Affairs, *distributed by* University Press of America Inc

Harvard Center for Middle Eastern Studies, *distributed by* Harvard University Press

Harvard Center for Population Studies, *distributed by* Harvard University Press

Harvard Center for the Study of World Religions, *distributed by* Harvard University Press

Harvard College Library, *distributed by* Harvard University Press

Harvard Common Press, *distributed by* Houghton Mifflin Harcourt Trade & Reference Division

The Harvard Common Press, *distributed by* Houghton Mifflin Harcourt

Harvard Department of Sanskrit & Indian Studies, *distributed by* Harvard University Press

Harvard Department of the Classics, *distributed by* Harvard University Press

Harvard Education Letter, *imprint of* Harvard Education Publishing Group

Harvard Education Press, *imprint of* Harvard Education Publishing Group

Harvard Education Publishing Group, *division of* Harvard University

Harvard Educational Review Reprint Series, *imprint of* Harvard Education Publishing Group

Harvard Ukrainian Research Institute, *subsidiary of* Harvard University, *distributed by* Harvard University Press

Harvard University Art Museums, *distributed by* Yale University Press

Harvard University Asia Center, *distributed by* Harvard University Press

Harvard University David Rockefeller Center for Latin American Studies, *distributed by* Harvard University Press

Harvard University Press, *distributor for* Dumbarton Oaks, Harvard Center for Middle Eastern Studies, Harvard Center for Population Studies, Harvard Center for the Study of World Religions, Harvard College Library (including Houghton Library Judaica division), Harvard Department of Sanskrit & Indian Studies, Harvard Department of the Classics, Harvard Ukrainian Research Institute, Harvard University Asia Center, Harvard University David Rockefeller Center for Latin American Studies, Harvard-Yenching Institute, Peabody Museum of Archaeology & Ethnology

Harvard-Yenching Institute, *distributed by* Harvard University Press

Harvest Hill Press, *distributed by* University Press of New England

Harvest House, *distributor for* Focus on the Family

Hatherleigh Press, *subsidiary of* Hatherleigh Co Ltd, Hatherleigh Co Ltd, *distributed by* Random House Distribution Services

Haven, *imprint of* Bridge-Logos Inc

Hawthorn Press, *distributed by* SteinerBooks

Hawthorne Press, *distributed by* Gryphon House Inc

Hay House Inc, *distributed by* Dempsey-Your Distributor Inc, Raincoast

Hayes, *distributed by* Perfection Learning Corp

Haynes, *distributed by* Delmar

Haynes Manuals Inc, *division of* The Haynes Publishing Group, *distributor for* G T Foulis, Haynes Owners Workshop Manuals, Oxford Illustrated Press, *distributed by* Motorbooks International

Haynes Owners Workshop Manuals, *distributed by* Haynes Manuals Inc

Nicolas Hays Inc, *distributed by* Red Wheel/Weiser/Conari

Hazamir, *imprint of* Transcontinental Music Publications

Hazelden/Johnson Institute, *imprint of* Hazelden Publishing

Hazelden/Keep Coming Back, *imprint of* Hazelden Publishing

Hazelden-Pittman Archives Press, *imprint of* Hazelden Publishing

Hazelden Publishing, *division of* Hazelden Foundation, *distributor for* Obsessive Anonymous, *distributed by* Health Communications Inc (trade)

HCI Books, *imprint of* Health Communications Inc

HCI Books Inc, *distributor for* Central Recovery Press (CRP)

HCI Teens, *imprint of* Health Communications Inc

Headwater Books, *distributed by* Stackpole Books

Healey Publishing, *distributed by* Sunbelt Publications Inc

Healing Arts Press, *imprint of* Inner Traditions International Ltd

Healing Tao Books, *distributed by* Tuttle Publishing

Health Administration Press, *division of* Foundation of the American College of Healthcare Executives

Health Books, *imprint of* Oxmoor House Inc

Health Communications Inc, *distributor for* Hazelden Publishing

Health Forum Inc, *subsidiary of* American Hospital Association

Health Information Network, *distributor for* Apollo Managed Care Inc

Health Information Press (HIP), *imprint of* Practice Management Information Corp (PMIC)

Health Professions Press, *division of* Paul H Brookes Publishing Co Inc, Brookes Publishing Co Inc, *subsidiary of* Brookes Publishing Co Inc, *distributed by* The Eurospan Group (Africa, Europe & Middle East), Footprint Books Pty Ltd (Australia, Fiji, New Zealand & Papua New Guinea), Login Brothers (Canada), Unifacmanu Trading Co Ltd (Taiwan)

Health Research GP Buyers UP, *division of* Public Citizen

Healthcare Performance Press, *imprint of* Productivity Press

Healthwatch, *imprint of* Players Press Inc

Healthy Living, *imprint of* Book Publishing Co

Healthy Living Books, *imprint of* Hatherleigh Press

Hearne Fine Art, *distributed by* The University of Arkansas Press

Hearst Books, *imprint of* HarperCollins Publishers, Sterling Publishing Co Inc

Hearthside Books, *distributed by* Closson Press

Hearts & Tummies Cookbook Co, *division of* Quixote Press, *imprint of* Quixote Press

Hearts 'n Tummies Cookbook Co, *imprint of* Hearts & Tummies Cookbook Co

HeatWave Romance, *subsidiary of* Awe-Struck Publishing

Heaven & Earth Press, *distributed by* Gem Guides Book Co

Heaven & Earth Publications, *distributed by* North Atlantic Books

Hebrew Union College Press, *division of* Hebrew Union College, *distributed by* Wayne State University Press

Heian International, *imprint of* Stone Bridge Press Inc

Heian International Inc, *imprint of* Stone Bridge Press Inc

Heimburger House Publishing Co, *distributor for* Black Dog & Leventhal, Book Sales Inc, Boyds Mills Press, Canadian Caboose Press, Carstens, Child's Play International, Evergreen Press, Firefly Books Ltd, Fitzhenry & Whiteside Ltd, Fordham University Press, Globe Pequot Press, Golden Hill Press, Harbour Publishing, HarperCollins, Johns Hopkins University Press, Hot Box Press, Houghton Mifflin Harcourt, Howling at the Moon Press, Iconografix, Indiana University Press, Kalmbach Publishing, Krause Publications, Motorbooks International, National Book Network, New York University Press, W W Norton & Co, Penquin Putnam Inc, Pictorial Histories Publishing Co, Sono Nis Press, Steam Passages Publishing, Sterling Publishing, Sugar Cane Press, Syracuse University Press, Thunder Bay Press, University of Minnesota Press, University of Scranton, Westcliffe Publishing, John Wiley & Sons

Heimdal, *distributed by* Casemate Publishers & Book Distributors LLC

William S Hein & Co Inc, *distributor for* Ashgate, Aspen, Butterworths, Sweet & Maxwell, John Wiley & Sons Inc

Heinemann, *division of* Houghton Mifflin Harcourt, *distributed by* ArtAge Publications, National Science Teachers Association (NSTA)

Heinemann Raintree, *division of* Capstone Publishers™

Heinle, *subsidiary of* Cengage Learning, *imprint of* Wadsworth Publishing

Heirloom Children's Book Publishers, *imprint of* Schiel & Denver Book Publishers

John Helde, *distributed by* EastBridge

Helion & Co Ltd, *distributed by* Casemate Publishers & Book Distributors LLC

Helios Press, *imprint of* Allworth Press

Hellgate Press, *imprint of* L & R Publishing, *distributed by* Midpoint Trade Books

Hendrick-Long Publishing Co, *distributor for* NES, The Official Tasp Study Guide

Henry Holt, *imprint of* Henry Holt and Company, LLC, *distributor for* Nevraumont Publishing Co

Ian Henry Publications, *distributed by* Empire Publishing Service

Joseph Henry Press, *imprint of* National Academies Press (NAP)

Herald Press, *imprint of* MennoMedia, *distributor for* Faith & Life Resources

Herald Publishing House, *division of* Community of Christ

Herbs & Spice, *imprint of* Crossquarter Publishing Group

Herder & Herder, *imprint of* The Crossroad Publishing Co

Here & Now, *imprint of* Gallopade International Inc

Editions Charles Herissey, *distributed by* Casemate Publishers & Book Distributors LLC

Heritage Books, *imprint of* Heritage Books Inc

Heritage Books Inc, *distributor for* Carroll County Genealogical Society, Fairfax Genealogical Society, National Genealogical Society, Virginia Genealogical Society

Heritage Builders, *imprint of* Focus on the Family

Heritage House, *distributor for* FineEdge.com

Nick Hern Books, *distributed by* Theatre Communications Group

Heroes & Helpers, *imprint of* Gallopade International Inc

Heroides Publishing, *imprint of* Joshua Tree Publishing

Hersilia, *distributed by* Dufour Editions Inc

Herzl Press, *subsidiary of* World Zionist Organization, *distributed by* Associated University Presses, Cornwal Books

Hes & De Graaf, *distributed by* Oak Knoll Press

Hesperia, *imprint of* ASCSA Publications

Hess Publications, *distributed by* Pilgrim Publications

Heuristic Books, *imprint of* Science & Humanities Press

Hewitt Homeschooling Resources, *division of* Hewitt Research Foundation

Hexagon Press, *distributed by* Gem Guides Book Co

Hi Willow Research & Publishing, *distributed by* LMC Source

Hidden Travel Series, *imprint of* Ulysses Press

HiddenSpring, *imprint of* Paulist Press

Higginson Book Co, *distributor for* Genealogical Publishing Co

High Museum of Art, *distributed by* Antique Collectors Club Ltd

High Tide Monograph Series, *imprint of* High Tide Press

High Tide Press, *subsidiary of* The Trinity Foundation

Highbridge Audio, *division of* Workman Publishing Co Inc, *imprint of* Algonquin Books of Chapel Hill, *distributed by* Penguin Audiobooks, Penguin Group (USA) LLC

Highgate Press, *imprint of* ECS Publishing Corp

HighRoads Media, *distributed by* Macmillan Audio

Highscope, *distributed by* Gryphon House Inc

hikingcamping.com, *distributed by* Sunbelt Publications Inc

Hill & Wang, *division of* Farrar, Straus & Giroux, LLC, *imprint of* Farrar, Straus & Giroux, LLC

Lawrence Hill Books, *imprint of* Chicago Review Press

Hill Winds Press, *distributed by* Enfield Publishing & Distribution Co

Hillenbrand Books, *imprint of* Liturgy Training Publications

Hillsdale College Press, *division of* Hillsdale College

Himalayan Institute Press, *division of* Himalayan International Institute of Yoga Science and Philosophy

Hindustan Book Agency, *distributed by* American Mathematical Society

Hinkler Books, *distributed by* Ideals Publications, a Guideposts Co

Hippocrates Publications, *imprint of* Book Publishing Co

Histoire & Collections, *distributed by* Casemate Publishers & Book Distributors LLC

Historic Idaho Series, *distributed by* Caxton Press

Historic New Orleans Collection, *distributed by* Oak Knoll Press

Historical Archive Press, *distributed by* Casemate Publishers & Book Distributors LLC

Historical Images, *imprint of* Bright Mountain Books Inc

Historical Indexes, *distributed by* Casemate Publishers & Book Distributors LLC

Historical Society of Pennsylvania, *distributed by* Diane Publishing Co

Historical Society of Western Pennsylvania, *distributed by* Stackpole Books

History Facts, *distributed by* Casemate Publishers & Book Distributors LLC

HMH Education Group, *imprint of* Houghton Mifflin Harcourt

HMH Franchise, *imprint of* Houghton Mifflin Harcourt Trade & Reference Division

HMH Trade and Reference Publishers, *imprint of* Houghton Mifflin Harcourt

Hoard's Dairyman Magazine, *imprint of* W D Hoard & Sons Co

Hobar Publications, *division of* Finney Company Inc, *distributor for* Drache Publications

Hobbes End Publishing LLC, *subsidiary of* Hobbes End Entertainment LLC

Hobblebush Books, *distributor for* Abelard Press, Oyster River Press, Plaidswede Publishing

Hochelaga, *distributor for* Cross-Cultural Communications, *distributed by* Cross-Cultural Communications

Hodder Education, *distributed by* Trans-Atlantic Publications Inc

Hogarth, *imprint of* Crown Publishing Group

Verlag Hans Huber Hogrefe AG, *distributed by* Hogrefe Publishing

Hogrefe Publishing, *distributor for* Verlag Hans Huber Hogrefe AG (Switzerland), Hogrefe Verlag (Germany)

Hogrefe Verlag, *distributed by* Hogrefe Publishing

Hohm Press, *subsidiary of* HSM LLC

Paul Holberton Publishing, *distributed by* Casemate Publishers & Book Distributors LLC

Holiday Bazaar Guide-OR, *imprint of* Goodluck Guides

Holiday Bazaar Guide-WA, *imprint of* Goodluck Guides

Hollywood Film Archive, *distributor for* R R Bowker

Holmes Publishing Group LLC, *distributor for* Capall-Bann (UK), Fulgur Ltd, Jerusalem Press, Starfire Publishing, Three Hands Press, Xoanon Publishing

Holmgren Design Services, *distributed by* Chelsea Green Publishing Co

Holocaust Library, *imprint of* United States Holocaust Memorial Museum

Holt Enterprises, *distributed by* Delmar

Henry Holt, *imprint of* Henry Holt and Company, LLC, *distributor for* Nevraumont Publishing Co

Henry Holt and Company, LLC, *division of* Macmillan, Macmillan

Holt McDougal, *division of* Houghton Mifflin Harcourt

Holt Paperbacks, *imprint of* Henry Holt and Company, LLC

Holy Cross Orthodox Press, *division of* Hellenic College Inc, Hellenic College Inc

Homa & Sekey Books, *distributor for* China Encyclopedia Publishing House, China Intercontinental Press, China Zhejiang Publishing United Group

Home Builders Press, *distributed by* Craftsman Book Co

Home Planners LLC, *subsidiary of* Hanley-Wood Inc, Hanley-Wood Inc, *distributed by* Creative Homeowner Press, H B Fenn & Co

Home Recording, *distributed by* Hal Leonard Corp

Homespun Tapes, *distributed by* Hal Leonard Corp

Homespun Video, *distributed by* Stackpole Books

Homestead Publishing, *affiliate of* Book Design Ltd

Homiletic & Pastoral Review, *subsidiary of* Ignatius Press

Honey Bear Books, *imprint of* Modern Publishing

Alan C Hood & Co Inc, *distributor for* Maryland Historical Society

Hooked on Phonics, *distributed by* Simon & Schuster, Inc

Hoop Tales®, *imprint of* The Globe Pequot Press

Hoover Institution Press, *subsidiary of* Hoover Institution on War, Revolution & Peace

Hoover's Business Press, *imprint of* Hoover's, Inc

Hoover's Handbooks, *imprint of* Hoover's, Inc

Hope Publishing House, *distributed by* Pelican Publishing Co

Johns Hopkins Aids Service, *distributed by* The Johns Hopkins University Press

Johns Hopkins University Press, *distributor for* Inter-American Development Bank, International Food Policy Research Institute, *distributed by* Heimburger House Publishing Co

Hops Press, *distributed by* Mountain Press Publishing Co

Horizon Publishers & Distributors Inc, *distributed by* Cedar Fort Inc

The Horse Health Care Library, *imprint of* Eclipse Press

Horse Latitudes Press, *imprint of* Crumb Elbow Publishing

Horticulture Books, *imprint of* Betterway Books

Hospital & Healthcare Compensation Service, *subsidiary of* John R Zabka Associates Inc, John R Zabka Associates Inc

Hot Box Press, *distributed by* Heimburger House Publishing Co

Houghton Mifflin Books for Children, *imprint of* Houghton Mifflin Harcourt Trade & Reference Division

Houghton Mifflin Harcourt, *imprint of* Houghton Mifflin Harcourt Trade & Reference Division, *distributor for* Chambers, Clarion Books, Harrap, The Harvard Common Press, Larousse Bilingual, Larousse Mexico, The Old Farmer's Almanac, Zest Books, *distributed by* Heimburger House Publishing Co

Houghton Mifflin Harcourt K-12 Publishers, *division of* Houghton Mifflin Harcourt

Houghton Mifflin Harcourt Publishing Company, *distributed by* Learning Links Inc

Houghton Mifflin Harcourt Trade & Reference Division, *division of* Houghton Mifflin Harcourt, Houghton Mifflin Harcourt Publishing Company, *distributor for* Harvard Common Press, Larausse, Old Farmers Almanac, *distributed by* Hachette Book Group

Hourglass, *imprint of* Baker Books

House of Collectibles, *imprint of* Random House Inc, Random House Information Group, Random House Reference/Random House Puzzles & Games/House of Collectibles

House to House Publications, *division of* DOVE Christian Fellowship International

Houston Publications, *distributed by* Hal Leonard Corp

HOW Books, *imprint of* F+W Media Inc, North Light Books

Howard Books, *imprint of* Atria Publishing Group

Howard University Press, *distributed by* The Johns Hopkins University Press

Howell Book House, *imprint of* John Wiley & Sons Inc

Howling at the Moon Press, *distributed by* Heimburger House Publishing Co

HPBooks, *imprint of* Berkley Publishing Group, Penguin Group (USA) LLC

HQN Books, *imprint of* Harlequin Enterprises Ltd

HRD Central, *distributor for* HRD Press

HRD Press, *distributed by* Ane Books (India), Centre for Customer Care (CCC) (Malaysia), Eurospan Ltd (Europe), HRD Central (Australia), IBS Buku SDN BHD (Malaysia), Knowledge Resources (South Africa), Management Learning Resources (United Kingdom), Multimedia HRD Pvt Ltd (India), PSI Consulting Inc (Korea), RV Crest International Inc/FDIX (Philippines), Trainco (South Africa), Training & Development Materials of Canada (Canada)

HSWF, *imprint of* Hard Shell Word Factory

Hub City Press, *distributed by* John F Blair Publisher

Huber, *distributed by* Alan Wofsy Fine Arts

Huckleberry House LLC, *distributed by* Sunbelt Publications Inc

Hudson Hills, *distributor for* National Gallery of Art

Hudson Hills Press Inc, *distributor for* American Federation of Arts

Hudson Hills Press LLC, *distributed by* National Book Network

Hudson Music, *distributed by* Hal Leonard Corp

Hudson Park Press, *distributed by* Publishers Group West

Hudson Street Press, *imprint of* Penguin Group (USA) LLC

Huia Publishers, *distributed by* University of Hawaii Press

Human Alchemy Publications, *distributed by* Crown House Publishing Co LLC

Human Rights Watch Books, *imprint of* Human Rights Watch

Humana Press, *imprint of* Springer

Humanity Books, *imprint of* Prometheus Books

Humanix Books LLC, *division of* NewsMaxx

Bruce Humphries, *imprint of* Branden Books

Lund Humphries, *imprint of* Ashgate Publishing Co

Hungry Goat Press, *imprint of* Gauthier Publications Inc

Hunter House Publishers, *distributed by* Gryphon House Inc

Karen Hunter Publishing, *imprint of* Gallery Books

Huntington Library, *distributed by* University of California Press

Huntington Library Press, *division of* Huntington Library, Art Collections & Botanical Gardens, *distributed by* University of California Press

Hurst, *distributed by* Oxford University Press USA

The Hutton Settlement, *distributed by* Washington State University Press

Hydra, *imprint of* Random House Inc, Random House Publishing Group

Hyperbole, *imprint of* San Diego State University Press

Hyperion, *distributor for* Alloy Entertainment, *distributed by* Hachette Book Group

Hyperion Audio, *imprint of* Hyperion

Hyperion Books for Children, *imprint of* Disney Publishing Worldwide

Hyperion eBooks, *imprint of* Hyperion

Hypermedia Inc, *imprint of* Frederic C Beil Publisher Inc

Hyphen Press, *distributed by* Princeton Architectural Press

I Love You, *imprint of* Modern Publishing

I&T Shop Service, *imprint of* Penton Media

IBC Publishing, *distributed by* Stone Bridge Press Inc

IBEX Press, *imprint of* Ibex Publishers

Ibex Publishers, *distributor for* Farhang Moaser

IBFD North America Inc (International Bureau of Fiscal Documentation), *division of* IBFD Foundation

IBS, *distributed by* Jonathan David Publishers Inc

IBS Buku SDN BHD, *distributor for* HRD Press

IchemE, *distributed by* American Institute of Chemical Engineers (AIChE)

Ichor Business Books, *imprint of* Purdue University Press

ICJ, *distributed by* United Nations Publications

ICLE, *imprint of* Institute of Continuing Legal Education

Iconografix, *distributed by* Heimburger House Publishing Co

Iconografix Inc, *distributed by* Motorbooks International

Idaho Center for the Book, *affiliate of* Library of Congress

Idea Bank, *distributed by* Fire Engineering Books & Videos

Ideals, *imprint of* Ideals Publications, a Guideposts Co

Ideals Children's Books, *imprint of* Ideals Publications, a Guideposts Co

Ideals Publications, a Guideposts Co, *distributor for* Hinkler Books, Rourke Publishing, Smart Ink, Smart Kidz, Someday Baby

Ides et Calendes, *distributed by* Alan Wofsy Fine Arts

Ides et Calendes SA, *distributed by* Wittenborn Art Books

IDRC, *distributed by* Stylus Publishing LLC

IEE, *imprint of* IET

IEEE Computer Society Press, *distributor for* American Society for Quality (ASQ)

IEEE Press, *division of* Institute of Electrical & Electronics Engineers Inc (IEEE), *distributed by* John Wiley & Sons Inc

IFSTA, *distributed by* Fire Engineering Books & Videos

Ignatius, *imprint of* Ignatius Press

Ignatius Press, *division of* Guadalupe Associates Inc, Guadalupe Associates Inc, *distributor for* Bethlehem Books, Veritas

IHS Jane's, *subsidiary of* IHS Inc

IIP Consumers Series, *imprint of* Independent Information Publications

Ikonographics, *imprint of* Franciscan Media, *distributed by* Franciscan Media

Ilchokak Publishers, *distributed by* Cheng & Tsui Co Inc

Illinois State Museum Society, *affiliate of* Illinois State Museum

Illuminating Engineering Society of North America (IES), *distributor for* McGraw-Hill, Taylor & Francis, John Wiley & Sons Inc

The Illustrated Bartsch, *imprint of* Abaris Books

ILR Press, *imprint of* Cornell University Press

Images Publications, *distributed by* Antique Collectors Club Ltd

Images Unlimited Publishing, *distributed by* Finney Company Inc

Imagine Publishing, *imprint of* Charlesbridge Publishing Inc

Imago Mundi, *imprint of* David R Godine Publisher Inc

ImaJinn Books, *imprint of* ImaJinn Books Inc

Immagine&Poesia, *distributed by* Cross-Cultural Communications

Immedium, *imprint of* Immedium Inc

IMP, *distributed by* Summy-Birchard Inc

Impact Books, *imprint of* North Light Books

Impact Publications/Development Concepts Inc, *distributed by* National Book Network

Impact Publishers Inc, *distributor for* STEP Publishers (Systematic Training for Effective Parenting)

Imperial College Press, *subsidiary of* World Scientific Publishing Co Inc

Imprint Academic, *distributed by* Philosophy Documentation Center

Impromptu Journaling Books, *imprint of* Stone Bridge Press Inc

Incentive Plus, *distributor for* MAR*CO Products Inc

Independence Press, *imprint of* Herald Publishing House

Independent Information Publications, *division of* Computing!, *distributed by* Pathway Book Service

Independent Music Press, *distributed by* Schirmer Trade Books

Independent Publishers Group, *division of* Chicago Review Press, *distributor for* Big Guy Books Inc, LaChance Publishing LLC

Independent Seaport Museum, *distributed by* Cornell Maritime Press Inc

Independent University of Moscow, *distributed by* American Mathematical Society

India Book House Ltd, *distributed by* Antique Collectors Club Ltd

Indian Culture Series, *imprint of* The Montana Council for Indian Education

Indiana University Press, *distributed by* Heimburger House Publishing Co

INDIGO, *imprint of* Genesis Press Inc

Indigo Love Spectrum, *imprint of* Genesis Press Inc

Indigo Vibe, *imprint of* Genesis Press Inc

Indo Editions, *distributed by* Casemate Publishers & Book Distributors LLC

Indulgence, *imprint of* Entangled Publishing

Industrial Press, *distributed by* NACE International, Society of Manufacturing Engineers

Indy-Tech Publishing, *imprint of* Sams Technical Publishing LLC

Infinitum Nihil, *imprint of* HarperCollins General Books Group

Information & Media Services, *division of* McGraw-Hill Financial

Information Today Books, *imprint of* Information Today, Inc

Information Today Inc, *distributor for* Association for Information Science & Technology (ASIS&T)

Infosential Press, *distributed by* EBL, netLibrary

Ingalls Publishing, *imprint of* Ingalls Publishing Group Inc (IPG)

Ingalls Publishing Group Inc (IPG), *distributor for* Southlore Press

Ingram Publisher Services, *distributor for* Fox Chapel Publishing Co Inc

Ingram Publisher Services/Spring Arbor, *distributor for* HarperCollins Publishers

Inkwater Press, *imprint of* Firstbooks.com Inc, Firstbooks.com Inc, Inkwater Press

Inland, *distributor for* World Citizens

Inlandia Institute, *imprint of* Heyday Books

Inner Traditions, *imprint of* Inner Traditions International Ltd

Inner Traditions/Bear & Company, *distributed by* Simon & Schuster, Inc

Inner Traditions en espanol, *imprint of* Inner Traditions International Ltd

Inner Traditions India, *imprint of* Inner Traditions International Ltd

Inner Worlds Music, *distributed by* Lotus Press

Innovation & Tourisms (INTO), *imprint of* Cognizant Communication Corp

Innovative Logistics, *distributor for* Visual Profile Books Inc

Innovative Marketing, *distributor for* Pentecostal Publishing House

innovativeKids®, *division of* Innovative USA® Inc, Innovative USA® Inc, *distributed by* Hachette Book Group

InnoVision Health Media, *distributed by* Square One Publishers Inc

Inprint Editions, *imprint of* Black Classic Press

Inservice Reviews, *imprint of* Oakstone Publishing LLC

Inside Pocket Publishing, *distributed by* Lerner Publishing Group Inc

Inside the Minds, *imprint of* Aspatore Books

Insiders' Guides®, *imprint of* The Globe Pequot Press

Insight Editions, *imprint of* Palace Press International, *distributed by* Welcome Books

Inspec, *imprint of* IET

Inspirational Art, *division of* Unarius Academy of Science Publications

Inspire Books, *imprint of* Peter Pauper Press, Inc

Instant Help, *imprint of* New Harbinger Publications Inc

Institute for Advanced Study in the Theatre Arts (IASTA), *distributed by* Fordham University Press

Institute for Mesoamerican Studies, *distributed by* University of Texas Press

Institute for Regional Studies of the Californias, *distributed by* San Diego State University Press

Institute for Research Information, *division of* PJD Publications Ltd

Institute for the Psychological Sciences Press (IPS), *distributed by* The Catholic University of America Press

Institute of Education, *distributed by* Stylus Publishing LLC

Institute of Governmental Studies, *subsidiary of* University of California, Berkeley

Institute of Materials, *distributed by* NACE International

Institute of Mathematical Geography, *division of* Arlinghaus Enterprises LLC

Institute of Police Technology & Management, *division of* University of North Florida

Institute Press, *distributed by* Crown House Publishing Co LLC

Institution of Chemical Engineers, *distributed by* Enfield Publishing & Distribution Co

The Institution of Engineering & Technology (IET), *subsidiary of* Stylus Publishing LLC, *distributed by* Stylus Publishing LLC

Instituto Monsa de Ediciones SA, *distributed by* Trans-Atlantic Publications Inc

INSTRAW, *distributed by* United Nations Publications

Integrating Instruction Series, *imprint of* Incentive Publications Inc

Intellect Publishing, *distributed by* Sunbelt Publications Inc

Inter-American Development Bank, *division of* Multilateral Development Bank, *distributed by* Johns Hopkins University Press

Inter Sports, *distributor for* Wilderness Adventures Press Inc

Inter-University Consortium for Political & Social Research (ICPSR), *affiliate of* University of Michigan Institute for Social Research

InterAmerican Press Books, *imprint of* R J Berg Publisher

Intercultural Press Inc, *division of* Nicholas Brealey Publishing, *distributed by* NBN

Interlink Books, *imprint of* Interlink Publishing Group Inc

Interlink Publishing Group Inc, *distributor for* Black & White Publishing (UK), Camerapix Publishers International, Georgina Campbell Guides (Ireland), Macmillan Caribbean (UK), Quartet Books (UK), Rucksack Readers (UK), Serif Publishing Ltd (UK), Sheldrake Press (UK), Signal Books (UK), Waverley Books (UK), Neil Wilson Publishing (UK), *distributed by* Publishers Group West (digital dist servs via Constellation)

InterMix, *imprint of* Penguin Group (USA) LLC

International Air Transport Association, *distributed by* J J Keller & Associates, Inc

International Book Centre Inc, *distributor for* Library du Liban (Lebanon), Stacey Intl Ltd (London), University of Michigan

International Brecht Society, *distributed by* University of Wisconsin Press

International Christian University Foundation, *distributed by* EastBridge

International Code Council, *distributed by* Professional Publications Inc (PPI)

International Communication Organization (ICO), *distributed by* Transaction Publishers Inc

International Conferences on the Unity of the Sciences, *distributed by* Paragon House

International Country Risk Guide, *imprint of* The PRS Group Inc

International Debate Education Association, *distributed by* Central European University Press

International Design Library®, *imprint of* Stemmer House Publishers Inc

International Energy Agency, *distributed by* Organization for Economic Cooperation & Development

International Food Policy Research Institute, *member of* Consultative Group on International Agricultural Research (CGIAR), *distributed by* Johns Hopkins University Press

International Jewelry Publications, *distributed by* Gem Guides Book Co

International Labor Offices, *distributed by* The Brookings Institution Press

International Law Institute, *distributed by* University Press of America Inc

International Marine Publishing, *imprint of* McGraw-Hill Professional

International Monetary Fund (IMF) Editorial & Publications Division, *division of* International Org (IGO)

International Pocket Library, *imprint of* Branden Books

International Press, *distributed by* American Mathematical Society

International Press of Boston Inc, *distributed by* AMS

International Transportation Forum, *distributed by* Organization for Economic Cooperation & Development

InterVarsity Press, *division of* InterVarsity Christian Fellowship/USA

Intervention, *division of* Scholastic Education

Intervention Press, *distributed by* Left Coast Press Inc

Interweave, *imprint of* F+W Media Inc

Interweave Press LLC, *unit of* Aspire Media LLC, *distributed by* Keith Ainsworth Pty Ltd, Australia, David Bateman Ltd, New Zealand, Search Press, UK

The Intrepid Traveler, *distributed by* National Book Network Inc (NBN)

IOM, *distributed by* United Nations Publications

Ione Press, *imprint of* ECS Publishing Corp

IPG, *distributor for* Linden Publishing Co Inc, Manning Publications Co, NBM Publishing Inc, Third World Press, Trafalgar Square Books

IRA, *distributed by* National Science Teachers Association (NSTA)

Iranbooks Press, *imprint of* Ibex Publishers

IRF Books, *imprint of* Paragon House

IRL, *distributed by* Oxford University Press USA

Iron Icon Books, *imprint of* Unveiled Media LLC

Ironclad Publishing, *distributed by* Casemate Publishers & Book Distributors LLC

Ironwood Press, *distributed by* The University of Arizona Press

Iroquois Press, *imprint of* Turner Publishing Co

Irvington Publishers, *distributed by* Ardent Media Inc

Irwin Professional, *imprint of* McGraw-Hill Professional

ISH Group, *distributed by* Empire Publishing Service

ISI Books, *imprint of* Intercollegiate Studies Institute Inc

Islamic Foundation, *distributed by* Kazi Publications Inc

Islamic Texts Society, *distributed by* Fons Vitae

Island, *imprint of* Random House Inc

Island Paradise Publishing, *distributed by* Sunbelt Publications Inc

Island Press, *distributor for* Environmental Law Institute, Environmental Law Institute (ELI), IUCN, Techne Press

Islander Group, *distributor for* Kamehameha Publishing

The Islander Group (TIG), *distributor for* Bess Press

The Islander Group Inc, *distributor for* Wide World Publishing

Islander Press, *imprint of* Shepard Publications

ISO, *distributed by* NACE International

iSong CD-ROMs, *distributed by* Hal Leonard Corp

IsraBook, *subsidiary of* Gefen Books

Isshin-Ryu Productions, *imprint of* The Linick Group Inc

Issues Press, *imprint of* Idyll Arbor Inc

It Books, *imprint of* HarperCollins General Books Group, HarperCollins Publishers

Italian School of East Asian Studies, *distributed by* Cheng & Tsui Co Inc

Itasca, *distributor for* BrickHouse Books Inc

It's About Time Inc, *distributor for* American Geological Institute (AGI)

IUCN, *distributed by* Island Press

iUniverse, *division of* Author Solutions Inc

IVP Academic, *imprint of* InterVarsity Press

IVP Books, *imprint of* InterVarsity Press

IVP Connect, *imprint of* InterVarsity Press

Ivy, *imprint of* Random House Inc

IWGIA, *distributed by* Transaction Publishers Inc

Jackson Square Press, *imprint of* Pelican Publishing Co

Jacobsville Books, *imprint of* Slipdown Mountain Publications LLC

Jade Rabbit, *imprint of* Quite Specific Media Group Ltd

Jaguar Tales, *distributed by* Sunbelt Publications Inc

Jam, *imprint of* Berkley Books

Janaway Publishing, *distributor for* Closson Press

Janus Library, *imprint of* Abaris Books

Japan Center for International Exchange, *distributed by* The Brookings Institution Press

Japan Publications Inc, *distributed by* Kodansha USA Inc

Japan Publications Trading Co Inc, *distributed by* Kodansha USA Inc

Japan Society, *distributed by* Yale University Press

Jawbone Press, *distributed by* Hal Leonard Corp

JayJo Books LLC, *subsidiary of* The Guidance Group

Jefferson Editions, *imprint of* Mage Publishers Inc

Jems, *imprint of* Elsevier, Health Sciences Division

Jenkins Publishing, *distributed by* Chelsea Green Publishing Co

Jersey Yarns, *imprint of* Quincannon Publishing Group

Jerusalem Press, *distributed by* Holmes Publishing Group LLC

Jerusalem Publications, *distributed by* Feldheim Publishers (Philipp Feldheim Inc)

Jesuit Consortium, *distributed by* Loyola Press

Jewish Lights Publishing, *division of* Longhill Partners Inc, Longhill Partners Inc

The Jewish Museum, *distributed by* Yale University Press

Jewish New Testament Publications, *distributed by* Lederer Books, Messianic Jewish Publishers

George R Jezek Photography, *distributed by* Gem Guides Book Co

Jhpiego, *affiliate of* The Johns Hopkins University

The Jim Henson Co, *distributed by* At a Glance, Walter Foster, Golden Books Family Entertainment, Grolier, KidsBooks, Penguin Group (USA) LLC, PK, Random House, Reader's Digest Children's Books, Running Press, Simon & Schuster

Jist, *distributor for* MAR*CO Products Inc

JIST Life, *imprint of* JIST Publishing

JIST Publishing, *division of* EMC Publishing

JIST Works, *imprint of* JIST Publishing

JKAP Publications, *distributed by* Jonathan David Publishers Inc

JMC Press, *distributed by* Vandamere Press

John Deere Publishing, *division of* Deere & Co

John Macrae Books, *imprint of* Henry Holt and Company, LLC

John Wiley & Sons Inc, *distributor for* Association for Information Science & Technology (ASIS&T), Center for Creative Leadership LLC, IEEE Press, R S Means, a Reed Construction Data Co, SAS Publishing, *distributed by* American Academy of Environmental Engineers, Center for Creative Leadership LLC, William S Hein & Co Inc, Illuminating Engineering Society of North America (IES), J J Keller & Associates, Inc, NACE International, SAS Publishing, Society of Manufacturing Engineers

Johns Hopkins University Press, *distributor for* Inter-American Development Bank, International Food Policy Research Institute, *distributed by* Heimburger House Publishing Co

The Johns Hopkins University Press, *affiliate of* The Johns Hopkins University, *distributor for* Baylor University Press, The Brookings Institution Press, Catholic University of America Press, Center for Talented Youth, Georgetown University Press, Johns Hopkins Aids Service, Howard University Press, Maryland Historical Society, Resources for the Future, University of Massachusetts Press, University of Pennsylvania Museum, University of Pennsylvania Press, University of Washington Press, The University Press of Kentucky, Urban Institute Press, The Woodrow Wilson Center Press, World Resources Institute

Johns Hopkins University Press Fullfillment Service, *distributor for* Baylor University Press

Johnson Books, *division of* Big Earth Publishing

Cy Johnson & Son, *distributed by* Gem Guides Book Co

Joint Center for Political & Economic Studies Press, *distributed by* University Press of America Inc

Joint Publishers, *distributed by* China Books

Jonathan David Publishers Inc, *distributor for* American-Israeli Cooperative, Emet Publishers, Feldheim, IBS, JKAP Publications, Purity Press, Seraphic Press

Jones & Bartlett Learning, *distributed by* Medical Group Management Association (MGMA)

Jones & Bartlett Learning LLC, *division of* Ascend Learning

Jones & Bartlett Publishers, *distributor for* American Academy of Orthopaedic Surgeons

The Fletcher Jones Foundation, *imprint of* University of California Press

Scott Jones Publishing, *distributed by* Delmar

Jordan Publishing, *imprint of* Evangel Publishing House

Joshua Tree Publishing, *imprint of* Joshua Tree Publishing

Jossey-Bass, *imprint of* John Wiley & Sons Inc, John Wiley & Sons Inc, *distributor for* Center for Creative Leadership LLC, *distributed by* Center for Creative Leadership LLC

Journal of Chinese Medicine Publications, *distributed by* Eastland Press

Journal Publishing, *division of* Slack Incorporated

Journalbytes.com, *imprint of* Oakstone Publishing LLC

JourneyForth Books, *division of* BJU Press, *imprint of* BJU Press

Jove, *imprint of* Berkley Books, Berkley Publishing Group, Penguin Group (USA) LLC

Joy Publishing Co, *division of* California Clock Co, California Clock Co

JPT America Inc, *distributed by* Cheng & Tsui Co Inc

JR Comics, *distributed by* Lerner Publishing Group Inc

Judeo Christian Ethics Series, *imprint of* PREP Publishing

Judson Press, *division of* American Baptist Churches in the USA, *distributed by* Abingdon Press

Juloya, *imprint of* Elva Resa Publishing

Jump at the Sun, *imprint of* Disney-Hyperion Books, Disney Publishing Worldwide

Jumpstart, *imprint of* Triumph Learning

Junebug Books, *imprint of* NewSouth Books

Juno Books, *distributed by* powerHouse Books

Jury Verdict Research; LRP Magazine Group, *division of* LRP Publications

Just Cause, *imprint of* Yard Dog Press

Just Think®, *imprint of* Thomas Geale Publications Inc

K A Publishing, *imprint of* Hobar Publications

Max Kade Institute for German-American Studies, *distributed by* University of Wisconsin Press

Kaeden Books, *imprint of* Kaeden Corp

Kaiser-Barlow, *imprint of* Schiffer Publishing Ltd

Kales Press, *distributed by* W W Norton & Company Inc

Kalindi Press, *imprint of* Hohm Press

Kalmbach Books, *imprint of* Madavor Media

Kalmbach Publishing, *distributed by* Heimburger House Publishing Co

Kamehameha Publishing, *division of* Kamehameha Schools, *imprint of* Kamehameha Publishing, *distributed by* Islander Group

Kamehameha Schools Press, *imprint of* Kamehameha Publishing

Kane Miller Books, *division of* Educational Development Corp, Educational Development Corp

The Kane Press, *distributed by* Lerner Publishing Group Inc

Kane Press Inc, *distributed by* Lerner Publishing Group

Kaplan Press, *distributed by* Gryphon House Inc

Kaplan Publishing, *unit of* Kaplan Inc, *distributed by* Simon & Schuster (S&S standard freight, credit, payment & returns policies apply), Simon & Schuster, Inc, Simon & Schuster Sales & Marketing

Kar-Ben Publishing, *division of* Lerner Publishing Group Inc, *distributed by* Beach Lloyd Publishers LLC

Karger, *distributor for* American Association of Blood Banks

Karnac Books, *distributed by* Stylus Publishing LLC

Karnak House, *imprint of* Red Sea Press Inc

KAV Books, *distributed by* Royal Fireworks Press

Kaynak, *distributed by* Tughra Books

Kazan Media, *imprint of* Volcano Press

Kazi Publications Inc, *distributor for* Foundation for Traditional Studies, Great Books of the Islamic World, Islamic Foundation

KC Publications Inc, *distributed by* Gem Guides Book Co

KCP Technologies Inc, *subsidiary of* Key Curriculum, A McGraw-Hill Education Company

Keen Custom Media, *imprint of* Clerisy Press

J J Keller & Associates, Inc, *distributor for* Chilton Book Co, International Air Transport Association, National Archives & Records Administration, National Institute of Occupational Safety & Health, Office of the Federal Register, Research & Special Programs Administration of the US Department of Transportation, John Wiley & Sons Inc, *distributed by* AMACOM Books

Kendall Hunt Publishing, *distributor for* Seedling Publications Inc

The Kenilworth Press Ltd, *distributed by* Half Halt Press Inc

Kennebec Large Print, *imprint of* Thorndike Press®

Kennedy Information Inc, *division of* Bureau of National Affairs (BNA), The Bureau of National Affairs Inc (BNA)

Kens Math, *imprint of* Young People's Press Inc (YPPI)

Kensington, *distributor for* Parachute Publishing LLC, *distributed by* Hachette Book Group

Kensington Books, *imprint of* Kensington Publishing Corp

Kensington Publishing Corp, *distributor for* Genesis Press, Marimba Books, New Horizon Press, Philosophical Library Inc, Urban Books, Vibe Books, *distributed by* Hachette Book Group USA, Penguin Group (USA) LLC

Kentucky Historical Society, *distributed by* The University Press of Kentucky

Kenyon Publications, *distributed by* Hal Leonard Corp

Kerem, *distributed by* Hachai Publishing

Kessinger Publishing®, *imprint of* Kessinger Publishing LLC

Key Education, *distributed by* Carson-Dellosa Publishing LLC

Keystone, *imprint of* National Publishing Co

Keystone Books, *imprint of* The Pennsylvania State University Press

Kid Help Publishing Co, *imprint of* Hearts & Tummies Cookbook Co

Kidhaven Press, *distributed by* Lucent Books®

KidHaven Press™, *imprint of* Gale

Kids Corner, *imprint of* Sundance/Newbridge Publishing

Kids Own Worship™, *imprint of* Group Publishing Inc

Kids' Stuff, *imprint of* Incentive Publications Inc

KidsBooks, *imprint of* Kidsbooks LLC, *distributor for* The Jim Henson Co

Kimani, *imprint of* Harlequin Enterprises Ltd

Kimbell Art Museum, *distributed by* Yale University Press

KinderMed Press, *imprint of* Iron Gate Publishing

Dorling Kindersley, *distributor for* Parachute Publishing LLC

Kinfolk, *distributed by* Simon & Schuster, Inc

Laurence King Publishing, *distributed by* Chronicle Books LLC

The King Legacy, *imprint of* Beacon Press

Kingsley Literary Services, *imprint of* Halcyon Press Ltd

Kiron Editions du Felin, *distributed by* Beach Lloyd Publishers LLC

KIT Publishers, *distributed by* Stylus Publishing LLC

Klutz, *division of* Scholastic Corp, *imprint of* Scholastic Trade Division

Wolters Kluwer Law & Business, *subsidiary of* Wolters Kluwer, Wolters Kluwer

Knack™, *imprint of* The Globe Pequot Press

Knickerbocker Press, *imprint of* Book Sales Inc

Knock-off Books, *imprint of* Ugly Duckling Presse

Alfred A Knopf, *imprint of* Random House Inc, *distributor for* Nevraumont Publishing Co

Alfred A Knopf Books for Young Readers, *imprint of* Random House Children's Books

Alfred A Knopf/Everyman's Library, *imprint of* Knopf Doubleday Publishing Group

Knopf Books for Young Readers, *imprint of* Random House Inc

Knopf Delacorte Dell Young Readers Group, *division of* Random House Children's Books

Knopf Guides, *imprint of* Random House Inc

Knossus Project, *distributed by* Chelsea Green Publishing Co

Knowledge Resources, *distributor for* American Society for Training & Development (ASTD), HRD Press

Kodansha, *distributed by* Oxford University Press USA

Kodansha America, *imprint of* Kodansha USA Inc

Kodansha Globe, *imprint of* Kodansha USA Inc

Kodansha International, *imprint of* Kodansha USA Inc

Kodansha USA Inc, *subsidiary of* Kodansha Ltd (Japan), Kodansha Ltd (Japan), *distributor for* Japan Publications Inc, Japan Publications Trading Co Inc, *distributed by* Oxford University Press

Kogan Page Publishers, *distributor for* Stanford University Press (distribute outside the Americas)

Kollath-Stensaas, *distributed by* Adventure Publications

Kolowalu Books, *imprint of* University of Hawaii Press

Kom Forlag, *distributed by* Enfield Publishing & Distribution Co

Konecky & Konecky (K&K), *imprint of* Konecky & Konecky LLC

Konecky & Konecky LLC, *distributor for* Octavo Editions

Koren, *imprint of* The Toby Press LLC

Kornfeld & Co, *distributed by* Alan Wofsy Fine Arts

Kornfeld (Switzerland), *distributed by* Picasso Project

Kosei Publishing Co, *imprint of* Tuttle Publishing, *distributed by* Tuttle Publishing

Kotan Publishing Inc, *imprint of* Tuttle Publishing, *distributed by* Tuttle Publishing

H J Kramer, *division of* New World Library

H J Kramer Inc, *affiliate of* New World Library

Krause Publications, *imprint of* F+W Media Inc, *distributed by* Heimburger House Publishing Co

Krause Publications Inc, *subsidiary of* F+W Media Inc, F+W Media Inc, *distributor for* Country Bumpkin, David & Charles, Colin Gower, Quarto Books

Kregel Academic & Professional, *imprint of* Kregel Publications

Kregel Classics, *imprint of* Kregel Publications

Kregel Kidzone, *imprint of* Kregel Publications

Kregel Publications, *division of* Kregel Inc, Kregel Inc, *imprint of* Kregel Publications, *distributor for* Candle Books, Monarch Books

De Krijger, *distributed by* Casemate Publishers & Book Distributors LLC

KTAV Publishing House Inc, *distributor for* Yeshiva University Press

KTeen, *imprint of* Kensington Publishing Corp

Kudzu House, *imprint of* Ariel Press, *distributed by* Ariel Press

KUED, *distributed by* The University of Utah Press

Kumarian Press, *division of* Lynne Rienner Publishers Inc, *distributor for* Management Sciences for Health

Scott G Kyle, *distributed by* Sunbelt Publications Inc

LaChance Publishing LLC, *distributed by* Independent Publishers Group

Ladders, *imprint of* Triumph Learning

Lady Fern Press, *imprint of* Crumb Elbow Publishing

LadybugPress, *division of* NewVoices Inc

Lake Claremont Press, *imprint of* Everything Goes Media LLC

Lake Forrest College Press, *distributed by* Northwestern University Press

Lakeshore Learning Materials, *distributor for* National Council of Teachers of Mathematics (NCTM)

Lalo Press, *distributed by* Bilingual Review Press/ Editorial Bilingue

Lancer Publishers, *distributed by* Casemate Publishers & Book Distributors LLC

Landfall Navigation, *distributor for* Marine Techniques Publishing

Landmark Audio Books, *distributor for* Eye in the Ear Children's Audio

Peter Lang Publishing Inc, *subsidiary of* Verlag Peter Lang AG (Switzerland), Verlag Peter Lang AG (Switzerland)

Lange Medical Books, *imprint of* McGraw-Hill Professional

Langenscheidt, *distributed by* Hagstrom Map & Travel Center

Langenscheidt Publishers Group, *distributed by* American Map Corp

Langenscheidt Publishing Group, *distributor for* Michelin Maps & Guides

Language Literacy Lessons, *imprint of* Incentive Publications Inc

Languages for Kids, *distributed by* Tralco-Lingo Fun

Lantern Books, *division of* Booklight Inc, *distributed by* SteinerBooks

LanternLight Library, *imprint of* University of Alaska Press

Larausse, *distributed by* Houghton Mifflin Harcourt Trade & Reference Division

Large Print Press, *imprint of* Thorndike Press®

Large Print Press™, *imprint of* Gale

Lark Books, *imprint of* Sterling Publishing Co Inc

Lark Crafts, *imprint of* Sterling Publishing Co Inc

Larousse Bilingual, *distributed by* Houghton Mifflin Harcourt

Larousse Mexico, *distributed by* Houghton Mifflin Harcourt

Latin American Literary Review Press, *distributed by* Bilingual Review Press/Editorial Bilingue

Latin American Review Press, *distributed by* Arte Publico Press

Latitude 20, *imprint of* University of Hawaii Press

JP Lattes, *distributed by* Beach Lloyd Publishers LLC

Laurel-Leaf, *imprint of* Random House Children's Books

Laurel Leaf Books, *imprint of* Random House Inc

Law Library Microform Consortium, *distributed by* Thomson Reuters Westlaw™

Law Tribune Books, *division of* American Lawyer Media

Merloyd Lawrence Inc, *distributed by* The Perseus Books Group

Lawtech Publishing, *distributed by* Sunbelt Publications Inc

LBKids, *imprint of* Little, Brown Books for Young Readers

Learn Roots Music, *distributed by* Mel Bay Publications Inc

Learning & Coloring Books, *imprint of* Quincannon Publishing Group

Learning Challenge, *imprint of* Kidsbooks LLC

The Learning Company, *imprint of* Houghton Mifflin Harcourt

Learning Fun, *imprint of* Incentive Publications Inc

Learning Links Inc, *distributor for* Harcourt, HarperCollins, Houghton Mifflin Harcourt Publishing Company, Little, Brown & Company, Penguin Group (USA) LLC, Random House Inc, Scholastic, Simon & Schuster

Learning Matters, *imprint of* SAGE Publications

Learning Media, *distributed by* Peoples Education Inc

LearningExpress, *imprint of* LearningExpress LLC, *distributed by* Delmar

LearningExpress LLC, *distributed by* National Book Network

Leaves of Healing, *imprint of* Progressive Press

Lectorum Publications Inc, *subsidiary of* Scholastic Inc

Leda, *imprint of* Norilana Books

Lederer Books, *division of* Messianic Jewish Publishers, *distributor for* Chosen People Ministries, First Fruits of Zion, Jewish New Testament Publications

Left Coast Press Inc, *distributor for* Intervention Press (Denmark), UCL Institute of Archaeology (UK)

Left To Write Press, *distributed by* Chelsea Green Publishing Co

Legacy Press, *imprint of* Rainbow Publishers

Legas Publishers, *distributed by* Cross-Cultural Communications

Dennis Lehane Books, *imprint of* HarperCollins General Books Group

Lehigh University Press, *affiliate of* Rowman & Littlefield Publishing Group (RLPG), *distributed by* Rowman & Littlefield

Leisure Arts Inc, *division of* Liberty Media, *distributor for* Oxmoor House Inc

The Lentz Leadership Institute, *imprint of* The Refractive Thinker Press, *distributed by* BCH Fulfillment & Distribution, Lightning Source

Hal Leonard, *distributed by* ArtAge Publications

Hal Leonard Corp, *distributor for* Amadeus Press, Applause Theatre & Cinema Books, Artistpro, Ashley Music, Backbeat Books, Beacon Music, Berklee Press, Fred Bock Music Company, Boosey & Hawkes, Centerstream Publications, Centerstream Publishing LLC, Cherry Lane Music Co, Cinema Books, Community Music Videos, Creative Concepts, DC Publications, Devine Entertainment Corp, Editions Durand, Editions Max Eschig, Editions Salabert, EM Books, EMI Christian, Faber Music Ltd, Guitar One, Guitar World, Home Recording, Homespun Tapes, Houston Publications, Hudson Music, iSong CD-ROMs, Jawbone Press, Kenyon Publications, Limelight Editions, Ashley Mark Publishing Co, Edward B Marks Music, Meredith Music, Modern Drummer Publications, Music Sales America, Musicians Institute Press, Musikverlage Han Sikorski, Christopher Parkening, Reader's Digest, Record Research, Ricordi, Lee Roberts Publications, Rubank Publications, G Schirmer Inc (Associated Music Publishers), Second Floor Music, Sing Out Corp, Star Licks Videos, Bernard Stein Music Co, String Letter Press, Tara Publications, Transcontinental Music, 21st Century Publications, Vintage Guitar, Word Music, Writer's Digest

Lerner Books UK, *division of* Lerner Publishing Group Inc

Lerner Publications, *division of* Lerner Publishing Group Inc, *imprint of* Lerner Publishing Group Inc

Lerner Publisher Services, *division of* Lerner Publishing Group Inc

Lerner Publishing, *distributor for* Red Chair Press

Lerner Publishing Group, *distributor for* Kane Press Inc

Lerner Publishing Group Inc, *distributor for* Andersen Press USA, Columbus Zoo, Gecko Press, Inside Pocket Publishing, JR Comics, The Kane Press, MVP Books, Red Chair Press, Stoke Books, We Do Listen

LernerClassroom, *division of* Lerner Publishing Group Inc, *imprint of* Lerner Publishing Group Inc

The Letter People®, *imprint of* Abrams Learning Trends

Letterland International Ltd, *distributed by* Enfield Publishing & Distribution Co

Leuven University Press, *distributed by* Cornell University Press

Lexington Books, *imprint of* Rowman & Littlefield Publishing Group, *distributor for* The Colonial Williamsburg Foundation

LexisNexis, *distributor for* Standard Publishing Corp

LexisNexis®, *division of* Reed Elsevier Inc

LexisNexis/Martindale-Hubbell, *member of* The Reed Elsevier Group

LexisNexis® Matthew Bender®, *member of* The LexisNexis Group, The LexisNexis® Group

Liberties Press, *distributed by* Dufour Editions Inc

Libraries Unlimited, *imprint of* ABC-CLIO

Libraries Unlimited/Linworth Publishing, *imprint of* ABC-CLIO

Library Company of Philadelphia, *distributed by* Diane Publishing Co

Library du Liban (Lebanon), *distributed by* International Book Centre Inc

The Library of America, *distributed by* Penguin Group (USA) LLC

Library of Congress-Center for the Book, *distributed by* Oak Knoll Press

Library of Contemporary Thought, *imprint of* Random House Inc

Library of Islam, *imprint of* Kazi Publications Inc

Library One Direct, *division of* Gareth Stevens Publishing

Libros Desafio, *imprint of* Faith Alive Christian Resources

Libros en Espanol, *imprint of* Touchstone

Libros Liguori, *imprint of* Liguori Publications

Libros Para Ninos, *imprint of* Simon & Schuster Children's Publishing

Life Cycle Books, *division of* Life Cycle Books Ltd (Canada)

Life on the Edge, *imprint of* Focus on the Family

Life Wisdom, *imprint of* Paragon House

LifeGuide Bible Studies, *imprint of* InterVarsity Press

LifeLearn, *distributor for* Teton NewMedia, *distributed by* Teton NewMedia

Lifestream, *imprint of* Beacon Hill Press of Kansas City

LifeTimes, *imprint of* Rayve Productions Inc

LifeWay Christian Resources, *distributor for* Casa Bautista de Publicaciones

The Liffey Press, *distributed by* Dufour Editions Inc

Lift Every Voice, *imprint of* Moody Publishers

The Light, *imprint of* Tughra Books

Light & Life, *distributor for* Conciliar Press, *distributed by* Conciliar Press

Light & Life Publishing Co, *distributor for* St Herman Press

Lighthouse Press, *imprint of* ProStar Publications Inc

Lightning Rod Press, *imprint of* American Philosophical Society

Lightning Source, *distributor for* Anaphora Literary Press, The Lentz Leadership Institute

Lightning Source/Ingram, *distributor for* Hard Shell Word Factory

Lightning Up Press, *distributed by* Enfield Publishing & Distribution Co

Liguori Publications, *distributor for* Redemptorist Publications

Liguori/Triumph, *imprint of* Liguori Publications

Philip E Lilienthal, *imprint of* University of California Press

Lillenas Publishing Co, *imprint of* Beacon Hill Press of Kansas City

Lilliput Press Ltd, *distributed by* Dufour Editions Inc

LIM Editrice SRL (Italy), *distributor for* Pendragon Press

Limelight Editions, *imprint of* Hal Leonard Books, Hal Leonard Performing Arts Publishing Group, Hal Leonard Performing Arts Publishing Group, *distributed by* Hal Leonard Corp, Hal Leonard Corp

Limestone Press, *distributed by* University of Alaska Press

Frances Lincoln, *distributed by* Antique Collectors Club Ltd, Quayside Publishing Group

Lincoln Record Society, *imprint of* Boydell & Brewer Inc

Linden Publishing Co Inc, *distributed by* IPG

Lindisfarne Books, *imprint of* SteinerBooks, SteinerBooks, *distributed by* Floris Books

Line by Line, *imprint of* Aspatore Books

John Liner Organization, *subsidiary of* Standard Publishing Corp

LinguaText Ltd, *distributor for* Juan de la Cuesta—Hispanic Monographs, European Masterpieces

The Linick Group Inc, *distributor for* Linick International, LKA Inc, National Association of Photo Sellers™, *distributed by* New World Press Books, Okinawan Kobujutsu Kyokai Association (OKKA)

Linick International, *distributed by* The Linick Group Inc

Linux Journal Press, *imprint of* Belltown Media, No Starch Press Inc

Linworth Learning, *imprint of* Linworth Publishing

Linworth Publishing, *imprint of* Libraries Unlimited

Lipper Marketplace, *division of* Thomson Reuters

Lippincott Williams & Wilkins, *unit of* Wolters Kluwer Health

Lippincott, Williams & Wilkins, *imprint of* Wolters Kluwer US Corp

Lips (Magazine & Press), *distributed by* Cross-Cultural Communications

LIS (Legal Information Services), *subsidiary of* CCH, a Wolters Kluwer business

Listening Library®, *division of* Books on Tape®, *imprint of* Books on Tape®, *distributed by* Books on Tape®

Literary House Press, *distributed by* Cornell Maritime Press Inc

Literary Reprint Series, *imprint of* University of Alaska Press

Literature & Thought, *imprint of* Perfection Learning Corp

Litigation GP, *division of* Public Citizen

Little America Publishing Co, *imprint of* Beautiful America Publishing Co

Little, Brown, *distributor for* Parachute Publishing LLC

Little, Brown & Co, *distributor for* Alloy Entertainment

Little, Brown & Company, *distributed by* Learning Links Inc

Little, Brown and Company, *division of* Hachette Book Group

Little, Brown Books for Young Readers, *division of* Hachette Book Group

The Little Entrepreneur, *imprint of* Harper Arrington Publishing, *distributed by* Harper Arrington Publishing

Little Imp Books, *imprint of* Impact Publishers Inc

Little Lucy & Friends™, *imprint of* Playhouse Publishing

Little Oak Press, *distributed by* Sunbelt Publications Inc

Little Patriot Press, *imprint of* Regnery Publishing Inc

Little Room Press, *distributed by* Fordham University Press

Little Shepherd, *imprint of* Scholastic Trade Division

Little Simon, *imprint of* Simon & Schuster Children's Publishing

Little Simon Inspirations, *imprint of* Simon & Schuster Children's Publishing

Little Toller Books, *distributed by* Dufour Editions Inc

Liturgical Press, *division of* The Order of St Benedict Inc, The Order of St Benedict Inc, *distributor for* Cistercian Publications Inc, Editorial Office

Liturgical Press Books, *imprint of* Liturgical Press

Liturgy Training Publications, *subsidiary of* Archdiocese of Chicago, *distributor for* United States Catholic Conference Publications

Live Oak, *imprint of* Greenleaf Book Group LLC

Liveright & Co, *imprint of* W W Norton & Company Inc

Living Books, *imprint of* Tyndale House Publishers Inc

Living Language, *imprint of* Random House Audio Publishing Group, Random House Inc

Livingston Press, *division of* University of West Alabama, *distributor for* Swallow's Tale Press

LKA Inc, *imprint of* The Linick Group Inc, *distributed by* The Linick Group Inc

Llewellyn Publications, *division of* Llewellyn Worldwide Ltd, *distributor for* Lo Scarabeo

Chris Lloyd, *distributor for* Cycle Publishing

LMC Source, *distributor for* Hi Willow Research & Publishing

LMD Inc, *distributor for* Council for Exceptional Children (CEC)

Lobster Press, *distributed by* Orca Book Publishers

Local Government & Public Service Reform Initiative, *distributed by* Central European University Press

Arlene Lochridge, *distributed by* Epicenter Press Inc

Locks Art Publications/Locks Gallery, *division of* Locks Gallery

Loft, *distributed by* Prestel Publishing

Loft Publications, *distributed by* Antique Collectors Club Ltd

Logan Brothers, *distributor for* Teton NewMedia

Login Brothers, *distributor for* Health Professions Press

Login Brothers Book Co, *distributor for* United States Pharmacopeia

Login Publishing Consortium, *distributor for* United States Pharmacopeia

Logion Press, *imprint of* Gospel Publishing House (GPH)

Logos, *imprint of* Bridge-Logos Inc

Logos Press, *imprint of* thinkBiotech LLC

Y Lolfa, *distributed by* Dufour Editions Inc

Lominger Inc, *distributed by* Center for Creative Leadership LLC

Lone Oak Press, *imprint of* Finney Company Inc

Lone Star Audio, *imprint of* Recorded Books LLC

Longman, *distributor for* Marriage Transformation LLC, *distributed by* Council for Exceptional Children (CEC), Trans-Atlantic Publications Inc

Look & Learn™, *imprint of* Playhouse Publishing

Look at Me, *imprint of* Modern Publishing

Looking Glass Books, *distributed by* John F Blair Publisher

Lookout Books, *distributed by* John F Blair Publisher

Looseleaf Law Publications Inc, *division of* Warodean Corp

The Lord's Press, *imprint of* Decent Hill Publishers LLC

Lorenz Educational Press, *division of* The Lorenz Corp

Lorimer, *distributed by* Casemate Publishers & Book Distributors LLC

James Lorimer & Co, *distributed by* Orca Book Publishers

Los Angeles Times Books, *distributed by* Angel City Press

Los Angeles Times Crosswords, *imprint of* Random House Reference/Random House Puzzles & Games/House of Collectibles

Lost Horse Press, *subsidiary of* The Academy of Northwest Writers & Publishers, *distributed by* University of Washington Press

Lothrop, Lee & Shepard Books, *imprint of* HarperCollins Publishers

Lotus Press, *division of* Lotus Brands Inc, Lotus Brands Inc, *distributor for* Back to Eden Books, Dipti, East West Cultural Center, Les Editions E T C, Inner Worlds Music, November Moon, S A B D A, Sadhana Publications, Samata Books, Sri Aurobindo Ashram, Star Sounds

The Lotus Seed Press (China), *distributed by* Blue Dolphin Publishing Inc

Louisiana Book Distributors, *imprint of* Pelican Publishing Co

Love Inspired, *imprint of* Love Inspired Books

Love Inspired Books, *imprint of* Harlequin Enterprises Ltd

Love Inspired Historical, *imprint of* Love Inspired Books

Love Inspired Suspense, *imprint of* Love Inspired Books

Love Publishing, *distributed by* Council for Exceptional Children (CEC)

Lovers, *imprint of* Bandanna Books

Loveswept, *imprint of* Random House Inc, Random House Publishing Group

Loving Guidance Inc, *distributed by* Gryphon House Inc

Loyola Press, *distributor for* Jesuit Consortium

LPC Group Inc, *distributor for* Dark Horse Comics

LRP Magazine Group, *subsidiary of* LRP Publications

LRS, *division of* Library Reproduction Service

Max Lucado Books, *imprint of* Thomas Nelson Inc

Lucent Books®, *imprint of* Gale, *distributor for* Greenhaven Press, Kidhaven Press, *distributed by* Greenhaven Imprints

Lucky Marble Books, *imprint of* PageSpring Publishing

Lumen, *imprint of* Brookline Books

Luna Books, *imprint of* Harlequin Enterprises Ltd

Lund Humphries/Ashgate, *distributor for* National Gallery of Art

Luster Editions, *imprint of* Circlet Press Inc

Lutheran University Press, *imprint of* Kirk House Publishers

LW Books, *imprint of* Schiffer Publishing Ltd

Lynn-Reinner Publishing, *distributor for* University of California Institute on Global Conflict & Cooperation

Lynx House Press, *distributed by* University of Washington Press

The Lyons Press, *imprint of* The Globe Pequot Press

M & H Type, *division of* The Arion Press

Pat MacKay Projects, *imprint of* Quite Specific Media Group Ltd

Mackinac Historic Parks, *distributed by* Michigan State University Press (MSU Press)

Macmillan, *subsidiary of* Verlagsgruppe Georg von Holtzbrinck GmbH, Verlagsgruppe Georg von Holtzbrinck GmbH, *imprint of* McGraw-Hill School Education Group, *distributor for* Bloomsbury Publishing, BNi Building News, The College Board, Tom Doherty Associates, LLC, Entangled Publishing, Papercutz, Rodale Books

Macmillan Audio, *division of* Macmillan, Macmillan Holdings, LLC, *distributor for* HighRoads Media, *distributed by* BBC Audiobooks America (library editions)

Macmillan Caribbean (UK), *distributed by* Interlink Publishing Group Inc

Macmillan Education (UK), *distributed by* Players Press Inc

Macmillan/McGraw-Hill, *imprint of* McGraw-Hill Education

Macmillan Publishing Co, *distributor for* National Association of Broadcasters (NAB)

Macmillan Reference USA™, *imprint of* Gale

Macmillan (UK), *distributed by* Scholium International Inc

MacroPrintBooks, *imprint of* Science & Humanities Press

MacVan Maps, *distributed by* Wide World of Maps Inc

'MAD' Books, *imprint of* DC Entertainment

Madavor Media, *distributed by* Publishers Group West (PGW)

Madison Area Community Supported Agriculture Coalition, *distributed by* Chelsea Green Publishing Co

Madison Books, *imprint of* Cooper Square Press

Madison House Publishers, *member of* Rowman & Littlefield Publishing Group, Rowman & Littlefield Publishing Group Inc, *distributor for* Center for Study of American Constitution

Magazine City, *distributor for* Eros Books

Magazine Line, *distributor for* Eros Books

Mage Publishers Inc, *distributed by* University of Toronto Press

Maggid, *imprint of* The Toby Press LLC

Maggies Music, *distributed by* Mel Bay Publications Inc

Magill's Choice, *imprint of* Salem Press Inc

Magnes Press, *distributed by* Gefen Books

MAGNI, *imprint of* The Magni Co

Magni Co, *distributed by* Book Publishing Co

The Magni Co, *subsidiary of* The Magni Group Inc

Maharishi University of Management Press, *subsidiary of* Maharishi University of Management, *distributed by* Fairfield Press, Penguin Group (USA) LLC

Maia Press, *distributed by* Dufour Editions Inc

Main Street Books, *imprint of* Random House Inc

Maisonneuve Press, *division of* Institute for Advanced Cultural Studies, *distributed by* Merlin Press (London, England)

Maize Press, *distributed by* Bilingual Review Press/Editorial Bilingue

JA Majors, *distributor for* MedBooks

Malley's, *distributed by* Mel Bay Publications Inc

Management Consultant International, *imprint of* Kennedy Information Inc

Management Learning Resources, *distributor for* HRD Press

Management Sciences for Health, *distributed by* Kumarian Press

ManagingSmart.com, *subsidiary of* BizBest Media Corp

Manchester University Press, *distributed by* Palgrave Macmillan, St Martin's Press, LLC

Mandala Publishing, *imprint of* Insight Editions

Mandate Press, *imprint of* William Carey Library Publishers

Manhattan GMAT, *distributed by* Simon & Schuster, Inc

Manhattan Prep, *distributed by* Simon & Schuster Sales & Marketing

Manhattan Publishing Co, *division of* US & Europe Books Inc, *distributor for* Council of Europe, European Court of Human Rights

Manning Publications Co, *distributed by* IPG, Pearson Education, Prentice Hall, TransQuest Publishers Pte Ltd

The Manuscript Society, *distributed by* Oak Knoll Press

Le Manuscrit, *distributed by* Beach Lloyd Publishers LLC

Many Hats Media, *distributor for* Sourced Media Books

Many Moons Press, *distributed by* Gem Guides Book Co

MAPART Publishing, *distributor for* Michelin Maps & Guides

Mapin, *distributed by* Antique Collectors Club Ltd

MAR*CO Products Inc, *distributor for* Boulden, Center for Youth Issues/STARS, Educational Media, HarperCollins, *distributed by* ASCA, Boulden Publishing, Burnell Books, Calloway House, Career Kids FYI, CFKR Career, Character Development, Community Intervention, Courage to Change, Cress Productions Co, EDU Reference, Educational Media Corp, Incentive Plus, Jist, Mental Health Resources, National Professional Resources, National Resource Center Youth Services, NIMCO Bookstore, Paperbacks for Educators, School Speciality, SourceResource, STARS-National Center for Youths, WRS Group, YouthLight Inc

Maren Green, *distributed by* Crabtree Publishing Co

Maren Green Publishing Inc, *distributed by* Crabtree Publishing Inc

Marick Press, *distributed by* Wayne State University Press

Marimba Books, *distributed by* Kensington Publishing Corp

Marine Education Textbooks Inc, *distributor for* Marine Techniques Publishing

Marine Survey Press, *imprint of* Marine Education Textbooks Inc

Marine Techniques Publishing, *distributor for* Academic Press, Best Publishing Co, Butterworth-Heinemann, Clarkson Research Services Ltd, Elsevier, Science & Technology Books, Focal Press, Gulf Professional Publishers, PennWell Business & Industrial Division, W B Saunders Co, Waterfront Soundings Productions, Witherby Seamanship International Ltd, *distributed by* Armchair Sailor Books & Charts, Baker, Lyman & Co, Bluewater Books & Charts, The Book House Inc, BooksXYZ.com, Brodart Books Co, Captain's Nautical Supplies, Coutts Library Services Inc, Elsevier Science, Technology & Business Books, Emery-Pratt Co, Follett Library Resources Inc, Landfall Navigation, Marine Education Textbooks Inc, MaritimeEmployment.com, Pilothouse Nautical Books & Charts, Seabreeze Books & Charts, Washington Book Distributors

Mariner Books, *imprint of* Houghton Mifflin Harcourt Trade & Reference Division

Marion Institute, *distributed by* Chelsea Green Publishing Co

Mariposa Press, *distributor for* Sylvan Dell Publishing

MaritimeEmployment.com, *distributor for* Marine Techniques Publishing

Ashley Mark Publishing Co, *imprint of* Hal Leonard Corp, *distributed by* Hal Leonard Corp

marketumbrella.org, *distributed by* Chelsea Green Publishing Co

MarketResearch.com, *distributor for* Apollo Managed Care Inc, Primary Research Group Inc

Markowski International Publishers, *distributed by* Executive Books, Moborbooks

Edward B Marks Music, *distributed by* Hal Leonard Corp

The Marlboro Press, *imprint of* Northwestern University Press

Marmac Publishing Co, *distributed by* Pelican Publishing Co

Loretta T Marra, *distributed by* Sunbelt Publications Inc

Marriage Transformation LLC, *distributed by* Barringer, Longman

Carole Marsh Books, *imprint of* Gallopade International Inc

Carole Marsh Mysteries, *imprint of* Gallopade International Inc

Marshall & Swift, *distributed by* McGraw-Hill Book Co

Marshall Cavendish Adult Trade, *imprint of* Marshall Cavendish Corp

Marshall Cavendish Benchmark, *imprint of* Marshall Cavendish Corp

Marshall Cavendish Corp, *member of* Times International Publishing Group, *distributed by* Marshall Cavendish Ltd (UK)

Marshall Cavendish Digital, *imprint of* Marshall Cavendish Corp

Marshall Cavendish Education, *imprint of* Marshall Cavendish Corp

Marshall Cavendish Ltd, *distributor for* Marshall Cavendish Corp

Marshall Cavendish Reference, *imprint of* Marshall Cavendish Corp

Marshall Editions, *distributed by* Antique Collectors Club Ltd

Marsilio, *imprint of* Rizzoli International Publications Inc

Darvin Martin CDs, *distributed by* Closson Press

Rux Martin Books, *imprint of* Houghton Mifflin Harcourt Trade & Reference Division

Marvel, *distributed by* Hachette Book Group

Helen Marx/Turtle Point, *imprint of* Turtle Point Press

Maryland Historical Society, *distributed by* Alan C Hood & Co Inc, The Johns Hopkins University Press

Maryland Historical Trust Press, *distributed by* Cornell Maritime Press Inc

Maryland History Press, *distributor for* Dogwood Ridge Books, Tapestry Press Ltd

Maryland Sea Grant Program, *distributed by* Cornell Maritime Press Inc

The Massachusetts Historical Society, *distributed by* University of Virginia Press

Master Books, *subsidiary of* New Leaf Publishing Group

Masters of Photography, *imprint of* Aperture Books

Masterwork Books, *imprint of* Kidsbooks LLC

Masthof Press, *distributor for* Closson Press

Math Products Plus, *imprint of* Wide World Publishing

Math Solutions®, *unit of* Scholastic Education

Mathematica Josephina, *distributed by* American Mathematical Society

The Mathematical Association of America, *distributed by* Cambridge University Press

Mathematical Society of Japan, *distributed by* American Mathematical Society

Matheson Trust, *distributed by* Fons Vitae

Adam Matthew, *imprint of* SAGE Publications

Maunsel & Co Publishers, *imprint of* Academica Press LLC

MBI, *distributor for* CarTech Inc

MBI Publishing Co, *division of* Keyside Publishing Group

Margaret K McElderry Books, *imprint of* Simon & Schuster Children's Publishing

McFarland & Co Ltd, Publishers (London, UK), *subsidiary of* McFarland

McGraw-Hill, *imprint of* McGraw-Hill Science, Engineering, Mathematics, *distributor for* Society of Manufacturing Engineers, *distributed by* American Academy of Environmental Engineers, American Water Works Association, Illuminating Engineering Society of North America (IES), NACE International, SAS Publishing, Society of Manufacturing Engineers

McGraw-Hill Book Co, *distributor for* Marshall & Swift

McGraw-Hill Career Education, *division of* McGraw-Hill Higher Education

McGraw-Hill Contemporary, *imprint of* McGraw-Hill Education

McGraw-Hill Contemporary Learning Series, *division of* McGraw-Hill Higher Education, *imprint of* McGraw-Hill Higher Education

McGraw-Hill Create, *division of* McGraw-Hill Higher Education, *imprint of* McGraw-Hill Education, McGraw-Hill Higher Education

McGraw-Hill Education, *division of* McGraw-Hill Financial

McGraw-Hill Education Australia, New Zealand & South Africa, *imprint of* McGraw-Hill Education

McGraw-Hill Education Europe, Middle East and Africa, *imprint of* McGraw-Hill Education

McGraw-Hill Education Latin America, *imprint of* McGraw-Hill Education

McGraw-Hill Education - Mexico, *imprint of* McGraw-Hill Education

McGraw-Hill Education - Spain, *imprint of* McGraw-Hill Education

McGraw-Hill Humanities, Social Sciences, Languages, *division of* McGraw-Hill Higher Education, *imprint of* McGraw-Hill Education, McGraw-Hill Higher Education

McGraw-Hill International, *distributor for* AMACOM Books

McGraw-Hill International Publishing Group, *division of* McGraw-Hill Education

McGraw-Hill/Irwin, *division of* McGraw-Hill Higher Education, *imprint of* McGraw-Hill Education, McGraw-Hill Higher Education

McGraw-Hill Learning Solutions, *imprint of* McGraw-Hill Higher Education

McGraw-Hill Professional, *division of* McGraw-Hill Education, McGraw-Hill Education, *imprint of* McGraw-Hill Education, *distributed by* Professional Publications Inc (PPI)

McGraw-Hill Professional Publishing, *distributor for* American Society for Quality (ASQ)

McGraw-Hill Ryerson, *imprint of* McGraw-Hill Education

McGraw-Hill School Education Group, *division of* McGraw-Hill Education

McGraw-Hill Science, Engineering, Mathematics, *division of* McGraw-Hill Higher Education, *imprint of* McGraw-Hill Education, McGraw-Hill Higher Education

McGraw-Hill Professional Development, *imprint of* McGraw-Hill Education

McIntosh & Otis, *subsidiary of* Louisiana State University Press

McKay Chess Library, *imprint of* Random House Reference/Random House Puzzles & Games/House of Collectibles

Anne McKinney Career Series, *imprint of* PREP Publishing

McKissick Museum, *distributed by* University of South Carolina Press

McPherson & Co, *imprint of* McPherson & Co

McWhiney Foundation Press/State House Press, *distributed by* Texas A&M University Press

Md Books, *imprint of* May Davenport Publishers

MDR, A D & B Co, *division of* Dun & Bradstreet Corp

Meadow Creek Press, *imprint of* Crumb Elbow Publishing

Meadowbrook Press, *distributed by* Simon & Schuster, Simon & Schuster, Inc, Simon & Schuster Sales & Marketing

Mean Free Path, *distributor for* American Society for Nondestructive Testing

R S Means, a Reed Construction Data Co, *subsidiary of* Reed Construction Data, *distributed by* John Wiley & Sons Inc

Measuring Up®, *imprint of* Peoples Education Inc

Mechling Associates, *distributor for* Western Pennsylvania Genealogical Society

MedBooks, *division of* Professional Education Workshops & Seminars, *distributed by* JA Majors

Medford Press, *imprint of* Plexus Publishing, Inc

Media Solutions, *distributor for* Ballinger Publishing

Medical Economics, *distributed by* OptumInsight™

Medical Group Management Association (MGMA), *distributor for* American Medical Association, Aspen Publishers, Greenbranch, HAP (Health Adminstration Press), Jones & Bartlett Learning, J Wiley & Sons

Medical Publishing (Gefen), *division of* Gefen Books

Medieval Institute Publications, *division of* Medieval Institute of Western Michigan University

Mel Bay Publications Inc, *distributor for* AcuTab Publications Inc, AMA, Chanterelle, Stefan Grossman's Guitar Workshop, Hardie Press, Learn Roots Music, Maggies Music, Malley's, Registry of Guitar Tutors (RGT), RGB Arte Visual, Scott's Highland Services, Voggenreiter Publishers, Walton's, SR Wheat

Melissa Media Associates Inc, *division of* Aristide D Caratzas, Publisher

Paul Mellon Centre, *distributed by* Yale University Press

Memoirs, *imprint of* American Philosophical Society

Memorable Meetings Press, *imprint of* R J Berg Publisher

Men at Arms, *imprint of* Osprey Publishing Inc

Menasha Ridge Press Inc, *division of* Keen Communications, Keen Communications LLC

C E Mendez Foundation Inc, *distributor for* Rocky River Publishers LLC

The Menil Collection, *distributed by* Yale University Press

Menil Foundation, *distributed by* University of Texas Press, Wittenborn Art Books

Menorah, *distributed by* Bloch Publishing Co

Mental Health Resources, *distributor for* American Counseling Association, MAR*CO Products Inc

Mercier, *distributed by* Dufour Editions Inc

Merck, *distributed by* Simon & Schuster Sales & Marketing

Merck Publishing, *distributed by* Simon & Schuster, Inc

Mercy Place, *distributed by* Destiny Image Inc

Meredith, *distributed by* Delmar

Meredith Music, *distributed by* Hal Leonard Corp

Merehurst Ltd, *imprint of* Tuttle Publishing

Merion Books, *distributed by* Enfield Publishing & Distribution Co

Merit Press Books, *imprint of* F+W Media Inc

Merlin Press (London, England), *distributor for* Maisonneuve Press

Merriam-Webster Inc, *subsidiary of* Encyclopaedia Britannica Inc

Merrick & Day, *distributed by* Antique Collectors Club Ltd

Frank Merriwell Inc, *subsidiary of* National Learning Corp

Merry Muse Press, *imprint of* Loft Press Inc

MerwinAsia, *distributed by* St Johann Press

Sonja Merz International, *distributor for* Stone Bridge Press Inc

Mesorah Publications Ltd, *distributor for* NCSY Publications

Messianic Jewish Publishers, *division of* Messianic Jewish Communications, *distributor for* Chosen People Ministries, First Fruits of Zion, Jewish New Testament Publications

Metamorphic Press, *distributed by* Chelsea Green Publishing Co

Metro Maps, *division of* Wide World of Maps Inc, *distributed by* Wide World of Maps Inc

Metropolitan Books, *imprint of* Henry Holt and Company, LLC

The Metropolitan Museum of Art, *distributed by* Yale University Press

MFA Publications, *imprint of* Museum of Fine Arts Boston, *distributed by* Art Books/D A P

MGI Management Institute Inc, *subsidiary of* SmartPros Ltd

MHS, *distributor for* ADD Warehouse

Micelle Press, *distributed by* Scholium International Inc

Michael di Capua Books, *imprint of* Disney-Hyperion Books, Scholastic Trade Division

Michelin Maps & Guides, *division of* Michelin North America Inc, *distributed by* Langenscheidt Publishing Group, MAPART Publishing

(CN only), NBN (guides for North America), Editions du Renouveau Pedagogique (French titles in Canada), Penguin Canada (English titles in Canada)

Michi Japanese Arts and Ways, *imprint of* Stone Bridge Press Inc

Michie, *imprint of* LexisNexis®

Michigan Municipal League, *affiliate of* National League of Cities, *distributor for* Crisp Books

Michigan State University Press (MSU Press), *division of* Michigan State University, *distributor for* Mackinac Historic Parks, MSU Museum, University of Alberta Press, University of Calgary Press, University of Manitoba Press, *distributed by* UBC Press, Canada

Microcosm Books, *imprint of* TFH Publications Inc

Microsoft Learning, *distributed by* Hachette Book Group

Microsoft Press, *division of* Microsoft Corp, *distributed by* O'Reilly Media (Asia, Australia, Europe, New Zealand, North America, UK), O'Reilly Media Inc, Shroff Publishers & Distributors (India)

Microsoft Press France, *subsidiary of* Microsoft Press

Microsoft Press Germany, *subsidiary of* Microsoft Press

Midewin Series, *imprint of* High Tide Press

Midnight Editions, *imprint of* Cleis Press

Midnight Ink, *imprint of* Llewellyn Publications

Midnight Marquee Press Inc, *affiliate of* Luminary Press

Midpoint Trade, *distributor for* Elite Books, Energy Psychology Press

Midpoint Trade Books, *distributor for* Hellgate Press

Midrashic Editions, *imprint of* Cross-Cultural Communications

Midwest Library Service, *distributor for* Business Research Services Inc, Do-It-Yourself Legal Publishers, Primary Research Group Inc, *distributed by* Trans-Atlantic Publications Inc

MidWest Plan Service (MWPS), *affiliate of* Iowa State University-Information Technology Services, *distributor for* Natural Resource Agriculture & Engineering Service, *distributed by* Natural Resource Agriculture & Engineering Service

Mike Murach & Associates Inc, *distributed by* Shroff Publishers (reprints)

Milady, *division of* Cengage Learning, *imprint of* Delmar

Milestone Documents, *division of* Schlager Group Inc

Milet Publishing Ltd, *imprint of* Tuttle Publishing, *distributed by* Tuttle Publishing

Military Illustrated, *distributed by* Casemate Publishers & Book Distributors LLC

Military Living Publications, *division of* Military Marketing Services Inc, Military Marketing Services Inc

Millbrook Press, *division of* Lerner Publishing Group Inc, *imprint of* Lerner Publishing Group Inc

Millennial Mind Publishing, *imprint of* American Book Publishing

Milliken Publishing Co, *division of* The Lorenz Corp, The Lorenz Corp

Mills & Boon Large Print, *distributed by* Thorndike Press®

Sally Milner, *distributed by* Sterling Publishing Co Inc

Minedition, *imprint of* Penguin Group (USA) LLC

The Minerals, Metals & Materials Society (TMS), *affiliate of* AIME

Minnesota Historical Society Press, *division of* Minnesota Historical Society

Minotaur, *imprint of* St Martin's Press, LLC

MIRA Books, *imprint of* Harlequin Enterprises Ltd

Miranda Press Trade Division, *imprint of* Cognizant Communication Corp

Miss Jackie Inc, *distributed by* Gryphon House Inc

Miss Rosen Edition, *imprint of* powerHouse Books

Mission San Juan Capistrano Women's Guild, *distributed by* Sunbelt Publications Inc

The Missionary Enterprise in Asia, *imprint of* EastBridge

Missouri History Museum, *distributed by* University of Missouri Press

MIT, *distributor for* The AEI Press

MIT List Visual Arts Center, *distributed by* DAP Distributed Art Publishers

MIT Press, *distributed by* DawnSignPress

The MIT Press, *distributor for* AAAI Press, Canadian Centre for Architecture, Zone Books, Zone Books dba Urzone Inc

Mitten Press, *imprint of* Spry Publishing

MJF Books, *imprint of* Fine Communications

MKSAP® Audio Companion, *imprint of* Oakstone Publishing LLC

MMP, *distributed by* Casemate Publishers & Book Distributors LLC

Farhang Moaser, *distributed by* Ibex Publishers

Mobipocket, *distributor for* Hard Shell Word Factory

Moborbooks, *distributor for* Markowski International Publishers

Modelling Manuals, *imprint of* Osprey Publishing Inc

Modelling Masterclass, *imprint of* Osprey Publishing Inc

Modern Drummer Publications, *distributed by* Hal Leonard Corp

Modern History Press, *imprint of* Loving Healing Press Inc

Modern Learning Press, *imprint of* EPS/School Specialty Literacy & Intervention

Modern Library, *imprint of* Random House Inc, Random House Publishing Group

Modern Masters, *imprint of* Abbeville Publishing Group

Modern Publishing, *division of* Kappa Books Publishers LLC, Unisystems Inc

MV Mojica & Associates Co, *distributor for* Sylvan Dell Publishing

Moleskine, *distributed by* Chronicle Books LLC

Moliere & Co, *imprint of* European Masterpieces, *distributed by* European Masterpieces

The Monacelli Press, *imprint of* Crown Publishing Group, Random House Inc, *distributed by* Penguin Group (USA) LLC

Monarch Books, *distributed by* Kregel Publications

Monarch Books of Canada, *distributor for* Price World Publishing LLC

Monarch Books of Canada Ltd, *distributor for* Boys Town Press

Mondadori Spanish Language, *distributed by* Random House Inc

Mondo, *imprint of* Mondo Publishing

Moneta Publications, *distributed by* Chelsea Green Publishing Co

Money Market Directories, *unit of* Standard & Poor's

Monjeu Press, *distributed by* Gryphon House Inc

Monostereo, *distributed by* Simon & Schuster Audio

Montana Historical Society Press, *distributed by* Globe Pequot Press, The Globe Pequot Press

Monthly Review Press, *division of* Monthly Review Foundation Inc, Monthly Review Foundation Inc, *distributed by* New York University Press

Moody Press, *distributor for* Focus on the Family

Moody Publishers, *affiliate of* Ministry of Moody Bible Institute

Moon City Press, *distributed by* The University of Arkansas Press

Moose Country Press, *distributed by* Enfield Publishing & Distribution Co

Morehouse Publishing, *imprint of* Church Publishing Inc, *distributor for* Gracewing (UK)

Morgan Kaufmann, *imprint of* Elsevier Inc

Morgan Kaufmann Publishers, *imprint of* Academic Press

Morrow Junior Books, *imprint of* HarperCollins Publishers

William Morrow, *imprint of* HarperCollins General Books Group, HarperCollins Publishers Sales, *distributor for* Nightingale-Conant

William Morrow Cookbooks, *imprint of* HarperCollins Publishers Sales

William Morrow Trade Paperbacks, *imprint of* HarperCollins General Books Group

Mosby, *imprint of* Elsevier, Health Sciences Division, *distributor for* OptumInsight™, *distributed by* Fire Engineering Books & Videos, OptumInsight™

Moser, *imprint of* Biblo-Moser

Motorbooks, *imprint of* MBI Publishing Co, Quayside Publishing Group

Motorbooks International, *distributor for* Haynes Manuals Inc, Iconografix Inc, *distributed by* Heimburger House Publishing Co

Paul Mould Publishing, *imprint of* Empire Publishing Service, *distributed by* Empire Publishing Service

Mt Blue, *imprint of* Genesis Press Inc

Mount Ida Press, *distributed by* State University of New York Press

Mount Olive College Press, *affiliate of* Mount Olive College

Mount Vernon Ladies Association, *distributed by* The University of Virginia Press

Mountain Air Books, *imprint of* Mountain n' Air Books

Mountain Biking Press/FineEdge.com, *imprint of* FineEdge.com

Mountain n' Air Books, *distributor for* Tom Harrison Cartography

Mountain Pond Publishing Corp, *distributed by* The Countryman Press

Mountain Press, *distributor for* Ericson Books

Mountain Press Publishing Co, *distributor for* Bucking Horse Books, Clark City Press, Companion Press, Cottonwood Publishing, Hops Press, Npustin Publishing, Western Edge Press

Mountain Sports Press Series, *imprint of* Mountain Press Publishing Co

Mountaineers Books, *distributor for* The American Alpine Club Press

The Mountaineers Books, *division of* The Mountaineers Club, *distributor for* The American Alpine Club Press, Colorado Mountain Club Press

De Gruyter Mouton, *imprint of* Walter de Gruyter GmbH & Co KG, Walter De Gruyter Inc, *distributed by* Walter de Gruyter Inc

Moyer Bell, *imprint of* Beaufort Books

Moznaim Publishing Corp, *distributor for* Avamra Institute, Breslov Research Institute, Red Wheel Weiser Inc

MRTS, *imprint of* Arizona Center for Medieval & Renaissance Studies (ACMRS)

MSS Information Corp, *distributed by* Ardent Media Inc

MSU Museum, *distributed by* Michigan State University Press (MSU Press)

MTI, *distributed by* NACE International

MTV Books, *imprint of* Gallery Books

MTV Press, *distributed by* powerHouse Books

Mudborn Press, *imprint of* Bandanna Books

Coleccion Mujeres de Palabra, *imprint of* University of Puerto Rico Press

Mulberry Books, *imprint of* HarperCollins Publishers

Mulholland Books, *imprint of* Little, Brown and Company

A G Muller & Cie, *distributed by* US Games Systems Inc

Lars Muller, *distributed by* Prestel Publishing

Multicultural Publications Inc, *subsidiary of* Making Education Reform Imperative Today Inc (MERIT)

Multimedia HRD Pvt Ltd, *distributor for* HRD Press

MultiMedia Reviews®, *imprint of* Oakstone Publishing LLC

Museum of American Folk Art, *distributed by* Antique Collectors Club Ltd

Museum of Early Southern Decorative Arts, *distributed by* The University of North Carolina Press

The Museum of Modern Art, *affiliate of* Circulating Film & Video Library, *distributed by* Distributed Art Publishers (DAP) (US & Canada only)

Museum of New Mexico Press, *unit of* New Mexico State Department of Cultural Affairs, *distributed by* University of New Mexico Press

Music/Culture, *imprint of* Wesleyan University Press

Music Sales, *distributed by* Welcome Books®

Music Sales America, *distributed by* Hal Leonard Corp

Music Sales Corp, *distributed by* Beekman Books Inc

Musical Kidz LLC, *distributed by* Palm Kids™

Musicians Institute Press, *imprint of* Hal Leonard Corp, *distributed by* Hal Leonard Corp

Musikverlage Han Sikorski, *distributed by* Hal Leonard Corp

MVP Books, *imprint of* Quayside Publishing Group, *distributed by* Lerner Publishing Group Inc

MyBizDaily.com, *subsidiary of* BizBest Media Corp

Mycroft & Moran, *imprint of* Arkham House Publishers Inc

Myklas Music Press, *distributed by* Alfred Publishing Company Inc

MyReportLinks.com Books, *imprint of* Enslow Publishers Inc

The Mysterious Press, *imprint of* Grove/Atlantic Inc

Mystic Books, *imprint of* Regal Crest Enterprises LLC

Mystic Oaks, *imprint of* Oak Tree Press

Mystic Seaport Museum Inc, *distributor for* Glencannon, Ten Pound Island Books

N & A, *imprint of* The Nautical & Aviation Publishing Co of America Inc

NACE International, *distributor for* ASM International, ASTM, AWS, Butterworth-Heinemann, Cambridge University Press, CASTI Publishing, Compass Publications, CRC Press, Marcel Dekker Inc, E&FN Spon, Elsevier Science Publishers, Gulf Publishing, Industrial Press, Institute of Materials, ISO, McGraw-Hill, MTI, Prentice Hall, Professional Publications, SSPC, Swedish Corrosion Institute, John Wiley & Sons Inc, *distributed by* Australasian Corrosion Association

NAL, *division of* Penguin Group (USA) LLC

Narosa Publishing House, *distributed by* American Mathematical Society

NASCO, *distributor for* National Council of Teachers of Mathematics (NCTM)

Nashville Division, *division of* Hachette Book Group

NASSP, *imprint of* National Association of Secondary School Principals (NASSP)

NASW Press, *division of* National Association of Social Workers (NASW)

Nataraj, *imprint of* New World Library

Nation Books, *imprint of* The Nation Institute, The Perseus Books Group

National Academies Press (NAP), *division of* National Academies

National Academy for Adult Jewish Studies, *imprint of* United Synagogue Book Service

The National Alliance Research Academy, *division of* The National Alliance for Insurance Education & Research

National Archives & Records Administration, *distributed by* J J Keller & Associates, Inc

National Association for Music Education, *distributed by* Rowman & Littlefield Education

National Association of Broadcasters (NAB), *distributed by* Allyn & Bacon, Lawrence Erlbaum Assoc, Focal Press, Macmillan Publishing Co, Tab Books, Wadsworth Inc

National Association of Home Builders (NAHB), *distributed by* BuilderBooks.com

National Association of Photo Sellers, *imprint of* Copywriter's Council of America (CCA), *distributed by* Copywriter's Council of America (CCA)

National Association of Photo Sellers™, *imprint of* The Linick Group Inc, *distributed by* The Linick Group Inc

National Book Co, *division of* Educational Research Associates

National Book Network, *distributor for* Blood Moon Productions Ltd, Brewers Publications, Bridge Works Publishing, Hudson Hills Press LLC, Impact Publications/Development Concepts Inc, LearningExpress LLC, Open Horizons Publishing Co, Welcome Rain Publishers LLC, *distributed by* Heimburger House Publishing Co

National Book Network (NBN), *distributor for* American Society for Training & Development (ASTD)

National Book Network Inc (NBN), *distributor for* The Intrepid Traveler

National Bureau of Economic Research, *distributed by* University of Chicago Press

National Center Early Childhood Workforce, *distributed by* Gryphon House Inc

National Center for Children in Poverty, *division of* Mailman School of Public Health at Columbia University

National Cooperative Highway Research Program, *imprint of* Transportation Research Board

National Council of Examiners for Engineering & Surveying, *distributed by* Professional Publications Inc (PPI)

National Council of Teachers of Mathematics (NCTM), *distributed by* Eric Armin Inc Education Ctr, Delta Education, Didax Educational Resources, Educators Outlet, ETA Cuisenaire, Lakeshore Learning Materials, NASCO, Spectrum

National Doll Society of America, *division of* Success Advertising & Publishing

National Farm Book Co, *division of* Hobar Publications

National Galleries of Scotland, *distributed by* Antique Collectors Club Ltd

National Gallery, London, *distributed by* Yale University Press

National Gallery of Art, *distributed by* Abrams, Bulfinch/Little, Cambridge University Press, Hudson Hills, Lund Humphries/Ashgate, OAP, Princeton University Press, Thames & Hudson, Yale University Press

National Gallery of Canada, *distributed by* University of Chicago Press

National Genealogical Society, *distributed by* Heritage Books Inc

National Geographic, *distributor for* The Colonial Williamsburg Foundation, *distributed by* Random House Inc

National Geographic Adventure Classics, *imprint of* National Geographic Books

National Geographic Adventure Press, *imprint of* National Geographic Books

National Geographic Books, *division of* National Geographic Society, *imprint of* National Geographic Books, *distributed by* PGUK / Hi Marketing (United Kingdom), Random House (Worldwide exc UK)

National Geographic Children's Books, *imprint of* National Geographic Books

National Geographic Directions, *imprint of* National Geographic Books

National Geographic Learning, *unit of* Cengage Learning

National Geographic Society, *distributed by* Random House

National Guitar Workshop, *distributed by* Alfred Publishing Company Inc

National Information Standards Organization, *distributor for* Niso Press

National Institute of Occupational Safety & Health, *distributed by* J J Keller & Associates, Inc

National Paper Trade Association, *distributor for* Grade Finders Inc

National Park Service Media Services, *subsidiary of* US Department of the Interior

National Poetry Foundation, *distributed by* University Press of New England

National Portrait Gallery, *distributed by* Antique Collectors Club Ltd

National Professional Resources, *distributor for* MAR*CO Products Inc

National Publishing Co, *subsidiary of* Courier Corp, *distributed by* Oxford University Press

National Ranching Heritage Center, *distributed by* Texas Tech University Press

National Register Publishing, *division of* Marquis Who's Who LLC

National Resource Center for Youth Services (NRCYS), *division of* University of Oklahoma-Outreach

National Resource Center Youth Services, *distributor for* MAR*CO Products Inc

National Science Teachers Association (NSTA), *distributor for* AAAS, BSCS, Corwin, Heinemann, IRA

National Society for the Study of Education, *distributed by* University of Chicago Press

National Teacher Examination Series, *imprint of* National Learning Corp

The National Trust, *distributed by* Antique Collectors Club Ltd

The National Underwriter Co, *division of* Summit Business Media

Native Voices, *imprint of* Book Publishing Co

Natural Heritage Press, *distributed by* Birch Brook Press

Natural Resource Agriculture & Engineering Service, *distributor for* MidWest Plan Service (MWPS), *distributed by* MidWest Plan Service (MWPS)

Naturegraph, *distributed by* Gem Guides Book Co

NaturEncyclopedia Series, *imprint of* Stemmer House Publishers Inc

Naval Institute Press, *division of* US Naval Institute, *distributed by* Publishers Group West (digital only)

NavPress, *imprint of* NavPress Publishing Group

NavPress Publishing Group, *division of* The Navigators

Nazarene Publishing House, *imprint of* Beacon Hill Press of Kansas City

NBM Publishing Inc, *distributed by* IPG

NBN, *distributor for* Intercultural Press Inc, Michelin Maps & Guides, Para Publishing LLC

NCP, *imprint of* New City Press

NCSY Publications, *distributed by* Mesorah Publications Ltd

NEA Professional Library, *imprint of* National Education Association (NEA)

Neal-Schuman Publishers Inc, *distributor for* Chandos, Facet

Near Eastern Press, *imprint of* Holmes Publishing Group LLC

E T Nedder Publishing, *imprint of* Paulist Press

Nefu Books, *imprint of* Africana Homestead Legacy Publishers Inc

Neibauer Press & Church Supplier, *division of* Louis Neibauer Co Inc, Louis Neibauer Co Inc

Nelson Canada, *distributed by* Peoples Education Inc

Grupo Nelson, *division of* Thomas Nelson Inc

Tommy Nelson, *division of* Thomas Nelson Inc, *distributor for* Focus on the Family

NES, The Official Tasp Study Guide, *distributed by* Hendrick-Long Publishing Co

The Netherlands Institute for Social Research, *distributed by* Transaction Publishers Inc

NetLearning, *imprint of* Delmar

netLibrary, *distributor for* Infosential Press

Nevada Publications, *distributor for* Gem Guides Book Co, *distributed by* Gem Guides Book Co

Nevraumont Publishing Co, *distributed by* Harry N Abrams Inc, Basic Books, Copernicus Press, Crown Publishing, W H Freeman, Harper Collins, Henry Holt, Alfred A Knopf, Pantheon Books, Penguin Putnam, Pi Press, Princeton University Press, Rizzoli International, Simon & Schuster, Texas A & M University Press, University of California Press, Westview Press, John Wiley & Sons, Yale University Press

New American Fiction Series, *imprint of* Green Integer

New American Library, *imprint of* NAL

New American Poetry Series, *imprint of* Green Integer

New Amsterdam Books, *imprint of* Ivan R Dee Publisher

New Architecture Group Ltd, *distributed by* Antique Collectors Club Ltd

New Beginnings Press, *imprint of* Hay House Inc

The New Careers Center, *division of* Finney Company Inc

New Cavendish Books Ltd, *distributed by* Antique Collectors Club Ltd

New City (Great Britain), *distributed by* New City Press

New City Press, *division of* Focolare Movement, *distributor for* Ciudad Nueva (Spain/Argentina), New City (Great Britain)

New Directions Publishing Corp, *distributed by* W W Norton & Company Inc, W W Norton Co

New England AEYC, *distributed by* Gryphon House Inc

New England Bibliographies, *distributed by* Oak Knoll Press

New England College, *distributed by* University Press of New England

New England History Press, *imprint of* Picton Press

New Falcon Publications, *imprint of* The Original Falcon Press

New Forest Press, *imprint of* Black Rabbit Books

New Harvest, *imprint of* Houghton Mifflin Harcourt Trade & Reference Division

New Holland Publishers Ltd, *distributed by* The Globe Pequot Press

New Horizon Press, *distributed by* Kensington Publishing Corp

New Horizons, *distributed by* Gryphon House Inc

New Horizons Book Publishing Co, *imprint of* World Citizens

New Island Books, *distributed by* Dufour Editions Inc

New Issues Poetry & Prose, *affiliate of* Western Michigan University

The New Jerusalem Bible, *imprint of* Random House Inc

New Leaf, *distributor for* Ash Tree Publishing

New Leaf Books, *distributor for* Blue Poppy Press

New Leaf Press Inc, *division of* New Leaf Publishing Group

New Marketplace, *imprint of* Oaklea Press

New Netherland Institute, *distributed by* State University of New York Press

New Pacific Press, *distributed by* North Atlantic Books

New Page Books, *imprint of* The Career Press Inc

New Path Learning, *distributed by* Peoples Education Inc

New Poets Series, *subsidiary of* BrickHouse Books Inc, *imprint of* BrickHouse Books Inc

New Readers Press, *division of* ProLiteracy, ProLiteracy, *distributor for* Teachers of English to Speakers of Other Languages Inc (TESOL)

The New South Co, *imprint of* C & M Online Media Inc

New Traditions, *imprint of* Gallopade International Inc

New Vanguard, *imprint of* Osprey Publishing Inc

New Voices, *imprint of* Florida Academic Press

New Win Publishing, *division of* Academic Learning Co LLC

New Wind Press, *distributed by* Stone & Scott Publishers

New Wine Press, *distributed by* Bridge-Logos Inc

New World Library, *division of* Whatever Publishing Inc, Whatever Publishing Inc

New World Paperbacks, *imprint of* International Publishers Co Inc

New World Press, *imprint of* Copywriter's Council of America (CCA), *distributed by* China Books

New World Press Books, *distributor for* The Linick Group Inc

New World Press (NWP), *imprint of* The Linick Group Inc

New York Academy of Sciences, *distributed by* Wiley Blackwell Publishers

The New York Botanical Garden Press, *division of* New York Botanical Garden, The New York Botanical Garden

New York Nights, *imprint of* Ugly Duckling Presse

New York University Press, *distributor for* Combined Academic Publishers Ltd, Footprint Books, Monthly Review Press, *distributed by* Heimburger House Publishing Co

New Yorker Desk Diary, *distributed by* Per Annum Inc

Newark Museum, *distributed by* Antique Collectors Club Ltd

Newbridge Communications Inc, *distributor for* Educational Impressions Inc

Newbridge Discovery Links, *imprint of* Sundance/Newbridge Publishing

Newbury Street Press, *imprint of* New England Historic Genealogical Society

The Newman Press, *imprint of* Paulist Press

Newmarket Press for It Books, *imprint of* HarperCollins General Books Group

News Books International, *imprint of* R J Berg Publisher

The News Group, *distributor for* Goodluck Guides

NewSouth Books, *imprint of* NewSouth Books, NewSouth Inc, *distributed by* John F Blair Publisher

NewSouth Classics, *imprint of* NewSouth Books

Newtona LLC, *distributed by* Sunbelt Publications Inc

Nexus Special Interests, *distributed by* Trans-Atlantic Publications Inc

NFPA, *distributed by* Delmar

Nibble Me Books™, *imprint of* Playhouse Publishing

Niche Publishing, *distributed by* John F Blair Publisher

Nicolin Fields Publishing, *distributed by* University Press of New England

Nightingale-Conant, *distributed by* William Morrow, Simon & Schuster

Nightingale-Conant (UK), *subsidiary of* Nightingale-Conant

Nightingale Editions, *imprint of* Cross-Cultural Communications

Nile Publishing, *distributed by* Tughra Books

Nilgiri Press, *division of* Blue Mountain Center of Meditation

Nimbus Publishing, *distributed by* Orca Book Publishers

Nimbus Publishing Ltd, *distributed by* Down East Books

NIMCO Bookstore, *distributor for* MAR*CO Products Inc

Nippon Foundation, *distributed by* EastBridge

Niso Press, *distributed by* National Information Standards Organization

NK Publications Inc, *affiliate of* Loukoumi Books

No Frills Buffalo, *distributed by* Aardvark

No Starch Press Inc, *distributed by* O'Reilly Media

Coleccion Clasicos No Tan Clasicos, *imprint of* University of Puerto Rico Press

Noble Porter Press, *imprint of* Dramaline® Publications LLC

Nodin Press, *distributed by* Adventure Publications

Noel Press, *imprint of* Nova Science Publishers Inc

Noetic Books, *imprint of* New Harbinger Publications Inc

NOLO, *subsidiary of* Internet Brands Inc

Nonpareil Books, *imprint of* David R Godine Publisher Inc

The Noontide Press, *imprint of* Legion for the Survival of Freedom

Nordic Africa Institute, *distributed by* Stylus Publishing LLC

Nordic Insititute of Asian Studies, *distributed by* University of Hawaii Press

Nortex Press, *imprint of* Eakin Press

North American Publishing, *distributor for* Grade Finders Inc

North Atlantic Books, *division of* Society for the Study of Native Arts & Sciences, *distributor for* DharmaCafe, Energy Arts, Ergos Institute, Frog Books, Heaven & Earth Publications, New Pacific Press, Rangjung Yeshe Publications, Sunfood Living

North Carolina Museum of Art, *distributed by* The University of North Carolina Press

North Castle Books, *imprint of* M E Sharpe Inc

North Country Books, *imprint of* North Country Books Inc

North Country Classics, *imprint of* North Country Books Inc

North Country Distributors, *distributor for* Cadence Jazz Books

North Light Books, *division of* F+W Media Inc, F+W Media Inc, *imprint of* F+W Media Inc

North Point Press, *imprint of* Farrar, Straus & Giroux, LLC

Northcross Books, *distributed by* Sunbelt Publications Inc

Northeastern University Press, *imprint of* University Press of New England

Northern Forest Center, *distributed by* Enfield Publishing & Distribution Co

Northfield Publishing, *imprint of* Moody Publishers

Northwest Fly Fishing, *distributed by* Stackpole Books

Northwestern University Press, *distributor for* Lake Forrest College Press, Third World Press, Tia Chucha Press

W W Norton, *distributor for* Allworth Press, Verso, *distributed by* Peoples Education Inc

W W Norton & Co, *distributor for* Dalkey Archive Press, Peace Hill Press, Persea Books, *distributed by* Heimburger House Publishing Co

W W Norton & Co Inc, *distributor for* The Countryman Press, Pushcart Press, Thames & Hudson

W W Norton & Company Inc, *distributor for* Airphoto International Ltd/Odyssey Publications, Albatross Publishing House, Arcade Publishing Inc, Atlas & Co, Blue Guides Ltd, George Braziller Inc, Chess Information & Research Center, Dalkey Archive Press, Fantagraphics Books, Kales Press, New Directions Publishing Corp, Ontario Review Press, Peace Hill Press, Pegasus Books, Persea Books Inc, Pushcart Press, Quantuck Lane Press, Skyhorse Publishing, Thames & Hudson, Winterthur Museum & Country Estate

W W Norton Co, *distributor for* New Directions Publishing Corp

Norvik Press, *distributed by* Dufour Editions Inc

Norwalk Press, *imprint of* Book Publishing Co

Nota Bell Books, *imprint of* Purdue University Press

Nova Biomedical Press, *imprint of* Nova Science Publishers Inc

Nova Global Affairs Press, *imprint of* Nova Science Publishers Inc

Nova History Press, *imprint of* Nova Science Publishers Inc

Nova Music, *imprint of* Nova Science Publishers Inc

Nova Science Books, *imprint of* Nova Science Publishers Inc

Nova Southeastern University, *distributed by* Gryphon House Inc

Novalis, *distributor for* Twenty-Third Publications, *distributed by* Twenty-Third Publications

Novel-Ties Study Guides, *imprint of* Learning Links Inc

November Moon, *distributed by* Lotus Press

Novinka Books, *imprint of* Nova Science Publishers Inc

NOW, *distributor for* The Perseus Books Group

NPC, *imprint of* National Publishing Co

Npustin Publishing, *distributed by* Mountain Press Publishing Co

NRH Press, *distributed by* Vandamere Press

NTC Contemporary Books, *imprint of* McGraw-Hill Professional

NTIS, *distributor for* Energy Information Administration (EIA)

Nuclear Energy Agency, *distributed by* Organization for Economic Cooperation & Development

Coleccion Nueve Pececitos, *imprint of* University of Puerto Rico Press

The Numata Center, *distributed by* University of Hawaii Press

Numismatics Books, *imprint of* Betterway Books

nursesbooks.org, The Publishing Program of ANA, *division of* American Nurses Association

Nutri-Books, *distributor for* Ash Tree Publishing

Nylabone Products, *division of* TFH Publications Inc

Oak Knoll Press, *distributor for* American Antiquarian Society, Bibliographical Society of America, Bibliographical Society of University of Virginia, The Bibliographical Society (UK), Block Museum, Boston College, John Carter Brown Library, Bryn Mawr College, Catalpa Press, Caxton Club, Center for Book Arts, Chapin Library, Fondation Custodia, The Grolier Club, Hes & De Graaf, Historic New Orleans Collection, Library of Congress-Center for the Book, The Manuscript Society, New England Bibliographies, Providence Athenaeum, Rivendale Press, Tate Galleries, Texas State Historical Association, Typophiles, Winterthur Museum, Yushodo Press

Oaklea Press, *unit of* Oaklea Press Inc, *imprint of* Oaklea Press

Oakstone Medical Publishing, *subsidiary of* Haights Cross Communications Inc

Oakstone Publishing LLC, *division of* Boston Ventures

Oak Tree Books, *imprint of* Oak Tree Press

OAP, *distributor for* National Gallery of Art

Obelisk Books, *imprint of* Whittier Publications Inc

Oberlin College Press, *subsidiary of* Oberlin College, *distributed by* University Press of New England (UPNE)

Oberon Books, *distributed by* Theatre Communications Group

Coleccion Obras Completas Eugenio Maria de Hostos, *imprint of* University of Puerto Rico Press

O'Brien Press, *distributed by* Dufour Editions Inc

Obsessive Anonymous, *distributed by* Hazelden Publishing

Obsidian, *imprint of* Genesis Press Inc

Occupational Competency Examination Series, *imprint of* National Learning Corp

Ocean Press, *distributed by* Consortium Book Sales & Distribution

Ocean Publishing, *division of* The Gromling Group Inc

Ocean Tree Books, *distributed by* Treasure Chest Books

Oceana®, *division of* Oxford University Press USA

Octavo Editions, *distributed by* Konecky & Konecky LLC

Octavo Press, *imprint of* Templegate Publishers

Octopus Books, *distributed by* Hachette Book Group

Odonian Press, *distributed by* Common Courage Press

Odyssey Books, *division of* The Ciletti Publishing Group Inc

OECD, *distributed by* The Brookings Institution Press

Off The Beaten Path®, *imprint of* The Globe Pequot Press

Office & Print Technologies, *division of* PJD Publications Ltd

Office of External Affairs, *division of* RAND Corp

Office of the Federal Register, *distributed by* J J Keller & Associates, Inc

Ohio State University Foreign Language Publications, *division of* Foreign Language Center

Ohio University Press, *distributor for* The Colonial Williamsburg Foundation

Okinawan Kobujutsu Kyokai Association (OKKA), *distributor for* The Linick Group Inc

Oklahoma State University, *distributor for* dbS Productions

Old Barn Publishing, *imprint of* Old Barn Enterprises Inc

Old Farmers Almanac, *distributed by* Houghton Mifflin Harcourt Trade & Reference Division

The Old Farmer's Almanac, *distributed by* Houghton Mifflin Harcourt

Old House, *imprint of* Osprey Publishing Inc

Old Kings Road Press, *imprint of* Athletic Guide Publishing

Olive Branch Press, *imprint of* Interlink Publishing Group Inc

Olive Tree Book Co, *imprint of* Greenleaf Book Group LLC

Oliver-Nelson (Atlanta, GA), *distributed by* Thomas Nelson Inc

Omnibus Press, *division of* Music Sales Ltd, *distributor for* Big Meteor, Gramophone

Omohundro Institute of Early American History & Culture, *distributed by* The University of North Carolina Press

On My Mind Series, *imprint of* The Globe Pequot Press

On My Own, *imprint of* Appletree Press Inc

140Main.com, *subsidiary of* BizBest Media Corp

1000 Readers, *imprint of* Gallopade International Inc

One World, *imprint of* Random House Inc, Random House Publishing Group

OneSource, *division of* Infogroup

Ontario Review Press, *distributed by* W W Norton & Company Inc, Persea Books

Ontos Verlag, *distributed by* Transaction Publishers Inc

ONWord, *imprint of* Delmar

Onyx, *imprint of* NAL, Penguin Group (USA) LLC

OPAMP Technical Books, *distributor for* Primary Research Group Inc

Open City, *imprint of* Grove/Atlantic Inc

Open City Books, *distributed by* Grove/Atlantic Inc

Open Court, *division of* Carus Publishing Co

Open Horizons Publishing Co, *distributed by* National Book Network

Open Road, *distributor for* Albert Whitman & Co, *distributed by* Simon & Schuster Sales & Marketing

Open Road Publishing, *distributed by* Simon & Schuster, Simon & Schuster, Inc

Open Scroll, *imprint of* Bridge-Logos Inc

Open Society Institute, *distributed by* Central European University Press

OpenRoadMedia.com, *distributor for* Philosophical Library Inc

OPIS/STALSBY Directories & Databases, *division of* United Communications Group

Options Publishing, *subsidiary of* Haights Cross Communications Inc

OptumInsight™, *distributor for* American Medical Association, Medical Economics, Mosby, *distributed by* American Medical Association, Mosby

Opus Communications, *imprint of* HCPro Inc

OR Books, *distributor for* CUNY Journalism Press

Oracle Press, *imprint of* McGraw-Hill Professional

Oral Biography Series, *imprint of* University of Alaska Press

Orange Grove Textbooks, *imprint of* University Press of Florida

Orb Books, *imprint of* Tom Doherty Associates, LLC

Orbis Books, *division of* Maryknoll Fathers & Brothers

Orbit, *division of* Hachette Book Group

Orbit Series, *imprint of* Krieger Publishing Co

Orca Book Publishers, *distributor for* The Book Publishing Co, Coteau Books, Creative Book Publishing, Formac Publishing, Lobster Press, James Lorimer & Co, Nimbus Publishing, Polestar Calendars, Second Story Press, 7th Generation, Sono Nis Pres, Sumach Press, Tradewind Books, Tuckamore Books, Tudor House

Orchard Books, *imprint of* Scholastic Trade Division

Orchard House Inc, *distributor for* Council for Exceptional Children (CEC)

Oregon Events Guide, *imprint of* Goodluck Guides

Oregon Fever Books, *imprint of* Crumb Elbow Publishing

Oregon River Watch, *imprint of* Crumb Elbow Publishing

Oregon Writers Colony, *distributed by* Washington State University Press

O'Reilly Media, *distributor for* Microsoft Press, No Starch Press Inc

O'Reilly Media Inc, *distributor for* Microsoft Press (North America)

OREP, *distributed by* Casemate Publishers & Book Distributors LLC

Organization for Economic Cooperation & Development, *division of* Organization for Economic Cooperation & Development (France), *distributor for* International Energy Agency (Imprint), International Transportation Forum, Nuclear Energy Agency (Imprint)

Oriental Institute, *distributed by* University of Chicago Press

Oriental Institute Publications, *division of* University of Chicago

Orion, *distributed by* Sterling Publishing Co Inc

Orpen Press, *distributed by* Dufour Editions Inc

Osprey, *imprint of* Osprey Publishing Inc

Osprey Modelling, *imprint of* Osprey Publishing Inc

Osprey Publishing Inc, *subsidiary of* Osprey Publishing Ltd, Osprey Publishing Ltd, *distributed by* Random House (US & CN)

Ostrich Editions, *imprint of* Cross-Cultural Communications

OSU Press, *distributed by* The University of Arizona Press

OTB Legacy Editions, *imprint of* Ocean Tree Books

The Other India Press (India), *distributed by* The Apex Press

Other Press LLC, *distributed by* Random House Inc

Otherworlds, *imprint of* Zumaya Publications LLC

Ottographics, *distributed by* Chelsea Green Publishing Co

Our Sunday Visitor Publishing, *division of* Our Sunday Visitor Inc

Out of This World Press, *distributed by* Gem Guides Book Co

Outdoor Books & Maps, *imprint of* Adler Publishing Inc

Outside America, *imprint of* The Globe Pequot Press

The Overlook Press, *subsidiary of* Peter Mayer Publishers Inc, Peter Mayer Publishers Inc, *distributed by* Penguin Group (USA) LLC

The Overmountain Press, *division of* Sabre Industries Inc, Sabre Industries Inc

Peter Owen Publishers, *distributed by* Trafalgar Square Books

Owlswick Press, *imprint of* Wildside Press

Oxbow (UK), *distributor for* Gorgias Press LLC

Oxfam Publishing, *distributed by* Stylus Publishing LLC

Oxford, *distributed by* SAS Publishing

Oxford Illustrated Press, *distributed by* Haynes Manuals Inc

Oxford University Press, *distributor for* The American Chemical Society, Fordham University Press, Kodansha USA Inc, National Publishing Co, *distributed by* Beach Lloyd Publishers LLC, Cheng & Tsui Co Inc, Delta Publishing Co

Oxford University Press Inc, *distributor for* Country Music Foundation Press

Oxford University Press USA, *division of* University of Oxford, *distributor for* The American Chemical Society, American University in Cairo, Arnold Clarendon, Cold Spring Harbor Laboratory Press, Engineering Press, Fordham University Press, Getty, Greenwich Medical Media, Grove Dictionaries, Hurst, IRL, Kodansha, Roxbury Publishing, Saunders, Thomson Publishing

Oxmoor House, *distributed by* Hachette Book Group

Oxmoor House Inc, *division of* Time Home Entertainment Inc, *distributed by* H B Fenn (Canada), Leisure Arts Inc

Oyinde Publishing, *imprint of* Africana Homestead Legacy Publishers Inc

Oyster River Press, *distributed by* Hobblebush Books

Ozark Publishing Inc, *distributed by* Amazon.com, Apple, Barnes & Noble, Econoclad, Follett, Gumdrop, Perma-Bound, Stay Bound

Ozark Society, *distributed by* The University of Arkansas Press

The P3 Press, *division of* Brown Books Publishing Group

Pace University Press, *unit of* Pace University

Pacific Boating Almanac, *imprint of* ProStar Publications Inc

Pacific Institute, *distributed by* Washington State University Press

Pacific Press Publishing Association, *division of* Seventh-Day Adventist Church

Packard Publishing, *distributed by* Antique Collectors Club Ltd

Pademelon Press, *distributed by* Gryphon House Inc

Pademelon Press Pty Ltd, *distributor for* Redleaf Press

Padua Playwrights Press, *distributed by* Theatre Communications Group

Kogan Page, *distributed by* Beekman Books Inc

Pagemill Press, *imprint of* Council Oak Books LLC

Painted Pony Inc, *subsidiary of* Wind River Development Fund

Painted Turtle Books, *imprint of* Wayne State University Press

PAJ Publications, *distributed by* Theatre Communications Group

PAKS-Parents & Kids, *imprint of* THE Learning Connection®

Paladin Press, *division of* Paladin Enterprises Inc, *distributed by* Amazon.com, Barnes & Noble, Borders

Paladin Timeless Books, *imprint of* Twilight Times Books

Joan Palevsky, *imprint of* University of California Press

Palgrave Macmillan, *division of* St Martin's Press, LLC, St Martin's Press, LLC, *distributor for* Berg Publishers, British Film Institute, Manchester University Press, Pluto Press, I B Tauris & Co Ltd, Zed Books, *distributed by* St Martin's Press, LLC

Pali Text Society, *imprint of* Wisdom Publications Inc

Palm Kids™, *division of* Palm Publishing LLC, *distributor for* Musical Kidz LLC

Pan Asian Publications, *distributed by* Cheng & Tsui Co Inc

Panda Books, *distributed by* China Books

Pandanus Books, *distributed by* University of Hawaii Press

Panmun Academic Services, *distributed by* Cheng & Tsui Co Inc

Panpac Education, *distributed by* Cheng & Tsui Co Inc

Pantheon Books, *imprint of* Random House Inc, *distributor for* Nevraumont Publishing Co

Pantheon Books/Schocken Books, *imprint of* Knopf Doubleday Publishing Group

Paperback Parade Collector Specials, *imprint of* Gryphon Books

Paperbacks for Educators, *distributor for* American Counseling Association, MAR*CO Products Inc

Papercutz, *distributed by* Macmillan, St Martin's Press, LLC

PaperStar, *imprint of* Penguin Group (USA) LLC, Penguin Young Readers Group, GP Putnam's Sons (Children's)

Paperweight Press, *distributed by* Tuttle Publishing

Papier-Mache Press, *imprint of* Beaufort Books

Papillion Publishing, *imprint of* Blue Dolphin Publishing Inc

Nelson Papucci, *distributed by* Sunbelt Publications Inc

Para Publishing LLC, *distributed by* NBN

Para Publishing Seminars, *division of* Para Publishing LLC

Para Research, *imprint of* Schiffer Publishing Ltd

Parabola, *distributed by* Fons Vitae

Parabola Books, *subsidiary of* Society for the Study of Myth & Tradition

Parachute Publishing LLC, *division of* Parachute Properties LLC, *distributed by* Bantam, Bendon, Berkley, Grosset, Harcourt, Harper Entertainment, HarperCollins, Kensington, Dorling Kindersley, Little, Brown, Pocket, Random House, Running Press, Scholastic, Simon & Schuster

Parachuting Publications, *imprint of* Para Publishing LLC

Paraclete Press Inc, *division of* Creative Joys Inc, *distributor for* Abbey of Saint Peter of Solesmes, Gloriae Dei Cantores

Paradigm Busters, *distributed by* Cheng & Tsui Co Inc

Paradigm Publications, *division of* Redwing Book Co

Paradigm Publishing Inc, *subsidiary of* EMC Publishing

Paragon, *distributed by* Fons Vitae

Paragon House, *distributor for* International Conferences on the Unity of the Sciences, Professors World Peace Academy, *distributed by* Bloomsbury Academic, Continuum International Publishing USA

Paralists, *division of* Para Publishing LLC

Parallax Press, *division of* Unified Buddhist Church

Paraview Pocket Books, *imprint of* Cosimo Inc

Paraview Press, *division of* Cosimo Inc

Pardey Publications, *imprint of* Paradise Cay Publications Inc

Parenting Press Inc, *distributor for* Raefield-Roberts, Publishers

Park Street Press, *imprint of* Inner Traditions International Ltd

Christopher Parkening, *distributed by* Hal Leonard Corp

Parker/Thomas Press, *imprint of* Tudor Publishers Inc

Parkscape Press, *imprint of* Channel Lake Inc

ParmenidesAudio™, *division of* Parmenides Publishing

ParmenidesFiction™, *division of* Parmenides Publishing

Partner Press, *distributed by* Gryphon House Inc

Partners, *distributor for* Ash Tree Publishing

Partners Book Distributing, *distributor for* Avery Color Studios

Partner's Book Distributing Inc, *distributor for* Blue Poppy Press

Partners Book Distributor, *distributor for* Wilderness Adventures Press Inc

Partners West, *distributor for* Goodluck Guides, Wilderness Adventures Press Inc

Partners/West, *distributor for* Pleasure Boat Studio: A Literary Press

Partner's/West Book Distributing Inc, *distributor for* Blue Poppy Press

Partnership Publications, *division of* House to House Publications

Parvardigar Press, *distributed by* Fons Vitae

Pasifika Press, *distributed by* University of Hawaii Press

Passages, *imprint of* Perfection Learning Corp

Passbooks, *imprint of* National Learning Corp

Gracie Passette Productions, *imprint of* Ephemera Bound Publishing

Pastoral Press, *imprint of* OCP, OCP Publications Inc, OCP Publications Inc

Pathway Book Service, *distributor for* Independent Information Publications

Pathway Books, *distributor for* Barcelona Publishers

Pauline Books & Media, *division of* Daughters of St Paul

Pauline Comics Series, *imprint of* Pauline Books & Media

Paws IV, *imprint of* Sasquatch Books

Payback Press, *distributed by* AK Press Distribution

PDR, *imprint of* Delmar

Peabody Essex Museum, *distributed by* Antique Collectors Club Ltd

Peabody Museum of Archaeology & Ethnology, *distributed by* Harvard University Press

Peabody Museum Press, *unit of* Peabody Museum of Archaeology & Ethnology, Peabody Museum of Archaeology & Ethnology, Harvard University

Peace Books, *distributed by* China Books

Peace Hill Press, *distributed by* W W Norton & Co, W W Norton & Company Inc

Peacewatch Editions, *imprint of* Ocean Tree Books

Peachpit Press, *division of* Pearson Education, Pearson Education Ltd (International)

Peachtree Jr, *imprint of* Peachtree Publishers

Pearson, *distributed by* Council for Exceptional Children (CEC)

Pearson Addison Wesley, *imprint of* Pearson Higher Education

Pearson Allyn & Bacon, *imprint of* Pearson Higher Education

Pearson Arts & Sciences, *division of* Pearson Education

Pearson Australia, *distributed by* Cheng & Tsui Co Inc

Pearson Australia-Schools Division, *distributor for* Boynton/Cook Publishers

Pearson Benjamin Cummings, *imprint of* Pearson Higher Education

Pearson Business Publishing, *unit of* Pearson Higher Education, Pearson Higher Education Division

Pearson Career, Health, Education & Technology, *division of* Pearson Education

Pearson Education, *distributor for* Manning Publications Co, *distributed by* American Academy of Environmental Engineers, Trans-Atlantic Publications Inc

Pearson Education Canada, *distributor for* Boynton/Cook Publishers

Pearson Education/ELT, *division of* Pearson Education

Pearson Higher Education, *division of* Pearson Education

Pearson Humanities & Social Sciences, *unit of* Pearson Higher Education, Pearson Higher Education Division

Pearson Learning Solutions, *unit of* Pearson Higher Education

Pearson Longman, *imprint of* Pearson Higher Education

Pearson New Zealand-Schools Division, *distributor for* Boynton/Cook Publishers

Pearson Prentice Hall, *imprint of* Pearson Higher Education

Pearson School, *unit of* Pearson Education

Pearson Technology, *distributed by* SkillPath Publications

Pearson Technology Group Canada, *distributed by* Penguin Books

Editions du Renouveau Pedagogique, *distributor for* Michelin Maps & Guides

T H Peek Publisher, *division of* Clearweave Corp

Bette L Pegas, *distributed by* Sunbelt Publications Inc

Pegasus Books, *distributed by* W W Norton & Company Inc

Pelican International Corp, *subsidiary of* Pelican Publishing Co

Pelican Pond Publishing, *imprint of* Blue Dolphin Publishing Inc

Pelican Publishing Co, *distributor for* Hope Publishing House, Marmac Publishing Co, Self-Help Success Books

A W Peller & Associates, *distributor for* Pieces of Learning

Pembroke Publishers, *distributed by* Stenhouse Publishers

Pen & Sword Books Ltd, *distributed by* Casemate Publishers & Book Distributors LLC

Pen & Sword Digital, *distributed by* Casemate Publishers & Book Distributors LLC

Pendragon Press, *subsidiary of* Camelot Publishing Co Inc, Camelot Publishing Co Inc, *distributor for* Croatian Musicological Society, *distributed by* LIM Editrice SRL (Italy), G Ricordi (Italy)

Penguin, *imprint of* Penguin Books, Penguin Group (USA) LLC, *distributor for* Verso

Penguin Audiobooks, *imprint of* Penguin Group (USA) LLC, *distributor for* Arkangel Complete Shakespeare, Highbridge Audio

Penguin Books, *imprint of* Penguin Group (USA) LLC, *distributor for* The Countryman Press, Pearson Technology Group Canada

Penguin Canada, *distributor for* Michelin Maps & Guides

Penguin Classics, *imprint of* Penguin Books, Penguin Group (USA) LLC

Penguin Compass, *imprint of* Penguin Books

Penguin Group (USA) LLC, *subsidiary of* Pearson plc, *distributor for* Alloy Entertainment, Arkangel, Bibli O'Phile, Consumer Guide/PIL, DAW Books Inc, Dream Works, Granta, HighBridge Audio, The Jim Henson Co, Kensington Publishing Corp, The Library of America, Maharishi University of Management Press, The Monacelli Press, The Overlook Press, Reader's Digest, Reader's Digest Trade Books, Rough Guides, *distributed by* Learning Links Inc

Penguin*HighBridge Audio, *imprint of* Penguin Audiobooks

The Penguin Press, *imprint of* Penguin Group (USA) LLC

Penguin Putnam, *distributor for* Nevraumont Publishing Co

Penguin 20th Century Classics, *imprint of* Penguin Books

Penguin Young Readers Group, *division of* Penguin Group (USA) LLC

Peninsula Publishing, *distributed by* Scitech Publishing Inc

Penn State University Press, *distributor for* University of California Institute on Global Conflict & Cooperation

Pennsylvania Historical & Museum Commission, *subsidiary of* The Commonwealth of Pennsylvania

Pennsylvania State Data Center, *subsidiary of* Institute of State & Regional Affairs

The Pennsylvania State University Press, *division of* The Pennsylvania State University

Pennwell, *distributed by* Gulf Publishing Co

PennWell Books, *division of* PennWell

PennWell Business & Industrial Division, *distributed by* Marine Techniques Publishing

Pennywell Press, *distributed by* John F Blair Publisher

Penobscot Press, *imprint of* Picton Press

PenQuill Press, *imprint of* Jonathan David Publishers Inc

Penquin Putnam Inc, *distributed by* Heimburger House Publishing Co

Pensiero Press, *imprint of* The Lentz Leadership Institute

Pentecostal Publishing House, *subsidiary of* United Pentecostal Church International, *distributed by* Anchor Distributors, Christian Network International, Innovative Marketing, Spring Arbor

Penton Price Digests, *imprint of* Penton Media

Peoples Education Inc, *subsidiary of* Peoples Educational Holdings Inc, *distributor for* Learning Media, Nelson Canada, New Path Learning, W W Norton, Rubicon, John Wiley & Sons

Linda Pequegnat, *distributed by* Sunbelt Publications Inc

Per Annum Inc, *distributor for* New Yorker Desk Diary

Peradam Press, *subsidiary of* The Center for Cultural & Naturalist Studies

Percheron Press, *imprint of* Eliot Werner Publications Inc

Peregrina Press, *distributed by* Cistercian Publications Inc, Editorial Office

Peter Peregrinus Ltd, *imprint of* IET

Peregrinzilla, *distributed by* Chelsea Green Publishing Co

Perennial, *imprint of* HarperCollins Publishers Sales

Perennial Currents, *imprint of* HarperCollins Publishers Sales

Perennial Dark Alley, *imprint of* HarperCollins Publishers Sales

Sophia Perennis, *distributed by* Fons Vitae

PerfectBound, *imprint of* HarperCollins Publishers Sales

Perfection Learning Corp, *distributor for* Abrams, Ace Books, Airmont, Annick Press, Archway, Atheneum, Baker Books, Ballantine, Bantam, Barrons, Berkley, Blake Books, Candlewick Press, Charlesbridge Press, Chelsea House, Children's Press, Chronicle Books, Crabtree Publishing, Crown, Disney Press, Distri Books, DK, Doubleday, Dutton, F+W Media Inc, Farrar, Straus & Giroux Inc, Fawcett, Firefly, First Avenue, Free Spirit, Fulcrum, Golden Books, Greenhaven Press Inc, Hammond Pub, Harcourt Inc, Hayes, Gareth Stevens, Frederick Warne

Perigee, *imprint of* Berkley Publishing Group, Penguin Group (USA) LLC

Perigee Books, *imprint of* Penguin Group (USA) LLC

Periplus Editions, *imprint of* Tuttle Publishing, *distributed by* Tuttle Publishing

Periscope, *distributed by* Prestel Publishing

Perma-Bound, *distributor for* Ozark Publishing Inc

Permanent Publications, *distributed by* Chelsea Green Publishing Co

Persea Books, *distributor for* Ontario Review Press, *distributed by* W W Norton & Co

Persea Books Inc, *distributed by* W W Norton & Company Inc

Persephone Books, *distributed by* Dufour Editions Inc

Persephone Press, *imprint of* Birch Brook Press, *distributed by* Birch Brook Press

Perseus (Addison Wesley Trade), *distributed by* HarperCollins Publishers

Perseus Books Group, *distributor for* Wide World Publishing

The Perseus Books Group, *distributor for* Da Capo Press Inc & Lifelong Books, Merloyd Lawrence Inc, *distributed by* NOW, Perseus Distribution Services

Perseus Distribution Services, *distributor for* The Perseus Books Group

Perseverance Press, *distributed by* John Daniel & Co

Personal Profiles, *division of* Brown Books Publishing Group

Peterson Institute for International Economics, *distributor for* Center for Global Development, *distributed by* DA Information Services (Australia, New Zealand & Papua New Guinea), East West Export Books (Cambodia, China, Indonesia, Japan, Philippines, Singapore, Taiwan, Thailand & Vietnam), The Eurospan Group (Africa, Eastern & Western Europe, Iran, Israel, Russia & Turkey), Renouf Bookstore (Canada), United Publishers Services Ltd (Japan & Republic of Korea), Viva Books PVT (Bangladesh, India, Nepal & Sri Lanka)

Peterson's/Pacesetter Books, *imprint of* Peterson's, a Nelnet Company

Petroleum Extension Service (PETEX), *division of* University of Texas

Pfeiffer, *imprint of* Jossey-Bass, John Wiley & Sons Inc

Pflaum Publishing Group, *division of* Peter Li Inc

PGUK / Hi Marketing, *distributor for* National Geographic Books

PGW/Perseus, *distributor for* Cobblestone Publishing

Phaeton Press, *imprint of* Gordian Press, *distributed by* Gordian Press

Phaidon Press, *distributed by* Hachette Book Group

Phaidon Press Inc, *subsidiary of* Phaidon Press Ltd, *distributor for* Mitchell Beazley, Electa

Phantom Books & Music, *imprint of* Empire Publishing Service

Phaze Books, *imprint of* Mundania Press LLC

Philadelphia Museum of Art, *distributed by* Antique Collectors Club Ltd, Yale University Press

Philedition, *distributed by* Casemate Publishers & Book Distributors LLC

Philomel, *imprint of* Penguin Group (USA) LLC, Penguin Young Readers Group

Philomel Books, *imprint of* Penguin Group (USA) LLC

Philosophical Library Inc, *distributed by* Kensington Publishing Corp (subs rts: Meryl Earl), OpenRoadMedia.com

Philosophy Documentation Center, *distributor for* Imprint Academic

Phoenix International, *distributed by* The University of Arkansas Press

Phoenix Mapping Service, *division of* Wide World of Maps Inc

Phoenix Press, *distributed by* AK Press Distribution, Sterling Publishing Co Inc

Pholiota Press Inc, *distributed by* Cross-Cultural Communications

Photofact®, *imprint of* Sams Technical Publishing LLC

Photolucida Book, *distributed by* Franklin, Beedle & Associates Inc

Pi Press, *distributor for* Nevraumont Publishing Co

Daniela Piazza Editore, *distributed by* Chelsea Green Publishing Co

Picador, *subsidiary of* Macmillan

Picaro Publishing, *distributed by* Sunbelt Publications Inc

Picasso Project, *division of* Alan Wofsy Fine Arts, Alan Wofsy Fine Arts, *distributor for* Cramer (Switzerland), Kornfeld (Switzerland), Ramie (France), *distributed by* Alan Wofsy Fine Arts

The Picasso Project, *imprint of* Alan Wofsy Fine Arts

Pickering & Chatto, *distributed by* Ashgate Publishing Co

Picton Press, *imprint of* Picton Press

Pictorial Histories Publishing Co, *distributed by* Heimburger House Publishing Co

Picture Me Books™, *imprint of* Playhouse Publishing

Picture, Play & Tote™, *imprint of* Playhouse Publishing

PictureProfits® Tool Kit, *distributed by* Copywriter's Council of America (CCA)

Picture Window Books, *imprint of* Capstone Publishers™

Picture Yearling, *imprint of* Random House Inc

Pie Books, *imprint of* Rizzoli International Publications Inc

Pieces of Learning, *division of* Creative Learning Consultants Inc, Creative Learning Consultants Inc, *distributed by* ALPS Publishing, A W Peller & Associates, Professional Associate Publishing, Prufrock Press Inc

Pikachu Press, *distributed by* Simon & Schuster, Inc

Pilgrim Publications, *distributor for* Christian Focus, Fox River Press, Hess Publications

Pilothouse Nautical Books & Charts, *distributor for* Marine Techniques Publishing

Pimlseur Language Programs, *imprint of* Recorded Books LLC

Pimsleur, *imprint of* Simon & Schuster Audio

Pinata Books, *imprint of* Arte Publico Press

Pine Forest Publishing, *distributed by* Finney Company Inc

Pine Forge Press, *subsidiary of* SAGE Publications Inc, *imprint of* SAGE Publications

Pine Street Books, *imprint of* University of Pennsylvania Press

Pine Winds Press, *imprint of* Idyll Arbor Inc

Pinnacle Books, *imprint of* Kensington Publishing Corp

Pinyon Publishing, *distributed by* Gem Guides Book Co

Pir Press, *distributed by* Fons Vitae

Pitch Publishing, *distributed by* Trafalgar Square Books

PJD Electronic Publishing, *division of* PJD Publications Ltd

PK, *distributor for* The Jim Henson Co

Plaidswede Publishing, *distributed by* Hobblebush Books

Planeta Peninsula, *distributed by* Sunbelt Publications Inc

Platinum Press, *imprint of* Adams Media

Plato Publishing, *distributed by* Halcyon Press Ltd

Play Bac Publishing, *distributed by* Black Dog & Leventhal Publishers Inc

Player Press A/Z Ltd, *division of* Players Press Inc

Player Press Ltd (UK), *division of* Players Press Inc

Players Press, *imprint of* Players Press Inc

Players Press (Canada), *division of* Players Press Inc

Players Press Inc, *distributor for* Camelion Plays, Garland-Clark Editors, Macmillan Education (UK), Preston Editions

Playwrights Canada Press, *distributed by* Theatre Communications Group

Pleasure Boat Studio: A Literary Press, *distributor for* Empty Bowl Press, *distributed by* Partners/West, Small Press Distribution

Plenum, *distributed by* ADD Warehouse

Plexus Books, *imprint of* Plexus Publishing, Inc

Plexus Publishing, Inc, *affiliate of* Information Today, Inc

PLI, *imprint of* Practising Law Institute, *distributor for* Practising Law Institute

The Plough Publishing House, *imprint of* Church Communities Foundation

Ploughshares, *subsidiary of* Ploughshares Inc

Plowshare Media, *imprint of* Plowshare Media

Plum Blossom Books, *imprint of* Parallax Press

Plum Tree Books, *imprint of* Classical Academic Press, Classical Academic Press LLC

Plumbago Books, *imprint of* Boydell & Brewer Inc

Plume, *division of* Penguin Group (USA) LLC, *imprint of* Penguin Group (USA) LLC

Pluto Press, *distributed by* Palgrave Macmillan

PMP, *imprint of* Paramount Market Publishing Inc

Pocket, *distributor for* Parachute Publishing LLC

Pocket Books Trade Paperback, *imprint of* Gallery Books

Pocket Guides Publishing, *distributed by* Adventure Publications

Pocket Paragon, *imprint of* David R Godine Publisher Inc

Pocket Star, *imprint of* Gallery Books

Pogo Press, *imprint of* Finney Company Inc

Pogo Press Inc, *imprint of* Finney Company Inc

Point, *imprint of* Scholastic Trade Division

Point Blank, *imprint of* Wildside Press

Poison Vine Books, *imprint of* Elderberry Press Inc, *distributed by* Elderberry Press Inc

Polestar Calendars, *distributed by* Orca Book Publishers

Policy Studies Associates (PSA), *imprint of* The Apex Press

Political Risk Services, *imprint of* The PRS Group Inc

Polka Dot Press, *imprint of* Adams Media

Pollyanna Productions, *distributed by* Gryphon House Inc

Polyface, *distributed by* Chelsea Green Publishing Co

PomegranateKids, *imprint of* Pomegranate Communications Inc

Pond Frog Editions, *imprint of* Red Moon Press

PopOut®, *imprint of* The Globe Pequot Press

Poppy, *imprint of* Little, Brown Books for Young Readers

Popular Press, *imprint of* University of Wisconsin Press

Popular Technology, *imprint of* Branden Books

Popular Woodworking Books, *imprint of* Betterway Books

Portavoz, *distributed by* Editorial Bautista Independiente

Portfolio, *subsidiary of* Penguin Group (USA) LLC, *imprint of* Penguin Group (USA) LLC

Portnoy Publishing, *distributed by* Dufour Editions Inc

Portraits of America, *imprint of* The Donning Company Publishers

Portsmouth Marine Society, *distributed by* Enfield Publishing & Distribution Co

Possibility Press, *imprint of* Markowski International Publishers

Potomac Books, *imprint of* University of Nebraska Press

Potomac Books Inc, *imprint of* University of Nebraska Press

Potter Craft, *imprint of* Clarkson Potter Publishers, Crown Publishing Group

Potter Style, *imprint of* Clarkson Potter Publishers, Crown Publishing Group

Power Kids Press, *imprint of* The Rosen Publishing Group Inc

powerHouse Books, *division of* powerHouse Cultural Entertainment Inc, *distributor for* Antinous Press, Juno Books, MTV Press, Throckmorton Press, VH1 Press, Vice Books, *distributed by* Random House Publisher Services

Poynter Consulting, *division of* Para Publishing LLC

PPC, *distributed by* Gryphon Books

Practical Action, *distributed by* Stylus Publishing LLC

Practical Reviews®, *imprint of* Oakstone Publishing LLC

The Practical Therapist Series, *imprint of* Impact Publishers Inc

Practising Law Institute, *distributed by* PLI

Practitioners Publishing Co, *distributor for* AICPA Professional Publications

Praeger, *imprint of* ABC-CLIO

Prairie Classics, *imprint of* Trails Books

Prairie Oak Press, *imprint of* Trails Books

Emory Pratt, *distributor for* Primary Research Group Inc

Prayer Book Press Inc, *subsidiary of* Media Judaica Inc, Media Judaica Inc

Premier Novels, *imprint of* Center Press

Prensa Pensar, *imprint of* Progressive Press

Prentice Hall, *distributor for* American Geological Institute (AGI), Manning Publications Co, *distributed by* American Academy of Environmental Engineers, NACE International, Society of Manufacturing Engineers

Prentice-Hall, *distributed by* SAS Publishing

Prentice Hall Press, *division of* Penguin Group (USA) LLC, *imprint of* Berkley Publishing Group

PREP Publishing, *subsidiary of* PREP Inc, PREP Inc

Presbyterian Publishing Corp, *distributor for* Epworth, SCM, *distributed by* Spring Arbor Distributors

Presidio Press, *imprint of* Random House Publishing Group

The Press at California State University, Fresno, *unit of* California State University, Fresno

The Press for Humanitarian Causes, *imprint of* Flying Pen Press LLC

Theodore Presser Co, *distributor for* Editions Orphee Inc

Prestel Publishing, *distributor for* Die Gestalten Verlag (DGV), Loft, Lars Muller, Periscope, Schirmer/Mosel

Preston Editions, *distributed by* Players Press Inc

Pretend & Play™, *imprint of* Playhouse Publishing

Price Stern Sloan, *imprint of* Penguin Group (USA) LLC, Penguin Young Readers Group

Price Stern Sloan Inc, *imprint of* Penguin Group (USA) LLC

Price World Publishing LLC, *distributed by* David Bateman Ltd (New Zealand), Cardinal Publisher's Group (US), Fortytwo Bookz Galaxy (India), Gazelle Book Services (UK), Monarch Books of Canada (CN), John Reed Books (Australia)

Prima Games, *imprint of* Random House Information Group

Primary Research Group Inc, *distributed by* Academic Book Center, Ambassador Books, The Book House, Coutts Library Service, Croft House Books, Eastern Book Company, MarketResearch.com, Midwest Library Service, OPAMP Technical Books, Emory Pratt, Research & Markets, Rittenhouse Book Distributors, Total Information, Yankee Book Peddler

Primary Source Media™, *imprint of* Gale

Prime Crime, *imprint of* Berkley Books, Berkley Publishing Group

Primer Publications, *distributed by* Gem Guides Book Co

Prince Press, *imprint of* Hendrickson Publishers Inc

Princeton Architectural Press, *distributor for* Balcony Press, Hyphen Press, *distributed by* Chronicle Books, Chronicle Books LLC

Princeton Book Co Publishers, *distributor for* Dance Books Ltd, Dance Notation Bureau, *distributed by* Dance Books Ltd

Princeton Review, *distributed by* Random House Inc

The Princeton Review, *imprint of* Random House Inc, Random House Information Group

Princeton University Art Museum, *distributed by* Yale University Press

Princeton University Press, *distributor for* National Gallery of Art, Nevraumont Publishing Co, University of California Institute on Global Conflict & Cooperation

Principia Press, *distributed by* The University of Akron Press

Principles in Practice, *imprint of* National Council of Teachers of English (NCTE)

Printing Industries of America, *distributor for* Grade Finders Inc

Pro Ed, *distributed by* Council for Exceptional Children (CEC)

Pro-Ed, *distributor for* Psychological Assessment Resources Inc (PAR), *distributed by* Psychological Assessment Resources Inc (PAR)

Pro Tactics™, *imprint of* The Globe Pequot Press

Proceedings, *imprint of* American Philosophical Society

Process Media, *imprint of* Feral House

Prodist, *imprint of* Watson Publishing International LLC

Productivity Press, *division of* Taylor & Francis Group, *distributor for* American Society for Quality (ASQ), Society of Manufacturing Engineers

Productivity Press Spanish Imprint, *imprint of* Productivity Press

ProEd, *distributor for* American Counseling Association

Professional Associate Publishing, *distributor for* Pieces of Learning

Professional Book Publishing, *division of* Slack Incorporated

Professional Development, *division of* Scholastic Education

The Professional Education Group Inc (PEG), *subsidiary of* CredibleLaw, *distributor for* ALI-ABA, American Bar Association, ASPEN, *distributed by* ALI-ABA, American Bar Association

Professional Practices, *imprint of* Krieger Publishing Co

Professional Publications, *distributed by* NACE International

Professional Publications Inc (PPI), *distributor for* American Association of State Highway & Transportation Officials, American Wood Council (American Forest & Paper Association) (National Design Specification for Wood Construction (NDS) & others), International Code Council, McGraw-Hill Professional (green building, design & construction titles, LEED titles), National Council of Examiners for Engineering & Surveying, Reg Review Inc (ASBOG geology exam review), SmartPros, Transportation Research Board Code, US Green Building Council (LEED reference guides)

Professional Resource Press, *imprint of* Professional Resource Exchange Inc

Professors World Peace Academy, *distributed by* Paragon House

Progressive Press, *imprint of* Progressive Press, *distributor for* Global Research

Prologue Books, *imprint of* F+W Media Inc

Prompt, *distributed by* Delmar

Proper Romance, *imprint of* Shadow Mountain

ProQuest LLC, *subsidiary of* Cambridge Information Group Inc

Provenance Press, *imprint of* Adams Media

Providence Athenaeum, *distributed by* Oak Knoll Press

Providence Press, *division of* Hope Publishing Co

Providence Publishing, *distributor for* Country Music Foundation Press

Prufrock Press, *distributed by* Sourcebooks Inc

Prufrock Press Inc, *distributor for* Pieces of Learning

Phil R Pryde, *distributed by* Sunbelt Publications Inc

PS&E Publications, *imprint of* Bartleby Press

PSG, *imprint of* Elsevier, Health Sciences Division

PSI Consulting Inc, *distributor for* HRD Press

PSS, *imprint of* Grosset & Dunlap, Penguin Young Readers Group

Psychological Assessment Resources Inc (PAR), *distributor for* American Guidance Service, Pro-Ed, The Psychological Corp, Riverside Publishing, Rorschach Workshops, *distributed by* ACER, Pro-Ed, The Psychological Corp, Riverside Publishing, Western Psychological Service

The Psychological Corp, *distributor for* Psychological Assessment Resources Inc (PAR), *distributed by* Psychological Assessment Resources Inc (PAR)

Psychology Press, *imprint of* Routledge/Taylor & Francis, Taylor & Francis Group, Taylor & Francis Inc

Public Access Broadcasting, *division of* Unarius Academy of Science Publications

Public Affairs, *distributed by* HarperCollins Publishers

Public Citizen, *distributed by* Addison Wesley, Simon & Schuster Pocket Books

Public History, *imprint of* Krieger Publishing Co

The Public Press, *distributed by* Enfield Publishing & Distribution Co

PublicAffairs, *member of* The Perseus Books Group, *imprint of* The Perseus Books Group

Publishers Group UK, *distributor for* Stone Bridge Press Inc

Publishers Group West, *distributor for* American Diabetes Association, Avalon Travel Publishing, Black Classic Press, Counterpoint Press LLC, Empire Press Media/Avant-Guide, Gault Millau Inc/Gayot Publications, Hudson Park Press, Interlink Publishing Group Inc, Naval Institute Press, Surrey Books, Tuttle Publishing, Ulysses Press, Wide World Publishing

Publishers Group West (PGW), *distributor for* Madavor Media

Publishers Group West/Perseus Distribution Co, *distributor for* Grove/Atlantic Inc

Publisher's Stone Publications, *distributed by* Florida Academic Press

Publishers Support Services, *division of* Five Star Publications Inc

Publishers Trade Secrets Library, *imprint of* Copywriter's Council of America (CCA)

Publishing Poynters Newsletter, *division of* Para Publishing LLC

Publishing Services, *division of* Scholastic Education

Pudding House Publications, *affiliate of* Pudding House Innovative Writers Programs

Pueblo Books, *imprint of* Liturgical Press

Coleccion Puertorriquena, *imprint of* University of Puerto Rico Press

Puffin, *imprint of* Penguin Group (USA) LLC

Puffin Books, *imprint of* Penguin Group (USA) LLC, Penguin Young Readers Group

Punch Press, *imprint of* Loft Press Inc

PUP Books, *imprint of* Purdue University Press

Purity Press, *distributed by* Jonathan David Publishers Inc

Purple House Press, *imprint of* Purple House Inc

Purple Mountain Press Ltd, *distributor for* Carmania Press London (North America only)

Purple Pomegranate Productions, *division of* Jews for Jesus

PUSH, *imprint of* Scholastic Trade Division

Pushcart Press, *distributed by* W W Norton & Co Inc, W W Norton & Company Inc

Pussywillow, *imprint of* Bandanna Books

Putnam, *imprint of* Penguin Group (USA) LLC, GP Putnam's Sons (Hardcover)

Putnam Adult, *imprint of* The Putnam Publishing Group

Putnam Berkley Audio, *imprint of* Penguin Group (USA) LLC, The Putnam Publishing Group, GP Putnam's Sons (Hardcover), *distributor for* Arkangel

Putnam Juvenile, *imprint of* The Putnam Publishing Group

The Putnam Publishing Group, *division of* Penguin Group (USA) LLC

G P Putnam's Sons, *imprint of* Penguin Young Readers Group

GP Putnam's Sons (Children's), *member of* Penguin Young Readers Group

GP Putnam's Sons (Hardcover), *imprint of* Penguin Group (USA) LLC

Puzzlewright Press, *imprint of* Sterling Publishing Co Inc

PWPA Books, *imprint of* Paragon House

PYO (Publish Your Own Co), *imprint of* Hearts & Tummies Cookbook Co

Pyr, *imprint of* Prometheus Books

QEB Publishing, *imprint of* Black Rabbit Books

QED Press, *imprint of* Comp-Type Inc

Qiblah Books, *distributed by* Fons Vitae

QMP, *imprint of* Quality Medical Publishing Inc

Quackenworth Publishing, *distributed by* BWI

Quality Books, *distributor for* Craftsman Book Co, Do-It-Yourself Legal Publishers

Quantuck Lane Press, *distributed by* W W Norton & Company Inc

Quarry Books, *imprint of* Indiana University Press, Quayside Publishing Group

Quartet Books (UK), *distributed by* Interlink Publishing Group Inc

Quarto Books, *distributed by* Krause Publications Inc

Quayside Publishing Group, *subsidiary of* The Quarto Group Inc, The Quarto Group Inc (London, UK), *distributor for* Aurum Press, Walter Foster Publishing, Frances Lincoln (adult trade list), RotoVision, Jacqui Small, *distributed by* Hachette US

Quest Books, *imprint of* Regal Crest Enterprises LLC, Theosophical Publishing House/Quest Books

Quick Reference Publishing, *distributed by* Sunbelt Publications Inc

QuickScan Reviews®, *imprint of* Oakstone Publishing LLC

Quill Driver Books, *imprint of* Linden Publishing Co Inc

Quill House Publishers, *imprint of* Kirk House Publishers

Quill Trade Paperbacks, *imprint of* HarperCollins Publishers

Quiller, *distributed by* Safari Press

Quiller Press Ltd, *distributed by* Stackpole Books

Quiller Publishing, *distributed by* Half Halt Press Inc

Quilliam Press, *distributed by* Fons Vitae

Quintessence Books, *imprint of* Quintessence Publishing Co Inc

Quintessence of Dental Technology, *imprint of* Quintessence Publishing Co Inc

Quintessence Pockets, *imprint of* Quintessence Publishing Co Inc

Quintessence Publishing Co Inc, *distributor for* Quintessence Publishing Co Ltd (Japan), Quintessence Publishing Ltd (London), Quintessence Verlags GmbH

Quintessence Publishing Co Ltd (Japan), *distributed by* Quintessence Publishing Co Inc

Quintessence Publishing Ltd (London), *distributed by* Quintessence Publishing Co Inc

Quintessence Verlags GmbH, *distributed by* Quintessence Publishing Co Inc

Quirk Books, *distributed by* Random House Publisher Services

Quite Specific Media Group Ltd, *distributor for* The Colonial Williamsburg Foundation

Quiver, *imprint of* Quayside Publishing Group

Quixote Press, *division of* Quixote Press, *imprint of* Hearts & Tummies Cookbook Co

Quiz Master Books, *imprint of* Trails Books

Quodlibetal Features, *distributed by* Vandamere Press

Qwikguide, *imprint of* Mel Bay Publications Inc

R & B Food & Culture Production, *distributed by* Sunbelt Publications Inc

RAB Desire, *imprint of* Riverdale Avenue Books (RAB)

RAB HSF, *imprint of* Riverdale Avenue Books (RAB)

RAB Pop, *imprint of* Riverdale Avenue Books (RAB)

RAB Truth, *imprint of* Riverdale Avenue Books (RAB)

Rabbinical Assembly of America, *distributed by* United Synagogue Book Service

Rabbit's Foot Press™, *imprint of* Blue Mountain Arts Inc

Radiant Books, *imprint of* Gospel Publishing House (GPH)

Radiant Life Curricular, *imprint of* Gospel Publishing House (GPH)

Radio Theatre, *imprint of* Focus on the Family

Radix Press, *subsidiary of* UGF/OR

Raefield-Roberts, Publishers, *distributed by* Parenting Press Inc

Ragged Mountain Press, *imprint of* McGraw-Hill Professional

Raid, *imprint of* Osprey Publishing Inc

Rainbow Book Agencies, *distributor for* Gem-Stone Press

Rainbow Bridge Publishing, *imprint of* Carson-Dellosa Publishing LLC

Rainbow Publishers, *imprint of* Rainbow Publishers

Rainbow Ridge Books, *distributed by* Square One Publishers Inc

Raincoast, *distributor for* Hay House Inc

Raincoast Books, *distributor for* Sourcebooks Inc

Rainsource Press, *distributed by* Chelsea Green Publishing Co

Raise the Dough in 30 Days Co, *imprint of* Quixote Press

Raising Lucy Studios LLC, *distributed by* Epicenter Press Inc

Ram Publishing, *distributed by* Gem Guides Book Co

Ram Publishing Co, *subsidiary of* Garrett Electronics

Ramakrishna Math, *distributed by* Vedanta Press

Ramanujan Mathematical Society, *distributed by* American Mathematical Society

Ramie (France), *distributed by* Picasso Project

Ramsey & Todd, *imprint of* Turner Publishing Co

Rand McNally, *distributor for* Wide World of Maps Inc, *distributed by* Wide World of Maps Inc

Rand McNally for Kids, *imprint of* Rand McNally

Peter E Randall Publisher, *distributed by* University Press of New England

Random House, *imprint of* Random House Inc, Random House Publishing Group, *distributor for* Clarkson Potter Publishers, The Jim Henson Co, National Geographic Books, National Geographic Society, Osprey Publishing Inc, Parachute Publishing LLC, Rizzoli International Publications Inc, Soho Press Inc, Universe Publishing, Welcome Books®, Wizards of the Coast LLC, *distributed by* Sunbelt Publications Inc

Random House Audio Publishing Group, *subsidiary of* Random House Inc

Random House Books for Young Readers, *imprint of* Random House Children's Books, Random House Inc

Random House Children's Books, *division of* Random House Inc, *distributor for* The Colonial Williamsburg Foundation

Random House Children's Publishing, *imprint of* Random House Inc

Random House Digital, *imprint of* Random House Inc

Random House Distribution Services, *distributor for* Hatherleigh Press

Random House/Golden Books Young Readers Group, *division of* Random House Children's Books

Random House Inc, *division of* Bertelsmann AG, *distributor for* Alloy Entertainment, Blue Apple Books, Karen Brown's Guides, Egmont USA, Mondadori Spanish Language, National Geographic, Other Press LLC, Princeton Review, Rizzoli, Rugged Land, Shambhala, Shambhala Publications Inc, Smithsonian Books, Soho Press, Steerforth Press, The Taunton Press, Ten Speed Press, Wizards of the Coast, *distributed by* DawnSignPress, Learning Links Inc

Random House Large Print, *division of* Random House Inc, *distributed by* Thorndike Press®

Random House Large Print Publishing, *imprint of* Random House Inc

Random House Publisher Services, *distributor for* Beacon Press, powerHouse Books, Quirk Books

Random House Publisher Services (RHPS), *distributor for* DC Entertainment

Random House Publishing Group, *division of* Random House Inc

Random House Reference & Information Publishing, *imprint of* Random House Inc

Random House Reference/Random House Puzzles & Games/House of Collectibles, *imprint of* Random House Audio Publishing Group, Random House Inc

Random House Websters, *imprint of* Random House Reference/Random House Puzzles & Games/House of Collectibles

Ranger Rick Science Program, *imprint of* Sundance/Newbridge Publishing

Rangjung Yeshe Publications, *distributed by* North Atlantic Books

Rasmuson Library Historical Translation Series, *imprint of* University of Alaska Press

Raven Press, *distributed by* Chelsea Green Publishing Co

Raven Productions Inc, *distributed by* Adventure Publications

Raven Tree Press, *division of* Delta Publishing

Shannon Ravenel Books, *imprint of* Algonquin Books of Chapel Hill

Ravenhawk™ Books, *division of* The 6DOF Group, The 6DOF Group

Rayo, *imprint of* HarperCollins Children's Books, HarperCollins General Books Group, HarperCollins Publishers Sales

Razorbill, *imprint of* Penguin Group (USA) LLC

RCE, *imprint of* Regal Crest Enterprises LLC

RCS Libri, *imprint of* Rizzoli International Publications Inc

RDV Books, *imprint of* Akashic Books

Reader's Digest, *distributed by* Fox Chapel Publishing Co Inc, Hal Leonard Corp, Penguin Group (USA) LLC

Reader's Digest Children's Books, *subsidiary of* The Reader's Digest Association Inc, *distributor for* The Jim Henson Co, *distributed by* Simon & Schuster Sales & Marketing

Reader's Digest Children's Publishing, *distributed by* Simon & Schuster, Inc

Reader's Digest General Books, *division of* The Reader's Digest Association Inc, The Reader's Digest Association Inc

Reader's Digest Trade Books, *division of* Reader's Digest Association Inc, The Reader's Digest Association Inc, *distributed by* Penguin Group (USA) LLC

Reader's Digest USA Select Editions, *division of* The Reader's Digest Association Inc

Read'n Run Books, *imprint of* Crumb Elbow Publishing

Ready Reader Storybooks, *imprint of* Modern Publishing

Ready to Learn, *imprint of* Incentive Publications Inc

REAL Phonics™, *imprint of* Broden Books LLC

Real Story Series, *distributed by* Common Courage Press

Rebel Inc, *distributed by* AK Press Distribution

Rebel Press, *distributed by* AK Press Distribution

Rebellion, *distributed by* Simon & Schuster Sales & Marketing

Rebellion Publishing, *distributed by* Simon & Schuster, Inc

Rebuilding Books, *imprint of* Impact Publishers Inc

Recommended Country Inns®, *imprint of* The Globe Pequot Press

The Reconstructionist Press, *distributed by* Fordham University Press

Record Research, *distributed by* Hal Leonard Corp

Recorded Books, *subsidiary of* Haights Cross Communications Inc

Recorded Books Audiolibros, *imprint of* Recorded Books LLC

Recorded Books Evergreen, *imprint of* Recorded Books LLC

Recorded Books Inspirational, *imprint of* Recorded Books LLC

Recorded Books LLC, *division of* Haights Cross Communications LLC, *distributor for* Buena Vista DVDs, The Film Movement DVDs

Recovered Classics, *imprint of* McPherson & Co

Recreation Sales, *distributed by* Gem Guides Book Co

Recruiting Trends, *imprint of* Kennedy Information Inc

Red Anvil Press, *imprint of* Elderberry Press Inc, *distributed by* Elderberry Press Inc

Red Brick Learning, *division of* Capstone Publishers™

Red Chair Press, *distributed by* Lerner Publishing, Lerner Publishing Group Inc

Red Dress Ink, *imprint of* Harlequin Enterprises Ltd

Red Lead Press, *imprint of* Dorrance Publishing Co Inc

Red Mansions Publishing, *distributed by* China Books

Red Portal Press, *imprint of* Scarletta

Red Wheel/Weiser/Conari, *distributor for* Nicolas Hays Inc

Red Wheel-Weiser Inc, *distributed by* Moznaim Publishing Corp

Red Wheel/Weiser LLC, *distributor for* Hampton Roads Publishing Co Inc

Charles Redd Center, *distributed by* Signature Books Publishing LLC

Redemptorist Publications, *distributed by* Liguori Publications

Redleaf Press, *division of* Think Small, *distributed by* Pademelon Press Pty Ltd (Australia)

Redwing Book Co, *distributor for* Blue Poppy Press

John Reed Books, *distributor for* Price World Publishing LLC

Referee Books, *imprint of* Referee Enterprises Inc

Reference Press, *distributor for* World Trade Press

Reg Review Inc, *distributed by* Professional Publications Inc (PPI)

Regal Books, *division of* Gospel Light

Regan Books, *imprint of* HarperCollins Publishers Sales

Regents External Degree Series, *imprint of* National Learning Corp

Regis External MBA Program, *imprint of* Bisk Education

Registry of Guitar Tutors (RGT), *distributed by* Mel Bay Publications Inc

Regnery, *imprint of* Regnery Publishing Inc

Regnery History, *imprint of* Regnery Publishing Inc

Regnery Publishing Inc, *subsidiary of* Eagle Publishing Inc

Regular Baptist Press, *division of* General Association of Regular Baptist Churches

RELS Press, *imprint of* Plowshare Media

Renaissance House, *imprint of* Laredo Publishing Co Inc, *distributed by* SRA/McGraw-Hill

Renegade Enterprises, *distributed by* Sunbelt Publications Inc

Renewing the Heart, *imprint of* Focus on the Family

Renouf Bookstore, *distributor for* Peterson Institute for International Economics

Research, *division of* Scholastic Education

Research & Markets, *distributor for* Primary Research Group Inc

Research & Special Programs Administration of the US Department of Transportation, *distributed by* J J Keller & Associates, Inc

Research Centrex, *imprint of* Crumb Elbow Publishing

Researchandmarkets.com, *distributor for* Apollo Managed Care Inc

Resilient Publishing LLC, *imprint of* Borderline Publishing

Resources for the Future, *distributed by* The Johns Hopkins University Press

Resurgence, *imprint of* Tyndale House Publishers Inc

Resurrection Press, *imprint of* Catholic Book Publishing Corp

The Retention Solutions Group, *division of* Dorland Healthcare Information

Retold Classics, *imprint of* Perfection Learning Corp

Retro Science Fiction, *imprint of* Gateways Books & Tapes

RetroRomance™, *imprint of* Samhain Publishing Ltd

Retrospect Publishing, *distributed by* Closson Press

Reunion Solutions Press, *imprint of* Iron Gate Publishing

Fleming H Revell, *division of* Baker Book House Co, Baker Book House Co

RGB Arte Visual, *distributed by* Mel Bay Publications Inc

Ribbits, *imprint of* Focus on the Family

Ricordi, *distributed by* Hal Leonard Corp

G Ricordi (Italy), *distributor for* Pendragon Press

Ridge Row Books, *imprint of* University of Scranton Press

Ridge Row Press, *subsidiary of* University of Scranton Press

Ridgetop Books, *imprint of* Bright Mountain Books Inc

Riebel-Roque, *distributed by* Casemate Publishers & Book Distributors LLC

Lynne Rienner Publishers Inc, *distributor for* Center for US-Mexican Studies, Ayebia Clarke Publishing Ltd (African lit), St Andrews Center for Syrian Studies

Rigby, *imprint of* Harcourt Achieve, Harcourt Inc

Riley & Johnson, *distributed by* Business Research Services Inc

Rincon Publishing Co, *distributed by* Sunbelt Publications Inc

Ringtaw Books, *imprint of* The University of Akron Press

Rio Chico, *imprint of* Rio Nuevo Publishers

Rio Grande Books, *imprint of* LPD Press

Ripley Entertainment, *distributed by* Simon & Schuster Sales & Marketing

Ripley Entertainment Inc, *distributed by* Simon & Schuster, Inc

Rittenhouse, *distributor for* Teton NewMedia

Rittenhouse Book Distributors, *distributor for* Primary Research Group Inc

Rivendale Press, *distributed by* Oak Knoll Press

River Books Co Ltd, *distributed by* Antique Collectors Club Ltd

River City Kids, *imprint of* River City Publishing LLC

River North, *imprint of* Moody Publishers

Riverdale Ave Books/Magnus Books, *imprint of* Riverdale Avenue Books (RAB)

Riverhead Books, *imprint of* Penguin Group (USA) LLC, The Putnam Publishing Group

Riverhead Books (Hardcover), *imprint of* Penguin Group (USA) LLC

Riverhead Books (Paperback), *imprint of* Berkley Publishing Group

Riverhead Books (Trade Paperback), *imprint of* Penguin Group (USA) LLC

Riverside Publishing, *subsidiary of* Houghton Mifflin Harcourt, Houghton Mifflin Harcourt Publishing Co, *distributor for* Psychological Assessment Resources Inc (PAR), *distributed by* Psychological Assessment Resources Inc (PAR)

RiverWood Books, *imprint of* White Cloud Press

Rizzoli, *distributed by* Random House Inc

Rizzoli First, *imprint of* Rizzoli International Publications Inc

Rizzoli International, *distributor for* Nevraumont Publishing Co

Rizzoli International Publications Inc, *subsidiary of* RCS Rizzoli Corp New York, RCS Rizzoli Corp New York, *distributor for* Editions Flammarion, Skira Editore, *distributed by* Random House

Rizzoli, New York, *imprint of* Rizzoli International Publications Inc

Road Dog Publications, *imprint of* Lost Classics Book Company LLC

Roadside Geology Series, *imprint of* Mountain Press Publishing Co

Roadside History Series, *imprint of* Mountain Press Publishing Co

Roaring Brook Press, *member of* Macmillan Children's Publishing Group

Lee Roberts Publications, *distributed by* Hal Leonard Corp

Robins Lane Press, *distributed by* Gryphon House Inc

Roc, *imprint of* NAL, Penguin Group (USA) LLC

The Rock Spring Collection of Japanese Literature, *imprint of* Stone Bridge Press Inc

Rockbottom Book Co, *distributor for* ABDO Publishing Group

Rockefeller Institute Press, *distributed by* State University of New York Press

The Rockefeller University Press, *unit of* Rockefeller University

Rockhurst University Press, *distributed by* Fordham University Press

Rockport Publishers, *imprint of* Quayside Publishing Group

Rocky River Publishers LLC, *distributed by* Follett Library Resources, C E Mendez Foundation Inc

Rodale, *distributor for* The Colonial Williamsburg Foundation, *distributed by* St Martin's Press, LLC

Rodale Books, *imprint of* Rodale Inc, *distributed by* Macmillan

Anita Roddick Publications, *distributed by* Chelsea Green Publishing Co

Roman Catholic Books, *division of* Catholic Media Apostolate Inc

Romantic Sounds Audio, *imprint of* Recorded Books LLC

Roncorp Music, *division of* Northeastern Music Publications

Roost Books, *imprint of* Shambhala Publications Inc

RoperPenberthy Publishing Ltd, *distributed by* Bridge-Logos Inc

Rorschach Workshops, *distributed by* Psychological Assessment Resources Inc (PAR)

Rose Dog Books, *imprint of* Dorrance Publishing Co Inc

Fr Seraphim Rose Foundation, *imprint of* St Herman Press

Rose Hill Books, *imprint of* Fordham University Press

Lois Rose Rose, *distributed by* Stone & Scott Publishers

Rosebud Books, *imprint of* Raven Productions Inc

Rosen Classroom Books & Materials, *division of* The Rosen Publishing Group Inc

Rossel Books, *distributed by* Behrman House Inc

Roth Family Foundation, *imprint of* University of California Press

Rothko Chapel, *distributed by* University of Texas Press

Fred B Rothman Publications, *imprint of* William S Hein & Co Inc

RotoVision, *distributed by* Quayside Publishing Group

Rough Guides, *subsidiary of* Pearson PLC, *distributed by* Penguin Group (USA) LLC

The Rough Notes Co Inc, *subsidiary of* Insurance Publishing Plus Corp, Insurance Publishing Plus Corp

Round Table Comics, *imprint of* Writers of the Round Table Press

Rourke Publishing, *distributed by* Ideals Publications, a Guideposts Co

Route, *distributed by* Dufour Editions Inc

Routledge, *imprint of* Routledge/Taylor & Francis, Taylor & Francis Inc

Routledge/Taylor & Francis, *member of* Taylor & Francis Group, *distributor for* David Fulton

Rowman & Littlefield, *distributor for* American Council on Education, Bucknell University Press, The Colonial Williamsburg Foundation, Fairleigh Dickinson University Press, Lehigh University Press, University of Delaware Press

Rowman & Littlefield Education, *distributor for* National Association for Music Education

Rowman & Littlefield Publishers Inc, *imprint of* Rowman & Littlefield Publishing Group, *distributor for* Smithsonian Scholarly Press

Roxbury Publishing, *distributed by* Oxford University Press USA

Roxbury Publishing Co, *imprint of* Oxford University Press, Oxford University Press USA

Royal Academy Publications, *distributed by* Harry N Abrams Inc

Royal Asiatic Society (Korea Branch), *distributed by* Cheng & Tsui Co Inc

Royal Fireworks Press, *distributor for* KAV Books, Silk Label Books, Trillium Press

Royal Historical Society, *imprint of* Boydell & Brewer Inc

Royal Society of Chemistry, *distributed by* The American Chemical Society

Royal Society of London, *distributed by* Scholium International Inc

Rubank Publications, *distributed by* Hal Leonard Corp

Rubicon, *distributed by* Peoples Education Inc

Rucksack Readers (UK), *distributed by* Interlink Publishing Group Inc

Rugged Land, *distributed by* Random House Inc

Raymond C Rumpf & Son Inc, *distributor for* Wilderness Adventures Press Inc

Rune-Tales, *imprint of* Quincannon Publishing Group

Running Press, *imprint of* The Perseus Books Group, Running Press Book Publishers, *distributor for* The Jim Henson Co, Parachute Publishing LLC

Running Press Book Publishers, *member of* The Perseus Books Group, *distributor for* Wine Enthusiast

Running Press Kids, *imprint of* Running Press Book Publishers

Running Press-Kids, *imprint of* The Perseus Books Group

Running Press Miniature Editions, *imprint of* Running Press Book Publishers

Running Press-Miniature Editions, *imprint of* The Perseus Books Group

Rural Science Institute, *distributed by* Chelsea Green Publishing Co

Michael Russell, *distributed by* Antique Collectors Club Ltd

Rutgers Series in Accounting Research, *imprint of* Markus Wiener Publishers Inc

Rutgers University Press, *division of* Rutgers, The State University

RV Crest International Inc/FDIX, *distributor for* HRD Press

RV Guides, *distributed by* American Map Corp

RV International Maps & Atlases, *distributed by* Hagstrom Map & Travel Center

Ryton Publications, *distributed by* Stackpole Books

RZM Publishing, *distributed by* Casemate Publishers & Book Distributors LLC

S A B D A, *distributed by* Lotus Press

S-A Design, *distributed by* CarTech Inc

S-A Design Books, *imprint of* CarTech Inc

S & B Books Ltd (Canada), *distributor for* Thorndike Press®

S I Publicaties BV, *distributed by* Casemate Publishers & Book Distributors LLC

Sacred Music Press, *imprint of* Transcontinental Music Publications

Saddleback Educational, *distributor for* Teachers of English to Speakers of Other Languages Inc (TESOL)

Saddleback Educational Publishing, *distributed by* Children's Plus, Delaney, Follett

Sadhana Publications, *distributed by* Lotus Press

Sadlier, *division of* William H Sadlier Inc

Sadlier-Oxford, *division of* William H Sadlier Inc

SAE (Society of Automotive Engineers International), *distributor for* Coordinating Research Council Inc

Safari Press, *distributor for* Quiller

Safer Society Press, *imprint of* Safer Society Foundation Inc

Sagamore Publishing LLC, *distributor for* American Academy for Park & Recreation Administration

Sage Books, *imprint of* Genesis Press Inc

SAGE UK Resources for Educators, *distributed by* Corwin, a Sage Co

St Andrews Center for Syrian Studies, *distributed by* Lynne Rienner Publishers Inc

Saint Andrews College Press, *subsidiary of* Saint Andrews Presbyterian College

St Augustine's Press Inc, *distributor for* Dumb Ox Books (publishes the Aristotelian Commentaries of Thomas Aquinas & like works), Fidelity Press (culture, history & politics from a Catholic viewpoint), Hardwood Press (trade books, mostly in sports & regional works), *distributed by* University of Chicago Press

St Bede's Publications, *distributed by* Fordham University Press

St Herman Press, *subsidiary of* Brotherhood of St Herman of Alaska, Brotherhood of St Herman of Alaska, *imprint of* St Herman Press, *distributed by* Light & Life Publishing Co

St James Press®, *imprint of* Gale

St Johann Press, *distributor for* MerwinAsia

St Louis Mercantile Library, *distributed by* University of Missouri Press

St Martin's Press, LLC, *subsidiary of* Macmillan, *distributor for* Berg Publishers, Bloomsbury USA, College Board, Manchester University Press, Palgrave Macmillan, Papercutz, Rodale, I B Tauris, Walker and Company, Zed Books

Saint Mary's Press, *subsidiary of* Christian Brothers Publications, *distributor for* Group Publishing

St Paisius Abbey, *imprint of* St Herman Press

St Paisius Missionary School, *imprint of* St Herman Press

St Pauls/Alba House, *division of* The Society of St Paul

St Vladimir's, *distributor for* Conciliar Press

St Xenia Skete, *imprint of* St Herman Press

The Saints Series, *imprint of* Pauline Books & Media

Salem Press, *distributor for* Schlager Group Inc

Salem Press Inc, *division of* EBSCO Publishing

Sales & Marketing, *division of* Scholastic Education

SalesSavvy.com, *subsidiary of* BizBest Media Corp

Salmon Poetry, *distributed by* Dufour Editions Inc

SaltRiver, *imprint of* Tyndale House Publishers Inc

Saltry Press, *distributed by* Epicenter Press Inc

Samata Books, *distributed by* Lotus Press

Sams Technical Publishing LLC, *division of* AGS Capital LLC, *imprint of* Quickfact®

San Antonio Express-News, *distributed by* Eakin Press

San Diego Architecture Foundation, *distributed by* Sunbelt Publications Inc

San Diego Association of Geologists, *distributed by* Sunbelt Publications Inc

San Diego City Works Press, *distributed by* Sunbelt Publications Inc

San Diego Natural History Museum, *distributed by* Sunbelt Publications Inc

San Diego Police Historical Association, *distributed by* Sunbelt Publications Inc

San Diego State University Press, *division of* San Diego State University Foundation, *distributor for* Institute for Regional Studies of the Californias

San Dieguit River Park Joint Powers Authority, *distributed by* Sunbelt Publications Inc

Coleccion San Pedrito, *imprint of* University of Puerto Rico Press

Sandala Productions, *distributed by* Fons Vitae

Sandcastle, *imprint of* ABDO Publishing Group

J S Sanders & Co, *imprint of* Ivan R Dee Publisher

Sandpiper, *imprint of* Houghton Mifflin Harcourt Trade & Reference Division

The Sandstone Press, *imprint of* Frederic C Beil Publisher Inc

Santillana, *imprint of* Santillana USA Publishing Co Inc

Santillana USA Publishing Co Inc, *division of* The Richmond Publishing Co Inc

Sapientia Press, *distributed by* The Catholic University of America Press

Saraland Press, *distributed by* University of South Carolina Press

Saroff Editions, *imprint of* McPherson & Co

SAS Publishing, *imprint of* SAS Institute Inc, *distributor for* AMACOM Books, Breakfast Communications, CRC Press, Duxbury, Harcourt, Harvard Business School Press, McGraw-Hill, Oxford, Prentice-Hall, Springer, John Wiley & Sons Inc, *distributed by* John Wiley & Sons Inc

Satas, *distributor for* Blue Poppy Press

Saunders, *imprint of* Elsevier, Health Sciences Division, *distributed by* Oxford University Press USA

Saunders Book Co, *distributor for* Sylvan Dell Publishing

W B Saunders, *distributor for* Current Medicine Group (CMG)

W B Saunders Co, *distributed by* Marine Techniques Publishing

The Sausage Maker, *distributed by* Stackpole Books

Savas Beatie, *distributed by* Casemate Publishers & Book Distributors LLC

Save Our Heritage Organization, *distributed by* Sunbelt Publications Inc

Alastair Sawday Publishing, *distributed by* The Globe Pequot Press

Saxon, *imprint of* Harcourt Inc

Saxon Publishers, *imprint of* Houghton Mifflin Harcourt, Houghton Mifflin Harcourt Publishing Company

Scala Publishers, *distributor for* American Federation of Arts, *distributed by* Antique Collectors Club Ltd

Scandalous, *imprint of* Entangled Publishing

Scarab Miniatures, *distributed by* Casemate Publishers & Book Distributors LLC

Lo Scarabeo, *distributed by* Llewellyn Publications

Scarecrow Press Inc, *imprint of* Rowman & Littlefield Publishing Group

Scarf Press, *distributed by* Bloch Publishing Co

Scarletta Junior Readers, *imprint of* Scarletta

Scarletta Kids, *imprint of* Scarletta

Scarletta Press, *imprint of* Scarletta

SCB Distributors, *distributor for* Circlet Press Inc, Damron Co

Schaum, *imprint of* McGraw-Hill Professional

Schiffer, *imprint of* Schiffer Publishing Ltd, *distributor for* Winterthur Museum & Country Estate

Schiffer Fashion Press, *imprint of* Schiffer Publishing Ltd

Schiffer LTD, *imprint of* Schiffer Publishing Ltd

Schiffer Military History, *imprint of* Schiffer Publishing Ltd

Schiffer Publishing Ltd, *distributor for* The Donning Co

Schirmer, *imprint of* Wadsworth Publishing

E C Schirmer Music Co, *imprint of* ECS Publishing Corp

G Schirmer Inc (Associated Music Publishers), *distributed by* Hal Leonard Corp

Schirmer/Mosel, *distributed by* Prestel Publishing

Schirmer Reference™, *imprint of* Gale

Schirmer Trade Books, *imprint of* Music Sales Corp, *distributor for* Big Meteor Publishing, Independent Music Press

Schlager Group Inc, *distributed by* Salem Press (ref books only)

A Naomi Schneider Book, *imprint of* University of California Press

Schocken Books, *imprint of* Pantheon Books/ Schocken Books, Random House Inc

Scholarly Digital Editions, *imprint of* Boydell & Brewer Inc

Scholarly Resources Inc, *imprint of* Gale

Scholars' Facsimiles & Reprints, *subsidiary of* Academic Resources Corp, Academic Resources Corp

Scholastic, *distributor for* Parachute Publishing LLC, *distributed by* Learning Links Inc

Scholastic Argentina SA, *subsidiary of* Scholastic International

Scholastic Australia Pty Ltd, *subsidiary of* Scholastic International

Scholastic Books, *distributor for* Alloy Entertainment

Scholastic Canada Ltd, *subsidiary of* Scholastic International

Scholastic Classroom & Community Group, *division of* Scholastic Inc

Scholastic Consumer & Professional Publishing, *division of* Scholastic Inc

Scholastic Education, *division of* Scholastic Inc

Scholastic Education Information Consulting (Shanghai) Co, Ltd, *subsidiary of* Scholastic International

Scholastic Education International (Singapore) Pvt Ltd, *subsidiary of* Scholastic International

Scholastic en Español, *imprint of* Scholastic Trade Division

Scholastic Grolier International Inc Indonesia, *subsidiary of* Scholastic International

Scholastic Hong Kong Ltd, *subsidiary of* Scholastic International

Scholastic Inc, *distributor for* The Colonial Williamsburg Foundation, Educational Impressions Inc

Scholastic India Private Ltd, *subsidiary of* Scholastic International

Scholastic International, *division of* Scholastic Inc

Scholastic Ireland Ltd, *subsidiary of* Scholastic International

Scholastic Ltd UK, *subsidiary of* Scholastic International

Scholastic Media, *division of* Scholastic Inc

Scholastic Mexico SA, *subsidiary of* Scholastic International

Scholastic New Zealand, *distributor for* Big Guy Books Inc

Scholastic New Zealand Ltd, *subsidiary of* Scholastic International

Scholastic Nonfiction, *imprint of* Scholastic Trade Division

Scholastic Paperbacks, *imprint of* Scholastic Trade Division

Scholastic Press, *imprint of* Scholastic Trade Division

Scholastic Reference, *imprint of* Scholastic Trade Division

Scholastic-Tab Publications, *distributor for* Educational Impressions Inc

Scholastic Trade Division, *division of* Scholastic Inc

Editions Scholasticae, *distributed by* Transaction Publishers Inc

Scholium International Inc, *distributor for* Dechema Series, Macmillan (UK), Micelle Press, Royal Society of London, Zuckschwerdt Verlag (Munich, Germany)

School of the Blues, *imprint of* Mel Bay Publications Inc

School of Government, *division of* The University of NC Chapel Hill

School Renaissance, *distributed by* Gryphon House Inc

School Speciality, *distributor for* MAR*CO Products Inc

Schwartz & Wade Books, *imprint of* Random House Inc

Schwartz and Wade Books, *imprint of* Random House Children's Books

Sci-Fi Audio, *imprint of* Recorded Books LLC

Science & Humanities Press, *subsidiary of* Banis & Associates

Science History Publications USA, *imprint of* Watson Publishing International LLC

Science, Naturally!™, *affiliate of* Platypus Media, Platypus Media LLC

Science of Mind Publications, *distributed by* De Vorss & Co

Science Press New York & Science Press Beijing, *distributed by* American Mathematical Society

Science Publishers Inc, *imprint of* Edenbridge Ltd, *distributed by* CRC Press

Scientific American, *imprint of* Farrar, Straus & Giroux, LLC

Scientific American Medicine, *distributor for* American College of Surgeons

Scitec Publications, *imprint of* Trans Tech Publications

Scitech Publishing Inc, *distributor for* Peninsula Publishing

SCM, *distributed by* Presbyterian Publishing Corp, Westminster John Knox Press

Scolari, *division of* SAGE Publications

Scots Plaid Press, *imprint of* Old Barn Enterprises Inc

Scott Publishing Co, *division of* AMOS Publishing Co

Scottish Text Society, *imprint of* Boydell & Brewer Inc

Scott's Highland Services, *distributed by* Mel Bay Publications Inc

Scribner, *imprint of* Scribner Publishing Group

Scribner Classics, *imprint of* Scribner

Scribner Poetry, *imprint of* Scribner

Charles Scribner's Sons®, *imprint of* Gale

Scripta Humanistica Publishing International, *subsidiary of* Brumar Communications

Scripta-Technica, *imprint of* John Wiley & Sons Inc

Scroll Saw Woodworking & Crafts, *imprint of* Fox Chapel Publishing Co Inc

Scythian Books, *imprint of* Berkeley Slavic Specialties

Sea-to-Sea Publishing, *imprint of* Black Rabbit Books

Seaboard Press, *imprint of* James A Rock & Co Publishers

Seabreeze Books & Charts, *distributor for* Marine Techniques Publishing

Seaforth Publishing, *distributed by* Casemate Publishers & Book Distributors LLC

Seal Press, *member of* Perseus Books Group, *imprint of* The Perseus Books Group

Sealife Research Alliance, *imprint of* Crumb Elbow Publishing

Search Institute Press®, *division of* Search Institute

Search Press, UK, *distributor for* Interweave Press LLC

Seastone, *imprint of* Ulysses Press

Second Chance Press, *imprint of* The Permanent Press

Second Floor Music, *distributed by* Hal Leonard Corp

Second Story Press, *distributed by* Orca Book Publishers

Secret Passage Press, *distributed by* Enfield Publishing & Distribution Co

Sedgwick Press, *imprint of* Grey House Publishing Inc™

Seed Savers, *distributed by* Chelsea Green Publishing Co

Seedling Publications Inc, *imprint of* Continental Press, Continental Press Inc, *distributed by* Kendall Hunt Publishing

Martin E Segal Theatre Center Publications, *distributed by* Theatre Communications Group

The Sektor Co, *distributed by* Sunbelt Publications Inc

Select, *imprint of* Oakstone Publishing LLC

Self-Esteem Shop, *distributor for* American Counseling Association

SelfHelp Success Books, *distributed by* Pelican Publishing Co

Selfhelpbooks.com, *imprint of* Wellness Institute/Self Help Books LLC

The Selfhelper Law Press of America, *imprint of* Do-It-Yourself Legal Publishers

SelfMadeHero, *imprint of* Harry N Abrams Inc

Seloc, *distributed by* Delmar

Sensation, *imprint of* Berkley Books, Berkley Publishing Group

Sense of Wonder Press, *imprint of* James A Rock & Co Publishers

Sentinel, *imprint of* Penguin Group (USA) LLC

Sephardic House, *distributed by* Bloch Publishing Co

Seraphic Press, *distributed by* Jonathan David Publishers Inc

Serendipity, *imprint of* Price Stern Sloan

Serif Publishing Ltd (UK), *distributed by* Interlink Publishing Group Inc

Serindia Publications, *distributed by* Art Media Resources Inc (US & CN)

Servant Books, *imprint of* Franciscan Media

Service Employees International Union, *distributed by* Chelsea Green Publishing Co

SESAP Audio Companion, *imprint of* Oakstone Publishing LLC

SETAC Press, *imprint of* Society of Environmental Toxicology & Chemistry

Seven Footer Kids, *imprint of* Seven Footer Press

Seven Footer Press, *subsidiary of* Seven Footer Entertainment LLC

Sevens Publishing, *imprint of* Borderline Publishing

7th Generation, *imprint of* Book Publishing Co, *distributed by* Orca Book Publishers

The Seventh Quarry, *imprint of* Cross-Cultural Communications

The Seventh Quarry Press, *imprint of* Cross-Cultural Communications, *distributed by* Cross-Cultural Communications

Sex-Kitten.Net Books, *imprint of* Ephemera Bound Publishing

Shaar Press, *imprint of* Mesorah Publications Ltd

Shabdaguchha (Magazine & Press), *distributed by* Cross-Cultural Communications

Shadow Mountain, *imprint of* Deseret Book Co

Shakespeare Playbooks, *imprint of* Bandanna Books

Shambhala, *distributed by* Random House Inc

Shambhala Publications Inc, *distributed by* Random House Inc

Shanghai Press, *distributed by* Tuttle Publishing

Shangri-La, *imprint of* Lotus Press

Sharpe Focus, *imprint of* M E Sharpe Inc

Sharpe Online Reference, *imprint of* M E Sharpe Inc

Sharpe Reference, *imprint of* M E Sharpe Inc

Shaw Books, *imprint of* WaterBrook Multnomah Publishing Group

Shaye Areheart Books, *imprint of* Random House Inc

Shearwater Books, *imprint of* Island Press

The Sheep Meadow Press, *distributed by* University Press of New England

Sheffield Phoenix Press, *distributed by* Society of Biblical Literature

Sheffield Publishing Co, *subsidiary of* Waveland Press Inc

Sheldrake Press (UK), *distributed by* Interlink Publishing Group Inc

Joyce Shellhart, *distributed by* Finney Company Inc

Shengold Books, *imprint of* Schreiber Publishing Inc

Shepard & Piper, *imprint of* Shepard Publications

Shepard Publications, *imprint of* Shepard Publications

W B Sheridan, *imprint of* Academica Press LLC

Shire, *imprint of* Osprey Publishing Inc

G Shirmer, *imprint of* Hal Leonard Corp

Shortfuse Press, *distributed by* Gem Guides Book Co

Iwasaki Shoten, *distributor for* Big Guy Books Inc

Showcase, *imprint of* Players Press Inc

ShowForth Videos, *division of* BJU Press, *imprint of* BJU Press

Shroff Publishers, *distributor for* Mike Murach & Associates Inc

Shroff Publishers & Distributors, *distributor for* Microsoft Press

Shufunotomo Co, *distributed by* Tuttle Publishing

Sicilia Parra, *distributed by* Cross-Cultural Communications

Side Street, *subsidiary of* BrickHouse Books Inc

Sierra Club Adult Books, *imprint of* Random House Inc

Sierra Club Books, *imprint of* Counterpoint Press LLC, *distributor for* Counterpoint Press, *distributed by* Chronicle Books (Sierra Club Calendars), Gibbs Smith (Sierra Club Books for Children), University of California Press

Sierra Club Books for Children, *division of* Sierra Club Books

Sierra Club Calendars, *division of* Sierra Club Books

Sierra Press, *distributed by* Gem Guides Book Co

Siete Cuentos Editorial, *imprint of* Seven Stories Press

Signal Books (UK), *distributed by* Interlink Publishing Group Inc

Signature Books, *imprint of* EastBridge

Signature Books Publishing LLC, *distributor for* Charles Redd Center, Tanner Trust Fund

Signatures Network, *distributed by* Andrews McMeel Publishing LLC

Signet, *imprint of* NAL, Penguin Group (USA) LLC

Signet Classics, *imprint of* NAL, Penguin Group (USA) LLC

Signum Verlag, *distributed by* Gallaudet University Press

Siles Press, *division of* Silman-James Press

Silhouette, *imprint of* Harlequin Enterprises Ltd

Silhouette Imprints, *imprint of* Crumb Elbow Publishing

Silk & Magic, *imprint of* ImaJinn Books Inc

Silk Label Books, *distributed by* Royal Fireworks Press

Silman-James Press, *distributed by* Codasat Canada Ltd

Siloam Press, *imprint of* Charisma Media

Silver Dagger Mysteries, *imprint of* The Overmountain Press

Silver Dragon Books, *imprint of* Regal Crest Enterprises LLC

Silver Oak, *distributed by* Sterling Publishing Co Inc

Silverplume, a Vertafore Co, *distributor for* Standard Publishing Corp

Simba Information, *division of* Market Research Group

Simcha Press, *imprint of* Health Communications Inc

Simon & Schuster, *imprint of* Simon & Schuster Publishing Group, *distributor for* Alloy Entertainment, Baen Publishing Enterprises, Beyond Words Publishing Inc, Cider Mill Press Book Publishers LLC, Good Books, The Jim Henson Co, Kaplan Publishing, Meadowbrook Press, Nevraumont Publishing Co, Nightingale-Conant, Open Road Publishing, Parachute Publishing LLC, *distributed by* ADD Warehouse, Cardoza Publishing, Gulf Publishing Co, Learning Links Inc

Simon & Schuster Audio, *division of* Simon & Schuster, Inc, *distributor for* Monostereo

Simon & Schuster Books for Young Readers, *imprint of* Simon & Schuster Children's Publishing

Simon & Schuster Children's Publishing, *division of* Simon & Schuster, Inc

Simon & Schuster Digital, *division of* Simon & Schuster, Inc

Simon & Schuster, Inc, *division of* CBS Corporation, *distributor for* Andrews McMeel Publishing LLC, Avatar Press, Backlist LLC (div of Chicken Soup for the Soul Publishing), Baen Books, Baseball America, BL Publishing (div of Games Workshop), Boom! Studios, Cardoza Publishing, Chicken Soup for the Soul Publishing, Cider Mill Press Book Publishers, Downtown Bookworks, Good Books, Harlequin Enterprises Ltd (billing only), Hooked on Phonics (Sandviks HOP Inc/Sandvik Publishing), Inner Traditions/Bear & Company, Kaplan Publishing, Kinfolk, Manhattan GMAT, Meadowbrook Press, Merck Publishing, Open Road Publishing, Pikachu Press (Pokemon Company International), Reader's Digest Children's Publishing, Rebellion Publishing, Ripley Entertainment Inc (Ripley's Believe it or Not), Tuttle Publishing, VIZ Media, Weldon Owen, World Almanac (div of Facts on File)

Simon & Schuster Mass Merchandise Sales Co, *distributor for* Harlequin Enterprises Ltd

Simon & Schuster Pocket Books, *distributor for* Public Citizen

Simon & Schuster Sales & Marketing, *division of* Simon & Schuster, Inc, *distributor for* Andrews McMeel Publishing LLC, Applesauce Press (children's), Avatar Press, Baen Books, Baseball America, Boom! Studios, Cardoza, Chicken Soup for the Soul, Cider Mill Press Book Publishers, Downtown Bookworks, Games Workshop, Harlequin (billing only), Kaplan Publishing, Manhattan Prep, Meadowbrook Press, Merck, Open Road, Reader's Digest Children's Books, Rebellion, Ripley Entertainment, VIZ Media, Weldon Owen, World Almanac (children's)

Simon Pulse, *imprint of* Simon & Schuster Children's Publishing

Simon Spotlight, *imprint of* Simon & Schuster Children's Publishing

Simple Productions, *imprint of* Shepard Publications

Simpson, *imprint of* University of California Press

Sing Out Corp, *distributed by* Hal Leonard Corp

Singapore University Press, *distributed by* University of Hawaii Press

Singing Dragon, *imprint of* Jessica Kingsley Publishers Inc

Singular, *imprint of* Delmar

Sisra Music Publishing, *imprint of* Empire Publishing Service

Byron Sistler, *distributor for* Ericson Books

6 x 6 Magazine, *imprint of* Ugly Duckling Presse

Six House, *subsidiary of* Gallopade International Inc

Sixth & Spring, *distributed by* Sterling Publishing Co Inc

Skateman Publications, *imprint of* World Citizens

Skidmore-Roth, *imprint of* Delmar

SkillPath Publications, *division of* The Graceland University Center for Professional Development & Lifelong Learning Inc, *distributor for* Franklin Covey, Pearson Technology, Thomson Publishing, John Wiley

SkillsTutor, *imprint of* Houghton Mifflin Harcourt

Skinner House Books, *imprint of* Unitarian Universalist Association

SkipJack Press, *imprint of* Finney Company Inc

Skipstone, *imprint of* The Mountaineers Books

Skira Editore, *distributed by* Rizzoli International Publications Inc

SkiraRizzoli Publishing, *imprint of* Rizzoli International Publications Inc

Skirt!®, *imprint of* The Globe Pequot Press

Sky Publishing, *distributed by* Sterling Publishing Co Inc

Skyhook Press, *imprint of* Shepard Publications

Skyhorse Publishing, *distributed by* W W Norton & Company Inc

Skylark, *imprint of* Random House Inc

SkyLight Paths Publishing, *division of* Longhill Partners Inc, LongHill Partners Inc

Slossen, *distributed by* ADD Warehouse

Slow Food Editore, *distributed by* Chelsea Green Publishing Co

Small Horizons, *imprint of* New Horizon Press

Jacqui Small, *distributed by* Quayside Publishing Group

Small Press Distribution, *distributor for* Ahsahta Press, Pleasure Boat Studio: A Literary Press

Small Press Distribution (SPD), *distributor for* Fugue State Press

Small Press United, *distributor for* Academy of Nutrition & Dietetics

SmallBusiness.tv, *subsidiary of* BizBest Media Corp

Smart Apple Media, *imprint of* Black Rabbit Books

Smart Ink, *distributed by* Ideals Publications, a Guideposts Co

Smart Kidz, *distributed by* Ideals Publications, a Guideposts Co

Smart Pop, *imprint of* BenBella Books Inc

Smart Sex Stuff for Kids, *imprint of* Gallopade International Inc

SmartLab, *distributed by* Chronicle Books LLC

Smartmaps®, *imprint of* VanDam Inc

SmartPros, *distributed by* Professional Publications Inc (PPI)

SmartsCo, *distributed by* Chronicle Books LLC

Smashwords, *distributor for* Hard Shell Word Factory

SMC Publishing, *distributed by* Cheng & Tsui Co Inc

Smiley Books, *imprint of* Hay House Inc

Smith & Kraus Books For Kids, *imprint of* Smith & Kraus Publishers Inc

Smith & Kraus Global, *subsidiary of* Smith & Kraus Publishers Inc

Smith-Pettit Foundation, *imprint of* Signature Books Publishing LLC

Smith Research Associates, *imprint of* Signature Books Publishing LLC

Smithsonian Books, *distributed by* Random House Inc

Smithsonian Library of the Solar System, *distributed by* Smithsonian Scholarly Press

Smithsonian Scholarly Press, *division of* Smithsonian Institution, *distributor for* Biological Diversity Handbook Series, Handbook of North American Indians, Smithsonian Library of the Solar System, Smithsonian Series in Archaeological Inquiry, Smithsonian Series in Comparative Evolutionary Biology, Smithsonian Series in Ethnographic Inquiry, *distributed by* Rowman & Littlefield Publishers Inc

Smithsonian Series in Archaeological Inquiry, *distributed by* Smithsonian Scholarly Press

Smithsonian Series in Comparative Evolutionary Biology, *distributed by* Smithsonian Scholarly Press

Smithsonian Series in Ethnographic Inquiry, *distributed by* Smithsonian Scholarly Press

Colin Smythe Ltd, *distributed by* Dufour Editions Inc

Snake Country Publishing, *distributed by* Caxton Press

Snaptail Press, *distributed by* Finney Company Inc

Snova Books, *imprint of* Nova Science Publishers Inc

Snow Lion, *imprint of* Shambhala Publications Inc

Snow Lion Publications Inc, *imprint of* Shambhala Publications, Shambhala Publications Inc

Snowy Owl Books, *imprint of* University of Alaska Press

Social Science Press, *distributed by* Berghahn Books

Social Sciences School Services, *distributor for* American Counseling Association

SocialMyBusiness.com, *subsidiary of* BizBest Media Corp

Societe Mathematique de France, *distributed by* American Mathematical Society

Society for American Baseball Research, *distributed by* University of Nebraska Press

Society of Biblical Literature, *distributor for* Brown Judaic Studies, Sheffield Phoenix Press

Society of Manufacturing Engineers, *distributor for* Free Press Division of MacMillan, Industrial Press, McGraw-Hill, Prentice Hall, John Wiley & Sons Inc, *distributed by* American Technical Publishers Inc, McGraw-Hill, Productivity Press

Society of the Cincinnati, *distributed by* University Press of America Inc

Soffietto Editions, *imprint of* Red Moon Press

Soft Skull Press, *imprint of* Counterpoint Press LLC

Sogang University Institute, *distributed by* Cheng & Tsui Co Inc

Soho Constable, *imprint of* Soho Press Inc

Soho Crime, *imprint of* Soho Press Inc

Soho Press, *distributed by* Random House Inc

Soho Press Inc, *distributed by* Random House

Soho Teen, *imprint of* Soho Press Inc

Solar Design Association, *distributed by* Chelsea Green Publishing Co

SOM Publishing, *subsidiary of* School of Metaphysics

Someday Baby, *distributed by* Ideals Publications, a Guideposts Co

Somerset Press, *division of* Hope Publishing Co

Somerville House USA, *imprint of* Grosset & Dunlap

Soncino, *distributed by* Bloch Publishing Co

Sono Nis Pres, *distributed by* Orca Book Publishers

Sono Nis Press, *distributed by* Heimburger House Publishing Co

Sopris West, *distributed by* Council for Exceptional Children (CEC)

Sopris West Educational Services, *imprint of* Cambium Learning Inc

Sorin Books, *imprint of* Ave Maria Press

Sotoportego Editore Venice, *distributed by* Edgewise Press Inc

Sound Ideas, *imprint of* Simon & Schuster Audio

Sound Library Audiobooks, *imprint of* AudioGO

SoundForth Music, *division of* BJU Press, *imprint of* BJU Press

Sourcebooks Casablanca, *imprint of* Sourcebooks Inc

Sourcebooks Fire, *imprint of* Sourcebooks Inc

Sourcebooks Inc, *distributor for* Prufrock Press, *distributed by* Raincoast Books

Sourcebooks Jabberwocky, *imprint of* Sourcebooks Inc

Sourcebooks Landmark, *imprint of* Sourcebooks Inc

Sourcebooks MediaFusion, *imprint of* Sourcebooks Inc

Sourced Media Books, *distributed by* Gibbs-Smith, Many Hats Media

SourceResource, *distributor for* MAR*CO Products Inc

South Carolina Bar Association, *distributed by* University of South Carolina Press

South Carolina Historical Society, *distributed by* University of South Carolina Press

South End Press, *affiliate of* Institute for Social & Cultural Change

South-Western, *imprint of* Wadsworth Publishing

South-Western Publishing, *distributor for* Course Technology

Southeastern Center for Contemporary Art, *distributed by* The University of North Carolina Press

Southeastern Cooperative Wildlife Disease Study, *distributed by* American Association for Vocational Instructional Materials

Southern Early Childhood Association, *distributed by* Gryphon House Inc

Southern Historical Press, *distributed by* Ericson Books

Southern Illinois University Press, *division of* Southern Illinois University

Southern Living Books, *imprint of* Oxmoor House Inc

Southern Methodist University Press, *distributed by* Texas A&M University Press

Southern Voices Audio, *imprint of* Recorded Books LLC

Southlore Press, *distributed by* Ingalls Publishing Group Inc (IPG)

Southwestern Studies, *imprint of* Texas Western Press

Sovereign World, *distributed by* Bridge-Logos Inc

Spark Avenue, *distributed by* Sunbelt Publications Inc

Sparkle Shapes, *imprint of* Playhouse Publishing

Speaker's Corner, *imprint of* Fulcrum Publishing Inc

Specialized Software, *imprint of* Lotus Press

Spectra, *imprint of* Random House Inc

Spectrum, *distributor for* National Council of Teachers of Mathematics (NCTM)

Sphinx Publishing, *division of* Sourcebooks Inc, *imprint of* Sourcebooks Inc

SPIE Press, *imprint of* SPIE

Spiegel & Grau, *imprint of* Random House Publishing Group

Spinsters Ink, *division of* Spinsters Ink Publishing Co

Spire Books, *imprint of* Fleming H Revell

Spirit, *imprint of* Norilana Books

Spirit Mountain Press, *distributed by* University of Alaska Press

Sporting News, *distributed by* Andrews McMeel Publishing LLC

Sports Collectors Digest, *imprint of* Betterway Books

SportsZONE, *imprint of* ABDO Publishing Group

Spotlight Books, *imprint of* Empire Publishing Service

Jack Spratt Choral Music, *imprint of* Empire Publishing Service

Spring Arbor, *distributor for* Faith Library Publications, Pentecostal Publishing House

Spring Arbor Distributors, *distributor for* BJU Press, Presbyterian Publishing Corp

Spring Freshet Press, *distributed by* University of Wisconsin Press

Spring Publications, *distributed by* Bloomsbury Academic

Springer, *subsidiary of* Springer Science+Business Media, *imprint of* Springer, *distributed by* SAS Publishing

Springer Healthcare, *imprint of* Springer

Springer Verlag, *distributor for* Current Medicine Group (CMG)

Springer-Verlag, *distributor for* American Institute of Physics

Springhouse Editions, *subsidiary of* White Pine Press, *distributed by* White Pine Press

Sproutman Publications, *distributed by* Book Publishing Co

Spyglass Books LLC, *distributed by* Biographical Publishing Co

Square One Publishers Inc, *distributor for* InnoVision Health Media, Rainbow Ridge Books, *distributed by* Thomas Allen & Son

SRA/McGraw-Hill, *division of* McGraw-Hill School Education Group, *imprint of* McGraw-Hill Education, *distributor for* Renaissance House

Sri Aurobindo Ashram, *distributed by* Lotus Press

Sri Lanka Institute of Traditional Studies, *distributed by* Fons Vitae

SSPC, *distributed by* NACE International

SSPC: The Society for Protective Coatings, *distributed by* Technical Publishing Co

ST Media Group Book Division, *division of* ST Media Group Intl

Stacey Intl Ltd (London), *distributed by* International Book Centre Inc

Stackpole Books, *distributor for* The Army War College Foundation Press, Barclay Creek Press, The Colonial Williamsburg Foundation, Headwater Books, Historical Society of Western Pennsylvania, Homespun Video, Northwest Fly Fishing, Quiller Press Ltd, Ryton Publications, The Sausage Maker, Stackpole Magazines, Swan Hill

Stackpole Magazines, *distributed by* Stackpole Books

Stadium Stories, *imprint of* The Globe Pequot Press

Stainer & Bell Ltd, *distributed by* ECS Publishing Corp

Standard & Poor's, *division of* McGraw-Hill Financial

Standard Educational Corp, *subsidiary of* The United Educators Inc

Standard Publishing Co, *distributor for* Focus on the Family

Standard Publishing Corp, *distributed by* LexisNexis, Silverplume, a Vertafore Co

Stanford Business Books, *imprint of* Stanford University Press

Stanford Security Studies, *imprint of* Stanford University Press

Stanford Law Books, *imprint of* Stanford University Press

Stanford General Books, *imprint of* Stanford University Press

Stanford University Press, *imprint of* Stanford University Press, *distributor for* The Woodrow Wilson Center Press, *distributed by* Kogan Page Publishers

Star Licks Videos, *distributed by* Hal Leonard Corp

Star Sounds, *distributed by* Lotus Press

Star Trek®, *imprint of* Gallery Books

Starbooks, *imprint of* STARbooks Press

STARbooks Press, *affiliate of* Florida Literary Foundation (FLF)

Starcrafts LLC, *imprint of* Starcrafts LLC

Starfire Publishing, *distributed by* Holmes Publishing Group LLC

Stargazer Books, *imprint of* Black Rabbit Books

Starrhill Press, *imprint of* River City Publishing LLC

STARS-National Center for Youths, *distributor for* MAR*CO Products Inc

Starscape, *imprint of* Tom Doherty Associates, LLC

StartupSmarts.com, *subsidiary of* BizBest Media Corp

State & National Parks Guides, *imprint of* Hunter Publishing Inc

State Experience, *imprint of* Gallopade International Inc

State Fair Books, *imprint of* R J Berg Publisher

State Stuff, *imprint of* Gallopade International Inc

State University of New York Press, *distributor for* Albany Institute of History & Art, Codhill Press, Samuel Dorsky Museum of Art, Mount Ida Press, New Netherland Institute, Rockefeller Institute Press, Uncrowned Queens

Stay Bound, *distributor for* Ozark Publishing Inc

Stay Focused Press, *imprint of* Abacus

STC Craft, *imprint of* Harry N Abrams Inc

Steam Passages Publishing, *distributed by* Heimburger House Publishing Co

Steam Press, *distributed by* Gryphon House Inc

Steck Vaughn, *imprint of* Harcourt Inc

Steeple Hill, *imprint of* Harlequin Enterprises Ltd

Steerforth Press, *distributed by* Random House Inc

Bernard Stein Music Co, *distributed by* Hal Leonard Corp

Rudolf Steiner Press UK, *distributor for* SteinerBooks

Rudolph Steiner Press, *distributed by* SteinerBooks

SteinerBooks, *distributor for* Chiron Publications, Clairview Books, Floris Books, Hawthorn Press, Lantern Books, Rudolph Steiner Press, Temple Lodge Publishing, *distributed by* Rudolf Steiner Press UK

Steinsaltz, *imprint of* The Toby Press LLC

Stemmer House Publishers Inc, *division of* Pathway Book Service

Stenhouse Publishers, *division of* Highlights for Children, *distributor for* Pembroke Publishers

STEP Publishers (Systematic Training for Effective Parenting), *distributed by* Impact Publishers Inc

Stephens Press™, *subsidiary of* Stephens Media LLC

Sterling, *imprint of* Sterling Publishing Co Inc

Sterling & Francine Clark Art Institute, *distributed by* Yale University Press

Sterling Epicure, *imprint of* Sterling Publishing Co Inc

Sterling Ethos, *imprint of* Sterling Publishing Co Inc

Sterling Innovation, *imprint of* Sterling Publishing Co Inc

Sterling Publishing, *distributed by* Heimburger House Publishing Co

Sterling Publishing Co Inc, *distributor for* Duncan Baird, Batsford (selected titles), Boxer Books, Brooklyn Botanic Garden (selected titles), Carlton Books, Cassell (selected titles), Collins & Brown (selected titles), Conway, Davis Publications (selected titles), Sally Milner (selected titles), Orion (selected titles), Phoenix Press (selected titles), Silver Oak, Sixth & Spring (selected titles), Sky Publishing, Watkins, Weidenfeld & Nicolson (selected titles), White Star Publishers

Sterling/Tamos, *imprint of* Sterling Publishing Co Inc

Sterling/Zambezi, *imprint of* Sterling Publishing Co Inc

Gareth Stevens, *distributed by* Perfection Learning Corp

Stewart, Tabori & Chang, *imprint of* Harry N Abrams Inc

Stimulus Books, *imprint of* Paulist Press

Stinging Fly Press, *distributed by* Dufour Editions Inc

Stoecklein Publishing, *distributed by* The Globe Pequot Press

Stoke Books, *distributed by* Lerner Publishing Group Inc

Stone & Scott Publishers, *distributor for* New Wind Press, Lois Rose Rose

Stone Arch Books, *imprint of* Capstone Publishers™

Stone Bridge Classics, *imprint of* Stone Bridge Press Inc

Stone Bridge Fiction, *imprint of* Stone Bridge Press Inc

Stone Bridge Press, *distributed by* Cheng & Tsui Co Inc

Stone Bridge Press Inc, *distributor for* IBC Publishing, *distributed by* Consortium Book Sales & Distribution Inc (US & CN), Sonja Merz International (China, Japan, Korea & Southeast Asia), Publishers Group UK (Europe & UK)

Stonefield Publishing, *distributed by* Chelsea Green Publishing Co

Stonewall, *subsidiary of* BrickHouse Books Inc, *imprint of* BrickHouse Books Inc

Storey Publishing, *division of* Workman Publishing Co Inc, *imprint of* Algonquin Books of Chapel Hill

Storey Publishing LLC, *distributed by* Workman Publishing Co Inc

The Story Plant, *division of* Studio Digital CT LLC

Strange Chemistry, *imprint of* Osprey Publishing Inc

Strebor Books, *imprint of* Atria Books

Stretch Think®, *imprint of* Thomas Geale Publications Inc

String Letter Press, *distributed by* Hal Leonard Corp

Strong Books, *imprint of* Book Marketing Works LLC

Stubs Guides, *distributed by* Hagstrom Map & Travel Center

Stubs Magazine, *distributed by* American Map Corp

Studien Verlag, *distributed by* Transaction Publishers Inc

Studio, *imprint of* Penguin Group (USA) LLC

Studio Mouse, *subsidiary of* Palm Kids™

Stylus Publishing LLC, *distributor for* Aeon Books, American Association for Higher Education, Cabi Books, Commonwealth Scientific & Industrial Research Organization (CSIRO), The Commonwealth Secretariat, Cork University Press, Global Professional Publishing, IDRC, Institute of Education, The Institution of Engineering & Technology (IET), Karnac Books, KIT Publishers, Nordic Africa Institute, Oxfam Publishing, Practical Action, Thorogood Publishing, Trentham Books Ltd, Women, Law & Development International (WLDI), World Health Organization (WHO)

Success Advertising, *division of* Success Advertising & Publishing

Success Advertising & Publishing, *division of* The Success Group

Suffolk Records Society, *imprint of* Boydell & Brewer Inc

Sugar Cane Press, *distributed by* Heimburger House Publishing Co

Sumach Press, *distributed by* Orca Book Publishers

Summit Beacon, *distributor for* Woodland Publishing Inc

Summit Books, *imprint of* Perfection Learning Corp

Summy-Birchard Inc, *subsidiary of* Warner/Chappell Music, *distributor for* Carisch SPA, IMP, *distributed by* Alfred Publications

Sun & Moon Classics, *imprint of* Green Integer

Sun Books, *division of* Sun Books - Sun Publishing Co, *imprint of* Sun Books - Sun Publishing Co, *distributed by* Sun Books - Sun Publishing Co

Sun Books - Sun Publishing Co, *division of* The Sun Companies, *distributor for* Far West Publishing Co, Sun Books

Sun Plans Inc, *distributed by* Chelsea Green Publishing Co

Sunbelt Publications Inc, *distributor for* Abbott Publishing, Alti Corp, Amaroma Ediciones (architectural & design publisher in Mexico), Amigos de Bolsa Chica, Anza-Borrego Foundation, W H Berger, Best Guides LLC, Bobolink Media, Joan Brady, California Sea Grant, Paul Douglas Campbell, Daddy's Heroes Inc, Dawsons Book Shop, Leland Fetzer, FineEdge.com, Flying Diamond, Fun Places Publishing, Jeffrey Garcia, Maureen Gilmer, Glove Pequot, Green Grass Press, Healey Publishing, hiking-camping.com, Huckleberry House LLC, Intellect Publishing, Island Paradise Publishing, Jaguar Tales, Scott G Kyle, Lawtech Publishing, Little Oak Press, Loretta T Marra, Mission San Juan Capistrano Women's Guild, Newtona LLC, Northcross Books, Nelson Papucci, Bette L Pegas, Linda Pequegnat, Picaro Publishing, Planeta Peninsula (Publisher from Mexico), Phil R Pryde, Quick Reference Publishing, R & B Food & Culture Production, Random House, Renegade Enterprises, Rincon Publishing Co, San Diego Architecture Foundation, San Diego Association of Geologists, San Diego City Works Press, San Diego Natural History Museum, San Diego Police Historical Association, San Dieguit River Park Joint Powers Authority, Save Our Heritage Organization, The Sektor Co, Spark Avenue, Surf Angel Publications, Trail Wisdom, Herbert B Turner, University of California Press, Armand Vallee, En Ville, Wigton Publishing, Wilderness Press, Wolf Water Press

Sunburst Paperbacks, *imprint of* Farrar, Straus & Giroux Books for Young Readers

Sundance/Newbridge Publishing, *division of* Rowman & Littlefield Publishing Group, *subsidiary of* Haights Cross Communications Inc

Sundial Books, *imprint of* Sunstone Press

Sunfood Living, *distributed by* North Atlantic Books

Sunrise Library, *imprint of* Theosophical University Press

Sunrise River Press, *affiliate of* Cartech Books/Specialty Press

Sunset Books, *imprint of* Oxmoor House Inc

SUNY Press, *distributor for* Codhill Press

SUP Publishing Logistics, *distributed by* Cheng & Tsui Co Inc

Super Sandcastle, *imprint of* ABDO Publishing Group

Superbrands Ltd, *distributed by* Antique Collectors Club Ltd

Sure Fire Press, *imprint of* Holmes Publishing Group LLC

Surf Angel Publications, *distributed by* Sunbelt Publications Inc

Surrey Books, *imprint of* Agate Publishing, *distributed by* Publishers Group West

Susquehanna University Press, *affiliate of* Associated University Presses, *distributed by* Associated University Presses

Sustainability Press, *distributed by* Chelsea Green Publishing Co

Suzuki Method International, *division of* Summy-Birchard Inc

Swagman Publishing, *imprint of* Adler Publishing Inc

Swallow Press, *imprint of* Ohio University Press

Swallow's Tale Press, *imprint of* Livingston Press, *distributed by* Livingston Press

Swan Books, *division of* Learning Links Inc

Swan Hill, *distributed by* Stackpole Books

Swan Isle Press, *distributed by* University of Chicago Press

Swedish Corrosion Institute, *distributed by* NACE International

Sweet & Maxwell, *distributed by* William S Hein & Co Inc

Swerve Editions, *imprint of* Zone Books dba Urzone Inc

Switchgrass Books, *imprint of* Northern Illinois University Press

Sword & Sorcery, *imprint of* White Wolf Publishing Inc

The Sword of Norilana, *imprint of* Norilana Books

SYBEX Inc, *division of* John Wiley & Sons Inc, John Wiley & Sons Inc, *distributed by* EMC Publishing

Sycamore Island Books, *imprint of* Paladin Press

Sylvan Dell Publishing, *distributed by* Mariposa Press (France), MV Mojica & Associates Co (Philippines), Saunders Book Co (Canada)

Symposium Publishing, *imprint of* Blue Dolphin Publishing Inc

Synergy, *imprint of* Bridge-Logos Inc

Syracuse University Press, *distributor for* Williams & Company Book Publishers, *distributed by* Alen House, Dedelas Press, Gryphon House Inc, Heimburger House Publishing Co

Tab Books, *distributor for* National Association of Broadcasters (NAB)

Tabard Press, *imprint of* Konecky & Konecky LLC

Tabernacle Publishing, *division of* Hope Publishing Co

Table Top Series, *imprint of* Incentive Publications Inc

The TAFT Group®, *imprint of* Gale

Yosifumi Taguchi, *distributed by* EastBridge

Tai Chi Foundation, *distributed by* Tuttle Publishing

Tale Blazers, *imprint of* Perfection Learning Corp

Taleka, *imprint of* Norilana Books

Nan A Talese, *imprint of* Random House Inc

Tamar Books, *imprint of* Mesorah Publications Ltd

Tamesis, *imprint of* Boydell & Brewer Inc

TAN Books, *imprint of* Saint Benedict Press LLC

T&T Clark International, *imprint of* Bloomsbury Publishing PLC

Tanner Trust Fund, *distributed by* Signature Books Publishing LLC

Tantor Audio, *imprint of* Tantor Media Inc

Tantor Media, *imprint of* Tantor Media Inc

The Tao of Books, *distributor for* Ash Tree Publishing

The S Mark Taper Foundation, *imprint of* University of California Press

Tapestry Press Ltd, *distributed by* Maryland History Press

Tara Publications, *distributed by* Hal Leonard Corp

Jeremy P Tarcher, *imprint of* Penguin Group (USA) LLC, The Putnam Publishing Group

Tarcher/Penguin, *imprint of* The Putnam Publishing Group

Taschen GmbH, *imprint of* Taschen America

Tastes Newsletter, *subsidiary of* Gault Millau Inc/Gayot Publications

Tata Institute of Fundamental Research, *distributed by* American Mathematical Society

Tata/McGraw-Hill, *imprint of* McGraw-Hill Education

Tate Galleries, *distributed by* Oak Knoll Press

Tate Publishing, *distributed by* Harry N Abrams Inc

Tattered Flag, *distributed by* Casemate Publishers & Book Distributors LLC

The Taunton Press, *distributed by* Random House Inc

The Taunton Press Inc, *distributor for* Academia Barilla

Taunton Sterling Dover, *distributed by* Fox Chapel Publishing Co Inc

I B Tauris, *distributed by* St Martin's Press, LLC

I B Tauris & Co Ltd, *distributed by* Palgrave Macmillan

Taurus, *imprint of* Santillana USA Publishing Co Inc

Taylor & Francis, *distributor for* The Fairmont Press Inc, *distributed by* Illuminating Engineering Society of North America (IES)

Taylor & Francis Asia Pacific, *imprint of* Taylor & Francis Inc

Taylor & Francis Books, *imprint of* Taylor & Francis Inc

Teachers College Press, *affiliate of* Teachers College, Columbia University

Teacher's Discovery, *division of* American Eagle Co Inc

Teachers License Examination Series, *imprint of* National Learning Corp

Teachers of English to Speakers of Other Languages Inc (TESOL), *distributed by* Alta Book Ctr, Delta Systems Inc, New Readers Press, Saddleback Educational

Teaching Strategies, *distributor for* Gryphon House, *distributed by* Gryphon House Inc

Techne Press, *distributed by* Island Press

Technical Publishing Co, *distributor for* SSPC: The Society for Protective Coatings

Technology, *division of* Scholastic Education

Katherine Tegen Books, *imprint of* HarperCollins Children's Books

Telfair Museums, *distributed by* University of Georgia Press

Telshare Publishing, *distributed by* Gryphon House Inc

Ellen Temple Publishing, *distributed by* Eakin Press

Temple Lodge Publishing, *distributed by* SteinerBooks

Temple University Press, *division of* Temple University of the Commonwealth System of Higher Education

Templeton Press, *subsidiary of* John Templeton Foundation

Temporal Mechanical Press, *division of* Enos Mills Cabin Museum & Gallery

Ten Pound Island Books, *distributed by* Mystic Seaport Museum Inc

Ten Speed Press, *imprint of* Crown Publishing Group, *distributed by* Random House Inc

Teora, *imprint of* Teora USA LLC

Terrace Books, *imprint of* University of Wisconsin Press

Terrapin Greetings, *imprint of* Down The Shore Publishing Corp

Tess Press, *imprint of* Black Dog & Leventhal Publishers Inc

Test Your Knowledge Books, *imprint of* National Learning Corp

Testament Books, *imprint of* Random House Inc

Teton NewMedia, *distributor for* LifeLearn, *distributed by* Blackwells, LifeLearn, Logan Brothers, Rittenhouse, Yankee

Tetra Press, *division of* Pfizer Inc, *distributed by* Voyageur Press

Texas A & M University Press, *distributor for* Nevraumont Publishing Co

Texas A&M University Press, *division of* Texas A&M University, *distributor for* Stephen F Austin State University Press, McWhiney Foundation Press/State House Press, Southern Methodist University Press, Texas Christian University Press, Texas Review Press, Texas State Historical Association, University of North Texas Press

Texas Christian University Press, *distributed by* Texas A&M University Press

Texas Memorial Museum, *distributed by* Bureau of Economic Geology, University of Texas at Austin

Texas Parks & Wildlife Department, *distributed by* University of Texas Press

Texas Review Press, *distributed by* Texas A&M University Press

Texas State Historical Association, *distributed by* Oak Knoll Press, Texas A&M University Press

Texas Tech University Press, *distributor for* The Colonial Williamsburg Foundation, National Ranching Heritage Center

University of Texas Press, *division of* University of Texas, *distributor for* Bat Conservation International, Institute for Mesoamerican Studies, Menil Foundation, Rothko Chapel, Texas Parks & Wildlife Department, Texas Western Press

Texas Western Press, *affiliate of* University of Texas at El Paso, *distributed by* University of Texas Press

TFH Publications Inc, *subsidiary of* Central Garden & Pet Corp

Thames & Hudson, *distributor for* National Gallery of Art, *distributed by* W W Norton & Co Inc, W W Norton & Company Inc

That Patchwork Place, *imprint of* Martingale®

That the World May Know, *imprint of* Focus on the Family

That VanDam Book, *imprint of* VanDam Inc

Theatre Communications Group, *distributor for* Absolute Classics, Aurora Metro Publications, Nick Hern Books, Oberon Books, Padua Playwrights Press, PAJ Publications, Playwrights Canada Press, Martin E Segal Theatre Center Publications, Ubu Repertory Theatre Publications

Theology of the Body Series, *imprint of* Pauline Books & Media

Theophilis, *imprint of* Transcontinental Music Publications

Theosophical Publishing House/Quest Books, *division of* The Theosophical Society in America

Theosophical University Press, *affiliate of* Theosophical Society (Pasadena)

Thesaurus Islamicus Foundation, *distributed by* Fons Vitae

Theta Books, *imprint of* Bridge Publications Inc

Theta Foundation of Bucharest, *distributed by* American Mathematical Society

Thieme, *distributor for* Current Medicine Group (CMG)

Thieme Medical Publishers Inc, *subsidiary of* Georg Thieme Verlag KG

Thing Quest®, *imprint of* Thomas Geale Publications Inc

Think, *imprint of* NavPress Publishing Group

Thinking Like a Scientist, *imprint of* Sundance/Newbridge Publishing

Third Millenium Publishing, *distributed by* Antique Collectors Club Ltd

Third World Press, *distributed by* IPG, Northwestern University Press

30 Degrees South Publishers, *distributed by* Casemate Publishers & Book Distributors LLC

Thistle Hill Publications, *distributed by* Enfield Publishing & Distribution Co

Thomas Nelson Inc, *subsidiary of* Faith Media, *distributor for* Discovery House, Oliver-Nelson (Atlanta, GA), *distributed by* Winston-Derek

Thomas Nelson Publishers, *division of* Thomas Nelson Inc

Thomson Publishing, *distributed by* Oxford University Press USA, SkillPath Publications

Thomson Reuters, *distributor for* AICPA Professional Publications

Thomson Reuters Westlaw™, *distributor for* Law Library Microform Consortium

Thorndike Large Print, *imprint of* Thorndike Press®

Thorndike Press®, *imprint of* Gale, *distributor for* Grand Central/Hachette Large Print, HarperLuxe, Mills & Boon Large Print, Random House Large Print, *distributed by* S & B Books Ltd (Canada)

Nelson Thornes, *distributed by* Trans-Atlantic Publications Inc

Thorogood Publishing, *distributed by* Stylus Publishing LLC

Three Forks®, *imprint of* The Globe Pequot Press

Three Hands Press, *distributed by* Holmes Publishing Group LLC

Three Rivers Press, *imprint of* Crown Publishing Group, Random House Inc

Threshold Editions, *imprint of* Gallery Books

Thresholds, *imprint of* Zumaya Publications LLC

Throckmorton Press, *distributed by* powerHouse Books

Thunder Bay Press, *distributed by* Heimburger House Publishing Co

Tia Chucha Press, *distributed by* Northwestern University Press

Tidewater Publishers, *imprint of* Cornell Maritime Press Inc, Schiffer Publishing Ltd

Tigris, *imprint of* Gorgias Press LLC

Tilbury House Publishers, *imprint of* WordSplice Studio LLC

Timber Press, *division of* Workman Publishing Co Inc, *imprint of* Algonquin Books of Chapel Hill, Timber Press Inc

Timber Press Inc, *subsidiary of* Workman Publishing Co, Workman Publishing Co Inc, *distributed by* Thomas Allen & Son

Timerberline Productions, *imprint of* Crumb Elbow Publishing

Time Being Books, *imprint of* Time Being Press

Time Inc Home Entertainment, *distributed by* Hachette Book Group

Timeless Love, *imprint of* Oak Tree Press

Times Books, *imprint of* Henry Holt and Company, LLC, Random House Inc

Megan Tingley Books, *imprint of* Little, Brown Books for Young Readers

Tit-Elation.com Books, *imprint of* Ephemera Bound Publishing

Toccata Press, *imprint of* Boydell & Brewer Inc

Today's Books, *imprint of* History Publishing Co LLC

TOKYOPOP, *imprint of* HarperCollins Children's Books

Tommy Nelson, *division of* Thomas Nelson Inc, *distributor for* Focus on the Family

Tonga Books, *imprint of* Europa Editions

Delos Toole, *distributed by* Gem Guides Book Co

Tools4Healing (Scott Mieras), *distributor for* Blue Poppy Press

TOP, *imprint of* Top Publications Ltd

Top of the Mountain Publishing, *division of* Powell Productions

Topaz, *imprint of* NAL, Penguin Group (USA) LLC

Topic Series, *imprint of* Oakstone Publishing LLC

Topics in World History, *imprint of* Markus Wiener Publishers Inc

Tor, *imprint of* Tom Doherty Associates, LLC

Tor Teen, *imprint of* Tom Doherty Associates, LLC

Torah Aura Productions, *distributor for* Free Spirit (selected titles)

Torah Umesorah Publications, *division of* Torah Umesorah-National Society for Hebrew Day Schools

Tory Corner Editions, *imprint of* Quincannon Publishing Group

Total Information, *distributor for* Primary Research Group Inc

Toucan Tales, *imprint of* Rayve Productions Inc

Touchstone, *imprint of* Scribner Publishing Group, Touchstone

Tourism Dynamic, *imprint of* Cognizant Communication Corp

Tourist Town Guides, *imprint of* Channel Lake Inc

Towers Maguire Publishing, *imprint of* The Local History Co

Trade Book Publishing, *division of* Slack Incorporated

Tradery House, *imprint of* Wimmer Cookbooks

Tradewind Books, *distributed by* Orca Book Publishers

Tradigital, *distributed by* Fons Vitae

Tradition Books, *imprint of* The Child's World Inc, *distributed by* The Child's World Inc

Trafalgar Square Books, *distributor for* J A Allen, Atlantic Books, Beautiful Books, Bene Factum Publishing, Elliott & Thompson, Peter Owen Publishers, Pitch Publishing, *distributed by* IPG

Trafford, *division of* Author Solutions Inc

Trail Wisdom, *distributed by* Sunbelt Publications Inc

Trailblazer Press, *distributed by* Chelsea Green Publishing Co

Trailblazer Publications, *distributed by* The Globe Pequot Press

Trails Books, *division of* Big Earth Publishing

Trails Books Guide, *imprint of* Trails Books

Oswald Train, *distributed by* Donald M Grant Publisher Inc

Trainco, *distributor for* HRD Press

Training & Development Materials of Canada, *distributor for* HRD Press

Trakker Maps Inc, *subsidiary of* American Map Corp, *distributed by* Hagstrom Map & Travel Center

Tralco, *distributor for* Beach Lloyd Publishers LLC

Tralco-Lingo Fun, *distributor for* Languages for Kids

Trans-Atlantic Publications Inc, *distributor for* Book Guild, Book House, Financial Times Publishing, Hodder Education, Instituto Monsa de Ediciones SA (art books from Spain), Longman, Midwest Library Service, Nexus Special Interests, Pearson Education, Nelson Thornes

Trans Tech Publications, *distributor for* Enfield Publishers, *distributed by* Curran Associates Inc, Enfield Publishing & Distribution Co, Yankee Book Peddler

Transaction Large Print, *imprint of* Transaction Publishers Inc

Transaction Publishers, *distributor for* University of California Institute on Global Conflict & Cooperation

Transaction Publishers Inc, *distributor for* Bridge 21, International Communication Organization (ICO), IWGIA, The Netherlands Institute for Social Research, Ontos Verlag, Editions Scholasticae, Studien Verlag, Witwatersrand University Press

Transactions, *imprint of* American Philosophical Society

Transcontinental Music, *distributed by* Hal Leonard Corp

Transcontinental Music Publications, *division of* Union for Reform Judaism

Transforming Press, *distributed by* Crown House Publishing Co LLC

Transit Cooperative Research Program, *imprint of* Transportation Research Board

The Transportation Book Service, *division of* Iconografix Inc

Transportation Research Board, *division of* National Academies, The National Academies

Transportation Research Board Code, *distributed by* Professional Publications Inc (PPI)

TransQuest Publishers Pte Ltd, *distributor for* Manning Publications Co

Travel Memories Press, *imprint of* R J Berg Publisher

Travelers' Tales, *subsidiary of* Solas House Inc

Traveling Pen Press, *imprint of* Flying Pen Press LLC

Treacle Press, *imprint of* McPherson & Co

Treasure Chest Books, *distributor for* Ocean Tree Books

Tree Frog Publications, *imprint of* Rada Press Inc

Tree of Life Books, *imprint of* Progressive Press

Treeline Press, *distributed by* Enfield Publishing & Distribution Co

Trees Co, *distributed by* Gem Guides Book Co

Trentham Books Ltd, *distributed by* Stylus Publishing LLC

Tri-Star Boze Books, *distributed by* Gem Guides Book Co

Triad Publishing Co, *imprint of* Triad Communications Ltd

Trident Reference, *imprint of* Standard International Media Holdings

The Trilateral Commission, *distributed by* The Brookings Institution Press

Trillium Mountain Productions, *imprint of* Crumb Elbow Publishing

Trillium Press, *distributed by* Royal Fireworks Press

Trinity University Press, *unit of* Trinity University, *distributed by* Bilingual Review Press/Editorial Bilingue

TriQuarterly Books, *imprint of* Northwestern University Press

TRISTAN OUTDOORS, *imprint of* TRISTAN Publishing

Triumph Books, *imprint of* Random House Publishing Group, *distributor for* United States Tennis Association

Triumph Entertainment, *imprint of* Triumph Books

Triumph Learning, *division of* Haights Cross Communications Inc, *subsidiary of* Haights Cross Communications Inc

Troitsa Books, *imprint of* Nova Science Publishers Inc

Troubador Press, *imprint of* Price Stern Sloan

Troubadour Books, *imprint of* Regal Crest Enterprises LLC

Truckload Carrier Assoc, *distributed by* Delmar

Truman State University Press, *unit of* Truman State University

Trust for Public Land, *distributed by* Chelsea Green Publishing Co

Tu Books, *imprint of* Lee & Low Books Inc

Tuckamore Books, *distributed by* Orca Book Publishers

Tudor House, *distributed by* Orca Book Publishers

Tufts University Press, *imprint of* University Press of New England

Tughra Books, *distributor for* Kaynak, Nile Publishing, Zambak

Tumbleweed Series, *imprint of* Mountain Press Publishing Co

Turnaround, *distributor for* Blood Moon Productions Ltd

Turnaround (London), *distributor for* Bella Books

Turner, *imprint of* Turner Publishing Co

Herbert B Turner, *distributed by* Sunbelt Publications Inc

Turtle Point, *imprint of* Turtle Point Press

Tusk Ivory, *imprint of* The Overlook Press

Tusk Paperbacks, *imprint of* The Overlook Press

Tuttle Publishing, *member of* Periplus Publishing Group, *distributor for* Healing Tao Books, Kosei Publishing Co, Kotan Publishing Inc, Milet Publishing Ltd, Paperweight Press, Periplus Editions, Shanghai Press, Shufunotomo Co, Tai Chi Foundation, *distributed by* Cheng & Tsui Co Inc, Publishers Group West (digital only), Simon & Schuster, Inc

TV Books, *distributed by* HarperCollins Publishers

Mark Twain Media, *distributed by* Carson-Dellosa Publishing LLC

Twayne Publishers™, *imprint of* Gale

Twelve, *imprint of* Grand Central Publishing

Twenty-First Century Books, *division of* Lerner Publishing Group Inc, *imprint of* Lerner Publishing Group Inc

21st Century Publications, *distributed by* Hal Leonard Corp

Twenty-Third Publications, *division of* Bayard Inc, *distributor for* Novalis (Canada), *distributed by* Columba (UK), John Garrett (Australia), Novalis (Canada)

Twilight Times Books, *distributed by* Brodart Co, BWI Books

Twilight Visions, *imprint of* Twilight Times Books

Two Wolf Press, *imprint of* White Wolf Publishing Inc

TwoDot®, *imprint of* The Globe Pequot Press

Tyee Press, *imprint of* Crumb Elbow Publishing

Tyndale Audio, *imprint of* Tyndale House Publishers Inc

Tyndale Entertainment, *imprint of* Tyndale House Publishers Inc

Tyndale House Publishers, *distributor for* Focus on the Family

Tyndale House Publishers Inc, *distributor for* Focus on the Family

Tyndale Kids, *imprint of* Tyndale House Publishers Inc

Tyndale Momentum, *imprint of* Tyndale House Publishers Inc

Tyndale Ninos, *imprint of* Tyndale House Publishers Inc

Type & Archetype Press, *imprint of* Type & Temperament Inc

Typophiles, *distributed by* Oak Knoll Press

Tyrus Books, *imprint of* F+W Media Inc

U X L™, *imprint of* Gale

UA Museum, *distributed by* University of Alaska Press

UBC Press, Canada, *distributor for* Michigan State University Press (MSU Press)

UBM Global Trade, *subsidiary of* United Business Media Ltd

Ubu Repertory Theatre Publications, *distributed by* Theatre Communications Group

UCL Institute of Archaeology, *distributed by* Left Coast Press Inc

UCLA Fowler Museum of Cultural History, *distributed by* University of Washington Press

UCLA/Hammer Museum, *distributed by* Wittenborn Art Books

Udig, *imprint of* Andrews McMeel Publishing LLC

Ugly Duckling Presse, *distributor for* United Artists

ULI, *imprint of* Urban Land Institute

The Ultra Violet Library, *imprint of* Circlet Press Inc

Ulysses Press, *distributed by* Publishers Group West

Unarius Academy of Science Publications, *division of* Unarius Educational Foundation

Unarius Video Productions, *division of* Unarius Academy of Science Publications

UNCITRAL, *distributed by* United Nations Publications

Uncrowned Queens, *distributed by* Excelsior Editions, State University of New York Press

Undergraduate Program Field Test Series, *imprint of* National Learning Corp

UNDP, *distributed by* United Nations Publications

UNFOLDS®, *imprint of* VanDam Inc

UNFPA, *distributed by* United Nations Publications

UNICEF, *distributed by* United Nations Publications

UNICRI, *distributed by* United Nations Publications

UNIDIR, *distributed by* United Nations Publications

UNIDO, *distributed by* United Nations Publications

Unifacmanu Trading Co Ltd, *distributor for* Health Professions Press

Union Square Press, *imprint of* Sterling Publishing Co Inc

Unique Books, *distributor for* Do-It-Yourself Legal Publishers

UNITAR, *distributed by* United Nations Publications

United Artists, *distributed by* Ugly Duckling Presse

The United Educators Inc, *subsidiary of* Standard Educational Corp

United Nations Publications, *distributor for* ICJ, INSTRAW, IOM, UNCITRAL, UNDP, UNFPA, UNICEF, UNICRI, UNIDIR, UNIDO, UNITAR, UNU

United Publishers Services Ltd, *distributor for* Peterson Institute for International Economics

United States Catholic Conference Publications, *distributed by* Liturgy Training Publications

United States Pharmacopeia, *distributed by* Consumer Reports, Login Brothers Book Co, Login Publishing Consortium

United States Tennis Association, *distributed by* Triumph Books, Universe Publishing, H O Zimman Inc

United Synagogue Book Service, *division of* United Synagogue of Conservative Judaism, *distributor for* Rabbinical Assembly of America

United Synagogue Commission on Jewish Education, *imprint of* United Synagogue Book Service

United Synagogue of Conservative Judaism, *imprint of* United Synagogue Book Service

Unity Books, *division of* Unity School of Christianity, *distributed by* De Vorss & Co

Univelt Inc, *affiliate of* American Astronautical Society, *distributor for* Astronautical Society of Western Australia, US Space Foundation

Universal Reference, *imprint of* Grey House Publishing Inc™

Universe, *imprint of* Rizzoli International Publications Inc, Universe Publishing, *distributor for* Country Music Foundation Press

Universe Calendars, *imprint of* Universe Publishing

Universe Publishing, *division of* Rizzoli International Publications Inc, *distributor for* United States Tennis Association, *distributed by* Random House

Universe Publishing Calendars, *distributed by* Andrews McMeel Publishing LLC

University College Dublin Press, *distributed by* Dufour Editions Inc

The University of Akron Press, *distributor for* Principia Press

University of Alabama Press, *distributor for* Fiction Collective Two Inc (FC2)

University of Alaska Press, *distributor for* Alaska Native Language Center, Alaska Quarterly Review, Alaska Sea Grant, Alutiiq Museum, Anchorage Museum Association, Anchorage Museum of Art History, Arctic Studies Center of the Smithsonian Museum, Far to the North Press, Geophysical Institute, Limestone Press, Spirit Mountain Press, UA Museum, Vanessapress

University of Alberta Press, *distributed by* Michigan State University Press (MSU Press)

The University of Arizona Press, *distributor for* Ironwood Press, OSU Press

The University of Arkansas Press, *division of* The University of Arkansas, *distributor for* Butler Center for Arkansas Studies, Hearne Fine Art, Moon City Press, Ozark Society, Phoenix International

University of Calgary Press, *distributed by* Michigan State University Press (MSU Press)

University of California Institute on Global Conflict & Cooperation, *subsidiary of* University of California, *distributed by* Brookings Institution Press, Columbia International Affairs Online (CIAO), Cornell University Press, Garland Publishers, Lynn-Reinner Publishing, Penn State University Press, Princeton University Press, Transaction Publishers, University of Michigan Press, Westview Press

University of California Press, *distributor for* artSITES, British Film Institute, Huntington Library, Huntington Library Press, Nevraumont Publishing Co, Sierra Club Books (adult trade), The Woodrow Wilson Center Press, *distributed by* Sunbelt Publications Inc

University of Chicago Press, *distributor for* Canadian Museum of Nature, Conservation International, CSLI Publications, Getty Publications, National Bureau of Economic Research, National Gallery of Canada, National Society for the Study of Education, Oriental Institute, St Augustine's Press Inc, Swan Isle Press

University of Chicago Press Distribution Center, *distributor for* University of Pittsburgh Press

University of Delaware Press, *distributed by* Rowman & Littlefield

University of Georgia Press, *distributor for* Golden Coast Publishing Co, Telfair Museums

University of Hawaii Press, *distributor for* Ateneo De Manila University Press, Global Oriental, Huia Publishers, Nordic Insititute of Asian Studies, The Numata Center, Pandanus Books, Pasifika Press, Singapore University Press, University of the Phillippines Press

University of Idaho Historical Manuscript Series, *distributed by* Caxton Press

University of Idaho Press, *distributed by* Caxton Press

University of Illinois Press, *unit of* University of Illinois

University of Manitoba Press, *distributed by* Michigan State University Press (MSU Press)

University of Massachusetts Press, *distributed by* The Johns Hopkins University Press

University of Michigan, *distributed by* International Book Centre Inc

University of Michigan Center for Japanese Studies, *unit of* University of Michigan

University of Michigan Press, *unit of* University of Michigan, *distributor for* Center for Chinese Studies, University of Michigan, Center for South & Southeast Asian Studies, University of Michigan, University of California Institute on Global Conflict & Cooperation, *distributed by* Eurospan (territory restricted to Europe, Africa & UK)

University of Minnesota Press, *distributed by* Heimburger House Publishing Co

University of Missouri Press, *distributor for* Missouri History Museum, St Louis Mercantile Library

University of Nebraska Press, *division of* University of Nebraska at Lincoln, *distributor for* Buros Institute, Caxton Press, Creighton University Press, Society for American Baseball Research

University of New Hampshire Press, *imprint of* University Press of New England

University of New Mexico, *distributor for* Avanyu Publishing, Fresco Fine Art Publications LLC, La Frontera Publishing, West End Press

University of New Mexico Press, *distributor for* Museum of New Mexico Press

The University of North Carolina Press, *distributor for* Museum of Early Southern Decorative Arts, North Carolina Museum of Art, Omohundro Institute of Early American History & Culture, Southeastern Center for Contemporary Art, Valentine Museum

University of North Texas Press, *distributed by* Texas A&M University Press

University of Oklahoma Press, *distributor for* Cherokee National Press, Chickasaw Press, Dakota Institute, Denver Art Museum, Gilcrease Museum, Vanderbilt University Press

University of Pennsylvania Libraries, *distributed by* Diane Publishing Co

University of Pennsylvania Museum, *distributed by* The Johns Hopkins University Press

University of Pennsylvania Museum of Archaeology & Anthropology, *division of* University of Pennsylvania

University of Pennsylvania Press, *distributed by* The Johns Hopkins University Press

University of Pittsburgh Press, *distributed by* University of Chicago Press Distribution Center

University of Puerto Rico Press, *subsidiary of* University of Puerto Rico

University of Rochester Press, *imprint of* Boydell & Brewer Inc, *affiliate of* Boydell & Brewer Inc

University of San Francisco Press, *distributed by* Fordham University Press

University of Scranton, *distributed by* Heimburger House Publishing Co

University of Scranton Press, *division of* University of Scranton

University of South Carolina Press, *affiliate of* University of South Carolina, *distributor for* McKissick Museum, Saraland Press, South Carolina Bar Association, South Carolina Historical Society

University of Texas Press, *division of* University of Texas, *distributor for* Bat Conservation International, Institute for Mesoamerican Studies, Menil Foundation, Rothko Chapel, Texas Parks & Wildlife Department, Texas Western Press

University of the Phillippines Press, *distributed by* University of Hawaii Press

University of Tokyo Press, *distributed by* Columbia University Press

University of Toronto Press, *distributor for* Central European University Press, Mage Publishers Inc

The University of Utah Press, *subsidiary of* University of Utah, *distributor for* BYU Museum of Peoples & Cultures, BYU Studies, Canyonlands Natural History Association, KUED (Utah PBS affiliate), Western Epics Publications

University of Vermont Press, *imprint of* University Press of New England

The University of Virginia Press, *affiliate of* University of Virginia, *distributor for* Colonial Society of Massachusetts, The Colonial Williamsburg Foundation, Mount Vernon Ladies Association

University of Virginia Press, *distributor for* The Massachusetts Historical Society

University of Washington Press, *imprint of* Combined Academic Publishers, *distributor for* American Federation of Arts, Lost Horse Press, Lynx House Press, UCLA Fowler Museum of Cultural History, *distributed by* The Johns Hopkins University Press

University of Wisconsin Press, *distributor for* The Center for the Study of Upper Midwestern Culture, Dryad Press, Elvehjem Museum of Art, International Brecht Society, Max Kade Institute for German-American Studies, Spring Freshet Press, Wisconsin Academy of Sciences, Arts & Letters, Wisconsin Historical Society Press, Wisconsin Veterans Museum

University Press, *distributed by* American Mathematical Society

University Press of America Inc, *member of* Rowman & Littlefield Publishing Group, Rowman & Littlefield Publishing Group, *distributor for* Atlantic Council, Center for National Policy Press, Harvard Center for International Affairs, International Law Institute, Joint Center for Political & Economic Studies Press, Society of the Cincinnati, White Burkett Miller Center

University Press of Colorado, *imprint of* Utah State University Press, *distributor for* Center for Literary Publishing, Colorado Historical Society

University Press of Florida, *affiliate of* State University System of Florida

The University Press of Kentucky, *distributor for* Kentucky Historical Society, *distributed by* The Johns Hopkins University Press

University Press of Maryland, *imprint of* CDL Press

University Press of New England, *distributor for* Beinecke Rare Book & Manuscript Library, Bibliopola Press, CavanKerry Press, Chipstone Foundation, The Colonial Williamsburg Foundation, Fence Books, Four Way Books, Isabella Stewart Gardner Museum, Harvest Hill Press, National Poetry Foundation, New England College, Nicolin Fields Publishing, Peter E Randall Publisher, The Sheep Meadow Press, Vermont Folklife Center, Wesleyan University Press, Winterthur Museum & Country Estate, Winterthur Museum Garden & Library

University Press of New England (UPNE), *distributor for* Oberlin College Press

University Science Books, *division of* University Books Inc, University Science Books

UNO Press, *division of* University of New Orleans, *distributed by* Biblio

UNU, *distributed by* United Nations Publications

Upper Access Books, *imprint of* Upper Access Inc

Upper Ohio Valley Books, *distributed by* John F Blair Publisher

Upper Room Books, *division of* The Upper Room, *imprint of* Abingdon Press, *distributed by* Abingdon Press

Upstart Books™, *imprint of* Highsmith Inc, Upstart Books

UpWrite Books, *imprint of* WinePress Publishing

Urban Books, *distributed by* Kensington Publishing Corp

Urban Institute Press, *distributed by* The Johns Hopkins University Press

Urim Publications, *division of* Lambda Publishers Inc

URJ Books & Music, *division of* Union for Reform Judaism

US Coast Pilot, *imprint of* ProStar Publications Inc

US Games Systems Inc, *distributor for* A G Muller & Cie

US Government Printing Office, *division of* US Government

US Green Building Council, *distributed by* Professional Publications Inc (PPI)

US International Publishing, *distributed by* Cheng & Tsui Co Inc

US Space Foundation, *distributed by* Univelt Inc

Usborne Books, *imprint of* EDC Publishing

Usborne Publishing, *distributed by* EDC Publishing

User's Guides, *imprint of* Basic Health Publications Inc

Utah Geological Survey, *division of* Utah Dept of Natural Resources, Utah Dept of Natural Resources

Utah State University Press, *division of* Utah State University

Vademecum, *imprint of* Landes Bioscience

Vagabond Voices, *distributed by* Dufour Editions Inc

Valaam Society of America, *imprint of* St Herman Press

Valentine Museum, *distributed by* The University of North Carolina Press

Armand Vallee, *distributed by* Sunbelt Publications Inc

Valuation Press, *imprint of* Marshall & Swift

Valusource, *imprint of* John Wiley & Sons Inc

Cardinal Van Thuan Series, *imprint of* Pauline Books & Media

V&A Publishing, *distributed by* Harry N Abrams Inc

Vandalia Press, *imprint of* West Virginia University Press

VanDam Advertising, *division of* VanDam Inc

VanDam Licensing, *division of* VanDam Inc

VanDam Publishing, *division of* VanDam Inc

Vandamere Press, *distributor for* ABI Professional Publications (non-exclusive), JMC Press (exclusive to trade), NRH Press (non-exclusive), Quodlibetal Features

Vanderbilt Library of American Philosophy, *imprint of* Vanderbilt University Press

Vanderbilt University Press, *division of* Vanderbilt University, *distributor for* Country Music Foundation Press, *distributed by* University of Oklahoma Press

Vanessapress, *distributed by* University of Alaska Press

Vanwell-Looking Back Press, *distributed by* Casemate Publishers & Book Distributors LLC

Vanwell Publishing, *distributed by* Casemate Publishers & Book Distributors LLC

Varlik, *subsidiary of* Cross-Cultural Communications

Yad Vashem, *distributed by* Berghahn Books

Vedanta Press, *subsidiary of* Vedanta Society of Southern California, *distributor for* Advaita Ashrama, Ananda Ashrama, Ramakrishna Math

Vegas Lit, *imprint of* Huntington Press Publishing

Velazquez Press, *division of* Academic Learning Co LLC

The Vendome Press, *distributed by* Harry N Abrams Inc

Venture Press, *imprint of* Williams & Company Book Publishers

Verba Mundi, *imprint of* David R Godine Publisher Inc

Veritas, *distributed by* ACTA Publications, Dufour Editions Inc, Ignatius Press

Verlag Valentin Koerner, *distributed by* Enfield Publishing & Distribution Co

Vermont Folklife Center, *distributed by* University Press of New England

Verso, *distributed by* W W Norton (USA), Penguin (Canada)

Vertigo, *imprint of* DC Entertainment

VH-1, *imprint of* Gallery Books

VH1 Press, *distributed by* powerHouse Books

Vibe Books, *distributed by* Kensington Publishing Corp

Vice Books, *distributed by* powerHouse Books

Victorian Heritage Press, *imprint of* Loving Healing Press Inc

Victory History of the Counties of England, *imprint of* Boydell & Brewer Inc

Victory in Grace Printing, *division of* Victory in Grace Ministries

Editorial Vida, *division of* Zondervan, A HarperCollins Company

Video Active Productions, *distributed by* Delmar

Vieweg Verlag Publications, *distributed by* American Mathematical Society

Viking, *imprint of* Penguin Group (USA) LLC

Viking Children's Books, *imprint of* Penguin Group (USA) LLC, Penguin Young Readers Group

Viking Compass, *imprint of* Penguin Group (USA) LLC, Viking

Viking Studio, *imprint of* Penguin Group (USA) LLC

Villard, *imprint of* Random House Publishing Group

Villard Books, *imprint of* Random House Inc

En Ville, *distributed by* Sunbelt Publications Inc

Vintage & Anchor Books, *imprint of* Knopf Doubleday Publishing Group

Vintage Books, *imprint of* Random House Inc

Vintage Guitar, *imprint of* Hal Leonard Corp, *distributed by* Hal Leonard Corp

Vintage Image, *imprint of* The Wine Appreciation Guild Ltd

Vireo Press, *distributed by* ECS Publishing Corp

Virginia Genealogical Society, *distributed by* Heritage Books Inc

Vision, *imprint of* Grand Central Publishing

VisionWorks, *distributor for* Ash Tree Publishing

Visit Britain, *distributed by* The Globe Pequot Press

Visual™, *imprint of* John Wiley & Sons Inc

Visual Profile Books Inc, *distributed by* Innovative Logistics (US & CN)

Vital Communities, *distributed by* Enfield Publishing & Distribution Co

Viva Books PVT, *distributor for* Peterson Institute for International Economics

Viva Editions, *imprint of* Cleis Press

VIZ Media, *distributed by* Simon & Schuster, Inc, Simon & Schuster Sales & Marketing

Voggenreiter Publishers, *distributed by* Mel Bay Publications Inc

Voices of Asia, *imprint of* EastBridge

Volo, *imprint of* Disney-Hyperion Books

Vows, *imprint of* Health Communications Inc

Voyage, *imprint of* Brigantine Media

Voyageur Press, *imprint of* MBI Publishing Co, Quayside Publishing Group, *distributor for* Tetra Press

W W Norton, *distributor for* Allworth Press, Verso, *distributed by* Peoples Education Inc

W W Norton & Co, *distributor for* Dalkey Archive Press, Peace Hill Press, Persea Books, *distributed by* Heimburger House Publishing Co

Wadsworth, *subsidiary of* Cengage Learning, *imprint of* Wadsworth Publishing

Wadsworth Athenaeum, *distributed by* Antique Collectors Club Ltd

Wadsworth Inc, *distributor for* National Association of Broadcasters (NAB)

Wadsworth Publishing, *division of* Cengage Learning, Cengage Learning™, *distributed by* Cengage Learning™

WAG Books, *distributed by* Casemate Publishers & Book Distributors LLC

Wageningen Academic Publishers, *distributed by* Enfield Publishing & Distribution Co

Walden Pond Press, *imprint of* HarperCollins Children's Books

Waldman House Press, *imprint of* TRISTAN Publishing

Walkabout Press, *distributed by* John F Blair Publisher

Walker & Co, *division of* Bloomsbury USA

Walker & Company, *imprint of* Bloomsbury Publishing

Walker and Company, *distributed by* St Martin's Press, LLC

Walker Books for Young Readers, *imprint of* Bloomsbury Publishing

Wall & Thompson, *distributed by* ADASI Publishing Co

Wallace Collection, *distributed by* Antique Collectors Club Ltd

Wallflower Press, *imprint of* Columbia University Press

Walton's, *distributed by* Mel Bay Publications Inc

Warboys LLC, *distributed by* Bridge-Logos Inc

Wargaming, *imprint of* Osprey Publishing Inc

Warlord Games, *distributed by* Casemate Publishers & Book Distributors LLC

Warman's, *imprint of* F+W Media Inc, Krause Publications Inc

Frederick Warne, *subsidiary of* Penguin Group (USA) LLC, *imprint of* Penguin Group (USA) LLC, Penguin Young Readers Group, *distributed by* Perfection Learning Corp

Warrior, *imprint of* Osprey Publishing Inc

Washington Book Distributors, *distributor for* Marine Techniques Publishing

Washington Events Guide, *imprint of* Goodluck Guides

Washington Post Crosswords, *imprint of* Random House Reference/Random House Puzzles & Games/House of Collectibles

Washington Service Bureau, *subsidiary of* CCH, a Wolters Kluwer business

Washington Square Press, *imprint of* Atria Books

Washington State Historical Society, *distributed by* Washington State University Press

Washington State University Press, *division of* Washington State University, *distributor for* The Hutton Settlement (single title), Oregon Writers Colony (single title), Pacific Institute (single title), Washington State Historical Society (single title), WSU Museum of Art

Water Resources Publications LLC, *distributor for* ASAE, ASCE

Water Row Books, *distributor for* Water Row Press, *distributed by* Water Row Press

Water Row Press, *subsidiary of* Water Row Books, *distributor for* Water Row Books, Weinberg Books, *distributed by* Water Row Books

Waterbrook Multnomah, *imprint of* Crown Publishing Group

WaterBrook Multnomah Publishing Group, *imprint of* Random House Inc

Waterford Press, *distributed by* The Globe Pequot Press

Waterfront Press (selected titles from all), *distributed by* Bilingual Review Press/Editorial Bilingue

Waterfront Soundings Productions, *distributed by* Marine Techniques Publishing

Watermark Press, *distributed by* Antique Collectors Club Ltd

Watersport Books, *imprint of* Aqua Quest Publications Inc

Watkins, *distributed by* Sterling Publishing Co Inc

Watson-Guptill, *imprint of* Crown Publishing Group

Watson-Guptill Publications, *imprint of* Crown Publishing Group, *distributor for* C & T Publishing Inc

Neale Watson Academic Publications, *imprint of* Watson Publishing International LLC

Waverley Books (UK), *distributed by* Interlink Publishing Group Inc

Wayne State University Press, *distributor for* Cranbrook Institute of Science, Detroit Institute of Arts, Hebrew Union College Press, Marick Press

The Waywiser Press, *distributed by* Dufour Editions Inc

WBusiness Books, *imprint of* New Win Publishing

We Do Listen, *distributed by* Lerner Publishing Group Inc

Weapon, *imprint of* Osprey Publishing Inc

Websters International Publishers, *distributed by* Antique Collectors Club Ltd

Wee Sing, *imprint of* Penguin Group (USA) LLC, Price Stern Sloan

Weidenfeld & Nicolson, *distributed by* Sterling Publishing Co Inc

Weight Watchers, *imprint of* St Martin's Press, LLC

Weinberg Books, *distributed by* Water Row Press

Weinstein Books, *imprint of* The Perseus Books Group

Welcome Books, *distributor for* Insight Editions

Welcome Books®, *imprint of* Welcome Enterprises, *distributor for* AAP, Cerf & Peterson, Music Sales, Zeke Holdings Ltd, *distributed by* Random House

Welcome Rain Publishers LLC, *distributed by* National Book Network

Weldon Owen, *distributed by* Simon & Schuster, Inc, Simon & Schuster Sales & Marketing

Wellfleet Press, *imprint of* Book Sales Inc

Wellington Press, *division of* BooksUPrint.com Inc

Welz, *distributed by* Alan Wofsy Fine Arts

Wendy Lamb Books, *imprint of* Random House Children's Books, Random House Inc

Wescott Cove Publishing Co, *imprint of* Far Horizons Media Co

Weseanne Publications, *distributed by* Gem Guides Book Co

Wesleyan Poetry, *imprint of* Wesleyan University Press

Wesleyan Publishing House, *division of* Wesleyan Church Corp, Wesleyan Church Corporation

Wesleyan University Press, *distributed by* University Press of New England

West, *imprint of* Delmar

West End Press, *distributed by* University of New Mexico

Westcliffe Publishers Inc, *imprint of* Big Earth Publishing

Westcliffe Publishing, *distributed by* Heimburger House Publishing Co

Western Edge Press, *imprint of* Sherman Asher Publishing, *distributed by* Mountain Press Publishing Co

Western Epics Publications, *distributed by* The University of Utah Press

Western Horseman, *distributed by* The Globe Pequot Press

Western Pennsylvania Genealogical Society, *distributed by* Mechling Associates

Western Psychological Service, *distributor for* Psychological Assessment Resources Inc (PAR)

Westminster John Knox Press, *division of* Presbyterian Publishing Corp, *imprint of* Presbyterian Publishing Corp, *distributor for* SCM

Westview Press, *member of* The Perseus Books Group, *imprint of* The Perseus Books Group, *distributor for* Nevraumont Publishing Co, University of California Institute on Global Conflict & Cooperation

WestWinds Press®, *imprint of* Graphic Arts Books

WH&O International, *division of* Meristem Systems Corp, Meristem Systems Corp

Wharncliffe, *distributed by* Casemate Publishers & Book Distributors LLC

What Do You Know About Books, *imprint of* National Learning Corp

SR Wheat, *distributed by* Mel Bay Publications Inc

Wheatherstone Press, *subsidiary of* Dickinson Consulting Group

Wheeler Publishing, *imprint of* Thorndike Press®

Wheeler Publishing™, *imprint of* Gale

Whitaker, *distributor for* Faith Library Publications

White Burkett Miller Center, *distributed by* University Press of America Inc

White Eagle Publishing Trust (England), *distributed by* De Vorss & Co

White Pine Press, *distributor for* Springhouse Editions

White Poppy Press, *imprint of* Modern Memoirs

White Rabbit Press, *distributed by* Cheng & Tsui Co Inc

White Star Publishers, *distributed by* Sterling Publishing Co Inc

White Thread Press, *distributed by* Fons Vitae

White Wolf Publishing Inc, *division of* CCP North America

Whitford Press, *imprint of* Schiffer Publishing Ltd

Whitney Museum of American Art, *distributed by* Yale University Press

Whittet, *distributed by* Diamond Farm Book Publishers

Whole Person Associates, *imprint of* Whole Person Associates Inc

Wicker Park Press, *distributed by* Academy Chicago Publishers

Wide World of Maps Inc, *distributor for* Benchmark Maps, Big Sky Maps, Franko Maps, MacVan Maps (Colorado Springs), Metro Maps, Rand McNally, *distributed by* Rand McNally

Wide World Publishing, *imprint of* Wide World Publishing, *distributed by* The Islander Group Inc, Perseus Books Group, Publishers Group West

Wide World Publishing/Tetra, *imprint of* Wide World Publishing

Wiggy Press, *imprint of* Dalton Publishing

Wigton Publishing, *distributed by* Sunbelt Publications Inc

Wildcat Canyon Press, *imprint of* Council Oak Books LLC

Wild Goose Co, *imprint of* Carson-Dellosa Publishing LLC

Wild Mountain Press, *imprint of* Crumb Elbow Publishing

Wild Oak, *imprint of* Oak Tree Press

Wilderness Adventures Press Inc, *distributed by* Angler's Book Supply, Books West, Inter Sports, Partners Book Distributor, Partners West, Raymond C Rumpf & Son Inc

Wilderness Press, *distributed by* Sunbelt Publications Inc

Wildflower Press, *affiliate of* Oakbrook Press

Wildlife Research Group, *imprint of* Crumb Elbow Publishing

WildStorm Productions, *imprint of* DC Entertainment

Wiley, *imprint of* Turner Publishing Co, John Wiley & Sons Inc, *distributed by* AICPA Professional Publications, Gulf Publishing Co

Wiley-IEEE Press, *imprint of* IEEE Press

Wiley-Blackwell, *distributor for* American Anthropological Association (AAA)

Wiley Blackwell Publishers, *distributor for* New York Academy of Sciences

Wiley-Heyden, *imprint of* John Wiley & Sons Inc

Wiley Interscience®, *imprint of* John Wiley & Sons Inc

J Wiley & Sons, *distributed by* Medical Group Management Association (MGMA)

John Wiley, *distributed by* SkillPath Publications

John Wiley & Sons, *imprint of* John Wiley & Sons Inc, *distributor for* The Electrochemical Society (ECS), Nevraumont Publishing Co, *distributed by* American Water Works Association, Heimburger House Publishing Co, Peoples Education Inc

John Wiley & Sons Inc, *distributor for* Association for Information Science & Technology (ASIS&T), Center for Creative Leadership LLC, IEEE Press, R S Means, a Reed Construction Data Co, SAS Publishing, *distributed by* American Academy of Environmental Engineers, Center for Creative Leadership LLC, William S Hein & Co Inc, Illuminating Engineering Society of North America (IES), J J Keller & Associates, Inc, NACE International, SAS Publishing, Society of Manufacturing Engineers

John Wiley & Sons Inc Higher Education, *division of* John Wiley & Sons Inc, John Wiley & Sons Inc

John Wiley & Sons Inc Professional/Trade Group, *division of* John Wiley & Sons Inc

John Wiley & Sons Inc Scientific, Technical, Medical & Scholarly (STMS), *division of* John Wiley & Sons Inc

Wiley-Liss, *imprint of* John Wiley & Sons Inc

Wiley-VCH, *imprint of* John Wiley & Sons Inc

William Carey Library Publishers, *division of* US Center for World Mission

William, James & Co, *imprint of* Franklin, Beedle & Associates Inc

William of Moerbeke Translation, *imprint of* St Augustine's Press Inc

Williams & Company Book Publishers, *distributed by* Syracuse University Press

Williams & Co Publishers, *imprint of* Williams & Company Book Publishers

Williams & Wilkins, *distributor for* Current Medicine Group (CMG)

Williamson Books, *imprint of* Ideals Publications, a Guideposts Co

Willow Bend Books, *imprint of* Heritage Books Inc

Willow Hill Press, *distributed by* John F Blair Publisher

Wilson Center Press, *imprint of* The Woodrow Wilson Center Press

H W Wilson, *imprint of* EBSCO Publishing

Neil Wilson Publishing (UK), *distributed by* Interlink Publishing Group Inc

Philip Wilson Publishers, *distributed by* Antique Collectors Club Ltd

Wimmer Cookbooks, *division of* Mercury Printing

Winchester Press, *imprint of* New Win Publishing

Wind Records, *distributed by* YMAA Publication Center

Windflower Press, *imprint of* Crumb Elbow Publishing

Windsor Books, *division of* Windsor Marketing Corp, Windsor Marketing Corp

Windward Publishing, *imprint of* Finney Company Inc

Wine Advisory Board, *imprint of* The Wine Appreciation Guild Ltd

Wine Enthusiast, *distributed by* Running Press Book Publishers

Wine Press, *imprint of* WinePress Publishing

Kelley Wingate Publications, *imprint of* Carson-Dellosa Publishing LLC

Wings Books, *imprint of* Random House Inc

WingSpread Publishers, *division of* Zur Ltd

Winston-Derek, *distributor for* Thomas Nelson Inc

Wintergreen/Orchard House Inc, *imprint of* Riverside Publishing

Winters Publishing, *distributor for* Anchors Away

Winterthur Museum, *distributed by* Oak Knoll Press

Winterthur Museum & Country Estate, *distributed by* Abrams, Acanthus, W W Norton & Company Inc, Schiffer, University Press of New England

Winterthur Museum Garden & Library, *distributed by* University Press of New England

Wisconsin Academy of Sciences, Arts & Letters, *distributed by* University of Wisconsin Press

Wisconsin Historical Society Press, *distributed by* University of Wisconsin Press

Wisconsin Veterans Museum, *distributed by* University of Wisconsin Press

Wisdom Archive, *division of* Wisdom Publications Inc

Wisdom Foundation, *distributed by* Fons Vitae

Paula Wiseman Books, *imprint of* Simon & Schuster Children's Publishing

Wish Publishing, *distributed by* Cardinal Publishers Group

Witherby Seamanship International Ltd, *distributed by* Marine Techniques Publishing

Wittenborn Art Books, *division of* Alan Wofsy Fine Arts, *distributor for* Ides et Calendes SA, Menil Foundation, UCLA/Hammer Museum, *distributed by* Alan Wofsy Fine Arts

George Wittenborn, *imprint of* Wittenborn Art Books

Witwatersrand University Press, *distributed by* Transaction Publishers Inc

Wizards of the Coast, *distributed by* Random House Inc

Wizards of the Coast LLC, *subsidiary of* Hasbro Inc, *distributed by* Random House

Alan Wofsy Fine Arts, *distributor for* Bora, Brusberg (Berlin), Cramer (Geneva), Huber, Ides et Calendes, Kornfeld & Co, Picasso Project, Welz, Wittenborn Art Books

Wolf Legal Publishers, *distributed by* Enfield Publishing & Distribution Co

Wolf Water Press, *distributed by* Sunbelt Publications Inc

Wolfe, *imprint of* Elsevier, Health Sciences Division

Wolters Kluwer US Corp, *subsidiary of* Wolters Kluwer NV (The Netherlands)

Women In Nontraditional Careers, *imprint of* Her Own Words LLC

Women, Law & Development International (WLDI), *distributed by* Stylus Publishing LLC

Women's Publications, *imprint of* Consumer Press

Marian Wood Books, *imprint of* GP Putnam's Sons (Hardcover)

Woodall Publications, *distributed by* The Globe Pequot Press

Woodbine House, *distributed by* ADD Warehouse

Woodcarving Illustrated Magazine, *imprint of* Fox Chapel Publishing Co Inc

Woodland Publishing Inc, *distributed by* Summit Beacon

The Woodrow Wilson Center Press, *division of* The Woodrow Wilson International Center for Scholars, Woodrow Wilson International Center for Scholars, *distributed by* Columbia University Press, The Johns Hopkins University Press, Stanford University Press, University of California Press

Woodrow Wilson Center Press/Johns Hopkins University Press, *imprint of* The Woodrow Wilson Center Press

Woodrow Wilson Center Press/Stanford University Press, *imprint of* The Woodrow Wilson Center Press

Word Aflame Press, *subsidiary of* Pentecostal Publishing House, *imprint of* Pentecostal Publishing House

Word & Quill Press, *distributed by* Cross-Cultural Communications

Word Dancer Press, *imprint of* Linden Publishing Co Inc

Word Music, *distributed by* Hal Leonard Corp

Wordsong, *imprint of* Boyds Mills Press

The Working Arts Library, *distributed by* Applause Theatre & Cinema Books

Workman Publishing, *distributor for* The Experiment

Workman Publishing Co Inc, *distributor for* Algonquin Books of Chapel Hill, Black Dog & Leventhal, Black Dog & Leventhal Publishers Inc, The Experiment, Greenwich Workshop Press Fearless Critic Media, Storey Publishing LLC

Workman Speakers Bureau, *division of* Workman Publishing Co Inc

Workout, *imprint of* Triumph Learning

World Almanac, *distributed by* Simon & Schuster, Inc, Simon & Schuster Sales & Marketing

World Almanac®, *imprint of* Infobase Learning

World Bank, *imprint of* World Bank Publications

World Bank Publications, *member of* The World Bank Group

World Book Inc, *subsidiary of* The Scott Fetzer Co

World Catholic Press, *imprint of* Catholic Book Publishing Corp

World Citizens, *affiliate of* Cinema Investments Co Inc, *distributed by* Inland

World Health Organization (WHO), *distributed by* Stylus Publishing LLC

World Literature Ministries, *imprint of* Faith Alive Christian Resources

World of Darkness, *imprint of* White Wolf Publishing Inc

World Reference Resources, *division of* Gareth Stevens Publishing

World Resources Institute, *distributed by* The Johns Hopkins University Press

World Trade Organization, *distributed by* The Brookings Institution Press

World Trade Press, *distributed by* Reference Press

World Vision Resources, *subsidiary of* World Vision International

World Wisdom, *distributed by* Fons Vitae

World Wrestling Entertainment, *imprint of* Gallery Books

The World's Largest Publishing Co, *subsidiary of* Gallopade International Inc

WorldTariff, *division of* FedEx Corp

Worth Publishers, *member of* Bedford, Freeman & Worth Publishing Group, LLC

The Wright Group/McGraw-Hill, *imprint of* McGraw-Hill Education

Wright Group/McGraw-Hill, *division of* McGraw-Hill School Education Group

Write Fuzzy, *imprint of* Write Bloody Publishing

Write Stuff®, *imprint of* Write Stuff Enterprises Inc

Writers & Artists on Photography Series, *imprint of* Aperture Books

Writer's Digest, *distributed by* Hal Leonard Corp

Writer's Digest Books, *imprint of* F+W Media Inc, F+W Media Inc

Wrox™, *imprint of* John Wiley & Sons Inc

WRS Group, *distributor for* MAR*CO Products Inc

WSU Museum of Art, *distributed by* Washington State University Press

www.simonandschuster.com, *imprint of* Simon & Schuster Digital

Wyrick & Co, *imprint of* Gibbs Smith Publisher

Xemplar, *imprint of* Crossquarter Publishing Group

Xeno Books, *imprint of* Red Hen Press

Xlibris Corp, *division of* Author Solutions Inc

XML Press, *subsidiary of* R L Hamilton & Associates LLC

Xoanon Publishing, *distributed by* Holmes Publishing Group LLC

Xpat Fiction, *imprint of* Franklin, Beedle & Associates Inc

YA Angst, *imprint of* Norilana Books

YA Books, *imprint of* Regal Crest Enterprises LLC

Yale Center for British Art, *distributed by* Yale University Press

Yale University Art Gallery, *distributed by* Yale University Press

Yale University Press, *division of* Yale University, *distributor for* Addison Gallery of American Art, Phillips Academy, American Federation of Arts, The Art Institute of Chicago, The Bard Graduate Center, The Colonial Williamsburg Foundation, Dallas Museum of Art, Harvard Art Museums, Harvard University Art Museums, Japan Society, The Jewish Museum, Kimbell Art Museum, Paul Mellon Centre, The Menil Collection, The Metropolitan Museum of Art, National Gallery, London, National Gallery of Art, National Gallery of Art (Washington, DC), Nevraumont Publishing Co, Philadelphia Museum of Art, Princeton University Art Museum, Sterling & Francine Clark Art Institute, Whitney Museum of American Art, Yale Center for British Art, Yale University Art Gallery, *distributed by* Cheng & Tsui Co Inc

Yankee, *distributor for* Teton NewMedia

Yankee Book Peddler, *distributor for* Primary Research Group Inc, Trans Tech Publications

Year Book, *imprint of* Elsevier, Health Sciences Division

Yearling, *imprint of* Random House Children's Books, Random House Inc

Yellow Books, *imprint of* Leadership Directories

Yellow 1, *imprint of* Wide World of Maps Inc

Yellow Rose Books, *imprint of* Regal Crest Enterprises LLC

Yellowback Mysteries, *imprint of* James A Rock & Co Publishers

Yelsraek Publishing, *distributed by* Adventures Unlimited Press

Yen Press, *imprint of* Orbit

Yes Books, *distributed by* Chelsea Green Publishing Co

Yeshiva University Museum Press, *distributed by* Gorgias Press LLC

Yeshiva University Press, *distributed by* KTAV Publishing House Inc

Yesterdays, *imprint of* Zumaya Publications LLC

YMAA Publication Center, *distributor for* Wind Records (Chinese healing music)

Yoga International, *imprint of* Himalayan Institute Press

York Medieval Press, *imprint of* Boydell & Brewer Inc

Yosemite Association, *imprint of* Heyday Books

You Can Teach Yourself, *imprint of* Mel Bay Publications Inc

Young Adult Resources, *division of* Gareth Stevens Publishing

Glenn Young Books, *distributed by* Applause Theatre & Cinema Books

Young Patriots Series, *imprint of* Patria Press Inc

Young Think®, *imprint of* Thomas Geale Publications Inc

Your Coach in a Box, *imprint of* Recorded Books LLC

YourBusinessMinute.com, *subsidiary of* BizBest Media Corp

Youth Specialties, *division of* Zondervan, A HarperCollins Company

YouthLight Inc, *distributor for* MAR*CO Products Inc

Yushodo Press, *distributed by* Oak Knoll Press

YWAM Publishing, *division of* Youth with a Mission, *distributor for* Emerald Books

Z140.com, *subsidiary of* BizBest Media Corp

Zahava Publications, *imprint of* Judaica Press Inc

Zak Books, *imprint of* Black Rabbit Books

Zambak, *distributed by* Tughra Books

Zaner-Bloser Inc, *subsidiary of* Highlights for Children Inc

Zaytuna Institute Press, *distributed by* Fons Vitae

Zebra Books, *imprint of* Kensington Publishing Corp

Zed Books, *distributed by* Palgrave Macmillan, St Martin's Press, LLC

Zeitgeist Films, *distributed by* Cheng & Tsui Co Inc

Zeke Holdings Ltd, *distributed by* Welcome Books®

Zenith Press, *imprint of* MBI Publishing Co, Quayside Publishing Group

Zeon, *distributed by* Gryphon Books

Zephyr Press, *imprint of* Chicago Review Press

Zest Books, *distributed by* Houghton Mifflin Harcourt

ZHealth Books, *imprint of* New Win Publishing

H O Zimman Inc, *distributor for* United States Tennis Association

Zinc Ink, *imprint of* Random House Publishing Group

Zoland Books, *imprint of* Steerforth Press

Zonderkidz, *division of* Zondervan, A HarperCollins Company

Zondervan, *distributor for* Focus on the Family

Zondervan, A HarperCollins Company, *division of* HarperCollins Publishers

Zone Books, *distributed by* The MIT Press

Zone Books dba Urzone Inc, *distributed by* The MIT Press

Zuckschwerdt Verlag (Munich, Germany), *distributed by* Scholium International Inc

Zumaya Publications LLC, *imprint of* eXtasy Books

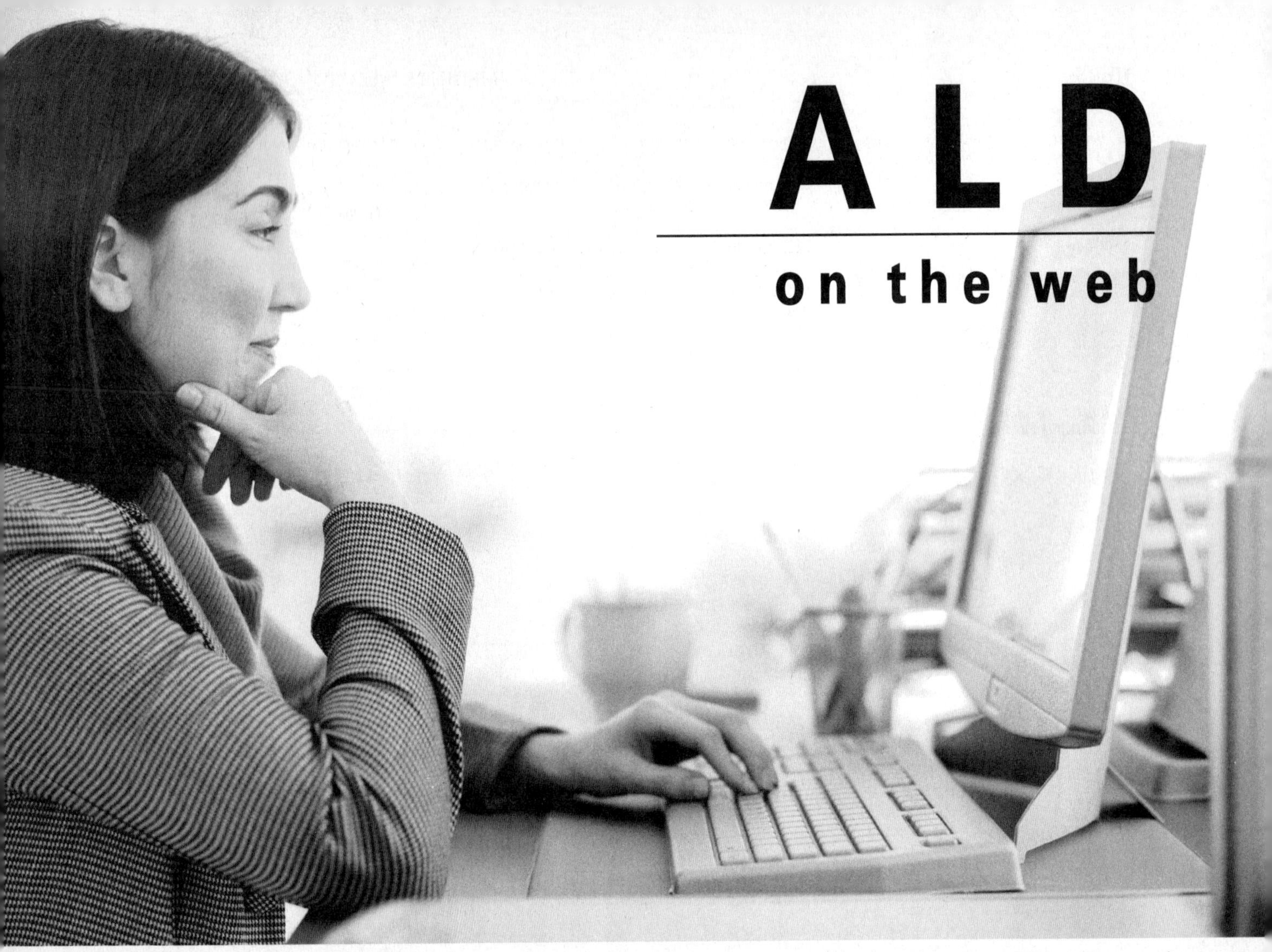

# Canadian Publishers

Listed in alphabetical order are those Canadian publishers that have reported to *LMP* that they produce an average of three or more books annually. Publishers that have appeared in a previous edition of *LMP*, but whose output currently does not meet our defined rate of activity, will be reinstated when their annual production reaches the required level. It should be noted that this rule of publishing activity does not apply to publishers of dictionaries, encyclopedias, atlases and braille books or to university presses.

The definition of a book is that used for *Books in Print* (Grey House Publishing, PO Box 56, Amenia, NY 12501-0056, USA) and excludes charts, pamphlets, folding maps, sheet music and material with stapled bindings. Publishers that make their titles available only in electronic or audio format are included if they meet the stated criteria. In the case of packages, the book must be of equal or greater importance than the accompanying piece. With few exceptions, new publishers are not listed prior to having published at least three titles within a year.

§ before the company name indicates those publishers involved in electronic publishing.

**ACTA Press**
2509 Dieppe Ave SW, Bldg B-6, Suite 101, Calgary, AB T3E 7J9
*Tel:* 403-288-1195 *Fax:* 403-247-6851
*E-mail:* journals@actapress.com; sales@actapress.com; calgary@iasted.org
*Web Site:* www.actapress.com
*Key Personnel*
Pres: Dr M H Hamza *E-mail:* hamza@iasted.org
Founded: 1972
Scientific & technical conference proceedings & journals; Computers, control & power systems, information technology, robotics, signal & image processing.
Publishes in English.
ISBN Prefix(es): 978-0-88986
Number of titles published annually: 50 Print; 50 CD-ROM
Total Titles: 900 Print; 50 CD-ROM

**Thomas Allen Publishers**
Division of Thomas Allen & Son Ltd
390 Steelcase Rd E, Markham, ON L3R 1G2
SAN: 115-1762
*Tel:* 905-475-9126 *Toll Free Tel:* 800-387-4333 (orders) *Fax:* 905-475-6747 *Toll Free Fax:* 800-458-5504 (orders)
*E-mail:* info@t-allen.com
*Web Site:* www.thomasallen.ca
*Key Personnel*
CEO & Pres: T James Allen *Tel:* 905-475-9126 ext 322 *E-mail:* jim.allen@t-allen.com
Natl Sales Mgr: Darryl Scott *Tel:* 905-475-9126 ext 327 *E-mail:* darryl.scott@t-allen.com
Founded: 2000
Seeks out & publishes quality literary fiction & nonfiction. Looking for original voices, fine writing & uncommon ideas with the intention to publish books of distinction & merit.
Publishes in English.
ISBN Prefix(es): 978-0-88762; 978-0-91902; 978-1-77102
Number of titles published annually: 12 Print; 6 E-Book
Total Titles: 152 Print; 88 E-Book
Distributor for Algonquin Books; Allworth; Arcade; Artisan; Basic Health; Black Dog & Leventhal; Charlesbridge/Imagine; Cormorant/Dancing Cat; Creative Homeowner; Fox Chapel; Harvard Common Press; Health Communications Inc; Heliconia Press; Highbridge Audio; Holiday House; Houghton Mifflin Harcourt; Innovative Kids; Larousse; Leisure Arts; Merriam-Webster; Midpoint; Ryland Peters & Small; Sky Pony; Skyhorse; Sports Publishing; Square One; Storey Publishing; Taunton Press; Timber Press; Tristan Publishing; Albert Whitman & Co; Willow Creek; Workman; Yankee; Zest
Membership(s): Canadian Booksellers Association; Canadian Publishers' Council

**The Althouse Press**
Unit of University of Western Ontario
Western University, 1137 Western Rd, London, ON N6G 1G7
SAN: 115-1142
*Tel:* 519-661-2096 *Fax:* 519-661-3714
*E-mail:* press@uwo.ca
*Web Site:* www.edu.uwo.ca/althousepress
*Key Personnel*
Dir: Dr Greg Dickinson *E-mail:* gdickins@uwo.ca
Mgr: Katherine Butson
Founded: 1977
Education, scholarly books & videotapes.
Publishes in English.
ISBN Prefix(es): 978-0-920354
Number of titles published annually: 5 Print
Total Titles: 54 Print
Distributed by SUNY Press; University of Chicago Press
Distributor for Lorimer; SUNY Press; Teachers College Press; University of Chicago Press

**Annick Press Ltd**
15 Patricia Ave, Toronto, ON M2M 1H9
SAN: 115-0065
*Tel:* 416-221-4802 *Fax:* 416-221-8400
*E-mail:* annickpress@annickpress.com
*Web Site:* www.annickpress.com
*Key Personnel*
Assoc Publr & Ed: Colleen MacMillan *E-mail:* colleenm@annickpress.com
Ed: Rick Wilks
Sales & Rts Mgr: Gayna Theophilus *E-mail:* gaynat@annickpress.com
Lib Sales Mgr, Firefly Books: Ann Quinn
Founded: 1975
Children's books.
Publishes in English, French.
ISBN Prefix(es): 978-0-920236; 978-0-920303; 978-1-55037; 978-1-55451
Number of titles published annually: 30 Print
Total Titles: 425 Print
*Branch Office(s)*
119 W Pender St, Suite 205, Vancouver, BC V6B 1S5 *Tel:* 604-718-1888 *Fax:* 604-687-4283
Distributed by Firefly Books Ltd; Open Road
U.S. Rep(s): Ian Booth; Nicholas Booth; Bob Ditter; Rachel Ginsburg; Tom Hamburg; Larry Hollern; David Lewis; Ted Lucia; Thomas Martin; Thomas J McFadden Associates; McLemore/Hollern & Associates Inc; Parisa Michailidis (spec sales); Kevin T Monahan; Frank Porter; Ann Quinn; Sirak & Sirak; Jennifer Sorensen (spec sales); Michael R Watson; Karen Winters; Debra Woodward; Karen Woodward
Foreign Rep(s): Ashton International Marketing Service (Asia); Cranbury International LLC (Caribbean, Latin America)
Foreign Rights: Diane Vanderkooy
Membership(s): Association of Canadian Publishers; Canadian Booksellers Association; CCI; Organization of Book Publishers of Ontario

**Anvil Press Publishers Inc**
278 E First Ave, Vancouver, BC V5T 1A6
Mailing Address: PO Box 3008, Vancouver, BC V6B 3X5
*Tel:* 604-876-8710 *Fax:* 604-879-2667
*E-mail:* info@anvilpress.com
*Web Site:* www.anvilpress.com
*Key Personnel*
Publr: Brian Kaufman
Founded: 1988
Literary, all genres; theatre & modern contemporary literature. Canadian authored titles only.
Publishes in English.
ISBN Prefix(es): 978-1-895636; 978-1-897535
Number of titles published annually: 10 Print
Total Titles: 90 Print
*Distribution Center:* University of Toronto Press, 10 Saint Mary St, Suite 700, Toronto, ON M4Y 2W8
Membership(s): Association of Book Publishers of British Columbia; Association of Canadian Publishers; Literary Press Group

**Aquila Communications Inc**
2642 Diab St, St-Laurent, QC H4S 1E8
*Tel:* 514-338-1065 *Toll Free Tel:* 800-667-7071 *Fax:* 514-338-1948 *Toll Free Fax:* 866-338-1948
*E-mail:* info2@aquilacommunications.com
*Web Site:* www.aquilacommunications.com
*Key Personnel*
Pres: Sami Kelada
Founded: 1970
High-interest/low-vocabulary readers for learners of French as a second language, grades 3 through college. Also, short humorous situational dialogues (1,200 words) in comic book format for kids & teens. Funny episodes of daily life of North American kids & teens (home & school).
Publishes in English, French.
ISBN Prefix(es): 978-0-88510
Number of titles published annually: 15 Print
Total Titles: 500 Print; 40 Audio
Imprints: Scaramouche
Distributed by Aquila Communications Ltd

**Arsenal Pulp Press**
211 E Georgia St, No 101, Vancouver, BC V6A 1Z6
*Tel:* 604-687-4233 *Toll Free Tel:* 888-600-PULP (600-7857) *Fax:* 604-687-4283
*E-mail:* info@arsenalpulp.com
*Web Site:* www.arsenalpulp.com
*Key Personnel*
Sales Dir & Assoc Publr: Robert Ballantyne
Mktg Dir: Janice Beley
Publr: Brian Lam
Prodn & Proj Mgr: Shyla Seller
Assoc Ed: Susan Safyan
Founded: 1982
Literary.

Publishes in English.
ISBN Prefix(es): 978-0-88978; 978-1-55152
Number of titles published annually: 20 Print
Total Titles: 260 Print
Imprints: Advance Editions; Pulp Press; Tillacum Library
Subsidiaries: Pulp Press
U.S. Rep(s): Consortium Book Sales & Distribution, The Keg House, Suite 101, 34 13 Ave NE, Minneapolis, MN 55413-1007, United States *Tel:* 612-746-2600 *Toll Free Tel:* 800-283-3572 (cust serv) *Fax:* 612-746-2606 *Web Site:* www.cbsd.com
*Distribution Center:* Consortium Book Sales & Distribution, The Keg House, Suite 101, 34 13 Ave NE, Minneapolis, MN 55413-1007, United States *Tel:* 612-746-2600 *Toll Free Tel:* 800-283-3572 (cust serv) *Fax:* 612-746-2606 *Web Site:* www.cbsd.com

**Association pour l'Avancement des Sciences et des Techniques de la Documentation**
2065 rue Parthenais, Bureau 387, Montreal, QC H2K 3T1
*Tel:* 514-281-5012 *Fax:* 514-281-8219
*E-mail:* info@asted.org
*Web Site:* www.asted.org
Founded: 1974
Association of specialists in information science.
Publishes in French.
ISBN Prefix(es): 978-2-921548
Number of titles published annually: 3 Print

**ASTED**, see Association pour l'Avancement des Sciences et des Techniques de la Documentation

**Athabasca University Press**
Edmonton Learning Ctr, Peace Hills Trust Tower, 1200, 10011-109 St, Edmonton, AB T5J 3S8
*Tel:* 780-497-3412 *Fax:* 780-421-3298
*E-mail:* aupress@athabascau.ca
*Web Site:* www.aupress.ca
*Key Personnel*
Acting Dir: Kathy Killoh *E-mail:* director.aupress@athabascau.ca
Sr Ed: Pamela Holway *E-mail:* editor.aupress@athabascau.ca
Mktg & Prodn: Morgan Tunzelmann *E-mail:* marketing.aupress@athabascau.ca
ISBN Prefix(es): 978-0-919737; 978-0-920982; 978-1-897425; 978-1-926836
*Distribution Center:* UBC Press, c/o UTP Distribution, 5201 Dufferin St, Toronto, ON M3H 5T8 *Tel:* 416-667-7791 *Toll Free Tel:* 800-565-9523 *Fax:* 416-667-7832 *Toll Free Fax:* 800-221-9985 *E-mail:* utpbooks@utpress.utoronto.ca
University of Washington Press, c/o Hopkins Fulfillment Service, PO Box 50370, Baltimore, MD 21211-4370, United States *Tel:* 410-516-6956 *Toll Free Tel:* 800-537-5487 *E-mail:* hfscustserv@press.jhu.edu
Eurospan Group, c/o Turpin Distribution, Pegasus Dr, Stratton Business Park, Biggleswade, Beds SG18 8TQ, United Kingdom (Africa, Europe, Middle East, UK) *Tel:* (01767) 604972 *Fax:* (01767) 601640 *E-mail:* eurospan@turpin-distribution.com

**B & B Publishing**
4823 Sherbrooke St W, Office 275, Westmount, QC H3Z 1G7
*Tel:* 514-932-9466 *Fax:* 514-932-5929
*E-mail:* editions@ebbp.ca
*Key Personnel*
Publr: Paul Beullac
Founded: 1996
Publisher of educational materials; books & wall maps for schools across Canada.
Publishes in English, French.
ISBN Prefix(es): 978-2-7615
Number of titles published annually: 10 Print
Total Titles: 400 Print
Distributed by Brault & Bouthillier Ltee; Brault & Bouthillier School Supplies
Foreign Rep(s): Bricolux (Belgium); Canada Ortho (France); Intelligence Insight LLP (Singapore); Wesco (France)
*Distribution Center:* 700, ave Beaumont, Montreal, QC H3N 1V5 *Tel:* 514-273-9186 *Fax:* 514-273-8627

**Banff Centre Press**
107 Tunnel Mountain Dr, Banff, AB T1L 1H5
Mailing Address: Box 1020, Banff, AB T1L 1H5
*Tel:* 403-762-6100 *Fax:* 403-762-6444
*E-mail:* press@banffcentre.ca
*Web Site:* www.banffcentre.ca/press
*Key Personnel*
Literary Arts Dir: Steven Ross Smith
Founded: 1995
Publisher of books on contemporary art & culture.
Publishes in English, French.
ISBN Prefix(es): 978-1-894773
Number of titles published annually: 4 Print
Total Titles: 41 Print; 2 CD-ROM
*Orders to:* ListDistCo, 100 Armstrong Ave, Georgetown, ON L7G 5S4 *Toll Free Tel:* 800-591-6250 *Fax:* 905-877-4410
*Returns:* ListDistCo, 100 Armstrong Ave, Georgetown, ON L7G 5S4 *Toll Free Tel:* 800-591-6250 *Fax:* 905-877-4410
*Warehouse:* ListDistCo, 100 Armstrong Ave, Georgetown, ON L7G 5S4 *Toll Free Tel:* 800-591-6250 *Fax:* 905-877-4410
*Distribution Center:* ListDistCo, 100 Armstrong Ave, Georgetown, ON L7G 5S4 *Toll Free Tel:* 800-591-6250 *Fax:* 905-877-4410
Membership(s): Book Publishers Association of Alberta; Literary Press Group

**Bayeux Arts Inc**
119 Stratton Crescent SW, Calgary, AB T3H 1T7
*E-mail:* mail@bayeux.com
*Web Site:* www.bayeux.com
*Key Personnel*
Co-Publr & Dir: Swapna Gupta
Co-Publr: Ashis Gupta *E-mail:* agupta@bayeux.com
Ed: Mercedes Batiz-Benet *E-mail:* mercedes@bayeux.com
Ed, Children's Lit: Judd Palmer *E-mail:* jpalmer@bayeux.com
Founded: 1994
ISBN Prefix(es): 978-1-896209; 978-1-897411
Number of titles published annually: 10 Print
Imprints: Alebrije; Gondolier; Odd Little Books; Rosencrantz Comics

**Beliveau Editeur**
920 rue Jean-Neveu, Longueuil, QC J4G 2M1
*Tel:* 514-253-0403; 450-679-1933 *Fax:* 450-679-6648
*E-mail:* admin@beliveauediteur.com
*Web Site:* www.beliveauediteur.com
*Key Personnel*
CEO & Pres: Mathieu Beliveau
Founded: 1975
Specialize in recovery, geopolitics & self-help, medicine, taxation & motivation.
Publishes in French.
ISBN Prefix(es): 978-2-89092
Number of titles published annually: 15 Print
Total Titles: 250 Print
Distributed by Iris Diffusion
Foreign Rights: Mme Pascale Patte-Wilbert (France); SDL Caravelle (Belgium); Transat (Switzerland)

**Between the Lines**
401 Richmond St W, No 277, Toronto, ON M5V 3A8
SAN: 115-0189
*Tel:* 416-535-9914 *Toll Free Tel:* 800-718-7201 *Fax:* 416-535-1484
*E-mail:* info@btlbooks.com
*Web Site:* www.btlbooks.com
*Key Personnel*
Mktg & Accts Mgr: Paula Brill
Mng Ed: Amanda Crocker
Publicist: Matthew Adams
Founded: 1977
Nonfiction, social, economic & political works dealing with international development issues & Canadian social issues.
Publishes in English.
ISBN Prefix(es): 978-0-919946; 978-0-921284; 978-1-896357; 978-1-897071
Number of titles published annually: 16 Print
Total Titles: 153 Print
U.S. Rep(s): SCB Distributors
Foreign Rep(s): Fernwood Books (Canada)
*Warehouse:* University of Toronto Press, 5201 Dufferin St, Downsview, ON M3H 5T8 *Toll Free Tel:* 800-565-9523 *Toll Free Fax:* 800-221-9985
*Distribution Center:* SCB Distributors, 15608 S New Century Dr, Gardena, CA 90248, United States (USA dist) *Tel:* 310-532-7001 *Toll Free Tel:* 800-729-6423

**Black Rose Books Ltd**
CP 35788 Succ Leo Pariseau, Montreal, QC H2X 0A4
SAN: 115-2653
*Tel:* 514-844-4076 *Toll Free Tel:* 800-565-9523 (orders) *Toll Free Fax:* 800-221-9985 (orders)
*E-mail:* info@blackrosebooks.net
*Web Site:* www.blackrosebooks.net
*Key Personnel*
Mktg Promo: Lucia Kowaluk
Edit Administrator: Robert Dollins
Founded: 1969
Politics, book & journal publishing in the social sciences & humanities.
Publishes in English.
ISBN Prefix(es): 978-0-919618; 978-0-919619; 978-0-920057; 978-0-921689; 978-1-55164
Number of titles published annually: 15 Print; 20 Online; 30 E-Book
Total Titles: 585 Print; 300 E-Book
*Branch Office(s)*
c/o University of Toronto Press, 2250 Military Rd, Tonawanda, NY 14150, United States *Tel:* 716-683-4547 *Fax:* 716-685-6895
*Foreign Office(s):* Book & Volume, PO Box 35, 3242 Birregurra, Victoria, Australia *Tel:* (03) 5236 2593 *Fax:* (03) 5236 2030 *E-mail:* info@bookandvolume.com.au *Web Site:* www.bookandvolume.com.au
c/o Central Books, 99 Wallis Rd, London E9 5LN, United Kingdom *Tel:* (020) 8986 4854 *Fax:* (020) 8533 5821 *E-mail:* orders@centralbooks.com *Web Site:* www.centralbooks.com
Distributed by University of Toronto Press
*Advertising Agency:* Central Books, 99 Wallis Rd, London E9 5LN, United Kingdom *Tel:* (020) 8986 4854 *Fax:* (020) 8533 5821 *E-mail:* orders@centralbooks.com
*Orders to:* Consortium Book Sales & Distribution, The Keg House, Suite 101, 34 13 Ave NE, Minneapolis, MN 55413-1007, United States, Sales Mgr: Julie Schaper *Tel:* 612-746-2600 *Toll Free Tel:* 800-283-3572 (cust serv) *Fax:* 612-746-2606 *E-mail:* consortium@cbsd.com *Web Site:* www.cbsd.com
*Returns:* Consortium Book Sales & Distribution, The Keg House, Suite 101, 34 13 Ave NE, Minneapolis, MN 55413-1007, United States, Sales Mgr: Julie Schaper *Tel:* 612-746-2600 *Toll Free Tel:* 800-283-3572 (cust serv) *Fax:* 612-746-2606 *E-mail:* consortium@cbsd.com *Web Site:* www.cbsd.com
*Shipping Address:* Consortium Book Sales & Distribution, The Keg House, Suite 101, 34 13

Ave NE, Minneapolis, MN 55413-1007, United States, Sales Mgr: Julie Schaper *Tel:* 612-746-2600 *Toll Free Tel:* 800-283-3572 (cust serv) *Fax:* 612-746-2606 *E-mail:* consortium@cbsd.com *Web Site:* www.cbsd.com
*Distribution Center:* Consortium Book Sales & Distribution, The Keg House, Suite 101, 34 13 Ave NE, Minneapolis, MN 55413-1007, United States, Sales Mgr: Julie Schaper *Tel:* 612-746-2600 *Toll Free Tel:* 800-283-3572 (cust serv) *Fax:* 612-746-2606 *E-mail:* consortium@cbsd.com *Web Site:* www.cbsd.com

**Blue Bike Books**
11919 125 St, Edmonton, AB T5L 0S3
*Tel:* 780-951-0032
*E-mail:* info@bluebikebooks.com
*Web Site:* www.bluebikebooks.com
*Key Personnel*
Publr: Nicholle Carriere *Tel:* 780-951-0032
Founded: 2005
Publish humor & trivia books. Large number of regional trivia titles as well as national ones.
Publishes in English.
ISBN Prefix(es): 978-1-897278; 978-0-9739116
Number of titles published annually: 10 Print
Total Titles: 40 Print
Distributed by Lone Pine Publishing
*Orders to:* Lone Pine Publishing, 10145 81 Ave, Edmonton, AB T6E 1W9, Contact: Jon Murphy *Toll Free Tel:* 800-661-9017 *E-mail:* sales@lonepinepublishing.com
*Returns:* 2002 80 Ave, Edmonton, AB T6P 1N2, Contact: Dawn Hogg *Tel:* 780-468-2259 *Fax:* 780-468-2844 *E-mail:* dhogg@lonepinepublishing.com
*Shipping Address:* 2002 80 Ave, Edmonton, AB T6P 1N2, Contact: Dawn Hogg *Tel:* 780-468-2259 *Fax:* 780-468-2844 *E-mail:* dhogg@lonepinepublishing.com
*Warehouse:* 2002 80 Ave, Edmonton, AB T6P 1N2, Contact: Dawn Hogg *Tel:* 780-468-2259 *Fax:* 780-468-2844 *E-mail:* dhogg@lonepinepublishing.com
*Distribution Center:* 2002 80 Ave, Edmonton, AB T6P 1N2, Contact: Dawn Hogg *Tel:* 780-468-2259 *Fax:* 780-468-2844 *E-mail:* dhogg@lonepinepublishing.com
Membership(s): Book Publishers Association of Alberta

**Editions du Bois-de-Coulonge**
1140 de Montigny, Sillery, QC G1S 3T7
*Tel:* 418-683-6332 *Fax:* 418-683-6332
*Web Site:* www.ebc.qc.ca
*Key Personnel*
Owner & Pres: Richard Leclerc, PhD
Founded: 1995
Publish & distribute books about music, multimedia, television & movies.
Publishes in French.
ISBN Prefix(es): 978-2-9801397
Number of titles published annually: 1 Print
Total Titles: 7 Print
Membership(s): Association for the Export of Canadian Books

**§Books We Love Ltd**
192 Lakeside Greens Dr, Chestermere, AB T1X 1C2
*Tel:* 403-710-4869
*E-mail:* bookswelove@shaw.ca
*Key Personnel*
Pres: Judith Pittman *E-mail:* judecalgary@shaw.ca
VP: Jamie Hill
Founded: 2010
Full service fiction publisher featuring romance, mystery, suspense, young adult, fantasy & science fiction. Royalty paying, non-subsidy publisher who specializes in works by established authors who have had their rights returned from major publishers & are interested in a publisher with a primarily online focus, but with the ability to bring their book out in print if desired. Provides extensive marketing & promotion assistance to its authors. Offers one of the most generous contracts in the industry & promotes its authors extensively.
Publishes in English.
ISBN Prefix(es): 978-1-927476
Number of titles published annually: 185 Print; 150 Online; 150 E-Book
Total Titles: 35 Print; 150 Online; 250 E-Book
Membership(s): Romance Writers of America

**Borealis Press Ltd**
8 Mohawk Crescent, Nepean, ON K2H 7G6
*Tel:* 613-829-0150 *Toll Free Tel:* 877-696-2585 *Fax:* 613-829-7783
*E-mail:* drt@borealispress.com
*Web Site:* www.borealispress.com
Founded: 1971
Canadian-oriented general titles of most types. No unsol mss, query first. Include synopsis &/or outline & sample chapter with SASE.
Publishes in English, French.
ISBN Prefix(es): 978-0-88887; 978-1-896133; 978-0-919594
Number of titles published annually: 24 Print
Subsidiaries: Tecumseh Press
Distributed by Blackwell; Dawson; EBSCO; Ex Libris; Hein; Swets

**The Boston Mills Press**
Division of Firefly Books Ltd
66 Leek Crescent, Richmond Hill, ON L4B 1H1
*Tel:* 416-499-8412 *Toll Free Tel:* 800-387-6192 *Fax:* 416-499-8313 *Toll Free Fax:* 800-450-0391
*E-mail:* service@fireflybooks.com
*Web Site:* www.fireflybooks.com
*Key Personnel*
Dir, Prodn & Co-Editions: Jacqueline Hope Raynor
Founded: 1974
Canadian & American history, guide books, large format colour photograph books.
Publishes in English.
ISBN Prefix(es): 978-0-919822; 978-0-919783; 978-1-55046
Number of titles published annually: 20 Print
Total Titles: 200 Print
Distributed by Firefly Books Ltd

**BPS Books**
Division of Bastian Publishing Services Ltd
42 Donalda Crescent, Toronto, ON M1S 1N7
*Tel:* 416-609-2004 *Fax:* 416-609-2936
*Web Site:* www.bpsbooks.com
*Key Personnel*
Publr & Ed-in-Chief: Donald G Bastian *E-mail:* dgbastian@sympatico.ca
Founded: 2007
Print-on-demand publisher of original & reprint trade paperbacks for the US, Canadian & UK markets via bookstore web sites such as the Amazon sites in all three countries. No unsol mss, query first using online form.
This publisher has indicated that 90% of their product is author subsidized.
Publishes in English, French.
ISBN Prefix(es): 978-1-926645; 978-0-9784402; 978-0-9809231; 978-1-927483
Number of titles published annually: 15 Print; 10 E-Book
Total Titles: 65 Print; 26 E-Book
Membership(s): Word Guild

**Brault & Bouthillier**
Division of B & B School Supplies
700 ave Beaumont, Montreal, QC H3N 1V5
*Tel:* 514-273-9186 *Toll Free Tel:* 800-361-0378 *Fax:* 514-273-8627 *Toll Free Fax:* 800-361-0378
*E-mail:* ventes@bb.ca
*Web Site:* www.braultbouthillier.com
*Key Personnel*
VP, Sales & Mktg: Yves Brault *Tel:* 514-273-9186 ext 219 *E-mail:* yvesbrault@bb.ca
Sales Dir: Claude Vaillancourt *Tel:* 514-273-9186 ext 227 *E-mail:* cvaillancourt@bb.ca
Sales & Mktg Coord: Maria Martinez *Tel:* 514-273-9186 ext 284 *E-mail:* mariamartinez@bb.ca
Founded: 1945
Pedagogical & scientific.
Publishes in English, French.
ISBN Prefix(es): 978-0-88537; 978-2-7615
Number of titles published annually: 100 Print
*Branch Office(s)*
150 Brittania Rd E, Unit 7, Mississauga, ON L4Z 2A4 *Tel:* 905-890-0404 *Toll Free Tel:* 800-668-1108 *Fax:* 905-890-7999 *Toll Free Fax:* 800-839-7718
Distributed by DPLU Inc (Montreal); B B Jocus (Toronto)

**Breakwater Books Ltd**
One Stamp's Lane, St Johns, NL A1C 6E6
Mailing Address: PO Box 2188, St Johns, NL A1C 6E6
*Tel:* 709-722-6680 *Toll Free Tel:* 800-563-3333 (orders) *Fax:* 709-753-0708
*E-mail:* info@breakwaterbooks.com
*Web Site:* www.breakwaterbooks.com
*Key Personnel*
Pres: Rebecca Rose
Founded: 1973
Books primarily about education & trade books.
Publishes in English, French.
ISBN Prefix(es): 978-0-919519; 978-0-919948; 978-0-920911; 978-1-55081
Number of titles published annually: 15 Print
Total Titles: 600 Print

**Brick Books**
Box 20081, 431 Boler Rd, London, ON N6K 4G6
*Tel:* 519-657-8579
*E-mail:* brick.books@sympatico.ca
*Web Site:* www.brickbooks.ca
*Key Personnel*
Gen Mgr: Kitty Lewis
Prodn Mgr: Alayna Munce
Founded: 1975
Publish poetry collections by Canadian authors.
Publishes in English.
ISBN Prefix(es): 978-0-919626; 978-1-894078
Number of titles published annually: 7 Print
Total Titles: 115 Print
*Distribution Center:* LitDistCo, 100 Armstrong Ave, Georgetown, ON L7G 5S4 *Toll Free Tel:* 800-591-6250 *Toll Free Fax:* 800-591-6251 *E-mail:* orders@litdistco.ca *Web Site:* www.litdistco.ca
Membership(s): Association of Canadian Publishers; Literary Press Group of Canada

**Brindle & Glass Ltd**
340-1105 Pandora Ave, Victoria, BC V8V 3P9
*Tel:* 250-360-0829
*E-mail:* info@brindleandglass.com
*Web Site:* www.brindleandglass.com
*Key Personnel*
Publr: Ruth Linka
Founded: 2001
Literary press.
Publishes in English.
ISBN Prefix(es): 978-1-897142; 978-0-9732481; 978-1-926972
Number of titles published annually: 8 Print
Total Titles: 65 Print
Foreign Rep(s): Ingram Book Co (USA); Literary Press Group of Canada (Canada)
Foreign Rights: Acacia House

*Distribution Center:* Heritage Group Distribution, 8-19272 96 Ave, Surrey, BC V4N 4C1 *Toll Free Tel:* 800-665-3302 *E-mail:* orders@hgdistribution.com

**Broadview Press**
280 Perry St, Unit 5, Peterborough, ON K9J 2J4
SAN: 115-6772
Mailing Address: PO Box 1243, Peterborough, ON K9J 7H5
*Tel:* 705-743-8990 *Fax:* 705-743-8353
*E-mail:* customerservice@broadviewpress.com
*Web Site:* www.broadviewpress.com
*Key Personnel*
CEO & Pres: Don Le Pan *Tel:* 250-824-5015 *Fax:* 250-824-5001 *E-mail:* don.lepan@broadviewpress.com
CFO: Carol Richardson *E-mail:* crichardson@broadviewpress.com
Mng Ed: Tara Lowes *Tel:* 705-743-7581 ext 30 *E-mail:* taralowes@broadviewpress.com
Accts Mgr: LeeAnna Dykstra *E-mail:* ldykstra@broadviewpress.com
Exam Copies Coord: Lisa Reid *E-mail:* examcopies@broadviewpress.com
Founded: 1985
Textbooks & nonfiction, arts & social sciences.
Publishes in English.
ISBN Prefix(es): 978-0-921149; 978-1-55111
Number of titles published annually: 70 Print
Total Titles: 400 Print
*Branch Office(s)*
15A Cork St E, Guelph, ON N1H 2W7 *Tel:* 519-821-2171 *Fax:* 519-821-0706
2-815 First St SW, Calgary, AB T2P 1N3 *Tel:* 403-232-6863 *Fax:* 403-233-0001 *E-mail:* broadview@broadviewpress.com
2215 Kenmore Ave, Buffalo, NY 14207, United States
U.S. Rep(s): Miller Trade Book Marketing; Anthony N Proe; Lois Shearer Associates; Nancy Suib
*Returns:* 2215 Kenmore Ave, Buffalo, NY 14207, United States

**Broken Jaw Press Inc**
Box 596, Sta A, Fredericton, NB E3B 5A6
*Tel:* 506-454-5127 *Fax:* 506-454-5134
*E-mail:* editors@brokenjaw.com
*Web Site:* www.brokenjaw.com
*Key Personnel*
Pres & Publr: Joe Blades *E-mail:* joeblades@nb.aibn.com
Founded: 1984 (incorporated 2003)
Publish mostly Canadian-authored literary books: poetry, fiction & creative nonfiction.
Publishes in English, French.
ISBN Prefix(es): 978-0-921411; 978-1-896647; 978-1-55391
Number of titles published annually: 6 Print; 1 Audio
Total Titles: 140 Print; 1 CD-ROM; 50 E-Book; 2 Audio
Imprints: Book Rat; Broken Jaw Press; Broken Jaw Press eBooks; Cauldron Books; Dead Sea Physh Products; Maritimes Arts Projects Productions; SpareTime Editions
Distributor for White Dwarf Editions (Montreal)

**Broquet Inc**
97-B Montee des Bouleaux, St Constant, QC J5A 1A9
*Tel:* 450-638-3338 *Fax:* 450-638-4338
*E-mail:* info@broquet.qc.ca
*Web Site:* www.broquet.qc.ca
*Key Personnel*
Pres: Antoine Broquet
Founded: 1979
Nature books & astronomy.
Publishes in English, French.
ISBN Prefix(es): 978-2-89000
Number of titles published annually: 80 Print; 1 CD-ROM
Total Titles: 800 Print; 1 CD-ROM
Distributed by Diffusion Prologue

**Brush Education Inc**
1220 Kensington Rd NW, Suite 210, Calgary, AB T2N 3P5
SAN: 115-0324
*Tel:* 403-283-0900 *Fax:* 403-283-6947
*E-mail:* contact@brusheducation.ca
*Web Site:* www.brusheducation.ca
*Key Personnel*
Partner: Fraser Seely
Founded: 1975
Wholly owned & operated by Brush Publishing & Media Services Inc. We offer a broad range of subjects including education, native studies, social sciences & Western Canadiana.
Publishes in English.
ISBN Prefix(es): 978-0-920490; 978-1-55059
Number of titles published annually: 17 Print; 17 Online; 5 E-Book
Total Titles: 250 Print; 17 Online; 5 E-Book
Distributed by Lone Pine
U.S. Rep(s): Lone Pine US
Membership(s): Association of Canadian Publishers; Book Publishers Association of Alberta

**Callawind Publications Inc**
3551 Sainte Charles Blvd, Suite 179, Kirkland, QC H9H 3C4
*Tel:* 514-685-9109
*E-mail:* info@callawind.com
*Web Site:* www.callawind.com
*Key Personnel*
Mktg: Pamela Carmen *E-mail:* pamela@callawind.com
Founded: 1995
Custom book publisher specializing in cookbooks & children's books.
This publisher has indicated that 100% of their product line is author subsidized.
Publishes in English.
ISBN Prefix(es): 978-1-896511
Number of titles published annually: 15 Print
Total Titles: 75 Print
*Distribution Center:* Biblio Distribution, 15200 NBN Way, Blue Ridge Summit, PA 17214, United States *Toll Free Tel:* 800-462-6420 *Toll Free Fax:* 800-338-4550 *E-mail:* custserv@nbnbooks.com *Web Site:* www.bibliodistribution.com
Membership(s): The Association of Publishers for Special Sales; IBPA, the Independent Book Publishers Association

**§Canada Law Book®**
Division of Thomson Reuters Canada Ltd
One Corporate Plaza, Toronto, ON M1T 3V4
*Tel:* 416-609-8000; 416-609-3800 (cust rel, Toronto, Intl); 905-713-4250 (tech support) *Toll Free Tel:* 800-387-5351 (cust rel, CN & US only); 866-614-7033 (tech support, CN & US only); 800-347-5164 (CN & US) *Fax:* 416-298-5082 (cust rel, Toronto) *Toll Free Fax:* 877-750-9041 (cust rel, CN only)
*Web Site:* www.canadalawbook.ca; www.carswell.com
Founded: 1855
Law books.
Publishes in English.
ISBN Prefix(es): 978-0-88804
Number of titles published annually: 50 Print; 3 CD-ROM; 3 E-Book
Total Titles: 480 Print; 25 CD-ROM; 40 Online; 9 E-Book
Subsidiaries: Canadian Lawyer/Law Times Media, A Thomson Reuters business
*Returns:* 245 Bartley Dr, Toronto, ON M4A 2V8

**Canadian Bible Society**
10 Carnforth Rd, Toronto, ON M4A 2S4
SAN: 112-5559
*Tel:* 416-757-4171 *Toll Free Tel:* 866-946-1711 *Fax:* 416-757-3376
*E-mail:* custserv@biblesociety.ca
*Web Site:* www.biblescanada.com; www.biblesociety.ca
*Key Personnel*
Dir, Scripture Resources: Joel Coppieters
Founded: 1804
Bibles, new testaments, scripture portions, selections; scriptures in foreign languages.
Publishes in English, French.
ISBN Prefix(es): 978-0-88834
Number of titles published annually: 20 Print; 3 CD-ROM; 3 Online; 5 Audio
Total Titles: 2,500 Print; 10 CD-ROM; 50 Audio
U.S. Publishers Represented: American Bible Society
Foreign Rep(s): United Bible Societies (Worldwide)
Membership(s): United Bible Societies

**Canadian Circumpolar Institute (CCI) Press**
Unit of Canadian Circumpolar Institute (CCI), University of Alberta
University of Alberta, Rm I-42 Pembina Hall, Edmonton, AB T6G 2H8
*Tel:* 780-492-4512 *Fax:* 780-492-1153
*E-mail:* cindy.mason@ualberta.ca
*Web Site:* www.cci.ualberta.ca
*Key Personnel*
Mng Ed: Elaine Louise Maloney *Tel:* 780-492-4999
Busn Mgr & Admin Asst: Cindy Mason *E-mail:* cindy.mason@ualberta.ca
Founded: 1960 (as Boreal Institute for Northern Studies; reconfigured & renamed 1990 as Canadian Circumpolar Institute)
Polar research, education, communications & outreach institute.
Publishes in English.
ISBN Prefix(es): 978-1-896445; 978-0-919058
Number of titles published annually: 5 Print; 1 CD-ROM
Total Titles: 92 Print; 1 CD-ROM
Membership(s): Association for the Export of Canadian Books; Association of Canadian Publishers; Book Publishers Association of Alberta

**The Canadian Council on Social Development**
190 O'Connor St, Suite 100, Ottawa, ON K2P 2R3
*Tel:* 613-236-8977 *Fax:* 613-236-2750
*E-mail:* council@ccsd.ca
*Web Site:* www.ccsd.ca
*Key Personnel*
CEO & Pres: Peggy Taillon *Tel:* 613-236-5868 ext 253 *E-mail:* taillon@ccsd.ca
VP, Res: Katherine Scott *Tel:* 613-236-5868 ext 245 *E-mail:* scott@ccsd.ca
Founded: 1920
Social policy, poverty, retirement, income security, economics, sustainable development self-help & aboriginal peoples.
Publishes in English, French.
ISBN Prefix(es): 978-0-88810
Number of titles published annually: 12 Print
Total Titles: 100 Print
Distributed by Renouf Publishing Ltd

**Canadian Energy Research Institute**
3512 33 St NW, Suite 150, Calgary, AB T2L 2A6
*Tel:* 403-282-1231 *Fax:* 403-284-4181
*E-mail:* info@ceri.ca
*Web Site:* www.ceri.ca
*Key Personnel*
CEO & Pres: Peter Howard
Exec Asst: Megan Murphy *Tel:* 403-220-2370 *Fax:* 403-220-9579 *E-mail:* mmurphy@ceri.ca
Founded: 1975

Energy research, conferences.
Publishes in English.
ISBN Prefix(es): 978-0-920522; 978-1-896091
Number of titles published annually: 5 Print
Total Titles: 150 Print

**Canadian Government Publishing**
Publishing & Depository Services, Public Works & Government Services Canada, Ottawa, ON K1A 0S5
*Tel:* 613-941-5995 *Toll Free Tel:* 800-635-7943 *Fax:* 613-954-5779 *Toll Free Fax:* 800-565-7757
*E-mail:* publications@tpsgc-pwgsc.gc.ca
*Web Site:* publications.gc.ca
*Key Personnel*
Dir: Joanne Joanisse
Official publisher for the government of Canada; active inventory of 22,000 titles in a wide variety of scientific, health, public policy, public administration, etc.
Publishes in English, French.
ISBN Prefix(es): 978-0-660; 978-0-662; 978-0-315
Number of titles published annually: 100 Print

**Canadian Institute of Chartered Accountants (L'Institut Canadien des Comptables Agrees)**
277 Wellington St W, Toronto, ON M5V 3H2
*Tel:* 416-977-3222 *Toll Free Tel:* 800-268-3793 (CN orders) *Fax:* 416-977-8585
*E-mail:* orders@cica.ca
*Web Site:* www.cica.ca
*Key Personnel*
CEO & Pres: Kevin Dancey *Tel:* 416-204-3333 *Fax:* 416-204-3405
Dir, Publg & Memb Servs: Brian Loney *Tel:* 416-204-3235 *Fax:* 416-204-3414 *E-mail:* brian.loney@cica.ca
Founded: 1917
Taxation, accounting, auditing, financial.
Publishes in English, French.
ISBN Prefix(es): 978-0-88800
Number of titles published annually: 15 Print
Total Titles: 200 Print; 40 CD-ROM

**Canadian Institute of Resources Law (Institut Canadien du Droit des Resources)**
Faculty of Law, University of Calgary, 2500 University Dr NW, MFH 3353, Calgary, AB T2N 1N4
*Tel:* 403-220-3200 *Fax:* 403-282-6182
*E-mail:* cirl@ucalgary.ca
*Web Site:* www.cirl.ca
*Key Personnel*
Info Resources Offr: Sue Parsons
Leading national centre of expertise on legal & policy issues relating to Canada's natural resources.
Publishes in English.
ISBN Prefix(es): 978-0-919269
Number of titles published annually: 3 Print; 4 Online
Total Titles: 45 Print; 33 Online

**Canadian Institute of Ukrainian Studies Press**
Division of Canadian Institute of Ukrainian Studies
University of Toronto, Rm 308, 256 McCaul St, Toronto, ON M5T 1W5
*Tel:* 416-946-7326 *Fax:* 416-978-2672
*E-mail:* cius@ualberta.ca
*Web Site:* www.ciuspress.com
*Key Personnel*
Exec Dir: Marko R Stech *E-mail:* m.stech@utoronto.ca
Founded: 1976
Publisher of scholarly works in Ukranian studies & Ukranian Canadian studies.
Publishes in English.
ISBN Prefix(es): 978-0-920862; 978-1-895571; 978-1-894865
Number of titles published annually: 5 Print
Total Titles: 180 Print
U.S. Rep(s): Baker & Taylor Books
*Orders to:* CIUS Press, University of Alberta, 430 Pembina Hall, Edmonton, AB T6G 2H8 *Tel:* 780-492-2973 *Fax:* 780-492-4967 *E-mail:* cius@ualberta.ca
*Returns:* CIUS Press, University of Alberta, 430 Pembina Hall, Edmonton, AB T6G 2H8 *Tel:* 780-492-2973 *Fax:* 780-492-4967 *E-mail:* cius@ualberta.ca
*Distribution Center:* CIUS Press, University of Alberta, 430 Pembina Hall, Edmonton, AB T6G 2H8, Contact: Iryna Fedoriw *Tel:* 780-492-2973 *Fax:* 780-492-4967 *E-mail:* cius@ualberta.ca

**Canadian Museum of Civilization**
100 Laurier St, Gatineau, QC K1A 0M8
Mailing Address: Box 3100, Sta B, Gatineau, QC J9X 4H2
*Tel:* 819-776-7000 *Toll Free Tel:* 800-555-5621 (North American orders only) *Fax:* 819-776-8393
*E-mail:* publications@civilization.ca
*Web Site:* www.civilization.ca
*Key Personnel*
VP: Chantal Schryer *Tel:* 819-776-8499 *E-mail:* chantal.schryer@civilization.ca
Publr: Rosemary Nugent *Tel:* 819-776-8389 *E-mail:* rosemary.nugent@civilization.ca
Founded: 1990
Museology, anthropology, archaeology, ethnology, folk culture, history, contemporary Native & Inuit art, native studies, CD-ROM.
Publishes in English, French.
ISBN Prefix(es): 978-0-660
Number of titles published annually: 15 Print
Total Titles: 400 Print; 8 CD-ROM
U.S. Rep(s): University of Washington Press
Membership(s): Association for the Export of Canadian Books; Association of Canadian Publishers; Canadian Booksellers Association

**Canadian Plains Research Center**
2 Research Dr, Regina, SK S4S 7H9
SAN: 115-0278
Mailing Address: University of Regina, 3737 Wascana Pkwy, Regina, SK S4S 0A2
*Tel:* 306-585-4758 *Toll Free Tel:* 866-874-2257 *Fax:* 306-585-4699
*E-mail:* canadian.plains@uregina.ca
*Web Site:* www.cprc.ca
*Key Personnel*
Exec Dir: Dr Polo Diaz *E-mail:* harry.diaz@uregina.ca
Pubns Mgr: Brian Mlazgar *Tel:* 306-585-4795 *E-mail:* brian.mlazgar@uregina.ca
Sr Ed: Donna Grant *Tel:* 306-585-4787 *E-mail:* donna.grant@uregina.ca
Founded: 1973
Scholarly paperbacks & hardcovers on cultural & economic development & history of Canadian Plains & western Canada.
Publishes in English, French.
ISBN Prefix(es): 978-0-88977
Number of titles published annually: 15 Print
Total Titles: 90 Print; 1 CD-ROM
*Distribution Center:* University of Toronto Press, 10 Saint Mary St, Suite 700, Toronto, ON M4Y 2W8 *Tel:* 416-978-2239 *Fax:* 416-978-4738 *Web Site:* www.utpress.utoronto.ca
Membership(s): Association of Canadian Publishers; Association of Canadian University Presses; Saskatchewan Publishers Group

**Canadian Poetry Press**
Western Univerisity, Dept of English, London, ON N6A 3K7
*Tel:* 519-673-1164; 519-661-2111 (ext 85834) *Fax:* 519-661-3776
*E-mail:* canadianpoetry@uwo.ca
*Web Site:* www.canadianpoetry.ca
*Key Personnel*
Dir & Gen Ed: D M R Bentley
Gen Mgr: Susan Bentley
Founded: 1986
Publishes in English.
ISBN Prefix(es): 978-0-921243
Number of titles published annually: 3 Print; 4 Online
Total Titles: 30 Print; 40 Online

**§Canadian Scholars' Press Inc**
Imprint of CSPI/Women's Press
180 Bloor St W, Suite 801, Toronto, ON M5S 2V6
SAN: 118-9484
*Tel:* 416-929-2774 *Toll Free Tel:* 800-463-1998 *Fax:* 416-929-1926
*E-mail:* info@cspi.org; editorial@cspi.org
*Web Site:* cspi.org; www.womenspress.ca
*Key Personnel*
Pres: Andrew Wayne
VP, Custom Publg: Drew Hawkins
VP, Book Publg: Rick Walker *Tel:* 416-929-2774 ext 17 *E-mail:* rick.walker@cspi.org
Prodn Mgr: Colleen Wormald
Founded: 1986
Scholarly books & texts for post-secondary education. Trade books-feminist orientation.
Publishes in English, French.
ISBN Prefix(es): 978-0-921627; 978-1-55130; 978-0-921881; 978-0-88961 (Women's Press); 978-1-89418; 978-1-894549 (Sumach Press)
Number of titles published annually: 24 Print; 10 E-Book
Total Titles: 400 Print; 6 CD-ROM; 80 E-Book
Imprints: Kellom Books; Sumach Press; Women's Press
*Orders to:* Gazelle Book Services Ltd, White Cross Mills, Hightown, Lancaster LA1 4XS, United Kingdom, Cust Serv Mgr: Ian Waterhouse *Tel:* (01524) 68765 *Fax:* (01524) 63232 *E-mail:* sales@gazellebooks.co.uk *Web Site:* www.gazellebooks.co.uk
*Returns:* Gazelle Book Services Ltd, White Cross Mills, Hightown, Lancaster LA1 4XS, United Kingdom, Cust Serv Mgr: Ian Waterhouse *Tel:* (01524) 68765 *Fax:* (01524) 63232 *E-mail:* sales@gazellebooks.co.uk *Web Site:* www.gazellebooks.co.uk
*Distribution Center:* Gazelle Book Services Ltd, White Cross Mills, Hightown, Lancaster LA1 4XS, United Kingdom, Cust Serv Mgr: Ian Waterhouse *Tel:* (01524) 68765 *Fax:* (01524) 63232 *E-mail:* sales@gazellebooks.co.uk *Web Site:* www.gazellebooks.co.uk
Membership(s): Association of Canadian Publishers; Organization of Book Publishers of Ontario

**Cape Breton University Press Inc (CBU Press)**
1250 Grand Lake Rd, Sydney, NS B1M 1A2
Mailing Address: PO Box 5300, Sydney, NS B1P 6L2
*Tel:* 902-563-1604 (orders & cust serv) *Fax:* 902-563-1177
*E-mail:* cbu_press@cbu.ca
*Web Site:* www.cbupress.ca
*Key Personnel*
Ed-in-Chief: Mike R Hunter *Tel:* 902-563-1955 *E-mail:* mike_hunter@cbu.ca
Founded: 1975
Nonfiction regional books; fiction, short stories, poetry, community economic development.
Publishes in English.
ISBN Prefix(es): 978-0-920336; 978-1-897009
Number of titles published annually: 3 Print
Total Titles: 84 Print
Distributed by Nimbus Publishing
*Orders to:* Nimbus Publishing, PO Box 9166, Halifax, NS B3K 5M8, Sales Mgr: Terrilee Bulger *Toll Free Tel:* 800-646-2879 *Toll Free*

*Fax:* 888-253-3133 *Web Site:* www.nimbus.ns.ca
*Distribution Center:* Nimbus Publishing, PO Box 9166, Halifax, NS B3K 5M8, Sales Mgr: Terrilee Bulger *Toll Free Tel:* 800-646-2879 *Toll Free Fax:* 888-253-3133 *Web Site:* www.nimbus.ns.ca
Membership(s): APMA; Association of Canadian Publishers

**Captus Press Inc**
1600 Steeles Ave W, Units 14-15, Concord, ON L4K 4M2
*Tel:* 416-736-5537 *Fax:* 416-736-5793
*E-mail:* info@captus.com
*Web Site:* www.captus.com
*Key Personnel*
Pres: Randy Hoffman *E-mail:* randy@captus.com
Mgr: Pauline Lai *E-mail:* pauline@captus.com
Accts Admin & Intl Rts: Lily Chu *E-mail:* lily@captus.com
Founded: 1987
Publication of textbooks, scholarly books, professional books, nonfiction trade books & multimedia Internet courses. Publishes in Spanish also.
Publishes in English, French.
ISBN Prefix(es): 978-0-921801; 978-1-896691; 978-1-895712; 978-1-55322
Number of titles published annually: 30 Print; 2 Online
Total Titles: 151 Print; 2 Online; 1 E-Book
Imprints: Captus Press; Captus University Publications; University Press of Canada

**Les Editions Caractere**
5800, rue Saint-Denis, bureau 900, Montreal, QC H2S 3L5
*Tel:* 514-273-1066 *Fax:* 514-276-0324
*E-mail:* caractere@tc.tc
*Web Site:* www.editionscaractere.com
Founded: 2004
ISBN Prefix(es): 978-2-923351; 978-2-89642; 978-2-89643
*Distribution Center:* Prologue Inc, 1650, Lionel Bertrand, Boisbriand, QC J7H 1N7 *Tel:* 450-434-0306 *Toll Free Tel:* 800-363-2864 *Fax:* 450-434-2627 *Toll Free Fax:* 800-361-7977

**Carswell**
Division of Thomson Reuters Canada Ltd
One Corporate Plaza, 2075 Kennedy Rd, Toronto, ON M1T 3V4
*Tel:* 416-609-8000; 416-298-5141; 416-609-3800 (cust rel) *Toll Free Tel:* 800-387-5164 (cust serv CN & US) *Fax:* 416-298-5094; 416-298-5082 (cust rel) *Toll Free Fax:* 877-750-9041 (CN only)
*E-mail:* carswell.customerrelations@thomson.com
*Web Site:* www.carswell.com
Founded: 1864
Canada's leading provider of specialized information & electronic research solutions to the legal, tax, accounting & human resources markets. Headquartered in Toronto, ON, Carswell provides integrated information in a range of formats, including books, looseleaf services, journals, newsletters, CD-ROMs & online. Carswell is a business within The Thomson Corporation.
Publishes in English, French.
ISBN Prefix(es): 978-0-459; 978-0-88820
Number of titles published annually: 100 Print
Total Titles: 1,113 Print; 10 Online
Imprints: Carswell; Richard De Boo
Divisions: Carswell Custom Printing
*Branch Office(s)*
430 rue St Pierre, Montreal, QC H2Y 2M5 *Tel:* 514-985-0824 *Fax:* 514-985-6605
Distributor for Australian Tax Practice; Editions Yvon Blai; Brooker's; Compu-Mark; Editorial Ararzadi; Ellis Publications; Fakta Info Direkt; Federal & State Government Printers; Forlaget Thomson; Foundation Press; GEE Publishing; W Green; Incorporated Council (London); IOB; Lahey; Lawbook Co; McGill University Air & Space Institute (Montreal); Native Law Center University of Saskatchewan; Professional Publishing (London); Provincial Government Printers; Research Institute of America; Round Hall Ltd; The Stationary Office (London); Sweet & Maxwell (Asia); Sweet & Maxwell Group; Thomson Tax Ltd (London); West Group
U.S. Publishers Represented: Research Institute of America; West

**§CCH Canadian Limited, A Wolters Kluwer Company**
Subsidiary of Wolters Kluwer NV (The Netherlands)
90 Sheppard Ave E, Suite 300, Toronto, ON M2N 6X1
*Tel:* 416-224-2224 *Toll Free Tel:* 800-268-4522 (CN & US cust serv) *Fax:* 416-224-2243 *Toll Free Fax:* 800-461-4131
*E-mail:* cservice@cch.ca (cust serv)
*Web Site:* www.cch.ca
*Key Personnel*
CEO & Pres: Doug Finley
VP, Fin & Admin: Allan Orr
VP, Technol: Marie Croteau
VP, Legal & Busn Mkts: Steve Monk
VP, Pubns, CCH Ltee: Guy Correau
Fin & Off Administrator: Karen Ali
Founded: 1946
Produce information products that help its customers take command of complex regulatory issues in tax, financial planning, business & law. One of Canada's largest & most respected professional information providers, producing leading-edge research materials & application software in both English & French. Products are available via the Internet as well as in CD-ROM & print formats. The company's long-standing success is based on technological innovation, information management expertise & a commitment to industry leadership. Works closely with experts from a variety of disciplines to provide insight & professional commentary that advances our customers' knowledge & productivity.
Publishes in English, French.
ISBN Prefix(es): 978-0-89366; 978-1-55141
Number of titles published annually: 50 Print
Total Titles: 800 Print
*Branch Office(s)*
Publications CCH Ltee, 7005 boul Taschereau bur 190, Brossard, QC J4Z 1A7 *Tel:* 450-678-4443
CCH Canadienne Limitee, 1120 rue Cherbourg, CP 2300, Sherbrooke, QC J1H 5N7 *Tel:* 819-566-2000
U.S. Publishers Represented: Aspen Publishers; CCH US

**Centre for Reformation & Renaissance Studies (CRRS)**
EJ Pratt Library, Rm 301, 71 Queen's Park Crescent E, Toronto, ON M5S 1K7
*Tel:* 416-585-4468 *Fax:* 416-585-4430 (attn: CRRS)
*E-mail:* crrs.publications@utoronto.ca
*Web Site:* www.crrs.ca
*Key Personnel*
Dir: Lynne Magnusson *Tel:* 416-585-4461
Pubns Mgr: Vanessa McCarthy *Tel:* 416-585-4465
Founded: 1965
Specialty library & academic publisher.
Publishes in English, French.
ISBN Prefix(es): 978-0-7727
Number of titles published annually: 10 Print
Total Titles: 102 Print
Imprints: Dovehouse Press

**Centre Franco-Ontarien de Ressources en Alphabetisation (Centre FORA)**
432 Ave Westmount, Unit H, Sudbury, ON P3A 5Z8
*Tel:* 705-524-3672 *Toll Free Tel:* 888-814-4422 (orders, CN only) *Fax:* 705-524-8535
*E-mail:* info@centrefora.on.ca
*Web Site:* www.centrefora.on.ca
*Key Personnel*
Dir: Yolande Clement *Tel:* 705-524-3672 ext 233 *E-mail:* yclement@centrefora.on.ca
Admin Secy: Monique Quesnel-Lafontaine *Tel:* 888-524-8569 ext 221 *E-mail:* mqlafontaine@centrefora.on.ca
Founded: 1989 (nonprofit organization)
Learning materials for adult literacy & distribute education materials for all ages.
Publishes in French.
ISBN Prefix(es): 978-2-921706
Number of titles published annually: 20 Print
Total Titles: 150 Print

**The Charlton Press**
Division of Charlton International Inc
PO Box 820, Sta Willowdale B, North York, ON M2K 2R1
*Tel:* 416-488-1418 *Toll Free Tel:* 800-442-6042 (North America) *Fax:* 416-488-4656 *Toll Free Fax:* 800-442-1542 (North America)
*E-mail:* chpress@charltonpress.com
*Web Site:* www.charltonpress.com
*Key Personnel*
CEO: William K Cross
Founded: 1952
Specialize in Royal Doulton, Royal Worcester etc. Collectibles & antiques, 20th century numismatics, sports cards, ceramics.
Publishes in English.
ISBN Prefix(es): 978-0-88968; 978-2-9800475
Number of titles published annually: 20 Print
Total Titles: 35 Print
*Orders to:* Book Systems Plus Ltd, 8 Hill St, 1st fl, Saffron Walden, Essex CB10 1JD, United Kingdom (UK & Europe) *Tel:* 524458 *Fax:* 524459 *E-mail:* bsp2b@aol.com
Membership(s): IBPA, the Independent Book Publishers Association

**ChemTec Publishing**
38 Earswick Dr, Toronto, ON M1E 1C6
*Tel:* 416-265-2603 *Fax:* 416-265-1399
*E-mail:* orderdesk@chemtec.org
*Web Site:* www.chemtec.org
*Key Personnel*
CEO: Anna Wypych
Circ Mgr: Anna Fox
Founded: 1988
Additives, blends, polymers, recycling & rheology.
Publishes in English.
ISBN Prefix(es): 978-1-895198
Number of titles published annually: 5 Print
Total Titles: 43 Print; 4 CD-ROM
Subsidiaries: ChemTec Laboratories Inc

**Cheneliere Education Inc**
5800 Saint Denis St, Montreal, QC H2S 3L5
*Tel:* 514-273-1066 *Toll Free Tel:* 800-565-5531 *Fax:* 514-276-0324 *Toll Free Fax:* 800-814-0324
*E-mail:* info@cheneliere.ca
*Web Site:* www.cheneliere.ca
*Key Personnel*
Pres: Jacques Rochefort *E-mail:* jrochefort@cheneliere.ca
Founded: 1971
School, college & university textbooks; vocational; French Immersion; teaching skills & book packaging (French & English languages).
Publishes in French.
ISBN Prefix(es): 978-2-89461; 978-2-7650
Number of titles published annually: 200 Print

Imprints: Beauchemin; Gaetan Morin Editeur; Graficor
U.S. Publishers Represented: McGraw-Hill Inc
*Warehouse:* McGraw-Hill Ryerson Limited, 300 Water St, Whitby, ON L1N 9B6
*See separate listing for:*
**Gaetan Morin Editeur**

**Chestnut Publishing Group Inc**
4005 Bayview Ave, Suite 610, Toronto, ON M2M 3Z9
*Tel:* 416-224-5824 *Fax:* 416-224-0595
*Web Site:* www.chestnutpublishing.com
*Key Personnel*
Pres: Stanley Starkman *E-mail:* sharkstark@sympatico.ca
VP, Publg: Dan de Souza *E-mail:* dan@readingahead.com
VP, Fin: Allan Goldbach *Tel:* 416-499-1253 *Fax:* 416-499-1652 *E-mail:* agoldbach@on.aibn.com
Founded: 2001
Publish education, school & college, trade, adult, children, juvenile, young adult & English as a second language titles.
Publishes in English, French.
ISBN Prefix(es): 978-1-894601; 978-1-894929; 978-0-9689522; 978-0-9731237; 978-1-897039; 978-0-9688946
Number of titles published annually: 20 Print; 4 CD-ROM; 3 Audio
Total Titles: 220 Print; 20 CD-ROM; 20 Audio
Imprints: Chestnut Publishing; Comfort Publishing; High Interest Publishing (HIP) (books for reluctant readers); Lynx Publishing (ESL); Patnor Publishing (books for reluctant readers & ESL)
Foreign Rep(s): Robinswood Press (UK)
Foreign Rights: INT Press (Australia, New Zealand)
*Warehouse:* TTS Distributing Inc, 45 Tyler St, Aurora, ON L4G 3L5, Contact: Rory Stewart *Tel:* 905-841-3898 *Fax:* 905-841-3026 *E-mail:* rstewart@ttsdistributing.com *Web Site:* www.ttsdistributing.com
Membership(s): Organization of Book Publishers of Ontario

**Chouette Publishing**
1001 Lenoir St, B-238, Montreal, QC H4C 2Z6
*Tel:* 514-925-3325 *Fax:* 514-925-3323
*E-mail:* info@editions-chouette.com
*Web Site:* www.chouettepublishing.com
*Key Personnel*
Publr & Ed: Christine L'Heureux
Founded: 1987
Produce children's books adapted to a stage of a child's development, from birth to age six.
Publishes in English, French.
ISBN Prefix(es): 978-2-921198; 978-2-89450
Number of titles published annually: 17 Print
U.S. Rep(s): Client Distribution Services
Foreign Rep(s): Christine L'Heureux
*Warehouse:* Heritage, 300 rue Arran, St-Lambert, QC J4R 1K5 *Tel:* 514-875-0327 *Fax:* 450-672-5448 *E-mail:* marketing@editions-chouette.com
*Distribution Center:* H B Fenn & Co, 34 Nixon Rd, Bolton, ON L7E 1W2 *Tel:* 905-951-6600 *Toll Free Tel:* 800-267-3366 *Fax:* 905-951-6601 *Toll Free Fax:* 800-465-3422 *E-mail:* sales@hbfenn.com *Web Site:* www.hbfenn.com

**Editions du CHU Sainte-Justine**
Unit of Direction de l'enseignement
3175 Cote-Saint-Catherine, Montreal, QC H3T 1C5
*Tel:* 514-345-4671 *Fax:* 514-345-4631
*E-mail:* edition.hsj@ssss.gouv.qc.ca
*Web Site:* www.editions-chu-sainte-justine.org
*Key Personnel*
Publg Dir: Marise Labrecque *Tel:* 514-345-7743 *E-mail:* marise.labreque.hsj@ssss.gouv.qc.ca
Sales Mgr: Jean-Francois Hebert *Tel:* 514-345-4931 ext 5541 *E-mail:* jean-francois.hebert.hsj@ssss.gouv.qc.ca
Ed: Marie-Eve Lefebvre *Tel:* 514-345-2350 *E-mail:* marie-eve.lefebvre.hsj@ssss.gouv.qc.ca
ISBN Prefix(es): 978-2-921215; 978-2-921858; 978-2-922770; 978-2-89619
Number of titles published annually: 12 Print
*Distribution Center:* Prologue, 1650 blvd Lionel-Bertrand, Boisbriand, QC J7H 1N7 *Tel:* 450-434-0306 *Toll Free Tel:* 800-363-2864 *Fax:* 450-434-2627 *Toll Free Fax:* 800-361-8088 *E-mail:* prologue@prologue.ca *Web Site:* www.prologue.ca
SDL La Caravelle, Rue du Pre-aux-oies, 303, 1130 Brussels, Belgium (Belgium & Luxembourg) *Tel:* (02) 240 93 08 *Fax:* (02) 216 35 98 *E-mail:* info@sdlcaravelle.com
Daudin Distribution, One rue Guynemer, 78114 Magny-les Hameaux, France *Tel:* 01 30 48 74 74 *Fax:* 01 34 98 02 44 *E-mail:* commandes@daudin.fr
Servidis, Chemin des chalets, 1279 Chavannes-de-Bogis, Switzerland *Tel:* (022) 960 95 32 *Fax:* (022) 960 95 77 *E-mail:* commande@servidis.ch

**Clements Publishing**
6021 Yonge St, Suite 213, Toronto, ON M2M 3W2
*Tel:* 647-477-2509 *Fax:* 647-477-2058
*E-mail:* info@clementspublishing.com
*Web Site:* www.clementspublishing.com
*Key Personnel*
Dir: Rob Clements
Founded: 2000
Christian publisher.
Publishes in English, French.
ISBN Prefix(es): 978-1-894667
Number of titles published annually: 10 Print
Total Titles: 30 Print; 7 Audio
*Orders to:* Spring Arbor; Ingram Book Co, One Ingram Blvd, La Vergne, TN 37086, United States *Tel:* 615-793-5000 *Toll Free Tel:* 800-937-8200 *E-mail:* customerservice@ingrambook.com *Web Site:* www.ingrambook.com
*Distribution Center:* Ingram Book Co, One Ingram Blvd, La Vergne, TN 37086, United States *Tel:* 615-793-5000 *Toll Free Tel:* 800-937-8200 *E-mail:* customerservice@ingrambook.com *Web Site:* www.ingrambook.com

**Coach House Books**
80 bpNichol Lane, Toronto, ON M5S 3J4
*Tel:* 416-979-2217 *Toll Free Tel:* 800-367-6360 (outside Toronto) *Fax:* 416-977-1158
*E-mail:* mail@chbooks.com
*Web Site:* www.chbooks.com
*Key Personnel*
Founder & Publr: Stan Bevington *E-mail:* stan@chbooks.com
Edit Dir: Alana Wilcox *E-mail:* alana@chbooks.com
Publicist: Evan Munday *E-mail:* evan@chbooks.com
Publg Asst: Leigh Nash *E-mail:* leigh@chbooks.com
Founded: 1965
Literary small press specializing in experimental fiction & poetry.
Publishes in English.
ISBN Prefix(es): 978-1-55245
Number of titles published annually: 16 Print; 5 Online
Total Titles: 140 Print; 60 Online
Foreign Rights: Amo Agency (Amo Noh) (South Korea); Anatolia Lit Agency (Amy Spangler) (Turkey); Sandra Bruna Agencia Literaria SL (Natalia Berenguer) (Portugal, Spain); English Agency Japan (Hamish Macaskill) (Japan); The Grayhawk Agency (Lora Fountain) (China, Taiwan); Mohr Books Literary Agency (Annelie Geissler) (Germany); Sandrine Paccher (France); Piergiorgio Nicolazzini Literary Agency (Maura Solinas) (Italy)
*Distribution Center:* LitDistCo, 100 Armstrong Ave, Georgetown, ON L7G 5S4 (CN orders) *Toll Free Tel:* 800-591-6250 *Toll Free Fax:* 800-591-6251 *E-mail:* orders@litdistco.ca *Web Site:* www.litdistco.ca
Small Press Distribution, 1341 Seventh St, Berkeley, CA 94710-1409, United States (US orders) *Toll Free Tel:* 800-869-7553 *Fax:* 510-524-0852 *E-mail:* spd@spdbooks.org *Web Site:* www.spdbooks.org
Consortium Book Sales & Distribution, The Keg House, 34 13 Ave NE, Suite 101, Minneapolis, MN 55413-1007, United States (US orders) *Tel:* 612-746-2600 *Fax:* 612-746-2606 *E-mail:* orderentry@perseusbooks.com *Web Site:* www.cbsd.com
Membership(s): Association of Canadian Publishers; Council of Literary Magazines & Presses; Literary Press Group

**Collector Grade Publications Inc**
PO Box 1046, Cobourg, ON K9A 4W5
*Tel:* 905-342-3434 *Fax:* 905-342-3688
*E-mail:* info@collectorgrade.com
*Web Site:* www.collectorgrade.com
*Key Personnel*
Pres: R Blake Stevens
Founded: 1979
Accurate, in-depth studies of modern small arms. Technical reference books.
Publishes in English.
ISBN Prefix(es): 978-0-88935
Number of titles published annually: 3 Print
Total Titles: 38 Print

**Company's Coming Publishing Ltd**
2311 96 St, Edmonton, AB T6N 1G3
*Tel:* 780-450-6223 *Toll Free Tel:* 800-875-7108 (US & CN) *Fax:* 780-450-1857
*E-mail:* info@companyscoming.com
*Web Site:* www.companyscoming.com
*Key Personnel*
Pres: Grant Lovig
VP, Mktg & Dist: Gail Lovig
Founded: 1981
Publish cookbooks, craft books & stationery products.
Publishes in English.
ISBN Prefix(es): 978-0-9690695; 978-0-9693322; 978-1-895455; 978-1-896891
Number of titles published annually: 25 Print
Total Titles: 200 Print

**The Continuing Legal Education Society of British Columbia (CLEBC)**
500-1155 W Pender St, Vancouver, BC V6E 2P4
*Tel:* 604-669-3544; 604-893-2121 (cust serv) *Toll Free Tel:* 800-663-0437 (CN) *Fax:* 604-669-9260
*E-mail:* custserv@cle.bc.ca
*Web Site:* www.cle.bc.ca
*Key Personnel*
CEO: Ron Friesen *Tel:* 604-893-2114 *E-mail:* rfriesen@cle.bc.ca
Dir, Pubns: Susan Munro *Tel:* 604-893-2106 *E-mail:* smunro@cle.bc.ca
Sales & Mktg Liaison: Karen Kerfoot *Tel:* 604-893-2110 *E-mail:* kkerfoot@cle.bc.ca
Founded: 1976
Publish course materials, practice manuals & case digests.
Publishes in English.
ISBN Prefix(es): 978-0-86504; 978-1-55258
Number of titles published annually: 50 Print
Total Titles: 267 Print; 1 CD-ROM; 37 Online
Imprints: CLEBC

**Cormorant Books Inc**
Affiliate of Thomas Allen & Sons

390 Steelcase Rd E, Markham, ON L3R 1G2
*Tel:* 905-475-9126 (Thomas Allen & Sons); 905-475-5571
*E-mail:* info@cormorantbooks.com
*Web Site:* www.cormorantbooks.com
*Key Personnel*
Pres & Publr, Cormorant Books: Marc Cote *E-mail:* m.cote@cormorantbooks.com
Assoc Publr, Cormorant Books & Publr, DCB/ Dancing Cat Books: Barry Jewett *E-mail:* b.jowett@cormorantbooks.com
Mktg: Bryan J Ibeas
Publicity: Meryl Howsam
Art & Cover Design: Angel Guerra
Interior Design: Tannice Goddard
Founded: 1986
Literary fiction & creative nonfiction for the adult market; poetry, children's illustrated; books for middle readers & young adults; Canadian authors only.
Publishes in English.
ISBN Prefix(es): 978-0-920953; 978-1-896951; 978-1-896332; 978-1-897151
Number of titles published annually: 22 Print
Total Titles: 160 Print; 1 Audio
Imprints: Dancing Cat Books (DCB); The Riverbank Press
Membership(s): Association of Canadian Publishers; Canadian Booksellers Association; Organization of Book Publishers of Ontario

**Coteau Books**
Division of Thunder Creek Publishing Co-operative
2517 Victoria Ave, Regina, SK S4P 0T2
SAN: 115-1037
*Tel:* 306-777-0170 *Toll Free Tel:* 800-440-4471 (CN only) *Fax:* 306-522-5152
*E-mail:* coteau@coteaubooks.com
*Web Site:* www.coteaubooks.com
*Key Personnel*
Mng Ed: Nik Burton
Founded: 1975
Only publish Canadian authors.
Publishes in English.
ISBN Prefix(es): 978-0-919926
Number of titles published annually: 12 Print; 8 E-Book
Total Titles: 130 Print; 15 E-Book
*Distribution Center:* Publishers Group Canada, 300-76 Stafford St, Toronto, ON M6J 2S1 *Tel:* 416-934-9900 *Fax:* 416-934-1410 *E-mail:* info@pgcbooks.ca

**La Courte Echelle**
5243 St Laurent Blvd, Montreal, QC H2T 1S4
*Tel:* 514-274-2004 *Toll Free Tel:* 800-387-6192 (orders only) *Fax:* 514-270-4160 *Toll Free Fax:* 800-450-0391 (orders only)
*E-mail:* info@courteechelle.com
*Web Site:* www.courteechelle.com
*Key Personnel*
Pres & Ed: Helene Derome
EVP & HR: Martine Benard
Dir, Sales & Mktg: Mia Caron
Founded: 1978
Children's, young adult & adult fiction. No unsol mss accepted.
Publishes in French.
ISBN Prefix(es): 978-2-89021
Number of titles published annually: 50 Print
Total Titles: 545 Print
U.S. Rep(s): Firefly Books
*Warehouse:* Firefly Books/Frontier, c/o CACHE, Tonawanda Commerce Ctr, 2221 Kenmore Ave, Tonawanda, NY 14207, United States *Fax:* 416-499-8313 *E-mail:* fireflybooks@globalserve.net
*Distribution Center:* Firefly Books Ltd, 66 Leek Crescent, Richmond Hill, ON L4B 1H1 *Tel:* 416-499-8412 *Toll Free Tel:* 800-450-0391 *Fax:* 416-499-8313 *Web Site:* www.fireflybooks.com

**§Crabtree Publishing Co Ltd**
Subsidiary of Crabtree Publishing Co (USA)
616 Welland Ave, St Catharines, ON L2M-5V6
SAN: 115-1436
*Tel:* 905-682-5221 *Toll Free Tel:* 800-387-7650 *Fax:* 905-682-7166 *Toll Free Fax:* 800-355-7166
*E-mail:* custserv@crabtreebooks.com; sales@crabtreebooks.com; orders@crabtreebooks.com
*Web Site:* www.crabtreebooks.com
*Key Personnel*
Pres: Peter A Crabtree
Publr: Bobbie Kalman
VP, Strategic Busn Devt: Sean Charlebois *E-mail:* sean_c@crabtreebooks.com
Edit Dir: Kathy Middleton *E-mail:* kathy_m@crabtreebooks.com
Dir, New Media: Rob MacGregor *E-mail:* rob_m@crabtreebooks.com
Prodn Dir: Craig Culliford *E-mail:* craig_c@crabtreebooks.com
Sales & Mktg Dir: Lisa Maisonneuve *E-mail:* lisa_m@crabtreebooks.com
Sales & Mktg Mgr: Julie Alguire *E-mail:* julie_a@crabtreebooks.com
Gen Mgr: John Siemens *E-mail:* john_s@crabtreebooks.com
Founded: 1978
Children's nonfiction & fiction, library binding & paperback for school & trade.
Publishes in English, French.
ISBN Prefix(es): 978-0-86505; 978-0-7787; 978-1-4271
Number of titles published annually: 201 Print; 634 E-Book; 48 Audio
Total Titles: 2,363 Print; 850 E-Book; 96 Audio
Imprints: Crabtree Look, Listen & Learn
Distributor for Bayard; Maren Green
Foreign Rep(s): BookSmart (China, Japan); INT Press (Australia, New Zealand); Roundhouse Group (European Union, UK); Titles (South Africa)
Membership(s): ABA; ALA; American Alliance of Museums; American Marketing Association; Association of Canadian Publishers; Canadian Booksellers Association; Educational Book & Media Association; National Science Teachers Association; Ontario Library Association

**CRRS**, see Centre for Reformation & Renaissance Studies (CRRS)

**§Database Directories**
588 Dufferin Ave, London, ON N6B 2A4
*Tel:* 519-433-1666 *Fax:* 519-430-1131
*E-mail:* mail@databasedirectory.com
*Web Site:* www.databasedirectory.com
*Key Personnel*
CEO: Lesley Classic *E-mail:* lclassic@databasedirectory.com
Pres: Robert Kasher
Founded: 1995
Directories & e-files on libraries, schools, colleges, universities, academic retailers & municipalities.
Publishes in English.
ISBN Prefix(es): 978-1-896537
Number of titles published annually: 3 Print; 4 CD-ROM; 4 Online
Total Titles: 10 Print; 10 CD-ROM; 4 Online
*Branch Office(s)*
1234-A Ninth Ave, Honolulu, HI 96816, United States

**Editions Le Dauphin Blanc Inc**
825, boul Lebourgneuf, Suite 125, Quebec, QC G2J 0B9
*Tel:* 418-845-4045 *Fax:* 418-845-1933
*E-mail:* info@dauphinblanc.com
*Web Site:* www.dauphinblanc.com
*Key Personnel*
CEO: Alain Williamson *E-mail:* alainwilliamson@dauphinblanc.com
Asst Dir & Prodn Mgr: Sonia Marois *E-mail:* soniamarois@dauphinblanc.com
Founded: 1991
ISBN Prefix(es): 978-2-89436
*Distribution Center:* Prologue Inc, 1650, Lionel-Bertrand, Boisbriand, QC J7H 1N7 *Tel:* 450-434-0306 *Toll Free Tel:* 800-363-2864 *Fax:* 450-434-2627 *Web Site:* www.prologue.ca
DG Diffusion, Zl de Bogues, 31750 Escalquens, France (Belgium & France) *Tel:* 05 61 00 09 99 *Fax:* 05 61 00 23 12 *E-mail:* adv@dgdiffusion.com *Web Site:* www.dgdiffusion.com
Diffusion Transat/Servidis, Chemin des Chalets 7, 1279 Chavannes-de-Bogis, Switzerland *Tel:* (022) 42 77 40 *Fax:* (022) 43 46 46 *E-mail:* transat@transatdiffusion.ch

**§DC Canada Education Publishing**
120 Slater St, Suite 960, Ottawa, ON K1P 6E2
*Tel:* 613-565-8885 *Toll Free Tel:* 888-565-0262 *Fax:* 613-565-8881
*E-mail:* info@dc-canada.ca
*Web Site:* www.dc-canada.ca
*Key Personnel*
Publg Dir: Mei Dang
Mng Ed: Debbie Gervais
Ed: Anja Pujic
Founded: 1995
ISBN Prefix(es): 978-0-9738439; 978-0-9738440; 978-0-9808816; 978-0-9810549; 978-1-926776
*Orders to:* 180 Metcalfe St, Suite 204, Ottawa, ON K2P 1P5

**Decker Publishing**
69 John St S, Suite 310, Hamilton, ON L8N 2B9
*Tel:* 905-522-8526 *Toll Free Tel:* 855-647-6511 *Fax:* 905-522-9273
*E-mail:* customercare@deckerpublishing.com
*Web Site:* www.deckerpublishing.com
*Key Personnel*
Pres: Ryan Decker
Mgr, Cust Care & Dist: Marie Moore *Tel:* 905-522-8526 ext 2233
Founded: 1982
Publishes textbooks & journals in all areas of medical & dental.
Publishes in English.
ISBN Prefix(es): 978-1-55009
Number of titles published annually: 2 Print; 3 CD-ROM; 15 Online
Total Titles: 3 Print; 25 Online
Distributed by Ebsco

**§Double Dragon Publishing Inc**
1-5762 Hwy 7 E, Markham, ON L3P 7Y4
Mailing Address: PO Box 54016, Markham, ON L3P 7Y4
*Tel:* 603-778-7191
*E-mail:* info@double-dragon-ebooks.com; sales@double-dragon-ebooks.com
*Web Site:* www.double-dragon-ebooks.com
*Key Personnel*
CEO & Publr: Deron Douglas
Founded: 2001
Publishes ebooks & trade paperbacks in the fantasy, science fiction, speculative fiction, horror & suspense genres. Established with the goal of building a Canadian-based publishing venue for the growing number of good but unpublished fiction writers around the world. Dedicated to publishing quality works of fiction & nonfiction & will continue to publish works in various genres in both the ebook & traditional paper book formats. Make special efforts to publish a specific number of works written by North American Aboriginal authors each year.
Publishes in English.
ISBN Prefix(es): 978-1-894841; 978-1-55404

Number of titles published annually: 40 Print; 100 E-Book
Total Titles: 40 Print; 125 E-Book
Imprints: Blood Moon Publishing; Carnal Desires Publishing; DDP Literary Press; Double Dragon eBooks; Double Dragon Media Group; Dragon Dance; Dragon Tooth Fantasy; Dragon's Heart Romance

**Doubleday Canada**
Imprint of Random House of Canada Limited
One Toronto St, Suite 300, Toronto, ON M5C 2V6
SAN: 115-0340
*Tel:* 416-364-4449 *Fax:* 416-364-6863
*Web Site:* www.randomhouse.ca
*Key Personnel*
CEO & Pres: Brad Martin
Chief Admin Offr & EVP: Douglas Foot *Tel:* 905-624-0672
EVP & Dir, Sales: Duncan Shields *Tel:* 905-624-0672
SVP & Dir, Mktg & Corp Communs: Tracey Turriff
SVP & Dir, Digital: Lisa Charters
VP & Dir, Mktg Strategy: Scott Sellers
VP, Creative Dir: Scott Richardson
VP, Prodn: Janine Laporte
VP & Publr, Double Day Canada Publg Group: Kristin Cochrane
Publg Dir, Double Day Canada Publg Group: Lynn Henry
Assoc Dir, Prodn: Carla Kean
Sr Ed, Double Day Canada Publg Group: Nina Pronovost; Tim Rostron
Founded: 1937
General trade nonfiction (current affairs, politics, business, sports); fiction, children's illustrated.
Random House Inc & its publishing entities are not accepting unsol submissions, proposals, mss, or submission queries via e-mail at this time.
Publishes in English.
ISBN Prefix(es): 978-0-385; 978-0-7704
Number of titles published annually: 60 Print
Total Titles: 45 Print
Imprints: Anchor Canada; Bond Street Books; Seal Books
Membership(s): Canadian Booksellers Association; Canadian Library Association; Canadian Publishers' Council

**Douglas & McIntyre**
Imprint of Harbour Publishing
2323 Quebec St, Suite 201, Vancouver, BC V5T 4S7
SAN: 115-1886
*Tel:* 604-254-7191 *Toll Free Tel:* 800-667-6902 (orders) *Fax:* 604-254-9099 *Toll Free Fax:* 800-668-5788 (orders CN)
*E-mail:* info@harbourpublishing.com
*Key Personnel*
COO: Jesse Finkelstein
Pres: Mark Scott
VP, Fin & Admin: David Cater
Publr: Trena White
New Society Publr: Rob Sanders *E-mail:* rob.sanders@greystonebooks.com
Founded: 1971
Douglas & McIntyre focuses on biographies, native art & history, architecture, literary fiction & cookbooks. New Society Publishers publishes books about the environment.
Publishes in English.
ISBN Prefix(es): 978-0-88894; 978-1-55044; 978-1-55365; 978-1-897408 (NSP); 978-0-86571 (NSP); 978-1-881699 (NSP); 978-1-55092 (NSP)
Number of titles published annually: 90 Print
Total Titles: 1,500 Print
*Branch Office(s)*
130 Spadina Ave, Suite 405, Toronto, ON M5V 2L4 *Tel:* 416-537-2501 *Fax:* 416-537-4647
U.S. Publishers Represented: Farrar Straus & Giroux
U.S. Rep(s): Publishers Group West (US orders)
*Distribution Center:* HarperCollins Canada Inc, 1995 Markham Rd, Scarborough, ON M1B 5M8 (orders in CN) *Tel:* 416-321-2241 *Toll Free Tel:* 800-387-0117 *Fax:* 416-321-3033 *Toll Free Fax:* 800-668-5788 *E-mail:* hcorder@harpercollins.com SAN: 115-026X
Membership(s): AAP; Association for the Export of Canadian Books; Association of Book Publishers of British Columbia; Association of Canadian Publishers; Canadian Booksellers Association

**Dundurn Press Ltd**
3 Church St, Suite 500, Toronto, ON M5E 1M2
SAN: 115-0359
*Tel:* 416-214-5544 *Fax:* 416-214-5556
*E-mail:* info@dundurn.com
*Web Site:* www.dundurn.com
*Key Personnel*
Pres & Publr: Kirk Howard *E-mail:* khoward@dundurn.com
Founded: 1972
Specialize in Canadian history, social sciences, some biography & art, fiction & mysteries.
Publishes in English.
ISBN Prefix(es): 978-0-919670; 978-1-55002; 978-0-88924; 978-0-88882; 978-1-55488
Number of titles published annually: 100 Print
Imprints: Boardwalk Books; Castle Street Mysteries; Dundurn; Hounslow (popular nonfiction); Napoleon & Co; Simon & Pierre (fiction)
Subsidiaries: Boardwalk Books; Hounslow Press; Simon & Pierre (fiction)
Foreign Rep(s): Gazelle Book Services (Europe)
*Distribution Center:* Ingram Publisher Services, One Ingram Blvd, La Vergne, TN 37086-1986, United States *Toll Free Tel:* 866-400-5351
University of Toronto Press, 10 Sainte Mary St, Suite 700, Toronto, ON M4Y 2W8 *Tel:* 416-978-2239 *Fax:* 416-978-4738 *Web Site:* www.utpress.utoronto.ca
Membership(s): Association of Canadian Publishers

**Ecrits des Forges**
992-A, rue Royale, Trois Rivieres, QC G9A 4H9
*Tel:* 819-840-8492 *Fax:* 819-376-0774
*E-mail:* ecritsdesforges@gmail.com
*Web Site:* www.ecritsdesforges.com
*Key Personnel*
Literary Ed: Bernard Pozier
Exec Dir: Patrick Boulanger
Cont: Edith Bourassa
Founded: 1971
Publish poetry.
Publishes in French.
ISBN Prefix(es): 978-2-89046
Number of titles published annually: 50 Print
Total Titles: 1,050 Print
Distributed by DCR; Prologue
Membership(s): ANEL

**ECW Press**
2120 Queen St E, Suite 200, Toronto, ON M4E 1E2
SAN: 115-1274
*Tel:* 416-694-3348 *Fax:* 416-698-9906
*E-mail:* info@ecwpress.com
*Web Site:* www.ecwpress.com
*Key Personnel*
Publr: Jack David *E-mail:* jack@ecwpress.com
Founded: 1974
Publishes in English.
ISBN Prefix(es): 978-0-920763; 978-1-55022; 978-0-920802
Number of titles published annually: 50 Print
Total Titles: 800 Print; 205 E-Book
Imprints: misFit
Foreign Rights: Bill Hanna (Worldwide exc Canada & USA)
Membership(s): Association of Canadian Publishers; Literary Press Group

**EDGE Science Fiction & Fantasy Publishing**
Imprint of Hades Publications Inc
PO Box 1714, Sta M, Calgary, AB T2P 2L7
*Tel:* 403-254-0160
*Web Site:* www.edgewebsite.com
*Key Personnel*
Pres & Publr: Brian Hades *E-mail:* publisher@hadespublications.com
Mktg Mgr: Janice Shoults
Founded: 1996
Encourage, produce & promote thought-provoking science fiction & fantasy & horror literature by "bringing the magic alive-one world at a time" with each new book released. Independent publisher of science fiction & fantasy novels in hard cover or trade paperback format. Produce high-quality books with lots of attention to detail & lots of marketing effort.
Publishes in English.
ISBN Prefix(es): 978-1-894063; 978-1-896944
Number of titles published annually: 8 Print
Total Titles: 87 Print; 1 Audio
Imprints: Absolute XPress; EDGE Science Fiction & Fantasy Publishing; Tesseract Books
U.S. Rep(s): Baker & Taylor; Fitzhenry & Whiteside; Ingram Book Co
*Distribution Center:* Fitzhenry & Whiteside, 195 Allstate Pkwy, Markham, ON L3R 4T8 *Toll Free Tel:* 800-387-9776 *Toll Free Fax:* 800-260-9777 *E-mail:* bookinfo@fitzhenry.ca
Membership(s): Book Publishers Association of Alberta; IBPA, the Independent Book Publishers Association; IPAC; PMA International

**Les Editions Alire**
120 Cote du Passage, Levis, QC G6V 5S9
*Tel:* 418-835-4441 *Fax:* 418-838-4443
*E-mail:* info@alire.com
*Web Site:* www.alire.com
*Key Personnel*
Admin Dir: Lorraine Bourassa *E-mail:* lorraine.bourassa@alire.com
Edit Dir: Jean Pettigrew *E-mail:* jean.pettigrew@alire.com
Dir, Sales: Louise Alain *E-mail:* louise.alain@alire.com
Founded: 1996
Publish French Canadian popular genre fiction.
Publishes in French.
ISBN Prefix(es): 978-2-922145; 978-2-89615
Number of titles published annually: 10 Print
Total Titles: 131 Print
*Billing Address:* Messageries ADP, 2315 rue de la Province, Longueuil, QC J4G 1G4 (Canada & US) *Tel:* 450-640-1237 *Fax:* 450-674-6237; Interforum Editis, 3 allee de la Seine Immeuble Paryseine, 94854 Ivry sur Seine, France (France & other countries) *Tel:* 01 49 59 11 56 *Fax:* 01 49 59 11 33
*Orders to:* Messageries ADP, 2315 rue de la Province, Longueuil, QC J4G 1G4 (Canada & US) *Tel:* 450-640-1237 *Fax:* 450-674-6237; Interforum Editis, 3 allee de la Seine Immeuble Paryseine, 94854 Ivry sur Seine, France (France & other countries) *Tel:* 01 49 59 11 56 *Fax:* 01 49 59 11 33
*Returns:* Messageries ADP, 2315 rue de la Province, Longueuil, QC J4G 1G4 (Canada & US) *Tel:* 450-640-1237 *Fax:* 450-674-6237; Interforum Editis, 3 allee de la Seine Immeuble Paryseine, 94854 Ivry sur Seine, France (France & other countries) *Tel:* 01 49 59 11 56 *Fax:* 01 49 59 11 33
*Distribution Center:* Messageries ADP, 2315 rue de la Province, Longueuil, QC J4G 1G4

(Canada & US) *Tel:* 450-640-1237 *Fax:* 450-674-6237
Membership(s): Association Nationale des Editeurs de Livres

**editions CERES Ltd/Le Moyen Francais**
CP 1089, Succursale B, Maison de la Poste, Montreal, QC H3B 3K9
*Tel:* 514-937-7138 *Fax:* 514-937-9875
*E-mail:* editionsceres@gmail.com
*Web Site:* www.editionsceres.ca
*Key Personnel*
Pres & Ed: G Di Stefano
Secy & Ed: R M Bidler
Founded: 1979
Dictionaries & erudite volumes on 14th, 15th & 16th centuries French language, literature & philology. Our authors are international. It is open to everyone who specializes in this discipline. University specialists & research libraries.
Publishes in English, French.
ISBN Prefix(es): 978-0-919089
Number of titles published annually: 2 Print
Total Titles: 86 Print

**Editions de la Pleine Lune**
223 34 Ave, Lachine, QC H8T 1Z4
*Tel:* 514-634-7954 *Fax:* 514-637-6366
*E-mail:* editpllune@videotron.ca
*Web Site:* www.pleinelune.qc.ca
*Key Personnel*
Pres & Dir: Marie-Madeleine Raoult
Media Rel: Ginette Beaulieu *E-mail:* ginette.beaulieu2@sympatico.ca
Founded: 1975
Publishes in French.
ISBN Prefix(es): 978-2-89024
Number of titles published annually: 8 Print
Total Titles: 185 Print
*Sales Office(s):* Diffusion Dimedia, 539 Lebeau Blvd, St-Laurent, QC H4N 1S2 *Tel:* 514-336-3941 *Fax:* 514-331-3916 *E-mail:* general@dimedia.qc.ca *Web Site:* www.dimedia.com
*Billing Address:* Diffusion Dimedia, 539 Lebeau Blvd, St-Laurent, QC H4N 1S2 *Tel:* 514-336-3941 *Fax:* 514-331-3916 *E-mail:* general@dimedia.qc.ca *Web Site:* www.dimedia.com
*Orders to:* Diffusion Dimedia, 539 Lebeau Blvd, St-Laurent, QC H4N 1S2 *Tel:* 514-336-3941 *Fax:* 514-331-3916 *E-mail:* general@dimedia.qc.ca *Web Site:* wwww.dimedia.com
*Returns:* Diffusion Dimedia, 539 Lebeau Blvd, St-Laurent, QC H4N 1S2 *Tel:* 514-336-3941 *Fax:* 514-331-3916 *E-mail:* general@dimedia.qc.ca *Web Site:* www.dimedia.com
*Distribution Center:* Exportlivre, 505, rue Belanger, bureau 223, Montreal, QC H2S 1G5 (elsewhere) *E-mail:* info@exportlivre.com *Web Site:* www.exportlivre.com
Diffusion Dimedia, 539 Lebeau Blvd, St-Laurent, QC H4N 1S2 *Tel:* 514-336-3941 *Fax:* 514-331-3916 *E-mail:* general@dimedia.qc.ca *Web Site:* www.dimedia.com
La Librairie du Quebec a Paris et DNM, 30, rue Gay Lussac, 75005 Paris, France *Tel:* 01 43 54 49 02 *Fax:* 01 43 54 39 15 *Web Site:* www.librairieduquebec.fr
Membership(s): ANEL

**Les Editions de l'Hexagone**
Division of Le Groupe Ville Marie Litterature
1010 rue de la Gauchetiere E, Montreal, QC H2L 2N5
*Tel:* 514-523-7993 (ext 4201) *Fax:* 514-282-7530
*E-mail:* vml@sogides.com
*Web Site:* www.edhexagone.com
*Key Personnel*
VP: Martin Balthazar
Lit Dir, Essays: Alain-Nicolas Renaud *E-mail:* alain.nicolas.renaud@groupevml.com
Lit Dir, Fiction: Danielle Fournier *E-mail:* danielle.fournier@groupevml.com
Ed: Stephane Berthomet *E-mail:* stephane.berthomet@groupevml.com
Prodn: Lucie Delemer *E-mail:* lucie.delemer@groupevml.com
Asst to the VP: Sylvia Briere *E-mail:* sylvie.briere@groupevml.com
Founded: 1953
Publishes in French.
ISBN Prefix(es): 978-2-89006
Number of titles published annually: 30 Print
Total Titles: 35 Print
*Orders to:* Messageries ADP, 2315 rue de la Province, Longueuil, QC J4G 1G4 *Tel:* 450-640-1234 *Toll Free Tel:* 800-771-3022 *Fax:* 450-640-1251 *Web Site:* www.messageries-adp.com
*Warehouse:* Messageries ADP, 2315 rue de la Province, Longueuil, QC J4G 1G4 *Tel:* 450-640-1234 *Toll Free Tel:* 800-771-3022 *Fax:* 450-640-1251 *Web Site:* www.messageries-adp.com

**Les Editions de Mortagne**
CP 116, Boucherville, QC J4B 5E6
*Tel:* 450-641-2387 *Fax:* 450-655-6092
*E-mail:* info@editionsdemortagne.com
*Web Site:* www.editionsdemortagne.com
*Key Personnel*
Founder & Pres: Max Permingeat
VP, Fin: Alexandra Pellerin
VP, Publg & Prodn: Caroline Pellerin
VP, R&D: Sandy Pellerin
Founded: 1979
Novels.
Publishes in French.
ISBN Prefix(es): 978-2-89074
Number of titles published annually: 15 Print
Total Titles: 15 Print
*Foreign Office(s):* BP 13, 16700 Ruffec, France *Tel:* 05 45 85 79 00
*Distribution Center:* Prologue, 1650 blvd Lionel-Bertrand, Broisbriand, QC J7N 1N7 *Tel:* 450-434-0306 *Toll Free Tel:* 800-363-2864 *Fax:* 450-434-2627 *Toll Free Fax:* 800-361-8088 *Web Site:* www.prologue.ca
SDL La Cravelle, 303 rue du pre aux oies, 1130 Brussels, Belgium *Tel:* (02) 240 93 00 *Fax:* (02) 216 35 98 *Web Site:* www.sdlcaravelle.com
Dilisco Distribution, Rte du Limousin BP 25, 23220 Cheniers, France *Tel:* 05 55 51 80 00 *Fax:* 05 55 62 17 39 *Web Site:* www.dilisco.fr
Dilisco Diffusion, Parc Mure 2-Bat 4-4, BP102, 128 Bis ave Jean-Jaures, 94208 Ivry-sur-Seine, France *Tel:* 01 49 59 50 50 *Fax:* 01 46 71 05 06 *Web Site:* www.dilisco.fr
Distribution Servidis, Chemin des Chalets 7, 1279 Chavannes-de-Bogis, Switzerland *Tel:* (022) 960-95-23 *Fax:* (022) 960-95-77 *Web Site:* www.servidis.ch
Membership(s): ANEL

**Editions Marcel Didier Inc**
Division of Editions Hurtubise HMH Ltee
1815 Ave de Lorimier, Montreal, QC H2K 3W6
*Tel:* 514-523-1523 *Toll Free Tel:* 800-361-1664 (Ontario to Maritimes) *Fax:* 514-523-9969
*E-mail:* marceldidier@hurtubisehmh.com
*Web Site:* www.hurtubisehmh.com
*Key Personnel*
CEO: Arnaud Foulon; Herve Foulon
Exec Dir: Johanne Livernoche *E-mail:* johanne.livernoche@distributionhmh.com
Founded: 1964
Literary essays, novels.
Publishes in English, French.
ISBN Prefix(es): 978-2-89144
Number of titles published annually: 60 Print
Distributed by Editions Hurtubise HMH; Librarie Du Quebec a Paris
U.S. Rep(s): Sosnowski Associates

**Les Editions du Ble**
340 Provencher Blvd, St Boniface, MB R2H 0G7
*Tel:* 204-237-8200 *Fax:* 204-233-8182
*E-mail:* direction@editionsduble.ca
*Web Site:* www.livres-disques.ca/editions_ble/home/index.cfm
*Key Personnel*
Admin Dir: Anne Molgat
Founded: 1974
Publish books in French (novels, essays, poetry) pertaining mainly to the Canadian West (but not exclusively).
Publishes in French.
ISBN Prefix(es): 978-2-921347
Number of titles published annually: 6 Print
Total Titles: 100 Print
*Distribution Center:* Diffusion Prologue, 1650 boul Lionel-Bertrand, Boisbriand, QC J7E 4H4 *Tel:* 450-434-0306 *Fax:* 450-434-2627

**Les Editions du Boreal**
4447, rue Saint-Denis, Montreal, QC H2J 2L2
*Tel:* 514-287-7401 *Fax:* 514-287-7664
*E-mail:* boreal@editionsboreal.qc.ca
*Web Site:* www.editionsboreal.qc.ca
*Key Personnel*
Dir Gen: Pascal Assathiany
Founded: 1963
General literature, essays, history, translations, children's & philosophy.
Publishes in French.
ISBN Prefix(es): 978-2-89052; 978-2-7646
Number of titles published annually: 70 Print
Total Titles: 1,370 Print
Distributed by Editions Du Seuil (Europe)
Foreign Rep(s): Agence AMV (Portugal, Spain); Ann-Christine Danielsson (Scandinavia); Niki Douge (Greece); Agence de l'Est (Bulgaria, Czech Republic, Estonia, Latvia, Lithuania, Poland, Romania, Slovakia); Imrie & Dervis (Australia, UK); Agnese Incisa Agenzia Letteraria (Italy); Japan UNI Agency (Japan); Anastasia Lester (Belarus, Russia, Ukraine); Liepman AG, Literary Agency (Germany); I Pikarski Ltd Literary Agency (Israel)
*Distribution Center:* Diffusion Dimedia, 539 Lebeau Blvd, St-Laurent, QC H4N 1S2 *Tel:* 514-336-3941 *Fax:* 514-331-3916 *Web Site:* www.dimedia.com
Volumen, 25, blvd Romain Rolland, CS 21418, 75993 Paris Cedex 14, France (Europe) *Tel:* 01 41 48 84 60 *E-mail:* volumen@volumen.fr

**§Les Editions du CRAM Inc**
1030, Cherrier, bureau 205, Montreal, QC H2L 1H9
*Tel:* 514-598-8547 *Fax:* 514-598-8788
*E-mail:* service@editionscram.com
*Web Site:* www.editionscram.com
Founded: 1988
ISBN Prefix(es): 978-2-89721; 978-2-922050; 978-2-9801489
Number of titles published annually: 20 Print
*Distribution Center:* Prologue, 1650 Lionel Bertrand, Boisbriand, QC J7H 1N7 *Tel:* 450-434-0306 *Fax:* 450-434-2627
SDL Caravelle, Rue du Pre-aux-geese, 303, 1130 Brussels, Belgium *Tel:* (02) 240 93 00 *Fax:* (02) 216 35 98
DG Diffusion, Zl de Bogues, 31750 Escalquens, France *Tel:* 05 61 00 09 99 *Fax:* 05 61 00 23 12
Transat Distribution SA, Chemin des Cottages, 1279 Chavannes de Bogis, Switzerland *Tel:* (022) 342 77 40 *Fax:* (022) 343 46 46 *E-mail:* transat@transatdiffusion.ch

**Editions du Noroit**
CP 156, Succersale de Lorimier, Montreal, QC H2H 2N6
*Tel:* 514-727-0005 *Fax:* 514-723-6660
*E-mail:* lenoroit@lenoroit.com
*Web Site:* www.lenoroit.com

*Key Personnel*
Lit Dir: Paul Belanger
Founded: 1971
Poetry.
Publishes in French.
ISBN Prefix(es): 978-2-89018
Number of titles published annually: 26 Print
Total Titles: 730 Print; 10 Audio
*Billing Address:* 4609 rue D'Iberville, Local 202, Montreal, QC H2H 2L9
*Distribution Center:* Diffusion Dimedia Inc, 539 Bd Lebeau, St-Laurent, QC H4N 1S2 *Tel:* 514-336-3941 *Fax:* 514-331-3916 *Web Site:* www.dimedia.com

**Les Editions du Remue-Menage**
La Maison Parent-Roback, 110 rue Ste-Therese, bureau 501, Montreal, QC H2Y 1E6
*Tel:* 514-876-0097 *Fax:* 514-876-7951
*E-mail:* info@editions-remuemenage.qc.ca
*Web Site:* www.editions-remuemenage.qc.ca
*Key Personnel*
Publr: Rachel Bedard
Dir: Ginette Peloquin
Ed: Elise Bergeron
Founded: 1976
Specialize in feminist books.
Publishes in English, French.
ISBN Prefix(es): 978-2-89091
Number of titles published annually: 15 Print
Total Titles: 170 Print
Distributed by Export Livre (Europe, US); Hushion House Publishing Ltd (USA, CN); Librarie du Quebec (France)
Foreign Rep(s): Library Plaisir (Egypt); S A Vander (Belgium)
*Distribution Center:* Diffusion Dimedia, 539 boul Lebeau, St-Laurent, QC H4N 1S2 *Tel:* 514-336-3941 *Fax:* 514-331-3916 *Toll Free Fax:* 800-667-3941 *E-mail:* commandes@dimedia.qc.ca
Membership(s): Association Nationale des Editeurs de Livres

**Editions du renouveau Pedagogique Inc (ERPI)**
Division of Pearson plc
5757 rue Cypihot, St Laurent, QC H4S 1R3
*Tel:* 514-334-2690 *Toll Free Tel:* 800-263-3678 *Fax:* 514-334-4720 *Toll Free Fax:* 800-643-4720
*E-mail:* erpidlm@erpi.com
*Web Site:* www.erpi.com
*Key Personnel*
Prodn Mgr: Helene Cousineau *Fax:* 514-334-9188 *E-mail:* helene.cousineau@erpi.com
Intl Rts: Lise Barras *Tel:* 514-334-2690 ext 445 *E-mail:* lise.barras@erpi.com
Founded: 1965
Textbooks.
Publishes in English, French.
ISBN Prefix(es): 978-2-7613
Number of titles published annually: 15 Print; 12 CD-ROM; 10 Online
Total Titles: 850 Print; 15 CD-ROM; 10 Online
Imprints: ERPI
Divisions: Diffusion du Livre Mirabel
Distributed by De Boeck; Pearson Education France; Penguin Readers; Village Mondial
Distributor for Addison-Wesley, Pearson Education (English as a second language series); Campus Press France; Duculot; Michelin North America (Canada) (French titles in Canada); Prentice-Hall
Membership(s): ANEL

**Les Editions du Septentrion**
1300 Maguire Ave, Sillery, QC G1T 1Z3
*Tel:* 418-688-3556 *Fax:* 418-527-4978
*E-mail:* sept@septentrion.qc.ca
*Web Site:* www.septentrion.qc.ca
*Key Personnel*
Pres & Publr: Denis Vaugeois
Mng Dir & Ed: Gilles Herman
Ed: Sophie Imbeault
Founded: 1988
Full service publisher.
Publishes in English, French.
ISBN Prefix(es): 978-2-89448
Number of titles published annually: 30 Print
Total Titles: 330 Print
*Distribution Center:* Dimedia, 539 boul Lebeau, St-Laurent, QC H4N 1S2

**Les Editions du Vermillon**
305 rue Sainte-Patrick, Ottawa, ON K1N 5K4
*Tel:* 613-241-4032 *Fax:* 613-241-3109
*E-mail:* leseditionsduvermillon@rogers.com
*Web Site:* leseditionsduvermillon.ca
*Key Personnel*
Pres: Jacques Flamand
Gen Dir: Monique Bertoli
Founded: 1982
Poetry, novels, children's books, textbooks, essays.
Publishes in English, French.
ISBN Prefix(es): 978-0-919925; 978-1-895873; 978-1-894547; 978-1-897058; 978-1-926628
Number of titles published annually: 15 Print
Total Titles: 372 Print
Foreign Rep(s): Diffusion Albert-le-Grand (Switzerland); Librairie du Quebec (France)
Foreign Rights: Montreal Contacts (Worldwide)
*Distribution Center:* Prologue Inc

**Les Editions Fides**
7333 place des Roseraies, bureau 100, Montreal, QC H1M 2X6
*Tel:* 514-745-4290 *Toll Free Tel:* 800-363-1451 (CN) *Fax:* 514-745-4299
*E-mail:* editions@fides.qc.ca
*Web Site:* www.editionsfides.com
*Key Personnel*
CEO & Dir Gen: Stephane Lavoie *Tel:* 514-745-4290 ext 351 *E-mail:* stephane.lavoie@fides.qc.ca
Ed: Bertin Dickner *Tel:* 514-745-4290 ext 356 *E-mail:* bertin.dickner@fides.qc.ca; Guylaine Girard *Tel:* 514-745-4290 ext 355; Michel Maille *Tel:* 514-745-4290 ext 352 *E-mail:* michel.maille@fides.qc.ca
Founded: 1937
Religion, philosophy, education, Canadian literature & history, dictionaries.
Publishes in French.
ISBN Prefix(es): 978-2-7621; 978-2-89007; 978-2-923989
Number of titles published annually: 60 Print
Total Titles: 2,000 Print
*Distribution Center:* Socadis, 420 rue Stinson, Ville St-Laurent, QC H4N 3L7 *Tel:* 514-331-3300 *Toll Free Tel:* 800-361-2847 *Fax:* 514-745-3282 *Toll Free Fax:* 866-803-5422 *E-mail:* socinfo@socadis.com

**Editions FouLire**
4339 rue des Becassines, Charlesbourg, QC G1G 1V5
*Tel:* 418-628-4029 *Toll Free Tel:* 877-628-4029 *Fax:* 418-628-4801
*E-mail:* info@foulire.com
*Web Site:* www.foulire.com
*Key Personnel*
Pres: Yvon Brochu *E-mail:* ybrochu@rdcreation.com
Mktg: Danielle Lajeunesse
Prodr: Lise Morin
Founded: 2005
Publishers of books for children.
Publishes in French.
ISBN Prefix(es): 978-2-89591
Number of titles published annually: 10 Print
Total Titles: 39 Print
*Distribution Center:* Prologue Inc, 1650 Lional Bertrand Blvd, Boisbriand, QC J7H 1N7 *Tel:* 450-434-0306 *Toll Free Tel:* 800-363-2864 *Fax:* 450-434-2627 *Toll Free Fax:* 800-361-8088 *E-mail:* prologue@prologue.ca

**Les Editions Ganesha Inc**
CP 484, Succursale Youville, Montreal, QC H2P 2W1
*Tel:* 450-641-2395 *Fax:* 450-641-2989
*E-mail:* courriel@editions-ganesha.qc.ca
*Web Site:* www.editions-ganesha.qc.ca
*Key Personnel*
Pres & Dir Gen: Andre Beaudoin
Founded: 1978
Publishes in French.
ISBN Prefix(es): 978-2-89145
Number of titles published annually: 4 Print
Total Titles: 56 Print

**Les Editions Heritage Inc**
300 Rue Arran, St-Lambert, QC J4R 1K5
*Tel:* 514-875-0327 *Toll Free Tel:* 800-561-3737 *Fax:* 450-672-5448
*Key Personnel*
CEO & Pres of the Council: Jacques Payette
Pres: Sylvie Payette
Founded: 1968
Juvenile & adult & French language.
Publishes in French.
ISBN Prefix(es): 978-2-7625
Number of titles published annually: 250 Print
Total Titles: 2,000 Print
Foreign Rights: Barbara Creary
Membership(s): Association for Canadian Publishers in the US

**Editions Hurtubise**
1815 De Lorimier Ave, Montreal, QC H2K 3W6
*Tel:* 514-523-1523 *Toll Free Tel:* 800-361-1664 (CN only) *Fax:* 514-523-9969
*Web Site:* www.editionshurtubise.com
*Key Personnel*
Pres: Herve Foulon
Gen Mgr: Arnaud Foulon
Rts Mgr: Alexandrine Foulon *Tel:* 514-523-1523 ext 220 *E-mail:* alexandrine.foulon@editionshurtubise.com
Founded: 1960
French Canadian publishing house. Fiction, nonfiction & textbooks.
Publishes in French.
ISBN Prefix(es): 978-2-89045; 978-2-89428; 978-2-89647
Number of titles published annually: 110 Print
Total Titles: 1,200 Print
Imprints: Bibliotheque Quebecoise (BQ)
Distributor for Marcel Didier Inc; Hurtubise HMH Ltee
*See separate listing for:*
**Editions Marcel Didier Inc**

**Les Editions JCL**
930 rue Jacques Cartier est, Chicoutimi, QC G7H 7K9
*Tel:* 418-696-0536 *Fax:* 418-696-3132
*E-mail:* jcl@jcl.qc.ca
*Web Site:* www.jcl.qc.ca
*Key Personnel*
Pres & Intl Rts: Jean-Claude Larouche
Founded: 1977
Novels & nonfiction.
Publishes in French.
ISBN Prefix(es): 978-2-920176; 978-2-89431
Number of titles published annually: 26 Print
Total Titles: 475 Print
Distributed by La Librairie du Quebec (French Europe); Transat (Switzerland)
Foreign Rights: Michael Wenzel (European Union)
*Distribution Center:* ADP, 2315 rue de la Province, Longueuil, QC J4G 1G4, Contact:

Jean-Pierre Elias *Toll Free Tel:* 800-771-3022 *Toll Free Fax:* 800-465-1237
Membership(s): ANEL

**Editions Marie-France**
9900 Avenue des Laurentides, Montreal, QC H1H 4V1
*Tel:* 514-329-3700 *Toll Free Tel:* 800-563-6644 (Canada) *Fax:* 514-329-0630
*E-mail:* editions@marie-france.qc.ca
*Web Site:* www.marie-france.qc.ca
*Key Personnel*
Pres: Jean Lachapelle
VP: Joanne Lacombe
Founded: 1977
School, kindergarten, elementary & secondary in French, natural sciences, human sciences, music, economic education & physics. Some titles in both French & English.
Publishes in English, French.
ISBN Prefix(es): 978-2-89168
Number of titles published annually: 25 Print
Total Titles: 1,001 Print
Membership(s): Association Nationale des Editeurs de Livres

**Les Editions Phidal Inc**
5740 Ferrier, Montreal, QC H4P 1M7
*Tel:* 514-738-0202 *Toll Free Tel:* 800-738-7349 *Fax:* 514-738-5102
*E-mail:* info@phidal.com; customer@phidal.com (sales & export)
*Web Site:* www.phidal.com
*Key Personnel*
Publr: Lionel Soussan
Founded: 1979
Full-service publisher.
Publishes in English, French.
ISBN Prefix(es): 978-2-89393; 978-2-7643
Number of titles published annually: 35 Print
Divisions: Edilivre Inc

**Editions Pierre Tisseyre**
155 rue Maurice, Rosemere, QC J7A 2S8
*Tel:* 514-335-0777 *Fax:* 514-335-6723
*E-mail:* info@edtisseyre.ca
*Web Site:* www.tisseyre.ca
*Key Personnel*
Pres: Charles Tisseyre
Dir & ISBN Contact: Sylvia De Angelis
Founded: 1947
French Canadian literature; adult & children's books.
Publishes in French.
ISBN Prefix(es): 978-2-7613; 978-2-89051; 978-2-89633
Number of titles published annually: 55 Print
Total Titles: 350 Print
Distributed by Diffusion du Livre Mirabel

**Editions Trecarre**
Subsidiary of Quebecor Media
La Tourelle, Bureau 800, 1055, Blvd Rene-Levesque E, Montreal, QC H2L 4S5
*Tel:* 514-849-5259 *Fax:* 514-849-1388
*Web Site:* www.edtrecarre.com
Founded: 1982
Coffee-table books, nature books, cookbooks, practical books.
Publishes in French.
ISBN Prefix(es): 978-2-89249; 978-2-89568
Number of titles published annually: 30 Print
Total Titles: 700 Print
*Warehouse:* 2185 Autoroute des Laurentides, Laval, QC H7S 1Z6

**Les Editions Un Monde Different Itee**
3905 Isabelle, bureau 101, Brossand, QC J4Y 2R2
Mailing Address: CP 51546 Succ Galeries Taschereau, Greenfield Park, QC J4V 3N8
*Tel:* 450-656-2660 *Toll Free Tel:* 800-443-2582 *Fax:* 450-659-9328
*E-mail:* info@umd.ca
*Web Site:* www.umd.ca
*Key Personnel*
Owner & Ed: Michel Ferron
Founded: 1977
Motivational & inspirational books.
Publishes in French.
ISBN Prefix(es): 978-2-89225
Number of titles published annually: 25 Print
Total Titles: 750 Print
*Distribution Center:* Messageries ADP, 2315 rue de la Province, Longueuil, QC J4G 1G4 *Tel:* 450-640-1234 *Fax:* 450-640-1251

**Editions Vents d'Ouest**
109 rue Wright, Gatineau, QC J8X 2G7
*Tel:* 819-770-6377 *Fax:* 819-770-0559
*E-mail:* info@ventsdouest.ca
*Web Site:* www.ventsdouest.ca
*Key Personnel*
Pres: Tolszczuk Benedict
VP: Pierre Cadieu
Coord: Michel Lavoie
Founded: 1993
Novels, short stories, history.
Publishes in French.
ISBN Prefix(es): 978-2-921603; 978-2-89537
Number of titles published annually: 18 Print
Total Titles: 218 Print
*Distribution Center:* Prologue Inc, 1650 Lionel-Bertrand Blvd, Boisbriand, QC J7H 1N7 *Tel:* 450-434-0306 *Toll Free Tel:* 800-363-2864 *Fax:* 450-434-2627 *Toll Free Fax:* 800-361-8088

**Les Editions XYZ inc**
1815 Ave de Lorimier, Montreal, QC H2K 3W6
*Tel:* 514-525-2170 *Fax:* 514-525-7537
*E-mail:* info@editionsxyz.com
*Web Site:* www.editionsxyz.com
*Key Personnel*
CEO: Dominique Lemay *Tel:* 514-523-1523 ext 259 *Fax:* 514-523-4237
Head, Communs: Alexandrine Foulon *E-mail:* alexandrine.foulon@editionsxyz.com
Prodn Mgr: Nathalie Tasse *E-mail:* nathalie.tasse@editionsxyz.com
Literary Mgr: Josee Bonneville *Tel:* 514-525-2170 ext 260 *E-mail:* josee.bonneville@editionsxyz.com
Literary Consultant: Andre Vanasse *Tel:* 514-525-2170 ext 260 *E-mail:* andre.vanasse@editionsxyz.com
Ed: Marie-Pierre Barathon *Tel:* 514-525-2170 ext 270 *E-mail:* marie-pierre.barathon@editionsxyz.com
Founded: 1985
Novels, short stories & essays on literature.
Publishes in French.
ISBN Prefix(es): 978-2-89261
Number of titles published annually: 25 Print
Total Titles: 457 Print
*Distribution Center:* HMH, 1815 Ave de Lorimier, Montreal, QC H2K 3W6 *Tel:* 514-523-1523 *Toll Free Tel:* 800-361-1664 *Fax:* 514-523-9969 *Web Site:* www.distributionhmh.com
Membership(s): Association of Canadian Publishers; Literary Press Group

**Editions Yvon Blais**
137 John, CP 180, Cowansville, QC J2K 3H6
Mailing Address: PO Box 180, Cowansville, QC J2K 3H6
*Tel:* 450-266-1086 *Toll Free Tel:* 800-363-3047 *Fax:* 450-263-9256
*E-mail:* editionsyvonblais.commentaires@thomson.com
*Web Site:* www.editionsyvonblais.qc.ca
*Key Personnel*
Dir, Publg & Intl Rts: Louis Busse
Gen Mgr: Charmian Harvey
Founded: 1978
Law books.
Publishes in French.
ISBN Prefix(es): 978-2-89073; 978-2-89451
Number of titles published annually: 30 Print
Total Titles: 500 Print
*Branch Office(s)*
430 St-Pierre, Montreal, QC H2Y 2M5

**ELS Editions**
University of Victoria, Dept of English, Victoria, BC V8W 3W1
Mailing Address: University of Victoria, PO Box 3070, Victoria, BC V8W 3W1
*Tel:* 250-721-7236 *Fax:* 250-721-6498
*E-mail:* els@uvic.ca
*Web Site:* english.uvic.ca/els
*Key Personnel*
Ed: Dr Luke Carson
Founded: 1975
Scholarly monographs related to literature.
Publishes in English.
ISBN Prefix(es): 978-0-9691436; 978-0-920604
Number of titles published annually: 5 Print
Total Titles: 107 Print

**Emond Montgomery Publications**
60 Shaftesbury Ave, Toronto, ON M4T 1A3
*Tel:* 416-975-3925 *Toll Free Tel:* 888-837-0815 *Fax:* 416-975-3924
*E-mail:* info@emp.ca; orders@emp.ca
*Web Site:* www.emp.ca
*Key Personnel*
Pres: D Paul Emond
Publr, School Group: Anthony Rezek *E-mail:* arezek@emp.ca
Mktg Mgr: Christine Davidson *E-mail:* cdavidson@emp.ca
Founded: 1978
Academic publisher.
Publishes in English.
ISBN Prefix(es): 978-0-920722; 978-1-55239
Number of titles published annually: 30 Print; 40 E-Book
Total Titles: 200 Print; 40 E-Book
*Returns:* c/o Canada Law Book, 240 Edward St, Aurora, ON L4G 3S9
*Warehouse:* 240 Edward St, Aurora, ON L4G 3S9 *Tel:* 905-841-6472 (Greater Toronto area) *Toll Free Tel:* 800-263-3269; 800-263-2037

**ERPI**, see Editions du renouveau Pedagogique Inc (ERPI)

**Fairwinds Press**
PO Box 668, Lions Bay, BC V0N 2E0
*Tel:* 604-913-0649
*E-mail:* orders@fairwinds-press.com
*Web Site:* www.fairwinds-press.com
*Key Personnel*
Publr & Intl Rts: Leslie Nolin *E-mail:* leslie@fairwinds-press.com
Founded: 1997
Publishes in English.
ISBN Prefix(es): 978-0-9682149; 978-0-9780974; 978-0-9881081
Number of titles published annually: 5 Print; 3 E-Book
Total Titles: 17 Print; 6 E-Book
Membership(s): Independent Publishers Association

**Fernwood Publishing**
32 Oceanvista Lane, Black Point, NS B0J 1B0
*Tel:* 902-857-1388 *Fax:* 902-857-1328
*E-mail:* info@fernpub.ca
*Web Site:* www.fernwoodpublishing.ca
*Key Personnel*
Co-Publr: Wayne Antony; Errol Sharpe *E-mail:* errol@fernpub.ca
Prodn Coord & Publr/Mng Ed: Roseway: Beverly Rach

Mng Ed: Jessica Antony; Candida Hadley
Promos Coord: Curran Faris; Nancy Malek
Founded: 1991
Social sciences & humanities, emphasizing labour studies, women's studies, gender studies, critical theory & research, political economy, cultural studies & social work for use in undergraduate courses in colleges & universities.
Publishes in English.
ISBN Prefix(es): 978-1-895686; 978-1-55266
Number of titles published annually: 29 Print
Total Titles: 340 Print
Imprints: Roseway Publishing
*Branch Office(s)*
748 Broadway Ave, Winnipeg, MB R3G 0X3, Contact: Wayne Antony *Tel:* 204-474-2958 *Fax:* 204-475-2813 *E-mail:* wayne@fernpub.ca
U.S. Rep(s): Independent Publishers Group
Foreign Rep(s): Merlin Press (Europe, Ireland, UK)
*Orders to:* Brunswick Books, 20 Maud St, Suite 303, Toronto, ON M5V 2M5 (North America) *Tel:* 416-703-3598 *Fax:* 416-703-6561 *E-mail:* orders@brunswickbooks.ca *Web Site:* www.brunswickbooks.ca; The Merlin Press/Central Books Ltd, 99 Wallis Rd, London E9 5LN, United Kingdom (UK & Europe) *Tel:* (020) 8966 4854 *Fax:* (020) 8533 5821 *E-mail:* orders@centralbooks.com *Web Site:* www.centralbooks.com
*Returns:* Brunswick Books, c/o TTS Distributing, 155 Edward St, Aurora, ON L4G IW3; First Choice/Brunswick Books, c/o JBF Express, 4392 Broadway, Depew, NY 14043, United States *Tel:* 716-683-9654

**Fifth House Publishers**
Division of Fitzhenry & Whiteside Limited
195 Allstate Pkwy, Markham, ON L3R 4T8
*Tel:* 905-477-9700 *Toll Free Tel:* 800-387-9776 *Toll Free Fax:* 800-260-9777
*E-mail:* godwit@fitzhenry.ca
*Web Site:* www.fitzhenry.ca/fifthhouse.aspx
*Key Personnel*
Publr: Tracey Dettman *E-mail:* tdettman@fitzhenry.ca
Founded: 1982
Trade publisher focusing on Western Canadian interest books; aviation, gardening.
Publishes in English, French.
ISBN Prefix(es): 978-0-920079; 978-1-895618; 978-1-894004; 978-1-894856
Number of titles published annually: 18 Print
Total Titles: 211 Print; 1 CD-ROM; 5 E-Book; 1 Audio
Distributed by Fitzhenry & Whiteside Ltd
Distributor for Glenbow Museum
*Orders to:* Ingram Publishing Services, 1210 Ingram Dr, Chambersburg, PA 17202, United States
*Returns:* Ingram Publishing Services, 1210 Ingram Dr, Chambersburg, PA 17202, United States
Membership(s): Book Publishers Association of Alberta

**Firefly Books Ltd**
50 Staples Ave, Unit 1, Richmond Hill, ON L4B 0A7
*Tel:* 416-499-8412 *Toll Free Tel:* 800-387-6192 (CN); 800-387-5085 (US) *Fax:* 416-499-8313 *Toll Free Fax:* 800-450-0391 (CN); 800-565-6034 (US)
*E-mail:* service@fireflybooks.com
*Web Site:* www.fireflybooks.com
*Key Personnel*
Pres: Lionel Koffler *E-mail:* lionel@fireflybooks.com
EVP: Leon Gouzoules
Lib Sales Dir: Ann Quinn *Tel:* 416-499-8412 ext 134 *E-mail:* annq@fireflybooks.com
Publicity Dir: Valerie Hatton *Tel:* 416-499-8412 ext 128 *E-mail:* valerie@fireflybooks.com
Rts & Contracts Mgr: Diane Vanderkooy *Tel:* 416-499-8412 ext 153 *E-mail:* dianevan@fireflybooks.com
Founded: 1977
Books & calendars.
Publishes in English.
ISBN Prefix(es): 978-0-920668; 978-1-895565; 978-1-55209; 978-1-55297; 978-1-55407
Number of titles published annually: 220 Print
Total Titles: 2,000 Print; 25 Online
Divisions: The Boston Mills Press
*Branch Office(s)*
8514 Long Canyon Dr, Austin, TX 78730-2183, United States, Contact: Thomas C Martin *Tel:* 512-372-8500 *Fax:* 512-372-2499 *E-mail:* fireflytom@mindspring.com
Distributor for Annick Press; Boston Mills Press; Camden House; Cottage Life; Firefly Books; The Genealogical Research Library Inc; Great North Books; Kiddy Chronicles; Mikaya Press; Robert Rose; Sound & Vision
Foreign Rep(s): Julian Ashton (Asia); Ethan Atkin (Caribbean, Latin America); Baccus Books (Owen Early) (South Africa, Sub-Saharan Africa); Angell Eurosales (Denmark, Finland, Iceland, Norway, Scandinavia, Sweden); Chris Lloyd (Northern Europe, UK); Anthony Moggach (East Africa, Eastern Europe, West Africa); Butler Peribo Pty Ltd (Australia); Joe Portelli (Greece, Italy, Malta, Portugal, Southern Europe, Spain); Anselm Robinon (Austria, Belgium, France, Germany, Switzerland, Western Europe); Butler Sims Ltd (Ireland)
Foreign Rights: Julian Ashton (Asia); Ethan Atkin (Caribbean, Latin America); Angell Eurosales (Denmark, Finland, Iceland, Norway, Scandinavia, Sweden); Chris Lloyd (Northern Europe, UK); Anthony Moggach (East Africa, Eastern Europe, West Africa); Butler Peribo Pty Ltd (Australia); Stephan Phillips (South Africa, Sub-Saharan Africa); Joe Portelli (Greece, Italy, Malta, Portugal, Southern Europe, Spain); Anselm Robinon (Austria, Belgium, France, Germany, Switzerland, Western Europe); Butler Sims Ltd (Ireland)
*Returns:* c/o Frontier Distributing, 1000 Young St, Suite 106, Tonawanda, NY 14150, United States
Membership(s): ABA; Association of Canadian Publishers; Canadian Booksellers Association
*See separate listing for:*
**The Boston Mills Press**

**Fitzhenry & Whiteside Limited**
195 Allstate Pkwy, Markham, ON L3R 4T8
SAN: 115-1444
*Tel:* 905-477-9700 *Toll Free Tel:* 800-387-9776 *Fax:* 905-477-9179 *Toll Free Fax:* 800-260-9777
*E-mail:* bookinfo@fitzhenry.ca; godwit@fitzhenry.ca
*Web Site:* www.fitzhenry.ca
*Key Personnel*
CFO: Peter Stubbs
Pres: Sharon Fitzhenry *Tel:* 905-477-9700 ext 228 *E-mail:* sfitz@fitzhenry.ca
Mgr, Cust Serv: Judy Ghoura *E-mail:* jghoura@fitzhenry.ca
Mgr, Opers: Holly Doll *E-mail:* hdoll@fitzhenry.ca
Mgr, Prodn: Uma Subramanian
Publr Rel: Sonya Gillis *E-mail:* sonya.gillis@fitzhenry.ca
Fin: Earl Leibovitch *E-mail:* earll@fitzhenry.ca
Founded: 1966
Trade, reference & children's books, educational material for elementary, high school & college.
Publishes in English.
ISBN Prefix(es): 978-0-88902; 978-1-55005; 978-1-55041; 978-1-894004; 978-1-894856; 978-0-88995; 978-1-55455
Number of titles published annually: 70 Print
Total Titles: 1,100 Print
Divisions: Fifth House; Red Deer Press Inc
Distributor for Capstone Press; Compass Point Books; Coughlan Publishing; EDGE Science Fiction & Fantasy Publishing; The Glenbow Museum; Good Books; Heinemann Raintree; Inhabit Media Inc; Japan Publishing Trading Co; Kodansha; Lee & Low Books; Mel Bay; Marshall Cavendish Children's Books; Meriwether Publishing Ltd; Annika Parance Publishing; Peachtree Publishers; Pelican Publishing Co; Picture Window Books; Pokeweed Press; Red Brick Learning; Stone Arch Books; Telos Publishing; TFH Publications Inc; Thirty Six Peonies Publishing; Tilbury House Publishers; Tradewind Books; Tundra & Associates; Verve Editions
U.S. Publishers Represented: The Beacon Press; Coteau Books; Kodansha International; Hal Leonard; Peachtree Publishers; Stackpole Books; Thistledown Press; Albert Whitman
U.S. Rep(s): Booklink; Eichkorn & Associates; Nor'East Sales; R&R Book Co
*Returns:* Ingram Publisher Services, 1210 Ingram Dr, Chambersburg, PA 17202, United States
*See separate listing for:*
**Fifth House Publishers**
**Red Deer Press**

**Flammarion Quebec**
375 Ave Laurier W, Montreal, QC H2V 2K3
*Tel:* 514-277-8807 *Fax:* 514-278-2085
*E-mail:* info@flammarion.qc.ca
*Web Site:* www.flammarion.qc.ca
*Key Personnel*
Gen Dir, Dist: Guy Gougeon
Publr: Louise Loiselle *E-mail:* lloiselle@flammarion.qc.ca
Founded: 1974
Best sellers, translations, Quebec literature, novels.
Publishes in French.
ISBN Prefix(es): 978-2-89077
Number of titles published annually: 20 Print
Total Titles: 286 Print
Imprints: Advenir; Bis (Pocket Book)
Distributor for A2C Medias; Acatos; ADEME; Agence Marc Praquin; APCE-ANCE; APEC; AQC (Agence Qualite Construction); Arcane Institut; Archibooks; Architectures a Vivre; Art Global; Art Lys; Arthaud; Association d'Economie Financiere; Aubier; Autrement; Batir Sain; Beaux-Arts Hors-Serie; Biotope; Bis; Braun; Des Bulles dans l'Ocean; Calvage et Mounet; Casterman; CEA; Centre Georges Pompidou; Centre Pompidou Jeunesse; Centre Technique Cuir Chaussure; CFPJ; Editorial Chessy; Clarysse; Climats; CMI (Centre de la Mobilite Internationale); Color Academy; Corroy; CRI (Centre de Ressources Interactif); CTC; Al Dante/Leo Scheer; Democratic Books; Jean Di Scuillo; Didier Vitrac; Le Dilettante; Editions d'Organisation; Dubos; Duculot; EDF; Edigo; Editeal; Edouard Valys; Ego Comme X; Editions 84; Elenbi; ENSTA (Ecole Nationale Superieure de Technologies Avancees); Esmod; Espaces Loisirs; Essec; Eyrolles; Eyrolles/Sang de la Terre; Flammarion; Fluide Glacial; Editions Geo Plein-Air; GEP; Green Travel Edition; Gremese; Groupe Action Scris; De l'Herne; Charles Herissey; Horay; Ideacom; Imbernon; INSEP; Ipso Facto; IRD; J'ai Lu; JNF; Journal des Finances; Jungle; Jury des Marques (CLSC); Kameleo; Lacurne; Ledoux Presse; Librio; Lignes & Manifestes; Links International; Litec; Ludetis; Ludion; Lux; Mae-Erti; La Maison de Paille; Les Editions Maison (LEM); La Maison Rustique; Editions du Management; Maxwell; Editions de Marque; Medieco; Melville; Michele Editions; MK2; Monsa; Musee du Quai Branly; Nature et Progres; Neopol; Nova; OEM; Paquet; La Pasteque; Pere Castor Flammarion; Le Petit Fute; Pif; Pix'N Love; Plume; La Presquile; La

Presse; Presses des Ponts et Chaussees; Profil Sante; Publitronic; Editions du Puits Fleuri; Pygmalion; Editions Retrouvees; Revue Cinema; Revue Fiduciaire; Revue Lignes & Manifestes; Rizzoli; RMN; RMN Jeunesse; Santesis; Sarbacane; Leo Scheer; Leo Scheer/Farrago; SEBTP; Septembre; Septembre Jeunesse; Seraqui; Shu-Book; Skira; Societe du Figaro Editions; Editions Sol 90; Somogy; Steinkis; Super Sellers; Tabary; La Tengo; Thircuir LD; 13e Note Editions; Tissot; UNFCM/Sedibois; Universalis; Vadrouilleur Edition; VDB; Ventana; Vermare; Vidal; Vie & Cie; Vinci; VM; Voix Paralleles
*Warehouse:* 420 Stinson, St-Laurent, QC H4N 2E9

**Flanker Press Ltd**
1243 Kenmount Rd, Unit A, Paradise, NL A1L 0V8
Mailing Address: PO Box 2522, Sta C, St John's, NL A1C 6K1
*Tel:* 709-739-4477 *Toll Free Tel:* 866-739-4420 *Fax:* 709-739-4420
*E-mail:* info@flankerpress.com
*Web Site:* www.flankerpress.com
*Key Personnel*
Pres: Garry Cranford *Tel:* 709-739-4477 ext 23
Mgr: Robert Woodworth *Tel:* 709-739-4477 ext 21
Prodn Mgr: Jerry Cranford *Tel:* 709-739-4477 ext 30
Digital Coord: Peter Hanes *Tel:* 709-739-4477 ext 29
Mktg & Publicity: Laura Cameron *Tel:* 709-739-4477 ext 24
Sales: Randy Drover *Tel:* 709-739-4477 ext 22
Founded: 1997
Wholly Canadian-owned trade book publisher.
Publishes in English.
ISBN Prefix(es): 978-0-9698767; 978-1-894463; 978-1-897317; 978-1-926881; 978-1-771170
Number of titles published annually: 20 Print; 20 E-Book
Imprints: Brazen Books; Flanker Press; Pennywell Books
Membership(s): Association of Canadian Publishers; Atlantic Publishers Marketing Association

**Folklore Publishing**
11717-9B Ave NW, Unit 2, Edmonton, AB T6J 7B7
*Tel:* 780-435-2376 *Fax:* 780-435-0674
*E-mail:* submissions@folklorepublishing.com (ms submissions)
*Web Site:* www.folklorepublishing.com
*Key Personnel*
Pres & Publr: Faye Boer *E-mail:* fboer@folklorepublishing.com
Founded: 2001
Publisher of popular history of North America & celebrity biographies.
Publishes in English.
ISBN Prefix(es): 978-1-894864; 978-1-897206
Number of titles published annually: 5 Print
Total Titles: 85 Print
Imprints: ICON Press
*Sales Office(s):* Lone Pine Publishing, 2311 96 St, Edmonton, AB T6N 1G3 *Tel:* 780-433-9333 *Toll Free Tel:* 800-661-9017 *Fax:* 780-433-9646 *Toll Free Fax:* 800-424-7173 *E-mail:* info@lonepinepublishing.com *Web Site:* www.lonepinepublishing.com
Distributed by Lone Pine Publishing/BookLogic
U.S. Rep(s): Lone Pine Publishing
Foreign Rep(s): Gazelle Book Services (UK & the continent); Lone Pine Publishing (USA)
*Billing Address:* Lone Pine Publishing, 2311 96 St, Edmonton, AB T6N 1G3 *Tel:* 780-433-9333 *Toll Free Tel:* 800-661-9017 *Toll Free Fax:* 800-424-7173 *E-mail:* accounts@lonepinepublishing.com *Web Site:* www.lonepinepublishing.com
*Orders to:* Lone Pine Publishing, 2311 96 St, Edmonton, AB T6N 1G3 *Tel:* 780-433-9333 *Toll Free Tel:* 800-661-9017 *Toll Free Fax:* 800-424-7173 *E-mail:* accounts@lonepinepublishing.com *Web Site:* www.lonepinepublishing.com
*Returns:* Lone Pine Publishing, 2311 96 St, Edmonton, AB T6N 1G3 *Tel:* 780-433-9333 *Toll Free Tel:* 800-661-9017 *Toll Free Fax:* 800-424-7173 *E-mail:* info@lonepinepublishing.com *Web Site:* www.lonepinepublishing.com
Membership(s): Book Publishers Association of Alberta

**The Fraser Institute**
1770 Burrard St, 4th fl, Vancouver, BC V6J 3G7
*Tel:* 604-688-0221 *Toll Free Tel:* 800-665-3558 *Fax:* 604-688-8539
*E-mail:* info@fraserinstitute.org; sales@fraserinstitute.org
*Web Site:* www.fraserinstitute.org
*Key Personnel*
Dir, Devt: Sherry Stein *E-mail:* sherry.stein@fraserinstitute.org
Dir, Communs: Dean Pelkey *E-mail:* dean.pelkey@fraserinstitute.org
Dir, Pubn Prodn: Kristin McCahon *Tel:* 604-688-0221 ext 583 *E-mail:* kristin.mccahon@fraserinstitute.org
Founded: 1974
Publish regulatory studies, health policy, social affairs, taxation, environmental studies, energy policy, immigration, welfare/poverty. Publish bi-monthly magazine *Fraser Forum* in English & Perspectives twice a year (in French). Also, publish current research in the form of books, monographs & Fraser Alerts.
Publishes in English, French.
ISBN Prefix(es): 978-0-88975
Number of titles published annually: 10 Print; 50 Online; 1 E-Book
Total Titles: 500 Print; 350 Online; 2 E-Book
*Branch Office(s)*
Lancaster Bldg, Suite 609-304, 8 Ave SW, Calgary, AB T2P 1C2 *Tel:* 403-216-7175 *Fax:* 403-234-9010
1491 Yonge St, Suite 401, Toronto, ON M4T 1Z4 *Tel:* 416-363-6575 *Fax:* 416-934-1639
Hermes Bldg, Tower B, Suite 252, 1470 Peel St, Montreal, QC H3A 1T1 *Tel:* 514-281-9550 *Fax:* 514-281-9464

**Gaetan Morin Editeur**
Imprint of Cheneliere Education Inc
5800 rue Ste-Denis, Bur 900, Montreal, QC H2S 3L5
*Tel:* 514-273-1066 *Toll Free Tel:* 800-565-5531 *Fax:* 514-276-0324 *Toll Free Fax:* 800-814-0324
*E-mail:* info@cheneliere.ca
*Web Site:* www.cheneliere.ca
*Key Personnel*
Pres & Mng Dir: Jacques Rochefort *E-mail:* jrochefort@cheneliere.ca
Founded: 1977
Textbooks, college, university & professional books.
Publishes in French.
ISBN Prefix(es): 978-2-89105
Number of titles published annually: 20 Print; 1 CD-ROM
Total Titles: 300 Print; 2 CD-ROM

**General Store Publishing House**
Division of IDP Group (Image Digital Printing)
499 O'Brien Rd, Renfrew, ON K7V 3Z3
*Tel:* 613-432-7697 *Toll Free Tel:* 800-465-6072 *Fax:* 613-432-7184
*E-mail:* orders@gsph.com (orders)
*Web Site:* www.gsph.com
*Key Personnel*
Founder & Publr: Tim Gordon *E-mail:* timgordon@gsph.com
Founded: 1981
Local history, sport books, senior fitness, military, history, poetry, cookbooks, self-help.
This publisher has indicated that 50% of their product line is author subsidized.
Publishes in English.
ISBN Prefix(es): 978-0-919431; 978-1-896182; 978-1-894263; 978-1-897113; 978-1-897508; 978-1-926962; 978-1-77123
Number of titles published annually: 25 Print; 15 E-Book
Total Titles: 900 Print; 15 E-Book
Membership(s): Association of Canadian Publishers; Organization of Book Publishers of Ontario

**Gilpin Publishing**
PO Box 597, Alliston, ON L9R 1V7
*Tel:* 705-424-6507 *Toll Free Tel:* 800-867-3281 *Fax:* 705-424-6507
*E-mail:* mail@gilpin.ca
*Web Site:* www.gilpin.ca
*Key Personnel*
Pres: Wayne Gilpin
Founded: 1987
Music publisher.
ISBN Prefix(es): 978-0-921046
Number of titles published annually: 4 Print; 1 CD-ROM
Total Titles: 35 Print; 1 CD-ROM

**Les Editions Goelette Inc**
1350 Marie-Victorin, St-Bruno-de-Montarville, Quebec, QC J3V 6B9
*Tel:* 450-653-1337 *Toll Free Tel:* 800-463-4961 *Fax:* 450-653-9924
*Web Site:* www.editionsgoelette.com
*Key Personnel*
Pres: Alain Delorme
Publr: Ingrid Remazeilles
Prodn Mgr: Caroline Coutu
Founded: 1997
ISBN Prefix(es): 978-2-9804941; 978-2-9806291; 978-2-922983; 978-2-89638; 978-2-89690
*Distribution Center:* Les Messageries ADP, 2315, rue de la Province, Longueuil, QC J4G 1G4 *Tel:* 450-640-1234 *Toll Free Tel:* 800-771-3022 *Fax:* 450-640-1251 *Toll Free Fax:* 800-603-0433

**Gold Eagle**
Imprint of Harlequin Enterprises Ltd
225 Duncan Mill Rd, 4th fl, Don Mills, ON M3B 3K9
*Tel:* 416-445-5860 *Fax:* 416-445-8655; 416-445-8736
*E-mail:* readgoldeagle@hotmail.com
*Web Site:* www.harlequin.com
Founded: 1982
Mass market fiction, science fiction, action & adventure.
Publishes in English.
ISBN Prefix(es): 978-0-373
Number of titles published annually: 36 Print
*Warehouse:* 3010 Walden Ave, Depew, NY 14043, United States

**Golden Meteorite Press**
Subsidiary of Golden Meteorite Press Ltd
126 Kingsway Garden, Edmonton, AB T5G 3G4
Mailing Address: PO Box 34181, Edmonton, AB T5G 3G4
*Tel:* 780-378-0063
*Web Site:* www.goldenmeteoritepress.com
*Key Personnel*
Ed & Lib Sales Dir: Austin Mardon *E-mail:* aamardon@yahoo.ca
Intl Rts: C Curry
Founded: 1989

Preferred submission is outline. Canadian SASE or IRC is required or else material is recycled. Accept fiction & nonfiction mss in all categories & genres. Submit to editor. Response in 12 weeks on all complete ms submissions. No phone calls please.
Publishes in English.
ISBN Prefix(es): 978-1-895385; 978-1-897
Number of titles published annually: 4 Print
Total Titles: 55 Print
Imprints: Golden Meteorite Press; RTAJ Fry Press; Shoestring Press

**Goose Lane Editions**
500 Beaverbrook Ct, Suite 330, Fredericton, NB E3B 5X4
SAN: 115-3420
*Tel:* 506-450-4251 *Toll Free Tel:* 888-926-8377 *Fax:* 506-459-4991
*E-mail:* info@gooselane.com
*Web Site:* www.gooselane.com
*Key Personnel*
Publr: Susanne Alexander
Art Dir & Prodn Mgr: Julie Scriver
Mng Ed: Akoulina Connell
Fiction Ed: Bethany Gibson
Poetry Ed: Ross Leckie
Founded: 1954
Primarily deal with Canadian authors. Submissions not accepted from outside of Canada.
Publishes in English.
ISBN Prefix(es): 978-0-920110; 978-0-919197; 978-0-86492
Number of titles published annually: 20 Print
Total Titles: 310 Print; 90 Audio
Imprints: BTC Audiobooks; Goose Lane Editions
Distributed by University of Toronto Press; University of Toronto Press Distribution (CN dist)
Distributor for StorySave
*Distribution Center:* University of Toronto Press Distribution, 2250 Military Rd, Tonawanda, NY 14150, United States (US dist) *Toll Free Tel:* 800-221-9523 *Toll Free Fax:* 800-221-9985 *E-mail:* utpbooks@utpress.utoronto.ca
Membership(s): American Audiobook Publishers Association; Association of Canadian Publishers; Atlantic Publishers Marketing Association; Literary Press Group of Canada

**Greystone Books**
2323 Quebec St, Suite 201, Vancouver, BC V5T 4S7
SAN: 115-1886
*Tel:* 604-254-9099 *Fax:* 604-254-9099
*E-mail:* info@greystonebooks.com
*Web Site:* www.greystonebooks.com; www.dmpibooks.com
*Key Personnel*
Publr: Rob Sanders *E-mail:* rob.sanders@greystonebooks.com
Assoc Publr: Nancy Flight
Mktg Dir: Emiko Morita
Founded: 1993
Publishes in English.
ISBN Prefix(es): 978-0-88894; 978-1-55054; 978-1-55365; 978-0-88833
Number of titles published annually: 30 Print
Total Titles: 400 Print
U.S. Rep(s): Publishers Group West
*Orders to:* Publishers Group West, United States (orders in the US) *Toll Free Tel:* 800-788-3123 *Fax:* 510-528-3444 SAN: 202-8522; Publishers Group World, United States (international orders) *Tel:* 858-457-2500 *Fax:* 858-812-6479; HarperCollins Canada (orders in CN) *Tel:* 416-321-2241 *Toll Free Tel:* 800-387-0117 *Fax:* 416-321-3033 *Toll Free Fax:* 800-668-5788 *E-mail:* hcorder@harpercollins.com SAN: 115-026X
Membership(s): AAP; Association for the Export of Canadian Books; Association of Book Publishers of British Columbia; Association of Canadian Publishers

**Groundwood Books**
Affiliate of House of Anansi Press Inc
110 Spadina Ave, Suite 801, Toronto, ON M5V 2K4
*Tel:* 416-363-4343 *Fax:* 416-363-1017
*E-mail:* genmail@groundwoodbooks.com
*Web Site:* www.houseofanansi.com
*Key Personnel*
Pres & Publr: Sarah MacLachlan
VP, Publg Opers & Royalties & Contracts: Matt Williams
VP, Sales: Barbara Howson
Publr: Sheila Barry
Mktg Dir: Laura Repas
Mktg Mgr: Fred Horler
Web Content Mgr: Trish Osuch
Publicist: Bridget Haines
Founded: 1978
Publish children's books, picture books, novels, nonfiction & folktales; publishes in Spanish also.
Publishes in English.
ISBN Prefix(es): 978-0-88899; 978-1-55498
Number of titles published annually: 25 Print
Total Titles: 500 Print
*Sales Office(s):* Martin & Associates Sales Agency, 594 Windermere Ave, Toronto, ON M6S 3L8 (Atlantic, ON & QC), Contact: Michael Martin *Tel:* 416-769-3947 *Toll Free Tel:* 866-225-3439 *Fax:* 416-769-5967 *E-mail:* memartin@interlog.com
Michael Reynolds & Associates, 339 Tenth Ave SE, Calgary, AB T2G 0W2 (AB, BC, MB & SK), Sales Rep: Heather Parsons *Tel:* 403-233-8771 *Fax:* 403-233-8772 *E-mail:* heather.parsons@shaw.ca
Michael Reynolds & Associates, 210-30 E Sixth Ave, Vancouver, BC V5T 1J4 (AB, BC, MB & SK), Sales Rep: Michael Reynolds *Tel:* 604-688-6918 *Fax:* 604-687-4624 *E-mail:* pubrep@telus.net
Michael Reynolds & Associates, 566 Montrose St, Winnipeg, MB R3M 2M1 (AB, BC, MB & SK), Sales Rep: Lisa Pearce *Tel:* 204-489-4409 *Fax:* 204-487-7314 *E-mail:* lpearce@mts.net
Foreign Rights: Bardon Media Agency (China); The Choicemaker Agency (Korea); The English Agency; Agence Litteraire Lora Fountain & Associates (France); Japan Uni Agency Inc (Japan)
*Returns:* HarperCollins Canada, 1995 Markham Rd, Scarborough, ON M1B 5M8 *Tel:* 416-321-2241 *Toll Free Tel:* 800-387-0117 *Fax:* 416-321-3033 *Toll Free Fax:* 800-668-5788
*Distribution Center:* HarperCollins Distribution & Fulfillment, 1995 Markham Rd, Scarborough, ON M1B 5M8 *Tel:* 416-321-2241 *Toll Free Tel:* 800-387-0117 *Fax:* 416-321-3033 *Toll Free Fax:* 800-668-5788
Membership(s): Association of Canadian Publishers; International Board on Books for Young People; Organization of Book Publishers of Ontario

**Groupe Educalivres Inc**
955, rue Bergar, Laval, QC H7L 4Z6
*Tel:* 514-334-8466 *Toll Free Tel:* 800-567-3671 (info serv) *Fax:* 514-334-8387
*E-mail:* commentaires@educalivres.com
*Web Site:* www.educalivres.com
*Key Personnel*
Owner & Pres: Jean-Guy Blanchette
EVP, Fin & Admin: Joe Cristofaro
Founded: 1992
School, college, university & professional textbooks.
Publishes in English, French.
ISBN Prefix(es): 978-2-7607; 978-0-03; 978-0-88586
Number of titles published annually: 3 Print
Divisions: COBA Management Software

**Groupe Sogides Inc**
Division of Groupe Livre Quebecor Media
955 rue Amherst, Montreal, QC H2L 3K4
*Tel:* 514-523-1182 *Toll Free Tel:* 800-361-4806 *Fax:* 514-597-0370
*E-mail:* edhomme@sogides.com
*Web Site:* www.sogides.com; www.edhomme.com
*Key Personnel*
Pres: Celine Massicotte *E-mail:* cmassicotte@groupehomme.com
VP, Publg: Pierre Bourdon *E-mail:* pbourdon@groupehomme.com
VP, Editions: Erwan Leseul *E-mail:* eleseul@groupehomme.com
Lib Dir: Stephane Masquida
Publr, France: Sylvain Neault *E-mail:* sylvain.neault@sogides.com
Rts & Perms: Mrs Florence Bisch *E-mail:* florence.bisch@groupehomme.com
Founded: 1967
Practical books, cookbooks, biographies, general interest books, popular psychology, art books, poetry, diaries, art calendars & stationery, novels, drama.
Publishes in French.
ISBN Prefix(es): 978-2-7619; 978-0-7760; 978-2-89026; 978-2-89194
Number of titles published annually: 150 Print
Total Titles: 2,000 Print
Imprints: Les Editions de l'Homme; Le Jour Editeur; Utilis
Subsidiaries: Le Groupe Ville-Marie Litterature; L'Hexagone; Messageries ADP; Quinze
Divisions: VLB Editeur
*Branch Office(s)*
Editions de l'Homme, Le Jour Editeur, Immeuble Paryseine, 3 Allee de la Seine, 94854 Ivry Cedex, France
Distributed by Distribution OLS-SA; Vivendi Universal Publishing
Distributor for Actif; Atlas; Berlitz Fixot; Chouette; Le Cri; Edimag; Editions Modus Vivendi; Fleuve Noir; Gault & Millau; Heritage; De L'Homme; Hors Collection; JCL; Albin Michel Jeunesse; Julliard; Robert Laffont; Langues pour tous; Albin Michel; Albin Michel Education; Nathan; Nathan Education; Option Sante; Olivier Orban; Perrin; Plon; Pocket; La Presse; Presses de la Cite (Poche); Presses de la Cite Litterature; Presses Libres; Michel Quintin; Quinze; Du Rocher; Rouge & Or; Seghers; Selection du Reader's Digest; Solar; Time-Life; Trapeze; Usborne; Claire Vigne; VLB; XYZ (Typo Seulement)
U.S. Publishers Represented: Reader's Digest
*Warehouse:* 1751 Richardson, Pointe St-Charles, Montreal, QC H3K 1G6

**Guerin Editeur Ltee**
4501 rue Drolet, Montreal, QC H2T 2G2
*Tel:* 514-842-3481 *Toll Free Tel:* 800-398-8337 *Fax:* 514-842-4923
*Web Site:* www.guerin-editeur.qc.ca
*Key Personnel*
Pres: Marc-Aime Guerin
VP: France Larochelle *E-mail:* france.larochelle@guerin-edi.qc.ca
Prodn Mgr: Janick Salvaille
Secy: Ginette Laperriere
Founded: 1970
Publishers of books for schools from kindergarten to university.
Publishes in English, French.
ISBN Prefix(es): 978-2-7601
Number of titles published annually: 80 Print; 2 Audio
Total Titles: 2,300 Print; 43 Audio
Distributed by Champlain Library (Ontario); Carme Pierre Yves Levy (Haiti); Library of Quebec (France); Library Prelagie (Maritimes); Servidis SA (Switzerland)

**Guernica Editions Inc**
489 Strathmore Blvd, Toronto, ON M4C 1N8
*Tel:* 416-576-9403 (orders & cust serv); 416-285-4067 (edit) *Fax:* 416-981-7606
*Web Site:* guernicaeditions.com
*Key Personnel*
Pres & Publr: Connie Guzzo McParland *E-mail:* conniemcparland@guernicaeditions.com
VP & Ed-In-Chief: Michael Mirolla *Tel:* 514-712-5304 *E-mail:* michaelmirolla@guernicaeditions.com
Publicist: Laura Carter *Tel:* 647-448-1926 *E-mail:* lauracarter@guernicaeditions.com
Founded: 1978
Literary press specializing in Canadian writing (prose, poetry, literary criticism, drama & social studies), translation into English, some foreign publications in the English language.
Publishes in English.
ISBN Prefix(es): 978-0-919349; 978-0-920717; 978-2-89135; 978-1-55071
Number of titles published annually: 25 Print
Total Titles: 450 Print
*Sales Office(s):* Literary Press Group, 501-192 Spadina Ave, Toronto, ON M5T 2C2, Natl Accts Mgr: Petra Morin *Tel:* 416-483-1321 ext 3 *Fax:* 416-483-2510 *E-mail:* pmorin@lpg.ca *Web Site:* www.lpg.ca
U.S. Rep(s): Small Press Distribution
*Shipping Address:* University of Toronto Press, 5201 Dufferin St, Downsview, ON M3H 5T8 *Tel:* 416-667-7846 *Toll Free Tel:* 800-565-9523 *Fax:* 416-667-7832
*Distribution Center:* Small Press Distribution, 1341 Seventh St, Berkeley, CA 94710-1409, United States, Sales & Mktg Mgr: Clay Banes *Tel:* 510-524-1668 *Toll Free Tel:* 800-869-7553 *Fax:* 510-524-0852 *E-mail:* clay@spdbooks.org *Web Site:* www.spdbooks.org

**Hancock House Publishers Ltd**
19313 Zero Ave, Surrey, BC V3S 9R9
Mailing Address: 1431 Harrison Ave, Blaine, WA 98230-5005, United States
*Tel:* 604-538-1114 *Toll Free Tel:* 800-938-1114 *Fax:* 604-538-2262 *Toll Free Fax:* 800-983-2262
*E-mail:* sales@hancockhouse.com
*Web Site:* www.hancockhouse.com
*Key Personnel*
Pres: David Hancock
Ed: Ingrid Luters
Founded: 1975
Biographical nature guide books.
Publishes in English.
ISBN Prefix(es): 978-0-88839; 978-0-919654
Number of titles published annually: 20 Print
Total Titles: 365 Print
Foreign Rep(s): Gazelle Book Services (UK)

**Harbour Publishing Co Ltd**
PO Box 219, Madeira Park, BC V0N 2H0
*Tel:* 604-883-2730 *Toll Free Tel:* 800-667-2988 *Fax:* 604-883-9451
*E-mail:* info@harbourpublishing.com
*Web Site:* www.harbourpublishing.com
*Key Personnel*
Publr: Howard White
Mktg Mgr: Marisa Alps
Prodn Coord: Anna Comfort
Founded: 1972
History & culture of British Columbia & West Coast, including fiction & poetry by Canadian authors.
Publishes in English.
ISBN Prefix(es): 978-0-920080; 978-1-55017
Number of titles published annually: 30 Print; 1 CD-ROM; 1 Audio
Total Titles: 600 Print; 1 CD-ROM; 5 Audio
Imprints: Douglas & McIntyre; Lost Moose
Distributor for Caitlin Press; Nightwood Editions
U.S. Rep(s): Graphic Arts Center Publishing Co; Robert Hale & Co; Ingram Book Co; Partners West
Foreign Rep(s): Gazelle Book Services Ltd (Eastern Europe, Ireland, UK, Western Europe)
*Orders to:* Harbour Publishing, Lagoon Rd, Madeira Park, BC V0N 2H0 *Toll Free Tel:* 800-667-2988 *E-mail:* orders@harbourpublishing.com
*Distribution Center:* Harbour Publishing, Lagoon Rd, Madeira Park, BC V0N 2H0
*See separate listing for:*
**Douglas & McIntyre**

**Harlequin Enterprises Ltd**
Subsidiary of Torstar Corp
225 Duncan Mill Rd, Don Mills, ON M3B 3K9
SAN: 115-3749
*Tel:* 416-445-5860 *Toll Free Tel:* 888-432-4879; 800-370-5838 (ebook inquiries) *Fax:* 416-445-8655
*E-mail:* CustomerService@harlequin.com
*Web Site:* www.harlequin.com
*Key Personnel*
COO: Craig Swinwood
CEO & Publr: Donna Hayes
EVP, Global Publg & Strategy: Loriana Sacilotto
EVP, Overseas: Stephen Miles
EVP, Direct to Consumer: Christina Clifford
CFO & SVP: Andrew Wright
VP, Opers & Admin: Jim Robinson
VP, Retail Sales: Alex Osuszek
VP & CIO Info Systems: Margaret Morrison
VP, Series Edit & Subs Rts: Dianne Moggy
EVP, Mktg & Digital: Brent Lewis
VP, Corp Reporting, Planning & Analysis: Kathy Vandervoort
VP, Overseas: Diego Castelli
VP, Gen Coun & Secy: Karen Louie
VP, HR: Trish Hewitt
Dir, Digital Prods: Farah Mullick
Dir, Harlequin Teen: Amy Jones
Dir, Overseas Publg Strategy: Emily Martin
Edit Dir, Carina Press: Angela James
Exec Ed, HQN & LUNA: Susan Swinwood
Mng Edit Coord, NY/Toronto: Beth Attwood
Sr Ed, HQN, LUNA & Teen: Margo Lipschultz
Sr Ed, MIRA: Nicole Brebner
Ed, Series: Adrienne Macintosh
Assoc Ed, Harlequin Superromance: Karen Reid
Asst Ed, HQN & MIRA: Leonore Waldrip
Asst Ed, MIRA: Michelle Venditti
Mgr, Online Engagement: Amy Wilkins
Author Liaison, Concierge Servs: Miranda Indrigo
Founded: 1949 (in Winnipeg, MB, CN)
Publishes in 31 languages in 111 international markets.
Publishes in English, French.
ISBN Prefix(es): 978-0-373
Number of titles published annually: 1,320 Print; 30 Online; 1,530 E-Book; 75 Audio
Total Titles: 30 Online; 1,850 E-Book; 95 Audio
Imprints: Carina Press (digital-first); Gold Eagle (action-adventure); Harlequin Books (series romance); Harlequin HQN (romance fiction); Harlequin Kimani Arabesque; Harlequin Kimani Press (African-American); Harlequin Kimani TRU; Harlequin LUNA (fantasy/paranormal); Harlequin MIRA (mainstream women's fiction); Harlequin Nonfiction (nonfiction); Harlequin Teen (young adult fiction); Love Inspired Books (inspirational romance); Silhouette Books (series romance); Spice (erotic fiction); Worldwide Library (mystery fiction); Worldwide Mystery
*Branch Office(s)*
233 Broadway, Suite 1001, New York, NY 10279, United States *Tel:* 212-553-4200 *Fax:* 212-227-8969 SAN: 200-2450
*Foreign Office(s):* Harlequin Mills & Boon, 18-24 Paradise Rd, Richmond, Surrey TW9 1SR, United Kingdom *Tel:* (0208) 288 2800 *Fax:* (0208) 288 2899
*Advertising Agency:* Vickers & Benson-Direct
*Distribution Center:* 3010 Walden Ave, Depew, NY 14043, United States
Membership(s): AAP; Association of Canadian Publishers; BISG
*See separate listing for:*
**Gold Eagle**
**Worldwide Library**

**HarperCollins Canada Ltd**
Division of HarperCollins Publishers Ltd
2 Bloor St E, 20th fl, Toronto, ON M4W 1A8
*Tel:* 416-975-9334 *Fax:* 416-975-9884
*E mail:* hccanada@harpercollins.com
*Web Site:* www.harpercollins.ca
*Key Personnel*
CEO & Pres: David Kent *Tel:* 416-975-9334 ext 212 *E-mail:* David.Kent@HarperCollins.com
VP & Publr: Iris Tupholme *Tel:* 416-975-9334 ext 123 *E-mail:* Iris.Tupholme@HarperCollins.com
VP, Fin: Wayne Playter *Tel:* 416-321-2241 ext 207 *E-mail:* Wayne.Playter@HarperCollins.com
VP, HR & Admin: Dianne Aquilina *Tel:* 416-975-9334 ext 216 *E-mail:* Dianne.Aquilina@HarperCollins.com
VP, Opers: Olive Khan *Tel:* 416-975-9334 ext 204 *E-mail:* Olive.Khan@HarperCollins.com
VP, Prodn: Neil Erickson *Tel:* 416-975-9334 ext 118 *E-mail:* Neil.Erickson@HarperCollins.com
VP, Sales & Mktg: Leo MacDonald *Tel:* 416-975-9334 ext 122 *E-mail:* Leo.MacDonald@HarperCollins.com
Publr, Patrick Crean Editions: Patrick Crean
Dir, Contracts & Legal Aff: Jeremy Rawlings *Tel:* 416-975-9334 ext 117 *E-mail:* Jeremy.Rawlings@HarperCollins.com
Dir, Publicity & Communs: Rob Firing *Tel:* 416-975-9334 ext 141 *E-mail:* Rob.Firing@HarperCollins.com
Dir, Subs Rts & List Mgmt: Lisa Rundle *Tel:* 416-975-9334 ext 113 *E-mail:* Lisa.Rundle@HarperCollins.com
Founded: 1989
Literary & commercial fiction, nonfiction, children's books, cookbooks, reference & spiritual books. Distribute for all HarperCollins companies in the US, UK & Australia.
Publishes in English.
ISBN Prefix(es): 978-1-55468
Number of titles published annually: 100 Print
Total Titles: 1,500 Print
Imprints: Phyllis Bruce Books; Collins Canada; Patrick Crean Editions; HarperCollins Publishers; HarperPerennialCanada; HarperTrophy Canada; HarperWeekend
Distributor for America's Test Kitchen; Douglas & McIntyre; ESPN Books; House of Anansi Press; Hyperion; Smithsonian Books; Tokyopop; Zondervan
*Warehouse:* 1995 Markham Rd, Scarborough, ON M1B 5M8 *Tel:* 416-321-2241 (orders) *Fax:* 416-321-3015

**Herald Press**
Imprint of MennoMedia
490 Dutton Dr, Unit C-8, Waterloo, ON N2L 6H7
*Tel:* 519-747-5722 *Toll Free Tel:* 800-631-6535 *Fax:* 519-747-5721
*E-mail:* hpcan@mpn.net
*Web Site:* www.heraldpress.com
*Key Personnel*
Sales & Mktg: Kathy Shantz *E-mail:* kathys@mennomedia.org
Founded: 1908
Christian books.
Publishes in English.
ISBN Prefix(es): 978-0-8361
Number of titles published annually: 20 Print
Total Titles: 450 Print
*Branch Office(s)*
718 N Main St, Newton, KS 67114, United States

*Tel:* 316-281-4412 *Toll Free Tel:* 800-245-7894 ext 220 *Fax:* 316-283-0454
1251 Virginia Ave, Harrisonburg, VA 22802-2434, United States *Toll Free Tel:* 800-999-3534 *Toll Free Fax:* 877-271-0760
Membership(s): Canadian Booksellers Association

**Heritage House Publishing Co Ltd**
1105 Pandora Ave, Victoria, BC V8V 3P9
*Tel:* 604-574-7067 *Toll Free Tel:* 800-665-3302 *Fax:* 604-574-9942 *Toll Free Fax:* 800-566-3336
*E-mail:* heritage@heritagehouse.ca; orders@heritagehouse.ca
*Web Site:* www.heritagehouse.ca
*Key Personnel*
Publr: Rodger Touchie
Mng Ed: Vivian Sinclair
Prodn Mgr: Susan Adamson *E-mail:* susan@heritagehouse.ca
Mktg Coord: Neil Wedin *Tel:* 250-580-1925
Founded: 1967
Publishes in English.
ISBN Prefix(es): 978-1-895811; 978-1-894384; 978-1-894974
Number of titles published annually: 30 Print
Total Titles: 175 Print
Distributor for Frank Amato; Bellerophon; Fine Edge Productions; Horsdal & Schubart; Sunfire; Whitecap
*Distribution Center:* Heritage Group Distribution, 19272 96 Ave, Suite 8, Surrey, BC V4N 4C1 *Fax:* 604-881-7068
Membership(s): Association of Book Publishers of British Columbia; Association of Canadian Publishers

**Les Heures bleues**
Sta Lorimier, PO Box 219, Montreal, QC H2H 2N6
*Tel:* 450-671-7718 *Fax:* 450-671-7718
*E-mail:* info@heuresbleues.com
*Web Site:* www.heuresbleues.com
*Key Personnel*
Pres: Rene Bonenfant
Founded: 1996
Publishes in French.
ISBN Prefix(es): 978-2-922265
Number of titles published annually: 6 Print
Total Titles: 50 Print
*Distribution Center:* Dimedia, 539 boul Lebeau, St-Laurent, QC H4N 1S2
Membership(s): Association Nationale des Editeurs de Livres

**House of Anansi Press Ltd**
Affiliate of Groundwood Books
110 Spadina Ave, Suite 801, Toronto, ON M5V 2K4
*Tel:* 416-363-4343 *Fax:* 416-363-1017
*E-mail:* customerservice@houseofanansi.com
*Web Site:* www.anansi.ca
*Key Personnel*
VP, Publg Opers & Royalties & Contracts - House of Anansi & Groundwood Books: Matt Williams
Pres & Publr: Sarah MacLachlan
VP, Sales: Barbara Howson
Opers Mgr: Mark Luk *Tel:* 416-363-4343 ext 221
Web Content Mgr: Trish Osuch
Mng Ed: Kelly Joseph
Ed: Meredith Dees
Founded: 1967
Literary publishing; fiction, poetry, criticism & belles lettres.
Publishes in English.
ISBN Prefix(es): 978-0-88784
Number of titles published annually: 25 Print
Total Titles: 200 Print
Imprints: Spiderlinc (crime fiction)
*Distribution Center:* Publishers Group West/Perseus Books Group, 1700 Fourth St, Berkeley, CA 94710, United States (US orders) *Toll Free Tel:* 800-343-4499 *Toll Free Fax:* 800-351-5073 *E-mail:* orderentry@perseusbooks.com
HarperCollins Canada Ltd, 1995 Markham Rd, Scarborough, ON M1B 5M8 (Canadian orders) *Tel:* 416-321-2241 *Toll Free Tel:* 800-387-0117 *E-mail:* hcorder@harpercollins.com

**C D Howe Institute**
67 Yonge St, Suite 300, Toronto, ON M5E 1J8
*Tel:* 416-865-1904 *Fax:* 416-865-1866
*E-mail:* cdhowe@cdhowe.org
*Web Site:* www.cdhowe.org
*Key Personnel*
CEO & Pres: William B P Robson
VP, Media & Ed: James Fleming *Tel:* 416-865-1904 ext 234 *E-mail:* jfleming@cdhowe.org
Info Servs Coord: Alyson Henry *E-mail:* ahenry@cdhowe.org
Founded: 1973
Economics & social policy studies.
Publishes in English, French.
ISBN Prefix(es): 978-0-88806
Number of titles published annually: 48 Print
Total Titles: 150 Print
Distributed by Renouf Publishing Co (Ottawa)

**Inclusion Press International**
47 Indian Trail, Toronto, ON M6R 1Z8
*Tel:* 416-658-5363 *Fax:* 416-658-5067
*E-mail:* inclusionpress@inclusion.com
*Web Site:* www.inclusion.com
*Key Personnel*
Founding Publr: Jack Pearpoint *E-mail:* jack@inclusion.com
Founded: 1989
Inclusion, change, diversity & community.
Publishes in English.
ISBN Prefix(es): 978-1-895418
Number of titles published annually: 1 Print; 2 CD-ROM; 2 E-Book
Total Titles: 34 Print; 7 CD-ROM; 2 E-Book

**Insomniac Press**
520 Princess Ave, London, ON N6B 2B8
*Tel:* 416-504-6270
*Web Site:* www.insomniacpress.com
*Key Personnel*
Prop & Publr: Mike O'Connor *E-mail:* mike@insomniacpress.com
Mng Ed: Dan Varrette *E-mail:* dan@insomniacpress.com
Founded: 1992
General trade publisher, fiction & nonfiction.
Publishes in English.
ISBN Prefix(es): 978-1-895837; 978-1-894663; 978-1-897178
Number of titles published annually: 16 Print
Total Titles: 235 Print
*Shipping Address:* Consortium Book Sales & Distribution, The Keg House, Suite 101, 34 13 Ave NE, Minneapolis, MN 55413-1007, United States *Tel:* 612-746-2600 *Toll Free Tel:* 800-283-3572 (cust serv) *Fax:* 612-746-2606 *Web Site:* www.cbsd.com
*Warehouse:* PGC, 250-A Carlton St, Toronto, ON M5A 2L1 *Toll Free Tel:* 800-663-5714 *Toll Free Fax:* 800-565-3770
Consortium Book Sales & Distribution, The Keg House, Suite 101, 34 13 Ave NE, Minneapolis, MN 55413-1007, United States *Tel:* 612-746-2600 *Toll Free Tel:* 800-283-3572 (cust serv) *Fax:* 612-746-2606 *Web Site:* www.cbsd.com

**Institut canadien du droit des ressources**, see Canadian Institute of Resources Law (Institut Canadien du Droit des Resources)

**The Institute for Research on Public Policy (IRPP)**
1470 Peel, Suite 200, Montreal, QC H3A 1T1
*Tel:* 514-985-2461 *Fax:* 514-985-2559
*E-mail:* irpp@irpp.org
*Web Site:* www.irpp.org
*Key Personnel*
VP, Opers: Suzanne Ostiguy McIntyre *Tel:* 514-787-0740 *E-mail:* smcintyre@irpp.org
Founded: 1972
Research on public policy.
Publishes in English, French.
ISBN Prefix(es): 978-0-88645
Number of titles published annually: 5 Print
Total Titles: 500 Print
U.S. Rep(s): Gower Publishing

**Institute of Intergovernmental Relations**
Queen's University, Robert Sutheland Hall, Rm 301, Kingston, ON K7L 3N6
*Tel:* 613-533-2080 *Fax:* 613-533-6868
*E-mail:* iigr@queensu.ca
*Web Site:* www.queensu.ca/iigr
*Key Personnel*
Dir: Andre Juneau
Pubns Coord & Secy: Mary Kennedy
Founded: 1965
Publish research & other scholarly work on Canadian federalism & intergovernmental relations; ethnicity, government & political science.
Publishes in English, French.
ISBN Prefix(es): 978-1-55339
Number of titles published annually: 4 Print
Total Titles: 96 Print
*Distribution Center:* McGill-Queen's University Press, Georgetown Terminal Warehouses, 34 Armstrong Ave, Georgetown, ON L7G 4R9 *Tel:* 905-873-2750 *Fax:* 905-873-6170

**Institute of Psychological Research, Inc.**
1304 Fleury St E, Montreal, QC H2C 1R3
*Tel:* 514-382-3000 *Toll Free Tel:* 800-363-7800 *Fax:* 514-382-3007 *Toll Free Fax:* 888-382-3007
*Web Site:* www.irpcanada.com
Founded: 1958 (Incorporated in 1963)
Psychological tests & materials.
Publishes in English, French.
ISBN Prefix(es): 978-0-88509; 978-2-89109
Number of titles published annually: 10 Print
Imprints: IPR, IRP
Distributed by Editions Editest (Belgium); Librairie du Quebec a Paris (France)
Distributor for Hans Huber (Rorschach only)
U.S. Publishers Represented: Academic Therapy Publications; American Orthopsychiatric; Behavior Sciences Systems; Martin M Bruce; Cardall Associates; Center for Psychological Services; Clinical Psychology Publishing; Nigel Cox; Educational & Clinical Publications; Educational Industrial Testing Service; Educational Performance Associate; Educators Publishing Services; Guidance Associates of Delaware; Harvard University Press; Industrial Psychology; Institute for Personality & Ability Testing; International Tests; Language Research Associates; National Foundation for Educational Research; Pacific Book; Psychological Assessment Resources; Psychological Test Specialists; Psychologists & Educators; Sheridan Psychological Services; Western Psychological Services

**Institute of Public Administration of Canada**
1075 Bay St, Suite 401, Toronto, ON M5S 2B1
*Tel:* 416-924-8787 *Fax:* 416-924-4992
*E-mail:* ntl@ipac.ca; ntl@iapc.ca
*Web Site:* www.ipac.ca; www.iapc.ca
*Key Personnel*
Chief Executive Officer: Robert Taylor *E-mail:* rtaylor@ipac.ca
Mng Ed: Megan Sproule-Jones *E-mail:* msproule-jones@ipac.ca
Ed: Evert A Lindquist
Founded: 1947
National bilingual English/French nonprofit organization, concerned with the theory & practice

of public management, with 20 regional groups across Canada. Provide networks & forums regionally, nationally & internationally. Specialize in political science, Canadian history & Canadian law.
Publishes in English, French.
ISBN Prefix(es): 978-0-919400; 978-0-920715; 978-0-919696; 978-1-55061
Number of titles published annually: 10 Print; 5 E-Book
Total Titles: 500 Print; 50 Online; 10 E-Book; 5 Audio

**International Development Research Centre (IDRC)**
150 Kent St, Ottawa, ON K1P 0B2
Mailing Address: PO Box 8500, Ottawa, ON K1G 3H9
*Tel:* 613-236-6163 *Fax:* 613-238-7230
*E-mail:* info@idrc.ca
*Web Site:* www.idrc.ca
*Key Personnel*
Publr: Bill Carman *Tel:* 613-236-6163 ext 2089
Founded: 1970
Publishes research results & scholarly studies on global & regional issues related to sustainable & equitable development.
Publishes in English, French.
ISBN Prefix(es): 978-0-88936; 978-1-55250
Number of titles published annually: 30 Print; 20 Online
Total Titles: 330 Print
Distributed by ITDG Publishing (Europe); Renouf Publishing Co Ltd (worldwide); Stylus Publishing Inc (Latin America & US)

**Irwin Law Inc**
14 Duncan St, Suite 206, Toronto, ON M5H 3G8
*Tel:* 416-862-7690 *Toll Free Tel:* 888-314-9014 *Fax:* 416-862-9236
*Web Site:* www.irwinlaw.com
*Key Personnel*
Pres & Publr: Jeffrey Miller *Tel:* 416-862-7690 ext 23 *E-mail:* jmiller@irwinlaw.com
VP: Alisa Posesorski *E-mail:* aposes@irwinlaw.com
Founded: 1996
Publisher of books & other material for lawyers & law students.
Publishes in English.
ISBN Prefix(es): 978-1-55221
Number of titles published annually: 20 Print; 20 E-Book
Total Titles: 150 Print; 75 E-Book
Distributed by Gaunt Inc
Distributor for The Federation Press (North America only)
Foreign Rep(s): Federation Press (Australia, New Zealand)
Membership(s): Organization of Book Publishers of Ontario

**ITMB Publishing Ltd**
12300 Bridgeport Rd, Richmond, BC V6V 1J5
*Tel:* 604-273-1400 *Fax:* 604-273-1488
*E-mail:* itmb@itmb.com
*Web Site:* www.itmb.com
Founded: 1980
Publisher/distributor of international maps.
Publishes in English.
ISBN Prefix(es): 978-1-5534
Number of titles published annually: 30 Print
Total Titles: 425 Print
Distributor for Borch; Freytag & Bernot; Gizi; National Geographic; Nelles; Rand McNally
Membership(s): International Map Trade Association

**Ivey Publishing**, see Richard Ivey School of Business

**Richard Ivey School of Business**
Division of Ivey Management Services
University of Western Ontario, 1151 Richmond St N, London, ON N6A 3K7
*Tel:* 519-661-3206 *Toll Free Tel:* 800-649-6355 *Fax:* 519-661-3485
*E-mail:* cases@ivey.uwo.ca
*Web Site:* www.iveycases.com; www.ivey.uwo.ca
*Key Personnel*
Busn Devt Coord: Shelli Hunter *Tel:* 519-661-4258 *E-mail:* shunter@ivey.uwo.ca
Founded: 1922
Publish business case studies for university business courses.
Publishes in English, French.
ISBN Prefix(es): 978-0-919534
Number of titles published annually: 200 Print
Total Titles: 2,500 Print
Distributed by Caseplace (The Aspen Institute's Centre for Business Education); Cengage Learning (USA); Centrale de Cas et de Medias Pedagogiques (CCMP) (Paris, France); College of Commerce (National Chengchi University, Taiwan); European Case Clearing House (ECCH) (UK); IESE Publishing (Spain); Institute for International Studies and Training (IIST) (Japan); LAD Publishing (USA); McGraw-Hill (USA); National Archive Publishing (USA); Pearson Custom Publishing (USA); Study.Net (USA); University Readers Inc (USA)
Distributor for China Europe International Business School (CEIBS); College of Commerce (National Chengchi University, Taiwan); Gordon Institute of Business Science (University of Pretoria, South Africa); Harvard Business School Publishing; Indian School of Business (India); Ivey Business Journal (reprints); Nanyang Business School (Singapore); Peking University (China); Thunderbird School of Business Management; Tsinghua University (China); Yonsei University (Korea; Harvard Business School cases & Harvard Business Review reprints)
U.S. Rep(s): Harvard Business School Publishing (case studies & HBR reprints)
Foreign Rep(s): European Case Clearing House (Europe)

**Kids Can Press Ltd**
Division of Corus Entertainment Inc
25 Dockside Dr, Toronto, ON M5A 0B5
*Tel:* 416-479-7000 *Toll Free Tel:* 800-265-0884 *Fax:* 416-960-5437
*E-mail:* info@kidscan.com; customerservice@kidscan.com
*Web Site:* www.kidscanpress.com; www.kidscanpress.ca
*Key Personnel*
Pres: Lisa Lyons
Cont: June Samms
VP, Brands, New Media & New Channel Revenue: Lisa Charters
Acting Publr: Lisa Lyons
Art Dir: Marie Bartholomew
Edit Dir: Yvette Ghione *Tel:* 416-479-7000 ext 36551
Assoc Publr: Semareh Al-Hillal
Rts Mgr: Adrienne Tang
Prodn Ed: Jennifer Grimbleby; DoEun Kwon
Cross Media Specialist: Danielle Mulhall
Graphic Designer: Mike Reis
Asst, Brands & New Busn: Allison MacLachlan
Founded: 1973
Books for children exclusively.
Publishes in English.
ISBN Prefix(es): 978-0-919964; 978-1-55074; 978-1-55337; 978-0-921103; 978-1-55453
Number of titles published annually: 75 Print
Total Titles: 500 Print
Imprints: Franklin; Kids Can Do It
*Branch Office(s)*
2250 Military Rd, Tonawanda, NY 14150, United States
Distributed by Open Road; University of Toronto Press
*Orders to:* University of Toronto Press
*Returns:* University of Toronto Press; 2250 Military Rd, Tonawanda, NY 14150, United States (US returns)
*Shipping Address:* University of Toronto Press
Membership(s): Children's Book Council

**Kindred Productions**
Division of Mennonite Brethren Church of Canada & United States
1310 Taylor Ave, Winnipeg, MB R3M 3Z6
*Tel:* 204-669-6575 *Toll Free Tel:* 800-545-7322 *Fax:* 204-654-1865
*E-mail:* custserv@kindredproductions.com
*Web Site:* www.kindredproductions.com
*Key Personnel*
Cust Serv Rep: Renita Kornelsen
Founded: 1982
Denominational material, Low German Bible, trade books & church resources.
Publishes in English, French.
ISBN Prefix(es): 978-0-919797; 978-0-921788; 978-1-894791
Number of titles published annually: 15 Print
Total Titles: 250 Print
*Branch Office(s)*
PO Box 421, Goessel, KS 67053, United States *Tel:* 620-367-3843
U.S. Publishers Represented: Kindred Productions

**Knopf Random Canada**
Division of Random House of Canada Limited
One Toronto St, Suite 300, Toronto, ON M5C 2V6
SAN: 201-3975
*Tel:* 416-364-4449 *Toll Free Tel:* 888-523-9292 *Fax:* 416-364-6863
*Web Site:* www.randomhouse.ca
*Key Personnel*
CEO & Pres: Brad Martin *Tel:* 905-624-0672
Chief Admin Offr & EVP: Doug Foot *Tel:* 905-624-0672
EVP & Exec Publr, Knopf Random Canada Publishing Group: Louise Dennys
EVP & Dir, Sales: Duncan Shields *Tel:* 905-624-0672
SVP & Dir, Digital: Lisa Charters *Tel:* 905-624-0672
SVP & Dir, Mktg & Corp Communs: Tracey Turriff
VP & Creative Dir: Scott Richardson
VP & Dir, Mktg Strategy: Scott Sellers
VP & Dir, Prodn: Janine Laporte
VP & Publr, Knopf Random Canada Publishing Group: Anne Collins
Publr, Vintage Canada & Assoc Publr, Knopf Random Canada: Marion Garner
Publr-at-Large: Diane Martin
Sr Mng Ed, Knopf Random Canada Publishing Group: Deidre Molina
Sr Ed, Knopf Random Canada Publishing Group: Pamela Murray; Paul Taunton
Sr Ed, Random House of Canada Limited: Craig Pyette
Assoc Ed: Amanda Lewis
Assoc Dir, Prodn: Carla Kean
Asst Prodn Mgr: Lindsay Jones
Off Mgr & Exec Asst, LD/Knopf Random Canada Publishing Group: Nina Ber-Donkor
Founded: 1991
Random House Inc & its publishing entities are not accepting unsol submissions, proposals, mss, or submission queries via e-mail at this time.
Publishes in English.
ISBN Prefix(es): 978-0-307; 978-0-676
Number of titles published annually: 40 Print
Imprints: Seal Books; Vintage Canada

Distributed by Random House of Canada Limited
*Orders to:* Random House of Canada Limited, 2775 Matheson Blvd E, Mississauga, ON L4W 4P7
*Shipping Address:* Random House of Canada Limited, 2775 Matheson Blvd E, Mississauga, ON L4W 4P7
Membership(s): Canadian Booksellers Association; Canadian Publishers' Council

**Laurier Books Ltd**
PO Box 2694, Sta D, Ottawa, ON K1P 5W6
SAN: 168-2806
*Tel:* 613-738-2163 *Fax:* 613-247-0256
*E-mail:* laurierbooks@yahoo.com
*Key Personnel*
Pres: L Marthe
Lib Sales Dir: R Lalwani
Founded: 1975
All foreign language dictionaries, Native American publications, annuals, bibliographic products, business directories, distribution, publishing, mail orders.
Publishes in English.
ISBN Prefix(es): 978-1-895959; 978-1-55394
Number of titles published annually: 15 Print
Total Titles: 3,000 Print
U.S. Rep(s): IBD Ltd

**§LexisNexis Canada Inc**
Member of The LexisNexis Group
123 Commerce Valley Dr E, Suite 700, Markham, ON L3T 7W8
*Tel:* 905-479-2665 *Toll Free Tel:* 800-668-6481; 800-387-0899 (cust serv) *Fax:* 905-479-2826 *Toll Free Fax:* 800-461-3275
*E-mail:* orders@lexisnexis.ca; service@lexisnexis.ca (cust serv)
*Web Site:* www.lexisnexis.ca
*Key Personnel*
Academic Solutions Specialist: Luc Meloche *E-mail:* luc.meloche@lexisnexis.ca
Mgr, Mktg Servs: Yolanda Majury *E-mail:* yolanda.majury@lexisnexis.ca
Dir, Training & Cust Retention: Jeff Morrison *E-mail:* jeff.morrison@lexisnexis.ca
Cust Serv Mgr: Barbara Brumwell *Tel:* 905-415-5816 *E-mail:* barbara.brumwell@lexisnexis.ca
Founded: 1912
Books, looseleaf services, newsletters, journals, legal publishing & online services.
Publishes in English, French.
ISBN Prefix(es): 978-0-409; 978-0-433
Number of titles published annually: 80 Print; 20 CD-ROM
Imprints: Butterworths
*Branch Office(s)*
355 Burrard St, Suite 920, Vancouver, BC V6C 2G8 *Tel:* 604-684-1462 *Fax:* 604-684-5581
112 Kent St, Suite 700, Ottawa, ON K1P 5P2 *Tel:* 613-238-3499 *Fax:* 613-238-7597
905 King St W, 4th fl, Suite 400, Toronto, ON M6K 3G9 *Tel:* 416-862-7656 *Fax:* 416-862-8073
215 Sainte-Jacques St, Suite 1111, Montreal, QC H2Y 1M6 *Tel:* 514-287-0339 *Toll Free Tel:* 800-227-9597 *Fax:* 514-287-0350

**Lidec Inc**
4350 Ave de l'Hotel-de-Ville, Montreal, QC H2W 2H5
Mailing Address: CP 5000, Succursale "C", Montreal, QC H2X 3M1
*Tel:* 514-843-5991 *Toll Free Tel:* 800-350-5991 (CN only) *Fax:* 514-843-5252
*E-mail:* lidec@lidec.qc.ca
*Web Site:* www.lidec.qc.ca
*Key Personnel*
Gen Mgr & ISBN Contact: Claude Legault
Founded: 1965
Publisher of school books.
Publishes in English, French.
ISBN Prefix(es): 978-2-7608
Number of titles published annually: 30 Print
Total Titles: 1,500 Print

**Life Cycle Books Ltd**
1085 Bellamy Rd N, Suite 20, Toronto, ON M1H 3C7
SAN: 110 8417
*Tel:* 416-690-5860 *Toll Free Tel:* 866-880-5860 *Fax:* 416-690-8532 *Toll Free Fax:* 866-690-8532
*E-mail:* orders@lifecyclebooks.com
*Web Site:* www.lifecyclebooks.com
*Key Personnel*
Founder & Pres: Paul Broughton *E-mail:* paulb@lifecyclebooks.com
Founded: 1973
Human life issues.
Publishes in English, French.
ISBN Prefix(es): 978-0-919225
Number of titles published annually: 3 Print
Total Titles: 41 Print
*Branch Office(s)*
PO Box 1008, Niagara Falls, NY 14304-1008, United States

**L'Instut Canadien des Comptables Agrees**, see Canadian Institute of Chartered Accountants (L'Institut Canadien des Comptables Agrees)

**Lone Pine Publishing**
2311 96 St, Edmonton, AB T6N 1G3
SAN: 115-4125
*Tel:* 780-433-9333 *Toll Free Tel:* 800-661-9017 *Fax:* 780-433-9646 *Toll Free Fax:* 800-424-7173
*E-mail:* info@lonepinepublishing.com
*Web Site:* www.lonepinepublishing.com
*Key Personnel*
Pres: Shane Kennedy
Dir, Mktg: Ken Davis
Sr Ed: Nancy Foulds
Founded: 1980
Natural history, travel, recreation, popular history, bird guides & gardening.
Publishes in English.
ISBN Prefix(es): 978-1-55105; 978-1-894877 (Ghost House Imprint)
Number of titles published annually: 30 Print
Total Titles: 800 Print
*Branch Office(s)*
1808 "B" St NW, Suite 140, Auburn, WA 98001, United States, Sales Mgr: Helen Ibach *Toll Free Tel:* 800-518-3541 *Toll Free Fax:* 800-548-1169 *E-mail:* hibach@lonepinepublishing.com
Distributor for Coteau Books; Folklore Publishing; InForum; Johnson & Gorman; Red Deer College Press
U.S. Rep(s): Baker & Taylor; Benjamin News; Book People; Ingram Book Co; Partners; Partners/West; Sunbelt

**James Lorimer & Co Ltd, Publishers**
317 Adelaide St W, Suite 1002, Toronto, ON M5V 1P9
SAN: 115-1134
*Tel:* 416-362-4762 *Fax:* 416-362-3939
*Web Site:* www.lorimer.ca
*Key Personnel*
Pres & Publr: James Lorimer
Promos: Kathy Chapman
Founded: 1970
Hardcover & paperback trade; business, economics, finance, history, politics; children's books; social sciences & sociology; cookbooks; illustrated history.
Publishes in English.
ISBN Prefix(es): 978-1-55028; 978-0-88862; 978-1-55277
Number of titles published annually: 20 Print
Total Titles: 500 Print
*Warehouse:* Formac Distributing, 5502 Atlantic St, Halifax, NS B3H 1G4 *Tel:* 902-421-7022 *Fax:* 902-425-0166 *Web Site:* www.formac.ca

**Lugus Publications**
Division of Lugus Productions Ltd
28 Industrial St, Studio 215, Toronto, ON M4G 1Y9
*Tel:* 416-342-9660
*E-mail:* studio203@distributel.net
*Web Site:* www.thestudio203.com
*Key Personnel*
Pres: Gethin James *E-mail:* james.gethin@gmail.com
Secy: Jacqueline James
Founded: 1981
Educational & trade publishing.
Publishes in English, French.
ISBN Prefix(es): 978-0-921633
Number of titles published annually: 5 Print
Total Titles: 120 Print
U.S. Publishers Represented: Blackwells North America

**Madison Press Books**
PO Box 239, Cannington, ON L0E 1E0
*Tel:* 416-360-0006
*E-mail:* info@madisonpressbooks.com
*Web Site:* www.madisonpressbooks.com
*Key Personnel*
Pres & Publr: Oliver Salzmann *E-mail:* osalzmann@madisonpressbooks.com
Founded: 1979
Illustrated nonfiction & calendars.
Publishes in English.
ISBN Prefix(es): 978-1-895892
Number of titles published annually: 10 Print
Total Titles: 15 Print

**Madonna House Publications**
RR 2, 2888 Dafoe Rd, Combermere, ON K0J 1L0
*Tel:* 613-756-3728 *Toll Free Tel:* 888-703-7110 *Fax:* 613-756-0103 *Toll Free Fax:* 877-717-2888
*E-mail:* publications@madonnahouse.org
*Web Site:* www.madonnahouse.org/publications
Founded: 1988
Publishes in English, French.
ISBN Prefix(es): 978-0-921440
Number of titles published annually: 4 Print; 2 Audio
Total Titles: 68 Print; 68 Online; 15 Audio
Membership(s): Catholic Publishers Association; CMN

**§Master Point Press**
331 Douglas Ave, Toronto, ON M5M 1H2
*Tel:* 416-781-0351 *Fax:* 416-781-1831
*E-mail:* info@masterpointpress.com
*Web Site:* www.masterpointpress.com; www.ebooksbridge.com (ebook sales); www.masteringbridge.com (bridge teacher/student support); www.bridgeblogging.com (author blogs & other feeds)
*Key Personnel*
Founder & Pres: Ray Lee
Founded: 1994
Books on games, especially contract bridge.
Publishes in English.
ISBN Prefix(es): 978-0-9698461; 978-1-894154; 978-1-897106; 978-1-55494
Number of titles published annually: 10 Print; 10 E-Book
Total Titles: 160 Print; 5 CD-ROM; 160 E-Book
Distributor for Better Bridge Now
U.S. Rep(s): Strauss Consultants, 45 Main St, Brooklyn, NY 11201, United States
Foreign Rep(s): Orca Book Services (Worldwide exc Australia & North America); Spade Deuce (Australia)

*Orders to:* Georgetown Terminal Warehouse Ltd, 34 Armstrong Ave, Georgetown, ON L7G 4R9 *Tel:* 905-873-2750 *Fax:* 905-873-6170 *E-mail:* info@gtwcanada.com *Web Site:* www.gtwcanada.com; Baker & Taylor, 2550 W Tyrola Rd, Suite 300, Charlotte, NC 28217, United States *Tel:* 704-998-3100 *Toll Free Tel:* 800-775-1800 *E-mail:* btinfo@btol.com *Web Site:* www.btol.com; Ingram Book Group, One Ingram Blvd, La Vergne, TN 37086, United States *Tel:* 615-793-5000 *Toll Free Tel:* 800-937-8200 *E-mail:* customer.service@ingrambook.com; Orca Book Services, 160 Milton Park, Abingdon OX14 4SD, United Kingdom *Tel:* (01235) 465500 *E-mail:* tradeorders@orcabookservices.co.uk *Web Site:* www.orcabookservices.co.uk
*Shipping Address:* Georgetown Terminal Warehouse Ltd, 34 Armstrong Ave, Georgetown, ON L7G 4R9

**McClelland & Stewart Ltd**
Division of Random House of Canada Limited
75 Sherbourne St, 5th fl, Toronto, ON M5A 2P9
SAN: 115-4192
*Tel:* 416-598-1114 *Fax:* 416-598-7764
*E-mail:* editorial@mcclelland.com
*Web Site:* www.mcclelland.com
*Key Personnel*
Pres & Publr: Douglas Pepper
SVP & Publr: Ellen Seligman
Publr, Fenn/McClelland & Stewart Ltd: Jordan Fenn
Exec Ed: Lara Hinchberger
Sr Ed: Anita Chong
Founded: 1906
Publishes in English.
ISBN Prefix(es): 978-0-7710
Number of titles published annually: 70 Print
Total Titles: 2,000 Print
*Sales Office(s):* Random House of Canada Limited, 2775 Matheson Blvd E, Mississauga, ON L4W 4P7 *Tel:* 905-624-0672 *Toll Free Tel:* 800-668-4247 *Fax:* 905-624-6217
*Orders to:* Random House of Canada Limited, 2775 Matheson Blvd E, Mississauga, ON L4W 4P7 *Tel:* 905-624-0672 *Toll Free Tel:* 800-668-4247 *Fax:* 905-624-6217
*Shipping Address:* Random House of Canada Limited, 2775 Matheson Blvd E, Mississauga, ON L4W 4P7 *Tel:* 905-624-0672 *Toll Free Tel:* 800-668-4247 *Fax:* 905-624-6217
*See separate listing for:*
**Tundra Books**

**McGill-Queen's University Press**
Imprint of Combined Academic Publishers
1010 Sherbrooke W, Suite 1720, Montreal, QC H3A 2R7
*Tel:* 514-398-3750 *Fax:* 514-398-4333
*E-mail:* mqup@mqup.ca
*Web Site:* www.mqup.ca
*Key Personnel*
Exec Dir: Philip Cercone *E-mail:* philip.cercone@mcgill.ca
Assoc Dir: Susan McIntosh *Tel:* 514-398-6306 *E-mail:* susan.mcintosh@mcgill.ca
Prodn & Design Mgr: Elena Goranescu McAdam *Tel:* 514-398-6996
Sr Ed, Montreal: John Zucchi *Tel:* 514-398-3968 *E-mail:* editorial1.mqup@mcgill.ca
Acqs Ed: James MacNevin
Founded: 1970
Original peer-reviewed, high-quality books in all areas of social sciences & humanities. Our emphasis is on providing an outlet for Canadian authors & scholarship. Publish authors from around the world.
Publishes in English, French.
ISBN Prefix(es): 978-0-88629; 978-0-7735
Number of titles published annually: 120 Print
Total Titles: 3,000 Print; 5 CD-ROM
*Branch Office(s)*
Queen's University, Kingston, ON K7L 3N6, Roger Martin *Tel:* 613-533-2155 *Fax:* 613-533-6822 *E-mail:* mqup@post.queensu.ca
Distributor for Acumen Publishing; Fontanus Monography Series; Institute for Research on Public Policy; Queen's Policy Studies Series; Les Editions du Septentrion (English titles)
Foreign Rep(s): East-West Export Books (Royden Muranaka) (Asia, Australia, New Zealand); Marston Book Services Ltd (Europe, Ireland, Middle East, North Africa, UK)
*Distribution Center:* c/o Georgetown Terminal Warehouses, 34 Armstrong Ave, Georgetown, ON L7G 4R9 (Canada distribution) *Tel:* 905-873-9781 *Toll Free Tel:* 877-864-8477 *Fax:* 905-873-6170 *Toll Free Fax:* 877-864-4272 *E-mail:* orders@gtwcanada.com
East-West Export Books, University of Hawaii Press, 2840 Kolowalu St, Honolulu, HI 96822, United States *Tel:* 808-856-6214 *Fax:* 808-988-6052 *E-mail:* eweb@hawaii.edu
CUP Services, PO Box 6525, Ithaca, NY 14851-6525, United States (United States distribution) *Toll Free Tel:* 800-666-2211 *Toll Free Fax:* 800-688-2877 *E-mail:* orderbook@cupserv.org
Marston Book Services Ltd, PO Box 269, Abingdon, Oxon OX14 4YN, United Kingdom (UK distribution) *Tel:* (01235) 465500 *Fax:* (01235) 465555 *E-mail:* tradeorders@marston.co.uk *Web Site:* www.pubeasy.com
Membership(s): American Association of University Presses; Association of Canadian Publishers; Association of Canadian University Presses

**McGraw-Hill Ryerson Limited**
Division of McGraw-Hill Education
300 Water St, Whitby, ON L1N 9B6
SAN: 115-060X
*Tel:* 905-430-5000 *Toll Free Tel:* 800-565-5758 (cust serv) *Fax:* 905-430-5020
*Web Site:* www.mcgrawhill.ca
*Key Personnel*
CEO & Pres: David Swail *E-mail:* davids@mcgrawhill.ca
VP & CFO: Brenda Arseneault *E-mail:* brendaa@mcgrawhill.ca
Pres, Higher Educ Div: Pat Ferrier *E-mail:* patf@mcgrawhill.ca
Pres, School Div: Nancy Gerrish *E-mail:* nancyg@mcgrawhill.ca
Founded: 1944
Publishes & distributes educational & professional products in both print & non-print media.
Publishes in English.
ISBN Prefix(es): 978-0-07
Number of titles published annually: 70 Print; 40 CD-ROM; 30 Online
Total Titles: 1,300 Print; 150 CD-ROM; 200 Online; 50 E-Book
Imprints: McGraw-Hill Ryerson
Distributed by McGraw-Hill Publishing Cos
Distributor for Glencoe/McGraw-Hill; Jamestown Education; McGraw-Hill; McGraw-Hill/Irwin; MedMaster Inc; Open Court; Osborne; Schaum's; SRA; Wright Group
U.S. Publishers Represented: The McGraw-Hill Companies
Membership(s): Canadian Educational Resources Council; Canadian Publishers' Council

**Mediaspaul**
3965 Henri-Bourassa E, Montreal-Nord, QC H1H 1L1
*Tel:* 514-322-7341 *Fax:* 514-322-4281
*E-mail:* info@mediaspaul.qc.ca; clientele@mediaspaul.qc.ca
*Web Site:* www.mediaspaul.qc.ca
Founded: 1975
Religious & photographic books.
Publisher has indicated that 20% of their product is author subsidized.
Publishes in French.
ISBN Prefix(es): 978-2-89129
Number of titles published annually: 20 Print
Total Titles: 300 Print

**Mi'kmaq-Maliseet Institute**
University of New Brunswick, Rm 343, Marshall d'Avray Hall, 10 MacKay Dr, Fredericton, NB E3B 5A3
*Tel:* 506-453-4840 *Fax:* 506-453-4784
*E-mail:* micmac@unb.ca
*Web Site:* www.unb.ca; www.unb.ca/fredericton/education/mmi
*Key Personnel*
Dir: Dr Lynda A Doige *E-mail:* ladoige@unb.ca
Coord: Andrea Belczewski *E-mail:* abelczew@unb.ca
Admin Asst: Shelley Chase
Founded: 1980
First Nations studies, languages & history offers programs for First Nations students at UNB, research, curriculum development, First Nations Business Administration Certificate Program, 4 year degree program.
Publishes in English.
Number of titles published annually: 1 Print; 1 Online
Total Titles: 12 Print; 2 Online
Distributed by Micmac Books

**Modus Vivendi Publishing Inc & Presses Aventure**
55 rue Jean-Talon ouest, 2nd fl, Montreal, QC H2R 2W8
*Tel:* 514-272-0433 *Fax:* 514-272-7234
*E-mail:* info@modusaventure.com
*Web Site:* www.modusaventure.com
*Key Personnel*
CEO: Marc Alain
Dir, Sales & Ed: Isabelle Jodoin
Founded: 1992
General trade publishing.
Publishes in French.
ISBN Prefix(es): 978-2-89523; 978-2-89543; 978-2-92372
Number of titles published annually: 200 Print
Divisions: Editions Bravo!; Editions Rouge; Presses Aventure
Distributed by Les Messageries ADP
*Distribution Center:* Les Messageries ADP, 2315 rue de la Province, Longueuil, QC J4G 1G4

**Moose Hide Books**
Imprint of Moose Enterprise Book & Theatre Play Publishing
684 Walls Rd, Prince Township, ON P6A 6K4
*Tel:* 705-779-3331 *Fax:* 705-779-3331
*E-mail:* mooseenterprises@on.aibn.com
*Web Site:* www.moosehidebooks.com
*Key Personnel*
Owner & Publr: Richard Mousseau *E-mail:* rmousseau@moosehidebooks.com
Ed: Edmond Alcid *E-mail:* ealcid@moosehidebooks.com
Book & theatre play publishing. Full author royalties paid. 90% of authors are new. House assists new first time authors.
This publisher has indicated that 50% of their product line is author subsidized.
Publishes in English.
ISBN Prefix(es): 978-1-894650
Number of titles published annually: 7 Print; 7 E-Book; 1 Audio
Total Titles: 200 Print; 100 Online; 25 E-Book; 1 Audio

**Editions MultiMondes**
930 rue Pouliot, Quebec, QC G1V 3N9

*Tel:* 418-651-3885 *Toll Free Tel:* 800-840-3029 *Fax:* 418-651-6822 *Toll Free Fax:* 888-303-5931
*E-mail:* multimondes@multim.com
*Web Site:* www.multimondes.qc.ca
*Key Personnel*
Pres: Jean-Marc Gagnon *E-mail:* jmgagnon@multim.com
VP: Lise Morin *E-mail:* lmorin@multim.com
Edit Asst. Melanie Beaulieu *E-mail:* mbeaulieu@multim.com
Founded: 1988
Books on science & the environment.
Publishes in English, French.
ISBN Prefix(es): 978-2-921146; 978-2-89544
Number of titles published annually: 20 Print
Total Titles: 200 Print
*Distribution Center:* Prologue, 1650, blvd Lionel-Bertrand, Boisbriand, QC J7H 1N7 (Canada) *Tel:* 450-434-0306 *Fax:* 450-434-2627 *E-mail:* prologue@prologue.ca
The SDL Caravelle, Rue du Pre aux Geese, 303, Brussels, Belgium (Belgium) *Tel:* (02) 240 93 00 *Fax:* (02) 216 35 98
Librairie du Quebec in Paris, 30, rue Gay Lussac, 75005 Paris, France (France) *Tel:* (01) 43 54 49 02 *Fax:* (01) 43 54 39 15 *E-mail:* direction@librairieduquebec.fr
Servidis SA, 7 Cottage Rd, CH-1279 Chavannes-de-Bogis, Switzerland (Switzerland) *Tel:* (021) 803 26 26 *Fax:* (021) 803 26 29 *E-mail:* pgavillet@servidis.ch

**Narada Press**
3165-133 Weber St N, Waterloo, ON N2J 3G9
*Tel:* 519-886-1969
Founded: 1993
General books on economic modeling & Vietnamese studies, including politics, arts & literature. Directories, reference books, foreign language & bilingual books, reprints, scholarly books, college textbooks, translations, Asian studies, developing countries, history, library & information sciences. Publishes in Vietnamese also.
Publishes in English.
ISBN Prefix(es): 978-1-895938
Number of titles published annually: 5 Print

**National Gallery of Canada, The Bookstore**
380 Sussex Dr, Ottawa, ON K1N 9N4
Mailing Address: PO Box 427, Sta A, Ottawa, ON K1N 9N4
*Tel:* 613-990-0962 (mail order sales) *Fax:* 613-990-1972
*E-mail:* ngcbook@gallery.ca
*Web Site:* www.national.gallery.ca
*Key Personnel*
Mgr, Opers: Patrick Aubin
Mail Order & E-Commerce Asst: Sophie Beaudoin Gabriel
Founded: 1980
Exhibition catalogues, monographs, permanent collection series, books on photography, exhibition handouts, videos & posters.
Publishes in English, French.
ISBN Prefix(es): 978-0-88884
Number of titles published annually: 4 Print
Total Titles: 38 Print
U.S. Rep(s): ABC Art Books
Membership(s): Canadian Booksellers Association; Canadian Museums Association; Museum Store Association

**Nelson Education Ltd**
Affiliate of Cengage Learning
1120 Birchmount Rd, Scarborough, ON M1K 5G4
*Tel:* 416-752-9100 *Toll Free Tel:* 800-268-2222 (cust serv) *Fax:* 416-752-8101 *Toll Free Fax:* 800-430-4445
*E-mail:* inquire@nelson.com
*Web Site:* www.nelson.com
*Key Personnel*
CEO & Pres: Greg Nordal
CFO: Michael Andrews
SVP, Media & Prodn Servs: Susan Cline
SVP, People & Engagement: Marlene Nyilassy
SVP & Mng Dir, Higher Educ Div: James Reeves
SVP & Mng Dir, School Div: Chris Besse
Founded: 1914
School, college, test, professional & reference.
Publishes in English.
ISBN Prefix(es): 978-0-17
Number of titles published annually: 700 Print
Total Titles: 11,864 Print; 30 CD-ROM; 30 E-Book; 100 Audio
U.S. Publishers Represented: American Technical Publishers Inc (ATP); Aseba; Brooks-Cole Publishing; Canada Housing & Mortgage Corp (CMHC); Centennial Press; Course Technology Inc; Craftsman; DC Heath Canada Ltd (school & college); Delmar Publishers Inc; Douglas & McIntyre; Duxbury Press; Exclusive; Goodheart Willcox; Great Source Educational; Groupe Beauchemin; HarperCollins; Heinemann; Heinle & Heinle Publishers Inc; Houghton Mifflin Harcourt Publishing Company (school, college & trade); Indigo Instrument; Industrial Press; International Thomson Publishing Services; Irwin Publishing; Learning Media Co; McDougall Littell & Co; Mondo; Nelson Thomson Learning; Nelson Thomson Learning Australia; Norbry; Peterson's; Phoenix Learning Resources; PWS Publishing; Reidmore Publishing; The Riverside Publishing Co; William H Sadlier; Scott Jones; South Western Education & College Publishing; Texere; Thomas Learning Asia; VideoActive Production; Wadsworth Publishers; West Publishing (educational product only); West Virginia University (FIT)
Membership(s): Canadian Educational Resources Council; Canadian Publishers' Council

**New Star Books Ltd**
107-3477 Commercial St, Vancouver, BC V5N 4E8
SAN: 115-1908
*Tel:* 604-738-9429 *Fax:* 604 738 9332
*E-mail:* info@newstarbooks.com; orders@newstarbooks.com
*Web Site:* www.newstarbooks.com
*Key Personnel*
Pres & Publr: Rolf Maurer
Founded: 1970
Social issues & current affairs, fiction, literary, history, international politics, labor, feminist, gay/lesbian studies & poetry. Emphasis on British Columbia & Western Canada.
Publishes in English.
ISBN Prefix(es): 978-0-919573; 978-0-921586; 978-1-55420; 978-0-96860
Number of titles published annually: 6 Print
Total Titles: 76 Print
Imprints: Longhouse
*Branch Office(s)*
1574 Gulf Rd, No 1517, Point Roberts, WA 98281, United States
Membership(s): Literary Press Group

**§New World Publishing**
PO Box 36075, Halifax, NS B3J 3S9
*Tel:* 902-576-2055 (inquiries) *Toll Free Tel:* 877-211-3334 (orders) *Fax:* 902-576-2095
*Web Site:* www.newworldpublishing.com
*Key Personnel*
Owner & Mng Ed: Dr Francis Mitchell *E-mail:* francis@newworldpublishing.com
Founded: 1995
Publishes in English.
ISBN Prefix(es): 978-1-895814
Number of titles published annually: 4 Print; 1 E-Book
Total Titles: 38 Print; 7 CD-ROM; 1 Online; 3 E-Book; 3 Audio
Distributed by Glen Margaret Publishing (most independent & gift stores in Maritimes)
*Returns:* 19 Frenchman's Rd, Oakfield, NS B2T 1A9 *E-mail:* nwp1@eastlink.ca
Membership(s): Atlantic Publishers Marketing Association; Canadian Booksellers Association

**NeWest Press**
8540 109 St, No 201, Edmonton, AB T6G 1E6
*Tel:* 780-432-9427 *Toll Free Tel:* 866-796-5473 *Fax:* 780-433-3179
*E-mail:* info@newestpress.com
*Web Site:* www.newestpress.com
*Key Personnel*
Gen Mgr: Paul Matwychuk
Mktg & Prodn Coord: Andrew Wilmot
Founded: 1977
Committed to developing & publishing first-time writers, as well as ensuring the availability of Canadian classics.
Publishes in English.
ISBN Prefix(es): 978-0-920316; 978-0-920897; 978-1-896300; 978-1-897126
Number of titles published annually: 13 Print
Total Titles: 140 Print
*Sales Office(s):* Literary Press Group, 192 Spadina Ave, Suite 501, Toronto, ON M5T 2C2, Sales Mgr: Martha Bucci *Tel:* 416-483-1321 *Fax:* 416-483-2510 *E-mail:* mbucci@lpg.ca
Foreign Rep(s): Acacia House Publishing Services Ltd; Bill & Frances Hanna
Foreign Rights: Bill & Frances Hanna
*Distribution Center:* LitDist Co, 100 Armstrong Ave, Georgetown, ON L7G 5S4 *Toll Free Tel:* 800-591-6250 *Toll Free Fax:* 800-591-6251 *E-mail:* orders@litdistco.ca
Membership(s): Association of Canadian Publishers; Book Publishers Association of Alberta; Canadian Booksellers Association; Crime Writers of Canada; Literary Press Group

**Nimbus Publishing Ltd**
3731 Mackintosh St, Halifax, NS B3K 5A5
SAN: 115-0685
*Tel:* 902-455-4286; 902-454-7404 *Toll Free Tel:* 800-NIMBUS9 (646-2879) *Fax:* 902-455-5440 *Toll Free Fax:* 888-253-3133
*E-mail:* customerservice@nimbus.ns.ca
*Web Site:* www.nimbus.ns.ca
*Key Personnel*
Sr Ed: Patrick Murphy *E-mail:* editorial@nimbus.ns.ca
Ed: Penelope Jackson *E-mail:* pjackson@nimbus.ns.ca
Prodn Mgr: Heather Bryan *E-mail:* hbryan@nimbus.ns.ca
Sales Mgr & Foreign Rts: Terrilee Bulger *Tel:* 902-455-2963 *E-mail:* tbulger@nimbus.ns.ca
Dist: Chester Legere
Billing: Phyllis Murray
Founded: 1978
Regional nonfiction books, relevant to the Atlantic-Canadian experience, social & natural history, children's books, cookbooks, travel, biography, photography & nautical.
Publishes in English.
ISBN Prefix(es): 978-0-920852; 978-0-919380; 978-0-921054; 978-0-921128; 978-1-55109
Number of titles published annually: 40 Print
Total Titles: 500 Print
Imprints: Nimbus; Vagrant Press (fiction)
Distributor for Acorn Press; Breton Books; Cape Breton University Press; MacIntyre Purcell Publishing Inc; Norwood Publishing; Pottersfield Press
U.S. Publishers Represented: Down East Books; Flat Hammock Press; Mystic Seaport Museum Inc; Sheridan House; Wooden Boat
U.S. Rep(s): Downeast Books

Membership(s): Association for the Export of Canadian Books; Association of Canadian Publishers; Atlantic Publishers Marketing Association; Canadian Booksellers Association; NEBA

**§The North-South Institute/Institut Nord-Sud**
55 Murray St, Suite 500, Ottawa, ON K1N 5M3
*Tel:* 613-241-3535 *Fax:* 613-241-7435
*E-mail:* nsi@nsi-ins.ca
*Web Site:* www.nsi-ins.ca
*Key Personnel*
Pres: Joseph K Ingram *E-mail:* jingram@nsi-ins.ca
Dir, Fin & Admin: Diane Guevremont *E-mail:* dguevremont@nsi-ins.ca
Info Mgr: Dina Shadid *E-mail:* dshadid@nsi-ins.ca
Founded: 1976
North-South relations & foreign aid, economics & trade, with emphasis on Canada & developing countries, foreign policy & multilateral cooperation, gender & development, human rights, civil society, conflict & human security, markets & social responsibility. Also publishes newsletters & Canadian Development Report (annual).
Publishes in English, French.
ISBN Prefix(es): 978-1-896770; 978-1-897358
Number of titles published annually: 10 Print; 15 Online
Total Titles: 60 Print; 6 CD-ROM; 450 Online

**Northern Canada Mission Distributors**, see Tribal Trails Books & Resources

**Northstone Publishing**
Imprint of Wood Lake Publishing Inc
9590 Jim Bailey Rd, Kelowna, BC V4V 1R2
SAN: 117-7346
*Tel:* 250-766-2778 *Toll Free Tel:* 800-299-2926; 800-663-2775 (orders) *Fax:* 250-766-2736 *Toll Free Fax:* 888-841-9991
*E-mail:* info@woodlakebooks.com
*Web Site:* www.woodlakebooks.com
*Key Personnel*
Pres & Mktg Dir: Mike Schwartzentruber
Founded: 1996
Books essential spirituality for our day.
Publishes in English.
ISBN Prefix(es): 978-1-55145; 978-1-896836
Number of titles published annually: 8 Print
Total Titles: 150 Print
Distributed by The Pilgrim Press
Distributor for The Pilgrim Press

**Novalis Publishing**
Division of Bayard Canada
10 Lower Spadina Ave, Suite 400, Toronto, ON M5V 2Z2
*Tel:* 416-363-3303 *Toll Free Tel:* 877-702-7773 *Fax:* 416-363-9409 *Toll Free Fax:* 877-702-7775
*E-mail:* books@novalis.ca
*Web Site:* www.novalis.ca
*Key Personnel*
Publr: Joseph Sinasac *E-mail:* joseph.sinasac@novalis.ca
Assoc Publr: Glenn Byer *E-mail:* glenn.byer@novalis.ca
Founded: 1936
Religious children's & adult books, periodicals & religious books (Catholic/Christian).
Publishes in English, French.
ISBN Prefix(es): 978-2-89088; 978-2-89507; 978-2-89646
Number of titles published annually: 30 Print
Total Titles: 360 Print
Distributor for Canterbury Press; Catholic Health Alliance of Canada (CHAC); Church House Publishing; Creative Communications for the Parish; Crossroad Publishing; Editions du Signe; Jewish Lights Publishing; Liguori Publications; Loyola Press; Morehouse Publishing/Church Publishing/Seabury; Orbis Books; Paulist Press; Pflaum Gospel Weeklies; Printery House; Random House/Doubleday/Image Books (religious titles only); Saint Mary's Press; St Vladimir Seminary Press; SCM Press; Twenty Third Publications
U.S. Publishers Represented: Creative Communications for the Parish; Jewish Lights Publishing; Orbis Books; Paulist Press; Pflaum Gospel Weeklies; Saint Mary's Press; Twenty-Third Publications
*Billing Address:* BND Distribution, 4475 Frontenac St, Montreal, QC H2H 2S2 *Tel:* 514-278-3020 *Toll Free Tel:* 800-387-7164 *Fax:* 514-278-3030 *Toll Free Fax:* 800-204-4140 *Web Site:* www.novalis.com
*Orders to:* BND Distribution, 4475 Frontenac St, Montreal, QC H2H 2S2 *Tel:* 514-278-3020 *Toll Free Tel:* 800-387-7164 *Fax:* 514-278-3030 *Toll Free Fax:* 800-204-4140 *Web Site:* www.novalis.com
*Returns:* BND Distribution, 4475 Frontenac St, Montreal, QC H2H 2S2 *Tel:* 514-278-3020 *Toll Free Tel:* 800-387-7164 *Fax:* 514-278-3030 *Toll Free Fax:* 800-204-4140 *Web Site:* www.novalis.com
*Shipping Address:* BND Distribution, 4475 Frontenac St, Montreal, QC H2H 2S2 *Tel:* 514-278-3020 *Toll Free Tel:* 800-387-7164 *Fax:* 514-278-3030 *Toll Free Fax:* 800-204-4140 *Web Site:* www.novalis.com
*Warehouse:* BND Distribution, 4475 Frontenac St, Montreal, QC H2H 2S2 *Tel:* 514-278-3020 *Toll Free Tel:* 800-387-7164 *Fax:* 514-278-3030 *Toll Free Fax:* 800-204-4140 *Web Site:* www.novalis.com

**Oberon Press**
145 Spruce St, Suite 205, Ottawa, ON K1R 6P1
SAN: 115-0723
*Tel:* 613-238-3275 *Fax:* 613-238-3275
*E-mail:* oberon@sympatico.ca
*Web Site:* www.oberonpress.ca
*Key Personnel*
Pres: Michael Macklem
VP & Gen Mgr: Nicholas Macklem
Secy & Treas: Dilshad Engineer
Founded: 1966
Canadiana, fiction, history, biography, poetry & travel.
Publishes in English.
ISBN Prefix(es): 978-0-88750; 978-0-7780
Number of titles published annually: 8 Print
Total Titles: 672 Print

**One Act Play Depot**
Box 335, 618 Memorial Dr, Spiritwood, SK S0J 2M0
*E-mail:* plays@oneactplays.net; orders@oneactplays.net
*Web Site:* oneactplays.net
*Key Personnel*
Mng Ed: Fraser MacFarlane
Ed: K Balvenie
Founded: 2002
Publication, sale & distribution of one-act plays. Orders ship within 24 hours. Accept submissions only in Feb of each year.
Publishes in English.
ISBN Prefix(es): 978-1-894910; 978-1-926849
Number of titles published annually: 10 Print
Total Titles: 110 Print

**Oolichan Books**
PO Box 2278, Fernie, BC V0B 1M0
SAN: 115-4680
*Tel:* 250-423-6113
*E-mail:* info@oolichan.com
*Web Site:* www.oolichan.com
*Key Personnel*
Publr: Randal Macnair
Ed: Ronald Smith
Consulting Ed: Pat Smith
Asst to the Publr: Christa Moffat
Founded: 1974
Publishers of literary fiction, poetry & literary nonfiction. Publish only Canadian authors.
Publishes in English.
ISBN Prefix(es): 978-0-88982
Number of titles published annually: 10 Print
Total Titles: 128 Print
*Shipping Address:* 542 B Second Ave, Fernie, BC V0B 1M0
*Distribution Center:* University of Toronto Press, 5201 Dufferin St, Toronto, ON M3H 5T8 *Toll Free Tel:* 800-565-9523 *E-mail:* utpbooks@utpress.utoronto.ca
Membership(s): Association of Book Publishers of British Columbia; Association of Canadian Publishers

**Owlkids Books Inc**
10 Lower Spadina Ave, Suite 400, Toronto, ON M5V 2Z2
*Tel:* 416-340-3700 *Fax:* 416-340-9769
*E-mail:* owlkids@owlkids.com
*Web Site:* www.owlkidsbooks.com
*Key Personnel*
Publr: Karen Boersma
Edit Dir: Karen Li
Dir, Sales & Mktg: Judy Brunsek
Founded: 1976
Award winning publisher of books for children ages 3-13.
Publishes in English.
ISBN Prefix(es): 978-1-897066; 978-1-897349; 978-1-926973
Number of titles published annually: 25 Print
Total Titles: 150 Print; 50 E-Book
*Orders to:* Publishers Group West/Perseus, 1094 Flex Dr, Jackson, TN 38301, United States *Toll Free Tel:* 800-343-4499 *Toll Free Fax:* 800-351-5073 *E-mail:* orderentry@perseusbooks.com *Web Site:* www.pgw.com

**Pacific Educational Press**
Unit of University of British Columbia
c/o University of British Columbia, Faculty of Education, 411-2389 Health Sciences Mall, Vancouver, BC V6T 1Z4
SAN: 115-1266
*Tel:* 604-822-5385 *Fax:* 604-822-6603
*E-mail:* pep.sales@ubc.ca
*Web Site:* www.pacificedpress.ca
*Key Personnel*
Dir: Catherine Edwards *Tel:* 604-822-6561 *E-mail:* catherine.edwards@ubc.ca
Mgr, Edit & Prodn Servs: Nadine Pedersen *Tel:* 604-827-4099 *E-mail:* nadine.pedersen@ubc.ca
Sr Ed: Barbara Kuhne *Tel:* 604-822-9499 *E-mail:* barbara.kuhne@ubc.ca
Founded: 1971
Textbooks for teacher education programs, education materials, materials which are generally used in classrooms or educational institutes, books on education topics & issues for a general readership.
Publishes in English.
ISBN Prefix(es): 978-0-88865; 978-1-895766
Number of titles published annually: 6 Print
Total Titles: 104 Print; 16 E-Book
Distributor for Critical Thinking Consortium (TC 2)
*Distribution Center:* Georgetown Terminal Warehouse, 34 Armstrong Ave, Georgetown, ON L7G 4R9 *Tel:* 905-873-9781 *Toll Free Tel:* 877-864-8477 (CN only) *Fax:* 905-873-6170 *Toll Free Fax:* 877-864-4272 (CN only) *E-mail:* orders@gtwcanada.com
Membership(s): Association of Book Publishers of British Columbia; Association of Canadian Publishers

**Palimpsest Press**
5 King St, Kingsville, ON N9Y 1H9
*Tel:* 519-563-9981
*E-mail:* info@palimpsestpress.ca
*Web Site:* www.palimpsestpress.ca
*Key Personnel*
Publr: Dawn Kresan *E-mail:* dawnkresan@palimpsestpress.ca
Asst: Sarah Jarvis
Founded: 2000
Publish poetry collections, nonfiction, essays, limited editions chapbooks & children's picture books.
Publishes in English.
ISBN Prefix(es): 978-0-9733952; 978-1-926794
Number of titles published annually: 5 Print
Total Titles: 30 Print
Imprints: Magpie Books (children's picture books, juvenile & young adult fiction)
*Sales Office(s):* Literary Press Group, 501-192 Spadina Ave, Toronto, ON M5T 2C2 *Tel:* 416-483-1321 *Fax:* 416-483-2510 *Web Site:* www.lpg.ca
*Orders to:* Literary Press Group, 501-192 Spadina Ave, Toronto, ON M5T 2C2 *Tel:* 416-483-1321 *Fax:* 416-483-2510 *Web Site:* www.lpg.ca
*Shipping Address:* LitDistCo, 100 Armstrong Ave, Georgetown, ON L7G 5S4
*Warehouse:* LitDistCo, 100 Armstrong Ave, Georgetown, ON L7G 5S4
*Distribution Center:* LitDistCo, 100 Armstrong Ave, Georgetown, ON L7G 5S4 *Toll Free Tel:* 800-591-6250 *Toll Free Fax:* 800-591-6251 *E-mail:* ordering@litdistco.ca *Web Site:* www.litdistco.ca
Membership(s): Association of Canadian Publishers; League of Canadian Poets; Literary Press Group of Canada

**Paulines Editions**
5610 rue Beaubien est, Montreal, QC H1T 1X5
*Tel:* 514-253-5610 *Fax:* 514-253-1907
*E-mail:* editions@paulines.qc.ca
*Web Site:* www.editions.paulines.qc.ca
*Key Personnel*
Dir & Intl Rts Contact: Vanda Salvador
Lib Sales Dir: Lucille Paradis
Founded: 1955
Religious books.
Publishes in English, French.
ISBN Prefix(es): 978-2-920912
Number of titles published annually: 4 Print
Total Titles: 60 Print
Distributed by Mediaspaul (Montreal)

**Pearson Education Canada**
Division of Pearson Canada Inc
26 Prince Andrew Place, Don Mills, ON M3C 2T8
SAN: 115-0022
*Tel:* 416-447-5101 *Toll Free Tel:* 800-263-9965 *Fax:* 416-443-0948 *Toll Free Fax:* 800-263-7733; 888-465-0536
*Web Site:* www.pearsoned.ca
*Key Personnel*
CEO: Dan Lee
Pres, School Div: Marty Keast *E-mail:* marty.keast@pearsoned.com
Higher Educ Div: Steve O'Hearn *E-mail:* steve.ohearn@pearsoned.com
Founded: 1966
Educational textbooks, trade, reference.
Publishes in English, French.
ISBN Prefix(es): 978-0-201
Total Titles: 5,700 Print
Imprints: Addison Wesley; Allyn & Bacon; Copp Clark; Benjamin Cummings; Ginn; Longman; Prentice Hall
*Orders to:* Pearson Education Operations Centre, PO Box 335, Newmarket, ON L3Y 4X7 *Toll Free Tel:* 800-567-3800 (cust serv); 800-361-6128 (school) *Toll Free Fax:* 800-236-7733 (cust serv); 800-563-9196 (school)
*Returns:* Pearson Education Operations Centre, PO Box 335, Newmarket, ON L3Y 4X7 *Toll Free Tel:* 800-567-3800 (cust serv); 800-361-6128 (school) *Toll Free Fax:* 800-236-7733 (cust serv); 800-563-9196 (school)
*Distribution Center:* 195 Harry Walker Pkwy, Newmarket, ON L3Y 7B3 *Tel:* 905-853-7888 *Fax:* 905-853-7865

**Pembroke Publishers Ltd**
538 Hood Rd, Markham, ON L3R 3K9
*Tel:* 905-477-0650 *Toll Free Tel:* 800-997-9807 *Fax:* 905-477-3691 *Toll Free Fax:* 800-339-5568
*Web Site:* www.pembrokepublishers.com
*Key Personnel*
Pres & Intl Rts: Mary Macchiusi *E-mail:* mary@pembrokepublishers.com
Mng Dir: Claudia Connolly
Founded: 1985
Educational books.
Publishes in English.
ISBN Prefix(es): 978-0-921217; 978-1-55138
Number of titles published annually: 15 Print
Total Titles: 230 Print
Distributor for Stenhouse Publishers
U.S. Publishers Represented: Stenhouse Publishers, 477 Congress St, Suite 4B, Portland, ME 04101-3417, United States
U.S. Rep(s): Stenhouse Publishers, 477 Congress St, Suite 4B, Portland, ME 04101-3417, United States
Foreign Rep(s): Curriculum Corp (Australia); Eurospan (UK); PMS (Singapore); Stenhouse Publishers (USA)
*Distribution Center:* Eurospan, 3 Henrietta St, Covent Garden, London WC2E 8LU, United Kingdom (UK)
Membership(s): Organization of Book Publishers of Ontario

**Pemmican Publications Inc**
150 Henry Ave, Winnipeg, MB R3B 0J7
SAN: 115-1657
*Tel:* 204-589-6346 *Fax:* 204-589-2063
*E-mail:* pemmican@pemmican.mb.ca
*Web Site:* www.pemmican.mb.ca
*Key Personnel*
Mng Ed: Randal McIlroy
Founded: 1980
Books of Metis & native concern, juvenile & young adult books, trade paperbacks, scholarly books. Submissions outside Canada must include international reply coupons.
Publishes in English, French.
ISBN Prefix(es): 978-0-919143; 978-0-921827
Number of titles published annually: 6 Print
Total Titles: 120 Print

**Penguin Books Canada Limited**, see Penguin Group (Canada)

**Penguin Group (Canada)**
Division of Pearson Penguin Canada Inc
90 Eglinton Ave E, Suite 700, Toronto, ON M4P 2Y3
SAN: 115-074X
*Tel:* 416-925-2249 *Fax:* 416-925-0068
*Web Site:* www.penguin.ca
*Key Personnel*
Chmn: Rob Prichard
COO: Barry Gallant
Pres & Publr: Nicole Winstanley
VP, Fin: Helena Hung
VP, HR: Ann Wood
Dir, Prodn: Janette Lush
VP, Sales: Don Robinson
Rts & Contracts Mgr: David Whiteside
VP, Mktg & Publicity: Yvonne Hunter
Contracts & Rts Coord: John Kruusi
Founded: 1974
General trade & paperback books, hardcover & classics, audio cassettes.
Publishes in English.
ISBN Prefix(es): 978-0-14; 978-0-452; 978-0-451; 978-0-453; 978-0-7214; 978-0-216
Number of titles published annually: 3,280 Print
Total Titles: 76,500 Print
Imprints: A&C Black UK; Ace; Albatross; Alpha Books; Arden; Arkana; Atlantic Books; Avery; BBC Children's Books; Berkley; Berkshire House; Bibli O'Phile; Bloomberg Press; Bloomsbury UK; Bloomsbury USA; Blue Hen; Boulevard; Callaway; Canongate; Celebra; Chamberlain Brothers; Children's High Level Group; Corinthian Books; The Countryman Press; Current; Dalkey Archive Press; DAW; Dial Books for Young Readers; Dutton; Dutton Children's Books; Europa Editions; Faber & Faber Ltd; Fig Tree; Firebird; Foul Play Press; Gotham Books; GP Putnam & Sons; Grosset & Dunlap; Hamish Hamilton; Hamish Hamilton Canada; Hamish Hamilton Juvenile; Heat; Hippocrene Books; Home; HP Books; Hudson Street Press; Humanity Books; Icon Books; Michael Joseph; Michael Joseph Juvenile; Jove; Kales Press; Ladybird; Allen Lane; Library of America; Liveright; Meridian; Methuen Canadian List; Minedition; Modern Gems; New Directions; Noah Publications; W W Norton; Onyx; Overlook Press; Peace Hill Press; Pegasus Books; Penguin Audio UK; Penguin Audio USA; Penguin Australia; Penguin Canada; Penguin Classics; Penguin Compass; Penguin 007; Penguin India; Penguin Ireland; Penguin New Zealand; Penguin Paperbacks; Penguin Press; Penguin South Africa; Penguin UK; Perigee; Persea Books; Philomel Books; Pi Press; Planet Dexter; Plume; Portfolio; Prentice Hall Cda; Prentice Hall Press; Price Stern Sloan; Price Stern Sloan Merchandise; Prime Crime; Profile Books; Prometheus Books; Puffin Canada; Puffin UK; Puffin USA; Pushcart Press; Putnam Audio; PYR Books; Quantuck Lane; Razorbill; Rose Reisman; Riverhead; Roadside Amusements; Roc; Screen Press Books; Sentinel; Short Books; Signet; Smithsonian; Speak; Tarcher; Thames & Hudson; Time Out Guides Ltd; Tusk/Ivories; Verso Press Canada; Verso Press UK; Verso Press USA; Viking Canada; Viking Children's Books; Viking Penguin Audio; Viking Studio; Viking UK; Viking UK Juvenile; Viking USA; Walting Street; Frederick Warne; Wee Sing; Which Books; Wizard Books
Distributor for Alpha Books; Arkangel; Atlantic Books; Avery; BBC Children's Books; Berkley Publishing; Bibli O'Phile; Bloomsbury Press; Callaway; Canongate; DAW; Dutton; Europa Editions; Faber & Faber Ltd; Fig Tree; Gotham Books; Hamish Hamilton; Hamish Hamilton Canada; Hippocrene Books; Hudson Street Press; Icon Books; Michael Joseph; Ladybird; Allen Lane; Library of America; Michelin North America (Canada) (English titles in Canada); New American Library; W W Norton; Overlook Press; Penguin Audio UK; Penguin Audio USA; Penguin Australia; Penguin Books USA; Penguin Canada; Penguin India; Penguin New Zealand; Penguin Press; Penguin South Africa; Penguin UK; Penguin Young Readers; Plume; Portfolio; Prometheus Books; Puffin Canada; Putnam; Rose Reisman; Verso Press USA; Viking Canada; Viking Penguin Audio; Viking USA; Frederick Warne; Which Book
*Distribution Center:* Pearson Canada Distribution Centre, 195 Harry Walker Pkwy, Newmarket, ON L3Y 7B4 *Tel:* 905-713-3852 *Toll Free Tel:* 800-399-6858 *Toll Free Fax:* 800-363-2665 *Web Site:* www.pearsoned.ca

**Pippin Publishing Corp**
PO Box 242, Don Mills, ON M3C 2S2

*Tel:* 416-510-2918 *Toll Free Tel:* 888-889-0001 *Fax:* 416-510-3359
*Web Site:* www.pippinpub.com
*Key Personnel*
Pres & Edit Dir: Jonathan Lovat Dickson *E-mail:* jld@pippinpub.com
Founded: 1995
Educational books: English as a foreign language; English language teaching, books for teachers & students. Also trade military memoirs.
Publishes in English.
ISBN Prefix(es): 978-0-88751
Number of titles published annually: 6 Print
Total Titles: 85 Print
Imprints: Dominie Press (CN)
Distributed by University of Toronto Press (CN & all other countries)
Foreign Rep(s): Gazelle Book Services Ltd (Africa, Europe, UK)
*Warehouse:* University of Toronto Press, 5201 Dufferin St, Toronto North York, ON M3H 5T8, Contact: Carol Trainor *Tel:* 416-667-7791 *Toll Free Tel:* 800-565-9523 *Fax:* 416-667-7832 *Toll Free Fax:* 800-221-9985 *E-mail:* utpbooks@utpress.utoronto.ca
University of Toronto Press, 2250 Military Rd, Tonawanda, NY 14150, United States

**Pontifical Institute of Mediaeval Studies, Dept of Publications**
59 Queens Park Crescent E, Toronto, ON M5S 2C4
SAN: 115-0804
*Tel:* 416-926-7142 *Fax:* 416-926-7292
*Web Site:* www.pims.ca
*Key Personnel*
Ed: Fred Unwalla *E-mail:* unwalla@chass.utoronto.ca
Founded: 1936
Scholarly material on the Middle Ages.
Publishes in English, French.
ISBN Prefix(es): 978-0-88844
Number of titles published annually: 5 Print
Total Titles: 250 Print

**Porcupine's Quill Inc**
68 Main St, Erin, ON N0B 1T0
Mailing Address: PO Box 160, Erin, ON N0B 1T0
*Tel:* 519-833-9158 *Fax:* 519-833-9845
*E-mail:* pql@sentex.net
*Web Site:* porcupinesquill.ca
*Key Personnel*
Publr: Tim Inkster
Founded: 1974
Modern Canadian literature, poetry & art.
Publishes in English.
ISBN Prefix(es): 978-0-88984
Number of titles published annually: 12 Print
Total Titles: 100 Print
U.S. Rep(s): University of Toronto Press
Membership(s): Association of Canadian Publishers; Canada Council for the Arts; Literary Press Group; Ontario Arts Council

**Portage & Main Press**
318 McDermot, Suite 100, Winnipeg, MB R3A 0A2
*Tel:* 204-987-3500 *Toll Free Tel:* 800-667-9673 *Fax:* 204-947-0080 *Toll Free Fax:* 866-734-8477
*E-mail:* books@portageandmainpress.com
*Web Site:* www.portageandmainpress.com
*Key Personnel*
Owner & Publr: Catherine Gerbasi
Edit Dir: Annalee Greenberg
Dir, Mktg: Kirsten Phillips
Founded: 1967
Educational resource (K-8), interior design.
Publishes in English.
ISBN Prefix(es): 978-0-919566; 978-0-920541; 978-1-895411; 978-1-894110; 978-1-55379; 978-0-96996; 978-0-9699032
Number of titles published annually: 14 Print
Total Titles: 200 Print
Imprints: Pegius Publishers

**Pottersfield Press**
83 Leslie Rd, East Lawrencetown, NS B2Z 1P8
SAN: 115-0790
*Toll Free Fax:* 888-253-3133
*Web Site:* www.pottersfieldpress.com
*Key Personnel*
Pres & Publr: Lesley Choyce *E-mail:* lchoyce@ns.sympatico.ca
Founded: 1979
Fiction, books about the sea, books of Atlantic & Canada; nonfiction, books of literary travel.
Publishes in English.
ISBN Prefix(es): 978-0-919001; 978-1-895900; 978-1-897426
Number of titles published annually: 6 Print
Total Titles: 104 Print; 2 CD-ROM; 4 Audio
Imprints: Atlantic Classics Series
Distributed by Nimbus Publishing
U.S. Rep(s): Nimbus Publishing
*Orders to:* c/o Nimbus Publishing, Box 9166, Halifax, NS B3K 5M8 *Toll Free Tel:* 800-646-2879 *Toll Free Fax:* 888-253-3133 *E-mail:* customerservice@nimbus.ca SAN: 115-0790
*Shipping Address:* c/o Nimbus Publishing, Box 9166, Halifax, NS B3K 5M8 *Tel:* 904-454-7404 *Toll Free Tel:* 800-646-2879 *Toll Free Fax:* 888-253-3133 *E-mail:* customerservice@nimbus.ca *Web Site:* www.nimbus.ca SAN: 115-0790
Membership(s): Association of Canadian Publishers

**PrairieView Press**
PO Box 460, Rosenort, MB R0G 0W0
*Tel:* 204-327-6543 *Toll Free Tel:* 800-477-7377 *Fax:* 204-327-6544
*Web Site:* www.prairieviewpress.com
*Key Personnel*
Owner & Pres: Chester Goossen
Mgr: Dalen Goossen
Secy: Darleen Loewen
Contact: Chad Goossen
Founded: 1968
Quality reading material for children & adults; songbooks. Over 1300 titles in distribution, listed in catalog.
Publishes in English.
ISBN Prefix(es): 978-0-920035; 978-1-896199; 978-1-897080
Number of titles published annually: 36 Print
Total Titles: 1,450 Print
*Branch Office(s)*
PO Box 88, Neche, ND 58265-0088, United States

**Les Presses de l'Université d'Ottawa**, see University of Ottawa Press (Presses de l'Université d'Ottawa)

**Les Presses de l'Universite du Quebec**
Division of Universite Du Quebec
2875 Boul Laurier, Suite 450, Quebec, QC G1V 2M2
*Tel:* 418-657-4399 *Fax:* 418-657-2096
*E-mail:* puq@puq.ca
*Web Site:* www.puq.ca
Founded: 1969
University press.
Publishes in English, French.
ISBN Prefix(es): 978-2-7605; 978-0-7770; 978-2-920073
Number of titles published annually: 80 Print
Total Titles: 1,300 Print
Distributor for Les editions Saint-Yves Inc; Figura; Imaginaire du Nord; Tele-Universite
*Distribution Center:* Prologue Inc, 1650 boul Lionel-Bertrand, Boisbriand, QC J7H 1N7
Patrimoine SPRL, rue du Noyer 168, 1030 Brussels, Belgium
SODIS SARL, 128 Ave du Marechal de Lattre de Tassigny, 77400 Thorigny-sur-Marne, France *Tel:* (01) 60 07 82 99 *Fax:* (01) 64 30 32 27 *E-mail:* portail@sodis.fr
SERVIDIS SA, Chemin des Chalets, 7-CH-1279 Chavannes-de-Bogis, Switzerland

**Les Presses De L'Universite Laval**
Division of Universite Du Quebec
Pavillon Maurice-Pollack, Suite 3103, 2305 University St, Quebec, QC G1V 0A6
*Tel:* 418-656-2803 *Fax:* 418-656-3305
*E-mail:* presses@pul.ulaval.ca
*Web Site:* www.pulaval.com
*Key Personnel*
Gen Dir: Denis Dion *E-mail:* denis.dion@pul.ulaval.ca
Gen Ed: Andre Baril *E-mail:* andr.baril@sympatico.ca; Dominique Gingras *E-mail:* dominique.gingras@pul.ulaval.ca
Founded: 1950
Books in the humanities & social sciences with an emphasis on subjects of interest in Quebec & Canada, administration, economy.
Publishes in French.
ISBN Prefix(es): 978-2-7637
Number of titles published annually: 100 Print; 60 Online; 60 E-Book
Total Titles: 10 Online; 10 E-Book
*Distribution Center:* Prologue Inc, 1650, blvd Lionel-Bertrand, Boisbriand, QC J7H 1N7 *Tel:* 450-434-0306 *Toll Free Tel:* 800-363-2864 *Fax:* 450-434-2627 *E-mail:* prologue@prologue.ca *Web Site:* www.prologue.ca

**Prise de Parole Inc**
109 Elm St, Suite 205, Sudbury, ON P3C 1T4
Mailing Address: CP 550, Sudbury, ON P3E 4R2
*Tel:* 705-675-6491 *Fax:* 705-673-1817
*E-mail:* info@prisedeparole.ca
*Web Site:* www.prisedeparole.ca
*Key Personnel*
Exec Dir: Denise Truax
Admin Dir: Alain Mayotte
Digital Shift Coord: Stephanie Cormier
Founded: 1973
Poetry, novels, drama, textbooks, essays.
Publishes in French.
ISBN Prefix(es): 978-0-920814; 978-0-921573; 978-2-89423
Number of titles published annually: 17 Print
Total Titles: 325 Print; 277 Online; 110 E-Book
*Distribution Center:* Diffusion Dimedia, 1650 boul Lionel-Bertrand, Boisbriand, QC J7H 1N7 *Tel:* 450-434-0306
Membership(s): ANEL; Regroupement des Editeurs Canadiens-Francais

**Productive Publications**
7-B Pleasant Blvd, Unit 1210, Toronto, ON M4T 1K2
SAN: 117-1712
Mailing Address: PO Box 7200, Sta A, Toronto, ON M5W 1X8
*Tel:* 416-483-0634 *Fax:* 416-322-7434
*Web Site:* www.productivepublications.com
*Key Personnel*
Owner & Pres: Iain Williamson
Founded: 1985
Paperback books-trade; business, finance, communications, computers, management, marketing, taxation, personal finance, entrepreneurship, self-help.
Publishes in English.
ISBN Prefix(es): 978-0-920847; 978-1-896210; 978-1-55270

Number of titles published annually: 28 Print
Total Titles: 147 Print

**Les Publications du Quebec**
1000, rte de l'Eqalise, Bureau 500, Quebec, QC G1V 3V9
*Tel:* 418-643-5150 *Toll Free Tel:* 800-463-2100 (Quebec province only) *Fax:* 418-643-6177 *Toll Free Fax:* 800 561 3479
*E-mail:* publicationsduquebec@cspq.gouv.qc.ca
*Web Site:* www.publicationsduquebec.gouv.qc.ca
*Key Personnel*
Dir: Sylvie Ferland
Founded: 1982
Government publications.
Publishes in English, French.
ISBN Prefix(es): 978-2-550; 978-2-551
Number of titles published annually: 200 Print; 20 Online
Total Titles: 4,000 Print; 100 Online
*Warehouse:* 2575 rue Watt, Quebec City, QC G1P 3T2, Pierre Otis

**Purich Publishing Ltd**
PO Box 23032, Market Mall Postal Outlet, Saskatoon, SK S7J 5H3
*Tel:* 306-373-5311 *Fax:* 306-373-5315
*E-mail:* purich@sasktel.net
*Web Site:* www.purichpublishing.com
*Key Personnel*
Publr: Karen Bolstad; Donald Purich
Founded: 1992
Books specializing in Aboriginal & social justice issues, law & Canadian history.
Publishes in English.
ISBN Prefix(es): 978-1-895830
Number of titles published annually: 4 Print
Total Titles: 34 Print
*Orders to:* Brunswick Books, 20 Maud St, Suite 303, Toronto, ON M5V 2M5 *Tel:* 416-703-3598 *Fax:* 416-703-6561 *E-mail:* orders@brunswickbooks.ca
*Returns:* Brunswick Books, c/o TTS Distributing, 45 Tyler St, Aurora, ON L4G 3L5
*Distribution Center:* Brunswick Books, 20 Maud St, Suite 303, Toronto, ON M5V 2M5 *Tel:* 416-703-3598 *Fax:* 416-703-6561 *E-mail:* orders@brunswickbooks.ca
Membership(s): Association of Canadian Publishers; Saskatchewan Publishers Group

**§QA International**
Division of Editions Quebec Amerique Inc
329 De la Commune W, 3rd fl, Montreal, QC H2Y 2E1
*Tel:* 514-499-3000 *Fax:* 514-499-3010
*Web Site:* www.qa-international.com
*Key Personnel*
Founder & CEO: Jacques Fortin
Rts Dir (Editions Quebec Amerique): Rita Biscotti
Dir of Busn Devt: Rossana Sommaruga
Founded: 1974
Create, develop & produce editorial content built around state-of-the-art computer images for publication in print & electronic media throughout the world.
Publishes in French.
Number of titles published annually: 60 Print
Total Titles: 770 Print

**Quebec Dans Le Monde**
CP 8503, succ Sainte-Foy, Quebec, QC G1V 4N5
SAN: 116-8657
*Tel:* 418-659-5540 *Fax:* 418-659-4143
*E-mail:* info@quebecmonde.com
*Web Site:* www.quebecmonde.com
*Key Personnel*
Dir Gen: Helene Thibault
Founded: 1983
Databases, guides & reference books on Quebec at large.
Publishes in French.
ISBN Prefix(es): 978-2-9801130; 978-2-91309
Number of titles published annually: 7 Print
Total Titles: 21 Print; 15 E-Book
Distributed by Librairie Du Quebec A Paris

**Editions Michel Quintin**
4770 rue Foster, Waterloo, QC J0E 2N0
SAN: 116-5356
*Tel:* 450-539-3774 *Fax:* 450-539-4905
*E-mail:* info@editionsmichelquintin.ca
*Web Site:* www.editionsmichelquintin.ca
*Key Personnel*
Pres: Michel Quintin
VP: Collette Dufresne
Founded: 1982
Nonfiction on fauna, nature, environment.
Publishes in French.
ISBN Prefix(es): 978-2-920438; 978-2-89435
Number of titles published annually: 30 Print
Total Titles: 200 Print
*Editorial Office(s):* PO Box 340, Waterloo, QC J0E 2N0
Distributed by Les Messageries ADP
Foreign Rep(s): Bacon & Hughes (Canada); Le Colporteur Diffusion (France); Multi Livres Diffusion (France); Servidis SA (Belgium)

**Random House of Canada Limited**
One Toronto St, Suite 300, Toronto, ON M5C 2V6
SAN: 201-3975
*Tel:* 416-364-4449 *Toll Free Tel:* 888-523-9292 (cust serv) *Fax:* 416-364-6863; 416-364-6653 (subs rts)
*Web Site:* www.randomhouse.ca
*Key Personnel*
CEO & Pres: Brad Martin
EVP: Louise Dennys
EVP & CFO: Douglas Foot *Tel:* 905-624-0672
EVP & Dir, Sales: Duncan Shields *Tel:* 905-624-0672
SVP, Random House of Canada Limited & Publr, Doubleday Canada: Kristin Cochrane
SVP & Dir, Mktg & Communs: Tracey Turriff
VP & Dir, Mktg Strategy: Scott Sellers
VP & Dir, Mktg & Ad: Constance Mackensie *Tel:* 905-624-0672
VP & Dir, Strategic Busn Devt: Robert Wheaton
VP, Prodn: Janine Laporte
Publr: Robert McCullough
Dir, eBooks & eProd Devt: Michael Bowles
Dir, Contracts: Samantha North
Prodn Mgr: Carla Kean
Sr Ed, Knopf & Random House: Paul Taunton
Founded: 1944
Random House of Canada Limited & its publishing entities are not accepting unsol submissions, proposals, mss, or submission queries via e-mail at this time.
Publishes in English.
ISBN Prefix(es): 978-0-307; 978-0-679; 978-0-553; 978-0-385; 978-0-7704; 978-0-345; 978-0-449; 978-0-676
Imprints: Anchor Canada; Bond Street Books; Doubleday Canada; Emblem Edition; Douglas Gibson Books; Knopf Canada; Random House Canada; Seal Books; Signal; Tundra Books; Vintage Canada
*Branch Office(s)*
One Toronto St, Suite 300, Toronto, ON M5C 2V6
Membership(s): Canadian Booksellers Association; Canadian Library Association; Canadian Publishers' Council
*See separate listing for:*
**Knopf Random Canada**
**McClelland & Stewart Ltd**
**Seal Books**

**Reader's Digest Association Canada ULC (Selection du Reader's Digest Canada SRL)**
1100 Rene Levesque Blvd W, Montreal, QC H3B 5H5
Mailing Address: PO Box 16500, Sta Westmount, Westmount, QC H3Z 0A4
*Tel:* 514-940-0751 *Toll Free Tel:* 866-236-7789 (cust serv) *Fax:* 514-940-3637
*E-mail:* customer.service@readersdigest.ca
*Web Site:* www.readersdigest.ca
*Key Personnel*
CEO & Pres: Tony Cioffi *Tel:* 514-940-0751 ext 302
Founded: 1943
Mail order & retail books on cookery, crafts, games & hobbies, money management, gardening, geography & geology, health & nutrition, history, house & home, how-to, law, general medicine, nature & science, travel; dictionaries, atlases, encyclopedias; fiction & general nonfiction in condensed form.
Publishes in English, French.
ISBN Prefix(es): 978-0-88850
Number of titles published annually: 100 Print
Total Titles: 450 Print
*Warehouse:* 300 Orenda Rd, Brampton, ON L6T 1G2

**Red Deer Press**
Division of Fitzhenry & Whiteside Limited
195 Allstate Pkwy, Markham, ON L3R 4T8
*Tel:* 905-477-9700 *Toll Free Tel:* 800-387-9776 (orders) *Fax:* 905-477-2834 *Toll Free Fax:* 800-260-9777 (orders)
*E-mail:* rdp@reddeerpress.com
*Web Site:* www.reddeerpress.com
*Key Personnel*
Publr: Richard Dionne *Tel:* 800-387-9776 ext 248 *E-mail:* dionne@reddeerpress.com
Promos: Cheryl Chen *Tel:* 800-387-9776 ext 258 *E-mail:* cheryl.chen@reddeerpress.com
Founded: 1975
Publishes in English, French.
ISBN Prefix(es): 978-0-88995
Number of titles published annually: 20 Print
Imprints: Northern Lights Books for Children; Robert J Sawyer Books
Membership(s): Book Publishers Association of Alberta; Literary Press Group of Canada

**Rocky Mountain Books Ltd (RMB)**
103-1075 Pendergast St, Victoria, BC V8V 0A1
*Tel:* 250-360-0829 *Fax:* 250-386-0829
*Web Site:* www.rmbooks.com
*Key Personnel*
Publr: Don Gorman *E-mail:* don@rmbooks.com
Sr Ed: Joe Wilderson *E-mail:* joe@rmbooks.com
Founded: 1979
Regional publisher of books on outdoor activities, mountain literature & mountain biographies.
Publishes in English.
ISBN Prefix(es): 978-0-9690038; 978-0-921102; 978-1-894765
Number of titles published annually: 20 Print
Total Titles: 188 Print
*Sales Office(s):* Heritage Group Distribution, 19272 96 Ave, Suite 8, Surrey, BC V4N 4C1 *Tel:* 604-881-7067 *Toll Free Tel:* 800-665-3302 *Fax:* 604-881-7068 *Toll Free Fax:* 800-566-3336 *Web Site:* www.hgdistribution.com
*Billing Address:* Heritage Group Distribution, 19272 96 Ave, Suite 8, Surrey, BC V4N 4C1 *Tel:* 604-881-7067 *Toll Free Tel:* 800-665-3302 *Fax:* 604-881-7068 *Toll Free Fax:* 800-566-3336 *Web Site:* www.hgdistribution.com
*Orders to:* Heritage Group Distribution, 19272 96 Ave, Suite 8, Surrey, BC V4N 4C1 *Tel:* 604-881-7067 *Toll Free Tel:* 800-665-3302 *Fax:* 604-881-7068 *Toll Free Fax:* 800-566-3336 *E-mail:* orders@hgdistribution.com *Web Site:* www.hgdistribution.com
*Returns:* Heritage Group Distribution, 19272 96 Ave, Suite 8, Surrey, BC V4N 4C1

*Tel:* 604-881-7067 *Toll Free Tel:* 800-665-3302 *Fax:* 604-881-7068 *Toll Free Fax:* 800-566-3336 *Web Site:* www.hgdistribution.com
*Shipping Address:* Heritage Group Distribution, 19272 96 Ave, Suite 8, Surrey, BC V4N 4C1 *Tel:* 604-881-7067 *Toll Free Tel:* 800-665-3302 *Fax:* 604-881-7068 *Toll Free Fax:* 800-566-3336 *Web Site:* www.hgdistribution.com
*Warehouse:* Heritage Group Distribution, 19272 96 Ave, Suite 8, Surrey, BC V4N 4C1 *Tel:* 604-881-7067 *Toll Free Tel:* 800-665-3302 *Fax:* 604-881-7068 *Toll Free Fax:* 800-566-3336 *Web Site:* www.hgdistribution.com
*Distribution Center:* Heritage Group Distribution, 19272 96 Ave, Suite 8, Surrey, BC V4N 4C1 *Tel:* 604-881-7067 *Toll Free Tel:* 800-665-3302 *Fax:* 604-881-7068 *Toll Free Fax:* 800-566-3336 *E-mail:* orders@hgdistribution.com *Web Site:* www.hgdistribution.com
Membership(s): Book Publishers Association of Alberta

**Ronsdale Press Ltd**
3350 W 21 Ave, Vancouver, BC V6S 1G7
SAN: 116-2454
*Tel:* 604-738-4688 *Toll Free Tel:* 855-738-4688 *Fax:* 604-731-4548
*E-mail:* ronsdale@shaw.ca
*Web Site:* ronsdalepress.com
*Key Personnel*
Dir & Intl Rts: Ronald Hatch
Lib Sales Dir: Veronica Hatch
Founded: 1988
Literary press, children's, history, literary & regional. Specialize in Canadian authors.
Publishes in English.
ISBN Prefix(es): 978-0-921870; 978-1-55380
Number of titles published annually: 12 Print; 12 E-Book
Total Titles: 210 Print
Foreign Rep(s): Literary Press Group (Tan Light) (USA)
*Distribution Center:* Raincoast Books, 2440 Viking Way, Richmond, BC V6V 1N2 *Toll Free Tel:* 800-663-5714 *Toll Free Fax:* 800-565-3770 *E-mail:* customerservice@raincoast.com *Web Site:* www.raincoast.com
Baker & Taylor, 2550 W Tyvola Rd, Suite 300, Charlotte, NC 28217, United States *Tel:* 704-998-3100 *Toll Free Tel:* 800-775-1800 *E-mail:* btinfo@baker-taylor.com *Web Site:* www.btol.com
Ingram, One Ingram Blvd, La Vergne, TN 37086, United States *Tel:* 615-793-5000 *E-mail:* inquiry@ingramcontent.com *Web Site:* www.ingramcontent.com
Gazelle Book Services, White Cross Mills, Hightown, Lancaster, Lancs LA1 4XS, United Kingdom (UK & Europe) *Tel:* (01524) 68765 *Web Site:* www.gazellebookservices.co.uk
Membership(s): Association of Book Publishers of British Columbia; Association of Canadian Publishers; Literary Press Group

**Robert Rose Inc**
120 Eglinton Ave E, Suite 800, Toronto, ON M4P 1E2
*Tel:* 416-322-6552 *Fax:* 416-322-6936
*Web Site:* www.robertrose.ca
Founded: 1995
ISBN Prefix(es): 978-1-896503; 978-0-7788
Total Titles: 150 Print
Distributed by Firefly Books Ltd

**Royal Ontario Museum Press**
100 Queen's Park, Toronto, ON M5S 2C6
*Tel:* 416-586-8000 *Fax:* 416-586-5642
*E-mail:* info@rom.on.ca
*Web Site:* www.rom.on.ca
Founded: 1912
Scholarly & general books on art, archaeology & sciences.
Publishes in English, French.
ISBN Prefix(es): 978-0-88854
Number of titles published annually: 8 Print
Total Titles: 100 Print
U.S. Rep(s): University of Toronto Press (NY)
*Warehouse:* University of Toronto Press, 5201 Dufferin St, Toronto, ON M3H 5T8, Contact: Carol Trainor *Tel:* 416-667-7791 *Toll Free Tel:* 800-565-9523 *Fax:* 416-667-7832 *E-mail:* utpbooks@utpress.utoronto.ca
*Distribution Center:* University of Toronto Press, 5201 Dufferin St, Toronto, ON M3H 5T8, Contact: Carol Trainor *Tel:* 416-667-7791 *Toll Free Tel:* 800-565-9523 *Fax:* 416-667-7832 *E-mail:* utpbooks@utpress.utoronto.ca

**Guy Saint-Jean Editeur Inc**
3440 Blvd Industriel, Laval, QC H7L 4R9
*Tel:* 450-663-1777 *Fax:* 450-663-6666
*E-mail:* info@saint-jeanediteur.com
*Web Site:* www.saint-jeanediteur.com
*Key Personnel*
Owner: Nicole Saint-Jean
VP, Publg: Marie-Claire Saint-Jean
VP, Opers: Jacques Frechette
Founded: 1981
Publishes in English, French.
ISBN Prefix(es): 978-2-920340; 978-2-89455
Number of titles published annually: 30 Print; 10 E-Book
Total Titles: 350 Print
Imprints: Green Frog Publishing
*Foreign Office(s):* Saint-Jean Editeur (France), 30-32 rue de Lappe, 75011 Paris, France, Contact: Christian Richard *Tel:* (01) 39 76 99 43 *Fax:* (01) 39 76 21 78 *E-mail:* gsj.editeur@free.fr
U.S. Publishers Represented: CDS
Foreign Rep(s): Int Press (Australia, New Zealand); Christian Richard (Europe)
Foreign Rights: Elizabeth Brayne (Europe)
Membership(s): ANEL

**Sara Jordan Publishing**
Division of Jordan Music Productions Inc
RPO Lakeport Box 28105, St Catharines, ON L2N 7P8
*Tel:* 905-938-5050 *Toll Free Tel:* 800-567-7733 *Fax:* 905-938-9970 *Toll Free Fax:* 800-229-3855
*Web Site:* www.sara-jordan.com
*Key Personnel*
Pres: Sara Jordan
Founded: 1990
Publish educational resources.
Publishes in English, French.
ISBN Prefix(es): 978-1-895523; 978-1-894262; 978-1-55386
Number of titles published annually: 6 Print
Total Titles: 60 Print
Membership(s): Association of Canadian Publishers

**Scholastic Canada Ltd**
Subsidiary of Scholastic Inc
604 King St W, Toronto, ON M5V 1E1
SAN: 115-5164
*Tel:* 905-887-7323 *Toll Free Tel:* 800-268-3848 (CN) *Fax:* 905-887-1131 *Toll Free Fax:* 866-346-1288
*Web Site:* www.scholastic.ca
*Key Personnel*
Pres: Linda Gosnell; Iole Lucchese
VP, Publg: Diane Kerner
VP, Mktg: Nancy Pearson *Tel:* 905-887-7323 ext 3515
VP, French Mktg & Publg: Chantale LaLonde
VP, Educ: Wendy Graham
VP, Book Fairs: Brigitte Birtch
Sr Dir, Trade: Kathy Goncharenko
Rts/Perms Mgr: Maral Maclagan *E-mail:* mmaclagan@scholastic.ca
Founded: 1957
Publish & distribute children's books & educational materials in both official languages.
Publishes in English, French.
ISBN Prefix(es): 978-0-590; 978-0-439; 978-0-7791; 978-1-55268; 978-0-545; 978-1-4431
Imprints: Les Editions Scholastic; North Winds Press; Scholastic Canada
Divisions: Scholastic Book Fairs Canada Inc
Distributor for Blue Sky Press (exclusive in CN); Cartwheel Books (exclusive in CN); Chicken House (exclusive in CN); Children's Press (exclusive in CN); Franklin Watts (US) (exclusive in CN); Grolier (exclusive in CN); Klutz (exclusive in CN); Arthur A Levine Books (exclusive in CN); Orchard Books (exclusive in CN); Scholastic en Espanol (exclusive in CN); Scholastic Graphix (exclusive in CN); Scholastic Nonfiction (exclusive in CN); Scholastic Paperbacks (exclusive in CN); Scholastic Press (exclusive in CN); Scholastic Reference (exclusive in CN)
U.S. Publishers Represented: Scholastic Inc
U.S. Rep(s): Scholastic Inc
Foreign Rights: Akcali Copyright Agency (Kezban Akcali) (Turkey); Bardon Chinese Media Agency (Cynthia Chang) (Taiwan); Marcin Biegaj (Poland); Sandra Bruna Agencia Literaria (Sandra Bruna) (Spain); JLM Literary Agency (Greece); Simona Kessler Agency (Adriana Marina) (Romania); Living Literary Agency (Elfriede Pexa) (Italy); Maxima Creative Agency (Santo Manurung) (Indonesia); Nika Literary Agency (Vania Kadiyska) (Bulgaria); I Pikarski Literary Agency (Israel); Karin Schindler Literary Agency (Brazil); Shinwon Agency Co (Yuni Lee) (Korea); Tuttle-Mori Agency Inc (Pimolporn Yutisri) (Thailand); Tuttle-Mori Agency Inc (Solan Natsume) (Japan)

**Seal Books**
Imprint of Random House of Canada Limited
One Toronto St, Suite 300, Toronto, ON M5C 2V6
SAN: 201-3975
*Tel:* 416-364-4449 *Toll Free Tel:* 888-523-9292 (order desk) *Fax:* 416-364-6863
*Web Site:* www.randomhouse.ca
*Key Personnel*
CEO & Pres: Brad Martin *Tel:* 905-624-0672
EVP & Dir, Sales: Duncan Shields *Tel:* 905-624-0672
EVP & Chief Admin Offr: Doug Foot *Tel:* 905-624-0672
SVP & Dir, Mktg & Corp Communs: Tracey Turriff
VP & Dir, Mktg Strategy: Scott Sellers
VP & Dir, Prodn: Janine Laporte
VP, Random House of Canada Limited & Publr, Doubleday Canada Publishing Group: Kristin Cochrane
Assoc Dir: Carla Kean
Founded: 1977
No unsol mss; prefer queries in advance from potential authors.
Publishes in English.
ISBN Prefix(es): 978-0-7704
Number of titles published annually: 18 Print
Membership(s): Canadian Booksellers Association; Canadian Library Association; Canadian Publishers' Council

**Second Story Feminist Press**
20 Maud St, Suite 401, Toronto, ON M5V 2M5
*Tel:* 416-537-7850 *Fax:* 416-537-0588
*E-mail:* info@secondstorypress.ca
*Web Site:* www.secondstorypress.ca
*Key Personnel*
Pres & Publr: Margie Wolfe
Mng Ed: Carolyn Jackson
Gen Mgr: Phuong Truong
Founded: 1988

Paperback & cloth books for juveniles & young adults, adult fiction & nonfiction.
Publishes in English.
ISBN Prefix(es): 978-0-925005; 978-1-896764; 978-1-897187
Number of titles published annually: 14 Print
Total Titles: 108 Print
Distributed by Book Publishing Co; University of Toronto Press
U.S. Rep(s): Orca Books (children's books)
*Orders to:* University of Toronto Press, 5201 Dufferin St, Downsview, ON M3H 5T8 *Tel:* 416-667-7791 *Toll Free Tel:* 800-565-9523 *Fax:* 416-667-7832
*Shipping Address:* University of Toronto Press, 5201 Dufferin St, Downsview, ON M3H 5T8 *Tel:* 416-667-7791 *Toll Free Tel:* 800-565-9523 *Fax:* 416-667-7832
*Distribution Center:* University of Toronto Press, 5201 Dufferin St, Downsview, ON M3H 5T8

**Second Story Press**, see Second Story Feminist Press

**Selection du Reader's Digest Canada SRL**, see Reader's Digest Association Canada ULC (Selection du Reader's Digest Canada SRL)

**J Gordon Shillingford Publishing Inc**
PO Box 86, RPO Corydon Ave, Winnipeg, MB R3M 3S3
*Tel:* 204-779-6967 *Fax:* 204-779-6970
*Web Site:* www.jgshillingford.com
*Key Personnel*
Pres & Publr: Gordon Shillingford
Founded: 1992
Primarily a literary publisher (drama & poetry), but also 3-4 nonfiction titles per year. Publish works of Canadian citizens only.
Publishes in English.
ISBN Prefix(es): 978-0-9689709; 978-0-920486; 978-1-896239; 978-0-9697261; 978-1-897289
Number of titles published annually: 12 Print
Total Titles: 248 Print
*Sales Office(s):* Canadian Manda Group, 165 Dufferin St, Toronto, ON M6K 3H6 *Tel:* 416-516-0911 *Fax:* 416-516-0917 *E-mail:* info@mandagroup.com *Web Site:* www.mandagroup.com
The Literary Press Group of Canada, 425 Adelaide St W, Suite 700, Toronto, ON M5V 2C1 (US Rep), Contact: Tan Light *Tel:* 416-483-1321 ext 3 *Fax:* 416-483-2510 *E-mail:* sales@lpg.ca
*Distribution Center:* University of Toronto Press, 5210 Dufferin St, Toronto, ON M3H 5T8 (CN) *Tel:* 416-667-7791 *Toll Free Tel:* 800-565-9523 *Toll Free Fax:* 800-221-9985 *E-mail:* utpbooks@utpres.utoronto.ca
University of Toronto Press, 2250 Military Rd, Tonawanda, NY 14150, United States (US) *Tel:* 416-667-7791 *Toll Free Tel:* 800-565-9523 *Fax:* 416-667-7832 *Toll Free Fax:* 800-221-9985 *E-mail:* utpbooks@utoronto.ca
Membership(s): Association of Canadian Publishers; Association of Manitoba Book Publishers; Literary Press Group

**Shoreline Press**
23 Sainte Anne, Ste Anne de Bellevue, QC H9X 1L1
SAN: 116-9564
*Tel:* 514-457-5733
*E-mail:* info@shorelinepress.ca
*Web Site:* shorelinepress.ca
*Key Personnel*
Sr Ed: Judith Isherwood
Founded: 1991
Publishes in English, French.
ISBN Prefix(es): 978-0-9695180; 978-0-9698752; 978-1-896754
Number of titles published annually: 5 Print
Total Titles: 60 Print
*Orders to:* Disticor Direct, 695 Westney Rd S, Unit 14, Ajax, ON L1S 6M9 *Toll Free Tel:* 866-679-2665 *E-mail:* ndalton@disticor.com
*Distribution Center:* Disticor Direct, 695 Westney Rd S, Unit 14, Ajax, ON L1S 6M9 *Toll Free Tel:* 866-679-2665 *E-mail:* ndalton@disticor.com
Membership(s): Association of Canadian Publishers; Association of English-language Publishers of Quebec; Quebec Library Association; Quebec Writer's Federation

**Signature Editions**
RPO Corydon, PO Box 206, Winnipeg, MB R3M 3S7
*Tel:* 204-779-7803 *Fax:* 204-779-6970
*E-mail:* signature@allstream.net
*Web Site:* www.signature-editions.com
*Key Personnel*
Publr: Karen Haughian
Founded: 1986
Literary publisher which publishes Canadian authors in the genres of fiction, nonfiction, poetry & drama.
Publishes in English.
ISBN Prefix(es): 978-0-921833; 978-1-897109
Number of titles published annually: 8 Print
Total Titles: 116 Print; 10 Audio
Distributor for Cyclops Press
*Orders to:* University of Toronto Press (UTP), 5201 Dufferin St, North York, ON M3H 5T8 *Tel:* 416-667-7791 *Toll Free Tel:* 800-565-9523 *Fax:* 416-667-7832 *Toll Free Fax:* 800-221-9985 *E-mail:* utpbooks@utpress.utoronto.ca
*Returns:* University of Toronto Press (UTP), 5201 Dufferin St, North York, ON M3H 5T8 *Tel:* 416-667-7791 *Toll Free Tel:* 800-565-9523 *Fax:* 416-667-7832 *Toll Free Fax:* 800-221-9985 *E-mail:* utpbooks@utpress.utoronto.ca
*Shipping Address:* University of Toronto Press (UTP), 2250 Military Rd, Tonawanda, NY 14150, United States; University of Toronto Press (UTP), 5201 Dufferin St, North York, ON M3H 5T8 *Tel:* 416-667-7791 *Toll Free Tel:* 800-565-9523 *Fax:* 416-667-7832 *Toll Free Fax:* 800-221-9985 *E-mail:* utpbooks@utpress.utoronto.ca
*Distribution Center:* University of Toronto Press (UTP), 5201 Dufferin St, North York, ON M3H 5T8 *Tel:* 416-667-7791 *Toll Free Tel:* 800-565-9523 *Fax:* 416-667-7832 *Toll Free Fax:* 800-221-9985 *E-mail:* utpbooks@utpress.utoronto.ca
Membership(s): Association of Canadian Publishers; Association of Manitoba Book Publishers; Literary Press Group of Canada

**Simon & Pierre Publishing Co Ltd**
Imprint of The Dundurn Group
3 Church St, Suite 500, Toronto, ON M5E 1M2
*Tel:* 416-214-5544 *Fax:* 416-214-5556
*E-mail:* info@dundurn.com
*Web Site:* www.dundurn.com
*Key Personnel*
Pres & Publr: J Kirk Howard *E-mail:* khoward@dundurn.com
Founded: 1972
Fiction.
Publishes in English.
ISBN Prefix(es): 978-1-55002; 978-0-88924
Number of titles published annually: 80 Print
Total Titles: 133 Print
Distributed by Dundurn Press

**§Simon & Schuster Canada**
Subsidiary of Simon & Schuster, Inc
166 King St E, Suite 300, Toronto, ON M5A 1J3
*Tel:* 647-427-8882 *Toll Free Tel:* 800-387-0446; 800-268-3216 (orders) *Fax:* 647-430-9446 *Toll Free Fax:* 888-849-8151 (orders)
*E-mail:* info@simonandschuster.ca
*Web Site:* www.simonsayscanada.com
*Key Personnel*
Pres & Publr: Kevin Hanson *E-mail:* kevin.hanson@simonandschuster.ca
VP, Sales & Mktg: David Millar *E-mail:* david.millar@simonandschuster.ca
Dir, Mktg: Felicia Quon *E-mail:* felicia.quon@simonandschuster.ca
Dir, Publicity: Amy Cormier *E-mail:* amy.cormier@simonandschuster.ca
Dir, Busn Aff: Kien Vuong *E-mail:* kien.vuong@simonandschuster.ca
Dir, Sales Opers: Alison Clarke *E-mail:* alison.clarke@simonandschuster.ca
Publishes in English.
Distributor for Andrews McMeel Publishing LLC; Baen Books; Baseball America; Black Library; Blue Heeler Books; Cardoza; Chicken Soup for the Soul; Cider Mill Press Book Publishers LLC; Downtown Books; Games Workshop; Good Books; Hooked on Phonics; Kaplan Publishing; KinFolk; John Locke Publishing; Manhattan Press; Merck; Open Road Press; Rebellion; Ripley's Publishing; Simon & Schuster; Viz; Weldon Owen Inc; World Almanac

**Simply Read Books**
501-5525 West Blvd, Vancouver, BC V6M 3W6
*Tel:* 604-727-2960
*E-mail:* go@simplyreadbooks.com
*Web Site:* www.simplyreadbooks.com
Founded: 2001
Our approach to illustrated children's books follows the finest publishing tradition & spirit with inspired content, extraordinary artwork, outstanding graphic design form & quality production. We introduce contemporary books with a modern appeal & fresh outlook & offer a careful selection of timeless stories that link the past with the present. We specialize in high-quality, unique picture books & fiction. Before submitting, please browse our web site, bookstores & libraries to look at & read what we publish. This will give you an idea of whether or not your story or illustrations would fit with our list.
Publishes in English, French.
ISBN Prefix(es): 978-1-894965; 978-0-9688768; 978-1-897476
Number of titles published annually: 25 Print
Total Titles: 100 Print
*Sales Office(s):* Publishers Group West, 1700 Fourth St, Berkeley, CA 94710, United States *Toll Free Tel:* 800-788-3123 *Fax:* 510-528-3614 *E-mail:* customerservice@pgw.com *Web Site:* www.pgw.com/customers
*Orders to:* Publishers Group West, 1700 Fourth St, Berkeley, CA 94710, United States *Toll Free Tel:* 800-788-3123 *Fax:* 510-528-3614 *E-mail:* customerservice@pgw.com *Web Site:* www.pgw.com/customers
*Returns:* Perseus Book Group, 1094 Flex Dr, Jackson, TN 38301, United States *Toll Free Tel:* 800-788-3123 *Fax:* 510-528-3614 *E-mail:* customerservice@pgw.com *Web Site:* www.pgw.com/customers
*Warehouse:* Raincoast, 9050 Shaughnessy St, Vancouver, BC V6P 6E5
*Distribution Center:* Perseus Book Group, 1094 Flex Dr, Jackson, TN 38301, United States *Toll Free Tel:* 800-543-4499
Membership(s): Association for Canadian Publishers in the US; IBPA, the Independent Book Publishers Association

**Gordon Soules Book Publishers Ltd**
1359 Amble Side Lane, West Vancouver, BC V7T 2Y9
SAN: 115-0987
*Tel:* 604-922-6588 *Fax:* 604-688-5442; 604-922-6574
*E-mail:* books@gordonsoules.com

*Web Site:* www.gordonsoules.com
*Key Personnel*
Pres: Gordon Soules
Founded: 1965
Publishers & distributors of high quality trade books.
Publishes in English.
ISBN Prefix(es): 978-0-919574; 978-1-894661
Number of titles published annually: 4 Print
Total Titles: 65 Print
*Branch Office(s)*
620-1916 Pike Place, Seattle, WA 98101, United States
Distributor for Aerie Publishing; AEW Services; Aldo Intrieri; Apple Communications; Arcadian Productions; The Ardent Angler Group; Artadvisory; John Baldwin; David Bates; Battle Street Books; Bilkin Enterprises Ltd; Blackbird Naturgraphics Inc; Blue Poppy Press; Christine Boehringer; Bradt Publications (England); British Columbia Waterfowl Society; Brian Burt; C-Van Productions; Children's Studio Books; Chrismar Mapping Services Inc; Community Arts Council of Vancouver; Crazyhorse Press; Cream Books; Creative Classics Publications Inc; Creative Solutions Inc; Crompton Books; Crossroads Press; Patty-Anne Cumpstone; Dewaal Media Productions; Dragon Fly Publications Inc; The Drawing-Room Graphics Services Ltd; Duo Consultants; Eaglet Publishing; Environment Canada; Federation of Mountain Clubs of BC; Fforbez Publications; Fjelltur Books; The Flag Shop; Fore Shore Publishing; Francis; Giesbrecht & Associates; Goodwin; Gordon Soules Book Publishers Ltd; Gregson Communications Ltd; Grove Cottage Press; Norman Hacking Publishers; Lesley Hasselfield; Heartwood Books; Hillpointe Publishing; Hillside Publishing; The Hip List Inc; Hockering Press; Impressions in Print; Innovative Publishing; Intelligent Patient Guide; ITMB Publishing; G M Johnson & Associates Inc; Joy Dee Marketing; Just Muffins Ltd; Kachina Press; KMB Publishing; The Laurier Institution; Liahona Press; Maps Unlimited; Marine Tapestry Publications; Meridian House; Mighton House Publishing & Distribution; Moody's Lookout Press; Morning Dawn Publishing Co; Mussio Ventures Ltd; N C Publishing; Naikoon Marine; New Century Books; North Shore Family Services Society; Okanagan Mountain Biking; Omega Press; Outdoor Recreation Council of BC; The Pacific Salmon Commission; Panorama Publications; Paper Works; Paradox Publishing; Carmen Patrick; Physicians for the Prevention of Nuclear War; Quadra Island Child Care Society; Qualy Publishing; Rainbow's End Company; Raser Enterprises; Raxas Books; Rychkun Recreation Publications; Sunporch Publishing; Syntax Books; Paul Tawrell; Tenisall Inc; Treeline Publishing; Tricouni Press; Vancouver Natural History Society; Varsity Outdoor Club; Walbourne Enterprises; Waterwheel Press; West Indies Trading Co; Sandra Wong Publishing; Bruce Woodsworth; World Wide Books & Maps; Yan's Variety; Yellow Hat Press
U.S. Publishers Represented: Berndtson & Berndtson; Lilac Press; Living Overseas Books; Orthopedic Physical Therapy Products; San Juan Enterprises Inc; US Games Systems Inc; The Vegetarian Resource Group

**Sport Books Publisher**
212 Robert St, side basement door, Toronto, ON M5S 2K7
*Tel:* 416-323-9438 *Fax:* 416-966-9022
*E-mail:* sbp@sportbookspub.com
*Web Site:* www.sportbookspub.com
*Key Personnel*
Pres: Dr Peter Klavora *E-mail:* peter.klavora@utoronto.ca
Exec Dir: Tania Klavora
Founded: 1983
Activity books, sports books & DVDs; subjects include physical education, exercise science text books & kinesiology. Orders accepted by mail, fax or online. Returns accepted if in mint condition.
Publishes in English, French.
ISBN Prefix(es): 978-0-920905
Number of titles published annually: 5 Print; 1 CD-ROM
Total Titles: 48 Print; 3 CD-ROM
*Foreign Office(s):* Cankarjeva c, 15b, Bled, Slovenia

**Statistics Canada**
Subsidiary of Canadian Government
150 Tunney's Pasture Driveway, Ottawa, ON K1A 0T6
*Tel:* 613-951-8116 (gen inquiries)
*Toll Free Tel:* 800-263-1136 (CN & US, gen inquiries); 800-267-6677 (prods & servs)
*Fax:* 613-951-0581 *Toll Free Fax:* 877-287-4369 (orders)
*E-mail:* infostats@statcan.gc.ca
*Web Site:* statcan.gc.ca
*Key Personnel*
Dir Gen: Claude Graziadie *Tel:* 613-951-1518 *Fax:* 613-951-0288
Founded: 1919
Federal government's principal data collection agency in Canada. Collects, analyzes & publishes statistical information on Canada's population, labor force, economy, education, housing, transportation & social cultural life. One of Canada's largest publishers, producing over 300 books a year.
Publishes in English, French.
ISBN Prefix(es): 978-0-660
Number of titles published annually: 60 Print
Total Titles: 300 Print; 1,013 CD-ROM; 1,764 Online
*Returns:* Distribution Ctr, Main Bldg, Rm 0505, Ottawa, ON K1A 0T6

**Sumach Press**
Imprint of Three O'Clock Press
425 Adelaide St W, Suite 200, Toronto, ON M5V 3C1
*Tel:* 416-929-2964 *Fax:* 416-929-1926
*E-mail:* info@sumachpress.com
*Web Site:* threeoclockpress.com
*Key Personnel*
Publr: Sarah Wayne
Founded: 2000
Presents writings by & about women.
Publishes in English.
ISBN Prefix(es): 978-1-896764; 978-1-894549; 978-0-929005
Number of titles published annually: 4 Print
Total Titles: 95 Print
*Sales Office(s):* Georgetown Terminal Warehouses, 34 Armstrong Ave, Georgetown, ON L7G 4R9 *Tel:* 905-873-2750 *Fax:* 905-873-6170 *E-mail:* orders@gtwcanada.com
Orca Book Publishers, PO Box 468, Custer, WA 98240-0468, United States *Toll Free Tel:* 800-210-5277 *Toll Free Fax:* 877-408-1551 *E-mail:* orca@orcabook.com *Web Site:* www.orcabook.com
Distributed by Orca Book Publishers (young adult titles in US)
*Billing Address:* Georgetown Terminal Warehouses, 34 Armstrong Ave, Georgetown, ON L7G 4R9 *Tel:* 905-873-2750 *Fax:* 905-873-6170 *E-mail:* orders@gtwcanada.com; Orca Book Publishers, PO Box 468, Custer, WA 98240-0468, United States *Toll Free Tel:* 800-210-5277 *Toll Free Fax:* 877-408-1551 *E-mail:* orca@orcabook.com *Web Site:* www.orcabook.com
*Orders to:* Georgetown Terminal Warehouses, 34 Armstrong Ave, Georgetown, ON L7G 4R9 *Tel:* 905-873-2750 *Fax:* 905-873-6170 *E-mail:* orders@gtwcanada.com; Orca Book Publishers, PO Box 468, Custer, WA 98240-0468, United States *Toll Free Tel:* 800-210-5277 *Toll Free Fax:* 877-408-1551 *E-mail:* orca@orcabook.com *Web Site:* www.orcabook.com; Gazelle Book Services Ltd, White Cross Mills, Hightown, Lancaster LA1 4XS, United Kingdom *Tel:* (01524) 68765 *Fax:* (01524) 63232 *E-mail:* sales@gazellebooks.co.uk
*Returns:* Georgetown Terminal Warehouses, 34 Armstrong Ave, Georgetown, ON L7G 4R9 *Tel:* 905-873-2750 *Fax:* 905-873-6170 *E-mail:* orders@gtwcanada.com; Orca Book Publishers, PO Box 468, Custer, WA 98240-0468, United States *Toll Free Tel:* 800-210-5277 *Toll Free Fax:* 877-408-1551 *E-mail:* orca@orcabook.com *Web Site:* www.orcabook.com
*Shipping Address:* Georgetown Terminal Warehouses, 34 Armstrong Ave, Georgetown, ON L7G 4R9 *Tel:* 905-873-2750 *Fax:* 905-873-6170 *E-mail:* orders@gtwcanada.com; Orca Book Publishers, PO Box 468, Custer, WA 98240-0468, United States *Toll Free Tel:* 800-210-5277 *Toll Free Fax:* 877-408-1551 *E-mail:* orca@orcabook.com *Web Site:* www.orcabook.com
*Warehouse:* Georgetown Terminal Warehouses, 34 Armstrong Ave, Georgetown, ON L7G 4R9 *Tel:* 905-873-2750 *Fax:* 905-873-6170 *E-mail:* orders@gtwcanada.com
Orca Book Publishers, PO Box 468, Custer, WA 98240-0468, United States *Toll Free Tel:* 800-210-5277 *Toll Free Fax:* 877-408-1551 *E-mail:* orca@orcabook.com *Web Site:* www.orcabook.com
*Distribution Center:* Georgetown Terminal Warehouses, 34 Armstrong Ave, Georgetown, ON L7G 4R9 *Tel:* 905-873-2750 *Fax:* 905-873-6170 *E-mail:* orders@gtwcanada.com
Orca Book Publishers, PO Box 468, Custer, WA 98240-0468, United States *Toll Free Tel:* 800-210-5277 *Toll Free Fax:* 877-408-1551 *E-mail:* orca@orcabook.com *Web Site:* www.orcabook.com
Membership(s): Association of Canadian Publishers; Organization of Book Publishers of Ontario

**Summerthought Publishing**
PO Box 2309, Banff, AB T1L 1C1
*Tel:* 403-762-0535 *Fax:* 403-762-3095
*Toll Free Fax:* 800-762-3095 (orders)
*E-mail:* info@summerthought.com; sales@summerthought.com
*Web Site:* www.summerthought.com
*Key Personnel*
Publr: Andrew Hempstead
Founded: 1971
Publisher of Canadian Rockies nonfiction books.
Publishes in English.
ISBN Prefix(es): 978-0-9782375; 978-0-9699732; 978-0-9811491
Number of titles published annually: 3 Print
Total Titles: 15 Print
Imprints: EJH Literary Enterprises
Foreign Rep(s): Cordee (UK); Freytag Berndt (Europe); Partners West (USA)
*Warehouse:* 536 Deer St, Banff, AB T1L 1C1

**Synaxis Press**
37323 Hawkins Pickle Rd, Dewdney, BC V0M 1H0
*Tel:* 604-826-9336
*E-mail:* synaxis@new-ostrog.org
*Web Site:* synaxispress.ca
*Key Personnel*
Illus: Vasili Novakshonoff
Ed: Lazar Puhalo
Founded: 1972
Theology for the Orthodox church & children's books.

Publishes in English, French.
ISBN Prefix(es): 978-0-919672
Number of titles published annually: 6 Print
Total Titles: 90 Print
Distributed by Light & Life Publishing Co

**TCP Press**
Imprint of The Communication Project
Legacy Ctr, 9 Lobraico Lane, Whitchurch-Stouffville, ON L4A 7X5
*Tel:* 905-640-8914 *Toll Free Tel:* 800-772-7765
*E-mail:* tcp@tcpnow.com
*Web Site:* www.tcppress.com
*Key Personnel*
Dir, Publg: Brian Puppa
Founded: 1984
Trade & educational books for both children & adults.
Publishes in English, French.
ISBN Prefix(es): 978-1-896232
Number of titles published annually: 4 Print; 1 CD-ROM; 5 E-Book; 1 Audio
Total Titles: 26 Print; 3 CD-ROM; 6 E-Book; 3 Audio
Membership(s): Independent Publishers Association

**Tecumseh Press**, see Borealis Press Ltd

**Theytus Books Ltd**
Subsidiary of Okanagan Indian Educational Resources Society
RR 2, Green Mountain Rd, Site 50, Comp 8, Lot 45, Penticton, BC V2A 6J7
SAN: 115-1517
*Tel:* 250-493-7181 *Fax:* 250-493-5302
*E-mail:* info@theytus.com
*Web Site:* www.theytus.com
*Key Personnel*
Publr: Anita Large
Founded: 1980
Native history, culture, politics & education & literature.
Publishes in English, French.
ISBN Prefix(es): 978-0-919441; 978-1-894778
Number of titles published annually: 8 Print; 2 CD-ROM
Total Titles: 68 Print; 3 CD-ROM
U.S. Rep(s):
*Advertising Agency:* Sandhill Book Marketing, Mill Crook Industrial Park, Unit 4, 3308 Appleosa Rd, Kelowna, BC V1V 2G9 (Alberta & BC only), Contact: Nancy Wise *Tel:* 250-491-1446 *Fax:* 250-491-4066 *E-mail:* info@sandhillbooks.com; University of Toronto Press, 5201 Dufferin St, North York, ON M3H 5T8 (rest of Canada) *Tel:* 416-667-7791 *Toll Free Tel:* 800-565-9523
Membership(s): Association of Canadian Publishers

**Thistledown Press**
118 20 St W, Saskatoon, SK S7N 0W6
SAN: 115-1061
*Tel:* 306-244-1722 *Fax:* 306-244-1762
*E-mail:* marketing@thistledownpress.com
*Web Site:* www.thistledownpress.com
*Key Personnel*
Owner & Publr: Allan Forrie
Publg & Prodn Mgr: Jackie Forrie
Founded: 1975
Poetry, fiction & nonfiction by Canadian authors; Irish poetry; fiction for young adults.
Publishes in English.
ISBN Prefix(es): 978-0-920066; 978-0-920633; 978-1-895449; 978-1-894345; 978-1-897235
Number of titles published annually: 14 Print
Total Titles: 250 Print
U.S. Rep(s): Amazon.com; Baker & Taylor; University of Toronto Press

*Distribution Center:* University of Toronto Press, 10 St Mary St, Suite 700, Toronto, ON M4Y 2W8 *Tel:* 416-978-2239 *Fax:* 416-978-4738 *Web Site:* www.utpress.utoronto.ca

**Thompson Educational Publishing Inc**
20 Ripley Ave, Toronto, ON M6S 3N9
*Tel:* 416-766-2763 (admin & orders) *Toll Free Tel:* 877-366-2763 *Fax:* 416-766-0398 (admin & orders)
*E-mail:* publisher@thompsonbooks.com
*Web Site:* www.thompsonbooks.com
*Key Personnel*
Pres: Keith Thompson
Founded: 1987
High school, college & university textbooks.
Publishes in English.
ISBN Prefix(es): 978-1-55077; 978-0-921332
Number of titles published annually: 6 Print
Total Titles: 90 Print
*Distribution Center:* UTP, 2250 Military Rd, Tonawanda, NY 14150, United States *Toll Free Tel:* 800-565-9523 *Toll Free Fax:* 800-221-9985 *E-mail:* utpbooks@utpress.utoronto.ca
Membership(s): Association of Canadian Publishers; Organization of Book Publishers of Ontario

**Thomson Groupe Modulo**
5800 Rue Saint-Denis, Bureau 1102, Montreal, QC H2S 3L5
*Tel:* 514-738-9818 *Toll Free Tel:* 888-738-9818 *Fax:* 514-738-5838 *Toll Free Fax:* 888-273-5247
*Web Site:* www.groupemodulo.com
*Key Personnel*
Gen Dir: Jean Bouchard
Translation: Dominique Lefort
Founded: 1975
School books, dictionaries, children's books, professional & technical textbooks.
Publishes in English, French.
ISBN Prefix(es): 978-2-8959
Number of titles published annually: 100 Print

**Tormont Publishing International**
Subsidiary of Kidzup Productions Inc
3305 Pitfield Blvd, St-Laurent, QC H4S 1H3
*Tel:* 514-954-1441 *Fax:* 514-954-1443
*Key Personnel*
Edit Dir: Danielle Robichaud *Tel:* 514-954-1441 ext 116
Ed: Sheima Benembarek
Founded: 1984
Our award winning educational music CDs have sold millions world wide. Our CDs teach early learning concepts to young children through music. Our teacher resources consist of award winning flash card kits, activity books with CD, DVDs & CDs. A wide variety of subjects including reading, writing, spelling, math, French, Spanish & much more are covered. Our books are innovative books formats combined with informative, educational & entertainment. They incorporate activities, puzzles, games, pianos, etc to challenge children's observation skills & intelligence. A wide variety of subjects including history, science, classics, educational & much more are covered.
Publishes in English, French.
ISBN Prefix(es): 978-2-921171; 978-2-920845; 978-0-760786
Number of titles published annually: 20 Print
Total Titles: 220 Print
Imprints: Kidzup Productions Inc; Tormont
Divisions: Product & Technology International

**TouchWood Editions**
103-1075 Pendergast St, Victoria, BC V8V 0A1
*Tel:* 250-360-0829 *Fax:* 250-386-0829
*E-mail:* info@touchwoodeditions.com
*Web Site:* www.touchwoodeditions.com
*Key Personnel*
Publr: Ruth Linka *E-mail:* ruth@touchwoodeditions.com
Founded: 1985
Publishes in English.
ISBN Prefix(es): 978-1-894898; 978-1-926741; 978-1-926971
Number of titles published annually: 12 Print; 18 E-Book
Total Titles: 224 Print; 170 E-Book
Foreign Rep(s): Gazelle (UK); Midpoint Sales (USA)
Foreign Rights: Acacia House (Bill Hanna)
*Orders to:* Heritage Group Distribution, 19272-96 Ave, Suite 8, Surrey, BC V4N 4C1 *Tel:* 604-881-7067 *Fax:* 604-881-7068 *E-mail:* orders@hgdistribution.com *Web Site:* www.hgdistribution.com
*Returns:* Heritage Group Distribution, 19272-96 Ave, Suite 8, Surrey, BC V4N 4C1 *Tel:* 604-881-7067 *Fax:* 604-881-7068 *E-mail:* orders@hgdistribution.com *Web Site:* www.hgdistribution.com
*Shipping Address:* Heritage Group Distribution, 19272-96 Ave, Suite 8, Surrey, BC V4N 4C1 *Tel:* 604-881-7067 *Fax:* 604-881-7068 *E-mail:* orders@hgdistribution.com *Web Site:* www.hgdistribution.com
*Warehouse:* Heritage Group Distribution, 19272-96 Ave, Suite 8, Surrey, BC V4N 4C1 *Tel:* 604-881-7067 *Fax:* 604-881-7068 *E-mail:* orders@hgdistribution.com *Web Site:* www.hgdistribution.com
*Distribution Center:* Heritage Group Distribution, 19272-96 Ave, Suite 8, Surrey, BC V4N 4C1 *Tel:* 604-881-7067 *Fax:* 604-881-7068 *E-mail:* orders@hgdistribution.com *Web Site:* www.hgdistribution.com
Membership(s): Association of Book Publishers of British Columbia; Association of Canadian Publishers

**Townson Publishing Co Ltd**
Affiliate of General Publishing Inc
PO Box 1404, Sta A, Vancouver, BC V6C 2P7
Mailing Address: PO Box 909, Blaine, WA 98231-0909, United States
*Tel:* 604 886 0594 (CN)
*E-mail:* townsonpublishing@gmail.com
*Web Site:* generalpublishing.co.uk
*Key Personnel*
Publr: Donald Townson
Founded: 1977
General trade books, literature in translation.
Publishes in English, French.
Number of titles published annually: 6 Print; 6 E-Book
Total Titles: 16 Print; 16 E-Book
Imprints: General Publishing; Townson Publishing; translatedbooks.com
Subsidiaries: Associated Merchandisers Inc (USA)
Foreign Rep(s): Associated Merchandisers Inc (UK, USA)

**Tradewind Books**
202-1807 Maritime Mews, Vancouver, BC V6H 3W7
*Fax:* 604-662-4405
*E-mail:* tradewindbooks@telus.net
*Web Site:* www.tradewindbooks.com
*Key Personnel*
Publr: Michael Katz *E-mail:* tradewindbooks@yahoo.com
Ed: Alison Acheson; Cynthia Nugent; R David Stephens; MaryAnn Thompson
Founded: 1994
Children's picture books, chapter books & young adults novels.
Publishes in English.
ISBN Prefix(es): 978-1-896580
Number of titles published annually: 8 Print
Total Titles: 65 Print

*Foreign Office(s):* Turnaround, Olympia Trading Estate, Unit 3, Coburg Rd, Wood Green, London N22 6TZ, United Kingdom *Tel:* (020) 8829-3000 *Fax:* (020) 8881-5088 *E-mail:* orders@turnaround-uk.com *Web Site:* www.turnaround-uk.com
Distributed by Fitzhenry & Whiteside (CN)
U.S. Rep(s): Orca Books
Foreign Rep(s): Tracey Dettman (Atlantic Canada, Ontario, Quebec, CN); Fitzhenry & Whiteside (Canada); Heather Parsons (Alberta, British Columbia, Manitoba, Saskatchewan); Penny Taylor (Atlantic Canada, Ontario, Quebec, CN); Jeff Wallace (Alberta, British Columbia, Manitoba, Saskatchewan, Western Canada)
*Orders to:* Fitzhenry & Whiteside, 195 Allstate Pkwy, Markham, ON L3R 4T8, Sonya Gillis *Tel:* 905-477-9700 *Toll Free Tel:* 800-387-9776 *Toll Free Fax:* 800-260-9777 *E-mail:* bookinfo@fitzhenry.ca *Web Site:* www.fitzhenry.ca
*Distribution Center:* Orca Books, PO Box 468, Custer, WA 98240-0468, United States (for US) *Toll Free Tel:* 800-210-5277 *Toll Free Fax:* 877-408-1551 *E-mail:* orca@orcabook.com
John Reed Book Distribution, Winbourne Estate, Unit 4-F, 9 Winbourne Rd, Brookvale, NSW 2100, Australia *Tel:* (02) 9939 3041 *Fax:* (02) 9453 4545 *E-mail:* johnmreed@johnreedbooks.com
Membership(s): Association of Book Publishers of British Columbia; Association of Canadian Publishers; Literary Press Group

**Tribal Trails Books & Resources**
Formerly Northern Canada Mission Distributors
Division of Northern Canada Evangelical Mission
PO Box 3030, Prince Albert, SK S6V 7V4
*Tel:* 306-764-4490 *Fax:* 306-764-3390
*E-mail:* missiondist@ncem.ca
*Web Site:* www.ncem.ca
*Key Personnel*
Bookstore Mgr: Lydia Goede
Founded: 1967
Publish books, pamphlets, tracts, Bibles, audio CDs. Subject specialty is native North American literature.
Publishes in English, French.
ISBN Prefix(es): 978-1-920731; 978-1-896968
Number of titles published annually: 3 Print
Total Titles: 111 Print
Membership(s): CBA: The Association for Christian Retail

**TSAR Publications**
PO Box 6996, Sta A, Toronto, ON M5W 1X7
*Tel:* 416-483-7191 *Fax:* 416-486-0706
*E-mail:* inquiries@tsarbooks.com
*Web Site:* www.tsarbooks.com
*Key Personnel*
Publr & Intl Rts: Ms Nurjehan Aziz *E-mail:* naziz@tsarbooks.com
Founded: 1985
Canadian literature, multicultural & international literature.
Publishes in English.
ISBN Prefix(es): 978-0-920661; 978-1-894770
Number of titles published annually: 8 Print
Total Titles: 101 Print
Imprints: TSAR
U.S. Rep(s): Small Press Distribution Inc, 1341 Seventh St, Berkeley, CA 94710, United States
*Distribution Center:* Small Press Distribution Inc, 1341 Seventh St, Berkeley, CA 94710, United States *Tel:* 510-524-1668 *Toll Free Tel:* 800-869-7553 *Fax:* 510-524-0852
Membership(s): Literary Press Group

**Tundra Books**
Division of McClelland & Stewart Ltd
One Toronto St, Suite 300, Toronto, ON M5C 2V6
SAN: 115-5415
*Tel:* 416-364-4449 *Toll Free Tel:* 888-523-9292 (orders); 800-588-1074 *Fax:* 416-598-0247 *Toll Free Fax:* 888-562-9924 (orders)
*E-mail:* tundra@mcclelland.com
*Web Site:* www.tundrabooks.com
*Key Personnel*
Publr: Kathy Lowinger *E-mail:* klowinger@mcclelland.com
Edit Dir: Tara Walker *Tel:* 416-364-4449 ext 813951
Mng Dir: Alison Morgan *Tel:* 416-598-4786 *E-mail:* amorgan@mcclelland.com
Founded: 1967
Children's books.
Publishes in English, French.
ISBN Prefix(es): 978-0-88776
Number of titles published annually: 50 Print
Total Titles: 350 Print
*Branch Office(s)*
Tundra Books of Northern New York, PO Box 1030, Plattsburgh, NY 12901, United States *Toll Free Tel:* 800-733-3000
Distributed by Everybody's Books Co; Forrester Books NZ Ltd; El Hombre de la Mancha; El Hormiguero; Prolongue Inc
U.S. Publishers Represented: Tundra Books of Northern New York
U.S. Rep(s): Jack Eichkorn & Associates Inc; R&R Book Co; Southern Territory Associates Inc; Nancy Suib & Associates
Foreign Rights: Cooke Agency International
*Orders to:* Random House of Canada Limited, 2775 Matheson Blvd E, Mississauga, ON L4W 4P7; Random House Inc - Distribution Center, 400 Hahn Rd, Westminster, MD 21157, United States *Toll Free Tel:* 800-726-0600 *Toll Free Fax:* 800-659-2436
*Returns:* Random House Inc, 1019 N State Rd 47, Crawfordsville, IN 47933, United States
*Warehouse:* Random House Inc - Distribution Center, 400 Hahn Rd, Westminster, MD 21157, United States *Toll Free Tel:* 800-726-0600 *Toll Free Fax:* 800-659-2436
Membership(s): ABA; ALA; Association of Booksellers for Children; International Board on Books for Young People

**Turnstone Press**
100 Arthur St, Unit 206, Winnipeg, MB R3B 1H3
SAN: 115-1096
*Tel:* 204-947-1555 *Toll Free Tel:* 888-363-7718 *Fax:* 204-942-1555
*E-mail:* info@turnstonepress.com
*Web Site:* www.turnstonepress.com
*Key Personnel*
Assoc Publr & Intl Rts: Jamis Paulson
Founded: 1976
Literary press including fiction, nonfiction, poetry, literary criticism, biography, travel fiction & adventure all with a strong Canadian focus.
Publishes in English.
ISBN Prefix(es): 978-0-88801
Number of titles published annually: 10 Print
Total Titles: 300 Print
Imprints: Ravenstone Books
*Distribution Center:* Fraser Direct, 100 Armstrong Ave, Georgetown, ON L7G 5S4 *Tel:* 905-877-4411

**UBC Press**, see University of British Columbia Press

**UCCB Press**, see Cape Breton University Press Inc (CBU Press)

**Ulysses Travel Guides**
4176 Saint Denis St, Montreal, QC H2W 2M5
*Tel:* 514-843-9447 (bookstore) *Fax:* 514-843-9448
*E-mail:* info@ulysses.ca
*Web Site:* www.ulyssesguides.com
*Key Personnel*
Pres: Daniel Desjardins *Tel:* 514-843-9447 ext 2224 *E-mail:* daniel@ulysses.ca
VP, Sales & Mktg: Claude Morneau *E-mail:* claude@ulysses.ca
Founded: 1980
Travel books.
Publishes in English, French.
ISBN Prefix(es): 978-2-921444; 978-2-89464
Number of titles published annually: 25 Print; 25 E-Book; 2 Audio
Total Titles: 175 Print; 175 E-Book; 2 Audio
Imprints: Guides de Voyage Ulyses; Ulysses Travel Guides
Distributor for A A Publications; Dakota; Footprint Handbooks; Editions Syvain Harvey; Hunter Publishing; ITMB Publishing Ltd; Odyssey Publications; PassPorter Travel Press; Rother Walking Guides; Trans Canada Trail Foundation; Vacation Works Publications

**University of Alberta Press**
Ring House 2, Edmonton, AB T6G 2E1
SAN: 118-9794
*Tel:* 780-492-3662 *Fax:* 780-492-0719
*Web Site:* www.uap.ualberta.ca
*Key Personnel*
Dir: Linda Cameron *Tel:* 780-492-0717 *E-mail:* linda.cameron@ualberta.ca
Mng Ed: Mary Lou Roy *Tel:* 780-492-9488 *E-mail:* marylou.roy@ualberta.ca
Acq Ed: Peter Midgley *Tel:* 780-492-7714 *E-mail:* pmidgley@ualberta.ca
Sales & Mktg Mgr: Cathie Crooks *Tel:* 780-492-5820 *E-mail:* ccrooks@ualberta.ca
Prodn & Designer: Alan Brownoff *Tel:* 780-492-8285 *E-mail:* abrownof@ualberta.ca
Off Mgr: Sharon Wilson *E-mail:* sharon.wilson@ualberta.ca
Founded: 1969
The UAP publishes in the areas of biography, history, language, literature, natural history, regional interest, native studies, travel narratives & reference books. UAP contributes to the intellectual & cultural life of Alberta & Canada by publishing well-edited, research-based knowledge & creative thought.
Publishes in English.
ISBN Prefix(es): 978-0-88864
Number of titles published annually: 25 Print; 10 E-Book
Total Titles: 260 Print; 44 E-Book; 1 Audio
U.S. Rep(s): Wayne State University Press
Foreign Rep(s): Gazelle Academic (Europe, South Africa, UK)
*Orders to:* Georgetown Terminal Warehouses, 34 Armstrong Ave, Georgetown, ON L7G 4R9 *Tel:* 905-873-9781 *Toll Free Tel:* 877-864-8477 *Fax:* 905-873-6170 *Toll Free Fax:* 877-864-4272 *E-mail:* orders@gtwcanada.com *Web Site:* gtwcanada.com
*Returns:* Georgetown Terminal Warehouses, 34 Armstrong Ave, Georgetown, ON L7G 4R9 *Tel:* 905-873-9781 *Toll Free Tel:* 877-864-8477 *Fax:* 905-873-6170 *Toll Free Fax:* 877-864-4272 *E-mail:* orders@gtwcanada.com *Web Site:* gtwcanada.com
*Shipping Address:* Georgetown Terminal Warehouses, 34 Armstrong Ave, Georgetown, ON L7G 4R9 *Tel:* 905-873-9781 *Toll Free Tel:* 877-864-8477 *Fax:* 905-873-6170 *Toll Free Fax:* 877-864-4272 *E-mail:* orders@gtwcanada.com *Web Site:* gtwcanada.com
*Warehouse:* Georgetown Terminal Warehouses, 34 Armstrong Ave, Georgetown, ON L7G 4R9 *Tel:* 905-873-9781 *Toll Free Tel:* 877-864-8477 *Fax:* 905-873-6170 *Toll Free Fax:* 877-864-4272 *E-mail:* orders@gtwcanada.com *Web Site:* gtwcanada.com
*Distribution Center:* Georgetown Terminal Warehouses, 34 Armstrong Ave, Georgetown,

ON L7G 4R9 *Tel:* 905-873-9781 *Toll Free Tel:* 877-864-8477 *Fax:* 905-873-6170 *Toll Free Fax:* 877-864-4272 *E-mail:* orders@gtwcanada.com *Web Site:* gtwcanada.com
Membership(s): Association of American University Presses; Association of Canadian Publishers; Association of Canadian University Presses; Book Publishers Association of Alberta

**University of British Columbia Press**
2029 West Mall, Vancouver, BC V6T 1Z2
SAN: 115-1118
*Tel:* 604-822-5959 *Toll Free Tel:* 877-377-9378 *Fax:* 604-822-6083 *Toll Free Fax:* 800-668-0821
*E-mail:* frontdesk@ubcpress.ca
*Web Site:* www.ubcpress.ca
*Key Personnel*
Dir: Melissa Pitts *Tel:* 604-822-6376 *E-mail:* pitts@ubcpress.ca
Asst Dir, Fin & Opers: Devni De Silva *Tel:* 604-822-8938 *E-mail:* desilva@ubcpress.ca
Asst Dir, Prodn & Edit Servs: Holly Keller *Tel:* 604-822-4545 *E-mail:* keller@ubcpress.ca
Sr Ed (Kelowna): Randy Schmidt *Tel:* 250-764-4761 *Fax:* 250-764-4709 *E-mail:* schmidt@ubcpress.ca
Sr Ed (Toronto): Emily Andrew *Tel:* 416-429-0322 *E-mail:* andrew@ubcpress.ca
Acqs Ed (Vancouver): Darcy Cullen *Tel:* 604-822-5744 *E-mail:* cullen@ubcpress.ca
Academic Mktg Mgr: Elizabeth Whitton *Tel:* 604-822-8226 *E-mail:* whitton@ubcpress.ca
Mgr, Exhibits, Reviews & Awards: Kerry Kilmartin *Tel:* 604-822-8244 *E-mail:* kilmartin@ubcpress.ca
Mgr, Inventory Data & Dist: Shari Martin *Tel:* 604-822-1221 *E-mail:* martin@ubcpress.ca
Mktg Mgr: Laraine Coates *Tel:* 604-822-6486
Ed: Megan Brand; Leslie Erickson; Ann MacKlem
Academic Mktg Mgr: Harmony Johnson *Tel:* 604-822-1978 *E-mail:* johnson@ubcpress.ca
Graphic Designer: Honey Mae Caffin *Tel:* 604-822-4546 *E-mail:* caffin@ubcpress.ca
Founded: 1971
Academic & scholarly publications; native studies, law & society, military history, northern studies, sexuality, political science & forestry.
Publishes in English.
ISBN Prefix(es): 978-0-7748
Number of titles published annually: 40 Print
Total Titles: 700 Print; 2 CD-ROM; 1 E-Book
Imprints: UBC Press
*Branch Office(s)*
587 Markham St, 2nd fl, Toronto, ON M6G 2L7 *Fax:* 416-535-9677
Distributed by University of Washington Press (US)
Distributor for Brookings Institution Press; Canadian Forest Service (worldwide); Canadian Wildlife Service (worldwide); Cavendish Publishing (UK); Earthscan; Edinboro University Press; Environmental Training Center; Hong Kong University Press; Jessica Kingsley Publishers; Manchester University Press; Oregon State University Press; Paradigm Publishers; Royal BC Museum (worldwide); Transaction Publishers; University of Arizona Press; University of Washington Press (includes Hong Kong UP, KITLV Press, National Gallery of Australia Press, Silkworm Books, UCLA Fowler Museum of Cultural History & Waanders Publishers); Washington State University Press; Western Geographical Press (worldwide); University of New England Press
U.S. Publishers Represented: Berghahn Books; Brookings Institution Press; Hong Kong University Press; Island Press; Jessica Kingsley Publishers; Manchester University Press; Oregon State University Press; Paradigm Publishers; Transaction Publishers; Tufts University Press; University of Arizona Press; University of Washington Press (includes Hong Kong UP, KITLV Press, National Gallery of Australia Press, Silkworm Books, UCLA Fowler Museum of Cultural History & Waanders Publishers); University Press of New England (includes Brandeis University Press, Dartmouth College Press, Northeastern University Press, University of New Hampshire Press & University of Vermont Press); Wesleyan University Press
U.S. Rep(s): University of Washington Press
Foreign Rep(s): Asia Publishers Services (Hong Kong, Singapore, Taiwan); East-West Export (Asia, Australia, Japan, New Zealand); Eurospan (Africa, Europe, Middle East, UK)
*Shipping Address:* UNI Press, 34 Armstrong Ave, Georgetown, ON L7G 4R9 *Tel:* 905-873-9781 *Toll Free Tel:* 877-864-8477 *Fax:* 905-873-6170 *Toll Free Fax:* 877-864-4272 *E-mail:* orders@gtwcanada.com
*Distribution Center:* 5201 Dufferin St, Toronto, ON M3H 5T8 *E-mail:* utpbooks@utpress.utoronto.ca

**University of Calgary Press**
2500 University Dr NW, Calgary, AB T2N 1N4
*Tel:* 403-220-7578 *Fax:* 403-282-0085
*Web Site:* www.uofcpress.com
*Key Personnel*
Dir: Donna Livingstone *Tel:* 403-220-3511 *E-mail:* livingsd@ucalgary.ca
Journals Mgr: Judy Powell *Tel:* 403-220-3512 *E-mail:* powell@ucalgary.ca
Mktg Assoc: Karen Buttner *Tel:* 403-220-3979 *E-mail:* kbuttner@ucalgary.ca
Founded: 1981
Specializing in scholarly books that make a difference. Series subjects include history, parks & protected areas, regional history, Northern studies, Africa, cinema studies, cultural studies, Canadian military & military history & communications studies.
Publishes in English, French.
ISBN Prefix(es): 978-0-919813; 978-1-895176; 978-1-55238
Number of titles published annually: 20 Print; 2 CD-ROM; 10 Online; 20 E-Book
Total Titles: 400 Print; 5 CD-ROM; 25 Online; 150 E-Book
*Sales Office(s):* Canada uniPRESSES, c/o Georgetown Terminal Warehouses, 34 Armstrong Ave, Georgetown, ON L7G 4R9 (World exc UK & Europe)
*Foreign Office(s):* Gazelle Book Services, White Cross Mills, High Town, Lancaster LA1 4XS, United Kingdom *Tel:* (020) 1524 68765 *Fax:* (020) 1524 63232
Distributor for Michigan State University Press
U.S. Rep(s): Michigan State University Press *Tel:* 517-355-9543 *Fax:* 517-432-2611 *Toll Free Fax:* 800-678-2120 *E-mail:* msupress@msu.edu
Foreign Rep(s): Gazelle (Europe, UK)
Foreign Rights: Roli Books (New Delhi)
*Billing Address:* Canada uniPRESSES, c/o Georgetown Terminal Warehouses, 34 Armstrong Ave, Georgetown, ON L7G 4R9 (World exc UK & Europe)
*Orders to:* Canada uniPRESSES, c/o Georgetown Terminal Warehouses, 34 Armstrong Ave, Georgetown, ON L7G 4R9 (World exc UK & Europe) *Toll Free Tel:* 877-864-8477 *Toll Free Fax:* 877-864-4272 *E-mail:* orders@gtwcanada.com
*Returns:* Canada uniPRESSES, c/o Georgetown Terminal Warehouses, 34 Armstrong Ave, Georgetown, ON L7G 4R9 (World exc UK & Europe) *Toll Free Tel:* 877-864-8477 *Toll Free Fax:* 877-864-4272
*Distribution Center:* Canada uniPRESSES, c/o Georgetown Terminal Warehouses, 34 Armstrong Ave, Georgetown, ON L7G 4R9 (World exc UK & Europe) *Tel:* 905-873-2750 *Toll Free Tel:* 877-864-8477 *Toll Free Fax:* 877-864-4272 *E-mail:* orders@gtwcanada.com
Membership(s): Association for Canadian Publishers in the US; Association of Canadian Publishers; Book Publishers Association of Alberta

**University of Manitoba Press**
University of Manitoba, 301 St Johns College, Winnipeg, MB R3T 2M5
SAN: 115-5474
*Tel:* 204-474-9495 *Fax:* 204-474-7566
*Web Site:* www.umanitoba.ca/uofmpress
*Key Personnel*
Dir: David Carr *Tel:* 204-474-9242 *E-mail:* carr@cc.umanitoba.ca
Mng Ed: Glenn Bergen *Tel:* 204-474-7338 *E-mail:* bergeng@cc.umanitoba.ca
Founded: 1967
Scholarly & general titles in humanities & social sciences; western Canadian history & native studies.
Publishes in English.
ISBN Prefix(es): 978-0-88755
Number of titles published annually: 8 Print
Total Titles: 120 Print
Distributed by University of Toronto Press (Canadian sales); Michigan State University Press (US sales)
*Shipping Address:* University of Toronto Press, 5201 Dufferin St, Toronto, ON M3H 5T8 *Tel:* 416-667-7791 *Toll Free Tel:* 800-565-9523 *Fax:* 416-667-7832 *Toll Free Fax:* 800-221-9985 *E-mail:* utpbooks@utpress.utoronto.ca; Michigan State University Press, 1405 S Harrison Rd, Suite 25, East Lansing, MI 48823, United States *Tel:* 517-355-9543 *Toll Free Fax:* 800-678-2120 *Web Site:* www.msupress.msu.edu

**University of Ottawa Press (Presses de l'Université d'Ottawa)**
Affiliate of University of Ottawa
542 King Edward Ave, Ottawa, ON K1N 6N5
*Tel:* 613-562-5246 *Fax:* 613-562-5247
*E-mail:* puo-oup@uottawa.ca
*Web Site:* www.press.uottawa.ca
*Key Personnel*
Dir: Lara Mainville *Tel:* 613-562-5663 *E-mail:* lara.mainville@uottawa.ca
Prodn Mgr: Marie Clausen *Tel:* 613-562-5800 ext 3064 *E-mail:* msec@uottawa.ca
Mktg Mgr: Jessica Clark *Tel:* 613-562-5800 ext 1311 *E-mail:* jessica.clark@uottawa.ca
Founded: 1936
Scholarly & trade books. University of Ottawa Press is the oldest francophone university press & only bilingual university press in North America.
Publishes in English, French.
ISBN Prefix(es): 978-0-7766; 978-2-7603
Number of titles published annually: 15 Print; 15 E-Book
Total Titles: 400 Print; 200 E-Book
Foreign Rep(s): CEDIF (France); Durnell Marketing (Europe exc UK); Lexa Publishers' Representatives (Canada (English-speaking)); Nouvelle Diffusion (Belgium); Oxford Publicity Partnership Ltd (UK); Prologue Inc (Canada (French-speaking)); Servidis (Switzerland)
*Distribution Center:* University of Toronto Press (UTP), 2250 Military Rd, Tonawanda, NY 14150, United States (English titles-US) *Toll Free Tel:* 800-565-9523 *Toll Free Fax:* 800-221-9985 *E-mail:* uptbooks@utpress.utoronto.ca *Web Site:* www.uptpress.utoronto.ca
University of Toronto Press (UTP), 5201 Dufferin St, North York, ON M3M 5T8 (English titles - CN) *Toll Free Tel:* 800-565-9523 *Toll Free Fax:* 800-221-9985 *E-mail:* utpbooks@utpress.utoronto.ca *Web Site:* www.utpress.utoronto.ca
Prologue Inc, 1650 boul Lionel-Bertrand, Boisbriand, QC J7H 1N7 (titles in French-

CN) *Tel:* 450-434-0306 *Toll Free Tel:* 800-363-2864 *Toll Free Fax:* 800-361-8088 *E-mail:* prologue@prologue.ca *Web Site:* www.prologue.ca
Distribution du Nouveau Monde, 30 rue Guy Lussac, 75005 Paris, France (titles in French - France, Belgium & Luxembourg) *Tel:* (01) 43 54 49 02 *Fax:* (01) 43 54 39 15 *E-mail:* dnm@librairieduquebec.fr *Web Site:* www.librairieduquebec.fr
Servidis SA, Chemin des Chalets, 1279 Chavannes-de-Bogis, Switzerland (titles in French-Switzerland) *Tel:* (022) 960 95 25 *Fax:* (022) 776 63 64 *E-mail:* commande@servidis.ch *Web Site:* www.servidis.ch
Marston Book Services Ltd, 160 Milton Park, Abingdon, Oxon OX14 4YN, United Kingdom (English titles - UK & Europe) *Tel:* (01235) 465521 *Fax:* (01235) 465555 *E-mail:* direct.orders@marston.co.uk *Web Site:* www.marston.co.uk
Membership(s): American Association of University Presses; ANEL; Association of Canadian Publishers; Association of Canadian University Presses

**§University of Toronto Press Inc**
Division of Multicultural History Society of Canada
10 Saint Mary St, Suite 700, Toronto, ON M4Y 2W8
*Tel:* 416-978-2239 *Fax:* 416-978-4738
*E-mail:* utpbooks@utpress.utoronto.ca
*Web Site:* www.utpress.utoronto.ca; www.utppublishing.com
*Key Personnel*
CEO & Pres: John Yates *Tel:* 416-667-7791 ext 222 *E-mail:* jyates@utpress.utoronto.ca
VP, Dist & MIS: Hamish Cameron *Tel:* 416-667-7773 *E-mail:* hcameron@utpress.utoronto.ca
VP, Higher Educ: Michael Harrison *Tel:* 519-837-0915 *Fax:* 519-767-1643 *E-mail:* mharrison@utphighereducation.com
VP, Journals: Anne Marie Corrigan *Tel:* 416-667-7838 *E-mail:* acorrigan@utpress.utoronto.ca
VP, Scholarly Publg: Lynn Fisher *Tel:* 416-978-2239 ext 243 *E-mail:* lfisher@utpress.utoronto.ca
Founded: 1901
Publisher, distributer & university bookstore.
Publishes in English.
ISBN Prefix(es): 978-0-8020; 978-1-4426
Number of titles published annually: 180 Print; 100 E-Book
Total Titles: 3,500 Print; 500 E-Book
Imprints: Rotman-UTP Publishing; University of Toronto
Divisions: University of Toronto Press Journals Division
*Branch Office(s)*
2250 Military Rd, Tonawanda, NY 14150, United States *Tel:* 716-693-2768 *Fax:* 716-693-2167
Distributor for Anvil Press; Ashlar House; Aspasia Books; Between the Lines; Black Rose Books; Canadian Museum of Nature; CAW/TCA Canada; Central European University Press KFT; Charter Press; Codasat Canada Ltd; Cornucopia Books; Dance Collection Danse; Dreamcatcher Publishing Co; Dundurn Group; G7 Funds; Goose Lane Editions; Great Plains Publications Ltd; Guernica Editions; Guidance Centre; Help...We've Got Kids; Integrative Leadership International Ltd; International Self-Council Press Ltd; ISSI; Jump Math; Kids Can Press; Knowledge Bureau; Lassonde Institute; Wilfrid Laurier University Press; Legas Publishing; Lobster Press Ltd; Mage Publishers; Manor House Publishing Inc; McDonald & Woodward Books; McGilligan Books; Multilingual Matters; National Museum of Science & Technology; Newbridge Press; NYC Nonprofits Project; OISE Press; Oolichan Books; Owlkids Books; Pajama Press; Penn State University Press; Pippin Publishing Corp; Playwrights Canada; Porcupine's Quill; Royal Ontario Museum; Second Story Press; Secret Mountain; Seraphim Editions; J Gordon Shillingford Publishers Inc; Signature Editions; Sister Vision Press; Subway Books Ltd; Teachers College Press; Theytus Books; Thistledown Press; Thompson Educational Publishing; TSAR Publications; Twin Guinep Ltd; University of British Columbia Press; University of Manitoba Press; University of Ottawa Press; University of Toronto Press-Higher Education; University of Toronto Press-Scholary Publishing Division; Wolsak & Wynn Publishers
U.S. Rep(s): Collins/Terry Associates (southwest coast); Roger Sauls, Book Traveler (southeast); Ben Schrager (northeast); Trim Associates (midwest); UTP Higher Education (CN & US coll rep)
Foreign Rep(s): APAC Cassidy & Associates Publishers Inc (China, Hong Kong, Indonesia, Korea, Malaysia, Singapore, Taiwan, Thailand, Vietnam); Ethan Atkin (Caribbean, Central America, Pakistan, South America); James Bennett Pty Ltd (Australia, New Zealand); Durnell Marketing Ltd (Europe); Oxford Publicity Partnership Ltd (UK); Segment Book Distributors (India); TBD (Canada, Middle East, North Africa, Turkey); United Publishers Services (Japan)
*Orders to:* 2250 Military Rd, Tonawanda, NY 14150, United States *Tel:* 716-693-2768 *Fax:* 716-693-2167; 5201 Dufferin St, Toronto, ON M3H 5T8 *Tel:* 416-667-7791 *Toll Free Tel:* 800-565-9523 *Toll Free Fax:* 800-221-9985 *E-mail:* utpbooks@utpress.utoronto.ca; InBooks (James Bennett Pty Ltd), 3 Narabong Way, Belrose, NSW 2085, Australia *Tel:* (02) 9986-7037 *Fax:* (02) 9986-7090 *E-mail:* marketing@inbooks.com.au; NBN International, Airport Business Ctr, 10 Thornbury Rd, Plymouth, United Kingdom *Tel:* (01752) 202301 *Fax:* (01752) 202333 *E-mail:* orders@nbninternational.com
*Returns:* 5201 Dufferin St, Toronto, ON M3H 5T8
*Warehouse:* 2250 Military Rd, Tonawanda, NY 14150, United States
5201 Dufferin St, Toronto, ON M3H 5T8
*Distribution Center:* 5201 Dufferin St, Toronto, ON M3H 5T8 *Tel:* 416-667-7791 *Toll Free Tel:* 800-565-9523 *Fax:* 416-667-7832 *Toll Free Fax:* 800-221-9985 *E-mail:* utpbooks@utpress.utoronto.ca
Membership(s): American Association of University Presses; Association of Canadian Publishers; Association of Canadian University Presses; Organization of Book Publishers of Ontario

**Vehicule Press**
PO Box 125, Place du Park Sta, Montreal, QC H2X 4A3
*Tel:* 514-844-6073 *Fax:* 514-844-7543
*E-mail:* vp@vehiculepress.com; admin@vehiculepress.com
*Web Site:* www.vehiculepress.com
*Key Personnel*
Publr & Gen Ed: Simon Dardick; Nancy Marrelli
Mng Ed: Vicki Marcok
Ed, Esplanade Books: Andrew Steinmetz
Ed, Signal Editions: Carmine Starnino
Mktg & Promos Mgr: Maya Assouad
Founded: 1973
Paperback trade; fiction, jazz, biography, literature, poetry. translation.
Publishes in English.
ISBN Prefix(es): 978-0-919890; 978-1-55065
Number of titles published annually: 14 Print
Total Titles: 350 Print
Imprints: Esplanade Books (fiction); Signal Editions (poetry)
U.S. Rep(s): IPG (Independent Publishers Group)
*Returns:* LitDistCo, 100 Armstrong Ave, Georgetown, ON L7G 5S4 *Tel:* 905-877-4411 *Toll Free Tel:* 800-591-6250 *Fax:* 905-877-4410 *Toll Free Fax:* 800-591-6251
*Shipping Address:* LitDistCo, 100 Armstrong Ave, Georgetown, ON L7G 5S4 *Tel:* 905-877-4411 *Toll Free Tel:* 800-591-6250 *Fax:* 905-877-4410 *Toll Free Fax:* 800-591-6251
*Distribution Center:* LitDistCo, 100 Armstrong Ave, Georgetown, ON L7G 5S4 *Tel:* 905-877-4411 *Toll Free Tel:* 800-591-6250 *Fax:* 905-877-4410 *Toll Free Fax:* 800-591-6251
Membership(s): Association of Canadian Publishers; Literary Press Group

**VLB Editeur Inc**
Division of Le Groupe Ville-Marie Litterature
1010 rue de la Gauchetiere E, Montreal, QC H2L 2N5
*Tel:* 514-523-7993 *Fax:* 514-282-7530
*Web Site:* www.edvlb.com
*Key Personnel*
Pres: Pierre Lesperance
VP, Publg & Ed: Jean-Yves Soucy
Literary Dir for Essays: Robert Laliberte
Asst Ed: Sylvie Briere *E-mail:* sylvie.briere@sogides.com
Founded: 1976
Publishes in French.
ISBN Prefix(es): 978-2-89005
Number of titles published annually: 30 Print
Total Titles: 900 Print
*Distribution Center:* 2315 Rue De La Province, Longueuil, QC J4G 1G4

**Weigl Educational Publishers Ltd**
6325 Tenth St SE, Calgary, AB T2H 2Z9
SAN: 115-1312
*Tel:* 403-233-7747 *Toll Free Tel:* 800-668-0766 *Fax:* 403-233-7769 *Toll Free Fax:* 866-449-3445
*E-mail:* info@weigl.com; orders@weigl.com
*Web Site:* www.weigl.ca; www.weigl.com
*Key Personnel*
Pres & Publr: Linda Weigl *E-mail:* linda@weigl.com
Founded: 1979
School library resources & textbooks for grades K-12 in English & French. Emphasis on: Canadian history, social studies & public affairs; science; multiculturalism; career/vocational/life management; distance education; books & guides for teachers.
Publishes in English.
ISBN Prefix(es): 978-0-919879; 978-1-896990; 978-1-55388
Number of titles published annually: 40 Print
Total Titles: 200 Print
*Branch Office(s)*
350 Fifth Ave, 59th fl, New York, NY 10118, United States *Toll Free Tel:* 866-649-3445 *Toll Free Fax:* 866-449-3445
Distributed by The Creative Co (United States); Rourke Publishing; Saunders Book Co (Canada); Smart Apple Media (United States)

**Whitecap Books Ltd**
314 W Cordova St, Suite 210, Vancouver, BC V6B 1E8
*Tel:* 604-681-6181 *Toll Free Tel:* 800-387-9776 *Toll Free Fax:* 800-260-9777
*Web Site:* www.whitecap.ca
*Key Personnel*
Pres: Nick Rundall *Tel:* 905-477-9700 ext 244 *E-mail:* nickr@whitecap.ca
Assoc Publr: Jesse Marchand *Tel:* 604-681-6181 ext 202 *E-mail:* jessem@whitecap.ca
Ed: Theresa Best *Tel:* 604-681-6181 ext 204 *E-mail:* theresab@whitecap.ca
Art Dir: Michelle Furbacher *Tel:* 604-681-6181 ext 203 *E-mail:* michellef@whitecap.ca

Publicist: Jeffrey Bryan *Tel:* 604-681-6181 ext 201 *E-mail:* jeffreyb@whitecap.ca
Founded: 1977
Trade books, photography, cookery, regional, gardening, outdoor guide books, natural history, juvenile nonfiction & illustrated children's books, juvenile fiction.
Publishes in English.
ISBN Prefix(es): 978-1-55110; 978-1-55285; 978-1-77050
Number of titles published annually: 85 Print
Total Titles: 480 Print
Imprints: Walrus Books
*Branch Office(s)*
195 Allstate Pkwy, Markham, ON L3R 4T8 *Tel:* 905-477-9700 *E-mail:* godwit@fitzhenry.ca *Web Site:* fitzhenry.ca
U.S. Rep(s): Midpoint Trade

**John Wiley & Sons Canada Ltd**
Subsidiary of John Wiley & Sons Inc
5353 Dundas St W, Suite 400, Toronto, ON M9B 6H8
*Tel:* 416-236-4433 *Toll Free Tel:* 800-467-4797 (orders only) *Fax:* 416-236-8743 (cust serv); 416-236-4447 *Toll Free Fax:* 800-565-6802 (orders)
*E-mail:* canada@wiley.com
*Web Site:* www.wiley.ca
*Key Personnel*
COO: Bill Zerter
Founded: 1968
Textbooks for colleges & universities; trade, professional & reference.
Publishes in English, French.
ISBN Prefix(es): 978-0-470; 978-0-471
Number of titles published annually: 50 Print
Total Titles: 600 Print
Distributor for John Wiley & Sons Inc

**Wilfrid Laurier University Press**
75 University Ave W, Waterloo, ON N2L 3C5
*Tel:* 519-884-0710 (ext 6124) *Toll Free Tel:* 866-836-5551 *Fax:* 519-725-1399
*E-mail:* press@wlu.ca
*Web Site:* www.wlupress.wlu.ca
*Key Personnel*
Dir: Brian Henderson *Tel:* 519-884-0710 ext 6123 *E-mail:* brian@press.wlu.ca
Mng Ed: Rob Kohlmeier *Tel:* 519-884-0710 ext 6119 *E-mail:* rob@press.wlu.ca
Acqs Ed: Ryan Chynces *Tel:* 519-884-0710 ext. 2034 *E-mail:* ryan@press.wlu.ca; Lisa Quinn *Tel:* 519-884-0710 ext 2843 *E-mail:* quinn@press.wlu.ca
Prodn Mgr: Heather Baine-Yanke *Tel:* 519-884-0710 ext 6122 *E-mail:* heather@press.wlu.ca
Sales & Mktg Mgr: Penelope Grows *Tel:* 519-884-0710 ext 6605 *E-mail:* pgrows@press.wlu.ca
Cust Serv & Dist Servs: Cheryl Beaupre *Tel:* 519-884-0710 ext 6124 *E-mail:* cheryl@press.wlu.ca
Founded: 1974
Publish scholarly & general interest books in the social sciences & humanities.
Publishes in English.
ISBN Prefix(es): 978-0-88920; 978-1-55458
Number of titles published annually: 30 Print; 30 Online
Total Titles: 416 Print; 400 Online
Distributor for Laurier Centre for Military Strategic & Disarmament Studies; Toronto International Film Festival
Foreign Rep(s): Blue4Books Inc (Midwestern States, Southeast, Southwest); Gazelle Book Services Ltd (Caribbean, Continental Europe, India, Ireland, Israel, Japan, Latin America, Middle East, South Africa, Southeast Asia, Sub-Saharan Africa, UK); Hargreaves, Fuller & Paton (Colin Fuller) (Alberta, British Columbia, Manitoba, Northwest Territories, Saskatchewan, Yukon); Hargreaves, Fuller & Paton (Terry Fernihough) (Ontario); Hargreaves, Fuller & Paton (Karen Stacey); Hargreaves, Fuller & Paton (Steve Paton) (Alberta, British Columbia, Manitoba, Northwest Territories, Saskatchewan, Yukon); Hill/Martin Associates (Western USA); Edward Makabenta (Philippines, Thailand); Ben Schrager (Northeast USA); Leona & Jerry Trainer (Eastern Canada); Woodslane Pty Ltd (Australia, Fiji, New Zealand, Pacific Islands, Papua New Guinea)
*Orders to:* University of Toronto Press Distribution, 5201 Dufferin Street, Toronto, ON M3H-5T8 (Canadian orders) *Toll Free Tel:* 800-565-9523 *Toll Free Fax:* 800-221-9985 *E-mail:* utpbooks@utpress.utoronto.ca; Edward Makabenta, 109 Talayan St, Quezon City 1104, Philippines (Bangkok, Thailand & Philippines) *Tel:* (02) 711-4548 *Fax:* (02) 740-0346 *E-mail:* edmak@pldtdsl.net; Gazelle Book Services Ltd, White Cross Mills, High Town, Lancaster LA1 4XS, United Kingdom (Continental Europe, India, Ireland, Israel, Japan, Latin America & the Caribbean, Middle East, South Africa, Southeast Asia, Sub-Saharan Africa & UK) *Tel:* (01524) 68765 *Fax:* (01524) 63232 *E-mail:* sales@gazellebooks.co.uk *Web Site:* www.gazellebookservices.co.uk; University of Toronto Press Distribution, 2250 Military Rd, Tonawanda, NY 14150, United States (US orders) *Toll Free Tel:* 800-565-9523 *Toll Free Fax:* 800-221-9985 *E-mail:* utpbooks@utpress.utoronto.ca
Membership(s): Association of American University Presses; Association of Canadian Publishers; Association of Canadian University Presses; Organization of Book Publishers of Ontario

**Wood Lake Publishing Inc**
9590 Jim Bailey Rd, Kelowna, BC V4V 1R2
*Tel:* 250-766-2778 *Toll Free Tel:* 800-663-2775 (orders) *Fax:* 250-766-2736 *Toll Free Fax:* 888-841-9991 (orders)
*E-mail:* info@woodlake.com; customerservice@woodlake.com
*Web Site:* www.woodlakebooks.com
*Key Personnel*
Pres & Acting Publr: Mike Schwartzentruber
Opers Mgr & HR: Patty Berube
Mktg Promos & Sales: Lynne Chilton *E-mail:* lynnec@woodlake.com
Founded: 1980
Books, church curriculum & periodicals.
Publishes in English.
ISBN Prefix(es): 978-1-55145; 978-0-919599; 978-0-929032
Number of titles published annually: 4 Print
Total Titles: 135 Print
Imprints: CopperHouse; Northstone; Wood Lake
Distributed by Augsburg Canada; Presbyterian Church of Canada; United Church of Canada
Distributor for Geneva Press; Northstone; The Pilgrim Press; The United Church Press; Westminster John Knox Press
U.S. Publishers Represented: Geneva Press; Westminster John Knox Press

**Worldwide Library**
Imprint of Harlequin Enterprises Ltd
225 Duncan Mill Rd, Don Mills, ON M3B 3K9
*Tel:* 416-445-5860 *Toll Free Tel:* 888-432-4879 *Fax:* 416-445-8655; 416-445-8736
*E-mail:* CustomerService@harlequin.com
*Web Site:* www.harlequin.com
*Key Personnel*
Exec Ed: Feroze Mohammed
Intl Rts: Jan Grammick
Founded: 1982
Mass market fiction.
Publishes in English.
ISBN Prefix(es): 978-0-373
Number of titles published annually: 78 Print
Imprints: Gold Eagle Books; Worldwide Mystery
Foreign Rights: Booklink (Europe)
*Warehouse:* 3010 Walden Ave, Depew, NY 14043, United States

Marketing Your Indexing Services
3rd Edition
Edited by Anne Leach
American Society for Indexing

Indexing for Editors and Authors
A Practical Guide to Understanding Indexes
American Society of Indexers

Information Today, Inc.

# Small Presses

Listed here, in alphabetical order, are U.S. & Canadian publishers who were not eligible to be listed in the sections covering U.S. Publishers or Canadian Publishers. Many of these publishers are new or offer distinctive titles they wish to make known to the users of *Literary Market Place*. Entries in this section are paid listings.

Publishers interested in participating in this section in future editions of LMP are invited to contact **Lauri Rimler, Advertising Sales** by e-mail at lwrimler@infotoday.com, by phone at 800-409-4929 ext 0088 or 908-219-0088, by fax at 908-219-0192 or by mail at Information Today, Inc., 630 Central Avenue, New Providence, NJ 07974.

**Adams-Pomeroy Press**
103 N Jackson St, Albany, WI 53502
Mailing Address: PO Box 189, Albany, WI 53502
*Tel:* 608-862-3645 *Toll Free Tel:* 877-862-3645 *Fax:* 608-862-3647
*E-mail:* adamspomeroy@tds.net
Founded: 1996
Adams-Pomeroy Press publishes books in the areas of education, multicultural nonfiction, juvenile fiction & fiction.
Titles include *Haunted Hill*; *How Big is Your Class?*; *Scrambled*
ISBN Prefix(es): 978-0-9661009
Distributed by Baker & Taylor Inc; Book Wholesalers Inc; Brodart; Follett
Membership(s): The Association of Publishers for Special Sales; Colorado Independent Publishers Association; IBPA, the Independent Book Publishers Association

**BCFL**
4806 Martinique Way, Naples, FL 34119
*Tel:* 908-447-3553 *Fax:* 239-596-8611
*E-mail:* BCFLGroup@gmail.com
*Web Site:* judgingfloraldesign.com
*Key Personnel*
Opers: Bill Whalen
Founded: 2012
Nonfiction publisher specializing in books on floral design for students, teachers, competitors, garden club arrangers, professional designers & judges.
Titles include *A Fresh Look at Judging Floral Design*
ISBN Prefix(es): 978-0-9854476
Membership(s): IBPA, the Independent Book Publishers Association

**Class Action Ink**
1300 NE 16 Ave, Suite 712, Portland, OR 97232-1483
*Tel:* 503-280-2448
*E-mail:* pam@classactionink.com
*Web Site:* www.classactionink.com
*Key Personnel*
Owner/Publr: Pam Glenn
Founded: 2009
Publishes literary fiction & poetry for mature, culturally savvy readers. Some projects may be partially author-subsidized.
Titles include *All the Wrong Places: Mrs. Frog's Improbable Search for Love*; *Barter World*; *Even As We Speak*; *What you least expect: selected poems 1980-2011*
ISBN Prefix(es): 978-0-9841530
Distributed by Amazon.com (Small Press Advantage program); Partners/West
Membership(s): IBPA, the Independent Book Publishers Association

DOUG BUTLER ENTERPRISES, INC.
FORGING FIRM FOUNDATIONS

**Doug Butler Enterprises, Inc**
495 Table Rd, Crawford, NE 69339
*Tel:* 308-665-1510 *Toll Free Tel:* 800-728-3826 *Fax:* 308-665-1520
*E-mail:* info@dougbutler.com
*Web Site:* www.dougbutler.com; www.essentialhorseshoeingbook.com
*Key Personnel*
Pres: Doug Butler
VP: Jacob Butler *E-mail:* jacob@dougbutler.com
Founded: 1974
Publish farrier science & horse foot care books, DVDs. New *Essential Principles of Horseshoeing* is 2013 IPPY Bronze Award Winner in "How-to" category! Also received Eric Hoffer Award, 2013, Honorable Mention in "Reference" category. See WorldCat & www.Essentialhorseshoeingbook.com for more information. Quantity discount prices available. Also new: Farrier Foundation Home Study (online) course – visit www.butlerprofessionalfarrierschool.com. All titles can be ordered directly from the publisher.
Titles include *Essential Principles of Horseshoeing*; *Horse Foot Care: A Horse Owners Guide to Humane Foot Care*; *Principles of Horseshoeing (P3)*; *Shoeing In Your Right Mind*; *Six-Figure Shoeing*; *The Cowboy Code: A Sure-fire Guide to Ridin' the Trails of Life*
ISBN Prefix(es): 978-0-916992
Distributed by Amazon.com

**Dreaming Publications LLC**
1938 Old Balsam Rd, Waynesville, NC 28786
SAN: 859-4333
*Tel:* 828-423-0226
*E-mail:* dreamingpublications@gmail.com
*Web Site:* dreamingpublications.com
*Key Personnel*
Pres: Lyn Marsh, PhD *E-mail:* lynmarshphd@gmail.com
Mktg Promos Dir: Glenda Kyle
Founded: 2010
Dreaming Publications LLC publishes juvenile & adult fiction & nonfiction. Our focus is to publish work that inspires new dreams & future visions, innovative thinking & imagination. We are currently focusing on eBook & paperback/softcover publishing.
Titles include *The Grand Tree (book 1 of 3 in the Rainbow Crystal series)*
ISBN Prefix(es): 978-0-9844495
Membership(s): IBPA, the Independent Book Publishers Association

**Filsinger & Company Ltd**
288 W 12 St, Suite 2R, New York, NY 10014
*Tel:* 212-243-7421
*E-mail:* filsingercompany@gmail.com
*Web Site:* www.filsingerco.com
*Key Personnel*
Pres: Cheryl Filsinger
Founded: 1974
Publisher of museum-quality children's books including the NEIGHBORS series.
Titles also available at BookHampton (Sag Harbor, East Hampton & Mattituck, NY), Little Marc Jacobs (NYC), Manhattan Books (NYC) & South Fork Natural History Museum (Bridgehampton, NY).
Titles include *NEIGHBORS The Yard Critters Book 1*; *NEIGHBORS The Yard Critters TOO*
ISBN Prefix(es): 978-0-916754
Distributed by Amazon.com; Baker & Taylor

**Heart and Mind Press**
3135 E Palo Verde Dr, Phoenix, AZ 85016
*Tel:* 602-790-4009
*E-mail:* info@heartandmindpress.com
*Web Site:* heartandmindpress.com
*Key Personnel*
Publr: Teresa Villegas
Founded: 2013
Heart and Mind Press is dedicated to helping parents & educators to inspire & cultivate conscious, empathetic, responsible children with an understanding of the natural world & how it impacts us on a deeper personal level. Exploring the interconnectedness of heart & mind is where we thrive.
Titles include *How We Became a Family (egg donor twins version)*; *How We Became a Family (sperm donor twins version)*
ISBN Prefix(es): 978-0-9884501

**Infusionmedia**
140 N Eighth St, Suite 214, The Apothecary, Lincoln, NE 68508-1353
SAN: 253-9136
*Tel:* 402-477-2065
*E-mail:* info@infusionmediadesign.com
*Web Site:* www.infusionmediadesign.com
*Key Personnel*
Pres: Cris Trautner *E-mail:* cris@infusionmediadesign.com
VP: Aaron Vacin *E-mail:* aaron@infusionmediadesign.com
Founded: 1994
In this rapidly changing publishing industry, you need to have a partner who still steer you in the right direction for your book or periodical & provide good counsel on the best way to publish based on your goals & definition of success. Infusionmedia has the experience (over 19 years & counting) to develop & execute a publishing solution that meets your needs & budget. We are a graphic design shop specializing in custom book design & publishing, e-book development, & web site design. Our expertise, resources & deep commitment to our craft make us an excellent choice to meet your custom publishing needs.

Titles include *A History of the World*; *The Loren Eiseley Reader*; *Put Your Mouth Where the Money Is: How to Refocus Your Marketing Communications for the Greatest Impact on Sales*; *Shafer's Nebraska Pheasant Hunting Almanac*; *Shortcuts to Gourmet Cooking & Family Favorites*
ISBN Prefix(es): 978-0-9704852; 978-0-9718677; 978-0-9796586
Imprints: Abbatia Press; Amanuent Press; Asteria Press; Infusionmedia Publishing; Plains Chronicles Press
Distributed by Baker & Taylor; Ingram
Membership(s): Better Business Bureau; IBPA, the Independent Book Publishers Association

**Lemon Grove Press**
1158 26 St, Suite 502, Santa Monica, CA 90403
*Tel:* 310-471-1740 *Fax:* 310-476-7627
*E-mail:* info@lemongrovepress.com
*Web Site:* www.thetakechargepatient.com
*Key Personnel*
Publr: Martine Ehrenclou
Asst: Christine Buffaloe
Founded: 2007
Boutique imprint specializing in adult self-help, health & nonfiction. No children's or young adult books.
Titles include *Critical Conditions: The Essential Hospital Guide to Get Your Loved One Out Alive*; *The Take-Charge Patient: How You Can Get the Best Medical Care*
ISBN Prefix(es): 978-0-9815240
Distributed by Baker & Taylor Inc; The Book House Inc; Bookmasters; Brodart Co Books & Automation; Emery-Pratt Co; Follett Library Resources Inc; Ingram Book Group; Midwest Library Service; Quality Books Inc; Unique Books Inc
Membership(s): IBPA, the Independent Book Publishers Association

**Little Pickle Press LLC**
PO Box 983, Belvedere, CA 94920
*Toll Free Tel:* 877-415-4488 *Fax:* 415-366-1520
*E-mail:* info@littlepicklepress.com
*Web Site:* www.littlepicklepress.com
*Key Personnel*
Chief Exec Pickle (CEO): Rana DiOrio *E-mail:* rana@littlepicklepress.com
Chief Mktg Pickle: Julie Fenton *Tel:* 401-699-4920 *E-mail:* julie@littlepicklepress.com
Founded: 2009
Little Pickle Press is dedicated to helping parents & educators cultivate conscious, responsible Little People by instilling core values, such as helping children in need, celebrating diversity & protecting the environment. A portion of our revenue is given to nonprofit affiliates that support our mission. We print & distribute our materials in an environmentally friendly manner. We seek & support emerging authors & artists.
Titles include *What Does It Mean To Be Global?*; *What Does It Mean To Be Green?*; *What Does It Mean To Be Present?*
ISBN Prefix(es): 978-0-9840806
Membership(s): The Association of Publishers for Special Sales; IBPA, the Independent Book Publishers Association; Society of Children's Book Writers & Illustrators

**Magic Hill Press LLC**
144 Magic Hill Rd, Hinesburg, VT 05461
*Tel:* 802-482-3287
*E-mail:* MagicHillPress@gmail.com
*Web Site:* www.MagicHillPress.com
*Key Personnel*
Principal: William H Schubart *E-mail:* Bill@Schubart.com
Founded: 2010
Magic Hill Publishing LLC is the imprint of novelist, short story & op-ed writer Bill Schubart. Titles available in print & electronically.
Titles include *I am Baybie: Based on the true story of the Reverend Baybie Hoover and her friend and Deaconess of Music Virginia Brown (novel)*; *Panhead: A Journey Home (novel)*
ISBN Prefix(es): 978-0-9834852
Distributed by Ingram Book Group; Lightning Source Inc
Membership(s): IBPA, the Independent Book Publishers Association; Independent Publishers of New England

**Magick Mirror Communications**
511 Avenue of the Americas, PMB 173, New York, NY 10011-8436
*Tel:* 212-255-2111; 212-208-2951 (voice mail) *Toll Free Tel:* 800-356-6796 *Fax:* 212-208-2951 (e-fax)
*E-mail:* MagickMirr@aol.com; Magickorders@aol.com
*Web Site:* magickmirror.com
*Key Personnel*
Artistic Dir: Eugenia Macer-Story
Founded: 1990
Publish poetry, playscripts & interdimensional journalism on supernatural & occult events.
Titles include *Applied Ecological Authority (playscript)*; *Battles with Dragons: Certain Tales of Political Yoga (short stories/occult)*; *The Bright Spidey Charm Book: Real Magick Both Talismanic & Philosophical (occult nonfiction)*; *Carrying Thunder (poetry)*; *Ceremonies 17 (playscript)*; *Crossing Jungle River (poetry)*; *The Dark Frontier (nonfiction occult)*; *Doing Business in the Adirondacks (nonfiction supernatural)*; *Fast Luck Botanica & Other Such Poems*; *The Fish Catcher Experiment (playscript)*; *M7 Bus (poetry)*; *The Merry Piper's Hollow Hills (poetry)*; *Mining the Sky (poetry)*; *OM/NADA (novel)*; *100 Crystal Arrows: The Bridge Of Many Voices (poetry)*; *Pulse of the Dragon: The Secret Knowledge of the Pirates (nonfiction)*; *Rat Tat Jazz Riddles: The Unmarked Crossroads (poetry)*; *The Sin of Love (novel)*; *Struck by Green Lightning aka Project Midas (novel)*; *Theatre Cosmos (poetry)*; *Three Roads: The Cosmic ATM (poetry)*; *Troll & Other Interdimensional Invasions (short stories)*; *Vanishing Questions (poetry)*
ISBN Prefix(es): 978-1-879980
Distributed by Amazon.com; Barnes & Noble (online); New Leaf Distributing Co
Membership(s): Council of Literary Magazines & Presses

**Moonstone Press LLC**
4816 Carrington Circle, Sarasota, FL 34243
SAN: 852-5625
*Tel:* 301-765-1081 *Fax:* 301-765-0510
*E-mail:* mazeprod@erols.com
*Web Site:* www.moonstonepress.net
*Key Personnel*
Publr: Stephanie Maze
Founded: 2001
Publishes quality photography-based books in English & Spanish for ages 3-12 & adults.
Titles include *Breastfeeding Around the World/Amamantar alrededor del mundo*; *Healthy Foods from A to Z/Comida sana de la A a la Z (for ages 3 & up)*; *Moments in the Wild/Momentos en el reino animal (4 title series for ages 3 & up)*
ISBN Prefix(es): 978-0-9707768; 978-0-9727697
Membership(s): IBPA, the Independent Book Publishers Association; White House Press Photogaphers Association

**New York Media Works**
Imprint of New York Media Works LLC
112 Franklin St, New York, NY 10013
SAN: 920-5187
*Tel:* 646-369-5681 *Fax:* 646-810-4033
*E-mail:* info@nymediaworks.com
*Web Site:* www.nymediaworks.com
*Key Personnel*
Owner: Julie Gribble *E-mail:* JGribble@nymediaworks.com
PR/Media: Kassia Graham *E-mail:* pr@nymediaworks.com
Media Strategy: Rachel Kent *E-mail:* pr@nymediaworks.com
Founded: 2012
New York Media Works is a publisher & content provider for new media & film located in the heart of Tribeca, NYC. We collaborate with artists & filmmakers from around the world to create inspiring & compelling stories to entertain audiences of all ages. Two new titles will be released in 2014.
Titles include *Bubblegum Princess*
ISBN Prefix(es): 978-0-9890914
Distributed by Brodart; London Candy Company; Quality Books Inc
Membership(s): AAP; Children's Literature Association; IBPA, the Independent Book Publishers Association

**Painted Hills Publishing**
16500 Dakota Ridge Rd, Longmont, CO 80503
*Tel:* 303-823-6642 *Fax:* 303-825-5119
*E-mail:* cw@livingimagescjw.com
*Web Site:* www.wildhoofbeats.com; www.horsephotographyworkshops.com
*Key Personnel*
Owner: Carol Walker
Founded: 2008
Publishes photography books on wild horses with the purpose of educating the public about the wild horse situation in the United States. Also publishes books on the techniques of photographing domestic & wild horses.
Titles include *Horse Photography: The Dynamic Guide for Horse Lovers*; *Wild Hoofbeats: America's Vanishing Wild Horses*
ISBN Prefix(es): 978-0-9817936
Distributed by Baker & Taylor; Books West; Gazelle International; Greenleaf Book Group; Quality Books
Membership(s): IBPA, the Independent Book Publishers Association; PPA

**Paraphrase LLC**
PO Box 56508, Sherman Oaks, CA 91413
SAN: 855-9643
*Tel:* 818-219-4377 *Toll Free Fax:* 888-863-4377
*E-mail:* books@paraphrasellc.com
*Web Site:* www.paraphrasellc.com
*Key Personnel*
Pres: Arnold Rudnick *E-mail:* arnold@paraphrasellc.com
Founded: 2006
Boutique publishing company dedicated to creating thought-provoking media that educates, entertains & inspires. Read a Book, Read a Mind®. Currently accepting queries & solicited mss.
Titles include *E S Pete: Sixth Grade Sense*; *Little Green*
ISBN Prefix(es): 978-0-9815879
Distributed by Amazon.com; Createspace Direct
Membership(s): IBPA, the Independent Book Publishers Association

**ProChain Press**
Imprint of ProChain Solutions Inc

3460 Commission Ct, No 301, Lake Ridge, VA 22192
*Tel:* 703-490-8821 *Fax:* 703-494-1414
*E-mail:* publishing@prochain.com
*Web Site:* prochain.com
*Key Personnel*
CEO: Robert Newbold *E-mail:* rnewbold@prochain.com
COO: William Lynch *E-mail:* blynch@prochain.com
Founded: 2008
Publish & manage books related primarily to project management & critical chain scheduling.
Titles include *Be Fast or Be Gone*; *The Billion Dollar Solution*
ISBN Prefix(es): 978-1-934979
Distributed by Amazon.com; Baker & Taylor; Barnes & Noble; Ingram
Membership(s): IBPA, the Independent Book Publishers Association

**Ransom Note Press**
PO Box 419, Ridgewood, NJ 07451
SAN: 257-4527
*Tel:* 201-835-2790
*E-mail:* editorial@ransomnotepress.com
*Web Site:* www.ransomnotepress.com
*Key Personnel*
Publr: Christian Alighieri
Sr Ed: Emily Marlowe
Publicist: Max St John
Founded: 2005
Ransom Note Press publishes modern & traditional mysteries & novels of suspense. Query via mail only, with descriptive letter, first 25 pages & SASE. No pet mysteries, serial killers or short story collections. We are interested only in novels that offer gripping story lines & well-executed plots. In general, we prefer novels in which the author has attempted to do something different to break from tradition & explore new ground.
Titles include *Circle of Assassins*; *Split*
ISBN Prefix(es): 978-0-9773787
Distributed by Baker & Taylor; Book Clearing House; Brodart Books
Membership(s): IBPA, the Independent Book Publishers Association

**Emma Right Books**
223 Nice Ct, Redwood City, CA 94065
*Tel:* 650-770-0993
*E-mail:* emmarightmarketing@gmail.com
*Web Site:* www.emmaright.com
*Key Personnel*
Author/Owner: Emma Right
Founded: 2013
Emma Right Books deal with young adult, middle grade & children's books that are fun, wholesome & hope to empower their readers in some manner.
Titles include *Keeper of Reign (ISBN: 978-1-939337-69-6)*
Distributed by Amazon.com; Barnes & Noble; Ingram Book Group; Lightning Source Inc; New Shelves (614 Fifth Ave, Troy, NY 12182)
Membership(s): The Association of Publishers for Special Sales; Christian Writers Guild; IBPA, the Independent Book Publishers Association

**Rivendell Books**
PO Box 9306, Richmond Heights, MO 63117-0306
SAN: 854-1531
*Tel:* 314-609-6534
*E-mail:* butch@rivendellbooks.com
*Web Site:* www.rivendellbooks.com
*Key Personnel*
Publr: Butch Drury
Founded: 2008
Rivendell Books is a very narrowly focused, niche publisher for a select group of authors who write nonfiction books that deal with freeing mankind from the tyranny of sincere ignorance, the ego & the destructive side of our animal natures.
Titles include *A Different Kind of Sentinel*
ISBN Prefix(es): 978-0-9797023
Distributed by Amazon.com; Baker & Taylor; Barnes & Noble (online); Ingram
Membership(s): IBPA, the Independent Book Publishers Association; St Louis Publishers Association; St Louis Writers Guild

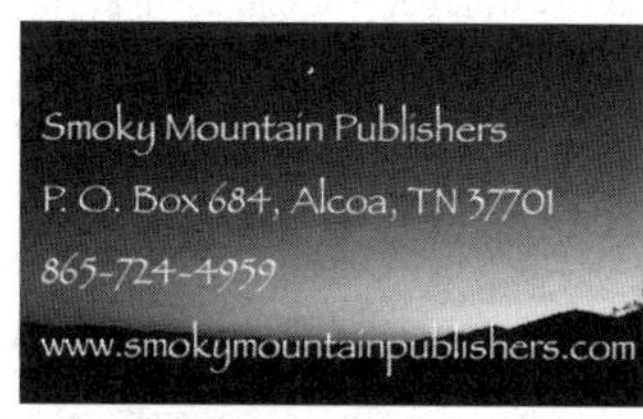


**Smoky Mountain Publishers**
PO Box 684, Alcoa, TN 37701
SAN: 857-992X
*Tel:* 865-724-4959
*Web Site:* smokymountainpublishers.com
*Key Personnel*
Owner: Dr Gail Palmer *E-mail:* lpalmer@utk.edu
Founded: 2005
Titles include *Great Smoky Mountains National Park: In the Beginning... Fact, Legend & Eminent Domain*; *Smoky Mountain Tales: Feuds, Murder & Mayhem (vol 1)*; *Smoky Mountain Tales: Feuds, Murder & Mayhem (vol 2)*
ISBN Prefix(es): 978-0-9823735
Distributed by Amazon.com
Membership(s): IBPA, the Independent Book Publishers Association

SPRING TREE PRESS

**Spring Tree Press**
571 Locust Point Rd, Locust, NJ 07760
Mailing Address: PO Box 461, Atlantic Highlands, NJ 07716
*Tel:* 732-872-8002 *Fax:* 732-872-6967
*E-mail:* springtreepress@gmail.com
*Web Site:* www.springtreepress.com; www.tyrrc.com
*Key Personnel*
Publr: Janine L Kimmel
Dir, Mktg & Publicity: Sara Sgariat *Tel:* 434-245-2272 *Fax:* 434-245-2272 *E-mail:* sgariatpublicity@comcast.net
Exec Asst: Danielle Nelson *E-mail:* danielle@sierrared.com
Founded: 2006
A small publisher specializing in quality books for the child, youth & young adult markets. Our latest title *The Yawning Rabbit River Chronicle* (ISBN: 978-0-9785007-1-9) is a beautifully illustrated story of an enchanted river & its heroes, both human & animal. This VOYA's Perfect Ten 2012 title is appropriate for ages 10-14.
Titles include *The Magic Gown*; *The Yawning Rabbit River Chronicle*
ISBN Prefix(es): 978-0-9785007
Distributed by Baker & Taylor; Brodart & Co; Follett Library Resource
Membership(s): IBPA, the Independent Book Publishers Association

**The Street Life Series**
c/o Xlibris Corp, 1663 Liberty Dr, Suite 200, Bloomington, IN 47403
*Toll Free Tel:* 888-795-4274 (orders thru Xlibris) *Fax:* 610-915-0294 (orders thru Xlibris)
*E-mail:* info@kevinmweeks.com
*Web Site:* www.kevinmweeks.com
*Key Personnel*
Author: Kevin M Weeks
Founded: 2006
The Street Life Series includes a collection of crime fiction novels & young adult historical fiction novels. Kevin M Weeks is the first African-American writer to receive literary awards from both the African-American Pavilion at BookExpo America & the Sons of Confederate Veterans Bonnie Blue Society. The Mom's Choice Awards named the debut young adult historical fiction novel among the best in family-friendly media, products & services. All titles are available for Kindle & NOOK Book.
Titles include *The Street Life Series: Is It Passion or Revenge? (ISBN: 978-1-4257-9712-6)*; *The Street Life Series: Is It Rags or Riches? (ISBN: 978-1-4415-6621-8)*; *The Street Life Series: Is It Suicide or Murder? (ISBN: 978-1-4257-1104-7)*; *The Street Life Series Youth Edition: Entangled in Freedom (978-1-4535-5525-5)*
Distributed by Amazon.com; Baker & Taylor; Barnes & Noble (online); Ingram
Membership(s): Georgia Writers Association; IBPA, the Independent Book Publishers Association; Military Writers Society of America; Mystery Writers of America; PEN American Center

**Surviving-Mental-Illness**
147-38 72 Ave, Flushing, NY 11367
*Tel:* 718 261-3772
*E-mail:* baronkatz@gmail.com
*Web Site:* www.surviving-mental-illness.com
Founded: 2012
Surviving-Mental-Illness was established to educate people with/without mental illness because of the many misconceptions about it. Linda Naomi Katz wrote & published the memoir *Surviving Mental Illness: My Story* (ISBN: 978-1-4327-8399-0, paperback) & created a web site through which the book can be purchased. This title has won ReadersFavorite.com's 2012 Non-Fiction: Autobiography Silver Award as well the 2012 Readers Views Literary Award (1st place) in the Memoir/Autobiography/Biography category. Linda runs her own peer support group for Jewish adults/families with mental health issues.
Titles include *Surviving Mental Illness: My Story*
Distributed by Amazon.com; Barnes & Noble; Outskirts Press Inc
Membership(s): IBPA, the Independent Book Publishers Association

**Telling Your Story Inc**
PO Box 668485, Pompano Beach, FL 33069
*Tel:* 954-249-1333; 954-970-9333
*Web Site:* www.telling-your-story.com
*Key Personnel*
Pres: Marjory D Lyons, PhD *E-mail:* marjory@telling-your-story.com
VP: Michael K Jefferson *Tel:* 928-963-0725 *E-mail:* michael@telling-your-story.com
Founded: 2001
Specialty publishing company writing, editing & producing books of memoirs & life stories

for private book clients. We interview, tape record, write & edit the story with the objective of producing 200 hard- or soft-cover books for distribution as the book client determines. Writers often submit mss of their life stories for further composition & editing. We provide excellent graphics & cover design & print-on-demand. All work based on contract for individualized service. Some books have been placed in libraries & historical museums. Call for one hour free consultation.
Titles include *Grandma Elaine's Story*; *Grandpa Merv's Memoir*; *Lucky Me*; *Memory Believes*; *Probing Darkness Finding Light*; *You Can Call Me Brooklyn*
ISBN Prefix(es): 978-0-9717283
*Branch Office(s)*
Sedona, AZ *Tel:* 928-274-2728
Membership(s): Florida Publishers Association Inc; IBPA, the Independent Book Publishers Association; National League of American Pen Women; The Writers' Network of South Florida

**Thompson Mill Press**
2865 S Eagle Rd, No 368, Newtown, PA 18940
*Tel:* 215-431-1424
*E-mail:* info@thompsonmillpress.com
*Web Site:* www.thompsonmillpress.com; www.KobeeManatee.com
*Key Personnel*
Principal: Bob Regan *E-mail:* bob.regan@thompsonmillpress.com
Founded: 2012
Located in the northern suburbs of Philadelphia, Thompson Mill Press focuses on the development, publishing & distribution of children's books containing anthropomorphic characters. Our initial plans for distribution include all of North America. Future distribution plans included Asia, Australia, Central & South America, Europe & Mexico.
Titles include *Kobee Manatee: Heading Home to Florida*
ISBN Prefix(es): 978-0-9883269
Distributed by Amazon.com; Ingram Book Group; Lightning Source Inc
Membership(s): IBPA, the Independent Book Publishers Association

**Three Wishes Publishing Company**
26500 W Agoura Rd, Suite 102-754, Calabasas, CA 91302
*Tel:* 818-878-0902 *Fax:* 818-878-1805
*E-mail:* Alva710@aol.com
*Web Site:* www.threewishespublishing.com
Founded: 2007
Children's book publisher.
Titles include *Circus Fever*; *I'm 5*; *On Your Mark, Get Set, Go!*
ISBN Prefix(es): 978-0-9796380
Imprints: Circus Fever
Distributed by Baker & Taylor
Membership(s): ALA; California Literary Arts Society; California School Library Association; Children's Literature Council; IBPA, the Independent Book Publishers Association; Society of Children's Book Writers & Illustrators

**TJ Publishers Inc**
PO Box 702701, Dallas, TX 75370
*Toll Free Tel:* 800-999-1168 *Fax:* 972-416-0944
*E-mail:* TJPubinc@aol.com
*Key Personnel*
Pres: T Patrick O'Rourke
Founded: 1978
Publisher & distributor of quality books, videotapes & other materials related to sign language & deafness including several best sellers.
Titles include *A Basic Course in American Sign Language (2nd ed)*; *A Basic Course in ASL Vocabulary Videotape*; *A Basic Vocabulary: American Sign Language for Parents and Children*; *From Mime to Sign*
ISBN Prefix(es): 978-0-932666

**Two Canoes Press**
PO Box 334, Hopkinton, MA 01568
SAN: 139-9853
*Tel:* 508-529-6034 *Fax:* 508-529-6005
*E-mail:* TwoCanoesPress@TwoCanoesPress.com; Singsalone@aol.com
*Web Site:* www.TwoCanoesPress.com
*Key Personnel*
Publr: C W Duncan *E-mail:* TwoCanoesPress@aol.com
Titles include *Double Time*
ISBN Prefix(es): 978-1-929590
Distributed by Partners Publishing Group
Membership(s): IBPA, the Independent Book Publishers Association

**Kevin M Weeks**, see The Street Life Series

**Worthy & James Publishing**
PO Box 362015, Milpitas, CA 95036
SAN: 852-5765
*Tel:* 408-945-3963
*E-mail:* worthy1234@sbcglobal.net; mail@worthyjames.com
*Web Site:* www.worthyjames.com
*Key Personnel*
Mgr: Diane James
Mgr/Author: Greg Mostyn
Founded: 2006
Publications in basic accounting, basic finance & basic math.
Titles include *Basic Accounting Concepts, Principles, and Procedures (vols 1 & 2)*
ISBN Prefix(es): 978-0-9791494
Membership(s): IBPA, the Independent Book Publishers Association

**York Press**
Imprint of The American Society for the Defense of Tradition, Family & Property (TFP)
1358 Jefferson Rd, Spring Grove, PA 17362
Mailing Address: PO Box 91, York New Salem, PA 17371-0091
*Tel:* 717-225-7147 *Toll Free Tel:* 888-317-5571 *Fax:* 717-225-7479
*Web Site:* www.returntoorder.org
*Key Personnel*
Author: John Horvat *Tel:* 717-225-7147 ext 227 *E-mail:* jh1908@aol.com
Secy: Benjamin Hiegert *Tel:* 717-225-7147 ext 222 *E-mail:* bhiegert@aol.com
Founded: 2012
Publish books about economy, society & Christianity.
Titles include *Return to Order: From a Frenzied Economy to an Organic Christian Society*
ISBN Prefix(es): 978-0-9882148
Distributed by Baker & Taylor Inc; Ingram Book Group

# Editorial Services & Agents

## Editorial Services — Activity Index

## CONDENSATIONS



## COPY-EDITING



## FACT CHECKING

## GHOST WRITING



## INDEXING

## INTERVIEWING



## LINE EDITING

## MANUSCRIPT ANALYSIS



## PERMISSIONS



## PHOTO RESEARCH

## PROOFREADING



## RESEARCH

## REWRITING



## SPECIAL ASSIGNMENT WRITING

## STATISTICS



## TECHNICAL WRITING



## TRANSCRIPTION EDITING



## TYPEMARKING

# Editorial Services

For information on other companies who provide services to the book industry, see **Consultants, Book Producers, Typing & Word Processing Services** and **Artists & Art Services**.

**A+ English LLC/Book-Editing.com**
Affiliate of Book-Editing.com
PO Box 1372, Mansfield, TX 76063
*Tel:* 469-789-3030
*E-mail:* editingnetwork@gmail.com
*Web Site:* www.editing-writing.com; www.book-editing.com; www.HelpWithStatistics; www.medical-writing-editing.com; www.apawriting.com
*Key Personnel*
Network Coord: Lynda Lotman
Founded: 1976
Serving writers (unpublished, published), publishers (mainstream, genre, trade, academic), agents, researchers & businesses. Ms evaluations, copy-editing, developmental editing, submission materials (query letters, book proposals), mentoring & ghostwriting. Work with fiction, nonfiction, medical/scientific/technical material, business documents & textbooks.
Membership(s): Science Fiction & Fantasy Writers of America

**A Westport Wordsmith**
101 Winfield St, Norwalk, CT 06855
*Tel:* 203-354-7309
*E-mail:* pj104daily@aol.com
*Key Personnel*
Prop: Peggy Daily
Founded: 1999
Proofreading (nonfiction & fiction) & indexing of trade books. Americanization.
Membership(s): American Society for Indexing; Editorial Freelancers Association

**AAA Photos**
401 Ocean Dr, Unit 804, Miami Beach, FL 33139
*Tel:* 305-534 0804
*Web Site:* www.photosphotos.net
*Key Personnel*
Pres: Jeff Greenberg *E-mail:* jeffreygreenberg@aol.com
Provides photos to tourism bureau, book publishers, magazine publishers, newspapers, travel publications, web sites & by assignment & stock.

**AAH Graphics Inc**
Subsidiary of Loft Press Inc
9293 Fort Valley Rd, Fort Valley, VA 22652-2020
*Tel:* 540-933-6211 *Fax:* 540-933-6523
*E-mail:* srh@aahgraphics.com
*Web Site:* www.aahgraphics.com
*Key Personnel*
Pres: Ann A Hunter
Founded: 1973
Complete editorial through production serving publishers & individuals. Design of text, jackets & covers, composition & production management through manufacturing.

**Aaron-Spear**
PO Box 42, Harborside, ME 04617
*Tel:* 207-326-8764
*Key Personnel*
Prop: Jody Spear
Developmental editing & copy-editing of scholarly mss in the humanities. Rewriting for style & sensibility as well as clarity, consistency & accuracy. Specialize in art history & environmental studies.

**About Books Inc**
1001 Taurus Dr, Colorado Springs, CO 80906
*Tel:* 719-632-8226 *Fax:* 719-213-2602
*Web Site:* www.about-books.com
*Key Personnel*
Owner & Pres: Debi Flora *E-mail:* debiflora@about-books.com
Owner & VP: Scott Flora
Sr Ed: Allan Burns
Founded: 1977
Complete writing, editorial & book development services: editing; cover & interior design; ebooks & print books; specialize in nonfiction books on all subjects.
Membership(s): The Association of Publishers for Special Sales

**Access Editorial Services**
1133 Broadway, Suite 528, New York, NY 10010
*Tel:* 212-255-7306 *Fax:* 212-255-7306
*E-mail:* wiseword@juno.com
*Key Personnel*
Dir: Louise Weiss
Founded: 1990
Services include travel writing.
Membership(s): The Authors Guild; New York Travel Writers Association; SATW; Toastmasters International

**Accurate Writing & More**
16 Barstow Lane, Hadley, MA 01035
*Tel:* 413-586-2388
*E-mail:* shel@principledprofit.com
*Web Site:* frugalmarketing.com; www.accuratewriting.com; www.grassrootsmarketingforauthors.com; www.greenandprofitable.com; www.frugalfun.com; www.twitter.com/shelhorowitz
*Key Personnel*
Owner & Dir: Shel Horowitz *E-mail:* shel@principledprofit.com
Dir: Dina Friedman
Founded: 1981
Advertising & promotion copy writing, ghost writing, interviewing, ms analysis, research, rewriting, special assignment writing & publishing consulting.
Membership(s): The Association of Publishers for Special Sales; IBPA, the Independent Book Publishers Association; Independent Publishers of New England; National Writers Union; Small Publishers, Artists & Writers Network; Western New England Editorial Freelancers Association

**J Adel Art & Design**
586 Ramapo Rd, Teaneck, NJ 07666
*Tel:* 201-836-2606
*E-mail:* jadelnj@aol.com
*Key Personnel*
Creative Dir: Judith Adel
Founded: 1985
Freelance copy, illustration & design services for publishers.

**AEIOU Inc**
894 Piermont Ave, Piermont, NY 10968
*Tel:* 845-680-5380 *Fax:* 845-680-5380
*Key Personnel*
Pres: Cynthia Crippen *E-mail:* ccrippen@verizon.net
Founded: 1976
Membership(s): American Society for Indexing

**AFS Wordstead**
1062 Vallee-a-Josaphat, Lac-des-Iles, QC J0W 1J0, Canada
*Tel:* 819-597-4072 *Fax:* 819-597-4547
*Web Site:* www.wordstead.com
*Key Personnel*
Owner & Sr Writer: Anthony F Shaker, PhD *E-mail:* afshaker@aol.com
Founded: 2001 (in the writing business since 1988)
Ghosting, rewriting, editing. Works in fiction & nonfiction (memoirs, autobiographies, biographies, business & self-improvement books, articles, scripts, book-to-screen adaptations). Works regularly with publishers on client projects & his own scholarly books.
For online query, please include full name, phone number, short description of project & nature of request (ghostwriting, editing, copywriting, etc).

**Rodelinde Albrecht**
PO Box 444, Lenox Dale, MA 01242-0444
*Tel:* 413-243-4350 *Toll Free Tel:* 800-370-5040 *Fax:* 413-243-3066
*E-mail:* rodelinde@earthlink.net
Founded: 1979
Full editorial services; scanning; copy/line editing (hardcopy/electronic); rewriting; castoff, typemarking; proofreading; proof-checking & consulting.

**AllWrite Advertising & Publishing**
260 Peachtree St NW, Suite 2200, Atlanta, GA 30303
Mailing Address: PO Box 1071, Atlanta, GA 30301
*Tel:* 678-691-9005 *Fax:* 530-689-6980
*E-mail:* questions@allwritepublishing.com
*Web Site:* www.allwritepublishing.com
*Key Personnel*
Pres & Publr: Annette R Johnson *E-mail:* annette@allwritepublishing.com
Founded: 1996
A conventional publisher that also offers editorial services for self-publishers & those who need promotional documents or materials, including booklets & brochures. Provides comprehensive editing & proofreading services: checking syntax, grammar, punctuation & style; & offering substantive/line editing, developmental editing & production editing. Get a free online quote at www.e-allwrite.com.
Membership(s): Writers Guild of America East

**Jeanette Almada**
3411 N Elaine Place, Unit 2, Chicago, IL 60657
*Tel:* 773-404-9350
*E-mail:* jmalmada@sbcglobal.net
Writer, reporter, editor. Rewrite, co-author or author any story for publication as a book, article, newsletter or brochure. Areas of research & writing interest include urban affairs & lifestyle; organic standards & organic consumer topics; slow & local food; corporate cultural issues & corporate profiles, land use & conservation; neighborhood or community development & other nonfiction topics.

**Ampersand Group**
12 Morenz Terr, Kanata, ON K2K 3G9, Canada
*Tel:* 613-435-5066
*Key Personnel*
Pres: Ed Matheson *E-mail:* ematheson@ball.net
Book publishing consultants for publishers, business, government & individuals with publishing problems. Specialize in project management, general book design & production.

**Joyce L Ananian**
25 Forest Circle, Waltham, MA 02452-4719
*Tel:* 781-894-4330
*E-mail:* jlananian@hotmail.com
Founded: 1981
Copy editing, fact checking, indexing, proofreading & line editing.

**Barbara S Anderson**
706 W Davis Ave, Ann Arbor, MI 48103-4855
*Tel:* 734-995-0125 *Toll Free Fax:* 866-859-2932
*E-mail:* bsa328@earthlink.net
*Key Personnel*
Owner: Barbara S Anderson
Admin Asst: Martin B Tittle *Tel:* 734-846-3864 *E-mail:* mtittle@umich.edu
Rewriting, proofreading, ms analysis & line editing. For related services see listing in Artists & Art Services.

**Denice A Anderson**
210 E Church St, Clinton, MI 49236
*Tel:* 517-456-4990 *Fax:* 517-456-4990
*E-mail:* deniceanderson@frontier.com
Founded: 1984
Copy-editing, line editing & proofreading; fiction & nonfiction; art, history, medical, legal, business, newspapers, journals & directories.
Membership(s): Editorial Freelancers Association

**Jim Anderson**
77 S Second St, Brooklyn, NY 11249
*Tel:* 718-388-1083
*E-mail:* jim.and@att.net

**Patricia Anderson PhD, Literary Consultant**
1489 Marine Dr, Suite 515, West Vancouver, BC V7T 1B8, Canada
*Tel:* 604-740-0805
*E-mail:* query@helpingyougetpublished.com; patriciaanderson@helpingyougetpublished.com
*Web Site:* www.helpingyougetpublished.com
*Key Personnel*
Literary Consultant: Dr Patricia Anderson, PhD
Founded: 1998 (online since 1999)
Ms assessment, editing & proofreading, book proposals, market research, book trailers & press releases for authors. Specialize in personalized writing & publishing strategies for emerging novelists & authors of book-length nonfiction.
Membership(s): The Authors Guild; Editors' Association of Canada/Association canadienne des reviseurs; The Writers' Union of Canada

**Angel Editing Services**
PO Box 2256, Sebastopol, CA 95473
*Tel:* 707-823-4146
*E-mail:* angel@stephaniemarohn.com
*Web Site:* www.stephaniemarohn.com
*Key Personnel*
Owner & Ed: Stephanie Marohn
Founded: 1993
Full range of editorial services, from developmental editing through copy-editing. Specializing in nonfiction trade books, particularly psychospiritual topics, metaphysics, natural medicine & other alternative thought.
Membership(s): Bay Area Editors' Forum

**Angel Publications**
3169 Quail Dr, Gloucester, ON K1T 1T9, Canada
*Tel:* 613-791-0979
*Key Personnel*
Pres: Diana Thistle Tremblay *E-mail:* dianathistle@live.ca
Children's writing.
Membership(s): Society of Children's Book Writers & Illustrators

**Angels Editorial Services**
1630 Main St, Suite 41, Coventry, CT 06238
*Tel:* 860-742-5279
*E-mail:* angelsus@aol.com
*Key Personnel*
Pres: Prof Claire Connelly, PhD
Founded: 1969
MS or disk: Counseling & psychotherapy, science & computers, textbooks, GLBT, fiction & nonfiction, animals.

**Aptara Inc**
3110 Fairview Park Dr, Suite 900, Falls Church, VA 22042
*Tel:* 703-352-0001
*E-mail:* info@aptaracorp.com
*Web Site:* www.aptaracorp.com
*Key Personnel*
CEO & Pres: Dev Ganesan
Liaison for complete or any combination of production services, ranging from simple 1-color to complex 4-color projects & copy-editing.

**ASJA Freelance Writer Search**
Affiliate of American Society of Journalists & Authors Inc
1501 Broadway, Suite 403, New York, NY 10036
*Tel:* 212-997-0947 *Fax:* 212-937-2315
*E-mail:* fws@asja.org
*Web Site:* www.freelancewritersearch.com
*Key Personnel*
Exec Dir: Alexandra Owens
Founded: 1948
Vital resource for anyone seeking the services of professsional writers for articles, books, book proposals, brochures, annual reports, speeches, TV & film scripts, advertising copy, publicity campaigns, corporate communications & more. Free, private listing service goes only to the 1,300 professional members of ASJA.

**Associated Editors**
27 W 96 St, New York, NY 10025
*Tel:* 212-662-9703
*Key Personnel*
Contact: Lynne Glasner *E-mail:* lyngla1@gmail.com; Maury Siegel
Copy-editing, rewriting, proofreading, indexing, research, developmental editing. Specialize in elementary & secondary textbooks; nonfiction trade books.

**Astor Indexers**
PO Box 950, Kent, CT 06757
*Tel:* 860-355-1066 *Toll Free Tel:* 800-848-2328 *Fax:* 860-355-1066
*Key Personnel*
Owner: Jane Farnol *E-mail:* bjfarnol@snet.net
Founded: 1970
Indexing is our only business. Staff handles all subjects; hard copy, e-mail or disk. Quality, speed & accuracy are our trademarks.

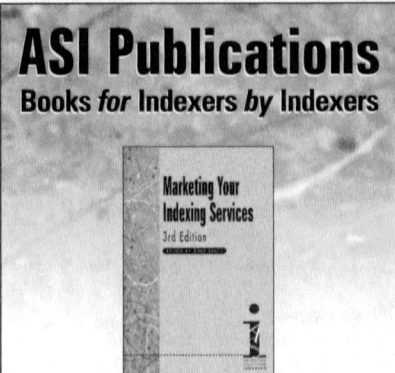

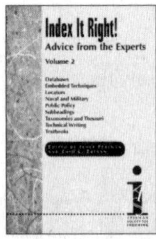

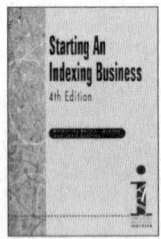

**Audrey Owen**
494 Eaglecrest Dr, Gibsons, BC V0N 1V8, Canada
*E-mail:* editor@writershelper.com
*Web Site:* www.writershelper.com
Founded: 2002
Besides the editing services offered by other agencies, I also specialize in educative edit-

ing that becomes a mini tutorial designed for, but is not restricted to, self-publishing writers.
Membership(s): Editors' Association of Canada/ Association canadienne des reviseurs; Federation of British Columbia Writers

**Sylvia Auerbach**
3890 Nobel Dr, No 506, San Diego, CA 92122
*Tel:* 858-597 8000
Writing assignments on relationships of parents & adult children, financial planning for older adults & book editing. Consultant to colleges & universities on book publishing courses. Lecturer on book publishing at Philadelphia Writers' Conference.
Membership(s): American Society of Journalists & Authors; The Authors Guild

**The Author's Friend**
548 Ocean Blvd, No 12, Long Branch, NJ 07740
*Tel:* 732-571-8051 *Toll Free Tel:* 877-485-7689 *Toll Free Fax:* 877-485-7689
*Key Personnel*
Prop: Judith Stein *E-mail:* jstein@panix.com
Founded: 1976
Copy & line editing, proofreading & transcription editing. Specialize in religion & spirituality, psychology, medicine, self-help, bibliographies & esoterica.

**Backman Writing & Communications**
32 Hillview Ave, Rensselaer, NY 12144
*Tel:* 518-449-4985 *Fax:* 518-449-7273
*Web Site:* www.backwrite.com
*Key Personnel*
Principal: John Backman *E-mail:* johnb@backwrite.com
Articles, blogs, advertising & marketing copy. Areas of focus: spirituality, higher education, engineering, financial services & generally making the complex simple.

**Baldwin Literary Services**
935 Hayes St, Baldwin, NY 11510-4834
*Tel:* 516-546-8338 *Fax:* 516-546-8338
*Key Personnel*
Pres: Marjorie Gillette Jones
Edit Dir: Pat Meglin
Founded: 1982
Creative writing courses. Specialize in novels, historical novels, autobiographies, medical, gardening & nature, spiritual.
Membership(s): International Women's Writing Guild

**Kathleen Barnes**
238 W Fourth St, Suite 3-C, New York, NY 10014
*Tel:* 212-924-8084
*E-mail:* kbarnes@compasscommunications.org
Writing, rewriting, line editing, copy-editing & proofreading.

**Melinda Barrett**
17110 Donmetz St, Granada Hills, CA 91344
*Tel:* 818-635-6865
*E-mail:* mbarrett_3@netzero.net
Founded: 1989
Copy-editing, proofreading, rewriting & special assignment writing.

**Diana Barth**
535 W 51 St, Suite 3-A, New York, NY 10019
*Tel:* 212-307-5465
*E-mail:* diabarth@juno.com
Founded: 1970
All subjects; specialize in performing arts, health, psychology, education & travel. Feature & ghost writer.

**Anita Bartholomew**
4237 Sarasota Ave, Sarasota, FL 34234
*Tel:* 941-358-0495
*E-mail:* anita@anitabartholomew.com
*Web Site:* www.anitabartholomew.com
Founded: 1993
Developmental editor. Specialize in fiction & narrative nonfiction. Have ghosted fiction & nonfiction. Co-authored a leading OB-GYN's award-winning memoir. Clients include authors (typically referred by their literary agents), publishers & nonprofits. Endorsements/testimonials available on web site & LinkedIn profile.
Membership(s): Editorial Freelancers Association

**Mark E Battersby**
PO Box 527, Ardmore, PA 19003
*Tel:* 610-924-9157 *Fax:* 610-924-9159
*E-mail:* mebatt12@earthlink.net
Founded: 1971
Freelance writer. Specialize in tax & financial features, columns, Web content & White Papers.

**Beaver Wood Associates**
655 Alstead Center Rd, Alstead, NH 03602
Mailing Address: PO Box 717, Alstead, NH 03602
*Tel:* 603-835-7900 *Fax:* 603-835-6279
*Web Site:* www.beaverwood.com
*Key Personnel*
Owner: Jeanne C Moody *E-mail:* jcmoody@beaverwood.com
Founded: 1985
Indexing, copy-editing, thesaurus construction.
Membership(s): American Society for Indexing

**Barbara Bergstrom MA LLC**
13 Stockton Way, Howell, NJ 07731
*Tel:* 732-363-8372
Offers complete editorial services: copy-editing, ms analysis, critique, development of mss, proofreading, research, revision, rewriting, condensations, copy fitting, writing, ghostwriting, indexing, newsletters, special assignment writing, speeches, transcription editing, project development & management, production services & editing for publishers, authors, academics, medical professionals, psychologists, businesses, public figures, associations & organizations. Act as publisher-author liaison, or as author's agent, full project management for publishers with mss needing copy-editing, revision &/or editor to work with author, or for self-publishing authors. Will travel to meet with authors to develop & edit mss. Meticulous editor (former university faculty) will copyedit Masters Thesis & Doctoral Dissertation, or we can prepare your ms for publication. Business, medical, psychological & technical writing, editing of user manuals into clearly understood English, project management & editing of in-house publications. Transcribe & edit books to tape. Special expertise in psychology, comparative literature, fiction, nonfiction, autobiography & memoirs, biography, art, art history, history, East Asian culture (China, Korea, Japan), Eastern philosophy & religions (Buddhism, Taoism, Confucianism, Shinto), T'ai Ch'i, martial arts, women's studies, natural healing, New Age, Native American, alternative healing sciences, meditation, "how-to", health & fitness, self-help, English, English as a Second Language (ESL) & more. ESL authors welcome. We are the editing/contracting agency for Dr Fred Penzel whose books include the award-winning *Obsessive-Compulsive Disorders: A Complete Guide to Getting Well and Staying Well* & *The Hair-Pulling Problem: A Complete Guide to Trichotillomania.* We also edited Jae Woong Kim's *Polishing the Diamond Enlightening the Mind.* Call before submitting mss. Ask about our specials. Also see listing under Consultants.

**Berlow Technical Communications Inc**
9 Prairie Ave, Suffern, NY 10901
*E-mail:* bteccinc@yahoo.com
*Key Personnel*
Pres: Lawrence H Berlow
Medical writing & editing, special assignment writing & secondary research.

**Jean Brodsky Bernard**
4609 Chevy Chase Blvd, Chevy Chase, MD 20815-5343
*Tel:* 301-654-8914
*E-mail:* dranreb@starpower.net
Founded: 1982

**Daniel Bial & Associates**
41 W 83 St, Suite 5-C, New York, NY 10024
*Tel:* 212-721-1786
*E-mail:* dbialagency@msn.com
*Web Site:* www.danielbialagency.com
*Key Personnel*
Founder & Prop: Daniel Bial
Founded: 1991
Creating, designing & producing illustrated el-hi & adult books; emphasis on reference sports.

**Bibliogenesis**
152 Coddington Rd, Ithaca, NY 14850
*Tel:* 607-277-9660
*Key Personnel*
Owner: Marian Hartman Rogers *E-mail:* mrogers@lightlink.com
Founded: 1987
Full editorial services encompassing all aspects of ms development: analysis, writing, rewriting, content editing, copy-editing, line editing, proofreading, fact checking, research & special assignment writing. Specialize in development, writing & editing of K-12 texts, teacher's editions & ancillaries in language arts, social studies, careers & other subject areas; scholarly works (classical & medieval studies, European history & literature, anthropology & gender studies, Middle Eastern studies, geography & travel); languages (French, German, Greek, Latin).

**Christopher Blackburn**
16 Purple Sageway, Toronto, ON M2H 2Z5, Canada
*Tel:* 416-491-4857
*E-mail:* cblackburn@rogers.com
Indexing of books, using appropriate software. Other skills include copy-editing & proofreading.
Membership(s): Indexing Society of Canada/Societe canadienne d'indexation

**Bloom Ink**
3497 Bennington Ct, Bloomfield Hills, MI 48301
*Tel:* 248-291-0370
*E-mail:* bbloom@bloomwriting.com
*Web Site:* www.bloomwriting.com
*Key Personnel*
Founder: Barbara Bloom
Founded: 2009
Provides a range of editing & publishing services including copyediting, developmental editing, audio abridgements (fiction, nonfiction), book proposals, ghost writing, book layout & design as well as assistance with self-publishing.
Membership(s): Editorial Freelancers Association

**Heidi Blough, Book Indexer**
502 Tanager Rd, St Augustine, FL 32086
*Tel:* 904-797-6572
*E-mail:* indexing@heidiblough.com
*Web Site:* www.heidiblough.com

*Key Personnel*
Owner: Heidi Blough
Founded: 2001
Indexing diverse topics that include: aerospace; biography; business, cooking, food & nutrition; engineering; general trade subjects; health & hospital administration; history, government & politics; how-to; maritime & transportation subjects.
Membership(s): American Society for Indexing

**Blue & Ude Writers' Services**
4249 Nuthatch Way, Clinton, WA 98236
Mailing Address: PO Box 145, Clinton, WA 98236-0145
*Tel:* 360-341-1630
*E-mail:* blueyude@whidbey.com
*Web Site:* www.blueudewritersservices.com
*Key Personnel*
Partner: Marian Blue; Wayne Ude
Founded: 1991
Provides all aspects of creative & technical writing & editing, including critiques, revisions & promotional copy, as well as grant writing.

**BookCrafters LLC**
Box C, Convent Station, NJ 07961
*Tel:* 973-984-7880
*Web Site:* bookcraftersllc.com
*Key Personnel*
Pres & Ed: Elizabeth Zack *E-mail:* ezack@bookcraftersllc.com
Founded: 2003
Specialize in ms development & editing. Offers services for published authors, literary agents & first-time writers from creating a marketable book proposal to fine-tuning a ms. The editor has over 23 years of experience in book publishing.

**The Bookmill**
501 Palisades Dr, No 315, Pacific Palisades, CA 90272-2848
*Tel:* 310-459-0190
*E-mail:* thebookmill1@verizon.net
*Web Site:* www.thebookmill.us
*Key Personnel*
Dir & Ed: Barbara Marinacci
Founded: 1982
MS critiques; developmental editing for books, articles; preparing queries & proposals; word processing; contacts with agents, editors & publishers; blurb writing, book "doctoring", proposals, restructuring & revising, transcribing.

**Boston Informatics**
35 Byard Lane, Westborough, MA 01581
*Tel:* 508-366-8176
*Web Site:* www.bostoninformatics.com
*Key Personnel*
Principal: M (May) H Hasso *E-mail:* mhsh2009@verizon.net
Founded: 2002
Provides indexing services for ebooks, databases, web & back of the book. Subjects covered include: business, finance & management, nutrition, health & allied sciences, social sciences, technology & engineering. Other services include taxonomy development, fact checking, information searching & word processing.
Membership(s): American Society for Indexing

**Boston Road Communications**
227 Boston Rd, Groton, MA 01450-1959
*Tel:* 978-448-8133
*Web Site:* www.bostonroadcommunications.com
*Key Personnel*
Owner: Christine R Lindemer *E-mail:* crlindemer@gmail.com
Founded: 2002
Indexing business, computer technology, quality management, project management, health care, history, agriculture, cookbooks, how-to, literary criticism & other subjects. Over 400 books indexed.
Membership(s): American Society for Indexing

**The Boston Word Works**
PO Box 56419, Sherman Oaks, CA 91413-1419
*Tel:* 818-904-9088 *Fax:* 818-787-1431
*Key Personnel*
Owner: Leslie Paul Boston
Founded: 1985
General fiction & nonfiction. Writing & editing. Evaluation, preparation of book proposals & sample chapters. Consultation on ideas, approaches & development.
Membership(s): Independent Writers of Southern California; National Writers Union

**bradylit**
81 Town Farm Hill, Hartland Four Corners, VT 05049
Mailing Address: PO Box 64, Hartland Four Corners, VT 05049
*Tel:* 802-436-2455 *Fax:* 802-436-2466
*Key Personnel*
Owner: Sally R Brady *E-mail:* sally@sallyryderbrady.com
Founded: 1988
Ms analysis, conceptual, developmental & line editing, book doctoring, rewriting; trade fiction & nonfiction; contacts with agents, editors & publishers. Work on a fee &/or percentage basis.

**Gordon Brumm**
1515 St Charles Ave, Lakewood, OH 44107
*Tel:* 216-226-6105 *Fax:* 216-226-1964
*E-mail:* brummg@cox.net
Founded: 1981

**Hilary R Burke**
59 Sparks St, Ottawa, ON K1P 6C3, Canada
Mailing Address: Box 133, Sta B, Ottawa, ON K1P 6C3, Canada
*Tel:* 613-237-4658
*E-mail:* hburke99@yahoo.com
Promotional writing of fiction & nonfiction.

**BZ/Rights & Permissions Inc**
145 W 86 St, New York, NY 10024
*Tel:* 212-924-3000 *Fax:* 212-924-2525
*E-mail:* info@bzrights.com
*Web Site:* www.bzrights.com
*Key Personnel*
Pres: Barbara Zimmerman *E-mail:* bz@bzrights.com
Founded: 1980
Clears rights for literary materials, music, film & TV clips, photos, art, celebrities for educational projects - printed textbooks, spoken word recordings, new electronic media, DVDs /videocassettes. Work with film & TV producers & ad agencies. Publisher of *The Mini-Encyclopedia of Public Domain Songs* & *They Never Renewed: Songs You Never Dreamed Were in the Public Domain.*
Membership(s): Association of Independent Music Publishers; Copyright Society of the USA; IBPA, the Independent Book Publishers Association; Media Communications Association

**Charles Carmony**
250 W 105 St, Suite 2-A, New York, NY 10025
*Tel:* 212-749-1835 *Fax:* 212-749-1835
*E-mail:* ccarmony@verizon.net
Indexing.

**Carpe Indexum**
364 Woodbine Ave, Syracuse, NY 13206-3324
*Tel:* 315-431-4949
*E-mail:* info@carpeindexum.com
*Web Site:* www.carpeindexum.com
*Key Personnel*
Owner: Michele Combs *E-mail:* mrothen2@twcny.rr.com
Founded: 2004
Provider of editing, indexing, research & writing & XML consulting services.
Membership(s): ALA; American Society for Indexing; Editorial Freelancers Association; Society of American Archivists

**R E Carsch, MS-Consultant**
1453 Rhode Island St, San Francisco, CA 94107-3248
*Tel:* 415-641-1095
*E-mail:* recarsch@mzinfo.com
*Key Personnel*
Consultant: R E Carsch
Founded: 1973
Full range editorial services including fact checking, interviewing, ms analysis, proofreading, research & industry overviews.
Membership(s): Art Libraries Society

**Anne Carson Associates**
3323 Nebraska Ave NW, Washington, DC 20016
*Tel:* 202-244-6679
*Key Personnel*
Ed-in-Chief: Anne Conover Carson
Founded: 1976
Proofreading, research, rewriting, special assignment writing, ms analysis. Specialize in Latin American culture & history, biographies of women & 20th century expats in Paris.
Membership(s): Academy of American Poets; The Authors Guild; MLA; National Coalition of Independent Scholars; National Press Club; Washington Independent Writers

**Carol Cartaino**
2000 Flat Run Rd, Seaman, OH 45679
*Tel:* 937-764-1303 *Fax:* 937-764-1303
*E-mail:* cartaino@aol.com
Founded: 1986
Content, developmental & line editing; ms analysis; rewriting & collaboration; development & packaging of book ideas & book programs. Nonfiction & selected fiction including how-to, self-help, reference, humorous & highly illustrated books. Also expert assistance of all kinds for self-publishers & solutions for problem mss.

**Claudia Caruana**
PO Box 654, Murray Hill Sta, New York, NY 10016
*Tel:* 516-488-5815
*E-mail:* ccaruana29@hotmail.com
Copy-editing, ms analysis, rights & permissions, picture search, proofreading, research, rewriting, special assignment writing, magazine photography.

**Angela M Casey**
42 Nathaniel Blvd, Delmar, NY 12054
*Tel:* 518-729-2693
*E-mail:* casey.angela.m@gmail.com
Founded: 2000
Book editing & ghost writing for established authors. Categories include psychology, health, diet, exercise & relationships. Advertising & promotion copy written for print & for web according to search engine optimization standards.

**Catalyst Communication Arts**
94 Chuparrosa Dr, San Luis Obispo, CA 93401
*Tel:* 805-235-2351 *Fax:* 805-543-7140
*Web Site:* www.sonsieconroy.com

*Key Personnel*
Owner: Sonsie Carbonara Conroy
*E-mail:* sconroy@slonet.org
Founded: 1980
Editorial services, specializing in indexing college textbooks, cookbooks, self-help, trade nonfiction.

**Catalyst Creative Services**
619 Marion Plaza, Palo Alto, CA 94301-4251
*Tel:* 650-325-1500
*Web Site:* www.CatalystCreative.us
*Key Personnel*
Owner & Chief Catalyst: Dennis Alan Briskin
*E-mail:* chief@catalystcreative.us
Founded: 1975
Our clients earn profits & get published. We offer complete editorial services, from the intelligent strategy (you must aim at the right target) to the structure, composition, revisions & final polish. Our business helps non-professional writers clarify, craft & publish their work for educated adult readers. We also ghostwrite for well-funded individuals with a story to tell or a cause to promote. (We respect academic integrity.) Writing is both an art & a craft. If you want to learn it, we can teach you the craft. We accept credit & debit cards.
Membership(s): Graphic Arts Association; National Writers Union

**Jeanne Cavelos Editorial Services**
PO Box 75, Mont Vernon, NH 03057
*Tel:* 603-673-6234
*Web Site:* www.jeannecavelos.com
*Key Personnel*
Owner: Jeanne Cavelos *E-mail:* jcavelos@sff.net
Founded: 1994
Published, best-selling writer & former senior editor at major publishing house. Full editorial services for publishers, book packagers, businesses, agents & authors. From line edit to thorough edit, to heavy edit. Detailed reader's reports. Book proposal doctoring. Editorial consulting, creative development. Newsletters, magazine articles, novelizations. Handle the full range of fiction & nonfiction. Specialize in thrillers, literary fiction, fantasy, science fiction, horror, popular culture, self-help, health & science.
Membership(s): Horror Writers Association; Science Fiction & Fantasy Writers of America

**CeciBooks Editorial & Publishing Consultation**
7057 26 Ave NW, Seattle, WA 98117
Mailing Address: PO Box 17229, Seattle, WA 98127
*Tel:* 206-706-9565
*E-mail:* cecibooks@gmail.com
*Web Site:* www.cecibooks.com
*Key Personnel*
Owner: Ceci Miller
Founded: 1988
Professional orientation to the world of publishing, as well as effective & respectful promotional writing & coaching. We develop publishing & marketing strategies that express our clients' best intentions. Whether an author or publisher wants advice on how best to position a book in the current market, seeks developmental or substantive editing, or needs a fresh marketing strategy, we offer guidance that is both reliable & affordable. E-mail to schedule a personal consultation by phone.
Membership(s): Northwest Independent Editors Guild; Pacific Northwest Writers Association; Society of Children's Book Writers & Illustrators; Women's Business Exchange

**Margaret Cheasebro**
246 Rd 2900, Aztec, NM 87410
*Tel:* 505-334-2869
*E-mail:* margaretcheasebro@yahoo.com
*Web Site:* www.wordsandwellness.com
Founded: 1986
Freelance writer. Specialize in articles about people, places & issues of the Four Corners area, nonfiction books about alternative healing & related subjects.
Membership(s): The Authors Guild; National Federation of Press Women; New Mexico Press Women

**Ruth Chernia**
198 Victor Ave, Toronto, ON M4K 1B2, Canada
*Tel:* 416-466-0164
*E-mail:* rchernia@editors.ca; rchernia@sympatico.ca
Founded: 1983
Provides professional editorial & publishing consultation to companies & individuals. Branch office in Toronto.
Membership(s): Editors' Association of Canada/Association canadienne des reviseurs

**Clear Concepts**
1329 Federal Ave, Suite 6, Los Angeles, CA 90025
*Tel:* 310-473-5453
*Key Personnel*
Owner: Karen Kleiner
Founded: 1986
Provides writing, substantive editing & research. Specializes in holistic health, fiction, children's books, technology & business. Owner holds BA from UCLA in Communication Studies.
Membership(s): Society for Technical Communication

**Clerical Plus**
97 Blueberry Lane, Shelton, CT 06484
*Tel:* 203-225-0879 *Fax:* 203-225-0879
*E-mail:* clericalplus@aol.com
*Web Site:* www.clericalplus.net
*Key Personnel*
Pres: Rose E Brown
Founded: 1990
Transcription/office support service company.

**Clotilde's Secretarial & Management Services**
PO Box 871926, New Orleans, LA 70187
*Tel:* 504-242-2912; 504-800-4863 (cell) *Fax:* 901-309-0664 (call first)
*E-mail:* elcsy58@aol.com; elcsy58@att.net
*Key Personnel*
Pres & Admin Mgr: Elvira C Sylve
Asst: Lillian Gail Tillman
Founded: 1989
Proofread & edit journals, newsletters, mss, research papers & medical documents. Specialize in preparing & typing research papers, grant proposals, medical & legal documents. Legal course work—Louisiana laws: briefs, business law, computer research & software, family law, interviewing, legal writing, litigation & researching in West Law.
Membership(s): American Health Information Management Association; National Association of Legal Assistants

**Coastside Editorial**
PO Box 181, Moss Beach, CA 94038
*E-mail:* bevjoe@pacific.net
*Key Personnel*
Contact: Beverly McGuire
Membership(s): Editcetera

**Robert L Cohen**
182-12 Horace Harding Expwy, Suite 2M, Fresh Meadows, NY 11365
*Tel:* 718-762-1195 *Toll Free Tel:* 866-EDITING (334-8464)
*E-mail:* wordsmith@sterlingmp.com
*Web Site:* www.rlcwordsandmusic.com; www.linkedin.com/in/robertcohen17
Copy, line (substantive) & developmental editing of academic, trade & reference books; editing & rewriting of public policy books/reports/policy briefs/newsletters/monographs; lexicography; radio & AV scriptwriting, speechwriting & other contract writing. Specialize in urban affairs & public policy, international relations (especially Middle East & related countries & regions), history & social sciences, politics & government, psychology & education, media & communications, Judaica & religion, music. Also writing coach & teacher for businesses, nonprofits & individuals.
Membership(s): American Society for Jewish Music; Cambridge Academic Editors Network; Editorial Freelancers Association

**Copywriter's Council of America (CCA)**
Division of The Linick Group Inc
CCA Bldg, 7 Putter Lane, Middle Island, NY 11953-1920
Mailing Address: PO Box 102, Dept LMP 11, Middle Island, NY 11953-0102
*Tel:* 631-924-8555 *Fax:* 631-924-8555
*E-mail:* cca4dmcopy@gmail.com
*Web Site:* www.AndrewLinickDirectMarketing.com/Copywriters-Council.html; www.NewWorldPressBooks.com
*Key Personnel*
Chmn, Consulting Group: Andrew S Linick, PhD
*E-mail:* andrew@asklinick.com
VP: Roger Dextor
Dir, Spec Projs: Barbara Deal
Over 25,000 freelance advertising copywriters, editors, communication specialists & journalists; covering publishing, Internet direct response/direct mail field for health, physical fitness, gourmet, how-to, martial arts, self improvement, travel & tourism, photography, sports & recreation, business communications & high tech for books, magazines, manuals, newsletters, in-house organs & courses. Marketing, research, rewriting, special assignment writing, copy-editing, indexing, proofreading, ms analysis; video production, audio-video news releases; interviews & profiles; rights & permissions. Also offer annual seminars, workshops & trade show to writers/editors who would like to increase their income. Phone consultation available. Provide comprehensive graphic re-design/new web site content development, interactive services with web site marketing makeover advice for first-time authors, self-publishers, professionals & entrepreneurs. Specializes in flash, animation, merchant accounts, online advertising/PR, links to top search engines, consulting on a 100% satisfaction guarantee. Free site evaluation for LMP readers.

**Corbett Gordon Co**
6 Fort Rachel Place, Mystic, CT 06355
*Tel:* 860-536-4108 *Fax:* 860-536-3732
*E-mail:* corbettgordon@comcast.net
*Key Personnel*
Owner: Rose Corbett Gordon
Creative research for books, book covers & exhibits. Fine art & historical research; experience includes wide range of subject areas, such as government, politics, social science & biological sciences. Also, art direction/commissioning of assignment photography.

**Course Crafters Inc**
3 Washington Sq, Haverhill, MA 01830
Mailing Address: PO Box 1058, Haverhill, MA 01831
*Tel:* 978-372-3446 *Fax:* 978-372-3660
*E-mail:* info@coursecrafters.com
*Web Site:* www.coursecrafters.com

*Key Personnel*
CEO & Publr: Lise B Ragan *Tel:* 978-372-3446 ext 228 *E-mail:* lragan@coursecrafters.com
Author & Ed: Dr Suzanne Irujo
Founded: 1993
Full-service development house & packager of educational materials, K-adult, with a unique focus in the growing English Language Learner Market (ELL). Specialize in English as a second language (ESL), bilingual education & literacy material for English language learners, their teachers & parents. Provide services to publishers in market research, consulting, conceptualizing, writing/editing, production, translation & developing marketing/sales plans. Also can develop customized materials for schools. Print, audio, video & multimedia in ESL & Spanish; professional development, instructional materials & assessment.

**Mark Crawford**
5101 Violet Lane, Madison, WI 53714
*Tel:* 608-240-4959
*E-mail:* mark.crawford@charter.net
Founded: 1995
Servicing all audiences including academic, technical, science, corporate & public relations. Additional services include: substantive editing, promotional writing & writing of corporate histories, business writing, marketing & communications, feature writing, editing & proofreading.

**Creative Freelancers Inc**
PO Box 366, Tallevast, FL 34270
*Tel:* 203-441-8144 *Toll Free Tel:* 800-398-9544
*Web Site:* www.freelancers1.com
*Key Personnel*
Pres: Marilyn Howard
Freelance copy & art services for publishing & advertising. Designers, artists, copy-editors, all creative areas, translations.

**Creative Inspirations Inc**
6203 Old Springville Rd, Pinson, AL 35126
Mailing Address: PO Box 100031, Irondale, AL 35210
*Web Site:* www.manuscriptcritique.com
*Key Personnel*
Pres: Michael Garrett *E-mail:* mike@manuscriptcritique.com
Founded: 1995
Editorial services for aspiring authors, including line edit & content evaluation.

**Ruth C Cross**
196 Melrose St, Unit 52, Brattleboro, VT 05301
*Tel:* 802-579-1368

**CS International Literary Agency**
43 W 39 St, New York, NY 10018
*Tel:* 212-921-1610; 212-391-9208
*E-mail:* query@csliterary.com; csliterary08@gmail.com
*Web Site:* www.csliterary.com
*Key Personnel*
Literary Agent: Cynthia Neesemann
Ms analysis, evaluation & agent representation available for nonfiction, fiction & screenplays. We assist writers in developing strategies to achieve ms publication or film production & to find the writing niche that suits their talents & personality in general or specialized markets. We are particularly responsive to helping beginning writers to improve their writing skills & style with suggestions for better plotting, characterization, dialogue & structure. Fees are very reasonable. Interests extend to full range of topics whether fact or fantasy, including international, occult, ethnic, political, historical & religious subjects, mysteries & comedies. Query with short synopsis of project.

**Cultural Studies & Analysis**
1123 Montrose St, Philadelphia, PA 19147-3721
*Tel:* 215-592-8544 *Fax:* 215-413-9041
*E-mail:* info@culturalanalysis.com
*Web Site:* www.culturalanalysis.com
*Key Personnel*
Dir: Margaret J King, PhD *E-mail:* mjking9@comcast.net
Sr Analyst: Jamie O'Boyle
Founded: 1994
Specialize in cultural analysis; identify consumer values & decision making. We do not provide novel writing.

**Culture Concepts Books**
69 Ashmount Crescent, Toronto, ON M9R 1C9, Canada
*Tel:* 416-245-8119
*E-mail:* cultureconcepts@rogers.com
*Web Site:* www.cultureconceptsbooks.ca; www.bookdoctor.ca
*Key Personnel*
Pres: Thelma Barer-Stein, PhD
Founded: 1980
Provides professional editorial services, ms evaluation, developmental & project editing, substantive editing, rewriting; line, copy & thesis editing.
Membership(s): Editors' Association of Canada/Association canadienne des reviseurs; The Writers' Union of Canada

**Cypress House**
Imprint of Comp-Type Inc
155 Cypress St, Fort Bragg, CA 95437
*Tel:* 707-964-9520 *Toll Free Tel:* 800-773-7782 *Fax:* 707-964-7531
*E-mail:* cypresshouse@cypresshouse.com
*Web Site:* www.cypresshouse.com
*Key Personnel*
Pres: Cynthia Frank *E-mail:* cynthia@cypresshouse.com
Prodn Mgr: Michael Brechner *E-mail:* unclemike@cypresshouse.com
Mng Ed: Joe Shaw *E-mail:* joeshaw@cypresshouse.com
Complete editorial, design, production, marketing & promotion services to independent publishers. Editorial services include ms evaluation, editing, rewriting, copymarking & proofing. Production services include book, cover & page design & make-up to camera-ready. Marketing & promotion services for selected titles.
Membership(s): ABA; Bay Area Independent Publishers Association; IBPA, the Independent Book Publishers Association; Northern California Independent Booksellers Association; Pacific Northwest Booksellers Association

**DanaRae Pomeroy**
139 Turner Circle, Greenville, SC 29609
*E-mail:* danarae@charter.net
*Web Site:* www.dana-rae.com
Founded: 1988
Ms critique; contact before sending mss for critique or editing.
Membership(s): National League of American Pen Women

**John M Daniel Literary Services**
PO Box 2790, McKinleyville, CA 95519
*Tel:* 707-839-3495 *Fax:* 707-839-3242
*E-mail:* jmd@danielpublishing.com
*Web Site:* www.danielpublishing.com/litserv.htm
*Key Personnel*
Ed: John M Daniel
Specialize in fiction & memoir.

**Darla Bruno Writer & Editor**
PO Box 243, Madison, NJ 07940
*E-mail:* editor@darlabruno.com
*Web Site:* www.darlabruno.com
Proofreading, copy-editing, developmental editing. Specialize in mainstream & literary fiction. Nonfiction subjects include self-help, health, travel, arts, memoir. Critiques mss & markets to literary agents.

**Suzanne B Davidson**
8084 N 44 St, Brown Deer, WI 53223
*Tel:* 414-355-6640
*E-mail:* davidson@milwpc.com
Founded: 1984
College texts, scholarly works, general nonfiction; law & criminal justice, business & finance, politics, public policy, history, social sciences, genealogy.

**Mari Lynch Dehmler**, see Fine Wordworking

**Christina Di Martino Literary Services**
139 Sandpiper Ave, Royal Palm Beach, FL 33411
*Tel:* 212-996-9086; 917-972-6012
*E-mail:* writealot@earthlink.net
*Web Site:* christinadimartino.com
*Key Personnel*
Owner: Christina Di Martino
Full book line services, collaboration of book projects, freelance writing for national magazines & teaching of writing.

**diacriTech Inc**
Formerly LaurelTech
250 Commercial St, Suite 2002, Manchester, NH 03101
*Tel:* 603-606-5800 *Fax:* 603-606-5838
*E-mail:* sales@diacritech.com
*Web Site:* www.diacritech.com
*Key Personnel*
CEO: Michael Hodges *E-mail:* m.hodges@diacritech.com
Founded: 1990
Specialize in meeting educational publishing needs. Full-service development & project management experience includes editorial, production, art & prepress services for textbooks & ancillaries. From developing, writing & editing mss to state-of-the-art page production, art rendering & prepress capabilities. In-house staff is experienced with all phases & disciplines of K-17.

**DK Research Inc**
14 Mohegan Lane, Commack, NY 11725
*Tel:* 631-543-5537 *Fax:* 631-543-5549
*Key Personnel*
Owner & Pres: Diane Kraut *E-mail:* dianekraut@att.net
Founded: 1993
Obtain copyright clearance for text material; negotiate photo & text permission fees; research & edit photos for use in textbooks.
Membership(s): Editorial Freelancers Association

**Double Play**
303 Hillcrest Rd, Belton, MO 64012-1852
*Tel:* 816-651-7118
*Key Personnel*
Pres: Lloyd Johnson
VP: Connie Johnson
Writing & research about baseball; sports, baseball museum consultant, exhibits; working on database of professional baseball.
Membership(s): Pro Football Researchers Association; Society for American Baseball Research

**Drennan Communications**
6 Robin Lane, East Kingston, NH 03827
*Tel:* 603-642-8002 *Fax:* 603-642-8002
*Key Personnel*
Pres & Edit Dir: William D Drennan
VP & Sr Ed: Christina L Drennan

Founded: 1980
Line editing, copy-editing, ms analysis, proofreading, rewriting, ghost writing, special assignment writing, condensations, typemarking, abstracting, fact checking, interviewing, research, advertising & promotion copywriting.

**Drummond Books**
2111 Cleveland St, Evanston, IL 60202
*Tel:* 847-302-2534
*E-mail:* drummondbooks@gmail.com
*Key Personnel*
Owner: Siobhan Drummond
Editorial & production services for web, print & ebooks, editorial management, project management from raw ms to finished book, copy editing, substantive editing, proofreading & indexing.

**DWJ BOOKS LLC**
Subsidiary of DWJ Television
22 Division St, 2nd fl, Sag Harbor, NY 11963
Mailing Address: PO Box 996, Sag Harbor, NY 11963
*Tel:* 631-899-4500 *Fax:* 631-899-4499
*E-mail:* info@dwjbooks.com
*Web Site:* www.dwjbooks.com
*Key Personnel*
EVP: Lauren Fedorko
Edit Dir: Darrell Kozlowski
Founded: 2005 (developing & packaging original content since 1988)
Full-service book & electronic development of large-scale projects & single titles for school, college, library & general reference publishing. Editorial services include: proposals, consulting, hiring of freelance staffs, writing, research, line & content editing, copy-editing, proofreading, indexing, fact checking, translating, special assignment writing, preparing files for print or online product.
Membership(s): ALA; American Book Producers Association; National Council for the Social Studies; National Council of Teachers of English

**Earth Edit**
PO Box 114, Maiden Rock, WI 54750
*Tel:* 715-448-3009
*Key Personnel*
Contact: George Dyke *E-mail:* gmdyke@gmail.com
Copy-editing & proofreading of earth science & geography texts.

**East Mountain Editing Services**
PO Box 1895, Tijeras, NM 87059-1895
*Tel:* 505-281-8422 *Fax:* 505-281-8422
*Web Site:* www.spanishindexing.com
*Key Personnel*
Mgr: Francine Cronshaw *E-mail:* cronshaw@nmia.com
Founded: 1992
Indexing (back-of-the-book) in Spanish or English. Also French, Italian & Portuguese. Special attention to Canadian editions. Consulting on bilingual or Spanish-language editions; copy-editing translations. For experience, see web site.
Membership(s): American Society for Indexing; New Mexico Translators & Interpreters Association

**EditAndPublishYourBook.com**
PO Box 2965, Nantucket, MA 02584-2965
*E-mail:* michaeltheauthor@yahoo.com
*Web Site:* www.editandpublishyourbook.com
*Key Personnel*
Principal: Michael Wells Glueck
Founded: 2002
Services offered include abstracting, condensations, copy-editing, interviewing, line editing, ms analysis, proofreading, rewriting, special assignment writing & transcription editing. Can also submit work to a reasonably priced subsidy publisher, shepherd it through the publication process & monitor online booksellers' web sites to make sure that it remains available for purchase, that they list it correctly & that the listing includes a front-cover photograph & other features. Can also suggest unorthodox but effective marketing techniques & write & submit reviews to online booksellers' web sites.
Recent projects include arranging online distribution for Donald E DeMarco's Nantucket Taste Memories: The DeMarco Restaurant Cookbook (self-published Oct 2007); as well as both writing & editing reviews for the Fictional Rome web site linked to the Richard Stockton College of New Jersey.

**Edit Etc**
12 Laurel Rd, Princeton, NJ 08540
*Tel:* 914-715-5849 *Fax:* 609-921-2025
*E-mail:* atkedit@cs.com
*Key Personnel*
Pres: Ann T Keene
Founded: 1985
Editing, writing, copywriting, research, photo research.
Membership(s): The Authors Guild

**Edit Resource LLC**
Division of Stanford Creative Services LLC
3578-E Hartsel Dr, Suite 387, Colorado Springs, CO 80920
*Tel:* 719-290-0757
*E-mail:* info@editresource.com (main)
*Web Site:* www.editresource.com (main); www.inspirationalghostwriting.com
*Key Personnel*
Owner: Elisa Stanford *E-mail:* elisa@editresource.com; Eric Stanford *E-mail:* eric@editresource.com
Founded: 1998
A writing & editing services provider.

**EditAmerica**
115 Jacobs Creek Rd, Ewing, NJ 08628
*Tel:* 609-882-5852
*Web Site:* www.editamerica.com; www.linkedin.com/in/PaulaPlantier
*Key Personnel*
Principal: Paula Plantier *E-mail:* paula@editamerica.com
Founded: 1979
Expert editing, rewriting/revising/repurposing, fact checking & proofreading of written communications in the areas of accounting, advertising, bibliography, biography, brochures, business, college application essays, company annual reports, cover letters, curricula vitae, education, finance, Form 10-Ks, Form 10-Qs, marketing, medicine, newsletters, news releases, peer-reviewed & refereed medical/scientific journal articles, pharmaceutics, press releases, religious treatises, resumes, theses/dissertations, user's manuals & web site content. Strict adherence to client-set deadlines. Satisfaction guaranteed for editorial services performed or there is no charge.

**Editcetera**
2034 Blake St, Suite 5, Berkeley, CA 94704
*Tel:* 510-849-1110 *Fax:* 510-848-1448
*E-mail:* info@editcetera.com
*Web Site:* www.editcetera.com
*Key Personnel*
Dir: Barbara Fuller
Founded: 1971
Association of freelance publishing professionals. Clients include authors, packagers, trade publishers, el-hi & college textbook publishers, self-publishers, computer companies (software & hardware) & corporations. Services available include production management from mss through bound books as well as writing, rewriting, developmental editing, copy-editing, coaching of writers, proofreading, indexing & web editing. Rigorous testing & review of all members.

**EditCraft Editorial Services**
422 Pine St, Grass Valley, CA 95945
*Tel:* 530-263-3688
*Web Site:* www.editcraft.com
*Key Personnel*
Prop: Eric W Engles, PhD *E-mail:* eric@editcraft.com
Founded: 1986
Editorial services for publishers, independent authors, scholars & technology companies.
Membership(s): Bay Area Editors' Forum; National Association of Science Writers

**The Editorial Dept LLC**
7650 E Broadway, Suite 308, Tucson, AZ 85710
*Tel:* 520-546-9992 *Fax:* 520-979-3408
*E-mail:* admin@editorialdepartment.com
*Web Site:* www.editorialdepartment.com
*Key Personnel*
Founder & Partner: Renni Browne
Pres: Ross Browne *E-mail:* rsb@editorialdepartment.com
Founded: 1980
Ms critique & evaluation, line & copy editing, novelizations & adaptations, book proposals, agent referral service, book cover design, book illustration, interior layout, e-book formatting, book/author marketing, publishing consultation, screenplay critique & consultation.

**The Editors Circle**
462 Grove St, Montclair, NJ 07043
*Tel:* 973-783-5082
*E-mail:* query@theeditorscircle.com
*Web Site:* www.theeditorscircle.com
*Key Personnel*
Ed: Bonny Fetterman *Tel:* 718-739-1057 *E-mail:* bvfetterman@aol.com; Rob Kaplan *Tel:* 914-736-7182 *E-mail:* robkaplan@optonline.net; Beth Lieberman *Tel:* 310-403-1602 *E-mail:* liebermanedit@socal.rr.com; John Paine *E-mail:* jpaine@johnpaine.com; Susan Schwartz *Tel:* 212-877-3211 *E-mail:* susan.sas22@gmail.com
Founded: 2005
A group of five independent book editors with more than 100 years of collective experience on-staff with major New York book publishers offering the following editorial services: editing & writing book proposals, query letters & complete mss; providing referrals to agents & publishers; consulting on self-publishing & digital publishing opportunities. Specialize in popular & scholarly nonfiction, memoirs & commercial & literary fiction.

**The Editor's Eye**
158-18 Riverside Dr W, Suite 6-E, New York, NY 10032
*Tel:* 212-740-6003 *Fax:* 212-740-6003
*E-mail:* editorseye@gmail.com
*Key Personnel*
Pres: Cheryll Y Greene
Founded: 1991
Develops companion publications for documentary films, public exhibitions & oral history projects; develops book, institutional & academic journal publication concepts; consults on fiction & nonfiction mss; line & copy-edits. Subjects include current events, history, gender issues, culture & arts. African American specialist.
Membership(s): PEN American Center

**EEI Communications**
7240 Parkway Dr, Suite 250, Hanover, MD 21076-1364
*Tel:* 410-309-8200 *Toll Free Tel:* 888-253-2762 *Fax:* 410-630-3980
*E-mail:* info@eeicom.com
*Web Site:* www.eeicom.com
*Key Personnel*
VP, Publg: John O'Brien
Substantive editing, copy-editing, writing, transcription, design, graphics, keyboarding, publications management, training in software & editorial skills; specialize in books & reports, government, technical/defense, management, communications & public health.
*Branch Office(s)*
962 Wayne Ave, Suite 310, Silver Spring, MD 20910

**Diane Eickhoff**
3808 Genessee St, Kansas City, MO 64111
*Tel:* 816-561-6693
*E-mail:* diane.eickhoff@gmail.com
Founded: 2000

**Irene Elmer**
2806 Cherry St, Berkeley, CA 94705-2310
*Tel:* 510-841-0466
*E-mail:* ielmer@earthlink.net
Founded: 1969
Rewriting, line editing & copy-editing of trade fiction & nonfiction, textbooks & scholarly works. Specialize in difficult rewrites, dialogue & lively presentation of difficult material. Special assignment writing of adult texts; trade nonfiction; high-interest, low-readability el-hi texts (fiction, drama, nonfiction).
Membership(s): Editcetera

**Catherine C Elverston ELS**
9 Red Bay Lane, Kitty Hawk, NC 27949-3307
*Tel:* 352-222-0625 (cell)
*E-mail:* celverston@gmail.com
All aspects of editing, preparing mss for publication, information research & retrieval. Also an agent.
Membership(s): American Medical Writers Association; Board of Editors in the Life Sciences

**R Elwell Indexing**
193 Main St, Cold Spring, NY 10516
*Tel:* 845-667-1036
*E-mail:* ruth.elwell@yahoo.com
Founded: 1975
Indexing.

**Enough Said**
3959 NW 29 Lane, Gainesville, FL 32606
*Tel:* 352-262-2971
*E-mail:* enoughsaid@cox.net
*Web Site:* users.navi.net/~heathlynn
*Key Personnel*
Owner & Ed: Ms Heath Lynn Silberfeld
Founded: 1984
Full range of hard-copy & electronic editorial services for nonfiction trade, mass market, textbook & self-publishing projects.

**Farrar Writing & Editing**
4638 Manchester Rd, Mound, MN 55364
*Tel:* 952-472-6874 *Fax:* 952-472-6874 (call first)
*Web Site:* www.writeandedit.net
*Key Personnel*
Freelance Writer & Ed: Amy E Farrar *E-mail:* amyfarrar@mchsi.com
Founded: 1999
Published book author (educational books for K-12 readers & general nonfiction); journalistic writing; book editor (copy-editing to substantive editing & rewriting); web site writing & editing. Clients include book publishers, nonprofits, magazines, newspapers & general businesses. Subjects include environmental, social, travel & health/medical.
Interested parties with book project in need of editing, send e-mail with synopsis of book, type of editorial service being sought, budget & deadline.
Membership(s): Professional Editors Network; Society of Children's Book Writers & Illustrators

**Lillian Mermin Feinsilver**
510 McCartney St, Easton, PA 18042
*Tel:* 610-252-7005
Membership(s): The Authors Guild

**Betsy Feist Resources**
140 E 81 St, Unit 8-G, New York, NY 10028-1875
*Tel:* 212-861-2014
*E-mail:* bfresources@rcn.com
*Key Personnel*
Pres: Betsy Feist
Complete editorial services, including development, writing, project management & editorial/production coordination. Specialize in instructional & informational materials.

**Jerry Felsen**
3960 NW 196 St, Miami Gardens, FL 33055-1869
*Tel:* 305-625-5012
*E-mail:* jfelsen0@att.net
*Web Site:* beatthemarket.org
Computer science, artificial intelligence, information systems & computer applications in business & investing; professional papers & business reports.

**Fine Wordworking**
PO Box 3041, Monterey, CA 93942-3041
*Tel:* 831-375-6278
*E-mail:* info@finewordworking.com
*Web Site:* marilynch.com
*Key Personnel*
Owner: Mari Lynch Dehmler
Founded: 1981
Writing, editing & proofreading of literary, business, personal & other material requiring top-level skills. Ghostwriting, collaborative writing & editing of adult, young adult & children's nonfiction books. Editing & proofreading of fiction. Well versed in Chicago style. Web content development & design collaboration. Interviewing, research & other support. Phone calls welcome.

**First Folio Resource Group Inc**
218 Adelaide St W, 2nd fl, Toronto, ON M5H 1W7, Canada
*Tel:* 416-368-7668 *Fax:* 416-368-9363
*E-mail:* mail@firstfolio.com
*Web Site:* www.firstfolio.com
*Key Personnel*
Mgr, Prodn Dept: Tom Dart
Proj Coord: Eileen Jung; Julie Kretchman; Debbie Smith; Bob Templeton
Complete editorial & production services: research, conceptual development, substantive editing, writing & rewriting, copy-editing, design & page layout, follow-up consultation & seminars.

**Richard A Flom**, see Lynn C Kronzek & Richard A Flom

**Focus Strategic Communications Inc**
2474 Waterford St, Oakville, ON L6L 5E6, Canada
*Tel:* 905-825-8757 *Toll Free Tel:* 866-263-6287 *Fax:* 905-825-5724 *Toll Free Fax:* 866-613-6287
*E-mail:* info@focussc.com
*Web Site:* www.focussc.com
*Key Personnel*
Dir: Adrianna Edwards *E-mail:* aedwards@focussc.com; Ron Edwards *E-mail:* redwards@focussc.com
Founded: 1988
Provide complete book development & production from concept & content to finished book. Innovative in assembling teams of experts to develop, write, edit, design & produce superior products. Specialty is education (textbooks, teacher resources, reference), focusing on social sciences, literacy & soft science. Trade books include kids & adult nonfiction on topics such as history, biography, science, how-to & business. Produce publisher-initiated titles as well as original books. Will work with other packagers to co-produce books.
Membership(s): AAP; American Book Producers Association; Association of Educational Publishers

**Foster Travel Publishing**
PO Box 5715, Berkeley, CA 94705-0715
*Tel:* 510-549-2202 *Fax:* 510-549-1131
*Web Site:* www.fostertravel.com
*Key Personnel*
Owner & Pres: Lee Foster *E-mail:* lee@fostertravel.com
Founded: 1970
Picture search, research, writing; travel (emphasizing locations, history, wine, nature). Specialize in Northern California, the West, Mexico-Baja, Europe, the Orient. Writing & photography available on web site (www.fostertravel.com). Provides travel writing/photography services for print & web editorial markets.
Membership(s): American Society of Media Photographers; Bay Area Travel Writers; SATW

**Sandi Frank**
8 Fieldcrest Ct, Cortlandt Manor, NY 10567
*Tel:* 914-739-7088
*E-mail:* sfrankmail@aol.com
Specialize in nonfiction in many disciplines, including textbooks, bibliographies, medical texts & journals, social sciences, scholarly material & cookbooks.
Membership(s): American Society for Indexing

**Frisbie/Communications**
631 N Dunton Ave, Arlington Heights, IL 60004
*Tel:* 847-253-4377 *Fax:* 847-253-4377
*Web Site:* www.richardfrisbie.net
*Key Personnel*
Pres: Richard Frisbie *E-mail:* richardfrisbie@sbcglobal.net
VP: Margery Frisbie *E-mail:* margeryfrisbie@sbcglobal.net
Founded: 1966
Creative direction & editorial work.
Membership(s): The Authors Guild; Society of Midland Authors

**Fromer Editorial Services**
1606 Noyes Dr, Silver Spring, MD 20910-2224
*Tel:* 301-585-8827 *Fax:* 301-585-1369
*Key Personnel*
Pres: Margot J Fromer *E-mail:* margotfromer@erols.com
Founded: 1980
Writing, rewriting & consultation in all aspects of health care & medicine; ms analysis, special assignment writing.
Membership(s): American Medical Writers Association; Science Writers' Association

**Sonia Elizabeth Fulop**
PO Box 978, Alamo, CA 94507
*Tel:* 847-736-4071
*Web Site:* www.soniafulop.com
Founded: 2005
A freelance developmental & copy editor of scholarly books & journals in the humanities & social sciences, Sonia received her training from the editing certificate program at the Graham School at the University of Chicago. She has worked with such publishers as Norton, Kent State University Press & Fordham University Press. Proficient in MLA, APA & Chicago & legal styles with a particular interest in legal studies & legal history, social work, literary criticism, visual culture, feminism & gender studies.
Membership(s): Cambridge Academic Editors Network; Council of Science Editors; Editorial Freelancers Association

**Diane Gallo**
49 Hilton St, Gilbertsville, NY 13776
Mailing Address: PO Box 106, Gilbertsville, NY 13776
*Tel:* 607-783-2386 *Fax:* 607-783-2386
*E-mail:* diane@dianegallo.com
*Web Site:* www.dianegallo.com
Interviewing & video scripts.

**Michael Garrett**, see Creative Inspirations Inc

**The Gary-Paul Agency**
1549 Main St, Stratford, CT 06615
*Tel:* 203-345-6167 *Fax:* 203-345-6167
*E-mail:* garret@thegarypaulagency.com
*Web Site:* www.thegarypaulagency.com; www.nutmegpictures.com
*Key Personnel*
Owner: Garret C Maynard *E-mail:* maynard@optonline.net
Founded: 1994
Literary agency that represents & promotes screenplays. Specialize in script development. WGAE Signator.
*Branch Office(s)*
27 Horseshoe Dr, Fayston, VT 05660 *Tel:* 203-556-8671
Membership(s): Writers Guild of America East

**Fred Gebhart**
2346 25 Ave, San Francisco, CA 94116-2337
*Tel:* 415-681-3018
*E-mail:* fgebhart@pobox.com
*Web Site:* www.fredgebhart.com
Founded: 1981
Editorial & advertorial writing. Specialize in business, consumer education, travel, healthcare, foreign countries, medicine, science, transportation, wine & spirits.
Membership(s): American Medical Writers Association; American Society of Journalists & Authors; International Society of Travel Medicine; National Association of Science Writers

**Gelles-Cole Literary Enterprises**
135 John Joy Rd, Woodstock, NY 12498-0341
*Tel:* 845-679-2452
*Web Site:* www.literaryenterprises.com
*Key Personnel*
Founder & Pres: Sandi Gelles-Cole *E-mail:* sandigc@aol.com
Founded: 1983
Editorial consultant ("Book Doctor") specializing in commercial fiction & nonfiction serving authors, publishers & literary agents; writing coach; consultant for self publishing authors, collaboration. Editorial specialty is development of concept & character development. Provide an intense word by word tutorial focusing on concept, style, voice, pace & characterization & for nonfiction, structure. Also offer help to experts & other authors developing their material for the general public. Also have small publishing arm. Soft spot - first novels.
Membership(s): Consulting Editors Alliance

**Nancy C Gerth PhD**
1431 Harlan's Trail, Sagle, ID 83860
*Tel:* 208-304-9066
*E-mail:* docnangee@nancygerth.com
*Web Site:* www.nancygerth.com
Founded: 2005
Freelance indexing & related services. Index specialities: law & scholarly. PhD in philsophy.
Providing information services since 1988.
Membership(s): American Society for Indexing; Pacific Northwest Chapter of American Society for Indexing

**GGP Publishing Inc**
105 Calvert St, Suite 201, Harrison, NY 10528-3138
*Tel:* 914-834-8896 *Fax:* 914-834-7566
*Web Site:* www.ggppublishing.com
*Key Personnel*
Pres: Generosa Gina Protano *E-mail:* ggprotano@ggppublishing.com
Founded: 1991
Packager for trade & educational publishers. All editorial, art & design, production & printing services—from concept to bound books or any segment(s) of this publishing process. Trade (fiction & nonfiction) & children's books, textbooks (el-hi, college & adult education), professional, reference & how-to books, cookbooks, audiotapes & videotapes, CDs & CD-ROMs. Specialize in the development of materials for the study of foreign languages (such as French, German, Italian, Japanese, Latin, Portuguese, Russian & Spanish) & English as a Second Language, as well as in the development of materials for bilingual education & language arts. In addition, we translate complete or partial programs from & into the various languages & act as literary agents & foreign publisher representatives.
Membership(s): American Book Producers Association

**Cathe Giffuni**, see Research Research

**Sheri Gilbert**
123 Van Voorhis Ave, Rochester, NY 14617
*Tel:* 585-342-0331 *Fax:* 585-323-1828
*E-mail:* gilbert@permissionseditor.com
*Web Site:* permissionseditor.com
Reviews mss for permissions identification; preparing permissions reports; obtaining permissions for text, art, photographs & song lyrics. Creating credit lines & source notes.

**Michael Wells Glueck**, see EditAndPublishYourBook.com

**Gold Leaf Press**
2229 Alter Rd, Detroit, MI 48215
*Tel:* 313-331-3571 *Fax:* 313-308-3063
*E-mail:* interest@goldleafpress.com
*Web Site:* www.goldleafpress.com
*Key Personnel*
Publr & Publg Consultant: Rebecca J Ensign *E-mail:* rebecca@goldleafpress.com
Founded: 1994
Independent publisher & publishing services provider to the trade, corporate & academic markets. Our proprietary publishing program, for qualifying works & authors, emphasizes editorial development for market worthiness. Through our services, Gold Leaf Press has edited, published & represented fiction & nonfiction titles & authors in a variety of genres, from scholarly works, autobiographies & company training manuals to corporate identity publications, self-help books & novels.

**Donald Goldstein**
1500 E 17 St, Brooklyn, NY 11230
*Tel:* 718-375-9346 *Fax:* 212-854-5640
*E-mail:* dgoldsbkyn@aol.com
Sports, sociology, American politics, the labor movement, Israel, Jewish related subjects; research, interviewing, copy-editing, rewriting, special assignment writing & proofreading.

**Robert M Goodman**
140 West End Ave, Unit 11-J, New York, NY 10023
*Tel:* 917-439-1097
*E-mail:* bobbybgood@gmail.com
Membership(s): Editorial Freelancers Association

**P M Gordon Associates Inc**
2115 Wallace St, Philadelphia, PA 19130
*Tel:* 215-769-2525 *Fax:* 215-769-5354
*E-mail:* pmga@pond1.net
*Web Site:* www.pmgordon.com
*Key Personnel*
Pres: Peggy M Gordon
VP: Douglas C Gordon
Founded: 1982
Developmental editing, rewriting & copy-editing for trade, text & corporate books; indexing. Complete design & production services.

**C+S Gottfried**
619 Cricklewood Dr, State College, PA 16803
*Tel:* 814-237-2580
*Web Site:* www.lookoutnow.com/index2.html
*Key Personnel*
Owner & Mktg Dir: Chet Gottfried *E-mail:* me@lookoutnow.com
Mgr: Susan Gottfried
Founded: 1988
From electronic or paper ms to camera copy, as well as printing-binding supervision.

**Sherry Gottlieb**
Unit of wordservices.com
4900 Dunes St, Oxnard, CA 93035
*Tel:* 805-382-3425
*E-mail:* writer@wordservices.com
*Web Site:* www.wordservices.com
Founded: 1991
Private editorial service that specialize in fiction & screenplays. Edited over 300 book mss, mostly fiction. Several clients have sold their books to major publishers.

**Graphic World Publishing Services**
Division of Graphic World Inc
11687 Adie Rd, St Louis, MO 63043
*Tel:* 314-567-9854 *Fax:* 314-567-7178
*E-mail:* quote@gwinc.com
*Web Site:* www.gwinc.com
*Key Personnel*
CEO & Pres: Kevin P Arrow
EVP, Technol: Andrew R Vosburgh *E-mail:* a.vosburgh@gwinc.com
EVP, Opers: Michael J Loomis *E-mail:* mike.loomis@gwps.com
Dir, Publg & Media Servs: Suzanne Kastner
VP of Sales: Dean Grantham *E-mail:* directorsales@gwinc.com
Complete editorial & project management services from ms through final files, including interior & cover design, composition services, electronic publishing services & art rendering.
*Branch Office(s)*
370 Seventh Ave, Suite 305, New York, NY 10001

**Paul Greenland Editorial Services**
9184 Longfellow Lane, Machesney Park, IL 61115
*Tel:* 815-540-0911
*Web Site:* www.paulgreenland.com
*Key Personnel*
Owner: Paul R Greenland
Services include writing, ghostwriting & collaboration, research, editing & proofreading. Published nonfiction author, marketing/communications professional & former senior editor of national business magazine. Contributor to many leading reference books (Gale Group, University of Chicago Press, St. James Press). Interview subjects include celebrities, athletes & leading business executives. Specialize in reference, business, biography & history. References available upon request.

**Rosemary F Gretton**
53 Grassland Ct, Danville, CA 94526
*Tel:* 925-336-0003 *Fax:* 925-336-0003
*E-mail:* rgretton@lyricism.ca
*Web Site:* www.lyricism.ca
Founded: 2003
Writing, editing & research services for publishers, government, business, nonprofit organizations & individuals. Specializes in copy writing, copy-editing, fact checking, line editing, proofreading, research & rewriting.
Membership(s): Editors' Association of Canada/Association canadienne des reviseurs

**Joan K Griffitts Indexing**
3909 W 71 St, Indianapolis, IN 46268-2257
*Tel:* 317-297-7312
*E-mail:* jkgriffitts@gmail.com
*Web Site:* www.joankgriffittsindexing.com
Founded: 1989
Indexing & proofreading of textbooks, tradebooks, reference books, technical documentation, catalogs & newspapers by former librarian. Most subjects; specialize in business, science, sports, gardening, computer science, library science, education, taxation & social science. Various computer formats & e-mail delivery.
Membership(s): American Society for Indexing

**Judith S Grossman**
715 Cherry Circle, Wynnewood, PA 19096
*Tel:* 610-642-0906
*E-mail:* stogiz@aol.com
Founded: 1973
Editing, ms evaluation & analysis, proofreading, rewriting; fiction, humanities, social sciences.

**Anne Hebenstreit**
20 Tip Top Way, Berkeley Heights, NJ 07922
*Tel:* 908-665-0536
Copy-editing & proofreading of el-hi & college texts & trade books.

**Helm Editorial Services**
707 SW Eighth Way, Fort Lauderdale, FL 33315
*Tel:* 954-525-5626
*E-mail:* lynnehelm12@aol.com
Freelance writing, line editing & publishing for executives & authors.

**Herr's Indexing Service**
PO Box 5378, Kailua Kona, HI 96745
*Tel:* 802-585-6844 *Fax:* 802-883-5415
*Web Site:* www.herrsindexing.com
*Key Personnel*
Owner: Linda Herr Hallinger *E-mail:* linda@herrsindexing.com
Founded: 1944
Provide quality & affordable indexes for a variety of topics. Specialize in medical books.
Membership(s): American Medical Writers Association; American Society for Indexing; Editorial Freelancers Association

**L Anne Hirschel DDS**
5990 Highgate Ave, East Lansing, MI 48823
*Tel:* 517-333-1748
*E-mail:* alicerichard@comcast.net
Medicine & dentistry, consumer/patient information, continuing education & editing for foreign speaking scientists.
Membership(s): American Dental Association; Medical Writers Association

**Burnham Holmes**
182 Lakeview Hill Rd, Poultney, VT 05764-9179
*Tel:* 802-287-9707 *Fax:* 802-287-9707 (computer fax/modem)
*E-mail:* burnham.holmes@castleton.edu
Founded: 1990
Write textbooks, fiction & general nonfiction, juvenile, young adult, plays & children's books.
Membership(s): The Authors Guild; League of Vermont Writers

**Henry Holmes Literary Agent/Book Publicist/Marketing Consultant**
PO Box 433, Swansea, MA 02777
*Tel:* 508-672-2258
*E-mail:* henryholmesandassociates@yahoo.com
*Key Personnel*
Pres & Literary Agent: Henry Holmes
Founded: 1997
Nonfiction: biography, business, education, law, health, history, sports, etc. Exclusive literary agent/book publicist for authors. Authors must present complete book proposal with SASE when submitting. Impeccable presentation is a must. Prefer books targeted at general audiences rather than an exclusive or limited market. Send letter with a good hook & a list of publishers you have contacted in the past. Do not send any spiral bound proposals; word count must be stated. Include past publicity & endorsement(s). Commission 15%. Contract must be signed. Upon receipt of signed contract, author will be sent a media portfolio with marketing data, tip sheet & full compliment of media contact listings. Professional consultation related to all media, freelance assignments, interviewing celebrities, professional athletes, musicians, political figures & other famous people.

**Nancy Humpheys Wordmaps**
600 Humboldt St, Richmond, CA 94805
*Tel:* 415-462-1844
*Web Site:* www.wordmapsindexing.com (book indexing); www.authormaps.com (book marketing)
*Key Personnel*
Principal & CEO: Nancy K Humphreys *E-mail:* nancy@wordmapsindexing.com
Founded: 1996
Indexes for self-published books, advice on book production & marketing; author of *Marketing Your Book to Libraries.*
Membership(s): American Society for Indexing; Indexing Society of Canada/Societe canadienne d'indexation

**Imagefinders Inc**
6101 Utah Ave NW, Washington, DC 20015
*Tel:* 202-244-4456 *Fax:* 202-244-3237
*Key Personnel*
Pres: Elisabeth M Hartjens *E-mail:* hartjens@erols.com
Founded: 1985
Photo & illustration research & editing; fact checking, information research. Specialize in Washington public domain sources.

**IndexEmpire Indexing Services**
16740 Orville Wright Dr, Riverside, CA 92518
*Tel:* 951-697-2819
*E-mail:* indexempire@gmail.com
*Key Personnel*
Contact: Jean F Middleton
Founded: 1999
Provides back-of-the-book indexes for nonfiction books of all types.
Membership(s): American Society for Indexing

**Indexing by the Book**
PO Box 12513, Tucson, AZ 85732
*Tel:* 520-750-8439
*E-mail:* indextran@cox.net
*Web Site:* www.indexingbythebook.com
*Key Personnel*
Indexer: Cynthia J Coan
Founded: 2003
Index books & serials. Subject specialties include health/medicine, history (especially Arizona/Southwest), education, language studies, library science, social sciences & psychology. Index adult, children's & Spanish language titles. Also translate print materials from Spanish & Swedish into English.
Membership(s): American Society for Indexing; ATA; National Council on Interpreting in Health Care

**InfoWorks Development Group**
2801 Cook Creek Dr, Ann Arbor, MI 48103-8962
*Tel:* 734-327-9669 *Fax:* 734-327-9686
*Key Personnel*
Partner: David E Salamie *E-mail:* desalamie@aol.com; Amy L Unterburger *E-mail:* aunterburg@aol.com
Founded: 1995
Full range of editorial services, including project management/editing, copy-editing, proofreading, SGML coding & bibliographies. Specialize in reference & general nonfiction projects.

**Integra Software Services Inc**
Division of Integra Software Services Pvt Ltd
1110 Jorie Blvd, Suite 200, Oak Brook, IL 60523
*Tel:* 630-586-2579 *Fax:* 630-586-2599
*Web Site:* www.integra.co.in
*Key Personnel*
SVP, North America: Mark Witman *E-mail:* mark.witman@integra.co.in
Dir, Opers & Edit Devt for Higher Educ: Ingrid Benson *E-mail:* ingrid.benson@integra.co.in
Tech Mgr: Jack Semens
Design Mgr: Emily Friel
Busn Mgr: Helen Fuller
Mng Ed: Miki Yamada; Karin Kipp
Founded: 1991
Project management, development & production support for book publishers. Full range of editorial & production services from ms through camera-ready copy, files or film. Services include text & art development, writing, copy-editing, proofreading, indexing, photo research, permissions, design, art & electronic composition, using QuarkXPress, Illustrator, Photoshop, Autopage & PowerMath. Specialty areas are business & economics, computer science, mathematics, science, history, English, medical & education texts.

**Jan Williams Indexing Services**
300 Dartmouth College Hwy, Lyme, NH 03768-3207
*Tel:* 603-795-4924 *Fax:* 603-795-4836
*Web Site:* www.janwilliamsindexing.com

*Key Personnel*
Prop: Jan Williams
Founded: 1998
Back-of-book indexes for trade, scholarly, reference & textbooks; database/online indexes for journals. Proofreading & copy-editing.
Membership(s): American Society for Indexing

**Jenkins Group Inc**
1129 Woodmere Ave, Suite B, Traverse City, MI 49686
*Tel:* 231-933-0445 *Toll Free Tel:* 800-706-4636 *Fax:* 231-933-0448
*E-mail:* info@bookpublishing.com
*Web Site:* www.bookpublishing.com
*Key Personnel*
CEO: Jerrold R Jenkins *Tel:* 231-933-0445 ext 1008 *E-mail:* jrj@bookpublishing.com
COO & Pres: James Kalajian *Tel:* 231-933-0445 ext 1006 *E-mail:* jjk@bookpublishing.com
Dir, Consulting & Mktg Servs: Kim Hornyak *Tel:* 231-933-0445 ext 1013 *E-mail:* khornyak@bookpublishing.com
Mng Ed, Independent Publisher Online: Jim Barnes *E-mail:* jimb@bookpublishing.com
Book Prodn Mgr: Leah Nicholson *Tel:* 231-933-0445 ext 1015 *E-mail:* lnicholson@bookpublishing.com
Founded: 1990
Full-service custom book publishing services for corporations, independent authors, organizations & small press publishers. Services include registrations, typesetting, cover design, color separations, ghost writing, illustration & photo placement, galley preparation & print management.

**JFE Editorial**
8425 Doreen Ave, Fort Worth, TX 76116-4922
*Tel:* 817-560-7018
*Web Site:* www.jfe-editorial.com
*Key Personnel*
Owner & Pres: June Ford *E-mail:* jford@jfe-editorial.com
Founded: 1987
Founded by Ms Ford - a nationally published author, ghostwriter, project manager, editor & proofreader. Focus includes: writing, ghostwriting, rewriting, special assignment writing; developmental, copy, line, style & content editing; proofreading; ms analysis; permissions, interviewing; fact checking; database research, coding, editing. Published in genres ranging from children's, trade & true crime to scholastic, self-help & sports books; also a variety of magazine articles. Coordinator of many high-dollar projects & extremely successful at transforming complex material into easily understood information. Ms Ford is a speaker for grades 3-12, universities & conferences. Also offers database research. Fax number provided upon request.
Membership(s): Association of Independent Information Professionals; Women's National Book Association

**JL Communications**
10205 Green Holly Terr, Silver Spring, MD 20902
*Tel:* 301-593-0640
*Key Personnel*
Writer, Ed & Poet: Joyce Eileen Latham
Founded: 1996

**Cliff Johnson & Associates**
10867 Fruitland Dr, Studio City, CA 91604
*Tel:* 818-761-5665 *Fax:* 818-761-9501
*E-mail:* quest543@yahoo.com
*Key Personnel*
Pres: Cliff Johnson
Founded: 1976
Nonfiction specialists (primarily medical, psychology, religious, self-help & philosophical books).

**Jouve North America Inc**
Division of Jouve Group (France)
70 Landmark Hill Dr, Brattleboro, VT 05301
Mailing Address: PO Box 1338, Brattleboro, VT 05302
*Tel:* 802-254-6073 *Toll Free Tel:* 800-451-4328
*Web Site:* www.jouve.com
*Key Personnel*
CEO & Pres: Emmanuel Benoit
Founded: 1997

**Just Creative Writing & Indexing Services (JCR)**
301 Wood Duck Dr, Greensboro, MD 21639
*Tel:* 410-482-6337
*E-mail:* jreveal@verizon.net; jreveal@justcreativewriting.com
*Web Site:* www.justcreativewriting.com
*Key Personnel*
Sole Proprietor: Judith Reveal
Founded: 2005
Provides editorial services for fiction & nonfiction; professional back-of-the-book indexing.
Membership(s): American Society for Indexing; Eastern Shore Writers' Association; Editorial Freelancers Association; Greensboro Business & Civic Association

**Sharon Kapnick**
185 West End Ave, New York, NY 10023-5547
*Tel:* 212-787-7231
Food & wine articles for magazines, web sites, newspapers & books.

**Ann T Keene**, see Edit Etc

**Keim Publishing**
66 Main St, Suite 807, Yonkers, NY 10701
*Tel:* 917-655-7190
*Key Personnel*
Owner & Pres: Betty Keim *E-mail:* blkeim@earthlink.net
Founded: 1985
Books & art catalogs, newsletters, brochures, electronic materials (eg, web sites, advertisements, etc), promotional items, reference books, production & design, line editing, copyediting, indexing, permissions, photo research, proofreading, reference assignments, research, rewriting, typemarking, special assignment writing. All subjects; specialize in art, broadcasting, history, literature, science, mathematics & music.

**Kessler Communications**
280 W 86 St, New York, NY 10024
*Tel:* 212-724-8610
*E-mail:* lmp@etk.mailbolt.com
*Web Site:* www.kesslercommunications.com
*Key Personnel*
Pres: Ellen Terry Kessler
Founded: 1986
Advertising & promotional copy, all types of editing & rewriting, brochures, catalogs, newsletters, book jackets, manuals, direct mail, advertorials, press releases, sales letters, special assignments, articles, interviewing, ghost writing.
Membership(s): Editorial Freelancers Association

**Jascha Kessler**
218 16 St, Santa Monica, CA 90402-2216
*Tel:* 310-393-7968 *Fax:* 310-393-7968 (by request only)
*E-mail:* jkessler@ucla.edu
*Web Site:* www.jfkessler.com; www.xlibris.com
Freelance reviews of poetry, fiction, history, philosophy, current affairs. Criticism as well as "cultural commentary" on the arts, theater & dance.
Membership(s): American Society of Composers, Authors and Publishers

**Theodore Knight PhD**
RockCliff Farm, Unit 101A, 40 Old Louisquisset Pike, North Smithfield, RI 02896
*Tel:* 401-597-6982
*E-mail:* tedknight1@cox.net
Founded: 1989
Editorial & project management for trade, textbook, university press & reference.

**Bill Koehnlein**
236 E Fifth St, New York, NY 10003-8545
*Tel:* 212-674-9145
*E-mail:* koehnlein.bill@gmail.com
Founded: 1982
Indexing & editing: all subjects, especially current affairs, social science, American labor & radical history, radical political movements & theory: socialism, Marxism, anarchism. Also food & nutrition issues, especially vegetarianism & veganism.

**Barry R Koffler**
Featherside, 14 Ginger Rd, High Falls, NY 12440
*Tel:* 845-687-9851
*E-mail:* barkof@feathersite.com
Founded: 1979
Indexing, Proofreading, Editing. Writing most subjects (including encyclopedic); specialize in popular & scientific works on animals & natural history.

**KOK Edit**
15 Hare Lane, East Setauket, NY 11733-3606
*Tel:* 631-474-1170 *Fax:* 631-474-9849
*E-mail:* editor@kokedit.com
*Web Site:* www.kokedit.com; twitter.com/#!/KOKEdit; www.facebook.com/K.OMooreKlopf; www.linkedin.com/in/kokedit; www.editor-mom.blogspot.com
*Key Personnel*
Owner: Katharine O'Moore-Klopf
Founded: 1995
Provides copyediting & substantive editing to authors & publishers of textbooks, professional books & journal articles (medicine, psychology, psychiatry, allied health) & nonfiction trade books (mainstream health care, alternative health care, child care, human sexuality, psychology, women's issues). Certified by the Board of Editors in the Life Sciences.
Membership(s): American Medical Writers Association; Board of Editors in the Life Sciences; Council of Science Editors; Editorial Freelancers Association; World Association of Medical Editors

**Kraft & Kraft**
40 Memorial Hwy, Apt 23-C, New Rochelle, NY 10801
*Tel:* 914-319-3320
*Web Site:* www.erickraft.com
*Key Personnel*
Owner & Edit Dir: Eric Kraft *E-mail:* eric-kraft@post.harvard.edu
Contact: Madeline Kraft
Founded: 1975
Design & development of educational materials.

**Eileen Kramer**
336 Great Rd, Stow, MA 01775
*Tel:* 978-897-4121
*E-mail:* kramer@tiac.net
*Web Site:* www.ekramer.com
Founded: 1985

Copyeditor/proofreader/ESL teacher/curriculum developer. Specialties include ESL textbooks & courseware; web, science, math, statistics, technical books, academic journals & textbooks.

**Lynn C Kronzek & Richard A Flom**
Affiliate of Lynn C Kronzek & Associates
145 S Glenoaks Blvd, Suite 240, Burbank, CA 91502
*Tel:* 818-768-7688 *Fax:* 818-768-7648
*Key Personnel*
Principal: Lynn C Kronzek *E-mail:* lckronzek@sbcglobal.net
Founded: 1989
Nonfiction writing & editorial services, with particular expertise in history, multicultural & Judaic studies, government/public affairs & religion. Affiliated with the National Council on Public History, American Association for State & Local History & the Rabbinical Assembly.

**Polly Kummel**
624 Boardman Rd, Aiken, SC 29803
*Tel:* 803-641-6831
*E-mail:* editor@amazinphrasin.com; pollyk1@msn.com
*Web Site:* www.amazinphrasin.com
Founded: 1990
Nonfiction (all subjects; trade & academic): copy-editing; substantive/developmental editing; coaching. Specialties: journalism, history, political science, memoir, equestrian subjects. Dissertation/thesis help for humanities grad students; electronic editing. More than 35 years of experience.

**Lachina Publishing Services Inc**
3793 S Green Rd, Cleveland, OH 44122
*Tel:* 216-292-7959 *Fax:* 216-292-3639
*E-mail:* info@lachina.com
*Web Site:* www.lachina.com
*Key Personnel*
Pres: Jeffrey A Lachina
Founded: 1978
Project management, editorial development, copy editing, biomedical illustration, indexing, page composition, book & jacket design, proofreading, technical illustration.

**Lynne Lackenbach Editorial Services**
31 Pillsbury Rd, East Hampstead, NH 03826
*Tel:* 603-329-8133
*E-mail:* lynnelack@gmail.com
Full line of editorial services to college & professional publishers. Specialize in scientific & technical material.

**Bob Land**, see Land on Demand

**Land on Demand**
20 Long Crescent Dr, Bristol, VA 24201
*Tel:* 276-642-0550
*E-mail:* landondemand@bvunet.net
*Web Site:* boblandedits.blogspot.com
*Key Personnel*
Proprietor & Proofreader: Bob Land
Founded: 1994 (Full-time freelancer since 1994; freelancer since 1986; full-time editor, writer, proofreader 1981-1994)
Editing, indexing, proofreading.

**LaurelTech**, see diacriTech Inc

**The Learning Source Ltd**
644 Tenth St, Brooklyn, NY 11215
*Tel:* 718-768-0231 (ext 10) *Fax:* 718-369-3467
*E-mail:* info@learningsourceltd.com
*Web Site:* www.learningsourceltd.com
*Key Personnel*
Dir: Gary W Davis; Wendy Davis
EVP: Brian Ableman
Provides a full range of editorial & book-producing services from concept through ms & design to film & bound book. Specialty areas include children's fiction & nonfiction, adult reference & nonfiction series & classroom materials. Sister company to Ivy Gate Books.

**Debra Lemonds**
PO Box 5516, Pasadena, CA 91117-0516
*Tel:* 626-844-9363
*E-mail:* dlemonds@earthlink.net
Founded: 1984
Photo editor. Layout & a bit of graphic design.
Membership(s): ASPP

**Elizabeth J Leppman**
631 Worcester Dr, Lexington, KY 40503
*Tel:* 859-245-4325 *Fax:* 859-245-4325
*E-mail:* ejleppman@windstream.net
*Web Site:* www.leppman.com
Founded: 1974
Published author & experienced book/journal editor will perform developmental, content & copy editing, ms reviewing, writing. Specialize in geography & map editing.

**Andrew S Linick PhD, The Copyologist®**
Subsidiary of The Linick Group Inc
Linick Bldg, 7 Putter Lane, Middle Island, NY 11953
Mailing Address: PO Box 102, Dept LMP 11, Middle Island, NY 11953-0102
*Tel:* 631-924-3888 *Fax:* 631-924-8555
*E-mail:* linickgroup@gmail.com
*Web Site:* www.AndrewLinickDirectMarketing.com/The-Copyologist.html; www.NewWorldPressBooks.com
*Key Personnel*
CEO & Creative Dir: Andrew S Linick, PhD *E-mail:* andrew@asklinick.com
VP: Roger Dextor
Founded: 1968
Complete editorial & copywriting services: copy analysis & line editing, research, rewriting for direct response, direct mail, mail order, sales promotions; specialize in newsletters, newspapers, magazines, house organs & seminars; catalog writing, business & consumer launch packages & in-house seminars on how to sell what you write; articles, nonfiction books & manuals. Phone consultation available; consumer, trade, business to business, all markets, media & subjects; ms analysis & development, proofreading, special assignment writing, ghostwriting, e-mail marketing campaigns for publishers. Provide comprehensive graphic re-design/new web site content development, interactive services with web site marketing makeover advice for first-time authors, self-publishers, professionals & entrepreneurs. Specializes in flash, animation, merchant accounts, online advertising/PR, links to top search engines, consulting on a 100% satisfaction guarantee. Free site evaluation for LMP readers. For over 43 years we have helped first-time authors & best-selling authors/publishers/entrepreneurs successfully promote books. Call for help today.
Membership(s): IBPA, the Independent Book Publishers Association

**Elliot Linzer**
126-10 Powells Cove Blvd, College Point, NY 11356
*Tel:* 718-353-1261 *Fax:* 814-253-1261
*E-mail:* elinzer@juno.com
Founded: 1971
Indexing (computer-assisted) of trade books, textbooks, reference books & scholarly books. Subject matter covered includes social sciences & computers.
Membership(s): American Society for Indexing; Editorial Freelancers Association

**E Trina Lipton**
60 E Eighth St, Suite 15-F, New York, NY 10003
*Tel:* 212-674-5558 (call first, messages); 917-327-6886 (cell) *Fax:* 212-674-3523
*E-mail:* trinalipton@hotmail.com
Thirty-six years experience of picture research & picture editing: historical & contemporary still photos & film footage, art illustrations. Photography: stock photos (B&W & color, all subjects). Also editorial research, fact checking & permissions interviewing.
Membership(s): National Press Photographers Association; New York Museum of Education Roundtable; UFT

**Eli Liss**
41 Viking Lane, Woodstock, NY 12498
*Tel:* 845-679-7173
*E-mail:* elibear88@aol.com
Founded: 1975
Indexing.

**Little Chicago Editorial Services**
154 Natural Tpke, Ripton, VT 05766
Mailing Address: PO Box 185, Ripton, VT 05766
*Tel:* 802-388-9782
*Web Site:* andreachesman.com
*Key Personnel*
Writer & Ed: Andrea Chesman *E-mail:* andreachesman@gmail.com
Editorial Services.

**Mari Lynch**, see Fine Wordworking

**Elizabeth Lyon**
3530 E Game Farm Rd, No 39, Springfield, OR 97477
*Tel:* 541-554-2082
*E-mail:* elyon123@comcast.net
*Web Site:* www.elizabethlyon.com
Founded: 1988
Full-time freelance book editor. Specialize in novels, memoirs, nonfiction books & proposals. Advises writers about how to write, connect with literary agents &, should 'Plan A' not succeed, how to successfully self-publish an ebook &/or print-on-demand. Over 60 writers have found publication with large publishers & small presses, while dozens have "gone indie," some to great success & acclaim. Edits query letters & synopses for clients. Has written 6 books on writing, including the bestsellers *Nonfiction Book Proposals Anybody Can Write* & *Manuscript Makeover*. *Writing Subtext* is the first in an e-booklet series, sold as Kindle singles & PDFs on the web site.
Membership(s): Oregon Writers Colony; Sisters in Crime; Williamette Writers Association

**Phyllis Manner**
17 Springdale Rd, New Rochelle, NY 10804
*Tel:* 914-834-4707 *Fax:* 914-834-4707
*E-mail:* pmanner@aol.com
Specialize in medicine, biochemistry & archeology.
Membership(s): American Society for Indexing; Archeological Institute of America

**Danny Marcus Word Worker**
Division of D M Enterprises
62 Washington St, Suite 2, Marblehead, MA 01945-3553
*Tel:* 781-631-3886; 781-290-9174 (cell) *Fax:* 781-631-3886
*E-mail:* emildanelle@yahoo.com
Founded: 1984

Proofreading, line editing & copy-editing. Specialize in politics, income taxes, government, history, current events, all kinds of fiction & general nonfiction.
Membership(s): Cambridge Academic Editors Network

**Joy Matkowski**
212 Ridge Hill Rd, Mechanicsburg, PA 17050
*Tel:* 717-620-8881
*E-mail:* jmatkowski1@comcast.net
Copy-editing & proofreading.

**Peter Mayeux**
RR 1, Box 242A3, 15660 Bobwhite Trail, Crete, NE 68333-0333
*Tel:* 402-826-5231
*E-mail:* pm41923@windstream.net
Broadcast commercial writing, textbooks, media scripts.

**McCarthy Creative Services**
625 Main St, Suite 834, New York, NY 10044-0035
*Tel:* 212-832-3428
*E-mail:* PaulMccarthy@MccarthyCreative.com
*Web Site:* www.mccarthycreative.com
*Key Personnel*
Founder & Pres: Prof Paul D McCarthy
Founded: 1999
The MCS Creative Editing division is the most popular of the 10 divisions of my global creativity company. My creative editing is customized & comprehensive, all forms of fiction & nonfiction, from concept to complete ms, for authors, agents & publishers. I've worked with 9 number 1 *New York Times* & international bestselling authors including Nelson Demille, Clive Cussler & Dr David Reuben. I have 36 years of combined experience as editor, agent, *New York Times* bestselling author & publisher. I am "The" Professor in Writing, Editing & Publishing at The University of Ulster, Ireland, 30,000 students. People from more than 120 countries have visited the MCS web site.
Membership(s): American Film Institute; American Society of Journalists & Authors; The Association of Publishers for Special Sales; The Authors Guild; The Grolier Club; The Princeton Club of New York; Women's National Book Association

**Anita D McClellan Associates**
464 Common St, Suite 142, Belmont, MA 02478-2704
*Tel:* 617-575-9203 *Fax:* 206-203-0829
*E-mail:* adm@anitamcclellan.com
*Web Site:* www.anitamcclellan.com
*Key Personnel*
Mng Dir: Anita D McClellan
Founded: 1988
Developmental editing, nonfiction proposal development, revising, restructuring, book doctoring, fiction & nonfiction.
Membership(s): The Authors Guild; Bay Area Editors' Forum; Bookbuilders of Boston; Cape Cod Writers Center; Editorial Freelancers Association; Independent Publishers of New England; International Women's Writing Guild; Sisters in Crime; Society of Children's Book Writers & Illustrators; Women's National Book Association

**Pamela Dittmer McKuen**
87 Tanglewood Dr, Glen Ellyn, IL 60137
*Tel:* 630-545-0867 *Fax:* 630-545-0868
*E-mail:* pmckuen@gmail.com
*Web Site:* www.allthewritethings.com; www.pamelamckuen.com
Special assignment writing, editorial & corporate projects, periodicals, copy-editing, interviewing & research.
Membership(s): Association of Women in Journalism; National Association of Real Estate Editors; National Federation of Press Women

**Pat McNees**
10643 Weymouth St, Suite 204, Bethesda, MD 20814
*Tel:* 301-897-8557
*E-mail:* pmcnees@nasw.org
*Web Site:* www.patmcnees.com; www.writersandeditors.com
Founded: 1971
Articles, books, photohistories. Specialize in memoirs, personal histories, biographies & organizational histories, especially in fields of medicine & psychiatry. Teach life story & legacy writing; do substantial editing, rewriting & book doctoring. Theme anthologies & stories about food, dancing & travel.
Membership(s): American Society of Journalists & Authors; Association of Health Care Journalists; Association of Personal Historians; The Authors Guild; Biographers International Organization; IBPA, the Independent Book Publishers Association; National Association of Science Writers; PEN International; Society for Technical Communication

**Barbara A Mele**
2525 Holland Ave, New York, NY 10467-8703
*Tel:* 718-654-8047 *Fax:* 718-654-8047
*E-mail:* bannmele@aol.com
Freelance permissions.

**Tom Mellers Publishing Services (TMPS)**
60 Second Ave, New York, NY 10003
*Tel:* 212-254-4958
*E-mail:* tmps71@yahoo.com
Comprehensive rights & permissions administration, acquiring & granting rights for text of all kinds, photos, art, video, film, music, spoken word. Acquiring services range from consulting with rightseekers, to evaluating permissionable material, setting up projects, sending & tracking requests, negotiating fees, preparing acknowledgments, administering payment & righting contracts. Granting services include drafting contracts, negotiating & collecting fees & preparing records (edit-in). Copyright registration. Specialize in literary estates. All subjects & media. Extensive editing & editorial services, from author consultation to ms analysis, fact checking & rewriting to project supervision (including typemarking, book design, line editing, copy-editing, proofreading). Ghost writing & special assignment writing, author representation & photo research, drafting contracts, image research & international work with museums.
*Branch Office(s)*
4629 Vestal Pkwy E, Vestal, NY 13850 *Tel:* 607-798-7994

**Fred C Mench Professor of Classics Emeritus**
207 Saint Martins Lane, Smyrna, TN 37167
*Tel:* 615-459-0765
*E-mail:* fmench@earthlink.net
Text editing, especially classical antiquity or English literature. Past projects included reading drafts of Roman historical novels for content & form, writing reviews of scholarly & fictional works (especially on ancient Rome). Book Review Editor of the journal Classical World for 15 years, involving extensive condensing of submitted texts. Special areas: Julius Caesar, Roman republic, Latin texts, the Bible, Greek mythology & G B Shaw. Also available for general editing.
Membership(s): American Philological Association

**Metropolitan Editorial & Writing Service**
Subsidiary of Metropolitan Research Co
4455 Douglas Ave, Riverdale, NY 10471
*Tel:* 718-549-5518
*Key Personnel*
Pres: Chauncey G Olinger, Jr
Founded: 1982
Editing, ms analysis, rewriting & restyling of general, professional & scholarly writing, especially in economics, business, social sciences, humanities, medicine & pharmacy. Specialize in editorial collaboration with authors; oral history interviewing.

**Susan T Middleton**
366-A Norton Hill Rd, Ashfield, MA 01330-9601
*Tel:* 413-628-4039
*E-mail:* smiddle@crocker.com
Founded: 1985
Book revision, collaboration, developmental & copy-editing for individuals & for trade & college markets primarily in the sciences.
Membership(s): Western New England Editorial Freelancers Association

**Robert J Milch**
9 Millbrook Dr, Stony Brook, NY 11790-2914
*Tel:* 631-689-8546 *Fax:* 631-689-8546
*E-mail:* milchedit@aol.com

**Stephen M Miller Inc**
15727 S Madison Dr, Olathe, KS 66062
*Tel:* 913-768-7997
*Web Site:* www.stephenmillerbooks.com
*Key Personnel*
Pres: Stephen M Miller *E-mail:* steve@stephenmillerbooks.com
Founded: 1994
Writing, editing; bible specialty & health subspecialty. Fulltime freelance writer & former editor, books, magazines & newspaper. Seminary & journalism school graduate, Kansas City area. Clientele of top national book publishers & magazines.
Membership(s): CBA; CBA: The Association for Christian Retail; Evangelical Christian Publishers Association; Society of Bible Literature; Wesleyan Theological Society

**Kathleen Mills Editorial Services**
PO Box 214, Chardon, OH 44024
*Tel:* 440-285-4347
*E-mail:* mills_edit@yahoo.com
*Key Personnel*
Edit Dir: Kathleen Mills
Founded: 1990
More than 30 years of publishing experience. Editing, indexing, writing, author liaison & project management. Arts & humanities, social sciences, technical, reference, medical, college, business, general nonfiction & web sites. Clients include the Cleveland Museum of Art, Western Reserve Historical Society, Case Western Reserve University, ASM International, UCLA & many others.

**Sondra Mochson**
18 Overlook Dr, Port Washington, NY 11050
*Tel:* 516-883-0961
All subjects, text & trade.

**Mary Mueller**
516 Bartram Rd, Moorestown, NJ 08057
*Tel:* 856-778-4769
*E-mail:* mamam49@aol.com

Abstracting, copy-editing, ghost writing, indexing, proofreading, rewriting & book reviewing-publicity. Specialize in consumer education, gardening, health, nutrition, house & home organizing, science & technology.

**Nina Neimark Editorial Services**
543 Third St, Brooklyn, NY 11215
*Tel:* 718-499-6804
*E-mail:* pneimark@hotmail.com
*Key Personnel*
Pres: Nina Neimark
Founded: 1965
Specializing in scholarly books & college texts on environmental issues, history, art, music, social sciences; also general nonfiction. Mss analysis & development, content & photo research, rewriting, copy-editing, proofreading, production editing & complete book packaging services.

**Nesbitt Graphics Inc**
555 Virginia Dr, Fort Washington, PA 19034
*Tel:* 215-591-9125 *Fax:* 215-591-9093
*Web Site:* www.nesbittgraphics.com
*Key Personnel*
Pres: Harry J Nesbitt, III *E-mail:* h_nesbitt@nesbittgraphics.com
VP, Technol: Bruce Nesbitt *E-mail:* b_nesbitt@nesbittgraphics.com
VP, Prodn Servs: Harry F Druding *E-mail:* h_druding@nesbittgraphics.com
Founded: 1998
Our school division offers complete PreK-12 educational publishing services including conceptual development, prototype development, research, writing, content editing, copy-editing, fact checking & production editing. Editorial expertise includes mathematics, science/health & reading/language arts. Extensive experience creating student & teacher's editions, alternative programs, supplemental materials, assessment, curriculum alignment, state customizations, correlations & professional developmental materials. Our higher education division provides expert full-service management for college, medical, nursing, allied health & scholarly publications. Production services for both school & higher education include instructional design, page layouts, art creation & art services, photo research/shoots, electronic composition & prepress services.
Membership(s): Book Industry Guild of New York; Bookbuilders of Boston; Midwest Publishing Association; National Association for the Education of Young Children; National Council of Supervisors of Mathematics; National Council of Teachers of Mathematics; National Science Teachers Association; Publishing Professionals Network

**Newgen North America Inc**
Subsidiary of Newgen KnowledgeWorks
2714 Bee Cave Rd, Suite 201, Austin, TX 78746
*Tel:* 512-478-5341 *Fax:* 512-476-4756
*Web Site:* www.newgen.co
*Key Personnel*
Pres: Maran Elancheran *E-mail:* maran@newgen.co
VP: Bill M Grosskopf *E-mail:* bill@newgen.co
Founded: 1955
Prepares project material for copy-editor, supervises the copy-editing, serves as liaison with the author, reviews the final ms & makes sure that all elements of the project are complete & ready to be turned over to a designer. Ensures that file conversions, coding & cleanup properly prepare book material for each stage in the process. Convert files to e-book formats. Scan printed books to prepare new print file & e-book files.

**Sue Newton**
1385 Cypress Point Lane, Suite 202, Ventura, CA 93003
*Tel:* 805-553-8087; 805-861-3923 (cell)
*E-mail:* sue.edit@gmail.com
Founded: 1995
Ms & line editing services including the correction of spelling errors, grammar, punctuation, syntax & consistency. Minor rewrites. 15 years experience in the publishing industry including fiction, nonfiction, autobiographies & advertising.
Membership(s): Small Publishers, Artists & Writers Network; Ventura County Writers Club

**Donald Nicholson-Smith**
PO Box 272, Knickerbocker Sta, New York, NY 10002
*E-mail:* mnr.dns@verizon.net
French-English literary translation.

**Northeastern Graphic Inc**
25 Old Kings Rd N, Suite 3B, Palm Coast, FL 32137-8245
*Tel:* 386-246-9942 *Fax:* 386-246-9698
*Web Site:* www.northeasterngraphic.com
*Key Personnel*
CFO: Kathryn Sussman
Pres: Kate Scully *E-mail:* kscully@northeasterngraphic.com
Founded: 1988
Copy-editing, fact checking, indexing, line editing, ms analysis, permissions, photo research, proofreading, rewriting & typemarking.

**nSight Inc**
One Van de Graaff Dr, Suite 202, Burlington, MA 01803
*Tel:* 781-273-6300 *Fax:* 781-273-6301
*E-mail:* nfritz@nsightworks.com
*Web Site:* www.nsightworks.com
*Key Personnel*
Founder & Chpn: Nan Fritz
CEO & Pres: Tom LeBlanc *E-mail:* tleblanc@nsightworks.com
VP, Mktg & Strategy: Dan Cote *E-mail:* dcote@nsightworks.com
VP, Publg & Edit Servs: Elizabeth St Germain *E-mail:* estgermain@nsightworks.com
Founded: 1982
Complete book & journal content development & production services: writing, copy-editing, developmental editing, indexing, proofreading; project management; abstracting, advertising & promotion copywriting, bibliographies, fact checking, interviewing, developmental editing, ms analysis, rewriting, special assignment writing, transcription editing; design, art rendering, photo research, covers & jackets; permissions; in-house composition as well as development of electronic publishing products, including HTML & XML coding & supervising printing. Online editing experts (visit EditExpress.com). Specialize in technical subject areas: college, medical & allied health, computer science, law, physical & life sciences & engineering.
Membership(s): Association of Educational Publishers; Bookbuilders of Boston

**Veronica Oliva**
PO Box 460365, San Francisco, CA 94146-0365
*Tel:* 415-337-7707
*E-mail:* veronicaoliva@sbcglobal.net; veronicaoliva.oliva@gmail.net
Founded: 1994
Permissions editor: Trade & educational publishers. Specialty: French, Spanish & Italian college-level textbooks.
Membership(s): Bay Area Editors' Forum; Media Alliance

**Orion Book Services**
751 South St, West Brattleboro, VT 05301-4234
*Tel:* 802-254-8783 (press 2) *Fax:* 802-254-8783 (call first)
*E-mail:* gr8books@myfairpoint.net
*Key Personnel*
Pres: Orion M Barber
Founded: 1984
Trade book development services; editorial & publishing consultation.

**Oyster River Press**
36 Oyster River Rd, Durham, NH 03824-3029
*Tel:* 603-868-5006
*E-mail:* oysterriverpress@comcast.net
*Web Site:* www.oysterriverpress.com
*Key Personnel*
Publr & Ed: Cicely Buckley
Interviewing, special assignment writing, translating services to/from French, Spanish, Russian, Polish.
Membership(s): New Hampshire Writers Project

**Pacific Publishing Services**
PO Box 1150, Capitola, CA 95010-1150
*Tel:* 831-476-8284 *Fax:* 831-476-8294
*E-mail:* pacpub@attglobal.net
*Key Personnel*
Pres: Albert Lee Strickland
Assoc: Lynne Ann De Spelder
Research, editorial & writing services for trade, text & corporate publications.

**Karen L Pangallo**
27 Buffum St, Salem, MA 01970
*Tel:* 978-744-8796
*E-mail:* pangallo@noblenet.org

**Diane Patrick**
140 Carver Loop, No 21A, Bronx, NY 10475-2954
*E-mail:* dpatrickediting@aol.com
*Web Site:* www.dianepatrick.net
Professional editor who polishes words for publishers, editors, agents, academics, legal professionals, entertainers & business owners. Especially enjoy working with biography.
Membership(s): ALA; International Women's Writing Guild; New York Association of Black Journalists

**Beth Penney Editorial Services**
PO Box 604, Pacific Grove, CA 93950-0604
*Tel:* 831-372-7625
*Key Personnel*
Pres: Beth Penney *E-mail:* bpenney@sonic.net
Founded: 1980
Membership(s): College Reading & Learning Association; MLA; National Council of Teachers of English

**PeopleSpeak**
25260-I La Paz Rd, Suite 1, Laguna Hills, CA 92653
*Tel:* 949-581-6190 *Fax:* 949-581-4958
*E-mail:* pplspeak@att.net
*Web Site:* www.detailsplease.com/peoplespeak
*Key Personnel*
Sr Ed: Sharon Goldinger
Founded: 1985
An eye for details. Copyediting; specialize in nonfiction mss, marketing materials, newsletters, directories.
Membership(s): IBPA, the Independent Book Publishers Association; Publishers Association of Los Angeles; San Diego Professional Editors Network

**Rebecca Pepper**
434 NE Floral Place, Portland, OR 97232
*Tel:* 503-236-5802
*E-mail:* rpepper@rpepper.net

Founded: 1986
Membership(s): Editcetera; Editorial Freelancers Association; Northwest Independent Editors Guild

**The Permissions Group Inc**
1247 Milwaukee Ave, Suite 303, Glenview, IL 60025
*Tel:* 847-635-6550 *Toll Free Tel:* 800-374-7985 *Fax:* 847-635-6968
*E-mail:* info@permissionsgroup.com
*Web Site:* www.permissionsgroup.com
*Key Personnel*
Dir: Sherry Hoesly *E-mail:* sherry_hoesly@permissionsgroup.com
Full-service copyright & permissions consulting company. Specializing in ms review & analysis, rights negotiation, individualized consulting.

**Elsa Peterson Ltd**
41 East Ave, Norwalk, CT 06851-3919
*Tel:* 203-846-8331
*E-mail:* epltd@earthlink.net
Founded: 1984
Offer a full range of editorial services personalized to your project: developmental or substantive editing, writing, rights clearance, picture research, translation (Spanish to English).
Membership(s): Association for Psychological Science; Connecticut Press Club; Editorial Freelancers Association; Text & Academic Authors

**Evelyn Walters Pettit**
PO Box 3073, Winter Park, FL 32790-3073
*Tel:* 407-620-0131 (cell); 407-644-1711 *Fax:* 407-644-1711
*E-mail:* bookseller@brandywinebooks.com
*Web Site:* www.brandywinebooks.com
Copy & line editing, rewriting & proofreading. Specialize in professional & reference books & journal articles & in general magazines & books. Experience in subjects ranging from social & biological sciences to engineering & mathematics to business.

**Meredith Phillips**
Subsidiary of Perseverance Editorial Services
4127 Old Adobe Rd, Palo Alto, CA 94306
*Tel:* 650-857-9555
*E-mail:* mphillips0743@comcast.net
Former author & award-nominated mystery publisher (Perseverance Press). Editing (developmental, line, copy), researching, fact checking, proofreading of trade books (fiction or nonfiction).

**PhotoEdit Inc**
3505 Cadillac Ave, Suite P-101, Costa Mesa, CA 92626
*Tel:* 714-434-5925 *Toll Free Tel:* 800-860-2098 *Fax:* 714-434-5937 *Toll Free Fax:* 800-804-3707
*E-mail:* sales@photoeditinc.com
*Web Site:* www.photoeditinc.com
*Key Personnel*
Pres: Raquel Rameriz
Founded: 1987
Photographers; large stock on hand.

**PhotoSource International**
Pine Lake Farm, 1910 35 Rd, Osceola, WI 54020-5602
*Tel:* 715-248-3800 (ext 21) *Toll Free Tel:* 800-624-0266 (ext 21) *Fax:* 715-248-3800 *Toll Free Fax:* 800-223-3860
*E-mail:* info@photosource.com; psi2@photosource.com
*Web Site:* www.photosource.com
*Key Personnel*
Dir: Rohn Engh
Mng Ed: Bruce Swenson
Ed & Photog: Dennis Carroll
Founded: 1976
Publisher, *The Photoletter*, *Photo Stock Notes*, *Photodaily*, market letter broadcasting photo needs of photo buyers to photographers, pictorial statitics.

**Pictures & Words Editorial Services**
3100 "B" Ave, Anacortes, WA 98221
*Tel:* 360-293-8476
*E-mail:* editor@picturesandwords.com
*Web Site:* www.picturesandwords.com/words
*Key Personnel*
Owner: Kristi Hein
Founded: 1995
Versatile generalist serving trade publishers & authors. Particular expertise in gardening, nature & environment, cookbooks, health & well-being, business, education, consumer interest, politics & fiction.
Membership(s): Bay Area Editors' Forum; Northwest Independent Editors Guild

**Caroline Pincus Book Midwife**
101 Wool St, San Francisco, CA 94110
*Tel:* 415-516-6206
*E-mail:* cpincus100@sbcglobal.net
*Key Personnel*
Book Midwife: Caroline Pincus
Founded: 1998
Ms development & book doctoring for the general trade. Specialize in health, personal growth, women's issues & narrative nonfiction.

**Marilyn Pincus Inc**
1320 W Bloomington Place, Tucson, AZ 85755-8773
*Tel:* 520-742-6699
*E-mail:* mpscribe@aol.com
*Web Site:* www.marilynpincus.info
*Key Personnel*
Pres: Marilyn Pincus
Author, ghostwriter & consultant-to-management. Books published in many languages. Works with clients on book development from A-Z. Ghostwrites some or all of clients' books. Highly skilled interviewer & researcher. Also originates or updates policies, procedures, job descriptions & related documents. Accepts some speaking invitations. See web site for bio & book titles.
Membership(s): The Authors Guild; International Association of Business Communicators; Women's Studies Advisory Council, University of Arizona

**J P Pochron Writer for Hire**
830 Lake Orchid Circle, No 203, Vero Beach, FL 32962
*Tel:* 772-569-2967
*E-mail:* hotwriter15@hotmail.com; jp_pochron@comcast.net
*Key Personnel*
Owner & Writer: J P Pochron
Over 35 years experience. Currently freelancing. Former editor, reporter & freelance writer, with marketing, advertising & public relations experience. Press releases, promotional copy, commercials, personal & business letter writing are services offered. Eight years library reference experience to assist with research.

**Wendy Polhemus-Annibell**
PO Box 464, Peconic, NY 11958
*Tel:* 631-276-0684
*E-mail:* wannibell@gmail.com; wannibel@suffolk.lib.ny.us
Founded: 1987
Freelance copy-editing, line editing, development editing, proofreading, project management (ms to prepress). Specialize in college textbooks (particularly English/grammar/writing/rhetoric texts) & fiction/nonfiction trade books, with an emphasis on editorial excellence.

**PreMediaGlobal**
4 Collins Ave, Plymouth, MA 02360
*Tel:* 508-746-0300 *Fax:* 508-746-3233
*E-mail:* info@premediaglobal.com
*Web Site:* www.premediaglobal.com
*Key Personnel*
CFO: John Chappell *Tel:* 508-746-0300 ext 304
EVP: Rick A Vayo *E-mail:* rvayo@premediaglobal.com
SVP: Jack Mitchell *E-mail:* jmitchell@premediaglobal.com
Founded: 2005
Providing full-service content creation, design/packaging & media delivery systems to publishers. Services include authoring/writing, editorial research & development, media development & production, editing, photo & text research/permissions, photography/photo shoot direction, indexing, proofreading, fact checking, design/design direction, art direction/editing, technical/illustrative art packages, photo manipulation & page make-up/composition services. Employs over 1,200 US & offshore resources specializing in content/media creation & make-up including file conversions/repurposing & content management & delivery services. All services are offered both in the US & at offshore facilities. Areas of specialization include school, higher education & professional publishing: mathematics (grade school/algebra/calculus/physics), foreign language (French/Spanish/German/Italian), English & English composition, history, political science, science (chemistry/biology/astronomy), social studies, computer science, business (economics/finance/marketing), engineering & technical trades as well as professional/reference material. Products range from simple one-color ancillaries components to highly complex design & art intensive core content.

**The Professional Writer**
175 W 12 St, Suite 6D, New York, NY 10011
*Tel:* 212-414-0188; 917-658-1946 (cell)
*E-mail:* paul@theprofessionalwriter.com
*Web Site:* www.theprofessionalwriter.com
*Key Personnel*
Owner: Paul Wisenthal
Founded: 1989
Book networking to the industry, book development-includes creative writing/editing, writer's block, project preparation. Copywriting for brochures, media kits, newsletters, business & investment proposals, writers coach & grants. Script writing, script doctor for TV/film/radio. Speechwriting. Youth market specialists.
Membership(s): The Authors Guild

**Pronk Media Inc**
PO Box 340, Beaverton, ON L0K 1A0, Canada
*Tel:* 416-441-3760
*E-mail:* info@pronk.com
*Web Site:* www.pronk.com
*Key Personnel*
Pres: Gord Pronk *Tel:* 416-441-3760 ext 203
Founded: 1981 (as Pronk & Associates Inc)
Offers complete PreK-12 educational publishing services including project management, writing, content editing, developmental editing, concept development, cover design, art direction, photo research, technical art, page composition, typography, page layout, Photoshop work, typesetting, complete prepress services, permissions, developmental editing, copy-editing, proofreading, indexing, fact checking & production editing for student resources, teacher editions & ancillaries. Expertise in mathe-

matics, science, social studies & language arts/reading materials for print, on CD-ROM, the Internet & design & production.

**Proofed to Perfection Editing Services**
PO Box 71851, Durham, NC 27722-1851
*Tel:* 919-732-8565
*E-mail:* inquiries@proofedtoperfection.com
*Web Site:* www.proofedtoperfection.com
*Key Personnel*
Sr Ed & Proj Coord: Pamela Guerrieri
*E-mail:* pamg@proofedtoperfection.com
Founded: 2006
Full-service editing company specializing in comprehensive, professional book editing. We offer proofreading, copy-editing, developmental editing, book critiques & book proposals at competitive rates. We hire editors with experience in the industry & guarantee personal, quality service. All new clients are offered a free sample edit & book critique.
Membership(s): American Christian Fiction Writers; Editorial Freelancers Association; Evangelical Christian Publishers Association

**Generosa Gina Protano Publishing**, see GGP Publishing Inc

**Publishing Resources Inc**
425 Carr 693, PMB 160, Dorado, PR 00646
*Tel:* 787-626-0607 *Toll Free Fax:* 866-547-3005
*E-mail:* pri@chevako.net
*Web Site:* www.publishingresources.net
*Key Personnel*
Pres: Ronald J Chevako
EVP & Ed: Anne W Chevako
Prodn: Jay A Chevako
Founded: 1978
Complete services including ms development, research, writing, translation (Spanish-English; English-Spanish), indexing, content editing & line editing by US trained professionals & full production services.

**Publishing Services**
525 E 86 St, Suite 8-E, New York, NY 10028
*Tel:* 212-628-9127 *Fax:* 212-988-1999
*E-mail:* publishingservices@mac.com
*Key Personnel*
Pres: Amy S Goldberger
Copy-editing, fact checking, line editing, photo research, ms analysis, permissions, research & rewriting.
Membership(s): Editorial Freelancers Association; Women's National Book Association

**Publishing Synthesis Ltd**
39 Crosby St, New York, NY 10013
*Tel:* 212-219-0135 *Fax:* 212-219-0136
*E-mail:* info@pubsyn.com
*Web Site:* www.pubsyn.com
*Key Personnel*
Pres: Otto H Barz *E-mail:* obarz@pubsyn.com
VP & Spec Projs Coord: Ellen Small
*E-mail:* esmall@pubsyn.com
Edit Dir: George Ernsberger
*E-mail:* gernsberger@pubsyn.com
Founded: 1975
Editing, design, typesetting & prepress production of college text & highly technical trade books.
Membership(s): Book Industry Guild of New York; IBPA, the Independent Book Publishers Association

**The Quarasan Group Inc**
405 W Superior St, Chicago, IL 60654
*Tel:* 312-981-2500
*E-mail:* info@quarasan.com
*Web Site:* www.quarasan.com
*Key Personnel*
Pres: Randi S Brill
SVP, Busn: Bob Taylor
Founded: 1982
From concept to completion, Quarasan provides planning, product conceptualization, complete customized publishing systems, editorial, design, marketing & product development services including original writing, substantive & content editing, correlations, focus/field testing, visual design, image procurement & all online & print delivery services for educational & edutainment products. Top caliber project management. Specialize in PreK-12 products in reading, literature, language arts, integrated curriculum programs, intervention, science, math, social studies, music, art, test prep & assessment/standardized tests.
Membership(s): ASCD; Association of Educational Publishers; International Reading Association; National Association for Music Education; National Council for the Social Studies; National Council of Teachers of English; National Council of Teachers of Mathematics; National Middle School Association; National Science Teachers Association; Teachers of English to Speakers of Other Languages

**Jane Rafal Editing Associates**
325 Forest Ridge Dr, Scottsville, VA 24590
*Tel:* 434-286-6949
*Key Personnel*
Owner: Jane Rafal *E-mail:* janerafal@ntelos.net
Founded: 1993
Developmental editing, cutting & book proposal development. Specialize in general trade fiction & nonfiction.

**Jerry Ralya**
7909 Vt Rte 14, Craftsbury Common, VT 05827
*Tel:* 802-586-7514
*E-mail:* jerry@jerryralya.com
Editing, development & indexing of trade, technical, medical & reference books. Specialties include computers, behavioral sciences & the humanities. Twenty-five years of experience.
Membership(s): American Society for Indexing; Editorial Freelancers Association

**The Reading Component**
1716 Clark Ave, PMB 195, Long Beach, CA 90815-3801
*Tel:* 562-438-0666
*Key Personnel*
Owner: Helen M Winton *E-mail:* hmwinton@outlook.com
Founded: 1994

**Research Research**
240 E 27 St, Suite 20-K, New York, NY 10016-9238
*Tel:* 212-779-9540 *Fax:* 212-779-9540
*E-mail:* ehtac@msn.com
*Key Personnel*
Pres: Cathe Giffuni
Founded: 1987

**Judith Riven Literary Agent LLC**
250 W 16 St, Suite 4F, New York, NY 10011
*Tel:* 212-255-1009 *Fax:* 212-255-8547
*E-mail:* rivenlitqueries@gmail.com
*Web Site:* rivenlit.com
*Key Personnel*
Owner & Pres: Judith Riven
Founded: 1993
Editorial consultation, developmental & structural editing, line editing, ms analysis.

**The Roberts Group**
12803 Eastview Curve, Apple Valley, MN 55124
*Tel:* 952-322-4005
*E-mail:* info@editorialservice.com
*Web Site:* www.editorialservice.com
*Key Personnel*
Owner: Sherry Roberts; Tony Roberts
Founded: 1990
Book design, production, editorial services & web development. A one-stop creative resource for quality interior book design, typesetting, editing, proofreading, indexing, Kindle & e-pub formatting. Serving established presses & self-publishers. Competitive prices. We pay attention to details & will work to meet your deadlines. Visit our web site for a complete description of services.
Membership(s): IBPA, the Independent Book Publishers Association; Midwest Independent Publishers Association; Professional Editors Network

**Peter Rooney**
332 Bleecker St, PMB X-6, New York, NY 10014-2980
*Tel:* 917-376-1792 *Fax:* 212-226-8047
*E-mail:* magnetix@ix.netcom.com
*Web Site:* www.magneticreports.com
Indexer, programmer/consultant for indexes, databases, directories, catalogues raisonnes. Large & small projects.
Membership(s): American Society for Indexing

**Dick Rowson**
4701 Connecticut Ave NW, Suite 503, Washington, DC 20008
*Tel:* 202-244-8104
*E-mail:* rcrowson2@aol.com
Helps authors find good publishers & appraise mss.

**Sachem Publishing Associates Inc**
402 W Lyon Farm Dr, Greenwich, CT 06831
Mailing Address: PO Box 4040, Greenwich, CT 06831
*Tel:* 203-813-3077 *Fax:* 203-531-2879
*E-mail:* sachempub@optonline.net
*Key Personnel*
Pres & Ed: Stephen P Elliott
Founded: 1974
Complete trade & mail order book preparation & packaging; editorial services, from concept to finished books. Specialize in consumer & educational reference books, including encyclopedias & dictionaries.

**Barbara S Salz LLC Photo Research**
127 Prospect Place, South Orange, NJ 07079
*Tel:* 973-762-6486
*E-mail:* bsalz.photo@gmail.com
Image research & permissions for books, magazines, exhibitions & advertising.
Membership(s): ASPP

**Pat Samples**
7152 Unity Ave N, Brooklyn Center, MN 55429
*Tel:* 763-560-5199 *Fax:* 763-560-5298
*E-mail:* patsamples@agingandcaregiving.com
*Web Site:* www.patsamples.com
Writing, research & editing for publishers, nonprofits & individuals.
Membership(s): The Authors Guild

**Paul Samuelson**
117 Oak Dr, San Rafael, CA 94901
*Tel:* 415-459-5352; 415-517-0700 *Fax:* 415-459-5352
*E-mail:* paul@storywrangler.com
*Web Site:* www.storywrangler.com
Also consults on narrative material & screenplays.

**Karen E Sardinas-Wyssling**
6 Bradford Lane, Plainsboro, NJ 08536-2326
*Tel:* 609-275-9148
*E-mail:* starchild240@comcast.net
Founded: 1976

Psychiatry, psychology, medicine, reference, children's literature, fiction. Medical books & journals, professional books, reference books, textbooks, children's books, testing material. IBM PC: Microsoft Word.

**C J Scheiner Books**
275 Linden Blvd, Suite B-2, Brooklyn, NY 11226
*Tel:* 718-469-1089 *Fax:* 718-469-1089
*Key Personnel*
Owner: C J Scheiner
Literature searches, special assignment writing, fact checking, research, photo research illustrations provided, bibliographies & source lists, text & introduction writing. Specialize in erotica, curiosa & sexology.

**Schoolhouse Network Inc**
PO Box 17676, Fountain Hills, AZ 85269
*Tel:* 973-206-1389
*E-mail:* info@schoolhousenetwork.com
*Web Site:* www.schoolhousenetwork.com
*Key Personnel*
Pres: Marilyn Greco *E-mail:* mgreco@schoolhousenetwork.com
Dir, Curriculum: Mary K Messick *E-mail:* mmessick@schoolhousenetwork.com
Founded: 1998
Provides a comprehensive range of editorial services to educational publishers, development groups, schools & other educational institutions for PreK, K-12 & college in both print & electronic media in the content areas of reading/language arts, ESL, literature, social studies, health & science. Develop student & teacher editions, leveled readers, fiction & nonfiction, graphic novels, literature searches, readability analyses, video scripts, animations, interactive Web-based content, software, educational games, workbooks, assessment components & state customizations with more than three decades of experience in the field of educational publishing.
Membership(s): Association of Educational Publishers; Editorial Freelancers Association; International Reading Association; National Association for the Education of Young Children; Teachers of English to Speakers of Other Languages

**Schroeder Indexing Services**
23 Camilla Pink Ct, Bluffton, SC 29909
*Tel:* 843-705-9779
*E-mail:* sanindex@schroederindexing.com
*Web Site:* www.schroederindexing.com
*Key Personnel*
Owner: Sandi Schroeder
Produce custom indexes using dedicated indexing software. Company web site includes current information on clients & titles indexed, information on planning an index, downloadable Project Information Sheet & request for an estimate.
Membership(s): American Society for Indexing

**Franklin L Schulaner**
PO Box 507, Kealakekua, HI 96750-0507
*Tel:* 808-322-3785
*E-mail:* fschulaner@hawaii.rr.com

**Sherri Schultz/Words with Grace**
1916 Pike Place, Suite 12, No 118, Seattle, WA 98101
*Tel:* 415-297-5708
*E-mail:* WordsWithGraceEditorial@gmail.com
*Web Site:* www.wordswithgrace.com
Founded: 1992
Experienced copyeditor & proofreader, primarily for nonfiction books, nonprofits & consultants. Works with clients around the country. Special expertise in travel, environment, politics, literary nonfiction & art. Refers fiction writers to other editors.
Membership(s): Bay Area Editors' Forum; Northwest Independent Editors Guild

**Scribendi Inc**
405 Riverview Dr, Chatham, ON N7M 5J5, Canada
*Tel:* 519-351-1626 (cust serv) *Fax:* 519-354-0192
*E-mail:* customerservice@scribendi.com
*Web Site:* www.scribendi.com
*Key Personnel*
Pres: Chandra Clarke *Tel:* 519-351-1626 ext 706 *E-mail:* chandra.clarke@scribendi.com
VP: Terence Johnson, MA *Tel:* 519-351-1626 ext 707 *E-mail:* terry@scribendi.com
Founded: 1997
On demand proofreading & editing services available 24/7. Web site offers instant quotes on all standard services; call or e-mail for special project quotes or long term arrangements.

**SDP Publishing Solutions LLC**
Formerly Sweet Dreams Publishing of MA
36 Captain's Way, East Bridgewater, MA 02333
*Tel:* 617-775-0656
*Web Site:* www.sdppublishingsolutions.com
*Key Personnel*
Publr & Agent: Lisa Akoury-Ross *E-mail:* lross@sdppublishing.com
Developmental Ed, Copyeditor & Proofreader: Shayla Perry
Developmental Ed & Copyeditor: Neysa Jensen; Shannon Miller; Lisa Schleifer
Ghost Writer: Aileen McDonough
Professional Proofreader/Proofchecker: Karen Grennan; Kim Sexton
Founded: 2009
Specialize in editorial services for all genres including fiction, nonfiction, memoirs, business books, children's books & more. Our business is designed to review mss & determine the best editorial approach for each author. From ghost writing, developmental editing, copy-editing & proofreading, we help our authors become better writers! We also write effective marketing kits, query letters, analysis of the competitive marketplace, along with the marketing & media landscape for those who wish to pitch to literary agents & traditional publishers. We offer optimal publishing solutions for authors worldwide from literary agency representation, to worldwide marketing, including international rights & independent publishing.

**Hank Searls**
Box 1877, 4435 Holly Lane NW, Gig Harbor, WA 98335
*Tel:* 253-851-9896 *Fax:* 253-851-9897
*E-mail:* hanksearls@comcast.net
Founded: 1986
Ms consultation & analysis. Screenplays, marketing counsel for authors. Previous publications includes Jaws 2, Jaws: The Revenge (Universal Pictures), The New Breed (Creator), Overboard (Norton), Kataki (McGraw-Hill), Sounding (Random House), Blood Song (Villard Books), The Hero Ship (NAC World), Firewind (Doubleday), The Crowded Sky (Harper), The Fugitive: Never Wave Goodbye (ABC).
Membership(s): The Authors Guild; National Writers Union; Writers Guild of America

**Richard Selman**
14 Washington Place, New York, NY 10003
*Tel:* 212-473-1874 *Fax:* 212-473-1875
Multimedia & electronic desktop publishing, advertising & promotional copywriting; fact checking, line editing, permissions, research, photo research, proofreading, ms analysis, bibliographies, copy-editing, interviewing, rewriting, special assignment writing, transcript editing, indexing, audio/video text.

**Alexa Selph**
4300 McClatchey Circle, Atlanta, GA 30342
*Tel:* 404-256-3717
*E-mail:* lexa101@aol.com

**Barry Sheinkopf**
c/o The Writing Ctr, 601 Palisade Ave, Englewood Cliffs, NJ 07632
*Tel:* 201-567-4017 *Fax:* 201-567-7202
*E-mail:* bsheinkopf@optonline.net
Founded: 1977
Trade, scholarly & professional publications, book design & self-publishing.
Membership(s): The Authors Guild; Mystery Writers of America

**Monika Shoffman-Graves**
70 Transylvania Ave, Key Largo, FL 33037
*Tel:* 305-451-1462 *Fax:* 305-451-1462
*E-mail:* keysmobill@earthlink.net
Indexing, ms analysis, proofreading & research.

**Roger W Smith**
59-67 58 Rd, Maspeth, NY 11378-3211
*Tel:* 718-416-1334
*E-mail:* roger.smith106@verizon.net
Founded: 1982
Membership(s): Editorial Freelancers Association

**P Gregory Springer**
206 Wood St, Urbana, IL 61801
*Tel:* 217-493-7986
*E-mail:* pgregory.springer@gmail.com
*Web Site:* tinyurl.com/3q8ngu4
Critical & narrative nonfiction.

**SSR Inc**
116 Fourth St SE, Washington, DC 20003
*Tel:* 202-543-1800 *Fax:* 202-544-7432
*E-mail:* ssr@ssrinc.com
*Web Site:* www.ssrinc.com
*Key Personnel*
Pres: Shirley Sirota Rosenberg
Writing, editing & design.

**Stackler Editorial Agency**
555 Lincoln Ave, Alameda, CA 94501
*Tel:* 510-814-9694 *Fax:* 510-814-9694
*E-mail:* stackler@aol.com
*Web Site:* www.fictioneditor.com
*Key Personnel*
Owner: Ed Stackler
Founded: 1996
Editorial services for novelists of crime, thriller & suspense fiction.

**Nancy Steele**
2210 Pine St, Philadelphia, PA 19103-6516
*Tel:* 215-732-5175
*E-mail:* nancy.steele.edits@gmail.com
Founded: 1999
Versatile, intuitive editor with 20 years of experience in editing nonfiction. Expertise in American art & antiques, anthologies, biographies & memoirs, business & technology, psychology, reference & illustrated books. Special interest in the arts of Japan.
Membership(s): National Association of Science Writers

**Sterling Media Productions LLC**, see Robert L Cohen

**Brooke C Stoddard**
Affiliate of Archon Editorial

815 King St, Suite 204, Alexandria, VA 22314
*Tel:* 703-838-1650
*E-mail:* stoddardbc@gmail.com
Founded: 1983
Magazine & book writing & editing. Can handle design & production.
Membership(s): American Independent Writers; American Society of Journalists & Authors; The Authors Guild; Editorial Freelancers Association; National Press Club

**Jean Stoess**
1600 Royal Dr, Reno, NV 89503
*Tel:* 775-322-5326
*E-mail:* jstoess@aol.com
Founded: 1977
Oral history transcription in all styles, cassette & CDs. Word processing for publishers & authors; oral history transcription rewriting. Type & revise mss from first through final draft. Editing when needed. Micro & regular tape cassettes. Wordperfect 11.0 & Microsoft Word 2003. APA style is a specialty.

**Jeri L Stolk**
2231 Rogene Dr, Suite 204, Baltimore, MD 21209
*Tel:* 410-864-8109
*E-mail:* jeri.stolk@comcast.net
Edit journals & books, especially academic.

**Vivian Sudhalter**
1202 Loma Dr, No 117, Ojai, CA 93023
*Tel:* 805-640-9737
*E-mail:* vivians09@att.net
Freelance editor specializing in fiction & nonfiction books on women's studies, as well other genres. I improve finished mss by copy-editing for good grammar, flow, punctuation, usage & consistency. I also help shape books from their inception by working with authors to create the structure that will best serve their vision. Having been in the book publishing industry for more than four decades, I provide insights into the publication process, whether conventional or POD. Contact by e-mail preferred.

**Fraser Sutherland**
39 Helena Ave, Toronto, ON M6G 2H3, Canada
*Tel:* 416-654-3636
*E-mail:* rodfrasers@gmail.com
Founded: 1970
General editorial services. Specialize in dictionaries & reference books (lexicography), ms analysis & rewriting.
Membership(s): Dictionary Society of North America; Editors' Association of Canada/Association canadienne des reviseurs; PEN Canada

**Sweet Dreams Publishing of MA**, see SDP Publishing Solutions LLC

**Textbook Writers Associates Inc**
275 Grove St, Suite 2-400, Newton, MA 02466
*Tel:* 781-209-0051 *Fax:* 781-209-2920
*Web Site:* www.textbookwriters.com
*Key Personnel*
Pres: Rose Sklare *E-mail:* rsklare@textbookwriters.com
Founded: 1993
Full service editorial/production company offering comprehensive scientific & professional book development & production. Provide extensive editorial work on medical journals; pharmaceutical writing of monographs, peer-reviewed articles & clinical trials. Services include project management, research, writing, online editing, design, art rendering, photo research, composition, proofreading, permissions, indexing. Specialize in medical, nursing & pharmaceutical sciences, as well as basic sciences, math & engineering.
Membership(s): American Medical Writers Association; Bookbuilders of Boston; Drug Information Association

**TexTech Inc**, see Jouve North America Inc

**Susan Thornton**
6090 Liberty Ave, Vermilion, OH 44089
*Tel:* 440-967-1757
*E-mail:* allenthornton@earthlink.net
*Key Personnel*
Freelance Copy Ed: Allen Thornton; Susan Thornton
Medical, technical, mathematics, university press, college text, reference, trade nonfiction & journals on hard copy & on disk.

**TSI Graphics**
1300 S Raney St, Effingham, IL 62401-4206
*Tel:* 217-347-7733; 217-347-7734 *Fax:* 217-342-9611
*E-mail:* info@tsigraphics.com
*Web Site:* www.tsigraphics.com
*Key Personnel*
Pres: Richard Whitsitt *Tel:* 908-532-0293 *E-mail:* rwhitsitt@tsigraphics.com
VP & Gen Mgr: David Nitsche *Tel:* 217-540-4100 *E-mail:* dnitsche@tsigraphics.com
VP, Admin & HR: Bob Berger *Tel:* 636-532-7301 *E-mail:* bberger@tsigraphics.com
VP, Busn Devt: David Paddick *E-mail:* dpaddick@tsigraphics.com
Cust Serv Mgr: Carolyn Bowlin *Tel:* 217-540-4135 *E-mail:* cbowlin@tsigraphics.com
All aspects of editorial functions, from development through indexing.
*Branch Office(s)*
7751 Kingspointe Pkwy, Suite 122, Orlando, FL 32819-6503 *Tel:* 407-351-0530
3100 Research Blvd, Kettering, OH 45420-4022 *Tel:* 937-531-4662

**Twin Oaks Indexing**
Division of Twin Oaks Community
138 Twin Oaks Rd, Suite W, Louisa, VA 23093
*Tel:* 540-894-5126 *Fax:* 540-894-4112
*Web Site:* www.twinoaks.org
*Key Personnel*
Mgr: Rachel Nishan
Founded: 1981
Subsidiaries: Twin Oaks Industries Inc

**Arlene S Uslander**, see Writeway Editing

**Visuals Unlimited**
27 Meadow Dr, Hollis, NH 03049
*Tel:* 603-465-3340 *Fax:* 603-465-3360
*E-mail:* staff@visualsunlimited.com
*Web Site:* visualsunlimited.com
*Key Personnel*
VP & Busn Devt Mgr, Ad: Robert Folz *E-mail:* rfolz@visualsunlimited.com
Dir: Shelly Folz *E-mail:* sfolz@visualsunlimited.com
Photo agent, photo research & stock agency.
Membership(s): Picture Agency Council of America

**Vocabula Communications Co**
5-A Holbrook Ct, Rockport, MA 01966
*Tel:* 978-546-3911
*E-mail:* info@vocabula.com
*Web Site:* www.vocabula.com; www.vocabulabooks.com (books)
*Key Personnel*
Pres: Robert Hartwell Fiske
Founded: 1986
Copy-editing, developmental editing, technical editing & writing, copywriting, special assignment writing, abstracting, interviewing, research, transcription editing, on-screen editing, html coding & editing, web site editing, proofreading & typemarking. Publisher of *The Vocabula Review* & Vocabula Books.

**Jayne Walker Literary Services**
1406 Euclid Ave, Suite 1, Berkeley, CA 94708
*Tel:* 510-843-8265
*Key Personnel*
Owner: Jayne Walker *E-mail:* jaynelwalker@earthlink.net
Founded: 1986
Editorial & marketing consultant. Specialize in active collaboration with authors: evaluation, developmental & line editing, copy-editing, research, rewriting & restyling of proposals & mss. Fiction & nonfiction; trade & academic books. Consulting on marketing, publicity & other publishing issues.

**Dorothy Wall, Writing Consultant**
3045 Telegraph Ave, Berkeley, CA 94705
*Tel:* 510-486-8008
*E-mail:* dorothy@dorothywall.com
*Web Site:* www.dorothywall.com
Founded: 1984
Ms analysis, substantive editing, marketing assistance for fiction & nonfiction.

**Wambtac Communications**
2323 N Tustin Ave, Suite C-202, Santa Ana, CA 92705
*Tel:* 714-954-0580 *Toll Free Tel:* 800-641-3936 *Fax:* 714-954-0793 (orders)
*E-mail:* wambtac@wambtac.com
*Web Site:* www.wambtac.com; claudiasuzanne.com (prof servs)
*Key Personnel*
Owner & Ghostwriter: Claudia Suzanne *E-mail:* claudia@wambtac.com
Founded: 1995
Book writing & publishing.
Membership(s): IBPA, the Independent Book Publishers Association

**WC Publishing**, see Wambtac Communications

**Anne Jones Weitzer**
Subsidiary of Weitzer & Associates
60 Sutton Place South, Suite 9-B South, New York, NY 10022-4168
*Tel:* 212-758-8149
*E-mail:* 47dehaven@msn.com; enamel@yahoo.com
Founded: 1989
Freelance writer & editor.
Membership(s): National Writers Union

**Toby Wertheim**
240 E 76 St, New York, NY 10021
*Tel:* 212-472-8587
*E-mail:* tobywertheim@yahoo.com
Research/editor.

**Rosemary Wetherold**
4507 Cliffstone Cove, Austin, TX 78735
*Tel:* 512-892-1606
*E-mail:* roses@ix.netcom.com
Founded: 1985
Copy editing, substantitive editing, desktop publishing. Varied subjects, including biological sciences & natural history.

**Helen Rippier Wheeler**
Subsidiary of Womanhood Media
1909 Cedar St, Suite 212, Berkeley, CA 94709-2037
*Tel:* 510-549-2970
*E-mail:* pen136@dslextreme.com
Consulting & professional development training.
Membership(s): Writers Guild of America

**Barbara Mlotek Whelehan**
7064 SE Cricket Ct, Stuart, FL 34997
*Tel:* 954-554-0765 (cell); 772-463-0818 (home)
*E-mail:* barbarawhelehan@bellsouth.net
More than 20 years of publishing experience. All subjects; specialize in personal finance, investments, mutual funds, business & consumer topics. Also copy-edit fiction.

**Martin L White**
10511 Preston St, Westchester, IL 60154-5311
*Tel:* 708-492-1253 *Fax:* 708-492-1253
*E-mail:* mlw@mlwindexing.com
*Web Site:* www.mlwindexing.com
*Key Personnel*
Owner: Martin L White
Founded: 1990
Book & journal indexing.
Membership(s): American Society for Indexing; Society for Technical Communication

**White Oak Editions**, see Carol Cartaino

**Whitehorse Productions**
2417 W 35 Ave, Denver, CO 80211
*Tel:* 303-433-4400
*Key Personnel*
Owner: Michael Haldeman
*E-mail:* michaelhaldeman@comcast.net
Founded: 1988
Indexing, editorial services, publication design & production, self-publishing assistance.
Membership(s): Rocky Mountain Publishing Professionals Guild

**Eleanor B Widdoes**
417 W 120 St, New York, NY 10027
*Tel:* 212-870-3051; 917-886-6401
Line editing, indexing, proofreading, research, bibliographies & newsletters.

**Windhaven®**
68 Hunting Rd, Auburn, NH 03032
*Tel:* 603-483-0929 *Fax:* 603-483-8022
*E-mail:* info@windhaven.com
*Web Site:* www.windhaven.com
*Key Personnel*
Dir & Ed: Nancy C Hanger *E-mail:* nhanger@windhaven.com
Ed & Consultant: Andrew V Phillips
*E-mail:* andrew@windhaven.com
Founded: 1985
Consulting & developmental editing, line editing, copy-editing, proofreading.
Membership(s): Editorial Freelancers Association; National Writers Union

**Winter Springs Editorial Services**
2263 Turk Rd, Doylestown, PA 18901-2964
*Tel:* 215-340-9052 *Fax:* 215-340-9052
*Key Personnel*
CEO & Ed: Carol H Munson
*E-mail:* chmunson@gmail.com
CFO: Lowell Munson
Founded: 1990
Editorial help from concept through ms to production; book proposals & permissions; book cover designs & images. Specialize in cookbooks, food, nutrition & health, textbooks.

**Wolf Pirate Project Inc**
337 Lost Lake Dr, Divide, CO 80814
*Tel:* 305-333-3186
*E-mail:* contact@wolfpiratebooks.com; workshop@wolfpiratebooks.com
*Web Site:* www.wolf-pirate.com
*Key Personnel*
Founder & Ed: Catherine Rudy
*E-mail:* catherinerudy@wolfpiratebooks.com
Ed: May Bestall *E-mail:* maybestall@wolfpiratebooks.com; Lois Tower
*E-mail:* loistower@wolfpiratebooks.com
Founded: 2010
Nonprofit company established to mentor, educate, develop & promote new writers & artists & focus on the general public to instill a desire to read for leisure. Fiction/nonfiction literary; content & development blue line edit. Service offered only through acceptance into the workshop. Otherwise online class is open to all at no cost & editors are available to answer questions.

**Nancy Wolff**
125 Gates Ave, No 14, Montclair, NJ 07042
*Tel:* 973-746-7415
*E-mail:* wolffindex@aol.com
Founded: 1991
Indexing, generalist; professional; prompt. Most fields: animals (Do Dogs Dream?); art (Durer & Beyond); biography (George F. Kennan); cookbooks (Chewy Gooey Crispy Crunchy... Cookies); history (China's Wings); memoir (Condoleezza Rice/No Higher Honor); music (No Such Thing as Silence [John Cage]); natural history & ecology (In Pursuit of Giants [fish]); young readers (Buffalo Bird Girl).

**WordCo Indexing Services Inc**
49 Church St, Norwich, CT 06360
*Tel:* 860-886-2532 *Toll Free Tel:* 877-WORDCO-3 (967-3263) *Fax:* 860-886-1155
*E-mail:* office@wordco.com
*Web Site:* www.wordco.com
*Key Personnel*
CEO & Pres: Stephen Ingle *E-mail:* sringle@wordco.com
Proj Coord: Melanie R Lozada
*E-mail:* mlozada@wordco.com
Founded: 1988
Since 1988, WordCo has completed thousands of thorough & accurate indexes in hundreds of subject areas for many major publishers. WordCo's in-house team of professionally trained indexers has the experience & capability to complete your indexing projects professionally & on time. Rush service & e-book indexing available.
Membership(s): American Society for Indexing; Bookbuilders of Boston

**WordForce Communications**
79 Jameson Ave, Suite 401, Toronto, ON M6K 2W7, Canada
*Tel:* 416-534-9881 *Toll Free Tel:* 866-WRD-FORCE (973-3672)
*E-mail:* info@wordforce.ca
*Web Site:* www.wordforce.ca
*Key Personnel*
Pres: Maja Rehou *E-mail:* mrehou@wordforce.ca
Founded: 2003
Provide editing, writing & consulting services to help engineers, scientists, lawyers, web developers & business professionals improve the effectiveness & profitability of their technical documents & marketing materials.
Membership(s): Editors' Association of Canada/Association canadienne des reviseurs; Toastmasters International

**Words into Print**
131 Fifth Ave, Suite 501, New York, NY 10003
*Tel:* 212-741-1393 *Fax:* 419-441-1393
*E-mail:* query@wordsintoprint.org
*Web Site:* www.wordsintoprint.org
*Key Personnel*
Ed: Marlene Adelstein *Tel:* 845-687-7224
*E-mail:* madelstein@aol.com; Martin Beiser
*Tel:* 973-202-9694 *E-mail:* martin.beiser@gmail.com; Linda Carbone *Tel:* 914-374-8790
*E-mail:* lindacarbone@optonline.net; Ruth Greenstein *E-mail:* rg@greenlinepublishing.com; Melanie Kroupa *Tel:* 781-329-1987
*E-mail:* mkroupa@verizon.net; Alice Peck
*Tel:* 917-494-7259 *E-mail:* alicepeck@alicepeck.com; Alice Rosengard *Tel:* 212-662-4323 *E-mail:* arosengard1@yahoo.com; Katharine Turok *E-mail:* kturok@gmail.com; Michael Wilde *Tel:* 518-672-7172
*E-mail:* michaelwildeeditorial@earthlink.net
Founded: 1998
An alliance of top New York publishing professionals who offer a broad range of editorial services to authors, publishers, literary agents, book packagers & content providers from around the world.

**Words with Grace**, see Sherri Schultz/Words with Grace

**Wordsworth Communication**
PO Box 9781, Alexandria, VA 22304-0468
*Tel:* 703-642-8775 *Fax:* 703-642-8775
*Key Personnel*
Pres: Franklin Wordsworth
Exec Dir: Paul Elliott
Founded: 1973
Special assignment & ghost writing, rewriting, copy & line editing, research, advertising & promotion copywriting, interviewing, condensations, abstracting, transcription editing.

**WordWitlox**
70 Grainger Crescent, Ajax, ON L1T 4Y6, Canada
*Tel:* 647-505-9673 *Fax:* 905-239-3604
*Web Site:* www.wordwitlox.com
*Key Personnel*
Copy Ed: Cathy Witlox *E-mail:* cathy@wordwitlox.com
Founded: 2004
Editing professionally since 1998, including 6-1/2 years full-time in-house experience copy editing for a large North American fiction publisher. WordWitlox is based near Toronto.
Membership(s): Editors' Association of Canada/Association canadienne des reviseurs

**Working With Words**
9720 SW Eagle Ct, Beaverton, OR 97008
*Tel:* 503-644-4317
*E-mail:* editor@zzz.com
*Key Personnel*
Owner: Sue Mann
Founded: 1985
Freelance editorial services. General trade, nonfiction. Subjects include children's, cookbooks, creativity, historical, inspirational, memoirs, self-help, spiritual, training. Substantive editing. Online & hard copy.
Membership(s): Northwest Independent Editors Guild; Northwest Writers & Publishers Association

**Wright Information Indexing Services**
PO Box 658, Sandia Park, NM 87047
*Tel:* 505-281-2600
*Web Site:* www.wrightinformation.com
*Key Personnel*
Owner & Pres: Jan C Wright *E-mail:* jancw@wrightinformation.com
Founded: 1991
Book, ebook & online indexing services, specializing in single-source publications; 2009 winner of H W Wilson Award for Excellence in Indexing.
Membership(s): American Society for Indexing

**The Write Way**
3048 Horizon Lane, Suite 1102, Naples, FL 34109
*Tel:* 239-273-9145
*E-mail:* darekane@gmail.com

*Key Personnel*
Pres: Roberta Kane
Also handle advertising & marketing.

**Writers Anonymous Inc**
1302 E Coronado Rd, Phoenix, AZ 85006
*Tel:* 602-256-2830 *Fax:* 602-256-2830
*Web Site:* writersanonymousinc.com
*Key Personnel*
Pres: Jordan Richman *E-mail:* jprich9231@aol.com
Edit Dir: Vita Richman
Substantive editing, scholarly, education, humanities, social science, environment, philosophy, music, art, literature, health, general science, medical, legal.
Membership(s): Editorial Freelancers Association; Indexers Unlimited

**Writers: Free-Lance Inc**
167 Bluff Rd, Strasburg, VA 22657
*Tel:* 540-635-4617
*Key Personnel*
Pres: Robert M Cullers *E-mail:* cullermama@yahoo.com
Founded: 1965
Over the past nearly 40 years we have been involved in the production of more than two dozen books plus thousands of specific writing & editing assignments running the gamut of subjects.

**The Writer's Lifeline Inc**
Subsidiary of AEI (Atchity Entertainment International Inc)
9601 Wilshire Blvd, Suite 1202, Beverly Hills, CA 90210
*Tel:* 323-932-0905 *Fax:* 323-932-0321
*E-mail:* questions@thewriterslifeline.com
*Web Site:* www.thewriterslifeline.com
*Key Personnel*
Chmn: Kenneth Atchity, PhD
Partner & Pres, Devt & Prodn: Chi-Li Wong
Founded: 1996
A full-service editorial company, providing nonfiction book writers, novelists, business, professional, technical & screenwriters with assistance in storytelling, mentoring, perfecting their style & craft, style-structure-concept-line editing, publishing consulting, development, translation, advertising & promotion, printing & self-publishing, distribution & research.
Membership(s): American Comparative Literature Association; The Authors Guild; CAPE; Directors Guild of America; PEN American Center; Women in Film; Writers Guild of America

**Writer's Relief, Inc**
207 Hackensack St, Wood-Ridge, NJ 07075
*Tel:* 201-641-3003 *Toll Free Tel:* 866-405-3003 *Fax:* 201-641-1253
*E-mail:* info@wrelief.com
*Web Site:* www.WritersRelief.com
*Key Personnel*
Pres: Ronnie L Smith *E-mail:* ronnie@wrelief.com
Founded: 1994
Don't have time to submit your writing? We can help. Submission leads & cover/query letter guidelines. Join the 30,000+ writers who subscribe to Submit Write Now, our free e-publication.

**Writeway Editing**
11256 Vista Sorrento Pkwy, Apt 102, San Diego, CA 92130
*Tel:* 858-925-7042 *Fax:* 209-532-2661
*Web Site:* www.uslander.net
*Key Personnel*
Owner & Freelance Book Ed: Arlene S Uslander *E-mail:* uslander.arlene@gmail.com
Founded: 1980
Editing services: whatever is necessary to prepare a ms to send to an agent or publisher, but no typing or ghost writing.
Membership(s): National Federation of Press Women; Publishers & Writers of San Diego; Small Publishers, Artists & Writers Network

**Wyman Indexing**
8526 Foxborough Dr, Suite 2-C, Savage, MD 20763
*Tel:* 443-336-5497
*Web Site:* www.wymanindexing.com
*Key Personnel*
Owner & Chief Indexer: Pilar Wyman *E-mail:* pilarw@wymanindexing.com
Founded: 1990
Freelance indexing & consulting (specialties include: medicine, technology, current events). Also provide Spanish-to-English translation services.
Membership(s): American Medical Writers Association; American Society for Indexing; Society for Technical Communication

**Zebra Communications**
230 Deerchase Dr, Woodstock, GA 30188-4438
*Tel:* 770-924-0528
*Web Site:* www.zebraeditor.com
*Key Personnel*
Owner: Bobbie Christmas *E-mail:* bobbie@zebraeditor.com
Founded: 1992
Editorial services that specialize in fiction & nonfiction books.
Membership(s): Atlanta Writers Club; Better Business Bureau; Florida Writers Association; Georgia Writers Association; International Guild of Professional Business Consultants; Society for the Preservation of English Language Literature; South Carolina Writers Workshop; Southeastern Writers Association; The Writers' Network

**Zeiders & Associates**
PO Box 670, Lewisburg, PA 17837
*Tel:* 570-524-4315 *Fax:* 570-524-4315
*Key Personnel*
Contact: Barbara Zeiders
All editorial work & complete book production. Specialize in math & physical, natural, medical & technical sciences at college & professional levels.

**Robert Zolnerzak**
101 Clark St, Unit 20-K, Brooklyn, NY 11201
*Tel:* 718-522-0591
*E-mail:* bobzolnerzak@verizon.net
Computer-assisted indexing for medical, scientific & computer science textbooks & journals since 1973.
Membership(s): American Society for Indexing; Editorial Freelancers Association

# Literary Agents

The agents listed here are among the most active in the field. Prior to obtaining a listing in *LMP*, potential entrants are required to submit verifiable references from publishers with whom they have placed titles. Letters in parentheses following the agency name indicate fields of activity:

(L)–Literary Agent (D)–Dramatic Agent (L-D)–Literary & Dramatic Agent

Those individuals who are members of the Association of Authors' Representatives are identified by the presence of (AAR) after their name.

Authors seeking literary representation are advised that some agents request a nominal reading fee that may be applied to the agent's commission upon representation. Other agencies may charge substantially higher fees which may not be applicable to a future commission and which are not refundable. The recommended course is to first send a query letter with an outline, sample chapter, and a self-addressed stamped envelope (SASE). Should an agent express interest in handling the manuscript, full details of fees and commissions should be obtained in writing before the complete manuscript is sent. Should an agency require significant advance payment from an author, the author is cautioned to make a careful investigation to determine the agency's standing in the industry before entering an agreement. The author should always retain a copy of the manuscript in his or her possession.

**AAA Books Unlimited** (L)
88 Greenbriar E Dr, Deerfield, IL 60015
*Tel:* 847-444-1220 *Fax:* 847-607-8335
*Web Site:* www.aaabooksunlimited.com
*Key Personnel*
Principal: Nancy Rosenfeld *E-mail:* nancy@aaabooksunlimited.com
Founded: 1993
Full service literary agency to provide clients with first class service "over & above" what normally is handled by a literary agency. We offer content-copy-line editing services. No unsol mss, query first.
Titles recently placed: *A Couple's Guide to Sexual Addiction: A Step-by-Step Plan to Rebuild Trust and Restore Intimacy*, Paldrom Catharine Collins, George N Collins, MA; *A Woman's Framework for a Successful Career and Life*, James Hamerstone, Lindsay Musser Hough; *AD/HD Success! Solutions for Boosting Self-Esteem (The Diary Method)*, Kerin B Adams, ACC; *An Introduction to Mozart: "The Music, The Man, The Myths"*, Roye E Wates, PhD; *Attached at the Heart: 8 Proven Parenting Principles for Raising Connected and Compassionate Children*, Barbara Nicholson, Lysa Parker; *Breaking the Cycle: Free Yourself From Sex Addiction, Porn Obsession, and Shame*, George N Collins, MA, Andrew Adleman, MA; *Do You Mind if I Order the Cheeseburger?*, Sherry F Colb, PhD; *Freedom of Assembly and Petition: The First Amendment: Its Constitutional History and the Contemporary Debate (Bill of Rights series)*, Margaret M Russell, David B Oppenheimer (series ed); *Hurakan*, Mike Stewart; *It Came from the '70s: from the Godfather to Apocalypse Now*, Connie Corcoran Wilson; *Jacob's Courage: A Holocaust Love Story (reprint)*, Charles S Weinblatt; *Justice Indicted*, Michael Shahnasarian; *Leviathan's Scales*, Jim Slusher; *Many Seconds Into the Future*, John J Clayton; *Milk and Oranges*, Charlene Wexler; *Mindfulness for Borderline Personality Disorder*, Blaise Aguirre, MD, Dr Gillian Galen; *Mitzvah Man (Modern Jewish Literature and Culture)*, John J Clayton; *Mood: Our Connection to the World*, Patrick M Burke, MB, BCH, PhD; *My Neck Hurts! Non-surgical Treatments for Neck and Upper Back Pain*, Martin Taylor, DO, PhD; *Negroes with Guns: The Dual Tradition of Nonviolent Social Change and Individual Self-Defense*, Nicholas Johnson; *Outsmarting Mother Nature: A Woman's Complete Guide to Plastic Surgery*, Iliana E Sweis, MD FACS; *Parenting Your Child with Autism: Practical Solutions, Strategies, and Advice for Helping Your Family*, M Anjali Sastry, PhD, Blaise Aguirre, MD; *Pryme Knumber*, Matthew J Flynn; *Searches and Seizures: The Fourth Amendment: Its Constitutional History and Contemporary Debate (Bill of Rights series)*, Cynthia Lee, David B Oppenheimer (series ed); *Sunder Breach*, Richard Fountain; *Survival to Growth*, Sam A Hout; *The Nun's Rabbi: The Rabbi-Psychiatrist and the Sisters of St Francis*, Abraham J Twerski, MD; *The Problem Was Me: How to End Negative Self-Talk and Take Your Life to a New Level*, Thomas Gagliano, Abraham J Twerski, MD; *The Prospective Spouse Checklist: Evaluating Your Potential Partner*, Isabelle Fox, PhD, Robert M Fox, JD; *Transparency in Government: Creating a More Open, Effective Democracy*, Donald Gordon; *Unfinished Business*, Lee Woodward; *Walls, a Metaphor*, Will Lonardo; *War and Sex: A Brief History of Men's Urge for Battle*, John V H Dippel; *Wayang*, Robert Harding; *Wrestling with Angels: New & Collected Stories*, John J Clayton

**The Aaland Agency** (L)
PO Box 849, Inyokern, CA 93527-0849
*Tel:* 760-384-3910
*Web Site:* www.the-aaland-agency.com
*Key Personnel*
Dir & Fiction/Nonfiction: Jo Ann Krueger *E-mail:* anniejo41@gmail.com
Foreign Rep, CN & Europe: Richard Allan
Nonfiction: Mitzi Rhone
Romance/Adventure: Susan Russell
Founded: 1991
Adult fiction & nonfiction. Author must submit in Times Roman, 12pt, one-inch margins & single spaced. Any format, e-mail file attachment, hardcopy or CD is acceptable (e-mail file attachment preferred). Crime drama, romance/adventure, children's stories, biographies & textbooks gladly accepted. No fees for ms review or evaluation. Complete ms or first three chapters. No unsol mss, query first.
Titles recently placed: *The Hydra Brief*, William Davison

**Dominick Abel Literary Agency Inc** (L)
146 W 82 St, Suite 1-A, New York, NY 10024
*Tel:* 212-877-0710 *Fax:* 212-595-3133
*Key Personnel*
Pres: Dominick Abel (AAR) *E-mail:* dominick@dalainc.com
Founded: 1975
Adult fiction & nonfiction. Handle film & TV rights. No unsol mss, query first by e-mail; no reading fee. Representatives in Hollywood & all major foreign countries.
Foreign Rep(s): Akcali Agency (Turkey); Luigi Bernabo & Associates (Italy); Big Apple Agency Inc (China, Indonesia, Malaysia, Taiwan, Vietnam); The Buckman Agency (Israel, Scandinavia); The English Agency (Japan); David Grossman Agency (UK Commonwealth); Korean Copyright Center (Korea); Lex Copyright Agency (Hungary); La Nouvelle Agence (France); Prava I Prevodi Agency (Eastern Europe, Greece, Russia, Ukraine); Lennart Sane Agency (Brazil, Central America, Netherlands, Portugal, South America, Spain); Thomas Schlueck Agency (Germany); Tuttle-Mori Agency Inc (Thailand)

**Abrams Artists Agency** (L-D)
275 Seventh Ave, 26th fl, New York, NY 10001
*Tel:* 646-486-4600 *Fax:* 646-486-2358
*E-mail:* literary@abramsartny.com
*Web Site:* www.abramsartists.com
*Key Personnel*
Dir, Book Div: Steve Ross
Literary Agent: Beth Blickers (AAR); Sarah L Douglas (AAR); Peter Hagan (AAR); Morgan Jenness; Charles Kopelman (AAR); Maura Teitelbaum (AAR)
Founded: 1977
Plays, screenplays, film & TV rights. No unsol mss, query first. Submit synopsis. No reading fee.
*Branch Office(s)*
9200 Sunset Blvd, 11th fl, Los Angeles, CA 90069, Contact: Norma Robbins *Tel:* 310-859-0625 *E-mail:* contactla@abramsartists.com

**Acacia House Publishing Services Ltd** (L)
51 Chestnut Ave, Brantford, ON N3T 4C3, Canada
*Tel:* 519-752-0978 *Fax:* 519-752-8349
*Key Personnel*
Mng Dir: Bill Hanna *E-mail:* bhanna.acacia@rogers.com
Founded: 1985
Adult fiction; no science fiction, occult, horror; most nonfiction. Handle film & TV rights for authors. Handle foreign rights for nine client publishers. Territories handled directly by Acacia include Czech Republic, Estonia, Latvia, Lithuania, Poland, Slovak Republic, Canada (English), USA, UK, Australia, Italy (fiction) & Scandinavia. No unsol mss, query first; submit outline & first 50 pages. Only typed, double spaced mss may be submitted with return postage. No reading fee. Fee charged for photocopying & postage or courier.
Foreign Rights: Akcali (Turkey); Carmen Balcells Agencia Literaria SA (Portugal, Spain); Big Apple Agency Inc (China, Hong Kong, Malaysia, Taiwan, Vietnam); Paul & Peter Fritz A G (Austria, Germany); Graal Literary Agency (Poland); Harris-Elon Agency (Ilana Kurshan) (Israel); International Literatuur Bureau BV (Netherlands); International Press Agency (South Africa); Japan UNI Agency Inc; Anna Jarota Agency (France); Katai & Bolza (Bosnia and Herzegovina, Croatia, Hungary, Montenegro, Serbia, Slovenia); Simona

Kessler (Romania); Duran Kim Agency (Korea); Alexander Korzhenevski (Russia); Maxima Creative Agency (Santo Manarung) (Indonesia); Daniela Micura Literary Services (Italy); Montreal Contact (Canada (French-speaking)); Read n' Right (Greece); Silk Road Agency (Thailand)

**AEI (Atchity Entertainment International Inc)** (L-D)
9601 Wilshire Blvd, Unit 1202, Beverly Hills, CA 90210
*Tel:* 323-932-0407 *Fax:* 323-932-0321
*E-mail:* submissions@aeionline.com
*Web Site:* www.aeionline.com
*Key Personnel*
CEO: Dr Kenneth Atchity
Pres & COO: Ms Chi-Li Wong
Submissions Coord: Jennifer Pope *E-mail:* jp@aeionline.com
Founded: 1996
E-mail & snail mail queries for novels, nonfiction book proposals, screenplays & treatments should consist of a compelling & businesslike letter giving us a brief overview of your story, the audience for which it is intended & a one sentence pitch. Screenplays submitted without SASE will not be returned.
Titles recently placed: *Dead Peasants*, Larry D Thompson; *Realms of Gold: Ritual to Romance*, Terry Stanfill; *The Messiah Matrix*, Kenneth John Atchity
Subsidiaries: The Writer's Lifeline Inc
Foreign Rights: Baror International (Worldwide exc Canada & USA)
Membership(s): The Authors Guild; Writers Guild of America

**Agency Chicago** (L-D)
332 S Michigan Ave, Suite 1032, No A600, Chicago, IL 60604
*E-mail:* ernsant@aol.com
*Key Personnel*
Owner: Ernest Santucci
Assoc: Shelly Chou
Founded: 1988
Professional & cross-over writers. No unsol mss; query letter first; handle film, stage & TV rights; no reading fee. True crime & investigations, Intelligence analysis, historical fiction, humor, politics, general wellness & food safety.

**Agency for the Performing Arts Inc**, see APA Talent & Literary Agency

**Agent's Ink** (L)
PO Box 4956, Fresno, CA 93744-4956
*Tel:* 559-438-1883 *Fax:* 559-438-8289
*Web Site:* agents-ink.com
*Key Personnel*
Owner/Dir: Sydney H Harriet, PhD
*E-mail:* sydharriet@yahoo.com
Founded: 1988
Health related nonfiction, business, cookbooks, sports, fiction, mystery, psychology, how-to & literary for medical & mental health professionals; no unsol mss-query first; send outline or sample chapters with a SASE; no phone or e-mail queries, query by mail only. No reading fee or monthly fee for representation. Marketing fee of $300 covers mailing, production, postage, phone calls, etc. Commission of 15%.
Titles recently placed: *I Got Caught Cheating! How Can I Save My Marriage?*, Dr Othniel Seiden, Jane L Bilett PhD; *I'm "Heeling" One Day at a Time*, Carole Brody Fleet
*Branch Office(s)*
9400 E Iliff Ave, Suite 361, Denver, CO 80231
*Tel:* 720-369-1851

**The Ahearn Agency Inc** (L)
2021 Pine St, New Orleans, LA 70118
*Tel:* 504-861-8395 *Fax:* 504-866-6434
*Web Site:* www.ahearnagency.com
*Key Personnel*
Pres: Pamela G Ahearn *E-mail:* pahearn@aol.com
Founded: 1992
General fiction, adult; no poetry, plays, young adult, articles or autobiographies. Specialize in women's fiction & suspense. No unsol mss, query first with SASE. No reading fee. Do not send attachments with e-mail queries unless requested.
Titles recently placed: *A Laird for Christmas*, Gerri Russell; *Blackstone's Bride*, Kate Moore; *Invisible*, Carla Buckley; *Lie Still*, Julia Haeberlin; *The Shogun's Daughter*, Laura Joh Rowland; *The Spanish Revenge*, Allan Topol; *What the Duke Desires*, Sabrina Jeffries
Foreign Rights: Lorella Belli Agency (Lorella Belli) (UK); Prava i Prevodi (Eastern Europe); Thomas Schluek (Germany)
Membership(s): International Thriller Writers Inc; Mystery Writers of America; Romance Writers of America

**Aitken Alexander Associates LLC** (L)
30 Vandam St, Suite 5A, New York, NY 10013
*Tel:* 212-929-4100
*Web Site:* www.aitkenalexander.co.uk
*Key Personnel*
Sr Agent: Anna Stein (AAR) *E-mail:* anna@aitkenalexander.com
Founded: 2009
Independent New York branch of the establish London-based Aitken Alexander Associates Ltd specializing in literary fiction & narrative nonfiction. No unsol mss, query first. No fees charged.
Titles recently placed: *Asunder*, Chloe Aridjis; *Goliath*, Max Blumenthal; *I Want to Show You More*, Jamie Quatro; *Kill Chain*, Andrew Cockburn; *Leaving the Atocha Station*, Ben Lerner; *Longbourn*, Jo Baker; *Love Me Back*, Merritt Tierce; *Panorama City*, Antoine Wilson; *Revenge*, Yoko Ogawa; *Salvation for a Saint*, Keigo Higashino; *Suddenly a Knock on the Door*, Etgar Keret; *The Butterfly Cabinet*, Bernie McGill; *The Free*, Willy Vlautin; *The Lady's Handbook for Her Mysterious Illness*, Sarah Ramsey; *The People in the Trees*, Hanya Yanagihara; *The Story of My Purity*, Francesco Pacifico; *The Unknowns*, Gabriel Roth; *The Virgins*, Pamela Erens; *Under the Sun: The Letters of Bruce Chatwin*, Bruce Chatwin; *Unremarried Widow*, Artis Henderson; *Where'd You Go Bernadette*, Maria Semple; *Winter King*, Tom Penn

**Akin & Randolph Agency** (L-D)
Literary Div, One Gateway Ctr, Suite 2600, Newark, NJ 07102
*Tel:* 973-353-8409; 973-623-6834 *Fax:* 973-353-8417
*E-mail:* info@akinandrandolph.com
*Web Site:* www.akinandrandolph.com
*Key Personnel*
Founding Agent: Wanda M Akin *E-mail:* wakin@akinandrandolph.com
Agent: Carol Randolph; Eric Easter; Angeli Rasbury
Founded: 1996 (by Wanda M Akin & Carol Randolph)
Specialize in nonfiction & fiction. Public affairs & African American interest; query first with SASE; handle film & TV rights; submit fiction-synopsis & sample chapters; nonfiction send proposal & sample chapters; no reading fee. Subs rights agent for Random House in some foreign countries, Genesis Press & Africa World Press. Mail or fax queries, submissions, etc to NJ mailing address.

**Linda Allen Literary Agency** (L)
1949 Green St, Suite 5, San Francisco, CA 94123
*Tel:* 415-921-6437
*Key Personnel*
Owner & Dir: Linda Allen (AAR)
*E-mail:* linda@lallenlitagency.com
Not taking new clients at this time. Projects by referral only.

**Miriam Altshuler Literary Agency** (L)
53 Old Post Rd N, Red Hook, NY 12571
*Tel:* 845-758-9408
*Web Site:* www.miriamaltshulerliteraryagency.com
*Key Personnel*
Pres: Miriam Altshuler (AAR)
Founded: 1994
Quality commercial & literary fiction & nonfiction, including children's books (young adult & middle grade). No unsol mss, query first. No fax; send queries by e-mail or regular mail. Submit synopsis & first chapter of book, pasted in body of e-mail. Handle film & TV rights. Representatives in all major countries. No reading fee.
Foreign Rights: AM Heath & Co (England, Europe); Tuttle-Mori Agency (China, Japan, Korea)

**Betsy Amster Literary Enterprises** (L)
6312 SW Capitol Hwy, No 503, Portland, OR 97239
*Tel:* 503-496-4007
*E-mail:* rights@amsterlit.com (rts inquiries); b.amster.assistant@gmail.com (adult book queries); b.amster.kidsbooks@gmail.com (children & young adult book queries)
*Web Site:* www.amsterlit.com
*Key Personnel*
Pres: Betsy Amster (AAR)
Agent, Children's & YA: Mary Cummings
Founded: 1992
Literary fiction, upscale commercial fiction (specifically mysteries/thrillers & women's fiction) & adult nonfiction. Subject areas of interest: narrative nonfiction (especially by journalists), travelogues, psychology, self-help, social issues, popular culture, cultural criticism, history, art & design, health, parenting, careers, lifestyle, cookbooks, gardening, gift books; no unsol mss. Handle film & TV rights for client book properties via co-agents; no reading fee. Address queries for adult books to b.amster.assistant@gmail.com & for children's & young adult titles to b.amster.kidsbooks@gmail.com. For fiction or memoirs, embed the first three pages in the body of your e-mail; for nonfiction, embed your proposal. Do not represent screenplays, poetry, western, fantasy, science fiction, action adventure, techno thrillers, spy capers, apocalyptic scenarios or political or religious arguments. We do not open attachments unless we have requested them; no phone, fax or snail mail queries.
*Branch Office(s)*
PO Box 27788, Los Angeles, CA 90027
Foreign Rights: Asli Karasuil Telif Literary Agency (Asli Ermis) (Turkey); Big Apple Agency Inc (China); Donatella d'Ormesson (France); The English Agency (Japan) Ltd (Japan); Japan Uni (Japan); Korea Copyright Center (KCC) (MiSook Hong) (Korea); Mohrbooks (Germany); Prava I Prevodi (Bulgaria, Croatia, Czech Republic, Estonia, Greece, Hungary, Latvia, Lithuania, Macedonia, Poland, Romania, Russia, Serbia, Slovakia, Slovenia); Lennart Sane Agency AB (Philip Sane) (Brazil, Holland, Portugal, Scandinavia, Spain, Spanish Latin America); Vicki Satlow (Italy); Abner Stein Agency (Arabella Stein) (UK)
Membership(s): PEN Center USA

**Marcia Amsterdam Agency** (L)
41 W 82 St, New York, NY 10024-5613
*Tel:* 212-873-4945
Founded: 1970
Adult & young adult fiction; horror, science fiction, suspense, mainstream, historical romance & contemporary women's etc. Handle film & TV rights. No unsol mss, query with SASE. Submit outline & first three chapters. No reading fee. Other fees: standard agency fees.
Foreign Rights: Daniel Bial Agency
Membership(s): Writers Guild of America

**Anderson Literary Management LLC** (L)
12 W 19 St, 2nd fl, New York, NY 10011
*Tel:* 212-645-6045 *Fax:* 212-741-1936
*E-mail:* info@andersonliterary.com
*Web Site:* www.andersonliterary.com
*Key Personnel*
Pres: Kathleen Anderson (AAR)
*E-mail:* kathleen@andersonliterary.com
Assoc Agent & Foreign Rts: Claire Anderson-Wheeler *E-mail:* claire@andersonliterary.com
Represents quality fiction & nonfiction (adult, young adult & middle-grade) for print, electronic, film & television.
Membership(s): PEN American Center

**Andy Ross Literary Agency** (L)
767 Santa Ray Ave, Oakland, CA 94610
*Tel:* 510-238-8965
*E-mail:* andyrossagency@hotmail.com
*Web Site:* www.andyrossagency.com
*Key Personnel*
Agent: Andy Ross (AAR)
Founded: 2008
Specialize in narrative nonfiction, journalism, history, current events, literary, commercial & young adult fiction.
Queries: send by e-mail only including "query" in the title header. Letters should be kept to 1/2 page. State the project category in the first sentence & provide a very brief description. Proposals: submit by e-mail only. See web site for additional query & proposal guidelines. No fees.
Titles recently placed: *A Country, Not a Bomb; North Korea Behind the Facade*, Andrew Lankov; *A Quantum Guide to Life*, Kunal Das; *Apex Predator: Orcas, Humans, and the Origins of Good and Evil*, Jeffrey Moussaleff Masson; *Broken Promises: How the AIDS Establishment Has Betrayed the Developing World*, Dr Edward Green; *Dead Love*, Lynda Watanabe McFerrin; *Dogs Make Us Human: A Global Family Album*, Jeffrey Moussaleff Masson (text), Art Wolfe (photography); *Drinking Water: The Past, Present and Future of Our Essential Ingredient*, David Sedlak; *Make Your Story a Movie*, John Marlow; *Maya Roads: One Woman's Journey Among the People of the Rainforest*, Mary Jo McConahay; *Mornings at the Stanton Street Shul: A Summer on the Lower East Side*, Dr Jonathan Boyarin; *No Simple Highway: The Life and Times of the Grateful Dead*, Peter Richardson; *Phoebe and the Ghost of Chagall*, Jill Koenigsdorf; *Salad Dressing: 50 Recipes*, Michele Anna Jordan; *The American Doomsday Machine*, Daniel Ellsberg; *The Dog Who Couldn't Stop Loving: How Dogs Have Captured Our Hearts for Thousands of Years*, Jeffrey Moussaleff Masson; *The Jersey Sting: Chris Christie & the Most Brazen Case of Jersey-Style Corruption—Ever*, Josh Margolin, Ted Sherman; *The Jewish Gospels*, Daniel Boyarin

**APA Talent & Literary Agency** (L-D)
405 S Beverly Dr, Beverly Hills, CA 90212
*Tel:* 310-888-4200 *Fax:* 310-888-4242
*Web Site:* www.apa-agency.com
*Key Personnel*
Owner: Lee Dinstman
SVP (Nashville): Steve Lassiter
Agent: David Saunders
Agent (Nashville): Frank Wing
Handle film & TV rights. No unsol mss; query first. Submit outline & sample chapters & SASE. No reading fee; 10% commission. Represent writers & producers.
*Branch Office(s)*
45 W 45 St, 4th fl, New York, NY 10036 *Tel:* 212-687-0092 *Fax:* 212-245-5062
3010 Poston Ave, Nashville, TN 37203 *Tel:* 615-297-0100 *Fax:* 615-297-5434

**Arcadia** (L)
31 Lake Place N, Danbury, CT 06810
*Tel:* 203-797-0993
*E-mail:* arcadialit@sbcglobal.net
*Key Personnel*
Pres: Victoria Gould Pryor (AAR)
Founded: 1986
Not seeking new clients.
Foreign Rights: Japan UNI Agency Inc (Japan); Barbara Levy Agency (UK); The Marsh Agency (translation)
Membership(s): The Authors Guild

**Arthur Pine Associates Inc**, see InkWell Management

**Atchity Entertainment International Inc**, see AEI (Atchity Entertainment International Inc)

**Author Author Literary Agency Ltd** (L)
130-1005 Columbia St, PO Box 42522, Columbia Sq, New Westminster, BC V3M 6H5, Canada
*Tel:* 604-415-0056 *Fax:* 604-415-0076
*Web Site:* www.authorauthor.ca
*Key Personnel*
Pres & CEO: Joan Rickard *E-mail:* joan@authorauthor.ca
Founded: 1991
Multi-service literary agency. Represents fiction & nonfiction for adults, young adults & children. No poetry, screenplays, magazine stories or articles. Visit web site for submission guidelines. Unpublished authors welcome. We also provide editing, ghostwriting & consulting services. An entry evaluation fee of $125 CDN charged per proposal. Editorial & ghostwriting service fee schedule available on web site. Currently accepting few new properties for marketing to publishers & focus on mentoring authors with evaluative feedback & literary guidance toward their writing endeavors.

**The Axelrod Agency** (L)
55 Main St, Chatham, NY 12037
Mailing Address: PO Box 357, Chatham, NY 12037
*Tel:* 518-392-2100
*Key Personnel*
Pres: Steven Axelrod (AAR) *E-mail:* steve@axelrodagency.com
Foreign Rts Dir: Lori Antonson *E-mail:* lori@axelrodagency.com
Founded: 1983
Fiction & nonfiction, film & TV rights. No unsol mss, query first; no reading fee.

**Elizabeth H Backman** (L)
86 Johnnycake Hollow Rd, Pine Plains, NY 12567
Mailing Address: PO Box 762, Pine Plains, NY 12567-0762
*Tel:* 518-398-9344 *Fax:* 518-398-6368
*E-mail:* bethcountry@fairpoint.net
*Key Personnel*
Owner: Elizabeth H Backman
Ad Serv: Donn King Potter
Founded: 1981
Literary & commercial fiction; nonfiction; current events, politics, business, biography, the arts, cooking, diet, health, sports, gardening, history, science, self-help & psychology; audio & video cassettes. Author representatives, consulting editors, advertising & promotion copywriters. No unsol mss, query first with SASE; submit introduction, cover letter, chapter by chapter outline or table of contents, three sample chapters & authors bio or complete ms with cover letter & author's bio. Reading fees: $100 for proposals, $500 for complete mss; 15% agency fee plus expenses (phone, mail, photocopying, etc). Handle film & TV rights.
Foreign Rights: Lennart Sane (Netherlands, Portugal, Scandinavia, Spain); Thomas Schlueck (Germany); Tuttle-Mori Agency Inc (Japan)

**Malaga Baldi Literary Agency** (L-D)
233 W 99, Suite 19C, New York, NY 10025
*Tel:* 212-222-3213
*E-mail:* baldibooks@gmail.com; info@baldibooks.com
*Web Site:* www.baldibooks.com
*Key Personnel*
Pres: Malaga Baldi
Founded: 1986
Cultural history, nonfiction & literary-edgy fiction. No unsol mss, query first with SASE; no reading fee.
Titles recently placed: *A Lexicon of Terror: Argentina & The Legacies of Torture, Rev*, Marguerite Feitlowitz; *A Queer & Pleasant Danger: The True Story of a Nice Jewish Boy Who Joins the Church of Scientology & Leaves Twelve Years Later to Become the Lovely Lady She is Today, A Memoir*, Kate Bornstein; *All or Nothing: The Life & Times of Romaine Brooks*, Cassandra Langer; *Body Geographic*, Barrie Jean Borich; *Erotic Awakening*, Barbara Carellas; *Fishing Dogs (revised)*, Ray Coppinger, Peter Pinardi; *Great Sex Made Simple: Tantric Tips to Deepen Intimacy & Heighten Pleasure*, Mark Michaels, Patricia Johnson; *Hello Georgeous: Becoming Barbra Streisand*, William J Mann; *Machiavelli: A Renaissance Life*, Joseph Markulin; *Mermaids (E-book ed)*, Patty Dann; *My New Gender Workbook: Now with More High Theory, Quizzes & Sex*, Kate Bornstein; *Promising Young Women*, Suzanne Scanlon; *PYG*, Russell Potter; *Robots & Pirates!*, Kate Bornstein; *Smart Casual: The Transformation of Gourmet Restaurant Style in America*, Alison Pearlman; *Starfish*, Patty Dann; *Three Minutes in Poland*, Glenn Kurtz; *Tinseltown: Murder Mayhem & Morphine in Hollywood*, William J Mann
Foreign Rights: Eliane Benisti Literary Agency (France); The Grayhawk Agency (Michelle Lin) (China, Taiwan); The Marsh Agency; Owls Agency (Japan); Abner Stein Agency (UK)

**The Balkin Agency Inc**, see Ward & Balkin Agency, Inc

**A Richard Barber/Peter Berinstein & Associates** (L)
60 E Eighth St, Suite 21-N, New York, NY 10003
*Tel:* 212-737-7266 *Fax:* 860-927-3942
*E-mail:* barberrich@aol.com
*Key Personnel*
Pres: A Richard Barber
Sr Assoc: Peter Berinstein
Handle software, film & TV rights. Specialize in fiction & nonfiction. No fees. No unsol mss, query first by mail (include SASE). No fax or e-mail submissions.
*Branch Office(s)*
80 N Main St, Kent, CT 06757-0887 *Tel:* 860-927-4911

**Baror International Inc** (L)
PO Box 868, Armonk, NY 10504-0868
*Tel:* 914-273-9199 *Fax:* 914-273-5058
*Web Site:* www.barorint.com
*Key Personnel*
Pres: Danny Baror *E-mail:* danny@barorint.com
Literary Agent: Heather Baror-Shapiro *E-mail:* heather@barorint.com
Specialize in international & domestic representation of literary works in both fiction & nonfiction ranging in genre including commercial fiction, literary titles, science fiction, fantasy, young adult & more. No unsol mss.

**Loretta Barrett Books Inc** (L)
220 E 23 St, 11th fl, New York, NY 10010
*Tel:* 212-242-3420
*E-mail:* query@lorettabarrettbooks.com
*Web Site:* www.lorettabarrettbooks.com
*Key Personnel*
Pres: Loretta A Barrett (AAR)
VP & Dir of Foreign Rts: Nick Mullendore (AAR)
Jr Agent: Jennifer Didik
Founded: 1990
Fiction & nonfiction. Handle film, TV & multimedia rights. No poetry or children's literature, no screenplays; no unsol mss, query first with SASE. Submit outlines, sample chapters, bio (nonfiction); synopsis, bio (fiction). Representatives on the West Coast & in all major foreign countries. No reading fee.

**Bella Pomer Agency Inc** (L)
355 St Clair Ave W, Suite 801, Toronto, ON M5P 1N5, Canada
*Tel:* 416-920-4949
*E-mail:* belpom@sympatico.ca
*Web Site:* bellapomeragency.com
*Key Personnel*
Pres: Bella Pomer
Founded: 1978
Full-length fiction (literary), historical & mystery fiction & general interest narrative nonfiction. Film & TV rights handled for books already represented; no original screenplays; no poetry. No unsol mss. Representation or direct sale in all principal countries. No reading fees. Note: this agent is not accepting new clients.
Titles recently placed: *A New Leaf*, Merilyn Simonds
Foreign Rights: Akcali & Tuna Copyright (Turkey); BMSR (Brazil); Duran Kim Agency (Korea); Grandi & Associate (Italy); Grayhawk Agency (Gray Tan) (China, Taiwan); International Editors' Co (Portugal, South America, Spain); Japan UNI Agency Inc (Japan); JLM Agency (Greece); Katai & Bolza (Hungary); Alexander Korschenevsky (Russia); Agence Michelle Lapautre (France); Liepman AG (Germany); Nurnberg (Netherlands); Prava & Prevoda (Czech Republic, Poland, Slovakia)

**Meredith Bernstein Literary Agency Inc** (L)
2095 Broadway, Suite 505, New York, NY 10023
*Tel:* 212-799-1007 *Fax:* 212-799-1145
*E-mail:* MGoodBern@aol.com
*Web Site:* www.meredithbernsteinliteraryagency.com
*Key Personnel*
Agent: Meredith Bernstein (AAR)
Adult fiction (commercial & literary) & nonfiction; memoirs, current events, biography, health & fitness, women's issues, mysteries & special projects; crafts & creative endeavors. No poetry or screenplays. No unsol mss, query first online (no attachments) or by mail (include SASE). For fiction submit a 1 page query letter; nonfiction send 1 page query letter, table of contents & information on why you are an expert in this field. Handle film & TV rights only for books represented. Representatives in foreign countries & on the west coast. No reading fee.
Membership(s): The Authors Guild; Sisters in Crime; Women's Media Group

**Bethel Agency** (L-D)
PO Box 21043, Park West Sta, New York, NY 10025
*Tel:* 212-864-4510
*Key Personnel*
Pres: Lewis R Chambers
Founded: 1967
Books & articles, fiction & nonfiction; stage plays, motion picture & TV properties; foreign & domestic. Represent photographers. Handle film & TV rights. No unsol mss, query first; submit outline & sample chapters. No reading fee.

**Daniel Bial Agency** (L-D)
41 W 83 St, Suite 5-C, New York, NY 10024
*Tel:* 212-721-1786
*E-mail:* dbialagency@msn.com
*Web Site:* www.danielbialagency.com
*Key Personnel*
Founder & Prop: Daniel Bial
Founded: 1991
Nonfiction: business, cookbooks, history, humor, languages, popular culture, psychology, reference, science, sports, travel; fiction: quality fiction. No juvenile, poetry, genre fiction, screenplays, textbooks. No unsol mss, query letter first with SASE or short e-mail (e-mail queries without attachments are fine). No reading fee.

**Vicky Bijur Literary Agency** (L-D)
333 West End Ave, Suite 5-B, New York, NY 10023
*Tel:* 212-580-4108
*E-mail:* queries@vickybijuragency.com
*Web Site:* www.vickybijuragency.com
*Key Personnel*
Agent: Vicky Bijur (AAR)
Founded: 1988
Adult fiction & nonfiction. No children's books, poetry, science fiction, fantasy or horror. No unsol mss, query first with SASE. Fiction: query, synopsis & first chapter. Nonfiction: query & proposal. If e-mailed, paste proposal into body of e-mail, no attachments. No phone or fax queries. If query by hard copy, include SASE for response. If material to be returned, include SASE large enough to contain pages. No reading fee. Agents in all principal foreign countries. Handle film & TV rights.
Titles recently placed: *A Fatal Winter*, G M Malliet; *And When She Was Good*, Laura Lippman; *Drive*, James Sallis; *Driven*, James Sallis; *Love Anthony*, Lisa Genova; *Others of My Kind*, James Sallis; *Pagan Spring*, G M Malliet; *Serious Eats*, Ed Levine; *The Buzzard Table*, Margaret Maron; *The Killer is Dying*, James Sallis; *Three-Day Town*, Margaret Maron
Foreign Rights: Agenzia Letteraria Internazionale (Italy); AnatoliaLit Agency (Turkey); The English Agency Japan (Japan); The Grayhawk Agency (China, Taiwan); The Deborah Harris Agency (Israel); Agence Michelle Lapautre (France); Lennart Sane Agency (Argentina, Brazil, Denmark, Finland, Holland, Norway, Portugal, Spain, Sweden); Liepman Agency AG (Germany); Maxima Creative Agency (Indonesia); Prava I Prevodi (Bulgaria, Czech Republic, Estonia, Greece, Hungary, Poland, Russia, Serbia, Slovakia); Abner Stein Agency (England); Tuttle Mori Agency Inc (Thailand); Eric Yang Agency (Korea)

**David Black Agency** (L-D)
Subsidiary of Black Inc
335 Adams St, 27th fl, Suite 2707, Brooklyn, NY 11201
*Tel:* 718-852-5500 *Fax:* 718-852-5539
*Web Site:* www.davidblackagency.com
*Key Personnel*
Pres: David Black (AAR) *E-mail:* dblack@dblackagency.com
Agent: Antonella Iannarino (AAR) *Tel:* 718-852-5535 *E-mail:* aiannarino@dblackagency.com; David Larabell *Tel:* 718-852-5526 *E-mail:* dlarabell@dblackagency.com; Linda Loewenthal *Tel:* 718-852-5523 *E-mail:* lloewenthal@dblackagency.com; Gary Morris *Tel:* 718-852-5518 *E-mail:* gmorris@dblackagency.com; Susan Raihofer *Tel:* 718-852-5542 *E-mail:* sraihofer@dblackagency.com; Sarah Smith *E-mail:* ssmith@dblackagency.com; Luke Thomas *Tel:* 718-852-5544 *E-mail:* lthomas@dblackagency.com; Joy Tutela *Tel:* 718-852-5533 *E-mail:* jtutela@dblackagency.com
Founded: 1990
Literary & commercial fiction & nonfiction, especially sports, politics, business, health, fitness, romance, parenting, psychology & social issues. No poetry. No unsol mss, query first with SASE. No reading fee. Agents in all principal foreign countries. Handle film & TV rights. No mysteries or thrillers.
Foreign Rights: Bardon-Chinese Media Agency (Ming-Ming Liu) (China); Eliane Benisti Agent Litteraire (Eliane Benisti & Noemi Rollet) (France); Luigi Bernabo Associates (Luigi Bernabo) (Italy); The Deborah Harris Agency (Efrat Lev) (Israel); International Editors' Co (Spanish) (Latin America, Spain); Katai & Bolza Literary Agents (Peter Bolza) (Hungary); Maxima Creative Agency (Santo Manurung) (Indonesia); Mohrbooks (Sabine Ibach, Bettina Kaufmann, Sebastian Ritscher & Cristina Uytiepo) (Germany); Prava I Prevodi Literary Agency (Milena Lukic, Ana Milenkovic & Jelena Todosijevic) (Bulgaria, Croatia, Czech Republic, Estonia, Greece, Latvia, Lithuania, Poland, Russia, Serbia, Slovenia); Riff Agency (Portuguese) (JP, Laura & Lucia Riff) (Brazil, Portugal); Sebes & van Gelderen Literary Agency (Paul Sebes) (Netherlands); Abner Stein (Abner & Arabella Stein, Caspian Dennis) (Australia, UK); Tuttle-Mori Agency Inc (Japan, Thailand); Eric Yang Agency (Sue Yang) (Korea)

**Bleecker Street Associates Inc** (L)
217 Thompson St, Suite 519, New York, NY 10012
*Tel:* 212-677-4492 *Fax:* 212-388-0001
*Key Personnel*
Pres: Agnes Birnbaum (AAR)
Founded: 1984
No unsol mss, query first about book project & author with SASE (cannot respond nor return materials without SASE). Do not query via e-mail, phone or fax. Handle film & TV rights for clients' own work only. Fiction & nonfiction; no poetry, plays or screenplays; handle magazine articles by book clients only. No reading fee.
Titles recently placed: *Four-Legged Miracles: Heart Warming Tales of Lost Dogs' Journeys Home*, Brad Steiger, Sherry Steiger; *Madame Curie*, Shelley Emling; *Real Ghosts, Restless Spirits, and Haunted Places*, Brad Steiger; *Sun Tzu at Gettysburg*, Bevin Alexander; *The Last Camel Charge*, Forrest Bryant Johnson; *The Magnificent Medills*, Megan McKinney; *Why Do Women Crave More Sex in the Summer*, Patricia Barnes-Svarney
Foreign Rights: Agenzia Letteraria Internazionale (Italy); Bookman (Netherlands, Scandinavia); The English Agency (Japan) Ltd (Japan); International Editors' Co (Portugal, South America, Spain); Thomas Schlueck (Germany); Abner Stein Agency (Arabella Stein) (British Commonwealth)

**Reid Boates Literary Agency** (L-D)
69 Cooks Crossroad, Pittstown, NJ 08867-0328
Mailing Address: PO Box 328, Pittstown, NJ 08867-0328
*Tel:* 908-797-8087
*E-mail:* reid.boates@gmail.com
*Key Personnel*
Sole Prop: Reid Boates
Founded: 1985
Narrative &/or how-to nonfiction, health, spirituality, wellness, business & sports. Handle film & TV rights. No fiction. Most new clients by referral. No reading fee. Agents in all major foreign markets. No unsol mss, submit written query with SASE.
Titles recently placed: *Mindfulness*, Joseph Goldstein; *Most Intimate*, Roshi Pat Enkyo O'Hara; *The Shambhala Principle*, Sakyong Mipham Rinpoche
Foreign Rep(s): Eliane Benisti (France); Raquel de la Concha (Spain); Michael Meller (Eastern Europe, Germany, UK); Owl's Agency (Japan) Ltd (Japan)

**Alison Bond Literary Agency** (L)
171 W 79 St, No 143, New York, NY 10024
*Key Personnel*
Principal: Alison M Bond *E-mail:* alison@bondlit.com
Founded: 1982
Literary fiction, memoir/biography, women's issues, food narratives & general nonfiction. No unsol mss; query first with SASE; for nonfiction projects, brief proposal & sample chapters, plus author's writing credits; not accepting new fiction writers at present time. Agents in most European countries. No fiction or genre categories. No fees charged.
Membership(s): Women's Media Group

**Bond Literary Agency** (L)
4340 E Kentucky Ave, Suite 471, Denver, CO 80246
*Tel:* 303-781-9305
*E-mail:* queries@bondliteraryagency.com
*Web Site:* bondliteraryagency.com
*Key Personnel*
Owner & Agent: Sandra Bond *E-mail:* sandra@bondliteraryagency.com
Founded: 1998
Specialize in adult commercial & literary fiction including mysteries & women's fiction (no romance, children's picture books, health, science fiction, adult fantasy or poetry); juvenile fiction; narrative nonfiction, science, memoir, biography & business. Talented, previously unpublished writers will be considered. Nonfiction authors must have excellent credentials & a strong platform. No unsol mss, query by e-mail first (letter in the body of the e-mail, no attachments). No phone calls please. Ms submissions by request only. Sell foreign & film/TV rights through subagents. No fees charged.
Titles recently placed: *Butch Cassidy: Beyond the Grave*, W C Jameson; *Claws of the Cat: A Shinobi Mystery*, Susan Spann; *Death in the 12th House: Where Neptune Rules*, Mitchell Scott Lewis; *Fatal Descent*, Beth Groundwater; *Her Story: A Timelin of the Women Who Changed America*, Charlotte S Waisman, Jill S Tietjen; *To Hell in a Handbasket*, Beth Groundwater; *Wicked Eddies*, Beth Groundwater

**BookEnds LLC** (L)
136 Long Hill Rd, Gillette, NJ 07933
*Web Site:* www.bookends-inc.com
*Key Personnel*
Owner & Literary Agent: Jessica H Faust (AAR) *E-mail:* jfsubmissions@bookends-inc.com
Agent: Jessica Alvarez (AAR) *E-mail:* jasubmissions@bookends-inc.com; Kim Lionetti (AAR) *E-mail:* klsubmissions@bookends-inc.com
Literary Asst & Rights Coord: Beth Campbell *E-mail:* submissions@bookends-inc.com
Dir, Digital Content: Bill Harris
Founded: 1999
Founded by former editors from Berkley Publishing, BookEnds is a literary agency that represents fiction & nonfiction for adult audiences. No unsol mss, query first. Review web site for submission instructions & get tips on queries & proposals. No fees.
Titles recently placed: *A Witch Before Dying*, Heather Blake; *An Heiress at Heart*, Jennifer Delamere; *Bedding Lord Ned*, Sally Mackenzie; *Buried in a Bog*, Sheila Connolly; *Cat Trick*, Sophie Kelly; *Chapter & Hearse: A Booktown Mystery*, Lorna Barrett; *Due or Die: A Library Mystery*, Jenn McKinlay; *Equilibrium*, Lorrie Thomson; *Every Trick in the Book*, Lucy Arlington; *Fire Kissed*, Erin Kellison; *Gotcha!*, Christie Craig; *Immortally Yours*, Angie Fox; *Killer Crab Cakes: The Fresh-Baked Mystery Series*, Livia Washburn; *Lady Outlaw*, Stacy Henrie; *More Than He Expected*, Andrea Laurence; *One Hot Murder*, Lorraine Bartlett; *Promise the Moon*, Elizabeth Joy Arnold; *The Farm*, Emily McKay; *The Medical Science of House*, Andrew Holtz; *The Reason is You*, Sharla Scroggs; *The Retail Doctor's Guide to Growing Your Business*, Bob Phibbs; *The Trouble with Cowboys*, Melissa Cutler
Membership(s): Mystery Writers of America; Romance Writers of America

**Books & Such** (L)
52 Mission Circle, Suite 122, PMB 170, Santa Rosa, CA 95409-5370
*Tel:* 707-538-4184
*Web Site:* booksandsuch.com
*Key Personnel*
Founder & Pres: Janet Kobobel Grant (AAR) *E-mail:* janet@booksandsuch.com
VP: Wendy Lawton *E-mail:* wendy@booksandsuch.com
Literary Agent, Adult Fiction, Nonfiction & Teen: Rachelle Gardner *E-mail:* rachelle@booksandsuch.com
Literary Agent, Adult Fiction & Nonfiction: Mary Keeley *E-mail:* mary@booksandsuch.com
Literary Agent, Teens, Twenties & Thirties: Rachel Kent *E-mail:* rachel@booksandsuch.com
Founded: 1997
Handles fiction & nonfiction. Submission by e-mail (no attachments). No phone calls. No unsol mss, query first. No fees.
Titles recently placed: *A Stitch in Crime*, Cathy Elliott; *Brides of London*, Melanie Dickerson; *Discovering the City of Sodom*, Stephen Collins, PhD, Latayne C Scott, PhD; *Firewall*, DiAnn Mills; *Flight of the Earls*, Michael Reynolds; *Leap Year*, Michelle DeRusha; *Pearl in the Night*, Atessa Afshar; *Take Joy*, Debbie Macomber; *The Good Girl's Guide to Breaking Bad Habits*, Cheri Gregory, Kathi Lipp; *Troubled Hearts*, Amy Simpson
*Branch Office(s)*
PO Box 1227, Hilmar, CA 95324-1227 *Tel:* 209-634-1913
Membership(s): Advanced Writers & Speakers Association; American Christian Fiction Writers; CBA; Romance Writers of America

**BookStop Literary Agency LLC** (L-D)
67 Meadow View Rd, Orinda, CA 94563
*E-mail:* info@bookstopliterary.com
*Web Site:* www.bookstopliterary.com
*Key Personnel*
CEO & Pres: Kendra Marcus
Literary Agent: Ms Minju Chang
Foreign Rts Coord: Isle Craane
Founded: 1984
Juvenile & young adult mss only (fiction & nonfiction) & illustration for children's books, especially humorous voices, intense young adult fiction, clever middle-grade & topics & mss for the Hispanic market in the U.S. Accept unsol mss. Submit full mss for picture books; first 10 pages for fiction; sample chapters & outline for nonfiction. See web site for additional submission information. No reading fee.
Titles recently placed: *Press Here*, Herve Tullet; *Scarlet*, A C Gaughen; *The Three Ninja Pigs*, Corey Schwartz

**Georges Borchardt Inc** (L-D)
136 E 57 St, New York, NY 10022
*Tel:* 212-753-5785
*E-mail:* georges@gbagency.com
*Web Site:* www.gbagency.com
*Key Personnel*
Founder & Pres: Georges Borchardt (AAR)
Founder: Anne Borchardt (AAR)
VP & Foreign Rts Dir: Valerie Borchardt *E-mail:* valerie@gbagency.com
VP & Sr Agent: Kate Johnson *E-mail:* kate@gbagency.com
Agent: Samantha Shea *E-mail:* samantha@gbagency.com
Foreign Rts Asst: Rachel Brooke *E-mail:* rachel@gbagency.com
Founded: 1967
Fiction & nonfiction. No unsol mss; handle film & TV rights & software. No fees charged.
Titles recently placed: *A Book of Voyages*, Patrick O'Brian; *Across the Pond: An Englishman's View of America*, Terry Eagleton; *Ancient Israel: The Former Prophets*, Robert Alter; *Butterfly People*, William Leach; *Darling: A Spiritual Autobiography*, Richard Rodríguez; *Franz Kafka: The Poet of Shame and Guilt*, Saul Friedlander; *Good Prose: The Art of Nonfiction*, Tracy Kidder, Richard Todd; *Gossip*, Joseph Epstein; *Henry Ford*, Vincent Curcio; *Inventing Wine*, Paul Lukacs; *Kissing the Sword: A Prison Memoir*, Shahrnush Parsipur; *Making It: A Novel of Madison Avenue*, Helen Klein Ross; *Memories of a Marriage*, Louis Begley; *My Brother, My Sister: Story of a Transformation*, Molly Haskell; *Pere Marie-Benoit and Jewish Rescue*, Suzan Zuccotti; *Quick Question*, John Ashbery; *Safe House*, Chris Ewan; *San Miguel*, T C Boyle; *The Abundance*, Amit Majmudar; *The Art of Fermentation*, Sandor Katz; *The House at Belle Fontaine*, Lily Tuck; *The Iron Curtain*, Anne Applebaum; *The Last Men on Top*, Susan Jacoby; *The Longings of Wayward Girls*, Karen Brown; *The Wolf and the Watchman: A Father, a Son, and the CIA*, Scott C Johnson; *The Woman Upstairs*, Claire Messud; *Ways of Forgetting*, John Dower; *What Art Is*, Arthur C Danto
Foreign Rights: The Asano Agency (Kiyoshi Asano) (Japanese); Carmen Balcells Agency (Maribel Luque) (Spanish); Bardon Chinese Media Agency (Ming-Ming Lui) (Chinese); Luigi Bernabo Associates SRL (Luigi Branabo) (Italian); English Agency (Junzo Sawa) (Japanese); Graal Literary Agency (Marcin Biegaj) (Polish); Deborah Harris Agency (Efrat Lev) (Israel); Japan UNI Agency (Miko Yamanouchi) (Japanese); JLM Agency (Nelly & John Moukakou) (Greek); Katai & Bolza (Peter Bolza) (Hungarian); Korean Copyright Center (Misook Hong) (Korean); Agence Michelle Lapautre (Michelle Lapautre) (French); Mohrbooks (Sabine Ibach & Sebastian Ritscher) (German); Andrew Nurnberg Associates (Kristine Shatrovska) (Baltic States); Andrew Nurnburg Associates (Anna Droumeva) (Bulgarian & Romanian); Andrew Nurnberg Associates (Ludmilla Sushkova) (Russian); Kristin Olson Literary Agency SRO (Kristin Olson) (Czech); RDC Agencia Literaria

(Raquel de la Concha) (Portuguese) (Portugal); Sane Toregard Agency (Ulf Toregard) (Scandinavia); Karin Schindler (Portuguese) (Brazil); Marianne Schoenbach Literary Agency BV (Marianne Schonbach) (Dutch); Sheil Land Associates (Vivien Green) (British); Telif Haklari Ajansi (Asli Karasuil) (Turkish); Tuttle-Mori Agency Inc (Asako Kawachi) (Japanese)

**The Barbara Bova Literary Agency LLC** (L)
3951 Gulf Shore Blvd N, Unit PH 1-B, Naples, FL 34103
*Tel:* 239-649-7237
*E-mail:* slushpile@yahoo.com
*Web Site:* www.barbarabovaliteraryagency.com
*Key Personnel*
Pres: Ben Bova
Mng Ed: Ken Bova *E-mail:* kenbova@barbarabovaliteraryagency.com
Sr Assoc
Agent: Michael Burke *E-mail:* michaelburke@barbarabovaliteraryagency.com
Audio Subrights Div Mgr: Stefan Rudnicki *E-mail:* stefanrudnicki@barbarabovaliteraryagency.com
Founded: 1974
Commercial fiction & nonfiction. No unsol mss, query first by e-mail. No reading fees. 15% commission on domestic sales & 20% commission on foreign sales. Fees for overseas postage & calls, photocopying & shipping. Short e-mail queries accepted (no attachments). Enter "query" in the subject line. Submit publishing history, an overview of the book, a word count & any pertinent information. A synopsis may be included. Seeking fiction & nonfiction, no scripts, poetry or children's books.

**Bradford Literary Agency** (L)
5694 Mission Center Rd, Suite 347, San Diego, CA 92108
*Tel:* 619-521-1201
*E-mail:* queries@bradfordlit.com
*Web Site:* www.bradfordlit.com
*Key Personnel*
Agent: Laura Bradford (AAR) *E-mail:* laura@bradfordlit.com; Natalie Lakosil *E-mail:* natalie@bradfordlit.com
Founded: 2001
A boutique agency offering a full range of representation services to authors, both published & pre-published. We are an editorial-focused agency & prefer to work closely with our authors in helping to build strong, sustainable careers. We believe the best author-agent relationships extend beyond making sales; in order to best serve our client's needs, we must also be a partner, advisor, a careful listener, a troubleshooter & an advocate.
We are currently acquiring fiction: romance (historical, romantic suspense, paranormal, category, contemporary, erotic), urban fantasy, women's fiction, mystery, thrillers & young adult. Also nonfiction: business, relationships, biography/memoir, self-help, parenting, narrative humor. We are not currently acquiring: poetry, screenplays, short stories, children's books, westerns, horror, new age, religion, crafts, cookbooks, gift books.
We accept unsol mss. Queries are accepted by e-mail only - send queries to queries@bradfordlit.com. We do not open e-mail attachments, unless specifically requested by an agent. Your entire submission must appear in the body of the e-mail & not as an attachment. The subject line should begin as follows: QUERY: (The title of the ms or any short message you would like us to see should follow). For fiction: Please e-mail a query letter along with the first chapter of your ms & a synopsis. Please be sure to include the genre & word count in your cover letter. For nonfiction: submit a book proposal including an outline, sample material, author bio & competitive survey. No fees.
Titles recently placed: *30 Days of No Gossip*, Stephanie Faris; *A Wedding She'll Never Forget*, Robyn Grady; *After Hours*, Cara McKenna; *Against the Ropes*, Sarah Castille; *Binding the Shadows*, Jenn Bennett; *Charmed Vengeance*, Suzanne Lazear; *Contaminated*, Em Garner; *Deep Deception*, Cathy Pegau; *Dirty Little Secret*, Jennifer Echols; *Enticing the Earl*, Christie Kelley; *Flirting With Texas*, Katie Lane; *For the Love of a Soldier*, Victoria Morgan; *Games People Play*, Shelby Reed; *Gilded*, Karina Cooper; *Going Under*, Lauren Dane; *Horde*, Ann Aguirre; *If I Lie*, Corrine Jackson; *In the Arms of the Heiress*, Maggie Robinson; *Legacy of the Clockwork Key*, Kristin Welker; *Looming Murder*, Carol Ann Martin; *Lush*, Lauren Dane; *Mission: Soldier to Daddy*, Soraya Lane; *Perdition*, Ann Aguirre; *Project Paper Doll: The Rules*, Stacey Kade; *Pushed*, Corrine Jackson; *Renegade*, J A Souders; *Round is a Tortilla*, Roseanne Thong; *Son of the Enemy*, Ana Barrons; *Tear You Apart*, Megan Hart; *The Favor*, Megan Hart; *The Second Chance Cafe*, Alison Kent; *True*, Erin McCarthy; *Uncommon Pleasure*, Anne Calhoun; *When I'm With You*, Beth Kery
Foreign Rights: Taryn Fagerness Agency (Taryn Fagerness) (Albania, Argentina, Australia, Brazil, Bulgaria, Canada, China, Croatia, Czech Republic, Denmark, Estonia, Finland, France, Germany, Greece, Hungary, Iceland, India, Indonesia, Israel, Italy, Japan, Korea, Latvia, Lithuania, Mexico, Netherlands, Norway, Poland, Portugal, Romania, Russia, Serbia, Slovakia, Spain, Sweden, Taiwan, Thailand, Turkey, Ukraine, UK, Vietnam)
Membership(s): ALA; Romance Writers of America; Society of Children's Book Writers & Illustrators

**Brandt & Hochman Literary Agents Inc** (L)
1501 Broadway, Suite 2310, New York, NY 10036
*Tel:* 212-840-5760 *Fax:* 212-840-5776
*Web Site:* brandthochman.com
*Key Personnel*
Pres: Gail Hochman (AAR) *E-mail:* ghochman@bromasite.com
Agent: Carl D Brandt (AAR) *E-mail:* books@bromasite.com; Charles Schlessiger (AAR) *E-mail:* cschlessiger@bromasite.com
Agent & Foreign Rts: Marianne Merola (AAR) *E-mail:* mmerola@bromasite.com
Agent: Bill Contardi (AAR) *E-mail:* bill@bromasite.com; Emily Forland *E-mail:* eforland@bromasite.com; Emma Patterson *E-mail:* epatterson@bromasite.com; Jody Klein *E-mail:* jklein@bromasite.com; Henry Thayer *E-mail:* hthayer@bromasite.com
Represents fiction & nonfiction, including mystery/thriller, memoir, narrative nonfiction, journalism, history, current affairs, health, science, pop culture, lifestyle, art history & children's books. No screenplays or textbooks. No unsol mss, query first by e-mail or regular mail. Responses to e-mailed queries not guaranteed. Queries limited to 2 pages. Include SASE if sending by regular mail. See web site for specific submission preferences for each agent. No reading fee. Fee charged for making copies & book/galley purchases. Co-agents in most foreign countries.

**The Joan Brandt Agency** (L)
788 Wesley Dr NW, Atlanta, GA 30305
*Tel:* 404-351-8877 *Fax:* 404-351-0068
*Key Personnel*
Pres: Joan Brandt Schwartz
Founded: 1990
Fiction & nonfiction (no science fiction, horror, fantasy, historical or romance), film & TV rights. No unsol mss, query first with SASE; submit letter plus brief synopsis. Agents present in all principal countries.

**The Helen Brann Agency Inc** (L)
94 Curtis Rd, Bridgewater, CT 06752
*Tel:* 860-354-9580 *Fax:* 860-355-2572
*Key Personnel*
Pres: Helen Brann (AAR) *E-mail:* hbrann@helenbrannagency.com
Assoc: Carol White *E-mail:* cwhite@helenbrannagency.com
Founded: 1973
No unsol mss, query first.
*Branch Office(s)*
Flora Roberts Inc, 275 Seventh Ave, 26th fl, New York, NY 10001, Sarah Douglas *Tel:* 646-486-4600 *Fax:* 646-486-2358
Foreign Rep(s): Carmen Balcells (Portugal, South America, Spain); Bardon-Chinese Media (China, Taiwan); Luigi Bernabo (Italy); Agence Michelle Lapautre (France); Leonhardt (Scandinavia); Sara Menguc (England); Mohrbooks (Germany); Andrew Nurnberg Associates Ltd (Eastern Europe); Onk Agency (Turkey); Tuttle-Mori Agency Inc (Japan)

**Barbara Braun Associates Inc** (L)
7 E 14 St, Suite 19F, New York, NY 10003
*Tel:* 212-604-9023
*Web Site:* www.barbarabraunagency.com
*Key Personnel*
Pres: Barbara Braun (AAR) *E-mail:* barbara@barbarabraunagency.com
Assoc: John F Baker
Founded: 1994
Represents both literary & commercial fiction as well as serious nonfiction, including memoir, biography, cultural history, women's issues, pop culture, art & architecture. Fiction is strong on stories for women, art-related fiction, historical & multicultural stories & mysteries & thrillers. Interested in narrative nonfiction & current affairs. No unsol mss, query first by e-mail to bbasubmissions@gmail.com. Include brief summary of book, word count, genre, any relevant publishing experience & first 5 pages of ms pasted into the body of the e-mail. No reading or other fees.
Foreign Rights: Jean V Naggar Literary Agency (Jennifer Weltz) (Worldwide)
Membership(s): The Authors Guild; PEN American Center

**M Courtney Briggs Esq, Authors Representative** (L)
Chase Tower, 28th fl, 100 N Broadway Ave, Oklahoma City, OK 73102
*Key Personnel*
Author's Rep: M Courtney Briggs
Founded: 1994
Fiction & nonfiction, adult & juvenile with emphasis on children's books, including picture books, middle-grade & young adult books. Represent authors & illustrators of trade books of all types. Handle film & TV rights. No unsol mss, query first by regular mail with SASE, include publishing history; published authors only; no reading fees.
Membership(s): Society of Children's Book Writers & Illustrators

**Brockman Inc** (L)
260 Fifth Ave, 10th fl, New York, NY 10001
*Tel:* 212-935-8900 *Fax:* 212-935-5535
*E-mail:* rights@brockman.com
*Web Site:* www.brockman.com
*Key Personnel*
Chmn & CEO: John Brockman
Pres: Katinka Matson
VP: Max Brockman

Rts Dir: Russell Weinberger
Literary & software agency. No unsol mss. Deal direct in all foreign markets. No fees charged.

**Curtis Brown Ltd** (L-D)
10 Astor Place, New York, NY 10003
*Tel:* 212-473-5400
*Web Site:* www.curtisbrown.com
*Key Personnel*
CEO: Timothy F Knowlton (AAR)
Pres: Peter L Ginsberg (AAR)
EVP & Book Agent: Ginger Knowlton (AAR)
SVP & Book Agent: Maureen Walters (AAR)
VP & Book Agent: Elizabeth Harding (AAR); Laura Blake Peterson (AAR)
Dir, Digital Strategy & Book Agent: Steve Kasdin (AAR)
Dir, Foreign Rts & Book Agent: Jonathan Lyons (AAR)
Book Agent: Ginger Clark (AAR); Katherine Fausset (AAR); Sarah La Polla (AAR); Mitchell Waters (AAR)
Film & TV Rts: Holly Frederick (AAR)
Founded: 1914
Handle general trade fiction & nonfiction, juvenile. No unsol mss, query first with SASE. Submit outline or sample chapters. No reading fee. Other fees charged (for photocopies, express mail, etc). Handle film & TV rights & merchandising & multimedia. No playwrights. Representatives in all major foreign countries.
*Branch Office(s)*
1750 Montgomery St, San Francisco, CA 94111 *Tel:* 415-954-8566

**Marie Brown Associates** (L)
412 W 154 St, New York, NY 10032
*Tel:* 212-939-9725 *Fax:* 212-939-9728
*E-mail:* mbrownlit@aol.com
*Key Personnel*
Owner & Pres: Marie D Brown
Founded: 1984
Adult & juvenile fiction & nonfiction. Handle film & TV rights through representatives in Hollywood. No unsol mss, query first; submit outline & sample chapters or full ms on request, 12-point, double-spaced, one-sided only, typed, white paper & unbound. Include SASE. No e-mail queries. No reading fee.

**Browne & Miller Literary Associates** (L)
410 S Michigan Ave, Suite 460, Chicago, IL 60605
*Tel:* 312-922-3063 *Fax:* 312-922-1905
*E-mail:* mail@browneandmiller.com
*Web Site:* www.browneandmiller.com
*Key Personnel*
Pres & Owner: Danielle Egan-Miller (AAR) *E-mail:* danielle@browneandmiller.com
Assoc Agent & Internship Coord: Joanna MacKenzie *E-mail:* joanna@browneandmiller.com
Founded: 1971
General adult trade fiction, nonfiction & young adult. No poetry, plays, short stories, horror, sci-fi novels or children's books. No unsol mss, query first with SASE or by e-mail; no reading fee.
Foreign Rep(s): Agence Eliane Benisti (Eliane Benisti) (France); Big Apple Agency Inc (China, Taiwan); Book Publishers Association of Israel (Shoshi Grajower) (Israel); The English Agency (Japan) Ltd (Japan); International Copyright Agency Ltd (Simona Kessler) (Romania); Japan UNI Agency Inc (Japan); KCBS Literary Agency (Hosung Maeng) (Korea); The Marsh Agency UK (Poland); Natoli, Stefan & Oliva (Roberta Oliva) (Italy); Andrew Nurnberg Associates Baltic (Tatjana Zoldnere) (Baltic States); Andrew Nurnberg Associates (Hungary); O A Literary Agency (Greece); Prava i Prevodi (Croatia, Montenegro, Serbia, Slovenia); Riff Agency (Brazil); Thomas Schluck Agency (Germany); Tuttle-Mori Agency Inc (Japan); Julio F Yanez Agencia Literaria (Montse F Yanez) (Mexico, South America, Spain); Eric Yang Agency (Korea)
Foreign Rights: Andrew Nurnberg Literary Agency (Liudmilla Sushkova) (Russia)
Membership(s): The Authors Guild; Midwest Writers Association; Mystery Writers of America; Romance Writers of America

**Don Buchwald & Associates Inc** (L)
10 E 44 St, New York, NY 10017
*Tel:* 212-867-1200 *Fax:* 212-867-2434
*E-mail:* info@buchwald.com
*Web Site:* www.buchwald.com
*Key Personnel*
CEO & Pres (NY): Don Buchwald *E-mail:* don@buchwald.com
CFO & VP: Stephen Fisher *E-mail:* steve@buchwald.com
EVP, Legal & Admin Aff: Richard Basch *E-mail:* richard@buchwald.com
Agent (NY): David Lewis *E-mail:* davidl@buchwald.com; Jonathan Mason *E-mail:* jmason@buchwald.com; Joanne Nici *E-mail:* jonici@buchwald.com; Rachel Sheedy *E-mail:* rachel@buchwald.com; Alan Willig *E-mail:* alanw@buchwald.com
Talent representatives & literary agency: TV, film, commercial, theatre & broadcasting. No unsol mss, query first. No reading fee.
*Branch Office(s)*
6500 Wilshire Blvd, Suite 2200, Los Angeles, CA 90048 *Tel:* 323-665-7400 *Fax:* 323-665-7470

**Howard Buck Agency** (L-D)
80 Eighth Ave, Suite 1107, New York, NY 10011
*Tel:* 212-924-9093
*Key Personnel*
Pres: Howard Buck
Contact: Mark Frisk
Founded: 1978
Fiction (no science fiction, fantasy, horror or screenplays) & nonfiction, adult; no juvenile or children's. No unsol mss, query first by letter with SASE. No original screenplays, teleplays or TV episodes. No reading fees; handle film rights.
Foreign Rep(s): A M Heath & Co Ltd (UK)

**Judith Buckner Literary Agency** (L-D)
12721 Hart St, North Hollywood, CA 91605
*Tel:* 818-982-8202 *Fax:* 818-764-6844
*Key Personnel*
Pres: Judith Buckner *E-mail:* jbuckner@pacbell.net
Founded: 1970
Handle commercial & literary fiction & nonfiction, some film & TV scripts. No children's, young adult, romance, science fiction or horror. No unsol mss; query first by letter or e-mail. No reading fee. Commission 15% domestic, 20% foreign. Handle film & TV rights. If invited to submit, for fiction send first fifty pages & brief synopsis of remainder. For nonfiction, send proposal including overview, target market, outline or table of contents, sample chapter, author's bio, survey of competition & reasons why your book is superior & marketing plan.

**The Bukowski Agency** (L-D)
14 Prince Arthur Ave, Suite 202, Toronto, ON M5R 1A9, Canada
*Tel:* 416-928-6728 *Fax:* 416-963-9978
*E-mail:* info@bukowskiagency.com
*Web Site:* www.bukowskiagency.com
*Key Personnel*
Pres & Primary Agent: Denise Bukowski
Founded: 1986
Adult trade except genre fiction by Canadian authors. No unsol mss, query first by regular mail. Submit proposal & sample for nonfiction; query & sample for fiction. No reading fees. Commission plus disbursements. Handle film & TV rights.
Foreign Rights: AJA Literary Agency (Anna Jarota) (France); Akcali Copyright Agency (Atilla Izgi Turgut) (Istanbul); Big Apple Agency (Vincent Lin) (China, Taiwan); The Foreign Office (Teresa Vilarrubla) (Latin America, Portugal, Spain); Graal Literary Agency (Filip Wojciechowski) (Eastern Europe, Poland); Grandi & Associati (Alessandra Mele) (Italy); The Deborah Harris Agency (Ilana Kurshan) (Israel); A M Heath & Co Ltd (Bill Hamilton) (UK); Japan UNI Agency Inc (Cecilia Kashiwamura) (Japan); JLM Literary Agency (Nelly Moukakou) (Greece); JLM Literary Agency (John Moukakou) (Greece); Katai & Bolza Literary Agents (Peter Bolza) (Hungary); Duran Kim Agency (Duran Kim) (Korea); Licht & Burr (Trine Licht) (Scandinavia); Mohrbooks AG (Annelie Geissler) (Germany); Agencia Literaria Riff (Joao Paulo Riff) (Brazil); Marianne Schoenbach Literary Agency (Marianne Schoenbach) (Holland); The Van Lear Agency (Elizabeth Van Lear) (Russia)

**Sheree Bykofsky Associates Inc** (L)
PO Box 706, Brigantine, NJ 08203
*E-mail:* submitbee@aol.com
*Web Site:* www.shereebee.com
*Key Personnel*
Pres & Agent: Sheree Bykofsky (AAR)
Founded: 1991
Adult trade & mass market nonfiction & fiction. No unsol mss, send e-query in body of e-mail to submitbee@aol.com. Handle film & TV rights through subagents. No fees.
Foreign Rep(s): Betty Anne Crawford
Foreign Rights: Big Apple Agency Inc (China); International Editors' Co (Spain); Alexander Korzhenevski (Russia); Piergiorgio Nicolazzini (Italy); Radoslav Trenev (Eastern Europe, Greece, Turkey); Tuttle-Mori Agency Inc (Japan); Diana Voigt (Germany); Eric Yang (Korea)
Membership(s): American Society of Journalists & Authors; The Authors Guild; North American Travel Journalists Association

**Cambridge Literary Associates** (L-D)
Division of Valentino Enterprises Inc
135 Beach Rd, Unit C-3, Salisbury, MA 01952
*Tel:* 978-499-0374 *Fax:* 978-499-9774
*Web Site:* www.cambridgeliterary.com
*Key Personnel*
Pres: Michael Valentino (AAR)
VP: Ralph Valentino (AAR)
Full literary agency. Fiction & nonfiction: action, mystery, romance, science fiction, screenplays. No unsol mss, query first with letter. No reading fee. Fee of $3 per page for editing.

**Carlisle & Co LLC**, see InkWell Management

**Maria Carvainis Agency Inc** (L)
Rockefeller Center, 1270 Avenue of the Americas, Suite 2320, New York, NY 10020
*Tel:* 212-245-6365 *Fax:* 212-245-7196
*E-mail:* mca@mariacarvainisagency.com
*Web Site:* mariacarvainisagency.com
*Key Personnel*
Pres: Maria Carvainis (AAR)
Assoc: Elizabeth Copps (AAR)
Contract & Subs Rts Mgr: Martha Guzman
Agent: Chelsea Gilmore
Founded: 1977
Literary & mainstream fiction: suspense/mystery, thriller, historical, contemporary women's fiction/romance, middle grade/young adult. Non-

fiction: business, biography, memoir, psychology, women's issues, popular science, history, pop culture. No screenplays, children's picture books, science fiction or poetry. Magazine rights handled for clients who are book authors. No unsol mss, query first with SASE, do not accept e-mailed or faxed submissions. Submit outline & sample chapters or full ms only on request. Handle film & TV rights. No reading fee. Signatory to Writers Guild of America (WGA). Representatives in Hollywood & all major foreign markets.
Titles recently placed: *A Winter Scandal*, Candace Camp; *Eternal Captive*, Laura Wright; *Last Man Standing*, Cindy Gerard; *Lethal*, Sandra Brown; *The Killing Song*, PJ Parrish; *The Secret Mistress*, Mary Balogh; *Until There Was You*, Kristan Higgins
Membership(s): ABA; The Authors Guild; International Thriller Writers Inc; Mystery Writers of America; Romance Writers of America

**Castiglia Literary Agency** (L)
1155 Camino Del Mar, Suite 510, Del Mar, CA 92014
*Tel:* 858-755-8761 *Fax:* 858-755-7063
*Web Site:* www.castiglialiteraryagency.com
*Key Personnel*
Pres & Agent: Julie Castiglia
Assoc Agent: Winifred Golden *E-mail:* win@castigliaagency.com
Founded: 1993
Ethnic, commercial & literary fiction, science, biography, psychology, women's issues, popular culture, health & niche books. No unsol mss; submit query letter with bio & one page writing sample of project, fiction or nonfiction, including SASE. No phone queries, only by e-mail. Represent books to TV & film rights. Specialize in science, health, biography, narrative nonfiction & literary fiction. No fees charged. Representives in all major foreign countries.
Titles recently placed: *Airbrushed Nation: The Lure and Loathing of Women's Magazines*, Jennifer Nelson; *Angels of Paris: An Architectural Tour Through the History of Paris*, Rosemary Flannery; *Barry Dixon Inspirations*, Brian Coleman; *Critical Companion to Jack London*, Jeanne Reesman; *Cuisine Nicoise*, Hillary Davis; *Fortuny Interiors*, Brian Coleman; *From Splendor to Revolution*, Julia P Gelardi; *Gloria Swanson: The Ultimate Star*, Stephen Michael Shearer; *Meringue*, Linda Jackson, Jennifer Evans Gardner; *Orphan's Journey*, Robert Buettner; *Overkill*, Robert Buettner; *Paris Wedding*, Kimberley Petyt; *Rocket Girl: The Story of America's First Female Rocket Scientist*, George P Morgan; *Salad for Dinner: Complete Meals for all Seasons*, Jeanne Kelley; *Stories in Stone New York*, Doug Keister; *The Art of the Visit*, Kathy Bertone; *The Two Krishnas*, Ghalib Shiraz Dhalla; *Undercurrents*, Robert Buettner
Foreign Rights: ACER Literary Agency (Spain); Asano Agency Inc (Japan); Lora Fountain Agence Litteraire (France); Grandi & Assoc (Italy); Imprima Korea Agency (Korea); MBA Literary Agents Ltd (UK); Michael Meller Agency (Germany); Svetlana Pironko (Russia); Vantage Copyright Agency (China)

**Jane Chelius Literary Agency Inc** (L)
548 Second St, Brooklyn, NY 11215
*Tel:* 718-499-0236; 718-499-0714 *Fax:* 718-832-7335
*E-mail:* queries@janechelius.com; rights@janechelius.com
*Web Site:* www.janechelius.com
*Key Personnel*
Pres: Jane Chelius (AAR) *E-mail:* jane@janechelius.com
Founded: 1995
Adult fiction & nonfiction including mystery, women's literature, humor, women's issues, medicine & science for a general audience, nature & natural world, biography. No children's books, poetry, stage plays or screenplays, science fiction, fantasy or category romance. No unsol mss. Query first with SASE; no e-mail queries with attachments. Paste one page synopsis, first 10 pages & short biography in body of e-mail. No reading fee; handle film & TV rights. Representation in all foreign markets.
Membership(s): International Association of Crime Writers; Mystery Writers of America; Women's Media Group

**Linda Chester Literary Agency** (L-D)
Rockefeller Ctr, Suite 2036, 630 Fifth Ave, New York, NY 10111
*Tel:* 212-218-3350 *Fax:* 212-218-3343
*E-mail:* submissions@lindachester.com
*Web Site:* www.lindachester.com
*Key Personnel*
Principal: Linda Chester (AAR)
Exec Off Mgr: Gary Jaffe *E-mail:* gjaffe@lindachester.com
West Coast Assoc: Laurie Fox *Tel:* 510-704-0971 *E-mail:* laurieannfox@comcast.net
Quality adult fiction & nonfiction. Handle film & TV rights. No reading fes; no unsol mss, query first.
*Branch Office(s)*
2342 Shattuck Ave, No 506, Berkeley, CA 94704, Contact: Laurie Fox *Tel:* 510-704-0971 *E-mail:* laurieannfox@comcast.net
Foreign Rights: The Fielding Agency LLC (Whitney Lee)

**Faith Childs Literary Agency Inc** (L)
915 Broadway, Suite 1009, New York, NY 10010
*Tel:* 212-995-9600 *Fax:* 212-995-9709
*E-mail:* assistant@faithchildsliteraryagencyinc.com
*Key Personnel*
Pres: Faith Hampton Childs (AAR)
Founded: 1990
Specialize in fiction & nonfiction film & TV rights. No unsol mss, queries or unreferred clients accepted. Agents in all principal countries.
Foreign Rep(s): Luigi Bernabo Associates SRL (Italy); The English Agency (Japan) Ltd (Japan); Lennart Sane (Austria, France, Germany, Netherlands, Scandinavia, Spain, Switzerland); Abner Stein Agency (England)

**Chinese Connection Agency** (L-D)
Division of The Yao Enterprises LLC
67 Banksville Rd, Armonk, NY 10504
*Tel:* 914-765-0296 *Fax:* 914-765-0297
*E-mail:* info@yaollc.com
*Web Site:* www.yaollc.com
*Key Personnel*
Pres: Mei C Yao
Founded: 1995
Translation rights sales of adult fiction & nonfiction, professional/business management books, college books, personal development, leisure books, etc. No unsol mss, query first (e-mail queries welcome). No reading fee. Handle software & film & TV rights.

**William F Christopher Publication Services** (L)
Unit of The Management Innovations Group
Kensington No 237, 1580 Geary Rd, Walnut Creek, CA 94597-2744
*Tel:* 925-943-5584 *Fax:* 925-943-5594
*E-mail:* wfcmgmt.innovations@yahoo.com
*Key Personnel*
Pres: William F (Bill) Christopher
Founded: 2000
Represent authors to place their books with publishers. Specialize only in business books & books on science & technology. No unsol mss, query first.
Membership(s): American Society for Quality; National Association of Business Economists; Society of Manufacturing Engineers; Society of Plastics Engineers; World Academy of Productivity Science

**Cine/Lit Representation** (L-D)
PO Box 802918, Santa Clarita, CA 91380-2918
*Tel:* 661-513-0268 *Fax:* 661-513-0915
*E-mail:* cinelit@att.net
*Key Personnel*
Partner: Anna Cottle (AAR); Mary Alice Kier (AAR)
Founded: 1991
Commercial & literary fiction & nonfiction. Emphasis in mainstream thrillers, suspense/mysteries, supernatural, horror & speculative. Nonfiction interest in narrative environmental, travel & pop culture. No unsol mss, query first with author's bio & brief synopsis. No reading fee. Representatives in all major foreign markets. Handle film & TV rights.
Membership(s): British Academy of Film & Television Arts/Los Angeles; Independent Film Project/West

**Wm Clark Associates** (L)
186 Fifth Ave, 2nd fl, New York, NY 10010
*Tel:* 212-675-2784 *Fax:* 347-649-9262
*E-mail:* general@wmclark.com
*Web Site:* www.wmclark.com
*Key Personnel*
Principal: William Clark (AAR) *E-mail:* wmclark@wmclark.com
Founded: 1999
Represents mainstream & literary fiction & quality nonfiction to the book publishing, motion picture, television & new media fields; e-mail queries only & should include a general description of the work, a synopsis/outline, biographical information & publishing history, if any. E-mails must be text only & e-mails with attachments will not be accepted. Unsol queries sent by any method other than through web site query page or e-mail to query@wmclark.com in the form described will be discarded unread. No reading fees; handle film & TV rights for books written by clients only; does not represent screenplays. Representatives in all major foreign countries.
Titles recently placed: *How Could This Happen? The Causes of the Holocaust*, Dan McMillan; *Marilyn: The Passion and the Paradox*, Lois Banner; *Paris Reborn: Napoleon III, Baron Haussmann and the Quest to Build a Modern City*, Stephane Kirkland; *Strange Stones: Dispatches from East to West*, Peter Hessler; *The Afterlife of Emerson Tang*, Paula Champa
Foreign Rights: Andrew Nurnberg Associates Ltd (Worldwide exc UK); Ed Victor Ltd (UK)
Membership(s): The Authors Guild; PEN International

**Collier Associates** (L)
416 Kelsey Park Dr, Palm Beach Gardens, FL 33410
Mailing Address: PO Box 20149, West Palm Beach, FL 33416
*Tel:* 561-514-6548 *Fax:* 561-799-4067
*E-mail:* dmccabooks@gmail.com
*Key Personnel*
Owner & Agent: Dianna Collier
Agent: Fred Warner
Founded: 1976
Fiction & nonfiction adult books. Fiction: war novels, mysteries, true crime, romance, contemporary & historical. Nonfiction: biographies & autobiographies of well-known people, popular works of political subjects & history, exposes, popular works on medical & scientific

subjects, finance, popular reference & how-to books, health, beauty & motherhood. Also handle film & TV rights for adult books only with co-agents. No unsol mss, query first with SASE; submit outline, sample chapters & bio; no reading fee for published authors of trade books, may charge fee for full length book mss for unpublished authors; charge cost of copying ms; submission postage; books ordered for subsidiary rights. Co-agents on West Coast & in many foreign countries.

Foreign Rep(s): Big Apple Agency Inc (Taiwan); International Literature Bureau BV (Netherlands); Johnson & Alcock Ltd (British Commonwealth); Mohrbooks AG (Austria, Germany, Switzerland); Tuttle-Mori Agency Inc (Japan); Julio F Yanez Agencia Literaria (Portugal, South America, Spain)

Foreign Rights: Agence Michelle Lapautre (France); Light & Burr (Denmark, Finland, Iceland, Norway, Sweden)

Membership(s): Mystery Writers of America

**Frances Collin Literary Agent** (L)
PO Box 33, Wayne, PA 19087
*E-mail:* queries@francescollin.com
*Web Site:* www.francescollin.com
*Key Personnel*
Owner: Frances Collin (AAR)
Assoc Agent: Sarah Yake *E-mail:* sarah@francescollin.com
Founded: 1948

Successor to Marie Rodell-Frances Collin Literary Agency (1975).

Trade fiction & nonfiction; no original screenplays. Special interest in the following areas: literary fiction, biography, history, travel, environmental, nature, memoir, mystery, fantasy/science fiction, young adult. No unsol mss, query via e-mail to queries@francescollin.com. Send query letter describing your project (text in the body of the e-mail only, e-mails with unsol attachments will be deleted unread). Handle film & TV rights through sub-agents; representatives in all foreign markets. No fees.

**Don Congdon Associates Inc** (L)
110 William St, Suite 2202, New York, NY 10038-3914
*Tel:* 212-645-1229 *Fax:* 212-727-2688
*E-mail:* dca@doncongdon.com
*Web Site:* www.doncongdon.com
*Key Personnel*
Agent: Cristina Concepcion (AAR); Michael Congdon (AAR); Katie Grimm; Katie Kotchman (AAR); Maura Kye-Casella (AAR); Susan Ramer (AAR)
Founded: 1983

Handle any & all trade books. Handle film & TV rights for regular clients. No unsol mss, query first with a one page synopsis of your work & relevant background & SASE or e-mail without attachments. In heading include "Query" & agent's full name. Include a sample chapter in body of e-mail. Now accepting new & professional authors. No reading fee.

Foreign Rep(s): AnatoliaLit Agency; Big Apple Agency Inc (China, Taiwan); Nurichan Kesim Literary Agency Inc; Agence Michelle Lapautre (France); Maxima Creative Agency (Indonesia); Andrew Nurnberg Associates (Eastern Europe, Germany, Russia); Owls Agency Inc (Japan); Read n' Right Agency (Greece); Lennart Sane Agency (Netherlands, Scandinavia); Vicki Satlow Literary Agency (Italy); Abner Stein Agency (UK); Tuttle-Mori Agency Inc (Japan); Julio F Yanez (Portugal, Spain); Eric Yang Agency (Korea)

**The Doe Coover Agency** (L)
PO Box 668, Winchester, MA 01890
*Tel:* 781-721-6000 *Fax:* 781-721-6727
*E-mail:* info@doecooveragency.com
*Web Site:* www.doecooveragency.com
*Key Personnel*
Pres: Doe Coover
Agent: Colleen Mohyde (AAR)
Assoc: Frances Kennedy
Founded: 1986

Nonfiction & fiction. Specialize in literary fiction, business, history & biography, science, health & medicine, cooking & food writing, gardening, humor, sports, music & politics, children's picture books, middle grade & young adult. No poetry, screenplays or unsol children's picture books. E-mail queries only - see web site for submission guidelines.

Handle film & TV rights on agency projects only. 15% commission.

Titles recently placed: *Chocopologie*, Fritz Knipschildt, Mary Goodody; *Eating for Total Health*, Duke University; *Esther's Hanukkah Disaster*, Jane Sutton; *Eyes on the Prize (25th anniversary ed)*, Juan Williams, Blackside Inc; *Finny and the Boy from Horse Mountain*, Andrea Young; *Generation V*, M L Brennan; *Jacques a la Minute*, Jacques Pepin; *Just Grill It*, Chris Schlesinger, John Willoughby; *LA Son: My Life, My City, My Food*, Roy Choi; *Man B Que: Meat, Beer and Rock 'n Roll*, John Carruthers, Jesse Valenciana; *Priest of Nature: The Religious Lives of Isaac Newton*, Robert Iliffe; *Rancho de Chimayo Cookbook (50th anniversary ed)*, Cheryl Jamison, Bill Jamison; *Rosemary Kennedy: The Legacy of a Life*, Kate Larson; *She Will Bring Us Home*, Diane Kiesel; *Silvana's Kitchen*, Silvana Nardone; *Skeletons in the Sand: The Story of a Dinosaur Expedition*, Paul Sereno; *Spain: Recipes and Traditions*, Jeff Koehler; *Spoils of War: The Fate of Culture in Times of Conflict*, Ricardo Elia; *Talking to Your Daughter about Puberty*, Lynda Madaras, Area Madaras; *The Approaching Great Transformation: Toward a Livable Post Carbon Economy*, Joel Magnuson; *The Bearing Tree*, Karen Fisher; *The Darjeeling Quartet*, Jeff Koehler; *The Last Love Song: A Biography of Joan Didion*, Tracy Daugherty; *The New England Cookbook*, Sarah Leah Chase; *The Tao of Gardening*, Carol Deppe; *Vegetarian Cooking for Everyone (revised ed)*, Deborah Madison

Foreign Rights: The English Agency (Japan) Ltd (Japan); The Marsh Agency (Europe); Abner Stein Agency (UK)

**Creative Media Agency Inc**, see Folio Literary Management LLC

**CreativeWell Inc** (L)
PO Box 3130, Memorial Sta, Upper Montclair, NJ 07043
*Tel:* 973-783-7575 *Toll Free Tel:* 800-743-9182 *Fax:* 973-783-7530
*E-mail:* info@creativewell.com
*Web Site:* www.creativewell.com
*Key Personnel*
Pres: George M Greenfield *E-mail:* george@creativewell.com
Founded: 2003

Fiction & nonfiction, film & TV rights. No unsol mss. No reading fee; other fees charged (for photocopies, express mail, etc). Representatives in principal foreign countries. Full-service lecture representation is also available.

**Crichton & Associates Inc** (L)
6940 Carroll Ave, Takoma Park, MD 20912
*Tel:* 301-495-9663
*E-mail:* cricht1@aol.com
*Web Site:* www.crichton-associates.com
*Key Personnel*
Pres: Sha-Shana Crichton
Founded: 2002

For fiction, submit first three chapters with synopsis & bio. For nonfiction, submit proposal with bio. No fees charged. Send queries to query@crichton-associates.com.

Membership(s): Romance Writers of America

**Richard Curtis Associates Inc** (L)
171 E 74 St, 2nd fl, New York, NY 10021
*Tel:* 212-772-7363 *Fax:* 212-772-7393
*Web Site:* www.curtisagency.com
*Key Personnel*
Pres: Richard Curtis *E-mail:* rcurtis@curtisagency.com
Founded: 1979

Commercial fiction/nonfiction. Nonfiction from previously published author only (must have been published by a major publisher). No stage plays or screenplays, short fiction, nonfiction or poetry. Handle film & TV rights. No unsol mss, query first with SASE. No e-mail or fax queries. No reading fee.

Foreign Rights: Baror International Inc (Worldwide exc USA)

Membership(s): Science Fiction & Fantasy Writers of America

**Darhansoff & Verrill** (L)
236 W 26 St, Suite 802, New York, NY 10001-6736
*Tel:* 917-305-1300 *Fax:* 917-305-1400
*E-mail:* info@dvagency.com
*Web Site:* www.dvagency.com
*Key Personnel*
Agent: Liz Darhansoff; Chuck Verrill
Rts Dir & Agent: Michele Mortimer
Off Mgr: Eric Amling
Founded: 1975

Fiction & nonfiction, literary fiction, young adult, memoirs, sophisticated suspense, history, science, biography, pop culture & current affairs. No theatrical plays or film scripts. No unsol mss, query first with SASE or by e-mail via submissions@dvagency.com. Film & TV rights handled by Los Angeles associates, Lynn Pleshette, Richard Green & UTA. Agents in many foreign countries. No fees charged.

Foreign Rights: Alkcali Copyright Agency (Ozgur Emir) (Turkey); Bardon-Chinese Media (Joanne Yang) (China), Eliane Benisti Agency (France); Luigi Bernabo Associates (Italy); The Book Publishers Association of Israel (Dalia Ever Hadani) (Israel); The English Agency (Hamish Macaskill) (Japan); Graal Literary Agency (Maria Strarz-Kanska) (Poland); International Copyrights Agency (Simona Kessler) (Romania); Interrights (Svetlana Stefanova) (Bulgaria); JLM Literarary Angency (John Moukakis) (Greece); Katai & Bolza (Peter Bolza) (Hungary); Licht & Burr (Trine Licht) (Scandinavia); Zvonimir Majdak (Croatia); Mohrbooks (Sebastian Ritscher) (Germany); Andrew Nurnberg Agency (Lumilla Shushkova) (Russia); Andrew Nurnberg Association Baltic (Tatjana Zoldnere) (Latvia); Kristin Olson Literary Agency (Kristin Olson) (Czech Republic); Agencia Riff (Laura Riff) (Brazil, Portugal); Agencia Riff (Joao Paulo Riff) (Brazil, Portugal); The Sayle Agency (Rachel Calder) (UK); Sebes & Van Gelderen Agency (Paul Sebes) (Holland); Shin Won Agency (Tae Kim) (Korea); Yanez Agencia Literaria (Montse F Yanez) (Spain)

**Liza Dawson Associates** (L)
350 Seventh Ave, Suite 2003, New York, NY 10001
*Tel:* 212-465-9071 *Fax:* 212-947-0460
*Web Site:* www.lizadawsonassociates.com
*Key Personnel*
CFO & Agent: Havis Dawson *E-mail:* queryhavis@lizadawsonassociates.com
Pres: Liza Dawson (AAR) *E-mail:* queryliza@lizadawsonassociates.com

Literary Agent: Caitlin Blasdell
*E-mail:* querycaitlin@lizadawsonassociates.com; Anna Olswanger *E-mail:* queryanna@lizadawsonassociates.com; Hannah Bowman *E-mail:* queryhannah@lizadawsonassociates.com
Literary Asst: Judith Engracia
*E-mail:* queryjudith@lizadawsonassociates.com
Assoc Agent: Monica Odom
*E-mail:* querymonica@lizadawsonassociates.com
Founded: 1996
Liza Dawson: Fiction, both literary & commercial. Nonfiction: strong narratives, history, psychology, memoirs, parenting & business books. No poetry, westerns or children's books.
Caitlin Blasdell: science fiction, fantasy, romance, women's fiction & young adult.
Havis Dawson: practical nonfiction, business, spiritual, thrillers & southern fiction.
No unsol mss. Send query letter first with SASE. No reading fee. Agents in Hollywood & all foreign countries.
Foreign Rights: Akcali Copyright Agency (Atilla Izgi Turgut) (Turkey); Eliane Benisti Agency (Leon de la Menadiere, sci-fi/fantasy only) (France); Graal Literary Agency (Marcin Biegaj) (Albania, Baltic States, Bulgaria, Greece, Hungary, Iceland, Macedonia, Poland, Romania, Serbia, Slovenia); The Grayhawk Agency (Gray Tan) (China, Taiwan, Thailand, Vietnam); Danny Hong Agency (Danny Hong) (Korea); Alexander Korzhenevski Agency (Alexander Korzhenevski) (Russia); Piergiorgio Nicollazzini Agency (Maura Solinas, sci-fi/fantasy only) (Italy); Kristin Olson Literary Agency (Kristin Olson) (Czech Republic); Thomas Schlueck GmbH (Bastian Schlueck, sci-fi/fantasy only) (Germany); Tuttle-Mori Agency Inc (Misa Morikawa, fiction; Manami Tamaoki, nonfiction) (Japan)
Membership(s): Women's Media Group

**The Jennifer DeChiara Literary Agency** (L)
31 E 32 St, Suite 300, New York, NY 10016
*Tel:* 212-481-8484 (ext 362) *Fax:* 212-481-9582
*Web Site:* www.jdlit.com
*Key Personnel*
Owner, Pres & Agent: Jennifer DeChiara
*E-mail:* jenndec@aol.com
Agent: Stephen Fraser *E-mail:* stephenafraser@verizon.net
Assoc Agent: Linda Epstein *E-mail:* linda.p.epstein@gmail.com; Marie Lamba
*E-mail:* marie.jdlit@gmail.com; Roseanne Wells *E-mail:* roseannelitagent@gmail.com
Film/TV Agent: Kimberly Guidone
Dir, JDLA Speakers Club: Arlynn Greenbaum
JDLA Workshop Coord: Stacy Mozer
Dir, Media Presentations: Diane DiResta
Foreign Rights Dir: Betty Anne Crawford
Busn Affs: Bill Bratton
Founded: 2001
Accepting queries in the following areas: children's books for every age (picture books, middle-grade & young adult), adult fiction & nonfiction in a wide range of genres. Accept e-mail queries only, with "Query" in the subject line; no attachments. Co-agents in every country. No fees.
Titles recently placed: *A Moose That Says Moo*, Jennifer Hamburg; *Not Young, Still Restless: My Life So Far*, Jeanne Cooper; *Openly Straight*, Bill Konigsberg; *Sitting Next to Jesus*, Carol Lynch Williams; *The One-Way Bridge*, Cathie Pelletier; *The Quantum League*, Matthew Kirby; *Whistle Root*, Christopher Pennell

**DeFiore and Company, LLC** (L)
47 E 19 St, 3rd fl, New York, NY 10003
*Tel:* 212-925-7744 *Fax:* 212-925-9803
*E-mail:* submissions@defioreandco.com; info@defioreandco.com
*Web Site:* www.defioreandco.com
*Key Personnel*
Founder & Pres: Brian DeFiore (AAR)
*E-mail:* querybrian@defioreandco.com
Literary Agent: Laurie Abkemeier (AAR)
*E-mail:* LMA@defioreandco.com; Debra Goldstein
Contracts Dir & Literary Agent: Kate Garrick
*E-mail:* kate@defioreandco.com
Foreign Rts Dir: Adam Schear *E-mail:* ajs@defioreandco.com
Literary Agent: Matthew Elblonk
*E-mail:* matthew@defioreandco.com; Caryn Karmatz Rudy (AAR) *E-mail:* ckr@defioreandco.com; Meredith Kaffel (AAR) *E-mail:* meredith@defioreandco.com; Rebecca Strauss *E-mail:* Rebecca@defioreandco.com
Founded: 1999
Handles mainstream fiction, suspense fiction, business, self-help, narrative nonfiction, cook books & memoirs.
Titles recently placed: *If You Were Here*, Jen Lancaster; *So Good They Can't Ignore You*, Cal Newport; *The 21-Day Weight Loss Kick Start*, Neal Barnard; *The Evolution of Bruno Littlemore*, Benjamin Hale; *The Fame Game*, Lauren Conrad; *When Parents Text*, Lauren Kaelin, Sophia Fraioli; *Wine to Water*, Doc Hendley
Foreign Rep(s): Gillon Aitken Associates (UK); Andrew Nurnberg Associates
Foreign Rights: Aitken Alexander Associates (Mary Pachnos) (UK); The Book Publishers Association of Israel (Delia Ever Hadani) (Israel); JLM Literary Agency (John Moukakos) (Greece); Kayi Agency (Dilek Kayi) (Turkey); Andrew Nurnberg Associates (Sabine Pfannenstiel, London) (Germany); Andrew Nurnberg Associates (Claire Anouchian, London) (France, Quebec, CN); Andrew Nurnberg Associates (Lucy Flynn) (Latin America exc Brazil, Portugal, Spain); Andrew Nurnberg Associates (Barbara Barbieri) (Brazil, Italy); Andrew Nurnberg Associates (Marei Pittner, London) (Netherlands, Scandinavia); Andrew Nurnberg Associates (Anna & Mira Droumeva, Sofia) (Bulgaria, Romania, Serbia); Andrew Nurnberg Associates (Petra Tobiskova & Jana Borovanova, Prague) (Czech Republic, Slovakia, Slovenia); Andrew Nurnberg Associates (Aleksandra Lapinska & Renata Paczewska, Warsaw) (Poland); Andrew Nurnberg Associates (Judit Hermann, Budapest) (Croatia, Hungary); Andrew Nurnberg Associates (Ludmilla Sushkova, Moscow) (Russia); Andrew Nurnberg Associates (Tatjana Zoldnere, Latvia) (Estonia, Latvia, Lithuania, Ukraine); Andrew Nurnberg Associates (Jackie Huang, Beijing) (China); Andrew Nurnberg Associates (Whitney Hsu, Taipei) (Taiwan); Tuttle-Mori Agency Inc (Ken Mori & Manami Tamaoki) (Japan); Tuttle-Mori Agency Inc (Thananchai Pandey, Bangkok) (Thailand); Eric Yang Agency (Henry Shin) (Korea)

**Joelle Delbourgo Associates Inc** (L)
101 Park St, Montclair, NJ 07042
*Tel:* 973-773-0836 (call only during standard business hours)
*Web Site:* www.delbourgo.com
*Key Personnel*
Founder & Pres, Agent & Consultant: Joelle Delbourgo (AAR) *Tel:* 973-773-0836
*E-mail:* joelle@delbourgo.com
Sr Agent: Jacqueline Flynn *Tel:* 201-981-4181
*E-mail:* jacqueline@delbourgo.com
Assoc Agent & Ed: Carrie Cantor *Tel:* 973-783-1005 *E-mail:* cantor.carrie@gmail.com
Ed: John Paine *E-mail:* jpaine@johnpaine.com; Fran Schumer *E-mail:* frannyrs2@gmail.com
Publicity Consultant: Jennifer Prost
*E-mail:* jennifer@delbourgo.com
Founded: 2000
Handle a wide range of adult fiction (literary & commercial) & nonfiction (practical & narrative): psychology, health, science, business, politics, lifestyle, health, parenting, cooking, spiritual. Also young adult & middle grade fiction. Hard copy submission with SASE or e-mail queries accepted, but check submission guidelines on web site. Materials will not be returned.
Titles recently placed: *Asking for It: The Culture of Rape*, Kate Harding; *Be Nobody*, Lama Marut; *Pink Ink*, Lindsey J Palmer; *Promise Bound*, Anne Greenwood Brown; *Searching for Sappho*, Philip Freeman; *Teach a Woman to Fish*, Ritu Sharma; *The French Cook: Soups and Stews*, Holly Herrick; *The Last Policeman #3*, Ben H Winters; *The Unofficial Guide to "Girls"*, Judy Gelman, Peter Zheutlin; *The Winged Herds of Anok*, Jennifer Alvarez
Foreign Rights: Duran Kim Agency (Korea); Maxima Agency (Indonesia); Jenny Meyer Literary Agency (Worldwide exc Asia); Andrew Nurnberg Associates Inc (China); Owls Agency Inc (Japan)
Membership(s): Women's Media Group

**D4EO Literary Agency** (L-D)
7 Indian Valley Rd, Weston, CT 06883
*Tel:* 203-544-7180 *Fax:* 203-544-7160
*Web Site:* www.d4eoliteraryagency.com
*Key Personnel*
Principal: Robert (Bob) G Diforio *E-mail:* bob@d4eo.com
Agent (YA & middle grade): Mandy Hubbard
*E-mail:* mandy@d4eo.com
Agent (picture books, middle grade & YA): Kristin Miller-Vincent *E-mail:* kristin@d4eo.com
Agent (children's, select genre adult, nonfiction, graphic novels): Bree Ogden *E-mail:* bree@d4eo.com
Agent (literary fiction, historical fiction, mystery, select YA): Samantha Dighton
*E-mail:* samantha@d4eo.com
Agent (mysteries, thrillers, romance & nonfiction): Joyce Holland *E-mail:* joyce@d4eo.com
Founded: 1989
Represent trade books of all types, fiction, nonfiction, business. Visit www.d4eoliteraryagency.com to see each agent's preferred method of submission. Only Bob Diforio is at the Weston, CT address. All agents prefer e-mail submissions.
Titles recently placed: *Echoes of My Soul*, Robert K Tanenbaum; *If You find Me*, Emily Murdoch; *Linked*, Imogene Howson; *Mirage*, Jack DuBrul, Clive Cussler; *Targets of Revenge*, Jeffrey S Stephens; *The Pandora Society*, Joy Hensley
Foreign Rep(s): Eliane Benisti (France)

**Sandra Dijkstra Literary Agency** (L)
1155 Camino del Mar, PMB 515, Del Mar, CA 92014-2605
*Web Site:* dijkstraagency.com
*Key Personnel*
Pres & Agent: Sandra Dijkstra (AAR)
Exec Asst & Agent: Elise Capron (AAR)
*Tel:* 858-755-3115 ext 100 *E-mail:* elise@dijkstraagency.com
Asst & Agent: Jennifer Azantian (AAR) *Tel:* 858-755-3115 ext 101 *E-mail:* jen@dijkstraagency.com; Thao Le (AAR) *Tel:* 858-755-3115 ext 105 *E-mail:* thao@dijkstraagency.com
Agent: Jill Marr (AAR) *Tel:* 858-755-3115 ext 108 *E-mail:* jmsubmissions@dijkstraagency.com
Founded: 1981
Fiction: contemporary, women's, literary, suspense, thrillers, science-fiction & fantasy. Nonfiction: narrative, history, business, psychology, self-help, science & memoir/biography. Works

in conjunction with foreign & film agents. E-mail submissions only. See web site for most up-to-date guidelines. No reading fee.
Foreign Rights: Bardon-Chinese Media Agency (China, Taiwan); Bernabo Assocs (Italy); Sandra Bruna Agencia Literaria (Portugal, Spain); The English Agency (Japan) Ltd (Japan); Graal Literary Agency (Poland); Agence Hoffman (Germany); Katai & Bolza (Hungary); Licht & Burr (Scandinavia); Maxima Creative Agency (Indonesia); La Nouvelle Agence (France); Onk Agency (Turkey); I Pikarski Agency (Israel); Prava I Prevodi (Eastern Europe); Sebes & Van Gelderen Literary Agency (Netherlands); Abner Stein Agency (UK); Synopsis Agency (Baltic States, Russia); Tuttle-Mori Agency Inc (Thailand); Eric Yang Agency (Korea)

**Donadio & Olson Inc** (L-D)
121 W 27 St, Suite 704, New York, NY 10001
*Tel:* 212-691-8077 *Fax:* 212-633-2837
*E-mail:* mail@donadio.com
*Web Site:* donadio.com
*Key Personnel*
Agent: Edward Hibbert; E Carrie Howland *E-mail:* carrie@donadio.com; Neil Olson (AAR)
Founded: 1969
Fiction, nonfiction & young adult. Handle film & TV rights for clients. No fees.
Foreign Rights: AnatoliaLit Agency (Amy Spangler) (Turkey); Agence Eliane Benisti (Noemie Rollet) (France); Luigi Bernabo Associates SRL (Luigi Bernabo) (Italy); Big Apple Agency Inc (Luc Kwanten) (China, Thailand); Paul & Peter Fritz AG (Christian Dittus) (Germany); The Deborah Harris Agency (Efrat Lev) (Israel); Japan Uni Agency (Miko Yamanouchi) (Japan); JLM Literary Agency (John Moukakos) (Greece); Korea Copyright Center (KCC) (Misun Kwon) (Korea); Licht & Burr (Trine Licht) (Denmark, Finland, Iceland, Norway, Sweden); MB Agencia Literaria (Monica Martin) (Catalan, Portugal, Spain); Andrew Nurnberg Associates (Mira Droumeva, Sofia) (Albania, Macedonia, Romania, Serbia); Andrew Nurnberg Associates (Judit Hermann) (Croatia, Hungary); Andrew Nurnberg Associates (Aleksandra Matuszak, Warsaw) (Poland); Andrew Nurnberg Associates (Ludmilla Sushkova) (Russia); Andrew Nurnberg Associates (Tatjana Zoldnere, Baltic) (Estonia, Latvia, Lithuania, Ukraine); Andrew Nurnberg Associates (Petra Tobiskova, Prague) (Czech Republic); The Riff Agency (Laura Riff) (Brazil); Marianne Schoenbach Literary Agency (Marianne Schoenbach) (Netherlands)

**Janis A Donnaud & Associates Inc** (L-D)
525 Broadway, 2nd fl, New York, NY 10012
*Tel:* 212-431-2663 *Fax:* 212-431-2667
*E-mail:* jdonnaud@aol.com
*Key Personnel*
Pres: Janis A Donnaud (AAR)
Founded: 1993
Nonfiction by experts in their fields: narrative nonfiction; healthcare & medicine; humor; cookbooks; women's issues; pop psychology, memoir; pop culture; Belle lettres & etymology. No unsol mss, query first; if requested, submit outline & sample chapters & curriculum vitae, with SASE with return postage or by e-mail, if return requested. No fiction. Handle film & TV rights. No phone calls. No reading fee.
Titles recently placed: *Jamie Deen at the Family Table*, Jamie Deen; *One Doctor*, Brendan Reilly, MD; *Oxford Companion to Spirits and Cocktails*, David Wondrich; *Real Korean Cooking*, Maangchi; *Yo Cuz!*, Steve Martorano
Foreign Rep(s): Abner Stein Agency (Worldwide)
Membership(s): The Authors Guild

**Jim Donovan Literary** (L)
5635 SMU Blvd, Suite 201, Dallas, TX 75206
*Tel:* 214-696-9411
*E-mail:* jdlqueries@sbcglobal.net
*Key Personnel*
Owner & Pres: Jim Donovan
Agent: Melissa Shultz
Founded: 1993
Literary & commercial fiction & nonfiction, especially biography, health, history, popular culture & sports. No poetry, short stories or children's. Accept unsol mss only with SASE. For nonfiction, query first with letter & SASE. For fiction, submit first 30-40 pages & synopsis with SASE. May query with e-mail, no attachments, response only if interested. No online submissions accepted. Handle film & TV rights for clients only. Agents in Hollywood & major foreign countries. No fees, 15% commission on monies earned.
Titles recently placed: *Below*, Ryan Lockwood; *Give Me a Fast Ship*, Tim Mc Grath; *Honor in the Dust*, Gregg Jones; *Manson*, Jeff Guinn; *The Lords of Apacheria*, Paul Andrew Hutton

**Doyen Literary Services Inc** (L)
1931 660 St, Newell, IA 50568
*Web Site:* www.barbaradoyen.com
*Key Personnel*
Pres: Barb J Doyen
Founded: 1988
Handles all types of trade nonfiction for adults; authors available to fill editorial needs in most topics. Specialize in business, health, fitness, how-to, psychology, self-improvement, cookbooks, narrative nonfiction, biography & memoir & many more. No fees charged. Only accepts e-mail queries through web site.
Titles recently placed: *Eating Clean for Dummies*, Jonathan Wright MD, Linda Larsen; *The Beginner's Guide to Growing Heirloom Vegetables*, Marie Iannotti

**Drennan Literary Agency** (L)
6 Robin Lane, East Kingston, NH 03827
*Tel:* 603-642-8002 *Fax:* 603-642-8002
*Key Personnel*
Pres: William D Drennan
Contact: Christina L Drennan
Founded: 1980
Scholarly only. No unsol mss, query first with outline & SASE. No reading fee.

**DSM Agency**, see Doris S Michaels Literary Agency Inc

**Dunham Literary Inc** (L)
110 William St, Suite 2202, New York, NY 10038
*Tel:* 212-929-0994
*Web Site:* dunhamlit.com
*Key Personnel*
Founder & Agent: Jennie Dunham (AAR)
Agent: Bridget Smith (AAR)
Founded: 2000
Represents literary fiction & nonfiction, children's book writers & illustrators. No plays or screenplays. Handle film & TV rights for books represented. No unsol mss, query letter first with SASE. No fax or e-mail queries. No reading fee.
Foreign Rights: A M Heath (Europe, UK); Shin-Won (Korea); Tuttle-Mori Agency Inc (Japan)
Membership(s): Society of Children's Book Writers & Illustrators

**Dunow, Carlson & Lerner Literary Agency Inc** (L)
27 W 20 St, Suite 1107, New York, NY 10011
*Tel:* 212-645-7606
*E-mail:* mail@dclagency.com
*Web Site:* www.dclagency.com
*Key Personnel*
Literary Agent: Jennifer Carlson (AAR); Henry Dunow (AAR); Erin Hosier; Amy Hughes; Eleanor Jackson; Julia Kenny; Betsy Lerner; Edward Necarsulmer, IV; Yishai Seidman
Founded: 2005
Query first, fiction & nonfiction. Handle film & TV rights. Agents in all foreign territories. Submit outlines & sample chapters with SASE. No reading fee.
Foreign Rights: Akcali Copyright Agency (Turkey); Big Apple Agency Inc (China, Taiwan); The English Agency (Japan); Grayhawk Agency (China, Taiwan); The Deborah Harris Agency (Israel); David Higham Associates (UK); JLM Literary Agency (Greece); Andrew Nurnberg Associates (Eastern Europe, Europe, Russia, South America); Owl Agency (Japan); Abner Stein Agency (UK); Tuttle-Mori Agency Inc (Japan); Eric Yang (Korea)

**Dupree, Miller & Associates Inc** (L)
100 Highland Park Village, Suite 350, Dallas, TX 75205
*Tel:* 214-559-2665 *Fax:* 214-559-7243
*E-mail:* editorial@dupreemiller.com
*Web Site:* www.dupreemiller.com
*Key Personnel*
Pres: Jan Miller *E-mail:* jmr@dupreemiller.com
EVP: Shannon Marven
Agent: Nena Madonia
Fiction & nonfiction. No children's, science fiction, fantasy, horror, short stories, poetry or screenplays. No unsol mss; accept query letter only, with SASE enclosed for reply. No fees. Market & promote own books both regionally & nationally.

**Dystel & Goderich Literary Management** (L-D)
One Union Sq W, Suite 904, New York, NY 10003
*Tel:* 212-627-9100 *Fax:* 212-627-9313
*Web Site:* www.dystel.com
*Key Personnel*
Pres & Partner: Jane Dystel (AAR)
Agent & Partner: Miriam Goderich *E-mail:* miriam@dystel.com
Agent: Michael Bourret (AAR) *E-mail:* mbourret@dystel.com
VP & Agent: Stacey Kendall Glick (AAR) *E-mail:* sglick@dystel.com
Sr Agent: Jim McCarthy (AAR) *E-mail:* jmccarthy@dystel.com
Subs Rts Dir & Agent: Lauren E Abramo *E-mail:* labramo@dystel.com
Agent: Jessica Papin *E-mail:* jpapin@dystel.com; John Rudolph *E-mail:* jrudolph@dystel.com; Michael Hoogland *E-mail:* mhoogland@dystel.com; Rachel Stout *E-mail:* rstout@dystel.com; Sharon Pelletier *E-mail:* spelletier@dystel.com
Royalties Mgr & Agent: Brenna Barr *E-mail:* bbarr@dystel.com
Ebook Proj Mgr & Agent: Yassine Belkacemi *E-mail:* ybelkacemi@dystel.com
Founded: 1994 (as Jane Dystel Literary Management)
General fiction & nonfiction, also cookbooks & children's books. No unsol mss, query letter or e-mail query with outline & first 50 pages. No reading fee. Handle film & TV rights. Firm also has a west coast office staffed by Michael Bourret (e-mail queries only).
Titles recently placed: *A Serving of Scandal*, Prue Leith; *All In*, Raine Miller; *An American Bride in Kabul*, Phyllis Chesler; *Autumn Bones*, Jacqueline Carey; *Because of Low*, Abbi Glines; *Bootstrapper*, Mardi Jo Link; *Brianna on the Brink*, Nicole McInnes; *Country Roads*, Nancy Herkness; *Covet*, Tracey Garvis Graves; *Crush*, Nicole Williams; *Dandelion Hunter*, Rebecca Lerner; *Darwen Arkwright*

*and the Insidious Bleck*, A J Hartley; *Darwen Arkwright and the Peregrine Pact*, A J Hartley; *Doctor Who*, Richelle Mead; *Fall for Me*, Sydney Landon; *Fiance by Friday*, Catherine Bybee; *First Class*, Allison Stewart; *Flour, Too*, Joanne Chang; *Gameboard of the Gods*, Richelle Mead; *Hothouse*, Boris Kachka; *How to Write Short*, Roy Peter Clark; *If I Should Die*, Amy Plum; *Indian Cooking Unfolded*, Raghavan Iyer; *Just For Now*, Abbi Glines; *Just Like Fate*, Suzanne Young, Cat Patrick; *Keep Your Eye on the Marshmallow*, Joachim de Posada, Bob Andelman; *Long Journey with Mr Jefferson*, William G Hyland, Jr; *Losing Hope*, Colleen Hoover; *Married by Monday*, Catherine Bybee; *Murder as a Fine Art*, David Morrell; *Naked*, Raine Miller; *Never Kiss a Rake*, Anne Stuart; *Not Planning On You*, Sydney Landon; *Not Quite Mine*, Catherine Bybee; *Small Changes, Big Results*, Ellie Krieger; *Tainted Angel*, Anne Cleeland; *Tap the Magic Tree*, Christie Matheson; *That's That*, Colin Broderick; *The Courage to Hope*, Shirley Sherrod; *The Dinnertime Survival Cookbook*, Debra Ponzek; *The Edge of Never*, J A Redmerski; *The Game Changer*, J Sterling; *The Prince of Paradise*, John Glatt; *The Program*, Suzanne Young; *The Real Skinny*, Katherine Brooking, Julie Upton; *The Sisterhood*, Helen Bryan; *Toms River*, Dan Fagin; *Weekends Required*, Sydney Landon; *What Would Brian Boitano Make?*, Brian Boitano; *While It Lasts*, Abbi Glines; *Wife by Wednesday*, Catherine Bybee; *Work Happy: What Great Bosses Know*, Jill Geisler; *Writers Rehab*, D B Gilles; *Yogalosophy*, Mandy Ingber

Foreign Rep(s): Ali (Italy); ANAW (Poland); Eliane Benisti (France); Big Apple Agency Inc (China); EAJ (Japan); International Editors' Co (Latin America, Spain); Kayi Literary (Turkey); Mohrbooks (Germany); Andrew Nurnberg (Eastern Europe); Read 'n' Right (Greece); Agencia Riff (Brazil); Sebes & Van Gelderen (Netherlands); Abner Stein Agency (UK); TBPAI (Israel); Ulf Toregard Agency (Scandinavia); Tuttle-Mori Agency Inc (Thailand); Eric Yang Agency (Korea)

**Anne Edelstein Literary Agency LLC** (L)
404 Riverside Dr, New York, NY 10025
*Tel:* 212-414-4923
*E-mail:* info@aeliterary.com; rights@aeliterary.com
*Web Site:* www.aeliterary.com
*Key Personnel*
Pres: Anne Edelstein (AAR)
Literary Agent & Rts Contact: Krista Ingebretson
Founded: 1990

Literary fiction & narrative nonfiction (including memoir, history, psychology, religion & culinary); handle film & TV rights; agents in all principal foreign countries.

No unsol mss, e-mail query first with outline & sample chapters. Include 25 pages (fiction) or proposal (nonfiction) in body of e-mail. If we are interested in seeing more, we will respond within 4 weeks. Because of the high number of submissions we receive, we cannot guarantee a response to those queries in which we are not interested. No phone queries or hard copies accepted. See web site for guideline details. No reading fee.

Foreign Rights: Akcali Copyright Agency (Turkey); AM Heath (Victoria Hobbs) (UK); L'Autre Agence (Corinne Marotte) (France); Silvia Bastos Agencia Literaria SL (Pau Centellas) (Spain); Luigi Bernabo Associates (Italy); Petra Eggers Agency (Petra Eggers) (Germany); The English Agency (Japan); The Grayhawk Agency (China, Taiwan); The Harris Agency (Efrat Lev) (Israel); Danny Hong Agency (Danny Hong) (Korea); Prava I Prevodi (Eastern Europe); The Riff Agency (Brazil); Marianne Schoenbach Literary Agency (Marianne Schoenbach) (Holland); Ulf Toregard Agency (Ulf Toregard) (Scandinavia); The Van Lear Agency (Russia)

Membership(s): The Authors Guild

**Educational Design Services LLC** (L)
5750 Bou Ave, Suite 1508, North Bethesda, MD 20852
*Tel:* 301-881-8611
*Web Site:* www.educationaldesignservices.com
*Key Personnel*
Pres: Bertram L Linder *E-mail:* blinder@educationaldesignservices.com
Founded: 1981

Materials for the el-hi & professional education market. Accept unsol mss with SASE, prefer query by e-submission first. Submit outline & sample chapter. No reading fee.

Titles recently placed: *Better Writing*, Travis Koll; *Bully Nation*, Susan Eva Porter; *Making a Difference in the Classroom*, Charlese E Brown; *Succes in Schools*, Susan Andres, Felicity Pines; *The Teachers' Lounge (Uncensored)*, Kelly Flynn; *Transparent Teaching of Adolescents*, Mindy Keller

**The Lisa Ekus Group LLC** (L)
57 North St, Hatfield, MA 01038
*Tel:* 413-247-9325 *Fax:* 413-247-9873
*E-mail:* lisaekus@lisaekus.com
*Web Site:* lisaekus.com
*Key Personnel*
Principal & Pres: Lisa Ekus (AAR)
*E-mail:* lisaekus@lisaekus.com
Founded: 1982

Since our inception in 1982, we have been helping both new & established authors & chefs make their mark on the culinary landscape. All of our nationally recognized culinary promotions are built on the same foundation: to create innovative strategies, pay meticulous attention to client needs & effectively & productively network across the culinary, media & publishing industries.

In 2000 we expanded our award-winning expertise to include author representation & literary agent services. Within 8 years, our literary agency has facilitated more than 150 book deals, representing over 90 authors & numerous leading publishers internationally.

We also offer comprehensive media training programs designed for authors, chefs, spokespeople, show hosts & food professionals & orchestrate creative partnerships between individuals & corporations in the culinary industry. Specialty areas include: food, nutrition, health & wine & spirit.

Accept unsol mss. Submissions should be in the form of a complete proposal & we provide detailed guidelines on our web site. No fees, clients are billed for expenses.

Titles recently placed: *125 Gluten-Free Vegetarian Recipes*, Carol Fenster PhD; *150 Best Donut Recipes*, George Geary; *150 Best Grilled Cheese Sandwiches*, Alison Lewis; *175 Best Babycakes*, Kathy Moore, Roxanne Wyss; *175 Best Babycakes Cupcake Maker Recipes*, Kathy Moore, Roxanne Wyss; *200 Mexican Recipes*, Kelley Cleary Coffeen; *300 Best Rice Cooker Recipes*, Katie Chin; *300 Sensational Soups*, Carla Snyder, Meredith Deeds; *A Spoonful of Promises*, T Susan Chang; *As American as Shoofly Pie*, William Woys Weaver; *Bake and Destroy: Good Food for Bad Vegans*, Natalie Slater; *Basic to Brillant, Y'all*, Virginia Willis; *Big Ranch, Big City*, Lou Lambert, June Naylor; *Bountiful Baby Purees*, Anni Daulter; *Championship BBQ Secrets for Real Smoked Food*, Karen Putnam, Judith Fertig; *Clean Eating for Busy Families*, Michelle Dudash, R.D.; *Come In, We're Closed*, Christine Carroll, Jody Eddy; *Cooking For Your Gluten-Free Teen*, Carlyn Berghoff, Sarah Berghoff McClure, Dr. Susanne P Nelson, Nancy Ross Ryan; *Easy Indian Cooking (second edition)*, Suneeta Vaswani; *Edible Brooklyn: The Cookbook*, Rachel Wharton; *Edible Dallas & Fort Worth*, Terri Taylor; *Farm Fresh Tennessee*, Paul Knipple, Angela Knipple; *Fire in My Belly*, Kevin Gillespie, David Joachim; *Gluten-Free Baking for the Holidays*, Jeanne Sauvage; *Gluten-Free Makeovers*, Beth Hillson; *Great Gluten-Free Vegan Eats from Around the World: Fantastic, Allergy-Free Ethnic Recipes*, Allyson Kramer; *Homemade Soda*, Andrew Schloss; *I Love Cinnamon Rolls!*, Judith Fertig; *Man Bites Dog*, Bruce Kraig, Patty Carroll; *My Kitchen Cure: How I Cooked My Way Out of Chronic Autoimmune Disease and Prevented Cancer with Whole Foods and Healing Recipes*, Mee Tracy McCormick; *Piece of Cake!*, Camilla V Saulsbury; *Pink Princess Party Cookbook*, Barbara Beery; *Pop-Out-and-Paint Horse Breeds*, Cindy A Littlefield; *Pretzel Making at Home*, Andrea Slonecker; *Put 'em Up! Fruit: A Preserving Guide & Cookbook*, Sherri Brooks Vinton; *Raising the Bar: The Future of Fine Chocolate*, Pam Williams, Jim Eber; *Roots The Definitive Compendium with More Than 225 Recipes*, Diane Morgan; *Rustic Italian Food*, Marc Vetri, Dave Joachim; *Salt Block Cooking: 70 Recipes for Grilling, Chilling, Searing, and Serving on Himalyan Salt Blocks*, Mark Bitterman; *Sunday Roasts*, Betty Rosbottom; *The Art of Beef Cutting*, Kari Underly; *The Back in the Swing Cookbook*, Barbara C Unell, Judith Fertig; *The Big Book of Babycakes Cake Pop Maker Recipes*, Kathy Moore, Roxanne Wyss; *The Big Book of Babycakes Cupcake Maker Recipes*, Kathy Moore, Roxanne Wyss; *The Complete Baking Cookbook*, George Geary; *The Dead Celebrity Cookbook Presents Christmas in Tinseltown: Celebrity Recipes and Hollywood Memories from Six Feet Under the Mistletoe*, Frank DeCaro; *The Dead Celebrity Cookbook: A Resurrection of Recipes from More Than 145 Stars of Stage and Screen*, Frank DeCaro; *The Fresh Honey Cookbook: 84 Recipes from a Beekeeper's Kitchen*, Laurey Masterton; *The Great Vegan Bean Book: More than 100 Delicious Plant-Based Dishes Packed with the Kindest Protein in Town! – Includes Soy-Free and Gluten-Free Recipes!*, Kathy Hester; *The Grown-Up Lunch Box*, Joy Manning; *The I Love Trader Joe's Around the World Cookbook*, Cherie Mercer Twohy; *The Karma Chow Ultimate Cookbook*, Melissa Costello; *The Meat Lover's Meatless Celebrations*, Kim O'Donnel; *The New Southern-Latino Table*, Sandra A Gutierrez; *The Paleo Summer Survival Guide: 12 Must-Have Recipes Plus Insider Tips for a Healthy, Happy Summer*, Charles Mayfield, Julie Mayfield; *The Tailgater's Cookbook*, David Joachim; *The Vetri Cookbook*, Marc Vetri, Dave Joachim, Jeff Benjamin; *Top 100 Step-by-Step Napkin Folds*, Denise Vivaldo; *Triple Slow Cooker Entertaining*, Kathy Moore, Roxanne Wyss; *Vegan Diner*, Julie Hasson; *Vegan Holiday Kitchen*, Nava Atlas; *Wicked Good Burgers*, Andy Husbands, Andrea Pyenson, Chris Hart; *Wild About Greens*, Nava Atlas; *Williams-Sonoma Rustic Italian*, Domenica Marchetti

Foreign Rights: The Jean V Naggar Literary Agency

Membership(s): International Association of Culinary Professionals; Women Presidents' Organization

**Ethan Ellenberg Literary Agency** (L)
548 Broadway, Suite 5-E, New York, NY 10012
*Tel:* 212-431-4554 *Fax:* 212-941-4652
*E-mail:* agent@ethanellenberg.com
*Web Site:* www.ethanellenberg.com
*Key Personnel*
Pres & Agent: Ethan Ellenberg (AAR)

Assoc Agent & Subs Rts: Evan Gregory
Founded: 1984
Commercial & literary fiction & nonfiction. Fiction: specialize in first novels, thrillers, romance & all women's fiction, children's books, mysteries, science fiction, fantasy. Nonfiction: specialize in health & spirituality, science, politics, cookbooks, pop culture & current affairs, history, biography, true crime. Accepting new clients, both published & unpublished. No reading fees; accept unsol submissions with SASE. E-mail submissions without attachments accepted, but prefer submissions by mail. For fiction: first 3 chapters, synopsis & SASE. For nonfiction: proposal, including outline & author bio, sample chapters, if available. Co-agents in Hollywood & all principal foreign countries.
Titles recently placed: *Bond of Passion*, Bertrice Small; *Bound by Blood*, Amanda Ashley; *Enslaved by a Viking*, Delilah Devlin; *Fatal Heat*, Lisa Marie Rice; *Heat Seeker*, Lucy Monroe; *His Duty to Protect*, Lindsay McKenna; *In Bed with the Opposition*, Kathie Denosky; *Inked Magic*, Jory Strong; *Lord of the Black Isle*, Elaine Coffmann; *Magebane*, Lee Arthur Chane; *Nightfire*, Lisa Marie Rice; *Not Your Ordinary Faerie Tale*, Christine Warren; *On the Prowl*, Christine Warren; *Redshirts*, John Scalzi; *Singularity*, Ian Douglas; *The Deep Zone*, James M Tabor; *The Dread*, Gail Z Martin; *The Gathering Storm*, Robin Bridges; *The Last Cowboy*, Lindsay McKenna; *The Search Committee*, Tim Owens; *The Shape of Desire*, Sharon Shinn; *Undead & Undermined*, MaryJanice Davidson; *Wizard Undercover*, K E Mills; *Wolf at the Door*, MaryJanice Davidson
Membership(s): International Association of Culinary Professionals; Mystery Writers of America; National Association of Science Writers; Novelists Inc; Romance Writers of America; Science Fiction & Fantasy Writers of America

**Nicholas Ellison Agency** (L)
Division of Sanford J Greenburger Associates Inc
55 Fifth Ave, 15th fl, New York, NY 10003
*Tel:* 212-206-5600 *Fax:* 212-463-8718
*Web Site:* greenburger.com/agent/nick-ellison
*Key Personnel*
Pres: Nicholas Ellison *E-mail:* nellison@sjga.com
Foreign Rts: Chloe Walker *E-mail:* cwalker@sjga.com
Founded: 1932
Fiction & narrative nonfiction (all subjects). No children's or science fiction. No unsol mss, query first. Submit sample chapters. Include a cover letter & brief synopsis of first 20 pgs of mss. Handle film & TV rights. Fees charged for photocopying & books ordered. Agents in principal foreign countries.

**Elaine P English PLLC** (L)
4710 41 St NW, Suite D, Washington, DC 20016
*Tel:* 202-362-5190 *Fax:* 202-362-5192
*E-mail:* foreignrights@elaineenglish.com
*Web Site:* www.elaineenglish.com
*Key Personnel*
Attorney & Literary Agent: Elaine English (AAR) *E-mail:* elaine@elaineenglish.com
Founded: 2006
Law firm & literary agency. Romance, women's fiction & cozy mystery stories only. No other genres accepted. No unsol mss, query first via e-mail. Electronic submissions strongly preferred. Detailed submission guidelines on web site. Charge no fees, standard commission & reimbursement of some expenses only. Not accepting submissions at this time.
Titles recently placed: *Art of Seduction*, Stephanie Julian; *Download Drama*, Celeste O Norfleet; *Last Chance Beauty Queen*, Hope Ramsey; *Sex, Lies & Valentines*, Tawny Weber; *Tall, Dark & Cowboy*, Joanne Kennedy; *The Preacher's Bride*, Laurie Kingery
Membership(s): Mystery Writers of America; Romance Writers of America; Sisters in Crime

**Felicia Eth Literary Representation** (L)
555 Bryant St, Suite 350, Palo Alto, CA 94301
*Tel:* 415 970 9717
*E-mail:* feliciaeth.literary@gmail.com
*Web Site:* www.ethliterary.com
*Key Personnel*
Pres: Felicia Eth (AAR)
Founded: 1989
Diverse nonfiction including narrative, psychology, health & popular science; including women's issues, investigative journalism & biography. Selective mainstream literary fiction. No unsol mss, query first for fiction, proposal for nonfiction. No discs, no files by e-mail. Handle film & TV rights for clients, books only through sub-agents in LA. No reading fee. Xeroxing costs & overseas mail, FedEx charged to client, $75 for full-length ms to cover mailing. Commission is 15% domestic & 20% foreign. Foreign rights agents in all major territories.
Titles recently placed: *Red Rover*, Roger Wiens; *The Memory Thief*, Emily Coin; *The Power of the Herd*, Linda Kohanov; *The World Is a Carpet*, Anna Badkhen

**Mary Evans Inc** (L)
242 E Fifth St, New York, NY 10003-8501
*Tel:* 212-979-0880 *Fax:* 212-979-5344
*E-mail:* info@maryevansinc.com
*Web Site:* www.maryevansinc.com
*Key Personnel*
Pres: Mary Evans (AAR)
Agent: Kaela Noel; Rosie Peele
Literary fiction, narrative nonfiction, commercial fiction, self-help, science & history, graphic novels & memoirs. Nonfiction should be submitted in proposal form & fiction with a query letter, a synopsis & three sample chapters, SASE required. Accept unsol mss. Handle film & TV rights, no reading fee.
Foreign Rights: Akcali Copyright Agency (Ozgur Emir) (Turkey); Berla and Griffini Rights Agency (Erica Berla) (Italy); The Book Publishers Association of Israel (Dalia Ever-Hadani) (Israel); Chandler Crawford Agency (Holland); The Grayhawk Agency (Gray Tan) (China, Taiwan); International Editors (Maru de Montserrat) (Portugal, Spain); LEX Copyright Office (Norbert Uzseka) (Hungary); Licht & Burr (Trine Licht) (Scandinavia); Liepman Agency (Mark Koralnik) (Germany); La Nouvelle Agence (Michele Kanonidis) (France); Andrew Nurnberg Associates (Ludmilla Sushkova) (Russia); Owls Agency Inc (Mario Tauchi) (Japan); Prava I Prevodi (Ana Milenkovic) (Eastern Europe, Greece); Riff Agency (Lauri Riff) (Brazil); Eric Yang Agency (Henry Shin) (Korea)

**Farber Literary Agency Inc** (L-D)
14 E 75 St, New York, NY 10021
*Tel:* 212-861-7075 *Fax:* 212-861-7076
*E-mail:* farberlit@aol.com; farberlit@gmail.com (submissions)
*Key Personnel*
Pres: Ann Farber
Attorney: Donald C Farber *Tel:* 212-861-2325 *E-mail:* donaldc142@gmail.com
Contact: Dr Seth Farber
Founded: 1990
Fiction, nonfiction, plays. Do not accept unsol mss. Handle film & TV rights. No reading fee.

**Farris Literary Agency Inc** (L)
PO Box 570069, Dallas, TX 75357-0069
*Tel:* 972-203-8804
*E-mail:* farris1@airmail.net
*Web Site:* www.farrisliterary.com
*Key Personnel*
Pres: Michael D Farris
Agent: Susan Morgan Farris
Founded: 2002
Handles fiction & nonfiction books, also occasional screenplay. Query first by e-mail or regular mail. If interested, we will request further submission. No fees charged.
Titles recently placed: *To Sketch a Thief*, Sharon Pape

**Feigenbaum Publishing Consultants Inc** (L)
61 Bounty Lane, Jericho, NY 11753
*Tel:* 516-647-8314 (cell) *Fax:* 516-935-0507
*E-mail:* readrover5@aol.com
*Key Personnel*
Pres: Laurie Feigenbaum *Tel:* 516-647-8314 (cell)
Founded: 1991
Contract negotiations & review, agenting, trademark & copyright registration, permissions clearance & general publishing advice. Expertise in book publishing & electronic publishing. No unsol mss, query first. Hourly fee or commission. Contracts negotiation, $95 per hour for contracts review, negotiation, trademark & copyright registration & permissions.

**Robert L Fenton PC; Entertainment Attorney & Literary Agent** (L)
Affiliate of Fenton Entertainment Group Inc
31800 Northwestern Hwy, Suite 204, Farmington Hills, MI 48334
*Tel:* 248-855-8780 *Fax:* 248-855-3302
*Web Site:* www.robertlfenton.com
*Key Personnel*
Literary Agent: Robert L Fenton
Founded: 1984
Specialize in nonfiction, fiction, women's fiction, historical romances, action & suspense; limited poetry, children's photographic books. Handle film & TV scripts. No unsol mss, preliminary letter or telephone call first. Submit outline & sample chapters. Reading fee: $350. Frequently charge an additional retainer along with a percentage if there is an agreement of representation. Extensive experience in all areas of publishing, film & TV. Producer at Universal Studios & 20th Century Fox; produced several feature films & Movies of the Week; published three best selling novels; Literary Guild, Doubleday Book-of-the-Month. Founded 1960. Writer's Workshop on Holland America Cruise Lines, Adjunct Professor, Creative Writing at Marygrove College, Detroit, MI; Writer's Digest Presents; The RLF Writer's Workshop on cruise lines, 2000; 1999 Guest Lecturer, Entertainment Law Seminar, University of MI Law School, April 1998. Mr Fenton prefers English but has limited working knowledge of French, Spanish, German & Russian. Will only represent seven or eight new writers each year. There is a waiting list.

**FinePrint Literary Management** (L)
115 W 29 St, 3rd fl, New York, NY 10001
*Tel:* 212-279-1282
*Web Site:* www.fineprintlit.com
*Key Personnel*
CEO: Peter Rubie (AAR) *E-mail:* peter@fineprintlit.com
Pres: Stephany Evans (AAR) *E-mail:* stephany@fineprintlit.com
In-House Subs Rts Dir: Jacqueline Murphy *E-mail:* jacqueline@fineprintlit.com
Agent: June Clark *E-mail:* june@fineprintlit.com; Rachel Coyne *E-mail:* rachel@fineprintlit.com; Janet Reid *E-mail:* janet@fineprintlit.com; Brooks Sherman *E-mail:* brooks@fineprintlit.com; Becky Vinter *E-mail:* becky@fineprintlit.

com; Laura Wood *E-mail:* laura@fineprintlit.com
Founded: 2000 (formed by the merger of the Peter Rubie Agency & the Imprint Agency)
High quality fiction & nonfiction. Handle film, TV & foreign rights through sub-agents. No unsol mss, query first. Submit outline & first two chapters with one page query letter & proposal. No reading fees. Photocopying fees. Some foreign mailing charges. Please send queries to the appropriate e-mail for the agent you wish to query.
Titles recently placed: *Better Homes and Hauntings*, Molly Harper; *Breathing Room*, Dr Melva Green, Lauren Rosenfeld; *California Quakes*, John Dvorak; *Chorus*, Emma Trevayne; *Combat-Ready Kitchen*, Anastacia Marx de Salcedo; *Dark Wolf*, Dani Harper; *Doped Up*, Sam Quinones; *Double Whammy*, Gretchen Archer; *Emergence*, Derek Rydall; *Gaining Ground*, Forrest Pritchard; *Gearwing*, Emma Trevayne; *Getting Back Out There*, Susan J Elliot; *How to Raise a Billionaire Genius*, Sean Campbell, D Horby; *I Am Otter*, Sam Garton; *I Don't Like Koala*, Sean Ferrell; *I Was M/ad Man*, Richard Gilbert; *Ice Cold Kill*, Dana Haynes; *Indefensible*, Lee Goodman; *It's In His Kiss*, Aimee Thurlo; *Lowcountry Bombshell*, Susan Boyer; *My Best Race*, Chris Cooper; *My Bluegrass Baby*, Molly Harper; *My First Kafka*, Matthue Roth; *Sacred Games*, Gary Corby; *Storm Warrior*, Dani Harper; *Tequila!*, Chantal Martineau; *The Beautiful Thing That Awaits Us All*, Laird Barron; *The Break-Up Artist*, Philip Siegel; *The Good Luck Cat*, Lissa Warren; *The Pawn Broker*, David Thurlo, Aimee Thurlo; *The Repeat Year*, Andrea Lochen; *The Tao and The Bard*, Phillip DePoy; *The Temporary Wife*, Jeannie Moon; *Thornbrook Park*, Sherri Erwin; *Trickster*, Jeff Somers; *Up Mud Creek*, Molly Harper
Foreign Rep(s): Lorella Belli (UK); Donatella d'Ormesson (France); Greyhawk Agency (China, Taiwan); International Editors (Latin America, Spain); Nurcihan Kesim (Turkey); Lennart Sane (Scandinavia, Spain); Piergiorgio Nicolazzini (Italy); Owl's Agency (Japan); Prava I Prevodi (Eastern Europe); Thomas Schlueck (Germany); Eric Yang Agency (Korea)

**The Fischer-Harbage Agency Inc** (L)
540 President St, 3rd fl, Brooklyn, NY 11215
*Tel:* 212-695-7105
*E-mail:* info@fischerharbage.com
*Web Site:* www.fischerharbage.com
*Key Personnel*
Pres: Ryan Fischer-Harbage
Founded: 2007
Full service boutique literary agency specializing in fiction, memoir, narrative nonfiction & current events. No unsol mss, query first with a short description, bio & first chapter of your book in the body of an e-mail to submissions@fischerharbage.com. No fees, standard commission paid.
Titles recently placed: *An American Caddie in St Andrews: Growing Up, Girls, and Looping on the Old Course*, Oliver Horovitz; *Angels Gate: A Shortcut Man Novel*, P G Sturges; *Domestic Affairs: A Novel*, Bridget Siegel; *Gray: A Novel*, Pete Wentz, James Montgomery; *Open Wound: The Tragic Obsession of Dr William Beaumont*, Jason Karlawish; *The Great Dissent: How Oliver Wendell Holmes Changed His Mind–and Changed the History of Free Speech in America*, Thomas Healy; *The Zombie Chasers 1*, John Kloepfer; *The Zombie Chasers 2: Undead Ahead*, John Kloepfer; *The Zombie Chasers 3: Sludgement Day*, John Kloepfer; *Tribulations of the Shortcut Man*, P G Sturges; *When We Wuz Famous*, Greg Takoudes
Foreign Rights: Linda Biagi Rights Management (Worldwide)

**Flaming Star Literary Enterprises LLC** (L)
111 Raup Rd, Chatham, NY 12037
*Web Site:* www.janisvallely.com
*Key Personnel*
Owner & Literary Agent: Janis Vallely *Tel:* 518-392-0897 *E-mail:* janisvallely@gmail.com; Joseph B Vallely *Tel:* 540-636-7076
Founded: 1985
Represents upscale commercial nonfiction: memoir, politics, self-help, diet, narrative nonfiction, popular psychology & health. No unsol mss; no phone calls, no reading fee. Submit query letter & book proposal by e-mail only. Representation on the West Coast & in foreign countries.
*Branch Office(s)*
320 Riverside Dr, New York, NY 10025 *Tel:* 212-666-1556
Foreign Rep(s): Anthea Literary Agency (Katalina Sabeva) (Bulgaria); Eliane Benisti Agent Litteraire (France); Luigi Bernabo Associates (Luigi Bernabo) (Italy); Big Apple Agency Inc (Grace Yang, Dr Luk Kwanten & Lily Chen) (China, Taiwan); Graal Literary Agency (Maria Strarz-Kanska) (Poland); International Copyright Agency Ltd (Simona Kessler) (Romania); International Editors' Co (Isabel Monteagudo) (Portugal, Spain); International Editors' Co (Nicolas Costa) (Argentina); International Editors' Co (Ms Flavia Sala) (Brazil, Portugal); Japan UNI (Miko Yamanouchi) (Japan); JLM Literary Agency (Nelly Moukakou) (Greece); Katai & Bolza (Peter Bolza) (Hungary); Linda Kohn International Literatuur (Netherlands); Nurcihan Kesim® Literary Agency (Filiz Karaman) (Turkey); Kristin Olson Literary Agency sro (Czech Republic); Ilana Pikarski Literary Agency (Ms Gal Pikarski) (Israel); Lennart Sane Agency SB (Lina Hammarling) (Scandinavia); Thomas Schlueck Literary & Art Agency (Tom Schluck) (Bulgaria); Thomas Schlueck Literary & Art Agency (Joachim Jessen) (Germany); Shin Won Agency (Eunja Beck, Mr Sang Hyung & Steve Yang) (Korea); Tuttle-Mori Agency Inc (Anongnard Podchanajun & Pimolporn Yutisri) (Thailand); Eric Yang Agency (Vince Baek) (Korea)

**Flannery Literary** (L)
1140 Wickfield Ct, Naperville, IL 60563
*Tel:* 630-428-2682
*Web Site:* flanneryliterary.com
*Key Personnel*
Owner: Jennifer Flannery *E-mail:* jennifer@flanneryliterary.com
Founded: 1992
Represents authors of books written for children & young adults. No unsol mss, query first with SASE or via e-mail. No fees.
Membership(s): ABA; ALA; Chicago Women in Publishing; International Reading Association; National Council of Teachers of English; Society of Children's Book Writers & Illustrators

**Peter Fleming Agency** (L)
PO Box 458, Pacific Palisades, CA 90272
*Tel:* 310-454-1373
*E-mail:* peterfleming@earthlink.net
*Key Personnel*
Pres: Peter Fleming
Nonfiction: undiscovered truths, exposes with upside potential, popular works on medical science & health discoveries, populist, contrarian, dissent, suppressed information overlooked or avoided by mainstream media (ex: corporate/political crimes), biographies & autobiographies of well known people. Interested in authors with strong platforms, web sites, blogs & seminar experience. No unsol mss, query first with SASE. Submit outline. No reading fee. Clients billed for major postage, FedEx, foreign communication & other pre-approved expenses.

**Sheldon Fogelman Agency Inc** (L)
10 E 40 St, Suite 3205, New York, NY 10016
*Tel:* 212-532-7250 *Fax:* 212-685-8939
*E-mail:* info@sheldonfogelmanagency.com
*Web Site:* sheldonfogelmanagency.com
*Key Personnel*
Pres & Literary Agent: Sheldon Fogelman
Literary Agent: Sean McCarthy
Asst Agent/Foreign Rts Mgr: Janine Hauber
Asst Agent: Amy Stern
Trade books of all types, fiction & nonfiction, adult & juvenile, including all rights. Handle film, TV, film & software rights. No unsol mss, query first, include publishing history. No reading fee.

**The Foley Literary Agency** (L)
34 E 38 St, Suite 1B, New York, NY 10016
*Tel:* 212-686-6930
*Key Personnel*
Partner: Joan Foley; Joseph Foley
Founded: 1961
Fiction & nonfiction books. No unsol mss, query first with SASE & brief outline. No reading fee. 10% sales commission, 15% foreign rights fees. Rare but occasional fees for phone, mail or copying. Handle film & TV rights for own authors' published books. Agents in all major European countries.

**Folio Jr**, see Folio Literary Management LLC

**Folio Literary Management LLC** (L)
The Film Center Bldg, 630 Ninth Ave, Suite 1101, New York, NY 10036
*Tel:* 212-400-1494 *Fax:* 212-967-0977
*Web Site:* www.foliolit.com
*Key Personnel*
Founding Partner & Agent: Scott Hoffman; Jeff Kleinman (AAR) *E-mail:* jkleinman@foliolit.com; Paige Wheeler (AAR) *E-mail:* paige@foliolit.com
SVP, Dir of Opers & Agent: Frank Weimann *E-mail:* frank@foliolit.com
SVP & Agent: Erin Niumata; Steve Troha (AAR) *E-mail:* steve@foliolitmanagement.com; Emily van Beek
Co-Dir of Intl Rts & Agent: Molly Jaffa (AAR) *E-mail:* molly@foliolit.com; Melissa Sarver *E-mail:* melissa@foliolit.com
Agent: Michelle Brower (AAR); Claudia Cross (AAR) *E-mail:* claudia@foliolitmanagement.com; Jita Fumich *E-mail:* jita@foliolit.com; Michael Harriot *E-mail:* michael@foliolit.com; Erin Harris; Katherine Latshaw *E-mail:* klatshaw@foliolitmanagement.com; Marcy Posner
Founded: 1997
Places both fiction & nonfiction. Seeking adult fiction appropriate for book club discussion, literary & commercial fiction. Also specializes in narrative nonfiction including memoirs. No poetry, stage plays or screen plays. Represents many first time authors as well as established authors. No unsol mss. E-mail queries only. For each agent's specialties, contact information & submission preference go to foliolit.com/folio-staff.
Folio Jr is a division devoted to representing outstanding children's book authors & artists. No fees.
Titles recently placed: *America's Most Haunted*, Eric Olsen, Theresa Argie; *Because Your Grandparents Love You*, Andrew Clement; *Bourbon Empire: Whiskey and the Story of America*, Reid Mitenbuler; *Broken Hearts, Fences, & Other Things to Mend*, Katie Finn; *Catch A Falling Star*, Kim Culbertson; *City Love*, Susan Colasanti; *Dumplin'*, Julie Murphy; *Firebird*, Misty Copeland, Christopher

Myer; *Glimpses of Life: The Story of Mary Cassatt*, Barbara Herkert; *Henry Holton Takes the Ice*, Sandra Bradley; *Little Green*, Roni Schotter; *Sadie Mac*, Sara O'Leary; *Sebastian and the Balloon*, Philip C Stead; *Soy Sauce For Beginners*, Kirstin Chen; *Tabula Rasa*, Kristen Lippert-Martin; *The Amazing Harvey*, Don Passman; *The Bollywood Bride*, Sonali Dev; *The Cheesy Vegan*, John Schlimm; *The Echoes of an Angel: A Mother's Journey Through Faith, Love, and Seeing the Unseen*, Aquanetta Gordon; *The Girls of Summer*, Morgan Matson; *The Maiden Tower*, Ella Leya; *The Reset Juice Cleanse Diet*, Lori Kenyon, Marra St Clair; *The United Hate of America*, Brooks Gibbs; *What Really Happened: John Edwards, Our Daughter, and Me*, Rielle Hunter; *When Santa Was a Baby*, Linda Bailey; *Wish*, Jake Smith

Foreign Rights: Asli Karasuil Telif Haklari (Turkey); Berla & Griffini (children's & women's fiction) (Italy); The Book Publishers Association of Israel (Israel); Graal Literary Agency (Poland); The Grayhawk Agency (China, Taiwan); Danny Hong Agency (Korea); IECO (Portugal, Spain); Iris Literary Agency (Catherine Fragou) (Greece); Japan Uni Agency (Japan); Michelle Lapautre Agency (France); Maxima Creative Agency (Indonesia); Prava I Prevodi Literary Agency (Czech Republic, Russia, Serbia); Riff Agency (Brazil); Schlueck Literary Agency (Germany); Marianne Schoenbach Literary Agency (Netherlands); Livia Stoia Literary Agency (Romania); Ulf Toregard Agency (Scandinavia); Tuttle-Mori Agency Inc (Thailand, Vietnam); Susanna Zevi Angezia Letteraria (Italy)

**Fort Ross Inc - International Rights** (L)
Division of Fort Ross Inc
26 Arthur Place, Yonkers, NY 10701
*Tel:* 914-375-6448; 718-775-8340
*E-mail:* fortross@optonline.net
*Web Site:* www.fortrossinc.com
*Key Personnel*
Pres & Exec Dir: Dr Vladimir P Kartsev *E-mail:* vkartsev2000@yahoo.com
Founded: 1992
Buys & sells publishing & translation rights for the books & illustrators of American & Russian authors & artists. Fiction: romance, mysteries, science fiction, fantasy, adventure. Nonfiction: popular science, self-help & biography. No unsol mss. Query first with brief synopsis, sample chapter & SASE; no fees.
Foreign Rep(s): Nova Littera (Baltic States, Belarus, Russia, Ukraine)

**Lynn C Franklin Associates Ltd** (L)
1350 Broadway, Suite 2015, New York, NY 10018
*Tel:* 212-868-6311 *Fax:* 212-868-6312
*E-mail:* agency@franklinandsiegal.com
*Key Personnel*
Pres & Agent: Lynn C Franklin (AAR)
Rts Mgr: Claudia Nys
Adult commercial & literary fiction; middle-grade & young adult fiction; & general nonfiction with special interest in self-help, health, psychology, personal growth & biographies, as well as current international affairs. No unsol mss, query e-mail (no attachments). No reading fee. Representatives in Hollywood & in all major foreign countries. Handle film & TV rights.
Titles recently placed: *The Book of Forgiving: The Four-Fold Path of Healing for Ourselves and Our World*, Desmond M Tutu, Mpho A Tutu; *The Customer Rules: The 39 Essential Rules for Delivering Sensational Service*, Lee Cockerell; *The Wahls Protocol*, Terry Wahls, MD, Eve Adamson
Foreign Rights: ACER Agencia Literaria (Elizabeth Atkins) (Portugal, Spain, Spanish Latin America); Eliane Benisti Literary Agency (France); Book Publishers Association of Israel (Israel); Chinese Connection Agency (China, Taiwan); Mary Clemmey Literary Agency (Mary Clemmey) (Australia, New Zealand, UK); The English Agency (Japan) Ltd (Japan); Fritz Agency (Germany); Graal Literary Agency (Poland); Berla e Griffini (Erica Berla) (Italy); Katai & Bolza (Hungary); Simona Kessler International Copyright Agency (Romania); Maxima Creative (Indonesia); Andrew Nurnberg Associates (Russia); Kristin Olson (Czech Republic); Prava & Prevodi Literary Agency (Bulgaria, Croatia, Montenegro, Serbia, Slovenia); Read n' Right Agency (Greece); Agencia Riff (Brazil); Lennart Sane Agency (Netherlands, Scandinavia); Eric Yang Agency (Korea)

**Jeanne Fredericks Literary Agency Inc** (L)
221 Benedict Hill Rd, New Canaan, CT 06840
*Tel:* 203-972-3011 *Fax:* 203-972-3011
*E-mail:* jeanne.fredericks@gmail.com (no unsol attachments)
*Web Site:* jeannefredericks.com
*Key Personnel*
Pres: Jeanne Fredericks (AAR)
Founded: 1997 (purchased assets of Susan P Urstadt Inc in May 1997)
Adult nonfiction only, especially practical popular reference, health & medical, gardening, business, travel, practical how-to, biography, antiques & decorative arts, sports, natural history, cookbooks, women's issues, history. No unsol mss, query first with SASE. If requested, submit proposal, author biography (including previous publishing history), detailed outline & sample chapters with SASE. Do not require signature for delivery. Handle film & TV rights with co-agent. No reading fee.
Titles recently placed: *25 Garden Projects*, Roger Marshall; *A Woman's Guide to Pelvic Health*, Beth Houser MD, Stephanie Hahn PT; *Amplified: The Art of the Contemporary Electric Guitar*, Robert Shaw; *My Scarlett: Margaret Mitchell and the Motion Picture Gone with the Wind*, John Wiley Jr; *Smart Guide to Single Malt Scotch Whisky*, Elizabeth Bell; *Smart Guide to Understanding Your Cat*, Carolyn Janik; *The Best There Ever Was: The Story of Dan Patch*, Sharon Smith; *The Creativity Cure*, Carrie Barron MD, Alton Barron MD; *Waking the Warrior Goddess (revised ed)*, Christine Horner MD; *Yoga Therapy*, Eden Goldman DC, Terra Gold DOM, Larry Payne PhD
Foreign Rep(s): Books Crossing Borders (Worldwide)
Membership(s): The Authors Guild

**Robert A Freedman Dramatic Agency Inc** (D)
1501 Broadway, Suite 2310, New York, NY 10036
*Tel:* 212-840-5760 *Fax:* 212-840-5776
*Key Personnel*
Pres: Robert A Freedman (AAR)
*E-mail:* rfreedmanagent@aol.com
SVP: Selma Luttinger (AAR)
VP & Agent: Marta Praeger (AAR)
Founded: 1928 (as Harold Freedman Brandt & Brandt Dramatic Department Inc, until 1981)
Dramatic scripts for stage, motion picture & TV. No unsol mss, query first. No reading fee. Material placed for production/publication is subject to 10% commission. Agents in all European countries. Will co-agent with literary agents to handle film rights & books.

**Samuel French Inc** (D)
45 W 25 St, New York, NY 10010-2751
*Tel:* 212-206-8990 *Toll Free Tel:* 866-598-8449 *Fax:* 212-206-1429
*E-mail:* info@samuelfrench.com
*Web Site:* www.samuelfrench.com
*Key Personnel*
Pres: Nate Collins *E-mail:* ncollins@samuelfrench.com
Dir, Opers: Kenneth Dingledine *E-mail:* kdingledine@samuelfrench.com
Literary Mgr: Amy Rose Marsh *E-mail:* amarsh@samuelfrench.com
Founded: 1830
Plays for publication & agency representation. Accept unsol mss, standard US play form. No reading fee. Handle film & TV rights for published works only. Send $4 for guidelines (recommended mss format).
*Branch Office(s)*
Samuel French Bookshop, 7623 Sunset Blvd, Hollywood, CA 90046
*Foreign Office(s):* Samuel French Ltd, 52 Fitzroy St, London W1T 5JR, United Kingdom, Opers Dir: David Webster *Tel:* (020) 7387 9373 *Fax:* (020) 7387 2161 *E-mail:* theatre@samuelfrench-london.co.uk *Web Site:* www.samuelfrench-london.co.uk

**Sarah Jane Freymann Literary Agency LLC** (L)
59 W 71 St, Suite 9-B, New York, NY 10023
*Tel:* 212-362-9277
*E-mail:* submissions@sarahjanefreymann.com
*Web Site:* www.sarahjanefreymann.com
*Key Personnel*
Owner & Agent: Sarah Jane Freymann *E-mail:* sarah@sarahjanefreymann.com
Assoc: Katharine Sands *Tel:* 212-751-8892 *E-mail:* katharinesands@nyc.rr.com; Steven Schwartz *Tel:* 212-362-1998 *E-mail:* steve@sarahjanefreymann.com; Jessica Sinsheimer *E-mail:* jessica@sarahjanefreymann.com
Founded: 1974
Represents book-length fiction & general nonfiction. Fiction: popular fiction plus quality mainstream, literary fiction & young adult. Nonfiction: spiritual/inspirational, psychology, self-help; women's/men's issues; health (conventional & alternative); cookbooks; narrative nonfiction, natural science, nature, memoirs, biography; current events, multicultural issues, popular culture; illustrated books, lifestyle, garden, design, architecture, humor, sports, travel & business. No unsol mss, query first with SASE. Handle film & TV rights with subagents. Representation in all foreign markets. No reading fee.
Titles recently placed: *Falling Under*, Gwen Hayes

**Fredrica S Friedman & Co Inc** (L)
136 E 57 St, 14th fl, New York, NY 10022
*Tel:* 212-829-9600 *Fax:* 212-829-9669
*E-mail:* info@fredricafriedman.com; submissions@fredricafriedman.com
*Web Site:* www.fredricafriedman.com
*Key Personnel*
Pres: Fredrica S Friedman (AAR)
Founded: 2000
Literary management firm that represents best selling & award winning authors. General nonfiction & fiction. No poetry, plays, screenplays, children's picture books, science fiction/fantasy or horror. No unsol mss-query first. Send all queries by e-mail, no attachments. See web site for detailed submission information. Hardcopy materials will not be returned; no fees.
Foreign Rep(s): Georges Borchardt Agency
Foreign Rights: Georges Borchardt Agency

**Candice Fuhrman Literary Agency** (L)
10 Cypress Hollow Dr, Tiburon, CA 94920
*Tel:* 415-383-1014
*E-mail:* candicef@pacbell.net
*Key Personnel*
Pres & Owner: Candice Fuhrman (AAR)

Nonfiction: health, memoir, psychology, women's issues, how-to & self-help; literary & commercial fiction. No unsol mss.
Currently not accepting new clients.
Foreign Rights: Jenny Meyer Literary Agency

**The Garamond Agency Inc** (L)
12 Horton St, Newburyport, MA 01950
*Fax:* 978-992-0265
*E-mail:* query@garamondagency.com
*Web Site:* www.garamondagency.com
*Key Personnel*
Dir: Lisa Adams; David Miller
Adult nonfiction, all subjects. No unsol mss, query by e-mail first. Submit cover letter, outline, synopsis, author bio & SASE. No reading fees. Handle TV & movie rights.
Foreign Rights: AnatoliaLit Agency (Turkey); Bardon-Chinese Media Agency (China, Taiwan); Berla & Griffini Rights Agency (Italy); Raquel de la Concha Agencia Literaria (Portugal, Spain); Graal Literary Agency (Poland); Anna Jarota Agency (France); Katai & Bolza Literary Agents (Hungary); Duran Kim Agency (Korea); Mo Literary Services (Netherlands); Mohrbooks (Germany); Andrew Nurnberg Association Sofia (Bulgaria); Andrew Nurnberg Literary Agency (Russia & former USSR); The Riff Agency (Brazil); Agentia literara Sun (Romania); Tuttle-Mori Agency Inc (Japan)
Membership(s): The Authors Guild

**Max Gartenberg Literary Agency** (L)
912 N Pennsylvania Ave, Yardley, PA 19067
*Tel:* 215-295-9230
*Web Site:* www.maxgartenberg.com
*Key Personnel*
Agent: Anne G Devlin *E-mail:* agdevlin@aol.com; Dirk Devlin *E-mail:* dirk_devlin1@yahoo.com
Founded: 1954
Adult nonfiction books & fiction. No unsol mss, query first. Submit formal book proposal, outline & sample as requested. No reading fee. Handle film & TV rights. Agents in all principal foreign markets.
Titles recently placed: *Arthritis and You: A Comprehensive Digest for Patients and Caregivers*, Naheed Ali MD; *Blazing Ice: Pioneering the 21st Century's Road to the South Pole*, John H Wright; *Everything A New Elementary School Teacher REALLY Needs to Know*, Otis Kreigel; *Land Your Dream Career: 11 Steps To Take In College*, Tori Randolph Terhune, Betsy A Hays; *Slaughter on North LaSalle*, Robert L Snow; *Surviving Your Bar/Bat Mitzvah: The Ultimate Insider's Guide*, Matt Axelrod; *The Spin Doctor*, Kirk Mitchell; *Verdi for Kids: His Life & Music*, Helen Bauer
Foreign Rights: International Editors' Co (Argentina); Mohrbooks AG, Literary Agency (Switzerland); La Nouvelle Agence (France); Pollinger Ltd (UK); Lennart Sane (Sweden); Tuttle-Mori Agency Inc (Japan)

**Gelfman/Schneider/ICM** (L)
Affiliate of John Farquharson Ltd
850 Seventh Ave, Suite 903, New York, NY 10019
*Tel:* 212-245-1993 *Fax:* 212-245-8678
*E-mail:* mail@gelfmanschneider.com
*Web Site:* gelfmanschneider.com
*Key Personnel*
Contact: Jane Gelfman (AAR); Deborah Schneider (AAR)
General trade fiction & nonfiction. Queries by mail only, no e-mail queries will be considered. No unsol mss, query first with SASE. Submit sample chapters & outline. Handle film & TV rights. No reading fee.
Foreign Rights: Curtis Brown Ltd (translation, UK)
Membership(s): The Authors Guild

**The Gersh Agency (TGA)** (L-D)
41 Madison Ave, 33rd fl, New York, NY 10010
*Tel:* 212-997-1818
*E-mail:* info@gershla.com
*Web Site:* gershagency.com
*Key Personnel*
Head of Books Dept: J Joseph Veltre, III (AAR)
Literary Agent: Phyllis Wender (AAR) *E-mail:* pwender@gershny.com; Susan Perlman Cohen *E-mail:* njcohen@aol.com
Founded: 2007 (1949 as talent agency)
Fiction, nonfiction, adult & juvenile, film & TV rights & plays. No unsol mss. Unsol materials will not be accepted or considered. No online submission unless requested. No reading fee.
*Branch Office(s)*
9465 Wilshire Blvd, 6th fl, Beverly Hills, CA 90212 (talent div) *Tel:* 310-274-6611
Foreign Rights: The English Agency (Japan) Ltd (Japan); Licht & Burr (Scandinavia); Mohrbooks (Germany); La Nouvelle Agence (France)

**GGP Publishing Inc** (L)
105 Calvert St, Suite 201, Harrison, NY 10528-3138
*Tel:* 914-834-8896 *Fax:* 914-834-7566
*Web Site:* www.ggppublishing.com
*Key Personnel*
Pres: Generosa Gina Protano *E-mail:* ggprotano@ggppublishing.com
Founded: 1991
Fiction & nonfiction; educational materials, English & foreign languages. Handle film & TV rights. No unsol mss, query first. Reading fees on all submissions, refundable from commission; fee charged for photocopying & postage or courier. Editorial & translation services also available.
Membership(s): American Book Producers Association

**The Gislason Agency** (L)
7400 University Ave NE, Fridley, MN 55432
*Tel:* 763-572-9297
*E-mail:* gislasonbj@aol.com
*Web Site:* www.thegislasonagency.com
*Key Personnel*
Attorney/Agent: Barbara J Gislason
Founded: 1992
The Gislason Agency is not considering unsol work & does not respond to inquiries.
Membership(s): American Bar Association; IBPA, the Independent Book Publishers Association; Minnesota Intellectual Property Lawyers Association; Minnesota State Bar Association; Mystery Writers of America; Science Fiction & Fantasy Writers of America

**Susan Gleason** (L)
325 Riverside Dr, Suite 41, New York, NY 10025
*Tel:* 212-662-3876 *Fax:* 212-864-3298
*E-mail:* sgleasonliteraryagent@gmail.com
Founded: 1992
Adult trade & mass market, fiction & nonfiction. No unsol mss, query first with SASE.
Handle film & TV rights, foreign rights. No reading fees.
Membership(s): International Women's Writing Guild

**Globo Libros Literary Agency** (L)
402 E 64 St, Suite 6-C, New York, NY 10065
*Tel:* 212-888-4655
*Web Site:* www.globo-libros.com; publishersmarketplace.com/members/dstockwell
*Key Personnel*
Founder: Diane Stockwell *E-mail:* dstockwell@nyc.rr.com
Founded: 2006
Specializes in Hispanic nonfiction authors from the US & abroad. Also represents works in English. Looking for compelling narrative nonfiction, cookbooks, memoir, biography, parenting & self-help by authors of any background. We also offer book length & short translations from Spanish into English. Query by e-mail only with a detailed summary of the project & author bio in the body of the message. No attachments. No fees charged.
Titles recently placed: *Buried Alive: The True Story of the Chilean Mining Disaster & the Extraordinary Rescue at Camp Hope*, Manuel Pino; *Cartel: The Coming Invasion of Mexico's Drug Wars*, Sylvia Longmire; *Cocino Latin*, Raquel Roque; *El Poder de Tu Cumpleanos*, Andrea Valeria; *El Salto: Aprovecha de las Nuevas Tecnologias y Alcance tu potencial*, Ariel Coro; *Killing the American Dream: How Anti-Immigrant Extremists are Destroying the Nation*, Pilar Marrero; *Los 10 Errores que las Mujeres Hacen en el Amor*, Maria Marin; *Volver a Morir*, Rosana Ubanell
Membership(s): The Authors Guild

**Krista Goering Literary Agency LLC** (L)
3514 Clinton Pkwy, Suite A-404, Lawrence, KS 66047
*Tel:* 785-841-0634 *Fax:* 785-841-8500
*E-mail:* query@kristagoering.com
*Web Site:* www.kristagoering.com
*Key Personnel*
Agent: Krista Goering
Founded: 2007
Specialize in nonfiction projects by authors with a platform who wish to build a brand with multiple projects. Nonfiction: send query by e-mail; no fees. No unsol mss, query first. While we are not accepting new clients, we are continuing to work with existing clients.
Titles recently placed: *101 Signs of Psychic Ability*, Melissa Alvarez; *101 Success Secrets for Gifted Kids*, Christine N Fonseca Ms Pps; *108 Spiritual Practices*, Debra Moffitt; *365 Ways to Raise Your Frequency*, Melissa Alvarez; *A Cure for Emma*, Julie Colvin; *Becoming Your Best Self: The Guide to Clarity, Inspiration & Healing*, Sara Wiseman; *Chemo: Secrets to Thriving*, Roxanne Brown, Barbara Mastej; *Community College Success: Networking Secrets for Winning Friends, Scholarships, Internships & Jobs*, Isa Adney; *Confessions of a Scroundel! From the Secret Memoirs of General James Wilkinson (1757-1825)*, Keith Thompson; *Full Cup, Thirsty Spirit: 6 Shifts to Nourish the Soul When Life's Too Busy & Too Much*, Karen Horneffer-Ginter PhD; *Homework Helpers: Essays & Term Papers*, Michelle Mclean; *Idol Hands*, Ted Scofield; *Say This Not That to Your Professor: 42 Talking Tips for College Success*, Ellen Bremen MA; *Slow Parenting Teens*, Molly Wingate, Marti Woodward; *That Should Still Be Us: The Flat World Myths That Are Keeping Us Flat on Our Backs*, Martin Sieff; *The Healthy Habit Plan*, Wes Cole; *The Little Book of Light: 100 Ways to Bring Light Into Your Life*, Mikaela Jones; *The Ultimate Guide for Creating Quick & Healthy Meals*, Franceen Friefeld Rd PH Ec; *Unchain the Pain*, Bob Livingstone Lcsw

**Goldfarb & Associates** (L-D)
721 Gibbon St, Alexandria, VA 22314
*Tel:* 202-466-3030 *Fax:* 703-836-5644
*E-mail:* rglawlit@gmail.com
*Web Site:* www.ronaldgoldfarb.com
*Key Personnel*
Founder & Owner: Ronald L Goldfarb
Literary Agent: Robbie Anna Hare

Founded: 1966
Only select new clients accepted. Fiction & serious nonfiction; no romance or sci-fi. No unsol mss, query first with letter, outline or synopsis, sample of best chapter, bio & SASE. Handle film & TV rights. No reading fee.
*Branch Office(s)*
177 Ocean Lane Dr, Suite 1101, Key Biscayne, FL 33149

**Frances Goldin Literary Agency, Inc** (L-D)
57 E 11 St, Suite 5-B, New York, NY 10003
*Tel:* 212-777-0047 *Fax:* 212-228-1660
*E-mail:* agency@goldinlit.com
*Web Site:* www.goldinlit.com
*Key Personnel*
Principal & Agent: Frances Goldin (AAR)
VP & Sr Agent: Ellen Geiger (AAR); Sam Stoloff (AAR)
Rts Dir & Agent: Matt McGowan (AAR) *E-mail:* mm@goldinlit.com
Assoc Agent & Off Mgr: Sarah Bridgins
Founded: 1977
No unsol mss or work previously submitted to publishers, query first with letter & SASE. No racist, sexist, agist, homophobic or pornographic material considered. Adult literary fiction & serious progressive nonfiction. Agents in Hollywood & all major foreign countries. No software. Handle film & TV rights. No reading fee.
Foreign Rep(s): Eliane Benisti (France); The English Agency (Japan) Ltd (Hamish Macaskill) (Japan); Graal Literary Agency (Maria Starz-Kanska) (Poland); David Grossman Literary Agency Ltd (David Grossman) (England, UK); International Editors' Co (Isabel Monteagudo) (Spain); International Editors' Co (Nicholas Costa) (Argentina); International Editors' Co (Flavia Sala) (Brazil); Jia-Xi Books (Gray Tan) (China, Taiwan); JLM Literary Agency (John L Moukakos) (Greece); Nurcihan Kesim Literary Agency Inc (Asli Karasuil) (Istanbul, Turkey); Ruth Liepman Agency (Ruth Weibel) (Germany); Living Literary Agency (Elfriede Pexa) (Italy); Jovan Milenkovic (Vuk Perisic) (Montenegro, Serbia); Kristin Olson Literary Agency (Kristin Olson) (Czech Republic); Pikarski Literary Agency Ltd (Gal Pikarski) (Israel); Lennart Sane Agency (Lennart Sane) (Iceland, Netherlands, Scandinavia, Sweden); Synopsis Literary Agency (Natalia Sanina) (Russia); Tuttle-Mori Agency Inc (Supanya Pratum) (Indonesia, Thailand, Vietnam); The Eric Yang Agency (Sue Yang) (Korea)

**Goodman-Andrew Agency Inc**, see Sasha Goodman Agency Inc

**Goodman Associates** (L)
500 West End Ave, New York, NY 10024
*Tel:* 212-873-4806
*Key Personnel*
Pres: Arnold P Goodman (AAR)
VP: Elise Simon Goodman
Founded: 1976
Adult book-length fiction & nonfiction. No plays, screenplays, poetry, textbooks, science fiction, children's books. No unsol mss, query first with SASE. No fees. Handle film & TV rights for clients' published materials. Representatives in Hollywood & major foreign markets. Accepting new clients by recommendation only.

**Irene Goodman Literary Agency** (L)
27 W 24 St, Suite 700B, New York, NY 10010
*Tel:* 212-604-0330
*E-mail:* queries@irenegoodman.com
*Web Site:* www.irenegoodman.com
*Key Personnel*
Pres: Irene Goodman (AAR)
*E-mail:* irenequeries@irenegoodman.com
VP: Miriam Kriss *E-mail:* miriamqueries@irenegoodman.com
Agent: Barbara Poelle *E-mail:* barbaraqueries@irenegoodman.com; Rachel Ekstrom *E-mail:* rachelqueries@irenegoodman.com
Mgr, Audio Rts: Sara Grubb
Founded: 1978
Commercial & literary fiction & nonfiction including mysteries, romance, women's fiction, thrillers & suspense. No poetry, inspirational fiction, screenplays or children's picture books. Handle film & TV rights through Steven Fisher in Los Angeles. No unsol mss, query first with first 10 pages & synopsis via e-mail. No snail mail. See web site under submission guidelines for each agent's preferences. No reading fee.
Foreign Rep(s): Danny Baror
Foreign Rights: Baror International Agency

**Sasha Goodman Agency Inc** (L)
6680 Colgate Ave, Los Angeles, CA 90048
*Tel:* 310-387-0242 *Fax:* 323-653-3457
*E-mail:* ukseg@sbcglobal.net
*Key Personnel*
Owner: Sasha Goodman
Founded: 2012
Fiction (commercial & literary) & nonfiction, all areas. No unsol mss, query first. Submit outline & 2 sample chapters. No telephone queries; no reading fees. 15% agency commission.
Foreign Rights: Linda Michaels Agency (Worldwide)

**Gotham Literary Agency** (L)
170 E 83 St, New York, NY 10028
*Tel:* 212-249-2615
*Key Personnel*
Mng Ed: Nathalie Scott *E-mail:* nathalie@gothamliteraryagency.com
Founded: 2004
Specialize in mystery/thriller, romance, memoir, bio, celebrity, new thoughts, psychological suspense, women's fiction & chic-lit. No sci-fi, fantasy, gay/lesbian, short stories, poetry or children's books. We are actively seeking action thrillers, suspense, historical & contemporary paranormal. Submit a synopsis & author bio, each no more than 1 page, 1 side, double-spaced. Do not staple pages. Include first 3 chapters for fiction or a proposal for nonfiction. Include a large SASE if you want your materials returned. No reading fee. If accepted for representation, there is a charge for agency costs to submit your ms: copies, priority mail & a one half hour agency fee per submission. We also offer editing services, proposal development, critique & Spanish translation.
Titles recently placed: *Eagle's Gold*, Vince De Paul Lupiano

**Doug Grad Literary Agency Inc** (L)
156 Prospect Park West, No 3L, Brooklyn, NY 11215
*Tel:* 718-788-6067
*E-mail:* query@dgliterary.com
*Web Site:* www.dgliterary.com
*Key Personnel*
Owner: Doug Grad *E-mail:* doug.grad@dgliterary.com
Assoc Agent: George Bick *Tel:* 212-861-5144 *E-mail:* george.bick@dgliterary.com
Founded: 2008
Commercial fiction & nonfiction in a wide variety of genres & subjects. See web site for additional information. Send cover letter only with brief description of book. Will ask to see more material if interested, via e-mail only to query@dgliterary.com. Do not send hard copies of proposals or mss. No fees.
Titles recently placed: *Gary Cooper Enduring Style*, G Bruce Boyer, Maria Cooper Janis; *Gordie Howe's Son: A Hall of Fame Life in the Shadow of Mr Hockey*, Mark Howe, Jay Greenberg; *Nailed: The Improbable Rise & Spectacular Collapse of Lenny Dykstra*, Christopher Frankie; *No Silent Night: The Christmas Battle for Bastogne*, Leo Barron, Don Cygan; *Pirate Alley: Commanding Task Force 151 Off Somalia*, Terry McKnight, Michael Hirsh; *Sleep Tight*, Jeff Jacobson; *Ten Days to Tehran: The Untold Story of Franklin D Roosevelt's Secret WWII Voyage & How It Changed the World*, L Douglas Keeney; *The Baseball Hall of Shame: The Best of Blooperstown*, Bruce Nash, Allan Zullo; *The Pointblank Directive: Three Generals & the Untold Story of the Daring Plan That Saved D-Day*, L Douglas Keeney; *Uncommon Youth: The Gilded Life and Tragic Times of J Paul Getty III*, Charles Fox; *World on a String: A Musical Memoir*, John Pizzarelli, Joseph Cosgriff
Foreign Rep(s): Baror International Inc (Danny Baror) (Worldwide)
Foreign Rights: Baror International Inc (Danny Baror) (Worldwide)

**Graham Agency** (D)
311 W 43 St, New York, NY 10036
*Tel:* 212-489-7730
*Key Personnel*
Prop: Earl Graham
Founded: 1971
Full-length stage plays & musicals only. No unsol mss, query by mail first. Submit brief description. No reading fee, 10% commission.

**Ashley Grayson Literary Agency** (L)
1342 W 18 St, San Pedro, CA 90732
*Tel:* 310-548-4672
*E-mail:* graysonagent@earthlink.net; rights@graysonagency.com
*Web Site:* graysonagency.com/blog/
*Key Personnel*
Dir & Agent: Ashley Grayson (AAR); Carolyn Grayson (AAR) *E-mail:* carolyngraysonagent@earthlink.net
Agent: Lois Winston *E-mail:* lois.graysonagent@earthlink.net
Founded: 1976
Literary & commercial fiction, nonfiction & young adult; no poetry or short stories. No reading fee. No unsol mss, query first with e-mail. Include letter, first 3 pages of ms or outline of proposal. If querying about children's picture book, submit entire ms. We prefer to receive queries from previously published authors. Handle film & TV rights for books already represented; no original screenplays. Represent literary rights in all principal countries, also represent international publishers in US & UK.
Foreign Rights: Bestun Korea Literary Agency (Yumi Chun) (Korea); Lora Fountain & Associates (France); Graal Literary Agency (Poland)
Membership(s): Romance Writers of America; Science Fiction & Fantasy Writers of America; Society of Children's Book Writers & Illustrators

**Sanford J Greenburger Associates Inc** (L)
55 Fifth Ave, 15th fl, New York, NY 10003
*Tel:* 212-206-5600 *Fax:* 212-463-8718
*Web Site:* www.greenburger.com
*Key Personnel*
VP: Heide Lange (AAR) *E-mail:* queryhl@sjga.com
Dir, Intl Rts: Stefanie Diaz *E-mail:* sdiaz@sjga.com
Dir, Intl Scouting Dept: Agnes Krup *Tel:* 212-206-5604 *E-mail:* akrup@sjga.com
Agent: Matthew Bialer *E-mail:* lribar@sjga.com; Brenda Bowen (AAR); Lisa Gallagher *E-mail:* lgsubmissions@sjga.com; Faith Hamlin (AAR) *E-mail:* fhamlin@sjga.com; Daniel

Mandel (AAR); Courtney Miller-Callihan
*E-mail:* cmiller@sjga.com
Founded: 1932
Fiction, nonfiction, handle film & TV rights. No unsol mss. Query first. Submit outline or synopsis & sample chapter. No reading fee. Copying fee. Agents in all principal foreign countries.

**Jill Grinberg Literary Management LLC** (L)
16 Court, Suite 3306, Brooklyn, NY 11241
*Tel:* 212-620-5883 *Fax:* 212-627-4725
*E-mail:* info@jillgrinbergliterary.com
*Web Site:* www.jillgrinbergliterary.com
*Key Personnel*
Pres: Jill Grinberg (AAR)

**Jill Grosjean Literary Agency** (L)
1390 Millstone Rd, Sag Harbor, NY 11963
*Tel:* 631-725-7419 *Fax:* 631-725-8632
*E-mail:* JillLit310@aol.com
*Key Personnel*
Owner & Literary Agent: Jill Grosjean
Founded: 1999
Literary fiction, mystery/suspense, women's fiction. No unsol mss, query first; e-mail queries preferred, no downloads or attachments. No fees charged. Foreign rights in UK, France, Italy, Spain, Netherlands, South America.
Titles recently placed: *A Capacity for Murder*, Bernadette Pajer; *A Single Thread*, Marie Bostwick; *A Spark of Death*, Bernadette Pajer; *A Thread So Thin*, Marie Bostwick; *Beating the Babushka*, Tim Maleeny; *Comfort & Joy*, Marie Bostwick; *Crossing Myself*, Greg Garrett; *Emma & the Vampires*, Wayne Josephson; *Fatal Induction*, Bernadette Pajer; *Fields of Gold*, Marie Bostwick; *I Love You Like a Tomato*, Marie Giordano; *Jump*, Tim Maleeny; *Nectar*, David Fickett; *No Idea*, Greg Garrett; *River's Edge*, Marie Bostwick; *Shame*, Greg Garrett; *Snow Angels*, Marie Bostwick; *Spectres in the Smoke*, Tony Broadbent; *Spun Tales*, Felicia Donovan; *Stealing the Dragon*, Tim Maleeny; *The Black Widow Agency*, Felicia Donovan; *The Reluctant Journey of David Connors*, Don Locke; *The Smoke*, Tony Broadbent; *The Summer the Wind Whispered My Name*, Don Locke; *Thread of Truth*, Marie Bostwick; *Threading the Needle*, Marie Bostwick; *Wings of the Morning*, Marie Bostwick

**Laura Gross Literary Agency Ltd** (L)
39 Chester St, Suite 301, Newton Highlands, MA 02461
Mailing Address: PO Box 610326, Newton Highlands, MA 02461
*Tel:* 617-964-2977 *Fax:* 617-964-3023
*E-mail:* query@lauragrossliteraryagency.com
*Web Site:* www.lg-la.com
*Key Personnel*
Pres: Laura Gross
Founded: 1988
No unsol mss. Query or e-mail first. Fiction, commercial & literary; nonfiction, serious topics, social, political, cultural issues & psychology. Include list of previous publications & bio. No reading fee.
Foreign Rights: Chandler Crawford (Worldwide exc UK)

**The Charlotte Gusay Literary Agency** (L-D)
10532 Blythe Ave, Los Angeles, CA 90064
*Tel:* 310-559-0831 *Fax:* 310-559-2639
*E-mail:* gusay1@ca.rr.com (queries only)
*Web Site:* www.gusay.com
Founded: 1988
Fiction & nonfiction, screenplay, children & adult, humor, parenting; crossover literary/commercial fiction; gardening, women's & men's issues, feminism, psychology, memoir, biography, travel. Handle film & TV rights. Represent selected illustrators, especially children's. No unsol mss, query first with SASE; ONLY when agency requests, submit one page synopsis & first three chapters or first 50 pages (for fiction); proposal (for nonfiction). Include SASE. No reading fee. For borderline queries we sometimes give prospective clients the benefit of the doubt & impose a nominal processing fee allowing the prospective clients to decide whether to submit their material or not. Once client is signed, client is responsible for providing agency hard copies of mss (as necessary) & shipping expenses (as necessary).
Titles recently placed: *Bar Flaubert*, Alexis Stamatis; *Chorus: A Literary Mixtape*, Saul Williams; *Forty-One Seconds to Freedom: An Insider's Account of the Lima Hostage Crisis, 1996-97*, Admiral Luis Giampietrei, Bill Salisbury, Lorena Ausejo; *Light a Penny Candle (film rts)*, Maeve Binchy; *Mother Ash*, Alexis Stamatis; *Outrageous Fortune: Growing Up at Leeds Castle*, Anthony Russell; *Richard Landry Estates*, Lynn Morgan; *What Angels Know: The Story of Elizabeth Barrett & Robert Browning*, Phil Davis (screenplay); *Wild West 2.0: How to Protect & Restore Your Reputation on the Untamed Social Frontier*, Michael Fertik, David Thompson
Foreign Rep(s): The Fielding Agency (Whitney Lee) (Worldwide)
Membership(s): The Authors Guild; PEN Center USA West; Writers Guild of America West

**The Mitchell J Hamilburg Agency** (L-D)
149 S Barrington Ave, Suite 732, Los Angeles, CA 90049
*Tel:* 310-471-4024 *Fax:* 310-471-9588
*Key Personnel*
Owner & Literary Agent: Michael Hamilburg
Fiction & nonfiction. No unsol mss, query first. Submit outline & two sample chapters, include SASE. Handle film & TV rights. No reading fee. No software.
Founded in the 1930's, literary agency since 1967.

**The Joy Harris Literary Agency Inc** (L)
381 Park Ave S, Suite 428, New York, NY 10016
*Tel:* 212-924-6269 *Fax:* 212-725-5275
*E-mail:* contact@jhlitagent.com
*Web Site:* www.joyharrisliterary.com
*Key Personnel*
Pres: Joy Harris (AAR) *E-mail:* joyharris@jhlitagent.com
No unsol mss, query first.

**Hartline Literary Agency LLC** (L)
123 Queenston Dr, Pittsburgh, PA 15235
*Toll Free Fax:* 888-279-6007
*Web Site:* www.hartlineliterary.com
*Key Personnel*
Owner & CEO: Joyce Hart *Tel:* 412-829-2483 *E-mail:* joyce@hartlineliterary.com
Agent: Terry Burns (AAR) *Tel:* 806-584-6464 *E-mail:* terry@hartlineliterary.com; Diana Flegal *Tel:* 412-915-1790 *E-mail:* diana@hartlineliterary.com; Linda Glaz *E-mail:* linda@hartlineliterary.com; Andy Scheer *Tel:* 719-282-3729 *E-mail:* andy@hartlineliterary.com
Founded: 1992
Advise clients on how to prepare proposals & advise them concerning what various publishers are looking for. Also help clients plan their literary careers. Our expertise is in the Christian market & we also work in the general market. Looking for clean, wholesome fiction for adults & inspiring nonfiction. Mss reflecting a Christian worldview preferred, even for the general market. Fiction: romance, romantic suspense, women's fiction, mystery/suspense, humor, chick/mom lit & general fiction. Nonfiction: self-help, Christian living, prayer, health, humor & business.
Accepts unsol mss. Submit cover letter, author bio, marketing analysis, summary & 3 sample chapters. If submitting via e-mail, send as an attachment & send the entire submission in one file. We do not accept submissions in multiple files. We accept e-mail, US mail, UPS & FedEx submissions. See web site for complete submission details. No fees.
Titles recently placed: *Bash & the Pirate Pig*, Burton Cole; *Black & White*, Ace Collins; *Catherine's Pursuit*, Lena Nelson Dooley; *Cooking the Books*, Bonnie Calhoun; *Dead Man's Hand*, Eddie Jones; *Deadliest in Show*, Christy Barritt; *Final Justice*, Christy Barritt; *Following Rain*, Darrel Nelson; *For Such a Time as This*, Kate Breslin; *Friend Me*, Jay Fabion; *Hollywood Dream*, Ace Collins; *Let's Talk Dementia*, Carol Howell; *Lifeline*, Christy Barritt; *Lonely...But Married*, Dr David Clarke; *Love Finds You in Lake Geneva, WI*, Pamela S Meyers; *Music for Your Heart*, Ace Collins; *Of Vines & Roses*, Linda Rondeau; *One Glorious Ambition*, Jane Kirkpatrick; *Petticoat Row*, Suzanne Woods Fisher; *Promise for Spring*, Jane Kirkpatrick; *Remants of Love*, Lorraine Beatty; *Ruth, Mother of Kings*, Diana Wallis Taylor; *Stolen Identity*, Lisa Harris; *The Bishop's Family (series)*, Suzanne Woods Fisher; *The Fruitcake Murders*, Ace Collins; *The Maze*, Jason Brannon; *The Preacher's Wife Wears Biker Boots*, Karla Akins; *The Quakers of New Gardon*, Jennifer Hudson Taylor, Claire Sanders, Ann Schrock, Susette Williams; *Wedding on the Rocks*, Rose Zediker
Membership(s): American Christian Fiction Writers

**John Hawkins & Associates Inc** (L)
71 W 23 St, Suite 1600, New York, NY 10010
*Tel:* 212-807-7040 *Fax:* 212-807-9555
*E-mail:* jha@jhalit.com
*Web Site:* jhalit.com
*Key Personnel*
Pres & Foreign Rts Dir: Moses Cardona (AAR) *E-mail:* moses@jhalit.com
VP: William Reiss (AAR) *E-mail:* reiss@jhalit.com
Assoc: Warren Frazier (AAR) *E-mail:* frazier@jhalit.com; Anne Hawkins (AAR) *E-mail:* ahawkins@jhalit.com
Perms & Rts: Liz Free *E-mail:* free@jhalit.com
No unsol mss, query first. Submit one-page bio & one- to three-page outline with SASE. No reading fee. Photocopy charges & fees for other services. Handle film & TV rights, software.
Foreign Rep(s): Sara Menguc Inc (UK)

**Heacock Literary Agency Inc** (L)
48 Villa Christina, La Luz, NM 88337
*Tel:* 575-437-1960 *Fax:* 575-437-1960 (call first)
*E-mail:* gracebooks@aol.com (for rights information concerning Elliot Abravanel, Wilferd Peterson, Audrey Wood, Don Wood)
*Web Site:* www.heacockliteraryagency.com
Founded: 1978 (by James B Heacock & Rosalie G Heacock Thompson, AAR)
No unsol mss, query first.
Titles recently placed: *Blue Sky*, Audrey Wood; *One Endless Hour*, Dan J Marlowe; *Puggy Times*, Audrey Wood, Don Wood; *The Birthday Queen*, Audrey Wood; *The Name of the Game is Death*, Dan J Marlowe
Foreign Rep(s): J E Bloch Literary Agency (Brazil); European American Information Services (France); Jeanne-Marie Herter (Switzerland); Richards Literary Agency (New Zealand); Saga Literia (Spain); Thomas Schlueck GmbH (Germany)
Membership(s): Association of Authors & Publishers; The Authors Guild; Society of Children's Book Writers & Illustrators

**The Jeff Herman Agency LLC** (L)
29 Park St, Stockbridge, MA 01262
Mailing Address: PO Box 1522, Stockbridge, MA 01262
*Tel:* 413-298-0077 *Fax:* 413-298-8188
*E-mail:* submissions@jeffherman.com
*Web Site:* www.jeffherman.com
*Key Personnel*
Pres: Jeffrey H Herman *E-mail:* jeff@jeffherman.com
VP: Deborah Levine
Founded: 1985
Nonfiction, reference, health, self-help, how-to business, technology, spirituality & textbooks. No unsol mss, query first with letter & SASE. No reading fee. Handle software, film & TV rights. Agents in all principal foreign countries.
Foreign Rep(s): Asano (Japan); De la Concha (Portugal, Spain)

**Susan Herner Rights Agency Inc** (L)
10 Upper Shad Rd, Pound Ridge, NY 10576
*Tel:* 914-234-2864 *Fax:* 914-234-2866
*E-mail:* sherneragency@optonline.net
*Key Personnel*
Pres: Susan N Herner
Founded: 1987
A full service literary agency representing a broad range of fiction & nonfiction authors. Not looking for new clients at the present time.

**Hill Nadell Literary Agency** (L)
8899 Beverly Blvd, Suite 805, Los Angeles, CA 90048
*Tel:* 310-860-9605 *Fax:* 310-860-9672
*Web Site:* www.hillnadell.com
*Key Personnel*
Pres: Bonnie Nadell
Founded: 1979
Adult fiction & nonfiction; film & TV rights only if handling the book. No unsol mss, query first with SASE. No reading fee. Agents in Hollywood & all foreign countries.
Titles recently placed: *The Pale King*, David Foster Wallace
Foreign Rep(s): Mary Clemmey (UK)
Foreign Rights: Andrew Nurnberg (Western Europe)

**The Barbara Hogenson Agency Inc** (L-D)
165 West End Ave, Suite 19-C, New York, NY 10023
*Tel:* 212-874-8084 *Fax:* 212-362-3011
*E-mail:* bhogenson@aol.com
*Key Personnel*
Pres: Barbara Hogenson (AAR)
Founded: 1994
Recommendation by clients only. Literary fiction, nonfiction, full length plays, consider some illustrated books. No screenplays or teleplays. No fees.
Membership(s): The Authors Guild; The Dramatists Guild of America; Society of Stage Directors & Choreographers; Writers Guild of America

**Henry Holmes Literary Agent/Book Publicist/Marketing Consultant** (L)
PO Box 433, Swansea, MA 02777
*Tel:* 508-672-2258
*E-mail:* henryholmesandassociates@yahoo.com
*Key Personnel*
Pres & Literary Agent: Henry Holmes
Founded: 1997
Nonfiction, no unsol mss, query first. Send query letter with chapters 1 & 2. If published, include past publicity, endorsement(s) etc. SASE. Ten mailings sent to preferred publishers via mss/CDs (this includes publisher research, query letter, packing, mailing, etc, at competitive rates. Independent of my representation, professional consultation via freelance assignments/project work would be based on involvement & duration of project based on competitive fees. Specialize in consulting, marketing, media publicity, talk show placement, etc. 15% standard commission. No reading fee. Retainer fee charged if ms is acceptable.

**Hornfischer Literary Management LP** (L)
PO Box 50544, Austin, TX 78763
*Tel:* 512-472-0011
*E-mail:* queries@hornfischerlit.com
*Web Site:* www.hornfischerlit.com
*Key Personnel*
Pres: Jim Hornfischer *E-mail:* jim@hornfischerlit.com
Founded: 2001
Quality narrative nonfiction, biography & autobiography, current events, US history, military history & world history, political & cultural subjects science, medicine/health, business/management/finance, academic writing & research that has a general-interest audience. No unsol mss; query first through e-mail, no longer accept queries through mail. No fees.
Titles recently placed: *500 Days*, Alex Kershaw; *Area 51*, Annie Jacobsen; *Brothers, Rivals, Victors*, Jonathan Jordan; *Outlaw Platoon*, Sean Parnell; *The Guerilla Factory*, Tony Schwalm; *The Second Nuclear Age*, Paul Bracken; *The Trident: The Forging of a SEAL Officer*, Jason Redman

**ICM/Sagalyn** (L)
Formerly The Sagalyn Literary Agency
4922 Fairmont Ave, Suite 200, Bethesda, MD 20814
*Tel:* 301-718-6440 *Fax:* 301-718-6444
*E-mail:* query@sagalyn.com
*Web Site:* www.sagalyn.com
*Key Personnel*
Owner: Raphael Sagalyn (AAR)
Dir, Dom Rts: Shannon O'Neill
Adult fiction & nonfiction. No unsol mss, query first with e-mail. Handle film & TV rights. No reading fee.
Foreign Rights: Carmen Balcells (Spain); Bardon-Chinese Media (China); Graal Literary Agency (Poland); Greene & Heaton (UK); Japan Uni Agency (Japan); JLM (Greece); Korea Copyright Center (Korea); Michelle Lapautre (France); Licht & Burr (Scandinavia); Mohrbooks (Germany); Lucia Riff (Brazil); Sebes & Van Gelderen Literary Agency (Netherlands); Synopsis Agency (Russia); Suzanne Zevi Agency (Italy)

**InkWell Management** (L)
521 Fifth Ave, 26th fl, New York, NY 10175
*Tel:* 212-922-3500 *Fax:* 212-922-0535
*E-mail:* info@inkwellmanagement.com; submissions@inkwellmanagement.com
*Web Site:* inkwellmanagement.com
*Key Personnel*
Founder & Pres: Michael Carlisle; Richard S Pine; Kim Witherspoon *E-mail:* kim@inkwellmanagement.com
Dir, Subs Rts: Lyndsey Blessing; Alexis Hurley *E-mail:* alexis@inkwellmanagement.com
Agent: David Forrer; George Lucas; Jacqueline Murphy; Charlie Olsen; David Hale Smith
Busn Mgr: Jennifer Witherell *E-mail:* jwitherell@inkwellmanagement.com
PR & Soc Media Strategist: Lisa Vanterpool
Founded: 2004 (created through the merger of Arthur Pine Associates Inc, Carlisle & Co LLC & Witherspoon Associates Inc)
General nonfiction & fiction books. No screenplays, plays, poetry. Motion picture, TV & foreign rights. No unsol mss, query first with SASE; submissions must be on an exclusive basis. No fees.
Foreign Rights: Anthea (Bulgaria); Graal Literary Agency (Poland); JLM (Greece); Katia & Bolza (Hungary); Simona Kessler (Romania); Korea Copyright Center (Korea); Michelle Lapautre (France); Maxima (Indonesia); MB Agency (Latin America, Portugal, Spain); Mohrbooks (Germany); Andrew Nurnberg Associates (China, Estonia, Latvia, Lithuania, Taiwan); Kristin Olson (Czech Republic, Slovakia); ONK Agency (Turkey); Pikarski (Israel); Prava I Prevodi (Albania, Croatia, Serbia, Slovenia); Riff (Brazil); Sane Toregard (Scandinavia); Roberto Santachiara (Italy); Serbes & van Golderen Literary Agency (Netherlands); Synopsis (Russia); Tuttle-Mori Agency Inc (Japan, Thailand, Vietnam); Eric Yang (Korea)

**InterLicense Ltd** (L)
110 Country Club Dr, Suite A, Mill Valley, CA 94941
*Tel:* 415-381-9780 *Fax:* 415-381-6485
*E-mail:* interlicense@sbcglobal.net; ilicense@aol.com
*Key Personnel*
Exec Dir: Manfred Mroczkowski
Subsidiary rights with focus on foreign rights agency & management, sales, administrations & on domestic subsidiary rights such as film, reprint, TV & merchandising rights. No unsol mss, query first. Handle software. Submit synopsis & sample chapters. Nonfiction. No reading fee. Charge for consultations.

**International Titles** (L)
931 E 56 St, Austin, TX 78751-1724
*Tel:* 512-909-2447
*Web Site:* www.internationaltitles.com
*Key Personnel*
Dir: Loris Essary *E-mail:* loris@internationaltitles.com
Represent all genres; primary emphasis on sales of foreign rights. No fees charged, no submission policy.

**International Transactions Inc** (L)
28 Alope Way, Gila, NM 88038
Mailing Address: PO Box 97, Gila, NM 88038
*Tel:* 845-373-9696 *Fax:* 480-393-5162
*E-mail:* info@intltrans.com
*Web Site:* www.intltrans.com
*Key Personnel*
Pres: Peter Riva *E-mail:* priva@intltrans.com
VP & Dir: Sandra Anne Riva *E-mail:* sriva@intltrans.com
Assoc Ed: JoAnn Collins *E-mail:* jcollins@intltrans.com
Founded: 1975
International literary & licensing agency. Specialize in nonfiction (including large projects), fiction, illustrated & children's. We cannot help every prospective author nor can we review every ms. Send a fiction submission query (only) to Submission-Fiction@IntlTrans.com. If, within three weeks, we are interested, we will call for more material. In the case of nonfiction authors, each query for submission must include a one-page summary of the book proposed as well as a brief description of the author's bona fides or expertise as author, including links to any media platform he or she may be able to employ. Send the nonfiction submission query to Submission-NonFiction@IntlTrans.com. Also handles film & TV rights. No fees.
Titles recently placed: *Aung Sung Suu Kyi*, Jesper Bengtsson; *Bell of the Desert*, Alan Gold; *Bringing Up Oscar*, Debra Ann Pawlak; *Drive on Moscow*, Niklas Zetterling; *Evil of the Age*, Allan Levine; *Fire Knife Dancing*, John Enright; *Flame Angels*, Robert Wintner; *Flypaper*, Chris Angus; *Neptune Speaks*, Robert Wintner; *One More River*, Mary Glickman; *Pago Pago*

*Tango*, John Enright; *Painting the Corners*, Bob Weintraub; *Sail of Stone*, Ake Edwardson; *Secret Heart: The Lives of Robert Ryan*, J R Jones; *The Black Hills*, Rod Thompson; *The Last Titanic Story*, Chris Angus; *The Sleeping & the Dead*, Jeff Crook; *The Square of Revenge*, Pieter Aspe; *The Tao of Joy Every Day: 365 Days of Tao Living*, Derek Lin
*Foreign Office(s):* Rechtsanwalt Roth, Gewurzmuhlstr 5, 80538 Munich, Germany *Tel:* (089) 55 26 26 55

**J de S Associates Inc** (L)
9 Shagbark Rd, South Norwalk, CT 06854
*Tel:* 203-838-7571 *Fax:* 203-866-2713
*Web Site:* www.jdesassociates.com
*Key Personnel*
Pres: Jacques de Spoelberch *E-mail:* jdespoel@aol.com
Founded: 1975
Fiction & nonfiction. No unsol mss, query first. Send outline & two sample chapters; no reading fee. Agents & film representatives in major foreign countries.

**JABberwocky Literary Agency Inc** (L)
24-16 Queens Plaza S, Suite 505, Long Island City, NY 11101-6250
*Tel:* 718-392-5985 *Fax:* 718-392-5987
*Web Site:* www.awfulagent.com
Founded: 1994
Full line of fiction & nonfiction trade books, particularly genre fiction (science fiction, fantasy, mystery, horror), literary fiction, young adult & middle grade & serious nonfiction (biography, science, history). No unsol mss, query first with biographical information & SASE. Will request mss after reviewing query if interested. Handle film & TV rights for regular clients. No reading fee. No fax or e-mail queries & always check web site to see which agents are currently accepting queries.
Titles recently placed: *Dead Ever After*, Charlaine Harris; *Gustav Gloom & the Nightmare Vault*, Adam-Troy Castro; *Limits of Power*, Elizabeth Moon; *Steelheart*, Brandon Sanderson; *The Daylight War*, Peter V Brett; *The Lost Fleet: Beyond the Frontier: Guardian*, Jack Campbell
Foreign Rep(s): AnatoliaLit Agency (Turkey); ANAW (Poland); Book Publishers Association (Israel); Bookman (Scandinavia); The English Agency (Japan) Ltd (Japan); Paul & Peter Fritz AG (Germany); The Grayhawk Agency (China, Taiwan); Danny Hong Agency (Korea); Agnese Incisa (Italy); Katai & Bolza (Hungary); Simona Kessler (Romania); Alexander Korzhenevski (Russia); Agence Litteraire Lenclud (France); Maxima Creative (Indonesia); Andrew Nurnberg (Baltic States); Kristin Olson (Czech Republic); Prava I Prevodi (Albania, Bulgaria, Croatia, Serbia, Slovenia); Read N Right (Greece); Karin Schindler (Brazil); Tuttle-Mori Agency Inc (Thailand, Vietnam); Julio F Yanez (Portugal, Spain); Zeno Agency Ltd (UK)
Membership(s): Science Fiction & Fantasy Writers of America

**Melanie Jackson Agency LLC** (L-D)
41 W 72 St, Suite 3F, New York, NY 10023
*Tel:* 212-873-3373 *Fax:* 212-799-5063
*Key Personnel*
Owner & Agent: Melanie Jackson
No unsol mss, query first.
Foreign Rep(s): Liepman Agency (Germany); Rogers, Coleridge & White (UK); Roberto Santachiara (Italy)

**James Peter Associates Inc** (L)
PO Box 358, New Canaan, CT 06840
*Tel:* 203-972-1070
*Web Site:* www.jamespeterassociates.com
*Key Personnel*
Pres: Gene Brissie *E-mail:* gene_brissie@msn.com
Founded: 1971
Nonfiction only, all subject areas. Handle software, film & TV rights through sub-agents in many foreign countries. No unsol mss, query first with SASE. Submit brief description of book, potential market, chapter outline, one sample chapter, competitive titles & author's credentials. No reading fee.

**Janklow & Nesbit Associates** (L)
445 Park Ave, New York, NY 10022
*Tel:* 212-421-1700 *Fax:* 212-980-3671
*E-mail:* info@janklow.com
*Web Site:* www.janklowandnesbit.com
*Key Personnel*
Sr Partner: Morton L Janklow
Partner: Lynn Nesbit
SVP: Anne Sibbald
VP & Dir, Foreign Rts: Cullen Stanley
Agent: Lucas W Janklow; Alexandra Machinist; P J Mark; Richard Morris
Founded: 1989 (successor to Morton L Janklow Assoc Inc founded in 1975)
General fiction & nonfiction. Handle film & TV rights for book represented; no reading fee.
*Foreign Office(s):* Janklow & Nesbit (UK) Ltd, 13-A Hillgate St, London W87SP, United Kingdom, Contact: Tim Glister *Tel:* (020) 7243 2975 *Fax:* (020) 7243 4339 *E-mail:* queries@janklow.co.uk *Web Site:* www.janklowandnesbit.co.uk

**Janus Literary Agency** (L)
201 Washington St, Groveland, MA 01834
*Tel:* 978-273-4227
*E-mail:* janusliteraryagency@gmail.com
*Web Site:* janusliteraryagency.blogspot.com
*Key Personnel*
Owner: Lenny Cavallaro
Founded: 1980
No new clients at this time. No reading fee. Possible handling fees if agency represents author & deals with editors via hard copy; none for electronic submissions. Provide editing, ghostwriting services &/or rewrites for a fee; also consultation on digital publication & POD/self-publication. No unsol mss, query first by e-mail only without attachments unless requested. Nonfiction: prospectus, outline, sample chapter. No longer handling fiction. Will reply only if interested.

**Jellinek & Murray Literary Agency** (L-D)
47-231 Kamakoi Rd, Kaneohe, HI 96744
*Tel:* 808-239-8451
*Key Personnel*
Pres: Roger Jellinek *E-mail:* rgr.jellinek@gmail.com
Founded: 1995
General adult fiction & nonfiction. No genre fiction. No unsol mss, query first with an e-mail. Submit proposal, outline, 2 sample chapters, author bio & credentials & platform, by e-mail. No reading fees. Handle film & TV rights.

**Carolyn Jenks Agency** (L-D)
69 Aberdeen Ave, Cambridge, MA 02138
*Tel:* 617-354-5099
*E-mail:* carolynjenks@comcast.net
*Web Site:* www.carolynjenksagency.com
*Key Personnel*
Owner & Dir: Carolyn Jenks
Digital Publg Dir: Jonathan Hu
Acqs Coord: Courtney Coats
Founded: 1979
Literary & commercial fiction & nonfiction. All genres. Theatre, film, artists, visual artists & screenwriters represented. Webmanager Metrocreate by Eric Wing. Contact by e-mail or via web site. Electronic submissions only; prefer query via web site. No fees charged.
Titles recently placed: *Sinners & the Sea*, Rebecca Kanner; *The Cool Elf*, Maria de Vivo; *The Dagger Quick*, Brian Eames; *The Dagger X*, Brian Eames; *Tragedy and Trust*, Thom Vines
Membership(s): Writers Guild of America

**JET Literary Associates Inc** (L)
941 Calle Mejia, Suite 507, Santa Fe, NM 87501
*Tel:* 212-971-2494 (NY voice mail); 505-780-0721
*E-mail:* query@jetliterary.com
*Web Site:* www.jetliterary.wordpress.com
*Key Personnel*
Pres (Austria off): Jim Trupin *E-mail:* jetlit@hotmail.com
VP: Elizabeth Trupin-Pulli *E-mail:* etp@jetliterary.com
Assoc Agent: Jessica Trupin *E-mail:* jessica@jetliterary.com
Founded: 1975
General book-length fiction & nonfiction. Specialize in adult & young adult fiction & commercial nonfiction; no science fiction or fantasy. No unsol mss, query first, preferably via e-mail. No reading fees. Mail & copying charges to be reimbursed. Full representation in all foreign markets.
*Branch Office(s)*
4519 Densmore Ave N, Seattle, WA 98103, Contact: Jessica Trupin *E-mail:* jessica@jetliterary.com
*Foreign Office(s):* Esterhazygasse 9A/26, 1060 Vienna, Austria *Tel:* (01) 587 0077 *Fax:* (01) 587 0077
Foreign Rep(s): Eliane Benisti (France); Big Apple Agency Inc (China); Educational Materials Enterprises (Greece); Fritz Agency (Germany); Nurcihan Kesim Literary Agency Inc (Turkey); Kohn (Netherlands); Lennart Sane (Sweden); Living Literary Agency (Italy); Tuttle-Mori Agency Inc (Japan); Julio F Yanez (Brazil, Spain)
Foreign Rights: Abner Stein Agency (UK)

**JMW Group Inc** (L)
One West Ave, Suite 219, Larchmont, NY 10538
*Tel:* 914-834-7800 *Fax:* 914-834-7824
*E-mail:* info@jmwgroup.net
*Web Site:* jmwgroup.net
*Key Personnel*
VP, Rts: Brice Diedrick *E-mail:* bdiedrick@att.net
Founded: 1949
Rights agenc; no fees charged.

**Jody Rein Books Inc** (L)
7741 S Ash Ct, Centennial, CO 80122
*Tel:* 303-694-9386
*Web Site:* www.jodyreinbooks.com
*Key Personnel*
Pres: Jody Rein (AAR) *E-mail:* jodyrein@jodyreinbooks.com
Literary Assoc & Off Mgr: Johnna Hietala *E-mail:* jhietala@jodyreinbooks.com
Founded: 1994
Author representation for existing clients only, no new agented clients. Specialize in adult narrative & commercial nonfiction. Some literary fiction. Handle film & TV rights through agents. See also Author Planet Publishing Services listing.
Titles recently placed: *Sensational Kids Revised Edition*, Lucy Jane Miller; *Teaching Savages to Fly*, Logan Ward; *The Diary of Attu*, Mark Obmascik; *The Feud: The All-American, No-Holds-Barred, Blood-&-Guts Story of the Hatfields & McCoys*, Dean H King
Foreign Rep(s): The English Agency (Japan); Grayhawk Agency (China, Taiwan); Japan UNI (Japan); Eric Yang Agency (Korea)

Foreign Rights: Jenny Meyer Literary Agency (Worldwide exc China, Japan, Korea, Thailand & USA)
Membership(s): The Authors Guild

**Jones Hutton Literary Associates** (L)
160 N Compo Rd, Westport, CT 06880-2102
*Tel:* 203-226-2588 *Fax:* 203-226-2588
*E-mail:* huttonbooks@hotmail.com
*Key Personnel*
Mng Ed: Caroline DuBois Hutton
*E-mail:* cdubh@optonline.net
Contact, Nonfiction: Roland Robitaille
Contact, Spanish Language: Roberta Fumega
Founded: 1994
Welcomes new & established writers. Will work closely with clients to get material into the best possible shape for presentation to editors at various publishing houses. Works with publishers both in the US & abroad. Handles mainly nonfiction in many categories, but always on the lookout for good new novels. Handles only a few authors at a time & gives to each the utmost personal attention. Turnaround time is short, usually less than two weeks. Earns fees from advances & royalties (15% domestic & 20% foreign sales). No reading or submission fees. For nonfiction, form for proposal may be e-mailed upon request. For fiction, a one- to two-page synopsis is required, as well as a short author's biography & two to three chapters of the novel. Please send all submissions by hard copy after first querying via e-mail. Affiliates in both editing & PR fields are available for referral.
Titles recently placed: *A Shift in the Wind*, Amuniddin Khan; *CannaCorn*, Cornelius Chapman; *Magic Needles: Feel Better & Live Longer with Accupuncture*, Jun Xu, MD LAC, Frank Murray; *Managing Your Money*, Thomas P Au; *Minimizing the Risk of Alzheimer's Disease*, Frank Murray; *Vitamin A & Beta Carotene are Miracle Workers*, Frank Murray

**The Karpfinger Agency** (L)
357 W 20 St, New York, NY 10011-3379
*Tel:* 212-691-2690 *Fax:* 212-691-7129
*E-mail:* info@karpfinger.com
*Web Site:* www.karpfinger.com
*Key Personnel*
Owner: Barney M Karpfinger
Foreign Rts Mgr: Cathy Jaque
Contact: Matt Spindler
Founded: 1985
Quality fiction & nonfiction. No unsol mss. Query first by mail only. See web site for specific instructions. No reading fee. Direct representation in all foreign markets.

**Keller Media Inc** (L)
578 Washington Blvd, No 745, Marina del Rey, CA 90292
*Toll Free Tel:* 800-278-8706
*E-mail:* query@kellermedia.com
*Web Site:* kellermedia.com/query
*Key Personnel*
Founder & CEO: Wendy Keller
Founded: 1989
Represent only nonfiction in these categories: business (sales, management, marketing); finance; self-help (parenting, women's issues, relationships, pop psychology); health (alternative & allopathic); metaphysical/spiritual/inspirational (never religious); nature, science, archaeology, reference, how-to (do anything). Do not send poetry, your memoir unless you are a celebrity, fiction, religious or juvenile books, or first person accounts of overcoming some medical condition. Most of agency's authors are either experts in their field, successful professional speakers, have their own radio, infomercial or television program, or are a household name. For best results, e-mail query first. No reading fee.
Titles recently placed: *Blue Mind*, Wallace J Nichols; *In the Garden of Thoughts*, Dodinsky; *Outsource Smart: Be Your Own Boss...Without Letting Your Business Become the Boss of You*, Daven Michaels; *Pimp My Childhood*, Holly Smith; *Running the Gauntlet*, Jeffrey W Hayzlett, Jim Eber; *Strategic Relationship Mastery*, Jody Robinett; *The Leadership Playbook*, Nathan Jamail; *The Millionaire Masterplan*, Roger James Hamilton; *The Wealth Choice: Success Secrets of Black Millionaires*, Dr Dennis Kimbro
Membership(s): National Association for Female Executives; National Speakers Association; United States Women's Chamber of Commerce

**Natasha Kern Literary Agency Inc** (L)
PO Box 1069, White Salmon, WA 98672
*Tel:* 509-493-3803
*E-mail:* agent@natashakern.com
*Web Site:* www.natashakern.com
*Key Personnel*
Pres: Natasha Kern *E-mail:* natasha@natashakern.com
Busn & Translation Rts Mgr: Jack Lauer
Agent: Athena Kern
Founded: 1986
Represent commercial adult fiction, inspirational fiction & young adult fiction. Actively represent all women's fiction; multicultural fiction; mainstream fiction; inspirational, historical & contemporary romance; romantic suspense, thrillers, mysteries, paranormal & young adult. DO NOT represent children's, horror, science fiction, short stories, poetry, sports, scholarly or coffee-table books. Handle film & TV rights only on represented books. Represented in all principal foreign countries as well as in Hollywood. No unsol mss, query first via e-mail (queries@natashakern.com). Please look at web site for submission info. Queries by mail are not accepted. Will respond only if interested. Include a 2-3 page synopsis & the first chapter of the novel.
Titles recently placed: *A Lasting Impression*, Tamera Alexander; *All Up In My Business*, Lutishia Lovely; *Ashes of the Earth*, Elliott Pattison; *Breaking Point*, Pamela Clare; *Daughter of Jerusalem*, Joan Wolf; *Evolutionaries: Unlocking the Spiritual and Cultural Potential of Science's Greatest Idea*, Carter Phipps; *Forbidden*, Leanna Ellis; *Four Sisters, All Queens*, Sherry Jones; *Hannah's Journey*, Jo Schmidt; *Last Chance Ranch*, Margaret Brownley; *Lord of Fire & Ice*, Connie Mason, Mia Marlowe; *Someone Like You*, Leigh Greenwood; *Trauma Plan*, Candace Calvert; *Wicked Edge*, Nina Bangs
Foreign Rep(s): Carmen Balcells (Spain); Agence Eliane Benisti (France); Luigi Bernabo (Italy); Phillip Chen (China, Taiwan); Prava i Prevodi (Eastern Europe); Lucia Riff (Brazil); Lennart Sane (Scandinavia); Junzo Sawa (Japan); Tom Schlueck (Germany); Lorna Soifer (Israel)

**Louise B Ketz Agency** (L)
414 E 78 St, Suite 1-B, New York, NY 10075
*Tel:* 212-249-0668
*E-mail:* ketzagency@aol.com
*Key Personnel*
Pres: Louise B Ketz
Founded: 1986
Nonfiction only: economics, science, reference, history. No unsol mss, query letter, chapter outline, table of contents, sample chapter, author biography. No reading fee.
Membership(s): Editorial Freelancers Association; National Association of Professional & Executive Women

**Virginia Kidd Agency Inc** (L)
PO Box 278, 538 E Harford St, Milford, PA 18337
*Tel:* 570-296-6205
*Web Site:* vk-agency.com
*Key Personnel*
Literary Agent, Foreign & Translation Rts: Christine M Cohen
Literary Agent, Ebooks, Contracts & Royalties: Vaughne L Hansen *E-mail:* vaughne@vk-agency.com
Founded: 1965
Specialize in fiction; special interest in science fiction, fantasy, speculative fiction. No unsol mss, query first via USPS (do not phone or e-mail queries); submit one-three page synopsis, with cover letter & SASE; no reading fee. Representative for dramatic rights: The William Morris Agency, Bill Contardi, New York contact. 15% commission; 15% higher commission on dramatic & foreign sales.
Titles recently placed: *Body Inc*, Alan Dean Foster; *Finding My Elegy*, Ursula K Le Guin; *The Land Across*, Gene Wolfe; *The Year's Best Science Fiction 29*, Gardner Dozois
Foreign Rep(s): Bardon Chinese Media Agency (China); Bridge Communications Co (Thailand); Paul & Peter Fritz AG (Germany); International Editors' Co (Portugal, South America, Spain); Alexander Korzhenevski (Estonia, Latvia, Lithuania, Russia); Agence Litteraire Lenclud (France); Agenzia Letteraria Internazionale (Italy); Pikarski Agency (Israel); Prava I Prevodi (Central Europe, Eastern Europe, Greece, Turkey); Lennart Sane (Netherlands, Scandinavia); Tuttle-Mori Agency Inc (Japan); Eric Yang Agency Inc (Korea)

**Kimberley Cameron & Associates** (L)
1550 Tiburon Blvd, Suite 704, Tiburon, CA 94920
*Tel:* 415-789-9191 *Fax:* 415-789-9177
*E-mail:* info@kimberleycameron.com
*Web Site:* www.kimberleycameron.com
*Key Personnel*
Pres & Literary Agent: Kimberley Cameron (AAR) *E-mail:* kimberley@kimberleycameron.com
Literary Agent: Elizabeth Krach
*E-mail:* elizabeth@kimberleycameron.com; Pooja Menon; Ethan Vaughn
Founded: 1957
Represent quality writing in book length fiction & nonfiction, including memoirs, biographies, literary fiction, mainstream fiction, science fiction, mysteries & thrillers. Do not handle screenplays, poetry or children's literature. Handle film & TV rights. E-mail all queries. For fiction, include one-page synopsis & first 50 pages as separate attachments. For nonfiction, send complete proposal including sample chapters. No fees charged. Additional office located in Paris.
Foreign Rights: The Fielding Agency (Whitney Lee) (Worldwide)
Membership(s): Sisters in Crime

**Kirchoff/Wohlberg Inc** (L)
897 Boston Post Rd, Madison, CT 06443
*Tel:* 203-245-7308 *Fax:* 203-245-3218
*Web Site:* www.kirchoffwohlberg.com
*Key Personnel*
Pres: Morris A Kirchoff
VP: Ronald P Zollshan *E-mail:* rzollshan@kirchoffwohlberg.com
Founded: 1974
Children & young adult fiction & nonfiction trade books only. Agency does not handle adult titles. No fees. Handle film & TV rights.
Membership(s): AIGA, the professional association for design; ALA; Book Industry Guild of New York; Bookbuilders of Boston; Inter-

national Reading Association; Society of Children's Book Writers & Illustrators; Society of Illustrators

**Harvey Klinger Inc** (L-D)
300 W 55 St, Suite 11-V, New York, NY 10019
*Tel:* 212-581-7068 *Fax:* 212-315-3823
*E-mail:* queries@harveyklinger.com
*Web Site:* www.harveyklinger.com
*Key Personnel*
Pres: Harvey Klinger (AAR) *E-mail:* harvey@harveyklinger.com
Agent: Sara Crowe *E-mail:* sara@harveyklinger.com; David Dunton *E-mail:* david@harveyklinger.com; Andrea Somberg *E-mail:* andrea@harveyklinger.com
Founded: 1977
Mainstream fiction & nonfiction. Handle film & TV rights. No unsol mss, faxes or e-mails; do not phone or fax; no reading fee. Representatives in Hollywood & all principal foreign countries. New clients obtained by referrals.
Foreign Rights: Eliane Benisti (France); Big Apple Agency Inc (Taiwan); David Grossman (UK); Daniela Micura (Italy); P & P (Eastern Europe, Russia); Lennart Sane (Latin America, Scandinavia, Spain); Thomas Schlueck GmbH (Germany); Tuttle-Mori Agency Inc (Japan); Sue Yang (Korea)
Membership(s): PEN Center USA

**Kneerim, Williams & Bloom Agency** (L-D)
90 Canal St, Boston, MA 02114
*Tel:* 617-303-1650
*Web Site:* www.kwlit.com
*Key Personnel*
Agency Administrator: Hope Denekamp *Tel:* 617-303-1651 *E-mail:* hope@kwblit.com
Partner: John Taylor "Ike" Williams *Tel:* 617-303-1658 *E-mail:* ike@kwblit.com
Mng Partner: Jill Kneerim *Tel:* 617-303-1653 *E-mail:* jill@kwblit.com
Mng Partner (NY): Brettne Bloom *Tel:* 212-645-2364 *E-mail:* bloom@kwblit.com
Agent: Kathryn Beaumont *Tel:* 617-303-1653 *E-mail:* beaumont@kwblit.com; Katherine Flynn *Tel:* 617-303-1659 *E-mail:* kflynn@kwblit.com
Founded: 1990
Handles books, film & television rights. Does not handle poetry, children's picture books & genre fiction; no romance, western or science fiction & fantasy. Does not charge fees. For dramatic rights inqury, contact Ike Williams or Kathryn Beaumont.
Titles recently placed: *A Border Passage*, Leila Ahmed; *A Garden in Africa*, Nina Sovich; *A Safeway in Arizona*, Tom Zoellner; *A Thousand Years With You*, Elizabeth Marshall Thomas; *Almost Normal*, Katherine Preston; *Arguably*, Christopher Hitchens; *Attuned to Customers*, Forrester Research; *Canton*, Steve Platt; *Culture Map*, Erin Meyer; *Debtor's Prison*, Robert Kuttner; *Decoded*, Brad Meltzer; *Eleanor & Hick*, Sue Quinn; *FDR at War*, Nigel Hamilton; *Fire and Light: How the Enlightenment Transformed Our World*, James MacGregor Burns; *Focus*, Ned Hallowell; *Homesick Texas: Friends & Family*, Lisa Fain; *Jimmy Carter*, Randall Balmer; *Letter to a Young Scientist*, E O Wilson; *Mindful Love*, Polly Young-Eisendrath; *More Than Just Sex*, Jim Downs; *Ninth Street Women*, Mary Gabriel; *No One Ever Told Me That*, John Spooner; *Paris versus New York*, Vahram Muratyan; *Smile at Strangers*, Susan Schorn; *Some Nerve*, Patty Chang Acker; *Taormina*, Patrick Somerville; *The Bad Job Fallacy*, Zeynep Ton; *The Dark of Morning*, Sarah Willis; *The Engagement*, J Courtney Sullivan; *The Life of Bobby Kennedy*, Larry Tye; *The Making of an Historian*, Joe Ellis; *The New Arabs*, Juan Cole; *The Oldest Living Things in the World*, Rachel Sussman; *The Singles*, Meredith Goldstein; *The Tower of Babel*, Ouroussoff; *To Be a Friend Is Fatal*, Kirk W Johnson; *X vs Y*, Eve & Leo Epstein
Foreign Rep(s): Baror International Inc
Foreign Rights: Baror International Inc

**The Knight Agency Inc** (L)
570 East Ave, Madison, GA 30650
*E-mail:* submissions@knightagency.net
*Web Site:* www.knightagency.net
*Key Personnel*
Owner & Pres: Deidre Knight (AAR)
VP: Judson Knight
VP, Sales & Agent: Pamela Harty (AAR)
Mktg Dir: Jia Gayles
Subs Rts Mgr & Agent: Elaine Spencer
Agent & Submissions Coord: Melissa Jeglinski
Agent: Lucienne Diver (AAR); Nephele Tempest (AAR)
Founded: 1996
Fiction: romance, women's fiction, commercial fiction, literary & multicultural fiction, young adult, science fiction & fantasy, middle-grade fiction. In nonfiction: business, self-help, finance, music/entertainment, media-related, pop culture, how-to, psychology, travel, health, inspirational/religious, reference & holiday books. No anthology collections, short stories or poetry. No unsol mss, query first by sending a brief summary or proposal, author info & first five pages by e-mail (no attachments). Allow a two to four week response time for queries. Upon request only submit the following: for fiction: first three chapters, synopsis or outline & copy of original query; nonfiction: proposal or outline, first one to three chapters, summary of author's qualifications, unique marketing opportunities & copy of original query. Allow 8-12 weeks for ms review. No reading fee. 15% commission on domestic sales, 15-25% on foreign. May use sub-agent for sale or film & foreign rights. Screenplays not accepted.
Titles recently placed: *Beauty's Beast*, Jenna Kernan; *Better Blood*, Rachel Caine; *Between*, Kerry Schafer; *Black Ops Rescues (series)*, Beth Cornelison; *Bundle of Joy*, Annie Jones; *Day Lighters*, Rachel Caine; *Dust and Light*, Carol Berg; *Fall of Knight*, Rachel Caine; *Gated*, Amy Christine Parker; *Heavenly Company*, Cecil Murphey, Twila Belk; *I Believe in Healing*, Cecil Murphey, Twila Belk; *Jensen Murphy: Ghost for Hire*, Christine Cody; *Nexus*, Ramez Naam; *The Havoc Machine*, Steven Harper; *The Trouble with Christmas*, Debbie Mazzuca; *Wakeworld*, Kerry Schafer
*Branch Office(s)*
Nephele Tempest, 14622 Ventura Blvd, No 785, Sherman Oaks, CA 91403
Lucienne Diver, PO Box 2659, Land O Lakes, FL 34639
Foreign Rights: Gabriella Ambrosioni (Italy); Graal Literary Agency (Poland); Katai & Bolza (Hungary); Whitney Lee (Asia); The Lenclud Agency (France); Lennart Sane Agency (Netherlands, Portugal, Scandinavia, Spain); Nova Littera (Russia); Andrew Nurnberg (Bulgaria); Kristin Olson (Czech Republic); I Pilarski (Israel); Thomas Schlueck GmbH (Germany); Julio F Yanez (Spain)
Membership(s): The Authors Guild; Mystery Writers of America; Romance Writers of America; Science Fiction & Fantasy Writers of America; Society of Children's Book Writers & Illustrators

**Paul Kohner Agency** (L-D)
9300 Wilshire Blvd, Suite 555, Beverly Hills, CA 90212
*Tel:* 310-550-1060 *Fax:* 310-276-1083
*Key Personnel*
Pres: Pearl Wexler
Literary Agent: Stephen Moore
Founded: 1938
Film & TV rights. No unsol mss, query first. No reading fee; fees for extensive copying or binding charges.

**Linda Konner Literary Agency** (L)
10 W 15 St, Suite 1918, New York, NY 10011
*Tel:* 212-691-3419 *Fax:* 212-691-0935
*Web Site:* www.lindakonnerliteraryagency.com
*Key Personnel*
Pres: Linda Konner (AAR) *E-mail:* ldkonner@cs.com
Founded: 1996
Health, nutrition, diet, relationships, sex, pop psychology, self-help, parenting, cookbooks, business & career/personal finance, celebrity/pop culture. No fiction, children's or memoir. No unsol mss, query first with one-page query & SASE or via e-mail. Submit outline & one to two sample chapters. No reading fee. 15% fee on US sales & up to 25% on foreign sales. One-time expense fee of $65, deducted from publisher's advance payment.
Titles recently placed: *A Sweet Taste of History*, Walter Staib; *Being Sober*, Harry Haroutunian, MD; *The Bliss List*, J P Hansen; *The Calorie Myth*, Jonathan Bailor
*Branch Office(s)*
Books Crossing Borders, 110 W 40 St, Suite 2305, New York, NY 10018 *E-mail:* bc@bookscrossingborders.com
Foreign Rights: Books Crossing Borders (Betty Anne Crawford) (Worldwide exc USA)
Membership(s): American Society of Journalists & Authors; The Authors Guild

**Elaine Koster Literary Agency LLC** (L)
55 Central Park West, Suite 6, New York, NY 10023
*Tel:* 212-362-9488 *Fax:* 212-712-0164
*Key Personnel*
Assoc Agent: Stephanie Lehmann (AAR)
Founded: 1998
Literary & quality commercial fiction, including medical, legal & young adult fiction, international thrillers, suspense, psychological suspense, contemporary fiction & women's fiction. Diverse nonfiction: psychology, science, self-help, cookbooks, popular culture, business, spirituality & inspiration, women's issues & health. No unsol mss, query first. Submit first 50 pages for fiction or a proposal for nonfiction. Queries & submissions must include SASE. No reading fee. Handle film & TV rights. Representatives on the West Coast & in major foreign countries. No longer taking on new clients.
Titles recently placed: *Those Across the River*, Christopher Buehlman
Foreign Rep(s): David Grossman Literary Agency (UK)
Foreign Rights: Chandler Crawford Agency (translations)
Membership(s): The Authors Guild; Mystery Writers of America; Women's Media Group

**Barbara S Kouts Literary Agency LLC** (L)
PO Box 560, Bellport, NY 11713
*Tel:* 631-286-1278 *Fax:* 631-286-1538
*E-mail:* bkouts@aol.com
*Key Personnel*
Owner: Barbara S Kouts (AAR)
Founded: 1980
Specialize in children's fiction & nonfiction. No unsol mss, query first. Submit synopsis or outline & sample chapters. No reading fee, but copy fees would apply, no software. Handle film & TV rights from sale of books. Agents in all principal foreign countries.
Membership(s): Society of Children's Book Writers & Illustrators

**Stuart Krichevsky Literary Agency Inc** (L)
381 Park Ave South, Suite 428, New York, NY 10016
*Tel:* 212-725-5288 *Fax:* 212-725-5275
*E-mail:* query@skagency.com
*Web Site:* skagency.com
*Key Personnel*
Pres: Stuart Krichevsky (AAR)
Literary Agent & Rts Dir: Shana Cohen (AAR)
*E-mail:* sc@skagency.com
Founded: 1995
Fiction & nonfiction. No reading fee. No unsol mss, query first; prefer e-mail queries (no attachments) to query@skagency.com. Include query letter & synopsis. To submit to Shana Cohen include letter, synopsis & first 2 pgs to SCquery@skagency.com.
Foreign Rights: Akcali Copyright Trade & Tourism Co Ltd (Turkey); The Deborah Harris Agency (Israel); Andrew Nurnberg Associates (China, Europe, South Africa); Tuttle-Mori Agency Inc (Japan); Eric Yang (Korea)

**Edite Kroll Literary Agency Inc** (L)
20 Cross St, Saco, ME 04072
*Tel:* 207-283-8797 *Fax:* 207-283-8799
*Key Personnel*
Pres: Edite Kroll *E-mail:* ekroll@maine.rr.com
Founded: 1981
Adult feminist general nonfiction & humor; children's fiction & picture books. No unsol mss, query first by e-mail.
Foreign Rights: ACER (Brazil, Portugal); ACER (children's) (Spain, Spanish Latin America); Agencia Litteraria Internazionale (Italy); Akcali (Turkey); IA Atterholm Agency (Scandinavia); Author Rights Agency (Estonia, Latvia, Russia); L'Autre Agence (France); Bardon Chinese Media (China); Big Apple (China); Book Publishers Association of Israel (Israel); Bookbank (adult) (Spain, Spanish Latin America); English Agency (Japan); David Grossman (adult) (UK); International Literatuur Bureau (Netherlands); JLM (Greece); Simona Kessler (Romania); Prava I Prevodi (Czech Republic, Estonia, Hungary, Montenegro, Poland, Serbia, Slovakia, Slovenia); Rights People (children's) (UK); Schlueck Agency (Germany); Eric Yang Agency (Korea)

**Lucy Kroll Agency**, see The Barbara Hogenson Agency Inc

**The LA Literary Agency** (L-D)
PO Box 46370, Los Angeles, CA 90046
*Tel:* 323-654-5288
*E-mail:* laliteraryagency@mac.com; mail@laliteraryagency.com
*Web Site:* www.laliteraryagency.com
*Key Personnel*
Literary Agent: Ann Cashman *E-mail:* ann@laliteraryagency.com; Eric Lasher *E-mail:* eric.laliterary@mac.com; Maureen Lasher *E-mail:* maureen.laliterary@mac.com
Founded: 1980
Specialize in narrative nonfiction, commercial & literary fiction. Accept unsol mss. Nonfiction: query, qualifications & proposal; Fiction: query & 50 pages. See web site for books, clients & submission information.

**Peter Lampack Agency Inc** (L)
350 Fifth Ave, Suite 5300, New York, NY 10118
*Tel:* 212-687-9106 *Fax:* 212-687-9109
*Web Site:* peterlampackagency.com
*Key Personnel*
Pres: Peter A Lampack
Agent & Foreign Rts: Rema Dilanyan *E-mail:* rema@peterlampackagency.com
Agent: Andrew Lampack *E-mail:* andrew@peterlampackagency.com
Office Mgr: Christie Russell *E-mail:* christie@peterlampackagency.com
Founded: 1977
Commercial & literary fiction; nonfiction by recognized experts in a given field (especially autobiography, biography, law, finance, politics, history). Handle motion picture & TV rights from book properties only. No stageplays, teleplays or screenplays. No unsol mss. Query with letter which describes the nature of the ms plus author's credentials if any, sample chapter & synopsis by e-mail only.
Titles recently placed: *Here & Now*, J M Coetzee, Paul Auster; *Mirage*, Clive Cussler, Jack Du Brul; *Poseidon's Arrow*, Clive Cussler, Dirk Cussler; *Raven*, Ted Bell; *The Childhood of Jesus*, J M Coetzee; *The Mayan Secrets*, Clive Cussler, Thomas Perry; *The Striker*, Clive Cussler, Justin Scott; *Zero Hour*, Clive Cussler, Graham Brown
Foreign Rep(s): Big Apple Agency Inc (China, Taiwan); Prava I Prevodi Literary Agency (Eastern Europe, Greece); Tuttle-Mori Agency Inc (Japan, Thailand); Eric Yang Agency (Korea)

**Michael Larsen/Elizabeth Pomada Literary Agents** (L)
1029 Jones St, San Francisco, CA 94109
*Tel:* 415-673-0939
*E-mail:* larsenpoma@aol.com
*Web Site:* www.larsenpomada.com
*Key Personnel*
Partner: Michael Larsen (AAR); Elizabeth Pomada (AAR)
Agent: Laurie McLean *E-mail:* queryagentsavant@gmail.com
Founded: 1972
General adult, book-length fiction & nonfiction. No unsol mss, query first. No attachments if submitting query by e-mail. See web site for detailed submission information. Fiction: literary, commercial, romance, mysteries, thrillers, historical, new voices. Nonfiction: business, psychology, biography, history, science, food, humor, how-to, reference, music, spirituality, futurism, technology, architecture, social issues, biographies, the arts, health, France, new ideas, memoirs, narrative nonfiction. No reading fee. Representatives in major foreign countries & in Hollywood. Handle film & TV rights for clients.
Titles recently placed: *Accepted*, Marni Bates; *Apocalypse To Go*, Katharine Kerr; *Awkward*, Marni Bates; *Blood of Eden*, Julie Kagawa; *Demons Do It Better*, Linda Wisdom; *Meet Jane Smith*, Marni Bates; *Of Cogs and Corsets*, Tee Morris, Pip Ballantine; *The Heat of the Day*, Jill Sorenson; *The Iron Fae (series)*, Julie Kagawa; *The Juliet Spell*, Douglas Rees; *The Travel Writer's Handbook: How to Write and Sell Your Own Travel Experiences (7th ed)*, Jacqueline Harmon Butler; *Tudor Historical #4*, D L Bogdan; *Wrayth*, Philippa Ballantine
Foreign Rep(s): David Grossman (England)
Foreign Rights: Chandler Crawford (Worldwide)
Membership(s): American Society of Journalists & Authors; The Authors Guild; National Speakers Association; Women's National Book Association

**Sarah Lazin Books** (L)
121 W 27 St, Suite 704, New York, NY 10001
*Tel:* 212-989-5757 *Fax:* 212-989-1393
*Web Site:* lazinbooks.com
*Key Personnel*
Pres: Sarah Lazin (AAR)
Founded: 1983
General nonfiction, fiction & illustrated books. Handle film, TV & theater rights. Domestic & foreign rights in all principal countries. No unsol mss, referral only. No fees.
Foreign Rights: Julio F-Yanez Agencia Literaria (Montse F-Yanez) (Brazil, Latin America, Portugal, Spain); Graal Literary Agency (Marcin Biegaj) (Poland); Katai & Bolza Literary Agents (Peter Bolza) (Hungary); Simona Kessler International Copyright Agency (Simona Kessler) (Romania); La Nouvelle Agence (Vanessa Kling) (France); Andrew Nurnberg Associates (Tatjana Zoldnere) (Estonia, Latvia, Lithuania); Kristin Olson Literary Agency (Thereza Dubova) (Czech Republic); Prava I Prevadi (Milena Kaplarevic) (Bulgaria, Croatia, Slovenia); Vicki Satlow Agency (Italy); Thomas Schlueck GmbH (Joachim Jessen) (Germany); Sebes & Van Gelderen Literary Agnecy (Paul Sebes & Mariska Kleinhoonte van Os) (Netherlands); Ulf Toregard Agency AB (Lina Hammerling) (Iceland, Scandinavia)

**The Ned Leavitt Agency** (L)
70 Wooster St, Suite 4-F, New York, NY 10012
*Tel:* 212-334-0999
*Web Site:* www.nedleavittagency.com
*Key Personnel*
Pres: Ned Leavitt (AAR)
Agent: Britta Alexander; Jillian Sweeney
Literary & commercial fiction & nonfiction, books on spirituality & psychology. No unsol mss. Submissions by recommendation only. Rejections not returned, no reading fee.

**Levine|Greenberg Literary Agency Inc** (L)
307 Seventh Ave, Suite 2407, New York, NY 10001
*Tel:* 212-337-0934 *Fax:* 212-337-0948
*Web Site:* www.levinegreenberg.com
*Key Personnel*
Principal: Daniel Greenberg (AAR) *E-mail:* dgreenberg@levinegreenberg.com; James Levine (AAR) *E-mail:* jlevine@levinegreenberg.com
Busn Mgr: Melissa Rowland *E-mail:* mrowland@levinegreenberg.com
Rts Mgr: Elizabeth Fisher *E-mail:* efisher@levinegreenberg.com
Agent: Lindsay Edgecombe (AAR) *E-mail:* ledgecombe@levinegreenberg.com; Stephanie Rostan (AAR) *E-mail:* srostan@levinegreenberg.com; Victoria Skurnick (AAR) *E-mail:* vskurnick@levinegreenberg.com; Danielle Svetcov *E-mail:* dsvetcov@levinegreenberg.com; Monika Verma *E-mail:* mverma@levinegreenberg.com
Assoc Agent: Kerry Sparks *E-mail:* ksparks@levinegreenberg.com
Agent-at-Large: Arielle Eckstut *E-mail:* aeckstut@levinegreenberg.com
Edit & Rts Asst: Tim Wojcik *E-mail:* ksparks@levinegreenberg.com
Founded: 1989
Narrative nonfiction, business, technology, psychology, parenting, health, humor, women's, men's, sexuality, education & social issues, popular culture, narrative nonfiction, fiction, cookbooks, sports. Online queries via the How To Submit page on web site or e-mail queries to submit@levinegreenberg.com. Attachments limited to 50 pages. Handle software, film & TV rights. No reading fee.
Foreign Rights: AnatoliaLit Copyright & Translation Agency (Turkey); Bardon-Chinese Media Agency (China, Taiwan); Eliane Benisti Agence Litteraire (France); The Book Publishers Association of Israel (Israel); Bridge Communications (Thailand); The English Agency (Japan); Ersilia Literary Agency (Greece); The Foreign Office (Latin America, Portugal, Spain); Graal Literary Agency (Czech Republic, Eastern Europe, Poland); Agence Hoffman (Germany); Internationaal Literatuur Bureau (Netherlands); Korea Copyright Center (KCC) (Korea); Maxima Creative Agency (Indonesia, Malaysia); Agencia Riff (Brazil); Vicki Satlow

Agency (Italy); Abner Stein Literary Agency (UK); Synopsis Literary Agency (Baltic States, Estonia, Russia); Ulf Toregard Agency (Scandinavia)

**Robert Lieberman Agency** (L)
Subsidiary of Ithaca Film Works
475 Nelson Rd, Ithaca, NY 14850
*Tel:* 607-273-8801
*Web Site:* www.kewgardensmovie.com/CUPeople/users/rhl10
*Key Personnel*
Pres: Robert H Lieberman *E-mail:* RHL10@cornell.edu
Founded: 1994
ABSOLUTELY NONFICTION ONLY! Specialize in college level textbooks by established & recognized academics in all fields, as well as trade books in science, math, economics, engineering, medicine, psychology, computers & other academic areas that would be of general or popular interest. Represent producers of CD-ROM/multimedia/software, film & videos that fall into these categories. Submissions can be proposals &/or sample chapters, resume & table of contents. No unsol mss, query first (prefer e-mail query); will give quick response by e-mail but will accept mail query with SASE; handle software; no reading fee.
Foreign Rep(s): East Communications (China)

**Literary & Creative Artists Inc** (L)
3543 Albemarle St NW, Washington, DC 20008-4213
*Tel:* 202-362-4688 *Fax:* 202-362-8875
*E-mail:* lca9643@lcadc.com (queries, no attachments)
*Web Site:* www.lcadc.com
*Key Personnel*
Founder & Pres: Muriel G Nellis (AAR)
VP: Jane F Roberts
Founded: 1981
Specialize in adult trade fiction & nonfiction credentialed authors only. No poetry or academic/technical work. No unsol mss, query first by mail addressed to Muriel Nellis with SASE or by e-mail (no attachments). Require exclusive review period of two to three weeks. No reading fee. Visit the submission page on our web site for more information.
Membership(s): ABA; American Bar Association; The Authors Guild

**Literary Artists Representatives** (L)
575 West End Ave, Suite GRC, New York, NY 10024-2711
*Tel:* 212-679-7788 *Fax:* 212-595-2098
*E-mail:* litartists@aol.com
*Key Personnel*
Pres: Madeline Perrone
VP: Samuel Fleishman
Founded: 1993
Emphasizes adult trade, nonfiction, (narrative, biography, memoir, current affairs, business, culture, history, how-to, film/TV, personal finance, sciences, sports, motivational). Handle film, TV electronic rights. Co-agents in Hollywood & other selected cities. No unsol mss, query first via e-mail, No fees.
Titles recently placed: *Disney U: How Disney University Develops the World's Most Engaged, Loyal, and Customer-Centric Employees*, Doug Lipp; *Financial Fitness Forever: 5 Steps to More Money, Less Risk & More Peace of Mind*, Paul Merriman, Richard Buck; *Golf's Holy War:*, Brett Cyrgalis; *Investment Mistakes Even Smart Investors Make & How to Avoid Them*, Larry E Swedroe, RC Balaban; *JFK in the Senate: Pathway to the Presidency*, John T Shaw; *Lady in the Dark: Iris Barry and the Art of Film*, Robert Sitton; *Saint Woody: The History & Fanaticism of Ohio State Football*, Bob Hunter; *Singularity Rising: Surviving & Thriving in a Smarter, Richer & More Dangerous World*, James D Miller; *Taking Charge with Value Investing: How to Choose the Best Investments According to Price, Performance, & Valuation to Build a Winning Portfolio*, Brian Nichols; *The $1,000 Challenge: How One Family Slashed Its Budget Without Moving Under a Bridge or Living on Government Cheese*, Brian J O'Connor; *The Quest for Alpha: The Holy Grail of Investing*, Larry E Swedroe; *The Soul of the Organization: How to Ignite Employee Engagement and Productivity at Every Level*, David B Zenoff; *Think, Act, and Invest Like Warren Buffett: The Winning Strategy to Help You Achieve Your Financial and Life Goals*, Larry Swedroe

**The Literary Group International**, see Folio Literary Management LLC

**Literary Management Group LLC** (L)
613 Crieve Rd, Nashville, TN 37220
Mailing Address: PO Box 40965, Nashville, TN 37204
*Tel:* 615-832-7231
*Web Site:* www.literarymanagementgroup.com; www.brucebarbour.com
*Key Personnel*
CEO & Pres: Bruce R Barbour *E-mail:* brucebarbour@literarymanagementgroup.com
VP, Fiction: Lavonne Stevens *E-mail:* lavonne@literarymanagementgroup.com
Founded: 1997
Nonfiction: Christian, motivational & inspirational. No unsol mss, query first with letter prior to submission of ms for review. Submit proposal, outline, sample chapters including return postage. E-mail queries preferred to brb@brucebarbour.com. Fiction: Submit proposals & sample chapters of adult Christian fiction to Jennifer Read at jennifer@literarymanagementgroup.com.
Membership(s): CBA: The Association for Christian Retail; Evangelical Christian Publishers Association

**Lowenstein Associates Inc** (L-D)
121 W 27 St, Suite 501, New York, NY 10001
*Tel:* 212-206-1630 *Fax:* 212-727-0280
*E-mail:* assistant@bookhaven.com (queries, no attachments)
*Web Site:* www.lowensteinassociates.com
*Key Personnel*
Pres: Barbara Lowenstein (AAR)
Agent, Contracts & Foreign Rts Mgr: Emily Gref *E-mail:* emily@bookhaven.com
Assoc Agent & Digital Strategist: Connor Goldsmith
Founded: 1976
Electronic queries (no attachments). No westerns, textbooks, children's picture books or books needing translation. Fiction: send a one page query with first 10 pages in the body of the e-mail; nonfiction: submit one page query, table of contents & a proposal (if available) in the body of the e-mail to assistant@bookhaven.com. Include the word QUERY & the project name in the subject line. Address the e-mail to the agent you want to consider your work. Visit our web site to find more information about each agent's interests. We will respond in 4-6 weeks. No reading fee.
Membership(s): Romance Writers of America

**Donald Maass Literary Agency** (L)
121 W 27 St, Suite 801, New York, NY 10001
*Tel:* 212-727-8383 *Fax:* 212-727-3271
*E-mail:* info@maassagency.com; rights@maassagency.com (subs rights inquiries)
*Web Site:* www.maassagency.com
*Key Personnel*
Pres: Donald Maass (AAR) *E-mail:* dmaass@maassagency.com
VP & Agent: Jennifer Jackson (AAR) *E-mail:* jjackson@maassagency.com
Rts Dir & Agent: Cameron McClure *E-mail:* cmcclure@maassagency.com
Agent: Stacia Decker *E-mail:* sdecker@maassagency.com; Amy Boggs
Agent & Rts Assoc: Katie Shea *E-mail:* kshea@maassagency.com
Agent & Asst to Pres: Jennifer Udden *E-mail:* judden@maassagency.com
Founded: 1980
Specialize in sci-fi, fantasy, mysteries, thrillers, romance, women's fiction, literary & mainstream, young adult & middle grade fiction as well as nonfiction. No poetry, picture books or screenplays. No unsol mss, query first. Electronic queries preferred. Include QUERY & title on subject line. Send a query letter, short synopsis & first 5 pages (no attachments). No phone or social media queries. Queries must be submitted to a specific agent. For each agent's preferences & query details, visit the agent profiles on our web site. Handle film & TV rights. No reading or evaluation fees.
Titles recently placed: *A Liaden Universe Constellation: Volume I*, Sharon Lee, Steve Miller; *Blue Blazes*, Chuck Wendig; *Dragon Justice*, Laura Anne Gilman; *Drift*, Jon McGoran; *Eight Million Gods*, Wen Spencer; *Elfhome*, Wen Spencer; *Elisha Barber*, E C Ambrose; *Emilie and the Hollow World*, Martha Wells; *Father Knows Death*, Jeffrey Allen; *Forever a Lady*, Delilah Marvelle; *Forged in Fire*, J A Pitts; *Ghost Ship*, Sharon Lee, Steve Miller; *I Travel by Night*, Robert McCammon; *Interrupt*, Jeff Carlson; *Murder for Choir*, Joelle Charbonneau; *Psalms of Isaak 4: Requiem*, Ken Scholes; *Revenge of a Not-So-Pretty Girl*, Carolita Blythe; *Silver*, Rhiannon Held; *Sister Mine*, Nalo Hopkinson; *Tarnished*, Rhiannon Held; *The Eighth Court*, Mike Shevdon; *The Hidden Life*, Adina Senft; *The Price of Peace*, Mike Shepherd; *The Testing*, Joelle Charbonneau; *This Dark Earth*, John Hornor Jacobs; *Under the Empyrean Sky*, Chuck Wendig; *Without a Summer*, Mary Robinette Kowal; *Woke Up Lonely*, Fiona Maazel
Foreign Rights: Book Publishers Association of Israel (Dalia Ever-Hadani) (Israel); The English Agency (Kohei Hattori) (Japan); The Grayhawk Agency (Gray Tan) (China, Taiwan); International Editors' Co (Falvia Sala & Nicolas Costa) (South America); International Editors' Co (Isabel Monteagudo & Maru du Monserrat) (Spain); Agenzia Letteraria Internazionale (Elisabetta Romano & Stefanie Fietta) (Italy); Anna Jarota Agency (Anna Jarota) (France); Ki Agency Ltd (Meg Davis) (UK); Alexander Korzhenevski Agency (Alexander Korzhenevski) (Russia); ONK Agency Ltd (Hatice Gok) (Turkey); Prava I Prevodi (Ana Milenkovic & Milena Kaplarevic) (Bulgaria, Czech Republic, Greece, Hungary, Poland, Romania, Serbia); Lennart Sane Agency AB (Lina Hammarling) (Denmark, Finland, Netherlands, Norway, Sweden); Thomas Schlueck GmbH (Thomas Schlueck & Bastian Schlueck) (Germany); Eric Yang Agency (Sue Yang & Jeannie Hwang) (Korea)
Membership(s): The Authors Guild; Mystery Writers of America; Romance Writers of America; Science Fiction & Fantasy Writers of America

**Gina Maccoby Literary Agency** (L)
PO Box 60, Chappaqua, NY 10514-0060
*Tel:* 914-238-5630
*E-mail:* query@maccobylit.com
*Web Site:* www.publishersmarketplace.com/members/GinaMaccoby

*Key Personnel*
Principal: Gina Maccoby (AAR)
Founded: 1986
High quality fiction & nonficton for adults & children. Handle film & TV rights for clients' work only. No screenplays. No unsol mss; query first. E-mail queries preferred. Include SASE if querying by regular mail. Owing to the volume of queries received, we will only respond if interested. No reading fee. May recover the cost of books purchased for submissions; airmail shipping of books overseas; overnight shipping domestically if requested by client; bank fees incurred related to transfers of payments; legal fees incurred with prior client approval. Co-agents in Hollywood & overseas.
Foreign Rep(s): Luigi Bernabo Associates (Italy); Big Apple Agency Inc (China); Mohrbooks (Germany); Andrew Nurnberg Associates (Bulgaria, Estonia, Latvia, Lithuania, Russia, Ukraine); Lennart Sane Agency (Brazil, Portugal, Scandinavia, Spain, Spanish Latin America)
Membership(s): The Authors Guild

**Carol Mann Agency** (L)
55 Fifth Ave, New York, NY 10003
*Tel:* 212-206-5635 *Fax:* 212-675-4809
*E-mail:* submissions@carolmannagency.com
*Web Site:* www.carolmannagency.com
*Key Personnel*
Pres: Carol Mann (AAR)
Agent: Eliza Dreier; Gareth Esersky; Myrsini Stephanides; Joanne Wyckoff; Laura Yorke
Founded: 1977
Literary & commercial fiction, no genre fiction, general nonfiction & memoir. Subs-agents in Los Angeles & for all foreign languages. No unsol mss, query first. E-mail queries only (no attachments). Mailed queries no longer accepted. For fiction & memoir, send a synopsis, brief bio & first 25 pages of ms. All other nonfiction, submit synopsis & brief bio. No reading fee. Handle film & TV rights for book clients only.
Foreign Rights: Ackali Copyright Agency (Atilla Izgi Turgut) (Turkey); Anthea Agency (Zlatka Paskaleva) (Bulgaria); Eliane Benisti Agency (France); Luigi Bernabo Associates (Italy); Big Apple Agency Inc (Vicky Chen) (Taiwan); Big Apple Agency Inc (Lily Chen) (China, Indonesia); Graal Literary Agency (Magdalena Cabajewska) (Poland); JLM Literary Agency (John Moukakos) (Greece); Katai & Bolza Literary Agents (Peter Bolza) (Hungary); Simona Kessler Intl Copyright Agency (Romania); Licht & Burr Literary Agency (Trine Licht) (Denmark, Iceland, Norway, Sweden); Meigas Agencia Literaria (Ruth Garcia-Lago) (Mexico); Mohrbooks (Sabine Ibach) (Germany); Andrew Nurnberg Associates Baltic (Kristine Supe) (Latvia); Andrew Nurnberg Literary Agency (Ludmilla Sushkova) (Russia); Kristin Olson Literary Agency (Czech Republic); I Pikarski Literary Agency (Gal Pikarski) (Israel); Prava I Prevodi Literary Agency (Ana Milenkovic) (Serbia); Guillermo Schavelzon & Associados (Jacoba Casier) (Spain); Karin Schindler (Brazil); Sebes & Van Gelderen Literary Agency (Paul Sebes) (Netherlands); Abner Stein Associates (Arabella Stein) (England); Tuttle-Mori Agency Inc (Manami Tamaoki) (Japan); Tuttle-Mori Agency Inc (Pimolporn Yutisri) (Thailand); Shin Won Agency (Tae Eun Kim) (Korea)

**Freya Manston Associates Inc** (L)
145 W 58 St, New York, NY 10019
*Tel:* 212-247-3075
*Key Personnel*
Pres: Freya Manston
Fiction & nonfiction. No unsol mss; not accepting new queries at this time. Agents in all principal countries. No fees charged.

**Manus & Associates Literary Agency Inc** (L)
425 Sherman Ave, Suite 200, Palo Alto, CA 94306
*Tel:* 650-470-5151 *Fax:* 650-470-5159
*E-mail:* manuslit@manuslit.com
*Web Site:* www.manuslit.com
*Key Personnel*
Pres: Jillian W Manus (AAR) *E-mail:* jillian@manuslit.com
Assoc: Jandy Nelson (AAR) *E-mail:* jandy@manuslit.com
General fiction & dramatic nonfiction books, TV & motion picture rights. No unsol mss. Fiction: query first with synopsis & first 30 pages. Nonfiction: query letter & proposal. No reading fee. Offices in NY & CA; representatives in all major foreign countries. The New York office does NOT accept any unsol mss.
Foreign Rep(s): Danny Baror (Worldwide)
Foreign Rights: Baror International Inc

**March Tenth Inc** (L)
24 Hillside Terr, Montvale, NJ 07645
*Tel:* 201-387-6551 *Fax:* 201-387-6552
*Web Site:* www.marchtenthinc.com
*Key Personnel*
Pres: Sandra Choron *E-mail:* schoron@aol.com
VP: Harry Choron *E-mail:* hchoron@aol.com
Founded: 1980
General nonfiction & fiction; specialize in popular culture. No children's or young adult novels, plays, screenplays or poetry. No unsol mss, query first. E-mail queries accepted. If mailing hard copy, include a SASE for materials you want returned. See web site for additional information. No reading fee. Book production services available. Handle film & TV rights. 15% commission.
Titles recently placed: *How Shakespeare Saved My Life*, Laura Bates; *Streets of Fire*, Eric Meola

**Denise Marcil Literary Agency Inc** (L)
483 Westover Rd, Stamford, CT 06902
*Tel:* 203-327-9970
*E-mail:* dmla@denisemarcilagency.com
*Web Site:* www.denisemarcilagency.com
*Key Personnel*
Pres & Agent: Denise Marcil (AAR)
Agent: Anne Marie O'Farrell (AAR) *E-mail:* annemarie@denisemarcilagency.com
Founded: 1977
Nonfiction: Personal growth, intelligent self-help & how-to's including mind-body-spirit, sports, business. careers. psychology & cookbooks. Send nonfiction e-mail queries to annemarie@denisemarcilagency.com.
Represents contemporary women's fiction & thrillers. Send fiction queries to dmla@denisemarcilagency.com. No unsol mss, query first. No fees charged. Subagents in all major countries.
Titles recently placed: *Discovering Vintage New York*, Mitch Broder; *Gratitude Prayers*, June Cotner; *Home to Seaview Key*, Sherryl Woods; *Idea Stormers, How To Lead and Inspire Creative Breakthroughs*, Bryan W Mattimore; *Sand Castle Bay*, Sherryl Woods; *Something About Sophie*, Mary Kay McComas; *Swinging '73, Baseball's Wildest Season*, Matthew Silverman; *The College Bound Organizer*, Anna Costaras, Gail Liss; *The Healthy Pregnancy Book*, William Sears, MD, Martha Sears, RN
Membership(s): The Authors Guild; Women's Media Group

**Barbara Markowitz** (L)
PO Box 41709, Los Angeles, CA 90041
*Tel:* 323-257-6188
Founded: 1980
No new submissions through Jan 31, 2014.
Agent only mid-level (8-11) & young adult (12-16) contemporary & historical fiction. No illustrated, science fiction or futuristic. No unsol mss; query first with SASE. Please state word count in query. No reading or other fees.

**Markson Thoma Literary Agency Inc** (L)
44 Greenwich Ave, New York, NY 10011
*Tel:* 212-243-8480 *Fax:* 212-691-9014
*E-mail:* info@marksonthoma.com
*Web Site:* www.marksonthoma.com
*Key Personnel*
Partner & Agent: Elaine Markson (AAR)
Dir, Subs Rts: Gary Johnson
Founded: 1972
Literary fiction & nonfiction. No unsol mss. No fees charged.
Foreign Rights: Liepman (Germany); MB Agencia Literaria (Latin America, Portugal, Spain); La Nouvelle Agence (France); Elizabeth Sheinkman (UK); Marco Vigevani (Italy)

**Mildred Marmur Associates Ltd** (L)
2005 Palmer Ave, PMB 127, Larchmont, NY 10538
*Tel:* 914-834-1170
*E-mail:* marmur@westnet.com
*Key Personnel*
Pres: Mildred Marmur (AAR)
Founded: 1987
Nonfiction only. No unsol mss; referrals only. Represented in Hollywood & foreign markets. Does not charge fees.
Membership(s): The Authors Guild

**Marsal Lyon Literary Agency LLC** (L)
665 San Rodolfo Dr, Suite 124, PMB 121, Solana Beach, CA 92075
*Tel:* 760-814-8507
*Web Site:* www.marsallyonliteraryagency.com
*Key Personnel*
Owner & Literary Agent: Kevan Lyon *E-mail:* kevan@marsalyonliteraryagency.com; Jill Marsal *E-mail:* jill@marsallyonliteraryagency.com
Literary Agent: Deborah Ritchken *E-mail:* deborah@marsallyonliteraryagency.com; Kathleen Rushall *E-mail:* kathleen@marsallyonliteraryagency.com
Founded: 2009
Dedicated to helping authors successfully place their work. Members have many years of experience in the publishing industry & possess a diverse & unique skill set. Have worked with many bestselling & award-winning authors, as well as first-time authors.
Fiction genres & categories represented: commercial, mainstream, multicultural, mystery, suspense, thriller, women's fiction, romance (all genres), young adult & middle grade. Nonfiction represented: biography, business/economics/investing/finance, diet, fitness & health, history/politics/current events, investigative journalism, lifestyle, memoirs, narrative nonfiction, parenting, pets/animals, pop culture & music, psychology, relationships/advice, science & nature, self-help, sports, women's issues. No unsol ms, query first. Writers are encouraged to visit the web site to determine who might be the best fit for your work. For electronic submissions (preferred), send query letter & write QUERY in the subject line of the e-mail. Hard copy submissions: for fiction, send cover letter, one-page synopsis of work & first 10 pages of ms; for nonfiction, include either cover letter or cover letter & complete proposal. No fees.

The Taryn Fagerness Agency represents foreign, audio & film subsidiary rights.
Titles recently placed: *A Convenient Bride*, Cheryl Ann Smith; *A Hometown Boy*, Janice Kay Johnson; *A Man of Privilege*, Sarah M Anderson; *A Rustic Chic Wedding*, Morgann Hill; *A Socialite Scorned*, Kerrie Droban; *An Affair of Vengeance*, Jamie Michele; *And Hell Followed with Her*, David Neiwert; *Back to You*, Robin Kaye; *Backhoe Joe*, Lori Alexander; *Beach Town Baking: An Endless Summer of Delicious Desserts*, Lee Shishak; *Behind the Lies*, Robin Perini; *Bleeding Talent: How the US Military Mismanages Great Leaders and Why it's Time for a Revolution*, Time Kane; *Bloodhound in Blue*, Adam Russ; *Buried Memories*, Katie Beers, Carolyn Gusoff; *Caged Warrior*, Lindsey Piper; *Call Me Zelda*, Ericka Robuck; *Dangerous Memories*, Angi Morgan; *Dangerous Waters*, Toni Anderson; *Dare You to*, Katie McGarry; *Dark Awakening*, Kendra Leigh Castle; *Dollface*, Renee Rosen; *Don't Look Back*, Jennifer Armentrout; *Essential Car Care for Women*, Jamie Little, Danielle McCormick; *Ex on the Beach*, Kim Law; *Exposed*, Laura Griffin; *Far Time Incident*, Neve Maslakovic; *Forest Fairy Crafts*, Lenka Vodicka, Asia Curry; *Freedom to Learn*, Peter Gray; *Gold Fire*, Starr Ambrose; *Hemingway's Girl*, Erika Robuck; *How to Deceive a Duke*, Lecia Cornwall; *Insomnia*, Jenn Johansson; *It Takes More than Talent*, Kristen Fischer; *It's Raining Bats and Frogs*, Rebecca Colby; *Life's a Witch*, Brittany Geragotelis; *Lone Wolf Terrorism*, Jeffrey Simon; *Mating Instinct*, Katie Reus; *Midnight Sacrifice*, Melinda Leigh; *My Migraine Miracle*, Joshua Turknett; *Out of All Knowing*, Jennifer Robson; *Profit from the Positive*, Margaret Greenberg, Senia Maymin; *Pushing the Limits*, Katie McGarry; *Rock Your Business*, David Fishof, Michael Levin; *Sacrifice*, Cayla Kluver; *Secrets of a Virgin*, Anna Randol; *Secrets of a Wedding Night*, Valerie Bowman; *She Can Scream*, Melinda Leigh; *She Can Tell*, Melinda Leigh; *Sinfully Yours*, Kendra Leigh Castle; *Sins of a Ruthless Rogue*, Anna Randol; *Starlight*, Carrie Lofty; *Sugar Springs*, Kim Law; *Summer in Napa*, Marina Adair; *Sweet Revenge*, Zoe Archer; *Targeted*, Katie Reus; *Temptation in a Kilt*, Victoria Roberts; *The Anatomist's Wife*, Anna Lee Huber; *The Baby Deal*, Kat Cantrell; *The Candidate*, Samuel Popkin; *The Challenger Sale*, Matthew Dixon, Brent Adamson; *The Chiefton*, Margaret Mallory; *The Claimed*, Caridad Pineiro; *The Darling Strumpet*, Gillian Bagwell; *The Delight Paradox*, Matthew Dixon, Nicholas Toman, Richard Delisi; *The Highlander's Prize*, Mary Wine; *The Joy Brigade*, Martin Limon; *The Last Time I Saw Paris*, Lynn Sheene; *The Love Dog*, Elsa Watson; *The Mango Bride*, Marivi Soliven; *The Price of Temptation*, Lecia Cornwall; *The Sinner*, Margaret Mallory; *The Valentine's Arrangement*, Kelsie Leverich; *The Van Winkle Project*, Karri Thompson; *The Vanishing Thief*, Kate Parker; *The Wisdom of Hair*, Kim Boykin; *Touch*, Jus Accardo; *Twisted*, Laura Griffin; *Unstoppable*, Laura Griffin; *Vagos, Mongols & Outlaws*, Charles Falco, Kerrie Droban; *Venus in Winter*, Gillian Bagwell; *Victorian Secret: What a Corset Taught Me about the Past, the Present, and Myself*, Sarah Chrisman; *Vinnie Gorgeous*, Anthony DeStefano; *Wait for You*, J Lynn; *Welcome Home Mama and Boris*, Carey Neesley, Michael Levin; *What Happens in Scotland*, Jennifer McQuiston; *What Makes Your Brain Happy & Why You Should Do the Opposite*, David DiSalvo; *What the Spell*, Brittany Geragotellis; *What's Wrong with Fat?*, Abigail Saguy; *Wild Princess*, Mary Hart Perry; *Witchy Crafts*, Lexa Olick; *Writing from the Senses*, Laura Deutsch; *X Marks the Scot*, Victoria Roberts
Foreign Rights: Taryn Fagerness Agency LLC (Albania, Argentina, Australia, Brazil, Bulgaria, Canada, China, Croatia, Czech Republic, Denmark, Estonia, Finland, France, Germany, Greece, Hungary, Iceland, India, Indonesia, Israel, Italy, Japan, Korea, Latvia, Lithuania, Mexico, Netherlands, Norway, Poland, Portugal, Romania, Russia, Serbia, Slovakia, Slovenia, Spain, Sweden, Taiwan, Thailand, Turkey, Ukraine, UK, Vietnam)
Membership(s): Romance Writers of America

**The Evan Marshall Agency** (L)
One Pacio Ct, Roseland, NJ 07068-1121
*Tel:* 973-287-6216 *Fax:* 973-488-7910
*Key Personnel*
Pres: Evan Marshall (AAR) *E-mail:* evan@evanmarshallagency.com
Founded: 1987
Representatives in Hollywood & foreign countries. No unsol mss; do not query or send submissions. Clients considered by professional referral only.
Membership(s): Mystery Writers of America; Sisters in Crime

**The Martell Agency** (L)
1350 Avenue of the Americas, Suite 1205, New York, NY 10019
*Tel:* 212-317-2672
*E-mail:* submissions@themartellagency.com
*Web Site:* www.themartellagency.com
*Key Personnel*
Owner: Alice Fried Martell
Contact: Stephanie Finman
Founded: 1985
Fiction & nonfiction. No screenplays or poetry. Handle film & TV rights. No unsol mss, query first. Submit query letters only, market analysis for nonfiction & author biography. Mss not returned; no reading fee. Represented in foreign markets.
Foreign Rep(s): Eliane Benisti (France); Bookbank SL (Alicia Gonzalez-Sterling) (Spain); Jill Hughes Agent (Eastern Europe, Greece, Middle East); Nurcihan Kesim Literary Agency Inc (Filiz Karaman) (Turkey); Lennart Sane Agency AB (Denmark, Finland, Holland, Norway, Sweden); Liepman AG Literary Agency (Eva Koralnik) (Germany, Switzerland); Sara Menguc Literary Agent (UK); Natoli Stefan & Oliva sa (Italy); Andrew Nurnberg Associates International (Whitney Hsu) (Taiwan); Andrew Nurnberg Associates International (Jackie Huang) (China); Tuttle-Mori Agency Inc (Japan); Tuttle-Mori Agency Inc (Thananchai Pandey) (Indonesia, Thailand); Julio F Yanez Agencia Literaria (Montse Yanez) (Brazil, Portugal); Eric Yang Agency (Henry Shin) (Korea)

**Martin Literary Management LLC** (L)
7683 SE 27 St, No 307, Mercer Island, WA 98040
*Tel:* 206-466-1773 (no queries) *Fax:* 206-466-1774
*Web Site:* www.martinliterarymanagement.com
*Key Personnel*
Literary Mgr & Agent: Sharlene Martin *E-mail:* sharlene@martinliterarymanagement.com
Founded: 2003
Nonfiction only. No poetry, short stories or screen plays. No unsol mss, query first. Now a "green agency", only e-mail queries (no attachments) will be accepted. No fees charged.
Titles recently placed: *A Craving for Noodles*, Christine Quinn; *Literary Fails: Totally (sic)!*, Sharlene Martin, Anthony Flacco; *Love Lies*, Amanda Lamb; *Special Agent Man*, Steve Moore; *The Pregnancy Project*, Gaby Rodriguez, Jenna Glatzer
Foreign Rights: Taryn Fagerness Agency (Worldwide exc Canada & US Territories)

**Martin-McLean Literary Associates LLC** (L)
5023 W 120 Ave, Suite 228, Broomfield, CO 80020
*Tel:* 303-465-2056 *Fax:* 303-465-2057
*E-mail:* martinmcleanlit@aol.com
*Web Site:* www.martinmcleanlit.com; www.mcleanlit.com
*Key Personnel*
CEO & Agent: Lisa Ann Martin, PhD
Founded: 1986
Literary fiction, nonfiction, health issues, psychology, how-to, self-help, sports, new thought, critical thinking, scholarly, biographies, memoirs, autobiographies & murder mystery. No unsol mss. Query first with letter, synopsis, total word count of ms & e-mail address to the agency's street address or by e-mail. Requirements: send proposal with SASE, follow submission directions on web site, or call for agency brochure. No evaluation or reading fee; work at $60/hr. New writers welcome.
Services: editing, proposal development & critique. Book development available. Ghostwriters can be matched to author. Agents worldwide with Internet access.
Titles recently placed: *A Bird in the Hand*, Jerry Banks; *Angel Kisses: The Gift of Infirmity*, Karen K Hoiland; *How to Avoid the Over-diagnosis and Over-treatment of Prostate Cancer*, Anthony H Horan, MD; *Indian Zero to American Hero: An Incredible Story of a Slumdog Scientist*, Dr B Vithal Shetty; *Mountains of Poetry: Colorado Poems by Colorado Kids*, Coyote Authors Club; *Pact of the Seven Stones: The Mist of Maletoc*, Kevin Cooke; *The Elements of Selling: Everyone Has Something to Sell*, Alan Zell; *The Feral Pistillate*, Warner Bair II; *The Fifth Estate*, Steven Berger; *The Magic Law of Increase: Tithing Your Way to Prosperity*, Lisa Ann Martin PhD; *The Second District*, Jerry Banks; *The Three R's Make the World go Around!*, Jade Martin, Dylan George, Kyra Mowry, Valerie Ulsh; *The Uncertain Believer*, Edward Correia; *Vulture Culture*, Eric Gerst; *Who Killed Public TV?*, Roger Smith; *Winter is Upon Us*, Kevin Cooke

**Harold Matson Co Inc** (L)
276 Fifth Ave, New York, NY 10001
*Tel:* 212-679-4490 *Fax:* 212-545-1224
*Key Personnel*
Agent: Ben Camardi (AAR); Jonathan Matson (AAR)
Founded: 1937
No unsol mss, query first with SASE. No reading fee. Handle film & TV rights. No screenplays.
Foreign Rep(s): Intercontinental Literary Agency (Europe); Abner Stein Agency (UK)
Membership(s): The Authors Guild

**Margret McBride Literary Agency** (L)
PO Box 9128, La Jolla, CA 92038
*Tel:* 858-454-1550 *Fax:* 858-454-2156
*E-mail:* staff@mcbridelit.com
*Web Site:* www.mcbrideliterary.com
*Key Personnel*
Owner & Pres: Margret McBride (AAR)
Founded: 1981
Specialize in commercial fiction, nonfiction, business, health & self-help No unsol mss. New clients by referral only. Submit query & synopsis or outline with SASE. No e-mail or fax queries. No poetry or romance. Allow 6-8 weeks for a response. No reading fee. Foreign rights sub-agents in all major countries.
Membership(s): The Authors Guild

**E J McCarthy Agency** (L)
1104 Shelter Bay Ave, Mill Valley, CA 94941
*Tel:* 415-383-6639 *Fax:* 415-383-6639
*E-mail:* ejmagency@gmail.com
*Web Site:* www.publishersmarketplace.com/members/ejmccarthy
*Key Personnel*
Owner: E J McCarthy
Founded: 2003
Independent literary agency. Subject specialties: history, military history, politics, sports, biography, media, memoir, thrillers & other nonfiction. Submissions should be double-spaced, single-sided, unbound pages. Use a standard serif typeface like Courier. Don't justify right margin. Type 25 lines of 60 characters or about 250 words per page. Number pages consecutively from beginning to end, not by chapter. No reading fee. Query first by e-mail or regular mail. Phone calls okay.
Titles recently placed: *Games of War*, Corey Mead; *Guerrilla Leader: T E Lawrence and the Arab Revolt*, James J Schneider; *The Heart and the Fist: The Education of a Humanitarian, the Making of a Navy SEAL*, Eric Greitens; *Two One Pony: An American Soldier's Year in Vietnam, 1969 (Stackpole Military History Series)*, Charles R Carr; *Wanted Dead or Alive: Manhunts from Geronimo to Bin Laden*, Benjamin Runkle

**Gerard McCauley Agency Inc** (L)
PO Box 844, Katonah, NY 10536-0844
*Tel:* 914-232-5700 *Fax:* 914-232-1506
*Key Personnel*
Pres: Gerard McCauley (AAR)
*E-mail:* gerrymccauley@earthlink.net
Founded: 1970
Nonfiction; educational materials. No unsol mss. Representatives in all major foreign countries. Not currently considering new mss. Does not charge fees.

**Anita D McClellan Associates** (L)
464 Common St, Suite 142, Belmont, MA 02478-2704
*Tel:* 617-575-9203 *Fax:* 206-203-0829
*E-mail:* adm@anitamcclellan.com
*Web Site:* www.anitamcclellan.com
*Key Personnel*
Agent: Anita McClellan (AAR)
Founded: 1988
General fiction & nonfiction, including feminism. No unsol mss, query first by e-mail without attachments, no work previously submitted to publishers. Submit outline or synopsis & first 2,500 words. No software. No reading fees charged.
Membership(s): The Authors Guild; Bay Area Editors' Forum; Bookbuilders of Boston; Cape Cod Writers Center; Editorial Freelancers Association; Grub Street; International Women's Writing Guild; Sisters in Crime; Society of Children's Book Writers & Illustrators; Women's National Book Association

**McIntosh & Otis Inc** (L)
353 Lexington Ave, New York, NY 10016-0900
*Tel:* 212-687-7400 *Fax:* 212-687-6894
*E-mail:* info@mcintoshandotis.com
*Web Site:* www.mcintoshandotis.com
*Key Personnel*
Owner & CEO: Eugene H Winick (AAR)
Pres & Sr Adult Agent: Elizabeth Winick Rubinstein (AAR)
Corp Secy & Agent: Ina H Winick
Agent & Dir, Subs Rts: Shira Hoffman (AAR)
Agent, Children's Dept: Christa Heschke
Royalty Admin: Alecia Douglas
Founded: 1928
Represent adult & juvenile fiction & nonfiction books. No unsol mss, query first via e-mail. See web site for instructions. No reading fees. Handle film & TV rights for represented clients only. Agents in most major foreign countries.
Foreign Rep(s): Anatolia Literary Agency (Turkey); Bardon-Chinese Media (Mainland China, Taiwan); Luigi Bernabo (Italy); Caroline Van Geldren (Netherlands); Japan UNI Agency Inc (Adult) (Japan); Mohrbooks (Germany); La Nouvelle Agence (France); Andrew Nurenburg (Eastern Europe); Prava I Prevodi Agency (Eastern Europe); Lennart Sane Agency (Denmark, Scandinavia); Abner Stein Agency (UK); Tuttle-Mori Agency Inc (children) (Japan); Julio F Yanez (Latin America, Portugal, Spain)

**McLean Literary Associates**, see Martin-McLean Literary Associates LLC

**Sally Hill McMillan LLC** (L)
429 E Kingston Ave, Charlotte, NC 28203
*Tel:* 704-334-0897
*E-mail:* mcmagency@aol.com
*Key Personnel*
Pres: Sally Hill McMillan (AAR)
Founded: 1990 (converted to a LLC in 2011)
Southern fiction & adult trade nonfiction; no unsol mss, query first & await further instructions. No sci-fi, military, horror, fantasy/adventure children's books or cookbooks. No reading fee. Handle film, TV, foreign & electronic rights through sub-agents.
Titles recently placed: *Pie Town*, Lynne Hinton; *The Armchair Birder: Discovering the Secret Lives of Familiar Birds*, John Yow
Foreign Rights: The Fielding Agency (all other territories); Thomas Schlueck GmbH (Germany)
Membership(s): Women's National Book Association

**Mendel Media Group LLC** (L)
115 W 30 St, Suite 800, New York, NY 10001
*Tel:* 646-239-9896 *Fax:* 212-685-4717
*Web Site:* www.mendelmedia.com
*Key Personnel*
Mng Partner: Scott Mendel (AAR)
*E-mail:* scott@mendelmedia.com
Founded: 2002
Represent nonfiction writers in most subject areas, from biography & serious history to health & relationships. Nonfiction clientele includes individual authors & institutions whose works, collections, archives, researchers &/or policy experts contribute to important public discussions & debates. Also represent more lighthearted nonfiction projects, when they suit the market particularly well. The agency's fiction writers principally write historical & contemporary multicultural fiction, contemporary thrillers & mainstream women's fiction. Do not accept fax or e-mail submissions. Submission guidelines are available on the web site. No fees.
Titles recently placed: *Agorafabulous!: Dispatches from My Bedroom*, Sara Benincasa; *Allah: The Biography*, Abbas Milani; *Aretha Franklin: The Queen of Soul*, Mark Bego; *Art Girls Are Easy*, Julie Klausner; *Great*, Sara Benincasa; *How to Exercise When You're Expecting*, Lindsay Brin; *How to Win at Everything*, Daniel Kibblesmith, Sam Weiner; *I Could Pee on This: And Other Poems by Cats*, Francesco Marciuliano; *I, Steve: Steve Jobs in His Own Words*, George Beahm; *Impatient Optimist: Bill Gates in His Own Words*, Lisa Rogak; *Off the Menu*, Stacey Ballis; *Our Man in the Dark*, Rashad Harrison; *Patient One*, Leonard Goldberg; *Slow Fire: The Beginner's Guide to Barbecue*, Ray "Dr BBQ" Lampe; *Super Boys: The Amazing Adventures of Jerry Siegel and Joe Shuster-the Creators of Superman*, Brad Ricca; *The Dogs of War: The Courage, Love, and Loyalty of Military Working Dogs*, Lisa Rogak; *The First Lady of Fleet Street: The Life, Fortune and Tragedy of Rachel Beer*, Yehuda Koren, Eilat Negev; *The King Whisperers: Power Behind the Throne, from Rasputin to Rove*, Kerwin Swint; *The March of the Bohemian Irregulars*, Peter Carlson; *The Raft*, S A Bodeen; *United Nations: A History*, Stanley Meisler; *Whitney Houston!: The Spectacular Rise and Tragic Fall of the Woman Whose Voice Inspired a Generation*, Mark Bego
Membership(s): American Association of University Professors; The Authors Guild; MLA; Mystery Writers of America; Romance Writers of America; Society of Children's Book Writers & Illustrators

**Scott Meredith Literary Agency LP** (L)
200 W 57 St, Suite 904, New York, NY 10019-3211
*Tel:* 646-274-1970 *Fax:* 212-977-5997
*E-mail:* info@scottmeredith.com
*Web Site:* www.scottmeredith.com
*Key Personnel*
Pres: Arthur M Klebanoff *Tel:* 646-274-1970 ext 102 *E-mail:* aklebanoff@rosettabooks.com
Dir, Subs Rts: Mary Jo Anne Valko-Warner
Founded: 1946
More than 1,500 titles in print. No unsol mss, query first. No fees charged.

**Mews Books Ltd** (L)
20 Bluewater Hill, Westport, CT 06880
*Tel:* 203-227-1836 *Fax:* 203-227-1144
*E-mail:* mewsbooks@aol.com
*Key Personnel*
Pres: Sidney B Kramer
Assoc: Valerie Seiling Jacobs *E-mail:* valerie@mewsbooks.com
Asst: Fran Pollak
Founded: 1975
Seeking professional quality edited works in all categories. In business for nearly 40 years, we offer full literary services. Mr. Kramer is an attorney & former publisher (Bantam Books co-founder & SVP & former president of New American Library) & offers legal consultation for authors with contractual issues.
Please send a one paragraph summary of your work, a second paragraph of your publishing history including full details of whether this submission was previously offered elsewhere & if needed, a third paragraph with other pertinent information. All queries should be submitted to mewsbooks@aol.com. We require an exclusive while reading. If we are interested, we will ask for a chapter by chapter overview, two sample chapters & a promotion plan. No fees.

**Doris S Michaels Literary Agency Inc** (L)
1841 Broadway, Suite 903, New York, NY 10023
*Tel:* 212-265-9474 *Fax:* 212-265-9480
*E-mail:* info@dsmagency.com
*Web Site:* www.dsmagency.com
*Key Personnel*
Pres: Doris S Michaels (AAR)
Asst: Pauline Hsia
Founded: 1994
Adult fiction: literary fiction that has a commercial appeal & strong screen potential. Adult nonfiction: business, current affairs, biography & memoirs, self-help, psychology, history, social services, gender, health, classical music, sports & women's issues. No romance, coffee table books, art books, trivia, pop culture, humor, westerns, occult & supernatural, horror, poetry, textbooks, children's books, picture books, film scripts, articles, cartoons or professional manuals. No unsol mss, query first with e-mail according to the submission guidelines on our web site & to determine the types

of books we are interested in representing before sending query. No regular mail or phone inquiries. Handle film & TV rights through Hollywood co-agents. No reading fee.
Titles recently placed: *The MELT Method*, Sue Hitzmann
Foreign Rights: Ahlbaeck Literary Agency (Elina Ahlbaeck) (Denmark, Finland, Iceland, Norway, Sweden); Bardon-Chinese Media Agency (Phillip C Chen & Joanne Yang) (China, Taiwan); Agence Eliane Benisti (Eliane Benisti) (France); The Book Publishers Association of Israel (Dalia Ever Hadani) (Israel); International Copyright Agency Ltd (Simona Kessler & Adriana Marina) (Romania); Japan UNI Agency Inc (Miko Yamanouchi) (Japan); Literarische Agentur (Thomas Schlueck, Bastian Schlueck & Joachim Jessen) (Germany); Piergiorgio Nicolazzini Literary Agency (Piergiorgio Nicolazzini & Maura Solinas) (Italy); OA Literary Agency (Michael Avramides) (Greece); Kristin Olson Literary Agency (Kristin Olson & Tereza Dubova) (Czech Republic, Slovakia); Onk Agency Ltd (Hatice Gok & Nazli Cokdu) (Turkey); PLIMA Literary Agency (Vuk & Mila Perisic) (Croatia, Serbia, Slovenia); RDC Agencia Lieraria SL (Raquel de la Concha & Marilu Casquero) (Latin America, Portugal, Spain); Marianne Schoenbach Literary Agency (Marianne Schoenbach) (Netherlands); Abner Stein Agency (Abner Stein, Kate McLennan & Caspian Dennis) (UK); Tuttle-Mori Agency Inc (Pimolporn Tutsiri) (Thailand, Vietnam); Eric Yang Agency (Sue Yang & Henry Shin) (Korea)
Membership(s): Women's National Book Association

**Martha Millard Literary Agency** (L)
420 Central Park W, Suite 5H, New York, NY 10025
*Tel:* 212-662-1030
*E-mail:* marmillink@aol.com
*Key Personnel*
Prop: Martha Millard (AAR)
Founded: 1980
Handle film & TV rights. Handle software subsidiary to book deals. No unsol mss. Not currently reading queries. No e-mail or fax queries. No fees. Representatives in principal countries.
Foreign Rep(s): Zeno Agency Ltd (UK)
Foreign Rights: Agenzia Letteraria Internazionale (Italy); AnatoliaLit Agency (Turkey); Lora Fountain Associates (France); Paul & Peter Fritz AG (Germany); International Editors' Co (Spain); International Literaatur Bureau (Netherlands); Prava I Prevodi (Eastern Europe); Tuttle-Mori Agency Inc (Japan)
Membership(s): The Authors Guild; Science Fiction & Fantasy Writers of America

**The Miller Agency Inc** (L)
630 Ninth Ave, Suite 1102, New York, NY 10036
*Tel:* 212-206-0913 *Fax:* 212-206-1473
*Key Personnel*
Contact: Sharon Bowers *E-mail:* sharon@mbgliterary.com; Jennifer Griffin *E-mail:* jennifer@mbgliterary.com; Angela Miller *E-mail:* angela@mbgliterary.com
Fiction & nonfiction. No unsol mss. Handle software, film & TV rights. No reading fee. Subagents in all principal foreign countries.

**Montreal-Contacts/The Rights Agency** (L)
1350 Sherbrooke St E, Suite 1, Montreal, QC H2L 1M4, Canada
*Tel:* 514-400-7075 *Fax:* 514-400-1045
*Web Site:* www.montreal-contacts.com/?lang=en
*Key Personnel*
Owner: Jean-Sebastien Dufresne
*E-mail:* jsdufresne@montreal-contacts.com
Founded: 1981
Represents publishers &/or literary agents exclusively for foreign rights. No author representation. Does not handle original mss. Representation in all principal countries through 20 corresponding agents covering 50 languages. Representing full catalogues or selected titles with new online promotional platform eMediaRights.

**Moore Literary Agency** (L)
10 State St, Suite 210, Newburyport, MA 01950
*Tel:* 978-465-9015 *Fax:* 978-465-6653
*Key Personnel*
Owner & Pres: Claudette Moore
*E-mail:* cmoore@moorelit.com
Founded: 1989
High tech books & select nonfiction. No unsol mss, query first. Submit proposal or outline & sample chapter. No reading fee, commission only.
Titles recently placed: *Windows® 7 Inside Out, Deluxe Edition*, Ed Bott, Carl Siechert, Craig Stinson

**Howard Morhaim Literary Agency Inc** (L)
30 Pierrepont St, Brooklyn, NY 11201-3371
*Tel:* 718-222-8400 *Fax:* 718-222-5056
*E-mail:* info@morhaimliterary.com
*Web Site:* www.morhaimliterary.com
*Key Personnel*
Pres: Howard Morhaim (AAR) *E-mail:* howard@morhaimliterary.com
Agent: Kate McKean (AAR) *E-mail:* kate@morhaimliterary.com
General adult & young adult fiction & nonfiction. Howard Morhaim is not accepting unsol mss. Kate McKean is open to submissions. E-mail your query letter along with three sample chapters (for fiction) or full proposal (for nonfiction). No reading fee. Handle film & TV rights. Representatives in all principal foreign markets.
Foreign Rep(s): Baror International (Worldwide exc Portugal, Spain & UK); The Gotham Group (Michael Prevett, film & TV); RDC Agencia Literaria (Portugal, Spain); Abner Stein Agency (UK)

**Henry Morrison Inc** (L)
PO Box 235, Bedford Hills, NY 10507-0235
*Tel:* 914-666-3500 *Fax:* 914-241-7846
*E-mail:* hmorrison1@aol.com
*Key Personnel*
Pres: Henry Morrison
Founded: 1965
Fiction & nonfiction. Handle film & TV rights. Accept unsol mss but must send query & outline first with SASE; no reading fee. Fee for ms copies, galleys, bound books for foreign & movie sales & ordering books for subs rights.
Titles recently placed: *The Plain Man*, Steve Englehart; *The Red Templar*, Paul Christopher; *The Thief*, Clive Cussler, Justin Scott

**Movable Type Management** (L)
610 Fifth Ave, Suite 1220, New York, NY 10185
*Tel:* 917-289-1089 *Fax:* 646-810-5757
*Web Site:* www.mtmgmt.net
*Key Personnel*
Pres: Jason Allen Ashlock *E-mail:* jashlock@movabletm.com
Sr Literary Mgr: Mary Kole *Tel:* 650-520-5287 *E-mail:* mkole@movabletm.com; Michele Matrisciani *E-mail:* mmatrisciani@movabletm.com
Founded: 2002
Provides inventive & expansive management services, working with authors in a wide variety of categories & genres to develop properties for distribution across platforms, devices & territories. A bicoastal management company, MTM performs in-house film. television & digital development, leveraging our relationships with digital start-ups & veteran producers to add value to an author's work at every opportunity.

**Muse Literary Management** (L)
189 Waverly Place, Unit 4, New York, NY 10014-3135
*Tel:* 212-925-3721
*E-mail:* museliterarymgmt@aol.com
*Web Site:* www.museliterary.com; twitter.com/museliterary
*Key Personnel*
Literary Agent: Deborah Carter
Founded: 1998 (formerly known as Mysterious Content Literary Agency, changed to Muse Literary Management in Dec 2005 to reflect interests beyond mysteries)
Focuses on ms development & sale & administration of print, performance & foreign rights to literary works. Seeking writers who have a readership in online & print journalism. Areas of interest: Writing with charisma in narrative nonfiction about extraordinary people & experiences in memoir/biography, history, home & lifestyle, travel, history, pop culture, music & the arts, New York, Americana, nostalgia, antiques & anything not mentioned here that writers think may be of interest. Not interested in topics related to medical, health, psychology, science, technology, finance, business, politics, religion/spirituality, abuse or victimhood, sports, pets, cooking, food or true crime. Also seeking literary fiction & short story collections with popular appeal, multicultural & international fiction, historical fiction, mysteries/thrillers with literary merit, action/adventure; not interested in religion/spirituality, romance, chick lit, sci fi/fantasy/horror, westerns. Also seeking children's fiction/nonfiction excluding sci fi/fantasy, vampires & such. No unsol mss, e-mail queries only. Charge postage to send books to foreign agents, preapproved by author.
Titles recently placed: *Adventures of Molly Whuppie & Other Appalachian Folktales (Taiwan)*, Anne Shelby; *Homeplace (McGraw-Hill Spanish Kindergarten kit)*, Anne Shelby; *What to Do About Pollution/South Korea*, Anne Shelby
Foreign Rights: Akacali Copyright Agency (Bengu Ayfer) (Turkey); Book Publishers of Israel (Beverley Levit) (Israel); EntersKorea Agency (Lauren Kim) (Korea); Jiaxi Books (China, Taiwan); Tuttle-Mori Agency Inc (Worapong Wilai) (Indonesia, Malaysia, Thailand, Vietnam); Jack Zhou (China, Taiwan)
Membership(s): Association of Booksellers for Children; The Authors Guild; Children's Literature Association; Historical Novel Society; International Thriller Writers Inc

**Bonnie Nadell Literary Agency**, see Hill Nadell Literary Agency

**Jean V Naggar Literary Agency Inc** (L)
216 E 75 St, Suite 1-E, New York, NY 10021
*Tel:* 212-794-1082
*E-mail:* jvnla@jvnla.com
*Web Site:* www.jvnla.com
*Key Personnel*
Pres: Jean V Naggar (AAR)
VP: Jennifer Weltz (AAR) *E-mail:* jweltz@jvnla.com
Sr Agent: Alice Tasman (AAR) *E-mail:* atasman@jvnla.com
Agent: Jessica Regel (AAR) *E-mail:* jregel@jvnla.com
Agent, Nonfiction: Elizabeth Evans *E-mail:* eevans@jvnla.com
Agent: Laura Biagi (AAR) *E-mail:* lbiagi@jvnla.com

Founded: 1978
Trade & mass market fiction & nonfiction. Motion picture, TV & foreign representation, film & TV rights for the books represented. No unsol mss, query first by e-mail; follow guidelines on web site. No reading fee. Commissions: 15% domestic, 20% UK & foreign translation.
Titles recently placed: *A Life in Men*, Gina Frangello; *Archetype*, M D Waters; *Beyond the Bear*, Dan Bigley, Debra McKinney; *Dark Lie*, Nancy Springer; *Dead Run*, Dan Schultz; *Every Never After*, Lesley Livingston; *Joone*, Emily Kate Moon; *Love With A Chance of Drowning*, Torre DeRoche; *Neverwas*, Kelly Moore, Tucker Reed, Larkin Reed; *On The Come Up*, Hannah Weyer; *Otis Dooda: Strange but True*, Ellen Potter, David Heatley; *Sleight of Hand*, Phillip Margolin; *Sugar Pop Moon*, John Florio; *The Bear Went Over the Mountain*, Iza Trapani; *The Bohemian Love Diaries*, Slash Coleman; *The Fate of Mercy Alban*, Wendy Webb; *The Heartbreak Messenger*, Alexander Vance; *The Land of Painted Caves*, Jean M Auel; *The Miseducation of Cameron Post*, Emily Danforth; *The Tudor Conspiracy*, C W Gortner; *We Only Know So Much*, Elizabeth Crane; *Work Like A Spy*, J C Carleson
Foreign Rep(s): Akcali Copyright Agency (Turkey); Luigi Bernabo Associates (Italy); Big Apple Agency (Mainland China, Taiwan); Graal Literary Agency (Poland); Greene & Heaton (UK); International Editors Co (Brazil, Latin America, Portugal, Spain); JLM Agency (Greece); Katai & Bolza Literary Agency (Hungary); Simona Kessler International Copyright Agency (Romania); Michelle Lapautre Agency (France); Licht & Burr Literary Agency (Scandinavia); Liepman Agency (Germany); Maxima Creative Agency (Indonesia); Andrew Nurnberg Literary Agency (Baltic States, Bulgaria, Czech Republic, Netherlands, Russia); Pikarski Agency (Israel); PLIMA (Montenegro, Serbia); Silkroad Publishers Agency (Thailand); Tuttle-Mori Agency Inc (Japan); Eric Yang Agency (Korea)

**BK Nelson Inc Literary Agency** (L-D)
Division of BK Nelson Inc
1565 Paseo Vida, Palm Springs, CA 92264
*Tel:* 760-778-8800 *Fax:* 760-778-6242
*E-mail:* bknelson4@cs.com
*Web Site:* www.bknelson.com; www.bknelsonlecturebureau.com; www.bknelsonmovieproduction.com
*Key Personnel*
CEO & Pres: Bonita K Nelson
CFO: Corp Reed
VP, West Coast: Leonard Ashbach
Edit Dir, East Coast: John W Benson
Acctg Dept: Erwin Rosenfeld
Founded: 1980
Fiction & nonfiction, business, self-help, autobiography, biography, political, children's, cookbooks, trivia; Lecture Bureau. No unsol mss, query with SASE. Prompt service. Deals directly with foreign publishers. Handle film & TV rights. Attend BEA, Cannes Film Festival & Frankfurt Book Fair.
Titles recently placed: *A Play on Words*, John Stark; *Chasing the Dragon*, Jane Miller Chai; *How to Buy Foreclosed Real Estate for a Fraction of Its Value, 3rd ed*, Theodore J Dallow, Don Ayer, Dick Pas, Esq; *Sons of Freedom*, John Stark; *Top Gun*, Michael Thompkins
*Branch Office(s)*
84 Woodland Rd, Pleasantville, NY 10570-1322 *Tel:* 914-741-1322 *Fax:* 914-741-1324
Foreign Rep(s): David Bolt Associates (England); Ulla Lohren Literary Agency (Scandinavia); McKee & Mouche (France, Germany); Tuttle-Mori Agency Inc (Japan)
Foreign Rights: Alexandra Chapman

Membership(s): American Association of University Women; The Authors Guild; The Dramatists Guild of America; Motion Picture Alliance; NACA

**Nelson Literary Agency LLC** (L)
1732 Wazee St, Suite 207, Denver, CO 80202-1284
*Tel:* 303-292-2805
*E-mail:* query@nelsonagency.com
*Web Site:* www.nelsonagency.com
*Key Personnel*
Pres & Sr Literary Agent: Kristin Nelson (AAR)
Literary Agent: Sara Megibow
Digital Liaison: Lori Bennett
Contracts & Royalties Mgr: Angie Hodapp
Submissions & Asian Territory Rts Coord: Anita Mumm
Founded: 2002
Accepts queries by e-mail only to query@nelsonagency.com. Represents fiction (literary, mainstream, women's, chick lit, romance, science fiction, fantasy, young adult, middle grade). No nonfiction, screenplays, short story collections, poetry, children's picture books, chapter books or Christian/inspirational. See web site for additional submission guidelines; no attachments, phone calls, postal mail or office visits. Some query letters & FAQs posted on web site. No fees charged.
Titles recently placed: *After*, Rhiannon Thomas; *Bird Box*, Josh Malerman; *Cold Stone Desire*, Eleri Stone; *Eddie Red Undercover: Mystery On Museum Mile*, Marcia Wells; *Embassy Row (series)*, Ally Carter; *Evernight*, Kristen Callihan; *Exposure Therapy*, Roni Loren; *Golden Boys*, Stacey Lee; *Hester*, Paula Reed; *Proof By Seduction*, Courtney Milan; *Rebel Mechanics*, Shanna Swendson; *Score*, Miranda Kenneally; *Shooting Stars*, Allison Rushby; *Soulless*, Gail Carriger; *The Bane Chronicles*, Cassandra Clare, Maureen Johnson, Sarah Rees Brennan; *The Cabinet of Curiosities*, Stefan Bachmann, Katherine Catmull, Claire Legrand, et al; *The Prize*, Jamie Ford; *The Siren*, Tiffany Reisz; *Tigerseye*, Jennifer Shaw Wolf; *Wool*, Hugh Howey; *Young Elites*, Marie Lu; *Younger Gods*, Michael Underwood
Foreign Rights: Jenny Meyer Literary Agency (Jenny Meyer) (Worldwide exc Asia)
Membership(s): Romance Writers of America; Science Fiction & Fantasy Writers of America; Society of Children's Book Writers & Illustrators

**New England Publishing Associates Inc** (L-D)
One Carver Place, Lawrenceville, GA 08648
Mailing Address: PO Box 66066, Lawrenceville, GA 08648-6066
*Tel:* 860-973-2439
*E-mail:* nepa@nepa.com; info@nepa.com; queries@nepa.com
*Web Site:* www.nepa.com
*Key Personnel*
Agent & Mng Dir: Roger S Williams (AAR)
Founded: 1983
No unsol mss, query first. See web site for details.
Foreign Rights: Rachel Calder (UK)
Membership(s): ABA; The Authors Guild; Organization of American Historians

**Regula Noetzli Literary Agent** (L)
Affiliate of Charlotte Sheedy Literary Agency Inc
2344 County Rte 83, Pine Plains, NY 12567
*Tel:* 518-398-6260
*E-mail:* Rregula@taconic.net; Regula@sheedylit.com
Adult fiction & nonfiction only with special interest in mysteries, biographies, psychology, popular science, sociology & environmental issues. Query first with outline & sample chapter. Representatives in Hollywood & most major foreign countries. No reading fees, no software.

**The Betsy Nolan Literary Agency** (L)
Division of The Nolan/Lehr Group Inc
214 W 29 St, Suite 1002, New York, NY 10001
*Tel:* 212-967-8200 *Fax:* 212-967-7292
*E-mail:* dblehr@cs.com
*Key Personnel*
Founding Partner: Betsy Nolan
Pres: Donald Lehr
Agent: Carla Glasser
Off Mgr: Jennifer Alperen
Nonfiction, popular culture, child care, psychology, cookbooks, how-to, biography, African-American & Judaica. No poetry. No unsol mss, query first; submit outline, no more than three sample chapters & author background; no reading fee; SASE.
Titles recently placed: *66 Square Feet*, Marie Viljoen; *Complete Herb Book*, Steven Orr; *Mad Hungry*, Lucinda Scala Quinn; *The Casserole Queens Cookbook: Put Some Lovin' in Your Oven with 100 Easy One-Dish Recipes*, Crystal Cook, Sandy Pollock

**Harold Ober Associates Inc** (L)
425 Madison Ave, New York, NY 10017
*Tel:* 212-759-8600 *Fax:* 212-759-9428
*Web Site:* www.haroldober.com
*Key Personnel*
Pres: Phyllis Westberg (AAR)
Agent: Jake Elwell (AAR)
Agent, Film Rts: Don Laventhall
Agent, Foreign Rts: Pamela Malpas (AAR)
Agent (backlist), Perms: Craig Tenney (AAR) *Tel:* 212-759-8600 ext 216
Founded: 1929
General fiction & nonfiction. No screenplays or plays. No e-mail queries. No unsol mss, query first with letter & SASE. Queries are accepted by postal mail & must be addressed to a specific agent for consideration. Enclose concise cover letter, the first five pages of the ms or proposal & SASE for reply. No reading fee.
Foreign Rep(s): David Higham Associates Ltd (UK)

**Objective Entertainment** (L-D)
609 Greenwich St, 6th fl, New York, NY 10014
*Tel:* 212-431-5454 *Fax:* 917-464-6394
*Web Site:* www.objectiveent.com
*Key Personnel*
COO: Jarred Weisfeld *E-mail:* Jarred@objectiveent.com
Pres: Ian Kleinert *E-mail:* IK@objectiveent.com
Head, Busn Aff: Mark S Frey *E-mail:* mfrey@marksfrey.com
Agent: Meghan Kilduff *E-mail:* mk@objectiveent.com; Leora Rosenberg *E-mail:* Leora@objectiveent.com
Founded: 2007
Full service management company specializing in book publishing, dramatic writing, talent & television packaging. Handles literary, dramatic & film rights, all commerical & adult trade publishing. No unsol mss. Submit query letter. No fees charged.

**Fifi Oscard Agency Inc** (L-D)
110 W 40 St, 16th fl, New York, NY 10018
*Tel:* 212-764-1100 *Fax:* 212-840-5019
*E-mail:* agency@fifioscard.com
*Web Site:* www.fifioscard.com
*Key Personnel*
Lit Agent: Carolyn French *E-mail:* cfrench@fifioscard.com; Carmen La Via *E-mail:* clavia@fifioscard.com; Kevin D McShane *E-mail:* kevin@fifioscard.com; Laura R Paperny *E-mail:* lrohman@fifioscard.com; Jerome Rudes *E-mail:* jh2001@aol.com; Peter Sawyer

*E-mail:* psawyer@fifioscard.com; Ivy Fischer Stone *E-mail:* ifischer@fifioscard.com
Founded: 1955
General fiction & nonfiction, all areas; film & TV rights; scripts for stage, motion picture & TV. Have always represented talent as well. No fees charged. No unsol mss, query first; submit outline & sample chapter if requested. See web site for more instruction.
Foreign Rep(s): Agenzia Letteraria Internazionale (Italy); Bardon-Chinese Media (China); Caroline Van Gelderan (Netherlands); Imprima Korea (Korea); Agence Michelle Lapautre (France); Thomas Schlueck (Germany); Abner Stein Agency (England); Julio F Yanez Agencia Literaria (Spain)

**Paraview Literary Agency** (L)
110 Martin Dr, Bracey, VA 23919
*Tel:* 434-636-4138
*Web Site:* www.paraviewliteraryagency.com
*Key Personnel*
Pres & Agent: Lisa Hagan
*E-mail:* paraview2000@yahoo.com
Founded: 1985
Business/investing/finance, health, memoir, mind/body/spirit, science, self-help, travel, political. No unsol mss, query first with letter & proposal. Submit outline & sample chapters. Handles film & TV rights. No fee charged.
Titles recently placed: *Heal Yourself*, Dr Lynne Zimmerman; *I See Your Soul Mate*, Sue Frederick; *Keep Out: Top Secret Places Governments Don't Want You to Know About*, Nick Redfern; *The Spiritual Girl's Guide to Dating*, Amy Leigh Mercree

**The Richard Parks Agency** (L)
PO Box 693, Salem, NY 12865
*Tel:* 518-854-9466 *Fax:* 518-854-9466
*E-mail:* rp@richardparksagency.com
*Key Personnel*
Contact: Richard Parks (AAR)
Founded: 1989
Fiction & nonfiction. No unsol mss, query first with SASE only, cannot respond to phone, fax or e-mail queries. No reading fee; fees for photocopies only at cost to us.
Foreign Rep(s): Barbara Levy Literary Agency (UK)
Foreign Rights: The Marsh Agency

**Kathi J Paton Literary Agency** (L)
Box 2236, Radio City Sta, New York, NY 10101-2236
*Tel:* 212-265-6586 *Fax:* 908-647-2117
*E-mail:* kjplitbiz@optonline.net
*Web Site:* www.patonliterary.com
*Key Personnel*
Owner: Kathi J Paton
Founded: 1987
Interested in biography, computers/technology, business/investing/finance, history, health, sports, science, literary fiction, parenting, Christian life & issues, popular culture, humor, investigative journalism & progressive politics/current affairs. No unsol mss; e-mail queries only with a brief description. If requested, e-mail proposal (nonfiction) or synopsis (fiction) & sample chapter. Sorry, no science fiction, horror, poetry, juvenile or self-published books. No reading fee. Subs-agents in all major foreign markets & Hollywood.
Titles recently placed: *Wild New Jersey: Nature Adventures in the Garden State*, David Wheeler, Margaret O'Gorman
Membership(s): The Authors Guild

**Pema Browne Ltd** (L)
71 Pine Rd, Woodbourne, NY 12788
*E-mail:* ppbltd@optonline.net
*Web Site:* www.pemabrowneltd.com
*Key Personnel*
Pres: Pema Browne
VP: Perry Browne
Founded: 1966
All subjects including genre romance, mass market & trade; fiction, nonfiction, business, how-to, cookbooks, health, reference, inspirational. Children's picture books, novelty, middle-grade, young adult, illustration. No unsol mss, query first (no fax, e-mail or phone queries). Submit cover letter, one page query with bio & SASE. Neat, wide margins, dark type, double-spaced, only one side of paper printed. We do NOT review mss that have previously been sent out to publishers. No reading fee. Work with foreign agents in major countries. Signatory to Writers Guild, Society of Children's Book Writers & Illustrators, Romance Writers of America.
Titles recently placed: *Fire and Smoke*, Susan Scott; *Never Kiss A Stranger*, Heather Grothaus; *Never Seduce A Scoundrel*, Heather Grothaus; *Salvation*, Susan Scott; *To Fight With Intrepidity*, JD Lock
Membership(s): Romance Writers of America; Society of Children's Book Writers & Illustrators; Writers Guild of America

**Dan Peragine Literary Agency** (L)
227 Beechwood Ave, Bogota, NJ 07603
*Tel:* 201-390-0468
*E-mail:* dpliterary@aol.com
*Key Personnel*
Owner & Pres: Dan Peragine (AAR)
EVP: Karen A Peragine
Founded: 1991
Specialize in behavioral sciences, biography, environment, history, Christian, inspirational, nonfiction, self-help, computers, sports, photography, all high school & college textbooks, Advanced placement & testing. Musical Groups, World War I, World War II, Handle software, film & TV rights. Represent photographic archives & books of all types. No unsol mss, query first with a complete proposal; if sending fiction, include any type of readers report or outside review with the submission; submit sample chapters single page, double spaced, or on disk (do not send by e-mail if it needs to be downloaded). No reading fees, fees charged for editorial development, re-writes, ghost writers, publishing consulting, full book packaging & book marketing.
Membership(s): ABA; ASPP; National Press Photographers Association; PPA

**Stephen Pevner Inc** (L-D)
382 Lafayette St, Suite 8, New York, NY 10003
*Tel:* 212-674-8403 *Fax:* 212-529-3692
*E-mail:* spidevelopment@gmail.com
*Key Personnel*
Pres: Stephen Pevner *E-mail:* spevner@aol.com
Founded: 1991
New fiction & general nonfiction, pop culture, humor, international film, TV & audio & electronic rights, plays, screenplays, independent producers & directors. No unsol mss or scripts, query first with SASE; submit outline & sample chapters or synopsis. No reading fees.

**Alison Picard Literary Agent** (L-D)
PO Box 2000, Cotuit, MA 02635
*Tel:* 508-477-7192 *Fax:* 508-477-7192 (call first)
*E-mail:* ajpicard@aol.com
Founded: 1985
Representing adult & juvenile/young adult fiction & nonfiction. Beginners welcome. No unsol mss, query first with letter & SASE; no phone or fax queries. Upon positive response, submit double-spaced complete ms. No fees charged.
Titles recently placed: *365 Days of Slow Cooker Recipes*, Stephanie O'Dea; *Curse of the Jade Lily*, David Housewright; *Decided on the Battlefield*, David Johnson; *Fear of Beauty*, Susan Froetschel; *Not Your Mother's Freezer Cookbook*, Jessica Fisher; *Seconds (new ed)*, David Ely; *The Efficiency Trap: Finding a Better Way to Achieve a Sustainable Energy Future*, Steve Hallett; *The Finest Hours (middle grade ed)*, Michael Tougias, Casey Sherman; *Three Cheers for Girls*, Sara Hunt; *Torn*, Stephanie Guerra; *Totally Together: Shortcuts to an Organized Life*, Stephanie O'Dea
Foreign Rights: John Pawsey (Europe)

**The Pimlico Agency Inc** (L)
PO Box 20490, New York, NY 10017
*Tel:* 212-628-9729 *Fax:* 212-535-7861
*Key Personnel*
Pres: Kay McCauley *E-mail:* kaymcc25@aol.com
Busn Mgr: Christopher Shepard
Agent: Kirby McCauley
Asst: Rose Carpio
Founded: 1974
Adult fiction & nonfiction. Motion picture & TV rights from book properties only. No unsol mss. Projects by referral only. No reading fee. Agents in all principal foreign countries.

**Pinder Lane & Garon-Brooke Associates Ltd** (L-D)
159 W 53 St, New York, NY 10019
*Tel:* 212-489-0880 *Fax:* 212-489-7104
*E-mail:* pinderlaneandgaronbrooke@gmail.com
*Web Site:* www.pinderlaneandgaronbrooke.com
*Key Personnel*
Owner & Agent: Dick Duane (AAR); Robert Thixton (AAR)
Founded: 1996
Fiction & nonfiction, film & TV rights. No unsol mss, query first. No reading fee. Submit short synopsis, double spaced & unbound. Representatives in Hollywood & all foreign markets.
Foreign Rep(s): Abner Stein Agency (UK)
Foreign Rights: Rights Unlimited

**Pippin Properties Inc** (L)
155 E 38 St, Suite 2-H, New York, NY 10016
*Tel:* 212-338-9310 *Fax:* 212-338-9579
*E-mail:* info@pippinproperties.com
*Web Site:* www.pippinproperties.com
*Key Personnel*
Founder & Owner: Holly M McGhee
Foreign Rts Dir: Alex Webb *E-mail:* alexwebb@rightspeople.com
Agent & Contracts Mgr: Joan Slattery
Agent & Mgr, Foreign & Audio Rts: Elena Mechlin *E-mail:* emechlin@pippinproperties.com
Agent: Julie Just
Represent authors & artists for children's picture books, middle-grade novels, chapter books & young adult novels. No unsol mss, query first with letter for lengthier submissions. For all submissions, include SASE. Handle film, TV & foreign rights. No fees charged.

**PMA Literary & Film Management Inc** (L-D)
Affiliate of Millennium Lion Inc & Global Lion Intellectual Properties Management Inc
PO Box 1817, Old Chelsea Sta, New York, NY 10113
*Tel:* 212-929-1222 *Fax:* 212-206-0238
*E-mail:* queries@pmalitfilm.com
*Web Site:* www.pmalitfilm.com
*Key Personnel*
Pres: Peter Miller
Dir, Subs Rts & Literary Mgr: Adrienne Rosado
Asst to the Pres: Christen Mecabe
Represents transformational & spiritual nonfiction, young adult, commercial fiction, nonfiction, true crime & celebrity books. Handles film & TV rights. Represent literary & film properties internationally. No unsol mss, query first. Submit one page synopsis or finished treatment & author bio. See web site for ad-

ditional submission guidelines. Co-agents in select foreign territories & deal directly with foreign publishers. Affiliate packages & produces feature films & TV. No fees charged.
Titles recently placed: *A Gift For My Sister*, Ann Pearlman; *Discover the Gift*, Shajen Joy Aziz, Demian Lichtenstein; *Divinity of Doubt*, Vincent Bugliosi; *Finding Your Element: How to Live a Life of Passion & Purpose*, Ken Robinson, Lou Aronica; *Pinkerton's War: Assassins, Insurgents & the Birth of the Secret Service*, Jay Bonansinga; *Secrets of the Dragon Gate*, Dr Steven Liu, Jonathan Blank; *Supreme Influence*, Niurka; *The Black Stiletto*, Raymond Benson; *The Colony*, A J Colucci; *The Devil & the Gunmaker*, M William Phelps; *The Fire Island Cookbook*, Mike De Simone, Jeff Jenssen; *The Invisible World*, Anthony De Stefano; *The Royal Treatment*, Dr Barbara Royal
Foreign Rep(s): Big Apple Agency Inc (China); Peter Bolza (Hungary); Tuttle-Mori Agency Inc (Japan)

**Poirot Literary Agency** (L)
3887 Nimbus Rd, Longmont, CO 80503
*Tel:* 303-494-0668 *Fax:* 303-494-9396
*E-mail:* poirotco@comcast.net
*Key Personnel*
Pres: Henry M Poirot
Founded: 1976
Nonfiction, no poetry. Handle film & TV rights. No unsol mss, query first. No reading fee.

**Pom Inc** (L-D)
21 Vista Dr, Great Neck, NY 11021
*Tel:* 516-487-3441
*Key Personnel*
Pres: Dan Green *E-mail:* dangreen@pomlit.com
Founded: 1990
Fiction & general nonfiction. No unsol mss. Please do not fax or e-mail. Handle electronic, film & TV rights. No reading fee.
Titles recently placed: *Elizabeth Patterson Bonaparte*, Charlene M Boyer Lewis; *The Fall of the House of Dixie: The Civil War and the Social Revolution That Transformed the South*, Bruce Levine; *The Scarlet Sisters: Sex, Scandal and Suffrage in the Gilded Age*, Myra MacPherson

**The Poynor Group** (L)
13454 Yorktown Dr, Bowie, MD 20715
*Tel:* 301-805-6788
*Key Personnel*
Pres: Jay Poynor *E-mail:* jpoynor@aol.com
Founded: 1985
Literary representation service & sales. Submit e-mail query first (mandatory). If agreeable, then send a synopsis & first three chapters. Commission: 15% of advance & royalties. No other fees.

**Linn Prentis Literary** (L)
6830 NE Bothell Way, PMB 496, Kenmore, WA 98028
*Tel:* 212-876-8557 *Fax:* 206-984-0837
*E-mail:* linn@linnprentis.com
*Web Site:* www.linnprentis.com
*Key Personnel*
Literary Agent: Linn Prentis
Fine fiction, limited nonfiction: special interest in speculative fiction, science fiction & fantasy. Special interest in family saga. Also mainstream, women's, literary, young adult & middle-reader, men's, mystery, suspense, historical, non-category romance. Literary nonfiction. Film rights only as outgrowth of book sales through Bill Contardi, New York. No phone, fax or e-mail queries; no unsol mss; query by mail with SASE; cover letter (credits, bio facts, word count, title & genre/target audience) 2 page synopsis, first 10 pages. Mss: double-spaced, unbound, one side of page, boxed with cover. No reading fee; 15% commission, 20% on dramatic & foreign sales. Founded as an affiliate of the Virginia Kidd Agency, now independent.
Foreign Rep(s): ALI (Italy); P & P Fritz (Germany); International Editors' Co (Portugal, South America, Spain); Korshenevski (Russia & former USSR); Lenclud (France); LEX (Hungary); MBA (Meg Davis) (UK); PIP (Eastern Europe); Lennart Sane (Scandinavia); Tuttle-Mori Agency Inc (Japan)
Membership(s): Science Fiction & Fantasy Writers of America

**The Aaron M Priest Literary Agency Inc** (L)
708 Third Ave, 23rd fl, New York, NY 10017-4201
*Tel:* 212-818-0344 *Fax:* 212-573-9417
*E-mail:* info@aaronpriest.com
*Web Site:* www.aaronpriest.com
*Key Personnel*
Pres & Agent: Aaron M Priest (AAR)
*E-mail:* querypriest@aaronpriest.com
Agent: Lucy Childs Baker (AAR)
*E-mail:* querychilds@aaronpriest.com; Nicole James (AAR) *E-mail:* queryjames@aaronpriest.com; Arleen Gradinger Priest; John Richmond; Lisa Erbach Vance (AAR) *E-mail:* queryvance@aaronpriest.com
Asst: Melissa Edwards *E-mail:* medwards@aaronpriest.com
Founded: 1974
Our agents are interested in the following. Aaron Priest: thrillers, general fiction. Lisa Erbach Vance: general fiction, mystery, thrillers, up market women's fiction, historical fiction, narrative nonfiction, memoir. Lucy Childs: literary & commercial fiction, historical fiction, memoir, edgy women's fiction. Nicole James: literary fiction, women's fiction, gay fiction, young adult fiction, pop culture & political nonfiction. For all agents: no poetry, no screenplays. The best way to query all agents is to submit a query letter via e-mail. The query should be about one page long describing your work as well as your background. No attachments, however a first chapter pasted into the body of an e-mail query is acceptable. Do not submit to more than one agent at a time at this agency (we urge you to consider each agent's emphasis before submitting). We will get back to you within four weeks, but only if interested. No fees are charged.

**Prospect Agency** (L)
285 Fifth Ave, PMB 445, Brooklyn, NY 11215
*Tel:* 718-788-3217 *Fax:* 718-360-9582
*Web Site:* www.prospectagency.com
*Key Personnel*
Founder & Literary Agent: Emily Sylvan Kim
*E-mail:* esk@prospectagency.com
Literary Agent: Teresa Kietlinski *E-mail:* tk@prospectagency.com; Rachel Orr *E-mail:* rko@prospectagency.com; Carrie Pestritto; Becca Stumpf *E-mail:* becca@prospectagency.com
Founded: 2005
Full service literary agency representing a range of fiction, nonfiction, illustrators, romance, literary fiction, middle grade fiction & picture books, adult commercial fiction, women's fiction & young adult titles. No unsol mss, query first via web. Only queries submitted through our web site are accepted. Queries sent by e-mail or regular mail not accepted. Send query letter, three chapters & a brief synopsis on web site. No fees charged. See web site for detailed submission guidelines.
Titles recently placed: *Badd*, Tim Tharp

*Branch Office(s)*
551 Valley Rd, PMB 377, Upper Montclair, NJ 07043
Foreign Rights: The Fielding Agency (Whitney Lee) (Worldwide)

**Generosa Gina Protano Publishing**, see GGP Publishing Inc

**Publishing Services** (L)
525 E 86 St, Suite 8-E, New York, NY 10028
*Tel:* 212-628-9127 *Fax:* 212-628-9128
*E-mail:* publishingservices@mac.com
*Key Personnel*
Pres: Amy S Goldberger
Upscale women's fiction & nonfiction. No unsol mss, query first with SASE. No phone calls. For fiction, send first 50 pages. For nonfiction, send outline & first three chapters. Handle film & TV rights. No reading fee.

**Puddingstone Literary, Authors' Agents** (L-D)
Subsidiary of Cohen Group LLC
11 Mabro Dr, Denville, NJ 07834-9607
*Tel:* 973-366-3622
*Key Personnel*
Dir: Alec Bernard
Sr Memb: Saul Cohen
Memb: Michael R Cohen
Contact: Eugenia Kielbicki
Founded: 1972
General trade & mass market fiction & nonfiction; motion picture scripts & teleplays. Handle film & TV rights. No unsol mss, query first with SASE. Submit outline & sample chapters. No reading fee. Representatives in Hollywood & foreign countries. Fee for ms copies, galleys & bound books for foreign & domestic submissions.

**Susan Rabiner Literary Agency Inc** (L)
315 W 39 St, Suite 1501, New York, NY 10018-3907
*Web Site:* RabinerLit.com
*Key Personnel*
Pres: Susan Rabiner *E-mail:* susan@rabiner.net
Agent: Holly Bemiss *E-mail:* hollyb@rabiner.net; Sydelle Kramer *E-mail:* sydellek@rabiner.net; Eric Nelson; Helena Schwarz *E-mail:* helens@rabiner.net
Founded: 1997
Serious nonfiction, narrative nonfiction, business, memoirs, sports, college texts; history, politics, economics, psychology, science, gender studies, popular culture, education, anthropology, archeology, law & biography. Represent trade authors trying to place their mss with the major commercial publishing houses. Also represent a limited number of college text authors. Primarily academics, journalists, scientists & independent scholars; query first by e-mail as an attachment, no faxes; no reading fees. No screenplays, poetry or fiction.
Titles recently placed: *A Fleece of Celestial Importance*, Greg Grandin; *Lady Bird & Lyndon*, Betty Caroli; *Paleocapitalism*, Jacob Hacker, Paul Pierson; *That Infamous Woman Polly Adler*, Debby Applegate; *The Age of Eisenhower*, William Hitchcock; *The Everyday Parenting Toolkit: The Kazdin Method for Easy, Step-by-Step, Lasting Change for You and Your Child*, Alan Kazdin, Carlo Rotella; *The Grid*, Gretchen Bakke; *The Indispensable Nation*, Vali Nasr; *The Signal & the Noise*, Nate Silver
Foreign Rights: The English Agency (Japan); Agence Hoffmann (Germany); Agnese Incisa (Italy)

**Raines & Raines** (L-D)
103 Kenyon Rd, Medusa, NY 12120
*Tel:* 518-239-8311 *Fax:* 518-239-6029

*Key Personnel*
Partner: Joan Raines; Theron Raines (AAR)
Assoc: Keith Korman
Founded: 1961
Handle film & TV rights. No unsol mss, query first; submit one page; no reading fee. Agents in all principal countries.
Foreign Rep(s): Agenzia Letteraria Internazionale; Balcells; Big Apple Agency Inc; Bookman; Campbell Thomson & McLaughlin; Fritz; Lapautre; Nurnberg; Tuttle-Mori Agency Inc

**Charlotte Cecil Raymond, Literary Agent** (L)
32 Bradlee Rd, Marblehead, MA 01945
*Tel:* 781-631-6722 *Fax:* 781-631-6722
*E-mail:* raymondliterary@gmail.com
Adult nonfiction & literary fiction; no juvenile, young adult, poetry, short stories, fantasy, science fiction or screenplays. No unsol mss, query first with SASE; submit outline & sample chapters. No reading fee.

**Rees Literary Agency** (L)
14 Beacon St, Suite 710, Boston, MA 02108
*Tel:* 617-227-9014 *Fax:* 617-227-8762
*E-mail:* reesagency@reesagency.com
*Web Site:* reesagency.com
*Key Personnel*
Agent: Ann Collette *E-mail:* agent10702@aol.com; Nicole LaBombard (AAR) *E-mail:* nicole@reesagency.com; Mr Lorin Rees (AAR) *E-mail:* lorin@reesagency.com
Founded: 1982
Literary fiction, nonfiction, business, biography, health, history, self-help, psychology, current affairs, humor, mystery, thrillers, etc. For fiction, include query letter &/or synopsis & the first three chapters. For nonfiction, enclose a complete book proposal or substantial treatment.
Titles recently placed: *A Hatred of Tulips*, Richard Lourie; *Andy Grove*, Richard Tedlow; *Art's Blood*, Vicki Lane; *Blood Makes the Grass Grow Green*, Johnny Rico; *Bone Factory*, Steve Sidor; *Busy Monsters*, William Giraldi; *Clair Fontaine, Crime Fighter*, Tracey Enright; *Driving Excellence: Management Principles From the Little Bus Company That Could*, Mark Aesch; *Girl Most Likely To*, Poonam Sharma; *Hot Spots*, Martin Fletcher; *Innovation Nation*, John Kao; *Leadership Therapy: Inside the Mind of Microsoft*, Anna Rowley; *Letter from Kabul*, Hamid Karzi; *Out Of Thin Air: The Book On Entrepreneurship*, Gregg Fairbrothers, Tessa Winter; *Primal Health*, William Meller; *Selling B2B Made Simple*, Geoffrey James; *Stirring it Up: How Business Can & Must Save the World*, Gary Hirshberg; *The Border Crosser*, Johnny Rico; *The Satisfied Customer*, Claes Fornell; *The Ultimate Sales Machine*, Chet Holmes; *Travel Writing*, Peter Ferry; *What Americans Really Want...Really*, Frank Luntz; *What Israel Means to Me*, Alan Dershowitz; *Who: Solve Your #1 Problem*, Geoff Smart, Randy Street; *Why Terrorism Works*, Alan Dershowitz; *Winning*, Jack Welch; *Words that Work*, Frank Luntz; *You Know When The Men Are Gone*, Siobhan Fallon
Foreign Rights: Taryn Fagerness (Albania, Argentina, Australia, Brazil, Bulgaria, Canada, China, Croatia, Czech Republic, Denmark, Estonia, Finland, France, Germany, Greece, Hungary, Iceland, India, Indonesia, Israel, Italy, Japan, Korea, Latvia, Lithuania, Mexico, Netherlands, Norway, Poland, Portugal, Romania, Russia, Serbia, Slovakia, Slovenia, Spain, Sweden, Taiwan, Thailand, Turkey, UK, Vietnam)
Membership(s): PEN American Center

**Marian Reiner** (L)
71 Disbrow Lane, New Rochelle, NY 10804
*Tel:* 914-235-7808 *Fax:* 914-576-1432
*E-mail:* mreinerlit@aol.com
Founded: 1963
Handle only work for children; fiction, nonfiction. No unsol mss. No online submissions. No new clients. No reading fee. Charge for photocopying & overseas phone & mail. Handle film & TV rights only for books agency sold.
Membership(s): The Authors Guild; Society of Authors & Illustrators; Society of Children's Book Writers & Illustrators

**Renaissance Literary & Talent** (L-D)
PO Box 17379, Beverly Hills, CA 90209
*Tel:* 323-848-8305
*E-mail:* query@renaissancemgmt.net
*Key Personnel*
Owner: Alan Nevins *E-mail:* alan@renaissancemgmt.net
Commercial fiction & nonfiction. Handle film & TV rights; novels. No unsol mss. Query first. Handle highly recommended mss. Submit outlines & sample chapters. No reading fee, 15% commission.

**The Amy Rennert Agency Inc** (L)
1550 Tiburon Blvd, Suite 302, Tiburon, CA 94920
*Tel:* 415-789-8955
*E-mail:* queries@amyrennert.com
*Web Site:* amyrennert.com
*Key Personnel*
Pres: Amy Rennert
Busn Mgr: Margie Perez
Assoc: Robyn Russell *E-mail:* robyn@amyrennert.com
Founded: 1999
The agency specializes in books that matter. Amy has spent more than 20 years in the publishing business, pursuing her passion for the written word. The agency represents a select group of quality fiction & nonfiction writers - many of them award-winners & dozens of agency books have been New York Times & national bestsellers. We provide career management for established & first time authors & our breadth of experience in many genres enables us to meet the needs of a diverse clientele. The agency has developed a reputation since its inception for a passionate commitment to agency writers. We are purposely a small organization to facilitate hands-on personalized service & attention to our authors & their books. We prefer to receive submissions via e-mail sent to queries@amyrennert.com. No reading fees. No submissions via phone or any other e-mail address. For nonfiction, submit cover letter in the body of an e-mail & attach a Word file with the proposal & first chapter. For fiction & sometimes memoir, send a cover letter in the body of an e-mail & attach a Word file with the first 10-20 pages. Due to the high volume of submissions, it is not possible to respond to each & every one. We are usually only able to respond to submissions we feel may be a good fit with our agency.
Foreign Rights: Chandler Crawford (Europe, Japan); Abner Stein Agency (England)
Membership(s): The Authors Guild

**Jodie Rhodes Literary Agency** (L)
8840 Villa La Jolla Dr, Suite 315, La Jolla, CA 92037
*E-mail:* jrhodesl@san.rr.com
*Web Site:* www.jodierhodesliterary.com
*Key Personnel*
Pres: Jodie Rhodes
Fiction Agent at Large: Clark McCutcheon
Nonfiction Agent at Large: Robert McCarter
Foreign Rts Agent: Jill Hughes
Founded: 1998
Established to bring talented new writers to the attention of publishers & establish a successful long term career for all writers. Interested in literary fiction, memoirs, intelligent, sophisticated mysteries, suspense & thrillers with fresh original plots, women's books with a unique story, quirky coming-of-age books, African American & multicultural literature, both fiction & nonfiction, politics, history, military, international affairs, science, medicine, health, fitness, women's issues, parenting. Have no interest in science fiction, fantasy, horror, erotica, religion, spiritual or inspiration books. Also do not handle children's books, only a few literary young adult/teen novels. Send query, brief synopsis, first 30 to 50 pages, SASE with stamps—not metered slip. No fees charged; handles film & TV rights. Do not call or e-mail us. We will contact you if your query &/or sample pages interest us. You do not have to enclose a SASE but we will not reply without a SASE unless your query has generated great interest - in case that occurs, always include your e-mail address with your query letter. Important: We cannot return any material that weights 13 ounces or more, even if you enclose a SASE – so if you send material that weights that much, keep in mind the material will not be returned to you.
Titles recently placed: *A Year of Cats & Dogs*, Margaret Hawkins; *Aging: Modern Theories & Therapies*, Joseph Panno; *Black Boy - White School*, Brian Walker; *Black Sea Twilight*, Domnica Radulescu; *Bombay Girl*, Kavita Daswani; *Broken Blue Line*, Connie Dial; *Combat Trama*, James D Johnson; *Computers and Creativity*, Robert Plotkin; *Computers, Internet & Society*, Robert Plotkin; *Computers, Internet and Society*, Robert Plotkin; *Confessions: A Memoir*, Jodie Rhodes; *Cosmic Numbers*, James D Stein, PhD; *Critical Components of J R R Tolkien*, Jay Ruud; *Dead Wrong*, Connie Dial; *Do You Really Need Back Surgery*, Aaron G Filler; *Encyclopedia of Enviromental Studies*, Marc Menetrez; *Encyclopedia of Science and Technology*, William Gough; *Fallen Angels*, Connie Dial; *Fighting for Dontae*, Mike Castan; *First Six Minutes of Life on Earth*, Christine Reed; *Forensic Science at Work*, Jay Siegal; *How to Survive a Natural Disaster*, Margaret Hawkins; *How We Got Barb Back*, Margaret Hawkins; *Impossible Problems, Ingenious Solutions: What Math and Science Do When They Hit the Wall*, James D Stein, PhD; *Internal Affairs*, Connie Dial; *Iran's Revolutionary Guard*, Stephen O'Hern; *Life of Earth*, Stanley A Rice; *Lovetorn*, Kavita Daswani; *My Beautiful Hippie*, Janet Nichols Lynch; *Nuclear Accidents and Disasters (Nuclear Power)*, James A Mahaffey; *Racing California*, Janet Nichols Lynch; *Straightening the Bell Curve: How Stereotypes about Black Masculinity Drive Research on Race and Intelligence*, Constance Hilliard; *Stranded*, J T Dutton; *The Alzheimer's Answer*, Marwan Sabbagh; *The Genie in the Machine*, Robert Plotkin; *The History of Nuclear Power*, James A Mahaffey; *The Night Battles*, M F Bloxam; *The Paranormal Equation: A New Scientific Perspective on Remote Viewing, Clairvoyance, and Other Inexplicable Phenomena*, James D Stein, PhD; *The Price of Loyalty*, Mike Castan; *The Red Flag in American Bathrooms*, Dr Wesley Jones; *Understanding Biodiversity*, Julie Casper
Foreign Rep(s): The English Agency (Japan); KCC Agency (Korea)
Foreign Rights: Jill Hughes Literary Agency (Worldwide)

**Rights Unlimited Inc** (L)
6 W 37 St, New York, NY 10001
*Tel:* 212-246-0900 *Fax:* 212-246-2114
*E-mail:* rightsunlimited@gmail.com
*Web Site:* rightsunlimited.com

*Key Personnel*
Pres: John Sansevere
International rights. No fees charged.

**John R Riina Literary Agency** (L)
1055 W Joppa Rd, Unit 651, Towson, MD 21204-3777
*Tel:* 410-296-1499
Founded: 1972
Nonfiction books: science, health, medicine, textbooks & how-to. No unsol mss, query first with author's bio, one paragraph synopsis & outline. No return of material without SASE. No reading fee. No phone queries.

**The Angela Rinaldi Literary Agency** (L)
PO Box 7877, Beverly Hills, CA 90212-7877
*Tel:* 310-842-7665 *Fax:* 310-837-8143
*Web Site:* www.rinaldiliterary.com
*Key Personnel*
Pres: Angela Rinaldi (AAR) *E-mail:* amr@rinaldiliterary.com
Founded: 1994
Commercial & literary fiction, nonfiction, lifestyle/travel/food. Accept unsol mss. Do not query by phone or fax. E-mail queries only, no attachments unless requested. Advise if sending out multiple submissions. Fiction submissions: Paste the first ten pages in the e-mail query. Nonfiction submissions: query with detailed covering letter. No reading fee. Representation in film & foreign markets for clients only.
Titles recently placed: *Beer, Food, and Flavor: A Guide to Tasting, Pairing, and the Culture of Craft Beer*, Schuyler Schultz; *Hand-Crafted Candy Bars: From-Scratch, All-Natural, Gloriously Grown-Up Confections*, Susan Heeger, Susie Norris; *Little Girl Gone*, Drusilla Campbell
Membership(s): PEN Center USA West

**Ann Rittenberg Literary Agency Inc** (L)
15 Maiden Lane, Suite 206, New York, NY 10038
*Tel:* 212-684-6936 *Fax:* 212-684-6929
*Web Site:* www.rittlit.com
*Key Personnel*
Pres: Ann Rittenberg (AAR)
Assoc Agent: Penn Whaling
Contact: Peri Halprin
Founded: 1992
Literary fiction & nonfiction; no genre fiction, no screenplays. Co-agents in all principal foreign countries as well as Hollywood. Query letter & first three chapters of double-spaced ms with SASE; no queries by fax.
Titles recently placed: *Back of Beyond*, C J Box; *Darkness All Around*, Doug Magee; *Hideout*, Kathleen George; *The Odds*, Kathleen George
Membership(s): The Authors Guild

**Judith Riven Literary Agent LLC** (L)
250 W 16 St, Suite 4F, New York, NY 10011
*Tel:* 212-255-1009 *Fax:* 212-255-8547
*E-mail:* rivenlitqueries@gmail.com
*Web Site:* rivenlit.com
*Key Personnel*
Owner & Pres: Judith Riven
Founded: 1993
Fiction & nonfiction. Handle film & TV rights for book clients only. One page query letter describing material with SASE. Unless requested, no mss accepted. E-mail queries are accepted but no attachments.
Titles recently placed: *Kneadlessly Simple: Fabulous, Fuss-Free, No-Knead Breads*, Nancy Baggett; *The Love-Lust Dilemma: Bridging the Gap Between Heart & Libido*, Stella Resnick, PhD; *The Sins of Brother Curtis: A Story of Betrayal, Conviction, and the Mormon Church*, Lisa Davis

**Riverside Literary Agency** (L)
41 Simon Keets Rd, Leyden, MA 01337
*Tel:* 413-772-0067 *Fax:* 413-772-0969
*E-mail:* rivlit@sover.net
*Web Site:* www.riversideliteraryagency.com
*Key Personnel*
Pres: Susan Lee Cohen
Founded: 1990
Adult fiction & nonfiction. No unsol mss, query first with SASE. No reading fees. Handle film & TV rights & foreign rights with co-agents.

**RLR Associates Ltd** (L-D)
7 W 51 St, New York, NY 10019
*Tel:* 212-541-8641 *Fax:* 212-262-7084
*Web Site:* www.rlrassociates.net
*Key Personnel*
Literary Agent: Scott Gould (AAR)
*E-mail:* sgould@rlrassociates.net
Founded: 1980
A boutique literary agency in Manhattan, representing fiction of all types (from genre to literary) & narrative nonfiction. No unsol mss; e-mail or regular mail query letters.

**RMA** (L)
612 Argyle Rd, Suite L-5, Brooklyn, NY 11230
*Tel:* 718-434-1893
*Web Site:* www.ricia.com
*Key Personnel*
Owner: Ricia Mainhardt *E-mail:* ricia@ricia.com
VP, West Coast Opers: Charla Mustard-Foote
Founded: 1987
Popular fiction, especially science fiction, fantasy, mystery, thriller, romance; nonfiction, especially pop culture, history & science. Do not accept poetry. No unsol mss. Query with SASE. Online submissions accepted. Submit query letter, brief synopsis & initial consecutive 2 or 3 chapters (20-30 pages). For e-mail, the same should be cut & pasted into the body of the e-mail, no attachments. Handle software for client's books only. Affiliates handle film & TV rights for client's books. No reading fee. Branch offices in Seattle & Hollywood.

**B J Robbins Literary Agency** (L)
5130 Bellaire Ave, North Hollywood, CA 91607
*E-mail:* robbinsliterary@gmail.com
*Key Personnel*
Owner & Pres: B J Robbins (AAR)
Agent: Amy Drake *E-mail:* amy.bjrobbinsliterary@gmail.com
Founded: 1992
Literary & commercial fiction, general nonfiction. Handle film & TV rights for agency clients only. E-mail queries accepted. No unsol attachments. Mailed submissions must include SASE.
Titles recently placed: *Headhunters on My Doorstep*, J Maarten Troost; *Shake Down the Stars*, Renee Swindle; *The Blood of Heroes*, James Donovan; *THe Blood of the Tiger*, J A Mills; *The Paris Deadline*, Max Byrd; *The Sinatra Club*, Sal Polisi, Steve Dougherty
Foreign Rights: The Marsh Agency (all other territories); Abner Stein Agency (UK)
Membership(s): PEN Center USA

**Rockmill & Company** (L)
647 Warren St, Brooklyn, NY 11217
*Tel:* 718-638-3990
*E-mail:* agentrockmill@yahoo.com
*Web Site:* www.rockmillandcompany.com
*Key Personnel*
Pres & Agent: Jayne Rockmill
Founded: 1989
Represents artists, photographers & writers, specializing in illustrated books & licensing. Initial submission is preferred by e-mail. For illustrated titles, submit a 1 page book summary, with sample text & illustrations along with author bio. For fiction & nonfiction book projects, submit a query letter with 3 sample chapters. Send SASE if anything needs to be returned. No fee charged to review project.
Titles recently placed: *Makeup for Ageless Beauty: More than 40 Colorful, Creative Looks for Women 40 and Over*, Linda Mason

**Linda Roghaar Literary Agency LLC** (L)
133 High Point Dr, Amherst, MA 01002
*Tel:* 413-256-1921 *Fax:* 413-256-2636
*E-mail:* contact@lindaroghaar.com
*Web Site:* www.lindaroghaar.com
*Key Personnel*
Owner & Pres: Linda L Roghaar (AAR)
*E-mail:* linda@lindaroghaar.com
Founded: 1996
Full-service agency handling mainly nonfiction; women's issues, religion & spirituality, history, self-help, memoir. Manage comprehensive rights. Query with SASE first. No reading fee. Domestic sales commission: 15%. No unsol mss.

**The Roistacher Literary Agency** (L)
545 W 111 St, Suite 7-J, New York, NY 10025
*Tel:* 212-222-1405
*Key Personnel*
Pres: Robert E Roistacher *E-mail:* rer41@columbia.edu
Founded: 1978
General nonfiction, especially journalism, social science & public policy. Literary fiction only from published writers. No unsol mss, query first. For nonfiction, submit prospectus, curriculum vitae, two sample chapters, chapter outline & table of contents. No reading fee.

**The Rosenberg Group** (L)
23 Lincoln Ave, Marblehead, MA 01945
*Tel:* 781-990-1341 *Fax:* 781-990-1344
*Web Site:* www.rosenberggroup.com
*Key Personnel*
Agent: Barbara Collins Rosenberg (AAR)
Founded: 1998
Representing romance & women's fiction, trade nonfiction & college level textbooks for the first & second year courses. Check web site for areas of nonfiction interest. No unsol ms, query first. No reading fee. No e-mail queries. Representatives in all foreign markets.
Membership(s): Romance Writers of America

**Rita Rosenkranz Literary Agency** (L)
440 West End Ave, Suite 15D, New York, NY 10024-5358
*Tel:* 212-873-6333 *Fax:* 212-873-5225
*Web Site:* www.ritarosenkranzliteraryagency.com
*Key Personnel*
Agent: Rita Rosenkranz (AAR)
*E-mail:* rrosenkranz@mindspring.com
Founded: 1990
Nonfiction, adult; no unsol mss, query first with SASE or via e-mail; no fees.
Membership(s): The Authors Guild; International Women's Writing Guild; Women's Media Group

**Jane Rotrosen Agency LLC** (L)
318 E 51 St, New York, NY 10022
*Tel:* 212-593-4330 *Fax:* 212-935-6985
*Web Site:* janerotrosen.com
*Key Personnel*
Founder: Jane Rotrosen Berkey (AAR)
Dir, Subs Rts: Peggy Gordijn *E-mail:* pgordijn@janerotrosen.com
Mgr, Contracts & Opers: Christina Prestia
*E-mail:* cprestia@janerotrosen.com
Agent: Andrea Cirillo *E-mail:* acirillo@janerotrosen.com; Christina Hogrebe *E-mail:* chogrebe@janerotrosen.com; Annelise Robey *E-mail:* arobey@janerotrosen.com; Meg

Ruley *E-mail:* mruley@janerotrosen.com; Amy Tannenbaum
Founded: 1974
Fiction & nonfiction. No unsol mss or queries. Query by referral only. Handle film & TV rights. No reading fee. 15% commission in USA & Canada. Co-represented abroad & on the West Coast.
Membership(s): The Authors Guild

**Damaris Rowland** (L)
420 E 23 St, Suite 6-F, New York, NY 10010
*Tel:* 212-475-8942
*E-mail:* nicholerowland5@mac.com
*Key Personnel*
Agent: Damaris Rowland (AAR)
Founded: 1994
Fiction & nonfiction. Handle film & TV rights. No unsol mss, query first with SASE. Submit outline & sample chapters.
Membership(s): The Authors Guild; Mystery Writers of America; Romance Writers of America

**Regina Ryan Books** (L)
251 Central Park W, Suite 7-D, New York, NY 10024
*Tel:* 212-787-5589
*E-mail:* queries@reginaryanbooks.com
*Web Site:* www.reginaryanbooks.com
*Key Personnel*
Pres: Regina Ryan (AAR) *E-mail:* reginaryan@reginaryanbooks.com
Founded: 1976
Book length works of nonfiction for the adult market. Specialize in narrative nonfiction, psychology, popular culture, cooking & food, health, diet & fitness, self-help, parenting, nature, gardening, pets, art, architecture, design, memoirs, general history & biography, science - especially natural history & cognitive neuroscience, women's issues. No poetry, screenplays or software. Query first, using the guidelines on our web site. No queries or follow-up by fax or phone. No reading fee; handle film, TV & foreign rights. Representation in all foreign countries.
Titles recently placed: *Backyard Birding: A Guide to Attracting and Identifying Birds*, Randi Minetor, Nic Minetor; *Banishing Math Anxiety*, Sheila Tobias, Victor Piercey; *Charles Dickens and the Street Children of London*, Andrea Warren; *Cookies for Grown-Ups*, Kelly Cooper; *Hardlucky: The Story of a Boy Who Learns How to Think Before He Acts*, Miriam Chaikin; *In Search of Sacco and Vanzetti: Double Lives, Troubled Times, and the Massachusetts Murder Case That Shook the World*, Susan Tejada; *Mingus Speaks*, John F Goodman; *So You Think You Know Baseball?: A Fan's Guide to the Official Rules*, Peter E Meltzer; *The Roof at the Bottom of the World: Discovering the Transantarctic Mountains*, Edmund Stump; *What's Wrong With My Vegetable Garden?: 100% Organic Solutions for All Your Vegetables, from Artichokes to Zucchini*, David Deardorff, Kathryn Wadsworth; *When Cancer Strikes a Friend: What to Say, What to Do, and How to Help*, Bonnie E Draeger; *When Johnny and Jane Come Marching Home: How All of Us Can Help Veterans*, Paula J Caplan
Foreign Rights: Books Crossing Borders (Worldwide exc UK); Abner Stein Agency (UK & Commonwealth)
Membership(s): The Authors Guild; PEN American Center; Women's Media Group

**The Sagalyn Literary Agency**, see ICM/Sagalyn

**Victoria Sanders & Associates LLC** (L)
241 Avenue of the Americas, Suite 11-H, New York, NY 10014
*Tel:* 212-633-8811 *Fax:* 212-633-0525
*E-mail:* queriesvsa@gmail.com
*Web Site:* www.victoriasanders.com
*Key Personnel*
Pres: Victoria Sanders (AAR)
Agent: Bernadette Baker-Baughman; Mr Chris Kepner; Tanya McKinnon
Founded: 1992
Always interested in new material & welcome all genres: literary & commercial fiction, nonfiction, memoir, women's fiction, thrillers, humor, science fiction/fantasy, graphic novels & self-help/motivational, just to name a few. No unsol mss, query first. E-mail queries only. Please include first 3 chapters (or about 25 pages) pasted into the body of the e-mail. Consult web site for further information. Handle film & TV rights & translation rights. No reading fees.
Titles recently placed: *Best Kept Secret*, Amy Hatvany; *Blood Makes Noise*, Gregory Widen; *Children of the Jacaranda Tree*, Sahar Delijani; *Confessions of a So Called Middle Child*, Maria Lennon; *Criminal*, Karin Slaughter; *Fallen*, Karin Slaughter; *How to Train a Train*, Jason Carter Eaton; *If I Had a Raptor*, George O'Connor; *If I Had a Triceratops*, George O'Connor; *Kill Me Once*, Jon Osborne; *Low Town*, Daniel Polansky; *Money Can't Buy Love*, Connie Briscoe; *Outside the Lines*, Amy Hatvany; *Perla*, Carolina De Robertis; *Shattered*, Kia DuPree; *Silenced*, Kia DuPree; *Skipping A Beat*, Sarah Pekkanen; *The Awesome Girls Guide to Dating Extraordinary Men*, Ernessa T Carter; *The Bed Bug Survival Guide: The Only Book You Need to Eliminate or Avoid This Pest Now*, Jeff Eisenberg; *The Hatchery*, Tom Isbell; *The Language of Sisters*, Amy Hatvany; *The Stranger You Seek*, Amanda Kyle Williams; *The Wedding Gift*, Marlen Suyapa Bodden; *These Girls*, Sarah Pekkanen; *Voted Most Likely*, Faith Erin Hicks; *Wasteland*, Susan Kim, Laurence Klavan; *Who We Be: The Colorization of America*, Jeff Chang
Foreign Rights: Chandler Crawford (Worldwide)

**Jack Scagnetti Talent & Literary Agency** (L-D)
5118 Vineland Ave, No 102, North Hollywood, CA 91601
*Tel:* 818-761-0580
*Web Site:* jackscagnettitalentandliteraryagency.books.officelive.com
*Key Personnel*
Owner: Jack Scagnetti *E-mail:* jack@jackscagnettiagency.com
Agent: David Goldman
Founded: 1974
Fiction & nonfiction books, sports, health & automobiles, how-to, no juveniles; screenplays, TV & film treatments. No unsol mss, query first. Submit synopsis, first chapter for books; paragraph or one-page synopsis for scripts. No reading fee, charge one-way postage for multiple submissions, 10% commission, 15% for books. Detailed critique & consultation services available for books on hourly basis. Signatory to Writer's Guild of America-West. Represented self in sale of 15 books which led to representing writer friends & others.
Membership(s): Academy of Television Arts & Sciences; Writers Guild of America West

**Schiavone Literary Agency Inc** (L-D)
236 Trails End, West Palm Beach, FL 33413-2135
*Tel:* 561-966-9294 *Fax:* 561-966-9294
*E-mail:* profschia@aol.com
*Web Site:* www.publishersmarketplace.com/members/profschia
*Key Personnel*
CEO: Dr James Schiavone
Pres, Bronx, NY Off: Jennifer Du Vall *E-mail:* jendu77@aol.com
Sr EVP, NY Off: Francine Edelman *E-mail:* francineedelman@aol.com
EVP, NY Off: Kevin McAdams *E-mail:* kvn.mcadams@yahoo.com
Founded: 1996
Fiction & nonfiction, all genres: children's & young adult, scholarly books, textbooks, business, motivational, advertising, marketing, specialize in celebrity biography & autobiography & memoirs. No poetry or children's picture books. No unsol mss. No queries via phone, fax or post. Accept only e-mail queries consisting of one page (no attachments). Query only one agent at the company. No fees; commissions: 15% domestic, 20% foreign. Representation in foreign markets. Send e-mail queries to individual personnel at their e-mail address noted. Also have offices in New York, NY.
Titles recently placed: *Beautiful Old Dogs*, David Tabatsky; *Brush With Darkness*, Erastes; *Conditional Futurism: New Perspective of End-Time Prophecy*, James Goetz; *Edwardian Cooking: 80 Recipes Inspired by Downton Abbey's Elegant Meals*, Larry Edwards; *Finding Jack: A Novel*, Gareth Crocker; *Get a Clue: Mystery Devotions for Kids*, Mark Littleton; *I Knew Him*, Erastes; *Junction X: A Novel*, Erastes; *Muffled Drum*, Erastes; *The Last Meal: Defending an Accused Mass Murderer*, Dennis Shere; *Through the New Testament: Devotions for Kids*, Mark Littleton; *Trust Me: A Memoir*, George Kennedy; *Unlikely Liberal: Sarah Palin's Curious Record as Alaska's Governor*, Matthew Zencey
*Branch Office(s)*
Bronx, NY 10463-1139, Pres: Jennifer Du Vall
New York, NY (contact Kevin McAdams for musical entertainment titles, Francine Edelman for all other genres - special interest in business, marketing, advertising & self-help)
Foreign Rights: Chloe Ataroff (Central Europe, France); Asli Ermis (Turkey); Feliz Karaman (Turkey); Hamish Mackaskill (Japan); Radoslav Trenev (Bulgaria, Eastern Europe); Annisa Waharyudisti (Indonesia, Vietnam); Yang Young-Chul (Korea)
Membership(s): National Education Association

**Wendy Schmalz Agency** (L)
402 Union St, Unit 831, Hudson, NY 12534
*Tel:* 518-672-7697
*E-mail:* wendy@schmalzagency.com
*Web Site:* www.schmalzagency.com
*Key Personnel*
Owner: Wendy Schmalz (AAR)
Founded: 2002
Adult & children's fiction & nonfiction. No unsol mss, e-mail queries only.
Titles recently placed: *Gracefully Grayson*, Ami Polonsky; *Lies My Girlfriend Told Me*, Julie Anne Peters; *Point Last Seen (series)*, April Henry; *Strands of Bronze and Gold*, Jane Nickerson; *Tales from My Closet*, Jennifer Moses; *The Half Life of Molly Pierce*, Katrina Leno; *The Secret of Ferrell Savage*, J Duddy Gill; *You Know What You Have to Do*, Bonnie Shimko
Foreign Rights: Rights People (Worldwide)

**Harold Schmidt Literary Agency** (L-D)
415 W 23 St, Suite 6-F, New York, NY 10011
*Tel:* 212-727-7473
*Key Personnel*
Pres: Harold D Schmidt (AAR) *E-mail:* hslanyc@aol.com
Specialize in book-length fiction & nonfiction. No unsol mss, query first by e-mail & include up to the first 5 pages of your book embedded in the e-mail; do not send as an attachment. Telephone queries not accepted. Do not send material through the mail unless requested. Representatives in Hollywood & in all principal foreign countries.

**Susan Schulman, A Literary Agency** (L-D)
454 W 44 St, New York, NY 10036
*Tel:* 212-713-1633 *Fax:* 212-581-8830
*E-mail:* schulmanagency@yahoo.com
*Web Site:* www.schulmanagency.com
*Key Personnel*
Owner: Susan Schulman (AAR)
Founded: 1980
Adult book-length genre & literary fiction & nonfiction especially women's studies, biography, psychology & the social sciences. No unsol mss. Query first with SASE or by e-mail. Submit outline & three sample chapters. No reading fee. Co-agent in all principal foreign countries. Handles film & TV rights for other agencies & individual titles.
Foreign Rep(s): ACER Agencia Literaria (Spain); Agenzia Letteraria Internazionale (Italy); Big Apple Agency Inc (China); Lora Fountain & Associates (France); Nurcihan Kesim Literary Agency Inc (Turkey); Korea Copyright Center (Korea); Leipman AG (Germany); Lennart Sane Agency (Sweden); Owl's Agency Inc (Japan); I Pikarski Literary Agency (Israel); Prava I Prevodi (Eastern Europe); The Rights Agency (Canada (French-speaking)); Susanna Zevi Agenzia Letteraria (Italy)
Membership(s): The Authors Guild; The Dramatists Guild of America; Society of Children's Book Writers & Illustrators; Women in Film; Women's Media Group; Writers Guild of America East

**A E Schwartz & Associates** (L-D)
13 Conversation Way, Stoughton, MA 02072
*Tel:* 781-436-5033
*E-mail:* info@aeschwartz.com
*Web Site:* aeschwartz.com
*Key Personnel*
CEO: Andrew E Schwartz
Founded: 1985
Comprehensive organization, business, rights & permissions, publishing; specialize in human resource development, organizational development & related training topics, management, training & business how-to's. No unsol mss; query first. Submit outline & sample chapters. Handle software. Assist authors on all facets of contracting with publishers. Evaluation fee: $125 (report).

**Laurens R Schwartz, Esquire** (L-D)
5 E 22 St, Suite 15-D, New York, NY 10010-5325
*Tel:* 212-228-2614
Founded: 1981
Full-service agency handling all media for all ages worldwide. No fees; standard commissions; WGA Signatory. No unsol mss, CD-ROMs, etc. Query first with synopsis of ONE project & resume. Also provide information relating to the project having been with other agents or shopped around. Enclose return mailer with postage. Require 4-week right-of-first refusal if request submission of entire project. Handle film, TV & L&M rights.
Membership(s): Writers Guild of America

**S©ott Treimel NY** (L)
434 Lafayette St, New York, NY 10003-6943
*Tel:* 212-505-8353
*Web Site:* scotttreimelny.com; scotttreimelny.blogspot.com
*Key Personnel*
Owner & Pres: Scott Treimel (AAR) *E-mail:* st.ny@verizon.net
Founded: 1995
Sells & administers intellectual property rights—foreign, dramatic, electronic, broadcast, merchandise, promotion—for children's book creators. Submission accepted only via web site submission form.
Titles recently placed: *Between Two Ends*, David Ward; *Boy + Bot*, Ame Dyckman; *Cherry Money Baby*, John M Cusick; *Fire in the Sky*, David Ward; *Five 4ths of July*, Pat Hughes; *I Need My Own Country!*, Rick Walton; *Laundry Day*, Maurie J Manning; *Old Robert and the Sea-Silly Cats*, Barbara Joosse; *Shotgun Serenade*, Gail Giles; *Sleeping Bootsie*, Maribeth Boelts; *The Clueless Girls Guide to Being a Genius*, Janice Repka; *The Fires of New SUN: A Blending Time Novel*, Michael Kinch; *Wiener Wolf*, Jeff Crosby; *Wink: The Ninja Who Wanted to Nap*, J C Phillipps
Foreign Rep(s): ACER Literaria (Argentina, Brazil, Central America, Spanish & Portuguese, Spanish languages, Spanish Latin America); Akcali Copyright (Turkey); Gabriella Ambrosioni (Italy); Donatalla d'Ormesson Agent Littéraire (France); Japan Uni (Japan); Barbara Kuper Literarische Agentur + Medienservice (Germany); Rights People (Bulgaria, China, Croatia, Czech Republic, Denmark, Finland, Greece, Hungary, Iceland, Indonesia, Israel, Korea, Lithuania, Poland, Romania, Russia, Scandinavia, Serbia, Slovakia, Slovenia, Sweden, Thailand, Vietnam)
Membership(s): The Authors Guild; Society of Children's Book Writers & Illustrators

**Scovil Galen Ghosh Literary Agency Inc** (L)
276 Fifth Ave, Suite 708, New York, NY 10001
*Tel:* 212-679-8686 *Fax:* 212-679-6710
*E-mail:* info@sgglit.com
*Web Site:* www.sgglit.com
*Key Personnel*
Pres: Russell Galen (AAR) *Fax:* 646-349-1868 *E-mail:* russellgalen@sgglit.com
Agent: Ann Behar *E-mail:* annbehar@sgglit.com; Anna Ghosh (AAR) *E-mail:* annaghosh@sgglit.com
Founded: 1993
All types fiction & nonfiction, adult & juvenile. Handle film & TV rights. No unsol mss, query first. Submit outline & sample chapters. E-mailed queries preferred but without attachments. Does not charge fees.
Titles recently placed: *An Echo in the Bone*, Diana Gabaldon
Foreign Rep(s): Baror International Inc (Worldwide exc USA)

**Lynn Seligman** (L)
400 Highland Ave, Upper Montclair, NJ 07043
*Tel:* 973-783-3631 *Fax:* 973-783-3691
*E-mail:* seliglit@aol.com
Founded: 1986
Adult & young adult fiction; adult nonfiction. Handle film & TV rights through agents in Hollywood. Submit letter describing project with short sample. No unsol mss; query first with SASE. No e-mail submissions. No reading fee.
Titles recently placed: *All Afternoon with a Scandalous Marquess (Lords of Vice series)*, Alexandra Hawkins; *Better Off Without Him*, Dee Ernst; *Dark World (series)*, Cara Lynn Shultz; *Dusk with a Dangerous Duke (Lords of Vice series)*, Alexandra Hawkins; *Not Quite What I Expected*, Dee Ernst; *Sunrise with a Notorious Lord (Lords of Vice series)*, Alexandra Hawkins; *Twilight with an Infamous Earl (Lords of Vice series)*, Alexandra Hawkins
Foreign Rights: Books Crossing Borders (Betty Anne Crawford) (Worldwide)
Membership(s): Women's Media Group

**Edythea Ginis Selman Literary Agency Inc** (L-D)
14 Washington Place, New York, NY 10003
*Tel:* 212-473-1874 *Fax:* 212-473-1875
*Key Personnel*
Pres & Agent: Edythea Ginis Selman (AAR)
VP & Electronic Publg Dir: Richard Selman (AAR)
Literary commercial fiction & serious issue-oriented narrative nonfiction. Selected children's fiction & young adult picture books, handles film & TV rights from adult novels & young adult (by referral only). No unsol mss, query first, only upon request (with SASE). Submit author bio, two sample chapters or 50 pages (nonfiction) or complete ms (fiction).
Foreign Rights: Antonella Antonelli (Italy); Eliane Benisti (France); David Grossman (England); Ruth Liepman (Germany); Isabel Monteagudo (Spain); Andrew Nurenburg (Japan); Uni
Membership(s): The Authors Guild; CSA; National Writers Union; PEN American Center; Society of Children's Book Writers & Illustrators; Women's National Book Association

**Seventh Avenue Literary Agency** (L)
2052 124 St, South Surrey, BC V4A 9K3, Canada
*Tel:* 604-538-7252 *Fax:* 604-538-7252
*E-mail:* info@seventhavenuelit.com
*Web Site:* www.seventhavenuelit.com
*Key Personnel*
Pres & Dir: Robert Mackwood *E-mail:* rmackwood@seventhavenuelit.com
Founded: 1974
Nonfiction agency representing international authors from a wide range of subjects & interests. No unsol mss, query first by e-mail; no fees charged.
Titles recently placed: *Great Companies Deserve Great Boards: A CEO's Guide to the Boardroom*, Beverly Behan; *Route 66 Still Kicks: Driving America's Main Street*, Rick Antonson; *Things That Must Not Be Forgotten: A Childhood in Wartime China (updated)*, Michael David Kwan; *Whole Foods to Thrive*, Brendan Brazier
Foreign Rights: Big Apple Agency Inc (Luc Kwantlen) (China, Indonesia, Taiwan); Fritz Agency (Christan Dittus) (Germany); Deborah Harris Agency (Ilana Kurshan) (Israel); Nurcihan Kesim Literary Agency (Dilek Kaya) (Turkey); Simona Kessler Agency (Adriana Marinara) (Romania); Korea Copyright Agency (Ms MiSook Hong) (Korea); Nova Littera Ltd (Daria Pridatkina) (Russia); Read n Right Agency (Nike Davarinou) (Greece); The Riff Agancy (Lucia Riff) (Brazil, Portugal); Sebes & Van Gelderen Literary Agency (Netherlands)

**The Seymour Agency**, see Mary Sue Seymour

**Mary Sue Seymour** (L-D)
475 Miner Street Rd, Canton, NY 13617
*Tel:* 315-386-1831
*Web Site:* www.theseymouragency.com
*Key Personnel*
Founder & Agent: Mary Sue Seymour (AAR) *E-mail:* marysue@twcny.rr.com
Sr Agent: Nicole Resciniti
Assoc Agent: Marisa Cleveland
Founded: 1992
Christian romance & women's fiction, nonfiction & secular romance.
Membership(s): The Authors Guild; Romance Writers of America; Writers Guild of America; Writers Guild of America East

**Charlotte Sheedy Literary Agency Inc** (L)
Affiliate of Sterling Lord Literistic Inc
928 Broadway, Suite 901, New York, NY 10010
*Tel:* 212-780-9800 *Fax:* 212-780-0308; 212-780-6095
*E-mail:* sheedy@sll.com
*Web Site:* www.sheedylit.com
*Key Personnel*
Owner: Charlotte Sheedy *E-mail:* charlotte@sheedylit.com

Asst: Mackenzie Brady *E-mail:* mackenzie@sheedylit.com
Fiction & nonfiction film & TV rights. No unsol mss, query first (no screenplays); submit outline & sample chapters; no reading fee. Agents in all principal countries.
Foreign Rep(s): The English Agency (Japan); Agnes Krup (Australia, Germany, Italy, Portugal, Switzerland); Lennart Sane (Netherlands, Scandinavia, Spain); Abner Stein Agency (England)

**The Shepard Agency** (L)
73 Kingswood Dr, Bethel, CT 06801
*Tel:* 203-790-4230; 203-790-1780 *Fax:* 203-798-2924
*E-mail:* shepardagey@mindspring.com
*Key Personnel*
Pres & Dir: Jean H Shepard
VP & Treas: Lance Hastings Shepard
Founded: 1986
Specialize in adult, children, general trade fiction & nonfiction, professional, reference & business. Handle film & TV rights. Not accepting mss at this time.

**The Robert E Shepard Agency** (L)
4804 Laurel Canyon Blvd, Box 592, Valley Village, CA 91607-3717
*E-mail:* mail@shepardagency.com
*Web Site:* www.shepardagency.com
*Key Personnel*
Owner & Pres: Robert E Shepard
Founded: 1994
Nonfiction only, most subject areas, except memoir & spirituality. Specialize in narrative nonfiction, history, current affairs, pop culture, business, science for lay people, health, parenting, some psychology, reference, Judaica & gay/lesbian. No unsol mss or proposals, query first with SASE. Prefer queries by e-mail (no attachments) or regular mail. Do not phone or fax. Submit overview, annotated outline, curriculum vitae & two sample chapters. See web site for guidelines. No reading fee. Handle film & TV rights.
Titles recently placed: *House of Stone: A Memoir of Home, Family, and a Lost Middle East*, Anthony Shadid; *How Not to Kill Your Baby*, Jacob Sager Weinstein; *Wealth of an Empire: The Treasure Shipments that Saved Britain and the World*, Robert Switky
Foreign Rights: Tuttle-Mori Agency Inc (Japan)
Membership(s): The Authors Guild

**Ken Sherman & Associates** (L-D)
1275 N Hayworth, Suite 103, Los Angeles, CA 90046
*Tel:* 310-273-8840 *Fax:* 310-271-2875
*E-mail:* kenshermanassociates@gmail.com
*Web Site:* www.kenshermanassociates.com
*Key Personnel*
Owner & Pres: Ken Sherman
Founded: 1989
Fiction & nonfiction books plus screenplays, teleplays, film & TV rights to books & life rights. No unsol mss or screenplays. Accept by referral only. Submit outline & minimum three sample chapters. No reading fee, ms copying charges if necessary. International Advisory Board Member, The Christopher Isherwood Foundation.
Deals in development include: Starhawk's "The Fifth Sacred Thing" as a feature; Tawni O'Dell's "Back Roads" (Oprah Book Club selection) as a feature & about to go to production (Infinity Media); David Guterson's "East of the Mountains" about to go into production. Multiple Anne Perry projects in film/TV development.
Titles recently placed: *East of the Mountains (film rights)*, David Guterson; *Jeff, One Lonely Guy*, Jeff Ragsdale, Michael Logan, David Shields; *Monk (series of books/ film-TV rights)*, Anne Perry; *The Witches of Eastwick-The Musical*, John Updike
Membership(s): Academy of Television Arts & Sciences; American Film Institute Third Decade Council; British Academy of Film & Television Arts/Los Angeles; PEN International

**Wendy Sherman Associates Inc** (L)
27 W 24 St, Suite 700-B, New York, NY 10010
*Tel:* 212-279-9027 *Fax:* 212-279-9027
*Web Site:* www.wsherman.com
*Key Personnel*
Pres: Wendy Sherman (AAR) *E-mail:* wendy@wsherman.com
Agent: Kimberly Perel *E-mail:* kim@wsherman.com
Founded: 1999
Represents a wide range of fiction & nonfiction. Literary & commercial fiction, including upmarket women's fiction; Nonfiction includes, memoir, narrative nonfiction, practical, self-help, popular psychology. No unsol mss, query first with SASE. E-mail queries preferred. For fiction, a letter & synopsis. For nonfiction, send proposal & two sample chapters. See web site for submission guidelines.
Titles recently placed: *Exposure*, Therese Fowler; *In Stitches*, Anthony Youn, MD; *ing Ransom Road: Confronting the Past, One Marathon at a Time*, Caleb Daniloff; *Lunch In Paris: A Love Story with Recipes*, Elizabeth Bard; *Raiders!: The Story of the Greatest Fan Film Ever Made*, Alan Eisenstock; *The Rules of Inheritance*, Claire Bidwell Smith; *Wasted*, Adam Minter
Foreign Rep(s): Jenny Meyer Literary Agency (Worldwide)
Foreign Rights: Duran Kim (Korea); Jenny Meyer Literary Agency (Worldwide exc Asia); Andrew Nurnberg (China); Owls Agency (Japan, Vietnam)
Membership(s): Women's Media Group

**Side by Side Literary Productions Inc** (L)
15 W 26 St, 2nd fl, New York, NY 10010
*Tel:* 646-442-2905 *Fax:* 212-888-3650
*Web Site:* sidebysidelit.com
*Key Personnel*
Founder & Pres: Laurie Bernstein *Fax:* 212-481-6037 *E-mail:* laurie@sidebysidelit.com
Founded: 2004
Literary agency handling general trade fiction & nonfiction as well as select juvenile titles. Specialize in popular health, medicine, self-help, parenting, popular culture, diet & narrative nonfiction. No unsol mss, query first. Will review hard copy & digital submissions. Handles film & TV rights.

**Rosalie Siegel, International Literary Agent Inc** (L)
One Abey Dr, Pennington, NJ 08534
*Tel:* 609-737-1007 *Fax:* 609-737-3708
*E-mail:* rsiegel@ix.netcom.com
*Web Site:* www.rosaliesiegel.com
*Key Personnel*
Pres: Rosalie Siegel (AAR)
Adult fiction, nonfiction & foreign books, film & TV rights. No unsol mss; query first; no reading fee. Representatives in all major European countries & Asian countries. Not actively seeking new clients.

**Irene Skolnick Literary Agency** (L)
2095 Broadway, Suite 307, New York, NY 10023
*Tel:* 212-727-3648 *Fax:* 212-727-1024
*E-mail:* office@skolnickliterary.com (queries)
*Web Site:* www.skolnickagency.com
*Key Personnel*
CEO: Irene Skolnick (AAR) *E-mail:* irene@skolnickliterary.com
Founded: 1994
Literary & historical fiction, thrillers; narrative nonfiction: memoir, biography, history, travel, humor; YA, middle grade. Handle film & TV rights. Representation in all major countries & Hollywood through co-agents. No unsol mss, query first. Send queries via e-mail or mail with SASE. Include/attach outline & sample chapter.
Titles recently placed: *Above the Waves*, Marie Mutsuki Mockett; *Anthony Hecht: The Poet and the Age*, David Yezzi; *Arcadia*, Allegra Goodman; *Give Me Everything You Have: On Being Stalked*, James Lasdun; *Love, Dishonor, Marry, Die; Cherish, Perish*, David Rakoff; *The Daily Dynamite*, Maiya Williams; *The Fifth Daughter of the Tsar*, Jennifer Laam; *The Long Shadow: The Great War and the Twentieth Century*, David Reynolds; *The Lost Episodes of Revie Bryson*, Bryan Furuness; *Where the Light Falls*, Katherine Keenum
Foreign Rights: Lippincott, Massie, McQuilkin (Maria Massie)
Membership(s): PEN American Center; Women's Media Group

**SLC Enterprises Inc** (L-D)
332 S Michigan Ave, No 1032-C216, Chicago, IL 60604
*Tel:* 616-942-2665 (answering serv & voice mail)
*Key Personnel*
Pres: Stephen Cogil Casari (AAR)
*E-mail:* scasari1@hotmail.com
Founded: 1985
Fiction & nonfiction; specialize in first novelists. Children's books, sports, baseball. No unsol mss, query first. Submit proposal, outline &/or sample chapters. Evaluation & discussion of publishability. Handle film & TV rights.
Titles recently placed: *Paige Goes to Philadelphia*, Diann Boehm

**Sligo Literary Agency LLC** (L)
425 Poa Place, San Luis Obispo, CA 93405
*Tel:* 805-550-1667 *Fax:* 805-783-2317
*E-mail:* editorial@mckennapubgrp.com
*Web Site:* sligolitagency.com
*Key Personnel*
Founder & Agent, Nonfiction: Eric Bollinger
*E-mail:* ric@mckennapubgrp.com
Agent, Fiction: Melinda Royer
Founded: 1998
Represent authors to publishers. Work with co-agents for TV movie rights. E-mail a query first. No reading or evaluation fee. Several foreign representatives in the UK.
Foreign Rep(s): Japan Uni Agency; Thomas Schlueck (Germany)

**Beverley Slopen Literary Agency** (L)
131 Bloor St W, Suite 711, Toronto, ON M5S 1S3, Canada
*Tel:* 416-964-9598 *Fax:* 416-921-7726
*E-mail:* beverley@slopenagency.ca
*Web Site:* www.slopenagency.ca
*Key Personnel*
Owner: Beverley Slopen *E-mail:* beverley@slopenagency.ca
Founded: 1973
Serious fiction & nonfiction. No children's books, illustrated books, science fiction or fantasy. No software, no film or TV rights handled. Query letter & brief proposal sent by mail with Canadian postage if you want it returned; not taking on many new clients.
Foreign Rep(s): Agenzia Letteraria Internazionale (Italy); Paul & Peter Fritz AG (Germany); David Grossman (UK); Alexander Korzhenevski (Russia); Michelle Lapautre (France); Licht & Burr Literary Agency (Scandinavia); Lucia Riff (Brazil); Tuttle-Mori Agency Inc (Japan); Julio F Yanez (Spain)
Foreign Rights: Gray Tan (China)

**Valerie Smith, Literary Agent** (L)
1746 Rte 44-55, Modena, NY 12548
*Tel:* 845-883-5848
*Key Personnel*
Contact: Valerie Smith
Founded: 1978
Fiction & nonfiction; special interest in fantasy & science fiction. No unsol mss, query first; no reading fee. Outline & 3 sample chapters. Representatives in Hollywood & all principal foreign countries.

**Michael Snell Literary Agency** (L)
Subsidiary of H Michael Snell Inc
PO Box 1206, Truro, MA 02666-1206
*Tel:* 508-349-3718
*E-mail:* snellliteraryagency@yahoo.com
*Web Site:* www.michaelsnellagency.com
*Key Personnel*
Pres & Edit Dir: H Michael Snell
VP: Patricia Smith *E-mail:* snell.patricia@gmail.com
Founded: 1978
Adult nonfiction; all levels of business & management from popular trade to professional reference; legal, medical, health, psychology, self-help & how-to books; animals & pets; women's issues in business, family & society; popular science & business; technical & scientific; professional & general computer books; parenting & relationships; project development & rewrite services. Welcome new authors. No unsol mss, query first. Submit outline, synopsis & up to 50 sample pages with SASE. Publication *How to Write a Book Proposal* available upon request with SASE, or consult Michael Snell's book, from *Book Idea to Bestseller* (Prima Publishing). Write for information on purchasing a model book proposal. Consider new clients on an exclusive basis. No reading fee, but do arrange for developmental editors & ghostwriters who do charge a fee.
Titles recently placed: *Barefoot Running Step by Step: Barefoot Ken Bob, the Guru of Shoeless Running, Shares His Personal Technique for Running with More Speed, Less Impact, Fewer Injuries and More Fun*, Roy M Wallack, Barefoot Ken Bob Saxton; *Business at the Speed of Now: Fire Up Your People, Thrill Your Customers, and Crush Your Competitors*, John M Bernard; *Glorybound*, Jessie van Eerden; *Now I Get It*, Donny Ebenstein; *Sun House*, David James Duncan; *The Gentle Art of Horseback Riding*, Gincy Self Bucklin; *The Sweet Science of Success*, G Richard Shell; *The Well-Balanced Leader: Interactive Learning Techniques to Help You Master the 9 Simple Behaviors of Outstanding Leadership*, Ron Roberts; *Tipping Sacred Cows: Kick the Bad Work Habits that Masquerade as Virtues*, Jake Breeden; *What Keeps Leaders Up at Night: Recognizing and Resolving Your Most Troubling Management Issues*, Nicole Lipkin

**Sobel Weber Associates Inc** (L)
146 E 19 St, New York, NY 10003-2404
*Tel:* 212-420-8585 *Fax:* 212-505-1017
*E-mail:* info@sobelweber.com
*Web Site:* www.sobelweber.com
*Key Personnel*
Principal: Nat Sobel; Judith Weber
Founded: 1970
General fiction & nonfiction. No unsol mss, query first with SASE, no electronic submissions. No reading fee. Handle film, TV & foreign rights; serialization & audio rights. Representatives on the West Coast & in all major foreign countries. Consult web site for submission guidelines & client list.
Titles recently placed: *Black Fridays*, Michael Sears; *Elsewhere*, Richard Russo; *Fobbit*, David Abrams; *Heart of Palm*, Laura Lee Smith; *I, Anna*, Elsa Lewin; *Information Retrieval*, Mark Allen Smith; *Jukebox Cadillac*, Doug Allyn; *Letters From Berlin: A Story of War, Survival, and the Redeeming Power of Love and Friendship*, Kerstin Lieff; *Magnificent Fraud: The Life of Anna Leonowens, Teacher at the Siamese Court*, Alfred Habegger; *Misfit*, Adam Braver; *Ratlines*, Stuart Neville; *Stealing Home*, Wiley Cash; *The Bathing Women*, Tie Ning; *The Forgetting Tree*, Tatjana Soli; *The Ghostman*, Roger Hobbs; *The Girl With a Clock for a Heart*, Peter Swanson; *The Rain Barrel*, Wiley Cash; *The Rules of Wolfe*, James Carlos Blake; *The Savage City: Race, Murder, and A Generation on the Edge*, T J English; *The Terror of Living*, Urban Waite; *The Tilted World*, Tom Franklin, Beth Ann Fennelly; *The Unremembered*, Peter Orullian
Foreign Rights: Abner Stein Agency (UK)

**Spectrum Literary Agency** (L)
320 Central Park W, Suite 1-D, New York, NY 10025
*Tel:* 212-362-4323 *Fax:* 212-362-4562
*Web Site:* www.spectrumliteraryagency.com
*Key Personnel*
Pres & Agent: Eleanor Wood
Agent: Justin Bell
Founded: 1976
Science fiction, mysteries, thrillers, horror & fantasy No unsol mss, query first with letter, synopsis, first ten pages & SASE. No reading fee. Agents in all principal foreign countries.
Titles recently placed: *Angel Condemned*, Mary Stanton; *Carnelians*, Catherine Asaro; *Fate of Worlds: Return from the Ringworld*, Larry Niven, Edward M Lerner; *In the Lion's Mouth*, Michael Flynn
Membership(s): Mystery Writers of America; Science Fiction & Fantasy Writers of America

**The Spieler Agency** (L)
154 W 57 St, Suite 135, New York, NY 10019
*Tel:* 212-757-4439 *Fax:* 212-333-2019
*E-mail:* spieleragency@spieleragency.com
*Key Personnel*
Agent: Eric Myers; Joseph Spieler
Nonfiction & literary fiction; children's books. Areas of interest include: environmental issues, business; women's issues; natural history & science for religious studies, psychology; health; history; biography. No unsol mss, query first with letter (prefer e-mail), first chapter/contents or detailed proposal. No phone queries. Submit author background, description of work & sample chapter with SASE. Handle film & TV rights only for book clients. No reading fee, only commissions.
Titles recently placed: *Pity the Billionaire: The Hard-Times Swindle and the Unlikely Comeback of the Right*, Thomas Frank; *The Financial Crisis Inquiry Report*; *The Lost Mona Lisa: The Extraordinary True Story of the Greatest Art Theft in History*, R A Scotti
Foreign Rights: The Marsh Agency (Continental Europe); Abner Stein Literary Agency (England)

**Philip G Spitzer Literary Agency Inc** (L)
50 Talmage Farm Lane, East Hampton, NY 11937
*Tel:* 631-329-3650 *Fax:* 631-329-3651
*E-mail:* spitzer516@aol.com
*Web Site:* www.spitzeragency.com
*Key Personnel*
Pres & Agent: Philip G Spitzer (AAR)
Mng Dir: Lukas Ortiz *E-mail:* lukas.ortiz@spitzeragency.com
Exec Asst: Luc Hunt *E-mail:* luc.hunt@spitzeragency.com
Founded: 1969
Literary fiction, suspense/thriller, general nonfiction, sports, politics, social issues, biography, film & TV rights. No unsol mss, query first with SASE, submit outline & sample chapters. No reading fee, photocopying fee. Foreign rights agents in all major markets.

**Nancy Stauffer Associates** (L)
30 Corbin Dr, Unit 1203, Darien, CT 06820
Mailing Address: PO Box 1203, Darien, CT 06820
*Tel:* 203-202-2500
*E-mail:* staufferassoc@optonline.net
*Web Site:* publishersmarketplace.com/members/nstauffer; staufferliterary.com
*Key Personnel*
Owner: Nancy Stauffer Cahoon *E-mail:* nancy@staufferliterary.com
Founded: 1989
Literary fiction, narrative nonfiction & young adult fiction. No mysteries, science fiction, fantasy, romance novels, screenplays or children's picture books. Query by e-mail only, with first 10 pages of your work. No attachments. Agents in all foreign markets.
Titles recently placed: *Benediction*, Kent Haruf; *Blasphemy, New & Selected Stories*, Sherman Alexie
Membership(s): The Authors Guild

**Michael Steinberg Literary Agent** (L)
PO Box 274, Glencoe, IL 60022-0274
*Tel:* 847-626-1000 *Fax:* 847-626-1002
*E-mail:* michael14steinberg@comcast.net
*Key Personnel*
Principal: Michael Steinberg
Founded: 1980
Book-length fiction (mystery, science fiction) & nonfiction (business topics). No unsol mss, query first. Submit outline & first three chapters (hardcopy). Will read only by personal reference from represented author or editor. $75 reading fee (waived for published authors) & other fees, including postage & phone. Handle software occasionally & rarely handle TV & film rights.
Titles recently placed: *All About Day Trading*, Jake Bernstein

**Sterling Lord Literistic Inc** (L)
65 Bleecker St, New York, NY 10012
*Tel:* 212-780-6050 *Fax:* 212-780-6095
*E-mail:* info@sll.com
*Web Site:* www.sll.com
*Key Personnel*
Chmn: Sterling Lord; Peter Matson
Pres: Philippa Brophy
VP: Laurie Liss (AAR)
Foreign Rts Mgr & Agent: Celeste Fine
Foreign Rts Mgr: Szilvia Molnar
Agent: Rebecca Friedman; Robert Guinsler; Judy Heiblum; Neeti Madan; George Nicholson; Jim Rutman; Ira Silverberg; Douglas Stewart
Fiction & nonfiction; film & TV rights. No unsol mss, query first; submit outline & sample chapters with SASE; no reading fee. Affiliated agency: Charlotte Sheedy Agency.
Foreign Rep(s): M B Agentia (Spain); Eliane Benisti (France); Luigi Bernabo (Italy); Paul & Peter Fritz (Germany); Deborah Harris Agency (Israel); JLM Literary (Greece); Korea Copyright Center (Korea); Licht & Burr (Scandinavia); Andrew Nurnberg Associates (Bulgaria, China, Czech Republic, Hungary, Latvia, Taiwan); Riff Agency (Brazil); Marianne Schonach (Netherlands); Tuttle-Mori Agency Inc (Japan, Thailand)

**Miriam Stern, Attorney-at-Law/Literary Agent** (L-D)
303 E 83 St, 20th fl, New York, NY 10028
*Tel:* 212-794-1289

Fiction & nonfiction. No unsol mss, call or letter query first. Submit finished mss, outlines with sample chapters when applicable. Negotiate motion picture rights for film & TV.

**The Joan Stewart Agency** (L)
885 Second Ave, 35th fl, New York, NY 10017
*Tel:* 212-418-7255 *Fax:* 212-832-3809
*Key Personnel*
Pres: Joan Stewart
Founded: 1983
Handle film & TV rights. No reading fee.

**Stimola Literary Studio Inc** (L)
308 Livingston Ct, Edgewater, NJ 07020
*Tel:* 201-945-9353 *Fax:* 201-945-9353
*E-mail:* info@stimolaliterarystudio.com
*Web Site:* www.stimolaliterarystudio.com
*Key Personnel*
Pres: Rosemary B Stimola (AAR)
Founded: 1997
Specialize in fiction & nonfiction, preschool through young adult. Queries via e-mail preferred. Respond only to those queries we wish to pursue further. No unsol attachments. See web site for submission guidelines. No fees.
Titles recently placed: *Courage Has No Color*, Tanya Lee Stone; *F*It List*, Julie Halpern; *Hiding Out at the Pancake Palace*, Nan Marino; *Revenge of the Girl with the Great Personality*, Elizabeth Eulberg; *Scare Scape*, Sam Fisher; *The Flying Beaver Brothers*, Maxwell Eaton III; *The REMNANT Trilogy*, Mary E Pearson; *Year of the Jungle*, Suzanne Collins, James Proimos
Foreign Rep(s): Intercontinental Literary Agency (translation); Schleuck Agency (Germany)
Foreign Rights: Rights People (UK)
Membership(s): ALA; National Council of Teachers of English; Society of Children's Book Writers & Illustrators

**Straus Literary** (L)
319 Lafayette St, Suite 220, New York, NY 10012
*Tel:* 646-843-9950 *Fax:* 646-390-3320
*Web Site:* www.strausliterary.com
*Key Personnel*
Agent: Jonah Straus *E-mail:* jonah@strausliterary.com
Founded: 2003
Focus on literary fiction, historical fiction, works in translation (especially Spanish & Portuguese), literary mystery & thriller, cookbooks, food & travel narratives, photography, politics, history, international affairs, biography, memoir.
Straus Literary acts as English sub-agent for: Editorial Everest, Spain; Mertin Agency (Nicole Witt), Germany; Riff Agency, Brazil.
Branch office in San Francisco, CA.
Titles recently placed: *1808: The Flight of the Emperor*, Laurentino Gomes, Andrew Nevins; *Crow-Blue*, Adriana Lisboa, Alison Entrekin; *Death & Co (Cocktail Book)*, David Kaplan, Nick Fauchald; *Di Palo's Italian Foods*, Lou Di Palo, Rachel Wharton; *Fidel & Gabo: A Portrait of the Legendary Friendship*, Angel Esteban, Stephanie Panichelli; *Jeni's Spendid Ice Creams at Home*, Jeni Britton Bauer; *Lockdown (Carandiru Station)*, Drauzio Varella; *P's Three Women*, Paulo Emilio Salles Gomes; *Poison Spring: The Secret History of the EPA*, Evaggelos Vallianatos; *Several Ways to Die in Mexico City*, Kurt Hollander; *The Cage: The Fight for Sri Lanka and the Last Days of the Tamil Tigers*, Gordon Weiss; *The Capitol Hill Playbook*, Nicholas Balthazar; *The Collected Poems of Carlos Drummond de Andrade*, Carlos Drummond de Andrade, Richard Zenith; *The Essential Book of Fermentation (Fermentation Nation)*, Jeff Cox; *The Girl in the Photograph*, Lygia Fagundes Telles; *The Street-Smart Salesman*, Anthony Belli, Janine Nichols; *Weaponized (Exile)*, Nicholas Mennuti, David Guggenheim
Foreign Rights: AK Agency (Alex Korzhenevski) (Baltic States, Russia, Ukraine); Amo Agency (Amo Noh) (Korea); Silvia Bastos Agency (Pau Centellas) (Latin America exc Brazil, Portugal, Spain); Big Apple Agency (Luc Kwanten) (China, Southeast Asia, Thailand); DS Budapest (Szabolcs Torok) (Hungary); ELST Literary Agency (Kalina Stefanova) (Bulgaria); The English Agency (Tsutomu Yawata) (Japan); Graal Literary Agency (Kamila Kanafa) (Poland); Deborah Harris Agency (Efrat Lev) (Israel); Iris Literary (Catherine Fragou) (Greece); Istanbul Copyright Agency (Barbaros Altug) (Turkey); Michelle Lapautre Agency (Catherine Lapautre) (France, Quebec, CN, Switzerland (French-speaking)); Lennart Sane Agency (Philip Sane) (Netherlands, Scandinavia); Michael Meller Agency (Regina Seitz) (Austria, Germany, Switzerland (German-speaking)); Andrew Nurnberg, Prague (Petra Tobiskova) (Czech Republic, Slovakia); Plima Literary (Vuk Perisic) (The Balkans exc Bulgaria, Greece & Turkey, Serbia); Riff Agency (Joao Paulo Riff) (Brazil); Susanna Zevi Agency (Susanna Zevi) (Italy)

**Robin Straus Agency Inc** (L)
229 E 79 St, Suite 5-A, New York, NY 10075
*Tel:* 212-472-3282 *Fax:* 212-472-3833
*E-mail:* info@robinstrausagency.com
*Web Site:* www.robinstrausagency.com
*Key Personnel*
Pres: Robin Straus (AAR) *E-mail:* robin@robinstrausagency.com
Founded: 1983
High quality fiction & nonfiction. Handle film & TV rights for represented clients' books. Foreign agents in all major foreign countries. No unsol mss, query first. No screenplays, plays, romance, westerns, science fiction, fantasy, horror, children's or poetry. Mail query with outline or synopsis, short author biography & sample chapters; SASE for response & return of mateireal must be included, or send brief e-mail letter describing book project (no downloads). No reading fees.
Foreign Rights: Deborah Harris (Israel); JLM Literary Agency (Greece); Andrew Nurnberg Associates (Worldwide exc Japan & Thailand); ONK Agency (Turkey); Tuttle-Mori Agency Inc (Japan, Thailand); Eric Yang Agency (Korea)

**Marianne Strong Literary Agency** (L)
65 E 96 St, New York, NY 10128
*Tel:* 212-249-1000 *Fax:* 212-831-3241
*Web Site:* stronglit.com
*Key Personnel*
Owner & Pres: Marianne Strong
*E-mail:* mariannestrong@stronglit.com
Agent: Nicole Lowary
Founded: 1978
In addition to select fiction, we handle general nonfiction, how-to books, biographies, gossip, society & entertainment, celebrity books, social history, life style, cookbooks, investigative biographies, mysteries, adventure, true crime fictionalized (or actual true crime), politics, self-help, inspirational, historic & memoirs. A separate service is provided that obtains assignments for professional writers. No fees charged; no unsol mss, query first with one page (no attachments) to mariannestrong@stronglit.com.
Titles recently placed: *Affirmed: The Last Triple Crown Winner*, Lou Sahadi; *Capital of the World : A Portrait of New York City in the Roaring Twenties*, David Wallace
Membership(s): The Authors Guild

**Strothman Agency LLC** (L)
PO Box 231132, Boston, MA 02123
*E-mail:* info@strothmanagency.com
*Web Site:* www.strothmanagency.com
*Key Personnel*
Principal & Agent: Wendy Strothman (AAR)
Agent: Lauren E MacLeod
Founded: 2003
Dedicated to promoting authors of significant books through the entire publishing cycle. No unsol mss, query first by e-mail only. Submit query letter, synopsis & SASE to strothmanagency@gmail.com, no attachments. Submissions will be acknowledged by an autoresponder. No fees charged.
Titles recently placed: *Frenzy & Untitled Book Two*, Robert Lettrick; *Lillian & Dash*, Sam Toperoff; *Mourning Lincoln*, Martha Hodes; *Of Horses & Humans*, Wendy Williams; *On the Edge: A Tiny Bird, An Ancient Crab, and An Epic Journey*, Deborah Cramer; *Origins of the British Empire*, Steve Pincus; *Real Mermaids Don't Sell Seashells (Real Mermaids Book 4)*, Helene Boudreau; *Serenading Earthworms: How Darwin Proved Darwin*, James Cost; *The Incarnate Trilogy*, Jodi Meadows; *The Pope & Mussolini*, David Kertzer; *Unequal Protections: The Last Legacy of Warren Burger's Court*, Linda Greenhouse, Michael Graetz
Membership(s): The Authors Guild

**Carolyn Swayze Literary Agency Ltd** (L)
15927 Pacific Place, White Rock, BC V4B 1S9, Canada
Mailing Address: PO Box 39588, RPO White Rock, Surrey, BC V4A 0A9, Canada
*Tel:* 604-538-3478
*Web Site:* www.swayzeagency.com
*Key Personnel*
Pres: Carolyn Swayze *E-mail:* carolyn@swayzeagency.com
Founded: 1994
Representing emerging & established authors of literary fiction, some commercial fiction, nonfiction, middle grade & YA books. No science fiction, no self-help, no picture books. An inquiry must include an author bio, a short description of the available project & short sample. No fees charged. Authors may consult web site for current submission guidelines. Mostly Canadian authors & US Pacific Northwest.
Titles recently placed: *Almost a Great Escape*, Tyler Trafford; *Assault on Juno*, Mark Zuehlke; *Audacious*, Gabrielle Prendergast; *Butterfly Winter*, W P Kinsella; *His Reluctant Rancher*, Roxanne Snopek; *Ortona Street Fight*, Mark Zuehlke; *Prisoner of Snowflake Falls*, John Lekich; *The Ballad of Jacob Peck*, Debra Komar; *The Break*, Nelsa Roberto; *The Evolution of Inanimate Objects*, Harry Karlinsky; *The Frail Days*, Gabrielle Prendergast; *The House on Sugarbush Road*, Meira Cook; *The Things They Said*, Kelli Deeth; *The Time We All Went Marching*, Arley McNeney; *Three River Ranch*, Roxanne Snopek
Foreign Rep(s): L'Autre Agence (Corinne Marotte) (France)
Foreign Rights: Elina Ahlback (Scandinavia); ALI (Stefania Fietta) (Italy); AM Heath & Co Ltd, Authors' Agents (UK); AMV Agencia Literaria (Spain); AnatoliaLit Copyright & Translation Agency (Turkey); Best Agency (Jeffrey Kim) (Korea); The Book Publishers Association of Israel (Dalia Ever Hadani) (Israel); Chinese Connection Agency (China, Taiwan); ELST Literary Agency (Kalina Stefanova) (Bulgaria); International Copyright Agency (Simona Kessler) (Moldova, Romania); Mo Literary Services (Netherlands); Mohr Books (Germany); Andrew Nurnberg Associates (Baltic States); O A Literary Agency (Greece); The Rights

Agency (Canada (French-speaking)); Maria Starz-Kanska (Poland); Tuttle-Mori Agency Inc (Japan)

**Robert E Tabian/Literary Agent** (L)
229 Paterson Ave, Suite 2, East Rutherford, NJ 07073
*Tel:* 631-987-2293 *Fax:* 201-438-1327
*E-mail:* retlit@mindspring.com
*Key Personnel*
Owner & Sole Prop: Bob E Tabian
Founded: 1992
Adult & young adult fiction, adult nonfiction; thrillers, mysteries, women's fiction, self-help, psychology, cookbooks, health & medicine, history, biography & popular culture & spirituality. No unsol mss, query first with SASE. Submit 100 pages (fiction) or outline & two sample chapters (nonfiction). Handle film & TV rights. Representatives in many foreign countries & Hollywood. No reading fee. Clients are charged ms copying & submission mailing charges.
Foreign Rights: Chandler Crawford Agency (Worldwide)

**Roslyn Targ Literary Agency Inc** (L)
105 W 13 St, Suite 15-E, New York, NY 10011
*Tel:* 212-206-9390 *Fax:* 212-989-6233
*E-mail:* roslyn@roslyntargagency.com
*Key Personnel*
Pres: Roslyn Targ (AAR)
Founded: 1970
No longer interested in acquiring domestic authors. Will continue to represent those authors already placed & will continue to represent foreign rights to my American clients. Not taking on any new clients & therefore, are not accepting any unsol mss or queries. Handle film & TV rights only to clients whose books we have sold. No screenplays or plays.

**Patricia Teal Literary Agency** (L)
2036 Vista del Rosa, Fullerton, CA 92831
*Tel:* 714-738-8333 *Fax:* 714-738-8333
*Key Personnel*
Owner & Pres: Patricia Teal (AAR)
Founded: 1978
Handle full-length category fiction & nonfiction; specialize in romance literature & women's mainstream literature. Commercial self-help & how-to in nonfiction. No short stories, articles, poetry, scripts or syndicated material. No fees charged, except for Xeroxing fee for mss circulated. No unsol mss, query first by mail. Not accepting new clients.
Titles recently placed: *Royal Wedding Bells*, Raye Morgan, Nina Harrington
Membership(s): The Authors Guild; Romance Writers of America

**Tessler Literary Agency LLC** (L)
27 W 20 St, Suite 1003, New York, NY 10011
*Tel:* 212-242-0466 *Fax:* 212-242-2366
*Web Site:* www.tessleragency.com
*Key Personnel*
Pres: Michelle Tessler (AAR)
Founded: 2004
Full-service boutique agency dedicated to writers of high quality fiction & nonfiction. Nonfiction list includes narrative, popular science, memoir, history, psychology, business, biography, food & travel. In fiction, represents literary, women's & commercial. No unsol mss, query first via web form. No fees charged.
Titles recently placed: *A Grand Complication: The Race to Build the World's Most Legendary Watch*, Stacy Perman; *Applied Minds: How Engineers Think*, Guru Madhavan; *Close Your Eyes*, Amanda Eyre Ward; *Duel with the Devil: The True Story of How Alexander Hamilton and Aaron Burr Teamed Up to Take on America's First Sensational Murder Mystery*, Paul Collins; *Emotional First Aid: Practical Strategies for Treating Failure, Rejection, Guilt, and Other Everyday Psychological Injuries*, Guy Winch, PhD; *Heir to the Empire City: New York and the Making of Theodore Roosevelt*, Edward Kohn; *Part Time Paleo*, Leanne Ely; *Straphanger: Saving Our Cities and Ourselves from the Automobile*, Taras Grescoe; *The Bonobo and the Atheist: In Search of Humanism Among the Primates*, Frans de Waal; *The Book of Immortality: The Science, Belief, and Magic Behind Living Forever*, Adam Gollner; *The Chemistry Between Us: Love, Sex, and the Science of Attraction*, Larry Young, PhD, Brian Alexander; *The Drunken Botanist*, Amy Stewart; *The Sleepwalker's Guide to Dancing*, Mira Jacob; *Underwater Dogs*, Seth Casteel; *Visit Sunny Chernobyl: And Other Adventures in the World's Most Polluted Places*, Andrew Blackwell
Foreign Rights: The Deborah Harris Agency (Israel); Andrew Nurnberg & Associates (China, Europe, Latin America); Tuttle-Mori Agency Inc (Japan); Eric Yang Agency (Korea)

**3 Seas Literary Agency** (L)
PO Box 8571, Madison, WI 53708
*Tel:* 608-834-9317
*Key Personnel*
Literary Agent: Michelle Grajkowski (AAR) *E-mail:* threeseaslit@aol.com; Cori Deyoe *E-mail:* cori@threeseaslit.com
Founded: 2000
E-mail queries only. For fiction titles, query with first chapter & synopsis embedded in the e-mail. For nonfiction, query with complete proposal attached. For picture books, query with complete text. Illustrations are not necessary. Considers simultaneous submissions. Responds within 1 month to e-mail submissions. No snail mail queries. 3 Seas will not respond to queries that are sent to e-mail addresses other than queries@threeseaslit.com. Obtains most new clients through recommendations from others & conferences. No fees charged.
Titles recently placed: *A Navy SEAL'S Surprise Baby*, Laura Marie Altom; *A Time For Home*, Alexis Morgan; *Captive*, KM Fawcett; *Changed By His Son*, Robin Gianakopoulus; *Do or Diner*, Christine Wenger; *Every Breath She Takes*, Norah Wilson; *Forever Friday*, Timothy Lewis; *Haley's Mountain Man*, Tracy Madison; *Her Perfect Cowboy*, Trish Milburn; *His Uptown Girl*, Liz Talley; *How to Write a Book in 30 Days*, Karen Wiesner; *Jimmie Joe Johnson: Manwhore*, Lindsey Brookes; *Just Perfect*, JoMarie DeGioia; *Must Love Dukes*, Elizabeth Michaels; *One Night with the Sheikh*, Kristi Gold; *Passion and Pretense*, Susan Gee Heino; *Queen of Song & Souls*, C L Wilson; *Queen of the Sylphs*, LJ McDonald; *Say It With Roses*, Devon Vaughn Archer; *Six Months Later*, Natalie D. Richards; *The Art of Stealing Time*, Katie MacAlister; *The Bride Next Door*, Winnie Griggs; *The Casanova Code*, Donna MacMeans; *The Champion*, Carla Capshaw; *The Rancher's Homecoming*, Cathy McDavid; *The Sister Season*, Jennifer Brown; *The Vampire With a Dragon Tattoo*, Kerrelyn Sparks; *The Winter King*, C L Wilson; *Thousand Words*, Jennifer Brown; *Three Days on Mimosa Lane*, Anna DeStefano
Foreign Rights: Ingo Stein (Germany); Marleen Seegers (China, France, Holland, Scandinavia)
Membership(s): Romance Writers of America

**Toad Hall Inc** (L-D)
74 Toad Hall Lane, Laceyville, PA 18623-8047
*Tel:* 570-869-2942
*Key Personnel*
Pres: Sharon Jarvis *E-mail:* sharonsj@frontiernet.net
Founded: 1983
Fiction & nonfiction, prefer nonfiction. No children's or young adult. No short material of any kind. Handle software, film & TV rights as outgrowth of book option. No unsol mss, query first with letter only. Submit letter, one-page synopsis or table of contents. No reading fee. Photocopy & legal fees. Affiliates Metropolitan, Rights Unlimited.
Foreign Rights: Rights Unlimited
Membership(s): The Association of Publishers for Special Sales; IBPA, the Independent Book Publishers Association

**The Tomasino Agency Inc** (L)
70 Chestnut St, Dobbs Ferry, NY 10522
*Tel:* 914-674-9659 *Fax:* 914-693-0381
*E-mail:* info@tomasinoagency.com
*Web Site:* www.tomasinoagency.com
*Key Personnel*
Pres: Christine K Tomasino
Founded: 1998
Commercial & literary fiction & nonfiction. Represent all subrights for book clients only. Specialize in conventional & mind/body health, women's issues, self-improvement, spirituality/esoterica, narrative nonfiction, lifestyle, adult illustrated & packaged books, sports. Translation of nonbook content into book-related formats for corporate & nonprofit organizational clients such as major web businesses & museums. No poetry, genre fiction, plays, science fiction or purely scholarly work. Foreign agents in all major markets. No unsol mss, query first. No e-mailed or faxed full-length proposals.

**Transatlantic Agency** (L)
2 Bloor St E, Ste 3500, Toronto, ON M4W-1A8, Canada
*Tel:* 416-488-9214
*E-mail:* info@transatlanticagency.com
*Web Site:* www.transatlanticagency.com
*Key Personnel*
Chmn: Don Sedgwick *E-mail:* don@transatlanticagency.com
Pres: David Bennett *E-mail:* david@transatlanticagency.com
VP: Lynn Bennett *E-mail:* lynn@transatlanticagency.com
Partner & Agent: Shaun Bradley *E-mail:* shaun@transatlanticagency.com; Marie Campbell *E-mail:* marie@transatlanticagency.com; Samantha Haywood *E-mail:* samantha@transatlanticagency.com
Agent: Fiona Kenshole *E-mail:* fiona@transatlanticagency.com; Meghan Macdonald *E-mail:* meghan@transatlanticagency.com; Patricia Ocampo *E-mail:* patricia@transatlanticagency.com; Jennifer Starkman *E-mail:* jennifer@transatlanticagency.com; Amy Tompkins *E-mail:* amy@transatlanticagency.com
Founded: 1993
Children's, adult literary fiction & literary nonfiction. Markets Canadian & American literary properties to English language publishers in the UK, USA & Canada & through sub-agents to publishers around the world. Handles film & TV rights for literary properties only: no film scripts or tele-plays. No unsol mss; initial letter of inquiry essential. No reading fees. See web site for individual agents' submission details.
Titles recently placed: *Annabel*, Kathleen Winter; *Bluefish*, Pat Schmatz; *Caroline - American Girl*, Kathleen Ernst; *Fat Angie*, E E Charlton-Trujillo; *Home and Away*, Dave Bidini; *McKenna - American Girl*, Mary Casanova; *Navigating Early*, Clare Vanderpool; *The Gypsy King*, Maureen Fergus; *The Metro Dogs of Moscow*, Rachelle Delaney; *The Neighbourhood*, Eric Walters; *The Selector of Souls*, Shauna Singh Baldwin; *The Truth About*

*Luck*, Iain Reid; *Why Men Lie*, Linden MacIntyre
Foreign Rights: The agency (Korea); Akcali Copyright (Turkey); ANAW Literary Agency (Poland); Berla & Griffini Rights Agency (Italy); The Book Publishers Association of Israel (Israel); ELST Literary Agency (Bulgaria); The English Agency (Japan) Ltd (Japan); Agence Litteraire Lora Fountain (France, Portugal, Spain); International Editors' Co (Spanish & Portuguese); Japan Uni Agency Inc (Japan); The Anna Jarota Agency (France); JLM Literary Agency (Greece); Katai & Bolza Literary Agents (Hungary); Liepman AG (Germany); Literarische Agentur+Medienservice (Germany); Mo Literary Services (Netherlands, Scandinavia); Andrew Nurnberg Associates International Ltd (China, Hong Kong, Taiwan); Kristin Olson Literary Agency sro (Czech Republic); Orange Agency (Korea); Agencia Literaria RIFF (Brazil); Shin Won Agency Co (Korea); Tuttle-Mori Agency Inc (Indonesia, Japan, Malaysia, Thailand, Vietnam); Young Agency (Korea)

**Treimel, S©ott, NY**, see S©ott Treimel NY

**TriadaUS Literary Agency** (L)
PO Box 561, Sewickley, PA 15143
*Tel:* 412-401-3376 *Fax:* 412-749-0842
*Web Site:* www.triadaus.com
*Key Personnel*
Agent: Dr Uwe Stender (AAR) *E-mail:* uwe@triadaus.com
Founded: 2004
Full service literary agency including fiction, nonfiction. Also international sales, film & TV options. No unsol mss, query first.
Titles recently placed: *Flight 93: The Story and the Legacy*, Tom McMillan; *Garden Therapy*, Stephanie Rose; *Hotter Than a Match Head*, Steve Boone, Tony Moss; *How to Barter for Your Dream Home-A Journey Around the World*, Michael Wigge; *How to Travel the World for Free*, Michael Wigge; *Love Isn't Supposed to Hurt*, Christi Paul; *Race-Baiter: How the Media Wields Dangerous Words to Divide a Nation*, Eric Deggans; *The Big Mix*, Dale McGowan; *The Kids' Outdoor Adventure Book: 448 Great Things to Do in Nature Before You Grow Up*, Stacy Tornio, Ken Keffer; *The Kids' Outdoor Myth Book*, Stacy Tornio, Ken Keffer; *The Reappearing Act*, Kate Fagan; *The Totally Sweet 90s: From Clear Cola to Furby, and Grunge to "Whatever", the Toys, Tastes, and Trends That Defined a Decade*, Gael Fashingbauer Cooper, Brian Bellmont; *The Tragedy Paper*, Elizabeth LaBan; *The Vigilante Poets of Selwyn Academy*, Kate Hattemer; *We Love Nature*, Stacy Tornio, Ken Keffer; *Wild Connection*, Dr Jennifer Verdolin

**Trident Media Group LLC** (L)
41 Madison Ave, 36th fl, New York, NY 10010
*Tel:* 212-262-4810 *Fax:* 212-262-4849
*Web Site:* www.tridentmediagroup.com
*Key Personnel*
Chmn: Robert Gottlieb
CEO: Daniel Strone
EVP & Lit Agent: Ellen Levine (AAR)
EVP: Scott Miller; John Silbersack
VP & Mng Dir, Foreign Rts: Claire Roberts
VP, Literary Agent: Kimberly Whalen
Assoc Dir, Foreign Rts: Jessica Olivo
Literary Agent: Eileen Cope; Don Fehr; Melissa Flashman; Alex Glass; Alanna Ramirez
Literary Agent, Women's Fiction: MacKenzie Fraser-Bub
Literary Agent: Erica Spellman-Silverman
Audio Rts Agent: Mark Gottlieb; Adrienne Lombardo
Foreign Rts Agent: Sylvie Rosokoff
Founded: 2000
General fiction & nonfiction. No unsol mss, query first by e-mail. Submit outline & sample chapters if requested. No reading fee. Handle film & TV rights for clients only. Representation in Hollywood.

**2M Communications Ltd** (L)
33 W 17 St, 11th fl, New York, NY 10011
*Tel:* 212-741-1509 *Fax:* 212-691-4460
*Web Site:* www.2mcommunications.com
*Key Personnel*
Pres: Madeleine Morel (AAR) *E-mail:* morel@2mcommunications.com
Founded: 1982
Only represent previously published ghostwriters & collaborators who work with platformed authors already represented by recognized literary agents or acquired by publishing houses. Numerous New York Times bestsellers but all confidential. No unsol mss, query first. Submit CV or resume.
Membership(s): Women's Media Group

**United Talent Agency** (L-D)
9560 Wilshire Blvd, Suite 500, Beverly Hills, CA 90212
*Tel:* 310-273-6700 *Fax:* 310-247-1111
*E-mail:* chanb@unitedtalent.com
*Web Site:* www.unitedtalent.com
*Key Personnel*
Owner: Gary C Cosay
Founded: 1991
Fiction, nonfiction. Handle film & TV rights. No unsol mss, query first; reading fee.

**Wales Literary Agency Inc** (L)
PO Box 9426, Seattle, WA 98109-0426
*Tel:* 206-284-7114
*E-mail:* waleslit@waleslit.com
*Web Site:* www.waleslit.com
*Key Personnel*
Owner & Literary Agent: Elizabeth Wales (AAR)
Asst Agent & Foreign Rts: Neal Swain
Founded: 1990
Specialize in quality fiction & nonfiction. Does not handle screenplays, children's books, genre fiction or most category nonfiction. No unsol mss, query first with cover letter & SASE or e-mail queries with no attachments. No phone or fax queries. Simultaneous submissions accepted. Response provided within 3 weeks to queries, 3 months to mss.
Titles recently placed: *American Savage: Insights, Slights, and Fights on Faith, Sex, Love, and Politics*, Dan Savage; *Badluck Way and the Wolf*, Bryce Andrews; *Dolls Behaving Badly*, Cinthia Ritchie; *Happiness is a Chemical in the Brain*, Lucia Perillo; *Heat: Adventures in the World's Fiery Places*, Bill Streever, PhD; *The Rocks Don't Lie: A Geologist Investigates Noah's Flood*, David Montgomery; *The Urban Bestiary: Encountering the Everyday Wild*, Lyanda Lynn Haupt
Foreign Rights: Antonella Antonelli Agenzia Letteraria (Italy); Big Apple Agency Inc (China); Nurcihan Kesim Literary & Licensing Agency (Turkey); Agence Lapautre (France); Mohrbooks Literary Agency (Austria, Germany, Switzerland); Sebes & van Gelderen Literary Agency (Netherlands); Shinwon Agency (Korea); Silk Road Agency (Thailand); Abner Stein Agency (UK); Ulf Toregard Agency AB (Sweden); Tuttle-Mori Agency Inc (Japan)

**Wallace Literary Agency Inc** (L)
301 E 79 St, No 14-J, New York, NY 10075-0951
*Tel:* 212-570-9090 *Fax:* 212-772-8979
*E-mail:* walliter@aol.com
*Key Personnel*
Pres: Lois Wallace
Founded: 1988
Handle film & TV rights for agency clients only. No unsol mss, query first with SASE, no reading fee.
Foreign Rights: A M Heath (UK); Michelle Lapautre (France); Andrew Nurnberg Associates (Europe); Tuttle-Mori Agency Inc (Japan)

**Ward & Balkin Agency, Inc** (L)
30 Brock Way, South Hadley, MA 01075
*Tel:* 413-322-8697
*Web Site:* www.wardbalkin.com
*Key Personnel*
Pres: Richard A Balkin (AAR)
*E-mail:* rick62838@crocker.com
Founded: 1972
Adult nonfiction fiction only. No unsol mss, query first. Submit outline & one sample chapter. No reading fee, 15% agency commission; 25% foreign rights. Currently not accepting new clients.
Clients of the late Christina (Kit) Ward are now handled by Colleen Mohyde at The Doe Coover Agency. Colleen can be reached at 718-721-6000 or colleen@doecooveragency.com.
Titles recently placed: *American Isis: A Biography of Sylvia Plath*, Carl Rollyson; *Apocalypse Forever*, Betsy Hartmann; *Changing Lives: Gustavo Dudamel, El Sistema, and the Transformative Power of Music*, Tricia Tunstall; *Newton Fever*, Sarah Dry; *The Approaching Great Transformation: Toward a Livable Post Carbon Economy*, Joel Magnuson; *The Wizard and the Prophet*, Charles Mann; *Why Geology Matters: Decoding the Past, Anticipating the Future*, Doug Macdougall
Foreign Rights: Taryn Fagerness Agency (Worldwide exc USA)

**Warwick Associates** (L)
18340 Sonoma Hwy, Sonoma, CA 95476
*Tel:* 707-939-9212 *Fax:* 707-938-3515
*E-mail:* warwick@vom.com
*Web Site:* www.warwickassociates.com
*Key Personnel*
Pres: Simon Warwick-Smith
Founded: 1985
A "one-stop" agency handling any or all parts of literary agenting through publicity & sales, etc. Specialize in spirituality, metaphysics, religion & psychology, celebrity memoirs, business & self-help, pop culture. Literary agent for a number of celebrity spiritual authors. No reading fee. Accept unsol mss. Query first with 2 chapters & SASE. No fiction or poetry.

**Waterside Productions Inc** (L)
2055 Oxford Ave, Cardiff, CA 92007
*Tel:* 760-632-9190 *Fax:* 760-632-9295
*E-mail:* admin@waterside.com
*Web Site:* www.waterside.com
*Key Personnel*
Founder & Pres: William Gladstone
*E-mail:* bgladstone@waterside.com
VP & Literary Agent: Carole Jelen McClendon
*Tel:* 925-930-0883 *E-mail:* carole@elenpub.com
Foreign Rts Dir: Neil Gudovitz *E-mail:* neilg@earthlink.net
Agent: Margot Maley Hutchison *Tel:* 858-483-0426 *E-mail:* mmaley@waterside.com; Lawrence Jackel *Tel:* 941-364-3601 *E-mail:* jackelpub1@verizon.net; Jill Kramer *E-mail:* editorjk2@aol.com; David C Nelson
Founded: 1982
Specialize in nonfiction. Professional how-to: technology, business, sftware, test-prep, etc. General: self-help, spiritual, health, human interest, etc. No phone calls. No unsol mss. Submit a full book proposal per guidelines found at, or query through, the web site form. No reading fee. Handles software, film & TV

rights with co-agents. In-house international division. Affiliations with PR agencies. Waterside now has its own print on demand & ebook publishing division at end of description of services.
Titles recently placed: *Conscious Money: Living, Creating & Investing with Your Values for a Sustainable New Prosperity*, Patricia Aburdene; *I Got a Name: The Jim Croce Story*, Ingrid Croce, Jimmy Rock; *The Crash of 2015*, Thom Hartmann; *The Golden Motorcycle Gang: A Story of Transformation*, Jack Canfield, William Gladstone; *The Steve Jobs Way: iLeadership for a New Generation*, Jay Elliot, William L Simon; *The Storm Before the Calm*, Neale Donald Walsch

**Watkins/Loomis Agency Inc** (L)
PO Box 20925, New York, NY 10025
*Tel:* 212-532-0080 *Fax:* 646-383-2449
*E-mail:* assistant@watkinsloomis.com
*Web Site:* www.watkinsloomis.com
*Key Personnel*
Pres: Gloria Loomis
Agent: Julia Masnik
Founded: 1908
Literary fiction, political nonfiction. No unsol material.
Foreign Rights: The Marsh Agency; Abner Stein Agency (UK)

**Waxman Literary Agency** (L)
Affiliate of Diversion Publishing Corp
80 Fifth Ave, Suite 1101, New York, NY 10011
*Tel:* 212-675-5556 *Fax:* 212-675-1381
*Web Site:* www.waxmanagency.com
*Key Personnel*
Pres & Agent: Scott Waxman
Agent: William Callahan; Byrd Leavell; Holly Root; Rachel Vogel
Founded: 1997
Fiction & nonfiction. No unsol mss, query first via e-mail. No reading fee, charge for reproductions.

**Cherry Weiner Literary Agency** (L)
28 Kipling Way, Manalapan, NJ 07726
*Tel:* 732-446-2096 *Fax:* 732-792-0506
*E-mail:* cherry8486@aol.com
*Key Personnel*
Owner: Cherry Weiner
Founded: 1977
Science fiction, general fiction & nonfiction. No unsol mss. Referred authors submit letter saying who referred. Submissions or recommendations only. Query letter where applicable, no downloads. No reading fee. Handle film & TV rights. Foreign representatives in England, Germany, Italy, Japan, Netherlands, Scandinavia, Russia, Spain, Eastern Europe & France.
Titles recently placed: *Alien Separation*, Gini Koch; *Escape from Hangtown*, Larry D Sweazy; *Night Terrors I & II*, Tim Waggoner; *The Assaults of Chaos*, S T Joshi; *Universal Alien*, Gini Koch; *Vengeance at Sundown*, Larry D Sweazy

**The Weingel-Fidel Agency** (L)
310 E 46 St, Suite 21-E, New York, NY 10017
*Tel:* 212-599-2959 *Fax:* 212-286-1986
*E-mail:* queries@theweingel-fidelagency.com
*Key Personnel*
Owner: Loretta Weingel-Fidel *E-mail:* lwf@theweingel-fidelagency.com
Founded: 1989
General fiction & nonfiction. Provide services to book authors/writers. No unsol mss, query first, by referral only; no reading fee.
Foreign Rep(s): Mary Clemmey (UK); Fritz Agency (Germany); Japan UNI (Japan); Michelle Lapautre (France); Lennart Sane (Netherlands, Scandinavia, Spain)
Foreign Rights: Jill Hughes (Albania, Bulgaria, Croatia, Estonia, Hungary, Latvia, Lithuania, Macedonia, Montenegro, Romania, Serbia, Slovakia, Slovenia)

**Westwood Creative Artists Ltd** (L)
94 Harbord St, Toronto, ON M5S 1G6, Canada
*Tel:* 416-964-3302 *Fax:* 416-975-9209
*E-mail:* wca_office@wcaltd.com
*Web Site:* www.wcaltd.com
*Key Personnel*
Chmn: Michael Levine
Pres: Bruce Westwood
Rts Dir: Natasha Daneman
Rts Mgr & Exec Asst: Chris Cassuccio
Agent & Asst to Pres: Carolyn Forde
Agent: Jackie Kaiser; Linda McKnight; Hilary McMahon; John Pearce
Admin Asst: Laura Cook; Lien De Nil
Founded: 1995
General trade fiction & nonfiction for international marketplace. Canadian authors only. No unsol mss, query first. Handle film & TV rights. No reading fee.
Foreign Rep(s): Akcali Copyright (Kezban Akcali) (Turkey); Akcali Copyright (Atilla Izgi Turgut) (Turkey); Sandra Bruna Literary Agency (Natalia Berenguer) (Brazil, Latin America, Portugal, Spain); Sandra Bruna Literary Agency (Sandra Bruna) (Brazil, Latin America, Portugal, Spain); The English Agency (Hamish Macaskill) (Japan); Graal Literary Agency (Maria Starz-Kanska) (Poland); Graal Literary Agency (Marcin Biegaj) (Poland); The Deborah Harris Agency (Efrat Lev) (Israel); International Copyright Agency (Simona Kessler) (Romania); Japan Uni Agency (Miko Suga Yamanouchi) (Japan); Anna Jarota (Anna Jarota) (France); Anna Jarota (Sandrine Bilan) (France); JLM Literary Agency (John Moukakos) (Greece); Katai & Bolza (Peter Bolza) (Hungary); Liepman Agency (Ruth Weibel) (Germany); Liepman Agency (Suzanne de Roche) (Germany); Maxima Creative Agency (Santo Manurung) (Indonesia); NiKa (Vania Kadiyska) (Bulgaria); Andrew Nurnberg & Associates (Lisa Brannstrom) (Netherlands, Scandinavia); Andrew Nurnberg & Associates (Eleonoora Kirk) (Netherlands, Scandinavia); Andrew Nurnberg Associates International (Whitney Hsu) (China); Kristin Olson (Czech Republic); PLIMA (Vuk Perisic) (Croatia, Serbia, Slovenia); Shin Won Agency (Tae Eun Kim) (Korea); Synopsis (Natalia Sanina) (Russia); Tuttle-Mori Agency Co Ltd (Thananchai Pandey) (Thailand); Tuttle-Mori Agency Inc (Ken Mori) (Japan); Marco Vigevani Agency (Italy)

**Rhoda Weyr Agency**, see Dunham Literary Inc

**Witherspoon Associates Inc**, see InkWell Management

**WME** (L-D)
1325 Avenue of the Americas, New York, NY 10019
*Tel:* 212-586-5100 *Fax:* 212-246-3583
*E-mail:* wma@interport.net
*Web Site:* www.wma.com
*Key Personnel*
Partner: Tina Bennett; Dorian Karchmar
Head, NY Lit Dept: Suzanne Gluck (AAR)
EVP, Co-Head: Jennifer Rudolph Walsh (AAR)
Dept Head: Eric Simonoff
Agent: Mel Berger (AAR); Tracy Fisher (AAR)
Contact: Jay Mandel (AAR)
All subjects; handle software, film & TV rights. No unsol mss, query first; no reading fee.
*Branch Office(s)*
9601 Wilshire Blvd, Beverly Hills, CA 90210 *Tel:* 310-285-9000 *Fax:* 310-285-9010
119 Washington Ave, Suite 400, Miami Beach, FL 33139 *Tel:* 305-938-2000 *Fax:* 305-938-2002
1600 Division St, Suite 300, Nashville, TN 37203 *Tel:* 615-963-3000 *Fax:* 615-963-3090
*Foreign Office(s):* Center Point, 103 New Oxford St, London WC1A 1DD, United Kingdom *Tel:* (020) 7534 6800 *Fax:* (020) 7534 6900

**Writers House** (L)
21 W 26 St, New York, NY 10010
*Tel:* 212-685-2400 *Fax:* 212-685-1781
*Web Site:* www.writershouse.com
*Key Personnel*
Chmn & CEO: Amy Berkower
Pres: Simon Lipskar (AAR)
EVP, Fiction & Nonfiction: Merrilee Heifetz (AAR)
VP & Dir, Juv & Young Adult: Susan Cohen (AAR)
Children's Subs Rts Dir: Cecelia de la Campa
Subs Rts Dir: Maja Nikolic
Dir, Digital Rts: Julie Trelstad
Sr Agent: Stephen Barr; Dan Conaway (AAR); Leigh Feldman; Susan Ginsburg; Dan Lazar (AAR) *E-mail:* dlazar@writershouse.com; Michele Rubin
Sr Agent, Juv & Young Adult: Jodi Reamer, Esq (AAR); Rebecca Sherman *E-mail:* rsherman@writershouse.com
Sr Agent, Mainstream Fiction & Nonfiction: Robin Rue (AAR)
Agent: Lisa DiMona; Brianne Johnson; Geri Thoma
Jr Agent: Kristy King
Founded: 1973
Represent trade books of all types, fiction & nonfiction, including all rights. Handle film & TV rights. No screenplays, teleplays or software. No unsol mss, query first with an intelligent one page letter stating what's wonderful about the book, what it's about & what background & experience you, as an author, bring to it. Queries generally responded to within 2 weeks & mss within 4 weeks. No reading fee.
Titles recently placed: *A World Without Heroes (Beyonders)*, Brandon Mull; *Adam; The Nightwalkers*, Jacquelyn Frank; *Deadly Sins*, Lora Leigh; *Devious*, Lisa Jackson; *Dork Diaries 5*, Rachel Renee Russell; *Eyes Wide Open*, Andrew Gross; *Family Storms*, VC Andrews; *Head Over Hills*, Jill Shalvis; *Hush*, Nancy Bush; *Lothaire*, Kresley Cole; *Massacre at Powder River*, William W Johnstone; *Moonlight in the Morning*, Jude Deveraux; *Nightborn*, Lynn Viehl; *Nowhere Near Respectable*, Mary Jo Putney; *One Lavender Lane*, JoAnn Ross; *Prey*, Linda Howard; *Secrets of the Lost Summer*, Carla Neggers; *Shadowfever*, Karen Marie Moning; *She Tempts the Duke*, Lorraine Heath; *Silenced*, Allison Brennan; *The Fault in Our Stars*, John Green; *The Jefferson Key*, Steve Berry; *The Other Side*, J D Robb; *Wicked Lies*, Lisa Jackson, Nancy Bush
*Branch Office(s)*
3368 Governor Dr, San Diego, CA 92122, Dir, Juv, Young Adult & Illus: Steven Malk *Tel:* 858-678-8767 *Fax:* 858-678-8530
Foreign Rep(s): Angharad Kowal (UK)
Foreign Rights: Ia Atterholm (Scandinavia); Bardon Agency (Taiwan); Eliane Benisti (France); Luigi Bernabo (Italy); Claude Choquette (Canada (French-speaking)); Raquel de la Concha (Portugal, Spain); DRT (Korea); Japan Uni (juv & young adult) (Japan); JLM Literary Agency (Greece); Simona Kessler (Romania); Ulla Lohren (Scandinavia); Aleksandra Matuszak (Poland); Jovan Milenkovic (Croatia, Montenegro, Serbia); Andrew Nurnberg Associates (Baltic States); The Owl's Agency (Japan); Ilana Pikarski Ltd (Israel); Katalina Sabeva (Bulgaria); Karin Schindler (Brazil); Thomas Schlueck (Germany); Sebes & Van

Gelderen Literary Agency (Netherlands); Synopsis Literary Agency (Russia); Petra Tobiskova (Czech Republic)

**Writers' Productions** (L-D)
PO Box 630, Westport, CT 06881-0630
*Tel:* 203-227-8199
*Key Personnel*
Owner & Pres: David L Meth *E-mail:* dlm67@mac.com
Founded: 1977
Literary quality fiction & nonfiction. Handle film, TV & licensing rights. Foreign Reps available as & where needed. No fees. No unsol mss; not accepting new clients. No mss or samples by fax or e-mail. No phone calls.
Membership(s): Academy of American Poets; The Dramatists Guild of America; Educational Theatre Association; PEN American Center

**Writers' Representatives LLC** (L)
116 W 14 St, 11th fl, New York, NY 10011-7305
*Tel:* 212-620-0023 *Fax:* 212-620-0023
*E-mail:* transom@writersreps.com
*Web Site:* www.writersreps.com
*Key Personnel*
Principal: Lynn Chu; Glen Hartley *E-mail:* glen@writersreps.com
Founded: 1985
Represents authors of book-length works of nonfiction & literary fiction for adults. Once WR agrees to represent an author, we give advice on how best to structure or edit an book proposal, discuss ideas for book projects & comment on finished ms material, with the goal of placing a book with the right publisher on the best possible terms for our author. We also discuss our authors' backgrounds & interests with publishers to promote upcoming projects or to find new ones. We sell to major publishers in the US & abroad.
Prefer to see ms material rather than synopses. Background about the author's professional experience, particularly that which is relevant to the book, as well as a list of previously published works. We respond within 2 to 5 weeks on average. We require that all authors fully advise us as to whether any project has been previously submitted to a publisher & what the response was & if the project has been submitted to another agent. Submissions should be accompanied by SASE; no reading fees.
Titles recently placed: *Social Animal: A Story of How Success Happens*, David Brooks; *The Anatomy of Influence: Literature as a Way of Life*, Harold Bloom
Foreign Rights: Agence Hoffman (Boris Hoffman) (France); Agencia Literaria Carmen Balcells (Anna Bofill) (Portugal); Agencia Literaria Carmen Balcells (Maribel Luque) (Spain); Tassy Barham Associates (Tassy Barham) (Brazil); Eggers & Landwehr KG (Petra Eggers) (Germany); Japan Uni Agency (Miko Yamanouchi) (Japan); Susanna Zevi Agencia Letteraria (Susanna Zevi) (Italy)

**The Wylie Agency Inc** (L)
250 W 57 St, Suite 2114, New York, NY 10107
*Tel:* 212-246-0069 *Fax:* 212-586-8953
*E-mail:* mail@wylieagency.com
*Web Site:* www.wylieagency.com
*Key Personnel*
Founder & Pres: Andrew Wylie
Literary Agent: Jin Auh; Sarah Chalfant; Jeffrey Posternak
Founded: 1980
Literary fiction & nonfiction; no unsol mss; query first with SASE. Handle film & TV rights. Contact for fee information.
*Foreign Office(s):* The Wylie Agency (UK) Ltd, 17 Bedford Sq, London WC1B 3JA, United Kingdom *Tel:* (020) 7908-5900 *Fax:* (020) 7908-5901 *E-mail:* mail@wylieagency.co.uk
Foreign Rights: The Wylie Agency (UK) Ltd (UK)

**Mary Yost Books** (L)
135 W 95 St, New York, NY 10025
*Tel:* 212-980-4988
*E-mail:* yostbooks59@aol.com
Founded: 1958
Psychology, women's topics. No unsol mss, query first. Submit outline & sample chapters. Representatives in many countries. Does not charge fees.
Foreign Rep(s): Abner Stein Agency (UK)
Foreign Rights: Ruth Liepman (Germany); Lennart Sane (Scandinavia)

**The Young Agency** (L)
115 W 29 St, 3rd fl, New York, NY 10001
*Tel:* 212-695-2431
*Key Personnel*
Prop: Marian Young
Founded: 1986
Fiction & nonfiction. No unsol mss; no reading fees. Handle film & TV rights after book is sold.

**Zachary Shuster Harmsworth Agency** (L-D)
1776 Broadway, Suite 1405, New York, NY 10019
*Tel:* 212-765-6900 *Fax:* 212-765-6490
*Web Site:* www.zshliterary.com
*Key Personnel*
Partner: Jennifer Gates *E-mail:* jgates@zshliterary.com; Esmond Harmsworth *E-mail:* eharmsworth@zshliterary.com; Todd Shuster *E-mail:* tshuster@zshliterary.com; Lane Zachary *E-mail:* lzachary@zshliterary.com
Literary Dir: Janet Silver *E-mail:* jsilver@zshliterary.com
At-Large Agent: Eve Bridburg
Affiliate Agent: Bridget Wagner
Literary, commercial & genre fiction & nonfiction (except no science fiction or fantasy), mystery, thriller, non-category romance, biography, current affairs, business, psychology, memoir, science & history. Some young adult; no children's. No unsol mss, e-mail only query letters, full plot; synopsis or detailed chapters summary plus three sample chapters up to 50 pages. No mss returned without SASE. No reading fee.
*Branch Office(s)*
535 Boylston St, 11th fl, Boston, MA 02116, Contact: MaryBeth Chappell *Tel:* 617-262-2400 *Fax:* 617-262-2468
Foreign Rep(s): Esmond Harmsworth (UK)
Foreign Rights: Big Apple Agency Inc (China); Agencia Literaria BMSR (Brazil); Sandra Bruna Agency (Spain); Ann-Christine Danielson Agency (Scandinavia); The English Agency (Japan); Agence Hoffman (Germany); Japan UNI (Japan); Asli Karasuil Telif Haklari Ajansi ve Tic AS (Ms Asli Karasuil) (Turkey); Alexander Korzhenevski Agency (Alexander Korzhenevski) (Russia); Michelle Lapautre (France); Owl's (Japan); I Pikarski Ltd (Israel); Prava I Prevodi (Eastern Europe, Greece); Tuttle-Mori Agency Inc (Japan); Eric Yang Agency (Korea)

**Barbara J Zitwer Agency** (L-D)
525 West End Ave, Unit 11-H, New York, NY 10024
*Tel:* 212-501-8423 *Fax:* 646-514-0497
*E-mail:* zitwer@gmail.com
*Key Personnel*
Pres: Barbara J Zitwer *E-mail:* bjzitwerag@aol.com
Founded: 1991
Fiction & popular nonfiction; memoir, pop culture, pop psychology. Look for international authors.
No unsol mss. Electronic queries only. Will look at ms on exclusive basis only. No reading fee. Handle software only in conjunction with ancillary rights of a book. Handle film & TV rights with co-agents in Hollywood.
Titles recently placed: *The Savior (The Sudarium Trilogy)*, Leonard Foglia, David Richards; *The Son (The Sudarium Trilogy)*, Leonard Foglia, David Richards; *The Surrogate (The Sudarium Trilogy)*, Leonard Foglia, David Richards
Foreign Rights: Gabriella Ambrosioni (Italy); Donatalla D'Ormesson (France); Anoukh Foerg Litteraire Agent (Germany); Grayhawk Agency (China, Taiwan); Imprima (Korea); International Editors' Co (Portugal, Spanish languages); I Pikarski Agency (Israel); Prava i Prevodi (Eastern Europe, Russia); Lenart Sane Agency (Scandinavia); Marianne Schoenbach Literary Agency; Tuttle-Mori Agency Inc (Japan)

# Illustration Agents

**Artists Associates**
4416 La Jolla Dr, Bradenton, FL 34210-3927
*Tel:* 941-756-8445
*Key Personnel*
Dir: Bill Erlacher
Represents 9 artists.

**Artworks Illustration**
325 W 38 St, Suite 1605, New York, NY 10018
*Tel:* 212-239-4946 *Fax:* 212-239-6106
*E-mail:* artworksillustration@earthlink.net
*Web Site:* www.artworksillustration.com
Founded: 1990
Represents 30 artists.
Membership(s): Society of Illustrators

**Carol Bancroft & Friends**
PO Box 2030, Danbury, CT 06813
*Tel:* 203-730-8270 *Fax:* 203-730-8275
*E-mail:* cbfriends@sbcglobal.net
*Web Site:* www.carolbancroft.com
*Key Personnel*
Owner: Joy Elton Tricarico
Founded: 1972
Represents many fine illustrators specializing in art for children of all ages. Servicing the publishing industry including, but not limited to: picture/mass market books & educational materials. We work with packagers, studios, toy companies & corporations in addition to licensing art to related products. Promotional packets sent upon request. Unsol artwork not accepted.
Membership(s): Graphic Artists Guild; NAEA; Society of Children's Book Writers & Illustrators; Society of Illustrators

**Benoit & Associates**
279 S Schuyler Ave, Kankakee, IL 60901
*Tel:* 815-932-2582 *Fax:* 815-932-2594
*E-mail:* benoitart@benoit-associates.com
*Web Site:* www.benoit-associates.com
*Key Personnel*
Pres: Michael J Benoit *E-mail:* mbenoit@benoit-associates.com
Full-service design & advertising studio: specialize in technical & color airbrush illustration & computer generated art (Mac & IBM) design, art direction, in-house photography, elementary through college textbook cover & newsletters, brochures, letterheads & annual reports; high volume, high quality, quick turnaround & satisfaction guaranteed.

**Bernstein & Andriulli Inc**
58 W 40 St, 6th fl, New York, NY 10018
*Tel:* 212-682-1490 *Fax:* 212-286-1890
*E-mail:* info@ba-reps.com
*Web Site:* www.ba-reps.com
*Key Personnel*
Illustration: Louisa St Pierre
Commercial illustration & photography.
Represents 70 artists.

**Bookmakers Ltd**
32 Parkview Ave, Wolfville, NS B4P 2K8, Canada
*Tel:* 575-776-5435 *Fax:* 505-776-2762
*Key Personnel*
Owner & Pres: Reg Ogilvie *E-mail:* reg@bookmakersltd.com
Owner & Contact: June Ogilvie *E-mail:* june@bookmakersltd.com
Founded: 1975
For more than 35 years Bookmakers Ltd has represented a group of the best children's book illustrators in the business & continues to also provide a full range of book production services. We've worked with most major publishers & design studios & look forward to helping create a success story with your next project.
Represents 25 artists.
Membership(s): Society of Children's Book Writers & Illustrators

**Byer-Sprinzeles Agency**
5800 Arlington Ave, Suite 16-C, Riverdale, NY 10471
*Tel:* 718-543-9399
*Web Site:* www.maggiebyersprinzeles.com
*Key Personnel*
Agent: Maggie Byer-Sprinzeles *E-mail:* maggie@maggiebyersprinzeles.com
Founded: 1991
Represents children's book illustrators.
Represents 27 artists.
Membership(s): Society of Children's Book Writers & Illustrators

**Cornell & McCarthy LLC**
2-D Cross Hwy, Westport, CT 06880
*Tel:* 203-454-4210
*E-mail:* contact@cmartreps.com
*Web Site:* www.cmartreps.com
*Key Personnel*
Partner: Merial Cornell; Pat McCarthy
Founded: 1989
Professional illustrators, specializing in the children's book markets; educational, trade & mass market. Representing over 35 artists with a variety of styles & techniques.
Membership(s): Graphic Artists Guild; Society of Children's Book Writers & Illustrators

**Craven Design Inc**
1202 Lexington Ave, Box 242, New York, NY 10028
*Tel:* 212-288-1022 *Fax:* 212-249-9910
*E-mail:* cravendesign@mac.com
*Web Site:* www.cravendesignstudios.com
*Key Personnel*
Artist Rep: Meryl Jones
Founded: 1981
Artist's representative: book illustration (text & trade), juvenile through adult; humorous, realistic, decorative & technical; maps, charts, graphs.
Represents 30 artists.

**Creative Arts of Ventura**
PO Box 684, Ventura, CA 93002-0684
*Tel:* 805-643-4160; 805-654-1927
*Web Site:* www.sculpture-museum.com
*Key Personnel*
Owner & Artist: Don Ulrich *E-mail:* ulrichxcal@aol.com; Lamia Ulrich
Founded: 1973 (gallery/studio)
Specialize in fine art, mixed media (from 2002-2005) wall sculptures curated by US State Department for the US Embassy in Riga Latvia. Painting & sculpture-abstract, public art sculpture design, lyric poetry, exhibitions & logos.
Represents 4 artists.

**Deborah Wolfe Ltd**
731 N 24 St, Philadelphia, PA 19130
*Tel:* 215-232-6666 *Fax:* 215-232-6585
*E-mail:* info@illustrationonline.com
*Web Site:* www.illustrationonline.com
Founded: 1978
Commercial illustrators & animators representative.
Represents 30 artists.

**Fort Ross Inc - International Representation for Artists**
Division of Fort Ross Inc
26 Arthur Place, Yonkers, NY 10701
*Tel:* 914-375-6448; 748-775-8340
*Web Site:* www.fortrossinc.com
*Key Personnel*
Exec Dir: Dr Vladimir P Kartsev *E-mail:* vkartsev2000@gmail.com
Founded: 1992
Foreign sales of secondary rights for illustrations, photographs & covers made by American & Canadian artists. Representation of Russian & East European artists & photographers in the USA & Canada.
Represents 42 artists.

**Foto Expression International (Toronto)**
266 Charlotte St, Suite 297, Peterborough, ON K9J 2V4, Canada
*Tel:* 705-745-5770
*E-mail:* operations@fotopressnews.org
*Web Site:* www.fotopressnews.org
*Key Personnel*
Owner & Opers Dir: John Milan Kubik
Founded: 1983

**Carol Guenzi Agents Inc**
Subsidiary of Artagent.com
865 Delaware St, Denver, CO 80204
*Tel:* 303-820-2599 *Toll Free Tel:* 800-417-5120 *Fax:* 303-820-2598
*E-mail:* info@artagent.com; art@artagent.com
*Web Site:* www.artagent.com
*Key Personnel*
Pres: Carol Guenzi
Founded: 1984
A wide selection of talent in all areas of visual communications.
Represents 30 artists.
Membership(s): American Institute of Graphic Arts; Art Directors Club of Denver

**The Charlotte Gusay Literary Agency**
10532 Blythe Ave, Los Angeles, CA 90064
*Tel:* 310-559-0831 *Fax:* 310-559-2639
*E-mail:* gusay1@ca.rr.com (queries only)
*Web Site:* www.gusay.com
Founded: 1988
Selectively represent children's book artists & illustrators.

**Herman Agency**
350 Central Park W, Apt 4I, New York, NY 10025
*Tel:* 212-749-4907
*Web Site:* www.hermanagencyinc.com
*Key Personnel*
Owner & Pres: Ronnie Ann Herman *E-mail:* ronnie@hermanagencyinc.com
Assoc Agent: Jill Corcoran *E-mail:* jill@hermanagencyinc.com
Co-Agent: Katia Herman *E-mail:* katia@hermanagencyinc.com
Founded: 1999
Represent illustrators, authors & author/illustrators of children's books, trade & educational.

Represents 35 artists.
Membership(s): The Authors Guild; Society of Children's Book Writers & Illustrators

**The Ivy League of Artists Inc**
7 Coventry Rd, Livingston, NJ 07039-5105
*Tel:* 973-992-4048 *Fax:* 973-992-4049
*E-mail:* ilartists@aol.com
*Key Personnel*
Owner & Pres: Ivy Mindlin
Illustration, spot drawings, calligraphy, cartoons, comps, storyboards, design & mechanical art.

**Levy Creative Management LLC**
425 E 58 St, Suite 37F, New York, NY 10022
*Tel:* 212-687-6463 *Fax:* 212-661-4839
*E-mail:* info@levycreative.com
*Web Site:* www.levycreative.com
*Key Personnel*
Pres & Founder: Sari Schorr *E-mail:* sari@levycreative.com
Founded: 1996
Boutique agency representing only award-winning international artists.

**Lindgren & Smith**
676-A Ninth Ave, New York, NY 10036
*Tel:* 212-397-7330
*E-mail:* representation@lindgrensmith.com
*Web Site:* www.lindgrensmith.com; www.redpaintbox.com
*Key Personnel*
Owner: Pat Lindgren *E-mail:* pat@lindgrensmith.com; Piper Smith *E-mail:* piper@lindgrensmith.com
Founded: 1987
Do not accept mss; examples of illustrator's work can be requested via e-mail.

**Lott Representatives**
PO Box 3607, New York, NY 10163
*Tel:* 212-755-5737
*Web Site:* www.lottreps.com
*Key Personnel*
Pres: Peter Lott *E-mail:* peter@lottreps.com
Represent commercial illustrators.

**MB Artists**
775 Sixth Ave, Suite 6, New York, NY 10001
*Tel:* 212-689-7830 *Fax:* 212-689-7829
*Web Site:* www.mbartists.com
*Key Personnel*
Pres & Agent: Mela Bolinao *E-mail:* mela@mbartists.com
Founded: 1986
Represents illustrators whose work is intended for juvenile market.
Represents 64 artists.
Membership(s): Children's Book Council; Graphic Artists Guild; Society of Children's Book Writers & Illustrators; Society of Illustrators

**Melissa Turk & the Artist Network**
9 Babbling Brook Lane, Suffern, NY 10901
*Tel:* 845-368-8606 *Fax:* 845-368-8608
*E-mail:* melissa@melissaturk.com
*Web Site:* www.melissaturk.com
*Key Personnel*
Contact: Dorothy Ziff
Founded: 1986
Represents professional artists supplying quality illustration, calligraphy & cartography. Specialize in children's trade & educational illustration as well as natural science illustration (wildlife, botanical, medical, etc), publishing & interpretive signage.
Represents 12 artists.
Membership(s): Graphic Artists Guild; Society of Children's Book Writers & Illustrators

**Morgan Gaynin Inc**
194 Third Ave, New York, NY 10003
*Tel:* 212-475-0440 *Fax:* 212-353-8538
*E-mail:* info@morgangaynin.com
*Web Site:* www.morgangaynin.com
*Key Personnel*
Principal, Rep: Gail Gaynin; Vicki Morgan
Rep: Kate Kelly
Founded: 1974
Illustrator's representative.
Represents 40 artists.
Membership(s): Graphic Artists Guild; Society of Children's Book Writers & Illustrators; Society of Illustrators

**Wanda Nowak Creative Illustrators Agency**
231 E 76 St, Suite 5-D, New York, NY 10021
*Tel:* 212-535-0438
*E-mail:* wanda@wandanow.com
*Web Site:* www.wandanow.com
*Key Personnel*
Pres: Wanda Nowak
Founded: 1995
Children's trade books, elementary & secondary textbook illustration & book cover illustration.
Represents 16 artists.

**Painted-Words Inc**
310 W 97 St, Suite 24, New York, NY 10025
*Tel:* 212-663-2311 *Fax:* 212-663-2891
*E-mail:* info@painted-words.com
*Web Site:* www.painted-words.com
*Key Personnel*
Agent: Lori Nowicki *E-mail:* lori@painted-words.com
Founded: 1992 (as Lori Nowicki & Associates)
Artist & literary agent.
Represents 41 artists.
Membership(s): Society of Children's Book Writers & Illustrators

**Pema Browne Ltd**
71 Pine Rd, Woodbourne, NY 12788
*E-mail:* info@pemabrowneltd.com
*Web Site:* www.pemabrowneltd.com
*Key Personnel*
Pres: Pema Browne
VP: Perry Browne
Founded: 1966
Illustration: realistic, humorous, fantasy, decorative, all ages; for publishing. Also literary agents for fiction & nonfiction, children's picture books, middle grade, young adult; romance, all genre business, health, how-to, cookbooks, inspirational, reference; no fax, e-mail or telephone queries. A SASE must be included for reply; only accepting limited new clients at this time.
Represents 3 artists.
Membership(s): Romance Writers of America; Society of Children's Book Writers & Illustrators; Writers Guild of America

**Portfolio Solutions LLC**
136 Jameson Hill Rd, Clinton Corners, NY 12514
*Tel:* 845-266-1001
*Web Site:* www.portfoliosolutionsllc.com
*Key Personnel*
Owner & Agent: Bernadette Szost *E-mail:* b.szost@portfoliosolutionsllc.com
Founded: 1999
Agency representing illustrators of children's books & related materials.
Represents 35 artists.
Membership(s): The Authors Guild; Society of Children's Book Writers & Illustrators

**Publishers' Graphics Inc**
231 Judd Rd, Easton, CT 06612-1025
*Tel:* 203-445-1511 *Fax:* 203-445-1411
*E-mail:* sales@publishersgraphics.com
*Web Site:* www.publishersgraphics.com
*Key Personnel*
Pres: Paige Gillies *E-mail:* paigeg@publishersgraphics.com
Founded: 1970
Represents 3 artists.

**Gerald & Cullen Rapp**
420 Lexington Ave, New York, NY 10170
*Tel:* 212-889-3337 *Fax:* 212-889-3341
*E-mail:* info@rappart.com
*Web Site:* www.rappart.com
*Key Personnel*
Rep: Nancy Moore *Tel:* 212-889-3337 ext 103 *E-mail:* nancy@rappart.com
Founded: 1944
Represent leading commercial illustrators on an exclusive basis. Sell to magazine & book publishers, ad agencies, design firms & major corporations.
Represents 60 artists.
Membership(s): Graphic Artists Guild; Society of Illustrators

**Kerry Reilly: Representatives**
1826 Asheville Place, Charlotte, NC 28203
*Tel:* 704-372-6007
*E-mail:* kerry@reillyreps.com
*Web Site:* www.reillyreps.com
Illustration & photography.
Represents 25 artists.

**Renaissance House**
Imprint of Laredo Publishing Co Inc
465 Westview Ave, Englewood, NJ 07631
*Tel:* 201-408-4048 *Fax:* 201-408-5011
*E-mail:* laredo@renaissancehouse.net; info@renaissancehouse.net
*Web Site:* www.renaissancehouse.net
Founded: 1991
Book developer that specializes in children's books, educational materials & bilingual market (English/Spanish). Represents illustrators who specialize in art for children that provide a wide variety of styles & techniques. Services the advertising & publishing industries, including children's books & educational materials. Multicultural artists are available. Promotional booklet sent upon request.
Represents 90 artists.

**Rosenthal Represents**
3850 Eddingham Ave, Calabasas, CA 91302
*Tel:* 818-222-5445 *Fax:* 818-222-5650
*E-mail:* eliselicenses@earthlink.net
*Web Site:* www.rosenthalrepresents.com
*Key Personnel*
Pres: Elise Rosenthal *E-mail:* elise@rosenthalrepresents.com
Sales & Mktg & Artists Rep: Neil Sandler
Founded: 1979
Illustrate book covers, children's & adult books. Licensing agents.
Represents 35 artists.
Membership(s): LIMA; Society of Illustrators

**Salzman International**
1751 Charles Ave, Arcata, CA 95521
*Tel:* 415-285-8267; 212-997-0115 (NY) *Fax:* 707-822-5500
*Web Site:* www.salzint.com
*Key Personnel*
Owner: Richard Salzman *E-mail:* rs@salzint.com
Founded: 1982
Agents for visual artists for educational & trade books specializing in art illustrators. Feature art for magazines & periodicals. Editorial services available.
Represents 25 artists.

**Richard W Salzman Artists' Representative**, see Salzman International

**The Schuna Group Inc**
1503 Briarknoll Dr, Arden Hills, MN 55112
*Tel:* 651-631-8480
*Web Site:* www.schunagroup.com
*Key Personnel*
Pres: Jo Anne Schuna *E-mail:* joanne@schunagroup.com
Represents 12 artists.

**Storybook Arts Inc**
414 Poplar Hill Rd, Dover Plains, NY 12522
Mailing Address: PO Box 672, Dover Plains, NY 12522
*Tel:* 845-877-3305
*Web Site:* www.storybookartsinc.com
*Key Personnel*
Owner & Pres: Janet De Carlo *E-mail:* janet@storybookartsinc.com
Founded: 2005
Artist representative agency.
Represents 25 artists.
Membership(s): Society of Children's Book Writers & Illustrators

**Christina A Tugeau Artist Agent LLC**
3009 Margaret Jones Lane, Williamsburg, VA 23185
*Tel:* 757-221-0666
*E-mail:* chris@catugeau.com
*Web Site:* www.catugeau.com
*Key Personnel*
Owner & Rep: Chris Tugeau
Founded: 1994
Represents North American illustrators for children's publishing: mass market & trade books, educational (preschool through young adult). Agency effectively closed to new artists but will view e-mail samples.
Represents 32 artists.
Membership(s): Society of Children's Book Writers & Illustrators

**Tugeau 2 Inc**
2231 Grandview Ave, Cleveland Heights, OH 44106
*Tel:* 216-707-0854 *Fax:* 216-795-8404
*Web Site:* www.tugeau2.com
*Key Personnel*
Owner: Nicole Tugeau *E-mail:* nicole@tugeau2.com
Founded: 2003
Agency for artist representation in the children's publishing industry.
Represents 35 artists.
Membership(s): Society of Children's Book Writers & Illustrators

**WendyLynn & Co**
504 Wilson Rd, Annapolis, MD 21401
*Tel:* 410-224-2729; 410-507-1059
*Web Site:* wendylynn.com
*Key Personnel*
Pres & Illustration Agent: Wendy Mays *E-mail:* wendy@wendylynn.com
Busn Mgr & Illustration Agent: Janice Onken *E-mail:* janice@wendylynn.com
Founded: 2002
Specialize in the children's publishing market. Represent & promote our illustrators to publishing companies which produce work for children & young adults.
Represents 35 artists.
Membership(s): Society of Children's Book Writers & Illustrators

**Wilkinson Studios Inc**
1121 E Main St, Suite 310, St Charles, IL 60174
*Tel:* 630-549-0504
*Web Site:* www.wilkinsonstudios.com
*Key Personnel*
Founder & Pres: Christine Wilkinson *E-mail:* chris@wilkinsonstudios.com
VP: Lisa O'Hara *E-mail:* lisa@wilkinsonstudios.com
Founded: 1999
Specializing in representing illustrators & managing art programs for educational, trade book & mass market publishing, children's magazines, games & related fields. Over 100 illustrators offering age appropriate artwork for pre-K through college in a wide range of styles, techniques & media, both conventional & electronic. Project management of large volume blackline or color illustration programs by dedicated staff with art & design backgrounds, working directly with the publisher or interfacing with design & development house vendors.
Represents 100 artists.
Membership(s): Graphic Artists Guild; Society of Children's Book Writers & Illustrators

# Lecture Agents

Listed below are some of the most active lecture agents who handle tours and single engagements for writers.

**American Program Bureau Inc**
313 Washington St, Suite 225, Newton, MA 02458
*Tel:* 617-965-6600 *Toll Free Tel:* 800-225-4575 *Fax:* 617-965-6610
*E-mail:* apb@apbspeakers.com
*Web Site:* www.apbspeakers.com
*Key Personnel*
VP, Speaker Rels & New Busn: Ken Eisenstein *Tel:* 617-614-1612 *E-mail:* keisenstein@apbspeakers.com
Founded: 1965
Lecture representation/speakers bureau. Branches located in Princeton, NJ & San Diego, CA.
Membership(s): International Association of Speakers Bureaus; NACA

**Authors Unlimited Inc**
31 E 32 St, Suite 300, New York, NY 10016
*Tel:* 212-481-8484 (ext 336) *Fax:* 212-481-9582
*Web Site:* www.authorsunlimited.com
*Key Personnel*
Pres: Arlynn Greenbaum *E-mail:* arlynnj@cs.com
Founded: 1991
Speakers bureau representing over 400 authors of adult, trade books. Arrange speaking engagements with colleges, libraries, corporations, trade associations & the like.

**The Barnabas Agency**
Division of The B&B Media Group Inc
109 S Main St, Corsicana, TX 75110
*Tel:* 903-872-0517 *Toll Free Tel:* 800-927-0517 *Fax:* 903-872-0518
*E-mail:* tbbmedia@tbbmedia.com
*Web Site:* www.tbbmedia.com
*Key Personnel*
Pres: Tina Jacobson *Tel:* 800-927-0517 ext 101 *E-mail:* tjacobson@tbbmedia.com
Founded: 2001
Objectives: To increase recognition of the client, his/her ministry, products & service; to establish client's credibility, help achieve long-term & short-term goals & help client develop a vision. Services range from consulting to full-scale personal management of the client & implementation of the various components of the campaign.

**Burns Entertainment & Sports Marketing**
820 Davis St, Suite 222, Evanston, IL 60201
*Tel:* 847-866-9400 *Fax:* 847-491-9778
*E-mail:* burnsl@burnsent.com
*Web Site:* burnsent.com
*Key Personnel*
CEO & COO: Bob Williams
Pres & Gen Counsel: Marc Ippolito
Pres: Doug Shabelman
Founded: 1970
Sports & entertainment marketing, match corporations with talent celebrities for appearances, speeches & endorsements.

**CreativeWell Inc**
PO Box 3130, Memorial Sta, Upper Montclair, NJ 07043
*Tel:* 973-783-7575 *Toll Free Tel:* 800-743-9182 *Fax:* 973-783-7530
*E-mail:* info@creativewell.com
*Web Site:* www.creativewell.com
*Key Personnel*
Pres: George M Greenfield *E-mail:* george@creativewell.com
Founded: 2003
Literary, lecture & arts management.

**The Fischer Ross Group Inc**
2 Greenwich Office Park, Suite 300, Greenwich, CT 06831
*Tel:* 203-622-4950 *Fax:* 203-531-4132
*E-mail:* frgstaff@frg-speakers.com
*Web Site:* www.frg-speakers.com
*Key Personnel*
Pres: Grada Fischer
Exclusive lecture agents for authors (fiction, nonfiction, trade) & journalists (print & broadcast), as well as nationally known celebrities & personalities. Arrange lecture tours, individual speaking engagements, product endorsements, public openings & appearances for the university, association & corporate markets.

**Greater Talent Network Inc**
437 Fifth Ave, New York, NY 10016
*Tel:* 212-645-4200 *Toll Free Tel:* 800-326-4211 *Fax:* 212-627-1471
*E-mail:* info@greatertalent.com
*Web Site:* www.greatertalent.com
*Key Personnel*
CEO: Don R Epstein *E-mail:* done@greatertalent.com
Founded: 1981
Exclusive lecture & entertainment management. Represent authors, journalists & nationally & internationally known individuals. Arrange speaking engagements & tours for corporations, associations, colleges & universities, town halls, hospitals & other organizations, as well as literary, motion picture, television & radio representation.
Membership(s): International Association of Speakers Bureaus

**International Entertainment Bureau**
3612 N Washington Blvd, Indianapolis, IN 46205-3592
*Tel:* 317-926-7566
*E-mail:* ieb@prodigy.net
*Key Personnel*
Founder: David Leonards
Founded: 1972
Database, resource center & clearing house. Information on speakers, celebrities & entertainers available in the marketplace. Planning, consulting, booking & producing.
Membership(s): Indiana Association of Fairs, Festivals & Events; Indiana Society of Association Executives; Meeting Professionals International

**Eddie Kritzer Productions**
Subsidiary of The Kritzer Entertainment Group
1112 Montana Ave, Suite 449, Santa Monica, CA 90403
*Tel:* 310-702-5356 *Fax:* 310-394-5770
*E-mail:* producedby@aol.com
*Web Site:* eddiekritzer.com
*Key Personnel*
CEO & Pres: Eddie Kritzer
Founded: 1983
Produce corporate shows for conventions & meetings. "A Night At The Improv" will write, create & produce comedy shows & corporate videos. Created Rockline Live National Radio Show. Produce shows worldwide, TV movies & movie specials. Accept submissions for mss, prefer nonfiction. Also produces movies. See web site for details.

**BK Nelson Inc Lecture Bureau**
Subsidiary of BK Nelson Inc
1565 Paseo Vida, Palm Springs, CA 92264
*Tel:* 760-778-8800 *Fax:* 760-778-6242
*E-mail:* bknelson4@cs.com
*Web Site:* www.bknelsonlecturebureau.com; www.bknelson.com; www.bknelsonmovieproduction.com
*Key Personnel*
CEO & Pres: Bonita K Nelson
CFO: Erv Rosenfeld
VP & Edit Dir, West Coast: John W Benson
Founded: 1988
Book authors & personalities, experts in diverse fields. Arrange seminars & keynote speaking engagements. Speechwriting/coaching. Publish B K Nelson's Speaker's Directory with photos each year. Online booking. Certification status granted by New York State Dept of Economic Development.
*Branch Office(s)*
84 Woodland Rd, Pleasantville, NY 10570 *Tel:* 914-741-1322 *Fax:* 914-741-1324 *Web Site:* bknelsonlecturebureau.com
Membership(s): American Association of University Women; The Authors Guild; BEA; NACA

**Random House Speakers Bureau**
1745 Broadway, Mail Drop 13-1, New York, NY 10019
*Tel:* 212-572-2013
*E-mail:* rhspeakers@randomhouse.com
*Web Site:* www.rhspeakers.com
*Key Personnel*
VP, Speakers Bureau: Robin Wolfson *Tel:* 212-572-2395 *E-mail:* rwolfson@randomhouse.com
Mktg Mgr: Stefanie Von Beoczy *Tel:* 212-572-2398 *E-mail:* svonbeoczy@randomhouse.com
Sr Agent: Jayme Boucher *Tel:* 212-572-7309 *E-mail:* jboucher@randomhouse.com
Agent Dir: Mary Coyne *Tel:* 212-572-2247 *E-mail:* mcoyne@randomhouse.com; Kathy Dunn *Tel:* 631-283-5923 *E-mail:* kdunn@randomhouse.com; Wade Lucas *Tel:* 212-572-6113 *E-mail:* walucas@randomhouse.com; Caitlin McCaskey *Tel:* 212-572-8661 *E-mail:* cmccaskey@randomhouse.com; Kim Thornton *Tel:* 212-572-2299 *E-mail:* kthornton@randomhouse.com; Elaine Trevorrow *Tel:* 212-572-2175 *E-mail:* etrevorrow@randomhouse.com
Coord: Jessie Garretson *Tel:* 212-572-2396 *E-mail:* jgarretson@randomhouse.com
Founded: 2006
Full-service lecture agency that represents best-selling authors, literary legends, cutting-edge thinkers & current tastemakers.
Membership(s): International Association of Speakers Bureaus

**Royce Carlton Inc**
866 United Nations Plaza, Suite 587, New York, NY 10017-1880
*Tel:* 212-355-7700 *Toll Free Tel:* 800-LECTURE (532-8873) *Fax:* 212-888-8659
*E-mail:* info@roycecarlton.com

*Web Site:* www.roycecarlton.com
*Key Personnel*
Pres: Carlton Sedgeley *Tel:* 212-822-0999
*E-mail:* carlton@roycecarlton.com
EVP: Lucy Lepage *Tel:* 212-822-0979
*E-mail:* lucy@roycecarlton.com
VP: Helen Churko *Tel:* 212-822-0981
*E-mail:* helen@roycecarlton.com
Founded: 1968
Agents, managers & brokers for speakers.

**Jodi Solomon Speakers Bureau**
295 Huntington Ave, Suite 211, Boston, MA 02115
*Tel:* 617-266-3450 *Fax:* 617-266-5660
*E-mail:* jodi@jodisolomon.biz
*Web Site:* www.jodisolomonspeakers.com

**The Tuesday Agency**
123 N Linn St, Suite 2-C, Iowa City, IA 52245
*Tel:* 319-338-7080
*E-mail:* trinity@tuesdayagency.com
*Web Site:* tuesdayagency.com
*Key Personnel*
Pres: Trinity Ray
VP: Kevin Mills
Exclusive speaker representation.

**World Class Speakers & Entertainers**
5200 Kanan Rd, Suite 210, Agoura Hills, CA 91301
*Tel:* 818-991-5400 *Fax:* 818-991-2226
*E-mail:* wcse@wcspeakers.com
*Web Site:* www.wcspeakers.com
*Key Personnel*
Pres: Joseph I Kessler *E-mail:* jkessler@wcspeakers.com
Founded: 1970
Represents world class speakers & entertainers. Database of 25,000 speakers & entertainers; directory/guide available.

**Writers' League of Texas (WLT)**
611 S Congress Ave, Suite 505, Austin, TX 78704
*Tel:* 512-499-8914
*E-mail:* wlt@writersleague.org
*Web Site:* www.writersleague.org
*Key Personnel*
Dir, Publicity & Progamming: Jennifer Ziegler
Off Administrator: Bethany Hegedus
*E-mail:* bethany@writersleague.org
Founded: 1981

# Associations, Events, Courses & Awards

## Book Trade & Allied Associations — Index

## LITERARY



## MAGAZINE & PRESS



## MEDIA - COMMUNICATIONS



## PUBLISHING

## PUBLISHING SERVICES



## WRITERS

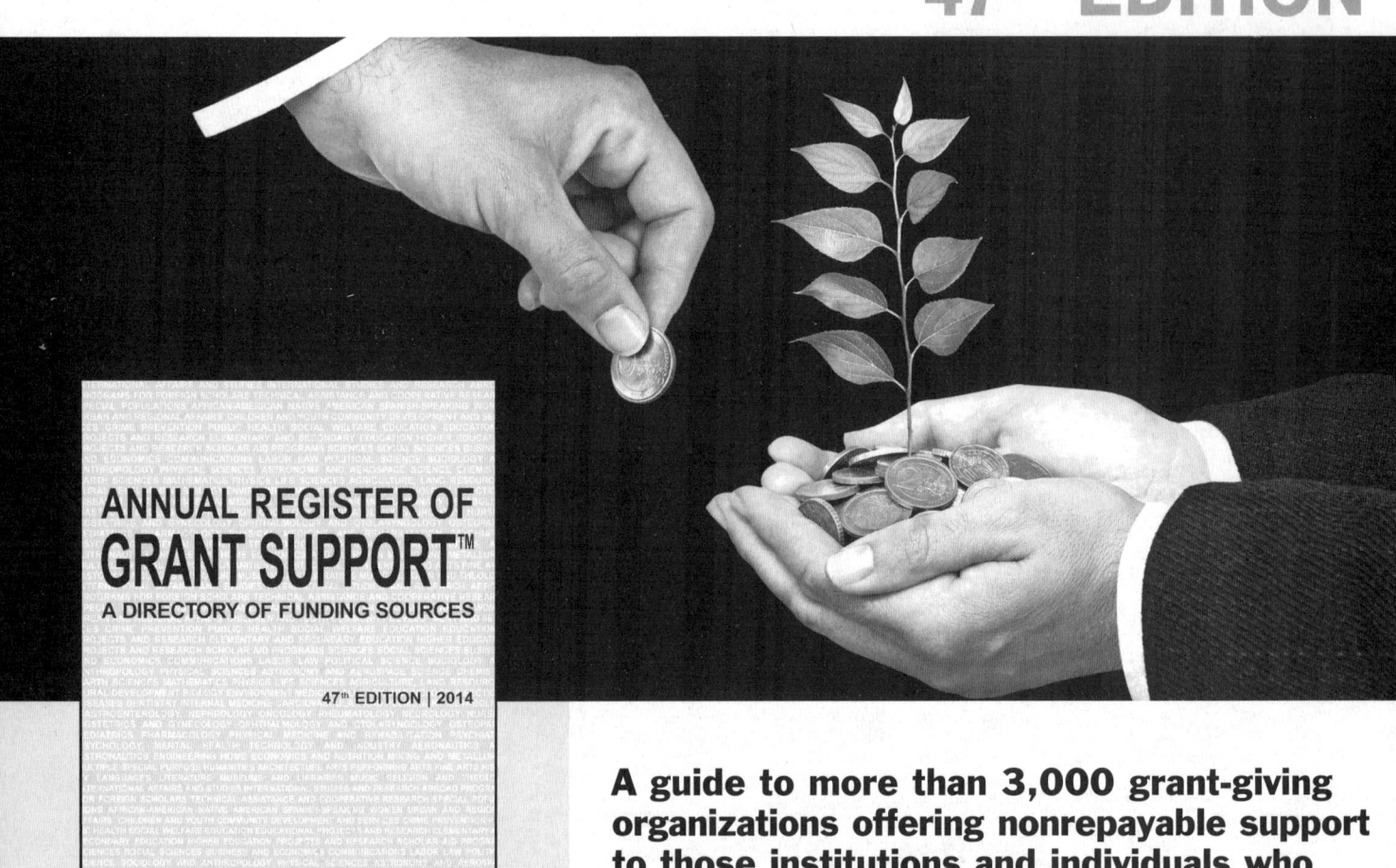

# Book Trade & Allied Associations

Listed here are associations and organizations that are concerned with books, literacy, language and speech, media and communications as well as groups who provide services to the publishing community.

**AAR**, see Association of Authors' Representatives Inc

**ABAC/ALAC**
368 Dalhousie St, Suite 301, Ottawa, ON K1N 7G3, Canada
*Tel:* 416-364-2376
*E-mail:* info@abac.org
*Web Site:* www.abac.org
*Key Personnel*
Pres: Liam McGahern
Treas: Michael Park
Founded: 1966
The association's aim is to foster an interest in rare books & mss & to maintain high standards in the antiquarian book trades.
Number of Members: 70
Publication(s): *ABAC/ALAC Membership Directory* (free by request)
Membership(s): International League of Antiquarian Booksellers

**The Academy of American Poets Inc**
75 Maiden Lane, Suite 901, New York, NY 10038
*Tel:* 212-274-0343 *Fax:* 212-274-9427
*E-mail:* academy@poets.org
*Web Site:* www.poets.org
*Key Personnel*
Pres & Exec Dir: Tree Swenson
Exec Dir: Jennifer Benka
Multimedia Prodr: Paul Legault *E-mail:* plegault@poets.org
Awards Coord & Exec Asst: Alex Dimitrov *Tel:* 212-274-0343 ext 15 *E-mail:* adimitrov@poets.org
Founded: 1934
The country's largest nonprofit association devoted to poetry. Sponsors the James Laughlin Poetry Award, Walt Whitman Award, Harold Morton Landon Translation Award, Wallace Stevens Award, Lenore Marshall Poetry Prize & annual college poetry prizes; workshops for high school students; award fellowship to American poets for distinguished poetic achievement; presents an annual national series of poetry readings & symposia. Publishes biannual journal. Also administers the National Poetry Month.
Number of Members: 6,000
Publication(s): *American Poet* (biannual)

**Academy of Motion Picture Arts & Sciences (AMPAS)**
8949 Wilshire Blvd, Beverly Hills, CA 90211
*Tel:* 310-247-3000 *Fax:* 310-859-9619
*E-mail:* ampas@oscars.org
*Web Site:* www.oscars.org
*Key Personnel*
CEO: Dawn Hudson
To advance the arts & sciences of motion pictures & to foster cooperation among the creative leadership of the motion picture industry for cultural, educational & technological progress. Confer annual awards of merit, serving as a constant incentive within the industry & focusing public attention upon the best in motion pictures.
Number of Members: 5,024
Publication(s): *Academy Players Directory, Annual Index to Motion Picture Credits, Nominations & Winners, List of Eligible Releases* (bulletin)

**Academy of Television Arts & Sciences (ATAS)**
5220 Lankershim Blvd, North Hollywood, CA 91601-3109
*Tel:* 818-754-2800 *Fax:* 818-761-2827
*Web Site:* www.emmys.tv
*Key Personnel*
CEO & Chmn of the Bd: Bruce Rosenblum
COO: Alan Perris
CFO: Frank Kohler
SVP, Awards: John Leverence
Founded: 1977
Organization for those involved in national television; bestows Emmy awards for excellence in television; college television awards & college internship program; inducts deserving individuals in "Television Academy Hall of Fame".
Number of Members: 17,000
Publication(s): *EMMY Magazine*

**Access Copyright, The Canadian Copyright Licensing Agency**
One Yonge St, Suite 800, Toronto, ON M5E 1E5, Canada
*Tel:* 416-868-1620 *Toll Free Tel:* 800-893-5777 *Fax:* 416-868-1621
*E-mail:* info@accesscopyright.ca
*Web Site:* www.accesscopyright.ca
*Key Personnel*
Exec Dir: Roanie Levy
Founded: 1988
Number of Members: 37
Publication(s): *Online Access* (quarterly, newsletter, free, electronic)
Membership(s): Book & Periodical Council; International Federation of Reproduction Rights Organizations

**Advertising Research Foundation (ARF)**
432 Park Ave S, 6th fl, New York, NY 10016-8013
*Tel:* 212-751-5656 *Fax:* 212-319-5265
*E-mail:* info@thearf.org; jar@thearf.org (edit)
*Web Site:* www.thearf.org; www.journalofadvertisingresearch.com
*Key Personnel*
Pres: Bob Barocci *Tel:* 212-751-5656 ext 210 *E-mail:* bb@thearf.org
EVP: Don Gloeckler
EVP, Digital: Ted McConnell
Ed-in-Chief: Geoffrey Precourt
Exec Ed: Douglas West
Mng Ed, Journal of Advertising Research: Catherine Gardner *Tel:* 646-465-5725 *E-mail:* catherine@thearf.org
Mgr, Forum Progs, Journal of Advertising Research: Zena Pagan *Tel:* 646-465-5721 *E-mail:* zena@thearf.org
Founded: 1936
Advertising research service trade association.
Publication(s): *Journal of Advertising Research (JAR)* (quarterly, $340 instns, $171 indivs, $80 academic - includes 1 yr print & online)

**AIGA, the professional association for design**
164 Fifth Ave, New York, NY 10010
*Tel:* 212-807-1990 *Fax:* 212-807-1799
*E-mail:* general@aiga.org
*Web Site:* www.aiga.org
*Key Personnel*
COO: Denise Wood *Tel:* 212-710-3135 *E-mail:* denise_wood@aiga.org
CEO & Exec Dir: Richard Grefe *Tel:* 212-710-3100 *E-mail:* grefe@aiga.org
Edit Dir: Rebecca Sears *Tel:* 212-710-3131
Founded: 1914
National nonprofit organization for graphic design profession. Organizes competitions, exhibitions, publications, educational activities & projects in the public interest to promote excellence in the graphic design industry.
Number of Members: 22,000
New Election: Annually in June

**ALA**, see The American Library Association (ALA)

**Alcuin Society**
PO Box 3216, Vancouver, BC V6B 3X8, Canada
*Tel:* 605-566-1502; 604-732-5403
*E-mail:* info@alcuinsociety.com
*Web Site:* www.alcuinsociety.com
Judges book design; publishes articles on book arts, collecting, typography, private presses, book collections, book binding.
Number of Members: 321
Publication(s): *Amphora* (3 issues/yr, journal, $50/yr membs, $75 instns)
Membership(s): Fellowship of American Bibliophilic Societies

**Alliance for Audited Media (AAM)**
Formerly Audit Bureau of Circulations
48 W Seegers Rd, Arlington Heights, IL 60005
*Tel:* 224-366-6939 *Fax:* 224-366-6949
*Web Site:* www.auditedmedia.com
*Key Personnel*
Pres & Mng Dir: Michael J Lavery *Tel:* 224-366-6500 *E-mail:* michael.lavery@auditedmedia.com
Cooperative association of advertisers, advertising agencies & publishers of newspapers, magazines, farm & business publications. Audit & report circulation, web site & additional digital edition analytics, including mobile application activity for publisher brands in North America.
Number of Members: 4,500
*Branch Office(s)*
122 E 42 St, Suite 807, New York, NY 10168-0899 *Tel:* 212-867-8992 *Fax:* 212-867-8947
151 Bloor St W, Suite 850, Toronto, ON M5S 1S4, Canada, VP & Gen Mgr: Joan Brehl *Tel:* 416-962-5840 *Fax:* 416-962-5844 *Web Site:* www.auditedmedia.com

**Alliance for Women in Media (AWM)**
Subsidiary of American Women in Radio & Television
1760 Old Meadow Rd, Suite 500, McLean, VA 22102
*Tel:* 703-506-3290 *Fax:* 703-506-3266
*E-mail:* info@awrt.org
*Web Site:* www.awrt.org
*Key Personnel*
Pres: Erin Fuller *E-mail:* efuller@allwomeninmedia.org
EVP: Amy B Lotz *E-mail:* alotz@allwomeninmedia.org

Founded: 1951
For members of the electronic & media industries.
Number of Members: 3,000
Publication(s): *Making Waves* (quarterly by mail, magazine); *News & Views* (monthly by e-mail, newsletter)

**American Academy of Arts & Sciences (AAAS)**
Norton's Woods, 136 Irving St, Cambridge, MA 02138-1996
*Tel:* 617-576-5000 *Fax:* 617-576-5050
*E-mail:* aaas@amacad.org
*Web Site:* www.amacad.org
*Key Personnel*
Pres: Leslie Berlowitz
Ed: Steven Marcus
Promote interchange of ideas through seminars & publications.
Number of Members: 6,000
Publication(s): *Daedalus*

**American Academy of Political & Social Science**
202 S 36 St, Philadelphia, PA 19104
*Tel:* 215-746-6500 *Fax:* 215-573-2667
*Web Site:* www.aapss.org
Founded: 1889
Education.
Publication(s): *The Annals of American Academy of Political & Social Science* (6 issues/yr, $109/yr indivs, $781/yr instns (e-access), $868/yr instns (print & e-access), $851/yr instns (print))

**American Antiquarian Society (AAS)**
185 Salisbury St, Worcester, MA 01609-1634
*Tel:* 508-755-5221 *Fax:* 508-753-3300
*Web Site:* www.americanantiquarian.org
*Key Personnel*
Pres: Ellen S Dunlap *Tel:* 508-471-2161 *E-mail:* edunlap@mwa.org
Dir, Book Pubn: Caroline F Sloat *Tel:* 508-471-2130 *E-mail:* csloat@mwa.org
Founded: 1812
Maintain research library in American history & culture through 1876.
Number of Members: 719

**American Association for the Advancement of Science**
1200 New York Ave NW, Washington, DC 20005
*Tel:* 202-326-6400 *Fax:* 202-371-9526
*E-mail:* webmaster@aaas.org
*Web Site:* www.aaas.org
*Key Personnel*
Chmn: Alice Huang
CEO: Alan Leschner
Dir, Exec Off Aff: Gretchen Seiler
Founded: 1848
Mission is to further the work of scientists, to facilitate cooperation among them, foster scientific freedom & responsibility, improve effectiveness of science in the promotion of human welfare & to increase public understanding & appreciation of the importance & promise of the methods of science in human progress. There are many membership organizations & professional societies which have similar aims or have interest in supporting these objectives. For further information, contact the AAAS Office of News & Information at the above address. US regional divisions: Arctic; Caribbean; Pacific; Southwest & Rocky Mountains.
2014 Meeting(s): Annual Meeting, Chicago, IL, Feb 13-17, 2014
Publication(s): *Science* (weekly, $10/issue, $135/yr prof rate)

**American Auto Racing Writers & Broadcasters**
922 N Pass Ave, Burbank, CA 91505
*Tel:* 818-842-7005 *Fax:* 818-842-7020
*Key Personnel*
Pres: Ms Dusty Brandel
Media people who cover auto racing.
Number of Members: 300

**American Book Producers Association (ABPA)**
151 W 19 St, 3rd fl, New York, NY 10011
*Tel:* 212-675-1363 *Fax:* 212-675-1364
*E-mail:* office@abpaonline.org
*Web Site:* www.abpaonline.org
*Key Personnel*
Pres: Richard Rothschild
VP: Nancy Hall
Treas & Bd of Dirs: Valerie Tomaselli
Bd of Dirs: Leslie Carola; Karen Matsu Greenberg; Susan Knopf
Founded: 1980
An organization of independent book producing companies in the US & CN.
Number of Members: 60
Publication(s): *Booknews* (membs only)

**American Booksellers Association**
333 Westchester Ave, Suite S202, White Plains, NY 10604
*Tel:* 914-406-7500 *Toll Free Tel:* 800-637-0037 *Fax:* 914-410-6297
*E-mail:* info@bookweb.org
*Web Site:* www.bookweb.org
*Key Personnel*
CEO: Oren Teicher *Tel:* 800-637-0037 ext 6611 *E-mail:* oren@bookweb.org
CFO: Eleanor Chang *Tel:* 800-637-0037 ext 6615 *E-mail:* ellie@bookweb.org
Content Offr: Dan Cullen *Tel:* 800-637-0037 ext 6660 *E-mail:* dan@bookweb.org
Devt Offr: Mark Nichols *Tel:* 800-637-0037 ext 6640 *E-mail:* mark@bookweb.org
Meetings & Planning Offr: Jill Perlstein *Tel:* 800-637-0037 ext 6642 *E-mail:* jill@bookweb.org
Membership & Mktg Offr: Meg Z Smith *Tel:* 800-637-0037 ext 6641 *E-mail:* meg@bookweb.org
Sr Prog Offr: Joy Dallanegra-Sanger *Tel:* 800-637-0037 ext 6618 *E-mail:* joy@bookweb.org
Dir, Memb Technol: Neil Strandberg *Tel:* 800-637-0037 ext 6627 *E-mail:* neil@bookweb.org
Mktg Mgr & Designer: Greg Galloway *Tel:* 800-637-0037 ext 6668 *E-mail:* greg@bookweb.org
Mgr, ABC Children's Group: Shannon O'Connor *Tel:* 800-637-0037 ext 6651 *E-mail:* shannon@bookweb.org
Founded: 1900
Trade organization representing independent booksellers.
Number of Members: 3,500
2014 Meeting(s): BookExpo America (BEA), Jacob K Javits Convention Center, 655 W 43 St, New York, NY, May 29-31, 2014
2015 Meeting(s): BookExpo America (BEA), Jacob K Javits Convention Center, 655 W 43 St, New York, NY, May 28-30, 2015
2016 Meeting(s): BookExpo America (BEA), Chicago, IL, May 12-14, 2016
Publication(s): *Book Buyers Handbook-Electronic*; *Bookselling This Week-Electronic*
Membership(s): BISG

**American Business Media**
675 Third Ave, 7th fl, New York, NY 10017-5704
*Tel:* 212-661-6360 *Fax:* 212-370-0736
*E-mail:* info@abmmail.com
*Web Site:* www.americanbusinessmedia.com
*Key Personnel*
CEO & Pres: Clark Pettit *Tel:* 212-661-6360 ext 3339 *E-mail:* c.pettit@abmmail
CFO & Gen Mgr: Todd Hittle *Tel:* 212-661-6360 ext 3323
Founded: 1906
Nonprofit, global association for business-to-business information providers, including producers of magazines, web site content/service providers, trade shows, newsletters, databases, custom publishers, as well as conventions, conferences, seminars & other ancillary media that build on the print medium. Call association for listing of events scheduled.
Number of Members: 283

**American Christian Writers Association**
PO Box 110390, Nashville, TN 37222-0390
*Tel:* 615-331-8668 *Toll Free Tel:* 800-21-WRITE (219-7483)
*Web Site:* www.acwriters.com
*Key Personnel*
Dir & Publr: Reg A Forder *E-mail:* regaforder@aol.com
2013 Meeting(s): Christian Writer's Conference, Caribbean Cruise, Nov 30-Dec 7, 2013
Membership(s): Evangelical Christian Publishers Association; Evangelical Press Association

**American Civil Liberties Union**
125 Broad St, 18th fl, New York, NY 10004
*Tel:* 212-549-2500 *Toll Free Tel:* 800-775-ACLU (orders)
*E-mail:* media@aclu.org
*Web Site:* www.aclu.org
*Key Personnel*
Pres: Susan N Herman
Exec Dir: Anthony D Romero
Communs Dir: Emily Tynes
Protection of constitutional rights & civil liberties through litigation, legislative lobbying & public education; 250 branch offices.
Number of Members: 500,000
Publication(s): *Civil Liberties* (biannual, newsletter)

**American Council on Education**
One Dupont Circle NW, Washington, DC 20036-1193
*Tel:* 202-939-9300 *Fax:* 202-939-9302
*Web Site:* www.acenet.edu
*Key Personnel*
Pres: Molly Corbett Broad
Pubns Coord: Don Hoyt *Tel:* 202-939-9380
Founded: 1918
The nation's major coordinating body for postsecondary education. Professional books & guides in higher education (special studies & reports on higher education).
Number of Members: 1,850
2014 Meeting(s): Annual Meeting, Manchester Grand Hyatt, San Diego, CA, March 8-11, 2014
Publication(s): *The Presidency* (3 issues/yr, $36/yr membs, $40/yr nonmembs)

**American Forest & Paper Association (AF&PA)**
1111 19 St NW, Suite 800, Washington, DC 20036
*Tel:* 202-463-2700 *Toll Free Tel:* 800-878-8878
*E-mail:* info@afandpa.org
*Web Site:* www.afandpa.org
*Key Personnel*
Pres & CEO: Donna A Harman
VP, Gen Coun & Corp Secy: Jan A Poling
Founded: 1993
National trade association; complete listing of publications available on web site.
Number of Members: 120
2014 Meeting(s): Paper2014, Jacob K Javits Convention Center, 655 W 43 St, New York, NY, March 2014

**American Independent Writers (AIW)**
7817 Evening Lane, Alexandria, VA 22306

*Tel:* 703-660-9336 *Fax:* 703-660-9321
*E-mail:* info@amerindywriters.org
*Web Site:* www.amerindywriters.org
*Key Personnel*
Exec Dir: Donald O Graul, Jr *E-mail:* donald@amerindywriters.org
Membership Mgr: Taryn Carrino *E-mail:* taryn@amerindywriters.org
Founded: 1975
Established to promote the mutual interests of freelance writers & to provide a variety of services to members.
Number of Members: 1,500
Publication(s): *The American Writer* (online monthly); *Directory of Members* (online only to membs)

**American Institute of Graphic Arts**, see AIGA, the professional association for design

**American Jewish Committee (AJC)**
Affiliate of Institute of Human Relations
Jacob Blaustein Bldg, 165 E 56 St, New York, NY 10022
Mailing Address: PO Box 705, New York, NY 10150
*Tel:* 212-751-4000; 212-891-1456 (membership) *Fax:* 212-891-1450
*Web Site:* www.ajc.org
*Key Personnel*
Pres: Robert Elman
Exec Dir: David A Harris *E-mail:* harrisd@ajc.org
Dir, Pubns: Lawrence Grossman *Tel:* 212-751-4000 ext 308 *E-mail:* grossmanl@ajc.org
Founded: 1906
Civic & religious rights of Jews in the USA & abroad; intergroup relations & human rights.
Number of Members: 43,000
Publication(s): *AJC Journal* (bimonthly, free to membs); *American Jewish Yearbook* ($30); *Commentary* ($4.50/issue)
*Branch Office(s)*
2027 Massachusetts Ave NW, Washington, DC 20036

**American Language Academy**, see American Literacy Council

**The American Library Association (ALA)**
50 E Huron St, Chicago, IL 60611
*Tel:* 312-944-6780; 312-280-4299 (memb & cust serv) *Toll Free Tel:* 800-545-2433 *Fax:* 312-440-9374
*E-mail:* ala@ala.org; customerservice@ala.org
*Web Site:* www.ala.org
*Key Personnel*
Exec Dir: Keith Michael Fiels *Tel:* 800-545-2433 ext 1392 *E-mail:* kfiels@ala.org
Lib Ref Specialist: Valerie Hawkins *Tel:* 312-280-2154 *E-mail:* vhawkins@ala.org
Founded: 1876
With over 60,000 members, ALA is the oldest & largest library association in the world. ALA promotes the highest quality library & information services & public access to information. Offers professional services & publications to members & nonmembers.
Number of Members: 60,000
2014 Meeting(s): Mid-Winter Meeting, Philadelphia, PA, Jan 24-28, 2014; National Library Week, Nationwide throughout the USA, April 13-19, 2014; Annual Conference, Las Vegas, NV, June 26-July 1, 2014
Publication(s): *American Libraries* (6 issues/yr, magazine, free to membs, $45/yr instns US & CN, $60/yr instns foreign)
*Branch Office(s)*
1615 New Hampshire Ave NW, 1st fl, Washington, DC 20009-2520 *Tel:* 202-628-8410 *Toll Free Tel:* 800-941-8478

**American Literacy Council**
1441 Mariposa Ave, Boulder, CO 80302
*Tel:* 303-440-7385
*E-mail:* presidentalc@americanliteracy.com
*Web Site:* www.americanliteracy.com
*Key Personnel*
Pres: Alan Mole *E-mail:* presidentalc4@americanliteracy.com
Dir & Opers Mgr: Joseph R Little *E-mail:* spellingprogress@americanliteracy.com
Founded: 1876
Produce & distribute literacy software & simpler spelling materials.
Number of Members: 12
Publication(s): *Sound-Write®* (free)

**American Literary Translators Association (ALTA)**
Affiliate of University of Texas Dallas
c/o The University of Texas at Dallas, 800 W Campbell Rd, Mail Sta JO51, Richardson, TX 75080-3021
*Tel:* 972-883-2093 *Fax:* 972-883-6303
*Web Site:* www.utdallas.edu/alta/
*Key Personnel*
Pres: Gary Racz *E-mail:* gregary.racz@liu.edu
Admin Asst: Maria Rosa Suarez *Tel:* 972-883-2092 *E-mail:* maria.suarez@utdallas.edu
Literary translation & translators.
Number of Members: 600
Publication(s): *Annotated Books Received: Annotation of Books in Translation* (biannual); *Newsletter* (3 issues/yr); *Translation Review* (biannual, $80/yr US & CN indivs, $100/yr intl indivs & joint household, $60/yr sr +65 indivs)

**American Management Association®**
1601 Broadway, New York, NY 10019-7420
*Tel:* 212-586-8100 *Toll Free Tel:* 877-566-9441 *Fax:* 212-903-8168; 518-891-0368
*E-mail:* customerservice@amanet.org
*Web Site:* www.amanet.org
*Key Personnel*
CEO & Pres: Edward T Reilly
Public Rel Mgr: Roger Kelleher *Tel:* 212-903-7976 *E-mail:* rkelleher@amanet.org
Over 140 seminars in 20 areas including management, project management, time management, leadership, finance, interpersonal skills, communication, supervisory skills & human resources.
Number of Members: 700,000
New Election: Annually in March

**American Marketing Association**
Division of Health Services Marketing Division
311 S Wacker Dr, Suite 5800, Chicago, IL 60606
*Tel:* 312-542-9000 *Toll Free Tel:* 800-AMA-1150 (262-1150) *Fax:* 312-542-9001
*E-mail:* info@ama.org
*Web Site:* www.marketingpower.com
*Key Personnel*
CEO: Dennis Dunlap
Mng Ed: Christopher Bartone *Tel:* 312-543-9000 ext 9029 *E-mail:* cbartone@ama.org
A nonprofit, educational institution. Offers online marketing info. Sponsors seminars, conferences & student marketing clubs & doctoral consortium. Publish books, journals, magazines & proceedings of conferences.
Number of Members: 38,000
Publication(s): *Journal of Marketing Research* (quarterly); *Journal of Public Policy & Marketing* (semiannual); *Marketing Health Services* (quarterly); *Marketing Management* (bimonthly); *Marketing News* (biweekly); *Marketing Research* (quarterly); *Proceedings of Conferences*

**American Medical Association**
515 N State St, Chicago, IL 60654
*Tel:* 312-464-5000 *Toll Free Tel:* 800-621-8335 *Fax:* 312-464-4184
*Web Site:* www.ama-assn.org
*Key Personnel*
CEO & EVP: Dr James Madara
VP, Busn Prods: Anthony J Frankos *Tel:* 312-464-5000 ext 5488
Promotes the science & art of medicine & betterment of public health. Association of physicians.
Publication(s): *American Medical News* (weekly); *Archives of Dermatology* (monthly); *Archives of General Psychiatry* (monthly); *Archives of Internal Medicine* (monthly); *Archives of Neurology* (monthly); *Archives of Opthalmology* (monthly); *Archives of Otolaryngology-Head & Neck Surgery* (monthly); *Archives of Pediatrics & Adolescent Medicine* (monthly); *Archives of Surgery* (monthly); *JAMA: The Journal of the American Medical Association* (weekly)
*Branch Office(s)*
119 Cherry Hill Rd, Parsippany, NJ 07054

**American Medical Writers Association (AMWA)**
30 W Gude Dr, Suite 525, Rockville, MD 20850-1161
*Tel:* 240-238-0940 *Fax:* 301-294-9006
*E-mail:* amwa@amwa.org
*Web Site:* www.amwa.org
*Key Personnel*
Exec Dir: Susan Krug *Tel:* 204-238-0940 ext 109 *E-mail:* skrug@amwa.org
Founded: 1940
Nonprofit association. Sponsors annual medical book awards & over 85 workshops at annual conference. Membership fees: indiv $160/yr, student $55/yr.
Number of Members: 5,300
2014 Meeting(s): Annual Conference, San Antonio, TX, Sept 25-27, 2014
2015 Meeting(s): Annual Conference, Memphis, TN, Oct 22-24, 2015
Publication(s): *AMWA Journal* (quarterly, journal, free to membs, $75/yr nonmembs); *AMWA Membership Directory* (annual, directory, $20 membs, $150 nonmembs); *Freelance Directory* (online, directory, $50/3 months, $75/6 months, $135/yr); *Jobs Online* (monthly, classified listing, $100-250 words, $175-600 words)

**American Political Science Association**
1527 New Hampshire Ave NW, Washington, DC 20036-1206
*Tel:* 202-483-2512 *Fax:* 202-483-2657
*E-mail:* apsa@apsanet.org
*Web Site:* www.apsanet.org
*Key Personnel*
Exec Dir: Michael Brintnall *E-mail:* brintnall@apsanet.org
Provide services to facilitate research, teaching & professional development in political science, including publications & services to assist college faculty, graduate students & researchers.
Number of Members: 15,000
2014 Meeting(s): Annual Meeting, Marriott Wardman Park/Omni Shoreham/Hilton, Washington, DC, Aug 28-31, 2014
2015 Meeting(s): Annual Meeting, Hilton/Hotel Nikko/Parc 55, San Francisco, CA, Sept 3-6, 2015
2016 Meeting(s): Annual Meeting, Pennsylvania Convention Center/Phildelphia Marriott, Philadelphia, PA, Sept 1-4, 2016
Publication(s): *American Political Science Review* (quarterly); *Perspectives on Politics* (quarterly); *PS: Political Science & Politics* (quarterly)

**American Printing History Association**
PO Box 4519, Grand Central Sta, New York, NY 10163-4519
*Tel:* 202-544-2422
*Web Site:* www.printinghistory.org

*Key Personnel*
Exec Dir: Jim Grossman
Proj Mgr: Christian Hale *Tel:* 202-544-2422 ext 133
Spec Proj Coord: Julia Brookins *Tel:* 202-544-2422 ext 119
Local chapters in New York City, New England, Inland, Chesapeake, Southern & Northern California.
Number of Members: 700
New Election: Annually in Jan
Publication(s): *The APHA Newsletter* (quarterly, newsletter, free to membs); *Printing History* (biannually, free to membs)

**American Psychological Association**
750 First St NE, Washington, DC 20002-4242
*Tel:* 202-336-5500 *Toll Free Tel:* 800-374-2721 *Fax:* 202-336-5620
*E-mail:* order@apa.org
*Web Site:* www.apa.org
*Key Personnel*
Publr & Exec Dir, Pubns & Databases: Gary R Vanden Bos, PhD *Tel:* 202-336-5795
Exec Dir, Sci Directorate: Steven J Breckler, PhD *Tel:* 202-336-5938
Exec Dir, Public & Memb Communs: Rhea K Farberman *Tel:* 202-336-5709
Publish numerous periodicals & books in the field of psychology.
Number of Members: 150,000
Publication(s): *American Psychologist* (monthly); *APA Membership Register* (annual); *APA Monitor* (monthly); *Directory of the APA* (1 issue/4 yrs, directory)

**American Public Human Services Association**
1133 19 St NW, Suite 400, Washington, DC 20036
*Tel:* 202-682-0100 *Fax:* 202-289-6555
*Web Site:* www.aphsa.org
*Key Personnel*
Dir, Membership & Communs: Jerome Uher *Tel:* 202-682-0100 ext 285 *E-mail:* jerome.uher@aphsa.org
Founded: 1930
Membership organization of public human services professionals.
Number of Members: 5,000
New Election: Annually in Dec
Publication(s): *NAPCWA Weekly Update* (online, newsletter, free to membs, $250/yr nonmembs); *Policy & Practice* (6 issues/yr, directory, $40 single copy, $45 single copy intl, $350/yr, $450/yr intl); *Public Human Services Directory* (annual, magazine, $200/yr membs, $225/yr nonmembs, $350/yr insts); *This Week In Washington* (weekly when Congress is in session, $285/yr membs, $300/yr nonmembs)

**American Society for Indexing Inc (ASI)**
10200 W 44 Ave, Suite 304, Wheat Ridge, CO 80033
*Tel:* 303-463-2887
*E-mail:* info@asindexing.org
*Web Site:* www.asindexing.org
*Key Personnel*
Exec Dir: Annette Rogers *E-mail:* arogers@asindexing.org
Founded: 1968
Educational programs for indexing field.
Number of Members: 950
New Election: Annually in May
Publication(s): *KeyWords* (quarterly, magazine, free to membs, $40 nonmembs)

**American Society for Information Science & Technology (ASIS&T)**, see Association for Information Science & Technology (ASIS&T)

**American Society of Composers, Authors & Publishers (ASCAP)**
One Lincoln Plaza, New York City, NY 10023
*Tel:* 212-621-6000 *Toll Free Tel:* 800-952-7227 *Fax:* 212-612-8453
*E-mail:* info@ascap.com
*Web Site:* www.ascap.com
*Key Personnel*
Chmn & Pres: Paul Williams *E-mail:* pwilliams@ascap.com
CEO: John Lo Frumento
Founded: 1914
License nondramatic right of public performance of members' copyrighted musical compositions & distribute royalties to members on basis of performances. Members are composers, lyricists & music publishers.
Number of Members: 435,000
*Branch Office(s)*
7920 W Sunset Blvd, 3rd fl, Los Angeles, CA 90046 *Tel:* 323-883-1000 *Fax:* 323-883-1049
420 Lincoln Rd, Suite 385, Miami Beach, FL 33139 *Tel:* 305-673-3446 *Fax:* 305-673-2446
950 Joseph E Lowery Blvd NW, Suite 23, Atlanta, GA 30318 *Tel:* 404-685-8699 *Fax:* 404-685-8701
Two Music Sq W, Nashville, TN 37203 *Tel:* 615-742-5000 *Fax:* 615-742-5020
Ave Martinez Nadal, c/ Hill Side 623, San Juan 00920, Puerto Rico *Tel:* 787-707-0782 *Fax:* 787-707-0783
8 Cork St, London W1S 3LJ, United Kingdom *Tel:* (020) 7439 0909 *Fax:* (020) 7434 0073

**American Society of Journalists and Authors (ASJA)**
1501 Broadway, Suite 403, New York, NY 10036
*Tel:* 212-997-0947 *Fax:* 212-937-2315
*Web Site:* asja.org
*Key Personnel*
Exec Dir: Alexandra Owens *E-mail:* director@asja.org
Founded: 1948
Service organization providing exchange of ideas, market information. Regular meetings with speakers from the industry, annual writers conference; medical plans available. Professional referral service, annual membership directory; first amendment advocacy group.
Number of Members: 1,400
Publication(s): *ASJA Monthly* (11 times/yr, newsletter, membs only); *Semi-Annual Membership Directory* (directory, $98)

**American Society of Magazine Editors (ASME)**
810 Seventh Ave, 24th fl, New York, NY 10019
*Tel:* 212-872-3700 *Fax:* 212-906-0128
*E-mail:* asme@magazine.org
*Web Site:* www.magazine.org/asme/index.aspx
*Key Personnel*
Chief Exec: Sid Holt
Prog Coord: Nina Fortuna *Tel:* 212-872-3737
Founded: 1963
Professional society for senior magazine editors. Sponsor the National Magazine Awards & Magazine Internship Program; hold monthly luncheons for members & conduct periodic seminars.
Number of Members: 700
New Election: Annually in April

**American Society of Media Photographers (ASMP)**
150 N Second St, Philadelphia, PA 19106
*Tel:* 215-451-2767 *Fax:* 215-451-0880
*E-mail:* info@asmp.org
*Web Site:* www.asmp.org
*Key Personnel*
Exec Dir: Eugene Mopsik *E-mail:* mopsik@asmp.org
Gen Mgr: Elena Goertz *E-mail:* goertz@asmp.org
Bookkeeper: Christine Chandler *Tel:* 215-451-2767 *E-mail:* chandler@asmp.org
Founded: 1944
Maintain & promote high professional standards & ethics in photography; cultivate mutual understanding among professional photographers; protect & promote interests of photographers whose work is for publication.
Number of Members: 5,500
Publication(s): *ASMP Professional Business Practices in Photography, 7th Ed* ($28 plus S&H; $20 membs); *Digital Photography Best Practices & Workflow & Handbook* ($20 membs); *Valuation of Lost Damaged Transparencies* ($14.95 plus S&H; $12 membs); *Working with an Architectural Photographer* ($15/10 issues plus $5 S&H, $10/10 issues plus $5 S&H membs; $45/50 issues plus $7 S&H , $40/50 issues plus $7 S&H membs; $75/100 issues plus $10 S&H, $70/100 issues plus $10 S&H membs); *Working with an Assignment Photographer* ($15/10 issues plus $5 S&H, $10/10 issues plus $5 S&H membs; $45/50 issues plus $7 S&H, $40/50 issues plus $7 S&H membs; $75/100 issues plus $10 S&H, $70/100 issues plus $10 S&H membs)

**American Sociological Association (ASA)**
1430 "K" St NW, Suite 600, Washington, DC 20005-4701
*Tel:* 202-383-9005 *Fax:* 202-638-0882
*E-mail:* customer@asanet.org
*Web Site:* www.asanet.org
*Key Personnel*
Exec Offr: Sally T Hillsman *Tel:* 202-383-9005 ext 316 *E-mail:* executive.office@asanet.org
Pubns Dir: Karen Gray Edwards *Tel:* 202-383-9005 ext 319 *E-mail:* publications@asanet.org
Founded: 1905
Nonprofit membership association dedicated to advancing sociology as a scientific discipline & profession serving the public good. Encompass sociologists who are faculty members at colleges & universities, researchers, practitioners & students.
Number of Members: 14,000
New Election: Annually in Aug
2014 Meeting(s): Annual Meeting, Hilton San Francisco & Parc55 Hotel, San Francisco, CA, Aug 16-19, 2014
Publication(s): *American Sociological Review* (bimonthly, $45 membs, $30 student membs, $370 instns (print/online), $334 instns (online only)); *Contemporary Sociology* (bimonthly, $45 membs, $30 student membs, $354 instns (print/online), $318 instns (online only)); *Contexts* (quarterly, magazine, $45 membs, $30 student membs, $260 instns (print/online), $234 instns (online only)); *Footnotes* (monthly exc July/Aug, Sept/Oct, May/June, free to membs, $30 nonmembs, $40 nonmemb instns); *Journal of Health & Social Behavior* (quarterly, $45 membs, $30 student membs, $310 instns (print/online), $278 instns (online only)); *Social Psychology Quarterly* ($45 membs, $30 student membs, $310 instns (print/online), $278 instns (online only)); *Sociological Methodology* (annual, $45 membs, $30 student membs, $360 instns (print/online), $330 instns (online only)); *Sociological Theory* (quarterly, $45 membs, $30 student membs, $370 instns (print/online), $334 instns (online only)); *Sociology of Education* (quarterly, $45 membs, $30 student membs, $310 instns (print/online), $278 instns (online only)); *Teaching Sociology* (quarterly, $45 membs, $30 student membs, $310 instns (print/online), $278 instns (online only))

**American Speech-Language-Hearing Association (ASHA)**
2200 Research Blvd, Rockville, MD 20850-3289

*Tel:* 301-296-5700 *Toll Free Tel:* 800-638-8255 (nonmembs); 800-498-2071 (membs) *Fax:* 301-296-5777; 301-296-8580
*E-mail:* actioncenter@asha.org
*Web Site:* www.asha.org
*Key Personnel*
Dir, Pubns: Gary Dunham *E-mail:* gdunham@asha.org
Founded: 1925
Membership organization for 150,000 speech-language pathologists & audiologists. Provide consumers with information & referral on speech, language & hearing. Publish information brochures & packets.
Number of Members: 150,000
New Election: Annually in Sept
Publication(s): *American Journal of Audiology* (2 issues/yr, $10/single article for 24 hours, $25 for entire site for 24 hours, journal, $49/yr electronic nonmembs, $137/yr electronic instns, $147/yr online archive nonmembs & instns); *American Journal of Speech-Language Pathology* (4 issues/yr, $10/single article for 24 hours, $25 for entire site for 24 hours, journal, $69/yr electonic nonmembs, $170/yr electronic instns, $147/yr online archives nonmembs & instns); *The ASHA Leader* (15 issues/mo, $10/single article for 24 hours, $25/entire site for 24 hours, newspaper); *Journal of Speech, Language & Hearing Research* (6 issues/yr, $10/single article for 24 hours, $25 for entire site for 24 hours, journal, $145/yr electronic nonmembs, $413/yr electronic instns, $423/yr online archives nonmembs & instns); *Language, Speech & Hearing Services In The Schools* (quarterly, $10/single article for 24 hours, $25 for entire site for 24 hours, journal, $69/yr electronic nonmembs, $170/yr electronic instns, $147/yr online archives nonmembs & instns)
*Branch Office(s)*
444 N Capitol St NW, Suite 715, Washington, DC 20001 *Tel:* 202-624-5884

**American Translators Association (ATA)**
225 Reinekers Lane, Suite 590, Alexandria, VA 22314
*Tel:* 703-683-6100 *Fax:* 703-683-6122
*E-mail:* ata@atanet.org
*Web Site:* www.atanet.org
*Key Personnel*
Pres: Dorothee Racette
Exec Dir: Walter W Bacak, Jr *Tel:* 703-683-6100 ext 3006 *E-mail:* walter@atanet.org
Founded: 1959
Membership consists of those professionally engaged in translating, interpreting or closely allied work, as well as those who are interested in these fields. Membership: $145/yr indivs, $300/yr corps.
Number of Members: 11,000
2014 Meeting(s): Annual Conference, Sheraton Hotel & Towers, Chicago, IL, Nov 5-8, 2014
2015 Meeting(s): Annual Conference, Hyatt Regency Hotel, Miami, FL, Nov 4-7, 2015
2016 Meeting(s): Annual Conference, San Francisco, CA, Nov 2-5, 2016
Publication(s): *ATA Chronicle* (11 issues/yr, $65, $90 CN & Mexico, $110 all other countries)
Membership(s): Federation of International Translators

**Antiquarian Booksellers' Association of America (ABAA)**
20 W 44 St, Suite 507, New York, NY 10036
*Tel:* 212-944-8291 *Fax:* 212-944-8293
*E-mail:* hq@abaa.org
*Web Site:* www.abaa.org
*Key Personnel*
Pres: John Thomson
Treas: Sam Hessel
VP & Secy: Tom Goldwasser
Exec Dir: Susan Benne *E-mail:* sbenne@abaa.org
Founded: 1949
Chapters: Northern California, Southern California, Midwest, Middle Atlantic, New England, Southeast, Southwest & Pacific Northwest. Membership open to antiquarian booksellers only. ABAA sponsors three or four international book fairs per year in Los Angeles & San Francisco (alternately) in mid-winter; in New York in the spring; in Boston in late autumn.
Number of Members: 470
2014 Meeting(s): California International Antiquarian Book Fair, Pasadena Convention Center, 300 E Green St, Pasadena, CA, Feb 7-9, 2014; New York International Antiquarian Book Fair, Park Avenue Armory, 643 Park Ave at 67 St, New York, NY, April 3-6, 2014
Publication(s): *Membership Directory* (annual, free)

**Antiquarian Booksellers' Association of Canada/Association de la Librairie Ancienne du Canada**, see ABAC/ALAC

**ASHA**, see American Speech-Language-Hearing Association (ASHA)

**Aspen Writers' Foundation**
110 E Hallam St, Suite 116, Aspen, CO 81611
*Tel:* 970-925-3122 *Fax:* 970-920-5700
*E-mail:* info@aspenwriters.org
*Web Site:* www.aspenwriters.org
*Key Personnel*
Creative Dir: Adrienne Brodeur *E-mail:* brodeur.adrienne@gmail.com
Dir: Maurice LaMee
Devt Assoc: Jamie Kravitz *E-mail:* jamie@aspenwriters.org
Progs Assoc: Sara Halterman *E-mail:* sara@aspenwriters.org
Progs Coord: Lauren Lowinger *E-mail:* lauren@aspenwriters.org
Founded: 1976
Program of the Aspen Institute. Encourages writers, inspires readers & connects people through the power of stories.
Meeting(s): Aspen Summer Words Writing Retreat & Literary Festival, Aspen, CO, June

**Associated Business Writers of America Inc**
Division of National Writers Association Inc
10940 S Parker Rd, Suite 508, Parker, CO 80134
*Tel:* 303-841-0246
*E-mail:* natlwritersassn@hotmail.com
*Web Site:* www.nationalwriters.com
*Key Personnel*
Exec Dir: Sandy Whelchel *E-mail:* authorsandy@hotmail.com
To help business writers & those seeking their services.
Number of Members: 100
Publication(s): *Professional Freelance Writers Directory* (directory, available free online)

**Associated Press Broadcast**
1100 13 St NW, Suite 700, Washington, DC 20005
*Tel:* 202-641-9000 *Toll Free Tel:* 800-821-4747 *Fax:* 202-370-2710
*Web Site:* www.ap.org
Number of Members: 5,800
Publication(s): *AP Broadcast Handbook* ($24.95)

**Association Canadienne des bibliotheques (ACB)**, see Canadian Library Association (CLA) (Association Canadienne des bibliotheques)

**Association canadienne des reviseurs**, see Editors' Association of Canada (Association canadienne des reviseurs)

**Association des Editeurs de Langue Anglaise du Quebec (AELAQ)**
1200 Atwater Ave, Suite 3, Westmount, QC H3Z 1X4, Canada
*Tel:* 514-932-5633
*E-mail:* admin@aelaq.org
*Web Site:* www.aelaq.org
*Key Personnel*
Exec Dir: Lara de Beaupre
Encourage publication, distribution & promotion of books published in English in Quebec.
Number of Members: 17
Publication(s): *Montreal Review of Books* (3 times/yr, report, free)

**Association des Libraires du Quebec**
407, blvd de Sainte Laurent Est, Bureau 801, Montreal, QC H2Y 2Y5, Canada
*Tel:* 514-526-3349 *Fax:* 514-526-3340
*E-mail:* info@alq.qc.ca
*Web Site:* www.alq.qc.ca
*Key Personnel*
Pres: Mary Ellen Vaugeois
Quebec association of booksellers.
Number of Members: 95

**Association for Information & Image Management International (AIIM)**
1100 Wayne Ave, Suite 1100, Silver Spring, MD 20910
*Tel:* 301-587-8202 *Toll Free Tel:* 800-477-2446 *Fax:* 301-587-2711
*E-mail:* aiim@aiim.org
*Web Site:* www.aiim.org
*Key Personnel*
Ed: Bryant Duhon *Tel:* 301-916-7182 *E-mail:* bduhon@aiim.org
Global association bringing together the users of document technologies with the providers of that technology.
Number of Members: 9,197

**Association for Information Science & Technology (ASIS&T)**
Formerly American Society for Information Science & Technology (ASIS&T)
1320 Fenwick Lane, Suite 510, Silver Spring, MD 20910
*Tel:* 301-495-0900 *Fax:* 301-495-0810
*E-mail:* asis@asis.org
*Web Site:* www.asis.org
*Key Personnel*
Exec Dir: Richard Hill *E-mail:* rhill@asis.org
To foster & lead the advancement of information science & technology.
Number of Members: 4,000
2014 Meeting(s): IA Summit, San Diego, CA, March 25-30, 2014; Annual Meeting, Sheraton Seattle, Seattle, WA, Oct 31-Nov 4, 2014
Publication(s): *Annual Review of Information Science & Technology*; *Bulletin*; *Journal*

**Association Media & Publishing**
12100 Sunset Hills Rd, Suite 130, Reston, VA 20190
*Tel:* 703-234-4063 *Fax:* 703-435-4390
*E-mail:* info@associationmediaandpublishing.org
*Web Site:* www.associationmediaandpublishing.org
*Key Personnel*
Exec Dir: Sarah Patterson *Tel:* 703-234-4107 *E-mail:* spatterson@associationmediaandpublishing.com
Edit Dir: Carla Kalogeridis *Tel:* 313-884-0988 *E-mail:* ckalogeridis@associationmediaandpublishing.org
Membership Coord: Kathryn Kovacs *Tel:* 703-234-4063 *E-mail:* kkovacs@associationmediaandpublishing.com
Coord, Mktg & Communs: Liz Jones *Tel:* 703-234-4112 *E-mail:* ejones@associationmediaandpublishing.com

Founded: 1963 (as Society of National Association Publications)
A nonprofit professional society that serves the needs of association & society publications & their staff to represent, promote & advance the common interest of periodicals of voluntary associations & societies.
Number of Members: 1,400
2014 Meeting(s): Annual Meeting, Sheraton Premier, Tyson's Corner, VA, May 19-21, 2014
Publication(s): *Association Publishing* (bimonthly)

**Association Nationale des Editeurs de Livres**
2514 boul Rosemont, Montreal, QC H1Y 1K4, Canada
*Tel:* 514-273-8130 *Toll Free Tel:* 866-900-ANEL (900-2635) *Fax:* 514-273-9657
*E-mail:* info@anel.qc.ca
*Web Site:* www.anel.qc.ca
*Key Personnel*
Dir Gen: Richard Prieur *E-mail:* prieur@anel.qc.ca
Memb Servs: Helene Letourneau *E-mail:* letourneau@anel.qc.ca
Founded: 1992
Professional association of French publishers in Canada.
Number of Members: 100

**Association of American Editorial Cartoonists**
3899 N Front St, Harrisburg, PA 17110
*Tel:* 717-703-3003 *Fax:* 717-703-3008
*E-mail:* aaec@pa-news.org
*Web Site:* www.editorialcartoonists.com
*Key Personnel*
Pres: Matt Wuerker
Gen Mgr: Teresa Shaak
Founded: 1957
Professional association.
Number of Members: 300
Publication(s): *Notebook* (quarterly, free to membs, $40/yr nonmembs)

**Association of American Publishers (AAP)**
71 Fifth Ave, 2nd fl, New York, NY 10003-3004
*Tel:* 212-255-0200 *Fax:* 212-255-7007
*Web Site:* www.publishers.org
*Key Personnel*
CEO & Pres: Tom Allen *Tel:* 202-220-4543 *Fax:* 202-347-3690
VP & Dir: Tina Jordan *Tel:* 212-255-0275 *E-mail:* tjordan@publishers.org
VP & Exec Dir, Prof Scholarly Publg: John Tagler *Tel:* 212-255-0200 ext 257
VP, Communs: Andi Sporkin
VP & Gen Counsel, Govt Aff: Allan R Adler *Tel:* 202-347-3375 *Fax:* 202-347-3690
Exec Dir, School Div: Jay Diskey *Tel:* 202-347-3375 *Fax:* 202-347-3690
Founded: 1970
Monitor & promote the USA publishing industry. Members: those actively engaged in the creation, publication & production of books, journals, electronic media, testing materials & a range of educational materials.
Number of Members: 300
2014 Meeting(s): Annual Meeting, March 2014
*Branch Office(s)*
455 Massachusetts Ave NW, Suite 700, Washington, DC 20001-2777, Dir, Communs & Pub Aff: Judith Platt *Tel:* 202-347-3375 *Fax:* 202-347-3690
Membership(s): BISG

**Association of American University Presses (AAUP)**
28 W 36 St, Suite 602, New York, NY 10018
*Tel:* 212-989-1010 *Fax:* 212-989-0275
*E-mail:* info@aaupnet.org
*Web Site:* www.aaupnet.org
*Key Personnel*
Exec Dir: Peter Berkery *Tel:* 212-989-1010 ext 29 *E-mail:* pberkery@aaupnet.org
Dir of Mktg & Communs: Brenna McLaughlin *Tel:* 518-436-3586 *E-mail:* bmclaughlin@aaupnet.org
Admin Mgr: Linda McCall *Tel:* 212-989-1010 ext 30 *E-mail:* lmccall@aaupnet.org
Membership & affiliation consists of university presses in North America & abroad that function as the publishing arms of their respective universities, issuing some 11,000 titles & more than 600 journals annually. AAUP helps these presses do their work more economically, creatively & effectively through its own activities in professional development; fund raising; statistical research & analysis; promoting the value of university presses; community & institutional relations & through its marketing programs.
Number of Members: 128
2014 Meeting(s): Annual Meeting, New Orleans Marriott, New Orleans, LA, June 22-24, 2014
2015 Meeting(s): Annual Meeting, Sheraton Denver Downtown, Denver, CO, June 18-20, 2015
Publication(s): *AAUP Book, Jacket & Journal Show* (catalog, $10); *Annual Directory* ($30); *The Exchange* (quarterly, newsletter, free); *University Press Books for Public & Secondary School Libraries* (annual, free)
Membership(s): BISG

**Association of Authors' Representatives Inc**
676-A Ninth Ave, Suite 312, New York, NY 10036
*Tel:* 212-840-5777
*Web Site:* www.aaronline.org
*Key Personnel*
Pres: Gail Hochman *E-mail:* president@aaronline.org
Treas: Jeff Gerecke
Founded: 1991
Voluntary & elective professional association of literary & play agents whose individual members subscribe to certain ethical practices. Members meet to discuss industry developments & problems of mutual interest.
Number of Members: 380
New Election: Annually in June

**Association of Book Publishers of British Columbia**
Affiliate of Association of Canadian Publishers
600-402 W Pender St, Vancouver, BC V6B 1T6, Canada
*Tel:* 604-684-0228 *Fax:* 604-684-5788
*E-mail:* admin@books.bc.ca
*Web Site:* www.books.bc.ca
*Key Personnel*
Exec Dir: Margaret Reynolds
Founded: 1974
Trade association representing the interests of BC owned & operated book publishing companies.
Number of Members: 50
New Election: Annually in April

**Association of Canadian Publishers (ACP)**
174 Spadina Ave, Suite 306, Toronto, ON M5T 2C2, Canada
*Tel:* 416-487-6116 *Fax:* 416-487-8815
*E-mail:* admin@canbook.org
*Web Site:* www.publishers.ca
*Key Personnel*
Exec Dir: Carolyn Wood *E-mail:* carolyn_wood@canbook.org
Progs Mgr: Kate Edwards *E-mail:* kate_edwards@canbook.org
Association of English-language Canadian-owned book publishing companies in Canada. Sponsor professional development seminars for book publishers. Publish membership directories, studies & reports.
Number of Members: 140
Publication(s): *Membership Directory* (annual)

**Association of Canadian University Presses**
10 St Mary St, Suite 700, Toronto, ON M4Y 2W8, Canada
*Tel:* 416-978-2239 ext 237 *Fax:* 416-978-4738
*Web Site:* www.acup.ca
*Key Personnel*
Admin: Charley La Rose *E-mail:* clarose@utpress.utoronto.ca
Founded: 1972
Number of Members: 15
New Election: Annually in Autumn

**Association of Catholic Publishers Inc**
4725 Dorsey Hall Dr, Suite A, PMB 709, Elliott City, MD 21042
*Tel:* 410-988-2926 *Fax:* 410-571-4946
*Web Site:* www.catholicsread.org; www.catholicpublishers.org; www.midatlanticcongress.org
*Key Personnel*
Pres: Jeff Smith
VP: Bret Thomas
Secy: Mary Beth Kunde-Anderson
Treas: Suann Fields
Exec Dir: Therese Brown
Facilitate the sharing of professional information, networking, cooperation & friendship among those involved in Catholic book publishing in the US & abroad. Offers trade co-op catalog, mailing list, Catholic bestsellers, advertising insert program & professional skills workshops.
Number of Members: 100
2014 Meeting(s): Mid-Atlantic Congress, Baltimore Hilton Hotel, Baltimore, MD, Feb 27-March 1, 2014
Publication(s): *Promotional Brochure* (annually)

**Association of College & University Printers**
Penn State University, 101 Hostetter Business Services Bldg, University Park, PA 16802
*Tel:* 814-865-7544 *Fax:* 814-863-6376
*Web Site:* www.multimediaprint.psu.edu
*Key Personnel*
Dir: Abbas Badani *Tel:* 814-865-8193 *E-mail:* atb10@psu.edu
Mgr: Theresa Roby *Tel:* 814-863-1980 *E-mail:* tlr7@psu.edu
Number of Members: 300

**The Association of Educational Publishers (AEP)**, see PreK-12 Learning Group

**Association of Free Community Papers (AFCP)**
7445 Morgan Rd, Suite 103, Liverpool, NY 13090
*Toll Free Tel:* 877-203-2327 *Fax:* 781-459-7770
*E-mail:* afcp@afcp.org
*Web Site:* www.afcp.org
*Key Personnel*
Exec Dir: Loren Colburn *E-mail:* loren@afcp.org
Founded: 1950
Organization of publishers serving the free-circulation community newspaper & shopping guide industry.
Number of Members: 250
Publication(s): *Freepaper Ink* (monthly, newsletter, free)

**Association of Jewish Libraries (AJL) Inc**
PO Box 1118, Teaneck, NJ 07666
*Tel:* 201-371-3255
*E-mail:* info@jewishlibraries.org
*Web Site:* www.jewishlibraries.org
*Key Personnel*
Pres: Heidi Estrin *E-mail:* president@jewishlibraries.org
Corresponding Secy & Contact: Elana Gensler

Member libraries in two divisions: Research Libraries, Archives & Special Collections, School & Center Libraries. Promote librarianship, services & standards in the field of Judaica.
Number of Members: 1,114
2014 Meeting(s): Annual Conference, Las Vegas, NV, June 22-25, 2014
Publication(s): *AJL News* (quarterly); *AJL Reviews* (quarterly); *Judaica Librarianship* (irregular)

**Association of Library Trustees, Advocates, Friends & Foundations (ALTAFF)**
109 S 13 St, Suite 3-N, Philadelphia, PA 19107
*Tel:* 312-280-2161 *Toll Free Tel:* 800-545-2433 (ext 2161) *Fax:* 215-545-3821
*E-mail:* altaff@ala.org
*Web Site:* www.ala.org/ala/mgrps/divs/altaff/index.cfm
*Key Personnel*
Exec Dir: Sally Gardner Reed *E-mail:* sreed@ala.org
Dir, Mktg & Communs: Beth Nawalinski *E-mail:* bnawalinski@ala.org
Founded: 2009
Resulting from the merger of Friends of Libraries USA (FOLUSA) & Association of Library Trustees & Advocates (ALTA) - this association serves as an expanded division of ALA. It is a national network of library supporters.
Number of Members: 5,000

**Association of Manitoba Book Publishers**
100 Arthur St, Suite 404, Winnipeg, MB R3B 1H3, Canada
*Tel:* 204-947-3335 *Fax:* 204-956-4689
*E-mail:* ambp@mts.net
*Web Site:* www.bookpublishers.mb.ca
*Key Personnel*
Exec Dir: Michelle Peters
Publishing industry association.
Number of Members: 13
Publication(s): *Prairie Books Now* (3 issues/yr, magazine, $20 US)

**Association of Medical Illustrators (AMI)**
201 E Main St, Suite 1405, Lexington, KY 40507
*Toll Free Tel:* 866-393-4264 *Fax:* 859-514-9166
*E-mail:* hq@ami.org
*Web Site:* www.ami.org
*Key Personnel*
Exec Dir: Melanie Bowzer
Founded: 1945
Promote the use of high-quality artwork in medical publications to advance medical education.
Number of Members: 850

**Association of Opinion Journalists (AOJ)**
3899 N Front St, Harrisburg, PA 17110
*Tel:* 717-703-3015 *Fax:* 717-703-3014
*E-mail:* ncew@pa-news.org
*Web Site:* www.ncew.org
*Key Personnel*
Mgr: Lisa Strohle
Founded: 1947
Sponsor seminars, regional critique meetings & annual foreign tours for members; also cosponsors the Wells Award for exemplary leadership in offering minorities employment in journalism; outreach (critique) service to members & nonmembers; annual convention; Publishes *The Masthead* (professional journal), circ 800.
Number of Members: 275
New Election: Annually in Sept
Publication(s): *The Masthead* (free online)

**Association of Publishers for Special Sales (APSS)**
Formerly Small Publishers Association of North America (SPAN)
PO Box 715, Avon, CT 06001-0715
*Tel:* 860-675-1344
*Web Site:* www.spannet.org
*Key Personnel*
Exec Dir: Brian Jud *E-mail:* brianjud@bookaapss.org
Busn Mgr: Debi Flora
A trade association for independent presses, self-publishers & pro-active authors who want to sell more books.
Publication(s): *The Sales Informer* (monthly)

**Association of Writers & Writing Programs (AWP)**
George Mason University, 4400 University Dr, MSN 1E3, Fairfax, VA 22030
*Tel:* 703-993-4301 *Fax:* 703-993-4302
*E-mail:* awp@awpwriter.org
*Web Site:* www.awpwriter.org
*Key Personnel*
Exec Dir: David W Fenza
Dir of Conferences: Christian Teresi
Dir, Devt: Amber Withycombe
Dir, Membership Servs: Diane Zinna
Dir, Pubns: Supriya Bhatnagar
Bookfair Mgr: Alana Hurley
Assoc Ed: Sara Flood
Conference Coord: Brenna Killeen
Founded: 1967
Magazine, publications, directory, competitions for awards (including publication), advocacy for literature & education, annual meeting, job placement.
Number of Members: 34,000
2014 Meeting(s): Annual Conference & Bookfair, Sheraton Seattle & Washington State Convention Center, Seattle, WA, Feb 26-March 1, 2014
2015 Meeting(s): Annual Conference & Bookfair, Hilton Minneapolis & Minneapolis Convention Center, Minneapolis, MN, April 8-11, 2015
2016 Meeting(s): Annual Conference & Bookfair, JW Marriott Los Angeles & Los Angeles Convention Center, Los Angeles, CA, March 30-April 2, 2016
2017 Meeting(s): Annual Conference & Bookfair, Washington Marriott Marquis & Washington Convention Center, Washington, DC, Feb 8-11, 2017
Publication(s): *The Writer's Chronicle* (6 issues/yr, free to membs)

**Association pour l'Avancement des Sciences et des Techniques de la Documentation**
2065 rue Parthenais, Bureau 387, Montreal, QC H2K 3T1, Canada
*Tel:* 514-281-5012 *Fax:* 514-281-8219
*E-mail:* info@asted.org
*Web Site:* www.asted.org
*Key Personnel*
Exec Dir: Suzanne Morin *Tel:* 514-281-5012 ext 234 *E-mail:* smorin@asted.org
Objective is the promotion of standards of excellence in the services & personnel of libraries, documentation & information centers.
Number of Members: 550
New Election: annually during congress
Publication(s): *Documentation et Bibliotheques* (quarterly, $65/yr CN, $85/yr elsewhere)

**ASTED**, see Association pour l'Avancement des Sciences et des Techniques de la Documentation

**Audit Bureau of Circulations**, see Alliance for Audited Media (AAM)

**Audit Bureau of Circulations (ABC), Canadian Office**
151 Bloor St W, Suite 850, Toronto, ON M5S 1S4, Canada
*Tel:* 416-962-5840 *Fax:* 416-962-5844
*Web Site:* www.accessabc.ca
*Key Personnel*
VP & Gen Mgr: Joan Brehl
Number of Members: 4,500

**The Authors Guild**
31 E 32 St, 7th fl, New York, NY 10016
*Tel:* 212-563-5904 *Fax:* 212-564-8363; 212-564-5363
*E-mail:* staff@authorsguild.org
*Web Site:* www.authorsguild.org
*Key Personnel*
Pres: Scott Turow
VP: Judy Blume
Exec Dir: Paul Aiken
Founded: 1912
National membership organization for nonfiction & fiction book authors & freelance journalists. Deals with the business & professional interests of authors in such fields as book contracts, copyright, subsidiary rights, free expression, taxes & others. Offer free contract reviews, web site development & hosting & health insurance.
Number of Members: 9,000
Publication(s): *The Bulletin* (quarterly)

**The Authors League Fund**
31 E 32 St, 7th fl, New York, NY 10016
*Tel:* 212-268-1208 *Fax:* 212-564-5363
*E-mail:* staff@authorsleaguefund.org
*Web Site:* www.authorsleaguefund.org
*Key Personnel*
Pres: Pat Cummings
VP: Sidney Offit
Exec Dir: Isabel Howe
Secy: Marian Seldes
Treas: James B Stewart
Founded: 1917
Provide interest-free loans to professional authors during personal hardship.
Number of Members: 900

**The Authors League of America Inc**, see The Authors Guild

**The Authors Registry Inc**
31 E 32 St, 7th fl, New York, NY 10016
*Tel:* 212-563-6920 *Fax:* 212-564-5363
*E-mail:* staff@authorsregistry.org
*Web Site:* www.authorsregistry.org
*Key Personnel*
Mng Dir: Terry King *E-mail:* tking@authorsregistry.org
A nonprofit corporation that provides a royalty collection & distribution service.
Number of Members: 40,000

**The Baker Street Irregulars (BSI)**
7938 Mill Stream Circle, Indianapolis, IN 46278
*Tel:* 317-293-2212; 317-384-4728 (cell)
*Web Site:* bakerstreetjournal.com
*Key Personnel*
Wiggins, Chmn: Michael F Whelan
Literary society with a small press operation including a quarterly journal with a Christmas, annual & 3-4 published books annually.
Number of Members: 300
Publication(s): *The Baker Street Journal* (quarterly & Xmas ann, $38.50/yr, $49.50/yr foreign)

**Before Columbus Foundation**
The Raymond House, Suite 302, 655 13 St, Oakland, CA 94612
SAN: 159-2955
*Tel:* 510-268-9775
*E-mail:* info@beforecolumbusfoundation.com
*Web Site:* www.beforecolumbusfoundation.org

*Key Personnel*
Exec Dir: Gundars Strads *Tel:* 510-642-7321
Founded: 1976
Provide information, research, consultation & promotional services for contemporary American multicultural writers & publishers. A nonprofit service organization that also sponsors classes, workshops, readings, public events & the annual American Book Awards.

**Bibliographical Society of America**
PO Box 1537, Lenox Hill Sta, New York, NY 10021-0043
*Tel:* 212-452-2710 *Fax:* 212-452-2710
*E-mail:* bsa@bibsocamer.org
*Web Site:* www.bibsocamer.org
*Key Personnel*
Pres: Claudia Funke *E-mail:* claudiafunke@mac.com
Treas: G Scott Clemons *E-mail:* scott.demons@bbh.com
VP: John Chrichton *E-mail:* jchrichton@brickrow.com
Exec Dir: Michele E Randall
Secy: Caroline Duroselle-Melish *E-mail:* cmelish@fas.harvard.edu
Sponsor short-term fellowships for bibliographic projects. Membership open to anyone interested in bibliographic projects & process.
Number of Members: 1,100
New Election: Annually in Jan
Meeting(s): Annual Meeting, New York, NY, Jan (Friday following the 4th Thursday)
Publication(s): *The Papers of the Bibliographical Society of America* (quarterly, $65 membership subscription fee, $20/yr for students providing proof of eligibility)

**Bibliographical Society of the University of Virginia**
c/o Alderman Library, University of Virginia, McCormick Rd, Charlottesville, VA 22904
Mailing Address: PO Box 400152, Charlottesville, VA 22904-4152
*Tel:* 434-924-7013 *Fax:* 434-924-1431
*E-mail:* bibsoc@virginia.edu
*Web Site:* bsuva.org
*Key Personnel*
Pres: G Thomas Tanselle
Exec Secy & Treas: Anne G Ribble *E-mail:* ar3g@virginia.edu
Founded: 1947
Scholarly society promoting the study of books as physical objects, the history of the book & of printing & publishing.
Number of Members: 550
Publication(s): *Studies in Bibliography* (annual, $55)

**Binding Industries Association (BIA)**
Affiliate of Printing Industries of America
200 Deer Run Rd, Sewickley, PA 15143
*Tel:* 412-741-6860 *Toll Free Tel:* 800-910-4283 *Fax:* 412-741-2311
*E-mail:* printing@printing.org
*Web Site:* www.printing.org
*Key Personnel*
CEO & Pres: Michael Makin *Tel:* 412-259-1777 *E-mail:* mmakin@printing.org
EVP: Mary Garnett *Tel:* 412-259-1801 *E-mail:* mgarnet@printing.org
Mgr, Mktg: Chrystal Kapanyko *Tel:* 412-259-1736 *E-mail:* ckapanyko@printing.org
Section/SIG Coord & Mgr: Justin Goldstein *Tel:* 412-259-1806 *E-mail:* jgoldstein@printing.org
Founded: 1955
Trade finishers & loose-leaf manufacturers united to conduct seminars, hold conventions, formulate & maintain industry standards. Bestow annual product of excellence awards.
Number of Members: 100
Publication(s): *The Binding Edge* (quarterly, magazine); *Membership Directory* (in print biennially & online, book)
*Branch Office(s)*
601 13 St NW, Suite 3505, Washington, DC 20005-3807 *Tel:* 202-730-7970

**BISG**, see Book Industry Study Group Inc (BISG)

**The Black Press of America**, see National Newspaper Publishers Assn (NNPA)

**BMI®**
7 World Trade Ctr, 250 Greenwich St, New York, NY 10007-0030
*Tel:* 212-586-2000; 212-220-3000 *Fax:* 212-246-2163
*E-mail:* foundation@bmi.com
*Web Site:* www.bmi.com
*Key Personnel*
CEO & Pres: Del R Bryant
VP, Corp Rel: Robbin Ahrold *E-mail:* rahrold@bmi.com
Founded: 1939
Secure & license the performing rights of music on behalf of its creators.
Number of Members: 300,000
Publication(s): *BMI MusicWorld* (quarterly)
*Branch Office(s)*
8730 Sunset Blvd, 3rd fl W, West Hollywood, CA 90069-2211 *Tel:* 310-659-9109 *E-mail:* losangeles@bmi.com
1691 Michigan Ave, Suite 350, Miami Beach, FL 33139 *Tel:* 305-673-5148
3340 Peachtree Rd NE, Suite 570, Atlanta, GA 30326 *Tel:* 404-261-5151 *E-mail:* atlanta@bmi.com
10 Music Sq E, Nashville, TN 37203-4399 *Tel:* 615-401-2000 *E-mail:* nashville@bmi.com
San Jose Bldg, Suite 1008, 1250 Ave Ponce de Leon, Santurce 00907, Puerto Rico *Tel:* 787-754-6490
84 Harley House, Marylebone Rd, London NW1 5HN, United Kingdom *Tel:* (020) 7846 2036 *E-mail:* london@bmi.com

**Book & Periodical Council (BPC)**
192 Spadina Ave, Suite 107, Toronto, ON M5T 2C2, Canada
*Tel:* 416-975-9366 *Fax:* 416-975-1839
*E-mail:* info@thebpc.ca
*Web Site:* www.thebpc.ca
*Key Personnel*
Chmn: Anita Purcell
Exec Dir: Anne McClelland
Umbrella organization representing associations of authors, editors, publishers, book manufacturers, distributors, booksellers & librarians in the book & periodical industries in Canada.
Number of Members: 32
Publication(s): *Dividends: The Value of Public Libraries in Canada* (free); *Freedom to Read Kit* (annual); *When the Censor Comes* (shipping charge or SASE)

**Book Industry Guild of New York**
PO Box 2001, New York, NY 10113-2001
*E-mail:* admin@bookindustryguildofny.org
*Web Site:* www.bookindustryguildofny.org
*Key Personnel*
Fin Secy & Webmaster: Emily Larsen *E-mail:* emily.larsen@gmail.com
Founded: 1926
For book publishing production, editorial, design & manufacturing people from the book community. Monthly dinner meetings, book show & educational seminars.
Number of Members: 800
New Election: May 2014

**Book Industry Study Group Inc (BISG)**
145 W 45 St, Suite 601, New York, NY 10036
*Tel:* 646-336-7141 *Fax:* 646-336-6214
*E-mail:* info@bisg.org
*Web Site:* www.bisg.org
*Key Personnel*
Exec Dir: Len Vlahos *E-mail:* len@bisg.org
Dir, Mktg: Mindy Im *Tel:* 646-336-7141 ext 11 *E-mail:* mindy@bisg.org
Proj Mgr, Res & Info: Nadine Vassallo *E-mail:* nadine@bisg.org
Founded: 1975
Trade association for policy, standards & research. The member-driven organization uniquely represents all segments of our industry from publishers & e-publishers to paper manufacturers, libraries, authors, printers, wholesalers, retailers & e-tailers, as well as organizations concerned with the book industry as a whole. For 30 years, BISG has provided a forum for all industry professionals to come together & efficiently address issues & concerns to advance the book community.
Number of Members: 200
New Election: Annually in Sept
Publication(s): *BookStats* (annual, $595 membs, $2,395 nonmembs, complimentary copies available for membs levels B & above)

**Book Manufacturers' Institute Inc (BMI)**
2 Armand Beach Dr, Suite 1B, Palm Coast, FL 32137-2612
*Tel:* 386-986-4552 *Fax:* 386-986-4553
*E-mail:* info@bmibook.com
*Web Site:* www.bmibook.org
*Key Personnel*
EVP: Daniel N Bach *E-mail:* dbach@dmibook.com
Founded: 1933
BMI is the leading nationally recognized trade association of the book manufacturing industry.
Number of Members: 80
2014 Meeting(s): Management Conference, Sanibel Harbour Marriott Resort & Spa, 17260 Harbour Point Dr, Fort Myers, FL, May 4-6, 2014
Membership(s): Book Industry Guild of New York; National Association of Manufacturers

**Book Publicists of Southern California**
714 Crescent Dr, Beverly Hills, CA 90210
*Tel:* 323-461-3921 *Fax:* 323-461-0917
*Key Personnel*
Founder & Pres, Emeritus: Irwin Zucker *E-mail:* irwin@promotioninmotion.net
Pres: Patty Weckbaugh
VP: Donna Larsen
Treas: Bruce Braunstein
Publicity: Devra Hill
Founded: 1976
Bimonthly meetings, varied, anything pertinent to promotion of books & authors.
Number of Members: 1,200
New Election: Annually in Nov
Publication(s): *Know Thy Shelf* (6 issues/yr, newsletter, free to membs)

**The Book Publishers Association of Alberta (BPAA)**
Affiliate of Association of Canadian Publishers (ACP)
10523 100 Ave, Edmonton, AB T5J 0A8, Canada
*Tel:* 780-424-5060 *Fax:* 780-424-7943
*E-mail:* info@bookpublishers.ab.ca
*Web Site:* www.bookpublishers.ab.ca
*Key Personnel*
Exec Dir: Kieran Leblanc *E-mail:* kleblanc@bookpublishers.ab.ca
Proj Coord: Donna White *E-mail:* dwhite@bookpublishers.ab.ca
Sponsor professional development seminars, workshops & Alberta Book Industry Awards.

Number of Members: 32
Publication(s): *Best of the West* (annual, free); *Membership Directory* (free)

**Bookbuilders of Boston**
44 Vinal Ave, Scituate, MA 02066
*Tel:* 781-378-1361 *Fax:* 419-821-2171
*E-mail:* office@bbboston.org
*Web Site:* www.bbboston.org
*Key Personnel*
Pres: Thomas Plain
Meetings, New England Book Show, seminars & scholarships; nonprofit organization.
New Election: Annually in April
Publication(s): *Directory* (annually, free)

**Bookbuilders West (BBW)**, see Publishing Professionals Network

**Books for Everybody**
111 Queen St E, Suite 320, Toronto, ON M5C 1S2, Canada
*Tel:* 416-364-3333 *Toll Free Tel:* 888-360-6658 *Fax:* 416-595-5415
*Web Site:* www.booksforeverybody.com
*Key Personnel*
Assoc Publr: Attila Berki *Tel:* 416-364-3333 ext 3160 *E-mail:* aberki@booksforeverybody.com
Founded: 1937
Publish consumer catalogues for independent book stores.
Publication(s): *Books for Everybody* (annual); *Books for Everybody British Columbia Edition*; *Books for Everybody Young Readers Edition*
Membership(s): Canadian Booksellers Association

**Boston Authors Club Inc**
45 Pine Crest Rd, Newton, MA 02459
*Tel:* 617-552-8457
*E-mail:* bostonauthors@aol.com
*Web Site:* www.bostonauthorsclub.org
*Key Personnel*
Pres: Alan Lawson *E-mail:* lawson@bc.edu
1st VP: Betty Lowry *Tel:* 508-358-4098 *E-mail:* bettylowry@aol.com
2nd VP: Sarah Lamstein *Tel:* 617-244-0646 *E-mail:* sml@sarahlamstein.com
Founded: 1899
Nonprofit organization promoting discourse & community among authors with various programs & gives annual awards.
Number of Members: 140
New Election: Annually in May
*Branch Office(s)*
79 Moore Rd, Wayland, MA 01778 *Tel:* 508-358-4098

**BPA Worldwide**
100 Beard Sawmill Rd, 6th fl, Shelton, CT 06484
*Tel:* 203-447-2800 *Fax:* 203-447-2900
*E-mail:* info@bpaww.com
*Web Site:* www.bpaww.com
*Key Personnel*
Pres & CEO: Glenn J Hansen *E-mail:* ghansen@bpaww.com
SVP, Busn Devt: Peter D Black
SVP, Auditing: Richard J Murphy
SVP, Fin & Admin: Doreen Castignoli
Founded: 1931
International, independent, not-for-profit organization whose membership consists of advertiser companies, advertising agencies & publications. Audit all-paid, all-controlled or any combination of paid & controlled circulation for more than 2,600 media properties including business, technical, professional publications, consumer magazines, newspapers, web sites, e-mail, newsletters & face-to-face events-expos & shows as well as more than 2,700 advertising & agency members.
Number of Members: 5,300
*Branch Office(s)*
10119 Maronda Dr, Riverview, FL 33578 *Tel:* 813-741-3142 *Fax:* 813-741-3162
One Concorde Gate, Suite 800, Toronto, ON M3C 3N6, Canada, Contact: Tim Peel *Tel:* 416-487-2418 *Fax:* 416-487-6405 *E-mail:* mpeel@bpaww.com
1010 Rue Sherbrooke Ouest, Bureau 1800, Montreal, QC H2A 2R7, Canada *Tel:* 514-845-0003 *Fax:* 514-845-0905 *E-mail:* mpasquale@bpaww.com
Suite 505, Bldg 4, China Central Palace, 89 Jianguo Rd, Chaoyang District, Beijing 100025, China *Tel:* (010) 8591 0691 *Fax:* (010) 8591 0589 *E-mail:* dchan@bpaww.com
Suite 2640, 26th fl, Anlian Bldg, 4018 Jintian Rd, Futian District, Shenzhen 518026, China *Tel:* (0755) 3395 5735 *Fax:* (0755) 3395 5999

**Broadcast Music Inc**, see BMI®

**Business Forms Management Association (BFMA)**
1147 Fleetwood Ave, Madison, WI 53716
*Toll Free Tel:* 888-367-3078
*E-mail:* bfma@bfma.org
*Web Site:* www.bfma.org
Founded: 1958
Sponsor professional training in all aspects of information resource management; classes are conducted in major cities in the US & CN. Bestow the association's highest award, the Jo Warner Award, to professionals in the information resources industry. Recipients do not have to be BFMA members.
Number of Members: 600

**Business Marketing Association (BMA)**
1833 Centre Point Circle, Suite 123, Naperville, IL 60563
*Tel:* 630-544-5054 *Fax:* 630-544-5055
*E-mail:* info@marketing.org
*Web Site:* www.marketing.org
*Key Personnel*
Principal & Exec Dir: Patrick Farrey *Tel:* 630-544-5054 ext 102 *E-mail:* pfarrey@marketing.org
Memb Servs Mgr: Lisa Schwarz *Tel:* 630-544-5054 ext 123 *E-mail:* lschwarz@marketing.org
Opers Mgr: Sarah Washburn *Tel:* 630-544-5054 ext 116 *E-mail:* swashburn@marketing.org
Prog Coord & Off Mgr: Donna Levy *Tel:* 630-544-5054 ext 115 *E-mail:* dlevy@marketing.org
Founded: 1922 (as National Industrial Advertising Association)
Provides information & resources to business-to-business marketers & marketing communicators.
Number of Members: 2,200
Publication(s): *The Business to Business Marketer* (6 issues/yr, magazine)

**Canada Council for the Arts (Conseil des Arts du Canada)**
350 Albert St, Ottawa, ON K1P 1A4, Canada
Mailing Address: PO Box 1047, Ottawa, ON K1P 5V8, Canada
*Tel:* 613-566-4414 *Toll Free Tel:* 800-263-5588 (CN only) *Fax:* 613-566-4390
*Web Site:* www.canadacouncil.ca
*Key Personnel*
Admin Coord: Lynne Lalonde *Tel:* 613-566-4414 ext 4531 *E-mail:* lynne.lalonde@canadacouncil.ca
Federal cultural granting agency for Canadian literature. See web site for various awards, prize contests, fellowships & grants.

**Canadian Authors Association (CAA)**
6 West St N, Suite 203, Orillia, ON L3V 5B8, Canada
*Tel:* 705-325-3926 *Toll Free Tel:* 866-216-6222 *Fax:* 705-653-0593
*E-mail:* admin@canauthors.org
*Web Site:* www.canauthors.org
*Key Personnel*
Exec Dir: Anita Purcell
Founded: 1921
Encourage & develop a climate favorable to the literary arts in Canada. Assistance to professional & emerging writers. Represent the concerns & interests of members.
Number of Members: 600
Publication(s): *Canadian Writers Guide* (biennial, $36); *National Newsline* (quarterly, complementary)

**Canadian Bookbinders and Book Artists Guild (CBBAG)**
80 Ward St, Suite 207, Toronto, ON M6H 4A6, Canada
*Tel:* 416-581-1071
*E-mail:* cbbag@cbbag.ca
*Web Site:* www.cbbag.ca
*Key Personnel*
Pres: Mary MacIntyre
Founded: 1983
Presents workshops & courses on a wide variety of topics, including bookbinding, box making, paper making & decorating, letterpress printing, paper conservation & more. Also maintains a reference library & an audio-visual catalogue.
Number of Members: 540
Publication(s): *Book Arts arts due livre* Canada (semiannual, May & Nov, magazine)

**Canadian Booksellers Association (CBA)**
1255 Bay St, Suite 902, Toronto, ON M5R 2A9, Canada
*Tel:* 416-467-7883 *Toll Free Tel:* 866-788-0790 *Fax:* 416-467-7886
*E-mail:* enquiries@cbabook.org
*Web Site:* www.cbabook.org
*Key Personnel*
Pres: Mark Lefebvre *E-mail:* lefebvre@mcmaster.ca
Sr Mgr: Jodi White *Tel:* 416-467-7883 ext 227 *E-mail:* jwhite@cbabook.org
Mktg & Communs Mgr: Stephanie Quinlan *Tel:* 416-467-7883 ext 230 *E-mail:* squinlan@cbabook.org
Founded: 1952
For firms or persons actively engaged in the retail sale of books & supplies.
Number of Members: 900
New Election: Annually in June
Publication(s): *Canadianbookseller* (quarterly, magazine, price varies)
Membership(s): Book & Periodical Council; BookNetCanada; Canadian Society of Association Executives; Retail Council of Canada

**Canadian Cataloguing in Publication Program**
Library & Archives Canada, 395 Wellington St, Ottawa, ON K1A 0N4, Canada
*Tel:* 613-996-5115 *Toll Free Tel:* 866-578-7777 (CN) *Fax:* 613-995-6274
*E-mail:* cip@lac-bac.gc.ca
*Web Site:* www.collectionscanada.ca
*Key Personnel*
CIP Coord: Luc Simard
Voluntary program of cooperation between publishers & libraries.
Publication(s): *Livres a Paraitre/Forthcoming Books* (monthly, free)

**Canadian Centre for Studies in Publishing**
Simon Fraser University Vancouver, 515 W Hastings St, Vancouver, BC V6B 5K3, Canada
*Tel:* 778-782-5242 *Fax:* 778-782-5239
*E-mail:* ccsp-info@sfu.ca
*Web Site:* www.harbour.sfu.ca/ccsp/; www.sfu.ca

*Key Personnel*
Prog Advisor: Jo-Anne Ray
Founded: 1987
Undergraduate, graduate & noncredit courses; research on digital publishing.
Publication(s): *Publishing Studies: Book Publishing 1* (book, $39.95)

**Canadian Children's Book Centre**
40 Orchard View Blvd, Suite 217, Toronto, ON M4R 1B9, Canada
*Tel:* 416-975-0010 *Fax:* 416-975-8970
*E-mail:* info@bookcentre.ca
*Web Site:* www.bookcentre.ca
*Key Personnel*
Exec Dir: Charlotte Teeple *E-mail:* charlotte@bookcentre.ca
Gen Mgr: Dawn Todd *E-mail:* dawn@bookcentre.ca
Lib Coord: Meghan Howe *E-mail:* meghan@bookcentre.ca
Prog Coord: Shannon Howe Barnes *E-mail:* shannon@bookcentre.ca
Sales & Mktg Mgr: Holly Kent *E-mail:* holly@bookcentre.ca
Founded: 1976
National not-for-profit organization to promote the reading, writing & illustrating of Canadian books for young readers. We provide programs, publications & resources for teachers, librarians, authors, illustrators, publishers, booksellers & parents.
Number of Members: 709
Publication(s): *Best Books for Kids & Teens* (semiannual, catalog, $5.95/issue); *Canadian Children's Book News* (4 times/yr, magazine, $4.95/issue, $24.95/single subn includes copies of Best Books for Kids & Teens)

**Canadian Education Association/Association canadienne d'education**
119 Spadina Ave, Suite 702, Toronto, ON M5V 2L1, Canada
*Tel:* 416-591-6300 *Toll Free Tel:* 866-803-9549 *Fax:* 416-591-5345
*E-mail:* info@cea-ace.ca
*Web Site:* www.cea-ace.ca
*Key Personnel*
CEO: Ron Canuel *Tel:* 416-591-6300 ext 236 *E-mail:* rcanuel@cea-ace.ca
COO: Gilles Latour *Tel:* 416-591-6300 ext 237 *E-mail:* glatour@cea-ace.ca
Dir, Communs: Max Cooke *Tel:* 416-591-6300 ext 225 *E-mail:* mcooke@cea-ace.ca
Founded: 1891
A national bilingual, charitable organization that promotes transformation in education.
Number of Members: 340
New Election: Annually in Sept or Oct
Publication(s): *Education Canada* (5 issues/yr, magazine, $64.95/yr US, $45.14/yr CN, $89.95/yr elsewhere; all prices CAD, price includes shipping & applicable taxes (CN only))

**Canadian ISBN Agency**
Unit of Library & Archives Canada
National Library of Canada, 395 Wellington St, Ottawa, ON K1A 0N4, Canada
*Tel:* 613-996-5115 *Toll Free Tel:* 866-578-7777 *Fax:* 613-995-6274
*E-mail:* isbn@lac-bac.gc.ca
*Web Site:* www.collectionscanada.ca
*Key Personnel*
Rep & CIP Coord: Luc Simard *Tel:* 819-994-6904

**Canadian Library Association (CLA) (Association Canadienne des bibliotheques)**
1150 Morrison Dr, Suite 400, Ottawa, ON K2H 8S9, Canada
*Tel:* 613-232-9625 *Fax:* 613-563-9895
*E-mail:* info@cla.ca
*Web Site:* www.cla.ca
*Key Personnel*
Exec Dir: Kelly Moore *Tel:* 613-232-9625 ext 306 *E-mail:* kmoore@cla.ca
Founded: 1946
National organization of personal & institutional members devoted to improving the quality of library & information service in Canada & developing higher standards of librarianship.
Number of Members: 3,000
2014 Meeting(s): National Conference & Trade Show, Victoria, BC, CN, May 28-31, 2014
2015 Meeting(s): National Conference & Trade Show, Ottawa, ON, CN, June 3-6, 2015
2016 Meeting(s): National Conference & Trade Show, Halifax, NS, CN, June 1-4, 2016
Publication(s): *Feliciter* (bimonthly, free to membs, $95/yr to nonmembs)

**Canadian Newspaper Association**
890 Yonge St, Suite 200, Toronto, ON M4W 3P4, Canada
*Tel:* 416-923-3567; 416-482-1090 *Toll Free Tel:* 877-305-2262 *Fax:* 416-923-7206; 416-482-1908
*E-mail:* info@cna-acj.ca
*Web Site:* www.cna-acj.ca
*Key Personnel*
CEO & Pres: John Hinds *Tel:* 416-923-3567 ext 244 *E-mail:* jhinds@cna-acj.ca
Asst to Pres: Adele Ritchie *Tel:* 416-923-3567 ext 235 *E-mail:* aritchie@cna-acj.ca
Founded: 1996
An organization providing service to its members in the area of marketing, member services & contesting legislation that is potentially harmful to newspapers & freedom of the press in general. The association brings the wisdom & dedication of all its members to foster & nurture a free press committed to providing the best possible service to its readers.
Number of Members: 99

**Canadian Printing Industries Association**
151 Slater St, Suite 1110, Ottawa, ON K1P 5H3, Canada
*Tel:* 613-236-7208 *Toll Free Tel:* 800-267-7280 *Fax:* 613-232-1334
*E-mail:* info@cpia-aci.ca
*Web Site:* www.cpia-aci.ca
*Key Personnel*
Pres: Bob Elliot *Tel:* 613-236-7208 ext 22 *E-mail:* belliott@cpia-aci.ca
Exec Asst: Cheri Nixon *Tel:* 613-236-7208 ext 21 *E-mail:* cheri@cpia-aci.ca
Founded: 1939
Publication(s): *National Impressions* (quarterly, newsletter, free to membs)

**Canadian Publishers' Council (CPC)**
250 Merton St, Suite 203, Toronto, ON M4S 1B1, Canada
*Tel:* 416-322-7011 *Fax:* 416-322-6999
*Web Site:* www.pubcouncil.ca
*Key Personnel*
Exec Dir, External Rel & Copyright: Jacqueline Hushion *Tel:* 416-322-7011 ext 222 *E-mail:* jhushion@pubcouncil.ca
Exec Dir, Trade & Higher Educ Groups: Colleen O'Neill *Tel:* 416-322-7011 ext 226 *E-mail:* coneill@pubcouncil.ca
Acctg Offr: Joanna Ames *Tel:* 416-322-7011 ext 228 *E-mail:* james@pubcouncil.ca
Founded: 1910
Promotion & advancement of the Canadian book industry.
Number of Members: 20
New Election: Annually in Feb
Publication(s): *Publishing: A View from the Inside* ($2 plus GST); *Who Buys Books?* ($45 plus GST)

**Canadian Society of Children's Authors Illustrators & Performers (CANSCAIP)**
104-40 Orchard View Blvd, Lower Level Entrance, Toronto, ON M4R 1B9, Canada
*Tel:* 416-515-1559
*E-mail:* office@canscaip.org
*Web Site:* www.canscaip.org
*Key Personnel*
Pres: Karen Krossing
VP: Catherine Rondina
Admin Dir: Jennifer Gordon
Founded: 1977
A group of professionals in the field of children's culture with members from all parts of Canada. For over 30 years, CANSCAIP has been instrumental in the support & promotion of children's literature through newsletters, workshops, meetings & other information programs for authors, parents, teachers, librarians, publishers & others. They have over 900 friends—teachers, librarians, parents & others—who are also interested in aspects of children's books, illustrations & performances.
Number of Members: 1,000
New Election: May 13, biennially
Meeting(s): Packaging Your Imagination, Toronto, Ontario, CN, annually in Nov
Publication(s): *Canscaip News* (quarterly, newsletter, $45/yr)

**CASW**, see Council for the Advancement of Science Writing (CASW)

**Catholic Library Association**
205 W Monroe, Suite 314, Chicago, IL 60606-5061
*Tel:* 312-739-1776 *Toll Free Tel:* 855-739-1776 *Fax:* 312-739-1778
*E-mail:* cla2@cathla.org
*Web Site:* www.cathla.org
*Key Personnel*
Pres: Malachy R McCarthy *E-mail:* mmccarthy@cathla.org
Founded: 1921
To promote literature & libraries of a Catholic nature & ecumenical spirit.
Number of Members: 1,000
2014 Meeting(s): CLA Convention, Pittsburgh, April 22-24, 2014
Publication(s): *Catholic Library World* (4 issues/yr, $100 nonmembs US; $140/yr foreign & $25 S&H)

**Catholic Press Association of the US & Canada**
205 W Monroe St, Suite 470, Chicago, IL 60606
*Tel:* 312-380-6789 *Fax:* 312-361-0256
*E-mail:* cathjourn@catholicpress.org
*Web Site:* www.catholicpress.org
*Key Personnel*
Exec Dir: Timothy Walter *E-mail:* twalter@catholicpress.org
Founded: 1911
Writing, publishing, advertising; all facets of publishing.
Number of Members: 800
2014 Meeting(s): Catholic Media Convention, Charlotte, NC, June 18-20, 2014
Publication(s): *The Catholic Journalist* (monthly); *Catholic Press Directory* (annual)

**CBA: The Association for Christian Retail**
9240 Explorer Dr, Suite 200, Colorado Springs, CO 80920
Mailing Address: PO Box 62000, Colorado Springs, CO 80962-2000
*Tel:* 719-265-9895 *Toll Free Tel:* 800-252-1950 *Fax:* 719-272-3510
*E-mail:* info@cbaonline.org
*Web Site:* www.cbaonline.org
*Key Personnel*
Exec Dir: Curtis Riskey
Founded: 1950

Association members are publishers, music publishers & gift houses.
Number of Members: 3,200
New Election: Annually in July
Publication(s): *CBA Retailers+Resources* (monthly, magazine, $49.95/yr membs, $59.95/yr nonmembs)

**CCAB Inc**
Division of BPA Worldwide
One Concorde Gate, Suite 800, Toronto, ON M3C 3N6, Canada
*Tel:* 416-487-2418 *Fax:* 416-487-6405
*E-mail:* info@bpaww.com
*Web Site:* www.bpaww.com
*Key Personnel*
VP: Tim Peel
Founded: 1935
Auditing of circulation.
Number of Members: 550

**The Center for Book Arts**
28 W 27 St, 3rd fl, New York, NY 10001
*Tel:* 212-481-0295 *Toll Free Fax:* 866-708-8994
*E-mail:* info@centerforbookarts.org
*Web Site:* www.centerforbookarts.org
*Key Personnel*
Exec Dir: Alexander Campos
Founded: 1974
Nonprofit, provides workspace, education, exhibitions & slide registry for book artists, hand papermakers & letter press printers; publication of fine art editions, lectures, outreach program.
Number of Members: 6,500
Publication(s): *Exhibition Catalogs*

**The Center for Exhibition Industry Research (CEIR)**
12700 Park Central Dr, Suite 308, Dallas, TX 75251
*Tel:* 972-687-9242 *Fax:* 972-692-6020
*E-mail:* info@ceir.org
*Web Site:* www.ceir.org
*Key Personnel*
CEO & Pres: Douglas L Ducate *Tel:* 972-687-9219 *E-mail:* dducate@ceir.org
Exec Dir: Cathy Breden *Tel:* 972-687-9201 *E-mail:* cbreden@ceir.org
Promote the exhibition industry by promoting the value & benefits of exhibitions in an integrated marketing program, through research, information & communications.
Number of Members: 600

**The Center for Fiction**
17 E 47 St, New York, NY 10017
*Tel:* 212-755-6710 *Fax:* 212-826-0831
*E-mail:* info@centerforfiction.org
*Web Site:* www.centerforfiction.org
*Key Personnel*
Chmn & Pres: Peter Ginna
Exec Dir: Noreen Tomassi *E-mail:* noreen@centerforfiction.org
Founded: 1820
Circulating library of mainly fiction titles. Monthly programs, literary lectures & readings. Writers' studio. Inquiries invited.
Number of Members: 500
Publication(s): *The Literarian* (quarterly, newsletter)

**The Center for the Book in the Library of Congress**
The Library of Congress, 101 Independence Ave SE, Washington, DC 20540-4920
*Tel:* 202-707-5221 *Fax:* 202-707-0269
*E-mail:* cfbook@loc.gov
*Web Site:* www.loc.gov/cfbook; www.read.gov.cfb
*Key Personnel*
Dir: John Y Cole *E-mail:* jcole@loc.gov
Communs Offr: Guy Lamolinara
Prog Offr: Anne Boni
Founded: 1977 (est by law)
Uses the influence & resources of the Library of Congress to stimulate public interest in books & reading & to encourage the study of books. Its program of symposia, projects, lectures, exhibitions & publications is supported by tax-deductible contributions from corporations & individuals. National reading promotion network includes more than 50 & DC affiliated state centers & more than 80 educational & civic organizations.

**Chicago Book Clinic**, see Midwest Publishing Association (MPA)

**Chicago Women in Publishing**
PO Box 268107, Chicago, IL 60626
*Tel:* 773-508-0351 *Fax:* 435-604-6049
*E-mail:* info@cwip.org
*Web Site:* www.cwip.org
*Key Personnel*
Pres: Jennifer Hull
Founded: 1972
Jobline employment listing service, monthly newsletter, monthly program meetings, freelance directory, annual conference, membership directory.
Number of Members: 500
Publication(s): *CWIP Clips* (monthly)

**The Children's Book Council (CBC)**
54 W 39 St, 14th fl, New York, NY 10018
*Tel:* 212-966-1990 *Fax:* 212-966-2073
*Toll Free Fax:* 888-807-9355 (orders only)
*E-mail:* cbc.info@cbcbooks.org
*Web Site:* www.cbcbooks.org
*Key Personnel*
Exec Dir: Robin Adelson *E-mail:* robin.adelson@cbcbooks.org
Communs Mgr: Nicole Deming *E-mail:* nicole.deming@cbcbooks.org
Founded: 1945
Nonprofit trade association of children's book publishers & related companies. Publish reading promotion display & informational materials. New electronic edition of Children's Books: Awards & Prizes; provides professional education & online member services.
Number of Members: 80
New Election: Annually in Sept
2014 Meeting(s): Children's Book Week, Nationwide across the USA, May 12-18, 2014
Publication(s): *Awards & Prizes Online* (online database, annual, $150); *CBC Features* (semiannual, $60 one-time charge)

**Christian Booksellers Association**, see CBA: The Association for Christian Retail

**CiP Program**, see Canadian Cataloguing in Publication Program

**City & Regional Magazine Association**
1970 E Grand Ave, Suite 330, El Segundo, CA 90245
*Tel:* 310-364-0193 *Fax:* 310-364-0196
*Web Site:* www.citymag.org
*Key Personnel*
Exec Dir: C James Dowden *Tel:* 310-364-0193 ext 811 *E-mail:* administrator@list.citymag.org
PR Coord: Bart Ortberg *E-mail:* bart.ort@dowdenmanagement.com
The purpose of the association is to facilitate professional development & training opportunities for member magazines & provide opportunities to exchange information & ideas. Also the sponsor of CRMA White Awards Competition, The City & Regional Magazine Award Program at the University of Missouri School of Journalism; city & regional magazine competition as well as an annual conference.
Number of Members: 89
Publication(s): *Enewsletter* (bimonthly, newsletter, free)

**Colorado Authors' League**
PO Box 24905, Denver, CO 80224
*Web Site:* www.coloradoauthors.org
*Key Personnel*
Pres: Vickie Bane *E-mail:* Vbane@comcast.net
Founded: 1931
Organization of independent, professional writers united to further members' success.
Number of Members: 250

**Committee On Scholarly Editions**
Subsidiary of Modern Language Association of America (MLA)
c/o Modern Language Association of America, 26 Broadway, 3rd fl, New York, NY 10004-1789
*Tel:* 646-576-5044 *Fax:* 646-458-0030
*Web Site:* www.mla.org
*Key Personnel*
Acqs Ed: James C Hatch *E-mail:* jhatch@mla.org
Founded: 1979
Assists editors & publishers in preparing reliable scholarly editions.
Number of Members: 9

**Connecticut Authors & Publishers Association (CAPA)**
PO Box 715, Avon, CT 06001-0715
*Tel:* 203-729-5335 *Fax:* 203-729-5335
*Web Site:* www.aboutcapa.com
*Key Personnel*
Founder: Brian Jud *E-mail:* brianjud@bookmarketing.com
Founded: 1994
Number of Members: 150
Meeting(s): Monthly Meeting, Avon Community Center, Avon, CT, 3rd Saturday of the month
Publication(s): *The Authority* (monthly, newsletter, free with membership)

**Conseil des Arts du Canada**, see Canada Council for the Arts (Conseil des Arts du Canada)

**Copywriter's Council of America (CCA)**
Division of The Linick Group Inc
CCA Bldg, 7 Putter Lane, Middle Island, NY 11953-1920
Mailing Address: PO Box 102, Middle Island, NY 11953-0102
*Tel:* 631-924-8555 *Fax:* 631-924-8555
*E-mail:* cca4dmcopy@gmail.com
*Web Site:* www.AndrewLinickDirectMarketing.com/Copywriters-Council.html; www.NewWorldPressBooks.com
*Key Personnel*
Chmn, Consulting Group: Andrew S Linick, PhD *E-mail:* andrew@asklinick.com
Pres: Gaylen Andrews
VP: Roger Dextor
Dir, Spec Projs: Barbara Deal
Freelance direct response advertising copywriters, direct marketing consultants, PR & communication specialists & marketing researchers. Cover business-to-business, consumer & industrial markets. Creative services covering all media, all products & services A-Z, e-commerce, e-marketing, e-targeted public relations. Provide comprehensive graphic re-design/new web site content development, interactive services with marketing web site makeover advice for first-time authors, self-publishers, professionals & entrepreneurs. Specialize in flash, animation, merchant accounts, online advertising/PR, links to top search engines, consulting on a 100% satisfaction guarantee. Free site evaluation for LMP readers.

Number of Members: 25,000
Publication(s): *The Digest* (quarterly, for membs only, ezine, $40)

**Corporation for Public Broadcasting (CPB)**
401 Ninth St NW, Washington, DC 20004-2129
*Tel:* 202-879-9600 *Toll Free Tel:* 800-272-2190 *Fax:* 202-879-9700
*E-mail:* info@cpb.org
*Web Site:* www.cpb.org
*Key Personnel*
CEO & Pres: Patricia de Stacy Harrison
COO & EVP: Vincent Curren
Support the nation's public TV & public radio industry through federally appropriated funds. Conduct support services & to stimulate the creation of programming on TV, radio & online.

**Corporation of Professional Librarians of Quebec**
1453, rue Beaubien Est, Bureau 215, Montreal, QC H2G 3C6, Canada
*Tel:* 514-845-3327 *Fax:* 514-845-1618
*E-mail:* info@cbpq.qc.ca
*Web Site:* www.cbpq.qc.ca
*Key Personnel*
Exec Dir: Regine Horinstein
Founded: 1969
Publications, continuing education for information professionals.
Number of Members: 700
Publication(s): *Argus* (3 issues/yr, $48 CN, $50 foreign)

**Council for Advancement & Support of Education (CASE)**
1307 New York Ave NW, Suite 1000, Washington, DC 20005-4701
*Tel:* 202-328-CASE (328-2273) *Fax:* 202-387-4973
*E-mail:* info@case.org; memberservicecenter@case.org
*Web Site:* www.case.org
*Key Personnel*
Pres: John Lippincott *Tel:* 202-478-5655 *E-mail:* lippincott@case.org
VP, Busn & Fin: Donald Falkenstein *Tel:* 202-478-5637 *E-mail:* falkenstein@case.org
Dir, Communs: Pam Russell *Tel:* 202-478-5680 *E-mail:* russell@case.org
Founded: 1974
Membership comprised of colleges, universities & independent schools.
Number of Members: 23,500
Publication(s): *Currents* (monthly except Aug & Dec, $100/yr)

**Council for the Advancement of Science Writing (CASW)**
PO Box 910, Hedgesville, WV 25427
*Tel:* 304-754-6786
*Web Site:* www.casw.org
*Key Personnel*
Exec Dir: Ben Patrusky *E-mail:* bpatrusky@aol.com
Administrator: Diane McGurgan *E-mail:* diane@casw.org
Founded: 1959
To advance science writing.
2014 Meeting(s): New Horizons in Science, Ohio State University, Columbus, OH, Oct 17-21, 2014

**Council of Literary Magazines & Presses (CLMP)**
154 Christopher St, Suite 3-C, New York, NY 10014-9110
*Tel:* 212-741-9110 *Fax:* 212-741-9112
*E-mail:* info@clmp.org
*Web Site:* www.clmp.org
*Key Personnel*
Exec Dir: Jeffrey Lependorf *Tel:* 212-741-9110 ext 14 *E-mail:* jlependorf@clmp.org
Progs Dir: Jamie Schwartz *Tel:* 212-741-9110 ext 12 *E-mail:* jschwartz@clmp.org
Founded: 1967
A national nonprofit organization that provides services to noncommercial literary magazines & book publishers, including technical assistance, various publications, marketing workshops, an annual directory of literary magazines & granting programs for literary magazines & presses.
Number of Members: 500

**CWA/SCA Canada**
Affiliate of The Newspaper Guild/Communication Workers of America (CWA) & Canadian Labour Congress
7B-1050 Baxter Rd, Ottawa, ON K2C 3P1, Canada
*Tel:* 613-820-9777 *Toll Free Tel:* 877-486-4292 *Fax:* 613-820-8188
*E-mail:* info@cwa-scacanada.ca
*Web Site:* www.cwa-scacanada.ca
*Key Personnel*
Dir: Martin O'Hanlon *Tel:* 613-820-8460 *E-mail:* mohanlon@cwa-scacanada.ca
Fin Offr: Joanne Scheel *E-mail:* jscheel@cwa-scacanada.ca
Founded: 1995
Union representing members in Canada.
Number of Members: 7,000

**Deadline Club**
Division of Society of Professional Journalists
c/o Salmagundi Club, 47 Fifth Ave, New York, NY 10003
*Tel:* 646-481-7584
*E-mail:* info@deadlineclub.org
*Web Site:* www.deadlineclub.org
*Key Personnel*
Pres: J Alex Tarquinio
Secy: Catherine Ginn
VP: Michael Arena; Nick Judd; Jacqueline Leo; Polly Whittell
Founded: 1925
Monthly meetings. Membership includes professionals working in print, broadcast, online & journalism education. Professional membership $30, associate membership $35.
Number of Members: 300
Publication(s): *Deadliner Express* (newsletter); *Quill* (magazine, free to membs, $72/yr); *SPJ Leads* (weekly, newsletter, free to membs)

**Digital Printing & Imaging Association**
Affiliate of Specialty Graphic Imaging Association International
10015 Main St, Fairfax, VA 22031-3489
*Tel:* 703-385-1335 *Toll Free Tel:* 888-385-3588 *Fax:* 703-273-0456
*E-mail:* sgia@sgia.org
*Web Site:* www.sgia.org
*Key Personnel*
CEO & Pres: Michael Robertson
Founded: 1992
Members are digital imaging producers, suppliers who sell to digital imagers & schools which teach digital imaging.
Number of Members: 900
Publication(s): *SGIA News* (monthly)

**Direct Marketing Association (DMA)**
1120 Avenue of the Americas, New York, NY 10036-6700
SAN: 692-6487
*Tel:* 212-768-7277 *Fax:* 212-302-6714
*E-mail:* dma@the-dma.org; consumer@the-dma.org; customerservice@the-dma.org
*Web Site:* the-dma.org
*Key Personnel*
CEO & Interim Pres: Linda A Woolley
Founded: 1917
A member organization representing the direct marketing business to legislators, regulators & the media, also offering educational & networking experiences for members.
2013 Meeting(s): NCDM 2013, Caesars Palace, 3570 Las Vegas Blvd S, Las Vegas, NV, Dec 9-11, 2013
2014 Meeting(s): DMA2014, San Diego, CA, Oct 26-28, 2014
Publication(s): *Direct from Washington* (weekly); *Point* (quarterly); *3D-DMA Daily Digest* (daily)
*Branch Office(s)*
1615 "L" St NW, Suite 1100, Washington, DC 20036 *Tel:* 202-955-5030 *Fax:* 202-955-0085

**Dog Writers' Association of America Inc (DWAA)**
173 Union Rd, Coatesville, PA 19320
*Tel:* 610-384-2436 *Fax:* 610-384-2471
*E-mail:* rhydowen@aol.com
*Web Site:* www.dwaa.org
*Key Personnel*
Pres: Carmen Battaglia, PhD
Secy: Pat Santi
Founded: 1935
Provide information about dogs (sport, breeding & ownership) & assist writers in gaining access to exhibitions.
Number of Members: 545
Meeting(s): Annual Meeting, Affinia Manhattan Hotel, New York, NY, Feb
Publication(s): *DWAA Newsletter* (monthly, free to membs)

**Editorial Freelancers Association (EFA)**
71 W 23 St, 4th fl, New York, NY 10010-4102
*Tel:* 212-929-5400 *Toll Free Tel:* 866-929-5425 *Fax:* 212-929-5439 *Toll Free Fax:* 866-929-5439
*E-mail:* info@the-efa.org; office@the-efa.org
*Web Site:* www.the-efa.org
*Key Personnel*
Exec: Margaret L Moser; J P Partland
Founded: 1970
A nonprofit, almost all-volunteer professional association of freelance editors, writers, copy editors, proofreaders, indexers, production specialists, researchers & translators. Provides job listing service, courses, dental & health insurance & related professional services. More than 16 chapters nationwide.
Number of Members: 1,900
Publication(s): *EFA Directory* (online, free); *EFA Newsletter* (6 issues/yr, newsletter, free to membs)

**Editors' Association of Canada (Association canadienne des reviseurs)**
502-27 Carlton St, Toronto, ON M5B 1L2, Canada
*Tel:* 416-975-1379 *Toll Free Tel:* 866-CAN-EDIT (226-3348) *Fax:* 416-975-1637
*E-mail:* info@editors.ca
*Web Site:* www.editors.ca; www.reviseurs.ca
*Key Personnel*
Exec Dir & Ed: Carolyn L Burke *E-mail:* carolyn.burke@editors.ca
Prof Devt Mgr: Helena Aalto *E-mail:* helena.aalto@editors.ca
Communs Mgr: Michelle Ou *E-mail:* michelle.ou@editors.ca
Membership Coord: Lianne Zwarenstein
Founded: 1979
Promotes professional editing as key in producing effective communication. Our members work with individuals in the corporate, technical, government, not-for-profit & publishing sectors. Sponsor professional development seminars, promotes & maintains high standards of editing

& publishing in Canada, establishes guidelines to help editors secure fair pay & good working conditions, helps both in-house & freelance editors to network & cooperates with other publishing associations in areas of common concern. The association is incorporated federally as a not-for-profit organization & is governed at the national level by an executive council.
Number of Members: 1,800
New Election: Annually in June
Publication(s): *Active Voice (La Voix Active)* (quarterly, newsletter, $38/yr, free to membs)
Membership(s): Book & Periodical Council; Canadian Conference of the Arts; Cultural Human Resources Council

**Education Writers Association (EWA)**
3516 Connecticut Ave NW, Washington, DC 20008-2401
*Tel:* 202-452-9830 *Fax:* 202-452-9837
*E-mail:* ewa@ewa.org
*Web Site:* www.ewa.org
*Key Personnel*
Exec Dir: Caroline Hendrie *E-mail:* chendrie@ewa.org
Prodr: Glen Baity
Founded: 1947
Conferences, seminars, newsletters, publications, employment services, freelance referral, workshops & national awards.
Number of Members: 3,000
Publication(s): *Education Reporter* (bimonthly, newsletter); *Standards for Education Reporters* ($12)

**Educational Book & Media Association (EBMA)**
37 Main St, Suite 203, Warrenton, VA 20186
Mailing Address: PO Box 3363, Warrenton, VA 20188
*Tel:* 540-318-7770 *Fax:* 202-962-3939
*E-mail:* info@edupaperback.org
*Web Site:* www.edupaperback.org
*Key Personnel*
Exec Dir: Brian Gorg
Meeting Mgr: Maureen Gelwicks
Founded: 1975
Regular membership consists of educational paperback book wholesalers; associate members are paperback publishers.
Number of Members: 125
2014 Meeting(s): Annual Meeting, Hilton La Jolla Torrey Pines, San Diego, CA, Jan 13-16, 2014

**Evangelical Christian Publishers Association (ECPA)**
9633 S 48 St, Suite 195, Phoenix, AZ 85044-5697
*Tel:* 480-966-3998 *Fax:* 480-966-1944
*E-mail:* info@ecpa.org
*Web Site:* www.ecpa.org
*Key Personnel*
Pres & CEO: Mark W Kuyper *E-mail:* mkuyper@ecpa.org
Founded: 1974
Trade association supporting Christian publishers worldwide. Provides professional seminars, compiles statistical studies & presents religious book awards.
Number of Members: 280
2014 Meeting(s): ECPA Leadership Summit, Colorado Springs, CO, April 28-30, 2014
Membership(s): BISG

**Evangelical Press Association (EPA)**
PO Box 20198, El Cajon, CA 92021
*Tel:* 619-609-0910 *Toll Free Tel:* 888-311-1731
*Web Site:* www.evangelicalpress.com
*Key Personnel*
Exec Dir: D'Arcy Maher
CFO: Lamar Keener
Founded: 1949
Professional Association of Christian freelancers, associates, magazines, newsletters, newspapers & content-rich web sites.
Number of Members: 300
2014 Meeting(s): Annual Convention, Sheraton Park Hotel at the Anaheim Resort, Anaheim, CA, May 4-6, 2014
Publication(s): *Liaison* (3x/yr, newsletter)

**Federation of BC Writers**
PO Box 3887, Sta Terminal, Vancouver, BC V6B 3Z3, Canada
*Tel:* 604-683-2057
*E-mail:* fedbcwriters@gmail.com
*Web Site:* www.bcwriters.ca
*Key Personnel*
Pres: Ben Nuttall-Smith
Founded: 1976
Not-for-profit organization established to contribute to a supportive environment for writing in the province. Writers of all levels working in all genres & specialties welcome. We publish a magazine & hold readings, workshops & literary competitions.
Number of Members: 500
New Election: Annually in May
Publication(s): *WordWorks* (quarterly)

**Florida Freelance Writers Association**
Affiliate of Cassell Network of Writers
45 Main St, North Stratford, NH 03590
Mailing Address: PO Box A, North Stratford, NH 03590
*Tel:* 603-922-8338 *Fax:* 603-922-8339
*E-mail:* ffwa@writers-editors.com; info@writers-editors.com
*Web Site:* www.writers-editors.com; www.ffwamembers.com
*Key Personnel*
Exec Dir: Dana K Cassell *E-mail:* dana@writers-editors.com
Founded: 1982
Network of freelance writers & editors, offering a job bank, Florida Markets directory, newsletter, etc.
Number of Members: 500
Publication(s): *Directory of Florida Markets for Writers* (newsletter & electronic formats, $35 or free with membership); *Freelance Writer's Report* (monthly, free with FFWA membership); *Guide to CNW/FFWA Writers* (continuously updated, free to qualified publishing companies & businesses)

**Florida Outdoor Writers Association Inc**
24 NW 33 Ct, Suite A, Gainesville, FL 32607
*E-mail:* info@fowa.org
*Web Site:* www.fowa.org
*Key Personnel*
Exec Dir: Tommy Thompson *E-mail:* execdir@fowa.org
Founded: 1946
501(c)(3) organization of outdoor writers.
Number of Members: 300
New Election: Annually in Sept
2014 Meeting(s): Annual Conference, Knoxville, TN, June 27-29, 2014
2015 Meeting(s): Annual Conference, McAllen, TX, May 22-24, 2015
Publication(s): *Market Edge Newsletter* (6 issues/yr, electronic, newsletter, free to membs)

**The Florida Publishers Association Inc (FPA)**
Affiliate of Association of American Publishers (AAP)
PO Box 916383, Longwood, FL 32791-6383
*Tel:* 863-647-5951 *Fax:* 863-647-5951
*E-mail:* fpabooks@gmail.com
*Web Site:* www.floridapublishersassociation.com
*Key Personnel*
Association Exec: Betsy Wright-Lampe
FPA Bd Memb: Mark Wayne Adams
Pres: Chris Angermann *E-mail:* c.angermann@verizon.net
Founded: 1979
Networking seminars, newsletter, publishing, book shows, workshops, small presses, independents & self-publishers; annual President's Book Award competition. Affiliate of Independent Book Publishers Association, Small Publishers Association of North American, Association of American Publishers, Florida Library Association & Florida Association for Media in Education.
Number of Members: 100
New Election: 2014
Publication(s): *FPA Sell More Books! Newsletter* (electronic, monthly, newsletter, free to membs, media, booksellers, libraries, reviewers)

**Florida Writers Association Inc**
PO Box 66069, St Pete Beach, FL 33736-6069
*Web Site:* www.floridawriters.net
*Key Personnel*
Pres: Chrissy Jackson *E-mail:* chrissyj@earthlink.net
Founded: 2001
Association of "writers helping writers" to improve writing skills, produce good work in all genres & successfully publish.
Number of Members: 1,200
Publication(s): *The Florida Writer* (quarterly, $4.95, free to membs)

**Foil & Specialty Effects Association (FSEA)**
2150 SW Westport Dr, Suite 101, Topeka, KS 66614
*Tel:* 785-271-5816 *Fax:* 785-271-6404
*Web Site:* www.fsea.com
*Key Personnel*
Exec Dir: Jeff Peterson *E-mail:* jeff@fsea.com
Asst Dir: Kym Conis *E-mail:* kym@fsea.com
Sales Dir: Gayla Peterson
Founded: 1992
Trade association for graphics finishing industry.
Number of Members: 325
Publication(s): *Inside Finishing Magazine* (quarterly)

**Follett Higher Education Group**
Division of Follett Corp
1818 Swift Dr, Oak Brook, IL 60523
*Tel:* 630-279-2330 *Toll Free Tel:* 800-323-4506 *Fax:* 630-279-2569
*Web Site:* www.fheg.follett.com
*Key Personnel*
Pres: Tom Christopher
CEO & Pres: Mary Lee Schneider
College bookstore: used textbook distribution company.

**La Fondation Emile Nelligan**
100 Sherbrooke St, Suite 202, Montreal, QC H2X 1C3, Canada
*Tel:* 514-278-4657 *Fax:* 514-278-1943
*E-mail:* info@fondation-nelligan.org
*Web Site:* www.fondation-nelligan.org
*Key Personnel*
CEO: Manon Gagnon
Pres: Michel Dallaire
Treas/Secy: Michel Gonneville
VP: Marie-Andree Beaudet
Founded: 1979
Sponsoring organization.
Number of Members: 1,000

**4A's (American Association of Advertising Agencies)**
1065 Avenue of the Americas, 16th fl, New York, NY 10018
*Tel:* 212-682-2500
*Web Site:* www.aaaa.org

*Key Personnel*
Pres & CEO: Nancy Hill *E-mail:* nhill@aaaa.org
EVP: Michael D Donahue *E-mail:* donahue@aaaa.org
HR: Barbara Bailey *E-mail:* barbarab@aaaa.org
Founded: 1917
National trade association for the advertising agency business.
Number of Members: 430
2014 Meeting(s): Transformation 2014, The Beverly Hilton, 9876 Wilshire Blvd, Beverly Hills, CA, March 16-19, 2014
*Branch Office(s)*
9595 Wilshire Blvd, Suite 900, Beverly Hills, CA 90212, EVP, Western Reg: Jerry McGee *Tel:* 310-300-3422 *Fax:* 310-300-3421 *E-mail:* jmcgee@aaaa.org
1203 19 St NW, 4th fl, Washington, DC 20036, EVP: Dick O'Brien *Tel:* 202-331-7345 *Fax:* 202-857-3675 *E-mail:* dobrien@aaaa.org
3050 Bellingrath Blvd, Roswell, GA 30076, VP, Agency Rel & Membership: Greg Walker *Tel:* 770-639-6720 (cell) *Fax:* 770-587-1217 *E-mail:* gwalker@aaaa.org
747 N Wabash Ave, Suite 902, Chicago, IL 60611, VP, Agency Rel & Membership: Laura Stern *Tel:* 312-388-7470 *E-mail:* lstearn@aaaa.org

**FPA**, see The Florida Publishers Association Inc (FPA)

**Garden Writers Association**
7809 FM 179, Shallowater, TX 79363-3637
*Tel:* 806-832-1870 *Fax:* 806-832-5244
*E-mail:* info@gardenwriters.org
*Web Site:* www.gardenwriters.org
*Key Personnel*
Exec Dir: Robert LaGasse *E-mail:* execdir@gardenwriters.org
Founded: 1948
Professional association garden communicators working as staff or freelance as newspaper columnists, magazine columnists, photographers & radio/TV hosts. Sponsor annual writer's contest & annual Garden Media award program for published articles or books, as well as a symposium every August.
Number of Members: 1,800
2014 Meeting(s): Annual Symposium, Westin Convention Center, Pittsburgh, PA, Aug 8-11, 2014
Publication(s): *Quill & Trowel* (bimonthly, newsletter)

**Graphic Artists Guild Inc**
32 Broadway, Suite 1114, New York, NY 10004-1612
*Tel:* 212-791-3400 *Fax:* 212-791-0333
*Web Site:* www.graphicartistsguild.org
*Key Personnel*
Pres: Haydn Adams *E-mail:* president@gag.org
Exec Dir: Patricia McKiernan *Tel:* 212-791-3400 ext 15 *E-mail:* admin@gag.org
Founded: 1967
Labor organization which advocates the advancement of artists' rights. Members are illustrators, graphic designers, surface & textile designers, computer graphics artists, cartoonists & others.
Number of Members: 1,100
Publication(s): *Pricing & Ethical Guidelines, 13th ed* (biannual, $39.99)

**Graphic Arts Show Company (GASC)**
1899 Preston White Dr, Reston, VA 20191-5468
*Tel:* 703-264-7200 *Fax:* 703-620-9187
*E-mail:* info@gasc.org
*Web Site:* www.gasc.org
*Key Personnel*
Pres: Ralph Happi *Tel:* 703-264-7200 ext 227
VP: Chris Price *Tel:* 703-264-7200 ext 221
Founded: 1982
Tradeshow management for printing, publishing & graphic communications events.
2014 Meeting(s): Graph Expo®, McCormick Place, 2301 S Lake Shore Dr, Chicago, IL, Sept 28-Oct 1, 2014
2015 Meeting(s): Graph Expo®, McCormick Place, 2301 S Lake Shore Dr, Chicago, IL, Sept 13-16, 2015

**Gravure Association of America Inc**
8281 Pine Lake Rd, Denver, NC 28037
*Tel:* 201-523-6042 *Fax:* 201-523-6048
*E-mail:* gaa@gaa.org
*Web Site:* www.gaa.org
*Key Personnel*
Exec Dir: Philip Pimlott *Tel:* 812-406-5434 *E-mail:* ppimlott@gaa.org
Exec Dir, GEF Foundation: Bernadette Carlson *Tel:* 847-331-1228 *E-mail:* bcarlson@gaa.org
Dir, Planning & Admin: Pamela W Schenk *Tel:* 585-288-2297 *E-mail:* pwschenk@gaa.org
Mktg & Communs: Sherre DeMao *Tel:* 704-483-2941 ext 13 *E-mail:* sherre@sldunlimited.com
Foster the advancement of gravure printing industry.
Number of Members: 250
Publication(s): *Gravure Magazine* (quarterly, free with membership)

**Great Lakes Graphics Association**
W232 N2950 Roundy Circle E, Suite 200, Pewaukee, WI 53072-4110
*Tel:* 262-522-2210 *Fax:* 262-522-2211
*E-mail:* info@piw.org
*Web Site:* www.piw.org
*Key Personnel*
Pres: Joe Lyman *Tel:* 262-522-2212
Number of Members: 175
Publication(s): *NewScan* (electronic, newsletter, free to membs)

**Guild of Book Workers**
521 Fifth Ave, 17th fl, New York, NY 10175-0038
*Tel:* 212-292-4444
*Web Site:* www.guildofbookworkers.org
*Key Personnel*
Pres: Mark Anderson *E-mail:* president@guildofbookworkers.org
Secy: Catherine Burkhard *Tel:* 214-363-7946 *E-mail:* secretary@guildofbookworkers.org
Founded: 1906
A national nonprofit educational organization which fosters the hand book arts: binding, calligraphy, illumination, paper decorating. Sponsor exhibits, lectures, workshops. See web site for membership fee information.
Number of Members: 900
Publication(s): *Journal* ($75 membs); *Newsletter* (bimonthly)

**Horror Writers Association (HWA)**
244 Fifth Ave, Suite 2767, New York, NY 10001
*E-mail:* hwa@horror.org
*Web Site:* www.horror.org
*Key Personnel*
Pres: Rocky Wood *E-mail:* president@horror.org
VP: Heather Graham
Admin: Lisa Morton *E-mail:* treasurer@horror.org
Monthly newsletter, online information, Hardship Fund, Grievance Committee, Bram Stoker Awards for Superior Achievement, a series of members-only anthologies, databases of agents, reviewers & book stores. Publication & $65/yr is required for membership.
Number of Members: 426
Publication(s): *Horror Writers Association Newsletter* (monthly, electronic, free)

**IBPA, the Independent Book Publishers Association**
1020 Manhattan Beach Blvd, Suite 204, Manhattan Beach, CA 90266
*Tel:* 310-546-1818 *Fax:* 310-546-3939
*E-mail:* info@ibpa-online.org
*Web Site:* www.ibpa-online.org
*Key Personnel*
COO: Terry Nathan *E-mail:* terry@ibpa-online.org
Exec Dir: Angela Bole
Asst Dir & Website Mgr: Lisa Krebs Magno *E-mail:* lisa@ibpa-online.org
Vendor Rel & Mktg: Chris Kahn *E-mail:* chris@ibpa-online.org
Founded: 1983
A national nonprofit publishers' co-operative which coordinates discounted participation in major book & library exhibits & trade shows throughout the country, as well as ad placement in major publications & direct mail programs. Sponsor workshops, awards & prizes.
Number of Members: 3,000
Publication(s): *IBPA Independent* (monthly, newsletter, free to membs, $60/yr nonmembs); *Membership & Service Directory* (annual)

**The Ibsen Society of America**
University of California, Dept of Scandinavian, 6303 Dwinelle Hall, No 2690, Berkeley, CA 94720-2690
*Tel:* 510-642-0927 *Fax:* 510-642-6220
*Web Site:* www.ibsensociety.liu.edu
*Key Personnel*
Pres: Mark Sandberg *E-mail:* sandberg@berkeley.edu
VP: Tanya Thresher
Ed, Ibsen News & Comment: Joan Templeton *E-mail:* joantemp@aol.com
Founded: 1978
A nonprofit corporation.
Number of Members: 250
Publication(s): *Ibsen News & Comment* (annual, newsletter, $15 libs, free to membs)

**IDEAlliance®**
1600 Duke St, Suite 420, Alexandria, VA 22314
*Tel:* 703-837-1070 *Fax:* 703-837-1072
*E-mail:* info@idealliance.org; registrar@idealliance.org
*Web Site:* www.idealliance.org
*Key Personnel*
CEO & Pres: David J Steinhardt *Tel:* 703-837-1066 *E-mail:* dsteinhardt@idealliance.org
Represent printing, publishing, newspapers, suppliers, government organizations & advertising agencies. Seek productivity & technical improvement in creation & distribution of printed & digital materials.
Number of Members: 200
2014 Meeting(s): PRIMEX Summit, Sheraton Sand Key Resort, Clearwater, FL, Feb 24-26, 2014; Print Distribution Conference, Sheraton Sand Key Resort, Clearwater, FL, May 6-7, 2014

**Independent Writers of Chicago (IWOC)**
28 E Jackson Bldg, Suite 1020, No W686, Chicago, IL 60604
*Toll Free Tel:* 800-804-IWOC (804-4962)
*E-mail:* info@iwoc.org
*Web Site:* www.iwoc.org
*Key Personnel*
Pres: David Epstein *E-mail:* david.m.epstein@earthlink.net
Monthly meetings, workshops & seminars dealing with the business aspects of independent writing. Writers' line job referral. Speakers' bureau.
Number of Members: 125
Publication(s): *Membership Directory* (annual, $10); *STET* (11 issues/yr, newsletter, $20/yr)

**InScribe Christian Writers' Fellowship (ICWF)**
PO Box 6201, Wetaskiwin, AB T2A 2E9, Canada
*E-mail:* query@inscribe.org; inscribe.mail@gmail.com
*Web Site:* www.inscribe.org
*Key Personnel*
Pres: Jack Popjes *E-mail:* jack_popjes@wfcliffe.ca
Founded: 1980
Number of Members: 150
Meeting(s): Spring WorDshop, Alberta, CN, Annually in April; Fall Conference, Annually last weekend in Sept
Publication(s): *FellowScript* (quarterly, newsletter, included with membership)

**Inter American Press Association (IAPA)**
Jules Dubois Bldg, 1801 SW Third Ave, Miami, FL 33129
*Tel:* 305-634-2465 *Fax:* 305-635-2272
*E-mail:* info@sipiapa.org
*Web Site:* www.sipiapa.org
*Key Personnel*
Pres: Milton Coleman
VP: Jaime Mantilla
Exec Dir: Julio E Munoz
Treas: Elizabeth Ballantine
To guard freedom of the press; to foster & protect the general & specific interests of the daily & periodical press of the Americas; to promote & maintain the dignity, rights & responsibilities of journalism; to encourage uniform standards of professional & business conduct; to exchange ideas & information which contribute to the cultural, material & technical development of the press; to foster a wider knowledge & greater interchange in support of the basic principles of a free society & individual liberty.
Number of Members: 1,300
Publication(s): *Hora de Cierre* (quarterly); *IAPA Annual Report* (annual); *IAPA News* (bimonthly); *Notisip* (quarterly)

**International Association of Business Communicators (IABC)**
601 Montgomery St, Suite 1900, San Francisco, CA 94111
*Tel:* 415-544-4700 *Toll Free Tel:* 800-776-4222 (US & CN) *Fax:* 415-544-4747
*E-mail:* service_center@iabc.com
*Web Site:* www.iabc.com
*Key Personnel*
Pres: Julie Freeman *E-mail:* jfreeman@iabc.com
SVP: Chris Grossgart *E-mail:* chrisgro@iabc.com
VP, Fin & HR: Maureen Lennon *E-mail:* mlennon@iabc.com
Founded: 1970
Communication association.
Number of Members: 13,500
2014 Meeting(s): World Conference, Sheraton Centre Toronto Hotel, 123 Queen St W, Toronto, ON, CN, June 8-11, 2014
2015 Meeting(s): World Conference, San Francisco Marriott Marquis, 55 Fourth St, San Francisco, CA, June 14-17, 2015
2016 Meeting(s): World Conference, Hilton New Orleans Riverside, 2 Poydras, New Orleans, LA, June 5-8, 2016
Publication(s): *Communication World* (bimonthly)

**International Association of Crime Writers Inc, North American Branch**
328 Eighth Ave, Suite 114, New York, NY 10001
*Tel:* 212-243-8966 *Fax:* 815-361-1477
*E-mail:* info@crimewritersna.org
*Web Site:* www.crimewritersna.org
*Key Personnel*
Pres: Steven Steinbock
Exec Dir: Mary A Frisque *E-mail:* mfrisque@igc.org
Secy-Treas: Jim Weikart
Secy: Johnny Temple
Founded: 1987
Promote communication among crime writers worldwide & enhance awareness & encourage translations of the genre in the US & abroad.
Number of Members: 285
Publication(s): *Border Patrol* (quarterly, free to membs)

**International Council for Adult Education**
55 Mont-Royal Ave W, Bureau 303, Montreal, QC H2J 2S4, Canada
*Tel:* 514-948-2044 *Toll Free Tel:* 877-948-2044 *Fax:* 514-948-2046
*E-mail:* icae@icea.qc.ca
*Web Site:* www.icea.qc.ca
*Key Personnel*
Pres: Lea Cousineau
Founded: 1972
Adult education lifelong learning.
Number of Members: 107
Publication(s): *ICAE News* (quarterly, newsletter, free to membs)

**International Digital Enterprise Alliance**, see IDEAlliance®

**International Encyclopedia Society**
PO Box 519, Baldwin Place, NY 10505-0519
*Tel:* 914-962-3287 *Fax:* 914-962-3287
*Web Site:* encyclopediasociety.com
*Key Personnel*
Pres: George Kurian *E-mail:* gtkurian@aol.com
Publication of books & journals; conferences; award of prizes.
Number of Members: 210
Publication(s): *Reference Desk Quarterly* ($29)

**International Publishing Management Association (IPMA)**
105 S Jefferson, Suite B-4, Kearney, MO 64060
*Tel:* 816-903-4762 *Fax:* 816-902-4766
*E-mail:* ipmainfo@ipma.org
*Web Site:* www.ipma.org
*Key Personnel*
Admin Dir: Carma Goin *E-mail:* cgoin@ipma.org
Founded: 1964
Membership for plant & mailing managers. Annual conference & trade show in late spring. Write or call for information.
Number of Members: 1,800
Publication(s): *Inside Edge* (monthly, newsletter)

**International Reading Association**
800 Barksdale Rd, Newark, DE 19711-3204
Mailing Address: PO Box 8139, Newark, DE 19714-8139
*Tel:* 302-731-1600 *Toll Free Tel:* 800-336-7323 (US & CN) *Fax:* 302-731-1057
*E-mail:* customerservice@reading.org
*Web Site:* www.reading.org
*Key Personnel*
Public Info Offr: Kathy Baughman *Tel:* 302-731-1600 ext 221 *E-mail:* kbaughman@reading.org
Exec Dir: Marcie Craig Post *E-mail:* mpost@reading.org
Conferences; publications, research, membership services; publications on reading & related topics; professional journals.
Number of Members: 90,000
2014 Meeting(s): Annual Convention, Ernest N Morial Convention Center, Halls D-E, New Orleans, LA, May 9-12, 2014

**International Society of Weekly Newspaper Editors**
Missouri Southern State University, 3950 E Newman Rd, Joplin, MO 64801-1595
*Tel:* 417-625-9736 *Fax:* 417-659-4445
*Web Site:* www.mssu.edu/iswne
*Key Personnel*
Exec Dir: Dr Chad Stebbins *E-mail:* stebbins-c@mssu.edu
Founded: 1955
Help those in weekly press to improve standards of editorial writing.
Number of Members: 300
Publication(s): *Grassroots Editor* (quarterly, $50/yr US & CN)

**International Standard Book Numbering (ISBN) US Agency, A Cambridge Information Group Co**
Affiliate of R R Bowker LLC
630 Central Ave, New Providence, NJ 07974
*Toll Free Tel:* 877-310-7333 *Fax:* 908-219-0188
*E-mail:* isbn-san@bowker.com
*Web Site:* www.isbn.org
Coordinate implementation of the ISBN, SAN & ISNI standards.
Number of Members: 120,000

**The International Women's Writing Guild (IWWG)**
317 Madison Ave, Suite 1704, New York, NY 10017
*Tel:* 917-720-6959
*E-mail:* iwwgquestions@gmail.com
*Web Site:* www.iwwg.org
*Key Personnel*
Exec Dir: Cynthia Fritts Stillwell *E-mail:* iwwgexecdir@gmail.com
Founded: 1976
Network for the empowerment of women through writing. Services include updated list of close to 35 literary agents, independent small presses & other writing services. Ten writing conferences & events annually, subn to the bimonthly 32-page newsletter *Network*, regional clusters & opportunities for publications. IWWG is a supportive network open to any woman regardless of portfolio. As such, it has established a remarkable record of achievement in the publishing world as well as in circles where lifelong learning & personal information are valued for their own sake.
Number of Members: 5,000
Publication(s): *Network* (quarterly, 32 pgs, free to members)

**Internet Alliance (IA)**
1615 L St NW, Suite 1100, Washington, DC 20036-5624
*Tel:* 202-861-2407
*Web Site:* www.internetalliance.org
*Key Personnel*
Exec Dir: Tammy Cota *E-mail:* tammy@internetalliance.org
State relations on Internet issues. Lobbyists.

**Investigative Reporters & Editors**
UMC School of Journalism, 138 Neff Annex, Columbia, MO 65211
*Tel:* 573-882-2042 *Fax:* 573-882-5431
*E-mail:* info@ire.org
*Web Site:* www.ire.org
*Key Personnel*
Exec Dir: Mark Horvit *E-mail:* mhorvit@ire.org
Founded: 1975
Nonprofit organization to improve the quality of investigative journalism.
Number of Members: 5,000
Publication(s): *The IRE Journal* (bimonthly, free with membership, $70/yr nonmembs, $125/yr instns, $85/yr coll libs in US, $90/yr foreign for electronic delivery, $150/yr foreign via regular mail)

**Jewish Book Council**
520 Eighth Ave, 4th fl, New York, NY 10018
*Tel:* 212-201-2920 *Fax:* 212-532-4952
*E-mail:* jbc@jewishbooks.org
*Web Site:* www.jewishbookcouncil.org

*Key Personnel*
Pres, Bd of Dirs: Lawrence J Krule
Dir: Carolyn Starman Hessel
*E-mail:* carolynhessel@jewishbooks.org
Dir, Progs: Mira Pomerantz Dauber
Dir, Web & Pubns: Naomi Firestone-Teeter
Founded: 1925
Sponsors programs based on its conviction that books of Jewish interest are an invaluable contribution to the welfare of the Jewish people. Works to promote the writing, publishing & reading of worthy books of Jewish content. Honors excellence in all fields of Jewish literary endeavor with awards to writers & citations to publishers. Serves as a resource providing guidance, program tools & publications; acts as a clearinghouse for information on all aspects of Jewish literature & publishing in North America.
Publication(s): *Jewish Book Month Poster*; *Jewish Book World* (4 issues/yr)

**The League of Canadian Poets**
192 Spadina Ave, Suite 312, Toronto, ON M5T 2C2, Canada
*Tel:* 416-504-1657 *Fax:* 416-504-0096
*E-mail:* readings@poets.ca
*Web Site:* www.poets.ca
*Key Personnel*
Exec Dir: Joanna Poblocka *E-mail:* joanna@poets.ca
Asst Dir: Ingel Madrus *E-mail:* readings@poets.ca
Admin & Communs Coord: Lesley Fletcher
*E-mail:* admin@poets.ca
Founded: 1966
Promote Canadian poetry & poets.
Number of Members: 600
New Election: Annually in June
Publication(s): *Poetry Markets for Canadians* (online only, $20/yr public, $100/yr schools or libraries)

**League of Vermont Writers**
PO Box 172, Underhill Center, VT 05490
*Tel:* 802-349-7475
*E-mail:* lvw@leaguevtwriters.org
*Web Site:* www.leagueofvermontwriters.org
*Key Personnel*
Pres: Deb Fennell
VP: Paula Diaco
Treas: Dan Close
Founded: 1929
Four meetings per year (Jan, April, July, Sept), reader & promotional services; occasional instructional seminars & workshops, publication of anthologies of members' work, writer's service.
Number of Members: 275
New Election: Annually in Jan
Publication(s): *League Lines* (quarterly, newsletter); *Vermont Voices Jubilee, 75th Anniversary Edition*; *Vermont Voices III, An Anthology* ($17/issue)

**League of Women Voters of the United States**
1730 "M" St NW, Suite 1000, Washington, DC 20036-4508
*Tel:* 202-429-1965 *Fax:* 202-429-0854; 202-429-4343
*E-mail:* lwv@lwv.org
*Web Site:* www.lwv.org
*Key Personnel*
Pres: Elisabeth MacNamara
Exec Dir: Nance E Tate
Sr Dir, Communs: Kelly Ceballos
Nonpartisan, grass roots political organization. Publish information on public policy issues in fields of natural resources, social policy, government, voter service & international relations.
Number of Members: 150,000
Publication(s): *The National Voter* (3 issues/yr, magazine); *Thinking Globally, Acting Locally: A Citizen's Guide to Community Education on Global Issues*; *Women in Action: Rebels and Reformers 1920-1980*

**Library Association of Alberta (LAA)**
80 Baker Crescent NW, Calgary, AB T2L 1R4, Canada
*Tel:* 403-284-5818 *Toll Free Tel:* 877-522-5550
*Fax:* 403-282-6646
*E-mail:* info@laa.ca
*Web Site:* www.laa.ca
*Key Personnel*
Pres: Diane Clark *E-mail:* president@laa.ca
1st VP: Lisa Hardy *E-mail:* 1stvicepresident@laa.ca
2nd VP: Lindsay Johnston
*E-mail:* 2ndvicepresident@laa.ca
Treas: Julia Reinhart *E-mail:* treasurer@laa.ca
Exec Dir/Conference Coord: Christine Sheppard
Nonprofit organization.
Number of Members: 625
2014 Meeting(s): Alberta Library Conference, Jasper Park Lodge, Jasper, AB, CN, April 24-27, 2014
Publication(s): *Letter of the LAA* (quarterly, for membs only)

**Library Binding Institute**
4440 PGA Blvd, Suite 600, Palm Beach Gardens, FL 33410
*Tel:* 561-745-6821 *Fax:* 561-472-8401
*E-mail:* info@lbibinders.org
*Web Site:* www.lbibinders.org
*Key Personnel*
Exec Dir: Debra S Nolan *E-mail:* dnolan@hardcoverbinders.org
Founded: 1935
Trade association for bookbinders. Hold annual meetings & workshops; provide information services, certification & technical review.
Number of Members: 80
Publication(s): *ShelfLife* (quarterly, $29 dom; $31 CN; $36 intl)

**Library of American Broadcasting**
Unit of University of Maryland Libraries
University of Maryland, Hornbake Library, College Park, MD 20742
*Tel:* 301-405-9160 *Fax:* 301-314-2634
*E-mail:* labcast@umd.edu
*Web Site:* www.lib.umd.edu/LAB
*Key Personnel*
Curator: Chuck Howell *Tel:* 301-314-0401
Founded: 1970
Library devoted to history of radio & television broadcasting. Contains 8,800 books; 320 vertical files of papers, documents & other print material; 225,000 photographs, 900 interviews & oral histories; 5,600 audiotapes; 8,000 discs; transcripts & scripts. Referral center to other sources of broadcast history.
Number of Members: 21
New Election: Annually in Nov
Publication(s): *Airwaves*

**Linguistic Society of America**
1325 18 St NW, Suite 211, Washington, DC 20036-6501
*Tel:* 202-835-1714 *Fax:* 202-835-1717
*E-mail:* lsa@lsadc.org
*Web Site:* www.linguisticsociety.org
*Key Personnel*
Pres: Ellen Kaisse
Exec Dir: Alyson Reed
Secy & Treas: Patrick Farrell
Ed: Greg Carlson
Founded: 1924
Number of Members: 5,000
New Election: Annually in Sept
Publication(s): *Language* (quarterly, $140-190/yr organizations, $95 indivs, $40 students, add $10 for foreign indivs); *LSA Meeting Handbook* (annual, $20)

**The Literary Press Group of Canada**
192 Spadina Ave, Suite 501, Toronto, ON M5T 2C2, Canada
*Tel:* 416-483-1321 *Fax:* 416-483-2510
*E-mail:* info@lpg.ca
*Web Site:* www.lpg.ca
*Key Personnel*
Exec Dir: Jack Illingworth *E-mail:* jack@lpg.ca
Sales & Mktg Mgr: Petra Morin
*E-mail:* pmorin@lpg.ca
National trade association providing cooperative sales, marketing, advertising & publicity services to members.
Number of Members: 52
New Election: Annually in May

**Literary Translators' Association of Canada**
Concordia University, LB 601, 1455 De Maisonneuve West, Montreal, QC H3G 1M8, Canada
*Tel:* 514-848-2424 (ext 8702)
*E-mail:* info@attlc-ltac.org
*Web Site:* www.attlc-ltac.org
*Key Personnel*
Pres: Jo-Anne Elder
Coord: Yves Dion
Founded: 1975
Promote & protect interests of literary translators in Canada; occasional meetings with local universities & occasional workshops, lobby for funding, organize readings & other events.
Number of Members: 150
New Election: Annually in June
Publication(s): *Transmission* (3 issues/yr online, free)

**Livestock Publications Council**
910 Currie St, Fort Worth, TX 76107
*Tel:* 817-336-1130 *Fax:* 817-232-4820
*Web Site:* www.livestockpublications.com
*Key Personnel*
Exec Dir: Diane E Johnson *E-mail:* diane@livestockpublications.com
Founded: 1974
A nonprofit organization designed to serve the livestock publishing industry.
Number of Members: 195
New Election: Annually in July
Publication(s): *Actiongram* (monthly, newsletter); *Membership Directory* (annually)

**Livres Canada Books**
One Nicholas, Suite 504, Ottawa, ON K1N 7B7, Canada
*Tel:* 613-562-2324 *Fax:* 613-562-2329
*E-mail:* aecb@aecb.org; info@livrescanadabooks.com
*Web Site:* www.aecb.org; www.livrescanadabooks.com
*Key Personnel*
Pres: Guy Frenette
Exec Dir: Francois Charette
As the only national trade association that connects English & French language publishers across Canada, Livres Canada Books has a mandate to foster Canadian publishers' export sales. Coordinates Canadian publishers' presence at international book fairs, promotes Canadian titles abroad through its catalogues, exhibits & web site, provides market intelligence & acts as a liaison between Canadian publishers & foreign buyers. Also assists the industry by providing funding assistance for Canadian publishers' international marketing strategies & activities.
Publication(s): *Canadian Studies Flyer* (annual, free); *Rights Canada Catalogue* (semiannual, free)

**Magazine Publishers of America**
810 Seventh Ave, 24th fl, New York, NY 10019
*Tel:* 212-872-3700 *Fax:* 212-888-4217
*E-mail:* mpa@magazine.org
*Web Site:* www.magazine.org
*Key Personnel*
Pres: Nina B Link
Dir, Mktg: Patty Bogie
Promote the value of magazines.
Number of Members: 220
*Branch Office(s)*
1211 Connecticut Ave NW, Washington, DC 20036, Contact: James Cregan *Tel:* 202-296-7277 *Fax:* 202-296-0343

**Magazines Canada**
425 Adelaide St W, Suite 700, Toronto, ON M5V 3C1, Canada
*Tel:* 416-504-0274 *Fax:* 416-504-0437
*E-mail:* info@magazinescanada.ca
*Web Site:* www.magazinescanada.ca
*Key Personnel*
CEO: Mark Jamison *E-mail:* mjamison@magazinescanada.ca
Exec Dir, Ad Servs: Gary Garland *E-mail:* ggarland@magazinescanada.ca
Exec Dir, Pub Aff: Jim Everson *Tel:* 613-488-9916 *Fax:* 613-488-2861 *E-mail:* jeverson@magazinescanada.ca
Mgr, Communs: Brianne DiAngelo *Tel:* 416-504-0274 ext 227 *E-mail:* bdiangelo@magazinescanada.ca
Founded: 1973
Distribution, promotion, professional development & lobbying for Canadian magazines.
Number of Members: 350
Publication(s): *Small Magazine Advertising* ($25 membs, $40 nonmembs, $28 students); *Small Magazine Business* ($25 membs, $45 nonmembs, $38 students); *Small Magazine Circulation* ($25 membs, $40 nonmembs, $28 students); *Small Magazine Editorial* ($25 membs, $40 nonmembs, $28 students); *Small Magazine Human Resources* ($25 membs, $40 nonmembs, $28 students)

**Maine Writers & Publishers Alliance**
314 Forest Ave, Rm 318, Portland, OR 04102
*Tel:* 207-228-8263 *Fax:* 207-228-8150
*E-mail:* info@mainewriters.org
*Web Site:* www.mainewriters.org
*Key Personnel*
VP: Jaed Coffin
Writing retreats, writing workshops, information services.
Number of Members: 800
Publication(s): *Maine In Print* (quarterly, $35/yr)

**Manitoba Arts Council**
525-93 Lombard Ave, Winnipeg, MB R3B 3B1, Canada
*Tel:* 204-945-2237 *Toll Free Tel:* 866-994-2787 (in Manitoba) *Fax:* 204-945-5925
*E-mail:* info@artscouncil.mb.ca
*Web Site:* www.artscouncil.mb.ca
*Key Personnel*
Assoc Dir, Policy, Planning & Partnerships & Writing & Publg Consultant: Patricia Sanders *Tel:* 204-945-0422 *E-mail:* psanders@artscouncil.mb.ca
Provincial arts council that funds professional Manitoban artists & arts organizations.

**The Manitoba Writers' Guild Inc**
218-100 Arthur St, Winnipeg, MB R3B 1H3, Canada
*Tel:* 204-944-8013
*E-mail:* info@mbwriter.mb.ca
*Web Site:* www.mbwriter.mb.ca
Founded: 1981
Membership $60/yr regular, $30/yr students & low income.
Number of Members: 550

**Media Alliance**
1904 Franklin St, Suite 818, Oakland, CA 94612
*Tel:* 510-832-9000 *Fax:* 510-238-8557
*E-mail:* info@media-alliance.org
*Web Site:* www.media-alliance.org
*Key Personnel*
Exec Dir: Tracy Rosenberg
Educational programs in editing, writing & journalism skills. Media relations & advocacy & hands-on computer skills. Job listings & resources, media watchdog activities.
Number of Members: 3,200
Publication(s): *Media How-to Guidebook* ($20)

**Media Coalition Inc**
19 Fulton St, Suite 407, New York, NY 10038
*Tel:* 212-587-4025 *Fax:* 212-587-2436
*Web Site:* www.mediacoalition.org
*Key Personnel*
Exec Dir: David Horowitz *Tel:* 212-587-4025 ext 3 *E-mail:* horowitz@mediacoalition.org
Founded: 1973
Trade association, defends first amendment rights to produce & distribute constitutionally-protected books, magazines, recordings, videos & video games.
Number of Members: 12
Publication(s): *Shooting the Messenger, Why Censorship Won't Stop Violence* ($1); *The Vanity of Bonfires* ($1.50)

**The Melville Society**
c/o Kent State Univ, Dept of English, Box 5190, Kent, OH 44242
*Key Personnel*
Pres: Dennis Berthold *E-mail:* d-berthold@tamu.edu
Treas: Gerald McGowan *E-mail:* gerald.mcgowan@mysticseaport.org
Ed, Leviathan: John Bryant *E-mail:* johnlbryant@hofstra.edu
Exec Secy: Mary K Bercaw Edwards *E-mail:* maryk.bercawedward@mysticseaport.org
Annual & special meetings & publications. Conferences in association with the Modern Language Association annual convention & American Literature Association annual convention.
Number of Members: 760
New Election: Annually in the Spring
Publication(s): *Leviathan* (3 issues/yr, free with membership)
*Branch Office(s)*
c/o Ed, Leviathan, Hofstra University, Dept of English, Hempstead, NY 11550

**Mental Health America (MHA)**
2000 N Beauregard St, 6th fl, Alexandria, VA 22311
*Tel:* 703-684-7722 *Toll Free Tel:* 800-969-6642 *Fax:* 703-684-5968
*Web Site:* mentalhealthamerica.net
*Key Personnel*
CEO & Pres: David L Shern, PhD *E-mail:* dshern@mentalhealthamerica.net
SVP, Opers: Dianne Felton *E-mail:* dfelton@mentalhealthamerica.net
Founded: 1909
Nonprofit dedicated to legislative advocacy, public education, healthcare reform, information & referral.
Number of Members: 1,000,000
Publication(s): *The Bell* (monthly); *Consumer Update* (monthly); *State Advocacy Update* (bimonthly)

**Metropolitan Lithographers Association Inc**
950 Third Ave, 14th fl, New York, NY 10022
*Tel:* 212-644-1010 *Fax:* 212-644-1936
*Key Personnel*
Pres: Kenneth Margolis
Multi-employer lithographic trade association active in collective bargaining, labor relations, management educational programs & public relations.
Number of Members: 7
New Election: Annually in Jan

**Midwest Independent Booksellers Association (MIBA)**
2355 Louisiana Ave N, Suite A, Golden Valley, MN 55427-3646
*Tel:* 763-544-2993 *Toll Free Tel:* 800-784-7522 *Fax:* 763-544-2266
*Web Site:* www.midwestbooksellers.org
*Key Personnel*
Exec Dir: Carrie Obry *E-mail:* carrie@midwestbooksellers.org
Association of independent bookstores in Midwest: Illinois, Iowa, Kansas, Minnesota, Missouri, Nebraska, North Dakota, South Dakota & Wisconsin. Annual trade show & meeting. Book catalog for member stores to use with consumers. Sponsors educational programs for booksellers, Spring meeting, Midwest Booksellers' Choice Awards & "Midwest Connections" regional marketing program.
Number of Members: 500
Publication(s): *MBA Trade Show Program* (annual); *Membership Directory* (online); *Midwest Booksellers Association Winter Catalog* (annual)

**Midwest Publishing Association (MPA)**
Formerly Chicago Book Clinic
310 W Lake St, Suite 111, Elmhurst, IL 60126
*Tel:* 630-833-4220 *Fax:* 630-563-9181
*E-mail:* info@midwestpublish.org
*Web Site:* www.midwestpublish.org
*Key Personnel*
Exec Dir: Kimberly LaBounty
Founded: 1936
Encourages excellence in publishing by providing a platform for educational, social & professional interaction. Members are professionals in book & media publishing, printing, editorial, design & all business aspects of our industry. Accomplishes mission through a variety of educational programs, publications & special events designed to promote the publishing media industry & its members.
Number of Members: 300
Publication(s): *MPA E-news* (weekly, free to membs)

**Midwest Travel Writers Association**
902 S Randall Rd, Suite C311, St Charles, IL 60174
*Toll Free Tel:* 888-551-8184
*E-mail:* admin@MTWA.org
*Web Site:* www.mtwa.org
*Key Personnel*
Pres: Mary Lu Laffey
Founded: 1951
To promote & practice travel writing as a profession. Subjects addressed include: food, wine, music, dance, theater, photography, sports, recreation, travel & resorts.
Number of Members: 100
Publication(s): *MTWA Directory* (annually, $100/CD)

**Miniature Book Society Inc**
702 Rosecrans St, San Diego, CA 92106-3013
*Tel:* 619-226-4441 *Fax:* 619-226-4441
*E-mail:* minibook@cox.net
*Web Site:* www.mbs.org
*Key Personnel*
Pres: Mark Palkovic
Secy: Edward Hoyenski

Founded: 1983
Number of Members: 302
Publication(s): *Miniature Book Society Newsletter* (3 issues/yr, newsletter, $40/yr)
Membership(s): Fellowship of American Bibliophilic Societies

**Modern Language Association of America (MLA)**
26 Broadway, 3rd fl, New York, NY 10004-1789
SAN: 202-6422
*Tel:* 646-576-5000 *Fax:* 646-458-0030
*E-mail:* convention@mla.org
*Web Site:* www.mla.org
*Key Personnel*
Dir of Convention Progs: Maribeth T Kraus *E-mail:* mkraus@mla.org
Exec Dir: Rosemary G Feal *Tel:* 646-576-5102 *E-mail:* execdirector@mla.org
Mktg & Sales Dir: Kathleen Hansen *Tel:* 646-576-5018 *E-mail:* khansen@mla.org
Convention; employment information, professional organization, scholarly publications.
Number of Members: 30,000
2014 Meeting(s): Annual Convention, Chicago, IL, Jan 9-12, 2014
Publication(s): *MLA International Bibliography* (annual, inquire); *MLA Newsletter* (quarterly, free to membs); *PMLA* (5 issues/yr, inquire); *Profession* (annual, free to membs; $7.50 nonmembs)

**Motion Picture Association of America Inc (MPAA)**
1600 "I" St NW, Washington, DC 20006
*Tel:* 202-293-1966 *Fax:* 202-293-1299
*E-mail:* motionpictureassociation@mpaa.org
*Web Site:* www.mpaa.org
*Key Personnel*
CEO & Pres: Christopher Dodd
EVP, External Affairs: John Feehery
VP, Corp Communs: Kate Spence
Founded: 1922
Trade association for the major motion picture producers & distributors. Administer motion picture industry's system of self-regulation & are spokespeople for production & distribution of motion pictures for theatrical, home video & TV use in the USA.
Number of Members: 60
*Branch Office(s)*
15301 Ventura Blvd, Bldg E, Sherman Oaks, CA 91403, VP, Corp Communs: Kori Bernards *Tel:* 818-995-6600 *Fax:* 818-285-4403
1010 Lake St, Suite 422, Oak Park, IL 60301 *Tel:* 708-660-0481 *Fax:* 708-660-0484
200 White Plains Rd, 1st fl, Tarrytown, NY 10591 *Tel:* 914-333-8892 *Fax:* 914-333-7541
1425 Greenway Dr, Suite 270, Irving, TX 75038 *Tel:* 972-756-9078 *Fax:* 972-756-9402
55 Saint Clair Ave W, Suite 210, Toronto, ON M4V 2Y7, Canada *Tel:* 416-961-1888 *Fax:* 416-968-1016 *Web Site:* www.mpa-canada.org
Avenue des Arts 46, Box 8, 1000 Brussels, Belgium *Tel:* (02) 778 27 11 *Fax:* (02) 778 27 00
Rua Jeronimo da Veiga, 45, Conj 121/122, 12th fl, Jardim Europa, 04536-000 Sao Paulo, SP, Brazil *Tel:* (011) 3667-2080 *Web Site:* www.mpaal.org.br
No 04-07 Central Mall, No 1 Magazine Rd, Singapore 059567, Singapore *Tel:* 6253 1033 *Fax:* 6255 1838 *Web Site:* www.moa-i.org

**Music Publishers' Association (MPA)**
243 Fifth Ave, Suite 236, New York, NY 10016
*Tel:* 212-327-4044
*E-mail:* admin@mpa.org
*Web Site:* host.mpa.org; www.mpa.org
*Key Personnel*
Pres: Kathleen Marsh
VP: Bryan Bradley
Treas: Bryndon Bay
Founded: 1895
Foster trade & commerce in the interest of those in the music publishing business & encourage understanding of & compliance with the copyright law to protect musical works against piracies & infringements.
Number of Members: 300
New Election: Annually, first week of July

**Mystery Writers of America (MWA)**
1140 Broadway, Suite 1507, New York, NY 10001
*Tel:* 212-888-8171
*E-mail:* mwa@mysterywriters.org
*Web Site:* www.mysterywriters.org
*Key Personnel*
Admin Dir: Margery Flax
The premier organization for mystery writers & other professionals in the mystery field. MWA watches developments in legislation & tax laws, sponsors symposia & mystery conferences, presents the Edgar Awards & provides information for mystery writers. Membership open to published authors, editors, screenwriters & other professionals in the field.
Number of Members: 3,000
Publication(s): *Mystery Writers Annual*; *The Third Degree* (10 issues/yr)

**NAPL**
One Meadowlands Plaza, Suite 1511, East Rutherford, NJ 07073
*Tel:* 201-634-9600 *Toll Free Tel:* 800-642-6275 *Fax:* 201-634-0324
*E-mail:* naplmemberservice@napl.org
*Web Site:* www.napl.org
*Key Personnel*
CEO & Pres: Joseph P Truncale, PhD *E-mail:* jtruncale@napl.org
VP & Chief Economist: Andrew D Paparozzi *E-mail:* apaparozzi@napl.org
Founded: 1933
Sponsor seminars/workshops each year throughout North America. Publish a variety of print-specific periodicals & retail books for the print community.
Number of Members: 3,600
Publication(s): *At Your Service* (quarterly); *The Economic Edge* (quarterly); *Journal of Graphic Communications Management* (quarterly); *Marketing Action Planner* (quarterly); *NAPL Business Review*; *NAPL/NAQP Quick & Small Commerical Printers Trends Reports* (newsletter); *NAPL White Papers*; *On the Job* (quarterly); *[P]Review* (magazine); *Print Profits* (quarterly); *Printing Business Conditions*; *[Re]View* (newsletter, semimonthly); *Sales Focus* (quarterly); *Special Reports* (5 issues/yr); *Tech Trends* (quarterly)

**NASW**, see National Association of Science Writers (NASW)

**National Association for Printing Leadership**, see NAPL

**National Association of Black Journalists (NABJ)**
1100 Knight Hall, Suite 3100, College Park, MD 20742
*Tel:* 301-405-0248 *Fax:* 301-314-1714
*E-mail:* nabj@nabj.org
*Web Site:* www.nabj.org
*Key Personnel*
Dir, Progs & Prof Devt: Ryan L Williams *Tel:* 301-405-0717 *E-mail:* rwilliams@nabj.org
Membership Mgr: Veronique Dodson *Tel:* 301-405-0554 *E-mail:* vdodson@nabj.org
Founded: 1975
To strengthen the ties between Blacks in the Black media & Blacks in the White media, eliminate racism, expand Black coverage & promote professionalism among Black journalists.
Number of Members: 3,300
New Election: Biennially, odd yrs
Publication(s): *NABJ Journal* (quarterly, journal)

**National Association of Broadcasters (NAB)**
1771 "N" St NW, Washington, DC 20036-2891
*Tel:* 202-429-5300 *Fax:* 202-429-4199
*E-mail:* nab@nab.org
*Web Site:* www.nab.org
*Key Personnel*
COO & CFO: Janet McGregor *Tel:* 202-429-5304
EVP, Conventions & Busn Opers: Mr Chris Brown
EVP, Mktg & Communs: Michelle Lehman *Tel:* 202-429-5444 *E-mail:* mlehman@nab.org
Trade association for radio & television stations. Provide products, publications (over 130) & other services related to broadcasting.
Number of Members: 9,000

**National Association of College Stores (NACS)**
500 E Lorain St, Oberlin, OH 44074
*Tel:* 440-775-7777 *Toll Free Tel:* 800-622-7498 *Fax:* 440-775-4769
*Web Site:* www.nacs.org
*Key Personnel*
Dir of Expositions: Mary Adler-Kozak *Tel:* 800-622-7498 ext 2265 *E-mail:* madler-kozak@nacs.org
Dir, Meetings: Jodie Wilmot *Tel:* 440-775-7777 ext 2272 *E-mail:* jwilmot@nacs.org
Exhibit Sales & Serv Rep: Linda Vargo *Tel:* 440-775-7777 ext 2302 *E-mail:* lvargo@nacs.org
Trade association for college store industry.
Number of Members: 3,700
2014 Meeting(s): CAMEX, Dallas, TX, March 7-11, 2014
Publication(s): *Campus Marketplace* (weekly online, newsletter); *The College Store* (bimonthly, magazine); *Directory of Colleges & College Stores* (annually); *List of School Openings & Other Dates* (annually); *The Torchlight* (semiannual, newsletter)
Membership(s): BISG

**National Association of Hispanic Publications Inc (NAHP)**
529 14 St NW, Suite 1126, Washington, DC 20045
*Tel:* 202-662-7250 *Fax:* 202-662-7251
*Web Site:* www.nahp.org
*Key Personnel*
Exec Dir: Mary Ann Gomez *Tel:* 202-662-7250 ext 1 *E-mail:* mgomez@nahp.org
Prog & Membership Asst: Cassandra Sherry *E-mail:* csherry@nahp.org
Founded: 1982
Promote Hispanic media.
Number of Members: 165
Publication(s): *The Hispanic Press* (quarterly, newsletter)

**National Association of Independent Publishers Representatives**
111 E 14 St, PMB 157, New York, NY 10003
*Tel:* 267-546-6561 *Toll Free Tel:* 888-624-7779
*Web Site:* naipr.org
*Key Personnel*
Exec Dir: Robert Rooney *E-mail:* robert.rooney@naipr.org
Founded: 1990
Information & promotion of commission selling for book publishers.
Seasonal offering of Publishers Frontlist trade catalogs.
Number of Members: 850
Publication(s): *The Call Report*™ (monthly, newsletter, free); *Marketing Advice for the*

*Very Small or Self-Publishers* (newsletter, free); *NAIPR News Online* (monthly, newsletter, free); *Selling on Commission* (free)

**National Association of Printing Ink Manufacturers (NAPIM)**
15 Technology Pkwy S, Peachtree Corners, GA 30092
*Tel:* 770-209-7289 *Fax:* 678-680-4920
*E-mail:* napim@napim.org
*Web Site:* www.napim.org
*Key Personnel*
Exec Dir: Brad Bergey *E-mail:* bbergey@napim.org
Trade association representing the printing ink industry & providing information & assistance to members to better manage their business.
Number of Members: 120
2014 Meeting(s): Annual Convention, Rancho Bernardo Inn, 17550 Bernardo Oaks Dr, San Diego, CA, March 22-26, 2014
Publication(s): *Introduction to Printing Ink* ($6 membs, $10 nonmembs); *Printing Ink Handbook, 6th ed* ($90 membs, $150 nonmembs); *Raw Material Data Handbook* ($100 membs, $250 nonmembs (vols 1-3), $400 membs, $400 nonmembs (vol 4, pigments))

**National Association of Real Estate Editors (NAREE)**
1003 NW Sixth Terr, Boca Raton, FL 33486-3455
*Tel:* 561-391-3599 *Fax:* 561-391-0099
*Web Site:* www.naree.org
*Key Personnel*
Pres: Harold Bubil
Exec Dir: Mary Doyle-Kimball
*E-mail:* madkimba@aol.com
Contact: David Kimball *E-mail:* dakimball@aol.com
Founded: 1929
Nonprofit professional association of writers Journalism Contest & seminars in winter, spring & fall; memberships active for journalists & associate for communications professionals. Bruss Real Estate Book Awards annual competition.
Number of Members: 650
2014 Meeting(s): Spring Real Estate Journalism Conference, Spring 2014
Publication(s): *NAREE Directory* (annually, directory, free to membs); *NAREE News* (quarterly, free to membs); *Spring Conference Book* (free to membs)

**National Association of Science Writers (NASW)**
PO Box 7905, Berkeley, CA 94707
*Tel:* 510-647-9500
*Web Site:* www.nasw.org
*Key Personnel*
Exec Dir: Tinsley Davis *E-mail:* director@nasw.org
Founded: 1934
Number of Members: 2,200
New Election: 2014
2014 Meeting(s): ScienceWriters, Columbus, OH, Oct 17-21, 2014
Publication(s): *ScienceWriters* (quarterly, magazine, free for membs)
Membership(s): World Federation of Science Journalists

**National Cable & Telecommunications Association (NCTA)**
25 Massachusetts Ave NW, Suite 100, Washington, DC 20001-1413
*Tel:* 202-222-2300 *Fax:* 202-222-2514
*Web Site:* www.ncta.com
*Key Personnel*
CEO & Pres: Michael Powell
SVP, Communs & Pub Aff: Rob Stoddard
*Tel:* 202-222-2350 *Fax:* 202-222-2351
*E-mail:* rstoddard@ncta.com
Represent the cable television industry & its program & equipment suppliers; inform leaders in Congress, the Federal Communications Commission & other federal agencies about industry positions, problems & policies; represent the complex interests of the cable television industry before courts of law & state regulatory agencies & in dialogues with other industry groups.
Publication(s): *A Cable Primer*; *Cable TV: All TV Should Be*; *Legislative History of the Cable Communications Policy Act*; *Producer's Source Book*

**National Cartoonists Society (NCS)**
341 N Maitland Ave, Suite 130, Maitland, FL 32751
*Tel:* 407-647-8839 *Fax:* 407-629-2502
*E-mail:* crowsgal@crowsgal.com; info@reuben.org
*Web Site:* www.reuben.org
*Key Personnel*
Pres: Tom Richmond
Exec Dir: Phil Pyster *E-mail:* phil@crowsegal.com
Fraternal Organization of Cartoonists.
Number of Members: 500
Publication(s): *The Cartoonist*

**National Coalition Against Censorship (NCAC)**
19 Fulton St, Suite 407, New York, NY 10038
*Tel:* 212-807-6222 *Fax:* 212-807-6245
*E-mail:* ncac@ncac.org
*Web Site:* www.ncac.org
*Key Personnel*
Exec Dir: Joan E Bertin
Communs & Coord, Youth Progs: Teresa Koberstein
Dir, Progs: Svetlana Mintcheva
Founded: 1974
Promote & defend free speech, inquiry & expression; monitor & publicize censorship incidents; sponsor public programs; assist in censorship controversies through advice, materials, contacts with local organizations & individuals. Membership is comprised of 50 national participating organizations; individuals may become NCAC friends for $30 or more. Reprints & informational materials available upon request.
New Election: Annually in Dec
Publication(s): *Censorship News* (4 issues/yr, $30/yr); *The Cyber-Library: Legal & Policy Issues Facing Public Libraries in the High-Tech Era* ($7.50); *Editorial Memorandum on Women, Censorship & "Pornography" 1993* ($5); *Meese Commission Exposed: Proceedings of a NCAC Public Information Briefing on the Attorney General's Commission on Pornography, Including Kurt Vonnegut Jr, Betty Friedan & Colleen Dewhurst* ($6); *Public Education, Democracy, Free Speech: the Ideas that Define & Unite Us* ($2.50); *A Report on Book Censorship Litigation in Public Schools, rev* ($4); *The Sex Panic, a conference report* ($3.50)

**National Coalition for Literacy**
PO Box 2932, Washington, DC 20013-2932
*Toll Free Tel:* 800-228-8813 *Toll Free Fax:* 866-738-3757
*E-mail:* ncl@ncladvocacy.org; ncl@national-coalition-literary.org
*Web Site:* www.national-coalition-literacy.org
*Key Personnel*
Pres: Marty Finsterbusch
Founded: 1981
A member organization made up of major service, research & policy organizations in adult education, family literacy & English Language Acquisition. NCL's mission is to advance adult education, family literacy & English language acquisition in America - from the most basic skills proficiency level across a continuum of services including the transition into postsecondary education & job training.
Number of Members: 44
Publication(s): *NCL Update* (monthly, newsletter, Free)

**National Communication Association**
1765 "N" St NW, Washington, DC 20036
*Tel:* 202-464-4622 *Fax:* 202-464-4600
*Web Site:* www.natcom.org
*Key Personnel*
Chief of Staff: Mark Fernando
*E-mail:* mfernando@natcom.org
Exec Dir: Nancy Kidd, PhD *Tel:* 202-534-1120
*E-mail:* nkidd@natcom.org
Founded: 1914
To promote effective & ethical communication.
Number of Members: 7,000
2014 Meeting(s): Annual Convention, Hilton Chicago/Palmer House Hilton, Chicago, IL, Nov 20-23, 2014
2015 Meeting(s): Annual Convention, Rio Hotel, Las Vegas, NV, Nov 19-22, 2015
Publication(s): *Communication Education* (quarterly); *Communication Monographs* (quarterly, journal); *Communication Teacher* (quarterly); *Critical Studies in Mass Communication* (journal); *Directory of Graduate Programs*; *Journal of International & Intercultural Communication*; *NCA Insider* (quarterly online, newsletter); *The Quarterly Journal of Speech*; *Text & Performance Quarterly* (journal)

**National Conference for Community & Justice**
1095 Day Hill Rd, Suite 100, Windsor, CT 06095
*Tel:* 860-683-1039 *Fax:* 860-683-1409
*E-mail:* info@nccjctwma.org
*Web Site:* www.nccjctwma.org
*Key Personnel*
Assoc, Dir, Communs & Instl Support: Amanda Gumbs *Tel:* 860-298-5313 *E-mail:* agumbs@nccj.org
A human relations organization dedicatd to fighting bias, bigotry & racism in America by promoting respect & understanding among all races, religions & cultures through advocacy, conflict resolution & education.
Number of Members: 200,000
Publication(s): *Actions Speak Louder*; *Big, Big World & the People in It*; *Hate: A Concept Examined*; *Intergroup Relations in the United States: Programs & Organizations*; *Intergroup Relations in the United States: Research Perspectives*; *Intergroup Relations in the United States: Seven Promising Practices*

**National Council of Teachers of English (NCTE)**
1111 W Kenyon Rd, Urbana, IL 61801-1096
*Tel:* 217-328-3870 *Toll Free Tel:* 877-369-6283 (cust serv) *Fax:* 217-328-9645
*E-mail:* public_info@ncte.org
*Web Site:* www.ncte.org
*Key Personnel*
Exec Dir: Kent Williamson *Tel:* 217-278-3601
Communs Specialist: Lori Bianchini
*Tel:* 217-278-3644 *Fax:* 217-278-3761
*E-mail:* lbianchini@ncte.org
Perms Coord: Shellie Elson *Tel:* 217-278-3638
*Fax:* 217-328-0977 *E-mail:* permissions@ncte.org
Founded: 1911
Focus on the major concerns of teachers of English & the language arts; offer teaching aids, advice, direction & guidance for members. Publish educational books, journals, pamphlets, research reports & position papers for all levels of the English teaching profession. Hold annual convention for members in November; sponsor conferences & workshops.
Number of Members: 35,000

Publication(s): *College Composition & Communication* (quarterly, journal, $75/yr, includes NCTE & CCCC membership); *College English* (6 times/yr, journal, $75/yr, includes NCTE membership); *English Education* (quarterly, journal, $75/yr, includes NCTE & CEE membership); *English Journal* (6 times/yr, $75/yr, includes NCTE membership); *English Leadership Quarterly* (journal, $75/yr, includes NCTE & CEL membership); *Language Arts* (6 times/yr, journal, $75/yr, includes NCTE membership); *Research in the Teaching of English* (quarterly, journal, $75/yr, includes NCTE membership); *Talking Points* (semiannual, journal, $75/yr, includes NCTE & WLU membership); *Teaching English in the Two-Year College* (quarterly, journal, $75/yr, includes NCTE & TYCA membership); *Voices from the Middle* (quarterly, journal, $75/yr, includes NCTE membership)

**National Education Association (NEA)**
1201 16 St NW, Washington, DC 20036-3290
*Tel:* 202-833-4000 *Fax:* 202-822-7974
*Web Site:* www.nea.org
*Key Personnel*
Secy/Treas: Rebecca "Becky" Pringle
Pres: Dennis Van Roekel
VP: Lily Eskelsen
Exec Dir: John C Stocks
Dir, PR: Andy Linebaugh *Tel:* 202-822-7218 *E-mail:* alinebaugh@nea.org
Professional association for over 3.2 million educators, with 14,000 local, 52 state & 6 regional affiliates.
Number of Members: 3,200,000
Publication(s): *The NEA Almanac of Higher Education* (annual); *NEA Today* (9 issues/yr); *Thought & Action* (2 issues/yr)

**National Federation of Advanced Information Services (NFAIS)**
1518 Walnut St, Suite 1004, Philadelphia, PA 19102-3403
*Tel:* 215-893-1561 *Fax:* 215-893-1564
*E-mail:* nfais@nfais.org
*Web Site:* www.nfais.org
*Key Personnel*
Dir, Commun & Planning: Jill O'Neill *Tel:* 215-893-1561 ext 14 *E-mail:* jilloneill@nfais.org
Sponsors research, carries out a comprehensive program of continuing education issues pertinent publications in all areas of documentation & information dissemination.
Number of Members: 60
Publication(s): *Enotes* (newsletter, free to membs); *Membership Directory* (online only, directory); *NFAIS E Notes* (online only)
Membership(s): CENDI; ICSTI; National Information Standards Organization

**National Federation of Press Women Inc (NFPW)**
PO Box 5556, Arlington, VA 22205-0056
*Tel:* 703-237-9804 *Toll Free Tel:* 800-780-2715 *Fax:* 703-237-9808
*E-mail:* presswomen@aol.com
*Web Site:* www.nfpw.org
Founded: 1936
Conduct seminars & workshops to increase knowledge & develop professional skills of working media women; youth projects.
Number of Members: 2,000
New Election: Annually in Sept
Publication(s): *Agenda* (quarterly)

**National Freedom of Information Coalition (NFOIC)**
Affiliate of Missouri School of Journalism
101 Reynolds Journalism Institute, Columbia, MO 65211-0012
*Tel:* 573-882-4856 *Fax:* 573-884-6204
*Web Site:* nfoic.org
*Key Personnel*
Exec Dir: Ken Bunting *Tel:* 573-882-3075 *E-mail:* buntingk@missouri.edu
Sr Info Specialist: Drew Griffith *Tel:* 573-882-3229 *E-mail:* griffithd@missouri.edu
Off Administator: Denise C Meyers *E-mail:* meyersd@missouri.edu
Grants & Contracts Asst: Le Anne Wiseman *E-mail:* wisemanl@missouri.edu
Founded: 1989 (as National Freedom of Information Assembly; 1991 changed to it's current name)
National membership organization for state freedom of information groups & academic centers as well as individuals supporting freedom of information. Offers $220,000 in grants semiannually for the creation & growth of State F01 Coalitions.
Number of Members: 62
Publication(s): *The FOI Advocate* (monthly, free by e-mail subn); *FOI Reports* (occasional, free to membs)

**National Government Publishing Association**
629 N Main St, Hattiesburg, MS 39401
*Tel:* 601-582-3330 *Fax:* 601-582-3354
*E-mail:* info@govpublishing.org
*Web Site:* www.govpublishing.org
*Key Personnel*
Pres: Douglas Beckham *E-mail:* dbeckham@mail.ls.state.ms.us
VP: Susie Barthel *E-mail:* susie.barthel@la.gov
Treas: John Wright *E-mail:* john_wright@legis.state.ak.us
Central Regl Dir: Timothy Smith *E-mail:* timothy.smith@wisconsin.gov
Southern Regl Dir: Tammy Golden *E-mail:* tammy.golden@tn.gov
Western Regl Dir: Mike Lincoln *E-mail:* mike.lincoln@state.co.us
Scholarship awarded to a college or university that has established a four-year program in printing & graphic arts. Information exchange central reference source & public arena for ongoing state publishing activities.
Number of Members: 100

**National Information Standards Organization**
One N Charles St, Suite 1905, Baltimore, MD 21201
*Tel:* 301-654-2512 *Toll Free Tel:* 866-957-1593 *Fax:* 410-685-5278
*E-mail:* nisohq@niso.org
*Web Site:* www.niso.org
*Key Personnel*
Mng Dir: Todd Carpenter *E-mail:* tcarpenter@niso.org
Busn Devt & Opers Mgr: Victoria Kinnear *E-mail:* vkinnear@niso.org
Developing, maintaining & publishing technical standards used by libraries, information services & publishers. Accredited by the American National Standards Institute.
Number of Members: 90
Publication(s): *Information Standards Quarterly (ISQ)* (4 issues/yr, $130/yr US, $165/yr CN & foreign, free to voting membs)

**National League of American Pen Women**
c/o National Pen Women-Scholarship, Pen Arts Bldg, 1300 17 St NW, Washington, DC 20036-1973
*Tel:* 202-785-1997 *Fax:* 202-452-8868
*E-mail:* contact@nlapw.org
*Web Site:* www.nlapw.org
*Key Personnel*
Natl Scholarship Chair: Mary B Barrer
Founded: 1897
Scholarships, letters, art & music workshops, awards & prizes. Must send SASE for information.
Number of Members: 3,500
Publication(s): *The Pen Woman* (4 issues/yr, $18/yr; free to membs)

**National Music Publishers' Association (NMPA)**
975 F St NW, Suite 315, Washington, DC 20004
*Tel:* 202-393-6672 *Fax:* 202-393-6673
*E-mail:* pr@nmpa.org
*Web Site:* www.nmpa.org
*Key Personnel*
CEO & Pres: David M Israelite
Founded: 1917
Trade association of American Music Publishers.
Number of Members: 3,000
*Branch Office(s)*
The Harry Fox Agency (HFA), 40 Wall St, 6th fl, New York, NY 10005-1344 *Tel:* 212-834-0100 *Fax:* 646-487-6779 *Web Site:* www.harryfox.com

**National Newspaper Association**
309 S Providence St, Columbia, MO 65203-4267
Mailing Address: PO Box 7540, Columbia, MO 65205-7540
*Tel:* 573-882-5800 *Toll Free Tel:* 800-829-4NNA (829-4662) *Fax:* 573-884-5490
*E-mail:* info@nna.org
*Web Site:* www.nnaweb.org
*Key Personnel*
CEO: Tonda F Rush *E-mail:* tonda@nna.org
Assoc Dir: Lynn Edinger
Progs & Outreach Mgr: Sara Dickson
Founded: 1885
Trade association.
Number of Members: 2,500
2014 Meeting(s): Annual Convention & Trade Show, Grand Hyatt San Antonio, San Antonio, TX, Oct 2-5, 2014
Publication(s): *Publishers Auxiliary* (monthly, $85/yr, $95/intl)
*Branch Office(s)*
2020 N 14 St, Suite 300, Arlington, VA 22201 *Tel:* 703-465-8808 *Fax:* 703-812-4555 *E-mail:* tonda@nna.org

**National Newspaper Publishers Assn (NNPA)**
1816 12 St NW, Washington, DC 20009
*Tel:* 202-588-8764 *Fax:* 202-588-8960
*E-mail:* info@blackpressusa.com; info@nnpa.org
*Web Site:* www.nnpa.org; www.blackpressusa.com
*Key Personnel*
Chmn: Cloves Cambell, Jr

**National Press Club (NPC)**
529 14 St NW, 13th fl, Washington, DC 20045
*Tel:* 202-662-7500 *Fax:* 202-662-7569
*E-mail:* infocenter@npcpress.org
*Web Site:* www.press.org
*Key Personnel*
Club Pres: Theresa Werner
Lib Dir: Julie Schoo *E-mail:* jschoo@press.org
Gen Mgr: Daisy Kings
Founded: 1908
Private professional organization for journalists. Sponsors workshops, rap sessions with authors, press forums, morning newsmakers, famous speaker luncheons; awards prizes for consumer journalism, environmental reporting; freedom of the press; diplomatic writing, Washington coverage & newsletters; book & art exhibits; computerized reference library; annual Book Fair & Authors' Night.
Number of Members: 4,000
Publication(s): *The Record* (weekly)

**National Press Club of Canada Foundation Inc**
150 Albert St, Ottawa, ON K1P 5G2, Canada
*Tel:* 613-567-9900 *Fax:* 613-233-5880
*E-mail:* manager@pressclub.on.ca
*Web Site:* pressclubcanada.ca
*Key Personnel*
Dir: Al Ottuum

Founded: 1928
Private club for reporters, journalists & media-related people; dining, bar & meeting facilities, catering for up to 150 people.
Number of Members: 450

**The National Press Foundation**
1211 Connecticut Ave NW, Suite 310, Washington, DC 20036
*Tel:* 202-663-7280
*Web Site:* www.nationalpress.org
*Key Personnel*
Pres & COO: Bob Meyers *E-mail:* bob@nationalpress.org
Dir of Progs: Linda Topping Streitfeld *E-mail:* linda@nationalpress.org
Dir of Opers: Kerry Buker *E-mail:* kerry@nationalpress.org
Progs Mgr: Maha Masud *E-mail:* maha@nationalpress.org
Founded: 1976
Provide all expenses paid educational programs to help journalists understand & report on complex topics in Washington, DC & around the world.

**National Press Photographers Association Inc (NPPA)**
3200 Croasdaile Dr, Suite 306, Durham, NC 27705
*Tel:* 919-383-7246 *Fax:* 919-383-7261
*E-mail:* info@nppa.org
*Web Site:* www.nppa.org
*Key Personnel*
Exec Dir: Mindy Hutchison *Tel:* 919-383-7246 ext 14 *E-mail:* director@nppa.org
IT Dir: Stephen Sample *Tel:* 919-383-7246 ext 11 *E-mail:* netgeek@nppa.org
Prof Servs Dir: Thomas Kenniff *Tel:* 919-383-7246 ext 16 *E-mail:* tkenniff@nppa.org
Founded: 1946
Number of Members: 10,004
Publication(s): *News Photographer Magazine* (monthly, free with membership)

**National Society of Newspaper Columnists (NSNC)**
1345 Fillmore St, Suite 507, San Francisco, CA 94115
Mailing Address: PO Box 411532, San Francisco, CA 94141
*Tel:* 415-488-NCNC (488-6762)
*Toll Free Tel:* 866-440-NSNC (440-6762)
*Fax:* 484-297-0336 *Toll Free Fax:* 866-635-5759
*E-mail:* staff@columnists.com
*Web Site:* www.columnists.com
*Key Personnel*
Pres: Ben Pollock
VP: Larry Cohen
Exec Dir: Luenna H Kim *Tel:* 415-563-5403 *E-mail:* director@columnists.com
Secy: Wayne Chan
Treas: James A Casto
Conference Chair: Ed Grisamore
Contest Chair: Mike Deupree
Membership Chair: Rose A Valenta
Newsletter Ed: Robert Haught
Archivist: Dave Astor
Number of Members: 500

**National Writers Association**
10940 S Parker Rd, Suite 508, Parker, CO 80134
*Tel:* 303-841-0246
*E-mail:* natlwritersassn@hotmail.com
*Web Site:* www.nationalwriters.com
*Key Personnel*
Exec Dir: Sandy Whelchel *E-mail:* authorsandy@hotmail.com
Founded: 1937
Nonprofit representative organization of new & established writers, serving freelance writers throughout the world.
Number of Members: 2,000
Publication(s): *Authorship* (quarterly, $20/yr); *NWA Newsletter* (monthly by e-mail only, newsletter)

**National Writers Union/UAW Local 1981**
Affiliate of UAW International, Technical, Office & Professional Division
256 W 38 St, Suite 703, New York, NY 10018
*Tel:* 212-254-0279 *Fax:* 212-254-0673
*E-mail:* nwu@nwu.org
*Web Site:* www.nwu.org/
*Key Personnel*
Pres: Larry Goldbetter
Founded: 1981
Organizing for better treatment of freelance writers by publishers; grievance procedures; negotiate union contracts with publishers; health insurance; conferences. Direct services include the Technical Writers Job Hotline & the Publication Rights Clearinghouse, a groundbreaking license fee collection system. National health insurance programs around the country; national grievance officers & contract advisors; agents database online for members; Authors Network, a Bed & Breakfast program for touring authors at over 160 sites throughout the country, including local reviewer's database, local press contacts & local bookstores/vendors.
Number of Members: 1,800
Publication(s): *local chapter newsletters* (free to members); *National Membership News* (monthly e-mail, newsletter, free to members)

**NCTA**, see Northern California Translators Association

**New England Independent Booksellers Association Inc (NEIBA)**
1955 Massachusetts Ave, Cambridge, MA 02140
*Web Site:* www.newenglandbooks.org
*Key Personnel*
Exec Dir: Steven Fischer *E-mail:* steve@neba.org
Admin Asst: Nan Sorensen *E-mail:* nan@neba.org
Trade association. Fall trade show annually in Sept or Oct; educational workshops, holiday gift catalog.
Number of Members: 500
Publication(s): *NEIBA News* (weekly, membs only)

**New England Poetry Club**
2 Farrar St, Cambridge, MA 02138
Mailing Address: PO Box 190076, Boston, MA 02119
*Tel:* 617-744-6034
*E-mail:* info@nepoetryclub.org
*Web Site:* www.nepoetryclub.org
*Key Personnel*
Pres: Diana Der-Hovanessian
VP: Sally Cragin; Daniel Tobin
Contest Chair: Ellin Sarot
Founded: 1915
Society for professional published poets. Sponsor various poetry contests & workshops. Workshops meet at the Yen Ching Institute (2 Divinity Ave Harvard Campus). Readings on first Monday, 7 pm at a location to be announced; workshops third Mondays 7:30 pm; monthly from Sept-May. Special programs at Longfellow House Sunday pm out of doors, $3,000 in prizes annually.
Number of Members: 500
Publication(s): *Writ* (semiannual, newsletter, free with annual dues)

*Branch Office(s)*
137 W Newton St, Boston, MA 02118 (inquiries on membership), Membership Chmn: Victor Howes

**New Hampshire Writers' Project**
2500 N River Rd, Manchester, NH 03106
*Tel:* 603-314-7980 *Fax:* 603-314-7981
*E-mail:* info@nhwritersproject.org
*Web Site:* www.nhwritersproject.org
*Key Personnel*
Exec Dir: George Geers *E-mail:* ggeers@nhwritersproject.org
Prog Dir: Carla Gericke *E-mail:* nhwp.carla@gmail.com
Off Mgr: Nicole Escobar
Pubns Asst: Dawn Coutu *E-mail:* dcoutu@nhwritersproject.com
Founded: 1988
Number of Members: 780
Publication(s): *NH Writer* (6/yr, newsletter); *NH Writers' Handbook* (special July/Aug issue of newsletter, biennial (2009, 2011), also sold to public, handbook)

**New Mexico Book Association (NMBA)**
1600 Lena St, Bldg C, Suite C-12, Santa Fe, NM 87505
Mailing Address: PO Box 1285, Santa Fe, NM 87504
*Tel:* 505-660-6357; 505-231-1755 *Fax:* 505-983-0899
*E-mail:* admin@nmbook.org
*Web Site:* www.nmbook.org
*Key Personnel*
Pres: James Mafchir *E-mail:* westernedge@santa-fe.net
VP: Paula Lozar *E-mail:* lozarpaula@cs.com
Exec Administrator: Stephanie Hiller
Sr Advisor: Richard Polese *Tel:* 505-231-1755 *E-mail:* richard@oceantree.com
Founded: 1994
Nonprofit association serving the interests of publishing, writing, designing, editing, selling & marketing for book professionals in New Mexico. Open to all involved in books &/or publishing. Need not be a resident of New Mexico.
Number of Members: 180
2013 Meeting(s): Holiday Fiesta & Awards Ceremony, Santa Fe, NM, Dec 2013
Publication(s): *LIBRO Book News* (bimonthly, newsletter, $65/yr membs)
Membership(s): The Association of Publishers for Special Sales; IBPA, the Independent Book Publishers Association; Publishers Association of the West

**Newspaper Association of America (NAA)**
4401 Wilson Blvd, Suite 900, Arlington, VA 22203
*Tel:* 571-366-1000 *Fax:* 571-366-1195
*Web Site:* www.naa.org
*Key Personnel*
CEO & Pres: John F Sturm *E-mail:* john.sturm@naa.org
VP, Communs: Cheryl Sadowski *Tel:* 571-366-1135 *E-mail:* cheryl.sadowski@naa.org
Serves newspapers & newspaper executives by working to advance the cause of a free press; to encourage the efficiency & economy of the newspaper publishing business in all departments & aspects; to engage in & promote research of use to newspapers; to gather & distribute among its member newspapers accurate, reliable & useful information about newspapers & their environment & to promote the highest standard of journalism.
Number of Members: 2,000
2014 Meeting(s): mediaXchange, Hyatt Regencey Denver at Colorado Convention Center, 650 15 St, Denver, CO, March 16-19, 2014
Publication(s): *Presstime* (weekly, membs only)

**The Newspaper Guild**
501 Third St NW, 6th fl, Washington, DC 20001-2797
*Tel:* 202-434-7177; 202-434-7162 (The Guild Reporter) *Fax:* 202-434-1472
*E-mail:* guild@cwa-union.org
*Web Site:* www.newsguild.org
*Key Personnel*
Pres: Bernard Lunzer
Ed, The Guild Reporter: Janell Hartman *E-mail:* jhartman@cwa-union.org
Founded: 1934
Labor union; AFL-CIO, CLC.
Number of Members: 26,000
Publication(s): *The Guild Reporter* (quarterly, free to membs, $20 subn rate nonmembs)

**North American Agricultural Journalists (NAAJ)**
6434 Hurta Lane, Bryan, TX 77808
*Tel:* 979-845-2872 *Fax:* 979-862-1202
*Web Site:* www.naaj.net
*Key Personnel*
Exec Secy & Treas: Kathleen Phillips *E-mail:* kaphillips@tamu.edu
Founded: 1952
Self-improvement seminars; annual writing contest for members & nonmembers.
Number of Members: 120
2014 Meeting(s): Spring Meeting, Washington, DC, April 2014
2015 Meeting(s): Spring Meeting, Washington, DC, April 2015
Publication(s): *NAAJ Newsletter* (varies/online to membs as needed)

**North American Bookdealers Exchange (NABE)**
PO Box 606, Cottage Grove, OR 97424-0026
*Tel:* 541-942-7455
*E-mail:* nabe@bookmarketingprofits.com
*Web Site:* www.bookmarketingprofits.com
*Key Personnel*
Exec Dir: Al Galasso
Promo Dir: Russ Von Hoelscher
Assoc Dir: Ingrid Crawford
Founded: 1980
International book marketing organization of independent publishers & mail order entrepreneurs. Activities include NABE Combined Book Exhibits at national & regional conventions serving the book, educational, gift & business trade. Publishers Preview Mail Order Program, National Press Release, Electronic Marketing plus complete publisher consultation services for printing, promoting & marketing books.
Number of Members: 1,000
Publication(s): *Book Dealers World* (quarterly, circ 10,000, $5/sample, $50/yr & $90/semiannual membership)

**North American Snowsports Journalists Association**
11728 SE Madison St, Portland, OR 97216-3849
*Tel:* 503-255-3771 *Fax:* 503-255-3771
*Web Site:* www.nasja.org
*Key Personnel*
Pres: Phil Johnson
VP, Communs: Dave Fonda *E-mail:* davefonda@videotron.ca
Exec Secy & Treas: Vicki Andersen *E-mail:* execsec@nasja.org
Founded: 1963 (first founded as the US Ski Writers Assn)
Professional group of writers, photographers, broadcasters, filmmakers, authors & editors who report ski & snowboard related news, info & features throughout the US & Canada.
Number of Members: 340
New Election: Annually in March
2014 Meeting(s): Annual Meeting, Killington, VT, March 23-28, 2014
2015 Meeting(s): Annual Meeting, Quebec, QC, CN, Feb 10-15, 2015

**North Carolina Writers' Network**
PO Box 21591, Winston-Salem, NC 27120-1591
*Tel:* 336-293-8844
*Web Site:* www.ncwriters.org
*Key Personnel*
Exec Dir: Ed Southern
Founded: 1985
Nonprofit, statewide.
Number of Members: 1,500
Publication(s): *Writers' Network News* (semiannual, newspaper, free to membs)

**Northern California Independent Booksellers Association (NCIBA)**
1007 General Kennedy Ave, San Francisco, CA 94129
Mailing Address: PO Box 29169, San Francisco, CA 94129
*Tel:* 415-561-7686 *Fax:* 415-561-7685
*E-mail:* office@nciba.com
*Web Site:* www.nciba.com
*Key Personnel*
VP: Calvin Crosby
Exec Dir: Hut Landon
Trade Show Mgr: Carol Seajay
Tradeshow, education seminars, collaborative advertising, regional holiday catalog. Special memberships for authors include mailing list on labels & e-blast discounts.
Number of Members: 500
Publication(s): *Holiday Catalog*; *Newsletter* (bimonthly, free with membership); *Northern California Rep Directory*
Membership(s): ABA

**Northern California Translators Association**
Affiliate of Chapter of the American Translators Association
PO Box 14015, Berkeley, CA 94712-5015
*Tel:* 510-845-8712 *Fax:* 510-845-8712
*E-mail:* ncta@ncta.org
*Web Site:* www.ncta.org
*Key Personnel*
Pres: Sonia Wichman
Admin: Juliet Viola
Founded: 1978
Professional translators & interpreters association with an annual membership directory & online referral service.
Number of Members: 600
New Election: Annually in Feb
Publication(s): *Translorial* (3 issues/yr, print & online, newsletter, free to membs at www.translorial.com; free PDF access for *Translorial Reader* registrants at www.ncta.org)

**Northwest Independent Editors Guild**
PO Box 1630, Snoqualmie, WA 98065
*E-mail:* info@edsguild.org
*Web Site:* www.edsguild.org
*Key Personnel*
Administrator: Toddie Downs
Founded: 1997
Professional association of more than 200 editors in WA, OR & the greater Northwest. Members work on all types of communication projects, from brochures & newsletters to books & web sites. The Editors Guild connects clients with professional editors, fosters community among its members & provides resources for editors' career development.
Number of Members: 225

**Northwest Territories Library Services**
Unit of Education, Culture & Employment
75 Woodland Dr, Hay River, NT X0E 1G1, Canada
*Tel:* 867-874-6531 *Toll Free Tel:* 866-297-0232 (CN) *Fax:* 867-874-3321
*Web Site:* www.ece.gov.nt.ca/public_library_services/index.html
*Key Personnel*
Territorial Libn: Alison Hopkins *E-mail:* alison_hopkins@gov.nt.ca

**Northwest Writers & Publishers Association (NWPA)**
Division of Papyrus Press LLC
21860 Willamette Dr, West Linn, OR 97068
*Web Site:* northwestwriterspublishers.weebly.com
*Key Personnel*
Pres: Dr Veronica Esagui *Tel:* 503-913-6006 *Fax:* 503-212-3275
Founded: 2012
Medium for networking between authors & publishers. Membership fees: $50/yr (includes 12 lectures), nonmemb attending meeting $10, member's guest $5, no fee for students under 18. Guest speakers at monthly meetings.
Number of Members: 80
Meeting(s): NWPA Monthly Meeting, Tualatin Public Lib, Tualatin, OR, 2nd Tues of month; NW Annual Book Festival, Pioneer Courthouse Sq, Portland, OR, Annually last Sat of July

**NPES The Association for Suppliers of Printing, Publishing & Converting Technologies**
1899 Preston White Dr, Reston, VA 20191
*Tel:* 703-264-7200 *Fax:* 703-620-0994
*E-mail:* npes@npes.org
*Web Site:* www.npes.org
*Key Personnel*
Pres: Ralph J Nappi *E-mail:* rnappi@npes.org
Dir, Communs & Mktg: Deborah Vieder *E-mail:* dvieder@npes.org
Founded: 1933
Represent manufacturers & distributors of equipment, supplies, systems & software for printing, publishing & converting.
Number of Members: 400
2014 Meeting(s): Graph Expo®, McCormick Place, 2301 S Lake Shore Dr, Chicago, IL, Sept 28-Oct 1, 2014
2015 Meeting(s): Graph Expo®, McCormick Place, 2301 S Lake Shore Dr, Chicago, IL, Sept 13-16, 2015
Publication(s): *NPES Pressroom Safety Manual*; *Safe Cleaning of Offset Sheetfed Presses*; *Safe Cleaning of Offset Webfed Presses*

**NPTA Alliance**
401 N Michigan Ave, Suite 2200, Chicago, IL 60611
*Tel:* 312-321-4092 *Toll Free Tel:* 800-355-NPTA (355-6782) *Fax:* 312-673-6736
*E-mail:* npta@gonpta.com
*Web Site:* www.gonpta.com
*Key Personnel*
CEO & Pres: Kevin Gammonley
Mgr, Membership Opers: Gretchen Fox
Founded: 1903
Trade Association.
Number of Members: 2,600
New Election: Annually in Autumn
Publication(s): *Paper & Packaging* (bi-monthly, magazine)
Membership(s): National Association of Wholesaler-Distributors

**Ontario Library Association**
50 Wellington St E, Suite 201, Toronto, ON M5E 1C8, Canada
*Tel:* 416-363-3388 *Toll Free Tel:* 866-873-9867 *Fax:* 416-941-9581 *Toll Free Fax:* 800-387-1181
*E-mail:* info@accessola.com

*Web Site:* www.accessola.com
*Key Personnel*
Exec Dir: Shelagh Paterson *Tel:* 416-363-3388 ext 24 *E-mail:* spaterson@accessola.com
Founded: 1900
Memberships available: Personal membership (for one individual, based on salary earned in library work, whether full-time or part-time) $40-$100, Institutional Membership (for one or two-persons, transferable within an institution) $145-$195, Associate Membership (for businesses/corporations to provide support) $195.
Number of Members: 5,300
New Election: Annually in Dec
Publication(s): *Access* (quarterly, magazine, $36 CN); *The Teaching Librarian* (3 issues/yr, $36 CN)

**Ordre des traducteurs, terminologues et interpretes agrees du quebec**
Affiliate of Conseil des traducteurs, terminologues et interpretes du Canada
2021 Union Ave, Suite 1108, Montreal, QC H3A 2S9, Canada
*Tel:* 514-845-4411 *Toll Free Tel:* 800-265-4815 *Fax:* 514-845-9903
*E-mail:* info@ottiaq.org
*Web Site:* www.ottiaq.org
*Key Personnel*
Exec Dir: Johanne Boucher *Tel:* 514-845-4411 ext 227 *E-mail:* direction@ottiaq.org
Communs Coord: Catherine Guillemette-Bedard *Tel:* 514-845-4411 ext 225 *E-mail:* cgbedard@ottiaq.org
Bring translators together to exchange information, send out offers of employment to members. Promote profession & protect public interest. Conferences, annual meeting, social activities, seminars, continuing education. Newsletter for membs only.
Number of Members: 2,073
Publication(s): *Circuit* (quarterly, $42 CN, $50 elsewhere); *L'antenne Express* (newsletter)

**Oregon Christian Writers (OCW)**
1075 Willow Lake Rd N, Keizer, OR 97303
*Tel:* 503-393-3356
*E-mail:* contact@oregonchristianwriters.org
*Web Site:* www.oregonchristianwriters.org
*Key Personnel*
Pres: Maxine Marsolini
Prog Chmn: Marilyn Rhoads
Summer Conference Dir: Lindy Jacobs *E-mail:* summerconf@oregonchristianwriters.org
Registrar & Busn Mgr: Sue Miholer
Founded: 1963
Workshops & seminars for beginning & advanced writers; guest speakers & critiques by professional writers.
Number of Members: 325
New Election: Annually in Oct
2014 Meeting(s): Oregon Christian Writers Seminar, Salem, OR, Feb 22, 2014; Oregon Christian Writers Seminar, Eugene, OR, May 17, 2014; Summer Coaching Conference, Jantzen Beach Red Lion Hotel, Portland, OR, Aug 4-7, 2014; Oregon Christian Writers Seminar, Portland, OR, Oct 12, 2014
Publication(s): *Oregon Christian Writers Newsletter* (3 issues/yr, newsletter)

**Organization of Book Publishers of Ontario**
20 Maud St, No 401, Toronto, ON M5V 2M5, Canada
*Tel:* 416-536-7584 *Fax:* 416-536-7692
*Web Site:* www.ontariobooks.ca
*Key Personnel*
Dir: Marg Anne Morrison
Informational, professional development, group marketing & lobbying services for members.
Number of Members: 43

**Overseas Press Club of America (OPC)**
40 W 45 St, New York, NY 10036
*Tel:* 212-626-9220 *Fax:* 212-626-9210
*Web Site:* www.opcofamerica.org
*Key Personnel*
Exec Dir: Sonya K Fry *E-mail:* sonya@opcofamerica.org
Founded: 1939
Maintain an international association of journalists, encourage professional skill & integrity of reportage, contribute to the freedom & independence of journalism & the press worldwide.
Number of Members: 425
New Election: Annually in Aug
Publication(s): *Bulletin* (monthly, newsletter, free to membs); *Dateline* (annual, magazine, free to membs)

**Pacific Northwest Booksellers Association**
338 W 11 Ave, Unit 108, Eugene, OR 97401
*Tel:* 541-683-4363 *Fax:* 541-683-3910
*E-mail:* info@pnba.org
*Web Site:* www.pnba.org; www.northwestbooklovers.org (public site)
*Key Personnel*
Exec Dir: Thom Chambliss *E-mail:* thom@pnba.org
Mktg Dir: Brian Juenemann *E-mail:* brian@pnba.org
Founded: 1965
Annual trade, lists of publishing companies' sales reps, educational seminars; work with local literacy groups & anticensorship organizations. Sponsor annual booksellers awards presented for books of exceptional quality by Northwest writers or publishers. Sponsor workshops & prizes. Rent mailing list of over 800 plus Northwest Bookstores.
Number of Members: 450
Publication(s): *Annual Rep List & Handbook* (annual online, handbook, free to membs); *Footnotes* (monthly e-mail, newsletter, free to membs)

**Pacific Northwest Writers Association**
1420 NW Gilman Blvd, Suite 2, PMB 2717, Issaquah, WA 98027
*Tel:* 425-673-2665 *Fax:* 425-961-0768
*E-mail:* pnwa@pnwa.org
*Web Site:* www.pnwa.org
*Key Personnel*
Pres: Pam Binder
Founded: 1956
Nonprofit association. Develops writing talent from pen to publication through education, accessibility to publishing industry & participation in a vital writer community.
Number of Members: 1,400

**Pacific Printing Industries Association**
Affiliate of Printing Industries of America
6825 SW Sandburg St, Portland, OR 97223
Mailing Address: PO Box 23575, Portland, OR 97281-3575
*Tel:* 503-221-3944 *Toll Free Tel:* 877-762-7742 *Fax:* 503-221-5691
*E-mail:* info@ppiassociation.org
*Web Site:* www.ppiassociation.org
*Key Personnel*
Exec Dir: Jules Van Sant *E-mail:* jules@ppiassociation.org
Trade association.
Number of Members: 230

**Palm Springs Writers Guild**
PO Box 947, Rancho Mirage, CA 92270-0947
*Web Site:* www.palmspringswritersguild.org
*Key Personnel*
Pres: James D McFarlin *Tel:* 775-530-2929 *E-mail:* president.pswg@gmail.com
VP, Membership: Diana Miller *Tel:* 760-574-4038 *E-mail:* vpmembership.pswg@gmail.com
Founded: 1977
Number of Members: 200

**PEN American Center**
Affiliate of International PEN
588 Broadway, Suite 303, New York, NY 10012
*Tel:* 212-334-1660 *Fax:* 212-334-2181
*E-mail:* info@pen.org
*Web Site:* www.pen.org
*Key Personnel*
Exec Dir: Suzanne Nossel
Pres: Peter Godwin
Intl Pres: John Ralston Saul
Dir, Membership, Marketing & Literary Awards: Paul Morris
Membership, Literary Awards & Writers' Fund Assoc: Arielle Anema *Tel:* 212-334-1660 ext 126 *E-mail:* arielle@pen.org
An association of writers working to advance literature, defend free expression & foster international literary fellowship.
Number of Members: 3,300
Publication(s): *Grants & Awards Available to American Writers* (online directory, $12)

**PEN Canada**
24 Ryerson Ave, Suite 301, Toronto, ON M5T 2P3, Canada
*Tel:* 416-703-8448 *Fax:* 416-703-3870
*E-mail:* queries@pencanada.ca
*Web Site:* www.pencanada.ca
*Key Personnel*
Pres: Charlie Foran
Exec Dir: Tasleem Thawar *Tel:* 416-703-8448 ext 22
Administrator: Kasey Coholan *Tel:* 416-703-8448 ext 25
Progs & Communs Coord: Brendan De Cairns *Tel:* 416-703-8448 ext 21
Founded: 1926
Number of Members: 1,000

**PEN Center USA**
Affiliate of International PEN
PO Box 6037, Beverly Hills, CA 90212
*Tel:* 323-424-4939 *Fax:* 323-424-4944
*E-mail:* pen@penusa.org
*Web Site:* www.penusa.org
*Key Personnel*
Bd Chair: Marvin Putnam
Secy & Treas: Robert Wallace
VP, Progs: Jamie Wolf
Exec Dir: Adam Somers
Progs Dir: Michelle Meyering
Founded: 1943
National association of poets, playwrights, screenwriters, essayists, editors, novelists, historians, critics, journalists & translators whose purpose is to foster a sense of community among writers in the Western US & to advance the freedom to write throughout the world.
Number of Members: 800
Publication(s): *Electric PEN* (biweekly); *Membership Directory* (annual)

**PEN New England**
Unit of PEN American Center
Massachusetts Institute of Technology, 77 Massachusetts Ave, 14-N-221A, Cambridge, MA 02139
*Tel:* 617-324-1729
*E-mail:* pen-newengland@mit.edu
*Web Site:* www.pen-ne.org
*Key Personnel*
Exec Dir: Karen Wulf
Advance the cause of literature & reading in New England & defending free expression everywhere.

**Periodical & Book Association of America Inc**
481 Eighth Ave, Suite 526, New York, NY 10001

*Tel:* 212-563-6502 *Fax:* 212-563-4098
*Web Site:* www.pbaa.net
*Key Personnel*
Exec Dir: Lisa Scott
Assoc Dir: Jose Cancio *E-mail:* jcancio@pbaa.net
Trade organization for newsstand publishers.
Number of Members: 102

**Photographic Society of America® (PSA®)**
3000 United Founders Blvd, Suite 103, Oklahoma City, OK 73112
*Tel:* 405-843-1437 *Toll Free Tel:* 855-PSA-INFO (855-772-4636) *Fax:* 405-843-1438
*E-mail:* hq@psa-photo.org
*Web Site:* www.psa-photo.org
*Key Personnel*
Opers Mgr: Kara Goodson
Sponsor workshops & awards for members.
Number of Members: 6,500
2014 Meeting(s): PSA® International Confernece of Photography, Albuquerque Marriott, 2101 Louisiana Blvd NE, Albuquerque, NM, Sept 27-Oct 3, 2014
2015 Meeting(s): PSA® International Confernece of Photography, Holiday Inn West Yellowstone, West Yellowstone, MT, Sept 27-Oct 3, 2015
Publication(s): *PSA Journal* (journal, $45/yr North America, $53/intl)

**Playwrights Guild of Canada**
215 Spadina Ave, Suite 210, Toronto, ON M5T 2C7, Canada
*Tel:* 416-703-0201 *Fax:* 416-703-0059
*E-mail:* info@playwrightsguild.ca
*Web Site:* www.playwrightsguild.ca
*Key Personnel*
Exec Dir: Robin Sokoloski
Membership Coord: Debra Anderson
Founded: 1982
Contracts, amateur agent productions, script service, readings.
Number of Members: 507
Membership(s): Professional Association of Canadian Playwrights

**Poetry Society of America (PSA)**
15 Gramercy Park S, New York, NY 10003
*Tel:* 212-254-9628 *Fax:* 212-673-2352
*Web Site:* www.poetrysociety.org
*Key Personnel*
Pres: Ruth Kaplan
Exec Dir: Alice Quinn
Mng Dir & Awards Coord: Brett Fletcher Lauer *E-mail:* brett@poetrysociety.org
Progs Dir: Darrel Alejandro Holnes
Founded: 1910
Contests, readings, lectures, symposia, seminars, weekly workshops for members.
Number of Members: 2,900
Publication(s): *Crossroads* (semiannual, free to membs)

**Poets & Writers Inc**
90 Broad St, Suite 2100, New York, NY 10004
*Tel:* 212-226-3586 *Fax:* 212-226-3963
*Web Site:* www.pw.org
*Key Personnel*
Exec Dir: Elliot Figman
Founded: 1970
A nonprofit organization which offers information, support & exposure to writers at all stages in their careers. Founded to foster the development of poets & fiction writers & to promote communication throughout the literary community. It publishes the bimonthly *Poets & Writers Magazine*, which delivers to its readers profiles of noted authors & publishing professionals, practical how-to articles, a comprehensive listing of grants & awards for writers & special sections on subjects ranging from small presses to writers conferences. The Readings/Workshops Program supports public literary events through matching grants to community organizations.
Distributed by Small Press Distribution
Publication(s): *Poets & Writers Magazine* (bimonthly, $19.95/yr, $38/2 yrs, $4.95 single copy 1999 forward; prior to 1999 $3.95)

**PreK-12 Learning Group**
Formerly The Association of Educational Publishers (AEP)
Division of Association of American Publishers (AAP)
325 Chestnut St, Suite 1110, Philadelphia, PA 19106
*Tel:* 267-351-4310 *Fax:* 267-351-4317
*E-mail:* prek12learning@publishers.org
*Web Site:* www.aepweb.org
*Key Personnel*
Exec Dir: Jay Diskey
Sr Dir: Susan Fletcher
Strategic Partnerships Exec: Jo-Ann McDevitt
Dir, Policy & Res: Julie Copty
Edit Dir: Stacey Pusey
Membership Dir: Colleen Quigley
Dir, Communs Technol & Proj Mgr, LRMI: Dave Gladney
Mktg Mgr: Laura Soule
Prog Mgr: Linda Swank
Communs Assoc: Brittany Lawrence
Communs Assoc, LRMI: John Micklos
Supports educational publishing through its programs & member services.
Number of Members: 350

**PRIMIR**, see Print Industries Market Information & Research Organization

**Print Industries Market Information & Research Organization**
Affiliate of NPES The Association for Suppliers of Printing, Publishing & Converting Technologies
1899 Preston White Dr, Reston, VA 20191
*Tel:* 703-264-7200 *Fax:* 703-620-0994
*E-mail:* info@primir.org
*Web Site:* www.primir.org; www.npes.org/primirresearch/primir.aspx
*Key Personnel*
Mng Dir: Jacqueline Bland *E-mail:* jbland@primir.org
Research association of the graphic arts industry; provide data & research to printers, publishers & manufacturers of equipment & supplies for the printing/publishing industry & converting industries.
Number of Members: 60
New Election: Annually in Dec

**Printing & Graphing Association MidAtlantic**
9685 Gerwig Lane, Columbia, MD 21046
*Tel:* 410-319-0900 *Toll Free Tel:* 877-319-0906 *Fax:* 410-319-0905
*E-mail:* info@pgama.com
*Web Site:* www.pgama.com
*Key Personnel*
Pres: Kerry C Stackpole *E-mail:* kerry@pgama.com
Founded: 1894
Number of Members: 360

**Printing Association of Florida Inc**
6275 Hazeltine National Dr, Orlando, FL 32822
*Tel:* 407-240-8009 *Toll Free Tel:* 800-331-0461 *Fax:* 407-240-8333
*Web Site:* www.pafgraf.org
*Key Personnel*
CEO & Pres: George Ryan
Dir, Membership & Pub Aff: Harold Yankelevitz
Founded: 1937
Trade association for the graphic arts industry.
Number of Members: 593
Publication(s): *Graphics Update* (monthly, free to membs)

**Printing Brokerage/Buyers Association**
1530 Locust St, Mezzanine 124, Philadelphia, PA 19102
*Tel:* 215-821-6581 *Fax:* 215-893-3671
*E-mail:* contactus@pbba.org
*Web Site:* pbba.org
*Key Personnel*
Dir: Vincent Mallardi *E-mail:* vince@pbba.org
Founded: 1985
Trade association for printing, sales brokerage & purchasing.
Number of Members: 830
Publication(s): *Brokerage* (monthly, newsletter, free to membs); *Hot Markets for Print Media* (annual, $995); *Law v. Print* ($395); *Why Use A Printing Independent* ($95)
*Branch Office(s)*
74-5576 Pawai Place, No 600, Kailua Kona, HI 96740 *Tel:* 808-339-0880

**Printing Industries of America**
200 Deer Run Rd, Sewickley, PA 15143-2600
*Tel:* 412-741-6860 *Toll Free Tel:* 800-910-4283 *Fax:* 412-741-2311
*E-mail:* printing@printing.org
*Web Site:* www.printing.org
*Key Personnel*
CEO & Pres: Michael Makin *E-mail:* mmakin@printing.org
Sr Custom Training & Consulting Specialist: Karen Keller *E-mail:* kkeller@printing.org
Founded: 1924
Member organization providing research, educational & technical services to printing industry worldwide.
Number of Members: 14,000
Publication(s): *The Magazine* (bimonthly, $75/yr); *Publications Catalog* (annual, free); *QC Catalog* (annual, free)

**Printing Industries Press**, see Printing Industries of America

**Printing Industry Association of the South**
305 Plus Park Blvd, Nashville, TN 37217
*Tel:* 615-366-1094 *Toll Free Tel:* 800-821-3138 *Fax:* 615-366-4192
*E-mail:* info@pias.org
*Web Site:* www.pias.org
*Key Personnel*
Pres: Ed Chalifoux
Provide services & support to the printing industry.
Number of Members: 500
Publication(s): *Print South* (monthly, magazine, free with membership)

**Professional Writers Association of Canada (PWAC)**
215 Spadina Ave, Suite 130, Toronto, ON M5T 2C7, Canada
*Tel:* 416-504-1645
*E-mail:* info@pwac.ca
*Web Site:* www.pwac.ca; www.writers.ca
*Key Personnel*
Exec Dir: Sandy Crawley
Gen Mgr: Margaret DeRosia *Tel:* 416-504-1645 ext 1
Protect & promote the interests of freelance writers in Canada, develop & maintain professional standards in editor-writer relationships, lobby for higher standard fees for freelancers, sponsor professional development workshops & offset freelancers' isolation by circulating news, information & market data on the industry.
Number of Members: 625

Publication(s): *PWAC Guide to Editing as a Sideline* (book, $21.40 per copy, GST included); *PWAC Guide to Roughing in the Market* (book, $24.60 per copy, plus postage)

**Protestant Church-Owned Publishers Association**
6631 Westbury Oaks Ct, Springfield, VA 22152
*Tel:* 703-220-5989
*Web Site:* www.pcpaonline.org
*Key Personnel*
Assoc Dir: Gary Mulder *E-mail:* mulder@pcpaonline.org
Founded: 1951
Number of Members: 40

**Public Relations Society of America Inc**
33 Maiden Lane, 11th fl, New York, NY 10038-5150
*Tel:* 212-460-1400 *Fax:* 212-995-0757
*Web Site:* www.prsa.org
*Key Personnel*
CFO: Philip Bonaventura *Tel:* 212-460-1440 *E-mail:* philip.bonaventura@prsa.org
COO & Pres: William Murray *Tel:* 212-460-1401 *E-mail:* william.murray@prsa.org
Founded: 1947
Association of public relations professionals dedicated to development & ethical practice of public relations.
Publication(s): *Public Relations Tactics* (monthly, $100/yr); *The Strategist* (quarterly, $150/yr)

**Publishers Association of the West (PubWest)**
17501 Hill Way, Lake Oswego, OR 97035
*Tel:* 503-635-0056 *Fax:* 602-234-3062
*E-mail:* executivedirector@pubwest.org
*Web Site:* www.pubwest.org
*Key Personnel*
Pres: Derek Lawrence
Exec Dir: Kent Watson *E-mail:* executivedirector@pubwest.org
Founded: 1977
Members are small & medium-sized book publishers located throughout North America. Supply marketing & technical information to members; conduct annual educational seminars; promote sales in the region. Trade show, including BEA, MPBA & PNBA. Publisher of the Huenefeld-PubWest Survey of Financial Operations.
Number of Members: 360
Publication(s): *The Endsheet* (quarterly, journal, free); *PubWest Membership Directory* (annual, directory, free to membs, $10 for nonmembs)

**Publishers Information Bureau (PIB)**
Division of Magazine Publishers of America
810 Seventh Ave, 24th fl, New York, NY 10019
*Tel:* 212-872-3700 *Fax:* 212-753-2768
*E-mail:* pib@magazine.org
*Web Site:* www.magazine.org
*Key Personnel*
Pres: Wayne Eadie *Tel:* 212-872-3722
Measure advertising pages & rate card revenues in consumer magazines & newspaper supplements.
Number of Members: 250

**Publishing Professionals Network**
Formerly Bookbuilders West (BBW)
9328 Elk Grove, Suite 105-250, Elk Grove, CA 95624
*Tel:* 916-320-0638
*E-mail:* operations@bookbuilders.org
*Web Site:* www.bookbuilders.org
*Key Personnel*
Pres: David Zielonka
Founded: 1969
Specialize in supporting the book publishing industry. Offers educational programs, seminars, scholarships. Produces an annual book show & has monthly dinner meetings.
Number of Members: 400
New Election: Annually in June
Publication(s): *Bookbuilders West Newsletter* (5 times/yr, newsletter)

**The Publishing Pros**, see Rocky Mountain Publishing Professionals Guild (RMPPG)

**PubWest**, see Publishers Association of the West (PubWest)

**Quebec Writers' Federation (QWF)**
1200 Atwater Ave, Suite 3, Westmount, QC H3Z 1X4, Canada
*Tel:* 514-933-0878
*E-mail:* info@qwf.org
*Web Site:* www.qwf.org
*Key Personnel*
Exec Dir: Lori Schubert *E-mail:* admin@qwf.org
Coord, Membership Servs & Communs: Julia Kater *E-mail:* julia@qwf.org
Association of Quebec writers to promote English language writing in Quebec through literary awards, writing workshops & literary events.
Number of Members: 545

**Reporters Committee for Freedom of the Press**
1101 Wilson Blvd, Suite 1100, Arlington, VA 22209-1817
*Tel:* 703-807-2100 *Toll Free Tel:* 800-336-4243 *Fax:* 703-807-2109
*E-mail:* rcfp@rcfp.org
*Web Site:* www.rcfp.org
*Key Personnel*
Exec Dir: Bruce Brown
Founded: 1970
Legal defense & research services for journalists & media lawyers.
Publication(s): *Access to Electronic Communications* (handbook, $3); *Access to Electronic Records* (handbook, $5); *Access to Juvenile Courts* (handbook, $3); *Access to Places* ($3); *Access to Police Records* (handbook, $3); *Agents of Discovery* (report, $3); *Alternative Dispute Resolution* (handbook, $3); *Anonymous Juries* (report, $3); *Campaign Reporting* (handbook, $3); *Can We Tape* ($3); *Compendium* (handbook, $50); *Confidential Sources & Information* (handbook, $3); *FERPA, HIPAA & DPPA* (handbook, $3); *First Amendment Handbook* ($7.50); *FOI Guide Book* (handbook, $10); *Gag Orders* (handbook, $3); *Grand Juries* (handbook, $3); *Homefront Confidential* (handbook, $10); *Judicial Speech* (handbook, $3); *Jury Proceedings & Records* (handbook, $3); *The Lost Stories* (handbook, $3); *The News Media & the Law* (quarterly, magazine, $30); *Off Base: Military Court Dockets* (handbook, $3); *Online Access to Plea Agreements* (handbook, $3); *Open Government Guide, 5th ed* ($10); *Photographer's Guide to Privacy* (handbook, $3); *Press Impasses* (handbook, $2); *The Privacy Paradox* ($3); *Private Eyes* (handbook, $3); *Privatization v the Public's Right to Know* (handbook, $3); *A Reporter's Field Guide* (handbook, $3); *A Reporter's Guide to American Indian Law* (handbook, $3); *A Reporter's Guide to Medical Privacy Law* (handbook, $3); *A Reporter's Guide to Military Justice* (handbook, $3); *Secret Docket* (handbook, $3); *Secret Juries* (handbook, $3); *Star Treatment* (handbook, $3); *Sunshine Inc* (handbook, $3); *Warrants & Wiretaps* (handbook, $3); *White Paper: Military Dockets* (handbook, $3)

**Rocky Mountain Publishing Professionals Guild (RMPPG)**
PO Box 19013, Boulder, CO 80308
*E-mail:* membership@rmppg.org
*Web Site:* thepublishingpros.org
*Key Personnel*
Pres: Jean Charney
VP: Robert Schram
Treas: Bobette Host
Communs Offr: Margaret Pevec
Founded: 1991
Professional nonprofit freelancers association of editors, designers, indexers, researchers, writers, proofreaders & marketing & production specialists. Promotes the business & professional interests of its members through contact with publishers, clients & colleagues, enhancement of skills & standards & encouragement of professional ethics. Dues $40 annually.
Number of Members: 75
Publication(s): *Membership Directory* (online)

**Romance Writers of America®**
14615 Benfer Rd, Houston, TX 77069
*Tel:* 832-717-5200 *Fax:* 832-717-5201
*E-mail:* info@rwa.org
*Web Site:* www.rwa.org
*Key Personnel*
Exec Dir: Allison Kelley *Tel:* 832-717-5200 ext 124 *E-mail:* allison.kelley@rwa.org
Romance Writers of America is dedicated to advancing the professional interests of career-focused romance writers through networking & advocacy.
Membership: $95/yr; $110/yr for 1st class postage. New member fee, $25.
Number of Members: 10,000
2014 Meeting(s): Annual Conference, San Antonio Marriott® Rivercenter & Marriott® Riverwalk, San Antonio, TX, July 23-26, 2014
2015 Meeting(s): Annual Conference, New York Marriott® Marquis, New York, NY, July 22-25, 2015
2016 Meeting(s): Annual Conference, San Diego Marriott Hotel and Marina, San Diego, CA, July 13-16, 2016
2017 Meeting(s): Annual Conference, Walt Disney World Swan and Dolphin, 1500 Epcot Resorts Blvd, Lake Buena Vista, FL, July 26-29, 2017
Publication(s): *Romance Writers Report* (monthly, magazine)

**SABEW**, see Society of American Business Editors & Writers Inc (SABEW)

**Saskatchewan Arts Board**
1355 Broad St, Regina, SK S4R 7V1, Canada
*Tel:* 306-787-4056 *Toll Free Tel:* 800-667-7526 (Saskatchewan only) *Fax:* 306-787-4199
*E-mail:* info@artsboard.sk.ca
*Web Site:* www.artsboard.sk.ca
*Key Personnel*
Exec Dir: David Kyle
Provide consultation, advice, grants, programs &/or services to individual artists, arts groups & organizations & members of the public. Programs support & encourage the development of artists, arts groups & organizations in the literary, performing, visual, media & multidisciplinary arts. Also develop & maintain a permanent collection of original works by Saskatchewan artists.

**Science Fiction & Fantasy Writers of America Inc (SFWA)**
PO Box 3238, Enfield, CT 06083-3238
*E-mail:* office@sfwa.org
*Web Site:* www.sfwa.org
*Key Personnel*
Pres: Steven Gould
VP: Rachel Swirsky
Founded: 1965

An organization of professional writers, editors, artists, agents & others in the science fiction & fantasy field.
Number of Members: 1,800
New Election: Annually in May
Publication(s): *Annual Membership Directory*; *SFWA Bulletin* (quarterly, $38/yr nonmembs, $48/yr foreign nonmembs)

**SF Canada**
7433 E River Rd, Washago, ON L0K 2B0, Canada
*Web Site:* www.sfcanada.org
*Key Personnel*
Pres: Steve Stanton
VP: Susan Forest
Treas & Secy: Sherry Ramsey
Founded: 1989
Exists to foster a sense of community among Canadian writers of speculative fiction, to improve communication between Canadian writers of speculative fiction, to foster the growth of quality writing in Canadian speculative fiction, to lobby on behalf of Canadian writers of speculative fiction & to encourage the translation of Canadian speculative fiction. Supports positive social action.
Number of Members: 150

**SHARP**, see Society for the History of Authorship, Reading & Publishing Inc (SHARP)

**SIBA**, see Southern Independent Booksellers Alliance

**Small Publishers, Artists & Writers Network (SPAWN)**
323 E Matilija St, Suite 110, PMB 123, Ojai, CA 93023
*Tel:* 805-646-3045 *Fax:* 805-640-8213
*Web Site:* www.spawn.org
*Key Personnel*
Pres: Susan Daffron *E-mail:* susan@spawn.org
Exec Dir: Patricia Fry *E-mail:* patricia@spawn.org
Founded: 1996
Number of Members: 200

**Small Publishers Association of North America (SPAN)**, see Association of Publishers for Special Sales (APSS)

**Social Sciences & Humanities Research Council of Canada (SSHRC)**
350 Albert St, Ottawa, ON K1P 6G4, Canada
Mailing Address: PO Box 1610, Ottawa, ON K1P 6G4, Canada
*Tel:* 613-992-0691 *Fax:* 613-992-1787
*E-mail:* z-info@sshrc.ca
*Web Site:* www.sshrc.ca
*Key Personnel*
Pres: Chad Gaffield *Tel:* 613-995-5488 *E-mail:* chad.gaffield@sshrc.ca
Founded: (SSHRC is a Federal Crown Corporation)
Offers two programs of support for scholarly publishing: aid to scholarly publication program, aid to research & transfer journal program. Only Canadian citizens or permanent residents of Canada are eligible to apply under either program.
Number of Members: 22

**Sociedad Interamericana de Prenza (SIP)**, see Inter American Press Association (IAPA)

**Society for Features Journalism (SFJ)**
University of Maryland, College of Journalism, 1100 Knight Hall, College Park, MD 20742
*Tel:* 301-314-2631 *Fax:* 301-314-9166
*Web Site:* featuresjournalism.org
*Key Personnel*
Bd Pres & Features Ed: Gretchen Day-Bryant *Tel:* 954-356-4718 *E-mail:* gday@sunsentinel.com
Exec Dir: Merrilee Cox *E-mail:* merrileesfj@gmail.com
Asst Mng Ed, Features: Alice Short *Tel:* 213-232-3408 *E-mail:* alice.short@latimes.com
Nonprofit trade association of Sunday & feature editors.
Number of Members: 250
Publication(s): *Style Magazine* (annual)

**Society for Scholarly Publishing (SSP)**
10200 W 44 Ave, Suite 304, Wheat Ridge, CO 80033-2840
*Tel:* 303-422-3914 *Fax:* 303-422-8894
*E-mail:* info@sspnet.org
*Web Site:* www.sspnet.org
*Key Personnel*
Exec Dir: Ann Mehan Crosse *Tel:* 303-422-8436 *E-mail:* amcross@resourcecenter.com
Founded: 1978
Professional association for people in scholarly publishing industry; 12-16 seminars/workshops sponsored each year. Top Management Roundtable.
Number of Members: 1,000
2014 Meeting(s): Annual Meeting, Westin™ Boston Waterfront, 425 Summer St, Boston, MA, May 28-30, 2014
Publication(s): *Directory* (annual, membs only)

**Society for Technical Communication**
9401 Lee Hwy, Suite 300, Fairfax, VA 22031
*Tel:* 703-522-4114 *Fax:* 703-522-2075
*E-mail:* stc@stc.org
*Web Site:* www.stc.org
*Key Personnel*
Exec Dir: Chris Lyons *Tel:* 571-366-1901 *E-mail:* chris.lyons@stc.org
Deputy Exec Dir: Lloyd Tucker *Tel:* 571-366-1904 *E-mail:* lloyd.tucker@stc.org
Professional society dedicated to the advancement of the theory & practice of technical communication in all media.
Number of Members: 15,000
Publication(s): *Intercom* (monthly, magazine, free to membs); *Technical Communication* (quarterly, journal, free to membs, $75/yr nonmembs)

**Society for the History of Authorship, Reading & Publishing Inc (SHARP)**
c/o The Johns Hopkins University Press, Journals Publishing Div, PO Box 19966, Baltimore, MD 21211-0966
*Tel:* 910-254-0308
*E-mail:* members@sharpweb.org
*Web Site:* www.sharpweb.org
*Key Personnel*
Pres: Leslie Howsam
Membership Secy: Eleanor F Shevlin
Promotes the study of book history among academics & non-academics. Publishing & scholarly attention to its history.
Number of Members: 1,175
Publication(s): *Book History* (annual, journal, included with individual membership, $55 in US & CN, $60 elsewhere); *SHARP News* (quarterly, included with membership); *SHARP Online Membership & Periodicals Directory* (annual, access to online included with membership)

**Society of American Business Editors & Writers Inc (SABEW)**
Walter Cronkite School of Journalism & Mass Communication, Arizona State University, 555 N Central Ave, Suite 302, Phoenix, AZ 85004-1248
*Tel:* 602-496-7862 *Fax:* 602-496-7041
*E-mail:* sabew@sabew.org
*Web Site:* sabew.org
*Key Personnel*
Exec Dir: Warren Watson *Tel:* 602-496-5186 *E-mail:* watson@sabew.org
Founded: 1964
Professional development. Sponsor regional workshops. Specialize in business journalism.
Number of Members: 3,200
2014 Meeting(s): Spring Conference, Walter Cronkite School of Journalism & Mass Communication, Arizona State University, Phoenix, AZ, March 27-29, 2014

**Society of American Travel Writers**
11950 W Lake Park Dr, Suite 320, Milwaukee, WI 53224-3049
*Tel:* 414-359-1625 *Fax:* 414-359-1671
*E-mail:* info@satw.org
*Web Site:* www.satw.org
Founded: 1959
Promote responsible journalism, provide professional support & development for our members, encourage the conservation & preservation of travel resources worldwide.
Number of Members: 1,100
Publication(s): *Directory of Members* (annual, $250/yr print or diskette)

**Society of Children's Book Writers & Illustrators (SCBWI)**
8271 Beverly Blvd, Los Angeles, CA 90048
*Tel:* 323-782-1010 *Fax:* 323-782-1892
*E-mail:* membership@scbwi.org; scbwi@scbwi.org
*Web Site:* www.scbwi.org
*Key Personnel*
Pres: Stephen Mooser *E-mail:* stephenmooser@scbwi.org
Exec Dir: Lin Oliver *E-mail:* linoliver@scbwi.org
Founded: 1971
An organization of children's writers & illustrators & others devoted to the interests of children's literature; annual workshops & conferences throughout the world.
Number of Members: 22,000
2014 Meeting(s): Winter Conference, Grand Hyatt New York, 109 E 42 St at Grand Central Terminal, New York, NY, Feb 21-23, 2014; Summer Conference, Los Angeles, CA, Aug 2014
Publication(s): *SCBWI Bulletin* (6 issues/yr, newsletter, with membership)

**Society of Illustrators (SI)**
128 E 63 St, New York, NY 10065
*Tel:* 212-838-2560 *Fax:* 212-838-2561
*E-mail:* info@societyillustrators.org
*Web Site:* www.societyillustrators.org
*Key Personnel*
Dir: Anelle Miller *E-mail:* anelle@societyillustrators.org
Founded: 1901
Museum of American Illustration.
Number of Members: 950
New Election: Annually in June
Publication(s): *American Illustrators* (annual, $45)

**The Society of Midland Authors (SMA)**
PO Box 10419, Chicago, IL 60610
*E-mail:* info@midlandauthors.com
*Web Site:* www.midlandauthors.com
*Key Personnel*
Pres: Robert Loerzel *E-mail:* loerzel@comcast.net
VP: Meg Tebo
Treas: Richard Bales
Corresponding Secy: Charles J Masters
Recording Secy: Anastasia Royal

Newsletter Ed: Tom Frisbie *E-mail:* tomfrisbie@aol.com
Webmaster: Mary Claire Hersh *E-mail:* maryclaire@prodigy.net
Founded: 1915
Nonprofit writer's association that seeks to stimulate creative efforts & closer association among Midwest writers; maintain collections of writer's works & encourage interest in reading, literature & writing in cooperation with other educational & cultural institutions. Members are qualified authors & co-authors of works from recognized publishers or associates (nonvoting) who live in Illinois, Indiana, Kansas, Michigan, Minnesota, Missouri & Nebraska. Monthly literary & professional programs, annual awards dinner, $500 & certificate, for best books of previous year in six categories: adult fiction & nonfiction, children's fiction & nonfiction, poetry & biography.
Number of Members: 400
Publication(s): *Literary License* (monthly, newsletter)

**Society of Motion Picture & Television Engineers (SMPTE)**
3 Barker Ave, 5th fl, White Plains, NY 10601
*Tel:* 914-761-1100 *Fax:* 914-761-3115
*Web Site:* www.smpte.org
*Key Personnel*
Exec Dir: Barbara Lange *Tel:* 914-205-2370
Dir, Engg: Peter Symes *Tel:* 914-205-2371
Founded: 1916
To advance theory & practice of engineering in film, TV, motion imaging & allied arts & sciences; establishment of standards & practices. Annual membership dues are $135.
Number of Members: 8,000
Publication(s): *SMPTE Motion Imaging Journal* (monthly, journal, free with membership or $140 subn US & $155 elsewhere)

**The Society of Professional Journalists**
Eugene S Pulliam National Journalism Ctr, 3909 N Meridian St, Indianapolis, IN 46208
*Tel:* 317-927-8000 *Fax:* 317-920-4789
*E-mail:* spj@spj.org
*Web Site:* www.spj.org
*Key Personnel*
Exec Dir: Joe Skeel *Tel:* 317-927-8000 ext 216 *E-mail:* jskeel@spj.org
Assoc Exec Dir: Chris Vachon *Tel:* 317-927-8000 ext 207 *E-mail:* cvachon@spj.org
Dir, Events: Heather Dunn *Tel:* 317-927-8000 ext 204 *E-mail:* hdunn@spj.org
Founded: 1909
Promote professional development in journalism.
Number of Members: 10,000
2014 Meeting(s): Excellence in Journalism, Gaylord Opryland Resort & Conference Ctr, 2800 Opryland Dr, Nashville, TN, Sept 4-6, 2014
Publication(s): *Quill* (6 times/yr, magazine, $75/yr, free for membs)

**The Society of Southwestern Authors (SSA)**
PO Box 30355, Tucson, AZ 85751-0355
*Tel:* 520-546-9382 *Fax:* 520-751-7877
*E-mail:* wporter202@aol.com
*Web Site:* www.ssa-az.org
*Key Personnel*
Pres: Penny Porter
Founded: 1972
Award one or more annual scholarships to promising new writers. Writers networking short story contest, 16 winning stories published in *The Story Teller* plus money prizes. Four first prizes for categories Short Fiction, Memoir, Poetry, Short Stories for Children ages 6-12.
Number of Members: 400
Publication(s): *The Write Word* (6 issues/yr, newsletter, free to membs)

**Software & Information Industry Association (SIIA)**
1090 Vermont Ave NW, 6th fl, Washington, DC 20005-4095
*Tel:* 202-289-7442 *Fax:* 202-289-7097
*E-mail:* info@siia.net
*Web Site:* www.siia.net
*Key Personnel*
Pres: Kenneth Wasch *Tel:* 202-789-4440
VP, Membership: Eric Fredell *Tel:* 202-789-4464
Principal trade association of the software & information industry.
Number of Members: 850
Publication(s): *Upgrade* (bimonthly, magazine, free to membs, $79 nonmembs)

**Southern Independent Booksellers Alliance**
3806 Yale Ave, Columbia, SC 29205
*Tel:* 803-994-9530 *Fax:* 309-410-0211
*E-mail:* info@sibaweb.com
*Web Site:* www.sibaweb.com
*Key Personnel*
Exec Dir: Wanda Jewell *E-mail:* wanda@sibaweb.com
Number of Members: 500
2014 Meeting(s): Southern Independent Booksellers Alliance Trade Show, Hilton, Norfolk, VA, Sept 19-21, 2014
Publication(s): *SEBA Holiday Catalog* (contact Ingram Book Co)

**Special Libraries Association (SLA)**
331 S Patrick St, Alexandria, VA 22314-3501
*Tel:* 703-647-4900 *Fax:* 703-647-4901
*E-mail:* sla@sla.org
*Web Site:* www.sla.org
*Key Personnel*
COO: Doug Newcomb *E-mail:* dnewcomb@sla.org
CEO: Janice R Lachance *Tel:* 703-647-4933 *E-mail:* janice@sla.org
Serial & nonserial publications; public relations; professional development; employment clearinghouse; resume referral service; computer-assisted, self-study programs; chapters, divisions, student groups & caucuses; government relations; fund development; scholarships; grants; honors & awards; annual conference & exhibit; winter meeting; information resources center.
Number of Members: 14,000
2014 Meeting(s): Annual Conference & INFO-EXPO, Vancouver, BC, CN, June 8-10, 2014
2015 Meeting(s): Annual Conference & INFO-EXPO, Boston, MA, June 14-16, 2015

**Specialized Information Publishers Association (SIPA)**
Division of Software & Information Industry Association (SIIA)
1090 Vermont Ave NW, 6th fl, Washington, DC 20005
*Tel:* 202-289-7442 *Fax:* 202-289-7097
*E-mail:* sipa@siia.net
*Web Site:* www.sipaonline.com
*Key Personnel*
Mng Ed: Ronn Levine
Members are subscription-based publishers representing small & large companies. Activities include e-mail, marketing, technical developments, copyright, business practices & editorial development.
Number of Members: 350
2014 Meeting(s): Annual Spring Conference, Washington, DC, June 5-7, 2014
Publication(s): *Hotline* (monthly, membs only)

**Tag & Label Manufacturers Institute Inc (TLMI)**
One Blackburn Ctr, Gloucester, MA 01930
*Tel:* 978-282-1400 *Fax:* 978-282-3238
*E-mail:* office@tlmi.com
*Web Site:* www.tlmi.com
*Key Personnel*
Pres: Frank Sablone *E-mail:* fas@tlmi.com
Founded: 1933
Number of Members: 300
2014 Meeting(s): Converter Meeting, The Resort at Pelican Hill, 22701 Pelican Hill Rd S, Newport Coast, CA, March 9-12, 2014; Annual Meeting, St Regis Monarch Beach, One Monarch Beach Resort, Dana Point, CA, Oct 12-15, 2014
Publication(s): *Hot Off The Press* (3 issues/yr, newsletter); *Illuminator Newsletter* (quarterly, newsletter)

**Teachers & Writers Collaborative**
520 Eighth Ave, Suite 2020, New York, NY 10018-4165
*Tel:* 212-691-6590 *Toll Free Tel:* 888-BOOKS-TW (266-5789) *Fax:* 212-675-0171
*E-mail:* info@twc.org; books@twc.org
*Web Site:* www.twc.org
*Key Personnel*
Dir: Amy Swauger *E-mail:* aswauger@twc.org
Founded: 1967
Information source for those interested in teaching writing & literary arts; publish books & magazines about creative writing; sponsor workshops. Basic annual membership: $35.
Publication(s): *Teachers & Writers* (quarterly, magazine, $20/yr)

**Technical Association of the Pulp & Paper Industry (TAPPI)**
15 Technology Pkwy S, Peachtree Corners, GA 30092
*Tel:* 770-446-1400 *Toll Free Tel:* 800-332-8686 (US); 800-446-9431 (CN) *Fax:* 770-446-6947
*E-mail:* memberconnection@tappi.org
*Web Site:* www.tappi.org
*Key Personnel*
VP, Opers: Eric Fletty *Tel:* 770-209-7535 *E-mail:* efletty@tappi.org
Press Opers Mgr: Jeff Wells *Tel:* 770-209-7228 *E-mail:* jwells@tappi.org
Founded: 1915
Professional society of executives, operating managers, engineers, scientists & technologists serving the pulp, paper & allied industries.
Number of Members: 8,000
2014 Meeting(s): PaperCon 2014, Nashville Convention Center, Nashville, TN, April 27-30, 2014
2015 Meeting(s): PaperCon 2015, Georgia World Congress Center, Atlanta, GA, April 19-22, 2015
2016 Meeting(s): TAPPI/AICC SuperCorrExpo®, Autumn 2016
Publication(s): *TAPPI JOURNAL* (monthly)

**Texas Institute of Letters (TIL)**
PO Box 609, Round Rock, TX 78680
*Tel:* 512-683-5640
*E-mail:* tilsecretary@yahoo.com
*Web Site:* www.texasinstituteofletters.org
*Key Personnel*
Pres: W K Stratton
VP: Andres Tijerina
Treas: James Hoggard
Secy: Jan Reid
Recording Secy: Betty Wiesepape
Sponsor awards for Texas-related books; cooperate in sponsorship of various writing fellowships.
Number of Members: 250
Publication(s): *Newsletter* (quarterly)

**United Nations Association of the United States of America**
801 Second Ave, 2nd fl, New York, NY 10017-4706
*Tel:* 212-907-1300 *Fax:* 212-682-9185

*E-mail:* unahq@unausa.org
*Web Site:* www.unausa.org
*Key Personnel*
Exec Dir: Patrick Madden
Founded: 1946
Publications, nonprofit information & educational services about international affairs & organizations.
Number of Members: 25,000

**US Board on Books For Young People (USBBY)**
Division of International Board on Books for Young People (IBBY)
5503 N El Adobe Dr, Fresno, CA 93711-2363
*Tel:* 559-351-6119
*E-mail:* executive.director@usbby.org
*Web Site:* www.usbby.org
*Key Personnel*
Exec Secy: V Ellis Vance *E-mail:* executive.secretary@usbby.org
Founded: 1953
Promotion of children's books & reading.
Number of Members: 500
Publication(s): *Bridges: A Publication of USBBY* (semiannual, $40)
Membership(s): ALA; Children's Book Council; International Reading Association; National Council of Teachers of English

**USBE: United States Book Exchange**
2969 W 25 St, Cleveland, OH 44113
*Tel:* 216-241-6960 *Fax:* 216-241-6966
*E-mail:* usbe@usbe.com
*Web Site:* www.usbe.com
*Key Personnel*
Mng Dir: John T Zubal; Marilyn Zubal
Redistribution of library materials to & from libraries.
Number of Members: 15,888

**Visual Artists & Galleries Association Inc (VAGA)**
350 Fifth Ave, Suite 2820, New York, NY 10118
*Tel:* 212-736-6666 *Fax:* 212-736-6767
*E-mail:* info@vagarights.com
*Web Site:* www.vagarights.com
*Key Personnel*
Exec Dir: Robert Panzer *E-mail:* rpanzer@vagarights.com
Licensing Exec: Andrea Mihavolic
Protects artists copyrights; provides art licensing & reproduction rights clearances & royalties collection for artists. Have archive of color transparencies & B&W images.
Number of Members: 18,000

**Visual Media Alliance (VMA)**
665 Third St, Suite 500, San Francisco, CA 94107-1926
*Tel:* 415-495-8242 *Toll Free Tel:* 800-659-3363 *Fax:* 415-543-7790 *Toll Free Fax:* 800-824-1911
*E-mail:* info@vma.bz
*Web Site:* vma.bz; www.visualmediaalliance.org
*Key Personnel*
Pres: Dan Nelson *Tel:* 415-489-7617 *E-mail:* dan@vma.bz
Trade association.
Number of Members: 950

**Web Offset Association (WOA)**
Division of Printing Industries of America
200 Deer Run Rd, Sewickley, PA 15143
*Tel:* 412-741-6860 *Toll Free Tel:* 800-910-4283 *Fax:* 412-741-2311
*E-mail:* printing@printing.org
*Web Site:* www.printing.org/weboffsetassociation
*Key Personnel*
EVP: Mary Garnett *E-mail:* mgarnett@printing.org
Printing Trade Association members work in Web Offset, printing. Meetings, publications & awards competition.
Number of Members: 8,000
New Election: Annually in Nov

**Western Writers of America Inc (WWA)**
271 CR 219, Encampment, WY 82325
*Tel:* 307-329-8942 *Fax:* 307-327-5465
*Web Site:* www.westernwriters.org
*Key Personnel*
Pres: Dusty Richards *E-mail:* dustyrichards@cox.net
VP: Sherry Monahan *E-mail:* sherry@sherrymonahan.com
Secy/Treas: Candy Moulton *E-mail:* wwa.moulton@gmail.com
Founded: 1953
Nonprofit confederation of professional writers of fiction & nonfiction pertaining to, or inspired by tradition, legends, development & history of the American West.
Number of Members: 650
2014 Meeting(s): Annual Convention, Sacramento, CA, June 24-28, 2014
Publication(s): *Roundup Magazine* (6 times/yr, $30/yr US, $50/yr foreign)

**Willamette Writers**
2108 Buck St, West Linn, OR 97068
*Tel:* 503-305-6729 *Fax:* 503-344-6174
*E-mail:* wilwrite@willamettewriters.com
*Web Site:* www.willamettewriters.com
*Key Personnel*
Pres: Val Mallinson
Off Mgr: Bill Johnson
Monthly meeting (open to public); critique groups; writer referrals; monthly newsletter; annual literary contest, annual conference.
Number of Members: 1,700
Publication(s): *The Willamette Writer* (monthly, free to membs)

**Women Who Write**
PO Box 652, Madison, NJ 07940-0652
*E-mail:* info@womenwhowrite.org
*Web Site:* www.womenwhowrite.org
*Key Personnel*
Pres: Ginger Pate
Writers' Notes Ed, Publicity: Maggie Roycraft
Founded: 1988
Writing groups, Writer's Conference, workshops, readings, literary events, newsletter & literary magazine.
Number of Members: 130
Publication(s): *Goldfinch: The Literary Magazine of Women Who Write* (annual); *Writers' Notes* (3 issues/yr, newsletter)

**Women's National Book Association Inc**
PO Box 237, FDR Sta, New York, NY 10150-0231
*Tel:* 212-208-4629 *Fax:* 212-208-4629
*E-mail:* publicity@bookbuzz.com; info@wnba.org
*Web Site:* www.wnba-books.org; www.NationalReadingGroupMonth.org
*Key Personnel*
Pres: Valerie Tomaselli
Natl Treas: Gloria Toler
Secy: Annette Marie Haley
PR: Susannah Greenberg
Founded: 1917
Increase opportunities for women & recognition of women in the world of books. Sponsor Women's National Book Association Award (formerly Constance Lindsay Skinner Award), Lucile Micheels Pannell Award & Ann Heidbreder Eastman Grant. Ten chapters: Atlanta, Binghamton, Boston, Dallas, Detroit, Los Angeles, Nashville, New York, San Francisco, Washington, DC.
Number of Members: 1,000
New Election: Biennially in May
Publication(s): *The Bookwoman* (3 issues/yr, free to membs)

**Writers' Alliance of Newfoundland & Labrador**
202-223 Duckworth St, St John's, NL A1C 6N1, Canada
*Tel:* 709-739-5215 *Toll Free Tel:* 866-739-5215 *Fax:* 709-739-5931
*E-mail:* wanl@nf.aibn.com
*Web Site:* wanl.ca
*Key Personnel*
Exec Dir: Thea Morash
Founded: 1987
Not-for-profit, member-based organization for writers & for those interested in writing.
Number of Members: 350
New Election: Annually in Sept

**Writers' Federation of Nova Scotia**
1113 Marginal Rd, Halifax, NS B3H 4P7, Canada
*Tel:* 902-423-8116 *Fax:* 902-422-0881
*E-mail:* talk@writers.ns.ca
*Web Site:* www.writers.ns.ca
*Key Personnel*
Exec Dir: Nate Crawford *E-mail:* director@writers.ns.ca
Founded: 1975
Number of Members: 800
New Election: Annually in June
Publication(s): *Eastword* (bimonthly, newsletter, $40)

**Writers Guild of Alberta**
11759 Groat Rd, Edmonton, AB T5M 3K6, Canada
*Tel:* 780-422-8174 *Toll Free Tel:* 800-665-5354 (AB only) *Fax:* 780-422-2663 (attn WGA)
*E-mail:* mail@writersguild.ab.ca
*Web Site:* www.writersguild.ab.ca
*Key Personnel*
Exec Dir: Carol Holmes *E-mail:* cholmes@writersguild.ab.ca
Communs & Partnerships Coord: Nicholas Mather *E-mail:* nmather@writersguild.ab.ca
Memb Servs Coord: Giorgia Severini
Progs Coord: Nichole Quiring *E-mail:* programs@writersguild.ab.ca
Founded: 1980
Our mission is to support, encourage & promote writers & writing, to safeguard the freedom to write & to read & to advocate for the well-being of writers.
Number of Members: 1,000
Publication(s): *WestWord* (bimonthly)
*Branch Office(s)*
Lord Denning House, 509 20 Ave SW, Calgary, AB T2S 0E7, Canada, Prog Coord: Samantha Warwick *Tel:* 403-265-2226 *E-mail:* swarwick@writersguild.ab.ca

**Writers Guild of America East (WGAE)**
250 Hudson St, New York, NY 10013
*Tel:* 212-767-7800 *Fax:* 212-582-1909
*E-mail:* info@wgae.org
*Web Site:* www.wgaeast.org
*Key Personnel*
Pres: Michael Winship
VP: Jeremy Pikser
Exec Dir: Lowell Peterson *Tel:* 212-767-7828 *E-mail:* lpeterson@wgaeast.org
Secy & Treas: Bob Schneider
Labor union representing professional writers in motion pictures, TV & radio. Membership available only through the sale of literary material or employment for writing services in one of these areas.
Number of Members: 4,200
New Election: Annually in Sept
Publication(s): *On Writing* (quarterly, magazine); *WGA East Newsletter* (bimonthly, newsletter, $22/yr)

**Writers Guild of America, West (WGAW)**
7000 W Third St, Los Angeles, CA 90048
*Tel:* 323-951-4000 *Toll Free Tel:* 800-548-4532 *Fax:* 323-782-4800
*Web Site:* www.wga.org
*Key Personnel*
Pres: Christopher Keyser
VP: Howard Rodman
Secy & Treas: Carl Gottlieb
Labor union: collective bargaining representation for film, TV broadcast, interactive & new media writers. Awards dinner & seminars (sometimes for public).
Number of Members: 9,000
Publication(s): *Written By Magazine* (monthly, exc Dec/Jan, $40/yr)

**Writers' Haven Writers (WHW)**
2244 Fourth Av, Suite A, San Diego, CA 92101-2119
*Tel:* 619-665-2712
*Key Personnel*
Natl Chmn: Michael Steven Gregory; Jean Jenkins *E-mail:* bjinkss@aol.com
Exec Dir: William H Martinez
State Dir, CO: John Stafford
State Dir, NY: Joe Renaldi
State Dir, OK: Joel Rizzo
Offers writers affiliation with a national organization; offer lifetime memberships & no dues. New members are nominated only by current WHWs in good standing. Workshops &/or informal gatherings of WHWs are sponsored by the WHWs involved, with the consent of their state director &/or the WHW headquarters in San Diego, whose officers gather weekly.
Number of Members: 200
Publication(s): *WHW Membership Directory* (members only, cost plus postage)

**Writers' League of Texas (WLT)**
611 S Congress Ave, Suite 505, Austin, TX 78704
*Tel:* 512-499-8914
*E-mail:* wlt@writersleague.org
*Web Site:* www.writersleague.org
*Key Personnel*
Exec Dir: Sheila Allee *E-mail:* sheila@writersleague.org
Workshops, seminars, classes, library resource center, technical assistance, audiotapes, newsletter, monthly programs, educational programs for young people. Memberships: $50 (basic), $15 (full-time students), $45 (seniors), $80 (couples).
Number of Members: 870
Publication(s): *Footnotes* (biweekly e-newsletter, newsletter, free); *Scribe* (blog)

**Writers' Union of Canada**
90 Richmond St E, Suite 200, Toronto, ON M5C 1P1, Canada
*Tel:* 416-703-8982 *Fax:* 416-504-9090
*E-mail:* info@writersunion.ca
*Web Site:* www.writersunion.ca
*Key Personnel*
Exec Dir: Kelly Duffin *Tel:* 416-703-8982 ext 221 *E-mail:* kduffin@writersunion.ca
Assoc Dir: Siobhan O'Connor *Tel:* 416-703-8982 ext 222 *E-mail:* soconnor@writersunion.ca
Off Administrator: Valerie Laws *Tel:* 416-703-8982 ext 224
Specialize in service for members & non-members including publications, newsletter, contract advice, competitions, ms evaluation & advocacy.
Number of Members: 2,000

# Foundations

Listed below are foundations that are closely affiliated with the book trade.

**Books for Asia**
Division of The Asia Foundation
2490 Verna Ct, San Leandro, CA 94577
Mailing Address: PO Box 193223, San Francisco, CA 94119-3223
*E-mail:* booksforasia@asiafound.org
*Web Site:* booksforasia.org
*Key Personnel*
Dir: Melody Zavala *Tel:* 510-667-6475 *Fax:* 510-351-2602 *E-mail:* mzavala@asiafound.org
Founded: 1954
A program of the Asia Foundation that has distributed well over 46 million books, journals & non-print educational resources to libraries, schools, universities & research centers in over 40 nations throughout Asia since 1954. Averages one million books per year in all educational fields at all educational levels sent to Asia Foundation field offices located throughout the region. Books are distributed by Foundation staff to recipient institutions based on requests received by our staff from representatives of those needy organizations. The overwhelming majority of books distributed are donated new books to the Asia Foundation by American publishers. Publishers may receive a tax deduction of up to twice the manufacturing cost for each book donated to qualified 501(c)(3) nonprofit organizations, such as the Asia Foundation. Monetary donations welcome.

**Bridge to Asia**
2140 Shattuck Ave, Berkeley, CA 97404-1222
*Tel:* 510-665-3998 *Fax:* 510-665-3988
*E-mail:* asianet@bridge.org
*Web Site:* www.bridge.org
*Key Personnel*
Pres: Jeffrey Smith *Tel:* 415-678-2994 *E-mail:* jasmith@well.com
VP: Newton Liu
Founded: 1987
A nonprofit book-donation program, which provides donated books, journals & Internet based research services to developing countries in Asia. Primary book-donors include members of the American Council of Learned Societies, the Nebraska Book Company, Follett Higher Education Group & several thousand individual book donors.
Membership(s): National Association of College Stores

**The Canadian Writers' Foundation Inc (La Fondation des Ecrivains Canadiens)**
PO Box 13281, Kanata Sta, Ottawa, ON K2K 1X4, Canada
*Tel:* 613-256-6937 *Fax:* 613-256-5457
*E-mail:* info@canadianwritersfoundation.org
*Web Site:* www.canadianwritersfoundation.org
*Key Personnel*
Pres: Marianne Scott *Tel:* 613-733-4223 *Fax:* 613-733-8752
Exec Secy: Suzanne Williams *E-mail:* smw.enterprises@sympatico.ca
Founded: 1931
Benevolent trust. Provides financial assistance to distinguished senior Canadian writers in need.

**The Century Foundation**
Division of The Century Foundation Inc
41 E 70 St, New York, NY 10021
*Tel:* 212-535-4441; 212-879-9197 *Fax:* 212-879-9197
*E-mail:* info@tcf.org
*Web Site:* www.tcf.org
*Key Personnel*
Pres: Janice Nittoli
VP & Dir, Pubns: Jason Renker *Tel:* 212-452-7715 *Fax:* 212-535-9883 *E-mail:* renker@tcf.org
Cont: Philip Li
Mgr, Spec Events: Loretta Ahlrich *Tel:* 212-452-7722 *Fax:* 212-535-7534 *E-mail:* ahlrich@tcf.org
Founded: 1919
Engaged in research & public education on significant contemporary policy issues. Emphasis on international political affairs, national, economic & social questions, government & media issues. No grants to institutions or individuals, but foundation will review independent project proposals within program guidelines as well as soliciting its own.

**La Foundation des Ecrivains Canadiens**, see The Canadian Writers' Foundation Inc (La Fondation des Ecrivains Canadiens)

**Graphic Arts Education & Research Foundation (GAERF)**
1899 Preston White Dr, Reston, VA 20191
*Tel:* 703-264-7200 *Toll Free Tel:* 866-381-9839 *Fax:* 703-620-3165
*E-mail:* gaerf@npes.org
*Web Site:* www.gaerf.org
*Key Personnel*
Pres: Ralph J Nappi
Dir: Eileen D Cassidy *E-mail:* ecassidy@npes.org
Founded: 1983
A major source of financial support for projects & programs designed to provide a graphic communications work force for the future.

**John Simon Guggenheim Memorial Foundation**
90 Park Ave, New York, NY 10016
*Tel:* 212-687-4470 *Fax:* 212-697-3248
*E-mail:* fellowships@gf.org
*Web Site:* www.gf.org
*Key Personnel*
Pres: Edward Hirsch
SVP & Secy: Andre Bernard
CFO & VP: Coleen Higgins-Jacob
Dir, Devt & PR: Richard W Hatter
Dir, Technol: Joseph Guruetz
Founded: 1925
Provide fellowships to further the development of scholars & artists by assisting them to engage in research in any field of knowledge & creation in any of the arts; awarded to persons who have already demonstrated exceptional capacity for productive scholarship or exceptional creative ability in the arts.

**The Heritage Foundation**
214 Massachusetts Ave NE, Washington, DC 20002-4999
*Tel:* 202-546-4400 *Toll Free Tel:* 800-544-4843 *Fax:* 202-546-8328
*E-mail:* info@heritage.org
*Web Site:* www.heritage.org
*Key Personnel*
Pres: Jim DeMint
EVP: Phil N Truluck
Creative Dir: Melissa Bluey
Founded: 1973
A tax exempt public policy research institute; complete publications list on request.

**The National Endowment for the Arts**
Nancy Hanks Ctr, Rm 703, 1100 Pennsylvania Ave NW, Washington, DC 20506-0001
*Tel:* 202-682-5400
*Web Site:* www.arts.gov; www.nea.gov
*Key Personnel*
Div Specialist: A Phil McNeal, II *Tel:* 202-682-5099 *E-mail:* mcnealp@arts.gov
Acting Dir, Lit: Amy Stolls
Grant-giving agency. Give grants to nonprofit literary organizations. Guidelines available on web site.

**Western States Arts Federation**
1743 Wazee St, Suite 300, Denver, CO 80202
*Tel:* 303-629-1166 *Toll Free Tel:* 888-562-7232 *Fax:* 303-629-9717
*E-mail:* staff@westaf.org
*Web Site:* www.westaf.org
*Key Personnel*
Exec Dir: Anthony Radich *E-mail:* anthony.radich@westaf.org
Dir, Mktg & Communs: Leah Horn *E-mail:* leah.horn@westaf.org
Sr Fin Assoc: Adrianne Devereux *E-mail:* adrianne.devereux@westaf.org
Assoc Dir: Seyan Lucero *E-mail:* seyan.lucero@westaf.org
Performing, visual & folk arts programs.

**H W Wilson Foundation**
10 Estes St, Ipswich, MA 01938
*Tel:* 978-356-6500 *Toll Free Tel:* 800-653-2726 (US & CN) *Fax:* 978-356-6565
*E-mail:* information@ebscohost.com
*Web Site:* www.ebscohost.com
*Key Personnel*
CEO & Pres: Harold Regan
Scholarship program for American Library Association accredited library schools & grants for library-related research.

# Calendar of Book Trade & Promotional Events—Alphabetical Index of Sponsors

# Calendar of Book Trade & Promotional Events—Alphabetical Index of Events

# Calendar of Book Trade & Promotional Events

Arranged chronologically by year and month, this section lists book trade events worldwide. Preceding this section are two indexes: the Sponsor Index is an alphabetical list of event sponsors and includes the names and dates of the events they sponsor; the Event Index is an alphabetical list of events along with the dates on which they are held.

## 2013

### NOVEMBER

**Feria Internacional del Libro de Guadalajara**
Av Alemania 1370, Colonia Moderna, 44190 Guadalajara, Jalisco, Mexico
*Tel:* (033) 3810 0331; (033) 3268 0900 *Fax:* (033) 3268 0921
*E-mail:* fil@fil.com.mx
*Web Site:* www.fil.com.mx
*Key Personnel*
Chmn: Raul Padilla Lopez
Gen Dir: Marisol Schulz *E-mail:* marisol.schulz@fil.com.mx
Contents Mgmt: Laura Niembro Diaz *E-mail:* laura.niembro@fil.com.mx
Exhibition Mgr: Veronica Mendoza Urista *E-mail:* veronica.mendoza@fil.com.mx
Location: Expo Guadalajara, Av Mariano Otero, 1499, Col Verde Valle, Guadalajara, Jalisco, Mexico
Nov 30-Dec 8, 2013

**Karlsruher Buecherschau (Karlsruhe Book Fair)**
Sponsored by Boersenverein des Deutschen Buchhandels, Landesverband Baden-Wuerttemberg eV (Association of Publishers & Booksellers in Baden-Wuerttemberg eV)
Paulinenstr 53, 70178 Stuttgart, Germany
*Tel:* (0711) 61941-0 *Fax:* (0711) 61941-44
*E-mail:* post@buchhandelsverband.de
*Web Site:* www.karlsruher-buecherschau.de; www.buchhandelsverband.de
*Key Personnel*
Contact: Silke Mueller *Tel:* (0711) 61941-26 *E-mail:* mueller@buchhandelsverband.de
Location: Karlsruhe, Germany
Nov 15-Dec 8, 2013

**Salon du Livre et de la Presse Jeunesse**
Sponsored by Reed Expositions France
52-54 quai de Dion-Bouton, CS 80001, 92806 Puteaux Cedex, France
*Tel:* 01 55 86 86 55 *Fax:* 01 48 57 04 62
*E-mail:* contact@slpj.fr
*Web Site:* www.salon-livre-presse-jeunesse.net
*Key Personnel*
Dir: Sylvie Vassallo
Leading publishing event dedicated to children's books, organized by Centre de promotion du livre de jeunesse.
Location: Montreuil, Seine-Saint-Denis, France
Nov 27-Dec 2, 2013

**Stuttgarter Buchwochen (Stuttgart Book Weeks)**
Sponsored by Boersenverein des Deutschen Buchhandels, Landesverband Baden-Wuerttemberg eV (Association of Publishers & Booksellers in Baden-Wuerttemberg eV)
Paulinenstr 53, 70178 Stuttgart, Germany
*Tel:* (0711) 61941-0 *Fax:* (0711) 61941-44
*E-mail:* post@buchhandelsverband.de
*Web Site:* www.stuttgarter-buchwochen.de; www.buchwochen.de; www.buchhandelsverband.de
*Key Personnel*
Contact: Andrea Baumann *Tel:* (0711) 61941-28 *E-mail:* baumann@buchhandelsverband.de
Location: Stuttgart, Germany
Nov 17-Dec 8, 2013

### DECEMBER

**NCDM 2013**
Sponsored by Direct Marketing Association (DMA)
1120 Avenue of the Americas, New York, NY 10036-6700
SAN: 692-6487
*Tel:* 212-768-7277 *Fax:* 212-302-6714
*E-mail:* dmaconferences@the-dma.org
*Web Site:* the-dma.org
*Key Personnel*
VP, Conferences & Membership: Kevin Fox *Tel:* 212-790-1468 *E-mail:* kfox@the-dma.org
NCDM - The Conference for Engaging Customers Using Data & Technology is where data-driven marketing professionals meet for three days of unprecedented access to sought after experts discussing industry trends & discovering new techniques for uncovering important customer insights from terabytes of online & offline data collected each year.
Location: Caesars Palace, 3570 Las Vegas Blvd S, Las Vegas, NV, USA
Dec 9-11, 2013

**Sofia International Book Fair**
Sponsored by Bulgarian Book Association
blvd Vitosha 64, 2nd fl, ap 4, 1463 Sofia, Bulgaria
*Tel:* (02) 958 15 25; (02) 958 92 11
*E-mail:* office@abk.bg
*Web Site:* www.abk.bg
*Key Personnel*
Event Promoter: Maria Popstefanova *E-mail:* m.popstefanova@abk.bg
The first Sofia International Book fair was organized in 1968. Since then it brings together over 40,000 visitors yearly to meet with exhibiting companies from Bulgaria & abroad & offers unrivalled access to the national & international book publishing & bookseller communities.
Location: National Palace of Culture, One Bulgaria Blvd, Sofia, Bulgaria
Dec 2013

## 2014

### JANUARY

**American Library Association Mid-Winter Meeting**
Sponsored by The American Library Association (ALA)
50 E Huron St, Chicago, IL 60611
*Toll Free Tel:* 800-545-2433 (ext 3223) *Fax:* 312-440-9374
*E-mail:* ala@ala.org
*Web Site:* www.ala.org/midwinter
*Key Personnel*
Conference/Events Coord: Alicia Babcock *Tel:* 800-545-2433 ext 3229 *E-mail:* ababcock@ala.org; Yvonne A McLean *Tel:* 800-545-2433 ext 3222 *E-mail:* ymclean@ala.org
Conference Supv: Amy R McGuigan *Tel:* 800-545-2433 ext 3226 *E-mail:* amcguigan@ala.org
Exhibit Mgr: Patrick Thomas Murphy *Tel:* 800-545-2433 ext 3218 *E-mail:* pmurphy@ala.org
Location: Philadelphia, PA, USA
Jan 24-28, 2014

**APE 2014**
Sponsored by digiprimo GmbH & Co KG
Lutherstr 18, 12167 Berlin, Germany
*Tel:* (030) 79 74 05 55 *Fax:* (030) 81 82 73 03
*E-mail:* info@digiprimo.com
*Web Site:* www.digiprimo.com
Location: Berlin, Germany
Jan 2014

**Football Writers Association of America Annual Meeting**
Sponsored by Football Writers Association of America (FWAA)
18652 Vista del Sol, Dallas, TX 75287
*Tel:* 972-713-6198
*Web Site:* www.sportswriters.net/fwaa; twitter.com/thefwaa
*Key Personnel*
Exec Dir: Steve Richardson *E-mail:* tiger@fwaa.com
Location: Newport Beach, CA, USA
Jan 3-7, 2014

**MLA Annual Convention**
Sponsored by Modern Language Association of America (MLA)
26 Broadway, 3rd fl, New York, NY 10004-1789
SAN: 202-6422
*Tel:* 646-576-5262; 646-576-5000 *Fax:* 646-458-0030
*E-mail:* convention@mla.org
*Web Site:* www.mla.org/convention
*Key Personnel*
Dir of Convention Progs: Maribeth T Kraus *E-mail:* mkraus@mla.org
Assoc Dir of Convention Progs: Karin Bagnall *E-mail:* kbagnall@mla.org
Location: Chicago, IL, USA
Jan 9-12, 2014

**Remainder & Promotional Book Fair**
Sponsored by Ciana Ltd
Rockholt, Ellimore Rd, Lustleigh, Newton Abbot TQ13 9TF, United Kingdom
*Tel:* (01626) 897 106 *Fax:* (01626) 897 107
*E-mail:* enquiries@ciana.co.uk
*Web Site:* www.ciana.co.uk
*Key Personnel*
Contact: Sarah Weedon; Robert Collie
Location: The Barbican Exhibition Hall, 2 Golden Lane, London, UK
Jan 19-20, 2014

## FEBRUARY

**Adelaide Festival**
Sponsored by Adelaide Festival Corp
Level 9, 33 King William St, Adelaide, SA 5000, Australia
Mailing Address: PO Box 8221, Station Arcade, Adelaide, SA 5000, Australia
*Tel:* (08) 8216 4444 *Fax:* (08) 8216 4455
*E-mail:* info@adelaidefestival.com.au
*Web Site:* www.adelaidefestival.com.au
*Key Personnel*
Artistic Dir: David Sefton
Prog Exec & Prodr: Jude Gun
Prog Dir: Lesley Newton
Spec Events Prodn Mgr: Adam Hornhardt
Annual event highlighting the arts, including literature. Adelaide Writers' Week is one of the high-profile events held during the festival.
Location: Adelaide's Central Business District, Adelaide, SA, Australia
Feb 28-March 16, 2014

**AWP Annual Conference & Bookfair**
Sponsored by Association of Writers & Writing Programs (AWP)
George Mason University, 4400 University Dr, MSN 1E3, Fairfax, VA 22030
*Tel:* 703-993-4301 *Fax:* 703-993-4302
*E-mail:* conference@awpwriter.org; awp@awpwriter.org
*Web Site:* www.aprwriter.org/conference; www.awpwriter.org
*Key Personnel*
Exec Dir: David W Fenza
Dir of Conferences: Christian Teresi
Conference Coord: Brenna Killeen
Assoc Dir of Cenferences: Cynthia Sherman
Conference Mgr: Sheri Sorvillo
Location: Washington State Convention Center & Sheraton Seattle Hotel, Seattle, WA, USA
Feb 26-March 1, 2014

**California International Antiquarian Book Fair**
Sponsored by Antiquarian Booksellers' Association of America (ABAA)
20 W 44 St, Suite 507, New York, NY 10036
*Tel:* 212-944-8291 *Fax:* 212-944-8293
*E-mail:* hq@abaa.org; info@winslowevents.com
*Web Site:* www.cabookfair.com; www.sfbookfair.com; www.abaa.org
*Key Personnel*
Exec Dir: Susan Benne *E-mail:* sbenne@abaa.org
Annual event co-sponsored by International League of Antiquarian Booksellers & managed by Winslow & Associates.
Location: Pasadena Convention Center, 300 E Green St, Pasadena, CA, USA
Feb 7-9, 2014

**Graphics of the Americas**
Sponsored by Printing Association of Florida Inc (PAF)
Affiliate of Printing Industries of America
6275 Hazeltine National Dr, Orlando, FL 32822
*Tel:* 407-240-8009 *Toll Free Tel:* 800-331-0461 *Fax:* 407-240-6942
*Web Site:* goaexpo.com
*Key Personnel*
Pres/CEO: George Ryan *Tel:* 407-240-8009 ext 114 *E-mail:* georger@flprint.org
Dir, Trade Show Opers: Adham Faltas *Tel:* 407-240-8009 ext 111 *E-mail:* adham@flprint.org
Location: Miami Beach Convention Center, 1901 Convention Center Dr, Miami Beach, FL, USA
Feb 27-March 1, 2014

**IS&T/SPIE Electronic Imaging Science & Technology**
Sponsored by IS&T/SPIE
c/o IS&T, 7003 Kilworth Lane, Springfield, VA 22151
*Tel:* 703-642-9090 *Fax:* 703-642-9094
*E-mail:* info@imaging.org; customerservice@spie.org
*Web Site:* spie.org/electronic-imaging.xml
*Key Personnel*
Exec Dir: Suzanne E Grinnan
Conference Prog Mgr: Diana Gonzalez
Exec Asst: Donna Smith
Location: Hilton San Francisco, Union Square, San Francisco, CA, USA
Feb 3-5, 2014

**PRIMEX Summit**
Sponsored by IDEAlliance®
1600 Duke St, Suite 420, Alexandria, VA 22314
*Tel:* 703-837-1070 *Fax:* 703-837-1072
*E-mail:* info@idealliance.org
*Web Site:* www.idealliance.org
*Key Personnel*
Mgr, Events & Membership: Georgia Volakis *Tel:* 703-837-1075 *E-mail:* gvolakis@idealliance.org
Location: Sheraton Sand Key Resort, Clearwater, FL, USA
Feb 24-26, 2014

**PSP Annual Conference**
Sponsored by Association of American Publishers (AAP)
71 Fifth Ave, 2nd fl, New York, NY 10003-3004
*Tel:* 212-255-0200 *Fax:* 212-255-7007
*Web Site:* www.publishers.org/psp
*Key Personnel*
VP & Exec Dir: John Tagler *Tel:* 212-255-1407 *E-mail:* jtagler@publishers.org
Dir: Sara Pinto *Tel:* 212-255-1716 *E-mail:* spinto@publishers.org
Location: Ritz Carlton Hotel, Washington, DC, USA
Feb 5-7, 2014

**Annual SCBWI Winter Conference**
Sponsored by Society of Children's Book Writers & Illustrators (SCBWI)
8271 Beverly Blvd, Los Angeles, CA 90048
*Tel:* 323-782-1010 *Fax:* 323-782-1892
*E-mail:* scbwi@scbwi.org
*Web Site:* www.scbwi.org
*Key Personnel*
Pres: Stephen Mooser *E-mail:* stephenmooser@scbwi.org
Exec Dir: Lin Oliver *E-mail:* linoliver@scbwi.org
Location: Grand Hyatt New York, 109 E 42 St at Grand Central Terminal, New York, NY, USA
Feb 21-23, 2014

**Texas Outdoor Writers Association Annual Conference**
Sponsored by Texas Outdoor Writers Association (TOWA)
PO Box 1753, Boerne, TX 78006
*Web Site:* www.towa.org
*Key Personnel*
Pres: David Sikes *Tel:* 361-886-3616 *E-mail:* dsikes@caller.com
Exec Dir: Lorraine Lawrence *Tel:* 210-833-0270 *E-mail:* director@towa.org
Location: New Braunfels, TX, USA
Feb 27-March 1, 2014

**WestPack®**
Sponsored by UBM Canon
2901 28 St, Suite 100, Santa Monica, CA 90405
*Tel:* 310-445-4200 *Fax:* 310-996-9499
*E-mail:* feedback@canontradeshows.com; packaginginfo@ubm.com
*Web Site:* www.canontradeshows.com; ubmcanon.com
Location: Anaheim Convention Center, 800 W Katella Ave, Anaheim, CA, USA
Feb 11-13, 2014

## SPRING

**IS&T Archiving Conference**
Sponsored by Society for Imaging Science & Technology (IS&T)
7003 Kilworth Lane, Springfield, VA 22151
*Tel:* 703-642-9090 *Fax:* 703-642-9094
*E-mail:* info@imaging.org
*Web Site:* www.imaging.org
*Key Personnel*
Exec Dir: Suzanne E Grinnan *E-mail:* sgrinnan@imaging.org
Conference Prog Mgr: Diana Gonzalez *E-mail:* dgonzalez@imaging.org
Location: Berlin, Germany
Spring 2014

**Xplor International Conference & Vendor Forum**
Sponsored by Xplor International
24156 State Rd 54, Suite 4, Lutz, FL 33559
*Tel:* 813-949-6170 *Toll Free Tel:* 800-669-7567 *Fax:* 813-949-9977
*E-mail:* info@xplor.org
*Web Site:* www.xplor.org
*Key Personnel*
Mktg Coord: Chad Henk *Tel:* 813-941-6171
Prog Coord: Jennifer J Smith
Location: FL, USA
Spring 2014

## MARCH

**The ARF Annual Convention & Insights Zone**
Sponsored by Advertising Research Foundation (ARF)
432 Park Ave S, 6th fl, New York, NY 10016-8013
*Tel:* 212-751-5656
*Web Site:* www.thearf.org
*Key Personnel*
Dir of Events: Kelly McSorley *Tel:* 646-465-5757 *E-mail:* kelly@thearf.org
Events Coord: Ronni Umles *Tel:* 646-465-5745 *E-mail:* ronni@thearf.org
Also known as Re:think.
Location: Marriott Marquis, New York, NY, USA
March 23-26, 2014

**Association of American Publishers Annual Meeting**
Sponsored by Association of American Publishers (AAP)
71 Fifth Ave, 2nd fl, New York, NY 10003-3004
*Tel:* 212-255-0200 *Fax:* 212-255-7007
*Web Site:* www.publishers.org
*Key Personnel*
VP & Dir: Tina Jordan *Tel:* 212-255-0275 *E-mail:* tjordan@publishers.org
March 2014

**Bologna Children's Book Fair**
Sponsored by BolognaFiere SpA
Piazza Costituzione, 6, 40128 Bologna, Italy
*Tel:* (051) 282 111 *Fax:* (051) 637 4011
*E-mail:* bookfair@bolognafiere.it
*Web Site:* www.bolognachildrensbookfair.com
*Key Personnel*
Contact: Marzia Sampaoli *Tel:* (051) 282 242 *E-mail:* marzia.sampaoli@bolognafiere.it;

Mariaelena Schiavo *Tel:* (051) 282 361
*E-mail:* mariaelena.schiavo@bolognafiere.it
Proj Mgr: Roberta Chinni *Tel:* (051) 282 269
*E-mail:* roberta.chinni@bolognafiere.it
Location: Bologna Fair Centre, Piazza Costituzione, 6, Bologna, Italy
March 24-27, 2014

**CAMEX**
Sponsored by National Association of College Stores (NACS)
500 E Lorain St, Oberlin, OH 44074
*Tel:* 440-775-7777 *Toll Free Tel:* 800-622-7498 *Fax:* 440-775-4769
*E-mail:* info@nacs.org
*Web Site:* www.camex.org; www.nacs.org
*Key Personnel*
CEO: Brian Cartier *Tel:* 800-622-7498 ext 2201 *E-mail:* bcartier@nacs.org
VP, Meetings & Expositions: Hugh Easley *Tel:* 800-622-7498 ext 2269 *E-mail:* heasley@nacs.org
Dir of Expositions: Mary Adler-Kozak *Tel:* 800-622-7498 ext 2265 *E-mail:* madler-kozak@nacs.org
Dir, PR: Charles E Schmidt *Tel:* 800-622-7498 ext 2351 *E-mail:* cschmidt@nacs.org
Conference & tradeshow dedicated exclusively to the more than $10 billion collegiate retailing industry.
Location: Dallas, TX, USA
March 7-11, 2014

**The Federation of Children's Book Groups Annual Conference**
Sponsored by The Federation of Children's Book Groups (FCBG)
Hampton Farm, Bowerhill, Melksham, Wilts SN12 6QZ, United Kingdom
*Tel:* (01225) 353710
*E-mail:* info@fcbg.org.uk
*Web Site:* www.fcbg.org.uk
Theme: Books and Beyond.
Location: Worth, UK
March 11-13, 2014

**The IA Summit**
Sponsored by Association for Information Science & Technology (ASIS&T)
1320 Fenwick Lane, Suite 510, Silver Spring, MD 20910
*Tel:* 301-495-0900 *Fax:* 301-495-0810
*E-mail:* meetings@asis.org; asis@asis.org
*Web Site:* www.asis.org
*Key Personnel*
Exec Dir: Richard Hill *E-mail:* rhill@asis.org
Dir of Meetings & Membership: Vanessa Foss *E-mail:* vfoss@asis.org
Location: San Diego, CA, USA
March 25-30, 2014

**IPA Congress**
Sponsored by International Publishers Association
23, ave de France, 1202 Geneva, Switzerland
*Tel:* (022) 704 18 20 *Fax:* (022) 704 18 21
*E-mail:* secretariat@internationalpublishers.org
*Web Site:* www.internationalpublishers.org
*Key Personnel*
Secy Gen: Mr Jens Bammel *E-mail:* bammel@internationalpublishers.org
Held every 2 years.
Location: Centara Grand at Central World, Bangkok, Thailand
March 25-27, 2014

**Leipzig Book Fair (Leipsiger Buchmesse)**
Sponsored by Leipziger Messe GmbH
Messe-Allee 1, 04356 Leipzig, Germany
Mailing Address: Postfach 10 07 20, 04007 Leipzig, Germany
*Tel:* (0341) 678-0 *Fax:* (0341) 678-8762
*E-mail:* info@leipziger-buchmesse.de
*Web Site:* www.leipziger-buchmesse.de
*Key Personnel*
Dir: Oliver Zille *Tel:* (0341) 678 8240
Held annually in conjunction with The Leipzig Antiquarian Book Fair.
Location: New Fair Ground, Leipzig, Germany
March 13-16, 2014

**mediaXchange**
Sponsored by Newspaper Association of America (NAA)
4401 Wilson Blvd, Suite 900, Arlington, VA 22203
*Tel:* 571-366-1000 *Fax:* 571-366-1195
*Web Site:* mediaxchange.naa.org; www.naa.org
*Key Personnel*
VP of Membership & Mktg: Missy Rentz *Tel:* 571-366-1140 *E-mail:* missy.rentz@naa.org
Dir of Communs: Marina Hendricks *Tel:* 571-366-1009 *E-mail:* marina.hendricks@naa.org
Annual technical exposition & conference for newspaper media executives.
Location: Hyatt Regency Denver at Colorado Convention Center, 650 15 St, Denver, CO, USA
March 16-19, 2014

**NAPIM Annual Convention**
Sponsored by National Association of Printing Ink Manufacturers (NAPIM)
15 Technology Pkwy S, Peachtree Corners, GA 30092
*Tel:* 770-209-7289 *Fax:* 678-680-4920
*E-mail:* napim@napim.org
*Web Site:* www.napim.org
*Key Personnel*
Exec Dir: Brad Bergey *E-mail:* bbergey@napim.org
Location: Rancho Bernardo Inn, 17550 Bernardo Oaks Dr, San Diego, CA, USA
March 22-25, 2014

**Paper2014**
Sponsored by American Forest & Paper Association (AF&PA)
1111 19 St NW, Suite 800, Washington, DC 20036
*Tel:* 202-463-2700 *Toll Free Tel:* 800-878-8878
*E-mail:* info@afandpa.org
*Web Site:* www.afandpa.org
*Key Personnel*
Dir of Meetings: Susan Van Eaton
Sr Mgr, Meetings & Member Servs: Kathy Smith
Co-hosted with the NPTA Alliance, this annual paper industry event offers participants access to decision makers from an impressive array of manufacturers, merchants, publishers, distributors of printing paper, packaging material & industrial material & supplies.
Location: Jacob K Javits Convention Center, 655 W 43 St, New York, NY, USA
March

**Salon du Livre de Paris**
(Paris Book Fair)
Sponsored by Reed Expositions France
Subsidiary of Reed Exhibition Companies
52-54 quai de Dion-Bouton, CS 80001, 92806 Puteaux Cedex, France
*Tel:* 01 47 56 64 31 *Fax:* 01 47 56 64 44
*E-mail:* livre@reedexpo.fr
*Web Site:* www.salondulivreparis.com
*Key Personnel*
Fair Mgr: Bertrand Morisset *E-mail:* bertrand.morisset@reedexpo.fr
Commun Coord: Carole Godefroy *E-mail:* carole.godefroy@reedexpo.fr
Annual international publishing event for publishers, booksellers, teachers & librarians. Open to the trade & the public.
Location: Paris Expo, Porte de Versailles, Paris, France
March 21-24, 2014

**Society of American Business Editors & Writers Spring Annual Conference**
Sponsored by Society of American Business Editors & Writers Inc (SABEW)
Walter Cronkite School of Journalism & Mass Communication, Arizona State University, 555 N Central Ave, Suite 302, Phoenix, AZ 85004-1248
*Tel:* 602-496-7862 *Fax:* 602-496-7041
*E-mail:* sabew@sabew.org
*Web Site:* sabew.org
*Key Personnel*
Exec Dir: Warren Watson *Tel:* 602-496-5186 *E-mail:* watson@sabew.org
Location: Walter Cronkite School of Journalism & Mass Communication, Arizona State University, Phoenix, AZ, USA
March 27-29, 2014

**Transformation 2014**
Sponsored by 4A's (American Association of Advertising Agencies)
1065 Avenue of the Americas, 16th fl, New York, NY 10018
*Tel:* 212-682-2500
*Web Site:* www.aaaa.org
*Key Personnel*
Pres & CEO: Nancy Hill *E-mail:* nhill@aaaa.org
VP, Events & Conferences: Brenda Major *Tel:* 212-850-0730 *E-mail:* bmajor@aaaa.org
Events Mgr: Troy Starwalt *Tel:* 212-850-0733 *E-mail:* tstarwalt@aaaa.org
Location: The Beverly Hilton, 9876 Wilshire Blvd, Beverly Hills, CA, USA
March 16-19, 2014

**Virginia Festival of the Book**
Sponsored by Virginia Foundation for the Humanities
145 Ednam Dr, Charlottesville, VA 22903
*Tel:* 434-924-3296 *Fax:* 434-296-4714
*E-mail:* vabook@virginia.edu
*Web Site:* www.vabook.org
*Key Personnel*
Prog Dir: Nancy Damon *Tel:* 434-924-7548
Annual public festival for children & adults featuring authors, illustrators, publishers, publicists, agents & other book professionals in panel discussions & readings. Most events are free. More than 200 authors invited annually.
Location: Charlottesville, VA, USA
March 19-23, 2014

## APRIL

**Alberta Library Conference**
Sponsored by Library Association of Alberta (LAA)
80 Baker Crescent NW, Calgary, AB T2L 1R4, Canada
*Tel:* 403-284-5818 *Toll Free Tel:* 877-522-5550 *Fax:* 403-282-6646
*E-mail:* info@laa.ca
*Web Site:* www.albertalibraryconference.com; www.laa.ca
*Key Personnel*
Exec Dir/Conference Coord: Christine Sheppard
Co-hosted by Alberta Library Trustees Association (ALTA).
Location: Jasper Park Lodge, Jasper, AB, CN
April 24-27, 2014

**Inter American Press Association Mid-Year Meeting**
Sponsored by Inter American Press Association (IAPA)
Jules Dubois Bldg, 1801 SW Third Ave, Miami, FL 33129
*Tel:* 305-634-2465 *Fax:* 305-635-2272
*E-mail:* info@sipiapa.org
*Web Site:* www.sipiapa.org
*Key Personnel*
Exec Dir: Julio E Munoz
Location: Hotel Hilton Resort, St Michael, Barbados
April 2014

**International Children's Book Day**
Sponsored by International Board on Books for Young People (IBBY)
Nonnenweg 12, Postfach, 4003 Basel, Switzerland
*Tel:* (061) 272 29 17 *Fax:* (061) 272 27 57
*E-mail:* ibby@ibby.org
*Web Site:* www.ibby.org
*Key Personnel*
Exec Dir: Liz Page *E-mail:* liz.page@ibby.org
Admin Asst: Ms Luzmaria Stauffenegger *E-mail:* luzmaria.stauffenegger@ibby.org
On Hans Christian Andersen's birthday, April 2nd, International Children's Book Day (ICBD) is celebrated to inspire a love of reading & to call attention to children's books. Each year a different national section has the opportunity to be the international sponsor. It decides upon a theme & invites a prominent author to write a message to the children of the world & a well-known illustrator to design a poster. These materials are used in different ways to promote books & reading around the world.
April 2, 2014

**Izmir Book Fair**
Sponsored by Tuyap Fairs & Exhibitions Organization Inc (Tuyap Fuar ve Sergiler A S)
E-5 Karayolu Uezeri, Guerpinar Kavsagi, Bueyuekcekmece, 34500 Istanbul, Turkey
*Tel:* (0212) 867 11 00 *Fax:* (0212) 886 66 98
*E-mail:* fairarea@tuyap.com.tr
*Web Site:* www.tuyap.com.tr
Annual event organized in cooperation with the Turkish Publishers Association.
Location: Culturepark Fair Ground, Izmir, Turkey
April 2014

**The London Book Fair**
Sponsored by Reed Exhibitions UK
Division of Reed Elsevier plc
Gateway House, 28 The Quadrant, Richmond, Surrey TW9 1DN, United Kingdom
*Tel:* (020) 8271 2124 *Fax:* (020) 8910 0728
*E-mail:* lbf.helpline@reedexpo.co.uk
*Web Site:* www.londonbookfair.co.uk
*Key Personnel*
Exhibition Coord: Sam D'Elia *Tel:* (020) 8910 7149 *Fax:* (020) 8334 0646 *E-mail:* sam.delia@reedexpo.co.uk
The London Book Fair is the global marketplace for rights negotiation & the sale & distribution of content across print, audio, TV, film & digital channels. Taking place every spring in the world's premier publishing & cultural capital, it is a unique opportunity to hear from authors, enjoy the vibrant atmosphere & explore innovations shaping the publishing world of the future. The London Book Fair brings you three days of focused access to customers, content & emerging markets.
Location: Earls Court Exhibition Centre, Warwick Rd, London, UK
April 8-10, 2014

**Los Angeles Times Festival of Books**
Sponsored by Los Angeles Times
Subsidiary of Tribune Co
202 W First St, Los Angeles, CA 90012
*Tel:* 213-237-5000 *Toll Free Tel:* 800-528-4637 *Fax:* 213-237-2335
*E-mail:* fobinfo@latimes.com
*Web Site:* events.latimes.com/festivalofbooks
Location: The University of Southern California (USC), Los Angeles, CA, USA
April 13-14, 2014

**National Library Week**
Sponsored by The American Library Association (ALA)
50 E Huron St, Chicago, IL 60611
*Toll Free Tel:* 800-545-2433 (ext 3223) *Fax:* 312-440-9374
*E-mail:* ala@ala.org
*Web Site:* www.ala.org/nlw
*Key Personnel*
Campaign Mgr: Megan G Humphrey *Tel:* 800-545-2433 ext 4020 *E-mail:* mhumphrey@ala.org
Campaign Coord: Megan McFarlane *Tel:* 800-545-2433 ext 2148 *E-mail:* mmcfarlane@ala.org
Location: Nationwide throughout the USA
April 13-19, 2014

**New York International Antiquarian Book Fair**
Sponsored by Antiquarian Booksellers' Association of America (ABAA)
20 W 44 St, Suite 507, New York, NY 10036
*Tel:* 212-944-8291 *Fax:* 212-944-8293
*E-mail:* hq@abaa.org
*Web Site:* www.nybookfair.com; www.abaa.org
*Key Personnel*
Exec Dir: Susan Benne *E-mail:* sbenne@abaa.org
Co-sponsored by International League of Antiquarian Booksellers (ILAB) & managed by Sanford L Smith & Associates.
Location: Park Avenue Armory, 643 Park Ave at 67 St, New York, NY, USA
April 3-6, 2014

**North American Agricultural Journalists Spring Meeting**
Sponsored by North American Agricultural Journalists (NAAJ)
6434 Hurta Lane, Bryan, TX 77808
*Tel:* 979-845-2872 *Fax:* 979-862-1202
*Web Site:* www.naaj.net
*Key Personnel*
Exec Secy & Treas: Kathleen Phillips *E-mail:* ka-phillips@tamu.edu
Location: Washington, DC, USA
April 2014

**PaperCon**
Sponsored by Technical Association of the Pulp & Paper Industry (TAPPI)
15 Technology Pkwy S, Peachtree Corners, GA 30092
*Tel:* 770-446-1400 *Toll Free Tel:* 800-332-8686 (US); 800-446-9431 (CN) *Fax:* 770-446-6947; 770-209-7206
*E-mail:* memberconnection@tappi.org
*Web Site:* www.papercon.org; www.tappi.org
*Key Personnel*
Meeting Mgr: Ed Robie *Tel:* 770-209-7243 *E-mail:* erobie@tappi.org
Dir of Mktg: Simona Marcellus *Tel:* 770-209-7293 *E-mail:* smarcellus@tappi.org
Location: Nashville Convention Center, Nashville, TN, USA
April 26-30, 2014

**The Quest for Excellence® Conference**
Sponsored by National Institute of Standards & Technology (NIST)
100 Bureau Dr, Gaithersburg, MD 20899
*Tel:* 301-975-2036 *Fax:* 301-948-3716
*E-mail:* baldrige@nist.gov
*Web Site:* www.nist.gov/baldrige/qe/index.cfm
*Key Personnel*
Conference Chair: Barbara Fischer *Tel:* 301-975-8942 *E-mail:* barbara.fischer@nist.gov
Official conference of the Baldridge Award, held in partnership with American Society for Quality (ASQ) & American Society for Training & Development (ASTD).
Location: Baltimore Marriott Waterfront, 400 Aliceanna St, Baltimore, MD, USA
April 7-9, 2014

**Southern Kentucky Book Fest**
1906 College Heights Blvd, WKU Libraries, Cravens 106, Bowling Green, KY 42101-1067
*Tel:* 270-745-4502 *Fax:* 270-745-6422
*Web Site:* www.sokybookfest.org
*Key Personnel*
Literary Outreach Coord: Kristie Lowry *Tel:* 270-745-4502 *E-mail:* kristie.lowry@wku.edu
The Southern Kentucky Book Fest is one of the state's largest literary events & is presented by WKU Libraries, Warren County Public Library & Barnes & Noble Booksellers. Book Fest is a fundraiser for the promotion of literacy in our community.
Location: Knicely Conference Center, Bowling Green, KY, USA
April 25-26, 2014

**SouthPack®**
Sponsored by UBM Canon
2901 28 St, Suite 100, Santa Monica, CA 90405
*Tel:* 310-445-4200 *Fax:* 310-996-9499
*E-mail:* feedback@canontradeshows.com; packaginginfo@ubm.com
*Web Site:* www.canontradeshows.com; ubmcanon.com
Location: Charlotte Convention Center, 501 S College St, Charlotte, NC, USA
April 15-16, 2014

**UKSG Annual Conference & Exhibition**
Sponsored by UKSG (United Kingdom Serials Group)
Bowman & Hillier Bldg, The Old Brewery, Priory Lane, Burford, Oxon OX18 4SG, United Kingdom
Mailing Address: PO Box 5594, Newbury RG20 0YD, United Kingdom
*Web Site:* www.uksg.org
*Key Personnel*
Busn Mgr: Alison Whitehorn *Tel:* (01635) 254292 *Fax:* (01635) 253826 *E-mail:* alison@uksg.org
Administrator: Karen Sadler *Tel:* (01865) 310834 *Fax:* (01865) 310834 *E-mail:* karen@uksg.org
Annual 3 day event open to everyone.
Location: Harrogate, N Yorks, UK
April 14-16, 2014

## MAY

**ASQ World Conference on Quality & Improvement**
Sponsored by American Society for Quality (ASQ)
600 N Plankinton Ave, Milwaukee, WI 53203
Mailing Address: PO Box 3005, Milwaukee, WI 53201-3005
*Tel:* 414-272-8575 *Toll Free Tel:* 800-248-1946 (US & CN) *Fax:* 414-272-1734
*E-mail:* help@asq.org
*Web Site:* www.asq.org
*Key Personnel*
CEO: Paul Borawski *E-mail:* pborawski@asq.org
Mgr, Event Mgmt: Shirley A Krentz *E-mail:* skrentz@asq.org

Location: Hilton Anatole, 2201 N Stemmons Fwy, Dallas, TX, USA
May 5-7, 2014

**BMI Management Conference**
Sponsored by Book Manufacturers' Institute Inc (BMI)
2 Armand Beach Dr, Suite 1B, Palm Coast, FL 32137-2612
*Tel:* 386-986-4552 *Fax:* 386-986-4553
*E-mail:* info@bmibook.com
*Web Site:* www.bmibook.org
*Key Personnel*
EVP: Daniel N Bach *E-mail:* dbach@dmibook.com
Off Mgr: Diane Morris
Conference Coord: Jackie Murray
Location: Sanibel Harbour Marriott Resort & Spa, 17260 Harbour Point Dr, Fort Myers, FL, USA
May 4-6, 2014

**BookExpo America (BEA)**
Sponsored by Reed Exhibitions USA
Division of Reed Elsevier plc
383 Main Ave, Norwalk, CT 06851
*Tel:* 203-840-4800 *Toll Free Tel:* 800-840-5614 *Fax:* 203-840-5805
*E-mail:* inquiry@bookexpoamerica.com
*Web Site:* bookexpoamerica.com
*Key Personnel*
Event Dir: Steven Rosato
Conference Mgr: Maggie Donovan *E-mail:* mdonovan@reedexpo.com
Conference Coord: Mackenzie Lynch *E-mail:* malynch@reedexpo.com
Produced & managed by Reed Exhibitions USA, BEA is sponsored by the American Booksellers Association (ABA), the Association of American Publishers Inc (AAP) & the Association of Authors' Representatives Inc (AAR).
Location: Jacob K Javits Convention Center, 655 W 43 St, New York, NY, USA
May 29-31, 2014

**Canadian Library Association National Conference & Trade Show**
Sponsored by Canadian Library Association (CLA) (Association Canadienne des bibliotheques)
1150 Morrison Dr, Suite 400, Ottawa, ON K2H 8S9, Canada
*Tel:* 613-232-9625 *Fax:* 613-563-9895
*E-mail:* info@cla.ca
*Web Site:* www.cla.ca
*Key Personnel*
Exec Dir: Kelly Moore *Tel:* 613-232-9625 ext 306 *E-mail:* kmoore@cla.ca
Conference & Events Mgr: Wendy Walton *Tel:* 613-232-9625 ext 302 *E-mail:* wwalton@cla.ca
Location: Victoria, BC, CN
May 28-31, 2014

**Children's Book Week**
Sponsored by The Children's Book Council (CBC)
54 W 39 St, 14th fl, New York, NY 10018
*Tel:* 212-966-1990 *Fax:* 212-966-2073
*E-mail:* cbc.info@cbcbooks.org
*Web Site:* www.bookweekonline.com; www.cbcbooks.org
*Key Personnel*
Exec Dir: Robin Adelson *E-mail:* robin.adelson@cbcbooks.org
Communs Mgr: Nicole Deming *E-mail:* nicole.deming@cbcbooks.org
Location: Nationwide across the USA
May 12-18, 2014

**EPA Annual Convention**
Sponsored by Evangelical Press Association (EPA)
PO Box 20198, El Cajon, CA 92021
*Tel:* 619-609-0910 *Toll Free Tel:* 888-311-1731
*Web Site:* www.evangelicalpress.com
*Key Personnel*
Exec Dir: D'Arcy Maher
CFO: Lamar Keener
Annual convention for editors, publishers, writers & other staff (print & online publications). Workshop tracks & plenary sessions, opportunities for networking & fellowship.
Location: Sheraton Park Hotel at the Anaheim Resort, Anaheim, CA, USA
May 4-6, 2014

**EXPOLIT (Exposicion de Literatura Cristiana Book Fair)**
Sponsored by Spanish Evangelical Publishers Association (SEPA)/Asociacion Evangelica espanola de Editores
1360 NW 88 Ave, Doral, FL 33172
*Tel:* 305-503-1191 *Fax:* 305-717-6886
*E-mail:* info@expolit.com
*Web Site:* www.expolit.com
*Key Personnel*
Supv: Jessica Hernandez *E-mail:* jessica@expolit.com
Media Coord: Tatyana Orozco *E-mail:* tatyana@expolit.com
Exhibit Coord: Mayra de Moya *E-mail:* mayra@expolit.com
Spanish Christian literature convention. Also sponsored by Editorial Unilit.
Location: Miami, FL, USA
May 2014

**IRA Annual Convention**
Sponsored by International Reading Association
800 Barksdale Rd, Newark, DE 19711-3204
Mailing Address: PO Box 8139, Newark, DE 19714-8139
*Tel:* 302-731-1600 *Toll Free Tel:* 800-336-7323 (US & CN) *Fax:* 302-731-1057
*E-mail:* customerservice@reading.org
*Web Site:* www.reading.org/convention.aspx; www.reading.org
*Key Personnel*
Exec Dir: Marcie Craig Post *E-mail:* mpost@reading.org
Exhibits & Devt Coord: Clavel Jones *Tel:* 302-731-3768 *E-mail:* cjones@reading.org
Location: Ernest N Morial Convention Center, Halls D-E, New Orleans, LA, USA
May 9-12, 2014

**Print Distribution Conference**
Sponsored by IDEAlliance®
1600 Duke St, Suite 420, Alexandria, VA 22314
*Tel:* 703-837-1070 *Fax:* 703-837-1072
*E-mail:* info@idealliance.org
*Web Site:* www.idealliance.org
*Key Personnel*
Mgr, Events & Membership: Georgia Volakis *Tel:* 703-837-1075 *E-mail:* gvolakis@idealliance.org
Location: Sheraton Sand Key Resort, Clearwater Beach, FL, USA
May 6-7, 2014

**Society for Scholarly Publishing Annual Meeting**
Sponsored by Society for Scholarly Publishing (SSP)
10200 W 44 Ave, Suite 304, Wheat Ridge, CO 80033-2840
*Tel:* 303-422-3914 *Fax:* 303-422-8894
*E-mail:* info@sspnet.org
*Web Site:* www.sspnet.org
*Key Personnel*
Exec Dir: Ann Mehan Crosse *Tel:* 720-881-6114 *E-mail:* amehan@resourcenter.com
Exec Asst, Meetings: Delfie Castro
Location: Westin™ Boston Waterfront, 425 Summer St, Boston, MA, USA
May 28-30, 2014

## JUNE

**AAUP Annual Meeting**
Sponsored by Association of American University Presses (AAUP)
28 W 36 St, Suite 602, New York, NY 10018
*Tel:* 212-989-1010 *Fax:* 212-989-0275
*E-mail:* info@aaupnet.org
*Web Site:* www.aaupnet.org
*Key Personnel*
Exec Dir: Peter Berkery *Tel:* 212-989-1010 ext 29 *E-mail:* pberkery@aaupnet.org
Asst Dir & Cont: Tim Muench *Tel:* 212-989-1010 ext 28 *E-mail:* tmuench@aaupnet.org
Dir of Mktg & Communs: Brenna McLaughlin *Tel:* 518-436-3586 *E-mail:* bmclaughlin@aaupnet.org
Admin Mgr: Linda McCall *Tel:* 212-989-1010 ext 30 *E-mail:* lmccall@aaupnet.org
Location: New Orleans Marriott, New Orleans, LA, USA
June 22-24, 2014

**American Library Association Annual Conference**
Sponsored by The American Library Association (ALA)
50 E Huron St, Chicago, IL 60611
*Toll Free Tel:* 800-545-2433 (ext 3223) *Fax:* 312-440-9374
*E-mail:* ala@ala.org
*Web Site:* www.ala.org
*Key Personnel*
Conference/Events Coord: Alicia Babcock *Tel:* 800-545-2433 ext 3229 *E-mail:* ababcock@ala.org; Yvonne A McLean *Tel:* 800-545-2433 ext 3222 *E-mail:* ymclean@ala.org
Conference Supv: Amy R McGuigan *Tel:* 800-545-2433 ext 3226 *E-mail:* amcguigan@ala.org
Exhibit Mgr: Patrick Thomas Murphy *Tel:* 800-545-2433 ext 3218 *E-mail:* pmurphy@ala.org
Location: Las Vegas, NV, USA
June 26-July 1, 2014

**Catholic Media Convention**
Sponsored by Catholic Press Association of the US & Canada
205 W Monroe St, Suite 470, Chicago, IL 60606
*Tel:* 312-380-6789 *Fax:* 312-361-0256
*Web Site:* www.catholicpress.org
*Key Personnel*
Exec Dir: Timothy Walter *E-mail:* twalter@catholicpress.org
Meeting Mgr: Sheila Lomax *E-mail:* slomax@catholicpress.org
Location: Charlotte, NC, USA
June 18-20, 2014

**Christian Resources Retailers & Suppliers Retreat**
Sponsored by Christian Resources Together
PO Box 995, Aylesbury, Bucks HP20 9HU, United Kingdom
*Tel:* (01296) 489860
*Web Site:* www.christianresourcestogether.co.uk
*Key Personnel*
Event Organizer: Steve Briars *E-mail:* steve@christianresourcestogether.co.uk
Location: Hayes Conference Centre, Swanwick, Alfreton, Derbyshire, UK
June 24-25, 2014

**EastPack®**
Sponsored by UBM Canon

2901 28 St, Suite 100, Santa Monica, CA 90405
*Tel:* 310-445-4200 *Fax:* 310-996-9499
*E-mail:* feedback@canontradeshows.com; packaginginfo@ubm.com
*Web Site:* www.canontradeshows.com; ubmcanon.com
Location: Jacob K Javits Convention Center, New York, NY, USA
June 10-12, 2014

**IABC World Conference**
Sponsored by International Association of Business Communicators (IABC)
601 Montgomery St, Suite 1900, San Francisco, CA 94111
*Tel:* 415-544-4700 *Toll Free Tel:* 800-776-4222 (US & CN) *Fax:* 415-544-4747
*E-mail:* conference@iabc.com
*Web Site:* www.iabc.com
*Key Personnel*
Events & Conferences Mgr: Charles Herrick *Tel:* 415-544-4745 *E-mail:* cherrick@iabc.com
Location: Sheraton Centre Toronto Hotel, 123 Queen St W, Toronto, ON, CN
June 8-11, 2014

**International Christian Retail Show**
Sponsored by CBA: The Association for Christian Retail
9240 Explorer Dr, Suite 200, Colorado Springs, CO 80920
*Tel:* 719-265-9895 *Toll Free Tel:* 800-252-1950 *Fax:* 719-272-3510
*E-mail:* info@cbaonline.org
*Web Site:* www.christianretailshow.com; www.cbaonline.org
*Key Personnel*
Exec Dir: Curtis Riskey
Meetings & Expositions Dir: Scott Graham *E-mail:* sgraham@cbaonline.org
For over 50 years, the annual International Christian Retail Show has been our industry's single-most impacting week. During this week, people of the industry from all over the world meet face-to-face for buying & selling, education, inspiration, fellowship & future planning. Here individuals unite to further the mission of seeing Christian products impact lives for God's Kingdom the world over. At this unique gathering, our industry's strength is most evident & our goals are most clearly in focus. It is, in short, the most important week in the ministry of your business & of the industry as a whole.
Location: Georgia World Congress Center, Atlanta, GA, USA
June 22-25, 2014

**Outdoor Writers Association of America Annual Conference**
Sponsored by Outdoor Writers Association of America
615 Oak St, Suite 201, Missoula, MT 59801
*Tel:* 406-728-7434
*E-mail:* info@owaa.org
*Web Site:* owaa.org
*Key Personnel*
Ed: Ashley Schroeder *E-mail:* editor@owaa.org
Membership & Conference Servs: Jessica Pollett *E-mail:* jpollett@owaa.org
Location: Knoxville, TN, USA
June 27-29, 2014

**PWAC National Conference & Annual General Meeting**
Sponsored by Professional Writers Association of Canada (PWAC)
215 Spadina Ave, Suite 130, Toronto, ON M5T 2C7, Canada
*Tel:* 416-504-1645
*E-mail:* info@pwac.ca
*Web Site:* www.pwac.ca
*Key Personnel*
Exec Dir: Sandy Crawley
Gen Mgr: Margaret DeRosia *Tel:* 416-504-1645 ext 1
Held in conjunction with Magazines Canada Annual Conference (MagNet).
Location: The Courtyard Toronto Downtown, 475 Yonge St, Toronto, ON, CN
June 3-6, 2014

**Singapore Book Fair**
Sponsored by Marshall Cavendish Business Information Pte Ltd
Member of Times Publishing Group
Times Centre, One New Industrial Rd, Singapore 536196, Singapore
*Tel:* 6213 9288 *Fax:* 6285 0161
*E-mail:* sbf@tpl.com.sg
*Web Site:* www.bookfair.com.sg
*Key Personnel*
Mgr, Exhibition Sales: Christine Ng *E-mail:* christineng@sg.marshallcavendish.com
Co-organized by Singapore Press Holdings, (Chinese Newspaper Division), this is the largest English & Chinese book fair in the region for publishers, distributors & retailers of children books, general & reference books, teachers' resource materials, best sellers, novels, comics, educational software, magazines, periodicals, online products, encyclopedias, IQ toys, stationery & arts & crafts.
Location: Suntec Singapore International Convention & Exhibition Centre, Singapore, Singapore
June 6-10, 2014

**SIPA'S Annual Spring Conference**
Sponsored by Specialized Information Publishers Association (SIPA)
Division of Software & Information Industry Association (SIIA)
1090 Vermont Ave NW, 6th fl, Washington, DC 20005
*Tel:* 202-289-7442 *Fax:* 202-289-7097
*E-mail:* sipa@siia.net
*Web Site:* www.sipaonline.com
*Key Personnel*
Exec Dir: Janine Hergesell
Mgr, Membership Servs: Julie Anthony
Location: Washington, DC, USA
June 5-7, 2014

**SLA Annual Conference & INFO-EXPO**
Sponsored by Special Libraries Association (SLA)
331 S Patrick St, Alexandria, VA 22314-3501
*Tel:* 703-647-4900 *Fax:* 703-647-4901
*Web Site:* www.sla.org
*Key Personnel*
CEO: Janice R Lachance *Tel:* 703-647-4933 *E-mail:* janice@sla.org
Dir, Events: Caroline Rives *Tel:* 703-647-4949 *E-mail:* crives@sla.org
Dir, Mktg & Exhibits: Jeff Leach *Tel:* 703-647-4922 *E-mail:* jleach@sla.org
Mktg/Events Assoc: Jarell D Grady *Tel:* 703-647-4941 *E-mail:* jgrady@sla.org
Location: Vancouver, BC, CN
June 8-10, 2014

## JULY

**Church & Synagogue Library Association Conference**
Sponsored by Church & Synagogue Library Association
10157 SW Barbur Blvd, No 102C, Portland, OR 97219
*Tel:* 503-244-6919 *Toll Free Tel:* 800-542-2752 (LIB-CSLA) *Fax:* 503-977-3734
*E-mail:* csla@worldaccessnet.com
*Web Site:* www.cslainfo.org
*Key Personnel*
Administrator: Judith Janzen
Location: Portland, OR, USA
July 28-30, 2014

**Hong Kong Book Fair**
Sponsored by Hong Kong Trade Development Council
c/o Exhibition Dept, Unit 13, Expo Galleria, Hong Kong Convention & Exhibition Centre, Wan Chai, Hong Kong
*Tel:* 1830 670; 1830 668 (cust serv) *Fax:* 2824 0026; 2824 0249
*E-mail:* exhibitions@hktdc.org
*Web Site:* hkbookfair.com/hktdc.com; hkbookfair.com/hktdc.com/en (English)
Location: Hong Kong Convention & Exhibition Center, One Expo Dr, Wan Chai, Hong Kong
July 2014

**IAML Annual Conference**
Sponsored by International Association of Music Libraries, Archives & Documentation Centres Inc (IAML)
c/o Gothenburg University, Academy of Music & Drama Library, Box 210, 405 30 Gothenburg, Sweden
*Tel:* (031) 786 40 57 *Fax:* (031) 786 40 59
*Web Site:* www.iaml.info
*Key Personnel*
Secy Gen: Pia Shekhter *E-mail:* secretary@iaml.info
Location: Antwerp, Belgium
July 13-19, 2014

**Romance Writers of America Annual Conference**
Sponsored by Romance Writers of America®
14615 Benfer Rd, Houston, TX 77069
*Tel:* 832-717-5200 *Fax:* 832-717-5201
*E-mail:* conference@rwa.org; info@rwa.org
*Web Site:* www.rwa.org
*Key Personnel*
Exec Dir: Allison Kelley *Tel:* 832-717-5200 ext 124 *E-mail:* allison.kelley@rwa.org
Location: San Antonio Marriott® Rivercenter & Marriott® Riverwalk, San Antonio, TX, USA
July 23-26, 2014

**TIBF: Tokyo International Book Fair**
Sponsored by Reed Exhibitions Japan Ltd
18F Shinjuku-Nomura Bldg, 1-26-2 Nishishinjuku, Shinjuku-ku, Toyko 163-0570, Japan
*Tel:* (03) 3349 8519 *Fax:* (03) 3349 8530
*E-mail:* tibf-eng@reedexpo.co.jp
*Web Site:* www.bookfair.jp; www.bookfair.jp/en (English)
Organized by Reed Exhibitions Japan Ltd, TIBF executive committee.
Location: Tokyo International Exhibition Center (Tokyo Big Sight), Tokyo, Japan
July 2014

## AUGUST

**Beijing International Book Fair**
Sponsored by China National Public Import & Export (Group) Corp (CNPIEC)
16 Gongti E Rd, Room 802, Chaoyang District, Beijing 100020, China
*Tel:* (010) 6586 6995; (010) 6506 3080 *Fax:* (010) 6508 9188
*Web Site:* www.bibf.net
*Key Personnel*
VChmn, Organizing Committee: Liu Bogen

Location: China International Exhibition Center, Beijing, China
Aug 27-31, 2014

**The Dorothy L Sayers Society Annual Convention**
Sponsored by The Dorothy L Sayers Society
Witham Library, 18 Newland St, Witham CM8 2AQ, United Kingdom
*Tel:* (01376) 519625
*E-mail:* info@sayers.org.uk
*Web Site:* www.sayers.org.uk
*Key Personnel*
Convention Admin: Simon Medd
Membership Secy: Lenelle Davis
Members only event.
Location: UK
Aug 2014

**Edinburgh International Book Festival**
5 Charlotte Sq, Edinburgh EH2 4DR, United Kingdom
*Tel:* (0131) 718 5666
*E-mail:* admin@edbookfest.co.uk
*Web Site:* www.edbookfest.co.uk
*Key Personnel*
Dir: Nick Barley
Mktg & PR Mgr: Amanda Barry
The festival takes place in Charlotte Square Gardens (just off the west end of Princes St) over 17 days each August. Over 800 world-class authors & thinkers gather to take part in events for people of all ages.
Location: Charlotte Square Gardens, Edinburgh, UK
Aug 9-25, 2014

**Garden Writers Association Annual Symposium**
Sponsored by Garden Writers Association
7809 FM 179, Shallowater, TX 79363-3637
*Tel:* 806-832-1870 *Fax:* 806-832-5244
*E-mail:* info@gardenwriters.org
*Web Site:* www.gardenwriters.org
*Key Personnel*
Pres: Debra Prinzing
Exec Dir: Robert LaGasse *E-mail:* execdir@gardenwriters.org
Location: Westin Convention Center, Pittsburgh, PA, USA
Aug 8-11, 2014

**IFLA World Library & Information Congress**
Sponsored by International Federation of Library Associations & Institutions (IFLA) (Federation internationale des associations de bibliothecaires et des bibliotheques)
Prins Willem-Alexanderhof 5, 2595 BE The Hague, Netherlands
Mailing Address: Postbus 95312, 2509 CH The Hague, Netherlands
*Tel:* (070) 3140884 *Fax:* (070) 3834827
*E-mail:* ifla@ifla.org
*Web Site:* www.ifla.org
*Key Personnel*
Secy Gen: Jennefer Nicholson
Mgr, Conferences & Busn Rel: Josche Ouwerkerk *E-mail:* josche.ouwerkerk@ifla.org
Held simultaneously with IFLA General Conference & Assembly.
Location: Lyon, France
Aug 16-22, 2014

**Annual SCBWI Summer Conference**
Sponsored by Society of Children's Book Writers & Illustrators (SCBWI)
8271 Beverly Blvd, Los Angeles, CA 90048
*Tel:* 323-782-1010 *Fax:* 323-782-1892
*E-mail:* scbwi@scbwi.org
*Web Site:* www.scbwi.org
*Key Personnel*
Pres: Stephen Mooser *E-mail:* stephenmooser@scbwi.org
Exec Dir: Lin Oliver *E-mail:* linoliver@scbwi.org
Location: Hyatt Regency Century Plaza, Los Angeles, CA, USA
Aug 2014

**South African Booksellers Association Annual Conference**
Sponsored by South African Booksellers Association (SABA)
WJ Louw Bldg, 7 Old Paarl Rd, Bellville, South Africa
Mailing Address: PO Box 870, Bellville 7535, South Africa
*Tel:* (021) 945 1572 *Fax:* (021) 945 2169
*E-mail:* saba@sabooksellers.com
*Web Site:* www.sabooksellers.com
*Key Personnel*
Natl Mgr: Frikkie Nel
Location: Vineyard Hotel, Newlands, Cape Town, South Africa
Aug 2014

**Swanwick: The Writers' Summer School**
Sponsored by Writers' Summer School
103, Jean Armour Dr, Mauchline, Ayrshire KA5 6DP, United Kingdom
*Tel:* (01290) 552248
*Web Site:* www.swanwickwritersschool.co.uk
*Key Personnel*
Secy: Miss Lesley Deschner *E-mail:* secretary@swanwickwritersschool.co.uk
A week-long residential writing school with top name speakers & tutors, plus informative panels, talks & discussion groups. Comfortable rooms with all meals & tuition included in the price. Open to everyone, from absolute beginners to published authors. Beautiful setting, licensed bar & evening entertainment. Believed to be the longest established residential writers' school in the world, Swanwick, held annually in August, is a must attend annual event in every writer's diary.
Location: The Hayes Conference Centre, Swanwick, Derbyshire, UK
Aug 2014

## AUTUMN

**Louisiana Book Festival**
Sponsored by Louisiana Center for the Book
Subsidiary of State Library of Louisiana
701 N Fourth St, Baton Rouge, LA 70802
*Tel:* 225-219-9503 *Fax:* 225-219-9840
*Web Site:* louisianabookfestival.org
*Key Personnel*
Dir: Jim Davis *Tel:* 225-342-9714 *E-mail:* jdavis@slol.lib.la.us
Asst Dir: Robert Wilson *E-mail:* rwilson@slol.lib.la.us
A free festival celebrating readers, writers & books with events for all ages & genres, food, music.
Location: State Library of Louisiana, Louisiana State Capitol, Louisiana State Museum & nearby locations, Baton Rouge, LA, USA
Autumn 2014

## SEPTEMBER

**AMWA Annual Conference**
Sponsored by American Medical Writers Association (AMWA)
30 W Gude Dr, Suite 525, Rockville, MD 20850-1161
*Tel:* 240-238-0940 *Fax:* 301-294-9006
*E-mail:* amwa@amwa.org
*Web Site:* www.amwa.org
*Key Personnel*
Conference Prog Mgr & Workshop Coord: Becky Phillips *Tel:* 240-238-0940 ext 103 *E-mail:* becky@amwa.org
Location: San Antonio, TX, USA
Sept 25-27, 2014

**Distripress Annual Congress**
Sponsored by Distripress
Seefeldstr 35, CH-8008 Zurich, Switzerland
*Tel:* (044) 202 41 21 *Fax:* (044) 202 10 25
*E-mail:* info@distripress.net
*Web Site:* www.distripress.net
*Key Personnel*
Mng Dir: David Owen *E-mail:* david.owen@distripress.net
Congress Coord: Susanne Jorg *E-mail:* susanne.joerg@distripress.net
Commun & Governing Bodies: Gabriela Rietmann *E-mail:* gabriela.rietmann@distripress.net
Annual event sponsored by Distripress, a non-profit association for the promotion of international press distribution.
Location: Cannes, France
Sept 29-Oct 2, 2014

**Excellence in Journalism**
Sponsored by The Society of Professional Journalists
Eugene S Pulliam National Journalism Ctr, 3909 N Meridian St, Indianapolis, IN 46208
*Tel:* 317-927-8000 *Fax:* 317-920-4789
*E-mail:* spj@spj.org
*Web Site:* excellenceinjournalism.org; www.spj.org
*Key Personnel*
Assoc Exec Dir: Chris Vachon *Tel:* 317-927-8000 ext 207 *E-mail:* cvachon@spj.org
Dir, Events: Heather Dunn *Tel:* 317-927-8000 ext 204 *E-mail:* hdunn@spj.org
Annual conference co-organized by Radio Television Digital News Association (RTDNA).
Location: Gaylord Opryland Resort & Conference Center, 2800 Opryland Dr, Nashville, TN, USA
Sept 4-6, 2014

**Goeteborg Book Fair**
Sponsored by Bok & Bibliotek i Norden AB
Maessans Gata 20, 412 94 Gothenburg, Sweden
*Tel:* (031) 708 84 00 *Fax:* (031) 20 91 03
*E-mail:* info@goteborg-bookfair.com; info@bokmassan.se
*Web Site:* www.bokmassan.se
*Key Personnel*
CEO: Anna Falck *E-mail:* af@goteborg-bookfair.com
Book Fair Dir: Maria Kaellsson *E-mail:* maka@goteborg-bookfair.com
Head of Prog: Gunilla Sandin *E-mail:* gs@goteborg-bookfair.com
Prog Coord: Anneli Jonasson *Tel:* (031) 708 84 03 *E-mail:* aj@goteborg-bookfair.com
Location: Gothenburg, Sweden
Sept 25-28, 2014

**Graph Expo®**
Sponsored by NPES The Association for Suppliers of Printing, Publishing & Converting Technologies
1899 Preston White Dr, Reston, VA 20191
*Tel:* 703-264-7200 *Fax:* 703-620-0994; 703-620-9187 (GASC)
*E-mail:* npes@npes.org; info@gasc.org
*Web Site:* www.npes.org; www.gasc.org
*Key Personnel*
Pres: Ralph J Nappi *E-mail:* rnappi@npes.org
VP (GASC): Chris Price *Tel:* 703-264-7200 ext 221 *E-mail:* cprice@gasc.org

Conference Mgr (GASC): Lilly Kinney *Tel:* 703-264-7200 ext 255 *E-mail:* lkinney@gasc.org
Produced by Graphic Arts Show Co Inc (GASC).
Location: McCormick Place, 2301 S Lake Shore Dr, Chicago, IL, USA
Sept 28-Oct 1, 2014

**IBBY International Congress**
Sponsored by International Board on Books for Young People (IBBY)
Nonnenweg 12, Postfach, 4003 Basel, Switzerland
*Tel:* (061) 272 29 17 *Fax:* (061) 272 27 57
*E-mail:* ibby@ibby.org
*Web Site:* www.ibby.org
*Key Personnel*
Exec Dir: Liz Page *E-mail:* liz.page@ibby.org
Admin Asst: Ms Luzmaria Stauffenegger *E-mail:* luzmaria.stauffenegger@ibby.org
IBBY's biennial international congresses, hosted by different countries, are the most important meeting points for IBBY members & other people involved in children's books & reading development. They are wonderful opportunities to make contacts, exchange ideas & open horizons.
Location: Mexico City, Mexico
Sept 10-13, 2014

**NAIBA Fall Conference**
Sponsored by New Atlantic Independent Booksellers Association (NAIBA)
2667 Hyacinth St, Westbury, NY 11590
*Tel:* 516-333-0681 *Fax:* 516-333-0689
*E-mail:* naibabooksellers@gmail.com
*Web Site:* www.newatlanticbooks.com
*Key Personnel*
Exec Dir: Eileen Dengler
Location: Hyatt Regency Crystal City, Arlington, VA, USA
Sept 19-21, 2014

**National Federation of Press Women Communications Conference**
Sponsored by National Federation of Press Women Inc (NFPW)
PO Box 5556, Arlington, VA 22205-0056
*Tel:* 703-237-9804 *Toll Free Tel:* 800-780-2715 *Fax:* 703-237-9808
*E-mail:* presswomen@aol.com
*Web Site:* www.nfpw.org
*Key Personnel*
Exec Dir: Carol Pierce
Membership Servs Mgr: Gloria Watkins *E-mail:* gwatkins@americanpressworks.com
Location: Greenville, SC, USA
Sept 4-6, 2014

**NIP: International Conference on Digital Printing Technologies**
Sponsored by Society for Imaging Science & Technology (IS&T)
7003 Kilworth Lane, Springfield, VA 22151
*Tel:* 703-642-9090 *Fax:* 703-642-9094
*E-mail:* info@imaging.org
*Web Site:* www.imaging.org
*Key Personnel*
Exec Dir: Suzanne E Grinnan *E-mail:* sgrinnan@imaging.org
Conference Prog Mgr: Diana Gonzalez *E-mail:* dgonzalez@imaging.org
Held in conjunction with Digital Fabrication Conference.
Location: Philadelphia, PA, USA
Sept 7-11, 2014

**PSA® International Conference of Photography**
Sponsored by Photographic Society of America® (PSA®)
3000 United Founders Blvd, Suite 103, Oklahoma City, OK 73112
*Tel:* 405-843-1437 *Toll Free Tel:* 855-PSA-INFO (855-772-4636) *Fax:* 405-843-1438
*E-mail:* hq@psa-photo.org
*Web Site:* www.psa-photo.org
*Key Personnel*
Conference VP: Janet Bigalke *E-mail:* conferencevp@psa-photo.org
Location: Albuquerque Marriott, 2101 Louisiana Blvd NE, Albuquerque, NM, USA
Sept 27-Oct 3, 2014

**Publishing Business Conference & Expo**
Sponsored by North American Publishing Co (NAPCO)
1500 Spring Garden St, 12th fl, Philadelphia, PA 19130
*Tel:* 215-238-5300 *Toll Free Tel:* 800-627-2689 *Fax:* 215-238-5384
*Web Site:* www.publishingbusiness.com
*Key Personnel*
Dir of Conferences & Events: Kate Leshko *E-mail:* kleshko@napco.com
Conference attendees enjoy highly targeted session content developed by the publisher of *Book Business* & *Publishing Executive* magazines & presented by some of the industry's most forward-thinking & accomplished leaders in print & digital publishing. Expo attendees get a first-hand look at publishing technology, solutions & services of more than 70 of the industry's leading suppliers.
Location: New York Marriott Marquis, 1535 Broadway, New York, NY, USA
Sept 22-24, 2014

**Southern Independent Booksellers Alliance Trade Show**
Sponsored by Southern Independent Booksellers Alliance
3806 Yale Ave, Columbia, SC 29205
*Tel:* 803-994-9530 *Fax:* 309-410-0211
*E-mail:* info@sibaweb.com
*Web Site:* www.tradeshow.sibaweb.com; www.sibaweb.com
*Key Personnel*
Exec Dir: Wanda Jewell *E-mail:* wanda@sibaweb.com
Members only event.
Location: Hilton, Norfolk, VA, USA
Sept 19-21, 2014

**TAPPI PEERS Conference**
Sponsored by Technical Association of the Pulp & Paper Industry (TAPPI)
15 Technology Pkwy S, Peachtree Corners, GA 30092
*Tel:* 770-446-1400 *Toll Free Tel:* 800-332-8686 (US); 800-446-9431 (CN) *Fax:* 770-446-6947; 770-209-7206
*E-mail:* memberconnection@tappi.org
*Web Site:* www.tappi.org
*Key Personnel*
Meeting Mgr: Ed Robie *Tel:* 770-209-7243 *E-mail:* erobie@tappi.org
Dir of Mktg: Simona Marcellus *Tel:* 770-209-7293 *E-mail:* smarcellus@tappi.org
Location: Hotel Murano, 1320 Broadway, Tacoma, WA, USA
Sept 14-17, 2014

**Worlddidac India**
Sponsored by Worlddidac Association
Bollwerk 21, 3011 Bern, Switzerland
*Tel:* (031) 311 76 82 *Fax:* (031) 312 17 44
*E-mail:* info@worlddidac.org
*Web Site:* www.worlddidacindia.com; www.worlddidac.org
*Key Personnel*
Dir Gen: Beat Jost *E-mail:* jost@worlddidac.org
Proj & Commun Mgr: Kateryna Schuetz *E-mail:* schuetz@worlddidac.org
International exhibition for education, training, technology & supply. Organized by Arclights Eventz Network Pvt Ltd.
Location: New Delhi, India
Sept 2014

## OCTOBER

**ACP/CMA National College Media Convention**
Sponsored by Associated Collegiate Press (ACP) Division of National Scholastic Press Association
2221 University Ave SE, Suite 121, Minneapolis, MN 55414
*Tel:* 612-625-8335 *Fax:* 612-626-0072
*E-mail:* info@studentpress.org
*Web Site:* www.studentpress.org; facebook.com/acpress; twitter.com/acpress
*Key Personnel*
Exec Dir, National Scholastic Press Association: Logan Aimone
Co-sponsored by College Media Association.
Location: Marriott, Philadelphia, PA, USA
Oct 29-Nov 2, 2014

**ASIS&T Annual Meeting**
Sponsored by Association for Information Science & Technology (ASIS&T)
1320 Fenwick Lane, Suite 510, Silver Spring, MD 20910
*Tel:* 301-495-0900 *Fax:* 301-495-0810
*E-mail:* meetings@asis.org; asis@asis.org
*Web Site:* www.asis.org
*Key Personnel*
Exec Dir: Richard Hill *E-mail:* rhill@asis.org
Dir of Meetings & Membership: Vanessa Foss *E-mail:* vfoss@asis.org
Location: Sheraton Seattle, Seattle, WA, USA
Oct 31-Nov 4, 2014

**DMA2014**
Sponsored by Direct Marketing Association (DMA)
1120 Avenue of the Americas, New York, NY 10036-6700
SAN: 692-6487
*Tel:* 212-768-7277 *Fax:* 212-302-6714
*E-mail:* dmaconferences@the-dma.org; info@the-dma.org
*Web Site:* the-dma.org
*Key Personnel*
VP, Conferences & Membership: Kevin Fox *Tel:* 212-790-1468 *E-mail:* kfox@the-dma.org
Data is the new currency. Integration is the best strategy. Relationships are the key. Real-time is the goal. Engagement is the reward. Learn it all at DMA2014, the global event for real-time marketers.
Location: San Diego, CA, USA
Oct 26-28, 2014

**Frankfurt Book Fair**
Sponsored by Ausstellungs-und Messe-GmbH des Boersenvereins des Deutschen Buchhandels
Braubachstr 16, 60311 Frankfurt am Main, Germany
Mailing Address: Postfach 100116, 60001 Frankfurt am Main, Germany
*Tel:* (069) 21020 *Fax:* (069) 2102 277
*E-mail:* info@book-fair.com
*Web Site:* www.book-fair.com; www.frankfurt-book-fair.com
*Key Personnel*
CEO & Dir: Juergen Boos
Largest international book & media fair attracting 7,500 exhibitors from over 110 countries & 280,000 visitors.
Location: Frankfurt Fairgrounds, Frankfurt, Germany
Oct 8-12, 2014

**Humanities Montana Festival of the Book**
Sponsored by Humanities Montana
311 Brantly, Missoula, MT 59812
*Tel:* 406-243-6022 *Toll Free Tel:* 800-624-6001 (MT only) *Fax:* 406-243-4836
*E-mail:* info@humanitiesmontana.org
*Web Site:* www.humanitiesmontana.org/
*Key Personnel*
Exec Dir: Ken Egan *E-mail:* ken.egan@humanitiesmontana.org
Assoc Dir for Progs: Kim Anderson *E-mail:* kim.anderson@humanitiesmontana.org
Two day, three night celebration featuring over 70 authors & 50 events.
Location: Missoula, MT
Oct 2014

**Inter American Press Association General Assembly**
Sponsored by Inter American Press Association (IAPA)
Jules Dubois Bldg, 1801 SW Third Ave, Miami, FL 33129
*Tel:* 305-634-2465 *Fax:* 305-635-2272
*E-mail:* info@sipiapa.org
*Web Site:* www.sipiapa.org
*Key Personnel*
Exec Dir: Julio E Munoz
Gathering of important international figures for workshops, seminars & other related activities, while offering networking opportunities for those interested on press/media freedom & freedom of expression issues.
Location: Santiago, Chile
Oct 2014

**LIBER Feria Internacional del Libro**
Sponsored by Federacion de Gremios de Editores de Espana (FGEE) (Spanish Association of Publishers Guilds)
Cea Bermudez, 44-2º, 28003 Madrid, Spain
*Tel:* 91 534 51 95 *Fax:* 91 535 26 25
*E-mail:* fgee@fge.es
*Web Site:* www.federacioneditores.org
*Key Personnel*
Executive Dir: Antonio Maria Avila
Location: Barcelona, Spain
Oct 1-3, 2014

**National Association of Science Writers Annual Meeting**
Sponsored by National Association of Science Writers (NASW)
PO Box 7905, Berkeley, CA 94707
*Tel:* 510-647-9500
*Web Site:* www.nasw.org
*Key Personnel*
Exec Dir: Tinsley Davis *E-mail:* director@nasw.org
Location: Columbus, OH, USA
Oct 17-21, 2014

**National Newspaper Association 127th Annual Convention & Trade Show**
Sponsored by National Newspaper Association
200 Little Falls St, Suite 405, Falls Church, VA 22046
Mailing Address: PO Box 7540, Columbia, MO 65205
*Tel:* 703-237-9802 *Toll Free Tel:* 800-829-4NNA (829-4662) *Fax:* 703-237-9808
*Web Site:* www.nnaweb.org
*Key Personnel*
CEO: Tonda F Rush *E-mail:* tonda@nna.org
Meeting Planner: Cindy Joy-Rodgers *Tel:* 540-891-5171 *Fax:* 509-696-5489 *E-mail:* cindy@nna.org
Location: Grand Hyatt San Antonio, San Antonio, TX, USA
Oct 2-5, 2014

**Texas Book Festival**
610 Brazos, Suite 200, Austin, TX 78701
*Tel:* 512-477-4055 *Fax:* 512-322-0722
*E-mail:* bookfest@texasbookfestival.org
*Web Site:* www.texasbookfestival.org
*Key Personnel*
Exec Dir: Lois Kim
Festival Coord: Kendall Miller
Off Mgr: Lisa Jones
The festival is a statewide program that promotes reading & literacy highlighted by a two-day festival, held annually in October, featuring authors from Texas & across the USA. Money raised from the festival is distributed as grants to public libraries throughout the state.
Location: State Capitol Bldg, Austin, TX, USA
Oct 2014

**Twin Cities Book Festival**
Sponsored by Rain Taxi
PO Box 3840, Minneapolis, MN 55403
*Tel:* 612-825-1528 *Fax:* 612-825-1528
*E-mail:* bookfest@raintaxi.com; info@raintaxi.com
*Web Site:* www.raintaxi.com/bookfest
*Key Personnel*
Dir: Eric Lorberer
Gala celebration of books, featuring large exhibition, author readings & signings, book art activities, panel discussions, used book sale & children's events.
Location: Minneapolis, MN, USA
Oct 2014

**Utah Humanities Book Festival**
Sponsored by Utah Humanities Council
Affiliate of Utah Center for the Book
202 W 300 N, Salt Lake City, UT 84103
*Tel:* 801-359-9670 *Toll Free Tel:* 866-864-8554 *Fax:* 801-531-7869
*Web Site:* www.utahhumanities.org/BookFestival.htm
*Key Personnel*
Exec Dir: Cynthia Buckingham *Tel:* 801-359-9670 ext 101 *E-mail:* buckingham@utahhumanities.org
Devt Dir: Kathleen Harmon Gardner *Tel:* 801-359-9670 ext 108 *E-mail:* gardner@utahhumanities.org
Lit Prog Offr: Michael McLane *Tel:* 801-359-9670 ext 104 *E-mail:* mclane@utahhumanities.org
Free literary event featuring national, regional & local authors held Oct 1-31 annually (National Book Month).
Location: Statewide, UT, USA
Oct 1-31, 2014

**WORLDDIDAC Basel**
Sponsored by Worlddidac Association
Bollwerk 21, 3011 Bern, Switzerland
*Tel:* (031) 311 76 82 *Fax:* (031) 312 17 44
*E-mail:* info@worlddidac.org
*Web Site:* www.worlddidacbasel.com; www.worlddidac.org
*Key Personnel*
Exhibition Dir: Claudia Kaeslin *E-mail:* claudia.kaeslin@worlddidacbasel.com
International exhibition for education, training, technology & supply. Held biennially in even numbered years.
Location: Basel, Switzerland
Oct 29-31, 2014

## NOVEMBER

**American Translators Association Annual Conference**
Sponsored by American Translators Association (ATA)
225 Reinekers Lane, Suite 590, Alexandria, VA 22314
*Tel:* 703-683-6100 *Fax:* 703-683-6122
*E-mail:* ata@atanet.org
*Web Site:* www.atanet.org
*Key Personnel*
Exec Dir: Walter W Bacak, Jr *Tel:* 703-683-6100 ext 3006 *E-mail:* walter@atanet.org
Meetings Mgr: Teresa C Kelly *Tel:* 703-683-6100 ext 3014 *E-mail:* teresak@atanet.org
Location: Sheraton Hotel & Towers, Chicago, IL, USA
Nov 5-8, 2014

**BMI Annual Conference**
Sponsored by Book Manufacturers' Institute Inc (BMI)
2 Armand Beach Dr, Suite 1B, Palm Coast, FL 32137-2612
*Tel:* 386-986-4552 *Fax:* 386-986-4553
*E-mail:* info@bmibook.com
*Web Site:* www.bmibook.org
*Key Personnel*
EVP: Daniel N Bach *E-mail:* dbach@dmibook.com
Off Mgr: Diane Morris
Conference Coord: Jackie Murray
Location: Hyatt Regency Coconut Point Resort & Spa, 5001 Coconut Rd, Bonita Springs, FL, USA
Nov 9-11, 2014

**Jewish Book Month**
Sponsored by Jewish Book Council
520 Eighth Ave, 4th fl, New York, NY 10018
*Tel:* 212-201-2920 *Fax:* 212-532-4952
*E-mail:* jbc@jewishbooks.org
*Web Site:* www.jewishbookcouncil.org; www.facebook.com/JewishBookCouncil; twitter.com/jewishbook
*Key Personnel*
Dir: Carolyn Starman Hessel *E-mail:* carolynhessel@jewishbooks.org
Assoc Dir: Naomi Firestone-Teeter
Location: Nationwide throughout the USA
Nov 17-Dec 17, 2014

**Miami Book Fair International**
Sponsored by Florida Center for the Literary Arts
c/o Miami Dade College, 401 NE Second Ave, Suite 4102, Miami, FL 33132
*Tel:* 305-237-3258 *Fax:* 305-237-3978
*E-mail:* wbookfair@mdc.edu
*Web Site:* www.miamibookfair.com
*Key Personnel*
Dir of Opers: Delia Lopez *Tel:* 305-237-3066 *E-mail:* delia.lopez@mdc.edu
Admin Asst: Giselle Hernandez *E-mail:* giselle.hernandez@mdc.edu
Miami Book Fair International is the largest event of its kind in the USA. For more than 30 years, the fair has been held over 8 days each November. In addition to readings by more than 400 authors from all over the world & the sale of thousands of books in many languages, the fair offers book-centered fun for children, panel discussions & writing classes in English & Spanish. For up to date information, call or visit the book fair web site at www.miamibookfair.com.
Location: Miami Dade College, Wolfson Campus, Miami, FL, USA
Nov 2014

**PACK EXPO International**
Sponsored by PMMI: The Association for Packaging and Processing Technologies
11911 Freedom Dr, Suite 600, Reston, VA 20190
*Tel:* 703-243-8555 *Toll Free Tel:* 888-ASK-PMMI (275-7664) *Fax:* 703-243-8556
*E-mail:* expo@pmmi.org
*Web Site:* www.packexpo.com
*Key Personnel*
VP, Trade Shows: Jim Pittas *Tel:* 571-612-3211 *E-mail:* jpittas@pmmi.org
Dir, Trade Show Opers: Dinah Sprouse *Tel:* 571-612-3215 *E-mail:* dinah@pmmi.org
Dir, Exhibitor Servs: Kim Beaulieu *Tel:* 571-612-3187 *E-mail:* kim@pmmi.org
Dir, Intl Tradeshows: Laura B Thompson *Tel:* 571-612-3217 *E-mail:* laura@pmmi.org
Mgr, Exhibitor Servs: Merideth Newman *Tel:* 571-612-3208 *E-mail:* merideth@pmmi.org
Biennial event.
Location: McCormick Place, 2301 S Lake Shore Dr, Chicago, IL, USA
Nov 2-5, 2014

**Salon du Livre de Montreal**
(Montreal Book Show)
300, rue du St-Secrement, Suite 430, Montreal, QC H2Y 1X4, Canada
*Tel:* 514-845-2365 *Fax:* 514-845-7119
*E-mail:* slm.info@videotron.ca
*Web Site:* www.salondulivredemontreal.com
*Key Personnel*
Gen Mgr: Francine Bois
Location: Place Bonaventure, Montreal, QC, CN
Nov 19-24, 2014

**Salon du Livre et de la Presse Jeunesse**
Sponsored by Reed Expositions France
52-54 quai de Dion-Bouton, CS 80001, 92806 Puteaux Cedex, France
*Tel:* 01 55 86 86 55 *Fax:* 01 48 57 04 62
*E-mail:* contact@slpj.fr
*Web Site:* www.salon-livre-presse-jeunesse.net
*Key Personnel*
Dir: Sylvie Vassallo
Leading publishing event dedicated to children's books, organized by Centre de promotion du livre de jeunesse.
Location: Montreuil, Seine-Saint-Denis, France
Nov 2014

# 2015

## JANUARY

**American Library Association Mid-Winter Meeting**
Sponsored by The American Library Association (ALA)
50 E Huron St, Chicago, IL 60611
*Toll Free Tel:* 800-545-2433 (ext 3223) *Fax:* 312-440-9374
*E-mail:* ala@ala.org
*Web Site:* www.ala.org/midwinter
*Key Personnel*
Conference/Events Coord: Alicia Babcock *Tel:* 800-545-2433 ext 3229 *E-mail:* ababcock@ala.org; Yvonne A McLean *Tel:* 800-545-2433 ext 3222 *E-mail:* ymclean@ala.org
Conference Supv: Amy R McGuigan *Tel:* 800-545-2433 ext 3226 *E-mail:* amcguigan@ala.org
Exhibit Mgr: Patrick Thomas Murphy *Tel:* 800-545-2433 ext 3218 *E-mail:* pmurphy@ala.org
Location: Chicago, IL, USA
Jan 23-27, 2015

**MLA Annual Convention**
Sponsored by Modern Language Association of America (MLA)
26 Broadway, 3rd fl, New York, NY 10004-1789
SAN: 202-6422
*Tel:* 646-576-5262; 646-576-5000 *Fax:* 646-458-0030
*E-mail:* convention@mla.org
*Web Site:* www.mla.org/convention
*Key Personnel*
Dir of Convention Progs: Maribeth T Kraus *E-mail:* mkraus@mla.org
Assoc Dir of Convention Progs: Karin Bagnall *E-mail:* kbagnall@mla.org
Location: Vancouver, BC, CN
Jan 8-11, 2015

## FEBRUARY

**Adelaide Festival**
Sponsored by Adelaide Festival Corp
Level 9, 33 King William St, Adelaide, SA 5000, Australia
Mailing Address: PO Box 8221, Station Arcade, Adelaide, SA 5000, Australia
*Tel:* (08) 8216 4444 *Fax:* (08) 8216 4455
*E-mail:* info@adelaidefestival.com.au
*Web Site:* www.adelaidefestival.com.au
*Key Personnel*
Artistic Dir: David Sefton
Prog Exec & Prodr: Jude Gun
Prog Dir: Lesley Newton
Spec Events Prodn Mgr: Adam Hornhardt
Annual event highlighting the arts, including literature. Adelaide Writers' Week is one of the high-profile events held during the festival.
Location: Adelaide's Central Business District, Adelaide, SA, Australia
Feb 27-March 15, 2015

**IS&T/SPIE Electronic Imaging Science & Technology**
Sponsored by IS&T/SPIE
c/o IS&T, 7003 Kilworth Lane, Springfield, VA 22151
*Tel:* 703-642-9090 *Fax:* 703-642-9094
*E-mail:* info@imaging.org; customerservice@spie.org
*Web Site:* spie.org/electronic-imaging.xml
*Key Personnel*
Exec Dir: Suzanne E Grinnan
Conference Prog Mgr: Diana Gonzalez
Exec Asst: Donna Smith
Location: San Francisco, CA, USA
Feb 15-19, 2015

**Jerusalem International Book Fair**
Sponsored by Ariel Municipal Co Ltd
PO Box 775, Jerusalem 91007, Israel
*Tel:* (02) 629 6415; (02) 629 7922 *Fax:* (02) 624 0663
*E-mail:* jerfair@jerusalem.muni.il
*Web Site:* www.jerusalembookfair.com
Biennial event.
Location: Jerusalem International Convention Center, Jerusalem, Israel
Feb 2015

## SPRING

**Poligrafia**
Sponsored by Poznan International Fair Ltd
ul Glogowska 14, 60-734 Poznan, Poland
*Tel:* (061) 869 20 00 *Fax:* (061) 869 29 99
*E-mail:* poligrafia@mtp.pl; info@mtp.pl
*Web Site:* www.poligrafiaexpo.pl/en (English); www.poligrafiaexpo.pl/pl (Polish)
*Key Personnel*
Proj Mgr: Piotr Kaminski *Tel:* (0603) 410 225 *E-mail:* piotr.kaminski@mtp.pl
International fair of printing machines, materials & services held biennially.
Location: Poznan International Fair Grounds, Poznan, Poland
Spring 2015

## MARCH

**Leipzig Book Fair (Leipsiger Buchmesse)**
Sponsored by Leipziger Messe GmbH
Messe-Allee 1, 04356 Leipzig, Germany
Mailing Address: Postfach 10 07 20, 04007 Leipzig, Germany
*Tel:* (0341) 678-0 *Fax:* (0341) 678-8762
*E-mail:* info@leipziger-buchmesse.de
*Web Site:* www.leipziger-buchmesse.de
*Key Personnel*
Dir: Oliver Zille *Tel:* (0341) 678 8240
Held annually in conjunction with The Leipzig Antiquarian Book Fair.
Location: New Fair Ground, Leipzig, Germany
March 12-15, 2015

**Virginia Festival of the Book**
Sponsored by Virginia Foundation for the Humanities
145 Ednam Dr, Charlottesville, VA 22903
*Tel:* 434-924-3296 *Fax:* 434-296-4714
*E-mail:* vabook@virginia.edu
*Web Site:* www.vabook.org
*Key Personnel*
Prog Dir: Nancy Damon *Tel:* 434-924-7548
Annual public festival for children & adults featuring authors, illustrators, publishers, publicists, agents & other book professionals in panel discussions & readings. Most events are free. More than 200 authors invited annually.
Location: Charlottesville, VA, USA
March 18-22, 2015

## APRIL

**AWP Annual Conference & Bookfair**
Sponsored by Association of Writers & Writing Programs (AWP)
George Mason University, 4400 University Dr, MSN 1E3, Fairfax, VA 22030
*Tel:* 703-993-4301 *Fax:* 703-993-4302
*E-mail:* conference@awpwriter.org; awp@awpwriter.org
*Web Site:* www.aprwriter.org/conference; www.awpwriter.org
*Key Personnel*
Exec Dir: David W Fenza
Dir of Conferences: Christian Teresi
Conference Coord: Brenna Killeen
Assoc Dir of Cenferences: Cynthia Sherman
Conference Mgr: Sheri Sorvillo
Location: Minneapolis Convention Center & Hilton Minneapolis Hotel, Minneapolis, MN, USA
April 8-11, 2015

**International Children's Book Day**
Sponsored by International Board on Books for Young People (IBBY)
Nonnenweg 12, Postfach, 4003 Basel, Switzerland
*Tel:* (061) 272 29 17 *Fax:* (061) 272 27 57
*E-mail:* ibby@ibby.org
*Web Site:* www.ibby.org

*Key Personnel*
Exec Dir: Liz Page *E-mail:* liz.page@ibby.org
Admin Asst: Ms Luzmaria Stauffenegger *E-mail:* luzmaria.stauffenegger@ibby.org
On Hans Christian Andersen's birthday, April 2nd, International Children's Book Day (ICBD) is celebrated to inspire a love of reading & to call attention to children's books. Each year a different national section has the opportunity to be the international sponsor. It decides upon a theme & invites a prominent author to write a message to the children of the world & a well-known illustrator to design a poster. These materials are used in different ways to promote books & reading around the world.
April 2, 2015

**Izmir Book Fair**
Sponsored by Tuyap Fairs & Exhibitions Organization Inc (Tuyap Fuar ve Sergiler A S)
E-5 Karayolu Uezeri, Guerpinar Kavsagi, Bueyuekcekmece, 34500 Istanbul, Turkey
*Tel:* (0212) 867 11 00 *Fax:* (0212) 886 66 98
*E-mail:* fairarea@tuyap.com.tr
*Web Site:* www.tuyap.com.tr
Annual event organized in cooperation with the Turkish Publishers Association.
Location: Culturepark Fair Ground, Izmir, Turkey
April 2015

**National Library Week**
Sponsored by The American Library Association (ALA)
50 E Huron St, Chicago, IL 60611
*Toll Free Tel:* 800-545-2433 (ext 3223) *Fax:* 312-440-9374
*E-mail:* ala@ala.org
*Web Site:* www.ala.org/nlw
*Key Personnel*
Campaign Mgr: Megan G Humphrey *Tel:* 800-545-2433 ext 4020 *E-mail:* mhumphrey@ala.org
Campaign Coord: Megan McFarlane *Tel:* 800-545-2433 ext 2148 *E-mail:* mmcfarlane@ala.org
Location: Nationwide throughout the USA
April 12-18, 2015

**North American Agricultural Journalists Spring Meeting**
Sponsored by North American Agricultural Journalists (NAAJ)
6434 Hurta Lane, Bryan, TX 77808
*Tel:* 979-845-2872 *Fax:* 979-862-1202
*Web Site:* www.naaj.net
*Key Personnel*
Exec Secy & Treas: Kathleen Phillips *E-mail:* ka-phillips@tamu.edu
Location: Washington, DC, USA
April 2015

**PaperCon**
Sponsored by Technical Association of the Pulp & Paper Industry (TAPPI)
15 Technology Pkwy S, Peachtree Corners, GA 30092
*Tel:* 770-446-1400 *Toll Free Tel:* 800-332-8686 (US); 800-446-9431 (CN) *Fax:* 770-446-6947; 770-209-7206
*E-mail:* memberconnection@tappi.org
*Web Site:* www.papercon.org; www.tappi.org
*Key Personnel*
Meeting Mgr: Ed Robie *Tel:* 770-209-7243 *E-mail:* erobie@tappi.org
Dir of Mktg: Simona Marcellus *Tel:* 770-209-7293 *E-mail:* smarcellus@tappi.org
Location: Georgia World Congress Center, Atlanta, GA, USA
April 18-22, 2015

**The Quest for Excellence® Conference**
Sponsored by National Institute of Standards & Technology (NIST)
100 Bureau Dr, Gaithersburg, MD 20899
*Tel:* 301-975-2036 *Fax:* 301-948-3716
*E-mail:* baldrige@nist.gov
*Web Site:* www.nist.gov/baldrige/qe/index.cfm
*Key Personnel*
Conference Chair: Barbara Fischer *Tel:* 301-975-8942 *E-mail:* barbara.fischer@nist.gov
Official conference of the Baldridge Award, held in partnership with American Society for Quality (ASQ) & American Society for Training & Development (ASTD).
Location: Baltimore Marriott Waterfront, 400 Aliceanna St, Baltimore, MD, USA
April 13-15, 2015

## MAY

**BookExpo America (BEA)**
Sponsored by Reed Exhibitions USA
Division of Reed Elsevier plc
383 Main Ave, Norwalk, CT 06851
*Tel:* 203-840-4800 *Toll Free Tel:* 800-840-5614 *Fax:* 203-840-5805
*E-mail:* inquiry@bookexpoamerica.com
*Web Site:* bookexpoamerica.com
*Key Personnel*
Event Dir: Steven Rosato
Conference Mgr: Maggie Donovan *E-mail:* mdonovan@reedexpo.com
Conference Coord: Mackenzie Lynch *E-mail:* malynch@reedexpo.com
Produced & managed by Reed Exhibitions USA, BEA is sponsored by the American Booksellers Association (ABA), the Association of American Publishers Inc (AAP) & the Association of Authors' Representatives Inc (AAR).
Location: Jacob K Javits Convention Center, 655 W 43 St, New York, NY, USA
May 28-30, 2015

**Outdoor Writers Association of America Annual Conference**
Sponsored by Outdoor Writers Association of America
615 Oak St, Suite 201, Missoula, MT 59801
*Tel:* 406-728-7434
*E-mail:* info@owaa.org
*Web Site:* owaa.org
*Key Personnel*
Ed: Ashley Schroeder *E-mail:* editor@owaa.org
Membership & Conference Servs: Jessica Pollett *E-mail:* jpollett@owaa.org
Location: McAllen, TX, USA
May 22-24, 2015

**PrintEx 2015**
Sponsored by Reed Exhibitions Australia Pty Ltd
Level 2, Tower 2, 475 Victoria Ave, Chatswood, NSW 2067, Australia
Mailing Address: Locked Bag 4500, Chatswood, NSW 2067, Australia
*Tel:* (02) 9422 2500
*E-mail:* inquiry@reedexhibitions.com.au
*Web Site:* www.printex.net.au
PrintEx brings the latest printing & graphic communications technologies to the industry. Sponsored by Graphic Arts Merchants Association of Australia Inc (GAMAA) & the Printing Industries Association of Australia (PIAA), this event is held every 4 years.
Location: Sydney Convention & Exhibition Centre, Darling Harbour, Sydney, NSW, Australia
May 5-8, 2015

## JUNE

**AAUP Annual Meeting**
Sponsored by Association of American University Presses (AAUP)
28 W 36 St, Suite 602, New York, NY 10018
*Tel:* 212-989-1010 *Fax:* 212-989-0275
*E-mail:* info@aaupnet.org
*Web Site:* www.aaupnet.org
*Key Personnel*
Exec Dir: Peter Berkery *Tel:* 212-989-1010 ext 29 *E-mail:* pberkery@aaupnet.org
Asst Dir & Cont: Tim Muench *Tel:* 212-989-1010 ext 28 *E-mail:* tmuench@aaupnet.org
Dir of Mktg & Communs: Brenna McLaughlin *Tel:* 518-436-3586 *E-mail:* bmclaughlin@aaupnet.org
Admin Mgr: Linda McCall *Tel:* 212-989-1010 ext 30 *E-mail:* lmccall@aaupnet.org
Location: Sheraton Denver Downtown, Denver, CO, USA
June 18-20, 2015

**American Library Association Annual Conference**
Sponsored by The American Library Association (ALA)
50 E Huron St, Chicago, IL 60611
*Toll Free Tel:* 800-545-2433 (ext 3223) *Fax:* 312-440-9374
*E-mail:* ala@ala.org
*Web Site:* www.ala.org
*Key Personnel*
Conference/Events Coord: Alicia Babcock *Tel:* 800-545-2433 ext 3229 *E-mail:* ababcock@ala.org; Yvonne A McLean *Tel:* 800-545-2433 ext 3222 *E-mail:* ymclean@ala.org
Conference Supv: Amy R McGuigan *Tel:* 800-545-2433 ext 3226 *E-mail:* amcguigan@ala.org
Exhibit Mgr: Patrick Thomas Murphy *Tel:* 800-545-2433 ext 3218 *E-mail:* pmurphy@ala.org
Location: San Francisco, CA, USA
June 25-30, 2015

**Canadian Library Association National Conference & Trade Show**
Sponsored by Canadian Library Association (CLA) (Association Canadienne des bibliotheques)
1150 Morrison Dr, Suite 400, Ottawa, ON K2H 8S9, Canada
*Tel:* 613-232-9625 *Fax:* 613-563-9895
*E-mail:* info@cla.ca
*Web Site:* www.cla.ca
*Key Personnel*
Exec Dir: Kelly Moore *Tel:* 613-232-9625 ext 306 *E-mail:* kmoore@cla.ca
Conference & Events Mgr: Wendy Walton *Tel:* 613-232-9625 ext 302 *E-mail:* wwalton@cla.ca
Location: Ottawa, ON, CN
June 3-6, 2015

**Christian Resources Retailers & Suppliers Retreat**
Sponsored by Christian Resources Together
PO Box 995, Aylesbury, Bucks HP20 9HU, United Kingdom
*Tel:* (01296) 489860
*Web Site:* www.christianresourcestogether.co.uk
*Key Personnel*
Event Organizer: Steve Briars *E-mail:* steve@christianresourcestogether.co.uk
Location: Hayes Conference Centre, Swanwick, Alfreton, Derbyshire, UK
June 30-July 1, 2015

**IABC World Conference**
Sponsored by International Association of Business Communicators (IABC)

601 Montgomery St, Suite 1900, San Francisco, CA 94111
*Tel:* 415-544-4700 *Toll Free Tel:* 800-776-4222 (US & CN) *Fax:* 415-544-4747
*E-mail:* conference@iabc.com
*Web Site:* www.iabc.com
*Key Personnel*
Events & Conferences Mgr: Charles Herrick *Tel:* 415-544-4745 *E-mail:* cherrick@iabc.com
Location: San Francisco Marriott Marquis, 55 Fourth St, San Francisco, CA, USA
June 14-17, 2015

**International Christian Retail Show**
Sponsored by CBA: The Association for Christian Retail
9240 Explorer Dr, Suite 200, Colorado Springs, CO 80920
*Tel:* 719-265-9895 *Toll Free Tel:* 800-252-1950 *Fax:* 719-272-3510
*E-mail:* info@cbaonline.org
*Web Site:* www.christianretailshow.com; www.cbaonline.org
*Key Personnel*
Exec Dir: Curtis Riskey
Meetings & Expositions Dir: Scott Graham *E-mail:* sgraham@cbaonline.org
For over 50 years, the annual International Christian Retail Show has been our industry's single-most impacting week. During this week, people of the industry from all over the world meet face-to-face for buying & selling, education, inspiration, fellowship & future planning. Here individuals unite to further the mission of seeing Christian products impact lives for God's Kingdom the world over. At this unique gathering, our industry's strength is most evident & our goals are most clearly in focus. It is, in short, the most important week in the ministry of your business & of the industry as a whole.
Location: Orange County Convention Center, Orlando, FL, USA
June 28-July 1, 2015

**SLA Annual Conference & INFO-EXPO**
Sponsored by Special Libraries Association (SLA)
331 S Patrick St, Alexandria, VA 22314-3501
*Tel:* 703-647-4900 *Fax:* 703-647-4901
*Web Site:* www.sla.org
*Key Personnel*
CEO: Janice R Lachance *Tel:* 703-647-4933 *E-mail:* janice@sla.org
Dir, Events: Caroline Rives *Tel:* 703-647-4949 *E-mail:* crives@sla.org
Dir, Mktg & Exhibits: Jeff Leach *Tel:* 703-647-4922 *E-mail:* jleach@sla.org
Mktg/Events Assoc: Jarell D Grady *Tel:* 703-647-4941 *E-mail:* jgrady@sla.org
Location: Boston, MA, USA
June 14-16, 2015

## JULY

**Romance Writers of America Annual Conference**
Sponsored by Romance Writers of America®
14615 Benfer Rd, Houston, TX 77069
*Tel:* 832-717-5200 *Fax:* 832-717-5201
*E-mail:* conference@rwa.org; info@rwa.org
*Web Site:* www.rwa.org
*Key Personnel*
Exec Dir: Allison Kelley *Tel:* 832-717-5200 ext 124 *E-mail:* allison.kelley@rwa.org
Location: New York Marriott® Marquis, New York, NY, USA
July 22-25, 2015

## AUGUST

**Swanwick: The Writers' Summer School**
Sponsored by Writers' Summer School
103, Jean Armour Dr, Mauchline, Ayrshire KA5 6DP, United Kingdom
*Tel:* (01290) 552248
*Web Site:* www.swanwickwritersschool.co.uk
*Key Personnel*
Secy: Miss Lesley Deschner *E-mail:* secretary@swanwickwritersschool.co.uk
A week-long residential writing school with top name speakers & tutors, plus informative panels, talks & discussion groups. Comfortable rooms with all meals & tuition included in the price. Open to everyone, from absolute beginners to published authors. Beautiful setting, licensed bar & evening entertainment. Believed to be the longest established residential writers' school in the world, Swanwick, held annually in August, is a must attend annual event in every writer's diary.
Location: The Hayes Conference Centre, Swanwick, Derbyshire, UK
Aug 2015

## SEPTEMBER

**Distripress Annual Congress**
Sponsored by Distripress
Seefeldstr 35, CH-8008 Zurich, Switzerland
*Tel:* (044) 202 41 21 *Fax:* (044) 202 10 25
*E-mail:* info@distripress.net
*Web Site:* www.distripress.net
*Key Personnel*
Mng Dir: David Owen *E-mail:* david.owen@distripress.net
Congress Coord: Susanne Jorg *E-mail:* susanne.joerg@distripress.net
Commun & Governing Bodies: Gabriela Rietmann *E-mail:* gabriela.rietmann@distripress.net
Annual event sponsored by Distripress, a non-profit association for the promotion of international press distribution.
Location: Brussels, Belgium
Sept 28-Oct 1, 2015

**Goteborg Book Fair**
Sponsored by Bok & Bibliotek i Norden AB
Maessans Gata 20, 412 94 Gothenburg, Sweden
*Tel:* (031) 708 84 00 *Fax:* (031) 20 91 03
*E-mail:* info@goteborg-bookfair.com; info@bokmassan.se
*Web Site:* www.bokmassan.se
*Key Personnel*
CEO: Anna Falck *E-mail:* af@goteborg-bookfair.com
Book Fair Dir: Maria Kaellsson *E-mail:* maka@goteborg-bookfair.com
Head of Prog: Gunilla Sandin *E-mail:* gs@goteborg-bookfair.com
Prog Coord: Anneli Jonasson *Tel:* (031) 708 84 03 *E-mail:* aj@goteborg-bookfair.com
Location: Gothenburg, Sweden
Sept 24-27, 2015

**Graph Expo®**
Sponsored by NPES The Association for Suppliers of Printing, Publishing & Converting Technologies
1899 Preston White Dr, Reston, VA 20191
*Tel:* 703-264-7200 *Fax:* 703-620-0994; 703-620-9187 (GASC)
*E-mail:* npes@npes.org; info@gasc.org
*Web Site:* www.npes.org; www.gasc.org
*Key Personnel*
Pres: Ralph J Nappi *E-mail:* rnappi@npes.org
VP (GASC): Chris Price *Tel:* 703-264-7200 ext 221 *E-mail:* cprice@gasc.org
Conference Mgr (GASC): Lilly Kinney *Tel:* 703-264-7200 ext 255 *E-mail:* lkinney@gasc.org
Produced by Graphic Arts Show Co Inc (GASC).
Location: McCormick Place, 2301 S Lake Shore Dr, Chicago, IL, USA
Sept 13-16, 2015

**National Federation of Press Women Communications Conference**
Sponsored by National Federation of Press Women Inc (NFPW)
PO Box 5556, Arlington, VA 22205-0056
*Tel:* 703-237-9804 *Toll Free Tel:* 800-780-2715 *Fax:* 703-237-9808
*E-mail:* presswomen@aol.com
*Web Site:* www.nfpw.org
*Key Personnel*
Exec Dir: Carol Pierce
Membership Servs Mgr: Gloria Watkins *E-mail:* gwatkins@americanpressworks.com
Location: Anchorage, AK, USA
Sept 10-12, 2015

**PACK EXPO Las Vegas**
Sponsored by PMMI: The Association for Packaging and Processing Technologies
11911 Freedom Dr, Suite 600, Reston, VA 20190
*Tel:* 703-243-8555 *Toll Free Tel:* 888-ASK-PMMI (275-7664) *Fax:* 703-243-8556
*E-mail:* expo@pmmi.org
*Web Site:* www.packexpo.com
*Key Personnel*
VP, Trade Shows: Jim Pittas *Tel:* 571-612-3211 *E-mail:* jpittas@pmmi.org
Dir, Trade Show Opers: Dinah Sprouse *Tel:* 571-612-3215 *E-mail:* dinah@pmmi.org
Dir, Exhibitor Servs: Kim Beaulieu *Tel:* 571-612-3187 *E-mail:* kim@pmmi.org
Mgr, Exhibitor Servs: Merideth Newman *Tel:* 571-612-3208 *E-mail:* merideth@pmmi.org
Biennial event.
Location: Las Vegas Convention Center, Las Vegas, NV, USA
Sept 28-30, 2015

**PSA® International Conference of Photography**
Sponsored by Photographic Society of America® (PSA®)
3000 United Founders Blvd, Suite 103, Oklahoma City, OK 73112
*Tel:* 405-843-1437 *Toll Free Tel:* 855-PSA-INFO (855-772-4636) *Fax:* 405-843-1438
*E-mail:* hq@psa-photo.org
*Web Site:* www.psa-photo.org
*Key Personnel*
Conference VP: Janet Bigalke *E-mail:* conferencevp@psa-photo.org
Location: Holiday Inn West Yellowstone, West Yellowstone, MT, USA
Sept 27-Oct 3, 2015

## OCTOBER

**ACP/CMA National College Media Convention**
Sponsored by Associated Collegiate Press (ACP) Division of National Scholastic Press Association
2221 University Ave SE, Suite 121, Minneapolis, MN 55414
*Tel:* 612-625-8335 *Fax:* 612-626-0072
*E-mail:* info@studentpress.org
*Web Site:* www.studentpress.org; facebook.com/acpress; twitter.com/acpress

*Key Personnel*
Exec Dir, National Scholastic Press Association: Logan Aimone
Co-sponsored by College Media Association.
Location: Hilton, Austin, TX, USA
Oct 28-Nov 1, 2015

**AMWA Annual Conference**
Sponsored by American Medical Writers Association (AMWA)
30 W Gude Dr, Suite 525, Rockville, MD 20850-1161
*Tel:* 240-238-0940 *Fax:* 301-294-9006
*E-mail:* amwa@amwa.org
*Web Site:* www.amwa.org
*Key Personnel*
Conference Prog Mgr & Workshop Coord: Becky Phillips *Tel:* 240-238-0940 ext 103 *E-mail:* becky@amwa.org
Location: Memphis, TN, USA
Oct 22-24, 2015

**Frankfurt Book Fair**
Sponsored by Ausstellungs-und Messe-GmbH des Boersenvereins des Deutschen Buchhandels
Braubachstr 16, 60311 Frankfurt am Main, Germany
Mailing Address: Postfach 100116, 60001 Frankfurt am Main, Germany
*Tel:* (069) 21020 *Fax:* (069) 2102 277
*E-mail:* info@book-fair.com
*Web Site:* www.book-fair.com; www.frankfurt-book-fair.com
*Key Personnel*
CEO & Dir: Juergen Boos
Largest international book & media fair attracting 7,500 exhibitors from over 110 countries & 280,000 visitors.
Location: Frankfurt Fairgrounds, Frankfurt, Germany
Oct 14-18, 2015

**Head, Heart, Hand: AIGA Design Conference**
Sponsored by AIGA, the professional association for design
164 Fifth Ave, New York, NY 10010
*Tel:* 212-807-1990
*E-mail:* general@aiga.org
*Web Site:* www.aiga.org
*Key Personnel*
Dir of Events: Jonathan Feinberg *Tel:* 212-710-3142
Conference Prodr: Katie Baker *Tel:* 212-710-3146
Biennial event.
Oct 2015

**LIBER Feria Internacional del Libro**
Sponsored by Federacion de Gremios de Editores de Espana (FGEE) (Spanish Association of Publishers Guilds)
Cea Bermudez, 44-2°, 28003 Madrid, Spain
*Tel:* 91 534 51 95 *Fax:* 91 535 26 25
*E-mail:* fgee@fge.es
*Web Site:* www.federacioneditores.org
*Key Personnel*
Executive Dir: Antonio Maria Avila
Location: Madrid, Spain
Oct 7-9, 2015

**Utah Humanities Book Festival**
Sponsored by Utah Humanities Council
Affiliate of Utah Center for the Book
202 W 300 N, Salt Lake City, UT 84103
*Tel:* 801-359-9670 *Toll Free Tel:* 866-864-8554 *Fax:* 801-531-7869
*Web Site:* www.utahhumanities.org/BookFestival.htm
*Key Personnel*
Exec Dir: Cynthia Buckingham *Tel:* 801-359-9670 ext 101 *E-mail:* buckingham@utahhumanities.org
Devt Dir: Kathleen Harmon Gardner *Tel:* 801-359-9670 ext 108 *E-mail:* gardner@utahhumanities.org
Lit Prog Offr: Michael McLane *Tel:* 801-359-9670 ext 104 *E-mail:* mclane@utahhumanities.org
Free literary event featuring national, regional & local authors held Oct 1-31 annually (National Book Month).
Location: Statewide, UT, USA
Oct 1-31, 2015

## NOVEMBER

**American Translators Association Annual Conference**
Sponsored by American Translators Association (ATA)
225 Reinekers Lane, Suite 590, Alexandria, VA 22314
*Tel:* 703-683-6100 *Fax:* 703-683-6122
*E-mail:* ata@atanet.org
*Web Site:* www.atanet.org
*Key Personnel*
Exec Dir: Walter W Bacak, Jr *Tel:* 703-683-6100 ext 3006 *E-mail:* walter@atanet.org
Meetings Mgr: Teresa C Kelly *Tel:* 703-683-6100 ext 3014 *E-mail:* teresak@atanet.org
Location: Hyatt Regency Hotel, Miami, FL, USA
Nov 4-7, 2015

# 2016

## JANUARY

**American Library Association Mid-Winter Meeting**
Sponsored by The American Library Association (ALA)
50 E Huron St, Chicago, IL 60611
*Toll Free Tel:* 800-545-2433 (ext 3223) *Fax:* 312-440-9374
*E-mail:* ala@ala.org
*Web Site:* www.ala.org/midwinter
*Key Personnel*
Conference/Events Coord: Alicia Babcock *Tel:* 800-545-2433 ext 3229 *E-mail:* ababcock@ala.org; Yvonne A McLean *Tel:* 800-545-2433 ext 3222 *E-mail:* ymclean@ala.org
Conference Supv: Amy R McGuigan *Tel:* 800-545-2433 ext 3226 *E-mail:* amcguigan@ala.org
Exhibit Mgr: Patrick Thomas Murphy *Tel:* 800-545-2433 ext 3218 *E-mail:* pmurphy@ala.org
Location: Boston, MA, USA
Jan 8-12, 2016

## FEBRUARY

**Adelaide Festival**
Sponsored by Adelaide Festival Corp
Level 9, 33 King William St, Adelaide, SA 5000, Australia
Mailing Address: PO Box 8221, Station Arcade, Adelaide, SA 5000, Australia
*Tel:* (08) 8216 4444 *Fax:* (08) 8216 4455
*E-mail:* info@adelaidefestival.com.au
*Web Site:* www.adelaidefestival.com.au
*Key Personnel*
Artistic Dir: David Sefton
Prog Exec & Prodr: Jude Gun
Prog Dir: Lesley Newton
Spec Events Prodn Mgr: Adam Hornhardt
Annual event highlighting the arts, including literature. Adelaide Writers' Week is one of the high-profile events held during the festival.
Location: Adelaide's Central Business District, Adelaide, SA, Australia
Feb 26-March 14, 2016

**IS&T/SPIE Electronic Imaging Science & Technology**
Sponsored by IS&T/SPIE
c/o IS&T, 7003 Kilworth Lane, Springfield, VA 22151
*Tel:* 703-642-9090 *Fax:* 703-642-9094
*E-mail:* info@imaging.org; customerservice@spie.org
*Web Site:* spie.org/electronic-imaging.xml
*Key Personnel*
Exec Dir: Suzanne E Grinnan
Conference Prog Mgr: Diana Gonzalez
Exec Asst: Donna Smith
Location: San Francisco, CA, USA
Feb 7-11, 2016

## MARCH

**AWP Annual Conference & Bookfair**
Sponsored by Association of Writers & Writing Programs (AWP)
George Mason University, 4400 University Dr, MSN 1E3, Fairfax, VA 22030
*Tel:* 703-993-4301 *Fax:* 703-993-4302
*E-mail:* conference@awpwriter.org; awp@awpwriter.org
*Web Site:* www.aprwriter.org/conference; www.awpwriter.org
*Key Personnel*
Exec Dir: David W Fenza
Dir of Conferences: Christian Teresi
Conference Coord: Brenna Killeen
Assoc Dir of Cenferences: Cynthia Sherman
Conference Mgr: Sheri Sorvillo
Location: Los Angeles Convention Center & JW Marriott Los Angeles, Los Angeles, CA, USA
March 30-April 2, 2016

**BookExpo America (BEA)**
Sponsored by Reed Exhibitions USA
Division of Reed Elsevier plc
383 Main Ave, Norwalk, CT 06851
*Tel:* 203-840-4800 *Toll Free Tel:* 800-840-5614 *Fax:* 203-840-5805
*E-mail:* inquiry@bookexpoamerica.com
*Web Site:* bookexpoamerica.com
*Key Personnel*
Event Dir: Steven Rosato
Conference Mgr: Maggie Donovan *E-mail:* mdonovan@reedexpo.com
Conference Coord: Mackenzie Lynch *E-mail:* malynch@reedexpo.com
Produced & managed by Reed Exhibitions USA, BEA is sponsored by the American Booksellers Association (ABA), the Association of American Publishers Inc (AAP) & the Association of Authors' Representatives Inc (AAR).
Location: Chicago, IL, USA
May 12-14, 2016

**Virginia Festival of the Book**
Sponsored by Virginia Foundation for the Humanities
145 Ednam Dr, Charlottesville, VA 22903
*Tel:* 434-924-3296 *Fax:* 434-296-4714
*E-mail:* vabook@virginia.edu
*Web Site:* www.vabook.org
*Key Personnel*
Prog Dir: Nancy Damon *Tel:* 434-924-7548

Annual public festival for children & adults featuring authors, illustrators, publishers, publicists, agents & other book professionals in panel discussions & readings. Most events are free. More than 200 authors invited annually.
Location: Charlottesville, VA, USA
March 16-20, 2016

## APRIL

**Christian Resources Retailers & Suppliers Retreat**
Sponsored by Christian Resources Together
PO Box 995, Aylesbury, Bucks HP20 9HU, United Kingdom
*Tel:* (01296) 489860
*Web Site:* www.christianresourcestogether.co.uk
*Key Personnel*
Event Organizer: Steve Briars *E-mail:* steve@christianresourcestogether.co.uk
Location: Hayes Conference Centre, Swanwick, Alfreton, Derbyshire, UK
April 5-6, 2016

**International Children's Book Day**
Sponsored by International Board on Books for Young People (IBBY)
Nonnenweg 12, Postfach, 4003 Basel, Switzerland
*Tel:* (061) 272 29 17 *Fax:* (061) 272 27 57
*E-mail:* ibby@ibby.org
*Web Site:* www.ibby.org
*Key Personnel*
Exec Dir: Liz Page *E-mail:* liz.page@ibby.org
Admin Asst: Ms Luzmaria Stauffenegger *E-mail:* luzmaria.stauffenegger@ibby.org
On Hans Christian Andersen's birthday, April 2nd, International Children's Book Day (ICBD) is celebrated to inspire a love of reading & to call attention to children's books. Each year a different national section has the opportunity to be the international sponsor. It decides upon a theme & invites a prominent author to write a message to the children of the world & a well-known illustrator to design a poster. These materials are used in different ways to promote books & reading around the world.
April 2, 2016

**National Library Week**
Sponsored by The American Library Association (ALA)
50 E Huron St, Chicago, IL 60611
*Toll Free Tel:* 800-545-2433 (ext 3223) *Fax:* 312-440-9374
*E-mail:* ala@ala.org
*Web Site:* www.ala.org/nlw
*Key Personnel*
Campaign Mgr: Megan G Humphrey *Tel:* 800-545-2433 ext 4020 *E-mail:* mhumphrey@ala.org
Campaign Coord: Megan McFarlane *Tel:* 800-545-2433 ext 2148 *E-mail:* mmcfarlane@ala.org
Location: Nationwide throughout the USA
April 10-16, 2016

## JUNE

**American Library Association Annual Conference**
Sponsored by The American Library Association (ALA)
50 E Huron St, Chicago, IL 60611
*Toll Free Tel:* 800-545-2433 (ext 3223) *Fax:* 312-440-9374
*E-mail:* ala@ala.org
*Web Site:* www.ala.org
*Key Personnel*
Conference/Events Coord: Alicia Babcock *Tel:* 800-545-2433 ext 3229 *E-mail:* ababcock@ala.org; Yvonne A McLean *Tel:* 800-545-2433 ext 3222 *E-mail:* ymclean@ala.org
Conference Supv: Amy R McGuigan *Tel:* 800-545-2433 ext 3226 *E-mail:* amcguigan@ala.org
Exhibit Mgr: Patrick Thomas Murphy *Tel:* 800-545-2433 ext 3218 *E-mail:* pmurphy@ala.org
Location: Orlando, FL, USA
June 23-28, 2016

**Canadian Library Association National Conference & Trade Show**
Sponsored by Canadian Library Association (CLA) (Association Canadienne des bibliotheques)
1150 Morrison Dr, Suite 400, Ottawa, ON K2H 8S9, Canada
*Tel:* 613-232-9625 *Fax:* 613-563-9895
*E-mail:* info@cla.ca
*Web Site:* www.cla.ca
*Key Personnel*
Exec Dir: Kelly Moore *Tel:* 613-232-9625 ext 306 *E-mail:* kmoore@cla.ca
Conference & Events Mgr: Wendy Walton *Tel:* 613-232-9625 ext 302 *E-mail:* wwalton@cla.ca
Location: Halifax, NS, CN
June 1-4, 2016

**IABC World Conference**
Sponsored by International Association of Business Communicators (IABC)
601 Montgomery St, Suite 1900, San Francisco, CA 94111
*Tel:* 415-544-4700 *Toll Free Tel:* 800-776-4222 (US & CN) *Fax:* 415-544-4747
*E-mail:* conference@iabc.com
*Web Site:* www.iabc.com
*Key Personnel*
Events & Conferences Mgr: Charles Herrick *Tel:* 415-544-4745 *E-mail:* cherrick@iabc.com
Location: Hilton New Orleans Riverside, 2 Poydras, New Orleans, LA, USA
June 5-8, 2016

## JULY

**Romance Writers of America Annual Conference**
Sponsored by Romance Writers of America®
14615 Benfer Rd, Houston, TX 77069
*Tel:* 832-717-5200 *Fax:* 832-717-5201
*E-mail:* conference@rwa.org; info@rwa.org
*Web Site:* www.rwa.org
*Key Personnel*
Exec Dir: Allison Kelley *Tel:* 832-717-5200 ext 124 *E-mail:* allison.kelley@rwa.org
Location: San Diego Marriott Hotel and Marina, San Diego, CA, USA
July 13-16, 2016

## AUGUST

**IBBY International Congress**
Sponsored by International Board on Books for Young People (IBBY)
Nonnenweg 12, Postfach, 4003 Basel, Switzerland
*Tel:* (061) 272 29 17 *Fax:* (061) 272 27 57
*E-mail:* ibby@ibby.org
*Web Site:* www.ibby.org
*Key Personnel*
Exec Dir: Liz Page *E-mail:* liz.page@ibby.org
Admin Asst: Ms Luzmaria Stauffenegger *E-mail:* luzmaria.stauffenegger@ibby.org
IBBY's biennial international congresses, hosted by different countries, are the most important meeting points for IBBY members & other people involved in children's books & reading development. They are wonderful opportunities to make contacts, exchange ideas & open horizons.
Location: Auckland, New Zealand
Aug 25-28, 2016

**Swanwick: The Writers' Summer School**
Sponsored by Writers' Summer School
103, Jean Armour Dr, Mauchline, Ayrshire KA5 6DP, United Kingdom
*Tel:* (01290) 552248
*Web Site:* www.swanwickwritersschool.co.uk
*Key Personnel*
Secy: Miss Lesley Deschner *E-mail:* secretary@swanwickwritersschool.co.uk
A week-long residential writing school with top name speakers & tutors, plus informative panels, talks & discussion groups. Comfortable rooms with all meals & tuition included in the price. Open to everyone, from absolute beginners to published authors. Beautiful setting, licensed bar & evening entertainment. Believed to be the longest established residential writers' school in the world, Swanwick, held annually in August, is a must attend annual event in every writer's diary.
Location: The Hayes Conference Centre, Swanwick, Derbyshire, UK
Aug 2016

## SEPTEMBER

**Excellence in Journalism**
Sponsored by The Society of Professional Journalists
Eugene S Pulliam National Journalism Ctr, 3909 N Meridian St, Indianapolis, IN 46208
*Tel:* 317-927-8000 *Fax:* 317-920-4789
*E-mail:* spj@spj.org
*Web Site:* excellenceinjournalism.org; www.spj.org
*Key Personnel*
Assoc Exec Dir: Chris Vachon *Tel:* 317-927-8000 ext 207 *E-mail:* cvachon@spj.org
Dir, Events: Heather Dunn *Tel:* 317-927-8000 ext 204 *E-mail:* hdunn@spj.org
Annual conference co-organized by Radio Television Digital News Association (RTDNA).
Location: Sheraton New Orleans, 500 Canal St, New Orleans, LA, USA
Sept 18-20, 2016

**Goteborg Book Fair**
Sponsored by Bok & Bibliotek i Norden AB
Maessans Gata 20, 412 94 Gothenburg, Sweden
*Tel:* (031) 708 84 00 *Fax:* (031) 20 91 03
*E-mail:* info@goteborg-bookfair.com; info@bokmassan.se
*Web Site:* www.bokmassan.se
*Key Personnel*
CEO: Anna Falck *E-mail:* af@goteborg-bookfair.com
Book Fair Dir: Maria Kaellsson *E-mail:* maka@goteborg-bookfair.com
Head of Prog: Gunilla Sandin *E-mail:* gs@goteborg-bookfair.com
Prog Coord: Anneli Jonasson *Tel:* (031) 708 84 03 *E-mail:* aj@goteborg-bookfair.com
Location: Gothenburg, Sweden
Sept 29-Oct 2, 2016

## OCTOBER

**Frankfurt Book Fair**
Sponsored by Ausstellungs-und Messe-GmbH des Boersenvereins des Deutschen Buchhandels
Braubachstr 16, 60311 Frankfurt am Main, Germany
Mailing Address: Postfach 100116, 60001 Frankfurt am Main, Germany
*Tel:* (069) 21020 *Fax:* (069) 2102 277
*E-mail:* info@book-fair.com
*Web Site:* www.book-fair.com; www.frankfurt-book-fair.com
*Key Personnel*
CEO & Dir: Juergen Boos
Largest international book & media fair attracting 7,500 exhibitors from over 110 countries & 280,000 visitors.
Location: Frankfurt Fairgrounds, Frankfurt, Germany
Oct 19-23, 2016

**TAPPI/AICC SuperCorrExpo® 2016**
Sponsored by Technical Association of the Pulp & Paper Industry (TAPPI)
15 Technology Pkwy S, Peachtree Corners, GA 30092
*Tel:* 770-446-1400 *Toll Free Tel:* 800-332-8686 (US); 800-446-9431 (CN) *Fax:* 770-446-6947; 770-209-7206
*E-mail:* memberconnection@tappi.org
*Web Site:* www.tappi.org
*Key Personnel*
Meeting Mgr: Ed Robie *Tel:* 770-209-7243 *E-mail:* erobie@tappi.org
Dir of Mktg: Simona Marcellus *Tel:* 770-209-7293 *E-mail:* smarcellus@tappi.org
Location: Orange County Convention Center, Orlando, FL, USA
Oct 17-20, 2016

**Utah Humanities Book Festival**
Sponsored by Utah Humanities Council
Affiliate of Utah Center for the Book
202 W 300 N, Salt Lake City, UT 84103
*Tel:* 801-359-9670 *Toll Free Tel:* 866-864-8554 *Fax:* 801-531-7869
*Web Site:* www.utahhumanities.org/BookFestival.htm
*Key Personnel*
Exec Dir: Cynthia Buckingham *Tel:* 801-359-9670 ext 101 *E-mail:* buckingham@utahhumanities.org
Devt Dir: Kathleen Harmon Gardner *Tel:* 801-359-9670 ext 108 *E-mail:* gardner@utahhumanities.org
Lit Prog Offr: Michael McLane *Tel:* 801-359-9670 ext 104 *E-mail:* mclane@utahhumanities.org
Free literary event featuring national, regional & local authors held Oct 1-31 annually (National Book Month).
Location: Statewide, UT, USA
Oct 1-31, 2016

## NOVEMBER

**American Translators Association Annual Conference**
Sponsored by American Translators Association (ATA)
225 Reinekers Lane, Suite 590, Alexandria, VA 22314
*Tel:* 703-683-6100 *Fax:* 703-683-6122
*E-mail:* ata@atanet.org
*Web Site:* www.atanet.org
*Key Personnel*
Exec Dir: Walter W Bacak, Jr *Tel:* 703-683-6100 ext 3006 *E-mail:* walter@atanet.org
Meetings Mgr: Teresa C Kelly *Tel:* 703-683-6100 ext 3014 *E-mail:* teresak@atanet.org
Location: San Francisco, CA, USA
Nov 2-5, 2016

# 2017

## JANUARY

**American Library Association Mid-Winter Meeting**
Sponsored by The American Library Association (ALA)
50 E Huron St, Chicago, IL 60611
*Toll Free Tel:* 800-545-2433 (ext 3223) *Fax:* 312-440-9374
*E-mail:* ala@ala.org
*Web Site:* www.ala.org/midwinter
*Key Personnel*
Conference/Events Coord: Alicia Babcock *Tel:* 800-545-2433 ext 3229 *E-mail:* ababcock@ala.org; Yvonne A McLean *Tel:* 800-545-2433 ext 3222 *E-mail:* ymclean@ala.org
Conference Supv: Amy R McGuigan *Tel:* 800-545-2433 ext 3226 *E-mail:* amcguigan@ala.org
Exhibit Mgr: Patrick Thomas Murphy *Tel:* 800-545-2433 ext 3218 *E-mail:* pmurphy@ala.org
Location: Atlanta, GA, USA
Jan 20-24, 2017

## FEBRUARY

**AWP Annual Conference & Bookfair**
Sponsored by Association of Writers & Writing Programs (AWP)
George Mason University, 4400 University Dr, MSN 1E3, Fairfax, VA 22030
*Tel:* 703-993-4301 *Fax:* 703-993-4302
*E-mail:* conference@awpwriter.org; awp@awpwriter.org
*Web Site:* www.aprwriter.org/conference; www.awpwriter.org
*Key Personnel*
Exec Dir: David W Fenza
Dir of Conferences: Christian Teresi
Conference Coord: Brenna Killeen
Assoc Dir of Cenferences: Cynthia Sherman
Conference Mgr: Sheri Sorvillo
Location: Washington Convention Center & Washington Marriott Marquis, Washington, DC, USA
Feb 8-11, 2017

## MARCH

**Virginia Festival of the Book**
Sponsored by Virginia Foundation for the Humanities
145 Ednam Dr, Charlottesville, VA 22903
*Tel:* 434-924-3296 *Fax:* 434-296-4714
*E-mail:* vabook@virginia.edu
*Web Site:* www.vabook.org
*Key Personnel*
Prog Dir: Nancy Damon *Tel:* 434-924-7548
Annual public festival for children & adults featuring authors, illustrators, publishers, publicists, agents & other book professionals in panel discussions & readings. Most events are free. More than 200 authors invited annually.
Location: Charlottesville, VA, USA
March 22-26, 2017

## MAY

**PacPrint 2017**
Sponsored by Reed Exhibitions Australia Pty Ltd
Level 2, Tower 2, 475 Victoria Ave, Chatswood, NSW 2067, Australia
Mailing Address: Locked Bag 4500, Chatswood, NSW 2067, Australia
*Tel:* (02) 9422 2500
*E-mail:* pacprint@reedexhibitions.com.au; inquiry@reedexhibitions.com.au
*Web Site:* www.pacprint.com.au
Sponsored by Graphic Arts Merchants Association of Australia Inc (GAMAA) & the Printing Industries Association of Australia (PIAA), this event is held every 4 years.
Location: Melbourne, Victoria, Australia
May 2017

## JUNE

**American Library Association Annual Conference**
Sponsored by The American Library Association (ALA)
50 E Huron St, Chicago, IL 60611
*Toll Free Tel:* 800-545-2433 (ext 3223) *Fax:* 312-440-9374
*E-mail:* ala@ala.org
*Web Site:* www.ala.org
*Key Personnel*
Conference/Events Coord: Alicia Babcock *Tel:* 800-545-2433 ext 3229 *E-mail:* ababcock@ala.org; Yvonne A McLean *Tel:* 800-545-2433 ext 3222 *E-mail:* ymclean@ala.org
Conference Supv: Amy R McGuigan *Tel:* 800-545-2433 ext 3226 *E-mail:* amcguigan@ala.org
Exhibit Mgr: Patrick Thomas Murphy *Tel:* 800-545-2433 ext 3218 *E-mail:* pmurphy@ala.org
Location: Chicago, IL, USA
June 22-27, 2017

## JULY

**Romance Writers of America Annual Conference**
Sponsored by Romance Writers of America®
14615 Benfer Rd, Houston, TX 77069
*Tel:* 832-717-5200 *Fax:* 832-717-5201
*E-mail:* conference@rwa.org; info@rwa.org
*Web Site:* www.rwa.org
*Key Personnel*
Exec Dir: Allison Kelley *Tel:* 832-717-5200 ext 124 *E-mail:* allison.kelley@rwa.org
Location: Walt Disney World Swan and Dolphin, 1500 Epcot Resorts Blvd, Lake Buena Vista, FL, USA
July 26-29, 2017

## SEPTEMBER

**PRINT®**
Sponsored by NPES The Association for Suppliers of Printing, Publishing & Converting Technologies
1899 Preston White Dr, Reston, VA 20191
*Tel:* 703-264-7200 *Fax:* 703-620-0994; 703-620-9187 (GASC)
*E-mail:* npes@npes.org; info@gasc.org
*Web Site:* www.npes.org; www.gasc.org
*Key Personnel*
Pres: Ralph J Nappi *E-mail:* rnappi@npes.org
VP (GASC): Chris Price *Tel:* 703-264-7200 ext 221 *E-mail:* cprice@gasc.org
Dir of Opers (GASC): Kelly Kliga *E-mail:* kkliga@gasc.org
Conference Mgr (GASC): Lilly Kinney *Tel:* 703-264-7200 ext 255 *E-mail:* lkinney@gasc.org
Quadrennial event produced by Graphic Arts Show Co Inc (GASC).
Location: McCormick Place, Chicago, IL, USA
Sept 10-14, 2017

## OCTOBER

**Frankfurt Book Fair**
Sponsored by Ausstellungs-und Messe-GmbH des Boersenvereins des Deutschen Buchhandels
Braubachstr 16, 60311 Frankfurt am Main, Germany
Mailing Address: Postfach 100116, 60001 Frankfurt am Main, Germany
*Tel:* (069) 21020 *Fax:* (069) 2102 277
*E-mail:* info@book-fair.com
*Web Site:* www.book-fair.com; www.frankfurt-book-fair.com
*Key Personnel*
CEO & Dir: Juergen Boos
Largest international book & media fair attracting 7,500 exhibitors from over 110 countries & 280,000 visitors.
Location: Frankfurt Fairgrounds, Frankfurt, Germany
Oct 11-15, 2017

**Utah Humanities Book Festival**
Sponsored by Utah Humanities Council
Affiliate of Utah Center for the Book
202 W 300 N, Salt Lake City, UT 84103
*Tel:* 801-359-9670 *Toll Free Tel:* 866-864-8554 *Fax:* 801-531-7869
*Web Site:* www.utahhumanities.org/BookFestival.htm
*Key Personnel*
Exec Dir: Cynthia Buckingham *Tel:* 801-359-9670 ext 101 *E-mail:* buckingham@utahhumanities.org
Devt Dir: Kathleen Harmon Gardner *Tel:* 801-359-9670 ext 108 *E-mail:* gardner@utahhumanities.org
Lit Prog Offr: Michael McLane *Tel:* 801-359-9670 ext 104 *E-mail:* mclane@utahhumanities.org
Free literary event featuring national, regional & local authors held Oct 1-31 annually (National Book Month).
Location: Statewide, UT, USA
Oct 1-31, 2017

# 2018

## FEBRUARY

**American Library Association Mid-Winter Meeting**
Sponsored by The American Library Association (ALA)
50 E Huron St, Chicago, IL 60611
*Toll Free Tel:* 800-545-2433 (ext 3223) *Fax:* 312-440-9374
*E-mail:* ala@ala.org
*Web Site:* www.ala.org/midwinter
*Key Personnel*
Conference/Events Coord: Alicia Babcock *Tel:* 800-545-2433 ext 3229 *E-mail:* ababcock@ala.org; Yvonne A McLean *Tel:* 800-545-2433 ext 3222 *E-mail:* ymclean@ala.org
Conference Supv: Amy R McGuigan *Tel:* 800-545-2433 ext 3226 *E-mail:* amcguigan@ala.org
Exhibit Mgr: Patrick Thomas Murphy *Tel:* 800-545-2433 ext 3218 *E-mail:* pmurphy@ala.org
Location: Denver, CO, USA
Feb 8-13, 2018

## MARCH

**Virginia Festival of the Book**
Sponsored by Virginia Foundation for the Humanities
145 Ednam Dr, Charlottesville, VA 22903
*Tel:* 434-924-3296 *Fax:* 434-296-4714
*E-mail:* vabook@virginia.edu
*Web Site:* www.vabook.org
*Key Personnel*
Prog Dir: Nancy Damon *Tel:* 434-924-7548
Annual public festival for children & adults featuring authors, illustrators, publishers, publicists, agents & other book professionals in panel discussions & readings. Most events are free. More than 200 authors invited annually.
Location: Charlottesville, VA, USA
March 21-25, 2018

## JUNE

**American Library Association Annual Conference**
Sponsored by The American Library Association (ALA)
50 E Huron St, Chicago, IL 60611
*Toll Free Tel:* 800-545-2433 (ext 3223) *Fax:* 312-440-9374
*E-mail:* ala@ala.org
*Web Site:* www.ala.org
*Key Personnel*
Conference/Events Coord: Alicia Babcock *Tel:* 800-545-2433 ext 3229 *E-mail:* ababcock@ala.org; Yvonne A McLean *Tel:* 800-545-2433 ext 3222 *E-mail:* ymclean@ala.org
Conference Supv: Amy R McGuigan *Tel:* 800-545-2433 ext 3226 *E-mail:* amcguigan@ala.org
Exhibit Mgr: Patrick Thomas Murphy *Tel:* 800-545-2433 ext 3218 *E-mail:* pmurphy@ala.org
Location: New Orleans, LA, USA
June 21-26, 2018

## OCTOBER

**Frankfurt Book Fair**
Sponsored by Ausstellungs-und Messe-GmbH des Boersenvereins des Deutschen Buchhandels
Braubachstr 16, 60311 Frankfurt am Main, Germany
Mailing Address: Postfach 100116, 60001 Frankfurt am Main, Germany
*Tel:* (069) 21020 *Fax:* (069) 2102 277
*E-mail:* info@book-fair.com
*Web Site:* www.book-fair.com; www.frankfurt-book-fair.com
*Key Personnel*
CEO & Dir: Juergen Boos
Largest international book & media fair attracting 7,500 exhibitors from over 110 countries & 280,000 visitors.
Location: Frankfurt Fairgrounds, Frankfurt, Germany
Oct 10-14, 2018

# Writers' Conferences & Workshops

The following lists workshops and seminars dealing with various aspects of the book trade. See **Courses for the Book Trade** for a list of college level programs and courses.

**Alice B Acheson's Workshops for Writers, Illustrators & Photographers**
Alice B Acheson
Unit of Acheson-Greub Inc
PO Box 735, Friday Harbor, WA 98250
*Tel:* 360-378-2815
*E-mail:* aliceba@aol.com
*Key Personnel*
Pres: Alice B Acheson
One or two day workshops on making a ms succeed in the market place. Writers utilize a pre-class assignment to determine techniques for finding & impressing an agent &/or publisher while class discussion includes discovering what's to come once the ms is under contract. Extensive written materials provided. Instructor shares 30 years of book publishing expertise in negotiating contracts, editing books & achieving award-winning book publicity.
*The Greatest Marketing Tool of all,* what works, what doesn't & why (Spring & Fall)
*Publishing Choices: Print-on-Demand, Self-Publishing, Traditional Publisher,* (Spring & Fall)
*You're Writing Your Manuscript, Now What?* (Spring & Fall).
Location: Book Passage, Corte Madera, CA
Date: Feb 28-March 2, 2014
Location: Richard Hugo House, Seattle, WA
Date: Spring 2014
Location: Field's End, Bainbridge Island, WA
Date: Spring 2014
Location: Field's End, Bainbridge Island, WA
Date: Autumn 2014
Location: Richard Hugo House, Seattle, WA
Date: Autumn 2014
Location: Book Passage, Corte Madera, CA
Date: Sept 19-21, 2014

**American Society of Journalists and Authors Annual Writers Conference**
American Society of Journalists and Authors (ASJA)
1501 Broadway, Suite 403, New York, NY 10036
*Tel:* 212-997-0947 *Fax:* 212-937-2315
*Web Site:* asja.org
*Key Personnel*
Exec Dir: Alexandra Owens *E-mail:* director@asja.org
Inside information from editors, agents & publishers, find inspiration & gain income-boosting ideas. Open to all, the conference features topics for newer & more experienced pros. New panels & workshops will enrich you no matter where you are in your writing career.

**AMWA Annual Conference**
American Medical Writers Association (AMWA)
30 W Gude Dr, Suite 525, Rockville, MD 20850-1161
*Tel:* 240-238-0940 *Fax:* 301-294-9006
*E-mail:* amwa@amwa.org
*Web Site:* www.amwa.org
*Key Personnel*
Educ Mgr: Dane Russo
Annual conference includes over 85 workshops.
Location: San Antonio, TX
Date: Sept 25-27, 2014
Location: Memphis, TN
Date: Oct 22-24, 2015

**Antioch Writers' Workshop**
Antioch University Midwest
900 Dayton St, Yellow Springs, OH 45387
*Tel:* 937-769-1803
*E-mail:* info@antiochwritersworkshop.com
*Web Site:* www.antiochwritersworkshop.com
*Key Personnel*
Pres: Rebecca Morean
Dir: Sharon Short
A week-long summer workshop featuring morning classes, midday presentations on writing profession, afternoon intensive seminars in a genre or type, evening faculty talks & readings. Non-refundable registration fee $125.

**Appalachian Writers' Workshop**
Hindman Settlement School
71 Center St, Hindman, KY 41822
Mailing Address: PO Box 844, Hindman, KY 41822-0844
*Tel:* 606-785-5475 *Fax:* 606-785-3499
*E-mail:* info@hindmansettlement.org
*Web Site:* www.hindmansettlement.org
*Key Personnel*
Interim Exec Dir: Jeanne Marie Hibberd
Poetry, nonfiction, short story, novel, dramatic writing & children's writing.

**Arkansas Writers' Conference**
Pioneer Branch of National League of American Pen Women/Arkansas Branch
Division of National League of American Pen Women
13005 Misty Creek Dr, Little Rock, AR 72211
*Tel:* 501-224-5823 *Fax:* 501-224-5823
*Web Site:* www.arkansaswritersconference.org
*Key Personnel*
Poet Laureate of AR & Contact: Peggy Vining *E-mail:* pvining@aristotle.net
Two-day annual conference; conference information available Feb 1. Thirty plus competitions are available. Write for brochure at above address & enclose SASE. Check web site for conference details.
Location: Presidential Holiday Inn, Little Rock, AR
Date: Annually first full weekend in June, Fri & Sat

**Artists & Writers Summer Fellowships**
The Constance Saltonstall Foundation for the Arts
435 Ellis Hollow Creek Rd, Ithaca, NY 14850
*Tel:* 607-539-3146
*E-mail:* artscolony@saltonstall.org
*Web Site:* www.saltonstall.org
*Key Personnel*
Dir: Lesley Williamson
Provide month long summer fellowships for New York state artists & writers May-Sept.

**Aspen Summer Words Writing Retreat & Literary Festival**
Aspen Writers' Foundation
110 E Hallam St, Suite 116, Aspen, CO 81611
*Tel:* 970-925-3122 *Fax:* 970-920-5700
*E-mail:* info@aspenwriters.org
*Web Site:* www.aspenwriters.org
*Key Personnel*
Exec Dir: Lisa Consiglio *Tel:* 970-925-3122 ext 1 *E-mail:* lisa@aspenwriters.org
Prog Mgr: Natalie Lacy *Tel:* 970-925-3122 ext 3 *E-mail:* natalie@aspenwriters.org
A 5-day writing retreat with morning workshops in fiction, poetry, memoir & essay complimented by a 5-day literary festival in the afternoons & evenings, featuring 20 events for readers & writers.

**The Association for Women In Communications**
The Association for Women in Communications
3337 Duke St, Alexandria, VA 22314
*Tel:* 703-370-7436 *Fax:* 703-342-4311
*E-mail:* info@womcom.org
*Web Site:* www.womcom.org
*Key Personnel*
Exec Dir: Pamela Valenzuela
Communs Mgr: Beth Veney *E-mail:* awcconnect@womcom.org
Professional development workshops & exposition in various areas of the communications field.

**Association pour l'Avancement des Sciences et des Techniques de la Documentation**
2065 rue Parthenais, Bureau 387, Montreal, QC H2K 3T1, Canada
*Tel:* 514-281-5012 *Fax:* 514-281-8219
*E-mail:* info@asted.org
*Web Site:* www.asted.org
*Key Personnel*
Exec Dir: Suzanne Morin *Tel:* 514-281-5012 ext 234 *E-mail:* smorin@asted.org

**Atlantic Center for the Arts Artists-in-Residence Program**
Atlantic Center for the Arts (ACA)
1414 Art Center Ave, New Smyrna Beach, FL 32168
*Tel:* 386-427-6975 *Toll Free Tel:* 800-393-6975 *Fax:* 386-427-5669
*E-mail:* program@atlanticcenterforthearts.org
*Web Site:* www.atlanticcenterforthearts.org
*Key Personnel*
Co-Dir/Community: Nancy Lowden Norman
Co-Dir/Residency: Jim Frost
Residency Dir: Nick Conroy
Dir of Fin & Acctg: Kevin Miller
Opers Mgr: Jim Zock
Mktg Mgr: Kathryn Peterson
Since 1982, Atlantic Center's residency program has provided artists from all artistic disciplines with spaces to live, work & collaborate during three-week residencies. Each residency session includes three master artists of different disciplines. The master artists each personally select a group of associates - talented, emerging artists - through an application process administered by ACA. During the residency, artists participate in informal sessions with their group, collaborate on projects & work independently on their own projects. The relaxed atmosphere & unstructured program provide considerable time for artistic regeneration & creation.

**Bard Society**
1358 Tiber Ave, Jacksonville, FL 32207
*Key Personnel*
Dir: Frank Green *E-mail:* frankgrn@comcast.net
Fiction writing workshop in existence for more than 35 years. Schedule: one workshop a week,

Wednesday evening, three hours; more than 40 books published by members. No fee but contributions welcome. All lovers of the written word welcome.

**Beyond the Book**
Copyright Clearance Center (CCC)
222 Rosewood Dr, Danvers, MA 01923
*Tel:* 978-750-8400 *Fax:* 978-646-8600
*E-mail:* beyondthebook@copyright.com
*Web Site:* www.copyright.com; beyondthebookcast.com
*Key Personnel*
HR: Meredith McCully
Programs also include online seminars & telephone conference calls with distinguished experts. Created with authors in mind, Beyond the Book seeks to provide information on the latest business issues facing the creative professions - from initial research to final publication & beyond. Your connection to leading editors, publishing analysts & information technology experts, as well as innovative authors.

**Big Apple Conference**
The International Women's Writing Guild (IWWG)
317 Madison Ave, Suite 1704, New York, NY 10017
*Tel:* 917-720-6959
*E-mail:* iwwgquestions@gmail.com
*Web Site:* www.iwwg.org
*Key Personnel*
Exec Dir: Cynthia Fritts Stillwell *E-mail:* iwwgexecdir@gmail.com
Held twice annually in April & Oct in New York, NY; includes a one day writing workshop on Sat & two open houses: Meet the Authors (morning) & Meet the Agents (afternoon) on Sun.

**Blockbuster Plots for Writers Retreat**
Martha Alderson
PO Box 1402, Capitola, CA 95010
*Tel:* 408-482-4678
*E-mail:* contact@blockbusterplots.com
*Web Site:* www.blockbusterplots.com
*Key Personnel*
Owner & Author: Martha Alderson
Four day writers retreat in the Santa Cruz mountains which provides simple techniques to help you grasp plot with ease & increase your chances of getting published. Whether you write screenplays, novels, short stories or memoirs, now is the time to learn what separates a blockbuster hit from a book that falls flat.

**Bread Loaf Writers' Conference**
Middlebury College
5525 Middlebury College, 14 Old Chapel Rd, Middlebury, VT 05753
*Tel:* 802-443-5286 *Fax:* 802-443-2087
*E-mail:* blwc@middlebury.edu
*Web Site:* www.middlebury.edu/blwc
*Key Personnel*
Dir: Michael Collier
Asst Dir: Jennifer Grotz
Admin Mgr: Noreen Cargill *E-mail:* ncargill@middlebury.edu
Ten-day conference for writers of poetry, fiction & nonfiction.

**Annual Cape Cod Writers' Center Conference**
Cape Cod Writers' Center
919 Main St, Osterville, MA 02655
Mailing Address: PO Box 408, Osterville, MA 02655
*Tel:* 508-420-0200 *Fax:* 508-420-0212
*E-mail:* writers@capecodwriterscenter.org
*Web Site:* www.capecodwriterscenter.org
*Key Personnel*
Pres: Kevin Symmons
Exec Dir: Nancy Robin Stuart
Busn & Mktg Mgr: Moira Powers
Hone skills as you learn from top professionals about your craft & the business of writing. In addition to classes in fiction, nonfiction, mystery, poetry, children's & other genres, the conference offers opportunities to meet with an editor-in-residence & agents-in-residence. Personal conferences & ms evaluations are available as well as a Young Writers Workshop. Many special events added for this year.

**Chautauqua Writers' Workshop**
The Writers' Center at Chautauqua
PO Box 28, Chautauqua, NY 14722-0408
*Tel:* 716-357-6316; 716-357-6250
*Toll Free Tel:* 800-836-ARTS (836-2787)
*Fax:* 716-269-7444
*Web Site:* writers.ciweb.org
*Key Personnel*
Prog Dir, Writer's Ctr: Clara Silverstein *E-mail:* clrsilver@gmail.com
Writing workshop in poetry & prose at 137 year-old Chautauqua Institution, international center for the arts, education, religion & recreation.
Location: Chautauqua Institution, Chautauqua, NY
Date: Last week in June-end of August

**Children's Book Conference**
Graduate School of Education
Affiliate of Portland State University, Summer Session
615 SW Harrison St, Portland, OR 97201
*Tel:* 503-725-9786 *Fax:* 503-725-5599
*Web Site:* www.pdx.edu/ceed/childrens-book-conference
*Key Personnel*
Prog Dir: Elizabeth Snyder *E-mail:* snydere@pdx.edu
College credit (optional), workshops in fiction, nonfiction, poetry; illustrator track available.

**Christian Writers' Conference**
American Christian Writers Association
PO Box 110390, Nashville, TN 37222-0390
*Tel:* 615-834-0450 *Toll Free Tel:* 800-21-WRITE (219-7483) *Fax:* 615-834-7736
*E-mail:* acwriters@aol.com
*Web Site:* www.acwriters.com
*Key Personnel*
Dir & Publr: Reg A Forder *E-mail:* regaforder@aol.com
Correspondence courses; 36 conferences annually, approximately three per month in major cities throughout the USA. Monthly magazine by subscription.
Location: Nashville Mentoring, Opryland Guest House, Nashville, TN
Date: April 4-5, 2014
Location: Oklahoma City Mentoring, La Quinta Hotel, Oklahoma City, OK
Date: April 11-12, 2014
Location: Grand Rapids Mentoring, Ramada Plaza Hotel, Grand Rapids, MI
Date: June 6-7, 2014
Location: Atlanta Mentoring, Hotel Indego, Atlanta, GA
Date: July 11-12, 2014
Location: Minneapolis Mentoring, Country Inn & Suites, Minneapolis, MN
Date: Aug 1-2, 2014
Location: Spokane Mentoring, Ramada Airport, Spokane, WA
Date: Sept 26-27, 2014
Location: Phoenix Mentoring, Grace Inn, Phoenix, AZ
Date: Oct 31-Nov 1, 2014
Location: Orlando Mentoring, Ramada Inn Disney, Orlando, FL
Date: Nov 21-22, 2014

**The Clarion Science Fiction & Fantasy Writers' Workshop**
The Clarion Foundation
Dept of Literature, Mail Code 0410, UC San Diego, 9500 Gilman Dr, La Jolla, CA 92093-0410
*Tel:* 858-534-2115
*E-mail:* clarion@ucsd.edu
*Web Site:* clarion.ucsd.edu
*Key Personnel*
Pres: Karen Joy Fowler
Prog Coord: Tania Mayer
Science fiction & fantasy writing workshop held for 6 weeks each summer.

**Creative Writing Day & Workshops**
Virginia Highlands Festival
335 Cummings St, Abingdon, VA 24210
Mailing Address: PO Box 801, Abingdon, VA 24212-0801
*Tel:* 276-623-5266 *Fax:* 276-676-3076
*E-mail:* vhf@eva.org
*Web Site:* www.vahighlandsfestival.org
*Key Personnel*
Chair: Tommy Bryant *E-mail:* tbryant@vhcc.edu
Lectures, readings & workshops in creative writing with noteworthy authors held each summer.

**Djerassi Resident Artists Program**
2325 Bear Gulch Rd, Woodside, CA 94062
*Tel:* 650-747-1250 *Fax:* 650-747-0105
*E-mail:* drap@djerassi.org
*Web Site:* www.djerassi.org
*Key Personnel*
Exec Dir: Margot Knight *Tel:* 650-747-1250 ext 14 *E-mail:* margot@djerassi.org
One-month residencies for writers & other artists.

**Education Writers Association Workshops**
Education Writers Association (EWA)
3516 Connecticut Ave NW, Washington, DC 20008-2401
*Tel:* 202-452-9830 *Fax:* 202-452-9837
*E-mail:* ewa@ewa.org
*Web Site:* www.ewa.org
*Key Personnel*
Exec Dir: Caroline Hendrie *E-mail:* chendrie@ewa.org
Prodr: Glen Baity
National seminar, regional meetings.

**Emerson College Literary Publishing Certificate Program**
Emerson College Professional Studies
Dept of Professional Studies, 120 Boylston St, Boston, MA 02116-8750
*Tel:* 617-824-8280 *Fax:* 617-824-8158
*E-mail:* continuing@emerson.edu
*Web Site:* www.emerson.edu/ce
*Key Personnel*
Exec Dir, Prof Studies: Hank Zappala *E-mail:* continuing@emerson.edu

**Festival & Conference on Poetry**
The Frost Place
158 Ridge Rd, Franconia, NH 03580
Mailing Address: PO Box 74, Franconia, NH 03580-0074
*Tel:* 603-823-5510
*E-mail:* frost@frostplace.org
*Web Site:* www.frostplace.org
*Key Personnel*
Exec Dir: Maudelle Driskell
Offers lectures, talks & craft panels by faculty in a seven-day program. See web site for details.

**Five Star Publishing & Marketing Secrets**
Five Star Publications Inc
4696 W Tyson St, Chandler, AZ 85226
Mailing Address: PO Box 6698, Dept LM, Chandler, AZ 85246-6698
*Tel:* 480-940-8182 *Toll Free Tel:* 866-471-0777 *Fax:* 480-940-8787
*E-mail:* info@fivestarpublications.com
*Web Site:* www.fivestarpublications.com; www.fivestarmarketingsecrets.com
*Key Personnel*
Pres: Linda F Radke
A six-hour publishing & marketing intensive workshop that teaches participants how to set up their own publishing company, produce well-designed printed books from a written ms, outsource ebook conversions, secure distribution for printed & electronic books, create a press kit & pitch it to the media & create & implement a marketing plan. The seminar is taught by Linda F Radke, President of Five Star Publications Inc. At times, Radke will be joined by other industry experts or executives of Five Star. The full-day workshop is divided into two three-hour segments with lunch in between. The first half focuses on publishing & the second half is dedicated to public relations & marketing. Participants may attend the first or second segment only at a reduced price. Groups are limited to 15 & one-on-one sessions are also available. Lunch is included. Participants receive two free hours of follow-up consultation with Radke & a free copy each of *Promote Like a Pro* & *The Economical Guide to Self-Publishing* when taking the full workshop. Call for location & date.

**Florida Writers Association Conference**
Florida Writers Association Inc
PO Box 66069, St Pete Beach, FL 33736-6069
*Web Site:* www.floridawriters.net
*Key Personnel*
Pres: Chrissy Jackson *E-mail:* chrissyj@earthlink.net
Assortment of workshops, networking, interviews with agents & editors, literary contest & banquet.
Location: Annual Conference
Date: Oct

**Fun in the Sun**
Florida Romance Writers Inc
Affiliate of Romance Writers of America
PO Box 430744, Miami, FL 33243
*Web Site:* www.frwriters.org
*Key Personnel*
Pres: Kristen Wallace
VP: Karen Kendall
Conference Chair: Aleka Nakis *Tel:* 954-663-9030 *E-mail:* aleka@alekanakis.com
Highlights include a full series of workshops on the art, craft & business of writing that will appeal to writers in all genres. Exclusive Q&A with our keynote speaker, live & silent auction & raffle, on-site bookstore, author book signing event, editor/agent appointments & more. Registration fees from $170-$200. Workshop speakers entitled to discounted registration fee. Group rates available for groups of 5 or more; special hotel rates for conference attendees also available. Use the mailing address for all conference correspondence.
Date: Jan

**The Gell Center of the Finger Lakes**
Writers & Books
740 University Ave, Rochester, NY 14607-1259
*Tel:* 585-473-2590 *Fax:* 585-442-9333
*Web Site:* www.wab.org
*Key Personnel*
Dir, Opers & Programming: Kathy Pottetti *Tel:* 585-473-2590 ext 103 *E-mail:* kathyp@wab.org
Meeting center that hosts classes, workshops, conferences, etc for groups of up to 50 people.

**Gettysburg Review Conference for Writers**
The Gettysburg Review
Subsidiary of Gettysburg College
300 N Washington St, Gettysburg, PA 17325
*Tel:* 717-337-6774 *Fax:* 717-337-6775
*E-mail:* getrev@hpb.com
*Web Site:* www.gettysburgreview.com/conference.html
*Key Personnel*
Conference Coord: Hope Maxwell Snyder
Five-day conference for writers featuring workshops, panel discussions, readings & ms consultations.

**The Glen Workshop**
Image Journal
3307 Third Ave W, Seattle, WA 98119
*Tel:* 206-281-2988 *Fax:* 206-281-2979
*E-mail:* glenworkshop@imagejournal.org
*Web Site:* www.imagejournal.org/page/events/the-glen-workshop
*Key Personnel*
Prog Dir: Anna Johnson *E-mail:* ajohnson@imagejournal.org
A week long arts workshop for writers & visual artists that combines an intensive learning experience with a lively festival of the arts.

**Gotham Writers' Workshop**
555 Eighth Ave, Suite 1402, New York, NY 10018-4358
*Tel:* 212-974-8377 *Toll Free Tel:* 877-974-8377 *Fax:* 212-307-6325
*E-mail:* office@write.org
*Web Site:* www.writingclasses.com
*Key Personnel*
Pres: Andre Becker
Professional writers teach acclaimed creative writing workshops online & in New York City throughout the year. NYC classes begin in Jan, April, July & Sept.

**Harvard Summer Writing Program**
Harvard University, Div of Continuing Education
51 Brattle St, Dept S760, Cambridge, MA 02138-3722
*Tel:* 617-495-4024 *Fax:* 617-495-9176
*E-mail:* summer@hudce.harvard.edu
*Web Site:* www.summer.harvard.edu
*Key Personnel*
Dir & Prog Contact: Dr Patricia Bellanca
Eight-week & four-week programs starting at the end of June; full-semester college-credit workshop courses in creative, professional & expository writing. These include: beginning fiction, poetry, journalism & screenwriting; advanced creative nonfiction; writing grant proposals, effective business communication, legal writing & principles of editing; cross-cultural expository writing, writing about social & ethical issues & writing about literature.

**Hedgebrook**
PO Box 1231, Freeland, WA 98249
*Tel:* 360-321-4786 *Fax:* 360-321-2171
*E-mail:* hedgebrook@hedgebrook.org
*Web Site:* www.hedgebrook.org
*Key Personnel*
Residency Dir: Vito Zingarelli *E-mail:* vitoz@hedgebrook.org
Residency Assoc: Kathryn Preiss *E-mail:* kathrynp@hedgebrook.org
Annual open house in September. Master Class Retreat Series workshops are scheduled throughout the year & combine the retreat experience with an educational/professional development component, providing participants the opportunity to be in residence & study with a Master Teacher. Participants receive five days of writing workshops, instructor-led constructive group feedback sessions, one-on-one sessions with the instructor & an additional day of retreat time. Meals are prepared by an on-site chef, featuring organic produce from Hedgebrook's garden. Writers at all levels of experience, published or not, are accepted into the Master Classes.

**Highland Summer Writers' Conference**
The Appalachian Regional Studies Center (ARSC)
Division of Radford University
PO Box 7014, Radford University, Radford, VA 24142
*Tel:* 540-831-5366; 540-831-6152 *Fax:* 540-831-5951
*Web Site:* www.radford.edu/~arsc
*Key Personnel*
Dir: Dr Theresa Burriss *Tel:* 540-831-6857 *E-mail:* tburriss@radford.edu
Instructor & ARSC Assoc: Ruth Derrick *E-mail:* rbderrick@radford.edu
Annual program based on Appalachian culture & writing; directed for two weeks by a fiction writer/poet/dramatist. Elective seminar-workshop combination offers the opportunity to study & practice creative & expository writing & earn 3 hours graduate/undergraduate credit.
Location: Radford University, Radford, VA

**Historical Novel Society North American Conference**
Historical Novel Society
400 Dark Star Ct, Fairbanks, AK 99709
*Tel:* 217-581-7538 *Fax:* 217-581-7534
*Web Site:* www.historicalnovelsociety.org
*Key Personnel*
US Membership Secy: Georgine Olson *E-mail:* georgine@mosquitonet.com
Location: London, UK
Date: Sept 2014

**How to be Published Workshops**
Michael Garrett
PO Box 100031, Birmingham, AL 35210
*Web Site:* www.writing2sell.com
*Key Personnel*
Pres: Michael Garrett *E-mail:* mike@writing2sell.com
Workshops teaching all aspects of how to be successfully published. See web site for dates & locations.

**Hurston/Wright Writer's Week**
The Zora Neale Hurston/Richard Wright Foundation
12138 Central Ave, Suite 209, Bowie, MD 20721
*Tel:* 301-459-2108 *Fax:* 301-277-1262
*E-mail:* info@hurstonwright.org
*Web Site:* www.hurstonwright.org
*Key Personnel*
Founder & Pres Emeritus: Marita Golden
Exec Dir: Clyde McElvene
Multi-genre Summer writer's workshop for writers of African descent. $20 submission fee.

**Idyllwild Arts Summer Workshops**
Idyllwild Arts Summer Program
52500 Temecula Dr, Idyllwild, CA 92549-0038
Mailing Address: PO Box 38, Idyllwild, CA 92549-0038
*Tel:* 951-659-2171 *Fax:* 951-659-4552
*E-mail:* summer@idyllwildarts.org
*Web Site:* www.idyllwildarts.org
*Key Personnel*
Summer Prog Registrar: Diane Dennis

*Tel:* 951-659-2171 ext 2365 *E-mail:* dianed@idyllwildarts.org
Five day workshops including creative nonfiction, fiction, chapbooks, poetry & visual representations of the American West.

**Indiana University Writers' Conference**
Indiana Universiy
Indiana University, 464 Ballantine Hall, Dept of English, 1020 E Kirkwood Ave, Bloomington, IN 47405
*Tel:* 812-855-1877 *Fax:* 812-855-9535
*E-mail:* writecon@indiana.edu
*Web Site:* www.indiana.edu/~writecon/
*Key Personnel*
Dir: Bob Bledsoe *E-mail:* rbledso@indiana.edu
Asst Dir: Caroline Diggins
Week-long, annual conference in June for writers of poetry, fiction, nonfiction & script writing. Second oldest such conference in the US. Past staff includes Raymond Carver, Allen Tate & Katherine Anne Porter.

**Iowa Summer Writing Festival**
Division of University of Iowa Continuing Education
University of Iowa, 215-C Seashore Hall, Iowa City, IA 52242
*Tel:* 319-335-4160 *Fax:* 319-335-4743
*E-mail:* iswfestival@uiowa.edu
*Web Site:* www.continuetolearn.uiowa.edu/iswfest
*Key Personnel*
Dir: Amy Margolis *E-mail:* amy-margolis@uiowa.edu
Annual week-long & weekend non-credit, intensive writing workshops in all genres; all welcome from age 21 & over.

**Jentel Artist Residency Program**
Jentel Foundation
130 Lower Piney Rd, Banner, WY 82832
*Tel:* 307-737-2311 *Fax:* 307-737-2305
*E-mail:* jentel@jentelarts.org
*Web Site:* www.jentelarts.org
*Key Personnel*
Exec Dir: Mary Jane Edwards
Offers one month residencies throughout the year to visual artists in all media & writers in fiction, creative nonfiction & poetry. Located on a working cattle ranch in the foothills of the Big Horn Moutains, 20 miles from Sheridan, WY. The award includes comfortable accommodations, a separate private studio & a stipend. Residents are invited to share their work through various outreach opportunities in the community. For more info or an application, see web site. Deadline is Sept 15 & Jan 15 each year.

**Juniper Summer Writing Institute**
Juniper Institute
c/o University Conference Services, 810 Campus Ctr, One Campus Ctr Way, Amherst, MA 01003
*Tel:* 413-545-5510
*E-mail:* juniperinstitute@hfa.umass.edu
*Web Site:* www.umass.edu/juniperinstitute
*Key Personnel*
Dir: Betsy Wheeler
Seven days of intensive writing workshops, craft sessions, readings & ms consultation in the beautiful Pioneer Valley. Scholarships available.

**Kentucky Women Writers Conference**
University of Kentucky
232 E Maxwell St, Lexington, KY 40506-0344
*Tel:* 859-257-2874
*E-mail:* kentuckywomenwriters@gmail.com
*Web Site:* www.uky.edu/wwk
*Key Personnel*
Dir: Julie Kuzneski Wrinn
Asst Dir: Vaughan Fielder
Founded in 1979, this is the oldest conference of its kind in the country featuring invited women writers offering workshops, reading & panel discussions.
Location: Lexington, KY
Date: Annually in Sept

**Kentucky Writers Conference**
Southern Kentucky Book Fest
1906 College Heights Blvd, Suite 11067, Bowling Green, KY 42101-1067
*Tel:* 270-745-4502
*Web Site:* www.sokybookfest.org
*Key Personnel*
Literary Outreach Coord: Kristie Lowry *Tel:* 270-745-4502 *E-mail:* kristie.lowry@wku.edu
Location: Carroll Knicely Conference Ctr
Date: April 25, 2014

**Key West Literary Seminar**
718 Love Lane, Key West, FL 33040
*Toll Free Tel:* 888-293-9291
*E-mail:* mail@kwls.org
*Web Site:* www.kwls.org
*Key Personnel*
Exec Dir: Miles Frieden
Media Dir: Arlo Haskell *Tel:* 305-293-9291
Annual literary seminar held in two parts with workshops taking place between the two sessions. The 2014 theme is The Dark Side: Mystery, Crime & the Literary Thriller. Writers' workshops take place Jan 12-16. See web site for details.
Location: Key West, FL
Date: Jan 9-12, 2014
Location: Key West, FL
Date: Jan 16-19, 2014

**Ligonier Valley Writers Conference**
Ligonier Valley Writers
PO Box B, Ligonier, PA 15658-1602
*Tel:* 724-238-3692
*Key Personnel*
Conference Dir: Judith Gallagher *E-mail:* jgallagher@lhtot.com
Contact: Mary Ann Mogus
Writers' Conference.

**Maine Writers Conference at Ocean Park**
Affiliate of Ocean Park Association
14 Temple Ave, Ocean Park, ME 04063
*Tel:* 401-598-1424
*E-mail:* www.opa@oceanpark.org
*Web Site:* www.oceanpark.org
*Key Personnel*
Dir: Dr Jim Brosnan
An eclectic, economical & intensive annual conference for writers of both poetry & prose of varying abilities & accomplishments.

**Maritime Writers' Workshops**
College of Extended Learning, University of New Brunswick, Fredericton
Affiliate of University of New Brunswick (Canada)
PO Box 4400, Fredericton, NB E3B 5A3, Canada
*Tel:* 506-458-7106 *Toll Free Tel:* 866-599-4646 *Fax:* 506-458-5012
*E-mail:* extend@unb.ca
*Web Site:* www.unb.ca/cel
*Key Personnel*
Prog Asst: Laurie Glenn Norris *E-mail:* laurie.norris@unb.ca
Maritime Writers' Workshops (MWW) will get you started or help you take your writing to the next level. Over its long history, hundreds of MWW participants have learned critical skills, found their voice & benefited from its comfortable & inviting atmosphere. You'll be actively involved & will receive helpful feedback in a supportive environment from instructors who are themselves successful writers. We offer workshops, retreats & rentings. Choose from a series of workshops suited to your particular interest or needs.
Also offer retreats & readings.

**Mark Twain Creative Writing Workshop**
New Letters
UMKC, University House, 5101 Rockhill Rd, Kansas City, MO 64110-2499
*Tel:* 816-235-1168 *Fax:* 816-235-2611
*E-mail:* newletters@umkc.edu
*Web Site:* www.newletters.org
*Key Personnel*
Admin Dir: Betsy Beasley *E-mail:* beasleym@umkc.edu
Ed-in-Chief: Robert Stewart *E-mail:* stewartr@umkc.edu
Edit Asst: Ashley Kaine *E-mail:* kainea@umkc.edu
Location: UMKC campus
Date: Annually in June

**McHugh's Rights/Permissions Workshop™**
John B McHugh Publishing Consultant
PO Box 170665, Milwaukee, WI 53217-8056
*Tel:* 414-351-3056
*E-mail:* jack@johnbmchugh.com
*Web Site:* www.johnbmchugh.com
*Key Personnel*
Principal & Consultant: John B McHugh
Provide on-site customized workshops in all aspects of publishing management.

**Mississippi River Creative Writing Workshop**
St Cloud State University, English Dept
720 Fourth Ave S, B-151, Rm 100, St Cloud, MN 56301-4498
*Tel:* 320-308-4947 *Fax:* 320-308-5524
*Web Site:* www.stcloudstate.edu
*Key Personnel*
Dir, Poet, Fiction Writer & Novelist: Bill Meissner *E-mail:* wjmeissner@stcloudstate.edu
Four-day workshop in poetry & fiction. Participants will develop creative writing skills & learn writing techniques & ideas. Includes presentation by professional published authors.

**Mt Chocorua Writing Workshop**
World Fellowship Center
PO Box 2280, Conway, NH 03818-2280
*Tel:* 603-447-2280 *Fax:* 603-447-1820
*E-mail:* reservations@worldfellowship.org
*Web Site:* www.worldfellowship.org
*Key Personnel*
Dir: Ellen Meeropol
An opportunity to create new poems & prose & apply what we know about craft to writing in need of revision. Writers of all levels encouraged to come.
Location: Conway (White Mountains), NH
Date: annually in July

**Mount Hermon Christian Writers Conference**
Mount Hermon Christian Camps & Conference Center
c/o Mount Hermon Association Inc, 37 Conference Dr, Mount Hermon, CA 95041
Mailing Address: c/o Mount Hermon Association Inc, PO Box 413, Mount Hermon, CA 95041
*Tel:* 831-335-4466 *Toll Free Tel:* 888-MH-CAMPS (642-2677 - registration) *Fax:* 831-335-9218
*E-mail:* info@mhcamps.org
*Web Site:* www.mounthermon.org/writers
*Key Personnel*
Dir: Rachel A Williams *Fax:* 831-335-9413 *E-mail:* rachel.williams@mounthermon.org
2 day Head Start Mentoring Clinic for beginning writers; 5 day Writers Conference for all abilities, including beginning to professional.

Location: Mount Hermon, CA
Date: April 9-15, 2014

**Mountain Writers Series**
2804 SE 27 Ave, Suite 2, Portland, OR 97202
*Tel:* 503-232-4517 *Fax:* 503-232-4517
*E-mail:* pdxmws@mountainwriters.org
*Web Site:* www.mountainwriters.org
*Key Personnel*
Artistic Dir: Sandra Williams
Work with nationally recognized poets, fiction writers, nonfiction writers, screenwriters & agents.

**MWG Writer Workshops**
Mississippi Writers Guild (MWG)
PO Box 3845, Meridian, MS 39303-3845
*Tel:* 601-880-1089
*Web Site:* www.mississippiwritersguild.com
*Key Personnel*
Pres: Robert Ray *E-mail:* robertray601@bellsouth.net
Events Coord: Richelle Putnam *E-mail:* richput@mywebemail.net
For information about this workshop, e-mail Richelle Putnam.

**Mystery Writers of America Workshops**
Mystery Writers of America (MWA)
1140 Broadway, Suite 1507, New York, NY 10001
*Tel:* 212-888-8171
*E-mail:* mwa@mysterywriters.org
*Web Site:* www.mysterywriters.org
*Key Personnel*
Admin Dir: Margery Flax
Mystery writing workshops given at various times throughout the year by regional chapters.

**Napa Valley Writers' Conference**
Napa Valley Community College
Upper Valley Campus, 1088 College Ave, St Helena, CA 94574
*Tel:* 707-967-2900 (ext 1611) *Fax:* 707-967-2909
*E-mail:* writecon@napavalley.edu
*Web Site:* www.napawritersconf.org
*Key Personnel*
Mng Dir: Andrea Bewick
Prog Dir: Anne Matlack Evans *Tel:* 707-253-3168 *E-mail:* abewick@napavalley.edu; John Leggett *Tel:* 707-253-3168
Poetry Prog Dir: Nan Cohen
Fiction Dir: Ms Lakin Khan
Admin Asst: Charlotte Morgan
Poetry & fiction sessions each year, offering small workshops, lectures & readings. Begins last Sunday in July & runs for one week.

**National Society of Newspaper Columnists Annual Conference**
National Society of Newspaper Columnists (NSNC)
1345 Fillmore St, Suite 507, San Francisco, CA 94115
Mailing Address: PO Box 411532, San Francisco, CA 94141
*Tel:* 415-488-NCNC (488-6762)
*Toll Free Tel:* 866-440-NSNC (440-6762)
*Fax:* 484-297-0336 *Toll Free Fax:* 866-635-5759
*Web Site:* www.columnists.com
*Key Personnel*
Pres: Ben Pollock
VP: Larry Cohen
Exec Dir: Luenna H Kim *Tel:* 415-563-5403 *E-mail:* director@columnists.com
Secy: Wayne Chan
Treas: James A Casto
Conference Chair: Brian O'Connor
Contest Chair: Mike Deupree
Membership Chair: Rose A Valenta
Newsletter Ed: Robert Haught
Archivist: Dave Astor
Annual conference & contest, occasional newsletter & networking with staff & syndicated columnists & regular freelance columnists.

**New York State Writers Institute**
State University of New York
Division of University at Albany/SUNY
University at Albany, Science Library 320, Albany, NY 12222
*Tel:* 518-442-5620 *Fax:* 518-442-5621
*E-mail:* writers@uamail.albany.edu
*Web Site:* www.albany.edu/writers-inst/
*Key Personnel*
Exec Dir: William Kennedy
Dir: Donald Faulkner
Asst Dir: Suzanne Lance
Literary program organization featuring year-round visiting writers, classic film, special literary events & conferences, writing courses & workshops. Write or see web site for dates & locations.

**North Carolina Writers' Network Annual Fall Conference**
North Carolina Writers' Network
PO Box 21591, Winston-Salem, NC 27120-1591
*Tel:* 336-293-8844
*E-mail:* mail@ncwriters.org
*Web Site:* www.ncwriters.org
*Key Personnel*
Exec Dir: Ed Southern
Workshops, readings, conferences, critiquing service & round table discussions, panels & meetings with agents, publishing workshops.
Date: Nov

**Northeast Texas Community College Annual Writers Conference**
Northeast Texas Community College
Continuing Education, PO Box 1307, Mount Pleasant, TX 75456-1307
*Tel:* 903-434-8134 *Toll Free Tel:* 800-870-0142 *Fax:* 903-572-6712
*Web Site:* www.ntcc.edu
*Key Personnel*
Pres: Dr Brad Johnson *E-mail:* bjohnson@ntcc.edu
Dir, Continuing Educ: Judy Jackson *E-mail:* jjackson@ntcc.edu

**Odyssey: The Summer Fantasy Writing Workshop**
PO Box 75, Mont Vernon, NH 03057
*Tel:* 603-673-6234 *Fax:* 603-673-6234
*Web Site:* www.odysseyworkshop.org
*Key Personnel*
Dir: Jeanne Cavelos *E-mail:* jcavelos@comcast.net
Intensive 6-week workshop for writers of fantasy, science fiction & horror. Dir Jeanne Cavelos is a former Sr Ed at Bantam Doubleday Dell Publishing & winner of the World Fantasy Award. Guest lecturers include some of the top writers in the field. College credit available. Application deadline: April 7.
Location: Saint Anselm College, Manchester, NH
Date: June 9-July 18, 2014

**Oregon Christian Writers Coaching Conference**
Oregon Christian Writers (OCW)
1075 Willow Lake Rd N, Keizer, OR 97303
*Tel:* 503-393-3356
*E-mail:* contact@oregonchristianwriters.org
*Web Site:* www.oregonchristianwriters.org
*Key Personnel*
Summer Conference Dir: Lindy Jacobs *E-mail:* summerconf@oregonchristianwriters.org
Registrar & Busn Mgr: Sue Miholer
Seven hours of hands-on help from well-published professionals, many specialized workshops, consultations with editors & networking with successful writers.
Location: Jantzen Beach Red Lion Hotel, Portland, OR
Date: Aug 4-7, 2014

**Oregon Christian Writers Seminar**
Oregon Christian Writers (OCW)
1075 Willow Lake Rd N, Keizer, OR 97303
*Tel:* 503-393-3356
*E-mail:* contact@oregonchristianwriters.org
*Web Site:* www.oregonchristianwriters.org
*Key Personnel*
Pres: Maxine Marsolini
Prog Chmn: Marilyn Rhoads
Registrar & Busn Mgr: Sue Miholer
Writers' workshops.
Location: Winter Conference, Salem, OR
Date: Feb 22, 2014
Location: Spring Conference, Eugene, OR
Date: May 17, 2014
Location: Fall Conference, Portland, OR
Date: Oct 11, 2014

**Orientation to the Graphic Arts**
Printing Industries of America
200 Deer Run Rd, Sewickley, PA 15143-2600
*Tel:* 412-259-1711 *Toll Free Tel:* 800-910-4283 *Fax:* 412-741-2311
*E-mail:* printing@printing.org
*Web Site:* www.printing.org
*Key Personnel*
CEO & Pres: Michael Makin *E-mail:* mmakin@printing.org
VP, Training: Jim Workman *E-mail:* jworkman@printing.org
Sr Custom Training & Consulting Specialist: Karen Keller *E-mail:* kkeller@printing.org

**Outdoor Writers Association of America Annual Conference**
Outdoor Writers Association of America
615 Oak St, Suite 201, Missoula, MT 59801
*Tel:* 406-728-7434 *Fax:* 406-728-7445
*E-mail:* info@owaa.org
*Web Site:* www.owaa.org
*Key Personnel*
Exec Dir: Robin Giner *E-mail:* rginer@owaa.org
Seminars & writing workshops; photography & controversial subjects.
Location: Knoxville, TN
Date: June 27-29, 2014
Location: McAllen, TX
Date: May 22-24, 2015

**Ozark Creative Writers Inc Annual Conference**
Ozark Creative Writers Inc
PO Box 424, Eureka Springs, AR 72632
*Tel:* 479-751-7246
*E-mail:* ozarkcreativewriters@gmail.com
*Web Site:* www.ozarkcreativewriters.org
*Key Personnel*
Chair: Dusty Richards *E-mail:* dustyrichards@cox.net
Writers' conference for beginners & professionals. Contest information in brochures available after May 1. Send No 10 SASE.
Location: Ozarks Convention Ctr, Eureka Springs, AR
Date: 2nd full weekend in Oct

**Pacific Northwest Children's Book Conference**
Portland State University Graduate School of Education
615 SW Harrison St, Portland, OR 97201
Mailing Address: PO Box 751, Portland, OR 97207
*Tel:* 503-725-9786 *Toll Free Tel:* 800-547-8887 (ext 9786) *Fax:* 503-725-5599

*Web Site:* www.pdx.edu/ceed/childrens-book-conference
*Key Personnel*
Contact: Elizabeth Snyder *E-mail:* snydere@pdx.edu
Focus on the craft of writing & illustrating for children & young people while working with an outstanding faculty of acclaimed editors, authors & illustrators. Housing & meals will be available on campus to allow more opportunities for networking & ongoing discussion with faculty & fellow students. Afternoon small-group, faculty-led workshops for writers & illustrators. Individual mss & portfolio reviews available. Undergraduate & graduate credit available through Portland State University.

**Pacific Northwest Summer Writers Conference**
Pacific Northwest Writers Association
1420 NW Gilman Blvd, Suite 2, PMB 2717, Issaquah, WA 98027
*Tel:* 425-673-2665
*E-mail:* pnwa@pnwa.org
*Web Site:* www.pnwa.org
*Key Personnel*
Pres: Pam Binder

**Pennwriters Conference**
Pennwriters Inc
406 Second St, Dalton, PA 18404
*Web Site:* www.pennwriters.org
*Key Personnel*
Conference Coord: Jessica Williams *E-mail:* jesswilliams06@verizon.net
Workshops, seminars with authors, agents & editors in romance, mystery, short story, nonfiction, poetry, read & critique sessions, hands-on workshops & contests, Agent/editor appointments.
Location: Eden Resort, Lancaster, PA
Date: May 16-18, 2014

**Philadelphia Writers' Conference**
PO Box 7171, Elkins Park, PA 19027-0171
*Tel:* 215-782-3288 *Fax:* 215-782-3288
*E-mail:* info@pwcwriters.org
*Web Site:* pwcwriters.org
*Key Personnel*
Trustee & Contact: Gloria T Delamar *E-mail:* delamarg@juno.com
Educational conferences for writers, workshops, critiques, contests, featured speakers, agents, editors.
Location: Philadelphia, PA
Date: random free forums
Location: Philadelphia, PA
Date: annual 3-day event; 2nd full weekend of June

**Pima Writers' Workshop**
Pima Community College
Pima College West Campus, 2202 W Anklam Rd, Tucson, AZ 85709-0170
*Tel:* 520-206-6084 *Fax:* 520-206-6020
*Web Site:* www.pima.edu
*Key Personnel*
Dir: Meg Files *E-mail:* mfiles@pima.edu
The three-day conference in May offers opportunities to meet with authors, editors & agents & to have mss critiqued.
Location: Pima Community College, West Campus, Tucson, AZ
Date: May 2014

**Poetry Flash Reading Series**
Poetry Flash
1450 Fourth St, Suite 4, Berkeley, CA 94710
*Tel:* 510-525-5476 *Fax:* 510-525-6752
*E-mail:* editor@poetryflash.org
*Web Site:* www.poetryflash.org
*Key Personnel*
Publr & Ed: Joyce Jenkins
Publication; conducts a reading & poetry series in conjunction with Moe's Books in Berkeley, CA & Diesel, A Bookstore in Oakland, CA. Host poets from all around the US.

**Port Townsend Writers' Conference**
Centrum Foundation
223 Battery Way, Port Townsend, WA 98368
Mailing Address: PO Box 1158, Port Townsend, WA 98368-0958
*Tel:* 360-385-3102 *Toll Free Tel:* 800-733-3608 (ticket off) *Fax:* 360-385-2470
*E-mail:* info@centrum.org
*Web Site:* www.centrum.org
*Key Personnel*
Artistic Dir: Erin Belieu
Workshops, lectures & readings.

**The Publishing Game**
Peanut Butter & Jelly Press LLC
PO Box 590239, Newton, MA 02459-0002
SAN: 299-7444
*Tel:* 617-630-0945 *Fax:* 617-630-0945 (call first)
*E-mail:* info@publishinggame.com; workshops@publishinggame.com
*Web Site:* www.publishinggame.com
*Key Personnel*
Off Mgr: Alyza Harris *E-mail:* alyza@publishinggame.com
All-day workshop covers how to find a literary agent, how to self-publish & how to successfully promote your book. Offered in 12 cities: New York, Boston, Philadelphia, DC, Boca Raton, Chicago, San Francisco, Los Angeles, Seattle, Phoenix, Dallas & several 'floating cities' each year. $195 includes workshop course binder. See www.publishinggame.com for latest locations, dates & details.

**Robert Quackenbush's Children's Book Writing & Illustration Workshops**
Robert Quackenbush Studios
223 E 78 St, New York, NY 10075
Mailing Address: 460 E 79 St, New York, NY 10075
*Tel:* 212-744-3822
*E-mail:* rqstudios@aol.com
*Web Site:* www.rquackenbush.com
Workshops at author/artists' studio; focus on planning children's books from concept to completion.
Location: New York, NY
Date: Second week in July annually (4 day intensive workshop)

**ReIMAGINE the MAGIC Annual Summer Conference**
The International Women's Writing Guild (IWWG)
317 Madison Ave, Suite 1704, New York, NY 10017
*Tel:* 917-720-6959
*E-mail:* iwwgquestions@gmail.com
*Web Site:* www.iwwg.org
*Key Personnel*
Exec Dir: Cynthia Fritts Stillwell *E-mail:* iwwgexecdir@gmail.com
For one week each summer, the Guild brings together close to 500 women in a shared-interest writing community, offering some 65 workshops each & every day. Call for further information.

**Romance Writers of America Annual Conference**
Romance Writers of America®
14615 Benfer Rd, Houston, TX 77069
*Tel:* 832-717-5200 *Fax:* 832-717-5201
*E-mail:* info@rwa.org
*Web Site:* www.rwa.org
*Key Personnel*
Exec Dir: Allison Kelley *Tel:* 832-717-5200 ext 124 *E-mail:* allison.kelley@rwa.org
Promote recognition of the genre of romance writing as a serious book form. Conduct workshops, sponsor national & regional conferences & awards for members.
Location: San Antonio Marriott® Rivercenter & Marriott® Riverwalk, San Antonio, TX
Date: July 23-26, 2014
Location: New York Marriott® Marquis, New York, NY
Date: July 22-25, 2015
Location: an Diego Marriott Hotel and Marina, San Diego, CA
Date: July 13-16, 2016
Location: Walt Disney World Swan and Dolphin, 1500 Epcot Resorts Blvd, Lake Buena Vista, FL
Date: July 26-29, 2017

**San Diego Christian Writers' Guild Conference**
San Diego Christian Writers' Guild
PO Box 270403, San Diego, CA 92198
*Tel:* 760-294-3269 *Fax:* 760-294-3269
*E-mail:* info@sandiegocwg.org
*Web Site:* www.sandiegocwg.org
*Key Personnel*
Pres: Jennie Gillespie; Robert Gillespie
One day seminar & workshops; personal consultations with editors. Journalism, magazine writing, fiction. Seminar is always the fourth Saturday in Sept.

**San Francisco Writers Conference**
1029 Jones St, San Francisco, CA 94109
*Tel:* 415-673-0939
*E-mail:* sfwriterscon@aol.com
*Web Site:* www.sfwriters.org
*Key Personnel*
Founder: Michael Larsen
Founder & Dir: Elizabeth Pomada
Craft & market oriented writers' conference covering fiction, nonfiction, children's books, film & poetry with name authors.

**Sandhills Writers' Series**
Augusta State University
Dept of Communications & Professional Writing, 2500 Walton Way, Augusta, GA 30904
*Tel:* 706-667-4437 *Fax:* 706-667-4770
*Web Site:* www.sandhills.aug.edu
*Key Personnel*
Dir & Professor of Creative Writing: Anthony Kellman *E-mail:* akellman@aol.com
Fiction, nonfiction, creative nonfiction & poetry craft-directed readings; participants meet in consultations with literary agents that represent commercial & literary fiction, nonfiction & children's books. Enrollment limited. Ms deadline Feb.

**Santa Barbara Book Promotion Workshop**
Para Publishing LLC
PO Box 8206-240, Santa Barbara, CA 93118-8206
SAN: 215-8981
*Tel:* 805-968-7277 *Toll Free Tel:* 800-727-2782 *Fax:* 805-968-1379
*E-mail:* info@parapublishing.com
*Web Site:* www.parapublishing.com
*Key Personnel*
Owner & Publr: Dan Poynter *E-mail:* danpoynter@parapublishing.com
Book marketing, promoting & distributing; four workshops per year.
Location: Santa Barbara, CA
Date: Jan, April, July, Oct; reservations required, attendance limited to 23

**Science Fiction Writers Workshop**
Center for the Study of Science Fiction
Division of University of Kansas
University of Kansas, Wescoe Hall, Rm 3001, Dept of English, 1445 Jayhawk Blvd, Lawrence, KS 66045-7590
*Tel:* 785-864-3380 *Fax:* 785-864-1159
*Web Site:* www.ku.edu/~sfcenter
*Key Personnel*
Founding Dir: James Gunn *E-mail:* jgunn@ku.edu
Dir: Chris McKitterick *E-mail:* cmckit@ku.edu
A noncredit, two-week intensive workshop offered in association with the Campbell Conference on science fiction by the Center for the Study of Science Fiction.
Location: University of Kansas, Lawrence, KS
Date: Summer

**Scribes & Scribblers Writing Camps for Kids**
Aspen Writers' Foundation
110 E Hallam St, Suite 116, Aspen, CO 81611
*Tel:* 970-925-3122 *Fax:* 970-920-5700
*E-mail:* info@aspenwriters.org
*Web Site:* www.aspenwriters.org
*Key Personnel*
Exec Dir: Lisa Consiglio *Tel:* 970-925-3122 ext 1 *E-mail:* lisa@aspenwriters.org
Helps kids discover writing is fun.
Location: Aspen, CO
Date: Annually July-Aug

**SDSU Writers' Conference**
San Diego State University College of Extended Studies
5250 Campanile Dr, Rm 2503, San Diego, CA 92182-1920
*Tel:* 619-594-2517 *Fax:* 619-594-8566
*E-mail:* sdsuwritersconference@mail.sdsu.edu
*Web Site:* www.neverstoplearning.net/writers
*Key Personnel*
Prog Dir: Becky Ryan *E-mail:* rjryan@mail.sdsu.edu
Annual weekend writers' conference. Topics include screenwriting, fiction, nonfiction, genre novels & children's writing. Personal editor & agent appointments available.
Location: Doubletree Hotel, Mission Valley, San Diego, CA
Date: Jan 24-26, 2014

**Hank Searls Authors Workshop**
4435 Holly Lane NW, Gig Harbor, WA 98335
Mailing Address: Box 1877, Suite 1-C, Gig Harbor, WA 98335
*Tel:* 253-851-9896 *Fax:* 253-851-9897
*E-mail:* hanksearls@comcast.net
*Key Personnel*
CEO & Pres: Hank Searls
Novel & full-length fiction writing, teaching & critiquing full-length fiction & nonfiction.
Location: Gig Harbor, WA

**See-More's Workshop Arts & Education Workshops**
The Shadow Box Theatre
325 West End Ave, Suite 12-B, New York, NY 10023
*Tel:* 212-724-0677 *Fax:* 212-724-0767
*E-mail:* sbt@shadowboxtheatre.org
*Web Site:* www.shadowboxtheatre.org
*Key Personnel*
Administrator: Elaine Brand *E-mail:* ebrand@shadowboxtheatre.org
Arts & Educ Dir: Carol Prud'homme Davis
Resident Workshops: Early learning through elementary grades, SBT's teaching artists guide students in the art of storytelling & curriculum exploration through puppetry, dramatics, dance & music. Professional Development Workshops: Hands-on staff development workshops provide classroom teachers with theatre & storytelling techniques. Author Workshops: Includes a trip or in-school SBT musical puppet show, our own storybooks with accompanying audio tapes/CDs & a meeting with playwright & author, Sandra Robbins. For more information contact us, as dates, times & locations change often.

**Sewanee Writers' Conference**
Stamler Ctr, 119 Gailor Hall, 735 University Ave, Sewanee, TN 37383-1000
*Tel:* 931-598-1141
*E-mail:* swc@sewanee.edu
*Web Site:* www.sewaneewriters.org
*Key Personnel*
Dir: Wyatt Prunty
Admissions & Creative Writing Administrator: Adam Latham *E-mail:* allatham@sewanee.edu
Administrator: Megan Roberts *E-mail:* mgroberts@sewanee.edu
Workshops in poetry, fiction & playwriting.
Location: The University of the South, Sewanee, TN
Date: Annually the last two weeks in July

**Society for Technical Communication's Annual Conference**
Society for Technical Communication
9401 Lee Hwy, Suite 300, Fairfax, VA 22031
*Tel:* 703-522-4114 *Fax:* 703-522-2075
*E-mail:* stc@stc.org
*Web Site:* www.stc.org
*Key Personnel*
Exec Dir: Chris Lyons *Tel:* 571-366-1901 *E-mail:* chris.lyons@stc.org
Deputy Exec Dir: Lloyd Tucker *Tel:* 571-366-1904 *E-mail:* lloyd.tucker@stc.org
Educational conference for technical communicators.

**Solid Gold Marketing Design Workshops**
Sparkle Presentations Inc
PO Box 2373, La Mesa, CA 91943-2373
*Tel:* 858-569-6555 *Toll Free Tel:* 800-932-0973
*Web Site:* www.sparklepresentations.com
*Key Personnel*
CEO & Pres: Sheryl Roush *E-mail:* sheryl@sparklepresentations.com
Design sessions teach creativity, design tactics, feedback & fun. Specializing in newsletters, brochures, flyers & presentation materials. Keynote addresses on attitude, creating a positive workplace. See web site for scheduled events.
Membership(s): IBPA, National Speakers Association & Toastmasters International.

**Southampton Writers' Conference**
Stony Brook Southampton
239 Montauk Hwy, Southampton, NY 11968
*Tel:* 631-632-5007
*E-mail:* southamptonwriters@notes.cc.sunysb.edu
*Web Site:* www.stonybrook.edu/writers
*Key Personnel*
Conference Coord: Christian McLean *E-mail:* christian.mclean@stonybrook.edu
Five & twelve day workshops including novel, short story, poetry, memoir & creative nonfiction, playwriting & screenwriting; also evening readings, performances & panels.

**Southern California Writers' Conference**
Southern California Writers' Conference (SCWC)
Division of Random Cove, ie
1010 University Ave, Suite 54, San Diego, CA 92103
*Tel:* 619-303-8185 *Fax:* 619-303-7462
*E-mail:* wewrite@writersconference.com
*Web Site:* www.writersconference.com
*Key Personnel*
Exec Dir: Michael Steven Gregory *Tel:* 619-906-7462 *Fax:* 253-390-8577 *E-mail:* msg@writersconference.com
Dir: Wes Albers *E-mail:* wes@writersconference.com
Asst Dir: Chrissie A Barnett *E-mail:* chrissie@writersconference.com
Annual writers conference & retreat. Fiction, nonfiction & scriptwriting mss eligible for advance critique submission before the conference followed by one-on-one consultation; awards given. Major speakers; banquet; workshops in fiction, nonfiction, scriptwriting, poetry, short story; conference emphasis on fiction & nonfiction; one agent panel to read & critique.
Location: San Diego, CA
Date: Feb 14-17, 2014

**SouthWest Writers Conference Series**
SouthWest Writers
3200 Carlisle Blvd NE, Suite 114, Albuquerque, NM 87110-1663
*Tel:* 505-830-6034
*E-mail:* swwriters@juno.com
*Web Site:* www.southwestwriters.com
*Key Personnel*
Pres: Kathy Kitts
Series of one-day conferences, annual writing contest (May 1 deadline), twice-monthly programs, bimonthly writing contest, workshops & writing classes.

**Spring Time Writers Creative Writing & Journaling Workshop**
Spring Time Writers
PO Box 512, Lyons, CO 80540-0512
*Tel:* 303-823-0997
*E-mail:* writers@springtimewriters.com
*Web Site:* www.springtimewriters.com
*Key Personnel*
Dir: Kathleen Spring
Creative writing & self discovery journaling workshops. Four days, including lodging, small classes, professional warm instruction in the Rocky Mountains in Colorado. Conferences held 2nd & 4th weekends June-Sept.

**Springfed Writers' Retreat**
Springfed Arts
PO Box 304, Royal Oak, MI 48068-0304
*Tel:* 248-589-3913
*Web Site:* www.springfed.org
*Key Personnel*
Dir: John D Lamb *E-mail:* johndlamb@ameritech.net
Poets & writers conference, good writers, food & accomodations.

**Squaw Valley Community of Writers Summer Workshops**
Community of Writers at Squaw Valley
PO Box 1416, Nevada City, CA 95959
*Tel:* 530-470-8440
*E-mail:* info@squawvalleywriters.org
*Web Site:* www.squawvalleywriters.org
*Key Personnel*
Exec Dir: Ms Brett Hall Jones
Dir, Fiction: Lisa Alvarez; Louis B Jones
Dir, Poetry Workshop: Robert Hass
Dir, Screenwriting: Diana Fuller
Summer writing workshops; each workshop is one week long.
Membership(s): Association of Writers & Writing Programs.

**The Summer Experience**
Sage Hill Writing Experience Inc
601 Spadina Crescent E, Suite 718, Saskatoon, SK S7K 3G8, Canada
Mailing Address: Box 1731, Saskatoon, SK S7K 3S1, Canada
*Tel:* 306-652-7395 *Fax:* 306-244-0255
*E-mail:* sage.hill@sasktel.net
*Web Site:* www.sagehillwriting.ca

*Key Personnel*
Exec Dir: Phillip Adams
Offers a special working & learning opportunity to writers at different stages of development. Top quality instruction, a low instructor-writer ratio & the rural Saskatchewan setting offer conditions ideal for the pursuit of excellence in the arts of fiction & poetry. Application to The Summer Experience is open to writers 19 years of age & older, regardless of city, province or country of residence.

**Summer Writers Program**
Hofstra University
CE, 250 Hofstra University, Hempstead, NY 11549-2500
*Tel:* 516-463-5016; 516-463-7200 *Fax:* 516-463-4833
*E-mail:* prpgse@hofstra.edu
*Web Site:* ccepa.hofstra.edu
*Key Personnel*
Dir: Richard Pioreck *Tel:* 516-463-0258 *E-mail:* richard.j.pioreck@hofstra.edu
Asst Dir: Jennifer Jokinen *Tel:* 516-463-7600 *E-mail:* jennifer.jokinen@hofstra.edu
Two week programs featuring writing classes, readings, special guest speakers & luncheon. Dorm rooms available.

**Taos Summer Writers' Conference**
University of New Mexico
University of New Mexico, Humanities Dept, Rm 253, Albuquerque, NM 87131-0001
SAN: 213-9588
Mailing Address: Dept of English Language & Literature, One University of New Mexico, MSC03 2170, Albuquerque, NM 81313-0001
*Tel:* 505-277-5572
*E-mail:* taosconf@unm.edu
*Web Site:* www.unm.edu/~taosconf
*Key Personnel*
Founding Dir: Sharon Oard Warner
Writing workshops & special events. All events associated with the conference - panels, presentations & readings are free & open to the public.
Location: Sagebrush Inn & Conference Center, Taos, NM

**Tony Hillerman Writers Conference**
WORDHARVEST LLC
1063 Willow Way, Santa Fe, NM 87507
*Tel:* 505-471-1565
*E-mail:* wordharvest@wordharvest.com
*Web Site:* www.wordharvest.com
*Key Personnel*
Founder: Anne Hillerman
Memb: Jean Schaumberg

**UCI Extension Writers' Program**
University of California, Irvine Extension
PO Box 6050, Irvine, CA 92616-6050
*Tel:* 949-824-5990 *Fax:* 949-824-3651
*Web Site:* www.unex.uci.edu
*Key Personnel*
Dir, Certificate Prog in Sustainability Leadership: Kirwan Rockefeller, PhD *Tel:* 949-824-6335 *E-mail:* kirwan.rockefeller@unx.uci.edu
Fiction, nonfiction & screen writing. Check catalogue for dates.
Location: University of California, Irvine Extension, Irvine, CA
Date: Check catalogue

**Unicorn Writers' Conference**
Unicorn Writers' Conference Inc
17 Church Hill Rd, Redding, CT 06896
*Tel:* 203-938-7405 *Fax:* 203-938-7405
*E-mail:* unicornwritersconference@gmail.com
*Web Site:* unicornwritersconference.com
*Key Personnel*
Chmn: Jan L Kardys *E-mail:* jan.kardys@gmail.com
Mktg Dir: Annie Sadlon
Sessions Dir: Emily Prescott
Following the keynote address, delivered by a best-selling author or celebrity. Offers 24 different sessions including fiction, nonfiction, memoir, mystery, poetry, screenwriting, writing for the childern's market & other major genres. How-to tutorials from publishing professionals educating writers on all aspects of publishing including contracts, copyrights, permissions, special sales, subsidiary rights, media training, promotion & platform, social media. self-publishing, book distribution & more. Features 2 agent panels & one editorial panel. One-to-one ms reviews available with editors, agents & faculty for an additional fee. Price $285, breakfast, lunch & dinner included. Welcome gift for all attendees. One-to-one sessions: $50 for a 30 minute session in-person private ms consultation with the faculty member, agent, editor of your choice. Query letter & book synopses reviews available also; 8:00am-7:30pm.
Location: St Clements Castle, Portland, CT
Date: March 22, 2014

**Visiting Writers Series**
University of Alaska Fairbanks
English Dept, PO Box 755720, Fairbanks, AK 99775-5720
*Tel:* 907-474-7193 *Fax:* 907-474-5247
*E-mail:* faengl@uaf.edu
*Web Site:* www.alaska.edu/english
*Key Personnel*
Assoc Professor: Derick Burleson *E-mail:* ffdwb@uaf.edu
Readings from & discussion of own writings; poetry, fiction, nonfiction. Other sponsors include: University of Alaska Foundation, Alaska State Council on the Arts, The National Endowment for the Arts, UAF College of Liberal Arts & UA President's Special Project Fund.
Location: Fairbanks, AK
Date: Contact for schedule

**The Voices Summer Writing Workshops**
Voices of Our Nations Art Foundation
Affiliate of University of San Francisco
c/o Community Initiatives Inc, 354 Pine St, Suite 700, San Francisco, CA 94104
*Toll Free Tel:* 866-202-6152
*E-mail:* info@voicesatvona.org
*Web Site:* www.voicesatvona.org
*Key Personnel*
Exec Dir: Diem Jones

**Wesleyan Writers Conference**
Wesleyan University
c/o Wesleyan University, 294 High St, Middletown, CT 06459
*Tel:* 860-685-3604 *Fax:* 860-685-2441
*Web Site:* www.wesleyan.edu/writing/conference
*Key Personnel*
Dir, Wesleyan Writers Conference: Anne Greene *E-mail:* agreene@wesleyan.edu
Seminars, readings, ms consultations & talks focused on novels, short stories, film, poetry, nonfiction, journalism, multi-media work, publishing; scholarships & fellowships. Participants are welcome to attend seminars in all genres; visits from editors & agents. Award-winning writers as faculty & guest speakers.
Location: Wesleyan University, Middletown, CT
Date: Annually during the third week in June

**Whidbey Island Writers Conference**
Whidbey Island Writers Association
5577 Vanbarr Place, Freeland, WA 98249
Mailing Address: PO Box 639, Freeland, WA 98249
*Tel:* 360-331-0307
*E-mail:* nila@whidbey.com
*Web Site:* www.nila.edu
*Key Personnel*
MFA Student Servs Coord: Asharaine Machala *E-mail:* mfa@nila.edu
Meet & learn from authors, editors & agents.

**Willamette Writers' Conference**
Willamette Writers
2108 Buck St, West Linn, OR 97068
*Tel:* 503-305-6729 *Fax:* 503-344-6174
*E-mail:* wilwrite@willamettewriters.com
*Web Site:* www.willamettewriters.com
*Key Personnel*
Pres: Val Mallinson
Off Mgr: Bill Johnson
Annual summer three-day conference: consultations with over 50 national agents, editors, film agents & producers; workshops (fiction, nonfiction, children's, screen/TV, genres, craft of writing); editing room available. Year-round: monthly meetings, writing contest, workshops, newsletter.

**Windbreak House Writing Retreats**
Windbreak House
PO Box 169, Hermosa, SD 57744-0169
*Tel:* 307-630-4003
*E-mail:* info@windbreakhouse.com
*Web Site:* www.windbreakhouse.com
*Key Personnel*
Owner & Writer in Residence: Linda M Hasselstrom
Asst: Tamara Rogers
Retreats scheduled to suit applicants.

**Winter Words Apres Ski for the Mind**
Aspen Writers' Foundation
110 E Hallam St, Suite 116, Aspen, CO 81611
*Tel:* 970-925-3122 *Fax:* 970-920-5700
*E-mail:* info@aspenwriters.org
*Web Site:* www.aspenwriters.org
*Key Personnel*
Exec Dir: Lisa Consiglio *Tel:* 970-925-3122 ext 1 *E-mail:* lisa@aspenwriters.org
Prog Mgr: Natalie Lacy *Tel:* 970-925-3122 ext 3 *E-mail:* natalie@aspenwriters.org
Series of readings with remarkable writers. Also includes book signings.

**Wisconsin Annual Fall Conferencee**
Society of Children's Book Writers & Illustrators, Wisconsin Chapter
PO Box 259303, Madison, WI 53725
*Tel:* 608-278-0692
*Web Site:* www.scbwi.org; www.scbwi-wi.com
*Key Personnel*
Co-Regl Advisor: Michael Kress-Russick; Jamie Swenson
Workshop on writing & illustrating for children. Includes ms or portfolio critique. Guest faculty includes award-winning writers & illustrators.

**Write on the Sound Writers' Conference**
City of Edmonds Art Commission
700 Main St, Edmonds, WA 98020
*Tel:* 425-771-0228 *Fax:* 425-771-0253
*E-mail:* wots@ci.edmonds.wa.us
*Web Site:* www.edmondswa.gov
*Key Personnel*
City of Edmonds Cultural Servs Mgr: Frances Chapin
Annual even with over 30 workshops by noted authors, educators & trade professionals. Features a keynote address, on-site book shop, ms critique appointments & a themed writing contest.

**The Writers' Colony at Dairy Hollow**
Subsidiary of Communication Arts Institute

515 Spring St, Eureka Springs, AR 72632
*Tel:* 479-253-7444 *Fax:* 479-253-9859
*E-mail:* director@writerscolony.org
*Web Site:* www.writerscolony.org
*Key Personnel*
Dir: Linda Caldwell
See web site for upcoming events & fellowships.

**Writers' League of Texas (WLT)**
611 S Congress Ave, Suite 505, Austin, TX 78704
*Tel:* 512-499-8914
*E-mail:* wlt@writersleague.org
*Web Site:* www.writersleague.org
*Key Personnel*
Off Administrator: Bethany Hegedus *E-mail:* bethany@writersleague.org
Conferences, workshops, seminars, classes, e-mail classes.
Location: Writer's League of Texas Resource Center/Library & other locations, ongoing programs throughout Texas
Date: Ongoing throughout year

**Writers Retreat Workshop (WRW)**
PO Box 4236, Louisville, KY 40204
*E-mail:* wrw04@netscape.net
*Web Site:* www.writersretreatworkshop.com
*Key Personnel*
Founder & Creative Dir: Gail Provost Stockwell *E-mail:* gail@writeit-sellit.com
Dir: Jason S Sitzes *E-mail:* jssitzes@aol.com
WRW Ed-in-Residence: Lorin Oberweger *E-mail:* loberweger@aol.com
Ten-day intensive workshop for writers of novels-in-progress, including private writing time & space, guest speakers & consultation with New York agent or editor, author instructor, as well as diagnostic sessions of participants' mss & daily assignments. Other retreats available, see web site for details.

**The Writers Workshop**
The Kenyon Review
Finn House, 102 W Wiggin St, Gambier, OH 43022
*Tel:* 740-427-5207 *Fax:* 740-427-5417
*E-mail:* kenyonreview@kenyon.edu
*Web Site:* www.kenyonreview.org
*Key Personnel*
Progs Dir, The Kenyon Review: Anna Duke Reach
Intensive writing workshops for adults & teens.

**Writers Workshop in Children's Literature**
Society of Children's Book Writers & Illustrators, Florida Region
125 E Merritt Island Causeway, Suite 209, Merritt Island, FL 32952
*Tel:* 321-338-7208
*Web Site:* www.scbwiflorida.com
*Key Personnel*
Regl Advisor: Linda Rodriguez Bernfeld *E-mail:* lindabernfeld@gmail.com
Workshops in writing & illustrating picture books, juvenile & young adult fiction & nonfiction, children's magazines & marketing, given by published authors, illustrators, editors & agents.
Location: SCBWI Florida Regional Conference
Date: Jan 17-19, 2014
Location: SCBWI Florida Mid-Year Workshop, Dolphin Hotel, Disney World, Orlando, FL
Date: June 6-7, 2014

**The Writing Center**
601 Palisade Ave, Englewood Cliffs, NJ 07632
*Tel:* 201-567-4017 *Fax:* 201-567-7202
*E-mail:* writingcenter@optonline.net
*Web Site:* www.thewritingcenternj.com
*Key Personnel*
Dir: Barry Sheinkopf *E-mail:* bsheinkopf@optonline.net
Writing seminars, editorial services, book design & publishing services.
Location: 601 Palisade Ave, Englewood Cliffs, NJ
Date: Year-round, 12-week writing seminars; Fall seminars begin Sept; Winter seminars begin Jan; Spring seminars begin April. Five week Summer session

**The Writing for Children Founders Workshops**
Highlights Foundation
814 Court St, Honesdale, PA 18431
*Tel:* 570-253-1192 *Fax:* 570-253-0179
*E-mail:* jolloyd@highlightsfoundation.org
*Web Site:* www.highlightsfoundation.org
*Key Personnel*
Exec Dir: Kent L Brown, Jr *E-mail:* klbrown@highlightsfoundation.org
For children's writers & illustrators seeking to sharpen their focus. Helps to improve your craft with the help of a master, finding the time & space in which to work & marketing yourself & your books. Cost of workshops range from $495 & up which includes tuition, meals, conference supplies & housing.

**Writing Workshops**
UC Davis Extension
Affiliate of University of California, Davis
1333 Research Park Dr, Davis, CA 95618
*Tel:* 510-642-6362
*E-mail:* extension@ucdavis.edu
*Web Site:* www.extension.ucdavis.edu; writing.ucdavis.edu
*Key Personnel*
Dir, Univ Writing Prog: Chris Thaiss *Tel:* 530-754-9197 *E-mail:* cjthaiss@ucdavis.edu
Workshops, courses & writing institutes.
Location: University of California, Davis & Sacramento, CA
Date: Year-round, call for dates

**Yaddo Artists Residency**
Yaddo
312 Union Ave, Saratoga Springs, NY 12866
Mailing Address: PO Box 395, Saratoga Springs, NY 12866-0395
*Tel:* 518-584-0746 *Fax:* 518-584-1312
*E-mail:* yaddo@yaddo.org
*Web Site:* www.yaddo.org
*Key Personnel*
Pres: Elaina Richardson *E-mail:* erichardson@yaddo.org
Prog Dir: Candace Wait *E-mail:* chwait@yaddo.org
An artists' community established in Saratoga Springs, New York in 1900 by the financier Spencer Trask & his poet wife, Katrina, to offer creative artists the rare gift of a supportive environment with uninterrupted time to think, experiment & create. Over the years, Yaddo has welcomed more than 6,000 artists working in one or more of the following media: choreography, film, literature, musical composition, painting, performance art, photography, printmaking, sculpture & video. About 220 artists are invited each year for residencies lasting up to 2 months. Application deadlines are Jan 1 & Aug 1.

**Young Writers' Workshop**
Cape Cod Writers' Center
919 Main St, Osterville, MA 02655
Mailing Address: PO Box 408, Osterville, MA 02655
*Tel:* 508-420-0200 *Fax:* 508-420-0212
*E-mail:* writers@capecodwriterscenter.org
*Web Site:* www.capecodwriterscenter.org
*Key Personnel*
Pres: Kevin Symmons
Exec Dir: Nancy Robin Stuart
Busn & Mktg Mgr: Moira Powers
Held concurrently with the annual Cape Cod Writers Conference in Aug, this program offers unique learning opportunities to young writers ages 12-18.

# Courses for the Book Trade

Various courses covering different phases of the book trade are given each year. Detailed information on any of these courses can be obtained by writing directly to the sponsoring organization. For up-to-date information on book trade courses, workshops and seminars, consult the calendar section of *Publishers Weekly* (PWxyz LLC, 71 W 23 Street, Suite 1608, New York, NY 10010). For related information see **Writers' Conferences & Workshops**.

**Arizona State University, Creative Writing Program**
851 S Cady Mall, Rm 542, Tempe, AZ 85287-0302
Mailing Address: Dept of English, Box 870302, Tempe, AZ 85287-0302
*Tel:* 480-965-6856 *Fax:* 480-965-3451
*Web Site:* www.asu.edu/clas/english/creativewriting
*Key Personnel*
Prog Dir: Peter Turchi *E-mail:* peter.turchi@asu.edu
Undergraduate & graduate courses in creative writing: workshops, theory & special topics.

**Arkansas State University Graphic Communications Program**
PO Box 1930, Dept of Journalism & Graphic Communications, State University, AR 72467-1930
*Tel:* 870-972-3114 *Fax:* 870-972-3321
*Web Site:* www.astate.edu
*Key Personnel*
Dept Chair: Dr Gilbert Fowler *E-mail:* gfowler@astate.edu
Instructor, Graphic Commun: Pradeep C Mishra *Tel:* 870-972-3075 *E-mail:* pmishra@astate.edu
Courses include Digital Pre-Press Workflow & File Creation
Electronic Innovations in Graphic Communications
Graphic Communications - Estimating & Schedules
Graphic Production Systems
Internet Communications
Internship
Intro to Digital Publishing
Intro to Visual Communication
Mass Communication in Modern Society
Multi-Media Production Techniques
News Design Publication
Photography

**Baylor University, Writing Program**
One Bear Place, Unit 97404, Waco, TX 76798-7404
*Tel:* 254-710-1768 *Fax:* 254-710-3894
*Web Site:* www.baylor.edu
*Key Personnel*
Chmn: Dianna Vitanza
Comprehensive writing program.
Courses include Advanced Argumentative & Persuasive Writing
Advanced Creative Writing: Poetry
Advanced Creative Writing: Prose
Advanced Expository Writing
Advanced Writing for the Popular Market
Creative Writing: Poetry
Creative Writing: Prose
Internship in Professional Writing
Professional & Technical Writing
Screenplay & Scriptwriting
Special Topics in Writing
Thinking & Writing, Freshman Course
Thinking, Writing & Research, Freshman Course
Writing for the Popular Market
Writing for the Workplace

**Binghamton University Creative Writing Program**
Division of State University of New York at Binghamton
c/o Dept of English, PO Box 6000, Binghamton, NY 13902-6000
*Tel:* 607-777-2168 *Fax:* 607-777-2408
*E-mail:* cwpro@binghamton.edu
*Web Site:* english.binghamton.edu/cwpro
*Key Personnel*
Dir, Prog: Maria Gillan
Assoc Dir, Creative Writing: Christine Gelineau
Distinguished Professor: John Vernon
Professor: Jaimee Wriston Colbert; Thomas Glave; Leslie Heywood; Liz Rosenberg
Asst Professor: Alexi Zentner
Lecturer: Joe Weil
Asst to Chmn, Eng: Colleen Burke
Undergraduate & graduate courses.
Courses include Advanced Workshops in Creative Writing
Fiction Workshop
Fundamentals of Creative Writing
Independent Study in Creative Writing
Intermediate Creative Writing
Poetry Workshop
Studies for Writers

**Boston University**
236 Bay State Rd, Boston, MA 02215
*Tel:* 617-353-2510 *Fax:* 617-353-3653
*E-mail:* crwr@bu.edu
*Web Site:* www.bu.edu/writing
*Key Personnel*
Prog Dir: Leslie Epstein *E-mail:* leslieep@bu.edu
Admin Coord: Caroline Woods
Contact: Prof Ha Jin *E-mail:* xjin@bu.edu; Prof Robert Pinsky *E-mail:* rpinsky@bu.edu; Prof Richard Schotter; Prof Kate Snodgrass; Prof Rosanna Warren *E-mail:* rosanna@bu.edu
Workshops. Offer a one-year Master's degree MSA in creative writing.
Courses include Fiction
Poetry

**Bowling Green State University, Creative Writing Program**
Dept of English, 211 East Hall, Bowling Green, OH 43403
*Tel:* 419-372-2576 *Fax:* 419-372-0333
*Web Site:* www.bgsu.edu/departments/creative-writing
*Key Personnel*
Dir & Advisor: Sharona Muir *E-mail:* smuir@bgsu.edu
Providers of comprehensive & rigorous education in professional writing, editing & marketing of poetry & fiction, since 1967.
Courses include Advanced Fiction Writing Workshop
Advanced Poetry Writing Workshop
Assistant Editing, Mid-American Review
Graduate Writers' Workshop in Poetry, Fiction
Studies in Contemporary Poetry, Fiction
Techniques of Fiction
Techniques of Poetry

**The Center for Book Arts**
28 W 27 St, 3rd fl, New York, NY 10001
*Tel:* 212-481-0295 *Toll Free Fax:* 866-708-8994
*E-mail:* info@centerforbookarts.org
*Web Site:* www.centerforbookarts.org
*Key Personnel*
Exec Dir: Alexander Campos *E-mail:* acampos@centerforbookarts.org
Offers classes & workshops during three semesters each year.
Courses include Hand Bookbinding
Hand Papermaking
Letterpress Printing

**Chicago Book Clinic Webinars**, see Midwest Publishing Association Webinars

**College of Liberal & Professional Studies, University of Pennsylvania**
3440 Market St, Suite 100, Philadelphia, PA 19104-3335
*Tel:* 215-898-7326 *Fax:* 215-573-2053
*E-mail:* lps@sas.upenn.edu
*Web Site:* www.sas.upenn.edu; www.sas.upenn.edu/lps
*Key Personnel*
Vice Dean & Assoc Dir: Nora Lewis *E-mail:* nlewis@sas.upenn.edu
Dir, Progs: Kristine Rabberman, PhD
Writing courses, beginning through advanced, taught by published authors; non-residential; fees vary; program catalog available for writing courses Sept-July.

**Columbia Publishing Course at Columbia University**
2950 Broadway, MC 3801, New York, NY 10027
*Tel:* 212-854-1898 *Fax:* 212-854-7618
*E-mail:* publishing@jrn.columbia.edu
*Web Site:* www.journalism.columbia.edu/publishing
*Key Personnel*
Dir: Lindy Hess *E-mail:* lah129@columbia.edu
Asst Dir: Susan Caplan *Tel:* 212-854-9775 *E-mail:* sc2719@columbia.edu
Provides an intensive introduction to book, magazine & digital publishing. Students learn the entire publishing process from established publishing professionals & gain hands-on experience from evaluations of original mss to the sales & marketing of finished products.
Courses include Book, Magazine & Digital Publishing

**Columbia University School of the Arts, Creative Writing Program**
Division of Columbia University
617 Kent Hall, New York, NY 10027
*Tel:* 212-854-3774 *Fax:* 212-854-7704
*E-mail:* writingprogram@columbia.edu
*Web Site:* www.columbia.edu/cu/writing
*Key Personnel*
Chair, Creative Writing: Binnie Kirshenbaum
Dir, Undergraduate Creative Writing: Stacey D'Erasmo
Prog Asst, Creative Writing: Dorla McIntosh
Courses include Fiction
Nonfiction
Poetry

**EEI Communications**
7240 Parkway Dr, Suite 250, Hanover, MD 21076-1364

*Tel:* 410-309-8200 *Toll Free Tel:* 888-253-2762 *Fax:* 410-630-3980
*E-mail:* info@eeicom.com
*Web Site:* www.eeicom.com
*Key Personnel*
Pres: James de Graffenreid *E-mail:* jdegraf@eeicom.com
VP, Busn Communs & Staffing Servs: John O'Brien *E-mail:* jobrien@eeicom.com
Dir, Training: Joe Robinson *E-mail:* jrobinson@eeicom.com
Publishing courses, basic through advanced level. Classes held in Alexandria, VA, Silver Spring, MD & Washington, DC & at client facilities. Visit our web site for schedule & fees.
*Branch Office(s)*
338 Clubhouse Rd, Hunt Valley, MD 21031
962 Wayne Ave, Suite 310, Silver Spring, MD 20910
Courses include Design
Desktop Publishing
Editing
Grammar
Graphics
Mac & PC Training
New Media
Photo Manipulation
Production
Proofreading
Publications Management & Newsletters
Web Site Development
Word Processing
Writing

**The Lisa Ekus Group LLC**
57 North St, Hatfield, MA 01038
*Tel:* 413-247-9325 *Fax:* 413-247-9873
*Web Site:* lisaekus.com
*Key Personnel*
Principal & Pres: Lisa Ekus *E-mail:* lisaekus@lisaekus.com
Assoc Dir, Media Training: Carl Raymond
Literary Assoc: Sally Ekus *E-mail:* sally@lisaekus.com
Comprehensive 1 or 2 day media training programs designed for cookbook authors, chefs, product spokespeople, show hosts & food professionals. Participants will spend their day(s) under the lights & in front of the camera, taping & critiquing actual television demonstrations of varying lengths. Courses are typically held in the professional kitchen of our Hatfield, MA, offices but off-site training is available. Visit culinarymediatraining.com to learn more.
Courses include Cookbook Publishing 101
Honing Your Edge: Media Training for Culinary Professionals
One-On-One Media Training

**Emerson College Dept of Writing, Literature & Publishing**
180 Tremont St, 10th fl, Boston, MA 02116
Mailing Address: 120 Boylston St, Boston, MA 02116-4624
*Tel:* 617-824-8750 *Fax:* 617-824-7856
*Web Site:* www.emerson.edu
*Key Personnel*
Chair: Jerald Walker
Graduate Prog Dir, MA in Publg: Lisa Diercks *E-mail:* lisa_diercks@emerson.edu
Offers BA, MA, BFA & MFA degrees in publishing & writing.
Courses include Applications for Publishing
Book Design & Production
Book Editing
Book Marketing & Sales
Book Publicity
Book Publishing Overview
Column Writing
Copyediting
Creating Electronic Publications
Digital Publishing for Tablets & Handheld Devices
Editor-Writer Relationship
Electronic Publishing Overview
Magazine Design & Production
Magazine Editing
Magazine Publishing Overview
Magazine Writing
Principles of Management for Publishing
Web Development for Electronic Publishing

**Fordham University, Graduate School of Business Administration**
Gabelli School of Business, 441 E Fordham Rd, Hughes Hall, Rm 516, Bronx, NY 10458
*Tel:* 718-817-1894
*Web Site:* www.bnet.fordham.edu
*Key Personnel*
Chair/Mktg: Dawn Lerman
Professor: Albert N Greco *E-mail:* agreco@fordham.edu
Offers MBA degree with a major in Communications & Media Management. MBA Graduate courses & additional MBA course work.
Courses include Accounting
Marketing with Public Relations
The Book Publishing Industry
Broadcast & Cable Marketing & Advertising Sales Business & Legal Aspects of Cable TV
Broadcast Management
Business & the Mass Media
Consumer Behavior
Coping with Global Corporate Crisis
Corporate Power & the Public
Direct Marketing
Economics
Executive Communications
Finance
Information & Communications Systems
International Marketing
Legal & Ethical Studies
Magazine Management
Managing Newspapers & Their Electronic Ventures
Marketing Management, Advertising & Media Planning
Mass Media in America
New Media & Mass Communications
Persuasion in Public Relations
Public Relations & Broadcasting
Public Relations as a Management Tool
Sales Management
Special Topics in Communications & Media Management: Book Publishing
The Press, the Law & the Corporation

**Gaylord College of Journalism & Mass Communication, Professional Writing Program**
Division of University of Oklahoma
c/o University of Oklahoma, 395 W Lindsey St, Rm 3534, Norman, OK 73019-0270
*Tel:* 405-325-2721 *Fax:* 405-325-7565
*Web Site:* www.ou.edu/gaylord
*Key Personnel*
Professor, Prof Writing: J Madison Davis *Tel:* 405-325-4171 *E-mail:* jmadisondavis@ou.edu
Coursework on writing for commercial publication.
Courses include Analyzing Category Fiction
Film Script Writing
Magazine Article Writing
Short Story Writing
Writing The Novel

**Graphic Artists Guild Inc**
32 Broadway, Suite 1114, New York, NY 10004-1612
*Tel:* 212-791-3400 *Fax:* 212-791-0333
*Web Site:* www.graphicartistsguild.org
*Key Personnel*
Pres: Haydn Adams *E-mail:* president@gag.org
Exec Dir: Patricia McKiernan *Tel:* 212-791-3400 ext 15 *E-mail:* admin@gag.org
Business workshops & seminars for professional graphic artists. Publish Graphic Artists Guild Handbook: Pricing & Ethical Guidelines. Chapters are located in Northern CA; Los Angeles, CA; Chicago, IL; Boston, MA; New York, NY, Seattle, WA & At Large Chapter.

**Graphic Arts Association**
1210 Northbrook Dr, Suite 250, Trevose, PA 19053
*Tel:* 215-396-2300 *Fax:* 215-396-9890
*E-mail:* gaa@gaa1900.com
*Web Site:* www.gaa1900.com
*Key Personnel*
Pres: Marge Baumhauer *E-mail:* margeb@gaa1900.com
Dir, Membership: Chris Gallagher
Regional trade association for the printing industry serving Pennsylvania, southern New Jersey & Delaware.
Courses include Computer Laptop Training
Estimating
Graphic Arts Fundamentals
Industrial Relations Training
Production
Sales & Management

**Hamilton College, English/Creative Writing**
English/Creative Writing Dept, 198 College Hill Rd, Clinton, NY 13323
*Tel:* 315-859-4370 *Fax:* 315-859-4390
*E-mail:* english@hamilton.edu
*Web Site:* www.hamilton.edu
*Key Personnel*
Chair, Dept of Eng: Onno Oerlemans *E-mail:* nstout@hamilton.edu
Professor of Eng: Catherine Kodat *E-mail:* ckodat@hamilton.edu
Assoc Professor of Eng: Doran Larson *E-mail:* dlarson@hamilton.edu
Asst Professor of Eng: Tina Hall *E-mail:* thall@hamilton.edu
Academic program; students may concentrate on creative writing. Three faculty members who specialize in creative writing courses.

**Hofstra University, English Dept**
204 Mason Hall, Hempstead, NY 11549
*Tel:* 516-463-5454 *Fax:* 516-463-6395
*Web Site:* www.hofstra.edu
*Key Personnel*
Chmn, English Dept: Joseph Fichtelberg, PhD *E-mail:* engjaf@hofstra.edu
Dir, Creative Writing Progs: Erik A Brogger *E-mail:* erik.a.brogger@hofstra.edu
Dir, Publg & Lit: Alexander Burke *E-mail:* alexander.j.burke@hofstra.edu
Undergraduate courses in all phases of publishing & creative writing, leading to a BA in English. MA in English Literature with concentration in creative writing.

**Hollins University-Jackson Center for Creative Writing**
PO Box 9677, Roanoke, VA 24020
*Tel:* 540-362-6317 *Fax:* 540-362-6097
*E-mail:* creative.writing@hollins.edu
*Web Site:* www.hollins.edu
*Key Personnel*
Dir: Prof Jeanne Larsen
BA degree in English with concentration in creative writing - 4 academic years; MFA in creative writing - 2-year program in residency.

**Louisiana State University Creative Writing Program MFA**
English Dept, 260 Allen Hall, Baton Rouge, LA 70803
*Tel:* 225-578-5922 *Fax:* 225-578-4129
*Web Site:* www.lsu.edu; www.english.lsu.edu/dept/programs/grad/creative_writing

*Key Personnel*
Dir, Creative Writing: James Wilcox *Tel:* 225-578-3049 *E-mail:* jwilcox1@lsu.edu
Asst Dir: Randolph Thomas *Tel:* 225-578-2830 *E-mail:* rndlpht@aol.com
A graduate program leading to the degree of Master of Fine Arts in creative writing.
Courses include Drama Workship, ENGL 7008
Fiction Workshop, ENGL 7006
Poetry Workshop, ENGL 7007
Screenwriting Workshop, ENGL 7009

**Manhattanville College Master of Arts in Writing Program**
2900 Purchase St, Purchase, NY 10577
*Tel:* 914-323-5239 *Fax:* 914-323-3122
*Web Site:* www.mville.edu/writing
*Key Personnel*
Dir, MAW Prog: Karen Sirabian *E-mail:* sirabiank@mville.edu
Offers courses with faculty who are well-known published writers & poets, all of whom are dedicated to helping writers explore their craft, sharpen their skills & take their writing to the next level - all within a thriving literary community. In addition, students can build on the skills gained in the editing & production course through work on our award-winning journal "Inkwell", which gives them the editorial & production experience to succeed in publishing.
Courses include Editing & Production Workshop
Fiction Workshop
Nonfiction Workshop
Poetry Workshop
Writing for Children & Young Adults
Writing the Contemporary Novel

**Massachusetts College of Art & Design Writing Children's Literature**
Affiliate of Massachusetts College of Art and Design Continuing Education Dept
621 Huntington Ave, Boston, MA 02115
*Tel:* 617-879-7200 *Fax:* 617-879-7171
*E-mail:* ce@massart.edu
*Web Site:* www.massart.edu/ce
*Key Personnel*
Dean, Prof & Continuing Educ: Anne Marie Stein College
Courses include Book Design
Computer Graphics
Design
Fine Arts
Illustrating Children's Books
Typography

**McNeese State University, Writing Program**
PO Box 92655, Lake Charles, LA 70609-0001
*Tel:* 337-475-5325; 337-475-5327
*Web Site:* www.mcneese.edu.com; www.mfa.mcneese.edu
*Key Personnel*
Dir, MFA Prog & Coord, Poetry Series: Amy Fleury *E-mail:* afleury@mcneese.edu
Asst Professor, Eng & Fiction: Alex Taylor *E-mail:* alextaylor1@mcneese.edu
MFA program in creative writing - 60 hour program.
Courses include Contemporary Novel
Contemporary Poetry
Creative Writing Workshop-Fiction
Creative Writing Workshop-Poetry
Form & Theory of Fiction I
Form & Theory of Fiction II
Form & Theory of Poetry I
Form & Theory of Poetry II

**Midwest Publishing Association Webinars**
Formerly Chicago Book Clinic Webinars
310 W Lake St, Suite 111, Elmhurst, IL 60126
*Tel:* 630-833-4220 *Fax:* 630-563-9181
*E-mail:* info@midwestpublish.org
*Web Site:* www.midwestpublish.org
*Key Personnel*
Exec Dir: Kimberly LaBounty
Various webinars for publishers, manufacturers, freelancers & printers involved in all publishing markets.

**Mississippi Review/University of Southern Mississippi, Center for Writers**
Affiliate of University of Southern Mississippi, Dept of English
118 College Dr 5144, Hattiesburg, MS 39406-0001
*Tel:* 601-266-5600 *Fax:* 601-266-5757
*Web Site:* www.usm.edu/english/c4w.html; www.usm.edu/english/mississippireview.html
*Key Personnel*
Ed-in-Chief: Andrew Milward
Graduate & undergraduate courses in fiction & poetry writing.
Mississippi Review.

**New York City College of Technology**
Division of City University of New York
300 Jay St, Brooklyn, NY 11201
*Tel:* 718-260-5500 *Fax:* 718-260-5198
*E-mail:* connect@citytech.cuny.edu
*Web Site:* www.citytech.cuny.edu
*Key Personnel*
Pres: Russell K Hotzler, PhD *Tel:* 718-260-5400 *E-mail:* rhotzler@citytech.cuny.edu
Dir, Graphic Arts Dept: Lloyd Carr *Tel:* 718-260-5822 *E-mail:* lcarr@citytech.cuny.edu
Two year or four year degree in graphic arts, certificates, associates or baccalaureate.
Courses include Advertising
Printing & Publishing

**New York University, Center for Publishing**
Affiliate of School of Continuing Education
Midtown Ctr, Rm 429, 11 W 42 St, New York, NY 10036
*Tel:* 212-992-3232 *Fax:* 212-992-3233
*E-mail:* pub.center@nyu.edu
*Web Site:* www.scps.nyu.edu/publishing
*Key Personnel*
Academic Prog Dir & Clinical Asst Professor: Andrea L Chambers
Asst Dir: Sarah McCarthy *E-mail:* sarah.mccarthy@nyu.edu
Offers a certificate in publishing, consisting of five courses. Individual courses may be taken. A total of 13 book, 14 magazine & 7 online publishing. Also offers a certificate in editing with 10 courses each year. The Summer Publishing Institute is an intensive residential program for recent college graduates, planning to enter the publishing industry. Consists of three week module in book publishing & three week module in magazine publishing, each including an overview of the industry, lectures, workshops, field trips & professional simulations, job fair & placement assistance. Application deadline; April 1 MS in publishing; contact Assoc Dir Alyssa Leal. Program consists of 42 graduate credits chosen from a required core of courses in the functional areas of publishing & a concentration in either book or magazine publishing. Courses are all offered in the evening.
Courses include Advanced Copyediting
Advanced Magazine Editing
Advanced Special Project in Publishing
Advertising in Magazines
Advertising Sales & Integrated Marketing for Business-to-Business Publishers
The Basics of the Book Publishing Industry: Today & Tomorrow
Book Design Strategies
Book Editing
Book Marketing
Book Packaging
Book Production & Manufacturing
Book Publicity, Promotion
Books from Writer to Reader: An Overview of the Publishing Process
Bookselling: From Publisher to Reader
The Business of Book Publishing: Financial Management in a Creative Environment
The Business of Business-to-Business Publishing
The Business of Online Publishing
The Business of Publishing for US Hispanic Markets
Children's Book Publishing
The Circulation Challenge: Newsstand, Retail & Speciality Outlets
Controlled Circulation
Cookbook Copyediting
Copyediting & Proofreading Fundamentals
Cross-Media Programs: The Future of Magazine Advertising Sales
Developmental Editing
Disk & Online Editing
The Economics of Magazine Publishing
Economics of Publishing
Editing Periodicals
Effective Marketing in Publishing Via the Digital Channels
Electronic Content Development
Electronic Publishing for Print & Online Part 1: Survey
Electronic Publishing for Print & Online Part II: Portfolio
E-mail Newsletters
The Evolving Business of Custom Publishing
Fact Checking
Financial Analysis I: Introduction to Financial Statement Analysis in Publishing
Financial Copyediting
Freelance Book Indexing
Fundamentals of Copyediting
Fundamentals of Proofreading
Globalization & the Web
Grammar for Publishing Professionals
How to Develop Your Career in Publishing
How to Market Your Freelance Editorial Services
How to Self-Publish Successfully & Profitably in Today's Market–An Intensive Two-Day Seminar
The Independent Publisher: How to Start, Sustain & Build a Small Press
Information Technology Management in Publishing
International Magazine Publishing
International Publishing
Internship
Journal Copyediting & Production
The Laws of Book Publishing: A Practical Guide to Contracts, Copyright & More
Legal Proofreading
Magazine Advertising Sales & Marketing
Magazine Branding & Franchise Development
Magazine Circulation
Magazine Copyediting
Magazine Editorial Planning & Management
Magazine Financial Management
Magazine Production & Manufacturing
Magazine Promotion, Events & Public Relations
Magazine Research: New Techniques to Accelerate Recovery Growth
Magazines from Mission to Magic & More: An Overview
Managing the Publishing Enterprise
Manuscript Editing
Marketing for Publishing
Media Ethics for Publishing Professionals
Mentored Academic Study
Multi-Channel Sales Promotion for Books
Multimedia Marketing & Product Development
ONIX: How Good Product Information Improves Sales
Online Publishing: Business, Technology & Strategy
Principles & Applications of Publishing on the Internet
Principles of Profitability in Book Publishing
Print Technology for Publishing

Production Editing
Professional Book & Information Publishing
Publishing: Books, Magazines & Multimedia
Publishing in Cyberspace: Legal & Practical Problems of Internet & Electronic Publishing
Publishing Law: Issues in Intellectual Property
Publishing On-Line
The Role of the Literary Agent in Book Publishing
Scientific, Technical & Medical Journal Copyediting
Scientific, Technical & Medical Journal Copyediting & Production
Scientific, Technical, Professional Publishing on the Internet
Secrets to Success in Magazine Freelance Writing & Editing
Special Sales, Licensing & Merchandising for Books
Starting a Small Book Publishing Co
Summer Institute in Book & Magazine Publishing
Trade & General Book Publishing
Usability: Information Architecture & the User Experience in Publishing
Web Marketing & E-Commerce
Web Page Development With HTML

**Ohio University, English Dept, Creative Writing Program**
Ohio University, English Dept, Ellis Hall, Athens, OH 45701
*Tel:* 740-593-2838 (English Dept) *Fax:* 740-593-2832
*E-mail:* english.department@ohio.edu
*Web Site:* english.ohiou.edu
*Key Personnel*
Dir: Dinty W Moore *E-mail:* moored4@ohio.edu
Offer PhD degree with creative writing emphasis.
Courses include Fiction
Form & Theory
Nonfiction
Novels
Poetry
Short Stories

**Pace University, Master of Science in Publishing**
Dept of Publishing, Rm 805-E, 551 Fifth Ave, New York, NY 10176
*Tel:* 212-346-1431 *Toll Free Tel:* 877-284-7670 *Fax:* 212-346-1165
*Web Site:* www.pace.edu/dyson/mspub
*Key Personnel*
Chmn & Dir, Publg Progs: Sherman Raskin *E-mail:* sraskin@pace.edu
Program educates its students in all pertinent aspects of the publishing business: books, magazines & digital publishing. Our graduates are equipped for the challenges facing the industry today.
Courses include Book Production & Design, PUB 606
Children's Book Publishing, PUB 634
Digital Issues in Publishing
Ebooks: Technology, Workflow & Business Model, PUB 621
Editorial Principles & Practices, PUB 634
Electronic Publishing for Publishers, PUB 636
Financial Aspects of Publishing, PUB 608
General Interest Books, PUB 610
Information Systems in Publishing, PUB 612
Legal Aspects of Publishing, PUB 618
Magazine Production & Design, PUB 607
Marketing Principles & Practices in Publishing, PUB 628
Modern Technology in Publishing, PUB 620
Publishing Comics & Graphic Novels, PUB 615
Subsidiary Rights, Acquisitions & the Function of the Literary Agent, PUB 610
The Future of Publishing: Transmedia, PUB 613

**Parsons School of Design, Continuing Education**
Division of New School University
66 Fifth Ave, New York, NY 10011
*Tel:* 212-229-8933 *Fax:* 212-229-5970
*E-mail:* ceinformation@newschool.edu; academy@newschool.edu
*Web Site:* www.parsons.edu/ce
Comprehensive courses & advanced courses appropriate for book, magazine & advertising design.
Courses include Graphic & Advertising Design

**Publishing Certificate Program at City College**
Division of Humanities NAC 5225, City College of New York, New York, NY 10031
*Tel:* 212-650-7925 *Fax:* 212-650-7912
*E-mail:* ccnypub@aol.com
*Web Site:* www.ccny.cuny.edu/publishing_certificate/index.html
*Key Personnel*
Dir: David Unger
Asst Dir: Retha Powers
Program for undergraduates. Take four of 20 courses offered & then qualify for a paid internship in a publishing house of your interest.
Courses include Books for Young Readers
Copyediting & Proofreading, etc
Ebooks & Digital Publishing
The Editorial Process
Introduction to Publishing I & II
Legal Issues in Publishing

**Rochester Institute of Technology, School of Print Media**
69 Lomb Memorial Dr, Rochester, NY 14623-5603
*Tel:* 585-475-2728; 585-475-5336 *Fax:* 585-475-5336
*E-mail:* spmofc@rit.edu
*Web Site:* cias.rit.edu/printmedia
*Key Personnel*
Chmn, School of Printing: Pat Sorce, PhD *Tel:* 585-475-2313 *E-mail:* psorce@mail.rit.edu
Classes in books & magazine production, typography, printing design, computer use, desktop prepress production, management, sales, finishing & bindery, quality control, marketing, finance & legal problems of publishing.
Courses include Computer Use
Desktop Prepress Production
Finance & Legal Problems of Publishing
Finishing & Bindery
Management
Marketing
Printing Design
Quality Control
Sales
Typography

**Rosemont College**
Graduate Publg Prog, 1400 Montgomery Ave, Rosemont, PA 19010
*Tel:* 610-527-0200 (ext 2336) *Fax:* 610-526-2964
*Web Site:* www.rosemont.edu
*Key Personnel*
Dir, Graduate Publg Progs: Anne Willkomm
Offers MA degree in publishing.
Courses include Design
Editing & Writing
Electronic Publishing
Legal Issues in Publishing
Literature
Marketing & Sales
Production & Design

**School of Visual Arts**
209 E 23 St, New York, NY 10010-3994
*Tel:* 212-592-2100 *Fax:* 212-592-2116
*Web Site:* www.sva.edu
*Key Personnel*
Exec Dir, Admissions & Student Aff: Javier Vega
Non-degree programs beginning in Sept, Jan & June, including intensive two-week workshops.
Courses include Advertising & Graphic Design
Artists' Books'
BFA Programs in Advertising & Graphic Design
Book Cover Design & Illustration Book Design
Book Illustration & Children's Book Writing & Illustration
Cartooning
Computer Art & Photography
Computer Graphics
Copywriting
Editorial Design
Fine Arts
Illustration & Cartooning
Interior Design & Photography
MAT in Art Education
MFA Programs in Fine Arts Illustration
Photographic Printing Processes
Type & Design Agency Skills
Video Recording & Editing

**Susquehanna University, Dept of English**
514 University Ave, Selinsgrove, PA 17870
*Tel:* 570-372-0101
*Key Personnel*
Professor, Eng: Laurence Roth
Assoc Professor, Communs: Katherine Hastings
Assoc Professor, Creative Writing: Karla Kelsey
Assoc Professor, Eng: Randy Robertson
Asst Professor, Creating Writing: Catherine Dent-Zobal
Courses include Editing, COMM:331 Intermediate focused subject course that focuses on the challenges & issues confronted in editing for journalism & teaches the process of editing a newspaper
Internship, ENGL:540 Working with internships available in publishing or editing either on- or off-campus
Introduction to Modern Publishing, ENGL:190 Introduces students to the history of modern publishing, to the process, art & business of producing books
Publishing: Entertainment, Art, Politics, Ethics, ENGL:388 Analyzes changes & continuities in the cultural role of publishing from the beginning of mass printing to the current day
Small Press Editing & Publishing, WRIT:270 Intermediate focused subject course that focuses on the challenges & issues faced by small literary presses. Students learn to edit fiction, poetry, nonfiction & memoirs

**Syracuse University Creative Writing Program**
401 Hall of Languages, Syracuse, NY 13244-1170
*Tel:* 315-443-2173 *Fax:* 315-443-3660
*Web Site:* english.syr.edu/creative_writing; www.syr.edu
*Key Personnel*
Dir: Christopher Kennedy *E-mail:* ckennedy@syr.edu
Assoc Dir: Sarah C Harwell *E-mail:* scharwel@syr.edu
Courses include Eastern European Poetry/Translation
The Essay
Fiction Workshop
The Forms of Fiction
The Forms of Poetry
Open Workshop - Fiction
Open Workshop - Poetry
Poetry Workshop
Prose Writing
Writing of Fiction
Writing of Poetry
Writing the Novella

**Syracuse University, SI Newhouse School of Public Communications**
215 University Place, Syracuse, NY 13244-2100

*Tel:* 315-443-3627 *Fax:* 315-443-3946
*E-mail:* newhouse@syr.edu
*Web Site:* newhouse.syr.edu
*Key Personnel*
Dean: Lorraine Branham
Undergraduate degrees in advertising; broadcast & arts journalism, magazine, newspaper & online journalism; public relations; television, radio, film; visual & interactive communications, photography & graphics; Master's degrees in advertising; magazine; newspaper; media administration; visual & interactive communications; public relations; television-radio & film. PhD degrees in mass communications.
Courses include Advertising
Broadcast, Magazine & Newspaper Journalism
Film
Media Administration
Photography
Public Relations
Radio
Television

**University of Alabama Program in Creative Writing**
Affiliate of University of Alabama, Dept of English
PO Box 870244, Tuscaloosa, AL 35487-0244
*Tel:* 205-348-5065 *Fax:* 205-348-1388
*E-mail:* english@ua.edu
*Web Site:* www.as.ua.edu/english
*Key Personnel*
Poet & Professor: Robin Behn *Tel:* 205-348-8488 *E-mail:* rbehn@english.as.ua.edu
Poet & Assoc Professor: Joel Brouwer *Tel:* 205-348-9524 *E-mail:* joel.brouwer@ua.edu
Poet & Asst Professor: Peter Streckfus *Tel:* 205-348-6265 *E-mail:* plstreckfus@bama.ua.edu
Fiction Writer & Professor: Michael Martone *Tel:* 205-348-5526 *E-mail:* mmartone@english.as.ua.edu
Fiction Writer & Assoc Professor: Wendy Rawlings *Tel:* 205-348-4507 *E-mail:* wendy.rawlings@ua.edu
Graduate Coord: Carol Appling *Tel:* 205-348-9493 *E-mail:* cappling@ua.edu
Three-year MFA degree program & creative writing course for undergraduates, minor in creative writing. See web site for details.

**University of Baltimore - College of Arts & Sciences, Ampersand Institute for Words & Images**
Division of School of Communications Design
1420 N Charles St, Baltimore, MD 21201-5779
*Tel:* 410-837-6022 *Fax:* 410-837-6029
*E-mail:* scd@ubalt.edu
*Web Site:* www.ubalt.edu
*Key Personnel*
Dir: Edwin Gold *E-mail:* egold@ubalt.edu
Academic Prog Specialist: Jaye Crooks
Sponsors Fall & Spring lecture series, conducts advanced seminars, workshops, mini-courses & conferences on publishing topics including writing, design; also supports through the School of Communications Design, a Masters of Arts program in Publications Design, an MFA in Integrated Design & an MFA in Creative Writing & Publishing Arts.

**University of California Extension Professional Sequence in Copyediting & Courses in Publishing**
1995 University Ave, Suite 110, Berkeley, CA 94720-7000
*Tel:* 510-642-6362 *Fax:* 510-643-0216
*E-mail:* letters@unex.berkeley.edu
*Web Site:* www.unex.berkeley.edu
*Key Personnel*
Prog Dir: Liz McDonough *Tel:* 510-643-1637
Certificate program in editing; evening/weekend courses & one-day seminars.
Courses include Editing
Management
Screenwriting
Writing (fiction, poetry, nonfiction)

**University of Chicago, Graham School of General Studies**
Division of Professional Programs
1427 E 60 St, Chicago, IL 60637
*Tel:* 773-702-1722 *Fax:* 773-702-6814
*Web Site:* www.grahamschool.uchicago.edu
*Key Personnel*
Prog Dir: Amber Neff *Tel:* 773-702-1682 *E-mail:* aneff@uchicago.edu
Noncredit courses.
Courses include Basic Creative Writing
Elements of Novel Writing
Getting the Story: Freelance Journalism Workshop
Intensive Short Story Workshop
Introduction to Freelance Journalism
Memoir Writing
Poetry Workshop: Outside the Self
Screenwriting Workshop
Writing Novels for Children & Young Adults
Writing the Novel 1
Writing the Novel 2
Writing the Personal Essay

**The University of Connecticut, The Realities of Publishing**
CLAS, 215 Glenbrook Rd, Unit 4025, Storrs, CT 06269-4025
*Tel:* 860-486-2141
*Web Site:* web.uconn.edu/english291
*Key Personnel*
Dept Head: Wayne Franklin *E-mail:* wayne.franklin@uconn.edu
This course provides a background for undergraduate students interested in professional careers in writing & publishing. Lectures by practitioners describe varied careers. Topics include: Professional Writing Format, Desktop Publishing, Journalism & Freelance Writing, Magazine & Book Publishing. Also offer Introduction to HTML, Ndesign & Dreamweaver.

**University of Denver Publishing Institute**
2000 E Asbury Ave, Denver, CO 80208
*Tel:* 303-871-2570 *Fax:* 303-871-2501
*Web Site:* www.du.edu/pi
*Key Personnel*
Dir: Joyce Meskis *E-mail:* joyce.meskis@du.edu; Jill N Smith *E-mail:* jill.smith@du.edu
Four-week graduate program in book publishing held July-Aug each year. Provides hands on workshops, lecture-teaching sessions on every phase of book publishing. Faculty consists of leading executives from publishing houses across the country. Emphasis on career counseling & job placement. Offers six quarter hours of graduate credit.
Courses include Children's Books
College Textbooks
E-Books
Economics of Publishing
Editing Workshop
Foreign Rights
Independent Presses
International Publishing
Marketing on the Internet
Marketing Workshop
Production & Design
Publicity & Promotion
Publishing & the Law
Reference Publishing in an Electronic World
Scholarly Books
Special Session on Magazine Publishing
Trade & Scholarly Books
University Presses

**University of Houston Creative Writing Program**
Affiliate of Hollins University Dept of English
229 Roy Cullen Bldg, Houston, TX 77204-5008
*Tel:* 713-743-2255 *Fax:* 713-743-3697
*E-mail:* cwp@uh.edu
*Web Site:* www.uh.edu/cwp
*Key Personnel*
Dir: Jay Kastely
Prog Coord: Shatera Anderson
Offers MA, MFA & PhD in creative writing.

**University of Illinois at Chicago, Program for Writers**
Affiliate of University of Illinois, Dept of English
College of Liberal Arts & Sciences, 2027 University Hall, 601 S Morgan St, Chicago, IL 60607-7120
*Tel:* 312-413-2200 (Eng Dept) *Fax:* 312-413-1005
*Web Site:* www.uic.edu
*Key Personnel*
Dir, Prog for Writers: Cris Mazza *Tel:* 312-413-2795 *E-mail:* cmazza@uic.edu
Graduate program for writers. Students in this program take literature classes as well as writing workshops. Offers MA & PhD in writing. Undergraduates seeking a BA in English may also specialize in writing.
Courses include Nonfiction
Novel
Poetry
Short Fiction

**University of Illinois, Dept of Journalism**
Unit of College of Communications, University of Illinois
Gregory Hall, Rm 120-A, 810 S Wright St, Urbana, IL 61801
*Tel:* 217-333-0709 *Fax:* 217-333-7931
*E-mail:* journ@uiuc.edu
*Web Site:* www.comm.uiuc.edu
*Key Personnel*
Dept Head: Prof Brian Johnson *Tel:* 217-333-2103 *E-mail:* bjk@illinois.edu
Master's degree program.
Courses include Graphics
Magazine Article Writing
News Editing
Photojournalism
Reporting I & II

**University of Iowa, Writers' Workshop, Graduate Creative Writing Program**
102 Dey House, 507 N Clinton St, Iowa City, IA 52242-1000
*Tel:* 319-335-0416 *Fax:* 319-335-0420
*Web Site:* www.uiowa.edu/~iww
*Key Personnel*
Dir: Lan Samantha Chang
Graduate: fiction & poetry workshops & seminars. Undergraduate: creative, fiction & poetry writing.

**University of Missouri-Kansas City, New Letters Weekend Writers Conference**
College of Arts & Sciences, Continuing Education Div, 5300 Rockhill Rd, Kansas City, MO 64110
*Tel:* 816-235-2736 *Fax:* 816-235-5279
*Web Site:* www.umkc.edu
*Key Personnel*
Admin Assoc: Kathi Wittfeld *Tel:* 816-235-2637 *E-mail:* wittfeldk@umkc.edu
State University: a variety of credit & noncredit courses on creative writing including fiction, poetry, essays & short stories.
Courses include Essay
Fiction
Poetry
Short Story

**University of Montana, Environmental Writing Institute**
Subsidiary of Environmental Studies Program
Environmental Studies, University of Montana, Missoula, MT 59812
*Tel:* 406-243-2904 *Fax:* 406-243-6090
*Web Site:* www.umt.edu/ewi
*Key Personnel*
Prog Mgr & Dir: Phil Condon *E-mail:* phil.condon@mso.umt.edu
Writing workshop for environmental & nature subjects.

**University of Southern California, Master of Professional Writing Program**
Mark Taper Hall, THH 355, 3501 Trousedale Pkwy, Los Angeles, CA 90089-0355
*Tel:* 213-740-3252 *Fax:* 213-740-5002
*E-mail:* mpw@college.usc.edu
*Web Site:* college.usc.edu/mpw
*Key Personnel*
Dir: Brighde Mullins
Prog Specialist: Howard Ho
Student Servs Advisor: Natalie Inouye
Multi-disciplinary Creative Writing Master's program & Master's of Arts degree in Professional Writing.
Courses include Creative Nonfiction
Fiction
New Media
Poetry
Writing for Stage & Screen

**University of Texas at Austin, Creative Writing Program**
Dept of English, PAR 108, One University Sta, Mailcode B5000, Austin, TX 78712-1164
*Tel:* 512-471-5132; 512-471-4991 *Fax:* 512-471-4909
*Web Site:* www.utexas.edu/cola/depts/english/creative-writing
*Key Personnel*
Chair, Poetry: Dean Young *E-mail:* deanyoung@mail.utexas.edu
Professor Emeritus: Zulfikar A Ghose *E-mail:* zulfj@mail.utexas.edu
Professor: Laura Furman *E-mail:* ljfurman@mail.utexas.edu; Kurt Heinzelman *E-mail:* kheinz@mail.utexas.edu; Rolando Hinojosa-Smith *E-mail:* rorro@mail.utexas.edu
Professor, Creative Writing: Peter N La Salle
Professor, Fiction: James Magnuson *E-mail:* magnuson@mail.utexas.edu
Professor: Thomas Whitbread *E-mail:* whitbread@mail.utexas.edu
Assoc Professor: Michael W Adams *E-mail:* adameve@austin.utexas.edu
Asst Professor: Oscar H Casares *E-mail:* ocasares@yahoo.com
Graduate Prog Coord I: Amy Stewart *Tel:* 512-471-5132 *E-mail:* amy.d.stewart@austin.utexas.edu
Graduate Prog Coord II: Patricia Schaub *E-mail:* gradeng@uts.cc.utexas.edu
A full range of poetry & fiction writing courses is offered, leading to the MA degree in English with concentration in creative writing.

**University of Texas at El Paso, Dept Creative Writing, MFA/Dept Creative Writing**
Liberal Arts 415 UTEP, 500 W University Ave, El Paso, TX 79968-9991
*Tel:* 915-747-5713 *Fax:* 915-747-5523
*Web Site:* www.utep.edu/cw
*Key Personnel*
Chair, Bilingual MFA: Prof Johnny Payne *Tel:* 915-747-5758 *E-mail:* jpayne@utep.edu
Dept Chair & Professor: Benjamin Alire Saenz *Tel:* 915-747-5721 *E-mail:* bsaenz@utep.edu
Professor: Luis Arturo Ramos *Tel:* 915-747-6511 *E-mail:* laramos@utep.edu
Assoc Professor: Rosa Alcala *Tel:* 915-747-7020 *E-mail:* ralcala1@utep.edu; Daniel Chacon *Tel:* 915-747-6255 *E-mail:* danchacon@utep.edu; Lex Williford *Tel:* 915-747-8806 *E-mail:* lex@utep.edu
Monolingual & bilingual workshops in fiction, poetry, playwriting, screenwriting, nonfiction & literary translation.

**UW-Madison, Division of Continuing Studies**
21 N Park St, 7th fl, Madison, WI 53715
*Tel:* 608-263-6320 *Toll Free Tel:* 877-336-7836 *Fax:* 608-262-1694
*E-mail:* liberalarts@dsc.wisc.edu
*Web Site:* continuingstudies.wisc.edu
*Key Personnel*
Faculty Assoc: Christine De Smet *Tel:* 608-262-3447 *E-mail:* cdesmet@dcs.wisc.edu
Professor Emeritus: Marshall Cook
Writing book trade & online writing courses offered, in-person retreats & conferences.
Courses include Writers Institute Conference
Critique Services
How to Write Feature Articles Online Course
Newsletter Workshop
Script Writing Workshop
Writing Retreats

**Vermont College of Fine Arts MFA in Writing for Children & Young Adults Program**
36 College St, Montpelier, VT 05602
*Tel:* 802-828-8637; 802-828-8696 *Toll Free Tel:* 866-934-VCFA (934-8232) *Fax:* 802-828-8649
*Web Site:* www.vcfa.edu
*Key Personnel*
Prog Dir: Melissa Fisher *E-mail:* melissa.fisher@vcfa.edu
Asst Prog Dir: Shannon Dixon *E-mail:* shannon.dixon@vcfa.edu
Writing for children & young adults. Intensive 10-day residencies & nonresident 6-month writing projects.

**Vermont College of Fine Arts, MFA in Writing Program**
36 College St, Montpelier, VT 05602
*Tel:* 802-828-8840; 802-828-8839 *Toll Free Tel:* 866-934-VCFA (934-8232) *Fax:* 802-828-8649
*Web Site:* www.vcfa.edu
*Key Personnel*
Prog Dir: Louise Crowley *E-mail:* louise.crowley@vcfa.edu
Asst Prog Dir: Rachel Muehlmann *Tel:* 802-828-8839 *E-mail:* rachel.muehlmann@vcfa.edu
Degree work in poetry, fiction, creative nonfiction.

**Warren Wilson College, MFA Program for Writers**
701 Warren Wilson Rd, Swannanoa, NC 28778
Mailing Address: PO Box 9000, Asheville, NC 28815-9000
*Tel:* 828-771-3717 *Fax:* 828-771-7005
*E-mail:* mfa@warren-wilson.edu
*Web Site:* www.warren-wilson.edu/~mfa
*Key Personnel*
Dir, MFA Prog: Debra Allberry
Full-time 2-year program with winter & summer semesters. Ten-day residency of classes, workshops & lectures on campus. The six-month project that follows is supervised through correspondence, with detailed ms criticism by faculty who are both accomplished writers & committed teachers.
Courses include Fiction
Poetry

**Writer's Digest University**
Division of F+W Media Inc
10151 Carver Rd, Suite 200, Blue Ash, OH 45242-4760
*Tel:* 513-531-2690 *Toll Free Tel:* 800-759-0963 *Fax:* 513-531-0798
*E-mail:* contact_us@fwmedia.com
*Web Site:* www.writersonlineworkshops.com
*Key Personnel*
Online Prodn Mgr: Kevin Quinn
Course workshops are taught by active, published writers in the appropriate area, such as fiction & nonfiction. Students participate online, via the Internet. Workshops range in length from 4 to 28 weeks. Correspondence; student has up to 2 years to complete; tuition installment plans available for most courses.
Courses include 28 Days to Your First WordPress Site, Nonfiction Writing
Advanced Poetry Writing, Specialty Workshops
Blogging 101, Marking and Building a Platform
Breaking into Copywriting, Freelance/Copywriting
Business Writing, Specialty Workshops
Character Development, Fiction Writing Workshops
Conflict and Suspense, Fiction Writing Workshops
Creativity & Expression, Getting Started
Description and Setting, Fiction Writing Workshops
Dialogue, Fiction Writing Workshops
Fiction Writing 101: Fundamentals, Fiction Writing Workshops
Fiction Writing 102: Building Your Novel, Fiction Writing Workshops
Fiction Writing 103: 12 Weeks to Your First Draft, Fiction Writing Workshops
Fiction Writing 104: Advanced Novel Writing, Fiction Writing Workshops
Fitting Writing Into Your Life, Getting Started
Focus on the Short Story, Short Story/Memoir
Form and Composition, Getting Started
Freelance Writing for Stay at Home Moms, Freelance/Copywriting
Fundamentals of Poetry Writing, Specialty Workshops
Getting Started in Writing, Getting Started
Ghostwriting, Freelance/Copywriting
Grammar and Mechanics, Getting Started
Magazine Article Writing, Freelance/Copywriting
Marketing Your Magazine Articles, Nonfiction Writing
Master in Fine Arts Application Preparation Workshop, Graduate Preparation Workshops
Outlining Your Novel, Getting Started
Plot and Structure, Fiction Writing Workshops
Revision & Self Editing, Preparing for Publication
Social Media 101, Nonfiction Writing
Successful Self-Publishing, Preparing for Publication
Technical Writing, Specialty Workshops
The Art of Storytelling 101: Storymapping and Pacing, Fiction Writing Workshops
Travel Writing, Specialty Workshops
Turning Your Personal Essays into a Memoir, Short Story/Memoir
Voice and Viewpoint, Fiction Writing Workshops
Writing a Memoir 101, Short Story/Memoir
Writing a Memoir 102, Short Story/Memoir
Writing a Religious Book, Specialty Workshops
Writing Nonfiction 101: Fundamentals, Nonfiction Writing
Writing Nonfiction 102: Advanced, Nonfiction Writing
Writing Nonfiction for Children, Graduate Preparation Workshops
Writing the Middle Grade Book, Specialty Workshops
Writing the Mystery Novel, Specialty Workshops
Writing the Nonfiction Book Proposal, Preparing for Publication
Writing the Novel Proposal, Preparing for Publication

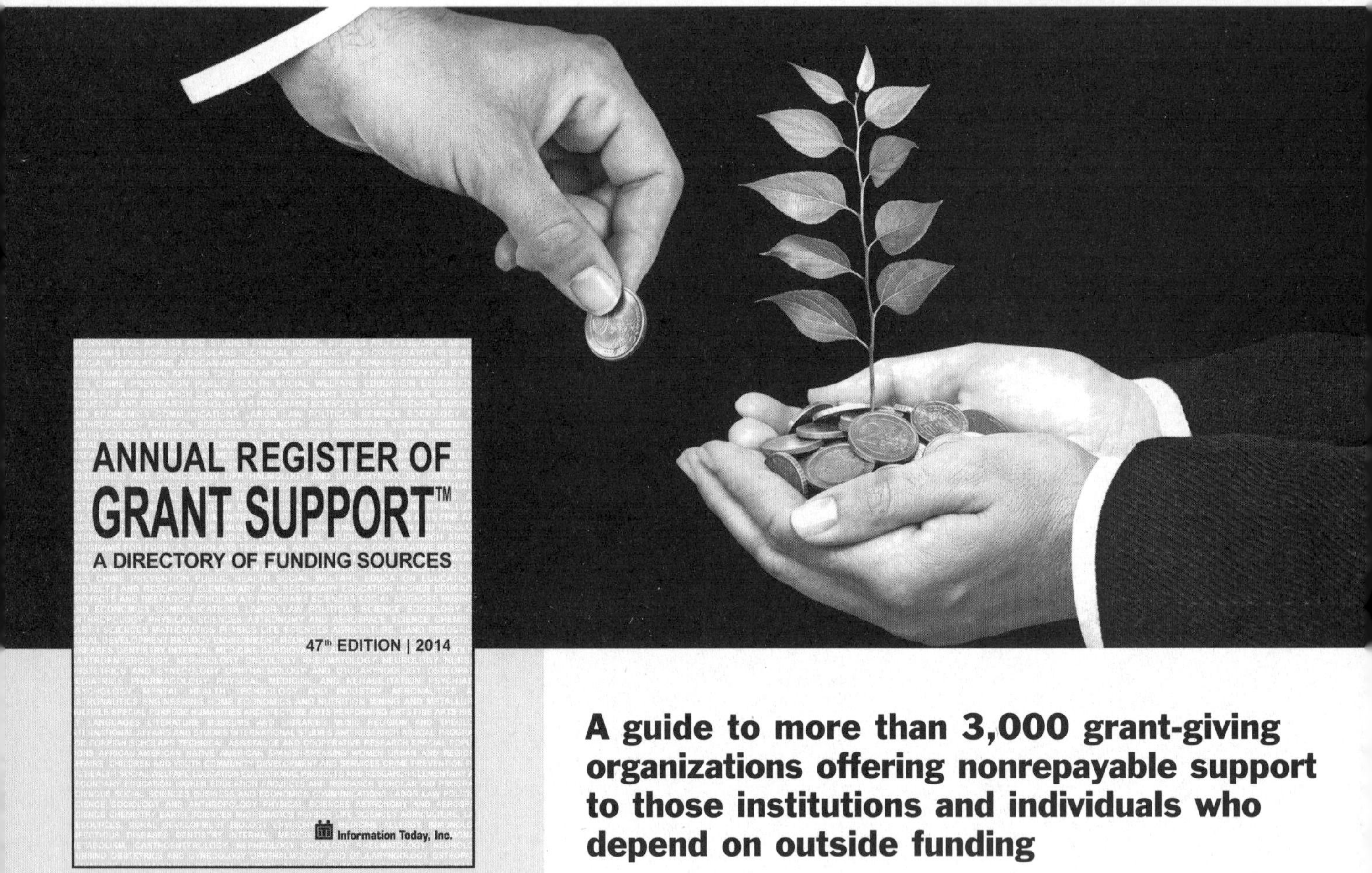

# Awards, Prize Contests, Fellowships & Grants

Major awards given to books, authors and publishers by various organizations are, for the most part, not open for application. However, many prize contests may be applied for by writing to the sponsor (for prompt response, always include a self-addressed, stamped envelope). Also included in this section is information relating to fellowships and grants that are primarily available to authors and students who are pursuing publishing related studies.

For more complete information about scholarships, fellowships and grants-in-aid, see *The Annual Register of Grant Support* (Information Today, Inc., 630 Central Avenue, New Providence, NJ 07974).

**AAUP Book, Jacket & Journal Design Show**
Association of American University Presses (AAUP)
28 W 36 St, Suite 602, New York, NY 10018
*Tel:* 212-989-1010 *Fax:* 212-989-0275
*E-mail:* info@aaupnet.org
*Web Site:* www.aaupnet.org
*Key Personnel*
Exec Dir: Peter Berkery *Tel:* 212-989-1010 ext 29 *E-mail:* pberkery@aaupnet.org
Dir of Mktg & Communs: Brenna McLaughlin *Tel:* 518-436-3586 *E-mail:* bmclaughlin@aaupnet.org
Admin Mgr: Linda McCall *Tel:* 212-989-1010 ext 30 *E-mail:* lmccall@aaupnet.org
Established: 1965
Excellence in design; competition limited to member presses in AAUP.
Award: Certificate, winning entries are displayed in a traveling exhibit
Presented: AAUP Annual Meeting, Annually in June

**ABZ First Book Poetry Prize**
ABZ Press
PO Box 2746, Huntington, WV 25727-2746
*Tel:* 304-638-5701
*Web Site:* abzpress.sharepoint.com
*Key Personnel*
Ed: John McKernan
Established: 2006
Contest for the first full-length book of poems. Reading fee is $30 which entitles the entrant to one copy of the winning book.
Closing Date: Annually, May 1-June 30

**Acclaim Film Script Competition**
Acclaim Film
300 Central Ave, Suite 501, St Petersburg, FL 33701
*Web Site:* acclaimscripts.com
*Key Personnel*
Contest Coord: Frank Drouzas
Open to all writers 18 & over.
Award: $1,000 (1st place), up-to-date books on writing & selling scripts (2nd place)
Closing Date: Ongoing

**Acclaim TV Script Competition**
Acclaim Film
300 Central Ave, Suite 501, St Petersburg, FL 33701
*Web Site:* acclaimscripts.com
*Key Personnel*
Contest Coord: Frank Drouzas
Open to all writers 18 & over. Must be original material of the author. Categories are Spec Scripts (for an existing show), Pilots & Movie of the Week.
Award: $500 for each category
Closing Date: Ongoing

**Milton Acorn Poetry Award**
Prince Edward Island Writers' Guild
115 Richmond St, Charlottetown, PE C1A 1H7, Canada
*Tel:* 902-368-4410 *Toll Free Tel:* 888-734-2784 *Fax:* 902-368-4418
*E-mail:* peiwritersguild@gmail.com
*Web Site:* www.peiwritersguild.com
*Key Personnel*
Exec Dir: Darrin White *Tel:* 902-368-6176 *E-mail:* dwhite@peica.ca
Maximum of 8-10 pages of poetry. May submit as many entries as they wish. The work must be original & unpublished. Typewritten & double-spaced on one side of the page only. Entry fee: $20. Contest is for Prince Edward Island residents only. Must be resident for six of the 12 months prior to the contest deadline. For further information call or e-mail.
Award: $400 (1st prize), $200 (2nd prize), $100 (3rd prize)

**Herbert Baxter Adams Prize**
American Historical Association
400 "A" St SE, Washington, DC 20003-3889
*Tel:* 202-544-2422 *Fax:* 202-544-8307
*E-mail:* awards@historians.org
*Web Site:* www.historians.org
Established: 1905
For a distinguished book by an American author in the field of European history, from ancient times through 1815. Entry must be the author's first substantial book; must have been published in 2013; must be citizen or permanent resident of the US or Canada. Submission of an entry may be made by an author or by a third party as well as by a publisher. Publishers may submit as many entries as they wish. Along with an application form, applicants must mail a copy of their book to each of the prize committee members who will be posted on our web site as the prize deadline approaches. All updated info on web site.
Award: Cash prize
Closing Date: May 15, 2014 (postmark)
Presented: AHA Annual Meeting

**Jane Addams Children's Book Award**
Jane Addams Peace Association
Subsidiary of Women's International League for Peace & Freedom (WILPF)
777 United Nations Plaza, 6th fl, New York, NY 10017
*Tel:* 212-682-8830 *Fax:* 212-286-8211
*E-mail:* japa@igc.org
*Web Site:* www.janeaddamspeace.org
*Key Personnel*
Award Comm Chpn: Prof Marianne Baker
Exec Dir: Linda Belle
Established: 1953
For a book that best combines literary merit with themes stressing peace, social justice, world community & the equality of the sexes & all races. Those applying must submit one copy to current committee chairperson.
Other Sponsor(s): Women's International League for Peace & Freedom (WILPF)
Award: Certificate; Cash
Closing Date: Annually, Dec 31
Presented: Announced April 28; ceremony held third Friday in Oct Annually

**AFCP's Annual Awards**
Association of Free Community Papers (AFCP)
7445 Morgan Rd, Suite 103, Liverpool, NY 13090
*Toll Free Tel:* 877-203-2327 *Fax:* 781-459-7770
*E-mail:* afcp@afcp.org
*Web Site:* www.afcp.org
*Key Personnel*
Exec Dir: Loren Colburn *E-mail:* loren@afcp.org
Established: 1970
Awards for excellence in 40 categories, revolving around the theme of free community papers.
Award: 1st, 2nd & 3rd place plaques, honorable mention certificates
Closing Date: Annually, Jan 31
Presented: AFCP's Annual Conference

**Agatha Awards**
Malice Domestic Ltd
PO Box 8007, Gaithersburg, MD 20898-8007
*E-mail:* malicedomesticpr@gmail.com
*Web Site:* www.malicedomestic.org
*Key Personnel*
Malice Dom Chair: Verena Rose *E-mail:* malicebodchair@malicedomestic.org
Agatha Awards Comm Memb: Marian Lesko *Tel:* 301-730-1675 *E-mail:* malice23agathas@aol.com
Established: 1989
Awards for best traditional mysteries of the calendar year. Awards given for best novel, best first novel, best nonfiction work, best short story, best children's/young adult novel.
Closing Date: Annually, Dec 31
Presented: Malice Domestic Conference, Agatha Awards Banquet, Annually in May

**Aggiornamento Award**
Catholic Library Association
205 W Monroe, Suite 314, Chicago, IL 60606-5061
*Tel:* 312-739-1776; 312-739-1776 *Toll Free Tel:* 855-739-1776 *Fax:* 312-739-1778; 312-739-1778
*E-mail:* cla2@cathla.org
*Web Site:* www.cathla.org
*Key Personnel*
Pres: Malachy R McCarthy *E-mail:* mmccarthy@cathla.org
Established: 1980
To recognize contributions made by an individual or an organization for the renewal of parish & community life in the spirit of Pope John XXIII.
Award: Plaque
Closing Date: None; in-house votes
Presented: CLA Annual Convention

**AIGA 50 Books/50 Covers**
AIGA, the professional association for design
164 Fifth Ave, New York, NY 10010
*Tel:* 212-807-1990 *Fax:* 212-807-1799
*E-mail:* competitions@aiga.org
*Web Site:* www.aiga.org
*Key Personnel*
Dir, Competitions & Exhibitions:

Gabriela Mirensky *Tel:* 212-710-3143
*E-mail:* gabriela_mirensky@aiga.org
Established: 1924
Annual award for excellence of design in books & book covers (complete sets of all books selected since 1924 at Columbia University Library - Rare Book Dept).
Award: Certificate of excellence, publication in AIGA annual, exhibition in 5th Avenue Gallery
Closing Date: Annually in March
Presented: Annually in Sept

**AJL Judaica Bibliography Award**
Association of Jewish Libraries (AJL) Inc
Affiliate of American Library Association (ALA)
PO Box 1118, Teaneck, NJ 07666
*Tel:* 201-371-3255
*E-mail:* ajlibs@osu.edu
*Web Site:* www.jewishlibraries.org
*Key Personnel*
Pres: Heidi Estrin *E-mail:* president@jewishlibraries.org
Ref & Bibliography Awards Comm Chair: Sharon Benamou *E-mail:* benamou@library.ucla.edu
Established: 1984
For best Judaica bibliography book published in previous calendar year.
Award: The seal of the Association
Closing Date: Annually in March
Presented: AJL Annual Convention, Annually in June

**AJL Judaica Reference Award**
Association of Jewish Libraries (AJL) Inc
Affiliate of American Library Association (ALA)
PO Box 1118, Teaneck, NJ 07666
*Tel:* 201-371-3255
*E-mail:* ajlibs@osu.edu
*Web Site:* www.jewishlibraries.org
*Key Personnel*
Pres: Heidi Estrin *E-mail:* president@jewishlibraries.org
Ref & Bibliography Awards Comm Chair: Sharon Benamou *E-mail:* benamou@library.ucla.edu
Established: 1984
Annual award for outstanding Judaica reference book published during previous calendar year.
Award: The seal of the Association
Closing Date: Annually in March
Presented: AJL Annual Convention, Annually in June

**AJL Scholarship**
Association of Jewish Libraries (AJL) Inc
Affiliate of American Library Association (ALA)
PO Box 1118, Teaneck, NJ 07666
*Web Site:* www.jewishlibraries.org
*Key Personnel*
Curator, Spec Collections: Shulamith Berger
In order to encourage students to train for & enter the field of Judaica librarianship, the Association of Jewish Libraries awards a scholarship to a student attending or planning to attend a graduate school of library & information science. Prospective candidates should have an interest in & demonstrate a potential for pursuing a career in Judaica librarianship. In addition, applicants must provide documentation showing participation in Judaica studies at an academic or less formal level &/or experience working in Judaica libraries.
Award: $1,000 per academic year
Closing Date: March 15-April 15 (varies by year)
Presented: AJL Annual Convention, June

**AKC Publications Fiction Contest**
American Kennel Club Publications
260 Madison Ave, New York, NY 10016
*Web Site:* www.akc.org/pubs/fictioncontest
Open to anyone. Entries must be original, unpublished stories that have not been offered to or accepted by any other publisher. Only one entry per author. The publisher retaines the right to publish the 3 prize-winning entries in an AKC publication. Entries may feature either a purebred or mixed breed dog. Maximum length is 2,000 words. Winners based on the style, content, originality & appeal of the story.
Award: $500 (1st place), $250 (2nd place), $100 (3rd place)

**Akron Poetry Prize**
The University of Akron Press
The University of Akron Press, 120 E Mill St, Suite 415, Akron, OH 44308
*Tel:* 330-972-6953 *Fax:* 330-972-8364
*E-mail:* uapress@uakron.edu
*Web Site:* www.uakron.edu/uapress/akron-poetry-prize
*Key Personnel*
Poetry Ed: Mary Biddinger
Edit & Design: Amy Freels *Tel:* 330-972-5342
*E-mail:* production@uakron.edu
Established: 1995
Open to all poets writing in English. Mss must be at least 48 pages. Entry fee: $25.
Award: $1,500 & publication
Closing Date: Annually postmarked April 15-June 15
Presented: online, Annually Sept 30

**Alabama Artists Fellowship Awards**
Alabama State Council on the Arts
201 Monroe St, Suite 110, Montgomery, AL 36130-1800
*Tel:* 334-242-4076 *Fax:* 334-240-3269
*Key Personnel*
Exec Dir: Albert B Head
Lit Prog Mgr: Anne Kimzey *Tel:* 334-242-4076 ext 236 *E-mail:* anne.kimzey@arts.alabama.gov
Awarded based on quality of work &/or career status, achievement & potential; two-year residency required.
Award: Cash; Two $5,000 fellowships
Closing Date: March 1
Presented: Annually, Oct 1

**Alberta Book Awards**
The Book Publishers Association of Alberta (BPAA)
10523 100 Ave, Edmonton, AB T5J 0A8, Canada
*Tel:* 780-424-5060 *Fax:* 780-424-7943
*E-mail:* info@bookpublishers.ab.ca
*Web Site:* www.bookpublishers.ab.ca
*Key Personnel*
Exec Dir: Kieran Leblanc *E-mail:* kleblanc@bookpublishers.ab.ca
Proj Coord: Donna White *E-mail:* dwhite@bookpublishers.ab.ca
Established: 1989
Excellence in writing & publishing within the province of Alberta.
Award: Sculpture, certificate
Closing Date: Jan
Presented: Annually in May

**Alcuin Society Awards in Excellence in Book Design in Canada**
Alcuin Society
PO Box 3216, Vancouver, BC V6B 3X8, Canada
*Tel:* 605-566-1502
*E-mail:* awards@alcuinsociety.com
*Web Site:* www.alcuinsociety.com
*Key Personnel*
Chair, Book Design Competition Comm: Leah Gordon *Tel:* 604-732-5403
Established: 1981
Recognizes the work of Canadian book designers & publishers through the Alcuin Citations awarded for excellence in book design & production. Must fulfill the following criteria: titles published exclusively in Canada or titles co-published with a publisher in another country but representing a book by a Canadian book designer. Categories are: children, limited editions, pictorial, poetry, prose fiction, prose nonfiction, prose nonfiction illustrated, reference.
Award: Certificate
Closing Date: Annually in March
Presented: Awards ceremony, Annually in Oct

**Nelson Algren Awards**
Chicago Tribune
Subsidiary of Tribune Co
Chicago Tribune, TT200, 435 N Michigan Ave, Chicago, IL 60611
*Toll Free Tel:* 800-874-2863 *Fax:* 312-222-5816
*E-mail:* nelsonalgren@tribune.com
*Web Site:* www.chicagotribune.com/about
*Key Personnel*
Book Ed: Elizabeth Taylor *E-mail:* etaylor@tribune.com
Established: 1982
Given for an outstanding unpublished short fiction, double-spaced & less than 10,000 words in length, by an American writer. No entry form or fee required. Entries will not be returned. Entries by mail only to Nelson Algren Awards at the above address: include cover letter with address, phone & e-mail, do not put name on the ms; no telephone or e-mail inquiries.
Award: $5,000 & three runners-up awards of $1,500 each
Closing Date: Annually in Feb
Presented: Chicago, IL, Annually in Autumn

**The Aliant Creative Writing Award for Young People**
Prince Edward Island Writers' Guild
115 Richmond St, Charlottetown, PE C1A 1H7, Canada
*Tel:* 902-368-4410 *Toll Free Tel:* 888-734-2784
*Fax:* 902-368-4418
*E-mail:* peiwritersguild@gmail.com
*Web Site:* www.peiwritersguild.com
*Key Personnel*
Exec Dir: Darrin White *Tel:* 902-368-6176
*E-mail:* dwhite@peica.ca
Elementary, junior & high school students may write on the topic of their choice & submit in 1 of 4 categories: Early Elementary (grades 1-3), Late Elementary (grades 4-6), Junior High (grades 7-9) & Senior High (grades 10-12). A maximum of five pages of poetry or 10 page short story will constitute an entry. No entry fee. Residents only. For more information contact PEI Council of the Arts at address above.
Award: $100 (1st prize), $75 (2nd prize), $50 (3rd prize)

**Alligator Juniper's National Writing Contest**
Prescott College, Alligator Juniper
220 Grove Ave, Prescott, AZ 86301
*Tel:* 928-350-2012
*E-mail:* alligatorjuniper@prescott.edu
*Web Site:* www.prescott.edu/alligatorjuniper
Established: 1995
Stories have a 30 page limit per entry or up to five poems. Entry fee $15; no e-mail submissions.
Award: $1,000 plus publication in fiction, creative nonfiction & poetry
Closing Date: Annually, Aug 15-Oct 1 (postmark)
Presented: Annually, Oct 1

**ALSC BWI/Summer Reading Program Grant**
Association for Library Service to Children (ALSC)
Division of American Library Association (ALA)
50 E Huron St, Chicago, IL 60611-2795
*Tel:* 312-280-2163 *Toll Free Tel:* 800-545-2433
*Fax:* 312-440-9374
*E-mail:* alsc@ala.org
*Web Site:* www.ala.org/alsc

*Key Personnel*
Exec Dir: Aimee Strittmatter *Tel:* 312-280-2162
*E-mail:* astrittmatter@ala.org
Awards Coord: Caroline Jewell
*E-mail:* alscawards@ala.org
Prog Coord: Marsha P Burgess
*E-mail:* mburgess@ala.org
Encourages reading programs for children in a public library. Applicant must plan & present an outline for a theme-based summer reading program in a public library.
Award: $3,000
Closing Date: Annually, Dec 1
Presented: ALA Midwinter Meeting, Annually in Jan

**American Association of University Women Award for Juvenile Literature**
AAUW, North Carolina Division
Affiliate of North Carolina Literary & Historical Association
4610 Mail Service Ctr, Raleigh, NC 27699-4610
*Tel:* 919-807-7290 *Fax:* 919-733-8807
*Key Personnel*
Awards Coord: Michael Hill *E-mail:* michael.hill@ncdcr.gov
Established: 1953
For a published work of juvenile fiction or nonfiction by a legal or actual resident of North Carolina for at least three years prior to the end of the contest period.
Other Sponsor(s): AAUW
Award: Cup
Closing Date: Annually, July 15
Presented: Raleigh, NC, Annually in Nov

**American Book Award**
Before Columbus Foundation
The Raymond House, Suite 302, 655 13 St, Oakland, CA 94612
SAN: 159-2955
*Tel:* 510-268-9775
*E-mail:* info@beforecolumbusfoundation.com
*Web Site:* www.beforecolumbusfoundation.org
*Key Personnel*
Exec Dir: Gundars Strads *Tel:* 510-642-7321
Established: 1978
To recognize outstanding literary achievement by contemporary American authors without restriction for race, sex, ethnic background or genre. The purpose is to acknowledge the excellence & multicultural diversity of American writing. The awards are nonprofit. There are no categories & all winners are accorded equal status. Award is given for books published within the current year. No application forms or fees. Must submit two copies of each entry.
Award: Plaque
Closing Date: Annually, Dec 31
Presented: Berkeley, CA, Annually in Oct

**American Illustration/American Photography**
Amilus Inc
Subsidiary of Fadner Media
15 E 32 St, 7th fl, New York, NY 10016
*Tel:* 212-470-0302 *Fax:* 212-532-2064
*E-mail:* info@ai-ap.com
*Web Site:* www.ai-ap.com
*Key Personnel*
Dir: Mark Heflin *E-mail:* mark@ai-ap.com
Established: 1985
For the finest illustrative work by students & professionals. Categories include: editorial, advertising & books, as well as unpublished work. Work will be published in the American Illustration annual & will include the artist's name, address & telephone. Also, similar competition & annual for photography called American Photography. Both books are published in Nov.
Closing Date: Annually, Feb 20 (illustration), Jan 23 (photography)
Presented: The Party, New York City, Nov, Annually in Nov

**The American Legion Fourth Estate Award**
The American Legion National Headquarters
700 N Pennsylvania St, Indianapolis, IN 46204
*Tel:* 317-630-1253 *Fax:* 317-630-1368
*E-mail:* pr@legion.org
*Web Site:* www.legion.org
*Key Personnel*
Dir: Joe March
Established: 1958
Annual award for excellence in journalism (any media). Material must have been published between Jan 1 & Dec 31 of prior year (ie 2014 award is for work published in 2013).
Award: 15-inch pylon ($2,000 stipend to defray expenses). Must accept award at national convention
Closing Date: Feb 18
Presented: The American Legion National Convention

**American Printing History Association Award**
American Printing History Association
PO Box 4519, Grand Central Sta, New York, NY 10163-4519
*Tel:* 202-544-2422
*Web Site:* www.printinghistory.org
*Key Personnel*
Exec Dir: Jim Grossman
Proj Mgr: Christian Hale *Tel:* 202-544-2422 ext 133
Spec Proj Coord: Julia Brookins *Tel:* 202-544-2422 ext 119
Established: 1976
For achievement in the printing world or in closely related fields.
Award: Two framed award certificates, one for an individual & one for an institution
Presented: APHA meeting, New York, NY, Annually in Jan

**AMWA Medical Book Awards**
American Medical Writers Association (AMWA)
30 W Gude Dr, Suite 525, Rockville, MD 20850-1161
*Tel:* 240-238-0940 *Fax:* 301-294-9006
*E-mail:* amwa@amwa.org
*Web Site:* www.amwa.org
*Key Personnel*
Awards Liaison: Rachel Spassiani
All medical books published in previous year are eligible for the current year's competition.
Award: Trophy

**Amy Writing Awards**
The Amy Foundation & World News Group
PO Box 16091, Lansing, MI 48901-6091
*Tel:* 517-323-6233 *Toll Free Tel:* 877-727-4262 *Fax:* 517-321-2572
*E-mail:* amyawards@worldmag.com
*Web Site:* www.worldmag.com/amyawards
*Key Personnel*
Pres: Jim Russell
Exec Dir: Mary Spagnuolo
Established: 1985
For writing that presents the Biblical position on issues affecting the world today. To be eligible, submitted articles must be published in a secular, non-religious journalistic outlet & contain a scriptural quote. Must have been published during current calendar year. See web site for submission form.
Award: $10,000 (1st prize), $5,000 (2nd prize), $4,000 (3rd prize), $3,000 (4th prize), $2,000 (5th prize), $1,000 (outstanding merit, 10 prizes)
Closing Date: Jan 31
Presented: The Amy Foundation, Lansing, MI

**Hans Christian Andersen Award**
US Board on Books For Young People (USBBY)
5503 N El Adobe Dr, Fresno, CA 93711-2363
*Tel:* 559-351-6119
*E-mail:* executive.director@usbby.org
*Web Site:* www.usbby.org
*Key Personnel*
Exec Secy: V Ellis Vance *E-mail:* executive.secretary@usbby.org
Established: 1956
Two medals are awarded biennially, one to an author & one to an illustrator, for their complete oeuvre. An Honor List is established with the books chosen by the National Sections of the International Board on Books for Young People (IBBY). Each section chooses three books from among those published in the country during the preceding biennium: for writing, illustrating & translating.
Award: Medals & honor list
Presented: IBBY Congress, Biennially in even-numbered years

**The Anisfield-Wolf Book Awards**
The Cleveland Foundation
1422 Euclid Ave, Suite 1300, Cleveland, OH 44115
*Tel:* 216-861-3810 *Fax:* 216-861-1729
*E-mail:* awinfo@clevefdn.org
*Web Site:* www.anisfield-wolf.org; www.clevelandfoundation.org
*Key Personnel*
CEO & Pres, Cleveland Foundation: Ronald B Richard
Jury Chmn: Henry Louis Gates, Jr
Mgr: Karen R Long
Established: 1935
Recognizes books that have made important contributions to our understanding of racism or our appreciation of the diversity of human cultures.
Award: $10,000 fiction prize (divided equally among fiction winners); $10,000 nonfiction prize (divided equally among nonfiction winners); $5,000 honorarium given to Lifetime Achievement winner
Closing Date: Dec 31

**R Ross Annett Award for Children's Literature**
Writers Guild of Alberta
11759 Groat Rd, Edmonton, AB T5M 3K6, Canada
*Tel:* 780-422-8174 *Toll Free Tel:* 800-665-5354 (AB only) *Fax:* 780-422-2663 (attn WGA)
*E-mail:* mail@writersguild.ab.ca
*Web Site:* www.writersguild.ab.ca
*Key Personnel*
Exec Dir: Carol Holmes *E-mail:* cholmes@writersguild.ab.ca
Communs & Partnerships Coord: Nicholas Mather *E-mail:* nmather@writersguild.ab.ca
Memb Servs Coord: Giorgia Severini
Progs Coord: Nichole Quiring
*E-mail:* programs@writersguild.ab.ca
Established: 1982
Alternates yearly between picture & chapter books. The 2013 award will be presented to the Alberta author of a children's picture book.
Award: $1,500
Closing Date: Annually, Dec 31
Presented: Alberta Literary Awards Gala
*Branch Office(s)*
Lord Denning House, 509 20 Ave SW, Calgary, AB T2S 0E7, Canada, Prog Coord: Samantha Warwick *Tel:* 403-265-2226
*E-mail:* swarwick@writersguild.ab.ca

**Annual Off Off Broadway Short Play Festival**
Samuel French Inc
45 W 25 St, New York, NY 10010-2751
*Tel:* 212-206-8990 *Toll Free Tel:* 866-598-8449 *Fax:* 212-206-1429
*E-mail:* oobfestival@samuelfrench.com
*Web Site:* oob.samuelfrench.com; www.samuelfrench.com

*Key Personnel*
Festival Coord: Billie Davis *E-mail:* bdavis@samuelfrench.com
Literary Coord: Amy Rose Marsh *E-mail:* amarsh@samuelfrench.com
Festival Mktg & Outreach: Katherine DiSavino *E-mail:* kdisavino@samuelfrench.com
Established: 1975
Selected plays are presented on the final day of the festival.
Award: Publication of top 6 plays
Closing Date: Mid Feb-late March
Presented: Annually in June or July during festival

**The Applegate/Jackson/Parks Future Teacher Scholarship**
National Institute for Labor Relations Research
5211 Port Royal Rd, Suite 510, Springfield, VA 22151
*Tel:* 703-321-9606 *Fax:* 703-321-7143
*E-mail:* research@nilrr.org
*Web Site:* www.nilrr.org
*Key Personnel*
Scholarship Administrator: Cathy Jones
Based solely on scholastic ability demonstrating an understanding of compulsory unionism in education.
Award: $1,000
Closing Date: Annually, Dec 31 (postmark or electronic submission)
Presented: Annually in April

**The May Hill Arbuthnot Honor Lecture Award**
Association for Library Service to Children (ALSC)
Division of American Library Association (ALA)
50 E Huron St, Chicago, IL 60611-2795
*Tel:* 312-280-2163 *Toll Free Tel:* 800-545-2433 *Fax:* 312-440-9374
*E-mail:* alsc@ala.org
*Web Site:* www.ala.org/alsc
*Key Personnel*
Exec Dir: Aimee Strittmatter *Tel:* 312-280-2162 *E-mail:* astrittmatter@ala.org
Awards Coord: Caroline Jewell *E-mail:* alscawards@ala.org
Prog Coord: Marsha P Burgess *E-mail:* mburgess@ala.org
Person appointed prepares a paper of significant contribution to the field of children's literature & delivers a lecture based on the paper in April. Libraries & other institutions apply to host the lecture. The paper is also published in the ALSC journal "Children & Libraries".
Award: $1000
Closing Date: Annually, May 1
Presented: The ALA Midwinter Meeting, Annually in Jan

**Arkansas Diamond Primary Book Award**
Arkansas State Library
Arkansas State Library, Suite 100, 900 W Capitol Ave, Little Rock, AR 72201-3108
*Tel:* 501-682-2860 *Fax:* 501-682-1693
*Web Site:* www.library.arkansas.gov; www.library.arkansas.gov
*Key Personnel*
Coord, Children's Progs: Cathy Howser *E-mail:* cathy@library.arkansas.gov
Established: 1999
To encourage reading for students in grades K-3. The Arkansas Department of Education & the Arkansas State Library support selected books that students all over Arkansas read or have read to them. The students vote for the one book they most enjoyed & the winning title recieves the award.
Other Sponsor(s): Arkansas Reading Association
Award: Medallion for first place, plaque for Honor Book
Closing Date: Annual vote in April
Presented: Little Rock, AR, Annually in Nov

**Artist Grants**
South Dakota Arts Council
Affiliate of Department of Tourism
711 E Wells Ave, Pierre, SD 57501-3369
*Tel:* 605-773-3301 *Fax:* 605-773-5977
*E-mail:* sdac@state.sd.us
*Web Site:* www.artscouncil.sd.gov/grants
*Key Personnel*
Dir: Michael Pangburn
Awards made to residents of South Dakota, based on the quality of art work.
Award: $1,000-$5,000
Closing Date: Annually, March 1

**Artist Projects Grants**
Arizona Commission on the Arts
417 W Roosevelt St, Phoenix, AZ 85003-1326
*Tel:* 602-771-6501 *Fax:* 602-256-0282
*E-mail:* info@azarts.gov
*Web Site:* www.azarts.gov
*Key Personnel*
Grants & IT Mgr: Ginny Berryhill *E-mail:* gberryhill@azarts.gov
Arizona poets, fiction & nonfiction writers only.
Award: Cash up to $5,500
Closing Date: Sept

**Artist Trust Fellowship**
Artist Trust
1835 12 Ave, Seattle, WA 98122
*Tel:* 206-467-8734 (ext 11) *Toll Free Tel:* 866-218-7878 (ext 11) *Fax:* 206-467-9633
*E-mail:* info@artisttrust.org
*Web Site:* www.artisttrust.org
*Key Personnel*
Exec Dir: Margit Rankin *Tel:* 206-467-8734 ext 12
Prog Mgr: Miguel Guillen *Tel:* 206-467-8734 ext 11
Established: 1988
Unrestricted grant to generative artists in Washington State. Fellowships will be awarded in music, media, literature & craft in even years. Fellowships will be awarded in dance, design, theatre & visual arts in odd years. Applications will be available in April & due early summer. Check web site for dates.
Award: $7,500

**Artists' Fellowships**
New York Foundation for the Arts
20 Jay St, 7th fl, Brooklyn, NY 11201
*Tel:* 212-366-6900 *Fax:* 212-366-1778
*E-mail:* info@nyfa.org
*Web Site:* www.nyfa.org
*Key Personnel*
Exec Dir: Michael Royce *E-mail:* mroyce@nfya.org
Interim Dir, Progs: Susan Ball *E-mail:* sball@nyfa.org
Fellowship, application limited to New York State residents. Applications in nonfiction literature & poetry; applications will be available online in mid-July. Grants awarded in 16 artistic disciplines.
Award: $7,000
Closing Date: Annually in Dec
Presented: New York, NY

**Athenaeum of Philadelphia Literary Award**
Athenaeum of Philadelphia
219 S Sixth St, Philadelphia, PA 19106
*Tel:* 215-925-2688 *Fax:* 215-925-3755
*Web Site:* www.philaathenaeum.org
*Key Personnel*
Circ Libn: Jill LeMin Lee *E-mail:* jilly@philaathenaeum.org
Established: 1950
In recognition & encouragement of outstanding literary achievement in Philadelphia & the vicinity.
Award: Citation
Closing Date: Annually, Dec 31
Presented: Annually in Spring

**Atlantic Poetry Prize**
Writers' Federation of Nova Scotia
1113 Marginal Rd, Halifax, NS B3H 4P7, Canada
*Tel:* 902-423-8116 *Fax:* 902-422-0881
*E-mail:* talk@writers.ns.ca
*Web Site:* www.writers.ns.ca
*Key Personnel*
Exec Dir: Nate Crawford *E-mail:* director@writers.ns.ca
Established: 1998
Presented to the best full-length book of poetry by an Atlantic Canadian in the previous calendar year.
Award: $2,000
Closing Date: Annually, 1st Friday in Dec
Presented: Halifax, NS, Canada, Annually in Oct

**Abrendal Austin National Writing Contest**
Black Penny Press
5198 Arlington Ave, Unit 923, Riverside, CA 92504
*Tel:* 951-214-5712; 951-741-7651
*E-mail:* shortstory@blackpennypresscontest.com; info@blackpennypress.com
*Web Site:* www.blackpennypresscontest.com
Maximum 2,500 words for short story or essay & up to 5 poems for each entrant. Stories or poems must belong to the original submitter. Original unpublished stories only. Entry fee $20.
Award: $500 (1st place), $250 (2nd place), 2 honorable mentions
Closing Date: Annually in May
Presented: Annually in Aug

**Autumn House Poetry, Fiction & Nonfiction Contests**
Autumn House Press
87 1/2 Westwood St, Pittsburgh, PA 15211
Mailing Address: PO Box 60100, Pittsburgh, PA 15211
*Web Site:* www.autumnhouse.org
Poetry Prize: All full-length collections of poetry 50-80 pages in length are eligible.
Fiction Contest: Submissions should be approximately 200-300 pages. All fiction sub-genres or any combination of sub-genres are eligible.
Nonfiction Contest: Submissions should be approximately 200-300 pages. All nonfiction subjects are eligible.
Enclose $30 handling fee for each prize. See web site for complete guidelines.
Award: $1,000, book publication, advance against royalties & $1,500 travel grant to participate in the Master Authors Series in Pittsburgh
Closing Date: Annually, June 30

**AWP Award Series**
Association of Writers & Writing Programs (AWP)
George Mason University, 4400 University Dr, MSN 1E3, Fairfax, VA 22030
*Tel:* 703-993-4301 *Fax:* 703-993-4302
*E-mail:* awp@awpwriter.org
*Web Site:* www.awpwriter.org
*Key Personnel*
Exec Dir: David W Fenza
Dir of Conferences: Christian Teresi
Dir, Devt: Amber Withycombe
Dir, Membership Servs: Diane Zinna
Dir, Pubns: Supriya Bhatnagar
Assoc Ed: Sara Flood
Conference Coord: Brenna Killeen
Established: 1967
An open competition for book-length mss in four categories: poetry, short fiction, novel & cre-

ative (nonfiction). Send business-size SASE after Nov 1 for submission guidelines.
Award: Publication by a major university press & an honorarium of $2,000 for nonfiction & novel. Donald Hall Prize in poetry-honorarium $5,000. Grace Paley Prize for short fiction-honorarium $5,000. One winner in each category
Closing Date: Annually, Feb 28 (postmark)

**Axiom Business Book Awards**
Independent Publisher Online
Division of Jenkins Group Inc
1129 Woodmere Ave, Suite B, Traverse City, MI 49686
*Tel:* 231-933-0445 *Toll Free Tel:* 800-706-4636 *Fax:* 231-933-0448
*E-mail:* info@axiomawards.com
*Web Site:* www.axiomawards.com
*Key Personnel*
CEO: Jerrold R Jenkins *E-mail:* jrj@bookpublishing.com
Pres: James Kalajian *Tel:* 800-706-4636 ext 1006 *E-mail:* jjk@bookpublishing.com
Mng Ed & Awards Dir: Jim Barnes *Tel:* 800-706-4636 ext 1011 *E-mail:* jimb@bookpublishing.com
Awards Coord: Amy Shamroe
Established: 2006
US-based award contest focused solely on business books. The goal of the awards is to celebrate the innovative, intelligent & creative aspects of the books that make us think, see & work differently every day. The awards offer no global boundaries, giving participants from every continent the opportunity to earn further recognition for their English-language titles. All publishers are eligible, ranging from large multi-title publishing houses to small one-title publishers. Publishers can be throughout North America & overseas publishers who publish English-language books intended for the American market. Print-on-demand & other independent authors are welcome to enter their books themselves.
Other Sponsor(s): Books Are Marketing Tools; Inc; Independent Publisher; Jenkins Group; Padilla Speer Beardsley
Award: Gold medal (1st place), silver medal (2nd place) & bronze medal (3rd place)
Closing Date: Annually in Jan
Presented: Book Expo America, Annually in May

**Marilyn Baillie Picture Book Award**
Canadian Children's Book Centre
40 Orchard View Blvd, Suite 217, Toronto, ON M4R 1B9, Canada
*Tel:* 416-975-0010 *Fax:* 416-975-8970
*E-mail:* info@bookcentre.ca
*Web Site:* www.bookcentre.ca
*Key Personnel*
Exec Dir: Charlotte Teeple *E-mail:* charlotte@bookcentre.ca
Gen Mgr: Dawn Todd *E-mail:* dawn@bookcentre.ca
Sales & Mktg Mgr: Holly Kent *E-mail:* holly@bookcentre.ca
Lib Coord: Meghan Howe *E-mail:* meghan@bookcentre.ca
Prog Coord: Shannon Howe Barnes *E-mail:* shannon@bookcentre.ca
Established: 2006
Awarded to a Canadian author & illustrator for excellence in the illustrated picture book format for children ages 3-8.
Other Sponsor(s): Charles Baillie
Award: $20,000 cash
Closing Date: Annually in mid-Dec

**Baker & Taylor/YALSA Conference Grants**
Young Adult Library Services Association (YALSA)
Division of American Library Association (ALA)
50 E Huron St, Chicago, IL 60611
*Tel:* 312-280-4390 *Toll Free Tel:* 800-545-2433 *Fax:* 312-280-5276; 312-664-7459
*E-mail:* yalsa@ala.org
*Web Site:* www.ala.org/yalsa/
*Key Personnel*
Exec Dir, YALSA: Beth Yoke *Tel:* 312-280-4391 *E mail:* byoke@ala.org
Prog Offr, Events & Conferences: Nichole Gilbert *Tel:* 312-280-4387 *Fax:* 312-280-1538 *E-mail:* ngilbert@ala.org
Established: 1983
This award is given to young adult librarians in public or school libraries to attend an ALA Annual Conference for the first time. Candidates must be members of YALSA & have one to ten years of library experience.
Award: $1,000 (2 given yearly)
Closing Date: Annually, Dec 1
Presented: ALA's midwinter meeting

**The Balcones Poetry Prize**
The Balcones Center for Creative Writing
Subsidiary of Austin Community College
1212 Rio Grande St, Austin, TX 78701
*Tel:* 512-828-9368
*Web Site:* www.austincc.edu/crw/balcones_prize.html
*Key Personnel*
Assoc Dir: John Herndon *E-mail:* jherndon@austincc.edu
Established: 1994
Recognizes an outstanding book of poetry published during the year. Books of poetry of 42 pgs or more may be submitted by author or publisher. Must bear a publication date between Jan 1, 2011 & Dec 31, 2012. $25 reading fee.
Award: $1,000
Closing Date: Jan 31

**Bancroft Prizes**
Columbia University
517 Butler Library, Mail Code 1101, 535 W 114 St, New York, NY 10027
*Tel:* 212-854-4746 *Fax:* 212-854-9099
*Web Site:* www.columbia.edu/cu/lweb/eguides/amerihist/bancroft.html
*Key Personnel*
Devt Offr: Matt Hampel
Established: 1948
Two awards presented annually for distinguished books in the fields of American history (including biography) & diplomacy. Award confined to books originally published in English or those with a published English translation. Books published in year preceding that in which award is made are eligible. Submit four copies & nominating letter.
Award: $10,000 each
Closing Date: Nov 1, page-proof copy may be submitted after Nov 1, provided the work will be published after that date & before Dec 31
Presented: Columbia University

**Barnard Women Poets Prize**
Barnard College
Barnard College, Women Poets at Barnard, 3009 Broadway, New York, NY 10027
*Tel:* 212-854-2116 *Fax:* 212-854-9498
*E-mail:* english@barnard.edu
*Web Site:* www.barnard.edu
*Key Personnel*
Dir, Women Poets & Assoc Professor, Eng: Saskia Hamilton *E-mail:* shamilton@barnard.edu
Given biennially for an exceptional 2nd collection of poems. Open to US women poets who have already published one book of poetry (the first collection should have been a full-length book, printed in an edition of 500 or more copies). Any ms under option or under contract to another publisher is not eligible. Entry fee is $20.
Award: $1,500 & publication by W W Norton & Co
Closing Date: Oct 15, 2014

**James P Barry Ohioana Award for Editorial Excellence**
Ohioana Library Association
274 E First Ave, Suite 300, Columbus, OH 43201
*Tel:* 614-466-3831 *Fax:* 614-728-6974
*E-mail:* ohioana@ohioana.org
*Web Site:* www.ohioana.org
*Key Personnel*
Exec Dir, Ohioana Library Association: Linda R Hengst *E-mail:* lhengst@ohioana.org
Established: 1979
Only Ohio-based serial (magazine, journal, newspaper, etc) that covers subjects of interest to the Ohioana Library, namely literature, history, culture, the arts or the general humanities. The award is given at the discretion of the Board of Trustees.
Closing Date: Annually, Dec 31
Presented: Ohioana Day Luncheon, Annually in Autumn

**Baskerville Publishers Poetry Award**
Texas Christian University
Texas Christian University, Dept of English, TCU Box 297270, Fort Worth, TX 76129
*Tel:* 817-257-5907 *Fax:* 817-257-7709
*E-mail:* descant@tcu.edu
*Web Site:* www.descant.tcu.edu
*Key Personnel*
Mng Ed: Dan Williams *E-mail:* d.e.williams@tcu.edu
Established: 2003
For an outstanding poem or poems by a single author in an issue. All published submissions are eligible for prize consideration. There is no application process.
Other Sponsor(s): descant Publication, Dept of English, TCU
Award: $250
Closing Date: Annually, Sept 1-April 1
Presented: Announced in journal, Annually in Summer

**The Mildred L Batchelder Award**
Association for Library Service to Children (ALSC)
Division of American Library Association (ALA)
50 E Huron St, Chicago, IL 60611-2795
*Tel:* 312-280-2163 *Toll Free Tel:* 800-545-2433 *Fax:* 312-440-9374
*E-mail:* alsc@ala.org
*Web Site:* www.ala.org/alsc
*Key Personnel*
Exec Dir: Aimee Strittmatter *Tel:* 312-280-2162 *E-mail:* astrittmatter@ala.org
Awards Coord: Caroline Jewell *E-mail:* alscawards@ala.org
Prog Coord: Marsha P Burgess *E-mail:* mburgess@ala.org
Established: 1966
Awarded to an American publisher for an outstanding book originally published in a foreign language in a foreign country & subsequently translated to English & published in the US during the previous year.
Award: Citation
Closing Date: Annually, Dec 31
Presented: ALSC Awards Program at the ALA Annual Conference, Annually in June

**The BC Book Prizes**
West Coast Book Prize Society
207 W Hastings St, Suite 901, Vancouver, BC V6B 1H7, Canada
*Tel:* 604-687-2405 *Fax:* 604-687-2435
*E-mail:* info@bcbookprizes.ca
*Web Site:* www.bcbookprizes.ca

*Key Personnel*
Exec Dir: Bryan Pike *E-mail:* bryan@rebuscreative.com
Gen Mgr: Val Mason *E-mail:* val@rebuscreative.com
Creative Publicity: Karen Green *E-mail:* karen@rebuscreative.com
Proj Coord: Kristie Poole *E-mail:* kristie@rebuscreative.com
Established: 1985
The following BC Book Prizes are awarded to a resident of BC or one who has lived in BC for 3 of the past 5 years: to the author of the best work of fiction; best book written for children 16 years & younger; best original nonfiction literary work; author of the best work of poetry. The following BC Book Prizes are also offered: originating publisher of the best book judged in terms of public appeal, initiative, design, production & content (publisher must have their head office in BC); author of the book which contributes most to the appreciation & understanding of BC (published anywhere & the author may reside outside BC); author & illustrator of the best picture book written for children (author/illustrator must be a BC/Yukon resident or have lived in BC or the Yukon for 3 of the past 5 years).
Other Sponsor(s): AbeBooks; Ampersand Inc; BC Teachers' Federation; British Columbia Booksellers Association; British Columbia Library Association; Friesens; Transcontinental Publishing; Webcom
Award: $2,000 & certificate
Closing Date: Annually, Dec 1, with exceptions made for books published in Dec
Presented: The British Columbia Book Prizes Banquet, Spring

**George Louis Beer Prize**
American Historical Association
400 "A" St SE, Washington, DC 20003-3889
*Tel:* 202-544-2422 *Fax:* 202-544-8307
*E-mail:* awards@historians.org
*Web Site:* www.historians.org
Established: 1923
Recognition of outstanding historical writing in European international history since 1895 that is submitted by a scholar who is a US citizen or permanent resident. Books published in 2013 are eligible. Only books of a high scholarly historical nature should be submitted. Along with an application form, applicants must mail a copy of their book to each of the prize committee members who will be posted on our web site as the prize deadline approaches. All updated info on web site.
Award: Cash prize
Closing Date: May 15, 2014 (postmark)
Presented: AHA Annual Meeting

**The Pura Belpre Award**
Association for Library Service to Children (ALSC)
Division of American Library Association (ALA)
50 E Huron St, Chicago, IL 60611-2795
*Tel:* 312-280-2163 *Toll Free Tel:* 800-545-2433 *Fax:* 312-440-9374
*E-mail:* alsc@ala.org
*Web Site:* www.ala.org/alsc
*Key Personnel*
Exec Dir: Aimee Strittmatter *Tel:* 312-280-2162 *E-mail:* astrittmatter@ala.org
Awards Coord: Caroline Jewell *E-mail:* alscawards@ala.org
Prog Coord: Marsha P Burgess *E-mail:* mburgess@ala.org
Established: 1996
Annual award presented to a Latino/Latina writer & illustrator whose children's work best celebrates the Latino cultural experience.
Other Sponsor(s): National Association to Promote Library & Information Services to Latinos & the Spanish Speaking (REFORMA)
Award: Medal
Closing Date: Annually, Dec 31
Presented: ALSC Awards Program at the ALA Annual Conference

**Benjamin Franklin Awards™**
IBPA, the Independent Book Publishers Association
1020 Manhattan Beach Blvd, Suite 204, Manhattan Beach, CA 90266
*Tel:* 310-546-1818 *Fax:* 310-546-3939
*E-mail:* info@ibpa-online.org
*Web Site:* www.ibpa-online.org; ibpabenjaminfranklinawards.com
*Key Personnel*
COO: Terry Nathan *E-mail:* terry@ibpa-online.org
Asst Dir & Website Mgr: Lisa Krebs Magno *E-mail:* lisa@ibpa-online.org
Vendor Rel & Mktg: Chris Kahn *E-mail:* chris@ibpa-online.org
Established: 1987
Excellence in independent publishing in specific genre & design (books, audio & video). Trophies are presented to the publishers during a gala awards ceremony on the last evening of the Publishing University prior to the opening of Book Expo America. Entry fee: membs $90/title/category; nonmembs-$190/first title (includes 1yr membership); $90/additional titles.
Award: Etched glass & wooden standing plaque
Closing Date: Sept 30 & Dec 31
Presented: April

**George Bennett Fellowship**
Phillips Exeter Academy
Phillips Exeter Academy, Office of the Dean of Faculty, 20 Main St, Exeter, NH 03833-2460
*Tel:* 603-772-4311 *Fax:* 603-777-4384
*E-mail:* teaching_opportunities@exeter.edu
*Web Site:* www.exeter.edu
*Key Personnel*
Coord, Selection Comm: Ralph Sneeden
Established: 1968
Established to provide support for one academic year for an individual contemplating or pursuing a career as a professional writer. Selection is based on the literary promise of the ms submitted. The committee favors applicants who have not yet published a book-length work with a major publisher. Send SASE for application or obtain from the Academy web site. Telephone inquiries strongly discouraged.
Award: $13,650, housing & board at the Academy for the academic year
Closing Date: Annually, Dec 1
Presented: Annually in April

**Naomi Berber Memorial Award**
Printing Industries of America
200 Deer Run Rd, Sewickley, PA 15143-2600
*Tel:* 412-259-1705 *Toll Free Tel:* 800-910-4283 (ext 705) *Fax:* 412-749-9890
*E-mail:* printing@printing.org
*Web Site:* www.printing.org
*Key Personnel*
CEO & Pres: Michael Makin *E-mail:* mmakin@printing.org
Asst to VP, Mktg: Sara Welsh *E-mail:* swelsh@printing.org
Established: 1976
Honors a woman who has made a major contribution to the development of the printing industry. A nominee must have worked in the printing industry for ten years or more. For more information, go to www.printing.org & click on Programs & Services then Awards & Recognition.
Other Sponsor(s): Printing Industries of America's Ben Franklin Society
Award: Engraved plaque
Presented: Printing Industries of America Fall Administrative Meetings

**Jessie Bernard Award**
American Sociological Association (ASA)
c/o Governance Office, 1430 "K" St NW, Suite 600, Washington, DC 20005
*Tel:* 202-383-9005 *Fax:* 202-638-0882
*E-mail:* governance@asanet.org
*Web Site:* www.asanet.org
*Key Personnel*
Dir, Governance: Michael Murphy *Tel:* 202-383-9005 ext 327
For scholarly contributions that enlarge the horizons of sociology to encompass fully the role of women in society. Winner announced through newsletter "Footnotes" an ASA publication. See web site for future awards.
Award: Certificate
Closing Date: Jan 31
Presented: ASA Annual Meeting, Montreal, QC, CN, Annually in Aug

**The Charles Bernheimer Prize**
American Comparative Literature Association (ACLA)
University of South Carolina, Dept of Languages, Literature & Cultures, Rm 813-A, 1620 College St, Columbia, SC 29208
*Tel:* 803-777-3021 *Fax:* 803-777-3041
*E-mail:* info@acla.org
*Web Site:* www.acla.org
*Key Personnel*
Secy & Treas: Alexander Beecroft
An outstanding dissertation in comparative literature completed by July 1. See web site for application details.
Award: $1,000 & a certificate, complimentary registration, a ticket to the banquet & a travel agent of $300 to facilitate the recipient attending the conference
Closing Date: Nov
Presented: Annual meeting, Spring following completed dissertation

**Doris Betts Fiction Prize**
North Carolina Writers' Network
c/o NC Literary Review, East Carolina University, Dept of English, Greenville, NC 27858-4353
*Tel:* 336-293-8844
*E-mail:* mail@ncwriters.org
*Web Site:* www.ncwriters.org
*Key Personnel*
Fiction Ed: Liza Wieland *E-mail:* wielandl@ecu.edu
The competition is open to any writer who is a legal resident of North Carolina or a member of NCWN. Entrants should submit two copies of a typed, original & unpublished story, not to exceed 6,000 words. Entrant fee for members of NCWN is $10, nonmembers $20. See www.ncwriters.org/programs-and-services/competitions/25-doris-betts-fiction-prize for full information.
Award: $250 1st prize, ten finalists considered for publication in the "North Carolina Literary Review"
Closing Date: Annually, Feb 1

**Beullah Rose Poetry Prize**
Smartish Pace
PO Box 22161, Baltimore, MD 21203
*Web Site:* www.smartishpace.com
*Key Personnel*
Assoc Ed: Clare Banks *E-mail:* cbsmartishpace@gmail.com
Established: 2005
Prize for exceptional poetry by women. All poems submitted for the prize will be considered

for publication in *Smartish Pace*. Online submissions at www.smartishpace.com. Postal submissions: submit 3 poems along with a $5 entry fee. Additional poems may be submitted for $1 per poem. No more than 20 poems may be submitted. All entries must include a bio. Include SASE with entry, include name, address, e-mail & telephone number on each page of poetry submitted. Write or print "Beullah Rose Poetry Prize" on top of each poem submitted.
Award: $200 & publication of winning poem in *Smartish Pace* (1st prize). All finalists will be published in *Smartish Pace*
Closing Date: Annually, Oct 1
Presented: Baltimore, MD

**Albert J Beveridge Award in American History**
American Historical Association
400 "A" St SE, Washington, DC 20003-3889
*Tel:* 202-544-2422 *Fax:* 202-544-8307
*E-mail:* awards@historians.org
*Web Site:* www.historians.org
Established: 1939
To promote & honor outstanding historical writing. The award is given for a distinguished book in English on the history of the US, Latin America, or Canada, from 1492 to the present. Books that employ new methodological or conceptual tools or that constitute significant re-examinations of important interpretive problems will be given preference. Literary merit is also an important criterion. Biographies, monographs & works of synthesis & interpretation are eligible; translations, anthologies & collections of documents are not. Books published in 2013 are eligible for the award; limited to five titles from any one publisher & must be submitted by sending a copy to each member of the committee. Along with an application form. All updated info on web site.
Award: Cash prize
Closing Date: May 15, 2014 (postmark)
Presented: AHA Annual Meeting

**Albert J Beveridge Grant for Research in the History of the Western Hemisphere**
American Historical Association
400 "A" St SE, Washington, DC 20003-3889
*Tel:* 202-544-2422 *Fax:* 202-544-8307
*E-mail:* awards@historians.org
*Web Site:* www.historians.org
To support research in the history of the Western hemisphere (United States, Canada & Latin America). Only members of the Association are eligible. The grants are intended to further research in progress & may be used for travel to a library or archive, for microfilms, photographs or photocopying - a list of purposes that is meant to be merely illustrative not exhaustive. Preference will be given to those with specific research needs, such as the completion of a project or completion of a discrete segment thereof; preference will be given to PhD candidates & junior scholars. Application forms available on web site. Applications must include application form with estimated budget, curriculum vita & statement of no more than 750 words. A one page bibliography of the most recent relevant, secondary works on the topic. Mailed & faxed submissions submissions are not accepted.
Award: Individual grants will not exceed $1,000; preference to PhD candidates & junior scholars
Closing Date: Annually, Feb 15

**BHTG - Competition for Youth Theatre Marilyn Hall Awards**
The Beverly Hills Theatre Guild
PO Box 148, Beverly Hills, CA 90213
*Tel:* 310-273-3390
*Web Site:* www.beverlyhillstheatreguild.com
*Key Personnel*
Pres: Carolyn Fried
Competition Coord: Candace Coster
Established: 1999
Playwright, children's theatre grade 6th-8th, 9th-12th grade.
Award: $1,200, $600
Closing Date: Annually, Jan 15 through last day of Feb (postmarked)
Presented: Los Angeles, CA, Annually, June 30

**BHTG - Julie Harris Playwright Award Competition**
The Beverly Hills Theatre Guild
PO Box 148, Beverly Hills, CA 90213
*Tel:* 310-273-3390
*Web Site:* www.beverlyhillstheatreguild.com
*Key Personnel*
Pres: Carolyn Fried
Competition Coord: Candace Coster
Established: 1978
For playwrights; Application & guidelines available upon request with SASE.
Award: $3,500, $2,500 & $1,500
Closing Date: Annually, Aug 1-Nov 1
Presented: Los Angeles, CA, Annually, June 30 (announcement)

**The Geoffrey Bilson Award for Historical Fiction for Young People**
Canadian Children's Book Centre
40 Orchard View Blvd, Suite 217, Toronto, ON M4R 1B9, Canada
*Tel:* 416-975-0010 *Fax:* 416-975-8970
*E-mail:* info@bookcentre.ca
*Web Site:* www.bookcentre.ca
*Key Personnel*
Exec Dir: Charlotte Teeple *E-mail:* charlotte@bookcentre.ca
Gen Mgr: Dawn Todd *E-mail:* dawn@bookcentre.ca
Sales & Mktg Mgr: Holly Kent *E-mail:* holly@bookcentre.ca
Lib Coord: Meghan Howe *E-mail:* meghan@bookcentre.ca
Prog Coord: Shannon Howe Barnes *E-mail:* shannon@bookcentre.ca
Established: 1988
Awarded to a Canadian author for an outstanding work of historical fiction for young people.
Award: $5,000
Closing Date: Annually, mid-Dec

**Bingham, Robert, Fellowships for Writers**, see PEN/Robert Bingham Fellowships for Writers

**Binghamton University John Gardner Fiction Book Award**
The Binghamton Center for Writers-State University of New York
Dept of English, General Literature & Rhetoric, Library N, Rm 1149, Vestal Pkwy E, Binghamton, NY 13902
Mailing Address: PO Box 6000, Binghamton, NY 13902-6000
*Tel:* 607-777-2713
*Web Site:* english.binghamton.edu/cwpro
*Key Personnel*
Dir: Maria Mazziotti Gillan *Tel:* 973-684-5904 *E-mail:* mgillan@binghamton.edu
Established: 2002
Selected by judges as the strongest novel or collection of fiction published in 2012. Minimum press run of 500 copies. Each book submitted must be accompanied by an application form; publishers may submit more than one book for prize consideration. Winners will be announced in "Poets & Writers".
Award: $1,000
Closing Date: Annually, March 1

**Binghamton University Milt Kessler Poetry Book Award**
The Binghamton Center for Writers-State University of New York
Dept of English, General Literature & Rhetoric, Library N, Rm 1149, Vestal Pkwy E, Binghamton, NY 13902
Mailing Address: PO Box 6000, Binghamton, NY 13902-6000
*Tel:* 607-777-2713
*Web Site:* english.binghamton.edu/cwpro
*Key Personnel*
Dir: Maria Mazziotti Gillan *Tel:* 973-684-5904 *E-mail:* mgillan@binghamton.edu
Established: 2002
For a book of poems, 48 pages or more in length selected by our judges as the strongest collection of poems by a poet over 40 published in 2012; must be accompanied by an application; publishers may submit more than 1 book for prize consideration; minimum press run of 500 copies. Winner announced in "Poets & Writers".
Award: $1,000
Closing Date: March 1

**Irma S & James H Black Award**
Bank Street College of Education
610 W 112 St, New York, NY 10025
*Tel:* 212-875-4458 *Fax:* 212-875-4558
*E-mail:* ccl@bankstreet.edu
*Web Site:* www.bankstreet.edu/center-childrens-literature
*Key Personnel*
Dir, Lib Servs: Kristin Freda *E-mail:* kfreda@bankstreet.edu
Established: 1972
For unified excellence of story line, language & illustration in a work for young children published during the previous year.
Award: Scroll & Gold Seals
Closing Date: Annually in Dec
Presented: Bank Street College of Education, Annually in May

**Black Warrior Review Fiction, Nonfiction & Poetry Contest**
Black Warrior Review
Office of Student Media, University of Alabama, Tuscaloosa, AL 35486-0027
Mailing Address: PO Box 870170, Tuscaloosa, AL 35487-0170
*Tel:* 205-348-4518
*Web Site:* www.bwr.ua.edu
*Key Personnel*
Mng Ed: Kirby Johnson *E-mail:* managingeditor.bwr@gmail.com
Fiction Ed: Jake Kinstler
Nonfiction Ed: Leia Wilson
Poetry Ed: Anne Betrelle
Established: 2005
Awards given to best nonfiction piece, short story & best poem entered. Submit one story (up to 7,500 words) or 3 poems. Entry fee $15 includes one-year subscription.
Award: $1,000 & publication (one for each category - poetry, nonfiction & fiction). Finalists noted & considered for publication
Closing Date: Annually, Sept 1 (submit online at bwrsubmissions.ua.edu)

**Neltje Blanchan Memorial Award**
Wyoming Arts Council
Division of Wyoming Department of Parks & Cultural Resources
2320 Capitol Ave, Cheyenne, WY 82002
*Tel:* 307-777-5234 *Fax:* 307-777-5499
*Web Site:* wyoarts.state.wy.us
*Key Personnel*
Literary, Visual & Performing Arts Specialist: Michael Shay *Tel:* 307-777-5234 *E-mail:* mshay@state.wy.us

Arts Council Mgr: Rita Basom *Tel:* 307-777-7473
*E-mail:* rbasom@state.wy.us
Established: 1988
Best writing in any genre inspired by a relationship with nature. Open to Wyoming residents only. Blind judges, single juror.
Other Sponsor(s): Neltje
Award: $1,000
Closing Date: Annually, Oct 31
Presented: ARTSPEAK Conference, Announced Nov 1

**Theodore C Blegen Award**
The Forest History Society Inc
701 William Vickers Ave, Durham, NC 27701-3162
*Tel:* 919-682-9319 *Fax:* 919-682-2349
*Web Site:* www.foresthistory.org
*Key Personnel*
Admin Asst: Andrea Anderson
*E-mail:* recluce2@duke.edu
Established: 1972
Recognizes the best scholarship in forest & conservation history published in a journal other than Environmental History.
Award: $500 & plaque
Closing Date: Early Spring but specific date can vary

**The James Boatwright III Prize for Poetry**
Shenandoah: The Washington & Lee University Review
Washington & Lee University, Mattingly House, 204 W Washington St, Lexington, VA 24450-2116
*Tel:* 540-458-8765
*E-mail:* shenandoah@wlu.edu
*Web Site:* shenandoahliterary.org; shenandoah.wlu.edu
*Key Personnel*
Ed: R T Smith *E-mail:* rodsmith@wlu.edu
Annual award for the best poem published in Shenandoah during a volume year.
Award: $1,000

**Frederick Bock Prize**
Poetry Magazine
444 N Michigan Ave, Suite 1850, Chicago, IL 60611-4034
*Tel:* 312-787-7070 *Fax:* 312-787-6650
*E-mail:* editors@poetrymagazine.org
*Web Site:* poetryfoundation.org
*Key Personnel*
Mng Ed: Valerie Johnson *E-mail:* vjohnson@poetrymagazine.org
Established: 1981
For poetry published during the preceding two volumes of Poetry. No application necessary.
Award: $500
Closing Date: No application necessary
Presented: Annually in Dec

**George Bogin Memorial Award**
Poetry Society of America (PSA)
15 Gramercy Park S, New York, NY 10003
*Tel:* 212-254-9628 *Fax:* 212-673-2352
*Web Site:* www.poetrysociety.org
*Key Personnel*
Pres: Ruth Kaplan
Exec Dir: Alice Quinn
Mng Dir & Awards Coord: Brett Fletcher Lauer
*E-mail:* brett@poetrysociety.org
Progs Dir: Darrel Alejandro Holnes
Established by the family & friends of George Bogin, for a selection of four or five poems that reflects the encounter of the ordinary & the extraordinary, uses language in an original way & takes a stand against oppression in any of its forms. No line limit; send No 10 SASE or see web site for more information.
Award: $500
Closing Date: Annually, Oct-Dec
Presented: Annual Awards Ceremony, New York, NY, Annually in Spring

**Bogle International Library Travel Fund**
International Relations Committee
Unit of American Library Association (ALA)
50 E Huron St, Chicago, IL 60611-2795
*Tel:* 312-280-3201 *Toll Free Tel:* 800-545-2433 (ext 3201) *Fax:* 312-280-4392
*E-mail:* intl@ala.org
*Web Site:* www.ala.org
*Key Personnel*
Dir, Off of Chapter & Intl Rel: Michael Dowling
Prog Offr: Delin Guerra *E-mail:* dguerra@ala.org
To librarians to travel abroad to study &/or attend first international conferences.
Award: $1,000
Closing Date: Annually in Dec
Presented: ALA Conference, Annually, Jan 1

**Laura Day Boggs Bolling Memorial**
The Poetry Society of Virginia
1194 Hume Rd, Hume, VA 22639-1806
*E-mail:* poetryinva@aol.com
*Web Site:* www.poetrysocietyofvirginia.org
*Key Personnel*
Pres: Judith K Bragg *E-mail:* musicsavy45@yahoo.com
Adult Contest Chair: Patsy Anne Bickerstaff
*E-mail:* granypatsy@yahoo.com; Guy Terrell
*E-mail:* ggterr@infionline.net
All entries must be in English, original & unpublished, Submit 2 copies, both copies must have the category name & number on top left of page. Entries will not be returned. Poem written by an adult for school-age children (10-12 yrs); any rhymed form; 20 line limit. Entry fee: $4 nonmembs.
Other Sponsor(s): Children of Laura Day Boggs Bolling: Alma, Flora & Glade
Award: $50 (1st prize), $30 (2nd prize), $20 (3rd prize)
Closing Date: Jan 19
Presented: Annual PSV Awards Luncheon, Richmond, VA, April

**Waldo M & Grace C Bonderman Playwriting for Youth National Competition & Symposium**, see Write Now

**Boston Globe-Horn Book Award**
The Boston Globe & The Horn Book Inc
56 Roland St, Suite 200, Boston, MA 02129
*Tel:* 617-628-0225 *Toll Free Tel:* 800-325-1170
*Fax:* 617-628-0882
*E-mail:* info@hbook.com
*Web Site:* www.hbook.com
*Key Personnel*
Ed-in-Chief, Horn Book Pubns: Roger Sutton
Asst Ed: Katrina Hedeen *Tel:* 617-628-0225 ext 222 *E-mail:* khedeen@hbook.com
Established: 1967
Honors excellence in children's & young adult literature in three categories: fiction & poetry, nonfiction & picture books. Published books only, mss not accepted.
Award: $500 each
Closing Date: Annually in May
Presented: Annually in Fall

**Boulevard Magazine Short Fiction Contest for Emerging Writers**
Boulevard Magazine
6614 Clayton Rd, PMB 325, Richmond Heights, MO 63117
*Tel:* 314-862-2643
*Web Site:* www.boulevardmagazine.org
*Key Personnel*
Founding Ed: Richard Burgin
*E-mail:* richardburgin@att.net
Mng Ed: Jessica Rogen *E-mail:* jessicarogen@boulevardmagazine.org
Open to writers who have not yet published a book of fiction, poetry or creative nonfiction with a nationally distributed press. Simultaneous submissions are allowed but previously accepted or published work is ineligible. Send typed, double-spaced mss & SAS postcard for acknowledgment of receipt. No mss will be returned. 8,000 word maximum length; cover sheets not necessary. Entry fee is $15 per story with no limit per author, includes one year subn.
Award: $1,500 & publication in the Spring or the Fall issue of Boulevard
Closing Date: Annually, Dec 31

**Bound to Stay Bound Books Scholarship**
Association for Library Service to Children (ALSC)
Division of American Library Association (ALA)
50 E Huron St, Chicago, IL 60611-2795
*Tel:* 312-280-2163 *Toll Free Tel:* 800-545-2433
*Fax:* 312-440-9374
*E-mail:* alsc@ala.org
*Web Site:* www.ala.org/alsc
*Key Personnel*
Exec Dir: Aimee Strittmatter *Tel:* 312-280-2162
*E-mail:* astrittmatter@ala.org
Awards Coord: Caroline Jewell
*E-mail:* alscawards@ala.org
Prog Coord: Marsha P Burgess
*E-mail:* mburgess@ala.org
For study in field of library service to children toward the MLS or beyond in an ALA-accredited program.
Award: $7,000 - 4 scholarships per yr
Closing Date: Annually, March 1
Presented: ALA Annual Conference, Annually in June

**Amber Bowerman Memorial Travel Writing Award**
Writers Guild of Alberta
11759 Groat Rd, Edmonton, AB T5M 3K6, Canada
*Tel:* 780-422-8174 *Toll Free Tel:* 800-665-5354 (AB only) *Fax:* 780-422-2663 (attn WGA)
*E-mail:* mail@writersguild.ab.ca
*Web Site:* www.writersguild.ab.ca
*Key Personnel*
Exec Dir: Carol Holmes *E-mail:* cholmes@writersguild.ab.ca
Communs & Partnerships Coord: Nicholas Mather *E-mail:* nmather@writersguild.ab.ca
Memb Servs Coord: Giorgia Severini
Progs Coord: Nichole Quiring
*E-mail:* programs@writersguild.ab.ca
Established: 2008
Open to unpublished travel essays by authors under 30; no longer than 3,000 words.
Award: $700
Closing Date: Annually, Dec 31
Presented: Alberta Literary Awards Gala
*Branch Office(s)*
Lord Denning House, 509 20 Ave SW, Calgary, AB T2S 0E7, Canada, Prog Coord: Samantha Warwick *Tel:* 403-265-2226
*E-mail:* swarwick@writersguild.ab.ca

**Barbara Bradley Prize**
New England Poetry Club
2 Farrar St, Cambridge, MA 02138
Mailing Address: PO Box 190076, Boston, MA 02119
*Tel:* 617-744-6034
*E-mail:* contests@nepoetryclub.org
*Web Site:* www.nepoetryclub.org
*Key Personnel*
Pres: Diana Der-Hovanessian
VP: Sally Cragin; Daniel Tobin
Contest Chair: Nazaleem Smith

Established: 1988
Prize for a poem in lyric form, under 21 lines, written by a woman. Mark name of contest on envelope, send to address above. Send poem in duplicate with name of writer on one only.
Award: $200
Closing Date: must be postmarked in April & May only
Presented: Public Library, Cambridge, MA, Annually in Autumn

**BrainStorm Poetry Contest for Mental Health Consumers**
Northern Initiative for Social Action (NISA)
680 Kirkwood Dr, Bldg 1, Sudbury, ON P3E 1X3, Canada
*Tel:* 705-222-6472 (ext 303)
*E-mail:* openminds@nisa.on.ca
*Web Site:* www.nisa.on.ca
*Key Personnel*
Publr & Ed: Dinah Laprairie
Established: 2003
Contest open only to people with lived experience of mental illness internationally. It aims to eliminate the stigma associated with mental illness by showcasing the talents & creativity of individuals living with mental illness. Contest details available after Dec 15 online. Contest runs Jan to end of March each year. Call or e-mail for entry form.
Award: $250 (1st prize), $150 (2nd prize), $75 (3rd prize), plus publication in *Open Minds Quarterly*
Closing Date: Annually Jan-March

**James Henry Breasted Prize**
American Historical Association
400 "A" St SE, Washington, DC 20003-3889
*Tel:* 202-544-2422 *Fax:* 202-544-8307
*E-mail:* awards@historians.org
*Web Site:* www.historians.org
Established: 1985
Best book in English in any field of history prior to 1000 AD. Different geographic area will be eligible each year. Entries must be published in 2013. Along with an application form, applicants must mail a copy of their book to each of the prize committee members who will be posted on our web site as the prize deadline approaches. All updated info on web site.
Award: Cash prize
Closing Date: May 15, 2014 (postmark)
Presented: AHA Annual Meeting

**The Briar Cliff Review Fiction, Poetry & Creative Nonfiction Contest**
The Briar Cliff Review-Briar Cliff University
3303 Rebecca St, Sioux City, IA 51104-2100
*Tel:* 712-279-1651 *Fax:* 712-279-5486
*Web Site:* www.briarcliff.edu/bcreview
*Key Personnel*
Mktg Dir: Judy Thompson
Ed: Tricia Currans-Sheehan
Poetry, creative nonfiction & fiction contest. Submit unpublished story, essay or 3 poems with $20. Entrants receive issue. No name on mss. Include cover page with title(s), name, address, e-mail, phone. Send SASE for results only.
Award: $1,000 each category & publication in Spring
Closing Date: Annually Nov 1

**Brick Road Poetry Book Contest**
Brick Road Poetry Press
PO Box 751, Columbus, GA 31902-0751
*Tel:* 706-649-3080
*Web Site:* brickroadpoetrypress.com
*Key Personnel*
Ed: Keith Badowski; Ron Self
Book-length poetry mss only, original collection of 50-80 pages of poetry, excluding cover page. Entry fee $25.
Award: $1,000, publication contract with Brick Road Poetry Press in both print & ebook formats & 25 copies of the printed book
Closing Date: Annually, Aug 1-Nov 1

**Brittingham & Pollak Prizes in Poetry**
University of Wisconsin Press
Dept of English, 600 N Park St, Madison, WI 53706
*Web Site:* www.wisc.edu/wisconsinpress
*Key Personnel*
Ed: Ronald Wallace
Established: 1985
Pollak & Brittingham are two prizes from one competition. For book-length mss of poetry. Mss not accepted before Aug 15 or after Sept 15; $25 reading fee required, check made payable to: University of Wisconsin Press. Mss not returned; send required business-size SASE for contest results. For guidelines check web site. Electronic submissions encouraged.
Other Sponsor(s): University of Wisconsin Creative Writing Program
Award: $1,000 & publication in University of Wisconsin Press Poetry Series for each book
Closing Date: Sept 15

**The Heywood Broun Award**
The Newspaper Guild
501 Third St NW, 6th fl, Washington, DC 20001-2797
*Tel:* 202-434-7177; 202-434-7162 (The Guild Reporter) *Fax:* 202-434-1472
*Web Site:* www.newsguild.org
*Key Personnel*
Ed: Janelle Hertman
Established: 1941
Journalism.
Award: $5,000
Closing Date: Last Friday in Jan
Presented: Washington, DC, Annually in May

**John Nicholas Brown Prize**
Medieval Academy of America
104 Mount Auburn St, 5th fl, Cambridge, MA 02138
*Tel:* 617-491-1622 *Fax:* 617-492-3303
*E-mail:* speculum@medievalacademy.org
*Web Site:* www.medievalacademy.org
*Key Personnel*
Exec Dir & Ed, Speculum: Eileen Gardiner *E-mail:* egardiner@themedievalacademy.org
Established: 1978
For a first book published four years prior to award date, in the field of medieval studies.
Award: $1,000
Closing Date: Annually, Oct 15
Presented: Annually in April

**Bucknell Seminar for Younger Poets**
Stadler Center for Poetry
Bucknell University, Bucknell Hall, Moore Ave, Lewisburg, PA 17837
*Tel:* 570-577-1853 *Fax:* 570-577-1885
*E-mail:* stadlercenter@bucknell.edu
*Web Site:* www.bucknell.edu/stadlercenter
*Key Personnel*
Dir: G C Waldrep
Mng Ed & Book Review Ed: Andrew Ciotola
Established: 1985
Three-week residence in writing for undergraduate poets. Applications should include an academic transcript, two supporting recommendations (at least one from a poetry-writing instructor) & a 10-12 page portfolio. A letter of self-presentation (letter of intro stressing commitment to poetry writing, experience & any publications) should accompany the application. Applications must be submitted online, see web site for details.
Closing Date: Jan 31 (postmark)
Presented: Stadler Center for Poetry, Bucknell University, Lewisburg, PA, June 8–29, 2014

**Georges Bugnet Award for Fiction**
Writers Guild of Alberta
11759 Groat Rd, Edmonton, AB T5M 3K6, Canada
*Tel:* 780-422-8174 *Toll Free Tel:* 800-665-5354 (AB only) *Fax:* 780-422-2663 (attn WGA)
*E-mail:* mail@writersguild.ab.ca
*Web Site:* www.writersguild.ab.ca
*Key Personnel*
Exec Dir: Carol Holmes *E-mail:* cholmes@writersguild.ab.ca
Communs & Partnerships Coord: Nicholas Mather *E-mail:* nmather@writersguild.ab.ca
Memb Servs Coord: Giorgia Severini
Progs Coord: Nichole Quiring *E-mail:* programs@writersguild.ab.ca
Established: 1982
Alberta Literary Award, author must be resident of Alberta.
Award: $1,500
Closing Date: Annually, Dec 31
Presented: Alberta Literary Awards Gala
*Branch Office(s)*
Lord Denning House, 509 20 Ave SW, Calgary, AB T2S 0E7, Canada, Prog Coord: Samantha Warwick *Tel:* 403-265-2226 *E-mail:* swarwick@writersguild.ab.ca

**Burnside Review Fiction Chapbook Competition**
Burnside Review
PO Box 1782, Portland, OR 97207
*Web Site:* burnsidereview.org
*Key Personnel*
Ed: Sid Miller *E-mail:* sid@burnsidereview.org
Established: 2006
Submit up to 10,000 words in the form of one long story or multiple shorter pieces. Outside judge is brought in. Contest results are announced via telephone, mail & on web site. Entry fee $15.
Award: $200 & 25 copies of the press run of at least 100
Closing Date: Annually, Dec 31
Presented: Annually, April 1

**The John Burroughs List of Nature Books for Young Readers**
John Burroughs Association Inc
15 W 77 St, New York, NY 10024
*Tel:* 212-769-5169 *Fax:* 212-313-7182
*Web Site:* research.amnh.org/burroughs
*Key Personnel*
Secy: Lisa Breslof *E-mail:* lbreslof@amnh.org
To recognize writers, artists & publishers who produce outstanding nature literature for children. Nonfiction subjects of natural history, ecology & environmental studies. Works may include poetry, travel, art, adventure, biography. No guide books to identification, science texts, or reference works. Submit five copies of each entry, addressed to: Secretary, The John Burroughs Association.
Award: John Burroughs Certificate of Recognition to authors, illustrators & publishers of each selected book
Closing Date: Annually, Nov 30
Presented: American Museum of Natural History, 1st Monday in April

**John Burroughs Medal**
John Burroughs Association Inc
15 W 77 St, New York, NY 10024
*Tel:* 212-769-5169 *Fax:* 212-313-7182
*Web Site:* research.amnh.org/burroughs
*Key Personnel*
Secy: Lisa Breslof *E-mail:* lbreslof@amnh.org
Established: 1926

Annual award for the year's best book in the field of natural history. The work of John Burroughs, a literary naturalist, is the standard for the general character of the books eligible. They should combine literary quality with accuracy & should be based on originality of observation & conclusion. Award is not given for compilations of others' findings. Submit six copies of each entry addressed to Secretary, The John Burroughs Association.
Award: Bronze medal
Closing Date: Annually, Oct 15
Presented: Luncheon at American Museum of Natural History, New York, NY, 1st Monday in April

**John Burroughs Outstanding Published Nature Essay Award**
John Burroughs Association Inc
15 W 77 St, New York, NY 10024
*Tel:* 212-769-5169 *Fax:* 212-313-7182
*Web Site:* research.amnh.org/burroughs
*Key Personnel*
Secy: Lisa Breslof *E-mail:* lbreslof@amnh.org
To recognize current authors of outstanding essays published in magazines & journals emphasizing John Burroughs Literary works, contributions & skill as an outstanding nature essayist; Submit seven copies of each entry addressed to "Secretary, The John Burroughs Association".
Award: Certificate of Recognition
Closing Date: Annually, Dec 31
Presented: Annual Meeting, 1st Monday in April

**CAA Award for Fiction**
Canadian Authors Association (CAA)
6 West St N, Suite 203, Orillia, ON L3V 5B8, Canada
*Tel:* 705-325-3926 *Toll Free Tel:* 866-216-6222
*E-mail:* admin@canauthors.org
*Web Site:* www.canauthors.org
*Key Personnel*
Exec Dir: Anita Purcell
Entries must be full-length English-language literature for adults by Canadian authors. Reprints are not eligible, nor is self-published work. Fee at $40 per entry to offset a portion of administrative costs.
Award: $2,000 & silver medal
Closing Date: Annually, Dec 15
Presented: CAA's Annual Conference, Awards Gala & Banquet, Annually in June

**CAA Emerging Writer Award**
Canadian Authors Association (CAA)
6 West St N, Suite 203, Orillia, ON L3V 5B8, Canada
*Tel:* 705-325-3926 *Toll Free Tel:* 866-216-6222
*E-mail:* admin@canauthors.org
*Web Site:* www.canauthors.org
*Key Personnel*
Exec Dir: Anita Purcell
Awarded to the Canadian writer under 30 yrs old deemed to show the most promise in the field of literary creation.
Award: $500 & 1 yr membership in Canadian Authors Association
Closing Date: Annually, March 31
Presented: CAA's Annual Conference, Awards Gala & Banquet, Annually in June

**CAA Lela Common Award for Canadian History**
Canadian Authors Association (CAA)
6 West St N, Suite 203, Orillia, ON L3V 5B8, Canada
*Tel:* 705-325-3926 *Toll Free Tel:* 866-216-6222
*E-mail:* admin@canauthors.org
*Web Site:* www.canauthors.org
*Key Personnel*
Exec Dir: Anita Purcell
Established: 1997
All entries must be historical nonfiction, on Canadian topics by Canadian authors. The books must be English-Language literature for adults (not "young adults"). Translations are not eligible. Fee of $40 per entry to offset a portion of administrative costs.
Award: $2,000 & silver medal
Closing Date: Annually, Dec 15
Presented: CAA's Annual Conference, Awards Gala & Banquet, Annually in June

**CAA Poetry Award**
Canadian Authors Association (CAA)
6 West St N, Suite 203, Orillia, ON L3V 5B8, Canada
*Tel:* 705-325-3926 *Toll Free Tel:* 866-216-6222
*E-mail:* admin@canauthors.org
*Web Site:* www.canauthors.org
*Key Personnel*
Exec Dir: Anita Purcell
For a volume of poetry by one poet. Entry fee $40 per title.
Award: $2000 & silver medal
Closing Date: Annually, Dec 15
Presented: CAA Annual Conference, Awards Gala & Banquet, Annually in June

**Gerald Cable Book Award**
Silverfish Review Press
PO Box 3541, Eugene, OR 97403
*Tel:* 541-344-5060
*E-mail:* sfrpress@earthlink.net
*Web Site:* www.silverfishreviewpress.com
*Key Personnel*
Ed & Publr: Rodger Moody
Established: 1995
Poetry Book; for author who has not yet published a collection; selection by March.
Award: $1,000 & publication by Silverfish Review Press & 25 copies of the book
Closing Date: Submit by Oct 15

**The Randolph Caldecott Medal**
Association for Library Service to Children (ALSC)
Division of American Library Association (ALA)
50 E Huron St, Chicago, IL 60611-2795
*Tel:* 312-280-2163 *Toll Free Tel:* 800-545-2433 *Fax:* 312-440-9374
*E-mail:* alsc@ala.org
*Web Site:* www.ala.org/alsc
*Key Personnel*
Exec Dir: Aimee Strittmatter *Tel:* 312-280-2162 *E-mail:* astrittmatter@ala.org
Prog Coord: Marsha P Burgess *E-mail:* mburgess@ala.org
Awards Coord: Caroline Jewell *E-mail:* alscawards@ala.org
Established: 1937
Given to the artist who created the most distinguished American picture book for children published in the US during the previous year. The artist must be a citizen or resident of the US.
Award: Medal
Closing Date: Annually, Dec 31
Presented: ALA Annual Conference, Annually in June

**California Book Awards**
Commonwealth Club of California
595 Market St, San Francisco, CA 94105
*Tel:* 415-597-6700 *Fax:* 415-597-6729
*E-mail:* bookawards@commonwealthclub.org
*Web Site:* www.commonwealthclub.org/bookawards
Established: 1931
Honors the exceptional literary merit of California writers & publishers. Awards are presented in the categories of fiction, nonfiction, poetry, first work of fiction, juvenile literature (up to age 10), adult literature (ages 11-16), Californiana, works in translation & notable contribution to publishing. To be eligible, author must be resident in California at the time of publication & books must be published under the year in consideration.
Award: Plaques with medallions for gold & silver awardees
Closing Date: Dec
Presented: Annually 1st Thurs in June

**Joe Pendleton Campbell Narrative Contest**
The Poetry Society of Virginia
1194 Hume Rd, Hume, VA 22639-1806
*E-mail:* poetryinva@aol.com
*Web Site:* www.poetrysocietyofvirginia.org
*Key Personnel*
Pres: Judith K Bragg *E-mail:* musicsavy45@yahoo.com
Adult Contest Chair: Patsy Anne Bickerstaff *E-mail:* granypatsy@yahoo.com; Guy Terrell *E-mail:* ggterr@infionline.net
All entries must be in English, original & unpublished. Submit 2 copies, each having the category name & number on top left of page. Any form; any subject; narrative poem; 64 line limit. Entry fee: $4 nonmembs.
Other Sponsor(s): Paula Savoy
Award: $50 (1st prize), $30 (2nd prize), $20 (3rd prize)
Closing Date: Jan 19
Presented: Annual PSV Awards Luncheon, Richmond, VA, April

**John W Campbell Memorial Award**
Center for the Study of Science Fiction
University of Kansas, Wescoe Hall, Rm 3001, Dept of English, 1445 Jayhawk Blvd, Lawrence, KS 66045-7590
*Tel:* 785-864-3380 *Fax:* 785-864-1159
*Web Site:* www.ku.edu/~sfcenter; ku.edu/campbell.htm
*Key Personnel*
Founding Dir: James Gunn *E-mail:* jgunn@ku.edu
Dir: Chris McKitterick *E-mail:* cmckit@ku.edu
Established: 1973
Selected by jury who produces a short list & votes on that list to select a winner. Science fiction novels published in English anywhere in the world in the year of eligibility. Publishers are encouraged to submit works for consideration by the jury.
Award: Trophy & expense paid trip to the conference to receive the award
Presented: Campbell Conference Awards Banquet, University of Kansas, Lawrence, KS

**Alexander Patterson Cappon Prize for Fiction**
New Letters
UMKC, University House, 5101 Rockhill Rd, Kansas City, MO 64110-2499
*Tel:* 816-235-1168 *Fax:* 816-235-2611
*E-mail:* newletters@umkc.edu
*Web Site:* www.newletters.org
Established: 1986
Literary contest. All entries considered for publication.
Award: $1,500 & publication
Closing Date: Annually, May 18

**Dorothy Churchill Cappon Prize for the Essay**
New Letters
UMKC, University House, 5101 Rockhill Rd, Kansas City, MO 64110-2499
*Tel:* 816-235-1168 *Fax:* 816-235-2611
*E-mail:* newletters@umkc.edu
*Web Site:* www.newletters.org
Established: 1986
Literary contest. All entries considered for publication.
Award: $1,500 & publication
Closing Date: Annually, May 18

**Carnegie-Whitney Award**
ALA Publishing Committee
Unit of American Library Association (ALA)
50 E Huron St, Chicago, IL 60611
*Tel:* 312-280-5416 *Toll Free Tel:* 800-545-2433
*Fax:* 312-280-5275; 312-440-9379
*Web Site:* www.ala.org
*Key Personnel*
Grant Administrator: Mary Jo Bolduc
*E-mail:* mbolduc@ala.org
For the preparation of bibliographic aids for research with scholarly intent & general applicability. Decisions made at Publishing Committee Meeting, each Jan. Completed proposals should be sent to Chair, ALA Publishing Committee at the above address.
Other Sponsor(s): James Gyman Whitney Fund, Andrew Carnegie Fund
Award: Up to $5,000 annually
Closing Date: Annually in Nov

**The Carter Prize For The Essay**
Shenandoah: The Washington & Lee University Review
Washington & Lee University, Mattingly House, 204 W Washington St, Lexington, VA 24450-2116
*Tel:* 540-458-8765
*E-mail:* shenandoah@wlu.edu
*Web Site:* shenandoahliterary.org; shenandoah.wlu.edu
*Key Personnel*
Ed: R T Smith *E-mail:* rodsmith@wlu.edu
Annual award for the best essay published in Shenandoah during a volume year.
Award: $1000

**Catholic Book Awards**
Catholic Press Association of the US & Canada
205 W Monroe St, Suite 470, Chicago, IL 60606
*Tel:* 312-380-6789 *Fax:* 312-361-0256
*E-mail:* cathjourn@catholicpress.org
*Web Site:* www.catholicpress.org
*Key Personnel*
Exec Dir: Timothy Walter *E-mail:* twalter@catholicpress.org
Opers Analyst: Barbara Mastrolia
Several awards for best Catholic books in different categories.
Award: Certificate
Closing Date: Jan
Presented: Annual Convention, June

**Catholic Press Association of the US & Canada Journalism Awards**
Catholic Press Association of the US & Canada
205 W Monroe St, Suite 470, Chicago, IL 60606
*Tel:* 312-380-6789 *Fax:* 312-361-0256
*E-mail:* cathjourn@catholicpress.org
*Web Site:* www.catholicpress.org
*Key Personnel*
Exec Dir: Timothy Walter *E-mail:* twalter@catholicpress.org
Opers Analyst: Barbara Mastrolia
Journalism entries from member publications.
Award: Certificates
Closing Date: Jan
Presented: Annual Convention, June

**CBA Libris Award for Author of the Year**
Canadian Booksellers Association (CBA)
1255 Bay St, Suite 902, Toronto, ON M5R 2A9, Canada
*Tel:* 416-467-7883 *Toll Free Tel:* 866-788-0790
*Fax:* 416-467-7886
*E-mail:* enquiries@cbabook.org
*Web Site:* www.cbabook.org
*Key Personnel*
Pres: Mark Lefebvre *E-mail:* lefebvre@mcmaster.ca
Sr Mgr: Jodi White *Tel:* 416-467-7883 ext 227
*E-mail:* jwhite@cbabook.org
Mktg & Communs Mgr: Stephanie Quinlan
*Tel:* 416-467-7883 ext 230 *E-mail:* squinlan@cbabook.org
Awarded to the Canadian author of an outstanding literary work in the previous year that is a contribution to Canadian culture & that combines readability with strong sales. An author who has offered strong support to the bookselling industry.
Closing Date: Annually in Feb
Presented: Libris Awards Presentation: National Conference, Annually in June

**CBA Libris Children's Picture Book of the Year**
Canadian Booksellers Association (CBA)
1255 Bay St, Suite 902, Toronto, ON M5R 2A9, Canada
*Tel:* 416-467-7883 *Toll Free Tel:* 866-788-0790
*Fax:* 416-467-7886
*E-mail:* enquiries@cbabook.org
*Web Site:* www.cbabook.org
*Key Personnel*
Pres: Mark Lefebvre *E-mail:* lefebvre@mcmaster.ca
Sr Mgr: Jodi White *Tel:* 416-467-7883 ext 227
*E-mail:* jwhite@cbabook.org
Mktg & Communs Mgr: Stephanie Quinlan
*Tel:* 416-467-7883 ext 230 *E-mail:* squinlan@cbabook.org
For a Canadian picture book from the previous year whose imaginative storyline & creative visuals engaged, entertained & delighted young children while generating customer attention & strong sales.
Closing Date: Annually in Feb
Presented: Libris Awards Presentation: National Conference, Annually in June

**CBA Libris Distributor of the Year**
Canadian Booksellers Association (CBA)
1255 Bay St, Suite 902, Toronto, ON M5R 2A9, Canada
*Tel:* 416-467-7883 *Toll Free Tel:* 866-788-0790
*Fax:* 416-467-7886
*E-mail:* enquiries@cbabook.org
*Web Site:* www.cbabook.org
*Key Personnel*
Pres: Mark Lefebvre *E-mail:* lefebvre@mcmaster.ca
Sr Mgr: Jodi White *Tel:* 416-467-7883 ext 227
*E-mail:* jwhite@cbabook.org
Mktg & Communs Mgr: Stephanie Quinlan
*Tel:* 416-467-7883 ext 230 *E-mail:* squinlan@cbabook.org
To a Canadian distributor in recognition of an outstanding support of the bookselling industry. Based on customer service, accuracy & speed of order fulfillment, correct invoicing, efficient handling of returns & credits.
Closing Date: Annually in Feb
Presented: Libris Awards Presentation: National Conference, Annually in June

**CBA Libris Editor of the Year**
Canadian Booksellers Association (CBA)
1255 Bay St, Suite 902, Toronto, ON M5R 2A9, Canada
*Tel:* 416-467-7883 *Toll Free Tel:* 866-788-0790
*Fax:* 416-467-7886
*E-mail:* enquiries@cbabook.org
*Web Site:* www.cbabook.org
*Key Personnel*
Pres: Mark Lefebvre *E-mail:* lefebvre@mcmaster.ca
Sr Mgr: Jodi White *Tel:* 416-467-7883 ext 227
*E-mail:* jwhite@cbabook.org
Mktg & Communs Mgr: Stephanie Quinlan
*Tel:* 416-467-7883 ext 230 *E-mail:* squinlan@cbabook.org
Awarded to an in-house editor in recognition of excellence in the field. Based on all-around skills, development of new authors, commitment to quality, commercial awareness & originality.
Closing Date: Annually in Feb
Presented: Libris Awards Presentation: National Conference, Annually in June

**CBA Libris Fiction Book of the Year**
Canadian Booksellers Association (CBA)
1255 Bay St, Suite 902, Toronto, ON M5R 2A9, Canada
*Tel:* 416-467-7883 *Toll Free Tel:* 866-788-0790
*Fax:* 416-467-7886
*E-mail:* enquiries@cbabook.org
*Web Site:* www.cbabook.org
*Key Personnel*
Pres: Mark Lefebvre *E-mail:* lefebvre@mcmaster.ca
Sr Mgr: Jodi White *Tel:* 416-467-7883 ext 227
*E-mail:* jwhite@cbabook.org
Mktg & Communs Mgr: Stephanie Quinlan
*Tel:* 416-467-7883 ext 230 *E-mail:* squinlan@cbabook.org
For a Canadian work of fiction published in the previous year that had an outstanding impact on the Canadian bookselling industry, created wide media attention, brought people into bookstores & had strong sales.
Closing Date: Annually in Feb
Presented: Libris Awards Presentation: National Conference, Annually in June

**CBA Libris Publisher of the Year**
Canadian Booksellers Association (CBA)
1255 Bay St, Suite 902, Toronto, ON M5R 2A9, Canada
*Tel:* 416-467-7883 *Toll Free Tel:* 866-788-0790
*Fax:* 416-467-7886
*E-mail:* enquiries@cbabook.org
*Web Site:* www.cbabook.org
*Key Personnel*
Pres: Mark Lefebvre *E-mail:* lefebvre@mcmaster.ca
Sr Mgr: Jodi White *Tel:* 416-467-7883 ext 227
*E-mail:* jwhite@cbabook.org
Mktg & Communs Mgr: Stephanie Quinlan
*Tel:* 416-467-7883 ext 230 *E-mail:* squinlan@cbabook.org
To a Canadian publisher in recognition of an outstanding contribution to the Canadian bookselling industry. Based on consistent high quality in author relations; editorial, production & marketing skills, retail support & commercial success.
Closing Date: Annually in Feb
Presented: Libris Awards Presentation: National Conference, Annually in June

**CBA Libris Sales Rep of the Year**
Canadian Booksellers Association (CBA)
1255 Bay St, Suite 902, Toronto, ON M5R 2A9, Canada
*Tel:* 416-467-7883 *Toll Free Tel:* 866-788-0790
*Fax:* 416-467-7886
*E-mail:* enquiries@cbabook.org
*Web Site:* www.cbabook.org
*Key Personnel*
Pres: Mark Lefebvre *E-mail:* lefebvre@mcmaster.ca
Sr Mgr: Jodi White *Tel:* 416-467-7883 ext 227
*E-mail:* jwhite@cbabook.org
Mktg & Communs Mgr: Stephanie Quinlan
*Tel:* 416-467-7883 ext 230 *E-mail:* squinlan@cbabook.org
Presented in memory of Gordon S Garner in recognition of excellence in the field. Based on all-around skills, development of new authors, commitment to quality, commercial awareness & originality.
Closing Date: Annually in Feb
Presented: Libris Awards Presentation: National Conference, Annually in June

**CBA Libris Small Press Publisher of the Year**
Canadian Booksellers Association (CBA)
1255 Bay St, Suite 902, Toronto, ON M5R 2A9, Canada
*Tel:* 416-467-7883 *Toll Free Tel:* 866-788-0790 *Fax:* 416-467-7886
*E-mail:* enquiries@cbabook.org
*Web Site:* www.cbabook.org
*Key Personnel*
Pres: Mark Lefebvre *E-mail:* lefebvre@mcmaster.ca
Sr Mgr: Jodi White *Tel:* 416-467-7883 ext 227 *E-mail:* jwhite@cbabook.org
Mktg & Communs Mgr: Stephanie Quinlan *Tel:* 416-467-7883 ext 230 *E-mail:* squinlan@cbabook.org
Awarded to a Canadian publisher in recognition of an outstanding contribution to the Canadian bookselling industry. Based on consistent high quality in author relations, editorial production & marketing skills, retail support & commercial success. Nominees must have published 25 or fewer new books the previous year.
Closing Date: Annually in Feb
Presented: Libris Awards Presentation: National Conference, Annually in June

**Center for Publishing Departmental Scholarships**
New York University, School of Continuing & Professional Studies
Midtown Ctr, Rm 429, 11 W 42 St, New York, NY 10036
*Tel:* 212-992-3232 *Fax:* 212-992-3233
*E-mail:* pub.center@nyu.edu; ms.publishing@nyu.edu
*Web Site:* www.scps.nyu.edu
*Key Personnel*
Assoc Dir: Sarah McCarthy *E-mail:* sarah.mccarthy@nyu.edu
Awarded to students enrolled in at least 6 credits in Master of Science in publishing program (not available to students in first semester). Need excellent academic record. Based on financial need & merit.
Award: $500 & up
Presented: Annually in Fall & Spring

**Jane Chambers Playwriting Award**
Women in Theatre Program, Association for Theatre in Higher Education
Georgetown University, 108 David Performing Arts Ctr, Box 571063, 37 & "O" St, NW, Washington, DC 20057-1063
*Tel:* 202-687-1327
*Web Site:* www.athe.org/displaycommon.cfm?an=1&subarticlenbr=25
*Key Personnel*
Contact: Maya E Roth *E-mail:* mer46@georgetown.edu
Established: 1984
Award for play or performance text by a woman which reflects a feminist perspective & contains a majority of opportunities for women performers. Scripts may be produced or unproduced; encourage experimentation with dramatic form; send SASE for application & full information or see web site; two bound copies of script required & not returned.
Award: $1,000 for reading of the winning piece at the award conference & free registration to the conference; student winner is also recognized
Closing Date: Feb 15
Presented: Annual ATHE National Conference

**The Alfred & Fay Chandler Book Award**
Harvard University
c/o Business History Review, Harvard Business School, Soldiers Field Rd, Boston, MA 02163
*Tel:* 617-495-1003 *Fax:* 617-495-0594
*E-mail:* bhr@hbs.edu
*Web Site:* www.hbs.edu/bhr
*Key Personnel*
Ed: Walter Friedman *E-mail:* wfriedman@hbs.edu
Established: 1964
Award given every three years for best book published in the US on the history of business. Selection by the editorial board of the Business History Review.
Award: A scroll

**G S Sharat Chandra Prize for Short Fiction**
BkMk Press - University of Missouri-Kansas City
5101 Rockhill Rd, Kansas City, MO 64110-2499
*Tel:* 816-235-2558 *Fax:* 816-235-2611
*E-mail:* bkmk@umkc.edu
*Web Site:* www.umkc.edu/bkmk
*Key Personnel*
Exec Ed: Robert Stewart *Tel:* 816-235-1120
Mng Ed: Ben Furnish
Assoc Ed: Michelle Boisseau *Tel:* 816-235-2561
Established: 2001
The best book-length ms of short fiction in English by a living author. Ms must be typed on standard-sized paper in English & should be 125-350 pages double-spaced. Entries must include two title pages: one with author name, address & phone number & one with no author information. Any acknowledgments should appear on a separate piece of paper. Entries must include a table of contents. Author's name must not appear anywhere on the ms. Do not submit your ms by fax or e-mail. A SASE should be included, for notification only. Note: No mss will be returned. A reading fee of $25 in US funds (check payable to BkMk Press) must accompany each ms. Entrants will receive a copy of the winning book when published.
Award: $1,000 plus book publication of winning ms by BkMk Press
Closing Date: Annually, Jan 15
Presented: Annually in Summer

**Chapter One Fiction Competition**
Bronx Council On the Arts
1738 Hone Ave, Bronx, NY 10461-1486
*Tel:* 718-931-9500 *Fax:* 718-409-6445
*E-mail:* info@bronxarts.org
*Web Site:* www.bronxarts.org
*Key Personnel*
Writers Ctr Dir: Maria Romano *Tel:* 718-931-9500 ext 21
Established: 1997
Awarded to five novelists from New York City for the first chapter of an unpublished novel & works in progress.
Award: $1,000 honorarium & a reading in the Bronx
Closing Date: Annually in Sept

**Chariton Review Short Fiction Prize**
Truman State University Press
100 E Normal Ave, Kirksville, MO 63501-4221
*Tel:* 660-785-7336 *Toll Free Tel:* 800-916-6802 *Fax:* 660-785-4480
*Web Site:* tsup.truman.edu
*Key Personnel*
Dir & Ed-in-Chief: Nancy Rediger *E-mail:* nancyr@truman.edu
Submit a story of up to 5,000 words with a $20 entry fee, which includes a copy of the prize issue. Refer to guidelines on web site.
Award: $1,000 & publication in Chariton Review
Closing Date: Annually, Sept 30

**Chicago Book Clinic Midwest Book & Media Show**, see MPA Midwest Publishing Award Show

**Children's Literature Association Article Award**
Children's Literature Association (ChLA)
1301 W 22 St, Suite 202, Oak Brook, IL 60523
*Tel:* 630-571-4520 *Fax:* 708-876-5598
*E-mail:* info@childlitassn.org
*Web Site:* www.childlitassn.org
Award for best literary criticism article published within a given year on the topic of children's literature. See web site for application requirements.
Award: $400 plus award certificate
Presented: ChLA Annual Conference, Annually in June

**Children's Literature Association Beiter Graduate Student Research Grants**
Children's Literature Association (ChLA)
1301 W 22 St, Suite 202, Oak Brook, IL 60523
*Tel:* 630-571-4520 *Fax:* 708-876-5598
*E-mail:* info@childlitassn.org
*Web Site:* www.childlitassn.org
*Key Personnel*
Grants Chair: Kenneth Kidd
Awarded for proposals of original scholarship with the expectation that the undertaking will lead to publication or a conference presentation & contribute to the field of children's literature criticism. Winners must either be members of the Children's Literature Association or join the association before they receive any funds. Applications & supporting materials should be written in or translated into English. Encouraging new scholars to enter the field, the scholarship is intended to enable "entry level" scholars (graduate students, instructors or assistant professors) to bring to a publishable level dissertations, theses or papers that they have written.
Award: $500-$1,500 (based on the number & needs of the winning applicants)
Closing Date: Annually, Feb 1
Presented: ChLA Annual Conference, Annually in June

**Children's Literature Association Book Award**
Children's Literature Association (ChLA)
1301 W 22 St, Suite 202, Oak Brook, IL 60523
*Tel:* 630-571-4520 *Fax:* 708-876-5598
*E-mail:* info@childlitassn.org
*Web Site:* www.childlitassn.org
Book awards given for best book on children's literature history, scholarship & criticism published as a book in a given year. See web site for application requirements.
Award: $800 plus award certificate
Presented: ChLA Annual Conference, Annually in June

**Children's Sequoyah Book Award**
Oklahoma Library Association
300 Hardy Dr, Edmond, OK 73013
*Tel:* 405-525-5100 *Fax:* 405-525-5103
*Web Site:* www.oklibs.org
*Key Personnel*
Exec Dir: Kay Boies *E-mail:* kboies@sbcglobal.net
Contact: Tracy Keeley
Established: 1959
School children's choice of a book published by a living US author from a selected list. Students grades 3-5 who have read/listened to at least 3 books from the Children's Masterlist are eligible to vote.
Award: Plaque/medal
Closing Date: Annually, March 1
Presented: OLA Annual Conference, Annually in April

**The Christopher Awards**
The Christophers
5 Hanover Sq, 22nd fl, New York, NY 10004-2751
*Tel:* 212-759-4050 *Toll Free Tel:* 888-298-4050 (orders) *Fax:* 212-838-5073
*E-mail:* mail@christophers.org
*Web Site:* www.christophers.org

*Key Personnel*
Prog Mgr & Event Prodr: Tony Rossi *E-mail:* t.rossi@christophers.org
Established: 1949
For adult (nonfiction only) & juvenile fiction & nonfiction published during the current calendar year. Themes must reflect "highest values of the human spirit" criteria.
Award: Bronze medallion
Closing Date: June 1 & Nov 1; books evaluated throughout the calendar year
Presented: New York, NY, Annually in May

**John Ciardi Prize for Poetry**
BkMk Press - University of Missouri-Kansas City
5101 Rockhill Rd, Kansas City, MO 64110-2499
*Tel:* 816-235-2558 *Fax:* 816-235-2611
*E-mail:* bkmk@umkc.edu
*Web Site:* www.umkc.edu/bkmk
*Key Personnel*
Exec Ed: Robert Stewart *Tel:* 816-235-1120
Mng Ed: Ben Furnish
Assoc Ed: Michelle Boisseau *Tel:* 816-235-2561
Established: 1998
Presented for the best full-length ms of poetry in English by a living author. Ms must be typed on standard-sized paper & should be approximately 50 pages minimum, 110 pages maximum, single-spaced. Entries must include two title pages: one with author name, address & phone & one with no author information. Any acknowledgements should appear on a separate piece of paper. Entries must include a table of contents. Author's name must not appear anywhere on the ms. Do not submit your ms by fax or e-mail. A SASE should be included, for notification only. Note: No mss will be returned. A reading fee of $25 in US funds (check made payable to BkMk Press) must accompany each ms. Entrants will receive a copy of the winning book when it is published.
Award: $1,000 plus publication by BkMk Press
Closing Date: Annually, Jan 15
Presented: Annually in Summer

**The City of Calgary W O Mitchell Book Prize**
Writers Guild of Alberta
11759 Groat Rd, Edmonton, AB T5M 3K6, Canada
*Tel:* 780-422-8174 *Toll Free Tel:* 800-665-5354 (AB only) *Fax:* 780-422-2663 (attn WGA)
*E-mail:* mail@writersguild.ab.ca
*Web Site:* www.writersguild.ab.ca
*Key Personnel*
Exec Dir: Carol Holmes *E-mail:* cholmes@writersguild.ab.ca
Communs & Partnerships Coord: Nicholas Mather *E-mail:* nmather@writersguild.ab.ca
Memb Servs Coord: Giorgia Severini
Progs Coord: Nichole Quiring *E-mail:* programs@writersguild.ab.ca
Recognizes literary achievement by Calgary authors. Types may be fiction, poetry, nonfiction, children's literature & drama.
Award: $5,000
Closing Date: Annually, Dec 31
Presented: Calgary Awards, Spring
*Branch Office(s)*
Lord Denning House, 509 20 Ave SW, Calgary, AB T2S 0E7, Canada, Prog Coord: Samantha Warwick *Tel:* 403-265-2226 *E-mail:* swarwick@writersguild.ab.ca

**City of Toronto Book Award**
City of Toronto
Subsidiary of City of Toronto (Municipality)
Toronto Protocol City Clerks Office, City Hall, 100 Queen St W, 2nd fl West, Toronto, ON M5H 2N2, Canada
*Tel:* 416-392-7805 *Fax:* 416-392-1247
*E-mail:* protocol@toronto.ca
*Web Site:* www.toronto.ca/book_awards
*Key Personnel*
Protocol Offr: Bev Kurmey *E-mail:* bkurmey@toronto.ca
Established: 1974
To honor authors of books of literary or artistic merit that are evocative of Toronto published in preceding year.
Other Sponsor(s): Toronto Public Library (in partnership)
Award: $15,000 annually, $1,000 to each short listed book, usually four to six books, remainder to winner
Closing Date: Last weekday in March
Presented: Toronto, Shortlist announced in Sept & winner in Oct

**City of Vancouver Book Award**
City of Vancouver, Cultural Services Dept
Woodward's Heritage Bldg, Suite 501, 111 W Hastings St, Vancouver, BC V6B 1H4, Canada
*Tel:* 604-871-6634 *Fax:* 604-871-6005
*E-mail:* culture@vancouver.ca
*Web Site:* vancouver.ca/bookaward
*Key Personnel*
Cultural Planner: Marnie Rice *E-mail:* marnie.rice@vancouver.ca
Established: 1989
Annual award for authors of books - any genre - that contribute to the appreciation & understanding of Vancouver's history, unique character or achievements of its residents.
Award: $2,000
Closing Date: Annually in May
Presented: The Mayor's Arts Awards, Annually in Sept

**CLA Book of the Year for Children Award**
Canadian Association of Children's Librarians, Canadian Library Association (Association Canadienne des Bibliotheques)
Subsidiary of Canadian Association of Public Libraries
1150 Morrison Dr, Suite 1100, Ottawa, ON K2H 8S9, Canada
*Tel:* 613-232-9625 *Fax:* 613-563-9895
*E-mail:* info@cla.ca
*Web Site:* www.cla.ca
*Key Personnel*
Contact: Myra Junyk *Tel:* 416-239-0766 *E-mail:* myrajunyk@yahoo.ca
Established: 1947
Awarded to the author of an outstanding Canadian children's book in English. Author must be a citizen or a resident of Canada.
Award: Leather-bound copy of winning book with award seal gold embossed on cover
Closing Date: Annually, Dec 31
Presented: CLA Annual Conference

**The Clarion Awards**
The Association for Women in Communications
3337 Duke St, Alexandria, VA 22314
*Tel:* 703-370-7436 *Fax:* 703-342-4311
*E-mail:* clarion@womcom.org
*Web Site:* www.womcom.org
*Key Personnel*
Exec Dir: Pamela Valenzuela
Communs Mgr: Beth Veney *E-mail:* awcconnect@womcom.org
Established: 1972
Honors excellence in more than 100 categories across all communications disciplines.
Award: Engraved crystal plaque, press releases, recognition at national conference
Closing Date: March (early bird), April (general entry)
Presented: National Conference Clarion Awards Banquet, Autumn

**Page Davidson Clayton Prize for Emerging Poets**
Michigan Quarterly Review
University of Michigan, 0576 Rackham Bldg, 915 E Washington St, Ann Arbor, MI 48109-1070
*Tel:* 734-764-9265
*E-mail:* mqr@umich.edu
*Web Site:* www.umich.edu/~mqr
*Key Personnel*
Mng Ed: Vicki Lawrence
Ed: Keith Taylor
Awarded annually to the best poet appearing in MQR who has not yet published a book.
Award: $500

**Cleveland State University Poetry Center Prizes**
Cleveland State University Poetry Center
2121 Euclid Ave, Cleveland, OH 44115-2214
*Tel:* 216-687-3986 *Fax:* 216-687-6943
*E-mail:* poetrycenter@csuohio.edu
*Web Site:* www.csuohio.edu/poetrycenter
*Key Personnel*
Dir: Michael Dumanis *E-mail:* csupc.mgr@gmail.com
Asst: Christopher Smith
Established: 1986
Poetry book mss, in two categories, First Book or Open Competition. Minimum 48 pages of poetry (one poem per page), SASE guidelines; readers fee required; simultaneous submissions permitted; mss not returned. Open competition is limited to poets who have published a full length collection, 48+ pp, 500+ copies.
Award: $1,000 & pubn in the Cleveland State University Poetry Center series
Closing Date: Feb 15 postmark
Presented: July

**David H Clift Scholarship**
ALA Scholarship Clearinghouse
Unit of American Library Association
50 E Huron St, Chicago, IL 60611
*Toll Free Tel:* 800-545-2433 (ext 4279) *Fax:* 312-280-3256
*E-mail:* scholarships@ala.org
*Web Site:* www.ala.org/scholarships
*Key Personnel*
Prog Off: Kimberly L Redd *E-mail:* klredd@ala.org
Established: 1969
Awarded annually to worthy US or Canadian citizen or permanent resident to begin an MLS degree in an ALA-accredited program.
Award: $3,000
Closing Date: Annually, March 1; applications available beginning in Oct

**Coal Hill Review Poetry Chapbook Contest**
Coal Hill Review
c/o Autumn House Press, PO Box 60100, Pittsburgh, PA 15211
*E-mail:* reviewcoalhill@gmail.com
*Web Site:* www.coalhillreview.com
*Key Personnel*
Ed: Michael Simms
Open to all poets writing in English. Ms may be submitted by attachment to our e-mail address. Submit a ms of 10-15 pages with a $20 entry fee.
Award: $1,000 & publication by Autumn House Press & Coal Hill Review
Closing Date: Nov 1

**CODiE Awards**
Software & Information Industry Association (SIIA)
1090 Vermont Ave NW, 6th fl, Washington, DC 20005-4095
*Tel:* 202-289-7442 *Fax:* 202-289-7097
*E-mail:* info@siia.net
*Web Site:* www.siia.net
*Key Personnel*
Pres: Kenneth Wasch *Tel:* 202-789-4440
Coord: Angel Scott *Tel:* 202-789-4458
Established: 1986

Honors excellence in the software & information industries.
Award: Trophy
Closing Date: Annually in Oct
Presented: SIIA CODiE Awards Gala, Annually in May

**Coe College Playwriting Festival**
Coe College
1220 First Ave NE, Cedar Rapids, IA 52402
*Tel:* 319-399-8624 *Fax:* 319-399-8557
*Web Site:* www.theatre.coe.edu; www.coe.edu/academics/theatrearts/theatrearts_playwritingfestival
*Key Personnel*
Prof, Theatre Arts & Scene & Costume Designer: Susan Wolverton *E-mail:* swolvert@coe.edu
Assoc Prof, Theatre Arts Chair: Steven Marc Weiss *E-mail:* sweiss@coe.edu
Established: 1992
Biennial playwriting award for new, full-length, original, unproduced & unpublished play. No musicals, adaptations, translations or collaborations. Only 1 entry/indiv.
Award: Publicly staged reading by students, faculty &/or individuals from the community, $500 & room, board, travel for one week residency
Closing Date: Nov 1 even years
Presented: Coe College, Cedar Rapids, IA, April

**Morton N Cohen Award for a Distinguished Edition of Letters**
Modern Language Association of America (MLA)
26 Broadway, 3rd fl, New York, NY 10004-1789
SAN: 202-6422
*Tel:* 646-576-5141 *Fax:* 646-458-0030
*E-mail:* awards@mla.org
*Web Site:* www.mla.org
*Key Personnel*
Coord, Book Prizes: Annie M Reiser *E-mail:* areiser@mla.org
Established: 1989
Biennial award for an outstanding edition of letters published in two years prior to competition deadline. Editions may be in single or multiple volumes. For consideration, submit four copies. Editors need not be members of the MLA.
Award: Cash award, certificate & a one year association membership
Closing Date: May 1, 2015
Presented: MLA Convention, Jan 2016

**The Victor Cohn Prize for Excellence in Medical Science Reporting**
Council for the Advancement of Science Writing (CASW)
PO Box 910, Hedgesville, WV 25427
*Tel:* 304-754-6786
*Web Site:* www.casw.org
Established: 2000
Medical science writing for the mass media within the last five years.
Award: $3,000
Closing Date: Annually, July 31
Presented: Gainesville, FL, Annually in Oct/Nov

**John M Collier Award for Forest History Journalism**
The Forest History Society Inc
701 William Vickers Ave, Durham, NC 27701-3162
*Tel:* 919-682-9319 *Fax:* 919-682-2349
*Web Site:* www.foresthistory.org
*Key Personnel*
Pres: Steven Anderson *E-mail:* stevena@duke.edu
Admin Asst: Andrea Anderson *E-mail:* recluce2@duke.edu
Established: 1987
Recognizes contributions to forest history that are published in newspapers, trade journals & other journalistic media. Open to any newspaper, or general circulation magazine, professional or freelance journalist in North America.
Award: $1,000 & expenses for a visit to The Forest History Society Library & Archives in Durham, NC & participation in an Institutes for Journalism in Natural Resources expedition
Closing Date: Annually, March 15

**Carr P Collins Award**
Texas Institute of Letters (TIL)
PO Box 609, Round Rock, TX 78680
*Tel:* 512-683-5640
*E-mail:* tilsecretary@yahoo.com
*Web Site:* www.texasinstituteofletters.org
*Key Personnel*
Pres: W K Stratton
VP: Andres Tijerina
Treas: James Hoggard
Secy: Jan Reid
Recording Secy: Betty Wiesepape
Annual award for the best nonfiction book by a Texan or about Texas. Guidelines on the web site.
Other Sponsor(s): Carr P Collins Foundation
Award: $5,000
Closing Date: Annually in Jan
Presented: TIL Awards Banquet, Annually in Spring

**The Winston Collins/Descant Prize for Best Canadian Poem**
Descant
50 Baldwin St, Toronto, ON M5T 1L4, Canada
Mailing Address: PO Box 314, Sta P, Toronto, ON M5S 2S8, Canada
*Tel:* 416-593-2557 *Fax:* 416-593-9362
*E-mail:* info@descant.ca
*Web Site:* www.descant.ca
*Key Personnel*
Ed-in-Chief: Karen Mulhallen *E-mail:* karenmulhallen@rogers.com
Established: 2006
Entry fee $30 (includes GST & 1 yr subn).
Award: $1,000 (1st prize) plus payment for publication in Descant
Closing Date: Oct
Presented: Spring

**Colorado Book Awards**
Colorado Humanities & Center for the Book
Division of Colorado Humanities
7935 E Prentice Ave, Suite 450, Greenwood Village, CO 80111
*Tel:* 303-894-7951 (ext 21) *Fax:* 303-864-9361
*E-mail:* info@coloradohumanities.org
*Web Site:* www.coloradohumanities.org
*Key Personnel*
Prog Coord: Christine Goff
Established: 1991
Cash prize to Colorado authors in fiction, nonfiction, young adult, children's, poetry, romance & additional categories vary from year to year.
Award: $250 (cash)
Closing Date: Annually in Jan
Presented: Colorado Book Awards Event, Annually in Summer

**Betsy Colquitt Award for Poetry**
Texas Christian University
Texas Christian University, Dept of English, TCU Box 297270, Fort Worth, TX 76129
*Tel:* 817-257-5907 *Fax:* 817-257-7709
*E-mail:* descant@tcu.edu
*Web Site:* www.descant.tcu.edu
*Key Personnel*
Mng Ed: Dan Williams *E-mail:* d.e.williams@tcu.edu
Established: 1996
Best poem or series of poems by a single author in a volume. No entry fee.
Other Sponsor(s): descant Publication, Dept of English, TCU
Award: $500
Closing Date: Annually, Sept 1-April 1
Presented: Announced in journal, Annually in Summer

**Miles Conrad Memorial Lecture**
National Federation of Advanced Information Services (NFAIS)
1518 Walnut St, Suite 1004, Philadelphia, PA 19102-3403
*Tel:* 215-893-1561 *Fax:* 215-893-1564
*E-mail:* nfais@nfais.org
*Web Site:* www.nfais.org
*Key Personnel*
Dir, Commun & Planning: Jill O'Neill *Tel:* 215-893-1561 ext 14 *E-mail:* jilloneill@nfais.org
Established: 1968
Annually given to an outstanding member of the information community who then delivers the "Miles Conrad Memorial Lecture" at the annual NFAIS Conference.
Award: Plaque & honorarium
Presented: Philadelphia, PA, Annually in Feb

**Constance Rooke Creative Non-Fiction Prize**
The Malahat Review
University of Victoria, Box 1700, Sta CSC, Victoria, BC V8W 2Y2, Canada
*Tel:* 250-721-8524 *Fax:* 250-472-5051
*E-mail:* malahat@uvic.ca
*Web Site:* malahatreview.ca
*Key Personnel*
Ed: John Barton
Invite entries from Canadian, American & overseas authors. Must be between 2,000-3,000 words. No restrictions as to subject matter. Entry fees: $35 Canadian entries, $40 US entries & $45 (US) for entries from Mexico & outside North America. See web site for additional details.
Award: One award of $1,000 CAD
Closing Date: Annually, Aug 1

**James Fenimore Cooper Prize**
Society of American Historians (SAH)
Affiliate of American Historical Association
603 Fayerweather, MC 2538, New York, NY 10027
*Tel:* 212-854-6495
*E-mail:* amhistsociety@columbia.edu
*Web Site:* sah.columbia.edu
*Key Personnel*
Pres: David W Blight
VP: David Nasaw
Exec Secy: Andie Tucher
Established: 1993
For a book of historical fiction on an American subject which makes a significant contribution to historical understanding, portrays authentically the people & events of the historical past & displays skills in narrative construction & prose style. Must be published & have a copyright within two years prior to prize year. Awarded biennially in odd-numbered years.
Award: $2,000 & a certificate
Closing Date: Jan 31, 2015
Presented: New York, NY, Biennially in May

**Cordon d'Or - Gold Ribbon International Annual Cook Book & Culinary Arts Culinary Academy Awards**
Cordon d'Or - Gold Ribbon Inc
7312 Sixth Ave N, St Petersburg, FL 33710
*Tel:* 727-347-2437
*E-mail:* culinaryparadise@aol.com
*Web Site:* www.cordondorcuisine.com; www.florida-americasculinaryparadise.com
*Key Personnel*
CEO & Pres: Noreen Kinney
Established: 2003
Literary Cook Book, Illustrated Cook Book & 'Potluck' Book (any genre) & 'Culinary Arts' Awards. Categories include cookbooks, photog-

raphers, food stylists, magazines, articles, web sites, recipes & menus. Full details available on the web site. Entry forms can be downloaded.
Award: $1,000 (overall winner), Crystal Globe Trophies (presented to winners in all categories)
Closing Date: Dec 31
Presented: St Petersburg, FL, Annually in Feb

**Albert B Corey Prize**
Canadian Historical Association-American Historical Association
c/o American Historical Association, 400 "A" St SE, Washington, DC 20003-3889
*Tel:* 202-544-2422 *Fax:* 202-544-8307
*E-mail:* cha-shc@cha-shc.ca
*Web Site:* www.historians.org/prizes; www.cha-shc.ca
*Key Personnel*
Exec Off Asst: Matthew Keough *Tel:* 202-544-2422 ext 100
Admin Asst: Jesse Pierce *Tel:* 202-544-2422 ext 106
Awarded biennially for the best book dealing with Canadian/American relations; awarded jointly with the American Historical Association. Books bearing an imprint of 2012 or 2013 are eligible for the 2014 prize. No application form, applicants must simply mail a copy of their book to each of the prize committee members who will be posted on our web site as the prize deadline approaches. All updated info on web site.
Award: $1,000 CAD
Closing Date: May 15, 2014
Presented: AHA Annual Meeting, New York, Jan 2015

**CPSA Prize in Comparative Politics**
Canadian Political Science Association
260 rue Dalhousie St, Suite 204, Ottawa, ON K1N 7E4, Canada
*Tel:* 613-562-1202 *Fax:* 613-241-0019
*E-mail:* cpsa-acsp@cpsa-acsp.ca
*Web Site:* www.cpsa-acsp.ca
*Key Personnel*
Administrator: Michelle Hopkins
Biennial prize awarded to the best book published in English or in French in the field of comparative politics. To be eligible, a book may be single or multi-authored. Single authored: author must be a Canadian citizen or a permanent resident of Canada or a member of the CPSA in the year the book was published. Multi-authored: at least one of the authors must be a Canadian citizen or a permanent resident of Canada or a member of the CPSA in the year the book was published. For the 2014 award, a book must have a copyright date of 2012 or 2013.
Award: Commemorative plaque & receive/share the set of books submitted to the CPSA office
Closing Date: Dec 10
Presented: Annual Conference, Biennially in May or June

**CPSA Prize in International Relations**
Canadian Political Science Association
260 rue Dalhousie St, Suite 204, Ottawa, ON K1N 7E4, Canada
*Tel:* 613-562-1202 *Fax:* 613-241-0019
*E-mail:* cpsa-acsp@cpsa-acsp.ca
*Web Site:* www.cpsa-acsp.ca
*Key Personnel*
Administrator: Michelle Hopkins
This is a biennial competition. The prize was established to recognize the contribution of Canadian political scientists to the study of international relations & to encourage the best Canadian scholarship in this field. Awarded to the best book published in English or in French in the field of international relations. Book may be single-authored or multi-authored. Single-authored: must be a Canadian citizen or a permanent resident of Canada or a member of the CPSA in the year the book was published. Multi-authored: at least one of the authors must be a Canadian citizen or a permanent resident of Canada or a member of the CPSA in the year the book was published. For the 2015 award the book must have a copyright date of 2013 or 2014.
Award: Commerative plaque & receive/share the set of books submitted to the CPSA for the 2015 prize
Presented: Annual Conference, Biennially in May or June

**The Crazyhorse Fiction Prize**
Crazyhorse
College of Charleston, Dept of English, 66 George St, Charleston, SC 29424
*Tel:* 843-953-7740 *Fax:* 843-953-7740
*E-mail:* crazyhorse@cofc.edu
*Web Site:* www.crazyhorsejournal.org
Award for best short story. Enter up to 25 pages fiction with $16 entry fee, which includes one-year subscription. Nationally prominent writer judges. See web site for complete instructions.
Award: $2,000 & publication in "Crazyhorse"
Closing Date: Annually, Jan 15

**Cunningham Commission for Youth Theatre**
The Theatre School, DePaul University
2135 N Kenmore Ave, Chicago, IL 60614-4100
*Tel:* 773-325-7932 *Fax:* 773-325-7920
*Web Site:* theatreschool.depaul.edu
*Key Personnel*
Assoc Dean & Chair, Theatre Studies: Dean Corrin *E-mail:* dcorrin@depaul.edu
Established: 1991
Playwriting commission, limited to writers whose primary residence is within 100 miles of Chicago's Loop.
Award: Up to $5,000 ($2,000 paid when the commission is contracted, $1,000 paid if the script moves to a workshop, $2,000 paid as royalty if the script is produced by The Theatre School)
Closing Date: Annually Dec 1
Presented: Presentation TBA, Winner notified by May 1

**Dana Awards**
Literary Competition, 200 Fosseway Dr, Greensboro, NC 27455
*E-mail:* danaawards@gmail.com
*Web Site:* www.danaawards.com
*Key Personnel*
Chair: Mary Elizabeth Parker
Established: 1996
For unpublished group of poems, short story, novel or novel-in-progress. Poetry: submit 5 poems of no more than 100 lines each with a $15 entry fee. Short story: submit up to 10,000 words with a $15 entry fee. Novel: the first 40 pages & a $25 entry fee. All types of novels accepted (no memoirs).
Award: $1,000 each competition (3 competitions: poetry, short fiction & novel
Closing Date: Annually, Oct 31
Presented: All awards, checks & notification are presented by mail or e-mail

**Robert Dana-Anhinga Prize for Poetry**
Anhinga Press
PO Box 3665, Tallahassee, FL 32315
*Tel:* 850-577-0745 *Fax:* 850-577-0745
*E-mail:* info@anhinga.org
*Web Site:* www.anhinga.org
*Key Personnel*
Dir: Rick Campbell
Established: 1983
Poetry book.
Award: $2,000 & publication
Closing Date: Annually, Feb 15-May 15
Presented: Tallahassee, FL

**The Danahy Fiction Prize**
Tampa Review
University of Tampa Press, 401 W Kennedy Blvd, Tampa, FL 33606
*Tel:* 813-253-6266
*E-mail:* utpress@ut.edu
*Web Site:* tampareview.ut.edu
*Key Personnel*
Ed: Richard Mathews
Edit Asst: Sean Donnelly
Established: 2006
Award: $1,000 & publication in "Tampa Review"
Closing Date: Nov 1

**Watson Davis & Helen Miles Davis Prize**
History of Science Society
Affiliate of American Council of Learned Societies
440 Geddes Hall, Notre Dame, IN 46556
*Tel:* 574-631-1194 *Fax:* 574-631-1533
*E-mail:* info@hssonline.org
*Web Site:* www.hssonline.org
*Key Personnel*
Exec Dir: Robert Jay Malone
Established: 1985
For the best book on the history of science directed to a broad public published during the preceding three years.
Award: $1,000 & certificate
Closing Date: April 1
Presented: Awards Banquet, Nov

**Dayton Literary Peace Prize**
Dayton Literary Peace Prize Foundation
25 Harman Terr, Dayton, OH 45419
Mailing Address: PO Box 461, Wright Brothers Branch, Dayton, OH 45409-0461
*Tel:* 937-298-5072
*Web Site:* daytonliterarypeaceprize.org
*Key Personnel*
DLPP Chair: Sharon Rab *E-mail:* sharon.rab@daytonliterarypeaceprize.org
Established: 2006
First & only annual US literary award recognizing the power of the written word to promote peace. This project is the recognition of adult fiction & nonfiction books that have led readers to a better understanding of other cultures, peoples, religions & political points of view.
Award: $10,000 each genre (fiction & nonfiction)
Closing Date: Annually in March
Presented: Benjamin & Marian Schuster Performing Arts Center, Dayton, OH, Annually in Nov

**Dayton Playhouse FutureFest**
The Dayton Playhouse
1301 E Siebenthaler Ave, Dayton, OH 45414
*Tel:* 937-424-8477 *Fax:* 937-424-0062
*E-mail:* dp_futurefest@yahoo.com
*Web Site:* www.daytonplayhouse.com
*Key Personnel*
Exec Dir: Wade Hamilton
FutureFest Prog Dir: Fran Pesch
Established: 1991
National Playwriting Competition; send SASE or see web site for submission guidelines.
Award: $1,000 (1st place), $100 (5 runners up) - all 6 finalists are provided travel to & housing for the FutureFest weekend
Closing Date: Annually, Oct 31
Presented: The Dayton Playhouse, Annually in May

**Delaware Division of the Arts Individual Artist Fellowships**
Carvel State Office Bldg, 4th fl, 820 N French St, Wilmington, DE 19801
*Tel:* 302-577-8278 *Fax:* 302-577-6561
*E-mail:* delarts@state.de.us
*Web Site:* www.artsdel.org

*Key Personnel*
Art & Artist Servs Coord: Kristin Pleasanton
Individual Artist Fellowships will be awarded to beginning or established poets & other creative writers. Applicants must be Delaware residents.
Award: A Masters Fellowship of $10,000 & established Professional Fellowships of $6,000 each & Emerging Professional Fellowships of $3,000
Closing Date: Annually, Aug 1
Presented: Annually (Master's awarded every three years in literature); winners notified in Dec

**Rick DeMarinis Short Story Award**
CUTTHROAT, A Journal of the Arts
PO Box 2414, Durango, CO 81302
*Tel:* 970-903-7914
*E-mail:* cutthroatmag@gmail.com
*Web Site:* www.cutthroatmag.com
*Key Personnel*
Ed-in-Chief: Pamela Uschuk
Mng Ed: Susan Foster
Fiction Ed: Beth Alvarado
Submit one unpublished short story (5000 word limit), any subject, any style. Mss must be 12 point font & double-spaced. Reading fee $17.
Award: $1,250 (1st place), $250 (2nd place), both include publication in *CUTTHROAT*
Closing Date: Annually in Oct
Presented: Annually in Dec

**Der-Hovanessian Translation Prize**
New England Poetry Club
2 Farrar St, Cambridge, MA 02138
Mailing Address: PO Box 190076, Boston, MA 02119
*Tel:* 617-744-6034
*E-mail:* contests@nepoetryclub.org
*Web Site:* www.nepoetryclub.org
*Key Personnel*
Pres: Diana Der-Hovanessian
VP: Sally Cragin; Daniel Tobin
Contest Chair: Nazaleem Smith
For translation from any language. Send a copy of original with the poem.
Award: $200
Closing Date: Annually, May 31
Presented: Public Library, Cambridge, MA, Annually in Autumn

**Alice Fay Di Castagnola Award**
Poetry Society of America (PSA)
15 Gramercy Park S, New York, NY 10003
*Tel:* 212-254-9628 *Fax:* 212-673-2352
*Web Site:* www.poetrysociety.org
*Key Personnel*
Pres: Ruth Kaplan
Exec Dir: Alice Quinn
Mng Dir & Awards Coord: Brett Fletcher Lauer *E-mail:* brett@poetrysociety.org
Progs Dir: Darrel Alejandro Holnes
Established: 1965
In honor of a friend & benefactor of the Society. For a ms in progress (poetry, prose or verse drama). Preliminary submission not to exceed 300 lines of sample verse if poetry or a sample chapter if prose; a sample scene if verse drama. Open to Society members only. Send No 10 SASE or see web site for complete information.
Award: $1,000
Closing Date: Annually, Oct-Dec
Presented: Annual Awards Ceremony, New York, NY, Annually in Spring

**Diagram Essay Contest**
DIAGRAM
University of Arizona, ML-445, PO Box 210067, Tucson, AZ 85721
*E-mail:* editor@thediagram.com
*Web Site:* www.thediagram.com/contest.html
*Key Personnel*
Ed: Ander Monson *E-mail:* editor@thediagram.com
Established: 2008
For an essay that incorporates writing in other genres or unique textual or visual elements. No particular aesthetic biases for this contest other than the name: we are looking for works of nonfiction that include hybrid elements - however you'd like to define. Submit an essay of up to 10,000 words. Entry fee $15.
Award: $1,000 & publication in Diagram
Closing Date: Annually in Oct

**Dickinson, Emily Award**, see The Writer Magazine/Emily Dickinson Award

**Annie Dillard Award for Creative Nonfiction**
The Bellingham Review
Mail Stop 9053, Western Washington University, Bellingham, WA 98225
*Tel:* 360-650-4863
*E-mail:* bhreview@wwu.edu
*Web Site:* www.bhreview.org
*Key Personnel*
Ed-in-Chief: Brenda Miller
Mng Ed: Marilyn Bruce
Established: 1983
Maximum length for prose is 6,000 words. Poems within a series of poems will each be treated as a separate entry. No previously published works, or works accepted for publication, are eligible. Work may be under consideration elsewhere, but must be withdrawn from the competition if accepted for publication. Make checks payable to: The Bellingham Review. All entries will receive a complimentary one-issue subscription. Entry fee for the first entry (one nonfiction work, one short story, or up to three poems) $20. Each additional entry, including each additional poem $10.
Award: $1,000 & publication in the Bellingham Review (1st prize), considered for publication (2nd, 3rd & finalists)
Closing Date: Annually, between Dec 1 & March 15
Presented: Annually in July

**Gordon W Dillon/Richard C Peterson Memorial Essay Prize**
American Orchid Society Inc
Fairfield Tropical Botanic Gardens, 10901 Old Cutler Rd, Coral Gables, FL 33156
*Tel:* 305-740-2010 *Fax:* 305-740-2011
*E-mail:* theaos@aos.org
*Web Site:* www.aos.org
*Key Personnel*
Dir, Pubns: James Watson *E-mail:* jwatson@aos.org
Established: 1985
Essay contest (orchid topics only; new theme announced each year).
Award: Cash award & a certificate of recognition. Winning essay published in the June issue of *Orchids* magazine the following year
Closing Date: Annually, Nov 30

**"Discovery"/Boston Review Poetry Contest**
Unterberg Poetry Center
Subsidiary of 92nd Street Y/Tisch Center for the Arts
1395 Lexington Ave, New York, NY 10128
*Tel:* 212-415-5760
*E-mail:* unterberg@92y.org
*Web Site:* www.92y.org/discovery
*Key Personnel*
Mng Dir: Ricardo Maldonado *E-mail:* rickymaldonado@92y.org
For poets who have not published a full-length poetry collection; for guidelines visit web site.
Other Sponsor(s): *Boston Review*
Award: Publication in *Boston Review*, reading at The Poetry Center & $500 each to the 4 winning authors
Closing Date: Jan 24, 2014
Presented: May 5, 2014

**Distinguished Book Award**
American Sociological Association (ASA)
c/o Governance Office, 1430 "K" St NW, Suite 600, Washington, DC 20005
*Tel:* 202-383-9005 *Fax:* 202-638-0882
*E-mail:* governance@asanet.org
*Web Site:* www.asanet.org
*Key Personnel*
Dir, Governance: Michael Murphy *Tel:* 202-383-9005 ext 327
This award is given for a single book published in the two calendar years preceding the award year. The winner of this award will be offered a lectureship known as the Sorokin Lecture. Regional & state sociological associations/societies may apply to ASA to receive this lecture at ASA's expense after the award recipient is announced. One member of the association must submit letters in support of each nomination for the award. Nominations should include name of author, title of book, date of publication, publisher & brief statements from two (differently located) sources as to why the book should be considered. Send nominations to: ASA office at above address.
Award: Certificate
Closing Date: Jan 31
Presented: ASA Annual Meeting, Montreal, Canada, Annually in Aug

**Dog Writers' Association of America Inc (DWAA) Annual Awards**
Dog Writers' Association of America Inc (DWAA)
173 Union Rd, Coatesville, PA 19320
*Tel:* 610-384-2436
*E-mail:* rhydowen@aol.com
*Web Site:* www.dwaa.org
*Key Personnel*
Pres: Carmen Battaglia, PhD
Secy: Pat Santi
Established: 1935
To give recognition to an individual, club or group which has done an outstanding job in the dog writing field in different categories.
Award: Over several thousand dollars in cash prizes; plaques & certificates
Closing Date: Annually in Sept
Presented: Annual Awards Banquet, Annually in Feb

**Dorothy Canfield Fisher Children's Book Award**
Vermont Department of Libraries
109 State St, Montpelier, VT 05609-0601
*Tel:* 802-828-6954 *Fax:* 802-828-1481
*E-mail:* cbec@state.vt.us
*Web Site:* www.dcfaward.org; libraries.vermont.gov/libraries
*Key Personnel*
Chpn: Mary Linney
Youth Servs Consultant: Grace Worcester Greene *E-mail:* grace.greene@state.vt.us
Established: 1956
For a book by a living American or Canadian author published one year previous, chosen by the children of Vermont, grades 4-8, from a master list of 30 titles.
Other Sponsor(s): Vermont PTA
Award: Illuminated scroll
Closing Date: Annually, Dec 1
Presented: Annually in May

**Dorset Prize**
Tupelo Press Inc
PO Box 1767, North Adams, MA 01247

SAN: 254-3281
*Tel:* 413-664-9611 *Fax:* 413-664-9711
*E-mail:* info@tupelopress.org
*Web Site:* www.tupelopress.org
*Key Personnel*
Mng Ed: Jim Schley
Established: 2003
An open book competition for poetry. Full guidelines on the web site.
Award: $3,000, publication & national distribution
Closing Date: Sept 1-Dec 31
Presented: Spring

**John Dos Passos Prize for Literature**
Longwood University
Dept of English & Modern Languages, 201 High St, Farmville, VA 23909
*Tel:* 434-395-2155 (dept) *Fax:* 434-395-2200
*Key Personnel*
Chpn, Dos Passos Comm & Assoc Prof: Mary Carroll-Hackett
Dept Chpn: Rhonda Brock-Servais
Established: 1980
To honor an imaginative prose writer. Preference given to those not previously honored. Winners are nominated & selected by a jury. Applications not accepted.
Award: $2,000 & a medallion
Presented: Longwood University, Farmville, VA, During Fall semester

**Frank Nelson Doubleday Memorial Award**
Wyoming Arts Council
Division of Wyoming Department of Parks & Cultural Resources
2320 Capitol Ave, Cheyenne, WY 82002
*Tel:* 307-777-5234 *Fax:* 307-777-5499
*Web Site:* wyoarts.state.wy.us
*Key Personnel*
Literary, Visual & Performing Arts Specialist: Michael Shay *Tel:* 307-777-5234 *E-mail:* mshay@state.wy.us
Arts Council Mgr: Rita Basom *Tel:* 307-777-7473 *E-mail:* rbasom@state.wy.us
Established: 1988
Best poetry, fiction, nonfiction or drama written by a woman author. Wyoming residents only. Blind judges & single juror.
Other Sponsor(s): Neltje
Award: $1,000
Closing Date: Annually, Oct 31
Presented: Announced Jan 1

**Carleton Drewry Memorial**
The Poetry Society of Virginia
1194 Hume Rd, Hume, VA 22639-1806
*E-mail:* poetryinva@aol.com
*Web Site:* www.poetrysocietyofvirginia.org
*Key Personnel*
Pres: Judith K Bragg *E-mail:* musicsavy45@yahoo.com
Adult Contest Chair: Patsy Anne Bickerstaff *E-mail:* granypatsy@yahoo.com; Guy Terrell *E-mail:* ggterr@infionline.net
Lyric or sonnet. Must be in English, original & unpublished. Submit 2 copies, each having the category name & number on top left of page. Entries will not be returned. Subject: mountains; 48 line limit. Entry fee: $4 nonmembs.
Award: $50 (1st prize), $30 (2nd prize), $20 (3rd prize)
Closing Date: Jan 19
Presented: Annual PSV Awards Luncheon, Richmond, VA, April

**Saint Katharine Drexel Award**
Catholic Library Association
205 W Monroe, Suite 314, Chicago, IL 60606-5061
*Tel:* 312-739-1776; 312-739-1776 *Toll Free Tel:* 855-739-1776 *Fax:* 312-739-1778; 312-739-1778
*E-mail:* cla2@cathla.org
*Web Site:* www.cathla.org
*Key Personnel*
Pres: Malachy R McCarthy *E-mail:* mmccarthy@cathla.org
Established: 1966
Recognizes an outstanding contribution to the growth of high school librarianship.
Award: Plaque
Closing Date: None; in-house votes
Presented: CLA Annual Convention

**Drury University One-Act Play Competition**
Drury University
900 N Benton Ave, Springfield, MO 65802-3344
*Tel:* 417-873-6821
*Web Site:* www.drury.edu
*Key Personnel*
Professor, Theatre: Dr Mick Sokol *E-mail:* msokol@drury.edu
Established: 1986
Biennial award for one-act plays. Open to all playwrights. Scripts are to be original, unpublished & unproduced; staged readings or workshop productions will not disqualify a script; musicals, monologues, children's plays & adaptations will not be considered; only stage plays will be judged; preference will be given to small cast, one-set shows with running times of no less than 20 & no more than 45 minutes; no more than one script per author; all scripts are to be typewritten & firmly bound; scripts cannot be acknowledged or returned unless accompanied by a SASE.
Award: $300 plus consideration for production by Drury University (1st prize); two honorable mentions $150 each
Closing Date: Dec 1 (even numbered years)
Presented: By mail no later than April 1 (odd numbered years)

**Dubuque Fine Arts Players Annual One Act Play Festival**
Dubuque Fine Arts Players
PO Box 1160, Dubuque, IA 52004-1160
*Tel:* 563-588-3438
*E-mail:* contact@dbqoneacts.org
*Web Site:* www.dbqoneacts.org
*Key Personnel*
Pres: Art Roche
Established: 1977
Annual national One-Act Playwriting Contest. Entry form & guidelines are available at the web site. Submit the entry form, two copies of the script, a synopsis of the play & entry fee. Plays may be submitted by US mail with a $15 entry fee. SASE should be enclosed if return of the reader evaluation forms &/or the scripts is desired. Plays may be submitted online for an entry fee of $20. The higher fee pays cost of printing & binding the play. Previously published or produced works, musicals & children's plays are not accepted.
Membership(s): Dubuque County Fine Arts Society.
Award: $600 (1st prize), $300 (2nd prize), $200 (3rd prize), production of first 3 winning plays unless production is beyond our capacity
Closing Date: Annually in Jan
Presented: Mindframe Theater, Annually late Aug

**John H Dunning Prize in United States History**
American Historical Association
400 "A" St SE, Washington, DC 20003-3889
*Tel:* 202-544-2422 *Fax:* 202-544-8307
*E-mail:* awards@historians.org
*Web Site:* www.historians.org
Established: 1927
Biennial award in recognition of outstanding historical writing in US history. To be awarded to a young scholar for an outstanding monograph in ms or in print on any subject relating to US history. To be eligible for consideration, an entry must be of a scholarly historical nature. It must be the author's first or second book, published in 2013 or 2014. Research accuracy, originality & literary merit are important factors. Along with an application form, applicants must mail a copy of their book to each of the prize committee members who will be posted on our web site as the prize deadline approaches. All updated info on web site.
Award: Cash prize
Closing Date: May 15, 2015 (postmark)
Presented: AHA Annual Meeting

**Eaton Literary Associates Literary Awards**
Eaton Literary Agency Inc
PO Box 49795, Sarasota, FL 34230-6795
*Tel:* 941-366-6589 *Fax:* 941-365-4679
*E-mail:* eatonlit@aol.com
*Web Site:* www.eatonliterary.com
*Key Personnel*
Pres: Ralph A Eaton
VP: Richard Lawrence
Established: 1984
Two awards are given, one for a book-length ms & one for a short story or article. These entries should not have been previously published.
Award: $2,500 (book-length program), $500 (short story or article program)
Closing Date: Annually, Aug 31 (book-length program), March 31 (short story or article program)
Presented: Annually in Sept (book-length program), April (short story or article program)

**Edelstein Prize**
Society for the History of Technology
Univ of Virginia, Dept of Science, Tech & Society, PO Box 400744, Charlottesville, VA 22904-4744
*Tel:* 434-987-6230 *Fax:* 434-975-2190 (attention: SHOT)
*E-mail:* shot@virginia.edu
*Web Site:* www.shot.jhu.edu
*Key Personnel*
Secy: Bernie Carlson
Established: 1968
For the best book published on the history of technology for a scholarly audience in the past three years.
Other Sponsor(s): Ruth Edelstein Barrish & Family in memory of Sidney Edelstein
Award: $3,500 & plaque
Closing Date: Annually, April 15
Presented: SHOT annual meeting, Cleveland, OH, Annually in Oct

**Education Awards of Excellence**
Printing Industries of America
200 Deer Run Rd, Sewickley, PA 15143-2600
*Tel:* 412-259-1705 *Toll Free Tel:* 800-910-4283 (ext 705) *Fax:* 412-749-9890
*E-mail:* printing@printing.org
*Web Site:* www.printing.org
*Key Personnel*
CEO & Pres: Michael Makin *E-mail:* mmakin@printing.org
Asst to VP, Mktg: Sara Welsh *E-mail:* swelsh@printing.org
Established: 1984
Honors one industry representative & one graphic arts educator who have each made outstanding contributions to graphic arts education & or training. Entry is free. For more information, go to www.printing.org & click on Programs & Services then Awards & Recognition.
Award: Engraved plaque
Presented: GASC/Printing Industries of America's Teacher's Conference

**Educators Award**
The Delta Kappa Gamma Society International
PO Box 1589, Austin, TX 78767-1589

*Tel:* 512-478-5748 *Toll Free Tel:* 888-762-4685 *Fax:* 512-478-3961
*E-mail:* societyexec@dkg.org
*Web Site:* www.dkg.org
*Key Personnel*
Info Servs Administrator: Linda Eller *Tel:* 512-478-5748 ext 120 *E-mail:* lindae@dkg.org
Annual award to the woman author(s) of a book whose work may influence the direction of thought & action necessary to meet the needs of today's complex society. The content must be of more than local interest with relationship, direct or implied, to education everywhere. The author must be a woman from Canada, Costa Rica, Denmark, El Salvador, Estonia, Finland, Germany, Great Britain, Guatemala, Iceland, Mexico, Netherlands, Norway, Puerto Rico, Sweden or the US; call, e-mail or download regulations. All nominations are made by publishers.
Award: $2,500
Closing Date: Feb 1 (postmark)
Presented: One of Five Regional Conferences or Society's International Convention, Summer

**Margaret A Edwards Award**
Young Adult Library Services Association (YALSA)
Division of American Library Association (ALA)
50 E Huron St, Chicago, IL 60611
*Tel:* 312-280-4390 *Toll Free Tel:* 800-545-2433 *Fax:* 312-280-5276
*E-mail:* yalsa@ala.org
*Web Site:* www.ala.org/yalsa/edwards
*Key Personnel*
Prog Offr, Events & Conferences: Nichole Gilbert *Tel:* 312-280-4387 *Fax:* 312-280-1538 *E-mail:* ngilbert@ala.org
Established: 1988
Given to an author for lifetime achievement in writing for teenagers.
Other Sponsor(s): School Library Journal
Award: $2,000 & citation
Closing Date: Annually in Dec
Presented: Announced at ALA's Midwinter Meeting. Winner honored & speaks during a luncheon at ALA's Annual Conference

**Wilfrid Eggleston Award for Nonfiction**
Writers Guild of Alberta
11759 Groat Rd, Edmonton, AB T5M 3K6, Canada
*Tel:* 780-422-8174 *Toll Free Tel:* 800-665-5354 (AB only) *Fax:* 780-422-2663 (attn WGA)
*E-mail:* mail@writersguild.ab.ca
*Web Site:* www.writersguild.ab.ca
*Key Personnel*
Exec Dir: Carol Holmes *E-mail:* cholmes@writersguild.ab.ca
Communs & Partnerships Coord: Nicholas Mather *E-mail:* nmather@writersguild.ab.ca
Memb Servs Coord: Giorgia Severini
Progs Coord: Nichole Quiring *E-mail:* programs@writersguild.ab.ca
Established: 1982
Alberta Literary Award, author must be resident of Alberta.
Award: $1,500 plus leather-bound copy of book
Closing Date: Annually, Dec 31
Presented: Alberta Literary Awards Gala
*Branch Office(s)*
Lord Denning House, 509 20 Ave SW, Calgary, AB T2S 0E7, Canada, Prog Coord: Samantha Warwick *Tel:* 403-265-2226 *E-mail:* swarwick@writersguild.ab.ca

**T S Eliot Prize for Poetry**
Truman State University Press
100 E Normal Ave, Kirksville, MO 63501-4221
*Tel:* 660-785-7336 *Toll Free Tel:* 800-916-6802 *Fax:* 660-785-4480
*E-mail:* tsup@truman.edu
*Web Site:* tsup.truman.edu
*Key Personnel*
Dir & Ed-in-Chief: Nancy Rediger *E-mail:* nancyr@truman.edu
Established: 1997
Annual award for the best unpublished book-length collection of poetry in English. Include a non-refundable reading fee of $25 for each ms submitted.
Award: $2,000 & publication
Closing Date: Oct 31
Presented: Jan

**Elliott Prize**
Medieval Academy of America
104 Mount Auburn St, 5th fl, Cambridge, MA 02138
*Tel:* 617-491-1622 *Fax:* 617-492-3303
*E-mail:* speculum@medievalacademy.org
*Web Site:* www.medievalacademy.org
*Key Personnel*
Exec Dir & Ed, Speculum: Eileen Gardiner *E-mail:* egardiner@themedievalacademy.org
Established: 1971
For a first article published two years prior to award date, in the field of medieval studies.
Award: $500
Closing Date: Annually, Oct 15
Presented: Annually in April

**Emerging Playwright Award**
Urban Stages
555 Eighth Ave, Suite 1800, New York, NY 10018
*Tel:* 212-421-1380 *Fax:* 212-421-1387
*E-mail:* urbanstage@aol.com
*Key Personnel*
Artistic Dir & Founder: Frances Hill
Literary Dir: Antoinette Mullins
Scripts not previously produced; scripts should have no more than 7 characters; well-written, imaginative situations & dialog; multicultural scripts are given special attention. Playwrights in & around NYC are given special attention. No processing fee & SASE with all submissions. Selected scripts are first given a staged reading. A select number of staged readings are given intensive workshops. A select number of workshopped plays are given full off-Broadway productions. Award given to playwrights of full productions at Urban Stages.
Award: $500
Closing Date: Year-round
Presented: New York

**The Ralph Waldo Emerson Award**
The Phi Beta Kappa Society
1606 New Hampshire Ave NW, Washington, DC 20009
*Tel:* 202-265-3808 *Fax:* 202-986-1601
*E-mail:* awards@pbk.org
*Web Site:* www.pbk.org/bookawards
*Key Personnel*
Coord, Society Events: Lucinda Morales *Tel:* 202-745-3235 *E-mail:* lmorales@pbk.org
Established: 1960
For scholarly studies that contribute to interpretations of the intellectual & cultural condition of humanity. To be eligible, must have been published in USA by American author. Works in history, philosophy, religion & related fields such as social sciences & anthropology are eligible. Nomination must come from publisher & be submitted online.
Award: $10,000
Closing Date: Annually in April
Presented: Washington, DC, Annually in Dec

**Empire State Award for Excellence in Literature for Young People**
New York Library Association
6021 State Farm Rd, Guilderland, NY 12084
*Tel:* 518-432-6952 *Toll Free Tel:* 800-252-6952 *Fax:* 518-427-1697
*E-mail:* info@nyla.org
*Web Site:* www.nyla.org
*Key Personnel*
Exec Dir: Michael Borges *Tel:* 518-432-6952 ext 101 *E-mail:* director@nyla.org
Deputy Dir: Jeremy Johannesen *E-mail:* events@nyla.org
Mktg & Communs Mgr: Cara Longobardi *E-mail:* marketing@nyla.org
Established: 1990
One-time award presented to a living author or illustrator currently residing in New York State. The award honors excellence in children's or young adult literature & a body of work that has made a significant contribution to literature for young people.
Award: Engraved medallion
Presented: Annual Conference, Annually in Oct

**Norma Epstein Foundation**
University of Toronto - University College
15 King's College Circle, UC 173, Toronto, ON M5S 3H7, Canada
*Tel:* 416-978-8083 *Fax:* 416-971-2027
*Web Site:* www.utoronto.ca
*Key Personnel*
Assoc Registra: Shelley Cornack
Academic Servs Asst: Khamla Sengthavy *E-mail:* khamla.sengthavy@utoronto.ca
Literary competition held every odd-numbered year. Three categories: fiction, drama & verse.
Award: $1,000 for each category
Closing Date: May 1, odd-numbered years
Presented: Toronto, Annually in Nov

**Erskine J Poetry Prize**
Smartish Pace
PO Box 22161, Baltimore, MD 21203
*Web Site:* www.smartishpace.com
*Key Personnel*
Founder & Ed: Stephen Reichert *E-mail:* sreichert@smartishpace.com
Established: 2001
All poems submitted for the prize will be considered for publication in *Smartish Pace*. Online submissions at www.smartishpace.com. Postal submissions: submit 3 poems along with a $5 entry fee. Additional poems may be submitted for $1 per poem. No more than 20 poems may be submitted. All entries must include bio. Include a SASE with entry & include name, address, e-mail & telephone number on each page of poetry submitted. Write or print "Erskine J" on the top of each poem submitted.
Award: $200 & publication of winning poem in *Smartish Pace* (1st prize). All finalists will be published in *Smartish Pace*
Closing Date: Annually, Sept 1
Presented: Baltimore, MD

**David W & Beatrice C Evans Biography & Handcart Awards**
Mountain West Center for Regional Studies
Division of College of Humanities & Social Sciences-Utah State University
0735 Old Main Hill, Logan, UT 84322-0735
*Tel:* 435-797-0299 *Fax:* 435-797-1092
*E-mail:* mwc@usu.edu
*Web Site:* www.mountainwest.usu.edu
*Key Personnel*
Prog Dir: Patricia Lambert
Established: 1983
For the best published biography or history with a significant biographical content of an individual associated with "Mormon Country" (a geographical, not religious, concept).
Award: $10,000 (The Evans Biography Award); $2,500 (The Evans Handcart Award)

Closing Date: Feb 1, 2014 for books published in 2013
Presented: Utah State University, Annually in Sept

**EXCEL Awards**
Association Media & Publishing
12100 Sunset Hills Rd, Suite 130, Reston, VA 20190
*Tel:* 703-234-4063 *Fax:* 703-435-4390
*E-mail:* info@associationmediaandpublishing.org
*Web Site:* www.associationmediaandpublishing.org
*Key Personnel*
Exec Dir: Sarah Patterson *Tel:* 703-234-4107 *E-mail:* spatterson@associationmediaandpublishing.com
Coord, Mktg & Communs: Liz Jones *Tel:* 703-234-4112 *E-mail:* ejones@associationmediaandpublishing.com
Service excellence awards program for association publishers. The EXCEL program judges over 1,200 magazines, newsletters, scholarly journals, electronic publications & web sites in the areas of editorial quality, design, general excellence, most improved & more.
Award: Gold Award (1st prize) brass statues; Silver & Bronze (2nd & 3rd prizes) framed certificates; EXTRA! Award, best of the gold, silver & bronze winners
Closing Date: Annually in Jan
Presented: Excel Awards Gala, Annual Meeting, Sheraton Premier, Tyson's Corner, VA, May 2014

**John K Fairbank Prize in East Asian History**
American Historical Association
400 "A" St SE, Washington, DC 20003-3889
*Tel:* 202-544-2422 *Fax:* 202-544-8307
*E-mail:* awards@historians.org
*Web Site:* www.historians.org
Established: 1968
Outstanding book on the history of China proper, Vietnam, Chinese Central Asia, Mongolia, Manchuria, Korea or Japan substantially after 1800; books published in 2013 will be eligible; anthologies, edited works & pamphlets are ineligible for the competition. Along with an application form, applicants must mail a copy of their book to each of the prize committee members who will be posted on our web site as the prize deadline approaches. All updated info on web site.
Award: Cash prize
Closing Date: May 15, 2014 (postmark)
Presented: AHA Annual Meeting

**Tom Fairley Award for Editorial Excellence**
Editors' Association of Canada (Association canadienne des reviseurs)
502-27 Carlton St, Toronto, ON M5B 1L2, Canada
*Tel:* 416-975-1379 *Toll Free Tel:* 866-CAN-EDIT (226-3348) *Fax:* 416-975-1637
*E-mail:* fairley_award@editors.ca
*Web Site:* www.editors.ca; www.reviseurs.ca
*Key Personnel*
Exec Dir & Ed: Carolyn L Burke *E-mail:* carolyn.burke@editors.ca
Communs Mgr: Michelle Ou *E-mail:* michelle.ou@editors.ca
Prof Devt Mgr: Helena Aalto *E-mail:* helena.aalto@editors.ca
Membership Coord: Lianne Zwarenstein
Established: 1983
Recognizes the editor's often invisible contribution to written communication.
Other Sponsor(s): Breakwater Books; HarperCollins; The C D Howe Institute; New Society Publishers; Orca Book Publishers; Random House of Canada; UBC Press, Madison; University of Calgary Press
Award: $2,000 cash

Closing Date: Jan of the year after the work took place
Presented: National Annual Conference, June of the year after the work took place

**Family Matters**
Glimmer Train Press Inc
PO Box 80430, Portland, OR 97280
*Tel:* 503-221-0836 *Fax:* 503-221-0837
*E-mail:* editors@glimmertrain.org
*Web Site:* www.glimmertrain.org
*Key Personnel*
Co-Ed: Susan Burmeister-Brown *E-mail:* susan@glimmertrain.org
Established: 2007
Open to all writers, family theme, 500-12,000 word count range. Winner notification takes place 2 months after the close of each competition.
Award: $1,500, pubn & 20 copies of that issue (1st place); $500 (2nd place); $300 (3rd place)
Closing Date: Annually in April & Oct

**Far Horizons Award for Poetry**
The Malahat Review
University of Victoria, Box 1700, Sta CSC, Victoria, BC V8W 2Y2, Canada
*Tel:* 250-721-8524 *Fax:* 250-472-5051
*E-mail:* malahat@uvic.ca
*Web Site:* www.malahatreview.ca
*Key Personnel*
Ed: John Barton
Open to writers whose poetry has yet to be published in book form. Awarded in alternate years. See web site for details.
Award: $1,000 CAD
Closing Date: May 1, even numbered yrs

**Far Horizons Award for Short Fiction**
The Malahat Review
University of Victoria, Box 1700, Sta CSC, Victoria, BC V8W 2Y2, Canada
*Tel:* 250-721-8524 *Fax:* 250-472-5051
*E-mail:* malahat@uvic.ca
*Web Site:* www.malahatreview.ca
*Key Personnel*
Ed: John Barton
Open to writers whose fiction has yet to be published in a book of their own. Limited to 3,500 words. Awarded in alternate years. See web site for details.
Award: $1,000 CAD
Closing Date: May 1, odd numbered yrs

**Norma Farber First Book Award**
Poetry Society of America (PSA)
15 Gramercy Park S, New York, NY 10003
*Tel:* 212-254-9628 *Fax:* 212-673-2352
*Web Site:* www.poetrysociety.org
*Key Personnel*
Pres: Ruth Kaplan
Exec Dir: Alice Quinn
Mng Dir & Awards Coord: Brett Fletcher Lauer *E-mail:* brett@poetrysociety.org
Progs Dir: Darrel Alejandro Holnes
For a first book of original poetry written by an American poet; publishers only may submit with entry form.
Award: $500
Closing Date: Annually, Oct-Dec
Presented: Annual Awards Ceremony, New York, NY, Annually in Spring

**Virginia Faulkner Award for Excellence in Writing**
Prairie Schooner
University of Nebraska, 123 Andrews Hall, Lincoln, NE 68588-0334
Mailing Address: PO Box 880334, Lincoln, NE 68588-0334
*Tel:* 402-472-0911 *Fax:* 402-472-9771
*Web Site:* prairieschooner.unl.edu
*Key Personnel*
Mng Ed: James Engelhardt *E-mail:* jengelhardt2@unl.edu
Ed: Kwame Dawes
Established: 1987
Annual writing prize for work published in *Prairie Schooner* magazine. Only work published in the previous year is considered.
Other Sponsor(s): Friends & family of Virginia Faulkner
Award: $1,000
Presented: Winners announced in Spring issue of *Prairie Schooner* magazine

**The FC2 Catherine Doctorow Innovative Fiction Prize**
Fiction Collective Two Inc (FC2)
University Ctr, Suite 310, 3007 N Ben Wilson St, Victoria, TX 77901
*Web Site:* www.fc2.org
Open to any US writer in English with at least 3 books of fiction published. Submissions may include a collection of short stories, one or more novellas or a novel of any length. Works that have previously appeared in magazines or in anthologies may be included.
Award: $15,000 & publication by FC2
Closing Date: Nov 1
Presented: May

**Fellowship & Scholarship Program for Writers**
Bread Loaf Writers' Conference
Middlebury College, Middlebury, VT 05753
*Tel:* 802-443-5286 *Fax:* 802-443-2087
*E-mail:* blwc@middlebury.edu
*Web Site:* www.middlebury.edu/blwc
*Key Personnel*
Dir: Michael Collier
Asst Dir: Jennifer Grotz
Admin Mgr: Noreen Cargill *E-mail:* ncargill@middlebury.edu
Work study scholarship to be used during conference in August.
Award: Fellowship provides tuition, room & board during 10-day conference; Scholarship provides tuition during conference
Closing Date: Annually, March 1
Presented: Ripton, VT, May

**Fellowship Program**
Rhode Island State Council on the Arts
Affiliate of Dept of Rhode Island State Government
One Capital Hill, 3rd fl, Providence, RI 02908
*Tel:* 401-222-3880 *Fax:* 401-222-3018
*Web Site:* www.arts.ri.gov
*Key Personnel*
Dir, Individual Artists Progs: Cristina DiChiera *E-mail:* cristina.dichiera@arts.ri.gov
Established: 1967
Applicants must be Rhode Island residents who are not students in an arts discipline. Fellowship recipients are selected by a regional panel of writers. Categories include fiction, poetry, playwriting/screenwriting. Guidelines & applications on web site.
Award: $5,000 recipient; $1,000 merit award
Closing Date: April 1
Presented: Annually

**Fellowships for Creative & Performing Artists & Writers**
American Antiquarian Society (AAS)
185 Salisbury St, Worcester, MA 01609-1634
*Tel:* 508-755-5221 *Fax:* 508-753-3311
*Web Site:* www.americanantiquarian.org
*Key Personnel*
Dir, Outreach: James David Moran *Tel:* 508-471-2131 *E-mail:* jmoran@mwa.org
Established: 1994
Award: $1,350 stipend for fellows residing on campus (rent free) in the Society's Scholars'

housing, $1,850 stipend for fellows residing off campus (no travel allowance)
Closing Date: Annually in Oct

**Fellowships for Historical Research**
American Antiquarian Society (AAS)
185 Salisbury St, Worcester, MA 01609-1634
*Tel:* 508-471-2131
*Web Site:* www.americanantiquarian.org
*Key Personnel*
Dir, Outreach: James David Moran *Tel:* 508-471-2131 *E-mail:* jmoran@mwa.org
Given to poets, fiction writers & creative nonfiction writers for monthlong residencies at the American Antiquarian Society in Worchester, MA, to research pre-twentieth century American history & culture. Submit 10 copies of up to 25 pages of poetry, fiction or creative nonfiction, a resume, 2 letters of recommendation & a 5-page project proposal.
Award: $1,350 stipend & on-campus housing provided; fellows residing off-campus receive $1,850
Closing Date: Annually, Oct 5

**Fence Modern Poets Series**
Fence Books
University at Albany, Science Library 320, 1400 Washington Ave, Albany, NY 12222
*Tel:* 518-591-8162
*E-mail:* fence.fencebooks@gmail.com
*Web Site:* www.fenceportal.org
*Key Personnel*
Publr & Ed: Rebecca Wolff *E-mail:* rebeccafence@gmail.com
Mng Ed: Rob Arnold *E-mail:* robfence@gmail.com
Established: 2001
For a poet writing in English at any stage of his or her publishing career.
Award: $1,000 & publication
Closing Date: Annually, Feb 28

**Shubert Fendrich Memorial Playwriting Contest**
Pioneer Drama Service Inc
PO Box 4267, Englewood, CO 80155-4267
*Tel:* 303-779-4035 *Toll Free Tel:* 800-333-7262 *Fax:* 303-779-4315
*E-mail:* playwrights@pioneerdrama.com
*Web Site:* www.pioneerdrama.com
*Key Personnel*
Submissions Ed: Lori Conary
Established: 1990
Presented for plays suitable for publication by Pioneer Drama Service Inc. Submission must include a full copy of your ms, a completed application, a recording of music (if applicable), proof of production & a SASE if you wish your material returned.
Award: $1,000 advance on royalties
Closing Date: Annually, Dec 31
Presented: Annually, June 1

**Fiction Open**
Glimmer Train Press Inc
PO Box 80430, Portland, OR 97280
*Tel:* 503-221-0836 *Fax:* 503-221-0837
*E-mail:* editors@glimmertrain.org
*Web Site:* www.glimmertrain.org
*Key Personnel*
Co-Ed: Susan Burmeister-Brown *E-mail:* susan@glimmertrain.org
Established: 1999
Open to all themes & all writers, 2,000 to 20,000 word count range. Winner notification takes place 2 months after the close of each competition.
Award: $2,500, publication & 20 copies of that issue (1st place), $1,000 (2nd place), $600 (3rd place)
Closing Date: Annually in March, June, Sept & Dec

**The Field Poetry Prize**
Oberlin College Press
Subsidiary of Oberlin College
50 N Professor St, Oberlin, OH 44074-1091
SAN: 212-1883
*Tel:* 440-775-8408 *Fax:* 440-775-8124
*E-mail:* oc.press@oberlin.edu
*Web Site:* www.oberlin.edu/ocpress; www.oberlin.edu/ocpress/prize.htm (guidelines)
*Key Personnel*
Mng Ed: Marco Wilkinson
Ed: David Walker; David Young
Established: 1996
Original poetry ms of 50 to 80 pages. Open to all poets whether or not they have previously published in book form. Reading fee $28 & includes one year subn to *Field*.
Award: $1,000 & publication in the Field Poetry Series
Closing Date: May 31
Presented: Aug (on web site)

**Findley Prize**, see Writers' Trust Engel/Findley Prize

**Fine Arts Work Center in Provincetown**
24 Pearl St, Provincetown, MA 02657
*Tel:* 508-487-9960 *Fax:* 508-487-8873
*E-mail:* general@fawc.org
*Web Site:* www.fawc.org
*Key Personnel*
Exec Dir: Michael Roberts *Tel:* 508-487-9960 ext 102 *E-mail:* mroberts@fawc.org
Established: 1968
Offer seven-month fellowships to ten artists & ten writers, Oct 1-May 1. The Center aims to aid emerging artists & writers at a critical stage of their careers. For application & brochure, see web site above or send SASE.
Award: Monthly stipends of up to $650 plus free rent for writers living at the Center; same for artists. Families welcome; no pets
Closing Date: Dec 1, writers; Feb 1, visual arts

**Finishing Line Press Prize in Poetry**, see Open Chapbook Competition

**Doug Fir Fiction Award**
Bear Deluxe Magazine
810 SE Belmont, Suite 5, Portland, OR 97214
*E-mail:* bear@orlo.org
*Web Site:* www.beardeluxe.org
*Key Personnel*
Ed: Tom Webb
A short story relating to a sense of place or the natural world, interpreted as broadly or narrowly as you wish. Multiple submissions are allowed but must be mailed separately with separate entry fees. Submit a story of up to 5,000 words. Ms must be typed & double-spaced. Author's name must not appear anywhere on the ms. Entry fee: $15.
Award: $1,000 & publication in the magazine & writer's residency
Closing Date: Annually in Sept (postmarked 1st Tues after Labor Day)

**Five Star Dragonfly Book Awards**
Five Star Publications Inc
4696 W Tyson St, Chandler, AZ 85226
Mailing Address: PO Box 6698, Dept LM, Chandler, AZ 85246-6698
*Tel:* 480-940-8182 *Toll Free Tel:* 866-471-0777 *Fax:* 480-940-8787
*E-mail:* info@fivestarpublications.com
*Web Site:* www.fivestarpublications.com; www.fivestarmarketingsecrets.com
*Key Personnel*
Pres: Linda F Radke
Established: 2009
Two contest to choose from.
The Purple Dragonfly Book Awards honor published authors of children's literature - fiction & nonfiction - with 37 distinct subject categories, ranging from books on the environment & cooking to books on sports & family. Looking for stories that inspire, inform, teach or entertain. The judging panel includes experts from the fields of editing, reviewing, bookselling & publishing, as well as industry experts in specific fields. Books entered in this contest can appeal to children of any age. No restriction on publication date as long as the book is still in print. Authors can enter both ebooks & printed books.
The Royal Dragonfly Book Awards honor published authors of all types of literature - fiction & nonfiction - in a wide variety of genres, including inspriational, how-to, environmental, travel, fantasy & science fiction, romance, children's books & more. The judging panel includes experts from the fields of editing, reviewing, bookselling & publishing, as well as industry experts in specific fields. Books in this category can appeal to readers of all ages. No restriction on publication date as long as the book is still in print. Authors can enter both ebooks & printed books.
Award: Grand prize winner $300; drawing from first place winners $100 (1 winner)
Closing Date: Purple Dragonfly: May 1, 2014; Royal Dragonfly: Aug 1, 2014 (early), Oct 1, 2014 (final)
Presented: Award is mailed, Purple Dragonfly: June 15, 2014

**Norma Fleck Award for Canadian Children's Non-Fiction**
Canadian Children's Book Centre
40 Orchard View Blvd, Suite 217, Toronto, ON M4R 1B9, Canada
*Tel:* 416-975-0010 *Fax:* 416-975-8970
*E-mail:* info@bookcentre.ca
*Web Site:* www.bookcentre.ca
*Key Personnel*
Exec Dir: Charlotte Teeple *E-mail:* charlotte@bookcentre.ca
Gen Mgr: Dawn Todd *E-mail:* dawn@bookcentre.ca
Lib Coord: Meghan Howe *E-mail:* meghan@bookcentre.ca
Prog Coord: Shannon Howe Barnes *E-mail:* shannon@bookcentre.ca
Sales & Mktg Mgr: Holly Kent *E-mail:* holly@bookcentre.ca
Established: 1999
Awarded to a Canadian author/illustrator for an outstanding work of nonfiction for young people.
Other Sponsor(s): Fleck Family Foundation
Award: $10,000
Closing Date: Mid Dec annually

**Florida Individual Artist Fellowships**
Florida Dept of State, Division of Cultural Affairs
500 S Bronough St, Tallahassee, FL 32399-0250
*Tel:* 850-245-6470 *Fax:* 850-245-6497
*E-mail:* info@florida-arts.org
*Web Site:* www.florida-arts.org
*Key Personnel*
Dir: Sandy Shaughnessy *E-mail:* sshaughnessy@dos.state.fl.us
Arts Administrator: Mrs Morgan Lewis *E-mail:* mblewis@dos.state.fl.us
Established: 1976
Awarded biennially (even years), this fellowship program supports the general artistic & career

advancement of individual artists & recognizes the creation of new artworks by these artists.
Award: $2,500 or $5,000 fellowship

**Fordham University, Graduate School of Business Administration**
113 W 60 St, New York, NY 10023
*Fax:* 212-636-7076
*Web Site:* www.bnet.fordham.edu
*Key Personnel*
Professor, Communs & Media Mgmt: Philip M Napoli *Tel:* 212-636-6196 *E-mail:* pnapoli@fordham.edu
Established: 1969
Offers MBA degree with a major in Communications & Media Management & Master of Science (MS) in Communications & Media Management for media & entertainment industries. Its mission is to educate business professionals who can manage effectively in a range of leadership roles & who are equipped for continuous growth in a changing global environment. A variety of assistantships, fellowships & scholarships are available to highly qualified MBA candidates, such as Graduate Assistantships; New York Times Foundation Scholarship; Hitachi Fellowship; Xerox Fellowship; National Black MBA Association Scholarships; Minority Business Students Alliance Scholarship & Alexis Welsh Memorial Scholarship.
Closing Date: Ongoing
Presented: Each trimester

**ForeWord Reviews Book of the Year Awards**
ForeWord Reviews
425 Boardman Ave, Suite B, Traverse City, MI 49684
*Tel:* 231-933-3699 *Fax:* 231-933-3899
*Web Site:* www.bookoftheyearawards.com
*Key Personnel*
Publr: Victoria Sutherland *E-mail:* victoria@forewordreviews.com
Any independently published titles in any format with a copyright date of the previous calendar year. Publishers should submit their entries as soon as possible. Winners named in 60 categories.
Award: $1,500 each given to best book in fiction, nonfiction & independent publisher of the year
Closing Date: Annually, Jan 15 for books published in previous calendar year
Presented: ALA Annual Conference

**Morris D Forkosch Prize**
American Historical Association
400 "A" St SE, Washington, DC 20003-3889
*Tel:* 202-544-2422 *Fax:* 202-544-8307
*E-mail:* awards@historians.org
*Web Site:* www.historians.org
In recognition of the best in English in the field of British, British Imperial or British Commonwealth history since 1485. Submissions of books relating to the shared common law heritage of the English-speaking world are particularly encouraged. Books on British, British Imperial or British Commonwealth history published in 2013 are eligible. Along with an application form, applicants must mail a copy of their book to each of the prize committee members who will be posted on our web site as the prize deadline approaches. All updated info on web site.
Closing Date: May 15, 2014 (postmark)
Presented: AHA Annual Meeting

**49th Parallel Poetry Award**
The Bellingham Review
Mail Stop 9053, Western Washington University, Bellingham, WA 98225
*Tel:* 360-650-4863
*E-mail:* bhreview@wwu.edu
*Web Site:* www.bhreview.org
*Key Personnel*
Ed-in-Chief: Brenda Miller
Mng Ed: Marilyn Bruce
Established: 1983
Maximum length for prose is 6,000 words. Poems within a series of poems will each be treated as a separate entry. No previously published works, or works accepted for publication, are eligible. Work may be under consideration elsewhere, but must be withdrawn from the competition if accepted for publication. Make checks payable to: The Bellingham Review. All entries will receive a complimentary one-issue subscription. Entry fee for the first entry $20. Additional entries $10.
Award: $1,000 & publication in the Bellingham Review (1st prize), considered for publication (2nd, 3rd & finalists)
Closing Date: Annually, between Dec 1 & March 15
Presented: Annually in July

**Foster City International Writer's Contest**
Foster City Parks & Recreation Dept
650 Shell Blvd, Foster City, CA 94404
*Tel:* 650-286-3386
*E-mail:* fostercity_writers@yahoo.com
*Web Site:* www.fostercity.org
*Key Personnel*
Comm Chair: Ilene Shaine
Contact: Manny Hernandez
Established: 1974
For fiction, humor, children's story & poetry & personal essay, rhymed verse, blank verse. Entries must be original, previously unpublished & in English. Fiction must be no more than 3,000 words; children's story no more than 3,000 words; poetry not to exceed two double-spaced typed pages in length. Open to all writers, no age or geographic limit. Send SASE for contest flyer. Nonrefundable entry fee: $20.
Award: $150 in each category (1st prize); $75 (2nd prize): children's, nonfiction, fiction, humor, poetry

**Dixon Ryan Fox Manuscript Prize**
New York State Historical Association
5798 State Hwy 80, Cooperstown, NY 13326
Mailing Address: PO Box 800, Cooperstown, NY 13326-0800
*Tel:* 607-547-1480 *Fax:* 607-547-1405
Established: 1974
Encourage original scholarship in the history of New York State. Award granted to the best unpublished ms on the history of New York State. Electronic submissions only.
Award: $3,000
Closing Date: Annually, Jan 2
Presented: New York State Historical Association Board of Trustees Annual Meeting, Cooperstown, NY, Annually in July

**Frances Henne YALSA/VOYA Research Grant**
Young Adult Library Services Association (YALSA)
Division of American Library Association (ALA)
50 E Huron St, Chicago, IL 60611
*Tel:* 312-280-4390 *Toll Free Tel:* 800-545-2433 *Fax:* 312-280-5276
*E-mail:* yalsa@ala.org
*Web Site:* www.ala.org/yalsa/
*Key Personnel*
Prog Offr, Events & Conferences: Nichole Gilbert *Tel:* 312-280-4387 *Fax:* 312-280-1538 *E-mail:* ngilbert@ala.org
Established: 1986
To provide seed money to an individual, institution or group for a project to encourage research in library service to young adults.
Other Sponsor(s): Scarecrow Press; Voice of Advocates
Award: $1000
Closing Date: Annually, Dec 1
Presented: ALA Midwinter Meeting, Annually in Jan

**H E Francis Award Short Story Competition**
University of Alabama Dept of English
UAH Huntsville Dept of English, Morton Hall 222, Huntsville, AL 35899
*Web Site:* www.uah.edu/colleges/liberal/english/hefrancis.contest
*Key Personnel*
Registrar: Mary B Hindman
Established: 1990
Mss must be unpublished & may not exceed 5000 words in length. Multiple submissions are acceptable so long as we are notified immediately in the event that a ms is selected by another competition or publication; submission must include $15 entry fee, cover sheet & 3 copies of ms.
Other Sponsor(s): Ruth Hindman Foundation
Award: $1,000
Closing Date: Annually, Dec 31
Presented: Annually in April

**Soeurette Diehl Fraser Translation Award**
Texas Institute of Letters (TIL)
PO Box 609, Round Rock, TX 78680
*Tel:* 512-683-5640
*E-mail:* tilsecretary@yahoo.com
*Web Site:* www.texasinstituteofletters.org
*Key Personnel*
Pres: W K Stratton
VP: Andres Tijerina
Treas: James Hoggard
Secy: Jan Reid
Recording Secy: Betty Wiesepape
Established: 1990
Biennial award given for the best book of translation by a Texan. Guidelines available on the web site.
Other Sponsor(s): Babette Fraser
Award: $1,000
Closing Date: Biennial in Jan, odd-numbered years
Presented: TIL Awards Banquet, Biennial in Spring

**George Freedley Memorial Award**
Theatre Library Association
Roundabout Theatre Co, 231 W 39 St, Suite 1200, New York, NY 10018
*Tel:* 212-719-9393 (ext 351)
*E-mail:* info@tla-online.org; tlabookawards@gmail.com
*Web Site:* www.tla-online.org
*Key Personnel*
Co-Chair: Linda Miles; Tiffany Nixon
Established: 1968
To the author of a book in the field of theater, published in the US, on the basis of scholarship, readability & general contribution to knowledge. Only books related to live performance (including Vaudeville, puppetry, pantomime & circus) will be considered.
Award: $500 (1st prize), $200 (Special Jury Prize); certificate
Closing Date: Feb 28
Presented: New York City, NY, Oct

**The Don Freeman Memorial Grant-In-Aid**
Society of Children's Book Writers & Illustrators (SCBWI)
8271 Beverly Blvd, Los Angeles, CA 90048
*Tel:* 323-782-1010 *Fax:* 323-782-1892
*E-mail:* membership@scbwi.org; scbwi@scbwi.org
*Web Site:* www.scbwi.org
*Key Personnel*
Pres: Stephen Mooser *E-mail:* stephenmooser@scbwi.org
Exec Dir: Lin Oliver *E-mail:* linoliver@scbwi.org
Established: 1977

To enable picture-book artists to further their understanding, training &/or work in any aspect of the picture-book genre. Grant may be used for the purchase of necessary materials, enrollment in illustrators' or writers' workshops or conferences, courses in advanced illustrating or writing techniques & travel for research or to expose work to publishers/art directors. Open to Society members only.
Award: $2,000 & $500 for runner-up
Closing Date: March
Presented: Aug

**The French-American Foundation & Florence Gould Foundation Annual Translation Prize**
The French-American Foundation
28 W 44 St, Suite 1420, New York, NY 10036
*Tel:* 212-829-8800 *Fax:* 212-829-8810
*E-mail:* translation@frenchamerican.org
*Web Site:* www.frenchamerican.org
*Key Personnel*
Pres: Charles Kopb *Tel:* 212-829-8801 *E-mail:* ckopb@frenchamerican.org
Prog Offr: Eugenie Briet *Tel:* 646-588-6791 *E-mail:* ebriet@frenchamerican.org
Established: 1986
Annual award for distinguished translations of fiction & nonfiction from French into English which have been published in the US. Translations must be submitted by the US publisher. Technical, poetry, scientific, reference works & children's literature are not accepted. Works must have been published between Jan 1 & Dec 31, 2013.
Other Sponsor(s): Florence Gould Foundation
Award: Two awards of $10,000, one for fiction; one for nonfiction
Closing Date: Dec 31
Presented: New York, NY, Spring

**Fresh Fish Award for Emerging Writers**
Writers' Alliance of Newfoundland and Labrador (WANL)/Literary Arts Foundation of Newfoundland and Labrador
Haymarket Sq, 208-223 Duckworth St, St John's, NL A1C 6N1, Canada
*Tel:* 709-739-5215
*E-mail:* wanl@nf.aibn.com
*Web Site:* wanl.ca
*Key Personnel*
Exec Dir: Alison Dyer
Exec Asst: Sheri Coombs *E-mail:* wanlassist@nf.aibn.com
Established: 2006
Intended to serve as an incentive for emerging writers in Newfoundland & Labrador by providing them with financial support, recognition & professional editing services for a book length ms in any genre. Must be registered members of WANL; writers may join WANL at the time of submission.
Award: $5,000, editing services of a professional editor valued at up to $1,000 & miniature sculpture
Closing Date: June, odd numbered years

**Friends of American Writers Awards**
Friends of American Writers
506 Rose Ave, Des Plaines, IL 60016
*Tel:* 847-827-8339
*Web Site:* www.fawchicago.org
*Key Personnel*
Pres: Vivian Mortensen *E-mail:* vmortens@comcast.net
Adult Literary Awards: April Nauman *E-mail:* adn1110@netzero.com
Established: 1922
For literary fiction & nonfiction books published in the current year. Book must be author's 1st, 2nd or 3rd work. Author must have lived for 5 years in the Midwest, currently living in the Midwest or book's setting must be Midwestern. No poetry or mss.
Award: Two cash prizes totaling $4,000
Closing Date: Dec 20
Presented: The Fortnightly, Chicago, IL, Annually in May

**Fulbright Scholar Program**
Council for International Exchange of Scholars
Division of The Institute of International Education
1400 "K" St NW, Washington, DC 20005
*Tel:* 202-686-4000 *Fax:* 202-362-3442
*E-mail:* scholars@iie.org
*Web Site:* www.iie.org/cies
*Key Personnel*
Dir, Scholar Progs: Debra Egan
Dir, Outreach & Pub Aff: Peter Van Derwater
Established: 1946
CIES cooperates with the US Dept of State, Bureau of Educational & Cultural Affairs, in the administration of the Fulbright scholar program, which offers approximately 800 grants annually to US faculty & professionals for university teaching &/or advanced research in more than 125 countries.
Award: Grant benefits, which vary by country, generally include a stipend & round-trip travel for the grantee
Closing Date: Aug 1

**Lewis Galantiere Translation Award**
American Translators Association (ATA)
225 Reinekers Lane, Suite 590, Alexandria, VA 22314
*Tel:* 703-683-6100 *Fax:* 703-683-6122
*E-mail:* ata@atanet.org
*Web Site:* www.atanet.org
*Key Personnel*
Exec Dir: Walter W Bacak, Jr *Tel:* 703-683-6100 ext 3006 *E-mail:* walter@atanet.org
Established: 1984
Awarded in even years for a distinguished book-length literary translation from any language, except German into English, published in the US.
Award: $1,000, a certificate of recognition & up to $500 toward expenses to attend the ATA Annual Conference
Closing Date: June 1 (even years)
Presented: ATA Annual Conference

**Gannon University's High School Poetry Contest**
Gannon University English Department
Gannon University, Dept of English, 109 University Sq, Erie, PA 16541
*Tel:* 814-871-7504
*Web Site:* www.gannon.edu/departmental/english/poetry.asp
*Key Personnel*
Professor, Eng: Berwyn Moore *E-mail:* moore001@gannon.edu
Established: 1985
HS students in grades 9-12 are invited to participate; must be original poetry.
Award: $100 (1st place), $75 (2nd place), $50 (3rd place), certificate (honorable mention)
Closing Date: Feb 1, 2014
Presented: Gannon University, Waldron Campus Ctr, Yehl Rm, Erie, PA, April 2014

**Francois-Xavier Garneau Medal**
Canadian Historical Association
130 Albert St, Suite 501, Ottawa, ON K1P 5G4, Canada
*Tel:* 613-233-7885 *Fax:* 613-565-5445
*E-mail:* cha-shc@cha-shc.ca
*Web Site:* www.cha-shc.ca
*Key Personnel*
Exec Coord: Michel Duquet *E-mail:* mduquet@cha-shc.ca
Established: 1980
Awarded every 5 years; commemorates the first Canadian Historian. Applicant should be a Canadian citizen or a legal immigrant. Given for the most outstanding scholarly book in the field of Canadian history within the previous five years.
Award: Minted medal & $2,000
Presented: 2015

**Alfred C Gary Memorial**
The Poetry Society of Virginia
1194 Hume Rd, Hume, VA 22639-1806
*E-mail:* poetryinva@aol.com
*Web Site:* www.poetrysocietyofvirginia.org
*Key Personnel*
Pres: Judith K Bragg *E-mail:* musicsavy45@yahoo.com
Adult Contest Chair: Patsy Anne Bickerstaff *E-mail:* granypatsy@yahoo.com; Guy Terrell *E-mail:* ggterr@infionline.net
All entries must be in English, original & unpublished. Submit 2 copies, each having the category name & number on top left of page. Entries will not be returned. Subject: a historic event that occurred between 1925 & 1992; iambic pentameter; 48 line limit. Entry fee: $4 nonmembs.
Other Sponsor(s): Claudia Gary
Award: $50 (1st prize), $30 (2nd prize), $20 (3rd prize)
Closing Date: Jan 19
Presented: Annual PSV Awards Luncheon, Richmond, VA, April

**John Gassner Memorial Playwriting Award**
The New England Theatre Conference Inc
215 Knob Hill Dr, Hamden, CT 06518
*Tel:* 617-851-8535 *Fax:* 203-288-5938
*E-mail:* mail@netconline.org
*Web Site:* www.netconline.org
Established: 1967
Playwriting contest for new full-length plays.
Award: $1,000 (1st prize), $500 (2nd prize)
Closing Date: Annually, April 15
Presented: NETC Annual Convention, Annually in Nov

**The Christian Gauss Award**
The Phi Beta Kappa Society
1606 New Hampshire Ave NW, Washington, DC 20009
*Tel:* 202-265-3808 *Fax:* 202-986-1601
*E-mail:* awards@pbk.org
*Web Site:* www.pbk.org/bookawards
*Key Personnel*
Coord, Society Events: Lucinda Morales *Tel:* 202-745-3235 *E-mail:* lmorales@pbk.org
Established: 1950
For outstanding books in the field of literary scholarship or criticism published in the USA. Nominations must come from publisher & be submitted online.
Award: $10,000
Closing Date: Annually in April
Presented: Washington, DC, Annually in Dec

**The Gaylactic Spectrum Awards**
Gaylactic Spectrum Awards Foundation
PO Box 73602, Washington, DC 20056-3602
*Tel:* 202-483-6369
*Web Site:* www.spectrumawards.org
*Key Personnel*
Exec Dir: Rob Gates
Established: 1998
Presented to outstanding works of science fiction, fantasy or horror with significant gay, lesbian, bisexual or transgender content.
Award: Statuette & cash prize for Best Novel & Best Short Fiction categories

Closing Date: Open between March 15 & April 30 for works released during the previous year
Presented: Varies - World Science Fiction Convention, Gaylaxicon or other, Fall

**Lionel Gelber Prize**
Lionel Gelber Foundation
University of Toronto, Munk School of Global Affairs, One Devonshire Place, Toronto, ON M5S 3K7, Canada
*Tel:* 416-946-8901 *Fax:* 416-946-8915
*E-mail:* events.munk@utoronto.ca
*Web Site:* www.utoronto.ca/mcis/gelber
Established: 1989
Given to the author of the year's most outstanding work of nonfiction in the field of international relations. Designed to encourage authors who write about international relations & to stimulate the audience for these books to grow. Open to authors of all nationalities. Six copies of each title must be submitted by the publisher. Books must be published between Jan 1 & Dec 31 in English or English translation.
Other Sponsor(s): Munk School of Global affairs
Award: $15,000
Closing Date: Oct
Presented: Short list announced Jan; prize award in Spring

**Georgetown Review Literary Prize**
Georgetown Review
Box 227, 400 E College St, Georgetown, KY 40324
*Web Site:* georgetownreview.georgetowncollege.edu
Established: 1993
For a single poem, a short story or an essay of any length. All entries are considered for publication. $10 entry fee, $5 for each additional entry.
Award: $1,000 & publication in Georgetown Review
Closing Date: Annually in Oct

**Leo Gershoy Award**
American Historical Association
400 "A" St SE, Washington, DC 20003-3889
*Tel:* 202-544-2422 *Fax:* 202-544-8307
*E-mail:* awards@historians.org
*Web Site:* www.historians.org
Established: 1975
In recognition of outstanding historical writing in 17th & 18th century Western European history. Books published in 2013 will be eligible. Along with an application form, applicants must mail a copy of their book (limited to three titles from any one publisher) to each of the prize committee members who will be posted on our web site as the prize deadline approaches. All updated info on web site.
Award: Cash prize
Closing Date: May 15, 2014 (postmark)
Presented: AHA Annual Meeting

**Charles M Getchell Award**, see Southeastern Theatre Conference New Play Project

**Allen Ginsberg Poetry Award**
The Poetry Center at Passaic County Community College
One College Blvd, Paterson, NJ 07505-1179
*Tel:* 973-684-6555 *Fax:* 973-523-6085
*Web Site:* www.pccc.edu/poetry
*Key Personnel*
Exec Dir: Maria Mazziotti Gillan *E-mail:* mgillan@pccc.edu
Asst Dir: Ashley Kesling *E-mail:* akesling@pccc.edu
Poem should not be more than 2 ms pages. Sheets which contain the poems should not contain the poet's name. Do not submit poems that imitate Allen Ginsberg's work. Entry fee $18.
Award: $1,000 (1st prize), $200 (2nd prize), $100 (3rd prize)
Closing Date: Annually, April 1

**Gival Press Novel Award**
Gival Press
PO Box 3812, Arlington, VA 22203
SAN: 852-0787
*Tel:* 703-351-0079 *Fax:* 703-351-0079
*E-mail:* givalpress@yahoo.com
*Web Site:* www.givalpress.com
*Key Personnel*
Publr & Ed: Robert L Giron
Established: 2005
For best literary novel.
Award: $3,000 & publication
Closing Date: Annually, May 30
Presented: Annually, Oct 1

**Gival Press Oscar Wilde Award**
Gival Press
PO Box 3812, Arlington, VA 22203
SAN: 852-0787
*Tel:* 703-351-0079 *Fax:* 703-351-0079
*E-mail:* givalpress@yahoo.com
*Web Site:* www.givalpress.com
*Key Personnel*
Publr & Ed: Robert L Giron
Established: 2002
For best GLBT poem.
Award: $100 & online publication
Closing Date: Annually, June 27
Presented: Annually, Sept 1

**Gival Press Short Story Award**
Gival Press
PO Box 3812, Arlington, VA 22203
SAN: 852-0787
*Tel:* 703-351-0079 *Fax:* 703-351-0079
*E-mail:* givalpress@yahoo.com
*Web Site:* www.givalpress.com
*Key Personnel*
Publr & Ed: Robert L Giron
Established: 2004
For best literary short story.
Award: $1,000 & online publication
Closing Date: Annually, Aug 8
Presented: Annually, Dec 1

**John Glassco Translation Prize**
Literary Translators' Association of Canada
Concordia University, LB 601, 1455 De Maisonneuve West, Montreal, QC H3G 1M8, Canada
*Tel:* 514-848-2424 (ext 8702)
*E-mail:* info@attlc-ltac.org
*Web Site:* www.attlc-ltac.org
*Key Personnel*
Pres: Jo-Anne Elder
Coord: Yves Dion
Established: 1982
For a first book-length literary translation into French or English published in Canada during the previous year. Must be Canadian citizen or permanent resident.
Award: $1,000
Closing Date: Annually, July 31
Presented: Annually, Sept 30

**GLCA New Writers Awards**
Great Lakes Colleges Association (GLCA)
535 W William St, Suite 301, Ann Arbor, MI 48103
*Tel:* 734-661-2350 *Fax:* 734-661-2349
*Web Site:* www.glca.org
*Key Personnel*
Dir, Prog Devt: Gregory R Wegner
Established: 1969
For a first published work of fiction or creative nonfiction or a first book of poetry. Submissions may be made only by publishers; one entry each, poetry, fiction or creative nonfiction. Submit 4 copies of the work & an author's statement agreeing to the terms. See web site for details.
Award: Reading engagements at up to 13 colleges & universities of the GLCA; each engagement includes $500 honorarium

**Danuta Gleed Literary Award**
Writers' Union of Canada
90 Richmond St E, Suite 200, Toronto, ON M5C 1P1, Canada
*Tel:* 416-703-8982 *Fax:* 416-504-9090
*E-mail:* info@writersunion.ca
*Web Site:* www.writersunion.ca
*Key Personnel*
Competitions Coord: Nancy MacLeod *Tel:* 416-703-8982 ext 226 *E-mail:* nmacleod@writersunion.ca
Off Administrator: Valerie Laws *Tel:* 416-703-8982 ext 224
Established: 1997
For best first collection of short fiction by a Canadian in 2012.
Award: $10,000 (1st prize); $500 (2nd & 3rd prizes)
Closing Date: Annually, Jan 31

**Golden Cylindar Awards**
Gravure Association of America Inc
8281 Pine Lake Rd, Denver, NC 28037
*Tel:* 201-523-6042 *Fax:* 201-523-6048
*E-mail:* gaa@gaa.org
*Web Site:* www.gaa.org
*Key Personnel*
Dir, Planning & Admin: Pamela W Schenk *Tel:* 585-288-2297 *E-mail:* pwschenk@gaa.org
Encourage highest quality gravure printing from design through production.
Award: Golden Cylinders on pedestals
Closing Date: Annually in April
Presented: Leadership Summit

**Golden Kite Awards**
Society of Children's Book Writers & Illustrators (SCBWI)
8271 Beverly Blvd, Los Angeles, CA 90048
*Tel:* 323-782-1010 *Fax:* 323-782-1892
*E-mail:* scbwi@scbwi.org; membership@scbwi.org
*Web Site:* www.scbwi.org
*Key Personnel*
Pres: Stephen Mooser *E-mail:* stephenmooser@scbwi.org
Exec Dir: Lin Oliver *E-mail:* linoliver@scbwi.org
Established: 1973
Four awards, one each for fiction, nonfiction, picture book text & picture book illustration, awarded each year to the most outstanding children's books published during that year & written or illustrated by members of the Society of Children's Book Writers & Illustrators. An honor book plaque is awarded in each category.
Award: Free transportation & accomodations to summer conference
Closing Date: Dec
Presented: Aug

**Golden Rose Award**
New England Poetry Club
2 Farrar St, Cambridge, MA 02138
Mailing Address: PO Box 190076, Boston, MA 02119
*Tel:* 617-744-6034
*E-mail:* contests@nepoetryclub.org
*Web Site:* www.nepoetryclub.org
*Key Personnel*
Pres: Diana Der-Hovanessian
VP: Sally Cragin; Daniel Tobin
Contest Chair: Ellin Sarot
Established: 1920

The oldest literary award given annually to poet who has done the most for poetry during previous year or in a lifetime. Chosen by board members.
Award: Rose sculpture
Closing Date: Annually, May 31
Presented: Longfellow Garden, Cambridge, MA, Annually in July

**Laurence Goldstein Poetry Prize**
Michigan Quarterly Review
University of Michigan, 0576 Rackham Bldg, 915 E Washington St, Ann Arbor, MI 48109-1070
*Tel:* 734-764-9265
*E-mail:* mqr@umich.edu
*Web Site:* www.umich.edu/~mqr
*Key Personnel*
Mng Ed: Vicki Lawrence
Ed: Keith Taylor
Awarded to the best poem published in MQR each year. No deadline or special application process.
Award: $500

**The Gracies®**
Alliance for Women in Media (AWM)
Subsidiary of American Women in Radio & Television
1760 Old Meadow Rd, Suite 500, McLean, VA 22102
*Tel:* 703-506-3290 *Fax:* 703-506-3266
*E-mail:* info@awrt.org
*Web Site:* www.awrt.org
*Key Personnel*
Pres: Erin Fuller *E-mail:* efuller@allwomeninmedia.org
EVP: Amy B Lotz *E-mail:* alotz@allwomeninmedia.org
Awarded for programming in all mediums which contributes to positive & realistic portrayals of women, addresses interests of concern to women, enhances women's image, position & welfare. For application information, contact Lesa Faris.
Award: Statue
Presented: Annually in May

**Grants for Artist Projects**
Artist Trust
1835 12 Ave, Seattle, WA 98122
*Tel:* 206-467-8734 (ext 11) *Toll Free Tel:* 866-218-7878 (ext 11) *Fax:* 206-467-9633
*E-mail:* info@artisttrust.org
*Web Site:* www.artisttrust.org
*Key Personnel*
Exec Dir: Margit Rankin *Tel:* 206-467-8734 ext 12
Prog Mgr: Miguel Guillen *Tel:* 206-467-8734 ext 11
Established: 1988
Project grant open to Washington State artists. Applications for the GAP will be available in winter. GAPs will be awarded in Fall in all artistic disciplines.
Award: Up to $1,500
Presented: Annually in June

**James H Gray Award for Short Nonfiction**
Writers Guild of Alberta
11759 Groat Rd, Edmonton, AB T5M 3K6, Canada
*Tel:* 780-422-8174 *Toll Free Tel:* 800-665-5354 (AB only) *Fax:* 780-422-2663 (attn WGA)
*E-mail:* mail@writersguild.ab.ca
*Web Site:* www.writersguild.ab.ca
*Key Personnel*
Exec Dir: Carol Holmes *E-mail:* cholmes@writersguild.ab.ca
Communs & Partnerships Coord: Nicholas Mather *E-mail:* nmather@writersguild.ab.ca
Memb Servs Coord: Giorgia Severini
Progs Coord: Nichole Quiring
*E-mail:* programs@writersguild.ab.ca
Established: 2009
Open to published & unpublished Alberta authors on any topic; no longer than 5,000 words.
Award: $700
Closing Date: Annually, Dec 31
*Branch Office(s)*
Lord Denning House, 509 20 Ave SW, Calgary, AB T2S 0E7, Canada, Prog Coord: Samantha Warwick *Tel:* 403-265-2226
*E-mail:* swarwick@writersguild.ab.ca

**The Green Rose Prize in Poetry**
New Issues Poetry & Prose
Western Michigan University, 1903 W Michigan Ave, Kalamazoo, MI 49008-5463
*Tel:* 269-387-8185 *Fax:* 269-387-2562
*E-mail:* new-issues@wmich.edu
*Web Site:* www.wmich.edu/newissues/greenroseprize.html
*Key Personnel*
Mng Ed: Kimberly Kolbe
Ed: William Olsen
Poets writing in English who have published one or more full-length collections of poetry. A $25 reading fee must accompany each ms; do not bind ms. Include a brief bio & relevant publication information, cover page with name, address, phone number, e-mail address & title of ms; include table of contents; enclose SASE.
Other Sponsor(s): Western Michigan University
Award: $2,000 & book publication
Closing Date: Sept 30

**Bess Gresham Memorial**
The Poetry Society of Virginia
1194 Hume Rd, Hume, VA 22639-1806
*E-mail:* poetryinva@aol.com
*Web Site:* www.poetrysocietyofvirginia.org
*Key Personnel*
Pres: Judith K Bragg *E-mail:* musicsavy45@yahoo.com
Adult Contest Chair: Patsy Anne Bickerstaff
*E-mail:* granypatsy@yahoo.com; Guy Terrell
*E-mail:* ggterr@infionline.net
All entries must be in English, original & unpublished. Submit 2 copies of each poem, each having the category name & number on top left of page. Only 1 poem per category; entries will not be returned. Subject: gardens; 48 line limit. Entry fee: $4 nonmembs.
Award: $50 (1st place), $30 (2nd place), $20 (3rd place)
Closing Date: Jan 19
Presented: Annual PSV Awards Luncheon, Richmond, VA, April

**Hackmatack Children's Choice Book Award**
Nova Scotia Department of Education
PO Box 34055, Scotia Square RPO, Halifax, NS B3J 3S1, Canada
*Tel:* 902-424-3774 *Fax:* 902-424-0613
*E-mail:* hackmatack@hackmatack.ca
*Web Site:* www.hackmatack.ca
*Key Personnel*
Hackmatack Coord: Kate Watson
Established: 1999
Atlantic Canadian Children's Choice Award for grades 4-6. Four categories: English fiction, English nonfiction, French fiction & French nonfiction.
Award: Plaques
Closing Date: Annually, Oct 15
Presented: Award ceremony, Annually in Spring

**Hackney Literary Awards**
1305 Second Ave N, Suite 103, Birmingham, AL 35203
*E-mail:* info@hackneyliteraryawards.org
*Web Site:* www.hackneyliteraryawards.org
Established: 1969
Short story, poetry & novel awards. Check web site or send SASE for contest guidelines. Entry fee: novels $30, short stories $20, poetry $15. Presented in Birmingham Arts Journal.
Award: $600 (1st place), $400 (2nd place), $250 (3rd place), plus a $5,000 prize sponsored by Morris Hackney for an unpublished novel
Closing Date: Annually, Nov 30 for short story & poetry entries; Annually, Sept 30 for novel entries
Presented: March 30

**Sarah Josepha Hale Award**
Trustees of the Richards Library
58 N Main, Newport, NH 03773
*Tel:* 603-863-3430
*E-mail:* rfl@newport.lib.nh.us
*Web Site:* www.newport.lib.nh.us
*Key Personnel*
Lib Dir & Award Administrator: Andrea Thorpe
*E-mail:* athorpe@newport.lib.nh.us
Established: 1956
A distinguished literary figure in some way associated with New England. Nominations or applications are not accepted.
Award: Bronze medal & $1,000
Presented: Newport, NH

**Loretta Dunn Hall Memorial**
The Poetry Society of Virginia
1194 Hume Rd, Hume, VA 22639-1806
*E-mail:* poetryinva@aol.com
*Web Site:* www.poetrysocietyofvirginia.org
*Key Personnel*
Pres: Judith K Bragg *E-mail:* musicsavy45@yahoo.com
Adult Contest Chair: Patsy Anne Bickerstaff
*E-mail:* granypatsy@yahoo.com; Guy Terrell
*E-mail:* ggterr@infionline.net
All entries must be in English, original & unpublished. Submit 2 copies, each having the category name & number on top left of page. Subject: family; any form; 24 line limit. VA residents only. Entry fee: $4 nonmembs.
Other Sponsor(s): Phyllis Hall Haislip
Award: $50 (1st prize), $30 (2nd prize), $20 (3rd prize)
Closing Date: Jan 19
Presented: Annual PSV Awards Luncheon, Richmond, VA, April

**Marilyn Hall Awards**, see BHTG - Competition for Youth Theatre Marilyn Hall Awards

**Handy Andy Prize**
The Poetry Society of Virginia
1194 Hume Rd, Hume, VA 22639-1806
*E-mail:* poetryinva@aol.com
*Web Site:* www.poetrysocietyofvirginia.org
*Key Personnel*
Pres: Judith K Bragg *E-mail:* musicsavy45@yahoo.com
Adult Contest Chair: Patsy Anne Bickerstaff
*E-mail:* granypatsy@yahoo.com; Guy Terrell
*E-mail:* ggterr@infionline.net
For a limerick. Must be in English, original & unpublished. Submit 2 copies, each having the category name & number on top left of page. Entry fee: $4 nonmembs.
Award: $25 (1st prize), $15 (2nd prize), $10 (3rd prize)
Closing Date: Jan 19
Presented: Annual PSV Awards Luncheon, Richmond, VA, April

**Clarence H Haring Prize**
American Historical Association
400 "A" St SE, Washington, DC 20003-3889
*Tel:* 202-544-2422 *Fax:* 202-544-8307
*E-mail:* awards@historians.org
*Web Site:* www.historians.org
For work by a Latin American in Latin American history during the preceding five years. Offered

quinquennially. There is no language limitation on works submitted. Along with an application form, applicants must mail a copy of their book to each of the prize committee members who will be posted on our web site as the prize deadline approaches. Books published 2011 through 2015 will be considered. All updated info on web site.
Award: Cash prize
Closing Date: May 16, 2016 (postmark)
Presented: AHA Annual Meeting, Denver, CO, Jan 5-8, 2017

**Joy Harjo Poetry Award**
CUTTHROAT, A Journal of the Arts
PO Box 2414, Durango, CO 81302
*Tel:* 970-903-7914
*E-mail:* cutthroatmag@gmail.com
*Web Site:* www.cutthroatmag.com
*Key Personnel*
Ed-in-Chief: Pamela Uschuk
Mng Ed: Susan Foster
Fiction Ed: Beth Alvarado; William Luvaas
Poetry Ed: William Pitt Root
Established: 2005
Submit online up to 3 unpublished poems (100 line limit for each). Writers may submit as often as they wish. No poems that have been previously published or have won contests are eligible; $17 reading fee.
Award: $1,250 (1st place), $250 (2nd place), both include publication in *CUTTHROAT*
Closing Date: Annually in Oct
Presented: Annually in Dec

**Aurand Harris Memorial Playwriting Award**
The New England Theatre Conference Inc
215 Knob Hill Dr, Hamden, CT 06518
*Tel:* 617-851-8535 *Fax:* 203-288-5938
*E-mail:* mail@netconline.org
*Web Site:* www.netconline.org
Established: 1997
Competition for new plays for young audiences. Scripts must be unpublished & unproduced. For guidelines, go to web site.
Award: $1,000 (1st prize), $500 (2nd prize)
Closing Date: Annually, May 1
Presented: NETC Annual Convention, Annually in Nov

**Julie Harris Playwright Award Competition**, see BHTG - Julie Harris Playwright Award Competition

**Haskins Medal Award**
Medieval Academy of America
104 Mount Auburn St, 5th fl, Cambridge, MA 02138
*Tel:* 617-491-1622 *Fax:* 617-492-3303
*E-mail:* speculum@medievalacademy.org
*Web Site:* www.medievalacademy.org
*Key Personnel*
Exec Dir & Ed, Speculum: Eileen Gardiner *E-mail:* egardiner@themedievalacademy.org
Established: 1940
For a book of outstanding importance in the medieval field published no earlier than six years prior to award date.
Award: Gold medal
Closing Date: Annually, Oct 15
Presented: Annually in Spring

**Headlands Center for the Arts Residency for Writers**
944 Fort Barry, Sausalito, CA 94965
*Tel:* 415-331-2787 *Fax:* 415-331-3857
*Web Site:* www.headlands.org
*Key Personnel*
Residency Mgr: Holly Blake *Tel:* 415-331-2787 ext 24 *E-mail:* hblake@headlands.org
Established: 1987
A one to ten week residency at Headlands is granted each year to writers of the Artist in Residency Program. Call or write the HCA for deadline & other information. See web site for application & more information.
Award: One, two or up to eleven week stay
Closing Date: June 4

**Drue Heinz Literature Prize**
University of Pittsburgh Press
Eureka Bldg, 5th fl, 3400 Forbes Ave, Pittsburgh, PA 15260
*Tel:* 412-383-2456 *Fax:* 412-383-2466
*E-mail:* info@upress.pitt.edu
*Web Site:* www.upress.pitt.edu
*Key Personnel*
Asst to Dir: Kelley H Johovic *E-mail:* kjohovic@upress.pitt.edu
Established: 1980
For a collection of short fiction 150-300 pages in length. Open to all writers who have published a book-length collection of short fiction or who have had three short stories or novellas published in commercial magazines or literary journals of national distribution. See web site for complete rules.
Other Sponsor(s): Drue Heinz & The Drue Heinz Trust
Award: $15,000 & publication by the University of Pittsburgh Press
Closing Date: Postmarked between May 1 & June 30
Presented: Pittsburgh, PA, Nov

**The Hemingway Foundation/PEN Award**
PEN New England
Massachusetts Institute of Technology, 77 Massachusetts Ave, 14-N-221A, Cambridge, MA 02139
*Tel:* 617-324-1729
*E-mail:* pen-newengland@mit.edu
*Web Site:* www.pen-ne.org
*Key Personnel*
Exec Dir: Karen Wulf
Award Administrator: Helene Atwan
Established: 1976
Given to a novel or book of short stories by an American writer who has not previously published a book of fiction. Entry fee: $35.
Award: $8,000 & one week residency in the Distinguished Visitors Series (Univ of Idaho)
Closing Date: Annually in Dec
Presented: JFK Library, Boston, MA, Annually in March

**Cecil Hemley Memorial Award**
Poetry Society of America (PSA)
15 Gramercy Park S, New York, NY 10003
*Tel:* 212-254-9628 *Fax:* 212-673-2352
*Web Site:* www.poetrysociety.org
*Key Personnel*
Pres: Ruth Kaplan
Exec Dir: Alice Quinn
Mng Dir & Awards Coord: Brett Fletcher Lauer *E-mail:* brett@poetrysociety.org
Progs Dir: Darrel Alejandro Holnes
Established: 1969
For an unpublished lyric poem on a philosophical theme, not to exceed 100 lines. Open to Society members only. Send No 10 SASE or see web site for more information.
Award: $500
Closing Date: Annually, Oct-Dec
Presented: Annual Awards Ceremony, New York, NY, Annually in Spring

**Henrico Theatre Company One-Act Playwriting Competition**
Henrico Recreation & Parks
PO Box 90775, Richmond, VA 23273-0775
*Tel:* 804-501-5138 *Fax:* 804-501-5284
*Key Personnel*
Sr Cultural Arts Coord: Amy Perdue *E-mail:* per22@co.henrico.va.us
Established: 1985
One-act playwriting.
Award: $300 & possible production (1st prize), $200 & possible production (2nd & 3rd prize)
Closing Date: Annually, July 1
Presented: Annually in Feb

**Brodie Herndon Memorial**
The Poetry Society of Virginia
1194 Hume Rd, Hume, VA 22639-1806
*E-mail:* poetryinva@aol.com
*Web Site:* www.poetrysocietyofvirginia.org
*Key Personnel*
Pres: Judith K Bragg *E-mail:* musicsavy45@yahoo.com
Adult Contest Chair: Patsy Anne Bickerstaff *E-mail:* granypatsy@yahoo.com; Guy Terrell *E-mail:* ggterr@infionline.net
Poems in any form about the sea; 48 line limit. Must be original, unpublished & in English. Submit 2 copies, each having the category name & number on top left of page. Entry fee: $4 nonmembs.
Award: $50 (1st prize), $30 (2nd prize)
Closing Date: Jan 19
Presented: Annual PSV Awards Luncheon, Richmond, VA, April

**Carl Hertzog Book Design Award**
Friends of the University Library
Subsidiary of University of Texas at El Paso
c/o Dir of the Library, University of Texas at El Paso, University Library, El Paso, TX 79968-0582
*Tel:* 915-747-5683 *Fax:* 915-747-5345
*Web Site:* libraryweb.utep.edu
*Key Personnel*
Assoc VP: Robert L Stakes *Tel:* 915-747-6710 *E-mail:* rlstakes@utep.edu
Biennial award for excellence in book design. There is a maximum number of 5 entries allowed & must have been printed Oct 2, 2011-Sept 2013. While a printer, publisher or designer may submit an entry, only the designer is eligible to receive the award.
Award: $1,000, bronze medallion & certificate
Closing Date: Oct 1, odd-numbered years
Presented: University of Texas, El Paso, Biennially in Feb/March

**Hidden River Arts Playwriting Award**
Hidden River™ Arts
PO Box 63927, Philadelphia, PA 19147
*Tel:* 610-764-0813
*E-mail:* hiddenriverarts@gmail.com
*Web Site:* www.hiddenriverarts.org
*Key Personnel*
Founding Dir: Debra Leigh Scott
Established: 2002
Annual award for an unpublished, unproduced full-length play. Entry fee: $17.
Award: $1,000 (awarded by mail) & anthology publication
Closing Date: Annually, June 30
Presented: Annually in Dec

**Highlights for Children Fiction Contest**
Highlights for Children Inc
803 Church St, Honesdale, PA 18431
*Tel:* 570-253-1080 *Fax:* 570-251-7847
*E-mail:* eds@highlights.com
*Web Site:* www.highlights.com
*Key Personnel*
Sr Ed: Joelle Dujardin
Established: 1980
Fiction for children, subject varies annually. Guidelines & contest topic available on web site under "About Us" area. Indicate word count in upper right-hand corner on the first

page of ms. No crime, violence or derogatory humor. Stories may be any length up to 750 words. Stories for beginning readers should not exceed 475 words.
Award: 3 prizes of $1,000 or tuition for any Highlights Foundation Workshop
Closing Date: Annually, Jan 1-Jan 31 (postmark)
Presented: Annually in June

**The Tony Hillerman Prize**
Wordharvest LLC
1063 Willow Way, Santa Fe, NM 87507
*Tel:* 505-471-1565
*E-mail:* wordharvest@wordharvest.com
*Web Site:* www.wordharvest.com
*Key Personnel*
Founder: Anne Hillerman; Jean Schaumberg
Established: 2007
Prize for best first mystery set in the Southwest.
Award: $10,000 & publication by St Martin's Press
Closing Date: Annually, June 1
Presented: Tony Hillerman Writers Conference, Annually

**Hillman Prizes in Journalism**
The Sidney Hillman Foundation
12 W 31 St, 12th fl, New York, NY 10001
*Tel:* 646-448-6413
*Web Site:* www.hillmanfoundation.org
*Key Personnel*
Pres: Bruce Raynor
Exec Dir: Alexandra Lescaze *Tel:* 917-696-2494 *E-mail:* alex@hillmanfoundation.org
Established: 1950
For journalism that fosters social & economic justice & for investigative journalism.
Award: $5,000 & certificate designed by New York cartoonist Edward Sorel
Closing Date: Jan 31
Presented: Award ceremony & cocktail party, New York, NY, Annually in Mid-May

**Eric Hoffer Award for Independent Books**
www.HofferAward.com
Subsidiary of The Eric Hoffer Project
PO Box 11, Titusville, NJ 08560
*Fax:* 609-964-1718
*E-mail:* info@hofferaward.com
*Web Site:* www.hofferaward.com
*Key Personnel*
Chmn & Exec Ed: Christopher Klim
Publr & Coord: E Martin
Established: 2002
Open to academic, small & self-published press books in the last 2 years. Results published in The US Review of Books (www.theusreview.com).
Award: $2,000 (Grand Prize); Best Academic, Small & Micro Press & Best Self-Published Awards; 16 category winners & runners-up
Closing Date: Annually, Jan 25
Presented: Annually in May

**Eric Hoffer Award for Short Prose**
www.HofferAward.com
Subsidiary of The Eric Hoffer Project
PO Box 11, Titusville, NJ 08560
*Fax:* 609-964-1718
*E-mail:* info@hofferaward.com
*Web Site:* www.hofferaward.com
*Key Personnel*
Chmn & Exec Ed: Christopher Klim
Ed: Danielle Evennou; Marjetta Geerling; Robert Gover; Christopher Helvey; Matt Ryan; Tim Waldron
Established: 2002
New fiction & creative nonfiction less than 10,000 words.
Award: $200 (Grand Prize); publication in Best New Writing (20-25 finalists)
Closing Date: Annually, March 31
Presented: Annually in Oct

**Bess Hokin Prize**
Poetry Magazine
444 N Michigan Ave, Suite 1850, Chicago, IL 60611-4034
*Tel:* 312-787-7070 *Fax:* 312-787-6650
*E-mail:* editors@poetrymagazine.org
*Web Site:* poetryfoundation.org
*Key Personnel*
Mng Ed: Valerie Johnson *E-mail:* vjohnson@poetrymagazine.org
Established: 1948
For poetry published in the preceding two volumes of Poetry. No application necessary.
Award: $1,000
Presented: Annually in Dec

**Honickman First Book Prize**
American Poetry Review
University of the Arts (UARTS), Hamilton Hall, 320 S Broad St, Rm 313, Philadelphia, PA 19102-4901
*Tel:* 215-717-6801 *Fax:* 215-717-6805
*Web Site:* www.aprweb.org
*Key Personnel*
Ed: Elizabeth Scanlon *E-mail:* escanlon@aprweb.org
Established: 1997
Awarded to any US citizen, writing in English & who has not published a book-length collection of poems with an ISBN. Poems previously published in periodicals or limited-edition chapbooks may be included in the ms, but the ms itself must not have been published as a book-length work exceeding 25 pages. No translations or multiple author entries accepted. Entry fee $25. Now accepting online submissions.
Award: $3,000
Closing Date: Oct 31 postmark
Presented: Announcement in March/April issue of the American Poetry Review, Feb 15

**Firman Houghton Prize**
New England Poetry Club
2 Farrar St, Cambridge, MA 02138
Mailing Address: PO Box 190076, Boston, MA 02119
*Tel:* 617-744-6034
*E-mail:* contests@nepoetryclub.org
*Web Site:* www.nepoetryclub.org
*Key Personnel*
Pres: Diana Der-Hovanessian
VP: Sally Cragin; Daniel Tobin
Contest Chair: Nazaleem Smith
Established: 1987
Award for a lyric poem in honor of the former president of the NEPC. $10 for 3 contest entries per poem entry & $3 for additional entries, free for members & students.
Award: $250
Closing Date: Annually, May 31
Presented: Public Library, Cambridge, MA, Annually in Autumn

**Amelia Frances Howard-Gibbon Illustrator's Award**
Canadian Library Association (CLA) (Association Canadienne des bibliotheques)
1150 Morrison Dr, Suite 400, Ottawa, ON K2H 8S9, Canada
*Tel:* 613-232-9625 *Fax:* 613-563-9895
*E-mail:* info@cla.ca
*Web Site:* www.cla.ca
Established: 1971
For outstanding work of illustration in current children's literature of Canada. Illustrator must be a Canadian citizen or resident of Canada. Nominations should be sent to Delilah Deane Cummings at the London Public Library, 251 Dundas St, London, ON N6A 6H9.
Award: $1,000 plus plaque
Closing Date: Annually, Dec 31
Presented: CLA Annual Conference

**Tom Howard/John H Reid Short Story Contest**
Tom Howard Books
351 Pleasant St, PMB 222, Northampton, MA 01060-3961
*Tel:* 413-320-1847 *Toll Free Tel:* 866-WINWRIT (946-9748) *Fax:* 413-280-0539
*Web Site:* www.winningwriters.com
*Key Personnel*
Pres: Adam Cohen *E-mail:* adam@winningwriters.com
VP: Jendi Reiter
Established: 1990
Submit short stories, essays or other works of prose, up to 5000 words each. Must be your own original work. Reading fee $16 per entry. Writers of all nations may enter, however, the works you submit should be in English. Both published & unpublished work accepted. Applications accepted July 15-April 30.
Award: $3,000 (1st prize), $1,000 (2nd prize), $400 (3rd prize), $250 (4th prize), $150 each (six Most Highly Commended Awards). Top 10 entries will be published on the Winning Writers web site
Closing Date: Annually, April 30 (postmark)
Presented: Annually, Sept 15 on web site

**Tom Howard/Margaret Reid Poetry Contest**
Tom Howard Books
351 Pleasant St, PMB 222, Northampton, MA 01060-3961
*Tel:* 413-320-1847 *Toll Free Tel:* 866-WINWRIT (946-9748) *Fax:* 413-280-0539
*Web Site:* www.winningwriters.com
*Key Personnel*
Pres: Adam Cohen *E-mail:* adam@winningwriters.com
VP: Jendi Reiter
Established: 2002
The Tom Howard Prize is awarded for a poem in any style or genre. The Margaret Reid Prize is awarded for a poem that rhymes or has a traditional style. Entry fee $8 for every 25 lines submitted. See web site for complete submission details & contest results. Both published & unpublished work accepted. Poets of all nations may enter, however, the works you submit should be in English.
Award: $2,000 & $500 runner-up for each plus publication on web site for all winners (five High Distinction Awards $100 each any category)
Closing Date: Annually, Sept 30
Presented: Annually, Feb 15 on web site

**Julia Ward Howe Book Awards**
Boston Authors Club Inc
45 Pine Crest Rd, Newton, MA 02459
*Tel:* 617-552-8457
*E-mail:* bostonauthors@aol.com
*Web Site:* www.bostonauthorsclub.org
*Key Personnel*
Pres: Alan Lawson *E-mail:* lawson@bc.edu
1st VP: Betty Lowry *Tel:* 508-358-4098 *E-mail:* bettylowry@aol.com
2nd VP: Sarah Lamstein *Tel:* 617-244-0646 *E-mail:* sml@sarahlamstein.com
Established: 1997
Awards for a trade book, a book for young readers, special award (varies) for book published previous year. Authors must live or have lived, worked or attended college within 100 miles of Boston. No submission fee.
Other Sponsor(s): Boston Public Library (Rare Books Div)

Award: $1,000 each for 2 books; certificates to finalists & authors of recommended books (number varies). All receive 1 year complimentary membership in the Club
Closing Date: Annually, Jan 15
Presented: Boston Public Library, 3rd Thursday in May

**L Ron Hubbard's Writers of the Future Contest**
Author Services Inc
PO Box 1630, Los Angeles, CA 90078
*Tel:* 323-466-3310 *Fax:* 323-466-6474
*E-mail:* contests@authorservicesinc.com
*Web Site:* www.writersofthefuture.com
*Key Personnel*
Coordinating Judge: K D Wentworth
Contest Dir: Joni Labaqui
Established: 1983
Short stories & novelettes (under 17,000 words) of science fiction & fantasy for new & amateur writers. No entry fee required, entrants retain all publication rights.
Award: Annually: Trophy & $5,000 (Grand prize); Quarterly: $1,000 (1st place), $750 (2nd place), $500 (3rd place)
Closing Date: Quarters: Dec 31, March 31, June 30, Sept 30

**Monica Hughes Award for Science Fiction & Fantasy**
Canadian Children's Book Centre
40 Orchard View Blvd, Suite 217, Toronto, ON M4R 1B9, Canada
*Tel:* 416-975-0010 *Fax:* 416-975-8970
*E-mail:* info@bookcentre.ca
*Web Site:* www.bookcentre.ca
*Key Personnel*
Exec Dir: Charlotte Teeple *E-mail:* charlotte@bookcentre.ca
Gen Mgr: Dawn Todd *E-mail:* dawn@bookcentre.ca
Sales & Mktg Mgr: Holly Kent *E-mail:* holly@bookcentre.ca
Lib Coord: Meghan Howe *E-mail:* meghan@bookcentre.ca
Prog Coord: Shannon Howe Barnes *E-mail:* shannon@bookcentre.ca
Established: 2011
Awarded to a Canadian author for excellence in science fiction & fantasy writing for children & adolescents.
Other Sponsor(s): HarperCollins Canada
Award: $5,000
Closing Date: Annually in mid Dec

**Lynda Hull Memorial Poetry Prize**
Crazyhorse
College of Charleston, Dept of English, 66 George St, Charleston, SC 29424
*Tel:* 843-953-7740 *Fax:* 843-953-7740
*E-mail:* crazyhorse@cofc.edu
*Web Site:* www.crazyhorsejournal.org
Award for best single poem. Enter 3 poems with $16 entry fee, which includes one-year subscription. Nationally prominent poet judges. See web site for complete instructions.
Award: $2,000 & publication in "Crazyhorse"
Closing Date: Annually, Jan 15

**Hurston/Wright Award for College Writers**
The Zora Neale Hurston/Richard Wright Foundation
12138 Central Ave, Suite 209, Bowie, MD 20721
*Tel:* 301-459-2108 *Fax:* 301-277-1262
*E-mail:* info@hurstonwright.org
*Web Site:* www.hurstonwright.org
*Key Personnel*
Founder & Pres Emeritus: Marita Golden
Exec Dir: Clyde McElvene
Established: 1990
Literary award presented to honor excellence in fiction writing by African American students enrolled as an undergraduate or graduate student in any college or university. Nonrefundable application fee of $10.
Award: $1,000 & story published in literary journal (1st prize), $500 (awarded to 2 runners-up)
Closing Date: Annually Jan 31
Presented: Annually in April

**Hurston/Wright Legacy Awards**
The Zora Neale Hurston/Richard Wright Foundation
12138 Central Ave, Suite 209, Bowie, MD 20721
*Tel:* 301-459-2108 *Fax:* 301-277-1262
*E-mail:* info@hurstonwright.org
*Web Site:* www.hurstonwright.org
*Key Personnel*
Founder & Pres Emeritus: Marita Golden
Exec Dir: Clyde McElvene
Established: 2000
Annual national literary award for debut fiction, fiction, nonfiction & poetry for published black writers. Application fee: $30.
Other Sponsor(s): Borders Books
Award: $10,000 for winners in 3 categories; $5,000 for 6 runners-up (2 in each category)

**IACP Cookbook Awards**
International Association of Culinary Professionals (IACP)
1100 Johnson Ferry Rd, Suite 300, Atlanta, GA 30342
*Tel:* 404-252-3663 *Fax:* 404-252-0774
*E-mail:* info@iacp.com
*Web Site:* www.iacp.com
*Key Personnel*
Prog Mgr: Vickie Mabry
Communs Specialist: Ericka Henderson
Established: 1985
Open to any food or beverage book published in the English language. Allows publishers to enter books in the category of their choice. Through a strict, two-tier system of judging & balloting, the entries are narrowed to three nominees in each category.
Closing Date: Nov
Presented: Annual Conference, location varies, Varies every year, usually held in April

**The Idaho Prize for Poetry**
Lost Horse Press
105 Lost Horse Lane, Sandpoint, ID 83864
*Tel:* 208-255-4410 *Fax:* 208-255-1560
*E-mail:* losthorsepress@mindspring.com
*Web Site:* www.losthorsepress.org
*Key Personnel*
Publr: Christine Holbert
Established: 2003
A national competition for a book-length poetry ms written by an American poet. Accompany ms with $25 reading fee (check or money order only). Books distributed by the University of Washington Press.
Award: $1,000 & publication
Closing Date: Annually, May 15
Presented: Annually, Aug 15

**John Phillip Immroth Memorial Award**
Intellectual Freedom Round Table (IFRT)
Unit of American Library Association (ALA)
50 E Huron St, Chicago, IL 60611
*Tel:* 312-280-4223 *Toll Free Tel:* 800-545-2433 *Fax:* 312-280-4227
*E-mail:* oif@ala.org
*Web Site:* www.ala.org/ifrt
*Key Personnel*
Prog Offr: Nanette Perez *Tel:* 312-280-4225 *E-mail:* nperez@ala.org
Admin Asst & Award Contact: Shumeca Pickett *Tel:* 312-280-4220 *E-mail:* spickett@ala.org
Established: 1976
Annual award for notable contribution to intellectual freedom & demonstrations of personal courage in defense of freedom of expression.
Award: $500 & citation
Closing Date: Annually, Dec 1
Presented: ALA Annual Conference, Annually in June

**The Independent Publisher Book Awards**
Independent Publisher Online
Division of Jenkins Group Inc
1129 Woodmere Ave, Suite B, Traverse City, MI 49686
*Tel:* 231-933-0445 *Toll Free Tel:* 800-706-4636 *Fax:* 231-933-0448
*Web Site:* www.independentpublisher.com/ipaward.lasso
*Key Personnel*
CEO: Jerrold R Jenkins *E-mail:* jrj@bookpublishing.com
Pres: James Kalajian *Tel:* 800-706-4636 ext 1006 *E-mail:* jjk@bookpublishing.com
Mng Ed & Awards Dir: Jim Barnes *Tel:* 800-706-4636 ext 1011 *E-mail:* jimb@bookpublishing.com
Awards Coord: Amy Shamroe
Established: 1996
Recognizes the works of independent publishers in 65 national & 10 regional categories, for excellence in literary merit, design & production, published during previous calendar year. E-books & audio books are welcome.
Other Sponsor(s): Jenkins Group
Award: Gold medal (1st place), silver medal (2nd place) & bronze medal (3rd place); foil seals available; winners featured in *Independent Publisher Magazine Online*
Closing Date: Annually in March
Presented: Book Expo America, Annually in May

**Indiana Review Fiction Prize**
Indiana Review
Ballantine Hall 465, 1020 E Kirkwood Ave, Bloomington, IN 47405
*Tel:* 812-855-3439
*E-mail:* inreview@indiana.edu
*Web Site:* indianareview.org
*Key Personnel*
Ed: Katie Moulton
Assoc Ed: Britt Ashley
Submit a short story of up to 8,000 words; only one story per entry, maximum 12 point font. Previously published works & works forthcoming elsewhere cannot be considered; $20 entry fee (which includes a subscription to Indiana Review).
Award: $1,000 & publication in Indiana Review
Closing Date: Annually in Oct

**Indie Publishing Contest**
San Francisco Writers Conference
1029 Jones St, San Francisco, CA 94109
*Tel:* 415-673-0939
*E-mail:* sfwriterscon@aol.com
*Web Site:* www.sfwriters.org
*Key Personnel*
Founder: Michael Larsen
Founder & Dir: Elizabeth Pomada
Contest Dir: Laurie McLean *E-mail:* laurie@agentsavant.com
All entries must be original, unpublished work not submitted to this contest in previous years & be in English. Complete an official entry form & attach to the entry. Entry fee: $35. Four catagories: adult fiction, nonfiction/memoir, poety & childrens/young adult.
Other Sponsor(s): San Francisco Writers University
Award: Indie Publishing Package (grand prize), Author Solutions Publisher Package (1st prize), 50% off Authors Solutions Publishing Package (honorable mention)

Closing Date: Annually in Dec
Presented: Annual conference, InterContinental Mark Hopkins Hotel

**Indies Choice Book Awards**
American Booksellers Association
333 Westchester Ave, Suite S202, White Plains, NY 10604
*Tel:* 914-406-7500 *Toll Free Tel:* 800-637-0037 *Fax:* 914-410-6297
*Web Site:* www.bookweb.org
*Key Personnel*
CEO: Oren Teicher *Tel:* 800-637-0037 ext 6611 *E-mail:* oren@bookweb.org
Devt Offr: Mark Nichols *Tel:* 800-637-0037 ext 6640 *E-mail:* mark@bookweb.org
Established: 1991
Book finalists will be picked by a bookseller jury, but the pool is limited to monthly Indie Next list selections. Categories have been revamped & expanded, now honoring the book of the year in the following categories: adult fiction, adult nonfiction, adult debut, young adults, middle reader, new picture book & most engaging author.
Presented: BookExpo America & ABA Convention

**Individual Artist Awards**
Maryland State Arts Council
Affiliate of Department of Business & Economic Development
175 W Ostend St, Suite E, Baltimore, MD 21230
*Tel:* 410-767-6555 *Fax:* 410-333-1062
*E-mail:* msac@msac.org
*Web Site:* www.msac.org
*Key Personnel*
Exec Dir: Theresa Colvin
Solely based on excellence of previous work. Must be a Maryland resident. Applications available. Award categories changed annually. Check with council for individual availability.
Award: $6,000 (1st prize), $3,000 (2nd prize) & $1,000 (3rd prize)
Closing Date: July (see web site for exact date)
Presented: Awards Reception, Early June

**Individual Artist Fellowships**
Maine Arts Commission
Division of State of Maine
25 State House Sta, 193 State St, Augusta, ME 04333-0025
*Tel:* 207-287-2726 *Fax:* 207-287-2725
*Web Site:* www.mainearts.com
*Key Personnel*
Dir: Donna McNeil *E-mail:* donna.mcneil@maine.gov
Established: 1987
Three prizes awarded annually to visual, performing & literary artists.
Award: $13,000
Closing Date: Visual & literary arts, May; Performing arts, June. Check web site
Presented: Fall

**Individual Artist Fellowships**
Nebraska Arts Council
Division of State of Nebraska
1004 Farnam, Plaza Level, Omaha, NE 68102
*Tel:* 402-595-2122 *Toll Free Tel:* 800-341-4067 *Fax:* 402-595-2334
*Web Site:* www.nebraskaartscouncil.org
*Key Personnel*
Artist Servs & Communs Mgr: Jayne Hutton *E-mail:* jayne.hutton@nebraska.gov
Established: 1991
Fellowship for Nebraska residents only; operates on a 3-yr cycle rotating with visual & performing arts & literature.
Award: $1,000-$5,000
Closing Date: Annually, Nov 15

**Individual Artist's Fellowships in Literature**
South Carolina Arts Commission (SCAC)
Division of State of South Carolina
1800 Gervais St, Columbia, SC 29201
*Tel:* 803-734-8696 *Fax:* 803-734-8526
*E-mail:* info@arts.sc.gov
*Web Site:* www.southcarolinaarts.com
*Key Personnel*
Communs Dir: Millie Hough *Tel:* 803-734-8698 *E-mail:* mhough@arts.sc.gov
Established: 2007
Non-matching funds for South Carolina residents only. Four fellowships, two in poetry & two in prose. Offered every other year.
Award: $5,000
Closing Date: Annually, Nov 1

**Individual Excellence Awards**
Ohio Arts Council
30 E Broad St, 33rd fl, Columbus, OH 43215
*Tel:* 614-466-2613 *Fax:* 614-466-4494
*Web Site:* www.oac.state.oh.us
*Key Personnel*
Exec Dir: Julie Henahan *E-mail:* julie.henahan@oac.state.oh.us
Prog Coord: Kathy Signorino *E-mail:* kathy.signorino@oac.state.oh.us
Indiv Prog: Ken Emerick *E-mail:* ken.emerick@oac.state.oh.us
Established: 1978
Award creativity to Ohio residents for creative writing (poetry, fiction, nonfiction), criticism, playwriting, visual arts, choreography, media arts, crafts, photography, music composition, design arts/illustration & interdisciplinary arts.
Award: $5,000 (determined by panel)
Closing Date: Biennually, Sept 1
Presented: Biennually

**Inkwell Journal Annual Fiction Competition**
Inkwell Journal
c/o Inkwell-Manhattanville College, 2900 Purchase St, Purchase, NY 10577
*Tel:* 914-323-7239 *Fax:* 914-323-3122
*E-mail:* inkwell@mville.edu
*Web Site:* www.inkwelljournal.org
*Key Personnel*
Ed-in-Chief: Tanya M Beltram
Established: 1999
Submit previously unpublished stories up to 5,000 words. SASE for contest notification only. Entry fee is $15 per story; limit 3 stories.
Award: $1,500 & publication in Spring issue of Inkwell
Closing Date: Aug 1-Oct 31
Presented: Spring

**Inkwell Journal Annual Poetry Competition**
Inkwell Journal
c/o Inkwell-Manhattanville College, 2900 Purchase St, Purchase, NY 10577
*Tel:* 914-323-7239 *Fax:* 914-323-3122
*E-mail:* inkwell@mville.edu
*Web Site:* www.inkwelljournal.org
*Key Personnel*
Ed-in-Chief: Tanya M Beltram
Established: 1999
Submit up to 5 previously unpublished poems, 40-line limit per poem. SASE for contest notification only. Entry fee is $10 for the first poem, $5 per each additional poem.
Award: $1,000 & publication in Spring issue of Inkwell
Closing Date: Aug 1-Oct 31
Presented: Spring

**Innis-Gerin Medal**
Royal Society of Canada
Walter House, 282 Somerset W, Ottawa, ON K2P 0J6, Canada
*Tel:* 613-991-6990 *Fax:* 613-991-6996
*E-mail:* nominations@rsc-src.ca
*Web Site:* www.rsc-src.ca
*Key Personnel*
Sr Offr, Memb Servs: Marie-Lyne Renaud *E-mail:* mlrenaud@rsc-src.ca
Established: 1966
Biennial award given in odd numbered years for a distinguished & sustained contribution to literature in social science, human geography & social psychology.
Award: Bronze medal
Closing Date: Dec 1
Presented: Quebec City, QC, CN, Nov

**Institute of Puerto Rican Culture**
PO Box 9024184, San Juan, PR 00902-1484
*Tel:* 787-724-0700 *Fax:* 787-724-8393
*E-mail:* www@icp.gobierno.pr
*Web Site:* www.icp.gobierno.pr
*Key Personnel*
Exec Dir: Mercedes Gomez Marrero
Dir: Carmen Viera
Established: 1955
Grant awarded to individual artists.
Award: Cash
Closing Date: Annually in April

**Intermediate Sequoyah Book Award**
Oklahoma Library Association
300 Hardy Dr, Edmond, OK 73013
*Tel:* 405-525-5100 *Fax:* 405-525-5103
*Web Site:* www.oklibs.org
*Key Personnel*
Exec Dir: Kay Boies *E-mail:* kboies@sbcglobal.net
Contact: Tracy Keeley
Established: 2010
Student choice award; students in grades 6-8 who have read/listened to at least 3 titles from the Intermediate Masterlist are eligible to vote.
Award: Plaque/medal
Closing Date: Annually, March 1
Presented: OLA Annual Conference, Annually in April

**International Latino Book Awards**
Latino Literacy Now
3445 Catalina Dr, Carlsbad, CA 92008
*Tel:* 760-434-1223 *Fax:* 760-434-7476
*E-mail:* jim@lbff.us
*Web Site:* www.lbff.us
Established: 1998
Celebrating Latino authors & their works.
Other Sponsor(s): Scholastic Libros Publishing
Closing Date: Annually, April 1
Presented: Annually in May

**International Poetry Competition**
Atlanta Review
PO Box 8248, Atlanta, GA 31106
*E-mail:* atlanta.review@yahoo.com
*Web Site:* www.atlantareview.com
*Key Personnel*
Publr & Ed: Dan Veach
Sr Ed: Lee Passarella; Memye Curtis Tucker
Literary Ed: A E Stallings
Established: 1996
Online entry at www.atlantareview.com.
Award: $1,000 (grand prize), publication in *Atlanta Review* (20 publication prizes)
Closing Date: Annually, March 1

**International Reading Association Children's & Young Adult's Book Award**
International Reading Association
800 Barksdale Rd, Newark, DE 19711-3204
Mailing Address: PO Box 8139, Newark, DE 19714-8139
*Tel:* 302-731-1600 *Toll Free Tel:* 800-336-7323 (US & CN) *Fax:* 302-731-1057
*E-mail:* committees@reading.org
*Web Site:* www.reading.org

*Key Personnel*
Public Info Offr: Kathy Baughman *Tel:* 302-731-1600 ext 221 *E-mail:* kbaughman@reading.org
Exec Dir: Marcie Craig Post *E-mail:* mpost@reading.org
Established: 1975
Six book awards will be offered for an author's first or second published children's book. Awards will be given for fiction & nonfiction in 3 categories: Primary (ages preschool-8), Intermediate (ages 9-13) & Young Adult (ages 14-17). This award is intended for newly published authors who show unusual promise in the children's book field. Books from any country & in any language copyrighted during the previous calendar year will be considered. Entries in a language other than English must include a one-page abstract in English & a translation into English of one chapter or similar selection that in the submitter's estimation is representative of the book. For guidelines, write to the executive office or e-mail: exec@reading.org.
Award: $800 per book
Closing Date: Annually in Nov
Presented: Annual Convention, Spring

**InterTech Technology Awards**
Printing Industries of America
200 Deer Run Rd, Sewickley, PA 15143-2600
*Tel:* 412-259-1782 *Toll Free Tel:* 800-910-4283 (ext 782) *Fax:* 412-741-2311
*E-mail:* intertechaward@printing.org
*Web Site:* www.printing.org/intertechawards
*Key Personnel*
CEO & Pres: Michael Makin *E-mail:* mmakin@printing.org
VP, Technol & Res: Dr Mark Bohan *Tel:* 412-259-1782 *E-mail:* mbohan@printing.org
Established: 1978
Honors innovative technology excellence for the graphic communications industry. The criteria for nomination stresses that the technology be recently developed, proved in industrial application, but not yet in widespread use.
Award: Lucite ™ Star
Closing Date: Annually, May 31
Presented: Printing Industries of America's Premier Print Awards Gala, Annually in the Fall

**IODE Violet Downey Book Award**
The National Chapter of Canada IODE
40 Orchard View Blvd, Suite 219, Toronto, ON M4R 1B9, Canada
*Tel:* 416-487-4416 *Toll Free Tel:* 866-827-7428 *Fax:* 416-487-4417
*E-mail:* iodecanada@bellnet.ca
*Web Site:* www.iode.ca
*Key Personnel*
Natl Pres: Ann Dyer
Established: 1984
Children's book award. Must be a Canadian author with text in English. At least 500 words & printed in Canada during previous calendar year. Suitable for children 13 years & under.
Award: $5,000
Closing Date: Annually, Dec 31
Presented: The National Annual Meeting, Annually, late May

**Iowa Poetry Prize**
University of Iowa Press
119 W Park Rd, 100 Kuhl House, Iowa City, IA 52242-1000
SAN: 282-4868
*Tel:* 319-335-2000 *Fax:* 319-335-2055
*E-mail:* uipress@uiowa.edu
*Web Site:* www.uiowapress.org
*Key Personnel*
Dir: James McCoy
Open to new as well as established poets for a book-length collection of poems written originally in English. Previous winners, current University of Iowa students & current & former University of Iowa Press employees are not eligible. Reading fee $20.
Award: Publication by the University of Iowa Press under a standard royalty agreement
Closing Date: Postmarked during April

**The Iowa Review Award**
University of Iowa-The Iowa Review
308 EPB, Iowa City, IA 52242-1408
*E-mail:* iowa-review@uiowa.edu
*Web Site:* www.iowareview.org
*Key Personnel*
Mng Ed: Lynne Nugent
Ed: Russell Valentino
Established: 2003
Fiction, poetry & nonfiction categories. Submit up to 25 pages of prose (double-spaced) or 10 pgs of poetry (1 poem or several, but no more than 1 poem per page). Work must be previously unpublished. There is a $20 entry fee; enclose an additional $10 for a yearlong subscription to the magazine (optional). Submissions between Jan 1-Jan 31.
Award: $1,500 & pubn in Dec issue of Iowa Review (1st place), $750 & pubn in the Dec issue of Iowa Review (1st runners-up)
Closing Date: Annually, Jan 31

**The Iowa Short Fiction Award**
Writers' Workshop, The University of Iowa
102 Dey House, 507 N Clinton St, Iowa City, IA 52242-1000
*Tel:* 319-335-0416 *Fax:* 319-335-0420
*Web Site:* www.uiowapress.org/authors/iowa-short-fiction.htm
*Key Personnel*
Prog Assoc: Connie Brothers
Dir, Writers' Workshop: Lan Samantha Chang
Established: 1970
For a previously unpublished collection of short stories of at least 150 typewritten pages by a writer who has not previously published a volume of prose fiction. Stories previously published in periodicals are eligible for inclusion. Include SASE. Write for further information.
Other Sponsor(s): University of Iowa Press
Award: Publication by University of Iowa Press
Closing Date: Aug 1-Sept 30

**Iowa Short Fiction Awards**
University of Iowa Press
119 W Park Rd, 100 Kuhl House, Iowa City, IA 52242-1000
SAN: 282-4868
*Tel:* 319-335-2000 *Fax:* 319-335-2055
*E-mail:* uipress@uiowa.edu
*Web Site:* www.uiowapress.org
*Key Personnel*
Dir: James McCoy
Any writer who has not previously published a volume of prose fiction is eligible to enter the competition. Previously entered mss that have been revised may be resubmitted. Writers are still eligible if they have published a volume of poetry or any work in a language other than English or if they have self-published any work in a small print run. Writers are still eligible if they are living abroad or are non-US citizens writing in English. Current University of Iowa students are not eligible.
Award: Publication by the University of Iowa Press under the Press's standard contract
Closing Date: Annually, Aug 1-Sept 30 (postmark)

**Jackie White Memorial National Children's Playwriting Contest**
Columbia Entertainment Co
309 Parkade Blvd, Columbia, MO 65202
*Tel:* 573-874-5628
*Web Site:* www.cectheatre.org
*Key Personnel*
Pres, Community Theatre: Judy Olson
Contest Dir: Betsy Phillips *E-mail:* bybetsy@yahoo.com
Established: 1988
The entry should be a full length play with speaking roles for at least seven characters. The entry may be an unpublished original work or an adaptation; $25 entry fee, send SASE for complete rules & entry form. Each author who enters the contest will receive a letter from the contest director discussing the strenghts & weaknesses of his or her play if a SASE is enclosed.
Other Sponsor(s): City of Columbia, Office of Cultural Affairs
Award: $500, production (possible, not guaranteed) for 1st place. We reserve the right to award the cash prize without production
Closing Date: Annually, June 1
Presented: Annually, Aug 31

**Joseph Henry Jackson Literary Award**
The San Francisco Foundation
One Embarcadero Ctr, Suite 1400, San Francisco, CA 94111
*Tel:* 415-733-8500 *Fax:* 415-477-2783
*E-mail:* info@sff.org
*Web Site:* www.sff.org
*Key Personnel*
Arts & Culture Prog Offr: Terezita Romo
Established: 1957
Award for the author of fiction (novel or short stories), nonfictional prose, poetry, spoken word. Awards are intended to encourage emerging artists not yet established in the genre who are either California-born or currently residing in Alameda, Contra Costa, Marin, San Francisco or San Mateo County, for an unpublished ms-in-progress. By nomination only.
Award: $2,000
Presented: Annually in Autumn

**J Franklin Jameson Fellowship in American History**
American Historical Association
400 "A" St SE, Washington, DC 20003-3889
*Tel:* 202-544-2422 *Fax:* 202-544-8307
*E-mail:* awards@historians.org
*Web Site:* www.historians.org
Established: 1980
To support significant scholarly research for one semester in the collections of the Library of Congress by new historians. At the time of application, applicants must hold the PhD degree or equivalent; must have received this degree within the last 5 years & must not have published or had accepted for publication a book-length historical work. The fellowship will not be awarded to permit completion of a doctoral dissertation. The applicant's project in American history must be one for which the general & special collections of the Library of Congress offer unique research support. Applicants should include a statement substantiating this relationship. Residency for at least three months at Library of Congress is required. Application instructions & all updated info available on web site.
Other Sponsor(s): Library of Congress
Award: Certificate
Closing Date: March 15 (postmark)

**Jamestown Prize**
Omohundro Institute of Early American History & Culture
Swem Library, Ground fl, 400 Landrum Dr, Williamsburg, VA 23185
Mailing Address: PO Box 8781, Williamsburg, VA 23187-8781 SAN: 201-5161
*Tel:* 757-221-1114 *Fax:* 757-221-1047

*E-mail:* ieahc1@wm.edu
*Web Site:* oieahc.wm.edu
*Key Personnel*
Dir: Karin A Wulf *Tel:* 757-221-1133
Ed, Pubns: Fredrika J Teute *Tel:* 757-221-1118 *E-mail:* fjteut@wm.edu
For an exceptional book length scholarly ms pertaining to the early history & culture of Anglo-America or to related developments in the British Isles, other North American colonial empires & their home countries, West Africa or the Caribbean. In short, any subject encompassing the Atlantic World circa 1450-1815 that bears upon the history & culture of what would & did become the United States.
Award: $3,000 & publication
Closing Date: April 30, 2015
Presented: Biennially

**Japan-US Friendship Commission Translation Prize**
Japan-US Friendship Commission
Affiliate of The Donald Keene Center of Japanese Culture
Columbia University, 507 Kent Hall, MC3920, New York, NY 10027
*Tel:* 212-854-5036 *Fax:* 212-854-4019
*Web Site:* www.keenecenter.org
*Key Personnel*
Faculty Dir: David B Lurie
Established: 1979
Prize is given for the best translation of a modern work of literature or for the best classical literary translation, or the prize is divided between a classical & a modern work. Translators of any nationality are welcome to apply. To qualify, works must be book-length translations of Japanese literary works: novels, collections of short stories, literary essays, memoirs, drama, or poetry. Submissions will be judged on the literary merit of the translation & the accuracy with which it reflects the spirit of the Japanese original. Applications are accepted from translators or their publishers. Previous winners are ineligible.
Award: $6,000 (either to one translator or divided between classical & modern)
Closing Date: Annually, Oct 31
Presented: Columbia University, Annually in April

**Jefferson Cup Award**
Youth Services Forum
Unit of Virginia Library Association (VLA)
c/o Virginia Library Association (VLA), PO Box 56312, Virginia Beach, VA 23456
*Tel:* 757-689-0594 *Fax:* 757-447-3478
*Web Site:* www.vla.org
*Key Personnel*
VLA Exec Dir: Lisa R Varga *E-mail:* vla.lisav@cox.net
Established: 1983
Honors a distinguished biography, historical fiction or American history book written especially for young people. Two awards given, one for books published for children & one for books published for young adults.
Award: $500 & engraved silver Jefferson Cup for each
Closing Date: Jan 31
Presented: Virginia Library Association (VLA) Annual Conference, Fall

**Jerome Award**
Catholic Library Association
205 W Monroe, Suite 314, Chicago, IL 60606-5061
*Tel:* 312-739-1776; 312-739-1776
*Toll Free Tel:* 855-739-1776 *Fax:* 312-739-1778; 312-739-1778
*E-mail:* cla2@cathla.org
*Web Site:* www.cathla.org
*Key Personnel*
Pres: Malachy R McCarthy *E-mail:* mmccarthy@cathla.org
Established: 1992
For outstanding work in Catholic scholarship; no unsol mss.
Award: Plaque
Closing Date: None; in-house votes
Presented: CLA Annual Convention

**Jerome Fellowship**
The Playwrights' Center
2301 Franklin Ave E, Minneapolis, MN 55406-1099
*Tel:* 612-332-7481 *Fax:* 612-332-6037
*E-mail:* info@pwcenter.org
*Web Site:* www.pwcenter.org
*Key Personnel*
Producing Artistic Dir: Jeremy Cohen *Tel:* 612-332-7481 ext 113 *E-mail:* jeremyc@pwcenter.org
Artistic Administrator: Amanda Robbins-Butcher *Tel:* 612-332-7481 ext 115 *E-mail:* amandar@pwcenter.org
Established: 1976
Fellowships awarded annually to emerging playwrights. Provides playwrights with funds & services to aid them in the development of their craft. One year in residence required, July 1 - June 30. Contact above for application & guidelines, or download from www.pwcenter.org.
Award: $16,000
Closing Date: See web site for details

**Jewel Box Theatre Playwriting Competition**
3700 N Walker, Oklahoma City, OK 73118-7031
*Tel:* 405-521-1786
*Web Site:* jewelboxtheatre.org
*Key Personnel*
Prodn Dir: Charles Tweed
Established: 1986
Original playwriting competition.
Award: $500
Closing Date: Jan 15
Presented: Banquet in Oklahoma City, May

**Anson Jones MD Award**
Texas Medical Association
401 W 15 St, Austin, TX 78701
*Tel:* 512-370-1300 *Fax:* 512-370-1630
*Web Site:* www.texmed.org
*Key Personnel*
Outreach Coord: Tammy Wishard
Established: 1957
Annual award in recognition of outstanding coverage of health & medical issues to the public by Texas Media.
Award: $500 cash award & plaque for winners
Closing Date: Jan 15

**Jesse H Jones Award**
Texas Institute of Letters (TIL)
PO Box 609, Round Rock, TX 78680
*Tel:* 512-683-5640
*E-mail:* tilsecretary@yahoo.com
*Web Site:* www.texasinstituteofletters.org
*Key Personnel*
Pres: W K Stratton
VP: Andres Tijerina
Treas: James Hoggard
Secy: Jan Reid
Recording Secy: Betty Wiesepape
Annual award for the best book of fiction by a Texan or about Texas. Guidelines on the web site.
Other Sponsor(s): Houston Endowment Inc
Award: $6,000
Closing Date: Annually in Jan
Presented: TIL Awards Banquet, Annually in Spring

**Judah, Sarah, Grace & Tom Memorial**
The Poetry Society of Virginia
1194 Hume Rd, Hume, VA 22639-1806
*E-mail:* poetryinva@aol.com
*Web Site:* www.poetrysocietyofvirginia.org
*Key Personnel*
Pres: Judith K Bragg *E-mail:* musicsavy45@yahoo.com
Adult Contest Chair: Patsy Anne Bickerstaff *E-mail:* granypatsy@yahoo.com; Guy Terrell *E-mail:* ggterr@infionline.net
All entries must be in English, original & unpublished. Submit 2 copies of each poem, both copies must have the category name & number on top left of page. Only one poem per category; entries will not be returned. Subject: encouraging reflection on inter-ethnic relations; any form; 48 line limit. Entry fee: $4 nonmembs.
Other Sponsor(s): Stuart & Linda Nottingham
Award: $50 (1st place), $30 (2nd place), $20 (3rd place)
Closing Date: Jan
Presented: Annual PSV Awards Luncheon, Richmond, VA, April

**Juniper Prize for Fiction**
University of Massachusetts Press
East Experiment Sta, 671 N Pleasant St, Amherst, MA 01003
*Tel:* 413-545-2217 *Fax:* 413-545-1226
*E-mail:* info@umpress.umass.edu
*Web Site:* www.umass.edu/umpress; www.umass.edu/umpress/juniper_fiction.html (description); www.umass.edu/umpress/juniper_fiction_guidelines.html
*Key Personnel*
Promos Mgr: Karen Fisk *E-mail:* kfisk@umpress.umass.edu
Established: 2004
Honor & publish outstanding works of literary fiction. Open to all writers in English, whether or not they are US Citizens. Entry fee is $25 (must be drawn on US bank).
Award: $1,500 upon publication
Closing Date: Annually, Aug 1-Sept 30 postmark
Presented: Online, Annually in April, announced online at web site

**Juniper Prize for Poetry**
University of Massachusetts Press
East Experiment Sta, 671 N Pleasant St, Amherst, MA 01003
*Tel:* 413-545-2217 *Fax:* 413-545-1226
*E-mail:* info@umpress.umass.edu
*Web Site:* www.umass.edu/umpress
*Key Personnel*
Promos Mgr: Karen Fisk *E-mail:* kfisk@umpress.umass.edu
Established: 1976
Awarded annually for an original ms of poems. In alternating years, the program is open to poets either with or without previously published books. Entry fee: $25.
Award: $1,500 & publication
Presented: Annually in April; publication by the following spring

**Juvenile Literary Awards/Young People's Literature Awards**
Friends of American Writers
506 Rose Ave, Des Plaines, IL 60016
*Tel:* 847-827-8339
*Web Site:* www.fawchicago.org
*Key Personnel*
Pres: Vivian Mortensen *E-mail:* vmortens@comcast.net
Juvenile Lit Awards Chair: Tanya Klasser *E-mail:* brujotal@aol.com
Established: 1960
For books written for young people from toddler through high school age & published in the current year, can only be author's 1st, 2nd

or 3rd book & the author must be from the Midwest &/or the book must be about the Midwest.
Award: Two $1500 prizes
Closing Date: Dec 20
Presented: The Fortnightly, Chicago, IL, Annually in May

**Frederick D Kagy Education Award of Excellence**
Printing Industries of America
200 Deer Run Rd, Sewickley, PA 15143-2600
*Tel:* 412-259-1705 *Toll Free Tel:* 800-910-4283 (ext 705) *Fax:* 412-749-9890
*E-mail:* printing@printing.org
*Web Site:* www.printing.org
*Key Personnel*
CEO & Pres: Michael Makin *E-mail:* mmakin@printing.org
Asst to VP, Mktg: Sara Welsh *E-mail:* swelsh@printing.org
Established: 1993
Honors a superior graphic communications program at the junior high, high school or community college level. School must be staffed by Printing Industries of America's teacher member (membership cost $49). Entry is free. For more information, go to www.printing.org & click on Programs & Services, then Awards & Recognition.
Other Sponsor(s): Printing Industries of America's Ben Franklin Society
Award: Engraved lithographic stone
Presented: Printing Industries of America Fall Administrative Meetings

**Ezra Jack Keats/Kerlan Memorial Fellowship**
Ezra Jack Keats Foundation
University of Minnesota, 113 Andersen Library, 222 21 Ave S, Minneapolis, MN 55455
*Tel:* 612-624-4576 *Fax:* 612-626-0377
*E-mail:* clrc@umn.edu
*Web Site:* www.ezra-jack-keats.org; special.lib.umn.edu/clrc
*Key Personnel*
Curator Kerlan Collection: Karen Hoyle
Awarded to a talented writer &/or illustrator of children's books who wish to use the Kerlan Collection to further his or her artistic development.
Award: $1,500
Closing Date: Jan 30

**Joan Kelly Memorial Prize in Women's History**
American Historical Association
400 "A" St SE, Washington, DC 20003-3889
*Tel:* 202-544-2422 *Fax:* 202-544-8307
*E-mail:* awards@historians.org
*Web Site:* www.historians.org
Established: 1984
For the book in women's history &/or feminist theory that best reflects the high intellectual & scholarly ideals exemplified by the life & work of Joan Kelly. Submissions shall be books in any chronological period, any geographical location, or in any area of feminist theory that incorporates an historical perspective. Books should demonstrate originality of research, creativity of insight, graceful stylistic presentation, analytical skills & a recognition of the important role of sex & gender in the historical process. The inter-relationship between women & the historical process should be addressed. Books published in 2013 are eligible. Along with an application form, one copy of each entry must be received by each of the five committee members. The Association will announce the recipients of prizes & awards at its annual meeting during the first week in Jan. All updated info on web site.
Award: Cash prize
Closing Date: May 15, 2014 (postmark)
Presented: AHA Annual Meeting

**Robert F Kennedy Book Awards**
Subsidiary of Robert F Kennedy Memorial
1300 19 St NW, Suite 750, Washington, DC 20036
*Tel:* 202-463-7575 *Fax:* 202-463-6606
*E-mail:* info@rfkcenter.org
*Web Site:* www.rfkcenter.org
*Key Personnel*
Contact: Christina Taylor *E-mail:* ctaylor@rfkcenter.org
Established: 1980
For a book of fiction or nonfiction that most faithfully & forcefully reflects Robert Kennedy's interests & concerns. Publishers or authors should send four copies of books published in the previous year along with a press release. See web site for further details.
Award: $2,500 & bust of Robert Kennedy
Closing Date: Feb 1
Presented: May

**Coretta Scott King Book Awards**
Ethnic Multicultural Information Exchange Round Table
Unit of The American Library Association
ALA Office for Literacy & Outreach Services, 50 E Huron St, Chicago, IL 60611
*Tel:* 312-280-4295; 312-280-4294
*Toll Free Tel:* 800-545-2433 *Fax:* 312-280-3256
*E-mail:* olos@ala.org
*Web Site:* www.ala.org/csk
*Key Personnel*
Dir, OLOS: Satia Orange *E-mail:* sorange@ala.org
Literacy Offr: Dale Lipschultz *E-mail:* dlipschultz@ala.org
Prog Coord: Elliot Mandel *E-mail:* emandel@ala.org
Established: 1970
To encourage the artistic expressions of the African-American experiences via literature & the graphic arts. Award to author & illustrator.
Other Sponsor(s): Book Wholesalers Inc; Johnson Publications, Encyclopedia Britannica, World Book
Award: Award plaque, $1,000 & set of encyclopedias to each awardee
Closing Date: Annually, Dec 1
Presented: Coretta Scott King Awards Breakfast at the ALA Annual Conference, June

**The Knight-Risser Prize for Western Environmental Journalism**
John S Knight Journalism Fellowships
Stanford University, 450 Serra Mall, Bldg 120, Rm 424, Stanford, CA 94305
*Tel:* 650-721-5955 *Fax:* 650-725-6154
*E-mail:* knightrisserprize@lists.stanford.edu
*Web Site:* knightrisser.stanford.edu
*Key Personnel*
Dir, Knight Fellowships: James R Bettinger *E-mail:* jimb@stanford.edu
Established: 2006
Recognizes excellence in reporting on such environmental issues as water, resource, land use & wild life, unique to the North American West, by print, broadcast & online journalists. Work must have been published in 2012. For more information, see web site.
Other Sponsor(s): Bill Lane Center for the Study of the North American West
Award: $5000 cash & participate in an awards event that includes a public symposium with journalists, academics & others about pressing Western environmental issues
Closing Date: March
Presented: Stanford University, Summer

**Knightville Poetry Contest**
The New Guard
PO Box 866, Wells, ME 04094
*E-mail:* info@newguardreview.com
*Web Site:* www.newguardreview.com
*Key Personnel*
Founding Ed & Publr: Shanna McNair
Established: 2009
Submit up to 3 poems of up to 300 lines. Online submissions preferred. For postal entries please include a short bio along with a $15 entry fee & SASE.
Award: $1,000 & publication in The New Guard
Closing Date: Varies

**E M Koeppel Short Fiction Award**
Writecorner Press
PO Box 140310, Gainesville, FL 32614
*Tel:* 352-338-7778
*E-mail:* contact@writecorner.com
*Web Site:* www.writecorner.com
*Key Personnel*
Ed: Robert B Gentry; Mary Sue Koeppel
Established: 2003
For best short fiction. Any theme or style with no more than 3,000 words. Only unpublished work is eligible. Winner published on www.writecorner.com literary web site. Guidelines on web site.
Other Sponsor(s): P L Titus Scholarship
Award: $1,100 (E M Koeppel Short Fiction Award), $100 (Editors Choice)
Closing Date: Annually, Oct 1-April 30
Presented: Annually in Summer

**Katherine Singer Kovacs Prize**
Modern Language Association of America (MLA)
26 Broadway, 3rd fl, New York, NY 10004-1789
SAN: 202-6422
*Tel:* 646-576-5141 *Fax:* 646-458-0030
*E-mail:* awards@mla.org
*Web Site:* www.mla.org
*Key Personnel*
Coord, Book Prizes: Annie M Reiser *E-mail:* areiser@mla.org
Established: 1990
Annual prize for an outstanding book published in year prior to competition in English in the field of Latin American & Spanish literature & cultures. Authors need not be members of MLA. For consideration, submit 6 copies.
Award: Cash award, certificate & a one year association membership
Closing Date: May 1
Presented: MLA Convention, Jan

**Michael Kraus Research Grant in History**
American Historical Association
400 "A" St SE, Washington, DC 20003-3889
*Tel:* 202-544-2422 *Fax:* 202-544-8307
*E-mail:* awards@historians.org
*Web Site:* www.historians.org
Grant given to a member of the association to recognize the most deserving proposal relating to works in progress on a research project in American colonial history, with particular reference to the intercultural aspects of American & European relations. The grants are intended to further research in progress & may be used for travel to a library or archive, for microfilms, photographs, or xeroxing. Preference will be given to those with specific research needs, such as the completion of a project or completion of a discrete segment thereof. Preference will be given to PhD candidates & junior scholars. Application forms & all updated info on web site. Applications must include application form with estimated budget, curriculum vitae, statement of no more than 750 words & a one-page bibliography of the most recent relevant, secondary works on the topic. Mailed &

faxed submissions are not accepted. Only members of the association are eligible to apply.
Award: Individual grants will not exceed $800
Closing Date: Annually, Feb 15

**The Robert Kroetsch City of Edmonton Book Prize**
Writers Guild of Alberta
11759 Groat Rd, Edmonton, AB T5M 3K6, Canada
*Tel:* 780-422-8174 *Toll Free Tel:* 800-665-5354 (AB only) *Fax:* 780-422-2663 (attn WGA)
*E-mail:* mail@writersguild.ab.ca
*Web Site:* www.writersguild.ab.ca
*Key Personnel*
Exec Dir: Carol Holmes *E-mail:* cholmes@writersguild.ab.ca
Communs & Partnerships Coord: Nicholas Mather *E-mail:* nmather@writersguild.ab.ca
Memb Servs Coord: Giorgia Severini
Progs Coord: Nichole Quiring *E-mail:* programs@writersguild.ab.ca
Entries must deal with some aspect of the City of Edmonton: history, geography, current affairs, its arts or its people or be written by an Edmonton author.
Award: $10,000 & leather-bound copy of book
Closing Date: Annually, Dec 31
Presented: Mayor's Evening for the Arts, Annually in Spring
*Branch Office(s)*
Lord Denning House, 509 20 Ave SW, Calgary, AB T2S 0E7, Canada, Prog Coord: Samantha Warwick *Tel:* 403-265-2226 *E-mail:* swarwick@writersguild.ab.ca

**Kumu Kahua/UHM Theatre & Dance Department Playwriting Contest**
Kumu Kahua/UHM Theatre & Dance Dept
46 Merchant St, Honolulu, HI 96813
*Tel:* 808-536-4441 (box off); 808-536-4222 *Fax:* 808-536-4226
*E-mail:* kumukahuatheatre@hawaiiantel.net
*Web Site:* www.kumukahua.org
*Key Personnel*
Artistic Dir: Harry L Wong, III
Hawaii Prize: open to residents of Hawaii & non-residents; full length (50 pages or more); play must be set in Hawaii &/or deal with the Hawaii experience.
Pacific Rim Prize: open to residents of Hawaii & non-residents; full length (50 pages or more); play must be set in &/or dealing with the Pacific Islands, Pacific Rim, or the Pacific/Asian-American experience.
Resident Prize: only open to residents of Hawaii; full length (50 pages or more) or one-acts; play can be on any topic.
Award: $600 (Hawaii Prize), $450 (Pacific Rim Prize), $250 (Resident Prize)
Closing Date: Jan 2
Presented: May

**W Kaye Lamb Award**
British Columbia Historical Federation
PO Box 5254, Sta B, Victoria, BC V8R 6N4, Canada
*E-mail:* info@bchistory.ca
*Web Site:* www.bchistory.ca
*Key Personnel*
Pres: Barbara Hynek *E-mail:* president@bchistory.ca
Contact: Marie Elliot
Scholarship offered for essays written by students in British Columbia colleges or universities on a topic relating to British Columbia history.
Award: $750 (1st or 2nd yr student), $1,000 (3rd or 4th yr student)
Closing Date: Annually, May 15

**Lambda Literary Awards (Lammys)**
Lambda Literary Foundation
5482 Wilshire Blvd, Suite 1595, Los Angeles, CA 90036
*Tel:* 213-568-3570 *Fax:* 213-568-3570
*E-mail:* info@lambdaliterary.org
*Web Site:* www.lambdaliterary.org
*Key Personnel*
Administrator: Kathleen DeBold
Exec Dir: Tony Valenzuela
Established: 1989
Annual award recognizing excellence in gay & lesbian literature. Entry fee required. Guidelines on the web site.
Award: Trophy & 2 $1,000 debut fiction awards
Closing Date: Annually, Dec 1
Presented: Various cities, Annually in May

**Gerald Lampert Memorial Award**
The League of Canadian Poets
192 Spadina Ave, Suite 312, Toronto, ON M5T 2C2, Canada
*Tel:* 416-504-1657 *Fax:* 416-504-0096
*E-mail:* readings@poets.ca
*Web Site:* www.poets.ca
*Key Personnel*
Exec Dir: Joanna Poblocka *E-mail:* joanna@poets.ca
Asst Dir: Ingel Madrus *E-mail:* readings@poets.ca
Admin & Communs Coord: Lesley Fletcher *E-mail:* admin@poets.ca
Annual award intended to recognize the work of a Canadian writer early in his or her career. Awarded for a first book of poetry published in the preceding year.
Award: $1,000
Closing Date: Annually, Nov 1
Presented: Annually in May or June

**Langum Prize in American Legal History or Biography**
The Langum Charitable Trust
2809 Berkeley Dr, Birmingham, AL 35242
*Tel:* 205-726-2424 *Fax:* 205-726-4216
*E-mail:* langumtrust@gmail.com
*Web Site:* www.langumtrust.org
*Key Personnel*
Dir: David J Langum, Sr *E-mail:* djlangum@samford.edu
Established: 2001
Awarded to a book published by a university press in the area of American legal history or American legal biography that is accessible to the educated general public, rooted in sound scholarship & with themes that touch upon matters of general concern to the American public, past or present.
Award: $1,000
Closing Date: Annually in Dec
Presented: Annually in March

**Langum Prize in Historical Fiction**
The Langum Charitable Trust
2809 Berkeley Dr, Birmingham, AL 35242
*Tel:* 205-726-2424 *Fax:* 205-726-4216
*Web Site:* www.langumtrust.org
*Key Personnel*
Dir: David J Langum, Sr *E-mail:* djlangum@samford.edu
Established: 2001
Awarded to a book published by any non-subsidy press for historical fiction set in the colonial or national periods that is both excellent fiction & excellent history.
Award: $1,000
Closing Date: Annually in Dec; also rolling submissions at our request
Presented: Annually in March

**Larew, Christian, Memorial Scholarship in Library & Information Technology**, see LITA/Christian Larew Memorial Scholarship in Library & Information Technology

**Lawrence Foundation Award**
Prairie Schooner
University of Nebraska, 123 Andrews Hall, Lincoln, NE 68588-0334
Mailing Address: PO Box 880334, Lincoln, NE 68588-0334
*Tel:* 402-472-0911 *Fax:* 402-472-9771
*E-mail:* jengelhardt2@unl.edu
*Web Site:* prairieschooner.unl.edu
*Key Personnel*
Ed: Kwame Dawes
Established: 1978
Annual writing prize for the best short story published in *Prairie Schooner* magazine; only work published in the previous year will be considered.
Other Sponsor(s): The Lawrence Foundation of New York City
Award: $1,000
Presented: Winners announced in Spring issue of *Prairie Schooner* magazine

**Lawrence Foundation Prize**
Michigan Quarterly Review
University of Michigan, 0576 Rackham Bldg, 915 E Washington St, Ann Arbor, MI 48109-1070
*Tel:* 734-764-9265
*E-mail:* mqr@umich.edu
*Web Site:* www.umich.edu/~mqr
*Key Personnel*
Mng Ed: Vicki Lawrence
Ed: Keith Taylor
Awarded to the best work of fiction published in MQR each year. No deadline or special application process.
Award: $1,000

**Stephen Leacock Memorial Medal for Humour**
Stephen Leacock Association
RR2, 4223 Line 12 N, Coldwater, ON L0K 1E0, Canada
*Tel:* 705-835-3218 *Fax:* 705-835-5171
*Web Site:* www.leacock.ca
*Key Personnel*
Chair, Award Comm: Judith Rapson *E-mail:* judith.rapson@gmail.com
Pres: Michael Hill
Contact: Don Reid *E-mail:* don_reid@sympatico.ca
Established: 1946
Humorous writing by Canadian authors. All entries must have been published in the year prior to the year the award is given. Ten copies of each book to be submitted should be sent along with $150 fee, authors bio & a 5x7 or larger B&W photograph. No ebooks accepted. Winner announced late April. Books are non-returnable.
Other Sponsor(s): Lakehead University; Sun Media
Award: $15,000 Canadian TD Bank Financial Group cash award & silver medal, each of 4 finalists receive $1,500 Canadian
Closing Date: Annually, Nov 30
Presented: Gala Award Dinner, Geneva Park, Orillia, ON, Annually, early June

**The Ledge Press Fiction Awards Competition**
The Ledge Press
40 Maple Ave, Bellport, NY 11713
*E-mail:* info@theledgemagazine.com
*Web Site:* theledgemagazine.com
*Key Personnel*
Publr & Ed-in-Chief: Timothy Monaghan
All stories must be previously unpublished & not exceed 7,500 words. Entry fee is $12 for the first story, $6 each additional story. $20 subscription (2 issues) to The Ledge gains free entry for the first story.
Award: $1,000 & pubn in *The Ledge Magazine* (1st), $250 & pubn (2nd), $100 & pubn (3rd)
Closing Date: Annually, Feb 28

**The Ledge Press Poetry Awards Competition**
The Ledge Press
40 Maple Ave, Bellport, NY 11713
*E-mail:* info@theledgemagazine.com
*Web Site:* theledgemagazine.com
*Key Personnel*
Publr & Ed-in-Chief: Timothy Monaghan
Established: 1995
All poems must be previously unpublished. Entry fee is $12 for first three poems; $3 each additional poem. $20 subscription (2 issues) to The Ledge gains free entry for the first three poems.
Award: $1,000 & pubn in *The Ledge Magazine* (1st), $250 & pubn (2nd), $100 & pubn (3rd)
Closing Date: Annually, April 30

**The Ledge Press Poetry Chapbook Competition**
The Ledge Press
40 Maple Ave, Bellport, NY 11713
*E-mail:* info@theledgemagazine.com
*Web Site:* theledgemagazine.com
*Key Personnel*
Publr & Ed-in-Chief: Timothy Monaghan
Established: 1994
Submit 16-28 pages of original poetry with title page, biographic note & acknowledgements, if any; open to all styles & forms of poetry. Entry fee: $18.
Award: $1,000 & 25 author copies of the published chapbook
Closing Date: Annually, Oct 31

**Waldo G Leland Prize**
American Historical Association
400 "A" St SE, Washington, DC 20003-3889
*Tel:* 202-544-2422 *Fax:* 202-544-8307
*E-mail:* awards@historians.org
*Web Site:* www.historians.org
Established: 1981
Offered every five years for the most outstanding reference tool in the field of history. Reference tool encompasses bibliographies, indexes, encyclopedias & other scholarly apparatus. The award is honorific. Books published between May 1, 2016 & April 30, 2021, will be eligible for consideration. No application form, applicant must simply mail a copy of their book to each of the prize committee members who will be posted on our web site as the prize deadline approaches. All updated info on web site.
Award: Cash prize
Closing Date: May 16, 2021 (postmark)
Presented: AHA Annual Meeting

**Vincent Lemieux Prize**
Canadian Political Science Association
260 rue Dalhousie St, Suite 204, Ottawa, ON K1N 7E4, Canada
*Tel:* 613-562-1202 *Fax:* 613-241-0019
*E-mail:* cpsa-acsp@cpsa-acsp.ca
*Web Site:* www.cpsa-acsp.ca
*Key Personnel*
Administrator: Michelle Hopkins
Established: 1997
This is a biennial competition awarded to the best thesis in any sub-field of political science submitted at a Canadian University, written in English or French, judged eminently worthy of publication in the form of a book or articles. A thesis is eligible only after nomination by the department of political science in which it was defended. For the 2015 award, a thesis must have been defended in 2013 or 2014.
Award: $1,000 & commemorative certificate
Presented: 2015 Annual Conference, Biennially in May or June

**Leopold-Hidy Award**
The Forest History Society Inc
701 William Vickers Ave, Durham, NC 27701-3162
*Tel:* 919-682-9319 *Fax:* 919-682-2349
*Web Site:* www.foresthistory.org
*Key Personnel*
Admin Asst: Andrea Anderson
*E-mail:* recluce2@duke.edu
Established: 1996
To honor the best article in the journal they co-publish, "Environmental History".
Other Sponsor(s): American Society for Environmental History

**Fenia & Yaakov Leviant Memorial Prize in Yiddish Studies**
Modern Language Association of America (MLA)
26 Broadway, 3rd fl, New York, NY 10004-1789
SAN: 202-6422
*Tel:* 646-576-5141 *Fax:* 646-458-0030
*E-mail:* awards@mla.org
*Web Site:* www.mla.org
*Key Personnel*
Coord, Book Prizes: Annie M Reiser
*E-mail:* areiser@mla.org
Established: 2000
Awarded alternately to an outstanding translation or an outstanding scholarly work in the field of Yiddish. In 2014, the prize will be awarded to an English translation of a Yiddish literary work published between 2010 & 2013. In 2016, the prize will be awarded to an outstanding scholarly work in English in the field of Yiddish published between 2012-2015. Authors need not be members of the MLA.
Award: Cash award, certificate & 1 year association membership
Closing Date: May 1, 2014
Presented: MLA Convention, Jan 2015

**Harry Levin Prize**
American Comparative Literature Association (ACLA)
University of South Carolina, Dept of Languages, Literature & Cultures, Rm 813-A, 1620 College St, Columbia, SC 29208
*Tel:* 803-777-3021 *Fax:* 803-777-3041
*E-mail:* info@acla.org
*Web Site:* www.acla.org
*Key Personnel*
Secy & Treas: Alexander Beecroft
Established: 1968
Prize recognizes outstanding work in literary history or criticism as opposed to theory published 2012-2014. See web site for nomination process.
Award: Complimentary conference registration, a banquet ticket & a travel grant to cover the cost of attending the annual meeting to receive the award in person
Closing Date: Sept 2014
Presented: ACLA Annual Meeting, Spring 2015

**Levinson Prize**
Poetry Magazine
444 N Michigan Ave, Suite 1850, Chicago, IL 60611-4034
*Tel:* 312-787-7070 *Fax:* 312-787-6650
*E-mail:* editors@poetrymagazine.org
*Web Site:* poetryfoundation.org
*Key Personnel*
Mng Ed: Valerie Johnson *E-mail:* vjohnson@poetrymagazine.org
Established: 1914
For poetry published in the preceding two volumes of Poetry. No application necessary.
Award: $500
Presented: Annually in Dec

**Levis Reading Prize**
Virginia Commonwealth University, Dept of English
PO Box 842005, Richmond, VA 23284-2005
*Tel:* 804-828-1331 *Fax:* 804-828-8684
*Web Site:* www.has.vcu.edu/eng/resources/levis_prize.htm
Established: 1997
In memory of Larry Levis, awarded for best first or second book of poetry.
Closing Date: Jan 15

**The Lieutenant-Governor's Awards for High Achievement in the Arts**
New Brunswick Arts Board (Conseil des arts du Nouveau-Brunswick)
61 Carleton St, Fredericton, NB E3B 3T2, Canada
*Tel:* 506-444-4444 *Toll Free Tel:* 866-460-ARTS (460-2787) *Fax:* 506-444-5543
*E-mail:* nbabcanb@artsnb.ca
*Web Site:* www.artsnb.ca
*Key Personnel*
Exec Dir: Luc Charette *E-mail:* lcharette@artsnb.ca
Prog Offr: Robert Bryar *Tel:* 506-444-5633
Established: 1989
Finance studies, provide subsistence allowance, up to $15,000 (creation grant).
Award: Excellence Awards, $20,000/year
Closing Date: Lieutenant Governor's Awards annually in June. Arts Scholarships & Artists in Residence annually in Feb
Presented: Fredericton, NB

**The Lieutenant-Governor's Medal for Historical Writing**
British Columbia Historical Federation
PO Box 5254, Sta B, Victoria, BC V8R 6N4, Canada
*E-mail:* writing@bchistory.ca
*Web Site:* www.bchistory.ca
*Key Personnel*
Pres: Barbara Hynek *E-mail:* president@bchistory.ca
Dir: William R Morrison
Outstanding book published in calendar year on British Columbia history. Books may be submitted by authors or publishers & published within the competition year.
Award: $600 & Governor's Medal, $400 (2nd place), $200 (3rd place)
Closing Date: Annually, Dec 31
Presented: Annual AGM, Annually in May

**Ruth Lilly Poetry Prize**
Poetry Foundation
444 N Michigan Ave, Suite 1850, Chicago, IL 60611-4034
*Tel:* 312-787-7070 *Fax:* 312-787-6650
*E-mail:* editors@poetrymagazine.org
*Web Site:* poetrymagazine.org
*Key Personnel*
Mng Ed: Valerie Johnson
Ed: Christian Wiman
Established: 1986
Awarded to a living United States poet, to recognize extraordinary artistic accomplishment.
Award: $100,000
Presented: Annually in May

**Joseph W Lippincott Award**
The American Library Association (ALA)
50 E Huron St, Chicago, IL 60611
*Tel:* 312-280-3247 *Toll Free Tel:* 800-545-2433 (ext 3247) *Fax:* 312-944-3897
*E-mail:* awards@ala.org
*Web Site:* www.ala.org
*Key Personnel*
Prog Offr: Cheryl M Malden *E-mail:* cmalden@ala.org
Established: 1938
Annual award presented to a librarian for distinguished service to the profession of librarianship, such service to include outstanding participation in the activities of professional library association, notable published profes-

sional writing or other significant activity on behalf of the profession & its aims.
Other Sponsor(s): Joseph W Lippincott III
Award: $1,000 & Citation
Closing Date: Annually, Dec 1
Presented: ALA Annual Conference, Annually in June

**LITA/Christian Larew Memorial Scholarship in Library & Information Technology**
Library & Information Technology Association (LITA)
Division of American Library Association (ALA)
c/o American Library Association, 50 E Huron St, Chicago, IL 60611-2795
*Toll Free Tel:* 800-545-2433 (ext 4270) *Fax:* 312-280-3257
*E-mail:* lita@ala.org
*Web Site:* www.ala.org/lita
*Key Personnel*
Prog Coord: Valerie A Edmonds-Merritt *Tel:* 312-280-4269 *E-mail:* vedmonds@ala.org
Established: 1999
Awarded jointly on an annual basis. The scholarship is designed to encourage the entry of qualified persons into the library & information technology field, who plan to follow a career in that field & who demonstrate academic excellence, leadership & a vision in pursuit of library & information technology. This scholarship is for study in an ALA Accredited Master of Library Science (MLS) program.
Other Sponsor(s): Baker & Taylor
Award: $3,000
Closing Date: Annually, March 1
Presented: LITA President's program held at the American Library Association Annual Conference, Annually in June

**LITA/LSSI Minority Scholarship in Library & Information Technology**
Library & Information Technology Association (LITA)
Division of American Library Association (ALA)
c/o American Library Association, 50 E Huron St, Chicago, IL 60611-2795
*Toll Free Tel:* 800-545-2433 (ext 4270) *Fax:* 312-280-3257
*E-mail:* lita@ala.org
*Web Site:* www.ala.org/lita
*Key Personnel*
Prog Coord: Valerie A Edmonds-Merritt *Tel:* 312-280-4269 *E-mail:* vedmonds@ala.org
Established: 1994
Scholarship is designed to encourage the entry of qualified minorities into the library & automation field who plan to follow a career in that field & who demonstrate potential in & have a strong commitment to the use of automated systems in libraries. Applicants must be qualified members of a principal minority group (American Indian or Alaskan native, Asian or Pacific Islander, African-American or Hispanic). The recipient must be a US or Canadian citizen. The scholarship is for study in an ALA Accredited Master of Library Science (MLS) program.
Other Sponsor(s): LSSI
Award: $2,500
Closing Date: Annually, March 1
Presented: LITA President's Program held at the American Library Association Annual Conference, Annually in June

**LITA/OCLC Minority Scholarship in Library & Information Technology**
Library & Information Technology Association (LITA)
Division of American Library Association (ALA)
c/o American Library Association, 50 E Huron St, Chicago, IL 60611-2795
*Toll Free Tel:* 800-545-2433 (ext 4270) *Fax:* 312-280-3257
*E-mail:* lita@ala.org
*Web Site:* www.ala.org/lita
*Key Personnel*
Prog Coord: Valerie A Edmonds-Merritt *Tel:* 312-280-4269 *E-mail:* vedmonds@ala.org
Established: 1991
For qualified members of a minority group. Must be US or Canadian citizen. For applicants who plan to enter a career in the library & automation field.
Other Sponsor(s): OCLC Inc
Award: $3,000
Closing Date: Annually, March 1
Presented: LITA President's Program at the American Library Association Annual Conference, Annually in June

**Literary Translation Projects**
National Endowment for the Arts
1100 Pennsylvania Ave NW, Rm 703, Washington, DC 20506
*Tel:* 202-682-5403; 202-682-5400; 202-682-5034 (lit fellowships hotline) *Fax:* 202-682-5609; 202-682-5610
*E-mail:* litfellowships@arts.gov
*Web Site:* www.arts.gov; www.nea.gov
*Key Personnel*
Grants Dir & Contracts Offr: Nicki Jacobs *Tel:* 202-682-5546 *E-mail:* jacobsn@arts.gov
Fellowships for published translators: for translations of published literary material into English. Applications accepted by genre. Guidelines available on web site.
Award: $12,500 or $25,000, depending on the artistic excellence & merit of the project
Closing Date: Annually in Jan
Presented: Notification by mail, Annually in Aug

**Literature Fellowship**
Idaho Commission on the Arts
2410 N Old Penitentiary Rd, Boise, ID 83712
Mailing Address: PO Box 83720, Boise, ID 83720-0008
*Tel:* 208-334-2119 *Toll Free Tel:* 800-ART-FUND (278-3863 within Idaho) *Fax:* 208-334-2488
*E-mail:* info@arts.idaho.gov
*Web Site:* www.arts.idaho.gov
*Key Personnel*
Lit Dir: Cort Conley *Tel:* 208-334-2119 ext 108 *E-mail:* cort.conley@arts.idaho.gov
Five fellowships awarded triennially for literary excellence. For Idaho residents only.
Award: $5,000
Closing Date: Annually in Jan
Presented: Annually in July

**Littleton-Griswold Prize in American Law & Society**
American Historical Association
400 "A" St SE, Washington, DC 20003-3889
*Tel:* 202-544-2422 *Fax:* 202-544-8307
*E-mail:* awards@historians.org
*Web Site:* www.historians.org
Established: 1985
Best book in any subject on the history of American law & society. Books published in 2013 will be eligible for consideration. Along with an application form, applicants must mail a copy of their book to each of the prize committee members who will be posted on our web site as the prize deadline approaches. All updated info on web site.
Award: Cash prize
Closing Date: May 15, 2014 (postmark)
Presented: AHA Annual Meeting

**Littleton-Griswold Research Grants**
American Historical Association
400 "A" St SE, Washington, DC 20003-3889
*Tel:* 202-544-2422 *Fax:* 202-544-8307
*E-mail:* awards@historians.org
*Web Site:* www.historians.org
For research in American legal history & the field of law & society. Only members of the Association are eligible. Applications must include application form with estimated budget, curriculum vitae & statement of no more than 750 words & a one-page bibliography of the most recent, relevant, secondary works on the topic. Application form & all updated info on web site. Preference will be given to junior scholars, PhD candidates & those without access to institutional funds.
Award: Individual grants will not exceed $1,000
Closing Date: Feb 15

**Locus Awards**
Locus Science Fiction Foundation Inc
Division of Locus Publications
PO Box 13305, Oakland, CA 94661-0305
*Tel:* 510-339-9196 *Fax:* 510-339-9198
*E-mail:* locus@locusmag.com
*Web Site:* www.locusmag.com
*Key Personnel*
Ed-in-Chief: Liza Groen Trombi
Mng Ed: Kirsten Gong-Wong
Established: 1971
Presented for the best science fiction novel, best fantasy novel, best first novel, best young-adult novel, best novella, best novelette, best short fiction, science fiction anthology, best nonfiction, art & artist, editor, magazine, best publisher & collection of the year.
Other Sponsor(s): EMP/SFM; Northwest Media Group; 1-2-3 Awards
Award: Trophy & free subscription
Presented: Science Fiction Museum

**The Gerald Loeb Awards**
Anderson School of Management at UCLA
Gold Hall, Suite B-305, 110 Westwood Plaza, Los Angeles, CA 90095-1481
*Tel:* 310-825-4478 *Fax:* 310-825-4479
*E-mail:* loeb@anderson.ucla.edu
*Web Site:* www.loeb.anderson.ucla.edu
*Key Personnel*
Prog Mgr: Jonathan Daillak
Established: 1957
Distinguished business & finance journalism in print & broadcast media.
Award: $2,000 winners; $500 honorable mention
Closing Date: Last Mon in Jan
Presented: Last week in June

**Loft-Mentor Series in Poetry & Creative Prose**
The Loft Literary Center
Open Book, Suite 200, 1011 Washington Ave S, Minneapolis, MN 55415
*Tel:* 612-215-2575 *Fax:* 612-215-2576
*E-mail:* loft@loft.org
*Web Site:* www.loft.org
*Key Personnel*
Prog Dir: Jerod Santek *Tel:* 612-215-2586 *E-mail:* jsantek@loft.org
Established: 1980
Annual award for poetry & fiction mss. Must be Minnesota State resident. Send SASE for current guidelines. Six different residencies scheduled throughout the year. Winners announced on web site. Open to poets, fiction writers & nonfiction writers.
Award: Stipend to defray costs of participating in the program & opportunity to study with six nationally known writer-mentors in brief residence during the course of the year
Closing Date: Mid-Spring
Presented: The Loft

**The Jack London Award**
Titan Press
Box 17897, Encino, CA 91416
*E-mail:* cwcsfv@gmail.com

*Key Personnel*
Mng Ed: Stefanya Wilson
Three quarterly competitions: fiction, poetry & nonfiction. Monthly nominations are made for publication & honorable mention. Of those, one is chosen for the annual Grand Prize. Published & unpublished mss are eligible. $65 annual dues ar allowed; one free submission per quarter; nonmembers; $15 reading fee per entry, up to 4 entries per quarter.
Award: Invitation to attend the biannual Writer's Conference, plaque commemorating winner as guest of honor (give a public reading of his work) & publication
Closing Date: Submissions accepted throughout the year
Presented: Biannual Writer's Conference

**Judy Lopez Memorial Award For Children's Literature**
Women's National Book Association/Los Angeles Chapter
1225 Selby Ave, Los Angeles, CA 90024
*Tel:* 310-474-9917 *Fax:* 310-474-6436
*Web Site:* www.wnba-books.org/la; www.judylopezbookaward.org
*Key Personnel*
Chair, Lopez Comm: Margaret Flanders
Pres: Rachelle Yousef
Chair, Selection Comm: Gail Kim
Established: 1986
For best books for young readers 9-12 years of age, submitted by publishers, written by US citizen/US resident in year that precedes the award.
Award: Bronze medal & cash honorarium
Closing Date: Annually, Feb 1
Presented: Dinner, UCLA Faculty Center, Los Angeles, CA, 2nd Sat or Sun in June

**Los Angeles Times Book Prizes**
Los Angeles Times
Subsidiary of Tribune Co
202 W First St, Los Angeles, CA 90012
*Tel:* 213-237-5775 *Toll Free Tel:* 800-528-4637 *Fax:* 213-237-7679
*Web Site:* www.latimesbookprizes.com
*Key Personnel*
CEO & Publr: David D Hiller
Administrator: Ann Binney *E-mail:* ann.binney@latimes.com
Established: 1980
Annual prizes to authors in the categories of fiction, first fiction, young adult fiction, mystery/thriller, biography, current interest, history, poetry, science & technology. No submissions accepted; nominations are done by committees of appointed judges.
Award: $1,000 & citation (in 9 different categories, plus 10th category, lifetime award - Distinguished Author)
Presented: Annually in April

**Louise Louis/Emily F Bourne Student Poetry Award**
Poetry Society of America (PSA)
15 Gramercy Park S, New York, NY 10003
*Tel:* 212-254-9628 *Fax:* 212-673-2352
*Web Site:* www.poetrysociety.org
*Key Personnel*
Pres: Ruth Kaplan
Exec Dir: Alice Quinn
Mng Dir & Awards Coord: Brett Fletcher Lauer *E-mail:* brett@poetrysociety.org
Progs Dir: Darrel Alejandro Holnes
Established: 1971
For an unpublished poem by an American high school or preparatory school student. Send No 10 SASE or visit web site for further guidelines.
Award: $250
Closing Date: Annually, Oct-Dec
Presented: Annual Awards Ceremony, New York, NY, Annually in Spring

**Louisville Grawemeyer Award in Religion**
Louisville Presbyterian Theological Seminary & University of Louisville
1044 Alta Vista Rd, Louisville, KY 40205-1798
*Tel:* 502-895-3411 *Toll Free Tel:* 800-264-1839 *Fax:* 502-894-2286
*E-mail:* grawemeyer@lpts.edu
*Web Site:* www.grawemeyer.org
*Key Personnel*
Dir: Shannon Craigo-Snell
Established: 1990
Given for a work presented or published in the eight years preceding the year of the award. Nominations are invited from religious organizations, appropriate academic associations, religious leaders & scholars, presidents of universities or schools of religion & publishers & editors of scholarly journals. Personal nominations accepted, self-nominations not accepted.
Award: $20,000 per year for 5 years
Closing Date: Nominations by Dec 1
Presented: Annually in Spring

**Love Creek Annual Short Play Festival**
Love Creek Productions
2144 45 Ave, Long Island City, NY 11101
*Tel:* 718-786-9397
*E-mail:* lovecreekle@aol.com; squaank@yahoo.com (submissions)
*Key Personnel*
Mng & Artistic Dir: Le Wilhelm
Lit Mgr: Becky Copley
Established: 1988
Annual one-act play festival for unpublished scripts unproduced in New York City in previous year. Send SASE for information/guidelines which must be followed exactly.
Award: Cash (1st prize), mini-showcase production (finalists)
Closing Date: Revolving (annual festival)
Presented: New York, NY, various midtown venues, Ongoing

**James Russell Lowell Prize**
Modern Language Association of America (MLA)
26 Broadway, 3rd fl, New York, NY 10004-1789
SAN: 202-6422
*Tel:* 646-576-5141 *Fax:* 646-458-0030
*E-mail:* awards@mla.org
*Web Site:* www.mla.org
*Key Personnel*
Coord, Book Prizes: Annie M Reiser *E-mail:* areiser@mla.org
Established: 1969
Awarded annually for an outstanding literary or linguistic study, or critical biography by an MLA member published in year prior to competition. Authors or publishers should submit 6 copies & confirmation of the author's membership in the MLA.
Award: Cash award & certificate
Closing Date: March 1
Presented: MLA Convention, Jan

**Pat Lowther Memorial Award**
The League of Canadian Poets
192 Spadina Ave, Suite 312, Toronto, ON M5T 2C2, Canada
*Tel:* 416-504-1657 *Fax:* 416-504-0096
*E-mail:* readings@poets.ca
*Web Site:* www.poets.ca
*Key Personnel*
Exec Dir: Joanna Poblocka *E-mail:* joanna@poets.ca
Asst Dir: Ingel Madrus *E-mail:* readings@poets.ca
Admin & Communs Coord: Lesley Fletcher *E-mail:* admin@poets.ca
Annual award for the best book of poetry written by a Canadian woman & published in the preceding year.
Award: $1,000
Closing Date: Annually, Nov 1
Presented: Annually in May or June

**Jeremiah Ludington Award**
Educational Book & Media Association (EBMA)
37 Main St, Suite 203, Warrenton, VA 20186
Mailing Address: PO Box 3363, Warrenton, VA 20188
*Tel:* 540-318-7770 *Fax:* 202-962-3939
*E-mail:* info@edupaperback.org
*Web Site:* www.edupaperback.org
*Key Personnel*
Exec Dir: Brian Gorg
Meeting Mgr: Maureen Gelwicks
Established: 1979
Presented to a person for distinguished work with young people & books; selected by EBMA committee & board; no application required.
Award: Citation & contribution to a cause chosen by recipient
Presented: Annually at EBMA meeting, Annually in Jan

**Hugh J Luke Award**
Prairie Schooner
University of Nebraska, 123 Andrews Hall, Lincoln, NE 68588-0334
Mailing Address: PO Box 880334, Lincoln, NE 68588-0334
*Tel:* 402-472-0911 *Fax:* 402-472-9771
*Web Site:* prairieschooner.unl.edu
*Key Personnel*
Mng Ed: James Engelhardt *E-mail:* jengelhardt2@unl.edu
Ed: Kwame Dawes
Established: 1989
Annual writing prize for best work published in the *Prairie Schooner* magazine in the previous year.
Other Sponsor(s): Friends & family of Hugh J Luke (in memoriam)
Award: $250
Presented: Winners announced in Spring issue of *Prairie Schooner* magazine

**Glenna Luschei Prairie Schooner Award**
Prairie Schooner
University of Nebraska, 123 Andrews Hall, Lincoln, NE 68588-0334
Mailing Address: PO Box 880334, Lincoln, NE 68588-0334
*Tel:* 402-472-0911 *Fax:* 402-472-9771
*Web Site:* prairieschooner.unl.edu
*Key Personnel*
Mng Ed: James Engelhardt *E-mail:* jengelhardt2@unl.edu
Ed: Kwame Dawes
Established: 1989
Annual writing prizes for best work published in the magazine. Only work published in *Prairie Schooner* in the previous year is considered.
Other Sponsor(s): Glenna Luschei
Award: $1,500 (first place), $250 (10 runners up)
Presented: Winners announced in Spring issue of *Prairie Schooner* magazine

**Lush Triumphant**
sub-TERRAIN Magazine
PO Box 3008, MPO, Vancouver, BC V6R 3X5, Canada
*Tel:* 604-876-8710 *Fax:* 604-879-2667
*E-mail:* subter@portal.ca
*Web Site:* www.subterrain.ca
Established: 2003
Annual literary award in 3 categories: fiction, poetry & nonfiction. Entry fee: $27.50.
Award: $750 CN (1st place in each category), 1st runner-up $250 & publication in Spring issue of following year

Closing Date: May 15
Presented: Vancouver, BC, Aug 15

**Thomas J Lyon Book Award in Western American Literary and Cultural Studies**
Western Literature Association
PO Box 6815, Logan, UT 84341
*Web Site:* www.westernlit.org/thomas-j-lyon-book-award-in-western-american-literary-and-cultural-studies/; www.westernlit.org
*Key Personnel*
Dir of Opers: Sabine Barcatta
*E-mail:* WLAoperations@gmail.com
Established: 1997
Honors outstanding single-author scholarly book on the literature & culture of the American West published in the previous year. Must submit a statement of support & three copies of the book.
Award: Certificate
Closing Date: June 15
Presented: Annual Conference

**Lyric Poetry Award**
Poetry Society of America (PSA)
15 Gramercy Park S, New York, NY 10003
*Tel:* 212-254-9628 *Fax:* 212-673-2352
*Web Site:* www.poetrysociety.org
*Key Personnel*
Pres: Ruth Kaplan
Exec Dir: Alice Quinn
Mng Dir & Awards Coord: Brett Fletcher Lauer
*E-mail:* brett@poetrysociety.org
Progs Dir: Darrel Alejandro Holnes
Established: 1972
For a lyric poem on any subject, not to exceed 50 lines. Open to Society members only. Send No 10 SASE or visit web site for further information.
Award: $500
Closing Date: Annually, Oct-Dec
Presented: Annual Awards Ceremony, New York, NY, Annually in Spring

**Lyric Poetry Prizes**
The Lyric
PO Box 110, Jericho, VT 05465
*Tel:* 802-899-3993 *Fax:* 802-899-3993
*E-mail:* themuse@thelyricmagazine.com
*Web Site:* thelyricmagazine.com
*Key Personnel*
Ed: Jean Mellichamp Milliken
Established: 1921
Awarded to undergraduates enrolled full time in an American or Canadian College. Awarded for poems published in "The Lyric" magazine. Winners of annual awards announced in the winter issue each year. Send SASE for guidelines. Sample copy of "The Lyric" $4; subn price $15/yr, $28/2 yrs, $38/3 yr, $2 extra per year for foreign & Canadian.
Award: Quarterly prize: $50. Annual awards: Lyric Memorial Prize $100, Lyric College Poetry Contest/Scholarship $500, Leslie Mellichamp Prize $100, Roberts Memorial Prize $100, Margaret Hailey Carpenter Prize $50, New England Prize $50, Fluvanna Prize $50. Honorable mentions, 1 yr subn to "The Lyric" magazine. Checks mailed to recipients
Closing Date: Dec 1 postmark
Presented: Quarterly prizes awarded in the following issue, annual prizes in the winter issue

**Macavity Award**
Mystery Readers International
7155 Marlborough Terr, Berkeley, CA 94705
Mailing Address: PO Box 8116, Berkeley, CA 94707
*Tel:* 510-845-3600
*Web Site:* www.mysteryreaders.org
*Key Personnel*
Dir: Janet Rudolph *E-mail:* janet@mysteryreaders.org
Established: 1986
Annually awarded for works nominated by & voted on by members of Mystery Readers International in categories: Best Novel, Best First Novel, Best Short Story, Best Nonfiction/Critical; Sue Feder Award for the Historical Mystery (all published in the US the previous year).
Award: Statue
Closing Date: No application necessary
Presented: Bouchercon, the World Mystery Convention, Oct

**Sir John A Macdonald Prize**
Canadian Historical Association
130 Albert St, Suite 501, Ottawa, ON K1P 5G4, Canada
*Tel:* 613-233-7885 *Fax:* 613-565-5445
*E-mail:* cha-shc@cha-shc.ca
*Web Site:* www.cha-shc.ca
*Key Personnel*
Exec Coord: Michel Duquet *E-mail:* mduquet@cha-shc.ca
Established: 1976
Awarded for the best book on Canadian history. See web site for application details.
Award: $5,000
Closing Date: Annually, Dec 1
Presented: Annual meeting, Canadian Historical Association, Annually in May

**The MacDowell Colony**
100 High St, Peterborough, NH 03458
*Tel:* 603-924-3886 *Fax:* 603-924-9142
*E-mail:* info@macdowellcolony.org; admissions@macdowellcolony.org
*Web Site:* www.macdowellcolony.org
*Key Personnel*
Exec Dir: Cheryl Young
Admissions Dir: Courtney Bethel
Communs Mgr: Jonathan Gourlay
Awarded for a career of outstanding contributions to the arts, including musical composition, visual arts or literature, architecture, film & video & interdisciplinary arts. Fellowships of up to eight weeks are available for writers, composers, film/video artists, visual artists, architects & interdisciplinary artists. Artists-in-residence receive room, board & exclusive use of a studio. The average length of stay is six weeks. Talent is the sole criterion for acceptance to the Colony. Established artists as well as emerging artists are encouraged to apply. Committees of distinguished professionals donate their time to judge applications, which include work samples, references & a brief project description. There are no residency fees. Grants for travel to & from the Colony are available based on need. Financial aid for writers is available through a special grant from a foundation. An aid application will be mailed following acceptance.
Award: The Edward MacDowell Medal; MacDowell Fellowships
Closing Date: For fellowships: Jan 15, April 15 & Sept 15, see application form & guidelines for details
Presented: Peterborough, NH, Annually in Aug
*Branch Office(s)*
163 E 81 St, New York, NY 10028 *Tel:* 212-535-9690 *Fax:* 212-737-3803

**Machigonne Fiction Contest**
The New Guard
PO Box 866, Wells, ME 04094
*E-mail:* info@newguardreview.com
*Web Site:* www.newguardreview.com
*Key Personnel*
Founding Ed & Publr: Shanna McNair
Established: 2009
Submit a short story or novel excerpt up to 7,500 words. Online submissions preferred. For postal mail entries, please include a short bio along with a $15 entry fee & SASE.
Award: $1,000 & publication in the New Guard
Closing Date: Varies

**C B MacPherson Prize**
Canadian Political Science Association
260 rue Dalhousie St, Suite 204, Ottawa, ON K1N 7E4, Canada
*Tel:* 613-562-1202 *Fax:* 613-241-0019
*E-mail:* cpsa-acsp@cpsa-acsp.ca
*Web Site:* www.cpsa-acsp.ca
*Key Personnel*
Administrator: Michelle Hopkins
Established: 1992
This is a biennial competition. Awarded to the best book published in English or in French in a field relating to the study of political theory. A book may be single-authored or multi-authored. Single-authored book: must be a Canadian citizen or a permanent resident of Canada or a member of the CPSA in the year the book was published. Multi-authored book: at least one of the authors must be a Canadian citizen or a permanent resident of Canada or a member of the CPSA in the year the book was published. For the 2014 award, a book must have a copyright date of 2012 or 2013.
Award: Commemorative plaque & also receive/share the set of books submitted to the CPSA office for the 2014 prize
Presented: Annual Conference, Biennially in May or June

**Magazine Merit Awards**
Society of Children's Book Writers & Illustrators (SCBWI)
8271 Beverly Blvd, Los Angeles, CA 90048
*Tel:* 323-782-1010 *Fax:* 323-782-1892
*E-mail:* membership@scbwi.org; scbwi@scbwi.org
*Web Site:* www.scbwi.org
*Key Personnel*
Pres: Stephen Mooser *E-mail:* stephenmooser@scbwi.org
Exec Dir: Lin Oliver *E-mail:* linoliver@scbwi.org
Established: 1988
For outstanding original magazine work for young people published during the calendar year & having been written or illustrated by SCBWI members.
Award: Four plaques (fiction, nonfiction, illustration, poetry), four honor certificates
Closing Date: Dec
Presented: April

**The Magazine of the Year Award**
Society of Publication Designers Inc
27 Union Sq W, Suite 207, New York, NY 10003
*Tel:* 212-223-3332 *Fax:* 212-223-5880
*E-mail:* mail@spd.org
*Web Site:* www.spd.org
*Key Personnel*
Exec Dir: Keisha Dean
Established: 1996
For continuing excellence in the field of publication design.
Closing Date: Jan
Presented: Annual Awards Gala, May

**J Russell Major Prize**
American Historical Association
400 "A" St SE, Washington, DC 20003-3889
*Tel:* 202-544-2422 *Fax:* 202-544-8307
*E-mail:* awards@historians.org
*Web Site:* www.historians.org
Established: 2001
Awarded for the best work in English on any aspect of French history. Books published in

2013 are eligible. Along with an application form, applicants must mail a copy of their book to each of the prize committee members who will be posted on our web site as the prize deadline approaches. All updated info on web site.
Award: Cash prize
Closing Date: May 1, 2014 (postmark)
Presented: AHA Annual Meeting

**Malahat Review Long Poem Prize**
The Malahat Review
University of Victoria, Box 1700, Sta CSC, Victoria, BC V8W 2Y2, Canada
*Tel:* 250-721-8524 *Fax:* 250-472-5051
*E-mail:* malahat@uvic.ca
*Web Site:* www.malahatreview.ca
*Key Personnel*
Ed: John Barton
Two awards for best long poem(s). See web site for details & entry fee. Contest runs every other year (in odd-numbered years). Alternates with Novella Prize.
Award: $1000 CAD (2 prizes)
Closing Date: Feb 1, odd numbered yrs

**Gene E & Adele R Malott Prize for Recording Community Activism**
The Langum Charitable Trust
2809 Berkeley Dr, Birmingham, AL 35242
*Tel:* 205-726-2424 *Fax:* 205-726-4216
*E-mail:* langumtrust@gmail.com
*Web Site:* www.langumtrust.org
*Key Personnel*
Dir: David J Langum, Sr *E-mail:* djlangum@samford.edu
Established: 2007
Biannual prize that recognizes the best literary depiction of an individual or small group of individuals whose efforts resulted in a significant improvement of their local community. Although the work of community improvement must be significant, the basis of the prize will be the skill & power of the literary or film depiction. Must have been published or released within the past 2 years of a prize cycle.
Award: $1,500 for the writer. If film, divided between the director & screenwriter; $1,000 if ongoing, the underlying project of community activism
Closing Date: Jan 1 for materials published or or released the previous 2 calendar years.

**Manheim, Ralph Medal for Translation**, see PEN/Ralph Manheim Medal for Translation

**Margaret Mann Citation**
Association for Library Collections & Technical Services (ALCTS)
Division of American Library Association
50 E Huron St, Chicago, IL 60611
SAN: 201-0062
*Tel:* 312-280-5037 *Toll Free Tel:* 800-545-2433 *Fax:* 312-280-5033
*E-mail:* alcts@ala.org
*Web Site:* www.ala.org/alcts
*Key Personnel*
Exec Dir: Charles Wilt *Tel:* 312-280-5030 *E-mail:* cwilt@ala.org
Pubns & Membership: Christine McConnell *Tel:* 312-280-5037 *E-mail:* cmcconnell@ala.org
Established: 1951
Award for outstanding professional achievement in cataloging or classification in a significant publication or by participation in a professional organization. Candidates are nominated. Citation recipient selected by jury.
Other Sponsor(s): OCLC
Award: Citation & $2,000 scholarship to the US or Canadian library school of winner's choice
Closing Date: Annually, Dec 1
Presented: ALA Annual Conference, Annually in June

**Many Voices Fellowships**
The Playwrights' Center
2301 Franklin Ave E, Minneapolis, MN 55406-1099
*Tel:* 612-332-7481 *Fax:* 612-332-6037
*E-mail:* info@pwcenter.org
*Web Site:* www.pwcenter.org
*Key Personnel*
Producing Artistic Dir: Jeremy Cohen *Tel:* 612-332-7481 ext 113 *E-mail:* jeremyc@pwcenter.org
Artistic Administrator: Amanda Robbins-Butcher *Tel:* 612-332-7481 ext 115 *E-mail:* amandar@pwcenter.org
For writers of color. Two distinct programs to serve writers of varying skill/experience levels both locally & nationally.
Award: Many Voices Mentorship: 2 Minnesota playwrights with little or no playwriting experience, $1,000 stipend; Many Voices Fellowship: 2 emerging playwrights receive a $5,650 stipend, $1,250 in play development funds & dramaturgical support. One must reside in Minnesota, the other may be a resident of any US state
Closing Date: See web site for details

**Marian Library Medal**
University of Dayton, Marian Library
300 College Park, Dayton, OH 45469-1390
*Tel:* 937-229-4214 *Fax:* 937-229-4258
*Web Site:* campus.udayton.edu/mary/mlmedal.html
*Key Personnel*
Libn: William Fackovec
Established: 1953
To scholars in any country for outstanding achievement in Marian research.
Award: Medal

**Marick Press Poetry Prize Competition**
Marick Press
PO Box 36253, Grosse Pointe Farms, MI 48236
*Tel:* 313-407-9236
*Web Site:* www.marickpress.com
*Key Personnel*
Mng Ed: Sandra Kuizenga *Tel:* 989-671-0403
Established: 2010
Submit a ms of 48-80 pages, 2 separate title pages, one with just the title & the other with full author info. Open competition for a poetry ms; submissions are accepted from anyone writing in the English language, whether living in the US or abroad (translations are not eligible). Entry fee: $15.
Award: $1,000 & publication by Marick Press
Closing Date: Annually in Oct
Presented: Annually in March

**Morton Marr Poetry Prize**
Southwest Review
6404 Robert Hyer Lane, Rm 307, Dallas, TX 75275-0374
Mailing Address: PO Box 750374, Dallas, TX 75275-0374
*Fax:* 214-768-1408
*E-mail:* swr@mail.smu.edu
*Web Site:* www.smu.edu/southwestreview
*Key Personnel*
Ed-in-Chief: Willard Spiegelman
Sr Ed: Jennifer Cranfill *Tel:* 214-768-1036
Open to writers who have not yet published a first book of poetry. Contestants may submit no more than 6 previously unpublished poems in a "traditional" form (eg sonnet, sestina, villanelle, rhymed stanzas, blank verse, etc). There is a $5 per poem entry/handling fee.
Award: $1,000 (1st prize), $500 (2nd prize)
Closing Date: Annually, Sept 30
Presented: Annually in Dec

**Helen & Howard R Marraro Prize in Italian History**
American Historical Association
400 "A" St SE, Washington, DC 20003-3889
*Tel:* 202-544-2422 *Fax:* 202-544-8307
*E-mail:* awards@historians.org
*Web Site:* www.historians.org
Established: 1973
Each award will be given for the book or article deemed best by the committee which treats Italian history in any epoch, Italian cultural history, or Italian-American relations. Each book must be published in 2013. Entries must first have been published in English by a historian whose usual residence is North America. Along with an application form, applicants must mail a copy of their book together with a curriculum vitae & bibliography of the author to each of the prize committee members who will be posted on our web site as the prize deadline approaches. All updated info on web site.
Other Sponsor(s): American Catholic Historical Association; Society for Italian Historical Studies
Award: Cash prize
Closing Date: May 15, 2014 (postmark)
Presented: AHA Annual Meeting

**Howard R Marraro Prize**
Modern Language Association of America (MLA)
26 Broadway, 3rd fl, New York, NY 10004-1789
SAN: 202-6422
*Tel:* 646-576-5141 *Fax:* 646-458-0030
*E-mail:* awards@mla.org
*Web Site:* www.mla.org
*Key Personnel*
Coord, Book Prizes: Annie M Reiser *E-mail:* areiser@mla.org
Established: 1973
For an outstanding study in Italian literature or comparative literature involving Italian by an MLA member; books or essays. The Prize is awarded each even-numbered year. The committee solicits submissions of works published in 2013 by current members. Submit 4 copies of the work & confirm author's membership in the MLA.
Award: Cash award & certificate
Closing Date: May 1, 2014
Presented: MLA Convention, Jan 2015

**Massachusetts Book Awards**
Massachusetts Center for the Book
Simons College - GSLIS, 300 The Fenway, Boston, MA 02115
*Tel:* 617-521-2719 *Fax:* 617-521-3035
*E-mail:* bookawards@massbook.org
*Web Site:* www.massbook.org
*Key Personnel*
Exec Dir: Sharon Shaloo *E-mail:* massbook@simmons.edu
Established: 2000
The MassBooks recognize significant achievements by Massachusetts writers in fiction, nonfiction, poetry & children's literature for the previous publishing year. Also awarded, the MA Book medal for creative publishing, programming or lifetime achievement in the Massachusetts book community. Visit web site for details.
Other Sponsor(s): Massachusetts Board of Library Commissioners; Massachusetts Cultural Council; Massachusetts Library Association; Massachusetts Library System; Simmons College Graduate School of Library & Information Science

**Masters Literary Awards**
Titan Press

PO Box 17897, Encino, CA 91416-7897
*Tel:* 818-377-4006
*E-mail:* titan91416@yahoo.com
*Web Site:* www.calwriterssfu.com
*Key Personnel*
Mng Ed: Stefanya Wilson
Established: 1981
Annual awards (including 4 quarterly prizes) for fiction, poetry & song lyrics & nonfiction. All quality published & unpublished mss are eligible, submitted from double-spaced photocopies or tearsheets. Guidelines available with No 10 SASE.
Award: $1,000 Grand Prize, 4 quarterly prizes of Honorable Mention
Closing Date: Submissions received prior to any award date are eligible for the subsequent award
Presented: Titan Press, March 15, June 15, Aug 15, Dec 15

**Matt Cohen Prize: In Celebration of a Writing Life**
The Writers' Trust of Canada
90 Richmond St E, Suite 200, Toronto, ON M5C 1P1, Canada
*Tel:* 416-504-8222 *Toll Free Tel:* 877-906-6548 *Fax:* 416-504-9090
*E-mail:* info@writerstrust.com
*Web Site:* www.writerstrust.com
*Key Personnel*
Exec Dir: Mary Osbourne *Tel:* 416-504-8222 ext 244
Established: 2001
Recognizes a lifetime of distinguished work by a Canadian writer, working in either poetry or prose, in either French or English. Generously sponsored by anonymous donors.
Award: $20,000
Presented: The Writers' Trust Awards, Toronto, ON, CN, Annually in Nov

**Mature Women Scholarship Grant - Art/Letters/Music**
National League of American Pen Women
c/o National Pen Women-Scholarship, Pen Arts Bldg, 1300 17 St NW, Washington, DC 20036-1973
*Tel:* 202-785-1997 *Fax:* 202-452-8868
*E-mail:* contact@nlapw.org
*Web Site:* www.nlapw.org
*Key Personnel*
Natl Scholarship Chair: Mary B Barrer
Established: 1976
Awarded biennially (even-numbered years). Judges in each category (art, letters, music) change for each award every award year. Must send SASE with inquiry for requirements. Include an $8 fee payable to NLAPW with entry.
Award: $1,000 (1st place), $750 (2nd place), $500 (3rd Place); $150 (Photography Award), $150 (Water Media Award), $100 (Jean Baber Memorial Art Fund)
Closing Date: Oct 1 of odd-numbered years
Presented: NLAPW Convention, Biennially in April (even-numbered years); March 15, mail notification

**Maxim Mazumdar New Play Competition**
Alleyway Theatre
One Curtain Up Alley, Buffalo, NY 14202-1911
*Tel:* 716-852-2600
*E-mail:* publicrelations@alleyway.com
*Web Site:* alleyway.com
*Key Personnel*
Founder, Alleyway Theatre: Neal Radice
Literary Mgr: Joyce Stilson *Tel:* 716-852-2600 ext 202 *E-mail:* jstilson@rocketmail.com
Contest limited to one submission per author, per year, per category. Entry must be a previously unproduced full-length (not less than 90 minutes) play or musical of any style, requiring no more than 8 performers & able to be presented on a unit or simple set, musicals must include CD, sheet music not necessary. One acts must be less than 25 minutes & no more than five actors. Entries will not be returned without SASE. Entry fee: $25.
Award: Cash & premiere production of entry at Alleyway Theatre
Closing Date: Annually, July 1

**Janet B McCabe Poetry Prize**
Ruminate Magazine
140 N Roosevelt Ave, Collins, CO 80521
*Tel:* 970-449-2726
*E-mail:* editor@ruminatemagazine.org
*Web Site:* www.ruminatemagazine.com
*Key Personnel*
Ed-in-Chief: Brianna Van Dyke
Sr Ed: Amy Lowe
Assoc Ed: Stephanie Lovegrove; Stefani Rossi
All submissions must be previously unpublished & submitted via online submission form. Up to 2 poems per entry, no longer than 40 lines each. Entry fee $18.
Award: $1,500 & publication in Fall issue (1st place), $500 & pubn (2nd place)
Closing Date: Annually, May 1

**John H McGinnis Memorial Award**
Southwest Review
6404 Robert Hyer Lane, Rm 307, Dallas, TX 75275-0374
Mailing Address: PO Box 750374, Dallas, TX 75275-0374
*Fax:* 214-768-1408
*E-mail:* swr@mail.smu.edu
*Web Site:* www.smu.edu/southwestreview
*Key Personnel*
Ed-in-Chief: Willard Spiegelman
Sr Ed: Jennifer Cranfill *Tel:* 214-768-1036
Established: 1960
For the best essay & story appearing in the Southwest Review during the preceding year.
Award: $500 (2-4 awards)
Presented: Annually in Jan

**Harold W McGraw Jr - Prize in Education**
McGraw-Hill Financial
1221 Avenue of the Americas, 47th fl, New York, NY 10020-1095
*Tel:* 212-904-2000; 212-512-2000 *Fax:* 212-512-3611
*Web Site:* www.mhfi.com
*Key Personnel*
Communs Assoc: Jo Ann Craig
Established: 1988
Honors three individuals whose accomplishments, programs & ideas can serve as effective models for the education of future generations.
Award: $50,000 & bronze sculpture award
Closing Date: Feb
Presented: Usually at New York Public Library, End of Sept

**McKnight Advancement Grants**
The Playwrights' Center
2301 Franklin Ave E, Minneapolis, MN 55406-1099
*Tel:* 612-332-7481 *Fax:* 612-332-6037
*E-mail:* info@pwcenter.org
*Web Site:* www.pwcenter.org
*Key Personnel*
Producing Artistic Dir: Jeremy Cohen *Tel:* 612-332-7481 ext 113 *E-mail:* jeremyc@pwcenter.org
Artistic Administrator: Amanda Robbins-Butcher *Tel:* 612-332-7481 ext 115 *E-mail:* amandar@pwcenter.org
Established: 1990
Grants to recognize mid-career playwrights whose work demonstrates exceptional artistic merit & potential. Playwright's primary residence must be in the state of Minnesota. Applicant must have had a minimum of one work fully produced by a professional theater at the time of application.
Award: Grants of $25,000 each
Presented: Annually in May

**McKnight Artist Fellowship for Writers**
The Loft Literary Center
Open Book, Suite 200, 1011 Washington Ave S, Minneapolis, MN 55415
*Tel:* 612-215-2575 *Fax:* 612-215-2576
*E-mail:* loft@loft.org
*Web Site:* www.loft.org
*Key Personnel*
Prog Dir: Jerod Santek *Tel:* 612-215-2586 *E-mail:* jsantek@loft.org
Established: 1982
Contest for Minnesota residents only.
Award: Four $25,000 awards which alternate annually between poetry & creative prose; one $25,000 award in children's literature which alternates annually between writing for children 8 & under & older children
Closing Date: Annually in late Fall
Presented: The Loft, Annually in Spring

**McKnight National Residency & Commission**
The Playwrights' Center
2301 Franklin Ave E, Minneapolis, MN 55406-1099
*Tel:* 612-332-7481 *Fax:* 612-332-6037
*E-mail:* info@pwcenter.org
*Web Site:* www.pwcenter.org
*Key Personnel*
Producing Artistic Dir: Jeremy Cohen *Tel:* 612-332-7481 ext 113 *E-mail:* jeremyc@pwcenter.org
Artistic Administrator: Amanda Robbins-Butcher *Tel:* 612-332-7481 ext 115 *E-mail:* amandar@pwcenter.org
Established: 1982
Playwrights whose work has made a significant impact on the contemporary theater. Applicant must be a US citizen or permanent resident & must have had a minimum of two different works fully produced by professional theaters. Call or check web site for application information & deadline guidelines. Minnesota-based playwrights are not eligible for the award. Proposals for the Residency & Commission must be agent/professional only. Send writers resume, a 2- or 3-page proposal & a full-length play script.
Award: $12,500
Closing Date: See web site for details

**McLaren Memorial Comedy Play Writing Competition**
Midland Community Theatre
2000 W Wadley Ave, Midland, TX 79705
*Tel:* 432-682-2544
*E-mail:* tracy@mctmidland.org
*Web Site:* www.mctmidland.org
*Key Personnel*
Prodn Mgr: Tracy Alexander *E-mail:* tracy@mctmidland.org
Established: 1990
All entries must be comedies for adults, teens, or children; musical comedies no longer accepted. Requirements: full-length play (70-90 minutes); one-act plays no longer accepted. See web site for competition guidelines & required brochure with entry form. Submissions accepted beginning Jan 1. Attn: McLaren Competition Chairman.
Closing Date: Annually, Feb 28
Presented: McLaren Festival, Annually in early Fall

**McLemore Prize**
Mississippi Historical Society

Affiliate of Mississippi Department of Archives & History
PO Box 571, Jackson, MS 39205-0571
*Tel:* 601-576-6850 *Fax:* 601-576-6975
*E-mail:* mhs@mdah.state.ms.us
*Web Site:* www.mdah.state.ms.us
*Key Personnel*
Pres: Charles Sullivan
VP: Ann Simmons
Secy & Treas, Historical Society: Elbert Hilliard
Public Info: Stephenie Morrisey
*E-mail:* morrisey@mdah.state.ms.us
Established: 1980
For distinguished scholarly book on a topic in Mississippi history or biography.
Award: $700
Closing Date: Annually, Nov 1
Presented: Annual meeting, Annually, 1st weekend in March

**John McMenemy Prize**
Canadian Political Science Association
260 rue Dalhousie St, Suite 204, Ottawa, ON K1N 7E4, Canada
*Tel:* 613-562-1202 *Fax:* 613-241-0019
*E-mail:* cpsa-acsp@cpsa-acsp.ca
*Web Site:* www.cpsa-acsp.ca
*Key Personnel*
Administrator: Michelle Hopkins
Established: 2000
To the author or authors of the best article in English or French, published in volume 46 of the "Canadian Journal of Political Science".
Other Sponsor(s): Societe Quebecoise de Science Politique
Award: Certificate of Award & memberships in the Canadian Political Science Association & the Societe Quebecoise de Science Politique
Presented: Annual Conference, Annually in May or June

**Medal of Honor for Literature**
National Arts Club
15 Gramercy Park S, New York, NY 10003
*E-mail:* literary@thenationalartsclub.org
*Web Site:* www.nationalartsclub.org
*Key Personnel*
Chair, Literary Comm: Cherry Provost
Established: 1967
Presented for a body of work of literary excellence; nominations within the committee only & awarded by the Board of Governors.
Award: Gold medal
Presented: Gala Black Tie Dinner, At discretion of recipient

**Lucille Medwick Memorial Award**
Poetry Society of America (PSA)
15 Gramercy Park S, New York, NY 10003
*Tel:* 212-254-9628 *Fax:* 212-673-2352
*Web Site:* www.poetrysociety.org
*Key Personnel*
Pres: Ruth Kaplan
Exec Dir: Alice Quinn
Mng Dir & Awards Coord: Brett Fletcher Lauer
*E-mail:* brett@poetrysociety.org
Progs Dir: Darrel Alejandro Holnes
Established: 1974
For an original poem in any form on a humanitarian theme, not to exceed 100 lines. Translations are ineligible. Open to Society members only. Send No 10 SASE for more information, or visit web site.
Award: $500
Closing Date: Annually, Oct-Dec
Presented: Annual Awards Ceremony, New York, NY, Annually in Spring

**Melcher Book Award**
Unitarian Universalist Association
25 Beacon St, Boston, MA 02108-2800
*Tel:* 617-948-4303 *Fax:* 617-367-3237
*E-mail:* info@uua.org
*Web Site:* www.uua.org
*Key Personnel*
Asst to EVP: Nancy Lawrence
*E-mail:* nlawrence@uua.org
Established: 1964
Given to a book making significant contribution to liberal religious thought.
Award: $1,000 & certificate
Closing Date: Dec 31
Presented: Boston, MA, Oct

**Frederic G Melcher Scholarship**
Association for Library Service to Children (ALSC)
Division of American Library Association (ALA)
50 E Huron St, Chicago, IL 60611-2795
*Tel:* 312-280-2163 *Toll Free Tel:* 800-545-2433
*Fax:* 312-440-9374
*E-mail:* alsc@ala.org
*Web Site:* www.ala.org/alsc
*Key Personnel*
Exec Dir: Aimee Strittmatter *Tel:* 312-280-2162
*E-mail:* astrittmatter@ala.org
Awards Coord: Caroline Jewell
*E-mail:* alscawards@ala.org
Prog Coord: Marsha P Burgess
*E-mail:* mburgess@ala.org
Established: 1956
To students entering the field of library service for graduate work in an ALA-accredited program & majoring in library service to children.
Award: $6,000 - 2 scholarships per yr
Closing Date: Annually, March 1
Presented: ALA Annual Conference, Annually in June

**The David Nathan Meyerson Prize for Fiction**
Southwest Review
6404 Robert Hyer Lane, Rm 307, Dallas, TX 75275-0374
Mailing Address: PO Box 750374, Dallas, TX 75275-0374
*Fax:* 214-768-1408
*E-mail:* swr@mail.smu.edu
*Web Site:* www.smu.edu/southwestreview
*Key Personnel*
Ed-in-Chief: Willard Spiegelman
Sr Ed: Jennifer Cranfill *Tel:* 214-768-1036
Open to writers who have not yet published a book of fiction, either a novel or collection of stories. Submissions must be no longer than 8,000 words. A $25 reading fee must accompany each submission.
Award: $1,000 & publication in *Southwest Review*
Closing Date: Annually, May 1
Presented: Annually in Fall

**Kenneth W Mildenberger Prize**
Modern Language Association of America (MLA)
26 Broadway, 3rd fl, New York, NY 10004-1789
SAN: 202-6422
*Tel:* 646-576-5141 *Fax:* 646-458-0030
*E-mail:* awards@mla.org
*Web Site:* www.mla.org
*Key Personnel*
Coord, Book Prizes: Annie M Reiser
*E-mail:* areiser@mla.org
Established: 1980
Biennial award for a work in the field of language, culture, literacy or literature with strong application to the teaching of languages other than English. For consideration submit 4 copies. Authors need not be members of the MLA. Awarded for a book published in 2013 or 2014.
Award: Cash award, certificate & one year association membership
Closing Date: May 1, 2015
Presented: MLA Convention, Jan 2016

**Milkweed National Fiction Prize**
Milkweed Editions
1011 Washington Ave S, Suite 300, Minneapolis, MN 55415-1246
*Tel:* 612-332-3192 *Toll Free Tel:* 800-520-6455
*Fax:* 612-215-2550
*E-mail:* submissions@milkweed.org
*Web Site:* www.milkweed.org
*Key Personnel*
CEO & Publr: Daniel Slager
Sales & Mktg Dir: Sue Ostfield
Content Mgr: Anna Weggel
Devt Mgr: Kate Strickland
Ed & Prog Mgr: Patrick Thomas
*E-mail:* patrick_thomas@milkweed.org
Assoc Ed: Allison Wigen
Publicist: Meredith Kessler
Established: 1988
Annual award for an unpublished novel or collection of short stories &/or one or more novellas. Awarded to the best work of fiction Milkweed accepts for publication during each calendar year by a writer not previously published by Milkweed Editions. Writers must request complete guidelines before submitting ms (send SASE or visit www. milkweed.org). Open year-round.
Award: $5,000 advance against royalties
Closing Date: Annually, Jan-March & July & Sept

**Mill Mountain Theatre**
Center in the Square, 2nd fl, One Market Sq SE, Roanoke, VA 24011-1437
*Tel:* 540-224-1250 (ext 7307)
*Web Site:* www.millmountain.org
*Key Personnel*
Dir, Devt: Paul M Mylott
Mng Dir & Dir Educ: Ginger Poole *Tel:* 540-224-1250 ext 7308
Prodn Mgr: Shelby Love
Established: 1964
Closing Date: Year-round
Presented: CenterPieces, Mill Mountain Theatre, Monthly exc Sept

**Isabel Miller Young Writers Award**
Writers Guild of Alberta
11759 Groat Rd, Edmonton, AB T5M 3K6, Canada
*Tel:* 780-422-8174 *Toll Free Tel:* 800-665-5354 (AB only) *Fax:* 780-422-2663 (attn WGA)
*E-mail:* mail@writersguild.ab.ca
*Web Site:* www.writersguild.ab.ca
*Key Personnel*
Exec Dir: Carol Holmes *E-mail:* cholmes@writersguild.ab.ca
Communs & Partnerships Coord: Nicholas Mather *E-mail:* nmather@writersguild.ab.ca
Memb Servs Coord: Giorgia Severini
Progs Coord: Nichole Quiring
*E-mail:* programs@writersguild.ab.ca
Cash prize or partial scholarship to attend Youth-Write, the WGA's summer writing camp for kids.
*Branch Office(s)*
Lord Denning House, 509 20 Ave SW, Calgary, AB T2S 0E7, Canada, Prog Coord: Samantha Warwick *Tel:* 403-265-2226
*E-mail:* swarwick@writersguild.ab.ca

**Milner Award**
Friends of the Atlanta-Fulton Public Library
One Margaret Mitchell Sq NW, Atlanta, GA 30303
*Tel:* 770-235-3645
*E-mail:* info@themilneraward.org
*Web Site:* www.themilneraward.org
*Key Personnel*
Exec Dir: Becky Hamilton
Established: 1983

For living American authors of children's books voted on by the children of Atlanta. No application process.
Other Sponsor(s): Milner Award Committee
Award: An honorarium & a glass sculpture (inkwell & pen) by Hans Frabel
Closing Date: Second week of Nov
Presented: Atlanta, GA

**Milton Dorfman Poetry Prize**
Rome Art & Community Center
308 W Bloomfield St, Rome, NY 13440
*Tel:* 315-336-1040 *Fax:* 315-336-1090
*E-mail:* racc2@cnymail.com
*Web Site:* www.romeart.org
*Key Personnel*
Exec Dir: Lauren Marie Getek
NY state residents only. Application fee per poem: $10.
Award: $150 (1st prize), $75 (2nd prize), $50 (3rd prize)
Closing Date: Aug 31
Presented: Rome Art & Community Center, Rome, NY

**Mississippi Review Prize**
University of Southern Mississippi Dept of English
118 College Dr, Box 5144, Hattiesburg, MS 39406-0001
*E-mail:* msreview@usm.edu
*Web Site:* www.usm.edu/english/mississippiireview.html
*Key Personnel*
Ed-in-Chief: Andrew Milward
Fiction & poetry prize open to all writers in English except current or former students or employees of the University of Southern Mississippi. Entry fee $15.
Award: Fiction & Poetry: $1,000 each & pubn in the print issue of *Mississippi Review* next Spring
Closing Date: Annually, Dec 1
Presented: Annually in May

**W O Mitchell Book Prize**, see The City of Calgary W O Mitchell Book Prize

**MLA Prize for a Bibliography, Archive or Digital Project**
Modern Language Association of America (MLA)
26 Broadway, 3rd fl, New York, NY 10004-1789
SAN: 202-6422
*Tel:* 646-576-5141 *Fax:* 646-458-0030
*E-mail:* awards@mla.org
*Web Site:* www.mla.org
*Key Personnel*
Coord, Book Prizes: Annie M Reiser *E-mail:* areiser@mla.org
Established: 1998
Awarded biennually for enumerative & descriptive bibliography, archive or digital project in 2 years prior to competition deadline. Criteria for determining excellence include evidence of analytical rigor, meticulous scholarship, intellectual creativity & subject range & depth. Editors need not be members of MLA. For consideration, submit 4 copies.
Award: Cash award, certificate & 1 year association membership
Closing Date: May 1, 2014
Presented: MLA Convention, Jan 2015

**MLA Prize for a First Book**
Modern Language Association of America (MLA)
26 Broadway, 3rd fl, New York, NY 10004-1789
SAN: 202-6422
*Tel:* 646-576-5141 *Fax:* 646-458-0030
*E-mail:* awards@mla.org
*Web Site:* www.mla.org
*Key Personnel*
Coord, Book Prizes: Annie M Reiser *E-mail:* areiser@mla.org
Awarded annually for an outstanding scholarly work published in year prior to competition as the first book-length publication by a current member of the MLA. For consideration, submit 6 copies.
Award: Cash award & certificate
Closing Date: April 1
Presented: MLA Convention, Jan

**MLA Prize for a Scholarly Edition**
Modern Language Association of America (MLA)
26 Broadway, 3rd fl, New York, NY 10004-1789
SAN: 202-6422
*Tel:* 646-576-5141 *Fax:* 646-458-0030
*E-mail:* awards@mla.org
*Web Site:* www.mla.org
*Key Personnel*
Coord, Book Prizes: Annie M Reiser *E-mail:* areiser@mla.org
Established: 1995
Biennial prize offered in odd-numbered years. Committee solicits submissions of editions published in previous biennium. A multivolume edition is eligible if at least one volume has been published during that period. The editor need not be a member of the MLA. Edition should be based on an examination of all available relevant textual sources; text should be accompanied by appropriate textual & other historical contextual information; the edition should exhibit the highest standards of accuracy in the presentation of its text & apparatus, which should be presented as accessibly & elegantly as possible. For consideration, submit 4 copies with letter.
Award: Cash award, certificate & one year membership in the association
Closing Date: May 1, 2015
Presented: MLA Convention, Jan 2016

**MLA Prize for Independent Scholars**
Modern Language Association of America (MLA)
26 Broadway, 3rd fl, New York, NY 10004-1789
SAN: 202-6422
*Tel:* 646-576-5141 *Fax:* 646-458-0030
*E-mail:* awards@mla.org
*Web Site:* www.mla.org
*Key Personnel*
Coord, Book Prizes: Annie M Reiser *E-mail:* areiser@mla.org
Established: 1983
Offered as a biennial prize with competitions in even numbered years for a distinguished scholarly book in the field of English or another modern language written by an independent scholar published in 2012 or 2013. Author enrolled in a program leading to an academic degree or holding a tenured, tenure-accruing, or tenure-track position in post-secondary education at the time of publication is not eligible. For consideration, submit 6 copies & application form.
Award: Cash award, certificate & one year association membership
Closing Date: May 1, 2014
Presented: MLA Convention, Jan 2015

**MLA Prize in United States Latina & Latino & Chicano & Chicano Literary & Cultural Studies**
Modern Language Association of America (MLA)
26 Broadway, 3rd fl, New York, NY 10004-1789
SAN: 202-6422
*Tel:* 646-576-5141 *Fax:* 646-458-0030
*E-mail:* awards@mla.org
*Web Site:* www.mla.org
*Key Personnel*
Coord, Book Prizes: Annie M Reiser *E-mail:* areiser@mla.org
Established: 2002
Biennial prize offered in odd-numbered years for an outstanding scholarly work published in the 2 years prior to competition deadline in the fields of Latina/Latino or Chicana/Chicano literary or cultural studies by a current member of the MLA. For consideration, submit 4 copies.
Award: Cash award, certificate & 1 year association membership
Closing Date: May 1, 2015
Presented: MLA Convention, Jan 2016

**Lucy Maud Montgomery Literature for Children Prize**
Prince Edward Island Writers' Guild
115 Richmond St, Charlottetown, PE C1A 1H7, Canada
*Tel:* 902-368-4410 *Toll Free Tel:* 888-734-2784 *Fax:* 902-368-4418
*E-mail:* peiwritersguild@gmail.com
*Web Site:* www.peiwritersguild.com
*Key Personnel*
Exec Dir: Darrin White *Tel:* 902-368-6176 *E-mail:* dwhite@peica.ca
The ms must be a story written for children 5 to 12 yrs of age. Maximum length 60 pages. May submit as many entries as they wish. Entry fee for each submission is $20. The work must be original & unpublished. Entry shall be typewritten & double spaced on one side of page only. Illustration may be submitted with the story. Contest for Prince Edward Island residents only. Call or e-mail for further information.
Award: $400 (1st prize), $200 (2nd prize), $100 (3rd prize)

**Cenie H Moon Prize**
The Poetry Society of Virginia
1194 Hume Rd, Hume, VA 22639-1806
*E-mail:* poetryinva@aol.com
*Web Site:* www.poetrysocietyofvirginia.org
*Key Personnel*
Pres: Judith K Bragg *E-mail:* musicsavy45@yahoo.com
Adult Contest Chair: Patsy Anne Bickerstaff *E-mail:* granypatsy@yahoo.com; Guy Terrell *E-mail:* ggterr@infionline.net
All entries must be in English, original & unpublished. Submit 2 copies of each poem, each having the category name & number on top left of page. Only one poem per category; entries will not be returned. Subject: woman or women; 48 line limit; any form. Entry fee: $4 nonmembs.
Award: $50 (1st prize), $30 (2nd prize), $20 (3rd prize)
Closing Date: Jan 19
Presented: Annual PSV Awards Luncheon, Richmond, VA, April

**Moonbeam Children's Book Awards**
Independent Publisher Online
Division of Jenkins Group Inc
1129 Woodmere Ave, Suite B, Traverse City, MI 49686
*Tel:* 231-933-0445 *Toll Free Tel:* 800-706-4636 *Fax:* 231-933-0448
*E-mail:* info@axiomawards.com
*Web Site:* www.moonbeamawards.com
*Key Personnel*
CEO: Jerrold R Jenkins *E-mail:* jrj@bookpublishing.com
Pres: James Kalajian *Tel:* 800-706-4636 ext 1006 *E-mail:* jjk@bookpublishing.com
Mng Ed & Awards Dir: Jim Barnes *Tel:* 800-706-4636 ext 1011 *E-mail:* jimb@bookpublishing.com
Awards Coord: Amy Shamroe
Established: 2007

Annual award celebrating youthful curiosity, discovery & learning through books & reading. Recognizes the best children's books published each year for the North American market. Authors, illustrators, publishers & self-publishers of children's books intended for the North American market may enter.
Other Sponsor(s): Jenkins Group Inc
Award: Gold medal (1st place), silver medal (2nd place) & bronze medal (3rd place)
Closing Date: Annually in Aug
Presented: Traverse City Children's Book Festival, Annually in Nov

**Jenny McKean Moore Writer-in-Washington**
George Washington University
English Dept, Rome Hall, 801 22 St NW, Suite 760, Washington, DC 20052
*Tel:* 202-994-6180 *Fax:* 202-994-7915
*E-mail:* engldept@gwu.edu
*Web Site:* www.gwu.edu/~english; departments.columbian.gwu.edu/english/openings (position details)
*Key Personnel*
Dir, Creative Writing: Lisa Page
*E-mail:* lpageinc@aol.com
Established: 1976
To be considered, applications must be made by letter indicating publications, teaching experience & a selection of published work. Genre alternates from year to year. Applications accepted between Oct 1 & Nov 1. Consult AWP job list for advertisement specifying genre.
Award: One year teaching position for approximately $58,000 plus benefits
Closing Date: Annually, Nov 1

**Ottoline Morrell Prize**
Formerly Motherwell Prize
Fence Books
University at Albany, Science Library 320, 1400 Washington Ave, Albany, NY 12222
*Tel:* 518-591-8162
*E-mail:* fence.fencebooks@gmail.com
*Web Site:* www.fenceportal.org
*Key Personnel*
Publr & Ed: Rebecca Wolff
*E-mail:* rebeccafence@gmail.com
Mng Ed: Rob Arnold *E-mail:* robfence@gmail.com
Established: 2013
For a book of poems by a woman writing in English who has previously published one or more books of poetry.
Award: Cash prize & publication

**William Morris Society in the United States Fellowships**
William Morris Society in the United States
PO Box 53263, Washington, DC 20009
*E-mail:* us@morrissociety.org
*Web Site:* www.morrissociety.org
*Key Personnel*
Pres: Margaretta S Frederick
Secy & Treas: Mark Samuels Lasner
Established: 1996
For scholarly or creative projects related to William Morris (1834-96); given to US citizens or permanent residents.
Award: Up to $1,000
Closing Date: Annually, Dec 1

**George L Mosse Prize**
American Historical Association
400 "A" St SE, Washington, DC 20003-3889
*Tel:* 202-544-2422 *Fax:* 202-544-8307
*E-mail:* awards@historians.org
*Web Site:* www.historians.org
Established: 2001
For an outstanding major work of extraordinary scholarly distinction, creativity & originality in the intellectual & cultural history of Europe since the Renaissance. Only books of a high scholarly distinction should be submitted. Research accuracy, originality & literary merit are important selection factors. Books published in 2013 are eligible. Along with an application form, applicants must mail a copy of their book to each of the prize committee members who will be posted on our web site as the prize deadline approaches. All updated info on web site.
Award: Cash prize
Closing Date: May 16, 2014 (postmark)
Presented: AHA Annual Meeting

**Most Significant Scholarly Book Award**
Texas Institute of Letters (TIL)
PO Box 609, Round Rock, TX 78680
*Tel:* 512-683-5640
*E-mail:* tilsecretary@yahoo.com
*Web Site:* www.texasinstituteofletters.org
*Key Personnel*
Pres: W K Stratton
VP: Andres Tijerina
Treas: James Hoggard
Secy: Jan Reid
Recording Secy: Betty Wiesepape
Annual award for the most useful & informative scholarly book contributing to general knowledge, by a Texan or about Texas. See web site for guidelines.
Other Sponsor(s): Friends of the Dallas Public Library
Award: $2,500
Closing Date: Annually in Jan
Presented: TIL Awards Banquet, Annually in Spring

**Motherwell Prize**, see Ottoline Morrell Prize

**Frank Luther Mott-Kappa Tau Alpha Research Award**
Kappa Tau Alpha
University of Missouri, School of Journalism, 76 Gannett Hall, Columbia, MO 65211-1200
*Tel:* 573-882-7685 *Fax:* 573-884-1720
*E-mail:* umcjourkta@missouri.edu
*Web Site:* www.kapataualpha.org
*Key Personnel*
Exec Dir: Keith P Sanders, PhD
Established: 1944
For the best research for books in journalism, exclusive of textbooks, published in the previous year.
Award: $1,000 & plaque (1st prize)
Closing Date: Dec (see web site)
Presented: Annually in Aug

**Sheila Margaret Motton Prize**
New England Poetry Club
2 Farrar St, Cambridge, MA 02138
Mailing Address: PO Box 190076, Boston, MA 02119
*Tel:* 617-744-6034
*E-mail:* contests@nepoetryclub.org
*Web Site:* www.nepoetryclub.org
*Key Personnel*
Pres: Diana Der-Hovanessian
VP: Sally Cragin; Daniel Tobin
Contest Chair: Nazaleem Smith
For a book of poems published in the last 2 years. Send 2 copies of the book with $5 handling fee for nonmembs.
Award: $500
Closing Date: Annually, May 31
Presented: Public Library, Cambridge, MA, Annually in Autumn

**MPA Midwest Publishing Award Show**
Formerly Chicago Book Clinic Midwest Book & Media Show
Midwest Publishing Association (MPA)
310 W Lake St, Suite 111, Elmhurst, IL 60126
*Tel:* 630-833-4220 *Fax:* 630-563-9181
*E-mail:* info@midwestpublish.org
*Web Site:* www.midwestpublish.org
*Key Personnel*
Exec Dir: Kimberly LaBounty
Established: 1949
Juried Show; 100 plus books, journals, magazines & ebooks selected each year. The goal is to demonstrate the outstanding quality of publishing in the midwest & recognize the importance of books or book design & multimedia in our society.
Award: Certificates of Award, photo & listing in show catalog & plaques
Closing Date: Varies
Presented: Downtown Chicago, 2nd Thursday in Oct

**Erika Mumford Prize**
New England Poetry Club
2 Farrar St, Cambridge, MA 02138
Mailing Address: PO Box 190076, Boston, MA 02119
*Tel:* 617-744-6034
*E-mail:* contests@nepoetryclub.org
*Web Site:* www.nepoetryclub.org
*Key Personnel*
Pres: Diana Der-Hovanessian
VP: Sally Cragin; Daniel Tobin
Contest Chair: Nazaleem Smith
Established: 1988
Contest for a poem about foreign culture or travel. Mark name of contest on envelope. Send poem in duplicate, name of writer on one only.
Award: $250
Closing Date: Annually, May 31
Presented: Public Library, Cambridge, MA, Annually in Autumn

**Municipal Chapter of Toronto IODE Jean Throop Book Award**
IODE Toronto
Division of IODE Canada & IODE Ontario
40 Orchard View Blvd, Suite 219, Toronto, ON M4R 1B9, Canada
*Tel:* 416-925-5078 *Fax:* 416-487-4417
*E-mail:* iodeontario@bellnet.ca
*Web Site:* www.iodeontario.ca
*Key Personnel*
Convenor: Mary K Anderson
Area VP: Margo Mackinnon
Established: 1974
Children's book (Toronto area author or illustrator).
Award: $1,000 & certificate
Closing Date: Annually, Feb 1
Presented: Annually in April

**Mythopoeic Awards**
Mythopoeic Society
Oklahoma State University, 306 Edmon Low Library, Stillwater, OK 74078
*Tel:* 405-744-9773
*E-mail:* awards@mythsoc.org
*Web Site:* www.mythsoc.org
*Key Personnel*
Awards Administrator: David Oberhelman
Established: 1967
Awards (two) honor scholarship in the Inklings (JRR Tolkien, CS Lewis, Charles Williams) & the general fields of myth & fantasy studies; each is given to the author of a book published in the previous three years. The Fantasy Awards (two) for adult & children's literature honor novels or single-author collections in the spirit of the Inklings; each is given to the author of a book published the previous year.
Award: Statuette
Closing Date: Members make nominations Jan-Feb, winners picked by late July (annually)
Presented: Mythcon 43, University of Berkeley, Berkeley, CA, Annually in Aug

**National Awards for Education Reporting**
Education Writers Association (EWA)
3516 Connecticut Ave NW, Washington, DC 20008-2401
*Tel:* 202-452-9830 *Fax:* 202-452-9837
*E-mail:* ewa@ewa.org
*Web Site:* www.ewa.org
*Key Personnel*
Exec Dir: Caroline Hendrie *E-mail:* chendrie@ewa.org
Prodr: Glen Baity
Established: 1960
Best education reporting in print & broadcast media.
Award: Grand prize, 1st prize, 2nd prize, special citation, in 19 categories; plaques & certificates
Closing Date: Annually in Jan
Presented: EWA National Seminar, Annually in Spring

**National Book Awards**
National Book Foundation
90 Broad St, Suite 604, New York, NY 10004
*Tel:* 212-685-0261 *Fax:* 212-213-6570
*E-mail:* nationalbook@nationalbook.org
*Web Site:* www.nationalbook.org
*Key Personnel*
Exec Dir: Harold Augerbraun
Dir, Technol: Meredith Andrews
Dir, Mktg & Spec Projs: Sherrie Young
Dir, Progs: Leslie Shipman
Mktg Media Mgr: Katie McDonough
Prog Mgr: Rebecca Keith
Established: 1950
Living American authors for books in USA, for fiction, nonfiction, poetry; young people's literature.
Award: $10,000 cash & bronze sculpture for winner in each genre
Closing Date: Annually in June
Presented: New York City, NY, Annually in Nov

**The National Business Book Award**
PwC
c/o Freedman & Associates Inc, 121 Richmond St W, Suite 605, Toronto, ON M5H 2K1, Canada
*Tel:* 416-868-4739
*Web Site:* www.nbbaward.com
Established: 1985
Excellence in business writing.
Other Sponsor(s): BMO Financial Group; Globe & Mail
Award: $20,000
Closing Date: Annually in Dec
Presented: Spring/early Summer

**National Endowment for the Humanities, Mellon Foundation & Folger Long-term Fellowships**
Folger Shakespeare Library
c/o Fellowship Committee, 201 E Capitol St SE, Washington, DC 20003
*Tel:* 202-544-4600 *Fax:* 202-544-4623
*E-mail:* institute@folger.edu
*Web Site:* www.folger.edu
*Key Personnel*
Dir: Dr Michael Witmore *Tel:* 202-675-0301
*E-mail:* mwitmore@folger.edu
Fellowship Admin: Carol Brobeck
*E-mail:* cbrobeck@folger.edu
Residential fellowships awarded to advanced scholars who have made substantial contributions in their fields of research & who are pursuing research projects appropriate to the collections of the Folger. Application form supported by four copies (short-term fellowship) or eight copies (long-term fellowship) of the applicant's curriculum vitae, four copies (short-term fellowship) or eight copies (long-term fellowship) of a 1,000-word description of the research project & three letters of recommendation.
Other Sponsor(s): National Endowment for the Humanities
Award: $2,500 per month (short-term fellowship), Mellon Foundations fellowships $50,000 stipend for NEH fellowships are $50,400
Closing Date: Nov 1, long-term fellowship; March 1, short-term fellowship

**National Federation of State Poetry Societies Annual Poetry Contest**
National Federation of State Poetry Societies (NFSPS)
PO Box 7842, Moore, OK 73153
*E-mail:* connpoetry@comcast.net
*Web Site:* www.NFSPS.com
*Key Personnel*
Pres: Russell H Strauss *E-mail:* rstrpoet@cs.com
Contest Chair: Mikki Pennington
Established: 1959
Fifty poetry contests, one for students only; rules & categories change, must have current rules provided on web site.
Other Sponsor(s): Individual states' poetry society as host society
Award: $10-$1,500
Closing Date: Annually March 15 (must not be postmarked before Jan 1)

**National Jewish Book Award-Children's & Young Adult Literature**
Jewish Book Council
520 Eighth Ave, 4th fl, New York, NY 10018
*Tel:* 212-201-2920 *Fax:* 212-532-4952
*E-mail:* jbc@jewishbooks.org
*Web Site:* www.jewishbookcouncil.org
*Key Personnel*
Pres, Bd of Dirs: Lawrence J Krule
Dir: Carolyn Starman Hessel
*E-mail:* carolynhessel@jewishbooks.org
Dir, Web & Pubns: Naomi Firestone-Teeter
Award: Citation & publicity
Closing Date: Annually in Sept
Presented: Center for Jewish History, Annually in March

**National Jewish Book Award-Contemporary Jewish Life & Practice**
Jewish Book Council
520 Eighth Ave, 4th fl, New York, NY 10018
*Tel:* 212-201-2920 *Fax:* 212-532-4952
*E-mail:* jbc@jewishbooks.org
*Web Site:* www.jewishbookcouncil.org
*Key Personnel*
Pres, Bd of Dirs: Lawrence J Krule
Dir: Carolyn Starman Hessel
*E-mail:* carolynhessel@jewishbooks.org
Dir, Web & Pubns: Naomi Firestone-Teeter
Award: Citation & publicity
Closing Date: Annually in Sept
Presented: Center for Jewish History, Annually in March

**National Jewish Book Award-History**
Jewish Book Council
520 Eighth Ave, 4th fl, New York, NY 10018
*Tel:* 212-201-2920 *Fax:* 212-532-4952
*E-mail:* jbc@jewishbooks.org
*Web Site:* www.jewishbookcouncil.org
*Key Personnel*
Pres, Bd of Dirs: Lawrence J Krule
Dir: Carolyn Starman Hessel
*E-mail:* carolynhessel@jewishbooks.org
Dir, Web & Pubns: Naomi Firestone-Teeter
Award: Citation & publicity
Closing Date: Annually in Sept
Presented: Center for Jewish History, Annually in March

**National Jewish Book Award-Illustrated Children's Book**
Jewish Book Council
520 Eighth Ave, 4th fl, New York, NY 10018
*Tel:* 212-201-2920 *Fax:* 212-532-4952
*E-mail:* jbc@jewishbooks.org
*Web Site:* www.jewishbookcouncil.org
*Key Personnel*
Pres, Bd of Dirs: Lawrence J Krule
Dir: Carolyn Starman Hessel
*E-mail:* carolynhessel@jewishbooks.org
Dir, Web & Pubns: Naomi Firestone-Teeter
Award: Citation & publicity
Closing Date: Annually in Sept
Presented: Center for Jewish History, Annually in March

**National Jewish Book Award-Modern Jewish Thought & Experience**
Jewish Book Council
520 Eighth Ave, 4th fl, New York, NY 10018
*Tel:* 212-201-2920 *Fax:* 212-532-4952
*E-mail:* jbc@jewishbooks.org
*Web Site:* www.jewishbookcouncil.org
*Key Personnel*
Pres, Bd of Dirs: Lawrence J Krule
Dir: Carolyn Starman Hessel
*E-mail:* carolynhessel@jewishbooks.org
Dir, Web & Pubns: Naomi Firestone-Teeter
Established: 1950
Award: Citation & publicity
Closing Date: Annually in Sept
Presented: Center for Jewish History, Annually in March

**National Jewish Book Award-Scholarship**
Jewish Book Council
520 Eighth Ave, 4th fl, New York, NY 10018
*Tel:* 212-201-2920 *Fax:* 212-532-4952
*E-mail:* jbc@jewishbooks.org
*Web Site:* www.jewishbookcouncil.org
*Key Personnel*
Pres, Bd of Dirs: Lawrence J Krule
Dir: Carolyn Starman Hessel
*E-mail:* carolynhessel@jewishbooks.org
Dir, Web & Pubns: Naomi Firestone-Teeter
Established: 1950
Closing Date: Annually in Sept
Presented: Center for Jewish History, Annually in March

**National Jewish Book Awards**
Jewish Book Council
520 Eighth Ave, 4th fl, New York, NY 10018
*Tel:* 212-201-2920 *Fax:* 212-532-4952
*E-mail:* jbc@jewishbooks.org
*Web Site:* www.jewishbookcouncil.org
*Key Personnel*
Pres, Bd of Dirs: Lawrence J Krule
Dir: Carolyn Starman Hessel
*E-mail:* carolynhessel@jewishbooks.org
Dir, Web & Pubns: Naomi Firestone-Teeter
Established: 1950
Twenty awards to authors & translators of books of outstanding scholarship & literary merit on Jewish themes for the general, no specialist reader. Writing based on archival material, visual arts, poetry, Jewish family via illustrated children's. Categories: Autobiography, Memoire, Children's Literature, Holocaust, Jewish History, (Gerrard & Ella Berman Award), Jewish Thought (Dorot Foundation Donor), Scholarship, Sephardic Culture (Mimi Frank Award), Jewish Education (Anonymous Donor), General Nonfiction, Fiction & Children's Awards, Eastern European Studies (Ronald Lauder Award), Children's & Young Adult's Books, American Jewish Studies, Women's Studies (Barbara Dobkin Award).
Award: Citation & publicity
Closing Date: Annually in Sept
Presented: Center for Jewish History, Annually in March

**National Magazine Awards**
National Magazine Awards Foundation

425 Adelaide St W, Suite 700, Toronto, ON M5V 3C1, Canada
*Tel:* 416-422-1358 *Fax:* 416-504-0437
*E-mail:* staff@magazine-awards.com
*Web Site:* www.magazine-awards.com
*Key Personnel*
Mng Dir: Barbara Gould *E-mail:* barbara-gould@rogers.com
Established: 1977
Honors excellence in Canadian magazine journalism with awards in 40 categories.
Award: $1000 Gold Award (1st place), $500 Silver Award (2nd place) in each category
Closing Date: Mid Jan annually
Presented: Early June

**National One-Act Playwriting Competition**
Little Theatre of Alexandria
600 Wolfe St, Alexandria, VA 22314
*Tel:* 703-683-5778 *Fax:* 703-683-1378
*E-mail:* asklta@thelittletheatre.com
*Web Site:* www.thelittletheatre.com
*Key Personnel*
Chmn, One-Act: Nancy L Owens *Tel:* 703-313-0614 *E-mail:* nancy.owens@gsa.gov
Established: 1978
One-Act Playwriting Competition. No more than two plays. Entries must be unpublished & unproduced as of date of entry. Entry fee: $20 per play.
Award: $350 (1st prize), $250 (2nd prize), $150 (3rd prize), usually stage readings of top plays
Closing Date: Annually, Oct 31

**National Outdoor Book Awards**
National Outdoor Book Awards Foundation Inc
921 S Eighth Ave, Stop 8128, Pocatello, ID 83209-8128
*Tel:* 208-282-3912 *Fax:* 208-282-2127
*Web Site:* www.noba-web.org
*Key Personnel*
Chair: Ron Watters *E-mail:* wattron@isu.edu
Established: 1995
Award recognizing the work of outstanding writers & publishers of outdoor books. Categories include history/biography, outdoor literature, instructional texts, outdoor adventure guides, nature guides, children's books, design/artistic merit & nature & environment. Guidelines on the web site.
Other Sponsor(s): Association of Outdoor Recreation & Education; National Outdoor Book Awards Foundation
Closing Date: Annually in Aug
Presented: International Conference on Outdoor Recreation & Education (Depending on the year, held in different locations in the US & Canada), Annually in early Nov

**National Poetry Series Open Competition**
National Poetry Series
57 Mountain Ave, Princeton, NJ 08540
*Tel:* 609-430-0999 *Fax:* 609-430-9933
*Web Site:* www.pw.org/content/open_competition
*Key Personnel*
Coord: Stephanie Stio
Established: 1978
For book-length typed ms of poetry, previously unpublished in book form; $30 entrance fee, payable to National Poetry Series; see web site for guidelines.
Award: Five books to be published by trade publishers, small presses & university publishers. $1,000 cash award for each winner
Closing Date: Annually, Jan 1-Feb 15 (postmark)
Presented: Annually in the Summer

**National Ten-Minute Play Contest**
Actors Theatre of Louisville
316 W Main St, Louisville, KY 40202-4218
*Tel:* 502-584-1265
*Web Site:* www.actorstheatre.org/participate/submit-a-play
*Key Personnel*
Literary Mgr: Sarah Lunnie
National ten-minute play contest. Submssion date begins Sept 1. Accept the first 500 plays submitted.
Award: $1,000 & possible production at Actors Theatre of Louisville
Closing Date: Annually, Nov 1

**National Translation Award**
American Literary Translators Association (ALTA)
Affiliate of University of Texas Dallas
c/o The University of Texas at Dallas, 800 W Campbell Rd, Mail Sta JO51, Richardson, TX 75080-3021
*Tel:* 972-883-2093 *Fax:* 972-883-6303
*Web Site:* www.utdallas.edu/alta/
*Key Personnel*
Admin Asst: Maria Rosa Suarez *Tel:* 972-883-2092 *E-mail:* maria.suarez@utdallas.edu
Established: 1991
Publishers are invited to nominate one book in each category of contemporary fiction, contemporary poetry, contemporary nonfiction & literature of the past. Must be a full-length book or anthology translated from another language into English & must have been published in the previous year. Send four copies of each book; $25 per entry.
Other Sponsor(s): University of Texas at Dallas
Award: $5,000
Closing Date: Annually, March 31
Presented: ALTA Conference, Philadelphia, PA, Annually in Nov

**National Writers Association Novel Contest**
National Writers Association
10940 S Parker Rd, Suite 508, Parker, CO 80134
*Tel:* 303-841-0246
*E-mail:* natlwritersassn@hotmail.com
*Web Site:* www.nationalwriters.com
*Key Personnel*
Exec Dir: Sandy Whelchel *E-mail:* authorsandy@hotmail.com
Established: 1937
Novel contest for unpublished works. Entry fee $35.
Award: $500 (1st prize), $250 (2nd prize), $150 (3rd prize)
Closing Date: Annually, April 1

**Nautilus Awards**
Marilyn McGuire & Associates Inc
378 Bromley Dr, Eastsound, WA 98245
Mailing Address: PO Box 1359, Eastsound, WA 98245
*Tel:* 360-376-2001
*Web Site:* www.nautilusbookawards.com
*Key Personnel*
Founder, Owner & Pres: Marilyn McGuire *E-mail:* marilyn@nautilusbookawards.com
Established: 2001
To recognize authors & titles that make a distinguished literary contribution to spiritual growth, conscious living & positive social change.
Mail book entries to PO Box 1359, Eastsound, WA 98245.
Closing Date: Jan 31

**Naylor, Phyllis Working Writer Fellowship**, see PEN/Phyllis Naylor Working Writer Fellowship

**NEA Literature Fellowships**
National Endowment for the Arts
1100 Pennsylvania Ave NW, Rm 703, Washington, DC 20506
*Tel:* 202-682-5034 (lit fellowships hotline); 202-682-5400; 202-682-5403 *Fax:* 202-682-5609; 202-682-5610
*E-mail:* litfellowships@arts.gov
*Web Site:* www.arts.gov; www.nea.gov
*Key Personnel*
Grants Dir & Contracts Offr: Nicki Jacobs *Tel:* 202-682-5546 *E-mail:* jacobsn@arts.gov
Established: 1967
Given to published writers of poetry, fiction & creative nonfiction; variable number of fellowships, based on available program funds. Applications accepted by genre (prose-odd yrs & poetry-even yrs). Applicants are restricted to applying in one fellowship category only in the same year. Must submit 9 copies as part of the application package. Guidelines available on web site.
Award: $25,000
Closing Date: Annually, March 1
Presented: Notifications to be sent by mail late Dec

**Nelligan Prize for Short Fiction**
Colorado Review
Colorado State Univ, Dept of Eng, Ctr for Literary Publg, 9105 Campus Delivery, Fort Collins, CO 80523-9105
*Tel:* 970-491-5449
*E-mail:* creview@colostate.edu
*Web Site:* nelliganprize.colostate.edu
*Key Personnel*
Dir: Stephanie G'Schwind
Established: 2004
Award to the author of an outstanding short story, previously unpublished. Entry fee $15 per story with no limit on number of entries. Stories must be under 50 pages. Online entry fee $17.
Award: $2,000 & pubn in Fall/Winter issue of *Colorado Review*
Closing Date: Annually, March 10

**Howard Nemerov Sonnet Award**
The Formalist
320 Hunter Dr, Evansville, IN 47711
*Web Site:* theformalist.evansville.edu/home.htm
*Key Personnel*
Dir: William Baer
Annual award given for the best unpublished sonnet (no translations).
Award: $1,000 & publication in *Measure: A Review of Formal Poetry*
Closing Date: Annually, Nov 15

**The Pablo Neruda Prize for Poetry**
Nimrod, The University of Tulsa
Subsidiary of The Nimrod Literary Awards
Nimrod International Journal, 800 S Tucker Dr, Tulsa, OK 74104
*Tel:* 918-631-3080 *Fax:* 918-631-3033
*E-mail:* nimrod@utulsa.edu
*Web Site:* www.utulsa.edu/nimrod
*Key Personnel*
Ed: Francine Ringold, PhD
Mng Ed: Eilis O'Neal
Established: 1978
No previously published works. Omit author's name on mss. Must have a US address by Oct to enter. Works must be in English or translated by the original author. Include a cover sheet containing major title & subtitles of the work, author's name, address & phone along with 3-10 pages of poetry: 1 long poem or several short poems. Mss will not be returned. Retain the rights to publish any contest submission. Works not accepted will be released. Winners & selected finalists will be published. Include SASE & a check for $20 (includes a one-year subscription & processing).
Award: $2,000 (1st prize), $1,000 (2nd prize); published writers receive two copies of the journal; winners will be flown to Tulsa for a conference & banquet
Closing Date: Annually April 30
Presented: Univ of Tulsa, Annually in Oct

**Neustadt International Prize for Literature**
World Literature Today
Affiliate of University of Oklahoma
University of Oklahoma, Suite 110, 630 Parrington Oval, Norman, OK 73019-4033
*Tel:* 405-325-4531 *Fax:* 405-325-7495
*Web Site:* www.worldliteraturetoday.org
*Key Personnel*
Exec Dir: Robert Con Davis-Undiano
*E-mail:* rcdavis@ou.edu
Asst Dir & Ed-in-Chief: Daniel Simon
*E-mail:* dsimon@ou.edu
Art Dir: Merleyn Bell *E-mail:* merleyn@ou.edu
Mng Ed: Michelle Johnson *E-mail:* lmjohnson@ou.edu
Book Reviews Ed: Marla Johnson
*E-mail:* mfjohnson@ou.edu
Mktg Dir, Progs & Devt: Terri Stubblefield
*E-mail:* tdstubb@ou.edu
Circ & Accts Specialist: Kay Blunck
*E-mail:* kblunck@ou.edu
Established: 1969
To a living writer for outstanding literary achievement; prize may honor a single major work or an entire oeuvre; writer's work must be available in a representative sample in English, Spanish or French; writer must accept the award in person in ceremonies at the University of Oklahoma; a special issue of *World Literature Today* is devoted to the laureate; Candidates must be nominated by a jury member.
Award: $50,000 & an eagle feather cast in silver
Presented: University of Oklahoma, Biennially (even-numbered years)

**Allan Nevins Prize**
Society of American Historians (SAH)
Affiliate of American Historical Association
603 Fayerweather, MC 2538, New York, NY 10027
*Tel:* 212-854-6495
*E-mail:* amhistsociety@columbia.edu
*Web Site:* sah.columbia.edu
*Key Personnel*
Pres: David W Blight
VP: David Nasaw
Exec Secy: Andie Tucher
Established: 1961
For the best written doctoral dissertation on an American subject. The dissertation must have been defended or the PhD degree received in the calendar year preceding the award presentation & must not have already been submitted for publication.
Award: $2,000, a certificate & publication by an award sponsoring publication house
Closing Date: Annually, Jan 31
Presented: New York, NY, Annually in May

**New England Book Awards**
New England Independent Booksellers Association Inc (NEIBA)
1955 Massachusetts Ave, Cambridge, MA 02140
*Tel:* 617-547-3642 *Fax:* 617-547-3759
*Web Site:* www.newenglandbooks.org/ne_awards.html
*Key Personnel*
Exec Dir: Steven Fischer *E-mail:* steve@neba.org
Admin Asst: Nan Sorensen *E-mail:* nan@neba.org
Established: 1990
Annual awards for fiction, nonfiction, children's & publishing are chosen by booksellers. Fiction, nonfiction & children's awards are awarded to specific titles either about New England, set in New England or by an author residing in New England, published between Sept 1 & Aug 31.
Award: $250 donation to charity or literary group chosen by each author
Closing Date: Annually in July
Presented: Fall trade show & conference, Annually in Sept/Oct

**New Hampshire Literary Awards**
New Hampshire Writers' Project
2500 N River Rd, Manchester, NH 03106
*Tel:* 603-314-7980 *Fax:* 603-314-7981
*E-mail:* info@nhwritersproject.org
*Web Site:* www.nhwritersproject.org
*Key Personnel*
Exec Dir: George Geers *E-mail:* ggeers@nhwritersproject.org
Prog Dir: Carla Gericke *E-mail:* nhwp.carla@gmail.com
Off Mgr: Nicole Escobar
Pubns Asst: Dawn Coutu *E-mail:* dcoutu@nhwritersproject.com
Established: 1992
Biennial award. Nominees must live in New Hampshire, be a native or deal with subject matter that is deemed by judges to be inherently connected with New Hampshire.
Closing Date: June 15
Presented: Nov

**New Issues Poetry Prize**
New Issues Poetry & Prose
Western Michigan University, 1903 W Michigan Ave, Kalamazoo, MI 49008-5463
*Tel:* 269-387-8185 *Fax:* 269-387-2562
*E-mail:* new-issues@wmich.edu
*Web Site:* www.wmich.edu/newissues
*Key Personnel*
Mng Ed: Kimberly Kolbe
Poets writing in English who have not previously published a full-length collection (48 plus pages) of poems. Submit ms minimum 48 pages, typed on one side, single spaced; do not bind ms. Include brief bio & relevant publication information; cover page with name, address, phone & title of ms; include table of contents. A $20 reading fee for each ms; enclose SASE.
Other Sponsor(s): Western Michigan University
Award: $2,000 & book publication
Closing Date: Nov 30

**New Jersey Council for the Humanities Book Award**
New Jersey Council for the Humanities
28 W State St, 6th fl, Trenton, NJ 08608
*Tel:* 609-695-4838 *Toll Free Tel:* 888-FYI-NJCH (394-6524) *Fax:* 609-695-4929
*E-mail:* njch@njch.org
*Web Site:* www.njch.org
*Key Personnel*
Exec Dir: Sharon Ann Holt *E-mail:* director@njch.org
Assoc Dir: Mary Rizzo *E-mail:* mrizzo@njch.org
Prog Offr: Robert Apgar *E-mail:* rapgar@njch.org
Established: 1988
Honors a nonfiction humanities book that balances scholarship with general public appeal. The book establishes a connection to New Jersey either through its subject or the author's birth, residence, or occupation. Nominations must be submitted by the publisher accompanied by six reading copies & a nomination form, which is available from the NJCH.
Award: $1,000 (Author); A gold seal imprinted with the award logo is available
Closing Date: See web site
Presented: Humanities Festival Week, Annual Awards Event, Annually in Oct

**New Letters Literary Awards**
New Letters
UMKC, University House, 5101 Rockhill Rd, Kansas City, MO 64110-2499
*Tel:* 816-235-1168 *Fax:* 816-235-2611
*E-mail:* newletters@umkc.edu
*Web Site:* www.newletters.org
Established: 1986
Annual literary contest.
Award: $1,500 & publication for each category - fiction, poetry & essay (1st prize). All entries considered for publication
Closing Date: Annually, May 18

**New Letters Prize for Poetry**
New Letters
UMKC, University House, 5101 Rockhill Rd, Kansas City, MO 64110-2499
*Tel:* 816-235-1168 *Fax:* 816-235-2611
*E-mail:* newletters@umkc.edu
*Web Site:* www.newletters.org
Established: 1986
Annual literary contest. All entries considered for publication.
Award: $1,500 & publication
Closing Date: May 18

**New Millennium Awards for Fiction, Poetry & Nonfiction**
New Millennium Writings
PO Box 2463, Knoxville, TN 37901
*Tel:* 865-428-0389 *Fax:* 865-428-0389
*Web Site:* newmillenniumwritings.com
*Key Personnel*
Publr & Ed: Don Williams
*E-mail:* donwilliams7@charter.net
Each fiction or nonfiction prize should total no more than 6,000 words (short-short fiction no more than 1,000 words). Each poetry entry may include up to 3 poems. A $17 reading fee is required for each entry. See web site for further information.
Award: $1,000 each for Poem, Fiction, Nonfiction & Short-Short Fiction plus publication
Closing Date: Annually in Jan

**New Women's Voices Chapbook Competition**
Finishing Line Press
PO Box 1626, Georgetown, KY 40324
*Tel:* 859-514-8966
*E-mail:* finishingbooks@aol.com; flpbookstore@aol.com
*Web Site:* www.finishinglinepress.com
*Key Personnel*
Publr: Leah Maines
Sr Ed: Christen Kincaid
Mng Ed: Kevin Murphy Maines
Established: 1998
Cash & publication of a chapbook of poems for women who have not yet published a full-length collection.
Award: $1,000 & publication
Closing Date: Annually, Feb 15

**New York City Book Awards**
The New York Society Library
53 E 79 St, New York, NY 10075
*Tel:* 212-288-6900 *Fax:* 212-744-5832
*E-mail:* events@nysoclib.org
*Web Site:* www.nysoclib.org
*Key Personnel*
Events Coord: Sara Holliday *Tel:* 212-288-6900 ext 222
Established: 1996
Given annually to the authors of the best books about New York City. Must submit copy of nominated book the same year of publication. $20 per book fee. Make check out to The New York Society Library.
Award: Plaque & varied monetary amount
Closing Date: Annually in Dec
Presented: The New York Society Library, Early May

**The New York Public Library Helen Bernstein Book Award for Excellence in Journalism**
The New York Public Library

Stephen A Schwarzman Bldg, Fifth Ave at 42 St, South Court Bldg, 3rd fl, New York, NY 10018-2788
*Tel:* 212-930-0876
*Web Site:* www.nypl.org
*Key Personnel*
Helen Bernstein Libn, Periodicals: Karen Gisonny *E-mail:* kgisonny@nypl.org
Established: 1988
Requires overall journalistic excellence & a published book that stems from the author's reportage & exemplifies outstanding work. Note: nominations are for books published during the calendar year & are solicited only from publishers & editors-in-chief of major newspapers, news magazines & book publishers nationwide.
Award: $15,000
Closing Date: Annually, Oct 1 for books published in calendar year
Presented: The New York Public Library, Annually in April/May

**New York State Edith Wharton Citation of Merit for Fiction Writers**
New York State Writers Institute
Subsidiary of University at Albany
University at Albany, SL 320, Albany, NY 12222
*Tel:* 518-442-5620 *Fax:* 518-442-5621
*E-mail:* writers@uamail.albany.edu
*Web Site:* www.albany.edu/writers-inst
*Key Personnel*
Exec Dir: William Kennedy
Dir: Donald Faulkner
Established: 1985
State author designation for a New York state fiction writer. Applications not accepted. Nominations by advisory panel only.
Award: $10,000
Presented: Albany, NY, Biennially

**New York State Walt Whitman Citation of Merit for Poets**
New York State Writers Institute
Subsidiary of University at Albany
University at Albany, SL 320, Albany, NY 12222
*Tel:* 518-442-5620 *Fax:* 518-442-5621
*E-mail:* writers@uamail.albany.edu
*Web Site:* www.albany.edu/writers-inst
*Key Personnel*
Exec Dir: William Kennedy
Dir: Donald Faulkner
Asst Dir: Suzanne Lance *Tel:* 518-442-5624 *E-mail:* slance@uamail.albany.edu
Established: 1985
State author designation for New York state poet. Applications not accepted. Nominations by advisory panel only.
Award: $10,000
Presented: Albany, NY, Biennially

**John Newbery Medal**
Association for Library Service to Children (ALSC)
Division of American Library Association (ALA)
50 E Huron St, Chicago, IL 60611-2795
*Tel:* 312-280-2163 *Toll Free Tel:* 800-545-2433 *Fax:* 312-440-9374
*E-mail:* alsc@ala.org
*Web Site:* www.ala.org/alsc
*Key Personnel*
Exec Dir: Aimee Strittmatter *Tel:* 312-280-2162 *E-mail:* astrittmatter@ala.org
Awards Coord: Caroline Jewell *E-mail:* alscawards@ala.org
Prog Coord: Marsha P Burgess *E-mail:* mburgess@ala.org
Established: 1922
Awarded annually to the author of the most distinguished writing in a children's book published during the preceding year. Restricted to authors who are citizens or residents of the US.
Award: Medal
Closing Date: Annually, Dec 31
Presented: ALA Annual Conference, Annually in June

**Newfoundland and Labrador Book Awards**
Writers' Alliance of Newfoundland and Labrador (WANL)/Literary Arts Foundation of Newfoundland and Labrador
Haymarket Sq, 208-223 Duckworth St, St John's, NL A1C 6N1, Canada
*Tel:* 709-739-5215
*E-mail:* wanl@nf.aibn.com
*Web Site:* wanl.ca
*Key Personnel*
Exec Dir: Alison Dyer
Exec Asst: Sheri Coombs *E-mail:* wanlassist@nf.aibn.com
Established: 1997
Honor excellence in Newfoundland & Labrador writing in 4 categories: fiction, nonfiction, poetry & children's/young adult literature.
Other Sponsor(s): The Bruneau Family (children's/young adult literature); Downhome Inc (fiction); Historic Sites Association (Heritage & History Book Award); Le Grow's Travel (poetry); Rogers Cable (nonfiction)
Award: $1,500 (1st prize), $500 (2 runners-up)
Closing Date: Jan
Presented: May

**Don & Gee Nicholl Fellowships in Screenwriting**
Academy of Motion Picture Arts & Sciences (AMPAS)
1313 Vine St, Hollywood, CA 90028
*Tel:* 310-247-3010 *Fax:* 310-247-3794
*E-mail:* nicholl@oscars.org
*Web Site:* www.oscars.org/nicholl
*Key Personnel*
Dir: Greg Beal
Established: 1986
Screenwriting; for information visit web site.
Award: Up to five awards of $35,000 each
Closing Date: Annually, May 1
Presented: Beverly Hills, CA, Annually in Nov

**John Frederick Nims Memorial Prize**
Poetry Magazine
444 N Michigan Ave, Suite 1850, Chicago, IL 60611-4034
*Tel:* 312-787-7070 *Fax:* 312-787-6650
*E-mail:* editors@poetrymagazine.org
*Web Site:* poetryfoundation.org
*Key Personnel*
Mng Ed: Valerie Johnson *E-mail:* vjohnson@poetrymagazine.org
Established: 1999
For poetry published in the preceding two volumes of Poetry Magazine. No application necessary.
Award: $500
Presented: Annually in Dec

**North Carolina Arts Council Writers Fellowships**
North Carolina Arts Council
Division of North Carolina State Government
109 E Jones St, Raleigh, NC 27601
Mailing Address: Dept of Cultural Resources, Mail Service Ctr 4632, Raleigh, NC 27699-4632
*Tel:* 919-807-6500 *Fax:* 919-807-6532
*E-mail:* ncarts@ncdcr.gov
*Web Site:* www.ncarts.org
*Key Personnel*
Exec Dir: Wayne Martin *Tel:* 919-807-6525 *E-mail:* wayne.martin@ncdcr.gov
Prog Dir, Lit: David Potorti *Tel:* 919-807-6512 *E-mail:* david.potorti@ncdcr.gov
Established: 1980
Fellowships are given every two years to poets & writers of fiction, literary nonfiction, literary translation playwrights & screenwriters. Writers who have lived in the state for at least one year as of application deadline & who intend to remain instate during the fellowship year are eligible.
Award: $10,000
Closing Date: Biennially, Nov 1st of even-numbered years
Presented: Biennially, Summer of odd-numbered years

**Northern California Book Awards**
Northern California Book Reviewers (NCBR)
c/o Poetry Flash, 1450 Fourth St, Suite 4, Berkeley, CA 94710
*Tel:* 510-525-5476 *Fax:* 510-525-6752
*E-mail:* editor@poetryflash.org
*Web Site:* www.poetryflash.org/ncba.html
*Key Personnel*
Chmn: Joyce Jenkins
Established: 1981
Awarded annually by category (fiction, poetry, nonfiction, children's literature & translation) for best book in category by a Northern California writer. Publishers Award given occasionally for special achievement by a Northern California publisher or a literary organization. Send 3 copies of book; no application or fee necessary.
Other Sponsor(s): The Center for the Art of Translation; Northern California Independent Booksellers Association; PEN West; Poetry Flash; San Francisco Public Library
Award: Cash & certificate
Closing Date: Dec 1
Presented: Koret Auditorium, San Francisco Main Public Library, April

**Notable Wisconsin Authors**
Wisconsin Library Association Inc
4610 S Biltmore Lane, Madison, WI 53718
*Tel:* 608-245-3640 *Fax:* 608-245-3646
*Web Site:* www.wla.lib.wi.us
*Key Personnel*
Exec Dir: Lisa K Strand *E-mail:* strand@scls.lib.wi.us
Memb Servs Coord: Brigitte Rupp Vacha *E-mail:* ruppvacha@scls.lib.wi.us
Established: 1973
Annual award Honoring Wisconsin authors, past & present, for their literary contributions.
Award: Printed brochure with biographical information on the notable author, including a list of authors' works
Presented: WLA Annual Conference, Annually Oct-Nov

**Novella Prize**
The Malahat Review
University of Victoria, Box 1700, Sta CSC, Victoria, BC V8W 2Y2, Canada
*Tel:* 250-721-8524 *Fax:* 250-472-5051
*E-mail:* malahat@uvic.ca
*Web Site:* www.malahatreview.ca
*Key Personnel*
Ed: John Barton
Awarded every other year (in even-numbered years) alternating with Long Poem Prize. See web site for details & entry fee.
Award: $1,500 CAD
Closing Date: Feb 1, even numbered yrs

**NSK Neustadt Prize for Children's Literature**
World Literature Today
University of Oklahoma, Suite 110, 630 Parrington Oval, Norman, OK 73019-4033
*Tel:* 405-325-4531 *Fax:* 405-325-7495
*Web Site:* www.worldliteraturetoday.org
*Key Personnel*
Exec Dir: Robert Con Davis-Undiano *E-mail:* rcdavis@ou.edu
Asst Dir & Ed-in-Chief: Daniel Simon *E-mail:* dsimon@ou.edu

Art Dir: Merleyn Bell *E-mail:* merleyn@ou.edu
Mng Ed: Michelle Johnson *E-mail:* lmjohnson@ou.edu
Book Reviews Ed: Marla Johnson *E-mail:* mfjohnson@ou.edu
Mktg Dir, Progs & Devt: Terri Stubblefield *E-mail:* tdstubb@ou.edu
Circ & Accts Specialist: Kay Blunck *E-mail:* kblunck@ou.edu
Established: 2003
An award intended to enhance the quality of children's literature by promoting writing that contributes to the quality of their lives. Awarded to a living writer with significant achievement, either over a lifetime or in a particular publication. The essential criterion for awarding this prize is that the writer's work is having a positive impact on the quality of children's literature.
Other Sponsor(s): Nancy Barcelo; Kathy Neustadt; Susan Neustadt Schwartz; The University of Oklahoma
Award: $25,000, medal & certificate
Closing Date: No outside nominations accepted, nominations by jury member only
Presented: The University of Oklahoma, Norman, OK, Biennially in Oct (odd-numbered years)

**Nuestras Voces National Playwriting Competition**
MetLife Foundation
138 E 27 St, New York, NY 10016
*Tel:* 212-225-9950 *Fax:* 212-225-9085
*Web Site:* www.repertorio.org
*Key Personnel*
Spec Projs Mgr: Allison Astor Vargas *E-mail:* aav@repertorio.org
Established: 2000
Award: $3,000 & full production (Winner), cash awards of $500-$3,000 (top 5), Stage Reading (top 10)
Closing Date: Annually in June

**Eli M Oboler Memorial Award**
Intellectual Freedom Round Table (IFRT)
Unit of American Library Association (ALA)
50 E Huron St, Chicago, IL 60611
*Tel:* 312-280-4223 *Toll Free Tel:* 800-545-2433 *Fax:* 312-280-4227
*E-mail:* oif@ala.org
*Web Site:* www.ala.org/ifrt
*Key Personnel*
Prog Offr: Nanette Perez *Tel:* 312-280-4225 *E-mail:* nperez@ala.org
Admin Asst & Award Contact: Shumeca Pickett *Tel:* 312-280-4220 *E-mail:* spickett@ala.org
Biennial award given to an author of a published work in English, or an English translation dealing with issues, events, questions or controversies in the area of intellectual freedom.
Award: $500 & certificate
Closing Date: Dec 1, odd numbered yrs, prior to ALA Conference
Presented: ALA Annual Conference, Anaheim, CA, Jan, even numbered yrs

**The Flannery O'Connor Award for Short Fiction**
University of Georgia Press
Main Library, 3rd fl, 320 S Jackson St, Athens, GA 30602
*Fax:* 706-369-6131
*Web Site:* www.ugapress.org
*Key Personnel*
Series Ed: Nancy Zafris
Acqs Ed: Sydney DuPre *Tel:* 706-542-1903 *E-mail:* sdupre@ugapress.uga.edu
Established: 1981
Collections of original short fiction. Ms should be 40,000-75,000 words & should be accompanied by a $25 submission fee; ms will not be returned. Submissions accepted between April 1 & May 31. Open to both published & unpublished writers. Applicants should visit The Press web site for guidelines. No phone calls regarding the award will be accepted. Accepting electronic submissions at georgiapress.submishmash.com.
Award: $1,000 & publication by the University of Georgia Press under a standard publishing contract
Closing Date: Annually, May 31

**Frank O'Connor Prize for Fiction**
Texas Christian University
Texas Christian University, Dept of English, TCU Box 297270, Fort Worth, TX 76129
*Tel:* 817-257-5907 *Fax:* 817-257-7709
*E-mail:* descant@tcu.edu
*Web Site:* www.descant.tcu.edu
*Key Personnel*
Mng Ed: Dan Williams *E-mail:* d.e.williams@tcu.edu
Established: 1957
Best published fiction in each volume of descant. No entry fee.
Other Sponsor(s): descant Publication, Dept of English, TCU
Award: $500
Closing Date: Annually, Sept 1-April 1
Presented: Announced in journal, Annually in Summer

**Scott O'Dell Award for Historical Fiction**
Hornbook, Suite 200, 56 Roland St, Boston, MA 02129
*Tel:* 617-628-8471 *Toll Free Tel:* 800-325-1170
*Web Site:* www.scottodell.com/odellaward.html
*Key Personnel*
Chair & Ed-in-Chief: Roger Sutton
Judge: Deborah Stevenson
Libn: Ann Carlson
Established: 1982
Presented for a work of historical fiction published in the previous year for children or young adults, by a US publisher & set in the New World. Winner is selected by O'Dell Award Committee.
Award: $5,000
Closing Date: Annually, Dec 31

**Dayne Ogilvie Prize**
The Writers' Trust of Canada
90 Richmond St E, Suite 200, Toronto, ON M5C 1P1, Canada
*Tel:* 416-504-8222 *Toll Free Tel:* 877-906-6548 *Fax:* 416-504-9090
*E-mail:* info@writerstrust.com
*Web Site:* www.writerstrust.com
*Key Personnel*
Exec Dir: Mary Osbourne *Tel:* 416-504-8222 ext 244
Established: 2007
Awarded to an emerging LGBT writer.
Other Sponsor(s): Robin Pacific
Award: $4,000
Presented: Pride Week, Toronto, ON, CN, Annually, early Summer

**Howard O'Hagan Award for Short Story**
Writers Guild of Alberta
11759 Groat Rd, Edmonton, AB T5M 3K6, Canada
*Tel:* 780-422-8174 *Toll Free Tel:* 800-665-5354 (AB only) *Fax:* 780-422-2663 (attn WGA)
*E-mail:* mail@writersguild.ab.ca
*Web Site:* www.writersguild.ab.ca
*Key Personnel*
Exec Dir: Carol Holmes *E-mail:* cholmes@writersguild.ab.ca
Communs & Partnerships Coord: Nicholas Mather *E-mail:* nmather@writersguild.ab.ca
Memb Servs Coord: Giorgia Severini
Progs Coord: Nichole Quiring *E-mail:* programs@writersguild.ab.ca
Established: 1982
Alberta Literary Award for published short stories only, author must be resident of Alberta; no longer than 5,000 words.
Award: $700
Closing Date: Annually, Dec 31
Presented: Alberta Literary Awards Gala
*Branch Office(s)*
Lord Denning House, 509 20 Ave SW, Calgary, AB T2S 0E7, Canada, Prog Coord: Samantha Warwick *Tel:* 403-265-2226 *E-mail:* swarwick@writersguild.ab.ca

**Ohioana Award for Children's Literature-Alice Louise Wood Memorial**
Ohioana Library Association
274 E First Ave, Suite 300, Columbus, OH 43201
*Tel:* 614-466-3831 *Fax:* 614-728-6974
*E-mail:* ohioana@ohioana.org
*Web Site:* www.ohioana.org
*Key Personnel*
Exec Dir, Ohioana Library Association: Linda R Hengst *E-mail:* lhengst@ohioana.org
Established: 1990
To an Ohio author of children's literature for a body of work or for a lifetime of contributions to children's literature. The Award is given at the discretion of the Board of Trustees.
Award: $1,000
Closing Date: Annually, Dec 31
Presented: Ohioana Day Luncheon, Annually in Autumn

**Ohioana Book Awards**
Ohioana Library Association
274 E First Ave, Suite 300, Columbus, OH 43201
*Tel:* 614-466-3831 *Fax:* 614-728-6974
*E-mail:* ohioana@ohioana.org
*Web Site:* www.ohioana.org
*Key Personnel*
Exec Dir, Ohioana Library Association: Linda R Hengst *E-mail:* lhengst@ohioana.org
Established: 1942
For the best books by Ohio authors in various fields of writing or books about Ohio or Ohioans. Submit two copies of a nominated book on or before its publication date.
Award: Citations & medals
Closing Date: Dec 31
Presented: Ohioana Day Luncheon, Oct

**Ohioana Career Award**
Ohioana Library Association
274 E First Ave, Suite 300, Columbus, OH 43201
*Tel:* 614-466-3831 *Fax:* 614-728-6974
*E-mail:* ohioana@ohioana.org
*Web Site:* www.ohioana.org
*Key Personnel*
Exec Dir, Ohioana Library Association: Linda R Hengst *E-mail:* lhengst@ohioana.org
Established: 1942
Awarded each year to a native-born Ohioan who has had an outstanding career in the arts & humanities. The recipient is an honored guest at Ohioana Day & must be present to receive the award. The award is given at the discretion of the Board of Trustees.
Closing Date: Annually, Dec 31
Presented: Ohioana Day Luncheon, Annually in Autumn

**Ohioana Citations**
Ohioana Library Association
274 E First Ave, Suite 300, Columbus, OH 43201
*Tel:* 614-466-3831 *Fax:* 614-728-6974
*E-mail:* ohioana@ohioana.org
*Web Site:* www.ohioana.org
*Key Personnel*
Exec Dir, Ohioana Library Association: Linda R Hengst *E-mail:* lhengst@ohioana.org
Established: 1945

For outstanding contributions & accomplishments in a specific field or area of the arts & humanities. Four Ohioana Citations, generally given in four different fields, including the Ohioana Music Citation, may be given each year. The recipient must have been born in Ohio or lived in Ohio for a minimum of 5 years. Citations are given at the discretion of the Board of Trustees.
Closing Date: Annually, Dec 31
Presented: Ohioana Day Luncheon, Annually in Autumn

**Ohioana Pegasus Award**
Ohioana Library Association
274 E First Ave, Suite 300, Columbus, OH 43201
*Tel:* 614-466-3831 *Fax:* 614-728-6974
*E-mail:* ohioana@ohioana.org
*Web Site:* www.ohioana.org
*Key Personnel*
Exec Dir, Ohioana Library Association: Linda R Hengst *E-mail:* lhengst@ohioana.org
Established: 1964
Given to recognize unique or outstanding contributions or achievements in the arts & humanities. Given at the discretion of the trustees of the association. Must have been born in Ohio or resided in Ohio for a minimum of 5 years.
Closing Date: Dec 31
Presented: Ohioana Day Luncheon, Oct

**Ohioana Poetry Award-Memorial to Helen & Laura Krout**
Ohioana Library Association
274 E First Ave, Suite 300, Columbus, OH 43201
*Tel:* 614-466-3831 *Fax:* 614-728-6974
*E-mail:* ohioana@ohioana.org
*Web Site:* www.ohioana.org
*Key Personnel*
Exec Dir, Ohioana Library Association: Linda R Hengst *E-mail:* lhengst@ohioana.org
Established: 1984
Award to an Ohio poet for a body of published work that has made & continues to make a significant contribution to poetry & through whose work as a writer, teacher, administrator or in community service, interest in poetry has been developed. The award is given at the descretion of the Board of Trustees.
Award: $1,000
Closing Date: Annually, Dec 31
Presented: Ohioana Day Luncheon, Annually in Autumn

**Ohioana Walter Rumsey Marvin Grant**
Ohioana Library Association
274 E First Ave, Suite 300, Columbus, OH 43201
*Tel:* 614-466-3831 *Fax:* 614-728-6974
*E-mail:* ohioana@ohioana.org
*Web Site:* www.ohioana.org
*Key Personnel*
Exec Dir, Ohioana Library Association: Linda R Hengst *E-mail:* lhengst@ohioana.org
Established: 1982
Writing competition; awarded to young, (30 yrs of age or younger) unpublished Ohio authors who were born or have lived in Ohio five years or more.
Award: $1,000
Closing Date: Jan 31
Presented: Ohioana Day Luncheon, Oct

**Chris O'Malley Fiction Prize**
The Madison Review
University of Wisconsin, 6193 Helen C White Hall, English Dept, 600 N Park St, Madison, WI 53706
*Tel:* 608-263-0566
*E-mail:* madisonrevw@gmail.com
*Web Site:* www.english.wisc.edu/madisonreview
*Key Personnel*
Chmn Dept: Prof Thomas Schaub
*E-mail:* thschaub@wisc.edu
Faculty Advisor & Prog Coord: Ronald Kuka
*E-mail:* rfkuka@wisc.edu
Size limit 30 pg maximum. Only one submission is allowed per person per contest. Mss must be previously unpublished & should be double-spaced with stardard 1" margins & 12-pt font. Entry fee $10.
Award: $1,000 & publication in the fall issue of The Madison Review
Closing Date: Annually, Feb 1

**Open Chapbook Competition**
Formerly Finishing Line Press Prize in Poetry
Finishing Line Press
PO Box 1626, Georgetown, KY 40324
*Tel:* 859-514-8966
*E-mail:* finishingbooks@aol.com; flpbookstore@aol.com
*Web Site:* www.finishinglinepress.com
*Key Personnel*
Publr: Leah Maines
Sr Ed: Christen Kincaid
Mng Ed: Kevin Murphy Maines
Established: 2002
Award for an unpublished chapbook of poems. Announced on web site & in *Poets & Writers Magazine*.
Award: $1,000 & publication
Closing Date: June 30

**Open Season Awards**
The Malahat Review
University of Victoria, Box 1700, Sta CSC, Victoria, BC V8W 2Y2, Canada
*Tel:* 250-721-8524 *Fax:* 250-472-5051
*E-mail:* malahat@uvic.ca
*Web Site:* malahatreview.ca
*Key Personnel*
Ed: John Barton
Established: 2009
Awards in 3 categories: poetry, short fiction & creative nonfiction. See web site for additional details.
Award: $1,000 CAD in each of three categories
Closing Date: Annually, Nov 1

**Opie Prize**
American Folklore Society/Children's Folklore Section
Ohio State Univ, Mershon Ctr, 1501 Neil Ave, Columbus, OH 43201-2602
*Tel:* 614-292-3375 *Fax:* 614-292-2407
*Web Site:* www.afsnet.org/aboutAFS/AFSprizes.cfm
*Key Personnel*
Exec Dir: Timothy Lloyd *E-mail:* lloyd.100@osu.edu
Section Convenor: Spencer Green
Annual award for the best book length treatment of children's folklore. Edited volumes, collections of folklore & authored studies published in English during previous two years are eligible. Authors or publishers should submit two copies of the book.
Award: $200
Closing Date: Varies
Presented: Oct

**George Orwell Award**
National Council of Teachers of English (NCTE)
1111 W Kenyon Rd, Urbana, IL 61801-1096
*Tel:* 217-328-3870 *Toll Free Tel:* 877-369-6283 (cust serv) *Fax:* 217-328-0977
*E-mail:* publiclangawards@ncte.org
*Web Site:* www.ncte.org
*Key Personnel*
Admin Liaison & Awards Contact: Linda Walters
Established: 1975
Recognizes individuals for distinguished contributions to honesty & clarity in public language.
Other Sponsor(s): NCTE Committee on Public Doublespeak
Award: Certificate
Closing Date: Annually, Sept 15
Presented: NCTE Annual Convention, Annually, late Nov

**Frank L & Harriet C Owsley Award**
Southern Historical Association
University of Georgia, Dept of History, Athens, GA 30602-1602
*Tel:* 706-542-8848 *Fax:* 706-542-2455
*Web Site:* sha.uga.edu
*Key Personnel*
Admin Asst: Shere Dendy *E-mail:* sdendy@uga.edu
Established: 1985
Awarded for most distinguished book in Southern history published in even-numbered years. Awarded in odd-numbered years.
Award: Cash
Closing Date: March 1
Presented: Annual meeting, Fall

**Pacific Northwest Book Awards**
Pacific Northwest Booksellers Association
338 W 11 Ave, Unit 108, Eugene, OR 97401
*Tel:* 541-683-4363 *Fax:* 541-683-3910
*E-mail:* info@pnba.org
*Web Site:* www.pnba.org
*Key Personnel*
Exec Dir: Thom Chambliss *E-mail:* thom@pnba.org
Mktg Dir: Brian Juenemann *E-mail:* brian@pnba.org
Established: 1965
Annual awards for authors who live in Washington, Oregon, Idaho, Alaska & Montana who have published exceptional books during the calendar year.
Award: Plaque & marketing to independent bookstores of the Pacific Northwest
Closing Date: Annually, Aug 30
Presented: Mid-March

**Pacific Northwest Young Reader's Choice Award**
Pacific Northwest Library Association (PNLA)
Vancouver Mall Community Library, 8700 NE Vancouver Mall Dr, Suite 285, Vancouver, WA 98662
*Tel:* 360-892-8256
*Web Site:* www.pnla.org/yrca
*Key Personnel*
Chair YRCA: Barbara Meisenheimer
*E-mail:* bmeisenheimer@fvrl.org
Established: 1940
Nominations taken only from children, teachers, parents & librarians of the Pacific Northwest (WA, OR, AK, ID, MT, BC & AB). Nominated titles were published 3 years previously in the US or CN. Only 4th to 12th graders in the Pacific Northwest vote on a selected list of titles. The categories are Junior grades 4-6, Intermediate grades 7-9 & senior grades 10-12. Awarded to the author of a book most popular with children. Send SASE for information or contact through e-mail address.
Award: Silver Medal
Closing Date: Annually, Feb 1
Presented: Pacific Northwest Library Association's Annual Conference, Annually in Aug

**PAGE International Screenwriting Awards**
Production Arts Group
7510 Sunset Blvd, Suite 610, Hollywood, CA 90046
*E-mail:* info@pageawards.com
*Web Site:* www.pageawards.com

*Key Personnel*
Admin Dir: Jennifer Berg
Contest Coord: Zoe Simmons
Established: 2003
Each year the judges present a total of 31 awards in 10 different categories.
Award: $25,000 (Grand Prize) plus Gold, Silver & Bronze Prizes in all 10 categories
Closing Date: Annually in May
Presented: Hollywood, CA, Annually in Oct

**Dobie Paisano Fellowship Program**
University of Texas at Austin, Texas Institute of Letters
Graduate School, 110 Inner Campus Dr, Stop G0400, Austin, TX 78712-0710
*Fax:* 512-471-7620
*Web Site:* www.utexas.edu/ogs/Paisano
*Key Personnel*
Dir: Dr Michael Adams *E-mail:* adameve@mail.utexas.edu
Established: 1967
Provides an opportunity for creative or nonfiction writers to live & write for an extended period in an environment that offers isolation & tranquility. At the time of application, the applicant must: be a native Texan; have lived in Texas at some time for at least 3 years; or have published significant work with a Texas subject. Criteria for making the awards include quality of work, character of the proposed project & suitability of the applicant for life at Paisano, the late J Frank Dobie's ranch near Austin, TX. Applications are available at the above web site or write for more information. Application fee: $20/1 fellowship, $30/both fellowships. Award: Ralph A Johnston Memorial Fellowship: $20,000 over four months; Jesse H Jones Writing Fellowship: $18,000 over five & a half months.
Closing Date: Annually in Jan
Presented: Annually in May

**Mildred & Albert Panowski Playwriting Award**
Northern Michigan University
Forest Roberts Theatre, 1401 Presque Isle Ave, Marquette, MI 49855-5364
*Tel:* 906-227-2553 *Fax:* 906-227-2567
*Web Site:* www.nmu.edu/theatre
*Key Personnel*
Dir: Ansley Valentine *E-mail:* avalentine@nmu.edu
Established: 1977
Provides students & faculty the unique opportunity to mount & produce an original work on the university stage. The playwright will benefit from seeing the work on its feet in front of an audience & from professional adjudication by guest critics. There is no restriction as to theme or genre; only one play per playwright may be entered.
Award: $2,000 cash, airline fare, room & board for the week of production
Closing Date: Annually, Oct 31 (receipt not postmark)
Presented: Forest Roberts Theatre, Northern Michigan Univ, Annually in April

**Francis Parkman Prize**
Society of American Historians (SAH)
Affiliate of American Historical Association
603 Fayerweather, MC 2538, New York, NY 10027
*Tel:* 212-854-6495
*E-mail:* amhistsociety@columbia.edu
*Web Site:* sah.columbia.edu
*Key Personnel*
Pres: David W Blight
VP: David Nasaw
Exec Secy: Andie Tucher
Established: 1957
For a nonfiction book, including biography, that is distinguished by its literary merit & makes an important contribution to the history of what is now the United States. The author need not be a citizen or resident of the United States & the book need not be published in the United States although must be published & copyrighted in the year preceding the award.
Award: $2,000, certificate & consideration of adoption by the History Book Club
Closing Date: Annually, Jan 31
Presented: New York, NY, Annually in May

**The Paterson Fiction Prize**
The Poetry Center at Passaic County Community College
One College Blvd, Paterson, NJ 07505-1179
*Tel:* 973-684-6555 *Fax:* 973-523-6085
*Web Site:* www.pccc.edu/poetry
*Key Personnel*
Exec Dir: Maria Mazziotti Gillan *E-mail:* mgillan@pccc.edu
Asst Dir: Ashley Kesling *E-mail:* akesling@pccc.edu
For a novel or collection of short fiction which, in the opinion of our judges, is the strongest work of fiction published in 2012. The author will be asked to participate in an awards ceremony & to give a reading at the Poetry Center. Each book submitted must be accompanied by an application form. Publisher may submit more than one book for prize consideration.
Award: $1,000
Closing Date: Annually, April 1

**The Paterson Poetry Prize**
The Poetry Center at Passaic County Community College
One College Blvd, Paterson, NJ 07505-1179
*Tel:* 973-684-6555 *Fax:* 973-523-6085
*Web Site:* www.pccc.edu/poetry
*Key Personnel*
Exec Dir: Maria Mazziotti Gillan *E-mail:* mgillan@pccc.edu
Asst Dir: Ashley Kesling *E-mail:* akesling@pccc.edu
For a book of poems, 48 pages or more in length, selected by our judges as the strongest collection of poems published in 2012. The poet will be asked to participate in an awards ceremony & to give a reading at the Poetry Center. Publisher may submit more than one book for prize consideration.
Award: $1,000
Closing Date: Annually, Feb 1

**The Paterson Prize for Books for Young People**
The Poetry Center at Passaic County Community College
One College Blvd, Paterson, NJ 07505-1179
*Tel:* 973-684-6555 *Fax:* 973-523-6085
*Web Site:* www.pccc.edu/poetry
*Key Personnel*
Exec Dir: Maria Mazziotti Gillan *E-mail:* mgillan@pccc.edu
Asst Dir: Ashley Kesling *E-mail:* akesling@pccc.edu
One book in each category will be selected for the most outstanding book for young people published in 2012.
Award: $500 in each category: PreK-Grade 3, Grades 4-6, Grades 7-12
Closing Date: Annually, March 15

**The Alicia Patterson Foundation Fellowship Program**
The Alicia Patterson Foundation
1090 Vermont Ave, Suite 1000, Washington, DC 20005
*Tel:* 202-393-5995 *Fax:* 301-951-8512
*E-mail:* info@aliciapatterson.org
*Web Site:* www.aliciapatterson.org
*Key Personnel*
Pres & Dir: Margaret Engel
Established: 1963
Yearly or 6 month stipend, not for academic study, for professional print journalist with five years experience & must be US citizen.
Award: $40,000 over 12 months, $20,000 over 6 months. Applicants choose whether they want 6 or 12 month grants
Closing Date: Annually, Oct 1
Presented: 1st week of Dec

**William Peden Prize in Fiction**
The Missouri Review
357 McReynolds Hall, Columbia, MO 65211
*Tel:* 573-882-4474 *Toll Free Tel:* 800-949-2505 *Fax:* 573-884-4671
*E-mail:* question@moreview.com
*Web Site:* www.missourireview.com
*Key Personnel*
Assoc Ed: Evelyn Somers *Tel:* 573-884-7839 *E-mail:* rogerses@missouri.edu
Awarded annually to the best story to appear in the magazine the previous volume year. Winner is selected by an outside judge. It is not a contest that writers can enter, since the winner is selected from stories already published in the magazine.
Other Sponsor(s): First National Bank of Columbia, MO
Award: $1,000
Presented: Columbia, MO

**The PEN Award for Poetry in Translation**
PEN American Center
Affiliate of International PEN
588 Broadway, Suite 303, New York, NY 10012
*Tel:* 212-334-1660 *Fax:* 212-334-2181
*E-mail:* awards@pen.org
*Web Site:* www.pen.org
*Key Personnel*
Exec Dir: Suzanne Nossel
Pres: Peter Godwin
Mgr, Membership & Literary Awards: Paul Morris *Tel:* 212-334-1660 ext 108 *E-mail:* paul@pen.org
Membership, Literary Awards & Writers' Fund Assoc: Arielle Anema *Tel:* 212-334-1660 ext 126 *E-mail:* arielle@pen.org
Recognizes book-length translations of poetry from any language into English, published during the current calendar year & is judged by a single translator of poetry appointed by the PEN Translation Committee. All books must have been published in the US, although translators may be of any nationality (US residency or citizenship is not required). No application form. May be submitted by publishers, agents or the translators themselves. Entry fee: $50.
Award: $3,000
Closing Date: Annually in Feb
Presented: PEN Literary Awards Ceremony, New York, NY, Annually in May

**PEN Center USA Literary Awards**
PEN Center USA
Affiliate of International PEN
269 S Beverly Dr, Suite 1163, Beverly Hills, CA 90212
Mailing Address: PO Box 6037, Beverly Hills, CA 90212
*Tel:* 323-424-4939 *Fax:* 323-424-4944
*E-mail:* awards@penusa.org
*Web Site:* www.penusa.org
Established: 1982
Literary awards for: fiction, creative nonfiction, nonfiction, poetry, translation, children's literature, drama, research nonfiction, screenplay, teleplay, journalism. Author must live west of Mississippi River. Work must have been published/produced in 2013.
Award: Cash awards $1,000

Closing Date: Book categories Dec 31, 2013, non-book categories Jan 31, 2014
Presented: Literary Awards Festival, Beverly Hills Hotel, Beverly Hills, CA, Autumn 2014

**PEN/Faulkner Award for Fiction**
PEN/Faulkner Foundation
Folger Shakespeare Library, 201 E Capitol St SE, Washington, DC 20003
*Tel:* 202-898-9063 *Fax:* 202-675-0360
*Web Site:* www.penfaulkner.org
*Key Personnel*
Exec Dir: Emma Snyder
Established: 1980
For a distinguished work of fiction published by an American citizen writer (for published work only). Send four copies of each book or four bound gallies for those being published in Nov & Dec.
Award: $15,000 (1st prize), $5,000 to each of four finalists
Closing Date: Annaully, Oct 31
Presented: Awards Ceremony, Washington, DC, Annually in May

**PEN/O. Henry Prize Stories**
Anchor Books
Division of Random House Inc
University of Texas at Austin, One University Sta B5000, Austin, TX 78712
*Tel:* 512-572-2428
*Web Site:* www.ohenryprizestories.com
*Key Personnel*
Series Ed: Laura Furman
Established: 1918
Annual collection of the best English language short stories published in American & Canadian magazines & written in the English language during the previous May 1-May 1. No submissions; selections made by the series editor from those published in the approximately 260 magazines with print editions submitted to the series.
Closing Date: May 1

**PEN/Phyllis Naylor Working Writer Fellowship**
PEN American Center
Affiliate of International PEN
588 Broadway, Suite 303, New York, NY 10012
*Tel:* 212-334-1660 *Fax:* 212-334-2181
*E-mail:* awards@pen.org
*Web Site:* www.pen.org
*Key Personnel*
Exec Dir: Suzanne Nossel
Pres: Peter Godwin
Mgr, Membership & Literary Awards: Paul Morris *Tel:* 212-334-1660 ext 108 *E-mail:* paul@pen.org
Membership, Literary Awards & Writers' Fund Assoc: Arielle Anema *Tel:* 212-334-1660 ext 126 *E-mail:* arielle@pen.org
Established: 2001
Award for an author of children's or young adult fiction. Provides a writer with a measure of financial sustenance in order to make possible an extended period of time to complete a book-length work-in-progress & to assist a writer at a crucial moment in his or her career when monetary support is particularly needed.
Award: $5,000
Closing Date: Annually in Feb
Presented: PEN Literary Awards Ceremony, New York, NY, Annually in May

**PEN/Ralph Manheim Medal for Translation**
PEN American Center
Affiliate of International PEN
588 Broadway, Suite 303, New York, NY 10012
*Tel:* 212-334-1660 *Fax:* 212-334-2181
*E-mail:* awards@pen.org
*Web Site:* www.pen.org
*Key Personnel*
Exec Dir: Suzanne Nossel
Pres: Peter Godwin
Mgr, Membership & Literary Awards: Paul Morris *Tel:* 212-334-1660 ext 108 *E-mail:* paul@pen.org
Membership, Literary Awards & Writers' Fund Assoc: Arielle Anema *Tel:* 212-334-1660 ext 126 *E-mail:* arielle@pen.org
Established: 1982
Given every 3 years to a translator who has demonstrated exceptional commitment to excellence throughout the body of his work. Candidates nominated by the PEN Translation Committee; internal nomination only. See web site for more information.
Award: Medal
Closing Date: None
Presented: PEN Literary Awards Ceremony, New York, NY, Every 3 years in May

**PEN/Robert Bingham Fellowships for Writers**
PEN American Center
Affiliate of International PEN
588 Broadway, Suite 303, New York, NY 10012
*Tel:* 212-334-1660 *Fax:* 212-334-2181
*E-mail:* awards@pen.org
*Web Site:* www.pen.org
*Key Personnel*
Exec Dir: Suzanne Nossel
Pres: Peter Godwin
Mgr, Membership & Literary Awards: Paul Morris *Tel:* 212-334-1660 ext 108 *E-mail:* paul@pen.org
Membership, Literary Awards & Writers' Fund Assoc: Arielle Anema *Tel:* 212-334-1660 ext 126 *E-mail:* arielle@pen.org
Honor an exceptionally talented fiction writer whose debut work–a first fiction novel or collection of short stories – represents distinguished literary achievement & suggests great promise. Nominations are welcome from any source. Candidates must be US residents but American citizenship is not required. Entry fee: $50.
Award: $35,000
Closing Date: Annually in Feb
Presented: PEN Literary Awards Ceremony, New York, NY, Annually in May

**PEN Translation Prize**
PEN American Center
Affiliate of International PEN
588 Broadway, Suite 303, New York, NY 10012
*Tel:* 212-334-1660 *Fax:* 212-334-2181
*E-mail:* awards@pen.org
*Web Site:* www.pen.org
*Key Personnel*
Exec Dir: Suzanne Nossel
Pres: Peter Godwin
Mgr, Membership & Literary Awards: Paul Morris *Tel:* 212-334-1660 ext 108 *E-mail:* paul@pen.org
Membership, Literary Awards & Writers' Fund Assoc: Arielle Anema *Tel:* 212-334-1660 ext 126 *E-mail:* arielle@pen.org
Established: 1963
For the best book-length translation into English from any language published in the US during the previous year. Technical, scientific or reference works are not eligible. See web site for more information. Entry fee: $50.
Award: $3,000
Closing Date: Annually in Feb
Presented: PEN Literary Awards Ceremony, New York, NY, Annually in May

**PEN Writers' Emergency Fund**
PEN American Center
Affiliate of International PEN
588 Broadway, Suite 303, New York, NY 10012
*Tel:* 212-334-1660 *Fax:* 212-334-2181
*Web Site:* www.pen.org
*Key Personnel*
Exec Dir: Suzanne Nossel
Pres: Peter Godwin
Intl Pres: Jiri Grusa
Coord: Arielle Anema *Tel:* 212-334-1660 ext 126 *E-mail:* arielle@pen.org
Established: 1921
Grants for professional published writers & produced playwrights in financial emergencies due to personal circumstances. These are not literary awards. Application form available online.
Award: Up to $2,000
Closing Date: Annually, Jan 15, March 15, June 15, Sept 15

**Perugia Press Prize for a First or Second Book by a Woman**
Perugia Press
PO Box 60364, Florence, MA 01062
*Tel:* 413-348-6635
*E-mail:* info@perugiapress.com
*Web Site:* www.perugiapress.com
*Key Personnel*
Dir: Susan Kan *E-mail:* susan@perugiapress.com
Established: 1997
For a first or second book of poetry by a woman.
Award: $1,000 & publication
Closing Date: Annually Nov 15
Presented: Announced annually by April 15

**Pfizer Award**
History of Science Society
Affiliate of American Council of Learned Societies
440 Geddes Hall, Notre Dame, IN 46556
*Tel:* 574-631-1194 *Fax:* 574-631-1533
*E-mail:* info@hssonline.org
*Web Site:* www.hssonline.org
*Key Personnel*
Exec Dir: Robert Jay Malone
Established: 1958
For an outstanding book in English, published during the preceding three years, on a topic related to the history of science.
Award: $2,500 & a medal
Closing Date: Annually, April 1
Presented: Annually in Oct or Nov

**James D Phelan Literary Award**
The San Francisco Foundation
One Embarcadero Ctr, Suite 1400, San Francisco, CA 94111
*Tel:* 415-733-8500 *Fax:* 415-477-2783
*E-mail:* info@sff.org
*Web Site:* www.sff.org
*Key Personnel*
Arts & Culture Prog Offr: Terezita Romo
Established: 1935
Award for the author of fiction (novel or short stories), nonfictional prose, poetry, spoken word. Awards are intended to encourage emerging artists not yet established in the genre who are either California-born or currently residing in Alaneda, Contra, Costa, Marin, San Francisco or Mateo County, for an unpublished ms-in-progress. By nomination only.
Award: $2,000
Presented: Annually in Autumn

**Phi Beta Kappa Award in Science**
The Phi Beta Kappa Society
1606 New Hampshire Ave NW, Washington, DC 20009
*Tel:* 202-265-3808 *Fax:* 202-986-1601
*E-mail:* awards@pbk.org
*Web Site:* www.pbk.org/bookawards
*Key Personnel*
Coord, Society Events: Lucinda Morales *Tel:* 202-745-3235 *E-mail:* lmorales@pbk.org
Established: 1959
For an outstanding interpretation of science written by a scientist & published in the US during

the previous year. Works in the physical & biological sciences & mathematics are eligible for the award. Highly technical works, monographs & reports on research are not eligible. Nominations must come from publisher & be submitted online.
Award: $10,000
Closing Date: Annually in April
Presented: Washington, DC, Annually in Dec

**Robert J Pickering Award for Playwriting Excellence**
Branch County Community Theatre
89 Division, Coldwater, MI 49036
*E-mail:* j7eden@aol.com
*Web Site:* www.branchcct.org
*Key Personnel*
Comm Chmn: J Richard Colbeck
Contact: Jennifer Colbeck
Established: 1984
Playwriting, Must be unproduced full length plays &/or musicals.
Award: $200 & production (1st prize), $50 (2nd prize), $25 (3rd prize)
Closing Date: Annually, Dec 31 (entries ongoing)
Presented: Tibbits Opera House, Coldwater, MI, Annually, Feb or March

**Lorne Pierce Medal**
Royal Society of Canada
Walter House, 282 Somerset W, Ottawa, ON K2P 0J6, Canada
*Tel:* 613-991-6990 *Fax:* 613-991-6996
*E-mail:* nominations@rsc-src.ca
*Web Site:* www.rsc-src.ca
*Key Personnel*
Sr Offr, Memb Servs: Marie-Lyne Renaud
*E-mail:* mlrenaud@rsc-src.ca
Established: 1926
Biennial award given in even-numbered years for an achievement of significance & conspicuous merit in imaginative or critical literature.
Award: Medal
Closing Date: Dec 1
Presented: Quebec City, QC, CN, Nov

**The Pinch Writing Awards in Fiction**
Hohenburg Foundation
University of Memphis, English Dept, 435 Patterson Hall, Memphis, TN 38152
*Tel:* 901-678-4190 *Fax:* 901-678-2226
*E-mail:* editor@thepinchjournal.com
*Web Site:* www.thepinchjournal.com
*Key Personnel*
Ed-in-Chief: Dr Kristen Iversen
*E-mail:* kiversen@memphis.edu
Mng Ed: Christopher Moyer
Established: 1987
Submit one previously unpublished story not to exceed 5,000 words accompanied by a $20 entrance fee, which includes a one-year subscription to "The Pinch." Additional entries are $10. Stories should be typed, double-spaced & include a cover sheet. The cover sheet must contain the author's name & full communication information. The author's name should not appear anywhere on the ms itself. Indicate contest entry & category on envelope. No mss will be returned.
Award: $1,000 & publication in the following Spring issue of *The Pinch* (1st prize), 2nd & 3rd place winners may also be published. All entrants receive one free copy of the journal
Closing Date: Annually, Dec 15-April 15
Presented: Annually, mid-Sept

**The Pinch Writing Awards in Poetry**
Hohenburg Foundation
University of Memphis, English Dept, 435 Patterson Hall, Memphis, TN 38152
*Tel:* 901-678-4190 *Fax:* 901-678-2226
*E-mail:* editor@thepinchjournal.com
*Web Site:* www.thepinchjournal.com
*Key Personnel*
Ed-in-Chief: Dr Kristen Iversen
*E-mail:* kiversen@memphis.edu
Mng Ed: Christopher Moyer
Established: 1987
Submit up to 3 unpublished poems accompanied by a $20 entrance fee. Additional groups of three poems may be submitted at $10 per group. Mss must be typed & accompanied by a cover letter. Mss themselves should not include the author's name. Indicate contest entry & category on envelope. No mss will be returned.
Award: $1,000 & publication in the subsequent issue of *The Pinch* will be awarded to the 1st place winner, 2nd & 3rd place winners may also be published. All entrants receive 1 free copy of the journal
Closing Date: Annually, Dec 15-April 15
Presented: Annually, Mid-Sept

**Playboy College Fiction Contest**
Playboy Enterprises Inc
9346 Civic Center Dr, Beverly Hills, CA 90210-3604
*Toll Free Tel:* 800-276-6048 (cust serv) *Fax:* 312-751-2818
*Web Site:* www.playboy.com
Established: 1985
Short story contest for accredited college/university students.
Award: $3,000 & publication in an upcoming issue (1st prize), $500 & an annual subscription (2nd prize), $200 & an annual subscription (3rd prize); open to all college students
Closing Date: Feb 15
Presented: Spring

**Playwright Discovery Award**
VSA
Affiliate of The John F Kennedy Center for the Performing Arts
818 Connecticut Ave NW, Suite 600, Washington, DC 20006
*Tel:* 202-628-2800 *Toll Free Tel:* 800-933-8721 *Fax:* 202-429-0868
*Web Site:* www.vsarts.org/playwrightdiscovery
*Key Personnel*
Dir, Performing Arts: Elena Widder
Established: 1984
Playwriting program for students with & without disabilities, grades 6-12. Script must somehow address the subject of disability.
Award: Attend performance of their script at JFK Center, scholarship funds
Closing Date: Annually, April 15
Presented: The John F Kennedy Center for Performing Arts

**Playwrights Project**
3675 Ruffin Rd, Suite 330, San Diego, CA 92123
*Tel:* 858-384-2970 *Fax:* 858-384-2974
*E-mail:* write@playwrightsproject.org
*Web Site:* www.playwrightsproject.org
*Key Personnel*
Exec Dir: Cecelia Kouma
Devt Mgr: Laurel Withers
Established: 1985
Playwriting contest for Californians under 19 years of age.
Award: Professional production (location to be announced), royalty
Closing Date: Annually, June 1
Presented: Annually, Jan-Feb following application

**The Plimpton Prize**
The Paris Review Foundation
62 White St, New York, NY 10013
*Tel:* 212-343-1333 *Fax:* 212-343-1988
*E-mail:* queries@theparisreview.org
*Web Site:* www.theparisreview.org
*Key Personnel*
Publr: Antonio Weiss
Mng Ed: Nicole Rudick
Sr Ed: Dierdre Foley-Mendelssohn
Awarded annually to the best work of fiction publishing in The Paris Review that year by an emerging or previously unpublished writer.
Award: $10,000
Presented: April

**PNWA Literary Contest**
Pacific Northwest Writers Association
1420 NW Gilman Blvd, Suite 2, PMB 2717, Issaquah, WA 98027
*Tel:* 425-673-2665
*E-mail:* pnwa@pnwa.org
*Web Site:* www.pnwa.org
*Key Personnel*
Pres: Pam Binder
Multiple categories by genre.
Closing Date: Annually in Feb
Presented: Annual Summer Conference

**Edgar Allan Poe Awards®**
Mystery Writers of America (MWA)
1140 Broadway, Suite 1507, New York, NY 10001
*Tel:* 212-888-8171
*E-mail:* mwa@mysterywriters.org
*Web Site:* www.mysterywriters.org
*Key Personnel*
Admin Dir: Margery Flax
Established: 1945
For the best mystery novel & best first novel by an American author. Also awards for best juvenile novel & young adult, motion picture, fact-crime writing, TV episode, short story, paperback original, critical/biographical work & play. The work must be published for the first time in the US in the calendar year prior to the award.
Award: Ceramic bust of Poe
Closing Date: Annually, Nov 30
Presented: New York, NY, Annually in late Spring

**Edgar Allan Poe Memorial**
The Poetry Society of Virginia
1194 Hume Rd, Hume, VA 22639-1806
*E-mail:* poetryinva@aol.com
*Web Site:* www.poetrysocietyofvirginia.org
*Key Personnel*
Pres: Judith K Bragg *E-mail:* musicsavy45@yahoo.com
Adult Contest Chair: Patsy Anne Bickerstaff *E-mail:* granypatsy@yahoo.com; Guy Terrell *E-mail:* ggterr@infionline.net
All entries must be in English, original & unpublished. Submit 2 copies of each poem, each having the category name & number on top left of page. Only one poem per category; entries will not be returned; any form; any subject; 48 line limit. Entry fee: $4 nonmembs.
Award: $100
Closing Date: Jan 19
Presented: Annual PSV Awards Luncheon, Richmond, VA, April

**A Poem With a Point of View**
The Poetry Society of Virginia
1194 Hume Rd, Hume, VA 22639-1806
*E-mail:* poetryinva@aol.com
*Web Site:* www.poetrysocietyofvirginia.org
*Key Personnel*
Pres: Judith K Bragg *E-mail:* musicsavy45@yahoo.com
Adult Contest Chair: Patsy Anne Bickerstaff *E-mail:* granypatsy@yahoo.com; Guy Terrell *E-mail:* ggterr@infionline.net
All entries must be in English, original & unpublished. Submit 2 copies, each having the category name & number on top left of page. Any form, any subject that express his or her strong

or particular feelings; 48 line limit. Entry fee: $4 nonmembs.
Other Sponsor(s): Angela Anselmo
Award: $50
Closing Date: Jan 19
Presented: Annual PSV Awards Luncheon, Richmond, VA, April

**Poetry Book Contest**
Accents Publishing
PO Box 910456, Lexington, KY 40591-0456
*Web Site:* www.accents-publishing.com/contest.html
*Key Personnel*
Founder & Sr Ed: Katerina Stoykova-Klemer
Established: 2010
Include submission form, ms, biography or CV & check or confirmation of payment. Ms should be 20-30 pgs of poetry & single spaced. Entry fee $10.
Award: $250 cash, pubn & 25 perfect-bound copies
Closing Date: Annually, Feb 1-June 30
Presented: Annually in July

**Poetry Center Book Award**
Poetry Center & American Poetry Archives at San Francisco State University
1600 Holloway Ave, San Francisco, CA 94132
*Tel:* 415-338-2227 *Fax:* 415-338-0966
*E-mail:* poetry@sfsu.edu
*Web Site:* www.sfsu.edu/~poetry
*Key Personnel*
Assoc Dir: Elise Ficarra
Established: 1980
For an outstanding book of poetry published in the year of the award. Volumes by individual authors; anthologies & translations not accepted. Poets or publishers should send one copy of each book & a $10 fee. Include a cover letter noting author name, book title(s), name of person issuing check & check number.
Award: $500 & an invitation to read in the Poetry Center's series
Closing Date: Jan 31
Presented: Fall

**Poetry Chapbook Contest**
Palettes & Quills
330 Knickerbocker Ave, Rochester, NY 14615
*Tel:* 585-458-0217
*E-mail:* palettesnquills@gmail.com
*Web Site:* www.palettesnquills.com
*Key Personnel*
Ed & Publr: Donna M Marbach
*E-mail:* dmmarbach@gmail.com
You must include a statement that all poems are your original work. Poems included in your ms may be previously published, but include an acknowledgement page listing specific publications. Entry fee per entry: $20. Translations not accepted. Poems longer than two pages are discouraged.
Award: Cash ($200) plus 50 copies of the published book
Closing Date: Biennially in Sept (even numbered years)
Presented: Online, Dec

**The George Polk Awards**
Long Island University
The Brooklyn Campus, One University Plaza, Brooklyn, NY 11201-5372
*Tel:* 718-488-1009; 718-488-1115
*Web Site:* www.liu.edu/polk
*Key Personnel*
Curator: John Darnton
Coord: Ralph Engelman *E-mail:* ralph.engelman@liu.edu
Established: 1949
For outstanding discernment & reporting of a news or feature story on the Internet, in newspapers, radio or television. Entries originating from publication offices, newsrooms or individual reporters are considered. Submit two copies of stories or tapes. No entry fees or application forms; entries will not be returned.
Award: Plaque
Closing Date: Jan 5
Presented: Spring

**Katherine Anne Porter Prize for Fiction**
Nimrod, The University of Tulsa
Subsidiary of The Nimrod Literary Awards
Nimrod International Journal, 800 S Tucker Dr, Tulsa, OK 74104
*Tel:* 918-631-3080 *Fax:* 918-631-3033
*E-mail:* nimrod@utulsa.edu
*Web Site:* www.utulsa.edu/nimrod
*Key Personnel*
Ed: Francine Ringold, PhD
Mng Ed: Eilis O'Neal
Established: 1978
Annual prize. 7500 words maximum. No previously published works or works accepted for publication elsewhere. Must have a US address by Oct to enter. Works must be in English or translated by original author. Author's name must not appear on ms. Include a cover sheet containing major title & subtitles, author's name, address, phone number & e-mail address. "Contest Entry" must be on envelope. Mss will not be returned. Nimrod retains the right to publish any submission. Works not accepted will be released; SASE for results only. $20 entry fee includes processing & one-year subscription.
Award: $2,000 (1st prize), $1,000 (2nd prize); plus each published writer receives two copies of the journal; winners are flown to Tulsa for a conference & banquet
Closing Date: April 30
Presented: Tulsa, OK, Oct

**Postcard Story Competition**
Writers' Union of Canada
90 Richmond St E, Suite 200, Toronto, ON M5C 1P1, Canada
*Tel:* 416-703-8982 *Fax:* 416-504-9090
*E-mail:* info@writersunion.ca
*Web Site:* www.writersunion.ca
*Key Personnel*
Competitions Coord: Nancy MacLeod *Tel:* 416-703-8982 ext 226 *E-mail:* nmacleod@writersunion.ca
Off Administrator: Valerie Laws *Tel:* 416-703-8982 ext 224
Best story under 250 words by a Canadian.
Award: $750
Closing Date: Annually, Feb 14

**Prairie Schooner Strousse Award**
Prairie Schooner
University of Nebraska, 123 Andrews Hall, Lincoln, NE 68588-0334
Mailing Address: PO Box 880334, Lincoln, NE 68588-0334
*Tel:* 402-472-0911 *Fax:* 402-472-9771
*Web Site:* prairieschooner.unl.edu
*Key Personnel*
Mng Ed: James Engelhardt
*E-mail:* jengelhardt2@unl.edu
Ed: Kwame Dawes
Established: 1975
For best poetry published in the magazine each year.
Other Sponsor(s): Friends & famliy of Fora Strousse
Award: $500
Presented: Prairie Schooner, Annually in March

**Derek Price/Rod Webster Prize Award**
History of Science Society
Affiliate of American Council of Learned Societies
440 Geddes Hall, Notre Dame, IN 46556
*Tel:* 574-631-1194 *Fax:* 574-631-1533
*E-mail:* info@hssonline.org
*Web Site:* www.hssonline.org
*Key Personnel*
Exec Dir: Robert Jay Malone
Established: 1978
For article appearing in Isis during the preceding three years.
Award: $1,000
Closing Date: Annually, April 1
Presented: Annual meeting, Late Oct or early Nov

**Printing Industries of America Premier Print Award**
Printing Industries of America
200 Deer Run Rd, Sewickley, PA 15143-2600
*Tel:* 412-741-6860 *Toll Free Tel:* 800-910-4283 *Fax:* 412-741-2311
*E-mail:* printing@printing.org
*Web Site:* www.printing.org
*Key Personnel*
Chmn of the Bd: William Gibson
CEO & Pres: Michael Makin *E-mail:* mmakin@printing.org
VP, Mktg: Lisa Rawa
Established: 1950
Awards competition for printed material.
Award: Plaques & certificates
Closing Date: Annually in May
Presented: Graph Expo, Annually in Sept or Oct

**Michael L Printz Award**
Young Adult Library Services Association (YALSA)
Division of American Library Association (ALA)
50 E Huron St, Chicago, IL 60611
*Tel:* 312-280-4390 *Toll Free Tel:* 800-545-2433 *Fax:* 312-280-5276
*E-mail:* yalsa@ala.org
*Web Site:* www.ala.org/yalsa/printz
*Key Personnel*
Prog Offr, Events & Conferences: Nichole Gilbert *Tel:* 312-280-4387 *Fax:* 312-280-1538 *E-mail:* ngilbert@ala.org
Established: 1999
Honors excellence in literature written for young adults. May be fiction, nonfiction, poetry or an anthology & must have been published during the preceding year & designated as young adult book or ages 12-18.
Other Sponsor(s): Booklist
Closing Date: Annually, Dec 1
Presented: YALSA Printz Reception during ALA Annual Conference

**PRISM international Literary Non-Fiction Contest**
PRISM international
University of British Columbia, Buch E462, 1866 Main Mall, Vancouver, BC V6T 1Z1, Canada
*Tel:* 778-822-2514 *Fax:* 778-822-3616
*E-mail:* prismwritingcontest@gmail.com
*Web Site:* www.prismmagazine.ca
*Key Personnel*
Exec Ed: Sierra Skye Gemma; Andrea Hoff
Prose Ed: Jane Campbell
Poetry Ed: Zach Mattison
Entry fee: $35 (includes a 1 yr subn); additional entries: $6.
Other Sponsor(s): University of British Columbia Bookstore
Award: $1,500 (grand prize), $300 (1st runner up), $200 (2nd runner up)
Closing Date: Annually in Nov (check web site for exact date)

**PRISM international Poetry Contest**
PRISM international

University of British Columbia, Buch E462, 1866 Main Mall, Vancouver, BC V6T 1Z1, Canada
*Tel:* 778-822-2514 *Fax:* 778-822-3616
*E-mail:* prismwritingcontest@gmail.com
*Web Site:* www.prismmagazine.ca
*Key Personnel*
Exec Ed: Sierra Skye Gemma; Andrea Hoff
Prose Ed: Jane Campbell
Poetry Ed: Zach Mattison
Established: 1986
Awarded for the best original, unpublished poem (3 poems, up to 25 pages). Works of translation are eligible. Entry fee $35 for 3 poems plus $5 for each additional entry.
Award: $1,500 grand prize, $300 (1st runner up), $200 (2nd runner up); all entries receive a 1 yr subn to *PRISM international*
Closing Date: Annually in Jan

**PRISM international Short Fiction Contest**
PRISM international
University of British Columbia, Buch E462, 1866 Main Mall, Vancouver, BC V6T 1Z1, Canada
*Tel:* 778-822-2514 *Fax:* 778-822-3616
*E-mail:* prismwritingcontest@gmail.com
*Web Site:* www.prismmagazine.ca
*Key Personnel*
Exec Ed: Sierra Skye Gemma; Andrea Hoff
Prose Ed: Jane Campbell
Poetry Ed: Zach Mattison
Established: 1986
Short fiction. Entry fee: $35 (CN), $40 (US), $45 (Intl).
Award: $2,000 (grand prize), $300 (1st runner up), $200 (2nd runner up)
Closing Date: Annually in Jan (check web site for exact date)

**Prix Alvine-Belisle**
Association pour l'Avancement des Sciences et des Techniques de la Documentation
2065 rue Parthenais, Bureau 387, Montreal, QC H2K 3T1, Canada
*Tel:* 514-281-5012 *Fax:* 514-281-8219
*E-mail:* info@asted.org
*Web Site:* www.asted.org
*Key Personnel*
Dir Gen: Francis Farley-Chevrier *E-mail:* ffc@asted.org
To the best books for young people published in French in Canada during the previous year.
Closing Date: Annually, end of June
Presented: Salon Du Livre, Montreal, QC, CN, Annually in Nov

**Prix Emile-Nelligan**
La Fondation Emile Nelligan
100 Sherbrooke St, Suite 202, Montreal, QC H2X 1C3, Canada
*Tel:* 514-278-4657 *Toll Free Tel:* 888-849-8540 *Fax:* 514-278-1943
*E-mail:* info@fondation-nelligan.org
*Web Site:* www.fondation-nelligan.org
*Key Personnel*
CEO: Manon Gagnon
Pres: Michel Dallaire
VP: Marie-Andree Beaudet
Treas/Secy: Michel Gonneville
Established: 1979
Collection must be published between Jan 1-Dec 31 of the preceding year.
Award: $7,500 & a bronze medal
Presented: Annually in May

**Prize for the Translation of Japanese Literature**, see Japan-US Friendship Commission Translation Prize

**Prometheus Awards**
Libertarian Futurist Society
650 Castro St, Suite 120-433, Mountain View, CA 94041
*Tel:* 650-968-6319
*E-mail:* info@lfs.org
*Web Site:* www.lfs.org
*Key Personnel*
Bd Pres: Bill Stoddard
VP: Rick Triplett
Dir: Charles Morrison
Asst Dir: Steve Burgauer
Established: 1979
Awarded to the best published novel of previous year that dramatizes the value of freedom. Hall of Fame—classic libertarian fiction.
Award: Prometheus one ounce gold coin mounted on an engraved plaque; Hall of Fame one-eighth ounce coin mounted on an engraved plaque
Closing Date: Annually, March 1st (Best Novel), Oct 1 (best Classic Fiction), Feb 1 (Special Awards)
Presented: World Science Fiction Convention or NASFIC, Labor Day weekend

**PROSE Awards**
Association of American Publishers (AAP)
71 Fifth Ave, 2nd fl, New York, NY 10003-3004
*Tel:* 212-255-0200 *Fax:* 212-255-7007
*Web Site:* www.proseawards.com; www.publishers.org
*Key Personnel*
Proj Mgr, Prof & Scholarly Publg: Kate Kolendo *Tel:* 212-255-0326 *E-mail:* kkolendo@publishers.org
Established: 1976
The PROSE Awards honor the very best in professional & scholarly publishing. With awards in over 45 catergories, PROSE is unique in it's breath & depth. AAP, PSP & AAUP members are eligible.
Award: Plaque & glass cubes
Closing Date: Annually, Oct 31
Presented: Annually in Feb

**The Publishing Triangle Literary Awards**
The Publishing Triangle
332 Bleecker St, Suite D-36, New York, NY 10014
*E-mail:* publishingtriangle@gmail.com
*Web Site:* www.publishingtriangle.org
Established: 1997
Contests for poetry, debut fiction & nonfiction. Books must be published in the US or Canada between Jan 1 & Dec 31. Entrants are accepted only between Oct 1 & Dec 1. General instructions, specific guidelines, for each award & submission form are available on web site starting Oct 1. For hard copy, send SASE or e-mail awards@publishingtriangle.org. Entry fee is $35.
Award: $1,000 for debut fiction & nonfiction, $500 for poetry
Closing Date: Dec 1
Presented: Ceremony in New York City, Late April/early May

**PubWest Book Design Awards**
Publishers Association of the West (PubWest)
17501 Hill Way, Lake Oswego, OR 97035
*Tel:* 503-635-0056 *Fax:* 602-234-3062
*Web Site:* www.pubwest.org
*Key Personnel*
Pres: Derek Lawrence
Exec Dir: Kent Watson *E-mail:* executivedirector@pubwest.org
Asst Dir: Amanda Fessler *E-mail:* amanda@pubwest.org
Established: 1977
Gold, silver & bronze awards are given in 20 categories. Trade book (illustrated), trade book (non-illustrated), children's/young adult (illustrated), artist's book, academic book/non-trade, guide/travel book, how-to book/crafts, cook book, art/photography book, sports/fitness/recreation book, reference book, short stories/poetry/anthologies, gift/holiday/specialty book, historical/biographical book, graphic novel/drawn book, jacket/cover design, digitally produced book-1 color, digitally produced book-4 color, best use of environmental materials & best of show.
Award: Medallions & glass award for best of show

**Pulitzer Prizes**
709 Journalism Bldg, Columbia University, 2950 Broadway, New York, NY 10027
*Tel:* 212-854-3841 *Fax:* 212-854-3342
*E-mail:* pulitzer@pulitzer.org
*Web Site:* www.pulitzer.org
*Key Personnel*
Admin: Sig Gissler
Established: 1917
Given to American authors for a distinguished book of fiction, performed play, history of the US, biography or autobiography, verse or general nonfiction, as well as journalism prizes for newspaper work in US dailies or weeklies, books must be first published in the calendar year.
Award: Gold medal for public service journalism category; $10,000 & certificate in all other categories
Closing Date: June 15 for bks published Jan 1-June 14, Oct 15 for bks published June 15-Dec 31 literary prizes, Feb 1 (journalism), Dec 31 (drama), Jan 15 (music)
Presented: Annually in Spring

**Pushcart Prize: Best of the Small Presses**
Pushcart Press
PO Box 380, Wainscott, NY 11975-0380
SAN: 202-9871
*Tel:* 631-324-9300
*Key Personnel*
Pres: Bill Henderson
Established: 1976
Awarded for works previously published by a small press or literary journal.
Award: Copies of the book *The Pushcart Prize: Best of the Small Presses*
Closing Date: Annually, Dec 1
Presented: Annually in Spring

**QWF Literary Awards**
Quebec Writers' Federation (QWF)
1200 Atwater Ave, Suite 3, Westmount, QC H3Z 1X4, Canada
*Tel:* 514-933-0878
*E-mail:* info@qwf.org
*Web Site:* www.qwf.org
*Key Personnel*
Exec Dir: Lori Schubert *E-mail:* admin@qwf.org
Coord, Membership Servs & Communs: Julia Kater *E-mail:* julia@qwf.org
Established: 1988
Literary for Quebec, English language authors. Request submission details.
Award: A M Klein Prize for Poetry: $2,000; Paragraphe Hugh MacLennan Prize for Fiction: $2,000; Mavis Gallant Prize for Nonfiction: $2,000; Concordia University First Book Prize: $2,000; Cole Foundation Prize for Translation: $2,000; QWF Prize for Children's & Young Adult Literature: $2,000
Closing Date: Annually, May 31
Presented: Annually in Nov

**Miriam Rachimi Memorial**
The Poetry Society of Virginia
1194 Hume Rd, Hume, VA 22639-1806
*E-mail:* poetryinva@aol.com
*Web Site:* www.poetrysocietyofvirginia.org

*Key Personnel*
Pres: Judith K Bragg *E-mail:* musicsavy45@yahoo.com
Adult Contest Chair: Patsy Anne Bickerstaff *E-mail:* granypatsy@yahoo.com; Guy Terrell *E-mail:* ggterr@infionline.net
All entries must be in English, original & unpublished. Submit 2 copies, each having the category name & number on top left of page. Subject: the spiritual impact of losing (or almost losing) a loved one; any form; 48 line limit. Entry fee: $4 nonmembs.
Other Sponsor(s): Ben Mahgerefteh; Michal Mahgerefteh
Award: $50 (1st prize), $30 (2nd prize), $20 (3rd prize)
Closing Date: Jan 19
Presented: Annual PSV Awards Luncheon, Richmond, VA, April

**Radcliffe Fellowship**
The Radcliffe Institute for Advanced Study
8 Garden St, Cambridge, MA 02138
*Tel:* 617-495-8212; 617-496-1324 (application office) *Fax:* 617-495-8136
*Web Site:* www.radcliffe.harvard.edu
*Key Personnel*
Administrator, Fellowships: Alison Ney
Radcliffe Institute fellowships are designed to support scholars, scientists, artists & writers of exceptional promise & demonstrated accomplishments who wish to pursue work in academic & professional fields & in the creative arts.
Award: Stipend & office space
Closing Date: Oct 1

**Thomas Head Raddall Atlantic Fiction Award**
Writers' Federation of Nova Scotia
1113 Marginal Rd, Halifax, NS B3H 4P7, Canada
*Tel:* 902-423-8116 *Fax:* 902-422-0881
*E-mail:* talk@writers.ns.ca
*Web Site:* www.writers.ns.ca
*Key Personnel*
Exec Dir: Nate Crawford *E-mail:* director@writers.ns.ca
Established: 1990
Presented to best fiction book, published by an Atlantic Canadian writer in previous calendar year.
Award: $20,000
Closing Date: Annually, 1st Friday in Dec
Presented: Halifax, NS, CN, Annually in Oct

**The Ragan Old North State Award Cup for Nonfiction**
North Carolina Literary & Historical Association
Affiliate of Historical Book Club of North Carolina
4610 Mail Service Ctr, Raleigh, NC 27699-4610
*Tel:* 919-807-7290 *Fax:* 919-733-8807
*Web Site:* www.history.ncdcr.gov/affiliates/lit-hist/awards/awards.htm
*Key Personnel*
Awards Coord: Michael Hill *E-mail:* michael.hill@ncdcr.gov
Established: 2003
For published book of nonfiction, not technical or scientific, by a legal or actual resident of North Carolina for at least three years prior to end of contest.
Award: Cup
Closing Date: Annually, July 15
Presented: Raleigh, NC, Annually in Nov

**Raiziss/de Palchi Fellowship**
The Academy of American Poets Inc
75 Maiden Lane, Suite 901, New York, NY 10038
*Tel:* 212-274-0343 *Fax:* 212-274-9427
*E-mail:* academy@poets.org
*Web Site:* www.poets.org
*Key Personnel*
Pres & Exec Dir: Tree Swenson
Exec Dir: Jennifer Benka
Multimedia Prodr: Paul Legault *E-mail:* plegault@poets.org
Awards Coord & Exec Asst: Alex Dimitrov *Tel:* 212-274-0343 ext 15 *E-mail:* adimitrov@poets.org
Established: 1995
Biennial award to recognize outstanding translations into English of modern Italian poetry. Given to enable an American translator of 20th century Italian poetry to travel, study, or otherwise advance a significant work-in-progress. For guidelines & entry form, send SASE in August of even-numbered years.
Award: $10,000 book prize & a $25,000 fellowship
Closing Date: Sept 1-Dec 31 (even-numbered years)
Presented: Jan (odd-numbered years)

**Sir Walter Raleigh Award for Fiction**
Historical Book Club of North Carolina
Affiliate of North Carolina Literary & Historical Association
4610 Mail Service Ctr, Raleigh, NC 27699-4610
*Tel:* 919-807-7290 *Fax:* 919-733-8807
*Key Personnel*
Awards Coord: Michael Hill *E-mail:* michael.hill@ncdcr.gov
Award for the best book of fiction by an author who has been a legal or actual resident of North Carolina for at least three years prior to the end of the contest.

**RBC Bronwen Wallace Award for Emerging Writers**
The Writers' Trust of Canada
90 Richmond St E, Suite 200, Toronto, ON M5C 1P1, Canada
*Tel:* 416-504-8222 *Toll Free Tel:* 877-906-6548 *Fax:* 416-504-9090
*E-mail:* info@writerstrust.com
*Web Site:* www.writerstrust.com
*Key Personnel*
Exec Dir: Mary Osbourne *Tel:* 416-504-8222 ext 244
Established: 1994
Awarded to a young author, 35 years of age & under, who has not been previously published in book form. The award alternates each year between short fiction & poetry.
Other Sponsor(s): RBC Foundation
Award: $5,000
Presented: Annually in Spring

**The Rea Award for the Short Story**
Dungannon Foundation
53 W Church Hill Rd, Washington, CT 06794
*Web Site:* reaaward.org
*Key Personnel*
Pres: Elizabeth R Rea
Established: 1986
Established by Michael M Rea to honor a living US or Canadian writer who has made a significant contribution to the short story form. No submissions accepted. The recipient is nominated & selected by a jury.
Award: $30,000

**Robert F Reed Technology Medal**
Printing Industries of America
200 Deer Run Rd, Sewickley, PA 15143-2600
*Tel:* 412-259-1705 *Toll Free Tel:* 800-910-4283 (ext 705) *Fax:* 412-749-9890
*E-mail:* printing@printing.org
*Web Site:* www.printing.org
*Key Personnel*
CEO & Pres: Michael Makin *E-mail:* mmakin@printing.org
Asst to VP, Mktg: Sara Welsh *E-mail:* swelsh@printing.org
Established: 1974
Acknowledges an individual who has made a major career contribution to the technical & scientific development of the graphic communications industry. For more information, go to www.printing.org & click on Programs & Services, then Awards & Recognition.
Other Sponsor(s): Printing Industries of America's Ben Franklin Society
Award: Engraved medal
Presented: TAGA Annual Technical Conference

**Regina Medal Award**
Catholic Library Association
205 W Monroe, Suite 314, Chicago, IL 60606-5061
*Tel:* 312-739-1776; 312-739-1776 *Toll Free Tel:* 855-739-1776 *Fax:* 312-739-1778; 312-739-1778
*E-mail:* cla2@cathla.org
*Web Site:* www.cathla.org
*Key Personnel*
Pres: Malachy R McCarthy *E-mail:* mmccarthy@cathla.org
Established: 1959
For continued distinguished lifetime contribution to children's literature; no unsol mss.
Award: Sterling silver medal
Closing Date: None; in-house votes
Presented: CLA Annual Convention

**Nathan Reingold Prize**
History of Science Society
Affiliate of American Council of Learned Societies
440 Geddes Hall, Notre Dame, IN 46556
*Tel:* 574-631-1194 *Fax:* 574-631-1533
*E-mail:* info@hssonline.org
*Web Site:* www.hssonline.org
*Key Personnel*
Exec Dir: Robert Jay Malone
Established: 1955
For an original essay, not to exceed 8,000 words, in history of science & its cultural influences. Open to graduate students only. Must send in three copies of essay with a detachable author/title page.
Award: $500 (& up to $500 travel reimbursement)
Closing Date: Annually, June 1
Presented: Annually in Oct or Nov

**Residency**
Millay Colony for the Arts
454 E Hill Rd, Austerlitz, NY 12017
Mailing Address: PO Box 3, Austerlitz, NY 12017-0003
*Tel:* 518-392-3103; 518-392-4144
*E-mail:* apply@millaycolony.org
*Web Site:* www.millaycolony.org
*Key Personnel*
Exec Dir: Caroline Crumpacker *E-mail:* director@millaycolony.org
Residency Dir: Calliope Nicholas *E-mail:* residency@millaycolony.org
Residencies for writers, composers & visual artists; send SASE to receive application & information; applications available by e-mail or on web site.
Award: One-month residencies offered including room, studio & meals; no cash award
Closing Date: Oct 1

**The Harold U Ribalow Prize**
Hadassah Magazine
50 W 58 St, 4th fl, New York, NY 10019
*Tel:* 212-451-6289 *Fax:* 212-451-6257
*E-mail:* ribalowprize@hadassah.org
*Web Site:* www.hadassah.org/magazine

*Key Personnel*
Exec Ed: Alan M Tigay
Established: 1983
Annual award for an outstanding English-language work of fiction on a Jewish theme by an author deserving of recognition.
Other Sponsor(s): Harold U Ribalow family
Award: $3,000
Closing Date: April of the year following publication
Presented: Autumn

**Evelyn Richardson Memorial Literary Trust Award**
Writers' Federation of Nova Scotia
1113 Marginal Rd, Halifax, NS B3H 4P7, Canada
*Tel:* 902-423-8116 *Fax:* 902-422-0881
*E-mail:* talk@writers.ns.ca
*Web Site:* www.writers.ns.ca
*Key Personnel*
Exec Dir: Nate Crawford *E-mail:* director@writers.ns.ca
Established: 1978
Presented to the best nonfiction book, published by a native or resident Nova Scotian in the previous calendar year.
Award: $2,000
Closing Date: Annually, 1st Friday in Dec
Presented: Halifax, NS, Canada, Annually in Oct

**Gwen Pharis Ringwood Award for Drama**
Writers Guild of Alberta
11759 Groat Rd, Edmonton, AB T5M 3K6, Canada
*Tel:* 780-422-8174 *Toll Free Tel:* 800-665-5354 (AB only) *Fax:* 780-422-2663 (attn WGA)
*E-mail:* mail@writersguild.ab.ca
*Web Site:* www.writersguild.ab.ca
*Key Personnel*
Exec Dir: Carol Holmes *E-mail:* cholmes@writersguild.ab.ca
Communs & Partnerships Coord: Nicholas Mather *E-mail:* nmather@writersguild.ab.ca
Memb Servs Coord: Giorgia Severini
Progs Coord: Nichole Quiring *E-mail:* programs@writersguild.ab.ca
Established: 1982
Alberta Literary Award, author must be resident of Alberta.
Award: $1,500 plus leather-bound copy of book
Closing Date: Annually, Dec 31
Presented: Alberta Literary Awards Gala
*Branch Office(s)*
Lord Denning House, 509 20 Ave SW, Calgary, AB T2S 0E7, Canada, Prog Coord: Samantha Warwick *Tel:* 403-265-2226 *E-mail:* swarwick@writersguild.ab.ca

**Roanoke-Chowan Award for Poetry**
North Carolina Literary & Historical Association
Affiliate of Historical Book Club of North Carolina
4610 Mail Service Ctr, Raleigh, NC 27699-4610
*Tel:* 919-807-7290 *Fax:* 919-733-8807
*Web Site:* www.history.ncdcr.gov/affiliates/lit-hist/awards/awards.htm
*Key Personnel*
Awards Coord: Michael Hill *E-mail:* michael.hill@ncdcr.gov
Established: 1953
Award for the best published book of poetry by a legal or actual resident of North Carolina for at least 3 years prior to the end of the contest period.
Award: Cup
Closing Date: Annually, July 15
Presented: Raleigh, NC, Annually in Nov

**The Roanoke Review Fiction Contest**
Roanoke College
221 College Lane, Salem, VA 24153
*E-mail:* review@roanoke.edu
*Web Site:* roanokereview.wordpress.com
*Key Personnel*
Ed: Paul Hanstedt *Tel:* 540-375-2380
Established: 2001
Award: $1,000, (1st prize), $500 (2nd prize)
Closing Date: Annually in Nov

**Rocky Mountain Book Award**
PO Box 42, Lethbridge, AB T1J 3Y3, Canada
*Tel:* 403-381-7164
*E-mail:* rockymountainbookaward@shaw.ca
*Web Site:* rmba.lethsd.ab.ca
*Key Personnel*
Contact: Michelle Dimnik
Established: 2001
Grade 4-7. An Alberta Children's Choice Book Award.
Closing Date: Jan 15
Presented: Announced electronically on Canada Book Day on April 23

**Rogers Writers' Trust Fiction Prize**
The Writers' Trust of Canada
90 Richmond St E, Suite 200, Toronto, ON M5C 1P1, Canada
*Tel:* 416-504-8222 *Toll Free Tel:* 877-906-6548 *Fax:* 416-504-9090
*E-mail:* info@writerstrust.com
*Web Site:* www.writerstrust.com
*Key Personnel*
Exec Dir: Mary Osbourne *Tel:* 416-504-8222 ext 244
Established: 1997
Awarded to the year's best novel or collection of short stories.
Other Sponsor(s): Rogers Communications
Award: $25,000
Presented: The Writers' Trust Awards, Toronto, ON, CN, Annually in Nov

**Sami Rohr Prize for Jewish Literature**
Jewish Book Council
520 Eighth Ave, 4th fl, New York, NY 10018
*Tel:* 212-201-2920 *Fax:* 212-532-4952
*E-mail:* jbc@jewishbooks.org
*Web Site:* www.jewishbookcouncil.org
*Key Personnel*
Pres, Bd of Dirs: Lawrence J Krule
Dir: Carolyn Starman Hessel *E-mail:* carolynhessel@jewishbooks.org
Dir, Web & Pubns: Naomi Firestone-Teeter
Established: 2006
Annual award which recognizes the unique role of contemporary writers in the transmission & examination of Jewish values & is intended to encourage & promote outstanding writing of Jewish interest. Rewards an emerging writer whose work has demonstrated a fresh vision & evidence of future potential. Recipients must have written a book of exceptional literary merit that stimulates an interest in themes of Jewish concern. Fiction & nonfiction books will be considered in alternate years.
Award: $100,000
Presented: Annually in Spring

**Romance Writers of America Awards**
Romance Writers of America®
14615 Benfer Rd, Houston, TX 77069
*Tel:* 832-717-5200 *Fax:* 832-717-5201
*E-mail:* info@rwa.org
*Web Site:* www.rwa.org
*Key Personnel*
Exec Dir: Allison Kelley *Tel:* 832-717-5200 ext 124 *E-mail:* allison.kelley@rwa.org
Deputy Exec Dir: Carol Ritter *Tel:* 832-717-5200 ext 127 *E-mail:* carol.ritter@rwa.org
Established: 1981
Golden Heart: for unpublished romance fiction mss; RITA Award: best published romance fiction mss for preceding year.
Award: Heart necklace for Golden Heart, Statue for RITA Award
Closing Date: Nov
Presented: Annual National Conference, Atlanta, GA, July

**Dorothy Sargent Rosenberg Poetry Prizes**
Dorothy Sargent Rosenberg Memorial Fund
PO Box 2306, Orinda, CA 94563
*Web Site:* www.dorothyprizes.org
*Key Personnel*
Trustee: Barr Rosenberg; Mary Rosenberg
Established: 2004
Awarded for the best lyric poems celebrating the human spirit. Up to 3 entries permitted per person. Entrants to be under the age of 40. Submitted poems to be previously unpublished, original & in English (no translations). Only one poem may be more than 30 lines. Prizes awarded as recommended by the judges. $10 entry fee. See web site for further details.
Award: Up to $25,000
Closing Date: Oct 5
Presented: Published on web site Feb

**Margaret W Rossiter History of Women in Science Prize**
History of Science Society
Affiliate of American Council of Learned Societies
440 Geddes Hall, Notre Dame, IN 46556
*Tel:* 574-631-1194 *Fax:* 574-631-1533
*E-mail:* info@hssonline.org
*Web Site:* www.hssonline.org
*Key Personnel*
Exec Dir: Robert Jay Malone
Recognition of an outstanding book (or, in even-numbered years, article) on the history of women in science. Books & articles published in the preceding four years are eligible.
Award: $1,000
Closing Date: April 1

**Lois Roth Award**
Modern Language Association of America (MLA)
26 Broadway, 3rd fl, New York, NY 10004-1789
SAN: 202-6422
*Tel:* 646-576-5141 *Fax:* 646-458-0030
*E-mail:* awards@mla.org
*Web Site:* www.mla.org
*Key Personnel*
Coord, Book Prizes: Annie M Reiser *E-mail:* areiser@mla.org
Established: 1999
Committee solicits submissions of translations into English of a book-length literary work. Translations published in year prior to competition are eligible. For consideration submit 6 copies & 12-15 pages of original text in its original language taken from the beginning, middle & end of the work & a litter identifying the translator, as well as the date of publication. Translators need not be members of the association. Offered in odd-numbered years.
Award: Cash award, certificate & one year association membership
Closing Date: April 1, 2015
Presented: MLA Convention, Jan 2016

**Lexi Rudnitsky Poetry Prize**
Persea Books
277 Broadway, Suite 708, New York, NY 10007
SAN: 212-8233
*Tel:* 212-260-9256 *Fax:* 212-267-3165
*E-mail:* info@perseabooks.com
*Web Site:* www.perseabooks.com
*Key Personnel*
Pres & Publr: Michael Braziller
VP & Edit Dir: Karen Braziller
Established: 2006
First book by an American woman poet.
Award: $1,000 plus publication
Closing Date: Oct 31

**William B Ruggles Journalism Scholarship**
National Institute for Labor Relations Research
5211 Port Royal Rd, Suite 510, Springfield, VA 22151
*Tel:* 703-321-9606 *Fax:* 703-321-7143
*E-mail:* research@nilrr.org
*Web Site:* www.nilrr.org
*Key Personnel*
Scholarship Administrator: Cathy Jones
Established: 1974
Scholarship grant for students majoring in journalism or related majors. Based on scholastic ability demonstrating an understanding of the economic, political & social implications of compulsory unionism.
Award: $2,000
Closing Date: Annually, Dec 31
Presented: Annually in April

**The Cornelius Ryan Award**
Overseas Press Club of America (OPC)
40 W 45 St, New York, NY 10036
*Tel:* 212-626-9220 *Fax:* 212-626-9210
*Web Site:* www.opcofamerica.org
*Key Personnel*
Exec Dir: Sonya K Fry
Awarded for best nonfiction book on international affairs.
Award: Certificate & cash award
Closing Date: Annually, last week of Jan
Presented: New York City, Annually in late April

**Saint Louis Literary Award**
Saint Louis University Library Associates
Pius XII Memorial Library, 3650 Lindell Blvd, St Louis, MO 63108
*Tel:* 314-977-3100 *Fax:* 314-977-3587
*E-mail:* slula@slu.edu
*Web Site:* www.slu.edu/libraries/associates
*Key Personnel*
Asst VP, Univ Libs: Gail M Staines, PhD *E-mail:* gstaines@slu.edu
Established: 1967
For body of author's work. No applications; awardee chosen by committee.
Award: Honorarium, Citation
Presented: Award Ceremony, Autumn

**The Carl Sandburg Literary Awards**
The Chicago Public Library Foundation
20 N Michigan Ave, Suite 520, Chicago, IL 60602
*Tel:* 312-201-9830 *Fax:* 312-201-9833
*Web Site:* www.chicagopubliclibraryfoundation.org
*Key Personnel*
CEO & Pres: Rhona Frazin *E-mail:* rfrazin@cplfoundation.org
Established: 2000
Honors a significant work or a body of work that has enhanced the public's awareness of the written word & reflects the Library's commitment to the freedom of all people to read, to learn & to discover.
Award: $10,000
Presented: The Forum, University of Illinois at Chicago, Annually in Oct

**The Ernest Sandeen & Richard Sullivan Prizes in Fiction & Poetry**
University of Notre Dame Press/ND Creative Writing Program, Dept of English
356 O'Shaughnessy Hall, Notre Dame, IN 46556
*Tel:* 574-631-7526 *Fax:* 574-631-4795
*E-mail:* creativewriting@nd.edu
*Web Site:* creativewriting.nd.edu
*Key Personnel*
Dir: Prof William O'Rourke
Awarded to authors who have published at least one volume of short fiction or one volume of poetry. Include a photocopy of the copyright & the title page of your previous volume. Vanity press publications do not fulfill this requirement. Please include a vita &/or a biographical statement which includes your publishing history. We will be glad to see a selection of reviews of the earlier collection. Submit two copies of your ms & inform us if the ms is available on computer disk. Include a SASE for acknowledgment of receipt of your submission. If you would like your ms returned, send a SASE. A $15 administrative fee should accompany submissions.
Award: $1,000 prize, $500 award & $500 advance against royalties from the Notre Dame Press
Closing Date: May 1-Sept 1, 2014 (Ernest Sandeen Prize), May 1-Sept 1, 2015 (Richard Sullivan Prize)

**Ada Sanderson Memorial**
The Poetry Society of Virginia
1194 Hume Rd, Hume, VA 22639-1806
*E-mail:* poetryinva@aol.com
*Web Site:* www.poetrysocietyofvirginia.org
*Key Personnel*
Pres: Judith K Bragg *E-mail:* musicsavy45@yahoo.com
Adult Contest Chair: Patsy Anne Bickerstaff *E-mail:* granypatsy@yahoo.com; Guy Terrell *E-mail:* ggterr@infionline.net
All entries must be in English, orginal & unpublished. Submit 2 copies, each having the category name & number on top left of page. Only one poem per category; entries will not be returned. Subject: nature; any form; 48 line limit. Entry fee: $4 nonmembs.
Award: $100
Closing Date: Jan 19
Presented: Annual PSV Awards Luncheon, Richmond, VA, April

**Mari Sandoz Award**
Nebraska Library Association
PO Box 21756, Lincoln, NE 68542-1756
*Tel:* 402-216-0727
*E-mail:* nebraskalibraries@gmail.com
*Web Site:* www.nebraskalibraries.org
*Key Personnel*
Exec Dir: Michael Straatmann *E-mail:* nlaexecutivedirector@gmail.com
Established: 1971
Given to a distinguished Nebraska author.
Award: Plaque
Closing Date: Annually, May 30
Presented: NLA/NEMA Fall Convention, Annually in late Oct

**May Sarton Award**
New England Poetry Club
2 Farrar St, Cambridge, MA 02138
Mailing Address: PO Box 190076, Boston, MA 02119
*Tel:* 617-744-6034
*E-mail:* contests@nepoetryclub.org
*Web Site:* www.nepoetryclub.org
*Key Personnel*
Pres: Diana Der-Hovanessian
VP: Sally Cragin; Daniel Tobin
Contest Chair: Nazaleem Smith
Honorary awards for work that inspires other poets. Chosen by board of directors.
Award: $250
Closing Date: Annually, May 31
Presented: Cambridge Library, Cambridge, MA, Annually in Spring

**Saturnalia Books Poetry Prize**
Saturnalia Books
105 Woodside Rd, Ardmore, PA 19003
*Tel:* 267-278-9541
*E-mail:* info@saturnaliabooks.com
*Web Site:* www.saturnaliabooks.com
*Key Personnel*
Publr: Henry Israeli
Established: 2003
Recognizes a poetry ms of high merit.
Award: $2,000 & publication
Closing Date: Annually, April 1

**SATW Foundation Lowell Thomas Travel Journalism Competition**
Society of American Travel Writers Foundation
6317 Crab Orchard Rd, Houston, TX 77057
*Tel:* 713-973-9985
*E-mail:* awards@satwf.com
*Web Site:* www.satwfoundation.org
*Key Personnel*
Pres: David G Molyneaux
Established: 1985
Premier awards for the best work in travel journalism. Competition is open to all North American journalists & is judged by leading schools of journalism. There are 20-plus categories, including individual & publication awards. Among them: Grand Award for Travel Journalist of the Year for a portfolio of work, Best Newspaper Travel sections (divided by circulation), Best Travel Magazine, Best Travel Coverage in Other Magazines, Best Guidebook, Best Travel Book, Best Online Travel Journalism Site & categories for writing, photography, audio broadcast, video broadcast, multimedia work & apps. For entry details & forms, see web site. New materials usually updated early Feb annually.
Award: Nearly $20,000 total in prize money: $1,500 (top prize), $500 (1st place)
Closing Date: April 1 (subject to change)
Presented: Location varies

**Aldo & Jeanne Scaglione Prize for a Translation of a Literary Work**
Modern Language Association of America (MLA)
26 Broadway, 3rd fl, New York, NY 10004-1789
SAN: 202-6422
*Tel:* 646-576-5141 *Fax:* 646-458-0030
*E-mail:* awards@mla.org
*Web Site:* www.mla.org
*Key Personnel*
Coord, Book Prizes: Annie M Reiser *E-mail:* areiser@mla.org
Awarded each even-numbered year for an outstanding translation into English of a book-length literary work; books must have been published in 2013. Translators need not be members of MLA. For consideration, submit 6 copies & 12-15 pages of original text.
Award: Cash award, certificate & 1 year association membership
Closing Date: April 1, 2014
Presented: MLA Convention, Jan 2015

**Aldo & Jeanne Scaglione Prize for a Translation of a Scholarly Study of Literature**
Modern Language Association of America (MLA)
26 Broadway, 3rd fl, New York, NY 10004-1789
SAN: 202-6422
*Tel:* 646-576-5141 *Fax:* 646-458-0030
*E-mail:* awards@mla.org
*Web Site:* www.mla.org
*Key Personnel*
Coord, Book Prizes: Annie M Reiser *E-mail:* areiser@mla.org
Awarded biennially for an outstanding translation into English of a book-length work of literary history, literary criticism, philology or literary theory published in two years prior to competition deadline. For consideration, submit 4 copies.
Award: Cash award, certificate & 1 yr association membership
Closing Date: May 1, 2015
Presented: MLA Convention, Jan 2016

**Aldo & Jeanne Scaglione Prize for Comparative Literary Studies**
Modern Language Association of America (MLA)
26 Broadway, 3rd fl, New York, NY 10004-1789
SAN: 202-6422
*Tel:* 646-576-5141 *Fax:* 646-458-0030
*E-mail:* awards@mla.org
*Web Site:* www.mla.org
*Key Personnel*
Coord, Book Prizes: Annie M Reiser *E-mail:* areiser@mla.org
Established: 1992
Prize awarded annually for an outstanding scholarly work by a member of the MLA in the field of comparative literary studies involving at least 2 literatures, published in year prior to competition. For consideration, submit 4 copies.
Award: Cash award & certificate
Closing Date: May 1
Presented: MLA Convention, Jan

**Aldo & Jeanne Scaglione Prize for French & Francophone Studies**
Modern Language Association of America (MLA)
26 Broadway, 3rd fl, New York, NY 10004-1789
SAN: 202-6422
*Tel:* 646-576-5141 *Fax:* 646-458-0030
*E-mail:* awards@mla.org
*Web Site:* www.mla.org
*Key Personnel*
Coord, Book Prizes: Annie M Reiser *E-mail:* areiser@mla.org
Established: 1992
Awarded annually for an outstanding scholarly work by a member of the MLA in the field of French or Francophone literary or linguistic studies published the previous year. For consideration, submit 4 copies.
Award: Cash award & certificate
Closing Date: May 1
Presented: MLA Convention, Jan

**Aldo & Jeanne Scaglione Prize for Italian Studies**
Modern Language Association of America (MLA)
26 Broadway, 3rd fl, New York, NY 10004-1789
SAN: 202-6422
*Tel:* 646-576-5141 *Fax:* 646-458-0030
*E-mail:* awards@mla.org
*Web Site:* www.mla.org
*Key Personnel*
Coord, Book Prizes: Annie M Reiser *E-mail:* areiser@mla.org
Established: 2000
Awarded biennially for an outstanding study in Italian literature or comparative literature involving Italian by an MLA member for books published in the year prior to competition deadline. For consideration, submit 4 copies.
Award: Cash award & certificate
Closing Date: May 1, 2015
Presented: MLA Convention, Jan 2016

**Aldo & Jeanne Scaglione Prize for Studies in Germanic Languages & Literature**
Modern Language Association of America (MLA)
26 Broadway, 3rd fl, New York, NY 10004-1789
SAN: 202-6422
*Tel:* 646-576-5141 *Fax:* 646-458-0030
*E-mail:* awards@mla.org
*Web Site:* www.mla.org
*Key Personnel*
Coord, Book Prizes: Annie M Reiser *E-mail:* areiser@mla.org
Awarded biennially only to members of the Association for an outstanding scholarly work on the linguistics or literatures of the Germanic languages including Danish, Dutch, German, Norwegian, Swedish & Yiddish & published in the 2 years prior to competition deadline. For consideration, submit 4 copies.
Award: Cash award & certificate
Closing Date: May 1, 2014
Presented: MLA Convention, Jan 2015

**Aldo & Jeanne Scaglione Prize for Studies in Slavic Languages & Literature**
Modern Language Association of America (MLA)
26 Broadway, 3rd fl, New York, NY 10004-1789
SAN: 202-6422
*Tel:* 646-576-5141
*E-mail:* awards@mla.org
*Web Site:* www.mla.org
*Key Personnel*
Coord, Book Prizes: Annie M Reiser *E-mail:* areiser@mla.org
Awarded biennially for an outstanding scholarly work on the linguistics or literatures of the Slavic languages & published in the 2 years prior to the competition deadline. Authors need not be members of the MLA. For consideration, submit 4 copies.
Award: Cash award, certificate & 1 year association membership
Closing Date: May 1, 2015
Presented: MLA Convention, Jan 2016

**Aldo & Jeanne Scaglione Publication Award for a Manuscript in Italian Literary Studies**
Modern Language Association of America (MLA)
26 Broadway, 3rd fl, New York, NY 10004-1789
SAN: 202-6422
*Tel:* 646-576-5141 *Fax:* 646-458-0030
*E-mail:* awards@mla.org
*Web Site:* www.mla.org
*Key Personnel*
Coord, Book Prizes: Annie M Reiser *E-mail:* areiser@mla.org
Awarded annually for an outstanding ms dealing with any aspect of the languages & literatures of Italy. Ms ready or accepted for publication by a member of the AAUP before award deadline; authors must be current members of the MLA residing in the US or CN. For consideration, submit 4 copies.
Award: Cash award & certificate
Closing Date: Aug 1
Presented: MLA Convention, Jan

**William Sanders Scarborough Prize**
Modern Language Association of America (MLA)
26 Broadway, 3rd fl, New York, NY 10004-1789
SAN: 202-6422
*Tel:* 646-576-5141 *Fax:* 646-458-0030
*E-mail:* awards@mla.org
*Web Site:* www.mla.org
*Key Personnel*
Coord, Book Prizes: Annie M Reiser *E-mail:* areiser@mla.org
Established: 2001
Annual prize for an outstanding scholarly study of Black American literature or culture published the previous year. Author need not be a member of the MLA. For consideration, submit 4 copies.
Award: Cash award, certificate & one year association membership
Closing Date: May 1
Presented: MLA Convention, Jan

**SCBWI Work-In-Progress Grants**
Society of Children's Book Writers & Illustrators (SCBWI)
8271 Beverly Blvd, Los Angeles, CA 90048
*Tel:* 323-782-1010 *Fax:* 323-782-1892
*E-mail:* membership@scbwi.org; scbwi@scbwi.org
*Web Site:* www.scbwi.org
*Key Personnel*
Pres: Stephen Mooser *E-mail:* stephenmooser@scbwi.org
Exec Dir: Lin Oliver *E-mail:* linoliver@scbwi.org
Established: 1978
The General Work-In-Progress Grant, the Work-In-Progress Grant for Nonfiction Research, the Work-In-Progress Grant for a Contemporary Novel for Young People & the Grant for a Work by an Author Who Has Never Been Published have been established to assist children's book writers in the completion of a specific project. Must be SCBWI member to qualify.
Award: $2,000 each & $500 for one runner-up in each category
Closing Date: March
Presented: Aug

**William D Schaeffer Environmental Award**
Printing Industries of America
200 Deer Run Rd, Sewickley, PA 15143-2600
*Tel:* 412-259-1705 *Toll Free Tel:* 800-910-4283 (ext 705) *Fax:* 412-749-9890
*E-mail:* printing@printing.org
*Web Site:* www.printing.org
*Key Personnel*
CEO & Pres: Michael Makin *E-mail:* mmakin@printing.org
PPA Coord: Sara Welsh *E-mail:* swelsh@printing.org
Honors significant contributions to environmental awareness by an individual in the printing industry. Entry is free. For more information, go to www.printing.org & click on Programs & Services, then Awards & Recognition.
Award: Engraved Plaque
Presented: National Environmental Health & Safety (NEHS) Conference

**Bernadotte E Schmitt Grants**
American Historical Association
400 "A" St SE, Washington, DC 20003-3889
*Tel:* 202-544-2422 *Fax:* 202-544-8307
*E-mail:* awards@historians.org
*Web Site:* www.historians.org
Awarded to support research in the history of Europe, Africa & Asia. Only members of the Association are eligible. The grants are intended to further research in progress & may be used for travel to a library or archive, for microfilms, photographs, or xeroxing, for coding & key punching. Preference will be given to those with specific research needs, such as the completion of a project or completion of a discrete segment thereof. Preference will be given to junior scholars, PhD candidates & those without access to institutional funds. Application form (online), CV & one page bibliography must be submitted by deadline. All updated info on web site.
Award: Individual grants will not exceed $1,000; Preference to PhD candidates & scholars
Closing Date: Annually, Feb 15

**Scholastic Library/National Library Week Grant**
The American Library Association (ALA)
50 E Huron St, Chicago, IL 60611
*Tel:* 312-280-2148 *Toll Free Tel:* 800-545-2433 (ext 2148) *Fax:* 312-280-5274
*Web Site:* www.ala.org/nlwgrant
*Key Personnel*
Coord, The Campaign for America's Libs: Megan McFarlane *E-mail:* mmcfarlane@ala.org
All types of libraries are encouraged to apply. Presented annually to a single library to support its National Library Week communications initiatives that use the National Library Week theme. See web site for more information & for electronic application submission.
Award: $3,000
Closing Date: Annually, Oct 1
Presented: Annually in Jan

**Ruth & Sylvia Schwartz Children's Book Award**
Ruth Schwartz Foundation

c/o Ontario Arts Council, 151 Bloor St W, 5th fl, Toronto, ON M5S 1T6, Canada
*Tel:* 416-961-1660 *Toll Free Tel:* 800-387-0058 (ON) *Fax:* 416-961-7447
*E-mail:* info@arts.on.ca
*Web Site:* www.arts.on.ca
*Key Personnel*
Exec Dir: Alan Walker *Tel:* 416-969-7413 *E-mail:* awalker@arts.on.ca
Assoc Dir: Sarah Milanes *Tel:* 416-969-7411 *E-mail:* smilanes@arts.on.ca
Awards Coord: Carolyn Gloude *Tel:* 416-969-7423 *E-mail:* cgloude@arts.on.ca
Established: 1975
Annual awards to recognize artistic excellence in writing & illustration in Canadian children's literature.
Other Sponsor(s): Ontario Arts Council; Ontario Arts Foundation
Award: $6,000 (CN) picture book, $6,000 (CN) young adult/middle reader
Presented: An Ontario public school, Annually in May

**Science in Society Journalism Awards**
National Association of Science Writers (NASW)
PO Box 7905, Berkeley, CA 94707
*Tel:* 510-647-9500
*Web Site:* www.nasw.org
*Key Personnel*
Exec Dir: Tinsley Davis *E-mail:* director@nasw.org
Established: 1972
Awarded annually to provide recognition for investigative reporting about the sciences & their impact for good & bad, for material published or broadcast between the period of Jan 1-Dec 31. Publishers & broadcasters will also receive certificates of recognition.
Award: $2,500, Certificate of Recognition in each category, travel to awards presentation for 1 author or representative
Closing Date: Feb 1 (postmark)
Presented: Oct

**The Robert S Sergeant Memorial**
The Poetry Society of Virginia
1194 Hume Rd, Hume, VA 22639-1806
*E-mail:* poetryinva@aol.com
*Web Site:* www.poetrysocietyofvirginia.org
*Key Personnel*
Pres: Judith K Bragg *E-mail:* musicsavy45@yahoo.com
Adult Contest Chair: Patsy Anne Bickerstaff *E-mail:* granypatsy@yahoo.com; Guy Terrell *E-mail:* ggterr@infionline.net
All entries must be in English, original & unpublished. Submit 2 copies, each having the category name & number on top left of page. Subject: birds; any form; 48 line limit. Entry fee: $4 nonmembs.
Other Sponsor(s): Alyssa Jenkins; Amber Jenkins; Annika Jenkins
Award: $50
Closing Date: Jan 19
Presented: Annual PSV Awards Luncheon, Richmond, VA, April

**SFWA Nebula Awards**
Science Fiction & Fantasy Writers of America Inc (SFWA)
PO Box 3238, Enfield, CT 06083-3238
*E-mail:* office@sfwa.org
*Web Site:* www.sfwa.org
*Key Personnel*
Pres: Steven Gould
Treas: Bud Sparhawk
VP: Rachel Swirsky
Established: 1965
Winners are selected by the members of the SFWA in the categories of novel, novella, novelette & short story. Andre Norton award for Outstanding Young Adult Fantasy or Science Fiction first presented in 2006. Also Grand Master for lifetime achievement in science fiction & fantasy, not necessarily awarded annually. Ray Bradbury Award for outstanding dramatic presentation first presented in April 2009.
Award: Lucite trophy for Grand Master & Norton; bronze sculpture for Ray Bradbury Award

**The Michael Shaara Book Prize**
Civil War Institute at Gettysburg College
Campus Box 435, 300 N Washington St, Gettysburg, PA 17325
*Tel:* 717-337-6590
*E-mail:* civilwar@gettysburg.edu
*Web Site:* www.gettysburg.edu
*Key Personnel*
Admin Asst: Diane Brennan
Established: 1997
Any novel about the Civil War published for the first time in the current calendar year to encourage fresh approaches to Civil War fiction is eligible. Self published books are not eligible. Publishers, critics & authors must submit books for consideration. No entry fee.
Award: $5,000
Closing Date: Annually, Dec 31

**Shaughnessy Cohen Prize for Political Writing**
The Writers' Trust of Canada
90 Richmond St E, Suite 200, Toronto, ON M5C 1P1, Canada
*Tel:* 416-504-8222 *Toll Free Tel:* 877-906-6548 *Fax:* 416-504-9090
*E-mail:* info@writerstrust.com
*Web Site:* www.writerstrust.com
*Key Personnel*
Exec Dir: Mary Osbourne *Tel:* 416-504-8222 ext 244
Established: 2000
Awarded for a nonfiction book that captures a political subject of relevance to the Canadian reader & enhances understanding of the issue. The winning work combines compelling new insights with depth of research & is of significant literary merit.
Other Sponsor(s): CTV
Award: $25,000
Presented: Politics & the Pen, Ottawa, ON, CN, Annually in Spring

**Mina P Shaughnessy Prize**
Modern Language Association of America (MLA)
26 Broadway, 3rd fl, New York, NY 10004-1789
SAN: 202-6422
*Tel:* 646-576-5141 *Fax:* 646-458-0030
*E-mail:* awards@mla.org
*Web Site:* www.mla.org
*Key Personnel*
Coord, Book Prizes: Annie M Reiser *E-mail:* areiser@mla.org
Established: 1980
Awarded annually for an outstanding publication in the field of language, culture, literacy, or literature with strong application to the teaching of English, published in 2012 or 2013. Authors need not be a member of the MLA. For consideration, submit 4 copies & a letter identifying each work submitted.
Award: Cash award, certificate & one-year membership in the association
Closing Date: May 1, 2014
Presented: MLA Convention, Jan 2015

**Short Prose Competition for Developing Writers**
Writers' Union of Canada
90 Richmond St E, Suite 200, Toronto, ON M5C 1P1, Canada
*Tel:* 416-703-8982 *Fax:* 416-504-9090
*E-mail:* info@writersunion.ca
*Web Site:* www.writersunion.ca
*Key Personnel*
Competitions Coord: Nancy MacLeod *Tel:* 416-703-8982 ext 226 *E-mail:* nmacleod@writersunion.ca
Off Administrator: Valerie Laws *Tel:* 416-703-8982 ext 224
Short prose up to 2,500 words by an unpublished Canadian writer.
Award: $2,500
Closing Date: Annually, Nov 3

**Short Story Award**
Prince Edward Island Writers' Guild
115 Richmond St, Charlottetown, PE C1A 1H7, Canada
*Tel:* 902-368-4410 *Toll Free Tel:* 888-734-2784 *Fax:* 902-368-4418
*E-mail:* peiwritersguild@gmail.com
*Web Site:* www.peiwritersguild.com
*Key Personnel*
Exec Dir: Darrin White *Tel:* 902-368-6176 *E-mail:* dwhite@peica.ca
One short story, maximum 2500 words, constitutes an entry. May submit as many entries as they wish. Work must be original & unpublished. Contest for Prince Edward Island residents only. Call for further information or e-mail. Entry fee for each submission $20.
Award: $400 (1st prize), $200 (2nd prize), $100 (3rd prize)

**Short Story Award for New Writers**
Glimmer Train Press Inc
PO Box 80430, Portland, OR 97280
*Tel:* 503-221-0836 *Fax:* 503-221-0837
*E-mail:* editors@glimmertrain.org
*Web Site:* www.glimmertrain.org
*Key Personnel*
Co-Ed: Susan Burmeister-Brown *E-mail:* susan@glimmertrain.org
Established: 1993
Open to writers whose fiction has not appeared in a print publication with a circulation over 5,000, with a 500-12,000 word count range. Winner notification takes place 2 months after the close of each competition.
Award: $1,500, publication & 20 copies of that issue (1st place), $500 (2nd place), $300 (3rd place)
Closing Date: Annually in Feb, May, Aug & Nov

**Edwin "Bud" Shrake Award for Best Short Nonfiction**
Texas Institute of Letters (TIL)
PO Box 609, Round Rock, TX 78680
*Tel:* 512-683-5640
*E-mail:* tilsecretary@yahoo.com
*Web Site:* www.texasinstituteofletters.org
*Key Personnel*
Pres: W K Stratton
VP: Andres Tijerina
Treas: James Hoggard
Secy: Jan Reid
Recording Secy: Betty Wiesepape
Annual award for best nonfiction writing appearing in a magazine, journal or other periodical or in a newspaper Sunday supplement. Only one story per entrant. Guidelines on the web site.
Award: $1,000
Closing Date: Annually in Jan
Presented: TIL Awards Banquet, Annually in Spring

**Robert F Sibert Informational Book Award**
Association for Library Service to Children (ALSC)
Division of American Library Association (ALA)
50 E Huron St, Chicago, IL 60611-2795
*Tel:* 312-280-2163 *Toll Free Tel:* 800-545-2433 *Fax:* 312-440-9374
*E-mail:* alsc@ala.org

*Web Site:* www.ala.org/alsc
*Key Personnel*
Exec Dir: Aimee Strittmatter *Tel:* 312-280-2162 *E-mail:* astrittmatter@ala.org
Awards Coord: Caroline Jewell *E-mail:* alscawards@ala.org
Prog Coord: Marsha P Burgess *E-mail:* mburgess@ala.org
Presented annually to the author of the most distinguished informational book published in English during the previous year for its significant contribution to children's literature.
Award: Medal
Closing Date: Annually, Dec 31
Presented: ALSC Membership Meeting held during ALA

**Dorothy Silver Playwriting Competition**
Mandel Jewish Community Center of Cleveland
26001 S Woodland Rd, Beachwood, OH 44122
*Tel:* 216-831-0700 *Fax:* 216-831-7796
*E-mail:* info@mandeljcc.org
*Web Site:* www.mandeljcc.org
*Key Personnel*
Competition Coord: Deborah Bobrow *Tel:* 216-593-6278 ext 1378 *E-mail:* dbobrow@mandeljcc.org
Established: 1982
Presented annually for Original works not previously produced at time of submission; suitable for full-length presentation; directly concerned with the Jewish experience.
Award: $1,000 plus staged reading
Closing Date: Dec 31
Presented: Jewish Community Center of Cleveland

**Silver Gavel Awards**
American Bar Association
321 N Clark St, Chicago, IL 60654
*Tel:* 312-988-5733 *Toll Free Tel:* 800-285-2221 (orders) *Fax:* 312-988-5494
*Web Site:* www.abanow.org; www.americanbar.org
*Key Personnel*
Staff Liaison: Howard Kaplan *E-mail:* howardkaplan@staff.abanet.org
Div Coord & Contact: Pamela Hollins *E-mail:* hollinsp@staff.abanet.org
Established: 1958
Media & arts awards competition to recognize communications media that have been exemplary in fostering public understanding of the law & the legal system during the previous calendar year.
Award: Silver Gavel, Honorable Mentions
Closing Date: Jan
Presented: July

**Francis B Simkins Award**
Southern Historical Association
University of Georgia, Dept of History, Athens, GA 30602-1602
*Tel:* 706-542-8848 *Fax:* 706-542-2455
*Web Site:* sha.uga.edu
*Key Personnel*
Admin Asst: Shere Dendy *E-mail:* sdendy@uga.edu
Established: 1977
Awarded for the most distinguished first book by an author in Southern history over a two-year period. Awarded in odd-numbered years for book published in two previous years.
Award: Cash
Closing Date: March 1
Presented: Annual meeting, Fall

**The John Simmons Short Fiction Award**
Writers' Workshop, The University of Iowa
102 Dey House, 507 N Clinton St, Iowa City, IA 52242-1000
*Tel:* 319-335-0416 *Fax:* 319-335-0420
Open to any writer who has not previously published a volume of prose fiction. Revised mss which have been previously entered may be resubmitted as well as writers who have published a volume of poetry are eligible. Mss must be a collection of short stories of at least 150 typewritten pages. Photo copies are acceptable; SASE return packaging must accompany the mss or these will not be returned. No cash, checks, or money orders accepted.
Award: Publication by University of Iowa Press
Closing Date: Annually, Aug 1-Sept 30
Presented: Annually in Autumn

**Charlie May Simon Children's Book Award**
Arkansas State Library
Arkansas State Library, Suite 100, 900 W Capitol Ave, Little Rock, AR 72201-3108
*Tel:* 501-682-2860 *Fax:* 501-682-1693
*Web Site:* www.library.arkansas.gov
*Key Personnel*
Coord, Children's Progs: Cathy Howser *E-mail:* cathy@library.arkansas.gov
Established: 1970
State of Arkansas upper elementary students read books selected by the award committee throughout the year & vote on favorite choice. Most popular book wins award (medallion) & second place award rewarded as Honor Book (plaque).
Other Sponsor(s): Arkansas Department of Education; Arkansas Reading Association
Award: CMS Medallion for first place, plaque for Honor Book
Closing Date: Annual vote in April
Presented: Little Rock, AR, Nov

**Skipping Stones Honor Awards**
Skipping Stones Inc
166 W 12 Ave, Eugene, OR 97401
Mailing Address: PO Box 3939, Eugene, OR 97403
*Tel:* 541-342-4956
*E-mail:* info@skippingstones.org
*Web Site:* www.skippingstones.org
*Key Personnel*
Exec Ed: Arun N Toke *E-mail:* editor@skippingstones.org
Established: 1993
Honors exceptional multicultural & international awareness books, nature/ecology books, bilingual books, teaching resources & educational videos/DVDs. A panel of parents, teachers, librarians, students & editors of Skipping Stones select the honors list in three categories. Entry fee is $50.
Award: Honor award certificates, award seals, reviews, press releases, e-releases, web site hyperlinks. Also displayed at NAME (National Association for Multicultural Education) Conference in Nov annually. Publicity in many educational journals
Closing Date: Annually, Feb 1
Presented: End of April, announced in May-Aug issue of Skipping Stones & on our web site

**Slipstream Annual Poetry Chapbook Contest**
Slipstream Press
PO Box 2071, Dept W-1, Niagara Falls, NY 14301
*Web Site:* www.slipstreampress.org
*Key Personnel*
Co-Ed: Dan Sicoli
Established: 1986
Prize awarded to best 40-page ms of poetry. $20 entry fee.
Award: $1,000 & 50 copies of book
Closing Date: Annually Dec 1

**Bernice Slote Award**
Prairie Schooner
University of Nebraska, 123 Andrews Hall, Lincoln, NE 68588-0334
Mailing Address: PO Box 880334, Lincoln, NE 68588-0334
*Tel:* 402-472-0911
*Web Site:* prairieschooner.unl.edu
*Key Personnel*
Mng Ed: James Engelhardt *E-mail:* jengelhardt2@unl.edu
Ed: Kwame Dawes
Established: 1985
Annual writing prize for best work by a beginning writer published in *Prairie Schooner* in the previous year.
Award: $500
Presented: Winners announced in Spring issue of *Prairie Schooner* magazine

**Donald Smiley Prize**
Canadian Political Science Association
260 rue Dalhousie St, Suite 204, Ottawa, ON K1N 7E4, Canada
*Tel:* 613-562-1202 *Fax:* 613-241-0019
*E-mail:* cpsa-acsp@cpsa-acsp.ca
*Web Site:* www.cpsa-acsp.ca
*Key Personnel*
Administrator: Michelle Hopkins
Established: 1995
Awarded to the best book published in French & the best book published in English in a field relating to the study of government & politics in Canada. To be eligible, a book may be single-authored or multi-authored. Single-authored book: author must be a Canadian citizen or a permanent resident of Canada or a member of the CPSA in the year the book was published. Multi-authored book: at least one of the authors must be a Canadian citizen or a permanent resident of Canada or a member of the CPSA in the year the book was published.
Award: Commemorative plaque & also receive/share the set of books submitted in the language of their own book
Closing Date: Annually, Dec 10
Presented: Annual Conference, Annually in May or June

**Helen C Smith Memorial Award**
Texas Institute of Letters (TIL)
PO Box 609, Round Rock, TX 78680
*Tel:* 512-683-5640
*E-mail:* tilsecretary@yahoo.com
*Web Site:* www.texasinstituteofletters.org
*Key Personnel*
Pres: W K Stratton
VP: Andres Tijerina
Treas: James Hoggard
Secy: Jan Reid
Recording Secy: Betty Wiesepape
Annual award for the first best book of poetry by a poet with a Texas association. Guidelines on the web site.
Other Sponsor(s): William Smith
Award: $1,200
Closing Date: Annually in Jan
Presented: TIL Awards Banquet, Annually in Spring

**The Jeffrey E Smith Editors' Prize**
The Missouri Review
357 McReynolds Hall, Columbia, MO 65211
*Tel:* 573-882-4474 *Toll Free Tel:* 800-949-2505 *Fax:* 573-884-4671
*Web Site:* www.missourireview.com
*Key Personnel*
Assoc Ed: Evelyn Somers *E-mail:* rogerses@missouri.edu
Established: 1991
Awarded annually in fiction, essay & poetry. Entry fee entitles entrant to one-year subscription. Writers should consult web site or send a SASE for guidelines.

Award: $5,000 (short fiction), $5,000 (essay), $5,000 (poetry) & publication in the Spring issue
Closing Date: Annually, Oct 1
Presented: Spring

**Kay Snow Literary Contest**
Willamette Writers
2108 Buck St, West Linn, OR 97068
*Tel:* 503-305-6729 *Fax:* 503-344-6174
*E-mail:* wilwrite@willamettewriters.com
*Web Site:* www.willamettewriters.com
*Key Personnel*
Pres: Val Mallinson
Off Mgr: Bill Johnson
Contest Coord: Lizzy Shannon
Established: 1971
Literary competition in six categories: fiction, nonfiction, juvenile, poetry, scriptwriting, student writer. Entry fee: $10-$15, free for students.
Award: $300 (1st prize), $150 (2nd prize), $50 (3rd prize)
Closing Date: Annually, April 23
Presented: Annual Conference, Annually in Aug

**The Society of Midland Authors Awards**
The Society of Midland Authors (SMA)
530 Michigan Ave, Evanston, IL 60202
Mailing Address: PO Box 10419, Chicago, IL 60610
*E-mail:* info@midlandauthors.com
*Web Site:* www.midlandauthors.com
*Key Personnel*
Pres: Robert Loerzel *E-mail:* loerzel@comcast.net
VP: Meg Tebo
Treas: Richard Bales
Corresponding Secy: Charles J Masters
Recording Secy: Anastasia Royal
Webmaster: Mary Claire Hersh *E-mail:* maryclaire@prodigy.net
Established: 1915
Juried award offers prizes in each of 6 literary categories: children's fiction, children's nonfiction, adult fiction & nonfiction, biography & poetry. Awarded to authors in any of the Midland states: Illinois, Indiana, Iowa, Kansas, Michigan, Minnesota, Missouri, Nebraska, North Dakota, South Dakota, Ohio & Wisconsin.
Award: Monetary award (varies, $500 minimum) & plaque
Closing Date: Annually, Feb 1
Presented: Chicago, IL, Annually, second Tuesday in May

**The Society of Southwestern Authors Writing Contest**
The Society of Southwestern Authors (SSA)
PO Box 30355, Tucson, AZ 85751-0355
*Tel:* 520-546-9382 *Fax:* 520-751-7877
*E-mail:* info@ssa-az.org
*Web Site:* www.ssa-az.org
*Key Personnel*
Contest Coord: Ashleen O'Gaea
Established: 1972
Annual awards for short fiction, 2,500 words max; personal essays & memoirs, 2,500 words; poetry, 40 lines; short stories for children ages 6-12, 1,500 words max.
Award: $250 (1st prize), $125 (2nd prize), $75 (3rd prize), $25 (honorable mention)
Closing Date: Oct 31
Presented: Sheraton Fourpoints, Tucson, AZ, Dec 18

**Sophie Kerr Prize**
Washington College
c/o College Relations Office, 300 Washington Ave, Chestertown, MD 21620
*Tel:* 410-778-2800 *Toll Free Tel:* 800-422-1782 *Fax:* 410-810-7150
*Web Site:* www.washcoll.edu
*Key Personnel*
Dir, Communs: Marcia Landskroener *Tel:* 410-778-7797 *E-mail:* mlandskroener2@washcoll.edu
Established: 1968
Literary award to graduating senior. Only open to undergraduates of Washington College.
Award: $61,000
Closing Date: Annually in April
Presented: Washington College Commencement, Chestertown, MD, Annually in May

**Southeast Review Narrative Nonfiction Contest**
The Southeast Review
Florida State University, Dept of English, Tallahassee, FL 32306
*E-mail:* southeastreview@gmail.com
*Web Site:* www.southeastreview.org
*Key Personnel*
Ed: Katie Cortese
Established: 1986
Best previously unpublished 6,000 word (max) nonfiction story. Include a brief (100 word) bio. All entries will be considered for publication. $16 entry fee per nonfiction entry.
Other Sponsor(s): FSU English Dept's Creative Writing Program
Award: $500
Closing Date: March

**Southeast Review's Gearhart Poetry Contest**
The Southeast Review
Florida State University, Dept of English, Tallahassee, FL 32306
*E-mail:* southeastreview@gmail.com
*Web Site:* www.southeastreview.org
*Key Personnel*
Ed: Katie Cortese
Established: 1996
Award for best poem. All entries will be considered for publication. $16 entry fee for up to 3 poems, no more than 10 pages total.
Other Sponsor(s): FSU English Dept's Creative Writing Program
Award: $500
Closing Date: March

**Southeastern Theatre Conference New Play Project**
Southeastern Theatre Conference (SETC)
1175 Revolution Mill Dr, Suite 14, Greensboro, NC 27405
*Tel:* 336-272-3645 *Fax:* 336-272-8810
*E-mail:* info@setc.org
*Web Site:* www.setc.org
*Key Personnel*
Chair, New Play Proj: Todd Ristau
New play contest.
Award: $1,000, travel & expenses publication in *Southern Threatre Magazine*
Closing Date: March-June
Presented: Southeastern Theatre Conference Convention, March of the following yr

**Southern Books Competition**
Southeastern Library Association
PO Box 950, Rex, GA 30273
*Tel:* 678-466-4339 *Fax:* 678-466-4349
*Web Site:* selaonline.org
*Key Personnel*
Chmn: Lorene Flanders
Admin Servs: Dr Gordon N Baker *E-mail:* gordonbaker@clayton.edu
Established: 1952
Recognition for excellence in bookmaking. Winners are displayed at SELA Conference & in a traveling exhibit available to institutions & organizations. It has been borrowed throughout the South, Canada, Scandinavia, Russia & South Africa.
Award: Published recognition list. Rotating & permanent display of winning books
Closing Date: Annually, date fluctuates
Presented: Biennial SELA Conference, Oct

**Southern Playwrights Competition**
Dept of English/Jacksonville State University
700 Pelham Rd N, Jacksonville, AL 36265-1602
*Tel:* 256-782-5498 *Fax:* 256-782-5441
*Web Site:* www.jsu.edu/depart/english/southpla.htm
*Key Personnel*
Coord: Sarah Moersch *E-mail:* smoersch@jsu.edu
Established: 1988
Drama.
Award: $1,000 honorarium & possible production of winning entry
Closing Date: Annually, Jan 15

**Sovereign Award for Writing**
The Jockey Club of Canada
Woodbine Sales Pavilion, 555 Rexdale Blvd, Rexdale, ON M9W 5L2, Canada
Mailing Address: PO Box 66, Sta B, Etobicoke, ON M9W 5K9, Canada
*Tel:* 416-675-7756 *Fax:* 416-675-6378
*E-mail:* jockeyclub@bellnet.ca
*Web Site:* www.jockeyclubcanada.com
*Key Personnel*
Exec Dir: Stacie Roberts
Established: 1975
Submissions must be of Canadian Thoroughbred Racing content. See guidelines on web site.
Award: Bronze statue of Saint Simon
Closing Date: Annually, Dec 31
Presented: Ontario, CN, Annually, the following April

**The Sow's Ear Poetry Prize & The Sow's Ear Chapbook Prize**
The Sow's Ear Poetry Review
Division of The Word Process Inc
217 Brookneill Dr, Winchester, VA 22602
Mailing Address: PO Box 127, Millwood, VA 22646
*Tel:* 540-955-3955
*Web Site:* sows-ear.kitenet.net
*Key Personnel*
Mng Ed: Robert G Lesman *E-mail:* rglesman@gmail.com
Ed: Kristin Zimet
Established: 1988
Single poem & chapbook.
Award: Poem $1,000; Chapbook $1,000 plus 25 copies
Closing Date: Annually, Nov 1 (poem), May 1 (chapbook)

**Sports Fiction & Essay Contest**
Winning Writers
351 Pleasant St, PMB 222, Northampton, MA 01060-3961
*Tel:* 413-320-1847 *Toll Free Tel:* 866-WINWRIT (946-9748) *Fax:* 413-280-0539
*Web Site:* www.winningwriters.com
*Key Personnel*
Pres: Adam Cohen *E-mail:* adam@winningwriters.com
VP: Jendi Reiter
Established: 2011
Entries accepted Nov 15-May 31. An entry is one story or essay on a sports-related theme. Entries should be original, unpublished, in English & may contain up to 6,000 words. May submit unlimited number of entries. Entry fee $15. Prize amounts are for each category.
Award: $1,000 cash (1st prize), $100 cash each (5 honorable mentions), plus publication on web site for all winners
Closing Date: Annually, May 31
Presented: Annually, Nov 15

**John Spray Mystery Award**
Canadian Children's Book Centre
40 Orchard View Blvd, Suite 217, Toronto, ON M4R 1B9, Canada
*Tel:* 416-975-0010 *Fax:* 416-975-8970
*E-mail:* info@bookcentre.ca
*Web Site:* www.bookcentre.ca
*Key Personnel*
Exec Dir: Charlotte Teeple *E-mail:* charlotte@bookcentre.ca
Gen Mgr: Dawn Todd *E-mail:* dawn@bookcentre.ca
Sales & Mktg Mgr: Holly Kent *E-mail:* holly@bookcentre.ca
Lib Coord: Meghan Howe *E-mail:* meghan@bookcentre.ca
Prog Coord: Shannon Howe Barnes *E-mail:* shannon@bookcentre.ca
Established: 2011
Awarded to a Canadian author for excellence in mystery writing for children & adolescents.
Other Sponsor(s): John Spray
Award: $5,000
Closing Date: Annually in mid Dec

**Spur Awards**
Western Writers of America Inc (WWA)
271 CR 219, Encampment, WY 82325
*Tel:* 307-329-8942 *Fax:* 307-327-5465
*E-mail:* wwa.moulton@gmail.com
*Web Site:* www.westernwriters.org
*Key Personnel*
Pres: Dusty Richards *E-mail:* dustyrichards@cox.net
VP: Sherry Monahan *E-mail:* sherry@sherrymonahan.com
Secy/Treas: Candy Moulton *E-mail:* wwa.moulton@gmail.com
Established: 1953
Various categories (western fiction/nonfiction).
Award: Plaques & recognition
Closing Date: Jan 4 of year following publication
Presented: Annual Convention, Annually in June

**The Edna Staebler Award for Creative Non-Fiction**
Wilfrid Laurier University
Office of the Dean, Faculty of Arts, 75 University Ave W, Waterloo, ON N2L 3C5, Canada
*Tel:* 519-884-1970 (ext 3891) *Fax:* 519-884-8854
*Key Personnel*
Dean: Michael Carroll *Tel:* 519-884-1970 ext 3891
Established: 1991
Annual literary award for a first or second published book of creative nonfiction published in the previous calendar year. Open to Canadian residents only to encourage new Canadian writers.
Award: $10,000
Closing Date: Annually, April 30 (received by)
Presented: Wilfrid Laurier University, Annually in Autumn

**Stanley Drama Award**
Wagner College
One Campus Rd, Staten Island, NY 10301
*Tel:* 718-390-3223 *Fax:* 718-390-3323
*Key Personnel*
Assoc Prof: Todd Alan Price *E-mail:* todd.price@wagner.edu
Established: 1957
Award given for original full-length play or musical which has not been professionally produced or received tradebook publication. Writers of musicals are urged to submit music on cassette tapes as well as books & lyrics. Consideration will also be given to a series of two or three thematically related one-act plays. Scripts must be accompanied by a SASE. Former winners are not eligible to compete. Applications are obtained by sending SASE, application fee of $30.00 must accompany submission.
Award: $2,000
Closing Date: Oct 31
Presented: Annually in April

**Edward Stanley Award**
Prairie Schooner
University of Nebraska, 123 Andrews Hall, Lincoln, NE 68588-0334
Mailing Address: PO Box 880334, Lincoln, NE 68588-0334
*Tel:* 402-472-0911 *Fax:* 402-472-9771
*Web Site:* prairieschooner.unl.edu
*Key Personnel*
Mng Ed: James Engelhardt *E-mail:* jengelhardt2@unl.edu
Ed: Kwame Dawes
Established: 1992
Annual writing prize for best poem or group of poems in the volume. Only contributors to the magazine are eligible.
Other Sponsor(s): Friends & family of Marion Edward Stanley (in memorium)
Award: $1,000
Presented: Winners announced in Spring issue of *Prairie Schooner* magazine

**Agnes Lynch Starrett Poetry Prize**
University of Pittsburgh Press
Eureka Bldg, 5th fl, 3400 Forbes Ave, Pittsburgh, PA 15260
*Tel:* 412-383-2456 *Fax:* 412-383-2466
*E-mail:* info@upress.pitt.edu
*Web Site:* www.upress.pitt.edu
*Key Personnel*
Asst to Dir: Kelley H Johovic *E-mail:* kjohovic@upress.pitt.edu
Established: 1981
Open to any poet who has not had a full-length book previously published. Submit typed 48-100 page poetry mss on white paper with SASE & check or money order of $25 for each ms submitted. See web site for complete rules.
Award: $5,000 & publication
Closing Date: March 1-April 30 (postmark)
Presented: Pittsburgh, PA, Autumn

**Stegner Fellowship**
Stanford University Creative Writing Program
Stanford Creative Writing Program, Dept of English, Stanford, CA 94305-2087
*Tel:* 650-723-0011 *Fax:* 650-723-3679
*Web Site:* creativewriting.stanford.edu
*Key Personnel*
Prog Asst: Christina Ablaza *E-mail:* stegnerfellowship@stanford.edu
Fellowship; residence required for two years at Stanford beginning autumn quarter each year.
Award: $26,000, required tuition & health insurance
Closing Date: Sept 1-Dec 1

**John Steinbeck Short Story Award**
Reed Magazine
San Jose State University, English Dept, One Washington Sq, San Jose, CA 95192-0090
*Tel:* 408-924-4458
*E-mail:* reed@email.sjsu.edu
*Web Site:* www.reedmag.org
All submissions must be through the online system with a common file format. Writers may submit multiple entries but each must be submitted separately & accompanied by a separate entry fee of $15.
Other Sponsor(s): Center for Steinbeck Studies; San Jose State University
Award: $1,000 & publication in Reed Magazine
Closing Date: June 1-Nov 1

**Stephan G Stephansson Award for Poetry**
Writers Guild of Alberta
11759 Groat Rd, Edmonton, AB T5M 3K6, Canada
*Tel:* 780-422-8174 *Toll Free Tel:* 800-665-5354 (AB only) *Fax:* 780-422-2663 (attn WGA)
*E-mail:* mail@writersguild.ab.ca
*Web Site:* www.writersguild.ab.ca
*Key Personnel*
Exec Dir: Carol Holmes *E-mail:* cholmes@writersguild.ab.ca
Communs & Partnerships Coord: Nicholas Mather *E-mail:* nmather@writersguild.ab.ca
Memb Servs Coord: Giorgia Severini
Progs Coord: Nichole Quiring *E-mail:* programs@writersguild.ab.ca
Established: 1982
Alberta Literary Award, author must be resident of Alberta.
Award: $1,500 plus leather-bound copy of book
Closing Date: Annually, Dec 31
Presented: Alberta Literary Awards Gala
*Branch Office(s)*
Lord Denning House, 509 20 Ave SW, Calgary, AB T2S 0E7, Canada, Prog Coord: Samantha Warwick *Tel:* 403-265-2226 *Fax:* 403-234-9532 (attn: WGA) *E-mail:* swarwick@writersguild.ab.ca

**Elizabeth Matchett Stover Memorial Award**
Southwest Review
6404 Robert Hyer Lane, Rm 307, Dallas, TX 75275-0374
Mailing Address: PO Box 750374, Dallas, TX 75275-0374
*Fax:* 214-768-1408
*E-mail:* swr@mail.smu.edu
*Web Site:* www.smu.edu/southwestreview
*Key Personnel*
Ed-in-Chief: Willard Spiegelman
Sr Ed: Jennifer Cranfill *Tel:* 214-768-1036
Established: 1978
Awarded annually to the author of the best poem or group of poems published in the Southwest Review during the preceding year.
Award: $300

**Jessamy Stursberg Poetry Contest for Youth**
The League of Canadian Poets
192 Spadina Ave, Suite 312, Toronto, ON M5T 2C2, Canada
*Tel:* 416-504-1657 *Fax:* 416-504-0096
*E-mail:* readings@poets.ca
*Web Site:* www.youngpoets.ca; www.poets.ca
*Key Personnel*
Exec Dir: Joanna Poblocka *E-mail:* joanna@poets.ca
Asst Dir: Ingel Madrus *E-mail:* readings@poets.ca
Admin & Communs Coord: Lesley Fletcher *E-mail:* admin@poets.ca
Established: 1995
Seeking poems by young poets across the country. Two age categories: Jr (grades 7-9) & Sr (grades 10-12). All winning poems will be published in the e-zine.
Award: $350 cash (1st place), $300 cash (2nd place), $250 cash (3rd place); all winners will receive certificates & student membership in the League for 1 yr
Closing Date: Annually, Jan 15
Presented: Young Poets Week each year (2nd week in April)

**Sudden Fiction Contest**
Berkeley Fiction Review
c/o ASUC Publications, Univ of California, 10-B Eshleman Hall, Berkeley, CA 94720-4500
*E-mail:* bfictionreview@yahoo.com
*Web Site:* www.ocf.berkeley.edu/~bfr/
*Key Personnel*
Mng Ed: Jennifer Brown; Brighton Early
All entries must be 1,000 words or less; typed, double-spaced, with a 12 pt font; include cover

letter & e-mail only. Entry fee $6 ($4 each additional story).
Award: $200 1st place; 1st, 2nd & 3rd place are published in upcoming newsletter

**The Sugarman Family Award for Jewish Children's Literature**
The District of Columbia Jewish Community Center
Irwin P Edlavitch Bldg, 1529 16 St NW, Washington, DC 20036
*Tel:* 202-518-9400 *Fax:* 202-518-9420
*Web Site:* www.washingtondcjcc.org
*Key Personnel*
Dir, Literary, Music & Dance Progs: Lili Kalish Gersch *Tel:* 202-777-3254
Established: 1994
Award for the best Jewish children's book published between Oct 1, 2012 & Oct 1, 2013. Submissions accepted starting Aug 1. Presented biennially; contact office for dates.
Presented: Jewish Literary Festival, Fall

**Ronald Sukenick American Book Review Innovative Fiction Prize**
Fiction Collective Two Inc (FC2)
University Ctr, Suite 310, 3007 N Ben Wilson St, Victoria, TX 77901
*Web Site:* www.fc2.org
Open to any US writer in English who has not previously published with Fiction Collective Two. Submissions may include a collection of short stories, one or more novellas or a novel of any length. Works that have previously appeared in magazines or in anthologies may be included.
Award: $1,500 & publication by FC2
Closing Date: Annually, Nov 1
Presented: May

**Hollis Summers Poetry Prize**
Ohio University Press
215 Columbus Rd, Suite 101, Athens, OH 45701-2979
*Tel:* 740-593-1157
*Web Site:* www.ohioswallow.com/poetry_prize
*Key Personnel*
Exec Ed: Kevin Haworth
This competition invites writers to submit unpublished collections of original poems. Individual collections must be the work of a single author. Translations are not accepted. Submit a ms of 60-95 pages of a poetry collection & a $25 entry fee.
Award: $1,000 & publication
Closing Date: Annually in Oct

**May Swenson Poetry Award**
Utah State University Press
Division of Utah State University
3078 Old Main Hill, Logan, UT 84322-3078
*Tel:* 435-797-1362 *Fax:* 435-797-0313
*Web Site:* www.usupress.org
*Key Personnel*
Dir: Michael Spooner *E-mail:* michael.spooner@usu.edu
Established: 1996
Submitted collections must be original poetry in English, 50 to 100 pages. No restrictions on form or subject. Submit one copy of the ms. Name/address on cover sheet only. Reading fee of $25 (includes copy of winning book). SASE for announcement of winner. Ms will not be returned. Judge reserves the right to declare no winner in any given year.
Award: $1,000, publication & royalties
Closing Date: Annually, Sept 30 (postmark)

**Sydney Taylor Book Awards**
Association of Jewish Libraries (AJL) Inc
PO Box 1118, Teaneck, NJ 07666
*Tel:* 973-744-3836
*E-mail:* chair@sydneytaylorbookaward.org
*Web Site:* www.sydneytaylorbookaward.org
*Key Personnel*
Pres: Heidi Estrin *E-mail:* president@jewishlibraries.org
Contact: Aimee Lurie
Established: 1968
Literary content for outstanding children's books in field of Jewish literature. Three categories of prizes: Younger Readers, Older Readers, Teen Readers.
Award: $500 prize for each category; $500 award to illustrator of Young Readers Award book
Closing Date: Annually, Dec 1
Presented: AJL Annual Convention, Annually in June

**Sydney Taylor Manuscript Award**
Association of Jewish Libraries (AJL) Inc
Affiliate of American Library Association (ALA)
204 Park St, Montclair, NJ 07042
*Tel:* 201-371-3255
*E-mail:* stmacajl@aol.com
*Web Site:* www.jewishlibraries.org
*Key Personnel*
Chpn: Aileen Grossberg
To encourage outstanding Jewish themed fiction written by an unpublished author. Story will appeal to all children ages 8-11 & to help launch new children's writers in their careers.
Award: $1,000
Closing Date: Annually, Sept 30
Presented: AJL Annual Convention, Annually in June

**Charles S Sydnor Award**
Southern Historical Association
University of Georgia, Dept of History, Athens, GA 30602-1602
*Tel:* 706-542-8848 *Fax:* 706-542-2455
*Web Site:* sha.uga.edu
*Key Personnel*
Admin Asst: Shere Dendy *E-mail:* sdendy@uga.edu
Established: 1956
Awarded for the most distinguished book in Southern history published in odd-numbered years. Awarded in even-numbered years.
Award: Cash
Closing Date: March 1
Presented: Annual meeting, Fall

**The Tampa Review Prize for Poetry**
Tampa Review
University of Tampa Press, 401 W Kennedy Blvd, Tampa, FL 33606
*Tel:* 813-253-6266
*E-mail:* utpress@ut.edu
*Web Site:* tampareview.ut.edu
*Key Personnel*
Ed: Richard Mathews
Edit Asst: Sean Donnelly
Established: 2001
Award: $2,000 & book publication in hardcover & paperback
Closing Date: Dec 31

**Rennie Taylor & Alton Blakeslee Fellowships in Science Writing**
Council for the Advancement of Science Writing (CASW)
PO Box 910, Hedgesville, WV 25427
*Tel:* 304-754-6786
*Web Site:* www.casw.org
*Key Personnel*
Exec Dir: Ben Patrusky *E-mail:* bpatrusky@aol.com
Established: 1975
For tuition & books for graduate study only.
Award: $5,000
Closing Date: July 1

**TD Canadian Children's Literature Award**
Canadian Children's Book Centre
40 Orchard View Blvd, Suite 217, Toronto, ON M4R 1B9, Canada
*Tel:* 416-975-0010 *Fax:* 416-975-8970
*E-mail:* info@bookcentre.ca
*Web Site:* www.bookcentre.ca
*Key Personnel*
Exec Dir: Charlotte Teeple *E-mail:* charlotte@bookcentre.ca
Gen Mgr: Dawn Todd *E-mail:* dawn@bookcentre.ca
Lib Coord: Meghan Howe *E-mail:* meghan@bookcentre.ca
Prog Coord: Shannon Howe Barnes *E-mail:* shannon@bookcentre.ca
Sales & Mktg Mgr: Holly Kent *E-mail:* holly@bookcentre.ca
Established: 2004
Awarded to a Canadian author/illustrator for the most distinguished book of the year.
Other Sponsor(s): TD Bank Group
Award: $25,000 cash, 1 to an English language book & 1 to a French language book, $10,000 to an English language honour book (maximum of 4), $10,000 to a French language honour book (maximum of 4), $2,500 to the publishers of the grand prize winning books for promotion & publicity purposes
Closing Date: Mid Dec annually

**Tennessee Arts Commission Fellowships**
Tennessee Arts Commission
401 Charlotte Ave, Nashville, TN 37243-0780
*Tel:* 615-741-1701 *Toll Free Tel:* 800-848-0299 *Fax:* 615-741-8559
*Web Site:* www.tn.gov/arts
*Key Personnel*
Dir, Literary Arts & Grants Analyst: Lee Baird *Tel:* 615-532-0493 *E-mail:* lee.baird@tn.gov
Annual literary fellowships given to Tennessee writers of every genre.
Award: $5,000
Closing Date: Annually, Jan 24

**The Texas Bluebonnet Award**
Texas Library Association
3355 Bee Cave Rd, Suite 401, Austin, TX 78746
*Tel:* 512-328-1518 *Toll Free Tel:* 800-580-2852 *Fax:* 512-328-8852
*Web Site:* www.txla.org
*Key Personnel*
Progs & Events Asst: Julie Serafini *E-mail:* julies@txla.org
Established: 1979
Awarded to favorite title on annual list, voted on by 200,000 children, grades 3-6.
Other Sponsor(s): Children's Round Table; Texas Association of School Librarians
Award: Medallion in desk mount
Closing Date: Aug 1
Presented: April

**Texas Institute of Letters Awards**
Texas Institute of Letters (TIL)
PO Box 609, Round Rock, TX 78680
*Tel:* 512-683-5640
*E-mail:* tilsecretary@yahoo.com
*Web Site:* www.texasinstituteofletters.org
*Key Personnel*
Pres: W K Stratton
VP: Andres Tijerina
Treas: James Hoggard
Secy: Jan Reid
Recording Secy: Betty Wiesepape
Established: 1936
Annual award for books published by Texas residents or on Texas-related subjects. Guidelines on the web site.
Award: Eleven cash awards, totalling $21,700

Closing Date: Annually in Jan
Presented: TIL Awards Banquet, Annually in Spring

**Theatre-Scriptworks**
Pennsylvania Council on the Arts
216 Finance Bldg, Harrisburg, PA 17120
*Tel:* 717-787-6883 *Fax:* 717-783-2538
*Web Site:* www.pacouncilonthearts.org
*Key Personnel*
Prog Dir: Jamie Dunlap *Tel:* 717-525-5542
*E-mail:* jadunlap@state.pa.us
Fellowships awarded every 3 years to playwrights who create & perform their own work. Must be PA resident. Biennial award, odd-numbered years.
Award: $5,000 or $10,000
Closing Date: Early Aug
Presented: Mid to late Jan

**3-Day Novel Contest**
The Geist Foundation
201-111 W Hastings St, Vancouver, BC V6B 1H4, Canada
*E-mail:* info@3daynovel.com
*Web Site:* www.3daynovel.com
Established: 1977
International novel writing competition. Entry fee of $50 ($35 early bird) for US & CN entries; may be postmarked up until one day before contest.
Award: Publication (1st prize), $500 (2nd prize), $100 (3rd prize)
Closing Date: Fri before Labor Day (postmark)
Presented: Annually Labor Day weekend

**Thurber Prize for American Humor**
Thurber House
77 Jefferson Ave, Columbus, OH 43215
*Tel:* 614-464-1032 *Fax:* 614-280-3645
*E-mail:* thurberhouse@thurberhouse.org
*Web Site:* www.thurberhouse.org
*Key Personnel*
Creative Dir: Susanne Jaffe
Mgr: Anne Touvell *Tel:* 614-464-1032 ext 10
Annual award for the most outstanding book of humor writing published in the United States. The award is presented by Thurber House, a nonprofit literary center in Columbus, OH & the former home of American humorist, author & New Yorker cartoonist James Thurber.
Award: $5,000, commemorative plaque & a nationwide media campaign
Closing Date: Annually, April 1
Presented: Caroline's Comedy Club on Broadway, New York City, Annually in the Fall

**Towson University Prize for Literature**
Towson University
English Dept, 8000 York Rd, Towson, MD 21252
*Tel:* 410-704-2000 *Fax:* 410-704-3999
*Web Site:* www.towson.edu/english
*Key Personnel*
Chair: Dr H George Hahn
Established: 1979
Annual award for a single book or book-length ms of fiction, poetry, drama or imaginative nonfiction by a young Maryland writer. Applicant must have resided in Maryland at least three years prior to applying & must be a Maryland resident when the prize is awarded.
Award: $1,000
Closing Date: Annually, June 15

**Translation Prize**
American-Scandinavian Foundation (ASF)
Scandinavia House, 58 Park Ave, New York, NY 10016
*Tel:* 212-879-9779 *Fax:* 212-686-2115
*E-mail:* grants@amscan.org
*Web Site:* www.amscan.org
*Key Personnel*
Dir, Fellowships: Valerie Hymas
*E-mail:* vhymas@amscan.org
Established: 1980
For translations of contemporary poetry or fiction by Danish, Finnish, Icelandic, Norwegian or Swedish authors born after 1800. Write to ASF or visit the ASF web site for full copy of rules.
Award: $2,000 (either poetry or fiction) & publication of excerpt in an issue of Scandinavian Review & commemorative bronze medallion . $1,000 Inger Sjoberg Prize for runner-up
Closing Date: Annually in June
Presented: Varies

**Trillium Book Award/Prix Trillium**
Ontario Media Development Corp (OMDC)
Division of Ministry of Culture, Ontario Government
South Tower, Suite 501, 175 Bloor St E, Toronto, ON M4W 3R8, Canada
*Tel:* 416-314-6858 (ext 698) *Fax:* 416-314-6876
*E-mail:* trillium23@omdc.on.ca
*Web Site:* www.omdc.on.ca
*Key Personnel*
Consultant, Industry Initiaves: Janet Hawkins
*Tel:* 416-642-6698 *E-mail:* jhawkins@omdc.on.ca
Established: 1987
Open to books in any genre; fiction, nonfiction, drama & children's books. There are no restrictions regarding the previous works of the author.
Award: $20,000 to winning authors in English & French; $2,500 to publishers of winning book in English & French
Closing Date: Jan
Presented: Award ceremony, Late Spring

**Harry S Truman Book Award**
Harry S Truman Library Institute for National & International Affairs
500 W US Hwy 24, Independence, MO 64050
*Tel:* 816-268-8248 *Fax:* 816-268-8299
*Web Site:* www.trumanlibrary.org
*Key Personnel*
Dir, Admin: Lisa Sullivan *E-mail:* lisa.sullivan@nara.gov
Established: 1963
For the best book published during the previous 2 years on the presidency of Harry S Truman. The book must deal with some aspect of the political, economic or social development of the US, principally between April 12, 1945 & Jan 20, 1953 or with the life or career of Truman. Submit 5 copies of the nominated book to Grants Administrator. Book must have been published between Jan 1, 2012 & Dec 31, 2013.
Award: $2,500
Closing Date: Annually in Jan
Presented: No later than May 8 (Truman's birthday) in even-numbered years

**Trustus Playwrights' Festival**
Trustus Theatre
520 Lady St, Columbia, SC 29201
Mailing Address: PO Box 11721, Columbia, SC 29211-1721
*Tel:* 803-254-9732 *Fax:* 803-771-9153
*E-mail:* trustus@trustus.org
*Web Site:* www.trustus.org
*Key Personnel*
Artistic Dir: Dewey Scott-Wiley
Mng Dir: Larry Hembree
Literary Mgr: Sarah Hammond
*E-mail:* shammond@trustus.org
Established: 1988
Experimental, hard-hitting, off-the-wall comedies or dramas suitable for open-minded audiences. No topic taboo, no musicals or plays for young audiences. Two copies of synopsis, resume & completed application. Send SASE for application & guidelines. Applications available on our web site.
Award: Selected play receives public staged reading & $250, followed by a one-year development period, full production, additional $500, plus travel/accommodations for Festival opening
Closing Date: Dec 1-Feb 1
Presented: Trustus, Aug, full production

**Kate Tufts Discovery Award**
Claremont Graduate University
Harper East, Unit B-7, 160 E Tenth St, Claremont, CA 91711-6165
*Tel:* 909-621-8974
*E-mail:* tufts@cgu.edu
*Web Site:* www.cgu.edu/tufts
*Key Personnel*
Poetry Award Coord: Susan Hampson
Established: 1993
Most worthy first book of poetry published between Sept 1, 2011 & Aug 31, 2012; Award presented for a first book by a poet of genuine promise.
Award: $10,000 cash
Closing Date: Annually, Sept 15
Presented: Claremont Graduate University, Annually in April

**Kingsley Tufts Poetry Award**
Claremont Graduate University
Harper East, Unit B-7, 160 E Tenth St, Claremont, CA 91711-6165
*Tel:* 909-621-8974
*E-mail:* tufts@cgu.edu
*Web Site:* www.cgu.edu/tufts
*Key Personnel*
Poetry Award Coord: Susan Hampson
Established: 1992
Most worthy book of poetry published between Sept 1, 2012 & Aug 31, 2013. Mss, CDs & chapbooks not accepted. This award honors an emerging poet, one who is past the very beginning, but has not yet reached the acknowledged pinnacle of his or her career.
Award: $100,000 cash
Closing Date: Annually, Sept 15
Presented: Claremont Graduate University, Claremont, CA, April

**Tupelo Press Poetry Contest for First or Second Books of Poetry**
Tupelo Press Inc
PO Box 1767, North Adams, MA 01247
SAN: 254-3281
*Tel:* 413-664-9611 *Fax:* 413-664-9711
*E-mail:* info@tupelopress.org
*Web Site:* www.tupelopress.org
*Key Personnel*
Mng Ed: Jim Schley
Established: 2000
An annual competition for first or second books of poetry. Full guidelines on the web site.
Award: $3,000 & publication & distribution
Closing Date: Jan 1-April 30
Presented: Summer

**Tupelo Press Snowbound Series Chapbook Award**
Tupelo Press Inc
PO Box 1767, North Adams, MA 01247
SAN: 254-3281
*Tel:* 413-664-9611 *Fax:* 413-664-9711
*E-mail:* info@tupelopress.org
*Web Site:* www.tupelopress.org
*Key Personnel*
Mng Ed: Jim Schley
Established: 2004
An annual open poetry chapbook competition. Full guidelines on the web site.
Award: $1,000 & publication

Closing Date: Annually Dec 1-Feb 28
Presented: Spring

**The Tusculum Review Prize for Fiction**
The Tusculum Review
60 Shiloh Rd, PO Box 5113, Greeneville, TN 37743
*Web Site:* www.tusculum.edu/tusculumreview
*Key Personnel*
Ed: Wayne Thomas *Tel:* 423-636-7300 ext 5285 *E-mail:* wthomas@tusculum.edu
Established: 2005
Award: $1,000 & publication in *The Tusculum Review*
Closing Date: March 15

**The 25 Most "Censored" Stories Annual**
Project Censored - Media Freedom Foundation
PO Box 571, Cotati, CA 94931
*Tel:* 707-874-2695
*Web Site:* www.projectcensored.org
*Key Personnel*
Pres, Media Freedom Foundation: Peter Phillips *E-mail:* peter@projectcensored.org
Dir, Project Censored: Mickey Huff *E-mail:* mickey@projectcensored.org
Established: 1976
Investigative journalism.
Award: Certificate
Presented: Annually, Oct 1

**Ucross Foundation Residency Program**
Ucross Foundation
30 Big Red Lane, Clearmont, WY 82835
*Tel:* 307-737-2291 *Fax:* 307-737-2322
*E-mail:* info@ucross.org
*Web Site:* www.ucrossfoundation.org
*Key Personnel*
Pres, Ucross Foundation: Sharon Dynak *E-mail:* sdynak@ucross.org
Residency Mgr: Ruth Salvatore *E-mail:* rsalvatore@ucross.org
Established: 1983
Artist & writer residency program. Approximately 85 individuals per year for 2-6 week lengths of time. Application fee: $40.
Award: Room, studio & board
Closing Date: Annually, March 1 (Fall session) & Oct 1 (Spring session)

**University of Iowa, Writer's Workshop**
University of Iowa, Writers' Workshop, Graduate Creative Writing Program
102 Dey House, 507 N Clinton St, Iowa City, IA 52242-1000
*Tel:* 319-335-0416 *Fax:* 319-335-0420
*Key Personnel*
Dir: Lan Samantha Chang
The Iowa Short Fiction Award; The John Simmons Short Fiction Award. For guidelines & further information send SASE.
Other Sponsor(s): The Iowa Arts Council; University of Iowa Press
Award: Publication
Closing Date: Sept 30
Presented: First quarter

**Utah Original Writing Competition**
Utah Division of Arts & Museums
Subsidiary of Utah State Department of Heritage & Arts
617 E South Temple, Salt Lake City, UT 84102
*Tel:* 801-236-7555 *Fax:* 801-236-7556
*Web Site:* arts.utah.gov
*Key Personnel*
Literary Arts Specialist: David Pace *Tel:* 801-533-5760 *E-mail:* davidpace@utah.gov
Established: 1958
Applicants must be Utah residents. Guidelines & forms posted on web site by April 1.
Award: $8,450 in prizes in 7 categories
Closing Date: June (the last Friday)
Presented: Salt Lake City, UT, Annually in Oct

**William Van Dyke Short Story Prize**
Ruminate Magazine
140 N Roosevelt Ave, Collins, CO 80521
*Tel:* 970-449-2726
*E-mail:* editor@ruminatemagazine.org
*Web Site:* www.ruminatemagazine.com
*Key Personnel*
Ed-in-Chief: Brianna Van Dyke
Sr Ed: Amy Lowe
Assoc Ed: Stephanie Lovegrove; Stefani Rossi
All submissions must be previously unpublished & submitted via online submission form. One short story per contest entry, 5,500 words or less. No limit on number of entries per person. Entry fee $15.
Award: $1,000 & pubn in Spring issue (1st place), pubn only (2nd place)
Closing Date: Annually in Oct

**The William Van Wert Memorial Fiction Award**
Hidden River™ Arts
PO Box 63927, Philadelphia, PA 19147
*Tel:* 610-764-0813
*E-mail:* hiddenriverarts@gmail.com
*Web Site:* www.hiddenriverarts.org
*Key Personnel*
Founding Dir: Debra Leigh Scott
Established: 2002
Annual award for a work of unpublished short story or novel excerpt of 25 pages or less. Entry fee: $17.
Award: $1,000 (awarded by mail) & anthology publication
Closing Date: Annually, June 30
Presented: Annually in Dec

**VanderMey Nonfiction Prize**
Ruminate Magazine
140 N Roosevelt Ave, Collins, CO 80521
*Tel:* 970-449-2726
*E-mail:* editor@ruminatemagazine.org
*Web Site:* www.ruminatemagazine.com
*Key Personnel*
Ed-in-Chief: Brianna Van Dyke
Sr Ed: Amy Lowe
Assoc Ed: Stephanie Lovegrove; Stefani Rossi
One nonfiction piece per entry, 5,500 words or less & must be previously unpublished. No limit on number of entries per person. Entry fee $15.
Award: $1,000 & publication in Spring issue
Closing Date: Annually in Feb

**Daniel Varoujan Award**
New England Poetry Club
2 Farrar St, Cambridge, MA 02138
Mailing Address: PO Box 190076, Boston, MA 02119
*Tel:* 617-744-6034
*E-mail:* contests@nepoetryclub.org
*Web Site:* www.nepoetryclub.org
*Key Personnel*
Pres: Diana Der-Hovanessian
VP: Sally Cragin; Daniel Tobin
Contest Chair: Nazaleem Smith
Established: 1979
Award for an unpublished poem (not a translation) in English worthy of the Armenian poet executed by the Turks in 1915 at the onset of the genocide of the Armenian population; $10 for up to 3 entries & $3 for each additional poem for nonmembs. Send poem in duplicate, name of writer on one only. Previous winners may not enter again.
Other Sponsor(s): Anthology of Armenian Poetry royalties from Diana Der Hovansessian
Award: $1,000
Closing Date: Annually, May 31
Presented: Harvard University, Cambridge, MA, Annually in Autumn

**Vermont Arts Council Grants**
Vermont Arts Council
136 State St, Montpelier, VT 05602
*Tel:* 802-828-5425 *Fax:* 802-828-3363
*E-mail:* info@vermontartscouncil.org
*Web Site:* www.vermontartscouncil.org
*Key Personnel*
Dir, Artist & Community Progs: Sonia Rae *Tel:* 802-828-5425 *E-mail:* srae@vermontartscouncil.org
Established: 1965
Individual grants are given to Vermont residents annually.
Award: $250-$1000 Artist Development Grant; $3000 Creation Grants
Closing Date: 1 deadline per year for Creation Grants; rolling deadline for Artist Development Grant

**Vermont Studio Center Writer's Program Fellowships**
Vermont Studio Center
80 Pearl St, Johnson, VT 05656
Mailing Address: PO Box 613, Johnson, VT 05656
*Tel:* 802-635-2727 *Fax:* 802-635-2730
*E-mail:* writing@vermontstudiocenter.org; info@vermontstudiocenter.org
*Web Site:* www.vermontstudiocenter.org
*Key Personnel*
Writing Prog Dir: Gary Clark *E-mail:* gclark@vermontstudiocenter.org
Prog Dir: Kathy Black *E-mail:* kblack@vermontstudiocenter.org
Accepts 12 writers per month year round fellowship awards are given as funds are available through the VSC Fellowship.
Award: 4-week residency
Closing Date: Feb 15, June 15, Oct 1, apply 6 months prior to residency date

**Very Short Fiction Award**
Glimmer Train Press Inc
PO Box 80430, Portland, OR 97280
*Tel:* 503-221-0836 *Fax:* 503-221-0837
*E-mail:* editors@glimmertrain.org
*Web Site:* www.glimmertrain.org
*Key Personnel*
Co-Ed: Susan Burmeister-Brown *E-mail:* susan@glimmertrain.org
Established: 1997
Open to short stories under 3,000 words. Winner notification takes place 2 months after the close of each competition.
Award: $1,500, publication & 20 copies of that issue (1st place), $500 (2nd place), $300 (3rd place)
Closing Date: Annually in Jan & July

**Jill Vickers Prize**
Canadian Political Science Association
260 rue Dalhousie St, Suite 204, Ottawa, ON K1N 7E4, Canada
*Tel:* 613-562-1202 *Fax:* 613-241-0019
*E-mail:* cpsa-acsp@cpsa-acsp.ca
*Web Site:* www.cpsa-acsp.ca
*Key Personnel*
Administrator: Michelle Hopkins
Awarded to the author or authors of the best paper presented in English or French on the topic of gender & politics.
Award: Commemorative certificate
Presented: Annual Conference, Annually in May or June

**Vicky Metcalf Award for Literature for Young People**
The Writers' Trust of Canada

90 Richmond St E, Suite 200, Toronto, ON M5C 1P1, Canada
*Tel:* 416-504-8222 *Toll Free Tel:* 877-906-6548 *Fax:* 416-504-9090
*E-mail:* info@writerstrust.com
*Web Site:* www.writerstrust.com
*Key Personnel*
Exec Dir: Mary Osbourne *Tel:* 416-504-8222 ext 244
Awarded to a Canadian writer of young people's literature for a body of work.
Other Sponsor(s): George Cedric Metcalf Foundation
Award: $20,000
Presented: The Writers' Trust Awards, Toronto, ON, CN, Annually in Nov

**Wag's Revue Writers' Contest**
Wag's Revue
2865 W Lyndale St, Suite 1, Chicago, IL 60647
*E-mail:* editors@wagsrevue.com
*Web Site:* www.wagsrevue.com
*Key Personnel*
Mng & Essays Ed: Sandra Allen *Tel:* 415-806-2698 *E-mail:* sandra@wagsrevue.com
Fiction Ed: William Litton *Tel:* 919-475-2497 *E-mail:* willylitt@wagsrevue.com
Poetry Ed: William Guzzardi *Tel:* 919-619-0673 *E-mail:* willguzzo@wagsrevue.com
Interface Developer: John Herr *E-mail:* john@wagsrevue.com
Established: 2009
Online only, twice-annual writers' contest (winter & summer).
Award: $1,000 & guaranteed publication in the forthcoming issue (1st prize), $500 (2nd prize), $100 (third prize); all submissions are considered for publication, unless otherwise announced on our web site
Presented: Feb 28 (Winter), Aug 31 (Summer)

**Richard Wall Memorial Award**
Theatre Library Association
Roundabout Theatre Co, 231 W 39 St, Suite 1200, New York, NY 10018
*Tel:* 212-719-9393 (ext 351)
*E-mail:* info@tla-online.org; tlabookawards@gmail.com
*Web Site:* www.tla-online.org
*Key Personnel*
Co-Chair: Linda Miles; Tiffany Nixon
Established: 1973
Honors books published in US in the field of recorded performance including motion picture, TV & radio. Ineligible books are: directories, collections from previously published sources & reprints.
Award: $500 (1st prize), $200 (Special Jury Prize); certificate
Closing Date: Feb 28
Presented: New York City, NY, Oct

**Edward Lewis Wallant Book Award**
Dr & Mrs Irving Waltman
3 Brighton Rd, West Hartford, CT 06117
*Tel:* 860-232-1421
*Key Personnel*
Sponsor of Award: Fran Waltman; Irving Waltman
Established: 1963
Awarded annually for a creative work of fiction (novel or collection of short stories) significant to American Jews. The author must be American & the book must have been published during the current year.
Award: $500 & scroll
Closing Date: Dec 31

**George Washington Book Prize**
Washington College, CV Starr Center for the Study of the American Experience
101 S Water St, Chestertown, MD 21620
*Tel:* 410-810-7165 *Fax:* 410-810-7175
*Web Site:* starrcenter.washcoll.edu/gw_book_prize
*Key Personnel*
Book Prize Coord: Lois Kitz *E-mail:* lkitz2@washcoll.edu
Established: 2005
Created to recognize outstanding published works that contribute to a greater understanding of America's Founding era. Books must be published in the year prior to the year prize is awarded. Announcement of finalists on George Washington's Birthday, Feb 22. Announcement of winner at Mount Vernon in May.
Other Sponsor(s): George Washington's Mount Vernon; Gilder Lehrman Institute of American History
Award: $50,000
Closing Date: Dec 1
Presented: Mount Vernon Estate & Gardens, Spring

**The Robert Watson Literary Prizes in Fiction & Poetry**
The Greensboro Review
MFA Writing Program, The Greensboro Review, UNC-Greensboro, 3302 MHRA Bldg, Greensboro, NC 27402-6170
*Tel:* 336-334-5459 *Fax:* 336-256-1470
*Web Site:* www.greensbororeview.org
*Key Personnel*
Ed: Jim Clark *E-mail:* jlclark@uncg.edu
Assoc Ed: Terry Kennedy *E-mail:* tlkenned@uncg.edu
Established: 1984
Short story - poetry.
Other Sponsor(s): MFA Writing Program at UNC Greensboro
Award: $1,000 (each category)
Closing Date: Annually, Sept 15

**Rene Wellek Prize**
American Comparative Literature Association (ACLA)
University of South Carolina, Dept of Languages, Literature & Cultures, Rm 813-A, 1620 College St, Columbia, SC 29208
*Tel:* 803-777-3021 *Fax:* 803-777-3041
*E-mail:* info@acla.org
*Web Site:* www.acla.org
*Key Personnel*
Secy & Treas: Alexander Beecroft
Established: 1968
To recognize an outstanding work in the field of literary & cultural theory published 2012-2014. See web site for nomination process.
Award: Complimentary conference registration & banquet ticket as well as travel grant to cover the cost of attending the annual meeting to receive the award in person
Closing Date: Sept 2014
Presented: ACLA Annual Meeting, Spring 2015

**Wergle Flomp Humor Poetry Contest**
Winning Writers
351 Pleasant St, PMB 222, Northampton, MA 01060-3961
*Tel:* 413-320-1847 *Toll Free Tel:* 866-WINWRIT (946-9748) *Fax:* 413-280-0539
*Web Site:* www.winningwriters.com
*Key Personnel*
Pres: Adam Cohen *E-mail:* adam@winningwriters.com
VP: Jendi Reiter
Established: 2001
Seeks best humor poems. Both published & unpublished works are welcome. Submit poems in English or inspired gibberish. No entry fee. Contestants may enter one poem per year. Poets from all nations welcome.
Award: $1,000 (1st prize), $100 (10 honorable mentions), plus publication on web site for all winners
Closing Date: Annually, April 1
Presented: Annually, Aug 15 on web site

**Wesley-Logan Prize in African Diaspora History**
American Historical Association
400 "A" St SE, Washington, DC 20003-3889
*Tel:* 202-544-2422 *Fax:* 202-544-8307
*E-mail:* awards@historians.org
*Web Site:* www.historians.org
Established: 1992
For an outstanding book in African Diaspora history. The prize is offered on some aspect of the history of the dispersion, settlement & adjustment & or return of peoples originally from Africa. Eligible for consideration are books in any chronological period & any geological location. Only books of high scholarly & literary merit will be considered. Along with an application form, applicants must mail a copy of their book to each of the prize committee members who will be posted on our web site as the prize deadline approaches. All updated info on web site. Books published in 2013 will be considered.
Other Sponsor(s): Association for the Study of Afro-American Life & History
Award: Cash
Closing Date: May 15, 2014 (postmark)
Presented: AHA Annual Meeting

**Western Heritage Awards (Wrangler Award)**
National Cowboy & Western Heritage Museum®
1700 NE 63 St, Oklahoma City, OK 73111
*Tel:* 405-478-2250 *Fax:* 405-478-4714
*E-mail:* info@nationalcowboymuseum.org
*Web Site:* www.nationalcowboymuseum.org
*Key Personnel*
Dir, PR & Museum Events: Shayla Simpson *E-mail:* ssimpson@nationalcowboymuseum.org
Established: 1961
Awarded annually honoring works in TV, film, literary & music which preserve the spirit of the American West.
Award: Bronze sculpture of a cowboy on horseback
Closing Date: Annually, Dec 31 (TV, Film & Literary)
Presented: Banquet & Awards Ceremonies, National Cowboy & Western Heritage Museum, Annually in April (must be in attendance to receive bronze sculpture)

**Western Magazine Awards Foundation**
875 Prairie Ave, Port Coquitlam, BC V3B 1R9, Canada
*Tel:* 604-945-3711
*E-mail:* wma@direct.ca
*Web Site:* www.westernmagazineawards.ca
*Key Personnel*
Pres: Rebecca Philps
Exec Dir: Corey Van't Haaf *E-mail:* corey@westernmagazineawards.ca
Established: 1983
Magazine awards honors editorial & artistic excellence in 26 categories; restricted to Western Canadian Publications.
Other Sponsor(s): CSME; Manitoba; Readers Digest; Saskatchewan Ministry of Tourism, Parks, Culture & Support; Amber Webb-Bowerman Memorial Foundation
Award: $1,000 in gold categories & $750 in written & visual categories
Closing Date: Annually in Jan
Presented: Vancouver, BC, Canada, June

**Hilary Weston Writers' Trust Prize for Nonfiction**
The Writers' Trust of Canada
90 Richmond St E, Suite 200, Toronto, ON M5C 1P1, Canada
*Tel:* 416-504-8222 *Toll Free Tel:* 877-906-6548 *Fax:* 416-504-9090

*E-mail:* info@writerstrust.com
*Web Site:* www.writerstrust.com
*Key Personnel*
Exec Dir: Mary Osbourne *Tel:* 416-504-8222 ext 244
Established: 1997
Awarded for literary exellence in nonfiction, which includes personal or journalistic essays, history, biography, memoirs, commentary & criticism, both social & political.
Award: $60,000 (1st prize), $5,000 (finalists)
Presented: Annually in Nov

**Charles A Weyerhauser Book Award**
The Forest History Society Inc
701 William Vickers Ave, Durham, NC 27701-3162
*Tel:* 919-682-9319 *Fax:* 919-682-2349
*Web Site:* www.foresthistory.org
*Key Personnel*
Admin Asst: Andrea Anderson
*E-mail:* recluce2@duke.edu
Established: 1977
Rewards superior scholarship in forest & conservation history. Award goes to an author who has exhibited fresh insight into a topic & whose narrative analysis is clear, inventive & thought-provoking.

**White, Jackie, Memorial National Children's Playwriting Contest**, see Jackie White Memorial National Children's Playwriting Contest

**William Allen White Children's Book Awards**
Emporia State University, William Allen White Library
William Allen White Library, 1200 Commercial St, Emporia, KS 66801-5092
Mailing Address: Emporia State University, Campus Box 4051, Emporia, KS 66801-5092
*Tel:* 620-341-5208 *Toll Free Tel:* 877-613-7323 *Fax:* 620-341-6208
*E-mail:* wawbookaward@emporia.edu
*Web Site:* waw.emporia.edu
*Key Personnel*
Dean: John Sheridan *E-mail:* jsherida@emporia.edu
Established: 1952
Two children's books are selected by the children of Kansas, grades 3-5 & 6-8, from two master lists of books chosen by a selection committee. When a student has read two books from either of the Master Lists, he or she is eligible to vote at their school (homeschooled vote at their local public library) for the annual White Award winners. Votes are recorded by each school, district or public library & submitted to the William Allen White Children Book Awards Program.
Other Sponsor(s): Trusler Foundation
Award: Two bronze medals, one for each grade level & a $2,500 check for each winner
Closing Date: Votes must be received by April 15 by the program
Presented: Emporia State University, Albert Taylor Hall, Announced late April & presented in Autumn

**Whiting Writers' Awards**
Mrs Giles Whiting Foundation
1133 Avenue of the Americas, 22nd fl, New York, NY 10036-6710
*Tel:* 212-336-2138
*E-mail:* info@whitingfoundation.org
*Web Site:* www.whitingfoundation.org
*Key Personnel*
Dir, Opers: Kellye Rosenheim
Dir, Writers' Prog: Barbara K Bristol
Established: 1985
For creative writing in fiction, nonfiction, poetry & plays. Applications not accepted by the foundation; confidential nominators propose candidates for selection committee consideration.
Award: Ten awards of $50,000 each
Presented: Whiting Writers' Awards, Annually, late Oct

**Walt Whitman Award**
The Academy of American Poets Inc
75 Maiden Lane, Suite 901, New York, NY 10038
*Tel:* 212-274-0343 *Fax:* 212-274-9427
*E-mail:* academy@poets.org
*Web Site:* www.poets.org
*Key Personnel*
Pres & Exec Dir: Tree Swenson
Exec Dir: Jennifer Benka
Multimedia Prodr: Paul Legault
*E-mail:* plegault@poets.org
Awards Coord & Exec Asst: Alex Dimitrov *Tel:* 212-274-0343 ext 15 *E-mail:* adimitrov@poets.org
Established: 1975
Annual award for a book-length ms of poetry by a living American poet who has not published a book of poetry. Visit academy web site for entry form & guidelines.
Award: First book publication $5,000 & a one-month residency at the Vermont Studio Center
Closing Date: Annually, Sept 15-Nov 15
Presented: Annually in Summer

**Whitman, Walt Award**, see Walt Whitman Award

**Jon Whyte Memorial Essay Prize**
Writers Guild of Alberta
11759 Groat Rd, Edmonton, AB T5M 3K6, Canada
*Tel:* 780-422-8174 *Toll Free Tel:* 800-665-5354 (AB only) *Fax:* 780-422-2663 (attn WGA)
*E-mail:* mail@writersguild.ab.ca
*Web Site:* www.writersguild.ab.ca
*Key Personnel*
Exec Dir: Carol Holmes *E-mail:* cholmes@writersguild.ab.ca
Communs & Partnerships Coord: Nicholas Mather *E-mail:* nmather@writersguild.ab.ca
Memb Servs Coord: Giorgia Severini
Progs Coord: Nichole Quiring
*E-mail:* programs@writersguild.ab.ca
Established: 1992
Awarded to an outstanding essay by an Alberta author that has Alberta at its heart: the province & its issues, its history or stories, its people or places; no longer than 3,000 words.
Award: $700
Closing Date: Annually, Dec 31
Presented: Alberta Literary Awards Gala
*Branch Office(s)*
Lord Denning House, 509 20 Ave SW, Calgary, AB T2S 0E7, Canada, Prog Coord: Samantha Warwick *Tel:* 403-265-2226
*E-mail:* swarwick@writersguild.ab.ca

**Wichita State University Playwriting Contest**
School of Performing Arts
Division of Wichita State University
1845 Fairmount St, Wichita, KS 67260-0153
*Tel:* 316-978-3360 *Fax:* 316-978-3202
*Web Site:* www.wichita.edu
*Key Personnel*
Admin Specialist: Renea Goforth *Tel:* 316-978-6634
For college students only (graduate or undergraduate).
Award: Production of play, transportation & housing for playwright to attend performance
Closing Date: Annually, Jan 15
Presented: Welsbacher Theatre, Wichita State University, Wichita, KS, Annually in Autumn

**The Laura Ingalls Wilder Medal**
Association for Library Service to Children (ALSC)
Division of American Library Association (ALA)
50 E Huron St, Chicago, IL 60611-2795
*Tel:* 312-280-2163 *Toll Free Tel:* 800-545-2433 *Fax:* 312-440-9374
*E-mail:* alsc@ala.org
*Web Site:* www.ala.org/alsc
*Key Personnel*
Exec Dir: Aimee Strittmatter *Tel:* 312-280-2162
*E-mail:* astrittmatter@ala.org
Awards Coord: Caroline Jewell
*E-mail:* alscawards@ala.org
Prog Coord: Marsha P Burgess
*E-mail:* mburgess@ala.org
Established: 1954
Biennial award presented to an author or illustrator whose books have made a substantial & lasting contribution to children's literature. The books must have been published in the US.
Award: Medal
Presented: ALA Conference

**William Flanagan Memorial Creative Persons Center**
Edward F Albee Foundation
14 Harrison St, New York, NY 10013
*Tel:* 212-226-2020 *Fax:* 212-226-5551
*E-mail:* info@albeefoundation.org
*Web Site:* www.albeefoundation.org
*Key Personnel*
Founder & Pres: Edward Albee
Foundation Secy: Jakob Holder
Residency program for writers & visual artists. The only requirements are talent & need.
Award: Room (Writers)/Room & Studio (Visual Artists)
Closing Date: Annually, Jan 1-March 1 for Summer season
Presented: The Barn, Montauk, Long Island, NY, Annually mid-May-mid-Oct, every writer or artist can choose 4 or 6 weeks, depending on availability

**Oscar Williams/Gene Derwood Award**
NY Community Trust
909 Third Ave, New York, NY 10022
*Tel:* 212-686-0010 *Fax:* 212-532-8528
*E-mail:* info@nycommunitytrust.org
*Web Site:* www.nycommunitytrust.org
*Key Personnel*
Pres: Lorie Slutsky *Tel:* 212-686-0010 ext 257
SVP: Joyce M Bove *Tel:* 212-686-0010 ext 552
VP, Communs: Ani F Hurwitz *Tel:* 212-686-0010 ext 224 *E-mail:* afh@nyct-cfi.org
Dir, Grants Budgeting: Liza Lagunoff *Tel:* 212-686-0010 ext 559 *E-mail:* ll@nyct-cfi.org
Exec Asst: Barbara Wybraniec *Tel:* 212-686-0010 ext 229
Established: 1971
Intended to help needy or worthy poets & artists who have had long & distinguished careers. Nominations or applications are not accepted in any form.
Award: Cash varies in amount
Presented: Annually

**William Carlos Williams Award**
Poetry Society of America (PSA)
15 Gramercy Park S, New York, NY 10003
*Tel:* 212-254-9628 *Fax:* 212-673-2352
*Web Site:* www.poetrysociety.org
*Key Personnel*
Pres: Ruth Kaplan
Exec Dir: Alice Quinn
Mng Dir & Awards Coord: Brett Fletcher Lauer
*E-mail:* brett@poetrysociety.org
Progs Dir: Darrel Alejandro Holnes
For a book of poetry published by a small press or a nonprofit or university press. Submissions, accompanied by an entry form, from publishers only. Send SASE for complete guidelines.

Award: Purchase prize between $500 & $1,000
Closing Date: Annually, Oct-Dec
Presented: Annually in April

**Gary Wilson Award for Short Fiction**
Texas Christian University
Texas Christian University, Dept of English, TCU Box 297270, Fort Worth, TX 76129
*Tel:* 817-257-5907 *Fax:* 817-257-7709
*E-mail:* descant@tcu.edu
*Web Site:* www.descant.tcu.edu
*Key Personnel*
Mng Ed: Dan Williams *E-mail:* d.e.williams@tcu.edu
Established: 2005
For an outstanding story in an issue. No application process, no entry fee; all published submissions are eligible for prize consideration. Submit work with a SASE.
Other Sponsor(s): descant Publication, Dept of English, TCU
Award: $250 cash
Closing Date: Annually, Sept 1-April 1
Presented: Announced in journal, Annually in Summer

**H W Wilson Co Indexing Award**
American Society for Indexing Inc (ASI)
10200 W 44 Ave, Suite 304, Wheat Ridge, CO 80033
*Tel:* 303-463-2887 *Fax:* 303-422-8894
*E-mail:* wilsonaward@asindexing.org
*Web Site:* www.asindexing.org
*Key Personnel*
Pres: Richard Shrout *E-mail:* president@asindexing.org
Exec Dir: Annette Rogers *E-mail:* arogers@asindexing.org
Established: 1978
Awarded to the indexer & the publisher of year's best monograph index.
Award: $1,000 & citation (indexer), citation (publisher)
Closing Date: Annually in Feb
Presented: Annual Conference

**The H W Wilson Library Staff Development Grant**
ALA Awards Program
Affiliate of American Library Association
50 E Huron St, Chicago, IL 60611
*Tel:* 312-280-3247 *Toll Free Tel:* 800-545-2433 (ext 3247) *Fax:* 312-944-3897; 312-440-9379
*E-mail:* awards@ala.org
*Web Site:* www.ala.org
*Key Personnel*
Prog Off: Cheryl Malden *E-mail:* cmalden@ala.org
To a library organization for a program to further its staff development goals & objectives.
Award: $3,500 & 24k gold-framed citation
Closing Date: Annually, Dec 1
Presented: ALA Annual Conference

**Herbert Warren Wind Book Award**
USGA Museum & Archives
77 Liberty Corner Rd, Far Hills, NJ 07931-0708
*Tel:* 908-234-2300 *Fax:* 908-470-5013
*Web Site:* www.usga.org
*Key Personnel*
Libn: Nancy Stulack *Tel:* 908-781-1107 *E-mail:* nstulack@usga.org
Established: 1987
Recognizes & honors outstanding contributions to golf literature. Named in honor of the famed golf writer, the award acknowledges & encourages outstanding research, writing & publishing about golf. The award attempts to broaden the public's interest & knowledge in the game of golf. Presented by the USGA Museum & Archives, the Book Award is the top literary prize awarded by the USGA.
Award: Silver inkwell with feather
Closing Date: Annually, Dec 31
Presented: Golf Writer's Association of America Annual Meeting, April

**The Laurence L & Thomas Winship/PEN New England Award**
Boston Globe & PEN New England
MIT 14N-221A, 77 Massachusetts Ave, Cambridge, MA 02139
*Tel:* 617-324-1729
*E-mail:* pen-ne@lesley.edu
*Web Site:* www.pen-ne.org
*Key Personnel*
Exec Dir: Karen Wulf
Established: 1975
For a US author who is of New England origin or whose work provides a New England theme or atmosphere. Submit 3 copies. Entry fee is $35.
Award: 3 $1,000 awards
Closing Date: Annually in Dec
Presented: Kennedy Presidential Library, Boston, MA, Annually, April 1

**Justin Winsor Prize for Library History Essay**
The Library History Round Table of the American Library Association
50 E Huron St, Chicago, IL 60611
*Tel:* 312-280-4283 *Toll Free Tel:* 800-545-2433 (ext 4283) *Fax:* 312-280-4392
*Web Site:* www.ala.org
*Key Personnel*
Prog Offr & LHRT Liaison: R Norman Rose *Tel:* 312-280-4283 ext 4283 *E-mail:* nrose@ala.org
To author of an outstanding essay embodying original historical research on a significant subject of library history.
Award: $100 & invitation to have paper considered for publication in Libraries & the Cultural Record
Closing Date: Jan

**Paul A Witty Short Story Award**
International Reading Association
800 Barksdale Rd, Newark, DE 19711-3204
Mailing Address: PO Box 8139, Newark, DE 19714-8139
*Tel:* 302-731-1600 *Toll Free Tel:* 800-336-7323 (US & CN) *Fax:* 302-731-1057
*E-mail:* committees@reading.org
*Web Site:* www.reading.org
*Key Personnel*
Public Info Offr: Kathy Baughman *Tel:* 302-731-1600 ext 221 *E-mail:* kbaughman@reading.org
Exec Dir: Marcie Craig Post *E-mail:* mpost@reading.org
Established: 1986
For an original story published for the first time during the calendar year in a periodical for children. The short story should serve as a literary standard that encourages young readers to read periodicals.
Award: $1,000
Closing Date: Annually, Nov 15
Presented: Association convention, Annually in Spring

**WLA Literary Award**
Wisconsin Library Association Inc
4610 S Biltmore Lane, Madison, WI 53718
*Tel:* 608-245-3640 *Fax:* 608-245-3646
*Web Site:* www.wla.lib.wi.us
*Key Personnel*
Exec Dir: Lisa K Strand *E-mail:* strand@scls.lib.wi.us
Memb Servs Coord: Brigitte Rupp Vacha *E-mail:* ruppvacha@scls.lib.wi.us
Established: 1974
To honor a work by a Wisconsin author for a book published in the preceding year that contributes to the world of literature & ideas.
Award: Monetary award
Closing Date: End of March
Presented: WLA Annual Conference, Annually Oct-Nov

**WNBA Pannell Award for Excellence in Children's Bookselling**
Women's National Book Association Inc
435 W 23 St, Suite 8-C, New York, NY 10011
Mailing Address: PO Box 237, FDR Sta, New York, NY 10150-0231
*Tel:* 212-242-6930
*E-mail:* pannellaward@gmail.com
*Web Site:* www.wnba-books.org; www.NationalReadingGroupMonth.org; www.wnba-books.org/awards
*Key Personnel*
Chair: Susan Knopf *E-mail:* susanknopf04@yahoo.com; Quinlan Lee *E-mail:* quinlan@adamsliterary.com
Established: 1981
Recognizes retail bookstores that excel at creatively bringing books & children together & inspiring children's interest in books & reading. One general book store with a children's section & one children's speciality store are selected each year by a jury of 5 book industry professionals based on creativity, responsiveness to community needs, passion & understanding of children's books & young readers. Supported by Penguin Books for Young Readers.
Award: $2,000 (2 at $1,000 each) plus 1 piece of original art for each recipient
Closing Date: Jan
Presented: BookExpo America

**Thomas Wolfe Fiction Prize**
North Carolina Writers' Network
PO Box 21591, Winston-Salem, NC 27120-1591
*E-mail:* mail@ncwriters.org
*Web Site:* www.ncwriters.org
*Key Personnel*
Exec Dir: Ed Southern
Competition is open to all writers regardless of geographical location or prior publication. Submit 2 copies of an unpublished fiction ms not to exceed 12 double-spaced pages. Entry fee $15 membs, $25 nonmembs. Submissions accepted Dec 1-Jan 30. Send submissions to Professor Tony Abbott, Davidson College, PO Box 7096, Davidson, NC 28035.
Award: $1,000 & possible pubn in *The Thomas Wolfe Review*
Closing Date: Annually, Jan 30

**Tobias Wolff Award for Fiction**
The Bellingham Review
Mail Stop 9053, Western Washington University, Bellingham, WA 98225
*Tel:* 360-650-4863
*E-mail:* bhreview@wwu.edu
*Web Site:* www.bhreview.org
*Key Personnel*
Ed-in-Chief: Brenda Miller
Mng Ed: Marilyn Bruce
Novel excerpts up to 6,000 words are accepted. Poems within a series of poems will each be treated as a separate entry. No previously published works, or works accepted for publication, are eligible. Work may be under consideration elsewhere, but must be withdrawn from the competition if accepted for publication. Make checks payable to: The Bellingham Review. All entries will receive a complimentary one-issue subscription. Entry fee for the first entry (one nonfiction work, one short story, or up to three poems) $20. Each additional entry including each additional poem $10.
Award: $1,000 & publication in the Bellingham Review (1st prize); considered for publication (2nd, 3rd & finalists)

Closing Date: Annually, between Dec 1 & March 15
Presented: Annually in July

**Women's National Book Association Award**
Women's National Book Association Inc
PO Box 237, FDR Sta, New York, NY 10150-0231
*Tel:* 212-208-4629 *Fax:* 212-208-4629
*E-mail:* publicity@bookbuzz.com
*Web Site:* www.wnba-books.org; www.NationalReadingGroupMonth.org
*Key Personnel*
Pres: Valerie Tomaselli
Natl Treas: Gloria Toler
Secy: Annette Marie Haley
PR: Susannah Greenberg
Established: 1940
Presented to a living American woman for her outstanding contribution to the world of books as well as society (through books). Offered alternate years in the even-number years.
Award: Citation
Presented: Varies, Biennially in even-numbered years

**The J Howard & Barbara M J Wood Prize**
Poetry Magazine
444 N Michigan Ave, Suite 1850, Chicago, IL 60611-4034
*Tel:* 312-787-7070 *Fax:* 312-787-6650
*E-mail:* editors@poetrymagazine.org
*Web Site:* poetryfoundation.org
*Key Personnel*
Mng Ed: Valerie Johnson *E-mail:* vjohnson@poetrymagazine.org
Established: 1994
For poetry published in the preceding two volumes of *Poetry*. No application necessary.
Award: $5,000
Presented: Annually in Dec

**Carter G Woodson Book Awards**
National Council for the Social Studies
8555 16 St, Suite 500, Silver Spring, MD 20910
*Tel:* 301-588-1800 *Toll Free Tel:* 800-296-7840; 800-683-0812 (pubn orders) *Fax:* 301-588-2049
*E-mail:* excellence@ncss.org; publications@ncss.org
*Web Site:* www.socialstudies.org
*Key Personnel*
Exec Dir: Susan Griffin *E-mail:* sgriffin@ncss.org
Dir, Meetings & Exhibits: David Bailor *Tel:* 301-588-1800 ext 109 *E-mail:* dbailor@ncss.org
Dir, Pubns: Michael Simpson *Tel:* 301-588-1800 ext 105 *E-mail:* msimpson@ncss.org
External Rel Council Communs Dir: Ana Post *Tel:* 301-588-1800 ext 114 *E-mail:* apost@ncss.org
Prog Mgr: Prema Cordeiro *Tel:* 301-588-1800 ext 106 *E-mail:* pcordeiro@ncss.org
Established: 1974
Annual award established by National Council for the Social Studies to recognize the most distinguished nonfiction books for young readers which depict ethnicity in the US. Eligible books deal with the experiences of one or more racial/ethnic minority groups in the US. Publisher must provide copy of each title for submission requirements.
Award: One elementary (K-6) & one middle level (5-8), one secondary (7-12) annual award, runner-up books designated Woodson Honor Books, seals are now available to publishers $.25 each for less than 1,000 & less for larger quantities
Closing Date: Annually, Sept 30
Presented: Awards Reception, NCSS Annual Conference

**Word Works Washington Prize**
The Word Works
Adirondack Community College, Dearlove Hall, 640 Bay Rd, Queensbury, NY 12804
Mailing Address: PO Box 42164, Washington, DC 20015
*Fax:* 301-581-9443
*E-mail:* editor@wordworksbooks.org
*Web Site:* www.wordworksbooks.org
*Key Personnel*
Pres & Chpn of Bd of Dirs: Karren L Alenier
Pres: Nancy White
Established: 1974
Annual prize for an unpublished ms of poetry. Submission may be made by any living American or Canadian writer. Include two title pages, one with & one without name, address, telephone number & e-mail. No entry form is required. Online submissions available. Submissions should be 48-64 pages, in English; please attach $25 entry fee, acknowledgment page & brief bio. Business sized SASE mandatory with entry. Visit web site for guidelines.
Award: $1,500 & publication
Closing Date: Annually, March 15

**World Fantasy Awards**
World Fantasy Awards Association
PO Box 43, Mukilteo, WA 98275-0043
*Web Site:* www.worldfantasy.org
*Key Personnel*
Pres: Peter Dennis Pautz *E-mail:* sfexecsec@gmail.com
To acknowledge excellence in fantasy writing & art.
Award: Trophy (bust of H P Lovecraft)
Closing Date: June 1
Presented: World Fantasy Convention, Halloween weekend

**World's Best Short-Short Story Contest**
The Southeast Review
Florida State University, Dept of English, Tallahassee, FL 32306
*E-mail:* southeastreview@gmail.com
*Web Site:* www.southeastreview.org
*Key Personnel*
Ed: Katie Cortese
Established: 1986
Best 500 word (max) previously unpublished short, short story. All entries will be considered for publication. $16 entry fee for up to 3 stories.
Other Sponsor(s): FSU English Dept's Creative Writing Program
Award: $500
Closing Date: March

**Write Now**
Formerly Waldo M & Grace C Bonderman Playwriting for Youth National Competition & Symposium
Indiana Repertory Theatre Inc
140 W Washington St, Indianapolis, IN 46204-3465
*Tel:* 317-635-5277 *Fax:* 317-236-0767
*Web Site:* www.irtlive.com/artists_information/playwrights/bonderman_introduction
*Key Personnel*
Founder: Dorothy Webb *E-mail:* dwebb@irtlive.com
Artistic Dir: Janet Allen *Tel:* 317-635-5277 ext 4800
Established: 1988
Biennial workshop to encourage writers to create artistic theatrical scripts for young audiences. A collaboration between Childsplay & Indiana Repertory Theatre.
Other Sponsor(s): Doris Duke Charitable Foundation
Award: $1,000, development workshop & rehearsed reading (up to 4 winners); certificates for semi-finalists & excerpts read at symposium
Closing Date: Biennially in June
Presented: Biennially in March

**Writer in Residence**
Idaho Commission on the Arts
2410 N Old Penitentiary Rd, Boise, ID 83712
Mailing Address: PO Box 83720, Boise, ID 83720-0008
*Tel:* 208-334-2119 *Toll Free Tel:* 800-ART-FUND (278-3863 within Idaho) *Fax:* 208-334-2488
*E-mail:* info@arts.idaho.gov
*Web Site:* www.arts.idaho.gov
*Key Personnel*
Lit Dir: Cort Conley *Tel:* 208-334-2119 ext 108 *E-mail:* cort.conley@arts.idaho.gov
Triennial Award. Recipient tours state & does readings (4 sites yearly). Open only to residents of Idaho; must have resided in Idaho at least one year. Award for artistic excellence, three year appointment.
Award: $10,000 plus travel expenses (distributed over 3 yr term)
Closing Date: Annually in Jan
Presented: Annually in July

**The Writer Magazine/Emily Dickinson Award**
Poetry Society of America (PSA)
15 Gramercy Park S, New York, NY 10003
*Tel:* 212-254-9628 *Fax:* 212-673-2352
*Web Site:* www.poetrysociety.org
*Key Personnel*
Pres: Ruth Kaplan
Exec Dir: Alice Quinn
Mng Dir & Awards Coord: Brett Fletcher Lauer *E-mail:* brett@poetrysociety.org
Progs Dir: Darrel Alejandro Holnes
Established: 1971
For a poem inspired by Dickinson (though not necessarily in her style), not to exceed 30 lines. Open to Society members only. Send No 10 SASE for guidelines, or visit web site.
Award: $250
Closing Date: Annually, Oct-Dec
Presented: Annual Awards Ceremony, New York, NY, Annually in Spring

**Writer's Digest Writing Competition**
Writer's Digest Books
Imprint of F+W Media Inc
10151 Carver Rd, Suite 200, Blue Ash, OH 45242
*Tel:* 513-531-2690 *Fax:* 513-531-0798
*E-mail:* writing-competition@fwmedia.com; writersdigest@fwmedia.com (edit)
*Web Site:* www.writersdigest.com
*Key Personnel*
Cust Serv: Nicole Florence
Established: 1931
Originally, unpublished mss in 10 categories: Inspirational writing (spiritual/religious); memoirs/personal essay; magazine feature article; genre short story (mystery, romance, etc); mainstream/literary short story; rhyming poetry; non- rhyming poetry; stage play; television/movie script & children's young adult fiction. Poems are $15 for the first entry; $10 for each additional poem submitted in the same online session. All other entries are $25 for the first ms; $15 for each additional ms submitted in the same online session. Refer to web site for current information.
Award: Trip to New York for the Writer's Digest Conference to meet with editors or agents (grand prize); cash, reference books & subscriptions. Refer to web site for current information
Closing Date: Annually in May
Presented: Annually in Oct

**Writers-Editors Network International Writing Competition**
Florida Freelance Writers Association

Affiliate of Cassell Network of Writers
45 Main St, North Stratford, NH 03590
Mailing Address: PO Box A, North Stratford, NH 03590
*Tel:* 603-922-8338 *Fax:* 603-922-8339
*E-mail:* contest@writers-editors.com
*Web Site:* www.writers-editors.com; www.ffwamembers.com
*Key Personnel*
Exec Dir: Dana K Cassell *E-mail:* dana@writers-editors.com
Established: 1984
Fiction, nonfiction, juvenile & poetry.
Award: Cash & certificate
Closing Date: Annually, March 15
Presented: Annually, May 31

**Writers Guild of America Awards**
Writers Guild of America, West (WGAW)
7000 W Third St, Los Angeles, CA 90048
*Tel:* 323-951-4000; 323-782-4569 *Fax:* 323-782-4800
*Web Site:* www.wga.org
*Key Personnel*
Pres: Christopher Keyser
VP: Howard Rodman
Secy & Treas: Carl Gottlieb
Awards: Jennifer Burt
Established: 1948
Annual, any eligible film exhibited for one week during calendar year; original screenplay; adapted screenplay. TV & radio awards. Only members can enter.
Award: Statuette
Closing Date: Annually, Sept 30
Presented: Annual Writer's Guild Award Show, Annually in Feb

**Writers' League of Texas Book Awards**
Writers' League of Texas (WLT)
611 S Congress Ave, Suite 505, Austin, TX 78704
*Tel:* 512-499-8914
*E-mail:* wlt@writersleague.org
*Web Site:* www.writersleague.org
*Key Personnel*
Off Administrator: Bethany Hegedus *E-mail:* bethany@writersleague.org
Established: 1991
Members of the Writers' League of Texas recognize outstanding books (fiction, nonfiction, poetry & literary prose, children's long & children's short) published in 2011 or 2012. Membership is not required. See web site for complete submission details.
Other Sponsor(s): University Co-op
Award: $1,000 each award, commemorative award & appearance at the Texas Book Festival
Closing Date: Annually in March
Presented: Annually in Oct

**Writers' Trust Engel/Findley Prize**
The Writers' Trust of Canada
90 Richmond St E, Suite 200, Toronto, ON M5C 1P1, Canada
*Tel:* 416-504-8222 *Toll Free Tel:* 877-906-6548 *Fax:* 416-504-9090
*E-mail:* info@writerstrust.com
*Web Site:* www.writerstrust.com
*Key Personnel*
Exec Dir: Mary Osbourne *Tel:* 416-504-8222 ext 244
Established: 1986
Presented to a Canadian writer in mid career. Writers are judged on their body of work-no less than 3 works of literary merit which are predominantly fiction rather than a single book. All Canadian writers are considered.
Award: $25,000
Presented: The Writers' Trust Awards, Toronto, ON, CN, Annually in Nov

**The Writers Trust/McClelland & Stewart Journey Prize**
The Writers' Trust of Canada
90 Richmond St E, Suite 200, Toronto, ON M5C 1P1, Canada
*Tel:* 416-504-8222 *Toll Free Tel:* 877-906-6548 *Fax:* 416-504-9090
*E-mail:* info@writerstrust.com
*Web Site:* www.writerstrust.com
*Key Personnel*
Exec Dir: Mary Osbourne *Tel:* 416-504-8222 ext 244
Established: 1988
Awarded to a new & developing writer of distinction for a short story published in a Canadian literary publication.
Other Sponsor(s): James A Michener (donation of his Canadian royalty earnings from his novel *Journey*)
Award: $10,000
Presented: The Writers' Trust Awards, Toronto, ON, CN, Annually in Nov

**WritersWeekly.com's 24-Hour Short Story Contest**
WritersWeekly
5726 Cortez Rd, Suite 349, Bradenton, FL 34210
*Fax:* 305-768-0261
*Web Site:* www.writersweekly.com
*Key Personnel*
Contact: Angela Hoy *E-mail:* angela@writersweekly.com
Held quarterly & limited to 500 entrants. You must be entered in the contest before the topic is posted in order to submit your story. Late stories are disqualified. Entry fee $5.
Award: $300 (1st prize), $250 (2nd place), $200 (3rd place); All winners will receive publication of their story on the WritersWeekly.com web site & 1 Freelance Income Kit. There will be 30 honorable mentions
Closing Date: 24 hours after contest start

**Writing for Children Competition**
Writers' Union of Canada
90 Richmond St E, Suite 200, Toronto, ON M5C 1P1, Canada
*Tel:* 416-703-8982 *Fax:* 416-504-9090
*E-mail:* info@writersunion.ca
*Web Site:* www.writersunion.ca
*Key Personnel*
Competitions Coord: Nancy MacLeod *Tel:* 416-703-8982 ext 226 *E-mail:* nmacleod@writersunion.ca
Off Administrator: Valerie Laws *Tel:* 416-703-8982 ext 224
Writing for children up to 1,500 words by an unpublished Canadian writer.
Award: $1,500
Closing Date: Annually, April 24

**Wyoming Arts Council Literature Fellowships**
Wyoming Arts Council
Division of Wyoming Department of Parks & Cultural Resources
2320 Capitol Ave, Cheyenne, WY 82002
*Tel:* 307-777-5234 *Fax:* 307-777-5499
*Web Site:* wyoarts.state.wy.us
*Key Personnel*
Literary, Visual & Performing Arts Specialist: Michael Shay *Tel:* 307-777-5234 *E-mail:* mshay@state.wy.us
Arts Council Mgr: Rita Basom *Tel:* 307-777-7473 *E-mail:* rbasom@state.wy.us
Established: 1986
Awarded annually for the most exciting new creative writing by Wyoming residents. Blind judges & one juror.
Award: $3,000 (three)
Closing Date: Annually, June 29
Presented: Casper College Literary Conference, Annually in Autumn

**Yale Series of Younger Poets**
Yale University Press
302 Temple St, New Haven, CT 06511
Mailing Address: PO Box 209040, New Haven, CT 06520-9040
*Tel:* 203-432-0960 *Fax:* 203-432-0948
*Web Site:* www.yalebooks.com
*Key Personnel*
Sr Ed: Eric Brandt
Admin Asst: Erica Dorpalen
Established: 1919
Awarded annually for poetry mss, 48-64 pages, by American writers under age 40 who have not previously had a volume of verse published. Submission fee $20. Visit web site for further details.
Award: Publication & royalties
Closing Date: Annually, Oct 1-Nov 15

**YALSA/VOYA Research Grant**, see Frances Henne YALSA/VOYA Research Grant

**YES New Play Festival**
Northern Kentucky University
205 FA Theatre Dept, Nunn Dr, Highland Heights, KY 41099-1007
*Tel:* 859-572-6303 *Fax:* 859-572-6057
*Key Personnel*
Proj Dir: Prof Sandra Forman *E-mail:* forman@nku.edu
Established: 1983
New play contest (biennial).
Award: $500 honoraria, travel & housing for 3 different playwrights to attend fully produced premiers of their plays
Closing Date: Plays accepted May 1-Sept 30 in even numbered years
Presented: April 2015

**The Young Adult Book Award**
Canadian Library Association (CLA) (Association Canadienne des bibliotheques)
1150 Morrison Dr, Suite 400, Ottawa, ON K2H 8S9, Canada
*Tel:* 613-232-9625 *Fax:* 613-563-9895
*E-mail:* info@cla.ca
*Web Site:* www.cla.ca
*Key Personnel*
Exec Dir: Kelly Moore *Tel:* 613-232-9625 ext 306 *E-mail:* kmoore@cla.ca
Mgr, Mktg & Communs: Judy Green *Tel:* 613-232-9625 ext 322 *E-mail:* jgreen@cla.ca
Established: 1980
Awarded to the author of an outstanding English language Canadian book which appeals to young adults between the ages of 13 & 18. Author must be citizen or resident of Canada.
Award: $1,000, cheque & plaques
Closing Date: Annually, Dec 31
Presented: CLA National Conference

**Young Lions Fiction Award**
New York Public Library
Office of Development, Rm 73, 11 W 40 St, New York, NY 10018
*Tel:* 212-930-0887 *Fax:* 212-930-0983
*E-mail:* younglions@nypl.org
*Web Site:* www.nypl.org
*Key Personnel*
Assoc Mgr, Young Lions Fiction Award: Isabel Yordan
Established: 2001
Given to an American writer age 35 or younger for either a novel or collection of short stories.
Award: $10,000
Closing Date: Annually in Aug
Presented: The New York Public Library, Annually in May

**Phyllis Smart-Young Poetry Prize**
The Madison Review

University of Wisconsin, 6193 Helen C White Hall, English Dept, 600 N Park St, Madison, WI 53706
*Tel:* 608-263-0566
*E-mail:* madisonrevw@gmail.com
*Web Site:* www.english.wisc.edu/madisonreview
*Key Personnel*
Chmn Dept: Prof Thomas Schaub
*E-mail:* thschaub@wisc.edu
Faculty Advisor & Prog Coord: Ronald Kuka
*E-mail:* rfkuka@wisc.edu
Mss must be previously unpublished & should be double-spaced with standard 1" margins & 12-pt font. There is a maximum of 15 pages for combined 3 poems. Only 1 submission is allowed per person per contest. Entry fee $10.
Award: $1,000 & publication in the fall issue of The Madison Review
Closing Date: Annually, Feb 1 (postmark)
Presented: Announced annually in March

**youngARTS**
National Foundation for Advancement in the Arts
777 Brickell Ave, Suite 370, Miami, FL 33131
*Tel:* 305-377-1140 *Toll Free Tel:* 800-970-ARTS (970-2787) *Fax:* 305-377-1149
*E-mail:* info@nfaa.org
*Web Site:* www.youngarts.org
*Key Personnel*
CEO & Pres (NFAA): Christina De Paul
*E-mail:* cdepaul@youngarts.org
Dir, Prodns: Roberta B Fliss *Tel:* 305-377-1140 ext 1700 *E-mail:* rfliss@youngarts.org
Established: 1981
Annual cash award & scholarship opportunities for 17-18 year old artists with demonstrated talent in dance, jazz, cinematic arts, music, photography, theater, visual arts, voice & writing. Registration fee: $35.
Award: Up to $10,000 in individual awards with potential for Presidential Scholar in the Arts Award
Closing Date: Annually, Oct 9
Presented: Alumni Performance & Awards Ceremony, The Olympia Theater at the Gunsman Center for the Performing Arts, Miami, FL, Annually in Jan

**The Youth Honor Award Progam**
Skipping Stones Inc
166 W 12 Ave, Eugene, OR 97401
Mailing Address: PO Box 3939, Eugene, OR 97403
*Tel:* 541-342-4956
*E-mail:* info@skippingstones.org
*Web Site:* www.skippingstones.org
*Key Personnel*
Exec Ed: Arun N Toke *E-mail:* editor@skippingstones.org
Established: 1993
Recognizes 10 creative & artistic works (writing, art, photo, essays, etc) by young people that promote multicultural & nature awareness. Entry fee $3. Everyone who enters the awards program receives the issue with 10 winners & a few noteworthy entries for free.
Award: Ten winners published in our Sept-Oct issue annually & receive an Honor Award Certificate, a subscription to *Skipping Stones* & five nature &/or multicultural books
Closing Date: Annually, June 25
Presented: Annually in Sept

**Anna Zornio Memorial Children's Theatre Playwriting Award**
University of New Hampshire Department of Theatre & Dance
Paul Creative Arts, Unit D-22, 30 Academic Way, Durham, NH 03824-3538
*Tel:* 603-862-3038 *Fax:* 603-862-0298
*Web Site:* www.unh.edu/theatre-dance/zornio
*Key Personnel*
Admin Mgr: Michael Wood *E-mail:* mike.wood@unh.edu
Theatre Chair: David Kaye
Established: 1980
Quadrennial award for well-written play or musical appropriate for young audiences, PreK-12.
Award: Cash award, up to $500 & play underwritten & produced by the UNH Theatre Department
Closing Date: March 2016
Presented: University of New Hampshire, Durham, NH, 2017-2018

# Books & Magazines for the Trade

## Reference Books for the Trade

**All-in-One Media Contacts Directory**
Published by Gebbie Press Inc
PO Box 1000, New Paltz, NY 12561-0017
*Tel:* 845-255-7560 *Toll Free Fax:* 888-345-2790
*E-mail:* gebbiepress@pipeline.com
*Web Site:* www.gebbieinc.com
*Key Personnel*
Pres: Mark Gebbie
Published in three sections. The Daily & Weekly Newspaper Directory section lists contact information for all US daily & weekly newspapers, including Black & Spanish language papers. The Radio & Television Directory section includes, radio & TV stations including Black & Spanish language stations & the Trade & Consumer Directory section includes a comprehensive listing of magazines available in various formats.
Annual.
42nd ed, 2013: 462 pp, $165 print, $395 online subn (each section available online separately for $155 each), $395 text files

**Almanac of Famous People**
Published by Gale
Division of Cengage Learning
27500 Drake Rd, Farmington Hills, MI 48331-3535
SAN: 213-4373
*Tel:* 248-699-4253 *Toll Free Tel:* 800-877-4253 *Fax:* 248-699-8062 *Toll Free Fax:* 800-414-5043 (orders)
*E-mail:* gale.galeord@cengage.com
*Web Site:* www.gale.cengage.com
*Key Personnel*
Ed: Jennifer Mossman
A guide to sources of biographical information on more than 30,000 prominent persons, past & present, famous & infamous, who are of popular interest. Entries include basic personal data for quick identifications, plus citations to material appearing in biographical sources. Vol 2 indexes the entries chronologically by year & day of birth & death, geographically using places of birth & death, alphabetically by occupation.
10th ed, 2011: 3,000 pp, $267/set
ISBN(s): 978-1-4144-4548-9

**American Book Prices Current**
Published by Bancroft Parkman Inc
PO Box 1236, Washington, CT 06793-0236
*Tel:* 860-868-7408; 212-737-2715 *Fax:* 860-868-0080
*E-mail:* abpc@snet.net
*Web Site:* www.bookpricescurrent.com
*Key Personnel*
Publr: Daniel J Leab
Exec Ed: Katharine Kyes Leab
Research price guide detailing prices realized at auction in the USA & abroad in the world of books, mss, autographs, maps, broadsides & charts. Also the proprietor of a series of databases dealing with the prices realized at auction of books recording missing books & mss. Now on CD-ROM only.
1,100 pp, Online price: libr or dealer $595, others $800, update $198.90
ISBN(s): 978-0-914022-38-1

**American Book Publishing Record® Annual**
Published by Grey House Publishing Inc™
4919 Rte 22, Amenia, NY 12501
Mailing Address: PO Box 56, Amenia, NY 12501-0056
*Tel:* 518-789-8700 *Toll Free Tel:* 800-562-2139 *Fax:* 518-789-0556
*E-mail:* books@greyhouse.com
*Web Site:* www.greyhouse.com
*Key Personnel*
Edit Dir: Laura Mars-Proietti *E-mail:* lmars@greyhouse.com
Provides immediate access to the 73,000 cataloging records for the entire year of 2010, for books published or distributed in the US.
Annual.
2013, $630/2 vol set
ISBN(s): 978-1-59237-697-1 (2 vol set)

**American Book Trade Directory**
Published by Information Today, Inc
630 Central Ave, New Providence, NJ 07974
*Toll Free Tel:* 800-824-2470 *Fax:* 813-855-2309
*E-mail:* custserv@infotoday.com
*Key Personnel*
Mgr, Tampa Edit Opers: Debra James *Tel:* 800-824-2470 ext 222 *E-mail:* djames@infotoday.com
Comprehensive directory of over 17,200 booksellers & wholesalers in the US & Canada, arranged by state/province & city; includes information on sidelines, appraisers, auctioneers & dealers in foreign-language books.
Annual.
59th ed, 2013-2014: 1,460 pp, $369.50 cloth
ISBN(s): 978-1-57387-464-9

**American Library Directory**
Published by Information Today, Inc
630 Central Ave, New Providence, NJ 07974
*Toll Free Tel:* 800-300-9868 (cust serv); 800-409-4929 (ext 0278) *Fax:* 908-219-0192
*E-mail:* custserv@infotoday.com
*Web Site:* www.americanlibrarydirectory.com
*Key Personnel*
Mng Ed: Beverley McDonough *Tel:* 908-219-0278 *E-mail:* bmcdonough@infotoday.com
Comprehensive directory of over 31,000 libraries throughout the United States & Canada. Also includes listings of library schools, networks, consortia, cooperative library organizations, state library agencies & US Armed Forces libraries overseas. Automation & database system vendor information, as well as e-mail addresses for libraries & library personnel included. Entries arranged geographically by state, province & city. Personnel Index section arranged alphabetically.
Annual.
66th ed, 2013-2014: 4,192 pp, $369.50/2 vol set cloth
ISBN(s): 978-1-57387-467-0 (2 vol set)

**American Reference Books Annual**
Published by Libraries Unlimited
Imprint of ABC-CLIO
130 Cremona Dr, Santa Barbara, CA 93117
Mailing Address: PO Box 1911, Santa Barbara, CA 93116-1911
*Tel:* 805-968-1911 *Toll Free Tel:* 800-368-6868 *Fax:* 805-685-9685 *Toll Free Fax:* 866-270-3856
*E-mail:* customerservice@abc-clio.com
*Web Site:* www.abc-clio.com; www.abc-clio.com
*Key Personnel*
Ed: Shannon Graff Hysell
The premier sources of information for the library & information community for more than three decades. Includes more than 1,800 descriptive & evaluative entries for recent reference publications. Reviews by subject experts of materials from more than 300 publishers & in nearly 500 subject areas. ARBA assists in answering everyday reference questions & in building a reference collection.
Annual.
Vol 44, 2013: 628 pp, $149
ISBN(s): 978-1-61069-367-7

**An Author's Guide to Children's Book Promotion**
Published by Raab Associates Inc
730 Yale Ave, Swarthmore, PA 19081
*Tel:* 914-241-2117
*E-mail:* info@raabassociates.com
*Web Site:* www.raabassociates.com
*Key Personnel*
Partner: Susan Raab
Provides authors & illustrators with the tools they need to get their books into the hands of key decision-makers: teachers, librarians, booksellers & reviewers. The book features a detailed directory of key associations, children's book information sources & trade & educational publications.
11th ed (rev), 2011: 87 pp, $14.95
ISBN(s): 978-096212-118-0

**The Art & Science of Book Publishing**
Published by Ohio University Press
215 Columbus Rd, Suite 101, Athens, OH 45701-2979
*Tel:* 740-593-1154 *Fax:* 740-593-4536
*Web Site:* www.ohioswallow.com
*Key Personnel*
Exec Ed: Kevin Haworth
Dir, Publicity: Jeff Kallet *Tel:* 740-593-1158 *E-mail:* kallet@ohio.edu
Author: Herbert S Bailey, Jr
Mktg Mgr: Sarah Welsch
Perms Spec: Sally Welch
Rts & Perms: Sally Welch
Introduction to basics of book publishing.
1993 ed: 234 pp, $14.95 paper
First published 1970
ISBN(s): 978-0-8214-0970-1

**The Association of American University Presses Directory**
Published by Association of American University Presses (AAUP)
28 W 36 St, Suite 602, New York, NY 10018
*Tel:* 212-989-1010 *Toll Free Tel:* 800-621-2736 (orders) *Fax:* 773-702-7212 (orders); 212-989-0275
*E-mail:* info@aaupnet.org
*Web Site:* www.aaupnet.org
*Key Personnel*
Exec Dir: Peter Berkery *Tel:* 212-989-1010 ext 29 *E-mail:* pberkery@aaupnet.org
Dir of Mktg & Communs: Brenna McLaughlin *Tel:* 518-436-3586 *E-mail:* bmclaughlin@aaupnet.org
Admin Mgr: Linda McCall *Tel:* 212-989-1010 ext 30 *E-mail:* lmccall@aaupnet.org
A detailed introduction to the structure & staff of the AAUP & to the publishing programs & personnel of member presses.
Annual.
2013: 256 pp, $30
ISBN(s): 978-0-945103-29-5 (print); 978-0-945103-30-1 (digital)

**AV Market Place**
Published by Information Today, Inc
630 Central Ave, New Providence, NJ 07974
*Tel:* 908-286-1090 *Toll Free Tel:* 800-409-4929; 800-300-9868 (cust serv) *Fax:* 908-219-0192
*E-mail:* custserv@infotoday.com
*Key Personnel*
Mng Ed: Karen Hallard *Tel:* 908-219-0277 *E-mail:* khallard@infotoday.com
A comprehensive directory of the AV market, listing the activities of almost 5,200 manufacturers, distributors & production service companies & over 1,250 products & services. Heavily indexed. Also contains information on related associations, state & local film & television commissions, awards & festivals, periodicals, reference books & AV-oriented conferences & exhibits. Covers all 50 states plus Canada.
Annual.
41st ed, 2013: 1,494 pp, $269.50 paper
ISBN(s): 978-1-57387-463-2

**Awards & Prizes Online**
Published by The Children's Book Council (CBC)
54 W 39 St, 14th fl, New York, NY 10018
*Tel:* 212-966-1990 *Fax:* 212-966-2073 *Toll Free Fax:* 888-807-9355 (orders only)
*E-mail:* cbc.info@cbcbooks.org; awardsandprizes@cbcbooks.org
*Web Site:* www.cbcbooks.org
*Key Personnel*
Exec Dir: Robin Adelson *E-mail:* robin.adelson@cbcbooks.org
Lists over 300 major US, British Commonwealth & international children's & young adult book awards; for teachers, librarians & universities with English, library or education schools teaching children's literature or creative writing. Includes indices, appendix & a list of information resources.
$150 online

**Banned in the USA: A Reference Guide to Book Censorship in Schools & Public Libraries Revised & Expanded Edition**
Published by Greenwood Press
Imprint of ABC-CLIO
130 Cremona Dr, Santa Barbara, CA 93117
Mailing Address: PO Box 1911, Santa Barbara, CA 93116-1911
*Tel:* 805-968-1911 *Toll Free Tel:* 800-368-6868 *Fax:* 805-685-9685 *Toll Free Fax:* 866-270-3856
*E-mail:* customerservice@abc-clio.com
*Web Site:* www.abc-clio.com
*Key Personnel*
CEO & Academic Publr: Ronald Boehm
Author: Herbert N Foerstel
Foerstel's book is the perfect book to hand to students writing papers on censorship or anyone doing research on the subject.
2002: 328 pp, $65 hardcover
ISBN(s): 978-0-313-31166-6

**Be the Media**
Published by Natural E Creative Group LLC
1110 Jericho Tpke, 2nd fl, New Hyde Park, NY 11040
*Tel:* 516-488-1143 *Fax:* 516-488-4111
*E-mail:* info@bethemedia.com
*Web Site:* www.bethemedia.com
1st ed: 536 pp, $34.95 US
First published 2009
ISBN(s): 978-0-9760814-5-6

**Biography & Genealogy Master Index**
Published by Gale
Division of Cengage Learning
27500 Drake Rd, Farmington Hills, MI 48331-3535
SAN: 213-4373
*Tel:* 248-699-4253 *Toll Free Tel:* 800-877-4253 *Fax:* 248-699-8074 *Toll Free Fax:* 800-414-5043 (orders)
*E-mail:* gale.galeord@cengage.com
*Web Site:* www.gale.cengage.com
*Key Personnel*
Ed: Jennifer Mossman
Provides more than 15 million citations compiled from more than 5,000 editions & volumes for approximately 1,700 current & retrospective biographical sources.
Two volumes annually; entries are cumulated every five years.
2011, $6110/vol; $1693
ISBN(s): 978-0-7876-4293-8 (supplements 2006-2010); 978-1-4144-3896-2 (vol 1); 978-1-4144-3897-9 (vol 2)

**Book Blitz, Getting Your Book in the News**
Published by Best Sellers
7456 Evergreen Dr, Goleta, CA 93117
*Tel:* 805-968-8567 *Fax:* 805-968-5747
*Key Personnel*
Author: Barbara Gaughen *E-mail:* bgaughenmu@aol.com; Ernest Weckbaugh
A hands-on publicity guide for authors; 60 steps for instant book success.
1996: 268 pp, $12.95
ISBN(s): 978-1-881474-02-9

**Book Fairs: An Exhibiting Guide for Publishers**
Published by Para Publishing LLC
PO Box 8206-240, Santa Barbara, CA 93118-8206
SAN: 215-8981
*Tel:* 805-968-7277 *Toll Free Tel:* 800-727-2782 *Fax:* 805-968-1379
*E-mail:* info@parapublishing.com
*Web Site:* www.parapublishing.com
*Key Personnel*
Owner & Publr: Dan Poynter *E-mail:* danpoynter@parapublishing.com
How to select, arrange & operate a booth at a book fair. Includes lists of fairs, exhibiting services, display materials & sources.
4th ed, 1986: 96 pp, $7.95 paper
ISBN(s): 978-0-915516-43-8

**Book Fulfillment: Order Entry, Picking, Packing and Shipping**
Published by Para Publishing LLC
PO Box 8206-240, Santa Barbara, CA 93118-8206
SAN: 215-8981
*Tel:* 805-968-7277 *Toll Free Tel:* 800-727-2782 *Fax:* 805-968-1379
*E-mail:* info@parapublishing.com
*Web Site:* www.parapublishing.com
*Key Personnel*
Owner & Publr: Dan Poynter *E-mail:* danpoynter@parapublishing.com
How to set up your publishing company & run your shipping department.
11th ed, 2011: 43 pp, $19.95 paper
ISBN(s): 978-1-56860-037-6

**Book Marketing: A New Approach**
Published by Para Publishing LLC
PO Box 8206-240, Santa Barbara, CA 93118-8206
SAN: 215-8981
*Tel:* 805-968-7277 *Toll Free Tel:* 800-727-2782 *Fax:* 805-968-1379
*E-mail:* info@parapublishing.com
*Web Site:* www.parapublishing.com
*Key Personnel*
Owner & Publr: Dan Poynter *E-mail:* danpoynter@parapublishing.com
How to sell books to bookstores, libraries & non-traditional markets.
Biennially.
13th ed, 2011: 76 pp, $14.95 paper
ISBN(s): 978-1-56860-029-1

**Book Review Index**
Published by Gale
Division of Cengage Learning
27500 Drake Rd, Farmington Hills, MI 48331-3535
SAN: 213-4373
*Tel:* 248-699-4253 *Toll Free Tel:* 800-877-4253 *Fax:* 248-699-8074 *Toll Free Fax:* 800-414-5043 (orders)
*E-mail:* gale.galeord@cengage.com
*Web Site:* www.gale.cengage.com
*Key Personnel*
Ed: Dana Ferguson
Provides review citations for approximately 600 publications. Available as 3 issue subscription or as an annual cumulation.
$513/set
ISBN(s): 978-1-4144-5810-6 (2011 set); 978-1-4144-5814-4 (2011 cumulation)

**Bookbinding Materials & Techniques 1700-1920**
Published by Canadian Bookbinders and Book Artists Guild (CBBAG)
80 Ward St, Suite 207, Toronto, ON M6H 4A6, Canada
*Tel:* 416-581-1071
*E-mail:* cbbag@cbbag.ca
*Web Site:* www.cbbag.ca
*Key Personnel*
Author: Margaret Lock
160 pp, $20
First published 2003
ISBN(s): 978-0-9695091-9-6

**Bookman's Price Index**
Published by Gale
Unit of Cengage Learning
27500 Drake Rd, Farmington Hills, MI 48331-3535
SAN: 213-4373
*Tel:* 248-699-4253 *Toll Free Tel:* 800-877-4253 *Fax:* 248-699-8075 *Toll Free Fax:* 800-414-5043 (orders)
*E-mail:* gale.galeord@cengage.com
*Web Site:* www.gale.cengage.com
*Key Personnel*
Ed: Jeffrey Wilson
A guide to the prices & availability of more rare or out-of-print antiquarian books as offered for sale in the catalogs of leading book dealers in the US, UK & Canada. Each volume lists approximately 15,000 titles. Volumes do not supersede previous volumes. Each volume covers catalogs from the previous 4-6 months. Each entry includes title, author, edition, year published, physical description (size, binding, illustrations), condition of the book & price.
Vol. 95-96, 2012, $625/vol
First published 1964
ISBN(s): 978-1-4144-0661-9 (vol 95); 978-1-4144-4565-6 (vol 96)

**Books in Print®**
Published by Grey House Publishing Inc™
4919 Rte 22, Amenia, NY 12501
Mailing Address: PO Box 56, Amenia, NY 12501-0056
*Tel:* 518-789-8700 *Toll Free Tel:* 800-562-2139 *Fax:* 518-789-0556
*E-mail:* books@greyhouse.com
*Web Site:* www.greyhouse.com
*Key Personnel*
Edit Dir: Laura Mars-Proietti *E-mail:* lmars@greyhouse.com
For over 50 years, Books In Print has served the library & book trade communities as the definitive bibliographic resource. This fully-updated edition features more than 401,000 new titles & more than 471,000 new ISBNs, to offer unparalleled coverage of the full range of books currently published or distributed in the US.
Annual.
2013-2014, $1,095/7 vol set
ISBN(s): 978-1-59237-714-5 (7 vol set)

**Books in Print Supplement®**
Published by Grey House Publishing Inc™
4919 Rte 22, Amenia, NY 12501
Mailing Address: PO Box 56, Amenia, NY 12501-0056
*Tel:* 518-789-8700 *Toll Free Tel:* 800-562-2139 *Fax:* 518-789-0556
*E-mail:* books@greyhouse.com
*Web Site:* www.greyhouse.com
*Key Personnel*
Edit Dir: Laura Mars-Proietti *E-mail:* lmars@greyhouse.com
This essential mid-year supplement to Books In Print® provides the latest book publishing updates for the past six months. This resource is crucial in ensuring that libraries & bookstores have access to the most accurate information throughout the year.
Annual.
2013-2014, $630/3 vol set
ISBN(s): 978-1-59237-690-2 (3 vol set)

**Books Out Loud™**
Published by Grey House Publishing Inc™
4919 Rte 22, Amenia, NY 12501
Mailing Address: PO Box 56, Amenia, NY 12501-0056
*Tel:* 518-789-8700 *Toll Free Tel:* 800-562-2139 *Fax:* 518-789-0556
*E-mail:* books@greyhouse.com
*Web Site:* www.greyhouse.com
*Key Personnel*
Edit Dir: Laura Mars-Proietti *E-mail:* lmars@greyhouse.com
With the increasing popularity of audiobooks, Books Out Loud™ is a must-have collection development & reference tool for your library or bookstore.
Annual.
2013, $400/2 vol set
ISBN(s): 978-1-59237-687-2 (2 vol set)

**BookStats**
Published by Book Industry Study Group Inc (BISG)
145 W 45 St, Suite 601, New York, NY 10036
*Tel:* 646-336-7141 *Fax:* 646-336-6214
*E-mail:* info@bisg.org; info@bookstats.org
*Web Site:* www.bisg.org; www.bookstats.org
*Key Personnel*
Proj Mgr, Standards & Best Practices: Julie Morris *E-mail:* julie@bisg.org
Statistics of book sales by market. Joint venture with Association of American Publishers (AAP).
Annual.
2013: 70 pp, PDF Summary Overview, free membs, $99 nonmembs, PDF Annual Report, $595 membs, $2,395 nonmembs

**Breathing Life Into Your Characters**
Published by Writer's Digest Books
Imprint of F+W Media Inc
10151 Carver Rd, Suite 200, Blue Ash, OH 45242
*Tel:* 513-531-2690 *Fax:* 513-531-0798
*E-mail:* writersdigest@fwmedia.com (edit)
*Web Site:* www.writersdigest.com; www.writersdigestshop.com
*Key Personnel*
Publr: Phil Sexton *E-mail:* phil.sexton@fwmedia.com
Learn techniques to help you tap your unconscious.
256 pp, $11.24
First published 2003
ISBN(s): 978-1-58297-597-9

**Business & Legal Forms for Authors & Self-Publishers**
Published by Allworth Press
Imprint of Skyhorse Publishing Inc
307 W 36 St, 11th fl, New York, NY 10018
*Tel:* 212-643-6816 *Fax:* 212-643-6819
*Web Site:* www.allworth.com
*Key Personnel*
Publr: Tad Crawford
Assoc Publr: Robert Porter *E-mail:* bporter@allworth.com
Publicity & Mktg Assoc: Cindy Peng
Contains 25 ready-to-use forms, negotiation checklist, extra tear-out forms & forms on CD-ROM.
3rd ed, 2005: 160 pp, $29.95 (includes CD-ROM)
ISBN(s): 978-1-58115-395-8

**Business Letters for Publishers: Creative Correspondence Outlines**
Published by Para Publishing LLC
PO Box 8206-240, Santa Barbara, CA 93118-8206
SAN: 215-8981
*Tel:* 805-968-7277 *Toll Free Tel:* 800-727-2782 *Fax:* 805-968-1379
*E-mail:* info@parapublishing.com
*Web Site:* www.parapublishing.com
*Key Personnel*
Owner & Publr: Dan Poynter *E-mail:* danpoynter@parapublishing.com
A collection of form letters conforming to publishing-industry procedures, designed to save time in drafting letters for sales, promotion, collections & other daily problems on disk.
82 pp, $29.95 CD or electronic version
ISBN(s): 978-0-915516-47-6

**Cabell's Directory of Publishing Opportunities in Accounting**
Published by Cabell Publishing Co
PO Box 5428, Beaumont, TX 77726-5428
*Tel:* 409-898-0575; 409-291-2936 (orders) *Fax:* 409-866-9554
*E-mail:* orders@cabells.com
*Web Site:* www.cabells.com
*Key Personnel*
Founder & Pres: David Cabell *E-mail:* dave@cabells.com
COO & Exec Mng Ed: Twyla George *E-mail:* twyla@cabells.com
Exec Dir & Sr Ed: Lacey Earle *E-mail:* lacey@cabells.com
Online directory of information on over 273 journals in accounting.
Annual.
$395
First published 1978
ISBN(s): 978-0-911753-58-5 (electronic only)

**Cabell's Directory of Publishing Opportunities in Business - College/Library Set**
Published by Cabell Publishing Co
PO Box 5428, Beaumont, TX 77726-5428
*Tel:* 409-898-0575; 409-291-2936 (orders) *Fax:* 409-866-9554
*E-mail:* orders@cabells.com
*Web Site:* www.cabells.com
*Key Personnel*
Founder & Pres: David Cabell *E-mail:* dave@cabells.com
COO & Exec Mng Ed: Twyla George *E-mail:* twyla@cabells.com
Exec Dir & Sr Ed: Lacey Earle *E-mail:* lacey@cabells.com
Online directory of information on over 2,522 academic journals in business.
Annual.
$945
First published 1978
ISBN(s): 978-0-911753-62-2 (electronic only)

**Cabell's Directory of Publishing Opportunities in Computer Science-Business Information Systems**
Published by Cabell Publishing Co
PO Box 5428, Beaumont, TX 77726-5428
*Tel:* 409-898-0575; 409-291-2936 (orders) *Fax:* 409-866-9554
*E-mail:* orders@cabells.com
*Web Site:* www.cabells.com
*Key Personnel*
Founder & Pres: David Cabell *E-mail:* dave@cabells.com
COO & Exec Mng Ed: Twyla George *E-mail:* twyla@cabells.com
Exec Dir & Sr Ed: Lacey Earle *E-mail:* lacey@cabells.com
Information on over 181 journals in computer science & business information systems.
Annual.
$395
ISBN(s): 978-0-911753-51-6 (electronic only)

**Cabell's Directory of Publishing Opportunities in Economics & Finance**
Published by Cabell Publishing Co
PO Box 5428, Beaumont, TX 77726-5428
*Tel:* 409-898-0575; 409-291-2936 (orders) *Fax:* 409-866-9554
*E-mail:* orders@cabells.com
*Web Site:* www.cabells.com
*Key Personnel*
Founder & Pres: David Cabell *E-mail:* dave@cabells.com

COO & Exec Mng Ed: Twyla George *E-mail:* twyla@cabells.com
Exec Dir & Sr Ed: Lacey Earle *E-mail:* lacey@cabells.com
Online directory of information on over 839 journals in economics & finance.
Annual.
$395
First published 1978
ISBN(s): 978-0-911753-59-2 (electronic only)

**Cabell's Directory of Publishing Opportunities in Education, Curriculum & Methods**
Published by Cabell Publishing Co
PO Box 5428, Beaumont, TX 77726-5428
*Tel:* 409-898-0575; 409-291-2936 (orders) *Fax:* 409-866-9554
*E-mail:* orders@cabells.com
*Web Site:* www.cabells.com
*Key Personnel*
Founder & Pres: David Cabell *E-mail:* dave@cabells.com
COO & Exec Mng Ed: Twyla George *E-mail:* twyla@cabells.com
Exec Dir & Sr Ed: Lacey Earle *E-mail:* lacey@cabells.com
Online indexes of over 490 journals on 28 different topic areas related to educational curriculum & methods.
Annual.
$315
First published 1981
ISBN(s): 978-0-911753-52-3 (electronic only)

**Cabell's Directory of Publishing Opportunities in Education Set**
Published by Cabell Publishing Co
PO Box 5428, Beaumont, TX 77726-5428
*Tel:* 409-898-0575; 409-291-2936 (orders) *Fax:* 409-866-9554
*E-mail:* orders@cabells.com
*Web Site:* www.cabells.com
*Key Personnel*
Founder & Pres: David Cabell *E-mail:* dave@cabells.com
COO & Exec Mng Ed: Twyla George *E-mail:* twyla@cabells.com
Exec Dir & Sr Ed: Lacey Earle *E-mail:* lacey@cabells.com
Information on over 1,000 journals in education. Electronic version only.
Annual.
$630
First published 2009

**Cabell's Directory of Publishing Opportunities in Educational Psychology & Administration**
Published by Cabell Publishing Co
PO Box 5428, Beaumont, TX 77726-5428
*Tel:* 409-898-0575; 409-291-2936 (orders) *Fax:* 409-866-9554
*E-mail:* orders@cabells.com
*Web Site:* www.cabells.com
*Key Personnel*
Founder & Pres: David Cabell *E-mail:* dave@cabells.com
COO & Exec Mng Ed: Twyla George *E-mail:* twyla@cabells.com
Exec Dir & Sr Ed: Lacey Earle *E-mail:* lacey@cabells.com
Online indexes of over 360 journals on 28 different topic areas related to educational psychology & administration.
Annual.
$315
First published 1981
ISBN(s): 978-0-911753-53-0 (electronic only)

**Cabell's Directory of Publishing Opportunities in Educational Technology & Library Science**
Published by Cabell Publishing Co
PO Box 5428, Beaumont, TX 77726-5428
*Tel:* 409-898-0575; 409-291-2936 (orders) *Fax:* 409-866-9554
*E-mail:* orders@cabells.com
*Web Site:* www.cabells.com
*Key Personnel*
Founder & Pres: David Cabell *E-mail:* dave@cabells.com
COO & Exec Mng Ed: Twyla George *E-mail:* twyla@cabells.com
Exec Dir & Sr Ed: Lacey Earle *E-mail:* lacey@cabells.com
Online directory of information on over 200 journals in educational technology & library science.
Annual.
$315
First published 2007
ISBN(s): 978-0-911753-54-7 (electronic only)

**Cabell's Directory of Publishing Opportunities in Health Administration**
Published by Cabell Publishing Co
PO Box 5428, Beaumont, TX 77726-5428
*Tel:* 409-898-0575; 409-291-2936 (orders) *Fax:* 409-866-9554
*E-mail:* orders@cabells.com
*Web Site:* www.cabells.com
*Key Personnel*
Founder & Pres: David Cabell *E-mail:* dave@cabells.com
COO & Exec Mng Ed: Twyla George *E-mail:* twyla@cabells.com
Exec Dir & Sr Ed: Lacey Earle *E-mail:* lacey@cabells.com
Information on 208 journals listed in health administration.
Annual.
$175
First published 2010
ISBN(s): 978-09-11753-56-1 (electronic only)

**Cabell's Directory of Publishing Opportunities in Management**
Published by Cabell Publishing Co
PO Box 5428, Beaumont, TX 77726-5428
*Tel:* 409-898-0575; 409-291-2936 (orders) *Fax:* 409-866-9554
*E-mail:* orders@cabells.com
*Web Site:* www.cabells.com
*Key Personnel*
Founder & Pres: David Cabell *E-mail:* dave@cabells.com
COO & Exec Mng Ed: Twyla George *E-mail:* twyla@cabells.com
Exec Dir & Sr Ed: Lacey Earle *E-mail:* lacey@cabells.com
Online directory of information on over 1,150 journals in management.
Annual.
$395
First published 1978
ISBN(s): 978-0-911753-60-8 (electronic only)

**Cabell's Directory of Publishing Opportunities in Marketing**
Published by Cabell Publishing Co
PO Box 5428, Beaumont, TX 77726-5428
*Tel:* 409-898-0575; 409-291-2936 (orders) *Fax:* 409-866-9554
*E-mail:* orders@cabells.com
*Web Site:* www.cabells.com
*Key Personnel*
Founder & Pres: David Cabell *E-mail:* dave@cabells.com
COO & Exec Mng Ed: Twyla George *E-mail:* twyla@cabells.com
Exec Dir & Sr Ed: Lacey Earle *E-mail:* lacey@cabells.com
Online directory of information on over 261 journals in marketing.
Annual.
$395
First published 1978
ISBN(s): 978-0-911753-61-5 (electronic only)

**Cabell's Directory of Publishing Opportunities in Nursing**
Published by Cabell Publishing Co
PO Box 5428, Beaumont, TX 77726-5428
*Tel:* 409-898-0575; 409-291-2936 (orders) *Fax:* 409-866-9554
*E-mail:* orders@cabells.com
*Web Site:* www.cabells.com
*Key Personnel*
Founder & Pres: David Cabell *E-mail:* dave@cabells.com
COO & Exec Mng Ed: Twyla George *E-mail:* twyla@cabells.com
Exec Dir & Sr Ed: Lacey Earle *E-mail:* lacey@cabells.com
Information on over 181 academic journals in nursing. Electronic version only.
Annual.
$175
First published 2010
ISBN(s): 978-0-911753-57-8 (electronic only)

**Cabell's Directory of Publishing Opportunities in Psychology & Psychiatry**
Published by Cabell Publishing Co
PO Box 5428, Beaumont, TX 77726-5428
*Tel:* 409-898-0575; 409-291-2936 (orders) *Fax:* 409-866-9554
*E-mail:* orders@cabells.com
*Web Site:* www.cabells.com
*Key Personnel*
Founder & Pres: David Cabell *E-mail:* dave@cabells.com
COO & Exec Mng Ed: Twyla George *E-mail:* twyla@cabells.com
Exec Dir & Sr Ed: Lacey Earle *E-mail:* lacey@cabells.com
Online directory of information on 600 journals listed in psychology & psychiatry.
Annual.
$400
First published 2002
ISBN(s): 978-0-911753-63-9 (electronic only)

**Catholic Press Directory**
Published by Catholic Press Association of the US & Canada
205 W Monroe St, Suite 470, Chicago, IL 60606
*Tel:* 312-380-6789 *Fax:* 312-361-0256
*E-mail:* cathjourn@catholicpress.org
*Web Site:* www.catholicpress.org
*Key Personnel*
Exec Dir: Timothy Walter *E-mail:* twalter@catholicpress.org
Opers Analyst: Barbara Mastrolia
Communs & Prodn Coord: Michelle Monckton
Complete listings of more than 600 Catholic newspapers, magazines, newsletters & foreign language publications in the USA & CN. Also includes Catholic book & general publishers; Diocesan directories.
Annual.
2013: 150 pp, $80

**CCOD**, see Consultants & Consulting Organizations Directory

**Chicago Guide to Preparing Electronic Manuscripts**
Published by University of Chicago Press
1427 E 60 St, Chicago, IL 60637-2954
SAN: 202-5280
*Tel:* 773-702-7700 *Toll Free Tel:* 800-621-2736 (orders) *Fax:* 773-702-9756
*E-mail:* marketing@press.uchicago.edu; custserv@press.uchicago.edu
*Web Site:* www.press.uchicago.edu

*Key Personnel*
Exec Ed: Susan Bielstein *Tel:* 773-702-7633 *E-mail:* sbielstein@press.uchicago.edu
A practical guide for authors & publishers who use computer disks & tapes for typesetting.
1987: 151 pp, $40 cloth, $15 paper
ISBN(s): 978-0-226-10392-1 (cloth); 978-0-226-10393-8 (paper)

**The Chicago Manual of Style**
Published by University of Chicago Press
1427 E 60 St, Chicago, IL 60637-2954
SAN: 202-5280
*Tel:* 773-702-7700; 773-753-3347 (cust serv, online ed - outside US & CN) *Toll Free Tel:* 800-621-2736 (orders); 877-705-1878 (cust serv, online ed - outside US & CN) *Fax:* 773-702-9756
*E-mail:* custserv@press.uchicago.edu; marketing@press.uchicago.edu; cmoshelpdesk@press.uchicago.edu
*Web Site:* www.press.uchicago.edu; www.chicagomanualofstyle.org
*Key Personnel*
Edit Dir, Ref: Paul Schellinger *Tel:* 773-702-2376 *E-mail:* pschellinger@press.uchicago.edu
Sr Ed: David Morrow
Style manual for authors, editors & copywriters. Revised every 10 years.
15th ed, revised & expanded, 2003: 984 pp, $55 cloth, $60 CD-ROM
ISBN(s): 978-0-226-10403-4 (cloth); 978-0-226-10404-1 (CD-ROM)

**Children's Books in Print®**
Published by Grey House Publishing Inc™
4919 Rte 22, Amenia, NY 12501
Mailing Address: PO Box 56, Amenia, NY 12501-0056
*Tel:* 518-789-8700 *Toll Free Tel:* 800-562-2139 *Fax:* 518-789-0556
*E-mail:* books@greyhouse.com
*Web Site:* www.greyhouse.com
*Key Personnel*
Edit Dir: Laura Mars-Proietti *E-mail:* lmars@greyhouse.com
Children's Books In Print® is the go-to source for locating children's & young adult titles in the US.
Annual.
2013, $505/2 vol set
ISBN(s): 978-1-59237-654-4 (2 vol set)

**Children's Literature Review**
Published by Gale
Unit of Cengage Learning
27500 Drake Rd, Farmington Hills, MI 48331-3535
SAN: 213-4373
*Tel:* 248-699-4253 *Toll Free Tel:* 800-877-4253 *Fax:* 248-699-8054 *Toll Free Fax:* 800-414-5043 (orders)
*E-mail:* gale.galeord@cengage.com
*Web Site:* www.gale.cengage.com
*Key Personnel*
Ed: Jelena Krstovic
Provides full texts from criticism on authors & illustrators of books for children & young adults. Includes indexes to titles, authors & nationality. A cumulative title index to the entire series is published seperately (included in subscription). Illustrations & photographs are included. Also available as an e-book.
Multiple vols/yr.
Vol 158-170, 2010-2012, $313/vol
ISBN(s): 978-1-4144-6215-8 (vol 158); 978-1-4144-6216-5 (vol 159); 978-1-4144-7311-6 (vol 160); 978-1-4144-7312-3 (vol 161); 978-1-4144-7313-0 (vol 162); 978-1-4144-7314-7 (vol 163); 978-1-4144-7315-4 (vol 164); 978-1-4144-7316-1 (vol 165); 978-1-4144-7317-8 (vol 166); 978-1-4144-7318-5 (vol 167); 978-1-4144-7319-2 (vol 168); 978-1-4144-7320-8 (vol 169); 978-1-4144-7321-5 (vol 170)

**Children's Writer's Word Book**
Published by Writer's Digest Books
Imprint of F+W Media Inc
10151 Carver Rd, Suite 200, Blue Ash, OH 45242
*Tel:* 513-531-2690 *Toll Free Tel:* 800-289-0963 *Fax:* 513-531-0798
*E-mail:* writersdigest@fwmedia.com (edit)
*Web Site:* www.writersdigest.com; www.writersdigestshop.com
*Key Personnel*
Publr: Phil Sexton *E-mail:* phil.sexton@fwmedia.com
Handy reference book to be used along with your dictionary or thesaurus. Gives guidelines for sentence length, word usage & theme at each reading level.
2nd ed: 352 pp, $11.48
First published 1999
ISBN(s): 978-1-58297-413-2

**Christian Book Writers' Marketing Guide**
Published by Joy Publishing Co
Division of California Clock Co
PO Box 9901, Fountain Valley, CA 92708
*Tel:* 714-545-4321 *Toll Free Tel:* 800-454-8228 *Fax:* 714-708-2099
*E-mail:* mail@joypublishing.com
*Web Site:* www.joypublishing.com
*Key Personnel*
Pres: Woody Young *E-mail:* woody@joypublishing.com
Info on publishers (books & periodicals).
2001: 273 pp, $19.95
ISBN(s): 973-0-939513-00-0

**Communicating Ideas: The Politics of Publishing in a Post-Industrial Society**
Published by Transaction Publishers Inc
10 Corporate Place S, Piscataway, NJ 08854
Mailing Address: 1247 State Rd, Princeton, NJ 08540
*Tel:* 732-445-2280 *Fax:* 732-445-3138
*Web Site:* www.transactionpub.com
*Key Personnel*
Chmn & Author: Irving Louis Horowitz *E-mail:* ihorowitz@transactionpub.com
View of publishing in America & abroad. Addresses the political implications of scholarly communication in the era of the new computerized technology. This title was originally published by Oxford University Press.
3rd ed, 2010: 356 pp, $27.95 (2nd ed) paper
First published 1988
ISBN(s): 978-0-88738-898-9 (2nd ed)

**The Complete Directory of Large Print Books & Serials™**
Published by Grey House Publishing Inc™
4919 Rte 22, Amenia, NY 12501
Mailing Address: PO Box 56, Amenia, NY 12501-0056
*Tel:* 518-789-8700 *Toll Free Tel:* 800-562-2139 *Fax:* 518-789-0556
*E-mail:* books@greyhouse.com
*Web Site:* www.greyhouse.com
*Key Personnel*
Edit Dir: Laura Mars-Proietti *E-mail:* lmars@greyhouse.com
The Complete Directory of Large Print Books & Serials™ is the single most important resource for building or managing a large print books or serials collection.
Annual.
2013, $435
ISBN(s): 978-1-59237-686-5

**The Complete Guide to Book Marketing**
Published by Allworth Press
Subsidiary of Allworth Communications Inc
Imprint of Skyhorse Publishing Inc
307 W 36 St, 11th fl, New York, NY 10018
*Tel:* 212-643-6816
*E-mail:* crawford@allworth.com
*Web Site:* www.allworth.com
*Key Personnel*
Author: David Cole
Publr: Tad Crawford
Assoc Publr: Robert Porter *E-mail:* bporter@allworth.com
Publicity & Mktg Assoc: Cindy Peng
Comprehensive resource book covering all aspects of book marketing.
2004 (rev): 256 pp, $19.95
ISBN(s): 978-1-58115-322-4

**The Complete Guide to Book Publicity**
Published by Allworth Press
Imprint of Skyhorse Publishing Inc
307 W 36 St, 11th fl, New York, NY 10018
*Tel:* 212-643-6816
*E-mail:* crawford@allworth.com
*Web Site:* www.allworth.com
*Key Personnel*
Publr: Tad Crawford
Assoc Publr: Robert Porter *E-mail:* bporter@allworth.com
Author: Jodee Blanco
Publicity & Mktg Assoc: Cindy Peng
A comprehensive resource book covering all aspects of book publicity.
2nd ed, 2004: 304 pp, $19.95
ISBN(s): 978-1-58115-349-1

**The Complete Guide to Self-Publishing**
Published by Writer's Digest Books
Imprint of F+W Media Inc
10151 Carver Rd, Suite 200, Blue Ash, OH 45242
*Tel:* 513-531-2690 *Toll Free Tel:* 800-289-0963 *Fax:* 513-531-0798
*E-mail:* writersdigest@fwmedia.com (edit)
*Web Site:* www.writersdigest.com; www.writersdigestshop.com
*Key Personnel*
Publr: Phil Sexton *E-mail:* phil.sexton@fwmedia.com
Everything you need to write, publish, promote & sell your book.
5th ed: 576 pp, $16.32 paper
First published 1991
ISBN(s): 978-1-58297-711-8

**The Complete Guide to Successful Publishing**
Published by Cardoza Publishing
5473 S Eastern Ave, Las Vegas, NV 89119
*Tel:* 702-870-7200 *Toll Free Tel:* 800-577-WINS (577-9467) *Fax:* 702-822-6500
*E-mail:* info@cardozabooks.com; cardozabooks@aol.com
*Web Site:* www.cardozabooks.com
*Key Personnel*
Publr & Author: Avery Cardoza
This step-by-step guide shows beginning & established publishers how to successfully produce professional-looking books that not only look good, but sell in the open market; readers learn how to find & develop ideas; set up the business from the ground up; design & layout a book; find authors, work contracts & negotiate deals; get distribution; expand a publishing company into a large enterprise & more.
3rd ed, April 2003: 416 pp, $19.95 paper
First published 1995
ISBN(s): 978-1-58042-097-6

**The Complete Handbook of Novel Writing**
Published by Writer's Digest Books
Imprint of F+W Media Inc

10151 Carver Rd, Suite 200, Blue Ash, OH 45242
*Tel:* 513-531-2690 *Toll Free Tel:* 800-289-0963 *Fax:* 513-531-0798
*E-mail:* writersdigest@fwmedia.com (edit)
*Web Site:* www.writersdigest.com; www.writersdigestshop.com
*Key Personnel*
Publr: Phil Sexton *E-mail:* phil.sexton@fwmedia.com
Everything you need to know about creating & selling your work.
1st ed: 400 pp, $7.20
First published 2002
ISBN(s): 978-1-58297-159-9

**Complete Television, Radio & Cable Industry Directory**
Published by Grey House Publishing Inc™
4919 Rte 22, Amenia, NY 12501
Mailing Address: PO Box 56, Amenia, NY 12501-0056
*Tel:* 518-789-8700 *Toll Free Tel:* 800-562-2139 *Fax:* 518-789-0556
*E-mail:* books@greyhouse.com
*Web Site:* www.greyhouse.com
*Key Personnel*
Edit Dir: Laura Mars-Proietti *E-mail:* lmars@greyhouse.com
Data & industry contacts on over 20,000 US & Canadian stations & organizations in the field: Television, Radio & Cable Stations, Programming Services & Technological Solutions, Brokers & Professional Services, Associations, Events, Education, Awards, Law & Regulation & Government Agencies.
Nov 2012: 2,000 pp, $350
ISBN(s): 978-1-61925-103-8

**Complete Video Directory™**
Published by Grey House Publishing Inc™
4919 Rte 22, Amenia, NY 12501
Mailing Address: PO Box 56, Amenia, NY 12501-0056
*Tel:* 518-789-8700 *Toll Free Tel:* 800-562-2139 *Fax:* 518-789-0556
*E-mail:* books@greyhouse.com
*Web Site:* www.greyhouse.com
*Key Personnel*
Edit Dir: Laura Mars-Proietti *E-mail:* lmars@greyhouse.com
Extensive listing of currently available entertainment titles along with education & special interest videos for home, school & business.
Annual.
March 2013: 7,900 pp, $655/4-vol set
ISBN(s): 978-1-61925-067-3

**Concise Dictionary of American Literary Biography**
Published by Gale
Unit of Cengage Learning
27500 Drake Rd, Farmington Hills, MI 48331-3535
SAN: 213-4373
*Tel:* 248-699-4253 *Toll Free Tel:* 800-877-4253 *Fax:* 248-699-8070 *Toll Free Fax:* 800-414-5043 (orders)
*E-mail:* gale.galeord@cengage.com
*Web Site:* www.gale.cengage.com
Organized chronologically, this set covers only the American authors most frequently studied in high school & college literature courses, extracts & fully updates essays in their entirety from the much larger Dictionary of Literary Biography series. A one volume supplement highlighting Modern American Writers is available seperately.
Volumes include: *Colonization to the American Renaissance, 1640-1865*
*Realism, Naturalism & Local Color, 1865-1917*
*The Twenties, 1917-1929*
*The Age of Maturity, 1929-1941*
*The New Consciousness, 1941-1968*
*Broadening Views, 1968-1988*
*Supplement: Modern American Writers.*
2,506 pp, $799/6 vol set
First published 1987
ISBN(s): 978-0-8103-1818-2 (6 vol set)

**Concise Dictionary of British Literary Biography**
Published by Gale
Unit of Cengage Learning
27500 Drake Rd, Farmington Hills, MI 48331-3535
SAN: 213-4373
*Tel:* 248-699-4253 *Toll Free Tel:* 800-347-4253 *Fax:* 248-699-8070 *Toll Free Fax:* 800-414-5043 (orders)
*E-mail:* gale.galeord@cengage.com
*Web Site:* www.gale.cengage.com
Illustrated set provides thorough coverage of major British literary figures of all eras. Vol 1: *Writers of the Middle Ages & Renaissance Before 1660*; Vol 2: *Writers of the Restoration & 18th Century 1660-1789*; Vol 3: *Writers of the Romantic Period 1789-1832*; Vol 4: *Victorian Writers, 1832-1890*; Vol 5: *Late Victorian & Edwardian Writers, 1890-1914*; Vol 6: *Modern Writers, 1914-1945*; Vol 7: *Writers After World War II, 1945-1960*; Vol 8: *Contemporary Writers, 1960-Present.*
1991: 24,000 pp, $1086/8 vol set
ISBN(s): 978-0-8103-7980-0

**Consultants & Consulting Organizations Directory**
Published by Gale
Unit of Cengage Learning
27500 Drake Rd, Farmington Hills, MI 48331-3535
SAN: 213-4373
*Tel:* 248-699-4253 *Toll Free Tel:* 800-877-4253 *Fax:* 248-699-8069 *Toll Free Fax:* 800-414-5043 (orders)
*E-mail:* gale.galeord@cengage.com
*Web Site:* www.gale.cengage.com
*Key Personnel*
Ed: Julie A Gough *E-mail:* julie.gough@cengage.com
Important details, including services offered, full contact information, date founded & principal business executives. More than 26,000 firms & individuals listed are arranged in subject sections under 14 general fields of consulting activity ranging from agriculture to marketing. More than 400 specialties are represented, including finance, computers, fund raising & others.
Annual.
37th ed, 2012, $1392
ISBN(s): 978-1-4144-5845-8

**Contemporary Authors**
Published by Gale
Unit of Cengage Learning
27500 Drake Rd, Farmington Hills, MI 48331-3535
SAN: 213-4373
*Tel:* 248-699-4253 *Toll Free Tel:* 800-877-4253 *Fax:* 248-699-8070 *Toll Free Fax:* 800-414-5043 (orders)
*E-mail:* gale.galeord@cengage.com
*Web Site:* www.gale.cengage.com
Find biographical information on more than 130,000 modern novelists, poets, playwrights, nonfiction writers, journalists & motion picture & television scriptwriters. A softcover cumulative index is published twice per year (included in subscription).
multiple vols/yr.
Vols 302-313, 2011, $293/vol
ISBN(s): 978-1-4144-6084-0 (vol 302); 978-1-4144-6085-7 (vol 303); 978-1-4144-6086-4 (vol 304); 978-1-4144-6087-1 (vol 305); 978-1-4144-6088-0 (vol 306); 978-1-4144-6089-5 (vol 307); 978-1-4144-6090-1 (vol 308); 978-1-4144-6091-8 (vol 309); 978-1-4144-6092-5 (vol 310); 978-1-4144-6093-2 (vol 311); 978-1-4144-6094-9 (vol 312); 978-1-4144-6095-6 (vol 313)

**Contemporary Literary Criticism**
Published by Gale
Unit of Cengage Learning
27500 Drake Rd, Farmington Hills, MI 48331-3535
SAN: 213-4373
*Tel:* 248-699-4253 *Toll Free Tel:* 800-877-4253 *Fax:* 248-699-8054 *Toll Free Fax:* 800-414-5043 (orders)
*E-mail:* gale.galeord@cengage.com
*Web Site:* www.gale.cengage.com
*Key Personnel*
Ed: Jeffrey Hunter
Each series volume contains full or excerpted texts from criticism & evaluations of about 6-8 major modern authors. Over 200 vols in print covering over 3,000 authors. *Cumulative Title Index* is published seperately.
Multiple vols/yr.
Vols 281-300, 2010-2011, $328/vol
ISBN(s): 978-1-4144-3977-8 (vol 281); 978-1-4144-3978-5 (vol 282); 978-1-4144-3979-2 (vol 283); 978-1-4144-3980-8 (vol 284); 978-1-4144-3981-5 (vol 285); 978-1-4144-3982-2 (vol 286); 978-1-4144-3983-9 (vol 287); 978-1-4144-3984-6 (vol 288); 978-1-4144-3985-3 (vol 289); 978-1-4144-3986-0 (vol 290); 978-1-4144-3987-7 (vol 291); 978-1-4144-4606-6 (vol 292); 978-1-4144-4607-3 (vol 293); 978-1-4144-4608-0 (vol 294); 978-1-4144-4609-7 (vol 295); 978-1-4144-4610-3 (vol 296); 978-1-4144-4611-0 (vol 297); 978-1-4144-4612-7 (vol 298); 978-1-4144-4613-4 (vol 299); 978-1-4144-4927-2 (vol 300)

**Copy Editing**
Published by Cambridge University Press
32 Avenue of the Americas, New York, NY 10013-2473
SAN: 200-206X
*Tel:* 212-924-3900 *Fax:* 212-691-3239
*E-mail:* newyork@cambridge.org
*Web Site:* www.cambridge.org/us
*Key Personnel*
Author: Judith Butcher
Edit Asst: David Jones *Tel:* 212-924-3900 ext 5072 *E-mail:* djou@cabridge.org
Copy Editing covers all aspects of the editorial process involved in converting an author's ms to the printed page. It covers the basics from how to mark a ms for the designer & typesetter, through the ground rules of house style & consistency, to how to read & correct proofs.
4th ed, 2006: 558 pp, $107
ISBN(s): 978-521-84713-1

**Copyediting: A Practical Guide**
Published by Axzo Press
Division of Thomson Learning
PO Box 25690, Rochester, NY 14625
*Toll Free Tel:* 888-534-5556 *Toll Free Fax:* 888-715-0220
*E-mail:* customerservice@axzopress.com
*Web Site:* www.axzopress.com
For authors, publishing personnel, writers, editors, journalists, teachers, desktop publishing & computer software workers.
3rd ed, 2001: 328 pp, $24.95
*Returns:* Axzo Press Distribution Center, One Executive Pkwy, Minster, OH 45865
ISBN(s): 978-1-56052-608-7

**Critical Insights: Authors**
Published by Grey House Publishing Inc™
4919 Rte 22, Amenia, NY 12501
Mailing Address: PO Box 56, Amenia, NY 12501-0056
*Tel:* 518-789-8700 *Toll Free Tel:* 800-562-2139 *Fax:* 518-789-0556
*E-mail:* books@greyhouse.com
*Web Site:* www.greyhouse.com
*Key Personnel*
Ed, Raymond Carver: James Plath
Ed, William Faulkner: Kathryn Stelmach Artuso
Ed, Zora Neale Hurston: Sharon Jones, PhD
Ed, Sylvia Plath: William Buckley
Ed, Philip Roth: Aimee Pozorski
Ed, Kurt Vonnegut: Rob Tally
Each volume contains 300 pgs & includes: General bibliography, chronology of author's life, complete list of author's works, publication dates of works, detailed bio of the editor & general subject index. Each volume published April/May 2013.
*Raymond Carver*
*William Faulkner*
*Zora Neale Hurston*
*Sylvia Plath*
*Philip Roth*
*Kurt Vonnegut.*
$85/vol (includes online access)
ISBN(s): 978-1-4298-3828-3 (William Faulkner); 978-1-4298-3829-0 (Philip Roth); 978-1-4298-3830-6 (Raymond Carver); 978-1-4298-3831-3 (Zora Neale Hurston); 978-1-4298-3832-0 (Kurt Vonnegut); 978-1-4298-3833-7 (Sylvia Plath); 978-1-4298-3844-3 (William Faulkner ebook); 978-1-4298-3845-0 (Philip Roth ebook); 978-1-4298-3846-7 (Raymond Carver ebook); 978-1-4298-3847-4 (Zora Neale Hurston ebook); 978-1-4298-3848-1 (Kurt Vonnegut ebook); 978-1-4298-3849-8 (Sylvia Plath ebook)

**Critical Insights: Themes**
Published by Grey House Publishing Inc™
Division of EBSCO Publishing
2 University Plaza, Suite 310, Hackensack, NJ 07601
SAN: 208-838X
*Tel:* 201-968-0500 *Toll Free Tel:* 866-550-8122 *Fax:* 201-968-0511
*E-mail:* csr@salempress.com
*Web Site:* salempress.com
Each of the 10 volumes contain 300 pages & explores a popular literary theme: Coming of Age, Cultural Encounters, Dystopia, Family, The Fantastic, Good & Evil, The Hero's Quest, Nature & the Environment, Technology & Humanity, War. Each volume published Sept 2012; ebooks available.
Sept 2012: 300 pp, $85/vol (includes online access)
ISBN(s): 978-1-4298-3731-6 (Coming of Age); 978-1-4298-3732-3 (Cultural Encounters); 978-1-4298-3733-0 (Dystopia); 978-1-4298-3734-7 (Family); 978-1-4298-3735-4 (The Fantasic); 978-1-4298-3736-1 (Good & Evil); 978-1-4298-3737-0 (The Hero's Quest); 978-1-4298-3738-5 (Nature & the Environment); 978-1-4298-3739-2 (Technology & Humanity); 978-1-4298-3740-8 (War)

**Critical Insights: Works**
Published by Grey House Publishing Inc™
4919 Rte 22, Amenia, NY 12501
Mailing Address: PO Box 56, Amenia, NY 12501-0056
*Tel:* 518-789-8700 *Toll Free Tel:* 800-562-2139 *Fax:* 518-789-0556
*E-mail:* books@greyhouse.com
*Web Site:* www.greyhouse.com
*Key Personnel*
Ed, Jane Eyre: Katie R Peel
Each essay is 5,000 words in length & offers comprehensive, in-depth coverage of a single work. Each volume is 300 pages & contains 16-18 essays that break down the work from several different perspectives & includes a brief biography of the author. Each volume published Dec 2013
*Brave New World* by Aldous Huxley
*Jane Eyre* by Charlotte Bronte.
$85/vol (includes online access)
ISBN(s): 978-1-61925-218-9 (Jane Eyre); 978-1-61925-219-6 (Jane Eyre ebook); 978-1-61925-238-7 (Brave New World); 978-1-61925-239-4 (Brave New World ebook)

**Critical Survey of Drama**
Published by Grey House Publishing Inc™
4919 Rte 22, Amenia, NY 12501
Mailing Address: PO Box 56, Amenia, NY 12501-0056
*Tel:* 518-789-8700 *Toll Free Tel:* 800-562-2139 *Fax:* 518-789-0556
*E-mail:* books@greyhouse.com
*Web Site:* www.greyhouse.com
*Key Personnel*
Ed: Carl Rollyson
Contains 602 essays that discuss individual dramatists & 64 cover overview topics. Authors covered represent all time periods & all areas of the world.
2nd ed (rev), 2003: 4,646 pp, $499/8 vol set
ISBN(s): 978-1-58765-102-1 (8 vol set)

**Critical Survey of Graphic Novels: Heroes & Superheroes**
Published by Grey House Publishing Inc™
4919 Rte 22, Amenia, NY 12501
Mailing Address: PO Box 56, Amenia, NY 12501-0056
*Tel:* 518-789-8700 *Toll Free Tel:* 800-562-2139 *Fax:* 518-789-0556
*E-mail:* books@greyhouse.com
*Web Site:* www.greyhouse.com
*Key Personnel*
Ed: Bart H Beaty; Stephen Weiner
Provides in-depth insight into over 130 of the most popular & studied graphic novels. Arranged alphabetically.
April 2012: 800 pp, $295/2 vol set (includes online access)
First published 2012
ISBN(s): 978-1-58765-865-5 (2 vol set); 978-1-58765-869-3 (ebook)

**Critical Survey of Graphic Novels: History, Theme & Technique**
Published by Grey House Publishing Inc™
4919 Rte 22, Amenia, NY 12501
Mailing Address: PO Box 56, Amenia, NY 12501-0056
*Tel:* 518-789-8700 *Toll Free Tel:* 800-562-2139 *Fax:* 518-789-0556
*E-mail:* books@greyhouse.com
*Web Site:* www.greyhouse.com
*Key Personnel*
Ed: Bart H Beaty; Stephen Weiner
Contains over 65 essays covering themes & concepts of graphic novels, including genres, time periods, foreign language traditions, social relevance & craftsmanship such as penciling & inking.
Oct 2012: 475 pp, $195 (includes online access)
First published 2012
ISBN(s): 978-1-58765-957-7; 978-1-58765-958-4 (ebook)

**Critical Survey of Graphic Novels: Independents & Underground Classics**
Published by Grey House Publishing Inc™
4919 Rte 22, Amenia, NY 12501
Mailing Address: PO Box 56, Amenia, NY 12501-0056
*Tel:* 518-789-8700 *Toll Free Tel:* 800-562-2139 *Fax:* 518-789-0556
*E-mail:* books@greyhouse.com
*Web Site:* www.greyhouse.com
*Key Personnel*
Ed: Bart H Beaty; Stephen Weiner
215 essays covering graphic novels & core comics series, focusing on the independents & underground genre.
May 2012: 1,500 pp, $395/3 vol set (includes online access)
First published 2012
ISBN(s): 978-1-58765-950-8 (3 vol set); 978-1-58765-954-6 (ebook)

**Critical Survey of Graphic Novels: Manga**
Published by Grey House Publishing Inc™
4919 Rte 22, Amenia, NY 12501
Mailing Address: PO Box 56, Amenia, NY 12501-0056
*Tel:* 518-789-8700 *Toll Free Tel:* 800-562-2139 *Fax:* 518-789-0556
*E-mail:* books@greyhouse.com
*Web Site:* www.greyhouse.com
*Key Personnel*
Ed: Bart H Beaty; Stephen Weiner
Provides in-depth insight for over 55 of the most popular manga graphic novels, ranging from metaseries to stand-alone books.
Sept 2012: 400 pp, $195 (includes online access)
First published 2012
ISBN(s): 978-1-58765-955-3; 978-1-58765-956-0 (ebook)

**Critical Survey of Long Fiction**
Published by Grey House Publishing Inc™
4919 Rte 22, Amenia, NY 12501
Mailing Address: PO Box 56, Amenia, NY 12501-0056
*Tel:* 518-789-8700 *Toll Free Tel:* 800-562-2139 *Fax:* 518-789-0556
*E-mail:* books@greyhouse.com
*Web Site:* www.greyhouse.com
*Key Personnel*
Ed: Carl Rollyson
581 original author essays as well as 97 new ones arranged alphabetically by author providing in-depth overviews of major authors in long fiction, both English language & foreign language.
Every 5-7 yrs.
4th ed, 2010: 6,056 pp, $995/10 vol set, (includes online access)
First published 1983
ISBN(s): 978-1-58765-535-7 (10 vol set); 978-1-58765-546-3 (ebook)

**Critical Survey of Mystery & Detective Fiction**
Published by Grey House Publishing Inc™
4919 Rte 22, Amenia, NY 12501
Mailing Address: PO Box 56, Amenia, NY 12501-0056
*Tel:* 518-789-8700 *Toll Free Tel:* 800-562-2139 *Fax:* 518-789-0556
*E-mail:* books@greyhouse.com
*Web Site:* www.greyhouse.com
*Key Personnel*
Ed: Carl Rollyson
Provides detailed analyses of the lives & writing of major contributors to the literary subgenre of mystery & detective fiction; Ebook also available.
Jan 2008 (rev): 2,388 pp, $399/5 vol set
ISBN(s): 978-1-58765-397-1 (5 vol set); 978-1-58765-444-2 (ebook)

**Critical Survey of Mythology & Folklore**
Published by Grey House Publishing Inc™
Division of EBSCO Publishing
2 University Plaza, Suite 310, Hackensack, NJ 07601
SAN: 208-838X

*Tel:* 201-968-0500 *Toll Free Tel:* 800-221-1592 *Fax:* 201-968-0511
*E-mail:* csr@salempress.com
*Web Site:* salempress.com
*Key Personnel*
Ed: Thomas J Sienkewicz
Each title offers familiar & unfamiliar myths, from a diverse range of countries & cultures as well as important retellings in the modern tradition. Upcoming titles in this series include: *Heroes & Heroines* (May 2013), *Deadly Battles & Warring Enemies* (Dec 2013), *Creation Myths* (May 2014), *Tales of the Family* (Dec 2014). Also available as ebook.
Jan 2013: 984 pp, $295/2 vol set
ISBN(s): 978-1-4298-3765-1; 978-1-4298-3768-2 (ebook)

**Critical Survey of Poetry**
Published by Grey House Publishing Inc™
4919 Rte 22, Amenia, NY 12501
Mailing Address: PO Box 56, Amenia, NY 12501-0056
*Tel:* 518-789-8700 *Toll Free Tel:* 800-562-2139 *Fax:* 518-789-0556
*E-mail:* books@greyhouse.com
*Web Site:* www.greyhouse.com
*Key Personnel*
Ed: Philip K Jason
An in depth resource covering 845 poets throughout history & the world. Organized into 5 subsets by geography & essay type. Published Jan 2011. All print sets include online access
*American Poets,* 4 vol set, 1860 pp, $495.
*British, Irish & Commonwealth Poets,* 3 vol set, 1390 pp, $395.
*European Poets,* 3 vol set, 1390 pp, $395.
*World Poets,* 1 vol, 465 pp, $150.
*Topical Essays,* 2 vol set, 930 pp, $295.
*Cumulative Indexes,* 1 vol, 464 pp, free with purchase of more than one subset.
4th ed, Jan 2011: 6,500 pp, $1,295/14 vol set
First published 2002
ISBN(s): 978-1-58765-582-1 (14 vol set); 978-1-58765-583-8 (American Poets); 978-1-58765-588-3 (British, Irish & Commonwealth Poets); 978-1-58765-592-0 (American Poets ebook set); 978-1-58765-593-7 (ebook set); 978-1-58765-755-9 (British, Irish & Commonwealth Poets ebook set); 978-1-58765-756-6 (European Poets); 978-1-58765-760-3 (European Poets ebook set); 978-1-58765-761-0 (World Poets); 978-1-58765-762-7 (World Poets ebook); 978-1-58765-763-4 (Topical Essays); 978-1-58765-766-5 (Topical Essays ebook set); 978-1-58765-767-2 (Cumulative Indexes)

**Critical Survey of Short Fiction**
Published by Grey House Publishing Inc™
4919 Rte 22, Amenia, NY 12501
Mailing Address: PO Box 56, Amenia, NY 12501-0056
*Tel:* 518-789-8700 *Toll Free Tel:* 800-562-2139 *Fax:* 518-789-0556
*E-mail:* books@greyhouse.com
*Web Site:* www.greyhouse.com
*Key Personnel*
Ed: Charles E May
625 essays arranged alphabetically by author providing in-depth overviews of short story writers.
Every 5-7 yrs.
4th ed, Jan 2012: 4,000 pp, $995/10 vol set
First published 2001
ISBN(s): 978-1-58765-789-4 (10 vol set); 978-1-58765-804-4 (ebook)

**Cyclopedia of Literary Characters**
Published by Grey House Publishing Inc™
4919 Rte 22, Amenia, NY 12501
Mailing Address: PO Box 56, Amenia, NY 12501-0056
*Tel:* 518-789-8700 *Toll Free Tel:* 800-562-2139 *Fax:* 518-789-0556
*E-mail:* books@greyhouse.com
*Web Site:* www.greyhouse.com
*Key Personnel*
Ed: Frank N Magill; A J Sobczak
Assoc Ed: Janet Long
Provides critical descriptions of more than 29,000 characters that appear in 3,294 works of literature.
Feb 1998 (rev): 2,483 pp, $368/5 vol set
ISBN(s): 978-0-89356-438-4 (5 vol set)

**Cyclopedia of World Authors**
Published by Grey House Publishing Inc™
4919 Rte 22, Amenia, NY 12501
Mailing Address: PO Box 56, Amenia, NY 12501-0056
*Tel:* 518-789-8700 *Toll Free Tel:* 800-562-2139 *Fax:* 518-789-0556
*E-mail:* books@greyhouse.com
*Web Site:* www.greyhouse.com
Provides concise introductions to the lives & works of 2,408 authors.
4th ed (rev), Nov 2003: 3,504 pp, $404/5 vol set
ISBN(s): 978-1-58765-122-9 (5 vol set)

**Dictionary of Literary Biography**
Published by Gale
Unit of Cengage Learning
27500 Drake Rd, Farmington Hills, MI 48331-3535
SAN: 213-4373
*Tel:* 248-699-4253 *Toll Free Tel:* 800-877-4253 *Fax:* 248-699-8070 *Toll Free Fax:* 800-414-5043 (orders)
*E-mail:* gale.galeord@cengage.com
*Web Site:* www.gale.cengage.com
Multi-volume series; each volume focuses on a specific literary movement or period. Series aims to encompass all who have contributed to literary history from the Elizabethan Era to 20th century English, American, Canadian, French & German literature, drama & history. Major biographical & critical essays are presented for the most important figures of each era. Each essay includes a career chronology, list of publications & a bibliography of works by & about the subject. Produced by Bruccoli, Clark & Layman for Gale. Also available online.
Multiple vols/yr.
Vols 355-361, 2010-2011, $315/vol
ISBN(s): 978-0-7876-8173-9 (vol 355); 978-0-7876-8174-6 (vol 356); 978-0-7876-8175-3 (vol 357); 978-0-7876-8176-0 (vol 358); 978-0-7876-8177-7 (vol 359); 978-0-7876-8178-4 (vol 360); 978-0-7876-8179-1 (vol 361)

**Dictionary of Modern English Usage**
Published by Oxford University Press USA
198 Madison Ave, New York, NY 10016
SAN: 202-5892
*Toll Free Tel:* 800-451-7556 (orders) *Fax:* 212-726-6453
*E-mail:* orders.us@oup.com
*Web Site:* www.oup.com/us
*Key Personnel*
Author: H W Fowler
2010 (Dec): 832 pp, $17.95
First published 2009
ISBN(s): 978-0-19-958589-2

**Direct Marketing Market Place®**
Published by National Register Publishing
Division of Marquis Who's Who LLC
300 Connell Dr, Suite 2000, Berkeley Heights, NJ 07922
*Toll Free Tel:* 800-473-7020 *Fax:* 908-673-1189
*E-mail:* NRPsales@marquiswhoswho.com (sales); NRPeditorial@marquiswhoswho.com (edit)
*Web Site:* www.nationalregisterpublishing.com
A comprehensive source of direct marketing, listing over 14,000 key personnel & almost 9,000 leading direct marketing companies, suppliers & creative sources. Includes e-mail & web site addresses.
Annual.
2014 ed, $365 paper
ISBN(s): 978-0-87217-023-0

**Directories in Print**
Published by Gale
Unit of Cengage Learning
27500 Drake Rd, Farmington Hills, MI 48331-3535
SAN: 213-4373
*Tel:* 248-699-4253 *Toll Free Tel:* 800-877-4253 *Fax:* 248-699-8074 *Toll Free Fax:* 800-414-5043 (orders)
*E-mail:* gale.galeord@cengage.com
*Web Site:* www.gale.cengage.com
*Key Personnel*
Ed: Matthew Miskelly *Tel:* 248-699-4253 ext 1744 *E-mail:* matthew.miskelly@cengage.com
Annotated guide to approximately 16,000 directories, rosters, lists & guides of all kinds. Contains completely updated entries, plus many new entries, including principal business & institutional directories from more than 80 countries. *DIP*-supplement, approximately 775 new entries.
Annual, with interedition supplement.
33rd-34th ed, $920 33rd ed; $966 34th ed
ISBN(s): 978-1-4144-5870-0 (33rd ed); 978-1-4144-6849-5 (34th ed)

**A Directory of American Poets & Writers**
Published by Poets & Writers Inc
90 Broad St, Suite 2100, New York, NY 10004
*Tel:* 212-226-3586 *Fax:* 212-226-3963
*E-mail:* directory@pw.org
*Web Site:* www.pw.org/directory
*Key Personnel*
Exec Dir: Elliot Figman
Asst Online Ed: Evan Smith Rakoff
Names, addresses, telephone numbers & e-mail addresses of over 9,000 contemporary American writers & poets. Available online only.
Free

**Directory of Business Information Resources**
Published by Grey House Publishing Inc™
4919 Rte 22, Amenia, NY 12501
Mailing Address: PO Box 56, Amenia, NY 12501-0056
*Tel:* 518-789-8700 *Toll Free Tel:* 800-562-2139 *Fax:* 518-789-0556
*E-mail:* books@greyhouse.com
*Web Site:* www.greyhouse.com
*Key Personnel*
Pres: Richard Gottlieb *Fax:* 518-789-0544 *E-mail:* rhg@greyhouse.com
Edit Dir: Laura Mars-Proietti *E-mail:* lmars@greyhouse.com
VP, Mktg: Jessica Moody *Tel:* 518-789-8700 ext 101 *E-mail:* jmoody@greyhouse.com
Publr: Leslie Mackenzie *E-mail:* lmackenzie@greyhouse.com
Source for contacts in nearly 100 business areas—from advertising & agriculture to utilities & wholesalers; the magazines & journals that are important to the trade, the conventions that are "must attends," databases, directories & industry web sites that provide access to must-have marketing resources. The over 22,000 detailed, informative entries, include contact names, phone & fax numbers, web sites & e-mail address along with descriptions, membership information, ordering details & more.
Annually in Jan.
2013: 2,000 pp, $495, $195 libs, call for online pricing
ISBN(s): 978-1-61925-009-3

**The Directory of Mail Order Catalogs**
Published by Grey House Publishing Inc™
4919 Rte 22, Amenia, NY 12501
Mailing Address: PO Box 56, Amenia, NY 12501-0056
*Tel:* 518-789-8700 *Toll Free Tel:* 800-562-2139 *Fax:* 518-789-0556
*E-mail:* books@greyhouse.com
*Web Site:* www.greyhouse.com
*Key Personnel*
Pres: Richard Gottlieb *Fax:* 518-789-0544 *E-mail:* rhg@greyhouse.com
VP, Mktg: Jessica Moody *Tel:* 518-789-8700 ext 101 *E-mail:* jmoody@greyhouse.com
Edit Dir: Laura Mars-Proietti *E-mail:* lmars@greyhouse.com
Publr: Leslie Mackenzie *E-mail:* lmackenzie@greyhouse.com
Complete listing of direct-to-consumer & business-to-business mail order catalogs for special sales & marketing managers, libraries, printers & more.
Annual.
2013: 1,300 pp, $250 libs, $450 other, call for online pricing
First published 1981
ISBN(s): 978-1-59237-878-4

**Directory of Mailing List Companies**
Published by Todd Publications
3500 NE Sixth Dr, Boca Raton, FL 33431
SAN: 207-0804
*Tel:* 561-910-0440 *Fax:* 561-910-0440
*E-mail:* toddpub@aol.com
*Key Personnel*
Owner & Publr: Barry Klein
Provides alphabetically, with addresses, phone numbers & zip codes, the names of more than 1100 list companies, specialists & brokers, together with their managers' names & telephones & other pertinent information.
18th ed, 2014: 150 pp, $95 paperback
ISBN(s): 978-0-87340-024-4

**Directory of Poetry Publishers**
Published by Dustbooks
PO Box 100, Paradise, CA 95967-0100
SAN: 204-1871
*Tel:* 530-877-6110 *Fax:* 530-877-0222
*E-mail:* publisher@dustbooks.com
*Web Site:* www.dustbooks.com
*Key Personnel*
Publr: Kathleen Glanville
Ed: Neil McIntyre
Publisher of poetry, books & magazines.
Annual (CD-ROM), continuously (online).
28th ed, 2012-2013: 300 pp, $21 CD-ROM; $49.95 indiv, $89.95 instns (online bundle with 3 other Dustbooks directories)
ISBN(s): 978-1-935742-12-8 (27th ed CD-ROM); 978-1-935742-22-7 (28th ed CD-ROM)

**Directory of Small Press-Magazine Editors & Publishers**
Published by Dustbooks
PO Box 100, Paradise, CA 95967-0100
SAN: 204-1871
*Tel:* 530-877-6110 *Fax:* 530-877-0222
*E-mail:* publisher@dustbooks.com
*Web Site:* www.dustbooks.com
*Key Personnel*
Publr: Kathleen Glanville
Ed: Neil McIntyre
Names & numbers in small publishing industry.
Annual (CD-ROM), continuously (online).
43rd ed, 2012-2013: 325 pp, $21.95 CD-ROM; $49.95 indiv, $89.95 instns (online bundle with 3 other Dustbooks directories)
ISBN(s): 978-1-935742-14-2 (42nd ed CD-ROM); 978-1-935742-19-7 (43rd ed CD-ROM)

**Directory of Special Libraries & Information Centers**
Published by Gale
Unit of Cengage Learning
27500 Drake Rd, Farmington Hills, MI 48331-3535
SAN: 213-4373
*Tel:* 248-699-4253 *Toll Free Tel:* 800-877-4253 *Fax:* 248-699-8075 *Toll Free Fax:* 800-414-5043 (orders)
*E-mail:* gale.galeord@cengage.com
*Web Site:* www.gale.cengage.com
*Key Personnel*
Ed: Matthew Miskelly *Tel:* 248-699-4253 ext 1744 *E-mail:* matthew.miskelly@cengage.com
Vol 1, in three parts, provides detailed contact & descriptive info on subject-specific resource collections maintained by various government agencies, businesses, publishers, educational & nonprofit organizations & associations around the world. Vol 2 contains geographical & personnel indexes.
Annual.
39th ed, $1,533
ISBN(s): 978-1-4144-5874-8

**The Directory of Venture Capital & Private Equity Firms**
Published by Grey House Publishing Inc™
4919 Rte 22, Amenia, NY 12501
Mailing Address: PO Box 56, Amenia, NY 12501-0056
*Tel:* 518-789-8700 *Toll Free Tel:* 800-562-2139 *Fax:* 518-789-0556
*E-mail:* books@greyhouse.com
*Web Site:* www.greyhouse.com
*Key Personnel*
Edit Dir: Laura Mars-Proietti *E-mail:* lmars@greyhouse.com
Contact & investment information on 2,300 VC Firms, over 10,000 Managing Partners & 11,500 VC Investments.
16th ed, March 2013: 1,100 pp, $750 paperback, $395 academic & lib
ISBN(s): 978-1-61925-112-0

**Do-It-Yourself Book Publicity Kit**
Published by Open Horizons Publishing Co
PO Box 2887, Taos, NM 87571
*Tel:* 575-751-3398 *Fax:* 575-751-3100
*E-mail:* info@bookmarket.com
*Web Site:* www.bookmarket.com
*Key Personnel*
Publr & Ed: John Kremer *E-mail:* johnkremer@bookmarket.com
How to write a news release, put together a media kit, get reviews, schedule interviews & get on-going national publicity.
2008: 256 pp, $30

**Drama Criticism**
Published by Gale
Unit of Cengage Learning
27500 Drake Rd, Farmington Hills, MI 48331-3535
SAN: 213-4373
*Tel:* 248-699-4253 *Toll Free Tel:* 800-877-4253 *Fax:* 248-699-8070 *Toll Free Fax:* 800-414-5043 (orders)
*E-mail:* gale.galeord@cengage.com
*Web Site:* www.gale.cengage.com
Wide variety of critical, biographical & bibliographical information on major plays & playwrights from all time periods. Substantial excerpts from significant commentary on the more widely-studied dramatists.
Annual.
37th-45th ed, 2010-2012, $223
ISBN(s): 978-1-4144-4929-6 (vol 37); 978-1-4144-5880-9 (vol 38); 978-1-4144-5881-6 (vol 39); 978-1-4144-5882-3 (vol 40); 978-1-4144-7097-9 (vol 41); 978-1-4144-7098-6 (vol 42); 978-1-4144-7099-3 (vol 43); 978-1-4144-7100-6 (vol 44); 978-1-4144-7101-3 (vol 45)

**Dynamic Characters**
Published by Writer's Digest Books
Imprint of F+W Media Inc
10151 Carver Rd, Suite 200, Blue Ash, OH 45242
*Tel:* 513-531-2690 *Toll Free Tel:* 800-289-0963 *Fax:* 513-531-0798
*E-mail:* writersdigest@fwmedia.com (edit)
*Web Site:* www.writersdigest.com; www.writersdigestshop.com
*Key Personnel*
Publr: Phil Sexton *E-mail:* phil.sexton@fwmedia.com
Explores the fundamental relationship between characterization & plot.
1st ed: 272 pp, $11.39 paper
First published 2004
ISBN(s): 978-0-89879-815-9 (hardcover); 978-1-58297-319-7 (paper)

**EFA On-Line Directory**
Published by Editorial Freelancers Association (EFA)
71 W 23 St, 4th fl, New York, NY 10010-4102
*Tel:* 212-929-5400 *Toll Free Tel:* 866-929-5400 *Fax:* 212-929-5439 *Toll Free Fax:* 866-929-5439
*E-mail:* info@the-efa.org; office@the-efa.org
*Web Site:* www.the-efa.org
*Key Personnel*
Exec: Margaret L Moser; J P Partland
National, nonprofit professional organization comprising editors, writers, indexers, proofreaders, researchers, translators & other self-employed workers in the publishing industry. Works to raise the professional status of its members & to make the freelance life more dynamic & rewarding. Online directory searchable by skills, subject matter, expertise & location.
2,000 pp, free (online)
ISBN(s): 978-1-880407-13-4

**El-Hi Textbooks & Serials in Print®**
Published by Grey House Publishing Inc™
4919 Rte 22, Amenia, NY 12501
Mailing Address: PO Box 56, Amenia, NY 12501-0056
*Tel:* 518-789-8700 *Toll Free Tel:* 800-562-2139 *Fax:* 518-789-0556
*E-mail:* books@greyhouse.com
*Web Site:* www.greyhouse.com
*Key Personnel*
Edit Dir: Laura Mars-Proietti *E-mail:* lmars@greyhouse.com
This edition of El-Hi Textbooks & Serials in Print® includes the in-print titles of publishers of textbooks & related materials. Publications listed & cross-referenced in different indexes like Subject, Title, Author & Series. Includes programmed learning & teachers' professional books. More than 195,000 textbooks (elementary, junior high & high school). Learning materials from over 17,000 publishers. Resources in different formats: audiovisual, tests, teaching aids, periodicals, maps & more. Save time ordering with complete publisher contact information on any of the products listed.
Annual.
2013, $450/2 vol set cloth
ISBN(s): 978-1-59237-694-0 (2 vol set)

**The Elements of Style**
Published by Pearson Arts & Sciences
Division of Pearson Education
51 Madison Ave, New York, NY 10010
*Tel:* 917-981-2200
*Web Site:* www.pearsonhighered.com

*Key Personnel*
Author: William Strunk; E B White
50th Anniversary, 2008: 105 pp, $19.95
First published 2008
ISBN(s): 978-0-205-63264-0 (cloth)

**Encyclopedia of Associations, National Organizations of the US**
Published by Gale
Unit of Cengage Learning
27500 Drake Rd, Farmington Hills, MI 48331-3535
SAN: 213-4373
*Tel:* 248-699-4253 *Toll Free Tel:* 800-877-4253 *Fax:* 248-699-8075 *Toll Free Fax:* 800-414-5043 (orders)
*E-mail:* gale.galeord@cengage.com
*Web Site:* www.gale.cengage.com
*Key Personnel*
Ed: Tara Atterberry *E-mail:* tara.atterberry@cengage.com
A guide to 25,048 US nonprofit membership organizations of national & international scope; includes trade & professional associations, social welfare & public affairs organizations, religious organizations, sports & hobby groups with voluntary members. Detailed entries furnish association name & complete contact information. This information is not duplicated anywhere in Encyclopedia of Associations. Name & keyword indexes accompany each volume. *Geographic & Executive Indexes* are available as a separate volume. A supplement is published between volumes.
Annual.
50th ed, 2011: 4,300 pp, $988; $770 for Geo/Exec Indexes; $817 for supplement
ISBN(s): 978-1-4144-4655-4 (geo & exec indexes); 978-1-4144-4656-1 (supplement); 978-1-4144-4657-8 (50th ed)

**Food & Beverage Market Place**
Published by Grey House Publishing Inc™
4919 Rte 22, Amenia, NY 12501
Mailing Address: PO Box 56, Amenia, NY 12501-0056
*Tel:* 518-789-8700 *Toll Free Tel:* 800-562-2139 *Fax:* 518-789-0556
*E-mail:* books@greyhouse.com
*Web Site:* www.greyhouse.com
*Key Personnel*
Edit Dir: Laura Mars-Proietti *E-mail:* lmars@greyhouse.com
Buying & marketing guide for the US food & beverage industry. 40,000 companies in 8 different industry groups: Manufacturers, Equipment Suppliers, Transportation, Warehouses, Wholesalers, Brokers, Importers & Exporters.
June 2013: 4,300 pp, $695/3-vol set, $595 academic & lib; $350 Vol 1 only; $250 each Vols 1 & 2
ISBN(s): 978-1-61925-128-1 (3-vol set); 978-1-61925-129-8 (Vol 1 Manufacturers); 978-1-61925-130-4 (Vol 2 Equipment & Supply Companies); 978-1-61925-131-1 (Vol 3 Third Party Logistics)

**45 Master Characters**
Published by Writer's Digest Books
Imprint of F+W Media Inc
10151 Carver Rd, Suite 200, Blue Ash, OH 45242
*Tel:* 513-531-2690 *Toll Free Tel:* 800-289-0963 *Fax:* 513-531-0798
*E-mail:* writersdigest@fwmedia.com (edit)
*Web Site:* www.writersdigest.com; www.writersdigestshop.com
*Key Personnel*
Publr: Phil Sexton *E-mail:* phil.sexton@fwmedia.com
Gives all the information you need to develop believable characters that resonate with every reader.
304 pp, $10.19 paper
First published 2001
ISBN(s): 978-1-58297-522-1

**Gale Directory of Databases**
Published by Gale
Unit of Cengage Learning
27500 Drake Rd, Farmington Hills, MI 48331-3535
SAN: 213-4373
*Tel:* 248-699-4253 *Toll Free Tel:* 800-347-4253 *Fax:* 248-699-8074 *Toll Free Fax:* 800-414-5043 (orders)
*E-mail:* gale.galeord@cengage.com
*Web Site:* www.gale.cengage.com
*Key Personnel*
Ed: Julie A Gough *E-mail:* julie.gough@cengage.com
Current information about more than 18,000 databases available worldwide in a variety of formats. Each edition is comprised of 2 volumes which include subject, geographic & master indexes.
Annual.
34th ed, $689
ISBN(s): 978-1-4144-4712-4 (2011)

**Gale Directory of Publications & Broadcast Media**
Published by Gale
Unit of Cengage Learning
27500 Drake Rd, Farmington Hills, MI 48331-3535
SAN: 213-4373
*Tel:* 248-699-4253 *Toll Free Tel:* 800-877-4253 *Fax:* 248-699-8075 *Toll Free Fax:* 800-414-5043 (orders)
*E-mail:* gale.galeord@cengage.com
*Web Site:* www.gale.cengage.com
*Key Personnel*
Ed: Matthew Miskelly *Tel:* 248-699-4253 ext 1744 *E-mail:* matthew.miskelly@cengage.com
This media directory contains thousands of listings for radio & television stations & cable companies. Print media entries list: address, phone & fax numbers & e-mail addresses, key personnel, including feature editors. Broadcast media entries: address, phone & fax numbers, e-mail addresses; key personnel, owner information, station call letter & channel, hours of operation; networks carries & more.
Semiannual (March & Dec).
147-148, $1297 147th ed; $1362 148th ed
ISBN(s): 978-1-4144-4715-5 (147th ed); 978-1-4144-5952-3 (148th ed)

**General Issues in Literacy/Illiteracy in the World: A Bibliography**
Published by Greenwood Press
Imprint of ABC-CLIO
130 Cremona Dr, Santa Barbara, CA 93117
Mailing Address: PO Box 1911, Santa Barbara, CA 93116-1911
*Tel:* 805-968-1911 *Toll Free Tel:* 800-368-6868 *Fax:* 805-685-9685 *Toll Free Fax:* 866-270-3856
*E-mail:* customerservice@abc-clio.com
*Web Site:* www.abc-clio.com
*Key Personnel*
CEO & Academic Publr: Ronald Boehm
Author: Betty Eller; William Eller; John Hladczuk; Sharon Hladczuk
Literacy-illiteracy; bibliography.
1st ed, 1990: 435 pp, $106.95 hardbound
ISBN(s): 978-0-313-27327-8

**Getting Into Print: The Decision-Making Process in Scholarly Publishing**
Published by University of Chicago Press
1427 E 60 St, Chicago, IL 60637-2954
SAN: 202-5280
*Tel:* 773-702-7700 *Toll Free Tel:* 800-621-2736 (orders) *Fax:* 773-702-9756
*E-mail:* custserv@press.uchicago.edu; marketing@press.uchicago.edu
*Web Site:* www.press.uchicago.edu
*Key Personnel*
Dir: Garrett P Kiely *Tel:* 773-702-8878 *E-mail:* gkiely@press.uchicago.edu
Edit Dir, Ref: Paul Schellinger *Tel:* 773-702-2376 *E-mail:* pschellinger@press.uchicago.edu
Exploration of two scholarly publishing companies & how editors select titles they sponsor.
1988: 282 pp, $38 cloth, $28 paper
ISBN(s): 978-0-226-67705-7 (cloth)

**Grammatically Correct**
Published by Writer's Digest Books
Imprint of F+W Media Inc
10151 Carver Rd, Suite 200, Blue Ash, OH 45242
*Tel:* 513-531-2690 *Toll Free Tel:* 800-289-0963 *Fax:* 513-531-0798
*E-mail:* writersdigest@fwmedia.com (edit)
*Web Site:* www.writersdigest.com; www.writersdigestshop.com
*Key Personnel*
Publr: Phil Sexton *E-mail:* phil.sexton@fwmedia.com
Easy to use, quick reference & most of all, comprehensive.
2nd ed: 352 pp, $11.98 paper
First published 1997
ISBN(s): 978-1-58297-616-7

**Grants & Awards**
Published by PEN American Center
Affiliate of International PEN
588 Broadway, Suite 303, New York, NY 10012
*Tel:* 212-334-1660 *Fax:* 212-334-2181
*E-mail:* info@pen.org
*Web Site:* www.pen.org
*Key Personnel*
Exec Dir: Suzanne Nossel
Pres: Peter Godwin
Website Ed: Antonio Aiello *Tel:* 212-334-1660 ext 114 *E-mail:* antonio@pen.org
Assoc Website Ed: Charles Leung *Tel:* 212-334-1660 ext 116 *E-mail:* chuck@pen.org
Database with nearly 15,000 domestic & foreign grants, literary awards, fellowships & residencies.
Online annual subn: $10 PEN membs, $12 nonmembs, $200 instns
*Branch Office(s)*
PEN New England, 29 Everett St, Cambridge, MA 02138, Exec Dir: Karen Wulf *Tel:* 617-349-8113 *E-mail:* pen_ne@vlesley.edu *Web Site:* www.pen-ne.org

**The Grey House Homeland Security Directory**
Published by Grey House Publishing Inc™
4919 Rte 22, Amenia, NY 12501
Mailing Address: PO Box 56, Amenia, NY 12501-0056
*Tel:* 518-789-8700 *Toll Free Tel:* 800-562-2139 *Fax:* 518-789-0556
*E-mail:* books@greyhouse.com
*Web Site:* www.greyhouse.com
*Key Personnel*
Edit Dir: Laura Mars-Proietti *E-mail:* lmars@greyhouse.com
National, state & local officials responsible for homeland security along with manufacturers of homeland security products & services.
March 2013: 1,000 pp, $195
ISBN(s): 978-1-61925-171-7

**The Grey House Performing Arts Directory**
Published by Grey House Publishing Inc™
4919 Rte 22, Amenia, NY 12501

Mailing Address: PO Box 56, Amenia, NY 12501-0056
*Tel:* 518-789-8700 *Toll Free Tel:* 800-562-2139 *Fax:* 518-789-0556
*E-mail:* books@greyhouse.com
*Web Site:* www.greyhouse.com
*Key Personnel*
Edit Dir: Laura Mars-Proietti *E-mail:* lmars@greyhouse.com
Over 8,500 listings, organized by discipline, of major performance organizations, facilities & information resources.
Dec 2012: 1,100 pp, $250 paperback, $195 academic & lib
ISBN(s): 978-1-59237-879-1

**A Guide to Academic Writing**
Published by Praeger
Imprint of ABC-CLIO
130 Cremona Dr, Santa Barbara, CA 93117
Mailing Address: PO Box 1911, Santa Barbara, CA 93116-1911
*Tel:* 805-968-1911 *Toll Free Tel:* 800-368-6868 *Fax:* 805-685-9685 *Toll Free Fax:* 866-270-3856
*E-mail:* custserv@abc-clio.com
*Web Site:* www.abc-clio.com
*Key Personnel*
CEO & Academic Publr: Ronald Boehm
Author: Jeffery A Cantor
A comprehensive guide to academic writing & publishing.
200 pp, $26.95 paper, $86.95 hardcover
ISBN(s): 978-0-275-94660-9 (paper); 978-0-313-29017-6 (hardcover)

**Guide to American & International Directories**
Published by Todd Publications
3500 NE Sixth Dr, Boca Raton, FL 33431
SAN: 207-0804
*Tel:* 561-910-0440 *Fax:* 561-910-0440
*E-mail:* toddpub@aol.com
*Key Personnel*
Owner & Publr: Barry Klein
Complete information on more than 12,000 directories, covering more than 300 trade, educational & professional categories. Index.
Annual.
22nd ed, 2013: 625 pp, $195 paperback
ISBN(s): 978-0-873400-22-4

**Guide to Literary Agents 2013**
Published by Writer's Digest Books
Imprint of F+W Media Inc
10151 Carver Rd, Suite 200, Blue Ash, OH 45242
*Tel:* 513-531-2690 *Toll Free Tel:* 800-289-0963 *Fax:* 513-531-0798
*E-mail:* writersdigest@fwmedia.com (edit)
*Web Site:* www.writersdigest.com; www.writersdigestshop.com
*Key Personnel*
Publr: Phil Sexton *E-mail:* phil.sexton@fwmedia.com
Author: Chuck Sambuchino
Annual.
368 pp, $17.13 paper
ISBN(s): 978-1-59963-597-2

**Guide to Writers Conferences & Writing Workshops**
Published by ShawGuides
PO Box 61569, Staten Island, NY 61569
*Tel:* 718-874-3311
*E-mail:* writing@shawguides.com
*Web Site:* shawguides.com
*Key Personnel*
Pres: Ron Janorkar
Online directory of conferences, seminars, workshops & retreats. Includes information about dates, facilities, faculty, writing specialties, daily activities, tuition, accommodations, refund policies, handicapped accessibility, nearby attractions. Includes information on organizations (dues, benefits, activities). Contents indexed by location (covers 50 states & 11 countries); specialties (nine genres); availability of college credit, continuing education credit & scholarships; writing contests, college writing programs. Available at writing.shawguides.com.

**Jeff Herman's Guide to Book Publishers, Editors, & Literary Agents 2013**
Published by Sourcebooks Inc
1935 Brookdale Rd, Suite 139, Naperville, IL 60563
SAN: 666-7864
Mailing Address: PO Box 4410, Naperville, IL 60567-4410
*Tel:* 630-961-3900 *Toll Free Tel:* 800-432-7444 *Fax:* 630-961-2168
*E-mail:* info@sourcebooks.com
*Web Site:* www.sourcebooks.com
*Key Personnel*
Author: Jeff Herman
Writing/reference book. Directory of publishers (US, University, Canada) & US literary agents. Includes interviews with editors & agents as well as additional information on submitting material to the publishing industry.
Annual.
23rd ed: 1,024 pp, $29.99 paper
First published 1990
ISBN(s): 978-1-4022-7199-1

**How to Get Your Book Published Free in Minutes & Marketed Worldwide in Days**
Published by Communication Unlimited
185 Shevelin Rd, Novato, CA 94947
*Tel:* 415-884-2941 *Toll Free Tel:* 800-563-1454 *Fax:* 415-883-5707
*E-mail:* gordon@gordonburgett.com
*Web Site:* www.gordonburgett.com
*Key Personnel*
Pres: Gordon Burgett *E-mail:* glburgett@aol.com
How-to information, step-by-step process & detailed examples of "ancillary" publishing.
1st ed, 2010: 208 pp, $15 paper, $10 digital download
ISBN(s): 978-0-9826635-0-9 (digital download); 978-0-9826635-1-6 (print)

**How to Publish & Market Your Own Book as an Independent African Heritage Book Publisher**
Published by ECA Associates Press
PO Box 15004, Chesapeake, VA 23328-0004
*Tel:* 757-547-5542 *Fax:* 757-547-5542 (call first)
*E-mail:* eca@bellsmill.net
*Key Personnel*
Pres: Dr E Curtis Alexander
Ed: Dr Mwalimu I Mwadilifu
1st ed: 140 pp, $15.95
ISBN(s): 978-0-938818-09-0

**How to Write a Book Proposal**
Published by Writer's Digest Books
Imprint of F+W Media Inc
10151 Carver Rd, Suite 200, Blue Ash, OH 45242
*Tel:* 513-531-2690 *Toll Free Tel:* 800-289-0963 *Fax:* 513-531-0798
*E-mail:* writersdigest@fwmedia.com (edit)
*Web Site:* www.writersdigest.com; www.writersdigestshop.com
*Key Personnel*
Publr: Phil Sexton *E-mail:* phil.sexton@fwmedia.com
Details how the industry works, where it's headed & how you can be part of it.
4th: 336 pp, $11.99 paper
First published 2003
ISBN(s): 978-1-58297-702-7

**Hudson's Washington News Media Contacts Directory**
Published by Grey House Publishing Inc™
4919 Rte 22, Amenia, NY 12501
Mailing Address: PO Box 56, Amenia, NY 12501-0056
*Tel:* 518-789-8700 *Toll Free Tel:* 800-562-2139 *Fax:* 518-789-0544
*E-mail:* books@greyhouse.com
*Web Site:* www.greyhouse.com
Comprehensive listing of Washington Press Corps.
Annual.
2013: 350 pp, $289 print, call for online pricing
ISBN(s): 978-1-61925-111-3

**Identities and Issues in Literature**
Published by Grey House Publishing Inc™
4919 Rte 22, Amenia, NY 12501
Mailing Address: PO Box 56, Amenia, NY 12501-0056
*Tel:* 518-789-8700 *Toll Free Tel:* 800-562-2139 *Fax:* 518-789-0556
*E-mail:* books@greyhouse.com
*Web Site:* www.greyhouse.com
*Key Personnel*
Ed: David Peck
Concentrates on how great social change can be traced in the literature of North America. Explores authors, works & subjects related to North American & world literatures.
Sept 1997: 1,104 pp, $236/3 vol set
ISBN(s): 978-0-89356-920-4 (2 vol set)

**International Directory of Children's Literature**
Published by George Kurian Reference Books
PO Box 519, Baldwin Place, NY 10505-0519
*Tel:* 914-962-3287
*Key Personnel*
Pres & Ed: George Kurian *E-mail:* gtkurian@aol.com
Information on children's literature around the world.
6th ed, 2008: 196 pp, $39.95 cloth
First published 1974
ISBN(s): 978-0-8160-1411-8

**International Directory of Little Magazines & Small Presses**
Published by Dustbooks
PO Box 100, Paradise, CA 95967-0100
SAN: 204-1871
*Tel:* 530-877-6110 *Toll Free Tel:* 800-477-6110 *Fax:* 530-877-0222
*E-mail:* publisher@dustbooks.com
*Web Site:* www.dustbooks.com
*Key Personnel*
Publr: Kathleen Glanville
Ed: Neil McIntyre
For libraries & writers; 4,000 small publishers with full data.
Annual (CD-ROM), continuously (online).
48th ed, 2012-2013: 800 pp, $37.95 CD-ROM; $49.95 indiv, $89.95 instns (online bundle with 3 other Dustbooks directories)
ISBN(s): 978-1-935742-18-0 (48th ed CD-ROM)

**International Literary Market Place**
Published by Information Today, Inc
630 Central Ave, New Providence, NJ 07974
*Tel:* 908-286-1090 *Toll Free Tel:* 800-409-4929; 800-300-9868 (cust serv) *Fax:* 908-219-0192
*E-mail:* custserv@infotoday.com
*Web Site:* www.literarymarketplace.com
*Key Personnel*
Mng Ed: Karen Hallard *Tel:* 908-219-0277 *E-mail:* khallard@infotoday.com
A comprehensive directory of current data on the book trade in 180 countries outside the US & Canada, with over 9,600 publishers & over 3,200 book organizations, including agents,

booksellers & library associations. Includes information basic to conducting business in each country. The US & Canada are covered by *Literary Market Place*. Also available online.
Annual.
47th ed, 2014: 1,880 pp, $299 paper, $399 online subn
ISBN(s): 978-1-57387-469-4

**Is There a Book Inside You?**
Published by Para Publishing LLC
PO Box 8206-240, Santa Barbara, CA 93118-8206
SAN: 215-8981
*Tel:* 805-968-7277 *Toll Free Tel:* 800-727-2782 *Fax:* 805-968-1379
*E-mail:* info@parapublishing.com
*Web Site:* www.parapublishing.com
*Key Personnel*
Owner & Publr: Dan Poynter *E-mail:* danpoynter@parapublishing.com
Author: Mindy Bingham
A step-by-step formula for researching & writing a book. How to find & work with collaborators.
5th ed, 1999: 236 pp, $14.95 paper
ISBN(s): 978-1-56860-046-8

**The Joy of Publishing!**
Published by Open Horizons Publishing Co
PO Box 2887, Taos, NM 87571
*Tel:* 575-751-3398 *Fax:* 575-751-3100
*E-mail:* info@bookmarket.com
*Web Site:* www.bookmarket.com
*Key Personnel*
Publr & Ed: John Kremer *E-mail:* johnkremer@bookmarket.com
Fascinating facts, anecdotes, curiosities & historic origins about books & authors, editors & publishers, bookmaking & bookselling.
2000: 256 pp, $29.99 (hardcover), $19.95 (internet special)
First published 1996
ISBN(s): 978-0-912411-47-7

**Jump Start Your Book Sales: A Money-Making Guide for Authors, Independent Publishers & Small Presses**
Published by Communication Creativity
4542 Melbourne Way, Highlands Ranch, CO 80130
*Tel:* 720-344-4388 *Toll Free Fax:* 866-685-0307
*Web Site:* www.selfpublishingresources.com (bookstore)
*Key Personnel*
Pres: Sue Collier *E-mail:* sue@selfpublishingresources.com
Sales & Ad Mgr: Doug Collier *E-mail:* doug@selfpublishingresources.com
Creative & money-making marketing ideas for authors & publishers.
1st ed, 1999: 358 pp, $19.95 paper
ISBN(s): 978-0-918880-41-3

**Keys to Great Writing**
Published by Writer's Digest Books
Imprint of F+W Media Inc
10151 Carver Rd, Suite 200, Blue Ash, OH 45242
*Tel:* 513-531-2690 *Toll Free Tel:* 800-289-0963 *Fax:* 513-531-0798
*E-mail:* writersdigest@fwmedia.com (edit)
*Web Site:* www.writersdigest.com; www.writersdigestshop.com
*Key Personnel*
Publr: Phil Sexton *E-mail:* phil.sexton@fwmedia.com
From grammar to revision strategies.
1st ed: 240 pp, $8.24 paper
ISBN(s): 978-1-58297-492-7

**Law Books & Serials in Print™**
Published by Grey House Publishing Inc™
4919 Rte 22, Amenia, NY 12501
Mailing Address: PO Box 56, Amenia, NY 12501-0056
*Tel:* 518-789-8700 *Toll Free Tel:* 800-562-2139 *Fax:* 518-789-0556
*E-mail:* books@greyhouse.com
*Web Site:* www.greyhouse.com
*Key Personnel*
Edit Dir: Laura Mars-Proietti *E-mail:* lmars@greyhouse.com
Law Books & Serials in Print™ provides immediate access to current legal books, serials & multimedia publications.
Annual.
2013, $1,155/3 vol set
ISBN(s): 978-1-59237-710-7 (3 vol set)

**The Library & Book Trade Almanac**
Published by Information Today, Inc
630 Central Ave, New Providence, NJ 07974
*Tel:* 908-286-1090 *Toll Free Tel:* 800-409-4929; 800-300-9868 (cust serv) *Fax:* 908-219-0192
*E-mail:* custserv@infotoday.com
*Key Personnel*
Ed: Dave Bogart *E-mail:* bogart@bogartandbarr.com
Almanac of US library & book trade statistics, standards, programs & major events of the year, as well as international statistics & developments. Includes lists of library & literary awards & prizes, notable books, library schools, scholarship sources; directory of book trade & library associations at state, regional, national & international levels; employment sources; calendar of events.
Annual.
58th ed, 2013: 790 pp, $249.95 hardbound
ISBN(s): 978-1-57387-468-7

**Literary Market Place**
Published by Information Today, Inc
630 Central Ave, New Providence, NJ 07974
*Tel:* 908-286-1090 *Toll Free Tel:* 800-409-4929; 800-300-9868 (cust serv) *Fax:* 908-219-0192
*E-mail:* custserv@infotoday.com
*Web Site:* www.literarymarketplace.com
*Key Personnel*
Mng Ed: Karen Hallard *Tel:* 908-219-0277 *E-mail:* khallard@infotoday.com
Directory of over 26,000 companies & individuals in US & Canadian publishing. Areas covered include book publishers; associations; book trade events; courses, conferences & contests; agents & agencies; services & suppliers; direct-mail promotion; review, selection & reference; radio & television; wholesale, export & import & book manufacturing. A two-volume set, each containing two alphabetical names & numbers indexes, one for key companies listed & one for individuals. The rest of the world is covered by *International Literary Market Place*. Also available online.
Annual.
74th ed, 2014: 1,776 pp, $379/2 vol set paper, $399 online subn
ISBN(s): 978-1-57387-473-1 (2 vol set)

**Magazines for Libraries**
Published by ProQuest LLC
Subsidiary of Cambridge Information Group Inc
630 Central Ave, New Providence, NJ 07974
*E-mail:* core_service@proquest.com
*Web Site:* www.proquest.com (publr); www.serialssolutions.com
*Key Personnel*
Gen Ed: Cheryl LaGuardia
Creator: Bill Katz
A critically annotated guide to magazine selection for public, college, school & special libraries, with approximately 6,000 periodicals critically evaluated by more than 200 subject specialists & classified under more than 160 subject headings. Includes journals (print & electronic) & newspapers.
22nd ed, 2014, $900 cloth
First published 1969
ISBN(s): 978-1-60030-645-7

**Magill's Literary Annual**
Published by Grey House Publishing Inc™
4919 Rte 22, Amenia, NY 12501
Mailing Address: PO Box 56, Amenia, NY 12501-0056
*Tel:* 518-789-8700 *Toll Free Tel:* 800-562-2139 *Fax:* 518-789-0556
*E-mail:* books@greyhouse.com
*Web Site:* www.greyhouse.com
Offers 200 major examples of serious literature published during the previous year, covering the best of the best in fiction, poetry & nonfiction; includes online access.
Annual.
June 2013: 600 pp, $195/2 vol set
First published 1954
ISBN(s): 978-1-4298-3809-2 (2 vol set); 978-1-4298-3812-2 (ebook)

**Magill's Survey of American Literature**
Published by Grey House Publishing Inc™
4919 Rte 22, Amenia, NY 12501
Mailing Address: PO Box 56, Amenia, NY 12501-0056
*Tel:* 518-789-8700 *Toll Free Tel:* 800-562-2139 *Fax:* 518-789-0556
*E-mail:* books@greyhouse.com
*Web Site:* www.greyhouse.com
*Key Personnel*
Ed: Steven G Kellman
Profiles of 339 major US & Canadian writers, of all genres, accompanied by analyses of their significant works.
Sept 2006: 2,904 pp, $499/6 vol set
First published 1991
ISBN(s): 978-1-58765-285-1 (6 vol set)

**Magill's Survey of World Literature**
Published by Grey House Publishing Inc™
4919 Rte 22, Amenia, NY 12501
Mailing Address: PO Box 56, Amenia, NY 12501-0056
*Tel:* 518-789-8700 *Toll Free Tel:* 800-562-2139 *Fax:* 518-789-0556
*E-mail:* books@greyhouse.com
*Web Site:* www.greyhouse.com
*Key Personnel*
Ed: Steven G Kellman
Profiles of major authors of fiction, drama, poetry & essays, each with sections on biography & analysis of the author's most important works-novels, short stories, poems & works of nonfiction.
Jan 2009 (rev): 3,032 pp, $499/6 vol set
ISBN(s): 978-1-58765-431-2 (6 vol set); 978-1-58765-446-6 (ebook)

**Mail Order Business Directory**
Published by Todd Publications
3500 NE Sixth Dr, Boca Raton, FL 33431
SAN: 207-0804
*Tel:* 561-910-0440 *Fax:* 561-910-0440
*E-mail:* toddpub@aol.com
*Key Personnel*
Owner & Publr: Barry Klein
Contains the names of the 5,500 most active mail order catalogs, listed by 40 product categories with Alphabetical Index & Merchandise Category Index.
Annual.
32nd ed, 2013: 445 pp, $195 paperback
ISBN(s): 978-0-873400-27-5

**Major 21st-Century Writers**
Published by Gale

Division of Cengage Learning
27500 Drake Rd, Farmington Hills, MI 48331-3535
SAN: 213-4373
*Tel:* 248-699-4253 *Toll Free Tel:* 800-347-4253 *Fax:* 248-699-8070 *Toll Free Fax:* 800-414-5043 (orders)
*E-mail:* gale.galeord@cengage.com
*Web Site:* www.gale.cengage.com
E book highlighting 21st century authors.
2006, $631
ISBN(s): 978-0-7876-7539-4

**Managing the Publishing Process: An Annotated Bibliography**
Published by Greenwood Press
Imprint of ABC-CLIO
130 Cremona Dr, Santa Barbara, CA 93117
Mailing Address: PO Box 1911, Santa Barbara, CA 93116-1911
*Tel:* 805-968-1911 *Toll Free Tel:* 800-368-6868 *Fax:* 805-685-9685 *Toll Free Fax:* 866-270-3856
*E-mail:* customerservice@abc-clio.com
*Web Site:* www.abc-clio.com
*Key Personnel*
CEO & Academic Publr: Ronald Boehm
Author: Bruce Speck
Cites & annotates more than 1200 books & articles on how to manage the publishing process.
1995: 360 pp, $110.95 hardcover
ISBN(s): 978-0-313-27956-0

**Manufacturing Standards & Specifications for (El-Hi) Textbooks (MSST)**
Published by State Instructional Materials Review Administrators (SIMRA)
2 Armand Beach Dr, Suite 1-B, Palm Coast, FL 32137
*Tel:* 386-986-4552 *Fax:* 386-986-4553
*E-mail:* info@bmibook.com
*Web Site:* www.bmibook.org
*Key Personnel*
Admin & Tech Dir, ACTS: Daniel N Bach
The official Advisory Commission on Textbook Specifications (ACTS) publication detailing the approved guidelines for the manufacture of elementary & high school textbooks.
Aug 2009: 92 pp, $35 looseleaf bound, adhesive bound or CD/per copy

**The Marshall Plan for Getting Your Novel Published**
Published by Writer's Digest Books
Imprint of F+W Media Inc
10151 Carver Rd, Suite 200, Blue Ash, OH 45242
*Tel:* 513-531-2690 *Toll Free Tel:* 800-289-0963 *Fax:* 513-531-0798
*E-mail:* writersdigest@fwmedia.com (edit)
*Web Site:* www.writersdigest.com; www.writersdigestshop.com
*Key Personnel*
Publr: Phil Sexton *E-mail:* phil.sexton@fwmedia.com
Learn how to find a hook, create a conflict, develop a protagonist & set things in motion.
1st ed: 240 pp, $10.18 paper
First published 1998
ISBN(s): 978-1-58297-062-2 (paperback)

**Masterplots**
Published by Grey House Publishing Inc™
4919 Rte 22, Amenia, NY 12501
Mailing Address: PO Box 56, Amenia, NY 12501-0056
*Tel:* 518-789-8700 *Toll Free Tel:* 800-562-2139 *Fax:* 518-789-0556
*E-mail:* books@greyhouse.com
*Web Site:* www.greyhouse.com
*Key Personnel*
Ed: Laurence W Mazzeno
4th ed (rev), Nov 2010: 7,316 pp, $1,200/12 vol set
First published 1976
ISBN(s): 978-1-58765-568-5 (12 vol set)

**Masterplots II: African American Literature**
Published by Grey House Publishing Inc™
4919 Rte 22, Amenia, NY 12501
Mailing Address: PO Box 56, Amenia, NY 12501-0056
*Tel:* 518-789-8700 *Toll Free Tel:* 800-562-2139 *Fax:* 518-789-0556
*E-mail:* books@greyhouse.com
*Web Site:* www.greyhouse.com
*Key Personnel*
Ed: Tyrone Williams
Essays on individual titles by great novelists, playwrights, memoirists, historians & critics as well as the bodies of work of major poets, short-story writers, essayists & orators.
Dec 2008 (rev): 2,160 pp, $404/4 vol set
ISBN(s): 978-1-58765-438-1 (4 vol set); 978-1-58765-447-3 (ebook)

**Masterplots II: American Fiction Series**
Published by Grey House Publishing Inc™
4919 Rte 22, Amenia, NY 12501
Mailing Address: PO Box 56, Amenia, NY 12501-0056
*Tel:* 518-789-8700 *Toll Free Tel:* 800-562-2139 *Fax:* 518-789-0556
*E-mail:* books@greyhouse.com
*Web Site:* www.greyhouse.com
*Key Personnel*
Ed: Steven G Kellman
Essays cover the most important works of fiction from the US, Canada & Latin America that are not covered in any other *Masterplots*.
Jan 2000 (rev): 2,975 pp, $446/6 vol set
ISBN(s): 978-0-89356-871-9 (6 vol set)

**Masterplots II: British and Commonwealth Fiction Series**
Published by Grey House Publishing Inc™
4919 Rte 22, Amenia, NY 12501
Mailing Address: PO Box 56, Amenia, NY 12501-0056
*Tel:* 518-789-8700 *Toll Free Tel:* 800-562-2139 *Fax:* 518-789-0556
*E-mail:* books@greyhouse.com
*Web Site:* www.greyhouse.com
*Key Personnel*
Ed: Frank N Magill
Reflects a growing awareness of a unique historical process: the development of English as an international language.
May 1987 (rev): 1,971 pp, $383/4 vol set
ISBN(s): 978-0-89356-468-1 (4 vol set)

**Masterplots II: Christian Literature**
Published by Grey House Publishing Inc™
4919 Rte 22, Amenia, NY 12501
Mailing Address: PO Box 56, Amenia, NY 12501-0056
*Tel:* 518-789-8700 *Toll Free Tel:* 800-562-2139 *Fax:* 518-789-0556
*E-mail:* books@greyhouse.com
*Web Site:* www.greyhouse.com
*Key Personnel*
Ed: John K Roth
Covers over 500 classic & contemporary works of Christian fiction, nonfiction, poetry & drama, providing a plot summary, analysis of Christian themes & an annotated bibliography for each title.
Sept 2007: 2,126 pp, $385/4 vol set
First published 2007
ISBN(s): 978-1-58765-379-7 (4 vol set); 978-1-58765-413-8 (ebook)

**Masterplots II: Drama Series**
Published by Grey House Publishing Inc™
4919 Rte 22, Amenia, NY 12501
Mailing Address: PO Box 56, Amenia, NY 12501-0056
*Tel:* 518-789-8700 *Toll Free Tel:* 800-562-2139 *Fax:* 518-789-0556
*E-mail:* books@greyhouse.com
*Web Site:* www.greyhouse.com
*Key Personnel*
Ed: Christian H Moe
Covers plays by important 20th Century playwrights. No other *Masterplots* covers these 345 plays.
Sept 2003 (rev): 1,850 pp, $404/4 vol set
ISBN(s): 978-1-58765-116-8 (4 vol set)

**Masterplots II: Juvenile & Young Adult Literature Supplement**
Published by Grey House Publishing Inc™
4919 Rte 22, Amenia, NY 12501
Mailing Address: PO Box 56, Amenia, NY 12501-0056
*Tel:* 518-789-8700 *Toll Free Tel:* 800-562-2139 *Fax:* 518-789-0556
*E-mail:* books@greyhouse.com
*Web Site:* www.greyhouse.com
*Key Personnel*
Ed: Frank N Magill
Authors address the thoughts & emotions of children.
March 1997: 1,502 pp, $289/3 vol set
ISBN(s): 978-0-89356-916-7 (3 vol set)

**Masterplots II: Nonfiction Series**
Published by Grey House Publishing Inc™
4919 Rte 22, Amenia, NY 12501
Mailing Address: PO Box 56, Amenia, NY 12501-0056
*Tel:* 518-789-8700 *Toll Free Tel:* 800-562-2139 *Fax:* 518-789-0556
*E-mail:* books@greyhouse.com
*Web Site:* www.greyhouse.com
*Key Personnel*
Ed: Frank N Magill
This series includes contributions from authors worldwide in the areas of autobiography, memoirs, philosophy, literary theory, anthropology, psychology & other subjects written for the nonspecialist.
March 1989: 1,762 pp, $383/4 vol set
ISBN(s): 978-0-89356-478-0 (4 vol set)

**Masterplots II: Poetry Series**
Published by Grey House Publishing Inc™
4919 Rte 22, Amenia, NY 12501
Mailing Address: PO Box 56, Amenia, NY 12501-0056
*Tel:* 518-789-8700 *Toll Free Tel:* 800-562-2139 *Fax:* 518-789-0556
*E-mail:* books@greyhouse.com
*Web Site:* www.greyhouse.com
*Key Personnel*
Ed: Philip K Jason
Provides the most comprehensive coverage of the important poems by both classic writers & contemporary poets.
Jan 2002 (rev): 4,545 pp, $499/8 vol set
ISBN(s): 978-1-58765-037-6 (8 vol set)

**Masterplots II: Short Story Series**
Published by Grey House Publishing Inc™
4919 Rte 22, Amenia, NY 12501
Mailing Address: PO Box 56, Amenia, NY 12501-0056
*Tel:* 518-789-8700 *Toll Free Tel:* 800-562-2139 *Fax:* 518-789-0556
*E-mail:* books@greyhouse.com
*Web Site:* www.greyhouse.com
*Key Personnel*
Ed: Charles E May
Penetrating discussions of the content, themes, structure & techniques of 1,490 stories by writers from every region in the world.

2nd ed (rev), Jan 2004: 4,944 pp, $599/8 vol set
ISBN(s): 978-1-58765-140-3 (8 vol set)

**Masterplots II, Women's Literature**
Published by Grey House Publishing Inc™
4919 Rte 22, Amenia, NY 12501
Mailing Address: PO Box 56, Amenia, NY 12501-0056
*Tel:* 518-789-8700 *Toll Free Tel:* 800-562-2139 *Fax:* 518-789-0556
*E-mail:* books@greyhouse.com
*Web Site:* www.greyhouse.com
*Key Personnel*
Ed: Frank N Magill
Essays examine novels & plays that also provide a genre category, identify the time period & setting of the plot & provide the principal characters with brief descriptions.
Feb 1995: 2,630 pp, $525/6 vol set
ISBN(s): 978-0-89356-898-6 (6 vol set)

**Medical & Health Care Books & Serials in Print™**
Published by Grey House Publishing Inc™
4919 Rte 22, Amenia, NY 12501
Mailing Address: PO Box 56, Amenia, NY 12501-0056
*Tel:* 518-789-8700 *Toll Free Tel:* 800-562-2139 *Fax:* 518-789-0556
*E-mail:* books@greyhouse.com
*Web Site:* www.greyhouse.com
*Key Personnel*
Edit Dir: Laura Mars-Proietti *E-mail:* lmars@greyhouse.com
*Medical & Health Care Books & Serials in Print™* provides immediate access to the highly specialized publishing activity in the health sciences & allied health fields.
Annual.
2013, $560/2 vol set
ISBN(s): 978-1-59237-707-7

**Metro California Media Directory**
Published by Cision North America
Division of Cision
332 S Michigan Ave, Suite 900, Chicago, IL 60604
*Tel:* 312-922-2400 *Toll Free Tel:* 866-639-5087 *Fax:* 312-922-9387
*E-mail:* info.us@cision.com
*Web Site:* cision.com
*Key Personnel*
CEO: Peter Granat
SVP, Busn Devt: Brett Safron
SVP, Devt: Greg Stam
SVP, Digital Content Mgmt: Scott Thompson
SVP, Global Content Licensing: Dawn Conway
SVP, Global & Prod Mktg: Vanessa Bugasch
SVP, North American Sales: Michael Renderman
Offers clients who target this region a more concise directory for their needs. This directory contains the same fields for each outlet/editor listing & the same structure as the Magazine/Newspaper & Radio/TV/Cable directories.
Annual.
2,200 pp, $445

**MLRC 50-State Survey: Employment Libel & Privacy Law**
Published by Oxford University Press USA
North Tower, 20th fl, 520 Eighth Ave, New York, NY 10018
*Tel:* 212-337-0200 *Fax:* 212-337-9893
*E-mail:* medialaw@medialaw.org
*Web Site:* www.medialaw.org
*Key Personnel*
VP, Mktg: Greg Bussy
Exec Dir: Sandra Baron
Easy-to-use compendiums of the law in all US jurisdictions, state & federal, used by journalists, lawyers, judges & law schools nationwide. Each state's chapter, prepared by experts in that jurisdiction, is presented in a uniform outline format & updated & published annually.
Annually in Jan.
1,150 pp, $225

**LLRC 50-State Survey: Media Libel Law**
Published by Oxford University Press USA
North Tower, 20th fl, 520 Eighth Ave, New York, NY 10018
*Tel:* 212-337-0200 *Fax:* 212-337-9893
*E-mail:* medialaw@medialaw.org
*Web Site:* www.medialaw.org
*Key Personnel*
VP, Mktg: Greg Bussy
Exec Dir: Sandra Baron
Easy-to-use compendiums of the law in all US jurisdictions, state & federal, used by journalists, lawyers, judges & law schools nationwide. Each state's chapter, prepared by experts in that jurisdiction, is presented in a uniform outline format & updated & published annually.
Annually in Nov.
1,500 pp, $225

**MLRC 50-State Survey: Media Privacy & Related Law**
Published by Oxford University Press USA
North Tower, 20th fl, 520 Eighth Ave, New York, NY 10018
*Tel:* 212-337-0200 *Fax:* 212-337-9893
*E-mail:* medialaw@medialaw.org
*Web Site:* www.medialaw.org
*Key Personnel*
VP, Mktg: Greg Bussy
Exec Dir: Sandra Baron
Easy-to-use compendiums of the law in all US jurisdictions, state & federal, used by journalists, lawyers, judges & law schools nationwide. Each state's chapter, prepared by experts in that jurisdiction, is presented in a uniform outline format & is updated & published annually.
Annually in July.
1,500 pp, $225

**National Trade and Professional Associations of the United States**
Published by Columbia Books & Information Services
8120 Woodmont Ave, Suite 110, Bethesda, MD 20814
*Tel:* 202-464-1662 *Toll Free Tel:* 888-265-0600 (cust serv) *Fax:* 202-464-1775
*E-mail:* info@columbiabooks.com
*Web Site:* www.columbiabooks.com
*Key Personnel*
Edit & Tech: Matt Ouzounian *Tel:* 202-464-1662 ext 110 *E-mail:* mouzounian@columbiabooks.com
Dir of Mktg: Brittany Carter *Tel:* 202-464-1662 ext 109 *E-mail:* bcarter@columbiabooks.com
Covers over 7,800 trade associations, professional societies & labor unions with national memberships with such data as chief executive, size of membership & staff, budget, telephone, facsimile number, e-mail address, publications, meeting data & historical background. Includes indexes by subject, geography, budget, acronym, chief executive officer & annual meeting location. Also available online at www.associationexecs.com.
Annual.
48th ed, 2013, $299 paper
First published 1965
ISBN(s): 978-0-9747322-9-9

**New York Publicity Outlets**
Published by Cision North America
332 S Michigan Ave, Suite 900, Chicago, IL 60604
*Tel:* 312-922-2400 *Toll Free Tel:* 866-639-5087 *Fax:* 312-922-3127
*E-mail:* info.us@cision.com
*Web Site:* us.cision.com
*Key Personnel*
SVP & Publr: Ruth McFarland *E-mail:* ruth.mcfarland@cision.com
SVP, Busn Devt: Brett Safron
Information about the dailies, magazines, newsletters, news services & syndicates, broadcast & cable stations & ethnic & community newspapers covering NY state & portions of CT & NJ.
Annually.
2,200 pp, $445

**The New York State Directory**
Published by Grey House Publishing Inc™
4919 Rte 22, Amenia, NY 12501
Mailing Address: PO Box 56, Amenia, NY 12501-0056
*Tel:* 518-789-8700 *Toll Free Tel:* 800-562-2139 *Fax:* 518-789-0556
*E-mail:* books@greyhouse.com
*Web Site:* www.greyhouse.com
*Key Personnel*
Edit Dir: Laura Mars-Proietti *E-mail:* lmars@greyhouse.com
Contact information for New York State government offices, public officials & private sector organizations.
Annual.
May 2013: 1,008 pp, $145
First published 1983
ISBN(s): 978-1-61925-125-0

**The New York Times Manual of Style & Usage**
Published by Three Rivers Press
Division of Random House Inc
1745 Broadway, New York, NY 10019
*Tel:* 212-782-9000 *Toll Free Tel:* 800-733-3000 (cust serv)
*Web Site:* www.randomhouse.com
*Key Personnel*
Author: William G Connolly; Allan M Siegal
Revised Edition 2002, $16.95
ISBN(s): 978-0-8129-6389-2

**Niche Publishing: Publish Profitably Every Time**
Published by Communication Unlimited
185 Shevelin Rd, Novato, CA 94947
*Tel:* 415-884-2941 *Toll Free Tel:* 800-563-1454 *Fax:* 415-883-5707
*E-mail:* gordon@gordonburgett.com
*Web Site:* www.gordonburgett.com
*Key Personnel*
Pres & Ed: Gordon Burgett *E-mail:* glburgett@aol.com
How-to information, step-by-step process & detailed example of niche publishing.
2008: 208 pp, $15 paper, $10 digital download
First published 2008
ISBN(s): 978-0-979629-525

**Nineteenth-Century Literature Criticism**
Published by Gale
Unit of Cengage Learning
27500 Drake Rd, Farmington Hills, MI 48331-3535
SAN: 213-4373
*Tel:* 248-699-4253 *Toll Free Tel:* 800-877-4253 *Fax:* 248-699-8054 *Toll Free Fax:* 800-414-5043 (orders)
*E-mail:* gale.galeord@cengage.com
*Web Site:* www.gale.cengage.com
*Key Personnel*
Ed: Kathy Darrow
Each volume in the series provides critical overviews of four to eight poets, novelists, short story writers, playwrights, philosophers & other creative writers, who died between 1800 & 1899. Most critical essays are full text. Every fourth volume covers literary topics including major literary movements, trends & other topics related to 19th-century literature.

A cumulative title index to the entire series is published seperately.
Multiple vols/yr.
Vols 235-257, $328/vol
ISBN(s): 978-1-4144-4919-7 (vol 235); 978-1-4144-4920-3 (vol 236); 978-1-4144-5799-4 (vol 237); 978-1-4144-7004-7 (vol 238); 978-1-4144-7005-4 (vol 239); 978-1-4144-7006-1 (vol 240); 978-1-4144-7007-8 (vol 241); 978-1-4144-7008-5 (vol 242); 978-1-4144-7009-2 (vol 243); 978-1-4144-7010-8 (vol 244); 978-1-4144-7011-5 (vol 245); 978-1-4144-7012-2 (vol 246); 978-1-4144-7013-9 (vol 247); 978-1-4144-7014-6 (vol 248); 978-1-4144-7015-3 (vol 249); 978-1-4144-7016-0 (vol 250); 978-1-4144-7017-7 (vol 251); 978-1-4144-7018-4 (vol 252); 978-1-4144-7019-1 (vol 253); 978-1-4144-7020-7 (vol 254); 978-1-4144-7021-4 (vol 255); 978-1-4144-7022-1 (vol 256); 978-1-4144-7023-8 (vol 257)

**No More Rejections**
Published by Writer's Digest Books
Imprint of F+W Media Inc
10151 Carver Rd, Suite 200, Blue Ash, OH 45242
*Tel:* 513-531-2690 *Toll Free Tel:* 800-289-0963 *Fax:* 513-531-0798
*E-mail:* writersdigest@fwmedia.com (edit)
*Web Site:* www.writersdigest.com; www.writersdigestshop.com
*Key Personnel*
Publr: Phil Sexton *E-mail:* phil.sexton@fwmedia.com
Secrets to writing a ms that sells. Thinking up original ideas, moving your story forward, developing characters with character, etc.
1st ed: 272 pp, $4.99
First published 2004
ISBN(s): 978-1-58297-285-5 (hardcover)

**O'Dwyer's Directory of Public Relations Firms**
Published by O'Dwyer Co
271 Madison Ave, Rm 600, New York, NY 10016
*Tel:* 212-679-2471 *Toll Free Tel:* 866-395-7710 *Fax:* 212 683 2750
*Web Site:* www.odwyerpr.com
*Key Personnel*
Publr & Ed-in-Chief: Jack O'Dwyer *E-mail:* jack@odwyerpr.com
A listing of more than 1,400 PR firms in the US & overseas.
Annual.
43rd ed, 2013: 322 pp, $95
First published 1970
ISBN(s): 978-0-941424-72-1

**100 Things Every Writer Needs to Know**
Published by Perigee Books
Imprint of Penguin Group (USA) LLC
375 Hudson St, New York, NY 10014
SAN: 282-5074
*Tel:* 212-366-2000 *Fax:* 212-366-2365
*Web Site:* www.penguin.com; us.penguingroup.com
*Key Personnel*
Publr: John Duff
Ed-in-Chief: Marian Lizzi
Author: Scott Edelstein
256 pp, $14.95
First published 1996
ISBN(s): 978-0-399-52508-7

**1001 Ways to Market Your Books**
Published by Open Horizons Publishing Co
PO Box 2887, Taos, NM 87571
*Tel:* 575-751-3398 *Fax:* 575-751-3100
*E-mail:* info@bookmarket.com
*Web Site:* www.bookmarket.com
*Key Personnel*
Publr & Ed: John Kremer *E-mail:* johnkremer@bookmarket.com
Outlines more than 1,000 different ways to market books. Uses many real-life examples describing how other publishers market their books. Includes planning & design, advertising & distribution, subsidiary rights & spinoffs.
6th ed, 2008: 704 pp, $27.95 paper
ISBN(s): 978-0-912411-49-X (paper)

**Photographer's Market**
Published by North Light Books
Division of F+W Media Inc
10151 Carver Rd, Suite 200, Blue Ash, OH 45242
*Tel:* 513-531-2690 *Toll Free Tel:* 800-666-0963 *Fax:* 513-891-7153
*E-mail:* photomarket@fwmedia.com
*Web Site:* www.artistsmarketonline.com
*Key Personnel*
Sr Content Developer: Mary Burzlaff Bostic
More than 1,500 listings of photo buyers with complete contact information; for freelance & stock photographers.
Annual.
37th ed, 2014: 688 pp, $34.99
ISBN(s): 978-1-4403-2942-5

**Play Index**
Published by H W Wilson
Imprint of EBSCO Publishing
10 Estes St, Ipswich, MA 01938
*Tel:* 978-356-6500 *Toll Free Tel:* 800-653-2726 (US & CN) *Fax:* 978-356-6565
*E-mail:* information@ebscohost.com
*Web Site:* www.ebscohost.com
*Key Personnel*
VP, Cataloging & Gen Ref Servs: Joseph Miller, MLS, PhD
Online publication including some 31,000 plays published from 1949 to the present as well as over 600 monologues.
contact for price information

**The Pocket Muse**
Published by Writer's Digest Books
Imprint of F+W Media Inc
10151 Carver Rd, Suite 200, Blue Ash, OH 45242
*Tel:* 513-531-2690 *Toll Free Tel:* 800-289-0963 *Fax:* 513-531-0798
*E-mail:* writersdigest@fwmedia.com (edit)
*Web Site:* www.writersdigest.com; www.writersdigestshop.com
*Key Personnel*
Publr: Phil Sexton *E-mail:* phil.sexton@fwmedia.com
Unique ideas for overcoming writer's block, creativity boosters, revision tips & more.
2004: 256 pp, $7.78 paper
ISBN(s): 978-1-58297-322-7

**Poetry Criticism**
Published by Gale
Unit of Cengage Learning
27500 Drake Rd, Farmington Hills, MI 48331-3535
SAN: 213-4373
*Tel:* 248-699-4253 *Toll Free Tel:* 800-347-4253 *Fax:* 248-699-8070 *Toll Free Fax:* 800-414-5043 (orders)
*E-mail:* gale.galeord@cengage.com
*Web Site:* www.gale.cengage.com
Covers four-eight major poets from all eras. Provides intro author biographical sketch, primary bibliography. annotated full text & excerpted criticism with additional readings.
multiple vols/yr.
Vols 112-126, $245/vol
ISBN(s): 978-1-4144-7124-2 (vol 112); 978-1-4144-7125-9 (vol 113); 978-1-4144-7126-6 (vol 114); 978-1-4144-7127-3 (vol 115); 978-1-4144-7128-0 (vol 116); 978-1-4144-7129-7 (vol 117); 978-1-4144-7130-3 (vol 118); 978-1-4144-7131-0 (vol 119); 978-1-4144-7132-7 (vol 120); 978-1-4144-7133-4 (vol 121); 978-1-4144-7134-1 (vol 122); 978-1-4144-7135-8 (vol 123); 978-1-4144-7136-5 (vol 124); 978-1-4144-7137-2 (vol 125); 978-1-4144-7138-9 (vol 126)

**Poets' Encyclopedia**
Published by Unmuzzled Ox Press
105 Hudson St, New York, NY 10013
*Tel:* 212-226-7170
*Key Personnel*
Ed: Michael Andre *E-mail:* mandreox@yahoo.com
Author: W H Auden; Dan Berrigan; John Cage; Allen Ginsberg
World's basic knowledge transformed by 225 poets, artists, musicians & novelists.
1st ed, 1979: 310 pp, $75 cloth, $40 paper
ISBN(s): 978-0-934450-02-7 (cloth); 978-0-934450-03-4 (paper)

**Poet's Market**
Published by Writer's Digest Books
Imprint of F+W Media Inc
10151 Carver Rd, Suite 200, Blue Ash, OH 45242
*Tel:* 513-531-2690 *Toll Free Tel:* 800-289-0963 *Fax:* 513-531-0798
*E-mail:* writersdigest@fwmedia.com (edit)
*Web Site:* www.writersdigest.com; www.writersdigestshop.com
*Key Personnel*
Publr: Phil Sexton *E-mail:* phil.sexton@fwmedia.com
Where & how to get poetry published; 1,800 US & international publisher listings, also includes contests & awards, writing colonies, organizations, conferences, workshops & publications useful to poets.
Annual.
2014: 512 pp, $29.99 paper
ISBN(s): 978-1-59963-730-3

**Professional Writing: Processes, Strategies & Tips for Publishing in Education Journals**
Published by Krieger Publishing Co
1725 Krieger Dr, Malabar, FL 32950
SAN: 202-6562
*Tel:* 321-724-9542 *Toll Free Tel:* 800-724-0025 *Fax:* 321-951-3671
*E-mail:* info@krieger-publishing.com
*Web Site:* www.krieger-publishing.com
*Key Personnel*
Author: Roger Hiemstra
Ad Mgr: Cheryl Stanton
Provides insights, tips, strategies & recommendations for publishing in educational periodicals.
1994: 152 pp, $27.50 cloth
First published 1993
ISBN(s): 978-0-89464-660-7

**Publish, Don't Perish: The Scholar's Guide to Academic Writing & Publishing**
Published by Praeger
Imprint of ABC-CLIO
130 Cremona Dr, Santa Barbara, CA 93117
Mailing Address: PO Box 1911, Santa Barbara, CA 93116-1911
*Tel:* 805-968-1911 *Toll Free Tel:* 800-368-6868 *Fax:* 805-685-9685 *Toll Free Fax:* 866-270-3856
*E-mail:* custserv@abc-clio.com
*Web Site:* www.abc-clio.com
*Key Personnel*
CEO & Academic Publr: Ronald Boehm
Author: Joseph M Moxley
Expressing a strongly positive view of the value of academic publishing that reaches far beyond

what is implied by the book title, Moxley offers informed suggestions to faculty members for conceiving, developing & publishing scholarly documents as books or journal articles.
224 pp, $27.95 paper, $72.95 hardcover
First published 1992
ISBN(s): 978-0-275-94453-6 (paper); 978-0-313-27735-1 (hardcover)

**Publishers Directory**
Published by Gale
Unit of Cengage Learning
27500 Drake Rd, Farmington Hills, MI 48331-3535
SAN: 213-4373
*Tel:* 248-699-4253 *Toll Free Tel:* 800-877-4253 *Fax:* 248-699-8074 *Toll Free Fax:* 800-414-5043 (orders)
*E-mail:* gale.galeord@cengage.com
*Web Site:* www.gale.cengage.com
*Key Personnel*
Ed: Verne Thompson
Contains over 30,000 US & Canadian publishers, distributors & wholesalers. Organizations listed are major publishing companies, small presses, special interest groups, museums, societies in the arts, science technology, history & genealogy, divisions within universities that issue field specific publications, religious institutions, government agencies & electronic & database publishers.
Annual.
36th-37th ed, $720 36th ed; $758 37th ed
ISBN(s): 978-1-4144-5988-2 (36th ed); 978-1-4144-5989-9 (37th ed)

**Publishers, Distributors & Wholesalers of the United States**
Published by Grey House Publishing Inc™
4919 Rte 22, Amenia, NY 12501
Mailing Address: PO Box 56, Amenia, NY 12501-0056
*Tel:* 518-789-8700 *Toll Free Tel:* 800-562-2139 *Fax:* 518-789-0556
*E-mail:* books@greyhouse.com
*Web Site:* www.greyhouse.com
*Key Personnel*
Edit Dir: Laura Mars-Proietti *E-mail:* lmars@greyhouse.com
Two information-packed volumes offering detailed data on 186,000 active US publishers, distributors, wholesalers & other related businesses.
Annual.
2013: 3,600 pp, $550/2 vol set hardcover
ISBN(s): 978-1-59237-729-9 (2 vol set)

**Publishers' International ISBN Directory**
Published by De Gruyter Saur
Imprint of Walter de Gruyter GmbH & Co KG
Mies-van-der-Rohe-Str 1, 80807 Munich, Germany
*Tel:* (089) 769 02-0 *Fax:* (089) 769 02-350
*E-mail:* info@degruyter.com
*Web Site:* www.degruyter.com
Annual.
39th ed, 2013: 7,448 pp, $1,299 EUR/6-vol set, $1,819 US/6-vol set; $1,399 EUR/6-vol set or eBookPLUS, $1,959 US/6-vol set or eBookPLUS; $2,090 EUR/6-vol set or eBookPLUS, $2,926 US/6-vol set & eBookPLUS
ISBN(s): 978-3-11-027418-9 (6-vol set); 978-3-11-027802-6 (eBookPLUS); 978-3-11-027803-3 (Groliet & EBook PLUS)

**Publishing as a Vocation: Studies of an Old Occupation in a New Technological Era**
Published by Transaction Publishers Inc
10 Corporate Place S, Piscataway, NJ 08854
Mailing Address: 1247 State Rd, Princeton, NJ 08540
*Tel:* 732-445-2280 *Fax:* 732-445-3138
*Web Site:* www.transactionpub.com
*Key Personnel*
Chmn & Author: Irving Louis Horowitz
*E-mail:* ihorowitz@transactionpub.com
Places publishing in America in its political & commercial setting. Addresses the political implications of scholary communication in the era of new computerized technology. Examines problems of political theory in the context of property rights versus the presumed right to know & the special strains involved in publishing as commerce versus information as a public trust.
1st ed, 2010: 167 pp, $37.95 paper
First published 2010
ISBN(s): 978-1-4128-1110-1

**Publishing Contracts, Sample Agreements for Book Publishers on Disk**
Published by Para Publishing LLC
PO Box 8206-240, Santa Barbara, CA 93118-8206
SAN: 215-8981
*Tel:* 805-968-7277 *Toll Free Tel:* 800-727-2782 *Fax:* 805-968-1379
*E-mail:* info@parapublishing.com
*Web Site:* www.parapublishing.com
*Key Personnel*
Owner & Publr: Dan Poynter
*E-mail:* danpoynter@parapublishing.com
Author: Charles Kent, Esq
22 different contracts covering every aspect of book publishing on disk, ready for computer customizing & printout.
5th ed, 2006: 127 pp, $29.95 disk
ISBN(s): 978-0-915516-46-9

**Publishing for the Pre K-12 Market**
Published by Simba Information
Division of Market Research Group
60 Long Ridge Rd, Suite 300, Stamford, CT 06902
SAN: 210-2021
*Tel:* 203-325-8193 *Toll Free Tel:* 888-297-4622 (cust serv) *Fax:* 203-325-8975
*E-mail:* customerservice@simbainformation.com
*Web Site:* www.simbainformation.com
*Key Personnel*
Mng Ed/Analyst: Kathy Mickey
Up-to-date descriptions & statistics on enrollments, demographic trends, in several categories; publishers' sales, forecasts, expenditures & profiles of the leading publishers in the K-12 market place.
Annual.
2013-2014: 186 pp, $3,450 print, $3,250 online, $3,850 online & print

**Publishing in the Information Age: A New Management Framework for the Digital Era**
Published by Praeger
Imprint of ABC-CLIO
130 Cremona Dr, Santa Barbara, CA 93117
Mailing Address: PO Box 1911, Santa Barbara, CA 93116-1911
*Tel:* 805-968-1911 *Toll Free Tel:* 800-368-6868 *Fax:* 805-685-9685 *Toll Free Fax:* 866-270-3856
*E-mail:* custserv@abc-clio.com
*Web Site:* www.abc-clio.com
*Key Personnel*
CEO & Academic Publr: Ronald Boehm
Author: Douglas M Eisenhart
A comprehensive single-volume study of the transformations underway in the publishing industry attributable to the penetration of digital information technologies & how publishers can benefit from them.
$39.95 paper, $107.95 hardcover
First published 1999
ISBN(s): 978-0-275-95696-7 (paper); 978-0-89930-847-0 (hardcover)

**Research Centers Directory**
Published by Gale
Unit of Cengage Learning
27500 Drake Rd, Farmington Hills, MI 48331-3535
SAN: 213-4373
*Tel:* 248-699-4253 *Toll Free Tel:* 800-877-4253 *Fax:* 248-699-8075 *Toll Free Fax:* 800-414-5043 (orders)
*E-mail:* gale.galeord@cengage.com
*Web Site:* www.gale.cengage.com
*Key Personnel*
Ed: Matthew Miskelly *Tel:* 248-699-4253 ext 1744 *E-mail:* matthew.miskelly@cengage.com; Sonya Hill
Directory describes more than 15,700 University affiliated & other nonprofit research centers in the US & Canada. Indexes: subject, geographic, personal name & master, including sponsoring organization, research center name & keywords.
Semiannual.
40th-41st ed, $1020 40th ed; $1071 41st ed
ISBN(s): 978-1-4144-4771-1 (40th ed); 978-1-4144-5990-5 (41st ed)

**The Self-Publishing Manual: How to Write, Print & Sell Your Own Book**
Published by Para Publishing LLC
PO Box 8206-240, Santa Barbara, CA 93118-8206
SAN: 215-8981
*Tel:* 805-968-7277 *Toll Free Tel:* 800-727-2782 *Fax:* 805-968-1379
*E-mail:* info@parapublishing.com
*Web Site:* www.parapublishing.com
*Key Personnel*
Owner & Publr: Dan Poynter
*E-mail:* danpoynter@parapublishing.com
How to write, publish & announce a book & get it listed. Emphasis on market targeting, advertising & distribution.
2009: 144 pp, $19.95 paper
ISBN(s): 978-1-56860-146-5

**Shakespearean Criticism**
Published by Gale
Unit of Cengage Learning
27500 Drake Rd, Farmington Hills, MI 48331-3535
SAN: 213-4373
*Tel:* 248-699-4253 *Toll Free Tel:* 800-877-4253 *Fax:* 248-699-8070 *Toll Free Fax:* 800-414-5043 (orders)
*E-mail:* gale.galeord@cengage.com
*Web Site:* www.gale.cengage.com
Thematically arranged essays from 1960 to the present of commentary on Shakespeare's plays & poems. Illustrated series provides support to students & teachers at high school & college levels. Beginning with Vol 60, presents topic entries that analyze various themes of Shakespeare's works. Each volume has a cumulative character index, a topic index & a topic index arranged by play title.
6 times/yr.
Vols 135-145, $328
ISBN(s): 978-1-4144-5995-0 (vol 135); 978-1-4144-5996-7 (vol 136); 978-1-4144-7139-6 (vol 137); 978-1-4144-7140-2 (vol 138); 978-1-4144-7141-9 (vol 139); 978-1-4144-7142-6 (vol 140); 978-1-4144-7143-3 (vol 141); 978-1-4144-7144-0 (vol 142); 978-1-4144-7145-7 (vol 143); 978-1-4144-7146-4 (vol 144); 978-1-4144-7147-1 (vol 145)

**Short Story Criticism**
Published by Gale
Unit of Cengage Learning
27500 Drake Rd, Farmington Hills, MI 48331-3535
SAN: 213-4373

*Tel:* 248-699-4253 *Toll Free Tel:* 800-877-4253 *Fax:* 248-699-8070 *Toll Free Fax:* 800-414-5043 (orders)
*E-mail:* gale.galeord@cengage.com
*Web Site:* www.gale.cengage.com
Series presenting critical views on the most widely studied writers of short fiction. Each volume includes overview of four to eight short story writers & a chronological historical survey of the critical response to his or her work. Most critical essays are full text.
Vols 144-157, $245
ISBN(s): 978-1-4144-7154-9 (vol 144); 978-1-4144-7155-6 (vol 145); 978-1-4144-7156-3 (vol 146); 978-1-4144-7157-0 (vol 147); 978-1-4144-7158-7 (vol 148); 978-1-4144-7159-4 (vol 149); 978-1-4144-7160-0 (vol 150); 978-1-4144-7161-7 (vol 151); 978-1-4144-7162-4 (vol 152); 978-1-4144-7163-1 (vol 153); 978-1-4144-7164-8 (vol 154); 978-1-4144-7165-5 (vol 155); 978-1-4144-7166-2 (vol 156); 978-1-4144-7167-9 (vol 157)

**Short Story Index**
Published by H W Wilson
Imprint of EBSCO Publishing
10 Estes St, Ipswich, MA 01938
*Tel:* 978-356-6500 *Toll Free Tel:* 800-653-2726 (US & CN) *Fax:* 978-356-6565
*E-mail:* information@ebscohost.com
*Web Site:* www.ebscohost.com
*Key Personnel*
VP, Cataloging & Gen Ref Servs: Joseph Miller, MLS, PhD
Ed: John Greenfieldt
Indexes short stories by author, title & subject in one alphabet. Basic Vol; Indexes 60,000 stories in 4,320 collections published from 1900-1949, $250. 5-yr Vol, 1950-1954: Indexes 9,575 stories in 549 collections, $250. 4-yr Vol, 1955-1958: Indexes 6,392 stories in 376 collections, $250. 5-yr Vol, 1959-1963: Indexes 9,068 stories in 582 collections, $250. 5-yr Vol, 1964-1968: Indexes 11,301 stories in 793 collections, $250. 5-yr Vol, 1969-1973: Indexes 11,561 stories in 805 collections, $250. 5-yr Vol, 1974-1978: Indexes 16,519 stories in 930 collections & 71 periodicals, $250. 5-yr Vol, 1979-1983: Indexes 16,633 stories in 904 collections & 67 periodicals, $250. 5-yr Vol, 1984-1988: Indexes 22,431 stories in 1,307 collections & periodicals, $250.
Annual, with five year cumulations.
349 pp, $250 US & CN, $310 foreign, available in electronic format
ISBN(s): 978-0-8242-0643-7

**Software and Intellectual Property Protection: Copyright and Patent Issues for Computer and Legal Professionals**
Published by Praeger
Imprint of ABC-CLIO
130 Cremona Dr, Santa Barbara, CA 93117
Mailing Address: PO Box 1911, Santa Barbara, CA 93116-1911
*Tel:* 805-968-1911 *Toll Free Tel:* 800-368-6868 *Fax:* 805-685-9685 *Toll Free Fax:* 866-270-3856
*E-mail:* custserv@abc-clio.com
*Web Site:* www.abc-clio.com
*Key Personnel*
CEO & Academic Publr: Ronald Boehm
Author: Bernard A Galler
A succinct, readable survey of the critical issues & cases in copyright & patent law applied to computer software, intended for computer professionals, academics & lawyers.
224 pp, $107.95 hardcover
ISBN(s): 978-0-89930-974-3

**Something About the Author**
Published by Gale
Unit of Cengage Learning
27500 Drake Rd, Farmington Hills, MI 48331-3535
SAN: 213-4373
*Tel:* 248-699-4253 *Toll Free Tel:* 800-877-4253 *Fax:* 248-699-8070 *Toll Free Fax:* 800-414-5043 (orders)
*E-mail:* gale.galeord@cengage.com
*Web Site:* www.gale.cengage.com
Heavily illustrated child-oriented reference tool. Each volume contains biographies on about 75 juvenile & young adult authors & illustrators. The series covers more than 12,000 authors. Entries include personal & career data, literary sidelights, complete bibliographies, critical comments & author portraits & book illustrations. A cumulative author index is included in each odd-numbered volume.
10 vols/yr.
Vols 220-236, $202/vol
ISBN(s): 978-1-4144-6123-6 (vol 220); 978-1-4144-6124-3 (vol 221); 978-1-4144-6125-0 (vol 222); 978-1-4144-6126-7 (vol 223); 978-1-4144-6127-4 (vol 224); 978-1-4144-6128-1 (vol 225); 978-1-4144-6129-8 (vol 226); 978-1-4144-6130-4 (vol 227); 978-1-4144-6131-1 (vol 228); 978-1-4144-6132-8 (vol 229); 978-1-4144-6133-5 (vol 230); 978-1-4144-6134-2 (vol 231); 978-1-4144-6135-9 (vol 232); 978-1-4144-6923-2 (vol 233); 978-1-4144-6924-9 (vol 234); 978-1-4144-6925-6 (vol 235); 978-1-4144-6926-3 (vol 236)

**Sports Market Place Directory**
Published by Grey House Publishing Inc™
4919 Rte 22, Amenia, NY 12501
Mailing Address: PO Box 56, Amenia, NY 12501-0056
*Tel:* 518-789-8700 *Toll Free Tel:* 800-562-2139 *Fax:* 518-789-0556
*E-mail:* books@greyhouse.com
*Web Site:* www.greyhouse.com
*Key Personnel*
Edit Dir: Laura Mars-Proietti *E-mail:* lmars@greyhouse.com
15,500 entries with key information about the people, organizations & events involving the sports industry.
April 2013: 2,300 pp, $250
ISBN(s): 978-1-61925-119-9

**Standard Periodical Directory**
Published by Oxbridge® Communications Inc
39 W 29 St, Suite 301, New York, NY 10001
*Tel:* 212-741-0231 *Toll Free Tel:* 800-955-0231 *Fax:* 212-633-2938
*E-mail:* info@oxbridge.com
*Web Site:* www.oxbridge.com
*Key Personnel*
CEO: Louis Hagood
Pres: Patricia Hagood
Over 63,000 US & Canadian periodicals arranged by subject matter into 262 classifications & indexed by title. Listings include publishing company, address, telephone number; names of editor, publisher, ad director; annotations; frequency, circulation, advertising & subscription rates; year established; trim size, print method, page count.
Annually in Jan.
36th ed, 2013: 2,306 pp, $1,995 hardcover, $995 digital, $1,995 single user CD-ROM, $2,995 print & CD-ROM
First published 1964
ISBN(s): 978-1-891783-59-3

**Subject Guide to Books in Print®**
Published by Grey House Publishing Inc™
4919 Rte 22, Amenia, NY 12501
Mailing Address: PO Box 56, Amenia, NY 12501-0056
*Tel:* 518-789-8700 *Toll Free Tel:* 800-562-2139 *Fax:* 518-789-0556
*E-mail:* books@greyhouse.com
*Web Site:* www.greyhouse.com
*Key Personnel*
Edit Dir: Laura Mars-Proietti *E-mail:* lmars@greyhouse.com
Master subject reference to titles, authors, publishers, wholesalers & distributors in the US.
Annual.
2013-2014: 15,312 pp, $800/6 vol set
ISBN(s): 978-1-59237-722-0 (6 vol set)

**Subject Guide to Children's Books in Print®**
Published by Grey House Publishing Inc™
4919 Rte 22, Amenia, NY 12501
Mailing Address: PO Box 56, Amenia, NY 12501-0056
*Tel:* 518-789-8700 *Toll Free Tel:* 800-562-2139 *Fax:* 518-789-0556
*E-mail:* books@greyhouse.com
*Web Site:* www.greyhouse.com
*Key Personnel*
Edit Dir: Laura Mars-Proietti *E-mail:* lmars@greyhouse.com
A natural complement to Children's Books In Print®, Subject Guide to Children's Books In Print® is a valuable tool when expanding children's literature collections & new curriculum areas.
Annual.
2013: 3,071 pp, $385
ISBN(s): 978-1-59237-657-5

**Training Guide to Frontline Bookselling**
Published by Paz & Associates
1417 Sadler Rd, PMB 274, Fernandina Beach, FL 32034
*Tel:* 904-277-2664 *Fax:* 904-261-6742
*E-mail:* mkaufman@pazbookbiz.com
*Web Site:* www.pazbookbiz.com
*Key Personnel*
Partner: Donna Paz Kaufman *E-mail:* dpaz@pazbookbiz.com
12 chapters on all aspects of bookstore operations, includes trainers outline.
3rd ed, Jan 2006: 125 pp, $189 plus shipping

**Travel Writer's Guide**
Published by Communication Unlimited
185 Shevelin Rd, Novato, CA 94947
*Tel:* 415-884-2941 *Toll Free Tel:* 800-563-1454 *Fax:* 415-883-5707
*E-mail:* gordon@gordonburgett.com
*Web Site:* www.gordonburgett.com
*Key Personnel*
Pres: Gordon Burgett *E-mail:* glburgett@aol.com
Writing/reference.
3rd ed (rev), updated 2005: 376 pp, $15 paper, $10 digital download
ISBN(s): 978-0-9708621-1-3

**Travel Writing**
Published by Writer's Digest Books
Imprint of F+W Media Inc
10151 Carver Rd, Suite 200, Blue Ash, OH 45242
*Tel:* 513-531-2690 *Toll Free Tel:* 800-289-0963 *Fax:* 513-531-0798
*E-mail:* writersdigest@fwmedia.com (edit)
*Web Site:* www.writersdigest.com; www.writersdigestshop.com
*Key Personnel*
Publr: Phil Sexton *E-mail:* phil.sexton@fwmedia.com
How to write engagingly about your travels, whether in journals for your own pleasure or articles for publications.
2nd ed, 2005: 320 pp, $8.24 paper
First published 2000
ISBN(s): 978-1-58297-381-4

**TRUMATCH Colorfinder**
Published by TRUMATCH Inc
122 Mill Pond Lane, Water Mill, NY 11976
Mailing Address: PO Box 501, Water Mill, NY 11976-0501
*Tel:* 631-204-9100 *Toll Free Tel:* 800-TRU-9100 (878-9100, US & CN) *Fax:* 631-204-0002
*E-mail:* info@trumatch.com
*Web Site:* www.trumatch.com
*Key Personnel*
Pres: Steven J Abramson
VP: Jane E Nichols *E-mail:* janen@trumatch.com
Digital guides for 4-color printing.
$85 paper for coated ed or uncoated ed

**Twentieth-Century Literary Criticism**
Published by Gale
Unit of Cengage Learning
27500 Drake Rd, Farmington Hills, MI 48331-3535
SAN: 213-4373
*Tel:* 248-699-4253 *Toll Free Tel:* 800-347-4253 *Fax:* 248-699-8054 *Toll Free Fax:* 800-414-5043 (orders)
*E-mail:* gale.galeord@cengage.com
*Web Site:* www.gale.cengage.com
*Key Personnel*
Ed: Linda Pavlovski
Each volume in the series presents overviews of 4-8 authors & furnishes full texts from representative criticism on the great novelists, poets & playwrights of the period 1900-1999. Every fourth volume covers literary topics including major literary movements, trends & other topics related to 20th century literature.
Multiple vols/yr.
Vols 245-268 2011-2012, $328/vol
ISBN(s): 978-1-4144-7025-2 (vol 245); 978-1-4144-7026-9 (vol 246); 978-1-4144-7027-6 (vol 247); 978-1-4144-7028-3 (vol 248); 978-1-4144-7029-0 (vol 249); 978-1-4144-7030-6 (vol 250); 978-1-4144-7031-3 (vol 251); 978-1-4144-7032-0 (vol 252); 978-1-4144-7033-7 (vol 253); 978-1-4144-7034-4 (vol 254); 978-1-4144-7035-1 (vol 255); 978-1-4144-7036-8 (vol 256); 978-1-4144-7037-5 (vol 257); 978-1-4144-7038-2 (vol 258); 978-1-4144-7039-9 (vol 259); 978-1-4144-7040-5 (vol 260); 978-1-4144-7041-2 (vol 261); 978-1-4144-7042-9 (vol 262); 978-1-4144-7043-6 (vol 263); 978-1-4144-7044-3 (vol 264); 978-1-4144-7045-0 (vol 265); 978-1-4144-7046-7 (vol 266); 978-1-4144-7047-4 (vol 267); 978-1-4144-7048-1 (vol 268)

**20 Master Plots**
Published by Writer's Digest Books
Imprint of F+W Media Inc
10151 Carver Rd, Suite 200, Blue Ash, OH 45242
*Tel:* 513-531-2690 *Toll Free Tel:* 800-289-0963 *Fax:* 513-531-0798
*E-mail:* writersdigest@fwmedia.com (edit)
*Web Site:* www.writersdigest.com; www.writersdigestshop.com
*Key Personnel*
Publr: Phil Sexton *E-mail:* phil.sexton@fwmedia.com
How to take timeless storytelling structures & make them immediate, now, for fiction that's universal in how it speaks to the reader's heart.
1st ed: 288 pp, $10.04 paper
First published 2003
ISBN(s): 987-1-59963-537-8

**2012 Survey of Compensation & Personnel Practices in the Publishing Industry**
Published by Association of American Publishers (AAP)
71 Fifth Ave, 2nd fl, New York, NY 10003-3004
*Tel:* 212-255-0200 *Fax:* 212-255-7007
*Web Site:* www.publishers.org
*Key Personnel*
CEO & Pres: Tom Allen *Tel:* 202-220-4543 *Fax:* 202-347-3690
VP & Dir: Tina Jordan *Tel:* 212-255-0275 *E-mail:* tjordan@publishers.org
VP & Exec Dir, Prof Scholarly Publg: John Tagler *Tel:* 212-255-0200 ext 257
VP, Communs: Andi Sporkin
VP & Gen Counsel, Govt Aff: Allan R Adler *Tel:* 202-347-3375 *Fax:* 202-347-3690
Exec Dir, School Div: Jay Diskey *Tel:* 202-347-3375 *Fax:* 202-347-3690
Survey report contains salary & personnel practices information for more than 120 benchmark jobs in the publishing industry.
Annual.
220 pp, Varies based on participation, company site & AAP membership status

**Ulrich's Periodicals Directory**
Published by ProQuest LLC
Subsidiary of Cambridge Information Group Inc
630 Central Ave, New Providence, NJ 07974
*Tel:* 908-795-3659 (edit) *Toll Free Tel:* 800-346-6049 (Ulrich's hotline, US only)
*E-mail:* ulrichs@proquest.com; core_service@proquest.com (orders)
*Web Site:* ulrichsweb.serialssolutions.com; www.proquest.com (publr); www.serialssolutions.com
*Key Personnel*
Edit Dir: Laurie Kaplan
Four-volume set, arranged by subject classification, includes periodicals, newsletters, newspapers, annuals & irregular serials published worldwide. Also available online.
Annual.
52nd ed, 2014: 11,500 pp, $2,175/4 vol set
First published 1932
ISBN(s): 978-1-60030-644-0 (4 vol set)

**Walden's Paper Catalog**
Published by Walden-Mott Corp
225 N Franklin Tpke, Ramsey, NJ 07446-1600
*Tel:* 201-818-8630 *Fax:* 201-818-8720
*E-mail:* info@papercatalog.com
*Web Site:* www.papercatalog.com
*Key Personnel*
Ed: Alfred F Walden *Tel:* 201-818-8630 ext 11
National directory of fine printing & writing papers. Alphabetical listing of brand names, their characteristics along with merchants that carry those manufacturers' grades. Sections: "Brand Name Index", "Paper Distributors", "Papers by Grade" & "How to Buy Paper".
2 issues/yr.
$85/yr
First published 1914

**Walden's Paper Handbook**
Published by Walden-Mott Corp
225 N Franklin Tpke, Ramsey, NJ 07446-1600
*Tel:* 201-818-8630 *Fax:* 201-818-8720
*E-mail:* info@papercatalog.com
*Web Site:* www.waldenmott.com
*Key Personnel*
Ed: Alfred F Walden *Tel:* 201-818-8630 ext 11
Pulp & paper industry pocket guide.
5th ed: 277 pp, $25

**Word Painting**
Published by Writer's Digest Books
Imprint of F+W Media Inc
10151 Carver Rd, Suite 200, Blue Ash, OH 45242
*Tel:* 513-531-2690 *Toll Free Tel:* 800-289-0963 *Fax:* 513-531-0798
*E-mail:* writersdigest@fwmedia.com (edit)
*Web Site:* www.writersdigest.com; www.writersdigestshop.com
*Key Personnel*
Publr: Phil Sexton *E-mail:* phil.sexton@fwmedia.com
Combines direct instruction with intriguing word exercises to teach you how to "paint" evocative descriptions that capture the images of your mind's eye & improve your writing.
1st ed: 256 pp, $8.34 paper
First published 2000
ISBN(s): 978-1-58297-025-7

**World Authors Series**
Published by H W Wilson
Imprint of EBSCO Publishing
10 Estes St, Ipswich, MA 01938
*Tel:* 978-356-6500 *Toll Free Tel:* 800-653-2726 (US & CN) *Fax:* 978-356-6565
*E-mail:* information@ebscohost.com
*Web Site:* www.ebscohost.com
*Key Personnel*
Dir, Mktg: Frank W Daly
*American Authors, 1600-1900*, $115.
*British Authors Before 1800*, $100.
*British Authors of the 19th Century*, $105.
*European Authors, 1000-1900*, $115.
*Junior Book of Authors*, $65 (2nd ed rev).
*More Junior Authors*, $60.
*Third Book of Junior Authors*, $65;
*Fourth Book 1978*, $70;
*Fifth Book 1983*, $80;
*Sixth Book 1989*, $80;
*Seventh Book 1996*, $80.
*Index to the Wilson Author Series 1997*, $50 (rev).
*World Authors 1900-1950* (4 vols), $590.
*World Authors 1950-1970*, $150; 1970-1975, $130; 1975-1980, $130; 1980-1985, $130;
*800 BC-Present*, (CD-ROM), $595;
*1900-Present*, (CD-ROM), $495;
*1950-Present*, (CD-ROM).
*Spanish American Authors: The Twentieth Century 1992*, $160.
*Eighth Book of Junior Authors, 2000*, $95.
*World Authors, 1985-1990*, $130.
*World Authors, 1990-1995*, $145.
*World Authors, 1995-2000*, $150.
*World Authors, 2000-2005*, $170.
Tenth Book of Junior Authors & Illustrators, $120.
All prices US & Canada, other countries higher.
800 pp, $170 US & CN, $185 foreign
ISBN(s): 978-0-8242-0001-5 (American Authors, 1600-1900); 978-0-8242-0006-0 (British Authors Before Eighteen Hundred); 978-0-8242-0007-7 (British Authors of the Nineteenth Century); 978-0-8242-0013-8 (European Authors 1000-1900); 978-0-8242-0028-2 (The Junior Book of Authors); 978-0-8242-0036-7 (More Junior Authors); 978-0-8242-0050-3 (Twentieth Century Authors: A Biographical Dictionary of Modern Literature); 978-0-8242-0408-2 (Third Book of Junior Authors); 978-0-8242-0568-3 (Fourth Book of Junior Authors & Illustrators); 978-0-8242-0640-6 (Greek & Latin Authors, 800BC-AD 1000: A Biographical Dictionary); 978-0-8242-0641-3 (World Authors: 1970-1975); 978-0-8242-0694-9 (Fifth Book of Junior Authors & Illustrators); 978-0-8242-0715-1 (World Authors, 1975-1980); 978-0-8242-0777-9 (Sixth Book of Junior Authors & Illustrators); 978-0-8242-0797-7 (World Authors, 1980-1985); 978-0-8242-0806-6 (Spanish American Authors: The Twentieth Century); 978-0-8242-0874-5 (The Professional Collection for Elementary Educators); 978-0-8242-0875-2 (World Authors, 1985-1990); 978-0-8242-0899-8 (World Authors, 1900-1950); 978-0-8242-0900-1 (Index to the Wilson Authors Series 1997); 978-0-8242-0956-8 (World Authors, 1990-1995); 978-0-8242-0968-1 (Eighth Book of Junior Authors & Illustrators); 978-0-8242-1032-8 (World Authors, 1995-2000); 978-0-8242-1066-3 (Tenth Book of Junior Authors & Illustrators); 978-0-8242-1077-9 (World Authors 2000-2005)

**World Literature Criticism: A Selection of Major Authors from Gale's Literary Criticism - Supplement**
Published by Gale
Unit of Cengage Learning
27500 Drake Rd, Farmington Hills, MI 48331-3535
SAN: 213-4373
*Tel:* 248-699-4253 *Toll Free Tel:* 800-877-4253 *Fax:* 248-699-8070 *Toll Free Fax:* 800-414-5043 (orders)
*E-mail:* gale.galeord@cengage.com
*Web Site:* www.gale.cengage.com
Updated supplement listing 20th Century authors collection of their biographical data, criticisms, list of principal works, historical survey of critical response to the author's works & sources for further study. Three indexes consist of authors, nationality & titles.
1997 supplement still in print.
961 pp, $231/2 vol set
ISBN(s): 978-07876-1696-0

**The Writer's Complete Fantasy Reference**
Published by Writer's Digest Books
Imprint of F+W Media Inc
10151 Carver Rd, Suite 200, Blue Ash, OH 45242
*Tel:* 513-531-2690 *Toll Free Tel:* 800-289-0963 *Fax:* 513-531-0798
*E-mail:* writersdigest@fwmedia.com (edit)
*Web Site:* www.writersdigest.com; www.writersdigestshop.com
*Key Personnel*
Publr: Phil Sexton *E-mail:* phil.sexton@fwmedia.com
Reveals the facts behind the fantasy, giving you the details you need to make your fiction vibrant, captivating & original.
304 pp, $10.79 paper
First published 2000
ISBN(s): 978-1-58297-026-4

**The Writer's Guide to Character Traits**
Published by Writer's Digest Books
Imprint of F+W Media Inc
10151 Carver Rd, Suite 200, Blue Ash, OH 45242
*Tel:* 513-531-2690 *Toll Free Tel:* 800-289-0963 *Fax:* 513-531-0798
*E-mail:* writersdigest@fwmedia.com (edit)
*Web Site:* www.writersdigest.com; www.writersdigestshop.com
*Key Personnel*
Publr: Phil Sexton *E-mail:* phil.sexton@fwmedia.com
Profiles the mental, emotional & physical qualities of dozens of different personality types.
384 pp, $11.43 paper
First published 1999
ISBN(s): 978-1-58297-390-6

**The Writer's Guide to Crafting Stories for Children**
Published by Writer's Digest Books
Imprint of F+W Media Inc
10151 Carver Rd, Suite 200, Blue Ash, OH 45242
*Tel:* 513-531-2690 *Toll Free Tel:* 800-289-0963 *Fax:* 513-531-0798
*E-mail:* writersdigest@fwmedia.com (edit)
*Web Site:* www.writersdigest.com; www.writersdigestshop.com
*Key Personnel*
Publr: Phil Sexton *E-mail:* phil.sexton@fwmedia.com
Insightful advice for mastering storytelling basics with dozens of examples that illustrate a variety of plot-building techniques.
1st ed: 192 pp, $10.67
First published 2001
ISBN(s): 978-1-58297-052-3

**The Writer's Idea Book 10th Anniversary Edition**
Published by Writer's Digest Books
Imprint of F+W Media Inc
10151 Carver Rd, Suite 200, Blue Ash, OH 45242
*Tel:* 513-531-2690 *Toll Free Tel:* 800-289-0963 *Fax:* 513-531-0798
*E-mail:* writersdigest@fwmedia.com (edit)
*Web Site:* www.writersdigest.com; www.writersdigestshop.com
*Key Personnel*
Publr: Phil Sexton *E-mail:* phil.sexton@fwmedia.com
Helps you to jump-start your creativity & develop original ideas.
1st ed: 352 pp, $13.39 paper
First published 2002
ISBN(s): 978-1-59963-386-2

**Writer's Market**
Published by Writer's Digest Books
Imprint of F+W Media Inc
10151 Carver Rd, Suite 200, Blue Ash, OH 45242
*Tel:* 513-531-2690 *Toll Free Tel:* 800-289-0963 *Fax:* 513-531-0798
*E-mail:* writersdigest@fwmedia.com (edit)
*Web Site:* www.writersmarket.com; www.fwmedia.com; www.writersdigestshop.com; www.writersdigestshop.com
*Key Personnel*
Publr: Phil Sexton *E-mail:* phil.sexton@fwmedia.com
Lists more than 4,000 places where freelance writers can sell articles, books, novels, stories, fillers & scripts.
Annual.
2014: 928 pp, $29.99 paper regular ed, $49.99 paper deluxe ed (includes online)
ISBN(s): 978-1-59963-732-7 (regular ed); 978-1-59963-733-4 (deluxe ed)

**The Writer's Market Guide to Getting Published**
Published by Writer's Digest Books
Imprint of F+W Media Inc
10151 Carver Rd, Suite 200, Blue Ash, OH 45242
*Tel:* 513-531-2690 *Toll Free Tel:* 800-289-0963 *Fax:* 513-531-0798
*E-mail:* writersdigest@fwmedia.com (edit)
*Web Site:* www.writersdigest.com; www.writersdigestshop.com
*Key Personnel*
Publr: Phil Sexton *E-mail:* phil.sexton@fwmedia.com
Sound information on professional writing issues, focusing on everything from contracts to creativity.
3rd ed, March 2010: 368 pp, $10.99 paper
First published 2004
ISBN(s): 978-1-58297-608-2

**Writer's Yearbook**
Published by F+W Media Inc
10151 Carver Rd, Suite 200, Blue Ash, OH 45242
*Tel:* 513-531-2690
*E-mail:* writersdigest@fwmedia.com
*Web Site:* www.writersdigest.com
*Key Personnel*
Exec Ed: Zachary Petit *E-mail:* zachary.petit@fwmedia.com
Includes lists of book & magazine article markets & how-to articles on writing & publishing.
Annual.
72 pp, $5.99 paper
First published 1990

**Writing Creative Nonfiction**
Published by Writer's Digest Books
Imprint of F+W Media Inc
10151 Carver Rd, Suite 200, Blue Ash, OH 45242
*Tel:* 513-531-2690 *Toll Free Tel:* 800-289-0963 *Fax:* 513-531-0798
*E-mail:* writersdigest@fwmedia.com (edit)
*Web Site:* www.writersdigest.com; www.writersdigestshop.com
*Key Personnel*
Publr: Phil Sexton *E-mail:* phil.sexton@fwmedia.com
More than thirty essays examining every key element of the craft, from researching ideas & structuring the story, to reportage & personal reflection.
400 pp, $12.70 paper
First published 2001
ISBN(s): 978-1-884910-50-0

**Writing Down the Bones: Freeing the Writer Within**
Published by Shambhala Publications Inc
Horticultural Hall, 300 Massachusetts Ave, Boston, MA 02115
SAN: 203-2481
*Tel:* 617-424-0030; 978-829-2599 (intl callers) *Toll Free Tel:* 888-424-2329 (cust serv); 866-424-0030 (off) *Fax:* 617-236-1563
*E-mail:* editorialdept@shambhala.com
*Web Site:* www.shambhala.com
*Key Personnel*
Owner & EVP: Sara Bercholz
Pres: Nikko Odiseos
Publr: Julie Saidenberg
Mng Ed: Liz Shaw
Author: Natalie Goldberg
Brings together Zen meditation & writing.
224 pp, $14 paper; $18.95 hardcover
First published 2005
ISBN(s): 978-1-59030-261-3 (paperback); 978-1-59030-794-6 (hardcover); 987-0-8348-2113-2 (e-book)

**Writing Life Stories**
Published by Writer's Digest Books
Imprint of F+W Media Inc
10151 Carver Rd, Suite 200, Blue Ash, OH 45242
*Tel:* 513-531-2690 *Toll Free Tel:* 800-289-0963 *Fax:* 513-531-0798
*E-mail:* writersdigest@fwmedia.com (edit)
*Web Site:* www.writersdigest.com; www.writersdigestshop.com
*Key Personnel*
Publr: Phil Sexton *E-mail:* phil.sexton@fwmedia.com
How to capture your own experiences & turn them into personal essays & book-length memoirs.
304 pp, $11.10 paper
First published 1998
ISBN(s): 978-1-58297-527-6

**Writing Mysteries**
Published by Writer's Digest Books
Imprint of F+W Media Inc
10151 Carver Rd, Suite 200, Blue Ash, OH 45242
*Tel:* 513-531-2690 *Toll Free Tel:* 800-289-0963 *Fax:* 513-531-0798
*E-mail:* writersdigest@fwmedia.com (edit)
*Web Site:* www.writersdigest.com; www.writersdigestshop.com
*Key Personnel*
Publr: Phil Sexton *E-mail:* phil.sexton@fwmedia.com
How to piece a perfect mystery together & create realistic stories that are taut, immediate & tense.
2nd ed: 256 pp, $11.43 paper
First published 2002
ISBN(s): 978-1-58297-102-5

**Writing the Breakout Novel**
Published by Writer's Digest Books
Imprint of F+W Media Inc
10151 Carver Rd, Suite 200, Blue Ash, OH 45242
*Tel:* 513-531-2690 *Fax:* 513-531-0798
*Web Site:* www.writersdigest.com; www.writersdigestshop.com
*Key Personnel*
Publr: Phil Sexton *E-mail:* phil.sexton@fwmedia.com
How to take your prose to the next level & write a breakout novel.
1st ed: 256 pp, $9.34 paper
First published 2001
ISBN(s): 978-1-58297-182-7

**Yearbook of Experts, Authorities & Spokespersons**
Published by Broadcast Interview Source Inc
2500 Wisconsin Ave NW, Suite 949, Washington, DC 20007-4132
*Tel:* 202-333-5000 *Fax:* 202-342-5411
*E-mail:* expertclick@gmail.com
*Web Site:* expertclick.com
*Key Personnel*
Publr & Ed: Mitchell P Davis *Tel:* 203-333-4904 *E-mail:* mitchell@yearbookofexperts.com
Listings of contacts at publishers, trade associations & public interest groups that welcome media contacts; for both print & broadcast journalist use.
Annual.
2012: 398 pp, $10.95 paper
ISBN(s): 978-0-934333-81-8

**You Can Write Children's Books Workbook**
Published by Writer's Digest Books
Imprint of F+W Media Inc
10151 Carver Rd, Suite 200, Blue Ash, OH 45242
*Tel:* 513-531-2690 *Toll Free Tel:* 800-289-0963 *Fax:* 513-531-0798
*E-mail:* writersdigest@fwmedia.com (edit)
*Web Site:* www.writersdigest.com; www.writersdigestshop.com
*Key Personnel*
Publr: Phil Sexton *E-mail:* phil.sexton@fwmedia.com
Provides hands-on instruction for finishing a ms, preparing it for publication & getting it published.
1st ed: 144 pp, $8.98 paper
First published 2004
ISBN(s): 978-1-58297-248-0

# Magazines for the Trade

The magazines listed have been selected because they are published specifically for the book trade industry (apart from book review and index journals, which are listed in **Book Review & Index Journals & Services** in volume 2) or because they are widely used in the industry for reference. Also included in this section are literary journals.

For a comprehensive international directory of periodicals, see *Ulrich's Periodicals Directory* (ProQuest LLC, 630 Central Avenue, New Providence, NJ 07974), which lists magazines by subject and includes notations indicating those that carry book reviews. See also the *International Directory of Little Magazines & Small Presses* (Dustbooks, PO Box 100, Paradise, CA 95967).

*Writer's Digest* (F+W Media, Inc., 10151 Carver Road, Suite 200, Blue Ash, OH 45242) publishes detailed magazine lists in certain issues. *Writer's Market* (Writer's Digest Books, 10151 Carver Road, Suite 200, Blue Ash, OH 45242) contains classified lists of writers' markets.

**Advertising Age**
Published by Crain Communications
Subsidiary of Crain Communications Inc
711 Third Ave, New York, NY 10017-4036
*Tel:* 212-210-0100 *Fax:* 212-210-0200 (NY)
*E-mail:* AdAgeEditor@adage.com
*Web Site:* adage.com
*Subscription Address:* 1155 Gratiot Ave, Detroit, MI 48207 *Tel:* 313-446-1665 *Fax:* 313-446-6777 *E-mail:* AdAgeSubscriptions@adage.com
*Key Personnel*
VP, Publg: Allison P Arden *Tel:* 212-210-0794 *E-mail:* aarden@adage.com
Ed-in-Chief, New York: Rance Crain *E-mail:* rcrain@crain.com
Exec Ed: Judann Pollack *Tel:* 212-210-0458 *E-mail:* jpollack@adage.com
Ed: Abbey Klaasen *E-mail:* aklaasen@adage.com
Covers advertising in business, media, trade newspapers & magazines. Also available online.
First published 1930
Frequency: Weekly
Circulation: 58,000
$4.99/issue
ISSN: 0001-8899 (print); 1557-7414 (online)

**Adweek**
Published by Prometheus Global Media LLC
770 Broadway, 7th fl, New York, NY 10003
*Tel:* 212-493-4100 *Fax:* 646-654-5637
*E-mail:* info@adweek.com
*Web Site:* www.adweek.com
*Key Personnel*
Edit Dir: Michael Wolff
Exec Ed: James Cooper
Mng Ed: Hillary Frey
Deputy Ed: Chip Bayers
Creative Dir: Nick Mrozowski
First published 1978
Frequency: 44 issues/yr
$149/yr print or digital
ISSN: 1549-9553

**American Journalism Review**
Published by The Phillip Merrill College of Journalism
Division of University of Maryland Foundation
University of Maryland, 1117 Journalism Bldg, College Park, MD 20742-7111
*Tel:* 301-405-8803 *Fax:* 301-405-8323
*E-mail:* editor@ajr.umd.edu
*Web Site:* www.ajr.org
*Key Personnel*
Pres: Kevin Klose
SVP & Ed: Rem Rieder
Edited for & by people working in the media & communications industry. Critiques journalism in all forms; including newspapers, TV, magazines, radio, cable TV, First Amendment issues & government regulation. Features book reviews, profiles, columns & news stories.
First published 1977
Frequency: Quarterly
Avg pages per issue: 72
Circulation: 25,000
ISSN: 1067-8654

**American Poetry Review**
University of the Arts (UARTS), Hamilton Hall, 320 S Broad St, Rm 313, Philadelphia, PA 19102-4901
*Tel:* 215-717-6801 *Fax:* 215-717-6805
*Web Site:* www.aprweb.org
*Key Personnel*
Busn Mgr: Michael Duffy
Ed: Stephen Berg; David Bonanno *E-mail:* dbonanno@aprweb.org; Elizabeth Scanlon *E-mail:* escanlon@aprweb.org
Poetry, general essays, fiction, translations, columns & interviews.
First published 1972
Book Use: Excerpts & serial rights, reviews
Frequency: Bimonthly
Avg pages per issue: 52
Circulation: 9,000
$4.50/issue, $25/yr
ISSN: 0360-3709
Ad Rates: Full page $950
Ad Closing Date(s): 45 days prior

**The American Spectator**
Published by The American Spectator Foundation
1611 N Kent St, Suite 901, Arlington, VA 22209
*Tel:* 703-807-2011 *Toll Free Tel:* 800-524-3469 *Fax:* 703-807-2013; 845-566-7020 (subns)
*E-mail:* editor@spectator.org
*Web Site:* www.spectator.org
*Subscription Address:* PO Box 638, Mount Morris, IL 61054
*Key Personnel*
Ed-in-Chief: R Emmett Tyrrell, Jr
Edit Dir: Wladyslaw Pleszczynski
Mng Ed: Kyle Peterson
Offers a unique blend of news reporting, social & political comment, humor pieces & cultural essays on the issues of the day.
First published 1924
Book Use: Book review section
Frequency: 10 issues/yr
Avg pages per issue: 82
Circulation: 50,000
$5.95/issue, $39/yr US, $59/yr, $109/2 yrs CN & elsewhere
ISSN: 0148-8414
Trim Size: 8 3/8 x 10 1/2
Ad Rates: 4-color full page $2,795; B&W full page $2,395
Ad Closing Date(s): 1st of each month

**ANQ: A Quarterly Journal of Short Articles, Notes & Reviews**
Published by Taylor & Francis Inc
325 Chestnut St, Suite 800, Philadelphia, PA 20036-1802
*Tel:* 215-625-8900 (ext 4) *Toll Free Tel:* 800-354-1420 (cust serv) *Fax:* 215-625-2940
*E-mail:* customer.service@taylorandfrancis.com
*Web Site:* www.tandfonline.com; www.routledge.com
*Key Personnel*
Ed: Sandro Jung *E-mail:* sandro.jung@ugent.be
English & American literature for an academic & library audience.
First published 1987
Book Use: Reviews
Frequency: Quarterly
Avg pages per issue: 64
Circulation: 500
$80/yr indivs (print & online), $204/yr instns (online only), $233/yr instns (print & online)
ISSN: 0895-769X
Trim Size: 6 x 9
Ad Rates: Full page $550; 1/2 page $350
Ad Closing Date(s): Winter Dec 1, Spring March 21, Summer June 18, Fall Sept 19

**The Artist's Magazine**
Published by F+W Media Inc
10151 Carver Rd, Suite 200, Blue Ash, OH 45242
*Tel:* 513-531-2690 *Fax:* 513-513 2696
*E-mail:* tamedit@fwmedia.com
*Web Site:* www.theartistsnetwork.com/the-artists-magazine
*Subscription Address:* 700 Estate St, Iola, WI 54990 *Toll Free Tel:* 800-258-0929
*Key Personnel*
Ed-in-Chief: Maureen Bloomfield
Mng Ed: Christine McHugh
Art instruction & advice for the working artist.
First published 1984
Book Use: Occasional book reviews (art-related titles only)
Frequency: 10 issues/yr
Avg pages per issue: 100
Circulation: 140,000
$20.96/yr US, $30.96 CN & foreign
ISSN: 0741-3351
Trim Size: 7 3/4 x 10 3/4

**AudioFile®**
Published by AudioFile® Publications Inc
37 Silver St, Portland, ME 04101
Mailing Address: PO Box 109, Portland, ME 04112-0109
*Tel:* 207-774-7563 *Toll Free Tel:* 800-506-1212 *Fax:* 207-775-3744
*E-mail:* info@audiofilemagazine.com; editorial@audiofilemagazine.com
*Web Site:* www.audiofilemagazine.com
*Key Personnel*
Publr & Ed: Robin F Whitten *E-mail:* robin@audiofilemagazine.com
Fin Offr: Patricia E Stickney *E-mail:* pat@audiofilemagazine.com
Mng Ed: Jennifer M Dowell *E-mail:* jennifer@audiofilemagazine.com

Review Ed: Elizabeth K Dodge *E-mail:* edodge@maine.edu
Art Dir: Jennifer Steele
Web Mgr: Mark Mattos *E-mail:* mark@audiofilemagazine.com
Web Admin: MaryBeth Walz *E-mail:* webadmin@audiofilemagazine.com
Asst Ed: Allison Adams
Edit Asst: Andrea Jackson-Darling; Kate Menendez
Cust Serv: Casey McManamy
For people who love audiobooks, is indispensable for anyone who enjoys spoken-word audio. We review nearly 400 audio books every 60 days, feature narrator & author profiles & award exceptional performances with AudioFile's Earphone Awards.
First published 1992
Frequency: Bimonthly
Avg pages per issue: 72
Circulation: 15,000
$6 US, $8 CN
ISSN: 1063-0244
Avg reviews per issue: 400
Trim Size: 8 3/8 x 10 7/8
Ad Rates: Full page $3,100

**Authorship**
Published by National Writers Association
10940 S Parker Rd, Suite 508, Parker, CO 80134
*Tel:* 303-841-0246
*E-mail:* natlwritersassn@hotmail.com
*Web Site:* www.nationalwriters.com
*Key Personnel*
Ed & Exec Dir: Sandy Whelchel *E-mail:* authorsandy@hotmail.com
Only take submissions dealing with writing. Also available online.
Book Use: Review books for writers (in-house staff)
Frequency: Quarterly
Avg pages per issue: 28
Circulation: 8,000
$20/yr
ISSN: 1092-9347

**Book Business**
Published by North American Publishing Co (NAPCO)
1500 Spring Garden St, 12th fl, Philadelphia, PA 19130
*Tel:* 215-238-5300; 215-238-5338 (cust serv)
*E-mail:* magazinecs@napco.com
*Web Site:* www.bookbusinessmag.com
*Key Personnel*
Publr: Matt Steinmetz
Edit Dir: Lynn Rosen
Ed-in-Chief: Brian Howard
Mng Ed: Jim Sturdivant
Provides both strategic & practical information publishers need to stay ahead of market trends, confront change proactively & run their businesses successfully & profitably. Book Business provides forward thinking for senior-level trade, education, association, business, children's, STM, independent & other book publishing executives. Also avalable onlinie.
First published 1998
Frequency: 6 issues/yr
free to individuals who meet pre-established demographic criteria
ISSN: 1558-9889

**Book Dealers World**
Published by North American Bookdealers Exchange (NABE)
PO Box 606, Cottage Grove, OR 97424-0026
*Tel:* 541-942-7455
*E-mail:* bookdealersworld@bookmarketingprofits.com
*Key Personnel*
Exec Dir: Al Galasso
Book marketing, self publishing, mail order.
First published 1980
Book Use: From NABE members
Frequency: Quarterly
Avg pages per issue: 32
Circulation: 10,000
$50/yr, sample $5
ISSN: 1098-8521

**Book Publishing Report**
Published by Simba Information
Division of Market Research Group
60 Long Ridge Rd, Suite 300, Stamford, CT 06902
SAN: 210-2021
*Tel:* 203-325-8193 *Toll Free Tel:* 888-297-4622 (cust serv) *Fax:* 203-325-8975
*E-mail:* customerservice@simbainformation.com
*Web Site:* www.simbainformation.com
*Key Personnel*
Sr Ed/Analyst: Michael Norris
Newsletter; every monthly issue monitors, analyzes & reports on trends & developments in book publishing & what they mean to you. It covers the deals, the financials, market data, legal developments, technological issues, distribution, people & more. Monitors book industry news from a strategic, product, financial & marketing perspective; particular attention to emerging book industry companies, especially those that are exploiting the trends & developments that shape entirely new products.
First published 1975
Frequency: Monthly
$695/yr
ISSN: 1086-1319
Trim Size: 8 1/2 x 11
Ad Rates: 4-color full page $2,550; 4-color 1/2 page $2,090; B&W full page $2,175; B&W 1/2 page $1,780

**BookPage**
Published by ProMotion Inc
2143 Belcourt Ave, Nashville, TN 37212
*Tel:* 615-292-8926 *Toll Free Tel:* 800-726-4242 *Fax:* 615-292-8249
*Web Site:* www.bookpage.com
*Key Personnel*
Pres & Publr: Michael A Zibart
Assoc Publr: Julia Steele *E-mail:* julia@bookpage.com
Subn Mgr: Elizabeth Herbert *Tel:* 615-292-8926 ext 34 *E-mail:* elizabeth@bookpage.com
Book reviews, author interviews; focus on general interest new releases. Monthly publication. Columns on romance, mystery, audio & paperback, plus individual reviews on books in all categories. Focus is completely on new releases; no backlist reviewed. HC & PB titles reviewed.
First published 1988
Book Use: Reviews
Frequency: Monthly
Avg pages per issue: 32
Circulation: 500,000

**Bookselling This Week**
Published by American Booksellers Association
333 Westchester Ave, Suite S202, White Plains, NY 10604
*Tel:* 914-406-7500 *Toll Free Tel:* 800-637-0037 *Fax:* 914-410-6297
*E-mail:* info@bookweb.org
*Web Site:* www.bookweb.org
*Key Personnel*
Dir, Content Devt: Rosemary Hawkins *Tel:* 914-406-7500 ext 7561 *E-mail:* rosemary@bookweb.org
Book industry news; ABA membership news. Available online only; no print edition.
Frequency: Weekly
Circulation: 13,000

**Bulletin**
Published by IDEAlliance®
1600 Duke St, Suite 420, Alexandria, VA 22314
*Tel:* 952-896-1908 *Fax:* 703-837-1072
*Web Site:* www.ipabulletin.com
*Key Personnel*
EVP & Publr: Steve Bonoff *E-mail:* sbonoff@idealliance.org
Ed: Chuck Lenatti *Tel:* 650-245-4434 *E-mail:* chuckl8899@aol.com
Management & technical information relating to graphic communication prepress & professional imaging segment of the graphic arts from creative & digital photography through digital & traditional printing. Available in print & online.
First published 1911
Book Use: Reviews & excerpts
Frequency: Bimonthly
Avg pages per issue: 52
Circulation: 3,500
$20/yr US & PR, $25/yr CN & foreign (surface), $60/yr air mail, $5 single copy
ISSN: 1539-137X
Trim Size: 8 1/4 x 10 3/4
Ad Rates: 4 color: full pg $1,800, 1/2 pg island $1,500, 1/2 pg $1,400, 1/4 pg $1,000
Ad Closing Date(s): 1st of month preceding pub month (Jan 1 for Feb issue, etc)

**Canadian Children's Book News**
Published by Canadian Children's Book Centre
40 Orchard View Blvd, Suite 217, Toronto, ON M4R 1B9, Canada
*Tel:* 416-975-0010 *Fax:* 416-975-8970
*E-mail:* info@bookcentre.ca
*Web Site:* www.bookcentre.ca
*Key Personnel*
Ed: Gillian O'Reilly *E-mail:* gillian@bookcentre.ca
News, book reviews (only review books by Canadian authors & illustrators), author & illustrator interviews, profiles of publishers & bookstores & information about the world of children's books in Canada. Visit web site for media kit. CCBN is available with membership to the Canadian Children's Book Centre; also available in bulk subscriptions & on newsstands across Canada.
First published 1977
Frequency: 4 issues/yr
Avg pages per issue: 40
Circulation: 7,000
ISSN: 1705-7809
Trim Size: 8 1/8 x 10 7/8

**Catholic Library World**
Published by Catholic Library Association
205 W Monroe, Suite 314, Chicago, IL 60606-5061
*Tel:* 312-739-1776 *Toll Free Tel:* 855-739-1776 *Fax:* 312-739-1778
*E-mail:* cla2@cathla.org
*Web Site:* www.cathla.org
*Key Personnel*
Pres: Malachy R McCarthy *E-mail:* mmccarthy@cathla.org
Gen Ed: Sigrid Kelsey *E-mail:* skelsey@lsu.edu
Articles, book & media reviews for library information professionals.
First published 1929
Book Use: Regularly publish reviews of books & other media
Frequency: Quarterly
Avg pages per issue: 90
Circulation: 1,100
Free to CLA membs, $100/yr nonmembs US, $125/yr + postage, back issues & single copies $25 + postage
ISSN: 0008-820X

Ad Rates: Full page $425; 2/3 page $360; 1/2 page $295; 1/3 page $230; 1/6 page $185; preferred space also available, color additional
Ad Closing Date(s): March issue, Jan 2; June issue, April 1; Sept issue, July 1; Dec issue, Oct 1

**CBA Retailers+Resources**
Published by CBA: The Association for Christian Retail
9240 Explorer Dr, Suite 200, Colorado Springs, CO 80920
*Tel:* 719-265-9895 *Toll Free Tel:* 800-252-1950 *Fax:* 719-272-3510
*E-mail:* info@cbaonline.org
*Web Site:* www.cbaonline.org
*Key Personnel*
Pubns Dir: Kathleen Samuelson *E-mail:* ksamuelson@cbaonline.org
Trade publication for the Christian retail industry; official publication of Christian Booksellers Association.
First published 1968
Book Use: Review, bestseller lists
Frequency: Monthly
Circulation: 6,700
$7.50/issue membs, $9.50/issue nonmembs, $59.95/yr nonmembs, $49.95/yr membs
ISSN: 0006-7563

**Chief Marketer**
Published by Penton Media Inc
249 W 17 St, New York, NY 10011
*Tel:* 212-204-4200 *Toll Free Tel:* 866-505-7173 (cust serv)
*Web Site:* chiefmarketer.com
*Key Personnel*
Group Publr: Leslie Bacon *Tel:* 203-358-4145 *E-mail:* leslie.bacon@penton.com
Exec Ed: Brian Quinton *E-mail:* brian.quinton@pentonmedia.com
Mng Ed: Beth Negus Viveiros *E-mail:* beth.negus@penton.com
Sr Ed: Richard Levey *E-mail:* richard.levey@penton.com; Patty Odell *E-mail:* patty.odell@penton.com; Larry Riggs *E-mail:* larry.riggs@penton.com
Covers the best in measurable marketing & helps marketing leaders navigate today's fast changing marketing landscape. Areas of emphasis: PROMO, Direct, Mobile, E-mail, Web, Social, Database/CRM, Lead Generation, B-to-B & Search.
Frequency: 16 issues/yr
Avg pages per issue: 92
$10/issue, $88/yr
ISSN: 2150-0037

**The Bulletin of the Center for Children's Books**
Published by The Johns Hopkins University Press
2715 N Charles St, Baltimore, MD 21218-4363
SAN: 202-7348
*Tel:* 410-516-6987 (journals outside US & CN) *Toll Free Tel:* 800-548-1784 (journal orders) *Fax:* 410-516-6968
*E-mail:* jrnlcirc@press.jhu.edu (journal orders)
*Web Site:* bccb.lis.illinois.edu
*Subscription Address:* PO Box 19966, Baltimore, MD 21211-0966
*Key Personnel*
Ed: Deborah Stevenson
For teachers, librarians, parents & booksellers.
First published 1947
Book Use: Reviews of children's & young adult books for teachers, librarians, parents & booksellers
Frequency: 11 issues/yr
Avg pages per issue: 40
Circulation: 6,500
$20/yr students, $55/yr indivs, $95/yr instns (print or online)
ISSN: 0008-9036

**Christian Retailing**
Published by Charisma Media
600 Rinehart Rd, Lake Mary, FL 32746
*Tel:* 407-333-0600 *Fax:* 407-333-7133
*E-mail:* christian.retailing@charismamedia.com
*Web Site:* www.charismamedia.com
*Key Personnel*
Mng Ed: Christine D Johnson *E-mail:* chris.johnson@charismamedia.com
News Ed: Eric Tiansay *E-mail:* eric.tiansay@charismamedia.com
A trade publication for the Christian retail market including industry news, books, music, inspirational gift & other market news, new releases & marketing & industry trends. Includes one supplement: Inspirational Gift Mart.
First published 1955
Book Use: News & reviews of New Releases
Frequency: Monthly
Avg pages per issue: 60
Circulation: 12,000
$40/yr, free to qualified retailers
ISSN: 0892-0281

**The Chronicle of Higher Education**
1255 23 St NW, Suite 700, Washington, DC 20037
*Tel:* 202-466-1000 *Fax:* 202-452-1033
*E-mail:* editor@chronicle.com
*Web Site:* chronicle.com
*Key Personnel*
Ed: Liz McMillan *E-mail:* liz.mcmillan@chronicle.com
Books Ed: Nina Ayoub *Tel:* 202-466-1020 *E-mail:* nina.ayoub@chronicle.com
Weekly newspaper covering higher education, including scholarly & publishing news.
First published 1966
Book Use: Articles on books of interest to an academic audience & on academic aspects of the publishing industry. Lists new books on higher education & new scholarly books; short & medium length excerpts from books on academic & literary issues
Frequency: Weekly (except for 2 issues in Dec & 1 in Aug)
Avg pages per issue: 100
Circulation: 350,000
$5.52/month print, $4.97/month digital ed
ISSN: 0009-5982

**College & Research Libraries Journal**
Published by Association of College & Research Libraries (ACRL)
Division of The American Library Association
50 E Huron St, Chicago, IL 60611
*Tel:* 312-280-2516 *Toll Free Tel:* 800-545-2433 (ext 2516) *Fax:* 312-280-2520
*E-mail:* acrl@ala.org
*Web Site:* www.ala.org/acrl
*Key Personnel*
Ed-in-Chief: Joseph Branin *E-mail:* joseph.branin@kaust.edu.sa
Prodn Ed: Dawn Mueller
Theory & research relevant to academic & research librarians. Check web site for submission information.
First published 1939
Book Use: Reviews
Frequency: Bimonthly
Avg pages per issue: 100
Circulation: 14,000
$75/yr nonmembs, $80/yr CN, $85/yr foreign
ISSN: 0010-0870

**Columbia Journalism Review**
Published by Columbia Graduate School of Journalism
Affiliate of Columbia University
Journalism Bldg, 2950 Broadway, New York, NY 10027
*Tel:* 212-854-1881; 212-854-2716 (busn) *Toll Free Tel:* 888-425-7782 (US subns) *Fax:* 212-854-8367
*E-mail:* cjr@columbia.edu
*Web Site:* www.cjr.org
*Key Personnel*
Acting Publr: Dennis Giza
Exec Ed: Mike Hoyt
Mng Ed: Brent Cunningham
Assoc Ed & Copy Mgr: Tom O'Neill
Monitors & assesses the performance of journalism in all forms.
First published 1961
Frequency: Bimonthly
Circulation: 30,000
$4.95/issue, $19.95/yr, $41.95/2 yrs
ISSN: 0010-194X

**Connections**
Published by Printing Industries of New England
5 Crystal Pond Rd, Southborough, MA 01772-1758
*Tel:* 508-804-4170 *Toll Free Tel:* 800-365-7463 *Fax:* 508-804-4119
*Web Site:* www.pine.org
*Key Personnel*
Publr: Tad Parker
Members only trade magazine for printing & graphic communication companies in New England.
First published 1938
Frequency: Bimonthly
Avg pages per issue: 48
Circulation: 1,200
Free to membs; must be a memb of Printing Industries of New England
ISSN: 0162-8771
Trim Size: 8 1/2 x 11
Ad Closing Date(s): Tenth of the month preceding publication

**Editors' Association of Canada - Online Directory of Editors**
Published by Editors' Association of Canada (Association canadienne des reviseurs)
502-27 Carlton St, Toronto, ON M5B 1L2, Canada
*Tel:* 416-975-1379 *Toll Free Tel:* 866-CAN-EDIT (226-3348) *Fax:* 416-975-1637
*E-mail:* info@editors.ca
*Web Site:* www.editors.ca
*Key Personnel*
Exec Dir & Ed: Carolyn L Burke *E-mail:* carolyn.burke@editors.ca
Communs Mgr: Michelle Ou *E-mail:* michelle.ou@editors.ca
Prof Devt Mgr: Helena Aalto *E-mail:* helena.aalto@editors.ca
Membership Coord: Lianne Zwarenstein
Online directory of descriptive listings of current association members indexed by specialty.

**Educational Marketer**
Published by Simba Information
Division of Market Research Group
60 Long Ridge Rd, Suite 300, Stamford, CT 06902
SAN: 210-2021
*Tel:* 203-325-8193 *Toll Free Tel:* 888-297-4622 (cust serv) *Fax:* 203-325-8975
*E-mail:* customerservice@simbainformation.com
*Web Site:* www.simbainformation.com
*Key Personnel*
Mng Ed/Analyst: Kathy Mickey
Newsletter; reports on educational publishing field (el-hi & college): enrollments, demographics, funding, mergers & acquisitions, new product developments & personnel changes. For pub-

lishers, suppliers & dealers in the educational market.
First published 1968
Frequency: 24 issues/yr
Avg pages per issue: 8
$695/yr
ISSN: 1013-1806
Ad Rates: 4-color full page $1,650; 4-color 1/2 page 1,320; B&W full page $1,150; B&W 1/2 page $1,150
Ad Closing Date(s): 12 days before publication date

**Electronic Education Report**
Published by Simba Information
Division of Market Research Group
60 Long Ridge Rd, Suite 300, Stamford, CT 06902
SAN: 210-2021
*Tel:* 203-325-8193 *Toll Free Tel:* 888-297-4622 (cust serv) *Fax:* 203-325-8975
*E-mail:* customerservice@simbainformation.com
*Web Site:* www.simbainformation.com
*Key Personnel*
Ed: Karen Meaney
Published twice each month to provide industry decision-makers with the problem-solving information they need to make prudent business decisions in a rapidly evolving, multibillion dollar market. Technologies covered include hardware, software, multimedia/CD-ROM, integrated learning systems, video, distance learning, online services & educational videocassettes News coverage includes sales & distribution trends, company rankings & financial profiles, trademark & rights issues, strategic alliances & mergers, site licensing & networks, etc. Analyzes K-12. Readers are upper & middle management textbook & software publishers, software distributors, online service providers, video publishers & computer hardware manufacturers.
First published 1994
Frequency: 24 issues/yr
$650/yr PDF download
ISSN: 1077-9949
Trim Size: 8 1/2 x 11
Ad Rates: 4-color full page $1,320; 4-color 1/2 page $1,060; B&W full page $1,120; B&W 1/2 page $920

**Event**
Published by Douglas College
700 Royal Ave, New Westminster, BC V3M 5Z5, Canada
Mailing Address: PO Box 2503, New Westminster, BC V3L 5B2, Canada
*Tel:* 604-527-5293 *Fax:* 604-527-5095
*E-mail:* event@douglascollege.ca
*Web Site:* eventmags.com
*Key Personnel*
Ed: Elizabeth Bachinsky
Mng Ed: Ian Cockfield
Fiction Ed: Christine Dewar
Poetry Ed: Gillian Jerome
Reviews Ed: Susan Waserman
Literary journal. Occasionally publish unsol reviews but should query first. Publish mostly Canadian writers, but are open to anyone writing in English. Do not read mss in Jan, July, Aug & Dec. Buy fiction, poetry, creative nonfiction.
First published 1971
Frequency: 3 issues/yr
Avg pages per issue: 128
Circulation: 1,200
$11.95/issue, $39.95/yr US, $29.95/yr CN
ISSN: 0315-3770
Trim Size: 6 x 9
Ad Rates: Full page $200; 1/2 page $100
Ad Closing Date(s): March 15 (Summer), July 15 (Fall/Winter), Nov 15 (Spring)

**Facilities Media Group**
Published by Bedrock Communications Inc
152 Madison Ave, Suite 802, New York, NY 10016
*Tel:* 212-532-4150 *Fax:* 212-213-6382
*Web Site:* www.facilitiesonline.com
*Key Personnel*
Assoc Publr: Michael Caffin *Tel:* 212-532-4150 ext 103 *E-mail:* mcaffin@facilitiesonline.com
Edit Dir: Timothy Herrick *Tel:* 212-532-4150 ext 105
Monthly trade magazine chronicling the facility, event & convention marketplace.
First published 1991
Frequency: Monthly
Avg pages per issue: 48
Circulation: 30,303
$4.95/issue, $48/yr

**Folio: The Magazine for Magazine Management**
Published by Red 7 Media LLC
10 Norden Place, Norwalk, CT 06855
*Tel:* 203-854-6730 *Fax:* 203-854-6735
*E-mail:* folioedit@foliomag.com
*Web Site:* www.foliomag.com
*Key Personnel*
CEO & Pres: Kerry Smith *E-mail:* ksmith@red7media.com
Publr & Ed: Tony Silber *E-mail:* tsilber@foliomag.com
Group Creative Dir: Dan Trombetto
Ed: Bill Mickey
News & articles for the magazine publishing executive.
First published 1972
Book Use: Excerpts & condensations
Frequency: Monthly
Avg pages per issue: 60
Circulation: 8,500
$96/yr, $106/yr CN & Mexico, $116/yr elsewhere, $8/issue newsstand
ISSN: 0046-4333

**Forecast**
Published by Baker & Taylor Inc
2550 W Tyvola Rd, Suite 300, Charlotte, NC 28217
Mailing Address: PO Box 6885, Bridgewater, NJ 08807
*Tel:* 704-998-3100 *Toll Free Tel:* 800-775-1800 *Fax:* 704-998-3319
*E-mail:* btinfo@baker-taylor.com
*Web Site:* www.baker-taylor.com
*Key Personnel*
Prodn Coord: Donna Heffner *Tel:* 908-541-7412
Prepublication announcements for booksellers & librarians containing bibliographic data & descriptions of forthcoming adult hardcover future bestsellers, noteworthy midlist titles, university & independent press releases; includes spoken-word audio.
First published 1969
Frequency: Monthly
Avg pages per issue: 135
Circulation: 50,000
Free for those who qualify

**ForeWord Reviews**
Division of ForeWord Magazine Inc
425 Boardman Ave, Suite B, Traverse City, MI 49684
*Tel:* 231-933-3699 *Fax:* 231-933-3899
*E-mail:* sales@forewordreviews.com
*Web Site:* www.forewordreviews.com
*Key Personnel*
Publr: Victoria Sutherland *E-mail:* victoria@forewordreviews.com
Exec Ed: Howard Lovy *E-mail:* howard@forewordreviews.com
Mng Ed: Matt Sutherland *E-mail:* matt@forewordreviews.com
Ad Sales: Stacy Price *E-mail:* stacy@forewordreviews.com
Review journal of books from independent presses, university presses & self-publishers. Distributed to librarians & booksellers for collection development.
First published 1998
Frequency: Quarterly
Avg pages per issue: 64
Circulation: 15,000
$19.95/yr US, $39.95/yr CN, $59.95/yr foreign (print), $9.99/yr (online)
ISSN: 1099-2642
Trim Size: 8 1/2 x 11
Ad Rates: B&W full page $2,257, 1/2 page $1,349
Ad Closing Date(s): 3 weeks prior to issue date

**Gateway Journalism Review/St Louis Journalism Review**
Published by St Louis Journalism Review (SJR)
Communications Bldg, 1100 Lincoln Dr, Mail Code 6601, Carbondale, IL 62901
*Tel:* 618-536-3361
*E-mail:* gatewayjr@siu.edu
*Web Site:* gatewayjr.org
*Key Personnel*
Publr: William Freivogel
Media critic of press & broadcasting - particularly of St Louis region & the Midwest, but also nationally.
First published 1970
Book Use: Book review & excerpts
Frequency: Quarterly
Avg pages per issue: 36
Circulation: 1,250
$32/yr, $50/2 yrs
ISSN: 0036-2972
Trim Size: 8 1/2 x 11
Ad Closing Date(s): 20th of each month

**Geist**
Published by The Geist Foundation
201-111 W Hastings St, Vancouver, BC V6B 1H4, Canada
*Tel:* 604-681-9161 *Toll Free Tel:* 888-GEIST-EH (434-7834) *Fax:* 604-677-6319
*E-mail:* geist@geist.com
*Web Site:* www.geist.com
*Key Personnel*
Publr: Stephen Osborne
Sr Ed: Mary Schendlinger
Canadian ideas & culture with a strong literary focus & a sense of humor. Must have Canadian angle (content or author residency). No e-mail submissions.
First published 1990
Frequency: Quarterly
Avg pages per issue: 86
Circulation: 7,000
$37.95/6 issues US & foreign, $29.95/6 issues CN, $45.50/8 issues US & foreign, $37.50/8 issues CN, $57.99/12 issues US & foreign, $49.99/12 issues CN
ISSN: 1181-6554
Ad Rates: Full page $970; 2/3 page $735; 1/2 page $685; 1/3 page $425; 1/6 page $270; ad rates decrease with frequent advertisement

**Graphic Monthly**
Published by North Island Publishing Ltd
1606 Sedlescomb Dr, Suite 8, Mississauga, ON L4X 1M6, Canada
*Tel:* 905-625-7070 *Toll Free Tel:* 800-331-7408 (US only) *Fax:* 905-625-4856
*Web Site:* www.graphicmonthly.ca
*Key Personnel*
Ed: Filomena Tamburri *Tel:* 905-625-7070 ext 258 *E-mail:* ftamburri@graphicmonthly.ca
Publr: Alexander Donald *Tel:* 905-625-7070 ext 230 *E-mail:* s.donald@northisland.ca
Graphic, printing info.
First published 1980

Frequency: Bimonthly
Avg pages per issue: 60
Circulation: 10,500
Free to qualified Canadian businesses
ISSN: 0227-2806

**Guild of Book Workers Newsletter**
Published by Guild of Book Workers
521 Fifth Ave, 17th fl, New York, NY 10175-0038
*Tel:* 212-292-4444
*Web Site:* www.guildofbookworkers.org
*Key Personnel*
Pres: Mark Anderson *E-mail:* president@guildofbookworkers.org
Newsletter Ed: Cindy Haller *E-mail:* newsletter@guildofbookworkers.org
Secy: Catherine Burkhard *Tel:* 214-363-7946 *E-mail:* secretary@guildofbookworkers.org
Articles, calendar of activities related to the book arts.
Frequency: Bimonthly
Avg pages per issue: 15
Circulation: 900
$5/issue

**The Horn Book Guide**
Published by Horn Book Inc
56 Roland St, Suite 200, Boston, MA 02129
*Tel:* 617-628-0225 *Toll Free Tel:* 800-325-1170 *Fax:* 617-628-0882
*E-mail:* info@hbook.com
*Web Site:* www.hbook.com
*Subscription Address:* 7585 Industrial Pkwy, Plain City, OH 43064 *Tel:* 614-873-7954 *Fax:* 614-873-7135 *E-mail:* subscribe@hbook.com
*Key Personnel*
Publr: Ian Singer *Tel:* 917-886-0718 *E-mail:* isinger@mediasourceinc.com
VP, Mktg: Andrew Thorne *Tel:* 614-873-7956 *E-mail:* athorne@hbook.com
Dir, Content & Digital Prod Devt, Media Source: Guy LeCharles Gonzalez *E-mail:* glgonzalez@mediasourceinc.com
Circ Dir: James Marinaccio *Tel:* 614-733-0312 *E-mail:* jmarinaccio@mediasourceinc.com
Ed-in-Chief: Roger Sutton
Exec Ed: Kitty Flynn *E-mail:* kflynn@hbook.com
Prodn Mgr & Designer: Lolly Robinson *Tel:* 617-628-0225 ext 226 *E-mail:* lrobinson@hbook.com
Brief, critical reviews of nearly every hardcover trade children's & young adult book published in the United States.
First published 1990
Book Use: Subject, series, reissues, new editions, author/illustrator & title indexes
Frequency: Semiannual
Avg pages per issue: 288
Circulation: 2,600
$35/issue, $60/yr
ISSN: 1044-405X
Trim Size: 8 3/8 x 11 1/16
Ad Rates: Color covers 2 & 3 $1690/each; color cover 4 $1740; B&W full page $1690
Ad Closing Date(s): Feb 1 for Spring issue, Aug 1 for Fall issue

**Horn Book Magazine**
Published by Horn Book Inc
56 Roland St, Suite 200, Boston, MA 02129
*Tel:* 617-628-0225 *Toll Free Tel:* 800-325-1170 *Fax:* 617-628-0882
*E-mail:* info@hbook.com
*Web Site:* www.hbook.com
*Subscription Address:* 7585 Industrial Pkwy, Plain City, OH 43064 *Tel:* 614-873-7954 *Fax:* 614-873-7135 *E-mail:* subscribe@hbook.com
*Key Personnel*
Publr: Ian Singer *Tel:* 917-886-0718 *E-mail:* isinger@mediasourceinc.com
VP, Mktg: Andrew Thorne *Tel:* 614-873-7956 *E-mail:* athorne@hbook.com
Dir, Content & Digital Prod Devt, Media Source: Guy LeCharles Gonzalez *E-mail:* glgonzalez@mediasourceinc.com
Circ Dir: James Marinaccio *Tel:* 614-733-0312 *E-mail:* jmarinaccio@mediasourceinc.com
Ed-in-Chief: Roger Sutton
Exec Ed: Martha V Parravano *E-mail:* mvp@hbook.com
Sr Ed: Elissa Gershowitz *E-mail:* egershowitz@hbook.com
Prodn Mgr & Designer: Lolly Robinson *Tel:* 617-628-0225 ext 226 *E-mail:* lrobinson@hbook.com
Circ & Fulfillment Mgr: Molly Donavan *Tel:* 614-873-7951 *E-mail:* mdonavan@hbook.com
Children's literature journal featuring reviews, articles, essays, columns, interviews with children's book authors & illustrators, current announcements.
First published 1924
Book Use: Reviews & occasional excerpts
Frequency: Bimonthly
Avg pages per issue: 128
Circulation: 8,500
$72/yr
ISSN: 0018-5078
Trim Size: 6 x 9
Ad Rates: Color covers 2, 3 & 4 $2,577/each; full page interior $2,150
Ad Closing Date(s): 2 months before pub date

**Independent Publisher**
Published by Jenkins Group Inc
1129 Woodmere Ave, Suite B, Traverse City, MI 49686
*Tel:* 231-933-0445 *Toll Free Tel:* 800-706-4636 *Fax:* 231-933-0448
*Web Site:* www.independentpublisher.com
*Key Personnel*
CEO: Jerrold R Jenkins *Tel:* 231-933-0445 ext 1008 *E-mail:* jrj@bookpublishing.com
COO & Pres: James Kalajian *Tel:* 231-933-0445 ext 1006 *E-mail:* jjk@bookpublishing.com
Mng Ed, Independent Publisher Online: Jim Barnes *E-mail:* jimb@bookpublishing.com
Article topics relevant to the business of book publishing, including marketing, promotion & distribution. Available online since 2000.
First published 1983
Book Use: Featured reviews & individual reviews from independently published works of the current year
Frequency: Monthly
Avg pages per issue: 80
Circulation: 40,000
Free online; sent monthly via e-mail
ISSN: 1098-5735
Avg reviews per issue: 40

**Information Today**
Published by Information Today, Inc
143 Old Marlton Pike, Medford, NJ 08055-8750
*Tel:* 609-654-6266 *Toll Free Tel:* 800-300-9868 (cust serv) *Fax:* 609-654-4309
*E-mail:* custserv@infotoday.com
*Web Site:* www.infotoday.com/IT/default.asp
*Key Personnel*
Ed-in-Chief: Barbara Brynko *E-mail:* bbrynko@infotoday.com
Publr/Pres & CEO: Thomas H Hogan
For users & producers of digital information services.
First published 1983
Frequency: 10 issues/yr
Avg pages per issue: 40
Circulation: 10,000+
$96.95/yr, $183/2yrs, $280/3yrs US; $125/yr, $235/2 yrs, $360/3 yrs CN & Mexico; $140 yr, $265/2 yrs, $403/3 yrs foreign; agencies $2 less
ISSN: 8755-6286
Trim Size: 9.5 x 11.75
Ad Rates: see web site for complete details

**Inkwell**
Published by Manhattanville College
2900 Purchase St, Purchase, NY 10577
*Tel:* 914-323-7239 *Fax:* 914-323-3122
*E-mail:* inkwell@mville.edu
*Web Site:* www.inkwelljournal.org
*Key Personnel*
Ed-in-Chief: Tanya M Beltram
Staffed by faculty & graduate students of the writing program, we are dedicated to providing a forum for emerging writers & to publishing high quality poems & short stories in a literary journal that also features nonfiction, artwork, essays & interviews on writing by established figures & yearly competitions in poetry & fiction. For our submission guidelines, see our web site.
First published 1995
Frequency: Semiannual (Spring & Fall)
Avg pages per issue: 150
Circulation: 500
$10
ISSN: 1085-0287
Trim Size: 8 1/2 x 5 1/2

**InPrint**
Published by New Jersey Press Association
840 Bear Tavern Rd, Suite 305, West Trenton, NJ 08628-1019
*Tel:* 609-406-0600 *Fax:* 609-406-0300
*E-mail:* njpress@njpa.org
*Web Site:* www.njpa.org
*Key Personnel*
Communs Mgr: Catherine Langley *Tel:* 609-406-0600 ext 17 *E-mail:* clangley@njpa.org
News of the NJ newspaper industry.
First published 1990
Book Use: No columns or frequent articles about books, no book review
Frequency: 5 issues/yr
Avg pages per issue: 16
Circulation: 1,300
$12/yr
ISSN: 1067-5132

**International Journal of Instructional Media (IJIM)**
Published by Westwood Press Inc
Subsidiary of CAL Industries
118 Five Mile River Rd, Darien, CT 06820
*Tel:* 203-656-8680
*Web Site:* www.adprima.com/ijim.htm
*Key Personnel*
Exec Ed: Dr Phillip J Sleeman *Tel:* 860-875-5484 *E-mail:* plsleeman@aol.com
Assoc Ed: Linda B Sleeman
Media Reviews: Dr John G Flores
Articles about programs in computer technology; computer mediated; communications including the Internet; distance education, including the Internet, ITV, video & audio conferencing; instructional media & technology; telecommunications; interactive video, videodisc & software applications; instructional media management; instructional development & systems; media research & evaluation; media research & communications. Guidelines on the web site.
First published 1973
Book Use: Media reviews, book & technology forums
Frequency: Quarterly
Avg pages per issue: 130
Circulation: 1,325
$225/yr (plus $20 shipping), $225/yr CN & elsewhere (plus $40 shipping)
ISSN: 0092-1815

**Journal of International Marketing**
Published by American Marketing Association

Division of Health Services Marketing Division
311 S Wacker Dr, Suite 5800, Chicago, IL 60606
*Tel:* 312-542-9000 *Toll Free Tel:* 800-AMA-1150 (262-1150) *Fax:* 312-542-9001
*E-mail:* info@ama.org
*Web Site:* www.marketingpower.com
*Key Personnel*
CEO: Dennis Dunlap
Ad Sales Dir: Richard Ballschmiede *Tel:* 312-542-9076 *E-mail:* rballschmiede@ama.org
Mng Ed: Christopher Bartone *Tel:* 312-542-9000 ext 9029 *E-mail:* cbartone@ama.org
Tech Ed: Andy Seagram
Ed: David A Griffith
Timely insights from executives along with reports on new trends & tactics. Each issue also features analysis of the latest marketing theories, in-depth articles by practitioners & coverage of new methods.
Frequency: Quarterly
Avg pages per issue: 144
Circulation: 1,300
$55/yr AMA membs, $120/yr indivs US, $126.75/yr indivs CN, $150/yr indivs foreign, $235/yr instns US, print/online combo rates available. Visit www.marketingpower.com for more options
ISSN: 1069-031X

**Journal of Marketing**
Published by American Marketing Association
Division of Health Services Marketing Division
311 S Wacker Dr, Suite 5800, Chicago, IL 60606
*Tel:* 312-542-9000 *Toll Free Tel:* 800-AMA-1150 (262-1150) *Fax:* 312-542-9001
*E-mail:* info@ama.org
*Web Site:* www.marketingpower.com
*Key Personnel*
CEO: Dennis Dunlap
Ad Sales Dir: Richard Ballschmiede *Tel:* 312-542-9076 *E-mail:* rballschmiede@ama.org
Mng Ed: Christopher Bartone *Tel:* 312-542-9000 ext 9029 *E-mail:* cbartone@ama.org
Tech Ed: Andy Seagram
Ed: Gary L Frazier *Tel:* 213-740-5032 *E-mail:* frazier@marshall.usc.edu
Thought-provoking, in-depth articles covering vital aspects of the marketing industry. You'll find original research on all aspects of marketing & you'll appreciate how the journal bridges the gap between theory & application.
First published 1936
Book Use: Some reviews & excerpts
Frequency: 6 times/yr
Avg pages per issue: 144
Circulation: 8,200
$60/yr membs, $135/yr indivs, $375/yr corps & instns, online & print/online combo rates available. Visit www.marketingpower.com/publications for more information
ISSN: 0022-2429

**Journal of Marketing Research**
Published by American Marketing Association
Division of Health Services Marketing Division
311 S Wacker Dr, Suite 5800, Chicago, IL 60606
*Tel:* 312-542-9000 *Toll Free Tel:* 800-AMA-1150 (262-1150) *Fax:* 312-542-9001
*E-mail:* info@ama.org
*Web Site:* www.marketingpower.com
*Key Personnel*
CEO: Dennis Dunlap
Ad Sales Dir: Richard Ballschmiede *Tel:* 312-542-9076 *E-mail:* rballschmiede@ama.org
Mng Ed: Christopher Bartone *Tel:* 312-542-9000 ext 9029 *E-mail:* cbartone@ama.org
Ed: Tulin Erdem *Tel:* 212-998-0404 *E-mail:* terdem@stern.nyu.edu
For the latest thinking in marketing research. The journal covers a wide range of marketing-research concepts, methods & applications. You'll read about new techniques; contributions to knowledge based on experimental methods; & developments in related fields that have a bearing on marketing research.
First published 1963
Book Use: Some reviews
Frequency: 6 times/yr
Avg pages per issue: 128
Circulation: 4,400
$60/yr membs, $135/yr indivs US, $141.75/yr indivs CN, $180/yr indivs foreign, $375/yr instns US, $393.75/yr instns CN, $420/yr instns foreign; online & print/online combo rates available. Visit www.marketingpower.com/publications for more options
ISSN: 0022-2437

**Journal of Scholarly Publishing**
Published by University of Toronto Press Journals Division
Division of University of Toronto Press Inc
5201 Dufferin St, Toronto, ON M3H 5T8, Canada
*Tel:* 416-667-7810 *Toll Free Tel:* 800-221-9985 (CN) *Fax:* 416-667-7881
*E-mail:* journals@utpress.utoronto.ca
*Web Site:* www.utpjournals.com
*Key Personnel*
VP, Journals, Univ of Toronto Press: Anne Marie Corrigan *Tel:* 416-667-7777 ext 7838 *E-mail:* acorrigan@utpress.utoronto.ca
Ed: Tom Radko
Ad & Mktg Coord: Audrey Greenwood *Tel:* 416-667-7777 ext 7766 *E-mail:* agreenwood@utpress.utoronto.ca
Articles on the writing, publication & use of serious nonfiction addressed to scholars, authors, publishers, reviewers, editors & librarians.
First published 1969
Book Use: Reviews of books relating to publishing
Frequency: Quarterly
Avg pages per issue: 64
Circulation: 800
$130/yr instns, $45/yr indivs, $40/yr membs; online version $115 instns, $35 indivs, $30 membs
ISSN: 1198-9742
Trim Size: 6 x 9
Ad Rates: Full page $350; 1/2 page $250; inside back cover $370; outside back cover $420; frequency discount; 30% 4 consecutive insertions, 20% for 3 & 10% for 2 inserts

**Journalism & Mass Communication Quarterly**
Published by SAGE Publications
2455 Teller Rd, Thousand Oaks, CA 91320
*Toll Free Tel:* 800-818-7243 *Toll Free Fax:* 800-583-2665
*E-mail:* journals@sagepub.com
*Web Site:* www.sagepub.com
*Key Personnel*
Ed: Daniel Riffe
Research in journalism & mass communication.
First published 1924
Frequency: Quarterly
Avg pages per issue: 1,000
Circulation: 5,000
$155 indiv, $294 instl, $300 instl (print& electronic); single issue $50 indiv, $81 instl
ISSN: 1077-6990 (print); 2161-430X (online)

**The Kenyon Review**
Subsidiary of Kenyon College
Finn House, 102 W Wiggin St, Gambier, OH 43022
*Tel:* 740-427-5208 *Fax:* 740-427-5417
*E-mail:* kenyonreview@kenyon.edu
*Web Site:* www.kenyonreview.org
*Key Personnel*
Mng Ed: Tyler Meier *Tel:* 740-427-5202 *E-mail:* meiert@kenyon.edu
Ed: David Lynn
Fiction, poetry, essays, book reviews, drama. See web site for details.
First published 1939
Book Use: Reviews of 12 books
Frequency: 4 issues/yr
Avg pages per issue: 185
Circulation: 6,500
$3.99/issue, $30/yr, $50/2 yrs, $70/3yrs
ISSN: 0163-075X
Trim Size: 7 x 10
Ad Rates: Full page $375
Ad Closing Date(s): Oct 10, Jan 10, April 10, July 10

**Knowledge Quest**
Published by American Association of School Librarians
Division of American Library Association
50 E Huron St, Chicago, IL 60611
*Tel:* 312-944-6780 *Toll Free Tel:* 800-545-2433 *Fax:* 312-280-5276
*E-mail:* aasl@ala.org
*Web Site:* www.ala.org/aasl/kqweb
*Key Personnel*
Mng Ed, Knowledge Quest: Markisan Naso *Tel:* 312-944-6780 ext 1396
Devoted to offering substantive information to assist in building-level library media specialists, supervisors, library educators & other decision makers concerned with the development of school library media programs & services. Articles address the integration of theory & practice in school librarianship & new developments in education, learning theory & relevant disciplines.
First published 1997
Frequency: 5 issues/yr
Avg pages per issue: 56
Circulation: 10,000
$12/issue, $50/yr nonmembs US, $60/yr nonmembs foreign
ISSN: 1094-9046

**Library Journal**
Published by Media Source Inc
160 Varick St, 11th fl, New York, NY 10013
*Tel:* 646-380-0752 *Toll Free Tel:* 800-588-1030 *Fax:* 646-380-0756
*E-mail:* ljinfo@mediasourceinc.com
*Web Site:* www.lj.libraryjournal.com
*Subscription Address:* PO Box 5881, Harlan, IA 51593 *Tel:* 515-247-2984 (outside US) *E-mail:* ljcustserv@cds-global.com
*Key Personnel*
VP, Group Publr: Ian Singer *Tel:* 646-380-0747 *E-mail:* isinger@mediasourceinc.com
Dir, Content & Digital Prod Devt: Guy Le Charles Gonzalez
Mng Ed: Bette-Lee Fox *Tel:* 646-380-0717 *E-mail:* blfox@mediasourceinc.com
Reviews are written & edited specifically to assess the value of a book for the library collection. Also, review DVDs, audiobook CDs, magazines, databases & web sites.
First published 1876
Book Use: Reviews, news
Frequency: Semimonthly (exc monthly during Jan, July, Aug & Dec)
Avg pages per issue: 144
Circulation: 18,000
$157.99/yr US, $199.99/yr CN & Mexico, $259.99/yr foreign
ISSN: 0363-0277

**Library Media Connection: The Professional Magazine for School Library Media & Technology Specialists**
Published by Linworth Publishing
Imprint of Libraries Unlimited
PO Box 292114, Kettering, OH 45429
*Toll Free Tel:* 800-607-4410 *Fax:* 937-890-0221
*E-mail:* lmc@librarymediaconnection.com
*Web Site:* www.librarymediaconnection.com
*Key Personnel*
Pres & Publr: Marlene Woo-Lun

Mng Ed: Wendy Medvetz *E-mail:* wmedvetz@librarymediaconnection.com
Ed: Gail Dickinson
K-12 school librarians & educators. See web site for information regarding ad rates & ad closing dates.
First published 1982
Book Use: Reviews; articles written by school librarians
Frequency: 7 issues/school yr
Avg pages per issue: 96
Circulation: 17,000
$69/yr
ISSN: 0731-4388

**The Library Quarterly**
Published by The University of Chicago Press, Journals Div
University of Maryland, College of Information Studies, 4105 Hornbake Bldg, South Wing, College Park, MD 20742
*Tel:* 310-405-3267 *Fax:* 301-314-9145
*E-mail:* lq@press.uchicago.edu
*Web Site:* www.journals.uchicago.edu
*Subscription Address:* PO Box 37005, Chicago, IL 60637
*Key Personnel*
Ed: John Carlo Bertot; Paul Jaeger
Reviews Section Ed: Leah Kim Gannett
Library & information science & related subjects.
First published 1931
Book Use: Reviews
Frequency: Quarterly
Avg pages per issue: 128
Circulation: 1,018
$17/issue indiv, $54/issue instns, $49/yr indivs combined print & online, $177/yr instns combined print & online
ISSN: 0024-2519
Ad Rates: Full page $607

**Locus: The Magazine of the Science Fiction & Fantasy Field**
Published by Locus Science Fiction Foundation Inc
PO Box 13305, Oakland, CA 94661-0305
*Tel:* 510-339-9196; 510-339-9198 *Fax:* 510-339-9198
*E-mail:* locus@locusmag.com
*Web Site:* www.locusmag.com
*Key Personnel*
Ed-in-Chief: Liza Groen Trombi
Mng Ed: Kirsten Gong-Wong
Includes news, awards, interviews & annual analysis of the science fiction field, monthly best-seller list & a complete monthly listing of new publications. Primarily a trade magazine for science fiction professionals, booksellers & libraries.
First published 1968
Book Use: Reviews
Frequency: Monthly
Avg pages per issue: 88
Circulation: 7,000
$6.95/issue, $60/yr indivs, $64/yr libs
ISSN: 0047-4959
Trim Size: 8 3/8 x 10 7/8
Ad Rates: B&W full page $1,000

**Marketing Management Magazine**
Published by American Marketing Association
Division of Health Services Marketing Division
311 S Wacker Dr, Suite 5800, Chicago, IL 60606
*Tel:* 312-542-9000 *Toll Free Tel:* 800-AMA-1150 (262-1150) *Fax:* 312-542-9001
*E-mail:* info@ama.org
*Web Site:* www.marketingpower.com
*Key Personnel*
CEO: Dennis Dunlap
Ad Sales Dir: Richard Ballschmiede *Tel:* 312-542-9076 *E-mail:* rballschmiede@ama.org
Mng Ed: Christopher Bartone *Tel:* 312-543-9000 ext 9029 *E-mail:* cbartone@ama.org
Ed-in-Chief: Gordon Wyner *E-mail:* gwyner@comcast.net
Focuses on strategic issues that marketing managers face every day. Covers brand management, CRM, product innovation, ROI, marketing effectiveness & B2B – to help managers keep pace with this rapidly changing field.
Frequency: 6 times/yr
Avg pages per issue: 55
Circulation: 12,000
$60/yr membs, $105/yr indivs US, $110.25/yr indivs CN, $150/yr indivs foreign, $135/yr instns US. See www.marketingpower.com/publications for more options
ISSN: 1061-3846

**Marketing Research: A Magazine of Management & Applications**
Published by American Marketing Association
Division of Health Services Marketing Division
311 S Wacker Dr, Suite 5800, Chicago, IL 60606
*Tel:* 312-542-9000 *Toll Free Tel:* 800-AMA-1150 (262-1150) *Fax:* 312-542-9001
*E-mail:* info@ama.org
*Web Site:* www.marketingpower.com
*Key Personnel*
Ad Sales Dir: Richard Ballschmiede *Tel:* 312-542-9076 *E-mail:* rballschmiede@ama.org
Mng Ed, Magazines & E-newsletters: Mary M Flory *E-mail:* mflory@ama.org
Each issue offers thought-provoking analyses of the latest trends & methodologies in marketing research applications & management. Written in clear, concise language with a focus on practical application *Marketing Research clearly shows how marketing research strategies affect real-world businesses.*
First published 1989
Book Use: Book & software reviews in each issue
Frequency: Quarterly
Avg pages per issue: 45
Circulation: 4,300
$55/yr AMA membs, $100/yr indivs US, $135/yr corps & instns US. Visit www.marketingpower.com/publications for more options
ISSN: 1040-8460
Ad Rates: Contact Ad Sales Dir for more information

**The Masthead**
Published by Association of Opinion Journalists (AOJ)
3899 N Front St, Harrisburg, PA 17110
*Tel:* 717-703-3015 *Fax:* 717-703-3014
*E-mail:* ncew@pa-news.org
*Web Site:* www.ncew.org
*Key Personnel*
Mgr: Lisa Strohle
All aspects of the work of professional opinion writers in all media, from determining editorial policy to writing, design & production.
First published 1948
Book Use: Reviews (select)
Frequency: Quarterly
Avg pages per issue: 36
Free online
ISSN: 0025-5122

**Medical Reference Services Quarterly**
Published by Routledge/Taylor & Francis
Member of Taylor & Francis Group
325 Chestnut St, Suite 800, Philadelphia, PA 19106
*Toll Free Tel:* 800-354-1420 (press 4) *Fax:* 215-625-2940
*Web Site:* www.tandfonline.com
*Key Personnel*
Ed: M Sandra Wood
Working tool journal for medical & health sciences librarians. Regularly publishes practice-oriented articles relating to medical reference services with an emphasis on online search services.
First published 1982
Book Use: Reviews
Frequency: Quarterly
Avg pages per issue: 116
Indiv: print & online $135, online only $125; Inst: print & online $523, online only $458
ISSN: 0276-3869 (print); 1540-9597 (online)

**Mergers & Acquisitions**
Published by Source Media
One State Street Plaza, 27th fl, New York, NY 10004
*Tel:* 212-803-6051 *Toll Free Tel:* 888-807-8667
*E-mail:* custserv@sourcemedia.com
*Web Site:* www.themiddlemarket.com
*Key Personnel*
Ed-in-Chief: Mary Kathleen Flynn *Tel:* 212-803-8708 *E-mail:* marykathleen.flynn@sourcemedia.com
Professional journal; covers the latest trends & influences impacting the buying & selling of businesses. Articles cover how to make money, save money & avoid disaster in the constantly changing merger & acquisition environment.
First published 1965
Frequency: Monthly
Avg pages per issue: 56
Circulation: 16,900
$995/yr, free 2 week trial available
ISSN: 0026-0010

**MLQ (Modern Language Quarterly): A Journal of Literary History**
Published by Duke University Press
University of Washington, English Dept, Box 354330, Seattle, WA 98195-4430
*Tel:* 206-543-6827 *Fax:* 206-685-2673
*E-mail:* mlq@u.washington.edu
*Web Site:* www.mlq.washington.edu; www.dukeupress.edu
*Subscription Address:* Duke University Press, Box 90660, Durham, NC 27708-0660 *Tel:* 919-687-3653 *E-mail:* subscriptions@dukeupress.edu
*Key Personnel*
Academic Ed: Marshall Brown
Acqs Ed, Journals: Erich Staib *Tel:* 919-687-3664
Edit & Admin Mgr: Rob Dilworth
Asst Ed: Heather Arvidson
Scholarly articles on literary history.
First published 1940
Book Use: Reviews
Frequency: Quarterly
Avg pages per issue: 130
Circulation: 1,350
$259/yr instns (print only); $226/yr instns (electronic); $266/yr instns (print & electronic); $35/yr indivs; $18/yr students add $12 postage & 7% GST for CN; $16 postage for outside US & CN
ISSN: 0026-7929 (print); 1527-1943 (online)
Ad Rates: B&W full page $250; B&W 1/2 page $175

**Multichannel Merchant**
Published by Penton Media Inc
11 River Bend Dr S, Stamford, CT 06907-0234
Mailing Address: PO Box 4949, Stamford, CT 06907-0242
*Tel:* 203-358-9900 *Fax:* 203-358-5823
*Web Site:* www.multichannelmerchant.com
*Key Personnel*
Ed-in-Chief: Melissa Dowling *E-mail:* melissa.dowling@penton.com
Sr Writer: Tim Parry *E-mail:* tim.parry@penton.com; Jim Tierney *E-mail:* jim.tierney@penton.com

Monthly marketing magazine covering TV marketing, catalogs, e-commerce, operations, fulfillment, telemarketing & more.
Frequency: Monthly
Circulation: 35,000
$10/issue, $85/yr US & CN, $218/yr elsewhere
ISSN: 1554-8961

**Network**
Published by The International Women's Writing Guild (IWWG)
317 Madison Ave, Suite 1704, New York, NY 10017
*Tel:* 917-720-6959
*E-mail:* iwwgquestions@gmail.com
*Web Site:* www.iwwg.org
*Key Personnel*
Exec Dir: Cynthia Fritts Stillwell
*E-mail:* iwwgexecdir@gmail.com
Member News, Regional Clusters, Correspondence Corner, Letters to the Editor, Environmental, Special Offerings, Profile of Guild Member, several hundred opportunities for publication & submission in every issue.
First published 1978
Frequency: Quarterly
Avg pages per issue: 32
Circulation: 3,000

**New Millennium Writings**
PO Box 2463, Knoxville, TN 37901
*Tel:* 865-428-0389 *Fax:* 865-428-0389
*E-mail:* npf@nationalpress.org
*Web Site:* newmillenniumwritings.com
*Key Personnel*
Publr & Ed: Don Williams
*E-mail:* donwilliams7@charter.net
Contains fiction, poetry & creative nonfiction by both emerging & well known writers. Regularly features profiles, interviews & essay on famous writers. Also includes writing tips & commentary by the editor.
First published 1996

**Newspapers & Technology**
Published by Conley Magazines LLC
1623 Blake St, Suite 250, Denver, CO 80202-1053
*Tel:* 303-575-9595 *Fax:* 303-575-9555
*E-mail:* letters@newsandtech.com
*Web Site:* www.newsandtech.com
*Key Personnel*
Publr: Mary L Van Meter *E-mail:* vanmeternt@aol.com
Ed-in-Chief: Chuck Moozakis
*E-mail:* cmoozakis@newsandtech.com
Ed: Tara McMeekin *E-mail:* tmcmeekin@newsandtech.com
Monthly trade publication for newspaper publishers & department managers involved in applying & integrating technology. Written by industry experts who provide regular coverage of the following departments: prepress, press, postpress & new media.
First published 1988
Frequency: Monthly
Avg pages per issue: 32
Circulation: 20,000
Free to qualified personnel
ISSN: 1052-5572

**North Carolina Literary Review (NCLR)**
Published by East Carolina University & North Carolina Literary & Historical Association
East Carolina University, English Dept, ECU Mailstop 555 English, Greenville, NC 27858-4353
*Tel:* 252-328-1537 *Fax:* 252-328-4889
*E-mail:* ncluser@ecu.edu
*Web Site:* www.nclr.ecu.edu
*Key Personnel*
Ed: Margaret Bauer *E-mail:* bauerm@ecu.edu
Sr Assoc Ed: Lorraine Hale Robinson
*E-mail:* robinsonlo@ecu.edu
Articles, essays, interviews, fiction/poetry by & about North Carolina writers & literature, culture & history.
First published 1992
Book Use: Excerpts from forthcoming books; essay reviews only - 2 or more books treated thematically
Frequency: Annual
Avg pages per issue: 200
Circulation: 650 + bookstore sales
$15/issue, $25/2 yr subn, $25/yr instn, $50/issue foreign, $50/yr subn foreign
ISSN: 1063-0724
Ad Rates: Full page $250; 1/2 page $150; 1/4 page $100
Ad Closing Date(s): Feb 1

**Poetics Today**
Published by Duke University Press
905 W Main St, Suite 18B, Durham, NC 27701
SAN: 201-3436
Mailing Address: PO Box 90660, Durham, NC 27708-0660
*Tel:* 919-688-5134 *Toll Free Tel:* 888-651-0122
*Fax:* 919-688-2615 *Toll Free Fax:* 888-651-0124
*E-mail:* subscriptions@dukeupress.edu
*Web Site:* www.dukeupress.edu
*Key Personnel*
CFO: Norris Langley
Edit & Admin Mgr: Rob Dilworth
Mktg Mgr, Journals Div: Cason Lynley
*E-mail:* jrnl_mktg_mgr@dukeupress.edu
Academic Ed: Meir Sternberg
Assoc Ed: Robert J Griffin
Asst Ed: Orly Lubin
Academics Exhibits & Publicity Coord: Emma Boyer
Book Use: Book reviews
Frequency: Quarterly
Avg pages per issue: 200
Circulation: 800
$40/yr indiv, $20/yr students (with photocopy of ID) $280/yr instns print only, $261/electronic only, $299/yr instns print & electronic
ISSN: 0333-5372 (print); 1527-5507 (online)
Ad Rates: B&W full page $250, B&W 1/2 page $200

**Poetry**
Published by Poetry Foundation
444 N Michigan Ave, Suite 1850, Chicago, IL 60611-4034
*Tel:* 312-787-7070 *Fax:* 312-787-6650
*E-mail:* editors@poetrymagazine.org
*Web Site:* www.poetryfoundation.org/poetrymagazine
*Subscription Address:* PO Box 421141, Palm Coast, FL 32142-1141
*Key Personnel*
Ed: Christian Wiman
Poetry, essays & book reviews. Complete submission guidelines can be found on the web site.
First published 1912
Frequency: Monthly
Avg pages per issue: 90
Circulation: 30,000
US: $3.75/issue, $35/yr indivs, $38/yr instns; Foreign: $47/yr indivs, $50/yr instns
ISSN: 0032-2032
Trim Size: 5 1/2 x 9
Ad Rates: Full page $800, 1/2 page $500, 1/4 page $375
Ad Closing Date(s): 15th of the 3rd month before issue date

**Poets & Writers Magazine**
Published by Poets & Writers Inc
90 Broad St, Suite 2100, New York, NY 10004
*Tel:* 212-226-3586 *Fax:* 212-226-3963
*E-mail:* editor@pw.org
*Web Site:* www.pw.org
*Key Personnel*
Edit Dir: Mary Gannon
Ed: Kevin Larimer
News for & about the contemporary literary community in the US. Pertinent articles, grants & awards, publishing opportunities, essays, interviews with writers.
First published 1973
Book Use: First serial, excerpts, author interviews
Frequency: Bimonthly
Avg pages per issue: 132
Circulation: 60,000
$5.95/issue, $19.95/yr
ISSN: 0891-6136

**Print**
Published by F+W Media Inc
38 E 29 St, 4th fl, New York, NY 10016
*Tel:* 212-447-1400 *Fax:* 212-447-5231
*E-mail:* info@printmag.com
*Web Site:* www.printmag.com
*Subscription Address:* PO Box 420235, Palm Coast, FL 32142-0235 *Tel:* 386-246-3361
*Toll Free Tel:* 877-860-9145 *E-mail:* print@palmcoastd.com
*Key Personnel*
Ed-in-Chief: Sarah Whitman
Mng Ed: Judith Grover
Art Dir: Ronson Slagle
Sales Dir: Elayne Recupero *Tel:* 267-247-5874
*E-mail:* elayne.recupero@gmail.com
Graphic design & visual communication for the creators of this material.
First published 1940
Book Use: Reviews
Frequency: 6 issues/yr
Avg pages per issue: 160
Circulation: 50,000
$40/yr US, 55/yr CN, $81/yr foreign; $19.95/yr digital
ISSN: 0032-8510

**PRISM international**
Published by University of British Columbia
Creative Writing Program UBC, 1866 Main Mall, Buch E-462, Vancouver, BC V6T 1Z1, Canada
*Tel:* 778-822-2514 *Fax:* 778-822-3616
*E-mail:* prismcirculation@gmail.com
*Web Site:* www.prismmagazine.ca
*Key Personnel*
Exec Ed, Circ: Andrea Hoff
Exec Ed, Fin: Sierra Skye Gemma
First published 1959
Frequency: Quarterly
Avg pages per issue: 90
Circulation: 1,200
$13/issue at newsstand; indivs: $35/yr, $55/2 yrs
Trim Size: 6 x 9
Ad Rates: Full page interior $300 (1 issue), $900 (1 yr, 4 issues); 1/2 page interior $200 (1 issue), $600 (1 yr, 4 issues); 1/4 page interior $100 (1 issue), $300 (1 yr, 4 issues); preprinted inserts $50/100

**Professional Photographer**
Published by PPA Publications & Events Inc
229 Peachtree St NE, Suite 2200, Atlanta, GA 30303
*Tel:* 404-522-8600 *Toll Free Tel:* 800-786-6277
*Fax:* 404-614-6406
*Web Site:* www.ppa.com; www.ppmag.com
*Key Personnel*
Dir, Pubns: Cameron Bishopp *E-mail:* cbishop@ppa.com
Illustrated feature articles about photographers, business & photographic techniques & trends; for practicing professional photographers (portrait, wedding, commercial, illustration, freelance, industrial, biomedical & scientific).
First published 1907

Frequency: Monthly
Avg pages per issue: 80
Circulation: 31,000 paid
$19.95/yr (digital), $29.95/yr US (digital & print combo), $45.95/yr CN (digital & print combo), $35.95/yr CN (print)

**Publishers Weekly**
Published by PWxyz LLC
71 W 23 St, Suite 1608, New York, NY 10010
*Tel:* 212-377-5500 *Fax:* 212-377-2733
*Web Site:* www.publishersweekly.com
*Subscription Address:* PO Box 16957, North Hollywood, CA 91615-6957 *Tel:* 818-487-2069 *Toll Free Tel:* 800-278-2991 *Fax:* 818-487-4550 *E-mail:* pw@pubservice.com
*Key Personnel*
Pres: George Slowik, Jr *E-mail:* george@publishersweekly.com
Publr: Cevin Bryerman *Tel:* 212-377-5703 *E-mail:* cbryerman@publishersweekly.com
Art Dir: Clive Chiu *E-mail:* cchiu@publishersweekly.com
Edit Dir: Michael Coffey *E-mail:* mcoffey@publishersweekly.com; Jim Milliot *Tel:* 212-377-5705 *E-mail:* jmilliot@publishersweekly.com
Reviews Dir: Louisa A Ermelino *E-mail:* lermelino@publishersweekly.com
Mng Ed: Sonia Jaffe Robbins *E-mail:* srobbins@publishersweekly.com
Sr Ed: Mark Rotella *E-mail:* mrotella@publishersweekly.com
Sr News Ed: Rachel Deahl *E-mail:* rdeahl@publishersweekly.com; Calvin Reid *E-mail:* creid@publishersweekly.com
Sr Ed, Children's Books: Diane Roback *E-mail:* roback@publishersweekly.com
Sr Religion Ed: Lynn Garrett *E-mail:* lgarrett@publishersweekly.com
Sr Reviews Ed: Peter Cannon *E-mail:* pcannon@publishersweekly.com; Sarah F Gold *E-mail:* sgold@publishersweekly.com
Sr Ed, Digital: Jonathan Segura *E-mail:* jsegura@publishersweekly.com
Deputy Reviews Ed: Mike Harvkey
Features Ed: Andrew R Albanese *E-mail:* aalbanese@publishersweekly.com
Ed, PW Select & Audio: Adam Boretz *E-mail:* aboretz@publishersweekly.com
Poetry Ed & Dir, Digital Opers: Craig Teicher *E-mail:* cteicher@publishersweekly.com
Reviews Ed: Rose Fox *E-mail:* rfox@publishersweekly.com
Mktg Mgr: Bryan Kinney *E-mail:* bkinney@publishersweekly.com
News for the book trade.
First published 1872
Book Use: Reviews, excerpts, news, features & statistics
Frequency: Weekly (51 issues/yr)
Avg pages per issue: 112
Circulation: 25,302
$8/issue, $249.99/yr print US, $180/yr digital US
ISSN: 0000-0019 (print); 2150-4000 (digital)
Trim Size: 7 7/8 x 10 1/2

**Publishing Executive**
Published by North American Publishing Co (NAPCO)
1500 Spring Garden St, 12th fl, Philadelphia, PA 19130
*Tel:* 215-238-5300; 215-238-5338 (cust serv)
*E-mail:* magazinecs@napco.com
*Web Site:* www.pubexec.com
*Key Personnel*
Publr: Matt Steinmetz
Edit Dir: Lynn Rosen
Mng Ed: Jim Sturdivant
Contributing Ed: Brian Howard
For publishing executives in b-to-b, consumer, association & government magazine publishing...how-to articles on business management, manufacturing, production & workflow.
First published 1987
Frequency: bimonthly
Avg pages per issue: 60
Circulation: 14,000
Free qualified/controlled circulation
ISSN: 1048-3055

**Publishing Poynters**
Published by Para Publishing LLC
PO Box 8206-240, Santa Barbara, CA 93118-8206
SAN: 215-8981
*Tel:* 805-968-7277 *Toll Free Tel:* 800-727-2782 *Fax:* 805-968-1379
*E-mail:* info@parapublishing.com
*Web Site:* www.parapublishing.com
*Key Personnel*
Owner & Publr: Dan Poynter *E-mail:* danpoynter@parapublishing.com
Book & information marketing news & ideas.
First published 1986
Book Use: Review copies on book publishing accepted
Frequency: Bimonthly
Avg pages per issue: 20
Circulation: 21,000
$9.95/2 yrs, free e-mail
ISSN: 1530-5694

**Quill & Quire**
Published by St Joseph Media Inc
Division of Key Media
111 Queen St E, Suite 320, Toronto, ON M5C 1S2, Canada
*Tel:* 416-364-3333 *Fax:* 416-595-5415
*Web Site:* www.quillandquire.com
*Key Personnel*
Publr: Alison Jones *Tel:* 416-364-3333 ext 3119 *E-mail:* ajones@quillandquire.com
Ed: Stuart Woods *E-mail:* swoods@quillandquire.com
Articles & features on book selling, publishing & Canadian libraries for writers, booksellers, publishers & librarians. Includes section, *Books for Young People*, with news & reviews of children's books & authors; review section for books for adults.
First published 1935
Book Use: Reviews
Frequency: Monthly
Avg pages per issue: 56
Circulation: 7,000
$79.50/yr CN, $130/2 yrs CN, $125/yr outside CN
ISSN: 0033-6491

**Quill & Scroll**
Published by Quill and Scroll Society
Univ of Iowa, School of Journalism, 100 Adler Journalism Bldg, Rm E-346, Iowa City, IA 52242
*Tel:* 319-335-3457 *Fax:* 319-335-3989
*E-mail:* quill-scroll@uiowa.edu
*Web Site:* www.uiowa.edu/~quill-sc
*Key Personnel*
Exec Dir & Publr: Vanessa Shelton *E-mail:* vanessa-shelton@uiowa.edu
Circ Mgr: Judy M Hauge
Scholastic journalism publishing, editing, writing, design, legal, ethics, broadcast & multimedia production.
First published 1926
Frequency: Semiannual during school yr
Avg pages per issue: 24
Circulation: 9,300
$5/issue, $17/yr, $30/2 yrs
ISSN: 0033-6505

**Quill Magazine**
Published by The Society of Professional Journalists
Eugene S Pulliam National Journalism Ctr, 3909 N Meridian St, Indianapolis, IN 46208
*Tel:* 317-927-8000 *Fax:* 317-920-4789
*E-mail:* spj@spj.org
*Web Site:* www.spj.org/quill.asp; www.spj.org
*Key Personnel*
Ed: Scott Leadingham *Tel:* 317-927-8000 ext 211 *E-mail:* sleadingham@spj.com
Examines the issues, changes & trends that influence the journalism profession.
Book Use: Book reviews
Frequency: 6 issues/yr
Circulation: 10,500
$75/yr, free for membs
ISSN: 0033-6475

**Radio-TV Interview Report**
Published by Bradley Communications Corp
390 Reed Rd, Broomall, PA 19008
*Tel:* 484-477-4220 *Toll Free Tel:* 800-989-1400 (ext 408) *Fax:* 610-541-0281
*E-mail:* info@rtir.com
*Web Site:* www.rtir.com; www.rtironline.com
*Key Personnel*
Publr: Steve Harrison
Lists authors, experts, celebrities, entrepreneurs & others available for radio & TV appearances.
Frequency: Biweekly
Circulation: 4,000
Free to qualified personnel

**Reference & Research Book News**
Published by Book News Inc
5739 NE Sumner St, Portland, OR 97218
*Tel:* 503-281-9230 *Fax:* 503-287-4485
*E-mail:* booknews@booknews.com
*Web Site:* www.booknews.com
*Key Personnel*
Publr: Fred Gullette
Ed: Eithne O'Leyne *E-mail:* eithne@booknews.com
Assoc Ed: Corinna Andrews
Periodical (now incorporating *SciTech Book News*) reviewing approximately 18,000 new books per year. Book News licenses its database of book reviews & annotations to booksellers & database providers. Current syndication includes: *Books in Print*; Baker & Taylor; YBP; Majors; EBSCO; ProQuest; Gale; Powell's; as well as a variety of online bookstores.
Frequency: Bimonthy (Feb, April, June, Aug, Oct, Dec)
Circulation: 1,200
ISSN: 0887-3763

**Reference & User Services Quarterly (RUSQ)**
Published by Reference & User Services Association
Division of American Library Association
50 E Huron St, Chicago, IL 60611
SAN: 201-0062
*Tel:* 312-280-4395 *Toll Free Tel:* 800-545-2433 *Fax:* 312-280-5273
*E-mail:* rusa@ala.org
*Web Site:* www.ala.org/rusa
*Key Personnel*
Exec Dir: Susan Hornung
First published 1960
Frequency: Quarterly
Avg pages per issue: 100
Circulation: 3,825 paid
$25/issue, $65/yr US, $70/yr CN & Mexico, $75/yr foreign
ISSN: 1094-9054

**Reference Desk**
Published by International Encyclopedia Society
PO Box 519, Baldwin Place, NY 10505-0519
*Tel:* 914-962-3287

*Key Personnel*
Pres & Ed: George Thomas Kurian
*E-mail:* gtkurian@aol.com
Articles on reference book publishing; reviews; quarterly record of reference books; publisher profiles.
First published 1991
Book Use: Book reviews; Index of publications
Frequency: Quarterly
Avg pages per issue: 32
Circulation: 902
$29/yr
ISSN: 1055-4777
Trim Size: 8 1/2 x 11
Ad Rates: Full page $300; 1/2 page $175
Ad Closing Date(s): March 30, June 30, Sept 30, Dec 30

**Rosebud Magazine**
Published by Rosebud Inc
PO Box 459, Cambridge, WI 53523
*Tel:* 608-423-9780
*Web Site:* www.rsbd.net
*Key Personnel*
Publr & Mng Ed: Roderick Clark
*E-mail:* jrodclark@rsbd.net
Short story, poetry & nonfiction.
First published 1993
Book Use: Excerpts
Frequency: 3 issues/yr
Avg pages per issue: 136
Circulation: 6,000
$6.95/issue, $20/yr, $35/2yrs
ISSN: 1072-1681

**Sales & Marketing Management Magazine**
Published by Mach1 Business Media LLC
27020 Noble Rd, Excelsior, MN 55331
Mailing Address: PO Box 247, Excelsior, MN 55331-0247
*Tel:* 952-401-1283 *Fax:* 952-401-7899
*Web Site:* www.salesandmarketing.com
*Key Personnel*
Pres & Publr: Mike Murrell *Tel:* 952-401-1283
*E-mail:* mike@salesandmarketing.com
Ed-in-Chief: Paul Nolan *Tel:* 763-350-3411
*E-mail:* paul@salesandmarketing.com
Mktg Mgr: Kris Stokes *E-mail:* kris@salesandmarketing.com
Online magazine providing information on major marketing, sales & management trends.
First published 1918
Book Use: Reviews
Frequency: Updated 2-3 times a week
Avg pages per issue: 36
Circulation: 25,000 print
free
ISSN: 0163-7517
Ad Rates: 2-page spread: $13,995 (1x), $13,695 (3x), $13,265 (6x); full page: $8,995 (1x), $8,695 (3x), $8,265 (6x); half page $6,075 (1x), $5,765 (3x), $5,460 (6x)

**School Library Journal**
Published by Media Source Inc
160 Varick St, 11th fl, New York, NY 10013
*Tel:* 646-380-0752 *Toll Free Tel:* 800-588-1030 *Fax:* 646-380-0757
*Web Site:* www.slj.com; www.facebook.com/schoollibraryjournal; twitter.com/#!/sljournal
*Subscription Address:* PO Box 5881, Harlan, IA 51593 *Tel:* 515-247-2984 (outside US)
*Key Personnel*
VP, Group Publr: Ian Singer *Tel:* 646-380-0747
*E-mail:* isinger@mediasourceinc.com
Dir, Content & Digital Prod Devt: Guy Le Charles Gonzalez
Edit Dir, Lib Journals: Rebecca T Miller
Mng Ed: Phyllis Levy Mandell *Tel:* 646-380-0733
*E-mail:* pmandell@mediasourceinc.com
Articles about library service to children & young adults; reviews of new books & multimedia products for children & young adults by school & public librarians.
First published 1954
Book Use: Reviews
Frequency: 15 issues/yr
Avg pages per issue: 115
Circulation: 38,000
$11/issue newsstand, $136.99/yr US, $199.99/yr CN, $259.99/yr foreign
ISSN: 0362-8930

**School Selection Guide**
Published by Baker & Taylor Inc
2550 W Tyvola Rd, Suite 300, Charlotte, NC 28217
Mailing Address: PO Box 6885, Bridgewater, NJ 08807
*Tel:* 704-998-3100 *Toll Free Tel:* 800-775-1800 *Fax:* 704-998-3319
*E-mail:* btinfo@baker-taylor.com
*Web Site:* www.baker-taylor.com
*Key Personnel*
Prodn Coord: Donna Heffner *Tel:* 908-541-7412
Recommended & high-demand titles for school libraries; available in print & on the web page.
Book Use: Selection for recommendation
Frequency: 3 issues/yr
Avg pages per issue: 200
Circulation: 50,000
Free

**Science & Technology Libraries**
Published by Routledge/Taylor & Francis
Member of Taylor & Francis Group
325 Chestnut St, Suite 800, Philadelphia, PA 19106
*Toll Free Tel:* 800-354-1420 (press 4) *Fax:* 215-625-2940
*Web Site:* www.tandfonline.com
*Key Personnel*
Ed-in-Chief: Tony Stankus
Topics relevant to management, operations, collections, services & staffing of specialized libraries in science & technology fields. Also available online.
First published 1980
Book Use: Reviews
Frequency: Quarterly
Avg pages per issue: 105
Circulation: 343
Indiv: print & online or print only $140, online only $130; Inst: print & online $602, online only $527
ISSN: 0194-262X (print); 1541-1109 (online)

**Scroll Original Artist Magazine**
Published by Scroll Publications Inc
646 Saint Vrain Ave, Las Animas, CO 81054
*Tel:* 719-469-4847
*E-mail:* scrollpubl@outlook.com
*Web Site:* www.scrolloriginalartistmagazine.com; twitter.com/scrollpublinc
*Key Personnel*
Pres & Publr: Cherylann Gray
Original works by original people from all over the world.
First published 2000
Frequency: 6 issues/yr
Circulation: 3,700
$9.95/issue, $54.50/yr
Ad Rates: $3 per CR inch
Ad Closing Date(s): 15th of every month

**The Serials Librarian**
Published by Routledge/Taylor & Francis
Member of Taylor & Francis Group
325 Chestnut St, Suite 800, Philadelphia, PA 19106
*Toll Free Tel:* 800-354-1420 (press 4) *Fax:* 215-625-2940
*Web Site:* www.tandfonline.com
*Key Personnel*
Ed: Louise Cole; Andrew Shroyer
Serials librarianship in academic, public, medical, law & other special libraries.
First published 1976
Book Use: Reviews
Frequency: Quarterly
Avg pages per issue: 124
Circulation: 712
Indiv: print & online $270, online only $245; Inst: print & online $1,018, online only $891
ISSN: 0361-526X (print); 1541-1095 (online)

**The Small Press Book Review**
Division of Greenfield Press
PO Box 176, Southport, CT 06890-0176
*Tel:* 203-332-7629 *Fax:* 203-332-7629
*Key Personnel*
Publr & Ed: Henry Berry
*E-mail:* henryberryinct@gmail.com
Electronic publication with book reviews for online users. Not copywrited, so can be downloaded by anyone. Finished books only; no galleys. Books in all categories, including university press books. Reviews of selected books appear 2-4 months after submission.
First published 1985
Book Use: Book reviews
Frequency: Monthly
Circulation: Internet
Free to online users

**Small Press Review/Small Magazine Review**
Published by Dustbooks
PO Box 100, Paradise, CA 95967-0100
SAN: 204-1871
*Tel:* 530-877-6110 *Fax:* 530-877-0222
*E-mail:* publisher@dustbooks.com
*Web Site:* www.dustbooks.com
*Key Personnel*
Publr: Kathleen Glanville
Ed: Susan Fulton Raymond
Assoc Ed: Tim Fulton
Online reviews, editorial opinion, lists of new publishers.
First published 1966
Book Use: Online reviews of books & magazines published by small, independent presses
Frequency: Bimonthly
Avg pages per issue: 24
Circulation: 3,500
$36/yr
ISSN: 0037-7228

**sub-TERRAIN Magazine**
PO Box 3008, MPO, Vancouver, BC V6R 3X5, Canada
*Tel:* 604-876-8710 *Fax:* 604-879-2667
*E-mail:* subter@portal.ca
*Web Site:* www.subterrain.ca
*Key Personnel*
Contact: Brian Kaufman
Literary magazine with the motto "Strong Words for a Polite Nation".
First published 1988
Frequency: 3 issues/yr
Avg pages per issue: 68
Circulation: 4,000
$18/yr indiv CN & US, $25 indiv foreign; $18/yr inst CN & US
ISSN: 0840-7533
Trim Size: 8 1/2 x 11
Ad Rates: Color 1/2 page $575; B&W full page $700, 1/2 page $475; Color inside front/back cover $800, back cover $900
Ad Closing Date(s): Feb 13, May 30, Oct 15

**Subtext**
Published by Open Book Publishing Inc
90 Holmes Ave, Darien, CT 06820
Mailing Address: PO Box 2228, Darien, CT 06820

*Tel:* 203-316-8008 *Fax:* 203-975-8469
*E-mail:* odasan@aol.com
*Web Site:* www.subtext.net
*Key Personnel*
Founder & Publr: Stephanie Oda; Glenn Sanislo
News & analysis on the book publishing & selling business, domestic & international.
First published 1995
Frequency: Biweekly
Avg pages per issue: 8
$499/yr

**Wag's Revue**
2865 W Lyndale St, Suite 1, Chicago, IL 60647
*E-mail:* editors@wagsrevue.com
*Web Site:* www.wagsrevue.com
*Key Personnel*
Mng & Essays Ed: Sandra Allen *Tel:* 415-806-2698 *E-mail:* sandra@wagsrevue.com
Fiction Ed: William Litton *Tel:* 919-475-2497 *E-mail:* willylitt@wagsrevue.com
Poetry Ed: William Guzzardi *Tel:* 919-619-0673 *E-mail:* willguzzo@wagsrevue.com
Interface Developer: John Herr *E-mail:* john@wagsrevue.com
Online only literary quarterly of fiction, poetry, essays & interviews. Release full, carefully edited issues, presenting content on a book-like page with the Internet's freedoms, creating something entirely new. All issues can be read for free online or downloaded at our web site. Submissions accepted from Dec 1-April 1 & July 1-Oct 1. We ask for first serial rights only, all other rights are retained by the author; no paper submissions. Refer to www.wagsrevue.com/submit.php.
First published 2009
Frequency: Quarterly
Avg pages per issue: 140
Free

**The Wordsworth Circle**
Published by New York University, Dept of English
19 University Place, Rm 536, New York, NY 10003
*Tel:* 212-998-8812 *Fax:* 212-995-4019
*Web Site:* www.nyu.edu/gsas/dept/english/journal/wordsworth/
*Key Personnel*
Ed: Marilyn Gaull *E-mail:* mg49@nyu.edu
Peer-reviewed essays on all areas of British Romanticism.
First published 1970
Frequency: Quarterly
Avg pages per issue: 64
Circulation: 2,200
$25/yr, $40/2 yrs, $60/3 yrs
ISSN: 0043-8006

**World Literature Today**
Published by University of Oklahoma
660 Parrington Oval, Suite 110, Norman, OK 73019-4033
*Tel:* 405-325-4531 *Fax:* 405-325-7495
*Web Site:* www.ou.edu/worldlit
*Key Personnel*
Exec Dir & Newstadt Prof: Robert Con Davis-Undiano
Brings you the whole world in every issue-covering over sixty of the world's literatures. With interviews, new poetry & fiction, lively essays on writers & regional trends, authors on books that changed their lives, travel writing, a column on children's literature & international book reviews, there is no better window to what is happening in world literature & culture.
First published 1927
Frequency: Bimonthly
Avg pages per issue: 80
Circulation: 6,600
$4.95/issue, $25/yr indiv, $50/yr CN & elsewhere, $125/yr instn, $150/yr instn CN & elsewhere

**The Writer**
Published by Madavor Media
85 Quincy Ave, Suite 2, Quincy, MA 02169
*Tel:* 617-706-9076 *Toll Free Tel:* 800-437-5828 (cust serv) *Fax:* 617-706-9110 (cust serv)
*Web Site:* www.writermag.com
*Key Personnel*
Publr: Susan Fitzgerald *E-mail:* sfitzgerald@madavor.com
Busn Opers: Courtney Carter *Fax:* 617-536-0102
Instructional articles on fiction, nonfiction & freelance writing, plus markets for ms sales. See guidelines on web site. Accept unsol mss.
First published 1887
Book Use: Regular book-review section
Frequency: Monthly
Avg pages per issue: 60
Circulation: 30,000
$6.95/issue, $32.95/yr US, $42.95/yr CN, $44.95/yr elsewhere
ISSN: 0043-9517

**Writer's Digest Magazine**
Published by F+W Media Inc
10151 Carver Rd, Suite 200, Blue Ash, OH 45242
*Tel:* 513-531-2690 *Fax:* 513-891-7153
*E-mail:* writersdigest@fwmedia.com
*Web Site:* www.writersdigest.com
*Subscription Address:* PO Box 421365, Palm Coast, FL 32142-7104
*Key Personnel*
Ed: Jessica Strawser *E-mail:* jessica.strawser@fwmedia.com
A publication focused on the craft & business of writing. Visit www.writersdigest.com/submissionguidelines for updated submission guidelines. No phone queries or snail mail.
First published 1920
Book Use: Reviews, excerpts, profiles of authors, tips & techniques
Frequency: 8 issues/yr
Avg pages per issue: 92
Circulation: 100,000
$19.96/yr US, $29.96/yr CN, $31.96/yr foreign
ISSN: 0043-9525
Trim Size: 7 3/4 x 10 3/4

# ASI Publications ..........................

## ···· Now Available for Your Favorite Ebook Reader

*Marketing Your Indexing Services, 3rd Edition*—Significantly revised and expanded, the third edition of ASI's best-selling guide to marketing for indexers includes nine new chapters covering an array of practical techniques and strategies. The book covers marketing in the new world of social media, offering critical advice for beginning indexers and start-up firms along with a wealth of ideas and tips for established professionals. This essential addition to any freelancer's library includes advice on these topics and more:

- Marketing action plans
- Résumé strategies and samples
- Self-promotion
- Marketing by word of mouth
- Websites
- Social network

**ASI member price $23.99** **Nonmember price $29.00**

*Starting an Indexing Business, 4th Edition*—This significantly revised edition of the must-have reference for new and aspiring freelance indexers includes advice on these topics and more:

- Setting up an indexing business
- How indexers learn their trade and stay up-to-date
- Finding clients and setting fees
- Packagers: Who are they and what do they do?
- Indexing while holding a full-time job
- Liability issues

The book also includes a sample Letter Agreement setting out terms between an indexer and author, a mini-salary survey with insight into the earnings potential in the field, and a handy business start-up checklist.

**ASI member price $20** **Nonmember price $25.00**

***Indexing for Editors and Authors: A Practical Guide to Understanding Indexes***—At last, an indexing guide for editors, authors, and designers who need to create, edit, format, or evaluate indexes and work with professional indexers. Three experienced indexer-authors explain the various types of indexes, the characteristics of good indexes, and common formatting considerations. They share dozens of practical tips and more than 100 examples of good and bad indexing practices. Publishing professionals will not only learn how to edit an index, but how to hire freelance indexers and maintain successful editor/author/indexer relationships. While geared to the needs of publishing professionals who are not indexers, the book will serve indexers as a guide to navigating the publishing process and explaining indexing processes to their clients.

**ASI member price $26.50** **Nonmember price $33.25**

143 Old Marlton Pike • Medford, NJ 08055

Phone: (800) 300-9868 or (609) 654-6266
Fax: (609) 654-4309
Email: custserv@infotoday.com
Order Online: infotoday.com

# Company Index

Included in this index are the names, addresses, telecommunication numbers and electronic addresses of the organizations included in this volume of *LMP*. Entries also include the page number(s) on which the listings appear.

Sections not represented in this index are **Imprints, Subsidiaries & Distributors; Calendar of Book Trade & Promotional Events; Reference Books for the Trade** and **Magazines for the Trade.**


A Better Be Write Publishing LLC, 9001 Ridge Hill St, Kernersville, NC 27284 *Tel:* 336-354-7173 *Fax:* 336-993-2497 *Web Site:* www.abetterbewrite.com, pg 1

A Cappela Publishing, PO Box 3691, Sarasota, FL 34230-3691 *Tel:* 941-351-2050 *Fax:* 941-351-4735 *E-mail:* acappub@aol.com *Web Site:* www.acappela.com, pg 1

A K Peters Ltd, 5 Commonwealth Rd, Suite 2-C, Natick, MA 01760-1526 *E-mail:* editorial@akpeters.com *Web Site:* www.akpeters.com, pg 1

A+ English LLC/Book-Editing.com, PO Box 1372, Mansfield, TX 76063 *Tel:* 469-789-3030 *E-mail:* editingnetwork@gmail.com *Web Site:* www.editing-writing.com; www.book-editing.com; www.HelpWithStatistics; www.medical-writing-editing.com; www.apawriting.com, pg 539

A-R Editions Inc, 8551 Research Way, Suite 180, Middleton, WI 53562 *Tel:* 608-836-9000 *Toll Free Tel:* 800-736-0070 (US book orders only) *Fax:* 608-831-8200 *E-mail:* info@areditions.com *Web Site:* www.areditions.com, pg 1

A Westport Wordsmith, 101 Winfield St, Norwalk, CT 06855 *Tel:* 203-354-7309 *E-mail:* pj104daily@aol.com, pg 539

AAA Books Unlimited, 88 Greenbriar E Dr, Deerfield, IL 60015 *Tel:* 847-444-1220 *Fax:* 847-607-8335 *Web Site:* www.aaabooksunlimited.com, pg 559

AAA Photos, 401 Ocean Dr, Unit 804, Miami Beach, FL 33139 *Tel:* 305-534-0804 *Web Site:* www.photosphotos.net, pg 539

AAAI Press, 2275 E Bayshore Rd, Suite 160, Palo Alto, CA 94303 *Tel:* 650-328-3123 *Fax:* 650-321-4457 *E-mail:* press12@aaai.org *Web Site:* www.aaaipress.org; www.aaai.org, pg 1

AACC International, 3340 Pilot Knob Rd, St Paul, MN 55121 *Tel:* 651-454-7250 *Fax:* 651-454-0766 *E-mail:* aacc@scisoc.org *Web Site:* www.aaccnet.org, pg 2

AAH Graphics Inc, 9293 Fort Valley Rd, Fort Valley, VA 22652-2020 *Tel:* 540-933-6211 *Fax:* 540-933-6523 *E-mail:* srh@aahgraphics.com *Web Site:* www.aahgraphics.com, pg 539

The Aaland Agency, PO Box 849, Inyokern, CA 93527-0849 *Tel:* 760-384-3910 *Web Site:* www.the-aaland-agency.com, pg 559

AAPG (American Association of Petroleum Geologists), 1444 S Boulder Ave, Tulsa, OK 74119 *Tel:* 918-584-2555 *Toll Free Tel:* 800-364-AAPG (364-2274) *Fax:* 918-580-2665 *Toll Free Fax:* 800-898-2274 *E-mail:* publications@aapg.org *Web Site:* www.aapg.org, pg 2

Aaron-Spear, PO Box 42, Harborside, ME 04617 *Tel:* 207-326-8764, pg 539

AAUP Book, Jacket & Journal Design Show, 28 W 36 St, Suite 602, New York, NY 10018 *Tel:* 212-989-1010 *Fax:* 212-989-0275 *E-mail:* info@aaupnet.org *Web Site:* www.aaupnet.org, pg 685

ABAC/ALAC, 368 Dalhousie St, Suite 301, Ottawa, ON K1N 7G3, Canada *Tel:* 416-364-2376 *E-mail:* info@abac.org *Web Site:* www.abac.org, pg 611

Abacus, 3413 Roger B Chaffee SE, Suite 101, Grand Rapids, MI 49546 *Tel:* 616-241-3404 *Fax:* 616-698-0325 *E-mail:* info@abacuspub.com *Web Site:* www.abacuspub.com, pg 2

Abaris Books, 70 New Canaan Ave, Norwalk, CT 06850 *Tel:* 203-838-8402 *Fax:* 203-857-0730 *E-mail:* abaris@abarisbooks.com *Web Site:* abarisbooks.com, pg 2

Abbeville Press, 137 Varick St, Suite 504, New York, NY 10013-1105 *Tel:* 212-366-5585 *Toll Free Tel:* 800-ARTBOOK (278-2665) *Fax:* 212-366-6966 *E-mail:* abbeville@abbeville.com *Web Site:* www.abbeville.com, pg 2

Abbeville Publishing Group, 137 Varick St, Suite 504, New York, NY 10013 *Tel:* 212-366-5585 *Toll Free Tel:* 800-ART-BOOK (278-2665) *Fax:* 212-366-6966 *E-mail:* abbeville@abbeville.com; marketing@abbeville.com; sales@abbeville.com; rights@abbeville.com *Web Site:* www.abbeville.com, pg 2

ABC-CLIO, 130 Cremona Dr, Santa Barbara, CA 93117 *Tel:* 805-968-1911 *Toll Free Tel:* 800-368-6868 *Fax:* 805-685-9685 *Toll Free Fax:* 866-270-3856 *E-mail:* sales@abc-clio.com; customerservice@abc-clio.com *Web Site:* www.abc-clio.com, pg 2

ABDO Publishing Group, 8000 W 78 St, Suite 310, Edina, MN 55439 *Tel:* 952-831-2120 (ext 223) *Toll Free Tel:* 800-800-1312 *Toll Free Fax:* 800-862-3480 *E-mail:* info@abdopublishing.com *Web Site:* www.abdopub.com, pg 2

Dominick Abel Literary Agency Inc, 146 W 82 St, Suite 1-A, New York, NY 10024 *Tel:* 212-877-0710 *Fax:* 212-595-3133, pg 559

Aberdeen Bay, 9301 Maple St, Manassas, VA 20110 *Tel:* 703-473-1392 *E-mail:* editor@aberdeenbay.com *Web Site:* www.aberdeenbay.com, pg 2

Abingdon Press, 201 Eighth Ave S, Nashville, TN 37203-3919 *Toll Free Tel:* 800-251-3320 *Toll Free Fax:* 800-836-7802 (orders) *E-mail:* orders@abingdonpress.com *Web Site:* www.abingdonpress.com, pg 3

About Books Inc, 1001 Taurus Dr, Colorado Springs, CO 80906 *Tel:* 719-632-8226 *Fax:* 719-213-2602 *Web Site:* www.about-books.com, pg 539

Abrams Artists Agency, 275 Seventh Ave, 26th fl, New York, NY 10001 *Tel:* 646-486-4600 *Fax:* 646-486-2358 *E-mail:* literary@abramsartny.com *Web Site:* www.abramsartists.com, pg 559

Harry N Abrams Inc, 115 W 18 St, 6th fl, New York, NY 10011 *Tel:* 212-206-7715 *Toll Free Tel:* 800-345-1359 *Fax:* 212-519-1210 *E-mail:* abrams@abramsbooks.com *Web Site:* www.abramsbooks.com, pg 3

Abrams Learning Trends, 16310 Bratton Lane, Suite 250, Austin, TX 78728-2403 *Toll Free Tel:* 800-227-9120 *Toll Free Fax:* 800-737-3322 *E-mail:* customerservice@abramslearningtrends.com (orders, cust serv) *Web Site:* www.abramslearningtrends.com (orders, cust serv), pg 3

Absey & Co Inc, 23011 Northcrest Dr, Spring, TX 77389 *Tel:* 281-257-2340 *Toll Free Tel:* 888-41-ABSEY (412-2739) *Fax:* 281-251-4676 *E-mail:* info@absey.biz *Web Site:* www.absey.biz, pg 3

ABZ First Book Poetry Prize, PO Box 2746, Huntington, WV 25727-2746 *Tel:* 304-638-5701 *Web Site:* abzpress.sharepoint.com, pg 685

Acacia House Publishing Services Ltd, 51 Chestnut Ave, Brantford, ON N3T 4C3, Canada *Tel:* 519-752-0978 *Fax:* 519-752-8349, pg 559

Academic Press, 525 "B" St, Suite 1800, San Diego, CA 92101 *Tel:* 619-231-6616 *Toll Free Tel:* 800-321-5068 (cust serv) *Fax:* 619-699-6715 *E-mail:* firstinitial.lastname@elsevier.com *Web Site:* www.elsevier.com, pg 3

Academica Press LLC, PO Box 60728, Cambridge Sta, Palo Alto, CA 94306 *Tel:* 650-329-0685 *Fax:* 650-329-0685 *E-mail:* academicapress@aol.com *Web Site:* www.academicapress.com, pg 3

Academy Chicago Publishers, 363 W Erie St, Suite 4-W, Chicago, IL 60654 *Tel:* 312-751-7300 *Toll Free Tel:* 800-248-READ (248-7323) *Fax:* 312-751-7306 *E-mail:* info@academychicago.com *Web Site:* www.academychicago.com, pg 4

The Academy of American Poets Inc, 75 Maiden Lane, Suite 901, New York, NY 10038 *Tel:* 212-274-0343 *Fax:* 212-274-9427 *E-mail:* academy@poets.org *Web Site:* www.poets.org, pg 611

Academy of Motion Picture Arts & Sciences (AMPAS), 8949 Wilshire Blvd, Beverly Hills, CA 90211 *Tel:* 310-247-3000 *Fax:* 310-859-9619 *E-mail:* ampas@oscars.org *Web Site:* www.oscars.org, pg 611

Academy of Nutrition & Dietetics, 120 S Riverside Plaza, Suite 2000, Chicago, IL 60606-6995 *Tel:* 312-899-0040 *Toll Free Tel:* 800-877-1600 *Fax:* 312-899-4757 *E-mail:* sales@eatright.org *Web Site:* www.eatright.org, pg 4

Academy of Television Arts & Sciences (ATAS), 5220 Lankershim Blvd, North Hollywood, CA 91601-3109 *Tel:* 818-754-2800 *Fax:* 818-761-2827 *Web Site:* www.emmys.tv, pg 611

Acanthus Publishing, 343 Commercial St, Unit 214, Boston, MA 02109 *Tel:* 617-230-2167 *Fax:* 215-243-7495 *E-mail:* info@acanthuspublishing.com *Web Site:* www.acanthuspublishing.com, pg 4

Accent Publications, 4050 Lee Vance View, Colorado Springs, CO 80918 *Tel:* 719-536-0100 *Toll Free Tel:* 800-708-5550; 800-535-2905 (cust serv); 800-323-7543 (main); 800-426-6596 (sales) *Fax:* 719-535-2928 *Toll Free Fax:* 800-430-0726 *Web Site:* www.davidcook.com, pg 4

Access Copyright, The Canadian Copyright Licensing Agency, One Yonge St, Suite 800, Toronto, ON M5E 1E5, Canada *Tel:* 416-868-1620 *Toll Free Tel:* 800-893-5777 *Fax:* 416-868-1621 *E-mail:* info@accesscopyright.ca *Web Site:* www.accesscopyright.ca, pg 611

Access Editorial Services, 1133 Broadway, Suite 528, New York, NY 10010 *Tel:* 212-255-7306 *Fax:* 212-255-7306 *E-mail:* wiseword@juno.com, pg 539

Acclaim Film Script Competition, 300 Central Ave, Suite 501, St Petersburg, FL 33701 *Web Site:* acclaimscripts.com, pg 685

Acclaim TV Script Competition, 300 Central Ave, Suite 501, St Petersburg, FL 33701 *Web Site:* acclaimscripts.com, pg 685

Accuity, a SourceMedia Co, 4709 W Golf Rd, Suite 600, Skokie, IL 60076-1253 *Tel:* 847-676-9600 *Toll Free Tel:* 800-321-3373 *Fax:* 847-933-8101 *E-mail:* custserv@accuitysolutions.com; support@accuitysolutions.com; sales@accuitysolutions.com; general@accuitysolutions.com *Web Site:* www.accuitysolutions.com, pg 4

Accurate Writing & More, 16 Barstow Lane, Hadley, MA 01035 *Tel:* 413-586-2388 *E-mail:* shel@principledprofit.com *Web Site:* frugalmarketing.com; www.accuratewriting.com; www.grassrootsmarketingforauthors.com; www.greenandprofitable.com; www.frugalfun.com; www.twitter.com/shelhorowitz, pg 539

Alice B Acheson's Workshops for Writers, Illustrators & Photographers, PO Box 735, Friday Harbor, WA 98250 *Tel:* 360-378-2815 *E-mail:* aliceba@aol.com, pg 667

Milton Acorn Poetry Award, 115 Richmond St, Charlottetown, PE C1A 1H7, Canada *Tel:* 902-368-4410 *Toll Free Tel:* 888-734-2784 *Fax:* 902-368-4418 *E-mail:* peiwritersguild@gmail.com *Web Site:* www.peiwritersguild.com, pg 685

Acres USA, 4031 Guadalupe St, Austin, TX 78751 *Tel:* 512-892-4400 *Toll Free Tel:* 800-355-5313 *Fax:* 512-892-4448 *E-mail:* orders@acresusa.com; editor@acresusa.com *Web Site:* www.acresusa.com, pg 4

ACTA Press, 2509 Dieppe Ave SW, Bldg B-6, Suite 101, Calgary, AB T3E 7J9, Canada *Tel:* 403-288-1195 *Fax:* 403-247-6851 *E-mail:* journals@actapress.com; sales@actapress.com; calgary@iasted.org *Web Site:* www.actapress.com, pg 493

ACTA Publications, 4848 N Clark St, Chicago, IL 60640 *Tel:* 773-271-1030 *Toll Free Tel:* 800-397-2282 *Fax:* 773-271-7399 *Toll Free Fax:* 800-397-0079 *E-mail:* info@actapublications.com *Web Site:* www.actapublications.com, pg 4

ACU Press, 1626 Campus Ct, Abilene, TX 79601 *Tel:* 325-674-2720 *Toll Free Tel:* 877-816-4455 *Fax:* 325-674-6471 *Web Site:* www.acupressbooks.com; www.leafwoodpublishers.com, pg 4

Adam Hill Publications, 2699 Stirling Rd, Suite B-301, Fort Lauderdale, FL 33312 *Tel:* 954-680-7639 *E-mail:* books@adamhilldesign.com *Web Site:* www.adamhilldesign.com, pg 4

Adams & Ambrose Publishing, PO Box 259684, Madison, WI 53725-9684 *Tel:* 608-257-5700 *Fax:* 608-257-5700 *E-mail:* info@adamsambrose.com, pg 4

Adams-Blake Publishing, 8041 Sierra St, Suite 102, Fair Oaks, CA 95628 *Tel:* 916-962-9296 *E-mail:* info@adams-blake.com *Web Site:* www.adams-blake.com, pg 5

Herbert Baxter Adams Prize, 400 "A" St SE, Washington, DC 20003-3889 *Tel:* 202-544-2422 *Fax:* 202-544-8307 *E-mail:* awards@historians.org *Web Site:* www.historians.org, pg 685

Adams Media, 57 Littlefield St, Avon, MA 02322 *Tel:* 508-427-7100 *Fax:* 508-427-6790 *Toll Free Fax:* 800-872-5627 *E-mail:* orders@adamsmedia.com *Web Site:* www.adamsmedia.com, pg 5

Adams-Pomeroy Press, 103 N Jackson St, Albany, WI 53502 *Tel:* 608-862-3645 *Toll Free Tel:* 877-862-3645 *Fax:* 608-862-3647 *E-mail:* adamspomeroy@tds.net, pg 527

ADASI Publishing Co, 6 Dover Point Rd, Suite B, Dover, NH 03820-4698 *Tel:* 603-866-9426 *E-mail:* info@adasi.com *Web Site:* www.adasi.com, pg 5

ADD Warehouse, 300 NW 70 Ave, Suite 102, Plantation, FL 33317 *Tel:* 954-792-8100 *Toll Free Tel:* 800-233-9273 *Fax:* 954-792-8545 *E-mail:* websales@addwarehouse.com *Web Site:* addwarehouse.com, pg 5

Jane Addams Children's Book Award, 777 United Nations Plaza, 6th fl, New York, NY 10017 *Tel:* 212-682-8830 *Fax:* 212-286-8211 *E-mail:* japa@igc.org *Web Site:* www.janeaddamspeace.org, pg 685

Addicus Books Inc, PO Box 45327, Omaha, NE 68145 *Tel:* 402-330-7493 *Toll Free Tel:* 800-352-2873 (orders) *Fax:* 402-330-1707 *E-mail:* info@addicusbooks.com; addicusbks@aol.com *Web Site:* www.addicusbooks.com, pg 5

J Adel Art & Design, 586 Ramapo Rd, Teaneck, NJ 07666 *Tel:* 201-836-2606 *E-mail:* jadelnj@aol.com, pg 539

Adirondack Mountain Club, 814 Goggins Rd, Lake George, NY 12845-4117 *Tel:* 518-668-4447 *Toll Free Tel:* 800-395-8080 *Fax:* 518-668-3746 *E-mail:* adkinfo@adk.org *Web Site:* www.adk.org, pg 5

Adler Publishing Inc, PO Box 2948, Parker, CO 80134 *Toll Free Tel:* 800-660-5107 (sales & orders) *Fax:* 303-688-4388 *E-mail:* mail@adlerpublishing.com *Web Site:* 4wdbooks.com, pg 5

Advance Publishing Inc, 6950 Fulton St, Houston, TX 77022 *Tel:* 713-695-0600 *Toll Free Tel:* 800-917-9630 *Fax:* 713-695-8585 *E-mail:* info@advancepublishing.com *Web Site:* www.advancepublishing.com, pg 5

Adventure House, 914 Laredo Rd, Silver Spring, MD 20901 *Tel:* 301-754-1589 *Web Site:* www.adventurehouse.com, pg 5

Adventure Publications, 820 Cleveland St, Cambridge, MN 55008 *Tel:* 763-689-9800 *Toll Free Tel:* 800-678-7006 *Fax:* 763-689-9039 *Toll Free Fax:* 877-374-9016 *E-mail:* custservice@adventurepublications.net *Web Site:* www.adventurepublications.net, pg 5

Adventures Unlimited Press, One Adventure Place, Kempton, IL 60946 *Tel:* 815-253-6390 *Fax:* 815-253-6300 *E-mail:* auphq@frontiernet.net; info@adventuresunlimitedpress.com *Web Site:* www.adventuresunlimitedpress.com, pg 5

Advertising Research Foundation (ARF), 432 Park Ave S, 6th fl, New York, NY 10016-8013 *Tel:* 212-751-5656 *Fax:* 212-319-5265 *E-mail:* info@thearf.org; jar@thearf.org (edit) *Web Site:* www.thearf.org; www.journalofadvertisingresearch.com, pg 611

Aegean Park Press, PO Box 2120, Walnut Creek, CA 94595 *Tel:* 925-947-2533 *Toll Free Tel:* 800-736-3587 (orders only) *E-mail:* aegeanparkpress@earthlink.net *Web Site:* www.aegeanparkpress.com, pg 6

Aegean Publishing Co, PO Box 6790, Santa Barbara, CA 93160 *Tel:* 805-964-6669 *Fax:* 805-683-4798 *E-mail:* info@aegeanpublishing.com *Web Site:* aegeanpublishing.com, pg 6

AEI (Atchity Entertainment International Inc), 9601 Wilshire Blvd, Unit 1202, Beverly Hills, CA 90210 *Tel:* 323-932-0407 *Fax:* 323-932-0321 *E-mail:* submissions@aeionline.com *Web Site:* www.aeionline.com, pg 560

The AEI Press, 1150 17 St NW, Washington, DC 20036 *Tel:* 202-862-5800 *Fax:* 202-862-7177 *Web Site:* www.aei.org, pg 6

AEIOU Inc, 894 Piermont Ave, Piermont, NY 10968 *Tel:* 845-680-5380 *Fax:* 845-680-5380, pg 539

Aerial Photography Services Inc, 2511 S Tryon St, Charlotte, NC 28203 *Tel:* 704-333-5143 *Fax:* 704-333-4911 *E-mail:* aps@aps-1.com *Web Site:* www.aps-1.com, pg 6

AFCP's Annual Awards, 7445 Morgan Rd, Suite 103, Liverpool, NY 13090 *Toll Free Tel:* 877-203-2327 *Fax:* 781-459-7770 *E-mail:* afcp@afcp.org *Web Site:* www.afcp.org, pg 685

Africa World Press Inc, 541 W Ingham Ave, Suite B, Trenton, NJ 08638 *Tel:* 609-695-3200 *Fax:* 609-695-6466 *E-mail:* customerservice@africaworldpressbooks.com *Web Site:* www.africaworldpressbooks.com, pg 6

African American Images, PO Box 1799, Chicago Heights, IL 60412 *Tel:* 708-672-4909 (cust serv) *Toll Free Tel:* 800-552-1991 (orders) *Fax:* 708-672-0466 *E-mail:* customer@africanamericanimages.com *Web Site:* www.africanamericanimages.com, pg 6

Africana Homestead Legacy Publishers Inc, 811 Church Rd, Suite 105, Cherry Hill, NJ 08002 *Tel:* 856-773-0694 *Toll Free Tel:* 866-250-8477 *Fax:* 856-486-1135 *Toll Free Fax:* 866-289-8681 *E-mail:* customer-service@ahlpub.com; sales@ahlpub.com (ordering info); editors@ahlpub.com (edit inquiries); public-relations@ahlpub.com *Web Site:* www.ahlpub.com, pg 6

AFS Wordstead, 1062 Vallee-a-Josaphat, Lac-des-Iles, QC J0W 1J0, Canada *Tel:* 819-597-4072 *Fax:* 819-597-4547 *Web Site:* www.wordstead.com, pg 539

Agatha Awards, PO Box 8007, Gaithersburg, MD 20898-8007 *E-mail:* malicedomesticpr@gmail.com *Web Site:* www.malicedomestic.org, pg 685

Ageless Press, 3759 Collins St, Sarasota, FL 34232 *Tel:* 941-365-1367 *Fax:* 941-365-1367 *E-mail:* irishope@comcast.net, pg 6

Agency Chicago, 332 S Michigan Ave, Suite 1032, No A600, Chicago, IL 60604 *E-mail:* ernsant@aol.com, pg 560

Agent's Ink, PO Box 4956, Fresno, CA 93744-4956 *Tel:* 559-438-1883 *Fax:* 559-438-8289 *Web Site:* agents-ink.com, pg 560

Aggiornamento Award, 205 W Monroe, Suite 314, Chicago, IL 60606-5061 *Tel:* 312-739-1776; 312-739-1776 *Toll Free Tel:* 855-739-1776 *Fax:* 312-739-1778; 312-739-1778 *E-mail:* cla2@cathla.org *Web Site:* www.cathla.org, pg 685

AHA Press, 155 N Wacker, Suite 400, Chicago, IL 60606 *Tel:* 312-893-6800 *Toll Free Tel:* 800-242-4890 *Toll Free Fax:* 866-516-5817 (orders) *Web Site:* www.healthforum.com, pg 6

The Ahearn Agency Inc, 2021 Pine St, New Orleans, LA 70118 *Tel:* 504-861-8395 *Fax:* 504-866-6434 *Web Site:* www.ahearnagency.com, pg 560

Ahsahta Press, Boise State University, Mail Stop 1525, 1910 University Dr, Boise, ID 83725-1525 *Tel:* 208-426-4373 *Fax:* 208-426-4373 *E-mail:* ahsahta@boisestate.edu *Web Site:* ahsahtapress.boisestate.edu, pg 6

AICPA Professional Publications, 220 Leigh Farm Rd, Durham, NC 27707 *Tel:* 919-402-4500 *Toll Free Tel:* 888-777-7077 *Fax:* 919-402-4505 *E-mail:* acquisitions@aicpa.org *Web Site:* www.aicpa.org, pg 6

AIGA 50 Books/50 Covers, 164 Fifth Ave, New York, NY 10010 *Tel:* 212-807-1990 *Fax:* 212-807-1799 *E-mail:* competitions@aiga.org *Web Site:* www.aiga.org, pg 685

AIGA, the professional association for design, 164 Fifth Ave, New York, NY 10010 *Tel:* 212-807-1990 *Fax:* 212-807-1799 *E-mail:* general@aiga.org *Web Site:* www.aiga.org, pg 611

AIMS Education Foundation, 1595 S Chestnut Ave, Fresno, CA 93702-4706 *Tel:* 559-255-4094 *Toll Free Tel:* 888-733-2467 *Fax:* 559-255-6396 *E-mail:* aimsed@aimsedu.org *Web Site:* www.aimsedu.org, pg 7

Aitken Alexander Associates LLC, 30 Vandam St, Suite 5A, New York, NY 10013 *Tel:* 212-929-4100 *Web Site:* www.aitkenalexander.co.uk, pg 560

AJL Judaica Bibliography Award, PO Box 1118, Teaneck, NJ 07666 *Tel:* 201-371-3255 *E-mail:* ajlibs@osu.edu *Web Site:* www.jewishlibraries.org, pg 686

AJL Judaica Reference Award, PO Box 1118, Teaneck, NJ 07666 *Tel:* 201-371-3255 *E-mail:* ajlibs@osu.edu *Web Site:* www.jewishlibraries.org, pg 686

AJL Scholarship, PO Box 1118, Teaneck, NJ 07666 *Web Site:* www.jewishlibraries.org, pg 686

AK Press Distribution, 674-A 23 St, Oakland, CA 94612 *Tel:* 510-208-1700 *Fax:* 510-208-1701 *E-mail:* info@akpress.org; sales@akpress.org; orders@akpress.org *Web Site:* www.akpress.org, pg 7

Akashic Books, 232 Third St, Suite A-115, Brooklyn, NY 11215 *Tel:* 718-643-9193 *Fax:* 718-643-9195 *E-mail:* info@akashicbooks.com *Web Site:* www.akashicbooks.com, pg 7

AKC Publications Fiction Contest, 260 Madison Ave, New York, NY 10016 *Web Site:* www.akc.org/pubs/fictioncontest, pg 686

Akin & Randolph Agency, Literary Div, One Gateway Ctr, Suite 2600, Newark, NJ 07102 *Tel:* 973-353-8409; 973-623-6834 *Fax:* 973-353-8417 *E-mail:* info@akinandrandolph.com *Web Site:* www.akinandrandolph.com, pg 560

Akron Poetry Prize, The University of Akron Press, 120 E Mill St, Suite 415, Akron, OH 44308 *Tel:* 330-972-6953 *Fax:* 330-972-8364 *E-mail:* uapress@uakron.edu *Web Site:* www.uakron.edu/uapress/akron-poetry-prize, pg 686

Alabama Artists Fellowship Awards, 201 Monroe St, Suite 110, Montgomery, AL 36130-1800 *Tel:* 334-242-4076 *Fax:* 334-240-3269, pg 686

Alaska Native Language Center, PO Box 757680, Fairbanks, AK 99775-7680 *Tel:* 907-474-7874 *Fax:* 907-474-6586 *E-mail:* fyanlp@uaf.edu (orders) *Web Site:* www.uaf.edu/anlc/, pg 7

Alban Publishing, 2121 Cooperative Way, Suite 100, Herndon, VA 20171 *Tel:* 703-964-2700 *Toll Free Tel:* 800-486-1318 *Fax:* 703-964-0370 *E-mail:* infocenter@alban.org *Web Site:* www.alban.org, pg 7

Albert Whitman & Co, 250 S Northwest Hwy, Suite 320, Park Ridge, IL 60068 *Tel:* 847-232-2800 *Toll Free Tel:* 800-255-7675 *Fax:* 847-581-0039 *E-mail:* mail@awhitmanco.com *Web Site:* www.albertwhitman.com, pg 7

Alberta Book Awards, 10523 100 Ave, Edmonton, AB T5J 0A8, Canada *Tel:* 780-424-5060 *Fax:* 780-424-7943 *E-mail:* info@bookpublishers.ab.ca *Web Site:* www.bookpublishers.ab.ca, pg 686

Rodelinde Albrecht, PO Box 444, Lenox Dale, MA 01242-0444 *Tel:* 413-243-4350 *Toll Free Tel:* 800-370-5040 *Fax:* 413-243-3066 *E-mail:* rodelinde@earthlink.net, pg 539

Alcuin Society, PO Box 3216, Vancouver, BC V6B 3X8, Canada *Tel:* 605-566-1502; 604-732-5403 *E-mail:* info@alcuinsociety.com *Web Site:* www.alcuinsociety.com, pg 611

Alcuin Society Awards in Excellence in Book Design in Canada, PO Box 3216, Vancouver, BC V6B 3X8, Canada *Tel:* 605-566-1502 *E-mail:* awards@alcuinsociety.com *Web Site:* www.alcuinsociety.com, pg 686

The Alexander Graham Bell Association for the Deaf & Hard of Hearing, 3417 Volta Place NW, Washington, DC 20007-2778 *Tel:* 202-337-5220 *Toll Free Tel:* 866-337-5220 (orders) *Fax:* 202-337-8314 *E-mail:* info@agbell.org; publications@agbell.org *Web Site:* www.agbell.org, pg 7

Alexander Street Press LLC, 3212 Duke St, Alexandria, VA 22314 *Tel:* 703-212-8520 *Toll Free Tel:* 800-889-5937 *Fax:* 703-940-6584 *E-mail:* sales@alexanderstreet.com; marketing@alexanderstreet.com *Web Site:* www.alexanderstreet.com, pg 7

Alfred Publishing Company Inc, PO Box 10003, Van Nuys, CA 91410-0003 *Tel:* 818-891-5999 *Toll Free Tel:* 800-292-6122 (dealer sales) *Fax:* 818-892-9239; 818-893-5560 *Toll Free Fax:* 800-632-1928 (dealer sales) *E-mail:* customerservice@alfred.com; sales@alfred.com *Web Site:* www.alfred.com, pg 7

Algonquin Books of Chapel Hill, 400 Silver Cedar Ct, Suite 300, Chapel Hill, NC 27514-1585 *Tel:* 919-967-0108 *Fax:* 919-933-0272 *E-mail:* inquiry@algonquin.com *Web Site:* www.workman.com/algonquin, pg 8

Algora Publishing, 222 Riverside Dr, Suite 16-D, New York, NY 10025-6809 *Tel:* 212-678-0232 *Fax:* 212-666-3682 *E-mail:* editors@algora.com *Web Site:* www.algora.com, pg 8

Nelson Algren Awards, Chicago Tribune, TT200, 435 N Michigan Ave, Chicago, IL 60611 *Toll Free Tel:* 800-874-2863 *Fax:* 312-222-5816 *E-mail:* nelsonalgren@tribune.com *Web Site:* www.chicagotribune.com/about, pg 686

ALI-ABA Continuing Professional Education, 4025 Chestnut St, Philadelphia, PA 19104 *Tel:* 215-243-1600 *Toll Free Tel:* 800-CLE-NEWS (253-6397) *Fax:* 215-243-1664; 215-243-1683 *Web Site:* www.ali-aba.org, pg 8

The Aliant Creative Writing Award for Young People, 115 Richmond St, Charlottetown, PE C1A 1H7, Canada *Tel:* 902-368-4410 *Toll Free Tel:* 888-734-2784 *Fax:* 902-368-4418 *E-mail:* peiwritersguild@gmail.com *Web Site:* www.peiwritersguild.com, pg 686

Alice James Books, 238 Main St, Farmington, ME 04938 *Tel:* 207-778-7071 *Fax:* 207-778-7766 *E-mail:* info@alicejamesbooks.org *Web Site:* www.alicejamesbooks.org, pg 8

All About Kids Publishing, PO Box 159, Gilroy, CA 95020 *Tel:* 408-337-1866 *E-mail:* mail@aakp.com *Web Site:* www.aakp.com, pg 8

All Things That Matter Press, 79 Jones Rd, Somerville, ME 04348 *E-mail:* allthingsthatmatterpress@gmail.com *Web Site:* www.allthingsthatmatterpress.com, pg 8

Allen D Bragdon Publishers Inc, 252 Great Western Rd, South Yarmouth, MA 02664-2210 *Tel:* 508-398-4440 *Toll Free Tel:* 877-876-2787 *Fax:* 508-760-2397 *E-mail:* admin@brainwaves.com *Web Site:* www.brainwaves.com, pg 8

Linda Allen Literary Agency, 1949 Green St, Suite 5, San Francisco, CA 94123 *Tel:* 415-921-6437, pg 560

Thomas Allen Publishers, 390 Steelcase Rd E, Markham, ON L3R 1G2, Canada *Tel:* 905-475-9126 *Toll Free Tel:* 800-387-4333 (orders) *Fax:* 905-475-6747 *Toll Free Fax:* 800-458-5504 (orders) *E-mail:* info@t-allen.com *Web Site:* www.thomasallen.ca, pg 493

Alliance for Audited Media (AAM), 48 W Seegers Rd, Arlington Heights, IL 60005 *Tel:* 224-366-6939 *Fax:* 224-366-6949 *Web Site:* www.auditedmedia.com, pg 611

Alliance for Women in Media (AWM), 1760 Old Meadow Rd, Suite 500, McLean, VA 22102 *Tel:* 703-506-3290 *Fax:* 703-506-3266 *E-mail:* info@awrt.org *Web Site:* www.awrt.org, pg 611

Alligator Juniper's National Writing Contest, 220 Grove Ave, Prescott, AZ 86301 *Tel:* 928-350-2012 *E-mail:* alligatorjuniper@prescott.edu *Web Site:* www.prescott.edu/alligatorjuniper, pg 686

Allium Press of Chicago, 1530 Elgin Ave, Forest Park, IL 60130 *Tel:* 708-689-9323 *E-mail:* info@alliumpress.com *Web Site:* www.alliumpress.com, pg 8

Alloy Entertainment, 151 W 26 St, 11th fl, New York, NY 10001 *Tel:* 212-244-4307 *E-mail:* nycassistant@alloyentertainment.com *Web Site:* www.alloyentertainment.com, pg 9

Allworth Press, 307 W 36 St, 11th fl, New York, NY 10018 *Tel:* 212-643-6816 *E-mail:* crawford@allworth.com *Web Site:* www.allworth.com, pg 9

AllWrite Advertising & Publishing, 260 Peachtree St NW, Suite 2200, Atlanta, GA 30303 *Tel:* 678-691-9005 *Fax:* 530-689-6980 *E-mail:* questions@allwritepublishing.com; support@allwritepublishing.com (orders & returns) *Web Site:* www.allwritepublishing.com, pg 9

AllWrite Advertising & Publishing, 260 Peachtree St NW, Suite 2200, Atlanta, GA 30303 *Tel:* 678-691-9005 *Fax:* 530-689-6980 *E-mail:* questions@allwritepublishing.com *Web Site:* www.allwritepublishing.com, pg 539

Allyn & Bacon, 75 Arlington St, Suite 300, Boston, MA 02116 *Tel:* 617-848-6000 *Toll Free Tel:* 800-526-0485 *Fax:* 617-848-6016 *Web Site:* www.pearsonhighered.com, pg 9

Jeanette Almada, 3411 N Elaine Place, Unit 2, Chicago, IL 60657 *Tel:* 773-404-9350 *E-mail:* jmalmada@sbcglobal.net, pg 539

Alpha, 375 Hudson St, New York, NY 10014 *Tel:* 212-366-2000, pg 9

ALPHA Publications of America Inc, 1830 E Broadway, Suite 124, Tucson, AZ 85719 *Tel:* 520-795-7100 *Toll Free Tel:* 800-528-3494 *Toll Free Fax:* 800-770-4329 *E-mail:* alphapublications@aol.com *Web Site:* www.alphapublications.com, pg 9

Alpine Publications Inc, 38262 Linman Rd, Crawford, CO 81415 *Tel:* 970-921-5005 *Toll Free Tel:* 800-777-7257 *Fax:* 970-921-5081 *E-mail:* editorial@alpinepub.com; customerservice@alpinepub.com *Web Site:* www.alpinepub.com, pg 9

ALSC BWI/Summer Reading Program Grant, 50 E Huron St, Chicago, IL 60611-2795 *Tel:* 312-280-2163 *Toll Free Tel:* 800-545-2433 *Fax:* 312-440-9374 *E-mail:* alsc@ala.org *Web Site:* www.ala.org/alsc, pg 686

AltaMira Press, 4501 Forbes Blvd, Suite 200, Lanham, MD 20706 *Tel:* 301-459-3366 *Toll Free Tel:* 800-462-6420 (cust serv) *Fax:* 301-429-5748 *E-mail:* custserv@rowman.com *Web Site:* www.altamirapress.com, pg 9

Althos Publishing, 1500 Piney Plains Rd, Suite 200, Carey, NC 27518 *Tel:* 919-557-2260 *Fax:* 919-557-2261 *E-mail:* info@althos.com *Web Site:* www.althosbooks.com, pg 9

The Althouse Press, Western University, 1137 Western Rd, London, ON N6G 1G7, Canada *Tel:* 519-661-2096 *Fax:* 519-661-3714 *E-mail:* press@uwo.ca *Web Site:* www.edu.uwo.ca/althousepress, pg 493

Miriam Altshuler Literary Agency, 53 Old Post Rd N, Red Hook, NY 12571 *Tel:* 845-758-9408 *Web Site:* www.miriamaltshulerliteraryagency.com, pg 560

AMACOM Books, 1601 Broadway, New York, NY 10019-7420 *Tel:* 212-586-8100; 518-891-5510 (orders) *Toll Free Tel:* 800-250-5308 (cust serv) *Fax:* 212-903-8083; 518-891-2372 (orders) *E-mail:* pubservice@amanet.org *Web Site:* www.amacombooks.org, pg 9

Amadeus Press/Hal Leonard Performing Arts Publishing Group, 33 Plymouth St, Suite 302, Montclair, NJ 07042 *Tel:* 973-337-5034 *Toll Free Tel:* 800-524-4425 *E-mail:* info@halleonardbooks.com *Web Site:* www.amadeuspress.com; www.halleonardbooks.com, pg 10

Frank Amato Publications Inc, 4040 SE Wister St, Portland, OR 97222 *Tel:* 503-653-8108 *Toll Free Tel:* 800-541-9498 *Fax:* 503-653-2766 *E-mail:* customerservice@amatobooks.com; info@amatobooks.com *Web Site:* www.amatobooks.com, pg 10

Amber Lotus Publishing, PO Box 11329, Portland, OR 97211 *Tel:* 503-284-6400 *Toll Free Tel:* 800-326-2375 (orders only) *Fax:* 503-284-6417 *E-mail:* info@amberlotus.com *Web Site:* www.amberlotus.com, pg 10

Amber Quill Press LLC, PO Box 265, Indian Hills, CO 80454 *E-mail:* business@amberquill.com *Web Site:* www.amberquill.com; www.amberheat.com (imprint); www.amberallure.com (imprint), pg 10

America West Publishers, PO Box 599, Hayden, ID 83835 *Tel:* 775-885-0700 *Toll Free Tel:* 800-729-4131 *Web Site:* www.nohoax.com, pg 10

American Academy of Arts & Sciences (AAAS), Norton's Woods, 136 Irving St, Cambridge, MA 02138-1996 *Tel:* 617-576-5000 *Fax:* 617-576-5050 *E-mail:* aaas@amacad.org *Web Site:* www.amacad.org, pg 612

American Academy of Environmental Engineers, 130 Holiday Ct, Suite 100, Annapolis, MD 21401 *Tel:* 410-266-3311 *Fax:* 410-266-7653 *E-mail:* info@aaee.net *Web Site:* www.aaee.net, pg 10

American Academy of Orthopaedic Surgeons, 6300 N River Rd, Rosemont, IL 60018-4262 *Tel:* 847-823-7186 *Toll Free Tel:* 800-346-2267 *Fax:* 847-823-8125 *Toll Free Fax:* 800-999-2939 *Web Site:* www.aaos.org, pg 10

American Academy of Pediatrics, 141 NW Point Blvd, Elk Grove Village, IL 60007-1098 *Tel:* 847-434-4000 *Toll Free Tel:* 888-227-1770 *Fax:* 847-434-8000 *E-mail:* pubs@aap.org *Web Site:* www.aap.org, pg 10

American Academy of Political & Social Science, 202 S 36 St, Philadelphia, PA 19104 *Tel:* 215-746-6500 *Fax:* 215-573-2667 *Web Site:* www.aapss.org, pg 612

The American Alpine Club Press, 710 Tenth St, Suite 100, Golden, CO 80401 *Tel:* 303-384-0110 *Fax:* 303-384-0111 *Web Site:* www.americanalpineclub.org, pg 10

American Anthropological Association (AAA), Publications Dept, Suite 600, 2200 Wilson Blvd, Arlington, VA 22201 *Tel:* 703-528-1902 *Fax:* 703-528-3546 *Web Site:* www.aaanet.org, pg 10

American Antiquarian Society (AAS), 185 Salisbury St, Worcester, MA 01609-1634 *Tel:* 508-755-5221 *Fax:* 508-753-3300 *Web Site:* www.americanantiquarian.org, pg 612

American Association for the Advancement of Science, 1200 New York Ave NW, Washington, DC 20005 *Tel:* 202-326-6400 *Fax:* 202-371-9526 *E-mail:* webmaster@aaas.org *Web Site:* www.aaas.org, pg 612

American Association for Vocational Instructional Materials, 220 Smithonia Rd, Winterville, GA 30683-9527 *Tel:* 706-742-5355 *Toll Free Tel:* 800-228-4689 *Fax:* 706-742-7005 *E-mail:* sales@aavim.com *Web Site:* www.aavim.com, pg 11

American Association of Blood Banks, 8101 Glenbrook Rd, Bethesda, MD 20814-2749 *Tel:* 301-907-6977 *Toll Free Tel:* 866-222-2498 (sales) *Fax:* 301-907-6895 *E-mail:* aabb@aabb.org; sales@aabb.org (ordering) *Web Site:* www.aabb.org, pg 11

American Association of Colleges for Teacher Education (AACTE), 1307 New York Ave NW, Suite 300, Washington, DC 20005-4701 *Tel:* 202-293-2450 *Fax:* 202-457-8095 *E-mail:* aacte@aacte.org *Web Site:* www.aacte.org, pg 11

American Association of Collegiate Registrars & Admissions Officers (AACRAO), One Dupont Circle NW, Suite 520, Washington, DC 20036-1135 *Tel:* 202-293-9161 *Fax:* 202-872-8857 *E-mail:* info@aacrao.org *Web Site:* www.aacrao.org, pg 11

American Association of University Women Award for Juvenile Literature, 4610 Mail Service Ctr, Raleigh, NC 27699-4610 *Tel:* 919-807-7290 *Fax:* 919-733-8807, pg 687

American Atheist Press, PO Box 158, Cranford, NJ 07016 *Tel:* 908-276-7300 *Fax:* 908-276-7402 *E-mail:* info@atheists.org *Web Site:* www.atheists.org, pg 11

American Auto Racing Writers & Broadcasters, 922 N Pass Ave, Burbank, CA 91505 *Tel:* 818-842-7005 *Fax:* 818-842-7020, pg 612

American Bar Association, 321 N Clark St, Chicago, IL 60654 *Tel:* 312-988-5000 *Toll Free Tel:* 800-285-2221 (orders) *Fax:* 312-988-6281 *E-mail:* orders@abanet.org *Web Site:* www.ababooks.org, pg 11

American Bible Society, 1865 Broadway, New York, NY 10023-7505 *Tel:* 212-408-1200 *Toll Free Tel:* 800-322-4253 *Fax:* 212-408-1512 *E-mail:* info@americanbible.org *Web Site:* www.americanbible.org, pg 11

American Biographical Institute, 5126 Bur Oak Circle, Raleigh, NC 27612 *Tel:* 919-781-8710 *Fax:* 919-781-8712 *E-mail:* abiinfo@abiworldwide.com *Web Site:* www.abiworldwide.com, pg 11

American Book Award, The Raymond House, Suite 302, 655 13 St, Oakland, CA 94612 *Tel:* 510-268-9775 *E-mail:* info@beforecolumbusfoundation.com *Web Site:* www.beforecolumbusfoundation.org, pg 687

American Book Producers Association (ABPA), 151 W 19 St, 3rd fl, New York, NY 10011 *Tel:* 212-675-1363 *Fax:* 212-675-1364 *E-mail:* office@abpaonline.org *Web Site:* www.abpaonline.org, pg 612

American Book Publishing, 14435-C Big Basin Way, No 155, Saratoga, CA 95070 *Tel:* 415-935-5082 *Toll Free Tel:* 800-684-8746 *E-mail:* info@american-book.com; orders@american-book.com *Web Site:* www.americanbookpublishing.com, pg 11

American Booksellers Association, 333 Westchester Ave, Suite S202, White Plains, NY 10604 *Tel:* 914-406-7500 *Toll Free Tel:* 800-637-0037 *Fax:* 914-410-6297 *E-mail:* info@bookweb.org *Web Site:* www.bookweb.org, pg 612

American Business Media, 675 Third Ave, 7th fl, New York, NY 10017-5704 *Tel:* 212-661-6360 *Fax:* 212-370-0736 *E-mail:* info@abmmail.com *Web Site:* www.americanbusinessmedia.com, pg 612

American Carriage House Publishing, PO Box 1130, Nevada City, CA 95959 *Tel:* 530-432-8860 *Toll Free Tel:* 866-986-2665 *Fax:* 530-432-7379 *E-mail:* editor@carriagehousepublishing.com *Web Site:* www.americancarriagehousepublishing.com, pg 11

American Catholic Press (ACP), 16565 S State St, South Holland, IL 60473 *Tel:* 708-331-5485 *Fax:* 708-331-5484 *E-mail:* acp@acpress.org *Web Site:* www.acpress.org, pg 11

The American Ceramic Society, 600 N Cleveland Ave, Suite 210, Westerville, OH 43082 *Tel:* 240-646-7054 *Toll Free Tel:* 866-721-3322 *Fax:* 614-794-5892 *E-mail:* customerservice@ceramics.org *Web Site:* www.ceramics.org, pg 12

The American Chemical Society, 1155 16 St NW, Washington, DC 20036 *Tel:* 202-872-4600 *Fax:* 202-872-6067 *E-mail:* help@acs.org *Web Site:* www.acs.org, pg 12

American Christian Writers Association, PO Box 110390, Nashville, TN 37222-0390 *Tel:* 615-331-8668 *Toll Free Tel:* 800-21-WRITE (219-7483) *Web Site:* www.acwriters.com, pg 612

American Civil Liberties Union, 125 Broad St, 18th fl, New York, NY 10004 *Tel:* 212-549-2500 *Toll Free Tel:* 800-775-ACLU (orders) *E-mail:* media@aclu.org *Web Site:* www.aclu.org, pg 612

American College, 270 S Bryn Mawr Ave, Bryn Mawr, PA 19010 *Tel:* 610-526-1000 *Toll Free Tel:* 888-263-7265 *Fax:* 610-526-1310 *Web Site:* www.theamericancollege.edu, pg 12

American College of Physician Executives, 400 N Ashley Dr, Suite 400, Tampa, FL 33602 *Tel:* 813-287-2000 *Toll Free Tel:* 800-562-8088 *Fax:* 813-287-8993 *E-mail:* acpe@acpe.org *Web Site:* www.acpe.org, pg 12

American College of Surgeons, 633 N Saint Clair St, Chicago, IL 60611-3211 *Tel:* 312-202-5000 *Fax:* 312-202-5001 *E-mail:* postmaster@facs.org *Web Site:* www.facs.org, pg 12

American Correctional Association, 206 N Washington St, Suite 200, Alexandria, VA 22314 *Tel:* 703-224-0000 *Toll Free Tel:* 800-222-5646 *Fax:* 703-224-0040 *Web Site:* www.aca.org, pg 12

American Council on Education, One Dupont Circle NW, Washington, DC 20036-1193 *Tel:* 202-939-9300; 301-632-6757 (orders) *Fax:* 202-939-9302 *E-mail:* pubs@acenet.edu *Web Site:* www.acenet.edu, pg 12

American Council on Education, One Dupont Circle NW, Washington, DC 20036-1193 *Tel:* 202-939-9300 *Fax:* 202-939-9302 *Web Site:* www.acenet.edu, pg 612

American Counseling Association, 5999 Stevenson Ave, Alexandria, VA 22304 *Tel:* 703-823-9800 (ext 222, book orders) *Toll Free Tel:* 800-422-2648 (ext 222, book orders); 800-347-6647 *Fax:* 703-823-0252 *Toll Free Fax:* 800-473-2329 *E-mail:* membership@counseling.org (book orders) *Web Site:* www.counseling.org, pg 12

American Diabetes Association, 1701 N Beauregard St, Alexandria, VA 22311 *Toll Free Tel:* 800-342-2383 *E-mail:* booksinfo@diabetes.org *Web Site:* www.diabetes.org, pg 12

American Federation of Arts, 305 E 47 St, 10th fl, New York, NY 10017 *Tel:* 212-988-7700 *Toll Free Tel:* 800-232-0270 *Fax:* 212-861-2487 *E-mail:* pubinfo@afaweb.org *Web Site:* www.afaweb.org, pg 12

American Federation of Astrologers Inc, 6535 S Rural Rd, Tempe, AZ 85283-3746 *Tel:* 480-838-1751 *Toll Free Tel:* 888-301-7630 *Fax:* 480-838-8293 *Web Site:* www.astrologers.com, pg 13

American Fisheries Society, 5410 Grosvenor Lane, Suite 110, Bethesda, MD 20814-2199 *Tel:* 301-897-8616; 703-661-1570 (book orders) *Fax:* 301-897-8096; 703-996-1010 (book orders) *E-mail:* main@fisheries.org *Web Site:* www.fisheries.org, pg 13

American Forest & Paper Association (AF&PA), 1111 19 St NW, Suite 800, Washington, DC 20036 *Tel:* 202-463-2700 *Toll Free Tel:* 800-878-8878 *E-mail:* info@afandpa.org *Web Site:* www.afandpa.org, pg 612

American Foundation for the Blind (AFB Press), 2 Penn Plaza, Suite 1102, New York, NY 10001 *Tel:* 212-502-7600; 412-741-1398 (orders) *Toll Free Tel:* 800-232-3044 (orders) *Fax:* 917-210-3979; 412-741-0609 (orders) *Toll Free Fax:* 888-545-8331 *E-mail:* press@afb.net; afborder@afb.net (orders); afbinfo@afb.net *Web Site:* www.afb.org, pg 13

American Geological Institute (AGI), 4220 King St, Alexandria, VA 22302-1502 *Tel:* 703-379-2480 *Fax:* 703-379-7563 *E-mail:* pubs@agiweb.org *Web Site:* www.agiweb.org, pg 13

American Geophysical Union (AGU), 2000 Florida Ave NW, Washington, DC 20009-1277 *Tel:* 202-462-6900 *Toll Free Tel:* 800-966-2481 (North America) *Fax:* 202-328-0566 *E-mail:* service@agu.org *Web Site:* www.agu.org, pg 13

American Girl Publishing, 8400 Fairway Place, Middleton, WI 53562 *Tel:* 608-836-4848; 608-360-1861 (US & CN); 608-831-5210 (outside US & CN) *Toll Free Tel:* 800-233-0264; 800-360-1861 *Fax:* 608-836-1999 *Web Site:* www.americangirl.com, pg 13

American Historical Association, 400 "A" St SE, Washington, DC 20003-3889 *Tel:* 202-544-2422 *Fax:* 202-544-8307 *E-mail:* aha@historians.org; awards@historians.org *Web Site:* www.historians.org, pg 13

American Illustration/American Photography, 15 E 32 St, 7th fl, New York, NY 10016 *Tel:* 212-470-0302 *Fax:* 212-532-2064 *E-mail:* info@ai-ap.com *Web Site:* www.ai-ap.com, pg 687

American Independent Writers (AIW), 7817 Evening Lane, Alexandria, VA 22306 *Tel:* 703-660-9336 *Fax:* 703-660-9321 *E-mail:* info@amerindywriters.org *Web Site:* www.amerindywriters.org, pg 612

American Industrial Hygiene Association - AIHA, 3141 Fairview Park Dr, Suite 777, Falls Church, VA 22042 *Tel:* 703-849-8888 *Fax:* 703-207-3561 *E-mail:* infonet@aiha.org *Web Site:* www.aiha.org, pg 13

American Institute for Economic Research (AIER), 250 Division St, Great Barrington, MA 01230 *Tel:* 413-528-1216 *Toll Free Tel:* 888-528-0103; 888-528-1216 (orders) *Fax:* 413-528-0103 *E-mail:* info@aier.org *Web Site:* www.aier.org, pg 13

American Institute of Aeronautics & Astronautics, 1801 Alexander Bell Dr, Suite 500, Reston, VA 20191-4344 *Tel:* 703-264-7500 *Toll Free Tel:* 800-639-AIAA (639-2422) *Fax:* 703-264-7551 *E-mail:* custserv@aiaa.org *Web Site:* www.aiaa.org, pg 14

American Institute of Chemical Engineers (AIChE), 3 Park Ave, 19th fl, New York, NY 10016-5991 *Tel:* 203-702-7660 *Toll Free Tel:* 800-242-4363 *Fax:* 203-775-5177 *E-mail:* custserv@aiche.org *Web Site:* www.aiche.org, pg 14

American Institute of Physics, 2 Huntington Quadrangle, Suite 1NO1, Melville, NY 11747 *Tel:* 516-576-2200; 301-209-3165 (orders) *Toll Free Tel:* 800-777-4643 (hardcover books) *Fax:* 516-349-7669; 301-209-0882 (orders) *E-mail:* aipinfo@aip.org *Web Site:* www.aip.org, pg 14

American Jewish Committee (AJC), Jacob Blaustein Bldg, 165 E 56 St, New York, NY 10022 *Tel:* 212-751-4000; 212-891-1456 (membership) *Fax:* 212-891-1450 *Web Site:* www.ajc.org, pg 613

American Law Institute, 4025 Chestnut St, Philadelphia, PA 19104-3099 *Tel:* 215-243-1600 *Toll Free Tel:* 800-253-6397 *Fax:* 215-243-1664; 215-243-1683 *Web Site:* www.ali.org, pg 14

The American Legion Fourth Estate Award, 700 N Pennsylvania St, Indianapolis, IN 46204 *Tel:* 317-630-1253 *Fax:* 317-630-1368 *E-mail:* pr@legion.org *Web Site:* www.legion.org, pg 687

The American Library Association (ALA), 50 E Huron St, Chicago, IL 60611 *Tel:* 312-944-6780 *Toll Free Tel:* 800-545-2433 *Fax:* 312-280-5275 *E-mail:* editionsmarketing@ala.org *Web Site:* www.alastore.ala.org, pg 14

The American Library Association (ALA), 50 E Huron St, Chicago, IL 60611 *Tel:* 312-944-6780; 312-280-4299 (memb & cust serv) *Toll Free Tel:* 800-545-2433 *Fax:* 312-440-9374 *E-mail:* ala@ala.org; customerservice@ala.org *Web Site:* www.ala.org, pg 613

American Literacy Council, 1441 Mariposa Ave, Boulder, CO 80302 *Tel:* 303-440-7385 *E-mail:* presidentalc@americanliteracy.com *Web Site:* www.americanliteracy.com, pg 613

American Literary Translators Association (ALTA), c/o The University of Texas at Dallas, 800 W Campbell Rd, Mail Sta JO51, Richardson, TX 75080-3021 *Tel:* 972-883-2093 *Fax:* 972-883-6303 *Web Site:* www.utdallas.edu/alta/, pg 613

American Management Association®, 1601 Broadway, New York, NY 10019-7420 *Tel:* 212-586-8100 *Toll Free Tel:* 877-566-9441 *Fax:* 212-903-8168; 518-891-0368 *E-mail:* customerservice@amanet.org *Web Site:* www.amanet.org, pg 613

American Map Corp, 36-36 33 St, 4th fl, Long Island City, NY 11106 *Tel:* 718-784-0055 *Toll Free Tel:* 888-774-7979 *Fax:* 718-784-0640 (admin); 718-784-1216 (sales & orders) *E-mail:* sales@americanmap.com *Web Site:* www.americanmap.com, pg 14

American Marketing Association, 311 S Wacker Dr, Suite 5800, Chicago, IL 60606 *Tel:* 312-542-9000 *Toll Free Tel:* 800-AMA-1150 (262-1150) *Fax:* 312-542-9001 *E-mail:* info@ama.org *Web Site:* www.marketingpower.com, pg 14, 613

American Mathematical Society, 201 Charles St, Providence, RI 02904-2294 *Tel:* 401-455-4000 *Toll Free Tel:* 800-321-4267 *Fax:* 401-331-3842; 401-455-4046 (cust serv) *E-mail:* ams@ams.org; cust-serv@ams.org *Web Site:* www.ams.org, pg 14

American Medical Association, 515 N State St, Chicago, IL 60654 *Tel:* 312-464-5000 *Toll Free Tel:* 800-621-8335 *Fax:* 312-464-4184 *Web Site:* www.ama-assn.org, pg 15, 613

American Medical Writers Association (AMWA), 30 W Gude Dr, Suite 525, Rockville, MD 20850-1161 *Tel:* 240-238-0940 *Fax:* 301-294-9006 *E-mail:* amwa@amwa.org *Web Site:* www.amwa.org, pg 613

American Numismatic Society, 75 Varick St, 11th fl, New York, NY 10013 *Tel:* 212-571-4470 *Fax:* 212-571-4479 *E-mail:* ans@numismatics.org *Web Site:* www.numismatics.org, pg 15

American Occupational Therapy Association Inc, 4720 Montgomery Lane, Bethesda, MD 20824 *Tel:* 301-652-2682 *Toll Free Tel:* 800-377-8555 *Fax:* 301-652-7711 *Web Site:* www.aota.org, pg 15

American Philosophical Society, 104 S Fifth St, Philadelphia, PA 19106 *Tel:* 215-440-3425 *Fax:* 215-440-3450 *E-mail:* dianepub@comcast.net *Web Site:* www.amphilsoc.org, pg 15

American Phytopathological Society (APS), 3340 Pilot Knob Rd, St Paul, MN 55121 *Tel:* 651-454-7250 *Toll Free Tel:* 800-328-7560 *Fax:* 651-454-0766 *E-mail:* aps@scisoc.org *Web Site:* www.apsnet.org, pg 15

American Political Science Association, 1527 New Hampshire Ave NW, Washington, DC 20036-1206 *Tel:* 202-483-2512 *Fax:* 202-483-2657 *E-mail:* apsa@apsanet.org *Web Site:* www.apsanet.org, pg 613

American Press, 60 State St, Suite 700, Boston, MA 02109 *Tel:* 617-247-0022 *E-mail:* americanpress@flash.net *Web Site:* www.americanpresspublishers.com, pg 15

American Printing History Association, PO Box 4519, Grand Central Sta, New York, NY 10163-4519 *Tel:* 202-544-2422 *Web Site:* www.printinghistory.org, pg 613

American Printing History Association Award, PO Box 4519, Grand Central Sta, New York, NY 10163-4519 *Tel:* 202-544-2422 *Web Site:* www.printinghistory.org, pg 687

American Printing House for the Blind Inc, 1839 Frankfort Ave, Louisville, KY 40206 *Tel:* 502-895-2405 *Toll Free Tel:* 800-223-1839 (cust serv) *Fax:* 502-899-2274 *E-mail:* info@aph.org *Web Site:* www.aph.org; shop.aph.org, pg 15

American Products Publishing Co, 8260 SW Nimbus Ave, Beaverton, OR 97008 *Tel:* 503-672-7502 *Toll Free Tel:* 800-668-8181 *Fax:* 503-672-7104 *E-mail:* info@american-products.com *Web Site:* www.american-products.com, pg 15

American Program Bureau Inc, 313 Washington St, Suite 225, Newton, MA 02458 *Tel:* 617-965-6600 *Toll Free Tel:* 800-225-4575 *Fax:* 617-965-6610 *E-mail:* apb@apbspeakers.com *Web Site:* www.apbspeakers.com, pg 605

American Psychiatric Publishing (APP), 1000 Wilson Blvd, Suite 1825, Arlington, VA 22209 *Tel:* 703-907-7322 *Toll Free Tel:* 800-368-5777 *Fax:* 703-907-1091 *E-mail:* appi@psych.org *Web Site:* www.appi.org; www.psychiatryonline.org, pg 15

American Psychological Association, 750 First St NE, Washington, DC 20002-4242 *Tel:* 202-336-5500 *Toll Free Tel:* 800-374-2721 *Fax:* 202-336-5620 *E-mail:* order@apa.org *Web Site:* www.apa.org/books, pg 16

American Psychological Association, 750 First St NE, Washington, DC 20002-4242 *Tel:* 202-336-5500 *Toll Free Tel:* 800-374-2721 *Fax:* 202-336-5620 *E-mail:* order@apa.org *Web Site:* www.apa.org, pg 614

American Public Human Services Association, 1133 19 St NW, Suite 400, Washington, DC 20036 *Tel:* 202-682-0100 *Fax:* 202-289-6555 *Web Site:* www.aphsa.org, pg 614

American Public Works Association, 2345 Grand Blvd, Suite 700, Kansas City, MO 64108-2625 *Tel:* 816-472-6100 *Toll Free Tel:* 800-848-2792 *Fax:* 816-472-1610 *Web Site:* www.apwa.net, pg 16

American Quilter's Society, 5801 Kentucky Dam Rd, Paducah, KY 42003-9323 *Tel:* 270-898-7903 *Toll Free Tel:* 800-626-5420 (orders) *Fax:* 270-898-1173 *Web Site:* www.americanquilter.com, pg 16

American Society for Indexing Inc (ASI), 10200 W 44 Ave, Suite 304, Wheat Ridge, CO 80033 *Tel:* 303-463-2887 *E-mail:* info@asindexing.org *Web Site:* www.asindexing.org, pg 614

American Society for Nondestructive Testing, 1711 Arlingate Lane, Columbus, OH 43228-0518 *Tel:* 614-274-6003 *Toll Free Tel:* 800-222-2768 *Fax:* 614-274-6899 *Web Site:* www.asnt.org, pg 16

American Society for Quality (ASQ), 600 N Plankinton Ave, Milwaukee, WI 53203 *Tel:* 414-272-8575 *Toll Free Tel:* 800-248-1946 (US & CN); 800-514-1564 (Mexico) *Fax:* 414-272-1734 *E-mail:* help@asq.org *Web Site:* www.asq.org, pg 16

American Society for Training & Development (ASTD), 1640 King St, Box 1443, Alexandria, VA 22313-1443 *Tel:* 703-683-8100 *Toll Free Tel:* 800-628-2783 *Fax:* 703-683-8103 *E-mail:* publications@astd.org *Web Site:* www.astd.org, pg 16

American Society of Agricultural Engineers (ASABE), 2950 Niles Rd, St Joseph, MI 49085-9659 *Tel:* 269-429-0300 *Fax:* 269-429-3852 *E-mail:* hq@asabe.org *Web Site:* www.asabe.org, pg 16

American Society of Agronomy, 5585 Guilford Rd, Madison, WI 53711-1086 *Tel:* 608-273-8080 *Fax:* 608-273-2021 *E-mail:* headquarters@sciencesocieties.org *Web Site:* www.agronomy.org, pg 16

American Society of Civil Engineers (ASCE), 1801 Alexander Bell Dr, Reston, VA 20191-4400 *Tel:* 703-295-6300 *Toll Free Tel:* 800-548-2723 *Fax:* 703-295-6278 *E-mail:* marketing@asce.org *Web Site:* www.asce.org, pg 16

American Society of Composers, Authors & Publishers (ASCAP), One Lincoln Plaza, New York City, NY 10023 *Tel:* 212-621-6000 *Toll Free Tel:* 800-952-7227 *Fax:* 212-612-8453 *E-mail:* info@ascap.com *Web Site:* www.ascap.com, pg 614

American Society of Electroneurodiagnostic Technologists Inc, 402 E Bannister Rd, Suite A, Kansas City, KS 64131-3019 *Tel:* 816-931-1120 *Fax:* 816-931-1145 *E-mail:* info@aset.org *Web Site:* www.aset.org, pg 17

American Society of Health-System Pharmacists, 7272 Wisconsin Ave, Bethesda, MD 20814 *Tel:* 301-657-3000; 301-664-8700 *Toll Free Tel:* 866-279-0681 (orders) *Fax:* 301-657-1251 (orders) *E-mail:* custserv@ashp.org *Web Site:* www.ashp.org, pg 17

American Society of Journalists and Authors (ASJA), 1501 Broadway, Suite 403, New York, NY 10036 *Tel:* 212-997-0947 *Fax:* 212-937-2315 *Web Site:* asja.org, pg 614

American Society of Journalists and Authors Annual Writers Conference, 1501 Broadway, Suite 403, New York, NY 10036 *Tel:* 212-997-0947 *Fax:* 212-937-2315 *Web Site:* asja.org, pg 667

American Society of Magazine Editors (ASME), 810 Seventh Ave, 24th fl, New York, NY 10019 *Tel:* 212-872-3700 *Fax:* 212-906-0128 *E-mail:* asme@magazine.org *Web Site:* www.magazine.org/asme/index.aspx, pg 614

American Society of Mechanical Engineers (ASME), 3 Park Ave, New York, NY 10016-5990 *Tel:* 212-591-7000 *Toll Free Tel:* 800-843-2763 (cust serv-US, CN & Mexico) *Fax:* 212-591-7674; 973-882-8113 (cust serv); 973-882-1717 (orders & inquiries) *E-mail:* infocentral@asme.org *Web Site:* www.asme.org, pg 17

American Society of Media Photographers (ASMP), 150 N Second St, Philadelphia, PA 19106 *Tel:* 215-451-2767 *Fax:* 215-451-0880 *E-mail:* info@asmp.org *Web Site:* www.asmp.org, pg 614

American Society of Plant Taxonomists, University of Michigan Herbarium, 3600 Varsity Dr, Ann Arbor, MI 48108-2228 *Tel:* 734-647-2812 *Fax:* 734-998-0038 *Web Site:* www.aspt.net, pg 17

American Sociological Association (ASA), 1430 "K" St NW, Suite 600, Washington, DC 20005-4701 *Tel:* 202-383-9005 *Fax:* 202-638-0882 *E-mail:* customer@asanet.org *Web Site:* www.asanet.org, pg 614

American Speech-Language-Hearing Association (ASHA), 2200 Research Blvd, Rockville, MD 20850-3289 *Tel:* 301-296-5700 *Toll Free Tel:* 800-638-8255 (nonmembs); 800-498-2071 (membs) *Fax:* 301-296-5777; 301-296-8580 *E-mail:* actioncenter@asha.org *Web Site:* www.asha.org, pg 614

American Technical Publishers Inc, 10100 Orland Pkwy, Suite 200, Orland Park, IL 60467-5756 *Tel:* 708-957-1100 *Toll Free Tel:* 800-323-3471 *Fax:* 708-957-1101 *E-mail:* service@americantech.net *Web Site:* www.go2atp.com, pg 17

American Translators Association (ATA), 225 Reinekers Lane, Suite 590, Alexandria, VA 22314 *Tel:* 703-683-6100 *Fax:* 703-683-6122 *E-mail:* ata@atanet.org *Web Site:* www.atanet.org, pg 615

American Water Works Association, 6666 W Quincy Ave, Denver, CO 80235 *Tel:* 303-794-7711 *Toll Free Tel:* 800-926-7337 *Fax:* 303-347-0804 *Web Site:* www.awwa.org, pg 17

Amherst Media Inc, 175 Rano St, Suite 200, Buffalo, NY 14207 *Tel:* 716-874-4450 *Toll Free Tel:* 800-622-3278 *Fax:* 716-874-4508 *E-mail:* marketing@amherstmedia.com *Web Site:* www.amherstmedia.com, pg 17

Amicus, PO Box 1329, Mankato, MN 56002 *Tel:* 507-388-9357 *Fax:* 507-388-1779 *E-mail:* info@amicuspublishing.us; orders@amicuspublishing.us *Web Site:* www.amicuspublishing.us, pg 17

AMMO Books LLC, 300 S Raymond Ave, Suite 3, Pasadena, CA 91105 *Tel:* 323-223-AMMO (223-2666) *Toll Free Tel:* 888-642-AMMO (642-2666) *Fax:* 323-978-4200 *Web Site:* www.ammobooks.com, pg 17

Ampersand Group, 12 Morenz Terr, Kanata, ON K2K 3G9, Canada *Tel:* 613-435-5066, pg 540

Ampersand Inc/Professional Publishing Services, 1050 N State St, Chicago, IL 60610 *Tel:* 312-280-8905 *Fax:* 312-944-1582 *E-mail:* info@ampersandworks.com *Web Site:* www.ampersandworks.com, pg 17

AMS Press Inc, Brooklyn Navy Yard, Unit 221, 63 Flushing Ave, Brooklyn, NY 11205-1005 *Tel:* 718-875-8100 *Fax:* 718-875-3800 *E-mail:* editorial@amspressinc.com *Web Site:* www.amspressinc.com, pg 18

Amsco School Publications Inc, 315 Hudson St, New York, NY 10013-1085 *Tel:* 212-886-6500; 212-886-6565 *Toll Free Tel:* 800-969-8398 *Fax:* 212-675-7010 *E-mail:* info@amscopub.com *Web Site:* www.amscopub.com, pg 18

Betsy Amster Literary Enterprises, 6312 SW Capitol Hwy, No 503, Portland, OR 97239 *Tel:* 503-496-4007 *E-mail:* rights@amsterlit.com (rts inquiries); b.amster.assistant@gmail.com (adult book queries); b.amster.kidsbooks@gmail.com (children & young adult book queries) *Web Site:* www.amsterlit.com, pg 560

Marcia Amsterdam Agency, 41 W 82 St, New York, NY 10024-5613 *Tel:* 212-873-4945, pg 561

AMWA Annual Conference, 30 W Gude Dr, Suite 525, Rockville, MD 20850-1161 *Tel:* 240-238-0940 *Fax:* 301-294-9006 *E-mail:* amwa@amwa.org *Web Site:* www.amwa.org, pg 667

AMWA Medical Book Awards, 30 W Gude Dr, Suite 525, Rockville, MD 20850-1161 *Tel:* 240-238-0940 *Fax:* 301-294-9006 *E-mail:* amwa@amwa.org *Web Site:* www.amwa.org, pg 687

Amy Writing Awards, PO Box 16091, Lansing, MI 48901-6091 *Tel:* 517-323-6233 *Toll Free Tel:* 877-727-4262 *Fax:* 517-321-2572 *E-mail:* amyawards@worldmag.com *Web Site:* www.worldmag.com/amyawards, pg 687

Joyce L Ananian, 25 Forest Circle, Waltham, MA 02452-4719 *Tel:* 781-894-4330 *E-mail:* jlananian@hotmail.com, pg 540

Anaphora Literary Press, 5755 E River Rd, No 2201, Tucson, AZ 85750 *Tel:* 520-425-4266 *Web Site:* anaphoraliterary.com, pg 18

Anchor Group Publishing, PO Box 551, Flushing, MI 48433 *E-mail:* anchorgrouppublishing@gmail.com *Web Site:* anchorgrouppublishing.com, pg 18

Hans Christian Andersen Award, 5503 N El Adobe Dr, Fresno, CA 93711-2363 *Tel:* 559-351-6119 *E-mail:* executive.director@usbby.org *Web Site:* www.usbby.org, pg 687

Barbara S Anderson, 706 W Davis Ave, Ann Arbor, MI 48103-4855 *Tel:* 734-995-0125 *Toll Free Fax:* 866-859-2932 *E-mail:* bsa328@earthlink.net, pg 540

Denice A Anderson, 210 E Church St, Clinton, MI 49236 *Tel:* 517-456-4990 *Fax:* 517-456-4990 *E-mail:* deniceanderson@frontier.com, pg 540

Jim Anderson, 77 S Second St, Brooklyn, NY 11249 *Tel:* 718-388-1083 *E-mail:* jim.and@att.net, pg 540

Anderson Literary Management LLC, 12 W 19 St, 2nd fl, New York, NY 10011 *Tel:* 212-645-6045 *Fax:* 212-741-1936 *E-mail:* info@andersonliterary.com *Web Site:* www.andersonliterary.com, pg 561

Patricia Anderson PhD, Literary Consultant, 1489 Marine Dr, Suite 515, West Vancouver, BC V7T 1B8, Canada *Tel:* 604-740-0805 *E-mail:* query@helpingyougetpublished.com; patriciaanderson@helpingyougetpublished.com *Web Site:* www.helpingyougetpublished.com, pg 540

Andrews McMeel Publishing LLC, 1130 Walnut St, Kansas City, MO 64106-2109 *Toll Free Tel:* 800-851-8923; 800-943-9839 (cust serv) *Toll Free Fax:* 800-943-9831 (orders) *Web Site:* www.andrewsmcmeel.com, pg 18

Andrews University Press, Sutherland House, 8360 W Campus Circle Dr, Berrien Springs, MI 49104-1700 *Tel:* 269-471-6915; 269-471-6134 (orders) *Toll Free Tel:* 800-467-6369 (Visa, MC & American Express orders only) *Fax:* 269-471-6224 *E-mail:* aupo@andrews.edu *Web Site:* www.universitypress.andrews.edu, pg 18

Andy Ross Literary Agency, 767 Santa Ray Ave, Oakland, CA 94610 *Tel:* 510-238-8965 *E-mail:* andyrossagency@hotmail.com *Web Site:* www.andyrossagency.com, pg 561

Angel City Press, 2118 Wilshire Blvd, Suite 880, Santa Monica, CA 90403 *Tel:* 310-395-9982 *Toll Free Tel:* 800-949-8039 *Fax:* 310-395-3353 *E-mail:* info@angelcitypress.com *Web Site:* www.angelcitypress.com, pg 18

Angel Editing Services, PO Box 2256, Sebastopol, CA 95473 *Tel:* 707-823-4146 *E-mail:* angel@stephaniemarohn.com *Web Site:* www.stephaniemarohn.com, pg 540

Angel Publications, 3169 Quail Dr, Gloucester, ON K1T 1T9, Canada *Tel:* 613-791-0979, pg 540

Angels Editorial Services, 1630 Main St, Suite 41, Coventry, CT 06238 *Tel:* 860-742-5279 *E-mail:* angelsus@aol.com, pg 540

Angelus Press, 2915 Forest Ave, Kansas City, MO 64109 *Tel:* 816-753-3150 *Toll Free Tel:* 800-966-7337 *Fax:* 816-753-3557 *E-mail:* info@angeluspress.org *Web Site:* www.angeluspress.org, pg 18

Anhinga Press, PO Box 3665, Tallahassee, FL 32315 *Tel:* 850-442-1408 *Fax:* 850-442-6323 *E-mail:* info@anhinga.org *Web Site:* www.anhinga.org, pg 18

The Anisfield-Wolf Book Awards, 1422 Euclid Ave, Suite 1300, Cleveland, OH 44115 *Tel:* 216-861-3810 *Fax:* 216-861-1729 *E-mail:* awinfo@clevefdn.org *Web Site:* www.anisfield-wolf.org; www.clevelandfoundation.org, pg 687

R Ross Annett Award for Children's Literature, 11759 Groat Rd, Edmonton, AB T5M 3K6, Canada *Tel:* 780-422-8174 *Toll Free Tel:* 800-665-5354 (AB only) *Fax:* 780-422-2663 (attn WGA) *E-mail:* mail@writersguild.ab.ca *Web Site:* www.writersguild.ab.ca, pg 687

Annick Press Ltd, 15 Patricia Ave, Toronto, ON M2M 1H9, Canada *Tel:* 416-221-4802 *Fax:* 416-221-8400 *E-mail:* annickpress@annickpress.com *Web Site:* www.annickpress.com, pg 493

Annual Off Off Broadway Short Play Festival, 45 W 25 St, New York, NY 10010-2751 *Tel:* 212-206-8990 *Toll Free Tel:* 866-598-8449 *Fax:* 212-206-1429 *E-mail:* oobfestival@samuelfrench.com *Web Site:* oob.samuelfrench.com; www.samuelfrench.com, pg 687

Annual Reviews, 4139 El Camino Way, Palo Alto, CA 94306 *Tel:* 650-493-4400 *Toll Free Tel:* 800-523-8635 *Fax:* 650-424-0910 *E-mail:* service@annualreviews.org *Web Site:* www.annualreviews.org, pg 18

ANR Publications University of California, 1301 S 46 St, Bldg 478 - MC 3580, Richmond, CA 94804 *Tel:* 510-665-2195 (cust serv) *Toll Free Tel:* 800-994-8849 *Fax:* 510-665-3427 *E-mail:* anrcatalog@ucdavis.edu *Web Site:* anrcatalog.ucanr.edu, pg 19

Antioch Writers' Workshop, 900 Dayton St, Yellow Springs, OH 45387 *Tel:* 937-769-1803 *E-mail:* info@antiochwritersworkshop.com *Web Site:* www.antiochwritersworkshop.com, pg 667

Antion & Associates, PO Box 9558, Virginia Beach, VA 23450 *Tel:* 757-431-1366 *Toll Free Tel:* 800-448-6280 *Fax:* 757-431-2050 *E-mail:* orders@antion.com *Web Site:* www.antion.com, pg 19

Antiquarian Booksellers' Association of America (ABAA), 20 W 44 St, Suite 507, New York, NY 10036 *Tel:* 212-944-8291 *Fax:* 212-944-8293 *E-mail:* hq@abaa.org *Web Site:* www.abaa.org, pg 615

Antique Collectors Club Ltd, 116 Pleasant St, Suite 18, East Hampton, MA 01027 *Tel:* 413-529-0861 *Toll Free Tel:* 800-252-5231 *Fax:* 413-529-0862 *E-mail:* sales@antiquecc.com *Web Site:* www.accdistribution.com, pg 19

Antique Trader Books, c/o Krause Publications, 700 E State St, Iola, WI 54990-0001 *Tel:* 715-445-2214 *Toll Free Tel:* 888-457-2873 *Fax:* 715-445-4087 *Web Site:* www.krause.com, pg 19

Antrim House, 21 Goodrich Rd, Simsbury, CT 06070-1804 *Tel:* 860-217-0023 *Fax:* 860-217-0023 *E-mail:* eds@antrimhousebooks.com *Web Site:* www.antrimhousebooks.com, pg 19

Anvil Press Publishers Inc, 278 E First Ave, Vancouver, BC V5T 1A6, Canada *Tel:* 604-876-8710 *Fax:* 604-879-2667 *E-mail:* info@anvilpress.com *Web Site:* www.anvilpress.com, pg 493

AOCS Press, 2710 S Boulder Dr, Urbana, IL 61802-6996 *Tel:* 217-359-2344 *Fax:* 217-351-8091 *E-mail:* general@aocs.org *Web Site:* www.aocs.org, pg 19

APA Planners Press, 205 N Michigan Ave, Suite 1200, Chicago, IL 60601 *Tel:* 312-431-9100 *Fax:* 312-786-6700 *E-mail:* customerservice@planning.org *Web Site:* www.planning.org, pg 19

APA Talent & Literary Agency, 405 S Beverly Dr, Beverly Hills, CA 90212 *Tel:* 310-888-4200 *Fax:* 310-888-4242 *Web Site:* www.apa-agency.com, pg 561

Aperture Books, 547 W 27 St, 4th fl, New York, NY 10001 *Tel:* 212-505-5555 *Toll Free Tel:* 800-929-2323 *Fax:* 212-979-7759 *E-mail:* info@aperture.org *Web Site:* www.aperture.org, pg 19

The Apex Press, 4501 Forbes Blvd, Suite 200, Lanham, MD 20706 *Tel:* 301-459-3366 *Toll Free Tel:* 800-462-6420 *Toll Free Fax:* 800-388-4450 *E-mail:* customercare@rowman.com, pg 19

The Apocryphile Press, 1700 Shattuck Ave, Suite 81, Berkeley, CA 94709 *Tel:* 510-290-4349 *E-mail:* apocryphile@earthlink.net *Web Site:* www.apocryphile.org, pg 20

Apogee Press, 2308 Sixth St, Berkeley, CA 94710 *E-mail:* editors.apogee@gmail.com *Web Site:* www.apogeepress.com, pg 20

Apollo Managed Care Inc, 1651 Foothill Blvd, Santa Ana, CA 92705 *Tel:* 805-969-2606 *Fax:* 805-969-3749 *E-mail:* apollomanagedcare@cox.net *Web Site:* www.apollomanagedcare.com, pg 20

APPA: The Association of Higher Education Facilities Officers, 1643 Prince St, Alexandria, VA 22314-2818 *Tel:* 703-684-1446 *Fax:* 703-549-2772 *Web Site:* www.appa.org, pg 20

Appalachian Mountain Club Books, 5 Joy St, Boston, MA 02108 *Tel:* 617-523-0655 *Fax:* 617-523-0722 *Web Site:* www.outdoors.org, pg 20

Appalachian Trail Conservancy, 799 Washington St, Harpers Ferry, WV 25425 *Tel:* 304-535-6331 *Toll Free Tel:* 888-287-8673 (orders only) *Fax:* 304-535-2667 *E-mail:* info@appalachiantrail.org *Web Site:* www.appalachiantrail.org; www.atctrailstore.org, pg 20

Appalachian Writers' Workshop, 71 Center St, Hindman, KY 41822 *Tel:* 606-785-5475 *Fax:* 606-785-3499 *E-mail:* info@hindmansettlement.org *Web Site:* www.hindmansettlement.org, pg 667

Applause Theatre & Cinema Books, 33 Plymouth St, Suite 302, Montclair, NJ 07042 *Tel:* 973-337-5034 *Toll Free Tel:* 800-637-2852 *Fax:* 973-337-5227 *E-mail:* info@applausepub.com *Web Site:* www.applausepub.com, pg 20

The Applegate/Jackson/Parks Future Teacher Scholarship, 5211 Port Royal Rd, Suite 510, Springfield, VA 22151 *Tel:* 703-321-9606 *Fax:* 703-321-7143 *E-mail:* research@nilrr.org *Web Site:* www.nilrr.org, pg 688

Appletree Press Inc, 151 Good Counsel Dr, Suite 125, Mankato, MN 56001 *Tel:* 507-345-4848 *Toll Free Tel:* 800-322-5679 *Fax:* 507-345-3002 *E-mail:* eatwell@hickorytech.net *Web Site:* www.appletreepress.com; www.appletree-press.com; www.letscookhealthymeals.com; www.appletree-press.us, pg 20

Applewood Books Inc, One River Rd, Carlisle, MA 01741 *Tel:* 781-271-0055 *Fax:* 781-271-0056 *E-mail:* applewood@awb.com *Web Site:* www.awb.com, pg 20

Appraisal Institute, 200 W Madison, Suite 1500, Chicago, IL 60606 *Tel:* 312-335-4100 *Toll Free Tel:* 888-756-4624 *Fax:* 312-335-4400 *Web Site:* www.appraisalinstitute.org, pg 21

Apprentice Shop Books LLC, 18 Wentworth Dr, Bedford, NH 03110 *Tel:* 603-472-8741 *Fax:* 603-472-2323 *E-mail:* info@apprenticeshopbooks.com *Web Site:* www.apprenticeshopbooks.com, pg 21

Apress Media LLC, 233 Spring St, New York, NY 10013 *Tel:* 212-460-1500 *Fax:* 212-460-1575 *E-mail:* editorial@apress.com *Web Site:* www.apress.com, pg 21

APS PRESS, 3340 Pilot Knob Rd, St Paul, MN 55121 *Tel:* 651-454-7250 *Toll Free Tel:* 800-328-7560 *Fax:* 651-454-0766 *E-mail:* aps@scisoc.org *Web Site:* www.shopapspress.org, pg 21

Aptara Inc, 3110 Fairview Park Dr, Suite 900, Falls Church, VA 22042 *Tel:* 703-352-0001 *E-mail:* info@aptaracorp.com *Web Site:* www.aptaracorp.com, pg 540

Aqua Quest Publications Inc, 486 Bayville Rd, Locust Valley, NY 11560-1209 *Tel:* 516-759-0476 *Toll Free Tel:* 800-933-8989 *Fax:* 516-759-4519 *E-mail:* info@aquaquest.com *Web Site:* www.aquaquest.com, pg 21

Aquila Communications Inc, 2642 Diab St, St-Laurent, QC H4S 1E8, Canada *Tel:* 514-338-1065 *Toll Free Tel:* 800-667-7071 *Fax:* 514-338-1948 *Toll Free Fax:* 866-338-1948 *E-mail:* info2@aquilacommunications.com *Web Site:* www.aquilacommunications.com, pg 493

The May Hill Arbuthnot Honor Lecture Award, 50 E Huron St, Chicago, IL 60611-2795 *Tel:* 312-280-2163 *Toll Free Tel:* 800-545-2433 *Fax:* 312-440-9374 *E-mail:* alsc@ala.org *Web Site:* www.ala.org/alsc, pg 688

Arbutus Press, 2364 Pinehurst Trail, Traverse City, MI 49696 *Tel:* 231-946-7240 *E-mail:* info@arbutuspress.com *Web Site:* www.arbutuspress.com, pg 21

Arcade Publishing Inc, 307 W 36 St, 11th fl, New York, NY 10018 *Tel:* 212-643-6816 *Fax:* 212-643-6819 *E-mail:* info@skyhorsepublishing.com (Subs & Foreign Rts) *Web Site:* www.arcadepub.com, pg 21

Arcadia, 31 Lake Place N, Danbury, CT 06810 *Tel:* 203-797-0993 *E-mail:* arcadialit@sbcglobal.net, pg 561

Arcadia Publishing Inc, 420 Wando Park Blvd, Mount Pleasant, SC 29464 *Tel:* 843-853-2070 *Toll Free Tel:* 888-313-2665 (orders only) *Fax:* 843-853-0044 *E-mail:* sales@arcadiapublishing.com *Web Site:* www.arcadiapublishing.com, pg 21

Arden Press Inc, PO Box 418, Denver, CO 80201-0418 *Tel:* 303-697-6766 *Fax:* 303-697-3443 *E-mail:* ardenpress@msn.com, pg 21

Ardent Media Inc, 522 E 82 St, Suite 1, New York, NY 10028 *Tel:* 212-861-1501 *Fax:* 212-861-0998 *E-mail:* ivyboxer@aol.com; ardentmedia@hotmail.com, pg 21

ARE Press, 215 67 St, Virginia Beach, VA 23451 *Tel:* 757-428-3588 *Toll Free Tel:* 800-333-4499 *Fax:* 757-491-0689 *Web Site:* www.edgarcayce.org, pg 21

Ariadne Press, 270 Goins Ct, Riverside, CA 92507 *Tel:* 951-684-9202 *Fax:* 951-779-0449 *E-mail:* ariadnepress@aol.com *Web Site:* www.ariadnebooks.com, pg 22

Ariel Press, 88 N Gate Station Dr, Suite 106, Marble Hill, GA 30148 *Tel:* 770-894-4226 *Fax:* 706-579-1274 *E-mail:* lig201@lightariel.com *Web Site:* www.lightariel.com, pg 22

Ariel Starr Productions Inc, PO Box 17, Demarest, NJ 07627-0017 *Tel:* 201-784-9148 *E-mail:* arielstarrprod@aol.com, pg 22

The Arion Press, The Presidio, 1802 Hays St, San Francisco, CA 94129 *Tel:* 415-668-2542 *Fax:* 415-668-2550 *E-mail:* arionpress@arionpress.com *Web Site:* www.arionpress.com, pg 22

Arizona State University, Creative Writing Program, 851 S Cady Mall, Rm 542, Tempe, AZ 85287-0302 *Tel:* 480-965-6856 *Fax:* 480-965-3451 *Web Site:* www.asu.edu/clas/english/creativewriting, pg 677

Arkansas Diamond Primary Book Award, Arkansas State Library, Suite 100, 900 W Capitol Ave, Little Rock, AR 72201-3108 *Tel:* 501-682-2860 *Fax:* 501-682-1693 *Web Site:* www.library.arkansas.gov; www.library.arkansas.gov, pg 688

Arkansas Research Inc, PO Box 303, Conway, AR 72033 *Tel:* 501-470-1120 *E-mail:* sales@arkansasresearch.com *Web Site:* www.arkansasresearch.com, pg 22

Arkansas State University Graphic Communications Program, PO Box 1930, Dept of Journalism & Graphic Communications, State University, AR 72467-1930 *Tel:* 870-972-3114 *Fax:* 870-972-3321 *Web Site:* www.astate.edu, pg 677

Arkansas Writers' Conference, 13005 Misty Creek Dr, Little Rock, AR 72211 *Tel:* 501-224-5823 *Fax:* 501-224-5823 *Web Site:* www.arkansaswritersconference.org, pg 667

Arkham House Publishers Inc, PO Box 546, Sauk City, WI 53583-0546 *Tel:* 608-643-4500 *Fax:* 608-643-5043 *E-mail:* sales@arkhamhouse.com *Web Site:* www.arkhamhouse.com, pg 22

ARO Publishing Co, 398 S 1100 W, Provo, UT 84601 *Tel:* 801-637-9115 *Fax:* 801-818-0616 *E-mail:* arobook@yahoo.com *Web Site:* www.arobookpublishing.com, pg 22

Jason Aronson Inc, 4501 Forbes Blvd, Suite 200, Lanham, MD 20706 *Tel:* 301-459-3366 *Toll Free Tel:* 800-462-6420 (orders) *Fax:* 301-429-5748 *Web Site:* www.jasonaronson.com, pg 22

Arsenal Pulp Press, 211 E Georgia St, No 101, Vancouver, BC V6A 1Z6, Canada *Tel:* 604-687-4233 *Toll Free Tel:* 888-600-PULP (600-7857) *Fax:* 604-687-4283 *E-mail:* info@arsenalpulp.com *Web Site:* www.arsenalpulp.com, pg 493

Art Image Publications, PO Box 160, Derby Line, VT 05830 *Toll Free Tel:* 800-361-2598 *Toll Free Fax:* 800-559-2598 *E-mail:* info@artimagepublications.com *Web Site:* www.artimagepublications.com, pg 22

The Art Institute of Chicago, 111 S Michigan Ave, Chicago, IL 60603-6404 *Tel:* 312-443-3600; 312-443-3540 (pubns) *Fax:* 312-443-1334 (pubns) *Web Site:* www.artic.edu; www.artinstituteshop.org, pg 22

Art of Living, PrimaMedia Inc, 1250 Bethlehem Pike, Suite 241, Hatfield, PA 19440 *Tel:* 215-660-5045 *Toll Free Tel:* 800-581-9020 *Fax:* 734-448-4125 *E-mail:* primamedia4@yahoo.com, pg 22

ArtAge Publications, PO Box 19955, Portland, OR 97280 *Tel:* 503-246-3000 *Toll Free Tel:* 800-858-4998 *Fax:* 503-246-3006 *Web Site:* www.seniortheatre.com, pg 23

ARTAMO Press, 11 W Anapamu St, Santa Barbara, CA 93101 *Tel:* 805-568-1400 *Fax:* 805-568-1400 *E-mail:* admin@artamopress.com *Web Site:* www.artamopress.com, pg 23

Arte Publico Press, University of Houston, Bldg 19, Rm 10, 4902 Gulf Fwy, Houston, TX 77204-2004 *Tel:* 713-743-2998 (sales) *Toll Free Tel:* 800-633-2783 *Fax:* 713-743-2847 (sales) *E-mail:* appinfo@uh.edu *Web Site:* www.arte.uh.edu; artepublicopress.com, pg 23

Artech House Inc, 685 Canton St, Norwood, MA 02062 *Tel:* 781-769-9750 *Toll Free Tel:* 800-225-9977 *Fax:* 781-769-6334 *E-mail:* artech@artechhouse.com *Web Site:* www.artechhouse.com, pg 23

Artisan Books, 225 Varick St, New York, NY 10014-4381 *Tel:* 212-254-5900 *Toll Free Tel:* 800-722-7202 *Fax:* 212-254-8098 *E-mail:* artisaninfo@workman.com; artisaninfo@artisanbooks.com *Web Site:* www.workman.com/artisanbooks/, pg 23

Artist Grants, 711 E Wells Ave, Pierre, SD 57501-3369 *Tel:* 605-773-3301 *Fax:* 605-773-5977 *E-mail:* sdac@state.sd.us *Web Site:* www.artscouncil.sd.gov/grants, pg 688

Artist Projects Grants, 417 W Roosevelt St, Phoenix, AZ 85003-1326 *Tel:* 602-771-6501 *Fax:* 602-256-0282 *E-mail:* info@azarts.gov *Web Site:* www.azarts.gov, pg 688

Artist Trust Fellowship, 1835 12 Ave, Seattle, WA 98122 *Tel:* 206-467-8734 (ext 11) *Toll Free Tel:* 866-218-7878 (ext 11) *Fax:* 206-467-9633 *E-mail:* info@artisttrust.org *Web Site:* www.artisttrust.org, pg 688

Artists & Writers Summer Fellowships, 435 Ellis Hollow Creek Rd, Ithaca, NY 14850 *Tel:* 607-539-3146 *E-mail:* artscolony@saltonstall.org *Web Site:* www.saltonstall.org, pg 667

Artists Associates, 4416 La Jolla Dr, Bradenton, FL 34210-3927 *Tel:* 941-756-8445, pg 601

Artists' Fellowships, 20 Jay St, 7th fl, Brooklyn, NY 11201 *Tel:* 212-366-6900 *Fax:* 212-366-1778 *E-mail:* info@nyfa.org *Web Site:* www.nyfa.org, pg 688

Artworks Illustration, 325 W 38 St, Suite 1605, New York, NY 10018 *Tel:* 212-239-4946 *Fax:* 212-239-6106 *E-mail:* artworksillustration@earthlink.net *Web Site:* www.artworksillustration.com, pg 601

ASCD, 1703 N Beauregard St, Alexandria, VA 22311-1714 *Tel:* 703-578-9600 *Toll Free Tel:* 800-933-2723 *Fax:* 703-575-5400 *E-mail:* member@ascd.org *Web Site:* www.ascd.org, pg 23

Ascend Books, 10101 W 87 St, Suite 200, Overland Park, KS 66212 *Tel:* 913-948-5500; 913-948-7634 (ordering) *Web Site:* www.ascendbooks.com, pg 23

Ascension Press, PO Box 1990, West Chester, PA 19380 *Tel:* 610-696-7795 *Toll Free Tel:* 800-376-0520 (sales & cust serv) *Fax:* 610-696-7796; 608-565-2025 (sales & cust serv) *E-mail:* info@ascensionpress.com *Web Site:* www.ascensionpress.com, pg 23

ASCP Press, 33 W Monroe St, Suite 1600, Chicago, IL 60603 *Tel:* 312-541-4999 *Toll Free Tel:* 800-267-2727 *Fax:* 312-541-4998 *Web Site:* www.ascp.org, pg 24

ASCSA Publications, American School of Classical Studies at Athens, 6-8 Charlton St, Princeton, NJ 08540-5232 *Tel:* 609-683-0000 *Fax:* 609-924-0578 *Web Site:* www.ascsa.edu.gr/publications, pg 24

Ash Tree Publishing, PO Box 64, Woodstock, NY 12498 *Tel:* 845-246-8081 *Fax:* 845-246-8081 *E-mail:* info@ashtreepublishing.com *Web Site:* www.ashtreepublishing.com, pg 24

Ashgate Publishing Co, 101 Cherry St, Suite 420, Burlington, VT 05401-4405 *Tel:* 802-865-7641 *Toll Free Tel:* 800-535-9544 *Fax:* 802-865-7847 *E-mail:* info@ashgate.com *Web Site:* www.ashgate.com, pg 24

Ashland Creek Press, 2305 Ashland St, Suite C417, Ashland, OR 97520 *Tel:* 760-300-3620 *Fax:* 253-550-2019 *E-mail:* editors@ashlandcreekpress.com *Web Site:* www.ashlandcreekpress.com, pg 24

Ashland Poetry Press, Ashland University, 401 College Ave, Ashland, OH 44805 *Tel:* 419-289-5957 *Fax:* 419-289-5255 *E-mail:* app@ashland.edu *Web Site:* www.ashland.edu/aupoetry, pg 24

ASIS International, 1625 Prince St, Alexandria, VA 22314 *Tel:* 703-519-6200 *Fax:* 703-519-6299 *E-mail:* asis@asisonline.org *Web Site:* www.asisonline.org, pg 24

ASJA Freelance Writer Search, 1501 Broadway, Suite 403, New York, NY 10036 *Tel:* 212-997-0947 *Fax:* 212-937-2315 *E-mail:* fws@asja.org *Web Site:* www.freelancewritersearch.com, pg 540

Aslan Publishing, 857 Post Rd, Suite 302, Fairfield, CT 06824 *Tel:* 203-372-0300 *Fax:* 203-374-4766 *E-mail:* information@aslanpublishing.com *Web Site:* www.aslanpublishing.com, pg 24

ASM International, 9639 Kinsman Rd, Materials Park, OH 44073-0002 *Tel:* 440-338-5151 *Toll Free Tel:* 800-336-5152; 800-368-9800 (Europe) *Fax:* 440-338-4634 *E-mail:* memberservicecenter@asminternational.org *Web Site:* asmcommunity.asminternational.org, pg 25

ASM Press, 1752 "N" St NW, Washington, DC 20036-2904 *Tel:* 202-737-3600 *Toll Free Tel:* 800-546-2416 *Fax:* 202-942-9342 *E-mail:* books@asmusa.org *Web Site:* estore.asm.org, pg 25

Aspatore Books, 35 Thomson Pl, Boston, MA 02210 *Toll Free Tel:* 866-ASPATORE (277-2867) *Fax:* 617-249-0219 *E-mail:* west.customer.service@thomsonreuters.com *Web Site:* www.aspatore.com, pg 25

Aspen Summer Words Writing Retreat & Literary Festival, 110 E Hallam St, Suite 116, Aspen, CO 81611 *Tel:* 970-925-3122 *Fax:* 970-920-5700 *E-mail:* info@aspenwriters.org *Web Site:* www.aspenwriters.org, pg 667

Aspen Writers' Foundation, 110 E Hallam St, Suite 116, Aspen, CO 81611 *Tel:* 970-925-3122 *Fax:* 970-920-5700 *E-mail:* info@aspenwriters.org *Web Site:* www.aspenwriters.org, pg 615

Associated Business Writers of America Inc, 10940 S Parker Rd, Suite 508, Parker, CO 80134 *Tel:* 303-841-0246 *E-mail:* natlwritersassn@hotmail.com *Web Site:* www.nationalwriters.com, pg 615

Associated Editors, 27 W 96 St, New York, NY 10025 *Tel:* 212-662-9703, pg 540

Associated Press Broadcast, 1100 13 St NW, Suite 700, Washington, DC 20005 *Tel:* 202-641-9000 *Toll Free Tel:* 800-821-4747 *Fax:* 202-370-2710 *Web Site:* www.ap.org, pg 615

Associated University Presses, 10 Schalks Crossing Rd, Suite 501-330, Plainsbury, NJ 08536 *Tel:* 609-269-8094 *Fax:* 609-269-8096 *E-mail:* aup440@aol.com *Web Site:* www.aupresses.com, pg 25

Association des Editeurs de Langue Anglaise du Quebec (AELAQ), 1200 Atwater Ave, Suite 3, Westmount, QC H3Z 1X4, Canada *Tel:* 514-932-5633 *E-mail:* admin@aelaq.org *Web Site:* www.aelaq.org, pg 615

Association des Libraires du Quebec, 407, blvd de Sainte Laurent Est, Bureau 801, Montreal, QC H2Y 2Y5, Canada *Tel:* 514-526-3349 *Fax:* 514-526-3340 *E-mail:* info@alq.qc.ca *Web Site:* www.alq.qc.ca, pg 615

Association for Computing Machinery, 2 Penn Plaza, Suite 701, New York, NY 10121-0701 *Tel:* 212-626-0500 *Toll Free Tel:* 800-342-6626 *Fax:* 212-944-1318 *E-mail:* acmhelp@acm.org *Web Site:* www.acm.org, pg 25

Association for Information & Image Management International (AIIM), 1100 Wayne Ave, Suite 1100, Silver Spring, MD 20910 *Tel:* 301-587-8202 *Toll Free Tel:* 800-477-2446 *Fax:* 301-587-2711 *E-mail:* aiim@aiim.org *Web Site:* www.aiim.org, pg 615

Association for Information Science & Technology (ASIS&T), 1320 Fenwick Lane, Suite 510, Silver Spring, MD 20910 *Tel:* 301-495-0900 *Fax:* 301-495-0810 *E-mail:* asis@asis.org *Web Site:* www.asis.org, pg 25, 615

The Association for Women In Communications, 3337 Duke St, Alexandria, VA 22314 *Tel:* 703-370-7436 *Fax:* 703-342-4311 *E-mail:* info@womcom.org *Web Site:* www.womcom.org, pg 667

Association Media & Publishing, 12100 Sunset Hills Rd, Suite 130, Reston, VA 20190 *Tel:* 703-234-4063 *Fax:* 703-435-4390 *E-mail:* info@associationmediaandpublishing.org *Web Site:* www.associationmediaandpublishing.org, pg 615

Association Nationale des Editeurs de Livres, 2514 boul Rosemont, Montreal, QC H1Y 1K4, Canada *Tel:* 514-273-8130 *Toll Free Tel:* 866-900-ANEL (900-2635) *Fax:* 514-273-9657 *E-mail:* info@anel.qc.ca *Web Site:* www.anel.qc.ca, pg 616

Association of American Editorial Cartoonists, 3899 N Front St, Harrisburg, PA 17110 *Tel:* 717-703-3003 *Fax:* 717-703-3008 *E-mail:* aaec@pa-news.org *Web Site:* www.editorialcartoonists.com, pg 616

Association of American Publishers (AAP), 71 Fifth Ave, 2nd fl, New York, NY 10003-3004 *Tel:* 212-255-0200 *Fax:* 212-255-7007 *Web Site:* www.publishers.org, pg 616

Association of American University Presses (AAUP), 28 W 36 St, Suite 602, New York, NY 10018 *Tel:* 212-989-1010 *Fax:* 212-989-0275 *E-mail:* info@aaupnet.org *Web Site:* www.aaupnet.org, pg 616

Association of Authors' Representatives Inc, 676-A Ninth Ave, Suite 312, New York, NY 10036 *Tel:* 212-840-5777 *Web Site:* www.aaronline.org, pg 616

Association of Book Publishers of British Columbia, 600-402 W Pender St, Vancouver, BC V6B 1T6, Canada *Tel:* 604-684-0228 *Fax:* 604-684-5788 *E-mail:* admin@books.bc.ca *Web Site:* www.books.bc.ca, pg 616

Association of Canadian Publishers (ACP), 174 Spadina Ave, Suite 306, Toronto, ON M5T 2C2, Canada *Tel:* 416-487-6116 *Fax:* 416-487-8815 *E-mail:* admin@canbook.org *Web Site:* www.publishers.ca, pg 616

Association of Canadian University Presses, 10 St Mary St, Suite 700, Toronto, ON M4Y 2W8, Canada *Tel:* 416-978-2239 ext 237 *Fax:* 416-978-4738 *Web Site:* www.acup.ca, pg 616

Association of Catholic Publishers Inc, 4725 Dorsey Hall Dr, Suite A, PMB 709, Elliott City, MD 21042 *Tel:* 410-988-2926 *Fax:* 410-571-4946 *Web Site:* www.catholicsread.org; www.catholicpublishers.org; www.midatlanticcongress.org, pg 616

Association of College & Research Libraries (ACRL), 50 E Huron St, Chicago, IL 60611 *Tel:* 312-280-2523 *Toll Free Tel:* 800-545-2433 (ext 2523) *Fax:* 312-280-2520 *E-mail:* acrl@ala.org *Web Site:* www.ala.org/acrl, pg 25

Association of College & University Printers, Penn State University, 101 Hostetter Business Services Bldg, University Park, PA 16802 *Tel:* 814-865-7544 *Fax:* 814-863-6376 *Web Site:* www.multimediaprint.psu.edu, pg 616

Association of Free Community Papers (AFCP), 7445 Morgan Rd, Suite 103, Liverpool, NY 13090 *Toll Free Tel:* 877-203-2327 *Fax:* 781-459-7770 *E-mail:* afcp@afcp.org *Web Site:* www.afcp.org, pg 616

Association of Jewish Libraries (AJL) Inc, PO Box 1118, Teaneck, NJ 07666 *Tel:* 201-371-3255 *E-mail:* info@jewishlibraries.org *Web Site:* www.jewishlibraries.org, pg 616

Association of Library Trustees, Advocates, Friends & Foundations (ALTAFF), 109 S 13 St, Suite 3-N, Philadelphia, PA 19107 *Tel:* 312-280-2161 *Toll Free Tel:* 800-545-2433 (ext 2161) *Fax:* 215-545-3821 *E-mail:* altaff@ala.org *Web Site:* www.ala.org/ala/mgrps/divs/altaff/index.cfm, pg 617

Association of Manitoba Book Publishers, 100 Arthur St, Suite 404, Winnipeg, MB R3B 1H3, Canada *Tel:* 204-947-3335 *Fax:* 204-956-4689 *E-mail:* ambp@mts.net *Web Site:* www.bookpublishers.mb.ca, pg 617

Association of Medical Illustrators (AMI), 201 E Main St, Suite 1405, Lexington, KY 40507 *Toll Free Tel:* 866-393-4264 *Fax:* 859-514-9166 *E-mail:* hq@ami.org *Web Site:* www.ami.org, pg 617

Association of Opinion Journalists (AOJ), 3899 N Front St, Harrisburg, PA 17110 *Tel:* 717-703-3015 *Fax:* 717-703-3014 *E-mail:* ncew@pa-news.org *Web Site:* www.ncew.org, pg 617

Association of Publishers for Special Sales (APSS), PO Box 715, Avon, CT 06001-0715 *Tel:* 860-675-1344 *Web Site:* www.spannet.org, pg 617

Association of Research Libraries, 21 Dupont Circle NW, Suite 800, Washington, DC 20036 *Tel:* 202-296-2296 *Fax:* 202-872-0884 *E-mail:* arlhq@arl.org *Web Site:* www.arl.org, pg 25

Association of School Business Officials International, 11401 N Shore Dr, Reston, VA 20190-4200 *Tel:* 703-478-0405 *Toll Free Tel:* 866-682-2729 *Fax:* 703-478-0205 *E-mail:* asboreq@asbointl.org; asbosba@asbointl.org *Web Site:* www.asbointl.org, pg 25

Association of Writers & Writing Programs (AWP), George Mason University, 4400 University Dr, MSN 1E3, Fairfax, VA 22030 *Tel:* 703-993-4301 *Fax:* 703-993-4302 *E-mail:* awp@awpwriter.org *Web Site:* www.awpwriter.org, pg 617

Association pour l'Avancement des Sciences et des Techniques de la Documentation, 2065 rue Parthenais, Bureau 387, Montreal, QC H2K 3T1, Canada *Tel:* 514-281-5012 *Fax:* 514-281-8219 *E-mail:* info@asted.org *Web Site:* www.asted.org, pg 494, 617, 667

Asta Publications LLC, PO Box 1735, Stockbridge, GA 30281 *Tel:* 678-814-1320 *Toll Free Tel:* 800-482-4190 *Fax:* 678-814-1370 *E-mail:* info@astapublications.com *Web Site:* www.astapublications.com, pg 25

ASTM International, 100 Barr Harbor Dr, West Conshohocken, PA 19428 *Tel:* 610-832-9500 *Fax:* 610-832-9555 *E-mail:* service@astm.org *Web Site:* www.astm.org, pg 25

Astor Indexers, PO Box 950, Kent, CT 06757 *Tel:* 860-355-1066 *Toll Free Tel:* 800-848-2328 *Fax:* 860-355-1066, pg 540

Astragal Press, 8075 215 St W, Lakeville, MN 55044 *Tel:* 952-469-6699 *Toll Free Tel:* 866-543-3045 *Fax:* 952-469-1968 *Toll Free Fax:* 800-330-6232 *E-mail:* info@astragalpress.com *Web Site:* www.astragalpress.com, pg 26

The Astronomical Society of the Pacific, 390 Ashton Ave, San Francisco, CA 94112 *Tel:* 415-337-1100 *Fax:* 415-337-5205 *Web Site:* www.astrosociety.org, pg 26

Athabasca University Press, Edmonton Learning Ctr, Peace Hills Trust Tower, 1200, 10011-109 St, Edmonton, AB T5J 3S8, Canada *Tel:* 780-497-3412 *Fax:* 780-421-3298 *E-mail:* aupress@athabascau.ca *Web Site:* www.aupress.ca, pg 494

Athenaeum of Philadelphia Literary Award, 219 S Sixth St, Philadelphia, PA 19106 *Tel:* 215-925-2688 *Fax:* 215-925-3755 *Web Site:* www.philaathenaeum.org, pg 688

Athletic Guide Publishing, PO Box 1050, Flagler Beach, FL 32136 *Tel:* 386-439-2250 *Toll Free Tel:* 800-255-1050 *Fax:* 386-439-2249 *E-mail:* agp@flaglernet.com *Web Site:* www.athleticguidepublishing.com, pg 26

Atlantic Center for the Arts Artists-in-Residence Program, 1414 Art Center Ave, New Smyrna Beach, FL 32168 *Tel:* 386-427-6975 *Toll Free Tel:* 800-393-6975 *Fax:* 386-427-5669 *E-mail:* program@atlanticcenterforthearts.org *Web Site:* www.atlanticcenterforthearts.org, pg 667

Atlantic Law Book Co, 22 Grassmere Ave, West Hartford, CT 06110-1215 *Tel:* 860-231-9300 *Fax:* 860-231-9242 *E-mail:* atlanticlawbooks@aol.com *Web Site:* www.atlanticlawbooks.com, pg 26

Atlantic Poetry Prize, 1113 Marginal Rd, Halifax, NS B3H 4P7, Canada *Tel:* 902-423-8116 *Fax:* 902-422-0881 *E-mail:* talk@writers.ns.ca *Web Site:* www.writers.ns.ca, pg 688

Atlantic Publishing Group Inc, 1210 SW 23 Place, Ocala, FL 34471 *Tel:* 352-622-1825 *Toll Free Tel:* 800-814-1132 *Fax:* 352-622-1875 *E-mail:* sales@atlantic-pub.com *Web Site:* www.atlantic-pub.com, pg 26

Atria Books, 1230 Avenue of the Americas, New York, NY 10020 *Tel:* 212-698-7000 *Fax:* 212-698-7007 *Web Site:* www.simonandschuster.com, pg 26

Atwood Publishing, PO Box 3185, Madison, WI 53704-0185 *Tel:* 608-242-7101 *Toll Free Tel:* 888-242-7101 *Fax:* 608-242-7102 *E-mail:* customerservice@atwoodpublishing.com *Web Site:* www.atwoodpublishing.com, pg 26

AudioGO, 42 Whitecap Dr, North Kingstown, RI 02852 *Tel:* 401-295-3800 *Toll Free Tel:* 800-621-0182 *Fax:* 401-295-3899 *Toll Free Fax:* 877-492-0873 *E-mail:* info@audiogo.com *Web Site:* www.audiogo.com, pg 26

Audit Bureau of Circulations (ABC), Canadian Office, 151 Bloor St W, Suite 850, Toronto, ON M5S 1S4, Canada *Tel:* 416-962-5840 *Fax:* 416-962-5844 *Web Site:* www.accessabc.ca, pg 617

Audrey Owen, 494 Eaglecrest Dr, Gibsons, BC V0N 1V8, Canada *E-mail:* editor@writershelper.com *Web Site:* www.writershelper.com, pg 540

Sylvia Auerbach, 3890 Nobel Dr, No 506, San Diego, CA 92122 *Tel:* 858-597-8000, pg 541

Augsburg Fortress Publishers, Publishing House of the Evangelical Lutheran Church in America, 100 S Fifth St, Suite 600, Minneapolis, MN 55402 *Tel:* 612-330-3300 *Toll Free Tel:* 800-426-0115 (ext 639, subns); 800-328-4648 (orders) *E-mail:* info@augsburgfortress.org; copyright@augsburgfortress.org (reprint permission requests); customercare@augsburgfortress.org *Web Site:* www.augsburgfortress.org, pg 27

August House Inc, 3500 Piedmont Rd NE, Suite 310, Atlanta, GA 30305 *Tel:* 404-442-4420 *Toll Free Tel:* 800-284-8784 *Fax:* 404-442-4435 *E-mail:* ahinfo@augusthouse.com *Web Site:* www.augusthouse.com, pg 27

Aum Publications, 86-10 Parsons Blvd, Jamaica, NY 11432-3314 *Tel:* 347-744-3199 *Web Site:* www.srichinmoybooks.com/us/aum_publications, pg 27

Abrendal Austin National Writing Contest, 5198 Arlington Ave, Unit 923, Riverside, CA 92504 *Tel:* 951-214-5712; 951-741-7651 *E-mail:* shortstory@blackpennypresscontest.com; info@blackpennypress.com *Web Site:* www.blackpennypresscontest.com, pg 688

Author Author Literary Agency Ltd, 130-1005 Columbia St, PO Box 42522, Columbia Sq, New Westminster, BC V3M 6H5, Canada *Tel:* 604-415-0056 *Fax:* 604-415-0076 *Web Site:* www.authorauthor.ca, pg 561

AuthorHouse, 1663 Liberty Dr, Bloomington, IN 47403 *Toll Free Tel:* 888-519-5121 *E-mail:* authorsupport@authorhouse.com *Web Site:* www.authorhouse.com, pg 27

Authorlink Press, 755 Laguna, Irving, TX 75039-3218 *Tel:* 972-402-0101 *Toll Free Fax:* 866-381-1587 *Web Site:* www.authorlink.com, pg 27

The Author's Friend, 548 Ocean Blvd, No 12, Long Branch, NJ 07740 *Tel:* 732-571-8051 *Toll Free Tel:* 877-485-7689 *Toll Free Fax:* 877-485-7689, pg 541

The Authors Guild, 31 E 32 St, 7th fl, New York, NY 10016 *Tel:* 212-563-5904 *Fax:* 212-564-8363; 212-564-5363 *E-mail:* staff@authorsguild.org *Web Site:* www.authorsguild.org, pg 617

The Authors League Fund, 31 E 32 St, 7th fl, New York, NY 10016 *Tel:* 212-268-1208 *Fax:* 212-564-5363 *E-mail:* staff@authorsleaguefund.org *Web Site:* www.authorsleaguefund.org, pg 617

The Authors Registry Inc, 31 E 32 St, 7th fl, New York, NY 10016 *Tel:* 212-563-6920 *Fax:* 212-564-5363 *E-mail:* staff@authorsregistry.org *Web Site:* www.authorsregistry.org, pg 617

Authors Unlimited Inc, 31 E 32 St, Suite 300, New York, NY 10016 *Tel:* 212-481-8484 (ext 336) *Fax:* 212-481-9582 *Web Site:* www.authorsunlimited.com, pg 605

Autism Asperger Publishing Co, 15490 Quivira Rd, Overland Park, KS 66223 *Tel:* 913-897-1004 *Toll Free Tel:* 877-277-8254 *Fax:* 913-681-9473 *E-mail:* aapcinfo@aapcpublishing.net *Web Site:* www.aapcpublishing.net, pg 27

Autumn House Poetry, Fiction & Nonfiction Contests, 87 1/2 Westwood St, Pittsburgh, PA 15211 *Web Site:* www.autumnhouse.org, pg 688

Autumn House Press, 87 1/2 Westwood St, Pittsburgh, PA 15211 *Tel:* 412-381-4261 *Web Site:* www.autumnhouse.org, pg 27

Avalon Travel Publishing, 1700 Fourth St, Berkeley, CA 94710-1711 *Tel:* 510-595-3664 *Fax:* 510-595-4228 *Web Site:* www.avalontravelbooks.com, pg 27

Ave Maria Press, PO Box 428, Notre Dame, IN 46556-0428 *Tel:* 574-287-2831 *Toll Free Tel:* 800-282-1865 *Fax:* 574-239-2904 *Toll Free Fax:* 800-282-5681 *E-mail:* avemariapress.1@nd.edu *Web Site:* www.avemariapress.com, pg 28

Avery, 375 Hudson St, New York, NY 10014 *Tel:* 212-366-2000 *Fax:* 212-366-2643 *E-mail:* online@penguinputnam.com *Web Site:* www.penguinputnam.com; us.penguingroup.com, pg 28

Avery Color Studios, 511 "D" Ave, Gwinn, MI 49841 *Tel:* 906-346-3908 *Toll Free Tel:* 800-722-9925 *Fax:* 906-346-3015 *E-mail:* averycolor@averycolorstudios.com, pg 28

Avisson Press Inc, 3007 Taliaferro Rd, Greensboro, NC 27408 *Tel:* 336-288-6989; 336-285-6763 *Fax:* 336-288-6989 *E-mail:* avisson4@aol.com, pg 28

AVKO Educational Research Foundation Inc, 3084 Willard Rd, Birch Run, MI 48415-9404 *Tel:* 810-686-9283 (orders & billing) *Toll Free Tel:* 866-AVKO612 (285-6612) *Fax:* 810-686-1101 *E-mail:* info@avko.org (gen inquiry) *Web Site:* www.avko.org; www.avko.blogspot.org, pg 28

Avotaynu Inc, 155 N Washington Ave, Bergenfield, NJ 07621 *Tel:* 201-387-7200 *Toll Free Tel:* 800-286-8296 *Fax:* 201-387-2855 *E-mail:* info@avotaynu.com *Web Site:* www.avotaynu.com, pg 28

Awe-Struck Publishing, 6457 Glenway Ave, Suite 109, Cincinnati, OH 45211-5222 *Toll Free Tel:* 888-232-0808 *Fax:* 513-598-9220 *E-mail:* inquiry@mundania.com; orders@mundania.com; submissions@awe-struck.net *Web Site:* www.awe-struck.net; www.mundania.com, pg 28

AWP Award Series, George Mason University, 4400 University Dr, MSN 1E3, Fairfax, VA 22030 *Tel:* 703-993-4301 *Fax:* 703-993-4302 *E-mail:* awp@awpwriter.org *Web Site:* www.awpwriter.org, pg 688

The Axelrod Agency, 55 Main St, Chatham, NY 12037 *Tel:* 518-392-2100, pg 561

Axiom Business Book Awards, 1129 Woodmere Ave, Suite B, Traverse City, MI 49686 *Tel:* 231-933-0445 *Toll Free Tel:* 800-706-4636 *Fax:* 231-933-0448 *E-mail:* info@axiomawards.com *Web Site:* www.axiomawards.com, pg 689

AZ Books LLC, 245 Eighth Ave, Suite 180, New York, NY 10011 *Toll Free Tel:* 888-945-7723 *Toll Free Fax:* 888-945-7724 *Web Site:* www.azbooksusa.com, pg 28

Azro Press, 1704 Llano St B, PMB 342, Santa Fe, NM 87505 *Tel:* 505-989-3272 *Fax:* 505-989-3832 *E-mail:* books@azropress.com *Web Site:* www.azropress.com, pg 28

B & B Publishing, 4823 Sherbrooke St W, Office 275, Westmount, QC H3Z 1G7, Canada *Tel:* 514-932-9466 *Fax:* 514-932-5929 *E-mail:* editions@ebbp.ca, pg 494

Babalu Inc, PO Box 23026, Santa Barbara, CA 93121 *Toll Free Tel:* 877-522-2258 *E-mail:* info@babaluinc.com *Web Site:* www.babaluinc.com, pg 28

Babbage Press, 8939 Canby Ave, Northridge, CA 91325-2702 *Tel:* 818-341-3161 *E-mail:* books@babbagepress.com *Web Site:* www.babbagepress.com, pg 29

Baby Tattoo Books, 6045 Longridge Ave, Van Nuys, CA 91401 *Tel:* 818-416-5314 *E-mail:* info@babytattoo.com *Web Site:* www.babytattoo.com, pg 29

Backbeat Books, 33 Plymouth St, Suite 302, Montclair, NJ 07042 *Tel:* 973-337-5034 *Toll Free Tel:* 800-637-2852 (Music Dispatch) *Fax:* 973-337-5227 *Web Site:* www.backbeatbooks.com, pg 29

Elizabeth H Backman, 86 Johnnycake Hollow Rd, Pine Plains, NY 12567 *Tel:* 518-398-9344 *Fax:* 518-398-6368 *E-mail:* bethcountry@fairpoint.net, pg 561

Backman Writing & Communications, 32 Hillview Ave, Rensselaer, NY 12144 *Tel:* 518-449-4985 *Fax:* 518-449-7273 *Web Site:* www.backwrite.com, pg 541

The Backwaters Press, 3502 N 52 St, Omaha, NE 68104-3506 *Tel:* 402-451-4052 *E-mail:* thebackwaterspress@gmail.com *Web Site:* www.thebackwaterspress.org, pg 29

Baen Publishing Enterprises, PO Box 1403, Riverdale, NY 10471-0605 *Tel:* 919-570-1640 *Fax:* 919-570-1644 *E-mail:* info@baen.com *Web Site:* www.baen.com, pg 29

Bagwyn Books, 975 S Myrtle Ave, Tempe, AZ 85281 *Tel:* 480-965-5900 *Fax:* 480-965-1681 *E-mail:* bagwynbooks@acmrs.org *Web Site:* acmrs.org/publications/bagwyn, pg 29

Baha'i Publishing, 415 Linden Ave, Wilmette, IL 60091 *Tel:* 847-425-7950 *Fax:* 847-425-7951 *E-mail:* bpt@usbnc.org *Web Site:* books.bahai.us, pg 29

Marilyn Baillie Picture Book Award, 40 Orchard View Blvd, Suite 217, Toronto, ON M4R 1B9, Canada *Tel:* 416-975-0010 *Fax:* 416-975-8970 *E-mail:* info@bookcentre.ca *Web Site:* www.bookcentre.ca, pg 689

Baker & Taylor/YALSA Conference Grants, 50 E Huron St, Chicago, IL 60611 *Tel:* 312-280-4390 *Toll Free Tel:* 800-545-2433 *Fax:* 312-280-5276; 312-664-7459 *E-mail:* yalsa@ala.org *Web Site:* www.ala.org/yalsa/, pg 689

Baker Books, 6030 E Fulton Rd, Ada, MI 49301 *Tel:* 616-676-9185 *Toll Free Tel:* 800-877-2665; 800-679-1957 *Fax:* 616-676-9573 *Toll Free Fax:* 800-398-3111 *Web Site:* www.bakerpublishinggroup.com, pg 29

The Baker Street Irregulars (BSI), 7938 Mill Stream Circle, Indianapolis, IN 46278 *Tel:* 317-293-2212; 317-384-4728 (cell) *Web Site:* bakerstreetjournal.com, pg 29, 617

Baker's Plays, 45 W 25 St, New York, NY 10010 *Toll Free Tel:* 866-598-8449 *Fax:* 212-206-1429 *E-mail:* info@bakersplays.com *Web Site:* www.bakersplays.com, pg 29

Balance Sports Publishing, 195 Lucero Way, Portola Valley, CA 94028 *Tel:* 650-561-9586 *Fax:* 650-391-9850 *E-mail:* info@balancesportspublishing.com *Web Site:* www.balancesportspublishing.com, pg 29

The Balcones Poetry Prize, 1212 Rio Grande St, Austin, TX 78701 *Tel:* 512-828-9368 *Web Site:* www.austincc.edu/crw/balcones_prize.html, pg 689

Malaga Baldi Literary Agency, 233 W 99, Suite 19C, New York, NY 10025 *Tel:* 212-222-3213 *E-mail:* baldibooks@gmail.com; info@baldibooks.com *Web Site:* www.baldibooks.com, pg 561

Baldwin Literary Services, 935 Hayes St, Baldwin, NY 11510-4834 *Tel:* 516-546-8338 *Fax:* 516-546-8338, pg 541

Ball-Stick-Bird Publications Inc, PO Box 429, Williamstown, MA 01267-0429 *Tel:* 413-664-0002 *Fax:* 413-664-0002 *E-mail:* info@ballstickbird.com *Web Site:* www.ballstickbird.com, pg 30

Ballinger Publishing, 41 N Jefferson St, Suite 402, Pensacola, FL 32502 *Tel:* 850-433-1166 *Fax:* 850-435-9174 *E-mail:* info@ballingerpublishing.com *Web Site:* www.ballingerpublishing.com, pg 30

Carol Bancroft & Friends, PO Box 2030, Danbury, CT 06813 *Tel:* 203-730-8270 *Fax:* 203-730-8275 *E-mail:* cbfriends@sbcglobal.net *Web Site:* www.carolbancroft.com, pg 601

Bancroft Press, 3209 Bancroft Rd, Baltimore, MD 21215 *Tel:* 410-358-0658 *Fax:* 410-764-1967 *Web Site:* www.bancroftpress.com, pg 30

Bancroft Prizes, 517 Butler Library, Mail Code 1101, 535 W 114 St, New York, NY 10027 *Tel:* 212-854-4746 *Fax:* 212-854-9099 *Web Site:* www.columbia.edu/cu/lweb/eguides/amerihist/bancroft.html, pg 689

Bandanna Books, 1212 Punta Gorda St, No 13, Santa Barbara, CA 93103 *Tel:* 805-899-2145 *E-mail:* bandanna@cox.net *Web Site:* www.bandannabooks.com; www.shakespeareplaybook.com; bookdoc.us, pg 30

B&H Publishing Group, One Lifeway Plaza, Nashville, TN 37234-0114 *Tel:* 615-251-2520 *Fax:* 615-251-5004 *Web Site:* www.bhpublishinggroup.com, pg 30

Banff Centre Press, 107 Tunnel Mountain Dr, Banff, AB T1L 1H5, Canada *Tel:* 403-762-6100 *Fax:* 403-762-6444 *E-mail:* press@banffcentre.ca *Web Site:* www.banffcentre.ca/press, pg 494

Banner of Truth, 63 E Louther St, Carlisle, PA 17013 *Tel:* 717-249-5747 *Toll Free Tel:* 800-263-8085 (orders) *Fax:* 717-249-0604 *E-mail:* info@banneroftruth.org *Web Site:* www.banneroftruth.co.uk; www.banneroftruth.org, pg 30

A Richard Barber/Peter Berinstein & Associates, 60 E Eighth St, Suite 21-N, New York, NY 10003 *Tel:* 212-737-7266 *Fax:* 860-927-3942 *E-mail:* barberrich@aol.com, pg 561

Barbour Publishing Inc, 1810 Barbour Dr, Uhrichsville, OH 44683 *Tel:* 740-922-6045 *Fax:* 740-922-5948 *E-mail:* info@barbourbooks.com *Web Site:* www.barbourbooks.com, pg 30

Barcelona Publishers, Pathway Book Service, 4 White Brook Rd, Gilsum, NH 03448 *Tel:* 603-357-0236 *Fax:* 603-357-2073 *E-mail:* pbs@pathwaybook.com; barcelonapublishers@gvtc.com *Web Site:* www.barcelonapublishers.com, pg 30

Bard Society, 1358 Tiber Ave, Jacksonville, FL 32207, pg 667

Barefoot Books, 2067 Massachusetts Ave, 5th fl, Cambridge, MA 02140 *Tel:* 617-576-0660 *Toll Free Tel:* 866-215-1756 (cust serv); 866-417-2369 (orders) *Fax:* 617-576-0049 *E-mail:* ussales@barefootbooks.com; help@barefootbooks.com *Web Site:* www.barefootbooks.com, pg 30

The Barnabas Agency, 109 S Main St, Corsicana, TX 75110 *Tel:* 903-872-0517 *Toll Free Tel:* 800-927-0517 *Fax:* 903-872-0518 *E-mail:* tbbmedia@tbbmedia.com *Web Site:* www.tbbmedia.com, pg 605

Barnard Women Poets Prize, Barnard College, Women Poets at Barnard, 3009 Broadway, New York, NY 10027 *Tel:* 212-854-2116 *Fax:* 212-854-9498 *E-mail:* english@barnard.edu *Web Site:* www.barnard.edu, pg 689

Kathleen Barnes, 238 W Fourth St, Suite 3-C, New York, NY 10014 *Tel:* 212-924-8084 *E-mail:* kbarnes@compasscommunications.org, pg 541

Barnhardt & Ashe Publishing, 444 Brickell Ave, Suite 51, PMB 432, Miami, FL 33131 *Toll Free Tel:* 800-283-6360 (orders) *E-mail:* barnhardtashe@aol.com *Web Site:* www.barnhardtashepublishing.com, pg 31

Baror International Inc, PO Box 868, Armonk, NY 10504-0868 *Tel:* 914-273-9199 *Fax:* 914-273-5058 *Web Site:* www.barorint.com, pg 562

Barranca Press, 1450 Couse St, No 10, Taos, NM 87571 *Tel:* 575-613-1026 *E-mail:* editor@barrancapress.com *Web Site:* www.barrancapress.com, pg 31

Loretta Barrett Books Inc, 220 E 23 St, 11th fl, New York, NY 10010 *Tel:* 212-242-3420 *E-mail:* query@lorettabarrettbooks.com *Web Site:* www.lorettabarrettbooks.com, pg 562

Melinda Barrett, 17110 Donmetz St, Granada Hills, CA 91344 *Tel:* 818-635-6865 *E-mail:* mbarrett_3@netzero.net, pg 541

Barricade Books Inc, 185 Bridge Plaza N, Suite 309, Fort Lee, NJ 07024 *Tel:* 201-944-7600 *Fax:* 201-917-4951 *E-mail:* customerservice@barricadebooks.com *Web Site:* www.barricadebooks.com, pg 31

Barringer Publishing, 3259 Sundance Circle, Naples, FL 34109 *Tel:* 239-514-7364 *Fax:* 239-596-8135 *E-mail:* info@barringerpublishing.com *Web Site:* www.barringerpublishing.com, pg 31

Barron's Educational Series Inc, 250 Wireless Blvd, Hauppauge, NY 11788 *Tel:* 631-434-3311 *Toll Free Tel:* 800-645-3476 *Fax:* 631-434-3723 *E-mail:* barrons@barronseduc.com *Web Site:* www.barronseduc.com, pg 31

James P Barry Ohioana Award for Editorial Excellence, 274 E First Ave, Suite 300, Columbus, OH 43201 *Tel:* 614-466-3831 *Fax:* 614-728-6974 *E-mail:* ohioana@ohioana.org *Web Site:* www.ohioana.org, pg 689

Barrytown/Station Hill Press, 120 Station Hill Rd, Barrytown, NY 12507 *Tel:* 845-758-5293 *E-mail:* publishers@stationhill.org *Web Site:* www.stationhill.org, pg 31

Diana Barth, 535 W 51 St, Suite 3-A, New York, NY 10019 *Tel:* 212-307-5465 *E-mail:* diabarth@juno.com, pg 541

Anita Bartholomew, 4237 Sarasota Ave, Sarasota, FL 34234 *Tel:* 941-358-0495 *E-mail:* anita@anitabartholomew.com *Web Site:* www.anitabartholomew.com, pg 541

Bartleby Press, 8600 Foundry St, Savage Mill Box 2043, Savage, MD 20763 *Tel:* 301-725-3906 *Toll Free Tel:* 800-953-9929 *Fax:* 301-725-0333 *E-mail:* inquiries@bartlebythepublisher.com *Web Site:* www.bartlebythepublisher.com, pg 31

Basic Books, 250 W 57 St, 15th fl, New York, NY 10107 *Tel:* 212-340-8164 *Fax:* 212-340-8135 *E-mail:* perseus.promos@perseusbooks.com *Web Site:* www.basicbooks.com; perseusbooks.com, pg 31

Basic Health Publications Inc, 28812 Top of the World Dr, Laguna Beach, CA 92651 *Tel:* 949-715-7327 *Toll Free Tel:* 800-575-8890 (orders) *Fax:* 949-715-7328 *E-mail:* info@basichealthpub.com *Web Site:* www.basichealthpub.com, pg 32

Baskerville Publishers Poetry Award, Texas Christian University, Dept of English, TCU Box 297270, Fort Worth, TX 76129 *Tel:* 817-257-5907 *Fax:* 817-257-7709 *E-mail:* descant@tcu.edu *Web Site:* www.descant.tcu.edu, pg 689

The Mildred L Batchelder Award, 50 E Huron St, Chicago, IL 60611-2795 *Tel:* 312-280-2163 *Toll Free Tel:* 800-545-2433 *Fax:* 312-440-9374 *E-mail:* alsc@ala.org *Web Site:* www.ala.org/alsc, pg 689

Mark E Battersby, PO Box 527, Ardmore, PA 19003 *Tel:* 610-924-9157 *Fax:* 610-924-9159 *E-mail:* mebatt12@earthlink.net, pg 541

Bay Tree Publishing LLC, 1400 Pinnacle Ct, Suite 406, Point Richmond, CA 94801-4178 *Tel:* 510-236-1475 *Toll Free Fax:* 866-552-7329 *Web Site:* www.baytreepublish.com, pg 32

Bayeux Arts Inc, 119 Stratton Crescent SW, Calgary, AB T3H 1T7, Canada *E-mail:* mail@bayeux.com *Web Site:* www.bayeux.com, pg 494

Baylor University Press, Baylor University, One Bear Place, Waco, TX 76798-7363 *Tel:* 254-710-3164 *Fax:* 254-710-3440 *Web Site:* www.baylorpress.com, pg 32

Baylor University, Writing Program, One Bear Place, Unit 97404, Waco, TX 76798-7404 *Tel:* 254-710-1768 *Fax:* 254-710-3894 *Web Site:* www.baylor.edu, pg 677

Baywood Publishing Co Inc, 26 Austin Ave, Amityville, NY 11701 *Tel:* 631-691-1270 *Toll Free Tel:* 800-638-7819 *Fax:* 631-691-1770 *E-mail:* baywood@baywood.com *Web Site:* www.baywood.com, pg 32

The BC Book Prizes, 207 W Hastings St, Suite 901, Vancouver, BC V6B 1H7, Canada *Tel:* 604-687-2405 *Fax:* 604-687-2435 *E-mail:* info@bcbookprizes.ca *Web Site:* www.bcbookprizes.ca, pg 689

BCFL, 4806 Martinique Way, Naples, FL 34119 *Tel:* 908-447-3553 *Fax:* 239-596-8611 *E-mail:* BCFLGroup@gmail.com *Web Site:* judgingfloraldesign.com, pg 527

Beach Lloyd Publishers LLC, 40 Cabot Dr, Wayne, PA 19087-5619 *Tel:* 610-407-9107 *Toll Free Tel:* 866-218-3253 (pin 8668) *Fax:* 775-254-0633 *E-mail:* beachlloyd@erols.com *Web Site:* www.beachlloyd.com, pg 32

Beacon Hill Press of Kansas City, PO Box 419527, Kansas City, MO 64141-6527 *Tel:* 816-931-1900 *Toll Free Tel:* 800-877-0700 (cust serv) *Fax:* 816-753-4071 *Web Site:* www.beaconhillbooks.com, pg 32

Beacon Press, 25 Beacon St, Boston, MA 02108 *Tel:* 617-742-2110 *Fax:* 617-723-3097; 617-742-2290 *Web Site:* www.beacon.org, pg 32

Bear & Co Inc, One Park St, Rochester, VT 05767 *Tel:* 802-767-3174 *Toll Free Tel:* 800-932-3277 *Fax:* 802-767-3726 *E-mail:* customerservice@InnerTraditions.com *Web Site:* InnerTraditions.com, pg 33

Beard Books Inc, 47 E South St, Suite 102, Frederick, MD 21701 *Tel:* 240-629-3300 *Toll Free Tel:* 888-563-4573 (book orders) *Fax:* 240-629-3360 *E-mail:* info@beardbooks.com; order@beardbooks.com *Web Site:* www.beardbooks.com; www.beardgroup.com, pg 33

Bearport Publishing Co Inc, 45 W 21 St, Suite 3B, New York, NY 10010 *Tel:* 212-337-8577 *Toll Free Tel:* 877-337-8577 *Fax:* 212-337-8557 *Toll Free Fax:* 866-337-8557 *E-mail:* info@bearportpublishing.com *Web Site:* www.bearportpublishing.com, pg 33

Beaufort Books, 27 W 20 St, Suite 1102, New York, NY 10011 *Tel:* 212-727-0222 *Fax:* 212-727-0195 *E-mail:* info@beaufortbooks.com *Web Site:* www.beaufortbooks.com, pg 33

Beautiful America Publishing Co, 2600 Progress Way, Woodburn, OR 97071 *Tel:* 503-982-4616 *Toll Free Tel:* 800-874-1233 *Fax:* 503-982-2825 *E-mail:* bapco@beautifulamericapub.com *Web Site:* www.beautifulamericapub.com, pg 33

Beaver Wood Associates, 655 Alstead Center Rd, Alstead, NH 03602 *Tel:* 603-835-7900 *Fax:* 603-835-6279 *Web Site:* www.beaverwood.com, pg 541

Beaver's Pond Press Inc, 7108 Ohms Lane, Edina, MN 55439-2129 *Tel:* 952-829-8818 *Web Site:* www.beaverspondpress.com, pg 33

Beckett Media LLC, 22840 Savi Ranch Pkwy, Suite 200, Yorba Linda, CA 92887 *Tel:* 714-939-9991 *Toll Free Tel:* 800-332-3330 *Fax:* 714-939-9909 *Toll Free Fax:* 800-249-7761 *Web Site:* www.beckettmedia.com, pg 33

Bedford, Freeman & Worth Publishing Group, LLC, 41 Madison Ave, 37th fl, New York, NY 10010 *Tel:* 212-576-9400 *Fax:* 212-689-2383 *Web Site:* www.macmillanhighered.com, pg 33

Bedford/St Martin's, 75 Arlington St, Boston, MA 02116 *Tel:* 617-399-4000 *Toll Free Tel:* 800-779-7440 *Fax:* 617-426-8582 *Web Site:* www.bedfordstmartins.com, pg 34

Beekman Books Inc, 300 Old All Angels Hill Rd, Wappingers Falls, NY 12590 *Tel:* 845-297-2690 *Fax:* 845-297-1002 *E-mail:* manager@beekmanbooks.com *Web Site:* www.beekmanbooks.com, pg 34

George Louis Beer Prize, 400 "A" St SE, Washington, DC 20003-3889 *Tel:* 202-544-2422 *Fax:* 202-544-8307 *E-mail:* awards@historians.org *Web Site:* www.historians.org, pg 690

Before Columbus Foundation, The Raymond House, Suite 302, 655 13 St, Oakland, CA 94612 *Tel:* 510-268-9775 *E-mail:* info@beforecolumbusfoundation.com *Web Site:* www.beforecolumbusfoundation.org, pg 617

Begell House Inc Publishers, 50 Cross Hwy, Redding, CT 06896 *Tel:* 203-938-1300 *Fax:* 203-938-1304 *E-mail:* orders@begellhouse.com *Web Site:* www.begellhouse.com, pg 34

Behrman House Inc, 11 Edison Place, Springfield, NJ 07081 *Tel:* 973-379-7200 *Toll Free Tel:* 800-221-2755 *Fax:* 973-379-7280 *E-mail:* behrmanhouse@gmail.com; customersupport@behrmanhouse.com *Web Site:* www.behrmanhouse.com, pg 34

Frederic C Beil Publisher Inc, 609 Whitaker St, Savannah, GA 31401 *Tel:* 912-233-2446 *E-mail:* books@beil.com *Web Site:* www.beil.com, pg 34

Beliveau Editeur, 920 rue Jean-Neveu, Longueuil, QC J4G 2M1, Canada *Tel:* 514-253-0403; 450-679-1933 *Fax:* 450-679-6648 *E-mail:* admin@beliveauediteur.com *Web Site:* www.beliveauediteur.com, pg 494

Bell Springs Publishing, PO Box 1240, Willits, CA 95490-1240 *Tel:* 707-459-6372 *Toll Free Tel:* 800-515-8050 *Fax:* 707-459-6372 *E-mail:* publisher@bellsprings.com *Web Site:* bellsprings.com; aboutpinball.com, pg 34

Bella Books, PO Box 10543, Tallahassee, FL 32302 *Tel:* 850-576-2370 *Toll Free Tel:* 800-729-4992 *Fax:* 850-576-3498 *E-mail:* info@bellabooks.com; orders@bellabooks.com; ebooks@bellabooks.com *Web Site:* www.bellabooks.com, pg 34

Bella Pomer Agency Inc, 355 St Clair Ave W, Suite 801, Toronto, ON M5P 1N5, Canada *Tel:* 416-920-4949 *E-mail:* belpom@sympatico.ca *Web Site:* bellapomeragency.com, pg 562

BelleBooks, PO Box 300921, Memphis, TN 38130 *Tel:* 901-344-9024 *Fax:* 901-344-9068 *E-mail:* bellebooks@bellebooks.com *Web Site:* www.bellebooks.com, pg 34

Bellerophon Books, PO Box 21307, Santa Barbara, CA 93121-1307 *Tel:* 805-965-7034 *Toll Free Tel:* 800-253-9943 *Fax:* 805-965-8286 *E-mail:* sales@bellerophonbooks.com *Web Site:* www.bellerophonbooks.com, pg 34

Belltown Media, PO Box 980985, Houston, TX 77098 *Tel:* 713-344-1956 *Fax:* 713-583-7956 *E-mail:* subs@linuxjournal.com *Web Site:* www.belltownmedia.com, pg 34

The Pura Belpre Award, 50 E Huron St, Chicago, IL 60611-2795 *Tel:* 312-280-2163 *Toll Free Tel:* 800-545-2433 *Fax:* 312-440-9374 *E-mail:* alsc@ala.org *Web Site:* www.ala.org/alsc, pg 690

Ben Yehuda Press, 430 Kensington Rd, Teaneck, NJ 07666 *Tel:* 201-833-5145 *Toll Free Tel:* 800-809-3505 *Fax:* 201-917-1278 *E-mail:* orders@benyehudapress.com; yudel@benyehudapress.com *Web Site:* www.benyehudapress.com, pg 34

BenBella Books Inc, 10300 N Central Expwy, Suite 400, Dallas, TX 75231 *Tel:* 214-750-3600 *Fax:* 214-750-3645 *E-mail:* feedback@benbellabooks.com *Web Site:* www.benbellabooks.com; www.smartpopbooks.com, pg 34

R James Bender Publishing, PO Box 23456, San Jose, CA 95153-3456 *Tel:* 408-225-5777 *Fax:* 408-225-4739 *E-mail:* order@bender-publishing.com *Web Site:* www.bender-publishing.com, pg 35

Benjamin Franklin Awards™, 1020 Manhattan Beach Blvd, Suite 204, Manhattan Beach, CA 90266 *Tel:* 310-546-1818 *Fax:* 310-546-3939 *E-mail:* info@ibpa-online.org *Web Site:* www.ibpa-online.org; ibpabenjaminfranklinawards.com, pg 690

John Benjamins Publishing Co, PO Box 27519, Philadelphia, PA 19118 *Tel:* 215-836-1200 *Toll Free Tel:* 800-562-5666 (orders) *Fax:* 215-836-1204 *E-mail:* service@benjamins.com *Web Site:* www.benjamins.com, pg 35

George Bennett Fellowship, Phillips Exeter Academy, Office of the Dean of Faculty, 20 Main St, Exeter, NH 03833-2460 *Tel:* 603-772-4311 *Fax:* 603-777-4384 *E-mail:* teaching_opportunities@exeter.edu *Web Site:* www.exeter.edu, pg 690

Benoit & Associates, 279 S Schuyler Ave, Kankakee, IL 60901 *Tel:* 815-932-2582 *Fax:* 815-932-2594 *E-mail:* benoitart@benoit-associates.com *Web Site:* www.benoit-associates.com, pg 601

Bentley Publishers, 1734 Massachusetts Ave, Cambridge, MA 02138-1804 *Tel:* 617-547-4170 *Toll Free Tel:* 800-423-4595 *Fax:* 617-876-9235 *E-mail:* sales@bentleypublishers.com *Web Site:* www.bentleypublishers.com, pg 35

BePuzzled, 2030 Harrison St, San Francisco, CA 94110 *Tel:* 415-503-1600 *Toll Free Tel:* 800-347-4818 *Fax:* 415-503-0085 *E-mail:* info@ugames.com *Web Site:* www.ugames.com, pg 35

Naomi Berber Memorial Award, 200 Deer Run Rd, Sewickley, PA 15143-2600 *Tel:* 412-259-1705 *Toll Free Tel:* 800-910-4283 (ext 705) *Fax:* 412-749-9890 *E-mail:* printing@printing.org *Web Site:* www.printing.org, pg 690

R J Berg Publisher, 79 Saint Paul St, Burlington, VT 05402-0369 *Tel:* 802-557-0928 *E-mail:* rjbergpublisher@gmail.com; rjberg@americanparksandresorts.com *Web Site:* www.americanparksandresorts.com, pg 35

Berghahn Books, 20 Jay St, Suite 512, Brooklyn, NY 11201 *Tel:* 212-233-6004 *Fax:* 212-233-6007 *E-mail:* info@berghahnbooks.com; salesus@berghahnbooks.com; editorial@journals.berghahnbooks.com *Web Site:* www.berghahnbooks.com, pg 35

Barbara Bergstrom MA LLC, 13 Stockton Way, Howell, NJ 07731 *Tel:* 732-363-8372, pg 541

Berkeley Slavic Specialties, PO Box 3034, Oakland, CA 94609-0034 *Tel:* 510-653-8048 *Fax:* 510-653-6313 *E-mail:* 71034.456@compuserve.com *Web Site:* www.berkslav.com, pg 35

Berkley Books, 375 Hudson St, New York, NY 10014 *Tel:* 212-366-2000 *Fax:* 212-366-2666 *E-mail:* online@penguinputnam.com *Web Site:* www.penguinputnam.com; us.penguingroup.com, pg 35

Berkley Publishing Group, 375 Hudson St, New York, NY 10014 *Tel:* 212-366-2000 *Fax:* 212-366-2385 *E-mail:* online@penguinputnam.com *Web Site:* us.penguingroup.com, pg 36

Berlow Technical Communications Inc, 9 Prairie Ave, Suffern, NY 10901 *E-mail:* bteccinc@yahoo.com, pg 541

Bernan, 4501 Forbes Blvd, Suite 200, Lanham, MD 20706 *Tel:* 301-459-7666 (cust serv & orders) *Fax:* 301-459-0056 *E-mail:* customercare@bernan.com *Web Site:* www.bernan.com, pg 36

Jean Brodsky Bernard, 4609 Chevy Chase Blvd, Chevy Chase, MD 20815-5343 *Tel:* 301-654-8914 *E-mail:* dranreb@starpower.net, pg 541

Jessie Bernard Award, c/o Governance Office, 1430 "K" St NW, Suite 600, Washington, DC 20005 *Tel:* 202-383-9005 *Fax:* 202-638-0882 *E-mail:* governance@asanet.org *Web Site:* www.asanet.org, pg 690

The Charles Bernheimer Prize, University of South Carolina, Dept of Languages, Literature & Cultures, Rm 813-A, 1620 College St, Columbia, SC 29208 *Tel:* 803-777-3021 *Fax:* 803-777-3041 *E-mail:* info@acla.org *Web Site:* www.acla.org, pg 690

Bernstein & Andriulli Inc, 58 W 40 St, 6th fl, New York, NY 10018 *Tel:* 212-682-1490 *Fax:* 212-286-1890 *E-mail:* info@ba-reps.com *Web Site:* www.ba-reps.com, pg 601

Meredith Bernstein Literary Agency Inc, 2095 Broadway, Suite 505, New York, NY 10023 *Tel:* 212-799-1007 *Fax:* 212-799-1145 *E-mail:* MGoodBern@aol.com *Web Site:* www.meredithbernsteinliteraryagency.com, pg 562

Berrett-Koehler Publishers Inc, 235 Montgomery St, Suite 650, San Francisco, CA 94104 *Tel:* 415-288-0260 *Fax:* 415-362-2512 *E-mail:* bkpub@bkpub.com *Web Site:* www.bkconnection.com, pg 36

Bess Press, 3565 Harding Ave, Honolulu, HI 96816 *Tel:* 808-734-7159; 808-734-7159 (ext 10, returns) *Toll Free Tel:* 800-910-2377 *Fax:* 808-732-3627 *E-mail:* sales@besspress.com *Web Site:* www.besspress.com, pg 36

A M Best Co, One Ambest Rd, Oldwick, NJ 08858 *Tel:* 908-439-2200 *Fax:* 908-439-3385 *E-mail:* customer_service@ambest.com; sales@ambest.com *Web Site:* www.ambest.com, pg 36

Bethany House Publishers, 11400 Hampshire Ave S, Bloomington, MN 55438 *Tel:* 952-829-2500 *Toll Free Tel:* 800-877-2665 (orders) *Fax:* 952-829-2568 *Toll Free Fax:* 800-398-3111 (orders) *Web Site:* www.bethanyhouse.com; www.bakerpublishinggroup.com, pg 36

Bethel Agency, PO Box 21043, Park West Sta, New York, NY 10025 *Tel:* 212-864-4510, pg 562

Bethlehem Books, 10194 Garfield St S, Bathgate, ND 58216 *Toll Free Tel:* 800-757-6831 *Fax:* 701-265-3716 *E-mail:* contact@bethlehembooks.com *Web Site:* www.bethlehembooks.com, pg 36

Betterway Books, 10151 Carver Rd, Suite 200, Blue Ash, OH 45242 *Tel:* 513-531-2690 *Toll Free Tel:* 800-666-0963 *Fax:* 513-891-7185 *Toll Free Fax:* 888-590-4082 *Web Site:* www.fwmedia.com, pg 36

Doris Betts Fiction Prize, c/o NC Literary Review, East Carolina University, Dept of English, Greenville, NC 27858-4353 *Tel:* 336-293-8844 *E-mail:* mail@ncwriters.org *Web Site:* www.ncwriters.org, pg 690

Between the Lines, 401 Richmond St W, No 277, Toronto, ON M5V 3A8, Canada *Tel:* 416-535-9914 *Toll Free Tel:* 800-718-7201 *Fax:* 416-535-1484 *E-mail:* info@btlbooks.com *Web Site:* www.btlbooks.com, pg 494

Beullah Rose Poetry Prize, PO Box 22161, Baltimore, MD 21203 *Web Site:* www.smartishpace.com, pg 690

Albert J Beveridge Award in American History, 400 "A" St SE, Washington, DC 20003-3889 *Tel:* 202-544-2422 *Fax:* 202-544-8307 *E-mail:* awards@historians.org *Web Site:* www.historians.org, pg 691

Albert J Beveridge Grant for Research in the History of the Western Hemisphere, 400 "A" St SE, Washington, DC 20003-3889 *Tel:* 202-544-2422 *Fax:* 202-544-8307 *E-mail:* awards@historians.org *Web Site:* www.historians.org, pg 691

Beyond the Book, 222 Rosewood Dr, Danvers, MA 01923 *Tel:* 978-750-8400 *Fax:* 978-646-8600 *E-mail:* beyondthebook@copyright.com *Web Site:* www.copyright.com; beyondthebookcast.com, pg 668

Beyond Words Publishing Inc, 20827 NW Cornell Rd, Suite 500, Hillsboro, OR 97124-9808 *Tel:* 503-531-8700 *Fax:* 503-531-8773 *Web Site:* www.beyondword.com, pg 37

Bhaktivedanta Book Trust (BBT), 9701 Venice Blvd, Suite 3, Los Angeles, CA 90034 *Tel:* 310-837-5283 *Toll Free Tel:* 800-927-4152 *Fax:* 310-837-1056 *E-mail:* store@krishna.com *Web Site:* www.krishna.com, pg 37

BHTG - Competition for Youth Theatre Marilyn Hall Awards, PO Box 148, Beverly Hills, CA 90213 *Tel:* 310-273-3390 *Web Site:* www.beverlyhillstheatreguild.com, pg 691

BHTG - Julie Harris Playwright Award Competition, PO Box 148, Beverly Hills, CA 90213 *Tel:* 310-273-3390 *Web Site:* www.beverlyhillstheatreguild.com, pg 691

Daniel Bial Agency, 41 W 83 St, Suite 5-C, New York, NY 10024 *Tel:* 212-721-1786 *E-mail:* dbialagency@msn.com *Web Site:* www.danielbialagency.com, pg 562

Daniel Bial & Associates, 41 W 83 St, Suite 5-C, New York, NY 10024 *Tel:* 212-721-1786 *E-mail:* dbialagency@msn.com *Web Site:* www.danielbialagency.com, pg 541

Bibliogenesis, 152 Coddington Rd, Ithaca, NY 14850 *Tel:* 607-277-9660, pg 541

Bibliographical Society of America, PO Box 1537, Lenox Hill Sta, New York, NY 10021-0043 *Tel:* 212-452-2710 *Fax:* 212-452-2710 *E-mail:* bsa@bibsocamer.org *Web Site:* www.bibsocamer.org, pg 618

Bibliographical Society of the University of Virginia, c/o Alderman Library, University of Virginia, McCormick Rd, Charlottesville, VA 22904 *Tel:* 434-924-7013 *Fax:* 434-924-1431 *E-mail:* bibsoc@virginia.edu *Web Site:* bsuva.org, pg 618

Bibliotheca Persica Press, 450 Riverside Dr, Suite 4, New York, NY 10027 *Tel:* 212-851-5723 *Fax:* 212-749-9524 *E-mail:* ey4@columbia.edu, pg 37

Biblo-Moser, PO Box 302, Cheshire, CT 06410-0302 *Tel:* 203-988-8100 *Fax:* 203-272-2308 *E-mail:* biblo.moser@snet.net, pg 37

Bick Publishing House, 16 Marion Rd, Branford, CT 06405 *Tel:* 203-208-5253 *Fax:* 203-208-5253 *E-mail:* bickpubhse@aol.com *Web Site:* www.bickpubhouse.com, pg 37

Big Apple Conference, 317 Madison Ave, Suite 1704, New York, NY 10017 *Tel:* 917-720-6959 *E-mail:* iwwgquestions@gmail.com *Web Site:* www.iwwg.org, pg 668

Big Apple Vision Publishing Inc, PO Box 722, Stone Ridge, NY 12484-0722 *Tel:* 845-616-1346 *Fax:* 845-339-9928 *E-mail:* info@bigapplevision.com *Web Site:* bigapplevision.com, pg 37

Big Guy Books Inc, 1042 N El Camino Real, Suite B-231, Encinitas, CA 92024 *Tel:* 760-652-5360 *Toll Free Tel:* 800-536-3030 (booksellers' cust serv) *Fax:* 760-652-5362 *E-mail:* info@bigguybooks.com *Web Site:* www.bigguybooks.com, pg 37

Vicky Bijur Literary Agency, 333 West End Ave, Suite 5-B, New York, NY 10023 *Tel:* 212-580-4108 *E-mail:* queries@vickybijuragency.com *Web Site:* www.vickybijuragency.com, pg 562

Bilingual Review Press/Editorial Bilingue, Arizona State Univ, Hispanic Research Ctr, Tempe, AZ 85287-2702 *Tel:* 480-965-3867 *Toll Free Tel:* 866-965-3867 *Fax:* 480-965-0315 *E-mail:* brp@asu.edu *Web Site:* www.asu.edu/brp, pg 37

The Geoffrey Bilson Award for Historical Fiction for Young People, 40 Orchard View Blvd, Suite 217, Toronto, ON M4R 1B9, Canada *Tel:* 416-975-0010 *Fax:* 416-975-8970 *E-mail:* info@bookcentre.ca *Web Site:* www.bookcentre.ca, pg 691

Binding Industries Association (BIA), 200 Deer Run Rd, Sewickley, PA 15143 *Tel:* 412-741-6860 *Toll Free Tel:* 800-910-4283 *Fax:* 412-741-2311 *E-mail:* printing@printing.org *Web Site:* www.printing.org, pg 618

Binghamton University Creative Writing Program, c/o Dept of English, PO Box 6000, Binghamton, NY 13902-6000 *Tel:* 607-777-2168 *Fax:* 607-777-2408 *E-mail:* cwpro@binghamton.edu *Web Site:* english.binghamton.edu/cwpro, pg 677

Binghamton University John Gardner Fiction Book Award, Dept of English, General Literature & Rhetoric, Library N, Rm 1149, Vestal Pkwy E, Binghamton, NY 13902 *Tel:* 607-777-2713 *Web Site:* english.binghamton.edu/cwpro, pg 691

Binghamton University Milt Kessler Poetry Book Award, Dept of English, General Literature & Rhetoric, Library N, Rm 1149, Vestal Pkwy E, Binghamton, NY 13902 *Tel:* 607-777-2713 *Web Site:* english.binghamton.edu/cwpro, pg 691

Biographical Publishing Co, 95 Sycamore Dr, Prospect, CT 06712-1493 *Tel:* 203-758-3661 *Fax:* 253-793-2618 *E-mail:* biopub@aol.com *Web Site:* www.biopub.us, pg 37

BioTechniques Books, 52 Vanderbilt Ave, 7th fl, New York, NY 10017 *Tel:* 212-520-2777 *Fax:* 212-520-2705 *Web Site:* www.biotechniques.com, pg 38

Birch Brook Press, PO Box 81, Delhi, NY 13753-0081 *Tel:* 607-746-7453 (book sales & prodn) *Fax:* 607-746-7453 *E-mail:* birchbrook@copper.net *Web Site:* www.birchbrookpress.info, pg 38

George T Bisel Co Inc, 710 S Washington Sq, Philadelphia, PA 19106-3519 *Tel:* 215-922-5760 *Toll Free Tel:* 800-247-3526 *Fax:* 215-922-2235 *E-mail:* gbisel@bisel.com *Web Site:* www.bisel.com, pg 38

Bishop Museum Press, 1525 Bernice St, Honolulu, HI 96817 *Tel:* 808-847-3511; 808-847-8291 *Fax:* 808-848-4147 *E-mail:* press@bishopmuseum.org *Web Site:* www.bishopmuseum.org/press, pg 38

Bisk Education, 9417 Princess Palm Ave, Suite 400, Tampa, FL 33619 *Tel:* 813-621-6200 *Toll Free Tel:* 800-874-7877 *Web Site:* www.bisk.com, pg 38

Bitingduck Press LLC, 1262 Sunnyoaks Cir, Altadena, CA 91001 *Tel:* 626-679-2494; 626-507-8033 *E-mail:* notifications@bitingduckpress.com *Web Site:* bitingduckpress.com, pg 38

BizBest Media Corp, 881 Alma Real Dr, Suite 220, Pacific Palisades, CA 90272 *E-mail:* info@bizbest.com *Web Site:* www.bizbest.com, pg 38

BJU Press, 1700 Wade Hampton Blvd, Greenville, SC 29614-0062 *Tel:* 864-242-5100 *Toll Free Tel:* 800-845-5731 *E-mail:* bjupinfo@bjupress.com *Web Site:* www.bjupress.com, pg 38

BkMk Press - University of Missouri-Kansas City, 5101 Rockhill Rd, Kansas City, MO 64110-2499 *Tel:* 816-235-2558 *Fax:* 816-235-2611 *E-mail:* bkmk@umkc.edu *Web Site:* www.umkc.edu/bkmk, pg 38

Black Classic Press, 3921 Vero Rd, Suite F, Baltimore, MD 21203-3414 *Tel:* 410-242-6954 *Toll Free Tel:* 800-476-8870 *Fax:* 410-242-6959 *E-mail:* email@blackclassicbooks.com; blackclassicpress@yahoo.com *Web Site:* www.blackclassicbooks.com; www.bcpdigital.com, pg 39

David Black Agency, 335 Adams St, 27th fl, Suite 2707, Brooklyn, NY 11201 *Tel:* 718-852-5500 *Fax:* 718-852-5539 *Web Site:* www.davidblackagency.com, pg 562

Black Dog & Leventhal Publishers Inc, 151 W 19 St, New York, NY 10011 *Tel:* 212-647-9336 *Toll Free Tel:* 800-722-7202 *Fax:* 212-647-9332 *E-mail:* info@blackdogandleventhal.com; orders@workman.com *Web Site:* www.blackdogandleventhal.com; blackdogonline.com, pg 39

Black Dome Press Corp, 649 Delaware Ave, Delmar, NY 12054 *Tel:* 518-439-6512 *Toll Free Tel:* 800-513-9013 (orders) *Fax:* 518-439-1309 *E-mail:* blackdomep@aol.com *Web Site:* www.blackdomepress.com, pg 39

Black Heron Press, PO Box 13396, Mill Creek, WA 98082-1396 *Tel:* 425-355-4929 *Fax:* 425-355-4929 *Web Site:* blackheron.mav.net, pg 39

Irma S & James H Black Award, 610 W 112 St, New York, NY 10025 *Tel:* 212-875-4458 *Fax:* 212-875-4558 *E-mail:* ccl@bankstreet.edu *Web Site:* www.bankstreet.edu/center-childrens-literature, pg 691

Black Mountain Press, PO Box 9907, Asheville, NC 28815 *Tel:* 828-273-3332 *Web Site:* www.theblackmountainpress.com, pg 39

Black Rabbit Books, 123 S Broad St, Mankato, MN 56001 *Tel:* 507-388-1609 *Fax:* 507-388-1364 *E-mail:* info@blackrabbitbooks.com; orders@blackrabbitbooks.com *Web Site:* www.blackrabbitbooks.com, pg 39

Black Rose Books Ltd, CP 35788 Succ Leo Pariseau, Montreal, QC H2X 0A4, Canada *Tel:* 514-844-4076 *Toll Free Tel:* 800-565-9523 (orders) *Toll Free Fax:* 800-221-9985 (orders) *E-mail:* info@blackrosebooks.net *Web Site:* www.blackrosebooks.net, pg 494

Black Warrior Review Fiction, Nonfiction & Poetry Contest, Office of Student Media, University of Alabama, Tuscaloosa, AL 35486-0027 *Tel:* 205-348-4518 *Web Site:* www.bwr.ua.edu, pg 691

Christopher Blackburn, 16 Purple Sageway, Toronto, ON M2H 2Z5, Canada *Tel:* 416-491-4857 *E-mail:* cblackburn@rogers.com, pg 541

The Blackburn Press, PO Box 287, Caldwell, NJ 07006-0287 *Tel:* 973-228-7077 *Fax:* 973-228-7276 *Web Site:* www.blackburnpress.com, pg 39

John F Blair Publisher, 1406 Plaza Dr, Winston-Salem, NC 27103 *Tel:* 336-768-1374 *Toll Free Tel:* 800-222-9796 *Fax:* 336-768-9194 *Web Site:* www.blairpub.com, pg 40

Neltje Blanchan Memorial Award, 2320 Capitol Ave, Cheyenne, WY 82002 *Tel:* 307-777-5234 *Fax:* 307-777-5499 *Web Site:* wyoarts.state.wy.us, pg 691

Bleecker Street Associates Inc, 217 Thompson St, Suite 519, New York, NY 10012 *Tel:* 212-677-4492 *Fax:* 212-388-0001, pg 562

Theodore C Blegen Award, 701 William Vickers Ave, Durham, NC 27701-3162 *Tel:* 919-682-9319 *Fax:* 919-682-2349 *Web Site:* www.foresthistory.org, pg 692

Bloch Publishing Co, 5875 Mining Terr, Suite 104, Jacksonville, FL 32257-3225 *Tel:* 904-880-7302 *Toll Free Tel:* 866-532-3977 *Fax:* 904-880-7307 *E-mail:* info@blochpub.com *Web Site:* www.blochpub.com, pg 40

Blockbuster Plots for Writers Retreat, PO Box 1402, Capitola, CA 95010 *Tel:* 408-482-4678 *E-mail:* contact@blockbusterplots.com *Web Site:* www.blockbusterplots.com, pg 668

Blood Moon Productions Ltd, 75 Saint Marks Place, Staten Island, NY 10301-1606 *Tel:* 718-556-9410 *E-mail:* editors@bloodmoonproductions.com *Web Site:* bloodmoonproductions.com, pg 40

Bloom Ink, 3497 Bennington Ct, Bloomfield Hills, MI 48301 *Tel:* 248-291-0370 *E-mail:* bbloom@bloomwriting.com *Web Site:* www.bloomwriting.com, pg 541

Bloom's Literary Criticism, 132 W 31 St, 17th fl, New York, NY 10001 *Toll Free Tel:* 800-322-8755 *Toll Free Fax:* 800-678-3633 *E-mail:* custserv@factsonfile.com *Web Site:* www.infobasepublishing.com, pg 40

Bloomsbury Academic, 80 Maiden Lane, Suite 704, New York, NY 10038 *Tel:* 212-953-5858 *Toll Free Tel:* 800-561-7704 *Fax:* 212-953-5944 *E-mail:* info@continuum-books.com *Web Site:* www.continuumbooks.com, pg 40

Bloomsbury Publishing, 175 Fifth Ave, New York, NY 10010 *Tel:* 212-674-5151 *Toll Free Tel:* 800-221-7945 *Fax:* 212-780-0115; 212-982-2837 *E-mail:* marketingusa@bloomsbury.com; adultpublicityusa.@bloomsbury.com *Web Site:* www.bloomsbury.com, pg 40

Heidi Blough, Book Indexer, 502 Tanager Rd, St Augustine, FL 32086 *Tel:* 904-797-6572 *E-mail:* indexing@heidiblough.com *Web Site:* www.heidiblough.com, pg 541

Blue & Ude Writers' Services, 4249 Nuthatch Way, Clinton, WA 98236 *Tel:* 360-341-1630 *E-mail:* blueyude@whidbey.com *Web Site:* www.bluedewritersservices.com, pg 542

Blue Apple Books, 515 Valley St, Suite 170, Maplewood, NJ 07040 *Tel:* 973-763-8191 *Toll Free Tel:* 800-722-6657; 800-733-3000 (orders) *Fax:* 973-763-5944 *E-mail:* info@blueapplebooks.com *Web Site:* blueapplebooks.com, pg 41

Blue Bike Books, 11919 125 St, Edmonton, AB T5L 0S3, Canada *Tel:* 780-951-0032 *E-mail:* info@bluebikebooks.com *Web Site:* www.bluebikebooks.com, pg 495

Blue Book Publications Inc, 8009 34 Ave S, Suite 250, Minneapolis, MN 55425 *Tel:* 952-854-5229 *Toll Free Tel:* 800-877-4867 *Fax:* 925-853-1486 *E-mail:* support@bluebookinc.com *Web Site:* www.bluebookofgunvalues.com; www.bluebookofguitarvalues.com, pg 41

Blue Crane Books, PO Box 380291, Cambridge, MA 02238 *Tel:* 617-926-8989 *Fax:* 617-926-0982 *E-mail:* bluecrane@arrow1.com, pg 41

Blue Dolphin Publishing Inc, 13340-D Grass Valley Ave, Grass Valley, CA 95945 *Tel:* 530-477-1503 *Toll Free Tel:* 800-643-0765 (orders) *Fax:* 530-477-8342 *E-mail:* bdolphin@bluedolphinpublishing.com *Web Site:* www.bluedolphinpublishing.com, pg 41

Blue Forge Press, 7419 Ebbert Dr SE, Port Orchard, WA 98367 *Tel:* 360-769-7174 *E-mail:* blueforgepress@gmail.com, pg 41

Blue Mountain Arts Inc, 2905 Wilderness Place, Boulder, CO 80301 *Tel:* 303-449-0536 *Toll Free Tel:* 800-525-0642 *Fax:* 303-417-6472 *Toll Free Fax:* 800-545-8573 *E-mail:* info@sps.com *Web Site:* www.sps.com, pg 41

Blue Note Publications Inc, 720 North Dr, Suite D, Melbourne, FL 32924 *Tel:* 321-799-2583 *Toll Free Tel:* 800-624-0401 (orders) *Fax:* 321-799-1942 *E-mail:* bluenotepress@gmail.com *Web Site:* www.bluenotebooks.com, pg 41

Blue Poppy Press, 1990 57 Ct, Unit A, Boulder, CO 80301 *Tel:* 303-447-8372 *Toll Free Tel:* 800-487-9296 *Fax:* 303-245-8362 *E-mail:* info@bluepoppy.com *Web Site:* www.bluepoppy.com, pg 41

Blue Rider Press, 375 Hudson St, New York, NY 10014 *Tel:* 212-366-2000, pg 41

BlueBridge, PO Box 601, Katonah, NY 10536 *Tel:* 914-301-5901 *Web Site:* www.bluebridgebooks.com, pg 42

Bristol Park Books, 252 W 38 St, Suite 206, New York, NY 10018 *Tel:* 212-842-0700 *Fax:* 212-842-1771 *E-mail:* ralexander@bbspublishingcorp.com, pg 48

Brittingham & Pollak Prizes in Poetry, Dept of English, 600 N Park St, Madison, WI 53706 *Web Site:* www.wisc.edu/wisconsinpress, pg 693

Broadview Press, 280 Perry St, Unit 5, Peterborough, ON K9J 2J4, Canada *Tel:* 705-743-8990 *Fax:* 705-743-8353 *E-mail:* customerservice@broadviewpress.com *Web Site:* www.broadviewpress.com, pg 496

Brockman Inc, 260 Fifth Ave, 10th fl, New York, NY 10001 *Tel:* 212-935-8900 *Fax:* 212-935-5535 *E-mail:* rights@brockman.com *Web Site:* www.brockman.com, pg 564

Broden Books LLC, 3824 Sunset Dr, Spring Park, MN 55384 *Tel:* 952-471-1066 *E-mail:* media@brodenbooks.com *Web Site:* www.brodenbooks.com, pg 48

Broken Jaw Press Inc, Box 596, Sta A, Fredericton, NB E3B 5A6, Canada *Tel:* 506-454-5127 *Fax:* 506-454-5134 *E-mail:* editors@brokenjaw.com *Web Site:* www.brokenjaw.com, pg 496

Brookes Publishing Co Inc, PO Box 10624, Baltimore, MD 21285-0624 *Tel:* 410-337-9580 (outside US & CN) *Toll Free Tel:* 800-638-3775 (US & CN) *Fax:* 410-337-8539 *E-mail:* custserv@brookespublishing.com *Web Site:* www.brookespublishing.com, pg 48

Brookhaven Press, PO Box 2287, La Crosse, WI 54602-2287 *Tel:* 608-781-0850 *Toll Free Tel:* 800-236-0850 *Fax:* 608-781-3883 *E-mail:* brookhaven@nmt.com *Web Site:* www.brookhavenpress.com, pg 48

The Brookings Institution Press, 1775 Massachusetts Ave NW, Washington, DC 20036-2188 *Tel:* 202-536-3600 *Toll Free Tel:* 800-537-5487 *Fax:* 202-536-3623 *E-mail:* permissions@brookings.edu *Web Site:* www.brookings.edu, pg 48

Brookline Books, 8 Trumbull Rd, Suite B-001, Northampton, MA 01060 *Tel:* 603-669-7032 (orders); 413-584-0184 *Toll Free Tel:* 800-666-2665 (orders) *Fax:* 413-584-6184 *E-mail:* brbooks@yahoo.com *Web Site:* www.brooklinebooks.com, pg 48

Brooklyn Publishers LLC, 211 First Ave SE, Suite 200, Cedar Rapids, IA 52401 *Tel:* 319-368-8012 *Toll Free Tel:* 888-473-8521 *Fax:* 319-368-8011 *E-mail:* customerservice@brookpub.com; editor@brookpub.com *Web Site:* www.brookpub.com, pg 48

Broquet Inc, 97-B Montee des Bouleaux, St Constant, QC J5A 1A9, Canada *Tel:* 450-638-3338 *Fax:* 450-638-4338 *E-mail:* info@broquet.qc.ca *Web Site:* www.broquet.qc.ca, pg 496

The Heywood Broun Award, 501 Third St NW, 6th fl, Washington, DC 20001-2797 *Tel:* 202-434-7177; 202-434-7162 (The Guild Reporter) *Fax:* 202-434-1472 *Web Site:* www.newsguild.org, pg 693

Brown Barn Books, 119 Kettle Creek Rd, Weston, CT 06883 *Tel:* 203-227-3387 *Fax:* 203-222-9673 *E-mail:* editorial@brownbarnbooks.com *Web Site:* www.brownbarnbooks.com, pg 48

Brown Books Publishing Group, 16250 Knoll Trail, Suite 205, Dallas, TX 75248 *Tel:* 972-381-0009 *Fax:* 972-248-4336 *E-mail:* publishing@brownbooks.com *Web Site:* www.brownbooks.com, pg 49

Curtis Brown Ltd, 10 Astor Place, New York, NY 10003 *Tel:* 212-473-5400 *Web Site:* www.curtisbrown.com, pg 565

John Nicholas Brown Prize, 104 Mount Auburn St, 5th fl, Cambridge, MA 02138 *Tel:* 617-491-1622 *Fax:* 617-492-3303 *E-mail:* speculum@medievalacademy.org *Web Site:* www.medievalacademy.org, pg 693

Karen Brown's Guides Inc, 16 E Third Ave, Suite 9, San Mateo, CA 94401 *Tel:* 650-342-9117 *Fax:* 650-342-9153 *E-mail:* orders@karenbrown.com *Web Site:* www.karenbrown.com, pg 49

Marie Brown Associates, 412 W 154 St, New York, NY 10032 *Tel:* 212-939-9725 *Fax:* 212-939-9728 *E-mail:* mbrownlit@aol.com, pg 565

Browne & Miller Literary Associates, 410 S Michigan Ave, Suite 460, Chicago, IL 60605 *Tel:* 312-922-3063 *Fax:* 312-922-1905 *E-mail:* mail@browneandmiller.com *Web Site:* www.browneandmiller.com, pg 565

Gordon Brumm, 1515 St Charles Ave, Lakewood, OH 44107 *Tel:* 216-226-6105 *Fax:* 216-226-1964 *E-mail:* brummg@cox.net, pg 542

Brush Education Inc, 1220 Kensington Rd NW, Suite 210, Calgary, AB T2N 3P5, Canada *Tel:* 403-283-0900 *Fax:* 403-283-6947 *E-mail:* contact@brusheducation.ca *Web Site:* www.brusheducation.ca, pg 496

Don Buchwald & Associates Inc, 10 E 44 St, New York, NY 10017 *Tel:* 212-867-1200 *Fax:* 212-867-2434 *E-mail:* info@buchwald.com *Web Site:* www.buchwald.com, pg 565

Howard Buck Agency, 80 Eighth Ave, Suite 1107, New York, NY 10011 *Tel:* 212-924-9093, pg 565

Bucknell Seminar for Younger Poets, Bucknell University, Bucknell Hall, Moore Ave, Lewisburg, PA 17837 *Tel:* 570-577-1853 *Fax:* 570-577-1885 *E-mail:* stadlercenter@bucknell.edu *Web Site:* www.bucknell.edu/stadlercenter, pg 693

Bucknell University Press, Taylor Hall, Bucknell University, Lewisburg, PA 17837 *Tel:* 570-577-3674 *E-mail:* aup440@aol.com *Web Site:* www.bucknell.edu/universitypress, pg 49

Judith Buckner Literary Agency, 12721 Hart St, North Hollywood, CA 91605 *Tel:* 818-982-8202 *Fax:* 818-764-6844, pg 565

Georges Bugnet Award for Fiction, 11759 Groat Rd, Edmonton, AB T5M 3K6, Canada *Tel:* 780-422-8174 *Toll Free Tel:* 800-665-5354 (AB only) *Fax:* 780-422-2663 (attn WGA) *E-mail:* mail@writersguild.ab.ca *Web Site:* www.writersguild.ab.ca, pg 693

BuilderBooks.com, 1201 15 St NW, Washington, DC 20005 *Tel:* 202-822-0200 *Toll Free Tel:* 800-223-2665 *Fax:* 202-266-8096 (edit) *E-mail:* builderbooks@nahb.com *Web Site:* www.builderbooks.com, pg 49

The Bukowski Agency, 14 Prince Arthur Ave, Suite 202, Toronto, ON M5R 1A9, Canada *Tel:* 416-928-6728 *Fax:* 416-963-9978 *E-mail:* info@bukowskiagency.com *Web Site:* www.bukowskiagency.com, pg 565

Bull Publishing Co, PO Box 1377, Boulder, CO 80306 *Tel:* 303-545-6350 *Toll Free Tel:* 800-676-2855 *Fax:* 303-545-6354 *E-mail:* bullpublishing@msn.com *Web Site:* www.bullpub.com, pg 49

Bunker Hill Publishing, 285 River Rd, Piermont, NH 03779 *Tel:* 603-272-9221 *Fax:* 603-283-7240 *E-mail:* mail@bunkerhillpublishing.com *Web Site:* www.bunkerhillpublishing.com, pg 49

The Bureau For At-Risk Youth, 303 Crossways Park Dr, Woodbury, NY 11797 *Tel:* 516-496-4863 *Fax:* 516-496-4050 *Web Site:* www.at-risk.com; www.guidance-group.com, pg 49

Bureau of Economic Geology, University of Texas at Austin, 10100 Burnet Rd, Bldg 130, Austin, TX 78758 *Tel:* 512-471-1534 *E-mail:* pubsales@beg.utexas.edu *Web Site:* www.beg.utexas.edu, pg 49

Burford Books, 101 E State St, No 301, Ithaca, NY 14850 *Tel:* 607-319-4373 *Fax:* 607-319-4373 *Toll Free Fax:* 866-212-7750 *E-mail:* info@burfordbooks.com *Web Site:* www.burfordbooks.com, pg 49

Hilary R Burke, 59 Sparks St, Ottawa, ON K1P 6C3, Canada *Tel:* 613-237-4658 *E-mail:* hburke99@yahoo.com, pg 542

Burns Archive Press, 140 E 38 St, New York, NY 10016 *Tel:* 212-889-1938 *Fax:* 212-481-9113 *Web Site:* www.burnsarchive.com, pg 49

Burns Entertainment & Sports Marketing, 820 Davis St, Suite 222, Evanston, IL 60201 *Tel:* 847-866-9400 *Fax:* 847-491-9778 *E-mail:* burnsl@burnsent.com *Web Site:* burnsent.com, pg 605

Burnside Review Fiction Chapbook Competition, PO Box 1782, Portland, OR 97207 *Web Site:* burnsidereview.org, pg 693

The John Burroughs List of Nature Books for Young Readers, 15 W 77 St, New York, NY 10024 *Tel:* 212-769-5169 *Fax:* 212-313-7182 *Web Site:* research.amnh.org/burroughs, pg 693

John Burroughs Medal, 15 W 77 St, New York, NY 10024 *Tel:* 212-769-5169 *Fax:* 212-313-7182 *Web Site:* research.amnh.org/burroughs, pg 693

John Burroughs Outstanding Published Nature Essay Award, 15 W 77 St, New York, NY 10024 *Tel:* 212-769-5169 *Fax:* 212-313-7182 *Web Site:* research.amnh.org/burroughs, pg 694

Business & Legal Reports Inc (BLR), 100 Winners Circle, Suite 300, Brentwood, CT 37027 *Tel:* 860-510-0100 *Toll Free Tel:* 800-727-5257 *E-mail:* service@blr.com *Web Site:* www.blr.com, pg 50

Business Expert Press, 222 E 46 St, New York, NY 10017-2906 *Tel:* 908-752-1257 *E-mail:* molly.hurford@businessexpertpress.com *Web Site:* www.businessexpertpress.com, pg 50

Business Forms Management Association (BFMA), 1147 Fleetwood Ave, Madison, WI 53716 *Toll Free Tel:* 888-367-3078 *E-mail:* bfma@bfma.org *Web Site:* www.bfma.org, pg 619

Business Marketing Association (BMA), 1833 Centre Point Circle, Suite 123, Naperville, IL 60563 *Tel:* 630-544-5054 *Fax:* 630-544-5055 *E-mail:* info@marketing.org *Web Site:* www.marketing.org, pg 619

Business Research Services Inc, 7720 Wisconsin Ave, Suite 213, Bethesda, MD 20814 *Tel:* 301-229-5561 *Toll Free Tel:* 800-845-8420 *Fax:* 301-229-6133 *E-mail:* brspubs@sba8a.com *Web Site:* www.sba8a.com; www.setasidealert.com, pg 50

Butte Publications Inc, PO Box 1328, Hillsboro, OR 97123-1328 *Tel:* 503-648-9791 *Toll Free Tel:* 866-312-8883 *Fax:* 503-693-9526 *Toll Free Fax:* 866-412-8883 (orders only) *E-mail:* service@buttepublications.com *Web Site:* www.buttepublications.com, pg 50

Byer-Sprinzeles Agency, 5800 Arlington Ave, Suite 16-C, Riverdale, NY 10471 *Tel:* 718-543-9399 *Web Site:* www.maggiebyersprinzeles.com, pg 601

Sheree Bykofsky Associates Inc, PO Box 706, Brigantine, NJ 08203 *E-mail:* submitbee@aol.com *Web Site:* www.shereebee.com, pg 565

Bywater Books, PO Box 3671, Ann Arbor, MI 48106-3671 *Tel:* 734-662-8815 *Web Site:* bywaterbooks.com, pg 50

BZ/Rights & Permissions Inc, 145 W 86 St, New York, NY 10024 *Tel:* 212-924-3000 *Fax:* 212-924-2525 *E-mail:* info@bzrights.com *Web Site:* www.bzrights.com, pg 542

C & M Online Media Inc, 3905 Meadow Field Lane, Raleigh, NC 27606 *Tel:* 919-233-8164 *E-mail:* support@cmonline.com *Web Site:* www.cmonline.com, pg 50

C & T Publishing Inc, 1651 Challenge Dr, Concord, CA 94520-5206 *Tel:* 925-677-0377 *Toll Free Tel:* 800-284-1114 *Fax:* 925-677-0373 *E-mail:* ctinfo@ctpub.com *Web Site:* www.ctpub.com, pg 50

CAA Award for Fiction, 6 West St N, Suite 203, Orillia, ON L3V 5B8, Canada *Tel:* 705-325-3926 *Toll Free Tel:* 866-216-6222 *E-mail:* admin@canauthors.org *Web Site:* www.canauthors.org, pg 694

CAA Emerging Writer Award, 6 West St N, Suite 203, Orillia, ON L3V 5B8, Canada *Tel:* 705-325-3926 *Toll Free Tel:* 866-216-6222 *E-mail:* admin@canauthors.org *Web Site:* www.canauthors.org, pg 694

CAA Lela Common Award for Canadian History, 6 West St N, Suite 203, Orillia, ON L3V 5B8, Canada *Tel:* 705-325-3926 *Toll Free Tel:* 866-216-6222 *E-mail:* admin@canauthors.org *Web Site:* www.canauthors.org, pg 694

CAA Poetry Award, 6 West St N, Suite 203, Orillia, ON L3V 5B8, Canada *Tel:* 705-325-3926 *Toll Free Tel:* 866-216-6222 *E-mail:* admin@canauthors.org *Web Site:* www.canauthors.org, pg 694

Capital Crime Press, PO Box 272904, Fort Collins, CO 80527 *Tel:* 970-481-4894 *Web Site:* www.capitalcrimepress.com, pg 51

Capital Enquiry Inc, 1034 Emerald Bay Rd, No 435, South Lake Tahoe, CA 96150 *Tel:* 916-442-1434 *Toll Free Tel:* 800-922-7486 *Fax:* 916-244-2704 *E-mail:* info@capenq.com *Web Site:* www.govbuddy.com, pg 51

Alexander Patterson Cappon Prize for Fiction, UMKC, University House, 5101 Rockhill Rd, Kansas City, MO 64110-2499 *Tel:* 816-235-1168 *Fax:* 816-235-2611 *E-mail:* newletters@umkc.edu *Web Site:* www.newletters.org, pg 694

Dorothy Churchill Cappon Prize for the Essay, UMKC, University House, 5101 Rockhill Rd, Kansas City, MO 64110-2499 *Tel:* 816-235-1168 *Fax:* 816-235-2611 *E-mail:* newletters@umkc.edu *Web Site:* www.newletters.org, pg 694

Capstone Publishers™, 1710 Roe Crest Dr, North Mankato, MN 56003 *Toll Free Tel:* 800-747-4992 (cust serv) *Toll Free Fax:* 888-262-0705 *Web Site:* www.capstonepress.com, pg 51

Captain Fiddle Music & Publications, 94 Wiswall Rd, Lee, NH 03824 *Tel:* 603-659-2658 *E-mail:* cfiddle@tiac.net *Web Site:* captainfiddle.com, pg 52

Captus Press Inc, 1600 Steeles Ave W, Units 14-15, Concord, ON L4K 4M2, Canada *Tel:* 416-736-5537 *Fax:* 416-736-5793 *E-mail:* info@captus.com *Web Site:* www.captus.com, pg 498

Les Editions Caractere, 5800, rue Saint-Denis, bureau 900, Montreal, QC H2S 3L5, Canada *Tel:* 514-273-1066 *Fax:* 514-276-0324 *E-mail:* caractere@tc.tc *Web Site:* www.editionscaractere.com, pg 498

Aristide D Caratzas, Publisher, PO Box 344H, Scarsdale, NY 10583 *Tel:* 914-725-4847 *Fax:* 914-725-4847 (call first) *E-mail:* contact@caratzas.com *Web Site:* www.caratzas.com, pg 52

Caravan Books, 6946 E Stevens Rd, Cave Creek, AZ 85331-8677 *Tel:* 480-575-9945 *E-mail:* sfandr@msn.com *Web Site:* www.scholarsbooklist.com, pg 52

Cardiotext Publishing, 3405 W 44 St, Minneapolis, MN 55410 *Tel:* 612-925-2053 *Toll Free Tel:* 888-999-9174 *Fax:* 612-922-7556 *E-mail:* info@cardiotextpublishing.com *Web Site:* www.cardiotextpublishing.com, pg 52

Cardoza Publishing, 5473 S Eastern Ave, Las Vegas, NV 89119 *Tel:* 702-870-7200 *Toll Free Tel:* 800-577-WINS (577-9467) *Fax:* 702-822-6500 *E-mail:* cardozabooks@aol.com; info@cardozabooks.com *Web Site:* www.cardozabooks.com, pg 52

Cardweb.com Inc®, 999 Vanderbilt Beach Rd, 2nd fl, Naples, FL 34108 *Tel:* 239-325-5300 *Toll Free Tel:* 800-874-8999 *Fax:* 239-236-0835 *Toll Free Fax:* 800-821-4627 *E-mail:* cardservices@cardweb.com; cardstaff@cardweb.com *Web Site:* www.cardweb.com, pg 52

The Career Press Inc, 220 W Parkway, Unit 12, Pompton Plains, NJ 07444 *Tel:* 201-848-0310 *Toll Free Tel:* 800-CAREER-1 (227-3371) *Fax:* 201-848-1727 *Web Site:* www.careerpress.com, pg 52

Caribe Betania Editores, PO Box 141000, Nashville, TN 37214-1000 *Tel:* 615-902-1893 *Toll Free Tel:* 800-322-7423 (ext 1893) *Fax:* 615-883-9376 *Web Site:* www.caribebetania.com, pg 52

Carlisle Press - Walnut Creek, 2673 Township Rd 421, Sugarcreek, OH 44681 *Tel:* 330-852-1900 *Toll Free Tel:* 800-852-4482 *Fax:* 330-852-3285, pg 52

Charles Carmony, 250 W 105 St, Suite 2-A, New York, NY 10025 *Tel:* 212-749-1835 *Fax:* 212-749-1835 *E-mail:* ccarmony@verizon.net, pg 542

Carnegie Mellon University Press, 5032 Forbes Ave, Pittsburgh, PA 15289-1021 *Tel:* 412-268-2861 *Toll Free Tel:* 800-666-2211 *Fax:* 412-268-8706 *E-mail:* carnegiemellonuniversitypress@gmail.com *Web Site:* www.cmu.edu/universitypress, pg 52

Carnegie-Whitney Award, 50 E Huron St, Chicago, IL 60611 *Tel:* 312-280-5416 *Toll Free Tel:* 800-545-2433 *Fax:* 312-280-5275; 312-440-9379 *Web Site:* www.ala.org, pg 695

Carolina Academic Press, 700 Kent St, Durham, NC 27701 *Tel:* 919-489-7486 *Toll Free Tel:* 800-489-7486 *Fax:* 919-493-5668 *E-mail:* cap@cap-press.com *Web Site:* www.cap-press.com; www.caplaw.com, pg 52

Carolrhoda Books, 241 First Ave N, Minneapolis, MN 55401 *Tel:* 612-332-3344 *Toll Free Tel:* 800-328-4929 *Fax:* 612-332-7615 *Toll Free Fax:* 800-332-1132 *E-mail:* info@lernerbooks.com *Web Site:* www.lernerbooks.com, pg 53

Carolrhoda Lab™, 241 First Ave N, Minneapolis, MN 55401 *Tel:* 612-332-3344 *Toll Free Tel:* 800-328-4929 *Fax:* 612-332-7615 *Toll Free Fax:* 800-332-1132 (US) *E-mail:* info@lernerbooks.com *Web Site:* www.lernerbooks.com, pg 53

Carpe Indexum, 364 Woodbine Ave, Syracuse, NY 13206-3324 *Tel:* 315-431-4949 *E-mail:* info@carpeindexum.com *Web Site:* www.carpeindexum.com, pg 542

Carroll Publishing, 4701 Sangamore Rd, Suite S-155, Bethesda, MD 20816 *Tel:* 301-263-9800 *Toll Free Tel:* 800-336-4240 *Fax:* 301-263-9801 *E-mail:* info@carrollpub.com *Web Site:* www.carrollpub.com, pg 53

R E Carsch, MS-Consultant, 1453 Rhode Island St, San Francisco, CA 94107-3248 *Tel:* 415-641-1095 *E-mail:* recarsch@mzinfo.com, pg 542

Anne Carson Associates, 3323 Nebraska Ave NW, Washington, DC 20016 *Tel:* 202-244-6679, pg 542

Carson-Dellosa Publishing LLC, PO Box 35665, Greensboro, NC 27425-5665 *Tel:* 336-632-0084 *Toll Free Tel:* 800-321-0943 *Fax:* 336-808-3273 *Toll Free Fax:* 800-535-2669 *E-mail:* custsvc@carsondellosa.com *Web Site:* www.carsondellosa.com, pg 53

Carstens Publications Inc, 108 Phil Hardin Rd, Newton, NJ 07860 *Tel:* 973-383-3355 *Toll Free Tel:* 888-526-5365 *Fax:* 973-383-4064 *E-mail:* carstens@carstens-publications.com *Web Site:* www.carstens-publications.com, pg 53

Carswell, One Corporate Plaza, 2075 Kennedy Rd, Toronto, ON M1T 3V4, Canada *Tel:* 416-609-8000; 416-298-5141; 416-609-3800 (cust rel) *Toll Free Tel:* 800-387-5164 (cust serv CN & US) *Fax:* 416-298-5094; 416-298-5082 (cust rel) *Toll Free Fax:* 877 750 9041 (CN only) *E-mail:* carswell.customerrelations@thomson.com *Web Site:* www.carswell.com, pg 498

Carol Cartaino, 2000 Flat Run Rd, Seaman, OH 45679 *Tel:* 937-764-1303 *Fax:* 937-764-1303 *E-mail:* cartaino@aol.com, pg 542

CarTech Inc, 39966 Grand Ave, North Branch, MN 55056 *Tel:* 651-277-1200 *Toll Free Tel:* 800-551-4754 *Fax:* 651-277-1203 *E-mail:* info@cartechbooks.com *Web Site:* www.cartechbooks.com, pg 53

Amon Carter Museum, 3501 Camp Bowie Blvd, Fort Worth, TX 76107-2695 *Tel:* 817-738-1933; 817-738-5065 (PR) *Toll Free Tel:* 800-573-1933 *Fax:* 817-336-1123 *E-mail:* pr@cartermuseum.org *Web Site:* www.cartermuseum.org, pg 53

The Carter Prize For The Essay, Washington & Lee University, Mattingly House, 204 W Washington St, Lexington, VA 24450-2116 *Tel:* 540-458-8765 *E-mail:* shenandoah@wlu.edu *Web Site:* shenandoahliterary.org; shenandoah.wlu.edu, pg 695

Claudia Caruana, PO Box 654, Murray Hill Sta, New York, NY 10016 *Tel:* 516-488-5815 *E-mail:* ccaruana29@hotmail.com, pg 542

Maria Carvainis Agency Inc, Rockefeller Center, 1270 Avenue of the Americas, Suite 2320, New York, NY 10020 *Tel:* 212-245-6365 *Fax:* 212-245-7196 *E-mail:* mca@mariacarvainisagency.com *Web Site:* mariacarvainisagency.com, pg 565

Casa Bautista de Publicaciones, 7000 Alabama Ave, El Paso, TX 79904 *Tel:* 915-566-9656 *Toll Free Tel:* 800-755-5958 (cust serv & orders) *Fax:* 915-562-6502; 915-565-9008 (orders) *Web Site:* www.casabautista.org; www.editorialmh.org, pg 53

Cascade Pass Inc, 4223 Glencoe Ave, Suite C-105, Marina Del Rey, CA 90292 *Tel:* 310-305-0210 *Toll Free Tel:* 888-837-0704 *Fax:* 310-305-7850 *Web Site:* www.cascadepass.com, pg 54

Casemate Publishers & Book Distributors LLC, 908 Darby Rd, Havertown, PA 19083 *Tel:* 610-853-9131 *Fax:* 610-853-9146 *E-mail:* casemate@casematepublishing.com *Web Site:* www.casematepublishing.com, pg 54

Angela M Casey, 42 Nathaniel Blvd, Delmar, NY 12054 *Tel:* 518-729-2693 *E-mail:* casey.angela.m@gmail.com, pg 542

Castiglia Literary Agency, 1155 Camino Del Mar, Suite 510, Del Mar, CA 92014 *Tel:* 858-755-8761 *Fax:* 858-755-7063 *Web Site:* www.castiglialiteraryagency.com, pg 566

Castle Connolly Medical Ltd, 42 W 24 St, 2nd fl, New York, NY 10010 *Tel:* 212-367-8400 *Toll Free Tel:* 800-339-DOCS (339-3627) *Fax:* 212-367-0964 *Web Site:* www.castleconnolly.com, pg 54

Catalyst Communication Arts, 94 Chuparrosa Dr, San Luis Obispo, CA 93401 *Tel:* 805-235-2351 *Fax:* 805-543-7140 *Web Site:* www.sonsieconroy.com, pg 542

Catalyst Creative Services, 619 Marion Plaza, Palo Alto, CA 94301-4251 *Tel:* 650-325-1500 *Web Site:* www.CatalystCreative.us, pg 543

Catholic Book Awards, 205 W Monroe St, Suite 470, Chicago, IL 60606 *Tel:* 312-380-6789 *Fax:* 312-361-0256 *E-mail:* cathjourn@catholicpress.org *Web Site:* www.catholicpress.org, pg 695

Catholic Book Publishing Corp, 77 West End Rd, Totowa, NJ 07512 *Tel:* 973-890-2400 *Toll Free Tel:* 877-228-2665 *Fax:* 973-890-2410 *E-mail:* info@catholicbookpublishing.com *Web Site:* www.catholicbookpublishing.com, pg 54

The Catholic Health Association of the United States, 4455 Woodson Rd, St Louis, MO 63134-3797 *Tel:* 314-427-2500 *Fax:* 314-253-0029 *E-mail:* servicecenter@chausa.org *Web Site:* www.chausa.org, pg 54

Catholic Library Association, 205 W Monroe, Suite 314, Chicago, IL 60606-5061 *Tel:* 312-739-1776 *Toll Free Tel:* 855-739-1776 *Fax:* 312-739-1778 *E-mail:* cla2@cathla.org *Web Site:* www.cathla.org, pg 620

Catholic Press Association of the US & Canada, 205 W Monroe St, Suite 470, Chicago, IL 60606 *Tel:* 312-380-6789 *Fax:* 312-361-0256 *E-mail:* cathjourn@catholicpress.org *Web Site:* www.catholicpress.org, pg 620

Catholic Press Association of the US & Canada Journalism Awards, 205 W Monroe St, Suite 470, Chicago, IL 60606 *Tel:* 312-380-6789 *Fax:* 312-361-0256 *E-mail:* cathjourn@catholicpress.org *Web Site:* www.catholicpress.org, pg 695

The Catholic University of America Press, 240 Leahy Hall, 620 Michigan Ave NE, Washington, DC 20064 *Tel:* 202-319-5052 *Toll Free Tel:* 800-537-5487 (orders only) *Fax:* 202-319-4985 *E-mail:* cua-press@cua.edu *Web Site:* cuapress.cua.edu, pg 54

Cato Institute, 1000 Massachusetts Ave NW, Washington, DC 20001-5403 *Tel:* 202-842-0200 *Toll Free Tel:* 800-767-1241 *Fax:* 202-842-3490 *E-mail:* catostore@cato.org *Web Site:* www.cato.org, pg 54

Jeanne Cavelos Editorial Services, PO Box 75, Mont Vernon, NH 03057 *Tel:* 603-673-6234 *Web Site:* www.jeannecavelos.com, pg 543

Caxton Press, 312 Main St, Caldwell, ID 83605-3299 *Tel:* 208-459-7421 *Toll Free Tel:* 800-657-6465 *Fax:* 208-459-7450 *E-mail:* publish@caxtonpress.com *Web Site:* www.caxtonpress.com, pg 54

CBA Libris Award for Author of the Year, 1255 Bay St, Suite 902, Toronto, ON M5R 2A9, Canada *Tel:* 416-467-7883 *Toll Free Tel:* 866-788-0790 *Fax:* 416-467-7886 *E-mail:* enquiries@cbabook.org *Web Site:* www.cbabook.org, pg 695

CBA Libris Children's Picture Book of the Year, 1255 Bay St, Suite 902, Toronto, ON M5R 2A9, Canada *Tel:* 416-467-7883 *Toll Free Tel:* 866-788-0790 *Fax:* 416-467-7886 *E-mail:* enquiries@cbabook.org *Web Site:* www.cbabook.org, pg 695

CBA Libris Distributor of the Year, 1255 Bay St, Suite 902, Toronto, ON M5R 2A9, Canada *Tel:* 416-467-7883 *Toll Free Tel:* 866-788-0790 *Fax:* 416-467-7886 *E-mail:* enquiries@cbabook.org *Web Site:* www.cbabook.org, pg 695

CBA Libris Editor of the Year, 1255 Bay St, Suite 902, Toronto, ON M5R 2A9, Canada *Tel:* 416-467-7883 *Toll Free Tel:* 866-788-0790 *Fax:* 416-467-7886 *E-mail:* enquiries@cbabook.org *Web Site:* www.cbabook.org, pg 695

CBA Libris Fiction Book of the Year, 1255 Bay St, Suite 902, Toronto, ON M5R 2A9, Canada *Tel:* 416-467-7883 *Toll Free Tel:* 866-788-0790 *Fax:* 416-467-7886 *E-mail:* enquiries@cbabook.org *Web Site:* www.cbabook.org, pg 695

CBA Libris Publisher of the Year, 1255 Bay St, Suite 902, Toronto, ON M5R 2A9, Canada *Tel:* 416-467-7883 *Toll Free Tel:* 866-788-0790 *Fax:* 416-467-7886 *E-mail:* enquiries@cbabook.org *Web Site:* www.cbabook.org, pg 695

CBA Libris Sales Rep of the Year, 1255 Bay St, Suite 902, Toronto, ON M5R 2A9, Canada *Tel:* 416-467-7883 *Toll Free Tel:* 866-788-0790 *Fax:* 416-467-7886 *E-mail:* enquiries@cbabook.org *Web Site:* www.cbabook.org, pg 695

CBA Libris Small Press Publisher of the Year, 1255 Bay St, Suite 902, Toronto, ON M5R 2A9, Canada *Tel:* 416-467-7883 *Toll Free Tel:* 866-788-0790 *Fax:* 416-467-7886 *E-mail:* enquiries@cbabook.org *Web Site:* www.cbabook.org, pg 696

CBA: The Association for Christian Retail, 9240 Explorer Dr, Suite 200, Colorado Springs, CO 80920 *Tel:* 719-265-9895 *Toll Free Tel:* 800-252-1950 *Fax:* 719-272-3510 *E-mail:* info@cbaonline.org *Web Site:* www.cbaonline.org, pg 620

CCAB Inc, One Concorde Gate, Suite 800, Toronto, ON M3C 3N6, Canada *Tel:* 416-487-2418 *Fax:* 416-487-6405 *E-mail:* info@bpaww.com *Web Site:* www.bpaww.com, pg 621

CCH, a Wolters Kluwer business, 2700 Lake Cook Rd, Riverwoods, IL 60015 *Tel:* 847-267-7000 *Toll Free Tel:* 800-525-3335 *Fax:* 773-866-3095 *Web Site:* www.cch.com, pg 55

CCH Canadian Limited, A Wolters Kluwer Company, 90 Sheppard Ave E, Suite 300, Toronto, ON M2N 6X1, Canada *Tel:* 416-224-2224 *Toll Free Tel:* 800-268-4522 (CN & US cust serv) *Fax:* 416-224-2243 *Toll Free Fax:* 800-461-4131 *E-mail:* cservice@cch.ca (cust serv) *Web Site:* www.cch.ca, pg 498

CDL Press, PO Box 34454, Bethesda, MD 20827 *Tel:* 301-762-2066 *Fax:* 253-484-5542 *E-mail:* cdlpress@erols.com *Web Site:* www.cdlpress.com, pg 55

CeciBooks Editorial & Publishing Consultation, 7057 26 Ave NW, Seattle, WA 98117 *Tel:* 206-706-9565 *E-mail:* cecibooks@gmail.com *Web Site:* www.cecibooks.com, pg 543

Cedar Fort Inc, 2373 W 700 S, Springville, UT 84663 *Tel:* 801-489-4084 *Toll Free Tel:* 800-SKY-BOOK (759-2665) *Fax:* 801-489-1097 *Toll Free Fax:* 800-388-3727 *E-mail:* brycemortimer@cedarfort.com *Web Site:* www.cedarfort.com, pg 55

Cedar Tree Books, PO Box 4256, Wilmington, DE 19807 *Tel:* 302-998-4171 *Fax:* 302-998-4185 *E-mail:* books@ctpress.com *Web Site:* www.cedartreebooks.com, pg 55

CEF Press, 17482 State Hwy M, Warrenton, MO 63383-0348 *Tel:* 636-456-4321 *Toll Free Tel:* 800-748-7710 (cust serv); 800-300-4033 (USA ministries) *Fax:* 636-456-9935 *E-mail:* cefexecutiveoffices@cefonline.com *Web Site:* www.cefonline.com, pg 55

Celebra, 375 Hudson St, New York, NY 10014 *Tel:* 212-366-2000 *Fax:* 212-366-2889, pg 55

Celebrity Profiles Publishing, PO Box 344, Stony Brook, NY 11790 *Tel:* 631-862-8555 *Fax:* 631-862-0139 *E-mail:* celebpro4@aol.com *Web Site:* www.richardgrudens.com, pg 55

Celestial Arts Publishing Co, 2625 Alcatraz Ave, Suite 505, Berkeley, CA 94705-2702 *Tel:* 510-285-3000 *Toll Free Tel:* 800-841-2665; 800-733-3000 (orders & cust serv) *Fax:* 510-599-1629 *E-mail:* csorders@randomhouse.com *Web Site:* www.tenspeed.com, pg 55

Cengage Learning, 200 First Stamford Place, Suite 400, Stamford, CT 06902 *Tel:* 203-965-8600 *Toll Free Tel:* 800-354-9706 *Fax:* 203-965-8599 *Toll Free Fax:* 800-487-8488 *E-mail:* esales@cengage.com *Web Site:* www.cengage.com, pg 55

The Center for Book Arts, 28 W 27 St, 3rd fl, New York, NY 10001 *Tel:* 212-481-0295 *Toll Free Fax:* 866-708-8994 *E-mail:* info@centerforbookarts.org *Web Site:* www.centerforbookarts.org, pg 621, 677

Center for Creative Leadership LLC, One Leadership Place, Greensboro, NC 27410-9427 *Tel:* 336-545-2810; 336-288-7210 *Fax:* 336-282-3284 *E-mail:* info@ccl.org *Web Site:* www.ccl.org/publications, pg 55

Center for East Asian Studies (CEAS), Western Washington University, 516 High St, Bellingham, WA 98225-9057 *Tel:* 360-650-3339 *Fax:* 360-650-6110 *E-mail:* easpress@wwu.edu *Web Site:* www.wwu.edu/eas, pg 56

The Center for Exhibition Industry Research (CEIR), 12700 Park Central Dr, Suite 308, Dallas, TX 75251 *Tel:* 972-687-9242 *Fax:* 972-692-6020 *E-mail:* info@ceir.org *Web Site:* www.ceir.org, pg 621

The Center for Fiction, 17 E 47 St, New York, NY 10017 *Tel:* 212-755-6710 *Fax:* 212-826-0831 *E-mail:* info@centerforfiction.org *Web Site:* www.centerforfiction.org, pg 621

Center for Futures Education Inc, 345 Erie St, Grove City, PA 16127 *Tel:* 724-458-5860 *Fax:* 724-458-5962 *E-mail:* info@thectr.com *Web Site:* www.thectr.com, pg 56

The Center for Learning, 29313 Clemens Rd, Suite 2-E, Westlake, OH 44145 *Tel:* 440-250-9341 *Fax:* 440-250-9715 *E-mail:* customerservice@centerforlearning.org *Web Site:* www.centerforlearning.org, pg 56

Center for Migration Studies of New York Inc (CMS), 27 Carmine St, New York, NY 10014-4423 *Tel:* 212-337-3080 *Fax:* 646-998-4625 *E-mail:* cms@cmsny.org *Web Site:* www.cmsny.org, pg 56

Center for Publishing Departmental Scholarships, Midtown Ctr, Rm 429, 11 W 42 St, New York, NY 10036 *Tel:* 212-992-3232 *Fax:* 212-992-3233 *E-mail:* pub.center@nyu.edu; ms.publishing@nyu.edu *Web Site:* www.scps.nyu.edu, pg 696

The Center for Thanatology Research & Education Inc, 391 Atlantic Ave, Brooklyn, NY 11217-1701 *Tel:* 718-858-3026 *Fax:* 718-852-1846 *E-mail:* thanatology@pipeline.com *Web Site:* www.thanatology.org, pg 56

The Center for the Book in the Library of Congress, The Library of Congress, 101 Independence Ave SE, Washington, DC 20540-4920 *Tel:* 202-707-5221 *Fax:* 202-707-0269 *E-mail:* cfbook@loc.gov *Web Site:* www.loc.gov/cfbook; www.read.gov.cfb, pg 621

Center for Women Policy Studies, 1776 Massachusetts Ave NW, Suite 450, Washington, DC 20036 *Tel:* 202-872-1770 *Fax:* 202-296-8962 *E-mail:* cwps@centerwomenpolicy.org *Web Site:* www.centerwomenpolicy.org, pg 56

Center Press, PO Box 6936, Thousand Oaks, CA 91360-6936 *Tel:* 818-889-7071 *Fax:* 818-889-7072 *E-mail:* center@centerbooks.com *Web Site:* centerbooks.com, pg 56

Center Street, 12 Cadillac Dr, Suite 480, Brentwood, TN 37027 *Tel:* 615-221-0996 *Web Site:* www.centerstreet.com, pg 56

Centering Corp, 7230 Maple St, Omaha, NE 68134 *Tel:* 402-553-1200 *Toll Free Tel:* 866-218-0101 *Fax:* 402-553-0507 *E-mail:* orders@centering.org *Web Site:* www.centering.org, pg 56

Centerstream Publishing LLC, PO Box 17878, Anaheim Hills, CA 92817-7878 *Tel:* 714-779-9390 *E-mail:* centerstrm@aol.com *Web Site:* www.centerstream-usa.com, pg 57

Central Conference of American Rabbis/CCAR Press, 355 Lexington Ave, 18th fl, New York, NY 10017 *Tel:* 212-972-3636 *Toll Free Tel:* 800-935-2227 *Fax:* 212-692-0819 *E-mail:* info@ccarnet.org *Web Site:* www.ccarnet.org/ccar-press, pg 57

Central European University Press, 224 W 57 St, 7th fl, New York, NY 10019 *Tel:* 212-547-6932 *Fax:* 646-557-2416 *Web Site:* www.ceupress.com, pg 57

Central Recovery Press (CRP), 3321 N Buffalo Dr, Suite 275, Las Vegas, NV 89129 *Tel:* 702-868-5830 *Fax:* 702-868-5831 *E-mail:* info@centralrecovery.com *Web Site:* centralrecoverypress.com, pg 57

Centre for Reformation & Renaissance Studies (CRRS), EJ Pratt Library, Rm 301, 71 Queen's Park Crescent E, Toronto, ON M5S 1K7, Canada *Tel:* 416-585-4468 *Fax:* 416-585-4430 (attn: CRRS) *E-mail:* crrs.publications@utoronto.ca *Web Site:* www.crrs.ca, pg 498

Centre Franco-Ontarien de Ressources en Alphabetisation (Centre FORA), 432 Ave Westmount, Unit H, Sudbury, ON P3A 5Z8, Canada *Tel:* 705-524-3672 *Toll Free Tel:* 888-814-4422 (orders, CN only) *Fax:* 705-524-8535 *E-mail:* info@centrefora.on.ca *Web Site:* www.centrefora.on.ca, pg 498

The Century Foundation, 41 E 70 St, New York, NY 10021 *Tel:* 212-535-4441; 212-879-9197 *Fax:* 212-879-9197 *E-mail:* info@tcf.org *Web Site:* www.tcf.org, pg 57, 641

Chain Store Guide (CSG), 3922 Coconut Palm Dr, Tampa, FL 33619 *Tel:* 813-627-6957 *Toll Free Tel:* 800-927-9292 (orders) *Fax:* 813-627-6888 *E-mail:* info@csgis.com *Web Site:* www.csgis.com, pg 57

Chalice Press, 483 E Lockwood Ave, Suite 100, St Louis, MO 63119 *Tel:* 314-231-8500 *Toll Free Tel:* 800-366-3383 *Fax:* 314-231-8524; 770-280-4039 (orders) *E-mail:* customerservice@chalicepress.com *Web Site:* www.chalicepress.com, pg 57

Jane Chambers Playwriting Award, Georgetown University, 108 David Performing Arts Ctr, Box 571063, 37 & "O" St, NW, Washington, DC 20057-1063 *Tel:* 202-687-1327 *Web Site:* www.athe.org/displaycommon.cfm?an=1&subarticlenbr=25, pg 696

Champion Writers Inc, 5676 Ridge View Dr, Alexandria, VA 22310 *Tel:* 703-473-1392 *Fax:* 703-778-0294 *Web Site:* www.championwriters.com, pg 57

The Alfred & Fay Chandler Book Award, c/o Business History Review, Harvard Business School, Soldiers Field Rd, Boston, MA 02163 *Tel:* 617-495-1003 *Fax:* 617-495-0594 *E-mail:* bhr@hbs.edu *Web Site:* www.hbs.edu/bhr, pg 696

G S Sharat Chandra Prize for Short Fiction, 5101 Rockhill Rd, Kansas City, MO 64110-2499 *Tel:* 816-235-2558 *Fax:* 816-235-2611 *E-mail:* bkmk@umkc.edu *Web Site:* www.umkc.edu/bkmk, pg 696

Channel Lake Inc, 238 E 30 St, No 1F, New York, NY 10016 *Tel:* 347-329-5576 *Toll Free Tel:* 800-592-1566 (orders) *Toll Free Fax:* 866-794-5507 *E-mail:* info@channellake.com *Web Site:* www.channellake.com; www.touristtown.com, pg 58

Channel Photographics, 980 Lincoln Ave, Suite 200-B, San Rafael, CA 94901 *Tel:* 415-456-2934 *Fax:* 415-456-4124 *Web Site:* www.channelphotographics.com, pg 58

Chaosium Inc, 22568 Mission Blvd, Suite 423, Hayward, CA 94541-5116 *Tel:* 510-583-1000 *Fax:* 510-583-1101 *Web Site:* www.chaosium.com, pg 58

Chapter One Fiction Competition, 1738 Hone Ave, Bronx, NY 10461-1486 *Tel:* 718-931-9500 *Fax:* 718-409-6445 *E-mail:* info@bronxarts.org *Web Site:* www.bronxarts.org, pg 696

Character Publishing, 23568 Montebella Rd, Pass Christian, MS 39571 *Tel:* 228-234-7651 *Fax:* 228-222-3321 *Web Site:* www.characterpublishing.org, pg 58

Charisma Media, 600 Rinehart Rd, Lake Mary, FL 32746 *Tel:* 407-333-0600 (all imprints) *Toll Free Tel:* 800-283-8494 (Charisma Media, Siloam Press, Creation House); 800-665-1468 *Fax:* 407-333-7100 (all imprints) *E-mail:* charisma@charismamedia.com *Web Site:* www.charismamedia.com, pg 58

CharismaLife Publishers, 600 Rinehart Rd, Lake Mary, FL 32746 *Tel:* 407-333-0600 *Toll Free Tel:* 800-451-4598 *Fax:* 407-333-7100 *E-mail:* charismalife@charismamedia.com *Web Site:* www.charismamedia.com, pg 58

Chariton Review Short Fiction Prize, 100 E Normal Ave, Kirksville, MO 63501-4221 *Tel:* 660-785-7336 *Toll Free Tel:* 800-916-6802 *Fax:* 660-785-4480 *Web Site:* tsup.truman.edu, pg 696

The Charles Press, Publishers, 230 N 21 St, Suite 202, Philadelphia, PA 19103 *Tel:* 215-561-2786 *Fax:* 215-561-0191 *E-mail:* mailbox@charlespresspub.com *Web Site:* www.charlespresspub.com, pg 58

Charles River Media, 20 Channel Center St, Boston, MA 02210 *Toll Free Tel:* 800-354-9706 *Toll Free Fax:* 800-487-8488 *E-mail:* crminfo@cengage.com *Web Site:* www.cengage.com; www.delmarlearning.com/charlesriver, pg 58

Charles Scribner's Sons®, 27500 Drake Rd, Farmington Hills, MI 48331-3535 *Toll Free Tel:* 800-877-4253 *Toll Free Fax:* 800-414-5043 *E-mail:* gale.galeord@cengage.com *Web Site:* www.gale.com/scribners, pg 58

Charlesbridge Publishing Inc, 85 Main St, Watertown, MA 02472 *Tel:* 617-926-0329 *Toll Free Tel:* 800-225-3214 *Fax:* 617-926-5720 *Toll Free Fax:* 800-926-5775 *E-mail:* books@charlesbridge.com *Web Site:* www.charlesbridge.com, pg 58

The Charlton Press, PO Box 820, Sta Willowdale B, North York, ON M2K 2R1, Canada *Tel:* 416-488-1418 *Toll Free Tel:* 800-442-6042 (North America) *Fax:* 416-488-4656 *Toll Free Fax:* 800-442-1542 (North America) *E-mail:* chpress@charltonpress.com *Web Site:* www.charltonpress.com, pg 498

Chautauqua Writers' Workshop, PO Box 28, Chautauqua, NY 14722-0408 *Tel:* 716-357-6316; 716-357-6250 *Toll Free Tel:* 800-836-ARTS (836-2787) *Fax:* 716-269-7444 *Web Site:* writers.ciweb.org, pg 668

Margaret Cheasebro, 246 Rd 2900, Aztec, NM 87410 *Tel:* 505-334-2869 *E-mail:* margaretcheasebro@yahoo.com *Web Site:* www.wordsandwellness.com, pg 543

Jane Chelius Literary Agency Inc, 548 Second St, Brooklyn, NY 11215 *Tel:* 718-499-0236; 718-499-0714 *Fax:* 718-832-7335 *E-mail:* queries@janechelius.com; rights@janechelius.com *Web Site:* www.janechelius.com, pg 566

Chelsea Green Publishing Co, 85 N Main St, Suite 120, White River Junction, VT 05001 *Tel:* 802-295-6300 *Toll Free Tel:* 800-639-4099 (cust serv, consumer & trade orders) *Fax:* 802-295-6444 *Web Site:* www.chelseagreen.com, pg 59

Chelsea House Publishers, 132 W 31 St, 17th fl, New York, NY 10001 *Tel:* 212-967-8800 *Toll Free Tel:* 800-322-8755 *Fax:* 917-339-0325; 917-339-0323 *Toll Free Fax:* 800-678-3633 *E-mail:* custserv@factsonfile.com *Web Site:* www.infobasepublishing.com; www.infobaselearning.com, pg 59

Chemical Education Resources Inc, 10 Davis Dr, Belmont, CA 94002 *Toll Free Tel:* 800-543-0487 (ext 1308, orders); 800-355-9983 (cust serv) *Fax:* 215-243-3786 (edit) *Toll Free Fax:* 800-451-3661 (orders) *Web Site:* www.cerlabs.com, pg 59

ChemTec Publishing, 38 Earswick Dr, Toronto, ON M1E 1C6, Canada *Tel:* 416-265-2603 *Fax:* 416-265-1399 *E-mail:* orderdesk@chemtec.org *Web Site:* www.chemtec.org, pg 498

Cheneliere Education Inc, 5800 Saint Denis St, Montreal, QC H2S 3L5, Canada *Tel:* 514-273-1066 *Toll Free Tel:* 800-565-5531 *Fax:* 514-276-0324 *Toll Free Fax:* 800-814-0324 *E-mail:* info@cheneliere.ca *Web Site:* www.cheneliere.ca, pg 498

Cheng & Tsui Co Inc, 25 West St, 2nd fl, Boston, MA 02111-1213 *Tel:* 617-988-2400 *Toll Free Tel:* 800-554-1963 *Fax:* 617-426-3669; 617-556-8964 *E-mail:* service@cheng-tsui.com; orders@cheng-tsui.com *Web Site:* www.cheng-tsui.com, pg 59

Ruth Chernia, 198 Victor Ave, Toronto, ON M4K 1B2, Canada *Tel:* 416-466-0164 *E-mail:* rchernia@editors.ca; rchernia@sympatico.ca, pg 543

Cherry Hill Publishing, 24344 Del Amo Rd, Ramona, CA 92065 *Tel:* 858-829-5550 *Toll Free Tel:* 800-407-1072 *Fax:* 760-203-1200 *E-mail:* operations@cherryhillpublishing.com; sales@cherryhillpublishing.com *Web Site:* www.cherryhillpublishing.com, pg 59

Cherry Lane Music Co, 315 Fifth Ave, Suite 801, New York, NY 10016 *Tel:* 646-470-3782 *Fax:* 212-251-0822 *Web Site:* www.cherrylaneprint.com, pg 59

Linda Chester Literary Agency, Rockefeller Ctr, Suite 2036, 630 Fifth Ave, New York, NY 10111 *Tel:* 212-218-3350 *Fax:* 212-218-3343 *E-mail:* submissions@lindachester.com *Web Site:* www.lindachester.com, pg 566

Chestnut Publishing Group Inc, 4005 Bayview Ave, Suite 610, Toronto, ON M2M 3Z9, Canada *Tel:* 416-224-5824 *Fax:* 416-224-0595 *Web Site:* www.chestnutpublishing.com, pg 499

Chicago Review Press, 814 N Franklin St, Chicago, IL 60610 *Tel:* 312-337-0747 *Toll Free Tel:* 800-888-4741 *Fax:* 312-337-5110 *E-mail:* frontdesk@chicagoreviewpress.com *Web Site:* www.chicagoreviewpress.com, pg 59

Chicago Spectrum Press, 12305 Westport Rd, Louisville, KY 40245 *Tel:* 502-899-1919 *Toll Free Tel:* 800-594-5190; 888-BOOKS-80 (266-5780) *Fax:* 502-896-0246 *E-mail:* request@evanstonpublishing.com; info@evanstonpublishing.com *Web Site:* www.evanstonpublishing.com, pg 60

Chicago Women in Publishing, PO Box 268107, Chicago, IL 60626 *Tel:* 773-508-0351 *Fax:* 435-604-6049 *E-mail:* info@cwip.org *Web Site:* www.cwip.org, pg 621

Child Welfare League of America (CWLA), 1726 "M" St, Suite 500, Washington, DC 20036 *Tel:* 202-688-4200 *Fax:* 202-833-1689 *Web Site:* www.cwla.org/pubs, pg 60

Children's Book Conference, 615 SW Harrison St, Portland, OR 97201 *Tel:* 503-725-9786 *Fax:* 503-725-5599 *Web Site:* www.pdx.edu/ceed/childrens-book-conference, pg 668

The Children's Book Council (CBC), 54 W 39 St, 14th fl, New York, NY 10018 *Tel:* 212-966-1990 *Fax:* 212-966-2073 *Toll Free Fax:* 888-807-9355 (orders only) *E-mail:* cbc.info@cbcbooks.org *Web Site:* www.cbcbooks.org, pg 621

Children's Book Press, 95 Madison Ave, Suite 1205, New York, NY 10016 *Tel:* 212-779-4400 *Fax:* 212-683-1894 *Web Site:* www.leeandlow.com, pg 60

Children's Literature Association Article Award, 1301 W 22 St, Suite 202, Oak Brook, IL 60523 *Tel:* 630-571-4520 *Fax:* 708-876-5598 *E-mail:* info@childlitassn.org *Web Site:* www.childlitassn.org, pg 696

Children's Literature Association Beiter Graduate Student Research Grants, 1301 W 22 St, Suite 202, Oak Brook, IL 60523 *Tel:* 630-571-4520 *Fax:* 708-876-5598 *E-mail:* info@childlitassn.org *Web Site:* www.childlitassn.org, pg 696

Children's Literature Association Book Award, 1301 W 22 St, Suite 202, Oak Brook, IL 60523 *Tel:* 630-571-4520 *Fax:* 708-876-5598 *E-mail:* info@childlitassn.org *Web Site:* www.childlitassn.org, pg 696

Children's Sequoyah Book Award, 300 Hardy Dr, Edmond, OK 73013 *Tel:* 405-525-5100 *Fax:* 405-525-5103 *Web Site:* www.oklibs.org, pg 696

Faith Childs Literary Agency Inc, 915 Broadway, Suite 1009, New York, NY 10010 *Tel:* 212-995-9600 *Fax:* 212-995-9709 *E-mail:* assistant@faithchildsliteraryagencyinc.com, pg 566

Child's Play®, 250 Minot Ave, Auburn, ME 04210 *Toll Free Tel:* 800-472-0099; 800-639-6404 *Toll Free Fax:* 800-854-6989 *E-mail:* chpmaine@aol.com; cplay@earthlink.net *Web Site:* www.childs-play.com/usa, pg 60

The Child's World Inc, 1980 Lookout Dr, Mankato, MN 56003 *Tel:* 507-385-1044 *Toll Free Tel:* 800-599-READ (599-7323) *Toll Free Fax:* 888-320-2329 *E-mail:* sales@childsworld.com *Web Site:* www.childsworld.com, pg 60

Childswork/Childsplay LLC, 303 Crossway Park Dr, Woodbury, NY 11797 *Toll Free Tel:* 800-962-1141 (cust serv) *Toll Free Fax:* 800-262-1886 (orders) *E-mail:* info@childswork.com *Web Site:* childswork.com, pg 60

China Books, 360 Swift Ave, Suite 48, South San Francisco, CA 94080 *Tel:* 650-872-7076 *Toll Free Tel:* 800-818-2017 (US only) *Fax:* 650-872-7808 *E-mail:* info@chinabooks.com *Web Site:* www.chinabooks.com, pg 60

Chinese Connection Agency, 67 Banksville Rd, Armonk, NY 10504 *Tel:* 914-765-0296 *Fax:* 914-765-0297 *E-mail:* info@yaollc.com *Web Site:* www.yaollc.com, pg 566

Chosen Books, PO Box 6287, Grand Rapids, MI 49516-6287 *Tel:* 616-676-9185 *Toll Free Tel:* 800-877-2665 (orders only) *Fax:* 616-676-9573 *Toll Free Fax:* 800-398-3111 (orders only) *Web Site:* www.bakerpublishinggroup.com, pg 60

Chouette Publishing, 1001 Lenoir St, B-238, Montreal, QC H4C 2Z6, Canada *Tel:* 514-925-3325 *Fax:* 514-925-3323 *E-mail:* info@editions-chouette.com *Web Site:* www.chouettepublishing.com, pg 499

Christian Liberty Press, 502 W Euclid Ave, Arlington Heights, IL 60004 *Tel:* 847-259-4444 *Toll Free Tel:* 800-832-2741 (cust serv) *Fax:* 847-259-2941 *E-mail:* custserv@christianlibertypress.com *Web Site:* www.shopchristianliberty.com, pg 60

Christian Light Publications Inc, 1050 Mount Clinton Pike, Harrisonburg, VA 22802 *Tel:* 540-434-1003 *Toll Free Tel:* 800-776-0478 *Fax:* 540-433-8896 *E-mail:* info@clp.org; orders@clp.org *Web Site:* www.clp.org, pg 60

Christian Schools International, 3350 E Paris Ave SE, Grand Rapids, MI 49512-3054 *Tel:* 616-957-1070 *Toll Free Tel:* 800-635-8288 *Fax:* 616-957-5022 *E-mail:* info@csionline.org *Web Site:* www.csionline.org, pg 61

The Christian Science Publishing Society, 210 Massachusettes Ave, Boston, MA 02115 *Tel:* 617-450-2000 *Toll Free Tel:* 800-288-7090 *Fax:* 617-450-7334 *Web Site:* www.spirituality.com, pg 61

Christian Writers' Conference, PO Box 110390, Nashville, TN 37222-0390 *Tel:* 615-834-0450 *Toll Free Tel:* 800-21-WRITE (219-7483) *Fax:* 615-834-7736 *E-mail:* acwriters@aol.com *Web Site:* www.acwriters.com, pg 668

The Christopher Awards, 5 Hanover Sq, 22nd fl, New York, NY 10004-2751 *Tel:* 212-759-4050 *Toll Free Tel:* 888-298-4050 (orders) *Fax:* 212-838-5073 *E-mail:* mail@christophers.org *Web Site:* www.christophers.org, pg 696

William F Christopher Publication Services, Kensington No 237, 1580 Geary Rd, Walnut Creek, CA 94597-2744 *Tel:* 925-943-5584 *Fax:* 925-943-5594 *E-mail:* wfcmgmt.innovations@yahoo.com, pg 566

Chronicle Books LLC, 680 Second St, San Francisco, CA 94107 *Tel:* 415-537-4200 *Toll Free Tel:* 800-759-0190 (cust serv) *Fax:* 415-537-4460 *Toll Free Fax:* 800-858-7787 (orders); 800-286-9471 (cust serv) *E-mail:* frontdesk@chroniclebooks.com *Web Site:* www.chroniclebooks.com, pg 61

Chronicle Guidance Publications Inc, 66 Aurora St, Moravia, NY 13118-3569 *Tel:* 315-497-0330 *Toll Free Tel:* 800-622-7284 *Fax:* 315-497-0339 *E-mail:* customerservice@chronicleguidance.com *Web Site:* www.chronicleguidance.com, pg 61

Editions du CHU Sainte-Justine, 3175 Cote-Saint-Catherine, Montreal, QC H3T 1C5, Canada *Tel:* 514-345-4671 *Fax:* 514-345-4631 *E-mail:* edition.hsj@ssss.gouv.qc.ca *Web Site:* www.editions-chu-sainte-justine.org, pg 499

John Ciardi Prize for Poetry, 5101 Rockhill Rd, Kansas City, MO 64110-2499 *Tel:* 816-235-2558 *Fax:* 816-235-2611 *E-mail:* bkmk@umkc.edu *Web Site:* www.umkc.edu/bkmk, pg 697

Cider Mill Press Book Publishers LLC, 12 Port Farm Rd, Kennebunkport, ME 04046 *Tel:* 207-967-8232 *Fax:* 207-967-8233 *Web Site:* www.cidermillpress.com, pg 61

Cinco Puntos Press, 701 Texas Ave, El Paso, TX 79901 *Tel:* 915-838-1625 *Toll Free Tel:* 800-566-9072 *Fax:* 915-838-1635 *E-mail:* info@cincopuntos.com *Web Site:* www.cincopuntos.com, pg 61

Cine/Lit Representation, PO Box 802918, Santa Clarita, CA 91380-2918 *Tel:* 661-513-0268 *Fax:* 661-513-0915 *E-mail:* cinelit@att.net, pg 566

Circlet Press Inc, 39 Hurlbut St, Cambridge, MA 02138 *Tel:* 617-864-0492 *Toll Free Tel:* 800-729-6423 (orders) *E-mail:* circletintern@gmail.com (edit queries); kjc@circlet.com (order fulfillment) *Web Site:* www.circlet.com, pg 61

Cistercian Publications Inc, Editorial Office, Saint John's Abbey, PO Box 7500, Collegeville, MN 56321 *Tel:* 320-363-2213 *Toll Free Tel:* 800-436-8431 *Fax:* 320-363-3299 *Toll Free Fax:* 800-445-5899 *E-mail:* editor@monks.org *Web Site:* www.cistercianpublications.org, pg 62

City & Regional Magazine Association, 1970 E Grand Ave, Suite 330, El Segundo, CA 90245 *Tel:* 310-364-0193 *Fax:* 310-364-0196 *Web Site:* www.citymag.org, pg 621

City Lights Publishers, 261 Columbus Ave, San Francisco, CA 94133 *Tel:* 415-362-8193 *Fax:* 415-362-4921 *E-mail:* staff@citylights.com *Web Site:* www.citylights.com, pg 62

The City of Calgary W O Mitchell Book Prize, 11759 Groat Rd, Edmonton, AB T5M 3K6, Canada *Tel:* 780-422-8174 *Toll Free Tel:* 800-665-5354 (AB only) *Fax:* 780-422-2663 (attn WGA) *E-mail:* mail@writersguild.ab.ca *Web Site:* www.writersguild.ab.ca, pg 697

City of Toronto Book Award, Toronto Protocol City Clerks Office, City Hall, 100 Queen St W, 2nd fl West, Toronto, ON M5H 2N2, Canada *Tel:* 416-392-7805 *Fax:* 416-392-1247 *E-mail:* protocol@toronto.ca *Web Site:* www.toronto.ca/book_awards, pg 697

City of Vancouver Book Award, Woodward's Heritage Bldg, Suite 501, 111 W Hastings St, Vancouver, BC V6B 1H4, Canada *Tel:* 604-871-6634 *Fax:* 604-871-6005 *E-mail:* culture@vancouver.ca *Web Site:* vancouver.ca/bookaward, pg 697

CLA Book of the Year for Children Award, 1150 Morrison Dr, Suite 1100, Ottawa, ON K2H 8S9, Canada *Tel:* 613-232-9625 *Fax:* 613-563-9895 *E-mail:* info@cla.ca *Web Site:* www.cla.ca, pg 697

The Clarion Awards, 3337 Duke St, Alexandria, VA 22314 *Tel:* 703-370-7436 *Fax:* 703-342-4311 *E-mail:* clarion@womcom.org *Web Site:* www.womcom.org, pg 697

Clarion Books, 215 Park Ave S, New York, NY 10003 *Tel:* 212-420-5883 *Toll Free Tel:* 800-225-3362 (orders) *Fax:* 212-420-5855 *Toll Free Fax:* 800-634-7568 (orders) *Web Site:* www.houghtonmifflinbooks.com, pg 62

The Clarion Science Fiction & Fantasy Writers' Workshop, Dept of Literature, Mail Code 0410, UC San Diego, 9500 Gilman Dr, La Jolla, CA 92093-0410 *Tel:* 858-534-2115 *E-mail:* clarion@ucsd.edu *Web Site:* clarion.ucsd.edu, pg 668

Clarity Press Inc, 3277 Roswell Rd NE, Suite 469, Atlanta, GA 30305 *Toll Free Tel:* 877-613-1495 (edit) *Toll Free Fax:* 877-613-7868 *E-mail:* claritypress@usa.net (foreign rts & perms) *Web Site:* www.claritypress.com, pg 62

Wm Clark Associates, 186 Fifth Ave, 2nd fl, New York, NY 10010 *Tel:* 212-675-2784 *Fax:* 347-649-9262 *E-mail:* general@wmclark.com *Web Site:* www.wmclark.com, pg 566

Clarkson Potter Publishers, c/o Random House Inc, 1745 Broadway, New York, NY 10019 *Tel:* 212-782-9000 *Toll Free Tel:* 888-264-1745 *Fax:* 212-572-6181 *Web Site:* www.clarksonpotter.com; www.randomhouse.com/crown/clarksonpotter, pg 62

Class Action Ink, 1300 NE 16 Ave, Suite 712, Portland, OR 97232-1483 *Tel:* 503-280-2448 *E-mail:* pam@classactionink.com *Web Site:* www.classactionink.com, pg 527

Classical Academic Press, 2151 Market St, Camp Hill, PA 17011 *Tel:* 717-730-0711 *Fax:* 717-730-0721 *E-mail:* info@classicalsubjects.com *Web Site:* www.classicalacademicpress.com, pg 62

Classroom Connect, 222 Berkeley St, Boston, MA 02116 *Tel:* 617-351-5000 *Toll Free Tel:* 800-638-1639 (cust support) *E-mail:* help@classroom.com *Web Site:* corporate.classroom.com; www.hmhinnovation.com, pg 62

Page Davidson Clayton Prize for Emerging Poets, University of Michigan, 0576 Rackham Bldg, 915 E Washington St, Ann Arbor, MI 48109-1070 *Tel:* 734-764-9265 *E-mail:* mqr@umich.edu *Web Site:* www.umich.edu/~mqr, pg 697

CLC Ministries, 701 Pennsylvania Ave, Fort Washington, PA 19034 *Tel:* 215-542-1240 *Toll Free Tel:* 800-659-1240 *Fax:* 215-542-7580 *E-mail:* orders@clcpublications.com *Web Site:* www.clcpublications.com, pg 62

Clear Concepts, 1329 Federal Ave, Suite 6, Los Angeles, CA 90025 *Tel:* 310-473-5453, pg 543

Clear Light Publishers, 823 Don Diego Ave, Santa Fe, NM 87505 *Tel:* 505-989-9590 *Toll Free Tel:* 800-253-2747 (orders) *Fax:* 505-989-9519 *E-mail:* market@clearlightbooks.com *Web Site:* www.clearlightbooks.com, pg 63

Clearfield Co Inc, 3600 Clipper Mill Rd, Suite 260, Baltimore, MD 21211 *Tel:* 410-837-8271 *Toll Free Tel:* 800-296-6687 (orders & cust serv) *Fax:* 410-752-8492 *E-mail:* sales@genealogical.com *Web Site:* www.genealogical.com, pg 63

Cleis Press, 2246 Sixth St, Berkeley, CA 94710 *Tel:* 510-845-8000 *Toll Free Tel:* 800-780-2279 (US) *Fax:* 510-845-8001 *E-mail:* orders@cleispress.com *Web Site:* www.cleispress.com; www.vivaeditions.com, pg 63

Clements Publishing, 6021 Yonge St, Suite 213, Toronto, ON M2M 3W2, Canada *Tel:* 647-477-2509 *Fax:* 647-477-2058 *E-mail:* info@clementspublishing.com *Web Site:* www.clementspublishing.com, pg 499

Clerical Plus, 97 Blueberry Lane, Shelton, CT 06484 *Tel:* 203-225-0879 *Fax:* 203-225-0879 *E-mail:* clericalplus@aol.com *Web Site:* www.clericalplus.net, pg 543

Clerisy Press, 306 Greenup St, Covington, KY 41011 *Tel:* 513-861-4045 *Toll Free Tel:* 888-604-4537 *Fax:* 859-291-9111 *E-mail:* info@clerisypress.com *Web Site:* www.clerisypress.com, pg 63

Cleveland State University Poetry Center Prizes, 2121 Euclid Ave, Cleveland, OH 44115-2214 *Tel:* 216-687-3986 *Fax:* 216-687-6943 *E-mail:* poetrycenter@csuohio.edu *Web Site:* www.csuohio.edu/poetrycenter, pg 697

David H Clift Scholarship, 50 E Huron St, Chicago, IL 60611 *Toll Free Tel:* 800-545-2433 (ext 4279) *Fax:* 312-280-3256 *E-mail:* scholarships@ala.org *Web Site:* www.ala.org/scholarships, pg 697

Clinical Laboratory & Standards Institute (CLSI), 950 W Valley Rd, Suite 2500, Wayne, PA 19087 *Tel:* 610-688-0100 *Toll Free Tel:* 877-447-1888 (orders) *Fax:* 610-688-0700 *E-mail:* customerservice@clsi.org *Web Site:* www.clsi.org, pg 63

Close Up Publishing, 1330 Braddock Place, Suite 400, Alexandria, VA 22314 *Tel:* 703-706-3300 *Toll Free Tel:* 800-CLOSE-UP (256-7387) *Fax:* 703-706-3564 *E-mail:* info@closeup.org *Web Site:* www.closeup.org, pg 63

Closson Press, 257 Delilah St, Apollo, PA 15613-1933 *Tel:* 724-337-4482 *Fax:* 724-337-9484 *E-mail:* clossonpress@comcast.net *Web Site:* www.clossonpress.com, pg 63

Clotilde's Secretarial & Management Services, PO Box 871926, New Orleans, LA 70187 *Tel:* 504-242-2912; 504-800-4863 (cell) *Fax:* 901-309-0664 (call first) *E-mail:* elcsy58@aol.com; elcsy58@att.net, pg 543

Clovernook Printing House for the Blind & Visually Impaired, 7000 Hamilton Ave, Cincinnati, OH 45231-5297 *Tel:* 513-522-3860 *Toll Free Tel:* 888-234-7156 *Fax:* 513-728-3946 (admin); 513-728-3950 (sales) *E-mail:* customerservice@clovernook.org *Web Site:* www.clovernook.org, pg 63

CN Times Books, 501 Fifth Ave, Suite 1708, New York, NY 10017 *Tel:* 212-867-8666 *Web Site:* cntimesbooks.com, pg 63

Coach House Books, 80 bpNichol Lane, Toronto, ON M5S 3J4, Canada *Tel:* 416-979-2217 *Toll Free Tel:* 800-367-6360 (outside Toronto) *Fax:* 416-977-1158 *E-mail:* mail@chbooks.com *Web Site:* www.chbooks.com, pg 499

Coaches Choice, 465 Reservation Rd, Marina, CA 93933 *Toll Free Tel:* 888-229-5745 *Fax:* 831-372-6075 *E-mail:* info@coacheschoice.com *Web Site:* www.coacheschoice.com, pg 63

Coachlight Press LLC, 1704 Craig's Store Rd, Afton, VA 22920-2017 *Tel:* 434-823-1692 *E-mail:* sales@coachlightpress.com *Web Site:* www.coachlightpress.com, pg 63

Coal Hill Review Poetry Chapbook Contest, c/o Autumn House Press, PO Box 60100, Pittsburgh, PA 15211 *E-mail:* reviewcoalhill@gmail.com *Web Site:* www.coalhillreview.com, pg 697

Coastside Editorial, PO Box 181, Moss Beach, CA 94038 *E-mail:* bevjoe@pacific.net, pg 543

Cobblestone Publishing, 30 Grove St, Suite C, Peterborough, NH 03458 *Tel:* 603-924-7209 *Toll Free Tel:* 800-821-0115 *Fax:* 603-924-7380 *E-mail:* customerservice@caruspub.com *Web Site:* www.cobblestonepub.com, pg 64

Codhill Press, One Arden Lane, New Paltz, NY 12561 *Tel:* 845-255-4060 *Fax:* 845-255-6784 *E-mail:* codhillpress@aol.com *Web Site:* www.codhill.com, pg 64

CODiE Awards, 1090 Vermont Ave NW, 6th fl, Washington, DC 20005-4095 *Tel:* 202-289-7442 *Fax:* 202-289-7097 *E-mail:* info@siia.net *Web Site:* www.siia.net, pg 697

Coe College Playwriting Festival, 1220 First Ave NE, Cedar Rapids, IA 52402 *Tel:* 319-399-8624 *Fax:* 319-399-8557 *Web Site:* www.theatre.coe.edu; www.coe.edu/academics/theatrearts/theatrearts_playwritingfestival, pg 698

Coffee House Press, 79 13 Ave NE, Suite 110, Minneapolis, MN 55413 *Tel:* 612-338-0125 *Fax:* 612-338-4004 *Web Site:* www.coffeehousepress.org, pg 64

Cognizant Communication Corp, 18 Peekskill Hollow Rd, Putnam Valley, NY 10597-3213 *Tel:* 845-603-6440; 845-603-6441 (warehouse & orders) *Fax:* 845-603-6442 *E-mail:* cogcomm@aol.com; sales@cognizantcommunication.com; inquiries@cognizantcommunication.com *Web Site:* www.cognizantcommunication.com, pg 64

Morton N Cohen Award for a Distinguished Edition of Letters, 26 Broadway, 3rd fl, New York, NY 10004-1789 *Tel:* 646-576-5141 *Fax:* 646-458-0030 *E-mail:* awards@mla.org *Web Site:* www.mla.org, pg 698

Robert L Cohen, 182-12 Horace Harding Expwy, Suite 2M, Fresh Meadows, NY 11365 *Tel:* 718-762-1195 *Toll Free Tel:* 866-EDITING (334-8464) *E-mail:* wordsmith@sterlingmp.com *Web Site:* www.rlcwordsandmusic.com; www.linkedin.com/in/robertcohen17, pg 543

The Victor Cohn Prize for Excellence in Medical Science Reporting, PO Box 910, Hedgesville, WV 25427 *Tel:* 304-754-6786 *Web Site:* www.casw.org, pg 698

Cold Spring Harbor Laboratory Press, 500 Sunnyside Blvd, Woodbury, NY 11797-2924 *Tel:* 516-422-4100; 516-422-4101 *Toll Free Tel:* 800-843-4388 *Fax:* 516-422-4097; 516-422-4092 (submissions) *E-mail:* cshpress@cshl.edu *Web Site:* www.cshlpress.com, pg 64

Collector Grade Publications Inc, PO Box 1046, Cobourg, ON K9A 4W5, Canada *Tel:* 905-342-3434 *Fax:* 905-342-3688 *E-mail:* info@collectorgrade.com *Web Site:* www.collectorgrade.com, pg 499

College & University Professional Association for Human Resources (CUPA-HR), 1811 Commons Point Dr, Knoxville, TN 37932 *Tel:* 865-637-7673 *Toll Free Tel:* 877-CUPA-HR4 (287-2474) *Fax:* 865-637-7674 *E-mail:* communications@cupahr.org *Web Site:* www.cupahr.org, pg 64

The College Board, 45 Columbus Ave, New York, NY 10023-6917 *Tel:* 212-713-8000 *Fax:* 212-713-8063 *Web Site:* www.collegeboard.com, pg 64

College of Liberal & Professional Studies, University of Pennsylvania, 3440 Market St, Suite 100, Philadelphia, PA 19104-3335 *Tel:* 215-898-7326 *Fax:* 215-573-2053 *E-mail:* lps@sas.upenn.edu *Web Site:* www.sas.upenn.edu; www.sas.upenn.edu/lps, pg 677

College Press Publishing Co, 2111 N Main St, Suite C, Joplin, MO 64801 *Tel:* 417-623-6280 *Toll Free Tel:* 800-289-3300 *Fax:* 417-623-1929 *E-mail:* books@collegepress.com *Web Site:* www.collegepress.com/storefront, pg 64

College Publishing, 12309 Lynwood Dr, Glen Allen, VA 23059 *Tel:* 804-364-8410 *Toll Free Tel:* 800-827-0723 *Fax:* 804-364-8408 *E-mail:* collegepub@mindspring.com *Web Site:* www.collegepublishing.us, pg 64

Collier Associates, 416 Kelsey Park Dr, Palm Beach Gardens, FL 33410 *Tel:* 561-514-6548 *Fax:* 561-799-4067 *E-mail:* dmccabooks@gmail.com, pg 566

John M Collier Award for Forest History Journalism, 701 William Vickers Ave, Durham, NC 27701-3162 *Tel:* 919-682-9319 *Fax:* 919-682-2349 *Web Site:* www.foresthistory.org, pg 698

Frances Collin Literary Agent, PO Box 33, Wayne, PA 19087 *E-mail:* queries@francescollin.com *Web Site:* www.francescollin.com, pg 567

Carr P Collins Award, PO Box 609, Round Rock, TX 78680 *Tel:* 512-683-5640 *E-mail:* tilsecretary@yahoo.com *Web Site:* www.texasinstituteofletters.org, pg 698

The Winston Collins/Descant Prize for Best Canadian Poem, 50 Baldwin St, Toronto, ON M5T 1L4, Canada *Tel:* 416-593-2557 *Fax:* 416-593-9362 *E-mail:* info@descant.ca *Web Site:* www.descant.ca, pg 698

The Colonial Williamsburg Foundation, PO Box 1776, Williamsburg, VA 23187-1776 *Tel:* 757-229-1000 *Toll Free Tel:* 800-HISTORY (447-8679) *Fax:* 757-220-7325 *E-mail:* cwres@cwf.org; geninfo@cwf.org *Web Site:* www.colonialwilliamsburg.org/publications, pg 64

Colorado Authors' League, PO Box 24905, Denver, CO 80224 *Web Site:* www.coloradoauthors.org, pg 621

Colorado Book Awards, 7935 E Prentice Ave, Suite 450, Greenwood Village, CO 80111 *Tel:* 303-894-7951 (ext 21) *Fax:* 303-864-9361 *E-mail:* info@coloradohumanities.org *Web Site:* www.coloradohumanities.org, pg 698

Colorado Geological Survey, Publications Section, 1313 Sherman St, Rm 715, Denver, CO 80203 *Tel:* 303-866-2611 *Fax:* 303-866-2461 (cust serv) *E-mail:* pubscgs@state.co.us (cust serv) *Web Site:* geosurvey.state.co.us, pg 65

Betsy Colquitt Award for Poetry, Texas Christian University, Dept of English, TCU Box 297270, Fort Worth, TX 76129 *Tel:* 817-257-5907 *Fax:* 817-257-7709 *E-mail:* descant@tcu.edu *Web Site:* www.descant.tcu.edu, pg 698

Columbia Books & Information Services, 8120 Woodmont Ave, Suite 110, Bethesda, MD 20814 *Tel:* 202-464-1662 *Toll Free Tel:* 888-265-0600 (cust serv) *Fax:* 202-464-1775 *E-mail:* info@columbiabooks.com *Web Site:* www.columbiabooks.com; www.lobbyists.info; www.associationexecs.com, pg 65

Columbia Publishing Course at Columbia University, 2950 Broadway, MC 3801, New York, NY 10027 *Tel:* 212-854-1898 *Fax:* 212-854-7618 *E-mail:* publishing@jrn.columbia.edu *Web Site:* www.journalism.columbia.edu/publishing, pg 677

Columbia University Press, 61 W 62 St, New York, NY 10023 *Tel:* 212-459-0600 *Toll Free Tel:* 800-944-8648 *Fax:* 212-459-3678 *E-mail:* cup_book@columbia.edu (orders & cust serv) *Web Site:* cup.columbia.edu, pg 65

Columbia University School of the Arts, Creative Writing Program, 617 Kent Hall, New York, NY 10027 *Tel:* 212-854-3774 *Fax:* 212-854-7704 *E-mail:* writingprogram@columbia.edu *Web Site:* www.columbia.edu/cu/writing, pg 677

Comex Systems Inc, 5 Cold Hill Rd, Suite 24, Mendham, NJ 07945 *Tel:* 973-543-2862 *Toll Free Tel:* 800-543-6959 *Fax:* 973-543-9644 *E-mail:* mail@comexsystems.com *Web Site:* www.comexsystems.com, pg 65

Committee On Scholarly Editions, c/o Modern Language Association of America, 26 Broadway, 3rd fl, New York, NY 10004-1789 *Tel:* 646-576-5044 *Fax:* 646-458-0030 *Web Site:* www.mla.org, pg 621

Common Courage Press, One Red Barn Rd, Monroe, ME 04951 *Tel:* 207-525-0900 *Toll Free Tel:* 800-497-3207 *Fax:* 207-525-3068 *E-mail:* orders-info@commoncouragepress.com *Web Site:* www.commoncouragepress.com, pg 65

Commonwealth Editions, One River Rd, Carlisle, MA 01741 *Tel:* 781-271-0055 *Toll Free Tel:* 800-277-5312 *Fax:* 781-271-0056 *E-mail:* customercare@awb.com *Web Site:* www.awb.com, pg 65

Communication Creativity, 4542 Melbourne Way, Highlands Ranch, CO 80130 *Tel:* 720-344-4388 *Toll Free Fax:* 866-685-0307 *Web Site:* www.selfpublishingresources.com (bookstore), pg 65

Community College Press, One Dupont Circle NW, Suite 410, Washington, DC 20036 *Tel:* 202-728-0200; 301-490-8116 (orders) *Toll Free Tel:* 800-250-6557 *Fax:* 202-223-9390 (edit); 301-604-0158 (orders); 202-833-2467 *E-mail:* aaccpub@ebrightkey.net *Web Site:* www.aacc.nche.edu/bookstore, pg 66

Company's Coming Publishing Ltd, 2311 96 St, Edmonton, AB T6N 1G3, Canada *Tel:* 780-450-6223 *Toll Free Tel:* 800-875-7108 (US & CN) *Fax:* 780-450-1857 *E-mail:* info@companyscoming.com *Web Site:* www.companyscoming.com, pg 499

Comprehensive Health Education Foundation (CHEF), 159 S Jackson St, Suite 510, Seattle, WA 98104 *Tel:* 206-824-2907 *Toll Free Tel:* 800-323-2433 *Fax:* 206-824-3072 *E-mail:* info@chef.org *Web Site:* www.chef.org, pg 66

Conciliar Press, 2747 Bond St, University Park, IL 60484 *Tel:* 219-728-2216 (outside US) *Toll Free Tel:* 800-967-7377 *Fax:* 708-534-7803 *Toll Free Fax:* 866-599-5208 *E-mail:* service@conciliarmedia.com *Web Site:* www.conciliarpress.com, pg 66

Concordia Publishing House, 3558 S Jefferson Ave, St Louis, MO 63118-3968 *Tel:* 314-268-1000 *Toll Free Tel:* 800-325-3040 (cust serv) *Toll Free Fax:* 800-490-9889 (cust serv) *E-mail:* order@cph.org *Web Site:* www.cph.org, pg 66

The Conference Board Inc, 845 Third Ave, New York, NY 10022-6679 *Tel:* 212-759-0900; 212-339-0345 (cust serv) *Fax:* 212-980-7014; 212-836-9740 (cust serv) *E-mail:* info@conference-board.org *Web Site:* www.conference-board.org, pg 66

Don Congdon Associates Inc, 110 William St, Suite 2202, New York, NY 10038-3914 *Tel:* 212-645-1229 *Fax:* 212-727-2688 *E-mail:* dca@doncongdon.com *Web Site:* www.doncongdon.com, pg 567

Connecticut Academy of Arts & Sciences, PO Box 208211, New Haven, CT 06520-8211 *Tel:* 203-432-3113 *Fax:* 203-432-5712 *E-mail:* caas@yale.edu *Web Site:* www.yale.edu/caas, pg 66

Connecticut Authors & Publishers Association (CAPA), PO Box 715, Avon, CT 06001-0715 *Tel:* 203-729-5335 *Fax:* 203-729-5335 *Web Site:* www.aboutcapa.com, pg 621

Miles Conrad Memorial Lecture, 1518 Walnut St, Suite 1004, Philadelphia, PA 19102-3403 *Tel:* 215-893-1561 *Fax:* 215-893-1564 *E-mail:* nfais@nfais.org *Web Site:* www.nfais.org, pg 698

Constance Rooke Creative Non-Fiction Prize, University of Victoria, Box 1700, Sta CSC, Victoria, BC V8W 2Y2, Canada *Tel:* 250-721-8524 *Fax:* 250-472-5051 *E-mail:* malahat@uvic.ca *Web Site:* malahatreview.ca, pg 698

Consumer Press, 13326 SW 28 St, Suite 102, Fort Lauderdale, FL 33330-1102 *Tel:* 954-370-9153 *Fax:* 954-472-1008 *E-mail:* info@consumerpress.com *Web Site:* consumerpress.com, pg 66

Consumertronics, 8400 Menaul NE, Suite A-199, Albuquerque, NM 87112 *Tel:* 505-321-1034 *E-mail:* wizguru@consumertronics.net *Web Site:* www.consumertronics.net, pg 66

Contemporary Publishing Co of Raleigh Inc, 5849 Lease Lane, Raleigh, NC 27617 *Tel:* 919-851-8221 *Fax:* 919-851-6666 *E-mail:* questions@contemporarypublishing.com *Web Site:* www.contemporarypublishing.com, pg 66

Continental AfrikaPublishers, 182 Stribling Circle, Spartanburg, SC 29301 *Tel:* 864-576-7992 *Fax:* 775-295-9699 *E-mail:* afrikalion@aol.com; afrikapharaoh@aol.com; afrikafiaga@aol.com; afrikadela@aol.com *Web Site:* www.writers.net/writers/22249, pg 66

The Continuing Legal Education Society of British Columbia (CLEBC), 500-1155 W Pender St, Vancouver, BC V6E 2P4, Canada *Tel:* 604-669-3544; 604-893-2121 (cust serv) *Toll Free Tel:* 800-663-0437 (CN) *Fax:* 604-669-9260 *E-mail:* custserv@cle.bc.ca *Web Site:* www.cle.bc.ca, pg 499

David C Cook, 4050 Lee Vance View, Colorado Springs, CO 80918 *Tel:* 719-536-0100 *Toll Free Tel:* 800-708-5550 *Fax:* 519-536-3269 *Web Site:* www.davidccook.com, pg 67

James Fenimore Cooper Prize, 603 Fayerweather, MC 2538, New York, NY 10027 *Tel:* 212-854-6495 *E-mail:* amhistsociety@columbia.edu *Web Site:* sah.columbia.edu, pg 698

Cooper Publishing Group LLC, PO Box 1129, Traverse City, MI 49685 *Tel:* 231-933-9958 *Fax:* 231-933-9964 *E-mail:* jr4239@att.net *Web Site:* www.cooperpublishinggroup.com, pg 67

Cooper Square Press, 5360 Manhattan Circle, Suite 101, Boulder, CO 80303 *Tel:* 303-543-7835 *Fax:* 303-543-0043 *Web Site:* www.rlpgbooks.com; www.rlpgtrade.com, pg 67

The Doe Coover Agency, PO Box 668, Winchester, MA 01890 *Tel:* 781-721-6000 *Fax:* 781-721-6727 *E-mail:* info@doecooveragency.com *Web Site:* www.doecooveragency.com, pg 567

Copley Custom Textbooks, 530 Great Rd, Acton, MA 01720 *Tel:* 978-263-9090 *Toll Free Tel:* 800-562-2147 *Fax:* 978-263-9190 *E-mail:* publish@copleycustom.com; textbook@copleypublishing.com *Web Site:* www.xanedu.com/copley, pg 67

Copper Canyon Press, Fort Worden State Park, Bldg 33, Port Townsend, WA 98368 *Tel:* 360-385-4925 *Toll Free Tel:* 877-501-1393 *Fax:* 360-385-4985 *E-mail:* poetry@coppercanyonpress.org *Web Site:* www.coppercanyonpress.org, pg 67

Copywriter's Council of America (CCA), CCA Bldg, 7 Putter Lane, Middle Island, NY 11953-1920 *Tel:* 631-924-3888 *Fax:* 631-924-8555 *E-mail:* cca4dmcopy@gmail.com *Web Site:* www.AndrewLinickDirectMarketing.com/Copywriters-Council.html; www.NewWorldPressBooks.com, pg 67

Copywriter's Council of America (CCA), CCA Bldg, 7 Putter Lane, Middle Island, NY 11953-1920 *Tel:* 631-924-8555 *Fax:* 631-924-8555 *E-mail:* cca4dmcopy@gmail.com *Web Site:* www.AndrewLinickDirectMarketing.com/Copywriters-Council.html; www.NewWorldPressBooks.com, pg 543, 621

Corbett Gordon Co, 6 Fort Rachel Place, Mystic, CT 06355 *Tel:* 860-536-4108 *Fax:* 860-536-3732 *E-mail:* corbettgordon@comcast.net, pg 543

Cordon d'Or - Gold Ribbon International Annual Cook Book & Culinary Arts Culinary Academy Awards, 7312 Sixth Ave N, St Petersburg, FL 33710 *Tel:* 727-347-2437 *E-mail:* culinaryparadise@aol.com *Web Site:* www.cordondorcuisine.com; www.florida-americasculinaryparadise.com, pg 698

Albert B Corey Prize, c/o American Historical Association, 400 "A" St SE, Washington, DC 20003-3889 *Tel:* 202-544-2422 *Fax:* 202-544-8307 *E-mail:* cha-shc@cha-shc.ca *Web Site:* www.historians.org/prizes; www.cha-shc.ca, pg 699

Cormorant Books Inc, 390 Steelcase Rd E, Markham, ON L3R 1G2, Canada *Tel:* 905-475-9126 (Thomas Allen & Sons); 905-475-5571 *E-mail:* info@cormorantbooks.com *Web Site:* www.cormorantbooks.com, pg 499

Cornell & McCarthy LLC, 2-D Cross Hwy, Westport, CT 06880 *Tel:* 203-454-4210 *E-mail:* contact@cmartreps.com *Web Site:* www.cmartreps.com, pg 601

Cornell Maritime Press Inc, 4880 Lower Valley Rd, Atglen, PA 19310 *Tel:* 610-593-1777 *Fax:* 610-593-2002 *E-mail:* info@schifferbooks.com *Web Site:* www.cmptp.com, pg 67

Cornell University Press, Sage House, 512 E State St, Ithaca, NY 14850 *Tel:* 607-277-2338 *Fax:* 607-277-2374 *E-mail:* cupressinfo@cornell.edu; cupress-sales@cornell.edu *Web Site:* www.cornellpress.cornell.edu, pg 67

Cornell University Southeast Asia Program Publications, 213 Kahin Ctr, 640 Stewart Ave, Ithaca, NY 14850 *Tel:* 607-277-2211 *Toll Free Tel:* 800-666-2211 *Fax:* 607-277-6292 *Toll Free Fax:* 800-688-2877 *E-mail:* seap-pubs@cornell.edu *Web Site:* www.einaudi.cornell.edu/southeastasia/publications, pg 68

Cornerstone Book Publishers, PO Box 24652, New Orleans, LA 70184 *E-mail:* info@cornerstonepublishers.com *Web Site:* www.cornerstonepublishers.com, pg 68

Corporation for Public Broadcasting (CPB), 401 Ninth St NW, Washington, DC 20004-2129 *Tel:* 202-879-9600 *Toll Free Tel:* 800-272-2190 *Fax:* 202-879-9700 *E-mail:* info@cpb.org *Web Site:* www.cpb.org, pg 622

Corporation of Professional Librarians of Quebec, 1453, rue Beaubien Est, Bureau 215, Montreal, QC H2G 3C6, Canada *Tel:* 514-845-3327 *Fax:* 514-845-1618 *E-mail:* info@cbpq.qc.ca *Web Site:* www.cbpq.qc.ca, pg 622

Cortina Institute of Languages, 7 Hollyhock Rd, Wilton, CT 06897 *Tel:* 203-762-2510 *Toll Free Tel:* 800-245-2145 *Fax:* 203-762-2514 *Web Site:* www.cortina-languages.com, pg 68

Cortina Learning International Inc (CLI), 7 Hollyhock Rd, Wilton, CT 06897-4414 *Tel:* 203-762-2510 *Toll Free Tel:* 800-245-2145 *Fax:* 203-762-2514 *E-mail:* info@cortinalearning.com *Web Site:* www.cortinalearning.com, pg 68

Corwin, a Sage Co, 2455 Teller Rd, Thousand Oaks, CA 91320 *Tel:* 805-499-9734 *Toll Free Tel:* 800-233-9936 *Fax:* 805-499-5323 *Toll Free Fax:* 800-417-2466 *E-mail:* info@corwin.com *Web Site:* www.corwin.com, pg 68

Cosimo Inc, Old Chelsea Sta, PO Box 416, New York, NY 10011 *Tel:* 212-989-3616 *Fax:* 212-989-3662 *E-mail:* info@cosimobooks.com *Web Site:* www.cosimobooks.com, pg 68

Coteau Books, 2517 Victoria Ave, Regina, SK S4P 0T2, Canada *Tel:* 306-777-0170 *Toll Free Tel:* 800-440-4471 (CN only) *Fax:* 306-522-5152 *E-mail:* coteau@coteaubooks.com *Web Site:* www.coteaubooks.com, pg 500

Cotsen Institute of Archaeology Press, 308 Charles E Young Dr N, Fowler A163, Box 951510, Los Angeles, CA 90024 *Tel:* 310-206-9384 *Fax:* 310-206-4723 *E-mail:* ioapubs@ioa.ucla.edu *Web Site:* www.ioa.ucla.edu, pg 68

Cottonwood Press, University of Kansas, Kansas Union, Rm 400, 1301 Jayhawk Blvd, Lawrence, KS 66045 *Tel:* 785-864-4520 *E-mail:* pwedge@ku.edu *Web Site:* www.cottonwoodmagazine.org, pg 68

Council for Advancement & Support of Education (CASE), 1307 New York Ave NW, Suite 1000, Washington, DC 20005-4701 *Tel:* 202-328-CASE (328-2273) *Fax:* 202-387-4973 *E-mail:* info@case.org; memberservicecenter@case.org *Web Site:* www.case.org, pg 622

Council for Exceptional Children (CEC), 2900 Crystal Dr, Suite 1000, Arlington, VA 22201 *Toll Free Tel:* 888-232-7733 (memb servs); 866-509-0219 *Fax:* 703-264-9494 *E-mail:* service@cec.sped.org *Web Site:* www.cec.sped.org, pg 69

Council for Research in Values & Philosophy (RVP), The Catholic University of America, Gibbons Hall, Rm B-12, 620 Michigan Ave NE, Washington, DC 20064 *Tel:* 202-319-6089 *Fax:* 202-319-6089 *E-mail:* cua-rvp@cua.edu *Web Site:* www.crvp.org, pg 69

Council for the Advancement of Science Writing (CASW), PO Box 910, Hedgesville, WV 25427 *Tel:* 304-754-6786 *Web Site:* www.casw.org, pg 622

Council Oak Books LLC, 2 W Sixth St, Suite 262, Tulsa, OK 74119 *Tel:* 918-743-BOOK (743-2665) *Toll Free Tel:* 800-247-8850 *Fax:* 918-743-4288 *E-mail:* publicity@counciloakbooks.com; order@counciloakbooks.com *Web Site:* www.counciloakbooks.com, pg 69

Council of Literary Magazines & Presses (CLMP), 154 Christopher St, Suite 3-C, New York, NY 10014-9110 *Tel:* 212-741-9110 *Fax:* 212-741-9112 *E-mail:* info@clmp.org *Web Site:* www.clmp.org, pg 622

Council of State Governments, 2760 Research Park Dr, Lexington, KY 40511 *Tel:* 859-244-8000 *Toll Free Tel:* 800-800-1910 *Fax:* 859-244-8001 *E-mail:* sales@csg.org *Web Site:* www.csg.org, pg 69

Council on Foreign Relations Press, The Harold Pratt House, 58 E 68 St, New York, NY 10065 *Tel:* 212-434-9400 *Fax:* 212-434-9800 *E-mail:* publications@cfr.org *Web Site:* www.cfr.org, pg 69

Council on Social Work Education (CSWE), 1701 Duke St, Suite 200, Alexandria, VA 22314-3457 *Tel:* 703-683-8080 *Fax:* 703-683-8493 *E-mail:* publications@cswe.org; info@cswe.org *Web Site:* www.cswe.org, pg 69

Counterpath Press, PO Box 18351, Denver, CO 80218 *E-mail:* editors@counterpathpress.org *Web Site:* www.counterpathpress.org, pg 69

Counterpoint Press LLC, 1919 Fifth St, Berkeley, CA 94710 *Tel:* 510-704-0230 *Fax:* 510-704-0268 *E-mail:* info@counterpointpress.com *Web Site:* www.counterpointpress.com; www.sierraclub.org/books; www.softskull.com, pg 69

Country Music Foundation Press, 222 Fifth Ave S, Nashville, TN 37203 *Tel:* 615-416-2001 *Fax:* 615-255-2245 *E-mail:* info@countrymusichalloffame.com *Web Site:* www.countrymusichalloffame.com, pg 69

The Countryman Press, 43 Lincoln Corners Way, Woodstock, VT 05091 *Tel:* 802-457-4826 *Toll Free Tel:* 800-245-4151 *Fax:* 802-457-1678 *E-mail:* countrymanpress@wwnorton.com *Web Site:* www.countrymanpress.com, pg 70

Course Crafters Inc, 3 Washington Sq, Haverhill, MA 01830 *Tel:* 978-372-3446 *Fax:* 978-372-3660 *E-mail:* info@coursecrafters.com *Web Site:* www.coursecrafters.com, pg 543

Course Technology, 20 Channel Center St, Boston, MA 02210 *Tel:* 617-757-7900 *Toll Free Tel:* 800-354-9706 (cust serv) *Fax:* 617-757-7969 *E-mail:* reply@course.com *Web Site:* www.cengage.com/coursetechnology; www.course.com, pg 70

La Courte Echelle, 5243 St Laurent Blvd, Montreal, QC H2T 1S4, Canada *Tel:* 514-274-2004 *Toll Free Tel:* 800-387-6192 (orders only) *Fax:* 514-270-4160 *Toll Free Fax:* 800-450-0391 (orders only) *E-mail:* info@courteechelle.com *Web Site:* www.courteechelle.com, pg 500

Covenant Communications Inc, 920 E State Rd, Suite F, American Fork, UT 84003-0416 *Tel:* 801-756-9966 *Toll Free Tel:* 800-662-9545 *Fax:* 801-756-1049 *E-mail:* info@covenant-lds.com *Web Site:* www.covenant-lds.com, pg 70

Cowley Publications, 4501 Forbes Blvd, Suite 200, Lanham, MD 20706 *Tel:* 301-459-3366 *Toll Free Tel:* 800-462-6420 *Fax:* 301-429-5748 *Toll Free Fax:* 800-338-4550 *E-mail:* custserv@rowman.com *Web Site:* rowman.com, pg 70

Coyote Press, PO Box 3377, Salinas, CA 93912-3377 *Tel:* 831-422-4912 *Fax:* 831-422-4913 *E-mail:* orders@coyotepress.com *Web Site:* www.coyotepress.com, pg 70

CPSA Prize in Comparative Politics, 260 rue Dalhousie St, Suite 204, Ottawa, ON K1N 7E4, Canada *Tel:* 613-562-1202 *Fax:* 613-241-0019 *E-mail:* cpsa-acsp@cpsa-acsp.ca *Web Site:* www.cpsa-acsp.ca, pg 699

CPSA Prize in International Relations, 260 rue Dalhousie St, Suite 204, Ottawa, ON K1N 7E4, Canada *Tel:* 613-562-1202 *Fax:* 613-241-0019 *E-mail:* cpsa-acsp@cpsa-acsp.ca *Web Site:* www.cpsa-acsp.ca, pg 699

CQ Press, 2300 "N" St NW, Suite 800, Washington, DC 20037 *Tel:* 202-729-1900 *Toll Free Tel:* 866-4CQ-PRESS (427-7737) *Fax:* 202-729-1923 *Toll Free Fax:* 800-380-3810 *E-mail:* customerservice@cqpress.com *Web Site:* www.cqpress.com, pg 70

Crabtree Publishing Co, 350 Fifth Ave, 59th fl, PMB 59051, New York, NY 10118 *Tel:* 212-496-5040 *Toll Free Tel:* 800-387-7650 *Toll Free Fax:* 800-355-7166 *E-mail:* custserv@crabtreebooks.com *Web Site:* www.crabtreebooks.com, pg 70

Crabtree Publishing Co Ltd, 616 Welland Ave, St Catharines, ON L2M-5V6, Canada *Tel:* 905-682-5221 *Toll Free Tel:* 800-387-7650 *Fax:* 905-682-7166 *Toll Free Fax:* 800-355-7166 *E-mail:* custserv@crabtreebooks.com; sales@crabtreebooks.com; orders@crabtreebooks.com *Web Site:* www.crabtreebooks.com, pg 500

Craftsman Book Co, 6058 Corte Del Cedro, Carlsbad, CA 92011 *Tel:* 760-438-7828 *Toll Free Tel:* 800-829-8123 *Fax:* 760-438-0398 *Web Site:* www.craftsman-book.com, pg 70

Craven Design Inc, 1202 Lexington Ave, Box 242, New York, NY 10028 *Tel:* 212-288-1022 *Fax:* 212-249-9910 *E-mail:* cravendesign@mac.com *Web Site:* www.cravendesignstudios.com, pg 601

Mark Crawford, 5101 Violet Lane, Madison, WI 53714 *Tel:* 608-240-4959 *E-mail:* mark.crawford@charter.net, pg 544

The Crazyhorse Fiction Prize, College of Charleston, Dept of English, 66 George St, Charleston, SC 29424 *Tel:* 843-953-7740 *Fax:* 843-953-7740 *E-mail:* crazyhorse@cofc.edu *Web Site:* www.crazyhorsejournal.org, pg 699

CRC Press LLC, 6000 Broken Sound Pkwy NW, Suite 300, Boca Raton, FL 33487 *Tel:* 561-994-0555 *Toll Free Tel:* 800-272-7737 *Fax:* 561-998-9784; 561-997-7249 (edit); 561-361-6057 (tax dept); 561-989-9732 (orders) *Toll Free Fax:* 800-643-9428 (sales); 800-374-3401 (orders) *E-mail:* orders@taylorandfrancis.com *Web Site:* www.crcpress.com, pg 71

Creating Crafts Group LLC, 741 Corporate Circle, Suite A, Golden, CO 80401 *Tel:* 303-215-5600 *E-mail:* editorial@creatingkeepsakes.com *Web Site:* www.creatingkeepsakes.com, pg 71

Creative Arts of Ventura, PO Box 684, Ventura, CA 93002-0684 *Tel:* 805-643-4160; 805-654-1927 *Web Site:* www.sculpture-museum.com, pg 601

Data Trace Publishing Co (DTP), 110 West Rd, Suite 227, Towson, MD 21204-2316 *Tel:* 410-494-4994 *Toll Free Tel:* 800-342-0454 (orders only) *Fax:* 410-494-0515 *E-mail:* info@datatrace.com; salesandmarketing@datatrace.com; editorial@datatrace.com; customerservice@datatrace.com *Web Site:* www.datatrace.com, pg 75

Database Directories, 588 Dufferin Ave, London, ON N6B 2A4, Canada *Tel:* 519-433-1666 *Fax:* 519-430-1131 *E-mail:* mail@databasedirectory.com *Web Site:* www.databasedirectory.com, pg 500

Editions Le Dauphin Blanc Inc, 825, boul Lebourgneuf, Suite 125, Quebec, QC G2J 0B9, Canada *Tel:* 418-845-4045 *Fax:* 418-845-1933 *E-mail:* info@dauphinblanc.com *Web Site:* www.dauphinblanc.com, pg 500

May Davenport Publishers, 26313 Purissima Rd, Los Altos Hills, CA 94022 *Tel:* 650-947-1275 *Fax:* 650-947-1373 *E-mail:* mdbooks@earthlink.net *Web Site:* www.maydavenportpublishers.com, pg 75

Suzanne B Davidson, 8084 N 44 St, Brown Deer, WI 53223 *Tel:* 414-355-6640 *E-mail:* davidson@milwpc.com, pg 544

Davies-Black Publishing, 20 Park Plaza, Suite 610, Boston, MA 02116 *Tel:* 617-523-3801 *Fax:* 617-523-3708 *E-mail:* info@nicholasbrealey.com *Web Site:* www.nicholasbrealey.com, pg 75

The Davies Group Publishers, PO Box 440140, Aurora, CO 80044-0140 *Tel:* 303-750-8374 *Fax:* 303-337-0952 *E-mail:* info@thedaviesgrouppublishers.com *Web Site:* www.thedaviesgrouppublishers.com, pg 75

Davies Publishing Inc, 32 S Raymond Ave, Suites 4 & 5, Pasadena, CA 91105-1961 *Tel:* 626-792-3046 *Toll Free Tel:* 877-792-0005 *Fax:* 626-792-5308 *E-mail:* info@daviespublishing.com *Web Site:* daviespublishing.com, pg 75

F A Davis Co, 1915 Arch St, Philadelphia, PA 19103 *Tel:* 215-568-2270 *Toll Free Tel:* 800-523-4049 *Fax:* 215-568-5065 *E-mail:* info@fadavis.com *Web Site:* www.fadavis.com, pg 76

Watson Davis & Helen Miles Davis Prize, 440 Geddes Hall, Notre Dame, IN 46556 *Tel:* 574-631-1194 *Fax:* 574-631-1533 *E-mail:* info@hssonline.org *Web Site:* www.hssonline.org, pg 699

DAW Books Inc, 375 Hudson St, 3rd fl, New York, NY 10014 *Tel:* 212-366-2096 *Fax:* 212-366-2090 *E-mail:* daw@us.penguingroup.com *Web Site:* us.penguingroup.com; www.dawbooks.com, pg 76

The Dawn Horse Press, 10336 Loch Lomond Rd, No 305, Middletown, CA 95461 *Tel:* 707-928-6590 *Toll Free Tel:* 877-770-0772 *Fax:* 707-928-6590 *E-mail:* dhp@adidam.org *Web Site:* www.dawnhorsepress.com, pg 76

Dawn Publications Inc, 12402 Bitney Springs Rd, Nevada City, CA 95959 *Tel:* 530-274-7775 *Toll Free Tel:* 800-545-7475 *Fax:* 530-274-7778 *E-mail:* nature@dawnpub.com; orders@dawnpub.com *Web Site:* www.dawnpub.com, pg 76

DawnSignPress, 6130 Nancy Ridge Dr, San Diego, CA 92121-3223 *Tel:* 858-625-0600 *Toll Free Tel:* 800-549-5350 *Fax:* 858-625-2336 *E-mail:* info@dawnsign.com *Web Site:* www.dawnsign.com, pg 76

Liza Dawson Associates, 350 Seventh Ave, Suite 2003, New York, NY 10001 *Tel:* 212-465-9071 *Fax:* 212-947-0460 *Web Site:* www.lizadawsonassociates.com, pg 567

Day Owl Press Corp, PO Box 3574, Lantana, FL 33465 *Toll Free Tel:* 866-806-6981 *Toll Free Fax:* 866-854-4375 *E-mail:* info@dayowl.net *Web Site:* www.dayowl.net; www.dayowlpresscorp.com, pg 76

Dayton Literary Peace Prize, 25 Harman Terr, Dayton, OH 45419 *Tel:* 937-298-5072 *Web Site:* daytonliterarypeaceprize.org, pg 699

Dayton Playhouse FutureFest, 1301 E Siebenthaler Ave, Dayton, OH 45414 *Tel:* 937-424-8477 *Fax:* 937-424-0062 *E-mail:* dp_futurefest@yahoo.com *Web Site:* www.daytonplayhouse.com, pg 699

dbS Productions, PO Box 94, Charlottesville, VA 22902 *Tel:* 434-293-5502 *Toll Free Tel:* 800-745-1581 *Fax:* 434-293-5502 *E-mail:* info@dbs-sar.com *Web Site:* www.dbs-sar.com, pg 76

DC Canada Education Publishing, 120 Slater St, Suite 960, Ottawa, ON K1P 6E2, Canada *Tel:* 613-565-8885 *Toll Free Tel:* 888-565-0262 *Fax:* 613-565-8881 *E-mail:* info@dc-canada.ca *Web Site:* www.dc-canada.ca, pg 500

DC Entertainment, 1700 Broadway, New York, NY 10019 *Tel:* 212-636-5400 *Toll Free Tel:* 800-887-6789 *Fax:* 212-636-5979 *E-mail:* dccomics@cambeywest.com *Web Site:* www.dccomics.com; www.madmag.com; www.dcentertainment.com, pg 76

DC Press LLC, 750 Powderhorn Circle, Lake Mary, FL 32746 *Tel:* 407-688-1156 *Web Site:* www.dcpressbooks.com, pg 76

Walter De Gruyter Inc, 121 High St, 3rd fl, Boston, MA 02110 *Tel:* 857-284-7073 *Fax:* 857-284-7358 *E-mail:* USinfo@degruyter.com *Web Site:* www.degruyter.com, pg 77

De Vorss & Co, 553 Constitution Ave, Camarillo, CA 93012-8510 *Tel:* 805-322-9010 *Toll Free Tel:* 800-843-5743 *Fax:* 805-322-9011 *E-mail:* service@devorss.com *Web Site:* www.devorss.com, pg 77

Deadline Club, c/o Salmagundi Club, 47 Fifth Ave, New York, NY 10003 *Tel:* 646-481-7584 *E-mail:* info@deadlineclub.org *Web Site:* www.deadlineclub.org, pg 622

Deborah Wolfe Ltd, 731 N 24 St, Philadelphia, PA 19130 *Tel:* 215-232-6666 *Fax:* 215-232-6585 *E-mail:* info@illustrationonline.com *Web Site:* www.illustrationonline.com, pg 601

Decent Hill Publishers LLC, 6100 Oak Tree Blvd, Suite 200, Cleveland, OH 44131 *Toll Free Tel:* 866-688-5325 *Toll Free Fax:* 866-688-5325 *E-mail:* support@decenthill.com *Web Site:* www.decenthill.com, pg 77

The Jennifer DeChiara Literary Agency, 31 E 32 St, Suite 300, New York, NY 10016 *Tel:* 212-481-8484 (ext 362) *Fax:* 212-481-9582 *Web Site:* www.jdlit.com, pg 568

Decker Publishing, 69 John St S, Suite 310, Hamilton, ON L8N 2B9, Canada *Tel:* 905-522-8526 *Toll Free Tel:* 855-647-6511 *Fax:* 905-522-9273 *E-mail:* customercare@deckerpublishing.com *Web Site:* www.deckerpublishing.com, pg 500

Ivan R Dee Publisher, 4501 Forbes Blvd, Suite 200, Lanham, MD 20706 *Tel:* 301-459-3366 *Toll Free Tel:* 800-462-6420 (cust serv) *Fax:* 301-429-5748 *Toll Free Fax:* 800-338-4550 (orders) *Web Site:* www.ivanrdee.com, pg 77

DeFiore and Company, LLC, 47 E 19 St, 3rd fl, New York, NY 10003 *Tel:* 212-925-7744 *Fax:* 212-925-9803 *E-mail:* submissions@defioreandco.com; info@defioreandco.com *Web Site:* www.defioreandco.com, pg 568

Delaware Division of the Arts Individual Artist Fellowships, Carvel State Office Bldg, 4th fl, 820 N French St, Wilmington, DE 19801 *Tel:* 302-577-8278 *Fax:* 302-577-6561 *E-mail:* delarts@state.de.us *Web Site:* www.artsdel.org, pg 699

Joelle Delbourgo Associates Inc, 101 Park St, Montclair, NJ 07042 *Tel:* 973-773-0836 (call only during standard business hours) *Web Site:* www.delbourgo.com, pg 568

Delmar, 5 Maxwell Dr, Clifton Park, NY 12065-2919 *Tel:* 518-348-2300 *Toll Free Tel:* 800-347-7707 (cust serv); 800-998-7498 *Fax:* 518-373-6200 *Toll Free Fax:* 800-487-8488 (cust serv) *Web Site:* www.cengage.com/delmar; www.delmarlearning.com, pg 77

DeLorme Publishing Co Inc, 2 DeLorme Dr, Yarmouth, ME 04096 *Tel:* 207-846-7000; 207-846-7111 (sales) *Toll Free Tel:* 800-561-5105; 800-511-2459 (cust serv) *Fax:* 207-846-7051 *Toll Free Fax:* 800-575-2244 *E-mail:* reseller@delorme.com *Web Site:* www.delorme.com, pg 77

Delphi Books, PO Box 6435, Lee's Summit, MO 64064 *Toll Free Tel:* 800-431-1579 (orders) *E-mail:* delphibks@yahoo.com *Web Site:* www.delphibooks.us, pg 77

Delphinium Books, PO Box 703, Harrison, NY 10528 *Tel:* 917-301-7496 (e-mail first) *E-mail:* contactform@delphiniumbooks.com *Web Site:* www.delphiniumbooks.com, pg 77

Delta Publishing Co, 1400 Miller Pkwy, McHenry, IL 60050-7030 *Tel:* 815-363-3582 *Toll Free Tel:* 800-323-8270 (orders) *Fax:* 815-363-2948 *Toll Free Fax:* 800-909-9901 *E-mail:* custsvc@deltapublishing.com *Web Site:* www.deltapublishing.com, pg 78

Rick DeMarinis Short Story Award, PO Box 2414, Durango, CO 81302 *Tel:* 970-903-7914 *E-mail:* cutthroatmag@gmail.com *Web Site:* www.cutthroatmag.com, pg 700

Demos Medical Publishing LLC, 11 W 42 St, New York, NY 10036 *Tel:* 212-683-0072 *Toll Free Tel:* 800-532-8663 *Fax:* 212-683-0118 *E-mail:* info@demosmedpub.com; orderdept@demosmedpub.com *Web Site:* www.demosmedpub.com, pg 78

Der-Hovanessian Translation Prize, 2 Farrar St, Cambridge, MA 02138 *Tel:* 617-744-6034 *E-mail:* contests@nepoetryclub.org *Web Site:* www.nepoetryclub.org, pg 700

Deseret Book Co, 57 W South Temple, Salt Lake City, UT 84101-1511 *Tel:* 801-517-3372; 801-534-1515 *Toll Free Tel:* 800-453-4532 (orders); 888-846-7302 (orders) *Fax:* 801-517-3126 *E-mail:* dbol@deseretbook.com *Web Site:* www.deseretbook.com, pg 78

DEStech Publications Inc, 439 N Duke St, Lancaster, PA 17602-4967 *Tel:* 717-290-1660 *Toll Free Tel:* 877-500-4337 *Fax:* 717-509-6100 *E-mail:* info@destechpub.com *Web Site:* www.destechpub.com, pg 78

Destiny Image Inc, 167 Walnut Bottom Rd, Shippensburg, PA 17257-0310 *Tel:* 717-532-3040 *Toll Free Tel:* 800-722-6774 (orders only) *Fax:* 717-532-9291 *E-mail:* sales@destinyimage.com *Web Site:* www.destinyimage.com, pg 78

Developmental Studies Center, 2000 Embarcadero, Suite 305, Oakland, CA 94606-5300 *Tel:* 510-533-0213 *Toll Free Tel:* 800-666-7270 *Fax:* 510-464-3670 *E-mail:* pubs@devstu.org; info@devstu.org *Web Site:* www.devstu.org, pg 78

Dewey Publications Inc, 1840 Wilson Blvd, Suite 203, Arlington, VA 22201 *Tel:* 703-524-1355 *Fax:* 703-524-1463 *E-mail:* deweypublications@gmail.com *Web Site:* www.deweypub.com, pg 78

Dharma Publishing, 35788 Hauser Bridge Rd, Cazadero, CA 95421 *Tel:* 707-847-3717 *Toll Free Tel:* 800-873-4276 *Fax:* 707-847-3380 *E-mail:* contact@dharmapublishing.com; customerservice@dharmapublishing.com *Web Site:* www.dharmapublishing.com, pg 78

Alice Fay Di Castagnola Award, 15 Gramercy Park S, New York, NY 10003 *Tel:* 212-254-9628 *Fax:* 212-673-2352 *Web Site:* www.poetrysociety.org, pg 700

Christina Di Martino Literary Services, 139 Sandpiper Ave, Royal Palm Beach, FL 33411 *Tel:* 212-996-9086; 917-972-6012 *E-mail:* writealot@earthlink.net *Web Site:* christinadimartino.com, pg 544

diacriTech Inc, 250 Commercial St, Suite 2002, Manchester, NH 03101 *Tel:* 603-606-5800 *Fax:* 603-606-5838 *E-mail:* sales@diacritech.com *Web Site:* www.diacritech.com, pg 544

Diagram Essay Contest, University of Arizona, ML-445, PO Box 210067, Tucson, AZ 85721 *E-mail:* editor@thediagram.com *Web Site:* www.thediagram.com/contest.html, pg 700

Dial Books for Young Readers, 345 Hudson St, New York, NY 10014 *Tel:* 212-366-2000 *Fax:* 212-414-3396 *E-mail:* online@penguinputnam.com *Web Site:* www.penguinputnam.com; us.penguingroup.com, pg 79

Diamond Farm Book Publishers, Bailey Settlement Rd, Alexandria Bay, NY 13607 *Tel:* 613-475-1771 *Toll Free Tel:* 800-481-1353 *Fax:* 613-475-3748 *Toll*

Dreaming Publications LLC, 1938 Old Balsam Rd, Waynesville, NC 28786 *Tel:* 828-423-0226 *E-mail:* dreamingpublications@gmail.com *Web Site:* dreamingpublications.com, pg 527

Drennan Communications, 6 Robin Lane, East Kingston, NH 03827 *Tel:* 603-642-8002 *Fax:* 603-642-8002, pg 544

Drennan Literary Agency, 6 Robin Lane, East Kingston, NH 03827 *Tel:* 603-642-8002 *Fax:* 603-642-8002, pg 569

Carleton Drewry Memorial, 1194 Hume Rd, Hume, VA 22639-1806 *E-mail:* poetryinva@aol.com *Web Site:* www.poetrysocietyofvirginia.org, pg 701

Saint Katharine Drexel Award, 205 W Monroe, Suite 314, Chicago, IL 60606-5061 *Tel:* 312-739-1776; 312-739-1776 *Toll Free Tel:* 855-739-1776 *Fax:* 312-739-1778; 312-739-1778 *E-mail:* cla2@cathla.org *Web Site:* www.cathla.org, pg 701

Drummond Books, 2111 Cleveland St, Evanston, IL 60202 *Tel:* 847-302-2534 *E-mail:* drummondbooks@gmail.com, pg 545

Drury University One-Act Play Competition, 900 N Benton Ave, Springfield, MO 65802-3344 *Tel:* 417-873-6821 *Web Site:* www.drury.edu, pg 701

Dubuque Fine Arts Players Annual One Act Play Festival, PO Box 1160, Dubuque, IA 52004-1160 *Tel:* 563-588-3438 *E-mail:* contact@dbqoneacts.org *Web Site:* www.dbqoneacts.org, pg 701

Dufour Editions Inc, PO Box 7, Chester Springs, PA 19425 *Tel:* 610-458-5005 *Toll Free Tel:* 800-869-5677 *Fax:* 610-458-7103 *E-mail:* info@dufoureditions.com *Web Site:* www.dufoureditions.com, pg 82

Duke University Press, 905 W Main St, Suite 18B, Durham, NC 27701 *Tel:* 919-688-5134 *Toll Free Tel:* 888-651-0122 *Fax:* 919-688-2615 *Toll Free Fax:* 888-651-0124 *E-mail:* orders@dukeupress.edu *Web Site:* www.dukeupress.edu, pg 82

Dumbarton Oaks, 1703 32 St NW, Washington, DC 20007 *Tel:* 202-339-6400 *Fax:* 202-339-6401; 202-298-8407 *E-mail:* doaksbooks@doaks.org *Web Site:* www.doaks.org, pg 82

Dun & Bradstreet, 103 JFK Pkwy, Short Hills, NJ 07078 *Tel:* 973-921-5500 *Toll Free Tel:* 800-526-0651; 800-234-3867 (cust serv) *E-mail:* custserv@dnb.com *Web Site:* www.dnb.com, pg 82

Dundurn Press Ltd, 3 Church St, Suite 500, Toronto, ON M5E 1M2, Canada *Tel:* 416-214-5544 *Fax:* 416-214-5556 *E-mail:* info@dundurn.com *Web Site:* www.dundurn.com, pg 501

Dunham Literary Inc, 110 William St, Suite 2202, New York, NY 10038 *Tel:* 212-929-0994 *Web Site:* dunhamlit.com, pg 569

Dunhill Publishing, 18340 Sonoma Hwy, Sonoma, CA 95476 *Tel:* 707-939-0570 *Fax:* 707-938-3515 *E-mail:* dunhill@vom.com *Web Site:* www.dunhillpublishing.com, pg 82

John H Dunning Prize in United States History, 400 "A" St SE, Washington, DC 20003-3889 *Tel:* 202-544-2422 *Fax:* 202-544-8307 *E-mail:* awards@historians.org *Web Site:* www.historians.org, pg 701

Dunow, Carlson & Lerner Literary Agency Inc, 27 W 20 St, Suite 1107, New York, NY 10011 *Tel:* 212-645-7606 *E-mail:* mail@dclagency.com *Web Site:* www.dclagency.com, pg 569

Dupree, Miller & Associates Inc, 100 Highland Park Village, Suite 350, Dallas, TX 75205 *Tel:* 214-559-2665 *Fax:* 214-559-7243 *E-mail:* editorial@dupreemiller.com *Web Site:* www.dupreemiller.com, pg 569

Duquesne University Press, 600 Forbes Ave, Pittsburgh, PA 15282 *Tel:* 412-396-6610 *Fax:* 412-396-5984 *E-mail:* dupress@duq.edu *Web Site:* www.dupress.duq.edu, pg 83

Dustbooks, PO Box 100, Paradise, CA 95967-0100 *Tel:* 530-877-6110 *Toll Free Tel:* 800-477-6110 *Fax:* 530-877-0222 *E-mail:* publisher@dustbooks.com; info@dustbooks.com *Web Site:* www.dustbooks.com, pg 83

Dutton, 375 Hudson St, New York, NY 10014 *Tel:* 212-366-2000 *Fax:* 212-366-2262 *E-mail:* online@penguinputnam.com *Web Site:* www.penguinputnam.com; us.penguingroup.com, pg 83

Dutton Children's Books, 345 Hudson St, New York, NY 10014 *Tel:* 212-366-2000 *E-mail:* online@penguinputnam.com *Web Site:* www.penguinputnam.com; us.penguingroup.com, pg 83

DWJ BOOKS LLC, 22 Division St, 2nd fl, Sag Harbor, NY 11963 *Tel:* 631-899-4500 *Fax:* 631-899-4499 *E-mail:* info@dwjbooks.com *Web Site:* www.dwjbooks.com, pg 545

DynaMinds Publishing, 6119 Nottingham Dr, Suite 1, Johnston, IA 50131 *Tel:* 515-270-5315 *Toll Free Tel:* 888-991-BOOK (991-2665) *Web Site:* www.dynamindspublishing.com, pg 83

Dystel & Goderich Literary Management, One Union Sq W, Suite 904, New York, NY 10003 *Tel:* 212-627-9100 *Fax:* 212-627-9313 *Web Site:* www.dystel.com, pg 569

E & E Publishing, 1001 Bridgeway, Suite 227, Sausalito, CA 94965 *Tel:* 415-331-4025 *Fax:* 415-331-4023 *E-mail:* eandegroup@eandegroup.com *Web Site:* www.eandegroup.com, pg 83

Eagan Press, 3340 Pilot Knob Rd, St Paul, MN 55121 *Tel:* 651-454-7250 *Toll Free Tel:* 800-328-7560 *Fax:* 651-454-0766 *E-mail:* aacc@scisoc.org *Web Site:* www.aaccnet.org, pg 83

Eagle's View Publishing, 6756 North Fork Rd, Liberty, UT 84310 *Tel:* 801-393-4555; 801-745-0905 (edit) *Toll Free Tel:* 800-547-3364 (orders over $100) *Fax:* 801-745-0903 (edit); 801-393-4647 *E-mail:* sales@eaglefeathertrading.com *Web Site:* www.eaglefeathertrading.com, pg 83

Eakin Press, 7005 Woodway Dr, Suite 114, Waco, TX 76712 *Tel:* 254-235-6161 *Toll Free Tel:* 800-880-8642 *Fax:* 254-235-6230 *E-mail:* sales@eakinpress.com *Web Site:* www.eakinpress.com, pg 83

Earth Aware Editions, 10 Paul Dr, San Rafael, CA 94903 *Tel:* 415-526-1370 *Fax:* 415-526-1394 *E-mail:* info@earthawareeditions.com, pg 83

Earth Edit, PO Box 114, Maiden Rock, WI 54750 *Tel:* 715-448-3009, pg 545

East Asian Legal Studies Program (EALSP), 500 W Baltimore St, Suite 411, Baltimore, MD 21201-1786 *Tel:* 410-706-3870 *Fax:* 410-706-1516 *E-mail:* eastasia@law.umaryland.edu *Web Site:* www.law.umaryland.edu/programs/international/eastasia, pg 83

East Mountain Editing Services, PO Box 1895, Tijeras, NM 87059-1895 *Tel:* 505-281-8422 *Fax:* 505-281-8422 *Web Site:* www.spanishindexing.com, pg 545

East West Discovery Press, PO Box 3585, Manhattan Beach, CA 90266 *Tel:* 310-545-3730 *Fax:* 310-545-3731 *E-mail:* info@eastwestdiscovery.com *Web Site:* www.eastwestdiscovery.com, pg 84

EastBridge, 70 New Canaan Ave, Norwalk, CT 06850 *Tel:* 203-855-9125 *Fax:* 203-857-0730 *E-mail:* asia@eastbridgebooks.org *Web Site:* www.eastbridgebooks.org, pg 84

Eastland Press, 1240 Activity Dr, Suite D, Vista, CA 92081 *Tel:* 206-217-0204 (edit); 760-598-9695 (orders) *Toll Free Tel:* 800-453-3278 (orders) *Fax:* 760-598-6083 (orders) *Toll Free Fax:* 800-241-3329 (orders) *E-mail:* info@eastlandpress.com; orders@eastlandpress.com (orders-credit cards only) *Web Site:* www.eastlandpress.com, pg 84

Easy Money Press, 5419 87 St, Lubbock, TX 79424 *Tel:* 806-543-5215 *E-mail:* easymoneypress@yahoo.com, pg 84

Eaton Literary Associates Literary Awards, PO Box 49795, Sarasota, FL 34230-6795 *Tel:* 941-366-6589 *Fax:* 941-365-4679 *E-mail:* eatonlit@aol.com *Web Site:* www.eatonliterary.com, pg 701

Eckankar, PO Box 2000, Chanhassen, MN 55317-2000 *Tel:* 952-380-2200 *Toll Free Tel:* 800-275-2606 *Fax:* 952-380-2295 *Toll Free Fax:* 800-510-3650 *E-mail:* eckbooks@eckankar.org *Web Site:* www.eckankar.org, pg 84

Eclipse Press, 3101 Beaumont Centre Circle, Lexington, KY 40513 *Tel:* 859-278-2361 *Toll Free Tel:* 800-866-2361 *Fax:* 859-276-6868 *E-mail:* editorial@eclipsepress.com; info@eclipsepress.com *Web Site:* www.eclipsepress.com, pg 84

Ecopress, 8075 215 St W, Lakeville, MN 55044 *Tel:* 952-469-6699 *Toll Free Tel:* 800-846-7027 *Fax:* 952-469-1968 *Toll Free Fax:* 800-330-6232 *E-mail:* info@finneyco.com *Web Site:* www.ecopress.com, pg 84

Ecrits des Forges, 992-A, rue Royale, Trois Rivieres, QC G9A 4H9, Canada *Tel:* 819-840-8492 *Fax:* 819-376-0774 *E-mail:* ecritsdesforges@gmail.com *Web Site:* www.ecritsdesforges.com, pg 501

ECS Publishing Corp, 615 Concord St, Framingham, MA 01702 *Tel:* 508-620-7400 *Toll Free Tel:* 800-777-1919 *Fax:* 508-620-7401 *E-mail:* office@ecspub.com *Web Site:* www.ecspublishing.com, pg 84

ECW Press, 2120 Queen St E, Suite 200, Toronto, ON M4E 1E2, Canada *Tel:* 416-694-3348 *Fax:* 416-698-9906 *E-mail:* info@ecwpress.com *Web Site:* www.ecwpress.com, pg 501

EDC Publishing, 10302 E 55 Place, Tulsa, OK 74146-6515 *Tel:* 918-622-4522 *Toll Free Tel:* 800-475-4522 *Fax:* 918-665-7919 *Toll Free Fax:* 800-743-5660 *E-mail:* edc@edcpub.com *Web Site:* www.edcpub.com, pg 84

Anne Edelstein Literary Agency LLC, 404 Riverside Dr, New York, NY 10025 *Tel:* 212-414-4923 *E-mail:* info@aeliterary.com; rights@aeliterary.com *Web Site:* www.aeliterary.com, pg 570

Edelstein Prize, Univ of Virginia, Dept of Science, Tech & Society, PO Box 400744, Charlottesville, VA 22904-4744 *Tel:* 434-987-6230 *Fax:* 434-975-2190 (attention: SHOT) *E-mail:* shot@virginia.edu *Web Site:* www.shot.jhu.edu, pg 701

EDGE Science Fiction & Fantasy Publishing, PO Box 1714, Sta M, Calgary, AB T2P 2L7, Canada *Tel:* 403-254-0160 *Web Site:* www.edgewebsite.com, pg 501

Edgewise Press Inc, 24 Fifth Ave, Suite 224, New York, NY 10011 *Tel:* 212-982-4818 *Fax:* 212-982-1364 *E-mail:* epinc@mindspring.com *Web Site:* www.edgewisepress.org, pg 84

ediciones Lerner, 241 First Ave N, Minneapolis, MN 55401 *Tel:* 612-332-3344 *Toll Free Tel:* 800-328-4929 *Fax:* 612-332-7615 *Toll Free Fax:* 800-332-1132 *E-mail:* info@lernerbooks.com *Web Site:* www.lernerbooks.com, pg 85

Ediciones Universal, 3090 SW Eighth St, Miami, FL 33135 *Tel:* 305-642-3234 *Fax:* 305-642-7978 *E-mail:* ediciones@ediciones.com *Web Site:* www.ediciones.com, pg 85

EditAndPublishYourBook.com, PO Box 2965, Nantucket, MA 02584-2965 *E-mail:* michaeltheauthor@yahoo.com *Web Site:* www.editandpublishyourbook.com, pg 545

Edit Etc, 12 Laurel Rd, Princeton, NJ 08540 *Tel:* 914-715-5849 *Fax:* 609-921-2025 *E-mail:* atkedit@cs.com, pg 545

Edit Resource LLC, 3578-E Hartsel Dr, Suite 387, Colorado Springs, CO 80920 *Tel:* 719-290-0757 *E-mail:* info@editresource.com (main) *Web Site:* www.editresource.com (main); www.inspirationalghostwriting.com, pg 545

EditAmerica, 115 Jacobs Creek Rd, Ewing, NJ 08628 *Tel:* 609-882-5852 *Web Site:* www.editamerica.com; www.linkedin.com/in/PaulaPlantier, pg 545

Editcetera, 2034 Blake St, Suite 5, Berkeley, CA 94704 *Tel:* 510-849-1110 *Fax:* 510-848-1448 *E-mail:* info@editcetera.com *Web Site:* www.editcetera.com, pg 545

EditCraft Editorial Services, 422 Pine St, Grass Valley, CA 95945 *Tel:* 530-263-3688 *Web Site:* www.editcraft.com, pg 545

Les Editions Alire, 120 Cote du Passage, Levis, QC G6V 5S9, Canada *Tel:* 418-835-4441 *Fax:* 418-838-4443 *E-mail:* info@alire.com *Web Site:* www.alire.com, pg 501

editions CERES Ltd/Le Moyen Francais, CP 1089, Succursale B, Maison de la Poste, Montreal, QC H3B 3K9, Canada *Tel:* 514-937-7138 *Fax:* 514-937-9875 *E-mail:* editionsceres@gmail.com *Web Site:* www.editionsceres.ca, pg 502

Editions de la Pleine Lune, 223 34 Ave, Lachine, QC H8T 1Z4, Canada *Tel:* 514-634-7954 *Fax:* 514-637-6366 *E-mail:* editpllune@videotron.ca *Web Site:* www.pleinelune.qc.ca, pg 502

Les Editions de l'Hexagone, 1010 rue de la Gauchetiere E, Montreal, QC H2L 2N5, Canada *Tel:* 514-523-7993 (ext 4201) *Fax:* 514-282-7530 *E-mail:* vml@sogides.com *Web Site:* www.edhexagone.com, pg 502

Les Editions de Mortagne, CP 116, Boucherville, QC J4B 5E6, Canada *Tel:* 450-641-2387 *Fax:* 450-655-6092 *E-mail:* info@editionsdemortagne.com *Web Site:* www.editionsdemortagne.com, pg 502

Editions Marcel Didier Inc, 1815 Ave de Lorimier, Montreal, QC H2K 3W6, Canada *Tel:* 514-523-1523 *Toll Free Tel:* 800-361-1664 (Ontario to Maritimes) *Fax:* 514-523-9969 *E-mail:* marceldidier@hurtubisehmh.com *Web Site:* www.hurtubisehmh.com, pg 502

Les Editions du Ble, 340 Provencher Blvd, St Boniface, MB R2H 0G7, Canada *Tel:* 204-237-8200 *Fax:* 204-233-8182 *E-mail:* direction@editionsduble.ca *Web Site:* www.livres-disques.ca/editions_ble/home/index.cfm, pg 502

Les Editions du Boreal, 4447, rue Saint-Denis, Montreal, QC H2J 2L2, Canada *Tel:* 514-287-7401 *Fax:* 514-287-7664 *E-mail:* boreal@editionsboreal.qc.ca *Web Site:* www.editionsboreal.qc.ca, pg 502

Les Editions du CRAM Inc, 1030, Cherrier, bureau 205, Montreal, QC H2L 1H9, Canada *Tel:* 514-598-8547 *Fax:* 514-598-8788 *E-mail:* service@editionscram.com *Web Site:* www.editionscram.com, pg 502

Editions du Noroit, CP 156, Succersale de Lorimier, Montreal, QC H2H 2N6, Canada *Tel:* 514-727-0005 *Fax:* 514-723-6660 *E-mail:* lenoroit@lenoroit.com *Web Site:* www.lenoroit.com, pg 502

Les Editions du Remue-Menage, La Maison Parent Roback, 110 rue Ste-Therese, bureau 501, Montreal, QC H2Y 1E6, Canada *Tel:* 514-876-0097 *Fax:* 514-876-7951 *E-mail:* info@editions-remuemenage.qc.ca *Web Site:* www.editions-remuemenage.qc.ca, pg 503

Editions du renouveau Pedagogique Inc (ERPI), 5757 rue Cypihot, St-Laurent, QC H4S 1R3, Canada *Tel:* 514-334-2690 *Toll Free Tel:* 800-263-3678 *Fax:* 514-334-4720 *Toll Free Fax:* 800-643-4720 *E-mail:* erpidlm@erpi.com *Web Site:* www.erpi.com, pg 503

Les Editions du Septentrion, 1300 Maguire Ave, Sillery, QC G1T 1Z3, Canada *Tel:* 418-688-3556 *Fax:* 418-527-4978 *E-mail:* sept@septentrion.qc.ca *Web Site:* www.septentrion.qc.ca, pg 503

Les Editions du Vermillon, 305 rue Sainte-Patrick, Ottawa, ON K1N 5K4, Canada *Tel:* 613-241-4032 *Fax:* 613-241-3109 *E-mail:* leseditionsduvermillon@rogers.com *Web Site:* leseditionsduvermillon.ca, pg 503

Les Editions Fides, 7333 place des Roseraies, bureau 100, Montreal, QC H1M 2X6, Canada *Tel:* 514-745-4290 *Toll Free Tel:* 800-363-1451 (CN) *Fax:* 514-745-4299 *E-mail:* editions@fides.qc.ca *Web Site:* www.editionsfides.com, pg 503

Editions FouLire, 4339 rue des Becassines, Charlesbourg, QC G1G 1V5, Canada *Tel:* 418-628-4029 *Toll Free Tel:* 877-628-4029 *Fax:* 418-628-4801 *E-mail:* info@foulire.com *Web Site:* www.foulire.com, pg 503

Les Editions Ganesha Inc, CP 484, Succursale Youville, Montreal, QC H2P 2W1, Canada *Tel:* 450-641-2395 *Fax:* 450-641-2989 *E-mail:* courriel@editions-ganesha.qc.ca *Web Site:* www.editions-ganesha.qc.ca, pg 503

Les Editions Heritage Inc, 300 Rue Arran, St-Lambert, QC J4R 1K5, Canada *Tel:* 514-875-0327 *Toll Free Tel:* 800-561-3737 *Fax:* 450-672-5448, pg 503

Editions Hurtubise, 1815 De Lorimier Ave, Montreal, QC H2K 3W6, Canada *Tel:* 514-523-1523 *Toll Free Tel:* 800-361-1664 (CN only) *Fax:* 514-523-9969 *Web Site:* www.editionshurtubise.com, pg 503

Les Editions JCL, 930 rue Jacques Cartier est, Chicoutimi, QC G7H 7K9, Canada *Tel:* 418-696-0536 *Fax:* 418-696-3132 *E-mail:* jcl@jcl.qc.ca *Web Site:* www.jcl.qc.ca, pg 503

Editions Marie-France, 9900 Avenue des Laurentides, Montreal, QC H1H 4V1, Canada *Tel:* 514-329-3700 *Toll Free Tel:* 800-563-6644 (Canada) *Fax:* 514-329-0630 *E-mail:* editions@marie-france.qc.ca *Web Site:* www.marie-france.qc.ca, pg 504

Editions Orphee Inc, 1240 Clubview Blvd N, Columbus, OH 43235-1226 *Tel:* 614-846-9517 *Fax:* 614-846-9794 *E-mail:* sales@editionsorphee.com *Web Site:* www.editionsorphee.com, pg 85

Les Editions Phidal Inc, 5740 Ferrier, Montreal, QC H4P 1M7, Canada *Tel:* 514-738-0202 *Toll Free Tel:* 800-738-7349 *Fax:* 514-738-5102 *E-mail:* info@phidal.com; customer@phidal.com (sales & export) *Web Site:* www.phidal.com, pg 504

Editions Pierre Tisseyre, 155 rue Maurice, Rosemere, QC J7A 2S8, Canada *Tel:* 514-335-0777 *Fax:* 514-335-6723 *E-mail:* info@edtisseyre.ca *Web Site:* www.tisseyre.ca, pg 504

Editions Trecarre, La Tourelle, Bureau 800, 1055, Blvd Rene-Levesque E, Montreal, QC H2L 4S5, Canada *Tel:* 514-849-5259 *Fax:* 514-849-1388 *Web Site:* www.edtrecarre.com, pg 504

Les Editions Un Monde Different Itee, 3905 Isabelle, bureau 101, Brossand, QC J4Y 2R2, Canada *Tel:* 450-656-2660 *Toll Free Tel:* 800-443-2582 *Fax:* 450-659-9328 *E-mail:* info@umd.ca *Web Site:* www.umd.ca, pg 504

Editions Vents d'Ouest, 109 rue Wright, Gatineau, QC J8X 2G7, Canada *Tel:* 819-770-6377 *Fax:* 819-770-0559 *E-mail:* info@ventsdouest.ca *Web Site:* www.ventsdouest.ca, pg 504

Les Editions XYZ inc, 1815 Ave de Lorimier, Montreal, QC H2K 3W6, Canada *Tel:* 514-525-2170 *Fax:* 514-525-7537 *E-mail:* info@editionsxyz.com *Web Site:* www.editionsxyz.com, pg 504

Editions Yvon Blais, 137 John, CP 180, Cowansville, QC J2K 3H6, Canada *Tel:* 450-266-1086 *Toll Free Tel:* 800-363-3047 *Fax:* 450-263-9256 *E-mail:* editionsyvonblais.commentaires@thomson.com *Web Site:* www.editionsyvonblais.qc.ca, pg 504

Editorial Bautista Independiente, 3417 Kenilworth Blvd, Sebring, FL 33870-4469 *Tel:* 863-382-6350 *Toll Free Tel:* 800-398-7187 (US) *Fax:* 863-382-8650 *E-mail:* info@ebi-bmm.org; ebiweb@ebi-bmm.org *Web Site:* www.ebi-bmm.org, pg 85

The Editorial Dept LLC, 7650 E Broadway, Suite 308, Tucson, AZ 85710 *Tel:* 520-546-9992 *Fax:* 520-979-3408 *E-mail:* admin@editorialdepartment.com *Web Site:* www.editorialdepartment.com, pg 545

Editorial Freelancers Association (EFA), 71 W 23 St, 4th fl, New York, NY 10010-4102 *Tel:* 212-929-5400 *Toll Free Tel:* 866-929-5425 *Fax:* 212-929-5439 *Toll Free Fax:* 866-929-5439 *E-mail:* info@the-efa.org; office@the-efa.org *Web Site:* www.the-efa.org, pg 622

Editorial Portavoz, 733 Wealthy St SE, Grand Rapids, MI 49503-5553 *Toll Free Tel:* 877-733-2607 (ext 206) *Fax:* 616-493-1790 *E-mail:* portavoz@portavoz.com *Web Site:* www.portavoz.com, pg 85

Editorial Unilit, 1360 NW 88 Ave, Miami, FL 33172 *Tel:* 305-592-6136 *Toll Free Tel:* 800-767-7726 *Fax:* 305-592-0087 *E-mail:* info@editorialunilit.com *Web Site:* www.editorialunilit.com, pg 85

Editors' Association of Canada (Association canadienne des reviseurs), 502-27 Carlton St, Toronto, ON M5B 1L2, Canada *Tel:* 416-975-1379 *Toll Free Tel:* 866-CAN-EDIT (226-3348) *Fax:* 416-975-1637 *E-mail:* info@editors.ca *Web Site:* www.editors.ca; www.reviseurs.ca, pg 622

The Editors Circle, 462 Grove St, Montclair, NJ 07043 *Tel:* 973-783-5082 *E-mail:* query@theeditorscircle.com *Web Site:* www.theeditorscircle.com, pg 545

The Editor's Eye, 158-18 Riverside Dr W, Suite 6-E, New York, NY 10032 *Tel:* 212-740-6003 *Fax:* 212-740-6003 *E-mail:* editorseye@gmail.com, pg 545

Education Awards of Excellence, 200 Deer Run Rd, Sewickley, PA 15143-2600 *Tel:* 412-259-1705 *Toll Free Tel:* 800-910-4283 (ext 705) *Fax:* 412-749-9890 *E-mail:* printing@printing.org *Web Site:* www.printing.org, pg 701

Education Writers Association (EWA), 3516 Connecticut Ave NW, Washington, DC 20008-2401 *Tel:* 202-452-9830 *Fax:* 202-452-9837 *E-mail:* ewa@ewa.org *Web Site:* www.ewa.org, pg 623

Education Writers Association Workshops, 3516 Connecticut Ave NW, Washington, DC 20008-2401 *Tel:* 202-452-9830 *Fax:* 202-452-9837 *E-mail:* ewa@ewa.org *Web Site:* www.ewa.org, pg 668

Educational Book & Media Association (EBMA), 37 Main St, Suite 203, Warrenton, VA 20186 *Tel:* 540-318-7770 *Fax:* 202-962-3939 *E-mail:* info@edupaperback.org *Web Site:* www.edupaperback.org, pg 623

Educational Design Services LLC, 5750 Bou Ave, Suite 1508, North Bethesda, MD 20852 *Tel:* 301-881-8611 *Web Site:* www.educationaldesignservices.com, pg 570

Educational Directories Inc (EDI), 1025 W Wise Rd, Suite 101, Schaumburg, IL 60193 *Tel:* 847-891-1250 *Toll Free Tel:* 800-357-6183 *Fax:* 847-891-0945 *E-mail:* info@ediusa.com *Web Site:* www.ediusa.com, pg 85

Educational Impressions Inc, 350 Ramapo Valley Rd, Oakland, NJ 07436 *Tel:* 973-423-4666 *Toll Free Tel:* 800-451-7450 *Fax:* 973-423-5569 *Web Site:* www.edimpressions.com; www.awpeller.com, pg 85

Educational Insights Inc, 152 W Walnut St, Suite 201, Gardena, CA 90248 *Toll Free Tel:* 800-933-3277 *Fax:* 847-281-2868 *Toll Free Fax:* 800-995-0506 *E-mail:* info@educationalinsights.com; cs@educationalinsights.com *Web Site:* www.educationalinsights.com, pg 85

Educators Award, PO Box 1589, Austin, TX 78767-1589 *Tel:* 512-478-5748 *Toll Free Tel:* 888-762-4685 *Fax:* 512-478-3961 *E-mail:* societyexec@dkg.org *Web Site:* www.dkg.org, pg 701

Educator's International Press Inc, 18 Colleen Rd, Troy, NY 12180 *Tel:* 518-271-9886 *Fax:* 518-266-9422 *Web Site:* www.edint.com, pg 85

Educators Progress Service Inc, 214 Center St, Randolph, WI 53956 *Tel:* 920-326-3126 *Toll Free Tel:* 888-951-4469 *Fax:* 920-326-3127 *E-mail:* epsinc@centurytel.net *Web Site:* www.freeteachingaids.com, pg 85

Edupress Inc, 4810 Forrest Run Rd, Madison, WI 53704 *Tel:* 608-241-1201 *Toll Free Tel:* 800-694-5827 *Toll Free Fax:* 800-835-2329 *E-mail:* edupress@highsmith.com *Web Site:* www.highsmith.com; www.edupressinc.com, pg 85

Margaret A Edwards Award, 50 E Huron St, Chicago, IL 60611 *Tel:* 312-280-4390 *Toll Free Tel:* 800-545-2433 *Fax:* 312-280-5276 *E-mail:* yalsa@ala.org *Web Site:* www.ala.org/yalsa/edwards, pg 702

EEI Communications, 7240 Parkway Dr, Suite 250, Hanover, MD 21076-1364 *Tel:* 410-309-8200 *Toll Free Tel:* 888-253-2762 *Fax:* 410-630-3980 *E-mail:* info@eeicom.com *Web Site:* www.eeicom.com, pg 546, 677

Wm B Eerdmans Publishing Co, 2140 Oak Industrial Dr NE, Grand Rapids, MI 49505 *Tel:* 616-459-4591 *Toll Free Tel:* 800-253-7521 *Fax:* 616-459-6540 *E-mail:* customerservice@eerdmans.com; sales@eerdmans.com *Web Site:* www.eerdmans.com, pg 85

Wilfrid Eggleston Award for Nonfiction, 11759 Groat Rd, Edmonton, AB T5M 3K6, Canada *Tel:* 780-422-8174 *Toll Free Tel:* 800-665-5354 (AB only)

*Fax:* 780-422-2663 (attn WGA) *E-mail:* mail@writersguild.ab.ca *Web Site:* www.writersguild.ab.ca, pg 702

Egmont USA, 443 Park Ave S, Suite 806, New York, NY 10016 *Tel:* 212-685-0102 *E-mail:* egmontusa@egmont.com *Web Site:* www.egmontusa.com, pg 86

Diane Eickhoff, 3808 Genessee St, Kansas City, MO 64111 *Tel:* 816-561-6693 *E-mail:* diane.eickhoff@gmail.com, pg 546

Eisenbrauns Inc, PO Box 275, Winona Lake, IN 46590-0275 *Tel:* 574-269-2011 *Fax:* 574-269-6788 *E-mail:* customer_service@eisenbrauns.com; publisher@eisenbrauns.com *Web Site:* www.eisenbrauns.com, pg 86

The Lisa Ekus Group LLC, 57 North St, Hatfield, MA 01038 *Tel:* 413-247-9325 *Fax:* 413-247-9873 *E-mail:* lisaekus@lisaekus.com *Web Site:* lisaekus.com, pg 570

The Lisa Ekus Group LLC, 57 North St, Hatfield, MA 01038 *Tel:* 413-247-9325 *Fax:* 413-247-9873 *Web Site:* lisaekus.com, pg 678

Elderberry Press Inc, 1393 Old Homestead Dr, Mezzanine, Oakland, OR 97462-9506 *Tel:* 541-459-6043 *Web Site:* www.elderberrypress.com, pg 86

The Electrochemical Society (ECS), 65 S Main St, Bldg D, Pennington, NJ 08534-2839 *Tel:* 609-737-1902 *Fax:* 609-737-2743 *E-mail:* ecs@electrochem.org *Web Site:* www.electrochem.org, pg 86

Edward Elgar Publishing Inc, The William Pratt House, 9 Dewey Ct, Northampton, MA 01060-3815 *Tel:* 413-584-5551 *Toll Free Tel:* 800-390-3149 (orders) *Fax:* 413-584-9933 *E-mail:* info@e-elgar.com *Web Site:* www.e-elgar.com, pg 86

T S Eliot Prize for Poetry, 100 E Normal Ave, Kirksville, MO 63501-4221 *Tel:* 660-785-7336 *Toll Free Tel:* 800-916-6802 *Fax:* 660-785-4480 *E-mail:* tsup@truman.edu *Web Site:* tsup.truman.edu, pg 702

Elite Books, PO Box 442, Fulton, CA 95439 *Tel:* 707-525-9292 *Toll Free Fax:* 800-330-9798 *Web Site:* www.elitebooks.biz, pg 86

Ethan Ellenberg Literary Agency, 548 Broadway, Suite 5-E, New York, NY 10012 *Tel:* 212-431-4554 *Fax:* 212-941-4652 *E-mail:* agent@ethanellenberg.com *Web Site:* www.ethanellenberg.com, pg 570

Elliot's Books, 799 Forest Rd, Northford, CT 06472 *Tel:* 203-484-2184 *Fax:* 203-484-7644 *E-mail:* outofprintbooks1@mindspring.com *Web Site:* www.elliotsbooks.com, pg 86

Elliott Prize, 104 Mount Auburn St, 5th fl, Cambridge, MA 02138 *Tel:* 617-491-1622 *Fax:* 617-492-3303 *E-mail:* speculum@medievalacademy.org *Web Site:* www.medievalacademy.org, pg 702

Nicholas Ellison Agency, 55 Fifth Ave, 15th fl, New York, NY 10003 *Tel:* 212-206-5600 *Fax:* 212-463-8718 *Web Site:* greenburger.com/agent/nick-ellison, pg 571

Ellora's Cave, 1056 Home Ave, Akron, OH 44310-3302 *Tel:* 330-253-3521 *E-mail:* service@ellorascave.com; comments@ellorascave.com *Web Site:* www.ellorascave.com, pg 86

Irene Elmer, 2806 Cherry St, Berkeley, CA 94705-2310 *Tel:* 510-841-0466 *E-mail:* ielmer@earthlink.net, pg 546

ELS Editions, University of Victoria, Dept of English, Victoria, BC V8W 3W1, Canada *Tel:* 250-721-7236 *Fax:* 250-721-6498 *E-mail:* els@uvic.ca *Web Site:* english.uvic.ca/els, pg 504

Elsevier Engineering Information (Ei), 360 Park Ave S, New York, NY 10010-1710 *Tel:* 212-989-5800 *Toll Free Tel:* 800-221-1044 *Fax:* 212-633-6380 *E-mail:* eicustomersupport@elsevier.com *Web Site:* www.ei.org, pg 86

Elsevier, Health Sciences Division, 1600 John F Kennedy Blvd, Suite 1800, Philadelphia, PA 19103-2899 *Tel:* 215-239-3900 *Toll Free Tel:* 800-523-1649 *Fax:* 215-239-3990 *Web Site:* www.elsevierhealth.com, pg 86

Elsevier Inc, 225 Wyman St, Waltham, MA 02144 *Tel:* 781-663-5200 *Fax:* 781-663-2262 *E-mail:* bookscustomerservice-usa@elsevier.com *Web Site:* www.elsevier.com, pg 87

Elva Resa Publishing, 8362 Tamarack Village, Suite 119-106, St Paul, MN 55125 *Tel:* 651-357-8770 *Fax:* 501-641-0777 *E-mail:* staff@elvaresa.com *Web Site:* www.elvaresa.com; www.almalittle.com, pg 87

Catherine C Elverston ELS, 9 Red Bay Lane, Kitty Hawk, NC 27949-3307 *Tel:* 352-222-0625 (cell) *E-mail:* celverston@gmail.com, pg 546

R Elwell Indexing, 193 Main St, Cold Spring, NY 10516 *Tel:* 845-667-1036 *E-mail:* ruth.elwell@yahoo.com, pg 546

EMC Publishing, 875 Montreal Way, St Paul, MN 55102 *Tel:* 651-290-2800 (corp) *Toll Free Tel:* 800-328-1452 *Fax:* 651-290-2899 *Toll Free Fax:* 800-328-4564 *E-mail:* educate@emcp.com *Web Site:* www.emcp.com, pg 87

Emerald Books, PO Box 55787, Seattle, WA 98155 *Tel:* 425-771-1153 *Toll Free Tel:* 800-922-2143 *Fax:* 425-775-2383 *E-mail:* books@ywampublishing.com *Web Site:* www.ywampublishing.com, pg 87

Emerging Playwright Award, 555 Eighth Ave, Suite 1800, New York, NY 10018 *Tel:* 212-421-1380 *Fax:* 212-421-1387 *E-mail:* urbanstage@aol.com, pg 702

Emerson College Dept of Writing, Literature & Publishing, 180 Tremont St, 10th fl, Boston, MA 02116 *Tel:* 617-824-8750 *Fax:* 617-824-7856 *Web Site:* www.emerson.edu, pg 678

Emerson College Literary Publishing Certificate Program, Dept of Professional Studies, 120 Boylston St, Boston, MA 02116-8750 *Tel:* 617-824-8280 *Fax:* 617-824-8158 *E-mail:* continuing@emerson.edu *Web Site:* www.emerson.edu/ce, pg 668

The Ralph Waldo Emerson Award, 1606 New Hampshire Ave NW, Washington, DC 20009 *Tel:* 202-265-3808 *Fax:* 202-986-1601 *E-mail:* awards@pbk.org *Web Site:* www.pbk.org/bookawards, pg 702

Emmaus Road Publishing Inc, 827 N Fourth St, Steubenville, OH 43952 *Tel:* 740-283-2880 (outside US) *Toll Free Tel:* 800-398-5470 (orders) *Fax:* 740-283-4011 (orders) *E-mail:* questions@emmausroad.org *Web Site:* www.emmausroad.org, pg 87

Emond Montgomery Publications, 60 Shaftesbury Ave, Toronto, ON M4T 1A3, Canada *Tel:* 416-975-3925 *Toll Free Tel:* 888-837-0815 *Fax:* 416-975-3924 *E-mail:* info@emp.ca; orders@emp.ca *Web Site:* www.emp.ca, pg 504

Empire Press Media/Avant-Guide, 244 Fifth Ave, Suite 2053, New York, NY 10001-7604 *Tel:* 917-512-3881 *Fax:* 212-202-7757 *E-mail:* info@avantguide.com; communications@avantguide.com; editor@avantguide.com *Web Site:* www.avantguide.com, pg 87

Empire Publishing Service, PO Box 1344, Studio City, CA 91614-0344 *Tel:* 818-784-8918 *E-mail:* empirepubsvc@att.net *Web Site:* www.ppeps.com, pg 87

Empire State Award for Excellence in Literature for Young People, 6021 State Farm Rd, Guilderland, NY 12084 *Tel:* 518-432-6952 *Toll Free Tel:* 800-252-6952 *Fax:* 518-427-1697 *E-mail:* info@nyla.org *Web Site:* www.nyla.org, pg 702

Enchanted Lion Books, 20 Jay St, Studio M-18, Brooklyn, NY 11231 *Tel:* 646-785-9272 *E-mail:* enchantedlion@gmail.com *Web Site:* www.enchantedlionbooks.com, pg 87

Encounter Books, 900 Broadway, Suite 601, New York, NY 10003 *Tel:* 212-871-6310 *Toll Free Tel:* 800-786-3839 *Fax:* 212-871-6311 *Toll Free Fax:* 877-811-1461 *E-mail:* read@encounterbooks.com *Web Site:* www.encounterbooks.com, pg 88

Encyclopaedia Britannica Inc, 331 N La Salle St, Chicago, IL 60654 *Tel:* 312-347-7159 (all other countries) *Toll Free Tel:* 800-323-1229 (US & CN) *Fax:* 312-294-2104 *E-mail:* editor@eb.com *Web Site:* www.eb.com; www.britannica.com, pg 88

Energy Information Administration (EIA), 1000 Independence Ave SW, Washington, DC 20585 *Tel:* 202-586-8800 *Fax:* 202-586-0727 *E-mail:* infoctr@eia.doe.gov *Web Site:* www.eia.doe.gov, pg 88

Energy Psychology Press, 1490 Mark West Springs Rd, Santa Rosa, CA 95404 *Tel:* 707-237-6951 *Toll Free Fax:* 800-330-9798 *Web Site:* www.energypsychologypress.com, pg 88

Enfield Publishing & Distribution Co, 234 May St, Enfield, NH 03748 *Tel:* 603-632-7377 *Fax:* 603-632-5611 *E-mail:* info@enfieldbooks.com *Web Site:* www.enfieldbooks.com, pg 88

Elaine P English PLLC, 4710 41 St NW, Suite D, Washington, DC 20016 *Tel:* 202-362-5190 *Fax:* 202-362-5192 *E-mail:* foreignrights@elaineenglish.com *Web Site:* www.elaineenglish.com, pg 571

Enigma Books, 360 E 116 St, New York, NY 10029 *Tel:* 212-933-1315 *E-mail:* editor@enigmabooks.com *Web Site:* www.enigmabooks.com, pg 88

Enough Said, 3959 NW 29 Lane, Gainesville, FL 32606 *Tel:* 352-262-2971 *E-mail:* enoughsaid@cox.net *Web Site:* users.navi.net/~heathlynn, pg 546

Enslow Publishers Inc, 40 Industrial Rd, Dept F-61, Berkeley Heights, NJ 07922 *Tel:* 908-771-9400 *Toll Free Tel:* 800-398-2504 *Fax:* 908-771-0925; 908-771-8400 (orders) *E-mail:* customerservice@enslow.com; orders@enslow.com *Web Site:* www.enslow.com; www.myreportlinks.com, pg 88

Entangled Publishing, 2614 S Timberline Rd, Suite 109, Fort Collins, CO 80525 *Tel:* 724-208-7888 (sales) *E-mail:* publisher@entangledpublishing.com *Web Site:* www.entangledpublishing.com, pg 89

Entomological Society of America, 10001 Derekwood Lane, Suite 100, Lanham, MD 20706-4876 *Tel:* 301-731-4535 *Fax:* 301-731-4538 *E-mail:* esa@entsoc.org *Web Site:* www.entsoc.org, pg 89

Environmental Law Institute, 2000 "L" St NW, Suite 620, Washington, DC 20036 *Tel:* 202-939-3800 *Fax:* 202-939-3868 *E-mail:* law@eli.org *Web Site:* www.eli.org, pg 89

Ephemera Bound Publishing, 719 Ninth St N, Fargo, ND 58102 *Toll Free Tel:* 888-642-3043 *Toll Free Fax:* 888-291-4052 (orders) *E-mail:* publish@ephemera-bound.com; sales@ephemera-bound.com *Web Site:* www.ephemera-bound.com, pg 89

Epicenter Press Inc, 6524 NE 181 St, Suite 2, Kenmore, WA 98028 *Tel:* 425-485-6822 (edit, mktg, busn off) *Toll Free Tel:* 800-950-6663 (orders) *Fax:* 425-481-8253 *E-mail:* info@epicenterpress.com *Web Site:* www.epicenterpress.com, pg 89

EPS/School Specialty Literacy & Intervention, 625 Mount Auburn St, 3rd fl, Cambridge, MA 02138-4555 *Tel:* 617-547-6706 *Toll Free Tel:* 800-225-5750 *Fax:* 617-547-0412 *Toll Free Fax:* 888-440-2665 *E-mail:* customerservice.eps@schoolspecialty.com *Web Site:* eps.schoolspecialty.com, pg 89

Norma Epstein Foundation, 15 King's College Circle, UC 173, Toronto, ON M5S 3H7, Canada *Tel:* 416-978-8083 *Fax:* 416-971-2027 *Web Site:* www.utoronto.ca, pg 702

Ericson Books, 1614 Redbud St, Nacogdoches, TX 75965-2936 *Tel:* 936-564-3625 *Fax:* 936-552-8999 *E-mail:* kissinkuzzins@suddenlink.net *Web Site:* www.ericsonbooks.com, pg 89

Ernst Publishing Co LLC, 99 Washington Ave, Suite 309, Albany, NY 12210 *Toll Free Tel:* 800-345-3822 *Toll Free Fax:* 800-252-0906 *E-mail:* clientservices@ernstpublishing.com *Web Site:* www.ernstpublishing.com, pg 89

Eros Books, 463 Barlow Ave, Staten Island, NY 10308 *Tel:* 718-317-7484 *Web Site:* www.eros.thecraze.com, pg 89

Erskine J Poetry Prize, PO Box 22161, Baltimore, MD 21203 *Web Site:* www.smartishpace.com, pg 702

ETC Publications, 1456 Rodeo Rd, Palm Springs, CA 92262 *Tel:* 760-316-9695 *Toll Free Tel:* 866-514-9969 *Fax:* 760-316-9681 *E-mail:* customer_service@etcpublications.com *Web Site:* www.etcpublications.com, pg 89

Felicia Eth Literary Representation, 555 Bryant St, Suite 350, Palo Alto, CA 94301 *Tel:* 415-970-9717 *E-mail:* feliciaeth.literary@gmail.com *Web Site:* www.ethliterary.com, pg 571

Etruscan Press, Wilkes University, 84 W South St, Wilkes-Barre, PA 18766 *Tel:* 570-408-4546 *Fax:* 570-408-3333 *E-mail:* books@etruscanpress.org *Web Site:* www.etruscanpress.org, pg 90

Europa Editions, 214 W 29 St, Suite 1003, New York, NY 10001 *Tel:* 212-868-6844 *Fax:* 212-868-6845 *E-mail:* info@europaeditions.com *Web Site:* www.europaeditions.com, pg 90

European Masterpieces, 103 Walker Way, Newark, DE 19711 *Tel:* 302-453-8695 *Fax:* 302-453-8601 *E-mail:* linguatext@juno.com *Web Site:* www.europeanmasterpieces.com, pg 90

Evan-Moor Educational Publishers, 18 Lower Ragsdale Dr, Monterey, CA 93940-5746 *Tel:* 831-649-5901 *Toll Free Tel:* 800-714-0971 (cust serv); 800-777-4362 (orders) *Fax:* 831-649-6256 *Toll Free Fax:* 800-777-4332 (orders) *E-mail:* sales@evan-moor.com; marketing@evan-moor.com *Web Site:* www.evan-moor.com, pg 90

Evangel Publishing House, 2000 Evangel Way, Nappanee, IN 46550 *Tel:* 574-773-3164 *Toll Free Tel:* 800-253-9315 (orders) *Fax:* 574-773-5934 *E-mail:* sales@evangelpublishing.com *Web Site:* www.evangelpublishing.com; www.evangelpress.com, pg 90

Evangelical Christian Publishers Association (ECPA), 9633 S 48 St, Suite 195, Phoenix, AZ 85044-5697 *Tel:* 480-966-3998 *Fax:* 480-966-1944 *E-mail:* info@ecpa.org *Web Site:* www.ecpa.org, pg 623

Evangelical Press Association (EPA), PO Box 20198, El Cajon, CA 92021 *Tel:* 619-609-0910 *Toll Free Tel:* 888-311-1731 *Web Site:* www.evangelicalpress.com, pg 623

David W & Beatrice C Evans Biography & Handcart Awards, 0735 Old Main Hill, Logan, UT 84322-0735 *Tel:* 435-797-0299 *Fax:* 435-797-1092 *E-mail:* mwc@usu.edu *Web Site:* www.mountainwest.usu.edu, pg 702

M Evans & Co Inc, 4501 Forbes Blvd, Suite 200, Lanham, MD 20706 *Tel:* 301-459-3366 *Fax:* 301-429-5743 *Web Site:* www.rlpgtrade.com, pg 90

Mary Evans Inc, 242 E Fifth St, New York, NY 10003-8501 *Tel:* 212-979-0880 *Fax:* 212-979-5344 *E-mail:* info@maryevansinc.com *Web Site:* www.maryevansinc.com, pg 571

Evanston Publishing Inc, 12305 Westport Rd, Suite 4, Louisville, KY 40245-2712 *Tel:* 502-899-1919 *Toll Free Tel:* 888-BOOKS80 (266-5780) *Fax:* 502-565-2507 *E-mail:* info@evanstonpublishing.com *Web Site:* www.evanstonpublishing.com, pg 90

Evergreen Pacific Publishing Ltd, 4204 Russell Rd, Suite M, Mukilteo, WA 98275-5424 *Tel:* 425-493-1451 *Fax:* 425-493-1453 *E-mail:* sales@evergreenpacific.com *Web Site:* www.evergreenpacific.com, pg 90

Excalibur Publications, PO Box 89667, Tucson, AZ 85752-9667 *Tel:* 520-575-9057 *E-mail:* excaliburpublications@centurylink.net, pg 90

EXCEL Awards, 12100 Sunset Hills Rd, Suite 130, Reston, VA 20190 *Tel:* 703-234-4063 *Fax:* 703-435-4390 *E-mail:* info@associationmediaandpublishing.org *Web Site:* www.associationmediaandpublishing.org, pg 703

Excelsior Editions, 22 Corporate Woods Blvd, 3rd fl, Albany, NY 12211-2504 *Tel:* 518-472-5000 *Toll Free Tel:* 877-204-6073 *Fax:* 518-472-5038 *Toll Free Fax:* 877-204-6074 *E-mail:* info@sunypress.edu *Web Site:* www.sunypress.edu, pg 90

The Experiment, 260 Fifth Ave, Suite 3 South, New York, NY 10001-6425 *Tel:* 212-889-1659 *E-mail:* info@theexperimentpublishing.com *Web Site:* www.theexperimentpublishing.com, pg 91

Eye in the Ear Children's Audio, 5 Crescent St, Portland, ME 04102 *Tel:* 207-780-1574 *Toll Free Tel:* 877-99-STORY (997-8679) *Fax:* 509-275-4252 *E-mail:* info@eyeintheear.com *Web Site:* www.eyeintheear.com, pg 91

Eye On Education, 6 Depot Way W, Larchmont, NY 10538 *Tel:* 914-833-0551 *Toll Free Tel:* 888-299-5350 *Fax:* 914-833-0761 *E-mail:* customer-service@eyeoneducation.com *Web Site:* www.eyeoneducation.com, pg 91

Faber & Faber Inc, 18 W 18 St, New York, NY 10011 *Tel:* 212-741-6900 *Fax:* 212-633-9385 *E-mail:* fsg.editorial@fsgbooks.com (edit inquiries) *Web Site:* us.macmillan.com/faberandfaber.aspx, pg 91

Facts On File, 132 W 31 St, 17th fl, New York, NY 10001 *Tel:* 212-967-8800 *Toll Free Tel:* 800-322-8755 *Fax:* 917-339-0323 *Toll Free Fax:* 800-678-3633 *E-mail:* custserv@factsonfile.com *Web Site:* infobasepublishing.com, pg 91

Fair Winds Press, 100 Cummings Ctr, Suite 406-L, Beverly, MA 01915 *Tel:* 978-282-9590 *Toll Free Tel:* 800-328-0590 (sales) *Fax:* 978-283-2742 *E-mail:* customerservice@quaysidepub.com *Web Site:* www.fairwindspress.com, pg 91

John K Fairbank Prize in East Asian History, 400 "A" St SE, Washington, DC 20003-3889 *Tel:* 202-544-2422 *Fax:* 202-544-8307 *E-mail:* awards@historians.org *Web Site:* www.historians.org, pg 703

Fairchild Books, 1385 Broadway, New York, NY 10018 *Tel:* 212-419-5292 *Toll Free Tel:* 800-932-4724; 888-330-8477 (orders) *E-mail:* orders@mpsvirginia.com *Web Site:* www.fairchildbooks.com, pg 91

Fairleigh Dickinson University Press, M-GH2-01, 285 Madison Ave, Madison, NJ 07940 *Tel:* 973-443-8564 *Fax:* 974-443-8364 *E-mail:* fdupress@fdu.edu *Web Site:* www.fdupress.org, pg 92

Tom Fairley Award for Editorial Excellence, 502-27 Carlton St, Toronto, ON M5B 1L2, Canada *Tel:* 416-975-1379 *Toll Free Tel:* 866-CAN-EDIT (226-3348) *Fax:* 416-975-1637 *E-mail:* fairley_award@editors.ca *Web Site:* www.editors.ca; www.reviseurs.ca, pg 703

The Fairmont Press Inc, 700 Indian Trail, Lilburn, GA 30047 *Tel:* 770-925-9388 *Fax:* 770-381-9865 *Web Site:* www.fairmontpress.com, pg 92

Fairwinds Press, PO Box 668, Lions Bay, BC V0N 2E0, Canada *Tel:* 604-913-0649 *E-mail:* orders@fairwinds-press.com *Web Site:* www.fairwinds-press.com, pg 504

Faith Alive Christian Resources, 2850 Kalamazoo Ave SE, Grand Rapids, MI 49560 *Tel:* 616-224-0728 *Toll Free Tel:* 800-333-8300 *Fax:* 616-224-0834 *Toll Free Fax:* 888-642-8606 *E-mail:* info@faithaliveresources.org; sales@faithaliveresources.org; editors@faithaliveresources.org *Web Site:* www.faithaliveresources.org, pg 92

Faith & Fellowship Press, 1020 W Alcott Ave, Fergus Falls, MN 56537 *Tel:* 218-736-7357; 218-736-2200 *Toll Free Tel:* 800-332-9232 *E-mail:* ffbooks@clba.org; ffpublishing@clba.org *Web Site:* www.faithandfellowship.org, pg 92

Faith & Life Resources, 1251 Virginia Ave, Harrisonburg, VA 22802-2434 *Toll Free Tel:* 800-245-7894 (orders & cust serv US); 800-631-6535 (orders & cust serv CN) *Toll Free Fax:* 877-271-0760 *E-mail:* mpcan@mpn.net *Web Site:* www.faithandliferesources.org; www.mpn.net, pg 92

Faith Library Publications, PO Box 50126, Tulsa, OK 74150-0126 *Tel:* 918-258-1588 (ext 2218) *Toll Free Tel:* 888-258-0999 (orders) *Fax:* 918-872-7710 (orders) *E-mail:* flp@rhema.org *Web Site:* www.rhema.org/store/wholesale, pg 92

FaithWalk Publishing, 5450 N Dixie Hwy, Lima, OH 45807 *Tel:* 419-227-1818 *Toll Free Tel:* 800-537-1030 (orders: non-bookstore mkts) *Fax:* 419-224-9184 *Web Site:* www.faithwalkpub.com, pg 92

FaithWords, 12 Cadillac Dr, Suite 480, Brentwood, TN 37027 *Tel:* 615-221-0996 *Fax:* 615-221-0962 *Web Site:* www.hachettebookgroup.com, pg 92

Family Matters, PO Box 80430, Portland, OR 97280 *Tel:* 503-221-0836 *Fax:* 503-221-0837 *E-mail:* editors@glimmertrain.org *Web Site:* www.glimmertrain.org, pg 703

F+W Media Inc, 10151 Carver Rd, Suite 200, Blue Ash, OH 45242 *Tel:* 513-531-2690 *Toll Free Tel:* 800-289-0963 (trade accts); 800-258-0929 (orders) *E-mail:* contact_us@fwmedia.com *Web Site:* www.fwmedia.com, pg 92

Far Horizons Award for Poetry, University of Victoria, Box 1700, Sta CSC, Victoria, BC V8W 2Y2, Canada *Tel:* 250-721-8524 *Fax:* 250-472-5051 *E-mail:* malahat@uvic.ca *Web Site:* www.malahatreview.ca, pg 703

Far Horizons Award for Short Fiction, University of Victoria, Box 1700, Sta CSC, Victoria, BC V8W 2Y2, Canada *Tel:* 250-721-8524 *Fax:* 250-472-5051 *E-mail:* malahat@uvic.ca *Web Site:* www.malahatreview.ca, pg 703

Farber Literary Agency Inc, 14 E 75 St, New York, NY 10021 *Tel:* 212-861-7075 *Fax:* 212-861-7076 *E-mail:* farberlit@aol.com; farberlit@gmail.com (submissions), pg 571

Norma Farber First Book Award, 15 Gramercy Park S, New York, NY 10003 *Tel:* 212-254-9628 *Fax:* 212-673-2352 *Web Site:* www.poetrysociety.org, pg 703

Farrar, Straus & Giroux Books for Young Readers, 175 Fifth Ave, New York, NY 10010 *Tel:* 212-741-6900; 646-307-5151 *Toll Free Tel:* 888-330-8477 (sales) *Fax:* 212-741-6973 *E-mail:* sales@fsgbooks.com; childrens.editorial@fsgbooks.com (edit inquiries) *Web Site:* us.macmillan.com/fsgyoungreaders.aspx; us.macmillan.com, pg 93

Farrar, Straus & Giroux, LLC, 18 W 18 St, New York, NY 10011 *Tel:* 212-741-6900 *Fax:* 212-633-9385 *E-mail:* fsg.publicity@fsgbooks.com *Web Site:* us.macmillan.com/fsg.aspx, pg 93

Farrar Writing & Editing, 4638 Manchester Rd, Mound, MN 55364 *Tel:* 952-472-6874 *Fax:* 952-472-6874 (call first) *Web Site:* www.writeandedit.net, pg 546

Farris Literary Agency Inc, PO Box 570069, Dallas, TX 75357-0069 *Tel:* 972-203-8804 *E-mail:* farris1@airmail.net *Web Site:* www.farrisliterary.com, pg 571

Father & Son Publishing Inc, 4909 N Monroe St, Tallahassee, FL 32303-7015 *Tel:* 850-562-2612 *Toll Free Tel:* 800-741-2712 (orders only) *Fax:* 850-562-0916 *Web Site:* www.fatherson.com, pg 93

Virginia Faulkner Award for Excellence in Writing, University of Nebraska, 123 Andrews Hall, Lincoln, NE 68588-0334 *Tel:* 402-472-0911 *Fax:* 402-472-9771 *Web Site:* prairieschooner.unl.edu, pg 703

Favorable Impressions, PO Box 69018, Pleasant Ridge, MI 48069 *Toll Free Tel:* 800-206-9513 *Fax:* 248-582-0912 *Web Site:* www.favimp.com, pg 93

FC&A Publishing, 103 Clover Green, Peachtree City, GA 30269 *Tel:* 770-487-6307 *Toll Free Tel:* 800-226-8024 *Fax:* 770-631-4357 *E-mail:* customer_service@fca.com *Web Site:* www.fca.com, pg 93

The FC2 Catherine Doctorow Innovative Fiction Prize, University Ctr, Suite 310, 3007 N Ben Wilson St, Victoria, TX 77901 *Web Site:* www.fc2.org, pg 703

Federal Bar Association, 1220 N Filmore St, Suite 444, Arlington, VA 22201 *Tel:* 571-481-9100 *Fax:* 571-481-9090 *E-mail:* fba@fedbar.org *Web Site:* www.fedbar.org, pg 93

Federal Buyers Guide Inc, 324 Palm Ave, Santa Barbara, CA 93101 *Tel:* 805-963-6524 *Fax:* 805-963-7478 *E-mail:* info@gov-world.com; info@fbgglobal.com *Web Site:* www.gov-world.com; www.federalbuyersguideinc.com; www.digitalsubs.com, pg 93

Federal Street Press, 25-13 Old Kings Hwy N, No 277, Darien, CT 06820 *Tel:* 203-852-1280 *Toll Free Tel:* 877-886-2830 *Fax:* 203-852-1389 *E-mail:* sales@federalstreetpress.com *Web Site:* www.federalstreetpress.com, pg 93

COMPANY INDEX

Federation of BC Writers, PO Box 3887, Sta Terminal, Vancouver, BC V6B 3Z3, Canada *Tel:* 604-683-2057 *E-mail:* fedbcwriters@gmail.com *Web Site:* www.bcwriters.ca, pg 623

Feigenbaum Publishing Consultants Inc, 61 Bounty Lane, Jericho, NY 11753 *Tel:* 516-647-8314 (cell) *Fax:* 516-935-0507 *E-mail:* readrover5@aol.com, pg 571

Lillian Mermin Feinsilver, 510 McCartney St, Easton, PA 18042 *Tel:* 610-252-7005, pg 546

Betsy Feist Resources, 140 E 81 St, Unit 8-G, New York, NY 10028-1875 *Tel:* 212-861-2014 *E-mail:* bfresources@rcn.com, pg 546

Feldheim Publishers (Philipp Feldheim Inc), 208 Airport Executive Park, Nanuet, NY 10954 *Tel:* 845-356-2282 *Toll Free Tel:* 800-237-7149 (orders) *Fax:* 845-425-1908 *E-mail:* sales@feldheim.com *Web Site:* www.feldheim.com, pg 94

Fellowship & Scholarship Program for Writers, Middlebury College, Middlebury, VT 05753 *Tel:* 802-443-5286 *Fax:* 802-443-2087 *E-mail:* blwc@middlebury.edu *Web Site:* www.middlebury.edu/blwc, pg 703

Fellowship Program, One Capital Hill, 3rd fl, Providence, RI 02908 *Tel:* 401-222-3880 *Fax:* 401-222-3018 *Web Site:* www.arts.ri.gov, pg 703

Fellowships for Creative & Performing Artists & Writers, 185 Salisbury St, Worcester, MA 01609-1634 *Tel:* 508-755-5221 *Fax:* 508-753-3311 *Web Site:* www.americanantiquarian.org, pg 703

Fellowships for Historical Research, 185 Salisbury St, Worcester, MA 01609-1634 *Tel:* 508-471-2131 *Web Site:* www.americanantiquarian.org, pg 704

Jerry Felsen, 3960 NW 196 St, Miami Gardens, FL 33055-1869 *Tel:* 305-625-5012 *E-mail:* jfelsen0@att.net *Web Site:* beatthemarket.org, pg 546

The Feminist Press at The City University of New York, 365 Fifth Ave, Suite 5406, New York, NY 10016 *Tel:* 212-817-7915 *Fax:* 212-817-1593 *E-mail:* info@feministpress.org *Web Site:* www.feministpress.org, pg 94

Fence Books, University at Albany, Science Library 320, 1400 Washington Ave, Albany, NY 12222 *Tel:* 518-591-8162 *E-mail:* fence.fencebooks@gmail.com *Web Site:* www.fenceportal.org, pg 94

Fence Modern Poets Series, University at Albany, Science Library 320, 1400 Washington Ave, Albany, NY 12222 *Tel:* 518-591-8162 *E-mail:* fence.fencebooks@gmail.com *Web Site:* www.fenceportal.org, pg 704

Shubert Fendrich Memorial Playwriting Contest, PO Box 4267, Englewood, CO 80155-4267 *Tel:* 303-779-4035 *Toll Free Tel:* 800-333-7262 *Fax:* 303-779-4315 *E-mail:* playwrights@pioneerdrama.com *Web Site:* www.pioneerdrama.com, pg 704

Robert L Fenton PC; Entertainment Attorney & Literary Agent, 31800 Northwestern Hwy, Suite 204, Farmington Hills, MI 48334 *Tel:* 248-855-8780 *Fax:* 248-855-3302 *Web Site:* www.robertlfenton.com, pg 571

Feral House, 1240 W Sims Way, Suite 124, Port Townsend, WA 98368 *Tel:* 323-666-3311 *Fax:* 323-297-4331 *E-mail:* info@feralhouse.com *Web Site:* feralhouse.com, pg 94

Ferguson Publishing, 132 W 31 St, 17th fl, New York, NY 10001 *Tel:* 212-967-8800 *Toll Free Tel:* 800-322-8755 *Fax:* 917-339-0323 *Toll Free Fax:* 800-678-3633 *E-mail:* custserv@factsonfile.com *Web Site:* infobasepublishing.com, pg 94

Fernwood Publishing, 32 Oceanvista Lane, Black Point, NS B0J 1B0, Canada *Tel:* 902-857-1388 *Fax:* 902-857-1328 *E-mail:* info@fernpub.ca *Web Site:* www.fernwoodpublishing.ca, pg 504

Howard Fertig, Publisher, 80 E 11 St, New York, NY 10003 *Tel:* 212-982-7922 *Fax:* 212-982-1099 *E-mail:* enquiries@hfertigbooks.com; orders@hfertigbooks.com *Web Site:* www.hfertigbooks.com, pg 94

Festival & Conference on Poetry, 158 Ridge Rd, Franconia, NH 03580 *Tel:* 603-823-5510 *E-mail:* frost@frostplace.org *Web Site:* www.frostplace.org, pg 668

Fiction Collective Two Inc (FC2), University Ctr, Suite 310, 3007 N Ben Wilson St, Victoria, TX 77901 *Tel:* 361-570-4200; 361-570-4207 *E-mail:* fc2cum@gmail.com *Web Site:* www.fc2.org; www.uhv.edu, pg 94

Fiction Open, PO Box 80430, Portland, OR 97280 *Tel:* 503-221-0836 *Fax:* 503-221-0837 *E-mail:* editors@glimmertrain.org *Web Site:* www.glimmertrain.org, pg 704

The Field Poetry Prize, 50 N Professor St, Oberlin, OH 44074-1091 *Tel:* 440-775-8408 *Fax:* 440-775-8124 *E-mail:* oc.press@oberlin.edu *Web Site:* www.oberlin.edu/ocpress; www.oberlin.edu/ocpress/prize.htm (guidelines), pg 704

Fifth Estate Publishing, 2795 County Hwy 57, Blounstville, AL 35031 *Toll Free Tel:* 855-299-2160 *E-mail:* admin@fifth-estate.net *Web Site:* fifthestatepub.com, pg 94

Fifth House Publishers, 195 Allstate Pkwy, Markham, ON L3R 4T8, Canada *Tel:* 905-477-9700 *Toll Free Tel:* 800-387-9776 *Toll Free Fax:* 800-260-9777 *E-mail:* godwit@fitzhenry.ca *Web Site:* www.fitzhenry.ca/fifthhouse.aspx, pg 505

Film-Video Publications/Circus Source Publications, 7944 Capistrano Ave, West Hills, CA 91304 *Tel:* 818-340-0175 *Fax:* 818-340-6770 *E-mail:* circussource@aol.com, pg 94

Filsinger & Company Ltd, 288 W 12 St, Suite 2R, New York, NY 10014 *Tel:* 212-243-7421 *E-mail:* filsingercompany@gmail.com *Web Site:* www.filsingerco.com, pg 527

Filter Press LLC, PO Box 95, Palmer Lake, CO 80133 *Tel:* 719-481-2420 *Toll Free Tel:* 888-570-2663 *Fax:* 719-481-2420 *E-mail:* info@filterpressbooks.com; orders@filterpressbooks.com *Web Site:* filterpressbooks.com, pg 95

Financial Executives Research Foundation Inc (FERF), West Tower, 7th fl, 1250 Headquarters Plaza, Morristown, NJ 07960-6837 *Tel:* 973-765-1000 *Fax:* 973-765-1023 *Web Site:* www.financialexecutives.org, pg 95

Financial Times Press & Wharton School Publishing, One Lake St, Upper Saddle River, NJ 07458 *Tel:* 201-236-7000 *Toll Free Tel:* 800-922-0579 (orders) *Web Site:* www.ftpress.com, pg 95

Fine Arts Work Center in Provincetown, 24 Pearl St, Provincetown, MA 02657 *Tel:* 508-487-9960 *Fax:* 508-487-8873 *E-mail:* general@fawc.org *Web Site:* www.fawc.org, pg 704

Fine Communications, 322 Eighth Ave, 15th fl, New York, NY 10001 *Tel:* 212-595-3500 *Fax:* 212-595-3779, pg 95

Fine Wordworking, PO Box 3041, Monterey, CA 93942-3041 *Tel:* 831-375-6278 *E-mail:* info@finewordworking.com *Web Site:* marilynch.com, pg 546

FineEdge.com, 14004 Biz Point Lane, Anacortes, WA 98221 *Tel:* 360-299-8500 *Fax:* 360-299-0535 *E-mail:* pub@fineedge.com *Web Site:* www.fineedge.com, pg 95

FinePrint Literary Management, 115 W 29 St, 3rd fl, New York, NY 10001 *Tel:* 212-279-1282 *Web Site:* www.fineprintlit.com, pg 571

Finney Company Inc, 8075 215 St W, Lakeville, MN 55044 *Tel:* 952-469-6699 *Toll Free Tel:* 800-846-7027 *Fax:* 952-469-1968 *Toll Free Fax:* 800-330-6232 *E-mail:* info@finneyco.com *Web Site:* www.finneyco.com, pg 95

Doug Fir Fiction Award, 810 SE Belmont, Suite 5, Portland, OR 97214 *E-mail:* bear@orlo.org *Web Site:* www.beardeluxe.org, pg 704

Fire Engineering Books & Videos, 1421 S Sheridan Rd, Tulsa, OK 74112 *Tel:* 918-831-9410 *Toll Free Tel:* 800-752-9764 *Fax:* 918-831-9555 *E-mail:* sales@pennwell.com *Web Site:* www.pennwellbooks.com/fire.html, pg 95

Firefly Books Ltd, 50 Staples Ave, Unit 1, Richmond Hill, ON L4B 0A7, Canada *Tel:* 416-499-8412 *Toll Free Tel:* 800-387-6192 (CN); 800-387-5085 (US) *Fax:* 416-499-8313 *Toll Free Fax:* 800-450-0391 (CN); 800-565-6034 (US) *E-mail:* service@fireflybooks.com *Web Site:* www.fireflybooks.com, pg 505

First Avenue Editions, 241 First Ave N, Minneapolis, MN 55401 *Tel:* 612-332-3344 *Toll Free Tel:* 800-328-4929 *Fax:* 612-332-7615 *Toll Free Fax:* 800-332-1132 *E-mail:* info@lernerbooks.com *Web Site:* www.lernerbooks.com, pg 95

First Folio Resource Group Inc, 218 Adelaide St W, 2nd fl, Toronto, ON M5H 1W7, Canada *Tel:* 416-368-7668 *Fax:* 416-368-9363 *E-mail:* mail@firstfolio.com *Web Site:* www.firstfolio.com, pg 546

The Fischer-Harbage Agency Inc, 540 President St, 3rd fl, Brooklyn, NY 11215 *Tel:* 212-695-7105 *E-mail:* info@fischerharbage.com *Web Site:* www.fischerharbage.com, pg 572

The Fischer Ross Group Inc, 2 Greenwich Office Park, Suite 300, Greenwich, CT 06831 *Tel:* 203-622-4950 *Fax:* 203-531-4132 *E-mail:* frgstaff@frg-speakers.com *Web Site:* www.frg-speakers.com, pg 605

Fitzhenry & Whiteside Limited, 195 Allstate Pkwy, Markham, ON L3R 4T8, Canada *Tel:* 905-477-9700 *Toll Free Tel:* 800-387-9776 *Fax:* 905-477-9179 *Toll Free Fax:* 800-260-9777 *E-mail:* bookinfo@fitzhenry.ca; godwit@fitzhenry.ca *Web Site:* www.fitzhenry.ca, pg 505

Five Star Dragonfly Book Awards, 4696 W Tyson St, Chandler, AZ 85226 *Tel:* 480-940-8182 *Toll Free Tel:* 866-471-0777 *Fax:* 480-940-8787 *E-mail:* info@fivestarpublications.com *Web Site:* www.fivestarpublications.com; www.fivestarmarketingsecrets.com, pg 704

Five Star Publications Inc, 4696 W Tyson St, Chandler, AZ 85226 *Tel:* 480-940-8182 *Toll Free Tel:* 866-471-0777 *Fax:* 480-940-8787 *E-mail:* info@fivestarpublications.com *Web Site:* www.fivestarpublications.com, pg 96

Five Star Publishing & Marketing Secrets, 4696 W Tyson St, Chandler, AZ 85226 *Tel:* 480-940-8182 *Toll Free Tel:* 866-471-0777 *Fax:* 480-940-8787 *E-mail:* info@fivestarpublications.com *Web Site:* www.fivestarpublications.com; www.fivestarmarketingsecrets.com, pg 669

FJH Music Co Inc, 2525 Davie Rd, Suite 360, Fort Lauderdale, FL 33317-7424 *Tel:* 954-382-6061 *Toll Free Tel:* 800-262-8744 *Fax:* 954-382-3073 *E-mail:* custserv@fjhmusic.com; sales@fjhmusic.com *Web Site:* www.fjhmusic.com, pg 96

Flaming Star Literary Enterprises LLC, 111 Raup Rd, Chatham, NY 12037 *Web Site:* www.janisvallely.com, pg 572

Flammarion Quebec, 375 Ave Laurier W, Montreal, QC H2V 2K3, Canada *Tel:* 514-277-8807 *Fax:* 514-278-2085 *E-mail:* info@flammarion.qc.ca *Web Site:* www.flammarion.qc.ca, pg 505

Flanker Press Ltd, 1243 Kenmount Rd, Unit A, Paradise, NL A1L 0V8, Canada *Tel:* 709-739-4477 *Toll Free Tel:* 866-739-4420 *Fax:* 709-739-4420 *E-mail:* info@flankerpress.com *Web Site:* www.flankerpress.com, pg 506

Flannery Literary, 1140 Wickfield Ct, Naperville, IL 60563 *Tel:* 630-428-2682 *Web Site:* flanneryliterary.com, pg 572

Flashlight Press, 527 Empire Blvd, Brooklyn, NY 11225 *Tel:* 718-288-8300 *Fax:* 718-972-6307 *E-mail:* editor@flashlightpress.com *Web Site:* www.flashlightpress.com, pg 96

Norma Fleck Award for Canadian Children's Non-Fiction, 40 Orchard View Blvd, Suite 217, Toronto, ON M4R 1B9, Canada *Tel:* 416-975-0010 *Fax:* 416-975-8970 *E-mail:* info@bookcentre.ca *Web Site:* www.bookcentre.ca, pg 704

FleetSeek, 500 Lafayette Blvd, Suite 230, Fredericksburg, VA 22401 *Tel:* 540-899-9872 *Toll Free Tel:* 888-ONLY-TTS (665-9887) *Fax:* 540-899-1948 *E-mail:* fleetseek@fleetseek.com *Web Site:* www.fleetseek.com, pg 96

Peter Fleming Agency, PO Box 458, Pacific Palisades, CA 90272 *Tel:* 310-454-1373 *E-mail:* peterfleming@earthlink.net, pg 572

Florida Academic Press, PO Box 357425, Gainesville, FL 32635 *Tel:* 352-332-5104 *E-mail:* fapress@gmail.com *Web Site:* www.floridaacademicpress.com, pg 96

Florida Freelance Writers Association, 45 Main St, North Stratford, NH 03590 *Tel:* 603-922-8338 *Fax:* 603-922-8339 *E-mail:* ffwa@writers-editors.com; info@writers-editors.com *Web Site:* www.writers-editors.com; www.ffwamembers.com, pg 623

Florida Funding Publications Inc, PO Box 561565, Miami, FL 33256 *Tel:* 305-251-2203 *Fax:* 305-251-2773 *E-mail:* info@floridafunding.com, pg 96

Florida Individual Artist Fellowships, 500 S Bronough St, Tallahassee, FL 32399-0250 *Tel:* 850-245-6470 *Fax:* 850-245-6497 *E-mail:* info@florida-arts.org *Web Site:* www.florida-arts.org, pg 704

Florida Outdoor Writers Association Inc, 24 NW 33 Ct, Suite A, Gainesville, FL 32607 *E-mail:* info@fowa.org *Web Site:* www.fowa.org, pg 623

The Florida Publishers Association Inc (FPA), PO Box 916383, Longwood, FL 32791-6383 *Tel:* 863-647-5951 *Fax:* 863-647-5951 *E-mail:* fpabooks@gmail.com *Web Site:* www.floridapublishersassociation.com, pg 623

Florida Writers Association Conference, PO Box 66069, St Pete Beach, FL 33736-6069 *Web Site:* www.floridawriters.net, pg 669

Florida Writers Association Inc, PO Box 66069, St Pete Beach, FL 33736-6069 *Web Site:* www.floridawriters.net, pg 623

Flying Pen Press LLC, 1660 Niagara St, Denver, CO 80220 *Tel:* 303-375-0499 *Fax:* 303-375-0499 *E-mail:* generalinquiries@flyingpenpress.com; bookorders@flyingpenpress.com; returns@flyingpenpress.com; info@flyingpenpress.com *Web Site:* www.flyingpenpress.com, pg 96

Focus on the Family, 8605 Explorer Dr, Colorado Springs, CO 80920-1051 *Tel:* 719-531-5181 *Toll Free Tel:* 800-A-FAMILY (232-6459) *Fax:* 719-531-3424 *Web Site:* focusonthefamily.com, pg 96

Focus Publishing/R Pullins Co Inc, PO Box 369, Newburyport, MA 01950 *Tel:* 978-462-7288 (edit) *Toll Free Tel:* 800-848-7236 (orders) *Fax:* 978-462-9035 (edit) *E-mail:* orders@pullins.com *Web Site:* www.pullins.com, pg 96

Focus Strategic Communications Inc, 2474 Waterford St, Oakville, ON L6L 5E6, Canada *Tel:* 905-825-8757 *Toll Free Tel:* 866-263-6287 *Fax:* 905-825-5724 *Toll Free Fax:* 866-613-6287 *E-mail:* info@focussc.com *Web Site:* www.focussc.com, pg 546

Fodor's Travel Publications, c/o Random House Inc, 1745 Broadway, New York, NY 10019 *Tel:* 212-829-6714 *Toll Free Tel:* 800-733-3000 *Fax:* 212-572-2248 *Web Site:* www.fodors.com, pg 96

Sheldon Fogelman Agency Inc, 10 E 40 St, Suite 3205, New York, NY 10016 *Tel:* 212-532-7250 *Fax:* 212-685-8939 *E-mail:* info@sheldonfogelmanagency.com *Web Site:* sheldonfogelmanagency.com, pg 572

Foil & Specialty Effects Association (FSEA), 2150 SW Westport Dr, Suite 101, Topeka, KS 66614 *Tel:* 785-271-5816 *Fax:* 785-271-6404 *Web Site:* www.fsea.com, pg 623

The Foley Literary Agency, 34 E 38 St, Suite 1B, New York, NY 10016 *Tel:* 212-686-6930, pg 572

Folio Literary Management LLC, The Film Center Bldg, 630 Ninth Ave, Suite 1101, New York, NY 10036 *Tel:* 212-400-1494 *Fax:* 212-967-0977 *Web Site:* www.foliolit.com, pg 572

Folklore Publishing, 11717-9B Ave NW, Unit 2, Edmonton, AB T6J 7B7, Canada *Tel:* 780-435-2376 *Fax:* 780-435-0674 *E-mail:* submissions@folklorepublishing.com (ms submissions) *Web Site:* www.folklorepublishing.com, pg 506

Follett Higher Education Group, 1818 Swift Dr, Oak Brook, IL 60523 *Tel:* 630-279-2330 *Toll Free Tel:* 800-323-4506 *Fax:* 630-279-2569 *Web Site:* www.fheg.follett.com, pg 623

La Fondation Emile Nelligan, 100 Sherbrooke St, Suite 202, Montreal, QC H2X 1C3, Canada *Tel:* 514-278-4657 *Fax:* 514-278-1943 *E-mail:* info@fondation-nelligan.org *Web Site:* www.fondation-nelligan.org, pg 623

Fons Vitae, 49 Mockingbird Valley Dr, Louisville, KY 40207-1366 *Tel:* 502-897-3641 *Fax:* 502-893-7373 *E-mail:* fonsvitaeky@aol.com *Web Site:* www.fonsvitae.com, pg 97

Fordham University, Graduate School of Business Administration, Gabelli School of Business, 441 E Fordham Rd, Hughes Hall, Rm 516, Bronx, NY 10458 *Tel:* 718-817-1894 *Web Site:* www.bnet.fordham.edu, pg 678

Fordham University, Graduate School of Business Administration, 113 W 60 St, New York, NY 10023 *Fax:* 212-636-7076 *Web Site:* www.bnet.fordham.edu, pg 705

Fordham University Press, 2546 Belmont Ave, University Box L, Bronx, NY 10458 *Tel:* 718-817-4795 *Fax:* 718-817-4785 *Web Site:* www.fordhampress.com, pg 97

ForeWord Reviews Book of the Year Awards, 425 Boardman Ave, Suite B, Traverse City, MI 49684 *Tel:* 231-933-3699 *Fax:* 231-933-3899 *Web Site:* www.bookoftheyearawards.com, pg 705

Morris D Forkosch Prize, 400 "A" St SE, Washington, DC 20003-3889 *Tel:* 202-544-2422 *Fax:* 202-544-8307 *E-mail:* awards@historians.org *Web Site:* www.historians.org, pg 705

Fort Ross Inc - International Representation for Artists, 26 Arthur Place, Yonkers, NY 10701 *Tel:* 914-375-6448; 748-775-8340 *Web Site:* www.fortrossinc.com, pg 601

Fort Ross Inc - International Rights, 26 Arthur Place, Yonkers, NY 10701 *Tel:* 914-375-6448; 718-775-8340 *E-mail:* fortross@optonline.net *Web Site:* www.fortrossinc.com, pg 573

Fort Ross Inc Russian-American Publishing Projects, 26 Arthur Place, Yonkers, NY 10701 *Tel:* 914-375-6448 *Fax:* 718-775-8340 *E-mail:* fortross@optonline.net *Web Site:* www.fortrossinc.com, pg 97

49th Parallel Poetry Award, Mail Stop 9053, Western Washington University, Bellingham, WA 98225 *Tel:* 360-650-4863 *E-mail:* bhreview@wwu.edu *Web Site:* www.bhreview.org, pg 705

The Forum Press Inc, 3100 W Warner Ave, Suite 7, Santa Ana, CA 92704 *Tel:* 714-545-3114 *Fax:* 714-545-3116 *E-mail:* theforumpress@cs.com *Web Site:* www.theforumpress.com, pg 97

Forum Publishing Co, 383 E Main St, Centerport, NY 11721 *Tel:* 631-754-5000 *Toll Free Tel:* 800-635-7654 *Fax:* 631-754-0630 *E-mail:* forumpublishing@aol.com *Web Site:* www.forum123.com, pg 97

Forward Movement Publications, 412 Sycamore St, Cincinnati, OH 45202-4110 *Tel:* 513-721-6659 *Toll Free Tel:* 800-543-1813 *Fax:* 513-721-0729 (orders) *E-mail:* orders@forwardmovement.org (orders & cust serv) *Web Site:* www.forwardmovement.org, pg 97

Foster City International Writer's Contest, 650 Shell Blvd, Foster City, CA 94404 *Tel:* 650-286-3386 *E-mail:* fostercity_writers@yahoo.com *Web Site:* www.fostercity.org, pg 705

Foster Travel Publishing, PO Box 5715, Berkeley, CA 94705-0715 *Tel:* 510-549-2202 *Fax:* 510-549-1131 *Web Site:* www.fostertravel.com, pg 546

Walter Foster Publishing Inc, 3 Wrigley, Suite A, Irvine, CA 92618 *Tel:* 949-380-7510 *Toll Free Tel:* 800-426-0099; 800-826-6600 (orders) *Fax:* 949-380-7575 *E-mail:* info@walterfoster.com *Web Site:* www.walterfoster.com, pg 97

Foto Expression International (Toronto), 266 Charlotte St, Suite 297, Peterborough, ON K9J 2V4, Canada *Tel:* 705-745-5770 *E-mail:* operations@fotopressnews.org *Web Site:* www.fotopressnews.org, pg 601

The Foundation Center, 79 Fifth Ave, New York, NY 10003-3076 *Tel:* 212-620-4230 *Toll Free Tel:* 800-424-9836 *Fax:* 212-807-3677 *E-mail:* order@foundationcenter.org *Web Site:* www.fdncenter.org; foundationcenter.org, pg 97

The Foundation for Economic Education Inc, 30 S Broadway, Irvington-on-Hudson, NY 10533 *Tel:* 914-591-7230 *Toll Free Tel:* 800-960-4FEE (960-4333) *Fax:* 914-591-8910 *E-mail:* freeman@fee.org (query/submit: attention Sheldon Richman, all others: attention Michael Nolan) *Web Site:* www.thefreemanonline.org; www.fee.org, pg 97

Foundation Press Inc, 395 Hudson St, New York, NY 10014 *Tel:* 212-367-6790 *Toll Free Tel:* 877-888-1330 *Fax:* 212-367-6799 *E-mail:* foundation-press@thomsonreuters.com *Web Site:* www.foundation-press.com, pg 98

Foundation Publications, 900 S Euclid St, La Habra, CA 90631 *Tel:* 714-879-2286 *Toll Free Tel:* 800-257-6272 *Fax:* 714-535-2164 *E-mail:* info@foundationpublications.com *Web Site:* www.foundationpublications.com, pg 98

4A's (American Association of Advertising Agencies), 1065 Avenue of the Americas, 16th fl, New York, NY 10018 *Tel:* 212-682-2500 *Web Site:* www.aaaa.org, pg 623

Fox Chapel Publishing Co Inc, 1970 Broad St, East Petersburg, PA 17520 *Tel:* 717-560-4703 *Toll Free Tel:* 800-457-9112 *Fax:* 717-560-4702 *E-mail:* customerservice@foxchapelpublishing.com *Web Site:* www.foxchapelpublishing.com, pg 98

Dixon Ryan Fox Manuscript Prize, 5798 State Hwy 80, Cooperstown, NY 13326 *Tel:* 607-547-1480 *Fax:* 607-547-1405, pg 705

Fox Run Press LLC, 7840 Bullet Rd, Peyton, OH 80831 *Tel:* 719-482-4035 *Fax:* 719-623-0254 *E-mail:* info@foxrunpress.com *Web Site:* www.foxrunpress.com, pg 98

FPMI Solutions Inc, 245 Business Park Rd, Suite A, Madison, AL 35758 *Tel:* 256-539-1850 *Toll Free Tel:* 888-644-3764 *Fax:* 256-539-0911 *E-mail:* info@fpmi.com *Web Site:* www.fpmisolutions.com; www.fpmi.com, pg 98

Frances Henne YALSA/VOYA Research Grant, 50 E Huron St, Chicago, IL 60611 *Tel:* 312-280-4390 *Toll Free Tel:* 800-545-2433 *Fax:* 312-280-5276 *E-mail:* yalsa@ala.org *Web Site:* www.ala.org/yalsa/, pg 705

H E Francis Award Short Story Competition, UAH Huntsville Dept of English, Morton Hall 222, Huntsville, AL 35899 *Web Site:* www.uah.edu/colleges/liberal/english/hefrancis.contest, pg 705

Franciscan Media, 28 W Liberty St, Cincinnati, OH 45202 *Tel:* 513-241-5615 *Toll Free Tel:* 800-488-0488 *Fax:* 513-241-0399 *E-mail:* books@americancatholic.org *Web Site:* www.americancatholic.org, pg 98

Sandi Frank, 8 Fieldcrest Ct, Cortlandt Manor, NY 10567 *Tel:* 914-739-7088 *E-mail:* sfrankmail@aol.com, pg 546

Franklin, Beedle & Associates Inc, 22462 SW Washington St, Sherwood, OR 97140 *Tel:* 503-625-4445 *Toll Free Tel:* 800-322-2665 *Fax:* 503-625-4434 *E-mail:* orderpro@fbeedle.com *Web Site:* www.fbeedle.com, pg 98

Lynn C Franklin Associates Ltd, 1350 Broadway, Suite 2015, New York, NY 10018 *Tel:* 212-868-6311 *Fax:* 212-868-6312 *E-mail:* agency@franklinandsiegal.com, pg 573

The Fraser Institute, 1770 Burrard St, 4th fl, Vancouver, BC V6J 3G7, Canada *Tel:* 604-688-0221 *Toll Free Tel:* 800-665-3558 *Fax:* 604-688-8539 *E-mail:* info@fraserinstitute.org; sales@fraserinstitute.org *Web Site:* www.fraserinstitute.org, pg 506

Soeurette Diehl Fraser Translation Award, PO Box 609, Round Rock, TX 78680 *Tel:* 512-683-5640 *E-mail:* tilsecretary@yahoo.com *Web Site:* www.texasinstituteofletters.org, pg 705

Frederick Fell Publishers Inc, 2131 Hollywood Blvd, Suite 305, Hollywood, FL 33020 *Tel:* 954-925-5242 *E-mail:* fellpub@aol.com (admin only) *Web Site:* www.fellpub.com, pg 98

Jeanne Fredericks Literary Agency Inc, 221 Benedict Hill Rd, New Canaan, CT 06840 *Tel:* 203-972-3011 *Fax:* 203-972-3011 *E-mail:* jeanne.fredericks@gmail.com (no unsol attachments) *Web Site:* jeannefredericks.com, pg 573

Free Spirit Publishing Inc, 217 Fifth Ave N, Suite 200, Minneapolis, MN 55401-1260 *Tel:* 612-338-2068 *Toll Free Tel:* 800-735-7323 *Fax:* 612-337-5050 *Toll Free Fax:* 866-419-5199 *E-mail:* help4kids@freespirit.com *Web Site:* www.freespirit.com, pg 99

George Freedley Memorial Award, Roundabout Theatre Co, 231 W 39 St, Suite 1200, New York, NY 10018 *Tel:* 212-719-9393 (ext 351) *E-mail:* info@tla-online.org; tlabookawards@gmail.com *Web Site:* www.tla-online.org, pg 705

Robert A Freedman Dramatic Agency Inc, 1501 Broadway, Suite 2310, New York, NY 10036 *Tel:* 212-840-5760 *Fax:* 212-840-5776, pg 573

The Don Freeman Memorial Grant-In-Aid, 8271 Beverly Blvd, Los Angeles, CA 90048 *Tel:* 323-782-1010 *Fax:* 323-782-1892 *E-mail:* membership@scbwi.org; scbwi@scbwi.org *Web Site:* www.scbwi.org, pg 705

W H Freeman and Co, 41 Madison Ave, 37th fl, New York, NY 10010 *Tel:* 212-576-9400 *Fax:* 212-689-2383 *Web Site:* www.whfreeman.com, pg 99

The French-American Foundation & Florence Gould Foundation Annual Translation Prize, 28 W 44 St, Suite 1420, New York, NY 10036 *Tel:* 212-829-8800 *Fax:* 212-829-8810 *E-mail:* translation@frenchamerican.org *Web Site:* www.frenchamerican.org, pg 706

Samuel French Inc, 45 W 25 St, New York, NY 10010-2751 *Tel:* 212-206-8990 *Toll Free Tel:* 866-598-8449 *Fax:* 212-206-1429 *E-mail:* info@samuelfrench.com *Web Site:* www.samuelfrench.com, pg 99, 573

Fresh Air Books, 1908 Grand Ave, Nashville, TN 37212 *Toll Free Tel:* 800-972-0433 (orders) *Fax:* 615-340-7266 *E-mail:* freshairbooks@me.com *Web Site:* www.bookstore.upperroom.org (orders), pg 99

Fresh Fish Award for Emerging Writers, Haymarket Sq, 208-223 Duckworth St, St John's, NL A1C 6N1, Canada *Tel:* 709-739-5215 *E-mail:* wanl@nf.aibn.com *Web Site:* wanl.ca, pg 706

Sarah Jane Freymann Literary Agency LLC, 59 W 71 St, Suite 9-B, New York, NY 10023 *Tel:* 212-362-9277 *E-mail:* submissions@sarahjanefreymann.com *Web Site:* www.sarahjanefreymann.com, pg 573

Fredrica S Friedman & Co Inc, 136 E 57 St, 14th fl, New York, NY 10022 *Tel:* 212-829-9600 *Fax:* 212-829-9669 *E-mail:* info@fredricafriedman.com; submissions@fredricafriedman.com *Web Site:* www.fredricafriedman.com, pg 573

Friends of American Writers Awards, 506 Rose Ave, Des Plaines, IL 60016 *Tel:* 847-827-8339 *Web Site:* www.fawchicago.org, pg 706

Friends United Press, 101 Quaker Hill Dr, Richmond, IN 47374 *Tel:* 765-962-7573 *Toll Free Tel:* 800-537-8839 *Fax:* 765-966-1293 *E-mail:* friendspress@fum.org *Web Site:* www.fum.org/shop, pg 99

Frisbie/Communications, 631 N Dunton Ave, Arlington Heights, IL 60004 *Tel:* 847-253-4377 *Fax:* 847-253-4377 *Web Site:* www.richardfrisbie.net, pg 546

Frog Books, 2526 Martin Luther King Jr Way, Berkeley, CA 94704 *Tel:* 510-549-4270 *Toll Free Tel:* 800-733-3000 (book orders only) *Fax:* 510-549-4276 *Toll Free Fax:* 800-659-2436 (orders) *E-mail:* orders@northatlanticbooks.com *Web Site:* www.northatlanticbooks.com, pg 99

Fromer Editorial Services, 1606 Noyes Dr, Silver Spring, MD 20910-2224 *Tel:* 301-585-8827 *Fax:* 301-585-1369, pg 546

Front Street, 815 Church St, Honesdale, PA 18431 *Tel:* 570-253-1164 *Toll Free Tel:* 800-490-5111 *E-mail:* contact@boydsmillspress.com *Web Site:* www.frontstreetbooks.com, pg 100

Fugue State Press, PO Box 80, Cooper Sta, New York, NY 10276 *E-mail:* info@fuguestatepress.com *Web Site:* www.fuguestatepress.com, pg 100

Candice Fuhrman Literary Agency, 10 Cypress Hollow Dr, Tiburon, CA 94920 *Tel:* 415-383-1014 *E-mail:* candicef@pacbell.net, pg 573

Fulbright Scholar Program, 1400 "K" St NW, Washington, DC 20005 *Tel:* 202-686-4000 *Fax:* 202-362-3442 *E-mail:* scholars@iie.org *Web Site:* www.iie.org/cies, pg 706

Fulcrum Publishing Inc, 4690 Table Mountain Dr, Suite 100, Golden, CO 80403 *Tel:* 303-277-1623 *Toll Free Tel:* 800-992-2908 *Fax:* 303-279-7111 *Toll Free Fax:* 800-726-7112 *E-mail:* info@fulcrumbooks.com; orders@fulcrumbooks.com *Web Site:* www.fulcrumbooks.com, pg 100

Sonia Elizabeth Fulop, PO Box 978, Alamo, CA 94507 *Tel:* 847-736-4071 *Web Site:* www.soniafulop.com, pg 547

Fun in the Sun, PO Box 430744, Miami, FL 33243 *Web Site:* www.frwriters.org, pg 669

FurnitureCore, 1385 Peachtree St NE, Suite 310, Atlanta, GA 30309 *Tel:* 404-961-3764 *Fax:* 404-961-3749 *E-mail:* info@furniturecore.com *Web Site:* www.furniturecore.com, pg 100

Future Horizons Inc, 721 W Abram St, Arlington, TX 76013 *Tel:* 817-277-0727 *Toll Free Tel:* 800-489-0727 *Fax:* 817-277-2270 *E-mail:* info@fhautism.com *Web Site:* www.fhautism.com, pg 100

Gaetan Morin Editeur, 5800 rue Ste-Denis, Bur 900, Montreal, QC H2S 3L5, Canada *Tel:* 514-273-1066 *Toll Free Tel:* 800-565-5531 *Fax:* 514-276-0324 *Toll Free Fax:* 800-814-0324 *E-mail:* info@cheneliere.ca *Web Site:* www.cheneliere.ca, pg 506

Gagosian Gallery, 980 Madison Ave, New York, NY 10075 *Tel:* 212-744-2313 *Fax:* 212-772-7962 *E-mail:* newyork@gagosian.com *Web Site:* www.gagosian.com, pg 100

Lewis Galantiere Translation Award, 225 Reinekers Lane, Suite 590, Alexandria, VA 22314 *Tel:* 703-683-6100 *Fax:* 703-683-6122 *E-mail:* ata@atanet.org *Web Site:* www.atanet.org, pg 706

Galaxy Press, 7051 Hollywood Blvd, Suite 200, Hollywood, CA 90028 *Tel:* 323-466-7815 *Toll Free Tel:* 877-8GALAXY (842-5299) *E-mail:* customers@galaxypress.com *Web Site:* www.galaxypress.com, pg 100

Galde Press Inc, PO Box 460, Lakeville, MN 55044 *Tel:* 952-891-5991 *Toll Free Tel:* 800-777-3454 *Fax:* 952-891-6091 *Web Site:* www.galdepress.com, pg 100

Gale, 27500 Drake Rd, Farmington Hills, MI 48331-3535 *Tel:* 248-699-4253 *Toll Free Tel:* 800-877-4253 *Fax:* 248-699-8049 *Toll Free Fax:* 800-414-5043 (orders) *E-mail:* gale.salesassistance@cengage.com *Web Site:* www.gale.cengage.com, pg 100

Galen Press Ltd, PO Box 64400, Tucson, AZ 85728-4400 *Tel:* 520-577-8363 *Fax:* 520-529-6459 *E-mail:* sales@galenpress.com *Web Site:* www.galenpress.com, pg 100

Gallaudet University Press, 800 Florida Ave NE, Washington, DC 20002-3695 *Tel:* 202-651-5488 *Fax:* 202-651-5489 *E-mail:* gupress@gallaudet.edu *Web Site:* gupress.gallaudet.edu, pg 100

Gallery Books, 1230 Avenue of the Americas, New York, NY 10020 *Toll Free Tel:* 800-456-6798 *Fax:* 212-698-7284 *E-mail:* consumer.customerservice@simonandschuster.com *Web Site:* www.simonsays.com, pg 101

Diane Gallo, 49 Hilton St, Gilbertsville, NY 13776 *Tel:* 607-783-2386 *Fax:* 607-783-2386 *E-mail:* diane@dianegallo.com *Web Site:* www.dianegallo.com, pg 547

Gallopade International Inc, 611 Hwy 74 S, Suite 2000, Peachtree City, GA 30269 *Tel:* 770-631-4222 *Toll Free Tel:* 800-536-2GET (536-2438) *Fax:* 770-631-4810 *Toll Free Fax:* 800-871-2979 *E-mail:* customerservice@gallopade.com *Web Site:* www.gallopade.com, pg 101

Gannon University's High School Poetry Contest, Gannon University, Dept of English, 109 University Sq, Erie, PA 16541 *Tel:* 814-871-7504 *Web Site:* www.gannon.edu/departmental/english/poetry.asp, pg 706

The Garamond Agency Inc, 12 Horton St, Newburyport, MA 01950 *Fax:* 978-992-0265 *E-mail:* query@garamondagency.com *Web Site:* www.garamondagency.com, pg 574

Garden Writers Association, 7809 FM 179, Shallowater, TX 79363-3637 *Tel:* 806-832-1870 *Fax:* 806-832-5244 *E-mail:* info@gardenwriters.org *Web Site:* www.gardenwriters.org, pg 624

Gareth Stevens Publishing, 111 E 14 St, Suite 349, New York, NY 10003 *Toll Free Tel:* 800-542-2595 *Toll Free Fax:* 877-542-2596 (cust serv) *E-mail:* customerservice@gspub.com *Web Site:* www.garethstevens.com, pg 101

Garland Science Publishing, 711 Third Ave, 8th fl, New York, NY 10017 *Tel:* 212-216-7800 *Fax:* 212-281-4487 *E-mail:* science@garland.com *Web Site:* www.garlandscience.com, pg 101

Francois-Xavier Garneau Medal, 130 Albert St, Suite 501, Ottawa, ON K1P 5G4, Canada *Tel:* 613-233-7885 *Fax:* 613-565-5445 *E-mail:* cha-shc@cha-shc.ca *Web Site:* www.cha-shc.ca, pg 706

Garrett Publishing Inc, 800 Fairway Dr, Suite 340, Deerfield Beach, FL 33441 *Tel:* 561-953-1322 *Fax:* 561-953-1940, pg 101

Max Gartenberg Literary Agency, 912 N Pennsylvania Ave, Yardley, PA 19067 *Tel:* 215-295-9230 *Web Site:* www.maxgartenberg.com, pg 574

Alfred C Gary Memorial, 1194 Hume Rd, Hume, VA 22639-1806 *E-mail:* poetryinva@aol.com *Web Site:* www.poetrysocietyofvirginia.org, pg 706

The Gary-Paul Agency, 1549 Main St, Stratford, CT 06615 *Tel:* 203-345-6167 *Fax:* 203-345-6167 *E-mail:* garret@thegarypaulagency.com *Web Site:* www.thegarypaulagency.com; www.nutmegpictures.com, pg 547

John Gassner Memorial Playwriting Award, 215 Knob Hill Dr, Hamden, CT 06518 *Tel:* 617-851-8535 *Fax:* 203-288-5938 *E-mail:* mail@netconline.org *Web Site:* www.netconline.org, pg 706

Gateways Books & Tapes, PO Box 370, Nevada City, CA 95959-0370 *Tel:* 530-271-2239 *Toll Free Tel:* 800-869-0658 *Fax:* 530-272-0184 *E-mail:* info@gatewaysbooksandtapes.com *Web Site:* www.gatewaysbooksandtapes.com; www.retrosf.com (Retro Science Fiction Imprint), pg 101

Gault Millau Inc/Gayot Publications, 4311 Wilshire Blvd, Suite 405, Los Angeles, CA 90010 *Tel:* 323-965-3529 *Fax:* 323-936-2883 *E-mail:* info@gayot.com *Web Site:* www.gayot.com, pg 101

The Christian Gauss Award, 1606 New Hampshire Ave NW, Washington, DC 20009 *Tel:* 202-265-3808 *Fax:* 202-986-1601 *E-mail:* awards@pbk.org *Web Site:* www.pbk.org/bookawards, pg 706

Gauthier Publications Inc, PO Box 806241, St Clair Shores, MI 48080 *Tel:* 313-458-7141 *Fax:* 586-279-1515 *E-mail:* info@gauthierpublications.com *Web Site:* www.gauthierpublications.com, pg 102

The Gaylactic Spectrum Awards, PO Box 73602, Washington, DC 20056-3602 *Tel:* 202-483-6369 *Web Site:* www.spectrumawards.org, pg 706

Gaylord College of Journalism & Mass Communication, Professional Writing Program, c/o University of Oklahoma, 395 W Lindsey St, Rm 3534, Norman, OK 73019-0270 *Tel:* 405-325-2721 *Fax:* 405-325-7565 *Web Site:* www.ou.edu/gaylord, pg 678

Fred Gebhart, 2346 25 Ave, San Francisco, CA 94116-2337 *Tel:* 415-681-3018 *E-mail:* fgebhart@pobox.com *Web Site:* www.fredgebhart.com, pg 547

Gefen Books, 11 Edison Place, Springfield, NJ 07081 *Tel:* 516-593-1234 *Toll Free Tel:* 800-477-5257 *Fax:* 516-295-2739 *E-mail:* info@gefenpublishing.com; gefenny@gefenpublishing.com *Web Site:* www.israelbooks.com, pg 102

Lionel Gelber Prize, University of Toronto, Munk School of Global Affairs, One Devonshire Place, Toronto, ON M5S 3K7, Canada *Tel:* 416-946-8901 *Fax:* 416-946-8915 *E-mail:* events.munk@utoronto.ca *Web Site:* www.utoronto.ca/mcis/gelber, pg 707

Gelfman/Schneider/ICM, 850 Seventh Ave, Suite 903, New York, NY 10019 *Tel:* 212-245-1993 *Fax:* 212-245-8678 *E-mail:* mail@gelfmanschneider.com *Web Site:* gelfmanschneider.com, pg 574

The Gell Center of the Finger Lakes, 740 University Ave, Rochester, NY 14607-1259 *Tel:* 585-473-2590 *Fax:* 585-442-9333 *Web Site:* www.wab.org, pg 669

Gelles-Cole Literary Enterprises, 135 John Joy Rd, Woodstock, NY 12498-0341 *Tel:* 845-679-2452 *Web Site:* www.literaryenterprises.com, pg 547

Gem Guides Book Co, 1275 W Ninth St, Upland, CA 91786 *Tel:* 626-855-1611 *Toll Free Tel:* 800-824-5118 (orders) *Fax:* 626-855-1610 *E-mail:* info@gemguidesbooks.com *Web Site:* www.gemguidesbooks.com, pg 102

GemStone Press, Sunset Farm Offices, Rte 4, Woodstock, VT 05091 *Tel:* 802-457-4000 *Toll Free Tel:* 800-962-4544 *Fax:* 802-457-4004 *E-mail:* sales@gemstonepress.com *Web Site:* www.gemstonepress.com, pg 102

Genealogical Publishing Co, 3600 Clipper Mill Rd, Suite 260, Baltimore, MD 21211 *Tel:* 410-837-8271 *Toll Free Tel:* 800-296-6687 *Fax:* 410-752-8492 *Web Site:* www.genealogical.com, pg 102

General Store Publishing House, 499 O'Brien Rd, Renfrew, ON K7V 3Z3, Canada *Tel:* 613-432-7697 *Toll Free Tel:* 800-465-6072 *Fax:* 613-432-7184 *E-mail:* orders@gsph.com (orders) *Web Site:* www.gsph.com, pg 506

Genesis Press Inc, PO Box 101, Columbus, MS 39701 *Toll Free Tel:* 888-463-4461 (orders only) *Web Site:* www.genesis-press.com, pg 102

Geological Society of America (GSA), 3300 Penrose Place, Boulder, CO 80301-1806 *Tel:* 303-357-1000 *Fax:* 303-357-1070 *E-mail:* pubs@geosociety.org (prodn); editing@geosociety.org (edit) *Web Site:* www.geosociety.org, pg 102

Geolytics Inc, 28 Brunswick Wood Dr, East Brunswick, NJ 08816 *Tel:* 732-651-2000 *Toll Free Tel:* 800-577-6717 *Fax:* 732-651-2721 *E-mail:* support@geolytics.com; questions@geolytics.com *Web Site:* www.geolytics.com, pg 102

Georgetown Review Literary Prize, Box 227, 400 E College St, Georgetown, KY 40324 *Web Site:* georgetownreview.georgetowncollege.edu, pg 707

Georgetown University Press, 3240 Prospect St NW, Suite 250, Washington, DC 20007 *Tel:* 202-687-5889 (busn) *Toll Free Tel:* 800-537-5487 *Fax:* 202-687-6340 (edit) *E-mail:* gupress@georgetown.edu *Web Site:* press.georgetown.edu, pg 102

The Gersh Agency (TGA), 41 Madison Ave, 33rd fl, New York, NY 10010 *Tel:* 212-997-1818 *E-mail:* info@gershla.com *Web Site:* gershagency.com, pg 574

Leo Gershoy Award, 400 "A" St SE, Washington, DC 20003-3889 *Tel:* 202-544-2422 *Fax:* 202-544-8307 *E-mail:* awards@historians.org *Web Site:* www.historians.org, pg 707

Nancy C Gerth PhD, 1431 Harlan's Trail, Sagle, ID 83860 *Tel:* 208-304-9066 *E-mail:* docnangee@nancygerth.com *Web Site:* www.nancygerth.com, pg 547

Gestalt Journal Press, PO Box 278, Gouldsboro, ME 04607-0278 *Tel:* 207-963-7064 *Toll Free Fax:* 866-460-8795 *E-mail:* press@gestalt.org *Web Site:* www.gestaltjournalpress.com, pg 103

Getty Publications, 1200 Getty Center Dr, Suite 500, Los Angeles, CA 90049-1682 *Tel:* 310-440-7365 *Toll Free Tel:* 800-223-3431 (orders) *Fax:* 310-440-7758 *E-mail:* pubsinfo@getty.edu *Web Site:* www.getty.edu/publications, pg 103

Gettysburg Review Conference for Writers, 300 N Washington St, Gettysburg, PA 17325 *Tel:* 717-337-6774 *Fax:* 717-337-6775 *E-mail:* getrev@hpb.com *Web Site:* www.gettysburgreview.com/conference.html, pg 669

GGP Publishing Inc, 105 Calvert St, Suite 201, Harrison, NY 10528-3138 *Tel:* 914-834-8896 *Fax:* 914-834-7566 *Web Site:* www.ggppublishing.com, pg 547, 574

GIA Publications Inc, 7404 S Mason Ave, Chicago, IL 60638 *Tel:* 708-496-3800 *Toll Free Tel:* 800-GIA-1358 (442-1358) *Fax:* 708-496-3828 *E-mail:* custserv@giamusic.com *Web Site:* www.giamusic.com, pg 103

Gibbs Smith Publisher, 1877 E Gentile St, Layton, UT 84041 *Tel:* 801-544-9800 *Toll Free Tel:* 800-748-5439; 800-835-4993 (orders) *Fax:* 801-544-5582 *Toll Free Fax:* 800-213-3023 (orders only) *E-mail:* info@gibbs-smith.com *Web Site:* www.gibbs-smith.com, pg 103

Gifted Education Press, 10201 Yuma Ct, Manassas, VA 20109 *Tel:* 703-369-5017 *Web Site:* www.giftededpress.com, pg 103

Sheri Gilbert, 123 Van Voorhis Ave, Rochester, NY 14617 *Tel:* 585-342-0331 *Fax:* 585-323-1828 *E-mail:* gilbert@permissionseditor.com *Web Site:* permissionseditor.com, pg 547

Gilpin Publishing, PO Box 597, Alliston, ON L9R 1V7, Canada *Tel:* 705-424-6507 *Toll Free Tel:* 800-867-3281 *Fax:* 705-424-6507 *E-mail:* mail@gilpin.ca *Web Site:* www.gilpin.ca, pg 506

Allen Ginsberg Poetry Award, One College Blvd, Paterson, NJ 07505-1179 *Tel:* 973-684-6555 *Fax:* 973-523-6085 *Web Site:* www.pccc.edu/poetry, pg 707

The Gislason Agency, 7400 University Ave NE, Fridley, MN 55432 *Tel:* 763-572-9297 *E-mail:* gislasonbj@aol.com *Web Site:* www.thegislasonagency.com, pg 574

Gival Press, 5200 N First St, Arlington, VA 22203 *Tel:* 703-351-0079 *Fax:* 703-351-0079 *E-mail:* givalpress@yahoo.com *Web Site:* www.givalpress.com, pg 103

Gival Press Novel Award, PO Box 3812, Arlington, VA 22203 *Tel:* 703-351-0079 *Fax:* 703-351-0079 *E-mail:* givalpress@yahoo.com *Web Site:* www.givalpress.com, pg 707

Gival Press Oscar Wilde Award, PO Box 3812, Arlington, VA 22203 *Tel:* 703-351-0079 *Fax:* 703-351-0079 *E-mail:* givalpress@yahoo.com *Web Site:* www.givalpress.com, pg 707

Gival Press Short Story Award, PO Box 3812, Arlington, VA 22203 *Tel:* 703-351-0079 *Fax:* 703-351-0079 *E-mail:* givalpress@yahoo.com *Web Site:* www.givalpress.com, pg 707

John Glassco Translation Prize, Concordia University, LB 601, 1455 De Maisonneuve West, Montreal, QC H3G 1M8, Canada *Tel:* 514-848-2424 (ext 8702) *E-mail:* info@attlc-ltac.org *Web Site:* www.attlc-ltac.org, pg 707

GLCA New Writers Awards, 535 W William St, Suite 301, Ann Arbor, MI 48103 *Tel:* 734-661-2350 *Fax:* 734-661-2349 *Web Site:* www.glca.org, pg 707

Susan Gleason, 325 Riverside Dr, Suite 41, New York, NY 10025 *Tel:* 212-662-3876 *Fax:* 212-864-3298 *E-mail:* sgleasonliteraryagent@gmail.com, pg 574

Danuta Gleed Literary Award, 90 Richmond St E, Suite 200, Toronto, ON M5C 1P1, Canada *Tel:* 416-703-8982 *Fax:* 416-504-9090 *E-mail:* info@writersunion.ca *Web Site:* www.writersunion.ca, pg 707

The Glen Workshop, 3307 Third Ave W, Seattle, WA 98119 *Tel:* 206-281-2988 *Fax:* 206-281-2979 *E-mail:* glenworkshop@imagejournal.org *Web Site:* www.imagejournal.org/page/events/the-glen-workshop, pg 669

Glenbridge Publishing Ltd, 19923 E Long Ave, Centennial, CO 80016-1969 *Tel:* 720-870-8381 *Toll Free Tel:* 800-986-4135 (orders) *Fax:* 720-230-1209 *E-mail:* glenbridge@qwestoffice.net *Web Site:* www.glenbridgepublishing.com, pg 103

Peter Glenn Publications, 306 NE Second St, 2nd fl, Delray Beach, FL 33483 *Tel:* 561-404-4290 *Toll Free Tel:* 888-332-6700 *Fax:* 561-892-5786 *Web Site:* www.pgdirect.com, pg 103

Glimmer Train Press Inc, PO Box 80430, Portland, OR 97280 *Tel:* 503-221-0836 *Fax:* 503-221-0837 *E-mail:* editors@glimmertrain.org *Web Site:* www.glimmertrain.org, pg 103

Glitterati Inc, 322 W 57 St, No 19T, New York, NY 10019 *Tel:* 212-362-9119 *Fax:* 646-607-4433 *E-mail:* info@glitteratiincorporated.com *Web Site:* glitteratiincorporated.com, pg 103

Global Authors Publications (GAP), 38 Bluegrass, Middleberg, FL 32068 *Tel:* 904-425-1608 *E-mail:* gapbook@yahoo.com, pg 104

Global Publishing, Sales & Distribution, 980 Lincoln Ave, Suite 200-B, San Rafael, CA 94901 *Tel:* 415-456-2934 *Fax:* 415-456-4124 *Web Site:* www.globalpsd.com, pg 104

Global Training Center Inc, PO Box 221977, El Paso, TX 79913-4977 *Tel:* 915-534-7900 *Toll Free Tel:* 800-860-5030 *Fax:* 915-534-7903 *E-mail:* contact@globaltrainingcenter.com *Web Site:* www.globaltrainingcenter.com, pg 104

The Globe Pequot Press, 246 Goose Lane, Guilford, CT 06437 *Tel:* 203-458-4500 *Toll Free Tel:* 800-243-0495 (orders only); 888-249-7586 (cust serv) *Fax:* 203-458-4601 *Toll Free Fax:* 800-820-2329 (orders & cust serv) *E-mail:* info@globepequot.com *Web Site:* www.globepequot.com, pg 104

Globo Libros Literary Agency, 402 E 64 St, Suite 6-C, New York, NY 10065 *Tel:* 212-888-4655 *Web Site:* www.globo-libros.com; publishersmarketplace.com/members/dstockwell, pg 574

David R Godine Publisher Inc, 15 Court Sq, Suite 320, Boston, MA 02108-4715 *Tel:* 617-451-9600 *Fax:* 617-350-0250 *E-mail:* pub@godine.com *Web Site:* www.godine.com, pg 104

Les Editions Goelette Inc, 1350 Marie-Victorin, St-Bruno-de-Montarville, Quebec, QC J3V 6B9, Canada *Tel:* 450-653-1337 *Toll Free Tel:* 800-463-4961 *Fax:* 450-653-9924 *Web Site:* www.editionsgoelette.com, pg 506

Krista Goering Literary Agency LLC, 3514 Clinton Pkwy, Suite A-404, Lawrence, KS 66047 *Tel:* 785-841-0634 *Fax:* 785-841-8500 *E-mail:* query@kristagoering.com *Web Site:* www.kristagoering.com, pg 574

Gold Eagle, 225 Duncan Mill Rd, 4th fl, Don Mills, ON M3B 3K9, Canada *Tel:* 416-445-5860 *Fax:* 416-445-8655; 416-445-8736 *E-mail:* readgoldeagle@hotmail.com *Web Site:* www.harlequin.com, pg 506

Gold Leaf Press, 2229 Alter Rd, Detroit, MI 48215 *Tel:* 313-331-3571 *Fax:* 313-308-3063 *E-mail:* interest@goldleafpress.com *Web Site:* www.goldleafpress.com, pg 547

Golden Cylindar Awards, 8281 Pine Lake Rd, Denver, NC 28037 *Tel:* 201-523-6042 *Fax:* 201-523-6048 *E-mail:* gaa@gaa.org *Web Site:* www.gaa.org, pg 707

Golden Kite Awards, 8271 Beverly Blvd, Los Angeles, CA 90048 *Tel:* 323-782-1010 *Fax:* 323-782-1892 *E-mail:* scbwi@scbwi.org; membership@scbwi.org *Web Site:* www.scbwi.org, pg 707

Golden Meteorite Press, 126 Kingsway Garden, Edmonton, AB T5G 3G4, Canada *Tel:* 780-378-0063 *Web Site:* www.goldenmeteoritepress.com, pg 506

Golden Rose Award, 2 Farrar St, Cambridge, MA 02138 *Tel:* 617-744-6034 *E-mail:* contests@nepoetryclub.org *Web Site:* www.nepoetryclub.org, pg 707

Golden West Cookbooks, 5738 N Central Ave, Phoenix, AZ 85012-1316 *Tel:* 602-234-1574 *Toll Free Tel:* 800-521-9221 *Fax:* 602-234-3062 *E-mail:* info@americantravelerpress.com *Web Site:* www.americantravelerpress.com, pg 104

Goldfarb & Associates, 721 Gibbon St, Alexandria, VA 22314 *Tel:* 202-466-3030 *Fax:* 703-836-5644 *E-mail:* rglawlit@gmail.com *Web Site:* www.ronaldgoldfarb.com, pg 574

Frances Goldin Literary Agency, Inc, 57 E 11 St, Suite 5-B, New York, NY 10003 *Tel:* 212-777-0047 *Fax:* 212-228-1660 *E-mail:* agency@goldinlit.com *Web Site:* www.goldinlit.com, pg 575

Donald Goldstein, 1500 E 17 St, Brooklyn, NY 11230 *Tel:* 718-375-9346 *Fax:* 212-854-5640 *E-mail:* dgoldsbkyn@aol.com, pg 547

Laurence Goldstein Poetry Prize, University of Michigan, 0576 Rackham Bldg, 915 E Washington St, Ann Arbor, MI 48109-1070 *Tel:* 734-764-9265 *E-mail:* mqr@umich.edu *Web Site:* www.umich.edu/~mqr, pg 708

Gollehon Press Inc, 3655 Glenn Dr SE, Grand Rapids, MI 49546 *Tel:* 616-949-3515 *Fax:* 616-949-8674 *Web Site:* www.gollehonbooks.com, pg 104

Good Books, 3518 Old Philadelphia Pike, Intercourse, PA 17534 *Tel:* 717-768-7171 *Toll Free Tel:* 800-762-7171 *Fax:* 717-768-3433 *Toll Free Fax:* 888-768-3433 *E-mail:* custserv@goodbks.com *Web Site:* www.goodbooks.com, pg 105

Good Parent Inc, One Regency Plaza, Suite 1001, Providence, RI 02903 *Tel:* 401-316-1322 *Toll Free Fax:* 866-718-0344 *Web Site:* www.goodparentinc.com, pg 105

Goodheart-Willcox Publisher, 18604 W Creek Dr, Tinley Park, IL 60477-6243 *Tel:* 708-687-5000 *Toll Free Tel:* 800-323-0440 *Fax:* 708-687-0315 *Toll Free Fax:* 888-409-3900 *E-mail:* custserv@g-w.com *Web Site:* www.g-w.com, pg 105

Goodluck Guides, 134 W Canyonview Dr, Longview, WA 98632 *Tel:* 360-575-1236 *Fax:* 360-885-1872, pg 105

Goodman Associates, 500 West End Ave, New York, NY 10024 *Tel:* 212-873-4806, pg 575

Irene Goodman Literary Agency, 27 W 24 St, Suite 700B, New York, NY 10010 *Tel:* 212-604-0330 *E-mail:* queries@irenegoodman.com *Web Site:* www.irenegoodman.com, pg 575

Robert M Goodman, 140 West End Ave, Unit 11-J, New York, NY 10023 *Tel:* 917-439-1097 *E-mail:* bobbybgood@gmail.com, pg 547

Sasha Goodman Agency Inc, 6680 Colgate Ave, Los Angeles, CA 90048 *Tel:* 310-387-0242 *Fax:* 323-653-3457 *E-mail:* ukseg@sbcglobal.net, pg 575

Goose Lane Editions, 500 Beaverbrook Ct, Suite 330, Fredericton, NB E3B 5X4, Canada *Tel:* 506-450-4251 *Toll Free Tel:* 888-926-8377 *Fax:* 506-459-4991 *E-mail:* info@gooselane.com *Web Site:* www.gooselane.com, pg 507

Goosebottom Books, 710 Portofino Lane, Foster City, CA 94404 *Tel:* 650-204-4076 *Toll Free Fax:* 888-407-5286 *E-mail:* info@goosebottombooks.com *Web Site:* goosebottombooks.com, pg 105

Gordian Press, 37 Crescent Ave, Staten Island, NY 10301 *Tel:* 718-273-8291, pg 105

P M Gordon Associates Inc, 2115 Wallace St, Philadelphia, PA 19130 *Tel:* 215-769-2525 *Fax:* 215-769-5354 *E-mail:* pmga@pond1.net *Web Site:* www.pmgordon.com, pg 547

Gorgias Press LLC, 954 River Rd, Piscataway, NJ 08854 *Tel:* 732-885-8900 *Fax:* 732-885-8908 *E-mail:* helpdesk@gorgiaspress.com *Web Site:* www.gorgiaspress.com, pg 105

Gospel Publishing House (GPH), 1445 Boonville Ave, Springfield, MO 65802 *Tel:* 417-862-2781 *Toll Free Tel:* 800-641-4310 *Fax:* 417-863-1874; 417-862-5881 *Toll Free Fax:* 800-328-0294 *E-mail:* custsrvreps@ag.org *Web Site:* www.gospelpublishing.com, pg 105

Gotham Books, 375 Hudson St, New York, NY 10014, pg 105

Gotham Literary Agency, 170 E 83 St, New York, NY 10028 *Tel:* 212-249-2615, pg 575

Gotham Writers' Workshop, 555 Eighth Ave, Suite 1402, New York, NY 10018-4358 *Tel:* 212-974-8377 *Toll Free Tel:* 877-974-8377 *Fax:* 212-307-6325 *E-mail:* office@write.org *Web Site:* www.writingclasses.com, pg 669

C+S Gottfried, 619 Cricklewood Dr, State College, PA 16803 *Tel:* 814-237-2580 *Web Site:* www.lookoutnow.com/index2.html, pg 547

Sherry Gottlieb, 4900 Dunes St, Oxnard, CA 93035 *Tel:* 805-382-3425 *E-mail:* writer@wordservices.com *Web Site:* www.wordservices.com, pg 547

Government Institutes (GI), 4501 Forbes Blvd, Suite 200, Lanham, MD 20706 *Tel:* 301-459-3366 (ext 5622) *Toll Free Tel:* 800-462-6420 *Fax:* 301-429-5748 *Toll Free Fax:* 800-338-4550 *Web Site:* www.govinstpress.com, pg 105

The Gracies®, 1760 Old Meadow Rd, Suite 500, McLean, VA 22102 *Tel:* 703-506-3290 *Fax:* 703-506-3266 *E-mail:* info@awrt.org *Web Site:* www.awrt.org, pg 708

Doug Grad Literary Agency Inc, 156 Prospect Park West, No 3L, Brooklyn, NY 11215 *Tel:* 718-788-6067 *E-mail:* query@dgliterary.com *Web Site:* www.dgliterary.com, pg 575

Grade Finders Inc, PO Box 944, Exton, PA 19341-0908 *Tel:* 610-269-7070 *Toll Free Tel:* 877-524-7080 *Fax:* 610-269-7077 *E-mail:* info@gradefinders.com *Web Site:* www.gradefinders.com, pg 105

The Graduate Group/Booksellers, 86 Norwood Rd, West Hartford, CT 06117-2236 *Tel:* 860-233-2330 *Toll Free Tel:* 800-484-7280 ext 3579 *Fax:* 860-233-2330 *E-mail:* graduategroup@hotmail.com *Web Site:* www.graduategroup.com, pg 106

Grafco Productions, 971 E Callaway Rd, Marietta, GA 30060 *Tel:* 770-436-1500 *Toll Free Tel:* 800-381-9169 *Fax:* 770-435-3793 *Web Site:* www.jackwboone.com, pg 106

Graham Agency, 311 W 43 St, New York, NY 10036 *Tel:* 212-489-7730, pg 575

Grand Central Publishing, 237 Park Ave, New York, NY 10017 *Tel:* 212-364-1100 *Web Site:* www.hachettebookgroup.com, pg 106

Donald M Grant Publisher Inc, PO Box 187, Hampton Falls, NH 03844-0187 *Tel:* 603-778-7191 *Fax:* 603-778-7191 *Web Site:* www.grantbooks.com, pg 106

Grants for Artist Projects, 1835 12 Ave, Seattle, WA 98122 *Tel:* 206-467-8734 (ext 11) *Toll Free Tel:* 866-218-7878 (ext 11) *Fax:* 206-467-9633 *E-mail:* info@artisttrust.org *Web Site:* www.artisttrust.org, pg 708

Graphic Artists Guild Inc, 32 Broadway, Suite 1114, New York, NY 10004-1612 *Tel:* 212-791-3400 *Fax:* 212-791-0333 *Web Site:* www.graphicartistsguild.org, pg 624, 678

Graphic Arts Association, 1210 Northbrook Dr, Suite 250, Trevose, PA 19053 *Tel:* 215-396-2300 *Fax:* 215-396-9890 *E-mail:* gaa@gaa1900.com *Web Site:* www.gaa1900.com, pg 678

Graphic Arts Books, 7820 NE Holman St, Suite B-9, Portland, OR 97218 *Tel:* 503-254-5591 *Fax:* 503-254-5609 *E-mail:* info-ga@graphicartsbooks.com *Web Site:* www.graphicartsbooks.com, pg 106

Graphic Arts Education & Research Foundation (GAERF), 1899 Preston White Dr, Reston, VA 20191 *Tel:* 703-264-7200 *Toll Free Tel:* 866-381-9839 *Fax:* 703-620-3165 *E-mail:* gaerf@npes.org *Web Site:* www.gaerf.org, pg 641

Graphic Arts Show Company (GASC), 1899 Preston White Dr, Reston, VA 20191-5468 *Tel:* 703-264-7200 *Fax:* 703-620-9187 *E-mail:* info@gasc.org *Web Site:* www.gasc.org, pg 624

Graphic Universe™, 241 First Ave N, Minneapolis, MN 55401 *Tel:* 612-332-3344 *Toll Free Tel:* 800-328-4929 *Fax:* 612-332-7615 *Toll Free Fax:* 800-332-1132 *E-mail:* info@lernerbooks.com *Web Site:* www.lernerbooks.com, pg 106

Graphic World Publishing Services, 11687 Adie Rd, St Louis, MO 63043 *Tel:* 314-567-9854 *Fax:* 314-567-7178 *E-mail:* quote@gwinc.com *Web Site:* www.gwinc.com, pg 547

Gravure Association of America Inc, 8281 Pine Lake Rd, Denver, NC 28037 *Tel:* 201-523-6042 *Fax:* 201-523-6048 *E-mail:* gaa@gaa.org *Web Site:* www.gaa.org, pg 624

Gray & Company Publishers, 1588 E 40 St, Suite 3-A, Cleveland, OH 44103 *Tel:* 216-431-2665 *Toll Free Tel:* 800-915-3609 *E-mail:* sales@grayco.com *Web Site:* www.grayco.com, pg 106

James H Gray Award for Short Nonfiction, 11759 Groat Rd, Edmonton, AB T5M 3K6, Canada *Tel:* 780-422-8174 *Toll Free Tel:* 800-665-5354 (AB only) *Fax:* 780-422-2663 (attn WGA) *E-mail:* mail@writersguild.ab.ca *Web Site:* www.writersguild.ab.ca, pg 708

Ashley Grayson Literary Agency, 1342 W 18 St, San Pedro, CA 90732 *Tel:* 310-548-4672 *E-mail:* graysonagent@earthlink.net; rights@graysonagency.com *Web Site:* graysonagency.com/blog/, pg 575

Graywolf Press, 250 Third Ave N, Suite 600, Minneapolis, MN 55401 *Tel:* 651-641-0077 *Fax:* 651-641-0036 *E-mail:* wolves@graywolfpress.org *Web Site:* www.graywolfpress.org, pg 106

Great Lakes Graphics Association, W232 N2950 Roundy Circle E, Suite 200, Pewaukee, WI 53072-4110 *Tel:* 262-522-2210 *Fax:* 262-522-2211 *E-mail:* info@piw.org *Web Site:* www.piw.org, pg 624

Great Potential Press Inc, 7025 E First Ave, Suite 5, Scottsdale, AZ 85251 *Tel:* 602-954-4200 *Toll Free Tel:* 877-954-4200 *Fax:* 602-954-0185 *Web Site:* www.greatpotentialpress.com, pg 106

Great Quotations Inc, 8102 S Lemont Rd, Suite 300, Woodridge, IL 60517 *Tel:* 630-985-2628 *Toll Free Tel:* 800-830-3020 *Fax:* 630-985-2610 *E-mail:* info@greatquotationsinc.com *Web Site:* greatquotationsinc.com, pg 107

Great Source Education Group, 181 Ballardvale St, Wilmington, MA 01887 *Tel:* 978-661-1471 *Toll Free Tel:* 800-289-4490 *Toll Free Fax:* 800-289-3994 *Web Site:* www.greatsource.com, pg 107

Greater Talent Network Inc, 437 Fifth Ave, New York, NY 10016 *Tel:* 212-645-4200 *Toll Free Tel:* 800-326-4211 *Fax:* 212-627-1471 *E-mail:* info@greatertalent.com *Web Site:* www.greatertalent.com, pg 605

Green Dragon Books, 12 S Dixie Hwy, Suite 202, Lake Worth, FL 33460 *Tel:* 561-533-6231 *Toll Free Tel:* 800-874-8844 *Fax:* 561-533-6233 *Toll Free Fax:* 888-874-8844 *E-mail:* info@greendragonbooks.com, pg 107

Green Eagle Press, PO Box 20329, New York, NY 10025 *Tel:* 212-663-2167 *Fax:* 212-316-7650 *E-mail:* mail@greeneagle.org *Web Site:* www.greeneagle.org, pg 107

Green Integer, 6022 Wilshire Blvd, Suite 202-C, Los Angeles, CA 90036 *Tel:* 323-857-1115 *Fax:* 323-857-0143 *E-mail:* info@greeninteger.com *Web Site:* www.greeninteger.com, pg 107

Green King Press, 4211 Fenwick Village Dr, Savannah, GA 31419 *Tel:* 843-325-6821, pg 107

The Green Rose Prize in Poetry, Western Michigan University, 1903 W Michigan Ave, Kalamazoo, MI 49008-5463 *Tel:* 269-387-8185 *Fax:* 269-387-2562 *E-mail:* new-issues@wmich.edu *Web Site:* www.wmich.edu/newissues/greenroseprize.html, pg 708

Green Sugar Press, 2200 E Devon Ave, Suite 340, Des Plaines, IL 60018-4503 *Tel:* 773-580-7780; 615-254-2402 (orders); 615-254-2488 (returns) *Fax:* 615-254-2405 (orders); 615-254-2405 (returns) *Toll Free Fax:* 866-270-4100 *E-mail:* order@greensugarpress.com *Web Site:* www.greensugarpress.com, pg 107

Sanford J Greenburger Associates Inc, 55 Fifth Ave, 15th fl, New York, NY 10003 *Tel:* 212-206-5600 *Fax:* 212-463-8718 *Web Site:* www.greenburger.com, pg 575

Greenhaven Press®, 27500 Drake Rd, Farmington Hills, MI 48331 *Toll Free Tel:* 800-877-4253 (cust serv & orders) *Fax:* 248-699-8051 (cust serv) *Toll Free Fax:* 800-414-5043 (orders only) *E-mail:* gale.customerservice@cengage.com; gale.galeord@thomson.com (orders) *Web Site:* www.gale.cengage.com/greenhaven, pg 107

Paul Greenland Editorial Services, 9184 Longfellow Lane, Machesney Park, IL 61115 *Tel:* 815-540-0911 *Web Site:* www.paulgreenland.com, pg 548

Greenleaf Book Group LLC, 4005 Banister Lane, Suite B, Austin, TX 78704 *Tel:* 512-891-6100 *Toll Free Tel:* 800-932-5420 *Fax:* 512-891-6150 *E-mail:* contact@greenleafbookgroup.com *Web Site:* www.greenleafbookgroup.com, pg 107

Greenwoman Publishing LLC, 1823 W Pikes Peak Ave, Colorado Springs, CO 80904-3844 *Tel:* 719-473-9237 *Fax:* 719-473-9237 *Web Site:* www.greenwomanpublishing.com, pg 108

Greenwood Research Books & Software, PO Box 12102, Wichita, KS 67277-2102 *Tel:* 316-214-5103 *Web Site:* greenray4ever.com (ordering), pg 108

Bess Gresham Memorial, 1194 Hume Rd, Hume, VA 22639-1806 *E-mail:* poetryinva@aol.com *Web Site:* www.poetrysocietyofvirginia.org, pg 708

Rosemary F Gretton, 53 Grassland Ct, Danville, CA 94526 *Tel:* 925-336-0003 *Fax:* 925-336-0003 *E-mail:* rgretton@lyricism.ca *Web Site:* www.lyricism.ca, pg 548

Grey House Publishing Inc™, 4919 Rte 22, Amenia, NY 12501 *Tel:* 518-789-8700 *Toll Free Tel:* 800-562-2139 *Fax:* 518-789-0556 *E-mail:* books@greyhouse.com *Web Site:* www.greyhouse.com, pg 108

Greystone Books, 2323 Quebec St, Suite 201, Vancouver, BC V5T 4S7, Canada *Tel:* 604-254-9099 *Fax:* 604-254-9099 *E-mail:* info@greystonebooks.com *Web Site:* www.greystonebooks.com; www.dmpibooks.com, pg 507

Griffin Publishing LLC, PO Box 28627, Santa Ana, CA 92799-8627 *Tel:* 714-556-7067 *Toll Free Tel:* 800-472-9741 *Fax:* 714-556-7067 *E-mail:* info@griffinpublishing.com *Web Site:* www.griffinpublishing.com, pg 108

Joan K Griffitts Indexing, 3909 W 71 St, Indianapolis, IN 46268-2257 *Tel:* 317-297-7312 *E-mail:* jkgriffitts@gmail.com *Web Site:* www.joankgriffittsindexing.com, pg 548

Jill Grinberg Literary Management LLC, 16 Court, Suite 3306, Brooklyn, NY 11241 *Tel:* 212-620-5883 *Fax:* 212-627-4725 *E-mail:* info@jillgrinbergliterary.com *Web Site:* www.jillgrinbergliterary.com, pg 576

Jill Grosjean Literary Agency, 1390 Millstone Rd, Sag Harbor, NY 11963 *Tel:* 631-725-7419 *Fax:* 631-725-8632 *E-mail:* JillLit310@aol.com, pg 576

Laura Gross Literary Agency Ltd, 39 Chester St, Suite 301, Newton Highlands, MA 02461 *Tel:* 617-964-2977 *Fax:* 617-964-3023 *E-mail:* query@lauragrossliteraryagency.com *Web Site:* www.lg-la.com, pg 576

Grosset & Dunlap, 345 Hudson St, New York, NY 10014 *Tel:* 212-366-2000 *E-mail:* online@penguinputnam.com *Web Site:* www.penguinputnam.com; us.penguingroup.com, pg 108

Judith S Grossman, 715 Cherry Circle, Wynnewood, PA 19096 *Tel:* 610-642-0906 *E-mail:* stogiz@aol.com, pg 548

Groundwood Books, 110 Spadina Ave, Suite 801, Toronto, ON M5V 2K4, Canada *Tel:* 416-363-4343 *Fax:* 416-363-1017 *E-mail:* genmail@groundwoodbooks.com *Web Site:* www.houseofanansi.com, pg 507

Group Publishing Inc, 1515 Cascade Ave, Loveland, CO 80538 *Tel:* 970-669-3836 *Toll Free Tel:* 800-447-1070 *Fax:* 970-292-4373 *E-mail:* info@group.com *Web Site:* www.group.com, pg 108

Groupe Educalivres Inc, 955, rue Bergar, Laval, QC H7L 4Z6, Canada *Tel:* 514-334-8466 *Toll Free Tel:* 800-567-3671 (info serv) *Fax:* 514-334-8387 *E-mail:* commentaires@educalivres.com *Web Site:* www.educalivres.com, pg 507

Groupe Sogides Inc, 955 rue Amherst, Montreal, QC H2L 3K4, Canada *Tel:* 514-523-1182 *Toll Free Tel:* 800-361-4806 *Fax:* 514-597-0370 *E-mail:* edhomme@sogides.com *Web Site:* www.sogides.com; www.edhomme.com, pg 507

Grove/Atlantic Inc, 841 Broadway, 4th fl, New York, NY 10003-4793 *Tel:* 212-614-7850 *Toll Free Tel:* 800-521-0178 *Fax:* 212-614-7886 *E-mail:* info@groveatlantic.com *Web Site:* www.groveatlantic.com, pg 108

Gryphon Books, PO Box 209, Brooklyn, NY 11228-0209 *E-mail:* gryphonbooks@att.net *Web Site:* www.gryphonbooks.com, pg 109

Gryphon Editions, PO Box 34461, Bethesda, MD 20827 *Tel:* 301-983-4171 *Toll Free Tel:* 800-633-8911 *Fax:* 301-983-8734 *E-mail:* gryphonedn@gmail.com *Web Site:* www.gryphoneditions.com, pg 109

Gryphon House Inc, 10770 Columbia Pike, Suite 201, Silver Spring, MD 20901 *Tel:* 301-595-9500 *Toll Free Tel:* 800-638-0928 *Fax:* 301-595-0051 *Toll Free Fax:* 877-638-7576 *E-mail:* info@ghbooks.com *Web Site:* www.gryphonhouse.com, pg 109

Carol Guenzi Agents Inc, 865 Delaware St, Denver, CO 80204 *Tel:* 303-820-2599 *Toll Free Tel:* 800-417-5120 *Fax:* 303-820-2598 *E-mail:* info@artagent.com; art@artagent.com *Web Site:* www.artagent.com, pg 601

Guerin Editeur Ltee, 4501 rue Drolet, Montreal, QC H2T 2G2, Canada *Tel:* 514-842-3481 *Toll Free Tel:* 800-398-8337 *Fax:* 514-842-4923 *Web Site:* www.guerin-editeur.qc.ca, pg 507

Guernica Editions Inc, 2250 Military Rd, Tonawanda, NY 14150-6000 *Tel:* 416-576-9403 *Fax:* 716-693-2667; 716-692-7479 *Toll Free Fax:* 800-221-9985 (orders) *E-mail:* guernicaeditions@cs.com *Web Site:* www.guernicaeditions.com, pg 109

Guernica Editions Inc, 489 Strathmore Blvd, Toronto, ON M4C 1N8, Canada *Tel:* 416-576-9403 (orders & cust serv); 416-285-4067 (edit) *Fax:* 416-981-7606 *Web Site:* guernicaeditions.com, pg 508

John Simon Guggenheim Memorial Foundation, 90 Park Ave, New York, NY 10016 *Tel:* 212-687-4470 *Fax:* 212-697-3248 *E-mail:* fellowships@gf.org *Web Site:* www.gf.org, pg 641

Guideposts Book & Inspirational Media, 16 E 34 St, 12th fl, New York, NY 10016 *Tel:* 212-251-8100 *Toll Free Tel:* 800-431-2344 (cust serv) *Fax:* 212-684-0689 *Web Site:* guideposts.org, pg 109

Guild of Book Workers, 521 Fifth Ave, 17th fl, New York, NY 10175-0038 *Tel:* 212-292-4444 *Web Site:* www.guildofbookworkers.org, pg 624

The Guilford Press, 72 Spring St, 4th fl, New York, NY 10012 *Tel:* 212-431-9800 *Toll Free Tel:* 800-365-7006 (ext 1, orders) *Fax:* 212-966-6708 *E-mail:* orders@guilford.com; info@guilford.com *Web Site:* www.guilford.com, pg 109

Gulf Publishing Co, 2 Greenway Plaza, Suite 1020, Houston, TX 77046 *Tel:* 713-529-4301 *Fax:* 713-520-4433 *E-mail:* books@gulfpub.com *Web Site:* www.gulfpub.com, pg 109

The Charlotte Gusay Literary Agency, 10532 Blythe Ave, Los Angeles, CA 90064 *Tel:* 310-559-0831 *Fax:* 310-559-2639 *E-mail:* gusay1@ca.rr.com (queries only) *Web Site:* www.gusay.com, pg 576, 601

Hachai Publishing, 527 Empire Blvd, Brooklyn, NY 11225 *Tel:* 718-633-0100 *Fax:* 718-633-0103 *E-mail:* info@hachai.com *Web Site:* www.hachai.com, pg 109

Hachette Book Group, 237 Park Ave, New York, NY 10017 *Tel:* 212-364-1100 *Toll Free Tel:* 800-759-0190 (cust serv) *Fax:* 212-364-0933 (intl orders) *Toll Free Fax:* 800-286-9471 (cust serv) *Web Site:* www.HachetteBookGroup.com, pg 110

Hachette Digital, 237 Park Ave, New York, NY 10017 *Tel:* 212-364-0600, pg 110

Hackett Publishing Co Inc, 3333 Massachusetts Ave, Indianapolis, IN 46218 *Tel:* 317-635-9250 (orders & cust serv) *Fax:* 317-635-9292 *Toll Free Fax:* 800-783-9213 *E-mail:* customer@hackettpublishing.com *Web Site:* www.hackettpublishing.com, pg 110

Hackmatack Children's Choice Book Award, PO Box 34055, Scotia Square RPO, Halifax, NS B3J 3S1, Canada *Tel:* 902-424-3774 *Fax:* 902-424-0613 *E-mail:* hackmatack@hackmatack.ca *Web Site:* www.hackmatack.ca, pg 708

Hackney Literary Awards, 1305 Second Ave N, Suite 103, Birmingham, AL 35203 *E-mail:* info@hackneyliteraryawards.org *Web Site:* www.hackneyliteraryawards.org, pg 708

Hadronic Press Inc, 35246 US 19 N, No 115, Palm Harbor, FL 34684 *Tel:* 727-934-9593 *Fax:* 727-934-9275 *E-mail:* hadronic@tampabay.rr.com *Web Site:* www.hadronicpress.com, pg 110

Hagstrom Map & Travel Center, 51 W 43 St, New York, NY 10036 *Toll Free Tel:* 800-432-MAPS (432-6277) *Fax:* 212-398-9856 *Web Site:* www.americanmap.com, pg 110

Haights Cross Communications Inc, 136 Madison Ave, 8th fl, New York, NY 10016 *Tel:* 212-209-0500 *Fax:* 212-209-0501 *E-mail:* info@haightscross.com *Web Site:* www.haightscross.com, pg 110

Hal Leonard Books, 33 Plymouth St, Suite 302, Montclair, NJ 07042 *Tel:* 973-337-5034 *Fax:* 973-337-5227, pg 110

Hal Leonard Corp, 7777 W Bluemound Rd, Milwaukee, WI 53213 *Tel:* 414-774-3630 *Toll Free Tel:* 800-524-4425 *Fax:* 414-774-3259 *E-mail:* sales@halleonard.com *Web Site:* www.halleonard.com; twitter.com/#!/HalleonardBooks, pg 110

Halcyon Press Ltd, 2206 N Gordon St, Suite D, Alvin, TX 77511 *Tel:* 281-585-9559 *Toll Free Tel:* 866-774-5786 *E-mail:* info@halcyon-press.com; editor@halcyonpress.com *Web Site:* www.halcyonpress.com, pg 111

Sarah Josepha Hale Award, 58 N Main, Newport, NH 03773 *Tel:* 603-863-3430 *E-mail:* rfl@newport.lib.nh.us *Web Site:* www.newport.lib.nh.us, pg 708

Half Halt Press Inc, 20042 Benevola Church Rd, Boonsboro, MD 21713 *Tel:* 301-733-7119 *Toll Free Tel:* 800-822-9635 (orders) *Fax:* 301-733-7408 *E-mail:* mail@halfhaltpress.com, pg 111

Loretta Dunn Hall Memorial, 1194 Hume Rd, Hume, VA 22639-1806 *E-mail:* poetryinva@aol.com *Web Site:* www.poetrysocietyofvirginia.org, pg 708

The Mitchell J Hamilburg Agency, 149 S Barrington Ave, Suite 732, Los Angeles, CA 90049 *Tel:* 310-471-4024 *Fax:* 310-471-9588, pg 576

Hamilton Books, 4501 Forbes Blvd, Suite 200, Lanham, MD 20706 *Tel:* 301-459-3366 *Toll Free Tel:* 800-462-6420 (cust serv) *Fax:* 301-429-5748 *Toll Free Fax:* 800-388-4550 (cust serv) *Web Site:* www.hamilton-books.com, pg 111

Hamilton College, English/Creative Writing, English/Creative Writing Dept, 198 College Hill Rd, Clinton, NY 13323 *Tel:* 315-859-4370 *Fax:* 315-859-4390 *E-mail:* english@hamilton.edu *Web Site:* www.hamilton.edu, pg 678

Hamilton Stone Editions, PO Box 43, Maplewood, NJ 07040 *Tel:* 973-378-8361 *E-mail:* hstone@hamiltonstone.org *Web Site:* www.hamiltonstone.org, pg 111

Hampton Press Inc, 307 Seventh Ave, Suite 506, New York, NY 10001 *Tel:* 646-638-3800 *Toll Free Tel:* 800-894-8955 *Fax:* 646-638-3802 *E-mail:* hamptonpr1@aol.com *Web Site:* www.hamptonpress.com, pg 111

Hampton Roads Publishing Co Inc, 211 E High St, Charlottesville, VA 22902 *Tel:* 978-465-0504 *Toll Free Tel:* 800-423-7087 (orders) *Fax:* 978-465-0243 *E-mail:* hrpub@rwwbooks.com *Web Site:* www.hamptonroadspub.com, pg 111

Hancock House Publishers, 1431 Harrison Ave, Blaine, WA 98230-5005 *Tel:* 604-538-1114 *Toll Free Tel:* 800-938-1114 *Fax:* 604-538-2262 *Toll Free Fax:* 800-983-2262 *E-mail:* sales@hancockhouse.com *Web Site:* www.hancockhouse.com, pg 111

Hancock House Publishers Ltd, 19313 Zero Ave, Surrey, BC V3S 9R9, Canada *Tel:* 604-538-1114 *Toll Free Tel:* 800-938-1114 *Fax:* 604-538-2262 *Toll Free Fax:* 800-983-2262 *E-mail:* sales@hancockhouse.com *Web Site:* www.hancockhouse.com, pg 508

Handprint Books Inc, 413 Sixth Ave, Brooklyn, NY 11215-3310 *Tel:* 718-768-3696 *Toll Free Tel:* 800-722-6657 (orders) *Fax:* 718-369-0844 *Toll Free Fax:* 800-858-7787 (orders) *E-mail:* info@handprintbooks.com *Web Site:* www.handprintbooks.com, pg 111

Handy Andy Prize, 1194 Hume Rd, Hume, VA 22639-1806 *E-mail:* poetryinva@aol.com *Web Site:* www.poetrysocietyofvirginia.org, pg 708

Hanging Loose Press, 231 Wyckoff St, Brooklyn, NY 11217 *Tel:* 347-529-4738 *Fax:* 347-227-8215 *E-mail:* print225@aol.com *Web Site:* www.hangingloosepress.com, pg 111

Hanley-Wood LLC, One Thomas Circle NW, Suite 600, Washington, DC 20005 *Tel:* 202-452-0800 *Fax:* 202-785-1974 *Web Site:* www.hanleywood.com, pg 112

Hannacroix Creek Books Inc, 1127 High Ridge Rd, No 110-B, Stamford, CT 06905-1203 *Tel:* 203-968-8098 *Fax:* 203-968-0193 *E-mail:* hannacroix@aol.com *Web Site:* www.hannacroixcreekbooks.com, pg 112

Hanser Publications LLC, 6915 Valley Ave, Cincinnati, OH 45244-3029 *Tel:* 513-527-8977 *Toll Free Tel:* 800-950-8977; 877-751-5052 (orders) *Fax:* 513-534-7803 *Toll Free Fax:* 800-527-8801 *E-mail:* info@hanserpublications.com *Web Site:* www.hanserpublications.com, pg 112

Harbour Publishing Co Ltd, PO Box 219, Madeira Park, BC V0N 2H0, Canada *Tel:* 604-883-2730 *Toll Free Tel:* 800-667-2988 *Fax:* 604-883-9451 *E-mail:* info@harbourpublishing.com *Web Site:* www.harbourpublishing.com, pg 508

Harcourt Achieve, 6277 Sea Harbor Dr, Orlando, FL 32887 *Tel:* 407-345-2000 *Toll Free Tel:* 800-531-5015 (cust serv/orders) *Toll Free Fax:* 800-699-9459 (cust serv/orders) *Web Site:* www.harcourtachieve.com, pg 112

Harcourt Inc, 6277 Sea Harbor Dr, Orlando, FL 32887 *Tel:* 407-345-2000 *Toll Free Tel:* 800-225-5425 (cust serv/orders) *Toll Free Fax:* 800-269-5232 (cust serv/orders) *Web Site:* www.hmhco.com, pg 112

Harcourt Mifflin School Publishers, 6277 Sea Harbor Dr, Orlando, FL 32887 *Tel:* 407-345-2000 *Toll Free Tel:* 800-225-5425 (cust serv) *Fax:* 407-345-3016 (cust serv) *Toll Free Fax:* 800-874-6418; 800-269-5232 (cust serv) *Web Site:* www.harcourtschool.com, pg 112

Hard Shell Word Factory, 6457 Glenway Ave, No 109, Cincinnati, OH 45211 *Toll Free Tel:* 888-232-0808 *Toll Free Fax:* 888-460-4752 *E-mail:* books@hardshell.com *Web Site:* www.hardshell.com, pg 112

Clarence H Haring Prize, 400 "A" St SE, Washington, DC 20003-3889 *Tel:* 202-544-2422 *Fax:* 202-544-8307 *E-mail:* awards@historians.org *Web Site:* www.historians.org, pg 708

Joy Harjo Poetry Award, PO Box 2414, Durango, CO 81302 *Tel:* 970-903-7914 *E-mail:* cutthroatmag@gmail.com *Web Site:* www.cutthroatmag.com, pg 709

Harlan Davidson Inc/Forum Press Inc, 773 Glenn Ave, Wheeling, IL 60090-6900 *Tel:* 847-541-9720 *Fax:* 847-541-9830 *E-mail:* harlandavidson@harlandavidson.com *Web Site:* www.harlandavidson.com, pg 112

Harlequin Enterprises Ltd, 233 Broadway, Suite 1001, New York, NY 10279 *Tel:* 212-553-4200 *Fax:* 212-227-8969 *E-mail:* CustomerService@harlequin.com *Web Site:* www.harlequin.com, pg 112

Harlequin Enterprises Ltd, 225 Duncan Mill Rd, Don Mills, ON M3B 3K9, Canada *Tel:* 416-445-5860 *Toll Free Tel:* 888-432-4879; 800-370-5838 (ebook inquiries) *Fax:* 416-445-8655 *E-mail:* CustomerService@harlequin.com *Web Site:* www.harlequin.com, pg 508

Harmonie Park Press, Liberty Professional Ctr, 35675 Mound Rd, Sterling Heights, MI 48310-4727 *Tel:* 586-979-2077; 586-979-1844 (cust serv) *Toll Free Tel:* 800-422-4880 *Fax:* 586-979-1786; 586-979-1863 (cust serv) *E-mail:* info@harmonieparkpress.com *Web Site:* harmonieparkpress.com, pg 113

HarperCollins Canada Ltd, 2 Bloor St E, 20th fl, Toronto, ON M4W 1A8, Canada *Tel:* 416-975-9334 *Fax:* 416-975-9884 *E-mail:* hccanada@harpercollins.com *Web Site:* www.harpercollins.ca, pg 508

HarperCollins Children's Books, 10 E 53 St, New York, NY 10022 *Tel:* 212-207-7000 *Web Site:* www.harpercollinschildrens.com, pg 113

HarperCollins General Books Group, 10 E 53 St, New York, NY 10022 *Tel:* 212-207-7000 *Fax:* 212-207-7633 *Web Site:* www.harpercollins.com, pg 113

HarperCollins Publishers, 10 E 53 St, New York, NY 10022 *Tel:* 212-207-7000 *Fax:* 212-207-7145 *Web Site:* www.harpercollins.com, pg 113

HarperCollins Publishers Sales, 10 E 53 St, New York, NY 10022 *Fax:* 212-207-7000 *Web Site:* www.harpercollins.com, pg 114

Harper's Magazine Foundation, 666 Broadway, 11th fl, New York, NY 10012 *Tel:* 212-420-5720 *Toll Free Tel:* 800-444-4653 *Fax:* 212-228-5889 *E-mail:* harpers@harpers.org *Web Site:* www.harpers.org, pg 114

Aurand Harris Memorial Playwriting Award, 215 Knob Hill Dr, Hamden, CT 06518 *Tel:* 617-851-8535 *Fax:* 203-288-5938 *E-mail:* mail@netconline.org *Web Site:* www.netconline.org, pg 709

The Joy Harris Literary Agency Inc, 381 Park Ave S, Suite 428, New York, NY 10016 *Tel:* 212-924-6269 *Fax:* 212-725-5275 *E-mail:* contact@jhlitagent.com *Web Site:* www.joyharrisliterary.com, pg 576

Harrison House Publishers, 7498 E 46 Place, Tulsa, OK 74145 *Tel:* 918-523-5700 *Toll Free Tel:* 800-888-4126 *Toll Free Fax:* 800-830-5688 *Web Site:* www.harrisonhouse.com, pg 114

Hartline Literary Agency LLC, 123 Queenston Dr, Pittsburgh, PA 15235 *Toll Free Fax:* 888-279-6007 *Web Site:* www.hartlineliterary.com, pg 576

Hartman Publishing Inc, 8529-A Indian School Rd NE, Albuquerque, NM 87112 *Tel:* 505-291-1274 *Toll Free Tel:* 800-999-9534 *Fax:* 505-291-1284 *Toll Free Fax:* 800-474-6106 *E-mail:* orders@hartmanonline.com; help@hartmanonline.com *Web Site:* www.hartmanonline.com, pg 114

Harvard Art Museums, 32 Quincy St, Cambridge, MA 02138 *Tel:* 617-495-1440; 617-496-6529 (edit) *Fax:* 617-495-9985 *E-mail:* am_shop@harvard.edu *Web Site:* www.harvardartmuseums.org, pg 114

Harvard Business Press, 300 N Beacon St, Watertown, MA 02472 *Tel:* 617-783-7400 *Fax:* 617-783-7489 *E-mail:* custserv@hbsp.harvard.edu *Web Site:* www.harvardbusiness.org, pg 114

The Harvard Common Press, 535 Albany St, Boston, MA 02118 *Tel:* 617-423-5803 *Toll Free Tel:* 888-657-3755 *Fax:* 617-695-9794 *E-mail:* orders@harvardcommonpress.com; info@harvardcommonpress.com *Web Site:* www.harvardcommonpress.com, pg 114

Harvard Education Publishing Group, 8 Story St, 1st fl, Cambridge, MA 02138 *Tel:* 617-495-3432 *Toll Free Tel:* 800-513-0763 (subns); 888-437-1437 (orders) *Fax:* 617-496-3584; 978-348-1233 (orders) *E-mail:* hepg@harvard.edu *Web Site:* www.hepg.org, pg 114

Harvard Square Editions, 2152 Beachwood Terr, Hollywood, CA 90068 *Tel:* 323-469-8932 *Fax:* 323-469-8932 *Web Site:* harvardsquareeditions.org, pg 114

Harvard Summer Writing Program, 51 Brattle St, Dept S760, Cambridge, MA 02138-3722 *Tel:* 617-495-4024 *Fax:* 617-495-9176 *E-mail:* summer@hudce.harvard.edu *Web Site:* www.summer.harvard.edu, pg 669

Harvard Ukrainian Research Institute, 34 Kirkland St, Cambridge, MA 02138 *Tel:* 617-495-4053 *Fax:* 617-495-8097 *E-mail:* huri@fas.harvard.edu *Web Site:* www.huri.harvard.edu, pg 114

Harvard University Press, 79 Garden St, Cambridge, MA 02138-1499 *Tel:* 617-495-2600; 401-531-2800 (intl orders) *Toll Free Tel:* 800-405-1619 (orders) *Fax:* 617-495-5898 (general); 617-496-4677 (edit & rts); 401-531-2801 (intl orders) *Toll Free Fax:* 800-406-9145 (orders) *E-mail:* contact_hup@harvard.edu *Web Site:* www.hup.harvard.edu, pg 114

Harvest Hill Press, PO Box 55, Salisbury Cove, ME 04672-0055 *Tel:* 207-288-8900 *Toll Free Tel:* 888-288-8900 *Fax:* 207-288-3611 *E-mail:* shop@harvesthillpress.com *Web Site:* www.harvesthillpress.com, pg 115

Harvest House Publishers Inc, 990 Owen Loop N, Eugene, OR 97402-9173 *Tel:* 541-343-0123 *Toll Free Tel:* 888-501-6991 *Fax:* 541-342-6410 *E-mail:* admin@harvesthousepublishers.com *Web Site:* www.harvesthousepublishers.com, pg 115

Haskins Medal Award, 104 Mount Auburn St, 5th fl, Cambridge, MA 02138 *Tel:* 617-491-1622 *Fax:* 617-492-3303 *E-mail:* speculum@medievalacademy.org *Web Site:* www.medievalacademy.org, pg 709

Hatherleigh Press, 522 46 Ave, Suite 200, Long Island City, NY 11101 *Tel:* 718-786-5338 *Toll Free Tel:* 800-367-2550 *Fax:* 718-706-6087 *Toll Free Fax:* 800-733-3000 (orders) *E-mail:* info@hatherleigh.com *Web Site:* www.hatherleighpress.com; www.hatherleigh.com, pg 115

John Hawkins & Associates Inc, 71 W 23 St, Suite 1600, New York, NY 10010 *Tel:* 212-807-7040 *Fax:* 212-807-9555 *E-mail:* jha@jhalit.com *Web Site:* jhalit.com, pg 576

Hay House Inc, 2776 Loker Ave W, Carlsbad, CA 92010 *Tel:* 760-431-7695 (ext 2, intl) *Toll Free Tel:* 800-654-5126 (ext 2, US) *Toll Free Fax:* 800-650-5115 *E-mail:* info@hayhouse.com; editorial@hayhouse.com *Web Site:* www.hayhouse.com, pg 115

Haynes Manuals Inc, 861 Lawrence Dr, Newbury Park, CA 91320 *Tel:* 805-498-6703 *Toll Free Tel:* 800-4-HAYNES (442-9637) *Fax:* 805-498-2867 *E-mail:* cstn@haynes.com *Web Site:* www.haynes.com, pg 115

Hazelden Publishing, 15251 Pleasant Valley Rd, Center City, MN 55012-0011 *Tel:* 651-213-4200 *Toll Free Tel:* 800-257-7810 *Fax:* 651-213-4590 *E-mail:* info@hazelden.org *Web Site:* www.hazelden.org, pg 116

HCPro Inc, 200 Hoods Lane, Marblehead, MA 01945 *Tel:* 781-639-1872 *Toll Free Tel:* 800-650-6787 *Toll Free Fax:* 800-639-8511 *E-mail:* customerservice@hcpro.com *Web Site:* www.hcpro.com, pg 116

Heacock Literary Agency Inc, 48 Villa Christina, La Luz, NM 88337 *Tel:* 575-437-1960 *Fax:* 575-437-1960 (call first) *E-mail:* gracebooks@aol.com (for rights information concerning Elliot Abravanel, Wilferd Peterson, Audrey Wood, Don Wood) *Web Site:* www.heacockliteraryagency.com, pg 576

Headlands Center for the Arts Residency for Writers, 944 Fort Barry, Sausalito, CA 94965 *Tel:* 415-331-2787 *Fax:* 415-331-3857 *Web Site:* www.headlands.org, pg 709

Health Administration Press, One N Franklin St, Suite 1700, Chicago, IL 60606-3491 *Tel:* 312-424-2800 *Fax:* 312-424-0014 *E-mail:* hap1@ache.org *Web Site:* www.ache.org; www.ache.org/hap.cfm (orders), pg 116

Health Communications Inc, 3201 SW 15 St, Deerfield Beach, FL 33442-8190 *Tel:* 954-360-0909 *Toll Free Tel:* 800-441-5569 (cust serv) *Fax:* 954-360-0034 *Web Site:* www.hcibooks.com; hci-online.com, pg 116

Health Forum Inc, 155 N Wacker Dr, Suite 400, Chicago, IL 60606 *Tel:* 312-893-6884 *Toll Free Tel:* 800-242-2626 *Fax:* 312-422-4600 *E-mail:* hfcustsvc@healthforum.com *Web Site:* www.ahaonlinestore.com; www.healthforum.com, pg 116

Health InfoNet Inc, 231 Market Place, No 331, San Ramon, CA 94583 *Tel:* 925-358-4370 *Toll Free Tel:* 800-446-1121 *Fax:* 925-358-4377 *E-mail:* hinbooks@aol.com *Web Site:* hinbooks.com, pg 116

Health Press NA Inc, 2920 Carlisle Blvd NE, Suite 111, Albuquerque, NM 87110 *Tel:* 505-888-1394 *Toll Free Tel:* 877-411-0707 *Fax:* 505-888-1521 *E-mail:* goodbooks@healthpress.com *Web Site:* www.healthpress.com, pg 116

Health Professions Press, 409 Washington Ave, Suite 500, Towson, MD 21204 *Tel:* 410-337-9585 *Toll Free Tel:* 888-337-8808 *Fax:* 410-337-8539 *E-mail:* custserv@healthpropress.com *Web Site:* www.healthpropress.com, pg 117

Health Research Books, 62 Seventh St, Pomeroy, WA 99347 *Tel:* 509-843-2385 *Toll Free Tel:* 888-844-2386 *Fax:* 509-843-2387 *E-mail:* publish@pomeroy-wa.com *Web Site:* www.healthresearchbooks.com, pg 117

Heart and Mind Press, 3135 E Palo Verde Dr, Phoenix, AZ 85016 *Tel:* 602-790-4009 *E-mail:* info@heartandmindpress.com *Web Site:* heartandmindpress.com, pg 527

HeartMath LLC, 14700 W Park Ave, Boulder Creek, CA 95006 *Tel:* 831-338-8700 *Toll Free Tel:* 800-450-9111 *Fax:* 831-338-9861 *E-mail:* inquiry@heartmath.com *Web Site:* www.heartmath.com, pg 117

Hearts & Tummies Cookbook Co, 3544 Blakslee St, Wever, IA 52658 *Tel:* 319-372-7480 *Toll Free Tel:* 800-571-2665 *Fax:* 319-372-7485 *E-mail:* quixotepress@gmail.com; heartsntummies@gmail.com *Web Site:* www.heartsntummies.com, pg 117

Anne Hebenstreit, 20 Tip Top Way, Berkeley Heights, NJ 07922 *Tel:* 908-665-0536, pg 548

Hebrew Union College Press, 3101 Clifton Ave, Cincinnati, OH 45220 *Tel:* 513-221-1875 *Fax:* 513-221-0321 *E-mail:* hucpress@huc.edu *Web Site:* huc.edu, pg 117

Hedgebrook, PO Box 1231, Freeland, WA 98249 *Tel:* 360-321-4786 *Fax:* 360-321-2171 *E-mail:* hedgebrook@hedgebrook.org *Web Site:* www.hedgebrook.org, pg 669

Heian International Inc, PO Box 8208, Berkeley, CA 94707 *Tel:* 510-524-8732 *Toll Free Tel:* 800-947-7271 *Fax:* 510-524-8711 *Toll Free Fax:* 888-411-8527 *E-mail:* sbp@stonebridge.com (gen & orders) *Web Site:* www.stonebridge.com, pg 117

Heimburger House Publishing Co, 7236 W Madison St, Forest Park, IL 60130 *Tel:* 708-366-1973 *Fax:* 708-366-1973 *E-mail:* info@heimburgerhouse.com *Web Site:* www.heimburgerhouse.com, pg 117

William S Hein & Co Inc, 2350 N Forest Rd, Getzville, NY 14068 *Tel:* 716-882-2600 *Toll Free Tel:* 800-828-7571 *Fax:* 716-883-8100 *E-mail:* mail@wshein.com; marketing@wshein.com *Web Site:* www.wshein.com, pg 117

Heinemann, 361 Hanover St, Portsmouth, NH 03801-3912 *Tel:* 603-431-7894 *Toll Free Tel:* 800-225-5800 (US) *Fax:* 603-431-2214 *Toll Free Fax:* 877-231-6980 (US) *E-mail:* custserv@heinemann.com *Web Site:* www.heinemann.com, pg 117

Drue Heinz Literature Prize, Eureka Bldg, 5th fl, 3400 Forbes Ave, Pittsburgh, PA 15260 *Tel:* 412-383-2456 *Fax:* 412-383-2466 *E-mail:* info@upress.pitt.edu *Web Site:* www.upress.pitt.edu, pg 709

Hellgate Press, PO Box 3531, Ashland, OR 97520 *Tel:* 541-973-5154 *Toll Free Tel:* 800-795-4059 *E-mail:* info@hellgatepress.com *Web Site:* www.hellgatepress.com, pg 117

Helm Editorial Services, 707 SW Eighth Way, Fort Lauderdale, FL 33315 *Tel:* 954-525-5626 *E-mail:* lynnehelm12@aol.com, pg 548

Helm Publishing, PO Box 9691, Treasure Island, FL 33740 *Tel:* 727-623-5014 *Web Site:* www.publishersdrive.com, pg 118

The Hemingway Foundation/PEN Award, Massachusetts Institute of Technology, 77 Massachusetts Ave, 14-N-221A, Cambridge, MA 02139 *Tel:* 617-324-1729 *E-mail:* pen-newengland@mit.edu *Web Site:* www.pen-ne.org, pg 709

Hemingway Western Studies Center, Boise State University, 1910 University Dr, Boise, ID 83725-1135 *Tel:* 208-426-1999; 208-426-1514 *Fax:* 208-426-4373 *E-mail:* books@booksboisestate.com *Web Site:* www.booksboisestate.com, pg 118

Cecil Hemley Memorial Award, 15 Gramercy Park S, New York, NY 10003 *Tel:* 212-254-9628 *Fax:* 212-673-2352 *Web Site:* www.poetrysociety.org, pg 709

Hendrick-Long Publishing Co, 10635 Tower Oaks, Suite D, Houston, TX 77070 *Tel:* 832-912-READ (912-7323) *Fax:* 832-912-7353 *E-mail:* hendrick-long@worldnet.att.net *Web Site:* www.hendricklongpublishing.com, pg 118

Hendrickson Publishers Inc, PO Box 3473, Peabody, MA 01961-3473 *Tel:* 978-532-6546 *Toll Free Tel:* 800-358-3111 *Fax:* 978-573-8111 *E-mail:* orders@hendrickson.com *Web Site:* www.hendrickson.com, pg 118

Henrico Theatre Company One-Act Playwriting Competition, PO Box 90775, Richmond, VA 23273-0775 *Tel:* 804-501-5138 *Fax:* 804-501-5284, pg 709

Hensley Publishing, 6116 E 32 St, Tulsa, OK 74135 *Tel:* 918-664-8520 *Toll Free Tel:* 800-288-8520 (orders only) *Fax:* 918-664-8562 *E-mail:* customerservice@hensleypublishing.com *Web Site:* www.hensleypublishing.com, pg 118

Her Own Words LLC, PO Box 5264, Madison, WI 53705-0264 *Tel:* 608-271-7083 *Fax:* 608-271-0209 *Web Site:* www.herownwords.com; www.nontraditionalcareers.com, pg 118

Herald Press, 1251 Virginia Ave, Harrisonburg, VA 22802-2434 *Toll Free Tel:* 800-245-7894 (orders-US); 800-999-3534; 800-631-6535 (orders-CN) *Toll Free Fax:* 877-271-0760 *E-mail:* info@MennoMedia.org *Web Site:* www.heraldpress.com; store.mennomedia.org, pg 118

Herald Press, 490 Dutton Dr, Unit C-8, Waterloo, ON N2L 6H7, Canada *Tel:* 519-747-5722 *Toll Free Tel:* 800-631-6535 *Fax:* 519-747-5721 *E-mail:* hpcan@mpn.net *Web Site:* www.heraldpress.com, pg 508

Herald Publishing House, 1001 W Walnut St, Independence, MO 64051 *Tel:* 816-521-3015 *Toll Free Tel:* 800-767-8181 *Fax:* 816-521-3066 *E-mail:* sales@heraldhouse.org *Web Site:* www.heraldhouse.org, pg 118

Heritage Books Inc, 100 Railroad Ave, Suite 104, Westminster, MD 21157-4826 *Tel:* 410-876-6101 *Toll Free Tel:* 800-876-6103 *Fax:* 410-558-6574 *E-mail:* info@heritagebooks.com; orders@heritagebooks.com *Web Site:* www.heritagebooks.com, pg 118

The Heritage Foundation, 214 Massachusetts Ave NE, Washington, DC 20002-4999 *Tel:* 202-546-4400 *Toll Free Tel:* 800-544-4843 *Fax:* 202-546-8328 *E-mail:* info@heritage.org *Web Site:* www.heritage.org, pg 118, 641

Heritage House Publishing Co Ltd, 1105 Pandora Ave, Victoria, BC V8V 3P9, Canada *Tel:* 604-574-7067 *Toll Free Tel:* 800-665-3302 *Fax:* 604-574-9942 *Toll Free Fax:* 800-566-3336 *E-mail:* heritage@heritagehouse.ca; orders@heritagehouse.ca *Web Site:* www.heritagehouse.ca, pg 509

Herman Agency, 350 Central Park W, Apt 4I, New York, NY 10025 *Tel:* 212-749-4907 *Web Site:* www.hermanagencyinc.com, pg 601

The Jeff Herman Agency LLC, 29 Park St, Stockbridge, MA 01262 *Tel:* 413-298-0077 *Fax:* 413-298-8188 *E-mail:* submissions@jeffherman.com *Web Site:* www.jeffherman.com, pg 577

Brodie Herndon Memorial, 1194 Hume Rd, Hume, VA 22639-1806 *E-mail:* poetryinva@aol.com *Web Site:* www.poetrysocietyofvirginia.org, pg 709

Susan Herner Rights Agency Inc, 10 Upper Shad Rd, Pound Ridge, NY 10576 *Tel:* 914-234-2864 *Fax:* 914-234-2866 *E-mail:* shemeragency@optonline.net, pg 577

Herr's Indexing Service, PO Box 5378, Kailua Kona, HI 96745 *Tel:* 802-585-6844 *Fax:* 802-883-5415 *Web Site:* www.herrsindexing.com, pg 548

Carl Hertzog Book Design Award, c/o Dir of the Library, University of Texas at El Paso, University Library, El Paso, TX 79968-0582 *Tel:* 915-747-5683 *Fax:* 915-747-5345 *Web Site:* libraryweb.utep.edu, pg 709

Heryin Books Inc, 1033 E Main St, Suite 202, Alhambra, CA 91801 *Tel:* 626-289-2238 *Fax:* 626-289-3865 *E-mail:* editor@heryin.com *Web Site:* www.heryin.com, pg 119

Herzl Press, 633 Third Ave, 21st fl, New York, NY 10017 *Tel:* 212-339-6020 *Fax:* 212-318-6176 *E-mail:* midstreamthf@aol.com *Web Site:* www.midstreamthf.com, pg 119

Heuer Publishing LLC, 211 First Ave SE, Suite 200, Cedar Rapids, IA 52401 *Tel:* 319-368-8008 *Toll Free Tel:* 800-950-7529 *Fax:* 319-368-8011 *E-mail:* editor@hitplays.com *Web Site:* www.hitplays.com, pg 119

Les Heures bleues, Sta Lorimier, PO Box 219, Montreal, QC H2H 2N6, Canada *Tel:* 450-671-7718 *Fax:* 450-671-7718 *E-mail:* info@heuresbleues.com *Web Site:* www.heuresbleues.com, pg 509

Hewitt Homeschooling Resources, 2103 Main St, Washougal, WA 98671 *Tel:* 360-835-8708 *Toll Free Tel:* 800-348-1750 *Fax:* 360-835-8697 *E-mail:* info@hewitthomeschooling.com *Web Site:* hewitthomeschooling.com, pg 119

Heyday Books, 1633 University Ave, Berkeley, CA 94703 *Tel:* 510-549-3564 *Fax:* 510-549-1889 *E-mail:* heyday@heydaybooks.com; orders@heydaybooks.com *Web Site:* www.heydaybooks.com, pg 119

Hi Willow Research & Publishing, PO Box 131266, Spring, TX 77393 *Toll Free Tel:* 800-873-3043 *Fax:* 936-271-4560 *E-mail:* lmcsourcesales@gmail.com *Web Site:* www.lmcsource.com, pg 119

Hidden River Arts Playwriting Award, PO Box 63927, Philadelphia, PA 19147 *Tel:* 610-764-0813 *E-mail:* hiddenriverarts@gmail.com *Web Site:* www.hiddenriverarts.org, pg 709

Higginson Book Co, 148 Washington St, Salem, MA 01970 *Tel:* 978-745-7170 *Fax:* 978-745-8025 *E-mail:* orders@higginsonbooks.com *Web Site:* www.higginsonbooks.com, pg 119

High Plains Press, 403 Cassa Rd, Glendo, WY 82213 *Tel:* 307-735-4370 *Toll Free Tel:* 800-552-7819 *Fax:* 307-735-4590 *E-mail:* editor@highplainspress.com *Web Site:* highplainspress.com, pg 119

High Tide Press, 1805 Ferro Rd, New Lenox, IL 60451 *Web Site:* www.hightidepress.com, pg 119

Highland Summer Writers' Conference, PO Box 7014, Radford University, Radford, VA 24142 *Tel:* 540-831-5366; 540-831-6152 *Fax:* 540-831-5951 *Web Site:* www.radford.edu/~arsc, pg 669

Highlights for Children, 1800 Watermark Dr, Columbus, OH 43215-1060 *Tel:* 614-486-0631 *Toll Free Tel:* 800-962-3661 (Highlights Club cust serv); 800-255-9517 (Highlights Magazine cust serv) *Web Site:* www.highlights.com, pg 119

Highlights for Children Fiction Contest, 803 Church St, Honesdale, PA 18431 *Tel:* 570-253-1080 *Fax:* 570-251-7847 *E-mail:* eds@highlights.com *Web Site:* www.highlights.com, pg 709

Hill & Wang, 18 W 18 St, New York, NY 10011 *Tel:* 212-741-6900 *Fax:* 212-633-9385 *E-mail:* fsg.publicity@fsgbooks.com; fsg.editorial@fsgbooks.com *Web Site:* us.macmillan.com/hillandwang.aspx, pg 119

Hill Nadell Literary Agency, 8899 Beverly Blvd, Suite 805, Los Angeles, CA 90048 *Tel:* 310-860-9605 *Fax:* 310-860-9672 *Web Site:* www.hillnadell.com, pg 577

The Tony Hillerman Prize, 1063 Willow Way, Santa Fe, NM 87507 *Tel:* 505-471-1565 *E-mail:* wordharvest@wordharvest.com *Web Site:* www.wordharvest.com, pg 710

Hillman Prizes in Journalism, 12 W 31 St, 12th fl, New York, NY 10001 *Tel:* 646-448-6413 *Web Site:* www.hillmanfoundation.org, pg 710

Hillsdale College Press, 33 E College St, Hillsdale, MI 49242 *Tel:* 517-437-7341 *Toll Free Tel:* 800-437-2268 *Fax:* 517-517-3923 *E-mail:* news@hillsdale.edu *Web Site:* www.hillsdale.edu, pg 120

Hillsdale Educational Publishers Inc, 39 North St, Hillsdale, MI 49242 *Tel:* 517-437-3179 *Fax:* 517-437-0531 *E-mail:* davestory@aol.com *Web Site:* www.hillsdalepublishers.com; michbooks.com, pg 120

Hilton Publishing, 1630 45 St, Suite B101, Munster, IN 46321 *Tel:* 219-922-4868 *Fax:* 219-922-6407 *E-mail:* orders@hiltonpub.com *Web Site:* www.hiltonpub.com, pg 120

Himalayan Institute Press, 952 Bethany Tpke, Honesdale, PA 18431-9706 *Tel:* 570-253-5551 *Toll Free Tel:* 800-822-4547 *Fax:* 570-253-4500 *E-mail:* info@himalayaninstitute.org *Web Site:* www.himalayaninstitute.org, pg 120

Hippocrene Books Inc, 171 Madison Ave, New York, NY 10016 *Tel:* 212-685-4373; 212-685-4375 *Fax:* 212-779-9338 *E-mail:* info@hippocrenebooks.com; orderdept@hippocrenebooks.com (orders); contact@hippocrenebooks.com *Web Site:* www.hippocrenebooks.com, pg 120

L Anne Hirschel DDS, 5990 Highgate Ave, East Lansing, MI 48823 *Tel:* 517-333-1748 *E-mail:* alicerichard@comcast.net, pg 548

The Historic New Orleans Collection, 533 Royal St, New Orleans, LA 70130 *Tel:* 504-523-4662 *Fax:* 504-598-7104 *E-mail:* wrc@hnoc.org *Web Site:* www.hnoc.org, pg 120

Historical Novel Society North American Conference, 400 Dark Star Ct, Fairbanks, AK 99709 *Tel:* 217-581-7538 *Fax:* 217-581-7534 *Web Site:* www.historicalnovelsociety.org, pg 669

History Publishing Co LLC, 173 Rte 9W, Palisades, NY 10964 *Tel:* 845-398-8161 *Fax:* 845-231-6167 *E-mail:* historypublish@aol.com; info@historypublishingco.com *Web Site:* www.historypublishingco.com, pg 120

W D Hoard & Sons Co, 28 W Milwaukee Ave, Fort Atkinson, WI 53538-2018 *Tel:* 920-563-5551 *Fax:* 920-563-7298 *E-mail:* hoards@hoards.com *Web Site:* www.hoards.com; www.hoardprinting.com, pg 120

Hobar Publications, 8075 215 St W, Lakeville, MN 55044 *Tel:* 952-469-6699 *Toll Free Tel:* 800-846-7027 *Fax:* 952-469-1968 *Toll Free Fax:* 800-330-6232 *E-mail:* info@finneyco.com *Web Site:* www.finney-hobar.com, pg 120

Hobbes End Publishing LLC, PO Box 193, Aubrey, TX 76227 *Tel:* 940-365-2230 *E-mail:* publisher@hobbesendpublishing.com *Web Site:* www.hobbesendpublishing.com, pg 120

Hobblebush Books, 17-A Old Milford Rd, Brookline, NH 03033 *Tel:* 603-672-4317 *Fax:* 603-672-4317 *E-mail:* hobblebush@charter.net *Web Site:* www.hobblebush.com, pg 121

Eric Hoffer Award for Independent Books, PO Box 11, Titusville, NJ 08560 *Fax:* 609-964-1718 *E-mail:* info@hofferaward.com *Web Site:* www.hofferaward.com, pg 710

Eric Hoffer Award for Short Prose, PO Box 11, Titusville, NJ 08560 *Fax:* 609-964-1718 *E-mail:* info@hofferaward.com *Web Site:* www.hofferaward.com, pg 710

Hofstra University, English Dept, 204 Mason Hall, Hempstead, NY 11549 *Tel:* 516-463-5454 *Fax:* 516-463-6395 *Web Site:* www.hofstra.edu, pg 678

The Barbara Hogenson Agency Inc, 165 West End Ave, Suite 19-C, New York, NY 10023 *Tel:* 212-874-8084 *Fax:* 212-362-3011 *E-mail:* bhogenson@aol.com, pg 577

Hogrefe Publishing, 38 Chauncy St, Suite 1002, Boston, MA 02111 *Toll Free Tel:* 866-823-4726 *Fax:* 617-354-6875 *E-mail:* publishing@hogrefe.com *Web Site:* www.hogrefe.com, pg 121

Hohm Press, PO Box 4410, Chino Valley, AZ 86323 *Tel:* 928-636-3331 *Toll Free Tel:* 800-381-2700 *Fax:* 928-636-7519 *E-mail:* hppublisher@cableone.net; hohmpresseditor@gmail.com *Web Site:* www.hohmpress.com, pg 121

Bess Hokin Prize, 444 N Michigan Ave, Suite 1850, Chicago, IL 60611-4034 *Tel:* 312-787-7070 *Fax:* 312-787-6650 *E-mail:* editors@poetrymagazine.org *Web Site:* poetryfoundation.org, pg 710

Holiday House Inc, 425 Madison Ave, New York, NY 10017 *Tel:* 212-688-0085 *Fax:* 212-421-6134 *E-mail:* holiday@holidayhouse.com *Web Site:* www.holidayhouse.com, pg 121

Hollins University-Jackson Center for Creative Writing, PO Box 9677, Roanoke, VA 24020 *Tel:* 540-362-6317 *Fax:* 540-362-6097 *E-mail:* creative.writing@hollins.edu *Web Site:* www.hollins.edu, pg 678

Hollym International Corp, 18 Donald Place, Elizabeth, NJ 07208 *Tel:* 908-353-1655 *Fax:* 908-353-0255 *E-mail:* contact@hollym.com *Web Site:* www.hollym.com, pg 121

Hollywood Film Archive, 8391 Beverly Blvd, PMB 321, Los Angeles, CA 90048 *Tel:* 323-655-4968 *Web Site:* hfarchive.com, pg 121

Holmes & Meier Publishers Inc, PO Box 943, Teaneck, NJ 07666 *Tel:* 201-833-2270 *Fax:* 201-833-2272 *E-mail:* info@holmesandmeier.com *Web Site:* www.holmesandmeier.com, pg 121

Burnham Holmes, 182 Lakeview Hill Rd, Poultney, VT 05764-9179 *Tel:* 802-287-9707 *Fax:* 802-287-9707 (computer fax/modem) *E-mail:* burnham.holmes@castleton.edu, pg 548

Henry Holmes Literary Agent/Book Publicist/ Marketing Consultant, PO Box 433, Swansea, MA 02777 *Tel:* 508-672-2258 *E-mail:* henryholmesandassociates@yahoo.com, pg 548, 577

Holmes Publishing Group LLC, PO Box 2370, Sequim, WA 98382 *Tel:* 360-681-2900 *Fax:* 360-351-9909 *E-mail:* holmespub@fastmail.fm *Web Site:* jdholmes.com, pg 121

Henry Holt and Company, LLC, 175 Fifth Ave, New York, NY 10010 *Tel:* 646-307-5151 *Toll Free Tel:* 888-330-8477 (orders) *Fax:* 646-307-5285 *E-mail:* firstname.lastname@hholt.com *Web Site:* www.henryholt.com, pg 122

Holt McDougal, 1900 S Batavia Ave, Geneva, IL 60134 *Tel:* 630-232-2550 *Toll Free Tel:* 800-462-6595 *Toll Free Fax:* 888-872-8380 *E-mail:* k12orders@hmco.com *Web Site:* holtmcdougal.hmhco.com/hm/home.htm, pg 122

Holy Cow! Press, PO Box 3170, Mount Royal Sta, Duluth, MN 55803 *Tel:* 218-724-1653 *Fax:* 218-724-1653 *E-mail:* holycow@holycowpress.org *Web Site:* www.holycowpress.org, pg 122

Holy Cross Orthodox Press, 50 Goddard Ave, Brookline, MA 02445 *Tel:* 617-731-3500 *Fax:* 617-850-1460 *E-mail:* press@hchc.edu *Web Site:* www.hchc.edu, pg 122

Homa & Sekey Books, 140 E Ridgewood Ave, Paramus, NJ 07652 *Tel:* 201-261-8810 *Toll Free Tel:* 800-870-HOMA (870-4662 orders) *Fax:* 201-261-8890 *E-mail:* info@homabooks.com *Web Site:* www.homabooks.com, pg 122

Home Planners LLC, 3275 W Ina Rd, Suite 260, Tucson, AZ 85741 *Tel:* 520-297-8200 *Toll Free Tel:* 800-521-6797 *Fax:* 520-297-6219 *Toll Free Fax:* 800-224-6699 *E-mail:* customerservice@eplans.com *Web Site:* www.eplans.com, pg 122

Homestead Publishing, Box 193, Moose, WY 83012-0193 *Tel:* 307-733-6248 *Fax:* 307-733-6248 *E-mail:* orders@homesteadpublishing.net *Web Site:* www.homesteadpublishing.net, pg 122

Honickman First Book Prize, University of the Arts (UARTS), Hamilton Hall, 320 S Broad St, Rm 313, Philadelphia, PA 19102-4901 *Tel:* 215-717-6801 *Fax:* 215-717-6805 *Web Site:* www.aprweb.org, pg 710

Hoover Institution Press, Stanford University, 434 Galvez Mall, Stanford, CA 94305-6010 *Tel:* 650-725-7146; 650-723-3373 *Toll Free Tel:* 800-935-2882 *Fax:* 650-723-8626 *E-mail:* hooverpress@stanford.edu *Web Site:* www.hoover.org; www.hooverpress.org, pg 122

Hoover's, Inc, 5800 Airport Blvd, Austin, TX 78752 *Tel:* 512-374-4500 *Toll Free Tel:* 866-307-3812 *Fax:* 512-374-4501 *E-mail:* info@hoovers.com *Web Site:* www.hoovers.com, pg 122

Hope Publishing Co, 380 S Main Place, Carol Stream, IL 60188 *Tel:* 630-665-3200 *Toll Free Tel:* 800-323-1049 *Fax:* 630-665-2552 *E-mail:* hope@hopepublishing.com *Web Site:* www.hopepublishing.com, pg 123

Horizon Publishers & Distributors Inc, 191 N 650 E, Bountiful, UT 84010-3628 *Tel:* 801-292-7102 *E-mail:* ldshorizonpublishers@gmail.com *Web Site:* www.ldshorizonpublishers.com, pg 123

Hornfischer Literary Management LP, PO Box 50544, Austin, TX 78763 *Tel:* 512-472-0011 *E-mail:* queries@hornfischerlit.com *Web Site:* www.hornfischerlit.com, pg 577

Horror Writers Association (HWA), 244 Fifth Ave, Suite 2767, New York, NY 10001 *E-mail:* hwa@horror.org *Web Site:* www.horror.org, pg 624

Hospital & Healthcare Compensation Service, 3 Post Rd FL, Suite 3, Oakland, NJ 07436 *Tel:* 201-405-0075 *Fax:* 201-405-2110 *E-mail:* allinfo@hhcsinc.com *Web Site:* www.hhcsinc.com, pg 123

Host Publications, 1000 E Seventh St, Suite 201, Austin, TX 78702 *Tel:* 512-236-1290 *Fax:* 512-236-1208 *Web Site:* www.hostpublications.com, pg 123

Firman Houghton Prize, 2 Farrar St, Cambridge, MA 02138 *Tel:* 617-744-6034 *E-mail:* contests@nepoetryclub.org *Web Site:* www.nepoetryclub.org, pg 710

Houghton Mifflin Harcourt, 222 Berkeley St, Boston, MA 02116-3764 *Tel:* 617-351-5000 *Toll Free Tel:* 800-225-5425 (Pre-K-8); 800-462-6595 (6–12; Advanced & Electives); 800-289-4490 (Specialized Curriculum: Great Source, Rigby, Saxon, Steck-Vaughn; Homeschool; Adult Ed); 800-323-9540 (Assessment: Riverside Publishing); 888-391-3245 (SkillsTutor); 888-242-6747 option 2 (Destination Series; Classroom Connect; Earobics; Edmark; Learning Village; Riverdeep); 800-225-3362 (Houghton Mifflin Harcourt Trade & Reference Publishers); 800-225-5800 (Heinemann) *Fax:* 617-351-1125 *Web Site:* www.hmhco.com, pg 123

Houghton Mifflin Harcourt K-12 Publishers, 222 Berkeley St, Boston, MA 02116-3764 *Tel:* 617-351-5000 *Toll Free Tel:* 800-225-5425 (cust serv) *Web Site:* www.hmhco.com; www.hmheducation.com, pg 123

Houghton Mifflin Harcourt Trade & Reference Division, 222 Berkeley St, Boston, MA 02116-3764 *Tel:* 617-351-5000 *Toll Free Tel:* 800-225-3362 *Web Site:* www.houghtonmifflinbooks.com, pg 123

House of Anansi Press Ltd, 110 Spadina Ave, Suite 801, Toronto, ON M5V 2K4, Canada *Tel:* 416-363-4343 *Fax:* 416-363-1017 *E-mail:* customerservice@houseofanansi.com *Web Site:* www.anansi.ca, pg 509

House of Collectibles, 1745 Broadway, New York, NY 10019 *Tel:* 212-782-9000 *Fax:* 212-572-4997 *Web Site:* www.houseofcollectibles.randomhouse.com; www.randomhouse.com, pg 124

House to House Publications, 11 Toll Gate Rd, Lititz, PA 17543 *Tel:* 717-627-1996 *Toll Free Tel:* 800-848-5892 *Fax:* 717-627-4004 *E-mail:* h2hp@dcfi.org *Web Site:* www.h2hp.com; www.dcfi.org, pg 124

Housing Assistance Council, 1025 Vermont Ave NW, Suite 606, Washington, DC 20005 *Tel:* 202-842-8600 *Fax:* 202-347-3441 *E-mail:* hac@ruralhome.org *Web Site:* www.ruralhome.org, pg 124

How to be Published Workshops, PO Box 100031, Birmingham, AL 35210 *Web Site:* www.writing2sell.com, pg 669

Howard Books, 216 Centerview Dr, Suite 303, Brentwood, TN 37027 *Tel:* 615-873-2080 *Fax:* 615-370-3834 *E-mail:* howardbooks@simonandschuster.com (info) *Web Site:* www.howardpublishing.com, pg 124

Amelia Frances Howard-Gibbon Illustrator's Award, 1150 Morrison Dr, Suite 400, Ottawa, ON K2H 8S9, Canada *Tel:* 613-232-9625 *Fax:* 613-563-9895 *E-mail:* info@cla.ca *Web Site:* www.cla.ca, pg 710

Tom Howard/John H Reid Short Story Contest, 351 Pleasant St, PMB 222, Northampton, MA 01060-3961 *Tel:* 413-320-1847 *Toll Free Tel:* 866-WINWRIT (946-9748) *Fax:* 413-280-0539 *Web Site:* www.winningwriters.com, pg 710

Tom Howard/Margaret Reid Poetry Contest, 351 Pleasant St, PMB 222, Northampton, MA 01060-3961 *Tel:* 413-320-1847 *Toll Free Tel:* 866-WINWRIT (946-9748) *Fax:* 413-280-0539 *Web Site:* www.winningwriters.com, pg 710

Howard University Press, 2225 Georgia Ave NW, Suite 718, Washington, DC 20059 *Tel:* 202-238-2570 *Fax:* 202-588-9849 *E-mail:* howardupress@howard.edu *Web Site:* www.hupress.howard.edu, pg 124

C D Howe Institute, 67 Yonge St, Suite 300, Toronto, ON M5E 1J8, Canada *Tel:* 416-865-1904 *Fax:* 416-865-1866 *E-mail:* cdhowe@cdhowe.org *Web Site:* www.cdhowe.org, pg 509

Julia Ward Howe Book Awards, 45 Pine Crest Rd, Newton, MA 02459 *Tel:* 617-552-8457 *E-mail:* bostonauthors@aol.com *Web Site:* www.bostonauthorsclub.org, pg 710

HPBooks, 375 Hudson St, New York, NY 10014 *Tel:* 212-366-2000 *E-mail:* online@penguinputnam.com *Web Site:* www.penguinputnam.com; us.penguingroup.com, pg 125

HRD Press, 22 Amherst Rd, Amherst, MA 01002-9709 *Tel:* 413-253-3488 *Toll Free Tel:* 800-822-2801 *Fax:* 413-253-3490 *E-mail:* info@hrdpress.com; customerservice@hrdpress.com *Web Site:* www.hrdpress.com, pg 125

L Ron Hubbard's Writers of the Future Contest, PO Box 1630, Los Angeles, CA 90078 *Tel:* 323-466-3310 *Fax:* 323-466-6474 *E-mail:* contests@authorservicesinc.com *Web Site:* www.writersofthefuture.com, pg 711

Hudson Hills Press LLC, 3556 Main St, Manchester, VT 05254 *Tel:* 802-362-6450 *Fax:* 802-362-6459 *E-mail:* artbooks@hudsonhills.com; editorial@hudsonhills.com (submissions) *Web Site:* www.hudsonhills.com, pg 125

Hudson Institute, 1015 15 St NW, 6th fl, Washington, DC 20005 *Tel:* 202-974-2400 *Toll Free Tel:* 888-554-1325 (bookstore inquiries) *Fax:* 202-974-2410 *E-mail:* info@hudson.org *Web Site:* www.hudson.org, pg 125

Hudson Park Press, 232 Madison Ave, Rm 1400, New York, NY 10016 *Tel:* 212-929-8898 *Fax:* 212-208-0946, pg 125

Monica Hughes Award for Science Fiction & Fantasy, 40 Orchard View Blvd, Suite 217, Toronto, ON M4R 1B9, Canada *Tel:* 416-975-0010 *Fax:* 416-975-8970 *E-mail:* info@bookcentre.ca *Web Site:* www.bookcentre.ca, pg 711

Lynda Hull Memorial Poetry Prize, College of Charleston, Dept of English, 66 George St, Charleston, SC 29424 *Tel:* 843-953-7740 *Fax:* 843-953-7740 *E-mail:* crazyhorse@cofc.edu *Web Site:* www.crazyhorsejournal.org, pg 711

Human Kinetics Inc, 1607 N Market St, Champaign, IL 61820 *Tel:* 217-351-5076 *Toll Free Tel:* 800-747-4457 *Fax:* 217-351-1549 (orders/cust serv) *E-mail:* info@hkusa.com *Web Site:* www.humankinetics.com, pg 125

Human Rights Watch, 350 Fifth Ave, 34th fl, New York, NY 10118-3299 *Tel:* 212-290-4700 *Fax:* 212-736-1300 *E-mail:* hrwnyc@hrw.org *Web Site:* www.hrw.org, pg 125

Humanix Books LLC, PO Box 20989, West Palm Beach, FL 33416 *Tel:* 561-459-5997 *Toll Free Tel:* 855-371-7810 *Fax:* 561-241-6448 *Toll Free Fax:* 855-371-7809 *E-mail:* info@humanixbooks.com *Web Site:* www.humanixbooks.com, pg 125

Nancy Humpheys Wordmaps, 600 Humboldt St, Richmond, CA 94805 *Tel:* 415-462-1844 *Web Site:* www.wordmapsindexing.com (book indexing); www.authormaps.com (book marketing), pg 548

Hungry? City Guides, 714 W Olympic Blvd, Suite 934, Los Angeles, CA 90015 *Fax:* 213-749-2080 *Web Site:* www.hungryguides.com, pg 125

Hunter House Publishers, 1515 1/2 Park St, Alameda, CA 94501 *Tel:* 510-865-5282 *Toll Free Tel:* 800-266-5592 *Fax:* 510-865-4295 *E-mail:* ordering@hunterhouse.com *Web Site:* www.hunterhouse.com, pg 125

Hunter Publishing Inc, 222 Clematis St, West Palm Beach, FL 33401 *Tel:* 561-835-2022 *Web Site:* www.amazingadventures.net, pg 126

Huntington Library Press, 1151 Oxford Rd, San Marino, CA 91108 *Tel:* 626-405-2172 *Fax:* 626-585-0794 *E-mail:* booksales@huntington.org *Web Site:* www.huntington.org, pg 126

Huntington Press Publishing, 3665 Procyon St, Las Vegas, NV 89103-1907 *Tel:* 702-252-0655 *Toll Free Tel:* 800-244-2224 *Fax:* 702-252-0675 *E-mail:* sales@huntingtonpress.com *Web Site:* www.huntingtonpress.com, pg 126

Hurston/Wright Award for College Writers, 12138 Central Ave, Suite 209, Bowie, MD 20721 *Tel:* 301-459-2108 *Fax:* 301-277-1262 *E-mail:* info@hurstonwright.org *Web Site:* www.hurstonwright.org, pg 711

Hurston/Wright Legacy Awards, 12138 Central Ave, Suite 209, Bowie, MD 20721 *Tel:* 301-459-2108 *Fax:* 301-277-1262 *E-mail:* info@hurstonwright.org *Web Site:* www.hurstonwright.org, pg 711

Hurston/Wright Writer's Week, 12138 Central Ave, Suite 209, Bowie, MD 20721 *Tel:* 301-459-2108 *Fax:* 301-277-1262 *E-mail:* info@hurstonwright.org *Web Site:* www.hurstonwright.org, pg 669

Hutton Electronic Publishing, 160 N Compo Rd, Westport, CT 06880-2102 *Tel:* 203-226-2588 *Fax:* 230-226-2588 *E-mail:* huttonbooks@hotmail.com, pg 126

Hyperion, 1500 Broadway, 3rd fl, New York, NY 10036 *Tel:* 212-536-6500 *Web Site:* hyperionbooks.com, pg 126

IACP Cookbook Awards, 1100 Johnson Ferry Rd, Suite 300, Atlanta, GA 30342 *Tel:* 404-252-3663 *Fax:* 404-252-0774 *E-mail:* info@iacp.com *Web Site:* www.iacp.com, pg 711

Ibex Publishers, PO Box 30087, Bethesda, MD 20824 *Tel:* 301-718-8188 *Toll Free Tel:* 888-718-8188 *Fax:* 301-907-8707 *E-mail:* info@ibexpub.com *Web Site:* www.ibexpublishers.com, pg 126

IBFD North America Inc (International Bureau of Fiscal Documentation), 8100 Boone Blvd, Suite 210, Vienna, VA 22182 *Tel:* 703-442-7757 *Fax:* 703-442-7758 *E-mail:* americas@ibfd.org *Web Site:* www.ibfd.org, pg 126

IBPA, the Independent Book Publishers Association, 1020 Manhattan Beach Blvd, Suite 204, Manhattan Beach, CA 90266 *Tel:* 310-546-1818 *Fax:* 310-546-3939 *E-mail:* info@ibpa-online.org *Web Site:* www.ibpa-online.org, pg 624

The Ibsen Society of America, University of California, Dept of Scandinavian, 6303 Dwinelle Hall, No 2690, Berkeley, CA 94720-2690 *Tel:* 510-642-0927 *Fax:* 510-642-6220 *Web Site:* www.ibsensociety.liu.edu, pg 624

ICM/Sagalyn, 4922 Fairmont Ave, Suite 200, Bethesda, MD 20814 *Tel:* 301-718-6440 *Fax:* 301-718-6444 *E-mail:* query@sagalyn.com *Web Site:* www.sagalyn.com, pg 577

Iconografix Inc, 1830-A Hanley Rd, Hudson, WI 54016 *Tel:* 715-381-9755 *Toll Free Tel:* 800-289-3504 (orders only) *Fax:* 715-381-9756 *E-mail:* info@iconografixinc.com *Web Site:* www.iconografixinc.com, pg 126

Idaho Center for the Book, Boise State University, 1910 University Dr, Boise, ID 83725 *Tel:* 208-426-1000 *Toll Free Tel:* 800-992-8398 (outside ID) *Fax:* 208-426-1243 *Web Site:* www.lili.org/icb; www.boisestatebooks.com (orders), pg 126

The Idaho Prize for Poetry, 105 Lost Horse Lane, Sandpoint, ID 83864 *Tel:* 208-255-4410 *Fax:* 208-255-1560 *E-mail:* losthorsepress@mindspring.com *Web Site:* www.losthorsepress.org, pg 711

IDEAlliance®, 1600 Duke St, Suite 420, Alexandria, VA 22314 *Tel:* 703-837-1070 *Fax:* 703-837-1072 *E-mail:* info@idealliance.org; registrar@idealliance.org *Web Site:* www.idealliance.org, pg 624

Ideals Publications, a Guideposts Co, 2630 Elm Hill Pike, Suite 100, Nashville, TN 37214 *Toll Free Tel:* 800-586-2572 (cust serv) *Fax:* 615-781-1447 *Web Site:* www.idealsbooks.com, pg 126

Idyll Arbor Inc, 39129 264 Ave SE, Enumclaw, WA 98022 *Tel:* 360-825-7797 *Fax:* 360-825-5670 *E-mail:* sales@idyllarbor.com *Web Site:* www.idyllarbor.com, pg 127

Idyllwild Arts Summer Workshops, 52500 Temecula Dr, Idyllwild, CA 92549-0038 *Tel:* 951-659-2171 *Fax:* 951-659-4552 *E-mail:* summer@idyllwildarts.org *Web Site:* www.idyllwildarts.org, pg 669

IEEE Computer Society, 2001 "L" St NW, Suite 700, Washington, DC 20036-4928 *Tel:* 202-371-0101 *Toll Free Tel:* 800-272-6657 (memb info) *Fax:* 202-728-9614 *E-mail:* help@computer.org *Web Site:* www.computer.org, pg 127

IEEE Press, 445 Hoes Lane, Piscataway, NJ 08854 *Tel:* 732-562-3418 *Fax:* 732-562-1746 *E-mail:* pressbooks@ieee.org (proposals & info) *Web Site:* www.ieee.org/press, pg 127

IET, c/o Inspec Inc, 379 Thornall St, Edison, NJ 08837-2225 *Tel:* 732-321-5575; 732-321-5579 *Fax:* 732-321-5702 *E-mail:* iee@inspecinc.com *Web Site:* www.theiet.org/inspec, pg 127

Ignatius Press, 1348 Tenth Ave, San Francisco, CA 94122-2304 *Tel:* 415-387-2324 *Toll Free Tel:* 800-651-1531 (orders) *Fax:* 415-387-0896 *E-mail:* info@ignatius.com *Web Site:* www.ignatius.com, pg 127

IHS Jane's, 110 N Royal St, Suite 200, Alexandria, VA 22314-1651 *Tel:* 703-683-3700 *Toll Free Tel:* 800-824-0768 (sales) *Fax:* 703-836-0297 *Toll Free Fax:* 800-836-0297 *E-mail:* customercare@ihs.com *Web Site:* www.ihs.com, pg 127

IHS Press, 222 W 21 St, Suite F-122, Norfolk, VA 23517 *Toll Free Tel:* 877-447-7737 *Toll Free Fax:* 877-447-7737 *E-mail:* info@ihspress.com; tradesales@ihspress.com (wholesale sales); order@ihspress.com *Web Site:* www.ihspress.com, pg 127

Illinois State Museum Society, 502 S Spring St, Springfield, IL 62706-5000 *Tel:* 217-782-7386 *Fax:* 217-782-1254 *E-mail:* editor@museum.state.il.us *Web Site:* www.museum.state.il.us, pg 127

Illuminating Engineering Society of North America (IES), 120 Wall St, 17th fl, New York, NY 10005-4001 *Tel:* 212-248-5000 *Fax:* 212-248-5017; 212-248-5018 *E-mail:* ies@ies.org *Web Site:* www.ies.org, pg 128

Illumination Arts Publishing, 808 Sixth St S, Suite 200, Kirkland, WA 98033 *Tel:* 425-968-5097 *Fax:* 425-968-5634 *E-mail:* liteinfo@illumin.com *Web Site:* www.illumin.com, pg 128

Imagefinders Inc, 6101 Utah Ave NW, Washington, DC 20015 *Tel:* 202-244-4456 *Fax:* 202-244-3237, pg 548

Imagination Publishing Group, PO Box 1304, Dunedin, FL 34697 *Toll Free Tel:* 888-701-6481 *Fax:* 727-736-1791 *E-mail:* info@dannythedragon.com *Web Site:* www.dannythedragon.com, pg 128

Imago Press, 3710 E Edison St, Tucson, AZ 85716 *Tel:* 520-327-0540 *Web Site:* www.oasisjournal.org, pg 128

ImaJinn Books Inc, PO Box 74274, Phoenix, AZ 85087-4274 *Toll Free Tel:* 877-625-3592 *E-mail:* orders@imajinnbooks.com *Web Site:* www.imajinnbooks.com, pg 128

Immedium, 535 Rockdale Dr, San Francisco, CA 94127 *Tel:* 415-452-8546 *Fax:* 360-937-6272 *E-mail:* orders@immedium.com; sales@immedium.com *Web Site:* www.immedium.com, pg 128

John Phillip Immroth Memorial Award, 50 E Huron St, Chicago, IL 60611 *Tel:* 312-280-4223 *Toll Free Tel:* 800-545-2433 *Fax:* 312-280-4227 *E-mail:* oif@ala.org *Web Site:* www.ala.org/ifrt, pg 711

Impact Publications/Development Concepts Inc, 9104 Manassas Dr, Suite N, Manassas Park, VA 20111-5211 *Tel:* 703-361-7300 *Toll Free Tel:* 800-361-1055 (cust serv) *Fax:* 703-335-9486 *E-mail:* query@impactpublications.com *Web Site:* www.impactpublications.com; www.ishoparoundtheworld.com; www.veteransworld.com; www.middleeasttravellover.com, pg 128

Impact Publishers Inc, PO Box 6016, Atascadero, CA 93423-6016 *Tel:* 805-466-5917 (opers & admin offs) *Toll Free Tel:* 800-246-7228 (orders) *Fax:* 805-466-5919 (opers & admin offs) *E-mail:* info@impactpublishers.com *Web Site:* www.impactpublishers.com; www.bibliotherapy.com, pg 128

Imprint Publications Inc, 207 E Ohio St, Suite 377, Chicago, IL 60611 *Tel:* 773-288-0782 *Fax:* 773-288-0792 *E-mail:* imppub@aol.com *Web Site:* www.imprint-chicago.com, pg 128

Incentive Publications Inc, 2400 Crestmoor Rd, Suite 211, Nashville, TN 37215 *Tel:* 615-385-2934 *Toll Free Tel:* 800-421-2830 *Fax:* 615-385-2967 *E-mail:* comments@incentivepublications.com *Web Site:* www.incentivepublications.com, pg 128

Inclusion Press International, 47 Indian Trail, Toronto, ON M6R 1Z8, Canada *Tel:* 416-658-5363 *Fax:* 416-658-5067 *E-mail:* inclusionpress@inclusion.com *Web Site:* www.inclusion.com, pg 509

Independent Information Publications, 3357 21 St, San Francisco, CA 94110 *Tel:* 415-643-8600 *E-mail:* linda@movedoc.com *Web Site:* www.movedoc.com, pg 129

Independent Institute, 100 Swan Way, Oakland, CA 94621-1428 *Tel:* 510-632-1366 *Toll Free Tel:* 800-927-8733 *Fax:* 510-568-6040 *E-mail:* orders@independent.org *Web Site:* www.independent.org, pg 129

The Independent Publisher Book Awards, 1129 Woodmere Ave, Suite B, Traverse City, MI 49686 *Tel:* 231-933-0445 *Toll Free Tel:* 800-706-4636 *Fax:* 231-933-0448 *Web Site:* www.independentpublisher.com/ipaward.lasso, pg 711

Independent Writers of Chicago (IWOC), 28 E Jackson Bldg, Suite 1020, No W686, Chicago, IL 60604 *Toll Free Tel:* 800-804-IWOC (804-4962) *E-mail:* info@iwoc.org *Web Site:* www.iwoc.org, pg 624

IndexEmpire Indexing Services, 16740 Orville Wright Dr, Riverside, CA 92518 *Tel:* 951-697-2819 *E-mail:* indexempire@gmail.com, pg 548

Indexing by the Book, PO Box 12513, Tucson, AZ 85732 *Tel:* 520-750-8439 *E-mail:* indextran@cox.net *Web Site:* www.indexingbythebook.com, pg 548

Indiana Historical Society Press (IHS Press), 450 W Ohio St, Indianapolis, IN 46202-3269 *Tel:* 317-232-1882; 317-234-0026 (orders); 317-234-2716 (edit) *Toll Free Tel:* 800-447-1830 (orders) *Fax:* 317-234-0562 (orders); 317-233-0857 (edit) *E-mail:* ihspress@indianahistory.org; orders@indianahistory.org (orders) *Web Site:* www.indianahistory.org; shop.indianahistory.org (orders), pg 129

Indiana Review Fiction Prize, Ballantine Hall 465, 1020 E Kirkwood Ave, Bloomington, IN 47405 *Tel:* 812-855-3439 *E-mail:* inreview@indiana.edu *Web Site:* indianareview.org, pg 711

Indiana University African Studies Program, Indiana University, 221 Woodburn Hall, Bloomington, IN 47405 *Tel:* 812-855-8284 *Fax:* 812-855-6734 *E-mail:* afrist@indiana.edu *Web Site:* www.indiana.edu/~afrist, pg 129

Indiana University Press, 601 N Morton St, Bloomington, IN 47404-3797 *Tel:* 812-855-8817 *Toll Free Tel:* 800-842-6796 (orders only) *Fax:* 812-855-7931; 812-855-8507 *E-mail:* iupress@indiana.edu; iuporder@indiana.edu (orders) *Web Site:* www.iupress.indiana.edu, pg 129

Indiana University Writers' Conference, Indiana University, 464 Ballantine Hall, Dept of English, 1020 E Kirkwood Ave, Bloomington, IN 47405 *Tel:* 812-855-1877 *Fax:* 812-855-9535 *E-mail:* writecon@indiana.edu *Web Site:* www.indiana.edu/~writecon/, pg 670

Indie Publishing Contest, 1029 Jones St, San Francisco, CA 94109 *Tel:* 415-673-0939 *E-mail:* sfwriterscon@aol.com *Web Site:* www.sfwriters.org, pg 711

Indies Choice Book Awards, 333 Westchester Ave, Suite S202, White Plains, NY 10604 *Tel:* 914-406-7500 *Toll Free Tel:* 800-637-0037 *Fax:* 914-410-6297 *Web Site:* www.bookweb.org, pg 712

Individual Artist Awards, 175 W Ostend St, Suite E, Baltimore, MD 21230 *Tel:* 410-767-6555 *Fax:* 410-333-1062 *E-mail:* msac@msac.org *Web Site:* www.msac.org, pg 712

Individual Artist Fellowships, 1004 Farnam, Plaza Level, Omaha, NE 68102 *Tel:* 402-595-2122 *Toll Free Tel:* 800-341-4067 *Fax:* 402-595-2334 *Web Site:* www.nebraskaartscouncil.org, pg 712

Individual Artist Fellowships, 25 State House Sta, 193 State St, Augusta, ME 04333-0025 *Tel:* 207-287-2726 *Fax:* 207-287-2725 *Web Site:* www.mainearts.com, pg 712

Individual Artist's Fellowships in Literature, 1800 Gervais St, Columbia, SC 29201 *Tel:* 803-734-8696 *Fax:* 803-734-8526 *E-mail:* info@arts.sc.gov *Web Site:* www.southcarolinaarts.com, pg 712

Individual Excellence Awards, 30 E Broad St, 33rd fl, Columbus, OH 43215 *Tel:* 614-466-2613 *Fax:* 614-466-4494 *Web Site:* www.oac.state.oh.us, pg 712

Industrial Press Inc, 989 Avenue of the Americas, 19th fl, New York, NY 10018 *Tel:* 212-889-6330 *Toll Free Tel:* 888-528-7852 *Fax:* 212-545-8327 *E-mail:* info@industrialpress.com *Web Site:* www.industrialpress.com, pg 129

Information Age Publishing Inc, PO Box 79049, Charlotte, NC 28271-7047 *Tel:* 704-752-9125 *Fax:* 704-752-9113 *E-mail:* infoage@infoagepub.com *Web Site:* www.infoagepub.com, pg 129

Information Gatekeepers Inc, 1340 Soldiers Field Rd, Suite 2, Boston, MA 02135 *Tel:* 617-782-5033 *Toll Free Tel:* 800-323-1088 *Fax:* 617-782-5735 *E-mail:* info@igigroup.com *Web Site:* www.igigroup.com, pg 129

Information Publications Inc, 2995 Woodside Rd, Suite 400-182, Woodside, CA 94062 *Tel:* 650-568-6170 *Toll Free Tel:* 877-544-4636 *Fax:* 650-568-6150 *Toll Free Fax:* 877-544-4635 *E-mail:* info@informationpublications.com *Web Site:* www.informationpublications.com, pg 130

Information Today, Inc, 143 Old Marlton Pike, Medford, NJ 08055-8750 *Tel:* 609-654-6266 *Toll Free Tel:* 800-300-9868 (cust serv) *Fax:* 609-654-4309 *E-mail:* custserv@infotoday.com *Web Site:* www.infotoday.com, pg 130

Infosential Press, 1162 Dominion Dr W, Mobile, AL 36695 *Tel:* 251-776-5656; 251-716-8178, pg 130

Infosources Publishing, 140 Norma Rd, Teaneck, NJ 07666 *Tel:* 201-836-7072 *Web Site:* www.infosourcespub.com, pg 130

InfoWorks Development Group, 2801 Cook Creek Dr, Ann Arbor, MI 48103-8962 *Tel:* 734-327-9669 *Fax:* 734-327-9686, pg 548

Infusionmedia, 140 N Eighth St, Suite 214, The Apothecary, Lincoln, NE 68508-1353 *Tel:* 402-477-2065 *E-mail:* info@infusionmediadesign.com *Web Site:* www.infusionmediadesign.com, pg 527

Ingalls Publishing Group Inc (IPG), PO Box 2500, Banner Elk, NC 28604 *Tel:* 828-297-6884 *Fax:* 828-297-6880 *E-mail:* sales@ingallspublishinggroup.com *Web Site:* www.ingallspublishinggroup.com, pg 130

Inkwater Press, 6750 SW Franklin St, Suite A, Portland, OR 97223 *Tel:* 503-968-6777 *Fax:* 503-968-6779 *E-mail:* orders@inkwaterbooks.com *Web Site:* www.inkwaterpress.com, pg 130

Inkwell Journal Annual Fiction Competition, c/o Inkwell-Manhattanville College, 2900 Purchase St, Purchase, NY 10577 *Tel:* 914-323-7239 *Fax:* 914-323-3122 *E-mail:* inkwell@mville.edu *Web Site:* www.inkwelljournal.org, pg 712

Inkwell Journal Annual Poetry Competition, c/o Inkwell-Manhattanville College, 2900 Purchase St, Purchase, NY 10577 *Tel:* 914-323-7239 *Fax:* 914-323-3122 *E-mail:* inkwell@mville.edu *Web Site:* www.inkwelljournal.org, pg 712

InkWell Management, 521 Fifth Ave, 26th fl, New York, NY 10175 *Tel:* 212-922-3500 *Fax:* 212-922-0535 *E-mail:* info@inkwellmanagement.com; submissions@inkwellmanagement.com *Web Site:* inkwellmanagement.com, pg 577

Inner Traditions International Ltd, One Park St, Rochester, VT 05767 *Tel:* 802-767-3174 *Toll Free Tel:* 800-246-8648 *Fax:* 802-767-3726 *E-mail:* customerservice@InnerTraditions.com *Web Site:* www.InnerTraditions.com, pg 130

Innis-Gerin Medal, Walter House, 282 Somerset W, Ottawa, ON K2P 0J6, Canada *Tel:* 613-991-6990 *Fax:* 613-991-6996 *E-mail:* nominations@rsc-src.ca *Web Site:* www.rsc-src.ca, pg 712

innovativeKids®, 50 Washington St, Suite 201, Norwalk, CT 06854 *Tel:* 203-838-6400 *E-mail:* info@innovativekids.com *Web Site:* www.innovativekids.com, pg 131

InScribe Christian Writers' Fellowship (ICWF), PO Box 6201, Wetaskiwin, AB T2A 2E9, Canada *E-mail:* query@inscribe.org; inscribe.mail@gmail.com *Web Site:* www.inscribe.org, pg 625

Insight Editions, 10 Paul Dr, San Rafael, CA 94903 *Tel:* 415-526-1370 *Toll Free Tel:* 800-809-3792 *E-mail:* info@insighteditions.com *Web Site:* www.insighteditions.com, pg 131

Insomniac Press, 520 Princess Ave, London, ON N6B 2B8, Canada *Tel:* 416-504-6270 *Web Site:* www.insomniacpress.com, pg 509

The Institute for Research on Public Policy (IRPP), 1470 Peel, Suite 200, Montreal, QC H3A 1T1, Canada *Tel:* 514-985-2461 *Fax:* 514-985-2559 *E-mail:* irpp@irpp.org *Web Site:* www.irpp.org, pg 509

Institute of Continuing Legal Education, 1020 Greene St, Ann Arbor, MI 48109-1444 *Tel:* 734-764-0533 *Toll Free Tel:* 877-229-4350 *Fax:* 734-763-2412 *Toll Free Fax:* 877-229-4351 *E-mail:* icle@umich.edu *Web Site:* www.icle.org, pg 131

Institute of Environmental Sciences and Technology - IEST, 2340 S Arlington Heights Rd, Suite 100, Arlington Heights, IL 60005-4516 *Tel:* 847-981-0100 *Fax:* 847-981-4130 *E-mail:* information@iest.org *Web Site:* www.iest.org, pg 131

Institute of Governmental Studies, 109 Moses Hall, Suite 2370, Berkeley, CA 94720-2370 *Tel:* 510-642-1428 *Fax:* 510-642-3020; 510-642-5537 (orders) *E-mail:* igspress@berkeley.edu *Web Site:* www.igs.berkeley.edu, pg 131

Institute of Intergovernmental Relations, Queen's University, Robert Sutheland Hall, Rm 301, Kingston, ON K7L 3N6, Canada *Tel:* 613-533-2080 *Fax:* 613-533-6868 *E-mail:* iigr@queensu.ca *Web Site:* www.queensu.ca/iigr, pg 509

Institute of Jesuit Sources (IJS), 3601 Lindell Blvd, St Louis, MO 63108 *Tel:* 314-633-4622 *Fax:* 314-633-4623 *E-mail:* ijs@jesuitsources.com *Web Site:* www.jesuitsources.com, pg 131

Institute of Mathematical Geography, 1964 Boulder Dr, Ann Arbor, MI 48104 *Tel:* 734-975-0246 *E-mail:* image@imagenet.org *Web Site:* www.imagenet.com, pg 131

Institute of Police Technology & Management, University Ctr, 12000 Alumni Dr, Jacksonville, FL 32224-2678 *Tel:* 904-620-4786 *Fax:* 904-620-2453 *E-mail:* info@iptm.org; orders@iptm.org *Web Site:* www.iptm.org, pg 131

Institute of Psychological Research, Inc., 1304 Fleury St E, Montreal, QC H2C 1R3, Canada *Tel:* 514-382-3000 *Toll Free Tel:* 800-363-7800 *Fax:* 514-382-3007 *Toll Free Fax:* 888-382-3007 *Web Site:* www.irpcanada.com, pg 509

Institute of Public Administration of Canada, 1075 Bay St, Suite 401, Toronto, ON M5S 2B1, Canada *Tel:* 416-924-8787 *Fax:* 416-924-4992 *E-mail:* ntl@ipac.ca; ntl@iapc.ca *Web Site:* www.ipac.ca; www.iapc.ca, pg 509

Institute of Puerto Rican Culture, PO Box 9024184, San Juan, PR 00902-1484 *Tel:* 787-724-0700 *Fax:* 787-724-8393 *E-mail:* www@icp.gobierno.pr *Web Site:* www.icp.gobierno.pr, pg 712

The Institutes™, 720 Providence Rd, Suite 100, Malvern, PA 19355-3433 *Tel:* 610-644-2100 *Toll Free Tel:* 800-644-2101 *Fax:* 610-640-9576 *E-mail:* customerservice@theinstitutes.org *Web Site:* www.theinstitutes.org, pg 131

Integra Software Services Inc, 1110 Jorie Blvd, Suite 200, Oak Brook, IL 60523 *Tel:* 630-586-2579 *Fax:* 630-586-2599 *Web Site:* www.integra.co.in, pg 548

Inter-American Development Bank, 1300 New York Ave NW, Washington, DC 20577 *Tel:* 202-623-1000 *Fax:* 202-623-3096 *E-mail:* pic@iadb.org *Web Site:* www.iadb.org/pub, pg 132

Inter American Press Association (IAPA), Jules Dubois Bldg, 1801 SW Third Ave, Miami, FL 33129 *Tel:* 305-634-2465 *Fax:* 305-635-2272 *E-mail:* info@sipiapa.org *Web Site:* www.sipiapa.org, pg 625

Inter-University Consortium for Political & Social Research (ICPSR), 330 Packard St, Ann Arbor, MI 48104 *Tel:* 734-647-5000 *Fax:* 734-647-8200 *E-mail:* netmail@icpsr.umich.edu *Web Site:* www.icpsr.umich.edu, pg 132

Intercultural Development Research Association (IDRA), 5815 Callaghan Rd, Suite 101, San Antonio, TX 78228 *Tel:* 210-444-1710 *Fax:* 210-444-1714 *E-mail:* contact@idra.org *Web Site:* www.idra.org, pg 132

Intercultural Press Inc, 20 Park Plaza, Suite 610, Boston, MA 02116 *Tel:* 617-523-3801 *Toll Free Tel:* 888-273-2539 *Fax:* 617-523-3708 *E-mail:* info@interculturalpress.com *Web Site:* www.interculturalpress.com, pg 132

InterLicense Ltd, 110 Country Club Dr, Suite A, Mill Valley, CA 94941 *Tel:* 415-381-9780 *Fax:* 415-381-6485 *E-mail:* interlicense@sbcglobal.net; ilicense@aol.com, pg 577

Interlink Publishing Group Inc, 46 Crosby St, Northampton, MA 01060 *Tel:* 413-582-7054 *Toll Free Tel:* 800-238-LINK (238-5465) *Fax:* 413-582-7057 *E-mail:* info@interlinkbooks.com *Web Site:* www.interlinkbooks.com, pg 132

Intermediate Sequoyah Book Award, 300 Hardy Dr, Edmond, OK 73013 *Tel:* 405-525-5100 *Fax:* 405-525-5103 *Web Site:* www.oklibs.org, pg 712

International Association of Business Communicators (IABC), 601 Montgomery St, Suite 1900, San Francisco, CA 94111 *Tel:* 415-544-4700 *Toll Free Tel:* 800-776-4222 (US & CN) *Fax:* 415-544-4747 *E-mail:* service_center@iabc.com *Web Site:* www.iabc.com, pg 625

International Association of Crime Writers Inc, North American Branch, 328 Eighth Ave, Suite 114, New York, NY 10001 *Tel:* 212-243-8966 *Fax:* 815-361-1477 *E-mail:* info@crimewritersna.org *Web Site:* www.crimewritersna.org, pg 625

International Book Centre Inc, 2391 Auburn Rd, Shelby Township, MI 48317 *Tel:* 586-254-7230 *Fax:* 586-254-7230 *E-mail:* ibc@ibcbooks.com *Web Site:* www.ibcbooks.com, pg 132

International City/County Management Association (ICMA), 777 N Capitol St NE, Suite 500, Washington, DC 20002-4201 *Tel:* 202-289-4262 *Toll Free Tel:* 800-745-8780 *Fax:* 202-962-3500 *E-mail:* customerservice@icma.org *Web Site:* icma.org, pg 132

International Code Council Inc, 5360 Workman Mill Rd, Whittier, CA 90601-2256 *Tel:* 562-699-0541 *Toll Free Tel:* 888-422-7233 *Fax:* 562-908-5524; 562-699-8031 *E-mail:* es@icc-es.org *Web Site:* www.iccsafe.org, pg 132

International Council for Adult Education, 55 Mont-Royal Ave W, Bureau 303, Montreal, QC H2J 2S4, Canada *Tel:* 514-948-2044 *Toll Free Tel:* 877-948-2044 *Fax:* 514-948-2046 *E-mail:* icae@icea.qc.ca *Web Site:* www.icea.qc.ca, pg 625

International Council of Shopping Centers (ICSC), 1221 Avenue of the Americas, 41st fl, New York, NY 10020-1099 *Tel:* 646-728-3800 *Fax:* 732-694-1755 *E-mail:* icsc@icsc.org *Web Site:* www.icsc.org, pg 132

International Development Research Centre (IDRC), 150 Kent St, Ottawa, ON K1P 0B2, Canada *Tel:* 613-236-6163 *Fax:* 613-238-7230 *E-mail:* info@idrc.ca *Web Site:* www.idrc.ca, pg 510

International Encyclopedia Society, PO Box 519, Baldwin Place, NY 10505-0519 *Tel:* 914-962-3287 *Fax:* 914-962-3287 *Web Site:* encyclopediasociety.com, pg 625

International Entertainment Bureau, 3612 N Washington Blvd, Indianapolis, IN 46205-3592 *Tel:* 317-926-7566 *E-mail:* ieb@prodigy.net, pg 605

International Evangelism Crusades Inc, 9101 Topanga Canyon Blvd, Unit 209, Chatsworth, CA 91311-5763 *Tel:* 818-882-0039 *Fax:* 818-998-6712, pg 132

International Food Policy Research Institute, 2033 "K" St NW, Washington, DC 20006-1002 *Tel:* 202-862-5600 *Fax:* 202-467-4439 *E-mail:* ifpri@cgiar.org *Web Site:* www.ifpri.org, pg 132

International Foundation of Employee Benefit Plans, 18700 W Bluemound Rd, Brookfield, WI 53045 *Tel:* 262-786-6700 *Toll Free Tel:* 888-334-3327 *Fax:* 262-786-8780 *E-mail:* editor@ifebp.org *Web Site:* www.ifebp.org, pg 133

The International Institute of Islamic Thought, 500 Grove St, Suite 200, Herndon, VA 20170 *Tel:* 703-471-1133 *Fax:* 703-471-3922 *E-mail:* iiit@iiit.org *Web Site:* www.iiit.org, pg 133

International Latino Book Awards, 3445 Catalina Dr, Carlsbad, CA 92008 *Tel:* 760-434-1223 *Fax:* 760-434-7476 *E-mail:* jim@lbff.us *Web Site:* www.lbff.us, pg 712

International Linguistics Corp, Learnables, 12220 Blue Ridge Blvd, Suite G, Grandview, MO 64030 *Tel:* 816-765-8855 *Toll Free Tel:* 800-237-1830 (orders) *Fax:* 816-765-2855 *E-mail:* learnables@sbcglobal.net *Web Site:* www.learnables.com, pg 133

International Monetary Fund (IMF) Editorial & Publications Division, 700 19 St NW, HQ1-7-124, Washington, DC 20431 *Tel:* 202-623-7430 *Fax:* 202-623-7201 *E-mail:* publications@imf.org *Web Site:* www.imfbookstore.org, pg 133

International Poetry Competition, PO Box 8248, Atlanta, GA 31106 *E-mail:* atlanta.review@yahoo.com *Web Site:* www.atlantareview.com, pg 712

International Press of Boston Inc, 387 Somerville Ave, Somerville, MA 02143 *Tel:* 617-623-3016 *Fax:* 617-623-3101 *E-mail:* ipb-info@intlpress.com; ipb-orders@intlpress.com *Web Site:* www.intlpress.com, pg 133

International Publishers Co Inc, 235 W 23 St, New York, NY 10011 *Tel:* 212-366-9816 *Fax:* 212-366-9820 *E-mail:* service@intpubnyc.com *Web Site:* www.intpubnyc.com, pg 133

International Publishing Management Association (IPMA), 105 S Jefferson, Suite B-4, Kearney, MO 64060 *Tel:* 816-903-4762 *Fax:* 816-902-4766 *E-mail:* ipmainfo@ipma.org *Web Site:* www.ipma.org, pg 625

International Reading Association, 800 Barksdale Rd, Newark, DE 19711-3204 *Tel:* 302-731-1600 *Toll Free Tel:* 800-336-7323 (US & CN) *Fax:* 302-731-1057 *E-mail:* customerservice@reading.org *Web Site:* www.reading.org, pg 133, 625

International Reading Association Children's & Young Adult's Book Award, 800 Barksdale Rd, Newark, DE 19711-3204 *Tel:* 302-731-1600 *Toll Free Tel:* 800-336-7323 (US & CN) *Fax:* 302-731-1057 *E-mail:* committees@reading.org *Web Site:* www.reading.org, pg 712

International Research Center for Energy & Economic Development, 850 Willowbrook Rd, Boulder, CO 80302 *Tel:* 303-442-4014 *Fax:* 303-442-5042 *E-mail:* info@iceed.org *Web Site:* www.iceed.org, pg 133

International Risk Management Institute Inc, 12222 Merit Dr, Suite 1450, Dallas, TX 75251-2276 *Tel:* 972-960-7693 *Fax:* 972-371-5120 *E-mail:* info27@irmi.com *Web Site:* www.irmi.com, pg 133

International Society for Technology in Education, 180 W Eighth Ave, Suite 300, Eugene, OR 97401-2916 *Tel:* 541-302-3777 (intl) *Toll Free Tel:* 800-336-5191 (US & CN) *Fax:* 541-302-3778 *E-mail:* iste@iste.org *Web Site:* www.iste.org; www.iste.org/bookstore (orders), pg 133

International Society of Automation (ISA), 67 T W Alexander Dr, Research Triangle Park, NC 27709-0185 *Tel:* 919-549-8411 *Fax:* 919-549-8288 *E-mail:* info@isa.org *Web Site:* www.isa.org, pg 133

International Society of Weekly Newspaper Editors, Missouri Southern State University, 3950 E Newman Rd, Joplin, MO 64801-1595 *Tel:* 417-625-9736 *Fax:* 417-659-4445 *Web Site:* www.mssu.edu/iswne, pg 625

International Standard Book Numbering (ISBN) US Agency, A Cambridge Information Group Co, 630 Central Ave, New Providence, NJ 07974 *Toll Free Tel:* 877-310-7333 *Fax:* 908-219-0188 *E-mail:* isbn-san@bowker.com *Web Site:* www.isbn.org, pg 625

International Titles, 931 E 56 St, Austin, TX 78751-1724 *Tel:* 512-909-2447 *Web Site:* www.internationaltitles.com, pg 577

International Transactions Inc, 28 Alope Way, Gila, NM 88038 *Tel:* 845-373-9696 *Fax:* 480-393-5162 *E-mail:* info@intltrans.com *Web Site:* www.intltrans.com, pg 577

International Wealth Success Inc, PO Box 186, Merrick, NY 11566-0186 *Tel:* 516-766-5850 *Toll Free Tel:* 800-323-0548 *Fax:* 516-766-5919 *E-mail:* admin@iwsmoney.com *Web Site:* www.iwsmoney.com, pg 134

The International Women's Writing Guild (IWWG), 317 Madison Ave, Suite 1704, New York, NY 10017 *Tel:* 917-720-6959 *E-mail:* iwwgquestions@gmail.com *Web Site:* www.iwwg.org, pg 625

Internet Alliance (IA), 1615 L St NW, Suite 1100, Washington, DC 20036-5624 *Tel:* 202-861-2407 *Web Site:* www.internetalliance.org, pg 625

InterTech Technology Awards, 200 Deer Run Rd, Sewickley, PA 15143-2600 *Tel:* 412-259-1782 *Toll Free Tel:* 800-910-4283 (ext 782) *Fax:* 412-741-2311 *E-mail:* intertechaward@printing.org *Web Site:* www.printing.org/intertechawards, pg 713

InterVarsity Press, 430 Plaza Dr, Westmont, IL 60559-1234 *Tel:* 630-734-4000 *Toll Free Tel:* 800-843-9487 *Fax:* 630-734-4200 *E-mail:* email@ivpress.com *Web Site:* www.ivpress.com, pg 134

Interweave Press LLC, 201 E Fourth St, Loveland, CO 80537 *Tel:* 970-669-7672 *Toll Free Tel:* 800-272-2193 *Fax:* 970-667-8317 *E-mail:* interweaveservice@interweave.com *Web Site:* www.interweave.com, pg 134

The Intrepid Traveler, 152 Saltonstall Pkwy, Rear Entrance, East Haven, CT 06512 *Tel:* 203-469-0214 *Fax:* 203-469-0430 *E-mail:* admin@intrepidtraveler.com *Web Site:* www.intrepidtraveler.com, pg 134

Investigative Reporters & Editors, UMC School of Journalism, 138 Neff Annex, Columbia, MO 65211 *Tel:* 573-882-2042 *Fax:* 573-882-5431 *E-mail:* info@ire.org *Web Site:* www.ire.org, pg 625

IODE Violet Downey Book Award, 40 Orchard View Blvd, Suite 219, Toronto, ON M4R 1B9, Canada *Tel:* 416-487-4416 *Toll Free Tel:* 866-827-7428 *Fax:* 416-487-4417 *E-mail:* iodecanada@bellnet.ca *Web Site:* www.iode.ca, pg 713

Iowa Poetry Prize, 119 W Park Rd, 100 Kuhl House, Iowa City, IA 52242-1000 *Tel:* 319-335-2000 *Fax:* 319-335-2055 *E-mail:* uipress@uiowa.edu *Web Site:* www.uiowapress.org, pg 713

The Iowa Review Award, 308 EPB, Iowa City, IA 52242-1408 *E-mail:* iowa-review@uiowa.edu *Web Site:* www.iowareview.org, pg 713

The Iowa Short Fiction Award, 102 Dey House, 507 N Clinton St, Iowa City, IA 52242-1000 *Tel:* 319-335-0416 *Fax:* 319-335-0420 *Web Site:* www.uiowapress.org/authors/iowa-short-fiction.htm, pg 713

Iowa Short Fiction Awards, 119 W Park Rd, 100 Kuhl House, Iowa City, IA 52242-1000 *Tel:* 319-335-2000 *Fax:* 319-335-2055 *E-mail:* uipress@uiowa.edu *Web Site:* www.uiowapress.org, pg 713

Iowa Summer Writing Festival, University of Iowa, 215-C Seashore Hall, Iowa City, IA 52242 *Tel:* 319-335-4160 *Fax:* 319-335-4743 *E-mail:* iswfestival@uiowa.edu *Web Site:* www.continuetolearn.uiowa.edu/iswfest, pg 670

Iron Gate Publishing, PO Box 999, Niwot, CO 80544 *Tel:* 303-530-2551 *Fax:* 303-530-5273 *E-mail:* editor@irongate.com; booknews@reunionsolutions.com *Web Site:* www.irongate.com; www.reunionsolutions.com, pg 134

Irwin Law Inc, 14 Duncan St, Suite 206, Toronto, ON M5H 3G8, Canada *Tel:* 416-862-7690 *Toll Free Tel:* 888-314-9014 *Fax:* 416-862-9236 *Web Site:* www.irwinlaw.com, pg 510

ISI Books, 3901 Centerville Rd, Wilmington, DE 19807-1938 *Tel:* 302-652-4600 *Toll Free Tel:* 800-526-7022 *Fax:* 302-652-1760 *E-mail:* info@isi.org; isibooks@isi.org *Web Site:* www.isibooks.org, pg 134

Island Press, 1718 Connecticut Ave NW, Suite 300, Washington, DC 20009 *Tel:* 202-232-7933 *Toll Free Tel:* 800-828-1302 *Fax:* 202-234-1328 *E-mail:* info@islandpress.org *Web Site:* www.islandpress.org, pg 134

Italica Press, 595 Main St, Suite 605, New York, NY 10044 *Tel:* 917-371-0563 *Fax:* 212-838-7812 *E-mail:* info@italicapress.com *Web Site:* www.italicapress.com, pg 134

ITMB Publishing Ltd, 12300 Bridgeport Rd, Richmond, BC V6V 1J5, Canada *Tel:* 604-273-1400 *Fax:* 604-273-1488 *E-mail:* itmb@itmb.com *Web Site:* www.itmb.com, pg 510

iUniverse, 1663 Liberty Dr, Bloomington, IN 47403 *Toll Free Tel:* 800-AUTHORS (288-4677) *Fax:* 812-355-4085 *Web Site:* www.iuniverse.com, pg 135

Richard Ivey School of Business, University of Western Ontario, 1151 Richmond St N, London, ON N6A 3K7, Canada *Tel:* 519-661-3206 *Toll Free Tel:* 800-649-6355 *Fax:* 519-661-3485 *E-mail:* cases@ivey.uwo.ca *Web Site:* www.iveycases.com; www.ivey.uwo.ca, pg 510

The Ivy League of Artists Inc, 7 Coventry Rd, Livingston, NJ 07039-5105 *Tel:* 973-992-4048 *Fax:* 973-992-4049 *E-mail:* ilartists@aol.com, pg 602

J de S Associates Inc, 9 Shagbark Rd, South Norwalk, CT 06854 *Tel:* 203-838-7571 *Fax:* 203-866-2713 *Web Site:* www.jdesassociates.com, pg 578

JABberwocky Literary Agency Inc, 24-16 Queens Plaza S, Suite 505, Long Island City, NY 11101-6250 *Tel:* 718-392-5985 *Fax:* 718-392-5987 *Web Site:* www.awfulagent.com, pg 578

Jackie White Memorial National Children's Playwriting Contest, 309 Parkade Blvd, Columbia, MO 65202 *Tel:* 573-874-5628 *Web Site:* www.cectheatre.org, pg 713

Joseph Henry Jackson Literary Award, One Embarcadero Ctr, Suite 1400, San Francisco, CA 94111 *Tel:* 415-733-8500 *Fax:* 415-477-2783 *E-mail:* info@sff.org *Web Site:* www.sff.org, pg 713

Melanie Jackson Agency LLC, 41 W 72 St, Suite 3F, New York, NY 10023 *Tel:* 212-873-3373 *Fax:* 212-799-5063, pg 578

Jain Publishing Co, PO Box 3523, Fremont, CA 94539 *Tel:* 510-659-8272 *Fax:* 510-659-0501 *E-mail:* mail@jainpub.com *Web Site:* www.jainpub.com, pg 135

James Peter Associates Inc, PO Box 358, New Canaan, CT 06840 *Tel:* 203-972-1070 *Web Site:* www.jamespeterassociates.com, pg 578

J Franklin Jameson Fellowship in American History, 400 "A" St SE, Washington, DC 20003-3889 *Tel:* 202-544-2422 *Fax:* 202-544-8307 *E-mail:* awards@historians.org *Web Site:* www.historians.org, pg 713

Jamestown Prize, Swem Library, Ground fl, 400 Landrum Dr, Williamsburg, VA 23185 *Tel:* 757-221-1114 *Fax:* 757-221-1047 *E-mail:* ieahc1@wm.edu *Web Site:* oieahc.wm.edu, pg 713

Jan Williams Indexing Services, 300 Dartmouth College Hwy, Lyme, NH 03768-3207 *Tel:* 603-795-4924 *Fax:* 603-795-4836 *Web Site:* www.janwilliamsindexing.com, pg 548

Janklow & Nesbit Associates, 445 Park Ave, New York, NY 10022 *Tel:* 212-421-1700 *Fax:* 212-980-3671 *E-mail:* info@janklow.com *Web Site:* www.janklowandnesbit.com, pg 578

Janus Literary Agency, 201 Washington St, Groveland, MA 01834 *Tel:* 978-273-4227 *E-mail:* janusliteraryagency@gmail.com *Web Site:* janusliteraryagency.blogspot.com, pg 578

Japan-US Friendship Commission Translation Prize, Columbia University, 507 Kent Hall, MC3920, New York, NY 10027 *Tel:* 212-854-5036 *Fax:* 212-854-4019 *Web Site:* www.keenecenter.org, pg 714

JayJo Books LLC, 303 Crossways Park Dr, Woodbury, NY 11797 *Tel:* 516-496-8492 *Toll Free Tel:* 800-999-6884 *Fax:* 516-496-4050 *Toll Free Fax:* 800-262-1886 *E-mail:* jayjobooks@guidance-group.com *Web Site:* www.guidance-group.com; www.jayjo.com, pg 135

Jefferson Cup Award, c/o Virginia Library Association (VLA), PO Box 56312, Virginia Beach, VA 23456 *Tel:* 757-689-0594 *Fax:* 757-447-3478 *Web Site:* www.vla.org, pg 714

Jellinek & Murray Literary Agency, 47-231 Kamakoi Rd, Kaneohe, HI 96744 *Tel:* 808-239-8451, pg 578

Jenkins Group Inc, 1129 Woodmere Ave, Suite B, Traverse City, MI 49686 *Tel:* 231-933-0445 *Toll Free Tel:* 800-706-4636 *Fax:* 231-933-0448 *E-mail:* info@bookpublishing.com *Web Site:* www.bookpublishing.com, pg 549

Carolyn Jenks Agency, 69 Aberdeen Ave, Cambridge, MA 02138 *Tel:* 617-354-5099 *E-mail:* carolynjenks@comcast.net *Web Site:* www.carolynjenksagency.com, pg 578

Jentel Artist Residency Program, 130 Lower Piney Rd, Banner, WY 82832 *Tel:* 307-737-2311 *Fax:* 307-737-2305 *E-mail:* jentel@jentelarts.org *Web Site:* www.jentelarts.org, pg 670

Jerome Award, 205 W Monroe, Suite 314, Chicago, IL 60606-5061 *Tel:* 312-739-1776; 312-739-1776 *Toll Free Tel:* 855-739-1776 *Fax:* 312-739-1778; 312-739-1778 *E-mail:* cla2@cathla.org *Web Site:* www.cathla.org, pg 714

Jerome Fellowship, 2301 Franklin Ave E, Minneapolis, MN 55406-1099 *Tel:* 612-332-7481 *Fax:* 612-332-6037 *E-mail:* info@pwcenter.org *Web Site:* www.pwcenter.org, pg 714

JET Literary Associates Inc, 941 Calle Mejia, Suite 507, Santa Fe, NM 87501 *Tel:* 212-971-2494 (NY voice mail); 505-780-0721 *E-mail:* query@jetliterary.com *Web Site:* www.jetliterary.wordpress.com, pg 578

Jewel Box Theatre Playwriting Competition, 3700 N Walker, Oklahoma City, OK 73118-7031 *Tel:* 405-521-1786 *Web Site:* jewelboxtheatre.org, pg 714

Jewish Book Council, 520 Eighth Ave, 4th fl, New York, NY 10018 *Tel:* 212-201-2920 *Fax:* 212-532-4952 *E-mail:* jbc@jewishbooks.org *Web Site:* www.jewishbookcouncil.org, pg 625

Jewish Lights Publishing, Sunset Farm Offices, Rte 4, Woodstock, VT 05091 *Tel:* 802-457-4000 *Toll Free Tel:* 800-962-4544 (orders only) *Fax:* 802-457-4004 *E-mail:* sales@jewishlights.com *Web Site:* www.jewishlights.com, pg 135

Jewish Publication Society, 2100 Arch St, 2nd fl, Philadelphia, PA 19103 *Tel:* 215-832-0600 *Toll Free Tel:* 800-234-3151 *Fax:* 215-568-2017 *E-mail:* jewishbook@jps.org *Web Site:* www.jps.org, pg 135

JFE Editorial, 8425 Doreen Ave, Fort Worth, TX 76116-4922 *Tel:* 817-560-7018 *Web Site:* www.jfe-editorial.com, pg 549

Jhpiego, 1615 Thames St, Baltimore, MD 21231-3492 *Tel:* 410-537-1800 *Fax:* 410-537-1473 *E-mail:* info@jhpiego.net; orders@jhpiego.net *Web Site:* www.jhpiego.org, pg 135

The Jim Henson Co, 1416 N La Brea Ave, Hollywood, CA 90028 *Tel:* 323-802-1500 *Fax:* 323-802-1825 *Web Site:* www.henson.com, pg 135

JIST Publishing, 875 Montreal Way, St Paul, MN 55102 *Tel:* 317-613-4200 *Toll Free Tel:* 800-328-1452 *Toll Free Fax:* 800-328-4564 *E-mail:* educate@emcp.com *Web Site:* jist.emcpublishingllc.com, pg 135

JL Communications, 10205 Green Holly Terr, Silver Spring, MD 20902 *Tel:* 301-593-0640, pg 549

JMW Group Inc, One West Ave, Suite 219, Larchmont, NY 10538 *Tel:* 914-834-7800 *Fax:* 914-834-7824 *E-mail:* info@jmwgroup.net *Web Site:* jmwgroup.net, pg 578

Jody Rein Books Inc, 7741 S Ash Ct, Centennial, CO 80122 *Tel:* 303-694-9386 *Web Site:* www.jodyreinbooks.com, pg 578

John Deere Publishing, 5440 Corporate Park Dr, Davenport, IA 52807 *Tel:* 309-765-4951 *Toll Free Tel:* 800-522-7448 (orders) *Fax:* 563-355-3690; 309-748-4083 *E-mail:* johndeerepublishing@johndeere.com *Web Site:* www.deere.com, pg 136

The Johns Hopkins University Press, 2715 N Charles St, Baltimore, MD 21218-4363 *Tel:* 410-516-6900; 410-516-6987 (journals outside US & CN) *Toll Free Tel:* 800-537-5487 (book orders & cust serv); 800-548-1784 (journal orders) *Fax:* 410-516-6968; 410-516-3866 (journal orders) *E-mail:* hfscustserv@press.jhu.edu (cust serv); jrnlcirc@press.jhu.edu (journal orders) *Web Site:* www.press.jhu.edu; muse.jhu.edu/about/subscriptions/index.html (Project Muse subns), pg 136

Johnson Books, 3005 Center Green Dr, Suite 225, Boulder, CO 80301 *Tel:* 303-443-9766 *Toll Free Tel:* 800-258-5830 *Fax:* 303-443-9687 *E-mail:* books@bigearthpublishing.com *Web Site:* www.bigearthpublishing.com; www.johnsonbooks.com, pg 136

Cliff Johnson & Associates, 10867 Fruitland Dr, Studio City, CA 91604 *Tel:* 818-761-5665 *Fax:* 818-761-9501 *E-mail:* quest543@yahoo.com, pg 549

Jonathan David Publishers Inc, 68-22 Eliot Ave, Middle Village, NY 11379 *Tel:* 718-456-8611 *Fax:* 718-894-2818 *E-mail:* info@jdbooks.com; customerservice@jdbooks.com *Web Site:* www.jdbooks.com, pg 136

Jones & Bartlett Learning LLC, 5 Wall St, Burlington, MA 01803 *Tel:* 978-443-5000 *Toll Free Tel:* 800-832-0034 *Fax:* 978-443-8000 *E-mail:* info@jblearning.com *Web Site:* www.jblearning.com, pg 136

Anson Jones MD Award, 401 W 15 St, Austin, TX 78701 *Tel:* 512-370-1300 *Fax:* 512-370-1630 *Web Site:* www.texmed.org, pg 714

Jones Hutton Literary Associates, 160 N Compo Rd, Westport, CT 06880-2102 *Tel:* 203-226-2588 *Fax:* 203-226-2588 *E-mail:* huttonbooks@hotmail.com, pg 579

Jesse H Jones Award, PO Box 609, Round Rock, TX 78680 *Tel:* 512-683-5640 *E-mail:* tilsecretary@yahoo.com *Web Site:* www.texasinstituteofletters.org, pg 714

Jones McClure Publishing, 3131 Eastside St, Suite 300, Houston, TX 77098 *Tel:* 713-335-8200 *Toll Free Tel:* 800-626-6667 *Fax:* 713-335-8201 *E-mail:* comments@jonesmcclure.com *Web Site:* www.jonesmcclure.com, pg 137

Joshua Tree Publishing, 1016 W Jackson Blvd, Suite 500, Chicago, IL 60607 *Tel:* 312-893-7525 *E-mail:* info@joshuatreepublishing.com *Web Site:* www.joshuatreepublishing.com; www.centaurbooks.com (imprint); www.chiralhouse.com (imprint), pg 137

Jossey-Bass, One Montgomery St, Suite 1200, San Francisco, CA 94104 *Tel:* 415-433-1740 *Toll Free Tel:* 800-956-7739 *Fax:* 415-433-0499 (edit/mktg) *Web Site:* www.josseybass.com; www.pfeiffer.com, pg 137

Journal of Roman Archaeology LLC, 95 Peleg Rd, Portsmouth, RI 02871 *Tel:* 401-683-1955 *Fax:* 401-683-1975 *E-mail:* jra@journalofromanarch.com *Web Site:* www.journalofromanarch.com, pg 137

Jouve North America Inc, 70 Landmark Hill Dr, Brattleboro, VT 05301 *Tel:* 802-254-6073 *Toll Free Tel:* 800-451-4328 *Web Site:* www.jouve.com, pg 549

Joy Publishing Co, PO Box 9901, Fountain Valley, CA 92708 *Tel:* 714-545-4321 *Toll Free Tel:* 800-454-8228 *Fax:* 714-708-2099 *Web Site:* www.joypublishing.com; www.kit-cat.com, pg 137

Joyce Media Inc, 3413 Soledad Canyon Rd, Acton, CA 93510-1974 *Tel:* 661-269-1169 *Fax:* 661-269-2139 *E-mail:* help@joycemediainc.com *Web Site:* www.joycemediainc.com, pg 137

Judah, Sarah, Grace & Tom Memorial, 1194 Hume Rd, Hume, VA 22639-1806 *E-mail:* poetryinva@aol.com *Web Site:* www.poetrysocietyofvirginia.org, pg 714

Judaica Press Inc, 123 Ditmas Ave, Brooklyn, NY 11218 *Tel:* 718-972-6200 *Toll Free Tel:* 800-972-6201 *Fax:* 718-972-6204 *E-mail:* info@judaicapress.com; orders@judaicapress.com *Web Site:* www.judaicapress.com, pg 137

Judson Press, 588 N Gulph Rd, King of Prussia, PA 19406 *Toll Free Tel:* 800-458-3766 *Fax:* 610-768-2107 *Web Site:* www.judsonpress.com, pg 137

Jump at the Sun, 114 Fifth Ave, New York, NY 10011 *Tel:* 212-633-4400 *Fax:* 212-633-4809 *Web Site:* disney.go.com, pg 137

Jungle Wagon Press, 5116 Didier Ave, Rockford, IL 61101 *Tel:* 815-988-9048 *E-mail:* junglewagonpress@gmail.com *Web Site:* www.junglewagonpress.com, pg 137

Juniper Prize for Fiction, East Experiment Sta, 671 N Pleasant St, Amherst, MA 01003 *Tel:* 413-545-2217 *Fax:* 413-545-1226 *E-mail:* info@umpress.umass.edu *Web Site:* www.umass.edu/umpress; www.umass.edu/umpress/juniper_fiction.html (description); www.umass.edu/umpress/juniper_fiction_guidelines.html, pg 714

Juniper Prize for Poetry, East Experiment Sta, 671 N Pleasant St, Amherst, MA 01003 *Tel:* 413-545-2217 *Fax:* 413-545-1226 *E-mail:* info@umpress.umass.edu *Web Site:* www.umass.edu/umpress, pg 714

Juniper Summer Writing Institute, c/o University Conference Services, 810 Campus Ctr, One Campus Ctr Way, Amherst, MA 01003 *Tel:* 413-545-5510 *E-mail:* juniperinstitute@hfa.umass.edu *Web Site:* www.umass.edu/juniperinstitute, pg 670

Just Creative Writing & Indexing Services (JCR), 301 Wood Duck Dr, Greensboro, MD 21639 *Tel:* 410-482-6337 *E-mail:* jreveal@verizon.net; jreveal@justcreativewriting.com *Web Site:* www.justcreativewriting.com, pg 549

JustUs & Associates, 1420 NW Gilman Blvd, Suite 2154, Issaquah, WA 98027-7001 *Tel:* 425-392-0897 *E-mail:* sales@horary.com *Web Site:* www.horary.com, pg 138

Juvenile Literary Awards/Young People's Literature Awards, 506 Rose Ave, Des Plaines, IL 60016 *Tel:* 847-827-8339 *Web Site:* www.fawchicago.org, pg 714

Kabbalah Publishing, 1100 S Robertson Blvd, Los Angeles, CA 90035 *Tel:* 310-601-1039; 310-657-7957 *E-mail:* kcla@kabbalah.com; customerservice@kabbalahpublishing.com *Web Site:* www.kabbalah.com; www.kabbalahpublishing.com, pg 138

Kaeden Corp, PO Box 16190, Rocky River, OH 44116-0190 *Tel:* 440-617-1400 *Toll Free Tel:* 800-890-7323 *Fax:* 440-617-1403 *E-mail:* info@kaeden.com *Web Site:* www.kaeden.com, pg 138

Frederick D Kagy Education Award of Excellence, 200 Deer Run Rd, Sewickley, PA 15143-2600 *Tel:* 412-259-1705 *Toll Free Tel:* 800-910-4283 (ext 705) *Fax:* 412-749-9890 *E-mail:* printing@printing.org *Web Site:* www.printing.org, pg 715

Kamehameha Publishing, 567 S King St, Suite 118, Honolulu, HI 96813 *Toll Free Tel:* 800-523-6200 *Fax:* 808-541-5305 *E-mail:* publishing@ksbe.edu *Web Site:* kamehamehapublishing.org, pg 138

Kane Miller Books, 4901 Morena Blvd, Suite 213, San Diego, CA 92117 *E-mail:* info@kanemiller.com *Web Site:* www.kanemiller.com, pg 138

Kane Press Inc, 350 Fifth Ave, Suite 7206, New York, NY 10118-7200 *Tel:* 212-268-1435 *E-mail:* info@kanepress.com *Web Site:* www.kanepress.com, pg 138

Kaplan Publishing, 395 Hudson St, 4th fl, New York, NY 10014 *Tel:* 212-618-2400 *Toll Free Tel:* 888-KAPLAN8 (527-5268) *Fax:* 917-344-2499 *Toll Free Fax:* 877-712-5487 *E-mail:* book.support@kaplan.com *Web Site:* www.kaplanpublishing.com, pg 138

Sharon Kapnick, 185 West End Ave, New York, NY 10023-5547 *Tel:* 212-787-7231, pg 549

Kapp Books LLC, 3602 Rocky Meadow Ct, Fairfax, VA 22033 *Tel:* 703-261-9171 *Fax:* 703-621-7162 *E-mail:* info@kappbooks.com *Web Site:* www.kappbooks.com, pg 138

Kar-Ben Publishing, 241 First Ave N, Minneapolis, MN 55401 *Tel:* 612-332-3344 *Toll Free Tel:* 800-4-KARBEN (452-7236) *Fax:* 612-332-7615 *Toll Free Fax:* 800-332-1132 *Web Site:* www.karben.com, pg 138

The Karpfinger Agency, 357 W 20 St, New York, NY 10011-3379 *Tel:* 212-691-2690 *Fax:* 212-691-7129 *E-mail:* info@karpfinger.com *Web Site:* www.karpfinger.com, pg 579

Kazi Publications Inc, 3023 W Belmont Ave, Chicago, IL 60618 *Tel:* 773-267-7001 *Fax:* 773-267-7002 *E-mail:* info@kazi.org *Web Site:* www.kazi.org, pg 138

Ezra Jack Keats/Kerlan Memorial Fellowship, University of Minnesota, 113 Andersen Library, 222 21 Ave S, Minneapolis, MN 55455 *Tel:* 612-624-4576 *Fax:* 612-626-0377 *E-mail:* clrc@umn.edu *Web Site:* www.ezra-jack-keats.org; special.lib.umn.edu/clrc, pg 715

Keim Publishing, 66 Main St, Suite 807, Yonkers, NY 10701 *Tel:* 917-655-7190, pg 549

J J Keller & Associates, Inc, 3003 Breezewood Lane, Neenah, WI 54957 *Tel:* 920-722-2848 *Toll Free Tel:* 877-564-2333 *Toll Free Fax:* 800-727-7516 *E-mail:* sales@jjkeller.com *Web Site:* www.jjkeller.com/jjk, pg 139

Keller Media Inc, 578 Washington Blvd, No 745, Marina del Rey, CA 90292 *Toll Free Tel:* 800-278-8706 *E-mail:* query@kellermedia.com *Web Site:* kellermedia.com/query, pg 579

Joan Kelly Memorial Prize in Women's History, 400 "A" St SE, Washington, DC 20003-3889 *Tel:* 202-544-2422 *Fax:* 202-544-8307 *E-mail:* awards@historians.org *Web Site:* www.historians.org, pg 715

Kelsey Street Press, 2824 Kelsey St, Berkeley, CA 94705 *Tel:* 510-845-2260 *Fax:* 510-548-9185 *E-mail:* info@kelseyst.com *Web Site:* www.kelseyst.com, pg 139

Kendall/Hunt Publishing Co, 4050 Westmark Dr, Dubuque, IA 52002-2624 *Tel:* 563-589-1000 *Toll Free Tel:* 800-228-0810 (orders) *Fax:* 563-589-1046 *Toll Free Fax:* 800-772-9165 *E-mail:* orders@kendallhunt.com *Web Site:* www.kendallhunt.com, pg 139

Kennedy Information Inc, One Phoenix Mill Lane, 3rd fl, Peterborough, NH 03458 *Tel:* 603-924-0900; 603-924-1006 *Toll Free Tel:* 800-531-0007 *Fax:* 603-924-4460 *E-mail:* bookstore@kennedyinfo.com; customerservice@kennedyinfo.com *Web Site:* www.kennedyinfo.com, pg 139

Robert F Kennedy Book Awards, 1300 19 St NW, Suite 750, Washington, DC 20036 *Tel:* 202-463-7575 *Fax:* 202-463-6606 *E-mail:* info@rfkcenter.org *Web Site:* www.rfkcenter.org, pg 715

Kensington Publishing Corp, 119 W 40 St, New York, NY 10018 *Tel:* 212-407-1500 *Toll Free Tel:* 800-221-2647 *Fax:* 212-935-0699 *Web Site:* www.kensingtonbooks.com, pg 139

Kent State University Press, 1118 University Library Bldg, 1125 Risman Dr, Kent, OH 44242 *Tel:* 330-672-7913; 419-281-1802 *Fax:* 330-672-3104 *E-mail:* ksupress@kent.edu *Web Site:* www.kentstateuniversitypress.com, pg 139

Kentucky Women Writers Conference, 232 E Maxwell St, Lexington, KY 40506-0344 *Tel:* 859-257-2874 *E-mail:* kentuckywomenwriters@gmail.com *Web Site:* www.uky.edu/wwk, pg 670

Kentucky Writers Conference, 1906 College Heights Blvd, Suite 11067, Bowling Green, KY 42101-1067 *Tel:* 270-745-4502 *Web Site:* www.sokybookfest.org, pg 670

Natasha Kern Literary Agency Inc, PO Box 1069, White Salmon, WA 98672 *Tel:* 509-493-3803 *E-mail:* agent@natashakern.com *Web Site:* www.natashakern.com, pg 579

Kessinger Publishing LLC, PO Box 1404, Whitefish, MT 59937 *E-mail:* books@kessingerpub.com *Web Site:* www.kessinger.net, pg 140

Kessler Communications, 280 W 86 St, New York, NY 10024 *Tel:* 212-724-8610 *E-mail:* lmp@etk.mailbolt.com *Web Site:* www.kesslercommunications.com, pg 549

Jascha Kessler, 218 16 St, Santa Monica, CA 90402-2216 *Tel:* 310-393-7968 *Fax:* 310-393-7968 (by request only) *E-mail:* jkessler@ucla.edu *Web Site:* www.jfkessler.com; www.xlibris.com, pg 549

Louise B Ketz Agency, 414 E 78 St, Suite 1-B, New York, NY 10075 *Tel:* 212-249-0668 *E-mail:* ketzagency@aol.com, pg 579

Key Curriculum, A McGraw-Hill Education Company, 1150 65 St, Emeryville, CA 94608 *Tel:* 510-595-7000 *Toll Free Tel:* 800-995-6284 *Fax:* 510-595-7040 (orders) *Toll Free Fax:* 800-541-2442 *Web Site:* www.keycurriculum.com, pg 140

Key West Literary Seminar, 718 Love Lane, Key West, FL 33040 *Toll Free Tel:* 888-293-9291 *E-mail:* mail@kwls.org *Web Site:* www.kwls.org, pg 670

Virginia Kidd Agency Inc, PO Box 278, 538 E Harford St, Milford, PA 18337 *Tel:* 570-296-6205 *Web Site:* vk-agency.com, pg 579

Kids Can Press Ltd, 25 Dockside Dr, Toronto, ON M5A 0B5, Canada *Tel:* 416-479-7000 *Toll Free Tel:* 800-265-0884 *Fax:* 416-960-5437 *E-mail:* info@kidscan.com; customerservice@kidscan.com *Web Site:* www.kidscanpress.com; www.kidscanpress.ca, pg 510

Kidsbooks LLC, 312 Stuart St, Boston, MA 02116 *Tel:* 617-425-0300 *Fax:* 617-425-0232 *E-mail:* sales@kidsbooks.com; customerservice@kidsbooks.com *Web Site:* www.kidsbooks.com, pg 140

Kimberley Cameron & Associates, 1550 Tiburon Blvd, Suite 704, Tiburon, CA 94920 *Tel:* 415-789-9191 *Fax:* 415-789-9177 *E-mail:* info@kimberleycameron.com *Web Site:* www.kimberleycameron.com, pg 579

Kindred Productions, 1310 Taylor Ave, Winnipeg, MB R3M 3Z6, Canada *Tel:* 204-669-6575 *Toll Free Tel:* 800-545-7322 *Fax:* 204-654-1865 *E-mail:* custserv@kindredproductions.com *Web Site:* www.kindredproductions.com, pg 510

Coretta Scott King Book Awards, ALA Office for Literacy & Outreach Services, 50 E Huron St, Chicago, IL 60611 *Tel:* 312-280-4295; 312-280-4294 *Toll Free Tel:* 800-545-2433 *Fax:* 312-280-3256 *E-mail:* olos@ala.org *Web Site:* www.ala.org/csk, pg 715

Jessica Kingsley Publishers Inc, 400 Market St, Suite 400, Philadelphia, PA 19106 *Tel:* 215-922-1161 *Toll Free Tel:* 866-416-1078 (cust serv) *Fax:* 215-922-1474 *E-mail:* orders@jkp.com *Web Site:* www.jkp.com, pg 140

Kinship Books, 781 Rte 308, Rhinebeck, NY 12572 *Tel:* 845-876-5840 (orders) *E-mail:* kinshipbooks@cs.com *Web Site:* www.kinshipny.com, pg 140

Kirchoff/Wohlberg Inc, 897 Boston Post Rd, Madison, CT 06443 *Tel:* 203-245-7308 *Fax:* 203-245-3218 *Web Site:* www.kirchoffwohlberg.com, pg 579

Kirk House Publishers, PO Box 390759, Minneapolis, MN 55439 *Tel:* 952-835-1828 *Toll Free Tel:* 888-696-1828 *Fax:* 952-835-2613 *E-mail:* publisher@kirkhouse.com *Web Site:* www.kirkhouse.com, pg 140

Kirkbride Bible Co Inc, 1102 Deloss St, Indianapolis, IN 46203 *Tel:* 317-633-1900 *Toll Free Tel:* 800-428-4385 *Fax:* 317-633-1444 *E-mail:* sales@kirkbride.com; info@kirkbride.com *Web Site:* www.kirkbride.com, pg 140

Kiva Publishing Inc, 10 Bella Loma, Santa Fe, NM 87506 *Tel:* 909-896-0518 *E-mail:* kivapub@aol.com *Web Site:* www.kivapub.com, pg 140

Harvey Klinger Inc, 300 W 55 St, Suite 11-V, New York, NY 10019 *Tel:* 212-581-7068 *Fax:* 212-315-3823 *E-mail:* queries@harveyklinger.com *Web Site:* www.harveyklinger.com, pg 580

Klutz, 450 Lambert Ave, Palo Alto, CA 94306 *Tel:* 650-857-0888 *Toll Free Tel:* 800-737-4123 *Fax:* 650-857-9110 *E-mail:* thefolks@klutz.com *Web Site:* www.klutz.com, pg 140

Wolters Kluwer Law & Business, 76 Ninth Ave, 7th fl, New York, NY 10011-5201 *Tel:* 212-771-0600 *Toll Free Tel:* 800-234-1660 (cust serv); 800-638-8437 (orders); 800-317-3113 (bookstore sales) *Toll Free Fax:* 800-901-9075 (cust serv); 800-561-4845 (bookstore sales) *Web Site:* www.aspenpublishers.com, pg 141

Kneerim, Williams & Bloom Agency, 90 Canal St, Boston, MA 02114 *Tel:* 617-303-1650 *Web Site:* www.kwlit.com, pg 580

The Knight Agency Inc, 570 East Ave, Madison, GA 30650 *E-mail:* submissions@knightagency.net *Web Site:* www.knightagency.net, pg 580

The Knight-Risser Prize for Western Environmental Journalism, Stanford University, 450 Serra Mall, Bldg 120, Rm 424, Stanford, CA 94305 *Tel:* 650-721-5955 *Fax:* 650-725-6154 *E-mail:* knightrisserprize@lists.stanford.edu *Web Site:* knightrisser.stanford.edu, pg 715

Theodore Knight PhD, RockCliff Farm, Unit 101A, 40 Old Louisquisset Pike, North Smithfield, RI 02896 *Tel:* 401-597-6982 *E-mail:* tedknight1@cox.net, pg 549

Knightville Poetry Contest, PO Box 866, Wells, ME 04094 *E-mail:* info@newguardreview.com *Web Site:* www.newguardreview.com, pg 715

Allen A Knoll Publishers, 200 W Victoria St, 2nd fl, Suite A, Santa Barbara, CA 93101-3627 *Tel:* 805-564-3377 *Toll Free Tel:* 800-777-7623 *Fax:* 805-966-6657 *E-mail:* bookinfo@knollpublishers.com *Web Site:* www.knollpublishers.com, pg 141

Alfred A Knopf/Everyman's Library, c/o Random House Inc, 1745 Broadway, New York, NY 10019 *Tel:* 212-751-2600 *Toll Free Tel:* 800-638-6460 *Fax:* 212-572-2593 *Web Site:* www.knopfdoubleday.com, pg 141

Knopf Random Canada, One Toronto St, Suite 300, Toronto, ON M5C 2V6, Canada *Tel:* 416-364-4449 *Toll Free Tel:* 888-523-9292 *Fax:* 416-364-6863 *Web Site:* www.randomhouse.ca, pg 510

Kodansha USA Inc, 451 Park Ave S, 7th fl, New York, NY 10016 *Tel:* 917-322-6200 *Fax:* 212-935-6929 *E-mail:* info@kodansha-usa.com *Web Site:* www.kodansha-intl.com, pg 141

Bill Koehnlein, 236 E Fifth St, New York, NY 10003-8545 *Tel:* 212-674-9145 *E-mail:* koehnlein.bill@gmail.com, pg 549

E M Koeppel Short Fiction Award, PO Box 140310, Gainesville, FL 32614 *Tel:* 352-338-7778 *E-mail:* contact@writecorner.com *Web Site:* www.writecorner.com, pg 715

Barry R Koffler, Featherside, 14 Ginger Rd, High Falls, NY 12440 *Tel:* 845-687-9851 *E-mail:* barkof@feathersite.com, pg 549

Kogan Page Publishers, 1518 Walnut St, Suite 1100, Philadelphia, PA 19102 *Tel:* 215-928-9112 *Fax:* 215-928-9113 *E-mail:* info@koganpage.com *Web Site:* www.koganpageusa.com, pg 141

Paul Kohner Agency, 9300 Wilshire Blvd, Suite 555, Beverly Hills, CA 90212 *Tel:* 310-550-1060 *Fax:* 310-276-1083, pg 580

Koho Pono LLC, 15024 SE Pinegrove Loop, Clackamas, OR 97015 *Tel:* 503-723-7392 *Toll Free Tel:* 800-937-8000 (orders) *Toll Free Fax:* 800-876-0186 (orders) *E-mail:* info@kohopono.com; orders@ingrambook.com *Web Site:* kohopono.com, pg 141

KOK Edit, 15 Hare Lane, East Setauket, NY 11733-3606 *Tel:* 631-474-1170 *Fax:* 631-474-9849 *E-mail:* editor@kokedit.com *Web Site:* www.kokedit.com; twitter.com/#!/KOKEdit; www.facebook.com/K.OMooreKlopf; www.linkedin.com/in/kokedit; www.editor-mom.blogspot.com, pg 549

Konecky & Konecky LLC, 72 Ayers Point Rd, Old Saybrook, CT 06475 *Tel:* 860-388-0878 *Fax:* 860-388-0273 *Web Site:* www.koneckyandkonecky.com, pg 142

Linda Konner Literary Agency, 10 W 15 St, Suite 1918, New York, NY 10011 *Tel:* 212-691-3419 *Fax:* 212-691-0935 *Web Site:* www.lindakonnerliteraryagency.com, pg 580

Elaine Koster Literary Agency LLC, 55 Central Park West, Suite 6, New York, NY 10023 *Tel:* 212-362-9488 *Fax:* 212-712-0164, pg 580

KotaPress, 135 Pony Soldier Rd, Sedona, AZ 86336-4613 *Tel:* 928-225-5416 *E-mail:* info@kotapress.com *Web Site:* kotapress.com, pg 142

Barbara S Kouts Literary Agency LLC, PO Box 560, Bellport, NY 11713 *Tel:* 631-286-1278 *Fax:* 631-286-1538 *E-mail:* bkouts@aol.com, pg 580

Katherine Singer Kovacs Prize, 26 Broadway, 3rd fl, New York, NY 10004-1789 *Tel:* 646-576-5141 *Fax:* 646-458-0030 *E-mail:* awards@mla.org *Web Site:* www.mla.org, pg 715

Kraft & Kraft, 40 Memorial Hwy, Apt 23-C, New Rochelle, NY 10801 *Tel:* 914-319-3320 *Web Site:* www.erickraft.com, pg 549

Eileen Kramer, 336 Great Rd, Stow, MA 01775 *Tel:* 978-897-4121 *E-mail:* kramer@tiac.net *Web Site:* www.ekramer.com, pg 549

H J Kramer Inc, PO Box 1082, Tiburon, CA 94920 *Tel:* 415-884-2100 (ext 10) *Toll Free Tel:* 800-972-6657 *Fax:* 415-435-5364 *E-mail:* hjkramer@jps.net *Web Site:* www.hjkramer.com; www.newworldlibrary.com, pg 142

Michael Kraus Research Grant in History, 400 "A" St SE, Washington, DC 20003-3889 *Tel:* 202-544-2422 *Fax:* 202-544-8307 *E-mail:* awards@historians.org *Web Site:* www.historians.org, pg 715

Krause Publications Inc, 700 E State St, Iola, WI 54990 *Tel:* 715-445-2214 *Toll Free Tel:* 800-258-0929 (cust serv); 888-457-2873 (orders) *Fax:* 715-445-4087 *E-mail:* bookorders@krause.com *Web Site:* www.krausebooks.com, pg 142

Kregel Publications, 733 Wealthy St SE, Grand Rapids, MI 49503-5553 *Tel:* 616-451-4775 *Toll Free Tel:* 800-733-2607 *Fax:* 616-451-9330 *E-mail:* kregelbooks@kregel.com *Web Site:* www.kregel.com, pg 142

Stuart Krichevsky Literary Agency Inc, 381 Park Ave South, Suite 428, New York, NY 10016 *Tel:* 212-725-5288 *Fax:* 212-725-5275 *E-mail:* query@skagency.com *Web Site:* skagency.com, pg 581

Krieger Publishing Co, 1725 Krieger Dr, Malabar, FL 32950 *Tel:* 321-724-9542 *Toll Free Tel:* 800-724-0025 *Fax:* 321-951-3671 *E-mail:* info@krieger-publishing.com *Web Site:* www.krieger-publishing.com, pg 142

Eddie Kritzer Productions, 1112 Montana Ave, Suite 449, Santa Monica, CA 90403 *Tel:* 310-702-5356 *Fax:* 310-394-5770 *E-mail:* producedby@aol.com *Web Site:* eddiekritzer.com, pg 605

The Robert Kroetsch City of Edmonton Book Prize, 11759 Groat Rd, Edmonton, AB T5M 3K6, Canada *Tel:* 780-422-8174 *Toll Free Tel:* 800-665-5354 (AB only) *Fax:* 780-422-2663 (attn WGA) *E-mail:* mail@writersguild.ab.ca *Web Site:* www.writersguild.ab.ca, pg 716

Edite Kroll Literary Agency Inc, 20 Cross St, Saco, ME 04072 *Tel:* 207-283-8797 *Fax:* 207-283-8799, pg 581

Lynn C Kronzek & Richard A Flom, 145 S Glenoaks Blvd, Suite 240, Burbank, CA 91502 *Tel:* 818-768-7688 *Fax:* 818-768-7648, pg 550

KTAV Publishing House Inc, 888 Newark Ave, Jersey City, NJ 07306 *Tel:* 201-963-9524 *Fax:* 201-963-0102 *E-mail:* orders@ktav.com *Web Site:* www.ktav.com, pg 142

Kumarian Press, 1800 30 St, Suite 314, Boulder, CO 80301 *Tel:* 303-444-6684 *Toll Free Tel:* 800-232-0223 (orders only) *Fax:* 303-444-0824 *E-mail:* questions@rienner.com *Web Site:* www.kpbooks.com, pg 142

Polly Kummel, 624 Boardman Rd, Aiken, SC 29803 *Tel:* 803-641-6831 *E-mail:* editor@amazinphrasin.com; pollyk1@msn.com *Web Site:* www.amazinphrasin.com, pg 550

Kumon Publishing North America, 300 Frank Burr Blvd, Suite 6, Teaneck, NJ 07666 *Tel:* 201-836-2105 *Fax:* 201-836-1559 *E-mail:* books@kumon.com *Web Site:* www.kumonbooks.com, pg 142

Kumu Kahua/UHM Theatre & Dance Department Playwriting Contest, 46 Merchant St, Honolulu, HI 96813 *Tel:* 808-536-4441 (box off); 808-536-4222 *Fax:* 808-536-4226 *E-mail:* kumukahuatheatre@hawaiiantel.net *Web Site:* www.kumukahua.org, pg 716

George Kurian Reference Books, PO Box 519, Baldwin Place, NY 10505-0519 *Tel:* 914-962-3287 *Fax:* 914-962-3287, pg 142

L & L Dreamspell, 376 W Quarry Rd, London, TX 76854 *Tel:* 281-703-2405 *E-mail:* publishing@lldreamspell.com *Web Site:* www.lldreamspell.com, pg 143

The LA Literary Agency, PO Box 46370, Los Angeles, CA 90046 *Tel:* 323-654-5288 *E-mail:* laliteraryagency@mac.com; mail@laliteraryagency.com *Web Site:* www.laliteraryagency.com, pg 581

LaChance Publishing LLC, 120 Bond St, Brooklyn, NY 11217 *Tel:* 917-855-7537 *Fax:* 646-390-1326 *E-mail:* info@lachancepublishing.com *Web Site:* www.lachancepublishing.com, pg 143

Lachina Publishing Services Inc, 3793 S Green Rd, Cleveland, OH 44122 *Tel:* 216-292-7959 *Fax:* 216-292-3639 *E-mail:* info@lachina.com *Web Site:* www.lachina.com, pg 550

Lynne Lackenbach Editorial Services, 31 Pillsbury Rd, East Hampstead, NH 03826 *Tel:* 603-329-8133 *E-mail:* lynnelack@gmail.com, pg 550

LadybugPress, 16964 Columbia River Dr, Sonora, CA 95370 *Tel:* 209-694-8340 *Toll Free Tel:* 888-892-5000 *Fax:* 209-694-8916 *E-mail:* ladybugpress@ladybugbooks.com *Web Site:* www.ladybugbooks.com, pg 143

Lake Claremont Press, 1026 W Van Buren St, 2nd fl, Chicago, IL 60607 *Tel:* 312-226-8400 *Fax:* 312-226-8420 *E-mail:* lcp@lakeclaremont.com *Web Site:* www.lakeclaremont.com, pg 143

Lake Superior Port Cities Inc, 310 E Superior St, Suite 125, Duluth, MN 55802 *Tel:* 218-722-5002 *Toll Free Tel:* 888-BIG-LAKE (244-5253) *Fax:* 218-722-4096 *E-mail:* reader@lakesuperior.com *Web Site:* www.lakesuperior.com, pg 143

LAMA Books, 2381 Sleepy Hollow Ave, Hayward, CA 94545-3429 *Tel:* 510-785-1091 *Toll Free Tel:* 888-452-6244 *Fax:* 510-785-1099 *Web Site:* www.lamabooks.com, pg 143

W Kaye Lamb Award, PO Box 5254, Sta B, Victoria, BC V8R 6N4, Canada *E-mail:* info@bchistory.ca *Web Site:* www.bchistory.ca, pg 716

Lambda Literary Awards (Lammys), 5482 Wilshire Blvd, Suite 1595, Los Angeles, CA 90036 *Tel:* 213-568-3570 *Fax:* 213-568-3570 *E-mail:* info@lambdaliterary.org *Web Site:* www.lambdaliterary.org, pg 716

Peter Lampack Agency Inc, 350 Fifth Ave, Suite 5300, New York, NY 10118 *Tel:* 212-687-9106 *Fax:* 212-687-9109 *Web Site:* peterlampackagency.com, pg 581

Gerald Lampert Memorial Award, 192 Spadina Ave, Suite 312, Toronto, ON M5T 2C2, Canada *Tel:* 416-504-1657 *Fax:* 416-504-0096 *E-mail:* readings@poets.ca *Web Site:* www.poets.ca, pg 716

Lanahan Publishers Inc, 324 Hawthorne Rd, Baltimore, MD 21210-2303 *Tel:* 410-366-2434 *Toll Free Tel:* 866-345-1949 *Fax:* 410-366-8798 *Toll Free Fax:* 888-345-7257 *E-mail:* info@lanahanpublishers.com *Web Site:* www.lanahanpublishers.com, pg 143

Land on Demand, 20 Long Crescent Dr, Bristol, VA 24201 *Tel:* 276-642-0550 *E-mail:* landondemand@bvunet.net *Web Site:* boblandedits.blogspot.com, pg 550

Landauer Corp, 3100 101 St, Suite A, Urbandale, IA 50322 *Tel:* 515-287-2144 *Toll Free Tel:* 800-557-2144 *Fax:* 515-276-5102 *E-mail:* info@landauercorp.com *Web Site:* www.landauercorp.com, pg 143

Landes Bioscience, 1806 Rio Grande St, Austin, TX 78701 *Tel:* 512-637-6050 *Toll Free Tel:* 800-736-9948 *Fax:* 512-637-6079 *E-mail:* info@landesbioscience.com *Web Site:* www.landesbioscience.com, pg 143

Peter Lang Publishing Inc, 29 Broadway, 18th fl, New York, NY 10006-3223 *Tel:* 212-647-7706 *Toll Free Tel:* 800-770-5264 (cust serv) *Fax:* 212-647-7707 *Web Site:* www.peterlang.com, pg 143

LangMarc Publishing, PO Box 90488, Austin, TX 78709-0488 *Tel:* 512-394-0989 *Toll Free Tel:* 800-864-1648 (orders) *Fax:* 512-394-0829 *E-mail:* langmarc@booksails.com *Web Site:* www.langmarc.com, pg 143

Langum Prize in American Legal History or Biography, 2809 Berkeley Dr, Birmingham, AL 35242 *Tel:* 205-726-2424 *Fax:* 205-726-4216 *E-mail:* langumtrust@gmail.com *Web Site:* www.langumtrust.org, pg 716

Langum Prize in Historical Fiction, 2809 Berkeley Dr, Birmingham, AL 35242 *Tel:* 205-726-2424 *Fax:* 205-726-4216 *Web Site:* www.langumtrust.org, pg 716

Lantern Books, 128 Second Place, Garden Suite, Brooklyn, NY 11231 *Tel:* 212-414-2275 *E-mail:* editorial@lanternbooks.com; info@lanternmedia.net *Web Site:* www.lanternbooks.com, pg 144

Laredo Publishing Co Inc, 465 Westview Ave, Englewood, NJ 07631 *Tel:* 201-408-4048 *Fax:* 201-408-5011 *E-mail:* info@laredopublishing.com *Web Site:* www.laredopublishing.com, pg 144

Lark Crafts, 67 Broadway, Asheville, NC 28801 *Tel:* 828-253-0467 *Fax:* 828-253-7952 *E-mail:* info@larkbooks.com *Web Site:* www.larkcrafts.com; www.larkbooks.com, pg 144

Michael Larsen/Elizabeth Pomada Literary Agents, 1029 Jones St, San Francisco, CA 94109 *Tel:* 415-673-0939 *E-mail:* larsenpoma@aol.com *Web Site:* www.larsenpomada.com, pg 581

Larson Publications, 4936 State Rte 414, Burdett, NY 14818 *Tel:* 607-546-9342 *Toll Free Tel:* 800-828-2197 *Fax:* 607-546-9344 *E-mail:* custserv@larsonpublications.com *Web Site:* www.larsonpublications.com, pg 144

Lasaria Creative Publishing, 4094 Majestic Lane, Suite 352, Fairfax, VA 22033 *E-mail:* submissions@lasariacreative.com *Web Site:* www.lasariacreative.com, pg 144

Latin American Literary Review Press, PO Box 17660, Pittsburgh, PA 15235-0860 *Tel:* 412-824-7903 *Fax:* 412-824-7909 *E-mail:* lalrp.editor@gmail.com *Web Site:* www.lalrp.org, pg 144

Laughing Elephant, 3645 Interlake N, Seattle, WA 98103 *Tel:* 206-447-9229 *Toll Free Tel:* 800-354-0400 *Fax:* 206-447-9189 *E-mail:* support@laughingelephant.com *Web Site:* www.laughingelephant.com, pg 144

Laurier Books Ltd, PO Box 2694, Sta D, Ottawa, ON K1P 5W6, Canada *Tel:* 613-738-2163 *Fax:* 613-247-0256 *E-mail:* laurierbooks@yahoo.com, pg 511

Law School Admission Council, 662 Penn St, Newtown, PA 18940 *Tel:* 215-968-1101 *E-mail:* lsacinfo@lsac.org *Web Site:* www.lsac.org, pg 144

Law Tribune Books, 201 Ann Uccello St, 4th fl, Hartford, CT 06103 *Tel:* 860-527-7900 *Fax:* 860-527-7433 *E-mail:* lawtribune@alm.com *Web Site:* www.ctlawtribune.com, pg 144

The Lawbook Exchange Ltd, 33 Terminal Ave, Clark, NJ 07066-1321 *Tel:* 732-382-1800 *Toll Free Tel:* 800-422-6686 *Fax:* 732-382-1887 *E-mail:* law@lawbookexchange.com *Web Site:* www.lawbookexchange.com, pg 144

Lawrence Foundation Award, University of Nebraska, 123 Andrews Hall, Lincoln, NE 68588-0334 *Tel:* 402-472-0911 *Fax:* 402-472-9771 *E-mail:* jengelhardt2@unl.edu *Web Site:* prairieschooner.unl.edu, pg 716

Lawrence Foundation Prize, University of Michigan, 0576 Rackham Bldg, 915 E Washington St, Ann Arbor, MI 48109-1070 *Tel:* 734-764-9265 *E-mail:* mqr@umich.edu *Web Site:* www.umich.edu/~mqr, pg 716

Merloyd Lawrence Inc, 102 Chestnut St, Boston, MA 02108 *Tel:* 617-523-5895 *Fax:* 617-252-5285, pg 145

Lawyers & Judges Publishing Co Inc, 917 N Swan Rd, Suite 300, Tucson, AZ 85711 *Tel:* 520-323-1500 *Toll Free Tel:* 800-209-7109 *Fax:* 520-323-0055 *Toll Free Fax:* 800-330-8795 *E-mail:* sales@lawyersandjudges.com *Web Site:* www.lawyersandjudges.com, pg 145

Sarah Lazin Books, 121 W 27 St, Suite 704, New York, NY 10001 *Tel:* 212-989-5757 *Fax:* 212-989-1393 *Web Site:* lazinbooks.com, pg 581

Stephen Leacock Memorial Medal for Humour, RR2, 4223 Line 12 N, Coldwater, ON L0K 1E0, Canada *Tel:* 705-835-3218 *Fax:* 705-835-5171 *Web Site:* www.leacock.ca, pg 716

Leadership Directories, 104 Fifth Ave, 3rd fl, New York, NY 10011 *Tel:* 212-627-4140 *Fax:* 212-645-0931 *E-mail:* info@leadershipdirectories.com *Web Site:* www.leadershipdirectories.com, pg 145

Leadership Ministries Worldwide/OBR, 3755 Pilot Point, Chattanooga, TN 37416 *Tel:* 423-855-2181 *Toll Free Tel:* 800-987-8790 *Fax:* 423-855-8616 *E-mail:* info@outlinebible.org *Web Site:* www.outlinebible.org, pg 145

The League of Canadian Poets, 192 Spadina Ave, Suite 312, Toronto, ON M5T 2C2, Canada *Tel:* 416-504-1657 *Fax:* 416-504-0096 *E-mail:* readings@poets.ca *Web Site:* www.poets.ca, pg 626

League of Vermont Writers, PO Box 172, Underhill Center, VT 05490 *Tel:* 802-349-7475 *E-mail:* lvw@leaguevtwriters.org *Web Site:* www.leagueofvermontwriters.org, pg 626

League of Women Voters of the United States, 1730 "M" St NW, Suite 1000, Washington, DC 20036-4508 *Tel:* 202-429-1965 *Fax:* 202-429-0854; 202-429-4343 *E-mail:* lwv@lwv.org *Web Site:* www.lwv.org, pg 626

Leaping Dog Press/Asylum Arts Press, PO Box 90473, Raleigh, NC 27675-0473 *Tel:* 919-809-9045 *E-mail:* sales@leapingdogpress.com *Web Site:* www.leapingdogpress.com, pg 145

THE Learning Connection®, 4100 Silverstar Rd, Suite D, Orlando, FL 32808 *Tel:* 407-292-2125 *Toll Free Tel:* 800-218-8489 *Fax:* 407-292-2123 *E-mail:* tlc@tlconnection.com *Web Site:* www.tlconnection.com, pg 145

Learning Links Inc, PO Box 326, Cranbury, NJ 08512 *Tel:* 516-437-9071 *Toll Free Tel:* 800-724-2616 *Fax:* 516-437-5392 *E-mail:* info@learninglinks.com *Web Site:* www.learninglinks.com, pg 145

The Learning Source Ltd, 644 Tenth St, Brooklyn, NY 11215 *Tel:* 718-768-0231 (ext 10) *Fax:* 718-369-3467 *E-mail:* info@learningsourceltd.com *Web Site:* www.learningsourceltd.com, pg 550

LearningExpress LLC, 2 Rector St, 26th fl, New York, NY 10006 *Tel:* 212-995-2566 *Toll Free Tel:* 800-295-9556 (ext 2) *Fax:* 212-995-5512 *E-mail:* customerservice@learningexpressllc.com (cust serv) *Web Site:* www.learningexpressllc.com, pg 145

The Ned Leavitt Agency, 70 Wooster St, Suite 4-F, New York, NY 10012 *Tel:* 212-334-0999 *Web Site:* www.nedleavittagency.com, pg 581

Lectorum Publications Inc, 205 Chubb Ave, Lyndhurst, NJ 07071 *Toll Free Tel:* 800-345-5946 *Fax:* 201-559-2201 *Toll Free Fax:* 877-532-8676 *E-mail:* lectorum@lectorum.com *Web Site:* www.lectorum.com, pg 145

Lederer Books, 6120 Day Long Lane, Clarksville, MD 21029 *Tel:* 410-531-6644 *Toll Free Tel:* 800-410-7367 (orders) *Fax:* 717-761-7273 *E-mail:* lederer@messianicjewish.net; customerservice@messianicjewish.net *Web Site:* www.messianicjewish.net, pg 146

The Ledge Press Fiction Awards Competition, 40 Maple Ave, Bellport, NY 11713 *E-mail:* info@theledgemagazine.com *Web Site:* theledgemagazine.com, pg 716

The Ledge Press Poetry Awards Competition, 40 Maple Ave, Bellport, NY 11713 *E-mail:* info@theledgemagazine.com *Web Site:* theledgemagazine.com, pg 717

The Ledge Press Poetry Chapbook Competition, 40 Maple Ave, Bellport, NY 11713 *E-mail:* info@theledgemagazine.com *Web Site:* theledgemagazine.com, pg 717

Lee & Low Books Inc, 95 Madison Ave, New York, NY 10016 *Tel:* 212-779-4400 *Toll Free Tel:* 888-320-3190 (ext 28, orders only) *Fax:* 212-683-1894 (orders only); 212-532-6035 *E-mail:* general@leeandlow.com *Web Site:* www.leeandlow.com, pg 146

Left Coast Press Inc, 1630 N Main St, Suite 400, Walnut Creek, CA 94596 *Tel:* 925-935-3380 *Fax:* 925-935-2916 *E-mail:* explore@lcoastpress.com *Web Site:* www.lcoastpress.com, pg 146

Lehigh University Press, B-040 Christmas-Saucon Hall, 14 E Packer Ave, Bethlehem, PA 18015 *Tel:* 610-758-3933 *Fax:* 610-758-6331 *E-mail:* inlup@lehigh.edu *Web Site:* inpress.sites.lehigh.edu, pg 146

Leilah Publications, PO Box 1863, Tempe, AZ 85280-1863 *Tel:* 480-241-4120 *E-mail:* leilah@leilahpublications.com *Web Site:* leilahpublications.com, pg 146

Leisure Arts Inc, 5701 Ranch Dr, Little Rock, AR 72223 *Tel:* 501-868-8800 *Toll Free Tel:* 800-643-8030 *Fax:* 501-868-8748 *Web Site:* www.leisurearts.com, pg 146

Waldo G Leland Prize, 400 "A" St SE, Washington, DC 20003-3889 *Tel:* 202-544-2422 *Fax:* 202-544-8307 *E-mail:* awards@historians.org *Web Site:* www.historians.org, pg 717

Vincent Lemieux Prize, 260 rue Dalhousie St, Suite 204, Ottawa, ON K1N 7E4, Canada *Tel:* 613-562-1202 *Fax:* 613-241-0019 *E-mail:* cpsa-acsp@cpsa-acsp.ca *Web Site:* www.cpsa-acsp.ca, pg 717

Lemon Grove Press, 1158 26 St, Suite 502, Santa Monica, CA 90403 *Tel:* 310-471-1740 *Fax:* 310-476-7627 *E-mail:* info@lemongrovepress.com *Web Site:* www.thetakechargepatient.com, pg 528

Debra Lemonds, PO Box 5516, Pasadena, CA 91117-0516 *Tel:* 626-844-9363 *E-mail:* dlemonds@earthlink.net, pg 550

The Lentz Leadership Institute, 9065 Big Plantation Ave, Las Vegas, NV 89143 *Tel:* 702-719-9214 *Toll Free Fax:* 877-298-5172 *E-mail:* orders@lentzleadership.com *Web Site:* www.lentzleadership.com; www.refractivethinker.com, pg 146

Leopold-Hidy Award, 701 William Vickers Ave, Durham, NC 27701-3162 *Tel:* 919-682-9319 *Fax:* 919-682-2349 *Web Site:* www.foresthistory.org, pg 717

Elizabeth J Leppman, 631 Worcester Dr, Lexington, KY 40503 *Tel:* 859-245-4325 *Fax:* 859-245-4325 *E-mail:* ejleppman@windstream.net *Web Site:* www.leppman.com, pg 550

Lerner Publications, 241 First Ave N, Minneapolis, MN 55401 *Tel:* 612-332-3344 *Toll Free Tel:* 800-328-4929 *Fax:* 612-332-7615 *Toll Free Fax:* 800-332-1132 *E-mail:* info@lernerbooks.com *Web Site:* www.lernerbooks.com, pg 146

Lerner Publishing Group Inc, 241 First Ave N, Minneapolis, MN 55401 *Tel:* 612-332-3344 *Toll Free Tel:* 800-328-4929 *Fax:* 612-332-7615 *Toll Free Fax:* 800-332-1132 *E-mail:* info@lernerbooks.com *Web Site:* www.lernerbooks.com, pg 146

LernerClassroom, 241 First Ave N, Minneapolis, MN 55401 *Tel:* 612-332-3344 *Toll Free Tel:* 800-328-4929 *Fax:* 612-332-7615 *Toll Free Fax:* 800-332-1132 *E-mail:* info@lernerbooks.com *Web Site:* www.lernerbooks.com, pg 147

Lessiter Publications, 225 Regency Ct, Suite 200, Brookfield, WI 53045 *Tel:* 262-782-4480 *Toll Free Tel:* 800-645-8455 *Fax:* 262-782-1252 *E-mail:* info@lesspub.com *Web Site:* www.lesspub.com, pg 147

Letterbox/Papyrus of London Publishers USA, 10501 Broom Hill Dr, Suite 1-F, Las Vegas, NV 89134-7339 *Tel:* 702-256-3838 *E-mail:* lb27383@cox.net, pg 147

Level 4 Press Inc, 13518 Jamul Dr, Jamul, CA 91935-1635 *Fax:* 619-374-7311 *E-mail:* sales@level4press.com *Web Site:* www.level4press.com, pg 147

Fenia & Yaakov Leviant Memorial Prize in Yiddish Studies, 26 Broadway, 3rd fl, New York, NY 10004-1789 *Tel:* 646-576-5141 *Fax:* 646-458-0030 *E-mail:* awards@mla.org *Web Site:* www.mla.org, pg 717

Harry Levin Prize, University of South Carolina, Dept of Languages, Literature & Cultures, Rm 813-A, 1620 College St, Columbia, SC 29208 *Tel:* 803-777-3021 *Fax:* 803-777-3041 *E-mail:* info@acla.org *Web Site:* www.acla.org, pg 717

Levine|Greenberg Literary Agency Inc, 307 Seventh Ave, Suite 2407, New York, NY 10001 *Tel:* 212-337-0934 *Fax:* 212-337-0948 *Web Site:* www.levinegreenberg.com, pg 581

Levinson Prize, 444 N Michigan Ave, Suite 1850, Chicago, IL 60611-4034 *Tel:* 312-787-7070 *Fax:* 312-787-6650 *E-mail:* editors@poetrymagazine.org *Web Site:* poetryfoundation.org, pg 717

Levis Reading Prize, PO Box 842005, Richmond, VA 23284-2005 *Tel:* 804-828-1331 *Fax:* 804-828-8684 *Web Site:* www.has.vcu.edu/eng/resources/levis_prize.htm, pg 717

Levy Creative Management LLC, 425 E 58 St, Suite 37F, New York, NY 10022 *Tel:* 212-687-6463 *Fax:* 212-661-4839 *E-mail:* info@levycreative.com *Web Site:* www.levycreative.com, pg 602

Lexington Books, 4501 Forbes Blvd, Suite 200, Lanham, MD 20706 *Tel:* 301-459-3366 *Fax:* 301-429-5749 *Web Site:* www.lexingtonbooks.com, pg 147

LexisNexis®, 701 E Water St, Charlottesville, VA 22902 *Tel:* 434-972-7600 *Toll Free Tel:* 800-446-3410 *Fax:* 434-961-5576 *E-mail:* customer.support@lexisnexis.com *Web Site:* www.lexisnexis.com, pg 147

LexisNexis Canada Inc, 123 Commerce Valley Dr E, Suite 700, Markham, ON L3T 7W8, Canada *Tel:* 905-479-2665 *Toll Free Tel:* 800-668-6481; 800-387-0899 (cust serv) *Fax:* 905-479-2826 *Toll Free Fax:* 800-461-3275 *E-mail:* orders@lexisnexis.ca; service@lexisnexis.ca (cust serv) *Web Site:* www.lexisnexis.ca, pg 511

LexisNexis/Martindale-Hubbell, 121 Chanlon Rd, New Providence, NJ 07974 *Tel:* 908-464-6800 *Toll Free Tel:* 800-526-4902 *Fax:* 908-464-3553 *E-mail:* info@martindale.com *Web Site:* www.martindale.com, pg 147

LexisNexis® Matthew Bender®, 1275 Broadway, Albany, NY 12204 *Tel:* 518-487-3000 *Toll Free Tel:* 800-424-4200 *Fax:* 518-487-3083 *Web Site:* bender.lexisnexis.com, pg 148

Liberty Fund Inc, 8335 Allison Pointe Trail, Suite 300, Indianapolis, IN 46250-1684 *Tel:* 317-842-0880 *Toll Free Tel:* 800-955-8335; 800-866-3520; 800-368-7897 ext 6069 (cust serv) *Fax:* 317-577-9067; 317-579-6060 (cust serv); 708-534-7803 *E-mail:* books@libertyfund.org; info@libertyfund.org *Web Site:* www.libertyfund.org, pg 148

Libraries Unlimited, 130 Cremona Dr, Santa Barbara, CA 93117 *Tel:* 805-968-1911 *Toll Free Tel:* 800-368-6868 *Fax:* 805-685-9685 *Toll Free Fax:* 866-270-3856 *E-mail:* customerservice@abc-clio.com *Web Site:* www.abc-clio.com; www.abc-clio.com, pg 148

Library Association of Alberta (LAA), 80 Baker Crescent NW, Calgary, AB T2L 1R4, Canada *Tel:* 403-284-5818 *Toll Free Tel:* 877-522-5550 *Fax:* 403-282-6646 *E-mail:* info@laa.ca *Web Site:* www.laa.ca, pg 626

Library Binding Institute, 4440 PGA Blvd, Suite 600, Palm Beach Gardens, FL 33410 *Tel:* 561-745-6821 *Fax:* 561-472-8401 *E-mail:* info@lbibinders.org *Web Site:* www.lbibinders.org, pg 626

The Library of America, 14 E 60 St, New York, NY 10022-1006 *Tel:* 212-308-3360 *Fax:* 212-750-8352 *E-mail:* info@loa.org *Web Site:* www.loa.org, pg 148

Library of American Broadcasting, University of Maryland, Hornbake Library, College Park, MD 20742 *Tel:* 301-405-9160 *Fax:* 301-314-2634 *E-mail:* labcast@umd.edu *Web Site:* www.lib.umd.edu/LAB, pg 626

Library of Virginia, 800 E Broad St, Richmond, VA 23219-8000 *Tel:* 804-692-3999; 804-692-3500 *Fax:* 804-692-3736 *Web Site:* www.lva.virginia.gov, pg 148

Lidec Inc, 4350 Ave de l'Hotel-de-Ville, Montreal, QC H2W 2H5, Canada *Tel:* 514-843-5991 *Toll Free Tel:* 800-350-5991 (CN only) *Fax:* 514-843-5252 *E-mail:* lidec@lidec.qc.ca *Web Site:* www.lidec.qc.ca, pg 511

Robert Lieberman Agency, 475 Nelson Rd, Ithaca, NY 14850 *Tel:* 607-273-8801 *Web Site:* www.kewgardensmovie.com/CUPeople/users/rhl10, pg 582

Mary Ann Liebert Inc, 140 Huguenot St, 3rd fl, New Rochelle, NY 10801-5215 *Tel:* 914-740-2100 *Toll Free Tel:* 800-654-3237 *Fax:* 914-740-2101 *E-mail:* info@liebertpub.com *Web Site:* www.liebertonline.com, pg 148

The Lieutenant-Governor's Awards for High Achievement in the Arts, 61 Carleton St, Fredericton, NB E3B 3T2, Canada *Tel:* 506-444-4444 *Toll Free Tel:* 866-460-ARTS (460-2787) *Fax:* 506-444-5543 *E-mail:* nbabcanb@artsnb.ca *Web Site:* www.artsnb.ca, pg 717

The Lieutenant-Governor's Medal for Historical Writing, PO Box 5254, Sta B, Victoria, BC V8R 6N4, Canada *E-mail:* writing@bchistory.ca *Web Site:* www.bchistory.ca, pg 717

Life Cycle Books, PO Box 799, Fort Collins, CO 80522 *Toll Free Tel:* 800-214-5849 *Toll Free Fax:* 888-690-8532 *E-mail:* orders@lifecyclebooks.com; support@lifecyclebooks.com *Web Site:* www.lifecyclebooks.com, pg 148

Life Cycle Books Ltd, 1085 Bellamy Rd N, Suite 20, Toronto, ON M1H 3C7, Canada *Tel:* 416-690-5860 *Toll Free Tel:* 866-880-5860 *Fax:* 416-690-8532 *Toll Free Fax:* 866-690-8532 *E-mail:* orders@lifecyclebooks.com *Web Site:* www.lifecyclebooks.com, pg 511

Light-Beams Publishing, 10 Toon Lane, Lee, NH 03861 *Tel:* 603-659-1300 *Toll Free Tel:* 800-397-7641 *E-mail:* info@light-beams.com *Web Site:* www.light-beams.com, pg 148

Light Technology Publishing, 4030 E Huntington Dr, Flagstaff, AZ 86004 *Tel:* 928-526-1345 *Toll Free Tel:* 800-450-0985 *Fax:* 928-714-1132 *E-mail:* publishing@lighttechnology.net *Web Site:* www.lighttechnology.com, pg 148

Lighthouse Publishing of the Carolinas, 2333 Barton Oaks Dr, Raleigh, NC 27614-7940 *E-mail:* lighthousepublishingcarolinas@gmail.com *Web Site:* lighthousepublishingofthecarolinas.com, pg 149

Ligonier Valley Writers Conference, PO Box B, Ligonier, PA 15658-1602 *Tel:* 724-238-3692, pg 670

Liguori Publications, One Liguori Dr, Liguori, MO 63057-1000 *Tel:* 636-464-2500 *Toll Free Tel:* 866-848-2492; 800-325-9521 *Fax:* 636-464-8449 *Web Site:* www.liguori.org, pg 149

Ruth Lilly Poetry Prize, 444 N Michigan Ave, Suite 1850, Chicago, IL 60611-4034 *Tel:* 312-787-7070 *Fax:* 312-787-6650 *E-mail:* editors@poetrymagazine.org *Web Site:* poetrymagazine.org, pg 717

Limelight Editions, 33 Plymouth St, Suite 302, Montclair, NJ 07042 *Tel:* 973-337-5034 *Fax:* 973-337-5227 *Web Site:* limelighteditions.com, pg 149

Linden Publishing Co Inc, 2006 S Mary St, Fresno, CA 93721 *Tel:* 559-233-6633 *Toll Free Tel:* 800-345-4447 (orders) *Fax:* 559-233-6933 *Web Site:* lindenpub.com, pg 149

Lindgren & Smith, 676-A Ninth Ave, New York, NY 10036 *Tel:* 212-397-7330 *E-mail:* representation@lindgrensmith.com *Web Site:* www.lindgrensmith.com; www.redpaintbox.com, pg 602

Lindisfarne Books, 610 Main St, Great Barrington, MA 01230 *Tel:* 413-528-8233 *Fax:* 413-528-8826 *E-mail:* service@lindisfarne.org *Web Site:* www.lindisfarne.org, pg 149

LinguaText Ltd, 103 Walker Way, Newark, DE 19711 *Tel:* 302-453-8695 *Fax:* 302-453-8695 *Toll Free Fax:* 800-784-4935 *E-mail:* linguatextext@juno.com *Web Site:* www.linguatextltd.com, pg 149

Linguistic Society of America, 1325 18 St NW, Suite 211, Washington, DC 20036-6501 *Tel:* 202-835-1714 *Fax:* 202-835-1717 *E-mail:* lsa@lsadc.org *Web Site:* www.linguisticsociety.org, pg 626

LinguiSystems Inc, 3100 Fourth Ave, East Moline, IL 61244 *Tel:* 309-755-2300 *Toll Free Tel:* 800-776-4332 *Fax:* 309-755-2377 *Toll Free Fax:* 800-577-4555 *E-mail:* service@linguisystems.com *Web Site:* www.linguisystems.com, pg 149

Andrew S Linick PhD, The Copyologist®, Linick Bldg, 7 Putter Lane, Middle Island, NY 11953 *Tel:* 631-924-3888 *Fax:* 631-924-8555

*E-mail:* linickgroup@gmail.com *Web Site:* www.AndrewLinickDirectMarketing.com/The-Copyologist.html; www.NewWorldPressBooks.com, pg 550

The Linick Group Inc, Linick Bldg, 7 Putter Lane, Middle Island, NY 11953 *Tel:* 631-924-3888; 631-924-8555 *Fax:* 631-924-8555 *E-mail:* linickgroup@gmail.com; andrew@AskLinick.com *Web Site:* www.AndrewLinickDirectMarketing.com/Publishers-Advice.html; www.NewWorldPressBooks.com, pg 149

Linworth Publishing, 130 Cremona Dr, Santa Barbara, CA 93117 *Tel:* 805-968-1911 *Toll Free Tel:* 800-368-6868 *Fax:* 805-685-9685 *Toll Free Fax:* 866-270-3856 *E-mail:* customerservice@abc-clio.com *Web Site:* www.abc-clio.com, pg 149

Elliot Linzer, 126-10 Powells Cove Blvd, College Point, NY 11356 *Tel:* 718-353-1261 *Fax:* 814-253-1261 *E-mail:* elinzer@juno.com, pg 550

LionHearted Publishing Inc, PO Box 618, Zephyr Cove, NV 89448-0618 *Tel:* 775-853-3221 *Toll Free Tel:* 888-546-6478 *Toll Free Fax:* 888-546-6478 *E-mail:* admin@lionhearted.com *Web Site:* www.lionhearted.com, pg 149

Lipper Marketplace, 195 Broadway, 5th fl, New York, NY 10007 *Tel:* 646-822-3450; 646-223-4000 (sales) *Toll Free Tel:* 800-782-5555 (orders) *E-mail:* general.info@thomsonreuters.com *Web Site:* www.lippermarketplace.com, pg 150

Joseph W Lippincott Award, 50 E Huron St, Chicago, IL 60611 *Tel:* 312-280-3247 *Toll Free Tel:* 800-545-2433 (ext 3247) *Fax:* 312-944-3897 *E-mail:* awards@ala.org *Web Site:* www.ala.org, pg 717

Lippincott Williams & Wilkins, 530 Walnut St, Philadelphia, PA 19106-3621 *Tel:* 215-521-8300 *Toll Free Tel:* 800-638-3030 (orders & cust serv) *E-mail:* orders@lww.com *Web Site:* www.lww.com, pg 150

E Trina Lipton, 60 E Eighth St, Suite 15-F, New York, NY 10003 *Tel:* 212-674-5558 (call first, messages); 917-327-6886 (cell) *Fax:* 212-674-3523 *E-mail:* trinalipton@hotmail.com, pg 550

Eli Liss, 41 Viking Lane, Woodstock, NY 12498 *Tel:* 845-679-7173 *E-mail:* elibear88@aol.com, pg 550

Listen & Live Audio Inc, PO Box 817, Roseland, NJ 07068-0817 *Tel:* 201-558-9000 *Toll Free Tel:* 800-653-9400 (orders) *Fax:* 201-558-9800 *Web Site:* www.listenandlive.com, pg 150

LITA/Christian Larew Memorial Scholarship in Library & Information Technology, c/o American Library Association, 50 E Huron St, Chicago, IL 60611-2795 *Toll Free Tel:* 800-545-2433 (ext 4270) *Fax:* 312-280-3257 *E-mail:* lita@ala.org *Web Site:* www.ala.org/lita, pg 718

LITA/LSSI Minority Scholarship in Library & Information Technology, c/o American Library Association, 50 E Huron St, Chicago, IL 60611-2795 *Toll Free Tel:* 800-545-2433 (ext 4270) *Fax:* 312-280-3257 *E-mail:* lita@ala.org *Web Site:* www.ala.org/lita, pg 718

LITA/OCLC Minority Scholarship in Library & Information Technology, c/o American Library Association, 50 E Huron St, Chicago, IL 60611-2795 *Toll Free Tel:* 800-545-2433 (ext 4270) *Fax:* 312-280-3257 *E-mail:* lita@ala.org *Web Site:* www.ala.org/lita, pg 718

Literary & Creative Artists Inc, 3543 Albemarle St NW, Washington, DC 20008-4213 *Tel:* 202-362-4688 *Fax:* 202-362-8875 *E-mail:* lca9643@lcadc.com (queries, no attachments) *Web Site:* www.lcadc.com, pg 582

Literary Artists Representatives, 575 West End Ave, Suite GRC, New York, NY 10024-2711 *Tel:* 212-679-7788 *Fax:* 212-595-2098 *E-mail:* litartists@aol.com, pg 582

Literary Management Group LLC, 613 Crieve Rd, Nashville, TN 37220 *Tel:* 615-832-7231 *Web Site:* www.literarymanagementgroup.com; www.brucebarbour.com, pg 582

The Literary Press Group of Canada, 192 Spadina Ave, Suite 501, Toronto, ON M5T 2C2, Canada *Tel:* 416-483-1321 *Fax:* 416-483-2510 *E-mail:* info@lpg.ca *Web Site:* www.lpg.ca, pg 626

Literary Translation Projects, 1100 Pennsylvania Ave NW, Rm 703, Washington, DC 20506 *Tel:* 202-682-5403; 202-682-5400; 202-682-5034 (lit fellowships hotline) *Fax:* 202-682-5609; 202-682-5610 *E-mail:* litfellowships@arts.gov *Web Site:* www.arts.gov; www.nea.gov, pg 718

Literary Translators' Association of Canada, Concordia University, LB 601, 1455 De Maisonneuve West, Montreal, QC H3G 1M8, Canada *Tel:* 514-848-2424 (ext 8702) *E-mail:* info@attlc-ltac.org *Web Site:* www.attlc-ltac.org, pg 626

Literature Fellowship, 2410 N Old Penitentiary Rd, Boise, ID 83712 *Tel:* 208-334-2119 *Toll Free Tel:* 800-ART-FUND (278-3863 within Idaho) *Fax:* 208-334-2488 *E-mail:* info@arts.idaho.gov *Web Site:* www.arts.idaho.gov, pg 718

Little, Brown and Company, 237 Park Ave, New York, NY 10017 *Tel:* 212-364-1100 *Fax:* 212-364-0952 *E-mail:* firstname.lastname@hbgusa.com *Web Site:* www.HachetteBookGroup.com, pg 150

Little, Brown Books for Young Readers, 237 Park Ave, New York, NY 10017 *Tel:* 212-364-1100 *Toll Free Tel:* 800-759-0190 (cust serv) *Web Site:* www.HachetteBookGroup.com, pg 150

Little Chicago Editorial Services, 154 Natural Tpke, Ripton, VT 05766 *Tel:* 802-388-9782 *Web Site:* andreachesman.com, pg 550

The Little Entrepreneur, c/o Harper-Arrington, 18701 Grand River, Suite 105, Detroit, MI 48223 *Toll Free Tel:* 888-435-9234 *Fax:* 248-281-0373 *E-mail:* info@harperarringtonmedia.com *Web Site:* www.thelittlee.com; www.harperarringtonmedia.com, pg 150

Little Pickle Press LLC, PO Box 983, Belvedere, CA 94920 *Toll Free Tel:* 877-415-4488 *Fax:* 415-366-1520 *E-mail:* info@littlepicklepress.com *Web Site:* www.littlepicklepress.com, pg 528

Littleton-Griswold Prize in American Law & Society, 400 "A" St SE, Washington, DC 20003-3889 *Tel:* 202-544-2422 *Fax:* 202-544-8307 *E-mail:* awards@historians.org *Web Site:* www.historians.org, pg 718

Littleton-Griswold Research Grants, 400 "A" St SE, Washington, DC 20003-3889 *Tel:* 202-544-2422 *Fax:* 202-544-8307 *E-mail:* awards@historians.org *Web Site:* www.historians.org, pg 718

Liturgical Press, PO Box 7500, St John's Abbey, Collegeville, MN 56321-7500 *Tel:* 320-363-2213 *Toll Free Tel:* 800-858-5450 *Fax:* 320-363-3299 *Toll Free Fax:* 800-445-5899 *E-mail:* sales@litpress.org *Web Site:* www.litpress.org, pg 150

Liturgy Training Publications, 3949 S Racine Ave, Chicago, IL 60609-2523 *Tel:* 773-579-4900 *Toll Free Tel:* 800-933-1800 (US & CN only orders) *Fax:* 773-486-7094 *Toll Free Fax:* 800-933-7094 (US & CN only orders) *E-mail:* orders@ltp.org *Web Site:* www.ltp.org, pg 151

The Live Oak Press LLC, PO Box 60036, Palo Alto, CA 94306-0036 *Tel:* 650-853-0197 *Fax:* 815-366-8205 *E-mail:* info@liveoakpress.com *Web Site:* www.liveoakpress.com, pg 151

Livestock Publications Council, 910 Currie St, Fort Worth, TX 76107 *Tel:* 817-336-1130 *Fax:* 817-232-4820 *Web Site:* www.livestockpublications.com, pg 626

Living Language, c/o Random House Inc, 1745 Broadway, New York, NY 10019 *Tel:* 212-782-9000 *Toll Free Tel:* 800-733-3000 (orders) *Toll Free Fax:* 800-659-2436 *E-mail:* livinglanguage@randomhouse.com *Web Site:* www.livinglanguage.com, pg 151

Living Stream Ministry (LSM), 2431 W La Palma Ave, Anaheim, CA 92801 *Tel:* 714-991-4681 *Fax:* 714-236-6005 *E-mail:* books@lsm.org *Web Site:* www.lsm.org, pg 151

Livingston Press, University of West Alabama, Sta 22, Livingston, AL 35470 *Tel:* 205-652-3470 *Fax:* 205-652-3717 *Web Site:* www.livingstonpress.uwa.edu, pg 151

Livres Canada Books, One Nicholas, Suite 504, Ottawa, ON K1N 7B7, Canada *Tel:* 613-562-2324 *Fax:* 613-562-2329 *E-mail:* aecb@aecb.org; info@livrescanadabooks.com *Web Site:* www.aecb.org; www.livrescanadabooks.com, pg 626

Llewellyn Publications, 2143 Wooddale Dr, Woodbury, MN 55125 *Tel:* 651-291-1970 *Toll Free Tel:* 800-843-6666 *Fax:* 651-291-1908 *E-mail:* publicity@llewellyn.com *Web Site:* www.llewellyn.com, pg 151

The Local History Co, 112 N Woodland Rd, Pittsburgh, PA 15232-2849 *Tel:* 412-362-2294 *Toll Free Tel:* 866-362-0789 (orders) *Fax:* 412-362-8192 *E-mail:* info@thelocalhistorycompany.com; sales@thelocalhistorycomany.com *Web Site:* www.thelocalhistorycompany.com, pg 151

Locks Art Publications/Locks Gallery, 600 Washington Sq S, Philadelphia, PA 19106 *Tel:* 215-629-1000 *E-mail:* info@locksgallery.com *Web Site:* www.locksgallery.com, pg 151

Locus Awards, PO Box 13305, Oakland, CA 94661-0305 *Tel:* 510-339-9196 *Fax:* 510-339-9198 *E-mail:* locus@locusmag.com *Web Site:* www.locusmag.com, pg 718

The Gerald Loeb Awards, Gold Hall, Suite B-305, 110 Westwood Plaza, Los Angeles, CA 90095-1481 *Tel:* 310-825-4478 *Fax:* 310-825-4479 *E-mail:* loeb@anderson.ucla.edu *Web Site:* www.loeb.anderson.ucla.edu, pg 718

Loft-Mentor Series in Poetry & Creative Prose, Open Book, Suite 200, 1011 Washington Ave S, Minneapolis, MN 55415 *Tel:* 612-215-2575 *Fax:* 612-215-2576 *E-mail:* loft@loft.org *Web Site:* www.loft.org, pg 718

Loft Press Inc, 9293 Fort Valley Rd, Fort Valley, VA 22652 *Tel:* 540-933-6210 *Fax:* 540-933-6523 *E-mail:* books@loftpress.com, pg 151

Logos Bible Software, 1313 Commercial St, Bellingham, WA 98225-4307 *Tel:* 360-527-1700 *Toll Free Tel:* 800-875-6467 *Fax:* 360-527-1707 *E-mail:* sales@logos.com *Web Site:* www.logos.com, pg 152

Logos Press, 3909 Witmer Rd, Suite 416, Niagara Falls, NY 14305 *Fax:* 815-346-3514 *E-mail:* info@logos-press.com *Web Site:* www.logos-press.com, pg 152

The Jack London Award, Box 17897, Encino, CA 91416 *E-mail:* cwcsfv@gmail.com, pg 718

Lone Pine Publishing, 2311 96 St, Edmonton, AB T6N 1G3, Canada *Tel:* 780-433-9333 *Toll Free Tel:* 800-661-9017 *Fax:* 780-433-9646 *Toll Free Fax:* 800-424-7173 *E-mail:* info@lonepinepublishing.com *Web Site:* www.lonepinepublishing.com, pg 511

Lonely Planet, 150 Linden St, Oakland, CA 94607 *Tel:* 510-893-8555 *Toll Free Tel:* 800-275-8555 (orders) *Fax:* 510-893-8563 *E-mail:* info@lonelyplanet.com *Web Site:* www.lonelyplanet.com, pg 152

Long River Press, 360 Swift Ave, Suite 48, South San Francisco, CA 94080 *Tel:* 650-872-7718 (ext 312) *Fax:* 650-872-7808 *E-mail:* info@longriverpress.com *Web Site:* www.chinabooks.com, pg 152

Looseleaf Law Publications Inc, 43-08 162 St, Flushing, NY 11358 *Tel:* 718-359-5559 *Toll Free Tel:* 800-647-5547 *Fax:* 718-539-0941 *E-mail:* info@looseleaf.com *Web Site:* www.looseleaflaw.com, pg 152

Judy Lopez Memorial Award For Children's Literature, 1225 Selby Ave, Los Angeles, CA 90024 *Tel:* 310-474-9917 *Fax:* 310-474-6436 *Web Site:* www.wnba-books.org/la; www.judylopezbookaward.org, pg 719

Lorenz Educational Press, 501 E Third St, Dayton, OH 45402 *Tel:* 937-228-6118 *Toll Free Tel:* 800-444-1144 *Fax:* 937-223-2042 *E-mail:* lep@lorenz.com *Web Site:* www.lorenzeducationalpress.com, pg 152

James Lorimer & Co Ltd, Publishers, 317 Adelaide St W, Suite 1002, Toronto, ON M5V 1P9, Canada *Tel:* 416-362-4762 *Fax:* 416-362-3939 *Web Site:* www.lorimer.ca, pg 511

Magazine Publishers of America, 810 Seventh Ave, 24th fl, New York, NY 10019 *Tel:* 212-872-3700 *Fax:* 212-888-4217 *E-mail:* mpa@magazine.org *Web Site:* www.magazine.org, pg 627

Magazines Canada, 425 Adelaide St W, Suite 700, Toronto, ON M5V 3C1, Canada *Tel:* 416-504-0274 *Fax:* 416-504-0437 *E-mail:* info@magazinescanada.ca *Web Site:* www.magazinescanada.ca, pg 627

Mage Publishers Inc, 1032 29 St NW, Washington, DC 20007 *Tel:* 202-342-1642 *Toll Free Tel:* 800-962-0922 *Fax:* 202-342-9269 *Web Site:* www.mage.com, pg 155

Magic Hill Press LLC, 144 Magic Hill Rd, Hinesburg, VT 05461 *Tel:* 802-482-3287 *E-mail:* MagicHillPress@gmail.com *Web Site:* www.MagicHillPress.com, pg 528

Magick Mirror Communications, 511 Avenue of the Americas, PMB 173, New York, NY 10011-8436 *Tel:* 212-255-2111; 212-208-2951 (voice mail) *Toll Free Tel:* 800-356-6796 *Fax:* 212-208-2951 (e-fax) *E-mail:* MagickMirr@aol.com; Magickorders@aol.com *Web Site:* magickmirror.com, pg 528

The Magni Co, 7106 Wellington Point Rd, McKinney, TX 75070 *Tel:* 972-540-2050 *Fax:* 972-540-1057 *E-mail:* sales@magnico.com; info@magnico.com *Web Site:* www.magnico.com, pg 155

Maharishi University of Management Press, 1000 N Fourth St, Dept 1155, Fairfield, IA 52557-1155 *Tel:* 641-472-1101 *Toll Free Tel:* 800-831-6523 *Fax:* 641-472-1122 *E-mail:* mumpress@mum.edu *Web Site:* www.mumpress.com, pg 155

Maine Writers & Publishers Alliance, 314 Forest Ave, Rm 318, Portland, OR 04102 *Tel:* 207-228-8263 *Fax:* 207-228-8150 *E-mail:* info@mainewriters.org *Web Site:* www.mainewriters.org, pg 627

Maine Writers Conference at Ocean Park, 14 Temple Ave, Ocean Park, ME 04063 *Tel:* 401-598-1424 *E-mail:* www.opa@oceanpark.org *Web Site:* www.oceanpark.org, pg 670

Maisonneuve Press, 6423 Adelphi Rd, Hyattsville, MD 20782 *Tel:* 301-277-7505 *Fax:* 301-277-2467 *Web Site:* www.maisonneuvepress.com, pg 155

J Russell Major Prize, 400 "A" St SE, Washington, DC 20003-3889 *Tel:* 202-544-2422 *Fax:* 202-544-8307 *E-mail:* awards@historians.org *Web Site:* www.historians.org, pg 720

Malahat Review Long Poem Prize, University of Victoria, Box 1700, Sta CSC, Victoria, BC V8W 2Y2, Canada *Tel:* 250-721-8524 *Fax:* 250-472-5051 *E-mail:* malahat@uvic.ca *Web Site:* www.malahatreview.ca, pg 721

Gene E & Adele R Malott Prize for Recording Community Activism, 2809 Berkeley Dr, Birmingham, AL 35242 *Tel:* 205-726-2424 *Fax:* 205-726-4216 *E-mail:* langumtrust@gmail.com *Web Site:* www.langumtrust.org, pg 721

Management Advisory Services & Publications (MASP), PO Box 81151, Wellesley Hills, MA 02481-0001 *Tel:* 781-235-2895 *Fax:* 781-235-5446 *E-mail:* info@masp.com *Web Site:* www.masp.com, pg 155

Management Concepts Inc, 8230 Leesburg Pike, Suite 800, Vienna, VA 22182 *Tel:* 703-790-9595 *Toll Free Tel:* 800 506-4450 *Fax:* 703-790-1371 *E-mail:* publications@managementconcepts.com *Web Site:* www.managementconcepts.com, pg 155

Management Sciences for Health, 784 Memorial Dr, Cambridge, MA 02139 *Tel:* 617-250-9500 *Fax:* 617-250-9090 *E-mail:* bookstore@msh.org *Web Site:* www.msh.org, pg 155

Mandala Publishing, 10 Paul Dr, San Rafael, CA 94903 *Tel:* 415-526-1370 *Fax:* 415-526-1394 *Toll Free Fax:* 866-509-0515 *E-mail:* info@insighteditions.com *Web Site:* www.mandalapublishing.com, pg 156

Manhattan Publishing Co, 670 White Plains Rd, Scarsdale, NY 10583 *Tel:* 914-472-4650 *Fax:* 914-472-4316 *E-mail:* coe@manhattanpublishing.com *Web Site:* www.manhattanpublishing.com, pg 156

Manhattanville College Master of Arts in Writing Program, 2900 Purchase St, Purchase, NY 10577 *Tel:* 914-323-5239 *Fax:* 914-323-3122 *Web Site:* www.mville.edu/writing, pg 679

Manic D Press Inc, 250 Banks St, San Francisco, CA 94110 *Tel:* 415-648-8288 *Fax:* 415-648-8288 *E-mail:* info@manicdpress.com *Web Site:* www.manicdpress.com, pg 156

Manitoba Arts Council, 525-93 Lombard Ave, Winnipeg, MB R3B 3B1, Canada *Tel:* 204-945-2237 *Toll Free Tel:* 866-994-2787 (in Manitoba) *Fax:* 204-945-5925 *E-mail:* info@artscouncil.mb.ca *Web Site:* www.artscouncil.mb.ca, pg 627

The Manitoba Writers' Guild Inc, 218-100 Arthur St, Winnipeg, MB R3B 1H3, Canada *Tel:* 204-944-8013 *E-mail:* info@mbwriter.mb.ca *Web Site:* www.mbwriter.mb.ca, pg 627

Carol Mann Agency, 55 Fifth Ave, New York, NY 10003 *Tel:* 212-206-5635 *Fax:* 212-675-4809 *E-mail:* submissions@carolmannagency.com *Web Site:* www.carolmannagency.com, pg 583

Margaret Mann Citation, 50 E Huron St, Chicago, IL 60611 *Tel:* 312-280-5037 *Toll Free Tel:* 800-545-2433 *Fax:* 312-280-5033 *E-mail:* alcts@ala.org *Web Site:* www.ala.org/alcts, pg 721

Phyllis Manner, 17 Springdale Rd, New Rochelle, NY 10804 *Tel:* 914-834-4707 *Fax:* 914-834-4707 *E-mail:* pmanner@aol.com, pg 550

Manning Publications Co, 20 Baldwin Rd, Shelter Island, NY 11964 *Toll Free Tel:* 800-294-4747 (orders) *E-mail:* orders@manning.com *Web Site:* www.manning.com, pg 156

Freya Manston Associates Inc, 145 W 58 St, New York, NY 10019 *Tel:* 212-247-3075, pg 583

Manus & Associates Literary Agency Inc, 425 Sherman Ave, Suite 200, Palo Alto, CA 94306 *Tel:* 650-470-5151 *Fax:* 650-470-5159 *E-mail:* manuslit@manuslit.com *Web Site:* www.manuslit.com, pg 583

Many Voices Fellowships, 2301 Franklin Ave E, Minneapolis, MN 55406-1099 *Tel:* 612-332-7481 *Fax:* 612-332-6037 *E-mail:* info@pwcenter.org *Web Site:* www.pwcenter.org, pg 721

MapEasy Inc, PO Box 80, Wainscott, NY 11975-0080 *Tel:* 631-537-6213 *Toll Free Tel:* 888-627-3279 *Fax:* 631-537-4541 *E-mail:* info@mapeasy.com *Web Site:* www.mapeasy.com, pg 156

MAR*CO Products Inc, 1443 Old York Rd, Warminster, PA 18974 *Tel:* 215-956-0313 *Toll Free Tel:* 800-448-2197 *Fax:* 215-956-9041 *E-mail:* help@marcoproducts.com *Web Site:* www.marcoproducts.com, pg 156

Marathon Press, 1500 Square Turn Blvd, Norfolk, NE 68701 *Tel:* 402-371-5040 *Toll Free Tel:* 800-228-0629 *Fax:* 402-371-9382 *Web Site:* www.marathonpress.com, pg 156

March Tenth Inc, 24 Hillside Terr, Montvale, NJ 07645 *Tel:* 201-387-6551 *Fax:* 201-387-6552 *Web Site:* www.marchtenthinc.com, pg 583

Denise Marcil Literary Agency Inc, 483 Westover Rd, Stamford, CT 06902 *Tel:* 203-327-9970 *E-mail:* dmla@denisemarcilagency.com *Web Site:* www.denisemarcilagency.com, pg 583

Danny Marcus Word Worker, 62 Washington St, Suite 2, Marblehead, MA 01945-3553 *Tel:* 781-631-3886; 781-290-9174 (cell) *Fax:* 781-631-3886 *E-mail:* emildanelle@yahoo.com, pg 550

Maren Green Publishing Inc, 5630 Memorial Ave N, Suite 3, Oak Park Heights, MN 55082 *Tel:* 651-439-4500 *Toll Free Tel:* 800-287-1512 *Fax:* 651-439-4532 *E-mail:* info@marengreen.com *Web Site:* www.marengreen.com, pg 156

Marian Library Medal, 300 College Park, Dayton, OH 45469-1390 *Tel:* 937-229-4214 *Fax:* 937-229-4258 *Web Site:* campus.udayton.edu/mary/mlmedal.html, pg 721

Marick Press, PO Box 36253, Grosse Pointe Farms, MI 48236 *Tel:* 313-407-9236 *E-mail:* orders@marickpress.com *Web Site:* www.marickpress.com, pg 157

Marick Press Poetry Prize Competition, PO Box 36253, Grosse Pointe Farms, MI 48236 *Tel:* 313-407-9236 *Web Site:* www.marickpress.com, pg 721

Marine Education Textbooks Inc, 124 N Van Ave, Houma, LA 70363-5895 *Tel:* 985-879-3866 *Fax:* 985-879-3911 *E-mail:* email@marineeducationtextbooks.com *Web Site:* www.marineeducationtextbooks.com, pg 157

Marine Techniques Publishing, 126 Western Ave, Suite 266, Augusta, ME 04330-7249 *Tel:* 207-622-7984 *E-mail:* info@marinetechpublishing.com; sales@marinetechpublishing.com *Web Site:* marinetechpublishing.com; www.groups.yahoo.com/group/marinetechniquespublishing, pg 157

Marion Street Press Inc, 4207 SE Woodstock Blvd, No 168, Portland, OR 97206 *Tel:* 503-888-4624 *Toll Free Fax:* 866-571-8359 *E-mail:* marionstreetpress@gmail.com *Web Site:* www.marionstreetpress.com, pg 157

Maritime Writers' Workshops, PO Box 4400, Fredericton, NB E3B 5A3, Canada *Tel:* 506-458-7106 *Toll Free Tel:* 866-599-4646 *Fax:* 506-458-5012 *E-mail:* extend@unb.ca *Web Site:* www.unb.ca/cel, pg 670

Mark Twain Creative Writing Workshop, UMKC, University House, 5101 Rockhill Rd, Kansas City, MO 64110-2499 *Tel:* 816-235-1168 *Fax:* 816-235-2611 *E-mail:* newletters@umkc.edu *Web Site:* www.newletters.org, pg 670

Marketscope Group Books LLC, PO Box 3118, Huntington Beach, CA 92605-3118 *Tel:* 562-343-5414 *Fax:* 562-343-5417 *E-mail:* info@marketscopegroup.com; fxtv@msn.com, pg 157

Barbara Markowitz, PO Box 41709, Los Angeles, CA 90041 *Tel:* 323-257-6188, pg 583

Markowski International Publishers, One Oakglade Circle, Hummelstown, PA 17036-9525 *Tel:* 717-566-0468 *E-mail:* info@possibilitypress.com *Web Site:* www.possibilitypress.com; www.aeronauticalpublishers.com, pg 157

Markson Thoma Literary Agency Inc, 44 Greenwich Ave, New York, NY 10011 *Tel:* 212-243-8480 *Fax:* 212-691-9014 *E-mail:* info@marksonthoma.com *Web Site:* www.marksonthoma.com, pg 583

Mildred Marmur Associates Ltd, 2005 Palmer Ave, PMB 127, Larchmont, NY 10538 *Tel:* 914-834-1170 *E-mail:* marmur@westnet.com, pg 583

Marquette Books, 3107 E 62 Ave, Spokane, WA 99223 *Tel:* 509-290-9240 *Fax:* 509-448-2191 *E-mail:* books@marquettebooks.com *Web Site:* www.marquettebooks.com, pg 157

Marquette University Press, 1415 W Wisconsin Ave, Milwaukee, WI 53233 *Tel:* 414-288-1564 *Toll Free Tel:* 800-247-6553 (cust serv) *Fax:* 414-288-7813 *Web Site:* www.marquette.edu/mupress, pg 157

Marquis Who's Who LLC, 300 Connell Dr, Suite 2000, Berkeley Heights, NJ 07922 *Tel:* 908-673-1000 *Toll Free Tel:* 800-473-7020 *Fax:* 908-673-1189 *E-mail:* customerservice@marquiswhoswho.com (cust serv, sales) *Web Site:* www.marquiswhoswho.com, pg 157

Morton Marr Poetry Prize, 6404 Robert Hyer Lane, Rm 307, Dallas, TX 75275-0374 *Fax:* 214-768-1408 *E-mail:* swr@mail.smu.edu *Web Site:* www.smu.edu/southwestreview, pg 721

Helen & Howard R Marraro Prize in Italian History, 400 "A" St SE, Washington, DC 20003-3889 *Tel:* 202-544-2422 *Fax:* 202-544-8307 *E-mail:* awards@historians.org *Web Site:* www.historians.org, pg 721

Howard R Marraro Prize, 26 Broadway, 3rd fl, New York, NY 10004-1789 *Tel:* 646-576-5141 *Fax:* 646-458-0030 *E-mail:* awards@mla.org *Web Site:* www.mla.org, pg 721

Marriage Transformation LLC, 2409 Hamill Rd, Hixson, TN 37343-4034 *Tel:* 423-599-0153 *E-mail:* staff@marriagetransformation.com *Web Site:* www.marriagetransformation.com, pg 157

Marsal Lyon Literary Agency LLC, 665 San Rodolfo Dr, Suite 124, PMB 121, Solana Beach, CA 92075 *Tel:* 760-814-8507 *Web Site:* www.marsallyonliteraryagency.com, pg 583

Marshall & Swift, 777 S Fiqueroa St, 12th fl, Los Angeles, CA 90017 *Tel:* 213-683-9000 *Toll Free Tel:* 800-544-2678 *Fax:* 213-683-9043 *E-mail:* csinquiry@marshallswift.com *Web Site:* www.marshallswift.com, pg 158

Marshall Cavendish Corp, 99 White Plains Rd, Tarrytown, NY 10591-9001 *Tel:* 914-332-8888 *Toll Free Tel:* 800-821-9881 *Fax:* 914-332-8102 *E-mail:* customerservice@marshallcavendish.com; mcc@marshallcavendish.com *Web Site:* marshallcavendish.us; marshallcavendishdigital.com; marshallcavendishebooks.com, pg 158

The Evan Marshall Agency, One Pacio Ct, Roseland, NJ 07068-1121 *Tel:* 973-287-6216 *Fax:* 973-488-7910, pg 584

The Martell Agency, 1350 Avenue of the Americas, Suite 1205, New York, NY 10019 *Tel:* 212-317-2672 *E-mail:* submissions@themartellagency.com *Web Site:* www.themartellagency.com, pg 584

Martin Literary Management LLC, 7683 SE 27 St, No 307, Mercer Island, WA 98040 *Tel:* 206-466-1773 (no queries) *Fax:* 206-466-1774 *Web Site:* www.martinliterarymanagement.com, pg 584

Martin-McLean Literary Associates LLC, 5023 W 120 Ave, Suite 228, Broomfield, CO 80020 *Tel:* 303-465-2056 *Fax:* 303-465-2057 *E-mail:* martinmcleanlit@aol.com *Web Site:* www.martinmcleanlit.com; www.mcleanlit.com, pg 584

Martingale®, 19021 120 Ave NE, Suite 102, Bothell, WA 98011 *Tel:* 425-483-3313 *Toll Free Tel:* 800-426-3126 *Fax:* 425-486-7596 *E-mail:* info@martingale-pub.com *Web Site:* www.martingale-pub.com, pg 158

Maryland Historical Society, 201 W Monument St, Baltimore, MD 21201 *Tel:* 410-685-3750 *Fax:* 410-385-2105 *Web Site:* www.mdhs.org, pg 158

Maryland History Press, PO Box 206, Fruitland, MD 21826-0206 *Tel:* 410-742-2682 *Toll Free Tel:* 877-742-2682 *Fax:* 410-505-4555 *E-mail:* sales@marylandhistorypress.com *Web Site:* www.marylandhistorypress.com, pg 158

Marymark Press, 45-08 Old Millstone Dr, East Windsor, NJ 08520 *Tel:* 609-443-0646, pg 158

Mason Crest Publishers, 370 Reed Rd, Suite 302, Broomall, PA 19008 *Tel:* 610-543-6200 *Toll Free Tel:* 866-MCP-BOOK (627-2665) *Fax:* 610-543-3878 *Web Site:* www.masoncrest.com, pg 158

Massachusetts Book Awards, Simons College - GSLIS, 300 The Fenway, Boston, MA 02115 *Tel:* 617-521-2719 *Fax:* 617-521-3035 *E-mail:* bookawards@massbook.org *Web Site:* www.massbook.org, pg 721

Massachusetts College of Art & Design Writing Children's Literature, 621 Huntington Ave, Boston, MA 02115 *Tel:* 617-879-7200 *Fax:* 617-879-7171 *E-mail:* ce@massart.edu *Web Site:* www.massart.edu/ce, pg 679

The Massachusetts Historical Society, 1154 Boylston St, Boston, MA 02215-3695 *Tel:* 617-536-1608 *Fax:* 617-859-0074 *E-mail:* publications@masshist.org *Web Site:* www.masshist.org, pg 158

Massachusetts Institute of Technology Libraries, 77 Massachusetts Ave, Bldg 14-S, Rm 0551, Cambridge, MA 02139-4307 *Tel:* 617-253-5651 *Fax:* 617-253-8894 *Web Site:* libraries.mit.edu/docs, pg 159

Master Books, PO Box 726, Green Forest, AR 72638-0726 *Tel:* 870-438-5288 *Fax:* 870-438-5120 *E-mail:* nlp@newleafpress.net *Web Site:* www.nlpg.com, pg 159

Master Point Press, 331 Douglas Ave, Toronto, ON M5M 1H2, Canada *Tel:* 416-781-0351 *Fax:* 416-781-1831 *E-mail:* info@masterpointpress.com *Web Site:* www.masterpointpress.com; www.ebooksbridge.com (ebook sales); www.masteringbridge.com (bridge teacher/student support); www.bridgeblogging.com (author blogs & other feeds), pg 511

Masters Literary Awards, PO Box 17897, Encino, CA 91416-7897 *Tel:* 818-377-4006 *E-mail:* titan91416@yahoo.com *Web Site:* www.calwriterssfu.com, pg 721

Materials Research Society, 506 Keystone Dr, Warrendale, PA 15086-7537 *Tel:* 724-779-3003 *Fax:* 724-779-8313 *E-mail:* info@mrs.org *Web Site:* www.mrs.org, pg 159

Math Solutions®, 150 Gate 5 Rd, Suite 101, Sausalito, CA 94965 *Tel:* 415-332-4181 *Toll Free Tel:* 800-868-9092 *Fax:* 415-331-1931 *Toll Free Fax:* 877-942-8837 *E-mail:* info@mathsolutions.com; orders@mathsolutions.com *Web Site:* www.mathsolutions.com, pg 159

Math Teachers Press Inc, 4850 Park Glen Rd, Minneapolis, MN 55416 *Tel:* 952-545-6535 *Toll Free Tel:* 800-852-2435 *Fax:* 952-546-7502 *E-mail:* info@movingwithmath.com *Web Site:* www.movingwithmath.com, pg 159

The Mathematical Association of America, 1529 18 St NW, Washington, DC 20036-1358 *Tel:* 202-387-5200 *Toll Free Tel:* 800-741-9415 *Fax:* 202-265-2384 *E-mail:* maahq@maa.org *Web Site:* www.maa.org, pg 159

Joy Matkowski, 212 Ridge Hill Rd, Mechanicsburg, PA 17050 *Tel:* 717-620-8881 *E-mail:* jmatkowski1@comcast.net, pg 551

Harold Matson Co Inc, 276 Fifth Ave, New York, NY 10001 *Tel:* 212-679-4490 *Fax:* 212-545-1224, pg 584

Matt Cohen Prize: In Celebration of a Writing Life, 90 Richmond St E, Suite 200, Toronto, ON M5C 1P1, Canada *Tel:* 416-504-8222 *Toll Free Tel:* 877-906-6548 *Fax:* 416-504-9090 *E-mail:* info@writerstrust.com *Web Site:* www.writerstrust.com, pg 722

Mature Women Scholarship Grant - Art/Letters/Music, c/o National Pen Women-Scholarship, Pen Arts Bldg, 1300 17 St NW, Washington, DC 20036-1973 *Tel:* 202-785-1997 *Fax:* 202-452-8868 *E-mail:* contact@nlapw.org *Web Site:* www.nlapw.org, pg 722

Maupin House Publishing, 2300 NW 71 Place, Gainesville, FL 32653 *Tel:* 352-373-5588 *Toll Free Tel:* 800-524-0634 *Fax:* 352-373-5546 *E-mail:* info@maupinhouse.com *Web Site:* www.maupinhouse.com, pg 159

Peter Mayeux, RR 1, Box 242A3, 15660 Bobwhite Trail, Crete, NE 68333-0333 *Tel:* 402-826-5231 *E-mail:* pm41923@windstream.net, pg 551

Mazda Publishers Inc, One Park Plaza, Suite 600, Irvine, CA 92614 *Tel:* 714-751-5252 *Fax:* 714-751-4805 *E-mail:* mazdapub@aol.com *Web Site:* www.mazdapub.com, pg 159

Maxim Mazumdar New Play Competition, One Curtain Up Alley, Buffalo, NY 14202-1911 *Tel:* 716-852-2600 *E-mail:* publicrelations@alleyway.com *Web Site:* alleyway.com, pg 722

MB Artists, 775 Sixth Ave, Suite 6, New York, NY 10001 *Tel:* 212-689-7830 *Fax:* 212-689-7829 *Web Site:* www.mbartists.com, pg 602

MBI Publishing Co, 400 First Ave N, Suite 300, Minneapolis, MN 55401 *Toll Free Tel:* 800-328-0590 *Fax:* 612-344-8691 *E-mail:* trade@mbipublishing.com (US trade orders & sales) *Web Site:* www.qbookshop.com, pg 159

McBooks Press Inc, ID Booth Bldg, 520 N Meadow St, Ithaca, NY 14850 *Tel:* 607-272-2114 *Fax:* 607-273-6068 *E-mail:* mcbooks@mcbooks.com *Web Site:* www.mcbooks.com, pg 159

Margret McBride Literary Agency, PO Box 9128, La Jolla, CA 92038 *Tel:* 858-454-1550 *Fax:* 858-454-2156 *E-mail:* staff@mcbridelit.com *Web Site:* www.mcbrideliterary.com, pg 584

Janet B McCabe Poetry Prize, 140 N Roosevelt Ave, Collins, CO 80521 *Tel:* 970-449-2726 *E-mail:* editor@ruminatemagazine.org *Web Site:* www.ruminatemagazine.com, pg 722

McCarthy Creative Services, 625 Main St, Suite 834, New York, NY 10044-0035 *Tel:* 212-832-3428 *E-mail:* PaulMccarthy@MccarthyCreative.com *Web Site:* www.mccarthycreative.com, pg 551

E J McCarthy Agency, 1104 Shelter Bay Ave, Mill Valley, CA 94941 *Tel:* 415-383-6639 *Fax:* 415-383-6639 *E-mail:* ejmagency@gmail.com *Web Site:* www.publishersmarketplace.com/members/ejmccarthy, pg 585

Gerard McCauley Agency Inc, PO Box 844, Katonah, NY 10536-0844 *Tel:* 914-232-5700 *Fax:* 914-232-1506, pg 585

McClanahan Publishing House Inc, 88 Cedar St, Kuttawa, KY 42055-0100 *Tel:* 270-388-9388 *Toll Free Tel:* 800-544-6959 *Fax:* 270-388-6186 *E-mail:* books@kybooks.com *Web Site:* www.kybooks.com, pg 160

Anita D McClellan Associates, 464 Common St, Suite 142, Belmont, MA 02478-2704 *Tel:* 617-575-9203 *Fax:* 206-203-0829 *E-mail:* adm@anitamcclellan.com *Web Site:* www.anitamcclellan.com, pg 551, 585

McClelland & Stewart Ltd, 75 Sherbourne St, 5th fl, Toronto, ON M5A 2P9, Canada *Tel:* 416-598-1114 *Fax:* 416-598-7764 *E-mail:* editorial@mcclelland.com *Web Site:* www.mcclelland.com, pg 512

McCutchan Publishing Corp, 3220 Blume Dr, Suite 197, Richmond, CA 94806 *Tel:* 510-758-5510 *Toll Free Tel:* 800-227-1540 *Fax:* 510-758-6078 *E-mail:* mccutchanpublish@sbcglobal.net *Web Site:* www.mccutchanpublishing.com, pg 160

The McDonald & Woodward Publishing Co, 431 E College St, Granville, OH 43023 *Tel:* 740-321-1140 *Toll Free Tel:* 800-233-8787 *Fax:* 740-321-1141 *E-mail:* mwpubco@mwpubco.com *Web Site:* www.mwpubco.com, pg 160

McFarland, 960 NC Hwy 88 W, Jefferson, NC 28640 *Tel:* 336-246-4460 *Toll Free Tel:* 800-253-2187 (orders) *Fax:* 336-246-5018; 336-246-4403 (orders) *E-mail:* info@mcfarlandpub.com *Web Site:* www.mcfarlandpub.com, pg 160

McGill-Queen's University Press, 1010 Sherbrooke W, Suite 1720, Montreal, QC H3A 2R7, Canada *Tel:* 514-398-3750 *Fax:* 514-398-4333 *E-mail:* mqup@mqup.ca *Web Site:* www.mqup.ca, pg 512

John H McGinnis Memorial Award, 6404 Robert Hyer Lane, Rm 307, Dallas, TX 75275-0374 *Fax:* 214-768-1408 *E-mail:* swr@mail.smu.edu *Web Site:* www.smu.edu/southwestreview, pg 722

Harold W McGraw Jr - Prize in Education, 1221 Avenue of the Americas, 47th fl, New York, NY 10020-1095 *Tel:* 212-904-2000; 212-512-2000 *Fax:* 212-512-3611 *Web Site:* www.mhfi.com, pg 722

McGraw-Hill Career Education, 1333 Burr Ridge Pkwy, Burr Ridge, IL 60527 *Tel:* 630-789-4000 *Toll Free Tel:* 800-338-3987 (cust serv) *Fax:* 630-789-5523; 614-755-5645 (cust serv) *Web Site:* www.mhhe.com, pg 160

McGraw-Hill Contemporary Learning Series, 501 Bell St, Dubuque, IA 52001 *Toll Free Tel:* 800-243-6532 *Web Site:* www.mhcls.com, pg 160

McGraw-Hill Create, 501 Bell St, Dubuque, IA 52001 *Tel:* 563-584-6000 *Fax:* 563-584-6600 *E-mail:* first_last@mcgraw-hill.com *Web Site:* www.mhhe.com, pg 160

McGraw-Hill Education, 2 Penn Plaza, New York, NY 10121-2298 *Tel:* 212-904-2000 *E-mail:* customer.service@mcgraw-hill.com *Web Site:* www.mheducation.com; www.mheducation.com/custserv.html, pg 160

McGraw-Hill Financial, 1221 Avenue of the Americas, 50th fl, New York, NY 10020 *Tel:* 212-512-2000 *Web Site:* www.mhfi.com, pg 161

McGraw-Hill Higher Education, 1333 Burr Ridge Pkwy, Burr Ridge, IL 60527 *Tel:* 630-789-4000 *Toll Free Tel:* 800-338-3987 (cust serv) *Fax:* 614-755-5645 (cust serv) *Web Site:* www.mhhe.com, pg 161

McGraw-Hill Humanities, Social Sciences, Languages, 2 Penn Plaza, 20th fl, New York, NY 10121 *Tel:* 212-904-2000 *Toll Free Tel:* 800-338-3987 (cust serv) *Fax:* 614-755-5645 (cust serv) *Web Site:* www.mhhe.com, pg 161

McGraw-Hill International Publishing Group, 2 Penn Plaza, New York, NY 10121 *Tel:* 212-904-2000 *Web Site:* www.mcgraw-hill.com, pg 161

McGraw-Hill/Irwin, 1333 Burr Ridge Pkwy, Burr Ridge, IL 60527 *Tel:* 630-789-4000 *Toll Free Tel:* 800-338-3987 (cust serv) *Fax:* 630-789-6942; 614-755-5645 (cust serv) *Web Site:* www.mhhe.com, pg 161

McGraw-Hill Professional, 1221 Avenue of the Americas, New York, NY 10020 *Tel:* 212-512-2000 *Web Site:* www.mhprofessional.com, pg 162

McGraw-Hill Ryerson Limited, 300 Water St, Whitby, ON L1N 9B6, Canada *Tel:* 905-430-5000 *Toll Free Tel:* 800-565-5758 (cust serv) *Fax:* 905-430-5020 *Web Site:* www.mcgrawhill.ca, pg 512

McGraw-Hill School Education Group, 8787 Orion Place, Columbus, OH 43240 *Tel:* 614-430-4000 *Toll Free Tel:* 800-848-1567 *Web Site:* www.mheducation.com, pg 162

McGraw-Hill Science, Engineering, Mathematics, 501 Bell St, Dubuque, IA 52001 *Tel:* 563-584-6000 *Toll Free Tel:* 800-338-3987 (cust serv) *Fax:* 614-755-5645 (cust serv) *Web Site:* www.mhhe.com, pg 162

McHugh's Rights/Permissions Workshop™, PO Box 170665, Milwaukee, WI 53217-8056 *Tel:* 414-351-3056 *E-mail:* jack@johnbmchugh.com *Web Site:* www.johnbmchugh.com, pg 670

McIntosh & Otis Inc, 353 Lexington Ave, New York, NY 10016-0900 *Tel:* 212-687-7400 *Fax:* 212-687-6894 *E-mail:* info@mcintoshandotis.com *Web Site:* www.mcintoshandotis.com, pg 585

McKenna Publishing Group, 425 POA Place, San Luis Obispo, CA 93405 *Tel:* 805-550-1667 *Web Site:* www.mckennapubgrp.com, pg 162

McKnight Advancement Grants, 2301 Franklin Ave E, Minneapolis, MN 55406-1099 *Tel:* 612-332-7481 *Fax:* 612-332-6037 *E-mail:* info@pwcenter.org *Web Site:* www.pwcenter.org, pg 722

McKnight Artist Fellowship for Writers, Open Book, Suite 200, 1011 Washington Ave S, Minneapolis, MN 55415 *Tel:* 612-215-2575 *Fax:* 612-215-2576 *E-mail:* loft@loft.org *Web Site:* www.loft.org, pg 722

McKnight National Residency & Commission, 2301 Franklin Ave E, Minneapolis, MN 55406-1099 *Tel:* 612-332-7481 *Fax:* 612-332-6037 *E-mail:* info@pwcenter.org *Web Site:* www.pwcenter.org, pg 722

Pamela Dittmer McKuen, 87 Tanglewood Dr, Glen Ellyn, IL 60137 *Tel:* 630-545-0867 *Fax:* 630-545-0868 *E-mail:* pmckuen@gmail.com *Web Site:* www.allthewritethings.com; www.pamelamckuen.com, pg 551

McLaren Memorial Comedy Play Writing Competition, 2000 W Wadley Ave, Midland, TX 79705 *Tel:* 432-682-2544 *E-mail:* tracy@mctmidland.org *Web Site:* www.mctmidland.org, pg 722

McLemore Prize, PO Box 571, Jackson, MS 39205-0571 *Tel:* 601-576-6850 *Fax:* 601-576-6975 *E-mail:* mhs@mdah.state.ms.us *Web Site:* www.mdah.state.ms.us, pg 722

John McMenemy Prize, 260 rue Dalhousie St, Suite 204, Ottawa, ON K1N 7E4, Canada *Tel:* 613-562-1202 *Fax:* 613-241-0019 *E-mail:* cpsa-acsp@cpsa-acsp.ca *Web Site:* www.cpsa-acsp.ca, pg 723

Sally Hill McMillan LLC, 429 E Kingston Ave, Charlotte, NC 28203 *Tel:* 704-334-0897 *E-mail:* mcmagency@aol.com, pg 585

Pat McNees, 10643 Weymouth St, Suite 204, Bethesda, MD 20814 *Tel:* 301-897-8557 *E-mail:* pmcnees@nasw.org *Web Site:* www.patmcnees.com; www.writersandeditors.com, pg 551

McNeese State University, Writing Program, PO Box 92655, Lake Charles, LA 70609-0001 *Tel:* 337-475-5325; 337-475-5327 *Web Site:* www.mcneese.edu.com; www.mfa.mcneese.edu, pg 679

McPherson & Co, 148 Smith Ave, Kingston, NY 12401 *Tel:* 845-331-5807 *Toll Free Tel:* 800-613-8219 *Fax:* 845-331-5807 *Toll Free Fax:* 800-613-8219 *E-mail:* bmcphersonco@gmail.com *Web Site:* www.mcphersonco.com, pg 162

McSweeney's Publishing, 849 Valencia St, San Francisco, CA 94110 *Tel:* 415-642-5609 (cust serv) *Web Site:* www.mcsweeneys.net, pg 162

MDR, A D & B Co, 6 Armstrong Rd, Suite 301, Shelton, CT 06484 *Tel:* 203-926-4800 *Toll Free Tel:* 800-333-8802 *E-mail:* mdrinfo@dnb.com *Web Site:* www.schooldata.com, pg 162

Meadowbrook Press, 6110 Blue Circle Dr, Suite 237, Minnetonka, MN 55343 *Toll Free Tel:* 800-338-2232 *Fax:* 952-930-1940 *E-mail:* info@meadowbrookpress.com *Web Site:* www.meadowbrookpress.com, pg 163

me+mi publishing inc, 400 S Knoll St, Suite B, Wheaton, IL 60187 *Tel:* 630-752-9951 *Toll Free Tel:* 888-251-1444 *Fax:* 630-588-9804 *E-mail:* rw@rosawesley.com *Web Site:* www.memima.com, pg 163

R S Means, a Reed Construction Data Co, 700 Longwater Dr, Norwell, MA 02061 *Tel:* 781-422-5000 *Toll Free Tel:* 800-334-3509 *Fax:* 781-585-8814 *Toll Free Fax:* 800-632-6701 *Web Site:* rsmeans.reedconstructiondata.com, pg 163

Medal of Honor for Literature, 15 Gramercy Park S, New York, NY 10003 *E-mail:* literary@thenationalartsclub.org *Web Site:* www.nationalartsclub.org, pg 723

Medals of America, 114 Southchase Blvd, Fountain Inn, SC 29644 *Toll Free Tel:* 800-605-4001 *Toll Free Fax:* 800-407-8640 *E-mail:* jholt@usmedals.com, pg 163

MedBooks, 101 W Buckingham Rd, Richardson, TX 75081-4802 *Tel:* 972-643-1809 *Toll Free Tel:* 800-443-7397 *Fax:* 972-994-0215 *E-mail:* medbooks@medbooks.com *Web Site:* www.medbooks.com, pg 163

Media Alliance, 1904 Franklin St, Suite 818, Oakland, CA 94612 *Tel:* 510-832-9000 *Fax:* 510-238-8557 *E-mail:* info@media-alliance.org *Web Site:* www.media-alliance.org, pg 627

Media Coalition Inc, 19 Fulton St, Suite 407, New York, NY 10038 *Tel.* 212-587-4025 *Fax:* 212-587-2436 *Web Site:* www.mediacoalition.org, pg 627

Mediaspaul, 3965 Henri-Bourassa E, Montreal-Nord, QC H1H 1L1, Canada *Tel:* 514-322-7341 *Fax:* 514-322-4281 *E-mail:* info@mediaspaul.qc.ca; clientele@mediaspaul.qc.ca *Web Site:* www.mediaspaul.qc.ca, pg 512

Medical Group Management Association (MGMA), 104 Inverness Terr E, Englewood, CO 80112-5306 *Tel:* 303-799-1111; 303-799-1111 (ext 1244, billing & returns); 303-799-1111 (ext 1295, dist ctr); 303-799-1111 (ext 1268, edit off); 303-799-1111 (ext 1888, book orders); 303-799-1111 (ext 1874, ad rates); 303-799-1111 (ext 1295, shipping & warehouse) *Toll Free Tel:* 877-275-6462 *Fax:* 303-784-6110 *E-mail:* support@mgma.com *Web Site:* www.mgma.com, pg 163

Medical Physics Publishing Corp (MPP), 4513 Vernon Blvd, Madison, WI 53705-4964 *Tel:* 608-262-4021 *Toll Free Tel:* 800-442-5778 (cust serv) *Fax:* 608-265-2121 *E-mail:* mpp@medicalphysics.org *Web Site:* www.medicalphysics.org, pg 163

Medieval Institute Publications, WMU East Campus, 100-E Walwood Hall, Kalamazoo, MI 49008 *Tel:* 269-387-8755 (orders) *Fax:* 269-387-8750 *Web Site:* www.wmich.edu/medieval/mip, pg 163

MedMaster Inc, 3337 Hollywood Oaks Dr, Fort Lauderdale, FL 33312 *Tel:* 954-962-8414 *Toll Free Tel:* 800-335-3480 *Fax:* 954-962-4508 *E-mail:* mmbks@aol.com *Web Site:* www.medmaster.net, pg 163

Lucille Medwick Memorial Award, 15 Gramercy Park S, New York, NY 10003 *Tel:* 212-254-9628 *Fax:* 212-673-2352 *Web Site:* www.poetrysociety.org, pg 723

The Russell Meerdink Co Ltd, 1555 S Park Ave, Neenah, WI 54956 *Tel:* 920-725-0955 *Toll Free Tel:* 800-635-6499 *Fax:* 920-725-0709 *E-mail:* questions@horseinfo.com *Web Site:* www.horseinfo.com, pg 163

Mehring Books Inc, PO Box 48377, Oak Park, MI 48237-5977 *Tel:* 248-967-2924 *Fax:* 248-967-3023 *E-mail:* sales@mehring.com *Web Site:* www.mehring.com, pg 164

Mel Bay Publications Inc, 4 Industrial Dr, Pacific, MO 63069-0066 *Tel:* 636-257-3970 *Toll Free Tel:* 800-863-5229 *Fax:* 636-257-5062 *Toll Free Fax:* 800-660-9818 *E-mail:* email@melbay.com *Web Site:* www.melbay.com, pg 164

Melcher Book Award, 25 Beacon St, Boston, MA 02108-2800 *Tel:* 617-948-4303 *Fax:* 617-367-3237 *E-mail:* info@uua.org *Web Site:* www.uua.org, pg 723

Frederic G Melcher Scholarship, 50 E Huron St, Chicago, IL 60611-2795 *Tel:* 312-280-2163 *Toll Free Tel:* 800-545-2433 *Fax:* 312-440-9374 *E-mail:* alsc@ala.org *Web Site:* www.ala.org/alsc, pg 723

Barbara A Mele, 2525 Holland Ave, New York, NY 10467-8703 *Tel:* 718-654-8047 *Fax:* 718-654-8047 *E-mail:* bannmele@aol.com, pg 551

Melissa Turk & the Artist Network, 9 Babbling Brook Lane, Suffern, NY 10901 *Tel:* 845-368-8606 *Fax:* 845-368-8608 *E-mail:* melissa@melissaturk.com *Web Site:* www.melissaturk.com, pg 602

The Mellen Poetry Press, 240 Portage Rd, Lewiston, NY 14092 *Tel:* 716-754-2266; 716-754-1400 (mktg); 716-754-2788 (order fulfillment) *Fax:* 716-754-4056; 716-754-1860 (fulfillment) *E-mail:* cservice@mellenpress.com *Web Site:* www.mellenpress.com, pg 164

Tom Mellers Publishing Services (TMPS), 60 Second Ave, New York, NY 10003 *Tel:* 212-254-4958 *E-mail:* tmps71@yahoo.com, pg 551

The Melville Society, c/o Kent State Univ, Dept of English, Box 5190, Kent, OH 44242, pg 627

Menasha Ridge Press Inc, 2204 First Ave S, Suite 102, Birmingham, AL 35233 *Tel:* 205-322-0439 *Toll Free Tel:* 888-604-4537 *Fax:* 205-326-1012 *E-mail:* info@menasharidge.com *Web Site:* www.menasharidge.com, pg 164

Fred C Mench Professor of Classics Emeritus, 207 Saint Martins Lane, Smyrna, TN 37167 *Tel:* 615-459-0765 *E-mail:* fmench@earthlink.net, pg 551

Mendel Media Group LLC, 115 W 30 St, Suite 800, New York, NY 10001 *Tel:* 646-239-9896 *Fax:* 212-685-4717 *Web Site:* www.mendelmedia.com, pg 585

Mental Health America (MHA), 2000 N Beauregard St, 6th fl, Alexandria, VA 22311 *Tel:* 703-684-7722 *Toll Free Tel:* 800-969-6642 *Fax:* 703-684-5968 *Web Site:* mentalhealthamerica.net, pg 627

Mercer University Press, 368 Orange St, Macon, GA 31201 *Tel:* 478-301-2880 *Toll Free Tel:* 866-895-1472 *Fax:* 478-301-2585 *E-mail:* mupressorders@mercer.edu *Web Site:* www.mupress.org, pg 164

Scott Meredith Literary Agency LP, 200 W 57 St, Suite 904, New York, NY 10019-3211 *Tel:* 646-274-1970 *Fax:* 212-977-5997 *E-mail:* info@scottmeredith.com *Web Site:* www.scottmeredith.com, pg 585

Merit Publishing International Inc, 6839 Villas Dr S, Boca Raton, FL 33433 *Tel:* 561-350-0329; 561-697-1116 (orders) *E-mail:* merituk@aol.com; meritpi@aol.com *Web Site:* www.meritpublishing.com, pg 164

Meriwether Publishing Ltd/Contemporary Drama Service, 885 Elkton Dr, Colorado Springs, CO 80907-3522 *Tel:* 719-594-4422 *Toll Free Tel:* 800-937-5297 *Fax:* 719-594-9916 *Toll Free Fax:* 888-594-4436 *E-mail:* customerservice@meriwether.com *Web Site:* www.meriwether.com, pg 164

Merriam Press, 133 Elm St, Suite 3R, Bennington, VT 05201-2250 *Tel:* 802-447-0313 *Web Site:* www.merriam-press.com, pg 165

Merriam-Webster Inc, 47 Federal St, Springfield, MA 01102 *Tel:* 413-734-3134 *Toll Free Tel:* 800-828-1880 (orders & cust serv) *Fax:* 413-731-5979 (sales) *E-mail:* support@merriam-webster.com *Web Site:* www.merriam-webster.com, pg 165

Mesorah Publications Ltd, 4401 Second Ave, Brooklyn, NY 11232 *Tel:* 718-921-9000 *Toll Free Tel:* 800-637-6724 *Fax:* 718-680-1875 *E-mail:* artscroll@mesorah.com *Web Site:* www.artscroll.com; www.mesorah.com, pg 165

Messianic Jewish Publishers, 6120 Day Long Lane, Clarksville, MD 21029 *Tel:* 410-531-6644 *Toll Free Tel:* 800-410-7367 (orders) *Fax:* 410-531-9440 (no orders) *E-mail:* lederer@messianicjewish.net; rightsandpermissions@messianicjewish.net (rights & perms) *Web Site:* messianicjewish.net, pg 165

Metropolitan Editorial & Writing Service, 4455 Douglas Ave, Riverdale, NY 10471 *Tel:* 718-549-5518, pg 551

Metropolitan Lithographers Association Inc, 950 Third Ave, 14th fl, New York, NY 10022 *Tel:* 212-644-1010 *Fax:* 212-644-1936, pg 627

The Metropolitan Museum of Art, 1000 Fifth Ave, New York, NY 10028 *Tel:* 212-879-5500; 212-570-3725 *Fax:* 212-396-5062 *E-mail:* editorial@metmuseum.org *Web Site:* www.metmuseum.org, pg 165

Mews Books Ltd, 20 Bluewater Hill, Westport, CT 06880 *Tel:* 203-227-1836 *Fax:* 203-227-1144 *E-mail:* mewsbooks@aol.com, pg 585

The David Nathan Meyerson Prize for Fiction, 6404 Robert Hyer Lane, Rm 307, Dallas, TX 75275-0374 *Fax:* 214-768-1408 *E-mail:* swr@mail.smu.edu *Web Site:* www.smu.edu/southwestreview, pg 723

MFA Publications, 465 Huntington Ave, Boston, MA 02115 *Tel:* 617-369-4233 *Fax:* 617-369-3459 *Web Site:* www.mfa.org/publications, pg 165

MGI Management Institute Inc, 12 Skyline Dr, Hawthorne, NY 10532 *Tel:* 914-428-6500 *Toll Free Tel:* 800-932-0191 *Fax:* 914-428-0773 *E-mail:* mgiusa@aol.com *Web Site:* www.mgi.org, pg 165

Doris S Michaels Literary Agency Inc, 1841 Broadway, Suite 903, New York, NY 10023 *Tel:* 212-265-9474 *Fax:* 212-265-9480 *E-mail:* info@dsmagency.com *Web Site:* www.dsmagency.com, pg 585

Michelin Maps & Guides, One Parkway S, Greenville, SC 29615-5022 *Tel:* 864-458-5565 *Fax:* 864-458-5665 *Toll Free Fax:* 866-297-0914; 888-773-7979 *E-mail:* orders@americanmap.com (orders) *Web Site:* www.michelintravel.com; www.michelinguide.com, pg 165

Michigan Municipal League, 1675 Green Rd, Ann Arbor, MI 48105 *Tel:* 734-662-3246 *Toll Free Tel:* 800-653-2483 *Fax:* 734-663-4496 *Web Site:* www.mml.org, pg 165

Michigan State University Press (MSU Press), 1405 S Harrison Rd, Suite 25, East Lansing, MI 48823 *Tel:* 517-355-9543 *Fax:* 517-432-2611 *Toll Free Fax:* 800-678-2120 *E-mail:* msupress@msu.edu *Web Site:* www.msupress.msu.edu, pg 165

Microsoft Press, One Microsoft Way, Redmond, WA 98052-6399 *Tel:* 425-882-8080 *Toll Free Tel:* 800-677-7377 *Fax:* 425-936-7329 *Web Site:* www.microsoft.com/learning/books, pg 166

Mid-List Press, 6524 Brownlee Dr, Nashville, TN 37205-3038 *Tel:* 615-822-3777 *Fax:* 612-823-8387 *E-mail:* guide@midlist.org *Web Site:* www.midlist.org, pg 166

Susan T Middleton, 366-A Norton Hill Rd, Ashfield, MA 01330-9601 *Tel:* 413-628-4039 *E-mail:* smiddle@crocker.com, pg 551

Midmarch Arts Press, 300 Riverside Dr, New York, NY 10025-5239 *Tel:* 212-666-6990 *Web Site:* midmarchartspress.org, pg 166

Midnight Marquee Press Inc, 9721 Britinay Lane, Baltimore, MD 21234 *Tel:* 410-665-1198 *E-mail:* mmarquee@aol.com *Web Site:* www.midmar.com, pg 166

Midwest Independent Booksellers Association (MIBA), 2355 Louisiana Ave N, Suite A, Golden Valley, MN 55427-3646 *Tel:* 763-544-2993 *Toll Free Tel:* 800-784-7522 *Fax:* 763-544-2266 *Web Site:* www.midwestbooksellers.org, pg 627

MidWest Plan Service (MWPS), Iowa State University, 122 Davidson Hall, Ames, IA 50011-3080 *Tel:* 515-294-4337 *Toll Free Tel:* 800-562-3618 *Fax:* 515-294-9589 *E-mail:* mwps@iastate.edu *Web Site:* www.mwps.org, pg 166

Midwest Publishing Association (MPA), 310 W Lake St, Suite 111, Elmhurst, IL 60126 *Tel:* 630-833-4220 *Fax:* 630-563-9181 *E-mail:* info@midwestpublish.org *Web Site:* www.midwestpublish.org, pg 627

Midwest Publishing Association Webinars, 310 W Lake St, Suite 111, Elmhurst, IL 60126 *Tel:* 630-833-4220 *Fax:* 630-563-9181 *E-mail:* info@midwestpublish.org *Web Site:* www.midwestpublish.org, pg 679

Midwest Travel Writers Association, 902 S Randall Rd, Suite C311, St Charles, IL 60174 *Toll Free Tel:* 888-551-8184 *E-mail:* admin@MTWA.org *Web Site:* www.mtwa.org, pg 627

Mike Murach & Associates Inc, 4340 N Knoll Ave, Fresno, CA 93722 *Tel:* 559-440-9071 *Toll Free Tel:* 800-221-5528 *Fax:* 559-440-0963 *E-mail:* murachbooks@murach.com *Web Site:* www.murach.com, pg 166

Mi'kmaq-Maliseet Institute, University of New Brunswick, Rm 343, Marshall d'Avray Hall, 10 MacKay Dr, Fredericton, NB E3B 5A3, Canada *Tel:* 506-453-4840 *Fax:* 506-453-4784 *E-mail:* micmac@unb.ca *Web Site:* www.unb.ca; www.unb.ca/fredericton/education/mmi, pg 512

Milady, Executive Woods, 5 Maxwell Dr, Clifton Park, NY 12065-2919 *Tel:* 518-348-2300 *Toll Free Tel:* 800-998-7498 *Fax:* 518-373-6309 *Web Site:* milady.cengage.com, pg 166

Robert J Milch, 9 Millbrook Dr, Stony Brook, NY 11790-2914 *Tel:* 631-689-8546 *Fax:* 631-689-8546 *E-mail:* milchedit@aol.com, pg 551

Kenneth W Mildenberger Prize, 26 Broadway, 3rd fl, New York, NY 10004-1789 *Tel:* 646-576-5141 *Fax:* 646-458-0030 *E-mail:* awards@mla.org *Web Site:* www.mla.org, pg 723

Military Info Publishing, PO Box 41211, Plymouth, MN 55442 *Tel:* 763-533-8627 *Fax:* 763-533-8627 *E-mail:* publisher@military-info.com *Web Site:* www.military-info.com, pg 166

Military Living Publications, 333 Maple Ave E, Suite 3130, Vienna, VA 22180-4717 *Tel:* 703-237-0203 (ext 1) *Toll Free Tel:* 877-363-4677 (ext 1) *Fax:* 703-997-8861 *E-mail:* customerservice@militaryliving.com *Web Site:* www.militaryliving.com, pg 166

Milkweed Editions, 1011 Washington Ave S, Suite 300, Minneapolis, MN 55415-1246 *Tel:* 612-332-3192 *Toll Free Tel:* 800-520-6455 *Fax:* 612-215-2550 *Web Site:* www.milkweed.org, pg 166

Milkweed National Fiction Prize, 1011 Washington Ave S, Suite 300, Minneapolis, MN 55415-1246 *Tel:* 612-332-3192 *Toll Free Tel:* 800-520-6455 *Fax:* 612-215-2550 *E-mail:* submissions@milkweed.org *Web Site:* www.milkweed.org, pg 723

Mill Mountain Theatre, Center in the Square, 2nd fl, One Market Sq SE, Roanoke, VA 24011-1437 *Tel:* 540-224-1250 (ext 7307) *Web Site:* www.millmountain.org, pg 723

Martha Millard Literary Agency, 420 Central Park W, Suite 5H, New York, NY 10025 *Tel:* 212-662-1030 *E-mail:* marmillink@aol.com, pg 586

Millbrook Press, 241 First Ave N, Minneapolis, MN 55401 *Tel:* 612-332-3344 *Toll Free Tel:* 800-328-4929 (US only) *Fax:* 612-332-7615 *Toll Free Fax:* 800-332-1132, pg 167

The Miller Agency Inc, 630 Ninth Ave, Suite 1102, New York, NY 10036 *Tel:* 212-206-0913 *Fax:* 212-206-1473, pg 586

Isabel Miller Young Writers Award, 11759 Groat Rd, Edmonton, AB T5M 3K6, Canada *Tel:* 780-422-8174 *Toll Free Tel:* 800-665-5354 (AB only) *Fax:* 780-422-2663 (attn WGA) *E-mail:* mail@writersguild.ab.ca *Web Site:* www.writersguild.ab.ca, pg 723

Richard K Miller Associates, 4132 Atlanta Hwy, Suite 110, Loganville, GA 30052 *Tel:* 770-466-9709 *Toll Free Tel:* 888-928-RKMA (928-7562) *Fax:* 770-466-6879 *Toll Free Fax:* 877-928-RKMA (928-7562) *Web Site:* rkma.com, pg 167

Robert Miller Gallery, 524 W 26 St, New York, NY 10001 *Tel:* 212-366-4774 *Fax:* 212-366-4454 *E-mail:* rmg@robertmillergallery.com *Web Site:* www.robertmillergallery.com, pg 167

Stephen M Miller Inc, 15727 S Madison Dr, Olathe, KS 66062 *Tel:* 913-768-7997 *Web Site:* www.stephenmillerbooks.com, pg 551

Milliken Publishing Co, 501 E Third St, Dayton, OH 45402 *Tel:* 937-228-6118 *Toll Free Tel:* 800-444-1144 *Fax:* 937-223-2042 *E-mail:* order@lorenz.com *Web Site:* www.lorenz.educationalpress.com, pg 167

Kathleen Mills Editorial Services, PO Box 214, Chardon, OH 44024 *Tel:* 440-285-4347 *E-mail:* mills_edit@yahoo.com, pg 551

Milner Award, One Margaret Mitchell Sq NW, Atlanta, GA 30303 *Tel:* 770-235-3645 *E-mail:* info@themilneraward.org *Web Site:* www.themilneraward.org, pg 723

Milton Dorfman Poetry Prize, 308 W Bloomfield St, Rome, NY 13440 *Tel:* 315-336-1040 *Fax:* 315-336-1090 *E-mail:* racc2@cnymail.com *Web Site:* www.romeart.org, pg 724

The Minerals, Metals & Materials Society (TMS), 184 Thorn Hill Rd, Warrendale, PA 15086 *Tel:* 724-776-9000 *Toll Free Tel:* 800-759-4867 *Fax:* 724-776-3770 *E-mail:* publications@tms.org (orders) *Web Site:* www.tms.org (orders), pg 167

Miniature Book Society Inc, 702 Rosecrans St, San Diego, CA 92106-3013 *Tel:* 619-226-4441 *Fax:* 619-226-4441 *E-mail:* minibook@cox.net *Web Site:* www.mbs.org, pg 627

Minnesota Historical Society Press, 345 Kellogg Blvd W, St Paul, MN 55102-1906 *Tel:* 651-259-3205; 651-259-3000 *Toll Free Tel:* 800-621-2736 (warehouse) *Fax:* 651-297-1345 *Toll Free Fax:* 800-621-8476 (warehouse) *E-mail:* info-mhspress@mnhs.org *Web Site:* www.mhspress.org, pg 167

Mississippi Review Prize, 118 College Dr, Box 5144, Hattiesburg, MS 39406-0001 *E-mail:* msreview@usm.edu *Web Site:* www.usm.edu/english/mississippiireview.html, pg 724

Mississippi Review/University of Southern Mississippi, Center for Writers, 118 College Dr 5144, Hattiesburg, MS 39406-0001 *Tel:* 601-266-5600 *Fax:* 601-266-5757 *Web Site:* www.usm.edu/english/c4w.html; www.usm.edu/english/mississippireview.html, pg 679

Mississippi River Creative Writing Workshop, 720 Fourth Ave S, B-151, Rm 100, St Cloud, MN 56301-4498 *Tel:* 320-308-4947 *Fax:* 320-308-5524 *Web Site:* www.stcloudstate.edu, pg 670

MIT List Visual Arts Center, MIT E 15-109, 20 Ames St, Cambridge, MA 02139 *Tel:* 617-253-4400; 617-253-4680 *Fax:* 617-258-7265 *E-mail:* mlinga@mit.edu *Web Site:* listart.mit.edu, pg 167

The MIT Press, 55 Hayward St, Cambridge, MA 02142 *Tel:* 617-253-5255 *Toll Free Tel:* 800-207-8354 (orders) *Fax:* 617-258-6779; 617-577-1545 (orders) *Web Site:* mitpress.mit.edu, pg 167

Mitchell Lane Publishers Inc, PO Box 196, Hockessin, DE 19707 *Tel:* 302-234-9426 *Toll Free Tel:* 800-814-5484 *Fax:* 302-234-4742 *Toll Free Fax:* 866-834-4164 *E-mail:* orders@mitchelllane.com *Web Site:* www.mitchelllane.com, pg 168

MLA Prize for a Bibliography, Archive or Digital Project, 26 Broadway, 3rd fl, New York, NY 10004-1789 *Tel:* 646-576-5141 *Fax:* 646-458-0030 *E-mail:* awards@mla.org *Web Site:* www.mla.org, pg 724

MLA Prize for a First Book, 26 Broadway, 3rd fl, New York, NY 10004-1789 *Tel:* 646-576-5141 *Fax:* 646-458-0030 *E-mail:* awards@mla.org *Web Site:* www.mla.org, pg 724

MLA Prize for a Scholarly Edition, 26 Broadway, 3rd fl, New York, NY 10004-1789 *Tel:* 646-576-5141 *Fax:* 646-458-0030 *E-mail:* awards@mla.org *Web Site:* www.mla.org, pg 724

MLA Prize for Independent Scholars, 26 Broadway, 3rd fl, New York, NY 10004-1789 *Tel:* 646-576-5141 *Fax:* 646-458-0030 *E-mail:* awards@mla.org *Web Site:* www.mla.org, pg 724

MLA Prize in United States Latina & Latino & Chicano & Chicano Literary & Cultural Studies, 26 Broadway, 3rd fl, New York, NY 10004-1789 *Tel:* 646-576-5141 *Fax:* 646-458-0030 *E-mail:* awards@mla.org *Web Site:* www.mla.org, pg 724

Mobility International USA, 132 E Broadway, Suite 343, Eugene, OR 97401 *Tel:* 541-343-1284 *Fax:* 541-343-6812 *E-mail:* info@miusa.org *Web Site:* www.miusa.org, pg 168

Sondra Mochson, 18 Overlook Dr, Port Washington, NY 11050 *Tel:* 516-883-0961, pg 551

Modern Language Association of America (MLA), 26 Broadway, 3rd fl, New York, NY 10004-1789 *Tel:* 646-576-5000 *Fax:* 646-458-0030 *E-mail:* info@mla.org *Web Site:* www.mla.org, pg 168

Modern Language Association of America (MLA), 26 Broadway, 3rd fl, New York, NY 10004-1789 *Tel:* 646-576-5000 *Fax:* 646-458-0030 *E-mail:* convention@mla.org *Web Site:* www.mla.org, pg 628

Modern Memoirs, 34 Main St, No 9, Amherst, MA 01002-2367 *Tel:* 413-253-2353 *Web Site:* www.modernmemoirs.com, pg 168

Modern Publishing, 155 E 55 St, New York, NY 10022 *Tel:* 212-826-0850 *Fax:* 212-759-9069 *Web Site:* www.modernpublishing.com, pg 168

Modus Vivendi Publishing Inc & Presses Aventure, 55 rue Jean-Talon ouest, 2nd fl, Montreal, QC H2R 2W8, Canada *Tel:* 514-272-0433 *Fax:* 514-272-7234 *E-mail:* info@modusaventure.com *Web Site:* www.modusaventure.com, pg 512

The Monacelli Press, 236 W 27 St, 4th fl, New York, NY 10001 *Tel:* 212-229-9925 *E-mail:* contact@monacellipress.com *Web Site:* www.monacellipress.com, pg 168

Mondial, 203 W 107 St, Suite 6-C, New York, NY 10025 *Tel:* 646-807-8031 *Fax:* 208-361-2863 *E-mail:* contact@mondialbooks.com *Web Site:* www.mondialbooks.com, pg 168

Mondo Publishing, 200 Sherwood Ave, Farmingdale, NY 11735 *Tel:* 212-268-3560 *Toll Free Tel:* 888-88-MONDO (886-6636) *Toll Free Fax:* 888-532-4492 *E-mail:* info@mondopub.com *Web Site:* www.mondopub.com, pg 168

Money Market Directories, 401 E Market St, Charlottesville, VA 22902 *Tel:* 434-977-1450 *Toll Free Tel:* 800-446-2810 *Fax:* 434-979-9962 *Web Site:* www.mmdwebaccess.com, pg 169

The Mongolia Society Inc, Indiana University, 322 Goodbody Hall, 1011 E Third St, Bloomington, IN 47405-7005 *Tel:* 812-855-4078 *Fax:* 812-855-4078 *E-mail:* monsoc@indiana.edu *Web Site:* www.mongoliasociety.org, pg 169

Monkfish Book Publishing Co, 22 E Market St, Suite 304, Rhinebeck, NY 12572 *Tel:* 845-876-4861 *E-mail:* monkfish@monkfishpublishing.com *Web Site:* www.monkfishpublishing.com, pg 169

The Montana Council for Indian Education, 1240 Burlington Ave, Billings, MT 59102-4224 *Tel:* 406-652-7598 (AM); 406-248-3465 (PM) *Fax:* 406-248-1297 *E-mail:* cie@cie-mt.org *Web Site:* www.cie-mt.org, pg 169

Montana Historical Society Press, Capitol Complex, 225 N Roberts St, Helena, MT 59620 *Tel:* 406-444-0090 (edit); 406-444-2890 (ordering/mktg); 406-444-2694 *Toll Free Tel:* 800-243-9900 *Fax:* 406-444-2696 (ordering/mktg) *Web Site:* www.montanahistoricalsociety.org, pg 169

Montemayor Press, 663 Hyland Hill Rd, Washington, VT 05675 *Tel:* 802-883-5081 *E-mail:* montepress@aol.com *Web Site:* www.montemayorpress.com, pg 169

Lucy Maud Montgomery Literature for Children Prize, 115 Richmond St, Charlottetown, PE C1A 1H7, Canada *Tel:* 902-368-4410 *Toll Free Tel:* 888-734-2784 *Fax:* 902-368-4418 *E-mail:* peiwritersguild@gmail.com *Web Site:* www.peiwritersguild.com, pg 724

Monthly Review Press, 146 W 29 St, Suite 6W, New York, NY 10001 *Tel:* 212-691-2555 *Toll Free Tel:* 800-670-9499 *Fax:* 212-727-3676 *E-mail:* mreview@igc.org *Web Site:* www.MonthlyReview.org, pg 169

Montreal-Contacts/The Rights Agency, 1350 Sherbrooke St E, Suite 1, Montreal, QC H2L 1M4, Canada *Tel:* 514-400-7075 *Fax:* 514-400-1045 *Web Site:* www.montreal-contacts.com/?lang=en, pg 586

Moody Publishers, 820 N La Salle Blvd, Chicago, IL 60610 *Tel:* 312-329-4000 *Toll Free Tel:* 800-678-8812 (cust serv) *Fax:* 312-329-2019 *Web Site:* www.moodypublishers.com, pg 169

Cenie H Moon Prize, 1194 Hume Rd, Hume, VA 22639-1806 *E-mail:* poetryinva@aol.com *Web Site:* www.poetrysocietyofvirginia.org, pg 724

Moonbeam Children's Book Awards, 1129 Woodmere Ave, Suite B, Traverse City, MI 49686 *Tel:* 231-933-0445 *Toll Free Tel:* 800-706-4636 *Fax:* 231-933-0448 *E-mail:* info@axiomawards.com *Web Site:* www.moonbeamawards.com, pg 724

Moonstone Press LLC, 4816 Carrington Circle, Sarasota, FL 34243 *Tel:* 301-765-1081 *Fax:* 301-765-0510 *E-mail:* mazeprod@erols.com *Web Site:* www.moonstonepress.net, pg 528

Jenny McKean Moore Writer-in-Washington, English Dept, Rome Hall, 801 22 St NW, Suite 760, Washington, DC 20052 *Tel:* 202-994-6180 *Fax:* 202-994-7915 *E-mail:* engldept@gwu.edu *Web Site:* www.gwu.edu/~english; departments.columbian.gwu.edu/english/openings (position details), pg 725

Moore Literary Agency, 10 State St, Suite 210, Newburyport, MA 01950 *Tel:* 978-465-9015 *Fax:* 978-465-6653, pg 586

Moose Hide Books, 684 Walls Rd, Prince Township, ON P6A 6K4, Canada *Tel:* 705-779-3331 *Fax:* 705-779-3331 *E-mail:* mooseenterprises@on.aibn.com *Web Site:* www.moosehidebooks.com, pg 512

Morehouse Publishing, 4775 Linglestown Rd, Harrisburg, PA 17112 *Tel:* 717-541-8130 *Toll Free Tel:* 800-877-0012 (orders only); 800-242-1918 (cust serv) *Fax:* 717-541-8136; 717-541-8128 (orders only) *Web Site:* www.morehousepublishing.com, pg 169

Morgan Gaynin Inc, 194 Third Ave, New York, NY 10003 *Tel:* 212-475-0440 *Fax:* 212-353-8538 *E-mail:* info@morgangaynin.com *Web Site:* www.morgangaynin.com, pg 602

Morgan James Publishing, 5 Penn Plaza, 23rd fl, New York, NY 10001 *Tel:* 212-655-5470 *Toll Free Tel:* 800-485-4943 *Fax:* 516-908-4496 *E-mail:* csauer@morganjamespublishing.com *Web Site:* www.morganjamespublishing.com, pg 169

Morgan Kaufmann, 225 Wyman St, Waltham, MA 02451 *Toll Free Tel:* 866-607-1417 *Fax:* 619-699-6310 *Web Site:* www.mkp.com, pg 170

Morgan Reynolds Publishing, 620 S Elm St, Suite 387, Greensboro, NC 27406 *Tel:* 336-275-1311 *Toll Free Tel:* 800-535-1504 *Fax:* 336-275-1152 *Toll Free Fax:* 800-535-5725 *E-mail:* editorial@morganreynolds.com *Web Site:* www.morganreynolds.com, pg 170

Howard Morhaim Literary Agency Inc, 30 Pierrepont St, Brooklyn, NY 11201-3371 *Tel:* 718-222-8400 *Fax:* 718-222-5056 *E-mail:* info@morhaimliterary.com *Web Site:* www.morhaimliterary.com, pg 586

Morning Sun Books Inc, PO Box 326, Kutztown, PA 19530-0326 *Tel:* 610-683-8566 *Fax:* 610-683-3287 *Web Site:* www.morningsunbooks.com, pg 170

Ottoline Morrell Prize, University at Albany, Science Library 320, 1400 Washington Ave, Albany, NY 12222 *Tel:* 518-591-8162 *E-mail:* fence.fencebooks@gmail.com *Web Site:* www.fenceportal.org, pg 725

William Morris Society in the United States Fellowships, PO Box 53263, Washington, DC 20009 *E-mail:* us@morrissociety.org *Web Site:* www.morrissociety.org, pg 725

Henry Morrison Inc, PO Box 235, Bedford Hills, NY 10507-0235 *Tel:* 914-666-3500 *Fax:* 914-241-7846 *E-mail:* hmorrison1@aol.com, pg 586

Morton Publishing Co, 925 W Kenyon Ave, Unit 12, Englewood, CO 80110 *Tel:* 303-761-4805 *Fax:* 303-762-9923 *E-mail:* contact@morton-pub.com *Web Site:* www.morton-pub.com, pg 170

Mosaic Press, 4500 Witmer Industrial Estates, PMB 145, Niagara Falls, NY 14305-1386 *Tel:* 905-825-2130 *Fax:* 905-825-2130 *E-mail:* info@mosaic-press.com *Web Site:* www.mosaic-press.com, pg 170

George L Mosse Prize, 400 "A" St SE, Washington, DC 20003-3889 *Tel:* 202-544-2422 *Fax:* 202-544-8307 *E-mail:* awards@historians.org *Web Site:* www.historians.org, pg 725

Most Significant Scholarly Book Award, PO Box 609, Round Rock, TX 78680 *Tel:* 512-683-5640 *E-mail:* tilsecretary@yahoo.com *Web Site:* www.texasinstituteofletters.org, pg 725

Motion Picture Association of America Inc (MPAA), 1600 "I" St NW, Washington, DC 20006 *Tel:* 202-293-1966 *Fax:* 202-293-1299 *E-mail:* motionpictureassociation@mpaa.org *Web Site:* www.mpaa.org, pg 628

Frank Luther Mott-Kappa Tau Alpha Research Award, University of Missouri, School of Journalism, 76 Gannett Hall, Columbia, MO 65211-1200 *Tel:* 573-882-7685 *Fax:* 573-884-1720 *E-mail:* umcjourkta@missouri.edu *Web Site:* www.kapataualpha.org, pg 725

Sheila Margaret Motton Prize, 2 Farrar St, Cambridge, MA 02138 *Tel:* 617-744-6034 *E-mail:* contests@nepoetryclub.org *Web Site:* www.nepoetryclub.org, pg 725

Mt Chocorua Writing Workshop, PO Box 2280, Conway, NH 03818-2280 *Tel:* 603-447-2280 *Fax:* 603-447-1820 *E-mail:* reservations@worldfellowship.org *Web Site:* www.worldfellowship.org, pg 670

Mount Hermon Christian Writers Conference, c/o Mount Hermon Association Inc, 37 Conference Dr, Mount Hermon, CA 95041 *Tel:* 831-335-4466 *Toll Free Tel:* 888-MH-CAMPS (642-2677 - registration) *Fax:* 831-335-9218 *E-mail:* info@mhcamps.org *Web Site:* www.mounthermon.org/writers, pg 670

Mount Olive College Press, 634 Henderson St, Mount Olive, NC 28365 *Tel:* 252-286-6851 *Fax:* 919-658-7180 *Web Site:* www.mountolivecollege.edu, pg 170

Mountain n' Air Books, 2947-A Honolulu Ave, La Crescenta, CA 91214 *Tel:* 818-248-9345 *Toll Free Tel:* 800-446-9696 *Fax:* 818-248-6516 *Toll Free Fax:* 800-303-5578 *Web Site:* www.mountain-n-air.com, pg 170

Mountain Press Publishing Co, 1301 S Third W, Missoula, MT 59801 *Tel:* 406-728-1900 *Toll Free Tel:* 800-234-5308 *Fax:* 406-728-1635 *E-mail:* info@mtnpress.com *Web Site:* www.mountain-press.com, pg 170

Mountain Writers Series, 2804 SE 27 Ave, Suite 2, Portland, OR 97202 *Tel:* 503-232-4517 *Fax:* 503-232-4517 *E-mail:* pdxmws@mountainwriters.org *Web Site:* www.mountainwriters.org, pg 671

The Mountaineers Books, 1001 SW Klickitat Way, Suite 201, Seattle, WA 98134 *Tel:* 206-223-6303 *Toll Free Tel:* 800-553-4453 *Fax:* 206-223-6306 *Toll Free Fax:* 800-568-7604 *E-mail:* mbooks@mountaineersbooks.org *Web Site:* www.mountaineersbooks.org, pg 170

De Gruyter Mouton, 121 High St, 3rd fl, Boston, MA 02110 *Tel:* 857-284-7073 *Fax:* 857-284-7358 *E-mail:* degruytermail@presswarehouse.com (orders & claims) *Web Site:* www.degruyter.com, pg 170

Movable Type Management, 610 Fifth Ave, Suite 1220, New York, NY 10185 *Tel:* 917-289-1089 *Fax:* 646-810-5757 *Web Site:* www.mtmgmt.net, pg 586

Moznaim Publishing Corp, 4304 12 Ave, Brooklyn, NY 11219 *Tel:* 718-438-7680 *Fax:* 718-438-1305 *E-mail:* sales@moznaim.com, pg 171

MPA Midwest Publishing Award Show, 310 W Lake St, Suite 111, Elmhurst, IL 60126 *Tel:* 630-833-4220 *Fax:* 630-563-9181 *E-mail:* info@midwestpublish.org *Web Site:* www.midwestpublish.org, pg 725

MRTS, PO Box 874402, Tempe, AZ 85287-4402 *Tel:* 480-727-6503 *Toll Free Tel:* 800-621-2736 (orders) *Fax:* 480-965-1681 *Toll Free Fax:* 800-621-8476 (orders) *E-mail:* mrts@asu.edu *Web Site:* www.acmrs.org/pubs, pg 171

Mary Mueller, 516 Bartram Rd, Moorestown, NJ 08057 *Tel:* 856-778-4769 *E-mail:* mamam49@aol.com, pg 551

Multicultural Publications Inc, 936 Slosson St, Akron, OH 44320 *Tel:* 330-865-9578 *Fax:* 330-865-9578 *E-mail:* multiculturalpub@prodigy.net, pg 171

Multimedia Larga, 900 S Boardman Dr, No G72, Gallup, NM 87301 *Tel:* 505-726-1720, pg 171

Editions MultiMondes, 930 rue Pouliot, Quebec, QC G1V 3N9, Canada *Tel:* 418-651-3885 *Toll Free Tel:* 800-840-3029 *Fax:* 418-651-6822 *Toll Free Fax:* 888-303-5931 *E-mail:* multimondes@multim.com *Web Site:* www.multimondes.qc.ca, pg 512

Erika Mumford Prize, 2 Farrar St, Cambridge, MA 02138 *Tel:* 617-744-6034 *E-mail:* contests@nepoetryclub.org *Web Site:* www.nepoetryclub.org, pg 725

Mundania Press LLC, 6457 Glenway Ave, Suite 109, Cincinnati, OH 45211-5222 *Tel:* 513-490-2822 *Fax:* 513-598-9220 *Toll Free Fax:* 888-460-4752 *E-mail:* books@mundania.com; inquiry@mundania.com *Web Site:* www.mundania.com, pg 171

Municipal Analysis Services Inc, PO Box 13453, Austin, TX 78711-3453 *Tel:* 512-327-3328 *Fax:* 413-740-1294 *E-mail:* munilysis@hotmail.com, pg 171

Municipal Chapter of Toronto IODE Jean Throop Book Award, 40 Orchard View Blvd, Suite 219, Toronto, ON M4R 1B9, Canada *Tel:* 416-925-5078 *Fax:* 416-487-4417 *E-mail:* iodeontario@bellnet.ca *Web Site:* www.iodeontario.ca, pg 725

Muse Literary Management, 189 Waverly Place, Unit 4, New York, NY 10014-3135 *Tel:* 212-925-3721 *E-mail:* museliterarymgmt@aol.com *Web Site:* www.museliterary.com; twitter.com/museliterary, pg 586

The Museum of Modern Art, 11 W 53 St, New York, NY 10019 *Tel:* 212-708-9443 *Fax:* 212-333-6575 *E-mail:* moma_publications@moma.org *Web Site:* www.moma.org, pg 171

Museum of New Mexico Press, 725 Camino Lejo, Suite C, Santa Fe, NM 87505 *Tel:* 505-476-1155; 505-272-7777 (orders) *Toll Free Tel:* 800-249-7737 (orders) *Fax:* 505-476-1156 *Toll Free Fax:* 800-622-8667 (orders) *Web Site:* www.mnmpress.org, pg 171

Music Publishers' Association (MPA), 243 Fifth Ave, Suite 236, New York, NY 10016 *Tel:* 212-327-4044 *E-mail:* admin@mpa.org *Web Site:* host.mpa.org; www.mpa.org, pg 628

Mutual Publishing, 1215 Center St, Suite 210, Honolulu, HI 96816 *Tel:* 808-732-1709 *Fax:* 808-734-4094 *E-mail:* info@mutualpublishing.com *Web Site:* www.mutualpublishing.com, pg 172

MWG Writer Workshops, PO Box 3845, Meridian, MS 39303-3845 *Tel:* 601-880-1089 *Web Site:* www.mississippiwritersguild.com, pg 671

Mystery Writers of America (MWA), 1140 Broadway, Suite 1507, New York, NY 10001 *Tel:* 212-888-8171 *E-mail:* mwa@mysterywriters.org *Web Site:* www.mysterywriters.org, pg 628

Mystery Writers of America Workshops, 1140 Broadway, Suite 1507, New York, NY 10001 *Tel:* 212-888-8171 *E-mail:* mwa@mysterywriters.org *Web Site:* www.mysterywriters.org, pg 671

Mystic Seaport Museum Inc, PO Box 6000, Mystic, CT 06355-0990 *Tel:* 860-572-5302; 860-572-0711 (visitor serv) *Toll Free Tel:* 800-248-1066 (wholesale orders only); 800-331-2665 (retail orders only) *Fax:* 860-572-5321 *E-mail:* info@mysticseaport.org *Web Site:* www.mysticseaport.org, pg 172

Mythopoeic Awards, Oklahoma State University, 306 Edmon Low Library, Stillwater, OK 74078 *Tel:* 405-744-9773 *E-mail:* awards@mythsoc.org *Web Site:* www.mythsoc.org, pg 725

NACE International, 1440 S Creek Dr, Houston, TX 77084-4906 *Tel:* 281-228-6200 *Toll Free Tel:* 800-797-NACE (797-6223) *Fax:* 281-228-6300 *E-mail:* firstservice@nace.org *Web Site:* www.nace.org, pg 172

Jean V Naggar Literary Agency Inc, 216 E 75 St, Suite 1-E, New York, NY 10021 *Tel:* 212-794-1082 *E-mail:* jvnla@jvnla.com *Web Site:* www.jvnla.com, pg 586

NAL, 375 Hudson St, New York, NY 10014 *Tel:* 212-366-2000 *E-mail:* online@penguinputnam.com *Web Site:* www.penguinputnam.com; us.penguingroup.com, pg 172

Napa Valley Writers' Conference, Upper Valley Campus, 1088 College Ave, St Helena, CA 94574 *Tel:* 707-967-2900 (ext 1611) *Fax:* 707-967-2909 *E-mail:* writecon@napavalley.edu *Web Site:* www.napawritersconf.org, pg 671

NAPL, One Meadowlands Plaza, Suite 1511, East Rutherford, NJ 07073 *Tel:* 201-634-9600 *Toll Free Tel:* 800-642-6275 *Fax:* 201-634-0324 *E-mail:* naplmemberservice@napl.org *Web Site:* www.napl.org, pg 628

Narada Press, 3165-133 Weber St N, Waterloo, ON N2J 3G9, Canada *Tel:* 519-886-1969, pg 513

The Narrative Press, 2041 E "A" St, Torrington, WY 82240 *Tel:* 307-532-3495 *Fax:* 307-532-3495 *E-mail:* service@narrativepress.com *Web Site:* www.narrativepress.com, pg 172

NASW Press, 750 First St NE, Suite 700, Washington, DC 20002 *Tel:* 202-408-8600 *Fax:* 203-336-8312 *E-mail:* press@naswdc.org *Web Site:* www.naswpress.org, pg 172

Nataraj Books, 7967 Twist Lane, Springfield, VA 22153 *Tel:* 703-455-4996 *Fax:* 703-455-4001 *E-mail:* nataraj@erols.com; orders@natarajbooks.com *Web Site:* www.natarajbooks.com, pg 172

Nation Books, 116 E 16 St, 8th fl, New York, NY 10003 *Tel:* 212-822-0264 *Fax:* 212-253-5356 *E-mail:* submissions@nationbooks.org *Web Site:* www.nationbooks.org, pg 172

National Academies Press (NAP), Lockbox 285, 500 Fifth St NW, Washington, DC 20001 *Tel:* 202-334-3313 *Toll Free Tel:* 888-624-8373 (cust serv) *Fax:* 202-334-2451 (cust serv); 202-334-2793 (mktg dept) *E-mail:* customer_service@nap.edu *Web Site:* www.nap.edu, pg 172

The National Alliance Research Academy, 3630 N Hills Dr, Austin, TX 78755 *Tel:* 512-345-7932 *Toll Free Tel:* 800-633-2165 *Fax:* 512-349-6194 *E-mail:* alliance@scic.com *Web Site:* www.scis.com/academy, pg 173

National Association for Music Education, 1806 Robert Fulton Dr, Reston, VA 20191 *Tel:* 703-860-4000 *Toll Free Tel:* 800-462-6420 (orders & returns); 800-336-3768 *Fax:* 703-860-1531 *Web Site:* www.menc.org; www.nafme.org, pg 173

National Association of Black Journalists (NABJ), 1100 Knight Hall, Suite 3100, College Park, MD 20742 *Tel:* 301-405-0248 *Fax:* 301-314-1714 *E-mail:* nabj@nabj.org *Web Site:* www.nabj.org, pg 628

National Association of Broadcasters (NAB), 1771 "N" St NW, Washington, DC 20036-2891 *Tel:* 202-429-5300 *Fax:* 202-429-4199 *E-mail:* nab@nab.org *Web Site:* www.nab.org, pg 173, 628

National Association of College Stores (NACS), 500 E Lorain St, Oberlin, OH 44074 *Tel:* 440-775-7777 *Toll Free Tel:* 800-622-7498 *Fax:* 440-775-4769 *Web Site:* www.nacs.org, pg 628

National Association of Hispanic Publications Inc (NAHP), 529 14 St NW, Suite 1126, Washington, DC 20045 *Tel:* 202-662-7250 *Fax:* 202-662-7251 *Web Site:* www.nahp.org, pg 628

National Association of Independent Publishers Representatives, 111 E 14 St, PMB 157, New York, NY 10003 *Tel:* 267-546-6561 *Toll Free Tel:* 888-624-7779 *Web Site:* naipr.org, pg 628

National Association of Insurance Commissioners, 2301 McGee St, Suite 800, Kansas City, MO 64108-2662 *Tel:* 816-842-3600; 816-783-8300 (cust serv) *Fax:* 816-783-8175; 816-460-7593 (cust serv) *E-mail:* prodserv@naic.org *Web Site:* www.naic.org, pg 173

National Association of Printing Ink Manufacturers (NAPIM), 15 Technology Pkwy S, Peachtree Corners, GA 30092 *Tel:* 770-209-7289 *Fax:* 678-680-4920 *E-mail:* napim@napim.org *Web Site:* www.napim.org, pg 629

National Association of Real Estate Editors (NAREE), 1003 NW Sixth Terr, Boca Raton, FL 33486-3455 *Tel:* 561-391-3599 *Fax:* 561-391-0099 *Web Site:* www.naree.org, pg 629

National Association of Science Writers (NASW), PO Box 7905, Berkeley, CA 94707 *Tel:* 510-647-9500 *Web Site:* www.nasw.org, pg 629

National Association of Secondary School Principals (NASSP), 1904 Association Dr, Reston, VA 20191-1537 *Tel:* 703-860-0200 *Toll Free Tel:* 800-253-7746 *Fax:* 703-476-5432 *E-mail:* membership@principals.org; sales@principals.org; publications2@nassp.org (communs & devt) *Web Site:* www.principals.org, pg 173

National Awards for Education Reporting, 3516 Connecticut Ave NW, Washington, DC 20008-2401 *Tel:* 202-452-9830 *Fax:* 202-452-9837 *E-mail:* ewa@ewa.org *Web Site:* www.ewa.org, pg 726

National Book Awards, 90 Broad St, Suite 604, New York, NY 10004 *Tel:* 212-685-0261 *Fax:* 212-213-6570 *E-mail:* nationalbook@nationalbook.org *Web Site:* www.nationalbook.org, pg 726

National Book Co, PO Box 8795, Portland, OR 97207-8795 *Tel:* 503-228-6345 *Fax:* 810-885-5811 *E-mail:* info@eralearning.com *Web Site:* www.eralearning.com, pg 173

National Braille Press, 88 Saint Stephen St, Boston, MA 02115-4302 *Tel:* 617-266-6160 *Toll Free Tel:* 800-548-7323 (cust serv); 888-965-8965 *Fax:* 617-437-0456 *E-mail:* orders@nbp.org *Web Site:* www.nbp.org, pg 173

The National Business Book Award, c/o Freedman & Associates Inc, 121 Richmond St W, Suite 605, Toronto, ON M5H 2K1, Canada *Tel:* 416-868-4739 *Web Site:* www.nbbaward.com, pg 726

National Cable & Telecommunications Association (NCTA), 25 Massachusetts Ave NW, Suite 100, Washington, DC 20001-1413 *Tel:* 202-222-2300 *Fax:* 202-222-2514 *Web Site:* www.ncta.com, pg 629

National Cartoonists Society (NCS), 341 N Maitland Ave, Suite 130, Maitland, FL 32751 *Tel:* 407-647-8839 *Fax:* 407-629-2502 *E-mail:* crowsgal@crowsgal.com; info@reuben.org *Web Site:* www.reuben.org, pg 629

National Catholic Educational Association, 1005 N Glebe Rd, Suite 525, Arlington, VA 22201 *Tel:* 571-257-0010 *Toll Free Tel:* 800-711-6232 *Fax:* 703-243-0025 *E-mail:* nceaadmin@ncea.org *Web Site:* www.ncea.org, pg 173

National Center for Children in Poverty, 215 W 125 St, 3rd fl, New York, NY 10027 *Tel:* 646-284-9600 *Fax:* 646-284-9623 *E-mail:* info@nccp.org *Web Site:* www.nccp.org, pg 173

National Center For Employee Ownership (NCEO), 1736 Franklin St, 8th fl, Oakland, CA 94612-3445 *Tel:* 510-208-1300 *Fax:* 510-272-9510 *E-mail:* customerservice@nceo.org *Web Site:* www.nceo.org, pg 174

National Coalition Against Censorship (NCAC), 19 Fulton St, Suite 407, New York, NY 10038 *Tel:* 212-807-6222 *Fax:* 212-807-6245 *E-mail:* ncac@ncac.org *Web Site:* www.ncac.org, pg 629

National Coalition for Literacy, PO Box 2932, Washington, DC 20013-2932 *Toll Free Tel:* 800-228-8813 *Toll Free Fax:* 866-738-3757 *E-mail:* ncl@ncladvocacy.org; ncl@national-coalition-literary.org *Web Site:* www.national-coalition-literacy.org, pg 629

National Communication Association, 1765 "N" St NW, Washington, DC 20036 *Tel:* 202-464-4622 *Fax:* 202-464-4600 *Web Site:* www.natcom.org, pg 629

National Conference for Community & Justice, 1095 Day Hill Rd, Suite 100, Windsor, CT 06095 *Tel:* 860-683-1039 *Fax:* 860-683-1409 *E-mail:* info@nccjctwma.org *Web Site:* www.nccjctwma.org, pg 629

National Conference of State Legislatures (NCSL), 7700 E First Place, Denver, CO 80230 *Tel:* 303-364-7700 *Fax:* 303-364-7800 *E-mail:* books@ncsl.org *Web Site:* www.ncsl.org, pg 174

National Council of Teachers of English (NCTE), 1111 W Kenyon Rd, Urbana, IL 61801-1096 *Tel:* 217-328-3870 *Toll Free Tel:* 877-369-6283 (cust serv) *Fax:* 217-328-9645 *E-mail:* orders@ncte.org *Web Site:* www.ncte.org, pg 174

National Council of Teachers of English (NCTE), 1111 W Kenyon Rd, Urbana, IL 61801-1096 *Tel:* 217-328-3870 *Toll Free Tel:* 877-369-6283 (cust serv) *Fax:* 217-328-9645 *E-mail:* public_info@ncte.org *Web Site:* www.ncte.org, pg 629

National Council of Teachers of Mathematics (NCTM), 1906 Association Dr, Reston, VA 20191-1502 *Tel:* 703-620-9840 *Toll Free Tel:* 800-235-7566 *Fax:* 703-476-2970 *E-mail:* nctm@nctm.org *Web Site:* www.nctm.org, pg 174

National Council on Radiation Protection & Measurements (NCRP), 7910 Woodmont Ave, Suite 400, Bethesda, MD 20814-3095 *Tel:* 301-657-2652 *Toll Free Tel:* 800-229-2652 *Fax:* 301-907-8768 *E-mail:* ncrppubs@ncrponline.org *Web Site:* www.ncrponline.org; www.ncrppublications.org, pg 174

National Crime Prevention Council, 2001 Jefferson Davis Hwy, Suite 901, Arlington, VA 22202 *Tel:* 202-466-6272 *Fax:* 202-296-1356 *E-mail:* ncpc@fulfills.org (orders) *Web Site:* www.ncpc.org, pg 174

National Education Association (NEA), 1201 16 St NW, Washington, DC 20036-3290 *Tel:* 202-833-4000 *Fax:* 202-822-7974 *Web Site:* www.nea.org, pg 174, 630

The National Endowment for the Arts, Nancy Hanks Ctr, Rm 703, 1100 Pennsylvania Ave NW, Washington, DC 20506-0001 *Tel:* 202-682-5400 *Web Site:* www.arts.gov; www.nea.gov, pg 641

National Endowment for the Humanities, Mellon Foundation & Folger Long-term Fellowships, c/o Fellowship Committee, 201 E Capitol St SE, Washington, DC 20003 *Tel:* 202-544-4600 *Fax:* 202-544-4623 *E-mail:* institute@folger.edu *Web Site:* www.folger.edu, pg 726

National Federation of Advanced Information Services (NFAIS), 1518 Walnut St, Suite 1004, Philadelphia, PA 19102-3403 *Tel:* 215-893-1561 *Fax:* 215-893-1564 *E-mail:* nfais@nfais.org *Web Site:* www.nfais.org, pg 630

National Federation of Press Women Inc (NFPW), PO Box 5556, Arlington, VA 22205-0056 *Tel:* 703-237-9804 *Toll Free Tel:* 800-780-2715 *Fax:* 703-237-9808 *E-mail:* presswomen@aol.com *Web Site:* www.nfpw.org, pg 630

National Federation of State Poetry Societies Annual Poetry Contest, PO Box 7842, Moore, OK 73153 *E-mail:* connpoetry@comcast.net *Web Site:* www.NFSPS.com, pg 726

National Freedom of Information Coalition (NFOIC), 101 Reynolds Journalism Institute, Columbia, MO 65211-0012 *Tel:* 573-882-4856 *Fax:* 573-884-6204 *Web Site:* nfoic.org, pg 630

National Gallery of Art, Fourth St & Pennsylvania Ave NW, Washington, DC 20565 *Tel:* 202-737-4215; 202-842-6480 *Fax:* 202-842-6733 *E-mail:* casva@nga.gov *Web Site:* www.nga.gov, pg 174

National Gallery of Canada, The Bookstore, 380 Sussex Dr, Ottawa, ON K1N 9N4, Canada *Tel:* 613-990-0962 (mail order sales) *Fax:* 613-990-1972 *E-mail:* ngcbook@gallery.ca *Web Site:* www.national.gallery.ca, pg 513

National Geographic Books, 1145 17 St NW, Washington, DC 20036-4688 *Tel:* 202-857-7000 *Fax:* 202-857-7670 *Web Site:* www.nationalgeographic.com, pg 174

National Geographic Learning, One Lower Ragsdale Dr, Bldg 1, Suite 200, Monterey, CA 93940 *Tel:* 831-625-3666 *Web Site:* www.ngl.cengage.com, pg 175

National Geographic Society, 1145 17 St NW, Washington, DC 20036-4688 *Tel:* 202-857-7000 *Fax:* 202-429-5727 *Web Site:* www.nationalgeographic.com, pg 175

National Golf Foundation, 1150 S US Hwy One, Suite 401, Jupiter, FL 33477 *Tel:* 561-744-6006 *Toll Free Tel:* 888-275-4643 *Fax:* 561-744-6107 *E-mail:* general@ngf.org *Web Site:* www.ngf.org, pg 175

National Government Publishing Association, 629 N Main St, Hattiesburg, MS 39401 *Tel:* 601-582-3330 *Fax:* 601-582-3354 *E-mail:* info@govpublishing.org *Web Site:* www.govpublishing.org, pg 630

National Information Standards Organization, One N Charles St, Suite 1905, Baltimore, MD 21201 *Tel:* 301-654-2512 *Toll Free Tel:* 866-957-1593 *Fax:* 410-685-5278 *E-mail:* nisohq@niso.org *Web Site:* www.niso.org, pg 175, 630

National Institute for Trial Advocacy (NITA), 1685 38 St, Suite 200, Boulder, CO 80301-2735 *Tel:* 720-890-4860 *Toll Free Tel:* 877-648-2632, 800-225-6482 (orders & returns) *Fax:* 720-890-7069 *E-mail:* info@nita.org *Web Site:* www.nita.org, pg 175

National Jewish Book Award-Children's & Young Adult Literature, 520 Eighth Ave, 4th fl, New York, NY 10018 *Tel:* 212-201-2920 *Fax:* 212-532-4952 *E-mail:* jbc@jewishbooks.org *Web Site:* www.jewishbookcouncil.org, pg 726

National Jewish Book Award-Contemporary Jewish Life & Practice, 520 Eighth Ave, 4th fl, New York, NY 10018 *Tel:* 212-201-2920 *Fax:* 212-532-4952 *E-mail:* jbc@jewishbooks.org *Web Site:* www.jewishbookcouncil.org, pg 726

National Jewish Book Award-History, 520 Eighth Ave, 4th fl, New York, NY 10018 *Tel:* 212-201-2920 *Fax:* 212-532-4952 *E-mail:* jbc@jewishbooks.org *Web Site:* www.jewishbookcouncil.org, pg 726

National Jewish Book Award-Illustrated Children's Book, 520 Eighth Ave, 4th fl, New York, NY 10018 *Tel:* 212-201-2920 *Fax:* 212-532-4952 *E-mail:* jbc@jewishbooks.org *Web Site:* www.jewishbookcouncil.org, pg 726

National Jewish Book Award-Modern Jewish Thought & Experience, 520 Eighth Ave, 4th fl, New York, NY 10018 *Tel:* 212-201-2920 *Fax:* 212-532-4952 *E-mail:* jbc@jewishbooks.org *Web Site:* www.jewishbookcouncil.org, pg 726

National Jewish Book Award-Scholarship, 520 Eighth Ave, 4th fl, New York, NY 10018 *Tel:* 212-201-2920 *Fax:* 212-532-4952 *E-mail:* jbc@jewishbooks.org *Web Site:* www.jewishbookcouncil.org, pg 726

National Jewish Book Awards, 520 Eighth Ave, 4th fl, New York, NY 10018 *Tel:* 212-201-2920 *Fax:* 212-532-4952 *E-mail:* jbc@jewishbooks.org *Web Site:* www.jewishbookcouncil.org, pg 726

National League of American Pen Women, c/o National Pen Women-Scholarship, Pen Arts Bldg, 1300 17 St NW, Washington, DC 20036-1973 *Tel:* 202-785-1997 *Fax:* 202-452-8868 *E-mail:* contact@nlapw.org *Web Site:* www.nlapw.org, pg 630

National League of Cities, 1301 Pennsylvania Ave NW, Washington, DC 20004-1763 *Tel:* 202-626-3100 *Fax:* 202-626-3043 *E-mail:* info@nlc.org *Web Site:* www.nlc.org, pg 175

National Learning Corp, 212 Michael Dr, Syosset, NY 11791 *Tel:* 516-921-8888 *Toll Free Tel:* 800-632-8888 *Fax:* 516-921-8743 *E-mail:* info@passbooks.com *Web Site:* www.passbooks.com, pg 175

National Magazine Awards, 425 Adelaide St W, Suite 700, Toronto, ON M5V 3C1, Canada *Tel:* 416-422-1358 *Fax:* 416-504-0437 *E-mail:* staff@magazine-awards.com *Web Site:* www.magazine-awards.com, pg 726

National Music Publishers' Association (NMPA), 975 F St NW, Suite 315, Washington, DC 20004 *Tel:* 202-393-6672 *Fax:* 202-393-6673 *E-mail:* pr@nmpa.org *Web Site:* www.nmpa.org, pg 630

National Newspaper Association, 309 S Providence St, Columbia, MO 65203-4267 *Tel:* 573-882-5800 *Toll Free Tel:* 800-829-4NNA (829-4662) *Fax:* 573-884-5490 *E-mail:* info@nna.org *Web Site:* www.nnaweb.org, pg 630

National Newspaper Publishers Assn (NNPA), 1816 12 St NW, Washington, DC 20009 *Tel:* 202-588-8764 *Fax:* 202-588-8960 *E-mail:* info@blackpressusa.com; info@nnpa.org *Web Site:* www.nnpa.org; www.blackpressusa.com, pg 630

National Notary Association (NNA), 9350 De Soto Ave, Chatsworth, CA 91311 *Tel:* 818-739-4000 *Toll Free Tel:* 800-876-6827 *Toll Free Fax:* 800-833-1211 *E-mail:* nna@nationalnotary.org *Web Site:* www.nationalnotary.org, pg 175

National One-Act Playwriting Competition, 600 Wolfe St, Alexandria, VA 22314 *Tel:* 703-683-5778 *Fax:* 703-683-1378 *E-mail:* asklta@thelittletheatre.com *Web Site:* www.thelittletheatre.com, pg 727

National Outdoor Book Awards, 921 S Eighth Ave, Stop 8128, Pocatello, ID 83209-8128 *Tel:* 208-282-3912 *Fax:* 208-282-2127 *Web Site:* www.noba-web.org, pg 727

National Park Service Media Services, 67 Mather Place, Harpers Ferry, WV 25425 *Tel:* 304-535-5050 *Fax:* 304-535-6176 *Web Site:* www.nps.gov/hfc, pg 175

National Poetry Series Open Competition, 57 Mountain Ave, Princeton, NJ 08540 *Tel:* 609-430-0999 *Fax:* 609-430-9933 *Web Site:* www.pw.org/content/open_competition, pg 727

National Press Club (NPC), 529 14 St NW, 13th fl, Washington, DC 20045 *Tel:* 202-662-7500 *Fax:* 202-662-7569 *E-mail:* infocenter@npcpress.org *Web Site:* www.press.org, pg 630

National Press Club of Canada Foundation Inc, 150 Albert St, Ottawa, ON K1P 5G2, Canada *Tel:* 613-567-9900 *Fax:* 613-233-5880 *E-mail:* manager@pressclub.on.ca *Web Site:* pressclubcanada.ca, pg 630

The National Press Foundation, 1211 Connecticut Ave NW, Suite 310, Washington, DC 20036 *Tel:* 202-663-7280 *Web Site:* www.nationalpress.org, pg 631

National Press Photographers Association Inc (NPPA), 3200 Croasdaile Dr, Suite 306, Durham, NC 27705 *Tel:* 919-383-7246 *Fax:* 919-383-7261 *E-mail:* info@nppa.org *Web Site:* www.nppa.org, pg 631

National Publishing Co, 11311 Roosevelt Blvd, Philadelphia, PA 19154-2105 *Tel:* 215-676-1863 *Toll Free Tel:* 888-333-1863 *Fax:* 215-673-8069 *Web Site:* www.courier.com, pg 175

National Register Publishing, 300 Connell Dr, Suite 2000, Berkeley Heights, NJ 07922 *Toll Free Tel:* 800-473-7020 *Fax:* 908-673-1189 *E-mail:* NRPsales@

marquiswhoswho.com (sales); NRPeditorial@ marquiswhoswho.com (edit) *Web Site:* www. nationalregisterpublishing.com, pg 175

National Resource Center for Youth Services (NRCYS), Schusterman Ctr, Bldg 4W, 4502 E 41 St, Tulsa, OK 74135-2512 *Tel:* 918-660-3700 *Toll Free Tel:* 800-274-2687 *Fax:* 918-660-3737 *Web Site:* www.nrcys.ou.edu, pg 175

National Science Teachers Association (NSTA), 1840 Wilson Blvd, Arlington, VA 22201-3000 *Tel:* 703-312-9205 *Toll Free Tel:* 800-722-NSTA; 800-277-5300 (orders) *Fax:* 703-526-9754 *Toll Free Fax:* 888-433-0526 (orders) *Web Site:* www.nsta.org/store, pg 176

National Society of Newspaper Columnists (NSNC), 1345 Fillmore St, Suite 507, San Francisco, CA 94115 *Tel:* 415-488-NCNC (488-6762) *Toll Free Tel:* 866-440-NSNC (440-6762) *Fax:* 484-297-0336 *Toll Free Fax:* 866-635-5759 *E-mail:* staff@columnists.com *Web Site:* www.columnists.com, pg 631

National Society of Newspaper Columnists Annual Conference, 1345 Fillmore St, Suite 507, San Francisco, CA 94115 *Tel:* 415-488-NCNC (488-6762) *Toll Free Tel:* 866-440-NSNC (440-6762) *Fax:* 484-297-0336 *Toll Free Fax:* 866-635-5759 *Web Site:* www.columnists.com, pg 671

National Ten-Minute Play Contest, 316 W Main St, Louisville, KY 40202-4218 *Tel:* 502-584-1265 *Web Site:* www.actorstheatre.org/participate/submit-a-play, pg 727

National Translation Award, c/o The University of Texas at Dallas, 800 W Campbell Rd, Mail Sta JO51, Richardson, TX 75080-3021 *Tel:* 972-883-2093 *Fax:* 972-883-6303 *Web Site:* www.utdallas.edu/alta/, pg 727

The National Underwriter Co, 5081 Olympic Blvd, Erlanger, KY 41018-3164 *Tel:* 859-692-2100 *Toll Free Tel:* 800-543-0874 *Fax:* 859-692-2289 *E-mail:* customerservice@nuco.com *Web Site:* www. nationalunderwriter.com, pg 176

National Writers Association, 10940 S Parker Rd, Suite 508, Parker, CO 80134 *Tel:* 303-841-0246 *E-mail:* natlwritersassn@hotmail.com *Web Site:* www. nationalwriters.com, pg 631

National Writers Association Novel Contest, 10940 S Parker Rd, Suite 508, Parker, CO 80134 *Tel:* 303-841-0246 *E-mail:* natlwritersassn@hotmail.com *Web Site:* www.nationalwriters.com, pg 727

National Writers Union/UAW Local 1981, 256 W 38 St, Suite 703, New York, NY 10018 *Tel:* 212-254-0279 *Fax:* 212-254-0673 *E-mail:* nwu@nwu.org *Web Site:* www.nwu.org/, pg 631

The Nautical & Aviation Publishing Co of America Inc, 845-A Lowcountry Blvd, Mount Pleasant, SC 29464 *Tel:* 843-856-0561 *Fax:* 843-856-3164 *Web Site:* www. nauticalandaviation.com, pg 176

Nautilus Awards, 378 Bromley Dr, Eastsound, WA 98245 *Tel:* 360-376-2001 *Web Site:* www. nautilusbookawards.com, pg 727

Naval Institute Press, 291 Wood Rd, Annapolis, MD 21402-5034 *Tel:* 410-268-6110 *Toll Free Tel:* 800-233-8764 *Fax:* 410-295-1084; 410-571-1703 (cust serv) *E-mail:* webmaster@navalinstitute.org; customer@ navalinstitute.org (cust serv); trade@usni.org *Web Site:* www.nip.org; www.usni.org, pg 176

NavPress Publishing Group, 3820 N 30 St, Colorado Springs, CO 80904 *Tel:* 719-548-9222 *Toll Free Tel:* 800-366-7788 *Toll Free Fax:* 800-343-3902 *E-mail:* customerservice@navpress.com *Web Site:* www.navpress.com, pg 176

NBM Publishing Inc, 40 Exchange Place, Suite 1308, New York, NY 10005 *Tel:* 212-643-5407 *Toll Free Tel:* 800-886-1223 *Fax:* 212-643-1545 *E-mail:* admin@nbmpub.com *Web Site:* www.nbmpub. com, pg 176

NEA Literature Fellowships, 1100 Pennsylvania Ave NW, Rm 703, Washington, DC 20506 *Tel:* 202-682-5034 (lit fellowships hotline); 202-682-5400; 202-682-5403 *Fax:* 202-682-5609; 202-682-5610 *E-mail:* litfellowships@arts.gov *Web Site:* www.arts. gov; www.nea.gov, pg 727

Neal-Schuman Publishers Inc, 100 William St, Suite 2004, New York, NY 10038 *Tel:* 212-925-8650 *Toll Free Tel:* 866-NS-BOOKS (672-6657) *Fax:* 212-219-8916 *Toll Free Fax:* 877-231-6980 *E-mail:* info@neal-schuman.com *Web Site:* www.neal-schuman.com, pg 176

NeDeo Press, PO Box 668, Robbins, NC 27325 *Web Site:* www.nedeopress.com, pg 176

Neibauer Press & Church Supplier, 20 Industrial Dr, Warminster, PA 18974 *Tel:* 215-322-6200 *Toll Free Tel:* 800-322-6203 *Fax:* 215-322-2495 *E-mail:* sales@neibauer.com; sales@churchsupplier. com *Web Site:* www.churchsupplier.com, pg 176

Nina Neimark Editorial Services, 543 Third St, Brooklyn, NY 11215 *Tel:* 718-499-6804 *E-mail:* pneimark@hotmail.com, pg 552

Nelligan Prize for Short Fiction, Colorado State Univ, Dept of Eng, Ctr for Literary Publg, 9105 Campus Delivery, Fort Collins, CO 80523-9105 *Tel:* 970-491-5449 *E-mail:* creview@colostate.edu *Web Site:* nelliganprize.colostate.edu, pg 727

BK Nelson Inc Lecture Bureau, 1565 Paseo Vida, Palm Springs, CA 92264 *Tel:* 760-778-8800 *Fax:* 760-778-6242 *E-mail:* bknelson4@cs.com *Web Site:* www. bknelsonlecturebureau.com; www.bknelson.com; www. bknelsonmovieproduction.com, pg 605

BK Nelson Inc Literary Agency, 1565 Paseo Vida, Palm Springs, CA 92264 *Tel:* 760-778-8800 *Fax:* 760-778-6242 *E-mail:* bknelson4@cs.com *Web Site:* www. bknelson.com; www.bknelsonlecturebureau.com; www. bknelsonmovieproduction.com, pg 587

Nelson Education Ltd, 1120 Birchmount Rd, Scarborough, ON M1K 5G4, Canada *Tel:* 416-752-9100 *Toll Free Tel:* 800-268-2222 (cust serv) *Fax:* 416-752-8101 *Toll Free Fax:* 800-430-4445 *E-mail:* inquire@nelson.com *Web Site:* www.nelson. com, pg 513

Nelson Literary Agency LLC, 1732 Wazee St, Suite 207, Denver, CO 80202-1284 *Tel:* 303-292-2805 *E-mail:* query@nelsonagency.com *Web Site:* www. nelsonagency.com, pg 587

Howard Nemerov Sonnet Award, 320 Hunter Dr, Evansville, IN 47711 *Web Site:* theformalist.evansville. edu/home.htm, pg 727

The Pablo Neruda Prize for Poetry, Nimrod International Journal, 800 S Tucker Dr, Tulsa, OK 74104 *Tel:* 918-631-3080 *Fax:* 918-631-3033 *E-mail:* nimrod@utulsa. edu *Web Site:* www.utulsa.edu/nimrod, pg 727

Nesbitt Graphics Inc, 555 Virginia Dr, Fort Washington, PA 19034 *Tel:* 215-591-9125 *Fax:* 215-591-9093 *Web Site:* www.nesbittgraphics.com, pg 552

Neustadt International Prize for Literature, University of Oklahoma, Suite 110, 630 Parrington Oval, Norman, OK 73019-4033 *Tel:* 405-325-4531 *Fax:* 405-325-7495 *Web Site:* www.worldliteraturetoday.org, pg 728

Allan Nevins Prize, 603 Fayerweather, MC 2538, New York, NY 10027 *Tel:* 212-854-6495 *E-mail:* amhistsociety@columbia.edu *Web Site:* sah. columbia.edu, pg 728

Nevraumont Publishing Co, 259 E 134 St, 2nd fl loft, Bronx, NY 10454-4405 *Tel:* 718-993-6192 *E-mail:* info@nevraumontpublishing.com *Web Site:* nevraumontpublishing.com, pg 176

New Canaan Publishing Co LLC, 2384 N Hwy 341, Rossville, GA 30741 *Tel:* 423-285-8672 *E-mail:* djm@newcanaanpublishing.com *Web Site:* www.newcanaanpublishing.com, pg 177

New City Press, 202 Comforter Blvd, Hyde Park, NY 12538 *Tel:* 845-229-0335 *Toll Free Tel:* 800-462-5980 (orders only) *Fax:* 845-229-0351 *E-mail:* info@ newcitypress.com *Web Site:* www.newcitypress.com, pg 177

New Concepts Publishing, 106-A W Hill Ave, Valdosta, GA 31636 *E-mail:* service@newconceptspublishing. com; submissions@newconceptspublishing.com *Web Site:* www.newconceptspublishing.com, pg 177

New Dimensions Publishing, 11248 N 11 St, Phoenix, AZ 85020 *Tel:* 602-861-2631 *Toll Free Tel:* 800-736-7367 *Fax:* 602-944-1235 *E-mail:* info@thedream.com *Web Site:* www.thedream.com, pg 177

New Directions Publishing Corp, 80 Eighth Ave, New York, NY 10011 *Tel:* 212-255-0230 *Fax:* 212-255-0231 *E-mail:* newdirections@ndbooks.com; editorial@ ndbooks.com *Web Site:* ndbooks.com, pg 177

New England Book Awards, 1955 Massachusetts Ave, Cambridge, MA 02140 *Tel:* 617-547-3642 *Fax:* 617-547-3759 *Web Site:* www.newenglandbooks.org/ ne_awards.html, pg 728

New England Independent Booksellers Association Inc (NEIBA), 1955 Massachusetts Ave, Cambridge, MA 02140 *Web Site:* www.newenglandbooks.org, pg 631

New England Poetry Club, 2 Farrar St, Cambridge, MA 02138 *Tel:* 617-744-6034 *E-mail:* info@nepoetryclub. org *Web Site:* www.nepoetryclub.org, pg 631

New England Publishing Associates Inc, One Carver Place, Lawrenceville, GA 08648 *Tel:* 860-973-2439 *E-mail:* nepa@nepa.com; info@nepa.com; queries@ nepa.com *Web Site:* www.nepa.com, pg 587

New Forums Press Inc, 1018 S Lewis St, Stillwater, OK 74074 *Tel:* 405-372-6158 *Toll Free Tel:* 800-606-3766 *Fax:* 405-377-2237 *E-mail:* submissions@newforums. com *Web Site:* www.newforums.com, pg 177

New Hampshire Literary Awards, 2500 N River Rd, Manchester, NH 03106 *Tel:* 603-314-7980 *Fax:* 603-314-7981 *E-mail:* info@nhwritersproject.org *Web Site:* www.nhwritersproject.org, pg 728

New Hampshire Writers' Project, 2500 N River Rd, Manchester, NH 03106 *Tel:* 603-314-7980 *Fax:* 603-314-7981 *E-mail:* info@nhwritersproject.org *Web Site:* www.nhwritersproject.org, pg 631

New Harbinger Publications Inc, 5674 Shattuck Ave, Oakland, CA 94609 *Tel:* 510-652-0215 *Toll Free Tel:* 800-748-6273 (orders only) *Fax:* 510-652-5472 *Toll Free Fax:* 800-652-1613 *E-mail:* nhhelp@ newharbinger.com; customerservice@newharbinger. com *Web Site:* www.newharbinger.com, pg 177

New Horizon Press, PO Box 669, Far Hills, NJ 07931-0669 *Tel:* 908-604-6311 *Toll Free Tel:* 800-533-7978 (orders only) *Fax:* 908-604-6330 *E-mail:* nhp@ newhorizonpressbooks.com *Web Site:* www. newhorizonpressbooks.com, pg 177

New Issues Poetry & Prose, Western Michigan University, 1903 W Michigan Ave, Kalamazoo, MI 49008-5463 *Tel:* 269-387-8185 *Fax:* 269-387-2562 *E-mail:* new-issues@wmich.edu *Web Site:* www. wmich.edu/newissues, pg 178

New Issues Poetry Prize, Western Michigan University, 1903 W Michigan Ave, Kalamazoo, MI 49008-5463 *Tel:* 269-387-8185 *Fax:* 269-387-2562 *E-mail:* new-issues@wmich.edu *Web Site:* www.wmich.edu/ newissues, pg 728

New Jersey Council for the Humanities Book Award, 28 W State St, 6th fl, Trenton, NJ 08608 *Tel:* 609-695-4838 *Toll Free Tel:* 888-FYI-NJCH (394-6524) *Fax:* 609-695-4929 *E-mail:* njch@njch.org *Web Site:* www.njch.org, pg 728

New Leaf Press Inc, 3142 Hwy 103 N, Green Forest, AR 72638-2233 *Tel:* 870-438-5288 *Toll Free Tel:* 800-999-3777 *Fax:* 870-438-5120 *E-mail:* nlp@ newleafpress.net *Web Site:* www.newleafpress.net, pg 178

New Letters Literary Awards, UMKC, University House, 5101 Rockhill Rd, Kansas City, MO 64110-2499 *Tel:* 816-235-1168 *Fax:* 816-235-2611 *E-mail:* newletters@umkc.edu *Web Site:* www. newletters.org, pg 728

New Letters Prize for Poetry, UMKC, University House, 5101 Rockhill Rd, Kansas City, MO 64110-2499 *Tel:* 816-235-1168 *Fax:* 816-235-2611 *E-mail:* newletters@umkc.edu *Web Site:* www. newletters.org, pg 728

North Carolina Writers' Network, PO Box 21591, Winston-Salem, NC 27120-1591 *Tel:* 336-293-8844 *Web Site:* www.ncwriters.org, pg 632

North Carolina Writers' Network Annual Fall Conference, PO Box 21591, Winston-Salem, NC 27120-1591 *Tel:* 336-293-8844 *E-mail:* mail@ncwriters.org *Web Site:* www.ncwriters.org, pg 671

North Country Books Inc, 220 Lafayette St, Utica, NY 13502-4312 *Tel:* 315-735-4877 *Toll Free Tel:* 800-342-7409 (orders) *Fax:* 315-738-4342 *E-mail:* ncbooks@verizon.net *Web Site:* www.northcountrybooks.com, pg 180

North Country Press, 126 Main St, Unity, ME 04988 *Tel:* 207-948-2208 *Fax:* 207-948-9000 *E-mail:* info@northcountrypress.com *Web Site:* www.northcountrypress.com, pg 180

North Light Books, 10151 Carver Rd, Suite 200, Blue Ash, OH 45242 *Tel:* 513-531-2690 *Toll Free Tel:* 800-666-0963 *Fax:* 513-891-7185 *Toll Free Fax:* 888-590-4082 *E-mail:* contact_us@fwmedia.com *Web Site:* www.fwmedia.com, pg 181

North Point Press, 18 W 18 St, 8th fl, New York, NY 10011 *Tel:* 212-741-6900 *Toll Free Tel:* 888-330-8477 *Fax:* 212-633-9385 *Web Site:* www.fsgbooks.com, pg 181

North River Press Publishing Corp, 27 Rosseter St, Great Barrington, MA 01230 *Tel:* 413-528-0034 *Toll Free Tel:* 800-486-2665 *Fax:* 413-528-3163 *Toll Free Fax:* 800-BOOK-FAX (266-5329) *E-mail:* info@northriverpress.com *Web Site:* www.northriverpress.com, pg 181

The North-South Institute/Institut Nord-Sud, 55 Murray St, Suite 500, Ottawa, ON K1N 5M3, Canada *Tel:* 613-241-3535 *Fax:* 613-241-7435 *E-mail:* nsi@nsi-ins.ca *Web Site:* www.nsi-ins.ca, pg 514

North Star Press of Saint Cloud Inc, PO Box 451, St Cloud, MN 56302-0451 *Tel:* 320-558-9062 *Toll Free Tel:* 888-820-1636 *Fax:* 320-558-9063 *E-mail:* info@northstarpress.com *Web Site:* www.northstarpress.com, pg 181

Northeast-Midwest Institute, 50 "F" St NW, Suite 950, Washington, DC 20001 *Tel:* 202-544-5200 *Fax:* 202-544-0043 *E-mail:* info@nemw.org *Web Site:* www.nemw.org, pg 181

Northeast Texas Community College Annual Writers Conference, Continuing Education, PO Box 1307, Mount Pleasant, TX 75456-1307 *Tel:* 903-434-8134 *Toll Free Tel:* 800-870-0142 *Fax:* 903-572-6712 *Web Site:* www.ntcc.edu, pg 671

Northeastern Graphic Inc, 25 Old Kings Rd N, Suite 3B, Palm Coast, FL 32137-8245 *Tel:* 386-246-9942 *Fax:* 386-246-9698 *Web Site:* www.northeasterngraphic.com, pg 552

Northern California Book Awards, c/o Poetry Flash, 1450 Fourth St, Suite 4, Berkeley, CA 94710 *Tel:* 510-525-5476 *Fax:* 510-525-6752 *E-mail:* editor@poetryflash.org *Web Site:* www.poetryflash.org/ncba.html, pg 729

Northern California Independent Booksellers Association (NCIBA), 1007 General Kennedy Ave, San Francisco, CA 94129 *Tel:* 415-561-7686 *Fax:* 415-561-7685 *E-mail:* office@nciba.com *Web Site:* www.nciba.com, pg 632

Northern California Translators Association, PO Box 14015, Berkeley, CA 94712-5015 *Tel:* 510-845-8712 *Fax:* 510-845-8712 *E-mail:* ncta@ncta.org *Web Site:* www.ncta.org, pg 632

Northern Illinois University Press, 2280 Bethany Rd, DeKalb, IL 60115 *Tel:* 815-753-1826; 815-753-1075 *Fax:* 815-753-1845 *Web Site:* www.niupress.niu.edu, pg 181

Northstone Publishing, 9590 Jim Bailey Rd, Kelowna, BC V4V 1R2, Canada *Tel:* 250-766-2778 *Toll Free Tel:* 800-299-2926; 800-663-2775 (orders) *Fax:* 250-766-2736 *Toll Free Fax:* 888-841-9991 *E-mail:* info@woodlakebooks.com *Web Site:* www.woodlakebooks.com, pg 514

Northwest Independent Editors Guild, PO Box 1630, Snoqualmie, WA 98065 *E-mail:* info@edsguild.org *Web Site:* www.edsguild.org, pg 632

Northwest Territories Library Services, 75 Woodland Dr, Hay River, NT X0E 1G1, Canada *Tel:* 867-874-6531 *Toll Free Tel:* 866-297-0232 (CN) *Fax:* 867-874-3321 *Web Site:* www.ece.gov.nt.ca/public_library_services/index.html, pg 632

Northwest Writers & Publishers Association (NWPA), 21860 Willamette Dr, West Linn, OR 97068 *Web Site:* northwestwriterspublishers.weebly.com, pg 632

Northwestern University Press, 629 Noyes St, Evanston, IL 60208-4210 *Tel:* 847-491-2046 *Toll Free Tel:* 800-621-2736 (orders only) *Fax:* 847-491-8150 *E-mail:* nupress@northwestern.edu *Web Site:* www.nupress.northwestern.edu, pg 181

W W Norton & Company Inc, 500 Fifth Ave, New York, NY 10110-0017 *Tel:* 212-354-5500 *Toll Free Tel:* 800-233-4830 (orders & cust serv) *Fax:* 212-869-0856 *Toll Free Fax:* 800-458-6515 *Web Site:* www.wwnorton.com, pg 181

Norwood House Press, PO Box 316598, Chicago, IL 60631 *Tel:* 773-467-0837 *Toll Free Tel:* 866-565-2900 *Fax:* 773-467-9686 *Toll Free Fax:* 866-565-2901 *E-mail:* customerservice@norwoodhousepress.com *Web Site:* www.norwoodhousepress.com, pg 182

Notable Wisconsin Authors, 4610 S Biltmore Lane, Madison, WI 53718 *Tel:* 608-245-3640 *Fax:* 608-245-3646 *Web Site:* www.wla.lib.wi.us, pg 729

Nova Press, 9058 Lloyd Place, West Hollywood, CA 90069 *Tel:* 310-275-3513 *Toll Free Tel:* 800-949-6175 *Fax:* 310-281-5629 *E-mail:* novapress@aol.com *Web Site:* www.novapress.net, pg 182

Nova Publishing Co, 1103 W College St, Carbondale, IL 62901 *Tel:* 618-457-3521 *Toll Free Tel:* 800-748-1175 (cust serv) *Fax:* 618-457-2552 *E-mail:* info@novapublishing.com *Web Site:* www.novapublishing.com, pg 182

Nova Science Publishers Inc, 400 Oser Ave, Suite 1600, Hauppauge, NY 11788-3619 *Tel:* 631-231-7269 *Fax:* 631-231-8175 *E-mail:* main@novapublishers.com *Web Site:* www.novapublishers.com, pg 182

Novalis Publishing, 10 Lower Spadina Ave, Suite 400, Toronto, ON M5V 2Z2, Canada *Tel:* 416-363-3303 *Toll Free Tel:* 877-702-7773 *Fax:* 416-363-9409 *Toll Free Fax:* 877-702-7775 *E-mail:* books@novalis.ca *Web Site:* www.novalis.ca, pg 514

Novella Prize, University of Victoria, Box 1700, Sta CSC, Victoria, BC V8W 2Y2, Canada *Tel:* 250-721-8524 *Fax:* 250-472-5051 *E-mail:* malahat@uvic.ca *Web Site:* www.malahatreview.ca, pg 729

Wanda Nowak Creative Illustrators Agency, 231 E 76 St, Suite 5-D, New York, NY 10021 *Tel:* 212-535-0438 *E-mail:* wanda@wandanow.com *Web Site:* www.wandanow.com, pg 602

NPES The Association for Suppliers of Printing, Publishing & Converting Technologies, 1899 Preston White Dr, Reston, VA 20191 *Tel:* 703-264-7200 *Fax:* 703-620-0994 *E-mail:* npes@npes.org *Web Site:* www.npes.org, pg 632

NPTA Alliance, 401 N Michigan Ave, Suite 2200, Chicago, IL 60611 *Tel:* 312-321-4092 *Toll Free Tel:* 800-355-NPTA (355-6782) *Fax:* 312-673-6736 *E-mail:* npta@gonpta.com *Web Site:* www.gonpta.com, pg 632

nSight Inc, One Van de Graaff Dr, Suite 202, Burlington, MA 01803 *Tel:* 781-273-6300 *Fax:* 781-273-6301 *E-mail:* nfritz@nsightworks.com *Web Site:* www.nsightworks.com, pg 552

NSK Neustadt Prize for Children's Literature, University of Oklahoma, Suite 110, 630 Parrington Oval, Norman, OK 73019-4033 *Tel:* 405-325-4531 *Fax:* 405-325-7495 *Web Site:* www.worldliteraturetoday.org, pg 729

Nuestras Voces National Playwriting Competition, 138 E 27 St, New York, NY 10016 *Tel:* 212-225-9950 *Fax:* 212-225-9085 *Web Site:* www.repertorio.org, pg 730

nursesbooks.org, The Publishing Program of ANA, 8515 Georgia Ave, Suite 400, Silver Spring, MD 20910-3492 *Tel:* 301-628-5000 *Toll Free Tel:* 800-924-9053; 800-637-0323 (orders) *Fax:* 301-628-5001 *E-mail:* anp@ana.org *Web Site:* www.nursesbooks.org; www.nursingworld.org, pg 182

Nystrom Herff Jones Education Division, 4719 W 62 St, Indianapolis, IN 46268-2593 *Tel:* 317-612-3901 *Toll Free Tel:* 800-621-8086 (cust serv) *Fax:* 317-329-3305 *E-mail:* info@nystromnet.com *Web Site:* www.nystromnet.com, pg 182

OAG Worldwide, 3025 Highland Pkwy, Suite 200, Downers Grove, IL 60515-5561 *Tel:* 630-515-5300 *Toll Free Tel:* 800-342-5624 (cust serv) *Fax:* 630-515-3251 *E-mail:* contactus@oag.com *Web Site:* www.oag.com, pg 182

Oak Knoll Press, 310 Delaware St, New Castle, DE 19720 *Tel:* 302-328-7232 *Toll Free Tel:* 800-996-2556 *Fax:* 302-328-7274 *E-mail:* oakknoll@oakknoll.com *Web Site:* www.oakknoll.com, pg 183

Oak Tree Press, 140 E Palmer St, Taylorville, IL 62568 *Tel:* 217-824-6500 *E-mail:* publisher@oaktreebooks.com; info@oaktreebooks.com; query@oaktreebooks.com; pressdept@oaktreebooks.com; bookorders@oaktreebooks.com *Web Site:* www.oaktreebooks.com; www.otpblog.blogspot.com, pg 183

Oaklea Press, 41 Old Mill Rd, Richmond, VA 23226-3111 *Tel:* 804-308-3906 *Fax:* 804-980-7057 *Web Site:* oakleapress.com, pg 183

Oakstone Publishing LLC, 100 Corporate Pkwy, Suite 600, Birmingham, AL 35242 *Toll Free Tel:* 800-633-4743 *Fax:* 205-995-1926 *E-mail:* service@oakstonemedical.com *Web Site:* www.oakstonepublishing.com; www.cmeonly.com; www.cdeonly.com, pg 183

Harold Ober Associates Inc, 425 Madison Ave, New York, NY 10017 *Tel:* 212-759-8600 *Fax:* 212-759-9428 *Web Site:* www.haroldober.com, pg 587

Oberlin College Press, 50 N Professor St, Oberlin, OH 44074-1091 *Tel:* 440-775-8408 *Fax:* 440-775-8124 *E-mail:* oc.press@oberlin.edu *Web Site:* www.oberlin.edu/ocpress, pg 183

Oberon Press, 145 Spruce St, Suite 205, Ottawa, ON K1R 6P1, Canada *Tel:* 613-238-3275 *Fax:* 613-238-3275 *E-mail:* oberon@sympatico.ca *Web Site:* www.oberonpress.ca, pg 514

Objective Entertainment, 609 Greenwich St, 6th fl, New York, NY 10014 *Tel:* 212-431-5454 *Fax:* 917-464-6394 *Web Site:* www.objectiveent.com, pg 587

Eli M Oboler Memorial Award, 50 E Huron St, Chicago, IL 60611 *Tel:* 312-280-4223 *Toll Free Tel:* 800-545-2433 *Fax:* 312-280-4227 *E-mail:* oif@ala.org *Web Site:* www.ala.org/ifrt, pg 730

Ocean Press, 511 Avenue of the Americas, Suite 96, New York, NY 10011-8436 *Tel:* 212-260-3690 *E-mail:* info@oceanbooks.com.au; orders@oceanbooks.com.au (orders only) *Web Site:* www.oceanbooks.com.au, pg 183

Ocean Publishing, PO Box 1080, Flagler Beach, FL 32136-1080 *Tel:* 386-517-1600 *E-mail:* publisher@oceanpublishing.org *Web Site:* www.oceanpublishing.org, pg 183

Ocean Tree Books, 1325 Cerro Gordo Rd, Santa Fe, NM 87501 *Tel:* 505-983-1412 *Fax:* 505-983-0899 *Web Site:* www.oceantree.com, pg 183

Oceana®, Law Division, 13th fl, 198 Madison Ave, New York, NY 10016-4314 *Tel:* 212-726-6000 *Toll Free Tel:* 800-451-7556 (orders only) *Fax:* 212-726-6457 (edit) *E-mail:* oxfordonline@oup.com; custserv.us@oup.com *Web Site:* www.oup.com/us, pg 184

Oceanview Publishing, CEO Center at Mediterranean Plaza, Suite 120-G, 595 Bay Isles Rd, Longboat Key, FL 34228 *Tel:* 941-387-8500 *Fax:* 941 387-0039 *Web Site:* www.oceanviewpub.com, pg 184

The Flannery O'Connor Award for Short Fiction, Main Library, 3rd fl, 320 S Jackson St, Athens, GA 30602 *Fax:* 706-369-6131 *Web Site:* www.ugapress.org, pg 730

Frank O'Connor Prize for Fiction, Texas Christian University, Dept of English, TCU Box 297270, Fort Worth, TX 76129 *Tel:* 817-257-5907 *Fax:* 817-257-7709 *E-mail:* descant@tcu.edu *Web Site:* www.descant.tcu.edu, pg 730

OCP, 5536 NE Hassalo St, Portland, OR 97213 *Tel:* 503-281-1191 *Toll Free Tel:* 800-548-8749 *Fax:* 503-282-3486 *Toll Free Fax:* 800-843-8181 *E-mail:* liturgy@ocp.org *Web Site:* www.ocp.org, pg 184

Octane Press, 808 Kinney Ave, Austin, TX 78704 *Tel:* 512-334-9441 *Fax:* 512-852-4737 *E-mail:* info@octanepress.com *Web Site:* www.octanepress.com, pg 184

Scott O'Dell Award for Historical Fiction, Hornbook, Suite 200, 56 Roland St, Boston, MA 02129 *Tel:* 617-628-8471 *Toll Free Tel:* 800-325-1170 *Web Site:* www.scottodell.com/odellaward.html, pg 730

Odyssey Books, 2421 Redwood Ct, Longmont, CO 80503-8155 *Tel:* 720-494-1473 *Fax:* 720-494-1471 *E-mail:* books@odysseybooks.net *Web Site:* cilettipublishinggroup.com, pg 184

Odyssey: The Summer Fantasy Writing Workshop, PO Box 75, Mont Vernon, NH 03057 *Tel:* 603-673-6234 *Fax:* 603-673-6234 *Web Site:* www.odysseyworkshop.org, pg 671

Dayne Ogilvie Prize, 90 Richmond St E, Suite 200, Toronto, ON M5C 1P1, Canada *Tel:* 416-504-8222 *Toll Free Tel:* 877-906-6548 *Fax:* 416-504-9090 *E-mail:* info@writerstrust.com *Web Site:* www.writerstrust.com, pg 730

Howard O'Hagan Award for Short Story, 11759 Groat Rd, Edmonton, AB T5M 3K6, Canada *Tel:* 780-422-8174 *Toll Free Tel:* 800-665-5354 (AB only) *Fax:* 780-422-2663 (attn WGA) *E-mail:* mail@writersguild.ab.ca *Web Site:* www.writersguild.ab.ca, pg 730

Ohio Genealogical Society, 611 State Rte 97 W, Bellville, OH 44813-8813 *Tel:* 419-886-1903 *Fax:* 419-886-0092 *E-mail:* ogs@ogs.org *Web Site:* www.ogs.org, pg 184

Ohio State University Foreign Language Publications, 198 Hagerty Hall, 1775 College Rd, Columbus, OH 43210-1340 *Tel:* 614-292-3838 *Toll Free Tel:* 800-678-6999 *Fax:* 614-688-3355 *E-mail:* flpubs@osu.edu *Web Site:* www.flpubs.osu.edu, pg 184

Ohio State University Press, 180 Pressey Hall, 1070 Carmack Rd, Columbus, OH 43210-1002 *Tel:* 614-292-6930 *Fax:* 614-292-2065 *Toll Free Fax:* 800-621-8476 *E-mail:* info@osupress.org *Web Site:* ohiostatepress.org, pg 184

Ohio University, English Dept, Creative Writing Program, Ohio University, English Dept, Ellis Hall, Athens, OH 45701 *Tel:* 740-593-2838 (English Dept) *Fax:* 740-593-2832 *E-mail:* english.department@ohio.edu *Web Site:* english.ohiou.edu, pg 680

Ohio University Press, 215 Columbus Rd, Suite 101, Athens, OH 45701-2979 *Tel:* 740-593-1154 *Fax:* 740-593-4536 *Web Site:* www.ohioswallow.com, pg 184

Ohioana Award for Children's Literature-Alice Louise Wood Memorial, 274 E First Ave, Suite 300, Columbus, OH 43201 *Tel:* 614-466-3831 *Fax:* 614-728-6974 *E-mail:* ohioana@ohioana.org *Web Site:* www.ohioana.org, pg 730

Ohioana Book Awards, 274 E First Ave, Suite 300, Columbus, OH 43201 *Tel:* 614-466-3831 *Fax:* 614-728-6974 *E-mail:* ohioana@ohioana.org *Web Site:* www.ohioana.org, pg 730

Ohioana Career Award, 274 E First Ave, Suite 300, Columbus, OH 43201 *Tel:* 614-466-3831 *Fax:* 614-728-6974 *E-mail:* ohioana@ohioana.org *Web Site:* www.ohioana.org, pg 730

Ohioana Citations, 274 E First Ave, Suite 300, Columbus, OH 43201 *Tel:* 614-466-3831 *Fax:* 614-728-6974 *E-mail:* ohioana@ohioana.org *Web Site:* www.ohioana.org, pg 730

Ohioana Pegasus Award, 274 E First Ave, Suite 300, Columbus, OH 43201 *Tel:* 614-466-3831 *Fax:* 614-728-6974 *E-mail:* ohioana@ohioana.org *Web Site:* www.ohioana.org, pg 731

Ohioana Poetry Award-Memorial to Helen & Laura Krout, 274 E First Ave, Suite 300, Columbus, OH 43201 *Tel:* 614-466-3831 *Fax:* 614-728-6974 *E-mail:* ohioana@ohioana.org *Web Site:* www.ohioana.org, pg 731

Ohioana Walter Rumsey Marvin Grant, 274 E First Ave, Suite 300, Columbus, OH 43201 *Tel:* 614-466-3831 *Fax:* 614-728-6974 *E-mail:* ohioana@ohioana.org *Web Site:* www.ohioana.org, pg 731

Old Barn Enterprises Inc, 600 Kelly Rd, Carthage, NC 28327 *Tel:* 910-947-2587 *Fax:* 480-287-9017 *E-mail:* jeffandpam@nynphotoschool.com *Web Site:* www.nynphotoschool.com, pg 184

Olde & Oppenheim Publishers, 3219 N Margate Place, Chandler, AZ 85224 *E-mail:* olde_oppenheim@hotmail.com *Web Site:* oldeandoppenheimpublishers.com, pg 185

Veronica Oliva, PO Box 460365, San Francisco, CA 94146-0365 *Tel:* 415-337-7707 *E-mail:* veronicaoliva@sbcglobal.net; veronicaoliva.oliva@gmail.net, pg 552

The Oliver Press Inc, Charlotte Sq, 5707 W 36 St, Minneapolis, MN 55416-2510 *Tel:* 952-926-8981 *Toll Free Tel:* 800-8-OLIVER (865-4837) *Fax:* 952-926-8965 *E-mail:* orders@oliverpress.com *Web Site:* www.oliverpress.com, pg 185

Chris O'Malley Fiction Prize, University of Wisconsin, 6193 Helen C White Hall, English Dept, 600 N Park St, Madison, WI 53706 *Tel:* 608-263-0566 *E-mail:* madisonrevw@gmail.com *Web Site:* www.english.wisc.edu/madisonreview, pg 731

OMNI Publishers Inc, 29131 Bulverde Rd, San Antonio, TX 78260 *Tel:* 210-778-4437 *Fax:* 830-438-4645 *Web Site:* www.omnipublishers.com; www.educatorethicsseries.com, pg 185

Omnibus Press, 257 Park Ave S, 20th fl, New York, NY 10010 *Tel:* 212-254-2100 *Toll Free Tel:* 800-431-7187 *Fax:* 212-254-2013 *Toll Free Fax:* 800-345-6842 *E-mail:* info-us@omnibuspress.com *Web Site:* www.musicsales.com; omnibuspressusa.com, pg 185

Omnidawn Publishing, 1632 Elm Ave, Richmond, CA 94805-1614 *Tel:* 510-237-5472 *Toll Free Tel:* 800-792-4957 *Fax:* 510-232-8525 *E-mail:* manager@omnidawn.com *Web Site:* www.omnidawn.com, pg 185

Omnigraphics Inc, 155 W Congress, Suite 200, Detroit, MI 48226 *Tel:* 313-961-1340 *Toll Free Tel:* 800-234-1340 (cust serv) *Fax:* 313-961-1383 *Toll Free Fax:* 800-875-1340 (cust serv) *E-mail:* info@omnigraphics.com *Web Site:* www.omnigraphics.com, pg 185

Omohundro Institute of Early American History & Culture, Swem Library, Ground fl, 400 Landrum Dr, Williamsburg, VA 23185 *Tel:* 757-221-1110 *Fax:* 757-221-1047 *E-mail:* ieahc1@wm.edu *Web Site:* oieahc.wm.edu, pg 185

One Act Play Depot, Box 335, 618 Memorial Dr, Spiritwood, SK S0J 2M0, Canada *E-mail:* plays@oneactplays.net; orders@oneactplays.net *Web Site:* oneactplays.net, pg 514

OneSource, 300 Baker Ave, Concord, MA 01742 *Tel:* 978-318-4300 *Toll Free Tel:* 866-354-6936 *Fax:* 978-318-4690 *E-mail:* sales@onesource.com *Web Site:* www.onesource.com, pg 185

Online Training Solutions Inc (OTSI), 2217 152 Ave NE, Redmond, WA 98052 *Toll Free Tel:* 888-308-6874 *Toll Free Fax:* 888-308-6875 *Web Site:* www.otsi.com, pg 185

Ontario Library Association, 50 Wellington St E, Suite 201, Toronto, ON M5E 1C8, Canada *Tel:* 416-363-3388 *Toll Free Tel:* 866-873-9867 *Fax:* 416-941-9581 *Toll Free Fax:* 800-387-1181 *E-mail:* info@accessola.com *Web Site:* www.accessola.com, pg 632

Oolichan Books, PO Box 2278, Fernie, BC V0B 1M0, Canada *Tel:* 250-423-6113 *E-mail:* info@oolichan.com *Web Site:* www.oolichan.com, pg 514

Ooligan Press, Portland State University, 369 Neuberger Hall, 724 SW Harrison St, Portland, OR 97201 *Tel:* 503-725-9748 *Fax:* 503-725-3561 *E-mail:* ooligan@ooliganpress.pdx.edu *Web Site:* ooligan.pdx.edu, pg 185

Open Chapbook Competition, PO Box 1626, Georgetown, KY 40324 *Tel:* 859-514-8966 *E-mail:* finishingbooks@aol.com; flpbookstore@aol.com *Web Site:* www.finishinglinepress.com, pg 731

Open Court, 70 E Lake St, Suite 300, Chicago, IL 60601 *Tel:* 312-701-1720 *Toll Free Tel:* 800-815-2280 (orders only) *Fax:* 312-701-1728 *E-mail:* opencourt@caruspub.com *Web Site:* www.opencourtbooks.com, pg 185

Open Horizons Publishing Co, PO Box 2887, Taos, NM 87571 *Tel:* 575-751-3398 *Fax:* 575-751-3100 *E-mail:* info@bookmarket.com *Web Site:* www.bookmarket.com, pg 186

Open Road Publishing, PO Box 284, Cold Spring Harbor, NY 11724-0284 *Tel:* 631-692-7172 *E-mail:* jopenroad@aol.com *Web Site:* www.openroadguides.com, pg 186

Open Season Awards, University of Victoria, Box 1700, Sta CSC, Victoria, BC V8W 2Y2, Canada *Tel:* 250-721-8524 *Fax:* 250-472-5051 *E-mail:* malahat@uvic.ca *Web Site:* malahatreview.ca, pg 731

Opie Prize, Ohio State Univ, Mershon Ctr, 1501 Neil Ave, Columbus, OH 43201-2602 *Tel:* 614-292-3375 *Fax:* 614-292-2407 *Web Site:* www.afsnet.org/aboutAFS/AFSprizes.cfm, pg 731

OPIS/STALSBY Directories & Databases, 3349 Hwy 138, Bldg D, Suite D, Wall, NJ 07719 *Tel:* 732-901-8800 *Toll Free Tel:* 800-275-0950 *Toll Free Fax:* 800-450-5864 *E-mail:* opisstalsbylistings@opisnet.com *Web Site:* www.opisnet.com, pg 186

Optometric Extension Program Foundation, 1921 E Carnegie Ave, Suite 3-L, Santa Ana, CA 92705-5510 *Tel:* 949-250-8070 *Fax:* 949-250-8157 *E-mail:* oep@oep.org *Web Site:* www.oepf.org, pg 186

OptumInsight™, 12125 Technology Dr, Eden Prairie, MN 55334 *Tel:* 952-833-7100 *Toll Free Tel:* 888-445-8745; 800-765-6713 *Fax:* 952-833-7201 *E-mail:* insight@optum.com *Web Site:* www.optuminsight.com, pg 186

Orange Frazer Press Inc, 37 1/2 W Main St, Wilmington, OH 45177 *Tel:* 937-382-3196 *Toll Free Tel:* 800-852-9332 (orders) *Fax:* 937-383-3159 *E-mail:* ofrazer@erinet.com *Web Site:* www.orangefrazer.com, pg 186

Orbis Books, Price Bldg, 85 Ryder Rd, Ossining, NY 10562 *Tel:* 914-941-7636 *Toll Free Tel:* 800-258-5838 (orders) *Fax:* 914-941-7005 *E-mail:* orbisbooks@maryknoll.org *Web Site:* www.orbisbooks.com, pg 186

Orbit, 237 Park Ave, New York, NY 10017 *Tel:* 212-364-1100 *Toll Free Tel:* 800-759-0190 *Web Site:* www.orbitbooks.net, pg 186

Orca Book Publishers, PO Box 468, Custer, WA 98240-0468 *Tel:* 250-380-1229 *Toll Free Tel:* 800-210-5277 *Fax:* 250-380-1892 *Toll Free Fax:* 877-408-1551 *E-mail:* orca@orcabook.com *Web Site:* www.orcabook.com, pg 186

Orchard Publications, 39510 Paseo Padre Pkwy, Suite 315, Fremont, CA 94538 *Tel:* 510-792-6077 *Fax:* 510-792-6097 *E-mail:* info@orchardpublications.com; orchard@orchardpublications.com *Web Site:* www.orchardpublications.com, pg 187

Orchises Press, PO Box 320533, Alexandria, VA 22320-4533 *Tel:* 703-683-1243 *Web Site:* mason.gmu.edu/~lathbury/, pg 187

Ordre des traducteurs, terminologues et interpretes agrees du quebec, 2021 Union Ave, Suite 1108, Montreal, QC H3A 2S9, Canada *Tel:* 514-845-4411 *Toll Free Tel:* 800-265-4815 *Fax:* 514-845-9903 *E-mail:* info@ottiaq.org *Web Site:* www.ottiaq.org, pg 633

Oregon Christian Writers (OCW), 1075 Willow Lake Rd N, Keizer, OR 97303 *Tel:* 503-393-3356 *E-mail:* contact@oregonchristianwriters.org *Web Site:* www.oregonchristianwriters.org, pg 633

Oregon Christian Writers Coaching Conference, 1075 Willow Lake Rd N, Keizer, OR 97303 *Tel:* 503-393-3356 *E-mail:* contact@oregonchristianwriters.org *Web Site:* www.oregonchristianwriters.org, pg 671

Oregon Christian Writers Seminar, 1075 Willow Lake Rd N, Keizer, OR 97303 *Tel:* 503-393-3356 *E-mail:* contact@oregonchristianwriters.org *Web Site:* www.oregonchristianwriters.org, pg 671

Oregon State University Press, 121 The Valley Library, Corvallis, OR 97331-4501 *Tel:* 541-737-3166 *Toll Free Tel:* 800-621-2736 (orders) *Fax:* 541-737-3170 *Toll Free Fax:* 800-426-3797 (orders) *E-mail:* osu.press@oregonstate.edu *Web Site:* oregonstate.edu/dept/press; osupress.oregonstate.edu, pg 187

O'Reilly Media Inc, 1005 Gravenstein Hwy N, Sebastopol, CA 95472 *Tel:* 707-827-7000; 707-827-7019 *Toll Free Tel:* 800-998-9938; 800-889-8969 *Fax:* 707-829-0104; 707-824-8268 *E-mail:* orders@oreilly.com *Web Site:* www.oreilly.com, pg 187

Organization for Economic Cooperation & Development, 2001 "L" St NW, Suite 650, Washington, DC 20036-4922 *Tel:* 202-785-6323 *Toll Free Tel:* 800-456-6323 (dist ctr/pubns orders) *Fax:* 202-785-0350 *E-mail:* washington.contact@oecd.org *Web Site:* www.oecdwash.org; www.oecd.org, pg 187

Organization of Book Publishers of Ontario, 20 Maud St, No 401, Toronto, ON M5V 2M5, Canada *Tel:* 416-536-7584 *Fax:* 416-536-7692 *Web Site:* www.ontariobooks.ca, pg 633

Oriental Institute Publications, 1155 E 58 St, Chicago, IL 60637 *Tel:* 773-702-5967 *Fax:* 773-702-9853 *E-mail:* oi-publications@uchicago.edu; oi-museum@uchicago.edu; oi-administration@uchicago.edu *Web Site:* oi.uchicago.edu, pg 188

Orientation to the Graphic Arts, 200 Deer Run Rd, Sewickley, PA 15143-2600 *Tel:* 412-259-1711 *Toll Free Tel:* 800-910-4283 *Fax:* 412-741-2311 *E-mail:* printing@printing.org *Web Site:* www.printing.org, pg 671

The Original Falcon Press, 1753 E Broadway Rd, No 101-277, Tempe, AZ 85282 *Tel:* 602-708-1409 *E-mail:* info@originalfalcon.com *Web Site:* www.originalfalcon.com, pg 188

Original Publications, PO Box 236, Old Beth Page, NY 11804 *Tel:* 516-605-0547 *Toll Free Tel:* 888-622-8581 *Fax:* 516-605-0549 *E-mail:* originalpub@aol.com *Web Site:* www.occult1.com, pg 188

Orion Book Services, 751 South St, West Brattleboro, VT 05301-4234 *Tel:* 802-254-8783 (press 2) *Fax:* 802-254-8783 (call first) *E-mail:* gr8books@myfairpoint.net, pg 552

ORO editions, 31 Commercial Blvd, Suite F, Novato, CA 94949 *Tel:* 415-883-3300 *Fax:* 415-883-3309 *E-mail:* info@oroeditions.com *Web Site:* www.oroeditions.com, pg 188

George Orwell Award, 1111 W Kenyon Rd, Urbana, IL 61801-1096 *Tel:* 217-328-3870 *Toll Free Tel:* 877-369-6283 (cust serv) *Fax:* 217-328-0977 *E-mail:* publiclangawards@ncte.org *Web Site:* www.ncte.org, pg 731

OSA, The Optical Society, 2010 Massachusetts Ave NW, Washington, DC 20036-1023 *Tel:* 202-223-8130 *Toll Free Tel:* 800-766-4672 *E-mail:* custserv@osa.org *Web Site:* www.osa.org, pg 188

Fifi Oscard Agency Inc, 110 W 40 St, 16th fl, New York, NY 10018 *Tel:* 212-764-1100 *Fax:* 212-840-5019 *E-mail:* agency@fifioscard.com *Web Site:* www.fifioscard.com, pg 587

Osprey Publishing Inc, 4301 21 St, Suite 220B, Long Island City, NY 11101 *Tel:* 718-433-4402 *Fax:* 718-433-4497 *E-mail:* ospreyusa@ospreypublishing.com *Web Site:* www.ospreypublishing.com, pg 188

Other Press LLC, 2 Park Ave, 24th fl, New York, NY 10016 *Tel:* 212-414-0054 *Toll Free Tel:* 877-843-6843 *Fax:* 212-414-0939 *E-mail:* editor@otherpress.com; rights@otherpress.com *Web Site:* www.otherpress.com, pg 188

OTTN Publishing, 16 Risler St, Stockton, NJ 08559 *Tel:* 609-397-4005 *Toll Free Tel:* 866-356-6886 *Fax:* 609-397-4007 *E-mail:* inquiries@ottnpublishing.com *Web Site:* www.ottnpublishing.com, pg 188

Our Sunday Visitor Publishing, 200 Noll Plaza, Huntington, IN 46750 *Tel:* 260-356-8400 *Toll Free Tel:* 800-348-2440 (orders) *Fax:* 260-356-8472 *Toll Free Fax:* 800-498-6709 *E-mail:* osvbooks@osv.com (book orders) *Web Site:* www.osv.com, pg 188

OUT OF YOUR MIND...AND INTO THE MARKETPLACE™, 13381 White Sand Dr, Tustin, CA 92780-4565 *Tel:* 714-544-0248 *Toll Free Tel:* 800-419-1513 *Fax:* 714-730-1414 *Web Site:* www.business-plan.com, pg 189

Outdoor Writers Association of America Annual Conference, 615 Oak St, Suite 201, Missoula, MT 59801 *Tel:* 406-728-7434 *Fax:* 406-728-7445 *E-mail:* info@owaa.org *Web Site:* www.owaa.org, pg 671

The Overlook Press, 141 Wooster St, Suite 4-B, New York, NY 10012 *Tel:* 212-673-2210; 845-679-6838 (orders & dist) *Fax:* 212-673-2296 *E-mail:* sales@overlookny.com (orders) *Web Site:* www.overlookpress.com, pg 189

The Overmountain Press, PO Box 1261, Johnson City, TN 37605-1261 *Tel:* 423-926-2691 *Toll Free Tel:* 800-992-2691 (orders) *Fax:* 423-232-1252 *E-mail:* orders@overmtn.com *Web Site:* www.overmtn.com, pg 189

Overseas Press Club of America (OPC), 40 W 45 St, New York, NY 10036 *Tel:* 212-626-9220 *Fax:* 212-626-9210 *Web Site:* www.opcofamerica.org, pg 633

Richard C Owen Publishers Inc, PO Box 585, Katonah, NY 10536-0585 *Tel:* 914-232-3903 *Toll Free Tel:* 800-336-5588 *Fax:* 914-232-3977 *E-mail:* rcostaff@rcowen.com *Web Site:* www.rcowen.com, pg 189

Owl About Books Publisher Inc, 1632 Royalwood Circle, Joshua, TX 76058 *Tel:* 682-553-9078 *Fax:* 817-558-8983 *E-mail:* owlaboutbooks@gmail.com *Web Site:* www.owlaboutbooks.com, pg 189

Owlkids Books Inc, 10 Lower Spadina Ave, Suite 400, Toronto, ON M5V 2Z2, Canada *Tel:* 416-340-3700 *Fax:* 416-340-9769 *E-mail:* owlkids@owlkids.com *Web Site:* www.owlkidsbooks.com, pg 514

Frank L & Harriet C Owsley Award, University of Georgia, Dept of History, Athens, GA 30602-1602 *Tel:* 706-542-8848 *Fax:* 706-542-2455 *Web Site:* sha.uga.edu, pg 731

Oxbridge® Communications Inc, 39 W 29 St, Suite 301, New York, NY 10001 *Tel:* 212-741-0231 *Toll Free Tel:* 800-955-0231 *Fax:* 212-633-2938 *E-mail:* info@oxbridge.com *Web Site:* www.oxbridge.com, pg 189

Oxford University Press USA, 198 Madison Ave, New York, NY 10016 *Tel:* 212-726-6000 *Toll Free Tel:* 800-451-7556 (orders); 800-445-9714 (cust serv) *Fax:* 919-677-1303 *E-mail:* custserv.us@oup.com *Web Site:* www.oup.com/us, pg 189

Oxmoor House Inc, 2100 Lakeshore Dr, Birmingham, AL 35209 *Tel:* 205-445-6000 *Toll Free Tel:* 800-366-4712; 888-891-8935 (cust serv); 800-765-6400 (orders) *Web Site:* www.oxmoorhouse.com, pg 190

Oyster River Press, 36 Oyster River Rd, Durham, NH 03824-3029 *Tel:* 603-868-5006 *E-mail:* oysterriverpress@comcast.net *Web Site:* www.oysterriverpress.com, pg 552

Ozark Creative Writers Inc Annual Conference, PO Box 424, Eureka Springs, AR 72632 *Tel:* 479-751-7246 *E-mail:* ozarkcreativewriters@gmail.com *Web Site:* www.ozarkcreativewriters.org, pg 671

Ozark Mountain Publishing Inc, PO Box 754, Huntsville, AR 72740-0754 *Tel:* 479-738-2348 *Toll Free Tel:* 800-935-0045 *Fax:* 479-738-2448 *E-mail:* info@ozarkmt.com *Web Site:* www.ozarkmt.com, pg 190

Ozark Publishing Inc, PO Box 228, Prairie Grove, AR 72753-0228 *Tel:* 479-595-9522 *Toll Free Tel:* 800-321-5671 *Fax:* 479-846-2843 *E-mail:* srg304@yahoo.com *Web Site:* www.ozarkpublishing.us, pg 190

P & R Publishing Co, 1102 Marble Hill Rd, Phillipsburg, NJ 08865 *Tel:* 908-454-0505 *Toll Free Tel:* 800-631-0094 *Fax:* 908-859-2390 *E-mail:* sales@prpbooks.com; generalinfo@prpbooks.com *Web Site:* prpbooks.com, pg 190

P R B Productions, 963 Peralta Ave, Albany, CA 94706-2144 *Tel:* 510-526-0722 *Fax:* 510-527-4763 *E-mail:* prbprdns@aol.com *Web Site:* www.prbmusic.com, pg 190

P S M J Resources Inc, 10 Midland Ave, Newton, MA 02458 *Tel:* 617-965-0055 *Toll Free Tel:* 800-537-7765 *Fax:* 617-965-5152 *E-mail:* info@psmj.com *Web Site:* www.psmj.com, pg 190

Pace University, Master of Science in Publishing, Dept of Publishing, Rm 805-E, 551 Fifth Ave, New York, NY 10176 *Tel:* 212-346-1431 *Toll Free Tel:* 877-284-7670 *Fax:* 212-346-1165 *Web Site:* www.pace.edu/dyson/mspub, pg 680

Pace University Press, Dept of Publishing, Rm 805-E, 551 Fifth Ave, New York, NY 10176 *Tel:* 212-346-1417 *Fax:* 212-346-1165 *Web Site:* www.pace.edu/press, pg 190

Pacific Educational Press, c/o University of British Columbia, Faculty of Education, 411-2389 Health Sciences Mall, Vancouver, BC V6T 1Z4, Canada *Tel:* 604-822-5385 *Fax:* 604-822-6603 *E-mail:* pep.sales@ubc.ca *Web Site:* www.pacificedpress.ca, pg 514

Pacific Northwest Book Awards, 338 W 11 Ave, Unit 108, Eugene, OR 97401 *Tel:* 541-683-4363 *Fax:* 541-683-3910 *E-mail:* info@pnba.org *Web Site:* www.pnba.org, pg 731

Pacific Northwest Booksellers Association, 338 W 11 Ave, Unit 108, Eugene, OR 97401 *Tel:* 541-683-4363 *Fax:* 541-683-3910 *E-mail:* info@pnba.org *Web Site:* www.pnba.org; www.northwestbooklovers.org (public site), pg 633

Pacific Northwest Children's Book Conference, 615 SW Harrison St, Portland, OR 97201 *Tel:* 503-725-9786 *Toll Free Tel:* 800-547-8887 (ext 9786) *Fax:* 503-725-5599 *Web Site:* www.pdx.edu/ceed/childrens-book-conference, pg 671

Pacific Northwest Summer Writers Conference, 1420 NW Gilman Blvd, Suite 2, PMB 2717, Issaquah, WA 98027 *Tel:* 425-673-2665 *E-mail:* pnwa@pnwa.org *Web Site:* www.pnwa.org, pg 672

Pacific Northwest Writers Association, 1420 NW Gilman Blvd, Suite 2, PMB 2717, Issaquah, WA 98027 *Tel:* 425-673-2665 *Fax:* 425-961-0768 *E-mail:* pnwa@pnwa.org *Web Site:* www.pnwa.org, pg 633

Pacific Northwest Young Reader's Choice Award, Vancouver Mall Community Library, 8700 NE Vancouver Mall Dr, Suite 285, Vancouver, WA 98662 *Tel:* 360-892-8256 *Web Site:* www.pnla.org/yrca, pg 731

Pacific Press Publishing Association, 1350 N Kings Rd, Nampa, ID 83687-3193 *Tel:* 208-465-2500 *Toll Free Tel:* 800-447-7377 *Fax:* 208-465-2531 *Web Site:* www.pacificpress.com, pg 190

Pacific Printing Industries Association, 6825 SW Sandburg St, Portland, OR 97223 *Tel:* 503-221-3944 *Toll Free Tel:* 877-762-7742 *Fax:* 503-221-5691 *E-mail:* info@ppiassociation.org *Web Site:* www.ppiassociation.org, pg 633

Pacific Publishing Services, PO Box 1150, Capitola, CA 95010-1150 *Tel:* 831-476-8284 *Fax:* 831-476-8294 *E-mail:* pacpub@attglobal.net, pg 552

PAGE International Screenwriting Awards, 7510 Sunset Blvd, Suite 610, Hollywood, CA 90046 *E-mail:* info@pageawards.com *Web Site:* www.pageawards.com, pg 731

Paintbox Press, 275 Madison Ave, Suite 600, New York, NY 10016 *Tel:* 212-878-6610 *Fax:* 212-202-6157 *E-mail:* info@paintboxpress.com *Web Site:* www.paintboxpress.com, pg 190

Painted Hills Publishing, 16500 Dakota Ridge Rd, Longmont, CO 80503 *Tel:* 303-823-6642 *Fax:* 303-825-5119 *E-mail:* cw@livingimagescjw.com *Web Site:* www.wildhoofbeats.com; www.horsephotographyworkshops.com, pg 528

Painted Pony Inc, 3 Ethete Rd, Fort Washakie, WY 82514 *Tel:* 307-335-7330 *Toll Free Tel:* 877-253-3824 *Fax:* 307-335-7332 *E-mail:* ppi@wrdf.org *Web Site:* www.paintedponyinc.com, pg 191

Painted-Words Inc, 310 W 97 St, Suite 24, New York, NY 10025 *Tel:* 212-663-2311 *Fax:* 212-663-2891 *E-mail:* info@painted-words.com *Web Site:* www.painted-words.com, pg 602

Dobie Paisano Fellowship Program, Graduate School, 110 Inner Campus Dr, Stop G0400, Austin, TX 78712-0710 *Fax:* 512-471-7620 *Web Site:* www.utexas.edu/ogs/Paisano, pg 732

Paladin Press, Gunbarrel Tech Ctr, 7077 Winchester Circle, Boulder, CO 80301 *Tel:* 303-443-7250 *Toll Free Tel:* 800-392-2400 *Fax:* 303-442-8741 *E-mail:* service@paladin-press.com *Web Site:* www.paladin-press.com, pg 191

Palgrave Macmillan, 175 Fifth Ave, Suite 200, New York, NY 10010 *Tel:* 646-307-5151 *Fax:* 212-777-6359 *E-mail:* firstname.lastname@palgrave-usa.com *Web Site:* us.macmillan.com/Palgrave.aspx, pg 191

Palimpsest Press, 5 King St, Kingsville, ON N9Y 1H9, Canada *Tel:* 519-563-9981 *E-mail:* info@palimpsestpress.ca *Web Site:* www.palimpsestpress.ca, pg 515

Palindrome Press, PO Box 4151, Fairfax, VA 22124-8151 *Tel:* 703-242-1734 *Fax:* 703-242-1734 *E-mail:* palindromepress@yahoo.com, pg 191

Palladium Books Inc, 39074 Webb Ct, Westland, MI 48185 *Tel:* 734-721-2903 (orders) *Fax:* 734-721-1238 *Web Site:* www.palladiumbooks.com, pg 191

Palm Island Press, 411 Truman Ave, Key West, FL 33040 *Tel:* 305-296-3102 *E-mail:* pipress2@gmail.com, pg 191

Palm Kids™, 50 Washington St, 12th fl, Norwalk, CT 06854 *Toll Free Tel:* 800-409-2457 *E-mail:* customercare@palmkids.com; sales@palmkids.com *Web Site:* www.palmkids.com, pg 191

Palm Springs Writers Guild, PO Box 947, Rancho Mirage, CA 92270-0947 *Web Site:* www.palmspringswritersguild.org, pg 633

Palmetto Bug Books, 121 N Hibiscus Dr, Miami Beach, FL 33139 *Tel:* 305-531-9813 *Fax:* 305-604-1516 *E-mail:* palmettobugbooks@gmail.com, pg 191

Pangaea Publications, 226 Wheeler St S, St Paul, MN 55105-1927 *Tel:* 651-226-2032 *Fax:* 651-226-2032 *E-mail:* info@pangaea.org *Web Site:* pangaea.org, pg 191

Karen L Pangallo, 27 Buffum St, Salem, MA 01970 *Tel:* 978-744-8796 *E-mail:* pangallo@noblenet.org, pg 552

Panoptic Enterprises, PO Box 11220, Burke, VA 22009-1220 *Tel:* 703-451-5953 *Toll Free Tel:* 800-594-4766 *Fax:* 703-451-5953 *E-mail:* panoptic@fedgovcontracts.com *Web Site:* www.fedgovcontracts.com, pg 191

Mildred & Albert Panowski Playwriting Award, Forest Roberts Theatre, 1401 Presque Isle Ave, Marquette, MI 49855-5364 *Tel:* 906-227-2553 *Fax:* 906-227-2567 *Web Site:* www.nmu.edu/theatre, pg 732

Pantheon Books/Schocken Books, c/o Random House Inc, 1745 Broadway, New York, NY 10019 *Tel:* 212-751-2600 *Toll Free Tel:* 800-638-6460 *Fax:* 212-572-6030, pg 191

Pants On Fire Press, 2062 Harbor Cove Way, Winter Garden, FL 34787 *Tel:* 863-546-0760 *E-mail:* submission@pantsonfirepress.com *Web Site:* www.pantsonfirepress.com, pg 192

Paper Thoughts Publishing, PO Box 13003, Coyote, CA 95013 *Tel:* 408-782-4407 *E-mail:* paperthougthspub@aol.com *Web Site:* paperthoughtspublishing.com, pg 192

Papercutz, 40 Exchange Place, Suite 1308, New York, NY 10005 *Tel:* 212-643-5407 *Toll Free Tel:* 800-886-1223 *Fax:* 212-643-1545 *E-mail:* papercutz@papercutz.com *Web Site:* www.papercutz.com, pg 192

Para Publishing LLC, PO Box 8206-240, Santa Barbara, CA 93118-8206 *Tel:* 805-968-7277 *Toll Free Tel:* 800-727-2782 *Fax:* 805-968-1379 *Web Site:* www.parapublishing.com, pg 192

Parabola Books, 20 W 20 St, 2nd fl, New York, NY 10011 *Tel:* 212-822-8806 *Toll Free Tel:* 800-592-2521 (subns) *Fax:* 212-822-8823 *E-mail:* info@parabola.org *Web Site:* www.parabola.org, pg 192

Parachute Publishing LLC, 322 Eighth Ave, Suite 702, New York, NY 10001 *Tel:* 212-691-1422 *Fax:* 212-645-8769 *E-mail:* tlabreglia@parachutepublishing.com *Web Site:* www.parachutepublishing.com, pg 192

Paraclete Press Inc, 36 Southern Eagle Cartway, Brewster, MA 02631 *Tel:* 508-255-4685 *Toll Free Tel:* 800-451-5006 *Fax:* 508-255-5705 *E-mail:* mail@paracletepress.com *Web Site:* www.paracletepress.com, pg 192

Paradigm Publications, 202 Bendix Dr, Taos, NM 87571 *Tel:* 575-758-7758 *Toll Free Tel:* 800-873-3946 (US); 888-873-3947 (CN) *Fax:* 575-758-7768 *Web Site:* www.paradigm-pubs.com; www.redwingbooks.com, pg 192

Paradigm Publishers, 5589 Arapahoe Ave, Suite 206A, Boulder, CO 80303 *Tel:* 303-245-9054 *Web Site:* www.paradigmpublishers.com, pg 193

Paradise Cay Publications Inc, 550 S "G" St, Suite 1, Arcata, CA 95521 *Tel:* 707-822-9063 *Toll Free Tel:* 800-736-4509 *Fax:* 707-822-9163 *E-mail:* info@paracay.com *Web Site:* www.paracay.com, pg 193

Paragon House, 1925 Oakcrest Ave, Suite 7, St Paul, MN 55113-2619 *Tel:* 651-644-3087 *Toll Free Tel:* 800-447-3709 *Fax:* 651-644-0997 *E-mail:* paragon@paragonhouse.com *Web Site:* www.paragonhouse.com, pg 193

Parallax Press, 2236-B Sixth St, Berkeley, CA 94710 *Tel:* 510-525-0101 *Toll Free Tel:* 800-863-5290 (orders) *Fax:* 510-525-7129 *E-mail:* info@parallax.org *Web Site:* www.parallax.org, pg 193

Paramount Market Publishing Inc, 950 Danby Rd, Suite 136, Ithaca, NY 14850 *Tel:* 607-275-8100 *Toll Free Tel:* 888-787-8100 *Fax:* 607-275-8101 *E-mail:* editors@paramountbooks.com *Web Site:* www.paramountbooks.com, pg 193

Paraphrase LLC, PO Box 56508, Sherman Oaks, CA 91413 *Tel:* 818-219-4377 *Toll Free Fax:* 888-863-4377 *E-mail:* books@paraphrasellc.com *Web Site:* www.paraphrasellc.com, pg 528

Paraview Literary Agency, 110 Martin Dr, Bracey, VA 23919 *Tel:* 434-636-4138 *Web Site:* www.paraviewliteraryagency.com, pg 588

Parenting Press Inc, 11065 Fifth Ave NE, Suite F, Seattle, WA 98125 *Tel:* 206-364-2900 *Toll Free Tel:* 800-99-BOOKS (992-6657) *Fax:* 206-364-0702 *E-mail:* office@parentingpress.com; marketing@parentingpress.com *Web Site:* www.parentingpress.com, pg 193

Park Genealogical Books, PO Box 130968, Roseville, MN 55113-0968 *Tel:* 651-488-4416 *Fax:* 651-488-2653 *Web Site:* www.parkbooks.com, pg 193

Park Place Publications, 591 Lighthouse Ave, Suite 10, Pacific Grove, CA 93950 *Tel:* 831-649-6640 *Toll Free Tel:* 888-702-4500 *E-mail:* publishingbiz@sbcglobal.net *Web Site:* www.parkplacepublications.com, pg 193

Francis Parkman Prize, 603 Fayerweather, MC 2538, New York, NY 10027 *Tel:* 212-854-6495 *E-mail:* amhistsociety@columbia.edu *Web Site:* sah.columbia.edu, pg 732

The Richard Parks Agency, PO Box 693, Salem, NY 12865 *Tel:* 518-854-9466 *Fax:* 518-854-9466 *E-mail:* rp@richardparksagency.com, pg 588

Parlay Press, 301 Central Ave, No 311, Hilton Head, SC 29926 *Toll Free Fax:* 888-301-3116 *E-mail:* mail@parlaypress.com *Web Site:* www.parlaypress.com, pg 194

Parmenides Publishing, 3753 Howard Hughes Pkwy, Suite 200, Las Vegas, NV 89169 *Tel:* 702-892-3934 *Fax:* 702-892-3939 *E-mail:* info@parmenides.com *Web Site:* www.parmenides.com, pg 194

Parsons School of Design, Continuing Education, 66 Fifth Ave, New York, NY 10011 *Tel:* 212-229-8933 *Fax:* 212-229-5970 *E-mail:* ceinformation@newschool.edu; academy@newschool.edu *Web Site:* www.parsons.edu/ce, pg 680

Pastoral Press, 5536 NE Hassalo, Portland, OR 97213-3638 *Tel:* 503-281-1191 *Toll Free Tel:* 800-548-8749 *Fax:* 503-282-3486 *Toll Free Fax:* 800-462-7329 *E-mail:* liturgy@ocp.org *Web Site:* www.ocp.org, pg 194

The Paterson Fiction Prize, One College Blvd, Paterson, NJ 07505-1179 *Tel:* 973-684-6555 *Fax:* 973-523-6085 *Web Site:* www.pccc.edu/poetry, pg 732

The Paterson Poetry Prize, One College Blvd, Paterson, NJ 07505-1179 *Tel:* 973-684-6555 *Fax:* 973-523-6085 *Web Site:* www.pccc.edu/poetry, pg 732

The Paterson Prize for Books for Young People, One College Blvd, Paterson, NJ 07505-1179 *Tel:* 973-684-6555 *Fax:* 973-523-6085 *Web Site:* www.pccc.edu/poetry, pg 732

Path Press Inc, 1229 Emerson St, Evanston, IL 60201 *Tel:* 847-492-0177 *E-mail:* pathpressinc@aol.com, pg 194

Pathfinder Publishing Inc, 120 S Houghton Rd, Suite 138, Tucson, AZ 85748 *Tel:* 520-647-0158 *Toll Free Tel:* 800-977-2282 *Fax:* 520-647-0160 *Web Site:* www.pathfinderpublishing.com, pg 194

Kathi J Paton Literary Agency, Box 2236, Radio City Sta, New York, NY 10101-2236 *Tel:* 212-265-6586 *Fax:* 908-647-2117 *E-mail:* kjplitbiz@optonline.net *Web Site:* www.patonliterary.com, pg 588

Patria Press Inc, PO Box 752, Carmel, IN 46082 *Tel:* 317-577-1321 *Fax:* 413-215-8030 *E-mail:* moreinfo@patriapress.com *Web Site:* www.patriapress.com; www.facebook.com/YoungPatriotsBooks; twitter.com/#!/kidsbios, pg 194

Diane Patrick, 140 Carver Loop, No 21A, Bronx, NY 10475-2954 *E-mail:* dpatrickediting@aol.com *Web Site:* www.dianepatrick.net, pg 552

The Alicia Patterson Foundation Fellowship Program, 1090 Vermont Ave, Suite 1000, Washington, DC 20005 *Tel:* 202-393-5995 *Fax:* 301-951-8512 *E-mail:* info@aliciapatterson.org *Web Site:* www.aliciapatterson.org, pg 732

Paul Dry Books, 1616 Walnut St, Suite 808, Philadelphia, PA 19103 *Tel:* 215-231-9939 *Fax:* 215-231-9942 *E-mail:* editor@pauldrybooks.com *Web Site:* www.pauldrybooks.com, pg 194

Pauline Books & Media, 50 Saint Paul's Ave, Boston, MA 02130 *Tel:* 617-522-8911 *Toll Free Tel:* 800-876-4463 (orders); 800-836-9723 (cust serv) *Fax:* 617-541-9805 *E-mail:* orderentry@pauline.org (cust serv); editorial@paulinemedia.com (ms submissions) *Web Site:* www.pauline.org, pg 194

Paulines Editions, 5610 rue Beaubien est, Montreal, QC H1T 1X5, Canada *Tel:* 514-253-5610 *Fax:* 514-253-1907 *E-mail:* editions@paulines.qc.ca *Web Site:* www.editions.paulines.qc.ca, pg 515

Paulist Press, 997 MacArthur Blvd, Mahwah, NJ 07430-9990 *Tel:* 201-825-7300 *Toll Free Tel:* 800-218-1903 *Fax:* 201-825-8345 *Toll Free Fax:* 800-836-3161 *E-mail:* info@paulistpress.com *Web Site:* www.paulistpress.com, pg 194

Peabody Museum Press, 11 Divinity Ave, Cambridge, MA 02138 *Tel:* 617-495-4255 *Fax:* 617-495-7535 *E-mail:* peapub@fas.harvard.edu *Web Site:* www.peabody.harvard.edu/publications, pg 195

Peace Hill Press, 18021 The Glebe Lane, Charles City, VA 23030 *Tel:* 804-829-5043 *Toll Free Tel:* 877-322-3445 (orders) *Fax:* 804-829-5704 *E-mail:* info@peacehillpress.com *Web Site:* www.peacehillpress.com, pg 195

Peachpit Press, 1249 Eighth St, Berkeley, CA 94710 *Tel:* 510-524-2178 *Toll Free Tel:* 800-283-9444 *Fax:* 510-524-2221 *E-mail:* info@peachpit.com *Web Site:* www.peachpit.com, pg 195

Peachtree Publishers, 1700 Chattahoochee Ave, Atlanta, GA 30318-2112 *Tel:* 404-876-8761 *Toll Free Tel:* 800-241-0113 *Fax:* 404-875-2578 *Toll Free Fax:* 800-875-8909 *E-mail:* hello@peachtree-online.com *Web Site:* www.peachtree-online.com, pg 195

Peanut Butter & Jelly Press LLC, PO Box 590239, Newton, MA 02459-0002 *Tel:* 617-630-0945 *Fax:* 617-630-0945 (call first) *E-mail:* info@pbjpress.com *Web Site:* www.publishinggame.com; www.pbjpress.com, pg 195

Pearson Arts & Sciences, 51 Madison Ave, New York, NY 10010 *Tel:* 917-981-2200 *Web Site:* www.pearsonhighered.com, pg 195

Pearson Benjamin Cummings, 1301 Sansome St, San Francisco, CA 94111-1122 *Tel:* 415-402-2500 *Toll Free Tel:* 800-922-0579 (orders) *Fax:* 415-402-2590 *E-mail:* question@aol.com *Web Site:* www.pearsonhighered.com, pg 195

Pearson Business Publishing, One Lake St, Upper Saddle River, NJ 07458 *Tel:* 201-236-7000 *Web Site:* www.pearsonhighered.com, pg 195

Pearson Career, Health, Education & Technology, One Lake St, Upper Saddle River, NJ 07458 *Tel:* 201-236-7000 *Fax:* 201-236-7755, pg 195

Pearson Education, 1900 E Lake Ave, Glenview, IL 60025 *Tel:* 847-729-3000 *Toll Free Tel:* 800-535-4391 (Midwest) *Fax:* 847-729-8910, pg 195

Pearson Education, One Lake St, Upper Saddle River, NJ 07458 *Tel:* 201-236-7000 *Fax:* 201-236-6549 *E-mail:* communications@pearsoned.com *Web Site:* www.pearsoned.com, pg 195

Pearson Education Canada, 26 Prince Andrew Place, Don Mills, ON M3C 2T8, Canada *Tel:* 416-447-5101 *Toll Free Tel:* 800-263-9965 *Fax:* 416-443-0948 *Toll Free Fax:* 800-263-7733; 888-465-0536 *Web Site:* www.pearsoned.ca, pg 515

Pearson Education/ELT, 10 Bank St, 9th fl, White Plains, NY 10606-1951 *Tel:* 914-287-8000 *Web Site:* www.pearsonelt.com, pg 195

Pearson Education International Group, One Lake St, Upper Saddle River, NJ 07458 *Tel:* 201-236-7000, pg 196

Pearson Higher Education, One Lake St, Upper Saddle River, NJ 07458 *Tel:* 201-236-7000 *Fax:* 201-236-3381 *Web Site:* www.pearsonhighered.com, pg 196

Pearson Humanities & Social Sciences, One Lake St, Upper Saddle River, NJ 07458 *Tel:* 201-236-7000 *Fax:* 201-236-3400, pg 196

Pearson Learning Solutions, 501 Boyleston St, Suite 900, Boston, MA 02116 *Tel:* 617-848-6300 *Toll Free Tel:* 800-428-4466 (orders) *Fax:* 617-848-6358 *E-mail:* pcp@pearsoncustom.com *Web Site:* www.pearsoned.com, pg 196

Pearson School, One Lake St, Upper Saddle River, NJ 07458 *Tel:* 201-236-7000 *Web Site:* www.pearsonschool.com, pg 196

William Peden Prize in Fiction, 357 McReynolds Hall, Columbia, MO 65211 *Tel:* 573-882-4474 *Toll Free Tel:* 800-949-2505 *Fax:* 573-884-4671 *E-mail:* question@moreview.com *Web Site:* www.missourireview.com, pg 732

T H Peek Publisher, PO Box 7406, Ann Arbor, MI 48107 *Tel:* 734-222-8205 *Fax:* 734-661-0136 *E-mail:* info@thpeekpublisher.com *Web Site:* www.thpeekpublisher.com, pg 196

Peel Productions Inc, 9415 NE Woodridge St, Vancouver, WA 98664 *Toll Free Tel:* 800-345-6665 *E-mail:* contact@drawbooks.com *Web Site:* www.peelbooks.com, pg 196

Pelican Publishing Co, 1000 Burmaster St, Gretna, LA 70053-2246 *Tel:* 504-368-1175 *Toll Free Tel:* 800-843-1724 *Fax:* 504-368-1195 *E-mail:* sales@pelicanpub.com (sales); office@pelicanpub.com (permission); promo@pelicanpub.com (publicity) *Web Site:* www.pelicanpub.com, pg 196

Pema Browne Ltd, 71 Pine Rd, Woodbourne, NY 12788 *E-mail:* ppbltd@optonline.net *Web Site:* www.pemabrowneltd.com, pg 588

Pema Browne Ltd, 71 Pine Rd, Woodbourne, NY 12788 *E-mail:* info@pemabrowneltd.com *Web Site:* www.pemabrowneltd.com, pg 602

Pembroke Publishers Ltd, 538 Hood Rd, Markham, ON L3R 3K9, Canada *Tel:* 905-477-0650 *Toll Free Tel:* 800-997-9807 *Fax:* 905-477-3691 *Toll Free Fax:* 800-339-5568 *Web Site:* www.pembrokepublishers.com, pg 515

Pemmican Publications Inc, 150 Henry Ave, Winnipeg, MB R3B 0J7, Canada *Tel:* 204-589-6346 *Fax:* 204-589-2063 *E-mail:* pemmican@pemmican.mb.ca *Web Site:* www.pemmican.mb.ca, pg 515

PEN American Center, 588 Broadway, Suite 303, New York, NY 10012 *Tel:* 212-334-1660 *Fax:* 212-334-2181 *E-mail:* info@pen.org *Web Site:* www.pen.org, pg 633

The PEN Award for Poetry in Translation, 588 Broadway, Suite 303, New York, NY 10012 *Tel:* 212-334-1660 *Fax:* 212-334-2181 *E-mail:* awards@pen.org *Web Site:* www.pen.org, pg 732

PEN Canada, 24 Ryerson Ave, Suite 301, Toronto, ON M5T 2P3, Canada *Tel:* 416-703-8448 *Fax:* 416-703-3870 *E-mail:* queries@pencanada.ca *Web Site:* www.pencanada.ca, pg 633

PEN Center USA, PO Box 6037, Beverly Hills, CA 90212 *Tel:* 323-424-4939 *Fax:* 323-424-4944 *E-mail:* pen@penusa.org *Web Site:* www.penusa.org, pg 633

PEN Center USA Literary Awards, 269 S Beverly Dr, Suite 1163, Beverly Hills, CA 90212 *Tel:* 323-424-4939 *Fax:* 323-424-4944 *E-mail:* awards@penusa.org *Web Site:* www.penusa.org, pg 732

PEN/Faulkner Award for Fiction, Folger Shakespeare Library, 201 E Capitol St SE, Washington, DC 20003 *Tel:* 202-898-9063 *Fax:* 202-675-0360 *Web Site:* www.penfaulkner.org, pg 733

PEN New England, Massachusetts Institute of Technology, 77 Massachusetts Ave, 14-N-221A, Cambridge, MA 02139 *Tel:* 617-324-1729 *E-mail:* pen-newengland@mit.edu *Web Site:* www.pen-ne.org, pg 633

PEN/O. Henry Prize Stories, University of Texas at Austin, One University Sta B5000, Austin, TX 78712 *Tel:* 512-572-2428 *Web Site:* www.ohenryprizestories.com, pg 733

PEN/Phyllis Naylor Working Writer Fellowship, 588 Broadway, Suite 303, New York, NY 10012 *Tel:* 212-334-1660 *Fax:* 212-334-2181 *E-mail:* awards@pen.org *Web Site:* www.pen.org, pg 733

PEN/Ralph Manheim Medal for Translation, 588 Broadway, Suite 303, New York, NY 10012 *Tel:* 212-334-1660 *Fax:* 212-334-2181 *E-mail:* awards@pen.org *Web Site:* www.pen.org, pg 733

PEN/Robert Bingham Fellowships for Writers, 588 Broadway, Suite 303, New York, NY 10012 *Tel:* 212-334-1660 *Fax:* 212-334-2181 *E-mail:* awards@pen.org *Web Site:* www.pen.org, pg 733

PEN Translation Prize, 588 Broadway, Suite 303, New York, NY 10012 *Tel:* 212-334-1660 *Fax:* 212-334-2181 *E-mail:* awards@pen.org *Web Site:* www.pen.org, pg 733

PEN Writers' Emergency Fund, 588 Broadway, Suite 303, New York, NY 10012 *Tel:* 212-334-1660 *Fax:* 212-334-2181 *Web Site:* www.pen.org, pg 733

Pendragon Press, 52 White Hill Lane, Hillsdale, NY 12529-5839 *Tel:* 518-325-6100 *Toll Free Tel:* 877-656-6381 (orders) *Fax:* 518-325-6102 *E-mail:* editor@pendragonpress.com *Web Site:* www.pendragonpress.com, pg 196

Penfield Books, 215 Brown St, Iowa City, IA 52245 *Tel:* 319-337-9998 *Toll Free Tel:* 800-728-9998 *Fax:* 319-351-6846 *E-mail:* penfield@penfieldbooks.com *Web Site:* www.penfieldbooks.com, pg 196

Penguin Audiobooks, 375 Hudson St, New York, NY 10014 *Tel:* 212-366-2000 *E-mail:* online@penguinputnam.com *Web Site:* www.penguinputnam.com; us.penguingroup.com, pg 196

Penguin Books, 375 Hudson St, New York, NY 10014 *Tel:* 212-366-2000 *E-mail:* online@penguinputnam.com *Web Site:* www.penguinputnam.com; www.penguinclassics.com; us.penguingroup.com, pg 196

Penguin Group (Canada), 90 Eglinton Ave E, Suite 700, Toronto, ON M4P 2Y3, Canada *Tel:* 416-925-2249 *Fax:* 416-925-0068 *Web Site:* www.penguin.ca, pg 515

Penguin Group (USA) LLC, 375 Hudson St, New York, NY 10014 *Tel:* 212-366-2000 *Toll Free Tel:* 800-847-5515 (inside sales); 800-631-8571 (cust serv) *Fax:* 212-366-2666; 607-775-4829 (inside sales) *E-mail:* online@us.penguingroup.com *Web Site:* www.penguin.com; us.penguingroup.com, pg 197

Penguin Group (USA) LLC Sales, 375 Hudson St, New York, NY 10014 *Tel:* 212-366-2000 *E-mail:* online@penguinputnam.com *Web Site:* us.penguingroup.com, pg 197

The Penguin Press, 375 Hudson St, New York, NY 10014, pg 197

Penguin Young Readers Group, 345 Hudson St, New York, NY 10014 *Tel:* 212-366-2000 *E-mail:* online@penguinputnam.com *Web Site:* www.penguinputnam.com; us.penguingroup.com, pg 197

Peninsula Publishing, 26666 Birch Hill Way, Los Altos Hills, CA 94022 *Tel:* 650-948-2511 *Fax:* 650-948-5004 *E-mail:* sales@peninsulapublishing.com *Web Site:* www.peninsulapublishing.com, pg 198

Beth Penney Editorial Services, PO Box 604, Pacific Grove, CA 93950-0604 *Tel:* 831-372-7625, pg 552

Pennsylvania Historical & Museum Commission, Commonwealth Keystone Bldg, 400 North St, Harrisburg, PA 17120-0053 *Tel:* 717-783-2618 *Toll Free Tel:* 800-747-7790 *Fax:* 717-787-8312 *E-mail:* ra-pabookstore@state.pa.us *Web Site:* www.pabookstore.com; www.phmc.state.pa.us, pg 198

Pennsylvania State Data Center, Penn State Harrisburg, 777 W Harrisburg Pike, Middletown, PA 17057-4898 *Tel:* 717-948-6336 *Fax:* 717-948-6754 *E-mail:* pasdc@psu.edu *Web Site:* pasdc.hbg.psu.edu, pg 198

The Pennsylvania State University Press, University Support Bldg 1, Suite C, 820 N University Dr, University Park, PA 16802-1003 *Tel:* 814-865-1327 *Toll Free Tel:* 800-326-9180 *Fax:* 814-863-1408 *Toll Free Fax:* 877-778-2665 *E-mail:* info@psupress.org *Web Site:* www.psupress.org, pg 198

PennWell Books, 1421 S Sheridan Rd, Tulsa, OK 74112 *Tel:* 918-831-9410 *Toll Free Tel:* 800-752-9764 *Fax:* 918-831-9555 *E-mail:* sales@pennwell.com *Web Site:* www.pennwellbooks.com, pg 198

Pennwriters Conference, 406 Second St, Dalton, PA 18404 *Web Site:* www.pennwriters.org, pg 672

Pentecostal Publishing House, 8855 Dunn Rd, Hazelwood, MO 63042 *Tel:* 314-837-7300 *Fax:* 314-336-1803 *E-mail:* pphordersdept@upci.org (orders) *Web Site:* www.pentecostalpublishing.com, pg 198

Penton Media, 9800 Metcalf Ave, Overland Park, KS 66212 *Tel:* 913-967-1719 *Toll Free Tel:* 800-262-1954 (cust serv) *Fax:* 913-967-1901 *Toll Free Fax:* 800-633-6219 *E-mail:* bookorders@penton.com *Web Site:* www.buypenton.com, pg 198

Peoples Education Inc, 299 Market St, Suite 240, Saddle Brook, NJ 07663 *Tel:* 201-712-0090 *Toll Free Tel:* 800-822-1080 *Fax:* 201-712-0045; 201-712-1016 *Web Site:* www.peopleseducation.com; www.peoplescollegeprep.com; www.measuringuplive.com; www.brightpointliteracy.com, pg 199

PeopleSpeak, 25260-I La Paz Rd, Suite 1, Laguna Hills, CA 92653 *Tel:* 949-581-6190 *Fax:* 949-581-4958 *E-mail:* pplspeak@att.net *Web Site:* www.detailsplease.com/peoplespeak, pg 552

Rebecca Pepper, 434 NE Floral Place, Portland, OR 97232 *Tel:* 503-236-5802 *E-mail:* rpepper@rpepper.net, pg 552

Per Annum Inc, 555 Eighth Ave, Suite 203, New York, NY 10018 *Tel:* 212-647-8700 *Toll Free Tel:* 800-548-1108 *Fax:* 212-647-8716 *E-mail:* info@perannum.com *Web Site:* www.perannum.com, pg 199

Peradam Press, PO Box 6, North San Juan, CA 95960-0006 *Tel:* 530-292-4266 *Fax:* 530-292-4266 *E-mail:* peradam@earthlink.net, pg 199

Dan Peragine Literary Agency, 227 Beechwood Ave, Bogota, NJ 07603 *Tel:* 201-390-0468 *E-mail:* dpliterary@aol.com, pg 588

Perfection Learning Corp, 2680 Berkshire Pkwy, Clive, IA 50325 *Tel:* 515-278-0133 *Toll Free Tel:* 800-762-2999 *Fax:* 515-278-2980 *Web Site:* perfectionlearning.com, pg 199

Perigee Books, 375 Hudson St, New York, NY 10014 *Tel:* 212-366-2000 *Fax:* 212-366-2365 *E-mail:* perigeebooks@us.penguingroup.com *Web Site:* www.penguin.com, pg 199

Periodical & Book Association of America Inc, 481 Eighth Ave, Suite 526, New York, NY 10001 *Tel:* 212-563-6502 *Fax:* 212-563-4098 *Web Site:* www.pbaa.net, pg 633

The Permanent Press, 4170 Noyac Rd, Sag Harbor, NY 11963 *Tel:* 631-725-1101 *Fax:* 631-725-8215 *E-mail:* info@thepermanentpress.com *Web Site:* www.thepermanentpress.com, pg 199

The Permissions Group Inc, 1247 Milwaukee Ave, Suite 303, Glenview, IL 60025 *Tel:* 847-635-6550 *Toll Free Tel:* 800-374-7985 *Fax:* 847-635-6968 *E-mail:* info@permissionsgroup.com *Web Site:* www.permissionsgroup.com, pg 553

Persea Books, 277 Broadway, Suite 708, New York, NY 10007 *Tel:* 212-260-9256 *Fax:* 212-267-3165 *E-mail:* info@perseabooks.com *Web Site:* www.perseabooks.com, pg 199

The Perseus Books Group, 387 Park Ave S, 12th fl, New York, NY 10016 *Tel:* 212-340-8100 *Toll Free Tel:* 800-343-4499 (cust serv) *Fax:* 212-340-8105 *Web Site:* www.perseusbooksgroup.com, pg 199

Perugia Press Prize for a First or Second Book by a Woman, PO Box 60364, Florence, MA 01062 *Tel:* 413-348-6635 *E-mail:* info@perugiapress.com *Web Site:* www.perugiapress.com, pg 733

Peter Pauper Press, Inc, 202 Mamaroneck Ave, White Plains, NY 10601-5376 *Tel:* 914-681-0144 *Fax:* 914-681-0389 *E-mail:* customerservice@peterpauper.com; orders@peterpauper.com *Web Site:* www.peterpauper.com, pg 199

Elsa Peterson Ltd, 41 East Ave, Norwalk, CT 06851-3919 *Tel:* 203-846-8331 *E-mail:* epltd@earthlink.net, pg 553

Peterson Institute for International Economics, 1750 Massachusetts Ave NW, Washington, DC 20036-1903 *Tel:* 202-328-9000 *Toll Free Tel:* 800-522-9139 (orders) *Fax:* 202-328-5432; 202-659-3225 *E-mail:* orders@petersoninstitute.org *Web Site:* www.petersoninstitute.org, pg 200

Peterson's, a Nelnet Company, Princeton Pike Corporate Ctr, 2000 Lenox Dr, Lawrenceville, NJ 08648 *Tel:* 609-896-1800 *E-mail:* sales@petersons.com *Web Site:* www.petersons.com, pg 200

Petroleum Extension Service (PETEX), University of Texas at Austin-PETEX, One University Sta, R8100, Austin, TX 78712-1100 *Tel:* 512-471-5940 *Toll Free Tel:* 800-687-4132 *Fax:* 512-471-9410 *Toll Free Fax:* 800-687-7839 *E-mail:* plach@www.utex.edu; petex@www.utexas.edu *Web Site:* www.utexas.edu/ce/petex, pg 200

Evelyn Walters Pettit, PO Box 3073, Winter Park, FL 32790-3073 *Tel:* 407-620-0131 (cell); 407-644-1711 *Fax:* 407-644-1711 *E-mail:* bookseller@brandywinebooks.com *Web Site:* www.brandywinebooks.com, pg 553

Stephen Pevner Inc, 382 Lafayette St, Suite 8, New York, NY 10003 *Tel:* 212-674-8403 *Fax:* 212-529-3692 *E-mail:* spidevelopment@gmail.com, pg 588

Pfizer Award, 440 Geddes Hall, Notre Dame, IN 46556 *Tel:* 574-631-1194 *Fax:* 574-631-1533 *E-mail:* info@hssonline.org *Web Site:* www.hssonline.org, pg 733

Pflaum Publishing Group, 2621 Dryden Rd, Suite 300, Dayton, OH 45439 *Tel:* 937-293-1415 *Toll Free Tel:* 800-543-4383; 800-523-4625 (sales) *Fax:* 937-293-1310 *Toll Free Fax:* 800-370-4450 *E-mail:* service@pflaum.com *Web Site:* pflaum.com, pg 200

Phaidon Press Inc, 180 Varick St, 14th fl, New York, NY 10014 *Tel:* 212-652-5400 *Toll Free Tel:* 800-759-0190 (cust serv) *Fax:* 212-652-5410 *Toll Free Fax:* 800-286-9471 (cust serv) *E-mail:* ussales@phaidon.com *Web Site:* www.phaidon.com, pg 200

James D Phelan Literary Award, One Embarcadero Ctr, Suite 1400, San Francisco, CA 94111 *Tel:* 415-733-8500 *Fax:* 415-477-2783 *E-mail:* info@sff.org *Web Site:* www.sff.org, pg 733

Phi Beta Kappa Award in Science, 1606 New Hampshire Ave NW, Washington, DC 20009 *Tel:* 202-265-3808 *Fax:* 202-986-1601 *E-mail:* awards@pbk.org *Web Site:* www.pbk.org/bookawards, pg 733

Phi Delta Kappa International®, 320 W Eighth St, Suite 216, Bloomington, IN 47405 *Tel:* 812-339-1156 *Toll Free Tel:* 800-766-1156 *Fax:* 812-339-0018 *E-mail:* customerservice@pdkintl.org *Web Site:* www.pdkintl.org, pg 200

Philadelphia Museum of Art, 2525 Pennsylvania Ave, Philadelphia, PA 19130 *Tel:* 215-684-7250 *Fax:* 215-235-8715 *Web Site:* www.philamuseum.org, pg 200

Philadelphia Writers' Conference, PO Box 7171, Elkins Park, PA 19027-0171 *Tel:* 215-782-3288 *Fax:* 215-782-3288 *E-mail:* info@pwcwriters.org *Web Site:* pwcwriters.org, pg 672

Meredith Phillips, 4127 Old Adobe Rd, Palo Alto, CA 94306 *Tel:* 650-857-9555 *E-mail:* mphillips0743@comcast.net, pg 553

Philomel, 345 Hudson St, New York, NY 10014 *Tel:* 212-366-2000, pg 201

Philosophical Library Inc, PO Box 251, New York, NY 10024 *Tel:* 212-886-1873; 212-873-6070 *Fax:* 212-873-6070 *E-mail:* editors@philosophicallibrary.com *Web Site:* philosophicallibrary.com, pg 201

Philosophy Documentation Center, PO Box 7147, Charlottesville, VA 22906-7147 *Tel:* 434-220-3300 *Toll Free Tel:* 800-444-2419 *Fax:* 434-220-3301 *E-mail:* order@pdcnet.org *Web Site:* www.pdcnet.org, pg 201

Phoenix Society for Burn Survivors, 1835 R W Berends Dr SW, Grand Rapids, MI 49519 *Tel:* 616-458-2773 *Toll Free Tel:* 800-888-BURN (888-2876) *Fax:* 616-458-2831 *E-mail:* info@phoenix-society.org *Web Site:* www.phoenix-society.org, pg 201

PhotoEdit Inc, 3505 Cadillac Ave, Suite P-101, Costa Mesa, CA 92626 *Tel:* 714-434-5925 *Toll Free Tel:* 800-860-2098 *Fax:* 714-434-5937 *Toll Free Fax:* 800-804-3707 *E-mail:* sales@photoeditinc.com *Web Site:* www.photoeditinc.com, pg 553

Photographic Society of America® (PSA®), 3000 United Founders Blvd, Suite 103, Oklahoma City, OK 73112 *Tel:* 405-843-1437 *Toll Free Tel:* 855-PSA-INFO (855-772-4636) *Fax:* 405-843-1438 *E-mail:* hq@psa-photo.org *Web Site:* www.psa-photo.org, pg 634

PhotoSource International, Pine Lake Farm, 1910 35 Rd, Osceola, WI 54020-5602 *Tel:* 715-248-3800 (ext 21) *Toll Free Tel:* 800-624-0266 (ext 21) *Fax:* 715-248-3800 *Toll Free Fax:* 800-223-3860 *E-mail:* info@photosource.com; psi2@photosource.com *Web Site:* www.photosource.com, pg 553

Piano Press, 1425 Ocean Ave, Suite 17, Del Mar, CA 92014 *Tel:* 619-884-1401 *Fax:* 858-755-1104 *E-mail:* pianopress@pianopress.com *Web Site:* www.pianopress.com, pg 201

Picador, 175 Fifth Ave, 19th fl, New York, NY 10010 *Tel:* 646-307-5151 *Fax:* 212-253-9627 *E-mail:* firstname.lastname@picadorusa.com *Web Site:* www.picadorusa.com, pg 201

Alison Picard Literary Agent, PO Box 2000, Cotuit, MA 02635 *Tel:* 508-477-7192 *Fax:* 508-477-7192 (call first) *E-mail:* ajpicard@aol.com, pg 588

Picasso Project, 1109 Geary Blvd, San Francisco, CA 94109 *Tel:* 415-292-6500 *Fax:* 415-292-6594 *E-mail:* editeur@earthlink.net (editorial); picasso@art-books.com (orders) *Web Site:* www.art-books.com, pg 201

Piccadilly Books Ltd, PO Box 25203, Colorado Springs, CO 80936-5203 *Tel:* 719-550-9887 *E-mail:* orders@piccadillybooks.com *Web Site:* www.piccadillybooks.com, pg 201

Robert J Pickering Award for Playwriting Excellence, 89 Division, Coldwater, MI 49036 *E-mail:* j7eden@aol.com *Web Site:* www.branchcct.org, pg 734

Picton Press, 814 E Elkcam Circle, Marco Island, FL 34145-2558 *Tel:* 239-970-2442 *E-mail:* sales@pictonpress.com (orders) *Web Site:* www.pictonpress.com, pg 201

Pictorial Histories Publishing Co, 521 Bickford St, Missoula, MT 59801 *Tel:* 406-549-8488 *Toll Free Tel:* 888-763-8350 *Fax:* 406-728-9280 *E-mail:* phpc@montana.com *Web Site:* www.pictorialhistoriespublishing.com, pg 201

Pictures & Words Editorial Services, 3100 "B" Ave, Anacortes, WA 98221 *Tel:* 360-293-8476 *E-mail:* editor@picturesandwords.com *Web Site:* www.picturesandwords.com/words, pg 553

Pie in the Sky Publishing LLC, 8031 E Phillips Circle, Centennial, CO 80112 *Tel:* 303-773-0851 *Fax:* 303-773-0851 *E-mail:* pieintheskypublishing@msn.com *Web Site:* www.pieintheskypublishing.com, pg 201

Pieces of Learning, 1990 Market Rd, Marion, IL 62959-8976 *Tel:* 618-964-9426 *Toll Free Tel:* 800-729-5137 *Toll Free Fax:* 800-844-0455 *E-mail:* piecesoflearning@verizon.net *Web Site:* www.piecesoflearning.com, pg 201

Lorne Pierce Medal, Walter House, 282 Somerset W, Ottawa, ON K2P 0J6, Canada *Tel:* 613-991-6990 *Fax:* 613-991-6996 *E-mail:* nominations@rsc-src.ca *Web Site:* www.rsc-src.ca, pg 734

The Pilgrim Press/United Church Press, 700 Prospect Ave, Cleveland, OH 44115-1100 *Toll Free Tel:* 800-537-3394 (cust serv-indivs); 800-654-5129 (cust serv-commercial accts) *Fax:* 216-736-2206 (orders) *E-mail:* proposals@thepilgrimpress.com *Web Site:* www.thepilgrimpress.com; www.unitedchurchpress.com, pg 202

Pilgrim Publications, PO Box 66, Pasadena, TX 77501-0066 *Tel:* 713-477-4261 *Fax:* 713-477-7561 *E-mail:* pilgrimpub@aol.com *Web Site:* members.aol.com/pilgrimpub/; www.pilgrimpublications.com, pg 202

Pima Writers' Workshop, Pima College West Campus, 2202 W Anklam Rd, Tucson, AZ 85709-0170 *Tel:* 520-206-6084 *Fax:* 520-206-6020 *Web Site:* www.pima.edu, pg 672

The Pimlico Agency Inc, PO Box 20490, New York, NY 10017 *Tel:* 212-628-9729 *Fax:* 212-535-7861, pg 588

The Pinch Writing Awards in Fiction, University of Memphis, English Dept, 435 Patterson Hall, Memphis, TN 38152 *Tel:* 901-678-4190 *Fax:* 901-678-2226 *E-mail:* editor@thepinchjournal.com *Web Site:* www.thepinchjournal.com, pg 734

The Pinch Writing Awards in Poetry, University of Memphis, English Dept, 435 Patterson Hall, Memphis, TN 38152 *Tel:* 901-678-4190 *Fax:* 901-678-2226 *E-mail:* editor@thepinchjournal.com *Web Site:* www.thepinchjournal.com, pg 734

Caroline Pincus Book Midwife, 101 Wool St, San Francisco, CA 94110 *Tel:* 415-516-6206 *E-mail:* cpincus100@sbcglobal.net, pg 553

Marilyn Pincus Inc, 1320 W Bloomington Place, Tucson, AZ 85755-8773 *Tel:* 520-742-6699 *E-mail:* mpscribe@aol.com *Web Site:* www.marilynpincus.info, pg 553

Pinder Lane & Garon-Brooke Associates Ltd, 159 W 53 St, New York, NY 10019 *Tel:* 212-489-0880 *Fax:* 212-489-7104 *E-mail:* pinderlaneandgaronbrooke@gmail.com *Web Site:* www.pinderlaneandgaronbrooke.com, pg 588

Pine Forge Press, 2455 Teller Rd, Thousand Oaks, CA 91320 *Tel:* 805-499-4224; 805-499-9774 (orders) *Fax:* 805-499-0871 (orders) *E-mail:* info@sagepub.com *Web Site:* www.sagepub.com; www.pineforge.com, pg 202

Pineapple Press Inc, PO Box 3889, Sarasota, FL 34230-3889 *Tel:* 941-706-2507 *Toll Free Tel:* 866-766-3850 (orders) *Fax:* 941-706-2509 *Toll Free Fax:* 800-838-1149 (orders) *E-mail:* info@pineapplepress.com; customer.service@ingrampublisherservices.com *Web Site:* www.pineapplepress.com, pg 202

Pioneer Publishing Co, Hwy 82 E, Carrolton, MS 38917 *Tel:* 662-237-6010 *E-mail:* pioneerse@tecinfo.com *Web Site:* www.pioneersoutheast.com, pg 202

Pippin Press, 229 E 85 St, New York, NY 10028 *Tel:* 212-288-4920 *Fax:* 908-237-2407, pg 202

Pippin Properties Inc, 155 E 38 St, Suite 2-H, New York, NY 10016 *Tel:* 212-338-9310 *Fax:* 212-338-9579 *E-mail:* info@pippinproperties.com *Web Site:* www.pippinproperties.com, pg 588

Pippin Publishing Corp, PO Box 242, Don Mills, ON M3C 2S2, Canada *Tel:* 416-510-2918 *Toll Free Tel:* 888-889-0001 *Fax:* 416-510-3359 *Web Site:* www.pippinpub.com, pg 515

PJD Publications Ltd, PO Box 966, Westbury, NY 11590-0966 *Tel:* 516-626-0650 *Fax:* 516-626-4456 *Web Site:* www.pjdonline.com, pg 202

Platinum Press LLC, 37 Rte 80, Killingworth, CT 06419 *Tel:* 860-663-3882 *Fax:* 718-875-5065, pg 202

Platypus Media LLC, 725 Eighth St SE, Washington, DC 20003 *Tel:* 202-546-1674 *Toll Free Tel:* 877-PLATYPS (752-8977) *Fax:* 202-546-2356 *E-mail:* info@platypusmedia.com *Web Site:* www.platypusmedia.com, pg 202

Playboy College Fiction Contest, 9346 Civic Center Dr, Beverly Hills, CA 90210-3604 *Toll Free Tel:* 800-276-6048 (cust serv) *Fax:* 312-751-2818 *Web Site:* www.playboy.com, pg 734

Players Press Inc, PO Box 1132, Studio City, CA 91614-0132 *Tel:* 818-789-4980 *E-mail:* playerspress@att.net *Web Site:* www.ppeps.com, pg 202

Playhouse Publishing, PO Box 1962, Cleveland, OH 44106 *Tel:* 330-926-1313 *Fax:* 330-475-8579 *E-mail:* info@picturemepress.com *Web Site:* www.picturemepress.com, pg 203

Playwright Discovery Award, 818 Connecticut Ave NW, Suite 600, Washington, DC 20006 *Tel:* 202-628-2800 *Toll Free Tel:* 800-933-8721 *Fax:* 202-429-0868 *Web Site:* www.vsarts.org/playwrightdiscovery, pg 734

Playwrights Guild of Canada, 215 Spadina Ave, Suite 210, Toronto, ON M5T 2C7, Canada *Tel:* 416-703-0201 *Fax:* 416-703-0059 *E-mail:* info@playwrightsguild.ca *Web Site:* www.playwrightsguild.ca, pg 634

Playwrights Project, 3675 Ruffin Rd, Suite 330, San Diego, CA 92123 *Tel:* 858-384-2970 *Fax:* 858-384-2974 *E-mail:* write@playwrightsproject.org *Web Site:* www.playwrightsproject.org, pg 734

Pleasure Boat Studio: A Literary Press, 201 W 89 St, New York, NY 10024 *Toll Free Tel:* 888-810-5308 *Toll Free Fax:* 888-810-5308 *E-mail:* pleasboat@nyc.rr.com *Web Site:* www.pleasureboatstudio.com, pg 203

Plexus Publishing, Inc, 143 Old Marlton Pike, Medford, NJ 08055 *Tel:* 609-654-6500 *Fax:* 609-654-4309 *E-mail:* info@plexuspublishing.com *Web Site:* www.plexuspublishing.com, pg 203

The Plimpton Prize, 62 White St, New York, NY 10013 *Tel:* 212-343-1333 *Fax:* 212-343-1988 *E-mail:* queries@theparisreview.org *Web Site:* www.theparisreview.org, pg 734

The Plough Publishing House, PO Box 903, Rifton, NY 12471-0903 *E-mail:* info@plough.com *Web Site:* www.plough.com, pg 203

Ploughshares, Emerson College, 120 Boylston St, Boston, MA 02116 *Tel:* 617-824-3757 *E-mail:* pshares@pshares.org *Web Site:* www.pshares.org, pg 203

Plowshare Media, 405 Vincente Way, La Jolla, CA 92037 *E-mail:* sales@plowsharemedia.com *Web Site:* plowsharemedia.com, pg 203

Plum Tree Books, 2151 Market St, Camp Hill, PA 17011 *Tel:* 717-730-0711 *Fax:* 717-730-0721 *E-mail:* info@classicalsubjects.com *Web Site:* www.plumtreebooks.com, pg 203

Plume, 375 Hudson St, New York, NY 10014 *Tel:* 212-366-2000 *Fax:* 212-366-2666 *E-mail:* online@penguinputnam.com *Web Site:* www.penguinputnam.com; us.penguingroup.com, pg 203

Plunkett Research Ltd, PO Drawer 541737, Houston, TX 77254-1737 *Tel:* 713-932-0000 *Fax:* 713-932-7080 *E-mail:* customersupport@plunkettresearch.com *Web Site:* www.plunkettresearch.com, pg 203

PMA Literary & Film Management Inc, PO Box 1817, Old Chelsea Sta, New York, NY 10113 *Tel:* 212-929-1222 *Fax:* 212-206-0238 *E-mail:* queries@pmalitfilm.com *Web Site:* www.pmalitfilm.com, pg 588

PNWA Literary Contest, 1420 NW Gilman Blvd, Suite 2, PMB 2717, Issaquah, WA 98027 *Tel:* 425-673-2665 *E-mail:* pnwa@pnwa.org *Web Site:* www.pnwa.org, pg 734

J P Pochron Writer for Hire, 830 Lake Orchid Circle, No 203, Vero Beach, FL 32962 *Tel:* 772-569-2967 *E-mail:* hotwriter15@hotmail.com; jp_pochron@comcast.net, pg 553

Pocket Press Inc, PO Box 25124, Portland, OR 97298-0124 *Toll Free Tel:* 888-237-2110 *Toll Free Fax:* 877-643-3732 *E-mail:* sales@pocketpressinc.com *Web Site:* www.pocketpressinc.com, pg 203

Pocol Press, 6023 Pocol Dr, Clifton, VA 20124-1333 *Tel:* 703-830-5862 *E-mail:* chrisandtom@erols.com *Web Site:* www.pocolpress.com, pg 204

Edgar Allan Poe Awards®, 1140 Broadway, Suite 1507, New York, NY 10001 *Tel:* 212-888-8171 *E-mail:* mwa@mysterywriters.org *Web Site:* www.mysterywriters.org, pg 734

Edgar Allan Poe Memorial, 1194 Hume Rd, Hume, VA 22639-1806 *E-mail:* poetryinva@aol.com *Web Site:* www.poetrysocietyofvirginia.org, pg 734

A Poem With a Point of View, 1194 Hume Rd, Hume, VA 22639-1806 *E-mail:* poetryinva@aol.com *Web Site:* www.poetrysocietyofvirginia.org, pg 734

Poetry Book Contest, PO Box 910456, Lexington, KY 40591-0456 *Web Site:* www.accents-publishing.com/contest.html, pg 735

Poetry Center Book Award, 1600 Holloway Ave, San Francisco, CA 94132 *Tel:* 415-338-2227 *Fax:* 415-338-0966 *E-mail:* poetry@sfsu.edu *Web Site:* www.sfsu.edu/~poetry, pg 735

Poetry Chapbook Contest, 330 Knickerbocker Ave, Rochester, NY 14615 *Tel:* 585-458-0217 *E-mail:* palettesnquills@gmail.com *Web Site:* www.palettesnquills.com, pg 735

Poetry Flash Reading Series, 1450 Fourth St, Suite 4, Berkeley, CA 94710 *Tel:* 510-525-5476 *Fax:* 510-525-6752 *E-mail:* editor@poetryflash.org *Web Site:* www.poetryflash.org, pg 672

Poetry Society of America (PSA), 15 Gramercy Park S, New York, NY 10003 *Tel:* 212-254-9628 *Fax:* 212-673-2352 *Web Site:* www.poetrysociety.org, pg 634

Poets & Writers Inc, 90 Broad St, Suite 2100, New York, NY 10004 *Tel:* 212-226-3586 *Fax:* 212-226-3963 *Web Site:* www.pw.org, pg 634

Pogo Press Inc, 8075 215 St W, Lakeville, MN 55044 *Tel:* 952-469-6699 *Toll Free Tel:* 800-846-7027 *Fax:* 952-469-1968 *Toll Free Fax:* 800-330-6232 *E-mail:* info@finneyco.com *Web Site:* www.pogopress.com, pg 204

Pointed Leaf Press, 136 Baxter St, New York, NY 10013 *Tel:* 212-941-1800 *Fax:* 212-941-1822 *E-mail:* info@pointedleafpress.com *Web Site:* www.pointedleafpress.com, pg 204

Poirot Literary Agency, 3887 Nimbus Rd, Longmont, CO 80503 *Tel:* 303-494-0668 *Fax:* 303-494-9396 *E-mail:* poirotco@comcast.net, pg 589

Poisoned Pen Press Inc, 6962 E First Ave, Suite 103, Scottsdale, AZ 85251 *Tel:* 480-945-3375 *Toll Free Tel:* 1-800-421-3976 *Fax:* 480-949-1707 *E-mail:* info@poisonedpenpress.com *Web Site:* www.poisonedpenpress.com, pg 204

Polar Bear & Co, 8 Brook St, Solon, ME 04979 *Tel:* 207-643-2795 *Web Site:* www.polarbearandco.com, pg 204

Wendy Polhemus-Annibell, PO Box 464, Peconic, NY 11958 *Tel:* 631-276-0684 *E-mail:* wannibell@gmail.com; wannibel@suffolk.lib.ny.us, pg 553

Police Executive Research Forum, 1120 Connecticut Ave NW, Suite 930, Washington, DC 20036 *Tel:* 202-466-7820 *Fax:* 202-466-7826 *E-mail:* perf@policeforum.org *Web Site:* www.policeforum.org, pg 204

The George Polk Awards, The Brooklyn Campus, One University Plaza, Brooklyn, NY 11201-5372 *Tel:* 718-488-1009; 718-488-1115 *Web Site:* www.liu.edu/polk, pg 735

Pom Inc, 21 Vista Dr, Great Neck, NY 11021 *Tel:* 516-487-3441, pg 589

Pomegranate Communications Inc, 19018 NE Portal Way, Portland, OR 97230 *Tel:* 503-328-6500 *Toll Free Tel:* 800-227-1428 *Fax:* 503-328-9330 *Toll Free Fax:* 800-848-4376 *E-mail:* info@pomegranate.com *Web Site:* www.pomegranate.com, pg 204

Pontifical Institute of Mediaeval Studies, Dept of Publications, 59 Queens Park Crescent E, Toronto, ON M5S 2C4, Canada *Tel:* 416-926-7142 *Fax:* 416-926-7292 *Web Site:* www.pims.ca, pg 516

Porcupine's Quill Inc, 68 Main St, Erin, ON N0B 1T0, Canada *Tel:* 519-833-9158 *Fax:* 519-833-9845 *E-mail:* pql@sentex.net *Web Site:* porcupinesquill.ca, pg 516

Port Townsend Writers' Conference, 223 Battery Way, Port Townsend, WA 98368 *Tel:* 360-385-3102 *Toll Free Tel:* 800-733-3608 (ticket off) *Fax:* 360-385-2470 *E-mail:* info@centrum.org *Web Site:* www.centrum.org, pg 672

Portage & Main Press, 318 McDermot, Suite 100, Winnipeg, MB R3A 0A2, Canada *Tel:* 204-987-3500 *Toll Free Tel:* 800-667-9673 *Fax:* 204-947-0080 *Toll Free Fax:* 866-734-8477 *E-mail:* books@portageandmainpress.com *Web Site:* www.portageandmainpress.com, pg 516

Katherine Anne Porter Prize for Fiction, Nimrod International Journal, 800 S Tucker Dr, Tulsa, OK 74104 *Tel:* 918-631-3080 *Fax:* 918-631-3033 *E-mail:* nimrod@utulsa.edu *Web Site:* www.utulsa.edu/nimrod, pg 735

Portfolio, 375 Hudson St, New York, NY 10014, pg 204

Portfolio Solutions LLC, 136 Jameson Hill Rd, Clinton Corners, NY 12514 *Tel:* 845-266-1001 *Web Site:* www.portfoliosolutionsllc.com, pg 602

Postcard Story Competition, 90 Richmond St E, Suite 200, Toronto, ON M5C 1P1, Canada *Tel:* 416-703-8982 *Fax:* 416-504-9090 *E-mail:* info@writersunion.ca *Web Site:* www.writersunion.ca, pg 735

Posterity Press Inc, 4948 Saint Elmo Ave, 3rd fl, Bethesda, MD 20814 *Tel:* 301-652-2384 *Fax:* 301-652-2543 *Web Site:* www.posteritypress.com, pg 204

Potomac Books Inc, 22841 Quicksilver Dr, Dulles, VA 20166 *Tel:* 703-661-1548 *Fax:* 703-661-1547 *E-mail:* pbimail@presswarehouse.com *Web Site:* www.potomacbooksinc.com, pg 204

The Professional Writer, 175 W 12 St, Suite 6D, New York, NY 10011 *Tel:* 212-414-0188; 917-658-1946 (cell) *E-mail:* paul@theprofessionalwriter.com *Web Site:* www.theprofessionalwriter.com, pg 553

Professional Writers Association of Canada (PWAC), 215 Spadina Ave, Suite 130, Toronto, ON M5T 2C7, Canada *Tel:* 416-504-1645 *E-mail:* info@pwac.ca *Web Site:* www.pwac.ca; www.writers.ca, pg 634

Progressive Press, 6200 Juniper Rd (entrance on Sunny Vista), Joshua Tree, CA 92252-4144 *Tel:* 760-366-3695 *Fax:* 760-366-3695 *E-mail:* info@progressivepress.com *Web Site:* www.progressivepress.com, pg 208

Prometheus Awards, 650 Castro St, Suite 120-433, Mountain View, CA 94041 *Tel:* 650-968-6319 *E-mail:* info@lfs.org *Web Site:* www.lfs.org, pg 736

Prometheus Books, 59 John Glenn Dr, Amherst, NY 14228-2119 *Tel:* 716-691-0133 *Toll Free Tel:* 800-421-0351 *Fax:* 716-691-0137 *E-mail:* marketing@prometheusbooks.com; editorial@prometheusbooks.com *Web Site:* www.Prometheusbooks.com, pg 208

Pronk Media Inc, PO Box 340, Beaverton, ON L0K 1A0, Canada *Tel:* 416-441-3760 *E-mail:* info@pronk.com *Web Site:* www.pronk.com, pg 553

Proofed to Perfection Editing Services, PO Box 71851, Durham, NC 27722-1851 *Tel:* 919-732-8565 *E-mail:* inquiries@proofedtoperfection.com *Web Site:* www.proofedtoperfection.com, pg 554

ProQuest LLC, 789 E Eisenhower Pkwy, Ann Arbor, MI 48108-3218 *Tel:* 734-761-4700 *Toll Free Tel:* 800-521-0600 *Fax:* 734-975-6486 *Toll Free Fax:* 800-864-0019 *E-mail:* info@proquest.com *Web Site:* www.proquest.com, pg 208

PROSE Awards, 71 Fifth Ave, 2nd fl, New York, NY 10003-3004 *Tel:* 212-255-0200 *Fax:* 212-255-7007 *Web Site:* www.proseawards.com; www.publishers.org, pg 736

Prospect Agency, 285 Fifth Ave, PMB 445, Brooklyn, NY 11215 *Tel:* 718-788-3217 *Fax:* 718-360-9582 *Web Site:* www.prospectagency.com, pg 589

ProStar Publications Inc, 3 Church Circle, Suite 109, Annapolis, MD 21401 *Tel:* 310-280-1010 *Toll Free Tel:* 800-481-6277 *Fax:* 310-280-1025 *Toll Free Fax:* 800-487-6277 *E-mail:* editor@prostarpublications.com *Web Site:* www.prostarpublications.com, pg 208

Protestant Church-Owned Publishers Association, 6631 Westbury Oaks Ct, Springfield, VA 22152 *Tel:* 703-220-5989 *Web Site:* www.pcpaonline.org, pg 635

The PRS Group Inc, 6320 Fly Rd, Suite 102, East Syracuse, NY 13057-9358 *Tel:* 315-431-0511 *Fax:* 315-431-0200 *E-mail:* custserv@prsgroup.com *Web Site:* www.prsgroup.com, pg 208

Prufrock Press, PO Box 8813, Waco, TX 76714-8813 *Tel:* 254-756-3337 *Toll Free Tel:* 800-998-2208 *Fax:* 254-756-3339 *Toll Free Fax:* 800-240-0333 *E-mail:* info@prufrock.com *Web Site:* www.prufrock.com, pg 208

Psychological Assessment Resources Inc (PAR), 16204 N Florida Ave, Lutz, FL 33549 *Tel:* 813-968-3003; 813-449-4065 *Toll Free Tel:* 800-331-8378 *Fax:* 813-968-2598; 813-961-2196 *Toll Free Fax:* 800-727-9329 *E-mail:* custsup@parinc.com *Web Site:* www4.parinc.com, pg 208

Psychology Press, 711 Third Ave, 8th fl, New York, NY 10017 *Tel:* 212-216-7800 *Toll Free Tel:* 800-634-7064 *Fax:* 212-563-2269 *Web Site:* www.psypress.com, pg 209

Public Citizen, 1600 20 St NW, Washington, DC 20009 *Tel:* 202-588-1000 *Fax:* 202-588-7798 *E-mail:* public_citizen@citizen.org *Web Site:* www.citizen.org, pg 209

Public Relations Society of America Inc, 33 Maiden Lane, 11th fl, New York, NY 10038-5150 *Tel:* 212-460-1400 *Fax:* 212-995-0757 *Web Site:* www.prsa.org, pg 635

PublicAffairs, 250 W 57 St, Suite 1321, New York, NY 10107 *Tel:* 212-397-6666 *Toll Free Tel:* 800-343-4499 (orders) *Fax:* 212-397-4277 *E-mail:* publicaffairs@perseusbooks.com *Web Site:* www.publicaffairsbooks.com, pg 209

Publication Consultants, 8370 Eleusis Dr, Anchorage, AK 99502 *Tel:* 907-349-2424 *Fax:* 907-349-2426 *E-mail:* books@publicationconsultants.com *Web Site:* www.publicationconsultants.com, pg 209

Les Publications du Quebec, 1000, rte de l'Eqalise, Bureau 500, Quebec, QC G1V 3V9, Canada *Tel:* 418-643-5150 *Toll Free Tel:* 800-463-2100 (Quebec province only) *Fax:* 418-643-6177 *Toll Free Fax:* 800-561-3479 *E-mail:* publicationsduquebec@cspq.gouv.qc.ca *Web Site:* www.publicationsduquebec.gouv.qc.ca, pg 517

Publications International Ltd, 7373 N Cicero Ave, Lincolnwood, IL 60712 *Tel:* 847-676-3470 *Fax:* 847-676-3671 *Web Site:* www.pilbooks.com, pg 209

Publishers Association of the West (PubWest), 17501 Hill Way, Lake Oswego, OR 97035 *Tel:* 503-635-0056 *Fax:* 602-234-3062 *E-mail:* executivedirector@pubwest.org *Web Site:* www.pubwest.org, pg 635

Publishers' Graphics Inc, 231 Judd Rd, Easton, CT 06612-1025 *Tel:* 203-445-1511 *Fax:* 203-445-1411 *E-mail:* sales@publishersgraphics.com *Web Site:* www.publishersgraphics.com, pg 602

Publishers Information Bureau (PIB), 810 Seventh Ave, 24th fl, New York, NY 10019 *Tel:* 212-872-3700 *Fax:* 212-753-2768 *E-mail:* pib@magazine.org *Web Site:* www.magazine.org, pg 635

Publishing Certificate Program at City College, Division of Humanities NAC 5225, City College of New York, New York, NY 10031 *Tel:* 212-650-7925 *Fax:* 212-650-7912 *E-mail:* ccnypub@aol.com *Web Site:* www.ccny.cuny.edu/publishing_certificate/index.html, pg 680

The Publishing Game, PO Box 590239, Newton, MA 02459-0002 *Tel:* 617-630-0945 *Fax:* 617-630-0945 (call first) *E-mail:* info@publishinggame.com; workshops@publishinggame.com *Web Site:* www.publishinggame.com, pg 672

Publishing Professionals Network, 9328 Elk Grove, Suite 105-250, Elk Grove, CA 95624 *Tel:* 916-320-0638 *E-mail:* operations@bookbuilders.org *Web Site:* www.bookbuilders.org, pg 635

Publishing Resources Inc, 425 Carr 693, PMB 160, Dorado, PR 00646 *Tel:* 787-626-0607 *Toll Free Fax:* 866-547-3005 *E-mail:* pri@chevako.net *Web Site:* www.publishingresources.net, pg 554

Publishing Services, 525 E 86 St, Suite 8-E, New York, NY 10028 *Tel:* 212-628-9127 *Fax:* 212-988-1999 *E-mail:* publishingservices@mac.com, pg 554

Publishing Services, 525 E 86 St, Suite 8-E, New York, NY 10028 *Tel:* 212-628-9127 *Fax:* 212-628-9128 *E-mail:* publishingservices@mac.com, pg 589

Publishing Synthesis Ltd, 39 Crosby St, New York, NY 10013 *Tel:* 212-219-0135 *Fax:* 212-219-0136 *E-mail:* info@pubsyn.com *Web Site:* www.pubsyn.com, pg 554

The Publishing Triangle Literary Awards, 332 Bleecker St, Suite D-36, New York, NY 10014 *E-mail:* publishingtriangle@gmail.com *Web Site:* www.publishingtriangle.org, pg 736

PubWest Book Design Awards, 17501 Hill Way, Lake Oswego, OR 97035 *Tel:* 503-635-0056 *Fax:* 602-234-3062 *Web Site:* www.pubwest.org, pg 736

Pudding House Publications, 81 Shadymere Lane, Columbus, OH 43213 *Tel:* 614-986-1881 *Web Site:* www.puddinghousepublications.com, pg 209

Puddingstone Literary, Authors' Agents, 11 Mabro Dr, Denville, NJ 07834-9607 *Tel:* 973-366-3622, pg 589

Puffin Books, 345 Hudson St, New York, NY 10014 *Tel:* 212-366-2000 *E-mail:* online@penguinputnam.com *Web Site:* www.penguinputnam.com; us.penguingroup.com, pg 209

Pulitzer Prizes, 709 Journalism Bldg, Columbia University, 2950 Broadway, New York, NY 10027 *Tel:* 212-854-3841 *Fax:* 212-854-3342 *E-mail:* pulitzer@pulitzer.org *Web Site:* www.pulitzer.org, pg 736

Purdue University Press, Stewart Ctr 370, 504 W State St, West Lafayette, IN 47907-2058 *Tel:* 765-494-2038 *Fax:* 765-496-2442 *E-mail:* pupress@purdue.edu *Web Site:* www.thepress.purdue.edu, pg 209

Pureplay Press, 195 26 Ave, No 2, San Francisco, CA 94121 *Tel:* 310-597-0328 *E-mail:* info@pureplaypress.com *Web Site:* www.pureplaypress.com, pg 209

Purich Publishing Ltd, PO Box 23032, Market Mall Postal Outlet, Saskatoon, SK S7J 5H3, Canada *Tel:* 306-373-5311 *Fax:* 306-373-5315 *E-mail:* purich@sasktel.net *Web Site:* www.purichpublishing.com, pg 517

Purple House Press, 8100 US Hwy 62 E, Cynthiana, KY 41031 *Tel:* 859-235-9970 *Web Site:* www.purplehousepress.com, pg 210

Purple Mountain Press Ltd, 1060 Main St, Fleischmanns, NY 12430 *Tel:* 845-254-4062 *Toll Free Tel:* 800-325-2665 (orders) *Fax:* 845-254-4476 *E-mail:* purple@catskill.net *Web Site:* www.catskill.net/purple, pg 210

Purple People Inc, 2301 W Hwy 89A, Suite 102, Sedona, AZ 86336 *Tel:* 928-204-6400 *Fax:* 928-282-2603 *E-mail:* info@purplepeople.com *Web Site:* www.purplepeople.com; www.bulliedtosilence.com, pg 210

Purple Pomegranate Productions, 60 Haight St, San Francisco, CA 94102 *Tel:* 415-864-2600 *Fax:* 415-552-8325 *E-mail:* sf@jewsforjesus.org *Web Site:* www.jewsforjesus.org, pg 210

Pushcart Press, PO Box 380, Wainscott, NY 11975-0380 *Tel:* 631-324-9300, pg 210

Pushcart Prize: Best of the Small Presses, PO Box 380, Wainscott, NY 11975-0380 *Tel:* 631-324-9300, pg 736

Putnam Berkley Audio, 375 Hudson St, New York, NY 10014 *Tel:* 212-366-2000 *Fax:* 212-366-2666 *E-mail:* online@penguinputnam.com *Web Site:* www.penguinputnam.com; us.penguingroup.com, pg 210

The Putnam Publishing Group, 375 Hudson St, New York, NY 10014 *Tel:* 212-366-2000 *Toll Free Tel:* 800-631-8571 *Fax:* 212-366-2643 *E-mail:* online@penguinputnam.com *Web Site:* www.penguinputnam.com; us.penguingroup.com, pg 210

GP Putnam's Sons (Children's), 345 Hudson St, New York, NY 10014 *Tel:* 212-366-2000 *Fax:* 212-414-3393 *E-mail:* online@penguinputnam.com *Web Site:* us.penguingroup.com, pg 210

GP Putnam's Sons (Hardcover), 375 Hudson St, New York, NY 10014 *Tel:* 212-366-2000 *E-mail:* online@penguinputnam.com *Web Site:* us.penguingroup.com, pg 210

Pyncheon House, 6 University Dr, Suite 105, Amherst, MA 01002, pg 210

QA International, 329 De la Commune W, 3rd fl, Montreal, QC H2Y 2E1, Canada *Tel:* 514-499-3000 *Fax:* 514-499-3010 *Web Site:* www.qa-international.com, pg 517

QED Press, 155 Cypress St, Fort Bragg, CA 95437 *Tel:* 707-964-9520 *Toll Free Tel:* 800-773-7782 *Fax:* 707-964-7531 *E-mail:* qedpress@mcn.org *Web Site:* www.cypresshouse.com, pg 210

Robert Quackenbush's Children's Book Writing & Illustration Workshops, 223 E 78 St, New York, NY 10075 *Tel:* 212-744-3822 *E-mail:* rqstudios@aol.com *Web Site:* www.rquackenbush.com, pg 672

Quackenworth Publishing, PO Box 4747, Culver City, CA 90231-4747 *Tel:* 310-945-5634 *Toll Free Tel:* 888-701-4991 *Fax:* 310-945-5709 *Toll Free Fax:* 888-892-6339 *E-mail:* info@quackenworth.com *Web Site:* www.quackenworth.com; www.wittybittybunch.com, pg 211

Quail Ridge Press, 101 Brooks Dr, Brandon, MS 39042 *Tel:* 601-825-2063 *Toll Free Tel:* 800-343-1583 *Fax:* 601-825-3091 *Toll Free Fax:* 800-864-1082 *E-mail:* info@quailridge.com *Web Site:* quailridge.com, pg 211

Quality Medical Publishing Inc, 2248 Welsch Industrial Ct, St Louis, MO 63146-4222 *Tel:* 314-878-7808 *Toll Free Tel:* 800-348-7808 *Fax:* 314-878-9937 *E-mail:* qmp@qmp.com *Web Site:* www.qmp.com, pg 211

The Quarasan Group Inc, 405 W Superior St, Chicago, IL 60654 *Tel:* 312-981-2500 *E-mail:* info@quarasan.com *Web Site:* www.quarasan.com, pg 554

Quayside Publishing Group, 400 First Ave N, Suite 300, Minneapolis, MN 55401 *Tel:* 612-344-8100 *Toll Free Tel:* 800-328-0590 (sales); 800-458-0454 *Fax:* 612-344-8691 *E-mail:* sales@creativepub.com *Web Site:* www.qbookshop.com, pg 211

Quebec Dans Le Monde, CP 8503, succ Sainte-Foy, Quebec, QC G1V 4N5, Canada *Tel:* 418-659-5540 *Fax:* 418-659-4143 *E-mail:* info@quebecmonde.com *Web Site:* www.quebecmonde.com, pg 517

Quebec Writers' Federation (QWF), 1200 Atwater Ave, Suite 3, Westmount, QC H3Z 1X4, Canada *Tel:* 514-933-0878 *E-mail:* info@qwf.org *Web Site:* www.qwf.org, pg 635

Quicksilver Productions, PO Box 340, Ashland, OR 97520-0012 *Tel:* 541-482-5343 *Fax:* 508-590-0099 *E-mail:* celestialcalendars@email.com *Web Site:* www.quicksilverproductions.com, pg 211

Quincannon Publishing Group, PO Box 8100, Glen Ridge, NJ 07028-8100 *Tel:* 973-380-9942 *E-mail:* editors@quincannongroup.com *Web Site:* www.quincannongroup.com, pg 211

Quintessence Publishing Co Inc, 4350 Chandler Dr, Hanover Park, IL 60133 *Tel:* 630-736-3600 *Toll Free Tel:* 800-621-0387 *Fax:* 630-736-3633 *E-mail:* contact@quintbook.com; service@quintbook.com *Web Site:* www.quintpub.com, pg 211

Editions Michel Quintin, 4770 rue Foster, Waterloo, QC J0E 2N0, Canada *Tel:* 450-539-3774 *Fax:* 450-539-4905 *E-mail:* info@editionsmichelquintin.ca *Web Site:* www.editionsmichelquintin.ca, pg 517

Quirk Books, 215 Church St, Philadelphia, PA 19106 *Tel:* 215-627-3581 *Fax:* 215-627-5220 *E-mail:* general@quirkbooks.com *Web Site:* www.quirkbooks.com, pg 211

Quite Specific Media Group Ltd, 7373 Pyramid Place, Hollywood, CA 90046 *Tel:* 323-851-5797 *Fax:* 323-851-5798 *E-mail:* info@quitespecificmedia.com *Web Site:* www.quitespecificmedia.com, pg 211

Quixote Press, 3544 Black St, Wever, IA 52658 *Tel:* 319-372-7480 *Toll Free Tel:* 800-571-2665 *Fax:* 319-372-7485 *E-mail:* heartsntummies@gmail.com; potpress@gmail.com, pg 212

QWF Literary Awards, 1200 Atwater Ave, Suite 3, Westmount, QC H3Z 1X4, Canada *Tel:* 514-933-0878 *E-mail:* info@qwf.org *Web Site:* www.qwf.org, pg 736

Susan Rabiner Literary Agency Inc, 315 W 39 St, Suite 1501, New York, NY 10018-3907 *Web Site:* RabinerLit.com, pg 589

Miriam Rachimi Memorial, 1194 Hume Rd, Hume, VA 22639-1806 *E-mail:* poetryinva@aol.com *Web Site:* www.poetrysocietyofvirginia.org, pg 736

Rada Press Inc, 1277 Fairmount Ave, St Paul, MN 55105 *Tel:* 651-645-3304 *E-mail:* info@radapress.com *Web Site:* www.radapress.com, pg 212

Radcliffe Fellowship, 8 Garden St, Cambridge, MA 02138 *Tel:* 617-495-8212; 617-496-1324 (application office) *Fax:* 617-495-8136 *Web Site:* www.radcliffe.harvard.edu, pg 737

Thomas Head Raddall Atlantic Fiction Award, 1113 Marginal Rd, Halifax, NS B3H 4P7, Canada *Tel:* 902-423-8116 *Fax:* 902-422-0881 *E-mail:* talk@writers.ns.ca *Web Site:* www.writers.ns.ca, pg 737

Radix Press, 11715 Bandlon Dr, Houston, TX 77072 *Tel:* 281-879-5688 *Web Site:* www.specialforcesbooks.com, pg 212

Jane Rafal Editing Associates, 325 Forest Ridge Dr, Scottsville, VA 24590 *Tel:* 434-286-6949, pg 554

The Ragan Old North State Award Cup for Nonfiction, 4610 Mail Service Ctr, Raleigh, NC 27699-4610 *Tel:* 919-807-7290 *Fax:* 919-733-8807 *Web Site:* www.history.ncdcr.gov/affiliates/lit-hist/awards/awards.htm, pg 737

Rainbow Books Inc, PO Box 430, Highland City, FL 33846 *Tel:* 863-648-4420 *Fax:* 863-647-5951 *E-mail:* info@rainbowbooksinc.com *Web Site:* www.rainbowbooksinc.com, pg 212

Rainbow Publishers, PO Box 261129, San Diego, CA 92196 *Tel:* 858-277-1167 *Toll Free Tel:* 800-323-7337 *Toll Free Fax:* 800-331-0297 *E-mail:* info@rainbowpublishers.com; editor@rainbowpublishers.com (edit dept) *Web Site:* www.rainbowpublishers.com, pg 212

Raines & Raines, 103 Kenyon Rd, Medusa, NY 12120 *Tel:* 518-239-8311 *Fax:* 518-239-6029, pg 589

Raiziss/de Palchi Fellowship, 75 Maiden Lane, Suite 901, New York, NY 10038 *Tel:* 212-274-0343 *Fax:* 212-274-9427 *E-mail:* academy@poets.org *Web Site:* www.poets.org, pg 737

Sir Walter Raleigh Award for Fiction, 4610 Mail Service Ctr, Raleigh, NC 27699-4610 *Tel:* 919-807-7290 *Fax:* 919-733-8807, pg 737

Jerry Ralya, 7909 Vt Rte 14, Craftsbury Common, VT 05827 *Tel:* 802-586-7514 *E-mail:* jerry@jerryralya.com, pg 554

Ram Publishing Co, 1881 W State St, Garland, TX 75042 *Tel:* 972-494-6151 *Toll Free Tel:* 800-527-4011 *Fax:* 972-494-1881 *E-mail:* sales@garrett.com *Web Site:* www.garrett.com, pg 212

RAND Corp, 1776 Main St, Santa Monica, CA 90407-2138 *Tel:* 310-393-0411 *Fax:* 310-393-4818 *Web Site:* www.rand.org, pg 212

Rand McNally, 9855 Woods Dr, Skokie, IL 60077 *Tel:* 847-329-8100 *Toll Free Tel:* 800-678-7263 *Fax:* 847-329-6139 *E-mail:* ctsales@randmcnally.com; mediarelations@randmcnally.com *Web Site:* www.randmcnally.com, pg 212

Random House Audio Publishing Group, 1745 Broadway, New York, NY 10019 *E-mail:* audio@randomhouse.com *Web Site:* www.randomhouse.com/audio, pg 212

Random House Children's Books, 1745 Broadway, New York, NY 10019 *Tel:* 212-782-9000 *Toll Free Tel:* 800-200-3552 *Fax:* 212-782-9452 *Web Site:* randomhousekids.com, pg 212

Random House Inc, 1745 Broadway, New York, NY 10019 *Tel:* 212-782-9000 *Toll Free Tel:* 800-726-0600 *Web Site:* www.randomhouse.com, pg 213

Random House Large Print, 1745 Broadway, New York, NY 10019 *Tel:* 212-782-9000 *Fax:* 212-782-9484, pg 214

Random House of Canada Limited, One Toronto St, Suite 300, Toronto, ON M5C 2V6, Canada *Tel:* 416-364-4449 *Toll Free Tel:* 888-523-9292 (cust serv) *Fax:* 416-364-6863; 416-364-6653 (subs rts) *Web Site:* www.randomhouse.ca, pg 517

Random House Publishing Group, 1745 Broadway, New York, NY 10019 *Toll Free Tel:* 800-200-3552 *Web Site:* atrandom.com, pg 214

Random House Reference/Random House Puzzles & Games/House of Collectibles, 1745 Broadway, New York, NY 10019 *Toll Free Tel:* 800-733-3000 *Toll Free Fax:* 800-659-2436 *E-mail:* words@random.com; puzzles@random.com, pg 214

Random House Speakers Bureau, 1745 Broadway, Mail Drop 13-1, New York, NY 10019 *Tel:* 212-572-2013 *E-mail:* rhspeakers@randomhouse.com *Web Site:* www.rhspeakers.com, pg 605

Ransom Note Press, PO Box 419, Ridgewood, NJ 07451 *Tel:* 201-835-2790 *E-mail:* editorial@ransomnotepress.com *Web Site:* www.ransomnotepress.com, pg 529

Gerald & Cullen Rapp, 420 Lexington Ave, New York, NY 10170 *Tel:* 212-889-3337 *Fax:* 212-889-3341 *E-mail:* info@rappart.com *Web Site:* www.rappart.com, pg 602

Rattapallax Press, 217 Thompson St, Suite 353, New York, NY 10012 *E-mail:* info@rattapallax.com *Web Site:* www.rattapallax.com, pg 214

Raven Productions Inc, PO Box 188, Ely, MN 55731 *Tel:* 218-365-3375 *Fax:* 678-306-3375 *E-mail:* raven@ravenwords.com; order@ravenwords.com *Web Site:* www.ravenwords.com, pg 214

Raven Publishing Inc, 125 Cherry Creek Rd, Norris, MT 59745 *Tel:* 406-685-3545 *Toll Free Tel:* 866-685-3545 *Fax:* 406-685-3599 *E-mail:* info@ravenpublishing.net *Web Site:* www.ravenpublishing.net, pg 214

Raven Tree Press, 1400 Miller Pkwy, McHenry, IL 60050-7030 *Tel:* 815-363-3582 *Toll Free Tel:* 800-323-8270 *Fax:* 815-363-2948 *Toll Free Fax:* 800-909-9901 *E-mail:* raven@raventreepress.com *Web Site:* www.raventreepress.com, pg 214

Ravenhawk™ Books, 7739 E Broadway Blvd, No 95, Tucson, AZ 85710 *Tel:* 520-296-4491 *Fax:* 520-296-4491 *E-mail:* ravenhawk6dof@yahoo.com *Web Site:* 6dofsolutions.com, pg 215

Charlotte Cecil Raymond, Literary Agent, 32 Bradlee Rd, Marblehead, MA 01945 *Tel:* 781-631-6722 *Fax:* 781-631-6722 *E-mail:* raymondliterary@gmail.com, pg 590

Rayve Productions Inc, PO Box 726, Windsor, CA 95492 *Tel:* 707-838-6200 *Toll Free Tel:* 800-852-4890 *Fax:* 707-838-2220 *E-mail:* rayvepro@aol.com *Web Site:* www.rayveproductions.com; www.foodandwinebooks.com, pg 215

Razorbill, 345 Hudson St, New York, NY 10014 *Tel:* 212-366-2000, pg 215

RBC Bronwen Wallace Award for Emerging Writers, 90 Richmond St E, Suite 200, Toronto, ON M5C 1P1, Canada *Tel:* 416-504-8222 *Toll Free Tel:* 877-906-6548 *Fax:* 416-504-9090 *E-mail:* info@writerstrust.com *Web Site:* www.writerstrust.com, pg 737

The Rea Award for the Short Story, 53 W Church Hill Rd, Washington, CT 06794 *Web Site:* reaaward.org, pg 737

Reader's Digest Association Canada ULC (Selection du Reader's Digest Canada SRL), 1100 Rene Levesque Blvd W, Montreal, QC H3B 5H5, Canada *Tel:* 514-940-0751 *Toll Free Tel:* 866-236-7789 (cust serv) *Fax:* 514-940-3637 *E-mail:* customer.service@readersdigest.ca *Web Site:* www.readersdigest.ca, pg 517

The Reader's Digest Association Inc, 750 Third Ave, New York, NY 10017 *Tel:* 914-238-1000; 646-293-6284 *Toll Free Tel:* 800-310-6261 (cust serv) *Fax:* 914-238-4559 *Web Site:* www.rd.com; www.rda.com, pg 215

Reader's Digest Children's Books, 44 S Broadway, White Plains, NY 10601 *Tel:* 914-238-1000 *Toll Free Tel:* 800-934-0977 *Web Site:* www.rdtradepublishing.com, pg 215

Reader's Digest General Books, Reader's Digest Rd, Pleasantville, NY 10570-7000 *Tel:* 914-238-1000 *Toll Free Tel:* 800-304-2807 (cust serv) *Fax:* 914-244-7436, pg 215

Reader's Digest Trade Books, 44 S Broadway, White Plains, NY 10601 *Tel:* 914-244-7503 *Fax:* 914-244-4841 *Web Site:* www.rd.com, pg 215

Reader's Digest USA Select Editions, 44 S Broadway, 7th fl, White Plains, NY 10601 *Tel:* 914-238-1000 *Toll Free Tel:* 800-304-2807 (cust serv) *Fax:* 914-831-1560 *Web Site:* www.rda.com/readers-digest-select-editions, pg 215

The Reading Component, 1716 Clark Ave, PMB 195, Long Beach, CA 90815-3801 *Tel:* 562-438-0666, pg 554

Recorded Books LLC, 270 Skipjack Rd, Prince Frederick, MD 20678 *Tel:* 410-535-5590 *Toll Free Tel:* 800-638-1304; 877-732-2898 *Fax:* 410-535-5499 *E-mail:* customerservice@recordedbooks.com *Web Site:* www.recordedbooks.com, pg 215

Red Chair Press, PO Box 333, South Egremont, MA 01258-0333 *Toll Free Tel:* 888-327-2141 (ext 110) *Toll Free Fax:* 888-533-4037 *E-mail:* info@redchairpress.com *Web Site:* www.redchairpress.com, pg 216

Red Deer Press, 195 Allstate Pkwy, Markham, ON L3R 4T8, Canada *Tel:* 905-477-9700 *Toll Free Tel:* 800-387-9776 (orders) *Fax:* 905-477-2834 *Toll Free Fax:* 800-260-9777 (orders) *E-mail:* rdp@reddeerpress.com *Web Site:* www.reddeerpress.com, pg 517

Red Dust Inc, 1148 Fifth Ave, New York, NY 10128 *Tel:* 212-348-4388 *Web Site:* www.reddustbooks.com, pg 216

Red Hen Press, PO Box 40820, Pasadena, CA 91114 *Tel:* 626-356-4760 *Fax:* 626-356-9974 *Web Site:* www.redhen.org, pg 216

Red Moon Press, PO Box 2461, Winchester, VA 22604-1661 *Tel:* 540-722-2156 *E-mail:* redmoon@shentel.net *Web Site:* www.redmoonpress.com, pg 216

Red Rock Press, 331 W 57 St, Suite 175, New York, NY 10019 *Tel:* 212-362-8304 *Fax:* 212-362-6216 *E-mail:* info@redrockpress.com *Web Site:* www.redrockpress.com, pg 216

Red Sea Press Inc, 541 W Ingham Ave, Suite B, Trenton, NJ 08638 *Tel:* 609-695-3200 *Fax:* 609-695-6466 *E-mail:* customerservice@africaworldpressbooks.com *Web Site:* www.africaworldpressbooks.com, pg 216

Red Wheel/Weiser/Conari, 65 Parker St, Suite 7, Newburyport, MA 01950 *Tel:* 978-465-0504 *Toll Free Tel:* 800-423-7087 (orders) *Fax:* 978-465-0243 *E-mail:* info@rwwbooks.com *Web Site:* www.redwheelweiser.com, pg 216

RedBone Press, PO Box 15571, Washington, DC 20003 *Tel:* 202-667-0392 *Fax:* 301-588-0588 *E-mail:* info@redbonepress.com *Web Site:* www.redbonepress.com, pg 216

Redleaf Press, 10 Yorkton Ct, St Paul, MN 55117 *Tel:* 651-641-0508 *Toll Free Tel:* 800-423-8309 *Toll Free Fax:* 800-641-0115 *Web Site:* www.redleafpress.org, pg 216

Robert D Reed Publishers, PO Box 1992, Bandon, OR 97411-1192 *Tel:* 541-347-9882 *Fax:* 541-347-9883 *E-mail:* 4bobreed@msn.com *Web Site:* www.rdrpublishers.com, pg 216

Robert F Reed Technology Medal, 200 Deer Run Rd, Sewickley, PA 15143-2600 *Tel:* 412-259-1705 *Toll Free Tel:* 800-910-4283 (ext 705) *Fax:* 412-749-9890 *E-mail:* printing@printing.org *Web Site:* www.printing.org, pg 737

Reedswain Inc, 88 Wells Rd, Spring City, PA 19475 *Tel:* 610-495-9578 *Toll Free Tel:* 800-331-5191 *Fax:* 610-495-6632 *E-mail:* orders@reedswain.com *Web Site:* www.reedswain.com, pg 217

Rees Literary Agency, 14 Beacon St, Suite 710, Boston, MA 02108 *Tel:* 617-227-9014 *Fax:* 617-227-8762 *E-mail:* reesagency@reesagency.com *Web Site:* reesagency.com, pg 590

The Re-evaluation Counseling Communities, 719 Second Ave N, Seattle, WA 98109 *Tel:* 206-284-0311 *Fax:* 206-284-8429 *E-mail:* ircc@rc.org *Web Site:* www.rc.org, pg 217

Referee Books, 2017 Lathrop Ave, Racine, WI 53405 *Tel:* 262-632-8855 *Toll Free Tel:* 800-733-6100 *Fax:* 262-632-5460 *E-mail:* questions@referee.com *Web Site:* www.referee.com, pg 217

Reference Publications Inc, 218 Saint Clair River Dr, Algonac, MI 48001 *Tel:* 810-794-5722 *Fax:* 810-794-7463 *E-mail:* referencepub@sbcglobal.net, pg 217

Reference Service Press, 5000 Windplay Dr, Suite 4, El Dorado Hills, CA 95762-9319 *Tel:* 916-939-9620 *Fax:* 916-939-9626 *E-mail:* info@rspfunding.com *Web Site:* www.rspfunding.com, pg 217

ReferencePoint Press Inc, 17150 Via del Campo, Suite 205, San Diego, CA 92127 *Tel:* 858-618-1314 *Toll Free Tel:* 888-479-6436 *Fax:* 858-618-1730 *E-mail:* orders@referencepointpress.com *Web Site:* www.referencepointpress.com, pg 217

Reformation Heritage Books, 2965 Leonard St NE, Grand Rapids, MI 49525 *Tel:* 616-977-0889 *Fax:* 616-285-3246 *E-mail:* orders@heritagebooks.org *Web Site:* www.heritagebooks.org, pg 217

Regal Books, 1957 Eastman Ave, Ventura, CA 93003 *Tel:* 805-644-9721 *Toll Free Tel:* 800-446-7735 (orders) *Web Site:* www.regalbooks.com; www.gospellight.com, pg 217

Regal Crest Enterprises LLC, 229 Sheridan Loop, Belton, TX 76513 *Tel:* 409-527-1188 *Toll Free Fax:* 866-294-9628 *E-mail:* info@regalcrestbooks.biz *Web Site:* www.regalcrest.biz, pg 217

Regina Medal Award, 205 W Monroe, Suite 314, Chicago, IL 60606-5061 *Tel:* 312-739-1776; 312-739-1776 *Toll Free Tel:* 855-739-1776 *Fax:* 312-739-1778; 312-739-1778 *E-mail:* cla2@cathla.org *Web Site:* www.cathla.org, pg 737

Regnery Publishing Inc, One Massachusetts Ave NW, Washington, DC 20001 *Tel:* 202-216-0600 *Toll Free Tel:* 888-219-4747 *Fax:* 202-216-0612 *Web Site:* www.regnery.com, pg 217

Regular Baptist Press, 1300 N Meacham Rd, Schaumburg, IL 60173-4806 *Tel:* 847-843-1600 *Toll Free Tel:* 800-727-4440 (orders only); 888-588-1600 *Fax:* 847-843-3757 *E-mail:* rbp@garbc.org *Web Site:* www.regularbaptistpress.org, pg 217

Kerry Reilly: Representatives, 1826 Asheville Place, Charlotte, NC 28203 *Tel:* 704-372-6007 *E-mail:* kerry@reillyreps.com *Web Site:* www.reillyreps.com, pg 602

ReIMAGINE the MAGIC Annual Summer Conference, 317 Madison Ave, Suite 1704, New York, NY 10017 *Tel:* 917-720-6959 *E-mail:* iwwgquestions@gmail.com *Web Site:* www.iwwg.org, pg 672

Marian Reiner, 71 Disbrow Lane, New Rochelle, NY 10804 *Tel:* 914-235-7808 *Fax:* 914-576-1432 *E-mail:* mreinerlit@aol.com, pg 590

Nathan Reingold Prize, 440 Geddes Hall, Notre Dame, IN 46556 *Tel:* 574-631-1194 *Fax:* 574-631-1533 *E-mail:* info@hssonline.org *Web Site:* www.hssonline.org, pg 737

Renaissance House, 465 Westview Ave, Englewood, NJ 07631 *Tel:* 201-408-4048 *Fax:* 201-408-5011 *E-mail:* info@renaissancehouse.net *Web Site:* www.renaissancehouse.net, pg 218

Renaissance House, 465 Westview Ave, Englewood, NJ 07631 *Tel:* 201-408-4048 *Fax:* 201-408-5011 *E-mail:* laredo@renaissancehouse.net; info@renaissancehouse.net *Web Site:* www.renaissancehouse.net, pg 602

Renaissance Literary & Talent, PO Box 17379, Beverly Hills, CA 90209 *Tel:* 323-848-8305 *E-mail:* query@renaissancemgmt.net, pg 590

The Amy Rennert Agency Inc, 1550 Tiburon Blvd, Suite 302, Tiburon, CA 94920 *Tel:* 415-789-8955 *E-mail:* queries@amyrennert.com *Web Site:* amyrennert.com, pg 590

Reporters Committee for Freedom of the Press, 1101 Wilson Blvd, Suite 1100, Arlington, VA 22209-1817 *Tel:* 703-807-2100 *Toll Free Tel:* 800-336-4243 *Fax:* 703-807-2109 *E-mail:* rcfp@rcfp.org *Web Site:* www.rcfp.org, pg 635

Research & Education Association (REA), 61 Ethel Rd W, Piscataway, NJ 08854 *Tel:* 732-819-8880 *Fax:* 732-819-8808 (orders) *E-mail:* info@rea.com *Web Site:* www.rea.com, pg 218

Research Press, 2612 N Mattis Ave, Champaign, IL 61822 *Tel:* 217-352-3273 *Toll Free Tel:* 800-519-2707 *Fax:* 217-352-1221 *E-mail:* rp@researchpress.com; orders@researchpress.com *Web Site:* www.researchpress.com, pg 218

Research Research, 240 E 27 St, Suite 20-K, New York, NY 10016-9238 *Tel:* 212-779-9540 *Fax:* 212-779-9540 *E-mail:* ehtac@msn.com, pg 554

Residency, 454 E Hill Rd, Austerlitz, NY 12017 *Tel:* 518-392-3103; 518-392-4144 *E-mail:* apply@millaycolony.org *Web Site:* www.millaycolony.org, pg 737

Resource Publications Inc, 160 E Virginia St, Suite 170, San Jose, CA 95112-5876 *Tel:* 408-286-8505 *Fax:* 408-287-8748 *E-mail:* orders@rpinet.com *Web Site:* www.rpinet.com, pg 218

Fleming H Revell, PO Box 6287, Grand Rapids, MI 49516-6287 *Tel:* 616-676-9185 *Toll Free Tel:* 800-877-2665; 800-679-1957 *Fax:* 616-676-9573 *Web Site:* www.revellbooks.com, pg 218

Review & Herald Publishing Association, 55 W Oak Ridge Dr, Hagerstown, MD 21740 *Tel:* 301-393-3000 *Toll Free Tel:* 800-234-7630 *Fax:* 301-393-4055 (edit); 301-393-3222 (book div) *E-mail:* editorial@rhpa.org *Web Site:* www.reviewandherald.com, pg 218

Rhemalda Publishing, PO Box 1790, Moses Lake, WA 98837 *E-mail:* editor@rhemalda.com; customer_service@rhemalda.com *Web Site:* rhemalda.com, pg 218

Jodie Rhodes Literary Agency, 8840 Villa La Jolla Dr, Suite 315, La Jolla, CA 92037 *E-mail:* jrhodesl@san.rr.com *Web Site:* www.jodierhodesliterary.com, pg 590

The Harold U Ribalow Prize, 50 W 58 St, 4th fl, New York, NY 10019 *Tel:* 212-451-6289 *Fax:* 212-451-6257 *E-mail:* ribalowprize@hadassah.org *Web Site:* www.hadassah.org/magazine, pg 737

Evelyn Richardson Memorial Literary Trust Award, 1113 Marginal Rd, Halifax, NS B3H 4P7, Canada *Tel:* 902-423-8116 *Fax:* 902-422-0881 *E-mail:* talk@writers.ns.ca *Web Site:* www.writers.ns.ca, pg 738

Lynne Rienner Publishers Inc, 1800 30 St, Suite 314, Boulder, CO 80301 *Tel:* 303-444-6684 *Fax:* 303-444-0824 *E-mail:* questions@rienner.com; cservice@rienner.com *Web Site:* www.rienner.com, pg 218

Rigby, 9205 Southpark Center Loop, Orlando, FL 32819 *Toll Free Tel:* 800-531-5015; 800-289-4490 *Toll Free Fax:* 800-289-3994 *Web Site:* rigby.hmhco.com/en/rigby.htm, pg 218

Emma Right Books, 223 Nice Ct, Redwood City, CA 94065 *Tel:* 650-770-0993 *E-mail:* emmarightmarketing@gmail.com *Web Site:* www.emmaright.com, pg 529

Rights Unlimited Inc, 6 W 37 St, New York, NY 10001 *Tel:* 212-246-0900 *Fax:* 212-246-2114 *E-mail:* rightsunlimited@gmail.com *Web Site:* rightsunlimited.com, pg 590

John R Riina Literary Agency, 1055 W Joppa Rd, Unit 651, Towson, MD 21204-3777 *Tel:* 410-296-1499, pg 591

The Angela Rinaldi Literary Agency, PO Box 7877, Beverly Hills, CA 90212-7877 *Tel:* 310-842-7665 *Fax:* 310-837-8143 *Web Site:* www.rinaldiliterary.com, pg 591

Gwen Pharis Ringwood Award for Drama, 11759 Groat Rd, Edmonton, AB T5M 3K6, Canada *Tel:* 780-422-8174 *Toll Free Tel:* 800-665-5354 (AB only) *Fax:* 780-422-2663 (attn WGA) *E-mail:* mail@writersguild.ab.ca *Web Site:* www.writersguild.ab.ca, pg 738

Rio Nuevo Publishers, 451 N Bonita Ave, Tucson, AZ 85745 *Tel:* 520-623-9558 *Toll Free Tel:* 800-969-9558 *Fax:* 520-624-5888 *Toll Free Fax:* 800-715-5888 *E-mail:* info@rionuevo.com (cust serv) *Web Site:* www.rionuevo.com, pg 218

Rising Sun Publishing, PO Box 70906, Marietta, GA 30007-0906 *Tel:* 770-518-0369 *Toll Free Tel:* 800-524-2813 *Fax:* 770-587-0862 *E-mail:* info@rspublishing.com *Web Site:* www.rspublishing.com, pg 219

Ann Rittenberg Literary Agency Inc, 15 Maiden Lane, Suite 206, New York, NY 10038 *Tel:* 212-684-6936 *Fax:* 212-684-6929 *Web Site:* www.rittlit.com, pg 591

Judith Riven Literary Agent LLC, 250 W 16 St, Suite 4F, New York, NY 10011 *Tel:* 212-255-1009 *Fax:* 212-255-8547 *E-mail:* rivenlitqueries@gmail.com *Web Site:* rivenlit.com, pg 554, 591

Rivendell Books, PO Box 9306, Richmond Heights, MO 63117-0306 *Tel:* 314-609-6534 *E-mail:* butch@rivendellbooks.com *Web Site:* www.rivendellbooks.com, pg 529

River City Publishing LLC, 1719 Mulberry St, Montgomery, AL 36106 *Tel:* 334-265-6753 *Fax:* 334-265-8880 *E-mail:* sales@rivercitypublishing.com *Web Site:* www.rivercitypublishing.com, pg 219

Riverdale Avenue Books (RAB), 5676 Riverdale Ave, Bronx, NY 10471 *Tel:* 212-279-6418 *Web Site:* www.riverdaleavebooks.com, pg 219

Riverhead Books (Hardcover), 375 Hudson St, New York, NY 10014 *Tel:* 212-366-2000 *E-mail:* online@penguinputnam.com *Web Site:* www.penguinputnam.com; us.penguingroup.com, pg 219

Riverhead Books (Trade Paperback), 375 Hudson St, New York, NY 10014 *Tel:* 212-366-2000 *E-mail:* online@penguinputnam.com *Web Site:* www.penguinputnam.com; us.penguingroup.com, pg 219

Riverside Literary Agency, 41 Simon Keets Rd, Leyden, MA 01337 *Tel:* 413-772-0067 *Fax:* 413-772-0969 *E-mail:* rivlit@sover.net *Web Site:* www.riversideliteraryagency.com, pg 591

Riverside Publishing, 3800 Golf Rd, Suite 200, Rolling Meadows, IL 60008 *Tel:* 630-467-7000 *Toll Free Tel:* 800-323-9540 *Fax:* 630-467-7192 (cust serv) *E-mail:* rpc_customer_service@hmhpub.com (cust serv) *Web Site:* www.riversidepublishing.com, pg 219

Rizzoli International Publications Inc, 300 Park Ave S, 4th fl, New York, NY 10010-5399 *Tel:* 212-387-3400 *Toll Free Tel:* 800-522-6657 (orders only) *Fax:* 212-387-3535 *E-mail:* publicity@rizzoliusa.com *Web Site:* www.rizzoliusa.com, pg 219

RLR Associates Ltd, 7 W 51 St, New York, NY 10019 *Tel:* 212-541-8641 *Fax:* 212-262-7084 *Web Site:* www.rlrassociates.net, pg 591

RMA, 612 Argyle Rd, Suite L-5, Brooklyn, NY 11230 *Tel:* 718-434-1893 *Web Site:* www.ricia.com, pg 591

The RoadRunner Press, 122 NW 32 St, Oklahoma City, OK 73118 *Tel:* 405-524-6205 *Fax:* 405-524-6312 *E-mail:* info@theroadrunnerpress.com; orders@theroadrunnerpress.com *Web Site:* www.theroadrunnerpress.com, pg 219

Roanoke-Chowan Award for Poetry, 4610 Mail Service Ctr, Raleigh, NC 27699-4610 *Tel:* 919-807-7290 *Fax:* 919-733-8807 *Web Site:* www.history.ncdcr.gov/affiliates/lit-hist/awards/awards.htm, pg 738

The Roanoke Review Fiction Contest, 221 College Lane, Salem, VA 24153 *E-mail:* review@roanoke.edu *Web Site:* roanokereview.wordpress.com, pg 738

Roaring Brook Press, 175 Fifth Ave, New York, NY 10010 *Tel:* 646-307-5151 *Web Site:* us.macmillan.com/roaringbrookpressaspx, pg 219

Roaring Forties Press, 1053 Santa Fe Ave, Berkeley, CA 94706 *Tel:* 510-527-5461 *E-mail:* info@roaringfortiespress.com *Web Site:* www.roaringfortiespress.com, pg 220

B J Robbins Literary Agency, 5130 Bellaire Ave, North Hollywood, CA 91607 *E-mail:* robbinsliterary@gmail.com, pg 591

The Roberts Group, 12803 Eastview Curve, Apple Valley, MN 55124 *Tel:* 952-322-4005 *E-mail:* info@editorialservice.com *Web Site:* www.editorialservice.com, pg 554

Rochester Institute of Technology, School of Print Media, 69 Lomb Memorial Dr, Rochester, NY 14623-5603 *Tel:* 585-475-2728; 585-475-5336 *Fax:* 585-475-5336 *E-mail:* spmofc@rit.edu *Web Site:* cias.rit.edu/printmedia, pg 680

James A Rock & Co Publishers, 900 S Irby St, Suite 508, Florence, SC 29501 *Toll Free Tel:* 800-411-2230 *Fax:* 843-395-5975 *E-mail:* jrock@rockpublishing.com *Web Site:* rockpublishing.com, pg 220

RockBench Publishing Corp, 6101 Stillmeadow Dr, Nashville, TN 37211-6518 *Tel:* 615-831-2277 *Fax:* 615-831-2212 *E-mail:* info@rockbench.com *Web Site:* www.rockbench.com, pg 220

The Rockefeller University Press, 1114 First Ave, 3rd fl, New York, NY 10065-8325 *Tel:* 212-327-7938 *Fax:* 212-327-8587 *E-mail:* rupress@rockefeller.edu *Web Site:* www.rupress.org, pg 220

Rockmill & Company, 647 Warren St, Brooklyn, NY 11217 *Tel:* 718-638-3990 *E-mail:* agentrockmill@yahoo.com *Web Site:* www.rockmillandcompany.com, pg 591

Rocky Mountain Book Award, PO Box 42, Lethbridge, AB T1J 3Y3, Canada *Tel:* 403-381-7164 *E-mail:* rockymountainbookaward@shaw.ca *Web Site:* rmba.lethsd.ab.ca, pg 738

Rocky Mountain Books Ltd (RMB), 103-1075 Pendergast St, Victoria, BC V8V 0A1, Canada *Tel:* 250-360-0829 *Fax:* 250-386-0829 *Web Site:* www.rmbooks.com, pg 517

Rocky Mountain Mineral Law Foundation, 9191 Sheridan Blvd, Suite 203, Westminister, CO 80031 *Tel:* 303-321-8100 *Fax:* 303-321-7657 *E-mail:* info@rmmlf.org *Web Site:* www.rmmlf.org, pg 220

Rocky Mountain Publishing Professionals Guild (RMPPG), PO Box 19013, Boulder, CO 80308 *E-mail:* membership@rmppg.org *Web Site:* thepublishingpros.org, pg 635

Rocky River Publishers LLC, PO Box 1679, Shepherdstown, WV 25443-1679 *Tel:* 304-876-1868 *Fax:* 304-263-2949 *E-mail:* rockyriverpublishers@citlink.net *Web Site:* www.rockyriver.com, pg 220

Rod & Staff Publishers Inc, Hwy 172, Crockett, KY 41413 *Tel:* 606-522-4348 *Fax:* 606-522-4896 *Toll Free Fax:* 800-643-1244 (ordering in US), pg 220

Rodale Books, 400 S Tenth St, Emmaus, PA 18098 *Tel:* 610-967-5171 *Toll Free Tel:* 800-848-4735 (cust serv) *E-mail:* customerservice@rodale.com *Web Site:* www.rodaleinc.com, pg 220

Rogers Writers' Trust Fiction Prize, 90 Richmond St E, Suite 200, Toronto, ON M5C 1P1, Canada *Tel:* 416-504-8222 *Toll Free Tel:* 877-906-6548 *Fax:* 416-504-9090 *E-mail:* info@writerstrust.com *Web Site:* www.writerstrust.com, pg 738

Linda Roghaar Literary Agency LLC, 133 High Point Dr, Amherst, MA 01002 *Tel:* 413-256-1921 *Fax:* 413-256-2636 *E-mail:* contact@lindaroghaar.com *Web Site:* www.lindaroghaar.com, pg 591

Sami Rohr Prize for Jewish Literature, 520 Eighth Ave, 4th fl, New York, NY 10018 *Tel:* 212-201-2920 *Fax:* 212-532-4952 *E-mail:* jbc@jewishbooks.org *Web Site:* www.jewishbookcouncil.org, pg 738

The Roistacher Literary Agency, 545 W 111 St, Suite 7-J, New York, NY 10025 *Tel:* 212-222-1405, pg 591

Roman Catholic Books, PO Box 2286, Fort Collins, CO 80522-2286 *Tel:* 970-490-2735 *Fax:* 904-212-1287 *Web Site:* www.booksforcatholics.com, pg 220

Romance Writers of America®, 14615 Benfer Rd, Houston, TX 77069 *Tel:* 832-717-5200 *Fax:* 832-717-5201 *E-mail:* info@rwa.org *Web Site:* www.rwa.org, pg 635

Romance Writers of America Annual Conference, 14615 Benfer Rd, Houston, TX 77069 *Tel:* 832-717-5200 *Fax:* 832-717-5201 *E-mail:* info@rwa.org *Web Site:* www.rwa.org, pg 672

Romance Writers of America Awards, 14615 Benfer Rd, Houston, TX 77069 *Tel:* 832-717-5200 *Fax:* 832-717-5201 *E-mail:* info@rwa.org *Web Site:* www.rwa.org, pg 738

Roncorp Music, PO Box 517, Glenmoore, PA 19343 *Tel:* 610-942-2370 *Fax:* 610-942-0660 *E-mail:* info@nemusicpub.com *Web Site:* www.nemusicpub.com, pg 220

Ronin Publishing Inc, PO Box 22900, Oakland, CA 94609 *Tel:* 510-420-3669 *Fax:* 510-420-3672 *E-mail:* ronin@roninpub.com *Web Site:* www.roninpub.com, pg 220

Ronsdale Press Ltd, 3350 W 21 Ave, Vancouver, BC V6S 1G7, Canada *Tel:* 604-738-4688 *Toll Free Tel:* 855-738-4688 *Fax:* 604-731-4548 *E-mail:* ronsdale@shaw.ca *Web Site:* ronsdalepress.com, pg 518

Peter Rooney, 332 Bleecker St, PMB X-6, New York, NY 10014-2980 *Tel:* 917-376-1792 *Fax:* 212-226-8047 *E-mail:* magnetix@ix.netcom.com *Web Site:* www.magneticreports.com, pg 554

Robert Rose Inc, 120 Eglinton Ave E, Suite 800, Toronto, ON M4P 1E2, Canada *Tel:* 416-322-6552 *Fax:* 416-322-6936 *Web Site:* www.robertrose.ca, pg 518

Rosemont College, Graduate Publg Prog, 1400 Montgomery Ave, Rosemont, PA 19010 *Tel:* 610-527-0200 (ext 2336) *Fax:* 610-526-2964 *Web Site:* www.rosemont.edu, pg 680

The Rosen Publishing Group Inc, 29 E 21 St, New York, NY 10010 *Tel:* 212-777-3017 *Toll Free Tel:* 800-237-9932 *Toll Free Fax:* 888-436-4643 *E-mail:* info@rosenpub.com *Web Site:* www.rosenpublishing.com, pg 221

Dorothy Sargent Rosenberg Poetry Prizes, PO Box 2306, Orinda, CA 94563 *Web Site:* www.dorothyprizes.org, pg 738

The Rosenberg Group, 23 Lincoln Ave, Marblehead, MA 01945 *Tel:* 781-990-1341 *Fax:* 781-990-1344 *Web Site:* www.rosenberggroup.com, pg 591

Rita Rosenkranz Literary Agency, 440 West End Ave, Suite 15D, New York, NY 10024-5358 *Tel:* 212-873-6333 *Fax:* 212-873-5225 *Web Site:* www.ritarosenkranzliteraryagency.com, pg 591

Rosenthal Represents, 3850 Eddingham Ave, Calabasas, CA 91302 *Tel:* 818-222-5445 *Fax:* 818-222-5650 *E-mail:* eliselicenses@earthlink.net *Web Site:* www.rosenthalrepresents.com, pg 602

Ross Books, PO Box 4340, Berkeley, CA 94704-0340 *Tel:* 510-841-2474 *Fax:* 510-295-2531 *E-mail:* sales@rossbooks.com *Web Site:* www.rossbooks.com, pg 221

Ross Publishing LLC, 392 Central Park W, Suite 20-C, New York, NY 10025-5878 *Tel:* 212-765-8200 *E-mail:* info@rosspub.com *Web Site:* www.rosspub.com, pg 221

Margaret W Rossiter History of Women in Science Prize, 440 Geddes Hall, Notre Dame, IN 46556 *Tel:* 574-631-1194 *Fax:* 574-631-1533 *E-mail:* info@hssonline.org *Web Site:* www.hssonline.org, pg 738

Lois Roth Award, 26 Broadway, 3rd fl, New York, NY 10004-1789 *Tel:* 646-576-5141 *Fax:* 646-458-0030 *E-mail:* awards@mla.org *Web Site:* www.mla.org, pg 738

Rothstein Associates Inc, 4 Arapaho Rd, Brookfield, CT 06804-3104 *Tel:* 203-740-7400 *Toll Free Tel:* 888-768-4783 *Fax:* 203-740-7401 *E-mail:* info@rothstein.com *Web Site:* www.rothstein.com, pg 221

Jane Rotrosen Agency LLC, 318 E 51 St, New York, NY 10022 *Tel:* 212-593-4330 *Fax:* 212-935-6985 *Web Site:* janerotrosen.com, pg 591

Rough Guides, 375 Hudson St, New York, NY 10014 *Toll Free Tel:* 800-631-8571 *E-mail:* mail@roughguides.com *Web Site:* www.roughguides.com, pg 221

The Rough Notes Co Inc, 11690 Technology Dr, Carmel, IN 46032-5600 *Tel:* 317-582-1600 *Toll Free Tel:* 800-428-4384 (cust serv) *Fax:* 317-816-1000 *Toll Free Fax:* 800-321-1909 *E-mail:* rnc@roughnotes.com *Web Site:* www.roughnotes.com, pg 221

Routledge/Taylor & Francis, 711 Third Ave, 8th fl, New York, NY 10017 *Tel:* 212-216-7800 *Toll Free Tel:* 800-634-7064 (orders) *Fax:* 212-564-7854 *Web Site:* www.routledge.com, pg 221

Damaris Rowland, 420 E 23 St, Suite 6-F, New York, NY 10010 *Tel:* 212-475-8942 *E-mail:* nicholerowland5@mac.com, pg 592

Rowman & Littlefield Publishers Inc, 4501 Forbes Blvd, Suite 200, Lanham, MD 20706 *Tel:* 301-459-3366 *Toll Free Tel:* 800-462-6420 (cust serv) *Fax:* 301-429-5748 *Web Site:* www.rowmanlittlefield.com, pg 221

Dick Rowson, 4701 Connecticut Ave NW, Suite 503, Washington, DC 20008 *Tel:* 202-244-8104 *E-mail:* rcrowson2@aol.com, pg 554

Roxbury Publishing Co, 2001 Evans Rd, Cary, NC 27513 *Toll Free Tel:* 800-280-0280; 800-451-7556 (orders); 800-455-9714 *Fax:* 919-677-8877; 919-677-1303 *E-mail:* highered.us@oup.com; custserv.us@oup.com *Web Site:* www.us.oup.com/us/catalog/he/; www.roxbury.net, pg 222

Royal Fireworks Press, First Ave, Unionville, NY 10988 *Tel:* 845-726-4444 *Fax:* 845-726-3824 *E-mail:* mail@rfwp.com *Web Site:* www.rfwp.com, pg 222

Royal Ontario Museum Press, 100 Queen's Park, Toronto, ON M5S 2C6, Canada *Tel:* 416-586-8000 *Fax:* 416-586-5642 *E-mail:* info@rom.on.ca *Web Site:* www.rom.on.ca, pg 518

Royce Carlton Inc, 866 United Nations Plaza, Suite 587, New York, NY 10017-1880 *Tel:* 212-355-7700 *Toll Free Tel:* 800-LECTURE (532-8873) *Fax:* 212-888-8659 *E-mail:* info@roycecarlton.com *Web Site:* www.roycecarlton.com, pg 605

Lexi Rudnitsky Poetry Prize, 277 Broadway, Suite 708, New York, NY 10007 *Tel:* 212-260-9256 *Fax:* 212-267-3165 *E-mail:* info@perseabooks.com *Web Site:* www.perseabooks.com, pg 738

William B Ruggles Journalism Scholarship, 5211 Port Royal Rd, Suite 510, Springfield, VA 22151 *Tel:* 703-321-9606 *Fax:* 703-321-7143 *E-mail:* research@nilrr.org *Web Site:* www.nilrr.org, pg 739

Running Press Book Publishers, 2300 Chestnut St, Philadelphia, PA 19103-4399 *Tel:* 215-567-5080 *Toll Free Tel:* 800-343-4499 (cust serv & orders) *Fax:* 215-568-2919 *Toll Free Fax:* 800-453-2884 (cust serv & orders) *E-mail:* perseus.promos@perseusbooks.com *Web Site:* www.runningpress.com, pg 222

Russell Sage Foundation, 112 E 64 St, New York, NY 10065 *Tel:* 212-750-6000 *Toll Free Tel:* 800-524-6401 *Fax:* 212-371-4761 *E-mail:* info@rsage.org *Web Site:* www.russellsage.org, pg 222

Russian Information Service Inc, PO Box 567, Montpelier, VT 05601 *Tel:* 802-223-4955 *E-mail:* editors@russianlife.com *Web Site:* www.russianlife.com, pg 222

Rutgers University Press, 106 Somerset St, 3rd fl, New Brunswick, NJ 08901 *Tel:* 858-445-7784 (edit); 848-445-7788 *Toll Free Tel:* 800-848-6224 (orders only) *Fax:* 732-745-4935 (acqs, edit, mktg, perms & prodn) *Toll Free Fax:* 800-272-6817 (fulfillment) *Web Site:* rutgerspress.rutgers.edu, pg 222

The Cornelius Ryan Award, 40 W 45 St, New York, NY 10036 *Tel:* 212-626-9220 *Fax:* 212-626-9210 *Web Site:* www.opcofamerica.org, pg 739

Regina Ryan Books, 251 Central Park W, Suite 7-D, New York, NY 10024 *Tel:* 212-787-5589 *E-mail:* queries@reginaryanbooks.com *Web Site:* www.reginaryanbooks.com, pg 592

Sachem Publishing Associates Inc, 402 W Lyon Farm Dr, Greenwich, CT 06831 *Tel:* 203-813-3077 *Fax:* 203-531-2879 *E-mail:* sachempub@optonline.net, pg 554

Saddleback Educational Publishing, 3120-A Pullman St, Costa Mesa, CA 92626 *Tel:* 714-640-5200 *Toll Free Tel:* 888-SDLBACK (735-2225); 800-637-8715 *Fax:* 714-640-5297 *Toll Free Fax:* 888-734-4010 *E-mail:* contact@sdlback.com *Web Site:* www.sdlback.com, pg 222

William H Sadlier Inc, 9 Pine St, New York, NY 10005 *Tel:* 212-227-2120 *Toll Free Tel:* 800-221-5175 (cust serv) *Fax:* 212-312-6080 *Web Site:* www.sadlier.com, pg 223

SAE (Society of Automotive Engineers International), 400 Commonwealth Dr, Warrendale, PA 15096-0001 *Tel:* 724-776-4841; 724-776-4970 (outside US & CN) *Toll Free Tel:* 877-606-7323 (cust serv) *Fax:* 724-776-0790 (cust serv) *E-mail:* publications@sae.org; customerservice@sae.org *Web Site:* www.sae.org, pg 223

Safari Press, 15621 Chemical Lane, Bldg B, Huntington Beach, CA 92649 *Tel:* 714-894-9080 *Toll Free Tel:* 800-451-4788 *Fax:* 714-894-4949 *E-mail:* info@safaripress.com *Web Site:* www.safaripress.com, pg 223

Safer Society Foundation Inc, 29 Union St, Brandon, VT 05733 *Tel:* 802-247-3132 *Fax:* 802-247-4233 *E-mail:* info@safersociety.org *Web Site:* www.safersociety.org, pg 223

Sagamore Publishing LLC, 1807 Federal Dr, Urbana, IL 61801 *Tel:* 217-359-5940 *Toll Free Tel:* 800-327-5557 (orders) *Fax:* 217-359-5975 *E-mail:* books@sagamorepub.com *Web Site:* www.sagamorepub.com, pg 223

SAGE Publications, 2455 Teller Rd, Thousand Oaks, CA 91320 *Toll Free Tel:* 800-818-7243 *Toll Free Fax:* 800-583-2665 *E-mail:* info@sagepub.com *Web Site:* www.sagepub.com, pg 223

Saint Andrews College Press, 1700 Dogwood Mile, Laurinburg, NC 28352-5598 *Tel:* 910-277-5310 *Fax:* 910-277-5020 *E-mail:* press@sapc.edu *Web Site:* www.sapc.edu/sapress, pg 223

St Augustine's Press Inc, PO Box 2285, South Bend, IN 46680-2285 *Tel:* 574-291-3500 *Toll Free Tel:* 888-997-4994 *Fax:* 574-291-3700 *Web Site:* www.staugustine.net, pg 223

St Herman Press, 10 Beegum Gorge Rd, Platina, CA 96076 *Tel:* 530-352-4430 *Fax:* 530-352-4432 *E-mail:* stherman@stherman.com *Web Site:* www.stherman.com, pg 224

St James Press®, 27500 Drake Rd, Farmington Hills, MI 48331-3535 *Tel:* 248-699-4253 *Toll Free Tel:* 800-877-4253 (orders) *Fax:* 248-699-8035 *Toll Free Fax:* 800-414-5043 (orders) *E-mail:* gale.galeord@cengage.com *Web Site:* www.gale.cengage.com, pg 224

Guy Saint-Jean Editeur Inc, 3440 Blvd Industriel, Laval, QC H7L 4R9, Canada *Tel:* 450-663-1777 *Fax:* 450-663-6666 *E-mail:* info@saint-jeanediteur.com *Web Site:* www.saint-jeanediteur.com, pg 518

St Johann Press, 315 Schraalenburgh Rd, Haworth, NJ 07641 *Tel:* 201-387-1529 *Fax:* 201-501-0698 *Web Site:* www.stjohannpress.com, pg 224

St Joseph's University Press, 5600 City Ave, Philadelphia, PA 19131-1395 *Tel:* 610-660-3402 *Fax:* 610-660-3412 *E-mail:* sjupress@sju.edu *Web Site:* www.sjupress.com, pg 224

Saint Louis Literary Award, Pius XII Memorial Library, 3650 Lindell Blvd, St Louis, MO 63108 *Tel:* 314-977-3100 *Fax:* 314-977-3587 *E-mail:* slula@slu.edu *Web Site:* www.slu.edu/libraries/associates, pg 739

St Martin's Press, LLC, 175 Fifth Ave, New York, NY 10010 *Tel:* 646-307-5151 *Fax:* 212-420-9314 *E-mail:* firstname.lastname@macmillan.com *Web Site:* www.stmartins.com, pg 224

Saint Mary's Press, 702 Terrace Heights, Winona, MN 55987-1318 *Tel:* 507-457-7900 *Toll Free Tel:* 800-533-8095 *Fax:* 507-457-7990 *Toll Free Fax:* 800-344-9225 *E-mail:* smpress@smp.org *Web Site:* www.smp.org, pg 224

Saint Nectarios Press, 10300 Ashworth Ave N, Seattle, WA 98133-9410 *Tel:* 206-522-4471 *Toll Free Tel:* 800-643-4233 *Fax:* 206-523-0550 *E-mail:* orders@stnectariospress.com *Web Site:* www.stnectariospress.com, pg 225

St Pauls/Alba House, 2187 Victory Blvd, Staten Island, NY 10314-6603 *Tel:* 718-761-0047 (edit & prodn); 718-698-2759 (mktg & billing) *Toll Free Tel:* 800-343-2522 *Fax:* 718-761-0057 *E-mail:* sales@stpauls.us; marketing@stpauls.us *Web Site:* www.stpauls.us; www.albahouse.org, pg 225

Sts Judes imPress, 5537 Waterman Blvd, Suite 2-W, St Louis, MO 63112 *Tel:* 314-454-0064 *E-mail:* stjudes1@att.net, pg 225

Salem Press Inc, 2 University Plaza, Suite 310, Hackensack, NJ 07601 *Tel:* 201-968-0500 *Toll Free Tel:* 800-221-1592; 866-550-8122 *Fax:* 201-968-0511 *E-mail:* csr@salempress.com *Web Site:* salempress.com, pg 225

Salina Bookshelf Inc, 3120 N Caden Ct, Suite 4, Flagstaff, AZ 86004 *Toll Free Tel:* 877-527-0070 *Fax:* 928-526-0386 *Web Site:* www.salinabookshelf.com, pg 225

Barbara S Salz LLC Photo Research, 127 Prospect Place, South Orange, NJ 07079 *Tel:* 973-762-6486 *E-mail:* bsalz.photo@gmail.com, pg 554

Salzman International, 1751 Charles Ave, Arcata, CA 95521 *Tel:* 415-285-8267; 212-997-0115 (NY) *Fax:* 707-822-5500 *Web Site:* www.salzint.com, pg 602

Samhain Publishing Ltd, 11821 Mason Montgomery Rd, Suite 4-B, Cincinnati, OH 45249 *Tel:* 513-453-4688 *Toll Free Tel:* 800-509-4158 (orders) *Fax:* 513-583-0191 *E-mail:* support@samhainpublishing.com *Web Site:* www.samhainpublishing.com, pg 225

Pat Samples, 7152 Unity Ave N, Brooklyn Center, MN 55429 *Tel:* 763-560-5199 *Fax:* 763-560-5298 *E-mail:* patsamples@agingandcaregiving.com *Web Site:* www.patsamples.com, pg 554

Sams Technical Publishing LLC, 9850 E 30 St, Indianapolis, IN 46229 *Tel:* 317-396-5336 *Toll Free Tel:* 800-428-7267 *Fax:* 317-489-3406 *Toll Free Fax:* 800-552-3910 *E-mail:* customercare@samswebsite.com *Web Site:* www.samswebsite.com, pg 225

Paul Samuelson, 117 Oak Dr, San Rafael, CA 94901 *Tel:* 415-459-5352; 415-517-0700 *Fax:* 415-459-5352 *E-mail:* paul@storywrangler.com *Web Site:* www.storywrangler.com, pg 554

San Diego Christian Writers' Guild Conference, PO Box 270403, San Diego, CA 92198 *Tel:* 760-294-3269 *Fax:* 760-294-3269 *E-mail:* info@sandiegocwg.org *Web Site:* www.sandiegocwg.org, pg 672

San Diego State University Press, Arts & Letters 283, 5500 Campanile Dr, San Diego, CA 92182-6020 *Tel:* 619-594-6220 (orders) *Web Site:* sdsupress.sdsu.edu, pg 225

San Francisco Writers Conference, 1029 Jones St, San Francisco, CA 94109 *Tel:* 415-673-0939 *E-mail:* sfwriterscon@aol.com *Web Site:* www.sfwriters.org, pg 672

The Carl Sandburg Literary Awards, 20 N Michigan Ave, Suite 520, Chicago, IL 60602 *Tel:* 312-201-9830 *Fax:* 312-201-9833 *Web Site:* www.chicagopubliclibraryfoundation.org, pg 739

The Ernest Sandeen & Richard Sullivan Prizes in Fiction & Poetry, 356 O'Shaughnessy Hall, Notre Dame, IN 46556 *Tel:* 574-631-7526 *Fax:* 574-631-4795 *E-mail:* creativewriting@nd.edu *Web Site:* creativewriting.nd.edu, pg 739

Victoria Sanders & Associates LLC, 241 Avenue of the Americas, Suite 11-H, New York, NY 10014 *Tel:* 212-633-8811 *Fax:* 212-633-0525 *E-mail:* queriesvsa@gmail.com *Web Site:* www.victoriasanders.com, pg 592

Ada Sanderson Memorial, 1194 Hume Rd, Hume, VA 22639-1806 *E-mail:* poetryinva@aol.com *Web Site:* www.poetrysocietyofvirginia.org, pg 739

Sandhills Writers' Series, Dept of Communications & Professional Writing, 2500 Walton Way, Augusta, GA 30904 *Tel:* 706-667-4437 *Fax:* 706-667-4770 *Web Site:* www.sandhills.aug.edu, pg 672

Sandlapper Publishing Inc, 1281 Amelia St NE, Orangeburg, SC 29115-5475 *Tel:* 803-531-1658 *Toll Free Tel:* 800-849-7263 (orders only) *Fax:* 803-534-5223 *Toll Free Fax:* 800-337-9420 *E-mail:* sales@sandlapperpublishing.com *Web Site:* www.sandlapperpublishing.com, pg 225

Mari Sandoz Award, PO Box 21756, Lincoln, NE 68542-1756 *Tel:* 402-216-0727 *E-mail:* nebraskalibraries@gmail.com *Web Site:* www.nebraskalibraries.org, pg 739

Santa Barbara Book Promotion Workshop, PO Box 8206-240, Santa Barbara, CA 93118-8206 *Tel:* 805-968-7277 *Toll Free Tel:* 800-727-2782 *Fax:* 805-968-1379 *E-mail:* info@parapublishing.com *Web Site:* www.parapublishing.com, pg 672

Santa Monica Press LLC, 215 S Hwy 101, Suite 110, Solana Beach, CA 92075 *Tel:* 858-793-1890 *Toll Free Tel:* 800-784-9553 *Fax:* 858-777-0444 *E-mail:* books@santamonicapress.com *Web Site:* www.santamonicapress.com, pg 226

Santillana USA Publishing Co Inc, 2023 NW 84 Ave, Doral, FL 33122 *Tel:* 305-591-9522 *Toll Free Tel:* 800-245-8584 *Fax:* 305-591-9145 *Toll Free Fax:* 888-248-9518 *E-mail:* customerservice@santillanausa.com *Web Site:* www.santillanausa.com; www.alfaguara.net, pg 226

Sara Jordan Publishing, RPO Lakeport Box 28105, St Catharines, ON L2N 7P8, Canada *Tel:* 905-938-5050 *Toll Free Tel:* 800-567-7733 *Fax:* 905-938-9970 *Toll Free Fax:* 800-229-3855 *Web Site:* www.sara-jordan.com, pg 518

Sarabande Books Inc, 2234 Dundee Rd, Suite 200, Louisville, KY 40205 *Tel:* 502-458-4028 *Fax:* 502-458-4065 *E-mail:* info@sarabandebooks.org *Web Site:* www.sarabandebooks.org, pg 226

Karen E Sardinas-Wyssling, 6 Bradford Lane, Plainsboro, NJ 08536-2326 *Tel:* 609-275-9148 *E-mail:* starchild240@comcast.net, pg 554

May Sarton Award, 2 Farrar St, Cambridge, MA 02138 *Tel:* 617-744-6034 *E-mail:* contests@nepoetryclub.org *Web Site:* www.nepoetryclub.org, pg 739

SAS Publishing, 100 SAS Campus Dr, Cary, NC 27513-2414 *Tel:* 919-677-8000 *Fax:* 919-677-4444 *E-mail:* saspress@sas.com *Web Site:* www.sas.com/publishing, pg 226

Saskatchewan Arts Board, 1355 Broad St, Regina, SK S4R 7V1, Canada *Tel:* 306-787-4056 *Toll Free Tel:* 800-667-7526 (Saskatchewan only) *Fax:* 306-787-4199 *E-mail:* info@artsboard.sk.ca *Web Site:* www.artsboard.sk.ca, pg 635

Sasquatch Books, 1904 S Main St, Suite 710, Seattle, WA 98101 *Tel:* 206-467-4300 *Toll Free Tel:* 800-775-0817 *Fax:* 206-467-4301 *E-mail:* custserv@sasquatchbooks.com *Web Site:* www.sasquatchbooks.com, pg 226

Saturnalia Books Poetry Prize, 105 Woodside Rd, Ardmore, PA 19003 *Tel:* 267-278-9541 *E-mail:* info@saturnaliabooks.com *Web Site:* www.saturnaliabooks.com, pg 739

SATW Foundation Lowell Thomas Travel Journalism Competition, 6317 Crab Orchard Rd, Houston, TX 77057 *Tel:* 713-973-9985 *E-mail:* awards@satwf.com *Web Site:* www.satwfoundation.org, pg 739

Satya House Publications, 22 Turkey St, Hardwick, MA 01037 *Tel:* 413-477-8743 *E-mail:* info@satyahouse.com; orders@satyahouse.com *Web Site:* www.satyahouse.com, pg 226

Savant Books & Publications LLC, 2630 Kapiolani Blvd, Suite 1601, Honolulu, HI 96826 *Tel:* 808-941-3927 *Fax:* 808-941-3927 *E-mail:* savantbooks@gmail.com *Web Site:* www.savantbooksandpublications.com, pg 226

Saxon Publishers, 9205 Southpark Center Loop, Orlando, FL 32819 *Toll Free Tel:* 800-289-4490 *Toll Free Fax:* 800-289-3994 *E-mail:* greatservice@hmhpub.com *Web Site:* saxonpublishers.hmhco.com, pg 226

Aldo & Jeanne Scaglione Prize for a Translation of a Literary Work, 26 Broadway, 3rd fl, New York, NY 10004-1789 *Tel:* 646-576-5141 *Fax:* 646-458-0030 *E-mail:* awards@mla.org *Web Site:* www.mla.org, pg 739

Aldo & Jeanne Scaglione Prize for a Translation of a Scholarly Study of Literature, 26 Broadway, 3rd fl, New York, NY 10004-1789 *Tel:* 646-576-5141 *Fax:* 646-458-0030 *E-mail:* awards@mla.org *Web Site:* www.mla.org, pg 739

Aldo & Jeanne Scaglione Prize for Comparative Literary Studies, 26 Broadway, 3rd fl, New York, NY 10004-1789 *Tel:* 646-576-5141 *Fax:* 646-458-0030 *E-mail:* awards@mla.org *Web Site:* www.mla.org, pg 740

Aldo & Jeanne Scaglione Prize for French & Francophone Studies, 26 Broadway, 3rd fl, New York, NY 10004-1789 *Tel:* 646-576-5141 *Fax:* 646-458-0030 *E-mail:* awards@mla.org *Web Site:* www.mla.org, pg 740

Aldo & Jeanne Scaglione Prize for Italian Studies, 26 Broadway, 3rd fl, New York, NY 10004-1789 *Tel:* 646-576-5141 *Fax:* 646-458-0030 *E-mail:* awards@mla.org *Web Site:* www.mla.org, pg 740

Aldo & Jeanne Scaglione Prize for Studies in Germanic Languages & Literature, 26 Broadway, 3rd fl, New York, NY 10004-1789 *Tel:* 646-576-5141 *Fax:* 646-458-0030 *E-mail:* awards@mla.org *Web Site:* www.mla.org, pg 740

Aldo & Jeanne Scaglione Prize for Studies in Slavic Languages & Literature, 26 Broadway, 3rd fl, New York, NY 10004-1789 *Tel:* 646-576-5141 *E-mail:* awards@mla.org *Web Site:* www.mla.org, pg 740

Aldo & Jeanne Scaglione Publication Award for a Manuscript in Italian Literary Studies, 26 Broadway, 3rd fl, New York, NY 10004-1789 *Tel:* 646-576-5141 *Fax:* 646-458-0030 *E-mail:* awards@mla.org *Web Site:* www.mla.org, pg 740

Jack Scagnetti Talent & Literary Agency, 5118 Vineland Ave, No 102, North Hollywood, CA 91601 *Tel:* 818-761-0580 *Web Site:* jackscagnettitalentandliteraryagency.books.officelive.com, pg 592

William Sanders Scarborough Prize, 26 Broadway, 3rd fl, New York, NY 10004-1789 *Tel:* 646-576-5141 *Fax:* 646-458-0030 *E-mail:* awards@mla.org *Web Site:* www.mla.org, pg 740

Scarecrow Press Inc, 4501 Forbes Blvd, Suite 200, Lanham, MD 20706 *Tel:* 301-459-3366 *Fax:* 301-429-5748 *Web Site:* www.scarecrowpress.com, pg 226

Scarletta, 10 S Fifth St, Suite 1105, Minneapolis, MN 55402 *Tel:* 612-455-0252 *Fax:* 612-338-4817 *E-mail:* info@scarlettapress.com *Web Site:* www.scarlettapress.com, pg 227

SCBWI Work-In-Progress Grants, 8271 Beverly Blvd, Los Angeles, CA 90048 *Tel:* 323-782-1010 *Fax:* 323-782-1892 *E-mail:* membership@scbwi.org; scbwi@scbwi.org *Web Site:* www.scbwi.org, pg 740

Scepter Publishers, PO Box 1391, New York, NY 10802 *Tel:* 212-354-0670 *Toll Free Tel:* 800-322-8773 *Fax:* 212-354-0736 *Web Site:* www.scepterpublishers.org, pg 227

William D Schaeffer Environmental Award, 200 Deer Run Rd, Sewickley, PA 15143-2600 *Tel:* 412-259-1705 *Toll Free Tel:* 800-910-4283 (ext 705) *Fax:* 412-749-9890 *E-mail:* printing@printing.org *Web Site:* www.printing.org, pg 740

Schaffner Press, PO Box 41567, Tucson, AZ 85717 *E-mail:* tim@schaffnerpress.com *Web Site:* www.schaffnerpress.com, pg 227

C J Scheiner Books, 275 Linden Blvd, Suite B-2, Brooklyn, NY 11226 *Tel:* 718-469-1089 *Fax:* 718-469-1089, pg 555

Schiavone Literary Agency Inc, 236 Trails End, West Palm Beach, FL 33413-2135 *Tel:* 561-966-9294 *Fax:* 561-966-9294 *E-mail:* profschia@aol.com *Web Site:* www.publishersmarketplace.com/members/profschia, pg 592

Schiel & Denver Book Publishers, 10685-B Hazelhurst Dr, Suite 8575, Houston, TX 77043 *Tel:* 832-699-0264 *Toll Free Tel:* 888-629-4449 *Toll Free Fax:* 888-224-2721 *E-mail:* enquiries@schieldenver.com *Web Site:* www.schieldenver.com, pg 227

Schiffer Publishing Ltd, 4880 Lower Valley Rd, Atglen, PA 19310 *Tel:* 610-593-1777 *Fax:* 610-593-2002 *E-mail:* schifferbk@aol.com *Web Site:* www.schifferbooks.com, pg 227

Schirmer Trade Books, 180 Madison Ave, 24th fl, New York, NY 10016 *Tel:* 212-254-2100 *Toll Free Tel:* 800-431-7187 (orders) *Fax:* 212-254-2013 *Web Site:* www.musicsales.com, pg 227

Schlager Group Inc, 2501 Oak Lawn Ave, Suite 440, Dallas, TX 75219 *Toll Free Tel:* 888-416-5727 *Fax:* 214-347-9469 *E-mail:* info@schlagergroup.com *Web Site:* www.schlagergroup.com, pg 227

Wendy Schmalz Agency, 402 Union St, Unit 831, Hudson, NY 12534 *Tel:* 518-672-7697 *E-mail:* wendy@schmalzagency.com *Web Site:* www.schmalzagency.com, pg 592

Harold Schmidt Literary Agency, 415 W 23 St, Suite 6-F, New York, NY 10011 *Tel:* 212-727-7473, pg 592

Bernadotte E Schmitt Grants, 400 "A" St SE, Washington, DC 20003-3889 *Tel:* 202-544-2422 *Fax:* 202-544-8307 *E-mail:* awards@historians.org *Web Site:* www.historians.org, pg 740

Scholars' Facsimiles & Reprints, 6946 E Stevens Rd, Cave Creek, AZ 85331-8677 *Tel:* 480-575-9945 *E-mail:* sfandr@msn.com *Web Site:* www.scholarsbooklist.com, pg 228

Scholastic Canada Ltd, 604 King St W, Toronto, ON M5V 1E1, Canada *Tel:* 905-887-7323 *Toll Free Tel:* 800-268-3848 (CN) *Fax:* 905-887-1131 *Toll Free Fax:* 866-346-1288 *Web Site:* www.scholastic.ca, pg 518

Scholastic Classroom & Community Group, 524 Broadway, New York, NY 10012 *Tel:* 212-343-6100 *Web Site:* www.scholastic.com, pg 228

Scholastic Consumer & Professional Publishing, 557 Broadway, New York, NY 10012 *Tel:* 212-343-6100 *Toll Free Tel:* 800-621-1115 *Fax:* 800-621-1115 *Web Site:* www.scholastic.com, pg 228

Scholastic Education, 524 Broadway, New York, NY 10012 *Tel:* 212-343-6100 *Fax:* 212-343-6189 *Web Site:* www.scholastic.com, pg 228

Scholastic Inc, 557 Broadway, New York, NY 10012 *Tel:* 212-343-6100 *Toll Free Tel:* 800-scholastic *Web Site:* www.scholastic.com, pg 228

Scholastic International, 557 Broadway, New York, NY 10012 *Tel:* 212-343-6100; 646-330-5288 (intl cust serv) *Toll Free Tel:* 800-SCHOLASTIC (800-724-6527) *Fax:* 646-837-7878 *E-mail:* international@scholastic.com, pg 228

Scholastic Library/National Library Week Grant, 50 E Huron St, Chicago, IL 60611 *Tel:* 312-280-2148 *Toll Free Tel:* 800-545-2433 (ext 2148) *Fax:* 312-280-5274 *Web Site:* www.ala.org/nlwgrant, pg 740

Scholastic Media, 524 Broadway, 5th fl, New York, NY 10012 *Tel:* 212-389-3900 *Fax:* 212-389-3886, pg 228

Scholastic Trade Division, 557 Broadway, New York, NY 10012 *Tel:* 212-343-6100; 212-343-4685 (export sales) *Fax:* 212-343-4714 (export sales) *Web Site:* www.scholastic.com, pg 228

Scholium International Inc, 151 Cow Neck Rd, Port Washington, NY 11050 *Tel:* 516-767-7171 *E-mail:* info@scholium.com *Web Site:* www.scholium.com, pg 229

Schonfeld & Associates Inc, 1931 Lynn Circle, Libertyville, IL 60048 *Tel:* 847-816-4870 *Toll Free Tel:* 800-205-0030 *Fax:* 847-816-4872 *E-mail:* saiinfo@saibooks.com *Web Site:* www.saibooks.com, pg 229

School for Advanced Research Press, 660 Garcia St, Santa Fe, NM 87505 *Tel:* 505-954-7206 *Toll Free Tel:* 888-390-6070 *Fax:* 505-954-7241 *E-mail:* press@sarsf.org *Web Site:* sarpress.sarweb.org, pg 229

School Guide Publications, 210 North Ave, New Rochelle, NY 10801 *Tel:* 914-632-1220 *Toll Free Tel:* 800-433-7771 *Fax:* 914-632-3412 *E-mail:* info@religiousministries.com *Web Site:* www.graduateguide.com; www.schoolguides.com; www.religiousministries.com, pg 229

School of Government, University of North Carolina, CB 3330, Chapel Hill, NC 27599-3330 *Tel:* 919-966-4119 *Fax:* 919-962-2707 *Web Site:* www.sog.unc.edu, pg 229

School of Visual Arts, 209 E 23 St, New York, NY 10010-3994 *Tel:* 212-592-2100 *Fax:* 212-592-2116 *Web Site:* www.sva.edu, pg 680

School Zone Publishing Co, 1819 Industrial Dr, Grand Haven, MI 49417 *Tel:* 616-846-5030 *Toll Free Tel:* 800-253-0564 *Fax:* 616-846-6181 *Toll Free Fax:* 800-550-4618 (orders only) *Web Site:* www.schoolzone.com, pg 229

Schoolhouse Network Inc, PO Box 17676, Fountain Hills, AZ 85269 *Tel:* 973-206-1389 *E-mail:* info@schoolhousenetwork.com *Web Site:* www.schoolhousenetwork.com, pg 555

Schreiber Publishing Inc, PO Box 4193, Rockville, MD 20849 *Tel:* 301-725-3906 *Toll Free Tel:* 800-296-1961 (sales) *Fax:* 301-725-0333 (orders) *E-mail:* schreiberpublishing@comcast.net *Web Site:* schreiberlanguage.com; shengold.com, pg 229

Schroeder Indexing Services, 23 Camilla Pink Ct, Bluffton, SC 29909 *Tel:* 843-705-9779 *E-mail:* sanindex@schroederindexing.com *Web Site:* www.schroederindexing.com, pg 555

Franklin L Schulaner, PO Box 507, Kealakekua, HI 96750-0507 *Tel:* 808-322-3785 *E-mail:* fschulaner@hawaii.rr.com, pg 555

Susan Schulman, A Literary Agency, 454 W 44 St, New York, NY 10036 *Tel:* 212-713-1633 *Fax:* 212-581-8830 *E-mail:* schulmanagency@yahoo.com *Web Site:* www.schulmanagency.com, pg 593

Sherri Schultz/Words with Grace, 1916 Pike Place, Suite 12, No 118, Seattle, WA 98101 *Tel:* 415-297-5708 *E-mail:* WordsWithGraceEditorial@gmail.com *Web Site:* www.wordswithgrace.com, pg 555

The Schuna Group Inc, 1503 Briarknoll Dr, Arden Hills, MN 55112 *Tel:* 651-631-8480 *Web Site:* www.schunagroup.com, pg 603

A E Schwartz & Associates, 13 Conversation Way, Stoughton, MA 02072 *Tel:* 781-436-5033 *E-mail:* info@aeschwartz.com *Web Site:* aeschwartz.com, pg 593

Laurens R Schwartz, Esquire, 5 E 22 St, Suite 15-D, New York, NY 10010-5325 *Tel:* 212-228-2614, pg 593

Ruth & Sylvia Schwartz Children's Book Award, c/o Ontario Arts Council, 151 Bloor St W, 5th fl, Toronto, ON M5S 1T6, Canada *Tel:* 416-961-1660 *Toll Free Tel:* 800-387-0058 (ON) *Fax:* 416-961-7447 *E-mail:* info@arts.on.ca *Web Site:* www.arts.on.ca, pg 740

Science & Humanities Press, 56 Summit Point, St Charles, MO 62201 *Tel:* 636-394-4950 *Web Site:* sciencehumanitiespress.com; beachhousebooks.com; macroprintbooks.com; earlyeditionsbooks.com; heuristicsbooks.com, pg 229

Science Fiction & Fantasy Writers of America Inc (SFWA), PO Box 3238, Enfield, CT 06083-3238 *E-mail:* office@sfwa.org *Web Site:* www.sfwa.org, pg 635

Science Fiction Writers Workshop, University of Kansas, Wescoe Hall, Rm 3001, Dept of English, 1445 Jayhawk Blvd, Lawrence, KS 66045-7590 *Tel:* 785-864-3380 *Fax:* 785-864-1159 *Web Site:* www.ku.edu/~sfcenter, pg 673

Science in Society Journalism Awards, PO Box 7905, Berkeley, CA 94707 *Tel:* 510-647-9500 *Web Site:* www.nasw.org, pg 741

Science, Naturally!™, 725 Eighth St SE, Washington, DC 20003 *Tel:* 202-465-4798 *Toll Free Tel:* 866-724-9876 *Fax:* 202-558-2132 *E-mail:* info@sciencenaturally.com *Web Site:* www.sciencenaturally.com, pg 229

Science Publishers Inc, PO Box 699, Enfield, NH 03748-0699 *Tel:* 603-632-7377 *Fax:* 603-632-5611 *E-mail:* info@scipub.net *Web Site:* www.scipub.net, pg 229

Scobre Press Corp, 2255 Calle Clara, La Jolla, CA 92037 *Toll Free Tel:* 877-726-2734 *Fax:* 858-551-1232 *E-mail:* info@scobre.com *Web Site:* www.scobre.com, pg 230

Scott Publishing Co, 911 S Vandemark Rd, Sidney, OH 45365 *Tel:* 937-498-0802 *Toll Free Tel:* 800-572-6885 (cust serv) *Fax:* 937-498-0807 *Toll Free Fax:* 800-488-5349 *E-mail:* cuserv@amospress.com *Web Site:* www.amosadvantage.com, pg 230

S©ott Treimel NY, 434 Lafayette St, New York, NY 10003-6943 *Tel:* 212-505-8353 *Web Site:* scotttreimelny.com; scotttreimelny.blogspot.com, pg 593

Scovil Galen Ghosh Literary Agency Inc, 276 Fifth Ave, Suite 708, New York, NY 10001 *Tel:* 212-679-8686 *Fax:* 212-679-6710 *E-mail:* info@sgglit.com *Web Site:* www.sgglit.com, pg 593

Scribendi Inc, 405 Riverview Dr, Chatham, ON N7M 5J5, Canada *Tel:* 519-351-1626 (cust serv) *Fax:* 519-354-0192 *E-mail:* customerservice@scribendi.com *Web Site:* www.scribendi.com, pg 555

Scribes & Scribblers Writing Camps for Kids, 110 E Hallam St, Suite 116, Aspen, CO 81611 *Tel:* 970-925-3122 *Fax:* 970-920-5700 *E-mail:* info@aspenwriters.org *Web Site:* www.aspenwriters.org, pg 673

Scribner, 1230 Avenue of the Americas, New York, NY 10020, pg 230

Scripta Humanistica Publishing International, 1383 Kersey Lane, Potomac, MD 20854 *Tel:* 301-294-7949 *Fax:* 301-424-9584 *E-mail:* info@scriptahumanistica.com *Web Site:* www.scriptahumanistica.com, pg 230

The Scriptural Research & Publishing Co Inc, 344 E Johnson Ave, Cheshire, CT 06410 *Tel:* 203-272-1780 *Fax:* 203-272-2296 *E-mail:* src1@srpublish.org *Web Site:* www.scripturalresearch.com, pg 230

Scurlock Publishing Co Inc, 1293 Myrtle Springs Rd, Texarkana, TX 75503 *Tel:* 903-832-4726 *Toll Free Tel:* 800-228-6389 (US & CN) *Fax:* 903-831-3177 *E-mail:* custserv@scurlockpublishing.com *Web Site:* muzzleloadermag.com; www.scurlockpublishing.com, pg 230

SDP Publishing Solutions LLC, 36 Captain's Way, East Bridgewater, MA 02333 *Tel:* 617-775-0656 *Web Site:* www.sdppublishingsolutions.com, pg 555

SDSU Writers' Conference, 5250 Campanile Dr, Rm 2503, San Diego, CA 92182-1920 *Tel:* 619-594-2517 *Fax:* 619-594-8566 *E-mail:* sdsuwritersconference@mail.sdsu.edu *Web Site:* www.neverstoplearning.net/writers, pg 673

Seal Books, One Toronto St, Suite 300, Toronto, ON M5C 2V6, Canada *Tel:* 416-364-4449 *Toll Free Tel:* 888-523-9292 (order desk) *Fax:* 416-364-6863 *Web Site:* www.randomhouse.ca, pg 518

Seal Press, 1700 Fourth St, Berkeley, CA 94710 *Tel:* 510-595-3664 *Fax:* 510-595-4228 *E-mail:* seal.press@perseusbooks.com *Web Site:* www.sealpress.com, pg 230

Search Institute Press®, The Banks Bldg, Suite 125, 615 First Ave NE, Minneapolis, MN 55413 *Tel:* 612-376-8955 *Toll Free Tel:* 800-888-7828 *Fax:* 612-692-5553 *E-mail:* si@search-institute.org *Web Site:* www.search-institute.org, pg 230

Hank Searls, Box 1877, 4435 Holly Lane NW, Gig Harbor, WA 98335 *Tel:* 253-851-9896 *Fax:* 253-851-9897 *E-mail:* hanksearls@comcast.net, pg 555

Hank Searls Authors Workshop, 4435 Holly Lane NW, Gig Harbor, WA 98335 *Tel:* 253-851-9896 *Fax:* 253-851-9897 *E-mail:* hanksearls@comcast.net, pg 673

Second Chance Press, 4170 Noyac Rd, Sag Harbor, NY 11963 *Tel:* 631-725-1101 *E-mail:* info@thepermanentpress.com *Web Site:* www.thepermanentpress.com, pg 230

Second Story Feminist Press, 20 Maud St, Suite 401, Toronto, ON M5V 2M5, Canada *Tel:* 416-537-7850 *Fax:* 416-537-0588 *E-mail:* info@secondstorypress.ca *Web Site:* www.secondstorypress.ca, pg 518

See-More's Workshop, 325 West End Ave, Suite 12-B, New York, NY 10023 *Tel:* 212-724-0677 *Fax:* 212-724-0767 *E-mail:* sbt@shadowboxtheatre.org *Web Site:* www.shadowboxtheatre.org, pg 231

See-More's Workshop Arts & Education Workshops, 325 West End Ave, Suite 12-B, New York, NY 10023 *Tel:* 212-724-0677 *Fax:* 212-724-0767 *E-mail:* sbt@shadowboxtheatre.org *Web Site:* www.shadowboxtheatre.org, pg 673

See Sharp Press, PO Box 1731, Tucson, AZ 85702-1731 *Tel:* 520-338-2151 *E-mail:* info@seesharppress.com *Web Site:* www.seesharppress.com, pg 231

Seedling Publications Inc, 520 E Bainbridge St, Elizabethtown, PA 17022 *Toll Free Tel:* 800-233-0759 *Toll Free Fax:* 888-834-1303 *E-mail:* info@continentalpress.com *Web Site:* www.continentalpress.com, pg 231

SelectBooks Inc, One Union Sq W, Suite 909, New York, NY 10003 *Tel:* 212-206-1997 *Fax:* 212-206-3815 *E-mail:* info@selectbooks.com *Web Site:* www.selectbooks.com, pg 231

Self-Counsel Press Ltd, 4152 Meridian St, Suite 105-471, Bellingham, WA 98226 *Toll Free Tel:* 800-663-3007 *E-mail:* orders@self-counsel.com *Web Site:* www.self-counsel.com, pg 231

Self-Realization Fellowship Publishers, 3208 Humboldt St, Los Angeles, CA 90031 *Tel:* 323-276-6002 *Toll Free Tel:* 888-773-8680 *Fax:* 323-927-1624 *Web Site:* www.srfpublishers.org, pg 231

Lynn Seligman, 400 Highland Ave, Upper Montclair, NJ 07043 *Tel:* 973-783-3631 *Fax:* 973-783-3691 *E-mail:* seliglit@aol.com, pg 593

Edythea Ginis Selman Literary Agency Inc, 14 Washington Place, New York, NY 10003 *Tel:* 212-473-1874 *Fax:* 212-473-1875, pg 593

Richard Selman, 14 Washington Place, New York, NY 10003 *Tel:* 212-473-1874 *Fax:* 212-473-1875, pg 555

Alexa Selph, 4300 McClatchey Circle, Atlanta, GA 30342 *Tel:* 404-256-3717 *E-mail:* lexa101@aol.com, pg 555

Sentient Publications LLC, 1113 Spruce St, Boulder, CO 80302 *Tel:* 303-443-2188 *Fax:* 303-381-2538 *E-mail:* contact@sentientpublications.com *Web Site:* www.sentientpublications.com, pg 231

The Robert S Sergeant Memorial, 1194 Hume Rd, Hume, VA 22639-1806 *E-mail:* poetryinva@aol.com *Web Site:* www.poetrysocietyofvirginia.org, pg 741

Serindia Publications, PO Box 10335, Chicago, IL 60610-0335 *Tel:* 312-664-5531 *Fax:* 312-664-4389 *E-mail:* info@serindia.com *Web Site:* www.serindia.com, pg 231

Seven Footer Kids, 247 W 30 St, 11th fl, New York, NY 10001-2824 *Tel:* 212-710-9340 *Fax:* 212-710-9344 *E-mail:* info@sevenfooter.com *Web Site:* www.sevenfooterpress.com, pg 231

Seven Footer Press, 247 W 30 St, 2nd fl, New York, NY 10001-2824 *Tel:* 212-710-9340 *Fax:* 212-710-9344 *E-mail:* info@sevenfooter.com *Web Site:* www.sevenfooterpress.com, pg 232

Seven Locks Press, 3100 W Warner Ave, Suite 8, Santa Ana, CA 97204 *E-mail:* sevenlocks@aol.com *Web Site:* www.sevenlockspublishing.com, pg 232

Seven Stories Press, 140 Watts St, New York, NY 10013 *Tel:* 212-226-8760 *Fax:* 212-226-1411 *E-mail:* info@sevenstories.com *Web Site:* www.sevenstories.com, pg 232

Seventh Avenue Literary Agency, 2052 124 St, South Surrey, BC V4A 9K3, Canada *Tel:* 604-538-7252 *Fax:* 604-538-7252 *E-mail:* info@seventhavenuelit.com *Web Site:* www.seventhavenuelit.com, pg 593

Sewanee Writers' Conference, Stamler Ctr, 119 Gailor Hall, 735 University Ave, Sewanee, TN 37383-1000 *Tel:* 931-598-1141 *E-mail:* swc@sewanee.edu *Web Site:* www.sewaneewriters.org, pg 673

Mary Sue Seymour, 475 Miner Street Rd, Canton, NY 13617 *Tel:* 315-386-1831 *Web Site:* www.theseymouragency.com, pg 593

SF Canada, 7433 E River Rd, Washago, ON L0K 2B0, Canada *Web Site:* www.sfcanada.org, pg 636

SFWA Nebula Awards, PO Box 3238, Enfield, CT 06083-3238 *E-mail:* office@sfwa.org *Web Site:* www.sfwa.org, pg 741

The Michael Shaara Book Prize, Campus Box 435, 300 N Washington St, Gettysburg, PA 17325 *Tel:* 717-337-6590 *E-mail:* civilwar@gettysburg.edu *Web Site:* www.gettysburg.edu, pg 741

Shadow Mountain, PO Box 30178, Salt Lake City, UT 84130 *Tel:* 801-534-1515 *Fax:* 801-517-3474 *E-mail:* submissions@shadowmountain.com *Web Site:* shadowmountain.com, pg 232

Shambhala Publications Inc, Horticultural Hall, 300 Massachusetts Ave, Boston, MA 02115 *Tel:* 617-424-0030 *Toll Free Tel:* 866-424-0030 (off); 888-424-2329 (cust serv) *Fax:* 617-236-1563 *E-mail:* customercare@shambhala.com *Web Site:* www.shambhala.com, pg 232

M E Sharpe Inc, 80 Business Park Dr, Suite 202, Armonk, NY 10504 *Tel:* 914-273-1800 *Toll Free Tel:* 800-541-6563 *Fax:* 914-273-2106 *E-mail:* info@mesharpe.com *Web Site:* www.mesharpe.com, pg 232

Shaughnessy Cohen Prize for Political Writing, 90 Richmond St E, Suite 200, Toronto, ON M5C 1P1, Canada *Tel:* 416-504-8222 *Toll Free Tel:* 877-906-6548 *Fax:* 416-504-9090 *E-mail:* info@writerstrust.com *Web Site:* www.writerstrust.com, pg 741

Mina P Shaughnessy Prize, 26 Broadway, 3rd fl, New York, NY 10004-1789 *Tel:* 646-576-5141 *Fax:* 646-458-0030 *E-mail:* awards@mla.org *Web Site:* www.mla.org, pg 741

Charlotte Sheedy Literary Agency Inc, 928 Broadway, Suite 901, New York, NY 10010 *Tel:* 212-780-9800 *Fax:* 212-780-0308; 212-780-6095 *E-mail:* sheedy@sll.com *Web Site:* www.sheedylit.com, pg 593

Sheffield Publishing Co, 9009 Antioch Rd, Salem, WI 53168 *Tel:* 262-843-2281 *Fax:* 262-843-3683 *E-mail:* info@spcbooks.com *Web Site:* www.spcbooks.com, pg 233

Barry Sheinkopf, c/o The Writing Ctr, 601 Palisade Ave, Englewood Cliffs, NJ 07632 *Tel:* 201-567-4017 *Fax:* 201-567-7202 *E-mail:* bsheinkopf@optonline.net, pg 555

Shenanigan Books, 84 River Rd, Summit, NJ 07901 *Tel:* 908-219-4275 *Fax:* 908-219-4485 *E-mail:* info@shenaniganbooks.com *Web Site:* www, shenaniganbooks.com, pg 233

Shen's Books, 1547 Palos Verdes Mall, Unit 291, Walnut Creek, CA 94597 *Tel:* 925-262-8108 *Toll Free Tel:* 800-456-6660 *Fax:* 925-415-6136 *Toll Free Fax:* 888-269-9092 *E-mail:* info@shens.com *Web Site:* www.shens.com, pg 233

The Shepard Agency, 73 Kingswood Dr, Bethel, CT 06801 *Tel:* 203-790-4230; 203-790-1780 *Fax:* 203-798-2924 *E-mail:* shepardagcy@mindspring.com, pg 594

Shepard Publications, PO Box 280, Friday Harbor, WA 98250 *Web Site:* www.shepardpub.com, pg 233

The Robert E Shepard Agency, 4804 Laurel Canyon Blvd, Box 592, Valley Village, CA 91607-3717 *E-mail:* mail@shepardagency.com *Web Site:* www.shepardagency.com, pg 594

Sherman Asher Publishing, 126 Candelario St, Santa Fe, NM 87501 *Tel:* 505-988-7214 *E-mail:* westernedge@santa-fe.net *Web Site:* www.shermanasher.com; www.westernedgepress.com, pg 233

Ken Sherman & Associates, 1275 N Hayworth, Suite 103, Los Angeles, CA 90046 *Tel:* 310-273-8840 *Fax:* 310-271-2875 *E-mail:* kenshermanassociates@gmail.com *Web Site:* www.kenshermanassociates.com, pg 594

Wendy Sherman Associates Inc, 27 W 24 St, Suite 700-B, New York, NY 10010 *Tel:* 212-279-9027 *Fax:* 212-279-9027 *Web Site:* www.wsherman.com, pg 594

Sheron Enterprises Inc, 1035 S Carley Ct, North Bellmore, NY 11710 *Tel:* 516-783-5885 *E-mail:* contact@longislandbookpublisher.com *Web Site:* www.longislandbookpublisher.com, pg 233

Shields Publications, PO Box 669, Eagle River, WI 54521-0669 *Tel:* 715-479-4810 *Fax:* 715-479-3905 *E-mail:* wormbooks@wormbooks.com *Web Site:* www.wormbooks.com, pg 233

J Gordon Shillingford Publishing Inc, PO Box 86, RPO Corydon Ave, Winnipeg, MB R3M 3S3, Canada *Tel:* 204-779-6967 *Fax:* 204-779-6970 *Web Site:* www.jgshillingford.com, pg 519

Monika Shoffman-Graves, 70 Transylvania Ave, Key Largo, FL 33037 *Tel:* 305-451-1462 *Fax:* 305-451-1462 *E-mail:* keysmobill@earthlink.net, pg 555

Shoreline Press, 23 Sainte Anne, Ste Anne de Bellevue, QC H9X 1L1, Canada *Tel:* 514-457-5733 *E-mail:* info@shorelinepress.ca *Web Site:* shorelinepress.ca, pg 519

Short Prose Competition for Developing Writers, 90 Richmond St E, Suite 200, Toronto, ON M5C 1P1, Canada *Tel:* 416-703-8982 *Fax:* 416-504-9090 *E-mail:* info@writersunion.ca *Web Site:* www.writersunion.ca, pg 741

Short Story Award, 115 Richmond St, Charlottetown, PE C1A 1H7, Canada *Tel:* 902-368-4410 *Toll Free Tel:* 888-734-2784 *Fax:* 902-368-4418 *E-mail:* peiwritersguild@gmail.com *Web Site:* www.peiwritersguild.com, pg 741

Short Story Award for New Writers, PO Box 80430, Portland, OR 97280 *Tel:* 503-221-0836 *Fax:* 503-221-0837 *E-mail:* editors@glimmertrain.org *Web Site:* www.glimmertrain.org, pg 741

Show What You Know® Publishing, A Lorenz Company, 501 E Third St, Dayton, OH 45402 *Tel:* 614-764-1211; 937-228-6118 *Toll Free Tel:* 877-PASSING (727-7464) *Fax:* 937-233-2042 *E-mail:* info@swykonline.com *Web Site:* www.swykonline.com; www.lorenzeducationalpress.com, pg 233

Edwin "Bud" Shrake Award for Best Short Nonfiction, PO Box 609, Round Rock, TX 78680 *Tel:* 512-683-5640 *E-mail:* tilsecretary@yahoo.com *Web Site:* www.texasinstituteofletters.org, pg 741

Robert F Sibert Informational Book Award, 50 E Huron St, Chicago, IL 60611-2795 *Tel:* 312-280-2163 *Toll Free Tel:* 800-545-2433 *Fax:* 312-440-9374 *E-mail:* alsc@ala.org *Web Site:* www.ala.org/alsc, pg 741

Side by Side Literary Productions Inc, 15 W 26 St, 2nd fl, New York, NY 10010 *Tel:* 646-442-2905 *Fax:* 212-888-3650 *Web Site:* sidebysidelit.com, pg 594

Rosalie Siegel, International Literary Agent Inc, One Abey Dr, Pennington, NJ 08534 *Tel:* 609-737-1007 *Fax:* 609-737-3708 *E-mail:* rsiegel@ix.netcom.com *Web Site:* www.rosaliesiegel.com, pg 594

Sierra Club Books, 85 Second St, 2nd fl, San Francisco, CA 94105 *Tel:* 415-977-5500 *Fax:* 415-977-5794 *E-mail:* books.publishing@sierraclub.org *Web Site:* www.sierraclubbooks.org, pg 233

Siglio, 2432 Medlow Ave, Los Angeles, CA 90041 *Tel:* 310-857-6935 *Fax:* 310-728-6844 *E-mail:* publisher@sigliopress.com *Web Site:* sigliopress.com, pg 233

Signalman Publishing, 3700 Commerce Blvd, Kissimmee, FL 34741 *Tel:* 407-504-4103 *Toll Free Tel:* 888-907-4423 *E-mail:* info@signalmanpublishing.com *Web Site:* www.signalmanpublishing.com, pg 233

Signature Books Publishing LLC, 564 W 400 N, Salt Lake City, UT 84116-3411 *Tel:* 801-531-1483 *Toll Free Tel:* 800-356-5687 (orders) *Fax:* 801-531-1488 *E-mail:* people@signaturebooks.com *Web Site:* www.signaturebooks.com; www.signaturebookslibrary.org, pg 233

Signature Editions, RPO Corydon, PO Box 206, Winnipeg, MB R3M 3S7, Canada *Tel:* 204-779-7803 *Fax:* 204-779-6970 *E-mail:* signature@allstream.net *Web Site:* www.signature-editions.com, pg 519

SIL International, 7500 W Camp Wisdom Rd, Dallas, TX 75236-5629 *Tel:* 972-708-7400 *Fax:* 972-708-7350 *E-mail:* publications_intl@sil.org *Web Site:* www.ethnologue.com; www.sil.org, pg 234

Silicon Press, 25 Beverly Rd, Summit, NJ 07901 *Tel:* 908-273-8919 *Fax:* 908-273-6149 *E-mail:* info@silicon-press.com *Web Site:* www.silicon-press.com, pg 234

Silman-James Press, 3624 Shannon Rd, Los Angeles, CA 90027 *Tel:* 323-661-9922 *Toll Free Tel:* 877-SJP-BOOK (757-2665) *Fax:* 323-661-9933 *E-mail:* info@silmanjamespress.com *Web Site:* www.silmanjamespress.com, pg 234

Dorothy Silver Playwriting Competition, 26001 S Woodland Rd, Beachwood, OH 44122 *Tel:* 216-831-0700 *Fax:* 216-831-7796 *E-mail:* info@mandeljcc.org *Web Site:* www.mandeljcc.org, pg 742

Silver Gavel Awards, 321 N Clark St, Chicago, IL 60654 *Tel:* 312-988-5733 *Toll Free Tel:* 800-285-2221 (orders) *Fax:* 312-988-5494 *Web Site:* www.abanow.org; www.americanbar.org, pg 742

Silver Leaf Books LLC, 13 Temi Rd, Holliston, MA 01746 *E-mail:* sales@silverleafbooks.com; editor@silverleafbooks.com; customerservice@silverleafbooks.com *Web Site:* www.silverleafbooks.com, pg 234

Silver Moon Press, 400 E 85 St, New York, NY 10028 *Toll Free Tel:* 800-874-3320 *Fax:* 212-988-8112 *E-mail:* mail@silvermoonpress.com *Web Site:* www.silvermoonpress.com, pg 234

SilverHouse Books, 555 NE 15 St, Suite 2-i, Miami, FL 33132 *Tel:* 305-747-1258 *E-mail:* info@silverhousebooks.com *Web Site:* www.silverhousebooks.com, pg 234

Simba Information, 60 Long Ridge Rd, Suite 300, Stamford, CT 06902 *Tel:* 203-325-8193 *Toll Free Tel:* 888-297-4622 (cust serv) *Fax:* 203-325-8975 *E-mail:* customerservice@simbainformation.com *Web Site:* www.simbainformation.com, pg 234

Simcha Press, 3201 SW 15 St, Deerfield Beach, FL 33442-8190 *Tel:* 954-360-0909 ext 212 *Toll Free Tel:* 800-851-9100 ext 212 *Toll Free Fax:* 800-424-7652 *E-mail:* simchapress@hcibooks.com *Web Site:* www.hcibooks.com, pg 234

Francis B Simkins Award, University of Georgia, Dept of History, Athens, GA 30602-1602 *Tel:* 706-542-8848 *Fax:* 706-542-2455 *Web Site:* sha.uga.edu, pg 742

The John Simmons Short Fiction Award, 102 Dey House, 507 N Clinton St, Iowa City, IA 52242-1000 *Tel:* 319-335-0416 *Fax:* 319-335-0420, pg 742

Simon & Pierre Publishing Co Ltd, 3 Church St, Suite 500, Toronto, ON M5E 1M2, Canada *Tel:* 416-214-5544 *Fax:* 416-214-5556 *E-mail:* info@dundurn.com *Web Site:* www.dundurn.com, pg 519

Simon & Schuster, 1230 Avenue of the Americas, New York, NY 10020 *Tel:* 212-698-7000 *Toll Free Tel:* 800-223-2348 (cust serv); 800-223-2336 (orders) *Toll Free Fax:* 800-943-9831 (orders) *Web Site:* www.simonandschuster.com, pg 234

Simon & Schuster Audio, 1230 Avenue of the Americas, New York, NY 10020 *Web Site:* audio.simonandschuster.com, pg 234

Simon & Schuster Canada, 166 King St E, Suite 300, Toronto, ON M5A 1J3, Canada *Tel:* 647-427-8882 *Toll Free Tel:* 800-387-0446; 800-268-3216 (orders) *Fax:* 647-430-9446 *Toll Free Fax:* 888-849-8151 (orders) *E-mail:* info@simonandschuster.ca *Web Site:* www.simonsayscanada.com, pg 519

Simon & Schuster Children's Publishing, 1230 Avenue of the Americas, New York, NY 10020 *Tel:* 212-698-7000 *Web Site:* KIDS.SimonandSchuster.com; TEEN.SimonandSchuster.com; simonandschuster.net; simonandschuster.biz, pg 235

Simon & Schuster Digital, 1230 Avenue of the Americas, New York, NY 10020 *Tel:* 212-698-7547 *Web Site:* www.simonandschuster.com; kids.simonandschuster.com; www.simonandschuster.ca; www.simonandschuster.co.uk; www.simonandschuster.net; www.simonandschuster.biz; www.tipsoncareerandmoney.com; www.tipsonhealthyliving.com; www.tipsonhomeandstyle.com; www.tipsonlifeandlove.com, pg 235

Simon & Schuster, Inc, 1230 Avenue of the Americas, New York, NY 10020 *Tel:* 212-698-7000 *Fax:* 212-698-7007 *E-mail:* firstname.lastname@simonandschuster.com *Web Site:* www.simonandschuster.com, pg 235

Simon & Schuster Sales & Marketing, 1230 Avenue of the Americas, New York, NY 10020 *Tel:* 212-698-7000, pg 236

Charlie May Simon Children's Book Award, Arkansas State Library, Suite 100, 900 W Capitol Ave, Little Rock, AR 72201-3108 *Tel:* 501-682-2860 *Fax:* 501-682-1693 *Web Site:* www.library.arkansas.gov, pg 742

Simply Read Books, 501-5525 West Blvd, Vancouver, BC V6M 3W6, Canada *Tel:* 604-727-2960 *E-mail:* go@simplyreadbooks.com *Web Site:* www.simplyreadbooks.com, pg 519

Sinauer Associates Inc, 23 Plumtree Rd, Sunderland, MA 01375 *Tel:* 413-549-4300 *Fax:* 413-549-1118 *E-mail:* publish@sinauer.com; orders@sinauer.com *Web Site:* www.sinauer.com, pg 236

Six Gallery Press, PO Box 90145, Pittsburgh, PA 15224-0545 *Web Site:* www.sixgallerypress.com, pg 236

Skandisk Inc, 6667 W Old Shakapee Rd, Suite 109, Bloomington, MN 55438-2622 *Tel:* 952-829-8998 *Toll Free Tel:* 800-468-2424 *Fax:* 952-829-8992 *E-mail:* tomten@skandisk.com *Web Site:* www.skandisk.com, pg 236

SkillPath Publications, PO Box 2768, Mission, KS 66201-2768 *Tel:* 913-362-3900 *Toll Free Tel:* 800-873-7545 *Fax:* 913-362-4241 *E-mail:* customercare@skillpath.net; products@skillpath.net *Web Site:* www.skillpath.com, pg 236

Skinner House Books, 25 Beacon St, Boston, MA 02108-2800 *Tel:* 617-742-2100 *Fax:* 617-742-7025 *E-mail:* skinnerhouse@uua.org *Web Site:* www.skinnerhouse.org, pg 236

Skipping Stones Honor Awards, 166 W 12 Ave, Eugene, OR 97401 *Tel:* 541-342-4956 *E-mail:* info@skippingstones.org *Web Site:* www.skippingstones.org, pg 742

Irene Skolnick Literary Agency, 2095 Broadway, Suite 307, New York, NY 10023 *Tel:* 212-727-3648 *Fax:* 212-727-1024 *E-mail:* office@skolnickliterary.com (queries) *Web Site:* www.skolnickagency.com, pg 594

Sky Oaks Productions Inc, 19544 Sky Oaks Way, Los Gatos, CA 95030 *Tel:* 408-395-7600 *Fax:* 408-395-8440 *E-mail:* tprworld@aol.com *Web Site:* www.tpr-world.com, pg 236

Sky Publishing, 90 Sherman St, Cambridge, MA 02140 *Tel:* 617-864-7360 *Toll Free Tel:* 866-644-1377 *Fax:* 617-864-6117 *E-mail:* info@skyandtelescope.com *Web Site:* www.skyandtelescope.com, pg 236

SkyLight Paths Publishing, Sunset Farm Offices, Rte 4, Woodstock, VT 05091 *Tel:* 802-457-4000 *Toll Free Tel:* 800-962-4544 *Fax:* 802-457-4004 *E-mail:* sales@skylightpaths.com *Web Site:* www.skylightpaths.com, pg 237

Slack Incorporated, 6900 Grove Rd, Thorofare, NJ 08086-9447 *Tel:* 856-848-1000 *Toll Free Tel:* 800-257-8290 *Fax:* 856-848-6091 *E-mail:* sales@slackinc.com *Web Site:* www.slackbooks.com, pg 237

SLC Enterprises Inc, 332 S Michigan Ave, No 1032-C216, Chicago, IL 60604 *Tel:* 616-942-2665 (answering serv & voice mail), pg 594

Sleeping Bear Press™, 315 Eisenhower Pkwy, Suite 200, Ann Arbor, MI 48108 *Toll Free Tel:* 800-487-2323 *Fax:* 734-794-0004 *E-mail:* sleepingbearpress@cengage.com *Web Site:* www.sleepingbearpress.com, pg 237

Sligo Literary Agency LLC, 425 Poa Place, San Luis Obispo, CA 93405 *Tel:* 805-550-1667 *Fax:* 805-783-2317 *E-mail:* editorial@mckennapubgrp.com *Web Site:* sligolitagency.com, pg 594

Slipdown Mountain Publications LLC, 28151 Quarry Lake Rd, Lake Linden, MI 49945 *Tel:* 906-523-4118 *Toll Free Tel:* 866-341-3705 *Toll Free Fax:* 866-341-3705 *E-mail:* books@jacobsvillebooks.com *Web Site:* www.jacobsvillebooks.com, pg 237

Slipstream Annual Poetry Chapbook Contest, PO Box 2071, Dept W-1, Niagara Falls, NY 14301 *Web Site:* www.slipstreampress.org, pg 742

Beverley Slopen Literary Agency, 131 Bloor St W, Suite 711, Toronto, ON M5S 1S3, Canada *Tel:* 416-964-9598 *Fax:* 416-921-7726 *E-mail:* beverley@slopenagency.ca *Web Site:* www.slopenagency.ca, pg 594

Bernice Slote Award, University of Nebraska, 123 Andrews Hall, Lincoln, NE 68588-0334 *Tel:* 402-472-0911 *Web Site:* prairieschooner.unl.edu, pg 742

Small Business Advisors Inc, 11 Franklin Ave, Hewlett, NY 11557 *Tel:* 516-374-1387; 914-260-1027 *Fax:* 516-374-1175; 720-294-3202 *E-mail:* info@smallbusinessadvice.com *Web Site:* www.smallbusinessadvice.com, pg 237

Small Publishers, Artists & Writers Network (SPAWN), 323 E Matilija St, Suite 110, PMB 123, Ojai, CA 93023 *Tel:* 805-646-3045 *Fax:* 805-640-8213 *Web Site:* www.spawn.org, pg 636

Donald Smiley Prize, 260 rue Dalhousie St, Suite 204, Ottawa, ON K1N 7E4, Canada *Tel:* 613-562-1202 *Fax:* 613-241-0019 *E-mail:* cpsa-acsp@cpsa-acsp.ca *Web Site:* www.cpsa-acsp.ca, pg 742

Smith & Kraus Publishers Inc, 40 Walch Dr, Portland, ME 04103 *Tel:* 207-523-2585 *Toll Free Tel:* 877-668-8680 *Fax:* 207-699-3698 *E-mail:* editor@smithandkraus.com *Web Site:* www.smithandkraus.com, pg 237

Helen C Smith Memorial Award, PO Box 609, Round Rock, TX 78680 *Tel:* 512-683-5640 *E-mail:* tilsecretary@yahoo.com *Web Site:* www.texasinstituteofletters.org, pg 742

The Jeffrey E Smith Editors' Prize, 357 McReynolds Hall, Columbia, MO 65211 *Tel:* 573-882-4474 *Toll Free Tel:* 800-949-2505 *Fax:* 573-884-4671 *Web Site:* www.missourireview.com, pg 742

M Lee Smith Publishers LLC, 5201 Virginia Way, Brentwood, TN 37027 *Tel:* 615-373-7517 *Toll Free Tel:* 800-274-6774 *Fax:* 615-373-5183 *E-mail:* custserv@mleesmith.com *Web Site:* www.mleesmith.com, pg 237

Roger W Smith, 59-67 58 Rd, Maspeth, NY 11378-3211 *Tel:* 718-416-1334 *E-mail:* roger.smith106@verizon.net, pg 555

Steve Smith Autosports, PO Box 11631, Santa Ana, CA 92711-1631 *Tel:* 714-639-7681 *Fax:* 714-639-9741 *Web Site:* www.stevesmithautosports.com, pg 237

Valerie Smith, Literary Agent, 1746 Rte 44-55, Modena, NY 12548 *Tel:* 845-883-5848, pg 595

Smithsonian Scholarly Press, Aerospace Bldg, 704-A, MRC 957, Washington, DC 20013 *Tel:* 202-633-3017 *Fax:* 202-633-6877 *E-mail:* schol_press@si.edu *Web Site:* www.scholarlypress.si.edu, pg 237

Smoky Mountain Publishers, PO Box 684, Alcoa, TN 37701 *Tel:* 865-724-4959 *Web Site:* smokymountainpublishers.com, pg 529

Smyth & Helwys Publishing Inc, 6316 Peake Rd, Macon, GA 31210-3960 *Tel:* 478-757-0564 *Toll Free Tel:* 800-747-3016 (orders only); 800-568-1248 (orders only) *Fax:* 478-757-1305 *E-mail:* information@helwys.com *Web Site:* www.helwys.com, pg 237

Michael Snell Literary Agency, PO Box 1206, Truro, MA 02666-1206 *Tel:* 508-349-3718 *E-mail:* snellliteraryagency@yahoo.com *Web Site:* www.michaelsnellagency.com, pg 595

Kay Snow Literary Contest, 2108 Buck St, West Linn, OR 97068 *Tel:* 503-305-6729 *Fax:* 503-344-6174 *E-mail:* wilwrite@willamettewriters.com *Web Site:* www.willamettewriters.com, pg 743

Snow Lion Publications Inc, 300 Massachusetts Ave, Boston, MA 02115 *Tel:* 617-236-0030 *Fax:* 617-236-1563 *E-mail:* customercare@shambhala.com *Web Site:* www.shambhala.com/snowlion, pg 238

Sobel Weber Associates Inc, 146 E 19 St, New York, NY 10003-2404 *Tel:* 212-420-8585 *Fax:* 212-505-1017 *E-mail:* info@sobelweber.com *Web Site:* www.sobelweber.com, pg 595

Social Sciences & Humanities Research Council of Canada (SSHRC), 350 Albert St, Ottawa, ON K1P 6G4, Canada *Tel:* 613-992-0691 *Fax:* 613-992-1787 *E-mail:* z-info@sshrc.ca *Web Site:* www.sshrc.ca, pg 636

Society for Features Journalism (SFJ), University of Maryland, College of Journalism, 1100 Knight Hall, College Park, MD 20742 *Tel:* 301-314-2631 *Fax:* 301-314-9166 *Web Site:* featuresjournalism.org, pg 636

Society for Human Resource Management (SHRM), 1800 Duke St, Alexandria, VA 22314 *Tel:* 703-548-3440 *Toll Free Tel:* 800-444-5006 (orders) *Fax:* 703-535-6490 *E-mail:* shrm@shrm.org; shrmstore@shrm.org *Web Site:* www.shrm.org, pg 238

Society for Industrial & Applied Mathematics, 3600 Market St, 6th fl, Philadelphia, PA 19104-2688 *Tel:* 215-382-9800 *Toll Free Tel:* 800-447-7426 *Fax:* 215-386-7999 *E-mail:* siambooks@siam.org *Web Site:* www.siam.org, pg 238

Society for Mining, Metallurgy & Exploration, 12999 E Adam Aircraft Circle, Englewood, CO 80112 *Tel:* 303-948-4200 *Toll Free Tel:* 800-763-3132 *Fax:* 303-973-3845 *E-mail:* cs@smenet.org *Web Site:* www.smenet.org, pg 238

Society for Scholarly Publishing (SSP), 10200 W 44 Ave, Suite 304, Wheat Ridge, CO 80033-2840 *Tel:* 303-422-3914 *Fax:* 303-422-8894 *E-mail:* info@sspnet.org *Web Site:* www.sspnet.org, pg 636

Society for Technical Communication, 9401 Lee Hwy, Suite 300, Fairfax, VA 22031 *Tel:* 703-522-4114 *Fax:* 703-522-2075 *E-mail:* stc@stc.org *Web Site:* www.stc.org, pg 636

Society for Technical Communication's Annual Conference, 9401 Lee Hwy, Suite 300, Fairfax, VA 22031 *Tel:* 703-522-4114 *Fax:* 703-522-2075 *E-mail:* stc@stc.org *Web Site:* www.stc.org, pg 673

Society for the History of Authorship, Reading & Publishing Inc (SHARP), c/o The Johns Hopkins University Press, Journals Publishing Div, PO Box 19966, Baltimore, MD 21211-0966 *Tel:* 910-254-0308 *E-mail:* members@sharpweb.org *Web Site:* www.sharpweb.org, pg 636

Society of American Archivists, 17 N State St, Suite 1425, Chicago, IL 60602-4061 *Tel:* 312-606-0722 *Toll Free Tel:* 866-722-7858 *Fax:* 312-606-0728 *E-mail:* info@archivists.org *Web Site:* www.archivists.org, pg 238

Society of American Business Editors & Writers Inc (SABEW), Walter Cronkite School of Journalism & Mass Communication, Arizona State University, 555 N Central Ave, Suite 302, Phoenix, AZ 85004-1248 *Tel:* 602-496-7862 *Fax:* 602-496-7041 *E-mail:* sabew@sabew.org *Web Site:* sabew.org, pg 636

Society of American Travel Writers, 11950 W Lake Park Dr, Suite 320, Milwaukee, WI 53224-3049 *Tel:* 414-359-1625 *Fax:* 414-359-1671 *E-mail:* info@satw.org *Web Site:* www.satw.org, pg 636

Society of Biblical Literature, The Luce Ctr, Suite 350, 825 Houston Mill Rd, Atlanta, GA 30329 *Tel:* 404-727-3100 *Fax:* 404-727-3101 (corp) *E-mail:* sbl@sbl-site.org *Web Site:* www.sbl-site.org, pg 238

Society of Children's Book Writers & Illustrators (SCBWI), 8271 Beverly Blvd, Los Angeles, CA 90048 *Tel:* 323-782-1010 *Fax:* 323-782-1892 *E-mail:* membership@scbwi.org; scbwi@scbwi.org *Web Site:* www.scbwi.org, pg 636

Society of Environmental Toxicology & Chemistry, 229 S Baylen St, 2nd fl, Pensacola, FL 32502 *Tel:* 850-469-1500 *Fax:* 850-469-9778 *E-mail:* setac@setac.org *Web Site:* www.setac.org, pg 238

Society of Exploration Geophysicists, 8801 S Yale Ave, Tulsa, OK 74137 *Tel:* 918-497-5500 *Fax:* 918-497-5557 *E-mail:* web@seg.org *Web Site:* www.seg.org, pg 238

Society of Illustrators (SI), 128 E 63 St, New York, NY 10065 *Tel:* 212-838-2560 *Fax:* 212-838-2561 *E-mail:* info@societyillustrators.org *Web Site:* www.societyillustrators.org, pg 636

Society of Manufacturing Engineers, One SME Dr, Dearborn, MI 48121 *Tel:* 313-425-3000 *Toll Free Tel:* 800-733-4763 (cust serv) *Fax:* 313-425-3400 *E-mail:* publications@sme.org *Web Site:* www.sme.org, pg 238

The Society of Midland Authors (SMA), PO Box 10419, Chicago, IL 60610 *E-mail:* info@midlandauthors.com *Web Site:* www.midlandauthors.com, pg 636

The Society of Midland Authors Awards, 530 Michigan Ave, Evanston, IL 60202 *E-mail:* info@midlandauthors.com *Web Site:* www.midlandauthors.com, pg 743

Society of Motion Picture & Television Engineers (SMPTE), 3 Barker Ave, 5th fl, White Plains, NY 10601 *Tel:* 914-761-1100 *Fax:* 914-761-3115 *Web Site:* www.smpte.org, pg 637

The Society of Naval Architects & Marine Engineers, 601 Pavonia Ave, Jersey City, NJ 07306-2907 *Tel:* 201-798-4800 *Toll Free Tel:* 800-798-2188 *Fax:* 201-798-4975 *Web Site:* www.sname.org, pg 238

The Society of Professional Journalists, Eugene S Pulliam National Journalism Ctr, 3909 N Meridian St, Indianapolis, IN 46208 *Tel:* 317-927-8000 *Fax:* 317-920-4789 *E-mail:* spj@spj.org *Web Site:* www.spj.org, pg 637

The Society of Southwestern Authors (SSA), PO Box 30355, Tucson, AZ 85751-0355 *Tel:* 520-546-9382 *Fax:* 520-751-7877 *E-mail:* wporter202@aol.com *Web Site:* www.ssa-az.org, pg 637

The Society of Southwestern Authors Writing Contest, PO Box 30355, Tucson, AZ 85751-0355 *Tel:* 520-546-9382 *Fax:* 520-751-7877 *E-mail:* info@ssa-az.org *Web Site:* www.ssa-az.org, pg 743

Software & Information Industry Association (SIIA), 1090 Vermont Ave NW, 6th fl, Washington, DC 20005-4095 *Tel:* 202-289-7442 *Fax:* 202-289-7097 *E-mail:* info@siia.net *Web Site:* www.siia.net, pg 637

Soho Press Inc, 853 Broadway, New York, NY 10003 *Tel:* 212-260-1900 *Fax:* 212-260-1902 *E-mail:* soho@sohopress.com; publicity@sohopress.com *Web Site:* www.sohopress.com, pg 239

Soil Science Society of America, 5585 Guilford Rd, Madison, WI 53711-5801 *Tel:* 608-273-8080 *Fax:* 608-273-2021 *E-mail:* headquarters@soils.org *Web Site:* www.soils.org, pg 239

Solano Press Books, PO Box 773, Point Arena, CA 95468 *Tel:* 707-884-4508 *Toll Free Tel:* 800-931-9373 *Fax:* 707-884-4109 *E-mail:* spbooks@solano.com *Web Site:* www.solano.com, pg 239

Solid Gold Marketing Design Workshops, PO Box 2373, La Mesa, CA 91943-2373 *Tel:* 858-569-6555 *Toll Free Tel:* 800-932-0973 *Web Site:* www.sparklepresentations.com, pg 673

Jodi Solomon Speakers Bureau, 295 Huntington Ave, Suite 211, Boston, MA 02115 *Tel:* 617-266-3450 *Fax:* 617-266-5660 *E-mail:* jodi@jodisolomon.biz *Web Site:* www.jodisolomonspeakers.com, pg 606

Solution Tree, 555 N Morton St, Bloomington, IN 47404 *Tel:* 812-336-7700 *Toll Free Tel:* 800-733-6786 *Fax:* 812-336-7790 *E-mail:* info@solution-tree.com *Web Site:* www.solution-tree.com, pg 239

SOM Publishing, 163 Moon Valley Rd, Windyville, MO 65783 *Tel:* 417-345-8411 *Fax:* 417-345-6668 *E-mail:* som@som.org; dreamschool@dreamschool.org *Web Site:* www.som.org; www.dreamschool.org, pg 239

Somerset Hall Press, 416 Commonwealth Ave, Suite 612, Boston, MA 02215 *Tel:* 617-236-5126 *E-mail:* info@somersethallpress.com *Web Site:* www.somersethallpress.com, pg 239

Soncino Press Ltd, 123 Ditmas Ave, Brooklyn, NY 11218 *Tel:* 718-972-6200 *Toll Free Tel:* 800-972-6201 *Fax:* 718-972-6204 *E-mail:* info@soncino.com *Web Site:* www.soncino.com, pg 239

Sophia Institute Press®, 522 Donald St, Unit 3, Bedford, NH 03110 *Tel:* 603-836-5505 *Toll Free Tel:* 800-888-9344 *Fax:* 603-641-8108 *Toll Free Fax:* 888-288-2259 *E-mail:* orders@sophiainstitute.com *Web Site:* www.sophiainstitute.com, pg 239

Sophie Kerr Prize, c/o College Relations Office, 300 Washington Ave, Chestertown, MD 21620 *Tel:* 410-778-2800 *Toll Free Tel:* 800-422-1782 *Fax:* 410-810-7150 *Web Site:* www.washcoll.edu, pg 743

Sopris West Educational Services, 17855 Dallas Pkwy, Suite 400, Dallas, TX 75287 *Tel:* 303-651-2829 *Toll Free Tel:* 800-547-6747 *Fax:* 303-776-5934 *Toll Free Fax:* 888-819-7767 *E-mail:* customerservice@sopriswest.com *Web Site:* www.sopriswest.com, pg 239

Soul Mate Publishing, PO Box 24, Macedon, NY 14502 *Tel:* 585-598-4791 *E-mail:* submissions@soulmatepublishing.com *Web Site:* www.soulmatepublishing.com, pg 239

Gordon Soules Book Publishers Ltd, 1359 Amble Side Lane, West Vancouver, BC V7T 2Y9, Canada *Tel:* 604-922-6588 *Fax:* 604-688-5442; 604-922-6574 *E-mail:* books@gordonsoules.com *Web Site:* www.gordonsoules.com, pg 519

Sound Feelings Publishing, 18375 Ventura Blvd, No 8000, Tarzana, CA 91356 *Tel:* 818-757-0600 *E-mail:* information@soundfeelings.com *Web Site:* www.soundfeelings.com, pg 239

Sounds True Inc, 413 S Arthur Ave, Louisville, CO 80027 *Tel:* 303-665-3151 *Toll Free Tel:* 800-333-9185 *E-mail:* customerservice@soundstrue.com *Web Site:* www.soundstrue.com, pg 239

Sourcebooks Inc, 1935 Brookdale Rd, Suite 139, Naperville, IL 60563 *Tel:* 630-961-3900 *Toll Free Tel:* 800-432-7444 *Fax:* 630-961-2168 *E-mail:* info@sourcebooks.com; customersupport@sourcebooks.com *Web Site:* www.sourcebooks.com, pg 240

Sourced Media Books, 29 Via Regalo, San Clemente, CA 92673 *Tel:* 949-813-0182 *E-mail:* info@sourcemediabooks.com *Web Site:* sourcedmediabooks.com, pg 240

South Carolina Bar, Continuing Legal Education Div, 950 Taylor St, Columbia, SC 29201 *Tel:* 803-799-6653 *Toll Free Tel:* 800-768-7787 *Fax:* 803-799-4118 *E-mail:* scbar-info@scbar.org *Web Site:* www.scbar.org, pg 240

South End Press, PO Box 382132, Cambridge, MA 02238 *Tel:* 718-874-0089 *Toll Free Fax:* 800-960-0078 *E-mail:* southend@southendpress.org; info@southendpress.org *Web Site:* www.southendpress.org, pg 240

South Platte Press, PO Box 163, David City, NE 68632-0163 *Tel:* 402-367-3554 *E-mail:* railroads@windstream.net *Web Site:* www.southplattepress.net, pg 240

Southampton Writers' Conference, 239 Montauk Hwy, Southampton, NY 11968 *Tel:* 631-632-5007 *E-mail:* southamptonwriters@notes.cc.sunysb.edu *Web Site:* www.stonybrook.edu/writers, pg 673

Southeast Review Narrative Nonfiction Contest, Florida State University, Dept of English, Tallahassee, FL 32306 *E-mail:* southeastreview@gmail.com *Web Site:* www.southeastreview.org, pg 743

Southeast Review's Gearhart Poetry Contest, Florida State University, Dept of English, Tallahassee, FL 32306 *E-mail:* southeastreview@gmail.com *Web Site:* www.southeastreview.org, pg 743

Southeastern Theatre Conference New Play Project, 1175 Revolution Mill Dr, Suite 14, Greensboro, NC 27405 *Tel:* 336-272-3645 *Fax:* 336-272-8810 *E-mail:* info@setc.org *Web Site:* www.setc.org, pg 743

Southern Books Competition, PO Box 950, Rex, GA 30273 *Tel:* 678-466-4339 *Fax:* 678-466-4349 *Web Site:* selaonline.org, pg 743

Southern California Writers' Conference, 1010 University Ave, Suite 54, San Diego, CA 92103 *Tel:* 619-303-8185 *Fax:* 619-303-7462 *E-mail:* wewrite@writersconference.com *Web Site:* www.writersconference.com, pg 673

Southern Historical Press Inc, 375 W Broad St, Greenville, SC 29601 *Tel:* 864-233-2346 *Toll Free Tel:* 800-233-0152 *Fax:* 864-233-2349, pg 240

Southern Illinois University Press, 1915 University Press Dr, SIUC Mail Code 6806, Carbondale, IL 62901-4323 *Tel:* 618-453-2281 *Fax:* 618-453-1221 *E-mail:* custserv@press.uchicago.edu; rights@siu.edu *Web Site:* www.siupress.com, pg 240

Southern Independent Booksellers Alliance, 3806 Yale Ave, Columbia, SC 29205 *Tel:* 803-994-9530 *Fax:* 309-410-0211 *E-mail:* info@sibaweb.com *Web Site:* www.sibaweb.com, pg 637

Southern Playwrights Competition, 700 Pelham Rd N, Jacksonville, AL 36265-1602 *Tel:* 256-782-5498 *Fax:* 256-782-5441 *Web Site:* www.jsu.edu/depart/english/southpla.htm, pg 743

SouthWest Writers Conference Series, 3200 Carlisle Blvd NE, Suite 114, Albuquerque, NM 87110-1663 *Tel:* 505-830-6034 *E-mail:* swwriters@juno.com *Web Site:* www.southwestwriters.com, pg 673

Sovereign Award for Writing, Woodbine Sales Pavilion, 555 Rexdale Blvd, Rexdale, ON M9W 5L2, Canada *Tel:* 416-675-7756 *Fax:* 416-675-6378 *E-mail:* jockeyclub@bellnet.ca *Web Site:* www.jockeyclubcanada.com, pg 743

The Sow's Ear Poetry Prize & The Sow's Ear Chapbook Prize, 217 Brookneill Dr, Winchester, VA 22602 *Tel:* 540-955-3955 *Web Site:* sows-ear.kitenet.net, pg 743

Soyinfo Center, PO Box 234, Lafayette, CA 94549-0234 *Tel:* 925-283-2991 *E-mail:* info@soyinfocenter.com *Web Site:* www.soyinfocenter.com, pg 240

Special Libraries Association (SLA), 331 S Patrick St, Alexandria, VA 22314-3501 *Tel:* 703-647-4900 *Fax:* 703-647-4901 *E-mail:* sla@sla.org *Web Site:* www.sla.org, pg 637

Specialized Information Publishers Association (SIPA), 1090 Vermont Ave NW, 6th fl, Washington, DC 20005 *Tel:* 202-289-7442 *Fax:* 202-289-7097 *E-mail:* sipa@siia.net *Web Site:* www.sipaonline.com, pg 637

Spectrum Literary Agency, 320 Central Park W, Suite 1-D, New York, NY 10025 *Tel:* 212-362-4323 *Fax:* 212-362-4562 *Web Site:* www.spectrumliteraryagency.com, pg 595

Sphinx Publishing, 1935 Brookdale Rd, Suite 139, Naperville, IL 60563 *Tel:* 630-961-3900 *Toll Free Tel:* 800-43-bright (432-7448) *Fax:* 630-961-2168 *E-mail:* info@sourcebooks.com *Web Site:* www.sourcebooks.com, pg 241

SPIE, 1000 20 St, Bellingham, WA 98225-6705 *Tel:* 360-676-3290 *Toll Free Tel:* 888-504-8171 *Fax:* 360-647-1445 *E-mail:* spie@spie.org *Web Site:* www.spie.org, pg 241

The Spieler Agency, 154 W 57 St, Suite 135, New York, NY 10019 *Tel:* 212-757-4439 *Fax:* 212-333-2019 *E-mail:* spieleragency@spieleragency.com, pg 595

Spinsters Ink, PO Box 242, Midway, FL 32343 *E-mail:* info@spinstersink.com; editorialdirector@spinstersink.com *Web Site:* www.spinstersink.com, pg 241

Philip G Spitzer Literary Agency Inc, 50 Talmage Farm Lane, East Hampton, NY 11937 *Tel:* 631-329-3650 *Fax:* 631-329-3651 *E-mail:* spitzer516@aol.com *Web Site:* www.spitzeragency.com, pg 595

Spizzirri Publishing Inc, PO Box 9397, Rapid City, SD 57709-9397 *Tel:* 605-348-2749 *Toll Free Tel:* 800-325-9819 *Fax:* 605-348-6251 *Toll Free Fax:* 800-322-9819 *E-mail:* spizzpub@aol.com *Web Site:* www.spizzirri.com, pg 241

Sport Books Publisher, 212 Robert St, side basement door, Toronto, ON M5S 2K7, Canada *Tel:* 416-323-9438 *Fax:* 416-966-9022 *E-mail:* sbp@sportbookspub.com *Web Site:* www.sportbookspub.com, pg 520

Sports Fiction & Essay Contest, 351 Pleasant St, PMB 222, Northampton, MA 01060-3961 *Tel:* 413-320-1847 *Toll Free Tel:* 866-WINWRIT (946-9748) *Fax:* 413-280-0539 *Web Site:* www.winningwriters.com, pg 743

John Spray Mystery Award, 40 Orchard View Blvd, Suite 217, Toronto, ON M4R 1B9, Canada *Tel:* 416-975-0010 *Fax:* 416-975-8970 *E-mail:* info@bookcentre.ca *Web Site:* www.bookcentre.ca, pg 744

Spring Time Writers Creative Writing & Journaling Workshop, PO Box 512, Lyons, CO 80540-0512 *Tel:* 303-823-0997 *E-mail:* writers@springtimewriters.com *Web Site:* www.springtimewriters.com, pg 673

Spring Tree Press, 571 Locust Point Rd, Locust, NJ 07760 *Tel:* 732-872-8002 *Fax:* 732-872-6967 *E-mail:* springtreepress@gmail.com *Web Site:* www.springtreepress.com; www.tyrrc.com, pg 529

Springer, 233 Spring St, New York, NY 10013-1578 *Tel:* 212-460-1500 *Toll Free Tel:* 800-SPRINGER (777-4643) *Fax:* 212-460-1575 *E-mail:* service-ny@springer.com *Web Site:* www.springer.com, pg 241

P Gregory Springer, 206 Wood St, Urbana, IL 61801 *Tel:* 217-493-7986 *E-mail:* pgregory.springer@gmail.com *Web Site:* tinyurl.com/3q8ngu4, pg 555

Springer Publishing Co LLC, 11 W 42 St, 15th fl, New York, NY 10036-8002 *Tel:* 212-431-4370 *Toll Free Tel:* 877-687-7476 *Fax:* 212-941-7842 *E-mail:* marketing@springerpub.com; cs@springerpub.com (orders); editorial@springerpub.com *Web Site:* www.springerpub.com, pg 241

Springfed Writers' Retreat, PO Box 304, Royal Oak, MI 48068-0304 *Tel:* 248-589-3913 *Web Site:* www.springfed.org, pg 673

Spry Publishing, 2500 S State St, Ann Arbor, MI 48104 *Tel:* 734-913-1700 *Toll Free Tel:* 877-722-2264 *Fax:* 734-913-1249 *E-mail:* info@sprypub.com *Web Site:* www.sprypub.com, pg 241

Spur Awards, 271 CR 219, Encampment, WY 82325 *Tel:* 307-329-8942 *Fax:* 307-327-5465 *E-mail:* wwa.moulton@gmail.com *Web Site:* www.westernwriters.org, pg 744

Square One Publishers Inc, 115 Herricks Rd, Garden City Park, NY 11040 *Tel:* 516-535-2010 *Toll Free Tel:* 877-900-BOOK (900-2665) *Fax:* 516-535-2014 *E-mail:* sq1publish@aol.com *Web Site:* www.squareonepublishers.com, pg 241

Squaw Valley Community of Writers Summer Workshops, PO Box 1416, Nevada City, CA 95959 *Tel:* 530-470-8440 *E-mail:* info@squawvalleywriters.org *Web Site:* www.squawvalleywriters.org, pg 673

SRA/McGraw-Hill, 8787 Orion Place, Columbus, OH 43240 *Tel:* 614-430-4000 *Fax:* 614-430-4303 *E-mail:* sra@mcgraw-hill.com *Web Site:* www.sraonline.com, pg 242

SSPC: The Society for Protective Coatings, 40 24 St, 6th fl, Pittsburgh, PA 15222-4656 *Tel:* 412-281-2331 *Toll Free Tel:* 877-281-7772 (US only) *Fax:* 412-281-9992 *E-mail:* info@sspc.org *Web Site:* www.sspc.org, pg 242

SSR Inc, 116 Fourth St SE, Washington, DC 20003 *Tel:* 202-543-1800 *Fax:* 202-544-7432 *E-mail:* ssr@ssrinc.com *Web Site:* www.ssrinc.com, pg 555

ST Media Group Book Division, 11262 Cornell Park Dr, Cincinnati, OH 45242 *Tel:* 513-421-2050 *Toll Free Tel:* 866-265-0954 *Fax:* 513-421-5144 *E-mail:* books@stmediagroup.com *Web Site:* www.stmediagroup.com, pg 242

Stackler Editorial Agency, 555 Lincoln Ave, Alameda, CA 94501 *Tel:* 510-814-9694 *Fax:* 510-814-9694 *E-mail:* stackler@aol.com *Web Site:* www.fictioneditor.com, pg 555

Stackpole Books, 5067 Ritter Rd, Mechanicsburg, PA 17055 *Tel:* 717-796-0411 *Toll Free Tel:* 800-732-3669 *Fax:* 717-796-0412 *Web Site:* www.stackpolebooks.com, pg 242

The Edna Staebler Award for Creative Non-Fiction, Office of the Dean, Faculty of Arts, 75 University Ave W, Waterloo, ON N2L 3C5, Canada *Tel:* 519-884-1970 (ext 3891) *Fax:* 519-884-8854, pg 744

Standard International Media Holdings, 568 Ninth St S, Suite 201, Naples, FL 34102-7336 *Tel:* 239-649-7077 *Fax:* 239-649-5832 *E-mail:* sales@standardinternationalmedia.com *Web Site:* www.standardinternationalmedia.com, pg 242

Standard Publications Inc, PO Box 2226, Champaign, IL 61825-2226 *Tel:* 217-898-7825 *Fax:* 630-214-0564 *E-mail:* spi@standardpublications.com *Web Site:* standardpublications.com, pg 242

Standard Publishing, 8805 Governors Hill Dr, Suite 400, Cincinnati, OH 45249 *Tel:* 513-931-4050 *Toll Free Tel:* 800-543-1353 *Fax:* 513-931-0950 *Toll Free Fax:* 877-867-5751 *E-mail:* customerservice@standardpub.com *Web Site:* www.standardpub.com, pg 242

Standard Publishing Corp, 155 Federal St, 13th fl, Boston, MA 02110 *Tel:* 617-457-0600 *Toll Free Tel:* 800-682-5759 *Fax:* 617-457-0608 *Web Site:* www.spcpub.com, pg 242

Stanford University Press, 1450 Page Mill Rd, Palo Alto, CA 94304-1124 *Tel:* 650-723-9434 *Fax:* 650-725-3457 *E-mail:* info@sup.org *Web Site:* www.sup.org, pg 242

Stanley Drama Award, One Campus Rd, Staten Island, NY 10301 *Tel:* 718-390-3223 *Fax:* 718-390-3323, pg 744

Edward Stanley Award, University of Nebraska, 123 Andrews Hall, Lincoln, NE 68588-0334 *Tel:* 402-472-0911 *Fax:* 402-472-9771 *Web Site:* prairieschooner.unl.edu, pg 744

Star Bright Books Inc, 13 Landsdowne St, Cambridge, MA 02139 *Tel:* 617-354-1300 *Fax:* 617-354-1399 *E-mail:* info@starbrightbooks.com; orders@starbrightbooks.com *Web Site:* www.starbrightbooks.com, pg 243

Star Publishing Co Inc, 650 El Camino Real, Redwood City, CA 94063 *Tel:* 650-591-3505 *Fax:* 650-591-3898 *E-mail:* mail@starpublishing.com *Web Site:* www.starpublishing.com, pg 243

STARbooks Press, PO Box 711612, Herndon, VA 20171 *E-mail:* contact@starbookspress.com *Web Site:* www.starbookspress.com, pg 243

Starcrafts LLC, 334-A Calef Hwy, Epping, NH 03042 *Tel:* 603-734-4300 *Toll Free Tel:* 866-953-8458 (24 hr message ctr) *Fax:* 603-734-4311 *E-mail:* astrosales@astrocom.com; starcrafts@comcast.net *Web Site:* www.astrocom.com; starcraftspublishing.com; acspublications.com, pg 243

Stargazer Publishing Co, 958 Stanislaus Dr, Corona, CA 92881 *Tel:* 951-898-4619 *Toll Free Tel:* 800-606-7895 (orders) *Fax:* 951-898-4633 *E-mail:* stargazer@stargazerpub.com; orders@stargazerpub.com *Web Site:* www.stargazerpub.com, pg 243

StarGroup International Inc, 1194 Old Dixie Hwy, Suite 201, West Palm Beach, FL 33413 *Tel:* 561-547-0667 *Fax:* 561-843-8530 *E-mail:* info@stargroupinternational.com *Web Site:* www.stargroupinternational.com, pg 243

Agnes Lynch Starrett Poetry Prize, Eureka Bldg, 5th fl, 3400 Forbes Ave, Pittsburgh, PA 15260 *Tel:* 412-383-2456 *Fax:* 412-383-2466 *E-mail:* info@upress.pitt.edu *Web Site:* www.upress.pitt.edu, pg 744

State University of New York Press, 22 Corporate Woods Blvd, 3rd fl, Albany, NY 12211-2504 *Tel:* 518-472-5000 *Toll Free Tel:* 877-204-6073 (orders) *Fax:* 518-472-5038 *Toll Free Fax:* 877-204-6074 (orders) *E-mail:* suny@presswarehouse.com (orders); info@sunypress.edu (edit off) *Web Site:* www.sunypress.edu, pg 243

Statistics Canada, 150 Tunney's Pasture Driveway, Ottawa, ON K1A 0T6, Canada *Tel:* 613-951-8116 (gen inquiries) *Toll Free Tel:* 800-263-1136 (CN & US, gen inquiries); 800-267-6677 (prods & servs) *Fax:* 613-951-0581 *Toll Free Fax:* 877-287-4369 (orders) *E-mail:* infostats@statcan.gc.ca *Web Site:* statcan.gc.ca, pg 520

Nancy Stauffer Associates, 30 Corbin Dr, Unit 1203, Darien, CT 06820 *Tel:* 203-202-2500 *E-mail:* staufferassoc@optonline.net *Web Site:* publishersmarketplace.com/members/nstauffer; staufferliterary.com, pg 595

Nancy Steele, 2210 Pine St, Philadelphia, PA 19103-6516 *Tel:* 215-732-5175 *E-mail:* nancy.steele.edits@gmail.com, pg 555

Steerforth Press, 45 Lyme Rd, Suite 208, Hanover, NH 03755-1222 *Tel:* 603-643-4787 *Fax:* 603-643-4788 *E-mail:* info@steerforth.com *Web Site:* www.steerforth.com, pg 244

Stegner Fellowship, Stanford Creative Writing Program, Dept of English, Stanford, CA 94305-2087 *Tel:* 650-723-0011 *Fax:* 650-723-3679 *Web Site:* creativewriting.stanford.edu, pg 744

John Steinbeck Short Story Award, San Jose State University, English Dept, One Washington Sq, San Jose, CA 95192-0090 *Tel:* 408-924-4458 *E-mail:* reed@email.sjsu.edu *Web Site:* www.reedmag.org, pg 744

Michael Steinberg Literary Agent, PO Box 274, Glencoe, IL 60022-0274 *Tel:* 847-626-1000 *Fax:* 847-626-1002 *E-mail:* michael14steinberg@comcast.net, pg 595

SteinerBooks, 610 Main St, Great Barrington, MA 01230 *Tel:* 413-528-8233 *Fax:* 413-528-8826 *E-mail:* friends@steinerbooks.org *Web Site:* www.steinerbooks.org, pg 244

Steller Publishing, 2114 S Live Oak Pkwy, Wilmington, NC 28403 *Tel:* 910-269-7444 *E-mail:* info@stellar-publishing.com *Web Site:* www.stellar-publishing.com, pg 244

Stemmer House Publishers Inc, 4 White Brook Rd, Gilsum, NH 03448 *Tel:* 603-357-0236 *Toll Free Tel:* 800-345-6665 *Fax:* 603-357-2073 *E-mail:* info@stemmer.com *Web Site:* www.stemmer.com, pg 244

Stenhouse Publishers, 480 Congress St, Portland, ME 04101-3451 *Tel:* 207-253-1600 *Toll Free Tel:* 888-363-0566 *Fax:* 207-253-5121 *Toll Free Fax:* 800-833-9164 *E-mail:* customerservice@stenhouse.com *Web Site:* www.stenhouse.com, pg 244

Stephan G Stephansson Award for Poetry, 11759 Groat Rd, Edmonton, AB T5M 3K6, Canada *Tel:* 780-422-8174 *Toll Free Tel:* 800-665-5354 (AB only) *Fax:* 780-422-2663 (attn WGA) *E-mail:* mail@writersguild.ab.ca *Web Site:* www.writersguild.ab.ca, pg 744

Stephens Press™, 1111 W Bonanza Rd, Las Vegas, NV 89106 *Tel:* 702-387-5260 *Toll Free Tel:* 888-951-2665 *Fax:* 702-387-2997 *E-mail:* info@stephenspress.com *Web Site:* www.stephenspress.com, pg 244

Sterling Lord Literistic Inc, 65 Bleecker St, New York, NY 10012 *Tel:* 212-780-6050 *Fax:* 212-780-6095 *E-mail:* info@sll.com *Web Site:* www.sll.com, pg 595

Sterling Publishing Co Inc, 387 Park Ave S, 11th fl, New York, NY 10016-8810 *Tel:* 212-532-7160 *Toll Free Tel:* 800-367-9692 *Fax:* 212-213-2495 *Web Site:* www.sterlingpub.com, pg 244

Miriam Stern, Attorney-at-Law/Literary Agent, 303 E 83 St, 20th fl, New York, NY 10028 *Tel:* 212-794-1289, pg 595

The Joan Stewart Agency, 885 Second Ave, 35th fl, New York, NY 10017 *Tel:* 212-418-7255 *Fax:* 212-832-3809, pg 596

Stewart, Tabori & Chang, 115 W 18 St, 6th fl, New York, NY 10011 *Tel:* 212-519-1200 *Fax:* 212-519-1210 *Web Site:* www.abramsbooks.com, pg 245

Stimola Literary Studio Inc, 308 Livingston Ct, Edgewater, NJ 07020 *Tel:* 201-945-9353 *Fax:* 201-945-9353 *E-mail:* info@stimolaliterarystudio.com *Web Site:* www.stimolaliterarystudio.com, pg 596

Sylvan Dell Publishing, 612 Johnnie Dodds Blvd, Suite A-2, Mount Pleasant, SC 29464 *Tel:* 843-971-6722 *Toll Free Tel:* 877-243-3457 *Fax:* 843-216-3804 *E-mail:* customerservice@sylvandellpublishing.com; info@sylvandellpublishing.com *Web Site:* www.sylvandellpublishing.com, pg 248

Synapse Information Resources Inc, 1247 Taft Ave, Endicott, NY 13760 *Tel:* 607-748-4145 *Toll Free Tel:* 888-SYN-CHEM (796-2436) *Fax:* 607-786-3966 *E-mail:* salesinfo@synapseinfo.com *Web Site:* www.synapseinfo.com, pg 249

Synaxis Press, 37323 Hawkins Pickle Rd, Dewdney, BC V0M 1H0, Canada *Tel:* 604-826-9336 *E-mail:* synaxis@new-ostrog.org *Web Site:* synaxispress.ca, pg 520

SynergEbooks, 948 New Hwy 7, Columbia, TN 38401 *Tel:* 931-223-5990 *E-mail:* synergebooks@aol.com *Web Site:* www.synergebooks.com, pg 249

Syracuse University Creative Writing Program, 401 Hall of Languages, Syracuse, NY 13244-1170 *Tel:* 315-443-2173 *Fax:* 315-443-3660 *Web Site:* english.syr.edu/creative_writing; www.syr.edu, pg 680

Syracuse University Press, 621 Skytop Rd, Suite 110, Syracuse, NY 13244-5290 *Tel:* 315-443-5534 *Toll Free Tel:* 800-365-8929 (cust serv) *Fax:* 315-443-5545 *E-mail:* supress@syr.edu *Web Site:* syracuseuniversitypress.syr.edu, pg 249

Syracuse University, SI Newhouse School of Public Communications, 215 University Place, Syracuse, NY 13244-2100 *Tel:* 315-443-3627 *Fax:* 315-443-3946 *E-mail:* newhouse@syr.edu *Web Site:* newhouse.syr.edu, pg 680

Robert E Tabian/Literary Agent, 229 Paterson Ave, Suite 2, East Rutherford, NJ 07073 *Tel:* 631-987-2293 *Fax:* 201-438-1327 *E-mail:* retlit@mindspring.com, pg 597

Tachyon Publications, 1459 18 St, Suite 139, San Francisco, CA 94107 *Tel:* 415-285-5615 *E-mail:* tachyon@tachyonpublications.com *Web Site:* www.tachyonpublications.com, pg 249

Tag & Label Manufacturers Institute Inc (TLMI), One Blackburn Ctr, Gloucester, MA 01930 *Tel:* 978-282-1400 *Fax:* 978-282-3238 *E-mail:* office@tlmi.com *Web Site:* www.tlmi.com, pg 637

Tahrike Tarsile Qur'an Inc, 80-08 51 Ave, Elmhurst, NY 11373 *Tel:* 718-446-6472 *Fax:* 718-446-4370 *E-mail:* read@koranusa.org *Web Site:* www.koranusa.org, pg 249

The Tampa Review Prize for Poetry, University of Tampa Press, 401 W Kennedy Blvd, Tampa, FL 33606 *Tel:* 813-253-6266 *E-mail:* utpress@ut.edu *Web Site:* tampareview.ut.edu, pg 745

TAN Books, PO Box 410487, Charlotte, NC 28241 *Toll Free Tel:* 800-437-5876 *Fax:* 815-226-7770 *E-mail:* customerservice@tanbooks.com *Web Site:* tanbooks.benedictpress.com; benedictpress.com, pg 249

T&T Clark International, 1385 Broadway, 5th fl, New York, NY 10018 *Tel:* 212-953-5858 *Toll Free Tel:* 800-561-7704 (orders) *Fax:* 212-953-5944 *Web Site:* www.continuumbooks.com, pg 249

Tanglewood Press, PO Box 3009, Terre Haute, IN 47803 *Tel:* 812-877-9488; 412-741-1579 (orders) *Toll Free Tel:* 800-836-4994 (orders) *Fax:* 412-741-0609 (orders) *Web Site:* www.tanglewoodbooks.com, pg 249

Tantor Media Inc, 2 Business Park, Old Saybrook, CT 06475 *Toll Free Tel:* 877-782-6867 *Toll Free Fax:* 888-782-7821 *Web Site:* www.tantor.com, pg 250

Taos Summer Writers' Conference, University of New Mexico, Humanities Dept, Rm 253, Albuquerque, NM 87131-0001 *Tel:* 505-277-5572 *E-mail:* taosconf@unm.edu *Web Site:* www.unm.edu/~taosconf, pg 674

Tapestry Press Ltd, 19 Nashoba Rd, Littleton, MA 01460 *Tel:* 978-486-0200 *Toll Free Tel:* 800-535-2007 *Fax:* 978-486-0244 *E-mail:* publish@tapestrypress.com *Web Site:* www.tapestrypress.com, pg 250

Taplinger Publishing Co Inc, PO Box 175, Marlboro, NJ 07746-0175 *Tel:* 305-256-7880 *Fax:* 305-256-7816 *E-mail:* taplingerpub@yahoo.com (rts & perms, edit, corp only), pg 250

Jeremy P Tarcher, 375 Hudson St, New York, NY 10014 *Tel:* 212-366-2000 *E-mail:* online@penguinputnam.com *Web Site:* www.penguinputnam.com; us.penguingroup.com, pg 250

Roslyn Targ Literary Agency Inc, 105 W 13 St, Suite 15-E, New York, NY 10011 *Tel:* 212-206-9390 *Fax:* 212-989-6233 *E-mail:* roslyn@roslyntargagency.com, pg 597

Taschen America, 6671 Sunset Blvd, Suite 1508, Los Angeles, CA 90028 *Tel:* 323-463-4441 *Toll Free Tel:* 888-TASCHEN (827-2436) *Fax:* 323-463-4442 *E-mail:* contact-us@taschen.com *Web Site:* www.taschen.com, pg 250

The Taunton Press Inc, 63 S Main St, Newtown, CT 06470 *Tel:* 203-426-8171 *Toll Free Tel:* 800-477-8727 (cust serv); 800-888-8286 (orders) *Fax:* 203-426-3434 *E-mail:* booksales@taunton.com *Web Site:* www.taunton.com, pg 250

Taylor & Francis Inc, 325 Chestnut St, Suite 800, Philadelphia, PA 20036-1802 *Tel:* 215-625-8900 *Toll Free Tel:* 800-354-1420 *Fax:* 215-625-2940 *E-mail:* customer.service@taylorandfrancis.com *Web Site:* www.taylorandfrancis.com, pg 250

Taylor-Dth Publishing, 108 Caribe Isle, Novato, CA 94949 *Tel:* 415-299-1087 *Web Site:* www.taylor-dth.com, pg 250

Rennie Taylor & Alton Blakeslee Fellowships in Science Writing, PO Box 910, Hedgesville, WV 25427 *Tel:* 304-754-6786 *Web Site:* www.casw.org, pg 745

TCP Press, Legacy Ctr, 9 Lobraico Lane, Whitchurch-Stouffville, ON L4A 7X5, Canada *Tel:* 905-640-8914 *Toll Free Tel:* 800-772-7765 *E-mail:* tcp@tcpnow.com *Web Site:* www.tcppress.com, pg 521

TD Canadian Children's Literature Award, 40 Orchard View Blvd, Suite 217, Toronto, ON M4R 1B9, Canada *Tel:* 416-975-0010 *Fax:* 416-975-8970 *E-mail:* info@bookcentre.ca *Web Site:* www.bookcentre.ca, pg 745

Teach Me Tapes Inc, 6016 Blue Circle Dr, Minnetonka, MN 55343 *Tel:* 952-933-8086 *Toll Free Tel:* 800-456-4656 *Fax:* 952-933-0512 *E-mail:* marie@teachmetapes.com *Web Site:* www.teachmetapes.com, pg 251

Teacher Created Resources Inc, 6421 Industry Way, Westminster, CA 92683 *Tel:* 714-891-7895 *Toll Free Tel:* 800-662-4321; 888-343-4335 *Fax:* 714-892-0283 *Toll Free Fax:* 800-525-1254 *E-mail:* custserv@teachercreated.com *Web Site:* www.teachercreated.com, pg 251

Teachers & Writers Collaborative, 520 Eighth Ave, Suite 2020, New York, NY 10018-4165 *Tel:* 212-691-6590 *Toll Free Tel:* 888-BOOKS-TW (266-5789) *Fax:* 212-675-0171 *E-mail:* info@twc.org; books@twc.org *Web Site:* www.twc.org, pg 637

Teachers College Press, 1234 Amsterdam Ave, New York, NY 10027 *Tel:* 212-678-3929 *Toll Free Tel:* 800-575-6566 *Fax:* 212-678-4149; 802-864-7626 *E-mail:* tcpress@tc.columbia.edu; tcp.orders@aidcvt.com (orders) *Web Site:* www.teacherscollegepress.com, pg 251

Teacher's Discovery, 2741 Paldan Dr, Auburn Hills, MI 48326 *Toll Free Tel:* 800-832-2437 *Toll Free Fax:* 800-287-4509 *E-mail:* foreignlanguage@teachersdiscovery.com; worldlanguage@teachersdiscovery.com *Web Site:* www.teachersdiscovery.com, pg 251

Teachers of English to Speakers of Other Languages Inc (TESOL), 1925 Ballenger Ave, Alexandria, VA 22314-6820 *Tel:* 703-836-0774 *Toll Free Tel:* 888-547-3369 *Fax:* 703-836-7864 *E-mail:* info@tesol.org *Web Site:* www.tesol.org, pg 251

Teaching & Learning Co, 501 E Third St, Dayton, OH 45402 *Tel:* 937-228-6118 *Toll Free Tel:* 800-444-1144 *Fax:* 937-223-2042 *E-mail:* info@lorenz.com, pg 251

Teaching Strategies, 7101 Wisconsin Ave, Suite 700, Bethesda, MD 20814 *Tel:* 301-634-0818 *Toll Free Tel:* 800-637-3652 *Fax:* 301-657-0250 *E-mail:* customerrelations@teachingstrategies.com *Web Site:* www.teachingstrategies.com, pg 251

Patricia Teal Literary Agency, 2036 Vista del Rosa, Fullerton, CA 92831 *Tel:* 714-738-8333 *Fax:* 714-738-8333, pg 597

Technical Association of the Pulp & Paper Industry (TAPPI), 15 Technology Pkwy S, Peachtree Corners, GA 30092 *Tel:* 770-446-1400 *Toll Free Tel:* 800-332-8686 (US); 800-446-9431 (CN) *Fax:* 770-446-6947 *E-mail:* memberconnection@tappi.org *Web Site:* www.tappi.org, pg 637

Telling Your Story Inc, PO Box 668485, Pompano Beach, FL 33069 *Tel:* 954-249-1333; 954-970-9333 *Web Site:* www.telling-your-story.com, pg 529

Temple University Press, 1852 N Tenth St, Philadelphia, PA 19122-6099 *Tel:* 215-926-2140 *Toll Free Tel:* 800-621-2736 *Fax:* 215-926-2141 *E-mail:* tempress@temple.edu *Web Site:* www.temple.edu/tempress, pg 251

Templegate Publishers, 302 E Adams St, Springfield, IL 62701 *Tel:* 217-522-3353 (edit & sales); 217-522-3354 (billing) *Toll Free Tel:* 800-367-4844 (orders only) *Fax:* 217-522-3362 *E-mail:* wisdom@templegate.com; orders@templegate.com (sales) *Web Site:* www.templegate.com, pg 252

Templeton Press, 300 Conshohocken State Rd, Suite 550, West Conshohocken, PA 19428 *Tel:* 484-531-8380 *Fax:* 484-531-8382 *E-mail:* tpinfo@templetonpress.org *Web Site:* www.templetonpress.org, pg 252

Temporal Mechanical Press, 6760 Hwy 7, Estes Park, CO 80517-6404 *Tel:* 970-586-4706 *E-mail:* enosmillscbn@earthlink.net *Web Site:* www.enosmills.com, pg 252

Ten Speed Press, 2625 Alcatraz Ave, Unit 505, Berkeley, CA 94705 *Tel:* 510-285-3000 *Toll Free Tel:* 800-841-BOOK (841-2665) *E-mail:* csorders@randomhouse.com *Web Site:* crownpublishing.com/imprint/ten-speed-press, pg 252

Tennessee Arts Commission Fellowships, 401 Charlotte Ave, Nashville, TN 37243-0780 *Tel:* 615-741-1701 *Toll Free Tel:* 800-848-0299 *Fax:* 615-741-8559 *Web Site:* www.tn.gov/arts, pg 745

Teora USA LLC, 505 Hampton Park Blvd, Unit G, Capitol Heights, MD 20743 *Tel:* 301-986-6990 *Toll Free Tel:* 800-974-2105 *Fax:* 301-350-5480 *Toll Free Fax:* 800-358-3754 *E-mail:* 2010@teora.com *Web Site:* www.teora.com, pg 252

Tessler Literary Agency LLC, 27 W 20 St, Suite 1003, New York, NY 10011 *Tel:* 212-242-0466 *Fax:* 212-242-2366 *Web Site:* www.tessleragency.com, pg 597

Teton NewMedia, 90 E Simpson, Suite 110, Jackson, WY 83001 *Tel:* 307-732-0028 *Toll Free Tel:* 877-306-9793 *Fax:* 307-734-0841 *E-mail:* sales@tetonnm.com *Web Site:* www.tetonnm.com, pg 252

Tetra Press, 3001 Commerce St, Blacksburg, VA 24060 *Tel:* 540-951-5400 *Toll Free Tel:* 800-526-0650 *Fax:* 540-951-5415 *E-mail:* consumer@tetra-fish.com *Web Site:* www.tetra-fish.com, pg 252

Texas A&M University Press, John H Lindsey Bldg, Lewis St, 4354 TAMU, College Station, TX 77843-4354 *Tel:* 979-845-1436 *Toll Free Tel:* 800-826-8911 (orders) *Fax:* 979-847-8752 *Toll Free Fax:* 888-617-2421 (orders) *E-mail:* upress@tamu.edu *Web Site:* www.tamupress.com, pg 252

The Texas Bluebonnet Award, 3355 Bee Cave Rd, Suite 401, Austin, TX 78746 *Tel:* 512-328-1518 *Toll Free Tel:* 800-580-2852 *Fax:* 512-328-8852 *Web Site:* www.txla.org, pg 745

Texas Christian University Press, 3000 Sandage Ave, Fort Worth, TX 76109 *Tel:* 817-257-7822 *Toll Free Tel:* 800-826-8911 *Fax:* 817-257-5075 *Web Site:* www.prs.tcu.edu, pg 253

Texas Institute of Letters (TIL), PO Box 609, Round Rock, TX 78680 *Tel:* 512-683-5640 *E-mail:* tilsecretary@yahoo.com *Web Site:* www.texasinstituteofletters.org, pg 637

Texas Institute of Letters Awards, PO Box 609, Round Rock, TX 78680 *Tel:* 512-683-5640 *E-mail:* tilsecretary@yahoo.com *Web Site:* www.texasinstituteofletters.org, pg 745

Texas State Historical Association, Stovall Hall 175, 1400 W Highland St, Denton, TX 76203 *Tel:* 940-369-5200 *Fax:* 940-369-5248 *Web Site:* www.tshaonline.org, pg 253

Texas Tech University Press, 2903 Fourth St, Suite 201, Lubbock, TX 79409 *Tel:* 806-742-2982 *Toll Free Tel:* 800-832-4042 *Fax:* 806-742-2979 *E-mail:* ttup@ttu.edu *Web Site:* www.ttupress.org, pg 253

University of Texas Press, 2100 Comal St, Austin, TX 78722 *Tel:* 512-471-7233 *Fax:* 512-232-7178 *E-mail:* utpress@uts.cc.utexas.edu *Web Site:* www.utexaspress.com, pg 253

Texas Western Press, c/o University of Texas at El Paso, 500 W University Ave, El Paso, TX 79968-0633 *Tel:* 915-747-5688 *Toll Free Tel:* 800-488-3798 (orders only) *Fax:* 915-747-7515 *E-mail:* twpress@utep.edu *Web Site:* twp.utep.edu, pg 253

Textbook Writers Associates Inc, 275 Grove St, Suite 2-400, Newton, MA 02466 *Tel:* 781-209-0051 *Fax:* 781-209-2920 *Web Site:* www.textbookwriters.com, pg 556

TFH Publications Inc, One TFH Plaza, Third & Union Aves, Neptune City, NJ 07753 *Tel:* 732-988-8400 *Toll Free Tel:* 800-631-2188 *Fax:* 732-776-8763 *E-mail:* info@tfh.com *Web Site:* www.tfh.com, pg 253

Thames & Hudson, 500 Fifth Ave, New York, NY 10110 *Tel:* 212-354-3763 *Toll Free Tel:* 800-233-4830 *Fax:* 212-398-1252 *E-mail:* bookinfo@thames.wwnorton.com *Web Site:* www.thamesandhudsonusa.com, pg 253

Theatre Communications Group, 520 Eighth Ave, 24th fl, New York, NY 10018-4156 *Tel:* 212-609-5900 *Fax:* 212-609-5901 *E-mail:* tcg@tcg.org *Web Site:* www.tcg.org, pg 254

Theatre-Scriptworks, 216 Finance Bldg, Harrisburg, PA 17120 *Tel:* 717-787-6883 *Fax:* 717-783-2538 *Web Site:* www.pacouncilonthearts.org, pg 746

Theosophical Publishing House/Quest Books, 306 W Geneva Rd, Wheaton, IL 60187 *Tel:* 630-665-0130 (ext 347) *Toll Free Tel:* 800-669-9425 (ext 347) *Fax:* 630-665-8791 *E-mail:* customerservice@questbooks.net *Web Site:* www.questbooks.net, pg 254

Theosophical University Press, PO Box C, Pasadena, CA 91109-7107 *Tel:* 626-798-3378 *Fax:* 626-798-4749 *E-mail:* tupress@theosociety.org *Web Site:* www.theosociety.org, pg 254

Theytus Books Ltd, RR 2, Green Mountain Rd, Site 50, Comp 8, Lot 45, Penticton, BC V2A 6J7, Canada *Tel:* 250-493-7181 *Fax:* 250-493-5302 *E-mail:* info@theytus.com *Web Site:* www.theytus.com, pg 521

Thieme Medical Publishers Inc, 333 Seventh Ave, 18th fl, New York, NY 10001 *Tel:* 212-760-0888 *Toll Free Tel:* 800-782-3488 *Fax:* 212-947-1112 *E-mail:* customerservice@thieme.com *Web Site:* www.thieme.com, pg 254

Thinkers' Press Inc, 1524 Le Claire St, Davenport, IA 52803 *Tel:* 563-271-6657 *E-mail:* info@chessbutler.com *Web Site:* www.thinkerspressinc.com, pg 254

Third World Press, 7822 S Dobson Ave, Chicago, IL 60619 *Tel:* 773-651-0700 *Fax:* 773-651-7286 *E-mail:* twpress3@aol.com *Web Site:* www.twpbooks.com, pg 254

Thistledown Press, 118 20 St W, Saskatoon, SK S7N 0W6, Canada *Tel:* 306-244-1722 *Fax:* 306-244-1762 *E-mail:* marketing@thistledownpress.com *Web Site:* www.thistledownpress.com, pg 521

Charles C Thomas Publisher Ltd, 2600 S First St, Springfield, IL 62704 *Tel:* 217-789-8980 *Toll Free Tel:* 800-258-8980 *Fax:* 217-789-9130 *E-mail:* books@ccthomas.com *Web Site:* www.ccthomas.com, pg 254

Thomas Geale Publications Inc, PO Box 370540, Montara, CA 94037-0540 *Tel:* 650-728-5219 *Toll Free Tel:* 800-554-5457 *Fax:* 650-728-0918 *E-mail:* justthink@comcast.net, pg 254

Thomas Nelson Inc, 501 Nelson Place, Nashville, TN 37214 *Tel:* 615-889-9000 *Toll Free Tel:* 800-251-4000 *Fax:* 615-902-1548 *E-mail:* publicity@thomasnelson.com *Web Site:* www.thomasnelson.com, pg 254

Thomas Nelson Publishers, PO Box 141000, Nashville, TN 37214-1000 *Tel:* 615-889-9000 *Toll Free Tel:* 800-251-4000 *Fax:* 615-902-2129 *Web Site:* www.thomasnelson.com, pg 255

Thomas Publications, 3245 Fairfield Rd, Gettysburg, PA 17325 *Tel:* 717-642-6600 *Toll Free Tel:* 800-840-6782 *Fax:* 717-642-5555 *E-mail:* info@thomaspublications.com *Web Site:* www.thomaspublications.com, pg 255

Thompson Educational Publishing Inc, 20 Ripley Ave, Toronto, ON M6S 3N9, Canada *Tel:* 416-766-2763 (admin & orders) *Toll Free Tel:* 877-366-2763 *Fax:* 416-766-0398 (admin & orders) *E-mail:* publisher@thompsonbooks.com *Web Site:* www.thompsonbooks.com, pg 521

Thompson Mill Press, 2865 S Eagle Rd, No 368, Newtown, PA 18940 *Tel:* 215-431-1424 *E-mail:* info@thompsonmillpress.com *Web Site:* www.thompsonmillpress.com; www.KobeeManatee.com, pg 530

Thomson Groupe Modulo, 5800 Rue Saint-Denis, Bureau 1102, Montreal, QC H2S 3L5, Canada *Tel:* 514-738-9818 *Toll Free Tel:* 888-738-9818 *Fax:* 514-738-5838 *Toll Free Fax:* 888-273-5247 *Web Site:* www.groupemodulo.com, pg 521

Thomson Reuters Westlaw™, 610 Opperman Dr, Eagan, MN 55123 *Tel:* 651-687-7000 *Toll Free Tel:* 800-328-9352 (sales); 800-328-4880 (cust serv) *Fax:* 651-687-7302 *Web Site:* store.westlaw.com, pg 255

Thorndike Press®, 10 Water St, Suite 310, Waterville, ME 04901 *Toll Free Tel:* 800-233-1244 (ext 4, cust serv/orders); 800-877-4253 (cust serv) *Toll Free Fax:* 877-363-4253 (cust serv); 800-558-4676 (orders) *E-mail:* gale.printorders@cengage.com; international@cengage.com (orders for customers outside US & CN) *Web Site:* thorndike.gale.com, pg 255

Susan Thornton, 6090 Liberty Ave, Vermilion, OH 44089 *Tel:* 440-967-1757 *E-mail:* allenthornton@earthlink.net, pg 556

3-Day Novel Contest, 201-111 W Hastings St, Vancouver, BC V6B 1H4, Canada *E-mail:* info@3daynovel.com *Web Site:* www.3daynovel.com, pg 746

3 Seas Literary Agency, PO Box 8571, Madison, WI 53708 *Tel:* 608-834-9317, pg 597

Three Wishes Publishing Company, 26500 W Agoura Rd, Suite 102-754, Calabasas, CA 91302 *Tel:* 818-878-0902 *Fax:* 818-878-1805 *E-mail:* Alva710@aol.com *Web Site:* www.threewishespublishing.com, pg 530

Thurber Prize for American Humor, 77 Jefferson Ave, Columbus, OH 43215 *Tel:* 614-464-1032 *Fax:* 614-280-3645 *E-mail:* thurberhouse@thurberhouse.org *Web Site:* www.thurberhouse.org, pg 746

Tide-mark Press, 176 Broad St, Windsor, CT 06095 *Tel:* 860-683-4499 *Toll Free Tel:* 888-461-4619 *Fax:* 860-683-4055 *E-mail:* customerservice@tide-mark.com *Web Site:* www.tidemarkpress.com, pg 255

Tiger Tales, 5 River Rd, Suite 128, Wilton, CT 06897 *Tel:* 920-387-2333 *Fax:* 920-387-9994 *Web Site:* www.tigertalesbooks.com, pg 255

Tilbury House Publishers, 103 Brunswick Ave, Gardiner, ME 04345 *Tel:* 207-582-1899 *Toll Free Tel:* 800-582-1899 (orders) *Fax:* 207-582-8227 *E-mail:* tilbury@tilburyhouse.com *Web Site:* www.tilburyhouse.com, pg 255

Timber Press Inc, 133 SW Second Ave, Suite 450, Portland, OR 97204 *Tel:* 503-227-2878 *Toll Free Tel:* 800-327-5680 *Fax:* 503-227-3070 *E-mail:* info@timberpress.com *Web Site:* www.timberpress.com, pg 255

Time Being Books, 10411 Clayton Rd, Suites 201-203, St Louis, MO 63131 *Tel:* 314-432-1771 *Fax:* 314-432-7939 *E-mail:* tbbooks@sbcglobal.net *Web Site:* www.timebeing.com, pg 255

TJ Publishers Inc, PO Box 702701, Dallas, TX 75370 *Toll Free Tel:* 800-999-1168 *Fax:* 972-416-0944 *E-mail:* TJPubinc@aol.com, pg 530

Toad Hall Inc, 74 Toad Hall Lane, Laceyville, PA 18623-8047 *Tel:* 570-869-2942, pg 597

The Toby Press LLC, 2 Great Pasture Rd, Danbury, CT 06810 *Tel:* 203-830-8508 *Fax:* 203-830-8512 *E-mail:* toby@tobypress.com *Web Site:* www.tobypress.com; www.korenpub.com, pg 256

Todd Publications, 3500 NE Sixth Dr, Boca Raton, FL 33431 *Tel:* 561-910-0440 *Fax:* 561-910-0440 *E-mail:* toddpub@aol.com, pg 256

The Tomasino Agency Inc, 70 Chestnut St, Dobbs Ferry, NY 10522 *Tel:* 914-674-9659 *Fax:* 914-693-0381 *E-mail:* info@tomasinoagency.com *Web Site:* www.tomasinoagency.com, pg 597

Tommy Nelson, 501 Nelson Place, Nashville, TN 37214 *Tel:* 615-889-9000 *Toll Free Tel:* 800-251-4000 *Fax:* 615-391-5225 *Web Site:* www.tommynelson.com, pg 256

Tony Hillerman Writers Conference, 1063 Willow Way, Santa Fe, NM 87507 *Tel:* 505-471-1565 *E-mail:* wordharvest@wordharvest.com *Web Site:* www.wordharvest.com, pg 674

Top of the Mountain Publishing, PO Box 2244, Pinellas Park, FL 33780-2244 *Tel:* 727-391-3958 *E-mail:* tag@abcinfo.com; info@abcinfo.com *Web Site:* abcinfo.com; www.topofthemountain.com, pg 256

Top Publications Ltd, 12221 Merit Dr, Suite 950, Dallas, TX 75251 *Tel:* 972-628-6414 *Fax:* 972-233-0713 *E-mail:* info@toppub.com *Web Site:* toppub.com, pg 256

Torah Aura Productions, 4423 Fruitland Ave, Los Angeles, CA 90058 *Tel:* 323-585-7312 *Toll Free Tel:* 800-238-6724 *Fax:* 323-585-0327 *E-mail:* misrad@torahaura.com; orders@torahaura.com *Web Site:* www.torahaura.com, pg 256

Torah Umesorah Publications, 620 Foster Ave, Brooklyn, NY 11230 *Tel:* 718-259-1223 *Fax:* 718-259-1795 *E-mail:* publications@torah-umesorah.org, pg 256

Tormont Publishing International, 3305 Pitfield Blvd, St-Laurent, QC H4S 1H3, Canada *Tel:* 514-954-1441 *Fax:* 514-954-1443, pg 521

Tortuga Press, 2777 Yulupa Ave, PMB 181, Santa Rosa, CA 95405 *Tel:* 707-544-4720 *Toll Free Tel:* 866-4TORTUGA (486-7884) *Fax:* 707-544-5609 *E-mail:* info@tortugapress.com *Web Site:* www.tortugapress.com, pg 256

TotalRecall Publications Inc, 1103 Middlecreek, Friendswood, TX 77546 *Tel:* 281-992-3131 *E-mail:* sales@totalrecallpress.com *Web Site:* www.totalrecallpress.com, pg 256

Touchstone, 1230 Avenue of the Americas, New York, NY 10020, pg 256

TouchWood Editions, 103-1075 Pendergast St, Victoria, BC V8V 0A1, Canada *Tel:* 250-360-0829 *Fax:* 250-386-0829 *E-mail:* info@touchwoodeditions.com *Web Site:* www.touchwoodeditions.com, pg 521

Tower Publishing Co, 588 Saco Rd, Standish, ME 04084 *Tel:* 207-642-5400 *Toll Free Tel:* 800-969-8693 *Fax:* 207-264-3870 *E-mail:* info@towerpub.com *Web Site:* www.towerpub.com, pg 257

Townson Publishing Co Ltd, PO Box 1404, Sta A, Vancouver, BC V6C 2P7, Canada *Tel:* 604-886-0594 (CN) *E-mail:* townsonpublishing@gmail.com *Web Site:* generalpublishing.co.uk, pg 521

Towson University Prize for Literature, English Dept, 8000 York Rd, Towson, MD 21252 *Tel:* 410-704-2000 *Fax:* 410-704-3999 *Web Site:* www.towson.edu/english, pg 746

Tracks Publishing, 140 Brightwood Ave, Chula Vista, CA 91910 *Tel:* 619-476-7125 *Toll Free Tel:* 800-443-3570 *Fax:* 619-476-8173 *E-mail:* tracks@cox.net *Web Site:* www.startupsports.com, pg 257

The University of Connecticut, The Realities of Publishing, CLAS, 215 Glenbrook Rd, Unit 4025, Storrs, CT 06269-4025 *Tel:* 860-486-2141 *Web Site:* web.uconn.edu/english291, pg 681

University of Delaware Press, 200A Morris Library, 181 S College Ave, Newark, DE 19717-5267 *Tel:* 302-831-1149 *Fax:* 302-831-6549 *E-mail:* ud-press@udel.edu *Web Site:* www2.lib.udel.edu/udpress, pg 265

University of Denver Publishing Institute, 2000 E Asbury Ave, Denver, CO 80208 *Tel:* 303-871-2570 *Fax:* 303-871-2501 *Web Site:* www.du.edu/pi, pg 681

University of Georgia Press, Main Library, 3rd fl, 320 S Jackson St, Athens, GA 30602 *Tel:* 706-369-6130 *Fax:* 706-369-6131; 706-369-6162 *E-mail:* books@ugapress.uga.edu (orders) *Web Site:* www.ugapress.org, pg 265

University of Hawaii Press, 2840 Kolowalu St, Honolulu, HI 96822 *Tel:* 808-956-8255 *Toll Free Tel:* 888-UHPRESS (847-7377) *Fax:* 808-988-6052 *Toll Free Fax:* 800-650-7811 *E-mail:* uhpbooks@hawaii.edu *Web Site:* www.uhpress.hawaii.edu, pg 265

University of Houston Creative Writing Program, 229 Roy Cullen Bldg, Houston, TX 77204-5008 *Tel:* 713-743-2255 *Fax:* 713-743-3697 *E-mail:* cwp@uh.edu *Web Site:* www.uh.edu/cwp, pg 681

University of Illinois at Chicago, Program for Writers, College of Liberal Arts & Sciences, 2027 University Hall, 601 S Morgan St, Chicago, IL 60607-7120 *Tel:* 312-413-2200 (Eng Dept) *Fax:* 312-413-1005 *Web Site:* www.uic.edu, pg 681

University of Illinois, Dept of Journalism, Gregory Hall, Rm 120-A, 810 S Wright St, Urbana, IL 61801 *Tel:* 217-333-0709 *Fax:* 217-333-7931 *E-mail:* journ@uiuc.edu *Web Site:* www.comm.uiuc.edu, pg 681

University of Illinois Press, 1325 S Oak St, MC-566, Champaign, IL 61820-6903 *Tel:* 217-333-0950 *Fax:* 217-244-8082 *E-mail:* uipress@uillinois.edu; journals@uillinois.edu *Web Site:* www.press.uillinois.edu, pg 265

University of Iowa Press, 119 W Park Rd, 100 Kuhl House, Iowa City, IA 52242-1000 *Tel:* 319-335-2000 *Toll Free Tel:* 800-621-2736 (orders only) *Fax:* 319-335-2055 *Toll Free Fax:* 800-621-8476 (orders only) *E-mail:* uipress@uiowa.edu *Web Site:* www.uiowapress.org, pg 266

University of Iowa, Writer's Workshop, 102 Dey House, 507 N Clinton St, Iowa City, IA 52242-1000 *Tel:* 319-335-0416 *Fax:* 319-335-0420, pg 747

University of Iowa, Writers' Workshop, Graduate Creative Writing Program, 102 Dey House, 507 N Clinton St, Iowa City, IA 52242-1000 *Tel:* 319-335-0416 *Fax:* 319-335-0420 *Web Site:* www.uiowa.edu/~iww, pg 681

University of Louisiana at Lafayette Press, PO Box 40831, UL, Lafayette, LA 70504-0831 *Tel:* 337-482-6027 *Fax:* 337-482-6028 *E-mail:* cls@louisiana.edu *Web Site:* www.ulpress.org, pg 266

University of Manitoba Press, University of Manitoba, 301 St Johns College, Winnipeg, MB R3T 2M5, Canada *Tel:* 204-474-9495 *Fax:* 204-474-7566 *Web Site:* www.umanitoba.ca/uofmpress, pg 523

University of Massachusetts Press, East Experiment Sta, 671 N Pleasant St, Amherst, MA 01003 *Tel:* 413-545-2217 *Fax:* 413-545-1226 *E-mail:* info@umpress.umass.edu *Web Site:* www.umass.edu/umpress, pg 266

University of Michigan Center for Japanese Studies, 1007 E Huron St, Ann Arbor, MI 48104-1690 *Tel:* 734-647-8885 *Fax:* 734-647-8886 *E-mail:* ii.cjspubs@umich.edu *Web Site:* www.cjspubs.lsa.umich.edu, pg 266

University of Michigan Press, 839 Greene St, Ann Arbor, MI 48104-3209 *Tel:* 734-764-4388 *Fax:* 734-615-1540 *E-mail:* esladmin@umich.edu *Web Site:* www.press.umich.edu, pg 266

University of Minnesota Press, 111 Third Ave S, Suite 290, Minneapolis, MN 55401-2520 *Tel:* 612-627-1970 *Fax:* 612-627-1980 *E-mail:* ump@umn.edu *Web Site:* www.upress.umn.edu, pg 266

University of Missouri-Kansas City, New Letters Weekend Writers Conference, College of Arts & Sciences, Continuing Education Div, 5300 Rockhill Rd, Kansas City, MO 64110 *Tel:* 816-235-2736 *Fax:* 816-235-5279 *Web Site:* www.umkc.edu, pg 681

University of Missouri Press, 2910 Le Mone Blvd, Columbia, MO 65201 *Tel:* 573-882-7641 *Toll Free Tel:* 800-621-2736 (orders) *Fax:* 573-884-4498 *Web Site:* press.umsystem.edu, pg 267

University of Montana, Environmental Writing Institute, Environmental Studies, University of Montana, Missoula, MT 59812 *Tel:* 406-243-2904 *Fax:* 406-243-6090 *Web Site:* www.umt.edu/ewi, pg 682

University of Nebraska at Omaha Center for Public Affairs Research, CPACS Bldg, Rm 108, 6001 Dodge St, Omaha, NE 68182 *Tel:* 402-554-2134 *Web Site:* www.unomaha.edu/cpar, pg 267

University of Nebraska Press, 1111 Lincoln Mall, Lincoln, NE 68588-0630 *Tel:* 402-472-3581; 919-966-7449 (cust serv & foreign orders) *Toll Free Tel:* 800-848-6224 (cust serv & US orders) *Fax:* 402-472-6214; 919-962-2704 (cust serv & foreign orders) *Toll Free Fax:* 800-526-2617 (cust serv & US orders) *E-mail:* pressmail@unl.edu *Web Site:* www.nebraskapress.unl.edu, pg 267

University of Nevada Press, University of Nevada, M/S 0166, Reno, NV 89557-0166 *Tel:* 775-784-6573 *Fax:* 775-784-6200 *Web Site:* www.unpress.nevada.edu, pg 267

University of New Mexico, University of New Mexico, Humanities Dept, Rm 253, Albuquerque, NM 87131-0001 *Tel:* 505-277-2346; 505-272-7777 (cust serv) *Toll Free Tel:* 800-249-7737 (orders only) *Fax:* 505-277-3343; 505-272-7778 (cust serv) *Toll Free Fax:* 800-622-8667 (orders only) *E-mail:* unmpress@unm.edu; custserv@upress.unm.edu (order dept) *Web Site:* unmpress.com, pg 267

The University of North Carolina Press, 116 S Boundary St, Chapel Hill, NC 27514-3808 *Tel:* 919-966-3561 *Fax:* 919-966-3829 *E-mail:* uncpress@unc.edu *Web Site:* www.uncpress.unc.edu, pg 267

University of North Texas Press, Stovall Hall, Suite 174, 1400 Highland St, Denton, TX 76201 *Tel:* 940-565-2142 *Fax:* 940-565-4590 *Web Site:* www.unt.edu/untpress, pg 268

University of Notre Dame Press, 310 Flanner Hall, Notre Dame, IN 46556 *Tel:* 574-631-6346 *Fax:* 574-631-8148 *E-mail:* undpress@nd.edu *Web Site:* www.undpress.nd.edu, pg 268

University of Oklahoma Press, 2800 Venture Dr, Norman, OK 73069-8216 *Tel:* 405-325-2000 *Toll Free Tel:* 800-627-7377 (orders) *Fax:* 405-364-5798 (orders) *Toll Free Fax:* 800-735-0476 (orders) *E-mail:* presscs@ou.edu *Web Site:* www.oupress.com, pg 268

University of Ottawa Press (Presses de l'Université d'Ottawa), 542 King Edward Ave, Ottawa, ON K1N 6N5, Canada *Tel:* 613-562-5246 *Fax:* 613-562-5247 *E-mail:* puo-oup@uottawa.ca *Web Site:* www.press.uottawa.ca, pg 523

University of Pennsylvania Museum of Archaeology & Anthropology, 3260 South St, Philadelphia, PA 19104-6324 *Tel:* 215-898-5723 *Fax:* 215-573-2497 *E-mail:* info@pennmuseum.org; publications@pennmuseum.org *Web Site:* www.penn.museum, pg 268

University of Pennsylvania Press, 3905 Spruce St, Philadelphia, PA 19104 *Tel:* 215-898-6261 *Fax:* 215-898-0404 *E-mail:* custserv@pobox.upenn.edu *Web Site:* www.pennpress.org, pg 268

University of Pittsburgh Press, Eureka Bldg, 5th fl, 3400 Forbes Ave, Pittsburgh, PA 15260 *Tel:* 412-383-2456 *Fax:* 412-383-2466 *E-mail:* info@upress.pitt.edu *Web Site:* www.upress.pitt.edu, pg 268

University of Puerto Rico Press, Edificio La Editorial (level 2), Carr No 1, KM 12.0, Jardin Botanico Norte, San Juan, PR 00927 *Tel:* 787-250-0435; 787-250-0550 *Toll Free Tel:* 877-338-7788 *Fax:* 787-753-9116 *E-mail:* info@laeditorialupr.com *Web Site:* www.laeditorialupr.com, pg 269

University of Rochester Press, 668 Mount Hope Ave, Rochester, NY 14620-2731 *Tel:* 585-275-0419 *Fax:* 585-271-8778 *E-mail:* boydell@boydellusa.net *Web Site:* www.urpress.com, pg 269

University of Scranton Press, 445 Madison Ave, Scranton, PA 18510 *Tel:* 570-941-4228 *Fax:* 570-941-7085 *E-mail:* salesoffice@scranton.edu *Web Site:* academic.scranton.edu/organization/upress, pg 269

University of South Carolina Press, 1600 Hampton St, Suite 544, Columbia, SC 29208 *Tel:* 803-777-5245 *Toll Free Tel:* 800-768-2500 (orders) *Fax:* 803-777-0160 *Toll Free Fax:* 800-868-0740 (orders) *Web Site:* www.sc.edu/uscpress, pg 269

University of Southern California, Master of Professional Writing Program, Mark Taper Hall, THH 355, 3501 Trousedale Pkwy, Los Angeles, CA 90089-0355 *Tel:* 213-740-3252 *Fax:* 213-740-5002 *E-mail:* mpw@college.usc.edu *Web Site:* college.usc.edu/mpw, pg 682

University of Tennessee Press, 110 Conference Center Bldg, 600 Henley St, Knoxville, TN 37996-4108 *Tel:* 865-974-3321 *Toll Free Tel:* 800-621-2736 (orders) *Fax:* 865-974-3724 *Toll Free Fax:* 800-621-8476 (orders) *E-mail:* custserv@utpress.org *Web Site:* www.utpress.org, pg 269

University of Texas at Arlington School of Urban & Public Affairs, 511 University Hall, 5th fl, 601 S Nedderman Dr, Arlington, TX 76010 *Tel:* 817-272-3071 *Fax:* 817-272-3415 *E-mail:* supa@uta.edu *Web Site:* www.uta.edu/supa, pg 269

University of Texas at Austin, Creative Writing Program, Dept of English, PAR 108, One University Sta, Mailcode B5000, Austin, TX 78712-1164 *Tel:* 512-471-5132; 512-471-4991 *Fax:* 512-471-4909 *Web Site:* www.utexas.edu/cola/depts/english/creative-writing, pg 682

University of Texas at El Paso, Dept Creative Writing, MFA/Dept Creative Writing, Liberal Arts 415 UTEP, 500 W University Ave, El Paso, TX 79968-9991 *Tel:* 915-747-5713 *Fax:* 915-747-5523 *Web Site:* www.utep.edu/cw, pg 682

University of Toronto Press Inc, 10 Saint Mary St, Suite 700, Toronto, ON M4Y 2W8, Canada *Tel:* 416-978-2239 *Fax:* 416-978-4738 *E-mail:* utpbooks@utpress.utoronto.ca *Web Site:* www.utpress.utoronto.ca; www.utppublishing.com, pg 524

The University of Utah Press, J Willard Marriott Library, Suite 5400, 295 S 1500 E, Salt Lake City, UT 84112-0860 *Tel:* 801-581-6771 *Toll Free Tel:* 800-621-2736 (orders) *Fax:* 801-581-3365 *Toll Free Fax:* 800-621-8471 *E-mail:* info@upress.utah.edu *Web Site:* www.uofupress.com, pg 269

The University of Virginia Press, PO Box 400318, Charlottesville, VA 22904-4318 *Tel:* 434-924-3468 (cust serv); 434-924-3469 (cust serv) *Toll Free Tel:* 800-831-3406 (orders) *Fax:* 434-982-2655 *Toll Free Fax:* 877-288-6400 *E-mail:* vapress@virginia.edu *Web Site:* www.upress.virginia.edu, pg 269

University of Washington Press, 433 Brooklyn Ave NE, Seattle, WA 98195-9570 *Tel:* 206-543-4050 *Toll Free Tel:* 800-537-5487 (orders) *Fax:* 206-543-3932; 410-516-6998 (orders) *E-mail:* uwpress@u.washington.edu *Web Site:* www.washington.edu/uwpress/, pg 270

University of Wisconsin Press, 1930 Monroe St, 3rd fl, Madison, WI 53711-2059 *Tel:* 608-263-0668 *Toll Free Tel:* 800-621-2736 (orders) *Fax:* 608-263-1173 *Toll Free Fax:* 800-621-2736 (orders) *E-mail:* uwiscpress@uwpress.wisc.edu (main off) *Web Site:* www.wisc.edu/wisconsinpress, pg 270

University of Wisconsin-School of Architecture & Urban Planning, 2131 E Hartford Ave, Rm 225, Milwaukee, WI 53211 *Tel:* 414-229-4014 *Fax:* 414-229-6976 *E-mail:* sarupead@uwm.edu *Web Site:* www.uwm.edu/SARUP, pg 270

University Press of America Inc, 4501 Forbes Blvd, Suite 200, Lanham, MD 20706 *Tel:* 301-459-3366 *Toll Free Tel:* 800-462-6420 *Fax:* 301-429-5748 *Toll Free Fax:* 800-338-4550 *Web Site:* www.univpress.com, pg 270

University Press of Colorado, 5589 Arapahoe Ave, Suite 206-C, Boulder, CO 80303 *Tel:* 720-406-8849 *Toll Free Tel:* 800-621-2736 (orders) *Fax:* 720-406-3443 *Web Site:* www.upcolorado.com, pg 270

University Press of Florida, 15 NW 15 St, Gainesville, FL 32603-2079 *Tel:* 352-392-1351 *Toll Free Tel:* 800-226-3822 (orders only) *Fax:* 352-392-0590 *Toll Free Fax:* 800-680-1955 (orders only) *E-mail:* info@upf.com *Web Site:* www.upf.com, pg 271

University Press of Kansas, 2502 Westbrooke Circle, Lawrence, KS 66045-4444 *Tel:* 785-864-4154; 785-864-4155 (orders) *Fax:* 785-864-4586 *E-mail:* upress@ku.edu; upkorders@ku.edu (orders) *Web Site:* www.kansaspress.ku.edu, pg 271

The University Press of Kentucky, 663 S Limestone St, Lexington, KY 40508-4008 *Tel:* 859-257-8400 *Fax:* 859-257-8481 *Web Site:* www.kentuckypress.com, pg 271

University Press of Mississippi, 3825 Ridgewood Rd, Jackson, MS 39211-6492 *Tel:* 601-432-6205 *Toll Free Tel:* 800-737-7788 (orders & cust serv) *Fax:* 601-432-6217 *E-mail:* press@mississippi.edu *Web Site:* www.upress.state.ms.us, pg 271

University Press of New England, One Court St, Suite 250, Lebanon, NH 03766 *Tel:* 603-448-1533 *Toll Free Tel:* 800-421-1561 (orders only) *Fax:* 603-448-7006; 603-643-1540 *E-mail:* university.press@dartmouth.edu *Web Site:* www.upne.com, pg 271

University Publishing Group, 219 W Washington St, Hagerstown, MD 21740 *Tel:* 240-420-0036 *Toll Free Tel:* 800-654-8188 *Fax:* 240-718-7100 *E-mail:* editorial@upgbooks.com; orders@upgbooks.com; sales@upgbooks.com *Web Site:* www.upgbooks.com, pg 272

University Publishing House, PO Box 1664, Mannford, OK 74044 *Tel:* 918-865-4726 *E-mail:* upub3@juno.com *Web Site:* www.universitypublishinghouse.net, pg 272

University Science Books, 20 Edgeshill Rd, Mill Valley, CA 94941 *Tel:* 415-332-5390 *Fax:* 415-383-3167 *E-mail:* univscibks@igc.org *Web Site:* www.uscibooks.com, pg 272

UnKnownTruths.com Publishing Co, 8815 Conroy Windermere Rd, Suite 190, Orlando, FL 32835 *Tel:* 407-929-9207 *Fax:* 407-876-3933 *E-mail:* info@unknowntruths.com *Web Site:* unknowntruths.com, pg 272

Unlimited Publishing LLC, Box 99, Nashville, IN 47448 *Tel:* 206-666-5484 *E-mail:* info@unlimitedpublishing.com; publish@unlimitedpublishing.com *Web Site:* www.unlimitedpublishing.com, pg 272

UNO Press, University of New Orleans Metro College, Educ Bldg, Suite 210, 2000 Lakeshore Dr, New Orleans, LA 70148 *Tel:* 504-280-7457 *Fax:* 504-280-7317 *E-mail:* unopress@uno.edu *Web Site:* unopress.org, pg 272

Unveiled Media LLC, PO Box 930463, Verona, WI 53593 *Tel:* 707-986-8345 *Web Site:* www.unveiledmedia.com, pg 272

W E Upjohn Institute for Employment Research, 300 S Westnedge Ave, Kalamazoo, MI 49007-4686 *Tel:* 269-343-5541; 269-343-4330 (pubns) *Toll Free Tel:* 888-227-8569 *Fax:* 269-343-7310 *E-mail:* publications@upjohninstitute.org *Web Site:* www.upjohn.org, pg 272

Upper Access Inc, 87 Upper Access Rd, Hinesburg, VT 05461 *Tel:* 802-482-2988 *Toll Free Tel:* 800-310-8320 *Fax:* 802-304-1005 *E-mail:* info@upperaccess.com *Web Site:* www.upperaccess.com, pg 272

Upper Room Books, 1908 Grand Ave, Nashville, TN 37212 *Tel:* 615-340-7200 *Toll Free Tel:* 800-972-0433 *Fax:* 615-340-7266 *E-mail:* urbooks@upperroom.org *Web Site:* www.upperroom.org, pg 273

Upstart Books™, 4810 Forest Run Rd, Madison, WI 53704 *Tel:* 608-241-1201 *Toll Free Tel:* 800-448-4887 (orders) *Toll Free Fax:* 800-448-5828 *E-mail:* custsvc@upstartpromotions.com *Web Site:* www.upstartbooks.com, pg 273

The Urban Institute Press, 2100 "M" St NW, Washington, DC 20037 *Tel:* 202-261-5885; 410-516-6956 (orders) *Toll Free Tel:* 877-UIPRESS (847-7377); 800-537-5487 (orders) *Fax:* 202-467-5775 *E-mail:* dinscoe@urban.org; hfscustserv@press.jhu.edu *Web Site:* www.uipress.org, pg 273

Urban Land Institute, 1025 Thomas Jefferson St NW, Suite 500-W, Washington, DC 20007 *Tel:* 202-624-7000 *Toll Free Tel:* 800-321-5011 (cust serv) *Fax:* 410-626-7140 *E-mail:* bookstore@uli.org; customerservice@uli.org *Web Site:* www.uli.org/books, pg 273

Urim Publications, c/o Lambda Publications Inc, 527 Empire Blvd, Brooklyn, NY 11225-3121 *Tel:* 718-972-5449 *Fax:* 718-972-6307 *E-mail:* publisher@urimpublications.com *Web Site:* urimpublications.com, pg 273

URJ Books & Music, 633 Third Ave, New York, NY 10017-6778 *Tel:* 212-650-4120 *Fax:* 212-650-4119 *E-mail:* press@urj.org *Web Site:* www.urjbooksandmusic.com, pg 273

US Board on Books For Young People (USBBY), 5503 N El Adobe Dr, Fresno, CA 93711-2363 *Tel:* 559-351-6119 *E-mail:* executive.director@usbby.org *Web Site:* www.usbby.org, pg 638

US Conference of Catholic Bishops, USCCB Publishing, 3211 Fourth St NE, Washington, DC 20017 *Tel:* 202-541-3090 *Toll Free Tel:* 800-235-8722 (orders only) *Fax:* 202-722-8709 *E-mail:* css@usccb.org; publications@usccb.org *Web Site:* www.usccbpublishing.org, pg 273

US Games Systems Inc, 179 Ludlow St, Stamford, CT 06902 *Tel:* 203-353-8400 *Toll Free Tel:* 800-54-GAMES (544-2637) *Fax:* 203-353-8431 *E-mail:* info@usgamesinc.com *Web Site:* www.usgamesinc.com, pg 273

US Government Printing Office, Superintendent of Documents, 732 N Capitol St NW, Washington, DC 20401 *Tel:* 202-512-1800 *Toll Free Tel:* 866-512-1800 (orders) *Fax:* 202-512-2104 *E-mail:* contactcenter@gpo.gov *Web Site:* bookstore.gpo.gov (sales), pg 273

USBE: United States Book Exchange, 2969 W 25 St, Cleveland, OH 44113 *Tel:* 216-241-6960 *Fax:* 216-241-6966 *E-mail:* usbe@usbe.com *Web Site:* www, usbe.com, pg 638

Utah Geological Survey, 1594 W North Temple, Suite 3110, Salt Lake City, UT 84116-3154 *Tel:* 801-537-3300 *Toll Free Tel:* 888-UTAH-MAP (882-4627 bookstore) *Fax:* 801-537-3400 *E-mail:* geostore@utah.gov *Web Site:* geology.utah.gov, pg 273

Utah Original Writing Competition, 617 E South Temple, Salt Lake City, UT 84102 *Tel:* 801-236-7555 *Fax:* 801-236-7556 *Web Site:* arts.utah.gov, pg 747

Utah State University Press, 3078 Old Main Hill, Logan, UT 84322-3078 *Tel:* 435-797-1362 *Fax:* 435-797-0313 *Web Site:* www.usupress.org, pg 274

UW-Madison, Division of Continuing Studies, 21 N Park St, 7th fl, Madison, WI 53715 *Tel:* 608-263-6320 *Toll Free Tel:* 877-336-7836 *Fax:* 608-262-1694 *E-mail:* liberalarts@dsc.wisc.edu *Web Site:* continuingstudies.wisc.edu, pg 682

William Van Dyke Short Story Prize, 140 N Roosevelt Ave, Collins, CO 80521 *Tel:* 970-449-2726 *E-mail:* editor@ruminatemagazine.org *Web Site:* www.ruminatemagazine.com, pg 747

The William Van Wert Memorial Fiction Award, PO Box 63927, Philadelphia, PA 19147 *Tel:* 610-764-0813 *E-mail:* hiddenriverarts@gmail.com *Web Site:* www.hiddenriverarts.org, pg 747

VanDam Inc, 11 W 20 St, 4th fl, New York, NY 10011-3704 *Tel:* 212-929-0416 *Toll Free Tel:* 800-UNFOLDS (863-6537) *Fax:* 212-929-0426 *E-mail:* info@vandam.com *Web Site:* www.vandam.com, pg 274

Vandamere Press, 3580 Morris St N, St Petersburg, FL 33713 *Tel:* 727-556-0950 *Toll Free Tel:* 800-551-7776 *Fax:* 727-556-2560 *E-mail:* orders@vandamere.com *Web Site:* www.vandamere.com, pg 274

Vanderbilt University Press, 2014 Broadway, Suite 320, Nashville, TN 37203 *Tel:* 615-322-3585 *Toll Free Tel:* 800-627-7377 (orders only) *Fax:* 615-343-8823 *Toll Free Fax:* 800-735-0476 (orders only) *E-mail:* vupress@vanderbilt.edu *Web Site:* www.vanderbiltuniversitypress.com, pg 274

VanderMey Nonfiction Prize, 140 N Roosevelt Ave, Collins, CO 80521 *Tel:* 970-449-2726 *E-mail:* editor@ruminatemagazine.org *Web Site:* www.ruminatemagazine.com, pg 747

Daniel Varoujan Award, 2 Farrar St, Cambridge, MA 02138 *Tel:* 617-744-6034 *E-mail:* contests@nepoetryclub.org *Web Site:* www.nepoetryclub.org, pg 747

Vault.com Inc, 75 Varick St, 8th fl, New York, NY 10013 *Tel:* 212-366-4212 *Fax:* 212-366-6117 *E-mail:* feedback@staff.vault.com *Web Site:* www.vault.com, pg 274

Vedanta Press, 1946 Vedanta Place, Hollywood, CA 90068 *Tel:* 323-960-1736 *Toll Free Tel:* 800-816-2242 *E-mail:* info@vedanta.com *Web Site:* www.vedanta.com, pg 274

Vehicule Press, PO Box 125, Place du Park Sta, Montreal, QC H2X 4A3, Canada *Tel:* 514-844-6073 *Fax:* 514-844-7543 *E-mail:* vp@vehiculepress.com; admin@vehiculepress.com *Web Site:* www.vehiculepress.com, pg 524

Velazquez Press, 9682 Telstar Ave, Suite 110, El Monte, CA 91731 *Tel:* 626-448-3448 *Fax:* 626-602-3817 *E-mail:* info@academiclearningcompany.com *Web Site:* www.velazquezpress.com, pg 274

The Vendome Press, 1334 York Ave, 3rd fl, New York, NY 10021 *Tel:* 212-737-5297 *Fax:* 212-737-5340 *E-mail:* info@vendomepress.com *Web Site:* www.vendomepress.com, pg 274

Venture Publishing Inc, 1999 Cato Ave, State College, PA 16801 *Tel:* 814-234-4561 *Fax:* 814-234-1651 *E-mail:* vpublish@venturepublish.com *Web Site:* www.venturepublish.com, pg 274

Vermont Arts Council Grants, 136 State St, Montpelier, VT 05602 *Tel:* 802-828-5425 *Fax:* 802-828-3363 *E-mail:* info@vermontartscouncil.org *Web Site:* www.vermontartscouncil.org, pg 747

Vermont College of Fine Arts MFA in Writing for Children & Young Adults Program, 36 College St, Montpelier, VT 05602 *Tel:* 802-828-8637; 802-828-8696 *Toll Free Tel:* 866-934-VCFA (934-8232) *Fax:* 802-828-8649 *Web Site:* www.vcfa.edu, pg 682

Vermont College of Fine Arts, MFA in Writing Program, 36 College St, Montpelier, VT 05602 *Tel:* 802-828-8840; 802-828-8839 *Toll Free Tel:* 866-934-VCFA (934-8232) *Fax:* 802-828-8649 *Web Site:* www.vcfa.edu, pg 682

Vermont Studio Center Writer's Program Fellowships, 80 Pearl St, Johnson, VT 05656 *Tel:* 802-635-2727 *Fax:* 802-635-2730 *E-mail:* writing@vermontstudiocenter.org; info@vermontstudiocenter.org *Web Site:* www.vermontstudiocenter.org, pg 747

Verso, 20 Jay St, Suite 1010, Brooklyn, NY 11201 *Tel:* 718-246-8160 *Fax:* 718-246-8165 *E-mail:* verso@versobooks.com *Web Site:* www.versobooks.com, pg 274

Very Short Fiction Award, PO Box 80430, Portland, OR 97280 *Tel:* 503-221-0836 *Fax:* 503-221-0837 *E-mail:* editors@glimmertrain.org *Web Site:* www.glimmertrain.org, pg 747

Jill Vickers Prize, 260 rue Dalhousie St, Suite 204, Ottawa, ON K1N 7E4, Canada *Tel:* 613-562-1202 *Fax:* 613-241-0019 *E-mail:* cpsa-acsp@cpsa-acsp.ca *Web Site:* www.cpsa-acsp.ca, pg 747

Vicky Metcalf Award for Literature for Young People, 90 Richmond St E, Suite 200, Toronto, ON M5C 1P1, Canada *Tel:* 416-504-8222 *Toll Free Tel:* 877-906-6548 *Fax:* 416-504-9090 *E-mail:* info@writerstrust.com *Web Site:* www.writerstrust.com, pg 747

Victory in Grace Printing, 60 Quentin Rd, Lake Zurich, IL 60047 *Tel:* 847-438-4494 *Toll Free Tel:* 800-78-GRACE (784-7223) *Fax:* 847-438-4232 *Web Site:* www.victoryingrace.org, pg 274

Viking, 375 Hudson St, New York, NY 10014 *Tel:* 212-366-2000 *E-mail:* online@penguinputnam.com *Web Site:* www.penguinputnam.com; us.penguingroup.com, pg 275

Viking Children's Books, 345 Hudson St, New York, NY 10014 *Tel:* 212-366-2000 *E-mail:* online@penguinputnam.com *Web Site:* www.penguinputnam.com; us.penguingroup.com, pg 275

Viking Studio, 375 Hudson St, New York, NY 10014 *Tel:* 212-366-2000 *E-mail:* online@penguinputnam.com *Web Site:* www.penguinputnam.com; us.penguingroup.com, pg 275

Carl Vinson Institute of Government, University of Georgia, 201 N Milledge Ave, Athens, GA 30602 *Tel:* 706-542-2736 *Fax:* 706-542-9301 *Web Site:* www.cviog.uga.edu, pg 275

Vintage & Anchor Books, c/o Random House Inc, 1745 Broadway, New York, NY 10019 *Tel:* 212-572-2420 *E-mail:* vintageanchorpublicity@randomhouse.com *Web Site:* vintage-anchor.knopfdoubleday.com, pg 275

Visible Ink Press®, 43311 Joy Rd, Suite 414, Canton, MI 48187-2075 *Tel:* 734-667-3211 *Fax:* 734-667-4311 *E-mail:* info@visibleink.com *Web Site:* www.visibleink.com, pg 275

Visiting Writers Series, English Dept, PO Box 755720, Fairbanks, AK 99775-5720 *Tel:* 907-474-7193 *Fax:* 907-474-5247 *E-mail:* faengl@uaf.edu *Web Site:* www.alaska.edu/english, pg 674

Visual Artists & Galleries Association Inc (VAGA), 350 Fifth Ave, Suite 2820, New York, NY 10118 *Tel:* 212-736-6666 *Fax:* 212-736-6767 *E-mail:* info@vagarights.com *Web Site:* www.vagarights.com, pg 638

Visual Media Alliance (VMA), 665 Third St, Suite 500, San Francisco, CA 94107-1926 *Tel:* 415-495-8242 *Toll Free Tel:* 800-659-3363 *Fax:* 415-543-7790 *Toll Free Fax:* 800-824-1911 *E-mail:* info@vma.bz *Web Site:* vma.bz; www.visualmediaalliance.org, pg 638

Visual Profile Books Inc, 302 Fifth Ave, New York, NY 10001 *Tel:* 212-279-7000 *Fax:* 212-279-7014 *Web Site:* www.visualreference.com, pg 275

Visuals Unlimited, 27 Meadow Dr, Hollis, NH 03049 *Tel:* 603-465-3340 *Fax:* 603-465-3360 *E-mail:* staff@visualsunlimited.com *Web Site:* visualsunlimited.com, pg 556

VLB Editeur Inc, 1010 rue de la Gauchetiere E, Montreal, QC H2L 2N5, Canada *Tel:* 514-523-7993 *Fax:* 514-282-7530 *Web Site:* www.edvlb.com, pg 524

Vocabula Communications Co, 5-A Holbrook Ct, Rockport, MA 01966 *Tel:* 978-546-3911 *E-mail:* info@vocabula.com *Web Site:* www.vocabula.com; www.vocabulabooks.com (books), pg 556

The Voices Summer Writing Workshops, c/o Community Initiatives Inc, 354 Pine St, Suite 700, San Francisco, CA 94104 *Toll Free Tel:* 866-202-6152 *E-mail:* info@voicesatvona.org *Web Site:* www.voicesatvona.org, pg 674

Volcano Press, 21496 National St, Volcano, CA 95689 *Tel:* 209-296-7989 *Toll Free Tel:* 800-879-9636 *Fax:* 209-296-4515 *E-mail:* sales@volcanopress.com *Web Site:* www.volcanopress.com, pg 275

Ludwig von Mises Institute, 518 W Magnolia Ave, Auburn, AL 36832 *Tel:* 334-321-2100 *Fax:* 334-321-2119 *E-mail:* info@mises.org *Web Site:* www.mises.org, pg 275

Wadsworth Publishing, 20 Davis Dr, Belmont, CA 94002 *Tel:* 650-595-2350 *Fax:* 650-592-3022 *Toll Free Fax:* 800-522-4923 *Web Site:* www.cengage.com, pg 275

Wag's Revue Writers' Contest, 2865 W Lyndale St, Suite 1, Chicago, IL 60647 *E-mail:* editors@wagsrevue.com *Web Site:* www.wagsrevue.com, pg 748

Wake Forest University Press, A5 Tribble Hall, Wake Forest University, Winston-Salem, NC 27109 *Tel:* 336-758-5448 *Fax:* 336-758-5636 *E-mail:* wfupress@wfu.edu *Web Site:* www.wfu.edu/wfupress, pg 276

Walch Education, 40 Walch Dr, Portland, ME 04103-1286 *Tel:* 207-772-2846 *Toll Free Tel:* 800-558-2846 *Fax:* 207-772-3105 *Toll Free Fax:* 888-991-5755 *E-mail:* customerservice@walch.com *Web Site:* www.walch.com, pg 276

Wales Literary Agency Inc, PO Box 9426, Seattle, WA 98109-0426 *Tel:* 206-284-7114 *E-mail:* waleslit@waleslit.com *Web Site:* www.waleslit.com, pg 598

Walker & Co, 175 Fifth Ave, 3rd fl, New York, NY 10010-7728 *Web Site:* www.walkerbooks.com, pg 276

Jayne Walker Literary Services, 1406 Euclid Ave, Suite 1, Berkeley, CA 94708 *Tel:* 510-843-8265, pg 556

Dorothy Wall, Writing Consultant, 3045 Telegraph Ave, Berkeley, CA 94705 *Tel:* 510-486-8008 *E-mail:* dorothy@dorothywall.com *Web Site:* www.dorothywall.com, pg 556

Richard Wall Memorial Award, Roundabout Theatre Co, 231 W 39 St, Suite 1200, New York, NY 10018 *Tel:* 212-719-9393 (ext 351) *E-mail:* info@tla-online.org; tlabookawards@gmail.com *Web Site:* www.tla-online.org, pg 748

Wallace Literary Agency Inc, 301 E 79 St, No 14-J, New York, NY 10075-0951 *Tel:* 212-570-9090 *Fax:* 212-772-8979 *E-mail:* walliter@aol.com, pg 598

Edward Lewis Wallant Book Award, 3 Brighton Rd, West Hartford, CT 06117 *Tel:* 860-232-1421, pg 748

Wambtac Communications, 2323 N Tustin Ave, Suite C-202, Santa Ana, CA 92705 *Tel:* 714-954-0580 *Toll Free Tel:* 800-641-3936 *Fax:* 714-954-0793 (orders) *E-mail:* wambtac@wambtac.com *Web Site:* www.wambtac.com; claudiasuzanne.com (prof servs), pg 556

Ward & Balkin Agency, Inc, 30 Brock Way, South Hadley, MA 01075 *Tel:* 413-322-8697 *Web Site:* www.wardbalkin.com, pg 598

Frederick Warne, 345 Hudson St, New York, NY 10014 *Tel:* 212-366-2000 *E-mail:* online@penguinputnam.com *Web Site:* www.penguinputnam.com; us.penguingroup.com, pg 276

Warren Communications News Inc, 2115 Ward Ct NW, Washington, DC 20037 *Tel:* 202-872-9200 *Toll Free Tel:* 800-771-9202 *Fax:* 202-293-3435; 202-318-8350 *E-mail:* info@warren-news.com; newsroom@warren-news.com *Web Site:* www.warren-news.com, pg 276

Warren Wilson College, MFA Program for Writers, 701 Warren Wilson Rd, Swannanoa, NC 28778 *Tel:* 828-771-3717 *Fax:* 828-771-7005 *E-mail:* mfa@warren-wilson.edu *Web Site:* www.warren-wilson.edu/~mfa, pg 682

Warwick Associates, 18340 Sonoma Hwy, Sonoma, CA 95476 *Tel:* 707-939-9212 *Fax:* 707-938-3515 *E-mail:* warwick@vom.com *Web Site:* www.warwickassociates.com, pg 598

George Washington Book Prize, 101 S Water St, Chestertown, MD 21620 *Tel:* 410-810-7165 *Fax:* 410-810-7175 *Web Site:* starrcenter.washcoll.edu/gw_book_prize, pg 748

Washington State University Press, Cooper Publications Bldg, Grimes Way, Pullman, WA 99164 *Tel:* 509-335-3518; 509-335-7880 (order fulfillment) *Toll Free Tel:* 800-354-7360 *Fax:* 509-335-8568 *E-mail:* wsupress@wsu.edu *Web Site:* wsupress.wsu.edu, pg 276

Water Environment Federation, 601 Wythe St, Alexandria, VA 22314-1994 *Tel:* 703-684-2400 *Toll Free Tel:* 800-666-0206 *Fax:* 703-684-2492 *E-mail:* csc@wef.org (cust serv) *Web Site:* www.wef.org, pg 276

Water Resources Publications LLC, PO Box 630026, Highlands Ranch, CO 80163-0026 *Tel:* 720-873-0171 *Toll Free Tel:* 800-736-2405 *Fax:* 720-873-0173 *Toll Free Fax:* 800-616-1971 *E-mail:* info@wrpllc.com *Web Site:* www.wrpllc.com, pg 277

Water Row Press, PO Box 438, Sudbury, MA 01776 *Tel:* 508-485-8515 *Fax:* 508-229-0885 *E-mail:* contact@waterrowbooks.com *Web Site:* www.waterrowbooks.com, pg 277

WaterBrook Multnomah Publishing Group, 12265 Oracle Blvd, Suite 200, Colorado Springs, CO 80921 *Tel:* 719-590-4999 *Toll Free Tel:* 800-603-7051 (orders) *Fax:* 719-590-8977 *Toll Free Fax:* 800-294-5686 (orders) *E-mail:* info@waterbrookmultnomah.com *Web Site:* waterbrookmultnomah.com, pg 277

Watermark Publishing, 1088 Bishop St, Suite 310, Honolulu, HI 96813 *Tel:* 808-587-7766 *Toll Free Tel:* 866-900-BOOK (900-2665) *Fax:* 808-521-3461 *E-mail:* info@bookshawaii.net *Web Site:* www.bookshawaii.net, pg 277

Waterside Productions Inc, 2055 Oxford Ave, Cardiff, CA 92007 *Tel:* 760-632-9190 *Fax:* 760-632-9295 *E-mail:* admin@waterside.com *Web Site:* www.waterside.com, pg 598

Watkins/Loomis Agency Inc, PO Box 20925, New York, NY 10025 *Tel:* 212-532-0080 *Fax:* 646-383-2449 *E-mail:* assistant@watkinsloomis.com *Web Site:* www.watkinsloomis.com, pg 599

Watson-Guptill Publications, c/o Random House Inc, 1745 Broadway, New York, NY 10019 *Tel:* 212-782-9000 *Fax:* 212-940-7381 *E-mail:* crownbiz@randomhouse.com *Web Site:* www.randomhouse.com/crown/watsonguptill, pg 277

Watson Publishing International LLC, PO Box 1240, Sagamore Beach, MA 02562-1240 *Tel:* 508-888-9113 *Fax:* 508-888-3733 *E-mail:* orders@watsonpublishing.com; orders@shpusa.com *Web Site:* www.shpusa.com; www.watsonpublishing.com, pg 277

The Robert Watson Literary Prizes in Fiction & Poetry, MFA Writing Program, The Greensboro Review, UNC-Greensboro, 3302 MHRA Bldg, Greensboro, NC 27402-6170 *Tel:* 336-334-5459 *Fax:* 336-256-1470 *Web Site:* www.greensbororeview.org, pg 748

Waveland Press Inc, 4180 IL Rte 83, Suite 101, Long Grove, IL 60047-9580 *Tel:* 847-634-0081 *Fax:* 847-634-9501 *E-mail:* info@waveland.com *Web Site:* www.waveland.com, pg 277

Waxman Literary Agency, 80 Fifth Ave, Suite 1101, New York, NY 10011 *Tel:* 212-675-5556 *Fax:* 212-675-1381 *Web Site:* www.waxmanagency.com, pg 599

Wayne State University Press, Leonard N Simons Bldg, 4809 Woodward Ave, Detroit, MI 48201-1309 *Tel:* 313-577-6120 *Toll Free Tel:* 800-978-7323 *Fax:* 313-577-6131 *Web Site:* www.wsupress.wayne.edu, pg 277

Wayside Publishing, 11 Jan Sebastian Dr, Suite 5, Sandwich, MA 02563 *Tel:* 508-833-5096 *Toll Free Tel:* 888-302-2519 *Fax:* 508-833-6284 *E-mail:* wayside@sprintmail.com *Web Site:* www.waysidepublishing.com, pg 277

Web Offset Association (WOA), 200 Deer Run Rd, Sewickley, PA 15143 *Tel:* 412-741-6860 *Toll Free Tel:* 800-910-4283 *Fax:* 412-741-2311 *E-mail:* printing@printing.org *Web Site:* www.printing.org/weboffsetassociation, pg 638

Weigl Educational Publishers Ltd, 6325 Tenth St SE, Calgary, AB T2H 2Z9, Canada *Tel:* 403-233-7747 *Toll Free Tel:* 800-668-0766 *Fax:* 403-233-7769 *Toll Free Fax:* 866-449-3445 *E-mail:* info@weigl.com; orders@weigl.com *Web Site:* www.weigl.ca; www.weigl.com, pg 524

Cherry Weiner Literary Agency, 28 Kipling Way, Manalapan, NJ 07726 *Tel:* 732-446-2096 *Fax:* 732-792-0506 *E-mail:* cherry8486@aol.com, pg 599

The Weingel-Fidel Agency, 310 E 46 St, Suite 21-E, New York, NY 10017 *Tel:* 212-599-2959 *Fax:* 212-286-1986 *E-mail:* queries@theweingel-fidelagency.com, pg 599

Anne Jones Weitzer, 60 Sutton Place South, Suite 9-B South, New York, NY 10022-4168 *Tel:* 212-758-8149 *E-mail:* 47dehaven@msn.com; enamel@yahoo.com, pg 556

Welcome Books®, 6 W 18 St, Unit 4B, New York, NY 10011 *Tel:* 212-989-3200 *Fax:* 212-989-3205 *E-mail:* info@welcomebooks.com *Web Site:* www.welcomebooks.com, pg 278

Welcome Rain Publishers LLC, 217 Thompson St, Suite 473, New York, NY 10012 *Tel:* 212-686-1909 *Web Site:* welcomerain.com, pg 278

Rene Wellek Prize, University of South Carolina, Dept of Languages, Literature & Cultures, Rm 813-A, 1620 College St, Columbia, SC 29208 *Tel:* 803-777-3021 *Fax:* 803-777-3041 *E-mail:* info@acla.org *Web Site:* www.acla.org, pg 748

Wellington Press, 9601-30 Miccosukee Rd, Tallahassee, FL 32309 *Tel:* 850-878-6500 *E-mail:* peacegames@aol.com *Web Site:* www.peacegames.com, pg 278

Wellness Institute/Self Help Books LLC, 515 W North St, Pass Christian, MS 39571-2605 *Tel:* 228-452-0770 *Fax:* 228-452-0775 *Web Site:* selfhelpbooks.com, pg 278

WendyLynn & Co, 504 Wilson Rd, Annapolis, MD 21401 *Tel:* 410-224-2729; 410-507-1059 *Web Site:* wendylynn.com, pg 603

Wergle Flomp Humor Poetry Contest, 351 Pleasant St, PMB 222, Northampton, MA 01060-3961 *Tel:* 413-320-1847 *Toll Free Tel:* 866-WINWRIT (946-9748) *Fax:* 413-280-0539 *Web Site:* www.winningwriters.com, pg 748

Eliot Werner Publications Inc, 31 Willow Lane, Clinton Corners, NY 12514 *Tel:* 845-266-4241 *Fax:* 845-266-3317 *E-mail:* eliotwerner@optonline.net *Web Site:* www.eliotwerner.com, pg 278

Toby Wertheim, 240 E 76 St, New York, NY 10021 *Tel:* 212-472-8587 *E-mail:* tobywertheim@yahoo.com, pg 556

Wescott Cove Publishing Co, 1227 S Florida Ave, Rockledge, FL 32955 *Tel:* 321-690-2224 *Fax:* 321-690-0853 *E-mail:* customerservice@farhorizonsmedia.com *Web Site:* www.farhorizonsmedia.com, pg 278

Wesley-Logan Prize in African Diaspora History, 400 "A" St SE, Washington, DC 20003-3889 *Tel:* 202-544-2422 *Fax:* 202-544-8307 *E-mail:* awards@historians.org *Web Site:* www.historians.org, pg 748

Wesleyan Publishing House, 13300 Olio Rd, Fishers, IN 46037 *Tel:* 317-774-3853 *Toll Free Tel:* 800-493-7539 *Fax:* 317-774-3865 *Toll Free Fax:* 800-788-3535 *E-mail:* wph@wesleyan.org *Web Site:* www.wesleyan.org/wph, pg 278

Wesleyan University Press, 215 Long Lane, Middletown, CT 06459-0433 *Tel:* 860-685-7711 *Fax:* 860-685-7712 *Web Site:* www.wesleyan.edu/wespress, pg 278

Wesleyan Writers Conference, c/o Wesleyan University, 294 High St, Middletown, CT 06459 *Tel:* 860-685-3604 *Fax:* 860-685-2441 *Web Site:* www.wesleyan.edu/writing/conference, pg 674

West Academic Publishing, 610 Opperman Dr, Eagan, MN 55123 *Tel:* 651-687-7000 *Toll Free Tel:* 800-328-2209 (bookstore orders); 800-313-WEST (313-9378) *Toll Free Fax:* 800-213-2323 (bookstore orders) *E-mail:* westacademic@thomsonreuters.com *Web Site:* www.westacademic.com, pg 278

West Virginia University Press, West Virginia University, PO Box 6295, Morgantown, WV 26506-6295 *Tel:* 304-293-8400 *Toll Free Tel:* 866-WVU-PRES (988-7737) *Fax:* 304-293-6585 *E-mail:* press@wvu.edu *Web Site:* www.wvupress.com, pg 278

Westcliffe Publishers Inc, 3360 Mitchell Lane, Suite E, Boulder, CO 80301 *Toll Free Tel:* 800-258-5830 *Fax:* 303-443-9687 *E-mail:* books@bigearthpublishing.com *Web Site:* www.bigearthpublishing.com/westcliffe-publishers, pg 279

Western Heritage Awards (Wrangler Award), 1700 NE 63 St, Oklahoma City, OK 73111 *Tel:* 405-478-2250 *Fax:* 405-478-4714 *E-mail:* info@nationalcowboymuseum.org *Web Site:* www.nationalcowboymuseum.org, pg 748

Western Magazine Awards Foundation, 875 Prairie Ave, Port Coquitlam, BC V3B 1R9, Canada *Tel:* 604-945-3711 *E-mail:* wma@direct.ca *Web Site:* www.westernmagazineawards.ca, pg 748

Western Pennsylvania Genealogical Society, 4400 Forbes Ave, Pittsburgh, PA 15213-4080 *Tel:* 412-687-6811 (answering machine) *E-mail:* info@wpgs.org *Web Site:* www.wpgs.org, pg 279

Western Reflections Publishing Co, 951 N Hwy 149, Lake City, CO 81235 *Tel:* 970-944-0110 *Toll Free Tel:* 800-993-4490 *Fax:* 970-944-0273 *E-mail:* publisher@westernreflectionspublishing.com *Web Site:* www.westernreflectionspublishing.com, pg 279

Western States Arts Federation, 1743 Wazee St, Suite 300, Denver, CO 80202 *Tel:* 303-629-1166 *Toll Free Tel:* 888-562-7232 *Fax:* 303-629-9717 *E-mail:* staff@westaf.org *Web Site:* www.westaf.org, pg 641

Western Writers of America Inc (WWA), 271 CR 219, Encampment, WY 82325 *Tel:* 307-329-8942 *Fax:* 307-327-5465 *Web Site:* www.westernwriters.org, pg 638

Westernlore Press, PO Box 35305, Tucson, AZ 85740-5305 *Tel:* 520-297-5491 *Fax:* 520-297-1722, pg 279

Westminster John Knox Press, 100 Witherspoon St, Louisville, KY 40202-1396 *Tel:* 502-569-5052 *Toll Free Tel:* 800-227-2872 (US only) *Fax:* 502-569-8308 *Toll Free Fax:* 800-541-5113 (US & CN) *E-mail:* wjk@wjkbooks.com; customer_service@wjkbooks.com *Web Site:* www.wjkbooks.com, pg 279

Hilary Weston Writers' Trust Prize for Nonfiction, 90 Richmond St E, Suite 200, Toronto, ON M5C 1P1, Canada *Tel:* 416-504-8222 *Toll Free Tel:* 877-906-6548 *Fax:* 416-504-9090 *E-mail:* info@writerstrust.com *Web Site:* www.writerstrust.com, pg 748

Westview Press, 2465 Central Ave, Boulder, CO 80301 *Tel:* 303-444-3541 *Fax:* 720-406-7336 *E-mail:* westview.orders@perseusbooks.com *Web Site:* www.perseusbooksgroup.com; www.westviewpress.com, pg 279

Westwood Creative Artists Ltd, 94 Harbord St, Toronto, ON M5S 1G6, Canada *Tel:* 416-964-3302 *Fax:* 416-975-9209 *E-mail:* wca_office@wcaltd.com *Web Site:* www.wcaltd.com, pg 599

Rosemary Wetherold, 4507 Cliffstone Cove, Austin, TX 78735 *Tel:* 512-892-1606 *E-mail:* roses@ix.netcom.com, pg 556

Charles A Weyerhauser Book Award, 701 William Vickers Ave, Durham, NC 27701-3162 *Tel:* 919-682-9319 *Fax:* 919-682-2349 *Web Site:* www.foresthistory.org, pg 749

WH&O International, 892 Worcester St, Suite 130, Wellesley, MA 02482 *Tel:* 508-525-5370 *Fax:* 508-525-5370 *E-mail:* whobooks@hotmail.com *Web Site:* www.whobooks.com, pg 279

Wheatherstone Press, PO Box 257, Portland, OR 97207-0257 *Tel:* 503-244-8929 *Fax:* 503-244-9795 *E-mail:* relocntr@nwlink.com *Web Site:* www.wheatherstonepress.com, pg 280

Helen Rippier Wheeler, 1909 Cedar St, Suite 212, Berkeley, CA 94709-2037 *Tel:* 510-549-2970 *E-mail:* pen136@dslextreme.com, pg 556

Barbara Mlotek Whelehan, 7064 SE Cricket Ct, Stuart, FL 34997 *Tel:* 954-554-0765 (cell); 772-463-0818 (home) *E-mail:* barbarawhelehan@bellsouth.net, pg 557

Whidbey Island Writers Conference, 5577 Vanbarr Place, Freeland, WA 98249 *Tel:* 360-331-0307 *E-mail:* nila@whidbey.com *Web Site:* www.nila.edu, pg 674

Whitaker House, 1030 Hunt Valley Circle, New Kensington, PA 15068 *Tel:* 724-334-7000 *Toll Free Tel:* 877-793-9800 *Fax:* 724-334-1200 *Toll Free Fax:* 800-765-1960 *E-mail:* publisher@whitakerhouse.com *Web Site:* whitakerhouse.com, pg 280

White Cloud Press, 300 E Hersey St, Suite 11, Ashland, OR 97520 *Tel:* 541-488-6415 *Toll Free Tel:* 800-380-8286 *Fax:* 541-482-7708 *E-mail:* info@whitecloudpress.com *Web Site:* www.whitecloudpress.com, pg 280

Martin L White, 10511 Preston St, Westchester, IL 60154-5311 *Tel:* 708-492-1253 *Fax:* 708-492-1253 *E-mail:* mlw@mlwindexing.com *Web Site:* www.mlwindexing.com, pg 557

White Pine Press, PO Box 236, Buffalo, NY 14201 *Tel:* 716-627-4665 *Fax:* 716-627-4665 *E-mail:* wpine@whitepine.org *Web Site:* www.whitepine.org, pg 280

William Allen White Children's Book Awards, William Allen White Library, 1200 Commercial St, Emporia, KS 66801-5092 *Tel:* 620-341-5208 *Toll Free Tel:* 877-613-7323 *Fax:* 620-341-6208 *E-mail:* wawbookaward@emporia.edu *Web Site:* waw.emporia.edu, pg 749

White Wolf Publishing Inc, 250 Ponce de Leon Ave, Suite 700, Decatur, GA 30030 *Tel:* 404-292-1819 *Toll Free Tel:* 800-454-9653 *E-mail:* questions@white-wolf.com *Web Site:* www.white-wolf.com, pg 280

Whitecap Books Ltd, 314 W Cordova St, Suite 210, Vancouver, BC V6B 1E8, Canada *Tel:* 604-681-6181 *Toll Free Tel:* 800-387-9776 *Toll Free Fax:* 800-260-9777 *Web Site:* www.whitecap.ca, pg 524

Whitehorse Press, 107 E Conway Rd, Center Conway, NH 03813-4012 *Tel:* 603-356-6556 *Toll Free Tel:* 800-531-1133 *Fax:* 603-356-6590 *E-mail:* customerservice@whitehorsepress.com *Web Site:* www.whitehorsebooks.com, pg 280

Whitehorse Productions, 2417 W 35 Ave, Denver, CO 80211 *Tel:* 303-433-4400, pg 557

Whiting Writers' Awards, 1133 Avenue of the Americas, 22nd fl, New York, NY 10036-6710 *Tel:* 212-336-2138 *E-mail:* info@whitingfoundation.org *Web Site:* www.whitingfoundation.org, pg 749

Walt Whitman Award, 75 Maiden Lane, Suite 901, New York, NY 10038 *Tel:* 212-274-0343 *Fax:* 212-274-9427 *E-mail:* academy@poets.org *Web Site:* www.poets.org, pg 749

Whittier Publications Inc, 3115 Long Beach Rd, Oceanside, NY 11572 *Tel:* 516-432-8120 *Toll Free Tel:* 800-897-TEXT (897-8398) *Fax:* 516-889-0341 *E-mail:* info@whitbooks.com, pg 280

Whole Person Associates Inc, 210 W Michigan St, Duluth, MN 55802-1908 *Tel:* 218-727-0500 *Toll Free Tel:* 800-247-6789 *Fax:* 218-727-0505 *E-mail:* books@wholeperson.com *Web Site:* www.wholeperson.com, pg 280

Jon Whyte Memorial Essay Prize, 11759 Groat Rd, Edmonton, AB T5M 3K6, Canada *Tel:* 780-422-8174 *Toll Free Tel:* 800-665-5354 (AB only) *Fax:* 780-422-2663 (attn WGA) *E-mail:* mail@writersguild.ab.ca *Web Site:* www.writersguild.ab.ca, pg 749

Wichita State University Playwriting Contest, 1845 Fairmount St, Wichita, KS 67260-0153 *Tel:* 316-978-3360 *Fax:* 316-978-3202 *Web Site:* www.wichita.edu, pg 749

Eleanor B Widdoes, 417 W 120 St, New York, NY 10027 *Tel:* 212-870-3051; 917-886-6401, pg 557

Wide World of Maps Inc, 2626 W Indian School Rd, Phoenix, AZ 85017 *Tel:* 602-279-2324 *Toll Free Tel:* 800-279-7654 *Fax:* 602-279-2350 *E-mail:* sales@maps4u.com *Web Site:* www.maps4u.com, pg 280

Wide World Publishing, PO Box 476, San Carlos, CA 94070-0476 *Tel:* 650-593-2839 *Fax:* 650-595-0802 *E-mail:* wwpbl@aol.com *Web Site:* wideworldpublishing.com, pg 280

Markus Wiener Publishers Inc, 231 Nassau St, Princeton, NJ 08542 *Tel:* 609-921-1141 *Fax:* 609-921-1140 *E-mail:* publisher@markuswiener.com *Web Site:* www.markuswiener.com, pg 280

Michael Wiese Productions, 12400 Ventura Blvd, No 1111, Studio City, CA 91604 *Tel:* 818-379-8799 *Toll Free Tel:* 800-833-5738 (orders) *Fax:* 818-986-3408 *E-mail:* mwpsales@mwp.com; fulfillment@portcity.com *Web Site:* www.mwp.com, pg 281

The Laura Ingalls Wilder Medal, 50 E Huron St, Chicago, IL 60611-2795 *Tel:* 312-280-2163 *Toll Free Tel:* 800-545-2433 *Fax:* 312-440-9374 *E-mail:* alsc@ala.org *Web Site:* www.ala.org/alsc, pg 749

Wilderness Adventures Press Inc, 45 Buckskin Rd, Belgrade, MT 59714 *Tel:* 406-388-0112 *Toll Free Tel:* 866-400-2012 *E-mail:* books@wildadvpress.com *Web Site:* store.wildadvpress.com, pg 281

Wildflower Press, Oakbrook Press, 3301 S Valley Dr, Rapid City, SD 57703 *Tel:* 605-381-6385 *Fax:* 605-343-8733 *E-mail:* info@wildflowerpress.org; bookorder@wildflowerpress.org *Web Site:* www.wildflowerpress.org, pg 281

Wildlife Education Ltd, 2418 Noyes St, Evanston, IL 60201 *Toll Free Tel:* 800-477-5034 *E-mail:* owls5@zoobooks.com; helpdesk@zoobooks.com *Web Site:* www.zoobooks.com; wildlife-ed.com, pg 281

Wildside Press, 414 Hungerford Dr, Suite 234, Rockville, MD 20850 *Tel:* 301-762-1305 *Fax:* 301-762-1306 *E-mail:* wildside@wildsidepress.com *Web Site:* www.wildsidebooks.com, pg 281

Wiley-Blackwell, Commerce Place, 350 Main St, Malden, MA 02148 *Tel:* 781-388-8200 *Fax:* 781-388-8210 *E-mail:* info@wiley.com *Web Site:* www.wiley.com, pg 281

John Wiley & Sons Canada Ltd, 5353 Dundas St W, Suite 400, Toronto, ON M9B 6H8, Canada *Tel:* 416-236-4433 *Toll Free Tel:* 800-467-4797 (orders only) *Fax:* 416-236-8743 (cust serv); 416-236-4447 *Toll Free Fax:* 800-565-6802 (orders) *E-mail:* canada@wiley.com *Web Site:* www.wiley.ca, pg 525

John Wiley & Sons Inc, 111 River St, Hoboken, NJ 07030-5774 *Tel:* 201-748-6000 *Toll Free Tel:* 800-225-5945 (cust serv) *Fax:* 201-748-6088 *E-mail:* info@wiley.com *Web Site:* www.wiley.com, pg 281

John Wiley & Sons Inc Higher Education, 111 River St, Hoboken, NJ 07030-5774 *Tel:* 201-748-6000 *Toll Free Tel:* 800-225-5945 (cust serv) *Fax:* 201-748-6008 *E-mail:* info@wiley.com *Web Site:* www.wiley.com, pg 281

John Wiley & Sons Inc Professional/Trade Group, 111 River St, Hoboken, NJ 07030 *Tel:* 201-748-6000 *Toll Free Tel:* 800-225-5945 (cust serv) *Fax:* 201-748-6088 *E-mail:* info@wiley.com *Web Site:* www.wiley.com, pg 281

John Wiley & Sons Inc Scientific, Technical, Medical & Scholarly (STMS), 111 River St, Hoboken, NJ 07030 *Tel:* 201-748-6000 *Toll Free Tel:* 800-225-5945 (cust serv) *Fax:* 201-748-6088 *E-mail:* info@wiley.com *Web Site:* www.wiley.com, pg 282

Wilfrid Laurier University Press, 75 University Ave W, Waterloo, ON N2L 3C5, Canada *Tel:* 519-884-0710 (ext 6124) *Toll Free Tel:* 866-836-5551 *Fax:* 519-725-1399 *E-mail:* press@wlu.ca *Web Site:* www.wlupress.wlu.ca, pg 525

Wilkinson Studios Inc, 1121 E Main St, Suite 310, St Charles, IL 60174 *Tel:* 630-549-0504 *Web Site:* www.wilkinsonstudios.com, pg 603

Willamette Writers, 2108 Buck St, West Linn, OR 97068 *Tel:* 503-305-6729 *Fax:* 503-344-6174 *E-mail:* wilwrite@willamettewriters.com *Web Site:* www.willamettewriters.com, pg 638

Willamette Writers' Conference, 2108 Buck St, West Linn, OR 97068 *Tel:* 503-305-6729 *Fax:* 503-344-6174 *E-mail:* wilwrite@willamettewriters.com *Web Site:* www.willamettewriters.com, pg 674

William Carey Library Publishers, 1605 E Elizabeth St, Pasadena, CA 91104 *Tel:* 626-720-8210 *Toll Free Tel:* 866-732-6657 (orders & cust serv) *E-mail:* assistant@wclbooks.com *Web Site:* www.missionbooks.org, pg 282

William Flanagan Memorial Creative Persons Center, 14 Harrison St, New York, NY 10013 *Tel:* 212-226-2020 *Fax:* 212-226-5551 *E-mail:* info@albeefoundation.org *Web Site:* www.albeefoundation.org, pg 749

William K Bradford Publishing Co Inc, 31 Main St, Maynard, MA 01754 *Toll Free Tel:* 800-421-2009 *Fax:* 978-897-1806 *E-mail:* wkb@wkbradford.com *Web Site:* www.wkbradford.com, pg 282

Williams & Company Book Publishers, 1317 Pine Ridge Dr, Savannah, GA 31406 *Tel:* 912-352-0404 *E-mail:* bookpub@comcast.net *Web Site:* www.pubmart.com, pg 282

Oscar Williams/Gene Derwood Award, 909 Third Ave, New York, NY 10022 *Tel:* 212-686-0010 *Fax:* 212-532-8528 *E-mail:* info@nycommunitytrust.org *Web Site:* www.nycommunitytrust.org, pg 749

William Carlos Williams Award, 15 Gramercy Park S, New York, NY 10003 *Tel:* 212-254-9628 *Fax:* 212-673-2352 *Web Site:* www.poetrysociety.org, pg 749

Willow Creek Press, 9931 Hwy 70 W, Minocqua, WI 54548 *Tel:* 715-358-7010 *Toll Free Tel:* 800-850-9453 *Fax:* 715-358-2807 *E-mail:* info@willowcreekpress.com *Web Site:* www.willowcreekpress.com, pg 282

Wilshire Book Co, 9731 Variel Ave, Chatsworth, CA 91311-4315 *Tel:* 818-700-1522 *Fax:* 818-700-1527 *Web Site:* www.mpowers.com, pg 282

Gary Wilson Award for Short Fiction, Texas Christian University, Dept of English, TCU Box 297270, Fort Worth, TX 76129 *Tel:* 817-257-5907 *Fax:* 817-257-7709 *E-mail:* descant@tcu.edu *Web Site:* www.descant.tcu.edu, pg 750

H W Wilson, 10 Estes St, Ipswich, MA 01938 *Tel:* 978-356-6500 *Toll Free Tel:* 800-653-2726 (US & CN) *Fax:* 978-356-6565 *E-mail:* information@ebscohost.com *Web Site:* www.ebscohost.com, pg 282

H W Wilson Co Indexing Award, 10200 W 44 Ave, Suite 304, Wheat Ridge, CO 80033 *Tel:* 303-463-2887 *Fax:* 303-422-8894 *E-mail:* wilsonaward@asindexing.org *Web Site:* www.asindexing.org, pg 750

H W Wilson Foundation, 10 Estes St, Ipswich, MA 01938 *Tel:* 978-356-6500 *Toll Free Tel:* 800-653-2726 (US & CN) *Fax:* 978-356-6565 *E-mail:* information@ebscohost.com *Web Site:* www.ebscohost.com, pg 641

The H W Wilson Library Staff Development Grant, 50 E Huron St, Chicago, IL 60611 *Tel:* 312-280-3247 *Toll Free Tel:* 800-545-2433 (ext 3247) *Fax:* 312-944-3897; 312-440-9379 *E-mail:* awards@ala.org *Web Site:* www.ala.org, pg 750

Wimbledon Music Inc & Trigram Music Inc, 1801 Century Park E, Suite 2400, Los Angeles, CA 90067 *Tel:* 310-556-9683 *Fax:* 310-277-1278 *E-mail:* irishmex127@gmail.com *Web Site:* www.wimbtri.net, pg 282

Wimmer Cookbooks, 4650 Shelby Air Dr, Memphis, TN 38118 *Tel:* 901-362-8900 *Toll Free Tel:* 800-363-1771 *E-mail:* wimmer@wimmerco.com *Web Site:* www.wimmerco.com, pg 282

Wind Canyon Books, PO Box 7035, Stockton, CA 95267 *Tel:* 209-956-1600 *Toll Free Tel:* 800-952-7007 *Fax:* 209-956-9424 *Toll Free Fax:* 888-289-7086 *E-mail:* books@windcanyonbooks.com *Web Site:* www.windcanyonbooks.com, pg 282

Herbert Warren Wind Book Award, 77 Liberty Corner Rd, Far Hills, NJ 07931-0708 *Tel:* 908-234-2300 *Fax:* 908-470-5013 *Web Site:* www.usga.org, pg 750

Windbreak House Writing Retreats, PO Box 169, Hermosa, SD 57744-0169 *Tel:* 307-630-4003 *E-mail:* info@windbreakhouse.com *Web Site:* www.windbreakhouse.com, pg 674

Windhaven®, 68 Hunting Rd, Auburn, NH 03032 *Tel:* 603-483-0929 *Fax:* 603-483-8022 *E-mail:* info@windhaven.com *Web Site:* www.windhaven.com, pg 557

Windsor Books, 260 Montauk Hwy, Suite 5, Bayshore, NY 11706 *Tel:* 631-665-6688 *Toll Free Tel:* 800-321-5934 *E-mail:* windsor.books@att.net *Web Site:* www.windsorpublishing.com, pg 282

Windward Publishing, 8075 215 St W, Lakeville, MN 55044 *Tel:* 952-469-6699 *Toll Free Tel:* 800-846-7027 *Fax:* 952-469-1968 *Toll Free Fax:* 800-330-6232 *E-mail:* info@finneyco.com *Web Site:* www.finneyco.com, pg 282

The Wine Appreciation Guild Ltd, 360 Swift Ave, Suites 30 & 34, South San Francisco, CA 94080 *Tel:* 650-866-3020 *Toll Free Tel:* 800-231-9463 *Fax:* 650-866-3513 *E-mail:* info@wineappreciation.com *Web Site:* www.wineappreciation.com, pg 283

WinePress Publishing, 1730 Railroad St, Enumclaw, WA 98022 *Tel:* 360-802-9758 *Toll Free Tel:* 800-326-4674 *Fax:* 360-802-9992 *Web Site:* www.winepresspublishing.com, pg 283

Wings Press, 627 E Guenther, San Antonio, TX 78210-1134 *Tel:* 210-271-7805 *Fax:* 210-271-7805 *E-mail:* press@wingspress.com *Web Site:* www.wingspress.com, pg 283

WingSpread Publishers, 2020 State Rd, Camp Hill, PA 17011 *Tel:* 717-761-7044 *Toll Free Tel:* 800-884-4571 *Fax:* 717-761-7273 *E-mail:* customerservice@echurchdepot.com *Web Site:* wingspreadpublishers.com, pg 283

The Laurence L & Thomas Winship/PEN New England Award, MIT 14N-221A, 77 Massachusetts Ave, Cambridge, MA 02139 *Tel:* 617-324-1729 *E-mail:* pen-ne@lesley.edu *Web Site:* www.pen-ne.org, pg 750

Justin Winsor Prize for Library History Essay, 50 E Huron St, Chicago, IL 60611 *Tel:* 312-280-4283 *Toll Free Tel:* 800-545-2433 (ext 4283) *Fax:* 312-280-4392 *Web Site:* www.ala.org, pg 750

Winter Springs Editorial Services, 2263 Turk Rd, Doylestown, PA 18901-2964 *Tel:* 215-340-9052 *Fax:* 215-340-9052, pg 557

Winter Words Apres Ski for the Mind, 110 E Hallam St, Suite 116, Aspen, CO 81611 *Tel:* 970-925-3122 *Fax:* 970-920-5700 *E-mail:* info@aspenwriters.org *Web Site:* www.aspenwriters.org, pg 674

Winters Publishing, 705 E Washington St, Greensburg, IN 47240 *Tel:* 812-663-4948 *Toll Free Tel:* 800-457-3230 *Fax:* 812-663-4948 *Toll Free Fax:* 800-457-3230 *E-mail:* winterspublishing@gmail.com *Web Site:* www.winterspublishing.com, pg 283

Winterthur Museum & Country Estate, 5105 Kennett Pike, Wilmington, DE 19735 *Tel:* 302-888-4663 *Toll Free Tel:* 800-448-3883 *Fax:* 302-888-4950 *Web Site:* www.winterthur.org, pg 283

Wisconsin Annual Fall Conferencee, PO Box 259303, Madison, WI 53725 *Tel:* 608-278-0692 *Web Site:* www.scbwi.org; www.scbwi-wi.com, pg 674

Wisconsin Dept of Public Instruction, 125 S Webster St, Madison, WI 53703 *Tel:* 608-266-2188 *Toll Free Tel:* 800-441-4563 *Fax:* 608-267-9110 *E-mail:* pubsales@dpi.state.wi.us *Web Site:* www.dpi.wi.gov/pubsales, pg 283

Wisdom Publications Inc, 199 Elm St, Somerville, MA 02144 *Tel:* 617-776-7416 *Toll Free Tel:* 800-272-4050 (orders) *Fax:* 617-776-7841 *E-mail:* info@wisdompubs.org *Web Site:* www.wisdompubs.org, pg 283

Wish Publishing, PO Box 10337, Terre Haute, IN 47801-0337 *Web Site:* www.wishpublishing.com, pg 283

Wittenborn Art Books, 1109 Geary Blvd, San Francisco, CA 94109 *Tel:* 415-292-6500 *Toll Free Tel:* 800-660-6403 *Fax:* 415-292-6594 *E-mail:* wittenborn@art-books.com *Web Site:* www.art-books.com, pg 284

Paul A Witty Short Story Award, 800 Barksdale Rd, Newark, DE 19711-3204 *Tel:* 302-731-1600 *Toll Free Tel:* 800-336-7323 (US & CN) *Fax:* 302-731-1057 *E-mail:* committees@reading.org *Web Site:* www.reading.org, pg 750

Wizards of the Coast LLC, 1600 Lind Ave SW, Renton, WA 98057-3305 *Tel:* 425-226-6500 *Web Site:* www.wizards.com/dnd/novels.aspx, pg 284

WLA Literary Award, 4610 S Biltmore Lane, Madison, WI 53718 *Tel:* 608-245-3640 *Fax:* 608-245-3646 *Web Site:* www.wla.lib.wi.us, pg 750

WME, 1325 Avenue of the Americas, New York, NY 10019 *Tel:* 212-586-5100 *Fax:* 212-246-3583 *E-mail:* wma@interport.net *Web Site:* www.wma.com, pg 599

WNBA Pannell Award for Excellence in Children's Bookselling, 435 W 23 St, Suite 8-C, New York, NY 10011 *Tel:* 212-242-6930 *E-mail:* pannellaward@gmail.com *Web Site:* www.wnba-books.org; www.NationalReadingGroupMonth.org; www.wnba-books.org/awards, pg 750

Alan Wofsy Fine Arts, 1109 Geary Blvd, San Francisco, CA 94109 *Tel:* 415-292-6500 *Toll Free Tel:* 800-660-6403 *Fax:* 415-292-6594 (off & cust serv); 415-512-0130 (acctg) *E-mail:* order@art-books.com (orders); editeur@earthlink.net (edit); beauxarts@earthlink.net (cust serv) *Web Site:* www.art-books.com, pg 284

Wolf Pirate Project Inc, 337 Lost Lake Dr, Divide, CO 80814 *Tel:* 305-333-3186 *E-mail:* contact@wolfpiratebooks.com; workshop@wolfpiratebooks.com *Web Site:* www.wolf-pirate.com, pg 557

Thomas Wolfe Fiction Prize, PO Box 21591, Winston-Salem, NC 27120-1591 *E-mail:* mail@ncwriters.org *Web Site:* www.ncwriters.org, pg 750

Nancy Wolff, 125 Gates Ave, No 14, Montclair, NJ 07042 *Tel:* 973-746-7415 *E-mail:* wolffindex@aol.com, pg 557

Tobias Wolff Award for Fiction, Mail Stop 9053, Western Washington University, Bellingham, WA 98225 *Tel:* 360-650-4863 *E-mail:* bhreview@wwu.edu *Web Site:* www.bhreview.org, pg 750

Wolters Kluwer US Corp, 2700 Lake Cook Rd, Riverwoods, IL 60015 *Tel:* 847-267-7000 *Fax:* 847-580-5192 *Web Site:* www.wolterskluwer.com, pg 284

Women Who Write, PO Box 652, Madison, NJ 07940-0652 *E-mail:* info@womenwhowrite.org *Web Site:* www.womenwhowrite.org, pg 638

Women's National Book Association Award, PO Box 237, FDR Sta, New York, NY 10150-0231 *Tel:* 212-208-4629 *Fax:* 212-208-4629 *E-mail:* publicity@bookbuzz.com *Web Site:* www.wnba-books.org; www.NationalReadingGroupMonth.org, pg 751

Women's National Book Association Inc, PO Box 237, FDR Sta, New York, NY 10150-0231 *Tel:* 212-208-4629 *Fax:* 212-208-4629 *E-mail:* publicity@bookbuzz.com; info@wnba.org *Web Site:* www.wnba-books.org; www.NationalReadingGroupMonth.org, pg 638

The J Howard & Barbara M J Wood Prize, 444 N Michigan Ave, Suite 1850, Chicago, IL 60611-4034 *Tel:* 312-787-7070 *Fax:* 312-787-6650 *E-mail:* editors@poetrymagazine.org *Web Site:* poetryfoundation.org, pg 751

Wood Lake Publishing Inc, 9590 Jim Bailey Rd, Kelowna, BC V4V 1R2, Canada *Tel:* 250-766-2778 *Toll Free Tel:* 800-663-2775 (orders) *Fax:* 250-766-2736 *Toll Free Fax:* 888-841-9991 (orders) *E-mail:* info@woodlake.com; customerservice@woodlake.com *Web Site:* www.woodlakebooks.com, pg 525

Woodbine House, 6510 Bells Mill Rd, Bethesda, MD 20817 *Tel:* 301-897-3570 *Toll Free Tel:* 800-843-7323 *Fax:* 301-897-5838 *E-mail:* info@woodbinehouse.com *Web Site:* www.woodbinehouse.com, pg 284

Woodland Publishing Inc, 515 S 700 E, Suite 2D, Salt Lake City, UT 84102 *Toll Free Tel:* 800-277-3243 *Fax:* 801-334-1913 *E-mail:* info@woodlandpublishing.com *Web Site:* www.woodlandpublishing.com, pg 284

The Woodrow Wilson Center Press, One Woodrow Wilson Plaza, 1300 Pennsylvania Ave NW, Washington, DC 20004-3027 *Tel:* 202-691-4000 *Fax:* 202-691-4001 *E-mail:* press@wilsoncenter.org *Web Site:* wilsoncenter.org, pg 284

Carter G Woodson Book Awards, 8555 16 St, Suite 500, Silver Spring, MD 20910 *Tel:* 301-588-1800 *Toll Free Tel:* 800-296-7840; 800-683-0812 (pubn orders) *Fax:* 301-588-2049 *E-mail:* excellence@ncss.org; publications@ncss.org *Web Site:* www.socialstudies.org, pg 751

WoodstockArts, PO Box 1342, Woodstock, NY 12498 *Tel:* 845-679-8111 *E-mail:* info@woodstockarts.com *Web Site:* www.woodstockarts.com, pg 284

Word Works Washington Prize, Adirondack Community College, Dearlove Hall, 640 Bay Rd, Queensbury, NY 12804 *Fax:* 301-581-9443 *E-mail:* editor@wordworksbooks.org *Web Site:* www.wordworksbooks.org, pg 751

WordCo Indexing Services Inc, 49 Church St, Norwich, CT 06360 *Tel:* 860-886-2532 *Toll Free Tel:* 877-WORDCO-3 (967-3263) *Fax:* 860-886-1155 *E-mail:* office@wordco.com *Web Site:* www.wordco.com, pg 557

WordForce Communications, 79 Jameson Ave, Suite 401, Toronto, ON M6K 2W7, Canada *Tel:* 416-534-9881 *Toll Free Tel:* 866-WRD-FORCE (973-3672) *E-mail:* info@wordforce.ca *Web Site:* www.wordforce.ca, pg 557

Words into Print, 131 Fifth Ave, Suite 501, New York, NY 10003 *Tel:* 212-741-1393 *Fax:* 419-441-1393 *E-mail:* query@wordsintoprint.org *Web Site:* www.wordsintoprint.org, pg 557

Wordsworth Communication, PO Box 9781, Alexandria, VA 22304-0468 *Tel:* 703-642-8775 *Fax:* 703-642-8775, pg 557

WordWitlox, 70 Grainger Crescent, Ajax, ON L1T 4Y6, Canada *Tel:* 647-505-9673 *Fax:* 905-239-3604 *Web Site:* www.wordwitlox.com, pg 557

Workers Compensation Research Institute, 955 Massachusetts Ave, Cambridge, MA 02139 *Tel:* 617-661-9274 *Fax:* 617-661-9284 *E-mail:* wcri@wcrinet.org *Web Site:* www.wcrinet.org, pg 284

Working With Words, 9720 SW Eagle Ct, Beaverton, OR 97008 *Tel:* 503-644-4317 *E-mail:* editor@zzz.com, pg 557

Workman Publishing Co Inc, 225 Varick St, 9th fl, New York, NY 10014-4381 *Tel:* 212-254-5900 *Toll Free Tel:* 800-722-7202 *Fax:* 212-254-8098 *E-mail:* info@workman.com *Web Site:* www.workman.com, pg 285

World Almanac®, 132 W 31 St, New York, NY 10001 *Toll Free Tel:* 800-322-8755 *E-mail:* almanac@factsonfile.com *Web Site:* www.worldalmanac.com, pg 285

World Bank Publications, Office of the Publisher, 1818 "H" St NW, U-11-1104, Washington, DC 20433 *Tel:* 202-458-4497 *Toll Free Tel:* 800-645-7247 (cust serv) *Fax:* 202-522-2631; 202-614-1237 *E-mail:* books@worldbank.org; pubrights@worldbank.org (foreign rts) *Web Site:* www.worldbank.org/publications; publications.worldbank.org, pg 285

World Book Inc, 233 N Michigan, Suite 2000, Chicago, IL 60601 *Tel:* 312-729-5800 *Toll Free Tel:* 800-967-5325 (consumer sales, US); 800-463-8845 (consumer sales, CN); 800-975-3250 (school & lib sales, US); 800-837-5365 (school & lib sales, CN); 866-866-5200 (web sales) *Fax:* 312-729-5600; 312-729-5606 *Toll Free Fax:* 800-433-9330 (school & lib sales, US); 888-690-4002 (school lib sales, CN) *Web Site:* www.worldbook.com, pg 285

World Citizens, PO Box 131, Mill Valley, CA 94942-0131 *Tel:* 415-380-8020 *Toll Free Tel:* 800-247-6553 (orders only), pg 285

World Class Speakers & Entertainers, 5200 Kanan Rd, Suite 210, Agoura Hills, CA 91301 *Tel:* 818-991-5400 *Fax:* 818-991-2226 *E-mail:* wcse@wcspeakers.com *Web Site:* www.wcspeakers.com, pg 606

World Fantasy Awards, PO Box 43, Mukilteo, WA 98275-0043 *Web Site:* www.worldfantasy.org, pg 751

World Resources Institute, 10 "G" St NE, Suite 800, Washington, DC 20002 *Tel:* 202-729-7600 *Fax:* 202-729-7610 *Web Site:* www.wri.org, pg 285

World Scientific Publishing Co Inc, 27 Warren St, Suite 401-402, Hackensack, NJ 07601 *Tel:* 201-487-9655 *Toll Free Tel:* 800-227-7562 *Fax:* 201-487-9656 *Toll Free Fax:* 888-977-2665 *E-mail:* wspc@wspc.com *Web Site:* www.wspc.com, pg 285

World Trade Press, 800 Lindberg Lane, Suite 190, Petaluma, CA 94952 *Tel:* 707-778-1124 *Toll Free Tel:* 800-833-8586 *Fax:* 707-778-1329 *Web Site:* www.worldtradepress.com, pg 286

World Vision Resources, 800 W Chestnut Ave, Monrovia, CA 91016-3198 *Tel:* 626-303-8811; 909-463-2998 (intl orders) *Toll Free Tel:* 800-777-7752 (US only) *Fax:* 909-463-2999 *E-mail:* wvresources@worldvision.org *Web Site:* www.worldvisionresources.com, pg 286

World's Best Short-Short Story Contest, Florida State University, Dept of English, Tallahassee, FL 32306 *E-mail:* southeastreview@gmail.com *Web Site:* www.southeastreview.org, pg 751

WorldTariff, 220 Montgomery St, Suite 448, San Francisco, CA 94104-3410 *Tel:* 415-391-7501; 415-591-6666 *Toll Free Tel:* 800-556-9334 *Fax:* 415-391-7537 (Fax/Modem) *Web Site:* www.worldtariff.com; ftn.fedex.com/wtonline, pg 286

Worldwide Library, 225 Duncan Mill Rd, Don Mills, ON M3B 3K9, Canada *Tel:* 416-445-5860 *Toll Free Tel:* 888-432-4879 *Fax:* 416-445-8655; 416-445-8736 *E-mail:* CustomerService@harlequin.com *Web Site:* www.harlequin.com, pg 525

Worth Publishers, 41 Madison Ave, 37th fl, New York, NY 10010 *Tel:* 212-576-9400 *Fax:* 212-561-8281 *Web Site:* www.worthpub.com, pg 286

Worthy & James Publishing, PO Box 362015, Milpitas, CA 95036 *Tel:* 408-945-3963 *E-mail:* worthy1234@sbcglobal.net; mail@worthyjames.com *Web Site:* www.worthyjames.com, pg 530

Wright Group/McGraw-Hill, 8787 Orion Place, Columbus, OH 43240 *Tel:* 614-430-4000 *Toll Free Tel:* 800-537-4740 *Web Site:* www.wrightgroup.com, pg 286

Wright Information Indexing Services, PO Box 658, Sandia Park, NM 87047 *Tel:* 505-281-2600 *Web Site:* www.wrightinformation.com, pg 557

Write Bloody Publishing, 2306 E Cesar Chavez, Suite 103, Austin, TX 78706 *E-mail:* writebloody@gmail.com *Web Site:* writebloody.com, pg 286

Write Now, 140 W Washington St, Indianapolis, IN 46204-3465 *Tel:* 317-635-5277 *Fax:* 317-236-0767 *Web Site:* www.irtlive.com/artists_information/playwrights/bonderman_introduction, pg 751

Write on the Sound Writers' Conference, 700 Main St, Edmonds, WA 98020 *Tel:* 425-771-0228 *Fax:* 425-771-0253 *E-mail:* wots@ci.edmonds.wa.us *Web Site:* www.edmondswa.gov, pg 674

Write Stuff Enterprises Inc, 1001 S Andrew Ave, Suite 120, Fort Lauderdale, FL 33316 *Tel:* 954-462-6657 *Toll Free Tel:* 800-900-2665 *Fax:* 954-462-6023 *E-mail:* legends@writestuffbooks.com *Web Site:* www.writestuffbooks.com, pg 286

The Write Way, 3048 Horizon Lane, Suite 1102, Naples, FL 34109 *Tel:* 239-273-9145 *E-mail:* darekane@gmail.com, pg 557

Writer in Residence, 2410 N Old Penitentiary Rd, Boise, ID 83712 *Tel:* 208-334-2119 *Toll Free Tel:* 800-ART-FUND (278-3863 within Idaho) *Fax:* 208-334-2488 *E-mail:* info@arts.idaho.gov *Web Site:* www.arts.idaho.gov, pg 751

The Writer Magazine/Emily Dickinson Award, 15 Gramercy Park S, New York, NY 10003 *Tel:* 212-254-9628 *Fax:* 212-673-2352 *Web Site:* www.poetrysociety.org, pg 751

Writers' Alliance of Newfoundland & Labrador, 202-223 Duckworth St, St John's, NL A1C 6N1, Canada *Tel:* 709-739-5215 *Toll Free Tel:* 866-739-5215 *Fax:* 709-739-5931 *E-mail:* wanl@nf.aibn.com *Web Site:* wanl.ca, pg 638

Writers Anonymous Inc, 1302 E Coronado Rd, Phoenix, AZ 85006 *Tel:* 602-256-2830 *Fax:* 602-256-2830 *Web Site:* writersanonymousinc.com, pg 558

Writer's AudioShop, 1316 Overland Stage Rd, Dripping Springs, TX 78620 *Tel:* 512-264-7067 *Fax:* 512-264-7067 *E-mail:* wrtaudshop@aol.com *Web Site:* www.writersaudio.com, pg 286

The Writers' Colony at Dairy Hollow, 515 Spring St, Eureka Springs, AR 72632 *Tel:* 479-253-7444 *Fax:* 479-253-9859 *E-mail:* director@writerscolony.org *Web Site:* www.writerscolony.org, pg 674

Writer's Digest Books, 10151 Carver Rd, Suite 200, Blue Ash, OH 45242 *Tel:* 513-531-2690 *Toll Free Tel:* 800-289-0963 *Fax:* 513-531-7185 *E-mail:* writersdigest@fwmedia.com (edit) *Web Site:* www.writersdigest.com, pg 286

The Youth Honor Award Progam, 166 W 12 Ave, Eugene, OR 97401 *Tel:* 541-342-4956 *E-mail:* info@skippingstones.org *Web Site:* www.skippingstones.org, pg 753

YWAM Publishing, PO Box 55787, Seattle, WA 98155-0787 *Tel:* 425-771-1153 *Toll Free Tel:* 800-922-2143 *Fax:* 425-775-2383 *E-mail:* books@ywampublishing.com *Web Site:* www.ywampublishing.com, pg 289

Zachary Shuster Harmsworth Agency, 1776 Broadway, Suite 1405, New York, NY 10019 *Tel:* 212-765-6900 *Fax:* 212-765-6490 *Web Site:* www.zshliterary.com, pg 600

Zagat Survey LLC, 76 Ninth Ave, 4th fl, New York, NY 10011 *Tel:* 212-977-6000 *Toll Free Tel:* 866-817-9947 (orders); 800-540-9609 *Fax:* 212-977-9760; 802-864-9846 (order related) *E-mail:* corpsales@zagat.com; shop@zagat.com *Web Site:* www.zagat.com, pg 289

Zaner-Bloser Inc, 1201 Dublin Rd, Columbus, OH 43215-1026 *Tel:* 614-486-0221 *Toll Free Tel:* 800-421-3018 (cust serv) *Toll Free Fax:* 800-992-6087 (orders) *E-mail:* zbcsd@zaner-bloser.com; international@zaner-bloser.com *Web Site:* www.zaner-bloser.com, pg 289

Zarahemla Books, 869 E 2680 N, Provo, UT 84604 *Tel:* 801-368-7374 *Fax:* 801-418-2081 *E-mail:* info@zarahemlabooks.com *Web Site:* zarahemlabooks.com, pg 289

Zebra Communications, 230 Deerchase Dr, Woodstock, GA 30188-4438 *Tel:* 770-924-0528 *Web Site:* www.zebraeditor.com, pg 558

Zeiders & Associates, PO Box 670, Lewisburg, PA 17837 *Tel:* 570-524-4315 *Fax:* 570-524-4315, pg 558

Zeig, Tucker & Theisen Inc, 3614 N 24 St, Phoenix, AZ 85016 *Tel:* 480-389-4342 *Toll Free Tel:* 800-666-2211 (orders) *Fax:* 602-944-8118 *E-mail:* marketing@zeigtucker.com *Web Site:* www.zeigtucker.com, pg 289

Zest Books, 35 Stillman St, Suite 121, San Francisco, CA 94107 *Tel:* 415-777-8654 *Fax:* 415-777-8653 *E-mail:* info@zestbooks.net; publicity@zestbooks.net *Web Site:* zestbooks.net, pg 289

Barbara J Zitwer Agency, 525 West End Ave, Unit 11-H, New York, NY 10024 *Tel:* 212-501-8423 *Fax:* 646-514-0497 *E-mail:* zitwer@gmail.com, pg 600

Robert Zolnerzak, 101 Clark St, Unit 20-K, Brooklyn, NY 11201 *Tel:* 718-522-0591 *E-mail:* bobzolnerzak@verizon.net, pg 558

Zondervan, A HarperCollins Company, 5300 Patterson Ave SE, Grand Rapids, MI 49530 *Tel:* 616-698-6900 *Toll Free Tel:* 800-226-1122; 800-727-1309 (retail orders) *Fax:* 616-698-3350 *Toll Free Fax:* 800-698-3256 (retail orders) *E-mail:* zinfo@zondervan.com *Web Site:* www.zondervan.com, pg 289

Zone Books dba Urzone Inc, 1226 Prospect Ave, Brooklyn, NY 11218 *Tel:* 718-686-0048 *Toll Free Tel:* 800-405-1619 (orders & cust serv) *Fax:* 718-686-9045 *Toll Free Fax:* 800-406-9145 (orders) *E-mail:* orders@triliteral.org *Web Site:* www.zonebooks.org, pg 289

Anna Zornio Memorial Children's Theatre Playwriting Award, Paul Creative Arts, Unit D-22, 30 Academic Way, Durham, NH 03824-3538 *Tel:* 603-862-3038 *Fax:* 603-862-0298 *Web Site:* www.unh.edu/theatre-dance/zornio, pg 753

ZOVA Books, PO Box 21833, Long Beach, CA 90801 *Tel:* 805-426-9682 *Fax:* 562-394-9568 *Web Site:* www.zovabooks.com, pg 290

Zumaya Publications LLC, 3209 S IH 35, Suite 1086, Austin, TX 78741 *Tel:* 512-402-5298 *Fax:* 253-660-2009 *E-mail:* acquisitions@zumayapublications.com *Web Site:* www.zumayapublications.com, pg 290

# Personnel Index

Included in this index are the personnel included in the entries in this volume of *LMP*, along with the page number(s) on which they appear. Not included in this index are those individuals associated with listings in the **Calendar of Book Trade & Promotional Events; Reference Books for the Trade** and **Magazines for the Trade** sections. Also, personnel associated with secondary addresses within listings (such as branch offices, sales offices, editorial offices, etc.) are not included.

Aalto, Helena, Editors' Association of Canada (Association canadienne des reviseurs), 502-27 Carlton St, Toronto, ON M5B 1L2, Canada *Tel:* 416-975-1379 *Toll Free Tel:* 866-CAN-EDIT (226-3348) *Fax:* 416-975-1637 *E-mail:* info@editors.ca *Web Site:* www.editors.ca; www.reviseurs.ca, pg 622

Aalto, Helena, Tom Fairley Award for Editorial Excellence, 502-27 Carlton St, Toronto, ON M5B 1L2, Canada *Tel:* 416-975-1379 *Toll Free Tel:* 866-CAN-EDIT (226-3348) *Fax:* 416-975-1637 *E-mail:* fairley_award@editors.ca *Web Site:* www.editors.ca; www.reviseurs.ca, pg 703

Aaronson, Deborah, Harry N Abrams Inc, 115 W 18 St, 6th fl, New York, NY 10011 *Tel:* 212-206-7715 *Toll Free Tel:* 800-345-1359 *Fax:* 212-519-1210 *E-mail:* abrams@abramsbooks.com *Web Site:* www.abramsbooks.com, pg 3

Abad, Kehaunani PhD, Kamehameha Publishing, 567 S King St, Suite 118, Honolulu, HI 96813 *Toll Free Tel:* 800-523-6200 *Fax:* 808-541-5305 *E-mail:* publishing@ksbe.edu *Web Site:* kamehamehapublishing.org, pg 138

Abbey, Caroline, Bloomsbury Publishing, 175 Fifth Ave, New York, NY 10010 *Tel:* 212-674-5151 *Toll Free Tel:* 800-221-7945 *Fax:* 212-780-0115; 212-982-2837 *E-mail:* marketingusa@bloomsbury.com; adultpublicityusa.@bloomsbury.com *Web Site:* www.bloomsbury.com, pg 40

Abdo, Jim, ABDO Publishing Group, 8000 W 78 St, Suite 310, Edina, MN 55439 *Tel:* 952-831-2120 (ext 223) *Toll Free Tel:* 800-800-1312 *Toll Free Fax:* 800-862-3480 *E-mail:* info@abdopublishing.com *Web Site:* www.abdopub.com, pg 2

Abdo, Paul, ABDO Publishing Group, 8000 W 78 St, Suite 310, Edina, MN 55439 *Tel:* 952-831-2120 (ext 223) *Toll Free Tel:* 800-800-1312 *Toll Free Fax:* 800-862-3480 *E-mail:* info@abdopublishing.com *Web Site:* www.abdopub.com, pg 2

Abdulhamid, Abusolayman, The International Institute of Islamic Thought, 500 Grove St, Suite 200, Herndon, VA 20170 *Tel:* 703-471-1133 *Fax:* 703-471-3922 *E-mail:* iiit@iiit.org *Web Site:* www.iiit.org, pg 133

Abe, Carol, University of Hawaii Press, 2840 Kolowalu St, Honolulu, HI 96822 *Tel:* 808-956-8255 *Toll Free Tel:* 888-UHPRESS (847-7377) *Fax:* 808-988-6052 *Toll Free Fax:* 800-650-7811 *E-mail:* uhpbooks@hawaii.edu *Web Site:* www.uhpress.hawaii.edu, pg 265

Abel, Dominick, Dominick Abel Literary Agency Inc, 146 W 82 St, Suite 1-A, New York, NY 10024 *Tel:* 212-877-0710 *Fax:* 212-595-3133, pg 559

Abfier, Mel, StarGroup International Inc, 1194 Old Dixie Hwy, Suite 201, West Palm Beach, FL 33413 *Tel:* 561-547-0667 *Fax:* 561-843-8530 *E-mail:* info@stargroupinternational.com *Web Site:* www.stargroupinternational.com, pg 243

Abkemeier, Laurie, DeFiore and Company, LLC, 47 E 19 St, 3rd fl, New York, NY 10003 *Tel:* 212-925-7744 *Fax:* 212-925-9803 *E-mail:* submissions@defioreandco.com; info@defioreandco.com *Web Site:* www.defioreandco.com, pg 568

Ablaza, Christina, Stegner Fellowship, Stanford Creative Writing Program, Dept of English, Stanford, CA 94305-2087 *Tel:* 650-723-0011 *Fax:* 650-723-3679 *Web Site:* creativewriting.stanford.edu, pg 744

Ableman, Brian, The Learning Source Ltd, 644 Tenth St, Brooklyn, NY 11215 *Tel:* 718-768-0231 (ext 10) *Fax:* 718-369-3467 *E-mail:* info@learningsourceltd.com *Web Site:* www.learningsourceltd.com, pg 550

Abraham, Ben, Urban Land Institute, 1025 Thomas Jefferson St NW, Suite 500-W, Washington, DC 20007 *Tel:* 202-624-7000 *Toll Free Tel:* 800-321-5011 (cust serv) *Fax:* 410-626-7140 *E-mail:* bookstore@uli.org; customerservice@uli.org *Web Site:* www.uli.org/books, pg 273

Abramo, Lauren E, Dystel & Goderich Literary Management, One Union Sq W, Suite 904, New York, NY 10003 *Tel:* 212-627-9100 *Fax:* 212-627-9313 *Web Site:* www.dystel.com, pg 569

Abramovitch, Ingrid, Artisan Books, 225 Varick St, New York, NY 10014-4381 *Tel:* 212-254-5900 *Toll Free Tel:* 800-722-7202 *Fax:* 212-254-8098 *E-mail:* artisaninfo@workman.com; artisaninfo@artisanbooks.com *Web Site:* www.workman.com/artisanbooks/, pg 23

Abrams, Joanne, Square One Publishers Inc, 115 Herricks Rd, Garden City Park, NY 11040 *Tel:* 516-535-2010 *Toll Free Tel:* 877-900-BOOK (900-2665) *Fax:* 516-535-2014 *E-mail:* sq1publish@aol.com *Web Site:* www.squareonepublishers.com, pg 242

Abrams, Liesa, Simon & Schuster Children's Publishing, 1230 Avenue of the Americas, New York, NY 10020 *Tel:* 212-698-7000 *Web Site:* KIDS.SimonandSchuster.com; TEEN.SimonandSchuster.com; simonandschuster.net; simonandschuster.biz, pg 235

Abrams, Robert E, Abbeville Publishing Group, 137 Varick St, Suite 504, New York, NY 10013 *Tel:* 212-366-5585 *Toll Free Tel:* 800-ART-BOOK (278-2665) *Fax:* 212-366-6966 *E-mail:* abbeville@abbeville.com; marketing@abbeville.com; sales@abbeville.com; rights@abbeville.com *Web Site:* www.abbeville.com, pg 2

Abramson, Karen, CCH, a Wolters Kluwer business, 2700 Lake Cook Rd, Riverwoods, IL 60015 *Tel:* 847-267-7000 *Toll Free Tel:* 800-525-3335 *Fax:* 773-866-3095 *Web Site:* www.cch.com, pg 55

Abreu, Carmen, Blue Note Publications Inc, 720 North Dr, Suite D, Melbourne, FL 32924 *Tel:* 321-799-2583 *Toll Free Tel:* 800-624-0401 (orders) *Fax:* 321-799-1942 *E-mail:* bluenotepress@gmail.com *Web Site:* www.bluenotebooks.com, pg 41

Accordino, Michael, Simon & Schuster, 1230 Avenue of the Americas, New York, NY 10020 *Tel:* 212-698-7000 *Toll Free Tel:* 800-223-2348 (cust serv); 800-223-2336 (orders) *Toll Free Fax:* 800-943-9831 (orders) *Web Site:* www.simonandschuster.com, pg 234

Achaibou, Amy, Chronicle Books LLC, 680 Second St, San Francisco, CA 94107 *Tel:* 415-537-4200 *Toll Free Tel:* 800-759-0190 (cust serv) *Fax:* 415-537-4460 *Toll Free Fax:* 800-858-7787 (orders); 800-286-9471 (cust serv) *E-mail:* frontdesk@chroniclebooks.com *Web Site:* www.chroniclebooks.com, pg 61

Acheson, Alice B, Alice B Acheson's Workshops for Writers, Illustrators & Photographers, PO Box 735, Friday Harbor, WA 98250 *Tel:* 360-378-2815 *E-mail:* aliceba@aol.com, pg 667

Acheson, Alison, Tradewind Books, 202-1807 Maritime Mews, Vancouver, BC V6H 3W7, Canada *Fax:* 604-662-4405 *E-mail:* tradewindbooks@telus.net *Web Site:* www.tradewindbooks.com, pg 521

Ackerman, John G, Cornell University Press, Sage House, 512 E State St, Ithaca, NY 14850 *Tel:* 607-277-2338 *Fax:* 607-277-2374 *E-mail:* cupressinfo@cornell.edu; cupress-sales@cornell.edu *Web Site:* www.cornellpress.cornell.edu, pg 67

Acland, Marigold, Cambridge University Press, 32 Avenue of the Americas, New York, NY 10013-2473 *Tel:* 212-924-3900; 212-337-5000 *Toll Free Tel:* 800-899-5222 *Fax:* 212-691-3239 *E-mail:* newyork@cambridge.org *Web Site:* www.cambridge.org/us, pg 51

Acton, Amy, Phoenix Society for Burn Survivors, 1835 R W Berends Dr SW, Grand Rapids, MI 49519 *Tel:* 616-458-2773 *Toll Free Tel:* 800-888-BURN (888-2876) *Fax:* 616-458-2831 *E-mail:* info@phoenix-society.org *Web Site:* www.phoenix-society.org, pg 201

Adamo, John, Random House Children's Books, 1745 Broadway, New York, NY 10019 *Tel:* 212-782-9000 *Toll Free Tel:* 800-200-3552 *Fax:* 212-782-9452 *Web Site:* randomhousekids.com, pg 213

Adams, Barry, Temple University Press, 1852 N Tenth St, Philadelphia, PA 19122-6099 *Tel:* 215-926-2140 *Toll Free Tel:* 800-621-2736 *Fax:* 215-926-2141 *E-mail:* tempress@temple.edu *Web Site:* www.temple.edu/tempress, pg 251

Adams, Ben, PublicAffairs, 250 W 57 St, Suite 1321, New York, NY 10107 *Tel:* 212-397-6666 *Toll Free Tel:* 800-343-4499 (orders) *Fax:* 212-397-4277 *E-mail:* publicaffairs@perseusbooks.com *Web Site:* www.publicaffairsbooks.com, pg 209

Adams, Beth, Howard Books, 216 Centerview Dr, Suite 303, Brentwood, TN 37027 *Tel:* 615-873-2080 *Fax:* 615-370-3834 *E-mail:* howardbooks@simonandschuster.com (info) *Web Site:* www.howardpublishing.com, pg 124

Adams, Chuck, Algonquin Books of Chapel Hill, 400 Silver Cedar Ct, Suite 300, Chapel Hill, NC 27514-1585 *Tel:* 919-967-0108 *Fax:* 919-933-0272 *E-mail:* inquiry@algonquin.com *Web Site:* www.workman.com/algonquin, pg 8

Adams, Haydn, Graphic Artists Guild Inc, 32 Broadway, Suite 1114, New York, NY 10004-1612 *Tel:* 212-791-3400 *Fax:* 212-791-0333 *Web Site:* www.graphicartistsguild.org, pg 624, 678

Adams, Jennifer, Clinical Laboratory & Standards Institute (CLSI), 950 W Valley Rd, Suite 2500, Wayne, PA 19087 *Tel:* 610-688-0100 *Toll Free Tel:* 877-447-1888 (orders) *Fax:* 610-688-0700 *E-mail:* customerservice@clsi.org *Web Site:* www.clsi.org, pg 63

Adams, Jennifer, Quirk Books, 215 Church St, Philadelphia, PA 19106 *Tel:* 215-627-3581 *Fax:* 215-627-5220 *E-mail:* general@quirkbooks.com *Web Site:* www.quirkbooks.com, pg 211

Adams, John, Florida Funding Publications Inc, PO Box 561565, Miami, FL 33256 *Tel:* 305-251-2203 *Fax:* 305-251-2773 *E-mail:* info@floridafunding.com, pg 96

Adams, Katie Henderson, W W Norton & Company Inc, 500 Fifth Ave, New York, NY 10110-0017 *Tel:* 212-354-5500 *Toll Free Tel:* 800-233-4830 (orders & cust serv) *Fax:* 212-869-0856 *Toll Free Fax:* 800-458-6515 *Web Site:* www.wwnorton.com, pg 182

Adams, Kelli, Counterpoint Press LLC, 1919 Fifth St, Berkeley, CA 94710 *Tel:* 510-704-0230 *Fax:* 510-704-0268 *E-mail:* info@counterpointpress.com *Web Site:* www.counterpointpress.com; www.sierraclub.org/books; www.softskull.com, pg 69

Adams, Lisa, The Garamond Agency Inc, 12 Horton St, Newburyport, MA 01950 *Fax:* 978-992-0265 *E-mail:* query@garamondagency.com *Web Site:* www.garamondagency.com, pg 574

Adams, Mark Wayne, The Florida Publishers Association Inc (FPA), PO Box 916383, Longwood, FL 32791-6383 *Tel:* 863-647-5951 *Fax:* 863-647-5951 *E-mail:* fpabooks@gmail.com *Web Site:* www.floridapublishersassociation.com, pg 623

Adams, Matthew, Between the Lines, 401 Richmond St W, No 277, Toronto, ON M5V 3A8, Canada *Tel:* 416-535-9914 *Toll Free Tel:* 800-718-7201 *Fax:* 416-535-1484 *E-mail:* info@btlbooks.com *Web Site:* www.btlbooks.com, pg 494

Adams, Dr Michael, Dobie Paisano Fellowship Program, Graduate School, 110 Inner Campus Dr, Stop G0400, Austin, TX 78712-0710 *Fax:* 512-471-7620 *Web Site:* www.utexas.edu/ogs/Paisano, pg 732

Adams, Michael W, University of Texas at Austin, Creative Writing Program, Dept of English, PAR 108, One University Sta, Mailcode B5000, Austin, TX 78712-1164 *Tel:* 512-471-5132; 512-471-4991 *Fax:* 512-471-4909 *Web Site:* www.utexas.edu/cola/depts/english/creative-writing, pg 682

Adams, Phillip, The Summer Experience, 601 Spadina Crescent E, Suite 718, Saskatoon, SK S7K 3G8, Canada *Tel:* 306-652-7395 *Fax:* 306-244-0255 *E-mail:* sage.hill@sasktel.net *Web Site:* www.sagehillwriting.ca, pg 674

Adams, Steven, American Institute for Economic Research (AIER), 250 Division St, Great Barrington, MA 01230 *Tel:* 413-528-1216 *Toll Free Tel:* 888-528-0103; 888-528-1216 (orders) *Fax:* 413-528-0103 *E-mail:* info@aier.org *Web Site:* www.aier.org, pg 13

Adams, Susan, Addicus Books Inc, PO Box 45327, Omaha, NE 68145 *Tel:* 402-330-7493 *Toll Free Tel:* 800-352-2873 (orders) *Fax:* 402-330-1707 *E-mail:* info@addicusbooks.com; addicusbks@aol.com *Web Site:* www.addicusbooks.com, pg 5

Adams, TaKisha, Gryphon House Inc, 10770 Columbia Pike, Suite 201, Silver Spring, MD 20901 *Tel:* 301-595-9500 *Toll Free Tel:* 800-638-0928 *Fax:* 301-595-0051 *Toll Free Fax:* 877-638-7576 *E-mail:* info@ghbooks.com *Web Site:* www.gryphonhouse.com, pg 109

Adams, Terry, Little, Brown and Company, 237 Park Ave, New York, NY 10017 *Tel:* 212-364-1100 *Fax:* 212-364-0952 *E-mail:* firstname.lastname@hbgusa.com *Web Site:* www.HachetteBookGroup.com, pg 150

Adams, William, University of South Carolina Press, 1600 Hampton St, Suite 544, Columbia, SC 29208 *Tel:* 803-777-5245 *Toll Free Tel:* 800-768-2500 (orders) *Fax:* 803-777-0160 *Toll Free Fax:* 800-868-0740 (orders) *Web Site:* www.sc.edu/uscpress, pg 269

Adamson, Susan, Heritage House Publishing Co Ltd, 1105 Pandora Ave, Victoria, BC V8V 3P9, Canada *Tel:* 604-574-7067 *Toll Free Tel:* 800-665-3302 *Fax:* 604-574-9942 *Toll Free Fax:* 800-566-3336 *E-mail:* heritage@heritagehouse.ca; orders@heritagehouse.ca *Web Site:* www.heritagehouse.ca, pg 509

Addicott, Lori, WaterBrook Multnomah Publishing Group, 12265 Oracle Blvd, Suite 200, Colorado Springs, CO 80921 *Tel:* 719-590-4999 *Toll Free Tel:* 800-603-7051 (orders) *Fax:* 719-590-8977 *Toll Free Fax:* 800-294-5686 (orders) *E-mail:* info@waterbrookmultnomah.com *Web Site:* waterbrookmultnomah.com, pg 277

Adel, Judith, J Adel Art & Design, 586 Ramapo Rd, Teaneck, NJ 07666 *Tel:* 201-836-2606 *E-mail:* jadelnj@aol.com, pg 539

Adelson, Robin, The Children's Book Council (CBC), 54 W 39 St, 14th fl, New York, NY 10018 *Tel:* 212-966-1990 *Fax:* 212-966-2073 *Toll Free Fax:* 888-807-9355 (orders only) *E-mail:* cbc.info@cbcbooks.org *Web Site:* www.cbcbooks.org, pg 621

Adelstein, Marlene, Words into Print, 131 Fifth Ave, Suite 501, New York, NY 10003 *Tel:* 212-741-1393 *Fax:* 419-441-1393 *E-mail:* query@wordsintoprint.org *Web Site:* www.wordsintoprint.org, pg 557

Adero, Malaika, Atria Books, 1230 Avenue of the Americas, New York, NY 10020 *Tel:* 212-698-7000 *Fax:* 212-698-7007 *Web Site:* www.simonandschuster.com, pg 26

Adjemian, Robert, Vedanta Press, 1946 Vedanta Place, Hollywood, CA 90068 *Tel:* 323-960-1736 *Toll Free Tel:* 800-816-2242 *E-mail:* info@vedanta.com *Web Site:* www.vedanta.com, pg 274

Adkins, David, Council of State Governments, 2760 Research Park Dr, Lexington, KY 40511 *Tel:* 859-244-8000 *Toll Free Tel:* 800-800-1910 *Fax:* 859-244-8001 *E-mail:* sales@csg.org *Web Site:* www.csg.org, pg 69

Adler, Allan R, Association of American Publishers (AAP), 71 Fifth Ave, 2nd fl, New York, NY 10003-3004 *Tel:* 212-255-0200 *Fax:* 212-255-7007 *Web Site:* www.publishers.org, pg 616

Adler, Cy A, Green Eagle Press, PO Box 20329, New York, NY 10025 *Tel:* 212-663-2167 *Fax:* 212-316-7650 *E-mail:* mail@greeneagle.org *Web Site:* www.greeneagle.org, pg 107

Adler, Ellen, The New Press, 38 Greene St, 4th fl, New York, NY 10013 *Tel:* 212-629-8802 *Toll Free Tel:* 800-343-4489 (orders) *Fax:* 212-629-8617 *Toll Free Fax:* 800-351-5073 (orders) *E-mail:* newpress@thenewpress.com *Web Site:* www.thenewpress.com, pg 178

Adler, Laina, HarperCollins General Books Group, 10 E 53 St, New York, NY 10022 *Tel:* 212-207-7000 *Fax:* 212-207-7633 *Web Site:* www.harpercollins.com, pg 113

Adler, William K, Reader's Digest General Books, Reader's Digest Rd, Pleasantville, NY 10570-7000 *Tel:* 914-238-1000 *Toll Free Tel:* 800-304-2807 (cust serv) *Fax:* 914-244-7436, pg 215

Adler-Kozak, Mary, National Association of College Stores (NACS), 500 E Lorain St, Oberlin, OH 44074 *Tel:* 440-775-7777 *Toll Free Tel:* 800-622-7498 *Fax:* 440-775-4769 *Web Site:* www.nacs.org, pg 628

Agnew, Tim, Concordia Publishing House, 3558 S Jefferson Ave, St Louis, MO 63118-3968 *Tel:* 314-268-1000 *Toll Free Tel:* 800-325-3040 (cust serv) *Toll Free Fax:* 800-490-9889 (cust serv) *E-mail:* order@cph.org *Web Site:* www.cph.org, pg 66

Agree, Peter A, University of Pennsylvania Press, 3905 Spruce St, Philadelphia, PA 19104 *Tel:* 215-898-6261 *Fax:* 215-898-0404 *E-mail:* custserv@pobox.upenn.edu *Web Site:* www.pennpress.org, pg 268

Aguilar, Enrique, Paulist Press, 997 MacArthur Blvd, Mahwah, NJ 07430-9990 *Tel:* 201-825-7300 *Toll Free Tel:* 800-218-1903 *Fax:* 201-825-8345 *Toll Free Fax:* 800-836-3161 *E-mail:* info@paulistpress.com *Web Site:* www.paulistpress.com, pg 195

Aguilo, Maria Jesus, Berrett-Koehler Publishers Inc, 235 Montgomery St, Suite 650, San Francisco, CA 94104 *Tel:* 415-288-0260 *Fax:* 415-362-2512 *E-mail:* bkpub@bkpub.com *Web Site:* www.bkconnection.com, pg 36

Ahearn, Pamela G, The Ahearn Agency Inc, 2021 Pine St, New Orleans, LA 70118 *Tel:* 504-861-8395 *Fax:* 504-866-6434 *Web Site:* www.ahearnagency.com, pg 560

Ahern, G Thomas, Capstone Publishers™, 1710 Roe Crest Dr, North Mankato, MN 56003 *Toll Free Tel:* 800-747-4992 (cust serv) *Toll Free Fax:* 888-262-0705 *Web Site:* www.capstonepress.com, pg 51

Ahlquist, Susan, Second Chance Press, 4170 Noyac Rd, Sag Harbor, NY 11963 *Tel:* 631-725-1101 *E-mail:* info@thepermanentpress.com *Web Site:* www.thepermanentpress.com, pg 230

Ahlrich, Loretta, The Century Foundation, 41 E 70 St, New York, NY 10021 *Tel:* 212-535-4441; 212-879-9197 *Fax:* 212-879-9197 *E-mail:* info@tcf.org *Web Site:* www.tcf.org, pg 57, 641

Ahrens, John, George T Bisel Co Inc, 710 S Washington Sq, Philadelphia, PA 19106-3519 *Tel:* 215-922-5760 *Toll Free Tel:* 800-247-3526 *Fax:* 215-922-2235 *E-mail:* gbisel@bisel.com *Web Site:* www.bisel.com, pg 38

Ahrold, Robbin, BMI®, 7 World Trade Ctr, 250 Greenwich St, New York, NY 10007-0030 *Tel:* 212-586-2000; 212-220-3000 *Fax:* 212-246-2163 *E-mail:* foundation@bmi.com *Web Site:* www.bmi.com, pg 618

Ahuja, Parveen, Kapp Books LLC, 3602 Rocky Meadow Ct, Fairfax, VA 22033 *Tel:* 703-261-9171 *Fax:* 703-621-7162 *E-mail:* info@kappbooks.com *Web Site:* www.kappbooks.com, pg 138

Aiken, Paul, The Authors Guild, 31 E 32 St, 7th fl, New York, NY 10016 *Tel:* 212-563-5904 *Fax:* 212-564-8363; 212-564-5363 *E-mail:* staff@authorsguild.org *Web Site:* www.authorsguild.org, pg 617

Aiossa, Nick, Adam Hill Publications, 2699 Stirling Rd, Suite B-301, Fort Lauderdale, FL 33312 *Tel:* 954-680-7639 *E-mail:* books@adamhilldesign.com *Web Site:* www.adamhilldesign.com, pg 4

Akers, Terric, Other Press LLC, 2 Park Ave, 24th fl, New York, NY 10016 *Tel:* 212-414-0054 *Toll Free Tel:* 877-843-6843 *Fax:* 212-414-0939 *E-mail:* editor@otherpress.com; rights@otherpress.com *Web Site:* www.otherpress.com, pg 188

Akin, Wanda M, Akin & Randolph Agency, Literary Div, One Gateway Ctr, Suite 2600, Newark, NJ 07102 *Tel:* 973-353-8409; 973-623-6834 *Fax:* 973-353-8417 *E-mail:* info@akinandrandolph.com *Web Site:* www.akinandrandolph.com, pg 560

Akoury-Ross, Lisa, SDP Publishing Solutions LLC, 36 Captain's Way, East Bridgewater, MA 02333 *Tel:* 617-775-0656 *Web Site:* www.sdppublishingsolutions.com, pg 555

Al-Hillal, Semareh, Kids Can Press Ltd, 25 Dockside Dr, Toronto, ON M5A 0B5, Canada *Tel:* 416-479-7000 *Toll Free Tel:* 800-265-0884 *Fax:* 416-960-5437 *E-mail:* info@kidscan.com; customerservice@kidscan.com *Web Site:* www.kidscanpress.com; www.kidscanpress.ca, pg 510

Al-Yemany, Riyad, The International Institute of Islamic Thought, 500 Grove St, Suite 200, Herndon, VA 20170 *Tel:* 703-471-1133 *Fax:* 703-471-3922 *E-mail:* iiit@iiit.org *Web Site:* www.iiit.org, pg 133

Alain, Louise, Les Editions Alire, 120 Cote du Passage, Levis, QC G6V 5S9, Canada *Tel:* 418-835-4441 *Fax:* 418-838-4443 *E-mail:* info@alire.com *Web Site:* www.alire.com, pg 501

Alain, Marc, Modus Vivendi Publishing Inc & Presses Aventure, 55 rue Jean-Talon ouest, 2nd fl, Montreal, QC H2R 2W8, Canada *Tel:* 514-272-0433 *Fax:* 514-272-7234 *E-mail:* info@modusaventure.com *Web Site:* www.modusaventure.com, pg 512

Alan, Yusuf, Tughra Books, 345 Clifton Ave, Clifton, NJ 07011 *Tel:* 973-777-2704 *Fax:* 973-457-7334 *E-mail:* info@tughrabooks.com *Web Site:* www.tughrabooks.com, pg 259

Albanese, Frank, HarperCollins Publishers, 10 E 53 St, New York, NY 10022 *Tel:* 212-207-7000 *Fax:* 212-207-7145 *Web Site:* www.harpercollins.com, pg 113

Albanese, Frank, HarperCollins Publishers Sales, 10 E 53 St, New York, NY 10022 *Fax:* 212-207-7000 *Web Site:* www.harpercollins.com, pg 114

Albee, Edward, William Flanagan Memorial Creative Persons Center, 14 Harrison St, New York, NY 10013 *Tel:* 212-226-2020 *Fax:* 212-226-5551 *E-mail:* info@albeefoundation.org *Web Site:* www.albeefoundation.org, pg 749

Albers, Wes, Southern California Writers' Conference, 1010 University Ave, Suite 54, San Diego, CA 92103 *Tel:* 619-303-8185 *Fax:* 619-303-7462 *E-mail:* wewrite@writersconference.com *Web Site:* www.writersconference.com, pg 673

Alberti, Milena, Random House Publishing Group, 1745 Broadway, New York, NY 10019 *Toll Free Tel:* 800-200-3552 *Web Site:* atrandom.com, pg 214

Alberti, Robert E, Impact Publishers Inc, PO Box 6016, Atascadero, CA 93423-6016 *Tel:* 805-466-5917 (opers & admin offs) *Toll Free Tel:* 800-246-7228 (orders) *Fax:* 805-466-5919 (opers & admin offs) *E-mail:* info@impactpublishers.com *Web Site:* www.impactpublishers.com; www.bibliotherapy.com, pg 128

Albi, Mary, Phaidon Press Inc, 180 Varick St, 14th fl, New York, NY 10014 *Tel:* 212-652-5400 *Toll Free Tel:* 800-759-0190 (cust serv) *Fax:* 212-652-5410 *Toll Free Fax:* 800-286-9471 (cust serv) *E-mail:* ussales@phaidon.com *Web Site:* www.phaidon.com, pg 200

Albrecht, Ms Geri, Heuer Publishing LLC, 211 First Ave SE, Suite 200, Cedar Rapids, IA 52401 *Tel:* 319-368-8008 *Toll Free Tel:* 800-950-7529 *Fax:* 319-368-8011 *E-mail:* editor@hitplays.com *Web Site:* www.hitplays.com, pg 119

Alcala, Rosa, University of Texas at El Paso, Dept Creative Writing, MFA/Dept Creative Writing, Liberal Arts 415 UTEP, 500 W University Ave, El Paso, TX 79968-9991 *Tel:* 915-747-5713 *Fax:* 915-747-5523 *Web Site:* www.utep.edu/cw, pg 682

Alcid, Edmond, Moose Hide Books, 684 Walls Rd, Prince Township, ON P6A 6K4, Canada *Tel:* 705-779-3331 *Fax:* 705-779-3331 *E-mail:* mooseenterprises@on.aibn.com *Web Site:* www.moosehidebooks.com, pg 512

Alcorn, Charles W PhD, Fiction Collective Two Inc (FC2), University Ctr, Suite 310, 3007 N Ben Wilson St, Victoria, TX 77901 *Tel:* 361-570-4200; 361-570-4207 *E-mail:* fc2cum@gmail.com *Web Site:* www.fc2.org; www.uhv.edu, pg 94

Alden, Laura, Judson Press, 588 N Gulph Rd, King of Prussia, PA 19406 *Toll Free Tel:* 800-458-3766 *Fax:* 610-768-2107 *Web Site:* www.judsonpress.com, pg 137

Alderson, Martha, Blockbuster Plots for Writers Retreat, PO Box 1402, Capitola, CA 95010 *Tel:* 408-482-4678 *E-mail:* contact@blockbusterplots.com *Web Site:* www.blockbusterplots.com, pg 668

Alenier, Karren L, Word Works Washington Prize, Adirondack Community College, Dearlove Hall, 640 Bay Rd, Queensbury, NY 12804 *Fax:* 301-581-9443 *E-mail:* editor@wordworksbooks.org *Web Site:* www.wordworksbooks.org, pg 751

Alesse, Craig, Amherst Media Inc, 175 Rano St, Suite 200, Buffalo, NY 14207 *Tel:* 716-874-4450 *Toll Free Tel:* 800-622-3278 *Fax:* 716-874-4508 *E-mail:* marketing@amherstmedia.com *Web Site:* www.amherstmedia.com, pg 17

Alewel, Rex, Marathon Press, 1500 Square Turn Blvd, Norfolk, NE 68701 *Tel:* 402-371-5040 *Toll Free Tel:* 800-228-0629 *Fax:* 402-371-9382 *Web Site:* www.marathonpress.com, pg 156

Alexander, Anne, National Geographic Books, 1145 17 St NW, Washington, DC 20036-4688 *Tel:* 202-857-7000 *Fax:* 202-857-7670 *Web Site:* www.nationalgeographic.com, pg 174

Alexander, Britta, The Ned Leavitt Agency, 70 Wooster St, Suite 4-F, New York, NY 10012 *Tel:* 212-334-0999 *Web Site:* www.nedleavittagency.com, pg 581

Alexander, Caitlin, Random House Publishing Group, 1745 Broadway, New York, NY 10019 *Toll Free Tel:* 800-200-3552 *Web Site:* atrandom.com, pg 214

Alexander, Francie, Scholastic Education, 524 Broadway, New York, NY 10012 *Tel:* 212-343-6100 *Fax:* 212-343-6189 *Web Site:* www.scholastic.com, pg 228

Alexander, Jill, Fair Winds Press, 100 Cummings Ctr, Suite 406-L, Beverly, MA 01915 *Tel:* 978-282-9590 *Toll Free Tel:* 800-328-0590 (sales) *Fax:* 978-283-2742 *E-mail:* customerservice@quaysidepub.com *Web Site:* www.fairwindspress.com, pg 91

Alexander, Jo, Oregon State University Press, 121 The Valley Library, Corvallis, OR 97331-4501 *Tel:* 541-737-3166 *Toll Free Tel:* 800-621-2736 (orders) *Fax:* 541-737-3170 *Toll Free Fax:* 800-426-3797 (orders) *E-mail:* osu.press@oregonstate.edu *Web Site:* oregonstate.edu/dept/press; osupress.oregonstate.edu, pg 187

Alexander, Karlee, McClanahan Publishing House Inc, 88 Cedar St, Kuttawa, KY 42055-0100 *Tel:* 270-388-9388 *Toll Free Tel:* 800-544-6959 *Fax:* 270-388-6186 *E-mail:* books@kybooks.com *Web Site:* www.kybooks.com, pg 160

Alexander, Kathy, The Johns Hopkins University Press, 2715 N Charles St, Baltimore, MD 21218-4363 *Tel:* 410-516-6900; 410-516-6987 (journals outside US & CN) *Toll Free Tel:* 800-537-5487 (book orders & cust serv); 800-548-1784 (journal orders) *Fax:* 410-516-6968; 410-516-3866 (journal orders) *E-mail:* hfscustserv@press.jhu.edu (cust serv); jrnlcirc@press.jhu.edu (journal orders) *Web Site:* www.press.jhu.edu; muse.jhu.edu/about/subscriptions/index.html (Project Muse subns), pg 136

Alexander, Neil M, Abingdon Press, 201 Eighth Ave S, Nashville, TN 37203-3919 *Toll Free Tel:* 800-251-3320 *Toll Free Fax:* 800-836-7802 (orders) *E-mail:* orders@abingdonpress.com *Web Site:* www.abingdonpress.com, pg 3

Alexander, Pamela, Oberlin College Press, 50 N Professor St, Oberlin, OH 44074-1091 *Tel:* 440-775-8408 *Fax:* 440-775-8124 *E-mail:* oc.press@oberlin.edu *Web Site:* www.oberlin.edu/ocpress, pg 183

Alexander, Patrick, The Pennsylvania State University Press, University Support Bldg 1, Suite C, 820 N University Dr, University Park, PA 16802-1003 *Tel:* 814-865-1327 *Toll Free Tel:* 800-326-9180 *Fax:* 814-863-1408 *Toll Free Fax:* 877-778-2665 *E-mail:* info@psupress.org *Web Site:* www.psupress.org, pg 198

Alexander, Ms Sandy, University Press of Mississippi, 3825 Ridgewood Rd, Jackson, MS 39211-6492 *Tel:* 601-432-6205 *Toll Free Tel:* 800-737-7788 (orders & cust serv) *Fax:* 601-432-6217 *E-mail:* press@mississippi.edu *Web Site:* www.upress.state.ms.us, pg 271

Alexander, Susanne, Goose Lane Editions, 500 Beaverbrook Ct, Suite 330, Fredericton, NB E3B 5X4, Canada *Tel:* 506-450-4251 *Toll Free Tel:* 888-926-8377 *Fax:* 506-459-4991 *E-mail:* info@gooselane.com *Web Site:* www.gooselane.com, pg 507

Alexander, Susanne M, Marriage Transformation LLC, 2409 Hamill Rd, Hixson, TN 37343-4034 *Tel:* 423-599-0153 *E-mail:* staff@marriagetransformation.com *Web Site:* www.marriagetransformation.com, pg 157

Alexander, Tracy, McLaren Memorial Comedy Play Writing Competition, 2000 W Wadley Ave, Midland, TX 79705 *Tel:* 432-682-2544 *E-mail:* tracy@mctmidland.org *Web Site:* www.mctmidland.org, pg 722

Algar, Liza, Chronicle Books LLC, 680 Second St, San Francisco, CA 94107 *Tel:* 415-537-4200 *Toll Free Tel:* 800-759-0190 (cust serv) *Fax:* 415-537-4460 *Toll Free Fax:* 800-858-7787 (orders); 800-286-9471 (cust serv) *E-mail:* frontdesk@chroniclebooks.com *Web Site:* www.chroniclebooks.com, pg 61

Alguire, Julie, Crabtree Publishing Co, 350 Fifth Ave, 59th fl, PMB 59051, New York, NY 10118 *Tel:* 212-496-5040 *Toll Free Tel:* 800-387-7650 *Toll Free Fax:* 800-355-7166 *E-mail:* custserv@crabtreebooks.com *Web Site:* www.crabtreebooks.com, pg 70

Alguire, Julie, Crabtree Publishing Co Ltd, 616 Welland Ave, St Catharines, ON L2M-5V6, Canada *Tel:* 905-682-5221 *Toll Free Tel:* 800-387-7650 *Fax:* 905-682-7166 *Toll Free Fax:* 800-355-7166 *E-mail:* custserv@crabtreebooks.com; sales@crabtreebooks.com; orders@crabtreebooks.com *Web Site:* www.crabtreebooks.com, pg 500

Ali, Karen, CCH Canadian Limited, A Wolters Kluwer Company, 90 Sheppard Ave E, Suite 300, Toronto, ON M2N 6X1, Canada *Tel:* 416-224-2224 *Toll Free Tel:* 800-268-4522 (CN & US cust serv) *Fax:* 416-224-2243 *Toll Free Fax:* 800-461-4131 *E-mail:* cservice@cch.ca (cust serv) *Web Site:* www.cch.ca, pg 498

Ali, Kazim, Oberlin College Press, 50 N Professor St, Oberlin, OH 44074-1091 *Tel:* 440-775-8408 *Fax:* 440-775-8124 *E-mail:* oc.press@oberlin.edu *Web Site:* www.oberlin.edu/ocpress, pg 183

Ali, Liaquat, Kazi Publications Inc, 3023 W Belmont Ave, Chicago, IL 60618 *Tel:* 773-267-7001 *Fax:* 773-267-7002 *E-mail:* info@kazi.org *Web Site:* www.kazi.org, pg 138

Aliaga, Roxanna, Insight Editions, 10 Paul Dr, San Rafael, CA 94903 *Tel:* 415-526-1370 *Toll Free Tel:* 800-809-3792 *E-mail:* info@insighteditions.com *Web Site:* www.insighteditions.com, pg 131

Alighieri, Christian, Ransom Note Press, PO Box 419, Ridgewood, NJ 07451 *Tel:* 201-835-2790 *E-mail:* editorial@ransomnotepress.com *Web Site:* www.ransomnotepress.com, pg 529

Aliotti, Tracee, International Society for Technology in Education, 180 W Eighth Ave, Suite 300, Eugene, OR 97401-2916 *Tel:* 541-302-3777 (intl) *Toll Free Tel:* 800-336-5191 (US & CN) *Fax:* 541-302-3778 *E-mail:* iste@iste.org *Web Site:* www.iste.org; www.iste.org/bookstore (orders), pg 133

Allan, Richard, The Aaland Agency, PO Box 849, Inyokern, CA 93527-0849 *Tel:* 760-384-3910 *Web Site:* www.the-aaland-agency.com, pg 559

Allberry, Debra, Warren Wilson College, MFA Program for Writers, 701 Warren Wilson Rd, Swannanoa, NC 28778 *Tel:* 828-771-3717 *Fax:* 828-771-7005 *E-mail:* mfa@warren-wilson.edu *Web Site:* www.warren-wilson.edu/~mfa, pg 682

Allday, Liana, Stewart, Tabori & Chang, 115 W 18 St, 6th fl, New York, NY 10011 *Tel:* 212-519-1200 *Fax:* 212-519-1210 *Web Site:* www.abramsbooks.com, pg 245

Allee, Sheila, Writers' League of Texas (WLT), 611 S Congress Ave, Suite 505, Austin, TX 78704 *Tel:* 512-499-8914 *E-mail:* wlt@writersleague.org *Web Site:* www.writersleague.org, pg 639

Allen, Chad, Chosen Books, PO Box 6287, Grand Rapids, MI 49516-6287 *Tel:* 616-676-9185 *Toll Free Tel:* 800-877-2665 (orders only) *Fax:* 616-676-9573 *Toll Free Fax:* 800-398-3111 (orders only) *Web Site:* www.bakerpublishinggroup.com, pg 60

Allen, Christopher, Summit University Press, 63 Summit Way, Gardiner, MT 59030-9314 *Tel:* 406-848-9742; 406-848-9500 *Toll Free Tel:* 800-245-5445 (retail orders) *Fax:* 406-848-9650 *Toll Free Fax:* 800-221-8307 *E-mail:* info@summituniversitypress.com *Web Site:* www.summituniversitypress.com, pg 246

Allen, Ms Desmond Walls, Arkansas Research Inc, PO Box 303, Conway, AR 72033 *Tel:* 501-470-1120 *E-mail:* sales@arkansasresearch.com *Web Site:* www.arkansasresearch.com, pg 22

Allen, Inge, Crystal Publishers Inc, 3460 Lost Hills Dr, Las Vegas, NV 89122 *Tel:* 702-434-3037 *Fax:* 702-434-3037 *Web Site:* www.crystalpub.com, pg 73

Allen, Janet, Write Now, 140 W Washington St, Indianapolis, IN 46204-3465 *Tel:* 317-635-5277 *Fax:* 317-236-0767 *Web Site:* www.irtlive.com/artists_information/playwrights/bonderman_introduction, pg 751

Allen, Keith, OSA, The Optical Society, 2010 Massachusetts Ave NW, Washington, DC 20036-1023 *Tel:* 202-223-8130 *Toll Free Tel:* 800-766-4672 *E-mail:* custserv@osa.org *Web Site:* www.osa.org, pg 188

Allen, Dr Leonard, ACU Press, 1626 Campus Ct, Abilene, TX 79601 *Tel:* 325-674-2720 *Toll Free Tel:* 877-816-4455 *Fax:* 325-674-6471 *Web Site:* www.acupressbooks.com; www.leafwoodpublishers.com, pg 4

Allen, Linda, Linda Allen Literary Agency, 1949 Green St, Suite 5, San Francisco, CA 94123 *Tel:* 415-921-6437, pg 560

Allen, Marc, New World Library, 14 Pamaron Way, Novato, CA 94949 *Tel:* 415-884-2100 *Toll Free Tel:* 800-227-3900 (ext 52, retail orders); 800-972-6657 *Fax:* 415-884-2199 *E-mail:* escort@newworldlibrary.com *Web Site:* www.newworldlibrary.com, pg 178

Allen, Mitch, Left Coast Press Inc, 1630 N Main St, Suite 400, Walnut Creek, CA 94596 *Tel:* 925-935-3380 *Fax:* 925-935-2916 *E-mail:* explore@lcoastpress.com *Web Site:* www.lcoastpress.com, pg 146

Allen, Rebecca, Texas Christian University Press, 3000 Sandage Ave, Fort Worth, TX 76109 *Tel:* 817-257-7822 *Toll Free Tel:* 800-826-8911 *Fax:* 817-257-5075 *Web Site:* www.prs.tcu.edu, pg 253

Allen, Robert, Macmillan Audio, 175 Fifth Ave, New York, NY 10010 *Tel:* 646-307-5151 *Toll Free Tel:* 888-330-8477 (cust serv) *Fax:* 917-534-0980 *E-mail:* firstname.lastname@macmillan.com *Web Site:* www.macmillanaudio.com, pg 154

Allen, Sandra, Wag's Revue Writers' Contest, 2865 W Lyndale St, Suite 1, Chicago, IL 60647 *E-mail:* editors@wagsrevue.com *Web Site:* www.wagsrevue.com, pg 748

Allen, T James, Thomas Allen Publishers, 390 Steelcase Rd E, Markham, ON L3R 1G2, Canada *Tel:* 905-475-9126 *Toll Free Tel:* 800-387-4333 (orders) *Fax:* 905-475-6747 *Toll Free Fax:* 800-458-5504 (orders) *E-mail:* info@t-allen.com *Web Site:* www.thomasallen.ca, pg 493

Allen, Tom, Association of American Publishers (AAP), 71 Fifth Ave, 2nd fl, New York, NY 10003-3004 *Tel:* 212-255-0200 *Fax:* 212-255-7007 *Web Site:* www.publishers.org, pg 616

Allen, Tom, Sterling Publishing Co Inc, 387 Park Ave S, 11th fl, New York, NY 10016-8810 *Tel:* 212-532-7160 *Toll Free Tel:* 800-367-9692 *Fax:* 212-213-2495 *Web Site:* www.sterlingpub.com, pg 244

Allen-Crowley, Mary, ANR Publications University of California, 1301 S 46 St, Bldg 478 - MC 3580, Richmond, CA 94804 *Tel:* 510-665-2195 (cust serv) *Toll Free Tel:* 800-994-8849 *Fax:* 510-665-3427 *E-mail:* anrcatalog@ucdavis.edu *Web Site:* anrcatalog.ucanr.edu, pg 19

Aller, Gary, Gallaudet University Press, 800 Florida Ave NE, Washington, DC 20002-3695 *Tel:* 202-651-5488 *Fax:* 202-651-5489 *E-mail:* gupress@gallaudet.edu *Web Site:* gupress.gallaudet.edu, pg 101

Allison, Kevin, Oxford University Press USA, 198 Madison Ave, New York, NY 10016 *Tel:* 212-726-6000 *Toll Free Tel:* 800-451-7556 (orders); 800-445-9714 (cust serv) *Fax:* 919-677-1303 *E-mail:* custserv.us@oup.com *Web Site:* www.oup.com/us, pg 189

Allison, Mark, Stackpole Books, 5067 Ritter Rd, Mechanicsburg, PA 17055 *Tel:* 717-796-0411 *Toll Free Tel:* 800-732-3669 *Fax:* 717-796-0412 *Web Site:* www.stackpolebooks.com, pg 242

Allison, Susan, Berkley Books, 375 Hudson St, New York, NY 10014 *Tel:* 212-366-2000 *Fax:* 212-366-2666 *E-mail:* online@penguinputnam.com *Web Site:* www.penguinputnam.com; us.penguingroup.com, pg 35

Allison, Susan, Berkley Publishing Group, 375 Hudson St, New York, NY 10014 *Tel:* 212-366-2000 *Fax:* 212-366-2385 *E-mail:* online@penguinputnam.com *Web Site:* us.penguingroup.com, pg 36

Almack, David, CLC Ministries, 701 Pennsylvania Ave, Fort Washington, PA 19034 *Tel:* 215-542-1240 *Toll Free Tel:* 800-659-1240 *Fax:* 215-542-7580 *E-mail:* orders@clcpublications.com *Web Site:* www.clcpublications.com, pg 62

Almqvist, Johan, Chronicle Books LLC, 680 Second St, San Francisco, CA 94107 *Tel:* 415-537-4200 *Toll Free Tel:* 800-759-0190 (cust serv) *Fax:* 415-537-4460 *Toll Free Fax:* 800-858-7787 (orders); 800-286-9471 (cust serv) *E-mail:* frontdesk@chroniclebooks.com *Web Site:* www.chroniclebooks.com, pg 61

Alongi, Pietro, Pearson Education/ELT, 10 Bank St, 9th fl, White Plains, NY 10606-1951 *Tel:* 914-287-8000 *Web Site:* www.pearsonelt.com, pg 195

Alperen, Jennifer, The Betsy Nolan Literary Agency, 214 W 29 St, Suite 1002, New York, NY 10001 *Tel:* 212-967-8200 *Fax:* 212-967-7292 *E-mail:* dblehr@cs.com, pg 587

Alps, Marisa, Harbour Publishing Co Ltd, PO Box 219, Madeira Park, BC V0N 2H0, Canada *Tel:* 604-883-2730 *Toll Free Tel:* 800-667-2988 *Fax:* 604-883-9451 *E-mail:* info@harbourpublishing.com *Web Site:* www.harbourpublishing.com, pg 508

Alter, George, Inter-University Consortium for Political & Social Research (ICPSR), 330 Packard St, Ann Arbor, MI 48104 *Tel:* 734-647-5000 *Fax:* 734-647-8200 *E-mail:* netmail@icpsr.umich.edu *Web Site:* www.icpsr.umich.edu, pg 132

Althouse, Jayne, House to House Publications, 11 Toll Gate Rd, Lititz, PA 17543 *Tel:* 717-627-1996 *Toll Free Tel:* 800-848-5892 *Fax:* 717-627-4004 *E-mail:* h2hp@dcfi.org *Web Site:* www.h2hp.com; www.dcfi.org, pg 124

Altinis-Kiraz, Christine PhD, Gorgias Press LLC, 954 River Rd, Piscataway, NJ 08854 *Tel:* 732-885-8900 *Fax:* 732-885-8908 *E-mail:* helpdesk@gorgiaspress.com *Web Site:* www.gorgiaspress.com, pg 105

Altman, David G, Center for Creative Leadership LLC, One Leadership Place, Greensboro, NC 27410-9427 *Tel:* 336-545-2810; 336-288-7210 *Fax:* 336-282-3284 *E-mail:* info@ccl.org *Web Site:* www.ccl.org/publications, pg 56

Altreuter, Judith, Modern Language Association of America (MLA), 26 Broadway, 3rd fl, New York, NY 10004-1789 *Tel:* 646-576-5000 *Fax:* 646-458-0030 *E-mail:* info@mla.org *Web Site:* www.mla.org, pg 168

Altshuler, Miriam, Miriam Altshuler Literary Agency, 53 Old Post Rd N, Red Hook, NY 12571 *Tel:* 845-758-9408 *Web Site:* www.miriamaltshulerliteraryagency.com, pg 560

Alvarado, Beth, Rick DeMarinis Short Story Award, PO Box 2414, Durango, CO 81302 *Tel:* 970-903-7914 *E-mail:* cutthroatmag@gmail.com *Web Site:* www.cutthroatmag.com, pg 700

Alvarado, Beth, Joy Harjo Poetry Award, PO Box 2414, Durango, CO 81302 *Tel:* 970-903-7914 *E-mail:* cutthroatmag@gmail.com *Web Site:* www.cutthroatmag.com, pg 709

Alvare, Susan, Hartman Publishing Inc, 8529-A Indian School Rd NE, Albuquerque, NM 87112 *Tel:* 505-291-1274 *Toll Free Tel:* 800-999-9534 *Fax:* 505-291-1284 *Toll Free Fax:* 800-474-6106 *E-mail:* orders@hartmanonline.com; help@hartmanonline.com *Web Site:* www.hartmanonline.com, pg 114

Alvarez, Amanda, Fire Engineering Books & Videos, 1421 S Sheridan Rd, Tulsa, OK 74112 *Tel:* 918-831-9410 *Toll Free Tel:* 800-752-9764 *Fax:* 918-831-9555 *E-mail:* sales@pennwell.com *Web Site:* www.pennwellbooks.com/fire.html, pg 95

Alvarez, Jessica, BookEnds LLC, 136 Long Hill Rd, Gillette, NJ 07933 *Web Site:* www.bookends-inc.com, pg 563

Alvarez, Lisa, Squaw Valley Community of Writers Summer Workshops, PO Box 1416, Nevada City, CA 95959 *Tel:* 530-470-8440 *E-mail:* info@squawvalleywriters.org *Web Site:* www.squawvalleywriters.org, pg 673

Alward, Kathy, Piano Press, 1425 Ocean Ave, Suite 17, Del Mar, CA 92014 *Tel:* 619-884-1401 *Fax:* 858-755-1104 *E-mail:* pianopress@pianopress.com *Web Site:* www.pianopress.com, pg 201

Amato, Frank W, Frank Amato Publications Inc, 4040 SE Wister St, Portland, OR 97222 *Tel:* 503-653-8108 *Toll Free Tel:* 800-541-9498 *Fax:* 503-653-2766 *E-mail:* customerservice@amatobooks.com; info@amatobooks.com *Web Site:* www.amatobooks.com, pg 10

Ambrosio, Dan, Da Capo Press Inc & Lifelong Books, 44 Farnsworth St, 3rd fl, Boston, MA 02210 *Tel:* 617-252-5200 *Toll Free Tel:* 800-343-4499 (orders) *Fax:* 617-252-5285 *Web Site:* www.perseusbooksgroup.com/dacapo, pg 74

Amendolara, Paula, Simon & Schuster Sales & Marketing, 1230 Avenue of the Americas, New York, NY 10020 *Tel:* 212-698-7000, pg 236

Ames, Joanna, Canadian Publishers' Council (CPC), 250 Merton St, Suite 203, Toronto, ON M4S 1B1, Canada *Tel:* 416-322-7011 *Fax:* 416-322-6999 *Web Site:* www.pubcouncil.ca, pg 620

Ames, Michael, Vanderbilt University Press, 2014 Broadway, Suite 320, Nashville, TN 37203 *Tel:* 615-322-3585 *Toll Free Tel:* 800-627-7377 (orders only) *Fax:* 615-343-8823 *Toll Free Fax:* 800-735-0476 (orders only) *E-mail:* vupress@vanderbilt.edu *Web Site:* www.vanderbiltuniversitypress.com, pg 274

Ames, Steve, World Citizens, PO Box 131, Mill Valley, CA 94942-0131 *Tel:* 415-380-8020 *Toll Free Tel:* 800-247-6553 (orders only), pg 285

Amini, Christina, Chronicle Books LLC, 680 Second St, San Francisco, CA 94107 *Tel:* 415-537-4200 *Toll Free Tel:* 800-759-0190 (cust serv) *Fax:* 415-537-4460 *Toll Free Fax:* 800-858-7787 (orders); 800-286-9471 (cust serv) *E-mail:* frontdesk@chroniclebooks.com *Web Site:* www.chroniclebooks.com, pg 61

Amitie, Julie, Scholastic Trade Division, 557 Broadway, New York, NY 10012 *Tel:* 212-343-6100; 212-343-4685 (export sales) *Fax:* 212-343-4714 (export sales) *Web Site:* www.scholastic.com, pg 229

Amling, Eric, Darhansoff & Verrill, 236 W 26 St, Suite 802, New York, NY 10001-6736 *Tel:* 917-305-1300 *Fax:* 917-305-1400 *E-mail:* info@dvagency.com *Web Site:* www.dvagency.com, pg 567

Ammons-Longtin, Cheryl, Oxford University Press USA, 198 Madison Ave, New York, NY 10016 *Tel:* 212-726-6000 *Toll Free Tel:* 800-451-7556 (orders); 800-445-9714 (cust serv) *Fax:* 919-677-1303 *E-mail:* custserv.us@oup.com *Web Site:* www.oup.com/us, pg 189

Amos, India, F+W Media Inc, 10151 Carver Rd, Suite 200, Blue Ash, OH 45242 *Tel:* 513-531-2690 *Toll Free Tel:* 800-289-0963 (trade accts); 800-258-0929 (orders) *E-mail:* contact_us@fwmedia.com *Web Site:* www.fwmedia.com, pg 92

Amsel, Andrew, Prayer Book Press Inc, 1363 Fairfield Ave, Bridgeport, CT 06605 *Tel:* 203-384-2284 *Fax:* 203-579-9109, pg 205

Amster, Betsy, Betsy Amster Literary Enterprises, 6312 SW Capitol Hwy, No 503, Portland, OR 97239 *Tel:* 503-496-4007 *E-mail:* rights@amsterlit.com (rts inquiries); b.amster.assistant@gmail.com (adult book queries); b.amster.kidsbooks@gmail.com (children & young adult book queries) *Web Site:* www.amsterlit.com, pg 560

Anastas, Greg, The Perseus Books Group, 387 Park Ave S, 12th fl, New York, NY 10016 *Tel:* 212-340-8100 *Toll Free Tel:* 800-343-4499 (cust serv) *Fax:* 212-340-8105 *Web Site:* www.perseusbooksgroup.com, pg 199

Anastas, Mara, Simon & Schuster Children's Publishing, 1230 Avenue of the Americas, New York, NY 10020 *Tel:* 212-698-7000 *Web Site:* KIDS.SimonandSchuster.com; TEEN.SimonandSchuster.com; simonandschuster.net; simonandschuster.biz, pg 235

Anders, Lou, Prometheus Books, 59 John Glenn Dr, Amherst, NY 14228-2119 *Tel:* 716-691-0133 *Toll Free Tel:* 800-421-0351 *Fax:* 716-691-0137 *E-mail:* marketing@prometheusbooks.com; editorial@prometheusbooks.com *Web Site:* www.Prometheusbooks.com, pg 208

Andersen, Peter, Doubleday/Nan A Talese, c/o Random House Inc, 1745 Broadway, New York, NY 10019 *Tel:* 212-751-2600 *Toll Free Tel:* 800-638-6460 *Fax:* 212-572-2593 *Web Site:* www.knopfdoubleday.com, pg 81

Andersen, Peter, Alfred A Knopf/Everyman's Library, c/o Random House Inc, 1745 Broadway, New York, NY 10019 *Tel:* 212-751-2600 *Toll Free Tel:* 800-638-6460 *Fax:* 212-572-2593 *Web Site:* www.knopfdoubleday.com, pg 141

Andersen, Vicki, North American Snowsports Journalists Association, 11728 SE Madison St, Portland, OR 97216-3849 *Tel:* 503-255-3771 *Fax:* 503-255-3771 *Web Site:* www.nasja.org, pg 632

Andersen-Zantop, Ashley, Capstone Publishers™, 1710 Roe Crest Dr, North Mankato, MN 56003 *Toll Free Tel:* 800-747-4992 (cust serv) *Toll Free Fax:* 888-262-0705 *Web Site:* www.capstonepress.com, pg 51

Anderson, Alison, University of Pennsylvania Press, 3905 Spruce St, Philadelphia, PA 19104 *Tel:* 215-898-6261 *Fax:* 215-898-0404 *E-mail:* custserv@pobox.upenn.edu *Web Site:* www.pennpress.org, pg 268

Anderson, Andrea, Theodore C Blegen Award, 701 William Vickers Ave, Durham, NC 27701-3162 *Tel:* 919-682-9319 *Fax:* 919-682-2349 *Web Site:* www.foresthistory.org, pg 692

Anderson, Andrea, John M Collier Award for Forest History Journalism, 701 William Vickers Ave, Durham, NC 27701-3162 *Tel:* 919-682-9319 *Fax:* 919-682-2349 *Web Site:* www.foresthistory.org, pg 698

Anderson, Andrea, Leopold-Hidy Award, 701 William Vickers Ave, Durham, NC 27701-3162 *Tel:* 919-682-9319 *Fax:* 919-682-2349 *Web Site:* www.foresthistory.org, pg 717

Anderson, Andrea, Charles A Weyerhauser Book Award, 701 William Vickers Ave, Durham, NC 27701-3162 *Tel:* 919-682-9319 *Fax:* 919-682-2349 *Web Site:* www.foresthistory.org, pg 749

Anderson, Ann-Marie, Temple University Press, 1852 N Tenth St, Philadelphia, PA 19122-6099 *Tel:* 215-926-2140 *Toll Free Tel:* 800-621-2736 *Fax:* 215-926-2141 *E-mail:* tempress@temple.edu *Web Site:* www.temple.edu/tempress, pg 251

Anderson, Barbara, Lynx House Press, 420 W 24 St, Spokane, WA 99203 *Tel:* 509-624-4894 *Web Site:* www.lynxhousepress.org, pg 154

Anderson, Barbara S, Barbara S Anderson, 706 W Davis Ave, Ann Arbor, MI 48103-4855 *Tel:* 734-995-0125 *Toll Free Fax:* 866-859-2932 *E-mail:* bsa328@earthlink.net, pg 540

Anderson, Becky, Gollehon Press Inc, 3655 Glenn Dr SE, Grand Rapids, MI 49546 *Tel:* 616-949-3515 *Fax:* 616-949-8674 *Web Site:* www.gollehonbooks.com, pg 104

Anderson, Christiane, American Society of Plant Taxonomists, University of Michigan Herbarium, 3600 Varsity Dr, Ann Arbor, MI 48108-2228 *Tel:* 734-647-2812 *Fax:* 734-998-0038 *Web Site:* www.aspt.net, pg 17

Anderson, Colleen, Balance Sports Publishing, 195 Lucero Way, Portola Valley, CA 94028 *Tel:* 650-561-9586 *Fax:* 650-391-9850 *E-mail:* info@balancesportspublishing.com *Web Site:* www.balancesportspublishing.com, pg 30

Anderson, Debra, Playwrights Guild of Canada, 215 Spadina Ave, Suite 210, Toronto, ON M5T 2C7, Canada *Tel:* 416-703-0201 *Fax:* 416-703-0059 *E-mail:* info@playwrightsguild.ca *Web Site:* www.playwrightsguild.ca, pg 634

Anderson, Duane, ACU Press, 1626 Campus Ct, Abilene, TX 79601 *Tel:* 325-674-2720 *Toll Free Tel:* 877-816-4455 *Fax:* 325-674-6471 *Web Site:* www.acupressbooks.com; www.leafwoodpublishers.com, pg 4

Anderson, Erik, University of Minnesota Press, 111 Third Ave S, Suite 290, Minneapolis, MN 55401-2520 *Tel:* 612-627-1970 *Fax:* 612-627-1980 *E-mail:* ump@umn.edu *Web Site:* www.upress.umn.edu, pg 267

Anderson, Gordon L, Paragon House, 1925 Oakcrest Ave, Suite 7, St Paul, MN 55113-2619 *Tel:* 651-644-3087 *Toll Free Tel:* 800-447-3709 *Fax:* 651-644-0997 *E-mail:* paragon@paragonhouse.com *Web Site:* www.paragonhouse.com, pg 193

Anderson, Heather, Walter De Gruyter Inc, 121 High St, 3rd fl, Boston, MA 02110 *Tel:* 857-284-7073 *Fax:* 857-284-7358 *E-mail:* USinfo@degruyter.com *Web Site:* www.degruyter.com, pg 77

Anderson, Heather, De Gruyter Mouton, 121 High St, 3rd fl, Boston, MA 02110 *Tel:* 857-284-7073 *Fax:* 857-284-7358 *E-mail:* degruytermail@presswarehouse.com (orders & claims) *Web Site:* www.degruyter.com, pg 170

Anderson, Jeff, Elite Books, PO Box 442, Fulton, CA 95439 *Tel:* 707-525-9292 *Toll Free Fax:* 800-330-9798 *Web Site:* www.elitebooks.biz, pg 86

Anderson, Jeff, Energy Psychology Press, 1490 Mark West Springs Rd, Santa Rosa, CA 95404 *Tel:* 707-237-6951 *Toll Free Fax:* 800-330-9798 *Web Site:* www.energypsychologypress.com, pg 88

Anderson, Jon, Simon & Schuster Children's Publishing, 1230 Avenue of the Americas, New York, NY 10020 *Tel:* 212-698-7000 *Web Site:* KIDS.SimonandSchuster.com; TEEN.SimonandSchuster.com; simonandschuster.net; simonandschuster.biz, pg 235

Anderson, Jon, Simon & Schuster, Inc, 1230 Avenue of the Americas, New York, NY 10020 *Tel:* 212-698-7000 *Fax:* 212-698-7007 *E-mail:* firstname.lastname@simonandschuster.com *Web Site:* www.simonandschuster.com, pg 235

Anderson, Kathleen, Anderson Literary Management LLC, 12 W 19 St, 2nd fl, New York, NY 10011 *Tel:* 212-645-6045 *Fax:* 212-741-1936 *E-mail:* info@andersonliterary.com *Web Site:* www.andersonliterary.com, pg 561

Anderson, Kent, Penguin Group (USA) LLC Sales, 375 Hudson St, New York, NY 10014 *Tel:* 212-366-2000 *E-mail:* online@penguinputnam.com *Web Site:* us.penguingroup.com, pg 197

Anderson, Kimberly, Chronicle Books LLC, 680 Second St, San Francisco, CA 94107 *Tel:* 415-537-4200 *Toll Free Tel:* 800-759-0190 (cust serv) *Fax:* 415-537-4460 *Toll Free Fax:* 800-858-7787 (orders); 800-286-9471 (cust serv) *E-mail:* frontdesk@chroniclebooks.com *Web Site:* www.chroniclebooks.com, pg 61

Anderson, Lydia, Wisdom Publications Inc, 199 Elm St, Somerville, MA 02144 *Tel:* 617-776-7416 *Toll Free Tel:* 800-272-4050 (orders) *Fax:* 617-776-7841 *E-mail:* info@wisdompubs.org *Web Site:* www.wisdompubs.org, pg 283

Anderson, Marc, Cambridge University Press, 32 Avenue of the Americas, New York, NY 10013-2473 *Tel:* 212-924-3900; 212-337-5000 *Toll Free Tel:* 800-899-5222 *Fax:* 212-691-3239 *E-mail:* newyork@cambridge.org *Web Site:* www.cambridge.org/us, pg 51

Anderson, Mark, Guild of Book Workers, 521 Fifth Ave, 17th fl, New York, NY 10175-0038 *Tel:* 212-292-4444 *Web Site:* www.guildofbookworkers.org, pg 624

Anderson, Mary, University of Washington Press, 433 Brooklyn Ave NE, Seattle, WA 98195-9570 *Tel:* 206-543-4050 *Toll Free Tel:* 800-537-5487 (orders) *Fax:* 206-543-3932; 410-516-6998 (orders) *E-mail:* uwpress@u.washington.edu *Web Site:* www.washington.edu/uwpress/, pg 270

Anderson, Mary K, Municipal Chapter of Toronto IODE Jean Throop Book Award, 40 Orchard View Blvd, Suite 219, Toronto, ON M4R 1B9, Canada *Tel:* 416-925-5078 *Fax:* 416-487-4417 *E-mail:* iodeontario@bellnet.ca *Web Site:* www.iodeontario.ca, pg 725

Anderson, Monty, Presbyterian Publishing Corp, 100 Witherspoon St, Louisville, KY 40202 *Tel:* 502-569-5000 *Toll Free Tel:* 800-523-1631 (US only) *Fax:* 502-569-5113 *E-mail:* ppcmail@presbypub.com *Web Site:* www.wjkbooks.com, pg 205

Anderson, Monty, Westminster John Knox Press, 100 Witherspoon St, Louisville, KY 40202-1396 *Tel:* 502-569-5052 *Toll Free Tel:* 800-227-2872 (US only) *Fax:* 502-569-8308 *Toll Free Fax:* 800-541-5113 (US & CN) *E-mail:* wjk@wjkbooks.com; customer_service@wjkbooks.com *Web Site:* www.wjkbooks.com, pg 279

Anderson, Dr Patricia PhD, Patricia Anderson PhD, Literary Consultant, 1489 Marine Dr, Suite 515, West Vancouver, BC V7T 1B8, Canada *Tel:* 604-740-0805 *E-mail:* query@helpingyougetpublished.com; patriciaanderson@helpingyougetpublished.com *Web Site:* www.helpingyougetpublished.com, pg 540

Anderson, Patricia PhD, Maryland Historical Society, 201 W Monument St, Baltimore, MD 21201 *Tel:* 410-685-3750 *Fax:* 410-385-2105 *Web Site:* www.mdhs.org, pg 158

Anderson, Peggy, Concordia Publishing House, 3558 S Jefferson Ave, St Louis, MO 63118-3968 *Tel:* 314-268-1000 *Toll Free Tel:* 800-325-3040 (cust serv) *Toll Free Fax:* 800-490-9889 (cust serv) *E-mail:* order@cph.org *Web Site:* www.cph.org, pg 66

Anderson, Richard, Encyclopaedia Britannica Inc, 331 N La Salle St, Chicago, IL 60654 *Tel:* 312-347-7159 (all other countries) *Toll Free Tel:* 800-323-1229 (US & CN) *Fax:* 312-294-2104 *E-mail:* editor@eb.com *Web Site:* www.eb.com; www.britannica.com, pg 88

Anderson, Shatera, University of Houston Creative Writing Program, 229 Roy Cullen Bldg, Houston, TX 77204-5008 *Tel:* 713-743-2255 *Fax:* 713-743-3697 *E-mail:* cwp@uh.edu *Web Site:* www.uh.edu/cwp, pg 681

Anderson, Steven, John M Collier Award for Forest History Journalism, 701 William Vickers Ave, Durham, NC 27701-3162 *Tel:* 919-682-9319 *Fax:* 919-682-2349 *Web Site:* www.foresthistory.org, pg 698

Anderson, William, Sagamore Publishing LLC, 1807 Federal Dr, Urbana, IL 61801 *Tel:* 217-359-5940 *Toll Free Tel:* 800-327-5557 (orders) *Fax:* 217-359-5975 *E-mail:* books@sagamorepub.com *Web Site:* www.sagamorepub.com, pg 223

Anderson-Wheeler, Claire, Anderson Literary Management LLC, 12 W 19 St, 2nd fl, New York, NY 10011 *Tel:* 212-645-6045 *Fax:* 212-741-1936 *E-mail:* info@andersonliterary.com *Web Site:* www.andersonliterary.com, pg 561

Andonian, Mr Aramais, Blue Crane Books, PO Box 380291, Cambridge, MA 02238 *Tel:* 617-926-8989 *Fax:* 617-926-0982 *E-mail:* bluecrane@arrow1.com, pg 41

Andreadis, Tina, HarperCollins General Books Group, 10 E 53 St, New York, NY 10022 *Tel:* 212-207-7000 *Fax:* 212-207-7633 *Web Site:* www.harpercollins.com, pg 113

Andreou, George, Alfred A Knopf/Everyman's Library, c/o Random House Inc, 1745 Broadway, New York, NY 10019 *Tel:* 212-751-2600 *Toll Free Tel:* 800-638-6460 *Fax:* 212-572-2593 *Web Site:* www.knopfdoubleday.com, pg 141

Andrew, Emily, University of British Columbia Press, 2029 West Mall, Vancouver, BC V6T 1Z2, Canada *Tel:* 604-822-5959 *Toll Free Tel:* 877-377-9378 *Fax:* 604-822-6083 *Toll Free Fax:* 800-668-0821 *E-mail:* frontdesk@ubcpress.ca *Web Site:* www.ubcpress.ca, pg 523

Andrewes, Lancelot, Wittenborn Art Books, 1109 Geary Blvd, San Francisco, CA 94109 *Tel:* 415-292-6500 *Toll Free Tel:* 800-660-6403 *Fax:* 415-292-6594 *E-mail:* wittenborn@art-books.com *Web Site:* www.art-books.com, pg 284

Andrews, Gaylen, Copywriter's Council of America (CCA), CCA Bldg, 7 Putter Lane, Middle Island, NY 11953-1920 *Tel:* 631-924-8555 *Fax:* 631-924-8555 *E-mail:* cca4dmcopy@gmail.com *Web Site:* www.AndrewLinickDirectMarketing.com/Copywriters-Council.html; www.NewWorldPressBooks.com, pg 621

Andrews, Hugh, Andrews McMeel Publishing LLC, 1130 Walnut St, Kansas City, MO 64106-2109 *Toll Free Tel:* 800-851-8923; 800-943-9839 (cust serv) *Toll Free Fax:* 800-943-9831 (orders) *Web Site:* www.andrewsmcmeel.com, pg 18

Andrews, Meredith, National Book Awards, 90 Broad St, Suite 604, New York, NY 10004 *Tel:* 212-685-0261 *Fax:* 212-213-6570 *E-mail:* nationalbook@nationalbook.org *Web Site:* www.nationalbook.org, pg 726

Andrews, Michael, Nelson Education Ltd, 1120 Birchmount Rd, Scarborough, ON M1K 5G4, Canada *Tel:* 416-752-9100 *Toll Free Tel:* 800-268-2222 (cust serv) *Fax:* 416-752-8101 *Toll Free Fax:* 800-430-4445 *E-mail:* inquire@nelson.com *Web Site:* www.nelson.com, pg 513

Andrews, Vaughn, Workman Publishing Co Inc, 225 Varick St, 9th fl, New York, NY 10014-4381 *Tel:* 212-254-5900 *Toll Free Tel:* 800-722-7202 *Fax:* 212-254-8098 *E-mail:* info@workman.com *Web Site:* www.workman.com, pg 285

Andrikanich, Chris, Gray & Company Publishers, 1588 E 40 St, Suite 3-A, Cleveland, OH 44103 *Tel:* 216-431-2665 *Toll Free Tel:* 800-915-3609 *E-mail:* sales@grayco.com *Web Site:* www.grayco.com, pg 106

Anema, Arielle, PEN American Center, 588 Broadway, Suite 303, New York, NY 10012 *Tel:* 212-334-1660 *Fax:* 212-334-2181 *E-mail:* info@pen.org *Web Site:* www.pen.org, pg 633

Arnold, Rob, Fence Books, University at Albany, Science Library 320, 1400 Washington Ave, Albany, NY 12222 *Tel:* 518-591-8162 *E-mail:* fence.fencebooks@gmail.com *Web Site:* www.fenceportal.org, pg 94

Arnold, Rob, Fence Modern Poets Series, University at Albany, Science Library 320, 1400 Washington Ave, Albany, NY 12222 *Tel:* 518-591-8162 *E-mail:* fence.fencebooks@gmail.com *Web Site:* www.fenceportal.org, pg 704

Arnold, Rob, Ottoline Morrell Prize, University at Albany, Science Library 320, 1400 Washington Ave, Albany, NY 12222 *Tel:* 518-591-8162 *E-mail:* fence.fencebooks@gmail.com *Web Site:* www.fenceportal.org, pg 725

Arnovitz, Benton M, United States Holocaust Memorial Museum, 100 Raoul Wallenberg Place SW, Washington, DC 20024-2126 *Tel:* 202-314-7837; 202-488-6144 (orders) *Toll Free Tel:* 800-259-9998 (orders) *Fax:* 202-479-9726; 202-488-0438 (orders) *E-mail:* cahs_publications@ushmm.org *Web Site:* www.ushmm.org, pg 262

Arnow, Ann, Bridge Publications Inc, 5600 E Olympic Blvd, Commerce City, CA 90022 *Tel:* 323-888-6200 *Toll Free Tel:* 800-722-1733 *Fax:* 323-888-6202 *E-mail:* info@bridgepub.com *Web Site:* www.bridgepub.com, pg 47

Arnow, Don, Bridge Publications Inc, 5600 E Olympic Blvd, Commerce City, CA 90022 *Tel:* 323-888-6200 *Toll Free Tel:* 800-722-1733 *Fax:* 323-888-6202 *E-mail:* info@bridgepub.com *Web Site:* www.bridgepub.com, pg 47

Aron, Paul, The Colonial Williamsburg Foundation, PO Box 1776, Williamsburg, VA 23187-1776 *Tel:* 757-229-1000 *Toll Free Tel:* 800-HISTORY (447-8679) *Fax:* 757-220-7325 *E-mail:* cwres@cwf.org; geninfo@cwf.org *Web Site:* www.colonialwilliamsburg.org/publications, pg 65

Aronica, Lou, The Story Plant, PO Box 4331, Stamford, CT 06907 *Tel:* 203-722-7920 *E-mail:* thestoryplant@thestoryplant.com *Web Site:* www.thestoryplant.com, pg 246

Aronson, Michael A, Harvard University Press, 79 Garden St, Cambridge, MA 02138-1499 *Tel:* 617-495-2600; 401-531-2800 (intl orders) *Toll Free Tel:* 800-405-1619 (orders) *Fax:* 617-495-5898 (general); 617-496-4677 (edit & rts); 401-531-2801 (intl orders) *Toll Free Fax:* 800-406-9145 (orders) *E-mail:* contact_hup@harvard.edu *Web Site:* www.hup.harvard.edu, pg 115

Aronson, Rosa, Teachers of English to Speakers of Other Languages Inc (TESOL), 1925 Ballenger Ave, Alexandria, VA 22314-6820 *Tel:* 703-836-0774 *Toll Free Tel:* 888-547-3369 *Fax:* 703-836-7864 *E-mail:* info@tesol.org *Web Site:* www.tesol.org, pg 251

Arriaza, David, UCLA Latin American Center Publications, UCLA Latin American Institute, 10343 Bunche Hall, Los Angeles, CA 90095 *Tel:* 310-825-4571 *Fax:* 310-206-6859 *E-mail:* latinamctr@international.ucla.edu *Web Site:* www.international.ucla.edu/lai, pg 261

Arrington, Jay, The Little Entrepreneur, c/o Harper-Arrington, 18701 Grand River, Suite 105, Detroit, MI 48223 *Toll Free Tel:* 888-435-9234 *Fax:* 248-281-0373 *E-mail:* info@harperarringtonmedia.com *Web Site:* www.thelittlee.com; www.harperarringtonmedia.com, pg 150

Arrow, Kevin P, Graphic World Publishing Services, 11687 Adie Rd, St Louis, MO 63043 *Tel:* 314-567-9854 *Fax:* 314-567-7178 *E-mail:* quote@gwinc.com *Web Site:* www.gwinc.com, pg 547

Arsenault, Jessica, Bear & Co Inc, One Park St, Rochester, VT 05767 *Tel:* 802-767-3174 *Toll Free Tel:* 800-932-3277 *Fax:* 802-767-3726 *E-mail:* customerservice@InnerTraditions.com *Web Site:* InnerTraditions.com, pg 33

Arsenault, Jessica, Inner Traditions International Ltd, One Park St, Rochester, VT 05767 *Tel:* 802-767-3174 *Toll Free Tel:* 800-246-8648 *Fax:* 802-767-3726 *E-mail:* customerservice@InnerTraditions.com *Web Site:* www.InnerTraditions.com, pg 130

Arseneault, Brenda, McGraw-Hill Ryerson Limited, 300 Water St, Whitby, ON L1N 9B6, Canada *Tel:* 905-430-5000 *Toll Free Tel:* 800-565-5758 (cust serv) *Fax:* 905-430-5020 *Web Site:* www.mcgrawhill.ca, pg 512

Arthur, Julie, Adventure Publications, 820 Cleveland St, Cambridge, MN 55008 *Tel:* 763-689-9800 *Toll Free Tel:* 800-678-7006 *Fax:* 763-689-9039 *Toll Free Fax:* 877-374-9016 *E-mail:* custservice@adventurepublications.net *Web Site:* www.adventurepublications.net, pg 5

Arthur, Michael, Beekman Books Inc, 300 Old All Angels Hill Rd, Wappingers Falls, NY 12590 *Tel:* 845-297-2690 *Fax:* 845-297-1002 *E-mail:* manager@beekmanbooks.com *Web Site:* www.beekmanbooks.com, pg 34

Arthur, Reagan, Little, Brown and Company, 237 Park Ave, New York, NY 10017 *Tel:* 212-364-1100 *Fax:* 212-364-0952 *E-mail:* firstname.lastname@hbgusa.com *Web Site:* www.HachetteBookGroup.com, pg 150

Artof, Susan, Center Press, PO Box 6936, Thousand Oaks, CA 91360-6936 *Tel:* 818-889-7071 *Fax:* 818-889-7072 *E-mail:* center@centerbooks.com *Web Site:* centerbooks.com, pg 56

Ascher, David, Scholastic Trade Division, 557 Broadway, New York, NY 10012 *Tel:* 212-343-6100; 212-343-4685 (export sales) *Fax:* 212-343-4714 (export sales) *Web Site:* www.scholastic.com, pg 228

Ash, Irene, Synapse Information Resources Inc, 1247 Taft Ave, Endicott, NY 13760 *Tel:* 607-748-4145 *Toll Free Tel:* 888-SYN-CHEM (796-2436) *Fax:* 607-786-3966 *E-mail:* salesinfo@synapseinfo.com *Web Site:* www.synapseinfo.com, pg 249

Ash, Michael, Synapse Information Resources Inc, 1247 Taft Ave, Endicott, NY 13760 *Tel:* 607-748-4145 *Toll Free Tel:* 888-SYN-CHEM (796-2436) *Fax:* 607-786-3966 *E-mail:* salesinfo@synapseinfo.com *Web Site:* www.synapseinfo.com, pg 249

Ashbach, Leonard, BK Nelson Inc Literary Agency, 1565 Paseo Vida, Palm Springs, CA 92264 *Tel:* 760-778-8800 *Fax:* 760-778-6242 *E-mail:* bknelson4@cs.com *Web Site:* www.bknelson.com; www.bknelsonlecturebureau.com; www.bknelsonmovieproduction.com, pg 587

Asher, James, McClanahan Publishing House Inc, 88 Cedar St, Kuttawa, KY 42055-0100 *Tel:* 270-388-9388 *Toll Free Tel:* 800-544-6959 *Fax:* 270-388-6186 *E-mail:* books@kybooks.com *Web Site:* www.kybooks.com, pg 160

Asher, Virginia Lee, Sky Oaks Productions Inc, 19544 Sky Oaks Way, Los Gatos, CA 95030 *Tel:* 408-395-7600 *Fax:* 408-395-8440 *E-mail:* tprworld@aol.com *Web Site:* www.tpr-world.com, pg 236

Ashfield, Keith, Kogan Page Publishers, 1518 Walnut St, Suite 1100, Philadelphia, PA 19102 *Tel:* 215-928-9112 *Fax:* 215-928-9113 *E-mail:* info@koganpage.com *Web Site:* www.koganpageusa.com, pg 141

Ashley, Britt, Indiana Review Fiction Prize, Ballantine Hall 465, 1020 E Kirkwood Ave, Bloomington, IN 47405 *Tel:* 812-855-3439 *E-mail:* inreview@indiana.edu *Web Site:* indianareview.org, pg 711

Ashlock, Jason Allen, Movable Type Management, 610 Fifth Ave, Suite 1220, New York, NY 10185 *Tel:* 917-289-1089 *Fax:* 646-810-5757 *Web Site:* www.mtmgmt.net, pg 586

Ashton, Stacey, Reader's Digest Children's Books, 44 S Broadway, White Plains, NY 10601 *Tel:* 914-238-1000 *Toll Free Tel:* 800-934-0977 *Web Site:* www.rdtradepublishing.com, pg 215

Ashton, Stacy, Reader's Digest Trade Books, 44 S Broadway, White Plains, NY 10601 *Tel:* 914-244-7503 *Fax:* 914-244-4841 *Web Site:* www.rd.com, pg 215

Ashwood, Shana, LearningExpress LLC, 2 Rector St, 26th fl, New York, NY 10006 *Tel:* 212-995-2566 *Toll Free Tel:* 800-295-9556 (ext 2) *Fax:* 212-995-5512 *E-mail:* customerservice@learningexpressllc.com (cust serv) *Web Site:* www.learningexpressllc.com, pg 145

Asiaghi, Anthony, American Society of Mechanical Engineers (ASME), 3 Park Ave, New York, NY 10016-5990 *Tel:* 212-591-7000 *Toll Free Tel:* 800-843-2763 (cust serv-US, CN & Mexico) *Fax:* 212-591-7674; 973-882-8113 (cust serv); 973-882-1717 (orders & inquiries) *E-mail:* infocentral@asme.org *Web Site:* www.asme.org, pg 17

Aspatore, Jonathan R, Aspatore Books, 35 Thomson Pl, Boston, MA 02210 *Toll Free Tel:* 866-ASPATORE (277-2867) *Fax:* 617-249-0219 *E-mail:* west.customer.service@thomsonreuters.com *Web Site:* www.aspatore.com, pg 25

Assathiany, Pascal, Les Editions du Boreal, 4447, rue Saint-Denis, Montreal, QC H2J 2L2, Canada *Tel:* 514-287-7401 *Fax:* 514-287-7664 *E-mail:* boreal@editionsboreal.qc.ca *Web Site:* www.editionsboreal.qc.ca, pg 502

Assouad, Maya, Vehicule Press, PO Box 125, Place du Park Sta, Montreal, QC H2X 4A3, Canada *Tel:* 514-844-6073 *Fax:* 514-844-7543 *E-mail:* vp@vehiculepress.com; admin@vehiculepress.com *Web Site:* www.vehiculepress.com, pg 524

Aster, Howard, Mosaic Press, 4500 Witmer Industrial Estates, PMB 145, Niagara Falls, NY 14305-1386 *Tel:* 905-825-2130 *Fax:* 905-825-2130 *E-mail:* info@mosaic-press.com *Web Site:* www.mosaic-press.com, pg 170

Astor, Dave, National Society of Newspaper Columnists (NSNC), 1345 Fillmore St, Suite 507, San Francisco, CA 94115 *Tel:* 415-488-NCNC (488-6762) *Toll Free Tel:* 866-440-NSNC (440-6762) *Fax:* 484-297-0336 *Toll Free Fax:* 866-635-5759 *E-mail:* staff@columnists.com *Web Site:* www.columnists.com, pg 631

Astor, Dave, National Society of Newspaper Columnists Annual Conference, 1345 Fillmore St, Suite 507, San Francisco, CA 94115 *Tel:* 415-488-NCNC (488-6762) *Toll Free Tel:* 866-440-NSNC (440-6762) *Fax:* 484-297-0336 *Toll Free Fax:* 866-635-5759 *Web Site:* www.columnists.com, pg 671

Atchity, Dr Kenneth, AEI (Atchity Entertainment International Inc), 9601 Wilshire Blvd, Unit 1202, Beverly Hills, CA 90210 *Tel:* 323-932-0407 *Fax:* 323-932-0321 *E-mail:* submissions@aeionline.com *Web Site:* www.aeionline.com, pg 560

Atchity, Kenneth PhD, The Writer's Lifeline Inc, 9601 Wilshire Blvd, Suite 1202, Beverly Hills, CA 90210 *Tel:* 323-932-0905 *Fax:* 323-932-0321 *E-mail:* questions@thewriterslifeline.com *Web Site:* www.thewriterslifeline.com, pg 558

Atkinson, Marisa, Graywolf Press, 250 Third Ave N, Suite 600, Minneapolis, MN 55401 *Tel:* 651-641-0077 *Fax:* 651-641-0036 *E-mail:* wolves@graywolfpress.org *Web Site:* www.graywolfpress.org, pg 106

Atkocaitis, John, Sundance/Newbridge Publishing, 33 Boston Post Rd W, Suite 440, Marlborough, MA 01752 *Toll Free Tel:* 888-200-2720; 800-343-8204 (Sundance cust serv & orders); 800-867-0307 (Newbridge cust serv & orders) *Toll Free Fax:* 800-456-2419 (orders) *E-mail:* info@sundancepub.com; info@newbridgeonline.com *Web Site:* www.sundancepub.com; www.newbridgeonline.com, pg 247

Attebery, Gerilyn, Lonely Planet, 150 Linden St, Oakland, CA 94607 *Tel:* 510-893-8555 *Toll Free Tel:* 800-275-8555 (orders) *Fax:* 510-893-8563 *E-mail:* info@lonelyplanet.com *Web Site:* www.lonelyplanet.com, pg 152

Attfield, Hilary, West Virginia University Press, West Virginia University, PO Box 6295, Morgantown, WV 26506-6295 *Tel:* 304-293-8400 *Toll Free Tel:* 866-WVU-PRES (988-7737) *Fax:* 304-293-6585 *E-mail:* press@wvu.edu *Web Site:* www.wvupress.com, pg 278

Attlee, James, University of Chicago Press, 1427 E 60 St, Chicago, IL 60637-2954 *Tel:* 773-702-7700; 773-702-7600 *Toll Free Tel:* 800-621-2736 (orders) *Fax:* 773-702-9756; 773-660-2235 (orders); 773-

PERSONNEL INDEX

702-2708 *E-mail:* custserv@press.uchicago.edu; marketing@press.uchicago.edu *Web Site:* www.press.uchicago.edu, pg 265

Attwood, Beth, Harlequin Enterprises Ltd, 233 Broadway, Suite 1001, New York, NY 10279 *Tel:* 212-553-4200 *Fax:* 212-227-8969 *E-mail:* CustomerService@harlequin.com *Web Site:* www.harlequin.com, pg 112

Attwood, Beth, Harlequin Enterprises Ltd, 225 Duncan Mill Rd, Don Mills, ON M3B 3K9, Canada *Tel:* 416-445-5860 *Toll Free Tel:* 888-432-4879; 800-370-5838 (ebook inquiries) *Fax:* 416-445-8655 *E-mail:* CustomerService@harlequin.com *Web Site:* www.harlequin.com, pg 508

Atwan, Helene, Beacon Press, 25 Beacon St, Boston, MA 02108 *Tel:* 617-742-2110 *Fax:* 617-723-3097; 617-742-2290 *Web Site:* www.beacon.org, pg 32

Atwan, Helene, The Hemingway Foundation/PEN Award, Massachusetts Institute of Technology, 77 Massachusetts Ave, 14-N-221A, Cambridge, MA 02139 *Tel:* 617-324-1729 *E-mail:* pen-newengland@mit.edu *Web Site:* www.pen-ne.org, pg 709

Atwood, Dr Christopher, The Mongolia Society Inc, Indiana University, 322 Goodbody Hall, 1011 E Third St, Bloomington, IN 47405-7005 *Tel:* 812-855-4078 *Fax:* 812-855-4078 *E-mail:* monsoc@indiana.edu *Web Site:* www.mongoliasociety.org, pg 169

Aubin, Patrick, National Gallery of Canada, The Bookstore, 380 Sussex Dr, Ottawa, ON K1N 9N4, Canada *Tel:* 613-990-0962 (mail order sales) *Fax:* 613-990-1972 *E-mail:* ngcbook@gallery.ca *Web Site:* www.national.gallery.ca, pg 513

Auerbach, Karen, Kensington Publishing Corp, 119 W 40 St, New York, NY 10018 *Tel:* 212-407-1500 *Toll Free Tel:* 800-221-2647 *Fax:* 212-935-0699 *Web Site:* www.kensingtonbooks.com, pg 139

Aufmuth, Christopher, Michelin Maps & Guides, One Parkway S, Greenville, SC 29615-5022 *Tel:* 864-458-5565 *Fax:* 864-458-5665 *Toll Free Fax:* 866-297-0914; 888-773-7979 *E-mail:* orders@americanmap.com (orders) *Web Site:* www.michelintravel.com; www.michelinguide.com, pg 165

Augerbraun, Harold, National Book Awards, 90 Broad St, Suite 604, New York, NY 10004 *Tel:* 212-685-0261 *Fax:* 212-213-6570 *E-mail:* nationalbook@nationalbook.org *Web Site:* www.nationalbook.org, pg 726

Auh, Jin, The Wylie Agency Inc, 250 W 57 St, Suite 2114, New York, NY 10107 *Tel:* 212-246-0069 *Fax:* 212-586-8953 *E-mail:* mail@wylieagency.com *Web Site:* www.wylieagency.com, pg 600

Aujla, Simmi, Houghton Mifflin Harcourt, 222 Berkeley St, Boston, MA 02116-3764 *Tel:* 617-351-5000 *Toll Free Tel:* 800-225-5425 (Pre-K-8); 800-462-6595 (6–12; Advanced & Electives); 800-289-4490 (Specialized Curriculum: Great Source, Rigby, Saxon, Steck-Vaughn; Homeschool; Adult Ed); 800-323-9540 (Assessment: Riverside Publishing); 888-391-3245 (SkillsTutor); 888-242-6747 option 2 (Destination Series; Classroom Connect; Earobics; Edmark; Learning Village; Riverdeep); 800-225-3362 (Houghton Mifflin Harcourt Trade & Reference Publishers); 800-225-5800 (Heinemann) *Fax:* 617-351-1125 *Web Site:* www.hmhco.com, pg 123

Aujla, Simmi, Houghton Mifflin Harcourt Trade & Reference Division, 222 Berkeley St, Boston, MA 02116-3764 *Tel:* 617-351-5000 *Toll Free Tel:* 800-225-3362 *Web Site:* www.houghtonmifflinbooks.com, pg 124

Ault, Charles, Temple University Press, 1852 N Tenth St, Philadelphia, PA 19122-6099 *Tel:* 215-926-2140 *Toll Free Tel:* 800-621-2736 *Fax:* 215-926-2141 *E-mail:* tempress@temple.edu *Web Site:* www.temple.edu/tempress, pg 251

Austin, Kurt, National Council of Teachers of English (NCTE), 1111 W Kenyon Rd, Urbana, IL 61801-1096 *Tel:* 217-328-3870 *Toll Free Tel:* 877-369-6283 (cust serv) *Fax:* 217-328-9645 *E-mail:* orders@ncte.org *Web Site:* www.ncte.org, pg 174

Avery, Laurie, Ohio State University Press, 180 Pressey Hall, 1070 Carmack Rd, Columbus, OH 43210-1002 *Tel:* 614-292-6930 *Fax:* 614-292-2065 *Toll Free Fax:* 800-621-8476 *E-mail:* info@osupress.org *Web Site:* ohiostatepress.org, pg 184

Avery, Marguerite, The MIT Press, 55 Hayward St, Cambridge, MA 02142 *Tel:* 617-253-5255 *Toll Free Tel:* 800-207-8354 (orders) *Fax:* 617-258-6779; 617-577-1545 (orders) *Web Site:* mitpress.mit.edu, pg 167

Avis, Ed, Health Administration Press, One N Franklin St, Suite 1700, Chicago, IL 60606-3491 *Tel:* 312-424-2800 *Fax:* 312-424-0014 *E-mail:* hap1@ache.org *Web Site:* www.ache.org; www.ache.org/hap.cfm (orders), pg 116

Awalt, Barbe, LPD Press, 925 Salamanca NW, Los Ranchos de Albuquerque, NM 87107-5647 *Tel:* 505-344-9382 *Fax:* 505-345-5129 *E-mail:* info@nmsantos.com *Web Site:* nmsantos.com, pg 153

Axelrod, Glen, TFH Publications Inc, One TFH Plaza, Third & Union Aves, Neptune City, NJ 07753 *Tel:* 732-988-8400 *Toll Free Tel:* 800-631-2188 *Fax:* 732-776-8763 *E-mail:* info@tfh.com *Web Site:* www.tfh.com, pg 253

Axelrod, Steven, The Axelrod Agency, 55 Main St, Chatham, NY 12037 *Tel:* 518-392-2100, pg 561

Axelson-Berry, Kitty, Modern Memoirs, 34 Main St, No 9, Amherst, MA 01002-2367 *Tel:* 413-253-2353 *Web Site:* www.modernmemoirs.com, pg 168

Axford, Elizabeth C, Piano Press, 1425 Ocean Ave, Suite 17, Del Mar, CA 92014 *Tel:* 619-884-1401 *Fax:* 858-755-1104 *E-mail:* pianopress@pianopress.com *Web Site:* www.pianopress.com, pg 201

Azantian, Jennifer, Sandra Dijkstra Literary Agency, 1155 Camino del Mar, PMB 515, Del Mar, CA 92014-2605 *Web Site:* dijkstraagency.com, pg 568

Azar, Phyllis, Tom Doherty Associates, LLC, 175 Fifth Ave, 14th fl, New York, NY 10010 *Tel:* 646-307-5151 *Toll Free Tel:* 800-455-0340 *Fax:* 212-388-0191 *E-mail:* firstname.lastname@tor.com *Web Site:* www.tor-forge.com, pg 80

Aziz, Ms Nurjehan, TSAR Publications, PO Box 6996, Sta A, Toronto, ON M5W 1X7, Canada *Tel:* 416-483-7191 *Fax:* 416-486-0706 *E-mail:* inquiries@tsarbooks.com *Web Site:* www.tsarbooks.com, pg 522

Azula, Carlos, Penguin Group (USA) LLC Sales, 375 Hudson St, New York, NY 10014 *Tel:* 212-366-2000 *E-mail:* online@penguinputnam.com *Web Site:* us.penguingroup.com, pg 197

Baake, Mike, Self-Realization Fellowship Publishers, 3208 Humboldt St, Los Angeles, CA 90031 *Tel:* 323-276-6002 *Toll Free Tel:* 888-773-8680 *Fax:* 323-927-1624 *Web Site:* www.srfpublishers.org, pg 231

Babb, Billy, Pentecostal Publishing House, 8855 Dunn Rd, Hazelwood, MO 63042 *Tel:* 314-837-7300 *Fax:* 314-336-1803 *E-mail:* pphordersdept@upci.org (orders) *Web Site:* www.pentecostalpublishing.com, pg 198

Babbitt, Sherry, Philadelphia Museum of Art, 2525 Pennsylvania Ave, Philadelphia, PA 19130 *Tel:* 215-684-7250 *Fax:* 215-235-8715 *Web Site:* www.philamuseum.org, pg 200

Babler, Linda, Atwood Publishing, PO Box 3185, Madison, WI 53704-0185 *Tel:* 608-242-7101 *Toll Free Tel:* 888-242-7101 *Fax:* 608-242-7102 *E-mail:* customerservice@atwoodpublishing.com *Web Site:* www.atwoodpublishing.com, pg 26

Baca, Lynn Thompson, School for Advanced Research Press, 660 Garcia St, Santa Fe, NM 87505 *Tel:* 505-954-7206 *Toll Free Tel:* 888-390-6070 *Fax:* 505-954-7241 *E-mail:* press@sarsf.org *Web Site:* sarpress.sarweb.org, pg 229

Bacak, Walter W Jr, American Translators Association (ATA), 225 Reinekers Lane, Suite 590, Alexandria, VA 22314 *Tel:* 703-683-6100 *Fax:* 703-683-6122 *E-mail:* ata@atanet.org *Web Site:* www.atanet.org, pg 615

Bacak, Walter W Jr, Lewis Galantiere Translation Award, 225 Reinekers Lane, Suite 590, Alexandria, VA 22314 *Tel:* 703-683-6100 *Fax:* 703-683-6122 *E-mail:* ata@atanet.org *Web Site:* www.atanet.org, pg 706

Bace, Marjan, Manning Publications Co, 20 Baldwin Rd, Shelter Island, NY 11964 *Toll Free Tel:* 800-294-4747 (orders) *E-mail:* orders@manning.com *Web Site:* www.manning.com, pg 156

Bach, Daniel N, Book Manufacturers' Institute Inc (BMI), 2 Armand Beach Dr, Suite 1B, Palm Coast, FL 32137-2612 *Tel:* 386-986-4552 *Fax:* 386-986-4553 *E-mail:* info@bmibook.com *Web Site:* www.bmibook.org, pg 618

Bacha, Diane, Madavor Media, 21027 Crossroads Circle, Waukesha, WI 53187-1612 *Tel:* 262-796-8776 *Toll Free Tel:* 800-533-6644 (cust serv & orders) *Fax:* 262-796-1615 (sales & cust serv); 262-798-6468 (edit) *Web Site:* www.kalmbach.com, pg 155

Bachman, Margie K, University of Pittsburgh Press, Eureka Bldg, 5th fl, 3400 Forbes Ave, Pittsburgh, PA 15260 *Tel:* 412-383-2456 *Fax:* 412-383-2466 *E-mail:* info@upress.pitt.edu *Web Site:* www.upress.pitt.edu, pg 268

Bachman, Tori, International Reading Association, 800 Barksdale Rd, Newark, DE 19711-3204 *Tel:* 302-731-1600 *Toll Free Tel:* 800-336-7323 (US & CN) *Fax:* 302-731-1057 *E-mail:* customerservice@reading.org *Web Site:* www.reading.org, pg 133

Back, Don, Riverside Publishing, 3800 Golf Rd, Suite 200, Rolling Meadows, IL 60008 *Tel:* 630-467-7000 *Toll Free Tel:* 800-323-9540 *Fax:* 630-467-7192 (cust serv) *E-mail:* rpc_customer_service@hmhpub.com (cust serv) *Web Site:* www.riversidepublishing.com, pg 219

Backhus, Craig, American Society of Mechanical Engineers (ASME), 3 Park Ave, New York, NY 10016-5990 *Tel:* 212-591-7000 *Toll Free Tel:* 800-843-2763 (cust serv-US, CN & Mexico) *Fax:* 212-591-7674; 973-882-8113 (cust serv); 973-882-1717 (orders & inquiries) *E-mail:* infocentral@asme.org *Web Site:* www.asme.org, pg 17

Backing, Janis, Moody Publishers, 820 N La Salle Blvd, Chicago, IL 60610 *Tel:* 312-329-4000 *Toll Free Tel:* 800-678-8812 (cust serv) *Fax:* 312-329-2019 *Web Site:* www.moodypublishers.com, pg 169

Backman, Elizabeth H, Elizabeth H Backman, 86 Johnnycake Hollow Rd, Pine Plains, NY 12567 *Tel:* 518-398-9344 *Fax:* 518-398-6368 *E-mail:* bethcountry@fairpoint.net, pg 561

Backman, John, Backman Writing & Communications, 32 Hillview Ave, Rensselaer, NY 12144 *Tel:* 518-449-4985 *Fax:* 518-449-7273 *Web Site:* www.backwrite.com, pg 541

Backus, Dr Charles, Texas A&M University Press, John H Lindsey Bldg, Lewis St, 4354 TAMU, College Station, TX 77843-4354 *Tel:* 979-845-1436 *Toll Free Tel:* 800-826-8911 (orders) *Fax:* 979-847-8752 *Toll Free Fax:* 888-617-2421 (orders) *E-mail:* upress@tamu.edu *Web Site:* www.tamupress.com, pg 252

Bacon, Stephanie, Idaho Center for the Book, Boise State University, 1910 University Dr, Boise, ID 83725 *Tel:* 208-426-1000 *Toll Free Tel:* 800-992-8398 (outside ID) *Fax:* 208-426-1243 *Web Site:* www.lili.org/icb; www.boisestatebooks.com (orders), pg 126

Badalian, Mrs Alvart, Blue Crane Books, PO Box 380291, Cambridge, MA 02238 *Tel:* 617-926-8989 *Fax:* 617-926-0982 *E-mail:* bluecrane@arrow1.com, pg 41

Badalov, Anar, The MIT Press, 55 Hayward St, Cambridge, MA 02142 *Tel:* 617-253-5255 *Toll Free Tel:* 800-207-8354 (orders) *Fax:* 617-258-6779; 617-577-1545 (orders) *Web Site:* mitpress.mit.edu, pg 167

Badani, Abbas, Association of College & University Printers, Penn State University, 101 Hostetter Business Services Bldg, University Park, PA 16802 *Tel:* 814-865-7544 *Fax:* 814-863-6376 *Web Site:* www.multimediaprint.psu.edu, pg 616

364-5798 (orders) *Toll Free Fax:* 800-735-0476 (orders) *E-mail:* presscs@ou.edu *Web Site:* www.oupress.com, pg 268

Baker-Baughman, Bernadette, Victoria Sanders & Associates LLC, 241 Avenue of the Americas, Suite 11-H, New York, NY 10014 *Tel:* 212-633-8811 *Fax:* 212-633-0525 *E-mail:* queriesvsa@gmail.com *Web Site:* www.victoriasanders.com, pg 592

Bakhtiar, Mary, Kazi Publications Inc, 3023 W Belmont Ave, Chicago, IL 60618 *Tel:* 773-267-7001 *Fax:* 773-267-7002 *E-mail:* info@kazi.org *Web Site:* www.kazi.org, pg 138

Bakke, Timothy O, Creative Homeowner, 24 Park Way, Upper Saddle River, NJ 07458-9960 *Tel:* 201-934-7100 *Toll Free Tel:* 800-631-7795 (cust serv) *Fax:* 201-934-7541; 201-934-8971 (orders) *E-mail:* info@creativehomeowner.com; customerservice@creativehomeowner.com *Web Site:* www.creativehomeowner.com, pg 71

Balachander, Bala, CTB/McGraw-Hill, 20 Ryan Ranch Rd, Monterey, CA 93940-5703 *Tel:* 831-393-0700 *Toll Free Tel:* 800-538-9547 *Fax:* 831-393-7825 *Web Site:* www.ctb.com, pg 73

Baldacci, Matthew, St Martin's Press, LLC, 175 Fifth Ave, New York, NY 10010 *Tel:* 646-307-5151 *Fax:* 212-420-9314 *E-mail:* firstname.lastname@macmillan.com *Web Site:* www.stmartins.com, pg 224

Baldi, Malaga, Malaga Baldi Literary Agency, 233 W 99, Suite 19C, New York, NY 10025 *Tel:* 212-222-3213 *E-mail:* baldibooks@gmail.com; info@baldibooks.com *Web Site:* www.baldibooks.com, pg 561

Baldwin, Margo, Chelsea Green Publishing Co, 85 N Main St, Suite 120, White River Junction, VT 05001 *Tel:* 802-295-6300 *Toll Free Tel:* 800-639-4099 (cust serv, consumer & trade orders) *Fax:* 802-295-6444 *Web Site:* www.chelseagreen.com, pg 59

Baldwin, Ruth, Nation Books, 116 E 16 St, 8th fl, New York, NY 10003 *Tel:* 212-822-0264 *Fax:* 212-253-5356 *E-mail:* submissions@nationbooks.org *Web Site:* www.nationbooks.org, pg 172

Bales, Richard, The Society of Midland Authors (SMA), PO Box 10419, Chicago, IL 60610 *E-mail:* info@midlandauthors.com *Web Site:* www.midlandauthors.com, pg 636

Bales, Richard, The Society of Midland Authors Awards, 530 Michigan Ave, Evanston, IL 60202 *E-mail:* info@midlandauthors.com *Web Site:* www.midlandauthors.com, pg 743

Balin, Sandy, C & T Publishing Inc, 1651 Challenge Dr, Concord, CA 94520-5206 *Tel:* 925-677-0377 *Toll Free Tel:* 800-284-1114 *Fax:* 925-677-0373 *E-mail:* ctinfo@ctpub.com *Web Site:* www.ctpub.com, pg 50

Balkcum, Gregg, Aerial Photography Services Inc, 2511 S Tryon St, Charlotte, NC 28203 *Tel:* 704-333-5143 *Fax:* 704-333-4911 *E-mail:* aps@aps-1.com *Web Site:* www.aps-1.com, pg 6

Balkin, Richard A, Ward & Balkin Agency, Inc, 30 Brock Way, South Hadley, MA 01075 *Tel:* 413-322-8697 *Web Site:* www.wardbalkin.com, pg 598

Ball, Christine, Dutton, 375 Hudson St, New York, NY 10014 *Tel:* 212-366-2000 *Fax:* 212-366-2262 *E-mail:* online@penguinputnam.com *Web Site:* www.penguinputnam.com; us.penguingroup.com, pg 83

Ball, Susan, Artists' Fellowships, 20 Jay St, 7th fl, Brooklyn, NY 11201 *Tel:* 212-366-6900 *Fax:* 212-366-1778 *E-mail:* info@nyfa.org *Web Site:* www.nyfa.org, pg 688

Ballantine, Elizabeth, Inter American Press Association (IAPA), Jules Dubois Bldg, 1801 SW Third Ave, Miami, FL 33129 *Tel:* 305-634-2465 *Fax:* 305-635-2272 *E-mail:* info@sipiapa.org *Web Site:* www.sipiapa.org, pg 625

Ballantyne, Robert, Arsenal Pulp Press, 211 E Georgia St, No 101, Vancouver, BC V6A 1Z6, Canada *Tel:* 604-687-4233 *Toll Free Tel:* 888-600-PULP (600-7857) *Fax:* 604-687-4283 *E-mail:* info@arsenalpulp.com *Web Site:* www.arsenalpulp.com, pg 493

Ballard, John, World Citizens, PO Box 131, Mill Valley, CA 94942-0131 *Tel:* 415-380-8020 *Toll Free Tel:* 800-247-6553 (orders only), pg 285

Ballard, Kimberly, National Braille Press, 88 Saint Stephen St, Boston, MA 02115-4302 *Tel:* 617-266-6160 *Toll Free Tel:* 800-548-7323 (cust serv); 888-965-8965 *Fax:* 617-437-0456 *E-mail:* orders@nbp.org *Web Site:* www.nbp.org, pg 173

Ballenger, Seale, Disney Publishing Worldwide, 44 S Broadway, 9th fl, White Plains, NY 10601-4411 *Tel:* 914-288-4100 *Web Site:* disney.go.com/books/index, pg 80

Balliett, Will, Thames & Hudson, 500 Fifth Ave, New York, NY 10110 *Tel:* 212-354-3763 *Toll Free Tel:* 800-233-4830 *Fax:* 212-398-1252 *E-mail:* bookinfo@thames.wwnorton.com *Web Site:* www.thamesandhudsonusa.com, pg 253

Ballinger, Malcolm, Ballinger Publishing, 41 N Jefferson St, Suite 402, Pensacola, FL 32502 *Tel:* 850-433-1166 *Fax:* 850-435-9174 *E-mail:* info@ballingerpublishing.com *Web Site:* www.ballingerpublishing.com, pg 30

Ballinger, Peter R, P R B Productions, 963 Peralta Ave, Albany, CA 94706-2144 *Tel:* 510-526-0722 *Fax:* 510-527-4763 *E-mail:* prbprdns@aol.com *Web Site:* www.prbmusic.com, pg 190

Balmuth, Deborah, Storey Publishing LLC, 210 MASS MoCA Way, North Adams, MA 01247 *Tel:* 413-346-2100 *Toll Free Tel:* 800-441-5700 (orders); 800-793-9396 (edit) *Fax:* 413-346-2199; 413-346-2196 (edit) *E-mail:* sales@storey.com *Web Site:* www.storey.com, pg 245

Balotro, April, BowTie Press®, 3 Burroughs, Irvine, CA 92618 *Tel:* 949-855-8822 *Toll Free Tel:* 888-738-2665 *Fax:* 949-458-3856 *E-mail:* bowtiepress@bowtieinc.com *Web Site:* www.bowtiepress.com, pg 44

Balsamo, Kathy, Pieces of Learning, 1990 Market Rd, Marion, IL 62959-8976 *Tel:* 618-964-9426 *Toll Free Tel:* 800-729-5137 *Toll Free Fax:* 800-844-0455 *E-mail:* piecesoflearning@verizon.net *Web Site:* www.piecesoflearning.com, pg 201

Balsamo, Stan, Pieces of Learning, 1990 Market Rd, Marion, IL 62959-8976 *Tel:* 618-964-9426 *Toll Free Tel:* 800-729-5137 *Toll Free Fax:* 800-844-0455 *E-mail:* piecesoflearning@verizon.net *Web Site:* www.piecesoflearning.com, pg 201

Balthazar, Martin, Les Editions de l'Hexagone, 1010 rue de la Gauchetiere E, Montreal, QC H2L 2N5, Canada *Tel:* 514-523-7993 (ext 4201) *Fax:* 514-282-7530 *E-mail:* vml@sogides.com *Web Site:* www.edhexagone.com, pg 502

Balvenie, K, One Act Play Depot, Box 335, 618 Memorial Dr, Spiritwood, SK S0J 2M0, Canada *E-mail:* plays@oneactplays.net; orders@oneactplays.net *Web Site:* oneactplays.net, pg 514

Bamford, Christopher, Lindisfarne Books, 610 Main St, Great Barrington, MA 01230 *Tel:* 413-528-8233 *Fax:* 413-528-8826 *E-mail:* service@lindisfarne.org *Web Site:* www.lindisfarne.org, pg 149

Bamford, Christopher, SteinerBooks, 610 Main St, Great Barrington, MA 01230 *Tel:* 413-528-8233 *Fax:* 413-528-8826 *E-mail:* friends@steinerbooks.org *Web Site:* www.steinerbooks.org, pg 244

Bandini, Lisa Kent, Developmental Studies Center, 2000 Embarcadero, Suite 305, Oakland, CA 94606-5300 *Tel:* 510-533-0213 *Toll Free Tel:* 800-666-7270 *Fax:* 510-464-3670 *E-mail:* pubs@devstu.org; info@devstu.org *Web Site:* www.devstu.org, pg 78

Bandos, Dr Kate, Bookhaven Press LLC, 302 Scenic Ct, Moon Township, PA 15108 *Tel:* 412-494-6926 *Toll Free Tel:* 800-782-7424 (orders only) *E-mail:* info@bookhavenpress.com; orders@bookhavenpress.com *Web Site:* bookhavenpress.com, pg 43

Banducci, Jo Anne, University of Nevada Press, University of Nevada, M/S 0166, Reno, NV 89557-0166 *Tel:* 775-784-6573 *Fax:* 775-784-6200 *Web Site:* www.unpress.nevada.edu, pg 267

Bane, Barbara S, NeDeo Press, PO Box 668, Robbins, NC 27325 *Web Site:* www.nedeopress.com, pg 176

Bane, Vickie, Colorado Authors' League, PO Box 24905, Denver, CO 80224 *Web Site:* www.coloradoauthors.org, pg 621

Banis, Robert J, Science & Humanities Press, 56 Summit Point, St Charles, MO 62201 *Tel:* 636-394-4950 *Web Site:* sciencehumanitiespress.com; beachhousebooks.com; macroprintbooks.com; earlyeditionsbooks.com; heuristicsbooks.com, pg 229

Bank, Josh, Alloy Entertainment, 151 W 26 St, 11th fl, New York, NY 10001 *Tel:* 212-244-4307 *E-mail:* nycassistant@alloyentertainment.com *Web Site:* www.alloyentertainment.com, pg 9

Banker, Rhea, Pearson Education/ELT, 10 Bank St, 9th fl, White Plains, NY 10606-1951 *Tel:* 914-287-8000 *Web Site:* www.pearsonelt.com, pg 195

Banks, Clare, Beullah Rose Poetry Prize, PO Box 22161, Baltimore, MD 21203 *Web Site:* www.smartishpace.com, pg 690

Banks, Renee, Chronicle Books LLC, 680 Second St, San Francisco, CA 94107 *Tel:* 415-537-4200 *Toll Free Tel:* 800-759-0190 (cust serv) *Fax:* 415-537-4460 *Toll Free Fax:* 800-858-7787 (orders); 800-286-9471 (cust serv) *E-mail:* frontdesk@chroniclebooks.com *Web Site:* www.chroniclebooks.com, pg 61

Bannon, Dr Joseph J Sr, Sagamore Publishing LLC, 1807 Federal Dr, Urbana, IL 61801 *Tel:* 217-359-5940 *Toll Free Tel:* 800-327-5557 (orders) *Fax:* 217-359-5975 *E-mail:* books@sagamorepub.com *Web Site:* www.sagamorepub.com, pg 223

Bannon, Peter L, Sagamore Publishing LLC, 1807 Federal Dr, Urbana, IL 61801 *Tel:* 217-359-5940 *Toll Free Tel:* 800-327-5557 (orders) *Fax:* 217-359-5975 *E-mail:* books@sagamorepub.com *Web Site:* www.sagamorepub.com, pg 223

Barathon, Marie-Pierre, Les Editions XYZ inc, 1815 Ave de Lorimier, Montreal, QC H2K 3W6, Canada *Tel:* 514-525-2170 *Fax:* 514-525-7537 *E-mail:* info@editionsxyz.com *Web Site:* www.editionsxyz.com, pg 504

Barb, Patrick, Watson-Guptill Publications, c/o Random House Inc, 1745 Broadway, New York, NY 10019 *Tel:* 212-782-9000 *Fax:* 212-940-7381 *E-mail:* crownbiz@randomhouse.com *Web Site:* www.randomhouse.com/crown/watsonguptill, pg 277

Barba, Susan, David R Godine Publisher Inc, 15 Court Sq, Suite 320, Boston, MA 02108-4715 *Tel:* 617-451-9600 *Fax:* 617-350-0250 *E-mail:* pub@godine.com *Web Site:* www.godine.com, pg 104

Barbee, Michael, Madavor Media, 21027 Crossroads Circle, Waukesha, WI 53187-1612 *Tel:* 262-796-8776 *Toll Free Tel:* 800-533-6644 (cust serv & orders) *Fax:* 262-796-1615 (sales & cust serv); 262-798-6468 (edit) *Web Site:* www.kalmbach.com, pg 155

Barber, A Richard, A Richard Barber/Peter Berinstein & Associates, 60 E Eighth St, Suite 21-N, New York, NY 10003 *Tel:* 212-737-7266 *Fax:* 860-927-3942 *E-mail:* barberrich@aol.com, pg 561

Barber, Orion M, Orion Book Services, 751 South St, West Brattleboro, VT 05301-4234 *Tel:* 802-254-8783 (press 2) *Fax:* 802-254-8783 (call first) *E-mail:* gr8books@myfairpoint.net, pg 552

Barbour, Bruce R, Literary Management Group LLC, 613 Crieve Rd, Nashville, TN 37220 *Tel:* 615-832-7231 *Web Site:* www.literarymanagementgroup.com; www.brucebarbour.com, pg 582

Barbour, Matthew, Omnigraphics Inc, 155 W Congress, Suite 200, Detroit, MI 48226 *Tel:* 313-961-1340 *Toll Free Tel:* 800-234-1340 (cust serv) *Fax:* 313-961-1383 *Toll Free Fax:* 800-875-1340 (cust serv) *E-mail:* info@omnigraphics.com *Web Site:* www.omnigraphics.com, pg 185

Barbour, Wanda, American Industrial Hygiene Association - AIHA, 3141 Fairview Park Dr, Suite 777, Falls Church, VA 22042 *Tel:* 703-849-8888 *Fax:* 703-207-3561 *E-mail:* infonet@aiha.org *Web Site:* www.aiha.org, pg 13

Barcatta, Sabine, Thomas J Lyon Book Award in Western American Literary and Cultural Studies, PO Box 6815, Logan, UT 84341 *Web Site:* www.westernlit.org/thomas-j-lyon-book-award-in-western-american-literary-and-cultural-studies/; www.westernlit.org, pg 720

Barer-Stein, Thelma PhD, Culture Concepts Books, 69 Ashmount Crescent, Toronto, ON M9R 1C9, Canada *Tel:* 416-245-8119 *E-mail:* cultureconcepts@rogers.com *Web Site:* www.cultureconceptsbooks.ca; www.bookdoctor.ca, pg 544

Barich, Steven, Alan Wofsy Fine Arts, 1109 Geary Blvd, San Francisco, CA 94109 *Tel:* 415-292-6500 *Toll Free Tel:* 800-660-6403 *Fax:* 415-292-6594 (off & cust serv); 415-512-0130 (acctg) *E-mail:* order@art-books.com (orders); editeur@earthlink.net (edit); beauxarts@earthlink.net (cust serv) *Web Site:* www.art-books.com, pg 284

Baril, Andre, Les Presses De L'Universite Laval, Pavillon Maurice-Pollack, Suite 3103, 2305 University St, Quebec, QC G1V 0A6, Canada *Tel:* 418-656-2803 *Fax:* 418-656-3305 *E-mail:* presses@pul.ulaval.ca *Web Site:* www.pulaval.com, pg 516

Barkan, Bebe, Cross-Cultural Communications, 239 Wynsum Ave, Merrick, NY 11566-4725 *Tel:* 516-868-5635 *Fax:* 516-379-1901 *E-mail:* info@cross-culturalcommunications.com; cccbarkan@optlonline.net; cccpoetry@aol.com *Web Site:* www.cross-culturalcommunications.com, pg 71

Barkan, Stanley H, Cross-Cultural Communications, 239 Wynsum Ave, Merrick, NY 11566-4725 *Tel:* 516-868-5635 *Fax:* 516-379-1901 *E-mail:* info@cross-culturalcommunications.com; cccbarkan@optlonline.net; cccpoetry@aol.com *Web Site:* www.cross-culturalcommunications.com, pg 71

Barker, Clyde F, American Philosophical Society, 104 S Fifth St, Philadelphia, PA 19106 *Tel:* 215-440-3425 *Fax:* 215-440-3450 *E-mail:* dianepub@comcast.net *Web Site:* www.amphilsoc.org, pg 15

Barker, Dr David, Bloomsbury Academic, 80 Maiden Lane, Suite 704, New York, NY 10038 *Tel:* 212-953-5858 *Toll Free Tel:* 800-561-7704 *Fax:* 212-953-5944 *E-mail:* info@continuum-books.com *Web Site:* www.continuumbooks.com, pg 40

Barker, Wayne G, Aegean Park Press, PO Box 2120, Walnut Creek, CA 94595 *Tel:* 925-947-2533 *Toll Free Tel:* 800-736-3587 (orders only) *E-mail:* aegeanparkpress@earthlink.net *Web Site:* www.aegeanparkpress.com, pg 6

Barnes, Catherine, Oxford University Press USA, 198 Madison Ave, New York, NY 10016 *Tel:* 212-726-6000 *Toll Free Tel:* 800-451-7556 (orders); 800-445-9714 (cust serv) *Fax:* 919-677-1303 *E-mail:* custserv.us@oup.com *Web Site:* www.oup.com/us, pg 189

Barnes, Jacqueline, BuilderBooks.com, 1201 15 St NW, Washington, DC 20005 *Tel:* 202-822-0200 *Toll Free Tel:* 800-223-2665 *Fax:* 202-266-8096 (edit) *E-mail:* builderbooks@nahb.com *Web Site:* www.builderbooks.com, pg 49

Barnes, Janet, Bentley Publishers, 1734 Massachusetts Ave, Cambridge, MA 02138-1804 *Tel:* 617-547-4170 *Toll Free Tel:* 800-423-4595 *Fax:* 617-876-9235 *E-mail:* sales@bentleypublishers.com *Web Site:* www.bentleypublishers.com, pg 35

Barnes, Jim, Axiom Business Book Awards, 1129 Woodmere Ave, Suite B, Traverse City, MI 49686 *Tel:* 231-933-0445 *Toll Free Tel:* 800-706-4636 *Fax:* 231-933-0448 *E-mail:* info@axiomawards.com *Web Site:* www.axiomawards.com, pg 689

Barnes, Jim, The Independent Publisher Book Awards, 1129 Woodmere Ave, Suite B, Traverse City, MI 49686 *Tel:* 231-933-0445 *Toll Free Tel:* 800-706-4636 *Fax:* 231-933-0448 *Web Site:* www.independentpublisher.com/ipaward.lasso, pg 711

Barnes, Jim, Jenkins Group Inc, 1129 Woodmere Ave, Suite B, Traverse City, MI 49686 *Tel:* 231-933-0445 *Toll Free Tel:* 800-706-4636 *Fax:* 231-933-0448 *E-mail:* info@bookpublishing.com *Web Site:* www.bookpublishing.com, pg 549

Barnes, Jim, Moonbeam Children's Book Awards, 1129 Woodmere Ave, Suite B, Traverse City, MI 49686 *Tel:* 231-933-0445 *Toll Free Tel:* 800-706-4636 *Fax:* 231-933-0448 *E-mail:* info@axiomawards.com *Web Site:* www.moonbeamawards.com, pg 724

Barnes, Shannon Howe, Marilyn Baillie Picture Book Award, 40 Orchard View Blvd, Suite 217, Toronto, ON M4R 1B9, Canada *Tel:* 416-975-0010 *Fax:* 416-975-8970 *E-mail:* info@bookcentre.ca *Web Site:* www.bookcentre.ca, pg 689

Barnes, Shannon Howe, The Geoffrey Bilson Award for Historical Fiction for Young People, 40 Orchard View Blvd, Suite 217, Toronto, ON M4R 1B9, Canada *Tel:* 416-975-0010 *Fax:* 416-975-8970 *E-mail:* info@bookcentre.ca *Web Site:* www.bookcentre.ca, pg 691

Barnes, Shannon Howe, Canadian Children's Book Centre, 40 Orchard View Blvd, Suite 217, Toronto, ON M4R 1B9, Canada *Tel:* 416-975-0010 *Fax:* 416-975-8970 *E-mail:* info@bookcentre.ca *Web Site:* www.bookcentre.ca, pg 620

Barnes, Shannon Howe, Norma Fleck Award for Canadian Children's Non-Fiction, 40 Orchard View Blvd, Suite 217, Toronto, ON M4R 1B9, Canada *Tel:* 416-975-0010 *Fax:* 416-975-8970 *E-mail:* info@bookcentre.ca *Web Site:* www.bookcentre.ca, pg 704

Barnes, Shannon Howe, Monica Hughes Award for Science Fiction & Fantasy, 40 Orchard View Blvd, Suite 217, Toronto, ON M4R 1B9, Canada *Tel:* 416-975-0010 *Fax:* 416-975-8970 *E-mail:* info@bookcentre.ca *Web Site:* www.bookcentre.ca, pg 711

Barnes, Shannon Howe, John Spray Mystery Award, 40 Orchard View Blvd, Suite 217, Toronto, ON M4R 1B9, Canada *Tel:* 416-975-0010 *Fax:* 416-975-8970 *E-mail:* info@bookcentre.ca *Web Site:* www.bookcentre.ca, pg 744

Barnes, Shannon Howe, TD Canadian Children's Literature Award, 40 Orchard View Blvd, Suite 217, Toronto, ON M4R 1B9, Canada *Tel:* 416-975-0010 *Fax:* 416-975-8970 *E-mail:* info@bookcentre.ca *Web Site:* www.bookcentre.ca, pg 745

Barnett, Chrissie A, Southern California Writers' Conference, 1010 University Ave, Suite 54, San Diego, CA 92103 *Tel:* 619-303-8185 *Fax:* 619-303-7462 *E-mail:* wewrite@writersconference.com *Web Site:* www.writersconference.com, pg 673

Barnett, Marilyn, Workman Publishing Co Inc, 225 Varick St, 9th fl, New York, NY 10014-4381 *Tel:* 212-254-5900 *Toll Free Tel:* 800-722-7202 *Fax:* 212-254-8098 *E-mail:* info@workman.com *Web Site:* www.workman.com, pg 285

Barnett, Nancy, House to House Publications, 11 Toll Gate Rd, Lititz, PA 17543 *Tel:* 717-627-1996 *Toll Free Tel:* 800-848-5892 *Fax:* 717-627-4004 *E-mail:* h2hp@dcfi.org *Web Site:* www.h2hp.com; www.dcfi.org, pg 124

Barney, Stacey, GP Putnam's Sons (Children's), 345 Hudson St, New York, NY 10014 *Tel:* 212-366-2000 *Fax:* 212-414-3393 *E-mail:* online@penguinputnam.com *Web Site:* us.penguingroup.com, pg 210

Barocci, Bob, Advertising Research Foundation (ARF), 432 Park Ave S, 6th fl, New York, NY 10016-8013 *Tel:* 212-751-5656 *Fax:* 212-319-5265 *E-mail:* info@thearf.org; jar@thearf.org (edit) *Web Site:* www.thearf.org; www.journalofadvertisingresearch.com, pg 611

Baron, Carole, Alfred A Knopf/Everyman's Library, c/o Random House Inc, 1745 Broadway, New York, NY 10019 *Tel:* 212-751-2600 *Toll Free Tel:* 800-638-6460 *Fax:* 212-572-2593 *Web Site:* www.knopfdoubleday.com, pg 141

Baron, Herman, Diane Publishing Co, 330 Pusey Ave, Suite 3 (rear), Collingdale, PA 19023-0617 *Tel:* 610-461-6200 *Toll Free Tel:* 800-782-3833 *Fax:* 610-461-6130 *Web Site:* www.dianepublishing.net, pg 79

Baror, Danny, Baror International Inc, PO Box 868, Armonk, NY 10504-0868 *Tel:* 914-273-9199 *Fax:* 914-273-5058 *Web Site:* www.barorint.com, pg 562

Baror-Shapiro, Heather, Baror International Inc, PO Box 868, Armonk, NY 10504-0868 *Tel:* 914-273-9199 *Fax:* 914-273-5058 *Web Site:* www.barorint.com, pg 562

Barot, Len, Bold Strokes Books Inc, PO Box 249, Valley Falls, NY 12185 *Tel:* 518-677-5127 *Fax:* 518-677-5291 *E-mail:* bsb@boldstrokesbooks.com *Web Site:* www.boldstrokesbooks.com, pg 42

Barr, Brenna, Dystel & Goderich Literary Management, One Union Sq W, Suite 904, New York, NY 10003 *Tel:* 212-627-9100 *Fax:* 212-627-9313 *Web Site:* www.dystel.com, pg 569

Barr, Stephen, Writers House, 21 W 26 St, New York, NY 10010 *Tel:* 212-685-2400 *Fax:* 212-685-1781 *Web Site:* www.writershouse.com, pg 599

Barr, Wayne, Barron's Educational Series Inc, 250 Wireless Blvd, Hauppauge, NY 11788 *Tel:* 631-434-3311 *Toll Free Tel:* 800-645-3476 *Fax:* 631-434-3723 *E-mail:* barrons@barronseduc.com *Web Site:* www.barronseduc.com, pg 31

Barrales-Saylor, Kelly, Albert Whitman & Co, 250 S Northwest Hwy, Suite 320, Park Ridge, IL 60068 *Tel:* 847-232-2800 *Toll Free Tel:* 800-255-7675 *Fax:* 847-581-0039 *E-mail:* mail@awhitmanco.com *Web Site:* www.albertwhitman.com, pg 7

Barras, Lise, Editions du renouveau Pedagogique Inc (ERPI), 5757 rue Cypihot, St-Laurent, QC H4S 1R3, Canada *Tel:* 514-334-2690 *Toll Free Tel:* 800-263-3678 *Fax:* 514-334-4720 *Toll Free Fax:* 800-643-4720 *E-mail:* erpidlm@erpi.com *Web Site:* www.erpi.com, pg 503

Barrer, Mary B, Mature Women Scholarship Grant - Art/Letters/Music, c/o National Pen Women-Scholarship, Pen Arts Bldg, 1300 17 St NW, Washington, DC 20036-1973 *Tel:* 202-785-1997 *Fax:* 202-452-8868 *E-mail:* contact@nlapw.org *Web Site:* www.nlapw.org, pg 722

Barrer, Mary B, National League of American Pen Women, c/o National Pen Women-Scholarship, Pen Arts Bldg, 1300 17 St NW, Washington, DC 20036-1973 *Tel:* 202-785-1997 *Fax:* 202-452-8868 *E-mail:* contact@nlapw.org *Web Site:* www.nlapw.org, pg 630

Barrett, Lauren, Ohio State University Foreign Language Publications, 198 Hagerty Hall, 1775 College Rd, Columbus, OH 43210-1340 *Tel:* 614-292-3838 *Toll Free Tel:* 800-678-6999 *Fax:* 614-688-3355 *E-mail:* flpubs@osu.edu *Web Site:* www.flpubs.osu.edu, pg 184

Barrett, Loretta A, Loretta Barrett Books Inc, 220 E 23 St, 11th fl, New York, NY 10010 *Tel:* 212-242-3420 *E-mail:* query@lorettabarrettbooks.com *Web Site:* www.lorettabarrettbooks.com, pg 562

Barrett, Sheila, Harvard University Press, 79 Garden St, Cambridge, MA 02138-1499 *Tel:* 617-495-2600; 401-531-2800 (intl orders) *Toll Free Tel:* 800-405-1619 (orders) *Fax:* 617-495-5898 (general); 617-496-4677 (edit & rts); 401-531-2801 (intl orders) *Toll Free Fax:* 800-406-9145 (orders) *E-mail:* contact_hup@harvard.edu *Web Site:* www.hup.harvard.edu, pg 115

Barrett, Skip, Crystal Clarity Publishers, 14618 Tyler Foote Rd, Nevada City, CA 95959 *Tel:* 530-478-7600 *Toll Free Tel:* 800-424-1055 *Fax:* 530-478-7610 *E-mail:* clarity@crystalclarity.com *Web Site:* www.crystalclarity.com, pg 73

Barron, Manuel H, Barron's Educational Series Inc, 250 Wireless Blvd, Hauppauge, NY 11788 *Tel:* 631-434-3311 *Toll Free Tel:* 800-645-3476 *Fax:* 631-434-3723 *E-mail:* barrons@barronseduc.com *Web Site:* www.barronseduc.com, pg 31

Barrs, Michael, HarperCollins General Books Group, 10 E 53 St, New York, NY 10022 *Tel:* 212-207-7000 *Fax:* 212-207-7633 *Web Site:* www.harpercollins.com, pg 113

Barry, Beth, Demos Medical Publishing LLC, 11 W 42 St, New York, NY 10036 *Tel:* 212-683-0072 *Toll Free Tel:* 800-532-8663 *Fax:* 212-683-0118 *E-mail:* info@demosmedpub.com; orderdept@demosmedpub.com *Web Site:* www.demosmedpub.com, pg 78

Barry, Graham, Chronicle Books LLC, 680 Second St, San Francisco, CA 94107 *Tel:* 415-537-4200 *Toll Free Tel:* 800-759-0190 (cust serv) *Fax:* 415-537-4460 *Toll Free Fax:* 800-858-7787 (orders); 800-286-9471 (cust serv) *E-mail:* frontdesk@chroniclebooks.com *Web Site:* www.chroniclebooks.com, pg 61

Barry, Jason, Paradigm Publishers, 5589 Arapahoe Ave, Suite 206A, Boulder, CO 80303 *Tel:* 303-245-9054 *Web Site:* www.paradigmpublishers.com, pg 193

Barry, Patrick, Houghton Mifflin Harcourt, 222 Berkeley St, Boston, MA 02116-3764 *Tel:* 617-351-5000 *Toll Free Tel:* 800-225-5425 (Pre-K-8); 800-462-6595 (6–12; Advanced & Electives); 800-289-4490 (Specialized Curriculum: Great Source, Rigby, Saxon, Steck-Vaughn; Homeschool; Adult Ed); 800-323-9540 (Assessment: Riverside Publishing); 888-391-3245 (SkillsTutor); 888-242-6747 option 2 (Destination Series; Classroom Connect; Earobics; Edmark; Learning Village; Riverdeep); 800-225-3362 (Houghton Mifflin Harcourt Trade & Reference Publishers); 800-225-5800 (Heinemann) *Fax:* 617-351-1125 *Web Site:* www.hmhco.com, pg 123

Barry, Patrick, Houghton Mifflin Harcourt Trade & Reference Division, 222 Berkeley St, Boston, MA 02116-3764 *Tel:* 617-351-5000 *Toll Free Tel:* 800-225-3362 *Web Site:* www.houghtonmifflinbooks.com, pg 124

Barry, Sheila, Groundwood Books, 110 Spadina Ave, Suite 801, Toronto, ON M5V 2K4, Canada *Tel:* 416-363-4343 *Fax:* 416-363-1017 *E-mail:* genmail@groundwoodbooks.com *Web Site:* www.houseofanansi.com, pg 507

Barsan, Corinna, Grove/Atlantic Inc, 841 Broadway, 4th fl, New York, NY 10003-4793 *Tel:* 212-614-7850 *Toll Free Tel:* 800-521-0178 *Fax:* 212-614-7886 *E-mail:* info@groveatlantic.com *Web Site:* www.groveatlantic.com, pg 108

Bartels, Lynn, Cup of Tea Books, 2671 Bristol Rd, Columbus, OH 43221 *Tel:* 614-264-5588 *E-mail:* sales@pagespringpublishing.com *Web Site:* www.cupofteabooks.com, pg 73

Bartels, Lynn, Lucky Marble Books, 2671 Bristol Rd, Columbus, OH 43221 *Tel:* 614-264-5588 *E-mail:* sales@pagespringpublishing.com *Web Site:* www.luckymarblebooks.com, pg 154

Barth, Ilene, Red Rock Press, 331 W 57 St, Suite 175, New York, NY 10019 *Tel:* 212-362-8304 *Fax:* 212-362-6216 *E-mail:* info@redrockpress.com *Web Site:* www.redrockpress.com, pg 216

Barth, Richard, Red Rock Press, 331 W 57 St, Suite 175, New York, NY 10019 *Tel:* 212-362-8304 *Fax:* 212-362-6216 *E-mail:* info@redrockpress.com *Web Site:* www.redrockpress.com, pg 216

Barthel, Susie, National Government Publishing Association, 629 N Main St, Hattiesburg, MS 39401 *Tel:* 601-582-3330 *Fax:* 601-582-3354 *E-mail:* info@govpublishing.org *Web Site:* www.govpublishing.org, pg 630

Bartholomew, Marie, Kids Can Press Ltd, 25 Dockside Dr, Toronto, ON M5A 0B5, Canada *Tel:* 416-479-7000 *Toll Free Tel:* 800-265-0884 *Fax:* 416-960-5437 *E-mail:* info@kidscan.com; customerservice@kidscan.com *Web Site:* www.kidscanpress.com; www.kidscanpress.ca, pg 510

Bartlett, Danielle, HarperCollins General Books Group, 10 E 53 St, New York, NY 10022 *Tel:* 212-207-7000 *Fax:* 212-207-7633 *Web Site:* www.harpercollins.com, pg 113

Bartlett, Timothy, Basic Books, 250 W 57 St, 15th fl, New York, NY 10107 *Tel:* 212-340-8164 *Fax:* 212-340-8135 *E-mail:* perseus.promos@perseusbooks.com *Web Site:* www.basicbooks.com; perseusbooks.com, pg 31

Bartok, Josh, Wisdom Publications Inc, 199 Elm St, Somerville, MA 02144 *Tel:* 617-776-7416 *Toll Free Tel:* 800-272-4050 (orders) *Fax:* 617-776-7841 *E-mail:* info@wisdompubs.org *Web Site:* www.wisdompubs.org, pg 283

Barton, John, Constance Rooke Creative Non-Fiction Prize, University of Victoria, Box 1700, Sta CSC, Victoria, BC V8W 2Y2, Canada *Tel:* 250-721-8524 *Fax:* 250-472-5051 *E-mail:* malahat@uvic.ca *Web Site:* malahatreview.ca, pg 698

Barton, John, Far Horizons Award for Poetry, University of Victoria, Box 1700, Sta CSC, Victoria, BC V8W 2Y2, Canada *Tel:* 250-721-8524 *Fax:* 250-472-5051 *E-mail:* malahat@uvic.ca *Web Site:* www.malahatreview.ca, pg 703

Barton, John, Far Horizons Award for Short Fiction, University of Victoria, Box 1700, Sta CSC, Victoria, BC V8W 2Y2, Canada *Tel:* 250-721-8524 *Fax:* 250-472-5051 *E-mail:* malahat@uvic.ca *Web Site:* www.malahatreview.ca, pg 703

Barton, John, Malahat Review Long Poem Prize, University of Victoria, Box 1700, Sta CSC, Victoria, BC V8W 2Y2, Canada *Tel:* 250-721-8524 *Fax:* 250-472-5051 *E-mail:* malahat@uvic.ca *Web Site:* www.malahatreview.ca, pg 721

Barton, John, Novella Prize, University of Victoria, Box 1700, Sta CSC, Victoria, BC V8W 2Y2, Canada *Tel:* 250-721-8524 *Fax:* 250-472-5051 *E-mail:* malahat@uvic.ca *Web Site:* www.malahatreview.ca, pg 729

Barton, John, Open Season Awards, University of Victoria, Box 1700, Sta CSC, Victoria, BC V8W 2Y2, Canada *Tel:* 250-721-8524 *Fax:* 250-472-5051 *E-mail:* malahat@uvic.ca *Web Site:* malahatreview.ca, pg 731

Barton, Laurence PhD, American College, 270 S Bryn Mawr Ave, Bryn Mawr, PA 19010 *Tel:* 610-526-1000 *Toll Free Tel:* 888-263-7265 *Fax:* 610-526-1310 *Web Site:* www.theamericancollege.edu, pg 12

Barton, Rick, Leisure Arts Inc, 5701 Ranch Dr, Little Rock, AR 72223 *Tel:* 501-868-8800 *Toll Free Tel:* 800-643-8030 *Fax:* 501-868-8748 *Web Site:* www.leisurearts.com, pg 146

Barton, Tim, Oxford University Press USA, 198 Madison Ave, New York, NY 10016 *Tel:* 212-726-6000 *Toll Free Tel:* 800-451-7556 (orders); 800-445-9714 (cust serv) *Fax:* 919-677-1303 *E-mail:* custserv.us@oup.com *Web Site:* www.oup.com/us, pg 189

Bartone, Christopher, American Marketing Association, 311 S Wacker Dr, Suite 5800, Chicago, IL 60606 *Tel:* 312-542-9000 *Toll Free Tel:* 800-AMA-1150 (262-1150) *Fax:* 312-542-9001 *E-mail:* info@ama.org *Web Site:* www.marketingpower.com, pg 14, 613

Baruth, Ruth, W H Freeman and Co, 41 Madison Ave, 37th fl, New York, NY 10010 *Tel:* 212-576-9400 *Fax:* 212-689-2383 *Web Site:* www.whfreeman.com, pg 99

Barz, Otto, YBK Publishers Inc, 39 Crosby St, New York, NY 10013 *Tel:* 212-219-0135 *Fax:* 212-219-0136 *E-mail:* info@ybkpublishers.com, pg 288

Barz, Otto H, Publishing Synthesis Ltd, 39 Crosby St, New York, NY 10013 *Tel:* 212-219-0135 *Fax:* 212-219-0136 *E-mail:* info@pubsyn.com *Web Site:* www.pubsyn.com, pg 554

Barzinji, Dr Jamal, The International Institute of Islamic Thought, 500 Grove St, Suite 200, Herndon, VA 20170 *Tel:* 703-471-1133 *Fax:* 703-471-3922 *E-mail:* iiit@iiit.org *Web Site:* www.iiit.org, pg 133

Basch, Richard, Don Buchwald & Associates Inc, 10 E 44 St, New York, NY 10017 *Tel:* 212-867-1200 *Fax:* 212-867-2434 *E-mail:* info@buchwald.com *Web Site:* www.buchwald.com, pg 565

Bashirrad, Avideh, Random House Publishing Group, 1745 Broadway, New York, NY 10019 *Toll Free Tel:* 800-200-3552 *Web Site:* atrandom.com, pg 214

Baskin, John, Orange Frazer Press Inc, 37 1/2 W Main St, Wilmington, OH 45177 *Tel:* 937-382-3196 *Toll Free Tel:* 800-852-9332 (orders) *Fax:* 937-383-3159 *E-mail:* ofrazer@erinet.com *Web Site:* www.orangefrazer.com, pg 186

Basmajian, Nancy, Ohio University Press, 215 Columbus Rd, Suite 101, Athens, OH 45701-2979 *Tel:* 740-593-1154 *Fax:* 740-593-4536 *Web Site:* www.ohioswallow.com, pg 184

Basmajian, Nancy, Swallow Press, 215 Columbus Rd, Suite 101, Athens, OH 45701 *Tel:* 740-593-1158 (Jeff Kallet) *Fax:* 740-593-4536 *Web Site:* www.ohioswallow.com, pg 248

Basom, Rita, Neltje Blanchan Memorial Award, 2320 Capitol Ave, Cheyenne, WY 82002 *Tel:* 307-777-5234 *Fax:* 307-777-5499 *Web Site:* wyoarts.state.wy.us, pg 692

Basom, Rita, Frank Nelson Doubleday Memorial Award, 2320 Capitol Ave, Cheyenne, WY 82002 *Tel:* 307-777-5234 *Fax:* 307-777-5499 *Web Site:* wyoarts.state.wy.us, pg 701

Basom, Rita, Wyoming Arts Council Literature Fellowships, 2320 Capitol Ave, Cheyenne, WY 82002 *Tel:* 307-777-5234 *Fax:* 307-777-5499 *Web Site:* wyoarts.state.wy.us, pg 752

Bass, Richard, Alban Publishing, 2121 Cooperative Way, Suite 100, Herndon, VA 20171 *Tel:* 703-964-2700 *Toll Free Tel:* 800-486-1318 *Fax:* 703-964-0370 *E-mail:* infocenter@alban.org *Web Site:* www.alban.org, pg 7

Bass, Suzanne, Chronicle Books LLC, 680 Second St, San Francisco, CA 94107 *Tel:* 415-537-4200 *Toll Free Tel:* 800-759-0190 (cust serv) *Fax:* 415-537-4460 *Toll Free Fax:* 800-858-7787 (orders); 800-286-9471 (cust serv) *E-mail:* frontdesk@chroniclebooks.com *Web Site:* www.chroniclebooks.com, pg 61

Bast, Tom, Triumph Books, 814 N Franklin St, Chicago, IL 60610 *Toll Free Tel:* 800-888-4741 (orders only) *Fax:* 312-663-3557 *Web Site:* www.triumphbooks.com, pg 259

Bastian, Donald G, BPS Books, 42 Donalda Crescent, Toronto, ON M1S 1N7, Canada *Tel:* 416-609-2004 *Fax:* 416-609-2936 *Web Site:* www.bpsbooks.com, pg 495

Basu, Anwesha, Workman Publishing Co Inc, 225 Varick St, 9th fl, New York, NY 10014-4381 *Tel:* 212-254-5900 *Toll Free Tel:* 800-722-7202 *Fax:* 212-254-8098 *E-mail:* info@workman.com *Web Site:* www.workman.com, pg 285

Bateman, Lewis, Cambridge University Press, 32 Avenue of the Americas, New York, NY 10013-2473 *Tel:* 212-924-3900; 212-337-5000 *Toll Free Tel:* 800-899-5222 *Fax:* 212-691-3239 *E-mail:* newyork@cambridge.org *Web Site:* www.cambridge.org/us, pg 51

Bates, Greg, Common Courage Press, One Red Barn Rd, Monroe, ME 04951 *Tel:* 207-525-0900 *Toll Free Tel:* 800-497-3207 *Fax:* 207-525-3068 *E-mail:* orders-info@commoncouragepress.com *Web Site:* www.commoncouragepress.com, pg 65

Bates, Vicki, University of South Carolina Press, 1600 Hampton St, Suite 544, Columbia, SC 29208 *Tel:* 803-777-5245 *Toll Free Tel:* 800-768-2500 (orders) *Fax:* 803-777-0160 *Toll Free Fax:* 800-868-0740 (orders) *Web Site:* www.sc.edu/uscpress, pg 269

Batiz-Benet, Mercedes, Bayeux Arts Inc, 119 Stratton Crescent SW, Calgary, AB T3H 1T7, Canada *E-mail:* mail@bayeux.com *Web Site:* www.bayeux.com, pg 494

Batmanglij, Mohammad, Mage Publishers Inc, 1032 29 St NW, Washington, DC 20007 *Tel:* 202-342-1642 *Toll Free Tel:* 800-962-0922 *Fax:* 202-342-9269 *Web Site:* www.mage.com, pg 155

Batmanglij, Najmieh, Mage Publishers Inc, 1032 29 St NW, Washington, DC 20007 *Tel:* 202-342-1642 *Toll Free Tel:* 800-962-0922 *Fax:* 202-342-9269 *Web Site:* www.mage.com, pg 155

Battaglia, Carmen PhD, Dog Writers' Association of America Inc (DWAA), 173 Union Rd, Coatesville, PA 19320 *Tel:* 610-384-2436 *Fax:* 610-384-2471 *E-mail:* rhydowen@aol.com *Web Site:* www.dwaa.org, pg 622

Battaglia, Carmen PhD, Dog Writers' Association of America Inc (DWAA) Annual Awards, 173 Union Rd, Coatesville, PA 19320 *Tel:* 610-384-2436 *E-mail:* rhydowen@aol.com *Web Site:* www.dwaa.org, pg 700

Battaglia, Emi, Grand Central Publishing, 237 Park Ave, New York, NY 10017 *Tel:* 212-364-1100 *Web Site:* www.hachettebookgroup.com, pg 106

Battista, Dino, The University of North Carolina Press, 116 S Boundary St, Chapel Hill, NC 27514-3808 *Tel:* 919-966-3561 *Fax:* 919-966-3829 *E-mail:* uncpress@unc.edu *Web Site:* www.uncpress.unc.edu, pg 267

Battista, Garth, Breakaway Books, PO Box 24, Halcottsville, NY 12438-0024 *Tel:* 607-326-4805 *Toll Free Tel:* 800-548-4348 (voicemail) *Fax:* 203-399-8073 *E-mail:* breakawaybooks@gmail.com *Web Site:* www.breakawaybooks.com, pg 46

Bauer, Susan Wise, Peace Hill Press, 18021 The Glebe Lane, Charles City, VA 23030 *Tel:* 804-829-5043 *Toll Free Tel:* 877-322-3445 (orders) *Fax:* 804-829-5704 *E-mail:* info@peacehillpress.com *Web Site:* www.peacehillpress.com, pg 195

Bauers, William, Penguin Group (USA) LLC Sales, 375 Hudson St, New York, NY 10014 *Tel:* 212-366-2000 *E-mail:* online@penguinputnam.com *Web Site:* us.penguingroup.com, pg 197

Baughman, Kathy, International Reading Association, 800 Barksdale Rd, Newark, DE 19711-3204 *Tel:* 302-731-1600 *Toll Free Tel:* 800-336-7323 (US & CN) *Fax:* 302-731-1057 *E-mail:* customerservice@reading.org *Web Site:* www.reading.org, pg 625

Baughman, Kathy, International Reading Association Children's & Young Adult's Book Award, 800 Barksdale Rd, Newark, DE 19711-3204 *Tel:* 302-731-1600 *Toll Free Tel:* 800-336-7323 (US & CN) *Fax:* 302-731-1057 *E-mail:* committees@reading.org *Web Site:* www.reading.org, pg 713

Baughman, Kathy, Paul A Witty Short Story Award, 800 Barksdale Rd, Newark, DE 19711-3204 *Tel:* 302-731-1600 *Toll Free Tel:* 800-336-7323 (US & CN) *Fax:* 302-731-1057 *E-mail:* committees@reading.org *Web Site:* www.reading.org, pg 750

Baum, Richard, New York Academy of Sciences, 7 World Trade, 40th fl, 250 Greenwich St, New York, NY 10007-2157 *Tel:* 212-298-8600 *Toll Free Tel:* 800-843-6927 *Fax:* 212-298-3644 *E-mail:* nyas@nyas.org; publications@nyas.org *Web Site:* www.nyas.org, pg 179

Baumann, Rebecca, Montana Historical Society Press, Capitol Complex, 225 N Roberts St, Helena, MT 59620 *Tel:* 406-444-0090 (edit); 406-444-2890 (ordering/mktg); 406-444-2694 *Toll Free Tel:* 800-243-9900 *Fax:* 406-444-2696 (ordering/mktg) *Web Site:* www.montanahistoricalsociety.org, pg 169

Baumgardner, Jennifer, The Feminist Press at The City University of New York, 365 Fifth Ave, Suite 5406, New York, NY 10016 *Tel:* 212-817-7915 *Fax:* 212-817-1593 *E-mail:* info@feministpress.org *Web Site:* www.feministpress.org, pg 94

Baumhauer, Marge, Graphic Arts Association, 1210 Northbrook Dr, Suite 250, Trevose, PA 19053 *Tel:* 215-396-2300 *Fax:* 215-396-9890 *E-mail:* gaa@gaa1900.com *Web Site:* www.gaa1900.com, pg 678

Baxter, Carol, The Mathematical Association of America, 1529 18 St NW, Washington, DC 20036-1358 *Tel:* 202-387-5200 *Toll Free Tel:* 800-741-9415 *Fax:* 202-265-2384 *E-mail:* maahq@maa.org *Web Site:* www.maa.org, pg 159

Bay, Bryndon, Mel Bay Publications Inc, 4 Industrial Dr, Pacific, MO 63069-0066 *Tel:* 636-257-3970 *Toll Free Tel:* 800-863-5229 *Fax:* 636-257-5062 *Toll Free Fax:* 800-660-9818 *E-mail:* email@melbay.com *Web Site:* www.melbay.com, pg 164

Bay, Bryndon, Music Publishers' Association (MPA), 243 Fifth Ave, Suite 236, New York, NY 10016 *Tel:* 212-327-4044 *E-mail:* admin@mpa.org *Web Site:* host.mpa.org; www.mpa.org, pg 628

Bay, Linda, Penguin Group (USA) LLC, 375 Hudson St, New York, NY 10014 *Tel:* 212-366-2000 *Toll Free Tel:* 800-847-5515 (inside sales); 800-631-8571 (cust serv) *Fax:* 212-366-2666; 607-775-4829 (inside sales) *E-mail:* online@us.penguingroup.com *Web Site:* www.penguin.com; us.penguingroup.com, pg 197

Bayer, Lisa, University of Georgia Press, Main Library, 3rd fl, 320 S Jackson St, Athens, GA 30602 *Tel:* 706-369-6130 *Fax:* 706-369-6131; 706-369-6162 *E-mail:* books@ugapress.uga.edu (orders) *Web Site:* www.ugapress.org, pg 265

Bayers, William, Harcourt Achieve, 6277 Sea Harbor Dr, Orlando, FL 32887 *Tel:* 407-345-2000 *Toll Free Tel:* 800-531-5015 (cust serv/orders) *Toll Free Fax:* 800-699-9459 (cust serv/orders) *Web Site:* www.harcourtachieve.com, pg 112

Bayers, William, Harcourt Inc, 6277 Sea Harbor Dr, Orlando, FL 32887 *Tel:* 407-345-2000 *Toll Free Tel:* 800-225-5425 (cust serv/orders) *Toll Free Fax:* 800-269-5232 (cust serv/orders) *Web Site:* www.hmhco.com, pg 112

Bayers, William, Houghton Mifflin Harcourt, 222 Berkeley St, Boston, MA 02116-3764 *Tel:* 617-351-5000 *Toll Free Tel:* 800-225-5425 (Pre-K-8); 800-462-6595 (6–12; Advanced & Electives); 800-289-4490 (Specialized Curriculum: Great Source, Rigby, Saxon, Steck-Vaughn; Homeschool; Adult Ed); 800-323-9540 (Assessment: Riverside Publishing); 888-391-3245 (SkillsTutor); 888-242-6747 option 2 (Destination Series; Classroom Connect; Earobics; Edmark; Learning Village; Riverdeep); 800-225-3362 (Houghton Mifflin Harcourt Trade & Reference Publishers); 800-225-5800 (Heinemann) *Fax:* 617-351-1125 *Web Site:* www.hmhco.com, pg 123

Bayless, Erin, Creating Crafts Group LLC, 741 Corporate Circle, Suite A, Golden, CO 80401 *Tel:* 303-215-5600 *E-mail:* editorial@creatingkeepsakes.com *Web Site:* www.creatingkeepsakes.com, pg 71

Bays, Susan, Arbutus Press, 2364 Pinehurst Trail, Traverse City, MI 49696 *Tel:* 231-946-7240 *E-mail:* info@arbutuspress.com *Web Site:* www.arbutuspress.com, pg 21

Bayuk, Michelle F, Albert Whitman & Co, 250 S Northwest Hwy, Suite 320, Park Ridge, IL 60068 *Tel:* 847-232-2800 *Toll Free Tel:* 800-255-7675 *Fax:* 847-581-0039 *E-mail:* mail@awhitmanco.com *Web Site:* www.albertwhitman.com, pg 7

Bazzy, William M, Artech House Inc, 685 Canton St, Norwood, MA 02062 *Tel:* 781-769-9750 *Toll Free Tel:* 800-225-9977 *Fax:* 781-769-6334 *E-mail:* artech@artechhouse.com *Web Site:* www.artechhouse.com, pg 23

Beach, Kristen, Liberty Fund Inc, 8335 Allison Pointe Trail, Suite 300, Indianapolis, IN 46250-1684 *Tel:* 317-842-0880 *Toll Free Tel:* 800-955-8335; 800-866-3520; 800-368-7897 ext 6069 (cust serv) *Fax:* 317-577-9067; 317-579-6060 (cust serv); 708-534-7803 *E-mail:* books@libertyfund.org; info@libertyfund.org *Web Site:* www.libertyfund.org, pg 148

Beacom, David, National Science Teachers Association (NSTA), 1840 Wilson Blvd, Arlington, VA 22201-3000 *Tel:* 703-312-9205 *Toll Free Tel:* 800-722-NSTA; 800-277-5300 (orders) *Fax:* 703-526-9754 *Toll Free Fax:* 888-433-0526 (orders) *Web Site:* www.nsta.org/store, pg 176

Beal, Greg, Don & Gee Nicholl Fellowships in Screenwriting, 1313 Vine St, Hollywood, CA 90028 *Tel:* 310-247-3010 *Fax:* 310-247-3794 *E-mail:* nicholl@oscars.org *Web Site:* www.oscars.org/nicholl, pg 729

Beale, Simon, ProQuest LLC, 789 E Eisenhower Pkwy, Ann Arbor, MI 48108-3218 *Tel:* 734-761-4700 *Toll Free Tel:* 800-521-0600 *Fax:* 734-975-6486 *Toll Free Fax:* 800-864-0019 *E-mail:* info@proquest.com *Web Site:* www.proquest.com, pg 208

Beams, Nan, Poisoned Pen Press Inc, 6962 E First Ave, Suite 103, Scottsdale, AZ 85251 *Tel:* 480-945-3375 *Toll Free Tel:* 1-800-421-3976 *Fax:* 480-949-1707 *E-mail:* info@poisonedpenpress.com *Web Site:* www.poisonedpenpress.com, pg 204

Bean, Susan, Northern Illinois University Press, 2280 Bethany Rd, DeKalb, IL 60115 *Tel:* 815-753-1826; 815-753-1075 *Fax:* 815-753-1845 *Web Site:* www.niupress.niu.edu, pg 181

Beard, Chris, Beard Books Inc, 47 E South St, Suite 102, Frederick, MD 21701 *Tel:* 240-629-3300 *Toll Free Tel:* 888-563-4573 (book orders) *Fax:* 240-629-3360 *E-mail:* info@beardbooks.com; order@beardbooks.com *Web Site:* www.beardbooks.com; www.beardgroup.com, pg 33

Beard, Morgan, Swedenborg Foundation Press, 320 N Church St, West Chester, PA 19380 *Tel:* 610-430-3222 *Toll Free Tel:* 800-355-3222 (cust serv) *Fax:* 610-430-7982 *E-mail:* info@swedenborg.com *Web Site:* www.swedenborg.com, pg 248

Beasley, Barbara, Paladin Press, Gunbarrel Tech Ctr, 7077 Winchester Circle, Boulder, CO 80301 *Tel:* 303-443-7250 *Toll Free Tel:* 800-392-2400 *Fax:* 303-442-8741 *E-mail:* service@paladin-press.com *Web Site:* www.paladin-press.com, pg 191

Beasley, Betsy, Mark Twain Creative Writing Workshop, UMKC, University House, 5101 Rockhill Rd, Kansas City, MO 64110-2499 *Tel:* 816-235-1168 *Fax:* 816-235-2611 *E-mail:* newletters@umkc.edu *Web Site:* www.newletters.org, pg 670

Beasley, J Malcolm, Professional Communications Inc, 20968 State Rd 22, Caddo, OK 74729 *Tel:* 580-367-9838 *Toll Free Tel:* 800-337-9838 *Fax:* 580-367-9989 *E-mail:* info@pcibooks.com *Web Site:* www.pcibooks.com, pg 207

Beaton, Jo, Zest Books, 35 Stillman St, Suite 121, San Francisco, CA 94107 *Tel:* 415-777-8654 *Fax:* 415-777-8653 *E-mail:* info@zestbooks.net; publicity@zestbooks.net *Web Site:* zestbooks.net, pg 289

Beaudet, Marie-Andree, La Fondation Emile Nelligan, 100 Sherbrooke St, Suite 202, Montreal, QC H2X 1C3, Canada *Tel:* 514-278-4657 *Fax:* 514-278-1943 *E-mail:* info@fondation-nelligan.org *Web Site:* www.fondation-nelligan.org, pg 623

Beaudet, Marie-Andree, Prix Emile-Nelligan, 100 Sherbrooke St, Suite 202, Montreal, QC H2X 1C3, Canada *Tel:* 514-278-4657 *Toll Free Tel:* 888-849-8540 *Fax:* 514-278-1943 *E-mail:* info@fondation-nelligan.org *Web Site:* www.fondation-nelligan.org, pg 736

Beaudoin, Andre, Les Editions Ganesha Inc, CP 484, Succursale Youville, Montreal, QC H2P 2W1, Canada *Tel:* 450-641-2395 *Fax:* 450-641-2989 *E-mail:* courriel@editions-ganesha.qc.ca *Web Site:* www.editions-ganesha.qc.ca, pg 503

Beaulieu, Ginette, Editions de la Pleine Lune, 223 34 Ave, Lachine, QC H8T 1Z4, Canada *Tel:* 514-634-7954 *Fax:* 514-637-6366 *E-mail:* editpllune@videotron.ca *Web Site:* www.pleinelune.qc.ca, pg 502

Beaulieu, Melanie, Editions MultiMondes, 930 rue Pouliot, Quebec, QC G1V 3N9, Canada *Tel:* 418-651-3885 *Toll Free Tel:* 800-840-3029 *Fax:* 418-651-6822 *Toll Free Fax:* 888-303-5931 *E-mail:* multimondes@multim.com *Web Site:* www.multimondes.qc.ca, pg 513

Beaumont, Kathryn, Kneerim, Williams & Bloom Agency, 90 Canal St, Boston, MA 02114 *Tel:* 617-303-1650 *Web Site:* www.kwlit.com, pg 580

Beaumont, Nancy, Society of American Archivists, 17 N State St, Suite 1425, Chicago, IL 60602-4061 *Tel:* 312-606-0722 *Toll Free Tel:* 866-722-7858 *Fax:* 312-606-0728 *E-mail:* info@archivists.org *Web Site:* www.archivists.org, pg 238

Beaupre, Cheryl, Wilfrid Laurier University Press, 75 University Ave W, Waterloo, ON N2L 3C5, Canada *Tel:* 519-884-0710 (ext 6124) *Toll Free Tel:* 866-836-5551 *Fax:* 519-725-1399 *E-mail:* press@wlu.ca *Web Site:* www.wlupress.wlu.ca, pg 525

Becerra, Nannette, Gem Guides Book Co, 1275 W Ninth St, Upland, CA 91786 *Tel:* 626-855-1611 *Toll Free Tel:* 800-824-5118 (orders) *Fax:* 626-855-1610 *E-mail:* info@gemguidesbooks.com *Web Site:* www.gemguidesbooks.com, pg 102

Becher, Bill, AuthorHouse, 1663 Liberty Dr, Bloomington, IN 47403 *Toll Free Tel:* 888-519-5121 *E-mail:* authorsupport@authorhouse.com *Web Site:* www.authorhouse.com, pg 27

Becher, Bill, iUniverse, 1663 Liberty Dr, Bloomington, IN 47403 *Toll Free Tel:* 800-AUTHORS (288-4677) *Fax:* 812-355-4085 *Web Site:* www.iuniverse.com, pg 135

Becher, Bill, Trafford, 1663 Liberty Dr, Bloomington, IN 47403 *Toll Free Tel:* 888-232-4444 *E-mail:* customersupport@trafford.com *Web Site:* www.trafford.com, pg 257

Becher, Bill, Xlibris Corp, 1663 Liberty Dr, Suite 200, Bloomington, IN 47403 *Toll Free Tel:* 888-795-4274 *Fax:* 610-915-0294 *E-mail:* info@xlibris.com *Web Site:* www.xlibris.com, pg 287

Beck, Eric, Seedling Publications Inc, 520 E Bainbridge St, Elizabethtown, PA 17022 *Toll Free Tel:* 800-233-0759 *Toll Free Fax:* 888-834-1303 *E-mail:* info@continentalpress.com *Web Site:* www.continentalpress.com, pg 231

Becker, Andre, Gotham Writers' Workshop, 555 Eighth Ave, Suite 1402, New York, NY 10018-4358 *Tel:* 212-974-8377 *Toll Free Tel:* 877-974-8377 *Fax:* 212-307-6325 *E-mail:* office@write.org *Web Site:* www.writingclasses.com, pg 669

Becker, Stephen, URJ Books & Music, 633 Third Ave, New York, NY 10017-6778 *Tel:* 212-650-4120 *Fax:* 212-650-4119 *E-mail:* press@urj.org *Web Site:* www.ujrbooksandmusic.com, pg 273

Becker, Ulrich, Mondial, 203 W 107 St, Suite 6-C, New York, NY 10025 *Tel:* 646-807-8031 *Fax:* 208-361-2863 *E-mail:* contact@mondialbooks.com *Web Site:* www.mondialbooks.com, pg 168

Beckham, Douglas, National Government Publishing Association, 629 N Main St, Hattiesburg, MS 39401 *Tel:* 601-582-3330 *Fax:* 601-582-3354 *E-mail:* info@govpublishing.org *Web Site:* www.govpublishing.org, pg 630

Beckman, Andrew, Timber Press Inc, 133 SW Second Ave, Suite 450, Portland, OR 97204 *Tel:* 503-227-2878 *Toll Free Tel:* 800-327-5680 *Fax:* 503-227-3070 *E-mail:* info@timberpress.com *Web Site:* www.timberpress.com, pg 255

Beckwith, Brian, Peoples Education Inc, 299 Market St, Suite 240, Saddle Brook, NJ 07663 *Tel:* 201-712-0090 *Toll Free Tel:* 800-822-1080 *Fax:* 201-712-0045; 201-712-1016 *Web Site:* www.peopleseducation.com; www.peoplescollegeprep.com; www.measuringuplive.com; www.brightpointliteracy.com, pg 199

Bedard, Rachel, Les Editions du Remue-Menage, La Maison Parent-Roback, 110 rue Ste-Therese, bureau 501, Montreal, QC H2Y 1E6, Canada *Tel:* 514-876-0097 *Fax:* 514-876-7951 *E-mail:* info@editions-remuemenage.qc.ca *Web Site:* www.editions-remuemenage.qc.ca, pg 503

Bedford, Stephen, Simon & Schuster, 1230 Avenue of the Americas, New York, NY 10020 *Tel:* 212-698-7000 *Toll Free Tel:* 800-223-2348 (cust serv); 800-223-2336 (orders) *Toll Free Fax:* 800-943-9831 (orders) *Web Site:* www.simonandschuster.com, pg 234

Bedick, Cara, The Experiment, 260 Fifth Ave, Suite 3 South, New York, NY 10001-6425 *Tel:* 212-889-1659 *E-mail:* info@theexperimentpublishing.com *Web Site:* www.theexperimentpublishing.com, pg 91

Beditz, Dr Joseph, National Golf Foundation, 1150 S US Hwy One, Suite 401, Jupiter, FL 33477 *Tel:* 561-744-6006 *Toll Free Tel:* 888-275-4643 *Fax:* 561-744-6107 *E-mail:* general@ngf.org *Web Site:* www.ngf.org, pg 175

Bednarik, Joseph, Copper Canyon Press, Fort Worden State Park, Bldg 33, Port Townsend, WA 98368 *Tel:* 360-385-4925 *Toll Free Tel:* 877-501-1393 *Fax:* 360-385-4985 *E-mail:* poetry@coppercanyonpress.org *Web Site:* www.coppercanyonpress.org, pg 67

Bedrick, Claudia, Enchanted Lion Books, 20 Jay St, Studio M-18, Brooklyn, NY 11231 *Tel:* 646-785-9272 *E-mail:* enchantedlion@gmail.com *Web Site:* www.enchantedlionbooks.com, pg 87

Beecroft, Alexander, The Charles Bernheimer Prize, University of South Carolina, Dept of Languages, Literature & Cultures, Rm 813-A, 1620 College St, Columbia, SC 29208 *Tel:* 803-777-3021 *Fax:* 803-777-3041 *E-mail:* info@acla.org *Web Site:* www.acla.org, pg 690

Beecroft, Alexander, Harry Levin Prize, University of South Carolina, Dept of Languages, Literature & Cultures, Rm 813-A, 1620 College St, Columbia, SC 29208 *Tel:* 803-777-3021 *Fax:* 803-777-3041 *E-mail:* info@acla.org *Web Site:* www.acla.org, pg 717

Beecroft, Alexander, Rene Wellek Prize, University of South Carolina, Dept of Languages, Literature & Cultures, Rm 813-A, 1620 College St, Columbia, SC 29208 *Tel:* 803-777-3021 *Fax:* 803-777-3041 *E-mail:* info@acla.org *Web Site:* www.acla.org, pg 748

Beeke, Joel R, Reformation Heritage Books, 2965 Leonard St NE, Grand Rapids, MI 49525 *Tel:* 616-977-0889 *Fax:* 616-285-3246 *E-mail:* orders@heritagebooks.org *Web Site:* www.heritagebooks.org, pg 217

Beeny, Martyn, University of Nebraska Press, 1111 Lincoln Mall, Lincoln, NE 68588-0630 *Tel:* 402-472-3581; 919-966-7449 (cust serv & foreign orders) *Toll Free Tel:* 800-848-6224 (cust serv & US orders) *Fax:* 402-472-6214; 919-962-2704 (cust serv & foreign orders) *Toll Free Fax:* 800-526-2617 (cust serv & US orders) *E-mail:* pressmail@unl.edu *Web Site:* www.nebraskapress.unl.edu, pg 267

Beers, Ron, Tyndale House Publishers Inc, 351 Executive Dr, Carol Stream, IL 60188 *Tel:* 630-668-8300 *Toll Free Tel:* 800-323-9400 *Web Site:* www.tyndale.com, pg 261

Begley, Charlotte, Clovernook Printing House for the Blind & Visually Impaired, 7000 Hamilton Ave, Cincinnati, OH 45231-5297 *Tel:* 513-522-3860 *Toll Free Tel:* 888-234-7156 *Fax:* 513-728-3946 (admin); 513-728-3950 (sales) *E-mail:* customerservice@clovernook.org *Web Site:* www.clovernook.org, pg 63

Behar, Ann, Scovil Galen Ghosh Literary Agency Inc, 276 Fifth Ave, Suite 708, New York, NY 10001 *Tel:* 212-679-8686 *Fax:* 212-679-6710 *E-mail:* info@sgglit.com *Web Site:* www.sgglit.com, pg 593

Behar, Mike, Leisure Arts Inc, 5701 Ranch Dr, Little Rock, AR 72223 *Tel:* 501-868-8800 *Toll Free Tel:* 800-643-8030 *Fax:* 501-868-8748 *Web Site:* www.leisurearts.com, pg 146

Behm, Melissa A, Brookes Publishing Co Inc, PO Box 10624, Baltimore, MD 21285-0624 *Tel:* 410-337-9580 (outside US & CN) *Toll Free Tel:* 800-638-3775 (US & CN) *Fax:* 410-337-8539 *E-mail:* custserv@brookespublishing.com *Web Site:* www.brookespublishing.com, pg 48

Behm, Melissa A, Health Professions Press, 409 Washington Ave, Suite 500, Towson, MD 21204 *Tel:* 410-337-9585 *Toll Free Tel:* 888-337-8808 *Fax:* 410-337-8539 *E-mail:* custserv@healthpropress.com *Web Site:* www.healthpropress.com, pg 117

Behn, Robin, University of Alabama Program in Creative Writing, PO Box 870244, Tuscaloosa, AL 35487-0244 *Tel:* 205-348-5065 *Fax:* 205-348-1388 *E-mail:* english@ua.edu *Web Site:* www.as.ua.edu/english, pg 681

Behrman, David, Behrman House Inc, 11 Edison Place, Springfield, NJ 07081 *Tel:* 973-379-7200 *Toll Free Tel:* 800-221-2755 *Fax:* 973-379-7280 *E-mail:* behrmanhouse@gmail.com; customersupport@behrmanhouse.com *Web Site:* www.behrmanhouse.com, pg 34

Behroozi, Cyrus, The Brookings Institution Press, 1775 Massachusetts Ave NW, Washington, DC 20036-2188 *Tel:* 202-536-3600 *Toll Free Tel:* 800-537-5487 *Fax:* 202-536-3623 *E-mail:* permissions@brookings.edu *Web Site:* www.brookings.edu, pg 48

Beier, Elizabeth, St Martin's Press, LLC, 175 Fifth Ave, New York, NY 10010 *Tel:* 646-307-5151 *Fax:* 212-420-9314 *E-mail:* firstname.lastname@macmillan.com *Web Site:* www.stmartins.com, pg 224

Beil, Frederic C, Frederic C Beil Publisher Inc, 609 Whitaker St, Savannah, GA 31401 *Tel:* 912-233-2446 *E-mail:* books@beil.com *Web Site:* www.beil.com, pg 34

Beilenson, Evelyn L, Peter Pauper Press, Inc, 202 Mamaroneck Ave, White Plains, NY 10601-5376 *Tel:* 914-681-0144 *Fax:* 914-681-0389 *E-mail:* customerservice@peterpauper.com; orders@peterpauper.com *Web Site:* www.peterpauper.com, pg 200

Beilenson, Laurence, Peter Pauper Press, Inc, 202 Mamaroneck Ave, White Plains, NY 10601-5376 *Tel:* 914-681-0144 *Fax:* 914-681-0389 *E-mail:* customerservice@peterpauper.com; orders@peterpauper.com *Web Site:* www.peterpauper.com, pg 199

Beiser, Martin, Words into Print, 131 Fifth Ave, Suite 501, New York, NY 10003 *Tel:* 212-741-1393 *Fax:* 419-441-1393 *E-mail:* query@wordsintoprint.org *Web Site:* www.wordsintoprint.org, pg 557

Beitzel, Tim, Kendall/Hunt Publishing Co, 4050 Westmark Dr, Dubuque, IA 52002-2624 *Tel:* 563-589-1000 *Toll Free Tel:* 800-228-0810 (orders) *Fax:* 563-589-1046 *Toll Free Fax:* 800-772-9165 *E-mail:* orders@kendallhunt.com *Web Site:* www.kendallhunt.com, pg 139

Bejarano, Laura, Lectorum Publications Inc, 205 Chubb Ave, Lyndhurst, NJ 07071 *Toll Free Tel:* 800-345-5946 *Fax:* 201-559-2201 *Toll Free Fax:* 877-532-8676 *E-mail:* lectorum@lectorum.com *Web Site:* www.lectorum.com, pg 145

Belanger, Paul, Editions du Noroit, CP 156, Succersale de Lorimier, Montreal, QC H2H 2N6, Canada *Tel:* 514-727-0005 *Fax:* 514-723-6660 *E-mail:* lenoroit@lenoroit.com *Web Site:* www.lenoroit.com, pg 503

Belasco, Leslie, ALI-ABA Continuing Professional Education, 4025 Chestnut St, Philadelphia, PA 19104 *Tel:* 215-243-1600 *Toll Free Tel:* 800-CLE-NEWS (253-6397) *Fax:* 215-243-1664; 215-243-1683 *Web Site:* www.ali-aba.org, pg 8

Belczewski, Andrea, Mi'kmaq-Maliseet Institute, University of New Brunswick, Rm 343, Marshall d'Avray Hall, 10 MacKay Dr, Fredericton, NB E3B 5A3, Canada *Tel:* 506-453-4840 *Fax:* 506-453-4784 *E-mail:* micmac@unb.ca *Web Site:* www.unb.ca; www.unb.ca/fredericton/education/mmi, pg 512

Belden, Kathy, Bloomsbury Publishing, 175 Fifth Ave, New York, NY 10010 *Tel:* 212-674-5151 *Toll Free Tel:* 800-221-7945 *Fax:* 212-780-0115; 212-982-2837 *E-mail:* marketingusa@bloomsbury.com; adultpublicityusa.@bloomsbury.com *Web Site:* www.bloomsbury.com, pg 40

Belderis, Ina, Theosophical University Press, PO Box C, Pasadena, CA 91109-7107 *Tel:* 626-798-3378 *Fax:* 626-798-4749 *E-mail:* tupress@theosociety.org *Web Site:* www.theosociety.org, pg 254

Belen, Lauren, Alban Publishing, 2121 Cooperative Way, Suite 100, Herndon, VA 20171 *Tel:* 703-964-2700 *Toll Free Tel:* 800-486-1318 *Fax:* 703-964-0370 *E-mail:* infocenter@alban.org *Web Site:* www.alban.org, pg 7

Beley, Janice, Arsenal Pulp Press, 211 E Georgia St, No 101, Vancouver, BC V6A 1Z6, Canada *Tel:* 604-687-4233 *Toll Free Tel:* 888-600-PULP (600-7857) *Fax:* 604-687-4283 *E-mail:* info@arsenalpulp.com *Web Site:* www.arsenalpulp.com, pg 493

Belfiglio, Brian, Scribner, 1230 Avenue of the Americas, New York, NY 10020, pg 230

Belfus, Linda, Elsevier, Health Sciences Division, 1600 John F Kennedy Blvd, Suite 1800, Philadelphia, PA 19103-2899 *Tel:* 215-239-3900 *Toll Free Tel:* 800-523-1649 *Fax:* 215-239-3990 *Web Site:* www.elsevierhealth.com, pg 87

Belieu, Erin, Port Townsend Writers' Conference, 223 Battery Way, Port Townsend, WA 98368 *Tel:* 360-385-3102 *Toll Free Tel:* 800-733-3608 (ticket off) *Fax:* 360-385-2470 *E-mail:* info@centrum.org *Web Site:* www.centrum.org, pg 672

Beliveau, Mathieu, Beliveau Editeur, 920 rue Jean-Neveu, Longueuil, QC J4G 2M1, Canada *Tel:* 514-253-0403; 450-679-1933 *Fax:* 450-679-6648 *E-mail:* admin@beliveauediteur.com *Web Site:* www.beliveauediteur.com, pg 494

Belkacemi, Yassine, Dystel & Goderich Literary Management, One Union Sq W, Suite 904, New York, NY 10003 *Tel:* 212-627-9100 *Fax:* 212-627-9313 *Web Site:* www.dystel.com, pg 569

Bell, Albert A, Ingalls Publishing Group Inc (IPG), PO Box 2500, Banner Elk, NC 28604 *Tel:* 828-297-6884 *Fax:* 828-297-6880 *E-mail:* sales@ingallspublishinggroup.com *Web Site:* www.ingallspublishinggroup.com, pg 130

Bell, Emily, Farrar, Straus & Giroux, LLC, 18 W 18 St, New York, NY 10011 *Tel:* 212-741-6900 *Fax:* 212-633-9385 *E-mail:* fsg.publicity@fsgbooks.com *Web Site:* us.macmillan.com/fsg.aspx, pg 93

Bell, Hannah, Schiel & Denver Book Publishers, 10685-B Hazelhurst Dr, Suite 8575, Houston, TX 77043 *Tel:* 832-699-0264 *Toll Free Tel:* 888-629-4449 *Toll Free Fax:* 888-224-2721 *E-mail:* enquiries@schieldenver.com *Web Site:* www.schieldenver.com, pg 227

Bell, Justin, Spectrum Literary Agency, 320 Central Park W, Suite 1-D, New York, NY 10025 *Tel:* 212-362-4323 *Fax:* 212-362-4562 *Web Site:* www.spectrumliteraryagency.com, pg 595

Bell, Merleyn, Neustadt International Prize for Literature, University of Oklahoma, Suite 110, 630 Parrington Oval, Norman, OK 73019-4033 *Tel:* 405-325-4531 *Fax:* 405-325-7495 *Web Site:* www.worldliteraturetoday.org, pg 728

Bell, Merleyn, NSK Neustadt Prize for Children's Literature, University of Oklahoma, Suite 110, 630 Parrington Oval, Norman, OK 73019-4033 *Tel:* 405-325-4531 *Fax:* 405-325-7495 *Web Site:* www.worldliteraturetoday.org, pg 730

Bellanca, Dr Patricia, Harvard Summer Writing Program, 51 Brattle St, Dept S760, Cambridge, MA 02138-3722 *Tel:* 617-495-4024 *Fax:* 617-495-9176 *E-mail:* summer@hudce.harvard.edu *Web Site:* www.summer.harvard.edu, pg 669

Belle, Linda, Jane Addams Children's Book Award, 777 United Nations Plaza, 6th fl, New York, NY 10017 *Tel:* 212-682-8830 *Fax:* 212-286-8211 *E-mail:* japa@igc.org *Web Site:* www.janeaddamspeace.org, pg 685

Beller, Laurence, Amsco School Publications Inc, 315 Hudson St, New York, NY 10013-1085 *Tel:* 212-886-6500; 212-886-6565 *Toll Free Tel:* 800-969-8398 *Fax:* 212-675-7010 *E-mail:* info@amscopub.com *Web Site:* www.amscopub.com, pg 18

Bellet, Danny, The Pennsylvania State University Press, University Support Bldg 1, Suite C, 820 N University Dr, University Park, PA 16802-1003 *Tel:* 814-865-1327 *Toll Free Tel:* 800-326-9180 *Fax:* 814-863-1408 *Toll Free Fax:* 877-778-2665 *E-mail:* info@psupress.org *Web Site:* www.psupress.org, pg 198

Bellew, Ib, Bunker Hill Publishing, 285 River Rd, Piermont, NH 03779 *Tel:* 603-272-9221 *Fax:* 603-283-7240 *E-mail:* mail@bunkerhillpublishing.com *Web Site:* www.bunkerhillpublishing.com, pg 49

Bellitto, Christopher, Paulist Press, 997 MacArthur Blvd, Mahwah, NJ 07430-9990 *Tel:* 201-825-7300 *Toll Free Tel:* 800-218-1903 *Fax:* 201-825-8345 *Toll Free Fax:* 800-836-3161 *E-mail:* info@paulistpress.com *Web Site:* www.paulistpress.com, pg 195

Bellow, Adam, HarperCollins General Books Group, 10 E 53 St, New York, NY 10022 *Tel:* 212-207-7000 *Fax:* 212-207-7633 *Web Site:* www.harpercollins.com, pg 113

Bellows, Melinda Gerosa, National Geographic Books, 1145 17 St NW, Washington, DC 20036-4688 *Tel:* 202-857-7000 *Fax:* 202-857-7670 *Web Site:* www.nationalgeographic.com, pg 174

Beltram, Tanya M, Inkwell Journal Annual Fiction Competition, c/o Inkwell-Manhattanville College, 2900 Purchase St, Purchase, NY 10577 *Tel:* 914-323-7239 *Fax:* 914-323-3122 *E-mail:* inkwell@mville.edu *Web Site:* www.inkwelljournal.org, pg 712

Beltram, Tanya M, Inkwell Journal Annual Poetry Competition, c/o Inkwell-Manhattanville College, 2900 Purchase St, Purchase, NY 10577 *Tel:* 914-323-7239 *Fax:* 914-323-3122 *E-mail:* inkwell@mville.edu *Web Site:* www.inkwelljournal.org, pg 712

Bembia, Hannah, OSA, The Optical Society, 2010 Massachusetts Ave NW, Washington, DC 20036-1023 *Tel:* 202-223-8130 *Toll Free Tel:* 800-766-4672 *E-mail:* custserv@osa.org *Web Site:* www.osa.org, pg 188

Bemis, Carol Stiles, W W Norton & Company Inc, 500 Fifth Ave, New York, NY 10110-0017 *Tel:* 212-354-5500 *Toll Free Tel:* 800-233-4830 (orders & cust serv) *Fax:* 212-869-0856 *Toll Free Fax:* 800-458-6515 *Web Site:* www.wwnorton.com, pg 182

Bemiss, Holly, Susan Rabiner Literary Agency Inc, 315 W 39 St, Suite 1501, New York, NY 10018-3907 *Web Site:* RabinerLit.com, pg 589

Benamou, Sharon, AJL Judaica Bibliography Award, PO Box 1118, Teaneck, NJ 07666 *Tel:* 201-371-3255 *E-mail:* ajlibs@osu.edu *Web Site:* www.jewishlibraries.org, pg 686

Benamou, Sharon, AJL Judaica Reference Award, PO Box 1118, Teaneck, NJ 07666 *Tel:* 201-371-3255 *E-mail:* ajlibs@osu.edu *Web Site:* www.jewishlibraries.org, pg 686

Benard, Martine, La Courte Echelle, 5243 St Laurent Blvd, Montreal, QC H2T 1S4, Canada *Tel:* 514-274-2004 *Toll Free Tel:* 800-387-6192 (orders only) *Fax:* 514-270-4160 *Toll Free Fax:* 800-450-0391 (orders only) *E-mail:* info@courteechelle.com *Web Site:* www.courteechelle.com, pg 500

Benard, Mary, Skinner House Books, 25 Beacon St, Boston, MA 02108-2800 *Tel:* 617-742-2100 *Fax:* 617-742-7025 *E-mail:* skinnerhouse@uua.org *Web Site:* www.skinnerhouse.org, pg 236

Benatar, Raquel, Laredo Publishing Co Inc, 465 Westview Ave, Englewood, NJ 07631 *Tel:* 201-408-4048 *Fax:* 201-408-5011 *E-mail:* info@laredopublishing.com *Web Site:* www.laredopublishing.com, pg 144

Benatar, Raquel, Renaissance House, 465 Westview Ave, Englewood, NJ 07631 *Tel:* 201-408-4048 *Fax:* 201-408-5011 *E-mail:* info@renaissancehouse.net *Web Site:* www.renaissancehouse.net, pg 218

Benbow, Ann E, American Geological Institute (AGI), 4220 King St, Alexandria, VA 22302-1502 *Tel:* 703-379-2480 *Fax:* 703-379-7563 *E-mail:* pubs@agiweb.org *Web Site:* www.agiweb.org, pg 13

Bender, Robert, Simon & Schuster, 1230 Avenue of the Americas, New York, NY 10020 *Tel:* 212-698-7000 *Toll Free Tel:* 800-223-2348 (cust serv); 800-223-2336 (orders) *Toll Free Fax:* 800-943-9831 (orders) *Web Site:* www.simonandschuster.com, pg 234

Bender, Roger J, R James Bender Publishing, PO Box 23456, San Jose, CA 95153-3456 *Tel:* 408-225-5777 *Fax:* 408-225-4739 *E-mail:* order@bender-publishing.com *Web Site:* www.bender-publishing.com, pg 35

Benedict, Holly, Quincannon Publishing Group, PO Box 8100, Glen Ridge, NJ 07028-8100 *Tel:* 973-380-9942 *E-mail:* editors@quincannongroup.com *Web Site:* www.quincannongroup.com, pg 211

Benedict, Tolszczuk, Editions Vents d'Ouest, 109 rue Wright, Gatineau, QC J8X 2G7, Canada *Tel:* 819-770-6377 *Fax:* 819-770-0559 *E-mail:* info@ventsdouest.ca *Web Site:* www.ventsdouest.ca, pg 504

Benembarek, Sheima, Tormont Publishing International, 3305 Pitfield Blvd, St-Laurent, QC H4S 1H3, Canada *Tel:* 514-954-1441 *Fax:* 514-954-1443, pg 521

Benezra, Mark, Original Publications, PO Box 236, Old Beth Page, NY 11804 *Tel:* 516-605-0547 *Toll Free Tel:* 888-622-8581 *Fax:* 516-605-0549 *E-mail:* originalpub@aol.com *Web Site:* www.occult1.com, pg 188

Benjamin, Dan, Do-It-Yourself Legal Publishers, 1588 Remsen Ave, Brooklyn, NY 11236 *Tel:* 718-684-4769 *Fax:* 718-684-4769 *E-mail:* ba07102@yahoo.com, pg 80

Benjamin, Sr Denise Cecilia, Pauline Books & Media, 50 Saint Paul's Ave, Boston, MA 02130 *Tel:* 617-522-8911 *Toll Free Tel:* 800-876-4463 (orders); 800-836-9723 (cust serv) *Fax:* 617-541-9805 *E-mail:* orderentry@pauline.org (cust serv); editorial@paulinemedia.com (ms submissions) *Web Site:* www.pauline.org, pg 194

Benjamin, Matthew, Touchstone, 1230 Avenue of the Americas, New York, NY 10020, pg 256

Benjey, Thomas R, Tuxedo Press, 546 E Springville Rd, Carlisle, PA 17015 *Tel:* 717-258-9733 *Fax:* 717-243-0074 *E-mail:* info@tuxedo-press.com *Web Site:* tuxedo-press.com, pg 260

Benka, Jennifer, The Academy of American Poets Inc, 75 Maiden Lane, Suite 901, New York, NY 10038 *Tel:* 212-274-0343 *Fax:* 212-274-9427 *E-mail:* academy@poets.org *Web Site:* www.poets.org, pg 611

Benka, Jennifer, Raiziss/de Palchi Fellowship, 75 Maiden Lane, Suite 901, New York, NY 10038 *Tel:* 212-274-0343 *Fax:* 212-274-9427 *E-mail:* academy@poets.org *Web Site:* www.poets.org, pg 737

Benka, Jennifer, Walt Whitman Award, 75 Maiden Lane, Suite 901, New York, NY 10038 *Tel:* 212-274-0343 *Fax:* 212-274-9427 *E-mail:* academy@poets.org *Web Site:* www.poets.org, pg 749

Benne, Susan, Antiquarian Booksellers' Association of America (ABAA), 20 W 44 St, Suite 507, New York, NY 10036 *Tel:* 212-944-8291 *Fax:* 212-944-8293 *E-mail:* hq@abaa.org *Web Site:* www.abaa.org, pg 615

Bennett, Barbara, Kensington Publishing Corp, 119 W 40 St, New York, NY 10018 *Tel:* 212-407-1500 *Toll Free Tel:* 800-221-2647 *Fax:* 212-935-0699 *Web Site:* www.kensingtonbooks.com, pg 139

Bennett, David, Transatlantic Agency, 2 Bloor St E, Ste 3500, Toronto, ON M4W-1A8, Canada *Tel:* 416-488-9214 *E-mail:* info@transatlanticagency.com *Web Site:* www.transatlanticagency.com, pg 597

Bennett, Jed, Penguin Young Readers Group, 345 Hudson St, New York, NY 10014 *Tel:* 212-366-2000 *E-mail:* online@penguinputnam.com *Web Site:* www.penguinputnam.com; us.penguingroup.com, pg 198

Bennett, John M, Luna Bisonte Prods, 137 Leland Ave, Columbus, OH 43214 *Tel:* 614-846-4126 *Web Site:* www.johnmbennett.net; www.lulu.com/spotlight/lunabisonteprods, pg 154

Bennett, Julie, Ten Speed Press, 2625 Alcatraz Ave, Unit 505, Berkeley, CA 94705 *Tel:* 510-285-3000 *Toll Free Tel:* 800-841-BOOK (841-2665) *E-mail:* csorders@randomhouse.com *Web Site:* crownpublishing.com/imprint/ten-speed-press, pg 252

Bennett, Lori, Nelson Literary Agency LLC, 1732 Wazee St, Suite 207, Denver, CO 80202-1284 *Tel:* 303-292-2805 *E-mail:* query@nelsonagency.com *Web Site:* www.nelsonagency.com, pg 587

Bennett, Lynn, Transatlantic Agency, 2 Bloor St E, Ste 3500, Toronto, ON M4W-1A8, Canada *Tel:* 416-488-9214 *E-mail:* info@transatlanticagency.com *Web Site:* www.transatlanticagency.com, pg 597

Bennett, Lyron, Sourcebooks Inc, 1935 Brookdale Rd, Suite 139, Naperville, IL 60563 *Tel:* 630-961-3900 *Toll Free Tel:* 800-432-7444 *Fax:* 630-961-2168 *E-mail:* info@sourcebooks.com; customersupport@sourcebooks.com *Web Site:* www.sourcebooks.com, pg 240

Bennett, Michael, Big Apple Vision Publishing Inc, PO Box 722, Stone Ridge, NY 12484-0722 *Tel:* 845-616-1346 *Fax:* 845-339-9928 *E-mail:* info@bigapplevision.com *Web Site:* bigapplevision.com, pg 37

Bennett, Millicent, Simon & Schuster, 1230 Avenue of the Americas, New York, NY 10020 *Tel:* 212-698-7000 *Toll Free Tel:* 800-223-2348 (cust serv); 800-223-2336 (orders) *Toll Free Fax:* 800-943-9831 (orders) *Web Site:* www.simonandschuster.com, pg 234

Bennett, Tina, WME, 1325 Avenue of the Americas, New York, NY 10019 *Tel:* 212-586-5100 *Fax:* 212-246-3583 *E-mail:* wma@interport.net *Web Site:* www.wma.com, pg 599

Bennett, Twila, Fleming H Revell, PO Box 6287, Grand Rapids, MI 49516-6287 *Tel:* 616-676-9185 *Toll Free Tel:* 800-877-2665; 800-679-1957 *Fax:* 616-676-9573 *Web Site:* www.revellbooks.com, pg 218

Bennie, Dale, University of Oklahoma Press, 2800 Venture Dr, Norman, OK 73069-8216 *Tel:* 405-325-2000 *Toll Free Tel:* 800-627-7377 (orders) *Fax:* 405-364-5798 (orders) *Toll Free Fax:* 800-735-0476 (orders) *E-mail:* presscs@ou.edu *Web Site:* www.oupress.com, pg 268

Benoit, Emmanuel, Jouve North America Inc, 70 Landmark Hill Dr, Brattleboro, VT 05301 *Tel:* 802-254-6073 *Toll Free Tel:* 800-451-4328 *Web Site:* www.jouve.com, pg 549

Benoit, Michael J, Benoit & Associates, 279 S Schuyler Ave, Kankakee, IL 60901 *Tel:* 815-932-2582 *Fax:* 815-932-2594 *E-mail:* benoitart@benoit-associates.com *Web Site:* www.benoit-associates.com, pg 601

Bensaid, Barbara, US Games Systems Inc, 179 Ludlow St, Stamford, CT 06902 *Tel:* 203-353-8400 *Toll Free Tel:* 800-54-GAMES (544-2637) *Fax:* 203-353-8431 *E-mail:* info@usgamesinc.com *Web Site:* www.usgamesinc.com, pg 273

Bensky, Dan, Eastland Press, 1240 Activity Dr, Suite D, Vista, CA 92081 *Tel:* 206-217-0204 (edit); 760-598-9695 (orders) *Toll Free Tel:* 800-453-3278 (orders) *Fax:* 760-598-6083 (orders) *Toll Free Fax:* 800-241-3329 (orders) *E-mail:* info@eastlandpress.com; orders@eastlandpress.com (orders-credit cards only) *Web Site:* www.eastlandpress.com, pg 84

Bensky, Lilian, Eastland Press, 1240 Activity Dr, Suite D, Vista, CA 92081 *Tel:* 206-217-0204 (edit); 760-598-9695 (orders) *Toll Free Tel:* 800-453-3278 (orders) *Fax:* 760-598-6083 (orders) *Toll Free Fax:* 800-241-3329 (orders) *E-mail:* info@eastlandpress.com; orders@eastlandpress.com (orders-credit cards only) *Web Site:* www.eastlandpress.com, pg 84

Benson, Ms Frances, Cornell University Press, Sage House, 512 E State St, Ithaca, NY 14850 *Tel:* 607-277-2338 *Fax:* 607-277-2374 *E-mail:* cupressinfo@cornell.edu; cupress-sales@cornell.edu *Web Site:* www.cornellpress.cornell.edu, pg 67

Benson, Ingrid, Integra Software Services Inc, 1110 Jorie Blvd, Suite 200, Oak Brook, IL 60523 *Tel:* 630-586-2579 *Fax:* 630-586-2599 *Web Site:* www.integra.co.in, pg 548

Benson, Jack, Water Environment Federation, 601 Wythe St, Alexandria, VA 22314-1994 *Tel:* 703-684-2400 *Toll Free Tel:* 800-666-0206 *Fax:* 703-684-2492 *E-mail:* csc@wef.org (cust serv) *Web Site:* www.wef.org, pg 277

Benson, John W, BK Nelson Inc Lecture Bureau, 1565 Paseo Vida, Palm Springs, CA 92264 *Tel:* 760-778-8800 *Fax:* 760-778-6242 *E-mail:* bknelson4@cs.com *Web Site:* www.bknelsonlecturebureau.com; www.bknelson.com; www.bknelsonmovieproduction.com, pg 605

Benson, John W, BK Nelson Inc Literary Agency, 1565 Paseo Vida, Palm Springs, CA 92264 *Tel:* 760-778-8800 *Fax:* 760-778-6242 *E-mail:* bknelson4@cs.com *Web Site:* www.bknelson.com; www.bknelsonlecturebureau.com; www.bknelsonmovieproduction.com, pg 587

Bentley, D M R, Canadian Poetry Press, Western Univeristy, Dept of English, London, ON N6A 3K7, Canada *Tel:* 519-673-1164; 519-661-2111 (ext 85834) *Fax:* 519-661-3776 *E-mail:* canadianpoetry@uwo.ca *Web Site:* www.canadianpoetry.ca, pg 497

Bentley, Michael, Bentley Publishers, 1734 Massachusetts Ave, Cambridge, MA 02138-1804 *Tel:* 617-547-4170 *Toll Free Tel:* 800-423-4595 *Fax:* 617-876-9235 *E-mail:* sales@bentleypublishers.com *Web Site:* www.bentleypublishers.com, pg 35

Bentley, Susan, Canadian Poetry Press, Western Univeristy, Dept of English, London, ON N6A 3K7, Canada *Tel:* 519-673-1164; 519-661-2111 (ext 85834) *Fax:* 519-661-3776 *E-mail:* canadianpoetry@uwo.ca *Web Site:* www.canadianpoetry.ca, pg 497

Benton, Lori, Scholastic Trade Division, 557 Broadway, New York, NY 10012 *Tel:* 212-343-6100; 212-343-4685 (export sales) *Fax:* 212-343-4714 (export sales) *Web Site:* www.scholastic.com, pg 228

Ber-Donkor, Nina, Knopf Random Canada, One Toronto St, Suite 300, Toronto, ON M5C 2V6, Canada *Tel:* 416-364-4449 *Toll Free Tel:* 888-523-9292 *Fax:* 416-364-6863 *Web Site:* www.randomhouse.ca, pg 510

Bercaw Edwards, Mary K, The Melville Society, c/o Kent State Univ, Dept of English, Box 5190, Kent, OH 44242, pg 627

Bercholz, Ivan, Shambhala Publications Inc, Horticultural Hall, 300 Massachusetts Ave, Boston, MA 02115 *Tel:* 617-424-0030 *Toll Free Tel:* 866-424-0030 (off); 888-424-2329 (cust serv) *Fax:* 617-236-1563 *E-mail:* customercare@shambhala.com *Web Site:* www.shambhala.com, pg 232

Bercholz, Samuel, Shambhala Publications Inc, Horticultural Hall, 300 Massachusetts Ave, Boston, MA 02115 *Tel:* 617-424-0030 *Toll Free Tel:* 866-424-0030 (off); 888-424-2329 (cust serv) *Fax:* 617-236-1563 *E-mail:* customercare@shambhala.com *Web Site:* www.shambhala.com, pg 232

Bercholz, Sara, Shambhala Publications Inc, Horticultural Hall, 300 Massachusetts Ave, Boston, MA 02115 *Tel:* 617-424-0030 *Toll Free Tel:* 866-424-0030 (off); 888-424-2329 (cust serv) *Fax:* 617-236-1563 *E-mail:* customercare@shambhala.com *Web Site:* www.shambhala.com, pg 232

Berchowitz, Gillian, Ohio University Press, 215 Columbus Rd, Suite 101, Athens, OH 45701-2979 *Tel:* 740-593-1154 *Fax:* 740-593-4536 *Web Site:* www.ohioswallow.com, pg 184

Berchowitz, Gillian, Swallow Press, 215 Columbus Rd, Suite 101, Athens, OH 45701 *Tel:* 740-593-1158 (Jeff Kallet) *Fax:* 740-593-4536 *Web Site:* www.ohioswallow.com, pg 248

Berchten, Rachel, University of California Press, 2120 Berkeley Way, Berkeley, CA 94704-1012 *Tel:* 510-642-4247 *Fax:* 510-643-7127 *E-mail:* askucp@ucpress.edu (books); customerservice@ucpressjournals.com (journals) *Web Site:* www.ucpress.edu, pg 264

Berens, Gayle, ULI-The Urban Land Institute, 1025 Thomas Jefferson St NW, Suite 500-W, Washington, DC 20007-5201 *Tel:* 202-624-7000; 410-626-7505 (cust serv outside US) *Toll Free Tel:* 800-321-5011 (cust serv) *Fax:* 202-624-7140; 410-626-7147 (orders only) *Toll Free Fax:* 800-248-4585 *E-mail:* bookstore@uli.org; customerservice@uli.org *Web Site:* www.uli.org, pg 262

Beresford, Lea, Bloomsbury Publishing, 175 Fifth Ave, New York, NY 10010 *Tel:* 212-674-5151 *Toll Free Tel:* 800-221-7945 *Fax:* 212-780-0115; 212-982-2837 *E-mail:* marketingusa@bloomsbury.com; adultpublicityusa.@bloomsbury.com *Web Site:* www.bloomsbury.com, pg 40

Berg, Jennifer, PAGE International Screenwriting Awards, 7510 Sunset Blvd, Suite 610, Hollywood, CA 90046 *E-mail:* info@pageawards.com *Web Site:* www.pageawards.com, pg 732

Berg, Patty, Crown Publishing Group, c/o Random House Inc, 1745 Broadway, New York, NY 10019 *Tel:* 212-782-9000 *Toll Free Tel:* 888-264-1745 *Fax:* 212-940-7408 *Web Site:* www.randomhouse.com/crown, pg 72

Berg, Rachel, Lonely Planet, 150 Linden St, Oakland, CA 94607 *Tel:* 510-893-8555 *Toll Free Tel:* 800-275-8555 (orders) *Fax:* 510-893-8563 *E-mail:* info@lonelyplanet.com *Web Site:* www.lonelyplanet.com, pg 152

Berge, Pablo Agrest, STOCKCERO Inc, 3785 NW 82 Ave, Suite 302, Doral, FL 33166 *Tel:* 305-722-7628 *Fax:* 305-477-5794 *E-mail:* sales@stockcero.com *Web Site:* www.stockcero.com, pg 245

Bergen, Glenn, University of Manitoba Press, University of Manitoba, 301 St Johns College, Winnipeg, MB R3T 2M5, Canada *Tel:* 204-474-9495 *Fax:* 204-474-7566 *Web Site:* www.umanitoba.ca/uofmpress, pg 523

Berger, Bob, TSI Graphics, 1300 S Raney St, Effingham, IL 62401-4206 *Tel:* 217-347-7733; 217-347-7734 *Fax:* 217-342-9611 *E-mail:* info@tsigraphics.com *Web Site:* www.tsigraphics.com, pg 556

Berger, Ellie, Scholastic Inc, 557 Broadway, New York, NY 10012 *Tel:* 212-343-6100 *Toll Free Tel:* 800-scholastic *Web Site:* www.scholastic.com, pg 228

Berger, Ellie, Scholastic Trade Division, 557 Broadway, New York, NY 10012 *Tel:* 212-343-6100; 212-343-4685 (export sales) *Fax:* 212-343-4714 (export sales) *Web Site:* www.scholastic.com, pg 228

Berger, Erin, Penguin Young Readers Group, 345 Hudson St, New York, NY 10014 *Tel:* 212-366-2000 *E-mail:* online@penguinputnam.com *Web Site:* www.penguinputnam.com; us.penguingroup.com, pg 198

Berger, Erin, Razorbill, 345 Hudson St, New York, NY 10014 *Tel:* 212-366-2000, pg 215

Berger, Dr John, Cambridge University Press, 32 Avenue of the Americas, New York, NY 10013-2473 *Tel:* 212-924-3900; 212-337-5000 *Toll Free Tel:* 800-899-5222 *Fax:* 212-691-3239 *E-mail:* newyork@cambridge.org *Web Site:* www.cambridge.org/us, pg 51

Berger, Karen, Quality Medical Publishing Inc, 2248 Welsch Industrial Ct, St Louis, MO 63146-4222 *Tel:* 314-878-7808 *Toll Free Tel:* 800-348-7808 *Fax:* 314-878-9937 *E-mail:* qmp@qmp.com *Web Site:* www.qmp.com, pg 211

Berger, Mel, WME, 1325 Avenue of the Americas, New York, NY 10019 *Tel:* 212-586-5100 *Fax:* 212-246-3583 *E-mail:* wma@interport.net *Web Site:* www.wma.com, pg 599

Berger, Pat, Vandamere Press, 3580 Morris St N, St Petersburg, FL 33713 *Tel:* 727-556-0950 *Toll Free Tel:* 800-551-7776 *Fax:* 727-556-2560 *E-mail:* orders@vandamere.com *Web Site:* www.vandamere.com, pg 274

Berger, Shulamith, AJL Scholarship, PO Box 1118, Teaneck, NJ 07666 *Web Site:* www.jewishlibraries.org, pg 686

Berger, Stacie, F+W Media Inc, 10151 Carver Rd, Suite 200, Blue Ash, OH 45242 *Tel:* 513-531-2690 *Toll Free Tel:* 800-289-0963 (trade accts); 800-258-0929 (orders) *E-mail:* contact_us@fwmedia.com *Web Site:* www.fwmedia.com, pg 92

Berger, Stacie, North Light Books, 10151 Carver Rd, Suite 200, Blue Ash, OH 45242 *Tel:* 513-531-2690 *Toll Free Tel:* 800-666-0963 *Fax:* 513-891-7185 *Toll Free Fax:* 888-590-4082 *E-mail:* contact_us@fwmedia.com *Web Site:* www.fwmedia.com, pg 181

Bergeron, Amanda, HarperCollins General Books Group, 10 E 53 St, New York, NY 10022 *Tel:* 212-207-7000 *Fax:* 212-207-7633 *Web Site:* www.harpercollins.com, pg 113

Bergeron, Catherine, The Johns Hopkins University Press, 2715 N Charles St, Baltimore, MD 21218-4363 *Tel:* 410-516-6900; 410-516-6987 (journals outside US & CN) *Toll Free Tel:* 800-537-5487 (book orders & cust serv); 800-548-1784 (journal orders) *Fax:* 410-516-6968; 410-516-3866 (journal orders) *E-mail:* hfscustserv@press.jhu.edu (cust serv); jrnlcirc@press.jhu.edu (journal orders) *Web Site:* www.press.jhu.edu; muse.jhu.edu/about/subscriptions/index.html (Project Muse subns), pg 136

Bergeron, Diane, Raven Tree Press, 1400 Miller Pkwy, McHenry, IL 60050-7030 *Tel:* 815-363-3582 *Toll Free Tel:* 800-323-8270 *Fax:* 815-363-2948 *Toll Free Fax:* 800-909-9901 *E-mail:* raven@raventreepress.com *Web Site:* www.raventreepress.com, pg 215

Bergeron, Elise, Les Editions du Remue-Menage, La Maison Parent-Roback, 110 rue Ste-Therese, bureau 501, Montreal, QC H2Y 1E6, Canada *Tel:* 514-876-0097 *Fax:* 514-876-7951 *E-mail:* info@editions-remuemenage.qc.ca *Web Site:* www.editions-remuemenage.qc.ca, pg 503

Bergey, Brad, National Association of Printing Ink Manufacturers (NAPIM), 15 Technology Pkwy S, Peachtree Corners, GA 30092 *Tel:* 770-209-7289 *Fax:* 678-680-4920 *E-mail:* napim@napim.org *Web Site:* www.napim.org, pg 629

841-9991 (orders) *E-mail:* info@woodlake.com; customerservice@woodlake.com *Web Site:* www.woodlakebooks.com, pg 525

Bess, Benjamin E, Bess Press, 3565 Harding Ave, Honolulu, HI 96816 *Tel:* 808-734-7159; 808-734-7159 (ext 10, returns) *Toll Free Tel:* 800-910-2377 *Fax:* 808-732-3627 *E-mail:* sales@besspress.com *Web Site:* www.besspress.com, pg 36

Besse, Chris, Nelson Education Ltd, 1120 Birchmount Rd, Scarborough, ON M1K 5G4, Canada *Tel:* 416-752-9100 *Toll Free Tel:* 800-268-2222 (cust serv) *Fax:* 416-752-8101 *Toll Free Fax:* 800-430-4445 *E-mail:* inquire@nelson.com *Web Site:* www.nelson.com, pg 513

Besser, Jennifer, GP Putnam's Sons (Children's), 345 Hudson St, New York, NY 10014 *Tel:* 212-366-2000 *Fax:* 212-414-3393 *E-mail:* online@penguinputnam.com *Web Site:* us.penguingroup.com, pg 210

Best, Theresa, Whitecap Books Ltd, 314 W Cordova St, Suite 210, Vancouver, BC V6B 1E8, Canada *Tel:* 604-681-6181 *Toll Free Tel:* 800-387-9776 *Toll Free Fax:* 800-260-9777 *Web Site:* www.whitecap.ca, pg 524

Bestall, May, Wolf Pirate Project Inc, 337 Lost Lake Dr, Divide, CO 80814 *Tel:* 305-333-3186 *E-mail:* contact@wolfpiratebooks.com; workshop@wolfpiratebooks.com *Web Site:* www.wolf-pirate.com, pg 557

Bestler, Emily, Atria Books, 1230 Avenue of the Americas, New York, NY 10020 *Tel:* 212-698-7000 *Fax:* 212-698-7007 *Web Site:* www.simonandschuster.com, pg 26

Betancourt, John, Wildside Press, 414 Hungerford Dr, Suite 234, Rockville, MD 20850 *Tel:* 301-762-1305 *Fax:* 301-762-1306 *E-mail:* wildside@wildsidepress.com *Web Site:* www.wildsidebooks.com, pg 281

Bethel, Courtney, The MacDowell Colony, 100 High St, Peterborough, NH 03458 *Tel:* 603-924-3886 *Fax:* 603-924-9142 *E-mail:* info@macdowellcolony.org; admissions@macdowellcolony.org *Web Site:* www.macdowellcolony.org, pg 720

Betrelle, Anne, Black Warrior Review Fiction, Nonfiction & Poetry Contest, Office of Student Media, University of Alabama, Tuscaloosa, AL 35486-0027 *Tel:* 205-348-4518 *Web Site:* www.bwr.ua.edu, pg 691

Betsch, Carol, University of Massachusetts Press, East Experiment Sta, 671 N Pleasant St, Amherst, MA 01003 *Tel:* 413-545-2217 *Fax:* 413-545-1226 *E-mail:* info@umpress.umass.edu *Web Site:* www.umass.edu/umpress, pg 266

Bettinger, James R, The Knight-Risser Prize for Western Environmental Journalism, Stanford University, 450 Serra Mall, Bldg 120, Rm 424, Stanford, CA 94305 *Tel:* 650-721-5955 *Fax:* 650-725-6154 *E-mail:* knightrisserprize@lists.stanford.edu *Web Site:* knightrisser.stanford.edu, pg 715

Betz, James L, George T Bisel Co Inc, 710 S Washington Sq, Philadelphia, PA 19106-3519 *Tel:* 215-922-5760 *Toll Free Tel:* 800-247-3526 *Fax:* 215-922-2235 *E-mail:* gbisel@bisel.com *Web Site:* www.bisel.com, pg 38

Betz, Sue Bradanini, Chicago Review Press, 814 N Franklin St, Chicago, IL 60610 *Tel:* 312-337-0747 *Toll Free Tel:* 800-888-4741 *Fax:* 312-337-5110 *E-mail:* frontdesk@chicagoreviewpress.com *Web Site:* www.chicagoreviewpress.com, pg 60

Beullac, Paul, B & B Publishing, 4823 Sherbrooke St W, Office 275, Westmount, QC H3Z 1G7, Canada *Tel:* 514-932-9466 *Fax:* 514-932-5929 *E-mail:* editions@ebbp.ca, pg 494

Bevington, Stan, Coach House Books, 80 bpNichol Lane, Toronto, ON M5S 3J4, Canada *Tel:* 416-979-2217 *Toll Free Tel:* 800-367-6360 (outside Toronto) *Fax:* 416-977-1158 *E-mail:* mail@chbooks.com *Web Site:* www.chbooks.com, pg 499

Bewick, Andrea, Napa Valley Writers' Conference, Upper Valley Campus, 1088 College Ave, St Helena, CA 94574 *Tel:* 707-967-2900 (ext 1611) *Fax:* 707-967-2909 *E-mail:* writecon@napavalley.edu *Web Site:* www.napawritersconf.org, pg 671

Bewley, Elizabeth, Little, Brown Books for Young Readers, 237 Park Ave, New York, NY 10017 *Tel:* 212-364-1100 *Toll Free Tel:* 800-759-0190 (cust serv) *Web Site:* www.HachetteBookGroup.com, pg 150

Bezalel, Lindsay, Avery, 375 Hudson St, New York, NY 10014 *Tel:* 212-366-2000 *Fax:* 212-366-2643 *E-mail:* online@penguinputnam.com *Web Site:* www.penguinputnam.com; us.penguingroup.com, pg 28

Bezalel, Lindsay, Gotham Books, 375 Hudson St, New York, NY 10014, pg 105

Bhatnagar, Supriya, Association of Writers & Writing Programs (AWP), George Mason University, 4400 University Dr, MSN 1E3, Fairfax, VA 22030 *Tel:* 703-993-4301 *Fax:* 703-993-4302 *E-mail:* awp@awpwriter.org *Web Site:* www.awpwriter.org, pg 617

Bhatnagar, Supriya, AWP Award Series, George Mason University, 4400 University Dr, MSN 1E3, Fairfax, VA 22030 *Tel:* 703-993-4301 *Fax:* 703-993-4302 *E-mail:* awp@awpwriter.org *Web Site:* www.awpwriter.org, pg 688

Biagi, Laura, Jean V Naggar Literary Agency Inc, 216 E 75 St, Suite 1-E, New York, NY 10021 *Tel:* 212-794-1082 *E-mail:* jvnla@jvnla.com *Web Site:* www.jvnla.com, pg 586

Bial, Daniel, Daniel Bial Agency, 41 W 83 St, Suite 5-C, New York, NY 10024 *Tel:* 212-721-1786 *E-mail:* dbialagency@msn.com *Web Site:* www.danielbialagency.com, pg 562

Bial, Daniel, Daniel Bial & Associates, 41 W 83 St, Suite 5-C, New York, NY 10024 *Tel:* 212-721-1786 *E-mail:* dbialagency@msn.com *Web Site:* www.danielbialagency.com, pg 541

Bialer, Matthew, Sanford J Greenburger Associates Inc, 55 Fifth Ave, 15th fl, New York, NY 10003 *Tel:* 212-206-5600 *Fax:* 212-463-8718 *Web Site:* www.greenburger.com, pg 575

Bialosky, Jill, W W Norton & Company Inc, 500 Fifth Ave, New York, NY 10110-0017 *Tel:* 212-354-5500 *Toll Free Tel:* 800-233-4830 (orders & cust serv) *Fax:* 212-869-0856 *Toll Free Fax:* 800-458-6515 *Web Site:* www.wwnorton.com, pg 182

Bianchini, Brian, International Press of Boston Inc, 387 Somerville Ave, Somerville, MA 02143 *Tel:* 617-623-3016 *Fax:* 617-623-3101 *E-mail:* ipb-info@intlpress.com; ipb-orders@intlpress.com *Web Site:* www.intlpress.com, pg 133

Bianchini, Lori, National Council of Teachers of English (NCTE), 1111 W Kenyon Rd, Urbana, IL 61801-1096 *Tel:* 217-328-3870 *Toll Free Tel:* 877-369-6283 (cust serv) *Fax:* 217-328-9645 *E-mail:* public_info@ncte.org *Web Site:* www.ncte.org, pg 629

Bick, George, Doug Grad Literary Agency Inc, 156 Prospect Park West, No 3L, Brooklyn, NY 11215 *Tel:* 718-788-6067 *E-mail:* query@dgliterary.com *Web Site:* www.dgliterary.com, pg 575

Bickel, Marla, Eclipse Press, 3101 Beaumont Centre Circle, Lexington, KY 40513 *Tel:* 859-278-2361 *Toll Free Tel:* 800-866-2361 *Fax:* 859-276-6868 *E-mail:* editorial@eclipsepress.com; info@eclipsepress.com *Web Site:* www.eclipsepress.com, pg 84

Bickerstaff, Patsy Anne, Laura Day Boggs Bolling Memorial, 1194 Hume Rd, Hume, VA 22639-1806 *E-mail:* poetryinva@aol.com *Web Site:* www.poetrysocietyofvirginia.org, pg 692

Bickerstaff, Patsy Anne, Joe Pendleton Campbell Narrative Contest, 1194 Hume Rd, Hume, VA 22639-1806 *E-mail:* poetryinva@aol.com *Web Site:* www.poetrysocietyofvirginia.org, pg 694

Bickerstaff, Patsy Anne, Carleton Drewry Memorial, 1194 Hume Rd, Hume, VA 22639-1806 *E-mail:* poetryinva@aol.com *Web Site:* www.poetrysocietyofvirginia.org, pg 701

Bickerstaff, Patsy Anne, Alfred C Gary Memorial, 1194 Hume Rd, Hume, VA 22639-1806 *E-mail:* poetryinva@aol.com *Web Site:* www.poetrysocietyofvirginia.org, pg 706

Bickerstaff, Patsy Anne, Bess Gresham Memorial, 1194 Hume Rd, Hume, VA 22639-1806 *E-mail:* poetryinva@aol.com *Web Site:* www.poetrysocietyofvirginia.org, pg 708

Bickerstaff, Patsy Anne, Loretta Dunn Hall Memorial, 1194 Hume Rd, Hume, VA 22639-1806 *E-mail:* poetryinva@aol.com *Web Site:* www.poetrysocietyofvirginia.org, pg 708

Bickerstaff, Patsy Anne, Handy Andy Prize, 1194 Hume Rd, Hume, VA 22639-1806 *E-mail:* poetryinva@aol.com *Web Site:* www.poetrysocietyofvirginia.org, pg 708

Bickerstaff, Patsy Anne, Brodie Herndon Memorial, 1194 Hume Rd, Hume, VA 22639-1806 *E-mail:* poetryinva@aol.com *Web Site:* www.poetrysocietyofvirginia.org, pg 709

Bickerstaff, Patsy Anne, Judah, Sarah, Grace & Tom Memorial, 1194 Hume Rd, Hume, VA 22639-1806 *E-mail:* poetryinva@aol.com *Web Site:* www.poetrysocietyofvirginia.org, pg 714

Bickerstaff, Patsy Anne, Cenie H Moon Prize, 1194 Hume Rd, Hume, VA 22639-1806 *E-mail:* poetryinva@aol.com *Web Site:* www.poetrysocietyofvirginia.org, pg 724

Bickerstaff, Patsy Anne, Edgar Allan Poe Memorial, 1194 Hume Rd, Hume, VA 22639-1806 *E-mail:* poetryinva@aol.com *Web Site:* www.poetrysocietyofvirginia.org, pg 734

Bickerstaff, Patsy Anne, A Poem With a Point of View, 1194 Hume Rd, Hume, VA 22639-1806 *E-mail:* poetryinva@aol.com *Web Site:* www.poetrysocietyofvirginia.org, pg 734

Bickerstaff, Patsy Anne, Miriam Rachimi Memorial, 1194 Hume Rd, Hume, VA 22639-1806 *E-mail:* poetryinva@aol.com *Web Site:* www.poetrysocietyofvirginia.org, pg 737

Bickerstaff, Patsy Anne, Ada Sanderson Memorial, 1194 Hume Rd, Hume, VA 22639-1806 *E-mail:* poetryinva@aol.com *Web Site:* www.poetrysocietyofvirginia.org, pg 739

Bickerstaff, Patsy Anne, The Robert S Sergeant Memorial, 1194 Hume Rd, Hume, VA 22639-1806 *E-mail:* poetryinva@aol.com *Web Site:* www.poetrysocietyofvirginia.org, pg 741

Bicknell, Liz, Candlewick Press, 99 Dover St, Somerville, MA 02144-2825 *Tel:* 617-661-3330 *Fax:* 617-661-0565 *E-mail:* bigbear@candlewick.com *Web Site:* www.candlewick.com, pg 51

Biddinger, Mary, Akron Poetry Prize, The University of Akron Press, 120 E Mill St, Suite 415, Akron, OH 44308 *Tel:* 330-972-6953 *Fax:* 330-972-8364 *E-mail:* uapress@uakron.edu *Web Site:* www.uakron.edu/uapress/akron-poetry-prize, pg 686

Bidler, R M, editions CERES Ltd/Le Moyen Francais, CP 1089, Succursale B, Maison de la Poste, Montreal, QC H3B 3K9, Canada *Tel:* 514-937-7138 *Fax:* 514-937-9875 *E-mail:* editionsceres@gmail.com *Web Site:* www.editionsceres.ca, pg 502

Bieker, Mike, The University of Arkansas Press, McIlroy House, 105 N McIlroy Ave, Fayetteville, AR 72701 *Tel:* 479-575-3246 *Toll Free Tel:* 800-626-0090 *Fax:* 479-575-6044 *E-mail:* uapress@uark.edu *Web Site:* www.uapress.com, pg 264

Biello, Lisa, F A Davis Co, 1915 Arch St, Philadelphia, PA 19103 *Tel:* 215-568-2270 *Toll Free Tel:* 800-523-4049 *Fax:* 215-568-5065 *E-mail:* info@fadavis.com *Web Site:* www.fadavis.com, pg 76

Bielstein, Susan, University of Chicago Press, 1427 E 60 St, Chicago, IL 60637-2954 *Tel:* 773-702-7700; 773-702-7600 *Toll Free Tel:* 800-621-2736 (orders) *Fax:* 773-702-9756; 773-660-2235 (orders); 773-702-2708 *E-mail:* custserv@press.uchicago.edu; marketing@press.uchicago.edu *Web Site:* www.press.uchicago.edu, pg 265

Biesel, David, St Johann Press, 315 Schraalenburgh Rd, Haworth, NJ 07641 *Tel:* 201-387-1529 *Fax:* 201-501-0698 *Web Site:* www.stjohannpress.com, pg 224

Biesel, Diane, St Johann Press, 315 Schraalenburgh Rd, Haworth, NJ 07641 *Tel:* 201-387-1529 *Fax:* 201-501-0698 *Web Site:* www.stjohannpress.com, pg 224

Bigelow, Christopher, Zarahemla Books, 869 E 2680 N, Provo, UT 84604 *Tel:* 801-368-7374 *Fax:* 801-418-2081 *E-mail:* info@zarahemlabooks.com *Web Site:* zarahemlabooks.com, pg 289

Biggins, Walter, University Press of Mississippi, 3825 Ridgewood Rd, Jackson, MS 39211-6492 *Tel:* 601-432-6205 *Toll Free Tel:* 800-737-7788 (orders & cust serv) *Fax:* 601-432-6217 *E-mail:* press@mississippi.edu *Web Site:* www.upress.state.ms.us, pg 271

Bijur, Vicky, Vicky Bijur Literary Agency, 333 West End Ave, Suite 5-B, New York, NY 10023 *Tel:* 212-580-4108 *E-mail:* queries@vickybijuragency.com *Web Site:* www.vickybijuragency.com, pg 562

Billeter, Michelle, Woodland Publishing Inc, 515 S 700 E, Suite 2D, Salt Lake City, UT 84102 *Toll Free Tel:* 800-277-3243 *Fax:* 801-334-1913 *E-mail:* info@woodlandpublishing.com *Web Site:* www.woodlandpublishing.com, pg 284

Billings, Hyacinth, World Resources Institute, 10 "G" St NE, Suite 800, Washington, DC 20002 *Tel:* 202-729-7600 *Fax:* 202-729-7610 *Web Site:* www.wri.org, pg 285

Billingsley, Joseph, Pelican Publishing Co, 1000 Burmaster St, Gretna, LA 70053-2246 *Tel:* 504-368-1175 *Toll Free Tel:* 800-843-1724 *Fax:* 504-368-1195 *E-mail:* sales@pelicanpub.com (sales); office@pelicanpub.com (permission); promo@pelicanpub.com (publicity) *Web Site:* www.pelicanpub.com, pg 196

Binder, Pam, Pacific Northwest Summer Writers Conference, 1420 NW Gilman Blvd, Suite 2, PMB 2717, Issaquah, WA 98027 *Tel:* 425-673-2665 *E-mail:* pnwa@pnwa.org *Web Site:* www.pnwa.org, pg 672

Binder, Pam, Pacific Northwest Writers Association, 1420 NW Gilman Blvd, Suite 2, PMB 2717, Issaquah, WA 98027 *Tel:* 425-673-2665 *Fax:* 425-961-0768 *E-mail:* pnwa@pnwa.org *Web Site:* www.pnwa.org, pg 633

Binder, Pam, PNWA Literary Contest, 1420 NW Gilman Blvd, Suite 2, PMB 2717, Issaquah, WA 98027 *Tel:* 425-673-2665 *E-mail:* pnwa@pnwa.org *Web Site:* www.pnwa.org, pg 734

Bine-Stock, Edward Z Esq, E & E Publishing, 1001 Bridgeway, Suite 227, Sausalito, CA 94965 *Tel:* 415-331-4025 *Fax:* 415-331-4023 *E-mail:* eandegroup@eandegroup.com *Web Site:* www.eandegroup.com, pg 83

Bine-Stock, Eve Heidi, E & E Publishing, 1001 Bridgeway, Suite 227, Sausalito, CA 94965 *Tel:* 415-331-4025 *Fax:* 415-331-4023 *E-mail:* eandegroup@eandegroup.com *Web Site:* www.eandegroup.com, pg 83

Bingham, Joan, Grove/Atlantic Inc, 841 Broadway, 4th fl, New York, NY 10003-4793 *Tel:* 212-614-7850 *Toll Free Tel:* 800-521-0178 *Fax:* 212-614-7886 *E-mail:* info@groveatlantic.com *Web Site:* www.groveatlantic.com, pg 108

Binney, Ann, Los Angeles Times Book Prizes, 202 W First St, Los Angeles, CA 90012 *Tel:* 213-237-5775 *Toll Free Tel:* 800-528-4637 *Fax:* 213-237-7679 *Web Site:* www.latimesbookprizes.com, pg 719

Binyominson, Yerachmiel, Hachai Publishing, 527 Empire Blvd, Brooklyn, NY 11225 *Tel:* 718-633-0100 *Fax:* 718-633-0103 *E-mail:* info@hachai.com *Web Site:* www.hachai.com, pg 109

Biolchini, Bob, PennWell Books, 1421 S Sheridan Rd, Tulsa, OK 74112 *Tel:* 918-831-9410 *Toll Free Tel:* 800-752-9764 *Fax:* 918-831-9555 *E-mail:* sales@pennwell.com *Web Site:* www.pennwellbooks.com, pg 198

Birkencamp, Dean, Paradigm Publishers, 5589 Arapahoe Ave, Suite 206A, Boulder, CO 80303 *Tel:* 303-245-9054 *Web Site:* www.paradigmpublishers.com, pg 193

Birkhead, Rob, Howard Books, 216 Centerview Dr, Suite 303, Brentwood, TN 37027 *Tel:* 615-873-2080 *Fax:* 615-370-3834 *E-mail:* howardbooks@simonandschuster.com (info) *Web Site:* www.howardpublishing.com, pg 124

Birkholz, Linda, Peradam Press, PO Box 6, North San Juan, CA 95960-0006 *Tel:* 530-292-4266 *Fax:* 530-292-4266 *E-mail:* peradam@earthlink.net, pg 199

Birnbaum, Agnes, Bleecker Street Associates Inc, 217 Thompson St, Suite 519, New York, NY 10012 *Tel:* 212-677-4492 *Fax:* 212-388-0001, pg 562

Biro, Martin, Kensington Publishing Corp, 119 W 40 St, New York, NY 10018 *Tel:* 212-407-1500 *Toll Free Tel:* 800-221-2647 *Fax:* 212-935-0699 *Web Site:* www.kensingtonbooks.com, pg 139

Birschel, Dee, International Foundation of Employee Benefit Plans, 18700 W Bluemound Rd, Brookfield, WI 53045 *Tel:* 262-786-6700 *Toll Free Tel:* 888-334-3327 *Fax:* 262-786-8780 *E-mail:* editor@ifebp.org *Web Site:* www.ifebp.org, pg 133

Birtch, Brigitte, Scholastic Canada Ltd, 604 King St W, Toronto, ON M5V 1E1, Canada *Tel:* 905-887-7323 *Toll Free Tel:* 800-268-3848 (CN) *Fax:* 905-887-1131 *Toll Free Fax:* 866-346-1288 *Web Site:* www.scholastic.ca, pg 518

Bisch, Mrs Florence, Groupe Sogides Inc, 955 rue Amherst, Montreal, QC H2L 3K4, Canada *Tel:* 514-523-1182 *Toll Free Tel:* 800-361-4806 *Fax:* 514-597-0370 *E-mail:* edhomme@sogides.com *Web Site:* www.sogides.com; www.edhomme.com, pg 507

Bischel, Dr Margaret, Apollo Managed Care Inc, 1651 Foothill Blvd, Santa Ana, CA 92705 *Tel:* 805-969-2606 *Fax:* 805-969-3749 *E-mail:* apollomanagedcare@cox.net *Web Site:* www.apollomanagedcare.com, pg 20

Biscotti, Rita, QA International, 329 De la Commune W, 3rd fl, Montreal, QC H2Y 2E1, Canada *Tel:* 514-499-3000 *Fax:* 514-499-3010 *Web Site:* www.qa-international.com, pg 517

Bisk, Nathan, Bisk Education, 9417 Princess Palm Ave, Suite 400, Tampa, FL 33619 *Tel:* 813-621-6200 *Toll Free Tel:* 800-874-7877 *Web Site:* www.bisk.com, pg 38

Bissette, Robyn, Grosset & Dunlap, 345 Hudson St, New York, NY 10014 *Tel:* 212-366-2000 *E-mail:* online@penguinputnam.com *Web Site:* www.penguinputnam.com; us.penguingroup.com, pg 108

Bixler, Gina, University of Notre Dame Press, 310 Flanner Hall, Notre Dame, IN 46556 *Tel:* 574-631-6346 *Fax:* 574-631-8148 *E-mail:* undpress@nd.edu *Web Site:* www.undpress.nd.edu, pg 268

Bjerke, Paisius, St Herman Press, 10 Beegum Gorge Rd, Platina, CA 96076 *Tel:* 530-352-4430 *Fax:* 530-352-4432 *E-mail:* stherman@stherman.com *Web Site:* www.stherman.com, pg 224

Black, Cynthia, Beyond Words Publishing Inc, 20827 NW Cornell Rd, Suite 500, Hillsboro, OR 97124-9808 *Tel:* 503-531-8700 *Fax:* 503-531-8773 *Web Site:* www.beyondword.com, pg 37

Black, David, David Black Agency, 335 Adams St, 27th fl, Suite 2707, Brooklyn, NY 11201 *Tel:* 718-852-5500 *Fax:* 718-852-5539 *Web Site:* www.davidblackagency.com, pg 562

Black, Kathy, Vermont Studio Center Writer's Program Fellowships, 80 Pearl St, Johnson, VT 05656 *Tel:* 802-635-2727 *Fax:* 802-635-2730 *E-mail:* writing@vermontstudiocenter.org; info@vermontstudiocenter.org *Web Site:* www.vermontstudiocenter.org, pg 747

Black, Kim, National Council of Teachers of English (NCTE), 1111 W Kenyon Rd, Urbana, IL 61801-1096 *Tel:* 217-328-3870 *Toll Free Tel:* 877-369-6283 (cust serv) *Fax:* 217-328-9645 *E-mail:* orders@ncte.org *Web Site:* www.ncte.org, pg 174

Black, Lindsay, Standard Publishing, 8805 Governors Hill Dr, Suite 400, Cincinnati, OH 45249 *Tel:* 513-931-4050 *Toll Free Tel:* 800-543-1353 *Fax:* 513-931-0950 *Toll Free Fax:* 877-867-5751 *E-mail:* customerservice@standardpub.com *Web Site:* www.standardpub.com, pg 242

Black, Peter D, BPA Worldwide, 100 Beard Sawmill Rd, 6th fl, Shelton, CT 06484 *Tel:* 203-447-2800 *Fax:* 203-447-2900 *E-mail:* info@bpaww.com *Web Site:* www.bpaww.com, pg 619

Black, Stephen, Simon & Schuster, Inc, 1230 Avenue of the Americas, New York, NY 10020 *Tel:* 212-698-7000 *Fax:* 212-698-7007 *E-mail:* firstname.lastname@simonandschuster.com *Web Site:* www.simonandschuster.com, pg 235

Blackburn, Celeste, Business & Legal Reports Inc (BLR), 100 Winners Circle, Suite 300, Brentwood, CT 37027 *Tel:* 860-510-0100 *Toll Free Tel:* 800-727-5257 *E-mail:* service@blr.com *Web Site:* www.blr.com, pg 50

Blackhall, Gail, The Globe Pequot Press, 246 Goose Lane, Guilford, CT 06437 *Tel:* 203-458-4500 *Toll Free Tel:* 800-243-0495 (orders only); 888-249-7586 (cust serv) *Fax:* 203-458-4601 *Toll Free Fax:* 800-820-2329 (orders & cust serv) *E-mail:* info@globepequot.com *Web Site:* www.globepequot.com, pg 104

Blackstock, Peter, Grove/Atlantic Inc, 841 Broadway, 4th fl, New York, NY 10003-4793 *Tel:* 212-614-7850 *Toll Free Tel:* 800-521-0178 *Fax:* 212-614-7886 *E-mail:* info@groveatlantic.com *Web Site:* www.groveatlantic.com, pg 108

Blades, Joe, Broken Jaw Press Inc, Box 596, Sta A, Fredericton, NB E3B 5A6, Canada *Tel:* 506-454-5127 *Fax:* 506-454-5134 *E-mail:* editors@brokenjaw.com *Web Site:* www.brokenjaw.com, pg 496

Blagowidow, George, Hippocrene Books Inc, 171 Madison Ave, New York, NY 10016 *Tel:* 212-685-4373; 212-685-4375 *Fax:* 212-779-9338 *E-mail:* info@hippocrenebooks.com; orderdept@hippocrenebooks.com (orders); contact@hippocrenebooks.com *Web Site:* www.hippocrenebooks.com, pg 120

Blair, Diane, Genesis Press Inc, PO Box 101, Columbus, MS 39701 *Toll Free Tel:* 888-463-4461 (orders only) *Web Site:* www.genesis-press.com, pg 102

Blair, Susan, National Geographic Books, 1145 17 St NW, Washington, DC 20036-4688 *Tel:* 202-857-7000 *Fax:* 202-857-7670 *Web Site:* www.nationalgeographic.com, pg 174

Blake, Corey Michael, Writers of the Round Table Press, 990 Bob-O-Link Rd, Highland Park, IL 60035 *Tel:* 949-375-1006 *Fax:* 815-346-2398 *E-mail:* mike@writersoftheroundtable.com *Web Site:* www.roundtablecompanies.com, pg 286

Blake, Gillian, Henry Holt and Company, LLC, 175 Fifth Ave, New York, NY 10010 *Tel:* 646-307-5151 *Toll Free Tel:* 888-330-8477 (orders) *Fax:* 646-307-5285 *E-mail:* firstname.lastname@hholt.com *Web Site:* www.henryholt.com, pg 122

Blake, Holly, Headlands Center for the Arts Residency for Writers, 944 Fort Barry, Sausalito, CA 94965 *Tel:* 415-331-2787 *Fax:* 415-331-3857 *Web Site:* www.headlands.org, pg 709

Blake, Tammy, Crown Publishing Group, c/o Random House Inc, 1745 Broadway, New York, NY 10019 *Tel:* 212-782-9000 *Toll Free Tel:* 888-264-1745 *Fax:* 212-940-7408 *Web Site:* www.randomhouse.com/crown, pg 72

Blakeslee, Kristine M, Michigan State University Press (MSU Press), 1405 S Harrison Rd, Suite 25, East Lansing, MI 48823 *Tel:* 517-355-9543 *Fax:* 517-432-2611 *Toll Free Fax:* 800-678-2120 *E-mail:* msupress@msu.edu *Web Site:* www.msupress.msu.edu, pg 165

Blanchard, Marshall, Hoover Institution Press, Stanford University, 434 Galvez Mall, Stanford, CA 94305-6010 *Tel:* 650-725-7146; 650-723-3373 *Toll Free Tel:* 800-935-2882 *Fax:* 650-723-8626 *E-mail:* hooverpress@stanford.edu *Web Site:* www.hoover.org; www.hooverpress.org, pg 122

Blanchette, Jean-Guy, Groupe Educalivres Inc, 955, rue Bergar, Laval, QC H7L 4Z6, Canada *Tel:* 514-334-8466 *Toll Free Tel:* 800-567-3671 (info serv)

Fax: 514-334-8387 E-mail: commentaires@educalivres.com Web Site: www.educalivres.com, pg 507

Bland, Jacqueline, Print Industries Market Information & Research Organization, 1899 Preston White Dr, Reston, VA 20191 Tel: 703-264-7200 Fax: 703-620-0994 E-mail: info@primir.org Web Site: www.primir.org; www.npes.org/primirresearch/primir.aspx, pg 634

Blandford, Clyde B Jr, FPMI Solutions Inc, 245 Business Park Rd, Suite A, Madison, AL 35758 Tel: 256-539-1850 Toll Free Tel: 888-644-3764 Fax: 256-539-0911 E-mail: info@fpmi.com Web Site: www.fpmisolutions.com; www.fpmi.com, pg 98

Blankensop, Mia, Chronicle Books LLC, 680 Second St, San Francisco, CA 94107 Tel: 415-537-4200 Toll Free Tel: 800-759-0190 (cust serv) Fax: 415-537-4460 Toll Free Fax: 800-858-7787 (orders); 800-286-9471 (cust serv) E-mail: frontdesk@chroniclebooks.com Web Site: www.chroniclebooks.com, pg 61

Blansfield, David, F+W Media Inc, 10151 Carver Rd, Suite 200, Blue Ash, OH 45242 Tel: 513-531-2690 Toll Free Tel: 800-289-0963 (trade accts); 800-258-0929 (orders) E-mail: contact_us@fwmedia.com Web Site: www.fwmedia.com, pg 92

Blansfield, David, Krause Publications Inc, 700 E State St, Iola, WI 54990 Tel: 715-445-2214 Toll Free Tel: 800-258-0929 (cust serv); 888-457-2873 (orders) Fax: 715-445-4087 E-mail: bookorders@krause.com Web Site: www.krausebooks.com, pg 142

Blaschko, Tom, Idyll Arbor Inc, 39129 264 Ave SE, Enumclaw, WA 98022 Tel: 360-825-7797 Fax: 360-825-5670 E-mail: sales@idyllarbor.com Web Site: www.idyllarbor.com, pg 127

Blasdell, Caitlin, Liza Dawson Associates, 350 Seventh Ave, Suite 2003, New York, NY 10001 Tel: 212-465-9071 Fax: 212-947-0460 Web Site: www.lizadawsonassociates.com, pg 568

Blatty, David, Harry N Abrams Inc, 115 W 18 St, 6th fl, New York, NY 10011 Tel: 212-206-7715 Toll Free Tel: 800-345-1359 Fax: 212-519-1210 E-mail: abrams@abramsbooks.com Web Site: www.abramsbooks.com, pg 3

Blau, Dan, Kidsbooks LLC, 312 Stuart St, Boston, MA 02116 Tel: 617-425-0300 Fax: 617-425-0232 E-mail: sales@kidsbooks.com; customerservice@kidsbooks.com Web Site: www.kidsbooks.com, pg 140

Bledsoe, Bob, Indiana University Writers' Conference, Indiana University, 464 Ballantine Hall, Dept of English, 1020 E Kirkwood Ave, Bloomington, IN 47405 Tel: 812-855-1877 Fax: 812-855-9535 E-mail: writecon@indiana.edu Web Site: www.indiana.edu/~writecon/, pg 670

Blelock, Julia, WoodstockArts, PO Box 1342, Woodstock, NY 12498 Tel: 845-679-8111 E-mail: info@woodstockarts.com Web Site: www.woodstockarts.com, pg 284

Blelock, Weston, WoodstockArts, PO Box 1342, Woodstock, NY 12498 Tel: 845-679-8111 E-mail: info@woodstockarts.com Web Site: www.woodstockarts.com, pg 284

Blessing, Lyndsey, InkWell Management, 521 Fifth Ave, 26th fl, New York, NY 10175 Tel: 212-922-3500 Fax: 212-922-0535 E-mail: info@inkwellmanagement.com; submissions@inkwellmanagement.com Web Site: inkwellmanagement.com, pg 577

Blevins, Tim, Augsburg Fortress Publishers, Publishing House of the Evangelical Lutheran Church in America, 100 S Fifth St, Suite 600, Minneapolis, MN 55402 Tel: 612-330-3300 Toll Free Tel: 800-426-0115 (ext 639, subns); 800-328-4648 (orders) E-mail: info@augsburgfortress.org; copyright@augsburgfortress.org (reprint permission requests); customercare@augsburgfortress.org Web Site: www.augsburgfortress.org, pg 27

Blickers, Beth, Abrams Artists Agency, 275 Seventh Ave, 26th fl, New York, NY 10001 Tel: 646-486-4600 Fax: 646-486-2358 E-mail: literary@abramsartny.com Web Site: www.abramsartists.com, pg 559

Blietz, Jeremy, Summy-Birchard Inc, 10585 Santa Monica Blvd, Los Angeles, CA 90025 Tel: 310-441-8600 Fax: 310-441-8780 Web Site: www.warnerchappell.com, pg 247

Blight, David W, James Fenimore Cooper Prize, 603 Fayerweather, MC 2538, New York, NY 10027 Tel: 212-854-6495 E-mail: amhistsociety@columbia.edu Web Site: sah.columbia.edu, pg 698

Blight, David W, Allan Nevins Prize, 603 Fayerweather, MC 2538, New York, NY 10027 Tel: 212-854-6495 E-mail: amhistsociety@columbia.edu Web Site: sah.columbia.edu, pg 728

Blight, David W, Francis Parkman Prize, 603 Fayerweather, MC 2538, New York, NY 10027 Tel: 212-854-6495 E-mail: amhistsociety@columbia.edu Web Site: sah.columbia.edu, pg 732

Bliss, Anthony A Jr, Aqua Quest Publications Inc, 486 Bayville Rd, Locust Valley, NY 11560-1209 Tel: 516-759-0476 Toll Free Tel: 800-933-8989 Fax: 516-759-4519 E-mail: info@aquaquest.com Web Site: www.aquaquest.com, pg 21

Bliss, Josefina A, Aqua Quest Publications Inc, 486 Bayville Rd, Locust Valley, NY 11560-1209 Tel: 516-759-0476 Toll Free Tel: 800-933-8989 Fax: 516-759-4519 E-mail: info@aquaquest.com Web Site: www.aquaquest.com, pg 21

Bloch, Mitchell, Bloch Publishing Co, 5875 Mining Terr, Suite 104, Jacksonville, FL 32257-3225 Tel: 904-880-7302 Toll Free Tel: 866-532-3977 Fax: 904-880-7307 E-mail: info@blochpub.com Web Site: www.blochpub.com, pg 40

Bloch, Sam, Herzl Press, 633 Third Ave, 21st fl, New York, NY 10017 Tel: 212-339-6020 Fax: 212-318-6176 E-mail: midstreamthf@aol.com Web Site: www.midstreamthf.com, pg 119

Block, Gwen M, Marine Education Textbooks Inc, 124 N Van Ave, Houma, LA 70363-5895 Tel: 985-879-3866 Fax: 985-879-3911 E-mail: email@marineeducationtextbooks.com Web Site: www.marineeducationtextbooks.com, pg 157

Block, Richard A, Marine Education Textbooks Inc, 124 N Van Ave, Houma, LA 70363-5895 Tel: 985-879-3866 Fax: 985-879-3911 E-mail: email@marineeducationtextbooks.com Web Site: www.marineeducationtextbooks.com, pg 157

Block, Dr Robert W, American Academy of Pediatrics, 141 NW Point Blvd, Elk Grove Village, IL 60007-1098 Tel: 847-434-4000 Toll Free Tel: 888-227-1770 Fax: 847-434-8000 E-mail: pubs@aap.org Web Site: www.aap.org, pg 10

Blom, Harry, Springer, 233 Spring St, New York, NY 10013-1578 Tel: 212-460-1500 Toll Free Tel: 800-SPRINGER (777-4643) Fax: 212-460-1575 E-mail: service-ny@springer.com Web Site: www.springer.com, pg 241

Blonshine, Christian, Health Communications Inc, 3201 SW 15 St, Deerfield Beach, FL 33442-8190 Tel: 954-360-0909 Toll Free Tel: 800-441-5569 (cust serv) Fax: 954-360-0034 Web Site: www.hcibooks.com; hci-online.com, pg 116

Blood, Michael, Avisson Press Inc, 3007 Taliaferro Rd, Greensboro, NC 27408 Tel: 336-288-6989; 336-285-6763 Fax: 336-288-6989 E-mail: avisson4@aol.com, pg 28

Bloom, Barbara, Bloom Ink, 3497 Bennington Ct, Bloomfield Hills, MI 48301 Tel: 248-291-0370 E-mail: bbloom@bloomwriting.com Web Site: www.bloomwriting.com, pg 541

Bloom, Brettne, Kneerim, Williams & Bloom Agency, 90 Canal St, Boston, MA 02114 Tel: 617-303-1650 Web Site: www.kwlit.com, pg 580

Bloom, Lexy, Vintage & Anchor Books, c/o Random House Inc, 1745 Broadway, New York, NY 10019 Tel: 212-572-2420 E-mail: vintageanchorpublicity@randomhouse.com Web Site: vintage-anchor.knopfdoubleday.com, pg 275

Bloom, Patience, Harlequin Enterprises Ltd, 233 Broadway, Suite 1001, New York, NY 10279 Tel: 212-553-4200 Fax: 212-227-8969 E-mail: CustomerService@harlequin.com Web Site: www.harlequin.com, pg 112

Bloomer, Paul, Redleaf Press, 10 Yorkton Ct, St Paul, MN 55117 Tel: 651-641-0508 Toll Free Tel: 800-423-8309 Toll Free Fax: 800-641-0115 Web Site: www.redleafpress.org, pg 216

Bloomfield, Mark, Regnery Publishing Inc, One Massachusetts Ave NW, Washington, DC 20001 Tel: 202-216-0600 Toll Free Tel: 888-219-4747 Fax: 202-216-0612 Web Site: www.regnery.com, pg 217

Bloomquist, John, Foundation Press Inc, 395 Hudson St, New York, NY 10014 Tel: 212-367-6790 Toll Free Tel: 877-888-1330 Fax: 212-367-6799 E-mail: foundation-press@thomsonreuters.com Web Site: www.foundation-press.com, pg 98

Blough, Heidi, Heidi Blough, Book Indexer, 502 Tanager Rd, St Augustine, FL 32086 Tel: 904-797-6572 E-mail: indexing@heidiblough.com Web Site: www.heidiblough.com, pg 542

Blount, Gregory James, Peter Glenn Publications, 306 NE Second St, 2nd fl, Delray Beach, FL 33483 Tel: 561-404-4290 Toll Free Tel: 888-332-6700 Fax: 561-892-5786 Web Site: www.pgdirect.com, pg 103

Blow, Nathan S PhD, BioTechniques Books, 52 Vanderbilt Ave, 7th fl, New York, NY 10017 Tel: 212-520-2777 Fax: 212-520-2705 Web Site: www.biotechniques.com, pg 38

Bloxson, Carrie, HarperCollins General Books Group, 10 E 53 St, New York, NY 10022 Tel: 212-207-7000 Fax: 212-207-7633 Web Site: www.harpercollins.com, pg 113

Blue, Marian, Blue & Ude Writers' Services, 4249 Nuthatch Way, Clinton, WA 98236 Tel: 360-341-1630 E-mail: blueyude@whidbey.com Web Site: www.blueudewritersservices.com, pg 542

Blue, Zach, AK Press Distribution, 674-A 23 St, Oakland, CA 94612 Tel: 510-208-1700 Fax: 510-208-1701 E-mail: info@akpress.org; sales@akpress.org; orders@akpress.org Web Site: www.akpress.org, pg 7

Bluey, Melissa, The Heritage Foundation, 214 Massachusetts Ave NE, Washington, DC 20002-4999 Tel: 202-546-4400 Toll Free Tel: 800-544-4843 Fax: 202-546-8328 E-mail: info@heritage.org Web Site: www.heritage.org, pg 119, 641

Blum, Michele, Westminster John Knox Press, 100 Witherspoon St, Louisville, KY 40202-1396 Tel: 502-569-5052 Toll Free Tel: 800-227-2872 (US only) Fax: 502-569-8308 Toll Free Fax: 800-541-5113 (US & CN) E-mail: wjk@wjkbooks.com; customer_service@wjkbooks.com Web Site: www.wjkbooks.com, pg 279

Blume, Judy, The Authors Guild, 31 E 32 St, 7th fl, New York, NY 10016 Tel: 212-563-5904 Fax: 212-564-8363; 212-564-5363 E-mail: staff@authorsguild.org Web Site: www.authorsguild.org, pg 617

Blumenfeld, Joe, Harcourt Achieve, 6277 Sea Harbor Dr, Orlando, FL 32887 Tel: 407-345-2000 Toll Free Tel: 800-531-5015 (cust serv/orders) Toll Free Fax: 800-699-9459 (cust serv/orders) Web Site: www.harcourtachieve.com, pg 112

Blumenfeld, Joe, Harcourt Inc, 6277 Sea Harbor Dr, Orlando, FL 32887 Tel: 407-345-2000 Toll Free Tel: 800-225-5425 (cust serv/orders) Toll Free Fax: 800-269-5232 (cust serv/orders) Web Site: www.hmhco.com, pg 112

Blumenthal, Scott, Scobre Press Corp, 2255 Calle Clara, La Jolla, CA 92037 Toll Free Tel: 877-726-2734 Fax: 858-551-1232 E-mail: info@scobre.com Web Site: www.scobre.com, pg 230

Blunck, Kay, Neustadt International Prize for Literature, University of Oklahoma, Suite 110, 630 Parrington Oval, Norman, OK 73019-4033 Tel: 405-325-4531 Fax: 405-325-7495 Web Site: www.worldliteraturetoday.org, pg 728

Blunck, Kay, NSK Neustadt Prize for Children's Literature, University of Oklahoma, Suite 110, 630 Parrington Oval, Norman, OK 73019-4033 *Tel:* 405-325-4531 *Fax:* 405-325-7495 *Web Site:* www.worldliteraturetoday.org, pg 730

Blythe, Rolph, Counterpoint Press LLC, 1919 Fifth St, Berkeley, CA 94710 *Tel:* 510-704-0230 *Fax:* 510-704-0268 *E-mail:* info@counterpointpress.com *Web Site:* www.counterpointpress.com; www.sierraclub.org/books; www.softskull.com, pg 69

Boates, Reid, Reid Boates Literary Agency, 69 Cooks Crossroad, Pittstown, NJ 08867-0328 *Tel:* 908-797-8087 *E-mail:* reid.boates@gmail.com, pg 563

Bobbitt, Michael D, Twilight Times Books, PO Box 3340, Kingsport, TN 37664-0340 *Tel:* 423-323-0183 *Fax:* 423-323-0183 *E-mail:* publisher@twilighttimes.com *Web Site:* www.twilighttimesbooks.com, pg 261

Bobco, Ann, Simon & Schuster Children's Publishing, 1230 Avenue of the Americas, New York, NY 10020 *Tel:* 212-698-7000 *Web Site:* KIDS.SimonandSchuster.com; TEEN.SimonandSchuster.com; simonandschuster.net; simonandschuster.biz, pg 235

Bobrow, Deborah, Dorothy Silver Playwriting Competition, 26001 S Woodland Rd, Beachwood, OH 44122 *Tel:* 216-831-0700 *Fax:* 216-831-7796 *E-mail:* info@mandeljcc.org *Web Site:* www.mandeljcc.org, pg 742

Bobst, Chuck, Pacific Press Publishing Association, 1350 N Kings Rd, Nampa, ID 83687-3193 *Tel:* 208-465-2500 *Toll Free Tel:* 800-447-7377 *Fax:* 208-465-2531 *Web Site:* www.pacificpress.com, pg 190

Boczkowski, Tricia, Gallery Books, 1230 Avenue of the Americas, New York, NY 10020 *Toll Free Tel:* 800-456-6798 *Fax:* 212-698-7284 *E-mail:* consumer.customerservice@simonandschuster.com *Web Site:* www.simonsays.com, pg 101

Bodack, Jeannine, SSPC: The Society for Protective Coatings, 40 24 St, 6th fl, Pittsburgh, PA 15222-4656 *Tel:* 412-281-2331 *Toll Free Tel:* 877-281-7772 (US only) *Fax:* 412-281-9992 *E-mail:* info@sspc.org *Web Site:* www.sspc.org, pg 242

Boehm, Ronald, ABC-CLIO, 130 Cremona Dr, Santa Barbara, CA 93117 *Tel:* 805-968-1911 *Toll Free Tel:* 800-368-6868 *Fax:* 805-685-9685 *Toll Free Fax:* 866-270-3856 *E-mail:* sales@abc-clio.com; customerservice@abc-clio.com *Web Site:* www.abc-clio.com, pg 2

Boehmer, Susan, Harvard University Press, 79 Garden St, Cambridge, MA 02138-1499 *Tel:* 617-495-2600; 401-531-2800 (intl orders) *Toll Free Tel:* 800-405-1619 (orders) *Fax:* 617-495-5898 (general); 617-496-4677 (edit & rts); 401-531-2801 (intl orders) *Toll Free Fax:* 800-406-9145 (orders) *E-mail:* contact_hup@harvard.edu *Web Site:* www.hup.harvard.edu, pg 115

Boer, Faye, Folklore Publishing, 11717-9B Ave NW, Unit 2, Edmonton, AB T6J 7B7, Canada *Tel:* 780-435-2376 *Fax:* 780-435-0674 *E-mail:* submissions@folklorepublishing.com (ms submissions) *Web Site:* www.folklorepublishing.com, pg 506

Boers, Jack, Baker Books, 6030 E Fulton Rd, Ada, MI 49301 *Tel:* 616-676-9185 *Toll Free Tel:* 800-877-2665; 800-679-1957 *Fax:* 616-676-9573 *Toll Free Fax:* 800-398-3111 *Web Site:* www.bakerpublishinggroup.com, pg 29

Boersma, Karen, Owlkids Books Inc, 10 Lower Spadina Ave, Suite 400, Toronto, ON M5V 2Z2, Canada *Tel:* 416-340-3700 *Fax:* 416-340-9769 *E-mail:* owlkids@owlkids.com *Web Site:* www.owlkidsbooks.com, pg 514

Bogaards, Paul, Alfred A Knopf/Everyman's Library, c/o Random House Inc, 1745 Broadway, New York, NY 10019 *Tel:* 212-751-2600 *Toll Free Tel:* 800-638-6460 *Fax:* 212-572-2593 *Web Site:* www.knopfdoubleday.com, pg 141

Boggs, Amy, Donald Maass Literary Agency, 121 W 27 St, Suite 801, New York, NY 10001 *Tel:* 212-727-8383 *Fax:* 212-727-3271 *E-mail:* info@maassagency.com; rights@maassagency.com (subs rights inquiries) *Web Site:* www.maassagency.com, pg 582

Boggs, Marcus, AltaMira Press, 4501 Forbes Blvd, Suite 200, Lanham, MD 20706 *Tel:* 301-459-3366 *Toll Free Tel:* 800-462-6420 (cust serv) *Fax:* 301-429-5748 *E-mail:* custserv@rowman.com *Web Site:* www.altamirapress.com, pg 9

Boggs, Marcus, Government Institutes (GI), 4501 Forbes Blvd, Suite 200, Lanham, MD 20706 *Tel:* 301-459-3366 (ext 5622) *Toll Free Tel:* 800-462-6420 *Fax:* 301-429-5748 *Toll Free Fax:* 800-338-4550 *Web Site:* www.govinstpress.com, pg 105

Boggs, Marcus, Scarecrow Press Inc, 4501 Forbes Blvd, Suite 200, Lanham, MD 20706 *Tel:* 301-459-3366 *Fax:* 301-429-5748 *Web Site:* www.scarecrowpress.com, pg 226

Bogie, Patty, Magazine Publishers of America, 810 Seventh Ave, 24th fl, New York, NY 10019 *Tel:* 212-872-3700 *Fax:* 212-888-4217 *E-mail:* mpa@magazine.org *Web Site:* www.magazine.org, pg 627

Bohan, Dr Mark, InterTech Technology Awards, 200 Deer Run Rd, Sewickley, PA 15143-2600 *Tel:* 412-259-1782 *Toll Free Tel:* 800-910-4283 (ext 782) *Fax:* 412-741-2311 *E-mail:* intertechaward@printing.org *Web Site:* www.printing.org/intertechawards, pg 713

Boies, Kay, Children's Sequoyah Book Award, 300 Hardy Dr, Edmond, OK 73013 *Tel:* 405-525-5100 *Fax:* 405-525-5103 *Web Site:* www.oklibs.org, pg 696

Boies, Kay, Intermediate Sequoyah Book Award, 300 Hardy Dr, Edmond, OK 73013 *Tel:* 405-525-5100 *Fax:* 405-525-5103 *Web Site:* www.oklibs.org, pg 712

Boisseau, Michelle, BkMk Press - University of Missouri-Kansas City, 5101 Rockhill Rd, Kansas City, MO 64110-2499 *Tel:* 816-235-2558 *Fax:* 816-235-2611 *E-mail:* bkmk@umkc.edu *Web Site:* www.umkc.edu/bkmk, pg 38

Boisseau, Michelle, G S Sharat Chandra Prize for Short Fiction, 5101 Rockhill Rd, Kansas City, MO 64110-2499 *Tel:* 816-235-2558 *Fax:* 816-235-2611 *E-mail:* bkmk@umkc.edu *Web Site:* www.umkc.edu/bkmk, pg 696

Boisseau, Michelle, John Ciardi Prize for Poetry, 5101 Rockhill Rd, Kansas City, MO 64110-2499 *Tel:* 816-235-2558 *Fax:* 816-235-2611 *E-mail:* bkmk@umkc.edu *Web Site:* www.umkc.edu/bkmk, pg 697

Boitnott, Sally, Pelican Publishing Co, 1000 Burmaster St, Gretna, LA 70053-2246 *Tel:* 504-368-1175 *Toll Free Tel:* 800-843-1724 *Fax:* 504-368-1195 *E-mail:* sales@pelicanpub.com (sales); office@pelicanpub.com (permission); promo@pelicanpub.com (publicity) *Web Site:* www.pelicanpub.com, pg 196

Bokermann, Bill, Chelsea Green Publishing Co, 85 N Main St, Suite 120, White River Junction, VT 05001 *Tel:* 802-295-6300 *Toll Free Tel:* 800-639-4099 (cust serv, consumer & trade orders) *Fax:* 802-295-6444 *Web Site:* www.chelseagreen.com, pg 59

Bol, Bob, Baker Books, 6030 E Fulton Rd, Ada, MI 49301 *Tel:* 616-676-9185 *Toll Free Tel:* 800-877-2665; 800-679-1957 *Fax:* 616-676-9573 *Toll Free Fax:* 800-398-3111 *Web Site:* www.bakerpublishinggroup.com, pg 29

Bol, Robert, Chosen Books, PO Box 6287, Grand Rapids, MI 49516-6287 *Tel:* 616-676-9185 *Toll Free Tel:* 800-877-2665 (orders only) *Fax:* 616-676-9573 *Toll Free Fax:* 800-398-3111 (orders only) *Web Site:* www.bakerpublishinggroup.com, pg 60

Bol, Robert, Fleming H Revell, PO Box 6287, Grand Rapids, MI 49516-6287 *Tel:* 616-676-9185 *Toll Free Tel:* 800-877-2665; 800-679-1957 *Fax:* 616-676-9573 *Web Site:* www.revellbooks.com, pg 218

Bolan, Michael, European Masterpieces, 103 Walker Way, Newark, DE 19711 *Tel:* 302-453-8695 *Fax:* 302-453-8601 *E-mail:* linguatext@juno.com *Web Site:* www.europeanmasterpieces.com, pg 90

Bolan, Michael, LinguaText Ltd, 103 Walker Way, Newark, DE 19711 *Tel:* 302-453-8695 *Fax:* 302-453-8695 *Toll Free Fax:* 800-784-4935 *E-mail:* linguatextext@juno.com *Web Site:* www.linguatextltd.com, pg 149

Bolchazy, Allan, Bolchazy-Carducci Publishers Inc, 1570 Baskin Rd, Mundelein, IL 60060 *Tel:* 847-526-4344 *Toll Free Tel:* 800-392-6453 *Fax:* 847-526-2867 *E-mail:* info@bolchazy.com; orders@bolchazy.com *Web Site:* www.bolchazy.com, pg 42

Bolchazy, Dr Marie Carducci PhD, Bolchazy-Carducci Publishers Inc, 1570 Baskin Rd, Mundelein, IL 60060 *Tel:* 847-526-4344 *Toll Free Tel:* 800-392-6453 *Fax:* 847-526-2867 *E-mail:* info@bolchazy.com; orders@bolchazy.com *Web Site:* www.bolchazy.com, pg 42

Boldrick, Penelope, Ignatius Press, 1348 Tenth Ave, San Francisco, CA 94122-2304 *Tel:* 415-387-2324 *Toll Free Tel:* 800-651-1531 (orders) *Fax:* 415-387-0896 *E-mail:* info@ignatius.com *Web Site:* www.ignatius.com, pg 127

Bolduc, Mary Jo, Carnegie-Whitney Award, 50 E Huron St, Chicago, IL 60611 *Tel:* 312-280-5416 *Toll Free Tel:* 800-545-2433 *Fax:* 312-280-5275; 312-440-9379 *Web Site:* www.ala.org, pg 695

Bole, Angela, IBPA, the Independent Book Publishers Association, 1020 Manhattan Beach Blvd, Suite 204, Manhattan Beach, CA 90266 *Tel:* 310-546-1818 *Fax:* 310-546-3939 *E-mail:* info@ibpa-online.org *Web Site:* www.ibpa-online.org, pg 624

Bolen, Dave, Highlights for Children, 1800 Watermark Dr, Columbus, OH 43215-1060 *Tel:* 614-486-0631 *Toll Free Tel:* 800-962-3661 (Highlights Club cust serv); 800-255-9517 (Highlights Magazine cust serv) *Web Site:* www.highlights.com, pg 119

Bolger, Loretta, Quincannon Publishing Group, PO Box 8100, Glen Ridge, NJ 07028-8100 *Tel:* 973-380-9942 *E-mail:* editors@quincannongroup.com *Web Site:* www.quincannongroup.com, pg 211

Bolinao, Mela, MB Artists, 775 Sixth Ave, Suite 6, New York, NY 10001 *Tel:* 212-689-7830 *Fax:* 212-689-7829 *Web Site:* www.mbartists.com, pg 602

Boling, John Mark, Grove/Atlantic Inc, 841 Broadway, 4th fl, New York, NY 10003-4793 *Tel:* 212-614-7850 *Toll Free Tel:* 800-521-0178 *Fax:* 212-614-7886 *E-mail:* info@groveatlantic.com *Web Site:* www.groveatlantic.com, pg 108

Bollinger, Becke, Indiana Historical Society Press (IHS Press), 450 W Ohio St, Indianapolis, IN 46202-3269 *Tel:* 317-232-1882; 317-234-0026 (orders); 317-234-2716 (edit) *Toll Free Tel:* 800-447-1830 (orders) *Fax:* 317-234-0562 (orders); 317-233-0857 (edit) *E-mail:* ihspress@indianahistory.org; orders@indianahistory.org (orders) *Web Site:* www.indianahistory.org; shop.indianahistory.org (orders), pg 129

Bollas, George, Cortina Institute of Languages, 7 Hollyhock Rd, Wilton, CT 06897 *Tel:* 203-762-2510 *Toll Free Tel:* 800-245-2145 *Fax:* 203-762-2514 *Web Site:* www.cortina-languages.com, pg 68

Bollas, George, Cortina Learning International Inc (CLI), 7 Hollyhock Rd, Wilton, CT 06897-4414 *Tel:* 203-762-2510 *Toll Free Tel:* 800-245-2145 *Fax:* 203-762-2514 *E-mail:* info@cortinalearning.com *Web Site:* www.cortinalearning.com, pg 68

Bollinger, Eric, McKenna Publishing Group, 425 POA Place, San Luis Obispo, CA 93405 *Tel:* 805-550-1667 *Web Site:* www.mckennapubgrp.com, pg 162

Bollinger, Eric, Sligo Literary Agency LLC, 425 Poa Place, San Luis Obispo, CA 93405 *Tel:* 805-550-1667 *Fax:* 805-783-2317 *E-mail:* editorial@mckennapubgrp.com *Web Site:* sligolitagency.com, pg 594

Bolm, Jennifer, Adventures Unlimited Press, One Adventure Place, Kempton, IL 60946 *Tel:* 815-253-6390 *Fax:* 815-253-6300 *E-mail:* auphq@frontiernet.net; info@adventuresunlimitedpress.com *Web Site:* www.adventuresunlimitedpress.com, pg 5

Bologna, James, Hudson Institute, 1015 15 St NW, 6th fl, Washington, DC 20005 *Tel:* 202-974-2400 *Toll Free Tel:* 888-554-1325 (bookstore inquiries) *Fax:* 202-974-2410 *E-mail:* info@hudson.org *Web Site:* www.hudson.org, pg 125

Bolotin, Susan, Workman Publishing Co Inc, 225 Varick St, 9th fl, New York, NY 10014-4381 *Tel:* 212-254-5900 *Toll Free Tel:* 800-722-7202 *Fax:* 212-254-8098 *E-mail:* info@workman.com *Web Site:* www.workman.com, pg 285

Bolstad, Karen, Purich Publishing Ltd, PO Box 23032, Market Mall Postal Outlet, Saskatoon, SK S7J 5H3, Canada *Tel:* 306-373-5311 *Fax:* 306-373-5315 *E-mail:* purich@sasktel.net *Web Site:* www.purichpublishing.com, pg 517

Bolte, Lynda, Shields Publications, PO Box 669, Eagle River, WI 54521-0669 *Tel:* 715-479-4810 *Fax:* 715-479-3905 *E-mail:* wormbooks@wormbooks.com *Web Site:* www.wormbooks.com, pg 233

Bolton, John, Interweave Press LLC, 201 E Fourth St, Loveland, CO 80537 *Tel:* 970-669-7672 *Toll Free Tel:* 800-272-2193 *Fax:* 970-667-8317 *E-mail:* interweaveservice@interweave.com *Web Site:* www.interweave.com, pg 134

Bonacum, Leslie, CCH, a Wolters Kluwer business, 2700 Lake Cook Rd, Riverwoods, IL 60015 *Tel:* 847-267-7000 *Toll Free Tel:* 800-525-3335 *Fax:* 773-866-3095 *Web Site:* www.cch.com, pg 55

Bonanno, Michelle, Houghton Mifflin Harcourt Trade & Reference Division, 222 Berkeley St, Boston, MA 02116-3764 *Tel:* 617-351-5000 *Toll Free Tel:* 800-225-3362 *Web Site:* www.houghtonmifflinbooks.com, pg 124

Bonaventura, Philip, Public Relations Society of America Inc, 33 Maiden Lane, 11th fl, New York, NY 10038-5150 *Tel:* 212-460-1400 *Fax:* 212-995-0757 *Web Site:* www.prsa.org, pg 635

Boncottie, John, Antique Collectors Club Ltd, 116 Pleasant St, Suite 18, East Hampton, MA 01027 *Tel:* 413-529-0861 *Toll Free Tel:* 800-252-5231 *Fax:* 413-529-0862 *E-mail:* sales@antiquecc.com *Web Site:* www.accdistribution.com, pg 19

Bond, Alison M, Alison Bond Literary Agency, 171 W 79 St, No 143, New York, NY 10024, pg 563

Bond, John H, Slack Incorporated, 6900 Grove Rd, Thorofare, NJ 08086-9447 *Tel:* 856-848-1000 *Toll Free Tel:* 800-257-8290 *Fax:* 856-848-6091 *E-mail:* sales@slackinc.com *Web Site:* www.slackbooks.com, pg 237

Bond, Sandra, Bond Literary Agency, 4340 E Kentucky Ave, Suite 471, Denver, CO 80246 *Tel:* 303-781-9305 *E-mail:* queries@bondliteraryagency.com *Web Site:* bondliteraryagency.com, pg 563

Bonelli, Kristen, Ave Maria Press, PO Box 428, Notre Dame, IN 46556-0428 *Tel:* 574-287-2831 *Toll Free Tel:* 800-282-1865 *Fax:* 574-239-2904 *Toll Free Fax:* 800-282-5681 *E-mail:* avemariapress.1@nd.edu *Web Site:* www.avemariapress.com, pg 28

Bonenberger, John, William H Sadlier Inc, 9 Pine St, New York, NY 10005 *Tel:* 212-227-2120 *Toll Free Tel:* 800-221-5175 (cust serv) *Fax:* 212-312-6080 *Web Site:* www.sadlier.com, pg 223

Bonenfant, Rene, Les Heures bleues, Sta Lorimier, PO Box 219, Montreal, QC H2H 2N6, Canada *Tel:* 450-671-7718 *Fax:* 450-671-7718 *E-mail:* info@heuresbleues.com *Web Site:* www.heuresbleues.com, pg 509

Bonessi, Edward, Houghton Mifflin Harcourt K-12 Publishers, 222 Berkeley St, Boston, MA 02116-3764 *Tel:* 617-351-5000 *Toll Free Tel:* 800-225-5425 (cust serv) *Web Site:* www.hmhco.com; www.hmheducation.com, pg 123

Boni, Anne, The Center for the Book in the Library of Congress, The Library of Congress, 101 Independence Ave SE, Washington, DC 20540-4920 *Tel:* 202-707-5221 *Fax:* 202-707-0269 *E-mail:* cfbook@loc.gov *Web Site:* www.loc.gov/cfbook; www.read.gov.cfb, pg 621

Bonk, Rich, Philadelphia Museum of Art, 2525 Pennsylvania Ave, Philadelphia, PA 19130 *Tel:* 215-684-7250 *Fax:* 215-235-8715 *Web Site:* www.philamuseum.org, pg 200

Bonnell, Jennifer, Puffin Books, 345 Hudson St, New York, NY 10014 *Tel:* 212-366-2000 *E-mail:* online@penguinputnam.com *Web Site:* www.penguinputnam.com; us.penguingroup.com, pg 209

Bonner, Pat, International Foundation of Employee Benefit Plans, 18700 W Bluemound Rd, Brookfield, WI 53045 *Tel:* 262-786-6700 *Toll Free Tel:* 888-334-3327 *Fax:* 262-786-8780 *E-mail:* editor@ifebp.org *Web Site:* www.ifebp.org, pg 133

Bonneville, Josee, Les Editions XYZ inc, 1815 Ave de Lorimier, Montreal, QC H2K 3W6, Canada *Tel:* 514-525-2170 *Fax:* 514-525-7537 *E-mail:* info@editionsxyz.com *Web Site:* www.editionsxyz.com, pg 504

Boomer, Helen, Penguin Young Readers Group, 345 Hudson St, New York, NY 10014 *Tel:* 212-366-2000 *E-mail:* online@penguinputnam.com *Web Site:* www.penguinputnam.com; us.penguingroup.com, pg 198

Boomhower, Ray, Indiana Historical Society Press (IHS Press), 450 W Ohio St, Indianapolis, IN 46202-3269 *Tel:* 317-232-1882; 317-234-0026 (orders); 317-234-2716 (edit) *Toll Free Tel:* 800-447-1830 (orders) *Fax:* 317-234-0562 (orders); 317-233-0857 (edit) *E-mail:* ihspress@indianahistory.org; orders@indianahistory.org (orders) *Web Site:* www.indianahistory.org; shop.indianahistory.org (orders), pg 129

Boone, Jack W, Grafco Productions, 971 E Callaway Rd, Marietta, GA 30060 *Tel:* 770-436-1500 *Toll Free Tel:* 800-381-9169 *Fax:* 770-435-3793 *Web Site:* www.jackwboone.com, pg 106

Boorstein, Amy, Crown Publishing Group, c/o Random House Inc, 1745 Broadway, New York, NY 10019 *Tel:* 212-782-9000 *Toll Free Tel:* 888-264-1745 *Fax:* 212-940-7408 *Web Site:* www.randomhouse.com/crown, pg 72

Boot, Chris, Aperture Books, 547 W 27 St, 4th fl, New York, NY 10001 *Tel:* 212-505-5555 *Toll Free Tel:* 800-929-2323 *Fax:* 212-979-7759 *E-mail:* info@aperture.org *Web Site:* www.aperture.org, pg 19

Booth, Doris, Authorlink Press, 755 Laguna, Irving, TX 75039-3218 *Tel:* 972-402-0101 *Toll Free Fax:* 866-381-1587 *Web Site:* www.authorlink.com, pg 27

Booth, Jessica, The University of Utah Press, J Willard Marriott Library, Suite 5400, 295 S 1500 E, Salt Lake City, UT 84112-0860 *Tel:* 801-581-6771 *Toll Free Tel:* 800-621-2736 (orders) *Fax:* 801-581-3365 *Toll Free Fax:* 800-621-8471 *E-mail:* info@upress.utah.edu *Web Site:* www.uofupress.com, pg 269

Booth, Linda, Herald Publishing House, 1001 W Walnut St, Independence, MO 64051 *Tel:* 816-521-3015 *Toll Free Tel:* 800-767-8181 *Fax:* 816-521-3066 *E-mail:* sales@heraldhouse.org *Web Site:* www.heraldhouse.org, pg 118

Booth, Tom, Oregon State University Press, 121 The Valley Library, Corvallis, OR 97331-4501 *Tel:* 541-737-3166 *Toll Free Tel:* 800-621-2736 (orders) *Fax:* 541-737-3170 *Toll Free Fax:* 800-426-3797 (orders) *E-mail:* osu.press@oregonstate.edu *Web Site:* oregonstate.edu/dept/press; osupress.oregonstate.edu, pg 187

Borchardt, Anne, Georges Borchardt Inc, 136 E 57 St, New York, NY 10022 *Tel:* 212-753-5785 *E-mail:* georges@gbagency.com *Web Site:* www.gbagency.com, pg 563

Borchardt, Georges, Georges Borchardt Inc, 136 E 57 St, New York, NY 10022 *Tel:* 212-753-5785 *E-mail:* georges@gbagency.com *Web Site:* www.gbagency.com, pg 563

Borchardt, Valerie, Georges Borchardt Inc, 136 E 57 St, New York, NY 10022 *Tel:* 212-753-5785 *E-mail:* georges@gbagency.com *Web Site:* www.gbagency.com, pg 563

Borchert, Scott, Monthly Review Press, 146 W 29 St, Suite 6W, New York, NY 10001 *Tel:* 212-691-2555 *Toll Free Tel:* 800-670-9499 *Fax:* 212-727-3676 *E-mail:* mreview@igc.org *Web Site:* www.MonthlyReview.org, pg 169

Bordon, Tony, Houghton Mifflin Harcourt, 222 Berkeley St, Boston, MA 02116-3764 *Tel:* 617-351-5000 *Toll Free Tel:* 800-225-5425 (Pre-K-8); 800-462-6595 (6–12; Advanced & Electives); 800-289-4490 (Specialized Curriculum: Great Source, Rigby, Saxon, Steck-Vaughn; Homeschool; Adult Ed); 800-323-9540 (Assessment: Riverside Publishing); 888-391-3245 (SkillsTutor); 888-242-6747 option 2 (Destination Series; Classroom Connect; Earobics; Edmark; Learning Village; Riverdeep); 800-225-3362 (Houghton Mifflin Harcourt Trade & Reference Publishers); 800-225-5800 (Heinemann) *Fax:* 617-351-1125 *Web Site:* www.hmhco.com, pg 123

Borgenicht, David, Quirk Books, 215 Church St, Philadelphia, PA 19106 *Tel:* 215-627-3581 *Fax:* 215-627-5220 *E-mail:* general@quirkbooks.com *Web Site:* www.quirkbooks.com, pg 211

Borges, Michael, Empire State Award for Excellence in Literature for Young People, 6021 State Farm Rd, Guilderland, NY 12084 *Tel:* 518-432-6952 *Toll Free Tel:* 800-252-6952 *Fax:* 518-427-1697 *E-mail:* info@nyla.org *Web Site:* www.nyla.org, pg 702

Boriack, Steve, Random House Publishing Group, 1745 Broadway, New York, NY 10019 *Toll Free Tel:* 800-200-3552 *Web Site:* atrandom.com, pg 214

Borland, Peter, Atria Books, 1230 Avenue of the Americas, New York, NY 10020 *Tel:* 212-698-7000 *Fax:* 212-698-7007 *Web Site:* www.simonandschuster.com, pg 26

Born, Bob, Pocket Press Inc, PO Box 25124, Portland, OR 97298-0124 *Toll Free Tel:* 888-237-2110 *Toll Free Fax:* 877-643-3732 *E-mail:* sales@pocketpressinc.com *Web Site:* www.pocketpressinc.com, pg 203

Borne, Joell Smith, Vanderbilt University Press, 2014 Broadway, Suite 320, Nashville, TN 37203 *Tel:* 615-322-3585 *Toll Free Tel:* 800-627-7377 (orders only) *Fax:* 615-343-8823 *Toll Free Fax:* 800-735-0476 (orders only) *E-mail:* vupress@vanderbilt.edu *Web Site:* www.vanderbiltuniversitypress.com, pg 274

Borque, Paul, Twenty-Third Publications, One Montauk Ave, Suite 200, New London, CT 06320 *Tel:* 860-437-3012 *Toll Free Tel:* 800-321-0411 (orders) *Toll Free Fax:* 800-572-0788 *E-mail:* 23ppweb@bayard-inc.com *Web Site:* www.twentythirdpublications.com, pg 260

Borsics, Angelin, Clarkson Potter Publishers, c/o Random House Inc, 1745 Broadway, New York, NY 10019 *Tel:* 212-782-9000 *Toll Free Tel:* 888-264-1745 *Fax:* 212-572-6181 *Web Site:* www.clarksonpotter.com; www.randomhouse.com/crown/clarksonpotter, pg 62

Bortz, Andrew, Bancroft Press, 3209 Bancroft Rd, Baltimore, MD 21215 *Tel:* 410-358-0658 *Fax:* 410-764-1967 *Web Site:* www.bancroftpress.com, pg 30

Bortz, Bruce L, Bancroft Press, 3209 Bancroft Rd, Baltimore, MD 21215 *Tel:* 410-358-0658 *Fax:* 410-764-1967 *Web Site:* www.bancroftpress.com, pg 30

Borzumato, Theresa M, Holiday House Inc, 425 Madison Ave, New York, NY 10017 *Tel:* 212-688-0085 *Fax:* 212-421-6134 *E-mail:* holiday@holidayhouse.com *Web Site:* www.holidayhouse.com, pg 121

Bosarge, Jerusha, Character Publishing, 23568 Montebella Rd, Pass Christian, MS 39571 *Tel:* 228-234-7651 *Fax:* 228-222-3321 *Web Site:* www.characterpublishing.org, pg 58

Bost, Laura, University of Texas Press, 2100 Comal St, Austin, TX 78722 *Tel:* 512-471-7233 *Fax:* 512-232-7178 *E-mail:* utpress@uts.cc.utexas.edu *Web Site:* www.utexaspress.com, pg 253

Boston, Les, Stone & Scott Publishers, PO Box 56419, Sherman Oaks, CA 91413-1419 *Tel:* 818-904-9088 *Fax:* 818-787-1431 *E-mail:* friday@stoneandscott.com *Web Site:* stoneandscott.com, pg 245

Boston, Leslie Paul, The Boston Word Works, PO Box 56419, Sherman Oaks, CA 91413-1419 *Tel:* 818-904-9088 *Fax:* 818-787-1431, pg 542

Bosveld, Jennifer, Pudding House Publications, 81 Shadymere Lane, Columbus, OH 43213 *Tel:* 614-986-1881 *Web Site:* www.puddinghousepublications.com, pg 209

Botton, Maury, The New Press, 38 Greene St, 4th fl, New York, NY 10013 *Tel:* 212-629-8802 *Toll Free Tel:* 800-343-4489 (orders) *Fax:* 212-629-8617 *Toll Free Fax:* 800-351-5073 (orders) *E-mail:* newpress@thenewpress.com *Web Site:* www.thenewpress.com, pg 178

Bottorff, Todd, Turner Publishing Co, 200 Fourth Ave N, Suite 950, Nashville, TN 37219 *Tel:* 615-255-BOOK (255-2665) *Fax:* 615-255-5081 *E-mail:* marketing@turnerpublishing.com; submissions@turnerpublishing.com *Web Site:* www.turnerpublishing.com, pg 260

Bottrell, Donna, The Wine Appreciation Guild Ltd, 360 Swift Ave, Suites 30 & 34, South San Francisco, CA 94080 *Tel:* 650-866-3020 *Toll Free Tel:* 800-231-9463 *Fax:* 650-866-3513 *E-mail:* info@wineappreciation.com *Web Site:* www.wineappreciation.com, pg 283

Botzman, Harvey, Cyclotour Guide Books, 160 Harvard St, Rochester, NY 14607 *Tel:* 585-244-6157 *E-mail:* cyclotour@cyclotour.com *Web Site:* www.cyclotour.com, pg 74

Bouchard, Jean, Thomson Groupe Modulo, 5800 Rue Saint-Denis, Bureau 1102, Montreal, QC H2S 3L5, Canada *Tel:* 514-738-9818 *Toll Free Tel:* 888-738-9818 *Fax:* 514-738-5838 *Toll Free Fax:* 888-273-5247 *Web Site:* www.groupemodulo.com, pg 521

Boucher, Jayme, Random House Speakers Bureau, 1745 Broadway, Mail Drop 13-1, New York, NY 10019 *Tel:* 212-572-2013 *E-mail:* rhspeakers@randomhouse.com *Web Site:* www.rhspeakers.com, pg 605

Boucher, Johanne, Ordre des traducteurs, terminologues et interpretes agrees du quebec, 2021 Union Ave, Suite 1108, Montreal, QC H3A 2S9, Canada *Tel:* 514-845-4411 *Toll Free Tel:* 800-265-4815 *Fax:* 514-845-9903 *E-mail:* info@ottiaq.org *Web Site:* www.ottiaq.org, pg 633

Boughton, Simon, Macmillan, 175 Fifth Ave, New York, NY 10010 *Tel:* 646-307-5151 *Fax:* 212-420-9314 *E-mail:* firstname.lastname@macmillan.com *Web Site:* www.macmillan.com, pg 154

Boughton, Simon, Roaring Brook Press, 175 Fifth Ave, New York, NY 10010 *Tel:* 646-307-5151 *Web Site:* us.macmillan.com/roaringbrookpressaspx, pg 219

Boulanger, Patrick, Ecrits des Forges, 992-A, rue Royale, Trois Rivieres, QC G9A 4H9, Canada *Tel:* 819-840-0492 *Fax:* 819-376-0774 *E-mail:* ecritsdesforges@gmail.com *Web Site:* www.ecritsdesforges.com, pg 501

Boulder, Sharon, Top of the Mountain Publishing, PO Box 2244, Pinellas Park, FL 33780-2244 *Tel:* 727-391-3958 *E-mail:* tag@abcinfo.com; info@abcinfo.com *Web Site:* abcinfo.com; www.topofthemountain.com, pg 256

Boulerice, Yvan, Art Image Publications, PO Box 160, Derby Line, VT 05830 *Toll Free Tel:* 800-361-2598 *Toll Free Fax:* 800-559-2598 *E-mail:* info@artimagepublications.com *Web Site:* www.artimagepublications.com, pg 22

Boulle, Philippe, White Wolf Publishing Inc, 250 Ponce de Leon Ave, Suite 700, Decatur, GA 30030 *Tel:* 404-292-1819 *Toll Free Tel:* 800-454-9653 *E-mail:* questions@white-wolf.com *Web Site:* www.white-wolf.com, pg 280

Boultinghouse, Philis, Howard Books, 216 Centerview Dr, Suite 303, Brentwood, TN 37027 *Tel:* 615-873-2080 *Fax:* 615-370-3834 *E-mail:* howardbooks@simonandschuster.com (info) *Web Site:* www.howardpublishing.com, pg 124

Bouman, Tom, Orbit, 237 Park Ave, New York, NY 10017 *Tel:* 212-364-1100 *Toll Free Tel:* 800-759-0190 *Web Site:* www.orbitbooks.net, pg 186

Bourassa, Edith, Ecrits des Forges, 992-A, rue Royale, Trois Rivieres, QC G9A 4H9, Canada *Tel:* 819-840-8492 *Fax:* 819-376-0774 *E-mail:* ecritsdesforges@gmail.com *Web Site:* www.ecritsdesforges.com, pg 501

Bourassa, Lorraine, Les Editions Alire, 120 Cote du Passage, Levis, QC G6V 5S9, Canada *Tel:* 418-835-4441 *Fax:* 418-838-4443 *E-mail:* info@alire.com *Web Site:* www.alire.com, pg 501

Bourbon Ramirez, Melissa, Entangled Publishing, 2614 S Timberline Rd, Suite 109, Fort Collins, CO 80525 *Tel:* 724-208-7888 (sales) *E-mail:* publisher@entangledpublishing.com *Web Site:* www.entangledpublishing.com, pg 89

Bourdon, Pierre, Groupe Sogides Inc, 955 rue Amherst, Montreal, QC H2L 3K4, Canada *Tel:* 514-523-1182 *Toll Free Tel:* 800-361-4806 *Fax:* 514-597-0370 *E-mail:* edhomme@sogides.com *Web Site:* www.sogides.com; www.edhomme.com, pg 507

Bouregy-Mickelsen, Ellen, Thomas Bouregy & Co Inc, 160 Madison Ave, 5th fl, New York, NY 10016 *Tel:* 212-598-0222 *Fax:* 212-979-1862, pg 44

Bourgault, Rochelle, Shambhala Publications Inc, Horticultural Hall, 300 Massachusetts Ave, Boston, MA 02115 *Tel:* 617-424-0030 *Toll Free Tel:* 866-424-0030 (off); 888-424-2329 (cust serv) *Fax:* 617-236-1563 *E-mail:* customercare@shambhala.com *Web Site:* www.shambhala.com, pg 232

Bourret, Michael, Dystel & Goderich Literary Management, One Union Sq W, Suite 904, New York, NY 10003 *Tel:* 212-627-9100 *Fax:* 212-627-9313 *Web Site:* www.dystel.com, pg 569

Boutote, Claudia, HarperCollins General Books Group, 10 E 53 St, New York, NY 10022 *Tel:* 212-207-7000 *Fax:* 212-207-7633 *Web Site:* www.harpercollins.com, pg 113

Bova, Ben, The Barbara Bova Literary Agency LLC, 3951 Gulf Shore Blvd N, Unit PH 1-B, Naples, FL 34103 *Tel:* 239-649-7237 *E-mail:* slushpile@yahoo.com *Web Site:* www.barbarabovaliteraryagency.com, pg 564

Bova, Ken, The Barbara Bova Literary Agency LLC, 3951 Gulf Shore Blvd N, Unit PH 1-B, Naples, FL 34103 *Tel:* 239-649-7237 *E-mail:* slushpile@yahoo.com *Web Site:* www.barbarabovaliteraryagency.com, pg 564

Bovay, Nicolas, United Nations Publications, 2 United Nations Plaza, Rm DC2-0853, New York, NY 10017 *Tel:* 212-963-8302 *Toll Free Tel:* 800-253-9646 *Fax:* 212-963-3489 *E-mail:* publications@un.org *Web Site:* unp.un.org, pg 262

Bove, Joyce M, Oscar Williams/Gene Derwood Award, 909 Third Ave, New York, NY 10022 *Tel:* 212-686-0010 *Fax:* 212-532-8528 *E-mail:* info@nycommunitytrust.org *Web Site:* www.nycommunitytrust.org, pg 749

Bowditch, Scottie, Penguin Young Readers Group, 345 Hudson St, New York, NY 10014 *Tel:* 212-366-2000 *E-mail:* online@penguinputnam.com *Web Site:* www.penguinputnam.com; us.penguingroup.com, pg 198

Bowe, William J, Encyclopaedia Britannica Inc, 331 N La Salle St, Chicago, IL 60654 *Tel:* 312-347-7159 (all other countries) *Toll Free Tel:* 800-323-1229 (US & CN) *Fax:* 312-294-2104 *E-mail:* editor@eb.com *Web Site:* www.eb.com; www.britannica.com, pg 88

Bowen, Arabella, Fodor's Travel Publications, c/o Random House Inc, 1745 Broadway, New York, NY 10019 *Tel:* 212-829-6714 *Toll Free Tel:* 800-733-3000 *Fax:* 212-572-2248 *Web Site:* www.fodors.com, pg 96

Bowen, Brenda, Sanford J Greenburger Associates Inc, 55 Fifth Ave, 15th fl, New York, NY 10003 *Tel:* 212-206-5600 *Fax:* 212-463-8718 *Web Site:* www.greenburger.com, pg 575

Bowen, Kelly, Algonquin Books of Chapel Hill, 400 Silver Cedar Ct, Suite 300, Chapel Hill, NC 27514-1585 *Tel:* 919-967-0108 *Fax:* 919-933-0272 *E-mail:* inquiry@algonquin.com *Web Site:* www.workman.com/algonquin, pg 8

Bowen, Stephanie, Sourcebooks Inc, 1935 Brookdale Rd, Suite 139, Naperville, IL 60563 *Tel:* 630-961-3900 *Toll Free Tel:* 800-432-7444 *Fax:* 630-961-2168 *E-mail:* info@sourcebooks.com; customersupport@sourcebooks.com *Web Site:* www.sourcebooks.com, pg 240

Bowers, Eddie, Eddie Bowers Publishing Co Inc, PO Box 130, Peosta, IA 52068-0130 *Tel:* 563-582-8333 *Toll Free Tel:* 800-747-2411 *Fax:* 563-582-8555 *E-mail:* eddiebowerspub@aol.com *Web Site:* www.eddiebowerspublishing.com, pg 44

Bowers, Linda, LinguiSystems Inc, 3100 Fourth Ave, East Moline, IL 61244 *Tel:* 309-755-2300 *Toll Free Tel:* 800-776-4332 *Fax:* 309-755-2377 *Toll Free Fax:* 800-577-4555 *E-mail:* service@linguisystems.com *Web Site:* www.linguisystems.com, pg 149

Bowers, Sharon, The Miller Agency Inc, 630 Ninth Ave, Suite 1102, New York, NY 10036 *Tel:* 212-206-0913 *Fax:* 212-206-1473, pg 586

Bowker, Scott, Houghton Mifflin Harcourt, 222 Berkeley St, Boston, MA 02116-3764 *Tel:* 617-351-5000 *Toll Free Tel:* 800-225-5425 (Pre-K-8); 800-462-6595 (6–12; Advanced & Electives); 800-289-4490 (Specialized Curriculum: Great Source, Rigby, Saxon, Steck-Vaughn; Homeschool; Adult Ed); 800-323-9540 (Assessment: Riverside Publishing); 888-391-3245 (SkillsTutor); 888-242-6747 option 2 (Destination Series; Classroom Connect; Earobics; Edmark; Learning Village; Riverdeep); 800-225-3362 (Houghton Mifflin Harcourt Trade & Reference Publishers); 800-225-5800 (Heinemann) *Fax:* 617-351-1125 *Web Site:* www.hmhco.com, pg 123

Bowler, Jim, Classroom Connect, 222 Berkeley St, Boston, MA 02116 *Tel:* 617-351-5000 *Toll Free Tel:* 800-638-1639 (cust support) *E-mail:* help@classroom.com *Web Site:* corporate.classroom.com; www.hmhinnovation.com, pg 62

Bowles, Michael, Random House of Canada Limited, One Toronto St, Suite 300, Toronto, ON M5C 2V6, Canada *Tel:* 416-364-4449 *Toll Free Tel:* 888-523-9292 (cust serv) *Fax:* 416-364-6863; 416-364-6653 (subs rts) *Web Site:* www.randomhouse.ca, pg 517

Bowlin, Carolyn, TSI Graphics, 1300 S Raney St, Effingham, IL 62401-4206 *Tel:* 217-347-7733; 217-347-7734 *Fax:* 217-342-9611 *E-mail:* info@tsigraphics.com *Web Site:* www.tsigraphics.com, pg 556

Bowman, Hannah, Liza Dawson Associates, 350 Seventh Ave, Suite 2003, New York, NY 10001 *Tel:* 212-465-9071 *Fax:* 212-947-0460 *Web Site:* www.lizadawsonassociates.com, pg 568

Bowman, Mary Ann, Frederic C Beil Publisher Inc, 609 Whitaker St, Savannah, GA 31401 *Tel:* 912-233-2446 *E-mail:* books@beil.com *Web Site:* www.beil.com, pg 34

Bowyer, Clifford B, Silver Leaf Books LLC, 13 Temi Rd, Holliston, MA 01746 *E-mail:* sales@silverleafbooks.com; editor@silverleafbooks.com; customerservice@silverleafbooks.com *Web Site:* www.silverleafbooks.com, pg 234

Bowzer, Melanie, Association of Medical Illustrators (AMI), 201 E Main St, Suite 1405, Lexington, KY 40507 *Toll Free Tel:* 866-393-4264 *Fax:* 859-514-9166 *E-mail:* hq@ami.org *Web Site:* www.ami.org, pg 617

Boyce, Jim, Victory in Grace Printing, 60 Quentin Rd, Lake Zurich, IL 60047 *Tel:* 847-438-4494 *Toll Free Tel:* 800-78-GRACE (784-7223) *Fax:* 847-438-4232 *Web Site:* www.victoryingrace.org, pg 274

Boyd, Jim, Financial Times Press & Wharton School Publishing, One Lake St, Upper Saddle River, NJ 07458 *Tel:* 201-236-7000 *Toll Free Tel:* 800-922-0579 (orders) *Web Site:* www.ftpress.com, pg 95

Boyd, Lindsay, Independent Institute, 100 Swan Way, Oakland, CA 94621-1428 *Tel:* 510-632-1366 *Toll Free Tel:* 800-927-8733 *Fax:* 510-568-6040 *E-mail:* orders@independent.org *Web Site:* www.independent.org, pg 129

Boyd, Stacy, Harlequin Enterprises Ltd, 233 Broadway, Suite 1001, New York, NY 10279 *Tel:* 212-553-4200 *Fax:* 212-227-8969 *E-mail:* CustomerService@harlequin.com *Web Site:* www.harlequin.com, pg 112

Boyer, Emma, Algonquin Books of Chapel Hill, 400 Silver Cedar Ct, Suite 300, Chapel Hill, NC 27514-1585 *Tel:* 919-967-0108 *Fax:* 919-933-0272 *E-mail:* inquiry@algonquin.com *Web Site:* www.workman.com/algonquin, pg 8

Boyko, Alan, Scholastic Inc, 557 Broadway, New York, NY 10012 *Tel:* 212-343-6100 *Toll Free Tel:* 800-scholastic *Web Site:* www.scholastic.com, pg 228

Boylan, Sue J, Zondervan, A HarperCollins Company, 5300 Patterson Ave SE, Grand Rapids, MI 49530 *Tel:* 616-698-6900 *Toll Free Tel:* 800-226-1122; 800-727-1309 (retail orders) *Fax:* 616-698-3350 *Toll Free Fax:* 800-698-3256 (retail orders) *E-mail:* zinfo@zondervan.com *Web Site:* www.zondervan.com, pg 289

Boyle, Aileen, Blue Rider Press, 375 Hudson St, New York, NY 10014 *Tel:* 212-366-2000, pg 42

Boyle, Candace, Bradford Publishing Co, 1743 Wazee St, Denver, CO 80202 *Tel:* 303-292-2590 *Toll Free Tel:* 800-446-2831 *Fax:* 303-298-5014 *E-mail:* marketing@bradfordpublishing.com; customerservice@bradfordpublishing.com *Web Site:* www.bradfordpublishing.com, pg 45

Boyle, David, HarperCollins Publishers, 10 E 53 St, New York, NY 10022 *Tel:* 212-207-7000 *Fax:* 212-207-7145 *Web Site:* www.harpercollins.com, pg 113

Boyle, Matt, American Society of Civil Engineers (ASCE), 1801 Alexander Bell Dr, Reston, VA 20191-4400 *Tel:* 703-295-6300 *Toll Free Tel:* 800-548-2723 *Fax:* 703-295-6278 *E-mail:* marketing@asce.org *Web Site:* www.asce.org, pg 16

Boyles, Julia, Interweave Press LLC, 201 E Fourth St, Loveland, CO 80537 *Tel:* 970-669-7672 *Toll Free Tel:* 800-272-2193 *Fax:* 970-667-8317 *E-mail:* interweaveservice@interweave.com *Web Site:* www.interweave.com, pg 134

Boyles, Sean, Clarkson Potter Publishers, c/o Random House Inc, 1745 Broadway, New York, NY 10019 *Tel:* 212-782-9000 *Toll Free Tel:* 888-264-1745 *Fax:* 212-572-6181 *Web Site:* www.clarksonpotter.com; www.randomhouse.com/crown/clarksonpotter, pg 62

Boynton-Trigg, Anne, Scholastic International, 557 Broadway, New York, NY 10012 *Tel:* 212-343-6100; 646-330-5288 (intl cust serv) *Toll Free Tel:* 800-SCHOLASTIC (800-724-6527) *Fax:* 646-837-7878 *E-mail:* international@scholastic.com, pg 228

Boys, Christina, Center Street, 12 Cadillac Dr, Suite 480, Brentwood, TN 37027 *Tel:* 615-221-0996 *Web Site:* www.centerstreet.com, pg 56

Boys, Christina, FaithWords, 12 Cadillac Dr, Suite 480, Brentwood, TN 37027 *Tel:* 615-221-0996 *Fax:* 615-221-0962 *Web Site:* www.hachettebookgroup.com, pg 92

Bozik, Tim, Pearson Higher Education, One Lake St, Upper Saddle River, NJ 07458 *Tel:* 201-236-7000 *Fax:* 201-236-3381 *Web Site:* www.pearsonhighered.com, pg 196

Bozzi, Debra, Yale University Press, 302 Temple St, New Haven, CT 06511-8909 *Tel:* 401-531-2800 (cust serv); 203-432-0960 *Toll Free Tel:* 800-405-1619 (cust serv) *Fax:* 203-432-0948; 401-531-2801 (cust serv) *Toll Free Fax:* 800-406-9145 (cust serv) *E-mail:* customer.care@trilateral.org (cust serv); language.yalepress@yale.edu *Web Site:* www.yalebooks.com, pg 287

Braaten, Douglas PhD, New York Academy of Sciences, 7 World Trade, 40th fl, 250 Greenwich St, New York, NY 10007-2157 *Tel:* 212-298-8600 *Toll Free Tel:* 800-843-6927 *Fax:* 212-298-3644 *E-mail:* nyas@nyas.org; publications@nyas.org *Web Site:* www.nyas.org, pg 179

Bracken, Don, History Publishing Co LLC, 173 Rte 9W, Palisades, NY 10964 *Tel:* 845-398-8161 *Fax:* 845-231-6167 *E-mail:* historypublish@aol.com; info@historypublishingco.com *Web Site:* www.historypublishingco.com, pg 120

Braddock, Joan PhD, University of Alaska Press, 794 University Ave, Suite 220, Fairbanks, AK 99709 *Tel:* 907-474-5831 *Toll Free Tel:* 888-252-6657 (US only) *Fax:* 907-474-5502 *E-mail:* fypress@uaf.edu *Web Site:* www.uaf.edu/uapress, pg 264

Bradford, Laura, Bradford Literary Agency, 5694 Mission Center Rd, Suite 347, San Diego, CA 92108 *Tel:* 619-521-1201 *E-mail:* queries@bradfordlit.com *Web Site:* www.bradfordlit.com, pg 564

Bradford, Maya, Harry N Abrams Inc, 115 W 18 St, 6th fl, New York, NY 10011 *Tel:* 212-206-7715 *Toll Free Tel:* 800-345-1359 *Fax:* 212-519-1210 *E-mail:* abrams@abramsbooks.com *Web Site:* www.abramsbooks.com, pg 3

Bradhering, Gary, MapEasy Inc, PO Box 80, Wainscott, NY 11975-0080 *Tel:* 631-537-6213 *Toll Free Tel:* 888-627-3279 *Fax:* 631-537-4541 *E-mail:* info@mapeasy.com *Web Site:* www.mapeasy.com, pg 156

Bradie, Ian R, Cambridge University Press, 32 Avenue of the Americas, New York, NY 10013-2473 *Tel:* 212-924-3900; 212-337-5000 *Toll Free Tel:* 800-899-5222 *Fax:* 212-691-3239 *E-mail:* newyork@cambridge.org *Web Site:* www.cambridge.org/us, pg 51

Bradley, Bryan, Music Publishers' Association (MPA), 243 Fifth Ave, Suite 236, New York, NY 10016 *Tel:* 212-327-4044 *E-mail:* admin@mpa.org *Web Site:* host.mpa.org; www.mpa.org, pg 628

Bradley, Cheryl, NASW Press, 750 First St NE, Suite 700, Washington, DC 20002 *Tel:* 202-408-8600 *Fax:* 203-336-8312 *E-mail:* press@naswdc.org *Web Site:* www.naswpress.org, pg 172

Bradley, Eric, Antique Trader Books, c/o Krause Publications, 700 E State St, Iola, WI 54990-0001 *Tel:* 715-445-2214 *Toll Free Tel:* 888-457-2873 *Fax:* 715-445-4087 *Web Site:* www.krause.com, pg 19

Bradley, Joanna, Fresh Air Books, 1908 Grand Ave, Nashville, TN 37212 *Toll Free Tel:* 800-972-0433 (orders) *Fax:* 615-340-7266 *E-mail:* freshairbooks@me.com *Web Site:* www.bookstore.upperroom.org (orders), pg 99

Bradley, Joanna, Upper Room Books, 1908 Grand Ave, Nashville, TN 37212 *Tel:* 615-340-7200 *Toll Free Tel:* 800-972-0433 *Fax:* 615-340-7266 *E-mail:* urbooks@upperroom.org *Web Site:* www.upperroom.org, pg 273

Bradley, Kevin J, Taylor & Francis Inc, 325 Chestnut St, Suite 800, Philadelphia, PA 20036-1802 *Tel:* 215-625-8900 *Toll Free Tel:* 800-354-1420 *Fax:* 215-625-2940 *E-mail:* customer.service@taylorandfrancis.com *Web Site:* www.taylorandfrancis.com, pg 250

Bradley, Linda, Learning Links Inc, PO Box 326, Cranbury, NJ 08512 *Tel:* 516-437-9071 *Toll Free Tel:* 800-724-2616 *Fax:* 516-437-5392 *E-mail:* info@learninglinks.com *Web Site:* www.learninglinks.com, pg 145

Bradley, Rosemary, Pearson Humanities & Social Sciences, One Lake St, Upper Saddle River, NJ 07458 *Tel:* 201-236-7000 *Fax:* 201-236-3400, pg 196

Bradley, Shaun, Transatlantic Agency, 2 Bloor St E, Ste 3500, Toronto, ON M4W-1A8, Canada *Tel:* 416-488-9214 *E-mail:* info@transatlanticagency.com *Web Site:* www.transatlanticagency.com, pg 597

Bradshaw, Alan, Palgrave Macmillan, 175 Fifth Ave, Suite 200, New York, NY 10010 *Tel:* 646-307-5151 *Fax:* 212-777-6359 *E-mail:* firstname.lastname@palgrave-usa.com *Web Site:* us.macmillan.com/Palgrave.aspx, pg 191

Bradshaw, Joel, University of Hawaii Press, 2840 Kolowalu St, Honolulu, HI 96822 *Tel:* 808-956-8255 *Toll Free Tel:* 888-UHPRESS (847-7377) *Fax:* 808-988-6052 *Toll Free Fax:* 800-650-7811 *E-mail:* uhpbooks@hawaii.edu *Web Site:* www.uhpress.hawaii.edu, pg 265

Brady, Elizabeth, Fine Communications, 322 Eighth Ave, 15th fl, New York, NY 10001 *Tel:* 212-595-3500 *Fax:* 212-595-3779, pg 95

Brady, Mackenzie, Charlotte Sheedy Literary Agency Inc, 928 Broadway, Suite 901, New York, NY 10010 *Tel:* 212-780-9800 *Fax:* 212-780-0308; 212-780-6095 *E-mail:* sheedy@sll.com *Web Site:* www.sheedylit.com, pg 594

Brady, Philip, Etruscan Press, Wilkes University, 84 W South St, Wilkes-Barre, PA 18766 *Tel:* 570-408-4546 *Fax:* 570-408-3333 *E-mail:* books@etruscanpress.org *Web Site:* www.etruscanpress.org, pg 90

Brady, Robert L, Business & Legal Reports Inc (BLR), 100 Winners Circle, Suite 300, Brentwood, CT 37027 *Tel:* 860-510-0100 *Toll Free Tel:* 800-727-5257 *E-mail:* service@blr.com *Web Site:* www.blr.com, pg 50

Brady, Sally R, bradylit, 81 Town Farm Hill, Hartland Four Corners, VT 05049 *Tel:* 802-436-2455 *Fax:* 802-436-2466, pg 542

Braeckel, Maria, Random House Publishing Group, 1745 Broadway, New York, NY 10019 *Toll Free Tel:* 800-200-3552 *Web Site:* atrandom.com, pg 214

Bragdon, Allen D, Allen D Bragdon Publishers Inc, 252 Great Western Rd, South Yarmouth, MA 02664-2210 *Tel:* 508-398-4440 *Toll Free Tel:* 877-876-2787 *Fax:* 508-760-2397 *E-mail:* admin@brainwaves.com *Web Site:* www.brainwaves.com, pg 8

Bragg, Judith K, Laura Day Boggs Bolling Memorial, 1194 Hume Rd, Hume, VA 22639-1806 *E-mail:* poetryinva@aol.com *Web Site:* www.poetrysocietyofvirginia.org, pg 692

Bragg, Judith K, Joe Pendleton Campbell Narrative Contest, 1194 Hume Rd, Hume, VA 22639-1806 *E-mail:* poetryinva@aol.com *Web Site:* www.poetrysocietyofvirginia.org, pg 694

Bragg, Judith K, Carleton Drewry Memorial, 1194 Hume Rd, Hume, VA 22639-1806 *E-mail:* poetryinva@aol.com *Web Site:* www.poetrysocietyofvirginia.org, pg 701

Bragg, Judith K, Alfred C Gary Memorial, 1194 Hume Rd, Hume, VA 22639-1806 *E-mail:* poetryinva@aol.com *Web Site:* www.poetrysocietyofvirginia.org, pg 706

Bragg, Judith K, Bess Gresham Memorial, 1194 Hume Rd, Hume, VA 22639-1806 *E-mail:* poetryinva@aol.com *Web Site:* www.poetrysocietyofvirginia.org, pg 708

Bragg, Judith K, Loretta Dunn Hall Memorial, 1194 Hume Rd, Hume, VA 22639-1806 *E-mail:* poetryinva@aol.com *Web Site:* www.poetrysocietyofvirginia.org, pg 708

Bragg, Judith K, Handy Andy Prize, 1194 Hume Rd, Hume, VA 22639-1806 *E-mail:* poetryinva@aol.com *Web Site:* www.poetrysocietyofvirginia.org, pg 708

Bragg, Judith K, Brodie Herndon Memorial, 1194 Hume Rd, Hume, VA 22639-1806 *E-mail:* poetryinva@aol.com *Web Site:* www.poetrysocietyofvirginia.org, pg 709

Bragg, Judith K, Judah, Sarah, Grace & Tom Memorial, 1194 Hume Rd, Hume, VA 22639-1806 *E-mail:* poetryinva@aol.com *Web Site:* www.poetrysocietyofvirginia.org, pg 714

Bragg, Judith K, Cenie H Moon Prize, 1194 Hume Rd, Hume, VA 22639-1806 *E-mail:* poetryinva@aol.com *Web Site:* www.poetrysocietyofvirginia.org, pg 724

Bragg, Judith K, Edgar Allan Poe Memorial, 1194 Hume Rd, Hume, VA 22639-1806 *E-mail:* poetryinva@aol.com *Web Site:* www.poetrysocietyofvirginia.org, pg 734

Bragg, Judith K, A Poem With a Point of View, 1194 Hume Rd, Hume, VA 22639-1806 *E-mail:* poetryinva@aol.com *Web Site:* www.poetrysocietyofvirginia.org, pg 734

Bragg, Judith K, Miriam Rachimi Memorial, 1194 Hume Rd, Hume, VA 22639-1806 *E-mail:* poetryinva@aol.com *Web Site:* www.poetrysocietyofvirginia.org, pg 737

Bragg, Judith K, Ada Sanderson Memorial, 1194 Hume Rd, Hume, VA 22639-1806 *E-mail:* poetryinva@aol.com *Web Site:* www.poetrysocietyofvirginia.org, pg 739

Bragg, Judith K, The Robert S Sergeant Memorial, 1194 Hume Rd, Hume, VA 22639-1806 *E-mail:* poetryinva@aol.com *Web Site:* www.poetrysocietyofvirginia.org, pg 741

Bramson, Ann, Artisan Books, 225 Varick St, New York, NY 10014-4381 *Tel:* 212-254-5900 *Toll Free Tel:* 800-722-7202 *Fax:* 212-254-8098 *E-mail:* artisaninfo@workman.com; artisaninfo@artisanbooks.com *Web Site:* www.workman.com/artisanbooks/, pg 23

Brent, Barbara, Two Thousand Three Associates, 4180 Saxon Dr, New Smyrna Beach, FL 32169 *Tel:* 386-690-2503 *E-mail:* ttta1@att.net *Web Site:* www.twothousandthree.com, pg 261

Brent, T David, University of Chicago Press, 1427 E 60 St, Chicago, IL 60637-2954 *Tel:* 773-702-7700; 773-702-7600 *Toll Free Tel:* 800-621-2736 (orders) *Fax:* 773-702-9756; 773-660-2235 (orders); 773-702-2708 *E-mail:* custserv@press.uchicago.edu; marketing@press.uchicago.edu *Web Site:* www.press.uchicago.edu, pg 265

Breschini, Gary PhD, Coyote Press, PO Box 3377, Salinas, CA 93912-3377 *Tel:* 831-422-4912 *Fax:* 831-422-4913 *E-mail:* orders@coyotepress.com *Web Site:* www.coyotepress.com, pg 70

Breslin, Ramsay, Kelsey Street Press, 2824 Kelsey St, Berkeley, CA 94705 *Tel:* 510-845-2260 *Fax:* 510-548-9185 *E-mail:* info@kelseyst.com *Web Site:* www.kelseyst.com, pg 139

Breslof, Lisa, The John Burroughs List of Nature Books for Young Readers, 15 W 77 St, New York, NY 10024 *Tel:* 212-769-5169 *Fax:* 212-313-7182 *Web Site:* research.amnh.org/burroughs, pg 693

Breslof, Lisa, John Burroughs Medal, 15 W 77 St, New York, NY 10024 *Tel:* 212-769-5169 *Fax:* 212-313-7182 *Web Site:* research.amnh.org/burroughs, pg 693

Breslof, Lisa, John Burroughs Outstanding Published Nature Essay Award, 15 W 77 St, New York, NY 10024 *Tel:* 212-769-5169 *Fax:* 212-313-7182 *Web Site:* research.amnh.org/burroughs, pg 694

Brettschneider, Cathie, The University of Virginia Press, PO Box 400318, Charlottesville, VA 22904-4318 *Tel:* 434-924-3468 (cust serv); 434-924-3469 (cust serv) *Toll Free Tel:* 800-831-3406 (orders) *Fax:* 434-982-2655 *Toll Free Fax:* 877-288-6400 *E-mail:* vapress@virginia.edu *Web Site:* www.upress.virginia.edu, pg 270

Breunig, Kevin, Appalachian Mountain Club Books, 5 Joy St, Boston, MA 02108 *Tel:* 617-523-0655 *Fax:* 617-523-0722 *Web Site:* www.outdoors.org, pg 20

Brewer, Andrew, University of California Press, 2120 Berkeley Way, Berkeley, CA 94704-1012 *Tel:* 510-642-4247 *Fax:* 510-643-7127 *E-mail:* askucp@ucpress.edu (books); customerservice@ucpressjournals.com (journals) *Web Site:* www.ucpress.edu, pg 264

Brewster, Alicia, Dragonfairy Press, 4355 Cobb Pkwy, Suite J116, Atlanta, GA 30339 *Tel:* 404-955-8150 *E-mail:* info@dragonfairypress.com *Web Site:* www.dragonfairypress.com, pg 81

Bricker, Megan, The American Ceramic Society, 600 N Cleveland Ave, Suite 210, Westerville, OH 43082 *Tel:* 240-646-7054 *Toll Free Tel:* 866-721-3322 *Fax:* 614-794-5892 *E-mail:* customerservice@ceramics.org *Web Site:* www.ceramics.org, pg 12

Bridburg, Eve, Zachary Shuster Harmsworth Agency, 1776 Broadway, Suite 1405, New York, NY 10019 *Tel:* 212-765-6900 *Fax:* 212-765-6490 *Web Site:* www.zshliterary.com, pg 600

Bridges, Shirin Yim, Goosebottom Books, 710 Portofino Lane, Foster City, CA 94404 *Tel:* 650-204-4076 *Toll Free Fax:* 888-407-5286 *E-mail:* info@goosebottombooks.com *Web Site:* goosebottombooks.com, pg 105

Bridgins, Sarah, Frances Goldin Literary Agency, Inc, 57 E 11 St, Suite 5-B, New York, NY 10003 *Tel:* 212-777-0047 *Fax:* 212-228-1660 *E-mail:* agency@goldinlit.com *Web Site:* www.goldinlit.com, pg 575

Briel, Barbara, Sourcebooks Inc, 1935 Brookdale Rd, Suite 139, Naperville, IL 60563 *Tel:* 630-961-3900 *Toll Free Tel:* 800-432-7444 *Fax:* 630-961-2168 *E-mail:* info@sourcebooks.com; customersupport@sourcebooks.com *Web Site:* www.sourcebooks.com, pg 240

Briem, Kit, Graywolf Press, 250 Third Ave N, Suite 600, Minneapolis, MN 55401 *Tel:* 651-641-0077 *Fax:* 651-641-0036 *E-mail:* wolves@graywolfpress.org *Web Site:* www.graywolfpress.org, pg 106

Briere, Sylvia, Les Editions de l'Hexagone, 1010 rue de la Gauchetiere E, Montreal, QC H2L 2N5, Canada *Tel:* 514-523-7993 (ext 4201) *Fax:* 514-282-7530 *E-mail:* vml@sogides.com *Web Site:* www.edhexagone.com, pg 502

Briere, Sylvie, VLB Editeur Inc, 1010 rue de la Gauchetiere E, Montreal, QC H2L 2N5, Canada *Tel:* 514-523-7993 *Fax:* 514-282-7530 *Web Site:* www.edvlb.com, pg 524

Briet, Eugenie, The French-American Foundation & Florence Gould Foundation Annual Translation Prize, 28 W 44 St, Suite 1420, New York, NY 10036 *Tel:* 212-829-8800 *Fax:* 212-829-8810 *E-mail:* translation@frenchamerican.org *Web Site:* www.frenchamerican.org, pg 706

Briggs, Barbara, University Press of New England, One Court St, Suite 250, Lebanon, NH 03766 *Tel:* 603-448-1533 *Toll Free Tel:* 800-421-1561 (orders only) *Fax:* 603-448-7006; 603-643-1540 *E-mail:* university.press@dartmouth.edu *Web Site:* www.upne.com, pg 271

Briggs, David, Philomel, 345 Hudson St, New York, NY 10014 *Tel:* 212-366-2000, pg 201

Briggs, David, GP Putnam's Sons (Children's), 345 Hudson St, New York, NY 10014 *Tel:* 212-366-2000 *Fax:* 212-414-3393 *E-mail:* online@penguinputnam.com *Web Site:* us.penguingroup.com, pg 210

Briggs, Harry, M E Sharpe Inc, 80 Business Park Dr, Suite 202, Armonk, NY 10504 *Tel:* 914-273-1800 *Toll Free Tel:* 800-541-6563 *Fax:* 914-273-2106 *E-mail:* info@mesharpe.com *Web Site:* www.mesharpe.com, pg 232

Briggs, John, Holiday House Inc, 425 Madison Ave, New York, NY 10017 *Tel:* 212-688-0085 *Fax:* 212-421-6134 *E-mail:* holiday@holidayhouse.com *Web Site:* www.holidayhouse.com, pg 121

Briggs, Laura, Potomac Books Inc, 22841 Quicksilver Dr, Dulles, VA 20166 *Tel:* 703-661-1548 *Fax:* 703-661-1547 *E-mail:* pbimail@presswarehouse.com *Web Site:* www.potomacbooksinc.com, pg 204

Briggs, M Courtney, M Courtney Briggs Esq, Authors Representative, Chase Tower, 28th fl, 100 N Broadway Ave, Oklahoma City, OK 73102, pg 564

Briggs, Michael, University Press of Kansas, 2502 Westbrooke Circle, Lawrence, KS 66045-4444 *Tel:* 785-864-4154; 785-864-4155 (orders) *Fax:* 785-864-4586 *E-mail:* upress@ku.edu; upkorders@ku.edu (orders) *Web Site:* www.kansaspress.ku.edu, pg 271

Bright, Cynthia F, Bright Mountain Books Inc, 206 Riva Ridge Dr, Fairview, NC 28730 *Tel:* 828-628-1768 *Toll Free Tel:* 800-437-3959 *Fax:* 828-628-1755 *E-mail:* booksbmb@charter.net *Web Site:* brightmountainbooks.com, pg 47

Bright, Harry, Maharishi University of Management Press, 1000 N Fourth St, Dept 1155, Fairfield, IA 52557-1155 *Tel:* 641-472-1101 *Toll Free Tel:* 800-831-6523 *Fax:* 641-472-1122 *E-mail:* mumpress@mum.edu *Web Site:* www.mumpress.com, pg 155

Brill, Calista, Roaring Brook Press, 175 Fifth Ave, New York, NY 10010 *Tel:* 646-307-5151 *Web Site:* us.macmillan.com/roaringbrookpressaspx, pg 219

Brill, L Chip, Peter Glenn Publications, 306 NE Second St, 2nd fl, Delray Beach, FL 33483 *Tel:* 561-404-4290 *Toll Free Tel:* 888-332-6700 *Fax:* 561-892-5786 *Web Site:* www.pgdirect.com, pg 103

Brill, Patricia, Harcourt Mifflin School Publishers, 6277 Sea Harbor Dr, Orlando, FL 32887 *Tel:* 407-345-2000 *Toll Free Tel:* 800-225-5425 (cust serv) *Fax:* 407-345-3016 (cust serv) *Toll Free Fax:* 800-874-6418; 800-269-5232 (cust serv) *Web Site:* www.harcourtschool.com, pg 112

Brill, Paula, Between the Lines, 401 Richmond St W, No 277, Toronto, ON M5V 3A8, Canada *Tel:* 416-535-9914 *Toll Free Tel:* 800-718-7201 *Fax:* 416-535-1484 *E-mail:* info@btlbooks.com *Web Site:* www.btlbooks.com, pg 494

Brill, Randi S, The Quarasan Group Inc, 405 W Superior St, Chicago, IL 60654 *Tel:* 312-981-2500 *E-mail:* info@quarasan.com *Web Site:* www.quarasan.com, pg 554

Brinati, Teresa, Society of American Archivists, 17 N State St, Suite 1425, Chicago, IL 60602-4061 *Tel:* 312-606-0722 *Toll Free Tel:* 866-722-7858 *Fax:* 312-606-0728 *E-mail:* info@archivists.org *Web Site:* www.archivists.org, pg 238

Brindle, Laura, Love Publishing Co, 9101 E Kenyon Ave, Suite 2200, Denver, CO 80237 *Tel:* 303-221-7333 *Toll Free Tel:* 877-240-6396 *Fax:* 303-221-7444 *E-mail:* lpc@lovepublishing.com *Web Site:* www.lovepublishing.com, pg 153

Brink, Matthew H, Butte Publications Inc, PO Box 1328, Hillsboro, OR 97123-1328 *Tel:* 503-648-9791 *Toll Free Tel:* 866-312-8883 *Fax:* 503-693-9526 *Toll Free Fax:* 866-412-8883 (orders only) *E-mail:* service@buttepublications.com *Web Site:* www.buttepublications.com, pg 50

Brinker, Spencer, Bearport Publishing Co Inc, 45 W 21 St, Suite 3B, New York, NY 10010 *Tel:* 212-337-8577 *Toll Free Tel:* 877-337-8577 *Fax:* 212-337-8557 *Toll Free Fax:* 866-337-8557 *E-mail:* info@bearportpublishing.com *Web Site:* www.bearportpublishing.com, pg 33

Brinley, Joseph F Jr, The Woodrow Wilson Center Press, One Woodrow Wilson Plaza, 1300 Pennsylvania Ave NW, Washington, DC 20004-3027 *Tel:* 202-691-4000 *Fax:* 202-691-4001 *E-mail:* press@wilsoncenter.org *Web Site:* wilsoncenter.org, pg 284

Brintnall, Michael, American Political Science Association, 1527 New Hampshire Ave NW, Washington, DC 20036-1206 *Tel:* 202-483-2512 *Fax:* 202-483-2657 *E-mail:* apsa@apsanet.org *Web Site:* www.apsanet.org, pg 613

Briskin, Dennis Alan, Catalyst Creative Services, 619 Marion Plaza, Palo Alto, CA 94301-4251 *Tel:* 650-325-1500 *Web Site:* www.CatalystCreative.us, pg 543

Brissie, Gene, James Peter Associates Inc, PO Box 358, New Canaan, CT 06840 *Tel:* 203-972-1070 *Web Site:* www.jamespeterassociates.com, pg 578

Bristol, Barbara K, Whiting Writers' Awards, 1133 Avenue of the Americas, 22nd fl, New York, NY 10036-6710 *Tel:* 212-336-2138 *E-mail:* info@whitingfoundation.org *Web Site:* www.whitingfoundation.org, pg 749

Britch, John, W H Freeman and Co, 41 Madison Ave, 37th fl, New York, NY 10010 *Tel:* 212-576-9400 *Fax:* 212-689-2383 *Web Site:* www.whfreeman.com, pg 99

Britch, John, Worth Publishers, 41 Madison Ave, 37th fl, New York, NY 10010 *Tel:* 212-576-9400 *Fax:* 212-561-8281 *Web Site:* www.worthpub.com, pg 286

Britson, Lowell, University of Pittsburgh Press, Eureka Bldg, 5th fl, 3400 Forbes Ave, Pittsburgh, PA 15260 *Tel:* 412-383-2456 *Fax:* 412-383-2466 *E-mail:* info@upress.pitt.edu *Web Site:* www.upress.pitt.edu, pg 268

Britton, Greg, The Johns Hopkins University Press, 2715 N Charles St, Baltimore, MD 21218-4363 *Tel:* 410-516-6900; 410-516-6987 (journals outside US & CN) *Toll Free Tel:* 800-537-5487 (book orders & cust serv); 800-548-1784 (journal orders) *Fax:* 410-516-6968; 410-516-3866 (journal orders) *E-mail:* hfscustserv@press.jhu.edu (cust serv); jrnlcirc@press.jhu.edu (journal orders) *Web Site:* www.press.jhu.edu; muse.jhu.edu/about/subscriptions/index.html (Project Muse subns), pg 136

Brizel, Michael A, Reader's Digest General Books, Reader's Digest Rd, Pleasantville, NY 10570-7000 *Tel:* 914-238-1000 *Toll Free Tel:* 800-304-2807 (cust serv) *Fax:* 914-244-7436, pg 215

Broad, Molly Corbett, American Council on Education, One Dupont Circle NW, Washington, DC 20036-1193 *Tel:* 202-939-9300; 301-632-6757 (orders) *Fax:* 202-939-9302 *E-mail:* pubs@acenet.edu *Web Site:* www.acenet.edu, pg 12

Broad, Molly Corbett, American Council on Education, One Dupont Circle NW, Washington, DC 20036-1193 *Tel:* 202-939-9300 *Fax:* 202-939-9302 *Web Site:* www.acenet.edu, pg 612

Brobeck, Carol, National Endowment for the Humanities, Mellon Foundation & Folger Long-term Fellowships, c/o Fellowship Committee, 201 E Capitol St SE, Washington, DC 20003 *Tel:* 202-544-4600 *Fax:* 202-544-4623 *E-mail:* institute@folger.edu *Web Site:* www.folger.edu, pg 726

Brochu, Yvon, Editions FouLire, 4339 rue des Becassines, Charlesbourg, QC G1G 1V5, Canada *Tel:* 418-628-4029 *Toll Free Tel:* 877-628-4029 *Fax:* 418-628-4801 *E-mail:* info@foulire.com *Web Site:* www.foulire.com, pg 503

Brock, John, Texas Tech University Press, 2903 Fourth St, Suite 201, Lubbock, TX 79409 *Tel:* 806-742-2982 *Toll Free Tel:* 800-832-4042 *Fax:* 806-742-2979 *E-mail:* ttup@ttu.edu *Web Site:* www.ttupress.org, pg 253

Brock, Sheila, PennWell Books, 1421 S Sheridan Rd, Tulsa, OK 74112 *Tel:* 918-831-9410 *Toll Free Tel:* 800-752-9764 *Fax:* 918-831-9555 *E-mail:* sales@pennwell.com *Web Site:* www.pennwellbooks.com, pg 198

Brock-Servais, Rhonda, John Dos Passos Prize for Literature, Dept of English & Modern Languages, 201 High St, Farmville, VA 23909 *Tel:* 434-395-2155 (dept) *Fax:* 434-395-2200, pg 701

Brockett, Louise, W W Norton & Company Inc, 500 Fifth Ave, New York, NY 10110-0017 *Tel:* 212-354-5500 *Toll Free Tel:* 800-233-4830 (orders & cust serv) *Fax:* 212-869-0856 *Toll Free Fax:* 800-458-6515 *Web Site:* www.wwnorton.com, pg 182

Brockman, John, Brockman Inc, 260 Fifth Ave, 10th fl, New York, NY 10001 *Tel:* 212-935-8900 *Fax:* 212-935-5535 *E-mail:* rights@brockman.com *Web Site:* www.brockman.com, pg 564

Brockman, Max, Brockman Inc, 260 Fifth Ave, 10th fl, New York, NY 10001 *Tel:* 212-935-8900 *Fax:* 212-935-5535 *E-mail:* rights@brockman.com *Web Site:* www.brockman.com, pg 564

Brodeur, Adrienne, Aspen Writers' Foundation, 110 E Hallam St, Suite 116, Aspen, CO 81611 *Tel:* 970-925-3122 *Fax:* 970-920-5700 *E-mail:* info@aspenwriters.org *Web Site:* www.aspenwriters.org, pg 615

Broesche, Jeffrey, Fine Communications, 322 Eighth Ave, 15th fl, New York, NY 10001 *Tel:* 212-595-3500 *Fax:* 212-595-3779, pg 95

Brogger, Erik A, Hofstra University, English Dept, 204 Mason Hall, Hempstead, NY 11549 *Tel:* 516-463-5454 *Fax:* 516-463-6395 *Web Site:* www.hofstra.edu, pg 678

Broida, Peter, Dewey Publications Inc, 1840 Wilson Blvd, Suite 203, Arlington, VA 22201 *Tel:* 703-524-1355 *Fax:* 703-524-1463 *E-mail:* deweypublications@gmail.com *Web Site:* www.deweypub.com, pg 78

Broikos, Anastasia, Boydell & Brewer Inc, 668 Mount Hope Ave, Rochester, NY 14620-2731 *Tel:* 585-275-0419 *Fax:* 585-271-8778 *E-mail:* boydell@boydellusa.net *Web Site:* www.boydellandbrewer.com, pg 45

Bromley, Carl, Nation Books, 116 E 16 St, 8th fl, New York, NY 10003 *Tel:* 212-822-0264 *Fax:* 212-253-5356 *E-mail:* submissions@nationbooks.org *Web Site:* www.nationbooks.org, pg 172

Bromley, Lizzy, Simon & Schuster Children's Publishing, 1230 Avenue of the Americas, New York, NY 10020 *Tel:* 212-698-7000 *Web Site:* KIDS.SimonandSchuster.com; TEEN.SimonandSchuster.com; simonandschuster.net; simonandschuster.biz, pg 235

Bronfin, Wendy, Houghton Mifflin Harcourt, 222 Berkeley St, Boston, MA 02116-3764 *Tel:* 617-351-5000 *Toll Free Tel:* 800-225-5425 (Pre-K-8); 800-462-6595 (6–12; Advanced & Electives); 800-289-4490 (Specialized Curriculum: Great Source, Rigby, Saxon, Steck-Vaughn; Homeschool; Adult Ed); 800-323-9540 (Assessment: Riverside Publishing); 888-391-3245 (SkillsTutor); 888-242-6747 option 2 (Destination Series; Classroom Connect; Earobics; Edmark; Learning Village; Riverdeep); 800-225-3362 (Houghton Mifflin Harcourt Trade & Reference Publishers); 800-225-5800 (Heinemann) *Fax:* 617-351-1125 *Web Site:* www.hmhco.com, pg 123

Brook, Susan Todd, Naval Institute Press, 291 Wood Rd, Annapolis, MD 21402-5034 *Tel:* 410-268-6110 *Toll Free Tel:* 800-233-8764 *Fax:* 410-295-1084; 410-571-1703 (cust serv) *E-mail:* webmaster@navalinstitute.org; customer@navalinstitute.org (cust serv); trade@usni.org *Web Site:* www.nip.org; www.usni.org, pg 176

Brooke, Peter, The Jim Henson Co, 1416 N La Brea Ave, Hollywood, CA 90028 *Tel:* 323-802-1500 *Fax:* 323-802-1825 *Web Site:* www.henson.com, pg 135

Brooke, Rachel, Georges Borchardt Inc, 136 E 57 St, New York, NY 10022 *Tel:* 212-753-5785 *E-mail:* georges@gbagency.com *Web Site:* www.gbagency.com, pg 563

Brookes, Jeffrey D, Brookes Publishing Co Inc, PO Box 10624, Baltimore, MD 21285-0624 *Tel:* 410-337-9580 (outside US & CN) *Toll Free Tel:* 800-638-3775 (US & CN) *Fax:* 410-337-8539 *E-mail:* custserv@brookespublishing.com *Web Site:* www.brookespublishing.com, pg 48

Brookes, Paul H, Brookes Publishing Co Inc, PO Box 10624, Baltimore, MD 21285-0624 *Tel:* 410-337-9580 (outside US & CN) *Toll Free Tel:* 800-638-3775 (US & CN) *Fax:* 410-337-8539 *E-mail:* custserv@brookespublishing.com *Web Site:* www.brookespublishing.com, pg 48

Brookins, Julia, American Printing History Association, PO Box 4519, Grand Central Sta, New York, NY 10163-4519 *Tel:* 202-544-2422 *Web Site:* www.printinghistory.org, pg 614

Brookins, Julia, American Printing History Association Award, PO Box 4519, Grand Central Sta, New York, NY 10163-4519 *Tel:* 202-544-2422 *Web Site:* www.printinghistory.org, pg 687

Brooks, Amy, Northeast-Midwest Institute, 50 "F" St NW, Suite 950, Washington, DC 20001 *Tel:* 202-544-5200 *Fax:* 202-544-0043 *E-mail:* info@nemw.org *Web Site:* www.nemw.org, pg 181

Brooks, Arthur, The AEI Press, 1150 17 St NW, Washington, DC 20036 *Tel:* 202-862-5800 *Fax:* 202-862-7177 *Web Site:* www.aei.org, pg 6

Brooks, Gabrielle, Alfred A Knopf/Everyman's Library, c/o Random House Inc, 1745 Broadway, New York, NY 10019 *Tel:* 212-751-2600 *Toll Free Tel:* 800-638-6460 *Fax:* 212-572-2593 *Web Site:* www.knopfdoubleday.com, pg 141

Brophy, Philippa, Sterling Lord Literistic Inc, 65 Bleecker St, New York, NY 10012 *Tel:* 212-780-6050 *Fax:* 212-780-6095 *E-mail:* info@sll.com *Web Site:* www.sll.com, pg 595

Broquet, Antoine, Broquet Inc, 97-B Montee des Bouleaux, St Constant, QC J5A 1A9, Canada *Tel:* 450-638-3338 *Fax:* 450-638-4338 *E-mail:* info@broquet.qc.ca *Web Site:* www.broquet.qc.ca, pg 496

Brosnan, Dr Jim, Maine Writers Conference at Ocean Park, 14 Temple Ave, Ocean Park, ME 04063 *Tel:* 401-598-1424 *E-mail:* www.opa@oceanpark.org *Web Site:* www.oceanpark.org, pg 670

Brosnan, Rosemary, HarperCollins Children's Books, 10 E 53 St, New York, NY 10022 *Tel:* 212-207-7000 *Web Site:* www.harpercollinschildrens.com, pg 113

Brothers, Connie, The Iowa Short Fiction Award, 102 Dey House, 507 N Clinton St, Iowa City, IA 52242-1000 *Tel:* 319-335-0416 *Fax:* 319-335-0420 *Web Site:* www.uiowapress.org/authors/iowa-short-fiction.htm, pg 713

Brothers, Ellen L, American Girl Publishing, 8400 Fairway Place, Middleton, WI 53562 *Tel:* 608-836-4848; 608-360-1861 (US & CN); 608-831-5210 (outside US & CN) *Toll Free Tel:* 800-233-0264; 800-360-1861 *Fax:* 608-836-1999 *Web Site:* www.americangirl.com, pg 13

Broude, Susan, Purple People Inc, 2301 W Hwy 89A, Suite 102, Sedona, AZ 86336 *Tel:* 928-204-6400 *Fax:* 928-282-2603 *E-mail:* info@purplepeople.com *Web Site:* www.purplepeople.com; www.bulliedtosilence.com, pg 210

Broughton, Paul, Life Cycle Books, PO Box 799, Fort Collins, CO 80522 *Toll Free Tel:* 800-214-5849 *Toll Free Fax:* 888-690-8532 *E-mail:* orders@lifecyclebooks.com; support@lifecyclebooks.com *Web Site:* www.lifecyclebooks.com, pg 148

Broughton, Paul, Life Cycle Books Ltd, 1085 Bellamy Rd N, Suite 20, Toronto, ON M1H 3C7, Canada *Tel:* 416-690-5860 *Toll Free Tel:* 866-880-5860 *Fax:* 416-690-8532 *Toll Free Fax:* 866-690-8532 *E-mail:* orders@lifecyclebooks.com *Web Site:* www.lifecyclebooks.com, pg 511

Brouwer, Joel, University of Alabama Program in Creative Writing, PO Box 870244, Tuscaloosa, AL 35487-0244 *Tel:* 205-348-5065 *Fax:* 205-348-1388 *E-mail:* english@ua.edu *Web Site:* www.as.ua.edu/english, pg 681

Brower, Michelle, Folio Literary Management LLC, The Film Center Bldg, 630 Ninth Ave, Suite 1101, New York, NY 10036 *Tel:* 212-400-1494 *Fax:* 212-967-0977 *Web Site:* www.foliolit.com, pg 572

Brown, Andy, Humanix Books LLC, PO Box 20989, West Palm Beach, FL 33416 *Tel:* 561-459-5997 *Toll Free Tel:* 855-371-7810 *Fax:* 561-241-6448 *Toll Free Fax:* 855-371-7809 *E-mail:* info@humanixbooks.com *Web Site:* www.humanixbooks.com, pg 125

Brown, Arthur, Vandamere Press, 3580 Morris St N, St Petersburg, FL 33713 *Tel:* 727-556-0950 *Toll Free Tel:* 800-551-7776 *Fax:* 727-556-2560 *E-mail:* orders@vandamere.com *Web Site:* www.vandamere.com, pg 274

Brown, Becky, Louisiana State University Press, 3990 W Lakeshore Dr, Baton Rouge, LA 70808 *Tel:* 225-578-6666 *Fax:* 225-578-6461 *E-mail:* lsupress@lsu.edu *Web Site:* lsupress.org, pg 153

Brown, Bridgett, Southern Illinois University Press, 1915 University Press Dr, SIUC Mail Code 6806, Carbondale, IL 62901-4323 *Tel:* 618-453-2281 *Fax:* 618-453-1221 *E-mail:* custserv@press.uchicago.edu; rights@siu.edu *Web Site:* www.siupress.com, pg 240

Brown, Brittan, The Jim Henson Co, 1416 N La Brea Ave, Hollywood, CA 90028 *Tel:* 323-802-1500 *Fax:* 323-802-1825 *Web Site:* www.henson.com, pg 135

Brown, Bruce, Reporters Committee for Freedom of the Press, 1101 Wilson Blvd, Suite 1100, Arlington, VA 22209-1817 *Tel:* 703-807-2100 *Toll Free Tel:* 800-336-4243 *Fax:* 703-807-2109 *E-mail:* rcfp@rcfp.org *Web Site:* www.rcfp.org, pg 635

Brown, Carl, Aum Publications, 86-10 Parsons Blvd, Jamaica, NY 11432-3314 *Tel:* 347-744-3199 *Web Site:* www.srichinmoybooks.com/us/aum_publications, pg 27

Brown, Cheri, Hackett Publishing Co Inc, 3333 Massachusetts Ave, Indianapolis, IN 46218 *Tel:* 317-635-9250 (orders & cust serv) *Fax:* 317-635-9292 *Toll Free Fax:* 800-783-9213 *E-mail:* customer@hackettpublishing.com *Web Site:* www.hackettpublishing.com, pg 110

Brown, Mr Chris, National Association of Broadcasters (NAB), 1771 "N" St NW, Washington, DC 20036-2891 *Tel:* 202-429-5300 *Fax:* 202-429-4199 *E-mail:* nab@nab.org *Web Site:* www.nab.org, pg 173, 628

Brown, Darlene, Harmonie Park Press, Liberty Professional Ctr, 35675 Mound Rd, Sterling Heights, MI 48310-4727 *Tel:* 586-979-2077; 586-979-1844 (cust serv) *Toll Free Tel:* 800-422-4880 *Fax:* 586-979-1786; 586-979-1863 (cust serv) *E-mail:* info@harmonieparkpress.com *Web Site:* harmonieparkpress.com, pg 113

Brown, Derrick, Write Bloody Publishing, 2306 E Cesar Chavez, Suite 103, Austin, TX 78706 *E-mail:* writebloody@gmail.com *Web Site:* writebloody.com, pg 286

Brown, Doug, Atlantic Publishing Group Inc, 1210 SW 23 Place, Ocala, FL 34471 *Tel:* 352-622-1825 *Toll Free Tel:* 800-814-1132 *Fax:* 352-622-1875 *E-mail:* sales@atlantic-pub.com *Web Site:* www.atlantic-pub.com, pg 26

Brunsek, Judy, Owlkids Books Inc, 10 Lower Spadina Ave, Suite 400, Toronto, ON M5V 2Z2, Canada *Tel:* 416-340-3700 *Fax:* 416-340-9769 *E-mail:* owlkids@owlkids.com *Web Site:* www.owlkidsbooks.com, pg 514

Bruscia, Kenneth E, Barcelona Publishers, Pathway Book Service, 4 White Brook Rd, Gilsum, NH 03448 *Tel:* 603-357-0236 *Fax:* 603-357-2073 *E-mail:* pbs@pathwaybook.com; barcelonapublishers@gvtc.com *Web Site:* www.barcelonapublishers.com, pg 30

Brutger, Molly, Meadowbrook Press, 6110 Blue Circle Dr, Suite 237, Minnetonka, MN 55343 *Toll Free Tel:* 800-338-2232 *Fax:* 952-930-1940 *E-mail:* info@meadowbrookpress.com *Web Site:* www.meadowbrookpress.com, pg 163

Bruton, Ben, HarperCollins General Books Group, 10 E 53 St, New York, NY 10022 *Tel:* 212-207-7000 *Fax:* 212-207-7633 *Web Site:* www.harpercollins.com, pg 113

Bryan, Heather, Nimbus Publishing Ltd, 3731 Mackintosh St, Halifax, NS B3K 5A5, Canada *Tel:* 902-455-4286; 902-454-7404 *Toll Free Tel:* 800-NIMBUS9 (646-2879) *Fax:* 902-455-5440 *Toll Free Fax:* 888-253-3133 *E-mail:* customerservice@nimbus.ns.ca *Web Site:* www.nimbus.ns.ca, pg 513

Bryan, Jeffrey, Whitecap Books Ltd, 314 W Cordova St, Suite 210, Vancouver, BC V6B 1E8, Canada *Tel:* 604-681-6181 *Toll Free Tel:* 800-387-9776 *Toll Free Fax:* 800-260-9777 *Web Site:* www.whitecap.ca, pg 525

Bryan, Nancy, University of Texas Press, 2100 Comal St, Austin, TX 78722 *Tel:* 512-471-7233 *Fax:* 512-232-7178 *E-mail:* utpress@uts.cc.utexas.edu *Web Site:* www.utexaspress.com, pg 253

Bryans, John B, Information Today, Inc, 143 Old Marlton Pike, Medford, NJ 08055-8750 *Tel:* 609-654-6266 *Toll Free Tel:* 800-300-9868 (cust serv) *Fax:* 609-654-4309 *E-mail:* custserv@infotoday.com *Web Site:* www.infotoday.com, pg 130

Bryans, John B, Plexus Publishing, Inc, 143 Old Marlton Pike, Medford, NJ 08055 *Tel:* 609-654-6500 *Fax:* 609-654-4309 *E-mail:* info@plexuspublishing.com *Web Site:* www.plexuspublishing.com, pg 203

Bryant, Del R, BMI®, 7 World Trade Ctr, 250 Greenwich St, New York, NY 10007-0030 *Tel:* 212-586-2000; 212-220-3000 *Fax:* 212-246-2163 *E-mail:* foundation@bmi.com *Web Site:* www.bmi.com, pg 618

Bryant, John, The Melville Society, c/o Kent State Univ, Dept of English, Box 5190, Kent, OH 44242, pg 627

Bryant, L J, Wildflower Press, Oakbrook Press, 3301 S Valley Dr, Rapid City, SD 57703 *Tel:* 605-381-6385 *Fax:* 605-343-8733 *E-mail:* info@wildflowerpress.org; bookorder@wildflowerpress.org *Web Site:* www.wildflowerpress.org, pg 281

Bryant, Tommy, Creative Writing Day & Workshops, 335 Cummings St, Abingdon, VA 24210 *Tel:* 276-623-5266 *Fax:* 276-676-3076 *E-mail:* vhf@eva.org *Web Site:* www.vahighlandsfestival.org, pg 668

Bryar, Robert, The Lieutenant-Governor's Awards for High Achievement in the Arts, 61 Carleton St, Fredericton, NB E3B 3T2, Canada *Tel:* 506-444-4444 *Toll Free Tel:* 866-460-ARTS (460-2787) *Fax:* 506-444-5543 *E-mail:* nbabcanb@artsnb.ca *Web Site:* www.artsnb.ca, pg 717

Bryerose, Cathy, Regal Crest Enterprises LLC, 229 Sheridan Loop, Belton, TX 76513 *Tel:* 409-527-1188 *Toll Free Fax:* 866-294-9628 *E-mail:* info@regalcrestbooks.biz *Web Site:* www.regalcrest.biz, pg 217

Bubil, Harold, National Association of Real Estate Editors (NAREE), 1003 NW Sixth Terr, Boca Raton, FL 33486-3455 *Tel:* 561-391-3599 *Fax:* 561-391-0099 *Web Site:* www.naree.org, pg 629

Buchanan, Mary (Ginjer), Berkley Books, 375 Hudson St, New York, NY 10014 *Tel:* 212-366-2000 *Fax:* 212-366-2666 *E-mail:* online@penguinputnam.com *Web Site:* www.penguinputnam.com; us.penguingroup.com, pg 36

Buchanan, Mary (Ginjer), Berkley Publishing Group, 375 Hudson St, New York, NY 10014 *Tel:* 212-366-2000 *Fax:* 212-366-2385 *E-mail:* online@penguinputnam.com *Web Site:* us.penguingroup.com, pg 36

Buchwald, Don, Don Buchwald & Associates Inc, 10 E 44 St, New York, NY 10017 *Tel:* 212-867-1200 *Fax:* 212-867-2434 *E-mail:* info@buchwald.com *Web Site:* www.buchwald.com, pg 565

Buck, Bethany, Simon & Schuster Children's Publishing, 1230 Avenue of the Americas, New York, NY 10020 *Tel:* 212-698-7000 *Web Site:* KIDS.SimonandSchuster.com; TEEN.SimonandSchuster.com; simonandschuster.net; simonandschuster.biz, pg 235

Buck, Howard, Howard Buck Agency, 80 Eighth Ave, Suite 1107, New York, NY 10011 *Tel:* 212-924-9093, pg 565

Buckles, Kristen, The University of Arizona Press, 355 S Euclid Ave, Suite 103, Tucson, AZ 85719-6654 *Tel:* 520-621-1441 *Toll Free Tel:* 800-426-3797 (orders) *Fax:* 520-621-8899 *Toll Free Fax:* 800-426-3797 *E-mail:* uap@uapress.arizona.edu *Web Site:* www.uapress.arizona.edu, pg 264

Buckley, Carol, Piano Press, 1425 Ocean Ave, Suite 17, Del Mar, CA 92014 *Tel:* 619-884-1401 *Fax:* 858-755-1104 *E-mail:* pianopress@pianopress.com *Web Site:* www.pianopress.com, pg 201

Buckley, Cicely, Oyster River Press, 36 Oyster River Rd, Durham, NH 03824-3029 *Tel:* 603-868-5006 *E-mail:* oysterriverpress@comcast.net *Web Site:* www.oysterriverpress.com, pg 552

Buckley, Kerri, Harlequin Enterprises Ltd, 233 Broadway, Suite 1001, New York, NY 10279 *Tel:* 212-553-4200 *Fax:* 212-227-8969 *E-mail:* CustomerService@harlequin.com *Web Site:* www.harlequin.com, pg 112

Buckley, Paul, Penguin Books, 375 Hudson St, New York, NY 10014 *Tel:* 212-366-2000 *E-mail:* online@penguinputnam.com *Web Site:* www.penguinputnam.com; www.penguinclassics.com; us.penguingroup.com, pg 197

Buckley, Paul, Viking, 375 Hudson St, New York, NY 10014 *Tel:* 212-366-2000 *E-mail:* online@penguinputnam.com *Web Site:* www.penguinputnam.com; us.penguingroup.com, pg 275

Buckner, Judith, Judith Buckner Literary Agency, 12721 Hart St, North Hollywood, CA 91605 *Tel:* 818-982-8202 *Fax:* 818-764-6844, pg 565

Buckner, Richard, Beacon Hill Press of Kansas City, PO Box 419527, Kansas City, MO 64141-6527 *Tel:* 816-931-1900 *Toll Free Tel:* 800-877-0700 (cust serv) *Fax:* 816-753-4071 *Web Site:* www.beaconhillbooks.com, pg 32

Budnick, Philip, Penguin Group (USA) LLC, 375 Hudson St, New York, NY 10014 *Tel:* 212-366-2000 *Toll Free Tel:* 800-847-5515 (inside sales); 800-631-8571 (cust serv) *Fax:* 212-366-2666; 607-775-4829 (inside sales) *E-mail:* online@us.penguingroup.com *Web Site:* www.penguin.com; us.penguingroup.com, pg 197

Budnick, Philip, Plume, 375 Hudson St, New York, NY 10014 *Tel:* 212-366-2000 *Fax:* 212-366-2666 *E-mail:* online@penguinputnam.com *Web Site:* www.penguinputnam.com; us.penguingroup.com, pg 203

Bufe, Charles, See Sharp Press, PO Box 1731, Tucson, AZ 85702-1731 *Tel:* 520-338-2151 *E-mail:* info@seesharppress.com *Web Site:* www.seesharppress.com, pg 231

Buffaloe, Christine, Lemon Grove Press, 1158 26 St, Suite 502, Santa Monica, CA 90403 *Tel:* 310-471-1740 *Fax:* 310-476-7627 *E-mail:* info@lemongrovepress.com *Web Site:* www.thetakechargepatient.com, pg 528

Bui, Francoise, Random House Children's Books, 1745 Broadway, New York, NY 10019 *Tel:* 212-782-9000 *Toll Free Tel:* 800-200-3552 *Fax:* 212-782-9452 *Web Site:* randomhousekids.com, pg 213

Buker, Kerry, The National Press Foundation, 1211 Connecticut Ave NW, Suite 310, Washington, DC 20036 *Tel:* 202-663-7280 *Web Site:* www.nationalpress.org, pg 631

Bukowski, Denise, The Bukowski Agency, 14 Prince Arthur Ave, Suite 202, Toronto, ON M5R 1A9, Canada *Tel:* 416-928-6728 *Fax:* 416-963-9978 *E-mail:* info@bukowskiagency.com *Web Site:* www.bukowskiagency.com, pg 565

Bulger, Joe, Simon & Schuster, Inc, 1230 Avenue of the Americas, New York, NY 10020 *Tel:* 212-698-7000 *Fax:* 212-698-7007 *E-mail:* firstname.lastname@simonandschuster.com *Web Site:* www.simonandschuster.com, pg 235

Bulger, Terrilee, Nimbus Publishing Ltd, 3731 Mackintosh St, Halifax, NS B3K 5A5, Canada *Tel:* 902-455-4286; 902-454-7404 *Toll Free Tel:* 800-NIMBUS9 (646-2879) *Fax:* 902-455-5440 *Toll Free Fax:* 888-253-3133 *E-mail:* customerservice@nimbus.ns.ca *Web Site:* www.nimbus.ns.ca, pg 513

Bull, James, Bull Publishing Co, PO Box 1377, Boulder, CO 80306 *Tel:* 303-545-6350 *Toll Free Tel:* 800-676-2855 *Fax:* 303-545-6354 *E-mail:* bullpublishing@msn.com *Web Site:* www.bullpub.com, pg 49

Bullas, Roslyn, North Atlantic Books, 2526 Martin Luther King Jr Way, Berkeley, CA 94704 *Tel:* 510-549-4270 *Fax:* 510-549-4276 *Web Site:* www.northatlanticbooks.com, pg 180

Buller, Bob, Society of Biblical Literature, The Luce Ctr, Suite 350, 825 Houston Mill Rd, Atlanta, GA 30329 *Tel:* 404-727-3100 *Fax:* 404-727-3101 (corp) *E-mail:* sbl@sbl-site.org *Web Site:* www.sbl-site.org, pg 238

Bumps, Susan, North Atlantic Books, 2526 Martin Luther King Jr Way, Berkeley, CA 94704 *Tel:* 510-549-4270 *Fax:* 510-549-4276 *Web Site:* www.northatlanticbooks.com, pg 180

Bunce, Cindy, Cedar Fort Inc, 2373 W 700 S, Springville, UT 84663 *Tel:* 801-489-4084 *Toll Free Tel:* 800-SKY-BOOK (759-2665) *Fax:* 801-489-1097 *Toll Free Fax:* 800-388-3727 *E-mail:* brycemortimer@cedarfort.com *Web Site:* www.cedarfort.com, pg 55

Bunch, Cindy, InterVarsity Press, 430 Plaza Dr, Westmont, IL 60559-1234 *Tel:* 630-734-4000 *Toll Free Tel:* 800-843-9487 *Fax:* 630-734-4200 *E-mail:* email@ivpress.com *Web Site:* www.ivpress.com, pg 134

Bunker, Jane, Northwestern University Press, 629 Noyes St, Evanston, IL 60208-4210 *Tel:* 847-491-2046 *Toll Free Tel:* 800-621-2736 (orders only) *Fax:* 847-491-8150 *E-mail:* nupress@northwestern.edu *Web Site:* www.nupress.northwestern.edu, pg 181

Bunker, Jane, TriQuarterly Books, 629 Noyes St, Evanston, IL 60201 *Toll Free Tel:* 800-621-2736 (orders only) *Fax:* 847-467-2096 *E-mail:* nupress@northwestern.edu *Web Site:* www.nupress.northwestern.edu, pg 259

Bunn, Anne, The MIT Press, 55 Hayward St, Cambridge, MA 02142 *Tel:* 617-253-5255 *Toll Free Tel:* 800-207-8354 (orders) *Fax:* 617-258-6779; 617-577-1545 (orders) *Web Site:* mitpress.mit.edu, pg 167

Bunting, Jennifer, Tilbury House Publishers, 103 Brunswick Ave, Gardiner, ME 04345 *Tel:* 207-582-1899 *Toll Free Tel:* 800-582-1899 (orders) *Fax:* 207-582-8227 *E-mail:* tilbury@tilburyhouse.com *Web Site:* www.tilburyhouse.com, pg 255

Bunting, Ken, National Freedom of Information Coalition (NFOIC), 101 Reynolds Journalism Institute, Columbia, MO 65211-0012 *Tel:* 573-882-4856 *Fax:* 573-884-6204 *Web Site:* nfoic.org, pg 630

Bunzel, Mark, FineEdge.com, 14004 Biz Point Lane, Anacortes, WA 98221 *Tel:* 360-299-8500 *Fax:* 360-299-0535 *E-mail:* pub@fineedge.com *Web Site:* www.fineedge.com, pg 95

Burch, Martin, Ocean Tree Books, 1325 Cerro Gordo Rd, Santa Fe, NM 87501 *Tel:* 505-983-1412 *Fax:* 505-983-0899 *Web Site:* www.oceantree.com, pg 183

Burch, Renee C, Wildlife Education Ltd, 2418 Noyes St, Evanston, IL 60201 *Toll Free Tel:* 800-477-5034 *E-mail:* owls5@zoobooks.com; helpdesk@zoobooks.com *Web Site:* www.zoobooks.com; wildlife-ed.com, pg 281

Burford, Peter, Burford Books, 101 E State St, No 301, Ithaca, NY 14850 *Tel:* 607-319-4373 *Fax:* 607-319-4373 *Toll Free Fax:* 866-212-7750 *E-mail:* info@burfordbooks.com *Web Site:* www.burfordbooks.com, pg 49

Burgauer, Steve, Prometheus Awards, 650 Castro St, Suite 120-433, Mountain View, CA 94041 *Tel:* 650-968-6319 *E-mail:* info@lfs.org *Web Site:* www.lfs.org, pg 736

Burgess, Angela R, IEEE Computer Society, 2001 "L" St NW, Suite 700, Washington, DC 20036-4928 *Tel:* 202-371-0101 *Toll Free Tel:* 800-272-6657 (memb info) *Fax:* 202-728-9614 *E-mail:* help@computer.org *Web Site:* www.computer.org, pg 127

Burgess, Daniel, Scribner, 1230 Avenue of the Americas, New York, NY 10020, pg 230

Burgess, Kathy, University Press of Mississippi, 3825 Ridgewood Rd, Jackson, MS 39211-6492 *Tel:* 601-432-6205 *Toll Free Tel:* 800-737-7788 (orders & cust serv) *Fax:* 601-432-6217 *E-mail:* press@mississippi.edu *Web Site:* www.upress.state.ms.us, pg 271

Burgess, Marsha P, ALSC BWI/Summer Reading Program Grant, 50 E Huron St, Chicago, IL 60611-2795 *Tel:* 312-280-2163 *Toll Free Tel:* 800-545-2433 *Fax:* 312-440-9374 *E-mail:* alsc@ala.org *Web Site:* www.ala.org/alsc, pg 687

Burgess, Marsha P, The May Hill Arbuthnot Honor Lecture Award, 50 E Huron St, Chicago, IL 60611-2795 *Tel:* 312-280-2163 *Toll Free Tel:* 800-545-2433 *Fax:* 312-440-9374 *E-mail:* alsc@ala.org *Web Site:* www.ala.org/alsc, pg 688

Burgess, Marsha P, The Mildred L Batchelder Award, 50 E Huron St, Chicago, IL 60611-2795 *Tel:* 312-280-2163 *Toll Free Tel:* 800-545-2433 *Fax:* 312-440-9374 *E-mail:* alsc@ala.org *Web Site:* www.ala.org/alsc, pg 689

Burgess, Marsha P, The Pura Belpre Award, 50 E Huron St, Chicago, IL 60611-2795 *Tel:* 312-280-2163 *Toll Free Tel:* 800-545-2433 *Fax:* 312-440-9374 *E-mail:* alsc@ala.org *Web Site:* www.ala.org/alsc, pg 690

Burgess, Marsha P, Bound to Stay Bound Books Scholarship, 50 E Huron St, Chicago, IL 60611-2795 *Tel:* 312-280-2163 *Toll Free Tel:* 800-545-2433 *Fax:* 312-440-9374 *E-mail:* alsc@ala.org *Web Site:* www.ala.org/alsc, pg 692

Burgess, Marsha P, The Randolph Caldecott Medal, 50 E Huron St, Chicago, IL 60611-2795 *Tel:* 312-280-2163 *Toll Free Tel:* 800-545-2433 *Fax:* 312-440-9374 *E-mail:* alsc@ala.org *Web Site:* www.ala.org/alsc, pg 694

Burgess, Marsha P, Frederic G Melcher Scholarship, 50 E Huron St, Chicago, IL 60611-2795 *Tel:* 312-280-2163 *Toll Free Tel:* 800-545-2433 *Fax:* 312-440-9374 *E-mail:* alsc@ala.org *Web Site:* www.ala.org/alsc, pg 723

Burgess, Marsha P, John Newbery Medal, 50 E Huron St, Chicago, IL 60611-2795 *Tel:* 312-280-2163 *Toll Free Tel:* 800-545-2433 *Fax:* 312-440-9374 *E-mail:* alsc@ala.org *Web Site:* www.ala.org/alsc, pg 729

Burgess, Marsha P, Robert F Sibert Informational Book Award, 50 E Huron St, Chicago, IL 60611-2795 *Tel:* 312-280-2163 *Toll Free Tel:* 800-545-2433 *Fax:* 312-440-9374 *E-mail:* alsc@ala.org *Web Site:* www.ala.org/alsc, pg 742

Burgess, Marsha P, The Laura Ingalls Wilder Medal, 50 E Huron St, Chicago, IL 60611-2795 *Tel:* 312-280-2163 *Toll Free Tel:* 800-545-2433 *Fax:* 312-440-9374 *E-mail:* alsc@ala.org *Web Site:* www.ala.org/alsc, pg 749

Burgin, Richard, Boulevard Magazine Short Fiction Contest for Emerging Writers, 6614 Clayton Rd, PMB 325, Richmond Heights, MO 63117 *Tel:* 314-862-2643 *Web Site:* www.boulevardmagazine.org, pg 692

Burk, Dale A, Stoneydale Press Publishing Co, 523 Main St, Stevensville, MT 59870-2839 *Tel:* 406-777-2729 *Toll Free Tel:* 800-735-7006 *Fax:* 406-777-2521 *Web Site:* www.stoneydale.com, pg 245

Burke, Alexander, Hofstra University, English Dept, 204 Mason Hall, Hempstead, NY 11549 *Tel:* 516-463-5454 *Fax:* 516-463-6395 *Web Site:* www.hofstra.edu, pg 678

Burke, Barbara, Jonathan David Publishers Inc, 68-22 Eliot Ave, Middle Village, NY 11379 *Tel:* 718-456-8611 *Fax:* 718-894-2818 *E-mail:* info@jdbooks.com; customerservice@jdbooks.com *Web Site:* www.jdbooks.com, pg 136

Burke, Carolyn L, Editors' Association of Canada (Association canadienne des reviseurs), 502-27 Carlton St, Toronto, ON M5B 1L2, Canada *Tel:* 416-975-1379 *Toll Free Tel:* 866-CAN-EDIT (226-3348) *Fax:* 416-975-1637 *E-mail:* info@editors.ca *Web Site:* www.editors.ca; www.reviseurs.ca, pg 622

Burke, Carolyn L, Tom Fairley Award for Editorial Excellence, 502-27 Carlton St, Toronto, ON M5B 1L2, Canada *Tel:* 416-975-1379 *Toll Free Tel:* 866-CAN-EDIT (226-3348) *Fax:* 416-975-1637 *E-mail:* fairley_award@editors.ca *Web Site:* www.editors.ca; www.reviseurs.ca, pg 703

Burke, Charlie, Bentley Publishers, 1734 Massachusetts Ave, Cambridge, MA 02138-1804 *Tel:* 617-547-4170 *Toll Free Tel:* 800-423-4595 *Fax:* 617-876-9235 *E-mail:* sales@bentleypublishers.com *Web Site:* www.bentleypublishers.com, pg 35

Burke, Colleen, Binghamton University Creative Writing Program, c/o Dept of English, PO Box 6000, Binghamton, NY 13902-6000 *Tel:* 607-777-2168 *Fax:* 607-777-2408 *E-mail:* cwpro@binghamton.edu *Web Site:* english.binghamton.edu/cwpro, pg 677

Burke, Craig, Berkley Books, 375 Hudson St, New York, NY 10014 *Tel:* 212-366-2000 *Fax:* 212-366-2666 *E-mail:* online@penguinputnam.com *Web Site:* www.penguinputnam.com; us.penguingroup.com, pg 35

Burke, Craig, Berkley Publishing Group, 375 Hudson St, New York, NY 10014 *Tel:* 212-366-2000 *Fax:* 212-366-2385 *E-mail:* online@penguinputnam.com *Web Site:* us.penguingroup.com, pg 36

Burke, Craig, NAL, 375 Hudson St, New York, NY 10014 *Tel:* 212-366-2000 *E-mail:* online@penguinputnam.com *Web Site:* www.penguinputnam.com; us.penguingroup.com, pg 172

Burke, Jennifer, Harmonie Park Press, Liberty Professional Ctr, 35675 Mound Rd, Sterling Heights, MI 48310-4727 *Tel:* 586-979-2077; 586-979-1844 (cust serv) *Toll Free Tel:* 800-422-4880 *Fax:* 586-979-1786; 586-979-1863 (cust serv) *E-mail:* info@harmonieparkpress.com *Web Site:* harmonieparkpress.com, pg 113

Burke, Katie, Pomegranate Communications Inc, 19018 NE Portal Way, Portland, OR 97230 *Tel:* 503-328-6500 *Toll Free Tel:* 800-227-1428 *Fax:* 503-328-9330 *Toll Free Fax:* 800-848-4376 *E-mail:* info@pomegranate.com *Web Site:* www.pomegranate.com, pg 204

Burke, Lori, Penguin Young Readers Group, 345 Hudson St, New York, NY 10014 *Tel:* 212-366-2000 *E-mail:* online@penguinputnam.com *Web Site:* www.penguinputnam.com; us.penguingroup.com, pg 198

Burke, Louise, Gallery Books, 1230 Avenue of the Americas, New York, NY 10020 *Toll Free Tel:* 800-456-6798 *Fax:* 212-698-7284 *E-mail:* consumer.customerservice@simonandschuster.com *Web Site:* www.simonsays.com, pg 101

Burke, Louise, Simon & Schuster, Inc, 1230 Avenue of the Americas, New York, NY 10020 *Tel:* 212-698-7000 *Fax:* 212-698-7007 *E-mail:* firstname.lastname@simonandschuster.com *Web Site:* www.simonandschuster.com, pg 235

Burke, Michael, The Barbara Bova Literary Agency LLC, 3951 Gulf Shore Blvd N, Unit PH 1-B, Naples, FL 34103 *Tel:* 239-649-7237 *E-mail:* slushpile@yahoo.com *Web Site:* www.barbarabovaliteraryagency.com, pg 564

Burke, Michele, Random House Children's Books, 1745 Broadway, New York, NY 10019 *Tel:* 212-782-9000 *Toll Free Tel:* 800-200-3552 *Fax:* 212-782-9452 *Web Site:* randomhousekids.com, pg 213

Burke, Sharon, Harvest House Publishers Inc, 990 Owen Loop N, Eugene, OR 97402-9173 *Tel:* 541-343-0123 *Toll Free Tel:* 888-501-6991 *Fax:* 541-342-6410 *E-mail:* admin@harvesthousepublishers.com *Web Site:* www.harvesthousepublishers.com, pg 115

Burke, Therese, DK, 375 Hudson St, 2nd fl, New York, NY 10014-3672 *Tel:* 212-213-4800 *Toll Free Tel:* 877-342-5357 (cust serv) *Fax:* 212-213-5202 *Web Site:* us.dk.com, pg 80

Burke, Thomas F, Pomegranate Communications Inc, 19018 NE Portal Way, Portland, OR 97230 *Tel:* 503-328-6500 *Toll Free Tel:* 800-227-1428 *Fax:* 503-328-9330 *Toll Free Fax:* 800-848-4376 *E-mail:* info@pomegranate.com *Web Site:* www.pomegranate.com, pg 204

Burke, Vincent J, The Johns Hopkins University Press, 2715 N Charles St, Baltimore, MD 21218-4363 *Tel:* 410-516-6900; 410-516-6987 (journals outside US & CN) *Toll Free Tel:* 800-537-5487 (book orders & cust serv); 800-548-1784 (journal orders) *Fax:* 410-516-6968; 410-516-3866 (journal orders) *E-mail:* hfscustserv@press.jhu.edu (cust serv); jrnlcirc@press.jhu.edu (journal orders) *Web Site:* www.press.jhu.edu; muse.jhu.edu/about/subscriptions/index.html (Project Muse subns), pg 136

Burke, William, Cummings & Hathaway Publishers, 395 Atlantic Ave, East Rockaway, NY 11518 *Tel:* 516-593-3607 *Fax:* 516-593-1401, pg 73

Burkhard, Catherine, Guild of Book Workers, 521 Fifth Ave, 17th fl, New York, NY 10175-0038 *Tel:* 212-292-4444 *Web Site:* www.guildofbookworkers.org, pg 624

Burkholder, Bruce, Editorial Bautista Independiente, 3417 Kenilworth Blvd, Sebring, FL 33870-4469 *Tel:* 863-382-6350 *Toll Free Tel:* 800-398-7187 (US) *Fax:* 863-382-8650 *E-mail:* info@ebi-bmm.org; ebiweb@ebi-bmm.org *Web Site:* www.ebi-bmm.org, pg 85

Burkholder, Courtney, International Society for Technology in Education, 180 W Eighth Ave, Suite 300, Eugene, OR 97401-2916 *Tel:* 541-302-3777 (intl) *Toll Free Tel:* 800-336-5191 (US & CN) *Fax:* 541-302-3778 *E-mail:* iste@iste.org *Web Site:* www.iste.org; www.iste.org/bookstore (orders), pg 133

Burks, Patrick C, American Geological Institute (AGI), 4220 King St, Alexandria, VA 22302-1502 *Tel:* 703-379-2480 *Fax:* 703-379-7563 *E-mail:* pubs@agiweb.org *Web Site:* www.agiweb.org, pg 13

Burleson, Derick, Visiting Writers Series, English Dept, PO Box 755720, Fairbanks, AK 99775-5720 *Tel:* 907-474-7193 *Fax:* 907-474-5247 *E-mail:* faengl@uaf.edu *Web Site:* www.alaska.edu/english, pg 674

Burley, Rachel, John Wiley & Sons Inc, 111 River St, Hoboken, NJ 07030-5774 *Tel:* 201-748-6000 *Toll Free Tel:* 800-225-5945 (cust serv) *Fax:* 201-748-6088 *E-mail:* info@wiley.com *Web Site:* www.wiley.com, pg 281

Burmeister-Brown, Susan, Family Matters, PO Box 80430, Portland, OR 97280 *Tel:* 503-221-0836 *Fax:* 503-221-0837 *E-mail:* editors@glimmertrain.org *Web Site:* www.glimmertrain.org, pg 703

Burmeister-Brown, Susan, Fiction Open, PO Box 80430, Portland, OR 97280 *Tel:* 503-221-0836 *Fax:* 503-221-0837 *E-mail:* editors@glimmertrain.org *Web Site:* www.glimmertrain.org, pg 704

Burmeister-Brown, Susan, Glimmer Train Press Inc, PO Box 80430, Portland, OR 97280 *Tel:* 503-221-0836 *Fax:* 503-221-0837 *E-mail:* editors@glimmertrain.org *Web Site:* www.glimmertrain.org, pg 103

Burmeister-Brown, Susan, Short Story Award for New Writers, PO Box 80430, Portland, OR 97280 *Tel:* 503-221-0836 *Fax:* 503-221-0837 *E-mail:* editors@glimmertrain.org *Web Site:* www.glimmertrain.org, pg 741

Butler, Adios, Alan Wofsy Fine Arts, 1109 Geary Blvd, San Francisco, CA 94109 *Tel:* 415-292-6500 *Toll Free Tel:* 800-660-6403 *Fax:* 415-292-6594 (off & cust serv); 415-512-0130 (acctg) *E-mail:* order@art-books.com (orders); editeur@earthlink.net (edit); beauxarts@earthlink.net (cust serv) *Web Site:* www.art-books.com, pg 284

Butler, Doug, Doug Butler Enterprises, Inc, 495 Table Rd, Crawford, NE 69339 *Tel:* 308-665-1510 *Toll Free Tel:* 800-728-3826 *Fax:* 308-665-1520 *E-mail:* info@dougbutler.com *Web Site:* www.dougbutler.com; www.essentialhorseshoeingbook.com, pg 527

Butler, Jacob, Doug Butler Enterprises, Inc, 495 Table Rd, Crawford, NE 69339 *Tel:* 308-665-1510 *Toll Free Tel:* 800-728-3826 *Fax:* 308-665-1520 *E-mail:* info@dougbutler.com *Web Site:* www.dougbutler.com; www.essentialhorseshoeingbook.com, pg 527

Butler, Leigh, Penguin Group (USA) LLC, 375 Hudson St, New York, NY 10014 *Tel:* 212-366-2000 *Toll Free Tel:* 800-847-5515 (inside sales); 800-631-8571 (cust serv) *Fax:* 212-366-2666; 607-775-4829 (inside sales) *E-mail:* online@us.penguingroup.com *Web Site:* www.penguin.com; us.penguingroup.com, pg 197

Butson, Katherine, The Althouse Press, Western University, 1137 Western Rd, London, ON N6G 1G7, Canada *Tel:* 519-661-2096 *Fax:* 519-661-3714 *E-mail:* press@uwo.ca *Web Site:* www.edu.uwo.ca/althousepress, pg 493

Buttner, Karen, University of Calgary Press, 2500 University Dr NW, Calgary, AB T2N 1N4, Canada *Tel:* 403-220-7578 *Fax:* 403-282-0085 *Web Site:* www.uofcpress.com, pg 523

Byer, Glenn, Novalis Publishing, 10 Lower Spadina Ave, Suite 400, Toronto, ON M5V 2Z2, Canada *Tel:* 416-363-3303 *Toll Free Tel:* 877-702-7773 *Fax:* 416-363-9409 *Toll Free Fax:* 877-702-7775 *E-mail:* books@novalis.ca *Web Site:* www.novalis.ca, pg 514

Byer-Sprinzeles, Maggie, Byer-Sprinzeles Agency, 5800 Arlington Ave, Suite 16-C, Riverdale, NY 10471 *Tel:* 718-543-9399 *Web Site:* www.maggiebyersprinzeles.com, pg 601

Bykofsky, Sheree, Sheree Bykofsky Associates Inc, PO Box 706, Brigantine, NJ 08203 *E-mail:* submitbee@aol.com *Web Site:* www.shereebee.com, pg 565

Byl, Craig, American Institute of Aeronautics & Astronautics, 1801 Alexander Bell Dr, Suite 500, Reston, VA 20191-4344 *Tel:* 703-264-7500 *Toll Free Tel:* 800-639-AIAA (639-2422) *Fax:* 703-264-7551 *E-mail:* custserv@aiaa.org *Web Site:* www.aiaa.org, pg 14

Byler, Joshua, Herald Press, 1251 Virginia Ave, Harrisonburg, VA 22802-2434 *Toll Free Tel:* 800-245-7894 (orders-US); 800-999-3534; 800-631-6535 (orders-CN) *Toll Free Fax:* 877-271-0760 *E-mail:* info@MennoMedia.org *Web Site:* www.heraldpress.com; store.mennomedia.org, pg 118

Bynum, Robert C, Travel Keys, PO Box 160691, Sacramento, CA 95816-0691 *Tel:* 916-452-5200 *Fax:* 916-452-5200, pg 258

Byram, John W, University of New Mexico, University of New Mexico, Humanities Dept, Rm 253, Albuquerque, NM 87131-0001 *Tel:* 505-277-2346; 505-272-7777 (cust serv) *Toll Free Tel:* 800-249-7737 (orders only) *Fax:* 505-277-3343; 505-272-7778 (cust serv) *Toll Free Fax:* 800-622-8667 (orders only) *E-mail:* unmpress@unm.edu; custserv@upress.unm.edu (order dept) *Web Site:* unmpress.com, pg 267

Byrd, Bobby, Cinco Puntos Press, 701 Texas Ave, El Paso, TX 79901 *Tel:* 915-838-1625 *Toll Free Tel:* 800-566-9072 *Fax:* 915-838-1635 *E-mail:* info@cincopuntos.com *Web Site:* www.cincopuntos.com, pg 61

Byrd, Lee, Cinco Puntos Press, 701 Texas Ave, El Paso, TX 79901 *Tel:* 915-838-1625 *Toll Free Tel:* 800-566-9072 *Fax:* 915-838-1635 *E-mail:* info@cincopuntos.com *Web Site:* www.cincopuntos.com, pg 61

Byrnes, David, Simon & Schuster, Inc, 1230 Avenue of the Americas, New York, NY 10020 *Tel:* 212-698-7000 *Fax:* 212-698-7007 *E-mail:* firstname.lastname@simonandschuster.com *Web Site:* www.simonandschuster.com, pg 235

Byrns, Bob, Paulist Press, 997 MacArthur Blvd, Mahwah, NJ 07430-9990 *Tel:* 201-825-7300 *Toll Free Tel:* 800-218-1903 *Fax:* 201-825-8345 *Toll Free Fax:* 800-836-3161 *E-mail:* info@paulistpress.com *Web Site:* www.paulistpress.com, pg 195

Cabasin, Linda, Fodor's Travel Publications, c/o Random House Inc, 1745 Broadway, New York, NY 10019 *Tel:* 212-829-6714 *Toll Free Tel:* 800-733-3000 *Fax:* 212-572-2248 *Web Site:* www.fodors.com, pg 96

Cabezas, Sue, Applewood Books Inc, One River Rd, Carlisle, MA 01741 *Tel:* 781-271-0055 *Fax:* 781-271-0056 *E-mail:* applewood@awb.com *Web Site:* www.awb.com, pg 20

Cabin, John, Vandamere Press, 3580 Morris St N, St Petersburg, FL 33713 *Tel:* 727-556-0950 *Toll Free Tel:* 800-551-7776 *Fax:* 727-556-2560 *E-mail:* orders@vandamere.com *Web Site:* www.vandamere.com, pg 274

Cadieu, Pierre, Editions Vents d'Ouest, 109 rue Wright, Gatineau, QC J8X 2G7, Canada *Tel:* 819-770-6377 *Fax:* 819-770-0559 *E-mail:* info@ventsdouest.ca *Web Site:* www.ventsdouest.ca, pg 504

Cady, Donald, Wesleyan Publishing House, 13300 Olio Rd, Fishers, IN 46037 *Tel:* 317-774-3853 *Toll Free Tel:* 800-493-7539 *Fax:* 317-774-3865 *Toll Free Fax:* 800-788-3535 *E-mail:* wph@wesleyan.org *Web Site:* www.wesleyan.org/wph, pg 278

Caffin, Honey Mae, University of British Columbia Press, 2029 West Mall, Vancouver, BC V6T 1Z2, Canada *Tel:* 604-822-5959 *Toll Free Tel:* 877-377-9378 *Fax:* 604-822-6083 *Toll Free Fax:* 800-668-0821 *E-mail:* frontdesk@ubcpress.ca *Web Site:* www.ubcpress.ca, pg 523

Caggiula, Sam, The Apex Press, 4501 Forbes Blvd, Suite 200, Lanham, MD 20706 *Tel:* 301-459-3366 *Toll Free Tel:* 800-462-6420 *Toll Free Fax:* 800-388-4450 *E-mail:* customercare@rowman.com, pg 20

Cahill, Brendan, Random House Inc, 1745 Broadway, New York, NY 10019 *Tel:* 212-782-9000 *Toll Free Tel:* 800-726-0600 *Web Site:* www.randomhouse.com, pg 213

Cahoon, Nancy Stauffer, Nancy Stauffer Associates, 30 Corbin Dr, Unit 1203, Darien, CT 06820 *Tel:* 203-202-2500 *E-mail:* staufferassoc@optonline.net *Web Site:* publishersmarketplace.com/members/nstauffer; staufferliterary.com, pg 595

Cain, Karen, Standard Publishing, 8805 Governors Hill Dr, Suite 400, Cincinnati, OH 45249 *Tel:* 513-931-4050 *Toll Free Tel:* 800-543-1353 *Fax:* 513-931-0950 *Toll Free Fax:* 877-867-5751 *E-mail:* customerservice@standardpub.com *Web Site:* www.standardpub.com, pg 242

Calamia, Joseph, Yale University Press, 302 Temple St, New Haven, CT 06511-8909 *Tel:* 401-531-2800 (cust serv); 203-432-0960 *Toll Free Tel:* 800-405-1619 (cust serv) *Fax:* 203-432-0948; 401-531-2801 (cust serv) *Toll Free Fax:* 800-406-9145 (cust serv) *E-mail:* customer.care@trilateral.org (cust serv); language.yalepress@yale.edu *Web Site:* www.yalebooks.com, pg 287

Calarco, Catherine, HeartMath LLC, 14700 W Park Ave, Boulder Creek, CA 95006 *Tel:* 831-338-8700 *Toll Free Tel:* 800-450-9111 *Fax:* 831-338-9861 *E-mail:* inquiry@heartmath.com *Web Site:* www.heartmath.com, pg 117

Calder, Kent, Texas State Historical Association, Stovall Hall 175, 1400 W Highland St, Denton, TX 76203 *Tel:* 940-369-5200 *Fax:* 940-369-5248 *Web Site:* www.tshaonline.org, pg 253

Caldwell, Amy, Beacon Press, 25 Beacon St, Boston, MA 02108 *Tel:* 617-742-2110 *Fax:* 617-723-3097; 617-742-2290 *Web Site:* www.beacon.org, pg 32

Caldwell, Linda, The Writers' Colony at Dairy Hollow, 515 Spring St, Eureka Springs, AR 72632 *Tel:* 479-253-7444 *Fax:* 479-253-9859 *E-mail:* director@writerscolony.org *Web Site:* www.writerscolony.org, pg 675

Caldwell, Madeline, Alfred A Knopf/Everyman's Library, c/o Random House Inc, 1745 Broadway, New York, NY 10019 *Tel:* 212-751-2600 *Toll Free Tel:* 800-638-6460 *Fax:* 212-572-2593 *Web Site:* www.knopfdoubleday.com, pg 141

Calhoun, Arlene S, American Biographical Institute, 5126 Bur Oak Circle, Raleigh, NC 27612 *Tel:* 919-781-8710 *Fax:* 919-781-8712 *E-mail:* abiinfo@abiworldwide.com *Web Site:* www.abiworldwide.com, pg 11

Calicchio, Rosemary, William H Sadlier Inc, 9 Pine St, New York, NY 10005 *Tel:* 212-227-2120 *Toll Free Tel:* 800-221-5175 (cust serv) *Fax:* 212-312-6080 *Web Site:* www.sadlier.com, pg 223

Calistro, Paddy, Angel City Press, 2118 Wilshire Blvd, Suite 880, Santa Monica, CA 90403 *Tel:* 310-395-9982 *Toll Free Tel:* 800-949-8039 *Fax:* 310-395-3353 *E-mail:* info@angelcitypress.com *Web Site:* www.angelcitypress.com, pg 18

Call, Jerry, Time Being Books, 10411 Clayton Rd, Suites 201-203, St Louis, MO 63131 *Tel:* 314-432-1771 *Fax:* 314-432-7939 *E-mail:* tbbooks@sbcglobal.net *Web Site:* www.timebeing.com, pg 255

Call, Pat, Wadsworth Publishing, 20 Davis Dr, Belmont, CA 94002 *Tel:* 650-595-2350 *Fax:* 650-592-3022 *Toll Free Fax:* 800-522-4923 *Web Site:* www.cengage.com, pg 276

Call, Susan, Jossey-Bass, One Montgomery St, Suite 1200, San Francisco, CA 94104 *Tel:* 415-433-1740 *Toll Free Tel:* 800-956-7739 *Fax:* 415-433-0499 (edit/mktg) *Web Site:* www.josseybass.com; www.pfeiffer.com, pg 137

Callahan, Alison, Doubleday/Nan A Talese, c/o Random House Inc, 1745 Broadway, New York, NY 10019 *Tel:* 212-751-2600 *Toll Free Tel:* 800-638-6460 *Fax:* 212-572-2593 *Web Site:* www.knopfdoubleday.com, pg 81

Callahan, Jack, McGraw-Hill Financial, 1221 Avenue of the Americas, 50th fl, New York, NY 10020 *Tel:* 212-512-2000 *Web Site:* www.mhfi.com, pg 161

Callahan, Kevin, HarperCollins General Books Group, 10 E 53 St, New York, NY 10022 *Tel:* 212-207-7000 *Fax:* 212-207-7633 *Web Site:* www.harpercollins.com, pg 113

Callahan, Laurie, New Directions Publishing Corp, 80 Eighth Ave, New York, NY 10011 *Tel:* 212-255-0230 *Fax:* 212-255-0231 *E-mail:* newdirections@ndbooks.com; editorial@ndbooks.com *Web Site:* ndbooks.com, pg 177

Callahan, Pat, University of South Carolina Press, 1600 Hampton St, Suite 544, Columbia, SC 29208 *Tel:* 803-777-5245 *Toll Free Tel:* 800-768-2500 (orders) *Fax:* 803-777-0160 *Toll Free Fax:* 800-868-0740 (orders) *Web Site:* www.sc.edu/uscpress, pg 269

Callahan, Tirzah, Cardweb.com Inc®, 999 Vanderbilt Beach Rd, 2nd fl, Naples, FL 34108 *Tel:* 239-325-5300 *Toll Free Tel:* 800-874-8999 *Fax:* 239-236-0835 *Toll Free Fax:* 800-821-4627 *E-mail:* cardservices@cardweb.com; cardstaff@cardweb.com *Web Site:* www.cardweb.com, pg 52

Callahan, William, Waxman Literary Agency, 80 Fifth Ave, Suite 1101, New York, NY 10011 *Tel:* 212-675-5556 *Fax:* 212-675-1381 *Web Site:* www.waxmanagency.com, pg 599

Callaway, MaryKatherine, Louisiana State University Press, 3990 W Lakeshore Dr, Baton Rouge, LA 70808 *Tel:* 225-578-6666 *Fax:* 225-578-6461 *E-mail:* lsupress@lsu.edu *Web Site:* lsupress.org, pg 153

Callery, Maryann, Plowshare Media, 405 Vincente Way, La Jolla, CA 92037 *E-mail:* sales@plowsharemedia.com *Web Site:* plowsharemedia.com, pg 203

Callison, Richard, Random House Publishing Group, 1745 Broadway, New York, NY 10019 *Toll Free Tel:* 800-200-3552 *Web Site:* atrandom.com, pg 214

Calvo, Roque J, The Electrochemical Society (ECS), 65 S Main St, Bldg D, Pennington, NJ 08534-2839 *Tel:* 609-737-1902 *Fax:* 609-737-2743 *E-mail:* ecs@electrochem.org *Web Site:* www.electrochem.org, pg 86

Camardi, Ben, Harold Matson Co Inc, 276 Fifth Ave, New York, NY 10001 *Tel:* 212-679-4490 *Fax:* 212-545 1224, pg 584

Cambell, Cloves Jr, National Newspaper Publishers Assn (NNPA), 1816 12 St NW, Washington, DC 20009 *Tel:* 202-588-8764 *Fax:* 202-588-8960 *E-mail:* info@blackpressusa.com; info@nnpa.org *Web Site:* www.nnpa.org; www.blackpressusa.com, pg 630

Cameron, Claire, Bull Publishing Co, PO Box 1377, Boulder, CO 80306 *Tel:* 303-545-6350 *Toll Free Tel:* 800-676-2855 *Fax:* 303-545-6354 *E-mail:* bullpublishing@msn.com *Web Site:* www.bullpub.com, pg 49

Cameron, Hamish, University of Toronto Press Inc, 10 Saint Mary St, Suite 700, Toronto, ON M4Y 2W8, Canada *Tel:* 416-978-2239 *Fax:* 416-978-4738 *E-mail:* utpbooks@utpress.utoronto.ca *Web Site:* www.utpress.utoronto.ca; www.utppublishing.com, pg 524

Cameron, Kimberley, Kimberley Cameron & Associates, 1550 Tiburon Blvd, Suite 704, Tiburon, CA 94920 *Tel:* 415-789-9191 *Fax:* 415-789-9177 *E-mail:* info@kimberleycameron.com *Web Site:* www.kimberleycameron.com, pg 579

Cameron, Laura, Flanker Press Ltd, 1243 Kenmount Rd, Unit A, Paradise, NL A1L 0V8, Canada *Tel:* 709-739-4477 *Toll Free Tel:* 866-739-4420 *Fax:* 709-739-4420 *E-mail:* info@flankerpress.com *Web Site:* www.flankerpress.com, pg 506

Cameron, Linda, University of Alberta Press, Ring House 2, Edmonton, AB T6G 2E1, Canada *Tel:* 780-492-3662 *Fax:* 780-492-0719 *Web Site:* www.uap.ualberta.ca, pg 522

Cameron, Shay, The University of Arizona Press, 355 S Euclid Ave, Suite 103, Tucson, AZ 85719-6654 *Tel:* 520-621-1441 *Toll Free Tel:* 800-426-3797 (orders) *Fax:* 520-621-8899 *Toll Free Fax:* 800-426-3797 *E-mail:* uap@uapress.arizona.edu *Web Site:* www.uapress.arizona.edu, pg 264

Cameron, Skyla Dawn, Mundania Press LLC, 6457 Glenway Ave, Suite 109, Cincinnati, OH 45211-5222 *Tel:* 513-490-2822 *Fax:* 513-598-9220 *Toll Free Fax:* 888-460-4752 *E-mail:* books@mundania.com; inquiry@mundania.com *Web Site:* www.mundania.com, pg 171

Camhi, Elaine, American Institute of Aeronautics & Astronautics, 1801 Alexander Bell Dr, Suite 500, Reston, VA 20191-4344 *Tel:* 703-264-7500 *Toll Free Tel:* 800-639-AIAA (639-2422) *Fax:* 703-264-7551 *E-mail:* custserv@aiaa.org *Web Site:* www.aiaa.org, pg 14

Campanella, Joseph, Amsco School Publications Inc, 315 Hudson St, New York, NY 10013-1085 *Tel:* 212-886-6500; 212-886-6565 *Toll Free Tel:* 800-969-8398 *Fax:* 212-675-7010 *E-mail:* info@amscopub.com *Web Site:* www.amscopub.com, pg 18

Campbell, Beth, BookEnds LLC, 136 Long Hill Rd, Gillette, NJ 07933 *Web Site:* www.bookends-inc.com, pg 563

Campbell, Bruce, Capital Enquiry Inc, 1034 Emerald Bay Rd, No 435, South Lake Tahoe, CA 96150 *Tel:* 916-442-1434 *Toll Free Tel:* 800-922-7486 *Fax:* 916-244-2704 *E-mail:* info@capenq.com *Web Site:* www.govbuddy.com, pg 51

Campbell, Colin G, The Colonial Williamsburg Foundation, PO Box 1776, Williamsburg, VA 23187-1776 *Tel:* 757-229-1000 *Toll Free Tel:* 800-HISTORY (447-8679) *Fax:* 757-220-7325 *E-mail:* cwres@cwf.org; geninfo@cwf.org *Web Site:* www.colonialwilliamsburg.org/publications, pg 64

Campbell, Jane, PRISM international Literary Non-Fiction Contest, University of British Columbia, Buch E462, 1866 Main Mall, Vancouver, BC V6T 1Z1, Canada *Tel:* 778-822-2514 *Fax:* 778-822-3616 *E-mail:* prismwritingcontest@gmail.com *Web Site:* www.prismmagazine.ca, pg 735

Campbell, Jane, PRISM international Poetry Contest, University of British Columbia, Buch E462, 1866 Main Mall, Vancouver, BC V6T 1Z1, Canada *Tel:* 778-822-2514 *Fax:* 778-822-3616 *E-mail:* prismwritingcontest@gmail.com *Web Site:* www.prismmagazine.ca, pg 736

Campbell, Jane, PRISM international Short Fiction Contest, University of British Columbia, Buch E462, 1866 Main Mall, Vancouver, BC V6T 1Z1, Canada *Tel:* 778-822-2514 *Fax:* 778-822-3616 *E-mail:* prismwritingcontest@gmail.com *Web Site:* www.prismmagazine.ca, pg 736

Campbell, Jennie, Water Resources Publications LLC, PO Box 630026, Highlands Ranch, CO 80163-0026 *Tel:* 720-873-0171 *Toll Free Tel:* 800-736-2405 *Fax:* 720-873-0173 *Toll Free Fax:* 800-616-1971 *E-mail:* info@wrpllc.com *Web Site:* www.wrpllc.com, pg 277

Campbell, Kristina, NASW Press, 750 First St NE, Suite 700, Washington, DC 20002 *Tel:* 202-408-8600 *Fax:* 203-336-8312 *E-mail:* press@naswdc.org *Web Site:* www.naswpress.org, pg 172

Campbell, Lakisha, BuilderBooks.com, 1201 15 St NW, Washington, DC 20005 *Tel:* 202-822-0200 *Toll Free Tel:* 800-223-2665 *Fax:* 202-266-8096 (edit) *E-mail:* builderbooks@nahb.com *Web Site:* www.builderbooks.com, pg 49

Campbell, Logan, Pearson Higher Education, One Lake St, Upper Saddle River, NJ 07458 *Tel:* 201-236-7000 *Fax:* 201-236-3381 *Web Site:* www.pearsonhighered.com, pg 196

Campbell, Marie, Transatlantic Agency, 2 Bloor St E, Ste 3500, Toronto, ON M4W-1A8, Canada *Tel:* 416-488-9214 *E-mail:* info@transatlanticagency.com *Web Site:* www.transatlanticagency.com, pg 597

Campbell, Marilyn A, Rutgers University Press, 106 Somerset St, 3rd fl, New Brunswick, NJ 08901 *Tel:* 858-445-7784 (edit); 848-445-7788 *Toll Free Tel:* 800-848-6224 (orders only) *Fax:* 732-745-4935 (acqs, edit, mktg, perms & prodn) *Toll Free Fax:* 800-272-6817 (fulfillment) *Web Site:* rutgerspress.rutgers.edu, pg 222

Campbell, Rick, Anhinga Press, PO Box 3665, Tallahassee, FL 32315 *Tel:* 850-442-1408 *Fax:* 850-442-6323 *E-mail:* info@anhinga.org *Web Site:* www.anhinga.org, pg 18

Campbell, Rick, Robert Dana-Anhinga Prize for Poetry, PO Box 3665, Tallahassee, FL 32315 *Tel:* 850-577-0745 *Fax:* 850-577-0745 *E-mail:* info@anhinga.org *Web Site:* www.anhinga.org, pg 699

Campbell, Thomas P, The Metropolitan Museum of Art, 1000 Fifth Ave, New York, NY 10028 *Tel:* 212-879-5500; 212-570-3725 *Fax:* 212-396-5062 *E-mail:* editorial@metmuseum.org *Web Site:* www.metmuseum.org, pg 165

Campfield, Charlene M, Campfield & Campfield Publishing, 6521 Cutler St, Philadelphia, PA 19126 *Toll Free Tel:* 888-518-2440 *Fax:* 215-224-6696 *E-mail:* info@campfieldspublishing.com *Web Site:* www.campfieldspublishing.com, pg 51

Campfield, Leon V Sr, Campfield & Campfield Publishing, 6521 Cutler St, Philadelphia, PA 19126 *Toll Free Tel:* 888-518-2440 *Fax:* 215-224-6696 *E-mail:* info@campfieldspublishing.com *Web Site:* www.campfieldspublishing.com, pg 51

Campi, Dr Alicia, The Mongolia Society Inc, Indiana University, 322 Goodbody Hall, 1011 E Third St, Bloomington, IN 47405-7005 *Tel:* 812-855-4078 *Fax:* 812-855-4078 *E-mail:* monsoc@indiana.edu *Web Site:* www.mongoliasociety.org, pg 169

Campion, Owen, Our Sunday Visitor Publishing, 200 Noll Plaza, Huntington, IN 46750 *Tel:* 260-356-8400 *Toll Free Tel:* 800-348-2440 (orders) *Fax:* 260-356-8472 *Toll Free Fax:* 800-498-6709 *E-mail:* osvbooks@osv.com (book orders) *Web Site:* www.osv.com, pg 188

Campo, Joan, Art of Living, PrimaMedia Inc, 1250 Bethlehem Pike, Suite 241, Hatfield, PA 19440 *Tel:* 215-660-5045 *Toll Free Tel:* 800-581-9020 *Fax:* 734-448-4125 *E-mail:* primamedia4@yahoo.com, pg 23

Campos, Alexander, The Center for Book Arts, 28 W 27 St, 3rd fl, New York, NY 10001 *Tel:* 212-481-0295 *Toll Free Fax:* 866-708-8994 *E-mail:* info@centerforbookarts.org *Web Site:* www.centerforbookarts.org, pg 621, 677

Canavan, Susan, Houghton Mifflin Harcourt Trade & Reference Division, 222 Berkeley St, Boston, MA 02116-3764 *Tel:* 617-351-5000 *Toll Free Tel:* 800-225-3362 *Web Site:* www.houghtonmifflinbooks.com, pg 124

Cancio, Jose, Periodical & Book Association of America Inc, 481 Eighth Ave, Suite 526, New York, NY 10001 *Tel:* 212-563-6502 *Fax:* 212-563-4098 *Web Site:* www.pbaa.net, pg 634

Candido, Arthur, Scholium International Inc, 151 Cow Neck Rd, Port Washington, NY 11050 *Tel:* 516-767-7171 *E-mail:* info@scholium.com *Web Site:* www.scholium.com, pg 229

Candido, Elena M, Scholium International Inc, 151 Cow Neck Rd, Port Washington, NY 11050 *Tel:* 516-767-7171 *E-mail:* info@scholium.com *Web Site:* www.scholium.com, pg 229

Canell, Pam, University of Washington Press, 433 Brooklyn Ave NE, Seattle, WA 98195-9570 *Tel:* 206-543-4050 *Toll Free Tel:* 800-537-5487 (orders) *Fax:* 206-543-3932; 410-516-6998 (orders) *E-mail:* uwpress@u.washington.edu *Web Site:* www.washington.edu/uwpress/, pg 270

Canfield, Doug, The Mountaineers Books, 1001 SW Klickitat Way, Suite 201, Seattle, WA 98134 *Tel:* 206-223-6303 *Toll Free Tel:* 800-553-4453 *Fax:* 206-223-6306 *Toll Free Fax:* 800-568-7604 *E-mail:* mbooks@mountaineersbooks.org *Web Site:* www.mountaineersbooks.org, pg 170

Canfield, Thomas, Starcrafts LLC, 334-A Calef Hwy, Epping, NH 03042 *Tel:* 603-734-4300 *Toll Free Tel:* 866-953-8458 (24 hr message ctr) *Fax:* 603-734-4311 *E-mail:* astrosales@astrocom.com; starcrafts@comcast.net *Web Site:* www.astrocom.com; starcraftspublishing.com; acspublications.com, pg 243

Cangelosi, Allegra, Northeast-Midwest Institute, 50 "F" St NW, Suite 950, Washington, DC 20001 *Tel:* 202-544-5200 *Fax:* 202-544-0043 *E-mail:* info@nemw.org *Web Site:* www.nemw.org, pg 181

Cannillo, Michelle, Herald Press, 1251 Virginia Ave, Harrisonburg, VA 22802-2434 *Toll Free Tel:* 800-245-7894 (orders-US); 800-999-3534; 800-631-6535 (orders-CN) *Toll Free Fax:* 877-271-0760 *E-mail:* info@MennoMedia.org *Web Site:* www.heraldpress.com; store.mennomedia.org, pg 118

Cannon, Chad, Thomas Nelson Inc, 501 Nelson Place, Nashville, TN 37214 *Tel:* 615-889-9000 *Toll Free Tel:* 800-251-4000 *Fax:* 615-902-1548 *E-mail:* publicity@thomasnelson.com *Web Site:* www.thomasnelson.com, pg 255

Cannon, Dolores, Ozark Mountain Publishing Inc, PO Box 754, Huntsville, AR 72740-0754 *Tel:* 479-738-2348 *Toll Free Tel:* 800-935-0045 *Fax:* 479-738-2448 *E-mail:* info@ozarkmt.com *Web Site:* www.ozarkmt.com, pg 190

Cannon, Pamela, Random House Publishing Group, 1745 Broadway, New York, NY 10019 *Toll Free Tel:* 800-200-3552 *Web Site:* atrandom.com, pg 214

Cannon, Tim, Houghton Mifflin Harcourt, 222 Berkeley St, Boston, MA 02116-3764 *Tel:* 617-351-5000 *Toll Free Tel:* 800-225-5425 (Pre-K-8); 800-462-6595 (6–12; Advanced & Electives); 800-289-4490 (Specialized Curriculum: Great Source, Rigby, Saxon, Steck-Vaughn; Homeschool; Adult Ed); 800-323-9540 (Assessment: Riverside Publishing); 888-391-3245 (SkillsTutor); 888-242-6747 option 2 (Destination Series; Classroom Connect; Earobics; Edmark; Learning Village; Riverdeep); 800-225-3362 (Houghton Mifflin Harcourt Trade & Reference Publishers); 800-225-5800 (Heinemann) *Fax:* 617-351-1125 *Web Site:* www.hmhco.com, pg 123

Canton, Alan N, Adams-Blake Publishing, 8041 Sierra St, Suite 102, Fair Oaks, CA 95628 *Tel:* 916-962-9296 *E-mail:* info@adams-blake.com *Web Site:* www.adams-blake.com, pg 5

Cantor, Carrie, Joelle Delbourgo Associates Inc, 101 Park St, Montclair, NJ 07042 *Tel:* 973-773-0836 (call only during standard business hours) *Web Site:* www.delbourgo.com, pg 568

Cantor, Jacqueline, Berkley Books, 375 Hudson St, New York, NY 10014 *Tel:* 212-366-2000 *Fax:* 212-366-2666 *E-mail:* online@penguinputnam.com *Web Site:* www.penguinputnam.com; us.penguingroup.com, pg 36

Cantor, Jacqueline, Berkley Publishing Group, 375 Hudson St, New York, NY 10014 *Tel:* 212-366-2000 *Fax:* 212-366-2385 *E-mail:* online@penguinputnam.com *Web Site:* us.penguingroup.com, pg 36

Canuel, Ron, Canadian Education Association/Association canadienne d'education, 119 Spadina Ave, Suite 702, Toronto, ON M5V 2L1, Canada *Tel:* 416-591-6300 *Toll Free Tel:* 866-803-9549 *Fax:* 416-591-5345 *E-mail:* info@cea-ace.ca *Web Site:* www.cea-ace.ca, pg 620

Canzoneri, Jennifer, BenBella Books Inc, 10300 N Central Expwy, Suite 400, Dallas, TX 75231 *Tel:* 214-750-3600 *Fax:* 214-750-3645 *E-mail:* feedback@benbellabooks.com *Web Site:* www.benbellabooks.com; www.smartpopbooks.com, pg 35

Caperton, Gaston, The College Board, 45 Columbus Ave, New York, NY 10023-6917 *Tel:* 212-713-8000 *Fax:* 212-713-8063 *Web Site:* www.collegeboard.com, pg 64

Capik, Gloria A, Paulist Press, 997 MacArthur Blvd, Mahwah, NJ 07430-9990 *Tel:* 201-825-7300 *Toll Free Tel:* 800-218-1903 *Fax:* 201-825-8345 *Toll Free Fax:* 800-836-3161 *E-mail:* info@paulistpress.com *Web Site:* www.paulistpress.com, pg 195

Caplan, David, Little, Brown Books for Young Readers, 237 Park Ave, New York, NY 10017 *Tel:* 212-364-1100 *Toll Free Tel:* 800-759-0190 (cust serv) *Web Site:* www.HachetteBookGroup.com, pg 150

Caplan, Susan, Columbia Publishing Course at Columbia University, 2950 Broadway, MC 3801, New York, NY 10027 *Tel:* 212-854-1898 *Fax:* 212-854-7618 *E-mail:* publishing@jrn.columbia.edu *Web Site:* www.journalism.columbia.edu/publishing, pg 677

Cappabianca, Rosemarie, McGraw-Hill Education, 2 Penn Plaza, New York, NY 10121-2298 *Tel:* 212-904-2000 *E-mail:* customer.service@mcgraw-hill.com *Web Site:* www.mheducation.com; www.mheducation.com/custserv.html, pg 160

Capps, Karen, Concordia Publishing House, 3558 S Jefferson Ave, St Louis, MO 63118-3968 *Tel:* 314-268-1000 *Toll Free Tel:* 800-325-3040 (cust serv) *Toll Free Fax:* 800-490-9889 (cust serv) *E-mail:* order@cph.org *Web Site:* www.cph.org, pg 66

Caprari, Gina, Davies Publishing Inc, 32 S Raymond Ave, Suites 4 & 5, Pasadena, CA 91105-1961 *Tel:* 626-792-3046 *Toll Free Tel:* 877-792-0005 *Fax:* 626-792-5308 *E-mail:* info@daviespublishing.com *Web Site:* daviespublishing.com, pg 75

Capron, Elise, Sandra Dijkstra Literary Agency, 1155 Camino del Mar, PMB 515, Del Mar, CA 92014-2605 *Web Site:* dijkstraagency.com, pg 568

Caras, Kathryn, Indiana University Press, 601 N Morton St, Bloomington, IN 47404-3797 *Tel:* 812-855-8817 *Toll Free Tel:* 800-842-6796 (orders only) *Fax:* 812-855-7931; 812-855-8507 *E-mail:* iupress@indiana.edu; iuporder@indiana.edu (orders) *Web Site:* www.iupress.indiana.edu, pg 129

Caratozzolo, Marie, Square One Publishers Inc, 115 Herricks Rd, Garden City Park, NY 11040 *Tel:* 516-535-2010 *Toll Free Tel:* 877-900-BOOK (900-2665) *Fax:* 516-535-2014 *E-mail:* sq1publish@aol.com *Web Site:* www.squareonepublishers.com, pg 242

Caratzas, Aristide D, Aristide D Caratzas, Publisher, PO Box 344H, Scarsdale, NY 10583 *Tel:* 914-725-4847 *Fax:* 914-725-4847 (call first) *E-mail:* contact@caratzas.com *Web Site:* www.caratzas.com, pg 52

Carbone, Becky, Para Publishing LLC, PO Box 8206-240, Santa Barbara, CA 93118-8206 *Tel:* 805-968-7277 *Toll Free Tel:* 800-727-2782 *Fax:* 805-968-1379 *Web Site:* www.parapublishing.com, pg 192

Carbone, Courtney, Random House Children's Books, 1745 Broadway, New York, NY 10019 *Tel:* 212-782-9000 *Toll Free Tel:* 800-200-3552 *Fax:* 212-782-9452 *Web Site:* randomhousekids.com, pg 213

Carbone, Linda, Words into Print, 131 Fifth Ave, Suite 501, New York, NY 10003 *Tel:* 212-741-1393 *Fax:* 419-441-1393 *E-mail:* query@wordsintoprint.org *Web Site:* www.wordsintoprint.org, pg 557

Carder, Sara, Jeremy P Tarcher, 375 Hudson St, New York, NY 10014 *Tel:* 212-366-2000 *E-mail:* online@penguinputnam.com *Web Site:* www.penguinputnam.com; us.penguingroup.com, pg 250

Cardona, Moses, John Hawkins & Associates Inc, 71 W 23 St, Suite 1600, New York, NY 10010 *Tel:* 212-807-7040 *Fax:* 212-807-9555 *E-mail:* jha@jhalit.com *Web Site:* jhalit.com, pg 576

Cardoza, Avery, Cardoza Publishing, 5473 S Eastern Ave, Las Vegas, NV 89119 *Tel:* 702-870-7200 *Toll Free Tel:* 800-577-WINS (577-9467) *Fax:* 702-822-6500 *E-mail:* cardozabooks@aol.com; info@cardozabooks.com *Web Site:* www.cardozabooks.com, pg 52

Carey, Jennifer, Mountain Press Publishing Co, 1301 S Third W, Missoula, MT 59801 *Tel:* 406-728-1900 *Toll Free Tel:* 800-234-5308 *Fax:* 406-728-1635 *E-mail:* info@mtnpress.com *Web Site:* www.mountain-press.com, pg 170

Carey, Mary Ann, Paulist Press, 997 MacArthur Blvd, Mahwah, NJ 07430-9990 *Tel:* 201-825-7300 *Toll Free Tel:* 800-218-1903 *Fax:* 201-825-8345 *Toll Free Fax:* 800-836-3161 *E-mail:* info@paulistpress.com *Web Site:* www.paulistpress.com, pg 195

Cargill, Noreen, Bread Loaf Writers' Conference, 5525 Middlebury College, 14 Old Chapel Rd, Middlebury, VT 05753 *Tel:* 802-443-5286 *Fax:* 802-443-2087 *E-mail:* blwc@middlebury.edu *Web Site:* www.middlebury.edu/blwc, pg 668

Cargill, Noreen, Fellowship & Scholarship Program for Writers, Middlebury College, Middlebury, VT 05753 *Tel:* 802-443-5286 *Fax:* 802-443-2087 *E-mail:* blwc@middlebury.edu *Web Site:* www.middlebury.edu/blwc, pg 703

Carispat, Gia, Art of Living, PrimaMedia Inc, 1250 Bethlehem Pike, Suite 241, Hatfield, PA 19440 *Tel:* 215-660-5045 *Toll Free Tel:* 800-581-9020 *Fax:* 734-448-4125 *E-mail:* primamedia4@yahoo.com, pg 22

Carkhuff, Robert W, HRD Press, 22 Amherst Rd, Amherst, MA 01002-9709 *Tel:* 413-253-3488 *Toll Free Tel:* 800-822-2801 *Fax:* 413-253-3490 *E-mail:* info@hrdpress.com; customerservice@hrdpress.com *Web Site:* www.hrdpress.com, pg 125

Carland-Adams, Bethany, F+W Media Inc, 10151 Carver Rd, Suite 200, Blue Ash, OH 45242 *Tel:* 513-531-2690 *Toll Free Tel:* 800-289-0963 (trade accts); 800-258-0929 (orders) *E-mail:* contact_us@fwmedia.com *Web Site:* www.fwmedia.com, pg 92

Carleo, John F, Industrial Press Inc, 989 Avenue of the Americas, 19th fl, New York, NY 10018 *Tel:* 212-889-6330 *Toll Free Tel:* 888-528-7852 *Fax:* 212-545-8327 *E-mail:* info@industrialpress.com *Web Site:* www.industrialpress.com, pg 129

Carlisle, Michael, InkWell Management, 521 Fifth Ave, 26th fl, New York, NY 10175 *Tel:* 212-922-3500 *Fax:* 212-922-0535 *E-mail:* info@inkwellmanagement.com; submissions@inkwellmanagement.com *Web Site:* inkwellmanagement.com, pg 577

Carlisle, Roy M, Independent Institute, 100 Swan Way, Oakland, CA 94621-1428 *Tel:* 510-632-1366 *Toll Free Tel:* 800-927-8733 *Fax:* 510-568-6040 *E-mail:* orders@independent.org *Web Site:* www.independent.org, pg 129

Carlson, Ann, Scott O'Dell Award for Historical Fiction, Hornbook, Suite 200, 56 Roland St, Boston, MA 02129 *Tel:* 617-628-8471 *Toll Free Tel:* 800-325-1170 *Web Site:* www.scottodell.com/odellaward.html, pg 730

Carlson, Bernadette, Gravure Association of America Inc, 8281 Pine Lake Rd, Denver, NC 28037 *Tel:* 201-523-6042 *Fax:* 201-523-6048 *E-mail:* gaa@gaa.org *Web Site:* www.gaa.org, pg 624

Carlson, Bernie, Edelstein Prize, Univ of Virginia, Dept of Science, Tech & Society, PO Box 400744, Charlottesville, VA 22904-4744 *Tel:* 434-987-6230 *Fax:* 434-975-2190 (attention: SHOT) *E-mail:* shot@virginia.edu *Web Site:* www.shot.jhu.edu, pg 701

Carlson, Bruce, Hearts & Tummies Cookbook Co, 3544 Blakslee St, Wever, IA 52658 *Tel:* 319-372-7480 *Toll Free Tel:* 800-571-2665 *Fax:* 319-372-7485 *E-mail:* quixotepress@gmail.com; heartsntummies@gmail.com *Web Site:* www.heartsntummies.com, pg 117

Carlson, Bruce, Quixote Press, 3544 Black St, Wever, IA 52658 *Tel:* 319-372-7480 *Toll Free Tel:* 800-571-2665 *Fax:* 319-372-7485 *E-mail:* heartsntummies@gmail.com; potpress@gmail.com, pg 212

Carlson, Carolyn, Viking, 375 Hudson St, New York, NY 10014 *Tel:* 212-366-2000 *E-mail:* online@penguinputnam.com *Web Site:* www.penguinputnam.com; us.penguingroup.com, pg 275

Carlson, Dale, Bick Publishing House, 16 Marion Rd, Branford, CT 06405 *Tel:* 203-208-5253 *Fax:* 203-208-5253 *E-mail:* bickpubhse@aol.com *Web Site:* www.bickpubhouse.com, pg 37

Carlson, Eydie, Epicenter Press Inc, 6524 NE 181 St, Suite 2, Kenmore, WA 98028 *Tel:* 425-485-6822 (edit, mktg, busn off) *Toll Free Tel:* 800-950-6663 (orders) *Fax:* 425-481-8253 *E-mail:* info@epicenterpress.com *Web Site:* www.epicenterpress.com, pg 89

Carlson, Greg, Linguistic Society of America, 1325 18 St NW, Suite 211, Washington, DC 20036-6501 *Tel:* 202-835-1714 *Fax:* 202-835-1717 *E-mail:* lsa@lsadc.org *Web Site:* www.linguisticsociety.org, pg 626

Carlson, Hannah, Bick Publishing House, 16 Marion Rd, Branford, CT 06405 *Tel:* 203-208-5253 *Fax:* 203-208-5253 *E-mail:* bickpubhse@aol.com *Web Site:* www.bickpubhouse.com, pg 37

Carlson, Jennifer, Dunow, Carlson & Lerner Literary Agency Inc, 27 W 20 St, Suite 1107, New York, NY 10011 *Tel:* 212-645-7606 *E-mail:* mail@dclagency.com *Web Site:* www.dclagency.com, pg 569

Carlson, John, Chronicle Books LLC, 680 Second St, San Francisco, CA 94107 *Tel:* 415-537-4200 *Toll Free Tel:* 800-759-0190 (cust serv) *Fax:* 415-537-4460 *Toll Free Fax:* 800-858-7787 (orders); 800-286-9471 (cust serv) *E-mail:* frontdesk@chroniclebooks.com *Web Site:* www.chroniclebooks.com, pg 61

Carlson, Linda, Parenting Press Inc, 11065 Fifth Ave NE, Suite F, Seattle, WA 98125 *Tel:* 206-364-2900 *Toll Free Tel:* 800-99-BOOKS (992-6657) *Fax:* 206-364-0702 *E-mail:* office@parentingpress.com; marketing@parentingpress.com *Web Site:* www.parentingpress.com, pg 193

Carlson, Lynn, Harper's Magazine Foundation, 666 Broadway, 11th fl, New York, NY 10012 *Tel:* 212-420-5720 *Toll Free Tel:* 800-444-4653 *Fax:* 212-228-5889 *E-mail:* harpers@harpers.org *Web Site:* www.harpers.org, pg 114

Carlson, Russ, Houghton Mifflin Harcourt, 222 Berkeley St, Boston, MA 02116-3764 *Tel:* 617-351-5000 *Toll Free Tel:* 800-225-5425 (Pre-K-8); 800-462-6595 (6–12; Advanced & Electives); 800-289-4490 (Specialized Curriculum: Great Source, Rigby, Saxon, Steck-Vaughn; Homeschool; Adult Ed); 800-323-9540 (Assessment: Riverside Publishing); 888-391-3245 (SkillsTutor); 888-242-6747 option 2 (Destination Series; Classroom Connect; Earobics; Edmark; Learning Village; Riverdeep); 800-225-3362 (Houghton Mifflin Harcourt Trade & Reference Publishers); 800-225-5800 (Heinemann) *Fax:* 617-351-1125 *Web Site:* www.hmhco.com, pg 123

Carlson, Stephen T, Upper Access Inc, 87 Upper Access Rd, Hinesburg, VT 05461 *Tel:* 802-482-2988 *Toll Free Tel:* 800-310-8320 *Fax:* 802-304-1005 *E-mail:* info@upperaccess.com *Web Site:* www.upperaccess.com, pg 272

Carman, Bill, International Development Research Centre (IDRC), 150 Kent St, Ottawa, ON K1P 0B2, Canada *Tel:* 613-236-6163 *Fax:* 613-238-7230 *E-mail:* info@idrc.ca *Web Site:* www.idrc.ca, pg 510

Carmen, Pamela, Callawind Publications Inc, 3551 Sainte Charles Blvd, Suite 179, Kirkland, QC H9H 3C4, Canada *Tel:* 514-685-9109 *E-mail:* info@callawind.com *Web Site:* www.callawind.com, pg 496

Carneal, Jeffrey J, Regnery Publishing Inc, One Massachusetts Ave NW, Washington, DC 20001 *Tel:* 202-216-0600 *Toll Free Tel:* 888-219-4747 *Fax:* 202-216-0612 *Web Site:* www.regnery.com, pg 217

Carney, Paul T, Fons Vitae, 49 Mockingbird Valley Dr, Louisville, KY 40207-1366 *Tel:* 502-897-3641 *Fax:* 502-893-7373 *E-mail:* fonsvitaeky@aol.com *Web Site:* www.fonsvitae.com, pg 97

Carola, Leslie, American Book Producers Association (ABPA), 151 W 19 St, 3rd fl, New York, NY 10011 *Tel:* 212-675-1363 *Fax:* 212-675-1364 *E-mail:* office@abpaonline.org *Web Site:* www.abpaonline.org, pg 612

Caron, Mia, La Courte Echelle, 5243 St Laurent Blvd, Montreal, QC H2T 1S4, Canada *Tel:* 514-274-2004 *Toll Free Tel:* 800-387-6192 (orders only) *Fax:* 514-270-4160 *Toll Free Fax:* 800-450-0391 (orders only) *E-mail:* info@courteechelle.com *Web Site:* www.courteechelle.com, pg 500

Carothers, Leslie, Environmental Law Institute, 2000 "L" St NW, Suite 620, Washington, DC 20036 *Tel:* 202-939-3800 *Fax:* 202-939-3868 *E-mail:* law@eli.org *Web Site:* www.eli.org, pg 89

Carpenter, Ken, Houghton Mifflin Harcourt Trade & Reference Division, 222 Berkeley St, Boston, MA 02116-3764 *Tel:* 617-351-5000 *Toll Free Tel:* 800-225-3362 *Web Site:* www.houghtonmifflinbooks.com, pg 124

Carpenter, Todd, National Information Standards Organization, One N Charles St, Suite 1905, Baltimore, MD 21201 *Tel:* 301-654-2512 *Toll Free Tel:* 866-957-1593 *Fax:* 410-685-5278 *E-mail:* nisohq@niso.org *Web Site:* www.niso.org, pg 175, 630

Carpio, Rose, The Pimlico Agency Inc, PO Box 20490, New York, NY 10017 *Tel:* 212-628-9729 *Fax:* 212-535-7861, pg 588

Carr, David, University of Manitoba Press, University of Manitoba, 301 St Johns College, Winnipeg, MB R3T 2M5, Canada *Tel:* 204-474-9495 *Fax:* 204-474-7566 *Web Site:* www.umanitoba.ca/uofmpress, pg 523

Carr, Gale, Parmenides Publishing, 3753 Howard Hughes Pkwy, Suite 200, Las Vegas, NV 89169 *Tel:* 702-892-3934 *Fax:* 702-892-3939 *E-mail:* info@parmenides.com *Web Site:* www.parmenides.com, pg 194

Carr, Julie, Counterpath Press, PO Box 18351, Denver, CO 80218 *E-mail:* editors@counterpathpress.org *Web Site:* www.counterpathpress.org, pg 69

Carr, Lloyd, New York City College of Technology, 300 Jay St, Brooklyn, NY 11201 *Tel:* 718-260-5500 *Fax:* 718-260-5198 *E-mail:* connect@citytech.cuny.edu *Web Site:* www.citytech.cuny.edu, pg 679

Carr, Rosalyn, University of Alabama Press, 200 Hackberry Lane, 2nd fl, Tuscaloosa, AL 35487 *Tel:* 205-348-5180 *Fax:* 205-348-9201 *Web Site:* www.uapress.ua.edu, pg 263

Carriere, Nicholle, Blue Bike Books, 11919 125 St, Edmonton, AB T5L 0S3, Canada *Tel:* 780-951-0032 *E-mail:* info@bluebikebooks.com *Web Site:* www.bluebikebooks.com, pg 495

Carrigan, Henry, Northwestern University Press, 629 Noyes St, Evanston, IL 60208-4210 *Tel:* 847-491-2046 *Toll Free Tel:* 800-621-2736 (orders only) *Fax:* 847-491-8150 *E-mail:* nupress@northwestern.edu *Web Site:* www.nupress.northwestern.edu, pg 181

Carrino, Taryn, American Independent Writers (AIW), 7817 Evening Lane, Alexandria, VA 22306 *Tel:* 703-660-9336 *Fax:* 703-660-9321 *E-mail:* info@amerindywriters.org *Web Site:* www.amerindywriters.org, pg 613

Carroll, Dennis, PhotoSource International, Pine Lake Farm, 1910 35 Rd, Osceola, WI 54020-5602 *Tel:* 715-248-3800 (ext 21) *Toll Free Tel:* 800-624-0266 (ext 21) *Fax:* 715-248-3800 *Toll Free Fax:* 800-223-3860 *E-mail:* info@photosource.com; psi2@photosource.com *Web Site:* www.photosource.com, pg 553

Carroll, Katie, Franciscan Media, 28 W Liberty St, Cincinnati, OH 45202 *Tel:* 513-241-5615 *Toll Free Tel:* 800-488-0488 *Fax:* 513-241-0399 *E-mail:* books@americancatholic.org *Web Site:* www.americancatholic.org, pg 98

Carroll, Kent, Europa Editions, 214 W 29 St, Suite 1003, New York, NY 10001 *Tel:* 212-868-6844 *Fax:* 212-868-6845 *E-mail:* info@europaeditions.com *Web Site:* www.europaeditions.com, pg 90

Carroll, Lisa, Allen A Knoll Publishers, 200 W Victoria St, 2nd fl, Suite A, Santa Barbara, CA 93101-3627 *Tel:* 805-564-3377 *Toll Free Tel:* 800-777-7623 *Fax:* 805-966-6657 *E-mail:* bookinfo@knollpublishers.com *Web Site:* www.knollpublishers.com, pg 141

Carroll, Mark T, ALI-ABA Continuing Professional Education, 4025 Chestnut St, Philadelphia, PA 19104 *Tel:* 215-243-1600 *Toll Free Tel:* 800-CLE-NEWS (253-6397) *Fax:* 215-243-1664; 215-243-1683 *Web Site:* www.ali-aba.org, pg 8

Carroll, Michael, The Edna Staebler Award for Creative Non-Fiction, Office of the Dean, Faculty of Arts, 75 University Ave W, Waterloo, ON N2L 3C5, Canada *Tel:* 519-884-1970 (ext 3891) *Fax:* 519-884-8854, pg 744

Carroll, Patrick, Princeton University Press, 41 William St, Princeton, NJ 08540-5237 *Tel:* 609-258-4900 *Toll Free Tel:* 800-777-4726 (orders) *Fax:* 609-258-6305 *Toll Free Fax:* 800-999-1958 *E-mail:* orders@cpfsinc.com *Web Site:* press.princeton.edu, pg 206

Carroll, Sydney, Sinauer Associates Inc, 23 Plumtree Rd, Sunderland, MA 01375 *Tel:* 413-549-4300 *Fax:* 413-549-1118 *E-mail:* publish@sinauer.com; orders@sinauer.com *Web Site:* www.sinauer.com, pg 236

Carroll Hackett, Mary, John Dos Passos Prize for Literature, Dept of English & Modern Languages, 201 High St, Farmville, VA 23909 *Tel:* 434-395-2155 (dept) *Fax:* 434-395-2200, pg 701

Carsch, R E, R E Carsch, MS-Consultant, 1453 Rhode Island St, San Francisco, CA 94107-3248 *Tel:* 415-641-1095 *E-mail:* recarsch@mzinfo.com, pg 542

Carson, Anne Conover, Anne Carson Associates, 3323 Nebraska Ave NW, Washington, DC 20016 *Tel:* 202-244-6679, pg 542

Carson, Carol, Alfred A Knopf/Everyman's Library, c/o Random House Inc, 1745 Broadway, New York, NY 10019 *Tel:* 212-751-2600 *Toll Free Tel:* 800-638-6460 *Fax:* 212-572-2593 *Web Site:* www.knopfdoubleday.com, pg 141

Carson, Cheryl, University of Tennessee Press, 110 Conference Center Bldg, 600 Henley St, Knoxville, TN 37996-4108 *Tel:* 865-974-3321 *Toll Free Tel:* 800-621-2736 (orders) *Fax:* 865-974-3724 *Toll Free Fax:* 800-621-8476 (orders) *E-mail:* custserv@utpress.org *Web Site:* www.utpress.org, pg 269

Carson, Dina C, Iron Gate Publishing, PO Box 999, Niwot, CO 80544 *Tel:* 303-530-2551 *Fax:* 303-530-5273 *E-mail:* editor@irongate.com; booknews@reunionsolutions.com *Web Site:* www.irongate.com; www.reunionsolutions.com, pg 134

Carson, Ken, Cengage Learning, 200 First Stamford Place, Suite 400, Stamford, CT 06902 *Tel:* 203-965-8600 *Toll Free Tel:* 800-354-9706 *Fax:* 203-965-8599 *Toll Free Fax:* 800-487-8488 *E-mail:* esales@cengage.com *Web Site:* www.cengage.com, pg 55

Carson, Dr Luke, ELS Editions, University of Victoria, Dept of English, Victoria, BC V8W 3W1, Canada *Tel:* 250-721-7236 *Fax:* 250-721-6498 *E-mail:* els@uvic.ca *Web Site:* english.uvic.ca/els, pg 504

Carstanjen, Lee Ann, Wayside Publishing, 11 Jan Sebastian Dr, Suite 5, Sandwich, MA 02563 *Tel:* 508-833-5096 *Toll Free Tel:* 888-302-2519 *Fax:* 508-833-6284 *E-mail:* wayside@sprintmail.com *Web Site:* www.waysidepublishing.com, pg 277

Carstens, Henry R, Carstens Publications Inc, 108 Phil Hardin Rd, Newton, NJ 07860 *Tel:* 973-383-3355 *Toll Free Tel:* 888-526-5365 *Fax:* 973-383-4064 *E-mail:* carstens@carstens-publications.com *Web Site:* www.carstens-publications.com, pg 53

Carswell, Christine, Chronicle Books LLC, 680 Second St, San Francisco, CA 94107 *Tel:* 415-537-4200 *Toll Free Tel:* 800-759-0190 (cust serv) *Fax:* 415-537-4460 *Toll Free Fax:* 800-858-7787 (orders); 800-286-9471 (cust serv) *E-mail:* frontdesk@chroniclebooks.com *Web Site:* www.chroniclebooks.com, pg 61

Carter, Dr Allyson, The University of Arizona Press, 355 S Euclid Ave, Suite 103, Tucson, AZ 85719-6654 *Tel:* 520-621-1441 *Toll Free Tel:* 800-426-3797 (orders) *Fax:* 520-621-8899 *Toll Free Fax:* 800-426-3797 *E-mail:* uap@uapress.arizona.edu *Web Site:* www.uapress.arizona.edu, pg 264

Carter, Anne, Palgrave Macmillan, 175 Fifth Ave, Suite 200, New York, NY 10010 *Tel:* 646-307-5151 *Fax:* 212-777-6359 *E-mail:* firstname.lastname@palgrave-usa.com *Web Site:* us.macmillan.com/Palgrave.aspx, pg 191

Carter, Brittany, Columbia Books & Information Services, 8120 Woodmont Ave, Suite 110, Bethesda, MD 20814 *Tel:* 202-464-1662 *Toll Free Tel:* 888-265-0600 (cust serv) *Fax:* 202-464-1775 *E-mail:* info@columbiabooks.com *Web Site:* www.columbiabooks.com; www.lobbyists.info; www.associationexecs.com, pg 65

Carter, Cherie, UnKnownTruths.com Publishing Co, 8815 Conroy Windermere Rd, Suite 190, Orlando, FL 32835 *Tel:* 407-929-9207 *Fax:* 407-876-3933 *E-mail:* info@unknowntruths.com *Web Site:* unknowntruths.com, pg 272

Carter, Deborah, Muse Literary Management, 189 Waverly Place, Unit 4, New York, NY 10014-3135 *Tel:* 212-925-3721 *E-mail:* museliterarymgmt@aol.com *Web Site:* www.museliterary.com; twitter.com/museliterary, pg 586

Carter, Jill, Crossway, 1300 Crescent St, Wheaton, IL 60187 *Tel:* 630-682-4300 *Toll Free Tel:* 800-635-7993 (orders); 800-543-1659 (cust serv) *Fax:* 630-682-4785 *E-mail:* info@crossway.org *Web Site:* www.crossway.org, pg 72

Carter, Laura, Guernica Editions Inc, 489 Strathmore Blvd, Toronto, ON M4C 1N8, Canada *Tel:* 416-576-9403 (orders & cust serv); 416-285-4067 (edit) *Fax:* 416-981-7606 *Web Site:* guernicaeditions.com, pg 508

Carvainis, Maria, Maria Carvainis Agency Inc, Rockefeller Center, 1270 Avenue of the Americas, Suite 2320, New York, NY 10020 *Tel:* 212-245-6365 *Fax:* 212-245-7196 *E-mail:* mca@mariacarvainisagency.com *Web Site:* mariacarvainisagency.com, pg 565

Carvalho, Julia, Chronicle Books LLC, 680 Second St, San Francisco, CA 94107 *Tel:* 415-537-4200 *Toll Free Tel:* 800-759-0190 (cust serv) *Fax:* 415-537-4460 *Toll Free Fax:* 800-858-7787 (orders); 800-286-9471 (cust serv) *E-mail:* frontdesk@chroniclebooks.com *Web Site:* www.chroniclebooks.com, pg 61

Carver, Holly, University of Iowa Press, 119 W Park Rd, 100 Kuhl House, Iowa City, IA 52242-1000 *Tel:* 319-335-2000 *Toll Free Tel:* 800-621-2736 (orders only) *Fax:* 319-335-2055 *Toll Free Fax:* 800-621-8476 (orders only) *E-mail:* uipress@uiowa.edu *Web Site:* www.uiowapress.org, pg 266

Casa, Delia, Allworth Press, 307 W 36 St, 11th fl, New York, NY 10018 *Tel:* 212-643-6816 *E-mail:* crawford@allworth.com *Web Site:* www.allworth.com, pg 9

Casal, Agustina, The Perseus Books Group, 387 Park Ave S, 12th fl, New York, NY 10016 *Tel:* 212-340-8100 *Toll Free Tel:* 800-343-4499 (cust serv) *Fax:* 212-340-8105 *Web Site:* www.perseusbooksgroup.com, pg 199

Casares, Oscar H, University of Texas at Austin, Creative Writing Program, Dept of English, PAR 108, One University Sta, Mailcode B5000, Austin, TX 78712-1164 *Tel:* 512-471-5132; 512-471-4991 *Fax:* 512-471-4909 *Web Site:* www.utexas.edu/cola/depts/english/creative-writing, pg 682

Casari, Stephen Cogil, SLC Enterprises Inc, 332 S Michigan Ave, No 1032-C216, Chicago, IL 60604 *Tel:* 616-942-2665 (answering serv & voice mail), pg 594

Cascardi, Andrea, Egmont USA, 443 Park Ave S, Suite 806, New York, NY 10016 *Tel:* 212-685-0102 *E-mail:* egmontusa@egmont.com *Web Site:* www.egmontusa.com, pg 86

Cascio, Laura, The Foundation Center, 79 Fifth Ave, New York, NY 10003-3076 *Tel:* 212-620-4230 *Toll Free Tel:* 800-424-9836 *Fax:* 212-807-3677 *E-mail:* order@foundationcenter.org *Web Site:* www.fdncenter.org; foundationcenter.org, pg 97

Casemore, Kristin, Ten Speed Press, 2625 Alcatraz Ave, Unit 505, Berkeley, CA 94705 *Tel:* 510-285-3000 *Toll Free Tel:* 800-841-BOOK (841-2665) *E-mail:* csorders@randomhouse.com *Web Site:* crownpublishing.com/imprint/ten-speed-press, pg 252

Casey, Adrianne, Channel Photographics, 980 Lincoln Ave, Suite 200-B, San Rafael, CA 94901 *Tel:* 415-456-2934 *Fax:* 415-456-4124 *Web Site:* www.channelphotographics.com, pg 58

Casey, Adrianne, Global Publishing, Sales & Distribution, 980 Lincoln Ave, Suite 200-B, San Rafael, CA 94901 *Tel:* 415-456-2934 *Fax:* 415-456-4124 *Web Site:* www.globalpsd.com, pg 104

Casey, Caroline, Coffee House Press, 79 13 Ave NE, Suite 110, Minneapolis, MN 55413 *Tel:* 612-338-0125 *Fax:* 612-338-4004 *Web Site:* www.coffeehousepress.org, pg 64

Casey, Maribeth, Storey Publishing LLC, 210 MASS MoCA Way, North Adams, MA 01247 *Tel:* 413-346-2100 *Toll Free Tel:* 800-441-5700 (orders); 800-793-9396 (edit) *Fax:* 413-346-2199; 413-346-2196 (edit) *E-mail:* sales@storey.com *Web Site:* www.storey.com, pg 246

Cash, Amy Opperman, Larson Publications, 4936 State Rte 414, Burdett, NY 14818 *Tel:* 607-546-9342 *Toll Free Tel:* 800-828-2197 *Fax:* 607-546-9344 *E-mail:* custserv@larsonpublications.com *Web Site:* www.larsonpublications.com, pg 144

Cash, Ellen, W H Freeman and Co, 41 Madison Ave, 37th fl, New York, NY 10010 *Tel:* 212-576-9400 *Fax:* 212-689-2383 *Web Site:* www.whfreeman.com, pg 99

Cash, Ellen, Worth Publishers, 41 Madison Ave, 37th fl, New York, NY 10010 *Tel:* 212-576-9400 *Fax:* 212-561-8281 *Web Site:* www.worthpub.com, pg 286

Cash, Mary, Holiday House Inc, 425 Madison Ave, New York, NY 10017 *Tel:* 212-688-0085 *Fax:* 212-421-6134 *E-mail:* holiday@holidayhouse.com *Web Site:* www.holidayhouse.com, pg 121

Cash, Susan L, Kent State University Press, 1118 University Library Bldg, 1125 Risman Dr, Kent, OH 44242 *Tel:* 330-672-7913; 419-281-1802 *Fax:* 330-672-3104 *E-mail:* ksupress@kent.edu *Web Site:* www.kentstateuniversitypress.com, pg 139

Cashman, Ann, The LA Literary Agency, PO Box 46370, Los Angeles, CA 90046 *Tel:* 323-654-5288 *E-mail:* laliteraryagency@mac.com; mail@laliteraryagency.com *Web Site:* www.laliteraryagency.com, pg 581

Caso, Adolf, Dante University of America Press Inc, PO Box 812158, Wellesley, MA 02482-0014 *Tel:* 781-235-3634 *Fax:* 781-790-1056 *E-mail:* danteu@danteuniversity.org *Web Site:* www.danteuniversity.org, pg 75

Caso, Adolph, Branden Books, PO Box 812094, Wellesley, MA 02482-0013 *Tel:* 781-235-3634 *E-mail:* branden@brandenbooks.com *Web Site:* www.brandenbooks.com, pg 45

Caso, Robert, Branden Books, PO Box 812094, Wellesley, MA 02482-0013 *Tel:* 781-235-3634 *E-mail:* branden@brandenbooks.com *Web Site:* www.brandenbooks.com, pg 45

Cason, Mary, Philadelphia Museum of Art, 2525 Pennsylvania Ave, Philadelphia, PA 19130 *Tel:* 215-684-7250 *Fax:* 215-235-8715 *Web Site:* www.philamuseum.org, pg 200

Cassanetti, Nico, Harry N Abrams Inc, 115 W 18 St, 6th fl, New York, NY 10011 *Tel:* 212-206-7715 *Toll Free Tel:* 800-345-1359 *Fax:* 212-519-1210 *E-mail:* abrams@abramsbooks.com *Web Site:* www.abramsbooks.com, pg 3

Cassell, Dana K, Florida Freelance Writers Association, 45 Main St, North Stratford, NH 03590 *Tel:* 603-922-8338 *Fax:* 603-922-8339 *E-mail:* ffwa@writers-editors.com; info@writers-editors.com *Web Site:* www.writers-editors.com; www.ffwamembers.com, pg 623

Cassell, Dana K, Writers-Editors Network International Writing Competition, 45 Main St, North Stratford, NH 03590 *Tel:* 603-922-8338 *Fax:* 603-922-8339 *E-mail:* contest@writers-editors.com *Web Site:* www.writers-editors.com; www.ffwamembers.com, pg 752

Cassels, John, NASW Press, 750 First St NE, Suite 700, Washington, DC 20002 *Tel:* 202-408-8600 *Fax:* 203-336-8312 *E-mail:* press@naswdc.org *Web Site:* www.naswpress.org, pg 172

Cassidy, Eileen D, Graphic Arts Education & Research Foundation (GAERF), 1899 Preston White Dr, Reston, VA 20191 *Tel:* 703-264-7200 *Toll Free Tel:* 866-381-9839 *Fax:* 703-620-3165 *E-mail:* gaerf@npes.org *Web Site:* www.gaerf.org, pg 641

Cassidy, John, Klutz, 450 Lambert Ave, Palo Alto, CA 94306 *Tel:* 650-857-0888 *Toll Free Tel:* 800-737-4123 *Fax:* 650-857-9110 *E-mail:* thefolks@klutz.com *Web Site:* www.klutz.com, pg 140

Cassidy, Kyran, HarperCollins Publishers, 10 E 53 St, New York, NY 10022 *Tel:* 212-207-7000 *Fax:* 212-207-7145 *Web Site:* www.harpercollins.com, pg 113

Cassidy, Lynda, UnKnownTruths.com Publishing Co, 8815 Conroy Windermere Rd, Suite 190, Orlando, FL 32835 *Tel:* 407-929-9207 *Fax:* 407-876-3933 *E-mail:* info@unknowntruths.com *Web Site:* unknowntruths.com, pg 272

Cassidy, Meg, Simon & Schuster, 1230 Avenue of the Americas, New York, NY 10020 *Tel:* 212-698-7000 *Toll Free Tel:* 800-223-2348 (cust serv); 800-223-2336 (orders) *Toll Free Fax:* 800-943-9831 (orders) *Web Site:* www.simonandschuster.com, pg 234

Cassity, Rebecca, Belltown Media, PO Box 980985, Houston, TX 77098 *Tel:* 713-344-1956 *Fax:* 713-583-7956 *E-mail:* subs@linuxjournal.com *Web Site:* www.belltownmedia.com, pg 34

Cassuccio, Chris, Westwood Creative Artists Ltd, 94 Harbord St, Toronto, ON M5S 1G6, Canada *Tel:* 416-964-3302 *Fax:* 416-975-9209 *E-mail:* wca_office@wcaltd.com *Web Site:* www.wcaltd.com, pg 599

Castellani, Mary Kate, Bloomsbury Publishing, 175 Fifth Ave, New York, NY 10010 *Tel:* 212-674-5151 *Toll Free Tel:* 800-221-7945 *Fax:* 212-780-0115; 212-982-2837 *E-mail:* marketingusa@bloomsbury.com; adultpublicityusa.@bloomsbury.com *Web Site:* www.bloomsbury.com, pg 40

Castellano, Giuseppe, Grosset & Dunlap, 345 Hudson St, New York, NY 10014 *Tel:* 212-366-2000 *E-mail:* online@penguinputnam.com *Web Site:* www.penguinputnam.com; us.penguingroup.com, pg 108

Castelli, Diego, Harlequin Enterprises Ltd, 225 Duncan Mill Rd, Don Mills, ON M3B 3K9, Canada *Tel:* 416-445-5860 *Toll Free Tel:* 888-432-4879; 800-370-5838 (ebook inquiries) *Fax:* 416-445-8655 *E-mail:* CustomerService@harlequin.com *Web Site:* www.harlequin.com, pg 508

Castiglia, Julie, Castiglia Literary Agency, 1155 Camino Del Mar, Suite 510, Del Mar, CA 92014 *Tel:* 858-755-8761 *Fax:* 858-755-7063 *Web Site:* www.castigliaagency.com, pg 566

Castignoli, Doreen, BPA Worldwide, 100 Beard Sawmill Rd, 6th fl, Shelton, CT 06484 *Tel:* 203-447-2800 *Fax:* 203-447-2900 *E-mail:* info@bpaww.com *Web Site:* www.bpaww.com, pg 619

Castillo, J, Multimedia Larga, 900 S Boardman Dr, No G72, Gallup, NM 87301 *Tel:* 505-726-1720, pg 171

Castillo, Johanna, Atria Books, 1230 Avenue of the Americas, New York, NY 10020 *Tel:* 212-698-7000 *Fax:* 212-698-7007 *Web Site:* www.simonandschuster.com, pg 26

Castle, John K, Castle Connolly Medical Ltd, 42 W 24 St, 2nd fl, New York, NY 10010 *Tel:* 212-367-8400 *Toll Free Tel:* 800-339-DOCS (339-3627) *Fax:* 212-367-0964 *Web Site:* www.castleconnolly.com, pg 54

Casto, James A, National Society of Newspaper Columnists (NSNC), 1345 Fillmore St, Suite 507, San Francisco, CA 94115 *Tel:* 415-488-NCNC (488-6762) *Toll Free Tel:* 866-440-NSNC (440-6762) *Fax:* 484-297-0336 *Toll Free Fax:* 866-635-5759 *E-mail:* staff@columnists.com *Web Site:* www.columnists.com, pg 631

Casto, James A, National Society of Newspaper Columnists Annual Conference, 1345 Fillmore St, Suite 507, San Francisco, CA 94115 *Tel:* 415-488-NCNC (488-6762) *Toll Free Tel:* 866-440-NSNC (440-6762) *Fax:* 484-297-0336 *Toll Free Fax:* 866-635-5759 *Web Site:* www.columnists.com, pg 671

Catalano, Kim, Galaxy Press, 7051 Hollywood Blvd, Suite 200, Hollywood, CA 90028 *Tel:* 323-466-7815 *Toll Free Tel:* 877-8GALAXY (842-5299) *E-mail:* customers@galaxypress.com *Web Site:* www.galaxypress.com, pg 100

Cater, David, Douglas & McIntyre, 2323 Quebec St, Suite 201, Vancouver, BC V5T 4S7, Canada *Tel:* 604-254-7191 *Toll Free Tel:* 800-667-6902 (orders) *Fax:* 604-254-9099 *Toll Free Fax:* 800-668-5788 (orders CN) *E-mail:* info@harbourpublishing.com, pg 501

Caulfield, Charlene, Wildflower Press, Oakbrook Press, 3301 S Valley Dr, Rapid City, SD 57703 *Tel:* 605-381-6385 *Fax:* 605-343-8733 *E-mail:* info@wildflowerpress.org; bookorder@wildflowerpress.org *Web Site:* www.wildflowerpress.org, pg 281

Cauti, Camille, Fine Communications, 322 Eighth Ave, 15th fl, New York, NY 10001 *Tel:* 212-595-3500 *Fax:* 212-595-3779, pg 95

Cauz, Jorge, Encyclopaedia Britannica Inc, 331 N La Salle St, Chicago, IL 60654 *Tel:* 312-347-7159 (all other countries) *Toll Free Tel:* 800-323-1229 (US & CN) *Fax:* 312-294-2104 *E-mail:* editor@eb.com *Web Site:* www.eb.com; www.britannica.com, pg 88

Cavallaro, Lenny, Janus Literary Agency, 201 Washington St, Groveland, MA 01834 *Tel:* 978-273-4227 *E-mail:* janusliteraryagency@gmail.com *Web Site:* janusliteraryagency.blogspot.com, pg 578

Cavanaugh, Molly, The Experiment, 260 Fifth Ave, Suite 3 South, New York, NY 10001-6425 *Tel:* 212-889-1659 *E-mail:* info@theexperimentpublishing.com *Web Site:* www.theexperimentpublishing.com, pg 91

Cavarretta, Joseph S, American Academy of Environmental Engineers, 130 Holiday Ct, Suite 100, Annapolis, MD 21401 *Tel:* 410-266-3311 *Fax:* 410-266-7653 *E-mail:* info@aaee.net *Web Site:* www.aaee.net, pg 10

Cavedon, Emily, Touchstone, 1230 Avenue of the Americas, New York, NY 10020, pg 257

Cavelos, Jeanne, Jeanne Cavelos Editorial Services, PO Box 75, Mont Vernon, NH 03057 *Tel:* 603-673-6234 *Web Site:* www.jeannecavelos.com, pg 543

Cavelos, Jeanne, Odyssey: The Summer Fantasy Writing Workshop, PO Box 75, Mont Vernon, NH 03057 *Tel:* 603-673-6234 *Fax:* 603-673-6234 *Web Site:* www.odysseyworkshop.org, pg 671

Cavenaugh, Drew, Frog Books, 2526 Martin Luther King Jr Way, Berkeley, CA 94704 *Tel:* 510-549-4270 *Toll Free Tel:* 800-733-3000 (book orders only) *Fax:* 510-549-4276 *Toll Free Fax:* 800-659-2436 (orders) *E-mail:* orders@northatlanticbooks.com *Web Site:* www.northatlanticbooks.com, pg 99

Ceballos, Kelly, League of Women Voters of the United States, 1730 "M" St NW, Suite 1000, Washington, DC 20036-4508 *Tel:* 202-429-1965 *Fax:* 202-429-0854; 202-429-4343 *E-mail:* lwv@lwv.org *Web Site:* www.lwv.org, pg 626

Cebik, Stephen, Yale University Press, 302 Temple St, New Haven, CT 06511-8909 *Tel:* 401-531-2800 (cust serv); 203-432-0960 *Toll Free Tel:* 800-405-1619 (cust serv) *Fax:* 203-432-0948; 401-531-2801 (cust serv) *Toll Free Fax:* 800-406-9145 (cust serv) *E-mail:* customer.care@trilateral.org (cust serv); language.yalepress@yale.edu *Web Site:* www.yalebooks.com, pg 287

Cecka, Melanie, Random House Children's Books, 1745 Broadway, New York, NY 10019 *Tel:* 212-782-9000 *Toll Free Tel:* 800-200-3552 *Fax:* 212-782-9452 *Web Site:* randomhousekids.com, pg 213

Cekola, Kim, Michigan Municipal League, 1675 Green Rd, Ann Arbor, MI 48105 *Tel:* 734-662-3246 *Toll Free Tel:* 800-653-2483 *Fax:* 734-663-4496 *Web Site:* www.mml.org, pg 165

Cella, Joe, MBI Publishing Co, 400 First Ave N, Suite 300, Minneapolis, MN 55401 *Toll Free Tel:* 800-328-0590 *Fax:* 612-344-8691 *E-mail:* trade@mbipublishing.com (US trade orders & sales) *Web Site:* www.qbookshop.com, pg 159

Centrello, Gina, Random House Inc, 1745 Broadway, New York, NY 10019 *Tel:* 212-782-9000 *Toll Free Tel:* 800-726-0600 *Web Site:* www.randomhouse.com, pg 213

Centrello, Gina, Random House Publishing Group, 1745 Broadway, New York, NY 10019 *Toll Free Tel:* 800-200-3552 *Web Site:* atrandom.com, pg 214

Cerbone, Will, Fordham University Press, 2546 Belmont Ave, University Box L, Bronx, NY 10458 *Tel:* 718-817-4795 *Fax:* 718-817-4785 *Web Site:* www.fordhampress.com, pg 97

Cercone, Philip, McGill-Queen's University Press, 1010 Sherbrooke W, Suite 1720, Montreal, QC H3A 2R7, Canada *Tel:* 514-398-3750 *Fax:* 514-398-4333 *E-mail:* mqup@mqup.ca *Web Site:* www.mqup.ca, pg 512

Cerruti, Laura, University of California Press, 2120 Berkeley Way, Berkeley, CA 94704-1012 *Tel:* 510-642-4247 *Fax:* 510-643-7127 *E-mail:* askucp@ucpress.edu (books); customerservice@ucpressjournals.com (journals) *Web Site:* www.ucpress.edu, pg 264

Cerullo, John, Amadeus Press/Hal Leonard Performing Arts Publishing Group, 33 Plymouth St, Suite 302, Montclair, NJ 07042 *Tel:* 973-337-5034 *Toll Free Tel:* 800-524-4425 *E-mail:* info@halleonardbooks.com *Web Site:* www.amadeuspress.com; www.halleonardbooks.com, pg 10

Cerullo, John, Applause Theatre & Cinema Books, 33 Plymouth St, Suite 302, Montclair, NJ 07042 *Tel:* 973-337-5034 *Toll Free Tel:* 800-637-2852 *Fax:* 973-337-5227 *E-mail:* info@applausepub.com *Web Site:* www.applausepub.com, pg 20

Cerullo, John, Backbeat Books, 33 Plymouth St, Suite 302, Montclair, NJ 07042 *Tel:* 973-337-5034 *Toll Free Tel:* 800-637-2852 (Music Dispatch) *Fax:* 973-337-5227 *Web Site:* www.backbeatbooks.com, pg 29

Cerullo, John, Hal Leonard Books, 33 Plymouth St, Suite 302, Montclair, NJ 07042 *Tel:* 973-337-5034 *Fax:* 973-337-5227, pg 110

Cerullo, John, Limelight Editions, 33 Plymouth St, Suite 302, Montclair, NJ 07042 *Tel:* 973-337-5034 *Fax:* 973-337-5227 *Web Site:* limelighteditions.com, pg 149

Chaban, Enid, Random House Children's Books, 1745 Broadway, New York, NY 10019 *Tel:* 212-782-9000 *Toll Free Tel:* 800-200-3552 *Fax:* 212-782-9452 *Web Site:* randomhousekids.com, pg 213

Chacon, Daniel, University of Texas at El Paso, Dept Creative Writing, MFA/Dept Creative Writing, Liberal Arts 415 UTEP, 500 W University Ave, El Paso, TX 79968-9991 *Tel:* 915-747-5713 *Fax:* 915-747-5523 *Web Site:* www.utep.edu/cw, pg 682

Chadwell, Fay, Oregon State University Press, 121 The Valley Library, Corvallis, OR 97331-4501 *Tel:* 541-737-3166 *Toll Free Tel:* 800-621-2736 (orders) *Fax:* 541-737-3170 *Toll Free Fax:* 800-426-3797 (orders) *E-mail:* osu.press@oregonstate.edu *Web Site:* oregonstate.edu/dept/press; osupress.oregonstate.edu, pg 187

Chadwick, Clare, Lonely Planet, 150 Linden St, Oakland, CA 94607 *Tel:* 510-893-8555 *Toll Free Tel:* 800-275-8555 (orders) *Fax:* 510-893-8563 *E-mail:* info@lonelyplanet.com *Web Site:* www.lonelyplanet.com, pg 152

Chait, Mark, HarperCollins General Books Group, 10 E 53 St, New York, NY 10022 *Tel:* 212-207-7000 *Fax:* 212-207-7633 *Web Site:* www.harpercollins.com, pg 113

Chalfant, Sarah, The Wylie Agency Inc, 250 W 57 St, Suite 2114, New York, NY 10107 *Tel:* 212-246-0069 *Fax:* 212-586-8953 *E-mail:* mail@wylieagency.com *Web Site:* www.wylieagency.com, pg 600

Chalifoux, Ed, Printing Industry Association of the South, 305 Plus Park Blvd, Nashville, TN 37217 *Tel:* 615-366-1094 *Toll Free Tel:* 800-821-3138 *Fax:* 615-366-4192 *E-mail:* info@pias.org *Web Site:* www.pias.org, pg 634

Chalker, Bob, NACE International, 1440 S Creek Dr, Houston, TX 77084-4906 *Tel:* 281-228-6200 *Toll Free Tel:* 800-797-NACE (797-6223) *Fax:* 281-228-6300 *E-mail:* firstservice@nace.org *Web Site:* www.nace.org, pg 172

Challender, Gary, Books In Motion, 9922 E Montgomery, Suite 31, Spokane Valley, WA 99206 *Tel:* 509-922-1646 *Toll Free Tel:* 800-752-3199 *Fax:* 509-922-1445 *E-mail:* info@booksinmotion.com *Web Site:* booksinmotion.biz, pg 44

Challice, John, Oxford University Press USA, 198 Madison Ave, New York, NY 10016 *Tel:* 212-726-6000 *Toll Free Tel:* 800-451-7556 (orders); 800-445-9714 (cust serv) *Fax:* 919-677-1303 *E-mail:* custserv.us@oup.com *Web Site:* www.oup.com/us, pg 189

Challman, Roger, TRISTAN Publishing, 2355 Louisiana Ave, Minneapolis, MN 55427 *Tel:* 763-545-1383 *Toll Free Tel:* 866-545-1383 *Fax:* 763-545-1387 *E-mail:* info@tristanpublishing.com *Web Site:* www.tristanpublishing.com, pg 259

Chambers, Andrea L, New York University, Center for Publishing, Midtown Ctr, Rm 429, 11 W 42 St, New York, NY 10036 *Tel:* 212-992-3232 *Fax:* 212-992-3233 *E-mail:* pub.center@nyu.edu *Web Site:* www.scps.nyu.edu/publishing, pg 679

Chambers, Bonita, A Cappela Publishing, PO Box 3691, Sarasota, FL 34230-3691 *Tel:* 941-351-2050 *Fax:* 941-351-4735 *E-mail:* acappub@aol.com *Web Site:* www.acappela.com, pg 1

Chambers, Lewis R, Bethel Agency, PO Box 21043, Park West Sta, New York, NY 10025 *Tel:* 212-864-4510, pg 562

Chambliss, Thom, Pacific Northwest Book Awards, 338 W 11 Ave, Unit 108, Eugene, OR 97401 *Tel:* 541-683-4363 *Fax:* 541-683-3910 *E-mail:* info@pnba.org *Web Site:* www.pnba.org, pg 731

Chambliss, Thom, Pacific Northwest Booksellers Association, 338 W 11 Ave, Unit 108, Eugene, OR 97401 *Tel:* 541-683-4363 *Fax:* 541-683-3910 *E-mail:* info@pnba.org *Web Site:* www.pnba.org; www.northwestbooklovers.org (public site), pg 633

Chamichian, Ani, The Experiment, 260 Fifth Ave, Suite 3 South, New York, NY 10001-6425 *Tel:* 212-889-1659 *E-mail:* info@theexperimentpublishing.com *Web Site:* www.theexperimentpublishing.com, pg 91

Chan, Ellen, Gallery Books, 1230 Avenue of the Americas, New York, NY 10020 *Toll Free Tel:* 800-456-6798 *Fax:* 212-698-7284 *E-mail:* consumer.customerservice@simonandschuster.com *Web Site:* www.simonsays.com, pg 101

Chan, Wayne, National Society of Newspaper Columnists (NSNC), 1345 Fillmore St, Suite 507, San Francisco, CA 94115 *Tel:* 415-488-NCNC (488-6762) *Toll Free Tel:* 866-440-NSNC (440-6762) *Fax:* 484-297-0336 *Toll Free Fax:* 866-635-5759 *E-mail:* staff@columnists.com *Web Site:* www.columnists.com, pg 631

Chan, Wayne, National Society of Newspaper Columnists Annual Conference, 1345 Fillmore St, Suite 507, San Francisco, CA 94115 *Tel:* 415-488-NCNC (488-6762) *Toll Free Tel:* 866-440-NSNC (440-6762) *Fax:* 484-297-0336 *Toll Free Fax:* 866-635-5759 *Web Site:* www.columnists.com, pg 671

Chanda, Justin, Simon & Schuster Children's Publishing, 1230 Avenue of the Americas, New York, NY 10020 *Tel:* 212-698-7000 *Web Site:* KIDS.SimonandSchuster.com; TEEN.SimonandSchuster.com; simonandschuster.net; simonandschuster.biz, pg 235

Chandlee, Chad M, Kendall/Hunt Publishing Co, 4050 Westmark Dr, Dubuque, IA 52002-2624 *Tel:* 563-589-1000 *Toll Free Tel:* 800-228-0810 (orders) *Fax:* 563-589-1046 *Toll Free Fax:* 800-772-9165 *E-mail:* orders@kendallhunt.com *Web Site:* www.kendallhunt.com, pg 139

Chandler, Beth, University of Missouri Press, 2910 Le Mone Blvd, Columbia, MO 65201 *Tel:* 573-882-7641 *Toll Free Tel:* 800-621-2736 (orders) *Fax:* 573-884-4498 *Web Site:* press.umsystem.edu, pg 267

Chandler, Christine, American Society of Media Photographers (ASMP), 150 N Second St, Philadelphia, PA 19106 *Tel:* 215-451-2767 *Fax:* 215-451-0880 *E-mail:* info@asmp.org *Web Site:* www.asmp.org, pg 614

Chaney, Margo, University of Illinois Press, 1325 S Oak St, MC-566, Champaign, IL 61820-6903 *Tel:* 217-333-0950 *Fax:* 217-244-8082 *E-mail:* uipress@uillinois.edu; journals@uillinois.edu *Web Site:* www.press.uillinois.edu, pg 266

Chang, Eleanor, American Booksellers Association, 333 Westchester Ave, Suite S202, White Plains, NY 10604 *Tel:* 914-406-7500 *Toll Free Tel:* 800-637-0037 *Fax:* 914-410-6297 *E-mail:* info@bookweb.org *Web Site:* www.bookweb.org, pg 612

Chang, Lan Samantha, The Iowa Short Fiction Award, 102 Dey House, 507 N Clinton St, Iowa City, IA 52242-1000 *Tel:* 319-335-0416 *Fax:* 319-335-0420 *Web Site:* www.uiowapress.org/authors/iowa-short-fiction.htm, pg 713

Chang, Lan Samantha, University of Iowa, Writer's Workshop, 102 Dey House, 507 N Clinton St, Iowa City, IA 52242-1000 *Tel:* 319-335-0416 *Fax:* 319-335-0420, pg 747

Chang, Lan Samantha, University of Iowa, Writers' Workshop, Graduate Creative Writing Program, 102 Dey House, 507 N Clinton St, Iowa City, IA 52242-1000 *Tel:* 319-335-0416 *Fax:* 319-335-0420 *Web Site:* www.uiowa.edu/~iww, pg 681

Chang, Melanie, Little, Brown Books for Young Readers, 237 Park Ave, New York, NY 10017 *Tel:* 212-364-1100 *Toll Free Tel:* 800-759-0190 (cust serv) *Web Site:* www.HachetteBookGroup.com, pg 150

Chang, Ms Minju, BookStop Literary Agency LLC, 67 Meadow View Rd, Orinda, CA 94563 *E-mail:* info@bookstopliterary.com *Web Site:* www.bookstopliterary.com, pg 563

Chapin, Amy, Avery Color Studios, 511 "D" Ave, Gwinn, MI 49841 *Tel:* 906-346-3908 *Toll Free Tel:* 800-722-9925 *Fax:* 906-346-3015 *E-mail:* averycolor@averycolorstudios.com, pg 28

Chapin, Frances, Write on the Sound Writers' Conference, 700 Main St, Edmonds, WA 98020 *Tel:* 425-771-0228 *Fax:* 425-771-0253 *E-mail:* wots@ci.edmonds.wa.us *Web Site:* www.edmondswa.gov, pg 674

Chapin, Wells, Avery Color Studios, 511 "D" Ave, Gwinn, MI 49841 *Tel:* 906-346-3908 *Toll Free Tel:* 800-722-9925 *Fax:* 906-346-3015 *E-mail:* averycolor@averycolorstudios.com, pg 28

Chaplin, Candice, Crown Publishing Group, c/o Random House Inc, 1745 Broadway, New York, NY 10019 *Tel:* 212-782-9000 *Toll Free Tel:* 888-264-1745 *Fax:* 212-940-7408 *Web Site:* www.randomhouse.com/crown, pg 72

Chaplin, Karen, HarperCollins Children's Books, 10 E 53 St, New York, NY 10022 *Tel:* 212-207-7000 *Web Site:* www.harpercollinschildrens.com, pg 113

Chapman, Guy, Kensington Publishing Corp, 119 W 40 St, New York, NY 10018 *Tel:* 212-407-1500 *Toll Free Tel:* 800-221-2647 *Fax:* 212-935-0699 *Web Site:* www.kensingtonbooks.com, pg 139

Chapman, Ian, Simon & Schuster, Inc, 1230 Avenue of the Americas, New York, NY 10020 *Tel:* 212-698-7000 *Fax:* 212-698-7007 *E-mail:* firstname.lastname@simonandschuster.com *Web Site:* www.simonandschuster.com, pg 235

Chapman, Jim, Houghton Mifflin Harcourt K-12 Publishers, 222 Berkeley St, Boston, MA 02116-3764 *Tel:* 617-351-5000 *Toll Free Tel:* 800-225-5425 (cust serv) *Web Site:* www.hmhco.com; www.hmheducation.com, pg 123

Chapman, Kathy, James Lorimer & Co Ltd, Publishers, 317 Adelaide St W, Suite 1002, Toronto, ON M5V 1P9, Canada *Tel:* 416-362-4762 *Fax:* 416-362-3939 *Web Site:* www.lorimer.ca, pg 511

Chapman, Natalie, Houghton Mifflin Harcourt Trade & Reference Division, 222 Berkeley St, Boston, MA 02116-3764 *Tel:* 617-351-5000 *Toll Free Tel:* 800-225-3362 *Web Site:* www.houghtonmifflinbooks.com, pg 124

Chappell, Gary, Nightingale-Conant, 6245 W Howard St, Niles, IL 60714 *Tel:* 847-647-0306 *Toll Free Tel:* 800-572-2770; 800-557-1660 (sales); 800-560-6081 (cust serv) *Fax:* 847-647-7145; 847-647-9143 (sales) *E-mail:* distributordivision@nightingale.com (orders) *Web Site:* www.nightingale.com, pg 179

Chappell, John, PreMediaGlobal, 4 Collins Ave, Plymouth, MA 02360 *Tel:* 508-746-0300 *Fax:* 508-746-3233 *E-mail:* info@premediaglobal.com *Web Site:* www.premediaglobal.com, pg 553

Chard, Lynn P, Institute of Continuing Legal Education, 1020 Greene St, Ann Arbor, MI 48109-1444 *Tel:* 734-764-0533 *Toll Free Tel:* 877-229-4350 *Fax:* 734-763-2412 *Toll Free Fax:* 877-229-4351 *E-mail:* icle@umich.edu *Web Site:* www.icle.org, pg 131

Charette, Francois, Livres Canada Books, One Nicholas, Suite 504, Ottawa, ON K1N 7B7, Canada *Tel:* 613-562-2324 *Fax:* 613-562-2329 *E-mail:* aecb@aecb.org; info@livrescanadabooks.com *Web Site:* www.aecb.org; www.livrescanadabooks.com, pg 626

Charette, Luc, The Lieutenant-Governor's Awards for High Achievement in the Arts, 61 Carleton St, Fredericton, NB E3B 3T2, Canada *Tel:* 506-444-4444 *Toll Free Tel:* 866-460-ARTS (460-2787) *Fax:* 506-444-5543 *E-mail:* nbabcanb@artsnb.ca *Web Site:* www.artsnb.ca, pg 717

Charkin, Richard, Bloomsbury Publishing, 175 Fifth Ave, New York, NY 10010 *Tel:* 212-674-5151 *Toll Free Tel:* 800-221-7945 *Fax:* 212-780-0115; 212-982-2837 *E-mail:* marketingusa@bloomsbury.com; adultpublicityusa.@bloomsbury.com *Web Site:* www.bloomsbury.com, pg 40

Charlebois, Sean, Crabtree Publishing Co, 350 Fifth Ave, 59th fl, PMB 59051, New York, NY 10118 *Tel:* 212-496-5040 *Toll Free Tel:* 800-387-7650 *Toll Free Fax:* 800-355-7166 *E-mail:* custserv@crabtreebooks.com *Web Site:* www.crabtreebooks.com, pg 70

Charlebois, Sean, Crabtree Publishing Co Ltd, 616 Welland Ave, St Catharines, ON L2M-5V6, Canada *Tel:* 905-682-5221 *Toll Free Tel:* 800-387-7650 *Fax:* 905-682-7166 *Toll Free Fax:* 800-355-7166 *E-mail:* custserv@crabtreebooks.com; sales@crabtreebooks.com; orders@crabtreebooks.com *Web Site:* www.crabtreebooks.com, pg 500

Charles, Kristi, National Resource Center for Youth Services (NRCYS), Schusterman Ctr, Bldg 4W, 4502 E 41 St, Tulsa, OK 74135-2512 *Tel:* 918-660-3700 *Toll Free Tel:* 800-274-2687 *Fax:* 918-660-3737 *Web Site:* www.nrcys.ou.edu, pg 176

Charlip, Christine, ASM Press, 1752 "N" St NW, Washington, DC 20036-2904 *Tel:* 202-737-3600 *Toll Free Tel:* 800-546-2416 *Fax:* 202-942-9342 *E-mail:* books@asmusa.org *Web Site:* estore.asm.org, pg 25

Charner, Kathleen, Gryphon House Inc, 10770 Columbia Pike, Suite 201, Silver Spring, MD 20901 *Tel:* 301-595-9500 *Toll Free Tel:* 800-638-0928 *Fax:* 301-595-0051 *Toll Free Fax:* 877-638-7576 *E-mail:* info@ghbooks.com *Web Site:* www.gryphonhouse.com, pg 109

Charney, Jean, Rocky Mountain Publishing Professionals Guild (RMPPG), PO Box 19013, Boulder, CO 80308 *E-mail:* membership@rmppg.org *Web Site:* thepublishingpros.org, pg 635

Charters, Lisa, Doubleday Canada, One Toronto St, Suite 300, Toronto, ON M5C 2V6, Canada *Tel:* 416-364-4449 *Fax:* 416-364-6863 *Web Site:* www.randomhouse.ca, pg 501

Charters, Lisa, Kids Can Press Ltd, 25 Dockside Dr, Toronto, ON M5A 0B5, Canada *Tel:* 416-479-7000 *Toll Free Tel:* 800-265-0884 *Fax:* 416-960-5437 *E-mail:* info@kidscan.com; customerservice@kidscan.com *Web Site:* www.kidscanpress.com; www.kidscanpress.ca, pg 510

Charters, Lisa, Knopf Random Canada, One Toronto St, Suite 300, Toronto, ON M5C 2V6, Canada *Tel:* 416-364-4449 *Toll Free Tel:* 888-523-9292 *Fax:* 416-364-6863 *Web Site:* www.randomhouse.ca, pg 510

Chasan, Gail, Harlequin Enterprises Ltd, 233 Broadway, Suite 1001, New York, NY 10279 *Tel:* 212-553-4200 *Fax:* 212-227-8969 *E-mail:* CustomerService@harlequin.com *Web Site:* www.harlequin.com, pg 112

Chase, Ron, Incentive Publications Inc, 2400 Crestmoor Rd, Suite 211, Nashville, TN 37215 *Tel:* 615-385-2934 *Toll Free Tel:* 800-421-2830 *Fax:* 615-385-2967 *E-mail:* comments@incentivepublications.com *Web Site:* www.incentivepublications.com, pg 128

Chase, Shelley, Mi'kmaq-Maliseet Institute, University of New Brunswick, Rm 343, Marshall d'Avray Hall, 10 MacKay Dr, Fredericton, NB E3B 5A3, Canada *Tel:* 506-453-4840 *Fax:* 506-453-4784 *E-mail:* micmac@unb.ca *Web Site:* www.unb.ca; www.unb.ca/fredericton/education/mmi, pg 512

Chatterjee, Jaya Aninda, Yale University Press, 302 Temple St, New Haven, CT 06511-8909 *Tel:* 401-531-2800 (cust serv); 203-432-0960 *Toll Free Tel:* 800-405-1619 (cust serv) *Fax:* 203-432-0948; 401-531-2801 (cust serv) *Toll Free Fax:* 800-406-9145 (cust serv) *E-mail:* customer.care@trilateral.org (cust serv); language.yalepress@yale.edu *Web Site:* www.yalebooks.com, pg 287

Chauncey, Caroline, Harvard Education Publishing Group, 8 Story St, 1st fl, Cambridge, MA 02138 *Tel:* 617-495-3432 *Toll Free Tel:* 800-513-0763 (subns); 888-437-1437 (orders) *Fax:* 617-496-3584; 978-348-1233 (orders) *E-mail:* hepg@harvard.edu *Web Site:* www.hepg.org, pg 114

Che, Kevin, Penguin Group (USA) LLC Sales, 375 Hudson St, New York, NY 10014 *Tel:* 212-366-2000 *E-mail:* online@penguinputnam.com *Web Site:* us.penguingroup.com, pg 197

Cheakalos, Christina, The Johns Hopkins University Press, 2715 N Charles St, Baltimore, MD 21218-4363 *Tel:* 410-516-6900; 410-516-6987 (journals outside US & CN) *Toll Free Tel:* 800-537-5487 (book orders & cust serv); 800-548-1784 (journal orders) *Fax:* 410-516-6968; 410-516-3866 (journal orders) *E-mail:* hfscustserv@press.jhu.edu (cust serv); jrnlcirc@press.jhu.edu (journal orders) *Web Site:* www.press.jhu.edu; muse.jhu.edu/about/subscriptions/index.html (Project Muse subns), pg 136

Checole, Kassahun, Africa World Press Inc, 541 W Ingham Ave, Suite B, Trenton, NJ 08638 *Tel:* 609-695-3200 *Fax:* 609-695-6466 *E-mail:* customerservice@africaworldpressbooks.com *Web Site:* www.africaworldpressbooks.com, pg 6

Checole, Kassahun, Red Sea Press Inc, 541 W Ingham Ave, Suite B, Trenton, NJ 08638 *Tel:* 609-695-3200 *Fax:* 609-695-6466 *E-mail:* customerservice@africaworldpressbooks.com *Web Site:* www.africaworldpressbooks.com, pg 216

Chelius, Jane, Jane Chelius Literary Agency Inc, 548 Second St, Brooklyn, NY 11215 *Tel:* 718-499-0236; 718-499-0714 *Fax:* 718-832-7335 *E-mail:* queries@janechelius.com; rights@janechelius.com *Web Site:* www.janechelius.com, pg 566

Chen, Cheryl, Red Deer Press, 195 Allstate Pkwy, Markham, ON L3R 4T8, Canada *Tel:* 905-477-9700 *Toll Free Tel:* 800-387-9776 (orders) *Fax:* 905-477-2834 *Toll Free Fax:* 800-260-9777 (orders) *E-mail:* rdp@reddeerpress.com *Web Site:* www.reddeerpress.com, pg 517

Chen, May, HarperCollins General Books Group, 10 E 53 St, New York, NY 10022 *Tel:* 212-207-7000 *Fax:* 212-207-7633 *Web Site:* www.harpercollins.com, pg 113

Chenault, Earlita, Counterpoint Press LLC, 1919 Fifth St, Berkeley, CA 94710 *Tel:* 510-704-0230 *Fax:* 510-704-0268 *E-mail:* info@counterpointpress.com *Web Site:* www.counterpointpress.com; www.sierraclub.org/books; www.softskull.com, pg 69

Cheng, Jill, Cheng & Tsui Co Inc, 25 West St, 2nd fl, Boston, MA 02111-1213 *Tel:* 617-988-2400 *Toll Free Tel:* 800-554-1963 *Fax:* 617-426-3669; 617-556-8964 *E-mail:* service@cheng-tsui.com; orders@cheng-tsui.com *Web Site:* www.cheng-tsui.com, pg 59

Cheng, Lisa, Running Press Book Publishers, 2300 Chestnut St, Philadelphia, PA 19103-4399 *Tel:* 215-567-5080 *Toll Free Tel:* 800-343-4499 (cust serv & orders) *Fax:* 215-568-2919 *Toll Free Fax:* 800-453-2884 (cust serv & orders) *E-mail:* perseus.promos@perseusbooks.com *Web Site:* www.runningpress.com, pg 222

Chernoff, Mitchell, Society for Industrial & Applied Mathematics, 3600 Market St, 6th fl, Philadelphia, PA 19104-2688 *Tel:* 215-382-9800 *Toll Free Tel:* 800-447-7426 *Fax:* 215-386-7999 *E-mail:* siambooks@siam.org *Web Site:* www.siam.org, pg 238

Cherry, Amy, W W Norton & Company Inc, 500 Fifth Ave, New York, NY 10110-0017 *Tel:* 212-354-5500 *Toll Free Tel:* 800-233-4830 (orders & cust serv) *Fax:* 212-869-0856 *Toll Free Fax:* 800-458-6515 *Web Site:* www.wwnorton.com, pg 182

Cherullo, Helen, The Mountaineers Books, 1001 SW Klickitat Way, Suite 201, Seattle, WA 98134 *Tel:* 206-223-6303 *Toll Free Tel:* 800-553-4453 *Fax:* 206-223-6306 *Toll Free Fax:* 800-568-7604 *E-mail:* mbooks@mountaineersbooks.org *Web Site:* www.mountaineersbooks.org, pg 170

Chesman, Andrea, Little Chicago Editorial Services, 154 Natural Tpke, Ripton, VT 05766 *Tel:* 802-388-9782 *Web Site:* andreachesman.com, pg 550

Chester, Linda, Linda Chester Literary Agency, Rockefeller Ctr, Suite 2036, 630 Fifth Ave, New York, NY 10111 *Tel:* 212-218-3350 *Fax:* 212-218-3343 *E-mail:* submissions@lindachester.com *Web Site:* www.lindachester.com, pg 566

Cheung, Anthony, Imprint Publications Inc, 207 E Ohio St, Suite 377, Chicago, IL 60611 *Tel:* 773-288-0782 *Fax:* 773-288-0792 *E-mail:* imppub@aol.com *Web Site:* www.imprint-chicago.com, pg 128

Chevako, Anne W, Publishing Resources Inc, 425 Carr 693, PMB 160, Dorado, PR 00646 *Tel:* 787-626-0607 *Toll Free Fax:* 866-547-3005 *E-mail:* pri@chevako.net *Web Site:* www.publishingresources.net, pg 554

Chevako, Jay A, Publishing Resources Inc, 425 Carr 693, PMB 160, Dorado, PR 00646 *Tel:* 787-626-0607 *Toll Free Fax:* 866-547-3005 *E-mail:* pri@chevako.net *Web Site:* www.publishingresources.net, pg 554

Chevako, Ronald J, Publishing Resources Inc, 425 Carr 693, PMB 160, Dorado, PR 00646 *Tel:* 787-626-0607 *Toll Free Fax:* 866-547-3005 *E-mail:* pri@chevako.net *Web Site:* www.publishingresources.net, pg 554

Childers, Kimberly B, Indiana University Press, 601 N Morton St, Bloomington, IN 47404-3797 *Tel:* 812-855-8817 *Toll Free Tel:* 800-842-6796 (orders only) *Fax:* 812-855-7931; 812-855-8507 *E-mail:* iupress@indiana.edu; iuporder@indiana.edu (orders) *Web Site:* www.iupress.indiana.edu, pg 129

Childress, David H, Adventures Unlimited Press, One Adventure Place, Kempton, IL 60946 *Tel:* 815-253-6390 *Fax:* 815-253-6300 *E-mail:* auphq@frontiernet.net; info@adventuresunlimitedpress.com *Web Site:* www.adventuresunlimitedpress.com, pg 5

Childs, Faith Hampton, Faith Childs Literary Agency Inc, 915 Broadway, Suite 1009, New York, NY 10010 *Tel:* 212-995-9600 *Fax:* 212-995-9709 *E-mail:* assistant@faithchildsliteraryagencyinc.com, pg 566

Chilton, Lynne, Wood Lake Publishing Inc, 9590 Jim Bailey Rd, Kelowna, BC V4V 1R2, Canada *Tel:* 250-766-2778 *Toll Free Tel:* 800-663-2775 (orders) *Fax:* 250-766-2736 *Toll Free Fax:* 888-841-9991 (orders) *E-mail:* info@woodlake.com; customerservice@woodlake.com *Web Site:* www.woodlakebooks.com, pg 525

Chilton, Robert, National Publishing Co, 11311 Roosevelt Blvd, Philadelphia, PA 19154-2105 *Tel:* 215-676-1863 *Toll Free Tel:* 888-333-1863 *Fax:* 215-673-8069 *Web Site:* www.courier.com, pg 175

Chin Aleong, Anne B, Mary Ann Liebert Inc, 140 Huguenot St, 3rd fl, New Rochelle, NY 10801-5215 *Tel:* 914-740-2100 *Toll Free Tel:* 800-654-3237 *Fax:* 914-740-2101 *E-mail:* info@liebertpub.com *Web Site:* www.liebertonline.com, pg 148

Chin, Kristine, American Institute of Chemical Engineers (AIChE), 3 Park Ave, 19th fl, New York, NY 10016-5991 *Tel:* 203-702-7660 *Toll Free Tel:* 800-242-4363 *Fax:* 203-775-5177 *E-mail:* custserv@aiche.org *Web Site:* www.aiche.org, pg 14

Chin, Oliver, Immedium, 535 Rockdale Dr, San Francisco, CA 94127 *Tel:* 415-452-8546 *Fax:* 360-937-6272 *E-mail:* orders@immedium.com; sales@immedium.com *Web Site:* www.immedium.com, pg 128

China, Wanda C, University of Hawaii Press, 2840 Kolowalu St, Honolulu, HI 96822 *Tel:* 808-956-8255 *Toll Free Tel:* 888-UHPRESS (847-7377) *Fax:* 808-988-6052 *Toll Free Fax:* 800-650-7811 *E-mail:* uhpbooks@hawaii.edu *Web Site:* www.uhpress.hawaii.edu, pg 265

Chinski, Eric, Farrar, Straus & Giroux, LLC, 18 W 18 St, New York, NY 10011 *Tel:* 212-741-6900 *Fax:* 212-633-9385 *E-mail:* fsg.publicity@fsgbooks.com *Web Site:* us.macmillan.com/fsg.aspx, pg 93

Chirichella, Christine, BNA Books, 1801 S Bell St, Arlington, VA 22202 *Toll Free Tel:* 800-372-1033 *Fax:* 732-346-1624 *E-mail:* books@bna.com *Web Site:* www.bnabooks.com, pg 42

Chirico, Anthony, Doubleday/Nan A Talese, c/o Random House Inc, 1745 Broadway, New York, NY 10019 *Tel:* 212-751-2600 *Toll Free Tel:* 800-638-6460 *Fax:* 212-572-2593 *Web Site:* www.knopfdoubleday.com, pg 81

Chirico, Anthony, Alfred A Knopf/Everyman's Library, c/o Random House Inc, 1745 Broadway, New York, NY 10019 *Tel:* 212-751-2600 *Toll Free Tel:* 800-638-6460 *Fax:* 212-572-2593 *Web Site:* www.knopfdoubleday.com, pg 141

Chirico, Tony, Random House Inc, 1745 Broadway, New York, NY 10019 *Tel:* 212-782-9000 *Toll Free Tel:* 800-726-0600 *Web Site:* www.randomhouse.com, pg 213

Chmiel, Barbara R, The Blackburn Press, PO Box 287, Caldwell, NJ 07006-0287 *Tel:* 973-228-7077 *Fax:* 973-228-7276 *Web Site:* www.blackburnpress.com, pg 39

Chng, Eng Leok, Marshall Cavendish Corp, 99 White Plains Rd, Tarrytown, NY 10591-9001 *Tel:* 914-332-8888 *Toll Free Tel:* 800-821-9881 *Fax:* 914-332-8102 *E-mail:* customerservice@marshallcavendish.com; mcc@marshallcavendish.com *Web Site:* marshallcavendish.us; marshallcavendishdigital.com; marshallcavendishebooks.com, pg 158

Choi, Grace, Human Rights Watch, 350 Fifth Ave, 34th fl, New York, NY 10118-3299 *Tel:* 212-290-4700 *Fax:* 212 736 1300 *E-mail:* hrwnyc@hrw.org *Web Site:* www.hrw.org, pg 125

Chong, Anita, McClelland & Stewart Ltd, 75 Sherbourne St, 5th fl, Toronto, ON M5A 2P9, Canada *Tel:* 416-598-1114 *Fax:* 416-598-7764 *E-mail:* editorial@mcclelland.com *Web Site:* www.mcclelland.com, pg 512

Chong, Michele, Michael Wiese Productions, 12400 Ventura Blvd, No 1111, Studio City, CA 91604 *Tel:* 818-379-8799 *Toll Free Tel:* 800-833-5738 (orders) *Fax:* 818-986-3408 *E-mail:* mwpsales@mwp.com; fulfillment@portcity.com *Web Site:* www.mwp.com, pg 281

Choron, Harry, March Tenth Inc, 24 Hillside Terr, Montvale, NJ 07645 *Tel:* 201-387-6551 *Fax:* 201-387-6552 *Web Site:* www.marchtenthinc.com, pg 583

Choron, Sandra, March Tenth Inc, 24 Hillside Terr, Montvale, NJ 07645 *Tel:* 201-387-6551 *Fax:* 201-387-6552 *Web Site:* www.marchtenthinc.com, pg 583

Chorpenning, Rev Joseph F, St Joseph's University Press, 5600 City Ave, Philadelphia, PA 19131-1395 *Tel:* 610-660-3402 *Fax:* 610-660-3412 *E-mail:* sjupress@sju.edu *Web Site:* www.sjupress.com, pg 224

Choteborsky, Mary, Crown Publishing Group, c/o Random House Inc, 1745 Broadway, New York, NY 10019 *Tel:* 212-782-9000 *Toll Free Tel:* 888-264-1745 *Fax:* 212-940-7408 *Web Site:* www.randomhouse.com/crown, pg 72

Chou, Arthur, New Win Publishing, 9682 Telstar Ave, Suite 110, El Monte, CA 91731 *Tel:* 626-448-3448 *Fax:* 626-602-3817 *E-mail:* info@academiclearningcompany.com *Web Site:* www.newwinpublishing.com; www.wbusinessbooks.com/, pg 178

Chou, Shelly, Agency Chicago, 332 S Michigan Ave, Suite 1032, No A600, Chicago, IL 60604 *E-mail:* ernsant@aol.com, pg 560

Chou, Yih-Fen, Heryin Books Inc, 1033 E Main St, Suite 202, Alhambra, CA 91801 *Tel:* 626-289-2238 *Fax:* 626-289-3865 *E-mail:* editor@heryin.com *Web Site:* www.heryin.com, pg 119

Chovnick, Lisa, Fine Communications, 322 Eighth Ave, 15th fl, New York, NY 10001 *Tel:* 212-595-3500 *Fax:* 212-595-3779, pg 95

Choyce, Lesley, Pottersfield Press, 83 Leslie Rd, East Lawrencetown, NS B2Z 1P8, Canada *Toll Free Fax:* 888-253-3133 *Web Site:* www.pottersfieldpress.com, pg 516

Chrichton, John, Bibliographical Society of America, PO Box 1537, Lenox Hill Sta, New York, NY 10021-0043 *Tel:* 212-452-2710 *Fax:* 212-452-2710 *E-mail:* bsa@bibsocamer.org *Web Site:* www.bibsocamer.org, pg 618

Chrisman, Ronald, University of North Texas Press, Stovall Hall, Suite 174, 1400 Highland St, Denton, TX 76201 *Tel:* 940-565-2142 *Fax:* 940-565-4590 *Web Site:* www.unt.edu/untpress, pg 268

Christian, Rick, Bondfire Books, 7680 Goddard St, Suite 220, Colorado Springs, CO 80920 *Tel:* 719-260-7080 *Web Site:* www.bondfirebooks.com, pg 43

Christiansen, Gayla, Texas A&M University Press, John H Lindsey Bldg, Lewis St, 4354 TAMU, College Station, TX 77843-4354 *Tel:* 979-845-1436 *Toll Free Tel:* 800-826-8911 (orders) *Fax:* 979-847-8752 *Toll Free Fax:* 888-617-2421 (orders) *E-mail:* upress@tamu.edu *Web Site:* www.tamupress.com, pg 252

Christianson, Julie, University of California Press, 2120 Berkeley Way, Berkeley, CA 94704-1012 *Tel:* 510-642-4247 *Fax:* 510-643-7127 *E-mail:* askucp@ucpress.edu (books); customerservice@ucpressjournals.com (journals) *Web Site:* www.ucpress.edu, pg 264

Christmas, Bobbie, Zebra Communications, 230 Deerchase Dr, Woodstock, GA 30188-4438 *Tel:* 770-924-0528 *Web Site:* www.zebraeditor.com, pg 558

Christofferson, Andrea, University of Wisconsin Press, 1930 Monroe St, 3rd fl, Madison, WI 53711-2059 *Tel:* 608-263-0668 *Toll Free Tel:* 800-621-2736 (orders) *Fax:* 608-263-1173 *Toll Free Fax:* 800-621-2736 (orders) *E-mail:* uwiscpress@uwpress.wisc.edu (main off) *Web Site:* www.wisc.edu/wisconsinpress, pg 270

Christopher, Julie, Simon & Schuster Children's Publishing, 1230 Avenue of the Americas, New York, NY 10020 *Tel:* 212-698-7000 *Web Site:* KIDS.SimonandSchuster.com; TEEN.SimonandSchuster.com; simonandschuster.net; simonandschuster.biz, pg 235

Christopher, Tom, Follett Higher Education Group, 1818 Swift Dr, Oak Brook, IL 60523 *Tel:* 630-279-2330 *Toll Free Tel:* 800-323-4506 *Fax:* 630-279-2569 *Web Site:* www.fheg.follett.com, pg 623

Christopher, William F (Bill), William F Christopher Publication Services, Kensington No 237, 1580 Geary Rd, Walnut Creek, CA 94597-2744 *Tel:* 925-943-5584 *Fax:* 925-943-5594 *E-mail:* wfcmgmt.innovations@yahoo.com, pg 566

Chu, Elaine, Immedium, 535 Rockdale Dr, San Francisco, CA 94127 *Tel:* 415-452-8546 *Fax:* 360-937-6272 *E-mail:* orders@immedium.com; sales@immedium.com *Web Site:* www.immedium.com, pg 128

Chu, Lily, Captus Press Inc, 1600 Steeles Ave W, Units 14-15, Concord, ON L4K 4M2, Canada *Tel:* 416-736-5537 *Fax:* 416-736-5793 *E-mail:* info@captus.com *Web Site:* www.captus.com, pg 498

Chu, Lynn, Writers' Representatives LLC, 116 W 14 St, 11th fl, New York, NY 10011-7305 *Tel:* 212-620-0023 *Fax:* 212-620-0023 *E-mail:* transom@writersreps.com *Web Site:* www.writersreps.com, pg 600

Chubinsky, Risa, AudioGO, 42 Whitecap Dr, North Kingstown, RI 02852 *Tel:* 401-295-3800 *Toll Free Tel:* 800-621-0182 *Fax:* 401-295-3899 *Toll Free Fax:* 877-492-0873 *E-mail:* info@audiogo.com *Web Site:* www.audiogo.com, pg 26

Chun, Stephanie, University of Hawaii Press, 2840 Kolowalu St, Honolulu, HI 96822 *Tel:* 808-956-8255 *Toll Free Tel:* 888-UHPRESS (847-7377) *Fax:* 808-988-6052 *Toll Free Fax:* 800-650-7811 *E-mail:* uhpbooks@hawaii.edu *Web Site:* www.uhpress.hawaii.edu, pg 265

Chung, Christopher, University of Chicago Press, 1427 E 60 St, Chicago, IL 60637-2954 *Tel:* 773-702-7700; 773-702-7600 *Toll Free Tel:* 800-621-2736 (orders) *Fax:* 773-702-9756; 773-660-2235 (orders); 773-702-2708 *E-mail:* custserv@press.uchicago.edu; marketing@press.uchicago.edu *Web Site:* www.press.uchicago.edu, pg 265

Church, Barbara J, Ashgate Publishing Co, 101 Cherry St, Suite 420, Burlington, VT 05401-4405 *Tel:* 802-865-7641 *Toll Free Tel:* 800-535-9544 *Fax:* 802-865-7847 *E-mail:* info@ashgate.com *Web Site:* www.ashgate.com, pg 24

Church, Dawson, Elite Books, PO Box 442, Fulton, CA 95439 *Tel:* 707-525-9292 *Toll Free Fax:* 800-330-9798 *Web Site:* www.elitebooks.biz, pg 86

Church, Dawson, Energy Psychology Press, 1490 Mark West Springs Rd, Santa Rosa, CA 95404 *Tel:* 707-237-6951 *Toll Free Fax:* 800-330-9798 *Web Site:* www.energypsychologypress.com, pg 88

Church, Doug, Pacific Press Publishing Association, 1350 N Kings Rd, Nampa, ID 83687-3193 *Tel:* 208-465-2500 *Toll Free Tel:* 800-447-7377 *Fax:* 208-465-2531 *Web Site:* www.pacificpress.com, pg 190

Churko, Helen, Royce Carlton Inc, 866 United Nations Plaza, Suite 587, New York, NY 10017-1880 *Tel:* 212-355-7700 *Toll Free Tel:* 800-LECTURE (532-8873) *Fax:* 212-888-8659 *E-mail:* info@roycecarlton.com *Web Site:* www.roycecarlton.com, pg 606

Chynces, Ryan, Wilfrid Laurier University Press, 75 University Ave W, Waterloo, ON N2L 3C5, Canada *Tel:* 519-884-0710 (ext 6124) *Toll Free Tel:* 866-836-5551 *Fax:* 519-725-1399 *E-mail:* press@wlu.ca *Web Site:* www.wlupress.wlu.ca, pg 525

Cianfarani, Nick, New City Press, 202 Comforter Blvd, Hyde Park, NY 12538 *Tel:* 845-229-0335 *Toll Free Tel:* 800-462-5980 (orders only) *Fax:* 845-229-0351 *E-mail:* info@newcitypress.com *Web Site:* www.newcitypress.com, pg 177

Ciechon, Mark, Palm Kids™, 50 Washington St, 12th fl, Norwalk, CT 06854 *Toll Free Tel:* 800-409-2457 *E-mail:* customercare@palmkids.com; sales@palmkids.com *Web Site:* www.palmkids.com, pg 191

Ciecierski, Andrea, Stylus Publishing LLC, 22883 Quicksilver Dr, Sterling, VA 20166-2012 *Tel:* 703-661-1504 (edit & sales) *Toll Free Tel:* 800-232-0223 (orders & cust serv) *Fax:* 703-661-1547 *E-mail:* stylusmail@presswarehouse.com (orders & cust serv); stylusinfo@styluspub.com *Web Site:* www.styluspub.com, pg 246

Ciletti, Barbara, Odyssey Books, 2421 Redwood Ct, Longmont, CO 80503-8155 *Tel:* 720-494-1473 *Fax:* 720-494-1471 *E-mail:* books@odysseybooks.net *Web Site:* cilettipublishinggroup.com, pg 184

Cilurso, Ed, Taylor & Francis Inc, 325 Chestnut St, Suite 800, Philadelphia, PA 20036-1802 *Tel:* 215-625-8900 *Toll Free Tel:* 800-354-1420 *Fax:* 215-625-2940 *E-mail:* customer.service@taylorandfrancis.com *Web Site:* www.taylorandfrancis.com, pg 250

Cimina, Dominique, Random House Children's Books, 1745 Broadway, New York, NY 10019 *Tel:* 212-782-9000 *Toll Free Tel:* 800-200-3552 *Fax:* 212-782-9452 *Web Site:* randomhousekids.com, pg 213

Ciminera, Siobhan, Simon & Schuster Children's Publishing, 1230 Avenue of the Americas, New York, NY 10020 *Tel:* 212-698-7000 *Web Site:* KIDS.SimonandSchuster.com; TEEN.SimonandSchuster.com; simonandschuster.net; simonandschuster.biz, pg 235

Cimino, Antoinette, Springer, 233 Spring St, New York, NY 10013-1578 *Tel:* 212-460-1500 *Toll Free Tel:* 800-SPRINGER (777-4643) *Fax:* 212-460-1575 *E-mail:* service-ny@springer.com *Web Site:* www.springer.com, pg 241

Cimino, Valerie, The Harvard Common Press, 535 Albany St, Boston, MA 02118 *Tel:* 617-423-5803 *Toll Free Tel:* 888-657-3755 *Fax:* 617-695-9794 *E-mail:* orders@harvardcommonpress.com; info@harvardcommonpress.com *Web Site:* www.harvardcommonpress.com, pg 114

Cioffi, Tony, Reader's Digest Association Canada ULC (Selection du Reader's Digest Canada SRL), 1100 Rene Levesque Blvd W, Montreal, QC H3B 5H5, Canada *Tel:* 514-940-0751 *Toll Free Tel:* 866-236-7789 (cust serv) *Fax:* 514-940-3637 *E-mail:* customer.service@readersdigest.ca *Web Site:* www.readersdigest.ca, pg 517

Ciommo, Dave, EPS/School Specialty Literacy & Intervention, 625 Mount Auburn St, 3rd fl, Cambridge, MA 02138-4555 *Tel:* 617-547-6706 *Toll Free Tel:* 800-225-5750 *Fax:* 617-547-0412 *Toll Free Fax:* 888-440-2665 *E-mail:* customerservice.eps@schoolspecialty.com *Web Site:* eps.schoolspecialty.com, pg 89

Ciotola, Andrew, Bucknell Seminar for Younger Poets, Bucknell University, Bucknell Hall, Moore Ave, Lewisburg, PA 17837 *Tel:* 570-577-1853 *Fax:* 570-577-1885 *E-mail:* stadlercenter@bucknell.edu *Web Site:* www.bucknell.edu/stadlercenter, pg 693

Circosta, Karey, Ave Maria Press, PO Box 428, Notre Dame, IN 46556-0428 *Tel:* 574-287-2831 *Toll Free Tel:* 800-282-1865 *Fax:* 574-239-2904 *Toll Free Fax:* 800-282-5681 *E-mail:* avemariapress.1@nd.edu *Web Site:* www.avemariapress.com, pg 28

Cirillo, Andrea, Jane Rotrosen Agency LLC, 318 E 51 St, New York, NY 10022 *Tel:* 212-593-4330 *Fax:* 212-935-6985 *Web Site:* janerotrosen.com, pg 591

Clague, Sue A, The Montana Council for Indian Education, 1240 Burlington Ave, Billings, MT 59102-4224 *Tel:* 406-652-7598 (AM); 406-248-3465 (PM) *Fax:* 406-248-1297 *E-mail:* cie@cie-mt.org *Web Site:* www.cie-mt.org, pg 169

Clain, Judy, Little, Brown and Company, 237 Park Ave, New York, NY 10017 *Tel:* 212-364-1100 *Fax:* 212-364-0952 *E-mail:* firstname.lastname@hbgusa.com *Web Site:* www.HachetteBookGroup.com, pg 150

Clark, Becky Brasington, The Johns Hopkins University Press, 2715 N Charles St, Baltimore, MD 21218-4363 *Tel:* 410-516-6900; 410-516-6987 (journals outside US & CN) *Toll Free Tel:* 800-537-5487 (book orders & cust serv); 800-548-1784 (journal orders) *Fax:* 410-516-6968; 410-516-3866 (journal orders) *E-mail:* hfscustserv@press.jhu.edu (cust serv); jrnlcirc@press.jhu.edu (journal orders) *Web Site:* www.press.jhu.edu; muse.jhu.edu/about/subscriptions/index.html (Project Muse subns), pg 136

Clark, Curtis L, University of Alabama Press, 200 Hackberry Lane, 2nd fl, Tuscaloosa, AL 35487 *Tel:* 205-348-5180 *Fax:* 205-348-9201 *Web Site:* www.uapress.ua.edu, pg 263

Clark, Denise, University of Washington Press, 433 Brooklyn Ave NE, Seattle, WA 98195-9570 *Tel:* 206-543-4050 *Toll Free Tel:* 800-537-5487 (orders) *Fax:* 206-543-3932; 410-516-6998 (orders) *E-mail:* uwpress@u.washington.edu *Web Site:* www.washington.edu/uwpress/, pg 270

Clark, Diane, Library Association of Alberta (LAA), 80 Baker Crescent NW, Calgary, AB T2L 1R4, Canada *Tel:* 403-284-5818 *Toll Free Tel:* 877-522-5550 *Fax:* 403-282-6646 *E-mail:* info@laa.ca *Web Site:* www.laa.ca, pg 626

Clark, Gary, Vermont Studio Center Writer's Program Fellowships, 80 Pearl St, Johnson, VT 05656 *Tel:* 802-635-2727 *Fax:* 802-635-2730 *E-mail:* writing@vermontstudiocenter.org; info@vermontstudiocenter.org *Web Site:* www.vermontstudiocenter.org, pg 747

Clark, Ginger, Curtis Brown Ltd, 10 Astor Place, New York, NY 10003 *Tel:* 212-473-5400 *Web Site:* www.curtisbrown.com, pg 565

Clark, James C, Penguin Group (USA) LLC, 375 Hudson St, New York, NY 10014 *Tel:* 212-366-2000 *Toll Free Tel:* 800-847-5515 (inside sales); 800-631-8571 (cust serv) *Fax:* 212-366-2666; 607-775-4829 (inside sales) *E-mail:* online@us.penguingroup.com *Web Site:* www.penguin.com; us.penguingroup.com, pg 197

Clark, Jan, Ernst Publishing Co LLC, 99 Washington Ave, Suite 309, Albany, NY 12210 *Toll Free Tel:* 800-345-3822 *Toll Free Fax:* 800-252-0906 *E-mail:* clientservices@ernstpublishing.com *Web Site:* www.ernstpublishing.com, pg 89

Clark, Jessica, University of Ottawa Press (Presses de l'Université d'Ottawa), 542 King Edward Ave, Ottawa, ON K1N 6N5, Canada *Tel:* 613-562-5246 *Fax:* 613-562-5247 *E-mail:* puo-oup@uottawa.ca *Web Site:* www.press.uottawa.ca, pg 523

Clark, Jim, The Robert Watson Literary Prizes in Fiction & Poetry, MFA Writing Program, The Greensboro Review, UNC-Greensboro, 3302 MHRA Bldg, Greensboro, NC 27402-6170 *Tel:* 336-334-5459 *Fax:* 336-256-1470 *Web Site:* www.greensbororeview.org, pg 748

Clark, June, FinePrint Literary Management, 115 W 29 St, 3rd fl, New York, NY 10001 *Tel:* 212-279-1282 *Web Site:* www.fineprintlit.com, pg 571

Clark, Kevin, American Public Works Association, 2345 Grand Blvd, Suite 700, Kansas City, MO 64108-2625 *Tel:* 816-472-6100 *Toll Free Tel:* 800-848-2792 *Fax:* 816-472-1610 *Web Site:* www.apwa.net, pg 16

Clark, Dr Laurel, SOM Publishing, 163 Moon Valley Rd, Windyville, MO 65783 *Tel:* 417-345-8411 *Fax:* 417-345-6668 *E-mail:* som@som.org; dreamschool@dreamschool.org *Web Site:* www.som.org; www.dreamschool.org, pg 239

Clark, Michiko, Pantheon Books/Schocken Books, c/o Random House Inc, 1745 Broadway, New York, NY 10019 *Tel:* 212-751-2600 *Toll Free Tel:* 800-638-6460 *Fax:* 212-572-6030, pg 192

Clark, Raymond C, Pro Lingua Associates Inc, 74 Cotton Mill Hill, Suite A-315, Brattleboro, VT 05301 *Tel:* 802-257-7779 *Toll Free Tel:* 800-366-4775 *Fax:* 802-257-5117 *E-mail:* info@prolinguaassociates.com *Web Site:* www.prolinguaassociates.com, pg 207

Clark, Sarah F, Yale University Press, 302 Temple St, New Haven, CT 06511-8909 *Tel:* 401-531-2800 (cust serv); 203-432-0960 *Toll Free Tel:* 800-405-1619 (cust serv) *Fax:* 203-432-0948; 401-531-2801 (cust serv) *Toll Free Fax:* 800-406-9145 (cust serv) *E-mail:* customer.care@trilateral.org (cust serv); language.yalepress@yale.edu *Web Site:* www.yalebooks.com, pg 287

Clark, Shaqunia, Stylus Publishing LLC, 22883 Quicksilver Dr, Sterling, VA 20166-2012 *Tel:* 703-661-1504 (edit & sales) *Toll Free Tel:* 800-232-0223 (orders & cust serv) *Fax:* 703-661-1547 *E-mail:* stylusmail@presswarehouse.com (orders & cust serv); stylusinfo@styluspub.com *Web Site:* www.styluspub.com, pg 246

Clark, Steve, Standard Publishing, 8805 Governors Hill Dr, Suite 400, Cincinnati, OH 45249 *Tel:* 513-931-4050 *Toll Free Tel:* 800-543-1353 *Fax:* 513-931-0950 *Toll Free Fax:* 877-867-5751 *E-mail:* customerservice@standardpub.com *Web Site:* www.standardpub.com, pg 242

Clark, William, Wm Clark Associates, 186 Fifth Ave, 2nd fl, New York, NY 10010 *Tel:* 212-675-2784 *Fax:* 347-649-9262 *E-mail:* general@wmclark.com *Web Site:* www.wmclark.com, pg 566

Clarke, Alison, Simon & Schuster Canada, 166 King St E, Suite 300, Toronto, ON M5A 1J3, Canada *Tel:* 647-427-8882 *Toll Free Tel:* 800-387-0446; 800-268-3216 (orders) *Fax:* 647-430-9446 *Toll Free Fax:* 888-849-8151 (orders) *E-mail:* info@simonandschuster.ca *Web Site:* www.simonsayscanada.com, pg 519

Clarke, Chandra, Scribendi Inc, 405 Riverview Dr, Chatham, ON N7M 5J5, Canada *Tel:* 519-351-1626 (cust serv) *Fax:* 519-354-0192 *E-mail:* customerservice@scribendi.com *Web Site:* www.scribendi.com, pg 555

Clarke, Erin, Random House Children's Books, 1745 Broadway, New York, NY 10019 *Tel:* 212-782-9000 *Toll Free Tel:* 800-200-3552 *Fax:* 212-782-9452 *Web Site:* randomhousekids.com, pg 213

Clarke, Harold, Reader's Digest Children's Books, 44 S Broadway, White Plains, NY 10601 *Tel:* 914-238-1000 *Toll Free Tel:* 800-934-0977 *Web Site:* www.rdtradepublishing.com, pg 215

Clarke, Harold, Reader's Digest Trade Books, 44 S Broadway, White Plains, NY 10601 *Tel:* 914-244-7503 *Fax:* 914-244-4841 *Web Site:* www.rd.com, pg 215

Clarke, Harold, Reader's Digest USA Select Editions, 44 S Broadway, 7th fl, White Plains, NY 10601 *Tel:* 914-238-1000 *Toll Free Tel:* 800-304-2807 (cust serv) *Fax:* 914-831-1560 *Web Site:* www.rda.com/readers-digest-select-editions, pg 215

Clarke, Lisa, Art of Living, PrimaMedia Inc, 1250 Bethlehem Pike, Suite 241, Hatfield, PA 19440 *Tel:* 215-660-5045 *Toll Free Tel:* 800-581-9020 *Fax:* 734-448-4125 *E-mail:* primamedia4@yahoo.com, pg 23

Clarke, Meghan, Taschen America, 6671 Sunset Blvd, Suite 1508, Los Angeles, CA 90028 *Tel:* 323-463-4441 *Toll Free Tel:* 888-TASCHEN (827-2436) *Fax:* 323-463-4442 *E-mail:* contact-us@taschen.com *Web Site:* www.taschen.com, pg 250

Clarke, Mia Barkan, Cross-Cultural Communications, 239 Wynsum Ave, Merrick, NY 11566-4725 *Tel:* 516-868-5635 *Fax:* 516-379-1901 *E-mail:* info@cross-culturalcommunications.com; cccbarkan@optonline.net; cccpoetry@aol.com *Web Site:* www.cross-culturalcommunications.com, pg 71

Clarke, Vicky, Utah Geological Survey, 1594 W North Temple, Suite 3110, Salt Lake City, UT 84116-3154 *Tel:* 801-537-3300 *Toll Free Tel:* 888-UTAH-MAP (882-4627 bookstore) *Fax:* 801-537-3400 *E-mail:* geostore@utah.gov *Web Site:* geology.utah.gov, pg 273

Classen, Jackelyn, Marshall Cavendish Corp, 99 White Plains Rd, Tarrytown, NY 10591-9001 *Tel:* 914-332-8888 *Toll Free Tel:* 800-821-9881 *Fax:* 914-332-8102 *E-mail:* customerservice@marshallcavendish.com; mcc@marshallcavendish.com *Web Site:* marshallcavendish.us; marshallcavendishdigital.com; marshallcavendishebooks.com, pg 158

Classic, Lesley, Database Directories, 588 Dufferin Ave, London, ON N6B 2A4, Canada *Tel:* 519-433-1666 *Fax:* 519-430-1131 *E-mail:* mail@databasedirectory.com *Web Site:* www.databasedirectory.com, pg 500

Clausen, Marie, University of Ottawa Press (Presses de l'Université d'Ottawa), 542 King Edward Ave, Ottawa, ON K1N 6N5, Canada *Tel:* 613-562-5246 *Fax:* 613-562-5247 *E-mail:* puo-oup@uottawa.ca *Web Site:* www.press.uottawa.ca, pg 523

Clay, Carolyn, Day Owl Press Corp, PO Box 3574, Lantana, FL 33465 *Toll Free Tel:* 866-806-6981 *Toll Free Fax:* 866-854-4375 *E-mail:* info@dayowl.net *Web Site:* www.dayowl.net; www.dayowlpresscorp.com, pg 76

Clayton, Douglas, Harvard Education Publishing Group, 8 Story St, 1st fl, Cambridge, MA 02138 *Tel:* 617-495-3432 *Toll Free Tel:* 800-513-0763 (subns); 888-437-1437 (orders) *Fax:* 617-496-3584; 978-348-1233 (orders) *E-mail:* hepg@harvard.edu *Web Site:* www.hepg.org, pg 114

Clayton, Keith, Random House Publishing Group, 1745 Broadway, New York, NY 10019 *Toll Free Tel:* 800-200-3552 *Web Site:* atrandom.com, pg 214

Clayton, Patricia Mulrane, Peter Lang Publishing Inc, 29 Broadway, 18th fl, New York, NY 10006-3223 *Tel:* 212-647-7706 *Toll Free Tel:* 800-770-5264 (cust serv) *Fax:* 212-647-7707 *Web Site:* www.peterlang.com, pg 143

Clayton, Susan, American Correctional Association, 206 N Washington St, Suite 200, Alexandria, VA 22314 *Tel:* 703-224-0000 *Toll Free Tel:* 800-222-5646 *Fax:* 703-224-0040 *Web Site:* www.aca.org, pg 12

Clemens, Michael, Blue Dolphin Publishing Inc, 13340-D Grass Valley Ave, Grass Valley, CA 95945 *Tel:* 530-477-1503 *Toll Free Tel:* 800-643-0765 (orders) *Fax:* 530-477-8342 *E-mail:* bdolphin@bluedolphinpublishing.com *Web Site:* www.bluedolphinpublishing.com, pg 41

Clemens, Paul M, Blue Dolphin Publishing Inc, 13340-D Grass Valley Ave, Grass Valley, CA 95945 *Tel:* 530-477-1503 *Toll Free Tel:* 800-643-0765 (orders) *Fax:* 530-477-8342 *E-mail:* bdolphin@bluedolphinpublishing.com *Web Site:* www.bluedolphinpublishing.com, pg 41

Clement, Yolande, Centre Franco-Ontarien de Ressources en Alphabetisation (Centre FORA), 432 Ave Westmount, Unit H, Sudbury, ON P3A 5Z8, Canada *Tel:* 705-524-3672 *Toll Free Tel:* 888-814-4422 (orders, CN only) *Fax:* 705-524-8535 *E-mail:* info@centrefora.on.ca *Web Site:* www.centrefora.on.ca, pg 498

Clemente, Stephen, Peterson's, a Nelnet Company, Princeton Pike Corporate Ctr, 2000 Lenox Dr, Lawrenceville, NJ 08648 *Tel:* 609-896-1800 *E-mail:* sales@petersons.com *Web Site:* www.petersons.com, pg 200

Clements, Pamela, Abingdon Press, 201 Eighth Ave S, Nashville, TN 37203-3919 *Toll Free Tel:* 800-251-3320 *Toll Free Fax:* 800-836-7802 (orders) *E-mail:* orders@abingdonpress.com *Web Site:* www.abingdonpress.com, pg 3

Clements, Rob, Clements Publishing, 6021 Yonge St, Suite 213, Toronto, ON M2M 3W2, Canada *Tel:* 647-477-2509 *Fax:* 647-477-2058 *E-mail:* info@clementspublishing.com *Web Site:* www.clementspublishing.com, pg 499

Clementson, Elizabeth, W W Norton & Company Inc, 500 Fifth Ave, New York, NY 10110-0017 *Tel:* 212-354-5500 *Toll Free Tel:* 800-233-4830 (orders & cust serv) *Fax:* 212-869-0856 *Toll Free Fax:* 800-458-6515 *Web Site:* www.wwnorton.com, pg 182

Clemons, G Scott, Bibliographical Society of America, PO Box 1537, Lenox Hill Sta, New York, NY 10021-0043 *Tel:* 212-452-2710 *Fax:* 212-452-2710 *E-mail:* bsa@bibsocamer.org *Web Site:* www.bibsocamer.org, pg 618

Cleveland, Marisa, Mary Sue Seymour, 475 Miner Street Rd, Canton, NY 13617 *Tel.* 315-386-1831 *Web Site:* www.theseymouragency.com, pg 593

Cleveland, Rob, August House Inc, 3500 Piedmont Rd NE, Suite 310, Atlanta, GA 30305 *Tel:* 404-442-4420 *Toll Free Tel:* 800-284-8784 *Fax:* 404-442-4435 *E-mail:* ahinfo@augusthouse.com *Web Site:* www.augusthouse.com, pg 27

Clifford, Carla, Penguin Group (USA) LLC Sales, 375 Hudson St, New York, NY 10014 *Tel:* 212-366-2000 *E-mail:* online@penguinputnam.com *Web Site:* us.penguingroup.com, pg 197

Clifford, Christina, Harlequin Enterprises Ltd, 225 Duncan Mill Rd, Don Mills, ON M3B 3K9, Canada *Tel:* 416-445-5860 *Toll Free Tel:* 888-432-4879; 800-370-5838 (ebook inquiries) *Fax:* 416-445-8655 *E-mail:* CustomerService@harlequin.com *Web Site:* www.harlequin.com, pg 508

Clift, Jeremy, International Monetary Fund (IMF) Editorial & Publications Division, 700 19 St NW, HQ1-7-124, Washington, DC 20431 *Tel:* 202-623-7430 *Fax:* 202-623-7201 *E-mail:* publications@imf.org *Web Site:* www.imfbookstore.org, pg 133

Cline, Susan, Nelson Education Ltd, 1120 Birchmount Rd, Scarborough, ON M1K 5G4, Canada *Tel:* 416-752-9100 *Toll Free Tel:* 800-268-2222 (cust serv) *Fax:* 416-752-8101 *Toll Free Fax:* 800-430-4445 *E-mail:* inquire@nelson.com *Web Site:* www.nelson.com, pg 513

Clingham, Greg, Bucknell University Press, Taylor Hall, Bucknell University, Lewisburg, PA 17837 *Tel:* 570-577-3674 *E-mail:* aup440@aol.com *Web Site:* www.bucknell.edu/universitypress, pg 49

Clockel, William, Educator's International Press Inc, 18 Colleen Rd, Troy, NY 12180 *Tel:* 518-271-9886 *Fax:* 518-266-9422 *Web Site:* www.edint.com, pg 85

Close, Amanda, Random House Publishing Group, 1745 Broadway, New York, NY 10019 *Toll Free Tel:* 800-200-3552 *Web Site:* atrandom.com, pg 214

Close, Ann, Alfred A Knopf/Everyman's Library, c/o Random House Inc, 1745 Broadway, New York, NY 10019 *Tel:* 212-751-2600 *Toll Free Tel:* 800-638-6460 *Fax:* 212-572-2593 *Web Site:* www.knopfdoubleday.com, pg 141

Close, Dan, League of Vermont Writers, PO Box 172, Underhill Center, VT 05490 *Tel:* 802-349-7475 *E-mail:* lvw@leaguevtwriters.org *Web Site:* www.leagueofvermontwriters.org, pg 626

Closson, Bob, Closson Press, 257 Delilah St, Apollo, PA 15613-1933 *Tel:* 724-337-4482 *Fax:* 724-337-9484 *E-mail:* clossonpress@comcast.net *Web Site:* www.clossonpress.com, pg 63

Closson, Marietta, Closson Press, 257 Delilah St, Apollo, PA 15613-1933 *Tel:* 724-337-4482 *Fax:* 724-337-9484 *E-mail:* clossonpress@comcast.net *Web Site:* www.clossonpress.com, pg 63

Clurman, Robert, United Synagogue Book Service, 820 Second Ave, New York, NY 10017 *Tel:* 212-533-7800 *Toll Free Tel:* 800-594-5617 (warehouse only) *Fax:* 212-253-5422 *E-mail:* booksvc@uscj.org *Web Site:* secure.uscj.org/bookservice, pg 263

Clute, Sharla, State University of New York Press, 22 Corporate Woods Blvd, 3rd fl, Albany, NY 12211-2504 *Tel:* 518-472-5000 *Toll Free Tel:* 877-204-6073 (orders) *Fax:* 518-472-5038 *Toll Free Fax:* 877-204-6074 (orders) *E-mail:* suny@presswarehouse.com (orders); info@sunypress.edu (edit off) *Web Site:* www.sunypress.edu, pg 243

Coalson, Lance, Father & Son Publishing Inc, 4909 N Monroe St, Tallahassee, FL 32303-7015 *Tel:* 850-562-2612 *Toll Free Tel:* 800-741-2712 (orders only) *Fax:* 850-562-0916 *Web Site:* www.fatherson.com, pg 93

Coan, Cynthia J, Indexing by the Book, PO Box 12513, Tucson, AZ 85732 *Tel:* 520-750-8439 *E-mail:* indextran@cox.net *Web Site:* www.indexingbythebook.com, pg 548

Coates, Damani, Black Classic Press, 3921 Vero Rd, Suite F, Baltimore, MD 21203-3414 *Tel:* 410-242-6954 *Toll Free Tel:* 800-476-8870 *Fax:* 410-242-6959 *E-mail:* email@blackclassicbooks.com; blackclassicpress@yahoo.com *Web Site:* www.blackclassicbooks.com; www.bcpdigital.com, pg 39

Coates, Laraine, University of British Columbia Press, 2029 West Mall, Vancouver, BC V6T 1Z2, Canada *Tel:* 604-822-5959 *Toll Free Tel:* 877-377-9378 *Fax:* 604-822-6083 *Toll Free Fax:* 800-668-0821 *E-mail:* frontdesk@ubcpress.ca *Web Site:* www.ubcpress.ca, pg 523

Coates, W Paul, Black Classic Press, 3921 Vero Rd, Suite F, Baltimore, MD 21203-3414 *Tel:* 410-242-6954 *Toll Free Tel:* 800-476-8870 *Fax:* 410-242-6959 *E-mail:* email@blackclassicbooks.com; blackclassicpress@yahoo.com *Web Site:* www.blackclassicbooks.com; www.bcpdigital.com, pg 39

Coats, Courtney, Carolyn Jenks Agency, 69 Aberdeen Ave, Cambridge, MA 02138 *Tel:* 617-354-5099 *E-mail:* carolynjenks@comcast.net *Web Site:* www.carolynjenksagency.com, pg 578

Cobb, David, The University Press of Kentucky, 663 S Limestone St, Lexington, KY 40508-4008 *Tel:* 859-257-8400 *Fax:* 859-257-8481 *Web Site:* www.kentuckypress.com, pg 271

Cobb, Michele, AudioGO, 42 Whitecap Dr, North Kingstown, RI 02852 *Tel:* 401-295-3800 *Toll Free Tel:* 800-621-0182 *Fax:* 401-295-3899 *Toll Free Fax:* 877-492-0873 *E-mail:* info@audiogo.com *Web Site:* www.audiogo.com, pg 26

Cobb, Steve, Crown Publishing Group, c/o Random House Inc, 1745 Broadway, New York, NY 10019 *Tel:* 212-782-9000 *Toll Free Tel:* 888-264-1745 *Fax:* 212-940-7408 *Web Site:* www.randomhouse.com/crown, pg 72

Cobb, Steve, WaterBrook Multnomah Publishing Group, 12265 Oracle Blvd, Suite 200, Colorado Springs, CO 80921 *Tel:* 719-590-4999 *Toll Free Tel:* 800-603-7051 (orders) *Fax:* 719-590-8977 *Toll Free Fax:* 800-294-5686 (orders) *E-mail:* info@waterbrookmultnomah.com *Web Site:* waterbrookmultnomah.com, pg 277

Cochran, Angela, American Society of Civil Engineers (ASCE), 1801 Alexander Bell Dr, Reston, VA 20191-4400 *Tel:* 703-295-6300 *Toll Free Tel:* 800-548-2723 *Fax:* 703-295-6278 *E-mail:* marketing@asce.org *Web Site:* www.asce.org, pg 16

Cochran, Marnie, Random House Publishing Group, 1745 Broadway, New York, NY 10019 *Toll Free Tel:* 800-200-3552 *Web Site:* atrandom.com, pg 214

Cochran, Terry, Sunbelt Publications Inc, 1256 Fayette St, El Cajon, CA 92020-1511 *Tel:* 619-258-4911 *Toll Free Tel:* 800-626-6579 (cust serv) *Fax:* 619-258-4916 *E-mail:* service@sunbeltpub.com; info@sunbeltpub.com *Web Site:* www.sunbeltbooks.com, pg 247

Cochran, Tracy, Parabola Books, 20 W 20 St, 2nd fl, New York, NY 10011 *Tel:* 212-822-8806 *Toll Free Tel:* 800-592-2521 (subns) *Fax:* 212-822-8823 *E-mail:* info@parabola.org *Web Site:* www.parabola.org, pg 192

Cochrane, Hank, Penguin Group (USA) LLC Sales, 375 Hudson St, New York, NY 10014 *Tel:* 212-366-2000 *E-mail:* online@penguinputnam.com *Web Site:* us.penguingroup.com, pg 197

Cochrane, Kristin, Doubleday Canada, One Toronto St, Suite 300, Toronto, ON M5C 2V6, Canada *Tel:* 416-364-4449 *Fax:* 416-364-6863 *Web Site:* www.randomhouse.ca, pg 501

Cochrane, Kristin, Random House of Canada Limited, One Toronto St, Suite 300, Toronto, ON M5C 2V6, Canada *Tel:* 416-364-4449 *Toll Free Tel:* 888-523-9292 (cust serv) *Fax:* 416-364-6863; 416-364-6653 (subs rts) *Web Site:* www.randomhouse.ca, pg 517

Cochrane, Kristin, Seal Books, One Toronto St, Suite 300, Toronto, ON M5C 2V6, Canada *Tel:* 416-364-4449 *Toll Free Tel:* 888-523-9292 (order desk) *Fax:* 416-364-6863 *Web Site:* www.randomhouse.ca, pg 518

Cochrell, Christie, Stanford University Press, 1450 Page Mill Rd, Palo Alto, CA 94304-1124 *Tel:* 650-723-9434 *Fax:* 650-725-3457 *E-mail:* info@sup.org *Web Site:* www.sup.org, pg 243

Cocks, Pamela, Tudor Publishers Inc, 3109 Shady Lawn Dr, Greensboro, NC 27408 *Tel:* 336-288-5395 *E-mail:* tudorpublishers@triad.rr.com, pg 259

Cody, Christine L, Boydell & Brewer Inc, 668 Mount Hope Ave, Rochester, NY 14620-2731 *Tel:* 585-275-0419 *Fax:* 585-271-8778 *E-mail:* boydell@boydellusa.net *Web Site:* www.boydellandbrewer.com, pg 45

Coe, Karen, Key Curriculum, A McGraw-Hill Education Company, 1150 65 St, Emeryville, CA 94608 *Tel:* 510-595-7000 *Toll Free Tel:* 800-995-6284 *Fax:* 510-595-7040 (orders) *Toll Free Fax:* 800-541-2442 *Web Site:* www.keycurriculum.com, pg 140

Coe, Karen, United States Holocaust Memorial Museum, 100 Raoul Wallenberg Place SW, Washington, DC 20024-2126 *Tel:* 202-314-7837; 202-488-6144 (orders) *Toll Free Tel:* 800-259-9998 (orders) *Fax:* 202-479-9726; 202-488-0438 (orders) *E-mail:* cahs_publications@ushmm.org *Web Site:* www.ushmm.org, pg 262

Coe, Richard, Hachette Book Group, 237 Park Ave, New York, NY 10017 *Tel:* 212-364-1100 *Toll Free Tel:* 800-759-0190 (cust serv) *Fax:* 212-364-0933 (intl orders) *Toll Free Fax:* 800-286-9471 (cust serv) *Web Site:* www.HachetteBookGroup.com, pg 110

Coffee, Margaret, Egmont USA, 443 Park Ave S, Suite 806, New York, NY 10016 *Tel:* 212-685-0102 *E-mail:* egmontusa@egmont.com *Web Site:* www.egmontusa.com, pg 86

Coffin, Christina, Yale University Press, 302 Temple St, New Haven, CT 06511-8909 *Tel:* 401-531-2800 (cust serv); 203-432-0960 *Toll Free Tel:* 800-405-1619 (cust serv) *Fax:* 203-432-0948; 401-531-2801 (cust serv) *Toll Free Fax:* 800-406-9145 (cust serv) *E-mail:* customer.care@trilateral.org (cust serv); language.yalepress@yale.edu *Web Site:* www.yalebooks.com, pg 287

Coffin, Jaed, Maine Writers & Publishers Alliance, 314 Forest Ave, Rm 318, Portland, OR 04102 *Tel:* 207-228-8263 *Fax:* 207-228-8150 *E-mail:* info@mainewriters.org *Web Site:* www.mainewriters.org, pg 627

Coghlan, Jennifer, BradyGames, 800 E 96 St, 3rd fl, Indianapolis, IN 46240 *Tel:* 317-428-3000 *Toll Free Tel:* 800-545-5912; 800-571-5840 (cust serv) *E-mail:* bradyquestions@pearsoned.com *Web Site:* www.bradygames.com, pg 45

Coglianese, Diana, Alfred A Knopf/Everyman's Library, c/o Random House Inc, 1745 Broadway, New York, NY 10019 *Tel:* 212-751-2600 *Toll Free Tel:* 800-638-6460 *Fax:* 212-572-2593 *Web Site:* www.knopfdoubleday.com, pg 141

Coglianese, Diana, Pantheon Books/Schocken Books, c/o Random House Inc, 1745 Broadway, New York, NY 10019 *Tel:* 212-751-2600 *Toll Free Tel:* 800-638-6460 *Fax:* 212-572-6030, pg 192

Cohan, Darcy, HarperCollins General Books Group, 10 E 53 St, New York, NY 10022 *Tel:* 212-207-7000 *Fax:* 212-207-7633 *Web Site:* www.harpercollins.com, pg 113

Cohen, Adam, Tom Howard/John H Reid Short Story Contest, 351 Pleasant St, PMB 222, Northampton, MA 01060-3961 *Tel:* 413-320-1847 *Toll Free Tel:* 866-WINWRIT (946-9748) *Fax:* 413-280-0539 *Web Site:* www.winningwriters.com, pg 710

Cohen, Adam, Tom Howard/Margaret Reid Poetry Contest, 351 Pleasant St, PMB 222, Northampton, MA 01060-3961 *Tel:* 413-320-1847 *Toll Free Tel:* 866-WINWRIT (946-9748) *Fax:* 413-280-0539 *Web Site:* www.winningwriters.com, pg 710

Cohen, Adam, Sports Fiction & Essay Contest, 351 Pleasant St, PMB 222, Northampton, MA 01060-3961 *Tel:* 413-320-1847 *Toll Free Tel:* 866-WINWRIT (946-9748) *Fax:* 413-280-0539 *Web Site:* www.winningwriters.com, pg 743

Cohen, Adam, Wergle Flomp Humor Poetry Contest, 351 Pleasant St, PMB 222, Northampton, MA 01060-3961 *Tel:* 413-320-1847 *Toll Free Tel:* 866-WINWRIT (946-9748) *Fax:* 413-280-0539 *Web Site:* www.winningwriters.com, pg 748

Cohen, Barbara, Oxford University Press USA, 198 Madison Ave, New York, NY 10016 *Tel:* 212-726-6000 *Toll Free Tel:* 800-451-7556 (orders); 800-445-9714 (cust serv) *Fax:* 919-677-1303 *E-mail:* custserv.us@oup.com *Web Site:* www.oup.com/us, pg 189

Cohen, Brett, Quirk Books, 215 Church St, Philadelphia, PA 19106 *Tel:* 215-627-3581 *Fax:* 215-627-5220 *E-mail:* general@quirkbooks.com *Web Site:* www.quirkbooks.com, pg 211

Cohen, Christine M, Virginia Kidd Agency Inc, PO Box 278, 538 E Harford St, Milford, PA 18337 *Tel:* 570-296-6205 *Web Site:* vk-agency.com, pg 579

Cohen, Craig, powerHouse Books, 37 Main St, Brooklyn, NY 11201 *Tel:* 212-604-9074 *Fax:* 212-366-5247 *E-mail:* info@powerhousebooks.com *Web Site:* www.powerhousebooks.com, pg 205

Cohen, David, Writers of the Round Table Press, 990 Bob-O-Link Rd, Highland Park, IL 60035 *Tel:* 949-375-1006 *Fax:* 815-346-2398 *E-mail:* mike@writersoftheroundtable.com *Web Site:* www.roundtablecompanies.com, pg 286

Cohen, Dr Emily-Jane, Stanford University Press, 1450 Page Mill Rd, Palo Alto, CA 94304-1124 *Tel:* 650-723-9434 *Fax:* 650-725-3457 *E-mail:* info@sup.org *Web Site:* www.sup.org, pg 243

Cohen, Erin, Writers of the Round Table Press, 990 Bob-O-Link Rd, Highland Park, IL 60035 *Tel:* 949-375-1006 *Fax:* 815-346-2398 *E-mail:* mike@writersoftheroundtable.com *Web Site:* www.roundtablecompanies.com, pg 286

Cohen, Herbert J, Platinum Press LLC, 37 Rte 80, Killingworth, CT 06419 *Tel:* 860-663-3882 *Fax:* 718-875-5065, pg 202

Cohen, Jeremy, Jerome Fellowship, 2301 Franklin Ave E, Minneapolis, MN 55406-1099 *Tel:* 612-332-7481 *Fax:* 612-332-6037 *E-mail:* info@pwcenter.org *Web Site:* www.pwcenter.org, pg 714

Cohen, Jeremy, Many Voices Fellowships, 2301 Franklin Ave E, Minneapolis, MN 55406-1099 *Tel:* 612-332-7481 *Fax:* 612-332-6037 *E-mail:* info@pwcenter.org *Web Site:* www.pwcenter.org, pg 721

Cohen, Jeremy, McKnight Advancement Grants, 2301 Franklin Ave E, Minneapolis, MN 55406-1099 *Tel:* 612-332-7481 *Fax:* 612-332-6037 *E-mail:* info@pwcenter.org *Web Site:* www.pwcenter.org, pg 722

Cohen, Jeremy, McKnight National Residency & Commission, 2301 Franklin Ave E, Minneapolis, MN 55406-1099 *Tel:* 612-332-7481 *Fax:* 612-332-6037 *E-mail:* info@pwcenter.org *Web Site:* www.pwcenter.org, pg 722

Cohen, Jonathan, Kensington Publishing Corp, 119 W 40 St, New York, NY 10018 *Tel:* 212-407-1500 *Toll Free Tel:* 800-221-2647 *Fax:* 212-935-0699 *Web Site:* www.kensingtonbooks.com, pg 139

Cohen, Judith, Cascade Pass Inc, 4223 Glencoe Ave, Suite C-105, Marina Del Rey, CA 90292 *Tel:* 310-305-0210 *Toll Free Tel:* 888-837-0704 *Fax:* 310-305-7850 *Web Site:* www.cascadepass.com, pg 54

Cohen, Katia Segre, Geolytics Inc, 28 Brunswick Wood Dr, East Brunswick, NJ 08816 *Tel:* 732-651-2000 *Toll Free Tel:* 800-577-6717 *Fax:* 732-651-2721 *E-mail:* support@geolytics.com; questions@geolytics.com *Web Site:* www.geolytics.com, pg 102

Cohen, Kelly, OSA, The Optical Society, 2010 Massachusetts Ave NW, Washington, DC 20036-1023 *Tel:* 202-223-8130 *Toll Free Tel:* 800-766-4672 *E-mail:* custserv@osa.org *Web Site:* www.osa.org, pg 188

Cohen, Larry, National Society of Newspaper Columnists (NSNC), 1345 Fillmore St, Suite 507, San Francisco, CA 94115 *Tel:* 415-488-NCNC (488-6762) *Toll Free Tel:* 866-440-NSNC (440-6762) *Fax:* 484-297-0336 *Toll Free Fax:* 866-635-5759 *E-mail:* staff@columnists.com *Web Site:* www.columnists.com, pg 631

Cohen, Larry, National Society of Newspaper Columnists Annual Conference, 1345 Fillmore St, Suite 507, San Francisco, CA 94115 *Tel:* 415-488-NCNC (488-6762) *Toll Free Tel:* 866-440-NSNC (440-6762) *Fax:* 484-297-0336 *Toll Free Fax:* 866-635-5759 *Web Site:* www.columnists.com, pg 671

Cohen, Linda, AICPA Professional Publications, 220 Leigh Farm Rd, Durham, NC 27707 *Tel:* 919-402-4500 *Toll Free Tel:* 888-777-7077 *Fax:* 919-402-4505 *E-mail:* acquisitions@aicpa.org *Web Site:* www.aicpa.org, pg 6

Cohen, Lord, Alan Wofsy Fine Arts, 1109 Geary Blvd, San Francisco, CA 94109 *Tel:* 415-292-6500 *Toll Free Tel:* 800-660-6403 *Fax:* 415-292-6594 (off & cust serv); 415-512-0130 (acctg) *E-mail:* order@art-books.com (orders); editeur@earthlink.net (edit); beauxarts@earthlink.net (cust serv) *Web Site:* www.art-books.com, pg 284

Cohen, Louis, Mason Crest Publishers, 370 Reed Rd, Suite 302, Broomall, PA 19008 *Tel:* 610-543-6200 *Toll Free Tel:* 866-MCP-BOOK (627-2665) *Fax:* 610-543-3878 *Web Site:* www.masoncrest.com, pg 158

Cohen, M, Players Press Inc, PO Box 1132, Studio City, CA 91614-0132 *Tel:* 818-789-4980 *E-mail:* playerspress@att.net *Web Site:* www.ppeps.com, pg 202

Cohen, Mark E, CDL Press, PO Box 34454, Bethesda, MD 20827 *Tel:* 301-762-2066 *Fax:* 253-484-5542 *E-mail:* cdlpress@erols.com *Web Site:* www.cdlpress.com, pg 55

Cohen, Michael R, Puddingstone Literary, Authors' Agents, 11 Mabro Dr, Denville, NJ 07834-9607 *Tel:* 973-366-3622, pg 589

Cohen, Mort, Riverside Publishing, 3800 Golf Rd, Suite 200, Rolling Meadows, IL 60008 *Tel:* 630-467-7000 *Toll Free Tel:* 800-323-9540 *Fax:* 630-467-7192 (cust serv) *E-mail:* rpc_customer_service@hmhpub.com (cust serv) *Web Site:* www.riversidepublishing.com, pg 219

Cohen, Nan, Napa Valley Writers' Conference, Upper Valley Campus, 1088 College Ave, St Helena, CA 94574 *Tel:* 707-967-2900 (ext 1611) *Fax:* 707-967-2909 *E-mail:* writecon@napavalley.edu *Web Site:* www.napawritersconf.org, pg 671

Cohen, Paul, Monkfish Book Publishing Co, 22 E Market St, Suite 304, Rhinebeck, NY 12572 *Tel:* 845-876-4861 *E-mail:* monkfish@monkfishpublishing.com *Web Site:* www.monkfishpublishing.com, pg 169

Cohen, Peter, Houghton Mifflin Harcourt, 222 Berkeley St, Boston, MA 02116-3764 *Tel:* 617-351-5000 *Toll Free Tel:* 800-225-5425 (Pre-K-8); 800-462-6595 (6–12; Advanced & Electives); 800-289-4490 (Specialized Curriculum: Great Source, Rigby, Saxon, Steck-Vaughn; Homeschool; Adult Ed); 800-323-9540 (Assessment: Riverside Publishing); 888-391-3245 (SkillsTutor); 888-242-6747 option 2 (Destination Series; Classroom Connect; Earobics; Edmark; Learning Village; Riverdeep); 800-225-3362 (Houghton Mifflin Harcourt Trade & Reference Publishers); 800-225-5800 (Heinemann) *Fax:* 617-351-1125 *Web Site:* www.hmhco.com, pg 123

Cohen, Peter, McGraw-Hill School Education Group, 8787 Orion Place, Columbus, OH 43240 *Tel:* 614-430-4000 *Toll Free Tel:* 800-848-1567 *Web Site:* www.mheducation.com, pg 162

Cohen, Philip, Mason Crest Publishers, 370 Reed Rd, Suite 302, Broomall, PA 19008 *Tel:* 610-543-6200 *Toll Free Tel:* 866-MCP-BOOK (627-2665) *Fax:* 610-543-3878 *Web Site:* www.masoncrest.com, pg 158

Cohen, Samantha, Simon & Schuster, Inc, 1230 Avenue of the Americas, New York, NY 10020 *Tel:* 212-698-7000 *Fax:* 212-698-7007 *E-mail:* firstname.lastname@simonandschuster.com *Web Site:* www.simonandschuster.com, pg 235

Collins, Blaire D, Bishop Museum Press, 1525 Bernice St, Honolulu, HI 96817 *Tel:* 808-847-3511; 808-847-8291 *Fax:* 808-848-4147 *E-mail:* press@bishopmuseum.org *Web Site:* www.bishopmuseum.org/press, pg 38

Collins, Christy, White Cloud Press, 300 E Hersey St, Suite 11, Ashland, OR 97520 *Tel:* 541-488-6415 *Toll Free Tel:* 800-380-8286 *Fax:* 541-482-7708 *E-mail:* info@whitecloudpress.com *Web Site:* www.whitecloudpress.com, pg 280

Collins, JoAnn, International Transactions Inc, 28 Alope Way, Gila, NM 88038 *Tel:* 845-373-9696 *Fax:* 480-393-5162 *E mail:* info@intltrans.com *Web Site:* www.intltrans.com, pg 577

Collins, Kate, Random House Publishing Group, 1745 Broadway, New York, NY 10019 *Toll Free Tel:* 800-200-3552 *Web Site:* atrandom.com, pg 214

Collins, Kelli, Ellora's Cave, 1056 Home Ave, Akron, OH 44310-3302 *Tel:* 330-253-3521 *E-mail:* service@ellorascave.com; comments@ellorascave.com *Web Site:* www.ellorascave.com, pg 86

Collins, Kevin F, HCPro Inc, 200 Hoods Lane, Marblehead, MA 01945 *Tel:* 781-639-1872 *Toll Free Tel:* 800-650-6787 *Toll Free Fax:* 800-639-8511 *E-mail:* customerservice@hcpro.com *Web Site:* www.hcpro.com, pg 116

Collins, Martha, Oberlin College Press, 50 N Professor St, Oberlin, OH 44074-1091 *Tel:* 440-775-8408 *Fax:* 440-775-8124 *E-mail:* oc.press@oberlin.edu *Web Site:* www.oberlin.edu/ocpress, pg 183

Collins, Nate, Samuel French Inc, 45 W 25 St, New York, NY 10010-2751 *Tel:* 212-206-8990 *Toll Free Tel:* 866-598-8449 *Fax:* 212-206-1429 *E-mail:* info@samuelfrench.com *Web Site:* www.samuelfrench.com, pg 99, 573

Collins, Teresa Wells, The University Press of Kentucky, 663 S Limestone St, Lexington, KY 40508-4008 *Tel:* 859-257-8400 *Fax:* 859-257-8481 *Web Site:* www.kentuckypress.com, pg 271

Colom, Wilbur O, Genesis Press Inc, PO Box 101, Columbus, MS 39701 *Toll Free Tel:* 888-463-4461 (orders only) *Web Site:* www.genesis-press.com, pg 102

Colonnese, Frank, The Center for Thanatology Research & Education Inc, 391 Atlantic Ave, Brooklyn, NY 11217-1701 *Tel:* 718-858-3026 *Fax:* 718-852-1846 *E-mail:* thanatology@pipeline.com *Web Site:* www.thanatology.org, pg 56

Colton, Tim, Carolina Academic Press, 700 Kent St, Durham, NC 27701 *Tel:* 919-489-7486 *Toll Free Tel:* 800-489-7486 *Fax:* 919-493-5668 *E-mail:* cap@cap-press.com *Web Site:* www.cap-press.com; www.caplaw.com, pg 52

Columbari, Bari, Pastoral Press, 5536 NE Hassalo, Portland, OR 97213-3638 *Tel:* 503-281-1191 *Toll Free Tel:* 800-548-8749 *Fax:* 503-282-3486 *Toll Free Fax:* 800-462-7329 *E-mail:* liturgy@ocp.org *Web Site:* www.ocp.org, pg 194

Columbus, Nadia, Nova Science Publishers Inc, 400 Oser Ave, Suite 1600, Hauppauge, NY 11788-3619 *Tel:* 631-231-7269 *Fax:* 631-231-8175 *E-mail:* main@novapublishers.com *Web Site:* www.novapublishers.com, pg 182

Colvin, Andrea, Andrews McMeel Publishing LLC, 1130 Walnut St, Kansas City, MO 64106-2109 *Toll Free Tel:* 800-851-8923; 800-943-9839 (cust serv) *Toll Free Fax:* 800-943-9831 (orders) *Web Site:* www.andrewsmcmeel.com, pg 18

Colvin, Rod, Addicus Books Inc, PO Box 45327, Omaha, NE 68145 *Tel:* 402-330-7493 *Toll Free Tel:* 800-352-2873 (orders) *Fax:* 402-330-1707 *E-mail:* info@addicusbooks.com; addicusbks@aol.com *Web Site:* www.addicusbooks.com, pg 5

Colvin, Theresa, Individual Artist Awards, 175 W Ostend St, Suite E, Baltimore, MD 21230 *Tel:* 410-767-6555 *Fax:* 410-333-1062 *E-mail:* msac@msac.org *Web Site:* www.msac.org, pg 712

Combs, Michele, Carpe Indexum, 364 Woodbine Ave, Syracuse, NY 13206-3324 *Tel:* 315-431-4949 *E-mail:* info@carpeindexum.com *Web Site:* www.carpeindexum.com, pg 542

Combs, Misty, Money Market Directories, 401 E Market St, Charlottesville, VA 22902 *Tel:* 434-977-1450 *Toll Free Tel:* 800-446-2810 *Fax:* 434-979-9962 *Web Site:* www.mmdwebaccess.com, pg 169

Comfort, Anna, Harbour Publishing Co Ltd, PO Box 219, Madeira Park, BC V0N 2H0, Canada *Tel:* 604-883-2730 *Toll Free Tel:* 800-667-2988 *Fax:* 604-883-9451 *E-mail:* info@harbourpublishing.com *Web Site:* www.harbourpublishing.com, pg 508

Como, Maureen, Liturgy Training Publications, 3949 S Racine Ave, Chicago, IL 60609-2523 *Tel:* 773-579-4900 *Toll Free Tel:* 800-933-1800 (US & CN only orders) *Fax:* 773-486-7094 *Toll Free Fax:* 800-933-7094 (US & CN only orders) *E-mail:* orders@ltp.org *Web Site:* www.ltp.org, pg 151

Comrie, Tim, YMAA Publication Center, PO Box 480, Wolfeboro, NH 03894 *Tel:* 603-569-7988 *Toll Free Tel:* 800-669-8892 *Fax:* 603-569-1889 *E-mail:* ymaa@aol.com *Web Site:* www.ymaa.com, pg 288

Conant, Vic, Nightingale-Conant, 6245 W Howard St, Niles, IL 60714 *Tel:* 847-647-0306 *Toll Free Tel:* 800-572-2770; 800-557-1660 (sales); 800-560-6081 (cust serv) *Fax:* 847-647-7145; 847-647-9143 (sales) *E-mail:* distributordivision@nightingale.com (orders) *Web Site:* www.nightingale.com, pg 179

Conary, Lori, Shubert Fendrich Memorial Playwriting Contest, PO Box 4267, Englewood, CO 80155-4267 *Tel:* 303-779-4035 *Toll Free Tel:* 800-333-7262 *Fax:* 303-779-4315 *E-mail:* playwrights@pioneerdrama.com *Web Site:* www.pioneerdrama.com, pg 704

Conaway, Dan, Writers House, 21 W 26 St, New York, NY 10010 *Tel:* 212-685-2400 *Fax:* 212-685-1781 *Web Site:* www.writershouse.com, pg 599

Concannon, Sean, CN Times Books, 501 Fifth Ave, Suite 1708, New York, NY 10017 *Tel:* 212-867-8666 *Web Site:* cntimesbooks.com, pg 63

Concepcion, Cristina, Don Congdon Associates Inc, 110 William St, Suite 2202, New York, NY 10038-3914 *Tel:* 212-645-1229 *Fax:* 212-727-2688 *E-mail:* dca@doncongdon.com *Web Site:* www.doncongdon.com, pg 567

Conde, Sidney, St Martin's Press, LLC, 175 Fifth Ave, New York, NY 10010 *Tel:* 646-307-5151 *Fax:* 212-420-9314 *E-mail:* firstname.lastname@macmillan.com *Web Site:* www.stmartins.com, pg 224

Condit, Carl Daniel, Sunstone Press, PO Box 2321, Santa Fe, NM 87504-2321 *Tel:* 505-988-4418 *Toll Free Tel:* 800-243-5644 *Fax:* 505-988-1025 (orders only) *Web Site:* www.sunstonepress.com, pg 247

Condon, Alicia, Kensington Publishing Corp, 119 W 40 St, New York, NY 10018 *Tel:* 212-407-1500 *Toll Free Tel:* 800-221-2647 *Fax:* 212-935-0699 *Web Site:* www.kensingtonbooks.com, pg 139

Condon, Phil, University of Montana, Environmental Writing Institute, Environmental Studies, University of Montana, Missoula, MT 59812 *Tel:* 406-243-2904 *Fax:* 406-243-6090 *Web Site:* www.umt.edu/ewi, pg 682

Condron, Dr Barbara, SOM Publishing, 163 Moon Valley Rd, Windyville, MO 65783 *Tel:* 417-345-8411 *Fax:* 417-345-6668 *E-mail:* som@som.org; dreamschool@dreamschool.org *Web Site:* www.som.org; www.dreamschool.org, pg 239

Conery, Leslie, International Society for Technology in Education, 180 W Eighth Ave, Suite 300, Eugene, OR 97401-2916 *Tel:* 541-302-3777 (intl) *Toll Free Tel:* 800-336-5191 (US & CN) *Fax:* 541-302-3778 *E-mail:* iste@iste.org *Web Site:* www.iste.org; www.iste.org/bookstore (orders), pg 133

Conescu, Nancy, Dial Books for Young Readers, 345 Hudson St, New York, NY 10014 *Tel:* 212-366-2000 *Fax:* 212-414-3396 *E-mail:* online@penguinputnam.com *Web Site:* www.penguinputnam.com; us.penguingroup.com, pg 79

Congdon, Michael, Don Congdon Associates Inc, 110 William St, Suite 2202, New York, NY 10038-3914 *Tel:* 212-645-1229 *Fax:* 212-727-2688 *E-mail:* dca@doncongdon.com *Web Site:* www.doncongdon.com, pg 567

Conine, Nancy, Transaction Publishers Inc, 10 Corporate Place S, 35 Berrue Circle, Piscataway, NJ 08854 *Tel:* 732-445-2280; 732-445-1245 (orders) *Toll Free Tel:* 888-999-6778 (dist ctr) *Fax:* 732-445-3138 *E-mail:* trans@transactionpub.com; orders@transactionpub.om *Web Site:* www.transactionpub.com, pg 258

Conis, Kym, Foil & Specialty Effects Association (FSEA), 2150 SW Westport Dr, Suite 101, Topeka, KS 66614 *Tel:* 785-271 5816 *Fax:* 785-271-6404 *Web Site:* www.fsea.com, pg 623

Conklin, Paul, Chelsea House Publishers, 132 W 31 St, 17th fl, New York, NY 10001 *Tel:* 212-967-8800 *Toll Free Tel:* 800-322-8755 *Fax:* 917-339-0325; 917-339-0323 *Toll Free Fax:* 800-678-3633 *E-mail:* custserv@factsonfile.com *Web Site:* www.infobasepublishing.com; www.infobaselearning.com, pg 59

Conley, Charlie, DeLorme Publishing Co Inc, 2 DeLorme Dr, Yarmouth, ME 04096 *Tel:* 207-846-7000; 207-846-7111 (sales) *Toll Free Tel:* 800-561-5105; 800-511-2459 (cust serv) *Fax:* 207-846-7051 *Toll Free Fax:* 800-575-2244 *E-mail:* reseller@delorme.com *Web Site:* www.delorme.com, pg 77

Conley, Cort, Literature Fellowship, 2410 N Old Penitentiary Rd, Boise, ID 83712 *Tel:* 208-334-2119 *Toll Free Tel:* 800-ART-FUND (278-3863 within Idaho) *Fax:* 208-334-2488 *E-mail:* info@arts.idaho.gov *Web Site:* www.arts.idaho.gov, pg 718

Conley, Cort, Writer in Residence, 2410 N Old Penitentiary Rd, Boise, ID 83712 *Tel:* 208-334-2119 *Toll Free Tel:* 800-ART-FUND (278-3863 within Idaho) *Fax:* 208-334-2488 *E-mail:* info@arts.idaho.gov *Web Site:* www.arts.idaho.gov, pg 751

Conley, Susan, Arden Press Inc, PO Box 418, Denver, CO 80201-0418 *Tel:* 303-697-6766 *Fax:* 303-697-3443 *E-mail:* ardenpress@msn.com, pg 21

Conley, Tricia, Viking, 375 Hudson St, New York, NY 10014 *Tel:* 212-366-2000 *E-mail:* online@penguinputnam.com *Web Site:* www.penguinputnam.com; us.penguingroup.com, pg 275

Conmy, Matt, Springer Publishing Co LLC, 11 W 42 St, 15th fl, New York, NY 10036-8002 *Tel:* 212-431-4370 *Toll Free Tel:* 877-687-7476 *Fax:* 212-941-7842 *E-mail:* marketing@springerpub.com; cs@springerpub.com (orders); editorial@springerpub.com *Web Site:* www.springerpub.com, pg 241

Connell, Akoulina, Goose Lane Editions, 500 Beaverbrook Ct, Suite 330, Fredericton, NB E3B 5X4, Canada *Tel:* 506-450-4251 *Toll Free Tel:* 888-926-8377 *Fax:* 506-459-4991 *E-mail:* info@gooselane.com *Web Site:* www.gooselane.com, pg 507

Connelly, Prof Claire PhD, Angels Editorial Services, 1630 Main St, Suite 41, Coventry, CT 06238 *Tel:* 860-742-5279 *E-mail:* angelsus@aol.com, pg 540

Conners, Peter, BOA Editions Ltd, 250 N Goodman St, Suite 306, Rochester, NY 14607 *Tel:* 585-546-3410 *Fax:* 585-546-3913 *E-mail:* contact@boaeditions.org *Web Site:* www.boaeditions.org, pg 42

Connolly, Carolyn, Simon & Schuster, Inc, 1230 Avenue of the Americas, New York, NY 10020 *Tel:* 212-698-7000 *Fax:* 212-698-7007 *E-mail:* firstname.lastname@simonandschuster.com *Web Site:* www.simonandschuster.com, pg 235

Connolly, Claudia, Pembroke Publishers Ltd, 538 Hood Rd, Markham, ON L3R 3K9, Canada *Tel:* 905-477-0650 *Toll Free Tel:* 800-997-9807 *Fax:* 905-477-3691 *Toll Free Fax:* 800-339-5568 *Web Site:* www.pembrokepublishers.com, pg 515

Connolly, John J EdD, Castle Connolly Medical Ltd, 42 W 24 St, 2nd fl, New York, NY 10010 *Tel:* 212-367-8400 *Toll Free Tel:* 800-339-DOCS (339-3627) *Fax:* 212-367-0964 *Web Site:* www.castleconnolly.com, pg 54

Connor, Fred, Cornell University Southeast Asia Program Publications, 213 Kahin Ctr, 640 Stewart Ave, Ithaca, NY 14850 *Tel:* 607-277-2211 *Toll Free Tel:* 800-666-2211 *Fax:* 607-277-6292 *Toll Free Fax:* 800-688-2877 *E-mail:* seap-pubs@cornell.edu *Web Site:* www.einaudi.cornell.edu/southeastasia/publications, pg 68

Connor, William J Jr, A Better Be Write Publishing LLC, 9001 Ridge Hill St, Kernersville, NC 27284 *Tel:* 336-354-7173 *Fax:* 336-993-2497 *Web Site:* www.abetterbewrite.com, pg 1

Connors, Dan, Twenty-Third Publications, One Montauk Ave, Suite 200, New London, CT 06320 *Tel:* 860-437-3012 *Toll Free Tel:* 800-321-0411 (orders) *Toll Free Fax:* 800-572-0788 *E-mail:* 23ppweb@bayard-inc.com *Web Site:* www.twentythirdpublications.com, pg 260

Conomos, Cynthia, Landes Bioscience, 1806 Rio Grande St, Austin, TX 78701 *Tel:* 512-637-6050 *Toll Free Tel:* 800-736-9948 *Fax:* 512-637-6079 *E-mail:* info@landesbioscience.com *Web Site:* www.landesbioscience.com, pg 143

Conover, Roger L, The MIT Press, 55 Hayward St, Cambridge, MA 02142 *Tel:* 617-253-5255 *Toll Free Tel:* 800-207-8354 (orders) *Fax:* 617-258-6779; 617-577-1545 (orders) *Web Site:* mitpress.mit.edu, pg 167

Conrad, Charles, Avery, 375 Hudson St, New York, NY 10014 *Tel:* 212-366-2000 *Fax:* 212-366-2643 *E-mail:* online@penguinputnam.com *Web Site:* www.penguinputnam.com; us.penguingroup.com, pg 28

Conrad, Charles, Gotham Books, 375 Hudson St, New York, NY 10014, pg 105

Conrad, Joanna, Texas Tech University Press, 2903 Fourth St, Suite 201, Lubbock, TX 79409 *Tel:* 806-742-2982 *Toll Free Tel:* 800-832-4042 *Fax:* 806-742-2979 *E-mail:* ttup@ttu.edu *Web Site:* www.ttupress.org, pg 253

Conrad, Kathryn, The University of Arizona Press, 355 S Euclid Ave, Suite 103, Tucson, AZ 85719-6654 *Tel:* 520-621-1441 *Toll Free Tel:* 800-426-3797 (orders) *Fax:* 520-621-8899 *Toll Free Fax:* 800-426-3797 *E-mail:* uap@uapress.arizona.edu *Web Site:* www.uapress.arizona.edu, pg 264

Conroy, Nick, Atlantic Center for the Arts Artists-in-Residence Program, 1414 Art Center Ave, New Smyrna Beach, FL 32168 *Tel:* 386-427-6975 *Toll Free Tel:* 800-393-6975 *Fax:* 386-427-5669 *E-mail:* program@atlanticcenterforthearts.org *Web Site:* www.atlanticcenterforthearts.org, pg 667

Conroy, Sonsie Carbonara, Catalyst Communication Arts, 94 Chuparrosa Dr, San Luis Obispo, CA 93401 *Tel:* 805-235-2351 *Fax:* 805-543-7140 *Web Site:* www.sonsieconroy.com, pg 543

Consiglio, Lisa, Aspen Summer Words Writing Retreat & Literary Festival, 110 E Hallam St, Suite 116, Aspen, CO 81611 *Tel:* 970-925-3122 *Fax:* 970-920-5700 *E-mail:* info@aspenwriters.org *Web Site:* www.aspenwriters.org, pg 667

Consiglio, Lisa, Scribes & Scribblers Writing Camps for Kids, 110 E Hallam St, Suite 116, Aspen, CO 81611 *Tel:* 970-925-3122 *Fax:* 970-920-5700 *E-mail:* info@aspenwriters.org *Web Site:* www.aspenwriters.org, pg 673

Consiglio, Lisa, Winter Words Apres Ski for the Mind, 110 E Hallam St, Suite 116, Aspen, CO 81611 *Tel:* 970-925-3122 *Fax:* 970-920-5700 *E-mail:* info@aspenwriters.org *Web Site:* www.aspenwriters.org, pg 674

Constable, Tina, Crown Publishing Group, c/o Random House Inc, 1745 Broadway, New York, NY 10019 *Tel:* 212-782-9000 *Toll Free Tel:* 888-264-1745 *Fax:* 212-940-7408 *Web Site:* www.randomhouse.com/crown, pg 72

Contardi, Bill, Brandt & Hochman Literary Agents Inc, 1501 Broadway, Suite 2310, New York, NY 10036 *Tel:* 212-840-5760 *Fax:* 212-840-5776 *Web Site:* brandthochman.com, pg 564

Conte, Pat, Gryphon House Inc, 10770 Columbia Pike, Suite 201, Silver Spring, MD 20901 *Tel:* 301-595-9500 *Toll Free Tel:* 800-638-0928 *Fax:* 301-595-0051 *Toll Free Fax:* 877-638-7576 *E-mail:* info@ghbooks.com *Web Site:* www.gryphonhouse.com, pg 109

Cook, Amy PhD, Sourced Media Books, 29 Via Regalo, San Clemente, CA 92673 *Tel:* 949-813-0182 *E-mail:* info@sourcemediabooks.com *Web Site:* sourcedmediabooks.com, pg 240

Cook, Charles, Kendall/Hunt Publishing Co, 4050 Westmark Dr, Dubuque, IA 52002-2624 *Tel:* 563-589-1000 *Toll Free Tel:* 800-228-0810 (orders) *Fax:* 563-589-1046 *Toll Free Fax:* 800-772-9165 *E-mail:* orders@kendallhunt.com *Web Site:* www.kendallhunt.com, pg 139

Cook, Cindy, Cengage Learning, 200 First Stamford Place, Suite 400, Stamford, CT 06902 *Tel:* 203-965-8600 *Toll Free Tel:* 800-354-9706 *Fax:* 203-965-8599 *Toll Free Fax:* 800-487-8488 *E-mail:* esales@cengage.com *Web Site:* www.cengage.com, pg 55

Cook, Dorothy M, W W Norton & Company Inc, 500 Fifth Ave, New York, NY 10110-0017 *Tel:* 212-354-5500 *Toll Free Tel:* 800-233-4830 (orders & cust serv) *Fax:* 212-869-0856 *Toll Free Fax:* 800-458-6515 *Web Site:* www.wwnorton.com, pg 181

Cook, Katie, Piano Press, 1425 Ocean Ave, Suite 17, Del Mar, CA 92014 *Tel:* 619-884-1401 *Fax:* 858-755-1104 *E-mail:* pianopress@pianopress.com *Web Site:* www.pianopress.com, pg 201

Cook, Kim, Trafalgar Square Books, 388 Howe Hill Rd, North Pomfret, VT 05053 *Tel:* 802-457-1911 *Toll Free Tel:* 800-423-4525 *Fax:* 802-457-1913 *E-mail:* tsquare@sover.net; info@trafalgarbooks.com *Web Site:* www.trafalgarbooks.com; www.horseandriderbooks.com, pg 257

Cook, Laura, Westwood Creative Artists Ltd, 94 Harbord St, Toronto, ON M5S 1G6, Canada *Tel:* 416-964-3302 *Fax:* 416-975-9209 *E-mail:* wca_office@wcaltd.com *Web Site:* www.wcaltd.com, pg 599

Cook, Marina, Berrett-Koehler Publishers Inc, 235 Montgomery St, Suite 650, San Francisco, CA 94104 *Tel:* 415-288-0260 *Fax:* 415-362-2512 *E-mail:* bkpub@bkpub.com *Web Site:* www.bkconnection.com, pg 36

Cook, Marshall, UW-Madison, Division of Continuing Studies, 21 N Park St, 7th fl, Madison, WI 53715 *Tel:* 608-263-6320 *Toll Free Tel:* 877-336-7836 *Fax:* 608-262-1694 *E-mail:* liberalarts@dsc.wisc.edu *Web Site:* continuingstudies.wisc.edu, pg 682

Cook, Martha, Trafalgar Square Books, 388 Howe Hill Rd, North Pomfret, VT 05053 *Tel:* 802-457-1911 *Toll Free Tel:* 800-423-4525 *Fax:* 802-457-1913 *E-mail:* tsquare@sover.net; info@trafalgarbooks.com *Web Site:* www.trafalgarbooks.com; www.horseandriderbooks.com, pg 257

Cook, Melinda, Classroom Connect, 222 Berkeley St, Boston, MA 02116 *Tel:* 617-351-5000 *Toll Free Tel:* 800-638-1639 (cust support) *E-mail:* help@classroom.com *Web Site:* corporate.classroom.com; www.hmhinnovation.com, pg 62

Cook, Tonya, Cornell University Press, Sage House, 512 E State St, Ithaca, NY 14850 *Tel:* 607-277-2338 *Fax:* 607-277-2374 *E-mail:* cupressinfo@cornell.edu; cupress-sales@cornell.edu *Web Site:* www.cornellpress.cornell.edu, pg 67

Cook, W Richard, University of Alabama Press, 200 Hackberry Lane, 2nd fl, Tuscaloosa, AL 35487 *Tel:* 205-348-5180 *Fax:* 205-348-9201 *Web Site:* www.uapress.ua.edu, pg 263

Cooke, Janet, Doubleday/Nan A Talese, c/o Random House Inc, 1745 Broadway, New York, NY 10019 *Tel:* 212-751-2600 *Toll Free Tel:* 800-638-6460 *Fax:* 212-572-2593 *Web Site:* www.knopfdoubleday.com, pg 81

Cooke, Janet, Alfred A Knopf/Everyman's Library, c/o Random House Inc, 1745 Broadway, New York, NY 10019 *Tel:* 212-751-2600 *Toll Free Tel:* 800-638-6460 *Fax:* 212-572-2593 *Web Site:* www.knopfdoubleday.com, pg 141

Cooke, Max, Canadian Education Association/Association canadienne d'education, 119 Spadina Ave, Suite 702, Toronto, ON M5V 2L1, Canada *Tel:* 416-591-6300 *Toll Free Tel:* 866-803-9549 *Fax:* 416-591-5345 *E-mail:* info@cea-ace.ca *Web Site:* www.cea-ace.ca, pg 620

Cookman, Whitney, Crown Publishing Group, c/o Random House Inc, 1745 Broadway, New York, NY 10019 *Tel:* 212-782-9000 *Toll Free Tel:* 888-264-1745 *Fax:* 212-940-7408 *Web Site:* www.randomhouse.com/crown, pg 72

Coolbaugh, Stephen, The Mathematical Association of America, 1529 18 St NW, Washington, DC 20036-1358 *Tel:* 202-387-5200 *Toll Free Tel:* 800-741-9415 *Fax:* 202-265-2384 *E-mail:* maahq@maa.org *Web Site:* www.maa.org, pg 159

Coolman, Marie, Bloomsbury Publishing, 175 Fifth Ave, New York, NY 10010 *Tel:* 212-674-5151 *Toll Free Tel:* 800-221-7945 *Fax:* 212-780-0115; 212-982-2837 *E-mail:* marketingusa@bloomsbury.com; adultpublicityusa.@bloomsbury.com *Web Site:* www.bloomsbury.com, pg 40

Coombs, Sheri, Fresh Fish Award for Emerging Writers, Haymarket Sq, 208-223 Duckworth St, St John's, NL A1C 6N1, Canada *Tel:* 709-739-5215 *E-mail:* wanl@nf.aibn.com *Web Site:* wanl.ca, pg 706

Coombs, Sheri, Newfoundland and Labrador Book Awards, Haymarket Sq, 208-223 Duckworth St, St John's, NL A1C 6N1, Canada *Tel:* 709-739-5215 *E-mail:* wanl@nf.aibn.com *Web Site:* wanl.ca, pg 729

Cooper, Alexandra, HarperCollins Children's Books, 10 E 53 St, New York, NY 10022 *Tel:* 212-207-7000 *Web Site:* www.harpercollinschildrens.com, pg 113

Cooper, Doris, Clarkson Potter Publishers, c/o Random House Inc, 1745 Broadway, New York, NY 10019 *Tel:* 212-782-9000 *Toll Free Tel:* 888-264-1745 *Fax:* 212-572-6181 *Web Site:* www.clarksonpotter.com; www.randomhouse.com/crown/clarksonpotter, pg 62

Cooper, I L, Cooper Publishing Group LLC, PO Box 1129, Traverse City, MI 49685 *Tel:* 231-933-9958 *Fax:* 231-933-9964 *E-mail:* jr4239@att.net *Web Site:* www.cooperpublishinggroup.com, pg 67

Cooper, Karen, Adams Media, 57 Littlefield St, Avon, MA 02322 *Tel:* 508-427-7100 *Fax:* 508-427-6790 *Toll Free Fax:* 800-872-5627 *E-mail:* orders@adamsmedia.com *Web Site:* www.adamsmedia.com, pg 5

Cooper, Karen, F+W Media Inc, 10151 Carver Rd, Suite 200, Blue Ash, OH 45242 *Tel:* 513-531-2690 *Toll Free Tel:* 800-289-0963 (trade accts); 800-258-0929 (orders) *E-mail:* contact_us@fwmedia.com *Web Site:* www.fwmedia.com, pg 92

Cooper, Kevin, New York University Press, 838 Broadway, 3rd fl, New York, NY 10003-4812 *Tel:* 212-998-2575 (edit) *Toll Free Tel:* 800-996-6987 (orders) *Fax:* 212-995-3833 (orders) *E-mail:* information@nyupress.org; customerservice@nyupress.org; orders@nyupress.org *Web Site:* www.nyupress.org, pg 179

Coorpender, Bruce, Pocket Press Inc, PO Box 25124, Portland, OR 97298-0124 *Toll Free Tel:* 888-237-2110 *Toll Free Fax:* 877-643-3732 *E-mail:* sales@pocketpressinc.com *Web Site:* www.pocketpressinc.com, pg 203

Coover, Doe, The Doe Coover Agency, PO Box 668, Winchester, MA 01890 *Tel:* 781-721-6000 *Fax:* 781-721-6727 *E-mail:* info@doecooveragency.com *Web Site:* www.doecooveragency.com, pg 567

Copan, Lil, Abingdon Press, 201 Eighth Ave S, Nashville, TN 37203-3919 *Toll Free Tel:* 800-251-3320 *Toll Free Fax:* 800-836-7802 (orders) *E-mail:* orders@abingdonpress.com *Web Site:* www.abingdonpress.com, pg 3

Cope, Christopher, Ascension Press, PO Box 1990, West Chester, PA 19380 *Tel:* 610-696-7795 *Toll Free Tel:* 800-376-0520 (sales & cust serv) *Fax:* 610-696-7796; 608-565-2025 (sales & cust serv) *E-mail:* info@ascensionpress.com *Web Site:* www.ascensionpress.com, pg 23

Cottle, Anna, Cine/Lit Representation, PO Box 802918, Santa Clarita, CA 91380-2918 *Tel:* 661-513-0268 *Fax:* 661-513-0915 *E-mail:* cinelit@att.net, pg 566

Cottrell, Sophie, Hachette Book Group, 237 Park Ave, New York, NY 10017 *Tel:* 212-364-1100 *Toll Free Tel:* 800-759-0190 (cust serv) *Fax:* 212-364-0933 (intl orders) *Toll Free Fax:* 800-286-9471 (cust serv) *Web Site:* www.HachetteBookGroup.com, pg 110

Cotts, Diane, University of Oklahoma Press, 2800 Venture Dr, Norman, OK 73069-8216 *Tel:* 405-325-2000 *Toll Free Tel:* 800-627-7377 (orders) *Fax:* 405-364-5798 (orders) *Toll Free Fax:* 800-735-0476 (orders) *E-mail:* presscs@ou.edu *Web Site:* www.oupress.com, pg 268

Cottter, Glenda, The University of Utah Press, J Willard Marriott Library, Suite 5400, 295 S 1500 E, Salt Lake City, UT 84112-0860 *Tel:* 801-581-6771 *Toll Free Tel:* 800-621-2736 (orders) *Fax:* 801-581-3365 *Toll Free Fax:* 800-621-8471 *E-mail:* info@upress.utah.edu *Web Site:* www.uofupress.com, pg 269

Coughlan, Robert, Capstone Publishers™, 1710 Roe Crest Dr, North Mankato, MN 56003 *Toll Free Tel:* 800-747-4992 (cust serv) *Toll Free Fax:* 888-262-0705 *Web Site:* www.capstonepress.com, pg 51

Counihan, Claire, Holiday House Inc, 425 Madison Ave, New York, NY 10017 *Tel:* 212-688-0085 *Fax:* 212-421-6134 *E-mail:* holiday@holidayhouse.com *Web Site:* www.holidayhouse.com, pg 121

Coupe, Carla, Wildside Press, 414 Hungerford Dr, Suite 234, Rockville, MD 20850 *Tel:* 301-762-1305 *Fax:* 301-762-1306 *E-mail:* wildside@wildsidepress.com *Web Site:* www.wildsidebooks.com, pg 281

Courrier, Kathleen, The Urban Institute Press, 2100 "M" St NW, Washington, DC 20037 *Tel:* 202-261-5885; 410-516-6956 (orders) *Toll Free Tel:* 877-UIPRESS (847-7377); 800-537-5487 (orders) *Fax:* 202-467-5775 *E-mail:* dinscoe@urban.org; hfscustserv@press.jhu.edu *Web Site:* www.uipress.org, pg 273

Court, Kathryn, Penguin Books, 375 Hudson St, New York, NY 10014 *Tel:* 212-366-2000 *E-mail:* online@penguinputnam.com *Web Site:* www.penguinputnam.com; www.penguinclassics.com; us.penguingroup.com, pg 196

Court, Kathryn, Penguin Group (USA) LLC, 375 Hudson St, New York, NY 10014 *Tel:* 212-366-2000 *Toll Free Tel:* 800-847-5515 (inside sales); 800-631-8571 (cust serv) *Fax:* 212-366-2666; 607-775-4829 (inside sales) *E-mail:* online@us.penguingroup.com *Web Site:* www.penguin.com; us.penguingroup.com, pg 197

Court, Kathryn, Plume, 375 Hudson St, New York, NY 10014 *Tel:* 212-366-2000 *Fax:* 212-366-2666 *E-mail:* online@penguinputnam.com *Web Site:* www.penguinputnam.com; us.penguingroup.com, pg 203

Cousens, Ellis E, John Wiley & Sons Inc, 111 River St, Hoboken, NJ 07030-5774 *Tel:* 201-748-6000 *Toll Free Tel:* 800-225-5945 (cust serv) *Fax:* 201-748-6088 *E-mail:* info@wiley.com *Web Site:* www.wiley.com, pg 281

Cousineau, Helene, Editions du renouveau Pedagogique Inc (ERPI), 5757 rue Cypihot, St-Laurent, QC H4S 1R3, Canada *Tel:* 514-334-2690 *Toll Free Tel:* 800-263-3678 *Fax:* 514-334-4720 *Toll Free Fax:* 800-643-4720 *E-mail:* erpidlm@erpi.com *Web Site:* www.erpi.com, pg 503

Cousineau, Lea, International Council for Adult Education, 55 Mont-Royal Ave W, Bureau 303, Montreal, QC H2J 2S4, Canada *Tel:* 514-948-2044 *Toll Free Tel:* 877-948-2044 *Fax:* 514-948-2046 *E-mail:* icae@icea.qc.ca *Web Site:* www.icea.qc.ca, pg 625

Coutu, Caroline, Les Editions Goelette Inc, 1350 Marie-Victorin, St-Bruno-de-Montarville, Quebec, QC J3V 6B9, Canada *Tel:* 450-653-1337 *Toll Free Tel:* 800-463-4961 *Fax:* 450-653-9924 *Web Site:* www.editionsgoelette.com, pg 506

Coutu, Dawn, New Hampshire Literary Awards, 2500 N River Rd, Manchester, NH 03106 *Tel:* 603-314-7980 *Fax:* 603-314-7981 *E-mail:* info@nhwritersproject.org *Web Site:* www.nhwritersproject.org, pg 728

Coutu, Dawn, New Hampshire Writers' Project, 2500 N River Rd, Manchester, NH 03106 *Tel:* 603-314-7980 *Fax:* 603-314-7981 *E-mail:* info@nhwritersproject.org *Web Site:* www.nhwritersproject.org, pg 631

Covell, John S, The MIT Press, 55 Hayward St, Cambridge, MA 02142 *Tel:* 617-253-5255 *Toll Free Tel:* 800-207-8354 (orders) *Fax:* 617-258-6779; 617-577-1545 (orders) *Web Site:* mitpress.mit.edu, pg 167

Covelli-Hunt, Robyn, Sun Books - Sun Publishing Co, PO Box 5588, Santa Fe, NM 87502-5588 *Tel:* 505-471-5177; 505-473-4161 *Toll Free Tel:* 877-849-0051 *Fax:* 505-473-4458 *E-mail:* info@sunbooks.com *Web Site:* www.sunbooks.com, pg 247

Cover, Arthur Byron, Babbage Press, 8939 Canby Ave, Northridge, CA 91325-2702 *Tel:* 818-341-3161 *E-mail:* books@babbagepress.com *Web Site:* www.babbagepress.com, pg 29

Cowell, Mary, Management Concepts Inc, 8230 Leesburg Pike, Suite 800, Vienna, VA 22182 *Tel:* 703-790-9595 *Toll Free Tel:* 800 506-4450 *Fax:* 703-790-1371 *E-mail:* publications@managementconcepts.com *Web Site:* www.managementconcepts.com, pg 155

Cowles, Lauren, Cambridge University Press, 32 Avenue of the Americas, New York, NY 10013-2473 *Tel:* 212-924-3900; 212-337-5000 *Toll Free Tel:* 800-899-5222 *Fax:* 212-691-3239 *E-mail:* newyork@cambridge.org *Web Site:* www.cambridge.org/us, pg 51

Cowlin, Scott, Peachpit Press, 1249 Eighth St, Berkeley, CA 94710 *Tel:* 510-524-2178 *Toll Free Tel:* 800-283-9444 *Fax:* 510-524-2221 *E-mail:* info@peachpit.com *Web Site:* www.peachpit.com, pg 195

Cox, Beth, McFarland, 960 NC Hwy 88 W, Jefferson, NC 28640 *Tel:* 336-246-4460 *Toll Free Tel:* 800-253-2187 (orders) *Fax:* 336-246-5018; 336-246-4403 (orders) *E-mail:* info@mcfarlandpub.com *Web Site:* www.mcfarlandpub.com, pg 160

Cox, Clare, Rowman & Littlefield Publishers Inc, 4501 Forbes Blvd, Suite 200, Lanham, MD 20706 *Tel:* 301-459-3366 *Toll Free Tel:* 800-462-6420 (cust serv) *Fax:* 301-429-5748 *Web Site:* www.rowmanlittlefield.com, pg 221

Cox, Clare, Scarecrow Press Inc, 4501 Forbes Blvd, Suite 200, Lanham, MD 20706 *Tel:* 301-459-3366 *Fax:* 301-429-5748 *Web Site:* www.scarecrowpress.com, pg 226

Cox, Clare, University Press of America Inc, 4501 Forbes Blvd, Suite 200, Lanham, MD 20706 *Tel:* 301-459-3366 *Toll Free Tel:* 800-462-6420 *Fax:* 301-429-5748 *Toll Free Fax:* 800-338-4550 *Web Site:* www.univpress.com, pg 270

Cox, Jon, Painted Pony Inc, 3 Ethete Rd, Fort Washakie, WY 82514 *Tel:* 307-335-7330 *Toll Free Tel:* 877-253-3824 *Fax:* 307-335-7332 *E-mail:* ppi@wrdf.org *Web Site:* www.paintedponyinc.com, pg 191

Cox, Jonathan, Simon & Schuster, 1230 Avenue of the Americas, New York, NY 10020 *Tel:* 212-698-7000 *Toll Free Tel:* 800-223-2348 (cust serv); 800-223-2336 (orders) *Toll Free Fax:* 800-943-9831 (orders) *Web Site:* www.simonandschuster.com, pg 234

Cox, Merrilee, Society for Features Journalism (SFJ), University of Maryland, College of Journalism, 1100 Knight Hall, College Park, MD 20742 *Tel:* 301-314-2631 *Fax:* 301-314-9166 *Web Site:* featuresjournalism.org, pg 636

Cox, Tom, Whitaker House, 1030 Hunt Valley Circle, New Kensington, PA 15068 *Tel:* 724-334-7000 *Toll Free Tel:* 877-793-9800 *Fax:* 724-334-1200 *Toll Free Fax:* 800-765-1960 *E-mail:* publisher@whitakerhouse.com *Web Site:* whitakerhouse.com, pg 280

Coyle, Lily, Beaver's Pond Press Inc, 7108 Ohms Lane, Edina, MN 55439-2129 *Tel:* 952-829-8818 *Web Site:* www.beaverspondpress.com, pg 33

Coyne, Christopher, Marshall Cavendish Corp, 99 White Plains Rd, Tarrytown, NY 10591-9001 *Tel:* 914-332-8888 *Toll Free Tel:* 800-821-9881 *Fax:* 914-332-8102 *E-mail:* customerservice@marshallcavendish.com; mcc@marshallcavendish.com *Web Site:* marshallcavendish.us; marshallcavendishdigital.com; marshallcavendishebooks.com, pg 158

Coyne, Frank, George T Bisel Co Inc, 710 S Washington Sq, Philadelphia, PA 19106-3519 *Tel:* 215-922-5760 *Toll Free Tel:* 800-247-3526 *Fax:* 215-922-2235 *E-mail:* gbisel@bisel.com *Web Site:* www.bisel.com, pg 38

Coyne, Mary, Random House Speakers Bureau, 1745 Broadway, Mail Drop 13-1, New York, NY 10019 *Tel:* 212-572-2013 *E-mail:* rhspeakers@randomhouse.com *Web Site:* www.rhspeakers.com, pg 605

Coyne, Rachel, FinePrint Literary Management, 115 W 29 St, 3rd fl, New York, NY 10001 *Tel:* 212-279-1282 *Web Site:* www.fineprintlit.com, pg 571

Craane, Isle, BookStop Literary Agency LLC, 67 Meadow View Rd, Orinda, CA 94563 *E-mail:* info@bookstopliterary.com *Web Site:* www.bookstopliterary.com, pg 563

Crabtree, Peter A, Crabtree Publishing Co, 350 Fifth Ave, 59th fl, PMB 59051, New York, NY 10118 *Tel:* 212-496-5040 *Toll Free Tel:* 800-387-7650 *Toll Free Fax:* 800-355-7166 *E-mail:* custserv@crabtreebooks.com *Web Site:* www.crabtreebooks.com, pg 70

Crabtree, Peter A, Crabtree Publishing Co Ltd, 616 Welland Ave, St Catharines, ON L2M-5V6, Canada *Tel:* 905-682-5221 *Toll Free Tel:* 800-387-7650 *Fax:* 905-682-7166 *Toll Free Fax:* 800-355-7166 *E-mail:* custserv@crabtreebooks.com; sales@crabtreebooks.com; orders@crabtreebooks.com *Web Site:* www.crabtreebooks.com, pg 500

Crabtree, Tamara, Abingdon Press, 201 Eighth Ave S, Nashville, TN 37203-3919 *Toll Free Tel:* 800-251-3320 *Toll Free Fax:* 800-836-7802 (orders) *E-mail:* orders@abingdonpress.com *Web Site:* www.abingdonpress.com, pg 3

Craft, Baird, Jones McClure Publishing, 3131 Eastside St, Suite 300, Houston, TX 77098 *Tel:* 713-335-8200 *Toll Free Tel:* 800-626-6667 *Fax:* 713-335-8201 *E-mail:* comments@jonesmcclure.com *Web Site:* www.jonesmcclure.com, pg 137

Cragin, Sally, Barbara Bradley Prize, 2 Farrar St, Cambridge, MA 02138 *Tel:* 617-744-6034 *E-mail:* contests@nepoetryclub.org *Web Site:* www.nepoetryclub.org, pg 692

Cragin, Sally, Der-Hovanessian Translation Prize, 2 Farrar St, Cambridge, MA 02138 *Tel:* 617-744-6034 *E-mail:* contests@nepoetryclub.org *Web Site:* www.nepoetryclub.org, pg 700

Cragin, Sally, Golden Rose Award, 2 Farrar St, Cambridge, MA 02138 *Tel:* 617-744-6034 *E-mail:* contests@nepoetryclub.org *Web Site:* www.nepoetryclub.org, pg 707

Cragin, Sally, Firman Houghton Prize, 2 Farrar St, Cambridge, MA 02138 *Tel:* 617-744-6034 *E-mail:* contests@nepoetryclub.org *Web Site:* www.nepoetryclub.org, pg 710

Cragin, Sally, Sheila Margaret Motton Prize, 2 Farrar St, Cambridge, MA 02138 *Tel:* 617-744-6034 *E-mail:* contests@nepoetryclub.org *Web Site:* www.nepoetryclub.org, pg 725

Cragin, Sally, Erika Mumford Prize, 2 Farrar St, Cambridge, MA 02138 *Tel:* 617-744-6034 *E-mail:* contests@nepoetryclub.org *Web Site:* www.nepoetryclub.org, pg 725

Cragin, Sally, New England Poetry Club, 2 Farrar St, Cambridge, MA 02138 *Tel:* 617-744-6034 *E-mail:* info@nepoetryclub.org *Web Site:* www.nepoetryclub.org, pg 631

Cragin, Sally, May Sarton Award, 2 Farrar St, Cambridge, MA 02138 *Tel:* 617-744-6034 *E-mail:* contests@nepoetryclub.org *Web Site:* www.nepoetryclub.org, pg 739

Cragin, Sally, Daniel Varoujan Award, 2 Farrar St, Cambridge, MA 02138 *Tel:* 617-744-6034 *E-mail:* contests@nepoetryclub.org *Web Site:* www.nepoetryclub.org, pg 747

Crahan, Eric, Princeton University Press, 41 William St, Princeton, NJ 08540-5237 *Tel:* 609-258-4900 *Toll Free Tel:* 800-777-4726 (orders) *Fax:* 609-258-6305 *Toll Free Fax:* 800-999-1958 *E-mail:* orders@cpfsinc.com *Web Site:* press.princeton.edu, pg 206

Craig, Bryce H, P & R Publishing Co, 1102 Marble Hill Rd, Phillipsburg, NJ 08865 *Tel:* 908-454-0505 *Toll Free Tel:* 800-631-0094 *Fax:* 908-859-2390 *E-mail:* sales@prpbooks.com; generalinfo@prpbooks.com *Web Site:* prpbooks.com, pg 190

Craig, Jo Ann, Harold W McGraw Jr - Prize in Education, 1221 Avenue of the Americas, 47th fl, New York, NY 10020-1095 *Tel:* 212-904-2000; 212-512-2000 *Fax:* 212-512-3611 *Web Site:* www.mhfi.com, pg 722

Craigo-Snell, Shannon, Louisville Grawemeyer Award in Religion, 1044 Alta Vista Rd, Louisville, KY 40205-1798 *Tel:* 502-895-3411 *Toll Free Tel:* 800-264-1839 *Fax:* 502-894-2286 *E-mail:* grawemeyer@lpts.edu *Web Site:* www.grawemeyer.org, pg 719

Crane, Edward H, Cato Institute, 1000 Massachusetts Ave NW, Washington, DC 20001-5403 *Tel:* 202-842-0200 *Toll Free Tel:* 800-767-1241 *Fax:* 202-842-3490 *E-mail:* catostore@cato.org *Web Site:* www.cato.org, pg 54

Cranfill, Jennifer, Morton Marr Poetry Prize, 6404 Robert Hyer Lane, Rm 307, Dallas, TX 75275-0374 *Fax:* 214-768-1408 *E-mail:* swr@mail.smu.edu *Web Site:* www.smu.edu/southwestreview, pg 721

Cranfill, Jennifer, John H McGinnis Memorial Award, 6404 Robert Hyer Lane, Rm 307, Dallas, TX 75275-0374 *Fax:* 214-768-1408 *E-mail:* swr@mail.smu.edu *Web Site:* www.smu.edu/southwestreview, pg 722

Cranfill, Jennifer, The David Nathan Meyerson Prize for Fiction, 6404 Robert Hyer Lane, Rm 307, Dallas, TX 75275-0374 *Fax:* 214-768-1408 *E-mail:* swr@mail.smu.edu *Web Site:* www.smu.edu/southwestreview, pg 723

Cranfill, Jennifer, Elizabeth Matchett Stover Memorial Award, 6404 Robert Hyer Lane, Rm 307, Dallas, TX 75275-0374 *Fax:* 214-768-1408 *E-mail:* swr@mail.smu.edu *Web Site:* www.smu.edu/southwestreview, pg 744

Cranford, Garry, Flanker Press Ltd, 1243 Kenmount Rd, Unit A, Paradise, NL A1L 0V8, Canada *Tel:* 709-739-4477 *Toll Free Tel:* 866-739-4420 *Fax:* 709-739-4420 *E-mail:* info@flankerpress.com *Web Site:* www.flankerpress.com, pg 506

Cranford, Jerry, Flanker Press Ltd, 1243 Kenmount Rd, Unit A, Paradise, NL A1L 0V8, Canada *Tel:* 709-739-4477 *Toll Free Tel:* 866-739-4420 *Fax:* 709-739-4420 *E-mail:* info@flankerpress.com *Web Site:* www.flankerpress.com, pg 506

Crary, Elizabeth, Parenting Press Inc, 11065 Fifth Ave NE, Suite F, Seattle, WA 98125 *Tel:* 206-364-2900 *Toll Free Tel:* 800-99-BOOKS (992-6657) *Fax:* 206-364-0702 *E-mail:* office@parentingpress.com; marketing@parentingpress.com *Web Site:* www.parentingpress.com, pg 193

Crary, Jonathan, Zone Books dba Urzone Inc, 1226 Prospect Ave, Brooklyn, NY 11218 *Tel:* 718-686-0048 *Toll Free Tel:* 800-405-1619 (orders & cust serv) *Fax:* 718-686-9045 *Toll Free Fax:* 800-406-9145 (orders) *E-mail:* orders@triliteral.org *Web Site:* www.zonebooks.org, pg 289

Craven, Kim, Oxford University Press USA, 198 Madison Ave, New York, NY 10016 *Tel:* 212-726-6000 *Toll Free Tel:* 800-451-7556 (orders); 800-445-9714 (cust serv) *Fax:* 919-677-1303 *E-mail:* custserv.us@oup.com *Web Site:* www.oup.com/us, pg 189

Craven, Robert H Jr, F A Davis Co, 1915 Arch St, Philadelphia, PA 19103 *Tel:* 215-568-2270 *Toll Free Tel:* 800-523-4049 *Fax:* 215-568-5065 *E-mail:* info@fadavis.com *Web Site:* www.fadavis.com, pg 76

Craven, Robert H Sr, F A Davis Co, 1915 Arch St, Philadelphia, PA 19103 *Tel:* 215-568-2270 *Toll Free Tel:* 800-523-4049 *Fax:* 215-568-5065 *E-mail:* info@fadavis.com *Web Site:* www.fadavis.com, pg 76

Crawford, Ann H, Geological Society of America (GSA), 3300 Penrose Place, Boulder, CO 80301-1806 *Tel:* 303-357-1000 *Fax:* 303-357-1070 *E-mail:* pubs@geosociety.org (prodn); editing@geosociety.org (edit) *Web Site:* www.geosociety.org, pg 102

Crawford, Betty Anne, The Jennifer DeChiara Literary Agency, 31 E 32 St, Suite 300, New York, NY 10016 *Tel:* 212-481-8484 (ext 362) *Fax:* 212-481-9582 *Web Site:* www.jdlit.com, pg 568

Crawford, Ingrid, North American Bookdealers Exchange (NABE), PO Box 606, Cottage Grove, OR 97424-0026 *Tel:* 541-942-7455 *E-mail:* nabe@bookmarketingprofits.com *Web Site:* www.bookmarketingprofits.com, pg 632

Crawford, Kristen, Arcadia Publishing Inc, 420 Wando Park Blvd, Mount Pleasant, SC 29464 *Tel:* 843-853-2070 *Toll Free Tel:* 888-313-2665 (orders only) *Fax:* 843-853-0044 *E-mail:* sales@arcadiapublishing.com *Web Site:* www.arcadiapublishing.com, pg 21

Crawford, Nate, Atlantic Poetry Prize, 1113 Marginal Rd, Halifax, NS B3H 4P7, Canada *Tel:* 902-423-8116 *Fax:* 902-422-0881 *E-mail:* talk@writers.ns.ca *Web Site:* www.writers.ns.ca, pg 688

Crawford, Nate, Thomas Head Raddall Atlantic Fiction Award, 1113 Marginal Rd, Halifax, NS B3H 4P7, Canada *Tel:* 902-423-8116 *Fax:* 902-422-0881 *E-mail:* talk@writers.ns.ca *Web Site:* www.writers.ns.ca, pg 737

Crawford, Nate, Evelyn Richardson Memorial Literary Trust Award, 1113 Marginal Rd, Halifax, NS B3H 4P7, Canada *Tel:* 902-423-8116 *Fax:* 902-422-0881 *E-mail:* talk@writers.ns.ca *Web Site:* www.writers.ns.ca, pg 738

Crawford, Nate, Writers' Federation of Nova Scotia, 1113 Marginal Rd, Halifax, NS B3H 4P7, Canada *Tel:* 902-423-8116 *Fax:* 902-422-0881 *E-mail:* talk@writers.ns.ca *Web Site:* www.writers.ns.ca, pg 638

Crawford, Tad, Allworth Press, 307 W 36 St, 11th fl, New York, NY 10018 *Tel:* 212-643-6816 *E-mail:* crawford@allworth.com *Web Site:* www.allworth.com, pg 9

Crawford, William R Sr, Military Living Publications, 333 Maple Ave E, Suite 3130, Vienna, VA 22180-4717 *Tel:* 703-237-0203 (ext 1) *Toll Free Tel:* 877-363-4677 (ext 1) *Fax:* 703-997-8861 *E-mail:* customerservice@militaryliving.com *Web Site:* www.militaryliving.com, pg 166

Crawford-Lee, Jeannie, Upper Room Books, 1908 Grand Ave, Nashville, TN 37212 *Tel:* 615-340-7200 *Toll Free Tel:* 800-972-0433 *Fax:* 615-340-7266 *E-mail:* urbooks@upperroom.org *Web Site:* www.upperroom.org, pg 273

Crawley, Sandy, Professional Writers Association of Canada (PWAC), 215 Spadina Ave, Suite 130, Toronto, ON M5T 2C7, Canada *Tel:* 416-504-1645 *E-mail:* info@pwac.ca *Web Site:* www.pwac.ca; www.writers.ca, pg 634

Creamer, Stacy, Simon & Schuster, Inc, 1230 Avenue of the Americas, New York, NY 10020 *Tel:* 212-698-7000 *Fax:* 212-698-7007 *E-mail:* firstname.lastname@simonandschuster.com *Web Site:* www.simonandschuster.com, pg 235

Creamer, Stacy, Touchstone, 1230 Avenue of the Americas, New York, NY 10020, pg 256

Crean, Patrick, HarperCollins Canada Ltd, 2 Bloor St E, 20th fl, Toronto, ON M4W 1A8, Canada *Tel:* 416-975-9334 *Fax:* 416-975-9884 *E-mail:* hccanada@harpercollins.com *Web Site:* www.harpercollins.ca, pg 508

Crecca, Paul J, Haights Cross Communications Inc, 136 Madison Ave, 8th fl, New York, NY 10016 *Tel:* 212-209-0500 *Fax:* 212-209-0501 *E-mail:* info@haightscross.com *Web Site:* www.haightscross.com, pg 110

Creehan, Tara, Chronicle Books LLC, 680 Second St, San Francisco, CA 94107 *Tel:* 415-537-4200 *Toll Free Tel:* 800-759-0190 (cust serv) *Fax:* 415-537-4460 *Toll Free Fax:* 800-858-7787 (orders); 800-286-9471 (cust serv) *E-mail:* frontdesk@chroniclebooks.com *Web Site:* www.chroniclebooks.com, pg 61

Crevier, Yvonne, University of Massachusetts Press, East Experiment Sta, 671 N Pleasant St, Amherst, MA 01003 *Tel:* 413-545-2217 *Fax:* 413-545-1226 *E-mail:* info@umpress.umass.edu *Web Site:* www.umass.edu/umpress, pg 266

Crewe, Jennifer, Columbia University Press, 61 W 62 St, New York, NY 10023 *Tel:* 212-459-0600 *Toll Free Tel:* 800-944-8648 *Fax:* 212-459-3678 *E-mail:* cup_book@columbia.edu (orders & cust serv) *Web Site:* cup.columbia.edu, pg 65

Crichton, Paul, Simon & Schuster Children's Publishing, 1230 Avenue of the Americas, New York, NY 10020 *Tel:* 212-698-7000 *Web Site:* KIDS.SimonandSchuster.com; TEEN.SimonandSchuster.com; simonandschuster.net; simonandschuster.biz, pg 235

Crichton, Sha-Shana, Crichton & Associates Inc, 6940 Carroll Ave, Takoma Park, MD 20912 *Tel:* 301-495-9663 *E-mail:* cricht1@aol.com *Web Site:* www.crichton-associates.com, pg 567

Crilly, Donna, Paulist Press, 997 MacArthur Blvd, Mahwah, NJ 07430-9990 *Tel:* 201-825-7300 *Toll Free Tel:* 800-218-1903 *Fax:* 201-825-8345 *Toll Free Fax:* 800-836-3161 *E-mail:* info@paulistpress.com *Web Site:* www.paulistpress.com, pg 195

Crim, Michele, Crown Publishing Group, c/o Random House Inc, 1745 Broadway, New York, NY 10019 *Tel:* 212-782-9000 *Toll Free Tel:* 888-264-1745 *Fax:* 212-940-7408 *Web Site:* www.randomhouse.com/crown, pg 72

Crim, Michele, Ten Speed Press, 2625 Alcatraz Ave, Unit 505, Berkeley, CA 94705 *Tel:* 510-285-3000 *Toll Free Tel:* 800-841-BOOK (841-2665) *E-mail:* csorders@randomhouse.com *Web Site:* crownpublishing.com/imprint/ten-speed-press, pg 252

Crippen, Cynthia, AEIOU Inc, 894 Piermont Ave, Piermont, NY 10968 *Tel:* 845-680-5380 *Fax:* 845-680-5380, pg 539

Crisp, Laura, Vintage & Anchor Books, c/o Random House Inc, 1745 Broadway, New York, NY 10019 *Tel:* 212-572-2420 *E-mail:* vintageanchorpublicity@randomhouse.com *Web Site:* vintage-anchor.knopfdoubleday.com, pg 275

Crispell, Chris, Beckett Media LLC, 22840 Savi Ranch Pkwy, Suite 200, Yorba Linda, CA 92887 *Tel:* 714-939-9991 *Toll Free Tel:* 800-332-3330 *Fax:* 714-939-9909 *Toll Free Fax:* 800-249-7761 *Web Site:* www.beckettmedia.com, pg 33

Crissman, Dan, The Overlook Press, 141 Wooster St, Suite 4-B, New York, NY 10012 *Tel:* 212-673-2210; 845-679-6838 (orders & dist) *Fax:* 212-673-2296 *E-mail:* sales@overlookny.com (orders) *Web Site:* www.overlookpress.com, pg 189

Crist, Steve, AMMO Books LLC, 300 S Raymond Ave, Suite 3, Pasadena, CA 91105 *Tel:* 323-223-AMMO (223-2666) *Toll Free Tel:* 888-642-AMMO (642-2666) *Fax:* 323-978-4200 *Web Site:* www.ammobooks.com, pg 17

Cristofaro, Joe, Groupe Educalivres Inc, 955, rue Bergar, Laval, QC H7L 4Z6, Canada *Tel:* 514-334-8466 *Toll Free Tel:* 800-567-3671 (info serv) *Fax:* 514-334-8387 *E-mail:* commentaires@educalivres.com *Web Site:* www.educalivres.com, pg 507

Critelli, Chris, Oxford University Press USA, 198 Madison Ave, New York, NY 10016 *Tel:* 212-726-6000 *Toll Free Tel:* 800-451-7556 (orders); 800-445-9714 (cust serv) *Fax:* 919-677-1303 *E-mail:* custserv.us@oup.com *Web Site:* www.oup.com/us, pg 189

Crocco, Kathy, MAR*CO Products Inc, 1443 Old York Rd, Warminster, PA 18974 *Tel:* 215-956-0313 *Toll Free Tel:* 800-448-2197 *Fax:* 215-956-9041 *E-mail:* help@marcoproducts.com *Web Site:* www.marcoproducts.com, pg 156

Croce, Mr Carmen R, St Joseph's University Press, 5600 City Ave, Philadelphia, PA 19131-1395 *Tel:* 610-660-3402 *Fax:* 610-660-3412 *E-mail:* sjupress@sju.edu *Web Site:* www.sjupress.com, pg 224

Crocker, Amanda, Between the Lines, 401 Richmond St W, No 277, Toronto, ON M5V 3A8, Canada *Tel:* 416-535-9914 *Toll Free Tel:* 800-718-7201 *Fax:* 416-535-1484 *E-mail:* info@btlbooks.com *Web Site:* www.btlbooks.com, pg 494

Crocker, Harry W III, Regnery Publishing Inc, One Massachusetts Ave NW, Washington, DC 20001 *Tel:* 202-216-0600 *Toll Free Tel:* 888-219 4747 *Fax:* 202-216-0612 *Web Site:* www.regnery.com, pg 217

Crockett, Barbara, Standard Publishing Corp, 155 Federal St, 13th fl, Boston, MA 02110 *Tel:* 617-457-0600 *Toll Free Tel:* 800-682-5759 *Fax:* 617-457-0608 *Web Site:* www.spcpub.com, pg 242

Croft, Charles R, Madavor Media, 21027 Crossroads Circle, Waukesha, WI 53187-1612 *Tel:* 262-796-8776 *Toll Free Tel:* 800-533-6644 (cust serv & orders) *Fax:* 262-796-1615 (sales & cust serv); 262-798-6468 (edit) *Web Site:* www.kalmbach.com, pg 155

Croft, Diane, National Braille Press, 88 Saint Stephen St, Boston, MA 02115-4302 *Tel:* 617-266-6160 *Toll Free Tel:* 800-548-7323 (cust serv); 888-965-8965 *Fax:* 617-437-0456 *E-mail:* orders@nbp.org *Web Site:* www.nbp.org, pg 173

Crompton, Linda, BoardSource, 750 Ninth St NW, Suite 650, Washington, DC 20001-4793 *Tel:* 202-349-2500 *Toll Free Tel:* 877-892-6273 *Fax:* 202-349-2599 *E-mail:* members@boardsource.org *Web Site:* www.boardsource.org, pg 42

Cronin, Dan, Peradam Press, PO Box 6, North San Juan, CA 95960-0006 *Tel:* 530-292-4266 *Fax:* 530-292-4266 *E-mail:* peradam@earthlink.net, pg 199

Cronin, Denise, Random House Publishing Group, 1745 Broadway, New York, NY 10019 *Toll Free Tel:* 800-200-3552 *Web Site:* atrandom.com, pg 214

Cronin, Denise, Viking Children's Books, 345 Hudson St, New York, NY 10014 *Tel:* 212-366-2000 *E-mail:* online@penguinputnam.com *Web Site:* www.penguinputnam.com; us.penguingroup.com, pg 275

Cronin, John, The Johns Hopkins University Press, 2715 N Charles St, Baltimore, MD 21218-4363 *Tel:* 410-516-6900; 410-516-6987 (journals outside US & CN) *Toll Free Tel:* 800-537-5487 (book orders & cust serv); 800-548-1784 (journal orders) *Fax:* 410-516-6968; 410-516-3866 (journal orders) *E-mail:* hfscustserv@press.jhu.edu (cust serv); jrnlcirc@press.jhu.edu (journal orders) *Web Site:* www.press.jhu.edu; muse.jhu.edu/about/subscriptions/index.html (Project Muse subns), pg 136

Cronin, Thomas, St Martin's Press, LLC, 175 Fifth Ave, New York, NY 10010 *Tel:* 646-307-5151 *Fax:* 212-420-9314 *E-mail:* firstname.lastname@macmillan.com *Web Site:* www.stmartins.com, pg 224

Cronk, Kevin, Fox Run Press LLC, 7840 Bullet Rd, Peyton, OH 80831 *Tel:* 719-482-4035 *Fax:* 719-623-0254 *E-mail:* info@foxrunpress.com *Web Site:* www.foxrunpress.com, pg 98

Cronshaw, Francine, East Mountain Editing Services, PO Box 1895, Tijeras, NM 87059-1895 *Tel:* 505-281-8422 *Fax:* 505-281-8422 *Web Site:* www.spanishindexing.com, pg 545

Cronyn, Melissa, National Park Service Media Services, 67 Mather Place, Harpers Ferry, WV 25425 *Tel:* 304-535-5050 *Fax:* 304-535-6176 *Web Site:* www.nps.gov/hfc, pg 175

Crooks, Cathie, University of Alberta Press, Ring House 2, Edmonton, AB T6G 2E1, Canada *Tel:* 780-492-3662 *Fax:* 780-492-0719 *Web Site:* www.uap.ualberta.ca, pg 522

Crooks, Jaye, University of Baltimore - College of Arts & Sciences, Ampersand Institute for Words & Images, 1420 N Charles St, Baltimore, MD 21201-5779 *Tel:* 410-837-6022 *Fax:* 410-837-6029 *E-mail:* scd@ubalt.edu *Web Site:* www.ubalt.edu, pg 681

Cropsey, Marvin, Abingdon Press, 201 Eighth Ave S, Nashville, TN 37203-3919 *Toll Free Tel:* 800-251-3320 *Toll Free Fax:* 800-836-7802 (orders) *E-mail:* orders@abingdonpress.com *Web Site:* www.abingdonpress.com, pg 3

Crosby, Calvin, Northern California Independent Booksellers Association (NCIBA), 1007 General Kennedy Ave, San Francisco, CA 94129 *Tel:* 415-561-7686 *Fax:* 415-561-7685 *E-mail:* office@nciba.com *Web Site:* www.nciba.com, pg 632

Crosby, Jeff, InterVarsity Press, 430 Plaza Dr, Westmont, IL 60559-1234 *Tel:* 630-734-4000 *Toll Free Tel:* 800 843-9487 *Fax:* 630-734-4200 *E-mail:* email@ivpress.com *Web Site:* www.ivpress.com, pg 134

Crosby, Lori R, Duquesne University Press, 600 Forbes Ave, Pittsburgh, PA 15282 *Tel:* 412-396-6610 *Fax:* 412-396-5984 *E-mail:* dupress@duq.edu *Web Site:* www.dupress.duq.edu, pg 83

Crosby, Patricia, University of Hawaii Press, 2840 Kolowalu St, Honolulu, HI 96822 *Tel:* 808-956-8255 *Toll Free Tel:* 888-UHPRESS (847-7377) *Fax:* 808-988-6052 *Toll Free Fax:* 800-650-7811 *E-mail:* uhpbooks@hawaii.edu *Web Site:* www.uhpress.hawaii.edu, pg 265

Cross, Claudia, Folio Literary Management LLC, The Film Center Bldg, 630 Ninth Ave, Suite 1101, New York, NY 10036 *Tel:* 212-400-1494 *Fax:* 212-967-0977 *Web Site:* www.foliolit.com, pg 572

Cross, Jamie, Math Solutions®, 150 Gate 5 Rd, Suite 101, Sausalito, CA 94965 *Tel:* 415-332-4181 *Toll Free Tel:* 800-868-9092 *Fax:* 415-331-1931 *Toll Free Fax:* 877-942-8837 *E-mail:* info@mathsolutions.com; orders@mathsolutions.com *Web Site:* www.mathsolutions.com, pg 159

Cross, Jeff, Hoover's, Inc, 5800 Airport Blvd, Austin, TX 78752 *Tel:* 512-374-4500 *Toll Free Tel:* 866-307-3812 *Fax:* 512-374-4501 *E-mail:* info@hoovers.com *Web Site:* www.hoovers.com, pg 122

Cross, John C Esq, Standard Publishing Corp, 155 Federal St, 13th fl, Boston, MA 02110 *Tel:* 617-457-0600 *Toll Free Tel:* 800-682-5759 *Fax:* 617-457-0608 *Web Site:* www.spcpub.com, pg 242

Cross, William K, The Charlton Press, PO Box 820, Sta Willowdale B, North York, ON M2K 2R1, Canada *Tel:* 416-488-1418 *Toll Free Tel:* 800-442-6042 (North America) *Fax:* 416-488-4656 *Toll Free Fax:* 800-442-1542 (North America) *E-mail:* chpress@charltonpress.com *Web Site:* www.charltonpress.com, pg 498

Crosse, Ann Mehan, Society for Scholarly Publishing (SSP), 10200 W 44 Ave, Suite 304, Wheat Ridge, CO 80033-2840 *Tel:* 303-422-3914 *Fax:* 303-422-8894 *E-mail:* info@sspnet.org *Web Site:* www.sspnet.org, pg 636

Crossley, Guy, Business & Legal Reports Inc (BLR), 100 Winners Circle, Suite 300, Brentwood, CT 37027 *Tel:* 860-510-0100 *Toll Free Tel:* 800-727-5257 *E-mail:* service@blr.com *Web Site:* www.blr.com, pg 50

Crossley, Guy, M Lee Smith Publishers LLC, 5201 Virginia Way, Brentwood, TN 37027 *Tel:* 615-373-7517 *Toll Free Tel:* 800-274-6774 *Fax:* 615-373-5183 *E-mail:* custserv@mleesmith.com *Web Site:* www.mleesmith.com, pg 237

Croteau, Marie, CCH Canadian Limited, A Wolters Kluwer Company, 90 Sheppard Ave E, Suite 300, Toronto, ON M2N 6X1, Canada *Tel:* 416-224-2224 *Toll Free Tel:* 800-268-4522 (CN & US cust serv) *Fax:* 416-224-2243 *Toll Free Fax:* 800-461-4131 *E-mail:* cservice@cch.ca (cust serv) *Web Site:* www.cch.ca, pg 498

Crouch, Anthony, University of California Press, 2120 Berkeley Way, Berkeley, CA 94704-1012 *Tel:* 510-642-4247 *Fax:* 510-643-7127 *E-mail:* askucp@ucpress.edu (books); customerservice@ucpressjournals.com (journals) *Web Site:* www.ucpress.edu, pg 264

Crouchet, Mike, Cardiotext Publishing, 3405 W 44 St, Minneapolis, MN 55410 *Tel:* 612-925-2053 *Toll Free Tel:* 888-999-9174 *Fax:* 612-922-7556 *E-mail:* info@cardiotextpublishing.com *Web Site:* www.cardiotextpublishing.com, pg 52

Crow, Dennis, Maisonneuve Press, 6423 Adelphi Rd, Hyattsville, MD 20782 *Tel:* 301-277-7505 *Fax:* 301-277-2467 *Web Site:* www.maisonneuvepress.com, pg 155

Crowe, Sara, Harvey Klinger Inc, 300 W 55 St, Suite 11-V, New York, NY 10019 *Tel:* 212-581-7068 *Fax:* 212-315-3823 *E-mail:* queries@harveyklinger.com *Web Site:* www.harveyklinger.com, pg 580

Crowe-Lile, Katie, Harcourt Mifflin School Publishers, 6277 Sea Harbor Dr, Orlando, FL 32887 *Tel:* 407-345-2000 *Toll Free Tel:* 800-225-5425 (cust serv) *Fax:* 407-345-3016 (cust serv) *Toll Free Fax:* 800-874-6418; 800-269-5232 (cust serv) *Web Site:* www.harcourtschool.com, pg 112

Crowley, James M, Society for Industrial & Applied Mathematics, 3600 Market St, 6th fl, Philadelphia, PA 19104-2688 *Tel:* 215-382-9800 *Toll Free Tel:* 800-447-7426 *Fax:* 215-386-7999 *E-mail:* siambooks@siam.org *Web Site:* www.siam.org, pg 238

Crowley, Louise, Vermont College of Fine Arts, MFA in Writing Program, 36 College St, Montpelier, VT 05602 *Tel:* 802-828-8840; 802-828-8839 *Toll Free Tel:* 866-934-VCFA (934-8232) *Fax:* 802-828-8649 *Web Site:* www.vcfa.edu, pg 682

Crowther, Duane S, Horizon Publishers & Distributors Inc, 191 N 650 E, Bountiful, UT 84010-3628 *Tel:* 801-292-7102 *E-mail:* ldshorizonpublishers@gmail.com *Web Site:* www.ldshorizonpublishers.com, pg 123

Crowther, Jean D, Horizon Publishers & Distributors Inc, 191 N 650 E, Bountiful, UT 84010-3628 *Tel:* 801-292-7102 *E-mail:* ldshorizonpublishers@gmail.com *Web Site:* www.ldshorizonpublishers.com, pg 123

Crum, Erin, HarperCollins Publishers, 10 E 53 St, New York, NY 10022 *Tel:* 212-207-7000 *Fax:* 212-207-7145 *Web Site:* www.harpercollins.com, pg 113

Crumly, Chuck, University of California Press, 2120 Berkeley Way, Berkeley, CA 94704-1012 *Tel:* 510-642-4247 *Fax:* 510-643-7127 *E-mail:* askucp@ucpress.edu (books); customerservice@ucpressjournals.com (journals) *Web Site:* www.ucpress.edu, pg 264

Crumpacker, Caroline, Residency, 454 E Hill Rd, Austerlitz, NY 12017 *Tel:* 518-392-3103; 518-392-4144 *E-mail:* apply@millaycolony.org *Web Site:* www.millaycolony.org, pg 737

Cruz, Ricky, US Games Systems Inc, 179 Ludlow St, Stamford, CT 06902 *Tel:* 203-353-8400 *Toll Free Tel:* 800-54-GAMES (544-2637) *Fax:* 203-353-8431 *E-mail:* info@usgamesinc.com *Web Site:* www.usgamesinc.com, pg 273

Cruz-Munoz, Mariana, Holiday House Inc, 425 Madison Ave, New York, NY 10017 *Tel:* 212-688-0085 *Fax:* 212-421-6134 *E-mail:* holiday@holidayhouse.com *Web Site:* www.holidayhouse.com, pg 121

Cryer, Bruce, HeartMath LLC, 14700 W Park Ave, Boulder Creek, CA 95006 *Tel:* 831-338-8700 *Toll Free Tel:* 800-450-9111 *Fax:* 831-338-9861 *E-mail:* inquiry@heartmath.com *Web Site:* www.heartmath.com, pg 117

Cubberley, William, Practising Law Institute, 810 Seventh Ave, New York, NY 10019 *Tel:* 212-824-5700 *Toll Free Tel:* 800-260-4PLI (260-4754 cust serv) *Fax:* 212-265-4742 (intl) *Toll Free Fax:* 800-321-0093 (local) *E-mail:* info@pli.edu *Web Site:* www.pli.edu, pg 205

Culhane, Sean, International Monetary Fund (IMF) Editorial & Publications Division, 700 19 St NW, HQ1-7-124, Washington, DC 20431 *Tel:* 202-623-7430 *Fax:* 202-623-7201 *E-mail:* publications@imf.org *Web Site:* www.imfbookstore.org, pg 133

Cull, Mark E, Red Hen Press, PO Box 40820, Pasadena, CA 91114 *Tel:* 626-356-4760 *Fax:* 626-356-9974 *Web Site:* www.redhen.org, pg 216

Cullen, Catherine, Crown Publishing Group, c/o Random House Inc, 1745 Broadway, New York, NY 10019 *Tel:* 212-782-9000 *Toll Free Tel:* 888-264-1745 *Fax:* 212-940-7408 *Web Site:* www.randomhouse.com/crown, pg 72

Cullen, Dan, American Booksellers Association, 333 Westchester Ave, Suite S202, White Plains, NY 10604 *Tel:* 914-406-7500 *Toll Free Tel:* 800-637-0037 *Fax:* 914-410-6297 *E-mail:* info@bookweb.org *Web Site:* www.bookweb.org, pg 612

Cullen, Darcy, University of British Columbia Press, 2029 West Mall, Vancouver, BC V6T 1Z2, Canada *Tel:* 604-822-5959 *Toll Free Tel:* 877-377-9378 *Fax:* 604-822-6083 *Toll Free Fax:* 800-668-0821 *E-mail:* frontdesk@ubcpress.ca *Web Site:* www.ubcpress.ca, pg 523

Cullers, Robert M, Writers: Free-Lance Inc, 167 Bluff Rd, Strasburg, VA 22657 *Tel:* 540-635-4617, pg 558

Culliford, Craig, Crabtree Publishing Co Ltd, 616 Welland Ave, St Catharines, ON L2M-5V6, Canada *Tel:* 905-682-5221 *Toll Free Tel:* 800-387-7650 *Fax:* 905-682-7166 *Toll Free Fax:* 800-355-7166 *E-mail:* custserv@crabtreebooks.com; sales@crabtreebooks.com; orders@crabtreebooks.com *Web Site:* www.crabtreebooks.com, pg 500

Cullinane, Mary, Houghton Mifflin Harcourt, 222 Berkeley St, Boston, MA 02116-3764 *Tel:* 617-351-5000 *Toll Free Tel:* 800-225-5425 (Pre-K-8); 800-462-6595 (6–12; Advanced & Electives); 800-289-4490 (Specialized Curriculum: Great Source, Rigby, Saxon, Steck-Vaughn; Homeschool; Adult Ed); 800-323-9540 (Assessment: Riverside Publishing); 888-391-3245 (SkillsTutor); 888-242-6747 option 2 (Destination Series; Classroom Connect; Earobics; Edmark; Learning Village; Riverdeep); 800-225-3362 (Houghton Mifflin Harcourt Trade & Reference Publishers); 800-225-5800 (Heinemann) *Fax:* 617-351-1125 *Web Site:* www.hmhco.com, pg 123

Culliton, Brendan, Touchstone, 1230 Avenue of the Americas, New York, NY 10020, pg 257

Cully, Christine French, Highlights for Children, 1800 Watermark Dr, Columbus, OH 43215-1060 *Tel:* 614-486-0631 *Toll Free Tel:* 800-962-3661 (Highlights Club cust serv); 800-255-9517 (Highlights Magazine cust serv) *Web Site:* www.highlights.com, pg 119

Culp, Rick, Pearson School, One Lake St, Upper Saddle River, NJ 07458 *Tel:* 201-236-7000 *Web Site:* www.pearsonschool.com, pg 196

Culpepper, Steve, The Globe Pequot Press, 246 Goose Lane, Guilford, CT 06437 *Tel:* 203-458-4500 *Toll Free Tel:* 800-243-0495 (orders only); 888-249-7586 (cust serv) *Fax:* 203-458-4601 *Toll Free Fax:* 800-820-2329 (orders & cust serv) *E-mail:* info@globepequot.com *Web Site:* www.globepequot.com, pg 104

Cumberland, Brian, Faith Library Publications, PO Box 50126, Tulsa, OK 74150-0126 *Tel:* 918-258-1588 (ext 2218) *Toll Free Tel:* 888-258-0999 (orders) *Fax:* 918-872-7710 (orders) *E-mail:* flp@rhema.org *Web Site:* www.rhema.org/store/wholesale, pg 92

Cummings, Mary, Betsy Amster Literary Enterprises, 6312 SW Capitol Hwy, No 503, Portland, OR 97239 *Tel:* 503-496-4007 *E-mail:* rights@amsterlit.com (rts inquiries); b.amster.assistant@gmail.com (adult book queries); b.amster.kidsbooks@gmail.com (children & young adult book queries) *Web Site:* www.amsterlit.com, pg 560

Cummings, Mary, Diversion Books, 80 Fifth Ave, Suite 1101, New York, NY 10011 *Tel:* 212-961-6390 (ext 7) *E-mail:* info@diversionbooks.com *Web Site:* www.diversionbooks.com, pg 80

Cummings, Pat, The Authors League Fund, 31 E 32 St, 7th fl, New York, NY 10016 *Tel:* 212-268-1208 *Fax:* 212-564-5363 *E-mail:* staff@authorsleaguefund.org *Web Site:* www.authorsleaguefund.org, pg 617

Cunningham, Kay, Psychological Assessment Resources Inc (PAR), 16204 N Florida Ave, Lutz, FL 33549 *Tel:* 813-968-3003; 813-449-4065 *Toll Free Tel:* 800-331-8378 *Fax:* 813-968-2598; 813-961-2196 *Toll Free Fax:* 800-727-9329 *E-mail:* custsup@parinc.com *Web Site:* www4.parinc.com, pg 208

Cunningham, Tammy, LearningExpress LLC, 2 Rector St, 26th fl, New York, NY 10006 *Tel:* 212-995-2566 *Toll Free Tel:* 800-295-9556 (ext 2) *Fax:* 212-995-5512 *E-mail:* customerservice@learningexpressllc.com (cust serv) *Web Site:* www.learningexpressllc.com, pg 145

Cunningham, Terri, DC Entertainment, 1700 Broadway, New York, NY 10019 *Tel:* 212-636-5400 *Toll Free Tel:* 800-887-6789 *Fax:* 212-636-5979 *E-mail:* dccomics@cambeywest.com *Web Site:* www.dccomics.com; www.madmag.com; www.dcentertainment.com, pg 76

Cuocci, Kerri, Sterling Publishing Co Inc, 387 Park Ave S, 11th fl, New York, NY 10016-8810 *Tel:* 212-532-7160 *Toll Free Tel:* 800-367-9692 *Fax:* 212-213-2495 *Web Site:* www.sterlingpub.com, pg 244

Curr, Judith, Atria Books, 1230 Avenue of the Americas, New York, NY 10020 *Tel:* 212-698-7000 *Fax:* 212-698-7007 *Web Site:* www.simonandschuster.com, pg 26

Curr, Judith, Simon & Schuster, Inc, 1230 Avenue of the Americas, New York, NY 10020 *Tel:* 212-698-7000 *Fax:* 212-698-7007 *E-mail:* firstname.lastname@simonandschuster.com *Web Site:* www.simonandschuster.com, pg 235

Curran, Randall, The Reader's Digest Association Inc, 750 Third Ave, New York, NY 10017 *Tel:* 914-238-1000; 646-293-6284 *Toll Free Tel:* 800-310-6261 (cust serv) *Fax:* 914-238-4559 *Web Site:* www.rd.com; www.rda.com, pg 215

Currans-Sheehan, Tricia, The Briar Cliff Review Fiction, Poetry & Creative Nonfiction Contest, 3303 Rebecca St, Sioux City, IA 51104-2100 *Tel:* 712-279-1651 *Fax:* 712-279-5486 *Web Site:* www.briarcliff.edu/bcreview, pg 693

Curren, Vincent, Corporation for Public Broadcasting (CPB), 401 Ninth St NW, Washington, DC 20004-2129 *Tel:* 202-879-9600 *Toll Free Tel:* 800-272-2190 *Fax:* 202-879-9700 *E-mail:* info@cpb.org *Web Site:* www.cpb.org, pg 622

Curry, Brendan, W W Norton & Company Inc, 500 Fifth Ave, New York, NY 10110-0017 *Tel:* 212-354-5500 *Toll Free Tel:* 800-233-4830 (orders & cust serv) *Fax:* 212-869-0856 *Toll Free Fax:* 800-458-6515 *Web Site:* www.wwnorton.com, pg 182

Curry, C, Golden Meteorite Press, 126 Kingsway Garden, Edmonton, AB T5G 3G4, Canada *Tel:* 780-378-0063 *Web Site:* www.goldenmeteoritepress.com, pg 506

Curtin, Thomas, Waveland Press Inc, 4180 IL Rte 83, Suite 101, Long Grove, IL 60047-9580 *Tel:* 847-634-0081 *Fax:* 847-634-9501 *E-mail:* info@waveland.com *Web Site:* www.waveland.com, pg 277

Curtis, Anthony, Huntington Press Publishing, 3665 Procyon St, Las Vegas, NV 89103-1907 *Tel:* 702-252-0655 *Toll Free Tel:* 800-244-2224 *Fax:* 702-252-0675 *E-mail:* sales@huntingtonpress.com *Web Site:* www.huntingtonpress.com, pg 126

Curtis, Carolyn, Pacific Press Publishing Association, 1350 N Kings Rd, Nampa, ID 83687-3193 *Tel:* 208-465-2500 *Toll Free Tel:* 800-447-7377 *Fax:* 208-465-2531 *Web Site:* www.pacificpress.com, pg 190

Curtis, Mary E, Transaction Publishers Inc, 10 Corporate Place S, 35 Berrue Circle, Piscataway, NJ 08854 *Tel:* 732-445-2280; 732-445-1245 (orders) *Toll Free Tel:* 888-999-6778 (dist ctr) *Fax:* 732-445-3138 *E-mail:* trans@transactionpub.com; orders@transactionpub.om *Web Site:* www.transactionpub.com, pg 258

Curtis, Nancy, High Plains Press, 403 Cassa Rd, Glendo, WY 82213 *Tel:* 307-735-4370 *Toll Free Tel:* 800-552-7819 *Fax:* 307-735-4590 *E-mail:* editor@highplainspress.com *Web Site:* highplainspress.com, pg 119

Curtis, Richard, Richard Curtis Associates Inc, 171 E 74 St, 2nd fl, New York, NY 10021 *Tel:* 212-772-7363 *Fax:* 212-772-7393 *Web Site:* www.curtisagency.com, pg 567

Curtis, William F PhD, Springer, 233 Spring St, New York, NY 10013-1578 *Tel:* 212-460-1500 *Toll Free Tel:* 800-SPRINGER (777-4643) *Fax:* 212-460-1575 *E-mail:* service-ny@springer.com *Web Site:* www.springer.com, pg 241

Cusack, John, St Martin's Press, LLC, 175 Fifth Ave, New York, NY 10010 *Tel:* 646-307-5151 *Fax:* 212-420-9314 *E-mail:* firstname.lastname@macmillan.com *Web Site:* www.stmartins.com, pg 224

Cussen, David M, Pineapple Press Inc, PO Box 3889, Sarasota, FL 34230-3889 *Tel:* 941-706-2507 *Toll Free Tel:* 866-766-3850 (orders) *Fax:* 941-706-2509 *Toll Free Fax:* 800-838-1149 (orders) *E-mail:* info@pineapplepress.com; customer.service@ingrampublisherservices.com *Web Site:* www.pineapplepress.com, pg 202

Cussen, June, Pineapple Press Inc, PO Box 3889, Sarasota, FL 34230-3889 *Tel:* 941-706-2507 *Toll Free Tel:* 866-766-3850 (orders) *Fax:* 941-706-2509 *Toll Free Fax:* 800-838-1149 (orders) *E-mail:* info@pineapplepress.com; customer.service@ingrampublisherservices.com *Web Site:* www.pineapplepress.com, pg 202

Cutler, Jean, Pennsylvania Historical & Museum Commission, Commonwealth Keystone Bldg, 400 North St, Harrisburg, PA 17120-0053 *Tel:* 717-783-2618 *Toll Free Tel:* 800-747-7790 *Fax:* 717-787-8312 *E-mail:* ra-pabookstore@state.pa.us *Web Site:* www.pabookstore.com; www.phmc.state.pa.us, pg 198

Cutler, Thomas, Naval Institute Press, 291 Wood Rd, Annapolis, MD 21402-5034 *Tel:* 410-268-6110 *Toll Free Tel:* 800-233-8764 *Fax:* 410-295-1084; 410-571-1703 (cust serv) *E-mail:* webmaster@navalinstitute.org; customer@navalinstitute.org (cust serv); trade@usni.org *Web Site:* www.nip.org; www.usni.org, pg 176

Cywinski, David, Hal Leonard Corp, 7777 W Bluemound Rd, Milwaukee, WI 53213 *Tel:* 414-774-3630 *Toll Free Tel:* 800-524-4425 *Fax:* 414-774-3259 *E-mail:* sales@halleonard.com *Web Site:* www.halleonard.com; twitter.com/#!/HalleonardBooks, pg 111

D'Acierno, Amanda, Books on Tape®, c/o Sales Dept, 3070 Bristol St, Suite 650, Costa Mesa, CA 92626 *Toll Free Tel:* 800-733-3000 (cust serv) *Toll Free Fax:* 800-940-7046 *Web Site:* www.booksontape.com, pg 44

D'Acierno, Amanda, Fodor's Travel Publications, c/o Random House Inc, 1745 Broadway, New York, NY 10019 *Tel:* 212-829-6714 *Toll Free Tel:* 800-733-3000 *Fax:* 212-572-2248 *Web Site:* www.fodors.com, pg 96

D'Acierno, Amanda, Living Language, c/o Random House Inc, 1745 Broadway, New York, NY 10019 *Tel:* 212-782-9000 *Toll Free Tel:* 800-733-3000 (orders) *Toll Free Fax:* 800-659-2436 *E-mail:* livinglanguage@randomhouse.com *Web Site:* www.livinglanguage.com, pg 151

D'Acierno, Amanda, Random House Audio Publishing Group, 1745 Broadway, New York, NY 10019 *E-mail:* audio@randomhouse.com *Web Site:* www.randomhouse.com/audio, pg 212

D'Acierno, Amanda, Random House Reference/Random House Puzzles & Games/House of Collectibles, 1745 Broadway, New York, NY 10019 *Toll Free Tel:* 800-733-3000 *Toll Free Fax:* 800-659-2436 *E-mail:* words@random.com; puzzles@random.com, pg 214

D'Agnes, Glenn, Workman Publishing Co Inc, 225 Varick St, 9th fl, New York, NY 10014-4381 *Tel:* 212-254-5900 *Toll Free Tel:* 800-722-7202 *Fax:* 212-254-8098 *E-mail:* info@workman.com *Web Site:* www.workman.com, pg 285

D'Agostino, Angela, R R Bowker LLC, 630 Central Ave, New Providence, NJ 07974 *Tel:* 908-286-1090 *Toll Free Tel:* 888-269-5372 (edit & cust serv, press 2 for returns) *Fax:* 908-219-0098; (020) 7832 1710 (UK for intl) *Toll Free Fax:* 877-337-7015 (domestic/US & CN) *E-mail:* orders@proquest.com (domestic orders); customer_service@proquest.co.uk (intl) *Web Site:* www.bowker.com, pg 44

D'Andrea, Deborah, Playhouse Publishing, PO Box 1962, Cleveland, OH 44106 *Tel:* 330-926-1313 *Fax:* 330-475-8579 *E-mail:* info@picturemepress.com *Web Site:* www.picturemepress.com, pg 203

Danielson, Krista, Finney Company Inc, 8075 215 St W, Lakeville, MN 55044 *Tel:* 952-469-6699 *Toll Free Tel:* 800-846-7027 *Fax:* 952-469-1968 *Toll Free Fax:* 800-330-6232 *E-mail:* info@finneyco.com *Web Site:* www.finneyco.com, pg 95

Danielson, Krista, Hobar Publications, 8075 215 St W, Lakeville, MN 55044 *Tel:* 952-469-6699 *Toll Free Tel:* 800-846-7027 *Fax:* 952-469-1968 *Toll Free Fax:* 800-330-6232 *E-mail:* info@finneyco.com *Web Site:* www.finney-hobar.com, pg 120

Danielson, Krista, Pogo Press Inc, 8075 215 St W, Lakeville, MN 55044 *Tel:* 952-469-6699 *Toll Free Tel:* 800-846-7027 *Fax:* 952-469-1968 *Toll Free Fax:* 800-330-6232 *E-mail:* info@finneyco.com *Web Site:* www.pogopress.com, pg 204

Danielson, Krista, Windward Publishing, 8075 215 St W, Lakeville, MN 55044 *Tel:* 952-469-6699 *Toll Free Tel:* 800-846-7027 *Fax:* 952-469-1968 *Toll Free Fax:* 800-330-6232 *E-mail:* info@finneyco.com *Web Site:* www.finneyco.com, pg 283

Danilson, Krista, Astragal Press, 8075 215 St W, Lakeville, MN 55044 *Tel:* 952-469-6699 *Toll Free Tel:* 866-543-3045 *Fax:* 952-469-1968 *Toll Free Fax:* 800-330-6232 *E-mail:* info@astragalpress.com *Web Site:* www.astragalpress.com, pg 26

Dannis, Joe, DawnSignPress, 6130 Nancy Ridge Dr, San Diego, CA 92121-3223 *Tel:* 858-625-0600 *Toll Free Tel:* 800-549-5350 *Fax:* 858-625-2336 *E-mail:* info@dawnsign.com *Web Site:* www.dawnsign.com, pg 76

Dano, Yvette, Penguin Group (USA) LLC, 375 Hudson St, New York, NY 10014 *Tel:* 212-366-2000 *Toll Free Tel:* 800-847-5515 (inside sales); 800-631-8571 (cust serv) *Fax:* 212-366-2666; 607-775-4829 (inside sales) *E-mail:* online@us.penguingroup.com *Web Site:* www.penguin.com; us.penguingroup.com, pg 197

Darby, Timothy, BNA Books, 1801 S Bell St, Arlington, VA 22202 *Toll Free Tel:* 800-372-1033 *Fax:* 732-346-1624 *E-mail:* books@bna.com *Web Site:* www.bnabooks.com, pg 42

Dardick, Simon, Vehicule Press, PO Box 125, Place du Park Sta, Montreal, QC H2X 4A3, Canada *Tel:* 514-844-6073 *Fax:* 514-844-7543 *E-mail:* vp@vehiculepress.com; admin@vehiculepress.com *Web Site:* www.vehiculepress.com, pg 524

Darhansoff, Liz, Darhansoff & Verrill, 236 W 26 St, Suite 802, New York, NY 10001-6736 *Tel:* 917-305-1300 *Fax:* 917-305-1400 *E-mail:* info@dvagency.com *Web Site:* www.dvagency.com, pg 567

Darling, Abigail, Laughing Elephant, 3645 Interlake N, Seattle, WA 98103 *Tel:* 206-447-9229 *Toll Free Tel:* 800-354-0400 *Fax:* 206-447-9189 *E-mail:* support@laughingelephant.com *Web Site:* www.laughingelephant.com, pg 144

Darling, Christina, Laughing Elephant, 3645 Interlake N, Seattle, WA 98103 *Tel:* 206-447-9229 *Toll Free Tel:* 800-354-0400 *Fax:* 206-447-9189 *E-mail:* support@laughingelephant.com *Web Site:* www.laughingelephant.com, pg 144

Darling, Harold, Laughing Elephant, 3645 Interlake N, Seattle, WA 98103 *Tel:* 206-447-9229 *Toll Free Tel:* 800-354-0400 *Fax:* 206-447-9189 *E-mail:* support@laughingelephant.com *Web Site:* www.laughingelephant.com, pg 144

Darling, Karen Merikangas, University of Chicago Press, 1427 E 60 St, Chicago, IL 60637-2954 *Tel:* 773-702-7700; 773-702-7600 *Toll Free Tel:* 800-621-2736 (orders) *Fax:* 773-702-9756; 773-660-2235 (orders); 773-702-2708 *E-mail:* custserv@press.uchicago.edu; marketing@press.uchicago.edu *Web Site:* www.press.uchicago.edu, pg 265

Darmiento, Grace, The Crossroad Publishing Co, 831 Chestnut Ridge Rd, Chestnut Ridge, NY 10977 *Tel:* 845-517-0180 *Toll Free Tel:* 800-888-4741 (orders) *Fax:* 845-517-0181 *Web Site:* www.CrossroadPublishing.com, pg 72

Darnton, John, The George Polk Awards, The Brooklyn Campus, One University Plaza, Brooklyn, NY 11201-5372 *Tel:* 718-488-1009; 718-488-1115 *Web Site:* www.liu.edu/polk, pg 735

Dart, Tom, First Folio Resource Group Inc, 218 Adelaide St W, 2nd fl, Toronto, ON M5H 1W7, Canada *Tel:* 416-368-7668 *Fax:* 416-368-9363 *E-mail:* mail@firstfolio.com *Web Site:* www.firstfolio.com, pg 546

Dattorre, Michael, Ash Tree Publishing, PO Box 64, Woodstock, NY 12498 *Tel:* 845-246-8081 *Fax:* 845-246-8081 *E-mail:* info@ashtreepublishing.com *Web Site:* www.ashtreepublishing.com, pg 24

Dauber, Mira Pomerantz, Jewish Book Council, 520 Eighth Ave, 4th fl, New York, NY 10018 *Tel:* 212-201-2920 *Fax:* 212-532-4952 *E-mail:* jbc@jewishbooks.org *Web Site:* www.jewishbookcouncil.org, pg 626

Daulton, Sue, Random House Audio Publishing Group, 1745 Broadway, New York, NY 10019 *E-mail:* audio@randomhouse.com *Web Site:* www.randomhouse.com/audio, pg 212

Davenport, Elaine, Writer's AudioShop, 1316 Overland Stage Rd, Dripping Springs, TX 78620 *Tel:* 512-264-7067 *Fax:* 512-264-7067 *E-mail:* wrtaudshop@aol.com *Web Site:* www.writersaudio.com, pg 286

Davenport, May, May Davenport Publishers, 26313 Purissima Rd, Los Altos Hills, CA 94022 *Tel:* 650-947-1275 *Fax:* 650-947-1373 *E-mail:* mdbooks@earthlink.net *Web Site:* www.maydavenportpublishers.com, pg 75

David, Jack, ECW Press, 2120 Queen St E, Suite 200, Toronto, ON M4E 1E2, Canada *Tel:* 416-694-3348 *Fax:* 416-698-9906 *E-mail:* info@ecwpress.com *Web Site:* www.ecwpress.com, pg 501

David, Kim, McGraw-Hill Higher Education, 1333 Burr Ridge Pkwy, Burr Ridge, IL 60527 *Tel:* 630-789-4000 *Toll Free Tel:* 800-338-3987 (cust serv) *Fax:* 614-755-5645 (cust serv) *Web Site:* www.mhhe.com, pg 161

David, Kim, McGraw-Hill Humanities, Social Sciences, Languages, 2 Penn Plaza, 20th fl, New York, NY 10121 *Tel:* 212-904-2000 *Toll Free Tel:* 800-338-3987 (cust serv) *Fax:* 614-755-5645 (cust serv) *Web Site:* www.mhhe.com, pg 161

David, Kim, McGraw-Hill/Irwin, 1333 Burr Ridge Pkwy, Burr Ridge, IL 60527 *Tel:* 630-789-4000 *Toll Free Tel:* 800-338-3987 (cust serv) *Fax:* 630-789-6942; 614-755-5645 (cust serv) *Web Site:* www.mhhe.com, pg 162

David, Kim, McGraw-Hill Science, Engineering, Mathematics, 501 Bell St, Dubuque, IA 52001 *Tel:* 563-584-6000 *Toll Free Tel:* 800-338-3987 (cust serv) *Fax:* 614-755-5645 (cust serv) *Web Site:* www.mhhe.com, pg 162

Davidson, Andrew J, Harlan Davidson Inc/Forum Press Inc, 773 Glenn Ave, Wheeling, IL 60090-6900 *Tel:* 847-541-9720 *Fax:* 847-541-9830 *E-mail:* harlandavidson@harlandavidson.com *Web Site:* www.harlandavidson.com, pg 112

Davidson, Angela E, Harlan Davidson Inc/Forum Press Inc, 773 Glenn Ave, Wheeling, IL 60090-6900 *Tel:* 847-541-9720 *Fax:* 847-541-9830 *E-mail:* harlandavidson@harlandavidson.com *Web Site:* www.harlandavidson.com, pg 112

Davidson, Christine, Emond Montgomery Publications, 60 Shaftesbury Ave, Toronto, ON M4T 1A3, Canada *Tel:* 416-975-3925 *Toll Free Tel:* 888-837-0815 *Fax:* 416-975-3924 *E-mail:* info@emp.ca; orders@emp.ca *Web Site:* www.emp.ca, pg 504

Davidson, Scott, McGraw-Hill Career Education, 1333 Burr Ridge Pkwy, Burr Ridge, IL 60527 *Tel:* 630-789-4000 *Toll Free Tel:* 800-338-3987 (cust serv) *Fax:* 630-789-5523; 614-755-5645 (cust serv) *Web Site:* www.mhhe.com, pg 160

Davies, Elizabeth B, The Davies Group Publishers, PO Box 440140, Aurora, CO 80044-0140 *Tel:* 303-750-8374 *Fax:* 303-337-0952 *E-mail:* info@thedaviesgrouppublishers.com *Web Site:* www.thedaviesgrouppublishers.com, pg 75

Davies, Jocelyn, HarperCollins Children's Books, 10 E 53 St, New York, NY 10022 *Tel:* 212-207-7000 *Web Site:* www.harpercollinschildrens.com, pg 113

Davies, Michael, Davies Publishing Inc, 32 S Raymond Ave, Suites 4 & 5, Pasadena, CA 91105-1961 *Tel:* 626-792-3046 *Toll Free Tel:* 877-792-0005 *Fax:* 626-792-5308 *E-mail:* info@daviespublishing.com *Web Site:* daviespublishing.com, pg 75

Davies, Shannon, Texas A&M University Press, John H Lindsey Bldg, Lewis St, 4354 TAMU, College Station, TX 77843-4354 *Tel:* 979-845-1436 *Toll Free Tel:* 800-826-8911 (orders) *Fax:* 979-847-8752 *Toll Free Fax:* 888-617-2421 (orders) *E-mail:* upress@tamu.edu *Web Site:* www.tamupress.com, pg 252

Davila, Randy, Hampton Roads Publishing Co Inc, 211 E High St, Charlottesville, VA 22902 *Tel:* 978-465-0504 *Toll Free Tel:* 800-423-7087 (orders) *Fax:* 978-465-0243 *E-mail:* hrpub@rwwbooks.com *Web Site:* www.hamptonroadspub.com, pg 111

Davis, Aida, American Institute of Aeronautics & Astronautics, 1801 Alexander Bell Dr, Suite 500, Reston, VA 20191-4344 *Tel:* 703-264-7500 *Toll Free Tel:* 800-639-AIAA (639-2422) *Fax:* 703-264-7551 *E-mail:* custserv@aiaa.org *Web Site:* www.aiaa.org, pg 14

Davis, Dr Alan, New Rivers Press, c/o Minnesota State University Moorhead, 1104 Seventh Ave S, Moorhead, MN 56563 *Tel:* 218-477-5870 *Fax:* 218-477-2236 *E-mail:* nrp@mnstate.edu *Web Site:* www.newriverspress.com; www.mnstate.edu/newriverspress, pg 178

Davis, Billie, Annual Off Off Broadway Short Play Festival, 45 W 25 St, New York, NY 10010-2751 *Tel:* 212-206-8990 *Toll Free Tel:* 866-598-8449 *Fax:* 212-206-1429 *E-mail:* oobfestival@samuelfrench.com *Web Site:* oob.samuelfrench.com; www.samuelfrench.com, pg 688

Davis, Carol Prud'homme, See-More's Workshop Arts & Education Workshops, 325 West End Ave, Suite 12-B, New York, NY 10023 *Tel:* 212-724-0677 *Fax:* 212-724-0767 *E-mail:* sbt@shadowboxtheatre.org *Web Site:* www.shadowboxtheatre.org, pg 673

Davis, Chris, American Occupational Therapy Association Inc, 4720 Montgomery Lane, Bethesda, MD 20824 *Tel:* 301-652-2682 *Toll Free Tel:* 800-377-8555 *Fax:* 301-652-7711 *Web Site:* www.aota.org, pg 15

Davis, Dawn, Atria Books, 1230 Avenue of the Americas, New York, NY 10020 *Tel:* 212-698-7000 *Fax:* 212-698-7007 *Web Site:* www.simonandschuster.com, pg 26

Davis, Dawn, HarperCollins General Books Group, 10 E 53 St, New York, NY 10022 *Tel:* 212-207-7000 *Fax:* 212-207-7633 *Web Site:* www.harpercollins.com, pg 113

Davis, Emily, Crown Publishing Group, c/o Random House Inc, 1745 Broadway, New York, NY 10019 *Tel:* 212-782-9000 *Toll Free Tel:* 888-264-1745 *Fax:* 212-940-7408 *Web Site:* www.randomhouse.com/crown, pg 72

Davis, Gary W, The Learning Source Ltd, 644 Tenth St, Brooklyn, NY 11215 *Tel:* 718-768-0231 (ext 10) *Fax:* 718-369-3467 *E-mail:* info@learningsourceltd.com *Web Site:* www.learningsourceltd.com, pg 550

Davis, H Leigh, BradyGames, 800 E 96 St, 3rd fl, Indianapolis, IN 46240 *Tel:* 317-428-3000 *Toll Free Tel:* 800-545-5912; 800-571-5840 (cust serv) *E-mail:* bradyquestions@pearsoned.com *Web Site:* www.bradygames.com, pg 45

Davis, J Madison, Gaylord College of Journalism & Mass Communication, Professional Writing Program, c/o University of Oklahoma, 395 W Lindsey St, Rm 3534, Norman, OK 73019-0270 *Tel:* 405-325-2721 *Fax:* 405-325-7565 *Web Site:* www.ou.edu/gaylord, pg 678

Davis, James B, Practice Management Information Corp (PMIC), 4727 Wilshire Blvd, Suite 300, Los Angeles, CA 90010 *Tel:* 323-954-0224 *Fax:* 323-954-0253 *Toll Free Fax:* 800-633-6556 (orders) *E-mail:* orders@medicalbookstore.com; customer.service@pmiconline.com *Web Site:* www.pmiconline.com, pg 205

de Groot, Ali, Modern Memoirs, 34 Main St, No 9, Amherst, MA 01002-2367 *Tel:* 413-253-2353 *Web Site:* www.modernmemoirs.com, pg 168

de Guzman, Beth, Grand Central Publishing, 237 Park Ave, New York, NY 10017 *Tel:* 212-364-1100 *Web Site:* www.hachettebookgroup.com, pg 106

de Jackmo, Nicole, Quirk Books, 215 Church St, Philadelphia, PA 19106 *Tel:* 215-627-3581 *Fax:* 215-627-5220 *E-mail:* general@quirkbooks.com *Web Site:* www.quirkbooks.com, pg 211

de la Campa, Cecelia, Writers House, 21 W 26 St, New York, NY 10010 *Tel:* 212-685-2400 *Fax:* 212-685-1781 *Web Site:* www.writershouse.com, pg 599

de la Cruz, Brent, Morgan Kaufmann, 225 Wyman St, Waltham, MA 02451 *Toll Free Tel:* 866-607-1417 *Fax:* 619-699-6310 *Web Site:* www.mkp.com, pg 170

de la Cuesta, Barbara, Birch Brook Press, PO Box 81, Delhi, NY 13753-0081 *Tel:* 607-746-7453 (book sales & prodn) *Fax:* 607-746-7453 *E-mail:* birchbrook@copper.net *Web Site:* www.birchbrookpress.info, pg 38

de la Hoz, Cindy, Running Press Book Publishers, 2300 Chestnut St, Philadelphia, PA 19103-4399 *Tel:* 215-567-5080 *Toll Free Tel:* 800-343-4499 (cust serv & orders) *Fax:* 215-568-2919 *Toll Free Fax:* 800-453-2884 (cust serv & orders) *E-mail:* perseus.promos@perseusbooks.com *Web Site:* www.runningpress.com, pg 222

de la Rosa, Denise, Palgrave Macmillan, 175 Fifth Ave, Suite 200, New York, NY 10010 *Tel:* 646-307-5151 *Fax:* 212-777-6359 *E-mail:* firstname.lastname@palgrave-usa.com *Web Site:* us.macmillan.com/Palgrave.aspx, pg 191

De Lima, Ana Paula, Touchstone, 1230 Avenue of the Americas, New York, NY 10020, pg 256

de Menil, Joy, Viking, 375 Hudson St, New York, NY 10014 *Tel:* 212-366-2000 *E-mail:* online@penguinputnam.com *Web Site:* www.penguinputnam.com; us.penguingroup.com, pg 275

De Mers, Martin, Algora Publishing, 222 Riverside Dr, Suite 16-D, New York, NY 10025-6809 *Tel:* 212-678-0232 *Fax:* 212-666-3682 *E-mail:* editors@algora.com *Web Site:* www.algora.com, pg 8

De Mier, Chrissy, Morton Publishing Co, 925 W Kenyon Ave, Unit 12, Englewood, CO 80110 *Tel:* 303-761-4805 *Fax:* 303-762-9923 *E-mail:* contact@morton-pub.com *Web Site:* www.morton-pub.com, pg 170

De Nil, Lien, Westwood Creative Artists Ltd, 94 Harbord St, Toronto, ON M5S 1G6, Canada *Tel:* 416-964-3302 *Fax:* 416-975-9209 *E-mail:* wca_office@wcaltd.com *Web Site:* www.wcaltd.com, pg 599

de Pablos, Jaime, Vintage & Anchor Books, c/o Random House Inc, 1745 Broadway, New York, NY 10019 *Tel:* 212-572-2420 *E-mail:* vintageanchorpublicity@randomhouse.com *Web Site:* vintage-anchor.knopfdoubleday.com, pg 275

De Pasture, Andrea, New Concepts Publishing, 106-A W Hill Ave, Valdosta, GA 31636 *E-mail:* service@newconceptspublishing.com; submissions@newconceptspublishing.com *Web Site:* www.newconceptspublishing.com, pg 177

De Pasture, Madris, New Concepts Publishing, 106-A W Hill Ave, Valdosta, GA 31636 *E-mail:* service@newconceptspublishing.com; submissions@newconceptspublishing.com *Web Site:* www.newconceptspublishing.com, pg 177

De Paul, Christina, youngARTS, 777 Brickell Ave, Suite 370, Miami, FL 33131 *Tel:* 305-377-1140 *Toll Free Tel:* 800-970-ARTS (970-2787) *Fax:* 305-377-1149 *E-mail:* info@nfaa.org *Web Site:* www.youngarts.org, pg 753

de Pree-Kajfez, Ariane, Stanford University Press, 1450 Page Mill Rd, Palo Alto, CA 94304-1124 *Tel:* 650-723-9434 *Fax:* 650-725-3457 *E-mail:* info@sup.org *Web Site:* www.sup.org, pg 243

de Rooy, Yolanda, Pearson Humanities & Social Sciences, One Lake St, Upper Saddle River, NJ 07458 *Tel:* 201-236-7000 *Fax:* 201-236-3400, pg 196

De Rosa, Maureen, American Academy of Pediatrics, 141 NW Point Blvd, Elk Grove Village, IL 60007-1098 *Tel:* 847-434-4000 *Toll Free Tel:* 888-227-1770 *Fax:* 847-434-8000 *E-mail:* pubs@aap.org *Web Site:* www.aap.org, pg 10

De Silva, Devni, University of British Columbia Press, 2029 West Mall, Vancouver, BC V6T 1Z2, Canada *Tel:* 604-822-5959 *Toll Free Tel:* 877-377-9378 *Fax:* 604-822-6083 *Toll Free Fax:* 800-668-0821 *E-mail:* frontdesk@ubcpress.ca *Web Site:* www.ubcpress.ca, pg 523

De Smet, Christine, UW-Madison, Division of Continuing Studies, 21 N Park St, 7th fl, Madison, WI 53715 *Tel:* 608-263-6320 *Toll Free Tel:* 877-336-7836 *Fax:* 608-262-1694 *E-mail:* liberalarts@dsc.wisc.edu *Web Site:* continuingstudies.wisc.edu, pg 682

de Souza, Dan, Chestnut Publishing Group Inc, 4005 Bayview Ave, Suite 610, Toronto, ON M2M 3Z9, Canada *Tel:* 416-224-5824 *Fax:* 416-224-0595 *Web Site:* www.chestnutpublishing.com, pg 499

De Souza, Kathleen, Mary Ann Liebert Inc, 140 Huguenot St, 3rd fl, New Rochelle, NY 10801-5215 *Tel:* 914-740-2100 *Toll Free Tel:* 800-654-3237 *Fax:* 914-740-2101 *E-mail:* info@liebertpub.com *Web Site:* www.liebertonline.com, pg 148

De Spelder, Lynne Ann, Pacific Publishing Services, PO Box 1150, Capitola, CA 95010-1150 *Tel:* 831-476-8284 *Fax:* 831-476-8294 *E-mail:* pacpub@attglobal.net, pg 552

de Spoelberch, Jacques, J de S Associates Inc, 9 Shagbark Rd, South Norwalk, CT 06854 *Tel:* 203-838-7571 *Fax:* 203-866-2713 *Web Site:* www.jdesassociates.com, pg 578

De Vinney, Karen, University of North Texas Press, Stovall Hall, Suite 174, 1400 Highland St, Denton, TX 76201 *Tel:* 940-565-2142 *Fax:* 940-565-4590 *Web Site:* www.unt.edu/untpress, pg 268

De Vivo, Frank, Practising Law Institute, 810 Seventh Ave, New York, NY 10019 *Tel:* 212-824-5700 *Toll Free Tel:* 800-260-4PLI (260-4754 cust serv) *Fax:* 212-265-4742 (intl) *Toll Free Fax:* 800-321-0093 (local) *E-mail:* info@pli.edu *Web Site:* www.pli.edu, pg 205

De Voll, Julie, Harvard Business Press, 300 N Beacon St, Watertown, MA 02472 *Tel:* 617-783-7400 *Fax:* 617-783-7489 *E-mail:* custserv@hbsp.harvard.edu *Web Site:* www.harvardbusiness.org, pg 114

De Welt, Chris, College Press Publishing Co, 2111 N Main St, Suite C, Joplin, MO 64801 *Tel:* 417-623-6280 *Toll Free Tel:* 800-289-3300 *Fax:* 417-623-1929 *E-mail:* books@collegepress.com *Web Site:* www.collegepress.com/storefront, pg 64

De Wit, Dave, Moody Publishers, 820 N La Salle Blvd, Chicago, IL 60610 *Tel:* 312-329-4000 *Toll Free Tel:* 800-678-8812 (cust serv) *Fax:* 312-329-2019 *Web Site:* www.moodypublishers.com, pg 169

De Witt, Marjorie, Other Press LLC, 2 Park Ave, 24th fl, New York, NY 10016 *Tel:* 212-414-0054 *Toll Free Tel:* 877-843-6843 *Fax:* 212-414-0939 *E-mail:* editor@otherpress.com; rights@otherpress.com *Web Site:* www.otherpress.com, pg 188

De Wolf, James S, The MIT Press, 55 Hayward St, Cambridge, MA 02142 *Tel:* 617-253-5255 *Toll Free Tel:* 800-207-8354 (orders) *Fax:* 617-258-6779; 617-577-1545 (orders) *Web Site:* mitpress.mit.edu, pg 167

Deal, Barbara, Copywriter's Council of America (CCA), CCA Bldg, 7 Putter Lane, Middle Island, NY 11953-1920 *Tel:* 631-924-8555 *Fax:* 631-924-8555 *E-mail:* cca4dmcopy@gmail.com *Web Site:* www.AndrewLinickDirectMarketing.com/Copywriters-Council.html; www.NewWorldPressBooks.com, pg 543, 621

Dean, Barbara, Island Press, 1718 Connecticut Ave NW, Suite 300, Washington, DC 20009 *Tel:* 202-232-7933 *Toll Free Tel:* 800-828-1302 *Fax:* 202-234-1328 *E-mail:* info@islandpress.org *Web Site:* www.islandpress.org, pg 134

Dean, John, Rizzoli International Publications Inc, 300 Park Ave S, 4th fl, New York, NY 10010-5399 *Tel:* 212-387-3400 *Toll Free Tel:* 800-522-6657 (orders only) *Fax:* 212-387-3535 *E-mail:* publicity@rizzoliusa.com *Web Site:* www.rizzoliusa.com, pg 219

Dean, Keisha, The Magazine of the Year Award, 27 Union Sq W, Suite 207, New York, NY 10003 *Tel:* 212-223-3332 *Fax:* 212-223-5880 *E-mail:* mail@spd.org *Web Site:* www.spd.org, pg 720

Dean, Mary Catherine, Abingdon Press, 201 Eighth Ave S, Nashville, TN 37203-3919 *Toll Free Tel:* 800-251-3320 *Toll Free Fax:* 800-836-7802 (orders) *E-mail:* orders@abingdonpress.com *Web Site:* www.abingdonpress.com, pg 3

Dean, Sheri, Business Expert Press, 222 E 46 St, New York, NY 10017-2906 *Tel:* 908-752-1257 *E-mail:* molly.hurford@businessexpertpress.com *Web Site:* www.businessexpertpress.com, pg 50

Dear, Sandra, Penguin Group (USA) LLC Sales, 375 Hudson St, New York, NY 10014 *Tel:* 212-366-2000 *E-mail:* online@penguinputnam.com *Web Site:* us.penguingroup.com, pg 197

Dears, Dion, American Anthropological Association (AAA), Publications Dept, Suite 600, 2200 Wilson Blvd, Arlington, VA 22201 *Tel:* 703-528-1902 *Fax:* 703-528-3546 *Web Site:* www.aaanet.org, pg 11

Deboer, Kathleen, Organization for Economic Cooperation & Development, 2001 "L" St NW, Suite 650, Washington, DC 20036-4922 *Tel:* 202-785-6323 *Toll Free Tel:* 800-456-6323 (dist ctr/pubns orders) *Fax:* 202-785-0350 *E-mail:* washington.contact@oecd.org *Web Site:* www.oecdwash.org; www.oecd.org, pg 187

deBoer, Margaret, Harcourt Mifflin School Publishers, 6277 Sea Harbor Dr, Orlando, FL 32887 *Tel:* 407-345-2000 *Toll Free Tel:* 800-225-5425 (cust serv) *Fax:* 407-345-3016 (cust serv) *Toll Free Fax:* 800-874-6418; 800-269-5232 (cust serv) *Web Site:* www.harcourtschool.com, pg 112

deBoer, Margaret, Houghton Mifflin Harcourt K-12 Publishers, 222 Berkeley St, Boston, MA 02116-3764 *Tel:* 617-351-5000 *Toll Free Tel:* 800-225-5425 (cust serv) *Web Site:* www.hmhco.com; www.hmheducation.com, pg 123

Debois, Muriel, Apprentice Shop Books LLC, 18 Wentworth Dr, Bedford, NH 03110 *Tel:* 603-472-8741 *Fax:* 603-472-2323 *E-mail:* info@apprenticeshopbooks.com *Web Site:* www.apprenticeshopbooks.com, pg 21

DeBold, Kathleen, Lambda Literary Awards (Lammys), 5482 Wilshire Blvd, Suite 1595, Los Angeles, CA 90036 *Tel:* 213-568-3570 *Fax:* 213-568-3570 *E-mail:* info@lambdaliterary.org *Web Site:* www.lambdaliterary.org, pg 716

Decalo, Dr Samuel, Florida Academic Press, PO Box 357425, Gainesville, FL 32635 *Tel:* 352-332-5104 *E-mail:* fapress@gmail.com *Web Site:* www.floridaacademicpress.com, pg 96

DeChiara, Jennifer, The Jennifer DeChiara Literary Agency, 31 E 32 St, Suite 300, New York, NY 10016 *Tel:* 212-481-8484 (ext 362) *Fax:* 212-481-9582 *Web Site:* www.jdlit.com, pg 568

Decker, Ryan, Decker Publishing, 69 John St S, Suite 310, Hamilton, ON L8N 2B9, Canada *Tel:* 905-522-8526 *Toll Free Tel:* 855-647-6511 *Fax:* 905-522-9273 *E-mail:* customercare@deckerpublishing.com *Web Site:* www.deckerpublishing.com, pg 500

Decker, Stacia, Donald Maass Literary Agency, 121 W 27 St, Suite 801, New York, NY 10001 *Tel:* 212-727-8383 *Fax:* 212-727-3271 *E-mail:* info@maassagency.com; rights@maassagency.com (subs rights inquiries) *Web Site:* www.maassagency.com, pg 582

Decter, Jackuelen, The Vendome Press, 1334 York Ave, 3rd fl, New York, NY 10021 *Tel:* 212-737-5297 *Fax:* 212-737-5340 *E-mail:* info@vendomepress.com *Web Site:* www.vendomepress.com, pg 274

Dee, Ivan R, Ivan R Dee Publisher, 4501 Forbes Blvd, Suite 200, Lanham, MD 20706 *Tel:* 301-459-3366 *Toll Free Tel:* 800-462-6420 (cust serv) *Fax:* 301-429-5748 *Toll Free Fax:* 800-338-4550 (orders) *Web Site:* www.ivanrdee.com, pg 77

Deemer, Joe, Printing Industries of America, 200 Deer Run Rd, Sewickley, PA 15143-2600 *Tel:* 412-741-6860; 412-259-1770 *E-mail:* membercentral@printing.org (orders) *Web Site:* www.printing.org, pg 207

Dees, Meredith, House of Anansi Press Ltd, 110 Spadina Ave, Suite 801, Toronto, ON M5V 2K4, Canada *Tel:* 416-363-4343 *Fax:* 416-363-1017 *E-mail:* customerservice@houseofanansi.com *Web Site:* www.anansi.ca, pg 509

DeFiore, Brian, DeFiore and Company, LLC, 47 E 19 St, 3rd fl, New York, NY 10003 *Tel:* 212-925-7744 *Fax:* 212-925-9803 *E-mail:* submissions@defioreandco.com; info@defioreandco.com *Web Site:* www.defioreandco.com, pg 568

Degan, Julia, Ozark Mountain Publishing Inc, PO Box 754, Huntsville, AR 72740-0754 *Tel:* 479-738-2348 *Toll Free Tel:* 800-935-0045 *Fax:* 479-738-2448 *E-mail:* info@ozarkmt.com *Web Site:* www.ozarkmt.com, pg 190

DeGennaro, Denise, Random House Children's Books, 1745 Broadway, New York, NY 10019 *Tel:* 212-782-9000 *Toll Free Tel:* 800-200-3552 *Fax:* 212-782-9452 *Web Site:* randomhousekids.com, pg 213

Degler, Mike, BradyGames, 800 E 96 St, 3rd fl, Indianapolis, IN 46240 *Tel:* 317-428-3000 *Toll Free Tel:* 800-545-5912; 800-571-5840 (cust serv) *E-mail:* bradyquestions@pearsoned.com *Web Site:* www.bradygames.com, pg 45

Dehmler, Mari Lynch, Fine Wordworking, PO Box 3041, Monterey, CA 93942-3041 *Tel:* 831-375-6278 *E-mail:* info@finewordworking.com *Web Site:* marilynch.com, pg 546

Deichert, Jerry, University of Nebraska at Omaha Center for Public Affairs Research, CPACS Bldg, Rm 108, 6001 Dodge St, Omaha, NE 68182 *Tel:* 402-554-2134 *Web Site:* www.unomaha.edu/cpar, pg 267

Deisinger, Robert D, American Technical Publishers Inc, 10100 Orland Pkwy, Suite 200, Orland Park, IL 60467-5756 *Tel:* 708-957-1100 *Toll Free Tel:* 800-323-3471 *Fax:* 708-957-1101 *E-mail:* service@americantech.net *Web Site:* www.go2atp.com, pg 17

Deitch, Lisa, F A Davis Co, 1915 Arch St, Philadelphia, PA 19103 *Tel:* 215-568-2270 *Toll Free Tel:* 800-523-4049 *Fax:* 215-568-5065 *E-mail:* info@fadavis.com *Web Site:* www.fadavis.com, pg 76

DeJesu, Betsy, Basic Books, 250 W 57 St, 15th fl, New York, NY 10107 *Tel:* 212-340-8164 *Fax:* 212-340-8135 *E-mail:* perseus.promos@perseusbooks.com *Web Site:* www.basicbooks.com; perseusbooks.com, pg 31

Dekker, Robert, Lippincott Williams & Wilkins, 530 Walnut St, Philadelphia, PA 19106-3621 *Tel:* 215-521-8300 *Toll Free Tel:* 800-638-3030 (orders & cust serv) *E-mail:* orders@lww.com *Web Site:* www.lww.com, pg 150

Deku, Prof Afrikadzata PhD, Continental AfrikaPublishers, 182 Stribling Circle, Spartanburg, SC 29301 *Tel:* 864-576-7992 *Fax:* 775-295-9699 *E-mail:* afrikalion@aol.com; afrikapharaoh@aol.com; afrikafiaga@aol.com; afrikadela@aol.com *Web Site:* www.writers.net/writers/22249, pg 66

Del'Isola, Rebeca, SilverHouse Books, 555 NE 15 St, Suite 2-i, Miami, FL 33132 *Tel:* 305-747-1258 *E-mail:* info@silverhousebooks.com *Web Site:* www.silverhousebooks.com, pg 234

Delacoste, Frederique, Cleis Press, 2246 Sixth St, Berkeley, CA 94710 *Tel:* 510-845-8000 *Toll Free Tel:* 800-780-2279 (US) *Fax:* 510-845-8001 *E-mail:* orders@cleispress.com *Web Site:* www.cleispress.com; www.vivaeditions.com, pg 63

Delamar, Gloria T, Philadelphia Writers' Conference, PO Box 7171, Elkins Park, PA 19027-0171 *Tel:* 215-782-3288 *Fax:* 215-782-3288 *E-mail:* info@pwcwriters.org *Web Site:* pwcwriters.org, pg 672

Delaney, Jennifer, David R Godine Publisher Inc, 15 Court Sq, Suite 320, Boston, MA 02108-4715 *Tel:* 617-451-9600 *Fax:* 617-350-0250 *E-mail:* pub@godine.com *Web Site:* www.godine.com, pg 104

Delaney, Jennifer, Intercultural Press Inc, 20 Park Plaza, Suite 610, Boston, MA 02116 *Tel:* 617-523-3801 *Toll Free Tel:* 888-273-2539 *Fax:* 617-523-3708 *E-mail:* info@interculturalpress.com *Web Site:* www.interculturalpress.com, pg 132

Delbourgo, Joelle, Joelle Delbourgo Associates Inc, 101 Park St, Montclair, NJ 07042 *Tel:* 973-773-0836 (call only during standard business hours) *Web Site:* www.delbourgo.com, pg 568

Delemer, Lucie, Les Editions de l'Hexagone, 1010 rue de la Gauchetiere E, Montreal, QC H2L 2N5, Canada *Tel:* 514-523-7993 (ext 4201) *Fax:* 514-282-7530 *E-mail:* vml@sogides.com *Web Site:* www.edhexagone.com, pg 502

Dellon, Hope, St Martin's Press, LLC, 175 Fifth Ave, New York, NY 10010 *Tel:* 646-307-5151 *Fax:* 212-420-9314 *E-mail:* firstname.lastname@macmillan.com *Web Site:* www.stmartins.com, pg 224

DeLong, Elizabeth, Seven Stories Press, 140 Watts St, New York, NY 10013 *Tel:* 212-226-8760 *Fax:* 212-226-1411 *E-mail:* info@sevenstories.com *Web Site:* www.sevenstories.com, pg 232

Delorme, Alain, Les Editions Goelette Inc, 1350 Marie-Victorin, St-Bruno-de-Montarville, Quebec, QC J3V 6B9, Canada *Tel:* 450-653-1337 *Toll Free Tel:* 800-463-4961 *Fax:* 450-653-9924 *Web Site:* www.editionsgoelette.com, pg 506

DeLuca, David, Bess Press, 3565 Harding Ave, Honolulu, HI 96816 *Tel:* 808-734-7159; 808-734-7159 (ext 10, returns) *Toll Free Tel:* 800-910-2377 *Fax:* 808-732-3627 *E-mail:* sales@besspress.com *Web Site:* www.besspress.com, pg 36

DeMao, Sherre, Gravure Association of America Inc, 8281 Pine Lake Rd, Denver, NC 28037 *Tel:* 201-523-6042 *Fax:* 201-523-6048 *E-mail:* gaa@gaa.org *Web Site:* www.gaa.org, pg 624

DeMarco, Michael, Peoples Education Inc, 299 Market St, Suite 240, Saddle Brook, NJ 07663 *Tel:* 201-712-0090 *Toll Free Tel:* 800-822-1080 *Fax:* 201-712-0045; 201-712-1016 *Web Site:* www.peopleseducation.com; www.peoplescollegeprep.com; www.measuringuplive.com; www.brightpointliteracy.com, pg 199

Demas, Jamie, Bedford, Freeman & Worth Publishing Group, LLC, 41 Madison Ave, 37th fl, New York, NY 10010 *Tel:* 212-576-9400 *Fax:* 212-689-2383 *Web Site:* www.macmillanhighered.com, pg 33

Demastus, Amanda, Howard Books, 216 Centerview Dr, Suite 303, Brentwood, TN 37027 *Tel:* 615-873-2080 *Fax:* 615-370-3834 *E-mail:* howardbooks@simonandschuster.com (info) *Web Site:* www.howardpublishing.com, pg 124

DeMayo, Joan, Random House Children's Books, 1745 Broadway, New York, NY 10019 *Tel:* 212-782-9000 *Toll Free Tel:* 800-200-3552 *Fax:* 212-782-9452 *Web Site:* randomhousekids.com, pg 213

Demers, Dr David, Marquette Books, 3107 E 62 Ave, Spokane, WA 99223 *Tel:* 509-290-9240 *Fax:* 509-448-2191 *E-mail:* books@marquettebooks.com *Web Site:* www.marquettebooks.com, pg 157

Deming, Nicole, The Children's Book Council (CBC), 54 W 39 St, 14th fl, New York, NY 10018 *Tel:* 212-966-1990 *Fax:* 212-966-2073 *Toll Free Fax:* 888-807-9355 (orders only) *E-mail:* cbc.info@cbcbooks.org *Web Site:* www.cbcbooks.org, pg 621

DeMint, Jim, The Heritage Foundation, 214 Massachusetts Ave NE, Washington, DC 20002-4999 *Tel:* 202-546-4400 *Toll Free Tel:* 800-544-4843 *Fax:* 202-546-8328 *E-mail:* info@heritage.org *Web Site:* www.heritage.org, pg 119, 641

Dempsey, Luke, Random House Publishing Group, 1745 Broadway, New York, NY 10019 *Toll Free Tel:* 800-200-3552 *Web Site:* atrandom.com, pg 214

Dendy, Shere, Frank L & Harriet C Owsley Award, University of Georgia, Dept of History, Athens, GA 30602-1602 *Tel:* 706-542-8848 *Fax:* 706-542-2455 *Web Site:* sha.uga.edu, pg 731

Dendy, Shere, Francis B Simkins Award, University of Georgia, Dept of History, Athens, GA 30602-1602 *Tel:* 706-542-8848 *Fax:* 706-542-2455 *Web Site:* sha.uga.edu, pg 742

Dendy, Shere, Charles S Sydnor Award, University of Georgia, Dept of History, Athens, GA 30602-1602 *Tel:* 706-542-8848 *Fax:* 706-542-2455 *Web Site:* sha.uga.edu, pg 745

Denehy, Debbie, Petroleum Extension Service (PETEX), University of Texas at Austin-PETEX, One University Sta, R8100, Austin, TX 78712-1100 *Tel:* 512-471-5940 *Toll Free Tel:* 800-687-4132 *Fax:* 512-471-9410 *Toll Free Fax:* 800-687-7839 *E-mail:* plach@www.utex.edu; petex@www.utexas.edu *Web Site:* www.utexas.edu/ce/petex, pg 200

Denekamp, Hope, Kneerim, Williams & Bloom Agency, 90 Canal St, Boston, MA 02114 *Tel:* 617-303-1650 *Web Site:* www.kwlit.com, pg 580

Dengler, M Heide, Information Today, Inc, 143 Old Marlton Pike, Medford, NJ 08055-8750 *Tel:* 609-654-6266 *Toll Free Tel:* 800-300-9868 (cust serv) *Fax:* 609-654-4309 *E-mail:* custserv@infotoday.com *Web Site:* www.infotoday.com, pg 130

Dennis, Diane, Idyllwild Arts Summer Workshops, 52500 Temecula Dr, Idyllwild, CA 92549-0038 *Tel:* 951-659-2171 *Fax:* 951-659-4552 *E-mail:* summer@idyllwildarts.org *Web Site:* www.idyllwildarts.org, pg 670

Dennis, Geoff, Crossway, 1300 Crescent St, Wheaton, IL 60187 *Tel:* 630-682-4300 *Toll Free Tel:* 800-635-7993 (orders); 800-543-1659 (cust serv) *Fax:* 630-682-4785 *E-mail:* info@crossway.org *Web Site:* www.crossway.org, pg 72

Dennis, Lane T, Crossway, 1300 Crescent St, Wheaton, IL 60187 *Tel:* 630-682-4300 *Toll Free Tel:* 800-635-7993 (orders); 800-543-1659 (cust serv) *Fax:* 630-682-4785 *E-mail:* info@crossway.org *Web Site:* www.crossway.org, pg 72

Dennis, Neil, IET, c/o Inspec Inc, 379 Thornall St, Edison, NJ 08837-2225 *Tel:* 732-321-5575; 732-321-5579 *Fax:* 732-321-5702 *E-mail:* iee@inspecinc.com *Web Site:* www.theiet.org/inspec, pg 127

Dennis, Stephanie, Running Press Book Publishers, 2300 Chestnut St, Philadelphia, PA 19103-4399 *Tel:* 215-567-5080 *Toll Free Tel:* 800-343-4499 (cust serv & orders) *Fax:* 215-568-2919 *Toll Free Fax:* 800-453-2884 (cust serv & orders) *E-mail:* perseus.promos@perseusbooks.com *Web Site:* www.runningpress.com, pg 222

Denny, Heather, Massachusetts Institute of Technology Libraries, 77 Massachusetts Ave, Bldg 14-S, Rm 0551, Cambridge, MA 02139-4307 *Tel:* 617-253-5651 *Fax:* 617-253-8894 *Web Site:* libraries.mit.edu/docs, pg 159

Dennys, Louise, Knopf Random Canada, One Toronto St, Suite 300, Toronto, ON M5C 2V6, Canada *Tel:* 416-364-4449 *Toll Free Tel:* 888-523-9292 *Fax:* 416-364-6863 *Web Site:* www.randomhouse.ca, pg 510

Dennys, Louise, Random House of Canada Limited, One Toronto St, Suite 300, Toronto, ON M5C 2V6, Canada *Tel:* 416-364-4449 *Toll Free Tel:* 888-523-9292 (cust serv) *Fax:* 416-364-6863; 416-364-6653 (subs rts) *Web Site:* www.randomhouse.ca, pg 517

Dent, Mary J, Resource Publications Inc, 160 E Virginia St, Suite 170, San Jose, CA 95112-5876 *Tel:* 408-286-8505 *Fax:* 408-287-8748 *E-mail:* orders@rpinet.com *Web Site:* www.rpinet.com, pg 218

Dent-Zobal, Catherine, Susquehanna University, Dept of English, 514 University Ave, Selinsgrove, PA 17870 *Tel:* 570-372-0101, pg 680

Deonarain, Renuka, The Brookings Institution Press, 1775 Massachusetts Ave NW, Washington, DC 20036-2188 *Tel:* 202-536-3600 *Toll Free Tel:* 800-537-5487 *Fax:* 202-536-3623 *E-mail:* permissions@brookings.edu *Web Site:* www.brookings.edu, pg 48

Der-Hovanessian, Diana, Barbara Bradley Prize, 2 Farrar St, Cambridge, MA 02138 *Tel:* 617-744-6034 *E-mail:* contests@nepoetryclub.org *Web Site:* www.nepoetryclub.org, pg 692

AndrewLinickDirectMarketing.com/Copywriters-Council.html; www.NewWorldPressBooks.com, pg 543, 621

Dextor, Roger, Andrew S Linick PhD, The Copyologist®, Linick Bldg, 7 Putter Lane, Middle Island, NY 11953 *Tel:* 631-924-3888 *Fax:* 631-924-8555 *E-mail:* linickgroup@gmail.com *Web Site:* www.AndrewLinickDirectMarketing.com/The-Copyologist.html; www.NewWorldPressBooks.com, pg 550

Deykerhoff, Paul, Penguin Group (USA) LLC Sales, 375 Hudson St, New York, NY 10014 *Tel:* 212-366-2000 *E-mail:* online@penguinputnam.com *Web Site:* us.penguingroup.com, pg 197

Deyoe, Cori, 3 Seas Literary Agency, PO Box 8571, Madison, WI 53708 *Tel:* 608-834-9317, pg 597

DeYoung, Neil, Hachette Digital, 237 Park Ave, New York, NY 10017 *Tel:* 212-364-0600, pg 110

Dhar, Uday K, Mondial, 203 W 107 St, Suite 6-C, New York, NY 10025 *Tel:* 646-807-8031 *Fax:* 208-361-2863 *E-mail:* contact@mondialbooks.com *Web Site:* www.mondialbooks.com, pg 168

Di Bello, John, W W Norton & Company Inc, 500 Fifth Ave, New York, NY 10110-0017 *Tel:* 212-354-5500 *Toll Free Tel:* 800-233-4830 (orders & cust serv) *Fax:* 212-869-0856 *Toll Free Fax:* 800-458-6515 *Web Site:* www.wwnorton.com, pg 182

di Capua, Michael, Scholastic Trade Division, 557 Broadway, New York, NY 10012 *Tel:* 212-343-6100; 212-343-4685 (export sales) *Fax:* 212-343-4714 (export sales) *Web Site:* www.scholastic.com, pg 228

di Cicco, Dennis, Sky Publishing, 90 Sherman St, Cambridge, MA 02140 *Tel:* 617-864-7360 *Toll Free Tel:* 866-644-1377 *Fax:* 617-864-6117 *E-mail:* info@skyandtelescope.com *Web Site:* www.skyandtelescope.com, pg 237

Di Cicco, Mark, Tyndale House Publishers Inc, 351 Executive Dr, Carol Stream, IL 60188 *Tel:* 630-668-8300 *Toll Free Tel:* 800-323-9400 *Web Site:* www.tyndale.com, pg 261

Di Gioia, Tony, George T Bisel Co Inc, 710 S Washington Sq, Philadelphia, PA 19106-3519 *Tel:* 215-922-5760 *Toll Free Tel:* 800-247-3526 *Fax:* 215-922-2235 *E-mail:* gbisel@bisel.com *Web Site:* www.bisel.com, pg 38

Di Martino, Christina, Christina Di Martino Literary Services, 139 Sandpiper Ave, Royal Palm Beach, FL 33411 *Tel:* 212-996-9086; 917-972-6012 *E-mail:* writealot@earthlink.net *Web Site:* christinadimartino.com, pg 544

Di Mattia, Nadia, Kane Press Inc, 350 Fifth Ave, Suite 7206, New York, NY 10118-7200 *Tel:* 212-268-1435 *E-mail:* info@kanepress.com *Web Site:* www.kanepress.com, pg 138

Di Piazza, Domenica, Twenty-First Century Books, 241 First Ave N, Minneapolis, MN 55401 *Tel:* 612-332-3344 *Toll Free Tel:* 800-328-4929 *Fax:* 612-332-7615 *Toll Free Fax:* 800-332-1132 *E-mail:* info@lernerbooks.com *Web Site:* www.lernerbooks.com, pg 260

Di Pietro, Chris, MFA Publications, 465 Huntington Ave, Boston, MA 02115 *Tel:* 617-369-4233 *Fax:* 617-369-3459 *Web Site:* www.mfa.org/publications, pg 165

Di Sarro, Lisa, Houghton Mifflin Harcourt K-12 Publishers, 222 Berkeley St, Boston, MA 02116-3764 *Tel:* 617-351-5000 *Toll Free Tel:* 800-225-5425 (cust serv) *Web Site:* www.hmhco.com; www.hmheducation.com, pg 123

Di Stefano, G, editions CERES Ltd/Le Moyen Francais, CP 1089, Succursale B, Maison de la Poste, Montreal, QC H3B 3K9, Canada *Tel:* 514-937-7138 *Fax:* 514-937-9875 *E-mail:* editionsceres@gmail.com *Web Site:* www.editionsceres.ca, pg 502

Di Vietro, Philip, American Society of Mechanical Engineers (ASME), 3 Park Ave, New York, NY 10016-5990 *Tel:* 212-591-7000 *Toll Free Tel:* 800-843-2763 (cust serv-US, CN & Mexico) *Fax:* 212-591-7674; 973-882-8113 (cust serv); 973-882-1717 (orders & inquiries) *E-mail:* infocentral@asme.org *Web Site:* www.asme.org, pg 17

Diaco, Paula, League of Vermont Writers, PO Box 172, Underhill Center, VT 05490 *Tel:* 802-349-7475 *E-mail:* lvw@leaguevtwriters.org *Web Site:* www.leagueofvermontwriters.org, pg 626

DiAngelo, Brianne, Magazines Canada, 425 Adelaide St W, Suite 700, Toronto, ON M5V 3C1, Canada *Tel:* 416-504-0274 *Fax:* 416-504-0437 *E-mail:* info@magazinescanada.ca *Web Site:* www.magazinescanada.ca, pg 627

Diaz, Jorge E, Casa Bautista de Publicaciones, 7000 Alabama Ave, El Paso, TX 79904 *Tel:* 915-566-9656 *Toll Free Tel:* 800-755-5958 (cust serv & orders) *Fax:* 915-562-6502; 915-565-9008 (orders) *Web Site:* www.casabautista.org; www.editorialmh.org, pg 53

Diaz, Katrina, Scribner, 1230 Avenue of the Americas, New York, NY 10020, pg 230

Diaz, Laly, Theosophical Publishing House/Quest Books, 306 W Geneva Rd, Wheaton, IL 60187 *Tel:* 630-665-0130 (ext 347) *Toll Free Tel:* 800-669-9425 (ext 347) *Fax:* 630-665-8791 *E-mail:* customerservice@questbooks.net *Web Site:* www.questbooks.net, pg 254

Diaz, Dr Polo, Canadian Plains Research Center, 2 Research Dr, Regina, SK S4S 7H9, Canada *Tel:* 306-585-4758 *Toll Free Tel:* 866-874-2257 *Fax:* 306-585-4699 *E-mail:* canadian.plains@uregina.ca *Web Site:* www.cprc.ca, pg 497

Diaz, Stefanie, Sanford J Greenburger Associates Inc, 55 Fifth Ave, 15th fl, New York, NY 10003 *Tel:* 212-206-5600 *Fax:* 212-463-8718 *Web Site:* www.greenburger.com, pg 575

Dibble, Jennifer, Zondervan, A HarperCollins Company, 5300 Patterson Ave SE, Grand Rapids, MI 49530 *Tel:* 616-698-6900 *Toll Free Tel:* 800-226-1122; 800-727-1309 (retail orders) *Fax:* 616-698-3350 *Toll Free Fax:* 800-698-3256 (retail orders) *E-mail:* zinfo@zondervan.com *Web Site:* www.zondervan.com, pg 289

DiChiera, Cristina, Fellowship Program, One Capital Hill, 3rd fl, Providence, RI 02908 *Tel:* 401-222-3880 *Fax:* 401-222-3018 *Web Site:* www.arts.ri.gov, pg 703

Dickerman, Colin, The Penguin Press, 375 Hudson St, New York, NY 10014, pg 197

Dickerson, Cindy, Cornell University Southeast Asia Program Publications, 213 Kahin Ctr, 640 Stewart Ave, Ithaca, NY 14850 *Tel:* 607-277-2211 *Toll Free Tel:* 800-666-2211 *Fax:* 607-277-6292 *Toll Free Fax:* 800-688-2877 *E-mail:* seap-pubs@cornell.edu *Web Site:* www.einaudi.cornell.edu/southeastasia/publications, pg 68

Dickerson, Donna, Peabody Museum Press, 11 Divinity Ave, Cambridge, MA 02138 *Tel:* 617-495-4255 *Fax:* 617-495-7535 *E-mail:* peapub@fas.harvard.edu *Web Site:* www.peabody.harvard.edu/publications, pg 195

Dickerson, Donya, McGraw-Hill Professional, 1221 Avenue of the Americas, New York, NY 10020 *Tel:* 212-512-2000 *Web Site:* www.mhprofessional.com, pg 162

Dickerson, Terese, Oxford University Press USA, 198 Madison Ave, New York, NY 10016 *Tel:* 212-726-6000 *Toll Free Tel:* 800-451-7556 (orders); 800-445-9714 (cust serv) *Fax:* 919-677-1303 *E-mail:* custserv.us@oup.com *Web Site:* www.oup.com/us, pg 189

Dickerson, Trisina, John F Blair Publisher, 1406 Plaza Dr, Winston-Salem, NC 27103 *Tel:* 336-768-1374 *Toll Free Tel:* 800-222-9796 *Fax:* 336-768-9194 *Web Site:* www.blairpub.com, pg 40

Dickinson, Dr Greg, The Althouse Press, Western University, 1137 Western Rd, London, ON N6G 1G7, Canada *Tel:* 519-661-2096 *Fax:* 519-661-3714 *E-mail:* press@uwo.ca *Web Site:* www.edu.uwo.ca/althousepress, pg 493

Dickinson, Jan, Wheatherstone Press, PO Box 257, Portland, OR 97207-0257 *Tel:* 503-244-8929 *Fax:* 503-244-9795 *E-mail:* relocntr@nwlink.com *Web Site:* www.wheatherstonepress.com, pg 280

Dickinson, Kimberly, Manning Publications Co, 20 Baldwin Rd, Shelter Island, NY 11964 *Toll Free Tel:* 800-294-4747 (orders) *E-mail:* orders@manning.com *Web Site:* www.manning.com, pg 156

Dickner, Bertin, Les Editions Fides, 7333 place des Roseraies, bureau 100, Montreal, QC H1M 2X6, Canada *Tel:* 514-745-4290 *Toll Free Tel:* 800-363-1451 (CN) *Fax:* 514-745-4299 *E-mail:* editions@fides.qc.ca *Web Site:* www.editionsfides.com, pg 503

Dickson, Jonathan Lovat, Pippin Publishing Corp, PO Box 242, Don Mills, ON M3C 2S2, Canada *Tel:* 416-510-2918 *Toll Free Tel:* 888-889-0001 *Fax:* 416-510-3359 *Web Site:* www.pippinpub.com, pg 516

Dickson, Sara, National Newspaper Association, 309 S Providence St, Columbia, MO 65203-4267 *Tel:* 573-882-5800 *Toll Free Tel:* 800-829-4NNA (829-4662) *Fax:* 573-884-5490 *E-mail:* info@nna.org *Web Site:* www.nnaweb.org, pg 630

Didier, Rebecca, Trafalgar Square Books, 388 Howe Hill Rd, North Pomfret, VT 05053 *Tel:* 802-457-1911 *Toll Free Tel:* 800-423-4525 *Fax:* 802-457-1913 *E-mail:* tsquare@sover.net; info@trafalgarbooks.com *Web Site:* www.trafalgarbooks.com; www.horseandriderbooks.com, pg 257

Didik, Jennifer, Loretta Barrett Books Inc, 220 E 23 St, 11th fl, New York, NY 10010 *Tel:* 212-242-3420 *E-mail:* query@lorettabarrettbooks.com *Web Site:* www.lorettabarrettbooks.com, pg 562

Didio, Dan, DC Entertainment, 1700 Broadway, New York, NY 10019 *Tel:* 212-636-5400 *Toll Free Tel:* 800-887-6789 *Fax:* 212-636-5979 *E-mail:* dccomics@cambeywest.com *Web Site:* www.dccomics.com; www.madmag.com; www.dcentertainment.com, pg 76

Diedrick, Brice, JMW Group Inc, One West Ave, Suite 219, Larchmont, NY 10538 *Tel:* 914-834-7800 *Fax:* 914-834-7824 *E-mail:* info@jmwgroup.net *Web Site:* jmwgroup.net, pg 578

Diehl, Debra, University Press of Kansas, 2502 Westbrooke Circle, Lawrence, KS 66045-4444 *Tel:* 785-864-4154; 785-864-4155 (orders) *Fax:* 785-864-4586 *E-mail:* upress@ku.edu; upkorders@ku.edu (orders) *Web Site:* www.kansaspress.ku.edu, pg 271

Dienstfrey, Patricia, Kelsey Street Press, 2824 Kelsey St, Berkeley, CA 94705 *Tel:* 510-845-2260 *Fax:* 510-548-9185 *E-mail:* info@kelseyst.com *Web Site:* www.kelseyst.com, pg 139

Diercks, Lisa, Emerson College Dept of Writing, Literature & Publishing, 180 Tremont St, 10th fl, Boston, MA 02116 *Tel:* 617-824-8750 *Fax:* 617-824-7856 *Web Site:* www.emerson.edu, pg 678

Diforio, Robert (Bob) G, D4EO Literary Agency, 7 Indian Valley Rd, Weston, CT 06883 *Tel:* 203-544-7180 *Fax:* 203-544-7160 *Web Site:* www.d4eoliteraryagency.com, pg 568

Diggins, Caroline, Indiana University Writers' Conference, Indiana University, 464 Ballantine Hall, Dept of English, 1020 E Kirkwood Ave, Bloomington, IN 47405 *Tel:* 812-855-1877 *Fax:* 812-855-9535 *E-mail:* writecon@indiana.edu *Web Site:* www.indiana.edu/~writecon/, pg 670

Dighton, Samantha, D4EO Literary Agency, 7 Indian Valley Rd, Weston, CT 06883 *Tel:* 203-544-7180 *Fax:* 203-544-7160 *Web Site:* www.d4eoliteraryagency.com, pg 568

Dijkstra, Sandra, Sandra Dijkstra Literary Agency, 1155 Camino del Mar, PMB 515, Del Mar, CA 92014-2605 *Web Site:* dijkstraagency.com, pg 568

Dilanyan, Rema, Peter Lampack Agency Inc, 350 Fifth Ave, Suite 5300, New York, NY 10118 *Tel:* 212-687-9106 *Fax:* 212-687-9109 *Web Site:* peterlampackagency.com, pg 581

Diley, Esther, Augsburg Fortress Publishers, Publishing House of the Evangelical Lutheran Church in America, 100 S Fifth St, Suite 600, Minneapolis, MN 55402 *Tel:* 612-330-3300 *Toll Free Tel:* 800-426-0115 (ext 639, subns); 800-328-4648 (orders) *E-mail:* info@augsburgfortress.org; copyright@augsburgfortress.

Dodson, Veronique, National Association of Black Journalists (NABJ), 1100 Knight Hall, Suite 3100, College Park, MD 20742 *Tel:* 301-405-0248 *Fax:* 301-314-1714 *E-mail:* nabj@nabj.org *Web Site:* www.nabj.org, pg 628

Doerr, Jennifer, Yale University Press, 302 Temple St, New Haven, CT 06511-8909 *Tel:* 401-531-2800 (cust serv); 203-432-0960 *Toll Free Tel:* 800-405-1619 (cust serv) *Fax:* 203-432-0948; 401-531-2801 (cust serv) *Toll Free Fax:* 800-406-9145 (cust serv) *E-mail:* customer.care@trilateral.org (cust serv); language.yalepress@yale.edu *Web Site:* www.yalebooks.com, pg 287

Doerr, Susan, University of Minnesota Press, 111 Third Ave S, Suite 290, Minneapolis, MN 55401-2520 *Tel:* 612-627-1970 *Fax:* 612-627-1980 *E-mail:* ump@umn.edu *Web Site:* www.upress.umn.edu, pg 266

Doherty, Kathleen, Tom Doherty Associates, LLC, 175 Fifth Ave, 14th fl, New York, NY 10010 *Tel:* 646-307-5151 *Toll Free Tel:* 800-455-0340 *Fax:* 212-388-0191 *E-mail:* firstname.lastname@tor.com *Web Site:* www.tor-forge.com, pg 80

Doherty, Ryan, Random House Publishing Group, 1745 Broadway, New York, NY 10019 *Toll Free Tel:* 800-200-3552 *Web Site:* atrandom.com, pg 214

Doherty, Thomas, Tom Doherty Associates, LLC, 175 Fifth Ave, 14th fl, New York, NY 10010 *Tel:* 646-307-5151 *Toll Free Tel:* 800-455-0340 *Fax:* 212-388-0191 *E-mail:* firstname.lastname@tor.com *Web Site:* www.tor-forge.com, pg 80

Doherty, Thomas, Macmillan, 175 Fifth Ave, New York, NY 10010 *Tel:* 646-307-5151 *Fax:* 212-420-9314 *E-mail:* firstname.lastname@macmillan.com *Web Site:* www.macmillan.com, pg 154

Doherty, Todd, Delmar, 5 Maxwell Dr, Clifton Park, NY 12065-2919 *Tel:* 518-348-2300 *Toll Free Tel:* 800-347-7707 (cust serv); 800-998-7498 *Fax:* 518-373-6200 *Toll Free Fax:* 800-487-8488 (cust serv) *Web Site:* www.cengage.com/delmar; www.delmarlearning.com, pg 77

Doherty, Tom, JIST Publishing, 875 Montreal Way, St Paul, MN 55102 *Tel:* 317-613-4200 *Toll Free Tel:* 800-328-1452 *Toll Free Fax:* 800-328-4564 *E-mail:* educate@emcp.com *Web Site:* jist.emcpublishingllc.com, pg 135

Dohle, Markus, Random House Inc, 1745 Broadway, New York, NY 10019 *Tel:* 212-782-9000 *Toll Free Tel:* 800-726-0600 *Web Site:* www.randomhouse.com, pg 213

Doige, Dr Lynda A, Mi'kmaq-Maliseet Institute, University of New Brunswick, Rm 343, Marshall d'Avray Hall, 10 MacKay Dr, Fredericton, NB E3B 5A3, Canada *Tel:* 506-453-4840 *Fax:* 506-453-4784 *E-mail:* micmac@unb.ca *Web Site:* www.unb.ca; www.unb.ca/fredericton/education/mmi, pg 512

Doiron, Paul, Down East Books, 680 Commercial St (US Rte 1), Rockport, ME 04856 *Tel:* 207-594-9544 *Toll Free Tel:* 800-685-7962 (US only orders); 800-766-1670 *Fax:* 207-594-7215 *E-mail:* submissions@downeast.com *Web Site:* www.downeast.com, pg 81

Dokmo, Charlie, NavPress Publishing Group, 3820 N 30 St, Colorado Springs, CO 80904 *Tel:* 719-548-9222 *Toll Free Tel:* 800-366-7788 *Toll Free Fax:* 800-343-3902 *E-mail:* customerservice@navpress.com *Web Site:* www.navpress.com, pg 176

Dolan, Deirdre F, W W Norton & Company Inc, 500 Fifth Ave, New York, NY 10110-0017 *Tel:* 212-354-5500 *Toll Free Tel:* 800-233-4830 (orders & cust serv) *Fax:* 212-869-0856 *Toll Free Fax:* 800-458-6515 *Web Site:* www.wwnorton.com, pg 182

Dolce, Holly, Harry N Abrams Inc, 115 W 18 St, 6th fl, New York, NY 10011 *Tel:* 212-206-7715 *Toll Free Tel:* 800-345-1359 *Fax:* 212-519-1210 *E-mail:* abrams@abramsbooks.com *Web Site:* www.abramsbooks.com, pg 3

Doll, Holly, Fitzhenry & Whiteside Limited, 195 Allstate Pkwy, Markham, ON L3R 4T8, Canada *Tel:* 905-477-9700 *Toll Free Tel:* 800-387-9776 *Fax:* 905-477-9179 *Toll Free Fax:* 800-260-9777 *E-mail:* bookinfo@fitzhenry.ca; godwit@fitzhenry.ca *Web Site:* www.fitzhenry.ca, pg 505

Dollar, Douglas, New Forums Press Inc, 1018 S Lewis St, Stillwater, OK 74074 *Tel:* 405-372-6158 *Toll Free Tel:* 800-606-3766 *Fax:* 405-377-2237 *E-mail:* submissions@newforums.com *Web Site:* www.newforums.com, pg 177

Dolled, Stephen, Marshall Cavendish Corp, 99 White Plains Rd, Tarrytown, NY 10591-9001 *Tel:* 914-332-8888 *Toll Free Tel:* 800-821-9881 *Fax:* 914-332-8102 *E-mail:* customerservice@marshallcavendish.com; mcc@marshallcavendish.com *Web Site:* marshallcavendish.us; marshallcavendishdigital.com; marshallcavendishebooks.com, pg 158

Dollins, Robert, Black Rose Books Ltd, CP 35788 Succ Leo Pariseau, Montreal, QC H2X 0A4, Canada *Tel:* 514-844-4076 *Toll Free Tel:* 800-565-9523 (orders) *Toll Free Fax:* 800-221-9985 (orders) *E-mail:* info@blackrosebooks.net *Web Site:* www.blackrosebooks.net, pg 494

Dols, Amy, The Child's World Inc, 1980 Lookout Dr, Mankato, MN 56003 *Tel:* 507-385-1044 *Toll Free Tel:* 800-599-READ (599-7323) *Toll Free Fax:* 888-320-2329 *E-mail:* sales@childsworld.com *Web Site:* www.childsworld.com, pg 60

Dombos, Juliet, The Pilgrim Press/United Church Press, 700 Prospect Ave, Cleveland, OH 44115-1100 *Toll Free Tel:* 800-537-3394 (cust serv-indivs); 800-654-5129 (cust serv-commercial accts) *Fax:* 216-736-2206 (orders) *E-mail:* proposals@thepilgrimpress.com *Web Site:* www.thepilgrimpress.com; www.unitedchurchpress.com, pg 202

Domenig, Kathleen, Strata Publishing Inc, PO Box 1303, State College, PA 16804 *Tel:* 814-234-8545 *Fax:* 814-238-7222 *E-mail:* stratapub@stratapub.com *Web Site:* www.stratapub.com, pg 246

Dominguez, Maria, Scholastic Trade Division, 557 Broadway, New York, NY 10012 *Tel:* 212-343-6100; 212-343-4685 (export sales) *Fax:* 212-343-4714 (export sales) *Web Site:* www.scholastic.com, pg 228

Domville, Sara, Betterway Books, 10151 Carver Rd, Suite 200, Blue Ash, OH 45242 *Tel:* 513-531-2690 *Toll Free Tel:* 800-666-0963 *Fax:* 513-891-7185 *Toll Free Fax:* 888-590-4082 *Web Site:* www.fwmedia.com, pg 36

Domville, Sara, F+W Media Inc, 10151 Carver Rd, Suite 200, Blue Ash, OH 45242 *Tel:* 513-531-2690 *Toll Free Tel:* 800-289-0963 (trade accts); 800-258-0929 (orders) *E-mail:* contact_us@fwmedia.com *Web Site:* www.fwmedia.com, pg 92

Domville, Sara, Krause Publications Inc, 700 E State St, Iola, WI 54990 *Tel:* 715-445-2214 *Toll Free Tel:* 800-258-0929 (cust serv); 888-457-2873 (orders) *Fax:* 715-445-4087 *E-mail:* bookorders@krause.com *Web Site:* www.krausebooks.com, pg 142

Domville, Sara, North Light Books, 10151 Carver Rd, Suite 200, Blue Ash, OH 45242 *Tel:* 513-531-2690 *Toll Free Tel:* 800-666-0963 *Fax:* 513-891-7185 *Toll Free Fax:* 888-590-4082 *E-mail:* contact_us@fwmedia.com *Web Site:* www.fwmedia.com, pg 181

Domville, Sara, Writer's Digest Books, 10151 Carver Rd, Suite 200, Blue Ash, OH 45242 *Tel:* 513-531-2690 *Toll Free Tel:* 800-289-0963 *Fax:* 513-531-7185 *E-mail:* writersdigest@fwmedia.com (edit) *Web Site:* www.writersdigest.com, pg 286

Don, Laurie, The Jim Henson Co, 1416 N La Brea Ave, Hollywood, CA 90028 *Tel:* 323-802-1500 *Fax:* 323-802-1825 *Web Site:* www.henson.com, pg 135

Donaher, Br Edward, St Pauls/Alba House, 2187 Victory Blvd, Staten Island, NY 10314-6603 *Tel:* 718-761-0047 (edit & prodn); 718-698-2759 (mktg & billing) *Toll Free Tel:* 800-343-2522 *Fax:* 718-761-0057 *E-mail:* sales@stpauls.us; marketing@stpauls.us *Web Site:* www.stpauls.us; www.albahouse.org, pg 225

Donahue, Jed, ISI Books, 3901 Centerville Rd, Wilmington, DE 19807-1938 *Tel:* 302-652-4600 *Toll Free Tel:* 800-526-7022 *Fax:* 302-652-1760 *E-mail:* info@isi.org; isibooks@isi.org *Web Site:* www.isibooks.org, pg 134

Donahue, Michael D, 4A's (American Association of Advertising Agencies), 1065 Avenue of the Americas, 16th fl, New York, NY 10018 *Tel:* 212-682-2500 *Web Site:* www.aaaa.org, pg 624

Donahue, Suzanne, Simon & Schuster, 1230 Avenue of the Americas, New York, NY 10020 *Tel:* 212-698-7000 *Toll Free Tel:* 800-223-2348 (cust serv); 800-223-2336 (orders) *Toll Free Fax:* 800-943-9831 (orders) *Web Site:* www.simonandschuster.com, pg 234

Donalty, Alison, HarperCollins Children's Books, 10 E 53 St, New York, NY 10022 *Tel:* 212-207-7000 *Web Site:* www.harpercollinschildrens.com, pg 113

Donatelli, Michael, The University of North Carolina Press, 116 S Boundary St, Chapel Hill, NC 27514-3808 *Tel:* 919-966-3561 *Fax:* 919-966-3829 *E-mail:* uncpress@unc.edu *Web Site:* www.uncpress.unc.edu, pg 267

Donatich, John, Yale University Press, 302 Temple St, New Haven, CT 06511-8909 *Tel:* 401-531-2800 (cust serv); 203-432-0960 *Toll Free Tel:* 800-405-1619 (cust serv) *Fax:* 203-432-0948; 401-531-2801 (cust serv) *Toll Free Fax:* 800-406-9145 (cust serv) *E-mail:* customer.care@trilateral.org (cust serv); language.yalepress@yale.edu *Web Site:* www.yalebooks.com, pg 287

Donato, Mariann, Macmillan, 175 Fifth Ave, New York, NY 10010 *Tel:* 646-307-5151 *Fax:* 212-420-9314 *E-mail:* firstname.lastname@macmillan.com *Web Site:* www.macmillan.com, pg 154

Donnaud, Janis A, Janis A Donnaud & Associates Inc, 525 Broadway, 2nd fl, New York, NY 10012 *Tel:* 212-431-2663 *Fax:* 212-431-2667 *E-mail:* jdonnaud@aol.com, pg 569

Donnelly, Maureen, Penguin Books, 375 Hudson St, New York, NY 10014 *Tel:* 212-366-2000 *E-mail:* online@penguinputnam.com *Web Site:* www.penguinputnam.com; www.penguinclassics.com; us.penguingroup.com, pg 197

Donnelly, Pat, AOCS Press, 2710 S Boulder Dr, Urbana, IL 61802-6996 *Tel:* 217-359-2344 *Fax:* 217-351-8091 *E-mail:* general@aocs.org *Web Site:* www.aocs.org, pg 19

Donnelly, Sean, The Danahy Fiction Prize, University of Tampa Press, 401 W Kennedy Blvd, Tampa, FL 33606 *Tel:* 813-253-6266 *E-mail:* utpress@ut.edu *Web Site:* tampareview.ut.edu, pg 699

Donnelly, Sean, The Tampa Review Prize for Poetry, University of Tampa Press, 401 W Kennedy Blvd, Tampa, FL 33606 *Tel:* 813-253-6266 *E-mail:* utpress@ut.edu *Web Site:* tampareview.ut.edu, pg 745

Donnelly, Susan, Harvard University Press, 79 Garden St, Cambridge, MA 02138-1499 *Tel:* 617-495-2600; 401-531-2800 (intl orders) *Toll Free Tel:* 800-405-1619 (orders) *Fax:* 617-495-5898 (general); 617-496-4677 (edit & rts); 401-531-2801 (intl orders) *Toll Free Fax:* 800-406-9145 (orders) *E-mail:* contact_hup@harvard.edu *Web Site:* www.hup.harvard.edu, pg 115

Donofrio, Caroline, Razorbill, 345 Hudson St, New York, NY 10014 *Tel:* 212-366-2000, pg 215

Donovan, Amy, United States Holocaust Memorial Museum, 100 Raoul Wallenberg Place SW, Washington, DC 20024-2126 *Tel:* 202-314-7837; 202-488-6144 (orders) *Toll Free Tel:* 800-259-9998 (orders) *Fax:* 202-479-9726; 202-488-0438 (orders) *E-mail:* cahs_publications@ushmm.org *Web Site:* www.ushmm.org, pg 262

Donovan, Jim, Jim Donovan Literary, 5635 SMU Blvd, Suite 201, Dallas, TX 75206 *Tel:* 214-696-9411 *E-mail:* jdlqueries@sbcglobal.net, pg 569

Donovan, John, McGraw-Hill International Publishing Group, 2 Penn Plaza, New York, NY 10121 *Tel:* 212-904-2000 *Web Site:* www.mcgraw-hill.com, pg 161

Donovan, Lisa, Simon & Schuster Children's Publishing, 1230 Avenue of the Americas, New York, NY 10020 *Tel:* 212-698-7000 *Web Site:* KIDS.SimonandSchuster.com; TEEN.SimonandSchuster.com; simonandschuster.net; simonandschuster.biz, pg 235

Donovan, Sharon, Counterpoint Press LLC, 1919 Fifth St, Berkeley, CA 94710 *Tel:* 510-704-0230 *Fax:* 510-704-0268 *E-mail:* info@counterpointpress.com *Web Site:* www.counterpointpress.com; www.sierraclub.org/books; www.softskull.com, pg 69

Dooley, Tim, OCP, 5536 NE Hassalo St, Portland, OR 97213 *Tel:* 503-281-1191 *Toll Free Tel:* 800-548-8749 *Fax:* 503-282-3486 *Toll Free Fax:* 800-843-8181 *E-mail:* liturgy@ocp.org *Web Site:* www.ocp.org, pg 184

Doorasamy, Sharon F, Morgan Reynolds Publishing, 620 S Elm St, Suite 387, Greensboro, NC 27406 *Tel:* 336-275-1311 *Toll Free Tel:* 800-535-1504 *Fax:* 336-275-1152 *Toll Free Fax:* 800-535-5725 *E-mail:* editorial@morganreynolds.com *Web Site:* www.morganreynolds.com, pg 170

Doornbos, Chris, David C Cook, 4050 Lee Vance View, Colorado Springs, CO 80918 *Tel:* 719-536-0100 *Toll Free Tel:* 800-708-5550 *Fax:* 519-536-3269 *Web Site:* www.davidccook.com, pg 67

Dore, Christine, Da Capo Press Inc & Lifelong Books, 44 Farnsworth St, 3rd fl, Boston, MA 02210 *Tel:* 617-252-5200 *Toll Free Tel:* 800-343-4499 (orders) *Fax:* 617-252-5285 *Web Site:* www.perseusbooksgroup.com/dacapo, pg 74

Dorff, Patricia, Council on Foreign Relations Press, The Harold Pratt House, 58 E 68 St, New York, NY 10065 *Tel:* 212-434-9400 *Fax:* 212-434-9800 *E-mail:* publications@cfr.org *Web Site:* www.cfr.org, pg 69

Dorfman, Debra, Scholastic Trade Division, 557 Broadway, New York, NY 10012 *Tel:* 212-343-6100; 212-343-4685 (export sales) *Fax:* 212-343-4714 (export sales) *Web Site:* www.scholastic.com, pg 228

Dorfman, Peter, Wimbledon Music Inc & Trigram Music Inc, 1801 Century Park E, Suite 2400, Los Angeles, CA 90067 *Tel:* 310-556-9683 *Fax:* 310-277-1278 *E-mail:* irishmex127@gmail.com *Web Site:* www.wimbtri.net, pg 282

Dorman, Dr Jessica, The Historic New Orleans Collection, 533 Royal St, New Orleans, LA 70130 *Tel:* 504-523-4662 *Fax:* 504-598-7104 *E-mail:* wrc@hnoc.org *Web Site:* www.hnoc.org, pg 120

Dorman, Mark, McGraw-Hill Education, 2 Penn Plaza, New York, NY 10121-2298 *Tel:* 212-904-2000 *E-mail:* customer.service@mcgraw-hill.com *Web Site:* www.mheducation.com; www.mheducation.com/custserv.html, pg 160

Dorman, Mark, McGraw-Hill International Publishing Group, 2 Penn Plaza, New York, NY 10121 *Tel:* 212-904-2000 *Web Site:* www.mcgraw-hill.com, pg 161

Dorman, Pamela, Viking, 375 Hudson St, New York, NY 10014 *Tel:* 212-366-2000 *E-mail:* online@penguinputnam.com *Web Site:* www.penguinputnam.com; us.penguingroup.com, pg 275

Dorning, Matthew, Conciliar Press, 2747 Bond St, University Park, IL 60484 *Tel:* 219-728-2216 (outside US) *Toll Free Tel:* 800-967-7377 *Fax:* 708-534-7803 *Toll Free Fax:* 866-599-5208 *E-mail:* service@conciliarmedia.com *Web Site:* www.conciliarpress.com, pg 66

Dorpalen, Erica, Yale Series of Younger Poets, 302 Temple St, New Haven, CT 06511 *Tel:* 203-432-0960 *Fax:* 203-432-0948 *Web Site:* www.yalebooks.com, pg 752

Dorpalen, Erica, Yale University Press, 302 Temple St, New Haven, CT 06511-8909 *Tel:* 401-531-2800 (cust serv); 203-432-0960 *Toll Free Tel:* 800-405-1619 (cust serv) *Fax:* 203-432-0948; 401-531-2801 (cust serv) *Toll Free Fax:* 800-406-9145 (cust serv) *E-mail:* customer.care@trilateral.org (cust serv); language.yalepress@yale.edu *Web Site:* www.yalebooks.com, pg 287

Dorr, Sharron, Theosophical Publishing House/Quest Books, 306 W Geneva Rd, Wheaton, IL 60187 *Tel:* 630-665-0130 (ext 347) *Toll Free Tel:* 800-669-9425 (ext 347) *Fax:* 630-665-8791 *E-mail:* customerservice@questbooks.net *Web Site:* www.questbooks.net, pg 254

Dorrance, Samuel R, Potomac Books Inc, 22841 Quicksilver Dr, Dulles, VA 20166 *Tel:* 703-661-1548 *Fax:* 703-661-1547 *E-mail:* pbimail@presswarehouse.com *Web Site:* www.potomacbooksinc.com, pg 204

Dosik, Anita, APPA: The Association of Higher Education Facilities Officers, 1643 Prince St, Alexandria, VA 22314-2818 *Tel:* 703-684-1446 *Fax:* 703-549-2772 *Web Site:* www.appa.org, pg 20

Doten, Mark, Soho Press Inc, 853 Broadway, New York, NY 10003 *Tel:* 212-260-1900 *Fax:* 212-260-1902 *E-mail:* soho@sohopress.com; publicity@sohopress.com *Web Site:* www.sohopress.com, pg 239

Dotto, Gabriel, Michigan State University Press (MSU Press), 1405 S Harrison Rd, Suite 25, East Lansing, MI 48823 *Tel:* 517-355-9543 *Fax:* 517-432-2611 *Toll Free Fax:* 800-678-2120 *E-mail:* msupress@msu.edu *Web Site:* www.msupress.msu.edu, pg 165

Doty, Jo, McClanahan Publishing House Inc, 88 Cedar St, Kuttawa, KY 42055-0100 *Tel:* 270-388-9388 *Toll Free Tel:* 800-544-6959 *Fax:* 270-388-6186 *E-mail:* books@kybooks.com *Web Site:* www.kybooks.com, pg 160

Dougan, Clark, University of Massachusetts Press, East Experiment Sta, 671 N Pleasant St, Amherst, MA 01003 *Tel:* 413-545-2217 *Fax:* 413-545-1226 *E-mail:* info@umpress.umass.edu *Web Site:* www.umass.edu/umpress, pg 266

Dougherty, Adria, Sterling Publishing Co Inc, 387 Park Ave S, 11th fl, New York, NY 10016-8810 *Tel:* 212-532-7160 *Toll Free Tel:* 800-367-9692 *Fax:* 212-213-2495 *Web Site:* www.sterlingpub.com, pg 244

Dougherty, Mary, Bedford/St Martin's, 75 Arlington St, Boston, MA 02116 *Tel:* 617-399-4000 *Toll Free Tel:* 800-779-7440 *Fax:* 617-426-8582 *Web Site:* www.bedfordstmartins.com, pg 34

Dougherty, Peter, Princeton University Press, 41 William St, Princeton, NJ 08540-5237 *Tel:* 609-258-4900 *Toll Free Tel:* 800-777-4726 (orders) *Fax:* 609-258-6305 *Toll Free Fax:* 800-999-1958 *E-mail:* orders@cpfsinc.com *Web Site:* press.princeton.edu, pg 206

Doughten, Kevin, Crown Publishing Group, c/o Random House Inc, 1745 Broadway, New York, NY 10019 *Tel:* 212-782-9000 *Toll Free Tel:* 888-264-1745 *Fax:* 212-940-7408 *Web Site:* www.randomhouse.com/crown, pg 72

Douglas, Alecia, McIntosh & Otis Inc, 353 Lexington Ave, New York, NY 10016-0900 *Tel:* 212-687-7400 *Fax:* 212-687-6894 *E-mail:* info@mcintoshandotis.com *Web Site:* www.mcintoshandotis.com, pg 585

Douglas, Deron, Double Dragon Publishing Inc, 1-5762 Hwy 7 E, Markham, ON L3P 7Y4, Canada *Tel:* 603-778-7191 *E-mail:* info@double-dragon-ebooks.com; sales@double-dragon-ebooks.com *Web Site:* www.double-dragon-ebooks.com, pg 500

Douglas, Diana R, Self-Counsel Press Ltd, 4152 Meridian St, Suite 105-471, Bellingham, WA 98226 *Toll Free Tel:* 800-663-3007 *E-mail:* orders@self-counsel.com *Web Site:* www.self-counsel.com, pg 231

Douglas, Sarah L, Abrams Artists Agency, 275 Seventh Ave, 26th fl, New York, NY 10001 *Tel:* 646-486-4600 *Fax:* 646-486-2358 *E-mail:* literary@abramsartny.com *Web Site:* www.abramsartists.com, pg 559

Douglas, Tyler, Self-Counsel Press Ltd, 4152 Meridian St, Suite 105-471, Bellingham, WA 98226 *Toll Free Tel:* 800-663-3007 *E-mail:* orders@self-counsel.com *Web Site:* www.self-counsel.com, pg 231

Douvris, Mara, Institute of Environmental Sciences and Technology - IEST, 2340 S Arlington Heights Rd, Suite 100, Arlington Heights, IL 60005-4516 *Tel:* 847-981-0100 *Fax:* 847-981-4130 *E-mail:* information@iest.org *Web Site:* www.iest.org, pg 131

Dove, Veronica, Bernan, 4501 Forbes Blvd, Suite 200, Lanham, MD 20706 *Tel:* 301-459-7666 (cust serv & orders) *Fax:* 301-459-0056 *E-mail:* customercare@bernan.com *Web Site:* www.bernan.com, pg 36

Dove, Veronica M, Government Institutes (GI), 4501 Forbes Blvd, Suite 200, Lanham, MD 20706 *Tel:* 301-459-3366 (ext 5622) *Toll Free Tel:* 800-462-6420 *Fax:* 301-429-5748 *Toll Free Fax:* 800-338-4550 *Web Site:* www.govinstpress.com, pg 105

Dowden, C James, City & Regional Magazine Association, 1970 E Grand Ave, Suite 330, El Segundo, CA 90245 *Tel:* 310-364-0193 *Fax:* 310-364-0196 *Web Site:* www.citymag.org, pg 621

Dowdy, Eric, Group Publishing Inc, 1515 Cascade Ave, Loveland, CO 80538 *Tel:* 970-669-3836 *Toll Free Tel:* 800-447-1070 *Fax:* 970-292-4373 *E-mail:* info@group.com *Web Site:* www.group.com, pg 108

Dowling, Michael, Bogle International Library Travel Fund, 50 E Huron St, Chicago, IL 60611-2795 *Tel:* 312-280-3201 *Toll Free Tel:* 800-545-2433 (ext 3201) *Fax:* 312-280-4392 *E-mail:* intl@ala.org *Web Site:* www.ala.org, pg 692

Downes, Terry, Disney Publishing Worldwide, 44 S Broadway, 9th fl, White Plains, NY 10601-4411 *Tel:* 914-288-4100 *Web Site:* disney.go.com/books/index, pg 80

Downey, Alessandra, Lynne Rienner Publishers Inc, 1800 30 St, Suite 314, Boulder, CO 80301 *Tel:* 303-444-6684 *Fax:* 303-444-0824 *E-mail:* questions@rienner.com; cservice@rienner.com *Web Site:* www.rienner.com, pg 218

Downey, Floann, West Virginia University Press, West Virginia University, PO Box 6295, Morgantown, WV 26506-6295 *Tel:* 304-293-8400 *Toll Free Tel:* 866-WVU-PRES (988-7737) *Fax:* 304-293-6585 *E-mail:* press@wvu.edu *Web Site:* www.wvupress.com, pg 278

Downs, Toddie, Northwest Independent Editors Guild, PO Box 1630, Snoqualmie, WA 98065 *E-mail:* info@edsguild.org *Web Site:* www.edsguild.org, pg 632

Doyel, Jade, Tyndale House Publishers Inc, 351 Executive Dr, Carol Stream, IL 60188 *Tel:* 630-668-8300 *Toll Free Tel:* 800-323-9400 *Web Site:* www.tyndale.com, pg 261

Doyen, Barb J, Doyen Literary Services Inc, 1931 660 St, Newell, IA 50568 *Web Site:* www.barbaradoyen.com, pg 569

Doyle, Kathy, St Martin's Press, LLC, 175 Fifth Ave, New York, NY 10010 *Tel:* 646-307-5151 *Fax:* 212-420-9314 *E-mail:* firstname.lastname@macmillan.com *Web Site:* www.stmartins.com, pg 224

Doyle, Linda, Johnson Books, 3005 Center Green Dr, Suite 225, Boulder, CO 80301 *Tel:* 303-443-9766 *Toll Free Tel:* 800-258-5830 *Fax:* 303-443-9687 *E-mail:* books@bigearthpublishing.com *Web Site:* www.bigearthpublishing.com; www.johnsonbooks.com, pg 136

Doyle, Linda, Trails Books, 3005 Center Green Dr, Suite 225, Boulder, CO 80301 *Tel:* 303-541-1506 *Toll Free Tel:* 800-258-5830 *E-mail:* books@bigearthpublishing.com *Web Site:* www.trailsbooks.com, pg 257

Doyle, Patricia, Barron's Educational Series Inc, 250 Wireless Blvd, Hauppauge, NY 11788 *Tel:* 631-434-3311 *Toll Free Tel:* 800-645-3476 *Fax:* 631-434-3723 *E-mail:* barrons@barronseduc.com *Web Site:* www.barronseduc.com, pg 31

Doyle, Timothy, Harvard University Press, 79 Garden St, Cambridge, MA 02138-1499 *Tel:* 617-495-2600; 401-531-2800 (intl orders) *Toll Free Tel:* 800-405-1619 (orders) *Fax:* 617-495-5898 (general); 617-496-4677 (edit & rts); 401-531-2801 (intl orders) *Toll Free Fax:* 800-406-9145 (orders) *E-mail:* contact_hup@harvard.edu *Web Site:* www.hup.harvard.edu, pg 115

Doyle-Kimball, Mary, National Association of Real Estate Editors (NAREE), 1003 NW Sixth Terr, Boca Raton, FL 33486-3455 *Tel:* 561-391-3599 *Fax:* 561-391-0099 *Web Site:* www.naree.org, pg 629

Dozier, Laura, Harry N Abrams Inc, 115 W 18 St, 6th fl, New York, NY 10011 *Tel:* 212-206-7715 *Toll Free Tel:* 800-345-1359 *Fax:* 212-519-1210 *E-mail:* abrams@abramsbooks.com *Web Site:* www.abramsbooks.com, pg 3

Drake, Amy, B J Robbins Literary Agency, 5130 Bellaire Ave, North Hollywood, CA 91607 *E-mail:* robbinsliterary@gmail.com, pg 591

Drake, David, Crown Publishing Group, c/o Random House Inc, 1745 Broadway, New York, NY 10019 *Tel:* 212-782-9000 *Toll Free Tel:* 888-264-1745 *Fax:* 212-940-7408 *Web Site:* www.randomhouse.com/crown, pg 72

Dreesen, Robert, Cambridge University Press, 32 Avenue of the Americas, New York, NY 10013-2473 *Tel:* 212-924-3900; 212-337-5000 *Toll Free Tel:* 800-899-5222 *Fax:* 212-691-3239 *E-mail:* newyork@cambridge.org *Web Site:* www.cambridge.org/us, pg 51

Drehs, Shana, Sourcebooks Inc, 1935 Brookdale Rd, Suite 139, Naperville, IL 60563 *Tel:* 630-961-3900 *Toll Free Tel:* 800-432-7444 *Fax:* 630-961-2168 *E-mail:* info@sourcebooks.com; customersupport@sourcebooks.com *Web Site:* www.sourcebooks.com, pg 240

Dreibelbis, Dana, Rutgers University Press, 106 Somerset St, 3rd fl, New Brunswick, NJ 08901 *Tel:* 858-445-7784 (edit); 848-445-7788 *Toll Free Tel:* 800-848-6224 (orders only) *Fax:* 732-745-4935 (acqs, edit, mktg, perms & prodn) *Toll Free Fax:* 800-272-6817 (fulfillment) *Web Site:* rutgerspress.rutgers.edu, pg 222

Dreier, Eliza, Carol Mann Agency, 55 Fifth Ave, New York, NY 10003 *Tel:* 212-206-5635 *Fax:* 212-675-4809 *E-mail:* submissions@carolmannagency.com *Web Site:* www.carolmannagency.com, pg 583

Dreisbach, Heather, Amicus, PO Box 1329, Mankato, MN 56002 *Tel:* 507-388-9357 *Fax:* 507-388-1779 *E-mail:* info@amicuspublishing.us; orders@amicuspublishing.us *Web Site:* www.amicuspublishing.us, pg 17

Drennan, Christina L, Drennan Communications, 6 Robin Lane, East Kingston, NH 03827 *Tel:* 603-642-8002 *Fax:* 603-642-8002, pg 544

Drennan, Christina L, Drennan Literary Agency, 6 Robin Lane, East Kingston, NH 03827 *Tel:* 603-642-8002 *Fax:* 603-642-8002, pg 569

Drennan, William D, Drennan Communications, 6 Robin Lane, East Kingston, NH 03827 *Tel:* 603-642-8002 *Fax:* 603-642-8002, pg 544

Drennan, William D, Drennan Literary Agency, 6 Robin Lane, East Kingston, NH 03827 *Tel:* 603-642-8002 *Fax:* 603-642-8002, pg 569

Dresner, Charles, Nicholas Brealey Publishing, 20 Park Plaza, Suite 610, Boston, MA 02116 *Tel:* 617-523-3801 *Toll Free Tel:* 888-BREALEY (273-2539) *Fax:* 617-523-3708 *E-mail:* info@nicholasbrealey.com *Web Site:* www.nicholasbrealey.com, pg 46

Dress, Erin, Abbeville Publishing Group, 137 Varick St, Suite 504, New York, NY 10013 *Tel:* 212-366-5585 *Toll Free Tel:* 800-ART-BOOK (278-2665) *Fax:* 212-366-6966 *E-mail:* abbeville@abbeville.com; marketing@abbeville.com; sales@abbeville.com; rights@abbeville.com *Web Site:* www.abbeville.com, pg 2

Dresser, Kate, Harlequin Enterprises Ltd, 233 Broadway, Suite 1001, New York, NY 10279 *Tel:* 212-553-4200 *Fax:* 212-227-8969 *E-mail:* CustomerService@harlequin.com *Web Site:* www.harlequin.com, pg 112

Drew, Stephanie, Springer Publishing Co LLC, 11 W 42 St, 15th fl, New York, NY 10036-8002 *Tel:* 212-431-4370 *Toll Free Tel:* 877-687-7476 *Fax:* 212-941-7842 *E-mail:* marketing@springerpub.com; cs@springerpub.com (orders); editorial@springerpub.com *Web Site:* www.springerpub.com, pg 241

Dreyer, Benjamin, Random House Publishing Group, 1745 Broadway, New York, NY 10019 *Toll Free Tel:* 800-200-3552 *Web Site:* atrandom.com, pg 214

Driskell, Maudelle, Festival & Conference on Poetry, 158 Ridge Rd, Franconia, NH 03580 *Tel:* 603-823-5510 *E-mail:* frost@frostplace.org *Web Site:* www.frostplace.org, pg 668

Drivdahl, Cheryl, EMC Publishing, 875 Montreal Way, St Paul, MN 55102 *Tel:* 651-290-2800 (corp) *Toll Free Tel:* 800-328-1452 *Fax:* 651-290-2899 *Toll Free Fax:* 800-328-4564 *E-mail:* educate@emcp.com *Web Site:* www.emcp.com, pg 87

Driver, Stephen, University Press of America Inc, 4501 Forbes Blvd, Suite 200, Lanham, MD 20706 *Tel:* 301-459-3366 *Toll Free Tel:* 800-462-6420 *Fax:* 301-429-5748 *Toll Free Fax:* 800-338-4550 *Web Site:* www.univpress.com, pg 270

Drollinger, Darrin, American Society of Agricultural Engineers (ASABE), 2950 Niles Rd, St Joseph, MI 49085-9659 *Tel:* 269-429-0300 *Fax:* 269-429-3852 *E-mail:* hq@asabe.org *Web Site:* www.asabe.org, pg 16

Drost, Susie, The Mongolia Society Inc, Indiana University, 322 Goodbody Hall, 1011 E Third St, Bloomington, IN 47405-7005 *Tel:* 812-855-4078 *Fax:* 812-855-4078 *E-mail:* monsoc@indiana.edu *Web Site:* www.mongoliasociety.org, pg 169

Drouzas, Frank, Acclaim Film Script Competition, 300 Central Ave, Suite 501, St Petersburg, FL 33701 *Web Site:* acclaimscripts.com, pg 685

Drouzas, Frank, Acclaim TV Script Competition, 300 Central Ave, Suite 501, St Petersburg, FL 33701 *Web Site:* acclaimscripts.com, pg 685

Drover, Randy, Flanker Press Ltd, 1243 Kenmount Rd, Unit A, Paradise, NL A1L 0V8, Canada *Tel:* 709-739-4477 *Toll Free Tel:* 866-739-4420 *Fax:* 709-739-4420 *E-mail:* info@flankerpress.com *Web Site:* www.flankerpress.com, pg 506

Druding, Harry F, Nesbitt Graphics Inc, 555 Virginia Dr, Fort Washington, PA 19034 *Tel:* 215-591-9125 *Fax:* 215-591-9093 *Web Site:* www.nesbittgraphics.com, pg 552

Druick, Douglas, The Art Institute of Chicago, 111 S Michigan Ave, Chicago, IL 60603-6404 *Tel:* 312-443-3600; 312-443-3540 (pubns) *Fax:* 312-443-1334 (pubns) *Web Site:* www.artic.edu; www.artinstituteshop.org, pg 22

Druliner, Karen G, University of Delaware Press, 200A Morris Library, 181 S College Ave, Newark, DE 19717-5267 *Tel:* 302-831-1149 *Fax:* 302-831-6549 *E-mail:* ud-press@udel.edu *Web Site:* www2.lib.udel.edu/udpress, pg 265

Drummond, Siobhan, Drummond Books, 2111 Cleveland St, Evanston, IL 60202 *Tel:* 847-302-2534 *E-mail:* drummondbooks@gmail.com, pg 545

Drury, Butch, Rivendell Books, PO Box 9306, Richmond Heights, MO 63117-0306 *Tel:* 314-609-6534 *E-mail:* butch@rivendellbooks.com *Web Site:* www.rivendellbooks.com, pg 529

Drury, Patricia, Quincannon Publishing Group, PO Box 8100, Glen Ridge, NJ 07028-8100 *Tel:* 973-380-9942 *E-mail:* editors@quincannongroup.com *Web Site:* www.quincannongroup.com, pg 211

Druskin, Julia, W W Norton & Company Inc, 500 Fifth Ave, New York, NY 10110-0017 *Tel:* 212-354-5500 *Toll Free Tel:* 800-233-4830 (orders & cust serv) *Fax:* 212-869-0856 *Toll Free Fax:* 800-458-6515 *Web Site:* www.wwnorton.com, pg 181

Dry, Paul, Paul Dry Books, 1616 Walnut St, Suite 808, Philadelphia, PA 19103 *Tel:* 215-231-9939 *Fax:* 215-231-9942 *E-mail:* editor@pauldrybooks.com *Web Site:* www.pauldrybooks.com, pg 194

Du Cane, John, Dragon Door Publications, 5 E Country Rd B, Suite 3, Little Canada, MN 55117 *Tel:* 651-487-2180 *Toll Free Tel:* 800-899-5111 (orders & cust serv) *E-mail:* support@dragondoor.com *Web Site:* www.dragondoor.com, pg 81

Du Vall, Jennifer, Schiavone Literary Agency Inc, 236 Trails End, West Palm Beach, FL 33413-2135 *Tel:* 561-966-9294 *Fax:* 561-966-9294 *E-mail:* profschia@aol.com *Web Site:* www.publishersmarketplace.com/members/profschia, pg 592

Duane, Dick, Pinder Lane & Garon-Brooke Associates Ltd, 159 W 53 St, New York, NY 10019 *Tel:* 212-489-0880 *Fax:* 212-489-7104 *E-mail:* pinderlaneandgaronbrooke@gmail.com *Web Site:* www.pinderlaneandgaronbrooke.com, pg 588

Dube, Matthew, Merriam-Webster Inc, 47 Federal St, Springfield, MA 01102 *Tel:* 413-734-3134 *Toll Free Tel:* 800-828-1880 (orders & cust serv) *Fax:* 413-731-5979 (sales) *E-mail:* support@merriam-webster.com *Web Site:* www.merriam-webster.com, pg 165

Dubin, Margaret, Heyday Books, 1633 University Ave, Berkeley, CA 94703 *Tel:* 510-549-3564 *Fax:* 510-549-1889 *E-mail:* heyday@heydaybooks.com; orders@heydaybooks.com *Web Site:* www.heydaybooks.com, pg 119

Dubin, Morgan, Harry N Abrams Inc, 115 W 18 St, 6th fl, New York, NY 10011 *Tel:* 212-206-7715 *Toll Free Tel:* 800-345-1359 *Fax:* 212-519-1210 *E-mail:* abrams@abramsbooks.com *Web Site:* www.abramsbooks.com, pg 3

Dublinski, Katie, Graywolf Press, 250 Third Ave N, Suite 600, Minneapolis, MN 55401 *Tel:* 651-641-0077 *Fax:* 651-641-0036 *E-mail:* wolves@graywolfpress.org *Web Site:* www.graywolfpress.org, pg 106

DuBosque, Douglas C, Peel Productions Inc, 9415 NE Woodridge St, Vancouver, WA 98664 *Toll Free Tel:* 800-345-6665 *E-mail:* contact@drawbooks.com *Web Site:* www.peelbooks.com, pg 196

DuBosque, Susan Joyce, Peel Productions Inc, 9415 NE Woodridge St, Vancouver, WA 98664 *Toll Free Tel:* 800-345-6665 *E-mail:* contact@drawbooks.com *Web Site:* www.peelbooks.com, pg 196

Ducate, Douglas L, The Center for Exhibition Industry Research (CEIR), 12700 Park Central Dr, Suite 308, Dallas, TX 75251 *Tel:* 972-687-9242 *Fax:* 972-692-6020 *E-mail:* info@ceir.org *Web Site:* www.ceir.org, pg 621

Dufault, Christopher, Random House Inc, 1745 Broadway, New York, NY 10019 *Tel:* 212-782-9000 *Toll Free Tel:* 800-726-0600 *Web Site:* www.randomhouse.com, pg 213

Dufay, Adrianna, HarperCollins General Books Group, 10 E 53 St, New York, NY 10022 *Tel:* 212-207-7000 *Fax:* 212-207-7633 *Web Site:* www.harpercollins.com, pg 113

Duff, John, HPBooks, 375 Hudson St, New York, NY 10014 *Tel:* 212-366-2000 *E-mail:* online@penguinputnam.com *Web Site:* www.penguinputnam.com; us.penguingroup.com, pg 125

Duff, John, Perigee Books, 375 Hudson St, New York, NY 10014 *Tel:* 212-366-2000 *Fax:* 212-366-2365 *E-mail:* perigeebooks@us.penguingroup.com *Web Site:* www.penguin.com, pg 199

Duff, John, Prentice Hall Press, 375 Hudson St, New York, NY 10014 *Tel:* 212-366-2000 *Fax:* 212-366-2666, pg 205

Duff, John, GP Putnam's Sons (Hardcover), 375 Hudson St, New York, NY 10014 *Tel:* 212-366-2000 *E-mail:* online@penguinputnam.com *Web Site:* us.penguingroup.com, pg 210

Duffin, Kelly, Writers' Union of Canada, 90 Richmond St E, Suite 200, Toronto, ON M5C 1P1, Canada *Tel:* 416-703-8982 *Fax:* 416-504-9090 *E-mail:* info@writersunion.ca *Web Site:* www.writersunion.ca, pg 639

Duffy, Trent, Artisan Books, 225 Varick St, New York, NY 10014-4381 *Tel:* 212-254-5900 *Toll Free Tel:* 800-722-7202 *Fax:* 212-254-8098 *E-mail:* artisaninfo@workman.com; artisaninfo@artisanbooks.com *Web Site:* www.workman.com/artisanbooks/, pg 23

Dufresne, Collette, Editions Michel Quintin, 4770 rue Foster, Waterloo, QC J0E 2N0, Canada *Tel:* 450-539-3774 *Fax:* 450-539-4905 *E-mail:* info@editionsmichelquintin.ca *Web Site:* www.editionsmichelquintin.ca, pg 517

Dufresne, Jean-Sebastien, Montreal-Contacts/The Rights Agency, 1350 Sherbrooke St E, Suite 1, Montreal, QC H2L 1M4, Canada *Tel:* 514-400-7075 *Fax:* 514-400-1045 *Web Site:* www.montreal-contacts.com/?lang=en, pg 586

Duggan, John, Workman Publishing Co Inc, 225 Varick St, 9th fl, New York, NY 10014-4381 *Tel:* 212-254-5900 *Toll Free Tel:* 800-722-7202 *Fax:* 212-254-8098 *E-mail:* info@workman.com *Web Site:* www.workman.com, pg 285

Duggins, Linda, Grand Central Publishing, 237 Park Ave, New York, NY 10017 *Tel:* 212-364-1100 *Web Site:* www.hachettebookgroup.com, pg 106

Duhon, Bryant, Association for Information & Image Management International (AIIM), 1100 Wayne Ave, Suite 1100, Silver Spring, MD 20910 *Tel:* 301-587-8202 *Toll Free Tel:* 800-477-2446 *Fax:* 301-587-2711 *E-mail:* aiim@aiim.org *Web Site:* www.aiim.org, pg 615

Dujack, Stephen, Environmental Law Institute, 2000 "L" St NW, Suite 620, Washington, DC 20036 *Tel:* 202-939-3800 *Fax:* 202-939-3868 *E-mail:* law@eli.org *Web Site:* www.eli.org, pg 89

Dujardin, Joelle, Highlights for Children Fiction Contest, 803 Church St, Honesdale, PA 18431 *Tel:* 570-253-1080 *Fax:* 570-251-7847 *E-mail:* eds@highlights.com *Web Site:* www.highlights.com, pg 709

Duke, Jacqueline, Eclipse Press, 3101 Beaumont Centre Circle, Lexington, KY 40513 *Tel:* 859-278-2361 *Toll Free Tel:* 800-866-2361 *Fax:* 859-276-6868 *E-mail:* editorial@eclipsepress.com; info@eclipsepress.com *Web Site:* www.eclipsepress.com, pg 84

Dukes, Paul, Psychology Press, 711 Third Ave, 8th fl, New York, NY 10017 *Tel:* 212-216-7800 *Toll Free Tel:* 800-634-7064 *Fax:* 212-563-2269 *Web Site:* www.psypress.com, pg 209

Dulber, Jill, Workman Publishing Co Inc, 225 Varick St, 9th fl, New York, NY 10014-4381 *Tel:* 212-254-5900 *Toll Free Tel:* 800-722-7202 *Fax:* 212-254-8098 *E-mail:* info@workman.com *Web Site:* www.workman.com, pg 285

Dumanis, Michael, Cleveland State University Poetry Center Prizes, 2121 Euclid Ave, Cleveland, OH 44115-2214 *Tel:* 216-687-3986 *Fax:* 216-687-6943 *E-mail:* poetrycenter@csuohio.edu *Web Site:* www.csuohio.edu/poetrycenter, pg 697

Dunbar, Linda, John Wiley & Sons Inc, 111 River St, Hoboken, NJ 07030-5774 *Tel:* 201-748-6000 *Toll Free Tel:* 800-225-5945 (cust serv) *Fax:* 201-748-6088 *E-mail:* info@wiley.com *Web Site:* www.wiley.com, pg 281

Duncan, C W, Two Canoes Press, PO Box 334, Hopkinton, MA 01568 *Tel:* 508-529-6034 *Fax:* 508-529-6005 *E-mail:* TwoCanoesPress@TwoCanoesPress.com; Singsalone@aol.com *Web Site:* www.TwoCanoesPress.com, pg 530

Duncan, Claudia, Caribe Betania Editores, PO Box 141000, Nashville, TN 37214-1000 *Tel:* 615-902-1893 *Toll Free Tel:* 800-322-7423 (ext 1893) *Fax:* 615-883-9376 *Web Site:* www.caribebetania.com, pg 52

Duncan, Michael, Cambridge University Press, 32 Avenue of the Americas, New York, NY 10013-2473 *Tel:* 212-924-3900; 212-337-5000 *Toll Free Tel:* 800-899-5222 *Fax:* 212-691-3239 *E-mail:* newyork@cambridge.org *Web Site:* www.cambridge.org/us, pg 51

Dunford, Martin, Rough Guides, 375 Hudson St, New York, NY 10014 *Toll Free Tel:* 800-631-8571 *E-mail:* mail@roughguides.com *Web Site:* www.roughguides.com, pg 221

Dungan, Tom III, Management Concepts Inc, 8230 Leesburg Pike, Suite 800, Vienna, VA 22182 *Tel:* 703-790-9595 *Toll Free Tel:* 800 506-4450 *Fax:* 703-790-1371 *E-mail:* publications@managementconcepts.com *Web Site:* www.managementconcepts.com, pg 155

Dunham, C Ryan, David C Cook, 4050 Lee Vance View, Colorado Springs, CO 80918 *Tel:* 719-536-0100 *Toll Free Tel:* 800-708-5550 *Fax:* 519-536-3269 *Web Site:* www.davidccook.com, pg 67

Dunham, Courtney, Basic Health Publications Inc, 28812 Top of the World Dr, Laguna Beach, CA 92651 *Tel:* 949-715-7327 *Toll Free Tel:* 800-575-8890 (orders) *Fax:* 949-715-7328 *E-mail:* info@basichealthpub.com *Web Site:* www.basichealthpub.com, pg 32

Dunham, Gary, American Speech-Language-Hearing Association (ASHA), 2200 Research Blvd, Rockville, MD 20850-3289 *Tel:* 301-296-5700 *Toll Free Tel:* 800-638-8255 (nonmembs); 800-498-2071 (membs) *Fax:* 301-296-5777; 301-296-8580 *E-mail:* actioncenter@asha.org *Web Site:* www.asha.org, pg 615

Dunham, Jennie, Dunham Literary Inc, 110 William St, Suite 2202, New York, NY 10038 *Tel:* 212-929-0994 *Web Site:* dunhamlit.com, pg 569

Dunlap, Dennis, American Marketing Association, 311 S Wacker Dr, Suite 5800, Chicago, IL 60606 *Tel:* 312-542-9000 *Toll Free Tel:* 800-AMA-1150 (262-1150) *Fax:* 312-542-9001 *E-mail:* info@ama.org *Web Site:* www.marketingpower.com, pg 14, 613

Dunlap, Ellen S, American Antiquarian Society (AAS), 185 Salisbury St, Worcester, MA 01609-1634 *Tel:* 508-755-5221 *Fax:* 508-753-3300 *Web Site:* www.americanantiquarian.org, pg 612

Dunlap, Jamie, Theatre-Scriptworks, 216 Finance Bldg, Harrisburg, PA 17120 *Tel:* 717-787-6883 *Fax:* 717-783-2538 *Web Site:* www.pacouncilonthearts.org, pg 746

Dunn, Craig, Marshall Cavendish Corp, 99 White Plains Rd, Tarrytown, NY 10591-9001 *Tel:* 914-332-8888 *Toll Free Tel:* 800-821-9881 *Fax:* 914-332-8102 *E-mail:* customerservice@marshallcavendish.com; mcc@marshallcavendish.com *Web Site:* marshallcavendish.us; marshallcavendishdigital.com; marshallcavendishebooks.com, pg 158

Dunn, Craig A, Wesleyan Publishing House, 13300 Olio Rd, Fishers, IN 46037 *Tel:* 317-774-3853 *Toll Free Tel:* 800-493-7539 *Fax:* 317-774-3865 *Toll Free Fax:* 800-788-3535 *E-mail:* wph@wesleyan.org *Web Site:* www.wesleyan.org/wph, pg 278

Dunn, Heather, The Society of Professional Journalists, Eugene S Pulliam National Journalism Ctr, 3909 N Meridian St, Indianapolis, IN 46208 *Tel:* 317-927-8000 *Fax:* 317-920-4789 *E-mail:* spj@spj.org *Web Site:* www.spj.org, pg 637

Dunn, Karen, Child Welfare League of America (CWLA), 1726 "M" St, Suite 500, Washington, DC 20036 *Tel:* 202-688-4200 *Fax:* 202-833-1689 *Web Site:* www.cwla.org/pubs, pg 60

Dunn, Kathy, Random House Speakers Bureau, 1745 Broadway, Mail Drop 13-1, New York, NY 10019 *Tel:* 212-572-2013 *E-mail:* rhspeakers@randomhouse.com *Web Site:* www.rhspeakers.com, pg 605

Dunn, Peter, Abrams Learning Trends, 16310 Bratton Lane, Suite 250, Austin, TX 78728-2403 *Toll Free Tel:* 800-227-9120 *Toll Free Fax:* 800-737-3322 *E-mail:* customerservice@abramslearningtrends.com (orders, cust serv) *Web Site:* www.abramslearningtrends.com (orders, cust serv), pg 3

Dunn, Ron, Cengage Learning, 200 First Stamford Place, Suite 400, Stamford, CT 06902 *Tel:* 203-965-8600 *Toll Free Tel:* 800-354-9706 *Fax:* 203-965-8599 *Toll Free Fax:* 800-487-8488 *E-mail:* esales@cengage.com *Web Site:* www.cengage.com, pg 55

Dunn, Ronald, Wadsworth Publishing, 20 Davis Dr, Belmont, CA 94002 *Tel:* 650-595-2350 *Fax:* 650-592-3022 *Toll Free Fax:* 800-522-4923 *Web Site:* www.cengage.com, pg 276

Dunn, Stephen P, W W Norton & Company Inc, 500 Fifth Ave, New York, NY 10110-0017 *Tel:* 212-354-5500 *Toll Free Tel:* 800-233-4830 (orders & cust serv) *Fax:* 212-869-0856 *Toll Free Fax:* 800-458-6515 *Web Site:* www.wwnorton.com, pg 181

Dunne, Thomas, St Martin's Press, LLC, 175 Fifth Ave, New York, NY 10010 *Tel:* 646-307-5151 *Fax:* 212-420-9314 *E-mail:* firstname.lastname@macmillan.com *Web Site:* www.stmartins.com, pg 224

Dunow, Henry, Dunow, Carlson & Lerner Literary Agency Inc, 27 W 20 St, Suite 1107, New York, NY 10011 *Tel:* 212-645-7606 *E-mail:* mail@dclagency.com *Web Site:* www.dclagency.com, pg 569

Dunphy, Dr Joan S, New Horizon Press, PO Box 669, Far Hills, NJ 07931-0669 *Tel:* 908-604-6311 *Toll Free Tel:* 800-533-7978 (orders only) *Fax:* 908-604-6330 *E-mail:* nhp@newhorizonpressbooks.com *Web Site:* www.newhorizonpressbooks.com, pg 177

Dunton, David, Harvey Klinger Inc, 300 W 55 St, Suite 11-V, New York, NY 10019 *Tel:* 212-581-7068 *Fax:* 212-315-3823 *E-mail:* queries@harveyklinger.com *Web Site:* www.harveyklinger.com, pg 580

Dunton, James R, The CSIS Press, 1800 "K" St NW, Washington, DC 20006 *Tel:* 202-887-0200 *Fax:* 202-775-3199 *E-mail:* books@csis.org *Web Site:* www.csis.org, pg 73

DuPont, Charles, Alan Wofsy Fine Arts, 1109 Geary Blvd, San Francisco, CA 94109 *Tel:* 415-292-6500 *Toll Free Tel:* 800-660-6403 *Fax:* 415-292-6594 (off & cust serv); 415-512-0130 (acctg) *E-mail:* order@art-books.com (orders); editeur@earthlink.net (edit); beauxarts@earthlink.net (cust serv) *Web Site:* www.art-books.com, pg 284

DuPre, Sydney, The Flannery O'Connor Award for Short Fiction, Main Library, 3rd fl, 320 S Jackson St, Athens, GA 30602 *Fax:* 706-369-6131 *Web Site:* www.ugapress.org, pg 730

Duquet, Michel, Francois-Xavier Garneau Medal, 130 Albert St, Suite 501, Ottawa, ON K1P 5G4, Canada *Tel:* 613-233-7885 *Fax:* 613-565-5445 *E-mail:* cha-shc@cha-shc.ca *Web Site:* www.cha-shc.ca, pg 706

Duquet, Michel, Sir John A Macdonald Prize, 130 Albert St, Suite 501, Ottawa, ON K1P 5G4, Canada *Tel:* 613-233-7885 *Fax:* 613-565-5445 *E-mail:* cha-shc@cha-shc.ca *Web Site:* www.cha-shc.ca, pg 720

Durakis, Tom, American Bible Society, 1865 Broadway, New York, NY 10023-7505 *Tel:* 212-408-1200 *Toll Free Tel:* 800-322-4253 *Fax:* 212-408-1512 *E-mail:* info@americanbible.org *Web Site:* www.americanbible.org, pg 11

Durand, Sarah, Atria Books, 1230 Avenue of the Americas, New York, NY 10020 *Tel:* 212-698-7000 *Fax:* 212-698-7007 *Web Site:* www.simonandschuster.com, pg 26

Durbin, Dean, Cengage Learning, 200 First Stamford Place, Suite 400, Stamford, CT 06902 *Tel:* 203-965-8600 *Toll Free Tel:* 800-354-9706 *Fax:* 203-965-8599 *Toll Free Fax:* 800-487-8488 *E-mail:* esales@cengage.com *Web Site:* www.cengage.com, pg 55

Durbin, Dean, Wadsworth Publishing, 20 Davis Dr, Belmont, CA 94002 *Tel:* 650-595-2350 *Fax:* 650-592-3022 *Toll Free Fax:* 800-522-4923 *Web Site:* www.cengage.com, pg 276

Durbin, Jon, W W Norton & Company Inc, 500 Fifth Ave, New York, NY 10110-0017 *Tel:* 212-354-5500 *Toll Free Tel:* 800-233-4830 (orders & cust serv) *Fax:* 212-869-0856 *Toll Free Fax:* 800-458-6515 *Web Site:* www.wwnorton.com, pg 182

Durepos, Joseph, Loyola Press, 3441 N Ashland Ave, Chicago, IL 60657 *Tel:* 773-281-1818 *Toll Free Tel:* 800-621-1008 *Fax:* 773-281-0555 (cust serv); 773-281-4129 (edit) *E-mail:* customerservice@loyolapress.com *Web Site:* www.loyolapress.com; www.spiritedtalk.org, pg 153

Durham, Anne, American Foundation for the Blind (AFB Press), 2 Penn Plaza, Suite 1102, New York, NY 10001 *Tel:* 212-502-7600; 412-741-1398 (orders) *Toll Free Tel:* 800-232-3044 (orders) *Fax:* 917-210-3979; 412-741-0609 (orders) *Toll Free Fax:* 888-545-8331 *E-mail:* press@afb.net; afborder@afb.net (orders); afbinfo@afb.net *Web Site:* www.afb.org, pg 13

Duroselle-Melish, Caroline, Bibliographical Society of America, PO Box 1537, Lenox Hill Sta, New York, NY 10021-0043 *Tel:* 212-452-2710 *Fax:* 212-452-2710 *E-mail:* bsa@bibsocamer.org *Web Site:* www.bibsocamer.org, pg 618

Duvall, Donna, Paladin Press, Gunbarrel Tech Ctr, 7077 Winchester Circle, Boulder, CO 80301 *Tel:* 303-443-7250 *Toll Free Tel:* 800-392-2400 *Fax:* 303-442-8741 *E-mail:* service@paladin-press.com *Web Site:* www.paladin-press.com, pg 191

Dworkin, Sharon, Prayer Book Press Inc, 1363 Fairfield Ave, Bridgeport, CT 06605 *Tel:* 203-384-2284 *Fax:* 203-579-9109, pg 205

Personnel Index

Fessler, Bill, Golden West Cookbooks, 5738 N Central Ave, Phoenix, AZ 85012-1316 *Tel:* 602-234-1574 *Toll Free Tel:* 800-521-9221 *Fax:* 602-234-3062 *E-mail:* info@americantravelerpress.com *Web Site:* www.americantravelerpress.com, pg 104

Fetterman, Bonny, The Editors Circle, 462 Grove St, Montclair, NJ 07043 *Tel:* 973-783-5082 *E-mail:* query@theeditorscircle.com *Web Site:* www.theeditorscircle.com, pg 545

Feuer, Lisa, Random House Publishing Group, 1745 Broadway, New York, NY 10019 *Toll Free Tel:* 800-200-3552 *Web Site:* atrandom.com, pg 214

Feuerhaken, P, New Victoria Publishers, PO Box 13173, Chicago, IL 60613-0173 *Tel:* 773-793-2244 *Toll Free Tel:* 888-530-4588 *E-mail:* newvictoriapub@att.net *Web Site:* www.newvictoria.com, pg 178

Feulner, Megan, Other Press LLC, 2 Park Ave, 24th fl, New York, NY 10016 *Tel:* 212-414-0054 *Toll Free Tel:* 877-843-6843 *Fax:* 212-414-0939 *E-mail:* editor@otherpress.com; rights@otherpress.com *Web Site:* www.otherpress.com, pg 188

Ficarra, Elise, Poetry Center Book Award, 1600 Holloway Ave, San Francisco, CA 94132 *Tel:* 415-338-2227 *Fax:* 415-338-0966 *E-mail:* poetry@sfsu.edu *Web Site:* www.sfsu.edu/~poetry, pg 735

Fichtelberg, Joseph PhD, Hofstra University, English Dept, 204 Mason Hall, Hempstead, NY 11549 *Tel:* 516-463-5454 *Fax:* 516-463-6395 *Web Site:* www.hofstra.edu, pg 678

Fickeisen, Cheryl L, Chronicle Guidance Publications Inc, 66 Aurora St, Moravia, NY 13118-3569 *Tel:* 315-497-0330 *Toll Free Tel:* 800-622-7284 *Fax:* 315-497-0339 *E-mail:* customerservice@chronicleguidance.com *Web Site:* www.chronicleguidance.com, pg 61

Fickeisen, Christopher D, Chronicle Guidance Publications Inc, 66 Aurora St, Moravia, NY 13118-3569 *Tel:* 315-497-0330 *Toll Free Tel:* 800-622-7284 *Fax:* 315-497-0339 *E-mail:* customerservice@chronicleguidance.com *Web Site:* www.chronicleguidance.com, pg 61

Fickeisen, Gary W, Chronicle Guidance Publications Inc, 66 Aurora St, Moravia, NY 13118-3569 *Tel:* 315-497-0330 *Toll Free Tel:* 800-622-7284 *Fax:* 315-497-0339 *E-mail:* customerservice@chronicleguidance.com *Web Site:* www.chronicleguidance.com, pg 61

Fidler, Patricia, Yale University Press, 302 Temple St, New Haven, CT 06511-8909 *Tel:* 401-531-2800 (cust serv); 203-432-0960 *Toll Free Tel:* 800-405-1619 (cust serv) *Fax:* 203-432-0948; 401-531-2801 (cust serv) *Toll Free Fax:* 800-406-9145 (cust serv) *E-mail:* customer.care@trilateral.org (cust serv); language.yalepress@yale.edu *Web Site:* www.yalebooks.com, pg 287

Field, Ty, Jones & Bartlett Learning LLC, 5 Wall St, Burlington, MA 01803 *Tel:* 978-443-5000 *Toll Free Tel:* 800-832-0034 *Fax:* 978-443-8000 *E-mail:* info@jblearning.com *Web Site:* www.jblearning.com, pg 136

Fielder, John, Westcliffe Publishers Inc, 3360 Mitchell Lane, Suite E, Boulder, CO 80301 *Toll Free Tel:* 800-258-5830 *Fax:* 303-443-9687 *E-mail:* books@bigearthpublishing.com *Web Site:* www.bigearthpublishing.com/westcliffe-publishers, pg 279

Fielder, Vaughan, Kentucky Women Writers Conference, 232 E Maxwell St, Lexington, KY 40506-0344 *Tel:* 859-257-2874 *E-mail:* kentuckywomenwriters@gmail.com *Web Site:* www.uky.edu/wwk, pg 670

Fields, Allyson, Rutgers University Press, 106 Somerset St, 3rd fl, New Brunswick, NJ 08901 *Tel:* 858-445-7784 (edit); 848-445-7788 *Toll Free Tel:* 800-848-6224 (orders only) *Fax:* 732-745-4935 (acqs, edit, mktg, perms & prodn) *Toll Free Fax:* 800-272-6817 (fulfillment) *Web Site:* rutgerspress.rutgers.edu, pg 222

Fields, Suann, Association of Catholic Publishers Inc, 4725 Dorsey Hall Dr, Suite A, PMB 709, Elliott City, MD 21042 *Tel:* 410-988-2926 *Fax:* 410-571-4946 *Web Site:* www.catholicsread.org; www.catholicpublishers.org; www.midatlanticcongress.org, pg 616

Fields, Suann, Liguori Publications, One Liguori Dr, Liguori, MO 63057-1000 *Tel:* 636-464-2500 *Toll Free Tel:* 866-848-2492; 800-325-9521 *Fax:* 636-464-8449 *Web Site:* www.liguori.org, pg 149

Fiels, Keith Michael, The American Library Association (ALA), 50 E Huron St, Chicago, IL 60611 *Tel:* 312-944-6780; 312-280-4299 (memb & cust serv) *Toll Free Tel:* 800-545-2433 *Fax:* 312-440-9374 *E-mail:* ala@ala.org; customerservice@ala.org *Web Site:* www.ala.org, pg 613

Fife, Bruce, Piccadilly Books Ltd, PO Box 25203, Colorado Springs, CO 80936-5203 *Tel:* 719-550-9887 *E-mail:* orders@piccadillybooks.com *Web Site:* www.piccadillybooks.com, pg 201

Figman, Elliot, Poets & Writers Inc, 90 Broad St, Suite 2100, New York, NY 10004 *Tel:* 212-226-3586 *Fax:* 212-226-3963 *Web Site:* www.pw.org, pg 634

Files, Meg, Pima Writers' Workshop, Pima College West Campus, 2202 W Anklam Rd, Tucson, AZ 85709-0170 *Tel:* 520-206-6084 *Fax:* 520-206-6020 *Web Site:* www.pima.edu, pg 672

Filling, Gregory, Pippin Press, 229 E 85 St, New York, NY 10028 *Tel:* 212-288-4920 *Fax:* 908-237-2407, pg 202

Filppi, Julie, OUT OF YOUR MIND...AND INTO THE MARKETPLACE™, 13381 White Sand Dr, Tustin, CA 92780-4565 *Tel:* 714-544-0248 *Toll Free Tel:* 800-419-1513 *Fax:* 714-730-1414 *Web Site:* www.business-plan.com, pg 189

Filsinger, Cheryl, Filsinger & Company Ltd, 288 W 12 St, Suite 2R, New York, NY 10014 *Tel:* 212-243-7421 *E-mail:* filsingercompany@gmail.com *Web Site:* www.filsingerco.com, pg 527

Filucci, Sierra, University of California Press, 2120 Berkeley Way, Berkeley, CA 94704-1012 *Tel:* 510-642-4247 *Fax:* 510-643-7127 *E-mail:* askucp@ucpress.edu (books); customerservice@ucpressjournals.com (journals) *Web Site:* www.ucpress.edu, pg 264

Finan, Bill, University of Pennsylvania Press, 3905 Spruce St, Philadelphia, PA 19104 *Tel:* 215-898-6261 *Fax:* 215-898-0404 *E-mail:* custserv@pobox.upenn.edu *Web Site:* www.pennpress.org, pg 268

Fine, Anton, Fine Communications, 322 Eighth Ave, 15th fl, New York, NY 10001 *Tel:* 212-595-3500 *Fax:* 212-595-3779, pg 95

Fine, Celeste, Sterling Lord Literistic Inc, 65 Bleecker St, New York, NY 10012 *Tel:* 212-780-6050 *Fax:* 212-780-6095 *E-mail:* info@sll.com *Web Site:* www.sll.com, pg 595

Fine, Glenn, Clinical Laboratory & Standards Institute (CLSI), 950 W Valley Rd, Suite 2500, Wayne, PA 19087 *Tel:* 610-688-0100 *Toll Free Tel:* 877-447-1888 (orders) *Fax:* 610-688-0700 *E-mail:* customerservice@clsi.org *Web Site:* www.clsi.org, pg 63

Fine, Kaethe, Fine Communications, 322 Eighth Ave, 15th fl, New York, NY 10001 *Tel:* 212-595-3500 *Fax:* 212-595-3779, pg 95

Fine, Michael J, Fine Communications, 322 Eighth Ave, 15th fl, New York, NY 10001 *Tel:* 212-595-3500 *Fax:* 212-595-3779, pg 95

Fine, Steve, Fine Communications, 322 Eighth Ave, 15th fl, New York, NY 10001 *Tel:* 212-595-3500 *Fax:* 212-595-3779, pg 95

Finegan, Patrick G Jr, Palindrome Press, PO Box 4151, Fairfax, VA 22124-8151 *Tel:* 703-242-1734 *Fax:* 703-242-1734 *E-mail:* palindromepress@yahoo.com, pg 191

Finer, Paul E, Classroom Connect, 222 Berkeley St, Boston, MA 02116 *Tel:* 617-351-5000 *Toll Free Tel:* 800-638-1639 (cust support) *E-mail:* help@classroom.com *Web Site:* corporate.classroom.com; www.hmhinnovation.com, pg 62

Fingerhut, Benjamin, St Augustine's Press Inc, PO Box 2285, South Bend, IN 46680-2285 *Tel:* 574-291-3500 *Toll Free Tel:* 888-997-4994 *Fax:* 574-291-3700 *Web Site:* www.staugustine.net, pg 223

Fingerhut, Bruce, St Augustine's Press Inc, PO Box 2285, South Bend, IN 46680-2285 *Tel:* 574-291-3500 *Toll Free Tel:* 888-997-4994 *Fax:* 574-291-3700 *Web Site:* www.staugustine.net, pg 223

Finkelman, Jamie, W W Norton & Company Inc, 500 Fifth Ave, New York, NY 10110-0017 *Tel:* 212-354-5500 *Toll Free Tel:* 800-233-4830 (orders & cust serv) *Fax:* 212-869-0856 *Toll Free Fax:* 800-458-6515 *Web Site:* www.wwnorton.com, pg 182

Finkelstein, Jesse, Douglas & McIntyre, 2323 Quebec St, Suite 201, Vancouver, BC V5T 4S7, Canada *Tel:* 604-254-7191 *Toll Free Tel:* 800-667-6902 (orders) *Fax:* 604-254-9099 *Toll Free Fax:* 800-668-5788 (orders CN) *E-mail:* info@harbourpublishing.com, pg 501

Finley, Doug, CCH Canadian Limited, A Wolters Kluwer Company, 90 Sheppard Ave E, Suite 300, Toronto, ON M2N 6X1, Canada *Tel:* 416-224-2224 *Toll Free Tel:* 800-268-4522 (CN & US cust serv) *Fax:* 416-224-2243 *Toll Free Fax:* 800-461-4131 *E-mail:* cservice@cch.ca (cust serv) *Web Site:* www.cch.ca, pg 498

Finman, Stephanie, The Martell Agency, 1350 Avenue of the Americas, Suite 1205, New York, NY 10019 *Tel:* 212-317-2672 *E-mail:* submissions@themartellagency.com *Web Site:* www.themartellagency.com, pg 584

Finn, Candace, Clarion Books, 215 Park Ave S, New York, NY 10003 *Tel:* 212-420-5883 *Toll Free Tel:* 800-225-3362 (orders) *Fax:* 212-420-5855 *Toll Free Fax:* 800-634-7568 (orders) *Web Site:* www.houghtonmifflinbooks.com, pg 62

Finsterbusch, Marty, National Coalition for Literacy, PO Box 2932, Washington, DC 20013-2932 *Toll Free Tel:* 800-228-8813 *Toll Free Fax:* 866-738-3757 *E-mail:* ncl@ncladvocacy.org; ncl@national-coalition-literary.org *Web Site:* www.national-coalition-literacy.org, pg 629

Firestone-Teeter, Naomi, Jewish Book Council, 520 Eighth Ave, 4th fl, New York, NY 10018 *Tel:* 212-201-2920 *Fax:* 212-532-4952 *E-mail:* jbc@jewishbooks.org *Web Site:* www.jewishbookcouncil.org, pg 626

Firestone-Teeter, Naomi, National Jewish Book Award-Children's & Young Adult Literature, 520 Eighth Ave, 4th fl, New York, NY 10018 *Tel:* 212-201-2920 *Fax:* 212-532-4952 *E-mail:* jbc@jewishbooks.org *Web Site:* www.jewishbookcouncil.org, pg 726

Firestone-Teeter, Naomi, National Jewish Book Award-Contemporary Jewish Life & Practice, 520 Eighth Ave, 4th fl, New York, NY 10018 *Tel:* 212-201-2920 *Fax:* 212-532-4952 *E-mail:* jbc@jewishbooks.org *Web Site:* www.jewishbookcouncil.org, pg 726

Firestone-Teeter, Naomi, National Jewish Book Award-History, 520 Eighth Ave, 4th fl, New York, NY 10018 *Tel:* 212-201-2920 *Fax:* 212-532-4952 *E-mail:* jbc@jewishbooks.org *Web Site:* www.jewishbookcouncil.org, pg 726

Firestone-Teeter, Naomi, National Jewish Book Award-Illustrated Children's Book, 520 Eighth Ave, 4th fl, New York, NY 10018 *Tel:* 212-201-2920 *Fax:* 212-532-4952 *E-mail:* jbc@jewishbooks.org *Web Site:* www.jewishbookcouncil.org, pg 726

Firestone-Teeter, Naomi, National Jewish Book Award-Modern Jewish Thought & Experience, 520 Eighth Ave, 4th fl, New York, NY 10018 *Tel:* 212-201-2920 *Fax:* 212-532-4952 *E-mail:* jbc@jewishbooks.org *Web Site:* www.jewishbookcouncil.org, pg 726

Firestone-Teeter, Naomi, National Jewish Book Award-Scholarship, 520 Eighth Ave, 4th fl, New York, NY 10018 *Tel:* 212-201-2920 *Fax:* 212-532-4952 *E-mail:* jbc@jewishbooks.org *Web Site:* www.jewishbookcouncil.org, pg 726

Firestone-Teeter, Naomi, National Jewish Book Awards, 520 Eighth Ave, 4th fl, New York, NY 10018 *Tel:* 212-201-2920 *Fax:* 212-532-4952 *E-mail:* jbc@jewishbooks.org *Web Site:* www.jewishbookcouncil.org, pg 726

Firestone-Teeter, Naomi, Sami Rohr Prize for Jewish Literature, 520 Eighth Ave, 4th fl, New York, NY 10018 *Tel:* 212-201-2920 *Fax:* 212-532-4952 *E-mail:* jbc@jewishbooks.org *Web Site:* www.jewishbookcouncil.org, pg 738

Firing, Rob, HarperCollins Canada Ltd, 2 Bloor St E, 20th fl, Toronto, ON M4W 1A8, Canada *Tel:* 416-975-9334 *Fax:* 416-975-9884 *E-mail:* hccanada@harpercollins.com *Web Site:* www.harpercollins.ca, pg 508

Fischbach, Christopher, Coffee House Press, 79 13 Ave NE, Suite 110, Minneapolis, MN 55413 *Tel:* 612-338-0125 *Fax:* 612-338-4004 *Web Site:* www.coffeehousepress.org, pg 64

Fischer, Amy-Lynn, University of California Press, 2120 Berkeley Way, Berkeley, CA 94704-1012 *Tel:* 510-642-4247 *Fax:* 510-643-7127 *E-mail:* askucp@ucpress.edu (books); customerservice@ucpressjournals.com (journals) *Web Site:* www.ucpress.edu, pg 264

Fischer, Craig, Police Executive Research Forum, 1120 Connecticut Ave NW, Suite 930, Washington, DC 20036 *Tel:* 202-466-7820 *Fax:* 202-466-7826 *E-mail:* perf@policeforum.org *Web Site:* www.policeforum.org, pg 204

Fischer, Grada, The Fischer Ross Group Inc, 2 Greenwich Office Park, Suite 300, Greenwich, CT 06831 *Tel:* 203-622-4950 *Fax:* 203-531-4132 *E-mail:* frgstaff@frg-speakers.com *Web Site:* www.frg-speakers.com, pg 605

Fischer, Shannon, Purple Pomegranate Productions, 60 Haight St, San Francisco, CA 94102 *Tel:* 415-864-2600 *Fax:* 415-552-8325 *E-mail:* sf@jewsforjesus.org *Web Site:* www.jewsforjesus.org, pg 210

Fischer, Steven, New England Book Awards, 1955 Massachusetts Ave, Cambridge, MA 02140 *Tel:* 617-547-3642 *Fax:* 617-547-3759 *Web Site:* www.newenglandbooks.org/ne_awards.html, pg 728

Fischer, Steven, New England Independent Booksellers Association Inc (NEIBA), 1955 Massachusetts Ave, Cambridge, MA 02140 *Web Site:* www.newenglandbooks.org, pg 631

Fischer, Tom, Timber Press Inc, 133 SW Second Ave, Suite 450, Portland, OR 97204 *Tel:* 503-227-2878 *Toll Free Tel:* 800-327-5680 *Fax:* 503-227-3070 *E-mail:* info@timberpress.com *Web Site:* www.timberpress.com, pg 255

Fischer-Harbage, Ryan, The Fischer-Harbage Agency Inc, 540 President St, 3rd fl, Brooklyn, NY 11215 *Tel:* 212-695-7105 *E-mail:* info@fischerharbage.com *Web Site:* www.fischerharbage.com, pg 572

Fisher, Agnes, Simon & Schuster, Inc, 1230 Avenue of the Americas, New York, NY 10020 *Tel:* 212-698-7000 *Fax:* 212-698-7007 *E-mail:* firstname.lastname@simonandschuster.com *Web Site:* www.simonandschuster.com, pg 235

Fisher, Allan, Crossway, 1300 Crescent St, Wheaton, IL 60187 *Tel:* 630-682-4300 *Toll Free Tel:* 800-635-7993 (orders); 800-543-1659 (cust serv) *Fax:* 630-682-4785 *E-mail:* info@crossway.org *Web Site:* www.crossway.org, pg 72

Fisher, Brad, The Charles Press, Publishers, 230 N 21 St, Suite 202, Philadelphia, PA 19103 *Tel:* 215-561-2786 *Fax:* 215-561-0191 *E-mail:* mailbox@charlespresspub.com *Web Site:* www.charlespresspub.com, pg 58

Fisher, Curtis, Diane Publishing Co, 330 Pusey Ave, Suite 3 (rear), Collingdale, PA 19023-0617 *Tel:* 610-461-6200 *Toll Free Tel:* 800-782-3833 *Fax:* 610-461-6130 *Web Site:* www.dianepublishing.net, pg 79

Fisher, Elizabeth, Levine|Greenberg Literary Agency Inc, 307 Seventh Ave, Suite 2407, New York, NY 10001 *Tel:* 212-337-0934 *Fax:* 212-337-0948 *Web Site:* www.levinegreenberg.com, pg 581

Fisher, John, Templegate Publishers, 302 E Adams St, Springfield, IL 62701 *Tel:* 217-522-3353 (edit & sales); 217-522-3354 (billing) *Toll Free Tel:* 800-367-4844 (orders only) *Fax:* 217-522-3362 *E-mail:* wisdom@templegate.com; orders@templegate.com (sales) *Web Site:* www.templegate.com, pg 252

Fisher, Lynn, University of Toronto Press Inc, 10 Saint Mary St, Suite 700, Toronto, ON M4Y 2W8, Canada *Tel:* 416-978-2239 *Fax:* 416-978-4738 *E-mail:* utpbooks@utpress.utoronto.ca *Web Site:* www.utpress.utoronto.ca; www.utppublishing.com, pg 524

Fisher, Maurice D, Gifted Education Press, 10201 Yuma Ct, Manassas, VA 20109 *Tel:* 703-369-5017 *Web Site:* www.giftededpress.com, pg 103

Fisher, Melissa, Vermont College of Fine Arts MFA in Writing for Children & Young Adults Program, 36 College St, Montpelier, VT 05602 *Tel:* 802-828-8637; 802-828-8696 *Toll Free Tel:* 866-934-VCFA (934-8232) *Fax:* 802-828-8649 *Web Site:* www.vcfa.edu, pg 682

Fisher, Michael G, Harvard University Press, 79 Garden St, Cambridge, MA 02138-1499 *Tel:* 617-495-2600; 401-531-2800 (intl orders) *Toll Free Tel:* 800-405-1619 (orders) *Fax:* 617-495-5898 (general); 617-496-4677 (edit & rts); 401-531-2801 (intl orders) *Toll Free Fax:* 800-406-9145 (orders) *E-mail:* contact_hup@harvard.edu *Web Site:* www.hup.harvard.edu, pg 115

Fisher, Stephen, Don Buchwald & Associates Inc, 10 E 44 St, New York, NY 10017 *Tel:* 212-867-1200 *Fax:* 212-867-2434 *E-mail:* info@buchwald.com *Web Site:* www.buchwald.com, pg 565

Fisher, Tracy, WME, 1325 Avenue of the Americas, New York, NY 10019 *Tel:* 212-586-5100 *Fax:* 212-246-3583 *E-mail:* wma@interport.net *Web Site:* www.wma.com, pg 599

Fisk, Karen, Juniper Prize for Fiction, East Experiment Sta, 671 N Pleasant St, Amherst, MA 01003 *Tel:* 413-545-2217 *Fax:* 413-545-1226 *E-mail:* info@umpress.umass.edu *Web Site:* www.umass.edu/umpress; www.umass.edu/umpress/juniper_fiction.html (description); www.umass.edu/umpress/juniper_fiction_guidelines.html, pg 714

Fisk, Karen, Juniper Prize for Poetry, East Experiment Sta, 671 N Pleasant St, Amherst, MA 01003 *Tel:* 413-545-2217 *Fax:* 413-545-1226 *E-mail:* info@umpress.umass.edu *Web Site:* www.umass.edu/umpress, pg 714

Fisk, Karen, University of Massachusetts Press, East Experiment Sta, 671 N Pleasant St, Amherst, MA 01003 *Tel:* 413-545-2217 *Fax:* 413-545-1226 *E-mail:* info@umpress.umass.edu *Web Site:* www.umass.edu/umpress, pg 266

Fisk, Raymond G, Down The Shore Publishing Corp, 638 Teal St, Cedar Run, NJ 08092 *Tel:* 609-978-1233 *Fax:* 609-597-0422 *E-mail:* dtsbooks@comcast.net; info@down-the-shore.com *Web Site:* www.down-the-shore.com, pg 81

Fiske, Robert Hartwell, Vocabula Communications Co, 5-A Holbrook Ct, Rockport, MA 01966 *Tel:* 978-546-3911 *E-mail:* info@vocabula.com *Web Site:* www.vocabula.com; www.vocabulabooks.com (books), pg 556

Fisketjon, Gary, Alfred A Knopf/Everyman's Library, c/o Random House Inc, 1745 Broadway, New York, NY 10019 *Tel:* 212-751-2600 *Toll Free Tel:* 800-638-6460 *Fax:* 212-572-2593 *Web Site:* www.knopfdoubleday.com, pg 141

Fitch, Ann, Tuxedo Press, 546 E Springville Rd, Carlisle, PA 17015 *Tel:* 717-258-9733 *Fax:* 717-243-0074 *E-mail:* info@tuxedo-press.com *Web Site:* tuxedo-press.com, pg 260

Fitterling, Michael Alan, Lost Classics Book Company LLC, 411 N Wales Dr, Lake Wales, FL 33853-3881 *Tel:* 863-678-3149 (edit off) *Fax:* 863-678-0802 *E-mail:* mgeditor@lostclassicsbooks.com *Web Site:* www.lostclassicsbooks.com, pg 152

Fitzgerald, Brenda, The University of Virginia Press, PO Box 400318, Charlottesville, VA 22904-4318 *Tel:* 434-924-3468 (cust serv); 434-924-3469 (cust serv) *Toll Free Tel:* 800-831-3406 (orders) *Fax:* 434-982-2655 *Toll Free Fax:* 877-288-6400 *E-mail:* vapress@virginia.edu *Web Site:* www.upress.virginia.edu, pg 270

Fitzgerald, Isaac, McSweeney's Publishing, 849 Valencia St, San Francisco, CA 94110 *Tel:* 415-642-5609 (cust serv) *Web Site:* www.mcsweeneys.net, pg 162

Fitzgerald, Lance, Simon & Schuster, 1230 Avenue of the Americas, New York, NY 10020 *Tel:* 212-698-7000 *Toll Free Tel:* 800-223-2348 (cust serv); 800-223-2336 (orders) *Toll Free Fax:* 800-943-9831 (orders) *Web Site:* www.simonandschuster.com, pg 234

Fitzgerald, Michelle, Palgrave Macmillan, 175 Fifth Ave, Suite 200, New York, NY 10010 *Tel:* 646-307-5151 *Fax:* 212-777-6359 *E-mail:* firstname.lastname@palgrave-usa.com *Web Site:* us.macmillan.com/Palgrave.aspx, pg 191

Fitzgerald, Patrick, Columbia University Press, 61 W 62 St, New York, NY 10023 *Tel:* 212-459-0600 *Toll Free Tel:* 800-944-8648 *Fax:* 212-459-3678 *E-mail:* cup_book@columbia.edu (orders & cust serv) *Web Site:* cup.columbia.edu, pg 65

Fitzgerald, Susan Kelly, Kinship Books, 781 Rte 308, Rhinebeck, NY 12572 *Tel:* 845-876-5840 (orders) *E-mail:* kinshipbooks@cs.com *Web Site:* www.kinshipny.com, pg 140

Fitzhenry, Sharon, Fitzhenry & Whiteside Limited, 195 Allstate Pkwy, Markham, ON L3R 4T8, Canada *Tel:* 905-477-9700 *Toll Free Tel:* 800-387-9776 *Fax:* 905-477-9179 *Toll Free Fax:* 800-260-9777 *E-mail:* bookinfo@fitzhenry.ca; godwit@fitzhenry.ca *Web Site:* www.fitzhenry.ca, pg 505

Fitzpatrick, Megan, Hachette Digital, 237 Park Ave, New York, NY 10017 *Tel:* 212-364-0600, pg 110

Fiyak-Burkley, Michele, University Press of Florida, 15 NW 15 St, Gainesville, FL 32603-2079 *Tel:* 352-392-1351 *Toll Free Tel:* 800-226-3822 (orders only) *Fax:* 352-392-0590 *Toll Free Fax:* 800-680-1955 (orders only) *E-mail:* info@upf.com *Web Site:* www.upf.com, pg 271

Fjestad, S P, Blue Book Publications Inc, 8009 34 Ave S, Suite 250, Minneapolis, MN 55425 *Tel:* 952-854-5229 *Toll Free Tel:* 800-877-4867 *Fax:* 925-853-1486 *E-mail:* support@bluebookinc.com *Web Site:* www.bluebookofgunvalues.com; www.bluebookofguitarvalues.com, pg 41

Flach, Andrew, Hatherleigh Press, 522 46 Ave, Suite 200, Long Island City, NY 11101 *Tel:* 718-786-5338 *Toll Free Tel:* 800-367-2550 *Fax:* 718-706-6087 *Toll Free Fax:* 800-733-3000 (orders) *E-mail:* info@hatherleigh.com *Web Site:* www.hatherleighpress.com; www.hatherleigh.com, pg 115

Flachman, Leonard, Kirk House Publishers, PO Box 390759, Minneapolis, MN 55439 *Tel:* 952-835-1828 *Toll Free Tel:* 888-696-1828 *Fax:* 952-835-2613 *E-mail:* publisher@kirkhouse.com *Web Site:* www.kirkhouse.com, pg 140

Flamand, Jacques, Les Editions du Vermillon, 305 rue Sainte-Patrick, Ottawa, ON K1N 5K4, Canada *Tel:* 613-241-4032 *Fax:* 613-241-3109 *E-mail:* leseditionsduvermillon@rogers.com *Web Site:* leseditionsduvermillon.ca, pg 503

Flamini, Michael, St Martin's Press, LLC, 175 Fifth Ave, New York, NY 10010 *Tel:* 646-307-5151 *Fax:* 212-420-9314 *E-mail:* firstname.lastname@macmillan.com *Web Site:* www.stmartins.com, pg 224

Flanagan, John F, Goodheart-Willcox Publisher, 18604 W Creek Dr, Tinley Park, IL 60477-6243 *Tel:* 708-687-5000 *Toll Free Tel:* 800-323-0440 *Fax:* 708-687-0315 *Toll Free Fax:* 888-409-3900 *E-mail:* custserv@g-w.com *Web Site:* www.g-w.com, pg 105

Flanagan, Marty, Ideals Publications, a Guideposts Co, 2630 Elm Hill Pike, Suite 100, Nashville, TN 37214 *Toll Free Tel:* 800-586-2572 (cust serv) *Fax:* 615-781-1447 *Web Site:* www.idealsbooks.com, pg 126

Flanders, Lorene, Southern Books Competition, PO Box 950, Rex, GA 30273 *Tel:* 678-466-4339 *Fax:* 678-466-4349 *Web Site:* selaonline.org, pg 743

Flanders, Margaret, Judy Lopez Memorial Award For Children's Literature, 1225 Selby Ave, Los Angeles, CA 90024 *Tel:* 310-474-9917 *Fax:* 310-474-6436 *Web Site:* www.wnba-books.org/la; www.judylopezbookaward.org, pg 719

Flanders, Tony, Sky Publishing, 90 Sherman St, Cambridge, MA 02140 *Tel:* 617-864-7360 *Toll Free Tel:* 866-644-1377 *Fax:* 617-864-6117 *E-mail:* info@skyandtelescope.com *Web Site:* www.skyandtelescope.com, pg 237

Flannery, Jennifer, Flannery Literary, 1140 Wickfield Ct, Naperville, IL 60563 *Tel:* 630-428-2682 *Web Site:* flanneryliterary.com, pg 572

Flashman, Melissa, Trident Media Group LLC, 41 Madison Ave, 36th fl, New York, NY 10010 *Tel:* 212-262-4810 *Fax:* 212-262-4849 *Web Site:* www.tridentmediagroup.com, pg 598

Flax, Margery, Mystery Writers of America (MWA), 1140 Broadway, Suite 1507, New York, NY 10001 *Tel:* 212-888-8171 *E-mail:* mwa@mysterywriters.org *Web Site:* www.mysterywriters.org, pg 628

Flax, Margery, Mystery Writers of America Workshops, 1140 Broadway, Suite 1507, New York, NY 10001 *Tel:* 212-888-8171 *E-mail:* mwa@mysterywriters.org *Web Site:* www.mysterywriters.org, pg 671

Flax, Margery, Edgar Allan Poe Awards®, 1140 Broadway, Suite 1507, New York, NY 10001 *Tel:* 212-888-8171 *E-mail:* mwa@mysterywriters.org *Web Site:* www.mysterywriters.org, pg 734

Flaxman, Jill, Crown Publishing Group, c/o Random House Inc, 1745 Broadway, New York, NY 10019 *Tel:* 212-782-9000 *Toll Free Tel:* 888-264-1745 *Fax:* 212-940-7408 *Web Site:* www.randomhouse.com/crown, pg 72

Fleck, Robert III, Oak Knoll Press, 310 Delaware St, New Castle, DE 19720 *Tel:* 302-328-7232 *Toll Free Tel:* 800-996-2556 *Fax:* 302-328-7274 *E-mail:* oakknoll@oakknoll.com *Web Site:* www.oakknoll.com, pg 183

Fleck, Robert D, Oak Knoll Press, 310 Delaware St, New Castle, DE 19720 *Tel:* 302-328-7232 *Toll Free Tel:* 800-996-2556 *Fax:* 302-328-7274 *E-mail:* oakknoll@oakknoll.com *Web Site:* www.oakknoll.com, pg 183

Fleet, Jani, Signature Books Publishing LLC, 564 W 400 N, Salt Lake City, UT 84116-3411 *Tel:* 801-531-1483 *Toll Free Tel:* 800-356-5687 (orders) *Fax:* 801-531-1488 *E-mail:* people@signaturebooks.com *Web Site:* www.signaturebooks.com; www.signaturebookslibrary.org, pg 234

Fleet, Xi Van, American Society of Civil Engineers (ASCE), 1801 Alexander Bell Dr, Reston, VA 20191-4400 *Tel:* 703-295-6300 *Toll Free Tel:* 800-548-2723 *Fax:* 703-295-6278 *E-mail:* marketing@asce.org *Web Site:* www.asce.org, pg 16

Flegal, Diana, Hartline Literary Agency LLC, 123 Queenston Dr, Pittsburgh, PA 15235 *Toll Free Fax:* 888-279-6007 *Web Site:* www.hartlineliterary.com, pg 576

Fleischer, Chip, Steerforth Press, 45 Lyme Rd, Suite 208, Hanover, NH 03755-1222 *Tel:* 603-643-4787 *Fax:* 603-643-4788 *E-mail:* info@steerforth.com *Web Site:* www.steerforth.com, pg 244

Fleishman, Samuel, Literary Artists Representatives, 575 West End Ave, Suite GRC, New York, NY 10024-2711 *Tel:* 212-679-7788 *Fax:* 212-595-2098 *E-mail:* litartists@aol.com, pg 582

Fleming, Connie, Oakstone Publishing LLC, 100 Corporate Pkwy, Suite 600, Birmingham, AL 35242 *Toll Free Tel:* 800-633-4743 *Fax:* 205-995-1926 *E-mail:* service@oakstonemedical.com *Web Site:* www.oakstonepublishing.com; www.cmeonly.com; www.cdeonly.com, pg 183

Fleming, Dr Deborah, Ashland Poetry Press, Ashland University, 401 College Ave, Ashland, OH 44805 *Tel:* 419-289-5957 *Fax:* 419-289-5255 *E-mail:* app@ashland.edu *Web Site:* www.ashland.edu/aupoetry, pg 24

Fleming, James, C D Howe Institute, 67 Yonge St, Suite 300, Toronto, ON M5E 1J8, Canada *Tel:* 416-865-1904 *Fax:* 416-865-1866 *E-mail:* cdhowe@cdhowe.org *Web Site:* www.cdhowe.org, pg 509

Fleming, Margo Beth, Stanford University Press, 1450 Page Mill Rd, Palo Alto, CA 94304-1124 *Tel:* 650-723-9434 *Fax:* 650-725-3457 *E-mail:* info@sup.org *Web Site:* www.sup.org, pg 243

Fleming, Peter, Peter Fleming Agency, PO Box 458, Pacific Palisades, CA 90272 *Tel:* 310-454-1373 *E-mail:* peterfleming@earthlink.net, pg 572

Fleming, Sue, Simon & Schuster Digital, 1230 Avenue of the Americas, New York, NY 10020 *Tel:* 212-698-7547 *Web Site:* www.simonandschuster.com; kids.simonandschuster.com; www.simonandschuster.ca; www.simonandschuster.co.uk; www.simonandschuster.net; www.simonandschuster.biz; www.tipsoncareerandmoney.com; www.tipsonhealthyliving.com; www.tipsonhomeandstyle.com; www.tipsonlifeandlove.com, pg 235

Fletcher, Lesley, Gerald Lampert Memorial Award, 192 Spadina Ave, Suite 312, Toronto, ON M5T 2C2, Canada *Tel:* 416-504-1657 *Fax:* 416-504-0096 *E-mail:* readings@poets.ca *Web Site:* www.poets.ca, pg 716

Fletcher, Lesley, The League of Canadian Poets, 192 Spadina Ave, Suite 312, Toronto, ON M5T 2C2, Canada *Tel:* 416-504-1657 *Fax:* 416-504-0096 *E-mail:* readings@poets.ca *Web Site:* www.poets.ca, pg 626

Fletcher, Lesley, Pat Lowther Memorial Award, 192 Spadina Ave, Suite 312, Toronto, ON M5T 2C2, Canada *Tel:* 416-504-1657 *Fax:* 416-504-0096 *E-mail:* readings@poets.ca *Web Site:* www.poets.ca, pg 719

Fletcher, Lesley, Jessamy Stursberg Poetry Contest for Youth, 192 Spadina Ave, Suite 312, Toronto, ON M5T 2C2, Canada *Tel:* 416-504-1657 *Fax:* 416-504-0096 *E-mail:* readings@poets.ca *Web Site:* www.youngpoets.ca; www.poets.ca, pg 744

Fletcher, Robert, Strategic Book Publishing & Rights Agency (SBPRA), 12620 FM 1960, Suite A-43 507, Houston, TX 77065 *Tel:* 703-637-6370 *Toll Free Tel:* 888-808-6190 *Web Site:* www.sbpra.com, pg 246

Fletcher, Sharon, NASW Press, 750 First St NE, Suite 700, Washington, DC 20002 *Tel:* 202-408-8600 *Fax:* 203-336-8312 *E-mail:* press@naswdc.org *Web Site:* www.naswpress.org, pg 172

Fletcher, Stephanie, Houghton Mifflin Harcourt Trade & Reference Division, 222 Berkeley St, Boston, MA 02116-3764 *Tel:* 617-351-5000 *Toll Free Tel:* 800-225-3362 *Web Site:* www.houghtonmifflinbooks.com, pg 124

Fletcher, Susan, PreK-12 Learning Group, 325 Chestnut St, Suite 1110, Philadelphia, PA 19106 *Tel:* 267-351-4310 *Fax:* 267-351-4317 *E-mail:* prek12learning@publishers.org *Web Site:* www.aepweb.org, pg 634

Fletty, Eric, Technical Association of the Pulp & Paper Industry (TAPPI), 15 Technology Pkwy S, Peachtree Corners, GA 30092 *Tel:* 770-446-1400 *Toll Free Tel:* 800-332-8686 (US); 800-446-9431 (CN) *Fax:* 770-446-6947 *E-mail:* memberconnection@tappi.org *Web Site:* www.tappi.org, pg 637

Fleury, Amy, McNeese State University, Writing Program, PO Box 92655, Lake Charles, LA 70609-0001 *Tel:* 337-475-5325; 337-475-5327 *Web Site:* www.mcneese.edu.com; www.mfa.mcneese.edu, pg 679

Flick-Nisbit, Andrea, Workman Publishing Co Inc, 225 Varick St, 9th fl, New York, NY 10014-4381 *Tel:* 212-254-5900 *Toll Free Tel:* 800-722-7202 *Fax:* 212-254-8098 *E-mail:* info@workman.com *Web Site:* www.workman.com, pg 285

Flickinger, Mike, Ascension Press, PO Box 1990, West Chester, PA 19380 *Tel:* 610-696-7795 *Toll Free Tel:* 800-376-0520 (sales & cust serv) *Fax:* 610-696-7796; 608-565-2025 (sales & cust serv) *E-mail:* info@ascensionpress.com *Web Site:* www.ascensionpress.com, pg 23

Flight, Nancy, Greystone Books, 2323 Quebec St, Suite 201, Vancouver, BC V5T 4S7, Canada *Tel:* 604-254-9099 *Fax:* 604-254-9099 *E-mail:* info@greystonebooks.com *Web Site:* www.greystonebooks.com; www.dmpibooks.com, pg 507

Flinchbaugh, Suzanne, The Johns Hopkins University Press, 2715 N Charles St, Baltimore, MD 21218-4363 *Tel:* 410-516-6900; 410-516-6987 (journals outside US & CN) *Toll Free Tel:* 800-537-5487 (book orders & cust serv); 800-548-1784 (journal orders) *Fax:* 410-516-6968; 410-516-3866 (journal orders) *E-mail:* hfscustserv@press.jhu.edu (cust serv); jrnlcirc@press.jhu.edu (journal orders) *Web Site:* www.press.jhu.edu; muse.jhu.edu/about/subscriptions/index.html (Project Muse subns), pg 136

Fliss, Roberta B, youngARTS, 777 Brickell Ave, Suite 370, Miami, FL 33131 *Tel:* 305-377-1140 *Toll Free Tel:* 800-970-ARTS (970-2787) *Fax:* 305-377-1149 *E-mail:* info@nfaa.org *Web Site:* www.youngarts.org, pg 753

Flood, Sara, Association of Writers & Writing Programs (AWP), George Mason University, 4400 University Dr, MSN 1E3, Fairfax, VA 22030 *Tel:* 703-993-4301 *Fax:* 703-993-4302 *E-mail:* awp@awpwriter.org *Web Site:* www.awpwriter.org, pg 617

Flood, Sara, AWP Award Series, George Mason University, 4400 University Dr, MSN 1E3, Fairfax, VA 22030 *Tel:* 703-993-4301 *Fax:* 703-993-4302 *E-mail:* awp@awpwriter.org *Web Site:* www.awpwriter.org, pg 688

Flora, Debi, About Books Inc, 1001 Taurus Dr, Colorado Springs, CO 80906 *Tel:* 719-632-8226 *Fax:* 719-213-2602 *Web Site:* www.about-books.com, pg 539

Flora, Debi, Association of Publishers for Special Sales (APSS), PO Box 715, Avon, CT 06001-0715 *Tel:* 860-675-1344 *Web Site:* www.spannet.org, pg 617

Flora, Scott, About Books Inc, 1001 Taurus Dr, Colorado Springs, CO 80906 *Tel:* 719-632-8226 *Fax:* 719-213-2602 *Web Site:* www.about-books.com, pg 539

Florence, Mari, Hungry? City Guides, 714 W Olympic Blvd, Suite 934, Los Angeles, CA 90015 *Fax:* 213-749-2080 *Web Site:* www.hungryguides.com, pg 125

Florence, Nicole, Writer's Digest Writing Competition, 10151 Carver Rd, Suite 200, Blue Ash, OH 45242 *Tel:* 513-531-2690 *Fax:* 513-531-0798 *E-mail:* writing-competition@fwmedia.com; writersdigest@fwmedia.com (edit) *Web Site:* www.writersdigest.com, pg 751

Florio, Marie, Gallery Books, 1230 Avenue of the Americas, New York, NY 10020 *Toll Free Tel:* 800-456-6798 *Fax:* 212-698-7284 *E-mail:* consumer.customerservice@simonandschuster.com *Web Site:* www.simonsays.com, pg 101

Florio, Marie, Simon & Schuster, 1230 Avenue of the Americas, New York, NY 10020 *Tel:* 212-698-7000 *Toll Free Tel:* 800-223-2348 (cust serv); 800-223-2336 (orders) *Toll Free Fax:* 800-943-9831 (orders) *Web Site:* www.simonandschuster.com, pg 234

Florio, Marie, Touchstone, 1230 Avenue of the Americas, New York, NY 10020, pg 256

Flounders, Emer, Harlequin Enterprises Ltd, 233 Broadway, Suite 1001, New York, NY 10279 *Tel:* 212-553-4200 *Fax:* 212-227-8969 *E-mail:* CustomerService@harlequin.com *Web Site:* www.harlequin.com, pg 112

Flower, Lauren, HarperCollins Children's Books, 10 E 53 St, New York, NY 10022 *Tel:* 212-207-7000 *Web Site:* www.harpercollinschildrens.com, pg 113

Flower, Richard, Bright Connections Media, A World Book Encyclopedia Company, 233 N Michigan Ave, Suite 2000, Chicago, IL 60601 *Tel:* 312-729-5800 *Fax:* 312-729-5610 *Web Site:* www.brightconnectionsmedia.com, pg 47

Flower, Richard, World Book Inc, 233 N Michigan, Suite 2000, Chicago, IL 60601 *Tel:* 312-729-5800 *Toll Free Tel:* 800-967-5325 (consumer sales, US); 800-463-8845 (consumer sales, CN); 800-975-3250 (school & lib sales, US); 800-837-5365 (school & lib sales, CN); 866-866-5200 (web sales) *Fax:* 312-729-5600; 312-729-5606 *Toll Free Fax:* 800-433-9330 (school & lib sales, US); 888-690-4002 (school lib sales, CN) *Web Site:* www.worldbook.com, pg 285

Forte, Deborah A, Scholastic Inc, 557 Broadway, New York, NY 10012 *Tel:* 212-343-6100 *Toll Free Tel:* 800-scholastic *Web Site:* www.scholastic.com, pg 228

Forte, Fran, The New Press, 38 Greene St, 4th fl, New York, NY 10013 *Tel:* 212-629-8802 *Toll Free Tel:* 800-343-4489 (orders) *Fax:* 212-629-8617 *Toll Free Fax:* 800-351-5073 (orders) *E-mail:* newpress@thenewpress.com *Web Site:* www.thenewpress.com, pg 178

Forte, Jeffrey L, Law Tribune Books, 201 Ann Uccello St, 4th fl, Hartford, CT 06103 *Tel:* 860-527-7900 *Fax:* 860-527-7433 *E-mail:* lawtribune@alm.com *Web Site:* www.ctlawtribune.com, pg 144

Fortgang, Adam, Princeton University Press, 41 William St, Princeton, NJ 08540-5237 *Tel:* 609-258-4900 *Toll Free Tel:* 800-777-4726 (orders) *Fax:* 609-258-6305 *Toll Free Fax:* 800-999-1958 *E-mail:* orders@cpfsinc.com *Web Site:* press.princeton.edu, pg 206

Fortier, C Azelie, Sinauer Associates Inc, 23 Plumtree Rd, Sunderland, MA 01375 *Tel:* 413-549-4300 *Fax:* 413-549-1118 *E-mail:* publish@sinauer.com; orders@sinauer.com *Web Site:* www.sinauer.com, pg 236

Fortin, Jacques, QA International, 329 De la Commune W, 3rd fl, Montreal, QC H2Y 2E1, Canada *Tel:* 514-499-3000 *Fax:* 514-499-3010 *Web Site:* www.qa-international.com, pg 517

Fortner, Shannon, International Reading Association, 800 Barksdale Rd, Newark, DE 19711-3204 *Tel:* 302-731-1600 *Toll Free Tel:* 800-336-7323 (US & CN) *Fax:* 302-731-1057 *E-mail:* customerservice@reading.org *Web Site:* www.reading.org, pg 133

Fortuna, Nina, American Society of Magazine Editors (ASME), 810 Seventh Ave, 24th fl, New York, NY 10019 *Tel:* 212-872-3700 *Fax:* 212-906-0128 *E-mail:* asme@magazine.org *Web Site:* www.magazine.org/asme/index.aspx, pg 614

Fortunato, Lisa, Rutgers University Press, 106 Somerset St, 3rd fl, New Brunswick, NJ 08901 *Tel:* 858-445-7784 (edit); 848-445-7788 *Toll Free Tel:* 800-848-6224 (orders only) *Fax:* 732-745-4935 (acqs, edit, mktg, perms & prodn) *Toll Free Fax:* 800-272-6817 (fulfillment) *Web Site:* rutgerspress.rutgers.edu, pg 222

Fortunato, Melissa, BePuzzled, 2030 Harrison St, San Francisco, CA 94110 *Tel:* 415-503-1600 *Toll Free Tel:* 800-347-4818 *Fax:* 415-503-0085 *E-mail:* info@ugames.com *Web Site:* www.ugames.com, pg 35

Foster, Cynthia, University Press of Mississippi, 3825 Ridgewood Rd, Jackson, MS 39211-6492 *Tel:* 601-432-6205 *Toll Free Tel:* 800-737-7788 (orders & cust serv) *Fax:* 601-432-6217 *E-mail:* press@mississippi.edu *Web Site:* www.upress.state.ms.us, pg 271

Foster, Frank, Medals of America, 114 Southchase Blvd, Fountain Inn, SC 29644 *Toll Free Tel:* 800-605-4001 *Toll Free Fax:* 800-407-8640 *E-mail:* jholt@usmedals.com, pg 163

Foster, Hal, Zone Books dba Urzone Inc, 1226 Prospect Ave, Brooklyn, NY 11218 *Tel:* 718-686-0048 *Toll Free Tel:* 800-405-1619 (orders & cust serv) *Fax:* 718-686-9045 *Toll Free Fax:* 800-406-9145 (orders) *E-mail:* orders@triliteral.org *Web Site:* www.zonebooks.org, pg 289

Foster, Lee, Foster Travel Publishing, PO Box 5715, Berkeley, CA 94705-0715 *Tel:* 510-549-2202 *Fax:* 510-549-1131 *Web Site:* www.fostertravel.com, pg 546

Foster, Susan, Bitingduck Press LLC, 1262 Sunnyoaks Cir, Altadena, CA 91001 *Tel:* 626-679-2494; 626-507-8033 *E-mail:* notifications@bitingduckpress.com *Web Site:* bitingduckpress.com, pg 38

Foster, Susan, Rick DeMarinis Short Story Award, PO Box 2414, Durango, CO 81302 *Tel:* 970-903-7914 *E-mail:* cutthroatmag@gmail.com *Web Site:* www.cutthroatmag.com, pg 700

Foster, Susan, Joy Harjo Poetry Award, PO Box 2414, Durango, CO 81302 *Tel:* 970-903-7914 *E-mail:* cutthroatmag@gmail.com *Web Site:* www.cutthroatmag.com, pg 709

Fotinos, Joel, GP Putnam's Sons (Hardcover), 375 Hudson St, New York, NY 10014 *Tel:* 212-366-2000 *E-mail:* online@penguinputnam.com *Web Site:* us.penguingroup.com, pg 210

Fotinos, Joel, Jeremy P Tarcher, 375 Hudson St, New York, NY 10014 *Tel:* 212-366-2000 *E-mail:* online@penguinputnam.com *Web Site:* www.penguinputnam.com; us.penguingroup.com, pg 250

Fott, Stacey Stonum, Stephens Press™, 1111 W Bonanza Rd, Las Vegas, NV 89106 *Tel:* 702-387-5260 *Toll Free Tel:* 888-951-2665 *Fax:* 702-387-2997 *E-mail:* info@stephenspress.com *Web Site:* www.stephenspress.com, pg 244

Foulds, Nancy, Lone Pine Publishing, 2311 96 St, Edmonton, AB T6N 1G3, Canada *Tel:* 780-433-9333 *Toll Free Tel:* 800-661-9017 *Fax:* 780-433-9646 *Toll Free Fax:* 800-424-7173 *E-mail:* info@lonepinepublishing.com *Web Site:* www.lonepinepublishing.com, pg 511

Foulon, Alexandrine, Editions Hurtubise, 1815 De Lorimier Ave, Montreal, QC H2K 3W6, Canada *Tel:* 514-523-1523 *Toll Free Tel:* 800-361-1664 (CN only) *Fax:* 514-523-9969 *Web Site:* www.editionshurtubise.com, pg 503

Foulon, Alexandrine, Les Editions XYZ inc, 1815 Ave de Lorimier, Montreal, QC H2K 3W6, Canada *Tel:* 514-525-2170 *Fax:* 514-525-7537 *E-mail:* info@editionsxyz.com *Web Site:* www.editionsxyz.com, pg 504

Foulon, Arnaud, Editions Marcel Didier Inc, 1815 Ave de Lorimier, Montreal, QC H2K 3W6, Canada *Tel:* 514-523-1523 *Toll Free Tel:* 800-361-1664 (Ontario to Maritimes) *Fax:* 514-523-9969 *E-mail:* marceldidier@hurtubisehmh.com *Web Site:* www.hurtubisehmh.com, pg 502

Foulon, Arnaud, Editions Hurtubise, 1815 De Lorimier Ave, Montreal, QC H2K 3W6, Canada *Tel:* 514-523-1523 *Toll Free Tel:* 800-361-1664 (CN only) *Fax:* 514-523-9969 *Web Site:* www.editionshurtubise.com, pg 503

Foulon, Herve, Editions Marcel Didier Inc, 1815 Ave de Lorimier, Montreal, QC H2K 3W6, Canada *Tel:* 514-523-1523 *Toll Free Tel:* 800-361-1664 (Ontario to Maritimes) *Fax:* 514-523-9969 *E-mail:* marceldidier@hurtubisehmh.com *Web Site:* www.hurtubisehmh.com, pg 502

Foulon, Herve, Editions Hurtubise, 1815 De Lorimier Ave, Montreal, QC H2K 3W6, Canada *Tel:* 514-523-1523 *Toll Free Tel:* 800-361-1664 (CN only) *Fax:* 514-523-9969 *Web Site:* www.editionshurtubise.com, pg 503

Fournier, Danielle, Les Editions de l'Hexagone, 1010 rue de la Gauchetiere E, Montreal, QC H2L 2N5, Canada *Tel:* 514-523-7993 (ext 4201) *Fax:* 514-282-7530 *E-mail:* vml@sogides.com *Web Site:* www.edhexagone.com, pg 502

Fournier, Holly, PennWell Books, 1421 S Sheridan Rd, Tulsa, OK 74112 *Tel:* 918-831-9410 *Toll Free Tel:* 800-752-9764 *Fax:* 918-831-9555 *E-mail:* sales@pennwell.com *Web Site:* www.pennwellbooks.com, pg 198

Fowler, Dr Gilbert, Arkansas State University Graphic Communications Program, PO Box 1930, Dept of Journalism & Graphic Communications, State University, AR 72467-1930 *Tel:* 870-972-3114 *Fax:* 870-972-3321 *Web Site:* www.astate.edu, pg 677

Fowler, Karen Joy, The Clarion Science Fiction & Fantasy Writers' Workshop, Dept of Literature, Mail Code 0410, UC San Diego, 9500 Gilman Dr, La Jolla, CA 92093-0410 *Tel:* 858-534-2115 *E-mail:* clarion@ucsd.edu *Web Site:* clarion.ucsd.edu, pg 668

Fowles, Cynthia, Bear & Co Inc, One Park St, Rochester, VT 05767 *Tel:* 802-767-3174 *Toll Free Tel:* 800-932-3277 *Fax:* 802-767-3726 *E-mail:* customerservice@InnerTraditions.com *Web Site:* InnerTraditions.com, pg 33

Fowles, Cynthia, Inner Traditions International Ltd, One Park St, Rochester, VT 05767 *Tel:* 802-767-3174 *Toll Free Tel:* 800-246-8648 *Fax:* 802-767-3726 *E-mail:* customerservice@InnerTraditions.com *Web Site:* www.InnerTraditions.com, pg 130

Fox, Anna, ChemTec Publishing, 38 Earswick Dr, Toronto, ON M1E 1C6, Canada *Tel:* 416-265-2603 *Fax:* 416-265-1399 *E-mail:* orderdesk@chemtec.org *Web Site:* www.chemtec.org, pg 498

Fox, Gretchen, NPTA Alliance, 401 N Michigan Ave, Suite 2200, Chicago, IL 60611 *Tel:* 312-321-4092 *Toll Free Tel:* 800-355-NPTA (355-6782) *Fax:* 312-673-6736 *E-mail:* npta@gonpta.com *Web Site:* www.gonpta.com, pg 632

Fox, Jim, Silman-James Press, 3624 Shannon Rd, Los Angeles, CA 90027 *Tel:* 323-661-9922 *Toll Free Tel:* 877-SJP-BOOK (757-2665) *Fax:* 323-661-9933 *E-mail:* info@silmanjamespress.com *Web Site:* www.silmanjamespress.com, pg 234

Fox, John C, The Perseus Books Group, 387 Park Ave S, 12th fl, New York, NY 10016 *Tel:* 212-340-8100 *Toll Free Tel:* 800-343-4499 (cust serv) *Fax:* 212-340-8105 *Web Site:* www.perseusbooksgroup.com, pg 199

Fox, Laurie, Linda Chester Literary Agency, Rockefeller Ctr, Suite 2036, 630 Fifth Ave, New York, NY 10111 *Tel:* 212-218-3350 *Fax:* 212-218-3343 *E-mail:* submissions@lindachester.com *Web Site:* www.lindachester.com, pg 566

Fox, Leisette, Wildflower Press, Oakbrook Press, 3301 S Valley Dr, Rapid City, SD 57703 *Tel:* 605-381-6385 *Fax:* 605-343-8733 *E-mail:* info@wildflowerpress.org; bookorder@wildflowerpress.org *Web Site:* www.wildflowerpress.org, pg 281

Fox, Marilyn L, American Academy of Orthopaedic Surgeons, 6300 N River Rd, Rosemont, IL 60018-4262 *Tel:* 847-823-7186 *Toll Free Tel:* 800-346-2267 *Fax:* 847-823-8125 *Toll Free Fax:* 800-999-2939 *Web Site:* www.aaos.org, pg 10

Fox, Nancy, Gem Guides Book Co, 1275 W Ninth St, Upland, CA 91786 *Tel:* 626-855-1611 *Toll Free Tel:* 800-824-5118 (orders) *Fax:* 626-855-1610 *E-mail:* info@gemguidesbooks.com *Web Site:* www.gemguidesbooks.com, pg 102

Fox, R K, American Press, 60 State St, Suite 700, Boston, MA 02109 *Tel:* 617-247-0022 *E-mail:* americanpress@flash.net *Web Site:* www.americanpresspublishers.com, pg 15

Fox, Steven A, Central Conference of American Rabbis/CCAR Press, 355 Lexington Ave, 18th fl, New York, NY 10017 *Tel:* 212-972-3636 *Toll Free Tel:* 800-935-2227 *Fax:* 212-692-0819 *E-mail:* info@ccarnet.org *Web Site:* www.ccarnet.org/ccar-press, pg 57

Foy, Fritz, Macmillan, 175 Fifth Ave, New York, NY 10010 *Tel:* 646-307-5151 *Fax:* 212-420-9314 *E-mail:* firstname.lastname@macmillan.com *Web Site:* www.macmillan.com, pg 154

Foy, Mr Pat, Health Forum Inc, 155 N Wacker Dr, Suite 400, Chicago, IL 60606 *Tel:* 312-893-6884 *Toll Free Tel:* 800-242-2626 *Fax:* 312-422-4600 *E-mail:* hfcustsvc@healthforum.com *Web Site:* www.ahaonlinestore.com; www.healthforum.com, pg 116

Fragnito, Michael, Sterling Publishing Co Inc, 387 Park Ave S, 11th fl, New York, NY 10016-8810 *Tel:* 212-532-7160 *Toll Free Tel:* 800-367-9692 *Fax:* 212-213-2495 *Web Site:* www.sterlingpub.com, pg 244

Franceschelli, Christopher, Handprint Books Inc, 413 Sixth Ave, Brooklyn, NY 11215-3310 *Tel:* 718-768-3696 *Toll Free Tel:* 800-722-6657 (orders) *Fax:* 718-369-0844 *Toll Free Fax:* 800-858-7787 (orders) *E-mail:* info@handprintbooks.com *Web Site:* www.handprintbooks.com, pg 111

Franceschelli, Joe, HarperCollins Publishers, 10 E 53 St, New York, NY 10022 *Tel:* 212-207-7000 *Fax:* 212-207-7145 *Web Site:* www.harpercollins.com, pg 113

Franceschi, Adrienne, Storey Publishing LLC, 210 MASS MoCA Way, North Adams, MA 01247 *Tel:* 413-346-2100 *Toll Free Tel:* 800-441-5700 (orders); 800-793-9396 (edit) *Fax:* 413-346-2199; 413-346-2196 (edit) *E-mail:* sales@storey.com *Web Site:* www.storey.com, pg 246

Franceschi, Adrienne, Timber Press Inc, 133 SW Second Ave, Suite 450, Portland, OR 97204 *Tel:* 503-227-2878 *Toll Free Tel:* 800-327-5680 *Fax:* 503-227-3070 *E-mail:* info@timberpress.com *Web Site:* www.timberpress.com, pg 255

Francet, Cris, Pants On Fire Press, 2062 Harbor Cove Way, Winter Garden, FL 34787 *Tel:* 863-546-0760 *E-mail:* submission@pantsonfirepress.com *Web Site:* www.pantsonfirepress.com, pg 192

Francis, Barbara, Pippin Press, 229 E 85 St, New York, NY 10028 *Tel:* 212-288-4920 *Fax:* 908-237-2407, pg 202

Francis, Casey, Thomas Nelson Inc, 501 Nelson Place, Nashville, TN 37214 *Tel:* 615-889-9000 *Toll Free Tel:* 800-251-4000 *Fax:* 615-902-1548 *E-mail:* publicity@thomasnelson.com *Web Site:* www.thomasnelson.com, pg 255

Francis, Mary C, University of California Press, 2120 Berkeley Way, Berkeley, CA 94704-1012 *Tel:* 510-642-4247 *Fax:* 510-643-7127 *E-mail:* askucp@ucpress.edu (books); customerservice@ucpressjournals.com (journals) *Web Site:* www.ucpress.edu, pg 264

Francis, Paul, American Society of Mechanical Engineers (ASME), 3 Park Ave, New York, NY 10016-5990 *Tel:* 212-591-7000 *Toll Free Tel:* 800-843-2763 (cust serv-US, CN & Mexico) *Fax:* 212-591-7674; 973-882-8113 (cust serv); 973-882-1717 (orders & inquiries) *E-mail:* infocentral@asme.org *Web Site:* www.asme.org, pg 17

Francis, Therese, Crossquarter Publishing Group, 1910 Sombra Ct, Santa Fe, NM 87505 *Tel:* 505-690-3923 *Fax:* 214-975-9715 *E-mail:* sales@crossquarter.com; info@crossquarter.com *Web Site:* www.crossquarter.com, pg 71

Frank, Charlotte, McGraw-Hill Education, 2 Penn Plaza, New York, NY 10121-2298 *Tel:* 212-904-2000 *E-mail:* customer.service@mcgraw-hill.com *Web Site:* www.mheducation.com; www.mheducation.com/custserv.html, pg 161

Frank, Cynthia, Cypress House, 155 Cypress St, Fort Bragg, CA 95437 *Tel:* 707-964-9520 *Toll Free Tel:* 800-773-7782 *Fax:* 707-964-7531 *E-mail:* cypresshouse@cypresshouse.com *Web Site:* www.cypresshouse.com, pg 74, 544

Frank, Cynthia, QED Press, 155 Cypress St, Fort Bragg, CA 95437 *Tel:* 707-964-9520 *Toll Free Tel:* 800-773-7782 *Fax:* 707-964-7531 *E-mail:* qedpress@mcn.org *Web Site:* www.cypresshouse.com, pg 211

Frank, Daniel, Pantheon Books/Schocken Books, c/o Random House Inc, 1745 Broadway, New York, NY 10019 *Tel:* 212-751-2600 *Toll Free Tel:* 800-638-6460 *Fax:* 212-572-6030, pg 192

Frank, Jerry, Vandamere Press, 3580 Morris St N, St Petersburg, FL 33713 *Tel:* 727-556-0950 *Toll Free Tel:* 800-551-7776 *Fax:* 727-556-2560 *E-mail:* orders@vandamere.com *Web Site:* www.vandamere.com, pg 274

Frankel, David, The Museum of Modern Art, 11 W 53 St, New York, NY 10019 *Tel:* 212-708-9443 *Fax:* 212-333-6575 *E-mail:* moma_publications@moma.org *Web Site:* www.moma.org, pg 171

Franki, Julene, ALI-ABA Continuing Professional Education, 4025 Chestnut St, Philadelphia, PA 19104 *Tel:* 215-243-1600 *Toll Free Tel:* 800-CLE-NEWS (253-6397) *Fax:* 215-243-1664; 215-243-1683 *Web Site:* www.ali-aba.org, pg 8

Frankl, Beth, Shambhala Publications Inc, Horticultural Hall, 300 Massachusetts Ave, Boston, MA 02115 *Tel:* 617-424-0030 *Toll Free Tel:* 866-424-0030 (off); 888-424-2329 (cust serv) *Fax:* 617-236-1563 *E-mail:* customercare@shambhala.com *Web Site:* www.shambhala.com, pg 232

Franklin, Lynn C, Lynn C Franklin Associates Ltd, 1350 Broadway, Suite 2015, New York, NY 10018 *Tel:* 212-868-6311 *Fax:* 212-868-6312 *E-mail:* agency@franklinandsiegal.com, pg 573

Franklin, Robert, McFarland, 960 NC Hwy 88 W, Jefferson, NC 28640 *Tel:* 336-246-4460 *Toll Free Tel:* 800-253-2187 (orders) *Fax:* 336-246-5018; 336-246-4403 (orders) *E-mail:* info@mcfarlandpub.com *Web Site:* www.mcfarlandpub.com, pg 160

Franklin, Wayne, The University of Connecticut, The Realities of Publishing, CLAS, 215 Glenbrook Rd, Unit 4025, Storrs, CT 06269-4025 *Tel:* 860-486-2141 *Web Site:* web.uconn.edu/english291, pg 681

Frankos, Anthony J, American Medical Association, 515 N State St, Chicago, IL 60654 *Tel:* 312-464-5000 *Toll Free Tel:* 800-621-8335 *Fax:* 312-464-4184 *Web Site:* www.ama-assn.org, pg 15, 613

Franks, Lainey, Lonely Planet, 150 Linden St, Oakland, CA 94607 *Tel:* 510-893-8555 *Toll Free Tel:* 800-275-8555 (orders) *Fax:* 510-893-8563 *E-mail:* info@lonelyplanet.com *Web Site:* www.lonelyplanet.com, pg 152

Frantz, Kristen, Berrett-Koehler Publishers Inc, 235 Montgomery St, Suite 650, San Francisco, CA 94104 *Tel:* 415-288-0260 *Fax:* 415-362-2512 *E-mail:* bkpub@bkpub.com *Web Site:* www.bkconnection.com, pg 36

Franzak, George, Rowman & Littlefield Publishers Inc, 4501 Forbes Blvd, Suite 200, Lanham, MD 20706 *Tel:* 301-459-3366 *Toll Free Tel:* 800-462-6420 (cust serv) *Fax:* 301-429-5748 *Web Site:* www.rowmanlittlefield.com, pg 221

Franzak, George, University Press of America Inc, 4501 Forbes Blvd, Suite 200, Lanham, MD 20706 *Tel:* 301-459-3366 *Toll Free Tel:* 800-462-6420 *Fax:* 301-429-5748 *Toll Free Fax:* 800-338-4550 *Web Site:* www.univpress.com, pg 270

Fraser, Caroline, Scholastic Media, 524 Broadway, 5th fl, New York, NY 10012 *Tel:* 212-389-3900 *Fax:* 212-389-3886, pg 228

Fraser, Malcolm, WinePress Publishing, 1730 Railroad St, Enumclaw, WA 98022 *Tel:* 360-802-9758 *Toll Free Tel:* 800-326-4674 *Fax:* 360-802-9992 *Web Site:* www.winepresspublishing.com, pg 283

Fraser, Simon, DK, 375 Hudson St, 2nd fl, New York, NY 10014-3672 *Tel:* 212-213-4800 *Toll Free Tel:* 877-342-5357 (cust serv) *Fax:* 212-213-5202 *Web Site:* us.dk.com, pg 80

Fraser, Stephen, The Jennifer DeChiara Literary Agency, 31 E 32 St, Suite 300, New York, NY 10016 *Tel:* 212-481-8484 (ext 362) *Fax:* 212-481-9582 *Web Site:* www.jdlit.com, pg 568

Fraser-Bub, MacKenzie, Trident Media Group LLC, 41 Madison Ave, 36th fl, New York, NY 10010 *Tel:* 212-262-4810 *Fax:* 212-262-4849 *Web Site:* www.tridentmediagroup.com, pg 598

Frautschi, Dylan, Iconografix Inc, 1830-A Hanley Rd, Hudson, WI 54016 *Tel:* 715-381-9755 *Toll Free Tel:* 800-289-3504 (orders only) *Fax:* 715-381-9756 *E-mail:* info@iconografixinc.com *Web Site:* www.iconografixinc.com, pg 126

Frazier, Felicia, Penguin Group (USA) LLC, 375 Hudson St, New York, NY 10014 *Tel:* 212-366-2000 *Toll Free Tel:* 800-847-5515 (inside sales); 800-631-8571 (cust serv) *Fax:* 212-366-2666; 607-775-4829 (inside sales) *E-mail:* online@us.penguingroup.com *Web Site:* www.penguin.com; us.penguingroup.com, pg 197

Frazier, Felicia, Penguin Group (USA) LLC Sales, 375 Hudson St, New York, NY 10014 *Tel:* 212-366-2000 *E-mail:* online@penguinputnam.com *Web Site:* us.penguingroup.com, pg 197

Frazier, Felicia, Penguin Young Readers Group, 345 Hudson St, New York, NY 10014 *Tel:* 212-366-2000 *E-mail:* online@penguinputnam.com *Web Site:* www.penguinputnam.com; us.penguingroup.com, pg 198

Frazier, Kathleen, Health Press NA Inc, 2920 Carlisle Blvd NE, Suite 111, Albuquerque, NM 87110 *Tel:* 505-888-1394 *Toll Free Tel:* 877-411-0707 *Fax:* 505-888-1521 *E-mail:* goodbooks@healthpress.com *Web Site:* www.healthpress.com, pg 116

Frazier, Ms Sunny, Oak Tree Press, 140 E Palmer St, Taylorville, IL 62568 *Tel:* 217-824-6500 *E-mail:* publisher@oaktreebooks.com; info@oaktreebooks.com; query@oaktreebooks.com; pressdept@oaktreebooks.com; bookorders@oaktreebooks.com *Web Site:* www.oaktreebooks.com; www.otpblog.blogspot.com, pg 183

Frazier, Warren, John Hawkins & Associates Inc, 71 W 23 St, Suite 1600, New York, NY 10010 *Tel:* 212-807-7040 *Fax:* 212-807-9555 *E-mail:* jha@jhalit.com *Web Site:* jhalit.com, pg 576

Frazin, Rhona, The Carl Sandburg Literary Awards, 20 N Michigan Ave, Suite 520, Chicago, IL 60602 *Tel:* 312-201-9830 *Fax:* 312-201-9833 *Web Site:* www.chicagopubliclibraryfoundation.org, pg 739

Frechette, Jacques, Guy Saint-Jean Editeur Inc, 3440 Blvd Industriel, Laval, QC H7L 4R9, Canada *Tel:* 450-663-1777 *Fax:* 450-663-6666 *E-mail:* info@saint-jeanediteur.com *Web Site:* www.saint-jeanediteur.com, pg 518

Freda, Kristin, Irma S & James H Black Award, 610 W 112 St, New York, NY 10025 *Tel:* 212-875-4458 *Fax:* 212-875-4558 *E-mail:* ccl@bankstreet.edu *Web Site:* www.bankstreet.edu/center-childrens-literature, pg 691

Fredell, Eric, Software & Information Industry Association (SIIA), 1090 Vermont Ave NW, 6th fl, Washington, DC 20005-4095 *Tel:* 202-289-7442 *Fax:* 202-289-7097 *E-mail:* info@siia.net *Web Site:* www.siia.net, pg 637

Frederick, Holly, Curtis Brown Ltd, 10 Astor Place, New York, NY 10003 *Tel:* 212-473-5400 *Web Site:* www.curtisbrown.com, pg 565

Frederick, Margaretta S, William Morris Society in the United States Fellowships, PO Box 53263, Washington, DC 20009 *E-mail:* us@morrissociety.org *Web Site:* www.morrissociety.org, pg 725

Fredericks, Jeanne, Jeanne Fredericks Literary Agency Inc, 221 Benedict Hill Rd, New Canaan, CT 06840 *Tel:* 203-972-3011 *Fax:* 203-972-3011 *E-mail:* jeanne.fredericks@gmail.com (no unsol attachments) *Web Site:* jeannefredericks.com, pg 573

Free, Liz, John Hawkins & Associates Inc, 71 W 23 St, Suite 1600, New York, NY 10010 *Tel:* 212-807-7040 *Fax:* 212-807-9555 *E-mail:* jha@jhalit.com *Web Site:* jhalit.com, pg 576

Freedman, Rana, Lonely Planet, 150 Linden St, Oakland, CA 94607 *Tel:* 510-893-8555 *Toll Free Tel:* 800-275-8555 (orders) *Fax:* 510-893-8563 *E-mail:* info@lonelyplanet.com *Web Site:* www.lonelyplanet.com, pg 152

Freedman, Robert A, Robert A Freedman Dramatic Agency Inc, 1501 Broadway, Suite 2310, New York, NY 10036 *Tel:* 212-840-5760 *Fax:* 212-840-5776, pg 573

Freeland, Abby, West Virginia University Press, West Virginia University, PO Box 6295, Morgantown, WV 26506-6295 *Tel:* 304-293-8400 *Toll Free Tel:* 866-WVU-PRES (988-7737) *Fax:* 304-293-6585 *E-mail:* press@wvu.edu *Web Site:* www.wvupress.com, pg 278

Freeland, Ronald, Judson Press, 588 N Gulph Rd, King of Prussia, PA 19406 *Toll Free Tel:* 800-458-3766 *Fax:* 610-768-2107 *Web Site:* www.judsonpress.com, pg 137

Freels, Amy, Akron Poetry Prize, The University of Akron Press, 120 E Mill St, Suite 415, Akron, OH 44308 *Tel:* 330-972-6953 *Fax:* 330-972-8364 *E-mail:* uapress@uakron.edu *Web Site:* www.uakron.edu/uapress/akron-poetry-prize, pg 686

Freeman, Fr Brendan, Cistercian Publications Inc, Editorial Office, Saint John's Abbey, PO Box 7500, Collegeville, MN 56321 *Tel:* 320-363-2213 *Toll Free Tel:* 800-436-8431 *Fax:* 320-363-3299 *Toll Free Fax:* 800-445-5899 *E-mail:* editor@monks.org *Web Site:* www.cistercianpublications.org, pg 62

Freeman, Darla, Kensington Publishing Corp, 119 W 40 St, New York, NY 10018 *Tel:* 212-407-1500 *Toll Free Tel:* 800-221-2647 *Fax:* 212-935-0699 *Web Site:* www.kensingtonbooks.com, pg 139

Freeman, Julie, International Association of Business Communicators (IABC), 601 Montgomery St, Suite 1900, San Francisco, CA 94111 *Tel:* 415-

Fry, Sonya K, The Cornelius Ryan Award, 40 W 45 St, New York, NY 10036 *Tel:* 212-626-9220 *Fax:* 212-626-9210 *Web Site:* www.opcofamerica.org, pg 739

Fryling, Robert A, InterVarsity Press, 430 Plaza Dr, Westmont, IL 60559-1234 *Tel:* 630-734-4000 *Toll Free Tel:* 800-843-9487 *Fax:* 630-734-4200 *E-mail:* email@ivpress.com *Web Site:* www.ivpress.com, pg 134

Fryman, Alona, Bloomsbury Publishing, 175 Fifth Ave, New York, NY 10010 *Tel:* 212-674-5151 *Toll Free Tel:* 800-221-7945 *Fax:* 212-780-0115; 212-982-2837 *E-mail:* marketingusa@bloomsbury.com; adultpublicityusa.@bloomsbury.com *Web Site:* www.bloomsbury.com, pg 40

Fuchs, Robert E, Wildflower Press, Oakbrook Press, 3301 S Valley Dr, Rapid City, SD 57703 *Tel:* 605-381-6385 *Fax:* 605-343-8733 *E-mail:* info@wildflowerpress.org; bookorder@wildflowerpress.org *Web Site:* www.wildflowerpress.org, pg 281

Fuersich, Larry, Visual Profile Books Inc, 302 Fifth Ave, New York, NY 10001 *Tel:* 212-279-7000 *Fax:* 212-279-7014 *Web Site:* www.visualreference.com, pg 275

Fuhrman, Candice, Candice Fuhrman Literary Agency, 10 Cypress Hollow Dr, Tiburon, CA 94920 *Tel:* 415-383-1014 *E-mail:* candicef@pacbell.net, pg 573

Fulks, Kira, The Forum Press Inc, 3100 W Warner Ave, Suite 7, Santa Ana, CA 92704 *Tel:* 714-545-3114 *Fax:* 714-545-3116 *E-mail:* theforumpress@cs.com *Web Site:* www.theforumpress.com, pg 97

Fuller, Barbara, Editcetera, 2034 Blake St, Suite 5, Berkeley, CA 94704 *Tel:* 510-849-1110 *Fax:* 510-848-1448 *E-mail:* info@editcetera.com *Web Site:* www.editcetera.com, pg 545

Fuller, Dale, Parabola Books, 20 W 20 St, 2nd fl, New York, NY 10011 *Tel:* 212-822-8806 *Toll Free Tel:* 800-592-2521 (subns) *Fax:* 212-822-8823 *E-mail:* info@parabola.org *Web Site:* www.parabola.org, pg 192

Fuller, Diana, Squaw Valley Community of Writers Summer Workshops, PO Box 1416, Nevada City, CA 95959 *Tel:* 530-470-8440 *E-mail:* info@squawvalleywriters.org *Web Site:* www.squawvalleywriters.org, pg 673

Fuller, Erin, Alliance for Women in Media (AWM), 1760 Old Meadow Rd, Suite 500, McLean, VA 22102 *Tel:* 703-506-3290 *Fax:* 703-506-3266 *E-mail:* info@awrt.org *Web Site:* www.awrt.org, pg 611

Fuller, Erin, The Gracies®, 1760 Old Meadow Rd, Suite 500, McLean, VA 22102 *Tel:* 703-506-3290 *Fax:* 703-506-3266 *E-mail:* info@awrt.org *Web Site:* www.awrt.org, pg 708

Fuller, Helen, Integra Software Services Inc, 1110 Jorie Blvd, Suite 200, Oak Brook, IL 60523 *Tel:* 630-586-2579 *Fax:* 630-586-2599 *Web Site:* www.integra.co.in, pg 548

Fuller, Dr Renee PhD, Ball-Stick-Bird Publications Inc, PO Box 429, Williamstown, MA 01267-0429 *Tel:* 413-664-0002 *Fax:* 413-664-0002 *E-mail:* info@ballstickbird.com *Web Site:* www.ballstickbird.com, pg 30

Fullington, Martha, Bright Mountain Books Inc, 206 Riva Ridge Dr, Fairview, NC 28730 *Tel:* 828-628-1768 *Toll Free Tel:* 800-437-3959 *Fax:* 828-628-1755 *E-mail:* booksbmb@charter.net *Web Site:* brightmountainbooks.com, pg 47

Fulton, Kevin, Green King Press, 4211 Fenwick Village Dr, Savannah, GA 31419 *Tel:* 843-325-6821, pg 107

Fumega, Roberta, Jones Hutton Literary Associates, 160 N Compo Rd, Westport, CT 06880-2102 *Tel:* 203-226-2588 *Fax:* 203-226-2588 *E-mail:* huttonbooks@hotmail.com, pg 579

Fumich, Jita, Folio Literary Management LLC, The Film Center Bldg, 630 Ninth Ave, Suite 1101, New York, NY 10036 *Tel:* 212-400-1494 *Fax:* 212-967-0977 *Web Site:* www.foliolit.com, pg 572

Fund, Ken, Fair Winds Press, 100 Cummings Ctr, Suite 406-L, Beverly, MA 01915 *Tel:* 978-282-9590 *Toll Free Tel:* 800-328-0590 (sales) *Fax:* 978-283-2742 *E-mail:* customerservice@quaysidepub.com *Web Site:* www.fairwindspress.com, pg 91

Fund, Ken, Quayside Publishing Group, 400 First Ave N, Suite 300, Minneapolis, MN 55401 *Tel:* 612-344-8100 *Toll Free Tel:* 800-328-0590 (sales); 800-458-0454 *Fax:* 612-344-8691 *E-mail:* sales@creativepub.com *Web Site:* www.qbookshop.com, pg 211

Funk, Susan, Mystic Seaport Museum Inc, PO Box 6000, Mystic, CT 06355-0990 *Tel:* 860-572-5302; 860-572-0711 (visitor serv) *Toll Free Tel:* 800-248-1066 (wholesale orders only); 800-331-2665 (retail orders only) *Fax:* 860-572-5321 *E-mail:* info@mysticseaport.org *Web Site:* www.mysticseaport.org, pg 172

Funke, Claudia, Bibliographical Society of America, PO Box 1537, Lenox Hill Sta, New York, NY 10021-0043 *Tel:* 212-452-2710 *Fax:* 212-452-2710 *E-mail:* bsa@bibsocamer.org *Web Site:* www.bibsocamer.org, pg 618

Furbacher, Michelle, Whitecap Books Ltd, 314 W Cordova St, Suite 210, Vancouver, BC V6B 1E8, Canada *Tel:* 604-681-6181 *Toll Free Tel:* 800-387-9776 *Toll Free Fax:* 800-260-9777 *Web Site:* www.whitecap.ca, pg 524

Furbush, Jake, The MIT Press, 55 Hayward St, Cambridge, MA 02142 *Tel:* 617-253-5255 *Toll Free Tel:* 800-207-8354 (orders) *Fax:* 617-258-6779; 617-577-1545 (orders) *Web Site:* mitpress.mit.edu, pg 167

Furman, Laura, PEN/O. Henry Prize Stories, University of Texas at Austin, One University Sta B5000, Austin, TX 78712 *Tel:* 512-572-2428 *Web Site:* www.ohenryprizestories.com, pg 733

Furman, Laura, University of Texas at Austin, Creative Writing Program, Dept of English, PAR 108, One University Sta, Mailcode B5000, Austin, TX 78712-1164 *Tel:* 512-471-5132; 512-471-4991 *Fax:* 512-471-4909 *Web Site:* www.utexas.edu/cola/depts/english/creative-writing, pg 682

Furney, Laura, University Press of Colorado, 5589 Arapahoe Ave, Suite 206-C, Boulder, CO 80303 *Tel:* 720-406-8849 *Toll Free Tel:* 800-621-2736 (orders) *Fax:* 720-406-3443 *Web Site:* www.upcolorado.com, pg 270

Furnish, Ben, BkMk Press - University of Missouri-Kansas City, 5101 Rockhill Rd, Kansas City, MO 64110-2499 *Tel:* 816-235-2558 *Fax:* 816-235-2611 *E-mail:* bkmk@umkc.edu *Web Site:* www.umkc.edu/bkmk, pg 38

Furnish, Ben, G S Sharat Chandra Prize for Short Fiction, 5101 Rockhill Rd, Kansas City, MO 64110-2499 *Tel:* 816-235-2558 *Fax:* 816-235-2611 *E-mail:* bkmk@umkc.edu *Web Site:* www.umkc.edu/bkmk, pg 696

Furnish, Ben, John Ciardi Prize for Poetry, 5101 Rockhill Rd, Kansas City, MO 64110-2499 *Tel:* 816-235-2558 *Fax:* 816-235-2611 *E-mail:* bkmk@umkc.edu *Web Site:* www.umkc.edu/bkmk, pg 697

Furr, Patty, FaithWalk Publishing, 5450 N Dixie Hwy, Lima, OH 45807 *Tel:* 419-227-1818 *Toll Free Tel:* 800-537-1030 (orders: non-bookstore mkts) *Fax:* 419-224-9184 *Web Site:* www.faithwalkpub.com, pg 92

Fusting, Donald W, Lanahan Publishers Inc, 324 Hawthorne Rd, Baltimore, MD 21210-2303 *Tel:* 410-366-2434 *Toll Free Tel:* 866-345-1949 *Fax:* 410-366-8798 *Toll Free Fax:* 888-345-7257 *E-mail:* info@lanahanpublishers.com *Web Site:* www.lanahanpublishers.com, pg 143

Futter, Deb, Grand Central Publishing, 237 Park Ave, New York, NY 10017 *Tel:* 212-364-1100 *Web Site:* www.hachettebookgroup.com, pg 106

G'Schwind, Stephanie, Nelligan Prize for Short Fiction, Colorado State Univ, Dept of Eng, Ctr for Literary Publg, 9105 Campus Delivery, Fort Collins, CO 80523-9105 *Tel:* 970-491-5449 *E-mail:* creview@colostate.edu *Web Site:* nelliganprize.colostate.edu, pg 727

Ga, Ellie, Ugly Duckling Presse, The Old American Can Factory, 232 Third St, Suite E002, Brooklyn, NY 11215 *Tel:* 347-948-5170 *E-mail:* udp_mailbox@yahoo.com; info@uglyducklingpresse.org *Web Site:* www.uglyducklingpresse.org, pg 261

Gabel, Claudia, HarperCollins Children's Books, 10 E 53 St, New York, NY 10022 *Tel:* 212-207-7000 *Web Site:* www.harpercollinschildrens.com, pg 113

Gabriel, Sophie Beaudoin, National Gallery of Canada, The Bookstore, 380 Sussex Dr, Ottawa, ON K1N 9N4, Canada *Tel:* 613-990-0962 (mail order sales) *Fax:* 613-990-1972 *E-mail:* ngcbook@gallery.ca *Web Site:* www.national.gallery.ca, pg 513

Gadd, Laurence, North River Press Publishing Corp, 27 Rosseter St, Great Barrington, MA 01230 *Tel:* 413-528-0034 *Toll Free Tel:* 800-486-2665 *Fax:* 413-528-3163 *Toll Free Fax:* 800-BOOK-FAX (266-5329) *E-mail:* info@northriverpress.com *Web Site:* www.northriverpress.com, pg 181

Gadiraju, Raju, Oxford University Press USA, 198 Madison Ave, New York, NY 10016 *Tel:* 212-726-6000 *Toll Free Tel:* 800-451-7556 (orders); 800-445-9714 (cust serv) *Fax:* 919-677-1303 *E-mail:* custserv.us@oup.com *Web Site:* www.oup.com/us, pg 189

Gadney, Alan, Film-Video Publications/Circus Source Publications, 7944 Capistrano Ave, West Hills, CA 91304 *Tel:* 818-340-0175 *Fax:* 818-340-6770 *E-mail:* circussource@aol.com, pg 94

Gadney, Nancy, Film-Video Publications/Circus Source Publications, 7944 Capistrano Ave, West Hills, CA 91304 *Tel:* 818-340-0175 *Fax:* 818-340-6770 *E-mail:* circussource@aol.com, pg 94

Gadsby, Oliver, Bloomsbury Academic, 80 Maiden Lane, Suite 704, New York, NY 10038 *Tel:* 212-953-5858 *Toll Free Tel:* 800-561-7704 *Fax:* 212-953-5944 *E-mail:* info@continuum-books.com *Web Site:* www.continuumbooks.com, pg 40

Gaffield, Chad, Social Sciences & Humanities Research Council of Canada (SSHRC), 350 Albert St, Ottawa, ON K1P 6G4, Canada *Tel:* 613-992-0691 *Fax:* 613-992-1787 *E-mail:* z-info@sshrc.ca *Web Site:* www.sshrc.ca, pg 636

Gage, Michael, Kirkbride Bible Co Inc, 1102 Deloss St, Indianapolis, IN 46203 *Tel:* 317-633-1900 *Toll Free Tel:* 800-428-4385 *Fax:* 317-633-1444 *E-mail:* sales@kirkbride.com; info@kirkbride.com *Web Site:* www.kirkbride.com, pg 140

Gagliano, Maria, Portfolio, 375 Hudson St, New York, NY 10014, pg 204

Gagnon, Debbie, Reader's Digest Trade Books, 44 S Broadway, White Plains, NY 10601 *Tel:* 914-244-7503 *Fax:* 914-244-4841 *Web Site:* www.rd.com, pg 215

Gagnon, Jean-Marc, Editions MultiMondes, 930 rue Pouliot, Quebec, QC G1V 3N9, Canada *Tel:* 418-651-3885 *Toll Free Tel:* 800-840-3029 *Fax:* 418-651-6822 *Toll Free Fax:* 888-303-5931 *E-mail:* multimondes@multim.com *Web Site:* www.multimondes.qc.ca, pg 513

Gagnon, Manon, La Fondation Emile Nelligan, 100 Sherbrooke St, Suite 202, Montreal, QC H2X 1C3, Canada *Tel:* 514-278-4657 *Fax:* 514-278-1943 *E-mail:* info@fondation-nelligan.org *Web Site:* www.fondation-nelligan.org, pg 623

Gagnon, Manon, Prix Emile-Nelligan, 100 Sherbrooke St, Suite 202, Montreal, QC H2X 1C3, Canada *Tel:* 514-278-4657 *Toll Free Tel:* 888-849-8540 *Fax:* 514-278-1943 *E-mail:* info@fondation-nelligan.org *Web Site:* www.fondation-nelligan.org, pg 736

Gagnon, Matt, Boom! Studios, 5670 Wilshire Blvd, Suite 450, Los Angeles, CA 90036 *Web Site:* www.boom-studios.com, pg 44

Gaio, Linda, Harlan Davidson Inc/Forum Press Inc, 773 Glenn Ave, Wheeling, IL 60090-6900 *Tel:* 847-541-9720 *Fax:* 847-541-9830 *E-mail:* harlandavidson@harlandavidson.com *Web Site:* www.harlandavidson.com, pg 112

Galassi, Donna, Avalon Travel Publishing, 1700 Fourth St, Berkeley, CA 94710-1711 *Tel:* 510-595-3664 *Fax:* 510-595-4228 *Web Site:* www.avalontravelbooks.com, pg 27

Galassi, Jonathan, Farrar, Straus & Giroux, LLC, 18 W 18 St, New York, NY 10011 *Tel:* 212-741-6900 *Fax:* 212-633-9385 *E-mail:* fsg.publicity@fsgbooks.com *Web Site:* us.macmillan.com/fsg.aspx, pg 93

Galassi, Jonathan, Macmillan, 175 Fifth Ave, New York, NY 10010 *Tel:* 646-307-5151 *Fax:* 212-420-9314 *E-mail:* firstname.lastname@macmillan.com *Web Site:* www.macmillan.com, pg 154

Galasso, Al, North American Bookdealers Exchange (NABE), PO Box 606, Cottage Grove, OR 97424-0026 *Tel:* 541-942-7455 *E-mail:* nabe@bookmarketingprofits.com *Web Site:* www.bookmarketingprofits.com, pg 632

Galat, Danielle, New World Library, 14 Pamaron Way, Novato, CA 94949 *Tel:* 415-884-2100 *Toll Free Tel:* 800-227-3900 (ext 52, retail orders); 800-972-6657 *Fax:* 415-884-2199 *E-mail:* escort@newworldlibrary.com *Web Site:* www.newworldlibrary.com, pg 178

Galbraith, Judy, Free Spirit Publishing Inc, 217 Fifth Ave N, Suite 200, Minneapolis, MN 55401-1260 *Tel:* 612-338-2068 *Toll Free Tel:* 800-735-7323 *Fax:* 612-337-5050 *Toll Free Fax:* 866-419-5199 *E-mail:* help4kids@freespirit.com *Web Site:* www.freespirit.com, pg 99

Galde, Phyllis, Galde Press Inc, PO Box 460, Lakeville, MN 55044 *Tel:* 952-891-5991 *Toll Free Tel:* 800-777-3454 *Fax:* 952-891-6091 *Web Site:* www.galdepress.com, pg 100

Gale, David, Simon & Schuster Children's Publishing, 1230 Avenue of the Americas, New York, NY 10020 *Tel:* 212-698-7000 *Web Site:* KIDS.SimonandSchuster.com; TEEN.SimonandSchuster.com; simonandschuster.net; simonandschuster.biz, pg 235

Gale, Kate, Red Hen Press, PO Box 40820, Pasadena, CA 91114 *Tel:* 626-356-4760 *Fax:* 626-356-9974 *Web Site:* www.redhen.org, pg 216

Gale, Meighan, Zone Books dba Urzone Inc, 1226 Prospect Ave, Brooklyn, NY 11218 *Tel:* 718-686-0048 *Toll Free Tel:* 800-405-1619 (orders & cust serv) *Fax:* 718-686-9045 *Toll Free Fax:* 800-406-9145 (orders) *E-mail:* orders@triliteral.org *Web Site:* www.zonebooks.org, pg 289

Galen, Russell, Scovil Galen Ghosh Literary Agency Inc, 276 Fifth Ave, Suite 708, New York, NY 10001 *Tel:* 212-679-8686 *Fax:* 212-679-6710 *E-mail:* info@sgglit.com *Web Site:* www.sgglit.com, pg 593

Gales, Kate, Simon & Schuster, 1230 Avenue of the Americas, New York, NY 10020 *Tel:* 212-698-7000 *Toll Free Tel:* 800-223-2348 (cust serv); 800-223-2336 (orders) *Toll Free Fax:* 800-943-9831 (orders) *Web Site:* www.simonandschuster.com, pg 234

Gall, John, Harry N Abrams Inc, 115 W 18 St, 6th fl, New York, NY 10011 *Tel:* 212-206-7715 *Toll Free Tel:* 800-345-1359 *Fax:* 212-519-1210 *E-mail:* abrams@abramsbooks.com *Web Site:* www.abramsbooks.com, pg 3

Gall, Robert, Blue Mountain Arts Inc, 2905 Wilderness Place, Boulder, CO 80301 *Tel:* 303-449-0536 *Toll Free Tel:* 800-525-0642 *Fax:* 303-417-6472 *Toll Free Fax:* 800-545-8573 *E-mail:* info@sps.com *Web Site:* www.sps.com, pg 41

Gallagher, Amy, North River Press Publishing Corp, 27 Rosseter St, Great Barrington, MA 01230 *Tel:* 413-528-0034 *Toll Free Tel:* 800-486-2665 *Fax:* 413-528-3163 *Toll Free Fax:* 800-BOOK-FAX (266-5329) *E-mail:* info@northriverpress.com *Web Site:* www.northriverpress.com, pg 181

Gallagher, Charles, The Perseus Books Group, 387 Park Ave S, 12th fl, New York, NY 10016 *Tel:* 212-340-8100 *Toll Free Tel:* 800-343-4499 (cust serv) *Fax:* 212-340-8105 *Web Site:* www.perseusbooksgroup.com, pg 199

Gallagher, Chris, Graphic Arts Association, 1210 Northbrook Dr, Suite 250, Trevose, PA 19053 *Tel:* 215-396-2300 *Fax:* 215-396-9890 *E-mail:* gaa@gaa1900.com *Web Site:* www.gaa1900.com, pg 678

Gallagher, Jim, OTTN Publishing, 16 Risler St, Stockton, NJ 08559 *Tel:* 609-397-4005 *Toll Free Tel:* 866-356-6886 *Fax:* 609-397-4007 *E-mail:* inquiries@ottnpublishing.com *Web Site:* www.ottnpublishing.com, pg 188

Gallagher, Judith, Ligonier Valley Writers Conference, PO Box B, Ligonier, PA 15658-1602 *Tel:* 724-238-3692, pg 670

Gallagher, Julia, Holiday House Inc, 425 Madison Ave, New York, NY 10017 *Tel:* 212-688-0085 *Fax:* 212-421-6134 *E-mail:* holiday@holidayhouse.com *Web Site:* www.holidayhouse.com, pg 121

Gallagher, Lisa, Sanford J Greenburger Associates Inc, 55 Fifth Ave, 15th fl, New York, NY 10003 *Tel:* 212-206-5600 *Fax:* 212-463-8718 *Web Site:* www.greenburger.com, pg 575

Gallagher, Mike, Penguin Group (USA) LLC, 375 Hudson St, New York, NY 10014 *Tel:* 212-366-2000 *Toll Free Tel:* 800-847-5515 (inside sales); 800-631-8571 (cust serv) *Fax:* 212-366-2666; 607-775-4829 (inside sales) *E-mail:* online@us.penguingroup.com *Web Site:* www.penguin.com; us.penguingroup.com, pg 197

Gallagher, Patricia, Liberty Fund Inc, 8335 Allison Pointe Trail, Suite 300, Indianapolis, IN 46250-1684 *Tel:* 317-842-0880 *Toll Free Tel:* 800-955-8335; 800-866-3520; 800-368-7897 ext 6069 (cust serv) *Fax:* 317-577-9067; 317-579-6060 (cust serv); 708-534-7803 *E-mail:* books@libertyfund.org; info@libertyfund.org *Web Site:* www.libertyfund.org, pg 148

Gallagher, Richard R, National Book Co, PO Box 8795, Portland, OR 97207-8795 *Tel:* 503-228-6345 *Fax:* 810-885-5811 *E-mail:* info@eralearning.com *Web Site:* www.eralearning.com, pg 173

Gallagher, Robert, TAN Books, PO Box 410487, Charlotte, NC 28241 *Toll Free Tel:* 800-437-5876 *Fax:* 815-226-7770 *E-mail:* customerservice@tanbooks.com *Web Site:* tanbooks.benedictpress.com; benedictpress.com, pg 249

Gallant, Barry, Penguin Group (Canada), 90 Eglinton Ave E, Suite 700, Toronto, ON M4P 2Y3, Canada *Tel:* 416-925-2249 *Fax:* 416-925-0068 *Web Site:* www.penguin.ca, pg 515

Gallegos, Anna, Museum of New Mexico Press, 725 Camino Lejo, Suite C, Santa Fe, NM 87505 *Tel:* 505-476-1155; 505-272-7777 (orders) *Toll Free Tel:* 800-249-7737 (orders) *Fax:* 505-476-1156 *Toll Free Fax:* 800-622-8667 (orders) *Web Site:* www.mnmpress.org, pg 171

Gallman, Amanda, Sandlapper Publishing Inc, 1281 Amelia St NE, Orangeburg, SC 29115-5475 *Tel:* 803-531-1658 *Toll Free Tel:* 800-849-7263 (orders only) *Fax:* 803-534-5223 *Toll Free Fax:* 800-337-9420 *E-mail:* sales@sandlapperpublishing.com *Web Site:* www.sandlapperpublishing.com, pg 226

Gallo, Irene, Tom Doherty Associates, LLC, 175 Fifth Ave, 14th fl, New York, NY 10010 *Tel:* 646-307-5151 *Toll Free Tel:* 800-455-0340 *Fax:* 212-388-0191 *E-mail:* firstname.lastname@tor.com *Web Site:* www.tor-forge.com, pg 80

Gallo, Vincent, William H Sadlier Inc, 9 Pine St, New York, NY 10005 *Tel:* 212-227-2120 *Toll Free Tel:* 800-221-5175 (cust serv) *Fax:* 212-312-6080 *Web Site:* www.sadlier.com, pg 223

Galloway, Greg, American Booksellers Association, 333 Westchester Ave, Suite S202, White Plains, NY 10604 *Tel:* 914-406-7500 *Toll Free Tel:* 800-637-0037 *Fax:* 914-410-6297 *E-mail:* info@bookweb.org *Web Site:* www.bookweb.org, pg 612

Gallup, Theresa, Amber Quill Press LLC, PO Box 265, Indian Hills, CO 80454 *E-mail:* business@amberquill.com *Web Site:* www.amberquill.com; www.amberheat.com (imprint); www.amberallure.com (imprint), pg 10

Galusha, Dale, Pacific Press Publishing Association, 1350 N Kings Rd, Nampa, ID 83687-3193 *Tel:* 208-465-2500 *Toll Free Tel:* 800-447-7377 *Fax:* 208-465-2531 *Web Site:* www.pacificpress.com, pg 190

Galvin, Mary Ellen, American Society of Mechanical Engineers (ASME), 3 Park Ave, New York, NY 10016-5990 *Tel:* 212-591-7000 *Toll Free Tel:* 800-843-2763 (cust serv-US, CN & Mexico) *Fax:* 212-591-7674; 973-882-8113 (cust serv); 973-882-1717 (orders & inquiries) *E-mail:* infocentral@asme.org *Web Site:* www.asme.org, pg 17

Galvin, Tom, Triumph Books, 814 N Franklin St, Chicago, IL 60610 *Toll Free Tel:* 800-888-4741 (orders only) *Fax:* 312-663-3557 *Web Site:* www.triumphbooks.com, pg 259

Galyan, Sheyna, Yotzeret Publishing, PO Box 18662, St Paul, MN 55118-0662 *Tel:* 651-470-3853 *Fax:* 651-224-7447 *E-mail:* info@yotzeretpublishing.com; orders@yotzeretpublishing.com *Web Site:* yotzeretpublishing.com, pg 288

Gamboa, Sharon, Penguin Group (USA) LLC Sales, 375 Hudson St, New York, NY 10014 *Tel:* 212-366-2000 *E-mail:* online@penguinputnam.com *Web Site:* us.penguingroup.com, pg 197

Gammonley, Kevin, NPTA Alliance, 401 N Michigan Ave, Suite 2200, Chicago, IL 60611 *Tel:* 312-321-4092 *Toll Free Tel:* 800-355-NPTA (355-6782) *Fax:* 312-673-6736 *E-mail:* npta@gonpta.com *Web Site:* www.gonpta.com, pg 632

Gammons, Keith, Smyth & Helwys Publishing Inc, 6316 Peake Rd, Macon, GA 31210-3960 *Tel:* 478-757-0564 *Toll Free Tel:* 800-747-3016 (orders only); 800-568-1248 (orders only) *Fax:* 478-757-1305 *E-mail:* information@helwys.com *Web Site:* www.helwys.com, pg 238

Gandiglio, Carla G, Hadronic Press Inc, 35246 US 19 N, No 115, Palm Harbor, FL 34684 *Tel:* 727-934-9593 *Fax:* 727-934-9275 *E-mail:* hadronic@tampabay.rr.com *Web Site:* www.hadronicpress.com, pg 110

Ganesan, Dev, Aptara Inc, 3110 Fairview Park Dr, Suite 900, Falls Church, VA 22042 *Tel:* 703-352-0001 *E-mail:* info@aptaracorp.com *Web Site:* www.aptaracorp.com, pg 540

Gann, Kirby, Sarabande Books Inc, 2234 Dundee Rd, Suite 200, Louisville, KY 40205 *Tel:* 502-458-4028 *Fax:* 502-458-4065 *E-mail:* info@sarabandebooks.org *Web Site:* www.sarabandebooks.org, pg 226

Gantz, Gabrielle, Picador, 175 Fifth Ave, 19th fl, New York, NY 10010 *Tel:* 646-307-5151 *Fax:* 212-253-9627 *E-mail:* firstname.lastname@picadorusa.com *Web Site:* www.picadorusa.com, pg 201

Garabedian, Peter, Macmillan, 175 Fifth Ave, New York, NY 10010 *Tel:* 646-307-5151 *Fax:* 212-420-9314 *E-mail:* firstname.lastname@macmillan.com *Web Site:* www.macmillan.com, pg 154

Garcia, Elisa, Harry N Abrams Inc, 115 W 18 St, 6th fl, New York, NY 10011 *Tel:* 212-206-7715 *Toll Free Tel:* 800-345-1359 *Fax:* 212-519-1210 *E-mail:* abrams@abramsbooks.com *Web Site:* www.abramsbooks.com, pg 3

Garcia, Patty, Tom Doherty Associates, LLC, 175 Fifth Ave, 14th fl, New York, NY 10010 *Tel:* 646-307-5151 *Toll Free Tel:* 800-455-0340 *Fax:* 212-388-0191 *E-mail:* firstname.lastname@tor.com *Web Site:* www.tor-forge.com, pg 80

Garcia, Ray, Celebra, 375 Hudson St, New York, NY 10014 *Tel:* 212-366-2000 *Fax:* 212-366-2889, pg 55

Gardiner, Eileen, John Nicholas Brown Prize, 104 Mount Auburn St, 5th fl, Cambridge, MA 02138 *Tel:* 617-491-1622 *Fax:* 617-492-3303 *E-mail:* speculum@medievalacademy.org *Web Site:* www.medievalacademy.org, pg 693

Gardiner, Eileen, Elliott Prize, 104 Mount Auburn St, 5th fl, Cambridge, MA 02138 *Tel:* 617-491-1622 *Fax:* 617-492-3303 *E-mail:* speculum@medievalacademy.org *Web Site:* www.medievalacademy.org, pg 702

Gardiner, Eileen, Haskins Medal Award, 104 Mount Auburn St, 5th fl, Cambridge, MA 02138 *Tel:* 617-491-1622 *Fax:* 617-492-3303 *E-mail:* speculum@medievalacademy.org *Web Site:* www.medievalacademy.org, pg 709

Gardiner, Eileen, Italica Press, 595 Main St, Suite 605, New York, NY 10044 *Tel:* 917-371-0563 *Fax:* 212-838-7812 *E-mail:* info@italicapress.com *Web Site:* www.italicapress.com, pg 134

Gardner, Catherine, Advertising Research Foundation (ARF), 432 Park Ave S, 6th fl, New York, NY 10016-8013 *Tel:* 212-751-5656 *Fax:* 212-319-5265 *E-mail:* info@thearf.org; jar@thearf.org (edit) *Web Site:* www.thearf.org; www.journalofadvertisingresearch.com, pg 611

Gardner, Jason, New World Library, 14 Pamaron Way, Novato, CA 94949 *Tel:* 415-884-2100 *Toll Free Tel:* 800-227-3900 (ext 52, retail orders); 800-972-6657 *Fax:* 415-884-2199 *E-mail:* escort@newworldlibrary.com *Web Site:* www.newworldlibrary.com, pg 178

Gardner, Joe, Child's Play®, 250 Minot Ave, Auburn, ME 04210 *Toll Free Tel:* 800-472-0099; 800-639-6404 *Toll Free Fax:* 800-854-6989 *E-mail:* chpmaine@aol.com; cplay@earthlink.net *Web Site:* www.childs-play.com/usa, pg 60

Gardner, Rachelle, Books & Such, 52 Mission Circle, Suite 122, PMB 170, Santa Rosa, CA 95409-5370 *Tel:* 707-538-4184 *Web Site:* booksandsuch.com, pg 563

Gardner, Thomas D, Reader's Digest General Books, Reader's Digest Rd, Pleasantville, NY 10570-7000 *Tel:* 914-238-1000 *Toll Free Tel:* 800-304-2807 (cust serv) *Fax:* 914-244-7436, pg 215

Garfield, Valerie, Simon & Schuster Children's Publishing, 1230 Avenue of the Americas, New York, NY 10020 *Tel:* 212-698-7000 *Web Site:* KIDS.SimonandSchuster.com; TEEN.SimonandSchuster.com; simonandschuster.net; simonandschuster.biz, pg 235

Garland, Ashley, HarperCollins General Books Group, 10 E 53 St, New York, NY 10022 *Tel:* 212-207-7000 *Fax:* 212-207-7633 *Web Site:* www.harpercollins.com, pg 113

Garland, Gary, Magazines Canada, 425 Adelaide St W, Suite 700, Toronto, ON M5V 3C1, Canada *Tel:* 416-504-0274 *Fax:* 416-504-0437 *E-mail:* info@magazinescanada.ca *Web Site:* www.magazinescanada.ca, pg 627

Garlick, Philip, OneSource, 300 Baker Ave, Concord, MA 01742 *Tel:* 978-318-4300 *Toll Free Tel:* 866-354-6936 *Fax:* 978-318-4690 *E-mail:* sales@onesource.com *Web Site:* www.onesource.com, pg 185

Garlid, Peter, Glitterati Inc, 322 W 57 St, No 19T, New York, NY 10019 *Tel:* 212-362-9119 *Fax:* 646-607-4433 *E-mail:* info@glitteratiincorporated.com *Web Site:* glitteratiincorporated.com, pg 103

Garner, Marion, Knopf Random Canada, One Toronto St, Suite 300, Toronto, ON M5C 2V6, Canada *Tel:* 416-364-4449 *Toll Free Tel:* 888-523-9292 *Fax:* 416-364-6863 *Web Site:* www.randomhouse.ca, pg 510

Garneski, Sally, American College of Surgeons, 633 N Saint Clair St, Chicago, IL 60611-3211 *Tel:* 312-202-5000 *Fax:* 312-202-5001 *E-mail:* postmaster@facs.org *Web Site:* www.facs.org, pg 12

Garnett, Mary, Binding Industries Association (BIA), 200 Deer Run Rd, Sewickley, PA 15143 *Tel:* 412-741-6860 *Toll Free Tel:* 800-910-4283 *Fax:* 412-741-2311 *E-mail:* printing@printing.org *Web Site:* www.printing.org, pg 618

Garnett, Mary, Web Offset Association (WOA), 200 Deer Run Rd, Sewickley, PA 15143 *Tel:* 412-741-6860 *Toll Free Tel:* 800-910-4283 *Fax:* 412-741-2311 *E-mail:* printing@printing.org *Web Site:* www.printing.org/weboffsetassociation, pg 638

Garonzik, Joe, Clearfield Co Inc, 3600 Clipper Mill Rd, Suite 260, Baltimore, MD 21211 *Tel:* 410-837-8271 *Toll Free Tel:* 800-296-6687 (orders & cust serv) *Fax:* 410-752-8492 *E-mail:* sales@genealogical.com *Web Site:* www.genealogical.com, pg 63

Garonzik, Joe, Genealogical Publishing Co, 3600 Clipper Mill Rd, Suite 260, Baltimore, MD 21211 *Tel:* 410-837-8271 *Toll Free Tel:* 800-296-6687 *Fax:* 410-752-8492 *Web Site:* www.genealogical.com, pg 102

Garretson, Jessie, Random House Speakers Bureau, 1745 Broadway, Mail Drop 13-1, New York, NY 10019 *Tel:* 212-572-2013 *E-mail:* rhspeakers@randomhouse.com *Web Site:* www.rhspeakers.com, pg 605

Garretson, Robin, Success Advertising & Publishing, 3419 Dunham Rd, Warsaw, NY 14569 *Tel:* 585-786-5663, pg 246

Garrett, Edward, Macmillan, 175 Fifth Ave, New York, NY 10010 *Tel:* 646-307-5151 *Fax:* 212-420-9314 *E-mail:* firstname.lastname@macmillan.com *Web Site:* www.macmillan.com, pg 154

Garrett, Jackie, Academic Press, 525 "B" St, Suite 1800, San Diego, CA 92101 *Tel:* 619-231-6616 *Toll Free Tel:* 800-321-5068 (cust serv) *Fax:* 619-699-6715 *E-mail:* firstinitial.lastname@elsevier.com *Web Site:* www.elsevier.com, pg 3

Garrett, Michael, Creative Inspirations Inc, 6203 Old Springville Rd, Pinson, AL 35126 *Web Site:* www.manuscriptcritique.com, pg 544

Garrett, Michael, How to be Published Workshops, PO Box 100031, Birmingham, AL 35210 *Web Site:* www.writing2sell.com, pg 669

Garrick, Kate, DeFiore and Company, LLC, 47 E 19 St, 3rd fl, New York, NY 10003 *Tel:* 212-925-7744 *Fax:* 212-925-9803 *E-mail:* submissions@defioreandco.com; info@defioreandco.com *Web Site:* www.defioreandco.com, pg 568

Garrido, Dr Marta, Merit Publishing International Inc, 6839 Villas Dr S, Boca Raton, FL 33433 *Tel:* 561-350-0329; 561-697-1116 (orders) *E-mail:* merituk@aol.com; meritpi@aol.com *Web Site:* www.meritpublishing.com, pg 164

Garrison, Deborah, Alfred A Knopf/Everyman's Library, c/o Random House Inc, 1745 Broadway, New York, NY 10019 *Tel:* 212-751-2600 *Toll Free Tel:* 800-638-6460 *Fax:* 212-572-2593 *Web Site:* www.knopfdoubleday.com, pg 141

Garrison, Deborah, Pantheon Books/Schocken Books, c/o Random House Inc, 1745 Broadway, New York, NY 10019 *Tel:* 212-751-2600 *Toll Free Tel:* 800-638-6460 *Fax:* 212-572-6030, pg 192

Garrison, Jessica, Dial Books for Young Readers, 345 Hudson St, New York, NY 10014 *Tel:* 212-366-2000 *Fax:* 212-414-3396 *E-mail:* online@penguinputnam.com *Web Site:* www.penguinputnam.com; us.penguingroup.com, pg 79

Garstein, Stacey, Markus Wiener Publishers Inc, 231 Nassau St, Princeton, NJ 08542 *Tel:* 609-921-1141 *Fax:* 609-921-1140 *E-mail:* publisher@markuswiener.com *Web Site:* www.markuswiener.com, pg 280

Garton, Keith, Red Chair Press, PO Box 333, South Egremont, MA 01258-0333 *Toll Free Tel:* 888-327-2141 (ext 110) *Toll Free Fax:* 888-533-4037 *E-mail:* info@redchairpress.com *Web Site:* www.redchairpress.com, pg 216

Garvey, Elaine, Templegate Publishers, 302 E Adams St, Springfield, IL 62701 *Tel:* 217-522-3353 (edit & sales); 217-522-3354 (billing) *Toll Free Tel:* 800-367-4844 (orders only) *Fax:* 217-522-3362 *E-mail:* wisdom@templegate.com; orders@templegate.com (sales) *Web Site:* www.templegate.com, pg 252

Garvey, Thomas M, Templegate Publishers, 302 E Adams St, Springfield, IL 62701 *Tel:* 217-522-3353 (edit & sales); 217-522-3354 (billing) *Toll Free Tel:* 800-367-4844 (orders only) *Fax:* 217-522-3362 *E-mail:* wisdom@templegate.com; orders@templegate.com (sales) *Web Site:* www.templegate.com, pg 252

Garych, Leslie, Scholastic Trade Division, 557 Broadway, New York, NY 10012 *Tel:* 212-343-6100; 212-343-4685 (export sales) *Fax:* 212-343-4714 (export sales) *Web Site:* www.scholastic.com, pg 229

Garza, Jennifer, Simon & Schuster, 1230 Avenue of the Americas, New York, NY 10020 *Tel:* 212-698-7000 *Toll Free Tel:* 800-223-2348 (cust serv); 800-223-2336 (orders) *Toll Free Fax:* 800-943-9831 (orders) *Web Site:* www.simonandschuster.com, pg 234

Gates, Henry Louis Jr, The Anisfield-Wolf Book Awards, 1422 Euclid Ave, Suite 1300, Cleveland, OH 44115 *Tel:* 216-861-3810 *Fax:* 216-861-1729 *E-mail:* awinfo@clevefdn.org *Web Site:* www.anisfield-wolf.org; www.clevelandfoundation.org, pg 687

Gates, Jennifer, Zachary Shuster Harmsworth Agency, 1776 Broadway, Suite 1405, New York, NY 10019 *Tel:* 212-765-6900 *Fax:* 212-765-6490 *Web Site:* www.zshliterary.com, pg 600

Gates, Rob, The Gaylactic Spectrum Awards, PO Box 73602, Washington, DC 20056-3602 *Tel:* 202-483-6369 *Web Site:* www.spectrumawards.org, pg 706

Gates, Tracy, Viking Children's Books, 345 Hudson St, New York, NY 10014 *Tel:* 212-366-2000 *E-mail:* online@penguinputnam.com *Web Site:* www.penguinputnam.com; us.penguingroup.com, pg 275

Gatt, Michelle, Slack Incorporated, 6900 Grove Rd, Thorofare, NJ 08086-9447 *Tel:* 856-848-1000 *Toll Free Tel:* 800-257-8290 *Fax:* 856-848-6091 *E-mail:* sales@slackinc.com *Web Site:* www.slackbooks.com, pg 237

Gatta, Gina, Damron Co, PO Box 422458, San Francisco, CA 94142-2458 *Tel:* 415-255-0404 *Toll Free Tel:* 800-462-6654 *Fax:* 415-703-9049 *E-mail:* info@damron.com *Web Site:* www.damron.com, pg 74

Gatten, Dave, Pacific Press Publishing Association, 1350 N Kings Rd, Nampa, ID 83687-3193 *Tel:* 208-465-2500 *Toll Free Tel:* 800-447-7377 *Fax:* 208-465-2531 *Web Site:* www.pacificpress.com, pg 190

Gauthier, Daniel J, Gauthier Publications Inc, PO Box 806241, St Clair Shores, MI 48080 *Tel:* 313-458-7141 *Fax:* 586-279-1515 *E-mail:* info@gauthierpublications.com *Web Site:* www.gauthierpublications.com, pg 102

Gauthier, Elizabeth, Gauthier Publications Inc, PO Box 806241, St Clair Shores, MI 48080 *Tel:* 313-458-7141 *Fax:* 586-279-1515 *E-mail:* info@gauthierpublications.com *Web Site:* www.gauthierpublications.com, pg 102

Gauthier, Mark, H W Wilson, 10 Estes St, Ipswich, MA 01938 *Tel:* 978-356-6500 *Toll Free Tel:* 800-653-2726 (US & CN) *Fax:* 978-356-6565 *E-mail:* information@ebscohost.com *Web Site:* www.ebscohost.com, pg 282

Gauvin, Rod, ProQuest LLC, 789 E Eisenhower Pkwy, Ann Arbor, MI 48108-3218 *Tel:* 734-761-4700 *Toll Free Tel:* 800-521-0600 *Fax:* 734-975-6486 *Toll Free Fax:* 800-864-0019 *E-mail:* info@proquest.com *Web Site:* www.proquest.com, pg 208

Gavin, Tara, Harlequin Enterprises Ltd, 233 Broadway, Suite 1001, New York, NY 10279 *Tel:* 212-553-4200 *Fax:* 212-227-8969 *E-mail:* CustomerService@harlequin.com *Web Site:* www.harlequin.com, pg 112

Gay, Elizabeth, Simon & Schuster, 1230 Avenue of the Americas, New York, NY 10020 *Tel:* 212-698-7000 *Toll Free Tel:* 800-223-2348 (cust serv); 800-223-2336 (orders) *Toll Free Fax:* 800-943-9831 (orders) *Web Site:* www.simonandschuster.com, pg 234

Gayles, Jia, The Knight Agency Inc, 570 East Ave, Madison, GA 30650 *E-mail:* submissions@knightagency.net *Web Site:* www.knightagency.net, pg 580

Gaynin, Gail, Morgan Gaynin Inc, 194 Third Ave, New York, NY 10003 *Tel:* 212-475-0440 *Fax:* 212-353-8538 *E-mail:* info@morgangaynin.com *Web Site:* www.morgangaynin.com, pg 602

Gayot, Alain, Gault Millau Inc/Gayot Publications, 4311 Wilshire Blvd, Suite 405, Los Angeles, CA 90010 *Tel:* 323-965-3529 *Fax:* 323-936-2883 *E-mail:* info@gayot.com *Web Site:* www.gayot.com, pg 101

Gayot, Andre, Gault Millau Inc/Gayot Publications, 4311 Wilshire Blvd, Suite 405, Los Angeles, CA 90010 *Tel:* 323-965-3529 *Fax:* 323-936-2883 *E-mail:* info@gayot.com *Web Site:* www.gayot.com, pg 101

Gazlay, Laura, The Library of America, 14 E 60 St, New York, NY 10022-1006 *Tel:* 212-308-3360 *Fax:* 212-750-8352 *E-mail:* info@loa.org *Web Site:* www.loa.org, pg 148

Geale, Nancy L, Thomas Geale Publications Inc, PO Box 370540, Montara, CA 94037-0540 *Tel:* 650-728-5219 *Toll Free Tel:* 800-554-5457 *Fax:* 650-728-0918 *E-mail:* justthink@comcast.net, pg 254

Geary, Judy, Ingalls Publishing Group Inc (IPG), PO Box 2500, Banner Elk, NC 28604 *Tel:* 828-297-6884 *Fax:* 828-297-6880 *E-mail:* sales@ingallspublishinggroup.com *Web Site:* www.ingallspublishinggroup.com, pg 130

Geck, Steve, Sourcebooks Inc, 1935 Brookdale Rd, Suite 139, Naperville, IL 60563 *Tel:* 630-961-3900 *Toll Free Tel:* 800-432-7444 *Fax:* 630-961-2168 *E-mail:* info@sourcebooks.com; customersupport@sourcebooks.com *Web Site:* www.sourcebooks.com, pg 240

Gedymin, Diane, Turner Publishing Co, 200 Fourth Ave N, Suite 950, Nashville, TN 37219 *Tel:* 615-255-BOOK (255-2665) *Fax:* 615-255-5081 *E-mail:* marketing@turnerpublishing.com; submissions@turnerpublishing.com *Web Site:* www.turnerpublishing.com, pg 260

Gee, Connie, BePuzzled, 2030 Harrison St, San Francisco, CA 94110 *Tel:* 415-503-1600 *Toll Free Tel:* 800-347-4818 *Fax:* 415-503-0085 *E-mail:* info@ugames.com *Web Site:* www.ugames.com, pg 35

Geerling, Marjetta, Eric Hoffer Award for Short Prose, PO Box 11, Titusville, NJ 08560 *Fax:* 609-964-1718 *E-mail:* info@hofferaward.com *Web Site:* www.hofferaward.com, pg 710

Geers, George, New Hampshire Literary Awards, 2500 N River Rd, Manchester, NH 03106 *Tel:* 603-314-7980 *Fax:* 603-314-7981 *E-mail:* info@nhwritersproject.org *Web Site:* www.nhwritersproject.org, pg 728

Geers, George, New Hampshire Writers' Project, 2500 N River Rd, Manchester, NH 03106 *Tel:* 603-314-7980 *Fax:* 603-314-7981 *E-mail:* info@nhwritersproject.org *Web Site:* www.nhwritersproject.org, pg 631

Gehani, Indu, Silicon Press, 25 Beverly Rd, Summit, NJ 07901 *Tel:* 908-273-8919 *Fax:* 908-273-6149 *E-mail:* info@silicon-press.com *Web Site:* www.silicon-press.com, pg 234

Gehringer, Richard, Columbia University Press, 61 W 62 St, New York, NY 10023 *Tel:* 212-459-0600 *Toll Free Tel:* 800-944-8648 *Fax:* 212-459-3678 *E-mail:* cup_book@columbia.edu (orders & cust serv) *Web Site:* cup.columbia.edu, pg 65

Geiger, Ellen, Frances Goldin Literary Agency, Inc, 57 E 11 St, Suite 5-B, New York, NY 10003 *Tel:* 212-777-0047 *Fax:* 212-228-1660 *E-mail:* agency@goldinlit.com *Web Site:* www.goldinlit.com, pg 575

Geiger, Rachel, Chronicle Books LLC, 680 Second St, San Francisco, CA 94107 *Tel:* 415-537-4200 *Toll Free Tel:* 800-759-0190 (cust serv) *Fax:* 415-537-4460 *Toll Free Fax:* 800-858-7787 (orders); 800-286-9471 (cust serv) *E-mail:* frontdesk@chroniclebooks.com *Web Site:* www.chroniclebooks.com, pg 61

Geist, Ken, Scholastic Trade Division, 557 Broadway, New York, NY 10012 *Tel:* 212-343-6100; 212-343-4685 (export sales) *Fax:* 212-343-4714 (export sales) *Web Site:* www.scholastic.com, pg 228

Gelardi, Salvatore, Academic Press, 525 "B" St, Suite 1800, San Diego, CA 92101 *Tel:* 619-231-6616 *Toll Free Tel:* 800-321-5068 (cust serv) *Fax:* 619-699-6715 *E-mail:* firstinitial.lastname@elsevier.com *Web Site:* www.elsevier.com, pg 3

Gelb, Eric, Small Business Advisors Inc, 11 Franklin Ave, Hewlett, NY 11557 *Tel:* 516-374-1387; 914-260-1027 *Fax:* 516-374-1175; 720-294-3202 *E-mail:* info@smallbusinessadvice.com *Web Site:* www.smallbusinessadvice.com, pg 237

Gelb, Joe, Small Business Advisors Inc, 11 Franklin Ave, Hewlett, NY 11557 *Tel:* 516-374-1387; 914-260-1027 *Fax:* 516-374-1175; 720-294-3202 *E-mail:* info@smallbusinessadvice.com *Web Site:* www.smallbusinessadvice.com, pg 237

Gelbach, Mary, F A Davis Co, 1915 Arch St, Philadelphia, PA 19103 *Tel:* 215-568-2270 *Toll Free Tel:* 800-523-4049 *Fax:* 215-568-5065 *E-mail:* info@fadavis.com *Web Site:* www.fadavis.com, pg 76

Gelbman, Leslie, Berkley Books, 375 Hudson St, New York, NY 10014 *Tel:* 212-366-2000 *Fax:* 212-366-2666 *E-mail:* online@penguinputnam.com *Web Site:* www.penguinputnam.com; us.penguingroup.com, pg 35

Gelbman, Leslie, Berkley Publishing Group, 375 Hudson St, New York, NY 10014 *Tel:* 212-366-2000 *Fax:* 212-366-2385 *E-mail:* online@penguinputnam.com *Web Site:* us.penguingroup.com, pg 36

Gelbman, Leslie, Penguin Group (USA) LLC, 375 Hudson St, New York, NY 10014 *Tel:* 212-366-2000 *Toll Free Tel:* 800-847-5515 (inside sales); 800-631-8571 (cust serv) *Fax:* 212-366-2666; 607-775-4829 (inside sales) *E-mail:* online@us.penguingroup.com *Web Site:* www.penguin.com; us.penguingroup.com, pg 197

Gelbman, Leslie, GP Putnam's Sons (Hardcover), 375 Hudson St, New York, NY 10014 *Tel:* 212-366-2000 *E-mail:* online@penguinputnam.com *Web Site:* us.penguingroup.com, pg 210

Gelfand, Dr Sergei, American Mathematical Society, 201 Charles St, Providence, RI 02904-2294 *Tel:* 401-455-4000 *Toll Free Tel:* 800-321-4267 *Fax:* 401-331-3842; 401-455-4046 (cust serv) *E-mail:* ams@ams.org; cust-serv@ams.org *Web Site:* www.ams.org, pg 14

Gelfman, Jane, Gelfman/Schneider/ICM, 850 Seventh Ave, Suite 903, New York, NY 10019 *Tel:* 212-245-1993 *Fax:* 212-245-8678 *E-mail:* mail@gelfmanschneider.com *Web Site:* gelfmanschneider.com, pg 574

Gelineau, Christine, Binghamton University Creative Writing Program, c/o Dept of English, PO Box 6000, Binghamton, NY 13902-6000 *Tel:* 607-777-2168 *Fax:* 607-777-2408 *E-mail:* cwpro@binghamton.edu *Web Site:* english.binghamton.edu/cwpro, pg 677

Geller, Sandra R, Practising Law Institute, 810 Seventh Ave, New York, NY 10019 *Tel:* 212-824-5700 *Toll Free Tel:* 800-260-4PLI (260-4754 cust serv) *Fax:* 212-265-4742 (intl) *Toll Free Fax:* 800-321-0093 (local) *E-mail:* info@pli.edu *Web Site:* www.pli.edu, pg 205

Gelles-Cole, Sandi, Gelles-Cole Literary Enterprises, 135 John Joy Rd, Woodstock, NY 12498-0341 *Tel:* 845-679-2452 *Web Site:* www.literaryenterprises.com, pg 547

Gelsomino, Tara, F+W Media Inc, 10151 Carver Rd, Suite 200, Blue Ash, OH 45242 *Tel:* 513-531-2690 *Toll Free Tel:* 800-289-0963 (trade accts); 800-258-0929 (orders) *E-mail:* contact_us@fwmedia.com *Web Site:* www.fwmedia.com, pg 92

Geltzeiler, Michael S, Reader's Digest General Books, Reader's Digest Rd, Pleasantville, NY 10570-7000 *Tel:* 914-238-1000 *Toll Free Tel:* 800-304-2807 (cust serv) *Fax:* 914-244-7436, pg 215

Gelwicks, Maureen, Educational Book & Media Association (EBMA), 37 Main St, Suite 203, Warrenton, VA 20186 *Tel:* 540-318-7770 *Fax:* 202-962-3939 *E-mail:* info@edupaperback.org *Web Site:* www.edupaperback.org, pg 623

Gelwicks, Maureen, Jeremiah Ludington Award, 37 Main St, Suite 203, Warrenton, VA 20186 *Tel:* 540-318-7770 *Fax:* 202-962-3939 *E-mail:* info@edupaperback.org *Web Site:* www.edupaperback.org, pg 719

Gemignani, Nathan, Cornell University Press, Sage House, 512 E State St, Ithaca, NY 14850 *Tel:* 607-277-2338 *Fax:* 607-277-2374 *E-mail:* cupressinfo@cornell.edu; cupress-sales@cornell.edu *Web Site:* www.cornellpress.cornell.edu, pg 67

Gemma, Sierra Skye, PRISM international Literary Non-Fiction Contest, University of British Columbia, Buch E462, 1866 Main Mall, Vancouver, BC V6T 1Z1, Canada *Tel:* 778-822-2514 *Fax:* 778-822-3616 *E-mail:* prismwritingcontest@gmail.com *Web Site:* www.prismmagazine.ca, pg 735

Gemma, Sierra Skye, PRISM international Poetry Contest, University of British Columbia, Buch E462, 1866 Main Mall, Vancouver, BC V6T 1Z1, Canada *Tel:* 778-822-2514 *Fax:* 778-822-3616 *E-mail:* prismwritingcontest@gmail.com *Web Site:* www.prismmagazine.ca, pg 736

Gemma, Sierra Skye, PRISM international Short Fiction Contest, University of British Columbia, Buch E462, 1866 Main Mall, Vancouver, BC V6T 1Z1, Canada *Tel:* 778-822-2514 *Fax:* 778-822-3616 *E-mail:* prismwritingcontest@gmail.com *Web Site:* www.prismmagazine.ca, pg 736

Genna, Vicki, Hill & Wang, 18 W 18 St, New York, NY 10011 *Tel:* 212-741-6900 *Fax:* 212-633-9385 *E-mail:* fsg.publicity@fsgbooks.com; fsg.editorial@fsgbooks.com *Web Site:* us.macmillan.com/hillandwang.aspx, pg 119

Genna, Victoria, Farrar, Straus & Giroux, LLC, 18 W 18 St, New York, NY 10011 *Tel:* 212-741-6900 *Fax:* 212-633-9385 *E-mail:* fsg.publicity@fsgbooks.com *Web Site:* us.macmillan.com/fsg.aspx, pg 93

Gensler, Elana, Association of Jewish Libraries (AJL) Inc, PO Box 1118, Teaneck, NJ 07666 *Tel:* 201-371-3255 *E-mail:* info@jewishlibraries.org *Web Site:* www.jewishlibraries.org, pg 616

Gentel, Gary, Houghton Mifflin Harcourt, 222 Berkeley St, Boston, MA 02116-3764 *Tel:* 617-351-5000 *Toll Free Tel:* 800-225-5425 (Pre-K-8); 800-462-6595 (6–12; Advanced & Electives); 800-289-4490 (Specialized Curriculum: Great Source, Rigby, Saxon, Steck-Vaughn; Homeschool; Adult Ed); 800-323-9540 (Assessment: Riverside Publishing); 888-391-3245 (SkillsTutor); 888-242-6747 option 2 (Destination Series; Classroom Connect; Earobics; Edmark; Learning Village; Riverdeep); 800-225-3362 (Houghton Mifflin Harcourt Trade & Reference Publishers); 800-225-5800 (Heinemann) *Fax:* 617-351-1125 *Web Site:* www.hmhco.com, pg 123

Gentel, Gary, Houghton Mifflin Harcourt Trade & Reference Division, 222 Berkeley St, Boston, MA 02116-3764 *Tel:* 617-351-5000 *Toll Free Tel:* 800-225-3362 *Web Site:* www.houghtonmifflinbooks.com, pg 124

Gentile, Deanna, Printing Industries of America, 200 Deer Run Rd, Sewickley, PA 15143-2600 *Tel:* 412-741-6860; 412-259-1770 *E-mail:* membercentral@printing.org (orders) *Web Site:* www.printing.org, pg 207

Gentillo, Eileen, Simon & Schuster Sales & Marketing, 1230 Avenue of the Americas, New York, NY 10020 *Tel:* 212-698-7000, pg 236

Gentry, Robert B, E M Koeppel Short Fiction Award, PO Box 140310, Gainesville, FL 32614 *Tel:* 352-338-7778 *E-mail:* contact@writecorner.com *Web Site:* www.writecorner.com, pg 715

George, Bob, FurnitureCore, 1385 Peachtree St NE, Suite 310, Atlanta, GA 30309 *Tel:* 404-961-3764 *Fax:* 404-961-3749 *E-mail:* info@furniturecore.com *Web Site:* www.furniturecore.com, pg 100

George, Keyleigh, Crown Publishing Group, c/o Random House Inc, 1745 Broadway, New York, NY 10019 *Tel:* 212-782-9000 *Toll Free Tel:* 888-264-1745 *Fax:* 212-940-7408 *Web Site:* www.randomhouse.com/crown, pg 72

George, Lee Anne, Association of Research Libraries, 21 Dupont Circle NW, Suite 800, Washington, DC 20036 *Tel:* 202-296-2296 *Fax:* 202-872-0884 *E-mail:* arlhq@arl.org *Web Site:* www.arl.org, pg 25

George, Patricia, Association of School Business Officials International, 11401 N Shore Dr, Reston, VA 20190-4200 *Tel:* 703-478-0405 *Toll Free Tel:* 866-682-2729 *Fax:* 703-478-0205 *E-mail:* asboreq@asbointl.org; asbosba@asbointl.org *Web Site:* www.asbointl.org, pg 25

Geraghty, Joe, Close Up Publishing, 1330 Braddock Place, Suite 400, Alexandria, VA 22314 *Tel:* 703-706-3300 *Toll Free Tel:* 800-CLOSE-UP (256-7387) *Fax:* 703-706-3564 *E-mail:* info@closeup.org *Web Site:* www.closeup.org, pg 63

Gerardi, Jan, Random House Children's Books, 1745 Broadway, New York, NY 10019 *Tel:* 212-782-9000 *Toll Free Tel:* 800-200-3552 *Fax:* 212-782-9452 *Web Site:* randomhousekids.com, pg 213

Gerardo, Donna, Tilbury House Publishers, 103 Brunswick Ave, Gardiner, ME 04345 *Tel:* 207-582-1899 *Toll Free Tel:* 800-582-1899 (orders) *Fax:* 207-582-8227 *E-mail:* tilbury@tilburyhouse.com *Web Site:* www.tilburyhouse.com, pg 255

Gerbasi, Catherine, Portage & Main Press, 318 McDermot, Suite 100, Winnipeg, MB R3A 0A2, Canada *Tel:* 204-987-3500 *Toll Free Tel:* 800-667-9673 *Fax:* 204-947-0080 *Toll Free Fax:* 866-734-8477 *E-mail:* books@portageandmainpress.com *Web Site:* www.portageandmainpress.com, pg 516

Gerecke, Jeff, Association of Authors' Representatives Inc, 676-A Ninth Ave, Suite 312, New York, NY 10036 *Tel:* 212-840-5777 *Web Site:* www.aaronline.org, pg 616

Gericke, Carla, New Hampshire Literary Awards, 2500 N River Rd, Manchester, NH 03106 *Tel:* 603-314-7980 *Fax:* 603-314-7981 *E-mail:* info@nhwritersproject.org *Web Site:* www.nhwritersproject.org, pg 728

Gericke, Carla, New Hampshire Writers' Project, 2500 N River Rd, Manchester, NH 03106 *Tel:* 603-314-7980 *Fax:* 603-314-7981 *E-mail:* info@nhwritersproject.org *Web Site:* www.nhwritersproject.org, pg 631

Gerli, Charles, Insight Editions, 10 Paul Dr, San Rafael, CA 94903 *Tel:* 415-526-1370 *Toll Free Tel:* 800-809-3792 *E-mail:* info@insighteditions.com *Web Site:* www.insighteditions.com, pg 131

Gerli, Jake, Insight Editions, 10 Paul Dr, San Rafael, CA 94903 *Tel:* 415-526-1370 *Toll Free Tel:* 800-809-3792 *E-mail:* info@insighteditions.com *Web Site:* www.insighteditions.com, pg 131

German, Donna, Sylvan Dell Publishing, 612 Johnnie Dodds Blvd, Suite A-2, Mount Pleasant, SC 29464 *Tel:* 843-971-6722 *Toll Free Tel:* 877-243-3457 *Fax:* 843-216-3804 *E-mail:* customerservice@sylvandellpublishing.com; info@sylvandellpublishing.com *Web Site:* www.sylvandellpublishing.com, pg 248

German, Lee, Sylvan Dell Publishing, 612 Johnnie Dodds Blvd, Suite A-2, Mount Pleasant, SC 29464 *Tel:* 843-971-6722 *Toll Free Tel:* 877-243-3457 *Fax:* 843-216-3804 *E-mail:* customerservice@sylvandellpublishing.com; info@sylvandellpublishing.com *Web Site:* www.sylvandellpublishing.com, pg 248

Gerrain, Dawn, Milady, Executive Woods, 5 Maxwell Dr, Clifton Park, NY 12065-2919 *Tel:* 518-348-2300 *Toll Free Tel:* 800-998-7498 *Fax:* 518-373-6309 *Web Site:* milady.cengage.com, pg 166

Gerrish, Nancy, McGraw-Hill Ryerson Limited, 300 Water St, Whitby, ON L1N 9B6, Canada *Tel:* 905-430-5000 *Toll Free Tel:* 800-565-5758 (cust serv) *Fax:* 905-430-5020 *Web Site:* www.mcgrawhill.ca, pg 512

Gersch, Lili Kalish, The Sugarman Family Award for Jewish Children's Literature, Irwin P Edlavitch Bldg, 1529 16 St NW, Washington, DC 20036 *Tel:* 202-518-9400 *Fax:* 202-518-9420 *Web Site:* www.washingtondcjcc.org, pg 745

Gershenowitz, Deborah, New York University Press, 838 Broadway, 3rd fl, New York, NY 10003-4812 *Tel:* 212-998-2575 (edit) *Toll Free Tel:* 800-996-6987 (orders) *Fax:* 212-995-3833 (orders) *E-mail:* information@nyupress.org; customerservice@nyupress.org; orders@nyupress.org *Web Site:* www.nyupress.org, pg 179

Gerth, Anne, InterVarsity Press, 430 Plaza Dr, Westmont, IL 60559-1234 *Tel:* 630-734-4000 *Toll Free Tel:* 800-843-9487 *Fax:* 630-734-4200 *E-mail:* email@ivpress.com *Web Site:* www.ivpress.com, pg 134

Gervais, Debbie, DC Canada Education Publishing, 120 Slater St, Suite 960, Ottawa, ON K1P 6E2, Canada *Tel:* 613-565-8885 *Toll Free Tel:* 888-565-0262 *Fax:* 613-565-8881 *E-mail:* info@dc-canada.ca *Web Site:* www.dc-canada.ca, pg 500

Gervasio, Janet, HarperCollins Publishers, 10 E 53 St, New York, NY 10022 *Tel:* 212-207-7000 *Fax:* 212-207-7145 *Web Site:* www.harpercollins.com, pg 113

Gesford, Mary, University Publishing Group, 219 W Washington St, Hagerstown, MD 21740 *Tel:* 240-420-0036 *Toll Free Tel:* 800-654-8188 *Fax:* 240-718-7100 *E-mail:* editorial@upgbooks.com; orders@upgbooks.com; sales@upgbooks.com *Web Site:* www.upgbooks.com, pg 272

Getek, Lauren Marie, Milton Dorfman Poetry Prize, 308 W Bloomfield St, Rome, NY 13440 *Tel:* 315-336-1040 *Fax:* 315-336-1090 *E-mail:* racc2@cnymail.com *Web Site:* www.romeart.org, pg 724

Gethers, Peter, Random House Inc, 1745 Broadway, New York, NY 10019 *Tel:* 212-782-9000 *Toll Free Tel:* 800-726-0600 *Web Site:* www.randomhouse.com, pg 213

Ghani, Rahim, Marshall Cavendish Corp, 99 White Plains Rd, Tarrytown, NY 10591-9001 *Tel:* 914-332-8888 *Toll Free Tel:* 800-821-9881 *Fax:* 914-332-8102 *E-mail:* customerservice@marshallcavendish.com; mcc@marshallcavendish.com *Web Site:* marshallcavendish.us; marshallcavendishdigital.com; marshallcavendishebooks.com, pg 158

Ghavami, Parvaneh, ADASI Publishing Co, 6 Dover Point Rd, Suite B, Dover, NH 03820-4698 *Tel:* 603-866-9426 *E-mail:* info@adasi.com *Web Site:* www.adasi.com, pg 5

Ghazarian, Ms Salpi H, Blue Crane Books, PO Box 380291, Cambridge, MA 02238 *Tel:* 617-926-8989 *Fax:* 617-926-0982 *E-mail:* bluecrane@arrow1.com, pg 41

Ghione, Yvette, Kids Can Press Ltd, 25 Dockside Dr, Toronto, ON M5A 0B5, Canada *Tel:* 416-479-7000 *Toll Free Tel:* 800-265-0884 *Fax:* 416-960-5437 *E-mail:* info@kidscan.com; customerservice@kidscan.com *Web Site:* www.kidscanpress.com; www.kidscanpress.ca, pg 510

Gholson, Kris, Eakin Press, 7005 Woodway Dr, Suite 114, Waco, TX 76712 *Tel:* 254-235-6161 *Toll Free Tel:* 800-880-8642 *Fax:* 254-235-6230 *E-mail:* sales@eakinpress.com *Web Site:* www.eakinpress.com, pg 83

Ghose, Zulfikar A, University of Texas at Austin, Creative Writing Program, Dept of English, PAR 108, One University Sta, Mailcode B5000, Austin, TX 78712-1164 *Tel:* 512-471-5132; 512-471-4991 *Fax:* 512-471-4909 *Web Site:* www.utexas.edu/cola/depts/english/creative-writing, pg 682

Ghosh, Anna, Scovil Galen Ghosh Literary Agency Inc, 276 Fifth Ave, Suite 708, New York, NY 10001 *Tel:* 212-679-8686 *Fax:* 212-679-6710 *E-mail:* info@sgglit.com *Web Site:* www.sgglit.com, pg 593

Ghoura, Judy, Fitzhenry & Whiteside Limited, 195 Allstate Pkwy, Markham, ON L3R 4T8, Canada *Tel:* 905-477-9700 *Toll Free Tel:* 800-387-9776 *Fax:* 905-477-9179 *Toll Free Fax:* 800-260-9777 *E-mail:* bookinfo@fitzhenry.ca; godwit@fitzhenry.ca *Web Site:* www.fitzhenry.ca, pg 505

Giagnocavo, Alan, Fox Chapel Publishing Co Inc, 1970 Broad St, East Petersburg, PA 17520 *Tel:* 717-560-4703 *Toll Free Tel:* 800-457-9112 *Fax:* 717-560-4702 *E-mail:* customerservice@foxchapelpublishing.com *Web Site:* www.foxchapelpublishing.com, pg 98

Giampietro, Frank, Alice James Books, 238 Main St, Farmington, ME 04938 *Tel:* 207-778-7071 *Fax:* 207-778-7766 *E-mail:* info@alicejamesbooks.org *Web Site:* www.alicejamesbooks.org, pg 8

Giangreco, Karen, The Experiment, 260 Fifth Ave, Suite 3 South, New York, NY 10001-6425 *Tel:* 212-889-1659 *E-mail:* info@theexperimentpublishing.com *Web Site:* www.theexperimentpublishing.com, pg 91

Gianino, Laura, Bloomsbury Publishing, 175 Fifth Ave, New York, NY 10010 *Tel:* 212-674-5151 *Toll Free Tel:* 800-221-7945 *Fax:* 212-780-0115; 212-982-2837 *E-mail:* marketingusa@bloomsbury.com; adultpublicityusa.@bloomsbury.com *Web Site:* www.bloomsbury.com, pg 41

Giarratano, Matt, Penguin Books, 375 Hudson St, New York, NY 10014 *Tel:* 212-366-2000 *E-mail:* online@penguinputnam.com *Web Site:* www.penguinputnam.com; www.penguinclassics.com; us.penguingroup.com, pg 197

Gibbons, Melissa, William H Sadlier Inc, 9 Pine St, New York, NY 10005 *Tel:* 212-227-2120 *Toll Free Tel:* 800-221-5175 (cust serv) *Fax:* 212-312-6080 *Web Site:* www.sadlier.com, pg 223

Gibson, Bethany, Goose Lane Editions, 500 Beaverbrook Ct, Suite 330, Fredericton, NB E3B 5X4, Canada *Tel:* 506-450-4251 *Toll Free Tel:* 888-926-8377 *Fax:* 506-459-4991 *E-mail:* info@gooselane.com *Web Site:* www.gooselane.com, pg 507

Gibson, George, Bloomsbury Publishing, 175 Fifth Ave, New York, NY 10010 *Tel:* 212-674-5151 *Toll Free Tel:* 800-221-7945 *Fax:* 212-780-0115; 212-982-2837 *E-mail:* marketingusa@bloomsbury.com; adultpublicityusa.@bloomsbury.com *Web Site:* www.bloomsbury.com, pg 40

Gibson, George L, Walker & Co, 175 Fifth Ave, 3rd fl, New York, NY 10010-7728 *Web Site:* www.walkerbooks.com, pg 276

Gibson, Jack, International Risk Management Institute Inc, 12222 Merit Dr, Suite 1450, Dallas, TX 75251-2276 *Tel:* 972-960-7693 *Fax:* 972-371-5120 *E-mail:* info27@irmi.com *Web Site:* www.irmi.com, pg 133

Gibson, Paul, Wolters Kluwer Law & Business, 76 Ninth Ave, 7th fl, New York, NY 10011-5201 *Tel:* 212-771-0600 *Toll Free Tel:* 800-234-1660 (cust serv); 800-638-8437 (orders); 800-317-3113 (bookstore sales) *Toll Free Fax:* 800-901-9075 (cust serv); 800-561-4845 (bookstore sales) *Web Site:* www.aspenpublishers.com, pg 141

Gibson, William, Printing Industries of America Premier Print Award, 200 Deer Run Rd, Sewickley, PA 15143-2600 *Tel:* 412-741-6860 *Toll Free Tel:* 800-910-4283 *Fax:* 412-741-2311 *E-mail:* printing@printing.org *Web Site:* www.printing.org, pg 735

Giddens, Mary, SteinerBooks, 610 Main St, Great Barrington, MA 01230 *Tel:* 413-528-8233 *Fax:* 413-528-8826 *E-mail:* friends@steinerbooks.org *Web Site:* www.steinerbooks.org, pg 244

Gifford, James M, The Jesse Stuart Foundation (JSF), 1645 Winchester Ave, Ashland, KY 41101 *Tel:* 606-326-1667 *Fax:* 606-325-2519 *E-mail:* jsf@jsfbooks.com *Web Site:* www.jsfbooks.com, pg 246

Giffuni, Cathe, Research Research, 240 E 27 St, Suite 20-K, New York, NY 10016-9238 *Tel:* 212-779-9540 *Fax:* 212-779-9540 *E-mail:* ehtac@msn.com, pg 554

Gigante, Alex, Penguin Group (USA) LLC, 375 Hudson St, New York, NY 10014 *Tel:* 212-366-2000 *Toll Free Tel:* 800-847-5515 (inside sales); 800-631-8571 (cust serv) *Fax:* 212-366-2666; 607-775-4829 (inside sales) *E-mail:* online@us.penguingroup.com *Web Site:* www.penguin.com; us.penguingroup.com, pg 197

Giganti, Edward J, The Catholic Health Association of the United States, 4455 Woodson Rd, St Louis, MO 63134-3797 *Tel:* 314-427-2500 *Fax:* 314-253-0029 *E-mail:* servicecenter@chausa.org *Web Site:* www.chausa.org, pg 54

Gilbert, Christina, Bloomsbury Publishing, 175 Fifth Ave, New York, NY 10010 *Tel:* 212-674-5151 *Toll Free Tel:* 800-221-7945 *Fax:* 212-780-0115; 212-982-2837 *E-mail:* marketingusa@bloomsbury.com; adultpublicityusa.@bloomsbury.com *Web Site:* www.bloomsbury.com, pg 40

Gilbert, Deborah, Soul Mate Publishing, PO Box 24, Macedon, NY 14502 *Tel:* 585-598-4791 *E-mail:* submissions@soulmatepublishing.com *Web Site:* www.soulmatepublishing.com, pg 239

Gilbert, Elizabeth, Walter Foster Publishing Inc, 3 Wrigley, Suite A, Irvine, CA 92618 *Tel:* 949-380-7510 *Toll Free Tel:* 800-426-0099; 800-826-6600 (orders) *Fax:* 949-380-7575 *E-mail:* info@walterfoster.com *Web Site:* www.walterfoster.com, pg 97

Gilbert, Jennifer G, Galen Press Ltd, PO Box 64400, Tucson, AZ 85728-4400 *Tel:* 520-577-8363 *Fax:* 520-529-6459 *E-mail:* sales@galenpress.com *Web Site:* www.galenpress.com, pg 100

Gilbert, Jon, Seven Stories Press, 140 Watts St, New York, NY 10013 *Tel:* 212-226-8760 *Fax:* 212-226-1411 *E-mail:* info@sevenstories.com *Web Site:* www.sevenstories.com, pg 232

Gilbert, Nichole, Baker & Taylor/YALSA Conference Grants, 50 E Huron St, Chicago, IL 60611 *Tel:* 312-280-4390 *Toll Free Tel:* 800-545-2433 *Fax:* 312-280-5276; 312-664-7459 *E-mail:* yalsa@ala.org *Web Site:* www.ala.org/yalsa/, pg 689

Gilbert, Nichole, Margaret A Edwards Award, 50 E Huron St, Chicago, IL 60611 *Tel:* 312-280-4390 *Toll Free Tel:* 800-545-2433 *Fax:* 312-280-5276 *E-mail:* yalsa@ala.org *Web Site:* www.ala.org/yalsa/edwards, pg 702

Gilbert, Nichole, Frances Henne YALSA/VOYA Research Grant, 50 E Huron St, Chicago, IL 60611 *Tel:* 312-280-4390 *Toll Free Tel:* 800-545-2433 *Fax:* 312-280-5276 *E-mail:* yalsa@ala.org *Web Site:* www.ala.org/yalsa/, pg 705

Gilbert, Nichole, Michael L Printz Award, 50 E Huron St, Chicago, IL 60611 *Tel:* 312-280-4390 *Toll Free Tel:* 800-545-2433 *Fax:* 312-280-5276 *E-mail:* yalsa@ala.org *Web Site:* www.ala.org/yalsa/printz, pg 735

Gilbert, Sheila E, DAW Books Inc, 375 Hudson St, 3rd fl, New York, NY 10014 *Tel:* 212-366-2096 *Fax:* 212-366-2090 *E-mail:* daw@us.penguingroup.com *Web Site:* us.penguingroup.com; www.dawbooks.com, pg 76

Gilbride, Tara, Crown Publishing Group, c/o Random House Inc, 1745 Broadway, New York, NY 10019 *Tel:* 212-782-9000 *Toll Free Tel:* 888-264-1745 *Fax:* 212-940-7408 *Web Site:* www.randomhouse.com/crown, pg 72

Gill, Alison, DC Entertainment, 1700 Broadway, New York, NY 10019 *Tel:* 212-636-5400 *Toll Free Tel:* 800-887-6789 *Fax:* 212-636-5979 *E-mail:* dccomics@cambeywest.com *Web Site:* www.dccomics.com; www.madmag.com; www.dcentertainment.com, pg 76

Gill, Craig, University Press of Mississippi, 3825 Ridgewood Rd, Jackson, MS 39211-6492 *Tel:* 601-432-6205 *Toll Free Tel:* 800-737-7788 (orders & cust serv) *Fax:* 601-432-6217 *E-mail:* press@mississippi.edu *Web Site:* www.upress.state.ms.us, pg 271

Gillan, Maria, Binghamton University Creative Writing Program, c/o Dept of English, PO Box 6000, Binghamton, NY 13902-6000 *Tel:* 607-777-2168 *Fax:* 607-777-2408 *E-mail:* cwpro@binghamton.edu *Web Site:* english.binghamton.edu/cwpro, pg 677

Gillan, Maria Mazziotti, Binghamton University John Gardner Fiction Book Award, Dept of English, General Literature & Rhetoric, Library N, Rm 1149, Vestal Pkwy E, Binghamton, NY 13902 *Tel:* 607-777-2713 *Web Site:* english.binghamton.edu/cwpro, pg 691

Gillan, Maria Mazziotti, Binghamton University Milt Kessler Poetry Book Award, Dept of English, General Literature & Rhetoric, Library N, Rm 1149, Vestal Pkwy E, Binghamton, NY 13902 *Tel:* 607-777-2713 *Web Site:* english.binghamton.edu/cwpro, pg 691

Gillan, Maria Mazziotti, Allen Ginsberg Poetry Award, One College Blvd, Paterson, NJ 07505-1179 *Tel:* 973-684-6555 *Fax:* 973-523-6085 *Web Site:* www.pccc.edu/poetry, pg 707

Gillan, Maria Mazziotti, The Paterson Fiction Prize, One College Blvd, Paterson, NJ 07505-1179 *Tel:* 973-684-6555 *Fax:* 973-523-6085 *Web Site:* www.pccc.edu/poetry, pg 732

Gillan, Maria Mazziotti, The Paterson Poetry Prize, One College Blvd, Paterson, NJ 07505-1179 *Tel:* 973-684-6555 *Fax:* 973-523-6085 *Web Site:* www.pccc.edu/poetry, pg 732

Gillan, Maria Mazziotti, The Paterson Prize for Books for Young People, One College Blvd, Paterson, NJ 07505-1179 *Tel:* 973-684-6555 *Fax:* 973-523-6085 *Web Site:* www.pccc.edu/poetry, pg 732

Gillespie, Christine, Alfred A Knopf/Everyman's Library, c/o Random House Inc, 1745 Broadway, New York, NY 10019 *Tel:* 212-751-2600 *Toll Free Tel:* 800-638-6460 *Fax:* 212-572-2593 *Web Site:* www.knopfdoubleday.com, pg 141

Gillespie, Christine, Pantheon Books/Schocken Books, c/o Random House Inc, 1745 Broadway, New York, NY 10019 *Tel:* 212-751-2600 *Toll Free Tel:* 800-638-6460 *Fax:* 212-572-6030, pg 192

Gillespie, Jennie, San Diego Christian Writers' Guild Conference, PO Box 270403, San Diego, CA 92198 *Tel:* 760-294-3269 *Fax:* 760-294-3269 *E-mail:* info@sandiegocwg.org *Web Site:* www.sandiegocwg.org, pg 672

Gillespie, Melanie, Comprehensive Health Education Foundation (CHEF), 159 S Jackson St, Suite 510, Seattle, WA 98104 *Tel:* 206-824-2907 *Toll Free Tel:* 800-323-2433 *Fax:* 206-824-3072 *E-mail:* info@chef.org *Web Site:* www.chef.org, pg 66

Gillespie, Robert, San Diego Christian Writers' Guild Conference, PO Box 270403, San Diego, CA 92198 *Tel:* 760-294-3269 *Fax:* 760-294-3269 *E-mail:* info@sandiegocwg.org *Web Site:* www.sandiegocwg.org, pg 672

Gillham, Will, Amon Carter Museum, 3501 Camp Bowie Blvd, Fort Worth, TX 76107-2695 *Tel:* 817-738-1933; 817-738-5065 (PR) *Toll Free Tel:* 800-573-1933 *Fax:* 817-336-1123 *E-mail:* pr@cartermuseum.org *Web Site:* www.cartermuseum.org, pg 53

Gillies, Paige, Publishers' Graphics Inc, 231 Judd Rd, Easton, CT 06612-1025 *Tel:* 203-445-1511 *Fax:* 203-445-1411 *E-mail:* sales@publishersgraphics.com *Web Site:* www.publishersgraphics.com, pg 602

Gilligan, Rev Michael PhD, American Catholic Press (ACP), 16565 S State St, South Holland, IL 60473 *Tel:* 708-331-5485 *Fax:* 708-331-5484 *E-mail:* acp@acpress.org *Web Site:* www.acpress.org, pg 12

Gilliland, Hap, The Montana Council for Indian Education, 1240 Burlington Ave, Billings, MT 59102-4224 *Tel:* 406-652-7598 (AM); 406-248-3465 (PM) *Fax:* 406-248-1297 *E-mail:* cie@cie-mt.org *Web Site:* www.cie-mt.org, pg 169

Gillis, Karen, St Martin's Press, LLC, 175 Fifth Ave, New York, NY 10010 *Tel:* 646-307-5151 *Fax:* 212-420-9314 *E-mail:* firstname.lastname@macmillan.com *Web Site:* www.stmartins.com, pg 224

Gillis, Sonya, Fitzhenry & Whiteside Limited, 195 Allstate Pkwy, Markham, ON L3R 4T8, Canada *Tel:* 905-477-9700 *Toll Free Tel:* 800-387-9776 *Fax:* 905-477-9179 *Toll Free Fax:* 800-260-9777 *E-mail:* bookinfo@fitzhenry.ca; godwit@fitzhenry.ca *Web Site:* www.fitzhenry.ca, pg 505

Gilly, Holly, Human Kinetics Inc, 1607 N Market St, Champaign, IL 61820 *Tel:* 217-351-5076 *Toll Free Tel:* 800-747-4457 *Fax:* 217-351-1549 (orders/cust serv) *E-mail:* info@hkusa.com *Web Site:* www.humankinetics.com, pg 125

Gilmer, E J, Amber Quill Press LLC, PO Box 265, Indian Hills, CO 80454 *E-mail:* business@amberquill.com *Web Site:* www.amberquill.com; www.amberheat.com (imprint); www.amberallure.com (imprint), pg 10

Gilmore, Chelsea, Maria Carvainis Agency Inc, Rockefeller Center, 1270 Avenue of the Americas, Suite 2320, New York, NY 10020 *Tel:* 212-245-6365 *Fax:* 212-245-7196 *E-mail:* mca@mariacarvainisagency.com *Web Site:* mariacarvainisagency.com, pg 565

Gilo, Jessica, Houghton Mifflin Harcourt, 222 Berkeley St, Boston, MA 02116-3764 *Tel:* 617-351-5000 *Toll Free Tel:* 800-225-5425 (Pre-K-8); 800-462-6595 (6–12; Advanced & Electives); 800-289-4490 (Specialized Curriculum: Great Source, Rigby, Saxon, Steck-Vaughn; Homeschool; Adult Ed); 800-323-9540 (Assessment: Riverside Publishing); 888-391-3245 (SkillsTutor); 888-242-6747 option 2 (Destination Series; Classroom Connect; Earobics; Edmark; Learning Village; Riverdeep); 800-225-3362 (Houghton Mifflin Harcourt Trade & Reference Publishers); 800-225-5800 (Heinemann) *Fax:* 617-351-1125 *Web Site:* www.hmhco.com, pg 123

Gilpin, R Wayne, Future Horizons Inc, 721 W Abram St, Arlington, TX 76013 *Tel:* 817-277-0727 *Toll Free Tel:* 800-489-0727 *Fax:* 817-277-2270 *E-mail:* info@fhautism.com *Web Site:* www.fhautism.com, pg 100

Gilpin, Wayne, Gilpin Publishing, PO Box 597, Alliston, ON L9R 1V7, Canada *Tel:* 705-424-6507 *Toll Free Tel:* 800-867-3281 *Fax:* 705-424-6507 *E-mail:* mail@gilpin.ca *Web Site:* www.gilpin.ca, pg 506

Gilson, Kristin, Puffin Books, 345 Hudson St, New York, NY 10014 *Tel:* 212-366-2000 *E-mail:* online@penguinputnam.com *Web Site:* www.penguinputnam.com; us.penguingroup.com, pg 209

Gimbel, Despina P, New York University Press, 838 Broadway, 3rd fl, New York, NY 10003-4812 *Tel:* 212-998-2575 (edit) *Toll Free Tel:* 800-996-6987 (orders) *Fax:* 212-995-3833 (orders) *E-mail:* information@nyupress.org; customerservice@nyupress.org; orders@nyupress.org *Web Site:* www.nyupress.org, pg 179

Giner, Robin, Outdoor Writers Association of America Annual Conference, 615 Oak St, Suite 201, Missoula, MT 59801 *Tel:* 406-728-7434 *Fax:* 406-728-7445 *E-mail:* info@owaa.org *Web Site:* www.owaa.org, pg 671

Gingerich, Amy, Faith & Life Resources, 1251 Virginia Ave, Harrisonburg, VA 22802-2434 *Toll Free Tel:* 800-245-7894 (orders & cust serv US); 800-631-6535 (orders & cust serv CN) *Toll Free Fax:* 877-271-0760 *E-mail:* mpcan@mpn.net *Web Site:* www.faithandliferesources.org; www.mpn.net, pg 92

Gingerich, Amy, Herald Press, 1251 Virginia Ave, Harrisonburg, VA 22802-2434 *Toll Free Tel:* 800-245-7894 (orders-US); 800-999-3534; 800-631-6535 (orders-CN) *Toll Free Fax:* 877-271-0760 *E-mail:* info@MennoMedia.org *Web Site:* www.heraldpress.com; store.mennomedia.org, pg 118

Gingold, Joel, Key Curriculum, A McGraw-Hill Education Company, 1150 65 St, Emeryville, CA 94608 *Tel:* 510-595-7000 *Toll Free Tel:* 800-995-6284 *Fax:* 510-595-7040 (orders) *Toll Free Fax:* 800-541-2442 *Web Site:* www.keycurriculum.com, pg 140

Gingras, Dominique, Les Presses De L'Universite Laval, Pavillon Maurice-Pollack, Suite 3103, 2305 University St, Quebec, QC G1V 0A6, Canada *Tel:* 418-656-2803 *Fax:* 418-656-3305 *E-mail:* presses@pul.ulaval.ca *Web Site:* www.pulaval.com, pg 516

Ginn, Catherine, Deadline Club, c/o Salmagundi Club, 47 Fifth Ave, New York, NY 10003 *Tel:* 646-481-7584 *E-mail:* info@deadlineclub.org *Web Site:* www.deadlineclub.org, pg 622

Ginna, Peter, Bloomsbury Publishing, 175 Fifth Ave, New York, NY 10010 *Tel:* 212-674-5151 *Toll Free Tel:* 800-221-7945 *Fax:* 212-780-0115; 212-982-2837 *E-mail:* marketingusa@bloomsbury.com; adultpublicityusa.@bloomsbury.com *Web Site:* www.bloomsbury.com, pg 40

Ginna, Peter, The Center for Fiction, 17 E 47 St, New York, NY 10017 *Tel:* 212-755-6710 *Fax:* 212-826-0831 *E-mail:* info@centerforfiction.org *Web Site:* www.centerforfiction.org, pg 621

Ginsberg, Peter L, Curtis Brown Ltd, 10 Astor Place, New York, NY 10003 *Tel:* 212-473-5400 *Web Site:* www.curtisbrown.com, pg 565

Ginsburg, Susan, Writers House, 21 W 26 St, New York, NY 10010 *Tel:* 212-685-2400 *Fax:* 212-685-1781 *Web Site:* www.writershouse.com, pg 599

Gipson, Scott, Caxton Press, 312 Main St, Caldwell, ID 83605-3299 *Tel:* 208-459-7421 *Toll Free Tel:* 800-657-6465 *Fax:* 208-459-7450 *E-mail:* publish@caxtonpress.com *Web Site:* www.caxtonpress.com, pg 54

Giraldi, Stephanie, Grove/Atlantic Inc, 841 Broadway, 4th fl, New York, NY 10003-4793 *Tel:* 212-614-7850 *Toll Free Tel:* 800-521-0178 *Fax:* 212-614-7886 *E-mail:* info@groveatlantic.com *Web Site:* www.groveatlantic.com, pg 108

Girard, Guylaine, Les Editions Fides, 7333 place des Roseraies, bureau 100, Montreal, QC H1M 2X6, Canada *Tel:* 514-745-4290 *Toll Free Tel:* 800-363-1451 (CN) *Fax:* 514-745-4299 *E-mail:* editions@fides.qc.ca *Web Site:* www.editionsfides.com, pg 503

Giron, Robert L, Gival Press, 5200 N First St, Arlington, VA 22203 *Tel:* 703-351-0079 *Fax:* 703-351-0079 *E-mail:* givalpress@yahoo.com *Web Site:* www.givalpress.com, pg 103

Giron, Robert L, Gival Press Novel Award, PO Box 3812, Arlington, VA 22203 *Tel:* 703-351-0079 *Fax:* 703-351-0079 *E-mail:* givalpress@yahoo.com *Web Site:* www.givalpress.com, pg 707

Godoff, Ann, Penguin Group (USA) LLC, 375 Hudson St, New York, NY 10014 *Tel:* 212-366-2000 *Toll Free Tel:* 800-847-5515 (inside sales); 800-631-8571 (cust serv) *Fax:* 212-366-2666; 607-775-4829 (inside sales) *E-mail:* online@us.penguingroup.com *Web Site:* www.penguin.com; us.penguingroup.com, pg 197

Godoff, Ann, The Penguin Press, 375 Hudson St, New York, NY 10014, pg 197

Godwin, Peter, PEN American Center, 588 Broadway, Suite 303, New York, NY 10012 *Tel:* 212-334-1660 *Fax:* 212-334-2181 *E-mail:* info@pen.org *Web Site:* www.pen.org, pg 633

Godwin, Peter, The PEN Award for Poetry in Translation, 588 Broadway, Suite 303, New York, NY 10012 *Tel:* 212-334-1660 *Fax:* 212-334-2181 *E-mail:* awards@pen.org *Web Site:* www.pen.org, pg 732

Godwin, Peter, PEN/Phyllis Naylor Working Writer Fellowship, 588 Broadway, Suite 303, New York, NY 10012 *Tel:* 212-334-1660 *Fax:* 212-334-2181 *E-mail:* awards@pen.org *Web Site:* www.pen.org, pg 733

Godwin, Peter, PEN/Ralph Manheim Medal for Translation, 588 Broadway, Suite 303, New York, NY 10012 *Tel:* 212-334-1660 *Fax:* 212-334-2181 *E-mail:* awards@pen.org *Web Site:* www.pen.org, pg 733

Godwin, Peter, PEN/Robert Bingham Fellowships for Writers, 588 Broadway, Suite 303, New York, NY 10012 *Tel:* 212-334-1660 *Fax:* 212-334-2181 *E-mail:* awards@pen.org *Web Site:* www.pen.org, pg 733

Godwin, Peter, PEN Translation Prize, 588 Broadway, Suite 303, New York, NY 10012 *Tel:* 212-334-1660 *Fax:* 212-334-2181 *E-mail:* awards@pen.org *Web Site:* www.pen.org, pg 733

Godwin, Peter, PEN Writers' Emergency Fund, 588 Broadway, Suite 303, New York, NY 10012 *Tel:* 212-334-1660 *Fax:* 212-334-2181 *Web Site:* www.pen.org, pg 733

Goede, Lydia, Tribal Trails Books & Resources, PO Box 3030, Prince Albert, SK S6V 7V4, Canada *Tel:* 306-764-4490 *Fax:* 306-764-3390 *E-mail:* missiondist@ncem.ca *Web Site:* www.ncem.ca, pg 522

Goehring, David, John Wiley & Sons Inc Professional/Trade Group, 111 River St, Hoboken, NJ 07030 *Tel:* 201-748-6000 *Toll Free Tel:* 800-225-5945 (cust serv) *Fax:* 201-748-6088 *E-mail:* info@wiley.com *Web Site:* www.wiley.com, pg 282

Goering, Krista, Krista Goering Literary Agency LLC, 3514 Clinton Pkwy, Suite A-404, Lawrence, KS 66047 *Tel:* 785-841-0634 *Fax:* 785-841-8500 *E-mail:* query@kristagoering.com *Web Site:* www.kristagoering.com, pg 574

Goertz, Elena, American Society of Media Photographers (ASMP), 150 N Second St, Philadelphia, PA 19106 *Tel:* 215-451-2767 *Fax:* 215-451-0880 *E-mail:* info@asmp.org *Web Site:* www.asmp.org, pg 614

Goff, Anthony, Hachette Digital, 237 Park Ave, New York, NY 10017 *Tel:* 212-364-0600, pg 110

Goff, Chris, HarperCollins Publishers, 10 E 53 St, New York, NY 10022 *Tel:* 212-207-7000 *Fax:* 212-207-7145 *Web Site:* www.harpercollins.com, pg 113

Goff, Christine, Colorado Book Awards, 7935 E Prentice Ave, Suite 450, Greenwood Village, CO 80111 *Tel:* 303-894-7951 (ext 21) *Fax:* 303-864-9361 *E-mail:* info@coloradohumanities.org *Web Site:* www.coloradohumanities.org, pg 698

Goff, Gordon, ORO editions, 31 Commercial Blvd, Suite F, Novato, CA 94949 *Tel:* 415-883-3300 *Fax:* 415-883-3309 *E-mail:* info@oroeditions.com *Web Site:* www.oroeditions.com, pg 188

Goff, Raoul, Earth Aware Editions, 10 Paul Dr, San Rafael, CA 94903 *Tel:* 415-526-1370 *Fax:* 415-526-1394 *E-mail:* info@earthawareeditions.com, pg 83

Goff, Raoul, Insight Editions, 10 Paul Dr, San Rafael, CA 94903 *Tel:* 415-526-1370 *Toll Free Tel:* 800-809-3792 *E-mail:* info@insighteditions.com *Web Site:* www.insighteditions.com, pg 131

Goff, Raoul, Mandala Publishing, 10 Paul Dr, San Rafael, CA 94903 *Tel:* 415-526-1370 *Fax:* 415-526-1394 *Toll Free Fax:* 866-509-0515 *E-mail:* info@insighteditions.com *Web Site:* www.mandalapublishing.com, pg 156

Goff, Steven, Channel Photographics, 980 Lincoln Ave, Suite 200-B, San Rafael, CA 94901 *Tel:* 415-456-2934 *Fax:* 415-456-4124 *Web Site:* www.channelphotographics.com, pg 58

Goff, Steven, Global Publishing, Sales & Distribution, 980 Lincoln Ave, Suite 200-B, San Rafael, CA 94901 *Tel:* 415-456-2934 *Fax:* 415-456-4124 *Web Site:* www.globalpsd.com, pg 104

Goforth, Renea, Wichita State University Playwriting Contest, 1845 Fairmount St, Wichita, KS 67260-0153 *Tel:* 316-978-3360 *Fax:* 316-978-3202 *Web Site:* www.wichita.edu, pg 749

Goin, Carma, International Publishing Management Association (IPMA), 105 S Jefferson, Suite B-4, Kearney, MO 64060 *Tel:* 816-903-4762 *Fax:* 816-902-4766 *E-mail:* ipmainfo@ipma.org *Web Site:* www.ipma.org, pg 625

Goin, Kenn, Bearport Publishing Co Inc, 45 W 21 St, Suite 3B, New York, NY 10010 *Tel:* 212-337-8577 *Toll Free Tel:* 877-337-8577 *Fax:* 212-337-8557 *Toll Free Fax:* 866-337-8557 *E-mail:* info@bearportpublishing.com *Web Site:* www.bearportpublishing.com, pg 33

Gojak, Linda M, National Council of Teachers of Mathematics (NCTM), 1906 Association Dr, Reston, VA 20191-1502 *Tel:* 703-620-9840 *Toll Free Tel:* 800-235-7566 *Fax:* 703-476-2970 *E-mail:* nctm@nctm.org *Web Site:* www.nctm.org, pg 174

Golan, Joan Marlow, Harlequin Enterprises Ltd, 233 Broadway, Suite 1001, New York, NY 10279 *Tel:* 212-553-4200 *Fax:* 212-227-8969 *E-mail:* CustomerService@harlequin.com *Web Site:* www.harlequin.com, pg 112

Golan, Joan Marlow, Love Inspired Books, 233 Broadway, Suite 1001, New York, NY 10279 *Tel:* 212-553-4200 *Fax:* 212-227-8969 *E-mail:* customer_service@harlequin.ca *Web Site:* www.loveinspiredbooks.com, pg 153

Gold, Edwin, University of Baltimore - College of Arts & Sciences, Ampersand Institute for Words & Images, 1420 N Charles St, Baltimore, MD 21201-5779 *Tel:* 410-837-6022 *Fax:* 410-837-6029 *E-mail:* scd@ubalt.edu *Web Site:* www.ubalt.edu, pg 681

Gold, Jennifer, Rough Guides, 375 Hudson St, New York, NY 10014 *Toll Free Tel:* 800-631-8571 *E-mail:* mail@roughguides.com *Web Site:* www.roughguides.com, pg 221

Gold, Jerry, Black Heron Press, PO Box 13396, Mill Creek, WA 98082-1396 *Tel:* 425-355-4929 *Fax:* 425-355-4929 *Web Site:* blackheron.mav.net, pg 39

Gold, Leslie J, P R B Productions, 963 Peralta Ave, Albany, CA 94706-2144 *Tel:* 510-526-0722 *Fax:* 510-527-4763 *E-mail:* prbprdns@aol.com *Web Site:* www.prbmusic.com, pg 190

Goldbach, Allan, Chestnut Publishing Group Inc, 4005 Bayview Ave, Suite 610, Toronto, ON M2M 3Z9, Canada *Tel:* 416-224-5824 *Fax:* 416-224-0595 *Web Site:* www.chestnutpublishing.com, pg 499

Goldbaum, Milton J, Alan Wofsy Fine Arts, 1109 Geary Blvd, San Francisco, CA 94109 *Tel:* 415-292-6500 *Toll Free Tel:* 800-660-6403 *Fax:* 415-292-6594 (off & cust serv); 415-512-0130 (acctg) *E-mail:* order@art-books.com (orders); editeur@earthlink.net (edit); beauxarts@earthlink.net (cust serv) *Web Site:* www.art-books.com, pg 284

Goldberg, Arthur, Abbeville Publishing Group, 137 Varick St, Suite 504, New York, NY 10013 *Tel:* 212-366-5585 *Toll Free Tel:* 800-ART-BOOK (278-2665) *Fax:* 212-366-6966 *E-mail:* abbeville@abbeville.com; marketing@abbeville.com; sales@abbeville.com; rights@abbeville.com *Web Site:* www.abbeville.com, pg 2

Goldberg, Franklin, Wm B Eerdmans Publishing Co, 2140 Oak Industrial Dr NE, Grand Rapids, MI 49505 *Tel:* 616-459-4591 *Toll Free Tel:* 800-253-7521 *Fax:* 616-459-6540 *E-mail:* customerservice@eerdmans.com; sales@eerdmans.com *Web Site:* www.eerdmans.com, pg 85

Goldberg, Glenn S, McGraw-Hill Financial, 1221 Avenue of the Americas, 50th fl, New York, NY 10020 *Tel:* 212-512-2000 *Web Site:* www.mhfi.com, pg 161

Goldberg, Harriet, MedMaster Inc, 3337 Hollywood Oaks Dr, Fort Lauderdale, FL 33312 *Tel:* 954-962-8414 *Toll Free Tel:* 800-335-3480 *Fax:* 954-962-4508 *E-mail:* mmbks@aol.com *Web Site:* www.medmaster.net, pg 163

Goldberg, Matthew, Basic Books, 250 W 57 St, 15th fl, New York, NY 10107 *Tel:* 212-340-8164 *Fax:* 212-340-8135 *E-mail:* perseus.promos@perseusbooks.com *Web Site:* www.basicbooks.com; perseusbooks.com, pg 31

Goldberg, Matty, The Perseus Books Group, 387 Park Ave S, 12th fl, New York, NY 10016 *Tel:* 212-340-8100 *Toll Free Tel:* 800-343-4499 (cust serv) *Fax:* 212-340-8105 *Web Site:* www.perseusbooksgroup.com, pg 199

Goldberg, Matty, Running Press Book Publishers, 2300 Chestnut St, Philadelphia, PA 19103-4399 *Tel:* 215-567-5080 *Toll Free Tel:* 800-343-4499 (cust serv & orders) *Fax:* 215-568-2919 *Toll Free Fax:* 800-453-2884 (cust serv & orders) *E-mail:* perseus.promos@perseusbooks.com *Web Site:* www.runningpress.com, pg 222

Goldberg, Michael, ASM Press, 1752 "N" St NW, Washington, DC 20036-2904 *Tel:* 202-737-3600 *Toll Free Tel:* 800-546-2416 *Fax:* 202-942-9342 *E-mail:* books@asmusa.org *Web Site:* estore.asm.org, pg 25

Goldberg, Michael H, URJ Books & Music, 633 Third Ave, New York, NY 10017-6778 *Tel:* 212-650-4120 *Fax:* 212-650-4119 *E-mail:* press@urj.org *Web Site:* www.ujrbooksandmusic.com, pg 273

Goldberg, Stephen, MedMaster Inc, 3337 Hollywood Oaks Dr, Fort Lauderdale, FL 33312 *Tel:* 954-962-8414 *Toll Free Tel:* 800-335-3480 *Fax:* 954-962-4508 *E-mail:* mmbks@aol.com *Web Site:* www.medmaster.net, pg 163

Goldberger, Amy S, Publishing Services, 525 E 86 St, Suite 8-E, New York, NY 10028 *Tel:* 212-628-9127 *Fax:* 212-988-1999 *E-mail:* publishingservices@mac.com, pg 554

Goldberger, Amy S, Publishing Services, 525 E 86 St, Suite 8-E, New York, NY 10028 *Tel:* 212-628-9127 *Fax:* 212-628-9128 *E-mail:* publishingservices@mac.com, pg 589

Goldbetter, Larry, National Writers Union/UAW Local 1981, 256 W 38 St, Suite 703, New York, NY 10018 *Tel:* 212-254-0279 *Fax:* 212-254-0673 *E-mail:* nwu@nwu.org *Web Site:* www.nwu.org/, pg 631

Golden, Lori, Health Communications Inc, 3201 SW 15 St, Deerfield Beach, FL 33442-8190 *Tel:* 954-360-0909 *Toll Free Tel:* 800-441-5569 (cust serv) *Fax:* 954-360-0034 *Web Site:* www.hcibooks.com; hci-online.com, pg 116

Golden, Marita, Hurston/Wright Award for College Writers, 12138 Central Ave, Suite 209, Bowie, MD 20721 *Tel:* 301-459-2108 *Fax:* 301-277-1262 *E-mail:* info@hurstonwright.org *Web Site:* www.hurstonwright.org, pg 711

Golden, Marita, Hurston/Wright Legacy Awards, 12138 Central Ave, Suite 209, Bowie, MD 20721 *Tel:* 301-459-2108 *Fax:* 301-277-1262 *E-mail:* info@hurstonwright.org *Web Site:* www.hurstonwright.org, pg 711

Golden, Marita, Hurston/Wright Writer's Week, 12138 Central Ave, Suite 209, Bowie, MD 20721 *Tel:* 301-459-2108 *Fax:* 301-277-1262 *E-mail:* info@hurstonwright.org *Web Site:* www.hurstonwright.org, pg 669

Golden, Tammy, National Government Publishing Association, 629 N Main St, Hattiesburg, MS 39401 *Tel:* 601-582-3330 *Fax:* 601-582-3354 *E-mail:* info@govpublishing.org *Web Site:* www.govpublishing.org, pg 630

Golden, Winifred, Castiglia Literary Agency, 1155 Camino Del Mar, Suite 510, Del Mar, CA 92014 *Tel:* 858-755-8761 *Fax:* 858-755-7063 *Web Site:* www.castiglialiteraryagency.com, pg 566

Goldenberg, Amy, American Anthropological Association (AAA), Publications Dept, Suite 600, 2200 Wilson Blvd, Arlington, VA 22201 *Tel:* 703-528-1902 *Fax:* 703-528-3546 *Web Site:* www.aaanet.org, pg 11

Goldfarb, Ronald L, Goldfarb & Associates, 721 Gibbon St, Alexandria, VA 22314 *Tel:* 202-466-3030 *Fax:* 703-836-5644 *E-mail:* rglawlit@gmail.com *Web Site:* www.ronaldgoldfarb.com, pg 574

Goldfind, Norman, Basic Health Publications Inc, 28812 Top of the World Dr, Laguna Beach, CA 92651 *Tel:* 949-715-7327 *Toll Free Tel:* 800-575-8890 (orders) *Fax:* 949-715-7328 *E-mail:* info@basichealthpub.com *Web Site:* www.basichealthpub.com, pg 32

Goldin, Frances, Frances Goldin Literary Agency, Inc, 57 E 11 St, Suite 5-B, New York, NY 10003 *Tel:* 212-777-0047 *Fax:* 212-228-1660 *E-mail:* agency@goldinlit.com *Web Site:* www.goldinlit.com, pg 575

Goldinger, Sharon, PeopleSpeak, 25260-I La Paz Rd, Suite 1, Laguna Hills, CA 92653 *Tel:* 949-581-6190 *Fax:* 949-581-4958 *E-mail:* pplspeak@att.net *Web Site:* www.detailsplease.com/peoplespeak, pg 552

Goldklang, Janice, The Globe Pequot Press, 246 Goose Lane, Guilford, CT 06437 *Tel:* 203-458-4500 *Toll Free Tel:* 800-243-0495 (orders only); 888-249-7586 (cust serv) *Fax:* 203-458-4601 *Toll Free Fax:* 800-820-2329 (orders & cust serv) *E-mail:* info@globepequot.com *Web Site:* www.globepequot.com, pg 104

Goldman, Barbara, ASM Press, 1752 "N" St NW, Washington, DC 20036-2904 *Tel:* 202-737-3600 *Toll Free Tel:* 800-546-2416 *Fax:* 202-942-9342 *E-mail:* books@asmusa.org *Web Site:* estore.asm.org, pg 25

Goldman, David, Jack Scagnetti Talent & Literary Agency, 5118 Vineland Ave, No 102, North Hollywood, CA 91601 *Tel:* 818 761-0580 *Web Site:* jackscagnettitalentandliteraryagency.books.officelive.com, pg 592

Goldman, Gloria, Judaica Press Inc, 123 Ditmas Ave, Brooklyn, NY 11218 *Tel:* 718-972-6200 *Toll Free Tel:* 800-972-6201 *Fax:* 718-972-6204 *E-mail:* info@judaicapress.com; orders@judaicapress.com *Web Site:* www.judaicapress.com, pg 137

Goldman, Gloria, Soncino Press Ltd, 123 Ditmas Ave, Brooklyn, NY 11218 *Tel:* 718-972-6200 *Toll Free Tel:* 800-972-6201 *Fax:* 718-972-6204 *E-mail:* info@soncino.com *Web Site:* www.soncino.com, pg 239

Goldman, Jeff, Barron's Educational Series Inc, 250 Wireless Blvd, Hauppauge, NY 11788 *Tel:* 631-434-3311 *Toll Free Tel:* 800-645-3476 *Fax:* 631-434-3723 *E-mail:* barrons@barronseduc.com *Web Site:* www.barronseduc.com, pg 31

Goldman, Jeffrey, Santa Monica Press LLC, 215 S Hwy 101, Suite 110, Solana Beach, CA 92075 *Tel:* 858-793-1890 *Toll Free Tel:* 800-784-9553 *Fax:* 858-777-0444 *E-mail:* books@santamonicapress.com *Web Site:* www.santamonicapress.com, pg 226

Goldman, Nicole, The Jim Henson Co, 1416 N La Brea Ave, Hollywood, CA 90028 *Tel:* 323-802-1500 *Fax:* 323-802-1825 *Web Site:* www.henson.com, pg 135

Goldsberry, Kristi, Ohio University Press, 215 Columbus Rd, Suite 101, Athens, OH 45701-2979 *Tel:* 740-593-1154 *Fax:* 740-593-4536 *Web Site:* www.ohioswallow.com, pg 184

Goldsberry, Kristi, Swallow Press, 215 Columbus Rd, Suite 101, Athens, OH 45701 *Tel:* 740-593-1158 (Jeff Kallet) *Fax:* 740-593-4536 *Web Site:* www.ohioswallow.com, pg 248

Goldsmith, Cathy, Random House Children's Books, 1745 Broadway, New York, NY 10019 *Tel:* 212-782-9000 *Toll Free Tel:* 800-200-3552 *Fax:* 212-782-9452 *Web Site:* randomhousekids.com, pg 213

Goldsmith, Connor, Lowenstein Associates Inc, 121 W 27 St, Suite 501, New York, NY 10001 *Tel:* 212-206-1630 *Fax:* 212-727-0280 *E-mail:* assistant@bookhaven.com (queries, no attachments) *Web Site:* www.lowensteinassociates.com, pg 582

Goldsmith, Keith, Vintage & Anchor Books, c/o Random House Inc, 1745 Broadway, New York, NY 10019 *Tel:* 212-572-2420 *E-mail:* vintageanchorpublicity@randomhouse.com *Web Site:* vintage-anchor.knopfdoubleday.com, pg 275

Goldsmith, Maureen, University of Pennsylvania Museum of Archaeology & Anthropology, 3260 South St, Philadelphia, PA 19104-6324 *Tel:* 215-898-5723 *Fax:* 215-573-2497 *E-mail:* info@pennmuseum.org; publications@pennmuseum.org *Web Site:* www.penn.museum, pg 268

Goldsmith, Michael, The Overlook Press, 141 Wooster St, Suite 4-B, New York, NY 10012 *Tel:* 212-673-2210; 845-679-6838 (orders & dist) *Fax:* 212-673-2296 *E-mail:* sales@overlookny.com (orders) *Web Site:* www.overlookpress.com, pg 189

Goldsmith, Richard, The Jim Henson Co, 1416 N La Brea Ave, Hollywood, CA 90028 *Tel:* 323-802-1500 *Fax:* 323-802-1825 *Web Site:* www.henson.com, pg 135

Goldstein, Cary, Simon & Schuster, 1230 Avenue of the Americas, New York, NY 10020 *Tel:* 212-698-7000 *Toll Free Tel:* 800-223-2348 (cust serv); 800-223-2336 (orders) *Toll Free Fax:* 800-943-9831 (orders) *Web Site:* www.simonandschuster.com, pg 234

Goldstein, Debra, DeFiore and Company, LLC, 47 E 19 St, 3rd fl, New York, NY 10003 *Tel:* 212-925-7744 *Fax:* 212-925-9803 *E-mail:* submissions@defioreandco.com; info@defioreandco.com *Web Site:* www.defioreandco.com, pg 568

Goldstein, Gary, Kensington Publishing Corp, 119 W 40 St, New York, NY 10018 *Tel:* 212-407-1500 *Toll Free Tel:* 800-221-2647 *Fax:* 212-935-0699 *Web Site:* www.kensingtonbooks.com, pg 139

Goldstein, Jeff, Trans-Atlantic Publications Inc, 311 Bainbridge St, Philadelphia, PA 19147 *Tel:* 215-925-5083 *Fax:* 215-925-1912 *Web Site:* www.transatlanticpub.com; www.businesstitles.com, pg 257

Goldstein, Justin, Binding Industries Association (BIA), 200 Deer Run Rd, Sewickley, PA 15143 *Tel:* 412-741-6860 *Toll Free Tel:* 800-910-4283 *Fax:* 412-741-2311 *E-mail:* printing@printing.org *Web Site:* www.printing.org, pg 618

Goldwasser, Tom, Antiquarian Booksellers' Association of America (ABAA), 20 W 44 St, Suite 507, New York, NY 10036 *Tel:* 212-944-8291 *Fax:* 212-944-8293 *E-mail:* hq@abaa.org *Web Site:* www.abaa.org, pg 615

Golembiewski, Joan, American Academy of Orthopaedic Surgeons, 6300 N River Rd, Rosemont, IL 60018-4262 *Tel:* 847-823-7186 *Toll Free Tel:* 800-346-2267 *Fax:* 847-823-8125 *Toll Free Fax:* 800-999-2939 *Web Site:* www.aaos.org, pg 10

Gollehon, John T, Gollehon Press Inc, 3655 Glenn Dr SE, Grand Rapids, MI 49546 *Tel:* 616-949-3515 *Fax:* 616-949-8674 *Web Site:* www.gollehonbooks.com, pg 104

Gollehon, Kathy, Gollehon Press Inc, 3655 Glenn Dr SE, Grand Rapids, MI 49546 *Tel:* 616-949-3515 *Fax:* 616-949-8674 *Web Site:* www.gollehonbooks.com, pg 104

Gollogly, Eugene, Lindisfarne Books, 610 Main St, Great Barrington, MA 01230 *Tel:* 413-528-8233 *Fax:* 413-528-8826 *E-mail:* service@lindisfarne.org *Web Site:* www.lindisfarne.org, pg 149

Gollogly, Gene, Lantern Books, 128 Second Place, Garden Suite, Brooklyn, NY 11231 *Tel:* 212-414-2275 *E-mail:* editorial@lanternbooks.com; info@lanternmedia.net *Web Site:* www.lanternbooks.com, pg 144

Gollogly, Gene, SteinerBooks, 610 Main St, Great Barrington, MA 01230 *Tel:* 413-528-8233 *Fax:* 413-528-8826 *E-mail:* friends@steinerbooks.org *Web Site:* www.steinerbooks.org, pg 244

Gollub, Matthew, Tortuga Press, 2777 Yulupa Ave, PMB 181, Santa Rosa, CA 95405 *Tel:* 707-544-4720 *Toll Free Tel:* 866-4TORTUGA (486-7884) *Fax:* 707-544-5609 *E-mail:* info@tortugapress.com *Web Site:* www.tortugapress.com, pg 256

Golob, Paul, Henry Holt and Company, LLC, 175 Fifth Ave, New York, NY 10010 *Tel:* 646-307-5151 *Toll Free Tel:* 888-330-8477 (orders) *Fax:* 646-307-5285 *E-mail:* firstname.lastname@hholt.com *Web Site:* www.henryholt.com, pg 122

Golski, Sara, Ten Speed Press, 2625 Alcatraz Ave, Unit 505, Berkeley, CA 94705 *Tel:* 510-285-3000 *Toll Free Tel:* 800-841-BOOK (841-2665) *E-mail:* csorders@randomhouse.com *Web Site:* crownpublishing.com/imprint/ten-speed-press, pg 252

Gomberg, David, Seven Footer Kids, 247 W 30 St, 11th fl, New York, NY 10001-2824 *Tel:* 212-710-9340 *Fax:* 212-710-9344 *E-mail:* info@sevenfooter.com *Web Site:* www.sevenfooterpress.com, pg 232

Gomberg, David, Seven Footer Press, 247 W 30 St, 2nd fl, New York, NY 10001-2824 *Tel:* 212-710-9340 *Fax:* 212-710-9344 *E-mail:* info@sevenfooter.com *Web Site:* www.sevenfooterpress.com, pg 232

Gomez, Eric, Beckett Media LLC, 22840 Savi Ranch Pkwy, Suite 200, Yorba Linda, CA 92887 *Tel:* 714-939-9991 *Toll Free Tel:* 800-332-3330 *Fax:* 714-939-9909 *Toll Free Fax:* 800-249-7761 *Web Site:* www.beckettmedia.com, pg 33

Gomez, Mary Ann, National Association of Hispanic Publications Inc (NAHP), 529 14 St NW, Suite 1126, Washington, DC 20045 *Tel:* 202-662-7250 *Fax:* 202-662-7251 *Web Site:* www.nahp.org, pg 628

Gomory, Stephanie, Abbeville Publishing Group, 137 Varick St, Suite 504, New York, NY 10013 *Tel:* 212-366-5585 *Toll Free Tel:* 800-ART-BOOK (278-2665) *Fax:* 212-366-6966 *E-mail:* abbeville@abbeville.com; marketing@abbeville.com; sales@abbeville.com; rights@abbeville.com *Web Site:* www.abbeville.com, pg 2

Goncalves, Andrea, United Nations Publications, 2 United Nations Plaza, Rm DC2-0853, New York, NY 10017 *Tel:* 212-963-8302 *Toll Free Tel:* 800-253-9646 *Fax:* 212-963-3489 *E-mail:* publications@un.org *Web Site:* unp.un.org, pg 262

Goncharenko, Kathy, Scholastic Canada Ltd, 604 King St W, Toronto, ON M5V 1E1, Canada *Tel:* 905-887-7323 *Toll Free Tel:* 800-268-3848 (CN) *Fax:* 905-887-1131 *Toll Free Fax:* 866-346-1288 *Web Site:* www.scholastic.ca, pg 518

Gong Stewart, Mrs Shane, University Press of Mississippi, 3825 Ridgewood Rd, Jackson, MS 39211-6492 *Tel:* 601-432-6205 *Toll Free Tel:* 800-737-7788 (orders & cust serv) *Fax:* 601-432-6217 *E-mail:* press@mississippi.edu *Web Site:* www.upress.state.ms.us, pg 271

Gong, Wakeford, Pureplay Press, 195 26 Ave, No 2, San Francisco, CA 94121 *Tel:* 310-597-0328 *E-mail:* info@pureplaypress.com *Web Site:* www.pureplaypress.com, pg 210

Gong-Wong, Kirsten, Locus Awards, PO Box 13305, Oakland, CA 94661-0305 *Tel:* 510-339-9196 *Fax:* 510-339-9198 *E-mail:* locus@locusmag.com *Web Site:* www.locusmag.com, pg 718

Gonnason, Hayley, Holiday House Inc, 425 Madison Ave, New York, NY 10017 *Tel:* 212-688-0085 *Fax:* 212-421-6134 *E-mail:* holiday@holidayhouse.com *Web Site:* www.holidayhouse.com, pg 121

Gonneville, Michel, La Fondation Emile Nelligan, 100 Sherbrooke St, Suite 202, Montreal, QC H2X 1C3, Canada *Tel:* 514-278-4657 *Fax:* 514-278-1943 *E-mail:* info@fondation-nelligan.org *Web Site:* www.fondation-nelligan.org, pg 623

Gore, Richard, LaChance Publishing LLC, 120 Bond St, Brooklyn, NY 11217 *Tel:* 917-855-7537 *Fax:* 646-390-1326 *E-mail:* info@lachancepublishing.com *Web Site:* www.lachancepublishing.com, pg 143

Gorelick, Amy, University Press of Florida, 15 NW 15 St, Gainesville, FL 32603-2079 *Tel:* 352-392-1351 *Toll Free Tel:* 800-226-3822 (orders only) *Fax:* 352-392-0590 *Toll Free Fax:* 800-680-1955 (orders only) *E-mail:* info@upf.com *Web Site:* www.upf.com, pg 271

Goretsky, Tal, Scribner, 1230 Avenue of the Americas, New York, NY 10020, pg 230

Gorg, Brian, Educational Book & Media Association (EBMA), 37 Main St, Suite 203, Warrenton, VA 20186 *Tel:* 540-318-7770 *Fax:* 202-962-3939 *E-mail:* info@edupaperback.org *Web Site:* www.edupaperback.org, pg 623

Gorg, Brian, Jeremiah Ludington Award, 37 Main St, Suite 203, Warrenton, VA 20186 *Tel:* 540-318-7770 *Fax:* 202-962-3939 *E-mail:* info@edupaperback.org *Web Site:* www.edupaperback.org, pg 719

Gorham, Sarah, Sarabande Books Inc, 2234 Dundee Rd, Suite 200, Louisville, KY 40205 *Tel:* 502-458-4028 *Fax:* 502-458-4065 *E-mail:* info@sarabandebooks.org *Web Site:* www.sarabandebooks.org, pg 226

Gorlinsky, Raelene, Ellora's Cave, 1056 Home Ave, Akron, OH 44310-3302 *Tel:* 330-253-3521 *E-mail:* service@ellorascave.com; comments@ellorascave.com *Web Site:* www.ellorascave.com, pg 86

Gorman, Don, Rocky Mountain Books Ltd (RMB), 103-1075 Pendergast St, Victoria, BC V8V 0A1, Canada *Tel:* 250-360-0829 *Fax:* 250-386-0829 *Web Site:* www.rmbooks.com, pg 517

Gorman, Maire, Houghton Mifflin Harcourt Trade & Reference Division, 222 Berkeley St, Boston, MA 02116-3764 *Tel:* 617-351-5000 *Toll Free Tel:* 800-225-3362 *Web Site:* www.houghtonmifflinbooks.com, pg 124

Gorzelski, David, Harmonie Park Press, Liberty Professional Ctr, 35675 Mound Rd, Sterling Heights, MI 48310-4727 *Tel:* 586-979-2077; 586-979-1844 (cust serv) *Toll Free Tel:* 800-422-4880 *Fax:* 586-979-1786; 586-979-1863 (cust serv) *E-mail:* info@harmonieparkpress.com *Web Site:* harmonieparkpress.com, pg 113

Gorzelski, Elaine, Harmonie Park Press, Liberty Professional Ctr, 35675 Mound Rd, Sterling Heights, MI 48310-4727 *Tel:* 586-979-2077; 586-979-1844 (cust serv) *Toll Free Tel:* 800-422-4880 *Fax:* 586-979-1786; 586-979-1863 (cust serv) *E-mail:* info@harmonieparkpress.com *Web Site:* harmonieparkpress.com, pg 113

Gosnell, Brice, Lonely Planet, 150 Linden St, Oakland, CA 94607 *Tel:* 510-893-8555 *Toll Free Tel:* 800-275-8555 (orders) *Fax:* 510-893-8563 *E-mail:* info@lonelyplanet.com *Web Site:* www.lonelyplanet.com, pg 152

Gosnell, Linda, Scholastic Canada Ltd, 604 King St W, Toronto, ON M5V 1E1, Canada *Tel:* 905-887-7323 *Toll Free Tel:* 800-268-3848 (CN) *Fax:* 905-887-1131 *Toll Free Fax:* 866-346-1288 *Web Site:* www.scholastic.ca, pg 518

Gosse, Jonathan F, American Technical Publishers Inc, 10100 Orland Pkwy, Suite 200, Orland Park, IL 60467-5756 *Tel:* 708-957-1100 *Toll Free Tel:* 800-323-3471 *Fax:* 708-957-1101 *E-mail:* service@americantech.net *Web Site:* www.go2atp.com, pg 17

Gossett, Bruce, American Society of Civil Engineers (ASCE), 1801 Alexander Bell Dr, Reston, VA 20191-4400 *Tel:* 703-295-6300 *Toll Free Tel:* 800-548-2723 *Fax:* 703-295-6278 *E-mail:* marketing@asce.org *Web Site:* www.asce.org, pg 16

Gottfried, Chet, C+S Gottfried, 619 Cricklewood Dr, State College, PA 16803 *Tel:* 814-237-2580 *Web Site:* www.lookoutnow.com/index2.html, pg 547

Gottfried, Susan, C+S Gottfried, 619 Cricklewood Dr, State College, PA 16803 *Tel:* 814-237-2580 *Web Site:* www.lookoutnow.com/index2.html, pg 547

Gottier, Aaron, P & R Publishing Co, 1102 Marble Hill Rd, Phillipsburg, NJ 08865 *Tel:* 908-454-0505 *Toll Free Tel:* 800-631-0094 *Fax:* 908-859-2390 *E-mail:* sales@prpbooks.com; generalinfo@prpbooks.com *Web Site:* prpbooks.com, pg 190

Gottlieb, Carl, Writers Guild of America Awards, 7000 W Third St, Los Angeles, CA 90048 *Tel:* 323-951-4000; 323-782-4569 *Fax:* 323-782-4800 *Web Site:* www.wga.org, pg 752

Gottlieb, Carl, Writers Guild of America, West (WGAW), 7000 W Third St, Los Angeles, CA 90048 *Tel:* 323-951-4000 *Toll Free Tel:* 800-548-4532 *Fax:* 323-782-4800 *Web Site:* www.wga.org, pg 639

Gottlieb, Mark, Trident Media Group LLC, 41 Madison Ave, 36th fl, New York, NY 10010 *Tel:* 212-262-4810 *Fax:* 212-262-4849 *Web Site:* www.tridentmediagroup.com, pg 598

Gottlieb, Richard, Grey House Publishing Inc™, 4919 Rte 22, Amenia, NY 12501 *Tel:* 518-789-8700 *Toll Free Tel:* 800-562-2139 *Fax:* 518-789-0556 *E-mail:* books@greyhouse.com *Web Site:* www.greyhouse.com, pg 108

Gottlieb, Robert, Trident Media Group LLC, 41 Madison Ave, 36th fl, New York, NY 10010 *Tel:* 212-262-4810 *Fax:* 212-262-4849 *Web Site:* www.tridentmediagroup.com, pg 598

Gottstein, Adam, Volcano Press, 21496 National St, Volcano, CA 95689 *Tel:* 209-296-7989 *Toll Free Tel:* 800-879-9636 *Fax:* 209-296-4515 *E-mail:* sales@volcanopress.com *Web Site:* www.volcanopress.com, pg 275

Gottstein, Ruth, Volcano Press, 21496 National St, Volcano, CA 95689 *Tel:* 209-296-7989 *Toll Free Tel:* 800-879-9636 *Fax:* 209-296-4515 *E-mail:* sales@volcanopress.com *Web Site:* www.volcanopress.com, pg 275

Gougeon, Guy, Flammarion Quebec, 375 Ave Laurier W, Montreal, QC H2V 2K3, Canada *Tel:* 514-277-8807 *Fax:* 514-278-2085 *E-mail:* info@flammarion.qc.ca *Web Site:* www.flammarion.qc.ca, pg 505

Goughnour, Kerrie, EMC Publishing, 875 Montreal Way, St Paul, MN 55102 *Tel:* 651-290-2800 (corp) *Toll Free Tel:* 800-328-1452 *Fax:* 651-290-2899 *Toll Free Fax:* 800-328-4564 *E-mail:* educate@emcp.com *Web Site:* www.emcp.com, pg 87

Gouhin, Patrick, International Society of Automation (ISA), 67 T W Alexander Dr, Research Triangle Park, NC 27709-0185 *Tel:* 919-549-8411 *Fax:* 919-549-8288 *E-mail:* info@isa.org *Web Site:* www.isa.org, pg 134

Gould, Barbara, National Magazine Awards, 425 Adelaide St W, Suite 700, Toronto, ON M5V 3C1, Canada *Tel:* 416-422-1358 *Fax:* 416-504-0437 *E-mail:* staff@magazine-awards.com *Web Site:* www.magazine-awards.com, pg 727

Gould, Robert, Big Guy Books Inc, 1042 N El Camino Real, Suite B-231, Encinitas, CA 92024 *Tel:* 760-652-5360 *Toll Free Tel:* 800-536-3030 (booksellers' cust serv) *Fax:* 760-652-5362 *E-mail:* info@bigguybooks.com *Web Site:* www.bigguybooks.com, pg 37

Gould, Scott, RLR Associates Ltd, 7 W 51 St, New York, NY 10019 *Tel:* 212-541-8641 *Fax:* 212-262-7084 *Web Site:* www.rlrassociates.net, pg 591

Gould, Steven, Science Fiction & Fantasy Writers of America Inc (SFWA), PO Box 3238, Enfield, CT 06083-3238 *E-mail:* office@sfwa.org *Web Site:* www.sfwa.org, pg 635

Gould, Steven, SFWA Nebula Awards, PO Box 3238, Enfield, CT 06083-3238 *E-mail:* office@sfwa.org *Web Site:* www.sfwa.org, pg 741

Goulding, Judy, Modern Language Association of America (MLA), 26 Broadway, 3rd fl, New York, NY 10004-1789 *Tel:* 646-576-5000 *Fax:* 646-458-0030 *E-mail:* info@mla.org *Web Site:* www.mla.org, pg 168

Gourlay, Jonathan, The MacDowell Colony, 100 High St, Peterborough, NH 03458 *Tel:* 603-924-3886 *Fax:* 603-924-9142 *E-mail:* info@macdowellcolony.org; admissions@macdowellcolony.org *Web Site:* www.macdowellcolony.org, pg 720

Gouzoules, Leon, Firefly Books Ltd, 50 Staples Ave, Unit 1, Richmond Hill, ON L4B 0A7, Canada *Tel:* 416-499-8412 *Toll Free Tel:* 800-387-6192 (CN); 800-387-5085 (US) *Fax:* 416-499-8313 *Toll Free Fax:* 800-450-0391 (CN); 800-565-6034 (US) *E-mail:* service@fireflybooks.com *Web Site:* www.fireflybooks.com, pg 505

Gover, Robert, Eric Hoffer Award for Short Prose, PO Box 11, Titusville, NJ 08560 *Fax:* 609-964-1718 *E-mail:* info@hofferaward.com *Web Site:* www.hofferaward.com, pg 710

Goyette, Cecile, Blue Apple Books, 515 Valley St, Suite 170, Maplewood, NJ 07040 *Tel:* 973-763-8191 *Toll Free Tel:* 800-722-6657; 800-733-3000 (orders) *Fax:* 973-763-5944 *E-mail:* info@blueapplebooks.com *Web Site:* blueapplebooks.com, pg 41

Grace, Judith, Cambridge University Press, 32 Avenue of the Americas, New York, NY 10013-2473 *Tel:* 212-924-3900; 212-337-5000 *Toll Free Tel:* 800-899-5222 *Fax:* 212-691-3239 *E-mail:* newyork@cambridge.org *Web Site:* www.cambridge.org/us, pg 51

Grace, Michelle, American Book Publishing, 14435-C Big Basin Way, No 155, Saratoga, CA 95070 *Tel:* 415-935-5082 *Toll Free Tel:* 800-684-8746 *E-mail:* info@american-book.com; orders@american-book.com *Web Site:* www.americanbookpublishing.com, pg 11

Grad, Doug, Doug Grad Literary Agency Inc, 156 Prospect Park West, No 3L, Brooklyn, NY 11215 *Tel:* 718-788-6067 *E-mail:* query@dgliterary.com *Web Site:* www.dgliterary.com, pg 575

Graddy, Julia, Maupin House Publishing, 2300 NW 71 Place, Gainesville, FL 32653 *Tel:* 352-373-5588 *Toll Free Tel:* 800-524-0634 *Fax:* 352-373-5546 *E-mail:* info@maupinhouse.com *Web Site:* www.maupinhouse.com, pg 159

Graddy, Robert, Maupin House Publishing, 2300 NW 71 Place, Gainesville, FL 32653 *Tel:* 352-373-5588 *Toll Free Tel:* 800-524-0634 *Fax:* 352-373-5546 *E-mail:* info@maupinhouse.com *Web Site:* www.maupinhouse.com, pg 159

Grady, Lynn, HarperCollins General Books Group, 10 E 53 St, New York, NY 10022 *Tel:* 212-207-7000 *Fax:* 212-207-7633 *Web Site:* www.harpercollins.com, pg 113

Grady, Thomas, Ave Maria Press, PO Box 428, Notre Dame, IN 46556-0428 *Tel:* 574-287-2831 *Toll Free Tel:* 800-282-1865 *Fax:* 574-239-2904 *Toll Free Fax:* 800-282-5681 *E-mail:* avemariapress.1@nd.edu *Web Site:* www.avemariapress.com, pg 28

Graff, Emily, Simon & Schuster, 1230 Avenue of the Americas, New York, NY 10020 *Tel:* 212-698-7000 *Toll Free Tel:* 800-223-2348 (cust serv); 800-223-2336 (orders) *Toll Free Fax:* 800-943-9831 (orders) *Web Site:* www.simonandschuster.com, pg 234

Grafton, John, Dover Publications Inc, 31 E Second St, Mineola, NY 11501-3852 *Tel:* 516-294-7000 *Toll Free Tel:* 800-223-3130 (orders) *Fax:* 516-742-6953; 516-742-5049 (orders) *Web Site:* store.doverdirect.com, pg 81

Graham, Bethany, Vanderbilt University Press, 2014 Broadway, Suite 320, Nashville, TN 37203 *Tel:* 615-322-3585 *Toll Free Tel:* 800-627-7377 (orders only) *Fax:* 615-343-8823 *Toll Free Fax:* 800-735-0476 (orders only) *E-mail:* vupress@vanderbilt.edu *Web Site:* www.vanderbiltuniversitypress.com, pg 274

Graham, Bonny, National Council of Teachers of English (NCTE), 1111 W Kenyon Rd, Urbana, IL 61801-1096 *Tel:* 217-328-3870 *Toll Free Tel:* 877-369-6283 (cust serv) *Fax:* 217-328-9645 *E-mail:* orders@ncte.org *Web Site:* www.ncte.org, pg 174

Graham, Earl, Graham Agency, 311 W 43 St, New York, NY 10036 *Tel:* 212-489-7730, pg 575

Graham, Heather, Horror Writers Association (HWA), 244 Fifth Ave, Suite 2767, New York, NY 10001 *E-mail:* hwa@horror.org *Web Site:* www.horror.org, pg 624

Graham, Jon, Bear & Co Inc, One Park St, Rochester, VT 05767 *Tel:* 802-767-3174 *Toll Free Tel:* 800-932-3277 *Fax:* 802-767-3726 *E-mail:* customerservice@InnerTraditions.com *Web Site:* InnerTraditions.com, pg 33

Graham, Jon, Inner Traditions International Ltd, One Park St, Rochester, VT 05767 *Tel:* 802-767-3174 *Toll Free Tel:* 800-246-8648 *Fax:* 802-767-3726 *E-mail:* customerservice@InnerTraditions.com *Web Site:* www.InnerTraditions.com, pg 130

Graham, Joseph, The American Chemical Society, 1155 16 St NW, Washington, DC 20036 *Tel:* 202-872-4600 *Fax:* 202-872-6067 *E-mail:* help@acs.org *Web Site:* www.acs.org, pg 12

Graham, Kassia, New York Media Works, 112 Franklin St, New York, NY 10013 *Tel:* 646-369-5681 *Fax:* 646-810-4033 *E-mail:* info@nymediaworks.com *Web Site:* www.nymediaworks.com, pg 528

Graham, Mary, Thomas Nelson Inc, 501 Nelson Place, Nashville, TN 37214 *Tel:* 615-889-9000 *Toll Free Tel:* 800-251-4000 *Fax:* 615-902-1548 *E-mail:* publicity@thomasnelson.com *Web Site:* www.thomasnelson.com, pg 255

Graham, Nan, Scribner, 1230 Avenue of the Americas, New York, NY 10020, pg 230

Graham, Phil, F+W Media Inc, 10151 Carver Rd, Suite 200, Blue Ash, OH 45242 *Tel:* 513-531-2690 *Toll Free Tel:* 800-289-0963 (trade accts); 800-258-0929 (orders) *E-mail:* contact_us@fwmedia.com *Web Site:* www.fwmedia.com, pg 92

Graham, Phil, North Light Books, 10151 Carver Rd, Suite 200, Blue Ash, OH 45242 *Tel:* 513-531-2690 *Toll Free Tel:* 800-666-0963 *Fax:* 513-891-7185 *Toll Free Fax:* 888-590-4082 *E-mail:* contact_us@fwmedia.com *Web Site:* www.fwmedia.com, pg 181

Graham, Phil, Writer's Digest Books, 10151 Carver Rd, Suite 200, Blue Ash, OH 45242 *Tel:* 513-531-2690 *Toll Free Tel:* 800-289-0963 *Fax:* 513-531-7185 *E-mail:* writersdigest@fwmedia.com (edit) *Web Site:* www.writersdigest.com, pg 286

Graham, Wendy, Scholastic Canada Ltd, 604 King St W, Toronto, ON M5V 1E1, Canada *Tel:* 905-887-7323 *Toll Free Tel:* 800-268-3848 (CN) *Fax:* 905-887-1131 *Toll Free Fax:* 866-346-1288 *Web Site:* www.scholastic.ca, pg 518

Grahek, Greg, AACC International, 3340 Pilot Knob Rd, St Paul, MN 55121 *Tel:* 651-454-7250 *Fax:* 651-454-0766 *E-mail:* aacc@scisoc.org *Web Site:* www.aaccnet.org, pg 2

Grahek, Greg, American Phytopathological Society (APS), 3340 Pilot Knob Rd, St Paul, MN 55121 *Tel:* 651-454-7250 *Toll Free Tel:* 800-328-7560 *Fax:* 651-454-0766 *E-mail:* aps@scisoc.org *Web Site:* www.apsnet.org, pg 15

Grahek, Greg, APS PRESS, 3340 Pilot Knob Rd, St Paul, MN 55121 *Tel:* 651-454-7250 *Toll Free Tel:* 800-328-7560 *Fax:* 651-454-0766 *E-mail:* aps@scisoc.org *Web Site:* www.shopapspress.org, pg 21

Grahek, Greg, Eagan Press, 3340 Pilot Knob Rd, St Paul, MN 55121 *Tel:* 651-454-7250 *Toll Free Tel:* 800-328-7560 *Fax:* 651-454-0766 *E-mail:* aacc@scisoc.org *Web Site:* www.aaccnet.org, pg 83

Grain, Tim, Birch Brook Press, PO Box 81, Delhi, NY 13753-0081 *Tel:* 607-746-7453 (book sales & prodn) *Fax:* 607-746-7453 *E-mail:* birchbrook@copper.net *Web Site:* www.birchbrookpress.info, pg 38

Grajkowski, Michelle, 3 Seas Literary Agency, PO Box 8571, Madison, WI 53708 *Tel:* 608-834-9317, pg 597

Grall, Shirley, McGraw-Hill Create, 501 Bell St, Dubuque, IA 52001 *Tel:* 563-584-6000 *Fax:* 563-584-6600 *E-mail:* first_last@mcgraw-hill.com *Web Site:* www.mhhe.com, pg 160

Gramaglia, Maria Pia, Rizzoli International Publications Inc, 300 Park Ave S, 4th fl, New York, NY 10010-5399 *Tel:* 212-387-3400 *Toll Free Tel:* 800-522-6657 (orders only) *Fax:* 212-387-3535 *E-mail:* publicity@rizzoliusa.com *Web Site:* www.rizzoliusa.com, pg 219

Grames, Juliet, Soho Press Inc, 853 Broadway, New York, NY 10003 *Tel:* 212-260-1900 *Fax:* 212-260-1902 *E-mail:* soho@sohopress.com; publicity@sohopress.com *Web Site:* www.sohopress.com, pg 239

Grammick, Jan, Worldwide Library, 225 Duncan Mill Rd, Don Mills, ON M3B 3K9, Canada *Tel:* 416-445-5860 *Toll Free Tel:* 888-432-4879 *Fax:* 416-445-8655; 416-445-8736 *E-mail:* CustomerService@harlequin.com *Web Site:* www.harlequin.com, pg 525

Grandstaff, Emily, The University of Virginia Press, PO Box 400318, Charlottesville, VA 22904-4318 *Tel:* 434-924-3468 (cust serv); 434-924-3469 (cust serv) *Toll Free Tel:* 800-831-3406 (orders) *Fax:* 434-982-2655 *Toll Free Fax:* 877-288-6400 *E-mail:* vapress@virginia.edu *Web Site:* www.upress.virginia.edu, pg 270

Granger, Heather, Law Tribune Books, 201 Ann Uccello St, 4th fl, Hartford, CT 06103 *Tel:* 860-527-7900 *Fax:* 860-527-7433 *E-mail:* lawtribune@alm.com *Web Site:* www.ctlawtribune.com, pg 144

Granitto, Diana, Institute of Environmental Sciences and Technology - IEST, 2340 S Arlington Heights Rd, Suite 100, Arlington Heights, IL 60005-4516 *Tel:* 847-981-0100 *Fax:* 847-981-4130 *E-mail:* information@iest.org *Web Site:* www.iest.org, pg 131

Grant, Ashley, A Cappela Publishing, PO Box 3691, Sarasota, FL 34230-3691 *Tel:* 941-351-2050 *Fax:* 941-351-4735 *E-mail:* acappub@aol.com *Web Site:* www.acappela.com, pg 1

Grant, Bob, Price World Publishing LLC, 1300 W Belmont Ave, Suite 20-G, Chicago, IL 60657 *Toll Free Tel:* 888-234-6896 *Fax:* 216-803-0350 *E-mail:* publishing@priceworldpublishing.com; info@priceworldpublishing.com *Web Site:* www.priceworldpublishing.com, pg 206

Grant, Darlene, The Pilgrim Press/United Church Press, 700 Prospect Ave, Cleveland, OH 44115-1100 *Toll Free Tel:* 800-537-3394 (cust serv-indivs); 800-654-5129 (cust serv-commercial accts) *Fax:* 216-736-2206 (orders) *E-mail:* proposals@thepilgrimpress.com *Web Site:* www.thepilgrimpress.com; www.unitedchurchpress.com, pg 202

Grant, Donna, Canadian Plains Research Center, 2 Research Dr, Regina, SK S4S 7H9, Canada *Tel:* 306-585-4758 *Toll Free Tel:* 866-874-2257 *Fax:* 306-585-4699 *E-mail:* canadian.plains@uregina.ca *Web Site:* www.cprc.ca, pg 497

Grant, Janet Kobobel, Books & Such, 52 Mission Circle, Suite 122, PMB 170, Santa Rosa, CA 95409-5370 *Tel:* 707-538-4184 *Web Site:* booksandsuch.com, pg 563

Grant, Jerome, Pearson Business Publishing, One Lake St, Upper Saddle River, NJ 07458 *Tel:* 201-236-7000 *Web Site:* www.pearsonhighered.com, pg 195

Grant, Penny, Sinauer Associates Inc, 23 Plumtree Rd, Sunderland, MA 01375 *Tel:* 413-549-4300 *Fax:* 413-549-1118 *E-mail:* publish@sinauer.com; orders@sinauer.com *Web Site:* www.sinauer.com, pg 236

Grantham, Charles E, Contemporary Publishing Co of Raleigh Inc, 5849 Lease Lane, Raleigh, NC 27617 *Tel:* 919-851-8221 *Fax:* 919-851-6666 *E-mail:* questions@contemporarypublishing.com *Web Site:* www.contemporarypublishing.com, pg 66

Grantham, Dean, Graphic World Publishing Services, 11687 Adie Rd, St Louis, MO 63043 *Tel:* 314-567-9854 *Fax:* 314-567-7178 *E-mail:* quote@gwinc.com *Web Site:* www.gwinc.com, pg 547

Granville, Chris, Basic Books, 250 W 57 St, 15th fl, New York, NY 10107 *Tel:* 212-340-8164 *Fax:* 212-340-8135 *E-mail:* perseus.promos@perseusbooks.com *Web Site:* www.basicbooks.com; perseusbooks.com, pg 31

Grathwohl, Casper, Oxford University Press USA, 198 Madison Ave, New York, NY 10016 *Tel:* 212-726-6000 *Toll Free Tel:* 800-451-7556 (orders); 800-445-9714 (cust serv) *Fax:* 919-677-1303 *E-mail:* custserv.us@oup.com *Web Site:* www.oup.com/us, pg 189

Gratz, Mike, Olde & Oppenheim Publishers, 3219 N Margate Place, Chandler, AZ 85224 *E-mail:* olde_oppenheim@hotmail.com *Web Site:* oldeandoppenheimpublishers.com, pg 185

Grau, Julie, Random House Publishing Group, 1745 Broadway, New York, NY 10019 *Toll Free Tel:* 800-200-3552 *Web Site:* atrandom.com, pg 214

Graul, Donald O Jr, American Independent Writers (AIW), 7817 Evening Lane, Alexandria, VA 22306 *Tel:* 703-660-9336 *Fax:* 703-660-9321 *E-mail:* info@amerindywriters.org *Web Site:* www.amerindywriters.org, pg 613

Grauman, Judith, The Guilford Press, 72 Spring St, 4th fl, New York, NY 10012 *Tel:* 212-431-9800 *Toll Free Tel:* 800-365-7006 (ext 1, orders) *Fax:* 212-966-6708 *E-mail:* orders@guilford.com; info@guilford.com *Web Site:* www.guilford.com, pg 109

Gray, Bob, Central Recovery Press (CRP), 3321 N Buffalo Dr, Suite 275, Las Vegas, NV 89129 *Tel:* 702-868-5830 *Fax:* 702-868-5831 *E-mail:* info@centralrecovery.com *Web Site:* centralrecoverypress.com, pg 57

Gray, David, Gray & Company Publishers, 1588 E 40 St, Suite 3-A, Cleveland, OH 44103 *Tel:* 216-431-2665 *Toll Free Tel:* 800-915-3609 *E-mail:* sales@grayco.com *Web Site:* www.grayco.com, pg 106

Gray, Jason, University of Wisconsin Press, 1930 Monroe St, 3rd fl, Madison, WI 53711-2059 *Tel:* 608-263-0668 *Toll Free Tel:* 800-621-2736 (orders) *Fax:* 608-263-1173 *Toll Free Fax:* 800-621-2736 (orders) *E-mail:* uwiscpress@uwpress.wisc.edu (main off) *Web Site:* www.wisc.edu/wisconsinpress, pg 270

Gray, Kevin, Trafford, 1663 Liberty Dr, Bloomington, IN 47403 *Toll Free Tel:* 888-232-4444 *E-mail:* customersupport@trafford.com *Web Site:* www.trafford.com, pg 257

Gray, Phil, Self-Realization Fellowship Publishers, 3208 Humboldt St, Los Angeles, CA 90031 *Tel:* 323-276-6002 *Toll Free Tel:* 888-773-8680 *Fax:* 323-927-1624 *Web Site:* www.srfpublishers.org, pg 231

Gray, Thomas, Upper Access Inc, 87 Upper Access Rd, Hinesburg, VT 05461 *Tel:* 802-482-2988 *Toll Free Tel:* 800-310-8320 *Fax:* 802-304-1005 *E-mail:* info@upperaccess.com *Web Site:* www.upperaccess.com, pg 272

Grayson, Ashley, Ashley Grayson Literary Agency, 1342 W 18 St, San Pedro, CA 90732 *Tel:* 310-548-4672 *E-mail:* graysonagent@earthlink.net; rights@graysonagency.com *Web Site:* graysonagency.com/blog/, pg 575

Grayson, Carolyn, Ashley Grayson Literary Agency, 1342 W 18 St, San Pedro, CA 90732 *Tel:* 310-548-4672 *E-mail:* graysonagent@earthlink.net; rights@graysonagency.com *Web Site:* graysonagency.com/blog/, pg 575

Graziadie, Claude, Statistics Canada, 150 Tunney's Pasture Driveway, Ottawa, ON K1A 0T6, Canada *Tel:* 613-951-8116 (gen inquiries) *Toll Free Tel:* 800-263-1136 (CN & US, gen inquiries); 800-267-6677 (prods & servs) *Fax:* 613-951-0581 *Toll Free Fax:* 877-287-4369 (orders) *E-mail:* infostats@statcan.gc.ca *Web Site:* statcan.gc.ca, pg 520

Grebenar, Sandy, Houghton Mifflin Harcourt Trade & Reference Division, 222 Berkeley St, Boston, MA 02116-3764 *Tel:* 617-351-5000 *Toll Free Tel:* 800-225-3362 *Web Site:* www.houghtonmifflinbooks.com, pg 124

Greco, Al, Carson-Dellosa Publishing LLC, PO Box 35665, Greensboro, NC 27425-5665 *Tel:* 336-632-0084 *Toll Free Tel:* 800-321-0943 *Fax:* 336-808-3273 *Toll Free Fax:* 800-535-2669 *E-mail:* custsvc@carsondellosa.com *Web Site:* www.carsondellosa.com, pg 53

Greco, Albert N, Fordham University, Graduate School of Business Administration, Gabelli School of Business, 441 E Fordham Rd, Hughes Hall, Rm 516, Bronx, NY 10458 *Tel:* 718-817-1894 *Web Site:* www.bnet.fordham.edu, pg 678

Greco, John, American Bible Society, 1865 Broadway, New York, NY 10023-7505 *Tel:* 212-408-1200 *Toll Free Tel:* 800-322-4253 *Fax:* 212-408-1512 *E-mail:* info@americanbible.org *Web Site:* www.americanbible.org, pg 11

Greco, Marilyn, Schoolhouse Network Inc, PO Box 17676, Fountain Hills, AZ 85269 *Tel:* 973-206-1389 *E-mail:* info@schoolhousenetwork.com *Web Site:* www.schoolhousenetwork.com, pg 555

Greeman, Amy, Storey Publishing LLC, 210 MASS MoCA Way, North Adams, MA 01247 *Tel:* 413-346-2100 *Toll Free Tel:* 800-441-5700 (orders); 800-793-9396 (edit) *Fax:* 413-346-2199; 413-346-2196 (edit) *E-mail:* sales@storey.com *Web Site:* www.storey.com, pg 246

Green, Anthony, Quackenworth Publishing, PO Box 4747, Culver City, CA 90231-4747 *Tel:* 310-945-5634 *Toll Free Tel:* 888-701-4991 *Fax:* 310-945-5709 *Toll Free Fax:* 888-892-6339 *E-mail:* info@quackenworth.com *Web Site:* www.quackenworth.com; www.wittybittybunch.com, pg 211

Green, Dan, Pom Inc, 21 Vista Dr, Great Neck, NY 11021 *Tel:* 516-487-3441, pg 589

Green, Erin, Boys Town Press, 14100 Crawford St, Boys Town, NE 68010 *Tel:* 402-498-1320 *Toll Free Tel:* 800-282-6657 *Fax:* 402-498-1310 *E-mail:* btpress@boystown.org *Web Site:* www.boystownpress.org, pg 45

Green, Frank, Bard Society, 1358 Tiber Ave, Jacksonville, FL 32207, pg 667

Green, George, America West Publishers, PO Box 599, Hayden, ID 83835 *Tel:* 775-885-0700 *Toll Free Tel:* 800-729-4131 *Web Site:* www.nohoax.com, pg 10

Green, James A, Greenwood Research Books & Software, PO Box 12102, Wichita, KS 67277-2102 *Tel:* 316-214-5103 *Web Site:* greenray4ever.com (ordering), pg 108

Green, Jane, PennWell Books, 1421 S Sheridan Rd, Tulsa, OK 74112 *Tel:* 918-831-9410 *Toll Free Tel:* 800-752-9764 *Fax:* 918-831-9555 *E-mail:* sales@pennwell.com *Web Site:* www.pennwellbooks.com, pg 198

Green, Judy, The Young Adult Book Award, 1150 Morrison Dr, Suite 400, Ottawa, ON K2H 8S9, Canada *Tel:* 613-232-9625 *Fax:* 613-563-9895 *E-mail:* info@cla.ca *Web Site:* www.cla.ca, pg 752

Green, Karen, The BC Book Prizes, 207 W Hastings St, Suite 901, Vancouver, BC V6B 1H7, Canada *Tel:* 604-687-2405 *Fax:* 604-687-2435 *E-mail:* info@bcbookprizes.ca *Web Site:* www.bcbookprizes.ca, pg 690

Green, Kate, Clarion Books, 215 Park Ave S, New York, NY 10003 *Tel:* 212-420-5883 *Toll Free Tel:* 800-225-3362 (orders) *Fax:* 212-420-5855 *Toll Free Fax:* 800-634-7568 (orders) *Web Site:* www.houghtonmifflinbooks.com, pg 62

Green, Mary, Martingale®, 19021 120 Ave NE, Suite 102, Bothell, WA 98011 *Tel:* 425-483-3313 *Toll Free Tel:* 800-426-3126 *Fax:* 425-486-7596 *E-mail:* info@martingale-pub.com *Web Site:* www.martingale-pub.com, pg 158

Green, Michael, Philomel, 345 Hudson St, New York, NY 10014 *Tel:* 212-366-2000, pg 201

Green, Nancy N, W W Norton & Company Inc, 500 Fifth Ave, New York, NY 10110-0017 *Tel:* 212-354-5500 *Toll Free Tel:* 800-233-4830 (orders & cust serv) *Fax:* 212-869-0856 *Toll Free Fax:* 800-458-6515 *Web Site:* www.wwnorton.com, pg 182

Green, Spencer, Opie Prize, Ohio State Univ, Mershon Ctr, 1501 Neil Ave, Columbus, OH 43201-2602 *Tel:* 614-292-3375 *Fax:* 614-292-2407 *Web Site:* www.afsnet.org/aboutAFS/AFSprizes.cfm, pg 731

Green, Susan, Huntington Library Press, 1151 Oxford Rd, San Marino, CA 91108 *Tel:* 626-405-2172 *Fax:* 626-585-0794 *E-mail:* booksales@huntington.org *Web Site:* www.huntington.org, pg 126

Greenbaum, Arlynn, Authors Unlimited Inc, 31 E 32 St, Suite 300, New York, NY 10016 *Tel:* 212-481-8484 (ext 336) *Fax:* 212-481-9582 *Web Site:* www.authorsunlimited.com, pg 605

Greenbaum, Arlynn, The Jennifer DeChiara Literary Agency, 31 E 32 St, Suite 300, New York, NY 10016 *Tel:* 212-481-8484 (ext 362) *Fax:* 212-481-9582 *Web Site:* www.jdlit.com, pg 568

Greenberg, Annalee, Portage & Main Press, 318 McDermot, Suite 100, Winnipeg, MB R3A 0A2, Canada *Tel:* 204-987-3500 *Toll Free Tel:* 800-667-9673 *Fax:* 204-947-0080 *Toll Free Fax:* 866-734-8477 *E-mail:* books@portageandmainpress.com *Web Site:* www.portageandmainpress.com, pg 516

Greenberg, Daniel, Levine|Greenberg Literary Agency Inc, 307 Seventh Ave, Suite 2407, New York, NY 10001 *Tel:* 212-337-0934 *Fax:* 212-337-0948 *Web Site:* www.levinegreenberg.com, pg 581

Greenberg, Jeff, AAA Photos, 401 Ocean Dr, Unit 804, Miami Beach, FL 33139 *Tel:* 305-534-0804 *Web Site:* www.photosphotos.net, pg 539

Greenberg, Karen Matsu, American Book Producers Association (ABPA), 151 W 19 St, 3rd fl, New York, NY 10011 *Tel:* 212-675-1363 *Fax:* 212-675-1364 *E-mail:* office@abpaonline.org *Web Site:* www.abpaonline.org, pg 612

Greenberg, Susannah, Women's National Book Association Award, PO Box 237, FDR Sta, New York, NY 10150-0231 *Tel:* 212-208-4629 *Fax:* 212-208-4629 *E-mail:* publicity@bookbuzz.com *Web Site:* www.wnba-books.org; www.NationalReadingGroupMonth.org, pg 751

Greenberg, Susannah, Women's National Book Association Inc, PO Box 237, FDR Sta, New York, NY 10150-0231 *Tel:* 212-208-4629 *Fax:* 212-208-4629 *E-mail:* publicity@bookbuzz.com; info@wnba.org *Web Site:* www.wnba-books.org; www.NationalReadingGroupMonth.org, pg 638

Greenberg, Zeke, Alan Wofsy Fine Arts, 1109 Geary Blvd, San Francisco, CA 94109 *Tel:* 415-292-6500 *Toll Free Tel:* 800-660-6403 *Fax:* 415-292-6594 (off & cust serv); 415-512-0130 (acctg) *E-mail:* order@art-books.com (orders); editeur@earthlink.net (edit); beauxarts@earthlink.net (cust serv) *Web Site:* www.art-books.com, pg 284

Greene, Alexander, Springer, 233 Spring St, New York, NY 10013-1578 *Tel:* 212-460-1500 *Toll Free Tel:* 800-SPRINGER (777-4643) *Fax:* 212-460-1575 *E-mail:* service-ny@springer.com *Web Site:* www.springer.com, pg 241

Greene, Anne, Wesleyan Writers Conference, c/o Wesleyan University, 294 High St, Middletown, CT 06459 *Tel:* 860-685-3604 *Fax:* 860-685-2441 *Web Site:* www.wesleyan.edu/writing/conference, pg 674

Greene, Cheryll Y, The Editor's Eye, 158-18 Riverside Dr W, Suite 6-E, New York, NY 10032 *Tel:* 212-740-6003 *Fax:* 212-740-6003 *E-mail:* editorseye@gmail.com, pg 545

Greene, Chip, Houghton Mifflin Harcourt, 222 Berkeley St, Boston, MA 02116-3764 *Tel:* 617-351-5000 *Toll Free Tel:* 800-225-5425 (Pre-K-8); 800-462-6595 (6–12; Advanced & Electives); 800-289-4490 (Specialized Curriculum: Great Source, Rigby, Saxon, Steck-Vaughn; Homeschool; Adult Ed); 800-323-9540 (Assessment: Riverside Publishing); 888-391-3245 (SkillsTutor); 888-242-6747 option 2 (Destination Series; Classroom Connect; Earobics; Edmark; Learning Village; Riverdeep); 800-225-3362 (Houghton Mifflin Harcourt Trade & Reference Publishers); 800-225-5800 (Heinemann) *Fax:* 617-351-1125 *Web Site:* www.hmhco.com, pg 123

Greene, Deirdre, Roaring Forties Press, 1053 Santa Fe Ave, Berkeley, CA 94706 *Tel:* 510-527-5461 *E-mail:* info@roaringfortiespress.com *Web Site:* www.roaringfortiespress.com, pg 220

Greene, Grace Worcester, Dorothy Canfield Fisher Children's Book Award, 109 State St, Montpelier, VT 05609-0601 *Tel:* 802-828-6954 *Fax:* 802-828-1481 *E-mail:* cbec@state.vt.us *Web Site:* www.dcfaward.org; libraries.vermont.gov/libraries, pg 700

Greene, Nick, Simon & Schuster, 1230 Avenue of the Americas, New York, NY 10020 *Tel:* 212-698-7000 *Toll Free Tel:* 800-223-2348 (cust serv); 800-223-2336 (orders) *Toll Free Fax:* 800-943-9831 (orders) *Web Site:* www.simonandschuster.com, pg 234

Greenfield, George M, CreativeWell Inc, PO Box 3130, Memorial Sta, Upper Montclair, NJ 07043 *Tel:* 973-783-7575 *Toll Free Tel:* 800-743-9182 *Fax:* 973-783-7530 *E-mail:* info@creativewell.com *Web Site:* www.creativewell.com, pg 567, 605

Greenfield, Ilan, Gefen Books, 11 Edison Place, Springfield, NJ 07081 *Tel:* 516-593-1234 *Toll Free Tel:* 800-477-5257 *Fax:* 516-295-2739 *E-mail:* info@gefenpublishing.com; gefenny@gefenpublishing.com *Web Site:* www.israelbooks.com, pg 102

Greenhalgh, Courtney, Workman Publishing Co Inc, 225 Varick St, 9th fl, New York, NY 10014-4381 *Tel:* 212-254-5900 *Toll Free Tel:* 800-722-7202 *Fax:* 212-254-8098 *E-mail:* info@workman.com *Web Site:* www.workman.com, pg 285

Greenhut, Carol, Schonfeld & Associates Inc, 1931 Lynn Circle, Libertyville, IL 60048 *Tel:* 847-816-4870 *Toll Free Tel:* 800-205-0030 *Fax:* 847-816-4872 *E-mail:* saiinfo@saibooks.com *Web Site:* www.saibooks.com, pg 229

Greenland, Paul R, Paul Greenland Editorial Services, 9184 Longfellow Lane, Machesney Park, IL 61115 *Tel:* 815-540-0911 *Web Site:* www.paulgreenland.com, pg 548

Greenleaf, Clint, Greenleaf Book Group LLC, 4005 Banister Lane, Suite B, Austin, TX 78704 *Tel:* 512-891-6100 *Toll Free Tel:* 800-932-5420 *Fax:* 512-891-6150 *E-mail:* contact@greenleafbookgroup.com *Web Site:* www.greenleafbookgroup.com, pg 107

Greenleaf, Lisa, Apprentice Shop Books LLC, 18 Wentworth Dr, Bedford, NH 03110 *Tel:* 603-472-8741 *Fax:* 603-472-2323 *E-mail:* info@apprenticeshopbooks.com *Web Site:* www.apprenticeshopbooks.com, pg 21

Greenspan, Elizabeth, Society for Industrial & Applied Mathematics, 3600 Market St, 6th fl, Philadelphia, PA 19104-2688 *Tel:* 215-382-9800 *Toll Free Tel:* 800-447-7426 *Fax:* 215-386-7999 *E-mail:* siambooks@siam.org *Web Site:* www.siam.org, pg 238

Greenspan, Jackie, Mondo Publishing, 200 Sherwood Ave, Farmingdale, NY 11735 *Tel:* 212-268-3560 *Toll Free Tel:* 888-88-MONDO (886-6636) *Toll Free Fax:* 888-532-4492 *E-mail:* info@mondopub.com *Web Site:* www.mondopub.com, pg 168

Greenspan, Shari Dash, Flashlight Press, 527 Empire Blvd, Brooklyn, NY 11225 *Tel:* 718-288-8300 *Fax:* 718-972-6307 *E-mail:* editor@flashlightpress.com *Web Site:* www.flashlightpress.com, pg 96

Greenspan, Shari Dash, Urim Publications, c/o Lambda Publications Inc, 527 Empire Blvd, Brooklyn, NY 11225-3121 *Tel:* 718-972-5449 *Fax:* 718-972-6307 *E-mail:* publisher@urimpublications.com *Web Site:* urimpublications.com, pg 273

Greenstein, Ruth, Words into Print, 131 Fifth Ave, Suite 501, New York, NY 10003 *Tel:* 212-741-1393 *Fax:* 419-441-1393 *E-mail:* query@wordsintoprint.org *Web Site:* www.wordsintoprint.org, pg 557

Greenwald, Martin, Central European University Press, 224 W 57 St, 7th fl, New York, NY 10019 *Tel:* 212-547-6932 *Fax:* 646-557-2416 *Web Site:* www.ceupress.com, pg 57

Greer, Jessica, Other Press LLC, 2 Park Ave, 24th fl, New York, NY 10016 *Tel:* 212-414-0054 *Toll Free Tel:* 877-843-6843 *Fax:* 212-414-0939 *E-mail:* editor@otherpress.com; rights@otherpress.com *Web Site:* www.otherpress.com, pg 188

Gref, Emily, Lowenstein Associates Inc, 121 W 27 St, Suite 501, New York, NY 10001 *Tel:* 212-206-1630 *Fax:* 212-727-0280 *E-mail:* assistant@bookhaven.com (queries, no attachments) *Web Site:* www.lowensteinassociates.com, pg 582

Grefe, Richard, AIGA, the professional association for design, 164 Fifth Ave, New York, NY 10010 *Tel:* 212-807-1990 *Fax:* 212-807-1799 *E-mail:* general@aiga.org *Web Site:* www.aiga.org, pg 611

Gregg, Richard, Phaidon Press Inc, 180 Varick St, 14th fl, New York, NY 10014 *Tel:* 212-652-5400 *Toll Free Tel:* 800-759-0190 (cust serv) *Fax:* 212-652-5410 *Toll Free Fax:* 800-286-9471 (cust serv) *E-mail:* ussales@phaidon.com *Web Site:* www.phaidon.com, pg 200

Gregory, Alexis, The Vendome Press, 1334 York Ave, 3rd fl, New York, NY 10021 *Tel:* 212-737-5297 *Fax:* 212-737-5340 *E-mail:* info@vendomepress.com *Web Site:* www.vendomepress.com, pg 274

Gregory, Debbie, Upper Room Books, 1908 Grand Ave, Nashville, TN 37212 *Tel:* 615-340-7200 *Toll Free Tel:* 800-972-0433 *Fax:* 615-340-7266 *E-mail:* urbooks@upperroom.org *Web Site:* www.upperroom.org, pg 273

Gregory, Evan, Ethan Ellenberg Literary Agency, 548 Broadway, Suite 5-E, New York, NY 10012 *Tel:* 212-431-4554 *Fax:* 212-941-4652 *E-mail:* agent@ethanellenberg.com *Web Site:* www.ethanellenberg.com, pg 571

Gregory, Kevin G, AuthorHouse, 1663 Liberty Dr, Bloomington, IN 47403 *Toll Free Tel:* 888-519-5121 *E-mail:* authorsupport@authorhouse.com *Web Site:* www.authorhouse.com, pg 27

Gregory, Kevin G, iUniverse, 1663 Liberty Dr, Bloomington, IN 47403 *Toll Free Tel:* 800-AUTHORS (288-4677) *Fax:* 812-355-4085 *Web Site:* www.iuniverse.com, pg 135

Gregory, Kevin G, Xlibris Corp, 1663 Liberty Dr, Suite 200, Bloomington, IN 47403 *Toll Free Tel:* 888-795-4274 *Fax:* 610-915-0294 *E-mail:* info@xlibris.com *Web Site:* www.xlibris.com, pg 287

Gregory, Michael Steven, Southern California Writers' Conference, 1010 University Ave, Suite 54, San Diego, CA 92103 *Tel:* 619-303-8185 *Fax:* 619-303-7462 *E-mail:* wewrite@writersconference.com *Web Site:* www.writersconference.com, pg 673

Gregory, Michael Steven, Writers' Haven Writers (WHW), 2244 Fourth Av, Suite A, San Diego, CA 92101-2119 *Tel:* 619-665-2712, pg 639

Greig, Bill T III, Regal Books, 1957 Eastman Ave, Ventura, CA 93003 *Tel:* 805-644-9721 *Toll Free Tel:* 800-446-7735 (orders) *Web Site:* www.regalbooks.com; www.gospellight.com, pg 217

Grench, Charles, The University of North Carolina Press, 116 S Boundary St, Chapel Hill, NC 27514-3808 *Tel:* 919-966-3561 *Fax:* 919-966-3829 *E-mail:* uncpress@unc.edu *Web Site:* www.uncpress.unc.edu, pg 267

Grennan, Karen, SDP Publishing Solutions LLC, 36 Captain's Way, East Bridgewater, MA 02333 *Tel:* 617-775-0656 *Web Site:* www.sdppublishingsolutions.com, pg 555

Gresch, Elise, BePuzzled, 2030 Harrison St, San Francisco, CA 94110 *Tel:* 415-503-1600 *Toll Free Tel:* 800-347-4818 *Fax:* 415-503-0085 *E-mail:* info@ugames.com *Web Site:* www.ugames.com, pg 35

Gress, Priti Chitnis, Hippocrene Books Inc, 171 Madison Ave, New York, NY 10016 *Tel:* 212-685-4373; 212-685-4375 *Fax:* 212-779-9338 *E-mail:* info@hippocrenebooks.com; orderdept@hippocrenebooks.com (orders); contact@hippocrenebooks.com *Web Site:* www.hippocrenebooks.com, pg 120

Greuel, Greg, Wayside Publishing, 11 Jan Sebastian Dr, Suite 5, Sandwich, MA 02563 *Tel:* 508-833-5096 *Toll Free Tel:* 888-302-2519 *Fax:* 508-833-6284 *E-mail:* wayside@sprintmail.com *Web Site:* www.waysidepublishing.com, pg 277

Gribble, Julie, New York Media Works, 112 Franklin St, New York, NY 10013 *Tel:* 646-369-5681 *Fax:* 646-810-4033 *E-mail:* info@nymediaworks.com *Web Site:* www.nymediaworks.com, pg 528

Griebeler, Pat, Theosophical Publishing House/Quest Books, 306 W Geneva Rd, Wheaton, IL 60187 *Tel:* 630-665-0130 (ext 347) *Toll Free Tel:* 800-669-9425 (ext 347) *Fax:* 630-665-8791 *E-mail:* customerservice@questbooks.net *Web Site:* www.questbooks.net, pg 254

Griffes, Peter L, ProStar Publications Inc, 3 Church Circle, Suite 109, Annapolis, MD 21401 *Tel:* 310-280-1010 *Toll Free Tel:* 800-481-6277 *Fax:* 310-280-1025 *Toll Free Fax:* 800-487-6277 *E-mail:* editor@prostarpublications.com *Web Site:* www.prostarpublications.com, pg 208

Griffin, Diana, Abbeville Press, 137 Varick St, Suite 504, New York, NY 10013-1105 *Tel:* 212-366-5585 *Toll Free Tel:* 800-ARTBOOK (278-2665) *Fax:* 212-366-6966 *E-mail:* abbeville@abbeville.com *Web Site:* www.abbeville.com, pg 2

Griffin, Jennifer, The Miller Agency Inc, 630 Ninth Ave, Suite 1102, New York, NY 10036 *Tel:* 212-206-0913 *Fax:* 212-206-1473, pg 586

Griffin, Jo Beth, Elsevier, Health Sciences Division, 1600 John F Kennedy Blvd, Suite 1800, Philadelphia, PA 19103-2899 *Tel:* 215-239-3900 *Toll Free Tel:* 800-523-1649 *Fax:* 215-239-3990 *Web Site:* www.elsevierhealth.com, pg 87

Griffin, John, National Geographic Society, 1145 17 St NW, Washington, DC 20036-4688 *Tel:* 202-857-7000 *Fax:* 202-429-5727 *Web Site:* www.nationalgeographic.com, pg 175

Griffin, Susan, Carter G Woodson Book Awards, 8555 16 St, Suite 500, Silver Spring, MD 20910 *Tel:* 301-588-1800 *Toll Free Tel:* 800-296-7840; 800-683-0812 (pubn orders) *Fax:* 301-588-2049 *E-mail:* excellence@ncss.org; publications@ncss.org *Web Site:* www.socialstudies.org, pg 751

Griffith, Drew, National Freedom of Information Coalition (NFOIC), 101 Reynolds Journalism Institute, Columbia, MO 65211-0012 *Tel:* 573-882-4856 *Fax:* 573-884-6204 *Web Site:* nfoic.org, pg 630

Griffor, Mariela, Marick Press, PO Box 36253, Grosse Pointe Farms, MI 48236 *Tel:* 313-407-9236 *E-mail:* orders@marickpress.com *Web Site:* www.marickpress.com, pg 157

Grilliot, Bob, JIST Publishing, 875 Montreal Way, St Paul, MN 55102 *Tel:* 317-613-4200 *Toll Free Tel:* 800-328-1452 *Toll Free Fax:* 800-328-4564 *E-mail:* educate@emcp.com *Web Site:* jist.emcpublishingllc.com, pg 135

Grillo, Scott, McGraw-Hill Professional, 1221 Avenue of the Americas, New York, NY 10020 *Tel:* 212-512-2000 *Web Site:* www.mhprofessional.com, pg 162

Grima, Tony, National Braille Press, 88 Saint Stephen St, Boston, MA 02115-4302 *Tel:* 617-266-6160 *Toll Free Tel:* 800-548-7323 (cust serv); 888-965-8965 *Fax:* 617-437-0456 *E-mail:* orders@nbp.org *Web Site:* www.nbp.org, pg 173

Grimbleby, Jennifer, Kids Can Press Ltd, 25 Dockside Dr, Toronto, ON M5A 0B5, Canada *Tel:* 416-479-7000 *Toll Free Tel:* 800-265-0884 *Fax:* 416-960-5437 *E-mail:* info@kidscan.com; customerservice@kidscan.com *Web Site:* www.kidscanpress.com; www.kidscanpress.ca, pg 510

Grimes, Alan, Greenleaf Book Group LLC, 4005 Banister Lane, Suite B, Austin, TX 78704 *Tel:* 512-891-6100 *Toll Free Tel:* 800-932-5420 *Fax:* 512-891-6150 *E-mail:* contact@greenleafbookgroup.com *Web Site:* www.greenleafbookgroup.com, pg 107

Grimes, Mark, American Academy of Pediatrics, 141 NW Point Blvd, Elk Grove Village, IL 60007-1098 *Tel:* 847-434-4000 *Toll Free Tel:* 888-227-1770 *Fax:* 847-434-8000 *E-mail:* pubs@aap.org *Web Site:* www.aap.org, pg 10

Grimm, Chris, The Globe Pequot Press, 246 Goose Lane, Guilford, CT 06437 *Tel:* 203-458-4500 *Toll Free Tel:* 800-243-0495 (orders only); 888-249-7586 (cust serv) *Fax:* 203-458-4601 *Toll Free Fax:* 800-820-2329 (orders & cust serv) *E-mail:* info@globepequot.com *Web Site:* www.globepequot.com, pg 104

Grimm, Katie, Don Congdon Associates Inc, 110 William St, Suite 2202, New York, NY 10038-3914 *Tel:* 212-645-1229 *Fax:* 212-727-2688 *E-mail:* dca@doncongdon.com *Web Site:* www.doncongdon.com, pg 567

Grimshaw, Sue, Random House Inc, 1745 Broadway, New York, NY 10019 *Tel:* 212-782-9000 *Toll Free Tel:* 800-726-0600 *Web Site:* www.randomhouse.com, pg 213

Grimshaw, Sue, Random House Publishing Group, 1745 Broadway, New York, NY 10019 *Toll Free Tel:* 800-200-3552 *Web Site:* atrandom.com, pg 214

Grinberg, Jill, Jill Grinberg Literary Management LLC, 16 Court, Suite 3306, Brooklyn, NY 11241 *Tel:* 212-620-5883 *Fax:* 212-627-4725 *E-mail:* info@jillgrinbergliterary.com *Web Site:* www.jillgrinbergliterary.com, pg 576

Grisamore, Ed, National Society of Newspaper Columnists (NSNC), 1345 Fillmore St, Suite 507, San Francisco, CA 94115 *Tel:* 415-488-NCNC (488-6762) *Toll Free Tel:* 866-440-NSNC (440-6762) *Fax:* 484-297-0336 *Toll Free Fax:* 866-635-5759 *E-mail:* staff@columnists.com *Web Site:* www.columnists.com, pg 631

Groban, Betsy, Houghton Mifflin Harcourt Trade & Reference Division, 222 Berkeley St, Boston, MA 02116-3764 *Tel:* 617-351-5000 *Toll Free Tel:* 800-225-3362 *Web Site:* www.houghtonmifflinbooks.com, pg 124

Groell, Anne, Random House Publishing Group, 1745 Broadway, New York, NY 10019 *Toll Free Tel:* 800-200-3552 *Web Site:* atrandom.com, pg 214

Gromling, Frank, Ocean Publishing, PO Box 1080, Flagler Beach, FL 32136-1080 *Tel:* 386-517-1600 *E-mail:* publisher@oceanpublishing.org *Web Site:* www.oceanpublishing.org, pg 183

Gros, Tobias, Octane Press, 808 Kinney Ave, Austin, TX 78704 *Tel:* 512-334-9441 *Fax:* 512-852-4737 *E-mail:* info@octanepress.com *Web Site:* www.octanepress.com, pg 184

Grosjean, Jill, Jill Grosjean Literary Agency, 1390 Millstone Rd, Sag Harbor, NY 11963 *Tel:* 631-725-7419 *Fax:* 631-725-8632 *E-mail:* JillLit310@aol.com, pg 576

Gross, Laura, Laura Gross Literary Agency Ltd, 39 Chester St, Suite 301, Newton Highlands, MA 02461 *Tel:* 617-964-2977 *Fax:* 617-964-3023 *E-mail:* query@lauragrossliteraryagency.com *Web Site:* www.lg-la.com, pg 576

Grossberg, Aileen, Sydney Taylor Manuscript Award, 204 Park St, Montclair, NJ 07042 *Tel:* 201-371-3255 *E-mail:* stmacajl@aol.com *Web Site:* www.jewishlibraries.org, pg 745

Grossgart, Chris, International Association of Business Communicators (IABC), 601 Montgomery St, Suite 1900, San Francisco, CA 94111 *Tel:* 415-544-4700 *Toll Free Tel:* 800-776-4222 (US & CN) *Fax:* 415-544-4747 *E-mail:* service_center@iabc.com *Web Site:* www.iabc.com, pg 625

Grossinger, Richard, Frog Books, 2526 Martin Luther King Jr Way, Berkeley, CA 94704 *Tel:* 510-549-4270 *Toll Free Tel:* 800-733-3000 (book orders only) *Fax:* 510-549-4276 *Toll Free Fax:* 800-659-2436 (orders) *E-mail:* orders@northatlanticbooks.com *Web Site:* www.northatlanticbooks.com, pg 99

Grossinger, Richard, North Atlantic Books, 2526 Martin Luther King Jr Way, Berkeley, CA 94704 *Tel:* 510-549-4270 *Fax:* 510-549-4276 *Web Site:* www.northatlanticbooks.com, pg 180

Grosskopf, Bill M, Newgen North America Inc, 2714 Bee Cave Rd, Suite 201, Austin, TX 78746 *Tel:* 512-478-5341 *Fax:* 512-476-4756 *Web Site:* www.newgen.co, pg 552

Grossman, Jim, American Historical Association, 400 "A" St SE, Washington, DC 20003-3889 *Tel:* 202-544-2422 *Fax:* 202-544-8307 *E-mail:* aha@historians.org; awards@historians.org *Web Site:* www.historians.org, pg 13

Grossman, Jim, American Printing History Association, PO Box 4519, Grand Central Sta, New York, NY 10163-4519 *Tel:* 202-544-2422 *Web Site:* www.printinghistory.org, pg 614

Grossman, Jim, American Printing History Association Award, PO Box 4519, Grand Central Sta, New York, NY 10163-4519 *Tel:* 202-544-2422 *Web Site:* www.printinghistory.org, pg 687

Grossman, Lawrence, American Jewish Committee (AJC), Jacob Blaustein Bldg, 165 E 56 St, New York, NY 10022 *Tel:* 212-751-4000; 212-891-1456 (membership) *Fax:* 212 891-1450 *Web Site:* www.ajc.org, pg 613

Grossman, Moshe, Feldheim Publishers (Philipp Feldheim Inc), 208 Airport Executive Park, Nanuet, NY 10954 *Tel:* 845-356-2282 *Toll Free Tel:* 800-237-7149 (orders) *Fax:* 845-425-1908 *E-mail:* sales@feldheim.com *Web Site:* www.feldheim.com, pg 94

Grosz-Ngate, Maria, Indiana University African Studies Program, Indiana University, 221 Woodburn Hall, Bloomington, IN 47405 *Tel:* 812-855-8284 *Fax:* 812-855-6734 *E-mail:* afrist@indiana.edu *Web Site:* www.indiana.edu/~afrist, pg 129

Groton, John, Quayside Publishing Group, 400 First Ave N, Suite 300, Minneapolis, MN 55401 *Tel:* 612-344-8100 *Toll Free Tel:* 800-328-0590 (sales); 800-458-0454 *Fax:* 612-344-8691 *E-mail:* sales@creativepub.com *Web Site:* www.qbookshop.com, pg 211

Grotz, Jennifer, Bread Loaf Writers' Conference, 5525 Middlebury College, 14 Old Chapel Rd, Middlebury, VT 05753 *Tel:* 802-443-5286 *Fax:* 802-443-2087 *E-mail:* blwc@middlebury.edu *Web Site:* www.middlebury.edu/blwc, pg 668

Grotz, Jennifer, Fellowship & Scholarship Program for Writers, Middlebury College, Middlebury, VT 05753 *Tel:* 802-443-5286 *Fax:* 802-443-2087 *E-mail:* blwc@middlebury.edu *Web Site:* www.middlebury.edu/blwc, pg 703

Grove, Susan Evans, The Society of Naval Architects & Marine Engineers, 601 Pavonia Ave, Jersey City, NJ 07306-2907 *Tel:* 201-798-4800 *Toll Free Tel:* 800-798-2188 *Fax:* 201-798-4975 *Web Site:* www.sname.org, pg 238

Grows, Penelope, Wilfrid Laurier University Press, 75 University Ave W, Waterloo, ON N2L 3C5, Canada *Tel:* 519-884-0710 (ext 6124) *Toll Free Tel:* 866-836-5551 *Fax:* 519-725-1399 *E-mail:* press@wlu.ca *Web Site:* www.wlupress.wlu.ca, pg 525

Grubb, Randell C, Theosophical University Press, PO Box C, Pasadena, CA 91109-7107 *Tel:* 626-798-3378 *Fax:* 626-798-4749 *E-mail:* tupress@theosociety.org *Web Site:* www.theosociety.org, pg 254

Grubb, Sara, Irene Goodman Literary Agency, 27 W 24 St, Suite 700B, New York, NY 10010 *Tel:* 212-604-0330 *E-mail:* queries@irenegoodman.com *Web Site:* www.irenegoodman.com, pg 575

Grubbauer, Melinda, De Vorss & Co, 553 Constitution Ave, Camarillo, CA 93012-8510 *Tel:* 805-322-9010 *Toll Free Tel:* 800-843-5743 *Fax:* 805-322-9011 *E-mail:* service@devorss.com *Web Site:* www.devorss.com, pg 77

Grucelski, John, University of Michigan Press, 839 Greene St, Ann Arbor, MI 48104-3209 *Tel:* 734-764-4388 *Fax:* 734-615-1540 *E-mail:* esladmin@umich.edu *Web Site:* www.press.umich.edu, pg 266

Grudens, Richard, Celebrity Profiles Publishing, PO Box 344, Stony Brook, NY 11790 *Tel:* 631-862-8555 *Fax:* 631-862-0139 *E-mail:* celebpro4@aol.com *Web Site:* www.richardgrudens.com, pg 55

Grunewald, Nancy, Washington State University Press, Cooper Publications Bldg, Grimes Way, Pullman, WA 99164 *Tel:* 509-335-3518; 509-335-7880 (order fulfillment) *Toll Free Tel:* 800-354-7360 *Fax:* 509-335-8568 *E-mail:* wsupress@wsu.edu *Web Site:* wsupress.wsu.edu, pg 276

Grusa, Jiri, PEN Writers' Emergency Fund, 588 Broadway, Suite 303, New York, NY 10012 *Tel:* 212-334-1660 *Fax:* 212-334-2181 *Web Site:* www.pen.org, pg 733

Guarin, Imelda, Marshall Cavendish Corp, 99 White Plains Rd, Tarrytown, NY 10591-9001 *Tel:* 914-332-8888 *Toll Free Tel:* 800-821-9881 *Fax:* 914-332-8102 *E-mail:* customerservice@marshallcavendish.com; mcc@marshallcavendish.com *Web Site:* marshallcavendish.us; marshallcavendishdigital.com; marshallcavendishebooks.com, pg 158

Guarnaschelli, Maria, W W Norton & Company Inc, 500 Fifth Ave, New York, NY 10110 0017 *Tel:* 212-354-5500 *Toll Free Tel:* 800-233-4830 (orders & cust serv) *Fax:* 212-869-0856 *Toll Free Fax:* 800-458-6515 *Web Site:* www.wwnorton.com, pg 182

Gubins, Samuel, Annual Reviews, 4139 El Camino Way, Palo Alto, CA 94306 *Tel:* 650-493-4400 *Toll Free Tel:* 800-523-8635 *Fax:* 650-424-0910 *E-mail:* service@annualreviews.org *Web Site:* www.annualreviews.org, pg 18

Gudovitz, Neil, Waterside Productions Inc, 2055 Oxford Ave, Cardiff, CA 92007 *Tel:* 760-632-9190 *Fax:* 760-632-9295 *E-mail:* admin@waterside.com *Web Site:* www.waterside.com, pg 598

Guenzi, Carol, Carol Guenzi Agents Inc, 865 Delaware St, Denver, CO 80204 *Tel:* 303-820-2599 *Toll Free Tel:* 800-417-5120 *Fax:* 303-820-2598 *E-mail:* info@artagent.com; art@artagent.com *Web Site:* www.artagent.com, pg 601

Guerin, Ken, Oxford University Press USA, 198 Madison Ave, New York, NY 10016 *Tel:* 212-726-6000 *Toll Free Tel:* 800-451-7556 (orders); 800-445-9714 (cust serv) *Fax:* 919-677-1303 *E-mail:* custserv.us@oup.com *Web Site:* www.oup.com/us, pg 189

Guerin, Marc-Aime, Guerin Editeur Ltee, 4501 rue Drolet, Montreal, QC H2T 2G2, Canada *Tel:* 514-842-3481 *Toll Free Tel:* 800-398-8337 *Fax:* 514-842-4923 *Web Site:* www.guerin-editeur.qc.ca, pg 507

Guernsey, Sarah E, The Art Institute of Chicago, 111 S Michigan Ave, Chicago, IL 60603-6404 *Tel:* 312-443-3600; 312-443-3540 (pubns) *Fax:* 312-443-1334 (pubns) *Web Site:* www.artic.edu; www.artinstituteshop.org, pg 22

Guerra, Angel, Cormorant Books Inc, 390 Steelcase Rd E, Markham, ON L3R 1G2, Canada *Tel:* 905-475-9126 (Thomas Allen & Sons); 905-475-5571 *E-mail:* info@cormorantbooks.com *Web Site:* www.cormorantbooks.com, pg 500

Guerra, Delin, Bogle International Library Travel Fund, 50 E Huron St, Chicago, IL 60611-2795 *Tel:* 312-280-3201 *Toll Free Tel:* 800-545-2433 (ext 3201) *Fax:* 312-280-4392 *E-mail:* intl@ala.org *Web Site:* www.ala.org, pg 692

Guerrero, Jessica, Glitterati Inc, 322 W 57 St, No 19T, New York, NY 10019 *Tel:* 212-362-9119 *Fax:* 646-607-4433 *E-mail:* info@glitteratiincorporated.com *Web Site:* glitteratiincorporated.com, pg 103

Guerrieri, Pamela, Proofed to Perfection Editing Services, PO Box 71851, Durham, NC 27722-1851 *Tel:* 919-732-8565 *E-mail:* inquiries@proofedtoperfection.com *Web Site:* www.proofedtoperfection.com, pg 554

Guerth, Jan-Erik, BlueBridge, PO Box 601, Katonah, NY 10536 *Tel:* 914-301-5901 *Web Site:* www.bluebridgebooks.com, pg 42

Guetebier, Amber, Red Wheel/Weiser/Conari, 65 Parker St, Suite 7, Newburyport, MA 01950 *Tel:* 978-465-0504 *Toll Free Tel:* 800-423-7087 (orders) *Fax:* 978-465-0243 *E-mail:* info@rwwbooks.com *Web Site:* www.redwheelweiser.com, pg 216

Guevara, Linda L, All About Kids Publishing, PO Box 159, Gilroy, CA 95020 *Tel:* 408-337-1866 *E-mail:* mail@aakp.com *Web Site:* www.aakp.com, pg 8

Guevara, Mike G, All About Kids Publishing, PO Box 159, Gilroy, CA 95020 *Tel:* 408-337-1866 *E-mail:* mail@aakp.com *Web Site:* www.aakp.com, pg 8

Guevin, John R, Biographical Publishing Co, 95 Sycamore Dr, Prospect, CT 06712-1493 *Tel:* 203-758-3661 *Fax:* 253-793-2618 *E-mail:* biopub@aol.com *Web Site:* www.biopub.us, pg 37

Guevremont, Diane, The North-South Institute/Institut Nord-Sud, 55 Murray St, Suite 500, Ottawa, ON K1N 5M3, Canada *Tel:* 613-241-3535 *Fax:* 613-241-7435 *E-mail:* nsi@nsi-ins.ca *Web Site:* www.nsi-ins.ca, pg 514

Guido, Umberto III, Peter Glenn Publications, 306 NE Second St, 2nd fl, Delray Beach, FL 33483 *Tel:* 561-404-4290 *Toll Free Tel:* 888-332-6700 *Fax:* 561-892-5786 *Web Site:* www.pgdirect.com, pg 103

Guidone, Kimberly, The Jennifer DeChiara Literary Agency, 31 E 32 St, Suite 300, New York, NY 10016 *Tel:* 212-481-8484 (ext 362) *Fax:* 212-481-9582 *Web Site:* www.jdlit.com, pg 568

Guild, Adam, Hungry? City Guides, 714 W Olympic Blvd, Suite 934, Los Angeles, CA 90015 *Fax:* 213-749-2080 *Web Site:* www.hungryguides.com, pg 125

Guilfoyle, Virginia, Federal Street Press, 25-13 Old Kings Hwy N, No 277, Darien, CT 06820 *Tel:* 203-852-1280 *Toll Free Tel:* 877-886-2830 *Fax:* 203-852-1389 *E-mail:* sales@federalstreetpress.com *Web Site:* www.federalstreetpress.com, pg 93

Guili, Lisa, Educational Insights Inc, 152 W Walnut St, Suite 201, Gardena, CA 90248 *Toll Free Tel:* 800-933-3277 *Fax:* 847-281-2868 *Toll Free Fax:* 800-995-0506 *E-mail:* info@educationalinsights.com; cs@educationalinsights.com *Web Site:* www.educationalinsights.com, pg 85

Guillemette-Bedard, Catherine, Ordre des traducteurs, terminologues et interpretes agrees du quebec, 2021 Union Ave, Suite 1108, Montreal, QC H3A 2S9, Canada *Tel:* 514-845-4411 *Toll Free Tel:* 800-265-4815 *Fax:* 514-845-9903 *E-mail:* info@ottiaq.org *Web Site:* www.ottiaq.org, pg 633

Guillen, Miguel, Artist Trust Fellowship, 1835 12 Ave, Seattle, WA 98122 *Tel:* 206-467-8734 (ext 11) *Toll Free Tel:* 866-218-7878 (ext 11) *Fax:* 206-467-9633 *E-mail:* info@artisttrust.org *Web Site:* www.artisttrust.org, pg 688

Guillen, Miguel, Grants for Artist Projects, 1835 12 Ave, Seattle, WA 98122 *Tel:* 206-467-8734 (ext 11) *Toll Free Tel:* 866-218-7878 (ext 11) *Fax:* 206-467-9633 *E-mail:* info@artisttrust.org *Web Site:* www.artisttrust.org, pg 708

Guinsler, Robert, Sterling Lord Literistic Inc, 65 Bleecker St, New York, NY 10012 *Tel:* 212-780-6050 *Fax:* 212-780-6095 *E-mail:* info@sll.com *Web Site:* www.sll.com, pg 595

Guiod, Suzanne, Boydell & Brewer Inc, 668 Mount Hope Ave, Rochester, NY 14620-2731 *Tel:* 585-275-0419 *Fax:* 585-271-8778 *E-mail:* boydell@boydellusa.net *Web Site:* www.boydellandbrewer.com, pg 45

Guiod, Suzanne, University of Rochester Press, 668 Mount Hope Ave, Rochester, NY 14620-2731 *Tel:* 585-275-0419 *Fax:* 585-271-8778 *E-mail:* boydell@boydellusa.net *Web Site:* www.urpress.com, pg 269

Gumbs, Amanda, National Conference for Community & Justice, 1095 Day Hill Rd, Suite 100, Windsor, CT 06095 *Tel:* 860-683-1039 *Fax:* 860-683-1409 *E-mail:* info@nccjctwma.org *Web Site:* www.nccjctwma.org, pg 629

Gunderson, Joanna, Red Dust Inc, 1148 Fifth Ave, New York, NY 10128 *Tel:* 212-348-4388 *Web Site:* www.reddustbooks.com, pg 216

Gundry, Stan, Zondervan, A HarperCollins Company, 5300 Patterson Ave SE, Grand Rapids, MI 49530 *Tel:* 616-698-6900 *Toll Free Tel:* 800-226-1122; 800-727-1309 (retail orders) *Fax:* 616-698-3350 *Toll Free Fax:* 800-698-3256 (retail orders) *E-mail:* zinfo@zondervan.com *Web Site:* www.zondervan.com, pg 289

Gunn, James, John W Campbell Memorial Award, University of Kansas, Wescoe Hall, Rm 3001, Dept of English, 1445 Jayhawk Blvd, Lawrence, KS 66045-7590 *Tel:* 785-864-3380 *Fax:* 785-864-1159 *Web Site:* www.ku.edu/~sfcenter; ku.edu/campbell.htm, pg 694

Gunn, James, Science Fiction Writers Workshop, University of Kansas, Wescoe Hall, Rm 3001, Dept of English, 1445 Jayhawk Blvd, Lawrence, KS 66045-7590 *Tel:* 785-864-3380 *Fax:* 785-864-1159 *Web Site:* www.ku.edu/~sfcenter, pg 673

Gunnison, John P, Adventure House, 914 Laredo Rd, Silver Spring, MD 20901 *Tel:* 301-754-1589 *Web Site:* www.adventurehouse.com, pg 5

Gupta, Ashis, Bayeux Arts Inc, 119 Stratton Crescent SW, Calgary, AB T3H 1T7, Canada *E-mail:* mail@bayeux.com *Web Site:* www.bayeux.com, pg 494

Gupta, Swapna, Bayeux Arts Inc, 119 Stratton Crescent SW, Calgary, AB T3H 1T7, Canada *E-mail:* mail@bayeux.com *Web Site:* www.bayeux.com, pg 494

Gurley, Brian, Triumph Learning, 136 Madison Ave, 7th fl, New York, NY 10016 *Tel:* 212-652-0200 *Toll Free Tel:* 800-221-9372 (cust serv) *Toll Free Fax:* 866-805-5723 *E-mail:* info@triumphlearning.com; customerservice@triumphlearning.com *Web Site:* www.triumphlearning.com, pg 259

Guruetz, Joseph, John Simon Guggenheim Memorial Foundation, 90 Park Ave, New York, NY 10016 *Tel:* 212-687-4470 *Fax:* 212-697-3248 *E-mail:* fellowships@gf.org *Web Site:* www.gf.org, pg 641

Gusinde-Duffy, Mick, University of Georgia Press, Main Library, 3rd fl, 320 S Jackson St, Athens, GA 30602 *Tel:* 706-369-6130 *Fax:* 706-369-6131; 706-369-6162 *E-mail:* books@ugapress.uga.edu (orders) *Web Site:* www.ugapress.org, pg 265

Guth, Robert E, The Reader's Digest Association Inc, 750 Third Ave, New York, NY 10017 *Tel:* 914-238-1000; 646-293-6284 *Toll Free Tel:* 800-310-6261 (cust serv) *Fax:* 914-238-4559 *Web Site:* www.rd.com; www.rda.com, pg 215

Gutierrez, Erika, Bedford/St Martin's, 75 Arlington St, Boston, MA 02116 *Tel:* 617-399-4000 *Toll Free Tel:* 800-779-7440 *Fax:* 617-426-8582 *Web Site:* www.bedfordstmartins.com, pg 34

Guttman, Joseph, University of Pennsylvania Press, 3905 Spruce St, Philadelphia, PA 19104 *Tel:* 215-898-6261 *Fax:* 215-898-0404 *E-mail:* custserv@pobox.upenn.edu *Web Site:* www.pennpress.org, pg 268

Guzman, Manuel, Cengage Learning, 200 First Stamford Place, Suite 400, Stamford, CT 06902 *Tel:* 203-965-8600 *Toll Free Tel:* 800-354-9706 *Fax:* 203-965-8599 *Toll Free Fax:* 800-487-8488 *E-mail:* esales@cengage.com *Web Site:* www.cengage.com, pg 55

Guzman, Martha, Maria Carvainis Agency Inc, Rockefeller Center, 1270 Avenue of the Americas, Suite 2320, New York, NY 10020 *Tel:* 212-245-6365 *Fax:* 212-245-7196 *E-mail:* mca@mariacarvainisagency.com *Web Site:* mariacarvainisagency.com, pg 565

Guzman, Robert, Egmont USA, 443 Park Ave S, Suite 806, New York, NY 10016 *Tel:* 212-685-0102 *E-mail:* egmontusa@egmont.com *Web Site:* www.egmontusa.com, pg 86

Guzzardi, William, Wag's Revue Writers' Contest, 2865 W Lyndale St, Suite 1, Chicago, IL 60647 *E-mail:* editors@wagsrevue.com *Web Site:* www.wagsrevue.com, pg 748

Gyurke, Jim, Psychological Assessment Resources Inc (PAR), 16204 N Florida Ave, Lutz, FL 33549 *Tel:* 813-968-3003; 813-449-4065 *Toll Free Tel:* 800-331-8378 *Fax:* 813-968-2598; 813-961-2196 *Toll Free Fax:* 800-727-9329 *E-mail:* custsup@parinc.com *Web Site:* www4.parinc.com, pg 208

Ha, Paul C, MIT List Visual Arts Center, MIT E 15-109, 20 Ames St, Cambridge, MA 02139 *Tel:* 617-253-4400; 617-253-4680 *Fax:* 617-258-7265 *E-mail:* mlinga@mit.edu *Web Site:* listart.mit.edu, pg 167

Haak, Kathleen, Dorrance Publishing Co Inc, 701 Smithfield St, Suite 301, Pittsburgh, PA 15222 *Toll Free Tel:* 800-695-9599; 800-788-7654 (gen cust orders); 888-840-8581 (bookstore orders & returns) *Fax:* 412-288-1786 *E-mail:* dorrinfo@dorrancepublishing.com *Web Site:* www.dorrancepublishing.com, pg 81

Haas, Mary Beth, Indiana University Press, 601 N Morton St, Bloomington, IN 47404-3797 *Tel:* 812-855-8817 *Toll Free Tel:* 800-842-6796 (orders only) *Fax:* 812-855-7931; 812-855-8507 *E-mail:* iupress@indiana.edu; iuporder@indiana.edu (orders) *Web Site:* www.iupress.indiana.edu, pg 129

Haase, H W, Quintessence Publishing Co Inc, 4350 Chandler Dr, Hanover Park, IL 60133 *Tel:* 630-736-3600 *Toll Free Tel:* 800-621-0387 *Fax:* 630-736-3633 *E-mail:* contact@quintbook.com; service@quintbook.com *Web Site:* www.quintpub.com, pg 211

Haav, Julia, Europa Editions, 214 W 29 St, Suite 1003, New York, NY 10001 *Tel:* 212-868-6844 *Fax:* 212-868-6845 *E-mail:* info@europaeditions.com *Web Site:* www.europaeditions.com, pg 90

Haav, Julia, Yale University Press, 302 Temple St, New Haven, CT 06511-8909 *Tel:* 401-531-2800 (cust serv); 203-432-0960 *Toll Free Tel:* 800-405-1619 (cust serv) *Fax:* 203-432-0948; 401-531-2801 (cust serv) *Toll Free Fax:* 800-406-9145 (cust serv) *E-mail:* customer.care@trilateral.org (cust serv); language.yalepress@yale.edu *Web Site:* www.yalebooks.com, pg 287

Habayeb, Amy, Little, Brown Books for Young Readers, 237 Park Ave, New York, NY 10017 *Tel:* 212-364-1100 *Toll Free Tel:* 800-759-0190 (cust serv) *Web Site:* www.HachetteBookGroup.com, pg 150

Habegger, Larry, Travelers' Tales, 2320 Bowdoin St, Palo Alto, CA 94306 *Tel:* 650-462-2110 *Fax:* 650-462-6305 *E-mail:* ttales@travelerstales.com *Web Site:* www.travelerstales.com, pg 258

Haber, Leo, Herzl Press, 633 Third Ave, 21st fl, New York, NY 10017 *Tel:* 212-339-6020 *Fax:* 212-318-6176 *E-mail:* midstreamthf@aol.com *Web Site:* www.midstreamthf.com, pg 119

Hachfeld, Linda, Appletree Press Inc, 151 Good Counsel Dr, Suite 125, Mankato, MN 56001 *Tel:* 507-345-4848 *Toll Free Tel:* 800-322-5679 *Fax:* 507-345-3002 *E-mail:* eatwell@hickorytech.net *Web Site:* www.appletreepress.com; www.appletree-press.com; www.letscookhealthymeals.com; www.appletree-press.us, pg 20

Hackinson, Frank J, FJH Music Co Inc, 2525 Davie Rd, Suite 360, Fort Lauderdale, FL 33317-7424 *Tel:* 954-382-6061 *Toll Free Tel:* 800-262-8744 *Fax:* 954-382-3073 *E-mail:* custserv@fjhmusic.com; sales@fjhmusic.com *Web Site:* www.fjhmusic.com, pg 96

Hackinson, Kyle, FJH Music Co Inc, 2525 Davie Rd, Suite 360, Fort Lauderdale, FL 33317-7424 *Tel:* 954-382-6061 *Toll Free Tel:* 800-262-8744 *Fax:* 954-382-3073 *E-mail:* custserv@fjhmusic.com; sales@fjhmusic.com *Web Site:* www.fjhmusic.com, pg 96

Hadde, Amilde, Modern Language Association of America (MLA), 26 Broadway, 3rd fl, New York, NY 10004-1789 *Tel:* 646-576-5000 *Fax:* 646-458-0030 *E-mail:* info@mla.org *Web Site:* www.mla.org, pg 168

Hades, Brian, EDGE Science Fiction & Fantasy Publishing, PO Box 1714, Sta M, Calgary, AB T2P 2L7, Canada *Tel:* 403-254-0160 *Web Site:* www.edgewebsite.com, pg 501

Hadley, Candida, Fernwood Publishing, 32 Oceanvista Lane, Black Point, NS B0J 1B0, Canada *Tel:* 902-857-1388 *Fax:* 902-857-1328 *E-mail:* info@fernpub.ca *Web Site:* www.fernwoodpublishing.ca, pg 505

Hafftka, Michael, Six Gallery Press, PO Box 90145, Pittsburgh, PA 15224-0545 *Web Site:* www.sixgallerypress.com, pg 236

Hagan, Lisa, Paraview Literary Agency, 110 Martin Dr, Bracey, VA 23919 *Tel:* 434-636-4138 *Web Site:* www.paraviewliteraryagency.com, pg 588

Hagan, Peter, Abrams Artists Agency, 275 Seventh Ave, 26th fl, New York, NY 10001 *Tel:* 646-486-4600 *Fax:* 646-486-2358 *E-mail:* literary@abramsartny.com *Web Site:* www.abramsartists.com, pg 559

Hagen, James, InterVarsity Press, 430 Plaza Dr, Westmont, IL 60559-1234 *Tel:* 630-734-4000 *Toll Free Tel:* 800-843-9487 *Fax:* 630-734-4200 *E-mail:* email@ivpress.com *Web Site:* www.ivpress.com, pg 134

Hagenberg, Mark, Perfection Learning Corp, 2680 Berkshire Pkwy, Clive, IA 50325 *Tel:* 515-278-0133 *Toll Free Tel:* 800-762-2999 *Fax:* 515-278-2980 *Web Site:* perfectionlearning.com, pg 199

Haggar, Darren, The Penguin Press, 375 Hudson St, New York, NY 10014, pg 197

Hagman, Lorri, University of Washington Press, 433 Brooklyn Ave NE, Seattle, WA 98195-9570 *Tel:* 206-543-4050 *Toll Free Tel:* 800-537-5487 (orders) *Fax:* 206-543-3932; 410-516-6998 (orders) *E-mail:* uwpress@u.washington.edu *Web Site:* www.washington.edu/uwpress/, pg 270

Hagood, Louis, Oxbridge® Communications Inc, 39 W 29 St, Suite 301, New York, NY 10001 *Tel:* 212-741-0231 *Toll Free Tel:* 800-955-0231 *Fax:* 212-633-2938 *E-mail:* info@oxbridge.com *Web Site:* www.oxbridge.com, pg 189

Hagood, Patricia, Oxbridge® Communications Inc, 39 W 29 St, Suite 301, New York, NY 10001 *Tel:* 212-741-0231 *Toll Free Tel:* 800-955-0231 *Fax:* 212-633-2938 *E-mail:* info@oxbridge.com *Web Site:* www.oxbridge.com, pg 189

Hagopian, Lori, Hal Leonard Corp, 7777 W Bluemound Rd, Milwaukee, WI 53213 *Tel:* 414-774-3630 *Toll Free Tel:* 800-524-4425 *Fax:* 414-774-3259 *E-mail:* sales@halleonard.com *Web Site:* www.halleonard.com; twitter.com/#!/HalleonardBooks, pg 111

Hague, Paige Stover Esq, Acanthus Publishing, 343 Commercial St, Unit 214, Boston, MA 02109 *Tel:* 617-230-2167 *Fax:* 215-243-7495 *E-mail:* info@acanthuspublishing.com *Web Site:* www.acanthuspublishing.com, pg 4

Hahn, Dr H George, Towson University Prize for Literature, English Dept, 8000 York Rd, Towson, MD 21252 *Tel:* 410-704-2000 *Fax:* 410-704-3999 *Web Site:* www.towson.edu/english, pg 746

Haidle, Micaela, McGraw-Hill Career Education, 1333 Burr Ridge Pkwy, Burr Ridge, IL 60527 *Tel:* 630-789-4000 *Toll Free Tel:* 800-338-3987 (cust serv) *Fax:* 630-789-5523; 614-755-5645 (cust serv) *Web Site:* www.mhhe.com, pg 160

Haigh, Liz, American Water Works Association, 6666 W Quincy Ave, Denver, CO 80235 *Tel:* 303-794-7711 *Toll Free Tel:* 800-926-7337 *Fax:* 303-347-0804 *Web Site:* www.awwa.org, pg 17

Haines, Bridget, Groundwood Books, 110 Spadina Ave, Suite 801, Toronto, ON M5V 2K4, Canada *Tel:* 416-363-4343 *Fax:* 416-363-1017 *E-mail:* genmail@groundwoodbooks.com *Web Site:* www.houseofanansi.com, pg 507

Halash, Amanda, Baker Books, 6030 E Fulton Rd, Ada, MI 49301 *Tel:* 616-676-9185 *Toll Free Tel:* 800-877-2665; 800-679-1957 *Fax:* 616-676-9573 *Toll Free Fax:* 800-398-3111 *Web Site:* www.bakerpublishinggroup.com, pg 29

Halata, Katie, Egmont USA, 443 Park Ave S, Suite 806, New York, NY 10016 *Tel:* 212-685-0102 *E-mail:* egmontusa@egmont.com *Web Site:* www.egmontusa.com, pg 86

Haldeman, Michael, Whitehorse Productions, 2417 W 35 Ave, Denver, CO 80211 *Tel:* 303-433-4400, pg 557

Hale, Charles, The MIT Press, 55 Hayward St, Cambridge, MA 02142 *Tel:* 617-253-5255 *Toll Free Tel:* 800-207-8354 (orders) *Fax:* 617-258-6779; 617-577-1545 (orders) *Web Site:* mitpress.mit.edu, pg 167

Hale, Christian, American Printing History Association, PO Box 4519, Grand Central Sta, New York, NY 10163-4519 *Tel:* 202-544-2422 *Web Site:* www.printinghistory.org, pg 614

Hale, Christian, American Printing History Association Award, PO Box 4519, Grand Central Sta, New York, NY 10163-4519 *Tel:* 202-544-2422 *Web Site:* www.printinghistory.org, pg 687

Hale, Nancy, Springer Publishing Co LLC, 11 W 42 St, 15th fl, New York, NY 10036-8002 *Tel:* 212-431-4370 *Toll Free Tel:* 877-687-7476 *Fax:* 212-941-7842 *E-mail:* marketing@springerpub.com; cs@springerpub.com (orders); editorial@springerpub.com *Web Site:* www.springerpub.com, pg 241

serv) *Fax:* 212-366-2666; 607-775-4829 (inside sales) *E-mail:* online@us.penguingroup.com *Web Site:* www.penguin.com; us.penguingroup.com, pg 197

Harris, Steve, Concordia Publishing House, 3558 S Jefferson Ave, St Louis, MO 63118-3968 *Tel:* 314-268-1000 *Toll Free Tel:* 800-325-3040 (cust serv) *Toll Free Fax:* 800-490-9889 (cust serv) *E-mail:* order@cph.org *Web Site:* www.cph.org, pg 66

Harrison, Colin, Scribner, 1230 Avenue of the Americas, New York, NY 10020, pg 230

Harrison, DeSales, Oberlin College Press, 50 N Professor St, Oberlin, OH 44074-1091 *Tel:* 440-775-8408 *Fax:* 440-775-8124 *E-mail:* oc.press@oberlin.edu *Web Site:* www.oberlin.edu/ocpress, pg 183

Harrison, Jack, University of Massachusetts Press, East Experiment Sta, 671 N Pleasant St, Amherst, MA 01003 *Tel:* 413-545-2217 *Fax:* 413-545-1226 *E-mail:* info@umpress.umass.edu *Web Site:* www.umass.edu/umpress, pg 266

Harrison, Joyce, Kent State University Press, 1118 University Library Bldg, 1125 Risman Dr, Kent, OH 44242 *Tel:* 330-672-7913; 419-281-1802 *Fax:* 330-672-3104 *E-mail:* ksupress@kent.edu *Web Site:* www.kentstateuniversitypress.com, pg 139

Harrison, Katherine, Dial Books for Young Readers, 345 Hudson St, New York, NY 10014 *Tel:* 212-366-2000 *Fax:* 212-414-3396 *E-mail:* online@penguinputnam.com *Web Site:* www.penguinputnam.com; us.penguingroup.com, pg 79

Harrison, Margaret, Oxford University Press USA, 198 Madison Ave, New York, NY 10016 *Tel:* 212-726-6000 *Toll Free Tel:* 800-451-7556 (orders); 800-445-9714 (cust serv) *Fax:* 919-677-1303 *E-mail:* custserv.us@oup.com *Web Site:* www.oup.com/us, pg 189

Harrison, Michael, University of Toronto Press Inc, 10 Saint Mary St, Suite 700, Toronto, ON M4Y 2W8, Canada *Tel:* 416-978-2239 *Fax:* 416-978-4738 *E-mail:* utpbooks@utpress.utoronto.ca *Web Site:* www.utpress.utoronto.ca; www.utppublishing.com, pg 524

Harrison, Nick, Harvest House Publishers Inc, 990 Owen Loop N, Eugene, OR 97402-9173 *Tel:* 541-343-0123 *Toll Free Tel:* 888-501-6991 *Fax:* 541-342-6410 *E-mail:* admin@harvesthousepublishers.com *Web Site:* www.harvesthousepublishers.com, pg 115

Harrison, Patricia de Stacy, Corporation for Public Broadcasting (CPB), 401 Ninth St NW, Washington, DC 20004-2129 *Tel:* 202-879-9600 *Toll Free Tel:* 800-272-2190 *Fax:* 202-879-9700 *E-mail:* info@cpb.org *Web Site:* www.cpb.org, pg 622

Harriss, Clarinda, BrickHouse Books Inc, 306 Suffolk Rd, Baltimore, MD 21218 *Tel:* 410-235-7690 *Fax:* 410-235-7690 *Web Site:* www.towson.edu/clarindaharriss; www.brickhousebooks.edu; www.brickhousebooks.wordpress.com, pg 47

Hart, Darlene, Riverside Publishing, 3800 Golf Rd, Suite 200, Rolling Meadows, IL 60008 *Tel:* 630-467-7000 *Toll Free Tel:* 800-323-9540 *Fax:* 630-467-7192 (cust serv) *E-mail:* rpc_customer_service@hmhpub.com (cust serv) *Web Site:* www.riversidepublishing.com, pg 219

Hart, Joyce, Hartline Literary Agency LLC, 123 Queenston Dr, Pittsburgh, PA 15235 *Toll Free Fax:* 888-279-6007 *Web Site:* www.hartlineliterary.com, pg 576

Harte, Lawrence, Althos Publishing, 1500 Piney Plains Rd, Suite 200, Carey, NC 27518 *Tel:* 919-557-2260 *Fax:* 919-557-2261 *E-mail:* info@althos.com *Web Site:* www.althosbooks.com, pg 9

Harting, Laurie, Palgrave Macmillan, 175 Fifth Ave, Suite 200, New York, NY 10010 *Tel:* 646-307-5151 *Fax:* 212-777-6359 *E-mail:* firstname.lastname@palgrave-usa.com *Web Site:* us.macmillan.com/Palgrave.aspx, pg 191

Hartjens, Elisabeth M, Imagefinders Inc, 6101 Utah Ave NW, Washington, DC 20015 *Tel:* 202-244-4456 *Fax:* 202-244-3237, pg 548

Hartley, Glen, Writers' Representatives LLC, 116 W 14 St, 11th fl, New York, NY 10011-7305 *Tel:* 212-620-0023 *Fax:* 212-620-0023 *E-mail:* transom@writersreps.com *Web Site:* www.writersreps.com, pg 600

Hartley, John, Peter Pauper Press, Inc, 202 Mamaroneck Ave, White Plains, NY 10601-5376 *Tel:* 914-681-0144 *Fax:* 914-681-0389 *E-mail:* customerservice@peterpauper.com; orders@peterpauper.com *Web Site:* www.peterpauper.com, pg 200

Hartman, Charles, National Council of Teachers of English (NCTE), 1111 W Kenyon Rd, Urbana, IL 61801-1096 *Tel:* 217-328-3870 *Toll Free Tel:* 877-369-6283 (cust serv) *Fax:* 217-328-9645 *E-mail:* orders@ncte.org *Web Site:* www.ncte.org, pg 174

Hartman, Dorothy, Herald Press, 1251 Virginia Ave, Harrisonburg, VA 22802-2434 *Toll Free Tel:* 800-245-7894 (orders-US); 800-999-3534; 800-631-6535 (orders-CN) *Toll Free Fax:* 877-271-0760 *E-mail:* info@MennoMedia.org *Web Site:* www.heraldpress.com; store.mennomedia.org, pg 118

Hartman, Janell, The Newspaper Guild, 501 Third St NW, 6th fl, Washington, DC 20001-2797 *Tel:* 202-434-7177; 202-434-7162 (The Guild Reporter) *Fax:* 202-434-1472 *E-mail:* guild@cwa-union.org *Web Site:* www.newsguild.org, pg 632

Hartman, Mark, Hartman Publishing Inc, 8529-A Indian School Rd NE, Albuquerque, NM 87112 *Tel:* 505-291-1274 *Toll Free Tel:* 800-999-9534 *Fax:* 505-291-1284 *Toll Free Fax:* 800-474-6106 *E-mail:* orders@hartmanonline.com; help@hartmanonline.com *Web Site:* www.hartmanonline.com, pg 114

Hartman, William, Quintessence Publishing Co Inc, 4350 Chandler Dr, Hanover Park, IL 60133 *Tel:* 630-736-3600 *Toll Free Tel:* 800-621-0387 *Fax:* 630-736-3633 *E-mail:* contact@quintbook.com; service@quintbook.com *Web Site:* www.quintpub.com, pg 211

Hartman-Seeskin, Sara, Free Spirit Publishing Inc, 217 Fifth Ave N, Suite 200, Minneapolis, MN 55401-1260 *Tel:* 612-338-2068 *Toll Free Tel:* 800-735-7323 *Fax:* 612-337-5050 *Toll Free Fax:* 866-419-5199 *E-mail:* help4kids@freespirit.com *Web Site:* www.freespirit.com, pg 99

Hartmann, Connie, Mel Bay Publications Inc, 4 Industrial Dr, Pacific, MO 63069-0066 *Tel:* 636-257-3970 *Toll Free Tel:* 800-863-5229 *Fax:* 636-257-5062 *Toll Free Fax:* 800-660-9818 *E-mail:* email@melbay.com *Web Site:* www.melbay.com, pg 164

Hartogh, Frances, Rocky Mountain Mineral Law Foundation, 9191 Sheridan Blvd, Suite 203, Westminister, CO 80031 *Tel:* 303-321-8100 *Fax:* 303-321-7657 *E-mail:* info@rmmlf.org *Web Site:* www.rmmlf.org, pg 220

Hartson, Kate, Center Street, 12 Cadillac Dr, Suite 480, Brentwood, TN 37027 *Tel:* 615-221-0996 *Web Site:* www.centerstreet.com, pg 56

Harty, Pamela, The Knight Agency Inc, 570 East Ave, Madison, GA 30650 *E-mail:* submissions@knightagency.net *Web Site:* www.knightagency.net, pg 580

Hartzler, John, Christian Light Publications Inc, 1050 Mount Clinton Pike, Harrisonburg, VA 22802 *Tel:* 540-434-1003 *Toll Free Tel:* 800-776-0478 *Fax:* 540-433-8896 *E-mail:* info@clp.org; orders@clp.org *Web Site:* www.clp.org, pg 60

Harvey, Dr Alan, Stanford University Press, 1450 Page Mill Rd, Palo Alto, CA 94304-1124 *Tel:* 650-723-9434 *Fax:* 650-725-3457 *E-mail:* info@sup.org *Web Site:* www.sup.org, pg 243

Harvey, Charmian, Editions Yvon Blais, 137 John, CP 180, Cowansville, QC J2K 3H6, Canada *Tel:* 450-266-1086 *Toll Free Tel:* 800-363-3047 *Fax:* 450-263-9256 *E-mail:* editionsyvonblais.commentaires@thomson.com *Web Site:* www.editionsyvonblais.qc.ca, pg 504

Harvey, Damien, Quackenworth Publishing, PO Box 4747, Culver City, CA 90231-4747 *Tel:* 310-945-5634 *Toll Free Tel:* 888-701-4991 *Fax:* 310-945-5709 *Toll Free Fax:* 888-892-6339 *E-mail:* info@quackenworth.com *Web Site:* www.quackenworth.com; www.wittybittybunch.com, pg 211

Harwell, Andrew, HarperCollins Children's Books, 10 E 53 St, New York, NY 10022 *Tel:* 212-207-7000 *Web Site:* www.harpercollinschildrens.com, pg 113

Harwell, Sarah C, Syracuse University Creative Writing Program, 401 Hall of Languages, Syracuse, NY 13244-1170 *Tel:* 315-443-2173 *Fax:* 315-443-3660 *Web Site:* english.syr.edu/creative_writing; www.syr.edu, pg 680

Harwood, Josh, Houghton Mifflin Harcourt Trade & Reference Division, 222 Berkeley St, Boston, MA 02116-3764 *Tel:* 617-351-5000 *Toll Free Tel:* 800-225-3362 *Web Site:* www.houghtonmifflinbooks.com, pg 124

Hasan, Syed, Springer, 233 Spring St, New York, NY 10013-1578 *Tel:* 212-460-1500 *Toll Free Tel:* 800-SPRINGER (777-4643) *Fax:* 212-460-1575 *E-mail:* service-ny@springer.com *Web Site:* www.springer.com, pg 241

Haskell, Arlo, Key West Literary Seminar, 718 Love Lane, Key West, FL 33040 *Toll Free Tel:* 888-293-9291 *E-mail:* mail@kwls.org *Web Site:* www.kwls.org, pg 670

Hass, Robert, Squaw Valley Community of Writers Summer Workshops, PO Box 1416, Nevada City, CA 95959 *Tel:* 530-470-8440 *E-mail:* info@squawvalleywriters.org *Web Site:* www.squawvalleywriters.org, pg 673

Hasselberger, Rich, Berkley Books, 375 Hudson St, New York, NY 10014 *Tel:* 212-366-2000 *Fax:* 212-366-2666 *E-mail:* online@penguinputnam.com *Web Site:* www.penguinputnam.com; us.penguingroup.com, pg 35

Hasselberger, Rich, Berkley Publishing Group, 375 Hudson St, New York, NY 10014 *Tel:* 212-366-2000 *Fax:* 212-366-2385 *E-mail:* online@penguinputnam.com *Web Site:* us.penguingroup.com, pg 36

Hasselberger, Rich, Dutton, 375 Hudson St, New York, NY 10014 *Tel:* 212-366-2000 *Fax:* 212-366-2262 *E-mail:* online@penguinputnam.com *Web Site:* www.penguinputnam.com; us.penguingroup.com, pg 83

Hasselberger, Rich, NAL, 375 Hudson St, New York, NY 10014 *Tel:* 212-366-2000 *E-mail:* online@penguinputnam.com *Web Site:* www.penguinputnam.com; us.penguingroup.com, pg 172

Hasselberger, Rich, GP Putnam's Sons (Hardcover), 375 Hudson St, New York, NY 10014 *Tel:* 212-366-2000 *E-mail:* online@penguinputnam.com *Web Site:* us.penguingroup.com, pg 210

Hasselstrom, Linda M, Windbreak House Writing Retreats, PO Box 169, Hermosa, SD 57744-0169 *Tel:* 307-630-4003 *E-mail:* info@windbreakhouse.com *Web Site:* www.windbreakhouse.com, pg 674

Hassler, Kurt, Orbit, 237 Park Ave, New York, NY 10017 *Tel:* 212-364-1100 *Toll Free Tel:* 800-759-0190 *Web Site:* www.orbitbooks.net, pg 186

Hasso, M (May) H, Boston Informatics, 35 Byard Lane, Westborough, MA 01581 *Tel:* 508-366-8176 *Web Site:* www.bostoninformatics.com, pg 542

Hastings, Deborah, Federal Street Press, 25-13 Old Kings Hwy N, No 277, Darien, CT 06820 *Tel:* 203-852-1280 *Toll Free Tel:* 877-886-2830 *Fax:* 203-852-1389 *E-mail:* sales@federalstreetpress.com *Web Site:* www.federalstreetpress.com, pg 93

Hastings, Katherine, Susquehanna University, Dept of English, 514 University Ave, Selinsgrove, PA 17870 *Tel:* 570-372-0101, pg 680

Hatch, James C, Committee On Scholarly Editions, c/o Modern Language Association of America, 26 Broadway, 3rd fl, New York, NY 10004-1789 *Tel:* 646-576-5044 *Fax:* 646-458-0030 *Web Site:* www.mla.org, pg 621

Hatch, Ronald, Ronsdale Press Ltd, 3350 W 21 Ave, Vancouver, BC V6S 1G7, Canada *Tel:* 604-738-4688 *Toll Free Tel:* 855-738-4688 *Fax:* 604-731-4548 *E-mail:* ronsdale@shaw.ca *Web Site:* ronsdalepress.com, pg 518

Hatch, Veronica, Ronsdale Press Ltd, 3350 W 21 Ave, Vancouver, BC V6S 1G7, Canada *Tel:* 604-738-4688 *Toll Free Tel:* 855-738-4688 *Fax:* 604-731-4548 *E-mail:* ronsdale@shaw.ca *Web Site:* ronsdalepress.com, pg 518

Hatcher, Lori, Urban Land Institute, 1025 Thomas Jefferson St NW, Suite 500-W, Washington, DC 20007 *Tel:* 202-624-7000 *Toll Free Tel:* 800-321-5011 (cust serv) *Fax:* 410-626-7140 *E-mail:* bookstore@uli.org; customerservice@uli.org *Web Site:* www.uli.org/books, pg 273

Hatter, Richard W, John Simon Guggenheim Memorial Foundation, 90 Park Ave, New York, NY 10016 *Tel:* 212-687-4470 *Fax:* 212-697-3248 *E-mail:* fellowships@gf.org *Web Site:* www.gf.org, pg 641

Hatton, Valerie, Firefly Books Ltd, 50 Staples Ave, Unit 1, Richmond Hill, ON L4B 0A7, Canada *Tel:* 416-499-8412 *Toll Free Tel:* 800-387-6192 (CN); 800-387-5085 (US) *Fax:* 416-499-8313 *Toll Free Fax:* 800-450-0391 (CN); 800-565-6034 (US) *E-mail:* service@fireflybooks.com *Web Site:* www.fireflybooks.com, pg 505

Hauber, Janine, Sheldon Fogelman Agency Inc, 10 E 40 St, Suite 3205, New York, NY 10016 *Tel:* 212-532-7250 *Fax:* 212-685-8939 *E-mail:* info@sheldonfogelmanagency.com *Web Site:* sheldonfogelmanagency.com, pg 572

Hauck, Michael T, DEStech Publications Inc, 439 N Duke St, Lancaster, PA 17602-4967 *Tel:* 717-290-1660 *Toll Free Tel:* 877-500-4337 *Fax:* 717-509-6100 *E-mail:* info@destechpub.com *Web Site:* www.destechpub.com, pg 78

Haughian, Karen, Signature Editions, RPO Corydon, PO Box 206, Winnipeg, MB R3M 3S7, Canada *Tel:* 204-779-7803 *Fax:* 204-779-6970 *E-mail:* signature@allstream.net *Web Site:* www.signature-editions.com, pg 519

Haught, Robert, National Society of Newspaper Columnists (NSNC), 1345 Fillmore St, Suite 507, San Francisco, CA 94115 *Tel:* 415-488-NCNC (488-6762) *Toll Free Tel:* 866-440-NSNC (440-6762) *Fax:* 484-297-0336 *Toll Free Fax:* 866-635-5759 *E-mail:* staff@columnists.com *Web Site:* www.columnists.com, pg 631

Haught, Robert, National Society of Newspaper Columnists Annual Conference, 1345 Fillmore St, Suite 507, San Francisco, CA 94115 *Tel:* 415-488-NCNC (488-6762) *Toll Free Tel:* 866-440-NSNC (440-6762) *Fax:* 484-297-0336 *Toll Free Fax:* 866-635-5759 *Web Site:* www.columnists.com, pg 671

Haupt, Jonathan, University of South Carolina Press, 1600 Hampton St, Suite 544, Columbia, SC 29208 *Tel:* 803-777-5245 *Toll Free Tel:* 800-768-2500 (orders) *Fax:* 803-777-0160 *Toll Free Fax:* 800-868-0740 (orders) *Web Site:* www.sc.edu/uscpress, pg 269

Haut, Judith, Random House Children's Books, 1745 Broadway, New York, NY 10019 *Tel:* 212-782-9000 *Toll Free Tel:* 800-200-3552 *Fax:* 212-782-9452 *Web Site:* randomhousekids.com, pg 213

Haven, Dr Stephen, Ashland Poetry Press, Ashland University, 401 College Ave, Ashland, OH 44805 *Tel:* 419-289-5957 *Fax:* 419-289-5255 *E-mail:* app@ashland.edu *Web Site:* www.ashland.edu/aupoetry, pg 24

Haver, Thomas M, William K Bradford Publishing Co Inc, 31 Main St, Maynard, MA 01754 *Toll Free Tel:* 800-421-2009 *Fax:* 978-897-1806 *E-mail:* wkb@wkbradford.com *Web Site:* www.wkbradford.com, pg 282

Havlish, Sue, Vanderbilt University Press, 2014 Broadway, Suite 320, Nashville, TN 37203 *Tel:* 615-322-3585 *Toll Free Tel:* 800-627-7377 (orders only) *Fax:* 615-343-8823 *Toll Free Fax:* 800-735-0476 (orders only) *E-mail:* vupress@vanderbilt.edu *Web Site:* www.vanderbiltuniversitypress.com, pg 274

Hawkins, Anne, John Hawkins & Associates Inc, 71 W 23 St, Suite 1600, New York, NY 10010 *Tel:* 212-807-7040 *Fax:* 212-807-9555 *E-mail:* jha@jhalit.com *Web Site:* jhalit.com, pg 576

Hawkins, Bob Jr, Harvest House Publishers Inc, 990 Owen Loop N, Eugene, OR 97402-9173 *Tel:* 541-343-0123 *Toll Free Tel:* 888-501-6991 *Fax:* 541-342-6410 *E-mail:* admin@harvesthousepublishers.com *Web Site:* www.harvesthousepublishers.com, pg 115

Hawkins, Drew, Canadian Scholars' Press Inc, 180 Bloor St W, Suite 801, Toronto, ON M5S 2V6, Canada *Tel:* 416-929-2774 *Toll Free Tel:* 800-463-1998 *Fax:* 416-929-1926 *E-mail:* info@cspi.org; editorial@cspi.org *Web Site:* cspi.org; www.womenspress.ca, pg 497

Hawkins, Janet, Trillium Book Award/Prix Trillium, South Tower, Suite 501, 175 Bloor St E, Toronto, ON M4W 3R8, Canada *Tel:* 416-314-6858 (ext 698) *Fax:* 416-314-6876 *E-mail:* trillium23@omdc.on.ca *Web Site:* www.omdc.on.ca, pg 746

Hawkins, Luvenia J, National Council on Radiation Protection & Measurements (NCRP), 7910 Woodmont Ave, Suite 400, Bethesda, MD 20814-3095 *Tel:* 301-657-2652 *Toll Free Tel:* 800-229-2652 *Fax:* 301-907-8768 *E-mail:* ncrppubs@ncrponline.org *Web Site:* www.ncrponline.org; www.ncrppublications.org, pg 174

Hawkins, Valerie, The American Library Association (ALA), 50 E Huron St, Chicago, IL 60611 *Tel:* 312-944-6780; 312-280-4299 (memb & cust serv) *Toll Free Tel:* 800-545-2433 *Fax:* 312-440-9374 *E-mail:* ala@ala.org; customerservice@ala.org *Web Site:* www.ala.org, pg 613

Hawley, Marcy, Orange Frazer Press Inc, 37 1/2 W Main St, Wilmington, OH 45177 *Tel:* 937-382-3196 *Toll Free Tel:* 800-852-9332 (orders) *Fax:* 937-383-3159 *E-mail:* ofrazer@erinet.com *Web Site:* www.orangefrazer.com, pg 186

Hawley, Sarah, Orange Frazer Press Inc, 37 1/2 W Main St, Wilmington, OH 45177 *Tel:* 937-382-3196 *Toll Free Tel:* 800-852-9332 (orders) *Fax:* 937-383-3159 *E-mail:* ofrazer@erinet.com *Web Site:* www.orangefrazer.com, pg 186

Haworth, Kevin, Ohio University Press, 215 Columbus Rd, Suite 101, Athens, OH 45701-2979 *Tel:* 740-593-1154 *Fax:* 740-593-4536 *Web Site:* www.ohioswallow.com, pg 184

Haworth, Kevin, Hollis Summers Poetry Prize, 215 Columbus Rd, Suite 101, Athens, OH 45701-2979 *Tel:* 740-593-1157 *Web Site:* www.ohioswallow.com/poetry_prize, pg 745

Hay, Deltina, Dalton Publishing, PO Box 242, Austin, TX 78767 *Tel:* 512-567-4955 *Fax:* 512-879-6814 *E-mail:* dpquery@daltonpublishing.com *Web Site:* www.daltonpublishing.com, pg 74

Hay, Louise L, Hay House Inc, 2776 Loker Ave W, Carlsbad, CA 92010 *Tel:* 760-431-7695 (ext 2, intl) *Toll Free Tel:* 800-654-5126 (ext 2, US) *Toll Free Fax:* 800-650-5115 *E-mail:* info@hayhouse.com; editorial@hayhouse.com *Web Site:* www.hayhouse.com, pg 115

Hayden, Cynthia, Lake Superior Port Cities Inc, 310 E Superior St, Suite 125, Duluth, MN 55802 *Tel:* 218-722-5002 *Toll Free Tel:* 888-BIG-LAKE (244-5253) *Fax:* 218-722-4096 *E-mail:* reader@lakesuperior.com *Web Site:* www.lakesuperior.com, pg 143

Hayden, Patrick Nielsen, Tom Doherty Associates, LLC, 175 Fifth Ave, 14th fl, New York, NY 10010 *Tel:* 646-307-5151 *Toll Free Tel:* 800-455-0340 *Fax:* 212-388-0191 *E-mail:* firstname.lastname@tor.com *Web Site:* www.tor-forge.com, pg 80

Hayden, Paul L, Lake Superior Port Cities Inc, 310 E Superior St, Suite 125, Duluth, MN 55802 *Tel:* 218-722-5002 *Toll Free Tel:* 888-BIG-LAKE (244-5253) *Fax:* 218-722-4096 *E-mail:* reader@lakesuperior.com *Web Site:* www.lakesuperior.com, pg 143

Hayden, Thomas K, National Notary Association (NNA), 9350 De Soto Ave, Chatsworth, CA 91311 *Tel:* 818-739-4000 *Toll Free Tel:* 800-876-6827 *Toll Free Fax:* 800-833-1211 *E-mail:* nna@nationalnotary.org *Web Site:* www.nationalnotary.org, pg 175

Haydis, Bill, Oxford University Press USA, 198 Madison Ave, New York, NY 10016 *Tel:* 212-726-6000 *Toll Free Tel:* 800-451-7556 (orders); 800-445-9714 (cust serv) *Fax:* 919-677-1303 *E-mail:* custserv.us@oup.com *Web Site:* www.oup.com/us, pg 189

Haydon, Roger, Cornell University Press, Sage House, 512 E State St, Ithaca, NY 14850 *Tel:* 607-277-2338 *Fax:* 607-277-2374 *E-mail:* cupressinfo@cornell.edu; cupress-sales@cornell.edu *Web Site:* www.cornellpress.cornell.edu, pg 67

Hayes, Donna, Harlequin Enterprises Ltd, 225 Duncan Mill Rd, Don Mills, ON M3B 3K9, Canada *Tel:* 416-445-5860 *Toll Free Tel:* 888-432-4879; 800-370-5838 (ebook inquiries) *Fax:* 416-445-8655 *E-mail:* CustomerService@harlequin.com *Web Site:* www.harlequin.com, pg 508

Hayes, Donna, Love Inspired Books, 233 Broadway, Suite 1001, New York, NY 10279 *Tel:* 212-553-4200 *Fax:* 212-227-8969 *E-mail:* customer_service@harlequin.ca *Web Site:* www.loveinspiredbooks.com, pg 153

Hayes, Kevin, Omnigraphics Inc, 155 W Congress, Suite 200, Detroit, MI 48226 *Tel:* 313-961-1340 *Toll Free Tel:* 800-234-1340 (cust serv) *Fax:* 313-961-1383 *Toll Free Fax:* 800-875-1340 (cust serv) *E-mail:* info@omnigraphics.com *Web Site:* www.omnigraphics.com, pg 185

Hayes, Regina, Viking Children's Books, 345 Hudson St, New York, NY 10014 *Tel:* 212-366-2000 *E-mail:* online@penguinputnam.com *Web Site:* www.penguinputnam.com; us.penguingroup.com, pg 275

Hayes, Ryan, Chronicle Books LLC, 680 Second St, San Francisco, CA 94107 *Tel:* 415-537-4200 *Toll Free Tel:* 800-759-0190 (cust serv) *Fax:* 415-537-4460 *Toll Free Fax:* 800-858-7787 (orders); 800-286-9471 (cust serv) *E-mail:* frontdesk@chroniclebooks.com *Web Site:* www.chroniclebooks.com, pg 61

Hayes, Todd, Oxford University Press USA, 198 Madison Ave, New York, NY 10016 *Tel:* 212-726-6000 *Toll Free Tel:* 800-451-7556 (orders); 800-445-9714 (cust serv) *Fax:* 919-677-1303 *E-mail:* custserv.us@oup.com *Web Site:* www.oup.com/us, pg 189

Hayford, Chuck, EastBridge, 70 New Canaan Ave, Norwalk, CT 06850 *Tel:* 203-855-9125 *Fax:* 203-857-0730 *E-mail:* asia@eastbridgebooks.org *Web Site:* www.eastbridgebooks.org, pg 84

Haynes, John, American Institute of Physics, 2 Huntington Quadrangle, Suite 1NO1, Melville, NY 11747 *Tel:* 516-576-2200; 301-209-3165 (orders) *Toll Free Tel:* 800-777-4643 (hardcover books) *Fax:* 516-349-7669; 301-209-0882 (orders) *E-mail:* aipinfo@aip.org *Web Site:* www.aip.org, pg 14

Haynes, John H, Haynes Manuals Inc, 861 Lawrence Dr, Newbury Park, CA 91320 *Tel:* 805-498-6703 *Toll Free Tel:* 800-4-HAYNES (442-9637) *Fax:* 805-498-2867 *E-mail:* cstn@haynes.com *Web Site:* www.haynes.com, pg 115

Hays, Carisa, Crown Publishing Group, c/o Random House Inc, 1745 Broadway, New York, NY 10019 *Tel:* 212-782-9000 *Toll Free Tel:* 888-264-1745 *Fax:* 212-940-7408 *Web Site:* www.randomhouse.com/crown, pg 72

Hays, John, Bear & Co Inc, One Park St, Rochester, VT 05767 *Tel:* 802-767-3174 *Toll Free Tel:* 800-932-3277 *Fax:* 802-767-3726 *E-mail:* customerservice@InnerTraditions.com *Web Site:* InnerTraditions.com, pg 33

Hays, John, Inner Traditions International Ltd, One Park St, Rochester, VT 05767 *Tel:* 802-767-3174 *Toll Free Tel:* 800-246-8648 *Fax:* 802-767-3726 *E-mail:* customerservice@InnerTraditions.com *Web Site:* www.InnerTraditions.com, pg 130

Hays, Michael, McGraw-Hill Higher Education, 1333 Burr Ridge Pkwy, Burr Ridge, IL 60527 *Tel:* 630-789-4000 *Toll Free Tel:* 800-338-3987 (cust serv) *Fax:* 614-755-5645 (cust serv) *Web Site:* www.mhhe.com, pg 161

Hayskar, Bonnie, Pangaea Publications, 226 Wheeler St S, St Paul, MN 55105-1927 *Tel:* 651-226-2032 *Fax:* 651-226-2032 *E-mail:* info@pangaea.org *Web Site:* pangaea.org, pg 191

Haywood, Samantha, Transatlantic Agency, 2 Bloor St E, Ste 3500, Toronto, ON M4W-1A8, Canada *Tel:* 416-488-9214 *E-mail:* info@transatlanticagency.com *Web Site:* www.transatlanticagency.com, pg 597

Hazuka, Heather L, Caddo Gap Press, 3145 Geary Blvd, PMB 275, San Francisco, CA 94118 *Tel:* 415-666-3012 *Fax:* 415-666-3552 *E-mail:* info@caddogap.com *Web Site:* www.caddogap.com, pg 50

Head, Albert B, Alabama Artists Fellowship Awards, 201 Monroe St, Suite 110, Montgomery, AL 36130-1800 *Tel:* 334-242-4076 *Fax:* 334-240-3269, pg 686

Healy, Nick, Capstone Publishers™, 1710 Roe Crest Dr, North Mankato, MN 56003 *Toll Free Tel:* 800-747-4992 (cust serv) *Toll Free Fax:* 888-262-0705 *Web Site:* www.capstonepress.com, pg 51

Healy, Sue, Leadership Directories, 104 Fifth Ave, 3rd fl, New York, NY 10011 *Tel:* 212-627-4140 *Fax:* 212-645-0931 *E-mail:* info@leadershipdirectories.com *Web Site:* www.leadershipdirectories.com, pg 145

Heard, Janet, Davies Publishing Inc, 32 S Raymond Ave, Suites 4 & 5, Pasadena, CA 91105-1961 *Tel:* 626-792-3046 *Toll Free Tel:* 877-792-0005 *Fax:* 626-792-5308 *E-mail:* info@daviespublishing.com *Web Site:* daviespublishing.com, pg 75

Heath, David, Redleaf Press, 10 Yorkton Ct, St Paul, MN 55117 *Tel:* 651-641-0508 *Toll Free Tel:* 800-423-8309 *Toll Free Fax:* 800-641-0115 *Web Site:* www.redleafpress.org, pg 216

Heathman, Kim A, LionHearted Publishing Inc, PO Box 618, Zephyr Cove, NV 89448-0618 *Tel:* 775-853-3221 *Toll Free Tel:* 888-546-6478 *Toll Free Fax:* 888-546-6478 *E-mail:* admin@lionhearted.com *Web Site:* www.lionhearted.com, pg 150

Hebel, Brad, Columbia University Press, 61 W 62 St, New York, NY 10023 *Tel:* 212-459-0600 *Toll Free Tel:* 800-944-8648 *Fax:* 212-459-3678 *E-mail:* cup_book@columbia.edu (orders & cust serv) *Web Site:* cup.columbia.edu, pg 65

Hebert, Jean-Francois, Editions du CHU Sainte-Justine, 3175 Cote-Saint-Catherine, Montreal, QC H3T 1C5, Canada *Tel:* 514-345-4671 *Fax:* 514-345-4631 *E-mail:* edition.hsj@ssss.gouv.qc.ca *Web Site:* www.editions-chu-sainte-justine.org, pg 499

Hechler, Kay, United States Institute of Peace Press, 2301 Constitution Ave NW, Washington, DC 20037 *Tel:* 202-457-1700 (edit); 703-661-1590 (cust serv) *Toll Free Tel:* 800-868-8064 (cust serv) *Fax:* 202-429-6063; 703-661-1501 (cust serv) *Web Site:* bookstore.usip.org, pg 262

Hecker, Helen, Twin Peaks Press, PO Box 8, Vancouver, WA 98666-0008 *Tel:* 360-694-2462 *Toll Free Tel:* 800-637-2256 *E-mail:* twinpeaks@pacifier.com *Web Site:* www.twinpeakspress.com, pg 261

Hecker, J L, Stipes Publishing LLC, 204 W University, Champaign, IL 61820 *Tel:* 217-356-8391 *Fax:* 217-356-5753 *E-mail:* stipes01@sbcglobal.net *Web Site:* www.stipes.com, pg 245

Hecker, Mel, United States Holocaust Memorial Museum, 100 Raoul Wallenberg Place SW, Washington, DC 20024-2126 *Tel:* 202-314-7837; 202-488-6144 (orders) *Toll Free Tel:* 800-259-9998 (orders) *Fax:* 202-479-9726; 202-488-0438 (orders) *E-mail:* cahs_publications@ushmm.org *Web Site:* www.ushmm.org, pg 262

Hedden, Andrew, Scholastic Inc, 557 Broadway, New York, NY 10012 *Tel:* 212-343-6100 *Toll Free Tel:* 800-scholastic *Web Site:* www.scholastic.com, pg 228

Hedeen, Katrina, Boston Globe-Horn Book Award, 56 Roland St, Suite 200, Boston, MA 02129 *Tel:* 617-628-0225 *Toll Free Tel:* 800-325-1170 *Fax:* 617-628-0882 *E-mail:* info@hbook.com *Web Site:* www.hbook.com, pg 692

Hee, Laurie, Lippincott Williams & Wilkins, 530 Walnut St, Philadelphia, PA 19106-3621 *Tel:* 215-521-8300 *Toll Free Tel:* 800-638-3030 (orders & cust serv) *E-mail:* orders@lww.com *Web Site:* www.lww.com, pg 150

Heffernan, Dick, Penguin Group (USA) LLC, 375 Hudson St, New York, NY 10014 *Tel:* 212-366-2000 *Toll Free Tel:* 800-847-5515 (inside sales); 800-631-8571 (cust serv) *Fax:* 212-366-2666; 607-775-4829 (inside sales) *E-mail:* online@us.penguingroup.com *Web Site:* www.penguin.com; us.penguingroup.com, pg 197

Heffernan, Dick, Penguin Group (USA) LLC Sales, 375 Hudson St, New York, NY 10014 *Tel:* 212-366-2000 *E-mail:* online@penguinputnam.com *Web Site:* us.penguingroup.com, pg 197

Heffron, Tom, Octane Press, 808 Kinney Ave, Austin, TX 78704 *Tel:* 512-334-9441 *Fax:* 512-852-4737 *E-mail:* info@octanepress.com *Web Site:* www.octanepress.com, pg 184

Heflin, Mark, American Illustration/American Photography, 15 E 32 St, 7th fl, New York, NY 10016 *Tel:* 212-470-0302 *Fax:* 212-532-2064 *E-mail:* info@ai-ap.com *Web Site:* www.ai-ap.com, pg 687

Hegedus, Bethany, Writers' League of Texas (WLT), 611 S Congress Ave, Suite 505, Austin, TX 78704 *Tel:* 512-499-8914 *E-mail:* wlt@writersleague.org *Web Site:* www.writersleague.org, pg 606, 675

Hegedus, Bethany, Writers' League of Texas Book Awards, 611 S Congress Ave, Suite 505, Austin, TX 78704 *Tel:* 512-499-8914 *E-mail:* wlt@writersleague.org *Web Site:* www.writersleague.org, pg 752

Hegeman, Ann, Rutgers University Press, 106 Somerset St, 3rd fl, New Brunswick, NJ 08901 *Tel:* 858-445-7784 (edit); 848-445-7788 *Toll Free Tel:* 800-848-6224 (orders only) *Fax:* 732-745-4935 (acqs, edit, mktg, perms & prodn) *Toll Free Fax:* 800-272-6817 (fulfillment) *Web Site:* rutgerspress.rutgers.edu, pg 222

Heiblum, Judy, Sterling Lord Literistic Inc, 65 Bleecker St, New York, NY 10012 *Tel:* 212-780-6050 *Fax:* 212-780-6095 *E-mail:* info@sll.com *Web Site:* www.sll.com, pg 595

Heider, Joe, John Wiley & Sons Inc Higher Education, 111 River St, Hoboken, NJ 07030-5774 *Tel:* 201-748-6000 *Toll Free Tel:* 800-225-5945 (cust serv) *Fax:* 201-748-6008 *E-mail:* info@wiley.com *Web Site:* www.wiley.com, pg 281

Heider, Joseph Sheridan, John Wiley & Sons Inc, 111 River St, Hoboken, NJ 07030-5774 *Tel:* 201-748-6000 *Toll Free Tel:* 800-225-5945 (cust serv) *Fax:* 201-748-6088 *E-mail:* info@wiley.com *Web Site:* www.wiley.com, pg 281

Heifetz, Merrilee, Writers House, 21 W 26 St, New York, NY 10010 *Tel:* 212-685-2400 *Fax:* 212-685-1781 *Web Site:* www.writershouse.com, pg 599

Heilman, Erica, Nicholas Brealey Publishing, 20 Park Plaza, Suite 610, Boston, MA 02116 *Tel:* 617-523-3801 *Toll Free Tel:* 888-BREALEY (273-2539) *Fax:* 617-523-3708 *E-mail:* info@nicholasbrealey.com *Web Site:* www.nicholasbrealey.com, pg 46

Heimberg, Justin, Seven Footer Kids, 247 W 30 St, 11th fl, New York, NY 10001-2824 *Tel:* 212-710-9340 *Fax:* 212-710-9344 *E-mail:* info@sevenfooter.com *Web Site:* www.sevenfooterpress.com, pg 232

Heimberg, Justin, Seven Footer Press, 247 W 30 St, 2nd fl, New York, NY 10001-2824 *Tel:* 212-710-9340 *Fax:* 212-710-9344 *E-mail:* info@sevenfooter.com *Web Site:* www.sevenfooterpress.com, pg 232

Heimbouch, Hollis, HarperCollins General Books Group, 10 E 53 St, New York, NY 10022 *Tel:* 212-207-7000 *Fax:* 212-207-7633 *Web Site:* www.harpercollins.com, pg 113

Heimburger, Donald J, Heimburger House Publishing Co, 7236 W Madison St, Forest Park, IL 60130 *Tel:* 708-366-1973 *Fax:* 708-366-1973 *E-mail:* info@heimburgerhouse.com *Web Site:* www.heimburgerhouse.com, pg 117

Heimert, Laura, Basic Books, 250 W 57 St, 15th fl, New York, NY 10107 *Tel:* 212-340-8164 *Fax:* 212-340-8135 *E-mail:* perseus.promos@perseusbooks.com *Web Site:* www.basicbooks.com; perseusbooks.com, pg 31

Hein, Kristi, Pictures & Words Editorial Services, 3100 "B" Ave, Anacortes, WA 98221 *Tel:* 360-293-8476 *E-mail:* editor@picturesandwords.com *Web Site:* www.picturesandwords.com/words, pg 553

Hein, William S Jr, William S Hein & Co Inc, 2350 N Forest Rd, Getzville, NY 14068 *Tel:* 716-882-2600 *Toll Free Tel:* 800-828-7571 *Fax:* 716-883-8100 *E-mail:* mail@wshein.com; marketing@wshein.com *Web Site:* www.wshein.com, pg 117

Heinle, Charles, EPS/School Specialty Literacy & Intervention, 625 Mount Auburn St, 3rd fl, Cambridge, MA 02138-4555 *Tel:* 617-547-6706 *Toll Free Tel:* 800-225-5750 *Fax:* 617-547-0412 *Toll Free Fax:* 888-440-2665 *E-mail:* customerservice.eps@schoolspecialty.com *Web Site:* eps.schoolspecialty.com, pg 89

Heinzelman, Kurt, University of Texas at Austin, Creative Writing Program, Dept of English, PAR 108, One University Sta, Mailcode B5000, Austin, TX 78712-1164 *Tel:* 512-471-5132; 512-471-4991 *Fax:* 512-471-4909 *Web Site:* www.utexas.edu/cola/depts/english/creative-writing, pg 682

Heise, Barbara, GemStone Press, Sunset Farm Offices, Rte 4, Woodstock, VT 05091 *Tel:* 802-457-4000 *Toll Free Tel:* 800-962-4544 *Fax:* 802-457-4004 *E-mail:* sales@gemstonepress.com *Web Site:* www.gemstonepress.com, pg 102

Heise, Judy, Naval Institute Press, 291 Wood Rd, Annapolis, MD 21402-5034 *Tel:* 410-268-6110 *Toll Free Tel:* 800-233-8764 *Fax:* 410-295-1084; 410-571-1703 (cust serv) *E-mail:* webmaster@navalinstitute.org; customer@navalinstitute.org (cust serv); trade@usni.org *Web Site:* www.nip.org; www.usni.org, pg 176

Heiser, Christopher, University of Chicago Press, 1427 E 60 St, Chicago, IL 60637-2954 *Tel:* 773-702-7700; 773-702-7600 *Toll Free Tel:* 800-621-2736 (orders) *Fax:* 773-702-9756; 773-660-2235 (orders); 773-702-2708 *E-mail:* custserv@press.uchicago.edu; marketing@press.uchicago.edu *Web Site:* www.press.uchicago.edu, pg 265

Heiserman, Alice, American Correctional Association, 206 N Washington St, Suite 200, Alexandria, VA 22314 *Tel:* 703-224-0000 *Toll Free Tel:* 800-222-5646 *Fax:* 703-224-0040 *Web Site:* www.aca.org, pg 12

Held, Ivan, Penguin Group (USA) LLC, 375 Hudson St, New York, NY 10014 *Tel:* 212-366-2000 *Toll Free Tel:* 800-847-5515 (inside sales); 800-631-8571 (cust serv) *Fax:* 212-366-2666; 607-775-4829 (inside sales) *E-mail:* online@us.penguingroup.com *Web Site:* www.penguin.com; us.penguingroup.com, pg 197

Held, Ivan, GP Putnam's Sons (Hardcover), 375 Hudson St, New York, NY 10014 *Tel:* 212-366-2000 *E-mail:* online@penguinputnam.com *Web Site:* us.penguingroup.com, pg 210

Held, Joe, The Reader's Digest Association Inc, 750 Third Ave, New York, NY 10017 *Tel:* 914-238-1000; 646-293-6284 *Toll Free Tel:* 800-310-6261 (cust serv) *Fax:* 914-238-4559 *Web Site:* www.rd.com; www.rda.com, pg 215

Helfand, Debra, Farrar, Straus & Giroux, LLC, 18 W 18 St, New York, NY 10011 *Tel:* 212-741-6900 *Fax:* 212-633-9385 *E-mail:* fsg.publicity@fsgbooks.com *Web Site:* us.macmillan.com/fsg.aspx, pg 93

Helgesen, Charles, The Oliver Press Inc, Charlotte Sq, 5707 W 36 St, Minneapolis, MN 55416-2510 *Tel:* 952-926-8981 *Toll Free Tel:* 800-8-OLIVER (865-4837) *Fax:* 952-926-8965 *E-mail:* orders@oliverpress.com *Web Site:* www.oliverpress.com, pg 185

Helgesen, Jeff, Research Press, 2612 N Mattis Ave, Champaign, IL 61822 *Tel:* 217-352-3273 *Toll Free Tel:* 800-519-2707 *Fax:* 217-352-1221 *E-mail:* rp@researchpress.com; orders@researchpress.com *Web Site:* www.researchpress.com, pg 218

Heller, Carol, Kent State University Press, 1118 University Library Bldg, 1125 Risman Dr, Kent, OH 44242 *Tel:* 330-672-7913; 419-281-1802 *Fax:* 330-672-3104 *E-mail:* ksupress@kent.edu *Web Site:* www.kentstateuniversitypress.com, pg 139

Helm, Dianne, Helm Publishing, PO Box 9691, Treasure Island, FL 33740 *Tel:* 727-623-5014 *Web Site:* www.publishersdrive.com, pg 118

Helm, Harry, Center Street, 12 Cadillac Dr, Suite 480, Brentwood, TN 37027 *Tel:* 615-221-0996 *Web Site:* www.centerstreet.com, pg 56

Helm, Harry, FaithWords, 12 Cadillac Dr, Suite 480, Brentwood, TN 37027 *Tel:* 615-221-0996 *Fax:* 615-221-0962 *Web Site:* www.hachettebookgroup.com, pg 92

Helus, Eric, NavPress Publishing Group, 3820 N 30 St, Colorado Springs, CO 80904 *Tel:* 719-548-9222 *Toll Free Tel:* 800-366-7788 *Toll Free Fax:* 800-343-3902 *E-mail:* customerservice@navpress.com *Web Site:* www.navpress.com, pg 176

Helvey, Christopher, Eric Hoffer Award for Short Prose, PO Box 11, Titusville, NJ 08560 *Fax:* 609-964-1718 *E-mail:* info@hofferaward.com *Web Site:* www.hofferaward.com, pg 710

Hembree, Larry, Trustus Playwrights' Festival, 520 Lady St, Columbia, SC 29201 *Tel:* 803-254-9732 *Fax:* 803-771-9153 *E-mail:* trustus@trustus.org *Web Site:* www.trustus.org, pg 746

Hemlock, Katherine, BradyGames, 800 E 96 St, 3rd fl, Indianapolis, IN 46240 *Tel:* 317-428-3000 *Toll Free Tel:* 800-545-5912; 800-571-5840 (cust serv) *E-mail:* bradyquestions@pearsoned.com *Web Site:* www.bradygames.com, pg 45

Hemperly, Becky S, Candlewick Press, 99 Dover St, Somerville, MA 02144-2825 *Tel:* 617-661-3330 *Fax:* 617-661-0565 *E-mail:* bigbear@candlewick.com *Web Site:* www.candlewick.com, pg 51

Hempstead, Andrew, Summerthought Publishing, PO Box 2309, Banff, AB T1L 1C1, Canada *Tel:* 403-762-0535 *Fax:* 403-762-3095 *Toll Free Fax:* 800-762-3095 (orders) *E-mail:* info@summerthought.com; sales@summerthought.com *Web Site:* www.summerthought.com, pg 520

Henahan, Julie, Individual Excellence Awards, 30 E Broad St, 33rd fl, Columbus, OH 43215 *Tel:* 614-466-2613 *Fax:* 614-466-4494 *Web Site:* www.oac.state.oh.us, pg 712

Henderson, Bill, Pushcart Press, PO Box 380, Wainscott, NY 11975-0380 *Tel:* 631-324-9300, pg 210

Henderson, Bill, Pushcart Prize: Best of the Small Presses, PO Box 380, Wainscott, NY 11975-0380 *Tel:* 631-324-9300, pg 736

Henderson, Brian, Wilfrid Laurier University Press, 75 University Ave W, Waterloo, ON N2L 3C5, Canada *Tel:* 519-884-0710 (ext 6124) *Toll Free Tel:* 866-836-5551 *Fax:* 519-725-1399 *E-mail:* press@wlu.ca *Web Site:* www.wlupress.wlu.ca, pg 525

Henderson, Diane, Homestead Publishing, Box 193, Moose, WY 83012-0193 *Tel:* 307-733-6248 *Fax:* 307-733-6248 *E-mail:* orders@homesteadpublishing.net *Web Site:* www.homesteadpublishing.net, pg 122

Henderson, Ericka, IACP Cookbook Awards, 1100 Johnson Ferry Rd, Suite 300, Atlanta, GA 30342 *Tel:* 404-252-3663 *Fax:* 404-252-0774 *E-mail:* info@iacp.com *Web Site:* www.iacp.com, pg 711

Henderson, Homer, Parenting Press Inc, 11065 Fifth Ave NE, Suite F, Seattle, WA 98125 *Tel:* 206-364-2900 *Toll Free Tel:* 800-99-BOOKS (992-6657) *Fax:* 206-364-0702 *E-mail:* office@parentingpress.com; marketing@parentingpress.com *Web Site:* www.parentingpress.com, pg 193

Henderson, Joe, The Jim Henson Co, 1416 N La Brea Ave, Hollywood, CA 90028 *Tel:* 323-802-1500 *Fax:* 323-802-1825 *Web Site:* www.henson.com, pg 135

Henderson, Paul, US Conference of Catholic Bishops, USCCB Publishing, 3211 Fourth St NE, Washington, DC 20017 *Tel:* 202-541-3090 *Toll Free Tel:* 800-235-8722 (orders only) *Fax:* 202-722-8709 *E-mail:* css@usccb.org; publications@usccb.org *Web Site:* www.usccbpublishing.org, pg 273

Hendrie, Caroline, Education Writers Association (EWA), 3516 Connecticut Ave NW, Washington, DC 20008-2401 *Tel:* 202-452-9830 *Fax:* 202-452-9837 *E-mail:* ewa@ewa.org *Web Site:* www.ewa.org, pg 623

Hendrie, Caroline, Education Writers Association Workshops, 3516 Connecticut Ave NW, Washington, DC 20008-2401 *Tel:* 202-452-9830 *Fax:* 202-452-9837 *E-mail:* ewa@ewa.org *Web Site:* www.ewa.org, pg 668

Hendrie, Caroline, National Awards for Education Reporting, 3516 Connecticut Ave NW, Washington, DC 20008-2401 *Tel:* 202-452-9830 *Fax:* 202-452-9837 *E-mail:* ewa@ewa.org *Web Site:* www.ewa.org, pg 726

Henebry, Martha, American Association of Collegiate Registrars & Admissions Officers (AACRAO), One Dupont Circle NW, Suite 520, Washington, DC 20036-1135 *Tel:* 202-293-9161 *Fax:* 202-872-8857 *E-mail:* info@aacrao.org *Web Site:* www.aacrao.org, pg 11

Hengst, Linda R, James P Barry Ohioana Award for Editorial Excellence, 274 E First Ave, Suite 300, Columbus, OH 43201 *Tel:* 614-466-3831 *Fax:* 614-728-6974 *E-mail:* ohioana@ohioana.org *Web Site:* www.ohioana.org, pg 689

Hengst, Linda R, Ohioana Award for Children's Literature-Alice Louise Wood Memorial, 274 E First Ave, Suite 300, Columbus, OH 43201 *Tel:* 614-466-3831 *Fax:* 614-728-6974 *E-mail:* ohioana@ohioana.org *Web Site:* www.ohioana.org, pg 730

Hengst, Linda R, Ohioana Book Awards, 274 E First Ave, Suite 300, Columbus, OH 43201 *Tel:* 614-466-3831 *Fax:* 614-728-6974 *E-mail:* ohioana@ohioana.org *Web Site:* www.ohioana.org, pg 730

Hengst, Linda R, Ohioana Career Award, 274 E First Ave, Suite 300, Columbus, OH 43201 *Tel:* 614-466-3831 *Fax:* 614-728-6974 *E-mail:* ohioana@ohioana.org *Web Site:* www.ohioana.org, pg 730

Hengst, Linda R, Ohioana Citations, 274 E First Ave, Suite 300, Columbus, OH 43201 *Tel:* 614-466-3831 *Fax:* 614-728-6974 *E-mail:* ohioana@ohioana.org *Web Site:* www.ohioana.org, pg 730

Hengst, Linda R, Ohioana Pegasus Award, 274 E First Ave, Suite 300, Columbus, OH 43201 *Tel:* 614-466-3831 *Fax:* 614-728-6974 *E-mail:* ohioana@ohioana.org *Web Site:* www.ohioana.org, pg 731

Hengst, Linda R, Ohioana Poetry Award-Memorial to Helen & Laura Krout, 274 E First Ave, Suite 300, Columbus, OH 43201 *Tel:* 614-466-3831 *Fax:* 614-728-6974 *E-mail:* ohioana@ohioana.org *Web Site:* www.ohioana.org, pg 731

Hengst, Linda R, Ohioana Walter Rumsey Marvin Grant, 274 E First Ave, Suite 300, Columbus, OH 43201 *Tel:* 614-466-3831 *Fax:* 614-728-6974 *E-mail:* ohioana@ohioana.org *Web Site:* www.ohioana.org, pg 731

Henoch, Larissa, Health Communications Inc, 3201 SW 15 St, Deerfield Beach, FL 33442-8190 *Tel:* 954-360-0909 *Toll Free Tel:* 800-441-5569 (cust serv) *Fax:* 954-360-0034 *Web Site:* www.hcibooks.com; hci-online.com, pg 116

Henry, Alyson, C D Howe Institute, 67 Yonge St, Suite 300, Toronto, ON M5E 1J8, Canada *Tel:* 416-865-1904 *Fax:* 416-865-1866 *E-mail:* cdhowe@cdhowe.org *Web Site:* www.cdhowe.org, pg 509

Henry, Brian, Strata Publishing Inc, PO Box 1303, State College, PA 16804 *Tel:* 814-234-8545 *Fax:* 814-238-7222 *E-mail:* stratapub@stratapub.com *Web Site:* www.stratapub.com, pg 246

Henry, Christie, University of Chicago Press, 1427 E 60 St, Chicago, IL 60637-2954 *Tel:* 773-702-7700; 773-702-7600 *Toll Free Tel:* 800-621-2736 (orders) *Fax:* 773-702-9756; 773-660-2235 (orders); 773-702-2708 *E-mail:* custserv@press.uchicago.edu; marketing@press.uchicago.edu *Web Site:* www.press.uchicago.edu, pg 265

Henry, Gray, Fons Vitae, 49 Mockingbird Valley Dr, Louisville, KY 40207-1366 *Tel:* 502-897-3641 *Fax:* 502-893-7373 *E-mail:* fonsvitaeky@aol.com *Web Site:* www.fonsvitae.com, pg 97

Henry, Jack, World Citizens, PO Box 131, Mill Valley, CA 94942-0131 *Tel:* 415-380-8020 *Toll Free Tel:* 800-247-6553 (orders only), pg 285

Henry, Karen, Bedford/St Martin's, 75 Arlington St, Boston, MA 02116 *Tel:* 617-399-4000 *Toll Free Tel:* 800-779-7440 *Fax:* 617-426-8582 *Web Site:* www.bedfordstmartins.com, pg 34

Henry, Lynn, Doubleday Canada, One Toronto St, Suite 300, Toronto, ON M5C 2V6, Canada *Tel:* 416-364-4449 *Fax:* 416-364-6863 *Web Site:* www.randomhouse.ca, pg 501

Henry, Sarah, Sourcebooks Inc, 1935 Brookdale Rd, Suite 139, Naperville, IL 60563 *Tel:* 630-961-3900 *Toll Free Tel:* 800-432-7444 *Fax:* 630-961-2168 *E-mail:* info@sourcebooks.com; customersupport@sourcebooks.com *Web Site:* www.sourcebooks.com, pg 240

Hensley, Neal, Hensley Publishing, 6116 E 32 St, Tulsa, OK 74135 *Tel:* 918-664-8520 *Toll Free Tel:* 800-288-8520 (orders only) *Fax:* 918-664-8562 *E-mail:* customerservice@hensleypublishing.com *Web Site:* www.hensleypublishing.com, pg 118

Hensley, Todd, C & T Publishing Inc, 1651 Challenge Dr, Concord, CA 94520-5206 *Tel:* 925-677-0377 *Toll Free Tel:* 800-284-1114 *Fax:* 925-677-0373 *E-mail:* ctinfo@ctpub.com *Web Site:* www.ctpub.com, pg 50

Hensley, Tony, C & T Publishing Inc, 1651 Challenge Dr, Concord, CA 94520-5206 *Tel:* 925-677-0377 *Toll Free Tel:* 800-284-1114 *Fax:* 925-677-0373 *E-mail:* ctinfo@ctpub.com *Web Site:* www.ctpub.com, pg 50

Henson, Brian, The Jim Henson Co, 1416 N La Brea Ave, Hollywood, CA 90028 *Tel:* 323-802-1500 *Fax:* 323-802-1825 *Web Site:* www.henson.com, pg 135

Henson, Lisa Esq, The Jim Henson Co, 1416 N La Brea Ave, Hollywood, CA 90028 *Tel:* 323-802-1500 *Fax:* 323-802-1825 *Web Site:* www.henson.com, pg 135

Henson, Noreen, Berghahn Books, 20 Jay St, Suite 512, Brooklyn, NY 11201 *Tel:* 212-233-6004 *Fax:* 212-233-6007 *E-mail:* info@berghahnbooks.com; salesus@berghahnbooks.com; editorial@journals.berghahnbooks.com *Web Site:* www.berghahnbooks.com, pg 35

Herbert, Karen Brown, Karen Brown's Guides Inc, 16 E Third Ave, Suite 9, San Mateo, CA 94401 *Tel:* 650-342-9117 *Fax:* 650-342-9153 *E-mail:* orders@karenbrown.com *Web Site:* www.karenbrown.com, pg 49

Herbig, Alice, University of Washington Press, 433 Brooklyn Ave NE, Seattle, WA 98195-9570 *Tel:* 206-543-4050 *Toll Free Tel:* 800-537-5487 (orders) *Fax:* 206-543-3932; 410-516-6998 (orders) *E-mail:* uwpress@u.washington.edu *Web Site:* www.washington.edu/uwpress/, pg 270

Herbst, John, Indiana Historical Society Press (IHS Press), 450 W Ohio St, Indianapolis, IN 46202-3269 *Tel:* 317-232-1882; 317-234-0026 (orders); 317-234-2716 (edit) *Toll Free Tel:* 800-447-1830 (orders) *Fax:* 317-234-0562 (orders); 317-233-0857 (edit) *E-mail:* ihspress@indianahistory.org; orders@indianahistory.org (orders) *Web Site:* www.indianahistory.org; shop.indianahistory.org (orders), pg 129

Herbst, Peggy Smith, Harcourt Mifflin School Publishers, 6277 Sea Harbor Dr, Orlando, FL 32887 *Tel:* 407-345-2000 *Toll Free Tel:* 800-225-5425 (cust serv) *Fax:* 407-345-3016 (cust serv) *Toll Free Fax:* 800-874-6418; 800-269-5232 (cust serv) *Web Site:* www.harcourtschool.com, pg 112

Herder, Dr Gwendolin, The Crossroad Publishing Co, 831 Chestnut Ridge Rd, Chestnut Ridge, NY 10977 *Tel:* 845-517-0180 *Toll Free Tel:* 800-888-4741 (orders) *Fax:* 845-517-0181 *Web Site:* www.CrossroadPublishing.com, pg 72

Herits, Noreen, Random House Children's Books, 1745 Broadway, New York, NY 10019 *Tel:* 212-782-9000 *Toll Free Tel:* 800-200-3552 *Fax:* 212-782-9452 *Web Site:* randomhousekids.com, pg 213

Herman, Cheryl, Books on Tape®, c/o Sales Dept, 3070 Bristol St, Suite 650, Costa Mesa, CA 92626 *Toll Free Tel:* 800-733-3000 (cust serv) *Toll Free Fax:* 800-940-7046 *Web Site:* www.booksontape.com, pg 44

Herman, Gilles, Les Editions du Septentrion, 1300 Maguire Ave, Sillery, QC G1T 1Z3, Canada *Tel:* 418-688-3556 *Fax:* 418-527-4978 *E-mail:* sept@septentrion.qc.ca *Web Site:* www.septentrion.qc.ca, pg 503

Herman, Jeffrey H, The Jeff Herman Agency LLC, 29 Park St, Stockbridge, MA 01262 *Tel:* 413-298-0077 *Fax:* 413-298-8188 *E-mail:* submissions@jeffherman.com *Web Site:* www.jeffherman.com, pg 577

Herman, Katia, Herman Agency, 350 Central Park W, Apt 4I, New York, NY 10025 *Tel:* 212-749-4907 *Web Site:* www.hermanagencyinc.com, pg 601

Herman, Rhonda, McFarland, 960 NC Hwy 88 W, Jefferson, NC 28640 *Tel:* 336-246-4460 *Toll Free Tel:* 800-253-2187 (orders) *Fax:* 336-246-5018; 336-246-4403 (orders) *E-mail:* info@mcfarlandpub.com *Web Site:* www.mcfarlandpub.com, pg 160

Herman, Ronnie Ann, Herman Agency, 350 Central Park W, Apt 4I, New York, NY 10025 *Tel:* 212-749-4907 *Web Site:* www.hermanagencyinc.com, pg 601

Herman, Susan N, American Civil Liberties Union, 125 Broad St, 18th fl, New York, NY 10004 *Tel:* 212-549-2500 *Toll Free Tel:* 800-775-ACLU (orders) *E-mail:* media@aclu.org *Web Site:* www.aclu.org, pg 612

Hermann, Sara, Parmenides Publishing, 3753 Howard Hughes Pkwy, Suite 200, Las Vegas, NV 89169 *Tel:* 702-892-3934 *Fax:* 702-892-3939 *E-mail:* info@parmenides.com *Web Site:* www.parmenides.com, pg 194

Hermes, Bill, Palm Kids™, 50 Washington St, 12th fl, Norwalk, CT 06854 *Toll Free Tel:* 800-409-2457 *E-mail:* customercare@palmkids.com; sales@palmkids.com *Web Site:* www.palmkids.com, pg 191

Hernandez, Manny, Foster City International Writer's Contest, 650 Shell Blvd, Foster City, CA 94404 *Tel:* 650-286-3386 *E-mail:* fostercity_writers@yahoo.com *Web Site:* www.fostercity.org, pg 705

Hernandez, Sulay, Other Press LLC, 2 Park Ave, 24th fl, New York, NY 10016 *Tel:* 212-414-0054 *Toll Free Tel:* 877-843-6843 *Fax:* 212-414-0939 *E-mail:* editor@otherpress.com; rights@otherpress.com *Web Site:* www.otherpress.com, pg 188

Herndon, John, The Balcones Poetry Prize, 1212 Rio Grande St, Austin, TX 78701 *Tel:* 512-828-9368 *Web Site:* www.austincc.edu/crw/balcones_prize.html, pg 689

Herner, Susan N, Susan Herner Rights Agency Inc, 10 Upper Shad Rd, Pound Ridge, NY 10576 *Tel:* 914-234-2864 *Fax:* 914-234-2866 *E-mail:* sherneragency@optonline.net, pg 577

Herr, John, Wag's Revue Writers' Contest, 2865 W Lyndale St, Suite 1, Chicago, IL 60647 *E-mail:* editors@wagsrevue.com *Web Site:* www.wagsrevue.com, pg 748

Herr, Staci, West Academic Publishing, 610 Opperman Dr, Eagan, MN 55123 *Tel:* 651-687-7000 *Toll Free Tel:* 800-328-2209 (bookstore orders); 800-313-WEST (313-9378) *Toll Free Fax:* 800-213-2323 (bookstore orders) *E-mail:* westacademic@thomsonreuters.com *Web Site:* www.westacademic.com, pg 278

Herrera, Aida, BenBella Books Inc, 10300 N Central Expwy, Suite 400, Dallas, TX 75231 *Tel:* 214-750-3600 *Fax:* 214-750-3645 *E-mail:* feedback@benbellabooks.com *Web Site:* www.benbellabooks.com; www.smartpopbooks.com, pg 35

Herron, Jerry, Wayne State University Press, Leonard N Simons Bldg, 4809 Woodward Ave, Detroit, MI 48201-1309 *Tel:* 313-577-6120 *Toll Free Tel:* 800-978-7323 *Fax:* 313-577-6131 *Web Site:* www.wsupress.wayne.edu, pg 277

Hersh, Mary Claire, The Society of Midland Authors (SMA), PO Box 10419, Chicago, IL 60610 *E-mail:* info@midlandauthors.com *Web Site:* www.midlandauthors.com, pg 637

Hersh, Mary Claire, The Society of Midland Authors Awards, 530 Michigan Ave, Evanston, IL 60202 *E-mail:* info@midlandauthors.com *Web Site:* www.midlandauthors.com, pg 743

Hershberger, Katy, Bloomsbury Publishing, 175 Fifth Ave, New York, NY 10010 *Tel:* 212-674-5151 *Toll Free Tel:* 800-221-7945 *Fax:* 212-780-0115; 212-982-2837 *E-mail:* marketingusa@bloomsbury.com; adultpublicityusa.@bloomsbury.com *Web Site:* www.bloomsbury.com, pg 40

Hershey, Jennifer, Random House Publishing Group, 1745 Broadway, New York, NY 10019 *Toll Free Tel:* 800-200-3552 *Web Site:* atrandom.com, pg 214

Hershon, Robert, Hanging Loose Press, 231 Wyckoff St, Brooklyn, NY 11217 *Tel:* 347-529-4738 *Fax:* 347-227-8215 *E-mail:* print225@aol.com *Web Site:* www.hangingloosepress.com, pg 111

Hertman, Janelle, The Heywood Broun Award, 501 Third St NW, 6th fl, Washington, DC 20001-2797 *Tel:* 202-434-7177; 202-434-7162 (The Guild Reporter) *Fax:* 202-434-1472 *Web Site:* www.newsguild.org, pg 693

Herz, Suzanne, Doubleday/Nan A Talese, c/o Random House Inc, 1745 Broadway, New York, NY 10019 *Tel:* 212-751-2600 *Toll Free Tel:* 800-638-6460 *Fax:* 212-572-2593 *Web Site:* www.knopfdoubleday.com, pg 81

Heschke, Christa, McIntosh & Otis Inc, 353 Lexington Ave, New York, NY 10016-0900 *Tel:* 212-687-7400 *Fax:* 212-687-6894 *E-mail:* info@mcintoshandotis.com *Web Site:* www.mcintoshandotis.com, pg 585

Hess, Dianne, Scholastic Trade Division, 557 Broadway, New York, NY 10012 *Tel:* 212-343-6100; 212-343-4685 (export sales) *Fax:* 212-343-4714 (export sales) *Web Site:* www.scholastic.com, pg 229

Hess, John W, Geological Society of America (GSA), 3300 Penrose Place, Boulder, CO 80301-1806 *Tel:* 303-357-1000 *Fax:* 303-357-1070 *E-mail:* pubs@geosociety.org (prodn); editing@geosociety.org (edit) *Web Site:* www.geosociety.org, pg 102

Hess, Lindy, Columbia Publishing Course at Columbia University, 2950 Broadway, MC 3801, New York, NY 10027 *Tel:* 212-854-1898 *Fax:* 212-854-7618 *E-mail:* publishing@jrn.columbia.edu *Web Site:* www.journalism.columbia.edu/publishing, pg 677

Hess, Peter, American Society of Mechanical Engineers (ASME), 3 Park Ave, New York, NY 10016-5990 *Tel:* 212-591-7000 *Toll Free Tel:* 800-843-2763 (cust serv-US, CN & Mexico) *Fax:* 212-591-7674; 973-882-8113 (cust serv); 973-882-1717 (orders & inquiries) *E-mail:* infocentral@asme.org *Web Site:* www.asme.org, pg 17

Hessel, Carolyn Starman, Jewish Book Council, 520 Eighth Ave, 4th fl, New York, NY 10018 *Tel:* 212-201-2920 *Fax:* 212-532-4952 *E-mail:* jbc@jewishbooks.org *Web Site:* www.jewishbookcouncil.org, pg 626

Hessel, Carolyn Starman, National Jewish Book Award-Children's & Young Adult Literature, 520 Eighth Ave, 4th fl, New York, NY 10018 *Tel:* 212-201-2920 *Fax:* 212-532-4952 *E-mail:* jbc@jewishbooks.org *Web Site:* www.jewishbookcouncil.org, pg 726

Hessel, Carolyn Starman, National Jewish Book Award-Contemporary Jewish Life & Practice, 520 Eighth Ave, 4th fl, New York, NY 10018 *Tel:* 212-201-2920 *Fax:* 212-532-4952 *E-mail:* jbc@jewishbooks.org *Web Site:* www.jewishbookcouncil.org, pg 726

Hessel, Carolyn Starman, National Jewish Book Award-History, 520 Eighth Ave, 4th fl, New York, NY 10018 *Tel:* 212-201-2920 *Fax:* 212-532-4952 *E-mail:* jbc@jewishbooks.org *Web Site:* www.jewishbookcouncil.org, pg 726

Hessel, Carolyn Starman, National Jewish Book Award-Illustrated Children's Book, 520 Eighth Ave, 4th fl, New York, NY 10018 *Tel:* 212-201-2920 *Fax:* 212-532-4952 *E-mail:* jbc@jewishbooks.org *Web Site:* www.jewishbookcouncil.org, pg 726

Hessel, Carolyn Starman, National Jewish Book Award-Modern Jewish Thought & Experience, 520 Eighth Ave, 4th fl, New York, NY 10018 *Tel:* 212-201-2920 *Fax:* 212-532-4952 *E-mail:* jbc@jewishbooks.org *Web Site:* www.jewishbookcouncil.org, pg 726

Hessel, Carolyn Starman, National Jewish Book Award-Scholarship, 520 Eighth Ave, 4th fl, New York, NY 10018 *Tel:* 212-201-2920 *Fax:* 212-532-4952 *E-mail:* jbc@jewishbooks.org *Web Site:* www.jewishbookcouncil.org, pg 726

Hessel, Carolyn Starman, National Jewish Book Awards, 520 Eighth Ave, 4th fl, New York, NY 10018 *Tel:* 212-201-2920 *Fax:* 212-532-4952 *E-mail:* jbc@jewishbooks.org *Web Site:* www.jewishbookcouncil.org, pg 726

Hessel, Carolyn Starman, Sami Rohr Prize for Jewish Literature, 520 Eighth Ave, 4th fl, New York, NY 10018 *Tel:* 212-201-2920 *Fax:* 212-532-4952 *E-mail:* jbc@jewishbooks.org *Web Site:* www.jewishbookcouncil.org, pg 738

Hessel, Sam, Antiquarian Booksellers' Association of America (ABAA), 20 W 44 St, Suite 507, New York, NY 10036 *Tel:* 212-944-8291 *Fax:* 212-944-8293 *E-mail:* hq@abaa.org *Web Site:* www.abaa.org, pg 615

Hester, Martin L, Avisson Press Inc, 3007 Taliaferro Rd, Greensboro, NC 27408 *Tel:* 336-288-6989; 336-285-6763 *Fax:* 336-288-6989 *E-mail:* avisson4@aol.com, pg 28

Hetrick, J Thomas, Pocol Press, 6023 Pocol Dr, Clifton, VA 20124-1333 *Tel:* 703-830-5862 *E-mail:* chrisandtom@erols.com *Web Site:* www.pocolpress.com, pg 204

Hettler, Kurt, Oxford University Press USA, 198 Madison Ave, New York, NY 10016 *Tel:* 212-726-6000 *Toll Free Tel:* 800-451-7556 (orders); 800-445-9714 (cust serv) *Fax:* 919-677-1303 *E-mail:* custserv.us@oup.com *Web Site:* www.oup.com/us, pg 189

Heustess, Todd, Peter Glenn Publications, 306 NE Second St, 2nd fl, Delray Beach, FL 33483 *Tel:* 561-404-4290 *Toll Free Tel:* 888-332-6700 *Fax:* 561-892-5786 *Web Site:* www.pgdirect.com, pg 103

Hewitt, Kristen, Chronicle Books LLC, 680 Second St, San Francisco, CA 94107 *Tel:* 415-537-4200 *Toll Free Tel:* 800-759-0190 (cust serv) *Fax:* 415-537-4460 *Toll Free Fax:* 800-858-7787 (orders); 800-286-9471 (cust serv) *E-mail:* frontdesk@chroniclebooks.com *Web Site:* www.chroniclebooks.com, pg 61

Hewitt, Trish, Harlequin Enterprises Ltd, 225 Duncan Mill Rd, Don Mills, ON M3B 3K9, Canada *Tel:* 416-445-5860 *Toll Free Tel:* 888-432-4879; 800-370-5838 (ebook inquiries) *Fax:* 416-445-8655 *E-mail:* CustomerService@harlequin.com *Web Site:* www.harlequin.com, pg 508

Heyboer, Bobbie Jo, Chosen Books, PO Box 6287, Grand Rapids, MI 49516-6287 *Tel:* 616-676-9185 *Toll Free Tel:* 800-877-2665 (orders only) *Fax:* 616-676-9573 *Toll Free Fax:* 800-398-3111 (orders only) *Web Site:* www.bakerpublishinggroup.com, pg 60

Heywood, Leslie, Binghamton University Creative Writing Program, c/o Dept of English, PO Box 6000, Binghamton, NY 13902-6000 *Tel:* 607-777-2168 *Fax:* 607-777-2408 *E-mail:* cwpro@binghamton.edu *Web Site:* english.binghamton.edu/cwpro, pg 677

Hibberd, Jeanne Marie, Appalachian Writers' Workshop, 71 Center St, Hindman, KY 41822 *Tel:* 606-785-5475 *Fax:* 606-785-3499 *E-mail:* info@hindmansettlement.org *Web Site:* www.hindmansettlement.org, pg 667

Hibbert, Edward, Donadio & Olson Inc, 121 W 27 St, Suite 704, New York, NY 10001 *Tel:* 212-691-8077 *Fax:* 212-633-2837 *E-mail:* mail@donadio.com *Web Site:* donadio.com, pg 569

Hicks, Patricia, Peradam Press, PO Box 6, North San Juan, CA 95960-0006 *Tel:* 530-292-4266 *Fax:* 530-292-4266 *E-mail:* peradam@earthlink.net, pg 199

Hicks, Tyler G, International Wealth Success Inc, PO Box 186, Merrick, NY 11566-0186 *Tel:* 516-766-5850 *Toll Free Tel:* 800-323-0548 *Fax:* 516-766-5919 *E-mail:* admin@iwsmoney.com *Web Site:* www.iwsmoney.com, pg 134

Hicks, William, River City Publishing LLC, 1719 Mulberry St, Montgomery, AL 36106 *Tel:* 334-265-6753 *Fax:* 334-265-8880 *E-mail:* sales@rivercitypublishing.com *Web Site:* www.rivercitypublishing.com, pg 219

Hiegert, Benjamin, York Press, 1358 Jefferson Rd, Spring Grove, PA 17362 *Tel:* 717-225-7147 *Toll Free Tel:* 888-317-5571 *Fax:* 717-225-7479 *Web Site:* www.returntoorder.org, pg 530

Hietala, Johnna, Jody Rein Books Inc, 7741 S Ash Ct, Centennial, CO 80122 *Tel:* 303-694-9386 *Web Site:* www.jodyreinbooks.com, pg 578

Higby, Maggie, Simon & Schuster, 1230 Avenue of the Americas, New York, NY 10020 *Tel:* 212-698-7000 *Toll Free Tel:* 800-223-2348 (cust serv); 800-223-2336 (orders) *Toll Free Fax:* 800-943-9831 (orders) *Web Site:* www.simonandschuster.com, pg 234

Higgins, Ron, Gulf Publishing Co, 2 Greenway Plaza, Suite 1020, Houston, TX 77046 *Tel:* 713-529-4301 *Fax:* 713-520-4433 *E-mail:* books@gulfpub.com *Web Site:* www.gulfpub.com, pg 109

Higgins-Jacob, Coleen, John Simon Guggenheim Memorial Foundation, 90 Park Ave, New York, NY 10016 *Tel:* 212-687-4470 *Fax:* 212-697-3248 *E-mail:* fellowships@gf.org *Web Site:* www.gf.org, pg 641

Highland, Kimberly, Penguin Group (USA) LLC Sales, 375 Hudson St, New York, NY 10014 *Tel:* 212-366-2000 *E-mail:* online@penguinputnam.com *Web Site:* us.penguingroup.com, pg 197

Hightower, Ms Dwan, Dream Catcher Publishing Inc, PO Box 33883, Decatur, GA 30033 *Tel:* 404-486-7703 *Toll Free Tel:* 888-771-2800 *Toll Free Fax:* 888-771-2800 *E-mail:* dcp@dreamcatcherpublishing.org *Web Site:* www.dreamcatcherpublishing.org, pg 82

Hilarian, Abbott, St Herman Press, 10 Beegum Gorge Rd, Platina, CA 96076 *Tel:* 530-352-4430 *Fax:* 530-352-4432 *E-mail:* stherman@stherman.com *Web Site:* www.stherman.com, pg 224

Hilbert, Lucas, F+W Media Inc, 10151 Carver Rd, Suite 200, Blue Ash, OH 45242 *Tel:* 513-531-2690 *Toll Free Tel:* 800-289-0963 (trade accts); 800-258-0929 (orders) *E-mail:* contact_us@fwmedia.com *Web Site:* www.fwmedia.com, pg 92

Hildebrand, Lloyd, Bridge-Logos Inc, Bldg 200, Suite 220, 17750 NW 115 Ave, Alachua, FL 32615 *Tel:* 386-462-2525 *Toll Free Tel:* 800-631-5802 (orders) *Fax:* 386-462-2535 *Toll Free Fax:* 800-935-6467 *E-mail:* customerservice@bridgelogos.com; info@bridgelogos.com *Web Site:* www.bridgelogos.com, pg 47

Hildreth, Mary Anne, Tower Publishing Co, 588 Saco Rd, Standish, ME 04084 *Tel:* 207-642-5400 *Toll Free Tel:* 800-969-8693 *Fax:* 207-264-3870 *E-mail:* info@towerpub.com *Web Site:* www.towerpub.com, pg 257

Hilferty, Daniel, Mason Crest Publishers, 370 Reed Rd, Suite 302, Broomall, PA 19008 *Tel:* 610-543-6200 *Toll Free Tel:* 866-MCP-BOOK (627-2665) *Fax:* 610-543-3878 *Web Site:* www.masoncrest.com, pg 158

Hill, Brandon, Ludwig von Mises Institute, 518 W Magnolia Ave, Auburn, AL 36832 *Tel:* 334-321-2100 *Fax:* 334-321-2119 *E-mail:* info@mises.org *Web Site:* www.mises.org, pg 275

Hill, David, Kregel Publications, 733 Wealthy St SE, Grand Rapids, MI 49503-5553 *Tel:* 616-451-4775 *Toll Free Tel:* 800-733-2607 *Fax:* 616-451-9330 *E-mail:* kregelbooks@kregel.com *Web Site:* www.kregel.com, pg 142

Hill, Devra, Book Publicists of Southern California, 714 Crescent Dr, Beverly Hills, CA 90210 *Tel:* 323-461-3921 *Fax:* 323-461-0917, pg 618

Hill, Frances, Emerging Playwright Award, 555 Eighth Ave, Suite 1800, New York, NY 10018 *Tel:* 212-421-1380 *Fax:* 212-421-1387 *E-mail:* urbanstage@aol.com, pg 702

Hill, Jamie, Books We Love Ltd, 192 Lakeside Greens Dr, Chestermere, AB T1X 1C2, Canada *Tel:* 403-710-4869 *E-mail:* bookswelove@shaw.ca, pg 495

Hill, Janet Muirhead, Raven Publishing Inc, 125 Cherry Creek Rd, Norris, MT 59745 *Tel:* 406-685-3545 *Toll Free Tel:* 866-685-3545 *Fax:* 406-685-3599 *E-mail:* info@ravenpublishing.net *Web Site:* www.ravenpublishing.net, pg 214

Hill, Karen, University of Michigan Press, 839 Greene St, Ann Arbor, MI 48104-3209 *Tel:* 734-764-4388 *Fax:* 734-615-1540 *E-mail:* esladmin@umich.edu *Web Site:* www.press.umich.edu, pg 266

Hill, Linda, Bella Books, PO Box 10543, Tallahassee, FL 32302 *Tel:* 850-576-2370 *Toll Free Tel:* 800-729-4992 *Fax:* 850-576-3498 *E-mail:* info@bellabooks.com; orders@bellabooks.com; ebooks@bellabooks.com *Web Site:* www.bellabooks.com, pg 34

Hill, Linda, Spinsters Ink, PO Box 242, Midway, FL 32343 *E-mail:* info@spinstersink.com; editorialdirector@spinstersink.com *Web Site:* www.spinstersink.com, pg 241

Hill, Michael, American Association of University Women Award for Juvenile Literature, 4610 Mail Service Ctr, Raleigh, NC 27699-4610 *Tel:* 919-807-7290 *Fax:* 919-733-8807, pg 687

Hill, Michael, Stephen Leacock Memorial Medal for Humour, RR2, 4223 Line 12 N, Coldwater, ON L0K 1E0, Canada *Tel:* 705-835-3218 *Fax:* 705-835-5171 *Web Site:* www.leacock.ca, pg 716

Hill, Michael, The Ragan Old North State Award Cup for Nonfiction, 4610 Mail Service Ctr, Raleigh, NC 27699-4610 *Tel:* 919-807-7290 *Fax:* 919-733-8807 *Web Site:* www.history.ncdcr.gov/affiliates/lit-hist/awards/awards.htm, pg 737

Hill, Michael, Sir Walter Raleigh Award for Fiction, 4610 Mail Service Ctr, Raleigh, NC 27699-4610 *Tel:* 919-807-7290 *Fax:* 919-733-8807, pg 737

Hill, Michael, Roanoke-Chowan Award for Poetry, 4610 Mail Service Ctr, Raleigh, NC 27699-4610 *Tel:* 919-807-7290 *Fax:* 919-733-8807 *Web Site:* www.history.ncdcr.gov/affiliates/lit-hist/awards/awards.htm, pg 738

Hill, Nancy, 4A's (American Association of Advertising Agencies), 1065 Avenue of the Americas, 16th fl, New York, NY 10018 *Tel:* 212-682-2500 *Web Site:* www.aaaa.org, pg 624

Hill, Richard, AHA Press, 155 N Wacker, Suite 400, Chicago, IL 60606 *Tel:* 312-893-6800 *Toll Free Tel:* 800-242-4890 *Toll Free Fax:* 866-516-5817 (orders) *Web Site:* www.healthforum.com, pg 6

Hill, Richard, Association for Information Science & Technology (ASIS&T), 1320 Fenwick Lane, Suite 510, Silver Spring, MD 20910 *Tel:* 301-495-0900 *Fax:* 301-495-0810 *E-mail:* asis@asis.org *Web Site:* www.asis.org, pg 25, 615

Hill, Rick, Health Forum Inc, 155 N Wacker Dr, Suite 400, Chicago, IL 60606 *Tel:* 312-893-6884 *Toll Free Tel:* 800-242-2626 *Fax:* 312-422-4600 *E-mail:* hfcustsvc@healthforum.com *Web Site:* www.ahaonlinestore.com; www.healthforum.com, pg 116

Hill, Stephen W, Kiva Publishing Inc, 10 Bella Loma, Santa Fe, NM 87506 *Tel:* 909-896-0518 *E-mail:* kivapub@aol.com *Web Site:* www.kivapub.com, pg 140

Hillebrand, Donald, SAE (Society of Automotive Engineers International), 400 Commonwealth Dr, Warrendale, PA 15096-0001 *Tel:* 724-776-4841; 724-776-4970 (outside US & CN) *Toll Free Tel:* 877-606-7323 (cust serv) *Fax:* 724-776-0790 (cust serv) *E-mail:* publications@sae.org; customerservice@sae.org *Web Site:* www.sae.org, pg 223

Hiller, David D, Los Angeles Times Book Prizes, 202 W First St, Los Angeles, CA 90012 *Tel:* 213-237-5775 *Toll Free Tel:* 800-528-4637 *Fax:* 213-237-7679 *Web Site:* www.latimesbookprizes.com, pg 719

Hiller, Stephanie, New Mexico Book Association (NMBA), 1600 Lena St, Bldg C, Suite C-12, Santa Fe, NM 87505 *Tel:* 505-660-6357; 505-231-1755 *Fax:* 505-983-0899 *E-mail:* admin@nmbook.org *Web Site:* www.nmbook.org, pg 631

Hillerman, Anne, The Tony Hillerman Prize, 1063 Willow Way, Santa Fe, NM 87507 *Tel:* 505-471-1565 *E-mail:* wordharvest@wordharvest.com *Web Site:* www.wordharvest.com, pg 710

Hillerman, Anne, Tony Hillerman Writers Conference, 1063 Willow Way, Santa Fe, NM 87507 *Tel:* 505-471-1565 *E-mail:* wordharvest@wordharvest.com *Web Site:* www.wordharvest.com, pg 674

Hilliard, Elbert, McLemore Prize, PO Box 571, Jackson, MS 39205-0571 *Tel:* 601-576-6850 *Fax:* 601-576-6975 *E-mail:* mhs@mdah.state.ms.us *Web Site:* www.mdah.state.ms.us, pg 723

Hillman, David, Simon & Schuster, Inc, 1230 Avenue of the Americas, New York, NY 10020 *Tel:* 212-698-7000 *Fax:* 212-698-7007 *E-mail:* firstname.lastname@simonandschuster.com *Web Site:* www.simonandschuster.com, pg 235

Hillman, Dennis, Kregel Publications, 733 Wealthy St SE, Grand Rapids, MI 49503-5553 *Tel:* 616-451-4775 *Toll Free Tel:* 800-733-2607 *Fax:* 616-451-9330 *E-mail:* kregelbooks@kregel.com *Web Site:* www.kregel.com, pg 142

Hillsman, Sally T, American Sociological Association (ASA), 1430 "K" St NW, Suite 600, Washington, DC 20005-4701 *Tel:* 202-383-9005 *Fax:* 202-638-0882 *E-mail:* customer@asanet.org *Web Site:* www.asanet.org, pg 614

Hilzen, Natalie, American Foundation for the Blind (AFB Press), 2 Penn Plaza, Suite 1102, New York, NY 10001 *Tel:* 212-502-7600; 412-741-1398 (orders) *Toll Free Tel:* 800-232-3044 (orders) *Fax:* 917-210-3979; 412-741-0609 (orders) *Toll Free Fax:* 888-545-8331 *E-mail:* press@afb.net; afborder@afb.net (orders); afbinfo@afb.net *Web Site:* www.afb.org, pg 13

Himmel, Eric, Harry N Abrams Inc, 115 W 18 St, 6th fl, New York, NY 10011 *Tel:* 212-206-7715 *Toll Free Tel:* 800-345-1359 *Fax:* 212-519-1210 *E-mail:* abrams@abramsbooks.com *Web Site:* www.abramsbooks.com, pg 3

Hinchberger, Lara, McClelland & Stewart Ltd, 75 Sherbourne St, 5th fl, Toronto, ON M5A 2P9, Canada *Tel:* 416-598-1114 *Fax:* 416-598-7764 *E-mail:* editorial@mcclelland.com *Web Site:* www.mcclelland.com, pg 512

Hindman, Mary B, H E Francis Award Short Story Competition, UAH Huntsville Dept of English, Morton Hall 222, Huntsville, AL 35899 *Web Site:* www.uah.edu/colleges/liberal/english/hefrancis.contest, pg 705

Hinds, John, Canadian Newspaper Association, 890 Yonge St, Suite 200, Toronto, ON M4W 3P4, Canada *Tel:* 416-923-3567; 416-482-1090 *Toll Free Tel:* 877-305-2262 *Fax:* 416-923-7206; 416-482-1908 *E-mail:* info@cna-acj.ca *Web Site:* www.cna-acj.ca, pg 620

Hines, Cammy, Green Sugar Press, 2200 E Devon Ave, Suite 340, Des Plaines, IL 60018-4503 *Tel:* 773-580-7780; 615-254-2402 (orders); 615-254-2488 (returns) *Fax:* 615-254-2405 (orders); 615-254-2405 (returns) *Toll Free Fax:* 866-270-4100 *E-mail:* order@greensugarpress.com *Web Site:* www.greensugarpress.com, pg 107

Hines, Thomas M, Summa Publications, PO Box 660725, Birmingham, AL 35266-0725 *Tel:* 205-822-0463 *Fax:* 205-822-0463 *Web Site:* summapub2.googlepages.com, pg 246

Hines, Tom, J J Keller & Associates, Inc, 3003 Breezewood Lane, Neenah, WI 54957 *Tel:* 920-722-2848 *Toll Free Tel:* 877-564-2333 *Toll Free Fax:* 800-727-7516 *E-mail:* sales@jjkeller.com *Web Site:* www.jjkeller.com/jjk, pg 139

Hiniker, Mary, Institute of Continuing Legal Education, 1020 Greene St, Ann Arbor, MI 48109-1444 *Tel:* 734-764-0533 *Toll Free Tel:* 877-229-4350 *Fax:* 734-763-2412 *Toll Free Fax:* 877-229-4351 *E-mail:* icle@umich.edu *Web Site:* www.icle.org, pg 131

Hinkel, Nancy, Random House Children's Books, 1745 Broadway, New York, NY 10019 *Tel:* 212-782-9000 *Toll Free Tel:* 800-200-3552 *Fax:* 212-782-9452 *Web Site:* randomhousekids.com, pg 213

Hinkelman, Edward G, World Trade Press, 800 Lindberg Lane, Suite 190, Petaluma, CA 94952 *Tel:* 707-778-1124 *Toll Free Tel:* 800-833-8586 *Fax:* 707-778-1329 *Web Site:* www.worldtradepress.com, pg 286

Hinkley, John, Moody Publishers, 820 N La Salle Blvd, Chicago, IL 60610 *Tel:* 312-329-4000 *Toll Free Tel:* 800-678-8812 (cust serv) *Fax:* 312-329-2019 *Web Site:* www.moodypublishers.com, pg 169

Hinojosa-Smith, Rolando, University of Texas at Austin, Creative Writing Program, Dept of English, PAR 108, One University Sta, Mailcode B5000, Austin, TX 78712-1164 *Tel:* 512-471-5132; 512-471-4991 *Fax:* 512-471-4909 *Web Site:* www.utexas.edu/cola/depts/english/creative-writing, pg 682

Hinsley, Erica, Alfred A Knopf/Everyman's Library, c/o Random House Inc, 1745 Broadway, New York, NY 10019 *Tel:* 212-751-2600 *Toll Free Tel:* 800-638-6460 *Fax:* 212-572-2593 *Web Site:* www.knopfdoubleday.com, pg 141

Hinz, Carol, Millbrook Press, 241 First Ave N, Minneapolis, MN 55401 *Tel:* 612-332-3344 *Toll Free Tel:* 800-328-4929 (US only) *Fax:* 612-332-7615 *Toll Free Fax:* 800-332-1132, pg 167

Hirashima, Steve, University of Hawaii Press, 2840 Kolowalu St, Honolulu, HI 96822 *Tel:* 808-956-8255 *Toll Free Tel:* 888-UHPRESS (847-7377) *Fax:* 808-988-6052 *Toll Free Fax:* 800-650-7811 *E-mail:* uhpbooks@hawaii.edu *Web Site:* www.uhpress.hawaii.edu, pg 265

Hirsch, Cheryl, Basic Health Publications Inc, 28812 Top of the World Dr, Laguna Beach, CA 92651 *Tel:* 949-715-7327 *Toll Free Tel:* 800-575-8890 (orders) *Fax:* 949-715-7328 *E-mail:* info@basichealthpub.com *Web Site:* www.basichealthpub.com, pg 32

Hirsch, Edward, John Simon Guggenheim Memorial Foundation, 90 Park Ave, New York, NY 10016 *Tel:* 212-687-4470 *Fax:* 212-697-3248 *E-mail:* fellowships@gf.org *Web Site:* www.gf.org, pg 641

Hirschhorn, Ellie, Simon & Schuster Digital, 1230 Avenue of the Americas, New York, NY 10020 *Tel:* 212-698-7547 *Web Site:* www.simonandschuster.com; kids.simonandschuster.com; www.simonandschuster.ca; www.simonandschuster.co.uk; www.simonandschuster.net; www.simonandschuster.biz; www.tipsoncareerandmoney.com; www.tipsonhealthyliving.com; www.tipsonhomeandstyle.com; www.tipsonlifeandlove.com, pg 235

Hirschhorn, Ellie, Simon & Schuster, Inc, 1230 Avenue of the Americas, New York, NY 10020 *Tel:* 212-698-7000 *Fax:* 212-698-7007 *E-mail:* firstname.lastname@simonandschuster.com *Web Site:* www.simonandschuster.com, pg 235

Hite, Robyn, Wimmer Cookbooks, 4650 Shelby Air Dr, Memphis, TN 38118 *Tel:* 901-362-8900 *Toll Free Tel:* 800-363-1771 *E-mail:* wimmer@wimmerco.com *Web Site:* www.wimmerco.com, pg 282

Hittle, Todd, American Business Media, 675 Third Ave, 7th fl, New York, NY 10017-5704 *Tel:* 212-661-6360 *Fax:* 212-370-0736 *E-mail:* info@abmmail.com *Web Site:* www.americanbusinessmedia.com, pg 612

Hivnor, Maggie, University of Chicago Press, 1427 E 60 St, Chicago, IL 60637-2954 *Tel:* 773-702-7700; 773-702-7600 *Toll Free Tel:* 800-621-2736 (orders) *Fax:* 773-702-9756; 773-660-2235 (orders); 773-702-2708 *E-mail:* custserv@press.uchicago.edu; marketing@press.uchicago.edu *Web Site:* www.press.uchicago.edu, pg 265

Ho, Howard, University of Southern California, Master of Professional Writing Program, Mark Taper Hall, THH 355, 3501 Trousedale Pkwy, Los Angeles, CA 90089-0355 *Tel:* 213-740-3252 *Fax:* 213-740-5002 *E-mail:* mpw@college.usc.edu *Web Site:* college.usc.edu/mpw, pg 682

Hoard, Trish, The Library of America, 14 E 60 St, New York, NY 10022-1006 *Tel:* 212-308-3360 *Fax:* 212-750-8352 *E-mail:* info@loa.org *Web Site:* www.loa.org, pg 148

Hoare, Steve, Black Dome Press Corp, 649 Delaware Ave, Delmar, NY 12054 *Tel:* 518-439-6512 *Toll Free Tel:* 800-513-9013 (orders) *Fax:* 518-439-1309 *E-mail:* blackdomep@aol.com *Web Site:* www.blackdomepress.com, pg 39

Hoban, Kathryn, Holiday House Inc, 425 Madison Ave, New York, NY 10017 *Tel:* 212-688-0085 *Fax:* 212-421-6134 *E-mail:* holiday@holidayhouse.com *Web Site:* www.holidayhouse.com, pg 121

Hobeika, Joelle, Alloy Entertainment, 151 W 26 St, 11th fl, New York, NY 10001 *Tel:* 212-244-4307 *E-mail:* nycassistant@alloyentertainment.com *Web Site:* www.alloyentertainment.com, pg 9

Hocherman, Riva, Henry Holt and Company, LLC, 175 Fifth Ave, New York, NY 10010 *Tel:* 646-307-5151 *Toll Free Tel:* 888-330-8477 (orders) *Fax:* 646-307-5285 *E-mail:* firstname.lastname@hholt.com *Web Site:* www.henryholt.com, pg 122

Hochman, Gail, Association of Authors' Representatives Inc, 676-A Ninth Ave, Suite 312, New York, NY 10036 *Tel:* 212-840-5777 *Web Site:* www.aaronline.org, pg 616

Hochman, Gail, Brandt & Hochman Literary Agents Inc, 1501 Broadway, Suite 2310, New York, NY 10036 *Tel:* 212-840-5760 *Fax:* 212-840-5776 *Web Site:* brandthochman.com, pg 564

Hochman, Sarah, Blue Rider Press, 375 Hudson St, New York, NY 10014 *Tel:* 212-366-2000, pg 42

Hodapp, Angie, Nelson Literary Agency LLC, 1732 Wazee St, Suite 207, Denver, CO 80202-1284 *Tel:* 303-292-2805 *E-mail:* query@nelsonagency.com *Web Site:* www.nelsonagency.com, pg 587

Hodges, Joanne, National Council of Teachers of Mathematics (NCTM), 1906 Association Dr, Reston, VA 20191-1502 *Tel:* 703-620-9840 *Toll Free Tel:* 800-235-7566 *Fax:* 703-476-2970 *E-mail:* nctm@nctm.org *Web Site:* www.nctm.org, pg 174

Hodges, Michael, diacriTech Inc, 250 Commercial St, Suite 2002, Manchester, NH 03101 *Tel:* 603-606-5800 *Fax:* 603-606-5838 *E-mail:* sales@diacritech.com *Web Site:* www.diacritech.com, pg 544

Hodgson, Kristen, Clinical Laboratory & Standards Institute (CLSI), 950 W Valley Rd, Suite 2500, Wayne, PA 19087 *Tel:* 610-688-0100 *Toll Free Tel:* 877-447-1888 (orders) *Fax:* 610-688-0700 *E-mail:* customerservice@clsi.org *Web Site:* www.clsi.org, pg 63

Hodus, Brett, Scobre Press Corp, 2255 Calle Clara, La Jolla, CA 92037 *Toll Free Tel:* 877-726-2734 *Fax:* 858-551-1232 *E-mail:* info@scobre.com *Web Site:* www.scobre.com, pg 230

Hoehner, Jane, Wayne State University Press, Leonard N Simons Bldg, 4809 Woodward Ave, Detroit, MI 48201-1309 *Tel:* 313-577-6120 *Toll Free Tel:* 800-978-7323 *Fax:* 313-577-6131 *Web Site:* www.wsupress.wayne.edu, pg 277

Hoerdeman, Sara, Northern Illinois University Press, 2280 Bethany Rd, DeKalb, IL 60115 *Tel:* 815-753-1826; 815-753-1075 *Fax:* 815-753-1845 *Web Site:* www.niupress.niu.edu, pg 181

Hoesly, Sherry, The Permissions Group Inc, 1247 Milwaukee Ave, Suite 303, Glenview, IL 60025 *Tel:* 847-635-6550 *Toll Free Tel:* 800-374-7985 *Fax:* 847-635-6968 *E-mail:* info@permissionsgroup.com *Web Site:* www.permissionsgroup.com, pg 553

Hofeldt, Sara E, Tapestry Press Ltd, 19 Nashoba Rd, Littleton, MA 01460 *Tel:* 978-486-0200 *Toll Free Tel:* 800-535-2007 *Fax:* 978-486-0244 *E-mail:* publish@tapestrypress.com *Web Site:* www.tapestrypress.com, pg 250

Hoff, Andrea, PRISM international Literary Non-Fiction Contest, University of British Columbia, Buch E462, 1866 Main Mall, Vancouver, BC V6T 1Z1, Canada *Tel:* 778-822-2514 *Fax:* 778-822-3616 *E-mail:* prismwritingcontest@gmail.com *Web Site:* www.prismmagazine.ca, pg 735

Hoff, Andrea, PRISM international Poetry Contest, University of British Columbia, Buch E462, 1866 Main Mall, Vancouver, BC V6T 1Z1, Canada *Tel:* 778-822-2514 *Fax:* 778-822-3616 *E-mail:* prismwritingcontest@gmail.com *Web Site:* www.prismmagazine.ca, pg 736

Hoff, Andrea, PRISM international Short Fiction Contest, University of British Columbia, Buch E462, 1866 Main Mall, Vancouver, BC V6T 1Z1, Canada *Tel:* 778-822-2514 *Fax:* 778-822-3616 *E-mail:* prismwritingcontest@gmail.com *Web Site:* www.prismmagazine.ca, pg 736

Hoffman, Joan, School Zone Publishing Co, 1819 Industrial Dr, Grand Haven, MI 49417 *Tel:* 616-846-5030 *Toll Free Tel:* 800-253-0564 *Fax:* 616-846-6181 *Toll Free Fax:* 800-550-4618 (orders only) *Web Site:* www.schoolzone.com, pg 229

Hoffman, Randy, Captus Press Inc, 1600 Steeles Ave W, Units 14-15, Concord, ON L4K 4M2, Canada *Tel:* 416-736-5537 *Fax:* 416-736-5793 *E-mail:* info@captus.com *Web Site:* www.captus.com, pg 498

Hoffman, Scott, Folio Literary Management LLC, The Film Center Bldg, 630 Ninth Ave, Suite 1101, New York, NY 10036 *Tel:* 212-400-1494 *Fax:* 212-967-0977 *Web Site:* www.foliolit.com, pg 572

Hoffman, Shira, McIntosh & Otis Inc, 353 Lexington Ave, New York, NY 10016-0900 *Tel:* 212-687-7400 *Fax:* 212-687-6894 *E-mail:* info@mcintoshandotis.com *Web Site:* www.mcintoshandotis.com, pg 585

Hoffman, Stuart A, Star Publishing Co Inc, 650 El Camino Real, Redwood City, CA 94063 *Tel:* 650-591-3505 *Fax:* 650-591-3898 *E-mail:* mail@starpublishing.com *Web Site:* www.starpublishing.com, pg 243

Hoffmeister, Emmaline, Rhemalda Publishing, PO Box 1790, Moses Lake, WA 98837 *E-mail:* editor@rhemalda.com; customer_service@rhemalda.com *Web Site:* rhemalda.com, pg 218

Hoffmeister, Rhett, Rhemalda Publishing, PO Box 1790, Moses Lake, WA 98837 *E-mail:* editor@rhemalda.com; customer_service@rhemalda.com *Web Site:* rhemalda.com, pg 218

Hoffnagle, Jerry, Rizzoli International Publications Inc, 300 Park Ave S, 4th fl, New York, NY 10010-5399 *Tel:* 212-387-3400 *Toll Free Tel:* 800-522-6657 (orders only) *Fax:* 212-387-3535 *E-mail:* publicity@rizzoliusa.com *Web Site:* www.rizzoliusa.com, pg 219

Hogan, Mary S, Plexus Publishing, Inc, 143 Old Marlton Pike, Medford, NJ 08055 *Tel:* 609-654-6500 *Fax:* 609-654-4309 *E-mail:* info@plexuspublishing.com *Web Site:* www.plexuspublishing.com, pg 203

Hogan, Michelle, Our Sunday Visitor Publishing, 200 Noll Plaza, Huntington, IN 46750 *Tel:* 260-356-8400 *Toll Free Tel:* 800-348-2440 (orders) *Fax:* 260-356-8472 *Toll Free Fax:* 800-498-6709 *E-mail:* osvbooks@osv.com (book orders) *Web Site:* www.osv.com, pg 189

Hogan, Thomas Jr, Information Today, Inc, 143 Old Marlton Pike, Medford, NJ 08055-8750 *Tel:* 609-654-6266 *Toll Free Tel:* 800-300-9868 (cust serv) *Fax:* 609-654-4309 *E-mail:* custserv@infotoday.com *Web Site:* www.infotoday.com, pg 130

Hogan, Thomas Jr, Plexus Publishing, Inc, 143 Old Marlton Pike, Medford, NJ 08055 *Tel:* 609-654-6500 *Fax:* 609-654-4309 *E-mail:* info@plexuspublishing.com *Web Site:* www.plexuspublishing.com, pg 203

Hogan, Thomas H Sr, Information Today, Inc, 143 Old Marlton Pike, Medford, NJ 08055-8750 *Tel:* 609-654-6266 *Toll Free Tel:* 800-300-9868 (cust serv) *Fax:* 609-654-4309 *E-mail:* custserv@infotoday.com *Web Site:* www.infotoday.com, pg 130

Hogan, Thomas H Sr, Plexus Publishing, Inc, 143 Old Marlton Pike, Medford, NJ 08055 *Tel:* 609-654-6500 *Fax:* 609-654-4309 *E-mail:* info@plexuspublishing.com *Web Site:* www.plexuspublishing.com, pg 203

Hoge, Steve, W W Norton & Company Inc, 500 Fifth Ave, New York, NY 10110-0017 *Tel:* 212-354-5500 *Toll Free Tel:* 800-233-4830 (orders & cust serv) *Fax:* 212-869-0856 *Toll Free Fax:* 800-458-6515 *Web Site:* www.wwnorton.com, pg 182

Hopkins, Michelle, Vincent Lemieux Prize, 260 rue Dalhousie St, Suite 204, Ottawa, ON K1N 7E4, Canada *Tel:* 613-562-1202 *Fax:* 613-241-0019 *E-mail:* cpsa-acsp@cpsa-acsp.ca *Web Site:* www.cpsa-acsp.ca, pg 717

Hopkins, Michelle, C B MacPherson Prize, 260 rue Dalhousie St, Suite 204, Ottawa, ON K1N 7E4, Canada *Tel:* 613-562-1202 *Fax:* 613-241-0019 *E-mail:* cpsa-acsp@cpsa-acsp.ca *Web Site:* www.cpsa-acsp.ca, pg 720

Hopkins, Michelle, John McMenemy Prize, 260 rue Dalhousie St, Suite 204, Ottawa, ON K1N 7E4, Canada *Tel:* 613-562-1202 *Fax:* 613-241-0019 *E-mail:* cpsa-acsp@cpsa-acsp.ca *Web Site:* www.cpsa-acsp.ca, pg 723

Hopkins, Michelle, Donald Smiley Prize, 260 rue Dalhousie St, Suite 204, Ottawa, ON K1N 7E4, Canada *Tel:* 613-562-1202 *Fax:* 613-241-0019 *E-mail:* cpsa-acsp@cpsa-acsp.ca *Web Site:* www.cpsa-acsp.ca, pg 742

Hopkins, Michelle, Jill Vickers Prize, 260 rue Dalhousie St, Suite 204, Ottawa, ON K1N 7E4, Canada *Tel:* 613-562-1202 *Fax:* 613-241-0019 *E-mail:* cpsa-acsp@cpsa-acsp.ca *Web Site:* www.cpsa-acsp.ca, pg 747

Hoppe, Anne, Clarion Books, 215 Park Ave S, New York, NY 10003 *Tel:* 212-420-5883 *Toll Free Tel:* 800-225-3362 (orders) *Fax:* 212-420-5855 *Toll Free Fax:* 800-634-7568 (orders) *Web Site:* www.houghtonmifflinbooks.com, pg 62

Hoppe, Joy, EMC Publishing, 875 Montreal Way, St Paul, MN 55102 *Tel:* 651-290-2800 (corp) *Toll Free Tel:* 800-328-1452 *Fax:* 651-290-2899 *Toll Free Fax:* 800-328-4564 *E-mail:* educate@emcp.com *Web Site:* www.emcp.com, pg 87

Hoppe, Joy, JIST Publishing, 875 Montreal Way, St Paul, MN 55102 *Tel:* 317-613-4200 *Toll Free Tel:* 800-328-1452 *Toll Free Fax:* 800-328-4564 *E-mail:* educate@emcp.com *Web Site:* jist.emcpublishingllc.com, pg 135

Hopper, Laura, Hyperion, 1500 Broadway, 3rd fl, New York, NY 10036 *Tel:* 212-536-6500 *Web Site:* hyperionbooks.com, pg 126

Horinstein, Regine, Corporation of Professional Librarians of Quebec, 1453, rue Beaubien Est, Bureau 215, Montreal, QC H2G 3C6, Canada *Tel:* 514-845-3327 *Fax:* 514-845-1618 *E-mail:* info@cbpq.qc.ca *Web Site:* www.cbpq.qc.ca, pg 622

Horler, Fred, Groundwood Books, 110 Spadina Ave, Suite 801, Toronto, ON M5V 2K4, Canada *Tel:* 416-363-4343 *Fax:* 416-363-1017 *E-mail:* genmail@groundwoodbooks.com *Web Site:* www.houseofanansi.com, pg 507

Horn, Leah, Western States Arts Federation, 1743 Wazee St, Suite 300, Denver, CO 80202 *Tel:* 303-629-1166 *Toll Free Tel:* 888-562-7232 *Fax:* 303-629-9717 *E-mail:* staff@westaf.org *Web Site:* www.westaf.org, pg 641

Hornburg, Michael, Grove/Atlantic Inc, 841 Broadway, 4th fl, New York, NY 10003-4793 *Tel:* 212-614-7850 *Toll Free Tel:* 800-521-0178 *Fax:* 212-614-7886 *E-mail:* info@groveatlantic.com *Web Site:* www.groveatlantic.com, pg 108

Hornby, Simon, Schiel & Denver Book Publishers, 10685-B Hazelhurst Dr, Suite 8575, Houston, TX 77043 *Tel:* 832-699-0264 *Toll Free Tel:* 888-629-4449 *Toll Free Fax:* 888-224-2721 *E-mail:* enquiries@schieldenver.com *Web Site:* www.schieldenver.com, pg 227

Hornfischer, Jim, Hornfischer Literary Management LP, PO Box 50544, Austin, TX 78763 *Tel:* 512-472-0011 *E-mail:* queries@hornfischerlit.com *Web Site:* www.hornfischerlit.com, pg 577

Hornik, Lauri, Dial Books for Young Readers, 345 Hudson St, New York, NY 10014 *Tel:* 212-366-2000 *Fax:* 212-414-3396 *E-mail:* online@penguinputnam.com *Web Site:* www.penguinputnam.com; us.penguingroup.com, pg 79

Hornstein, Gabriel, AMS Press Inc, Brooklyn Navy Yard, Unit 221, 63 Flushing Ave, Brooklyn, NY 11205-1005 *Tel:* 718-875-8100 *Fax:* 718-875-3800 *E-mail:* editorial@amspressinc.com *Web Site:* www.amspressinc.com, pg 18

Hornyak, Kim, Jenkins Group Inc, 1129 Woodmere Ave, Suite B, Traverse City, MI 49686 *Tel:* 231-933-0445 *Toll Free Tel:* 800-706-4636 *Fax:* 231-933-0448 *E-mail:* info@bookpublishing.com *Web Site:* www.bookpublishing.com, pg 549

Horowitz, Beverly, Random House Children's Books, 1745 Broadway, New York, NY 10019 *Tel:* 212-782-9000 *Toll Free Tel:* 800-200-3552 *Fax:* 212-782-9452 *Web Site:* randomhousekids.com, pg 213

Horowitz, Craig, BowTie Press®, 3 Burroughs, Irvine, CA 92618 *Tel:* 949-855-8822 *Toll Free Tel:* 888-738-2665 *Fax:* 949-458-3856 *E-mail:* bowtiepress@bowtieinc.com *Web Site:* www.bowtiepress.com, pg 44

Horowitz, David, Media Coalition Inc, 19 Fulton St, Suite 407, New York, NY 10038 *Tel:* 212-587-4025 *Fax:* 212-587-2436 *Web Site:* www.mediacoalition.org, pg 627

Horowitz, Irving Louis, Transaction Publishers Inc, 10 Corporate Place S, 35 Berrue Circle, Piscataway, NJ 08854 *Tel:* 732-445-2280; 732-445-1245 (orders) *Toll Free Tel:* 888-999-6778 (dist ctr) *Fax:* 732-445-3138 *E-mail:* trans@transactionpub.com; orders@transactionpub.om *Web Site:* www.transactionpub.com, pg 258

Horowitz, Mitchell, Jeremy P Tarcher, 375 Hudson St, New York, NY 10014 *Tel:* 212-366-2000 *E-mail:* online@penguinputnam.com *Web Site:* www.penguinputnam.com; us.penguingroup.com, pg 250

Horowitz, Shel, Accurate Writing & More, 16 Barstow Lane, Hadley, MA 01035 *Tel:* 413-586-2388 *E-mail:* shel@principledprofit.com *Web Site:* frugalmarketing.com; www.accuratewriting.com; www.grassrootsmarketingforauthors.com; www.greenandprofitable.com; www.frugalfun.com; www.twitter.com/shelhorowitz, pg 539

Horowitz, Valerie, The Lawbook Exchange Ltd, 33 Terminal Ave, Clark, NJ 07066-1321 *Tel:* 732-382-1800 *Toll Free Tel:* 800-422-6686 *Fax:* 732-382-1887 *E-mail:* law@lawbookexchange.com *Web Site:* www.lawbookexchange.com, pg 145

Horton, Boe, ProQuest LLC, 789 E Eisenhower Pkwy, Ann Arbor, MI 48108-3218 *Tel:* 734-761-4700 *Toll Free Tel:* 800-521-0600 *Fax:* 734-975-6486 *Toll Free Fax:* 800-864-0019 *E-mail:* info@proquest.com *Web Site:* www.proquest.com, pg 208

Horton, David, Bethany House Publishers, 11400 Hampshire Ave S, Bloomington, MN 55438 *Tel:* 952-829-2500 *Toll Free Tel:* 800-877-2665 (orders) *Fax:* 952-829-2568 *Toll Free Fax:* 800-398-3111 (orders) *Web Site:* www.bethanyhouse.com; www.bakerpublishinggroup.com, pg 36

Horvat, John, York Press, 1358 Jefferson Rd, Spring Grove, PA 17362 *Tel:* 717-225-7147 *Toll Free Tel:* 888-317-5571 *Fax:* 717-225-7479 *Web Site:* www.returntoorder.org, pg 530

Horvath, Dave, Jason Aronson Inc, 4501 Forbes Blvd, Suite 200, Lanham, MD 20706 *Tel:* 301-459-3366 *Toll Free Tel:* 800-462-6420 (orders) *Fax:* 301-429-5748 *Web Site:* www.jasonaronson.com, pg 22

Horvath, Dave, Lexington Books, 4501 Forbes Blvd, Suite 200, Lanham, MD 20706 *Tel:* 301-459-3366 *Fax:* 301-429-5749 *Web Site:* www.lexingtonbooks.com, pg 147

Horvath, Dave, University Press of America Inc, 4501 Forbes Blvd, Suite 200, Lanham, MD 20706 *Tel:* 301-459-3366 *Toll Free Tel:* 800-462-6420 *Fax:* 301-429-5748 *Toll Free Fax:* 800-338-4550 *Web Site:* www.univpress.com, pg 270

Horvit, Mark, Investigative Reporters & Editors, UMC School of Journalism, 138 Neff Annex, Columbia, MO 65211 *Tel:* 573-882-2042 *Fax:* 573-882-5431 *E-mail:* info@ire.org *Web Site:* www.ire.org, pg 625

Horwege, Richard, The Donning Company Publishers, 184 Business Park Dr, Suite 206, Virginia Beach, VA 23462 *Tel:* 757-497-1789 *Toll Free Tel:* 800-296-8572 *Fax:* 757-497-2542 *Web Site:* www.donning.com, pg 80

Hosier, Erin, Dunow, Carlson & Lerner Literary Agency Inc, 27 W 20 St, Suite 1107, New York, NY 10011 *Tel:* 212-645-7606 *E-mail:* mail@dclagency.com *Web Site:* www.dclagency.com, pg 569

Host, Bobette, Rocky Mountain Publishing Professionals Guild (RMPPG), PO Box 19013, Boulder, CO 80308 *E-mail:* membership@rmppg.org *Web Site:* thepublishingpros.org, pg 635

Hotchkiss, Erin, Harry N Abrams Inc, 115 W 18 St, 6th fl, New York, NY 10011 *Tel:* 212-206-7715 *Toll Free Tel:* 800-345-1359 *Fax:* 212-519-1210 *E-mail:* abrams@abramsbooks.com *Web Site:* www.abramsbooks.com, pg 3

Hottensen, Judy, Grove/Atlantic Inc, 841 Broadway, 4th fl, New York, NY 10003-4793 *Tel:* 212-614-7850 *Toll Free Tel:* 800-521-0178 *Fax:* 212-614-7886 *E-mail:* info@groveatlantic.com *Web Site:* www.groveatlantic.com, pg 108

Hottenstein, Alex, Bedford, Freeman & Worth Publishing Group, LLC, 41 Madison Ave, 37th fl, New York, NY 10010 *Tel:* 212-576-9400 *Fax:* 212-689-2383 *Web Site:* www.macmillanhighered.com, pg 33

Hotzler, Russell K PhD, New York City College of Technology, 300 Jay St, Brooklyn, NY 11201 *Tel:* 718-260-5500 *Fax:* 718-260-5198 *E-mail:* connect@citytech.cuny.edu *Web Site:* www.citytech.cuny.edu, pg 679

Houder, Daniel, Kennedy Information Inc, One Phoenix Mill Lane, 3rd fl, Peterborough, NH 03458 *Tel:* 603-924-0900; 603-924-1006 *Toll Free Tel:* 800-531-0007 *Fax:* 603-924-4460 *E-mail:* bookstore@kennedyinfo.com; customerservice@kennedyinfo.com *Web Site:* www.kennedyinfo.com, pg 139

Hough, Millie, Individual Artist's Fellowships in Literature, 1800 Gervais St, Columbia, SC 29201 *Tel:* 803-734-8696 *Fax:* 803-734-8526 *E-mail:* info@arts.sc.gov *Web Site:* www.southcarolinaarts.com, pg 712

Houghton, Daniel, Lonely Planet, 150 Linden St, Oakland, CA 94607 *Tel:* 510-893-8555 *Toll Free Tel:* 800-275-8555 (orders) *Fax:* 510-893-8563 *E-mail:* info@lonelyplanet.com *Web Site:* www.lonelyplanet.com, pg 152

Houghton, Harmon, Clear Light Publishers, 823 Don Diego Ave, Santa Fe, NM 87505 *Tel:* 505-989-9590 *Toll Free Tel:* 800-253-2747 (orders) *Fax:* 505-989-9519 *E-mail:* market@clearlightbooks.com *Web Site:* www.clearlightbooks.com, pg 63

Houle, Linda, L & L Dreamspell, 376 W Quarry Rd, London, TX 76854 *Tel:* 281-703-2405 *E-mail:* publishing@lldreamspell.com *Web Site:* www.lldreamspell.com, pg 143

Hourigan, Katherine, Doubleday/Nan A Talese, c/o Random House Inc, 1745 Broadway, New York, NY 10019 *Tel:* 212-751-2600 *Toll Free Tel:* 800-638-6460 *Fax:* 212-572-2593 *Web Site:* www.knopfdoubleday.com, pg 81

Hourigan, Katherine, Alfred A Knopf/Everyman's Library, c/o Random House Inc, 1745 Broadway, New York, NY 10019 *Tel:* 212-751-2600 *Toll Free Tel:* 800-638-6460 *Fax:* 212-572-2593 *Web Site:* www.knopfdoubleday.com, pg 141

Householder, Stacy, National Conference of State Legislatures (NCSL), 7700 E First Place, Denver, CO 80230 *Tel:* 303-364-7700 *Fax:* 303-364-7800 *E-mail:* books@ncsl.org *Web Site:* www.ncsl.org, pg 174

Housley, Jim, Bloom's Literary Criticism, 132 W 31 St, 17th fl, New York, NY 10001 *Toll Free Tel:* 800-322-8755 *Toll Free Fax:* 800-678-3633 *E-mail:* custserv@factsonfile.com *Web Site:* www.infobasepublishing.com, pg 40

Housley, Jim, Chelsea House Publishers, 132 W 31 St, 17th fl, New York, NY 10001 *Tel:* 212-967-8800 *Toll Free Tel:* 800-322-8755 *Fax:* 917-339-0325; 917-339-

0323 *Toll Free Fax:* 800-678-3633 *E-mail:* custserv@factsonfile.com *Web Site:* www.infobasepublishing.com; www.infobaselearning.com, pg 59

Housley, Jim, Facts On File, 132 W 31 St, 17th fl, New York, NY 10001 *Tel:* 212-967-8800 *Toll Free Tel:* 800-322-8755 *Fax:* 917-339-0323 *Toll Free Fax:* 800-678-3633 *E-mail:* custserv@factsonfile.com *Web Site:* infobasepublishing.com, pg 91

Housley, Jim, Ferguson Publishing, 132 W 31 St, 17th fl, New York, NY 10001 *Tel:* 212-967-8800 *Toll Free Tel:* 800-322-8755 *Fax:* 917-339-0323 *Toll Free Fax:* 800-678-3633 *E-mail:* custserv@factsonfile.com *Web Site:* infobasepublishing.com, pg 94

Houtz, Julie, ASCD, 1703 N Beauregard St, Alexandria, VA 22311-1714 *Tel:* 703-578-9600 *Toll Free Tel:* 800-933-2723 *Fax:* 703-575-5400 *E-mail:* member@ascd.org *Web Site:* www.ascd.org, pg 23

Hovemann, Glenn, Dawn Publications Inc, 12402 Bitney Springs Rd, Nevada City, CA 95959 *Tel:* 530-274-7775 *Toll Free Tel:* 800-545-7475 *Fax:* 530-274-7778 *E-mail:* nature@dawnpub.com; orders@dawnpub.com *Web Site:* www.dawnpub.com, pg 76

Hovey, Kim, Random House Publishing Group, 1745 Broadway, New York, NY 10019 *Toll Free Tel:* 800-200-3552 *Web Site:* atrandom.com, pg 214

Hoving, Allan, Tantor Media Inc, 2 Business Park, Old Saybrook, CT 06475 *Toll Free Tel:* 877-782-6867 *Toll Free Fax:* 888-782-7821 *Web Site:* www.tantor.com, pg 250

Howard, Assuanta, Asta Publications LLC, PO Box 1735, Stockbridge, GA 30281 *Tel:* 678-814-1320 *Toll Free Tel:* 800-482-4190 *Fax:* 678-814-1370 *E-mail:* info@astapublications.com *Web Site:* www.astapublications.com, pg 25

Howard, Brent, NAL, 375 Hudson St, New York, NY 10014 *Tel:* 212-366-2000 *E-mail:* online@penguinputnam.com *Web Site:* www.penguinputnam.com; us.penguingroup.com, pg 172

Howard, Elise, Algonquin Books of Chapel Hill, 400 Silver Cedar Ct, Suite 300, Chapel Hill, NC 27514-1585 *Tel:* 919-967-0108 *Fax:* 919-933-0272 *E-mail:* inquiry@algonquin.com *Web Site:* www.workman.com/algonquin, pg 8

Howard, Gerry, Doubleday/Nan A Talese, c/o Random House Inc, 1745 Broadway, New York, NY 10019 *Tel:* 212-751-2600 *Toll Free Tel:* 800-638-6460 *Fax:* 212-572-2593 *Web Site:* www.knopfdoubleday.com, pg 81

Howard, Glenda, Harlequin Enterprises Ltd, 233 Broadway, Suite 1001, New York, NY 10279 *Tel:* 212-553-4200 *Fax:* 212-227-8969 *E-mail:* CustomerService@harlequin.com *Web Site:* www.harlequin.com, pg 112

Howard, J Kirk, Simon & Pierre Publishing Co Ltd, 3 Church St, Suite 500, Toronto, ON M5E 1M2, Canada *Tel:* 416-214-5544 *Fax:* 416-214-5556 *E-mail:* info@dundurn.com *Web Site:* www.dundurn.com, pg 519

Howard, Kathy, Graphic Arts Books, 7820 NE Holman St, Suite B-9, Portland, OR 97218 *Tel:* 503-254-5591 *Fax:* 503-254-5609 *E-mail:* info-ga@graphicartsbooks.com *Web Site:* www.graphicartsbooks.com, pg 106

Howard, Kirk, Dundurn Press Ltd, 3 Church St, Suite 500, Toronto, ON M5E 1M2, Canada *Tel:* 416-214-5544 *Fax:* 416-214-5556 *E-mail:* info@dundurn.com *Web Site:* www.dundurn.com, pg 501

Howard, Laura, McSweeney's Publishing, 849 Valencia St, San Francisco, CA 94110 *Tel:* 415-642-5609 (cust serv) *Web Site:* www.mcsweeneys.net, pg 162

Howard, Marilyn, Creative Freelancers Inc, PO Box 366, Tallevast, FL 34270 *Tel:* 203-441-8144 *Toll Free Tel:* 800-398-9544 *Web Site:* www.freelancers1.com, pg 544

Howard, Meredith, Columbia University Press, 61 W 62 St, New York, NY 10023 *Tel:* 212-459-0600 *Toll Free Tel:* 800-944-8648 *Fax:* 212-459-3678 *E-mail:* cup_book@columbia.edu (orders & cust serv) *Web Site:* cup.columbia.edu, pg 65

Howard, Peter, Canadian Energy Research Institute, 3512 33 St NW, Suite 150, Calgary, AB T2L 2A6, Canada *Tel:* 403-282-1231 *Fax:* 403-284-4181 *E-mail:* info@ceri.ca *Web Site:* www.ceri.ca, pg 496

Howard, Roy, Cantos Para Todos, 2524 N Welgate Circle, Wichita, KS 67226 *Tel:* 316-239 6477 *Web Site:* www.cantos.org, pg 51

Howe, Isabel, The Authors League Fund, 31 E 32 St, 7th fl, New York, NY 10016 *Tel:* 212-268-1208 *Fax:* 212-564-5363 *E-mail:* staff@authorsleaguefund.org *Web Site:* www.authorsleaguefund.org, pg 617

Howe, Mark, Cengage Learning, 200 First Stamford Place, Suite 400, Stamford, CT 06902 *Tel:* 203-965-8600 *Toll Free Tel:* 800-354-9706 *Fax:* 203-965-8599 *Toll Free Fax:* 800-487-8488 *E-mail:* esales@cengage.com *Web Site:* www.cengage.com, pg 55

Howe, Meghan, Marilyn Baillie Picture Book Award, 40 Orchard View Blvd, Suite 217, Toronto, ON M4R 1B9, Canada *Tel:* 416-975-0010 *Fax:* 416-975-8970 *E-mail:* info@bookcentre.ca *Web Site:* www.bookcentre.ca, pg 689

Howe, Meghan, The Geoffrey Bilson Award for Historical Fiction for Young People, 40 Orchard View Blvd, Suite 217, Toronto, ON M4R 1B9, Canada *Tel:* 416-975-0010 *Fax:* 416-975-8970 *E-mail:* info@bookcentre.ca *Web Site:* www.bookcentre.ca, pg 691

Howe, Meghan, Canadian Children's Book Centre, 40 Orchard View Blvd, Suite 217, Toronto, ON M4R 1B9, Canada *Tel:* 416-975-0010 *Fax:* 416-975-8970 *E-mail:* info@bookcentre.ca *Web Site:* www.bookcentre.ca, pg 620

Howe, Meghan, Norma Fleck Award for Canadian Children's Non-Fiction, 40 Orchard View Blvd, Suite 217, Toronto, ON M4R 1B9, Canada *Tel:* 416-975-0010 *Fax:* 416-975-8970 *E-mail:* info@bookcentre.ca *Web Site:* www.bookcentre.ca, pg 704

Howe, Meghan, Monica Hughes Award for Science Fiction & Fantasy, 40 Orchard View Blvd, Suite 217, Toronto, ON M4R 1B9, Canada *Tel:* 416-975-0010 *Fax:* 416-975-8970 *E-mail:* info@bookcentre.ca *Web Site:* www.bookcentre.ca, pg 711

Howe, Meghan, John Spray Mystery Award, 40 Orchard View Blvd, Suite 217, Toronto, ON M4R 1B9, Canada *Tel:* 416-975-0010 *Fax:* 416-975-8970 *E-mail:* info@bookcentre.ca *Web Site:* www.bookcentre.ca, pg 744

Howe, Meghan, TD Canadian Children's Literature Award, 40 Orchard View Blvd, Suite 217, Toronto, ON M4R 1B9, Canada *Tel:* 416-975-0010 *Fax:* 416-975-8970 *E-mail:* info@bookcentre.ca *Web Site:* www.bookcentre.ca, pg 745

Howell, Christopher, Lynx House Press, 420 W 24 St, Spokane, WA 99203 *Tel:* 509-624-4894 *Web Site:* www.lynxhousepress.org, pg 154

Howell, Chuck, Library of American Broadcasting, University of Maryland, Hornbake Library, College Park, MD 20742 *Tel:* 301-405-9160 *Fax:* 301-314-2634 *E-mail:* labcast@umd.edu *Web Site:* www.lib.umd.edu/LAB, pg 626

Howey, Linda, National Geographic Books, 1145 17 St NW, Washington, DC 20036-4688 *Tel:* 202-857-7000 *Fax:* 202-857-7670 *Web Site:* www.nationalgeographic.com, pg 174

Howland, Bob, Griffin Publishing LLC, PO Box 28627, Santa Ana, CA 92799-8627 *Tel:* 714-556-7067 *Toll Free Tel:* 800-472-9741 *Fax:* 714-556-7067 *E-mail:* info@griffinpublishing.com *Web Site:* www.griffinpublishing.com, pg 108

Howland, Bryan, Griffin Publishing LLC, PO Box 28627, Santa Ana, CA 92799-8627 *Tel:* 714-556-7067 *Toll Free Tel:* 800-472-9741 *Fax:* 714-556-7067 *E-mail:* info@griffinpublishing.com *Web Site:* www.griffinpublishing.com, pg 108

Howland, E Carrie, Donadio & Olson Inc, 121 W 27 St, Suite 704, New York, NY 10001 *Tel:* 212-691-8077 *Fax:* 212-633-2837 *E-mail:* mail@donadio.com *Web Site:* donadio.com, pg 569

Howland, Robin, Griffin Publishing LLC, PO Box 28627, Santa Ana, CA 92799-8627 *Tel:* 714-556-7067 *Toll Free Tel:* 800-472-9741 *Fax:* 714-556-7067 *E-mail:* info@griffinpublishing.com *Web Site:* www.griffinpublishing.com, pg 108

Howry, Michelle, Touchstone, 1230 Avenue of the Americas, New York, NY 10020, pg 256

Howsam, Leslie, Society for the History of Authorship, Reading & Publishing Inc (SHARP), c/o The Johns Hopkins University Press, Journals Publishing Div, PO Box 19966, Baltimore, MD 21211-0966 *Tel:* 910-254-0308 *E-mail:* members@sharpweb.org *Web Site:* www.sharpweb.org, pg 636

Howsam, Meryl, Cormorant Books Inc, 390 Steelcase Rd E, Markham, ON L3R 1G2, Canada *Tel:* 905-475-9126 (Thomas Allen & Sons); 905-475-5571 *E-mail:* info@cormorantbooks.com *Web Site:* www.cormorantbooks.com, pg 500

Howser, Cathy, Arkansas Diamond Primary Book Award, Arkansas State Library, Suite 100, 900 W Capitol Ave, Little Rock, AR 72201-3108 *Tel:* 501-682-2860 *Fax:* 501-682-1693 *Web Site:* www.library.arkansas.gov; www.library.arkansas.gov, pg 688

Howser, Cathy, Charlie May Simon Children's Book Award, Arkansas State Library, Suite 100, 900 W Capitol Ave, Little Rock, AR 72201-3108 *Tel:* 501-682-2860 *Fax:* 501-682-1693 *Web Site:* www.library.arkansas.gov, pg 742

Howson, Barbara, Groundwood Books, 110 Spadina Ave, Suite 801, Toronto, ON M5V 2K4, Canada *Tel:* 416-363-4343 *Fax:* 416-363-1017 *E-mail:* genmail@groundwoodbooks.com *Web Site:* www.houseofanansi.com, pg 507

Howson, Barbara, House of Anansi Press Ltd, 110 Spadina Ave, Suite 801, Toronto, ON M5V 2K4, Canada *Tel:* 416-363-4343 *Fax:* 416-363-1017 *E-mail:* customerservice@houseofanansi.com *Web Site:* www.anansi.ca, pg 509

Howson, Diedra, The New York Botanical Garden Press, 2900 Southern Blvd, Bronx, NY 10458-5126 *Tel:* 718-817-8721 *Fax:* 718-817-8842 *E-mail:* nybgpress@nybg.org *Web Site:* www.nybgpress.org, pg 179

Hoy, Angela, WritersWeekly.com's 24-Hour Short Story Contest, 5726 Cortez Rd, Suite 349, Bradenton, FL 34210 *Fax:* 305-768-0261 *Web Site:* www.writersweekly.com, pg 752

Hoyem, Andrew, The Arion Press, The Presidio, 1802 Hays St, San Francisco, CA 94129 *Tel:* 415-668-2542 *Fax:* 415-668-2550 *E-mail:* arionpress@arionpress.com *Web Site:* www.arionpress.com, pg 22

Hoyenski, Edward, Miniature Book Society Inc, 702 Rosecrans St, San Diego, CA 92106-3013 *Tel:* 619-226-4441 *Fax:* 619-226-4441 *E-mail:* minibook@cox.net *Web Site:* www.mbs.org, pg 627

Hoyle, Karen, Ezra Jack Keats/Kerlan Memorial Fellowship, University of Minnesota, 113 Andersen Library, 222 21 Ave S, Minneapolis, MN 55455 *Tel:* 612-624-4576 *Fax:* 612-626-0377 *E-mail:* clrc@umn.edu *Web Site:* www.ezra-jack-keats.org; special.lib.umn.edu/clrc, pg 715

Hoyt, Debra Morton, W W Norton & Company Inc, 500 Fifth Ave, New York, NY 10110-0017 *Tel:* 212-354-5500 *Toll Free Tel:* 800-233-4830 (orders & cust serv) *Fax:* 212-869-0856 *Toll Free Fax:* 800-458-6515 *Web Site:* www.wwnorton.com, pg 181

Hoyt, Don, American Council on Education, One Dupont Circle NW, Washington, DC 20036-1193 *Tel:* 202-939-9300; 301-632-6757 (orders) *Fax:* 202-939-9302 *E-mail:* pubs@acenet.edu *Web Site:* www.acenet.edu, pg 12

Hoyt, Don, American Council on Education, One Dupont Circle NW, Washington, DC 20036-1193 *Tel:* 202-939-9300 *Fax:* 202-939-9302 *Web Site:* www.acenet.edu, pg 612

Hruska, Bronwen, Soho Press Inc, 853 Broadway, New York, NY 10003 *Tel:* 212-260-1900 *Fax:* 212-260-1902 *E-mail:* soho@sohopress.com; publicity@sohopress.com *Web Site:* www.sohopress.com, pg 239

Hsia, Pauline, Doris S Michaels Literary Agency Inc, 1841 Broadway, Suite 903, New York, NY 10023 *Tel:* 212-265-9474 *Fax:* 212-265-9480 *E-mail:* info@dsmagency.com *Web Site:* www.dsmagency.com, pg 585

Hsu, Ellen, InterVarsity Press, 430 Plaza Dr, Westmont, IL 60559-1234 *Tel:* 630-734-4000 *Toll Free Tel:* 800-843-9487 *Fax:* 630-734-4200 *E-mail:* email@ivpress.com *Web Site:* www.ivpress.com, pg 134

Hu, Jonathan, Carolyn Jenks Agency, 69 Aberdeen Ave, Cambridge, MA 02138 *Tel:* 617-354-5099 *E-mail:* carolynjenks@comcast.net *Web Site:* www.carolynjenksagency.com, pg 578

Huang, Alice, American Association for the Advancement of Science, 1200 New York Ave NW, Washington, DC 20005 *Tel:* 202-326-6400 *Fax:* 202-371-9526 *E-mail:* webmaster@aaas.org *Web Site:* www.aaas.org, pg 612

Hubbard, Loretta, Crystal Productions, 1812 Johns Dr, Glenview, IL 60025 *Tel:* 847-657-8144 *Toll Free Tel:* 800-255-8629 *Toll Free Fax:* 800-657-8149 *E-mail:* custserv@crystalproductions.com *Web Site:* www.crystalproductions.com, pg 73

Hubbard, Mandy, D4EO Literary Agency, 7 Indian Valley Rd, Weston, CT 06883 *Tel:* 203-544-7180 *Fax:* 203-544-7160 *Web Site:* www.d4eoliteraryagency.com, pg 568

Hubbard, Peter, HarperCollins General Books Group, 10 E 53 St, New York, NY 10022 *Tel:* 212-207-7000 *Fax:* 212-207-7633 *Web Site:* www.harpercollins.com, pg 113

Hubbard, Sarah, Professional Publications Inc (PPI), 1250 Fifth Ave, Belmont, CA 94002 *Tel:* 650-593-9119 *Toll Free Tel:* 800-426-1178 (orders) *Fax:* 650-592-4519 *E-mail:* info@ppi2pass.com *Web Site:* www.ppi2pass.com, pg 207

Hubbart, Dustin, University of Illinois Press, 1325 S Oak St, MC-566, Champaign, IL 61820-6903 *Tel:* 217-333-0950 *Fax:* 217-244-8082 *E-mail:* uipress@uillinois.edu; journals@uillinois.edu *Web Site:* www.press.uillinois.edu, pg 266

Hubbs, Roger A, Cornell University Press, Sage House, 512 E State St, Ithaca, NY 14850 *Tel:* 607-277-2338 *Fax:* 607-277-2374 *E-mail:* cupressinfo@cornell.edu; cupress-sales@cornell.edu *Web Site:* www.cornellpress.cornell.edu, pg 67

Hubenthal, Dayna, Koho Pono LLC, 15024 SE Pinegrove Loop, Clackamas, OR 97015 *Tel:* 503-723-7392 *Toll Free Tel:* 800-937-8000 (orders) *Toll Free Fax:* 800-876-0186 (orders) *E-mail:* info@kohopono.com; orders@ingrambook.com *Web Site:* kohopono.com, pg 141

Huber, Elizabeth A, American Mathematical Society, 201 Charles St, Providence, RI 02904-2294 *Tel:* 401-455-4000 *Toll Free Tel:* 800-321-4267 *Fax:* 401-331-3842; 401-455-4046 (cust serv) *E-mail:* ams@ams.org; cust-serv@ams.org *Web Site:* www.ams.org, pg 14

Huber, Fred, Penguin Group (USA) LLC Sales, 375 Hudson St, New York, NY 10014 *Tel:* 212-366-2000 *E-mail:* online@penguinputnam.com *Web Site:* us.penguingroup.com, pg 197

Huck, Kathryn, St Martin's Press, LLC, 175 Fifth Ave, New York, NY 10010 *Tel:* 646-307-5151 *Fax:* 212-420-9314 *E-mail:* firstname.lastname@macmillan.com *Web Site:* www.stmartins.com, pg 224

Hudson, Christopher, The Museum of Modern Art, 11 W 53 St, New York, NY 10019 *Tel:* 212-708-9443 *Fax:* 212-333-6575 *E-mail:* moma_publications@moma.org *Web Site:* www.moma.org, pg 171

Hudson, Dawn, Academy of Motion Picture Arts & Sciences (AMPAS), 8949 Wilshire Blvd, Beverly Hills, CA 90211 *Tel:* 310-247-3000 *Fax:* 310-859-9619 *E-mail:* ampas@oscars.org *Web Site:* www.oscars.org, pg 611

Hudson, Ken, Schiel & Denver Book Publishers, 10685-B Hazelhurst Dr, Suite 8575, Houston, TX 77043 *Tel:* 832-699-0264 *Toll Free Tel:* 888-629-4449 *Toll Free Fax:* 888-224-2721 *E-mail:* enquiries@schieldenver.com *Web Site:* www.schieldenver.com, pg 227

Hudson, Suzan, Herald Publishing House, 1001 W Walnut St, Independence, MO 64051 *Tel:* 816-521-3015 *Toll Free Tel:* 800-767-8181 *Fax:* 816-521-3066 *E-mail:* sales@heraldhouse.org *Web Site:* www.heraldhouse.org, pg 118

Hudson, Travis L, American Geological Institute (AGI), 4220 King St, Alexandria, VA 22302-1502 *Tel:* 703-379-2480 *Fax:* 703-379-7563 *E-mail:* pubs@agiweb.org *Web Site:* www.agiweb.org, pg 13

Huelsing, Kristi, Coaches Choice, 465 Reservation Rd, Marina, CA 93933 *Toll Free Tel:* 888-229-5745 *Fax:* 831-372-6075 *E-mail:* info@coacheschoice.com *Web Site:* www.coacheschoice.com, pg 63

Huff, Mickey, The 25 Most "Censored" Stories Annual, PO Box 571, Cotati, CA 94931 *Tel:* 707-874-2695 *Web Site:* www.projectcensored.org, pg 747

Hughes, Amy, Dunow, Carlson & Lerner Literary Agency Inc, 27 W 20 St, Suite 1107, New York, NY 10011 *Tel:* 212-645-7606 *E-mail:* mail@dclagency.com *Web Site:* www.dclagency.com, pg 569

Hughes, Andrew W, Doubleday/Nan A Talese, c/o Random House Inc, 1745 Broadway, New York, NY 10019 *Tel:* 212-751-2600 *Toll Free Tel:* 800-638-6460 *Fax:* 212-572-2593 *Web Site:* www.knopfdoubleday.com, pg 81

Hughes, Andrew W, Alfred A Knopf/Everyman's Library, c/o Random House Inc, 1745 Broadway, New York, NY 10019 *Tel:* 212-751-2600 *Toll Free Tel:* 800-638-6460 *Fax:* 212-572-2593 *Web Site:* www.knopfdoubleday.com, pg 141

Hughes, Andy, Pantheon Books/Schocken Books, c/o Random House Inc, 1745 Broadway, New York, NY 10019 *Tel:* 212-751-2600 *Toll Free Tel:* 800-638-6460 *Fax:* 212-572-6030, pg 192

Hughes, Brigid, Graywolf Press, 250 Third Ave N, Suite 600, Minneapolis, MN 55401 *Tel:* 651-641-0077 *Fax:* 651-641-0036 *E-mail:* wolves@graywolfpress.org *Web Site:* www.graywolfpress.org, pg 106

Hughes, Connie, Lippincott Williams & Wilkins, 530 Walnut St, Philadelphia, PA 19106-3621 *Tel:* 215-521-8300 *Toll Free Tel:* 800-638-3030 (orders & cust serv) *E-mail:* orders@lww.com *Web Site:* www.lww.com, pg 150

Hughes, Doug, McGraw-Hill Contemporary Learning Series, 501 Bell St, Dubuque, IA 52001 *Toll Free Tel:* 800-243-6532 *Web Site:* www.mhcls.com, pg 160

Hughes, Doug, McGraw-Hill Higher Education, 1333 Burr Ridge Pkwy, Burr Ridge, IL 60527 *Tel:* 630-789-4000 *Toll Free Tel:* 800-338-3987 (cust serv) *Fax:* 614-755-5645 (cust serv) *Web Site:* www.mhhe.com, pg 161

Hughes, Doug, McGraw-Hill Humanities, Social Sciences, Languages, 2 Penn Plaza, 20th fl, New York, NY 10121 *Tel:* 212-904-2000 *Toll Free Tel:* 800-338-3987 (cust serv) *Fax:* 614-755-5645 (cust serv) *Web Site:* www.mhhe.com, pg 161

Hughes, Doug, McGraw-Hill/Irwin, 1333 Burr Ridge Pkwy, Burr Ridge, IL 60527 *Tel:* 630-789-4000 *Toll Free Tel:* 800-338-3987 (cust serv) *Fax:* 630-789-6942; 614-755-5645 (cust serv) *Web Site:* www.mhhe.com, pg 162

Hughes, Doug, McGraw-Hill Science, Engineering, Mathematics, 501 Bell St, Dubuque, IA 52001 *Tel:* 563-584-6000 *Toll Free Tel:* 800-338-3987 (cust serv) *Fax:* 614-755-5645 (cust serv) *Web Site:* www.mhhe.com, pg 162

Hughes, Eileen, The Brookings Institution Press, 1775 Massachusetts Ave NW, Washington, DC 20036-2188 *Tel:* 202-536-3600 *Toll Free Tel:* 800-537-5487 *Fax:* 202-536-3623 *E-mail:* permissions@brookings.edu *Web Site:* www.brookings.edu, pg 48

Hughes, Georgia, New World Library, 14 Pamaron Way, Novato, CA 94949 *Tel:* 415-884-2100 *Toll Free Tel:* 800-227-3900 (ext 52, retail orders); 800-972-6657 *Fax:* 415-884-2199 *E-mail:* escort@newworldlibrary.com *Web Site:* www.newworldlibrary.com, pg 178

Hughes, Heather, Sleeping Bear Press™, 315 Eisenhower Pkwy, Suite 200, Ann Arbor, MI 48108 *Toll Free Tel:* 800-487-2323 *Fax:* 734-794-0004 *E-mail:* sleepingbearpress@cengage.com *Web Site:* www.sleepingbearpress.com, pg 237

Hughes, Jessie, W W Norton & Company Inc, 500 Fifth Ave, New York, NY 10110-0017 *Tel:* 212-354-5500 *Toll Free Tel:* 800-233-4830 (orders & cust serv) *Fax:* 212-869-0856 *Toll Free Fax:* 800-458-6515 *Web Site:* www.wwnorton.com, pg 182

Hughes, Jill, Jodie Rhodes Literary Agency, 8840 Villa La Jolla Dr, Suite 315, La Jolla, CA 92037 *E-mail:* jrhodes1@san.rr.com *Web Site:* www.jodierhodesliterary.com, pg 590

Hughes, Larry, Simon & Schuster, 1230 Avenue of the Americas, New York, NY 10020 *Tel:* 212-698-7000 *Toll Free Tel:* 800-223-2348 (cust serv); 800-223-2336 (orders) *Toll Free Fax:* 800-943-9831 (orders) *Web Site:* www.simonandschuster.com, pg 234

Hughes, Nicki, Castle Connolly Medical Ltd, 42 W 24 St, 2nd fl, New York, NY 10010 *Tel:* 212-367-8400 *Toll Free Tel:* 800-339-DOCS (339-3627) *Fax:* 212-367-0964 *Web Site:* www.castleconnolly.com, pg 54

Hughes, Patrick, Central Recovery Press (CRP), 3321 N Buffalo Dr, Suite 275, Las Vegas, NV 89129 *Tel:* 702-868-5830 *Fax:* 702-868-5831 *E-mail:* info@centralrecovery.com *Web Site:* centralrecoverypress.com, pg 57

Huisingh, Rosemary, LinguiSystems Inc, 3100 Fourth Ave, East Moline, IL 61244 *Tel:* 309-755-2300 *Toll Free Tel:* 800-776-4332 *Fax:* 309-755-2377 *Toll Free Fax:* 800-577-4555 *E-mail:* service@linguisystems.com *Web Site:* www.linguisystems.com, pg 149

Huizenga, Alan, Tyndale House Publishers Inc, 351 Executive Dr, Carol Stream, IL 60188 *Tel:* 630-668-8300 *Toll Free Tel:* 800-323-9400 *Web Site:* www.tyndale.com, pg 261

Hulbert, Jonathan, Wadsworth Publishing, 20 Davis Dr, Belmont, CA 94002 *Tel:* 650-595-2350 *Fax:* 650-592-3022 *Toll Free Fax:* 800-522-4923 *Web Site:* www.cengage.com, pg 276

Hulburt, Stephen, Prestel Publishing, 900 Broadway, Suite 603, New York, NY 10003 *Tel:* 212-995-2720 *Toll Free Tel:* 888-463-6110 (cust serv) *Fax:* 212-995-2733 *E-mail:* sales@prestel-usa.com *Web Site:* www.prestel.com, pg 205

Hulkower, Lynda, Midmarch Arts Press, 300 Riverside Dr, New York, NY 10025-5239 *Tel:* 212-666-6990 *Web Site:* midmarchartspress.org, pg 166

Hull, Donna, American Society of Agricultural Engineers (ASABE), 2950 Niles Rd, St Joseph, MI 49085-9659 *Tel:* 269-429-0300 *Fax:* 269-429-3852 *E-mail:* hq@asabe.org *Web Site:* www.asabe.org, pg 16

Hull, Jennifer, Chicago Women in Publishing, PO Box 268107, Chicago, IL 60626 *Tel:* 773-508-0351 *Fax:* 435-604-6049 *E-mail:* info@cwip.org *Web Site:* www.cwip.org, pg 621

Hull, Stephen, University Press of New England, One Court St, Suite 250, Lebanon, NH 03766 *Tel:* 603-448-1533 *Toll Free Tel:* 800-421-1561 (orders only) *Fax:* 603-448-7006; 603-643-1540 *E-mail:* university.press@dartmouth.edu *Web Site:* www.upne.com, pg 271

Hullett, James, Hackett Publishing Co Inc, 3333 Massachusetts Ave, Indianapolis, IN 46218 *Tel:* 317-635-9250 (orders & cust serv) *Fax:* 317-635-9292 *Toll Free Fax:* 800-783-9213 *E-mail:* customer@hackettpublishing.com *Web Site:* www.hackettpublishing.com, pg 110

Hullinger, Margret S, BNA Books, 1801 S Bell St, Arlington, VA 22202 *Toll Free Tel:* 800-372-1033 *Fax:* 732-346-1624 *E-mail:* books@bna.com *Web Site:* www.bnabooks.com, pg 42

Hulsey, Dave, Indiana University Press, 601 N Morton St, Bloomington, IN 47404-3797 *Tel:* 812-855-8817 *Toll Free Tel:* 800-842-6796 (orders only) *Fax:* 812-

855-7931; 812-855-8507 *E-mail:* iupress@indiana.edu; iuporder@indiana.edu (orders) *Web Site:* www.iupress.indiana.edu, pg 129

Hultenschmidt, Leah, Sourcebooks Inc, 1935 Brookdale Rd, Suite 139, Naperville, IL 60563 *Tel:* 630-961-3900 *Toll Free Tel:* 800-432-7444 *Fax:* 630-961-2168 *E-mail:* info@sourcebooks.com; customersupport@sourcebooks.com *Web Site:* www.sourcebooks.com, pg 240

Hummel, Kermit, The Countryman Press, 43 Lincoln Corners Way, Woodstock, VT 05091 *Tel:* 802-457-4826 *Toll Free Tel:* 800-245-4151 *Fax:* 802-457-1678 *E-mail:* countrymanpress@wwnorton.com *Web Site:* www.countrymanpress.com, pg 70

Humphrey, Doug, Cambridge Educational, 132 W 31 St, 17th fl, New York, NY 10001 *Toll Free Tel:* 800-322-8755 *Fax:* 609-671-0266 *Toll Free Fax:* 800-329-6687 *E-mail:* custserve@films.com *Web Site:* cambridge.films.com, pg 51

Humphrey, Harv, University of Notre Dame Press, 310 Flanner Hall, Notre Dame, IN 46556 *Tel:* 574-631-6346 *Fax:* 574-631-8148 *E-mail:* undpress@nd.edu *Web Site:* www.undpress.nd.edu, pg 268

Humphrey, John H, Journal of Roman Archaeology LLC, 95 Peleg Rd, Portsmouth, RI 02871 *Tel:* 401-683-1955 *Fax:* 401-683-1975 *E-mail:* jra@journalofromanarch.com *Web Site:* www.journalofromanarch.com, pg 137

Humphreys, Nancy K, Nancy Humpheys Wordmaps, 600 Humboldt St, Richmond, CA 94805 *Tel:* 415-462-1844 *Web Site:* www.wordmapsindexing.com (book indexing); www.authormaps.com (book marketing), pg 548

Hundley, Amy, Grove/Atlantic Inc, 841 Broadway, 4th fl, New York, NY 10003-4793 *Tel:* 212-614-7850 *Toll Free Tel:* 800-521-0178 *Fax:* 212-614-7886 *E-mail:* info@groveatlantic.com *Web Site:* www.groveatlantic.com, pg 108

Hung, Helena, Penguin Group (Canada), 90 Eglinton Ave E, Suite 700, Toronto, ON M4P 2Y3, Canada *Tel:* 416-925-2249 *Fax:* 416-925-0068 *Web Site:* www.penguin.ca, pg 515

Hunt, Katrina W, School of Government, University of North Carolina, CB 3330, Chapel Hill, NC 27599-3330 *Tel:* 919-966-4119 *Fax:* 919-962-2707 *Web Site:* www.sog.unc.edu, pg 229

Hunt, Luc, Philip G Spitzer Literary Agency Inc, 50 Talmage Farm Lane, East Hampton, NY 11937 *Tel:* 631-329-3650 *Fax:* 631-329-3651 *E-mail:* spitzer516@aol.com *Web Site:* www.spitzeragency.com, pg 595

Hunt, Rebecca, Harlequin Enterprises Ltd, 233 Broadway, Suite 1001, New York, NY 10279 *Tel:* 212-553-4200 *Fax:* 212-227-8969 *E-mail:* CustomerService@harlequin.com *Web Site:* www.harlequin.com, pg 112

Hunt, Richard, Clerisy Press, 306 Greenup St, Covington, KY 41011 *Tel:* 513-861-4045 *Toll Free Tel:* 888-604-4537 *Fax:* 859-291-9111 *E-mail:* info@clerisypress.com *Web Site:* www.clerisypress.com, pg 63

Hunt, Steve, Michelin Maps & Guides, One Parkway S, Greenville, SC 29615-5022 *Tel:* 864-458-5565 *Fax:* 864-458-5665 *Toll Free Fax:* 866-297-0914; 888-773-7979 *E-mail:* orders@americanmap.com (orders) *Web Site:* www.michelintravel.com; www.michelinguide.com, pg 165

Hunter, Ann A, AAH Graphics Inc, 9293 Fort Valley Rd, Fort Valley, VA 22652-2020 *Tel:* 540-933-6211 *Fax:* 540-933-6523 *E-mail:* srh@aahgraphics.com *Web Site:* www.aahgraphics.com, pg 539

Hunter, Ann A, Loft Press Inc, 9293 Fort Valley Rd, Fort Valley, VA 22652 *Tel:* 540-933-6210 *Fax:* 540-933-6523 *E-mail:* books@loftpress.com, pg 151

Hunter, Michael, Hunter Publishing Inc, 222 Clematis St, West Palm Beach, FL 33401 *Tel:* 561-835-2022 *Web Site:* www.amazingadventures.net, pg 126

Hunter, Mike R, Cape Breton University Press Inc (CBU Press), 1250 Grand Lake Rd, Sydney, NS B1M 1A2, Canada *Tel:* 902-563-1604 (orders & cust serv) *Fax:* 902-563-1177 *E-mail:* cbu_press@cbu.ca *Web Site:* www.cbupress.ca, pg 497

Hunter, Shelli, Richard Ivey School of Business, University of Western Ontario, 1151 Richmond St N, London, ON N6A 3K7, Canada *Tel:* 519-661-3206 *Toll Free Tel:* 800-649-6355 *Fax:* 519-661-3485 *E-mail:* cases@ivey.uwo.ca *Web Site:* www.iveycases.com; www.ivey.uwo.ca, pg 510

Hunter, Stephen R, Loft Press Inc, 9293 Fort Valley Rd, Fort Valley, VA 22652 *Tel:* 540-933-6210 *Fax:* 540-933-6523 *E-mail:* books@loftpress.com, pg 151

Hunter, Yvonne, Penguin Group (Canada), 90 Eglinton Ave E, Suite 700, Toronto, ON M4P 2Y3, Canada *Tel:* 416-925-2249 *Fax:* 416-925-0068 *Web Site:* www.penguin.ca, pg 515

Huot, Mary, Houghton Mifflin Harcourt Trade & Reference Division, 222 Berkeley St, Boston, MA 02116-3764 *Tel:* 617-351-5000 *Toll Free Tel:* 800-225-3362 *Web Site:* www.houghtonmifflinbooks.com, pg 124

Hupping, Carol, Jewish Publication Society, 2100 Arch St, 2nd fl, Philadelphia, PA 19103 *Tel:* 215-832-0600 *Toll Free Tel:* 800-234-3151 *Fax:* 215-568-2017 *E-mail:* jewishbook@jps.org *Web Site:* www.jps.org, pg 135

Hurd, Charlie, CLC Ministries, 701 Pennsylvania Ave, Fort Washington, PA 19034 *Tel:* 215-542-1240 *Toll Free Tel:* 800-659-1240 *Fax:* 215-542-7580 *E-mail:* orders@clcpublications.com *Web Site:* www.clcpublications.com, pg 62

Hurdle, Priscilla, Cornell University Press, Sage House, 512 E State St, Ithaca, NY 14850 *Tel:* 607-277-2338 *Fax:* 607-277-2374 *E-mail:* cupressinfo@cornell.edu; cupress-sales@cornell.edu *Web Site:* www.cornellpress.cornell.edu, pg 67

Hurley, Alana, Association of Writers & Writing Programs (AWP), George Mason University, 4400 University Dr, MSN 1E3, Fairfax, VA 22030 *Tel:* 703-993-4301 *Fax:* 703-993-4302 *E-mail:* awp@awpwriter.org *Web Site:* www.awpwriter.org, pg 617

Hurley, Alexis, InkWell Management, 521 Fifth Ave, 26th fl, New York, NY 10175 *Tel:* 212-922-3500 *Fax:* 212-922-0535 *E-mail:* info@inkwellmanagement.com; submissions@inkwellmanagement.com *Web Site:* inkwellmanagement.com, pg 577

Hurley, Cheryl, The Library of America, 14 E 60 St, New York, NY 10022-1006 *Tel:* 212-308-3360 *Fax:* 212-750-8352 *E-mail:* info@loa.org *Web Site:* www.loa.org, pg 148

Hurley, Solera, Allen A Knoll Publishers, 200 W Victoria St, 2nd fl, Suite A, Santa Barbara, CA 93101-3627 *Tel:* 805-564-3377 *Toll Free Tel:* 800-777-7623 *Fax:* 805-966-6657 *E-mail:* bookinfo@knollpublishers.com *Web Site:* www.knollpublishers.com, pg 141

Hurrle, Lou, Sams Technical Publishing LLC, 9850 E 30 St, Indianapolis, IN 46229 *Tel:* 317-396-5336 *Toll Free Tel:* 800-428-7267 *Fax:* 317-489-3406 *Toll Free Fax:* 800-552-3910 *E-mail:* customercare@samswebsite.com *Web Site:* www.samswebsite.com, pg 225

Hurston, Vernita, The Guilford Press, 72 Spring St, 4th fl, New York, NY 10012 *Tel:* 212-431-9800 *Toll Free Tel:* 800-365-7006 (ext 1, orders) *Fax:* 212-966-6708 *E-mail:* orders@guilford.com; info@guilford.com *Web Site:* www.guilford.com, pg 109

Hurwitz, Ani F, Oscar Williams/Gene Derwood Award, 909 Third Ave, New York, NY 10022 *Tel:* 212-686-0010 *Fax:* 212-532-8528 *E-mail:* info@nycommunitytrust.org *Web Site:* www.nycommunitytrust.org, pg 749

Hushion, Jacqueline, Canadian Publishers' Council (CPC), 250 Merton St, Suite 203, Toronto, ON M4S 1B1, Canada *Tel:* 416-322-7011 *Fax:* 416-322-6999 *Web Site:* www.pubcouncil.ca, pg 620

Hussein, Afzal, Federal Buyers Guide Inc, 324 Palm Ave, Santa Barbara, CA 93101 *Tel:* 805-963-6524 *Fax:* 805-963-7478 *E-mail:* info@gov-world.com; info@fbgglobal.com *Web Site:* www.gov-world.com; www.federalbuyersguideinc.com; www.digitalsubs.com, pg 93

Hussey, John P, The University Press of Kentucky, 663 S Limestone St, Lexington, KY 40508-4008 *Tel:* 859-257-8400 *Fax:* 859-257-8481 *Web Site:* www.kentuckypress.com, pg 271

Hussey, Mark, Pace University Press, Dept of Publishing, Rm 805-E, 551 Fifth Ave, New York, NY 10176 *Tel:* 212-346-1417 *Fax:* 212-346-1165 *Web Site:* www.pace.edu/press, pg 190

Hussey, Mary-Theresa, Harlequin Enterprises Ltd, 233 Broadway, Suite 1001, New York, NY 10279 *Tel:* 212-553-4200 *Fax:* 212-227-8969 *E-mail:* CustomerService@harlequin.com *Web Site:* www.harlequin.com, pg 112

Hutchings, Linda, The Fairmont Press Inc, 700 Indian Trail, Lilburn, GA 30047 *Tel:* 770-925-9388 *Fax:* 770-381-9865 *Web Site:* www.fairmontpress.com, pg 92

Hutchison, Margot Maley, Waterside Productions Inc, 2055 Oxford Ave, Cardiff, CA 92007 *Tel:* 760-632-9190 *Fax:* 760-632-9295 *E-mail:* admin@waterside.com *Web Site:* www.waterside.com, pg 598

Hutchison, Mindy, National Press Photographers Association Inc (NPPA), 3200 Croasdaile Dr, Suite 306, Durham, NC 27705 *Tel:* 919-383-7246 *Fax:* 919-383-7261 *E-mail:* info@nppa.org *Web Site:* www.nppa.org, pg 631

Hutchison-Cleaves, Geoffrey MA, Letterbox/Papyrus of London Publishers USA, 10501 Broom Hill Dr, Suite 1-F, Las Vegas, NV 89134-7339 *Tel:* 702-256-3838 *E-mail:* lb27383@cox.net, pg 147

Hutson, Sarah, The Penguin Press, 375 Hudson St, New York, NY 10014, pg 197

Hutto, Alicia, South Carolina Bar, Continuing Legal Education Div, 950 Taylor St, Columbia, SC 29201 *Tel:* 803-799-6653 *Toll Free Tel:* 800-768-7787 *Fax:* 803-799-4118 *E-mail:* scbar-info@scbar.org *Web Site:* www.scbar.org, pg 240

Hutton, Caroline DuBois, Hutton Electronic Publishing, 160 N Compo Rd, Westport, CT 06880-2102 *Tel:* 203-226-2588 *Fax:* 230-226-2588 *E-mail:* huttonbooks@hotmail.com, pg 126

Hutton, Caroline DuBois, Jones Hutton Literary Associates, 160 N Compo Rd, Westport, CT 06880-2102 *Tel:* 203-226-2588 *Fax:* 203-226-2588 *E-mail:* huttonbooks@hotmail.com, pg 579

Hutton, Daisy, Thomas Nelson Inc, 501 Nelson Place, Nashville, TN 37214 *Tel:* 615-889-9000 *Toll Free Tel:* 800-251-4000 *Fax:* 615-902-1548 *E-mail:* publicity@thomasnelson.com *Web Site:* www.thomasnelson.com, pg 255

Hutton, Daisy, Thomas Nelson Publishers, PO Box 141000, Nashville, TN 37214-1000 *Tel:* 615-889-9000 *Toll Free Tel:* 800-251-4000 *Fax:* 615-902-2129 *Web Site:* www.thomasnelson.com, pg 255

Hutton, Daisy, Zondervan, A HarperCollins Company, 5300 Patterson Ave SE, Grand Rapids, MI 49530 *Tel:* 616-698-6900 *Toll Free Tel:* 800-226-1122; 800-727-1309 (retail orders) *Fax:* 616-698-3350 *Toll Free Fax:* 800-698-3256 (retail orders) *E-mail:* zinfo@zondervan.com *Web Site:* www.zondervan.com, pg 289

Hutton, Eileen, Brilliance Audio, 1704 Eaton Dr, Grand Haven, MI 49417 *Tel:* 616-846-5256 *Toll Free Tel:* 800-648-2312 (orders only) *Fax:* 616-846-0630 *E-mail:* customerservice@brillianceaudio.com *Web Site:* www.brillianceaudio.com, pg 47

Hutton, Jayne, Individual Artist Fellowships, 1004 Farnam, Plaza Level, Omaha, NE 68102 *Tel:* 402-595-2122 *Toll Free Tel:* 800-341-4067 *Fax:* 402-595-2334 *Web Site:* www.nebraskaartscouncil.org, pg 712

Hvide, Brit, Simon & Schuster, 1230 Avenue of the Americas, New York, NY 10020 *Tel:* 212-698-7000 *Toll Free Tel:* 800-223-2348 (cust serv); 800-223-2336 (orders) *Toll Free Fax:* 800-943-9831 (orders) *Web Site:* www.simonandschuster.com, pg 234

Irwin-Diehl, Rebecca, Judson Press, 588 N Gulph Rd, King of Prussia, PA 19406 *Toll Free Tel:* 800-458-3766 *Fax:* 610-768-2107 *Web Site:* www.judsonpress.com, pg 137

Isaac, Joanne, American Numismatic Society, 75 Varick St, 11th fl, New York, NY 10013 *Tel:* 212-571-4470 *Fax:* 212-571-4479 *E-mail:* ans@numismatics.org *Web Site:* www.numismatics.org, pg 15

Isaacs, Suzanne T, Ampersand Inc/Professional Publishing Services, 1050 N State St, Chicago, IL 60610 *Tel:* 312-280-8905 *Fax:* 312-944-1582 *E-mail:* info@ampersandworks.com *Web Site:* www.ampersandworks.com, pg 17

Isaacson, Dana, Random House Publishing Group, 1745 Broadway, New York, NY 10019 *Toll Free Tel:* 800-200-3552 *Web Site:* atrandom.com, pg 214

Isenberg, Joy, Farrar, Straus & Giroux, LLC, 18 W 18 St, New York, NY 10011 *Tel:* 212-741-6900 *Fax:* 212-633-9385 *E-mail:* fsg.publicity@fsgbooks.com *Web Site:* us.macmillan.com/fsg.aspx, pg 93

Iserson, Mary Lou, Galen Press Ltd, PO Box 64400, Tucson, AZ 85728-4400 *Tel:* 520-577-8363 *Fax:* 520-529-6459 *E-mail:* sales@galenpress.com *Web Site:* www.galenpress.com, pg 100

Isherwood, Judith, Shoreline Press, 23 Sainte Anne, Ste Anne de Bellevue, QC H9X 1L1, Canada *Tel:* 514-457-5733 *E-mail:* info@shorelinepress.ca *Web Site:* shorelinepress.ca, pg 519

Israeli, Henry, Saturnalia Books Poetry Prize, 105 Woodside Rd, Ardmore, PA 19003 *Tel:* 267-278-9541 *E-mail:* info@saturnaliabooks.com *Web Site:* www.saturnaliabooks.com, pg 739

Israelite, David M, National Music Publishers' Association (NMPA), 975 F St NW, Suite 315, Washington, DC 20004 *Tel:* 202-393-6672 *Fax:* 202-393-6673 *E-mail:* pr@nmpa.org *Web Site:* www.nmpa.org, pg 630

Ivers, Mitchell, Gallery Books, 1230 Avenue of the Americas, New York, NY 10020 *Toll Free Tel:* 800-456-6798 *Fax:* 212-698-7284 *E-mail:* consumer.customerservice@simonandschuster.com *Web Site:* www.simonsays.com, pg 101

Iversen, Dr Kristen, The Pinch Writing Awards in Fiction, University of Memphis, English Dept, 435 Patterson Hall, Memphis, TN 38152 *Tel:* 901-678-4190 *Fax:* 901-678-2226 *E-mail:* editor@thepinchjournal.com *Web Site:* www.thepinchjournal.com, pg 734

Iversen, Dr Kristen, The Pinch Writing Awards in Poetry, University of Memphis, English Dept, 435 Patterson Hall, Memphis, TN 38152 *Tel:* 901-678-4190 *Fax:* 901-678-2226 *E-mail:* editor@thepinchjournal.com *Web Site:* www.thepinchjournal.com, pg 734

Iverson, Anne, Mountain Press Publishing Co, 1301 S Third W, Missoula, MT 59801 *Tel:* 406-728-1900 *Toll Free Tel:* 800-234-5308 *Fax:* 406-728-1635 *E-mail:* info@mtnpress.com *Web Site:* www.mountain-press.com, pg 170

Ivester, Stan, University of Tennessee Press, 110 Conference Center Bldg, 600 Henley St, Knoxville, TN 37996-4108 *Tel:* 865-974-3321 *Toll Free Tel:* 800-621-2736 (orders) *Fax:* 865-974-3724 *Toll Free Fax:* 800-621-8476 (orders) *E-mail:* custserv@utpress.org *Web Site:* www.utpress.org, pg 269

Jabbari, Dr Ahmad, Mazda Publishers Inc, One Park Plaza, Suite 600, Irvine, CA 92614 *Tel:* 714-751-5252 *Fax:* 714-751-4805 *E-mail:* mazdapub@aol.com *Web Site:* www.mazdapub.com, pg 159

Jackel, Lawrence, Waterside Productions Inc, 2055 Oxford Ave, Cardiff, CA 92007 *Tel:* 760-632-9190 *Fax:* 760-632-9295 *E-mail:* admin@waterside.com *Web Site:* www.waterside.com, pg 598

Jackolin, Jennena, Waveland Press Inc, 4180 IL Rte 83, Suite 101, Long Grove, IL 60047-9580 *Tel:* 847-634-0081 *Fax:* 847-634-9501 *E-mail:* info@waveland.com *Web Site:* www.waveland.com, pg 277

Jackson, Bobby L, Multicultural Publications Inc, 936 Slosson St, Akron, OH 44320 *Tel:* 330-865-9578 *Fax:* 330-865-9578 *E-mail:* multiculturalpub@prodigy.net, pg 171

Jackson, Carolyn, Second Story Feminist Press, 20 Maud St, Suite 401, Toronto, ON M5V 2M5, Canada *Tel:* 416-537-7850 *Fax:* 416-537-0588 *E-mail:* info@secondstorypress.ca *Web Site:* www.secondstorypress.ca, pg 518

Jackson, Chrissy, Florida Writers Association Conference, PO Box 66069, St Pete Beach, FL 33736-6069 *Web Site:* www.floridawriters.net, pg 669

Jackson, Chrissy, Florida Writers Association Inc, PO Box 66069, St Pete Beach, FL 33736-6069 *Web Site:* www.floridawriters.net, pg 623

Jackson, Christopher, Random House Publishing Group, 1745 Broadway, New York, NY 10019 *Toll Free Tel:* 800-200-3552 *Web Site:* atrandom.com, pg 214

Jackson, Danielle, Sourcebooks Inc, 1935 Brookdale Rd, Suite 139, Naperville, IL 60563 *Tel:* 630-961-3900 *Toll Free Tel:* 800-432-7444 *Fax:* 630-961-2168 *E-mail:* info@sourcebooks.com; customersupport@sourcebooks.com *Web Site:* www.sourcebooks.com, pg 240

Jackson, David B, Stanford University Press, 1450 Page Mill Rd, Palo Alto, CA 94304-1124 *Tel:* 650-723-9434 *Fax:* 650-725-3457 *E-mail:* info@sup.org *Web Site:* www.sup.org, pg 243

Jackson, Eleanor, Dunow, Carlson & Lerner Literary Agency Inc, 27 W 20 St, Suite 1107, New York, NY 10011 *Tel:* 212-645-7606 *E-mail:* mail@dclagency.com *Web Site:* www.dclagency.com, pg 569

Jackson, Heather, Crown Publishing Group, c/o Random House Inc, 1745 Broadway, New York, NY 10019 *Tel:* 212-782-9000 *Toll Free Tel:* 888-264-1745 *Fax:* 212-940-7408 *Web Site:* www.randomhouse.com/crown, pg 72

Jackson, Jennifer, Doubleday/Nan A Talese, c/o Random House Inc, 1745 Broadway, New York, NY 10019 *Tel:* 212-751-2600 *Toll Free Tel:* 800-638-6460 *Fax:* 212-572-2593 *Web Site:* www.knopfdoubleday.com, pg 81

Jackson, Jennifer, Alfred A Knopf/Everyman's Library, c/o Random House Inc, 1745 Broadway, New York, NY 10019 *Tel:* 212-751-2600 *Toll Free Tel:* 800-638-6460 *Fax:* 212-572-2593 *Web Site:* www.knopfdoubleday.com, pg 141

Jackson, Jennifer, Donald Maass Literary Agency, 121 W 27 St, Suite 801, New York, NY 10001 *Tel:* 212-727-8383 *Fax:* 212-727-3271 *E-mail:* info@maassagency.com; rights@maassagency.com (subs rights inquiries) *Web Site:* www.maassagency.com, pg 582

Jackson, Joe, University of Chicago Press, 1427 E 60 St, Chicago, IL 60637-2954 *Tel:* 773-702-7700; 773-702-7600 *Toll Free Tel:* 800-621-2736 (orders) *Fax:* 773-702-9756; 773-660-2235 (orders); 773-702-2708 *E-mail:* custserv@press.uchicago.edu; marketing@press.uchicago.edu *Web Site:* www.press.uchicago.edu, pg 265

Jackson, Judy, Northeast Texas Community College Annual Writers Conference, Continuing Education, PO Box 1307, Mount Pleasant, TX 75456-1307 *Tel:* 903-434-8134 *Toll Free Tel:* 800-870-0142 *Fax:* 903-572-6712 *Web Site:* www.ntcc.edu, pg 671

Jackson, Kate, HarperCollins Children's Books, 10 E 53 St, New York, NY 10022 *Tel:* 212-207-7000 *Web Site:* www.harpercollinschildrens.com, pg 113

Jackson, Lauren, Harlequin Enterprises Ltd, 233 Broadway, Suite 1001, New York, NY 10279 *Tel:* 212-553-4200 *Fax:* 212-227-8969 *E-mail:* CustomerService@harlequin.com *Web Site:* www.harlequin.com, pg 112

Jackson, Marie Marr, United States Institute of Peace Press, 2301 Constitution Ave NW, Washington, DC 20037 *Tel:* 202-457-1700 (edit); 703-661-1590 (cust serv) *Toll Free Tel:* 800-868-8064 (cust serv) *Fax:* 202-429-6063; 703-661-1501 (cust serv) *Web Site:* bookstore.usip.org, pg 262

Jackson, Melanie, Melanie Jackson Agency LLC, 41 W 72 St, Suite 3F, New York, NY 10023 *Tel:* 212-873-3373 *Fax:* 212-799-5063, pg 578

Jackson, Penelope, Nimbus Publishing Ltd, 3731 Mackintosh St, Halifax, NS B3K 5A5, Canada *Tel:* 902-455-4286; 902-454-7404 *Toll Free Tel:* 800-NIMBUS9 (646-2879) *Fax:* 902-455-5440 *Toll Free Fax:* 888-253-3133 *E-mail:* customerservice@nimbus.ns.ca *Web Site:* www.nimbus.ns.ca, pg 513

Jackson, Robert, Good Parent Inc, One Regency Plaza, Suite 1001, Providence, RI 02903 *Tel:* 401-316-1322 *Toll Free Fax:* 866-718-0344 *Web Site:* www.goodparentinc.com, pg 105

Jacob, Chris, HeartMath LLC, 14700 W Park Ave, Boulder Creek, CA 95006 *Tel:* 831-338-8700 *Toll Free Tel:* 800-450-9111 *Fax:* 831-338-9861 *E-mail:* inquiry@heartmath.com *Web Site:* www.heartmath.com, pg 117

Jacob, Leonard R, Institute of Police Technology & Management, University Ctr, 12000 Alumni Dr, Jacksonville, FL 32224-2678 *Tel:* 904-620-4786 *Fax:* 904-620-2453 *E-mail:* info@iptm.org; orders@iptm.org *Web Site:* www.iptm.org, pg 131

Jacob, Mary Ann, Texas A&M University Press, John H Lindsey Bldg, Lewis St, 4354 TAMU, College Station, TX 77843-4354 *Tel:* 979-845-1436 *Toll Free Tel:* 800-826-8911 (orders) *Fax:* 979-847-8752 *Toll Free Fax:* 888-617-2421 (orders) *E-mail:* upress@tamu.edu *Web Site:* www.tamupress.com, pg 253

Jacob, Michele, Basic Books, 250 W 57 St, 15th fl, New York, NY 10107 *Tel:* 212-340-8164 *Fax:* 212-340-8135 *E-mail:* perseus.promos@perseusbooks.com *Web Site:* www.basicbooks.com; perseusbooks.com, pg 31

Jacobs, Andrea, The Globe Pequot Press, 246 Goose Lane, Guilford, CT 06437 *Tel:* 203-458-4500 *Toll Free Tel:* 800-243-0495 (orders only); 888-249-7586 (cust serv) *Fax:* 203-458-4601 *Toll Free Fax:* 800-820-2329 (orders & cust serv) *E-mail:* info@globepequot.com *Web Site:* www.globepequot.com, pg 104

Jacobs, Ben, Bloom's Literary Criticism, 132 W 31 St, 17th fl, New York, NY 10001 *Toll Free Tel:* 800-322-8755 *Toll Free Fax:* 800-678-3633 *E-mail:* custserv@factsonfile.com *Web Site:* www.infobasepublishing.com, pg 40

Jacobs, Ben, Chelsea House Publishers, 132 W 31 St, 17th fl, New York, NY 10001 *Tel:* 212-967-8800 *Toll Free Tel:* 800-322-8755 *Fax:* 917-339-0325; 917-339-0323 *Toll Free Fax:* 800-678-3633 *E-mail:* custserv@factsonfile.com *Web Site:* www.infobasepublishing.com; www.infobaselearning.com, pg 59

Jacobs, Ben, Facts On File, 132 W 31 St, 17th fl, New York, NY 10001 *Tel:* 212-967-8800 *Toll Free Tel:* 800-322-8755 *Fax:* 917-339-0323 *Toll Free Fax:* 800-678-3633 *E-mail:* custserv@factsonfile.com *Web Site:* infobasepublishing.com, pg 91

Jacobs, Ben, Ferguson Publishing, 132 W 31 St, 17th fl, New York, NY 10001 *Tel:* 212-967-8800 *Toll Free Tel:* 800-322-8755 *Fax:* 917-339-0323 *Toll Free Fax:* 800-678-3633 *E-mail:* custserv@factsonfile.com *Web Site:* infobasepublishing.com, pg 94

Jacobs, Ben, World Almanac®, 132 W 31 St, New York, NY 10001 *Toll Free Tel:* 800-322-8755 *E-mail:* almanac@factsonfile.com *Web Site:* www.worldalmanac.com, pg 285

Jacobs, Danielle, Arkham House Publishers Inc, PO Box 546, Sauk City, WI 53583-0546 *Tel:* 608-643-4500 *Fax:* 608-643-5043 *E-mail:* sales@arkhamhouse.com *Web Site:* www.arkhamhouse.com, pg 22

Jacobs, Donald, Georgetown University Press, 3240 Prospect St NW, Suite 250, Washington, DC 20007 *Tel:* 202-687-5889 (busn) *Toll Free Tel:* 800-537-5487 *Fax:* 202-687-6340 (edit) *E-mail:* gupress@georgetown.edu *Web Site:* press.georgetown.edu, pg 103

Jacobs, Laurence, Craftsman Book Co, 6058 Corte Del Cedro, Carlsbad, CA 92011 *Tel:* 760-438-7828 *Toll Free Tel:* 800-829-8123 *Fax:* 760-438-0398 *Web Site:* www.craftsman-book.com, pg 70

Janusz, Julie, ProQuest LLC, 789 E Eisenhower Pkwy, Ann Arbor, MI 48108-3218 *Tel:* 734-761-4700 *Toll Free Tel:* 800-521-0600 *Fax:* 734-975-6486 *Toll Free Fax:* 800-864-0019 *E-mail:* info@proquest.com *Web Site:* www.proquest.com, pg 208

Jao, Jonathan, Random House Publishing Group, 1745 Broadway, New York, NY 10019 *Toll Free Tel:* 800-200-3552 *Web Site:* atrandom.com, pg 214

Japikse, Carl, Ariel Press, 88 N Gate Station Dr, Suite 106, Marble Hill, GA 30148 *Tel:* 770-894-4226 *Fax:* 706-579-1274 *E-mail:* lig201@lightariel.com *Web Site:* www.lightariel.com, pg 22

Jaque, Cathy, The Karpfinger Agency, 357 W 20 St, New York, NY 10011-3379 *Tel:* 212-691-2690 *Fax:* 212-691-7129 *E-mail:* info@karpfinger.com *Web Site:* www.karpfinger.com, pg 579

Jaquith, George, Wind Canyon Books, PO Box 7035, Stockton, CA 95267 *Tel:* 209-956-1600 *Toll Free Tel:* 800-952-7007 *Fax:* 209-956-9424 *Toll Free Fax:* 888-289-7086 *E-mail:* books@windcanyonbooks.com *Web Site:* www.windcanyonbooks.com, pg 282

Jaramillo, Raquel, Workman Publishing Co Inc, 225 Varick St, 9th fl, New York, NY 10014-4381 *Tel:* 212-254-5900 *Toll Free Tel:* 800-722-7202 *Fax:* 212-254-8098 *E-mail:* info@workman.com *Web Site:* www.workman.com, pg 285

Jarrad, Mary Beth, New York University Press, 838 Broadway, 3rd fl, New York, NY 10003-4812 *Tel:* 212-998-2575 (edit) *Toll Free Tel:* 800-996-6987 (orders) *Fax:* 212-995-3833 (orders) *E-mail:* information@nyupress.org; customerservice@nyupress.org; orders@nyupress.org *Web Site:* www.nyupress.org, pg 179

Jarvis, Michael, Chain Store Guide (CSG), 3922 Coconut Palm Dr, Tampa, FL 33619 *Tel:* 813-627-6957 *Toll Free Tel:* 800-927-9292 (orders) *Fax:* 813-627-6888 *E-mail:* info@csgis.com *Web Site:* www.csgis.com, pg 57

Jarvis, Sarah, Palimpsest Press, 5 King St, Kingsville, ON N9Y 1H9, Canada *Tel:* 519-563-9981 *E-mail:* info@palimpsestpress.ca *Web Site:* www.palimpsestpress.ca, pg 515

Jarvis, Sharon, Toad Hall Inc, 74 Toad Hall Lane, Laceyville, PA 18623-8047 *Tel:* 570-869-2942, pg 597

Jasmine, Michelle, Random House Publishing Group, 1745 Broadway, New York, NY 10019 *Toll Free Tel:* 800-200-3552 *Web Site:* atrandom.com, pg 214

Javsicas, Aaron, W W Norton & Company Inc, 500 Fifth Ave, New York, NY 10110-0017 *Tel:* 212-354-5500 *Toll Free Tel:* 800-233-4830 (orders & cust serv) *Fax:* 212-869-0856 *Toll Free Fax:* 800-458-6515 *Web Site:* www.wwnorton.com, pg 182

Jayo, James, The Globe Pequot Press, 246 Goose Lane, Guilford, CT 06437 *Tel:* 203-458-4500 *Toll Free Tel:* 800-243-0495 (orders only); 888-249-7586 (cust serv) *Fax:* 203-458-4601 *Toll Free Fax:* 800-820-2329 (orders & cust serv) *E-mail:* info@globepequot.com *Web Site:* www.globepequot.com, pg 104

Jefferson, Michael K, Telling Your Story Inc, PO Box 668485, Pompano Beach, FL 33069 *Tel:* 954-249-1333; 954-970-9333 *Web Site:* www.telling-your-story.com, pg 529

Jeffrey, Douglas A, Hillsdale College Press, 33 E College St, Hillsdale, MI 49242 *Tel:* 517-437-7341 *Toll Free Tel:* 800-437-2268 *Fax:* 517-517-3923 *E-mail:* news@hillsdale.edu *Web Site:* www.hillsdale.edu, pg 120

Jeglinski, Melissa, The Knight Agency Inc, 570 East Ave, Madison, GA 30650 *E-mail:* submissions@knightagency.net *Web Site:* www.knightagency.net, pg 580

Jellinek, Roger, Jellinek & Murray Literary Agency, 47-231 Kamakoi Rd, Kaneohe, HI 96744 *Tel:* 808-239-8451, pg 578

Jenkins, Jean, Writers' Haven Writers (WHW), 2244 Fourth Av, Suite A, San Diego, CA 92101-2119 *Tel:* 619-665-2712, pg 639

Jenkins, Jerrold R, Axiom Business Book Awards, 1129 Woodmere Ave, Suite B, Traverse City, MI 49686 *Tel:* 231-933-0445 *Toll Free Tel:* 800-706-4636 *Fax:* 231-933-0448 *E-mail:* info@axiomawards.com *Web Site:* www.axiomawards.com, pg 689

Jenkins, Jerrold R, The Independent Publisher Book Awards, 1129 Woodmere Ave, Suite B, Traverse City, MI 49686 *Tel:* 231-933-0445 *Toll Free Tel:* 800-706-4636 *Fax:* 231-933-0448 *Web Site:* www.independentpublisher.com/ipaward.lasso, pg 711

Jenkins, Jerrold R, Jenkins Group Inc, 1129 Woodmere Ave, Suite B, Traverse City, MI 49686 *Tel:* 231-933-0445 *Toll Free Tel:* 800-706-4636 *Fax:* 231-933-0448 *E-mail:* info@bookpublishing.com *Web Site:* www.bookpublishing.com, pg 549

Jenkins, Jerrold R, Moonbeam Children's Book Awards, 1129 Woodmere Ave, Suite B, Traverse City, MI 49686 *Tel:* 231-933-0445 *Toll Free Tel:* 800-706-4636 *Fax:* 231-933-0448 *E-mail:* info@axiomawards.com *Web Site:* www.moonbeamawards.com, pg 724

Jenkins, John, CQ Press, 2300 "N" St NW, Suite 800, Washington, DC 20037 *Tel:* 202-729-1900 *Toll Free Tel:* 866-4CQ-PRESS (427-7737) *Fax:* 202-729-1923 *Toll Free Fax:* 800-380-3810 *E-mail:* customerservice@cqpress.com *Web Site:* www.cqpress.com, pg 70

Jenkins, John, The MIT Press, 55 Hayward St, Cambridge, MA 02142 *Tel:* 617-253-5255 *Toll Free Tel:* 800-207-8354 (orders) *Fax:* 617-258-6779; 617-577-1545 (orders) *Web Site:* mitpress.mit.edu, pg 168

Jenkins, Joyce, Northern California Book Awards, c/o Poetry Flash, 1450 Fourth St, Suite 4, Berkeley, CA 94710 *Tel:* 510-525-5476 *Fax:* 510-525-6752 *E-mail:* editor@poetryflash.org *Web Site:* www.poetryflash.org/ncba.html, pg 729

Jenkins, Joyce, Poetry Flash Reading Series, 1450 Fourth St, Suite 4, Berkeley, CA 94710 *Tel:* 510-525-5476 *Fax:* 510-525-6752 *E-mail:* editor@poetryflash.org *Web Site:* www.poetryflash.org, pg 672

Jenks, Carolyn, Carolyn Jenks Agency, 69 Aberdeen Ave, Cambridge, MA 02138 *Tel:* 617-354-5099 *E-mail:* carolynjenks@comcast.net *Web Site:* www.carolynjenksagency.com, pg 578

Jenness, Morgan, Abrams Artists Agency, 275 Seventh Ave, 26th fl, New York, NY 10001 *Tel:* 646-486-4600 *Fax:* 646-486-2358 *E-mail:* literary@abramsartny.com *Web Site:* www.abramsartists.com, pg 559

Jennings, Marc, Hagstrom Map & Travel Center, 51 W 43 St, New York, NY 10036 *Toll Free Tel:* 800-432-MAPS (432-6277) *Fax:* 212-398-9856 *Web Site:* www.americanmap.com, pg 110

Jensen, Chris, IEEE Computer Society, 2001 "L" St NW, Suite 700, Washington, DC 20036-4928 *Tel:* 202-371-0101 *Toll Free Tel:* 800-272-6657 (memb info) *Fax:* 202-728-9614 *E-mail:* help@computer.org *Web Site:* www.computer.org, pg 127

Jensen, Connie, Saint Mary's Press, 702 Terrace Heights, Winona, MN 55987-1318 *Tel:* 507-457-7900 *Toll Free Tel:* 800-533-8095 *Fax:* 507-457-7990 *Toll Free Fax:* 800-344-9225 *E-mail:* smpress@smp.org *Web Site:* www.smp.org, pg 224

Jensen, Jack, Chronicle Books LLC, 680 Second St, San Francisco, CA 94107 *Tel:* 415-537-4200 *Toll Free Tel:* 800-759-0190 (cust serv) *Fax:* 415-537-4460 *Toll Free Fax:* 800-858-7787 (orders); 800-286-9471 (cust serv) *E-mail:* frontdesk@chroniclebooks.com *Web Site:* www.chroniclebooks.com, pg 61

Jensen, Neysa, SDP Publishing Solutions LLC, 36 Captain's Way, East Bridgewater, MA 02333 *Tel:* 617-775-0656 *Web Site:* www.sdppublishingsolutions.com, pg 555

Jensen, Renee, National Association of Insurance Commissioners, 2301 McGee St, Suite 800, Kansas City, MO 64108-2662 *Tel:* 816-842-3600; 816-783-8300 (cust serv) *Fax:* 816-783-8175; 816-460-7593 (cust serv) *E-mail:* prodserv@naic.org *Web Site:* www.naic.org, pg 173

Jewell, Caroline, ALSC BWI/Summer Reading Program Grant, 50 E Huron St, Chicago, IL 60611-2795 *Tel:* 312-280-2163 *Toll Free Tel:* 800-545-2433 *Fax:* 312-440-9374 *E-mail:* alsc@ala.org *Web Site:* www.ala.org/alsc, pg 687

Jewell, Caroline, The May Hill Arbuthnot Honor Lecture Award, 50 E Huron St, Chicago, IL 60611-2795 *Tel:* 312-280-2163 *Toll Free Tel:* 800-545-2433 *Fax:* 312-440-9374 *E-mail:* alsc@ala.org *Web Site:* www.ala.org/alsc, pg 688

Jewell, Caroline, The Mildred L Batchelder Award, 50 E Huron St, Chicago, IL 60611-2795 *Tel:* 312-280-2163 *Toll Free Tel:* 800-545-2433 *Fax:* 312-440-9374 *E-mail:* alsc@ala.org *Web Site:* www.ala.org/alsc, pg 689

Jewell, Caroline, The Pura Belpre Award, 50 E Huron St, Chicago, IL 60611-2795 *Tel:* 312-280-2163 *Toll Free Tel:* 800-545-2433 *Fax:* 312-440-9374 *E-mail:* alsc@ala.org *Web Site:* www.ala.org/alsc, pg 690

Jewell, Caroline, Bound to Stay Bound Books Scholarship, 50 E Huron St, Chicago, IL 60611-2795 *Tel:* 312-280-2163 *Toll Free Tel:* 800-545-2433 *Fax:* 312-440-9374 *E-mail:* alsc@ala.org *Web Site:* www.ala.org/alsc, pg 692

Jewell, Caroline, The Randolph Caldecott Medal, 50 E Huron St, Chicago, IL 60611-2795 *Tel:* 312-280-2163 *Toll Free Tel:* 800-545-2433 *Fax:* 312-440-9374 *E-mail:* alsc@ala.org *Web Site:* www.ala.org/alsc, pg 694

Jewell, Caroline, Frederic G Melcher Scholarship, 50 E Huron St, Chicago, IL 60611-2795 *Tel:* 312-280-2163 *Toll Free Tel:* 800-545-2433 *Fax:* 312-440-9374 *E-mail:* alsc@ala.org *Web Site:* www.ala.org/alsc, pg 723

Jewell, Caroline, John Newbery Medal, 50 E Huron St, Chicago, IL 60611-2795 *Tel:* 312-280-2163 *Toll Free Tel:* 800-545-2433 *Fax:* 312-440-9374 *E-mail:* alsc@ala.org *Web Site:* www.ala.org/alsc, pg 729

Jewell, Caroline, Robert F Sibert Informational Book Award, 50 E Huron St, Chicago, IL 60611-2795 *Tel:* 312-280-2163 *Toll Free Tel:* 800-545-2433 *Fax:* 312-440-9374 *E-mail:* alsc@ala.org *Web Site:* www.ala.org/alsc, pg 742

Jewell, Caroline, The Laura Ingalls Wilder Medal, 50 E Huron St, Chicago, IL 60611-2795 *Tel:* 312-280-2163 *Toll Free Tel:* 800-545-2433 *Fax:* 312-440-9374 *E-mail:* alsc@ala.org *Web Site:* www.ala.org/alsc, pg 749

Jewell, Wanda, Southern Independent Booksellers Alliance, 3806 Yale Ave, Columbia, SC 29205 *Tel:* 803-994-9530 *Fax:* 309-410-0211 *E-mail:* info@sibaweb.com *Web Site:* www.sibaweb.com, pg 637

Jewett, Barry, Cormorant Books Inc, 390 Steelcase Rd E, Markham, ON L3R 1G2, Canada *Tel:* 905-475-9126 (Thomas Allen & Sons); 905-475-5571 *E-mail:* info@cormorantbooks.com *Web Site:* www.cormorantbooks.com, pg 500

Jimenez, Kathy, Santillana USA Publishing Co Inc, 2023 NW 84 Ave, Doral, FL 33122 *Tel:* 305-591-9522 *Toll Free Tel:* 800-245-8584 *Fax:* 305-591-9145 *Toll Free Fax:* 888-248-9518 *E-mail:* customerservice@santillanausa.com *Web Site:* www.santillanausa.com; www.alfaguara.net, pg 226

Jin, Prof Ha, Boston University, 236 Bay State Rd, Boston, MA 02215 *Tel:* 617-353-2510 *Fax:* 617-353-3653 *E-mail:* crwr@bu.edu *Web Site:* www.bu.edu/writing, pg 677

Joanisse, Joanne, Canadian Government Publishing, Publishing & Depository Services, Public Works & Government Services Canada, Ottawa, ON K1A 0S5, Canada *Tel:* 613-941-5995 *Toll Free Tel:* 800-635-7943 *Fax:* 613-954-5779 *Toll Free Fax:* 800-565-7757 *E-mail:* publications@tpsgc-pwgsc.gc.ca *Web Site:* publications.gc.ca, pg 497

Jodoin, Isabelle, Modus Vivendi Publishing Inc & Presses Aventure, 55 rue Jean-Talon ouest, 2nd fl, Montreal, QC H2R 2W8, Canada *Tel:* 514-272-0433 *Fax:* 514-272-7234 *E-mail:* info@modusaventure.com *Web Site:* www.modusaventure.com, pg 512

Keller, Holly, University of British Columbia Press, 2029 West Mall, Vancouver, BC V6T 1Z2, Canada *Tel:* 604-822-5959 *Toll Free Tel:* 877-377-9378 *Fax:* 604-822-6083 *Toll Free Fax:* 800-668-0821 *E-mail:* frontdesk@ubcpress.ca *Web Site:* www.ubcpress.ca, pg 523

Keller, Jim, J J Keller & Associates, Inc, 3003 Breezewood Lane, Neenah, WI 54957 *Tel:* 920-722-2848 *Toll Free Tel:* 877-564-2333 *Toll Free Fax:* 800-727-7516 *E-mail:* sales@jjkeller.com *Web Site:* www.jjkeller.com/jjk, pg 139

Keller, Karen, Orientation to the Graphic Arts, 200 Deer Run Rd, Sewickley, PA 15143-2600 *Tel:* 412-259-1711 *Toll Free Tel:* 800-910-4283 *Fax:* 412-741-2311 *E-mail:* printing@printing.org *Web Site:* www.printing.org, pg 671

Keller, Karen, Printing Industries of America, 200 Deer Run Rd, Sewickley, PA 15143-2600 *Tel:* 412-741-6860 *Toll Free Tel:* 800-910-4283 *Fax:* 412-741-2311 *E-mail:* printing@printing.org *Web Site:* www.printing.org, pg 634

Keller, Marc, Triumph Learning, 136 Madison Ave, 7th fl, New York, NY 10016 *Tel:* 212-652-0200 *Toll Free Tel:* 800-221-9372 (cust serv) *Toll Free Fax:* 866-805-5723 *E-mail:* info@triumphlearning.com; customerservice@triumphlearning.com *Web Site:* www.triumphlearning.com, pg 259

Keller, Matthew A, Capstone Publishers™, 1710 Roe Crest Dr, North Mankato, MN 56003 *Toll Free Tel:* 800-747-4992 (cust serv) *Toll Free Fax:* 888-262-0705 *Web Site:* www.capstonepress.com, pg 51

Keller, Michael, Stanford University Press, 1450 Page Mill Rd, Palo Alto, CA 94304-1124 *Tel:* 650-723-9434 *Fax:* 650-725-3457 *E-mail:* info@sup.org *Web Site:* www.sup.org, pg 243

Keller, Robert L, J J Keller & Associates, Inc, 3003 Breezewood Lane, Neenah, WI 54957 *Tel:* 920-722-2848 *Toll Free Tel:* 877-564-2333 *Toll Free Fax:* 800-727-7516 *E-mail:* sales@jjkeller.com *Web Site:* www.jjkeller.com/jjk, pg 139

Keller, Wendy, Keller Media Inc, 578 Washington Blvd, No 745, Marina del Rey, CA 90292 *Toll Free Tel:* 800-278-8706 *E-mail:* query@kellermedia.com *Web Site:* kellermedia.com/query, pg 579

Keller-Krikava, Marne, J J Keller & Associates, Inc, 3003 Breezewood Lane, Neenah, WI 54957 *Tel:* 920-722-2848 *Toll Free Tel:* 877-564-2333 *Toll Free Fax:* 800-727-7516 *E-mail:* sales@jjkeller.com *Web Site:* www.jjkeller.com/jjk, pg 139

Kelley, Allison, Romance Writers of America®, 14615 Benfer Rd, Houston, TX 77069 *Tel:* 832-717-5200 *Fax:* 832-717-5201 *E-mail:* info@rwa.org *Web Site:* www.rwa.org, pg 635

Kelley, Allison, Romance Writers of America Annual Conference, 14615 Benfer Rd, Houston, TX 77069 *Tel:* 832-717-5200 *Fax:* 832-717-5201 *E-mail:* info@rwa.org *Web Site:* www.rwa.org, pg 672

Kelley, Allison, Romance Writers of America Awards, 14615 Benfer Rd, Houston, TX 77069 *Tel:* 832-717-5200 *Fax:* 832-717-5201 *E-mail:* info@rwa.org *Web Site:* www.rwa.org, pg 738

Kelley, Lynn, Kane Miller Books, 4901 Morena Blvd, Suite 213, San Diego, CA 92117 *E-mail:* info@kanemiller.com *Web Site:* www.kanemiller.com, pg 138

Kelley, Pamela, University of Hawaii Press, 2840 Kolowalu St, Honolulu, HI 96822 *Tel:* 808-956-8255 *Toll Free Tel:* 888-UHPRESS (847-7377) *Fax:* 808-988-6052 *Toll Free Fax:* 800-650-7811 *E-mail:* uhpbooks@hawaii.edu *Web Site:* www.uhpress.hawaii.edu, pg 265

Kelley, Dr Suzzanne, New Rivers Press, c/o Minnesota State University Moorhead, 1104 Seventh Ave S, Moorhead, MN 56563 *Tel:* 218-477-5870 *Fax:* 218-477-2236 *E-mail:* nrp@mnstate.edu *Web Site:* www.newriverspress.com; www.mnstate.edu/newriverspress, pg 178

Kellman, Anthony, Sandhills Writers' Series, Dept of Communications & Professional Writing, 2500 Walton Way, Augusta, GA 30904 *Tel:* 706-667-4437 *Fax:* 706-667-4770 *Web Site:* www.sandhills.aug.edu, pg 672

Kellogg, David, Council on Foreign Relations Press, The Harold Pratt House, 58 E 68 St, New York, NY 10065 *Tel:* 212-434-9400 *Fax:* 212-434-9800 *E-mail:* publications@cfr.org *Web Site:* www.cfr.org, pg 69

Kelly, Barbara, PJD Publications Ltd, PO Box 966, Westbury, NY 11590-0966 *Tel:* 516-626-0650 *Fax:* 516-626-4456 *Web Site:* www.pjdonline.com, pg 202

Kelly, Burta, Ashgate Publishing Co, 101 Cherry St, Suite 420, Burlington, VT 05401-4405 *Tel:* 802-865-7641 *Toll Free Tel:* 800-535-9544 *Fax:* 802-865-7847 *E-mail:* info@ashgate.com *Web Site:* www.ashgate.com, pg 24

Kelly, Dervla, Harry N Abrams Inc, 115 W 18 St, 6th fl, New York, NY 10011 *Tel:* 212-206-7715 *Toll Free Tel:* 800-345-1359 *Fax:* 212-519-1210 *E-mail:* abrams@abramsbooks.com *Web Site:* www.abramsbooks.com, pg 3

Kelly, Donna E, North Carolina Office of Archives & History, Historical Publications Section, 4622 Mail Service Ctr, Raleigh, NC 27699-4622 *Tel:* 919-733-7442 (ext 225) *Fax:* 919-733-1439 *Web Site:* www.ncpublications.com; nc-historical-publications.stores.yahoo.net (online store), pg 180

Kelly, Frances, Eye in the Ear Children's Audio, 5 Crescent St, Portland, ME 04102 *Tel:* 207-780-1574 *Toll Free Tel:* 877-99-STORY (997-8679) *Fax:* 509-275-4252 *E-mail:* info@eyeintheear.com *Web Site:* www.eyeintheear.com, pg 91

Kelly, Jean Marie, HarperCollins Publishers, 10 E 53 St, New York, NY 10022 *Tel:* 212-207-7000 *Fax:* 212-207-7145 *Web Site:* www.harpercollins.com, pg 113

Kelly, Kate, Morgan Gaynin Inc, 194 Third Ave, New York, NY 10003 *Tel:* 212-475-0440 *Fax:* 212-353-8538 *E-mail:* info@morgangaynin.com *Web Site:* www.morgangaynin.com, pg 602

Kelly, Kevin, Practising Law Institute, 810 Seventh Ave, New York, NY 10019 *Tel:* 212-824-5700 *Toll Free Tel:* 800-260-4PLI (260-4754 cust serv) *Fax:* 212-265-4742 (intl) *Toll Free Fax:* 800-321-0093 (local) *E-mail:* info@pli.edu *Web Site:* www.pli.edu, pg 205

Kelly, Laurence A, Eye in the Ear Children's Audio, 5 Crescent St, Portland, ME 04102 *Tel:* 207-780-1574 *Toll Free Tel:* 877-99-STORY (997-8679) *Fax:* 509-275-4252 *E-mail:* info@eyeintheear.com *Web Site:* www.eyeintheear.com, pg 91

Kelly, Neil K, F A Davis Co, 1915 Arch St, , Philadelphia, PA 19103 *Tel:* 215-568-2270 *Toll Free Tel:* 800-523-4049 *Fax:* 215-568-5065 *E-mail:* info@fadavis.com *Web Site:* www.fadavis.com, pg 76

Kelly, Patricia, Crown Publishing Group, c/o Random House Inc, 1745 Broadway, New York, NY 10019 *Tel:* 212-782-9000 *Toll Free Tel:* 888-264-1745 *Fax:* 212-940-7408 *Web Site:* www.randomhouse.com/crown, pg 72

Kelly, Patrick, The Experiment, 260 Fifth Ave, Suite 3 South, New York, NY 10001-6425 *Tel:* 212-889-1659 *E-mail:* info@theexperimentpublishing.com *Web Site:* www.theexperimentpublishing.com, pg 91

Kelly, Robert, Goodheart-Willcox Publisher, 18604 W Creek Dr, Tinley Park, IL 60477-6243 *Tel:* 708-687-5000 *Toll Free Tel:* 800-323-0440 *Fax:* 708-687-0315 *Toll Free Fax:* 888-409-3900 *E-mail:* custserv@g-w.com *Web Site:* www.g-w.com, pg 105

Kelly, Ryan, Chronicle Books LLC, 680 Second St, San Francisco, CA 94107 *Tel:* 415-537-4200 *Toll Free Tel:* 800-759-0190 (cust serv) *Fax:* 415-537-4460 *Toll Free Fax:* 800-858-7787 (orders); 800-286-9471 (cust serv) *E-mail:* frontdesk@chroniclebooks.com *Web Site:* www.chroniclebooks.com, pg 61

Kelly, Timothy T, National Geographic Society, 1145 17 St NW, Washington, DC 20036-4688 *Tel:* 202-857-7000 *Fax:* 202-429-5727 *Web Site:* www.nationalgeographic.com, pg 175

Kelly, Virginia A, F A Davis Co, 1915 Arch St, Philadelphia, PA 19103 *Tel:* 215-568-2270 *Toll Free Tel:* 800-523-4049 *Fax:* 215-568-5065 *E-mail:* info@fadavis.com *Web Site:* www.fadavis.com, pg 76

Kelly-Pye, Laurie, The Career Press Inc, 220 W Parkway, Unit 12, Pompton Plains, NJ 07444 *Tel:* 201-848-0310 *Toll Free Tel:* 800-CAREER-1 (227-3371) *Fax:* 201-848-1727 *Web Site:* www.careerpress.com, pg 52

Kelsey, Karla, Susquehanna University, Dept of English, 514 University Ave, Selinsgrove, PA 17870 *Tel:* 570-372-0101, pg 680

Kelty, John, Copywriter's Council of America (CCA), CCA Bldg, 7 Putter Lane, Middle Island, NY 11953-1920 *Tel:* 631-924-3888 *Fax:* 631-924-8555 *E-mail:* cca4dmcopy@gmail.com *Web Site:* www.AndrewLinickDirectMarketing.com/Copywriters-Council.html; www.NewWorldPressBooks.com, pg 67

Kemnitz, Dr Tom M, Royal Fireworks Press, First Ave, Unionville, NY 10988 *Tel:* 845-726-4444 *Fax:* 845-726-3824 *E-mail:* mail@rfwp.com *Web Site:* www.rfwp.com, pg 222

Kemp, Jaemellah, Naval Institute Press, 291 Wood Rd, Annapolis, MD 21402-5034 *Tel:* 410-268-6110 *Toll Free Tel:* 800-233-8764 *Fax:* 410-295-1084; 410-571-1703 (cust serv) *E-mail:* webmaster@navalinstitute.org; customer@navalinstitute.org (cust serv); trade@usni.org *Web Site:* www.nip.org; www.usni.org, pg 176

Kempker, Debra, Prima Games, 3000 Lava Ridge Ct, Roseville, CA 95661 *Tel:* 916-787-7000 *Fax:* 916-787-7001 *Web Site:* www.primagames.com, pg 206

Kempster, Rachel, DK, 375 Hudson St, 2nd fl, New York, NY 10014-3672 *Tel:* 212-213-4800 *Toll Free Tel:* 877-342-5357 (cust serv) *Fax:* 212-213-5202 *Web Site:* us.dk.com, pg 80

Kendall, Josh, Little, Brown and Company, 237 Park Ave, New York, NY 10017 *Tel:* 212-364-1100 *Fax:* 212-364-0952 *E-mail:* firstname.lastname@hbgusa.com *Web Site:* www.HachetteBookGroup.com, pg 150

Kendall, Karen, Fun in the Sun, PO Box 430744, Miami, FL 33243 *Web Site:* www.frwriters.org, pg 669

Keneston, Fran, State University of New York Press, 22 Corporate Woods Blvd, 3rd fl, Albany, NY 12211-2504 *Tel:* 518-472-5000 *Toll Free Tel:* 877-204-6073 (orders) *Fax:* 518-472-5038 *Toll Free Fax:* 877-204-6074 (orders) *E-mail:* suny@presswarehouse.com (orders); info@sunypress.edu (edit off) *Web Site:* www.sunypress.edu, pg 243

Kennedy, Christopher, Syracuse University Creative Writing Program, 401 Hall of Languages, Syracuse, NY 13244-1170 *Tel:* 315-443-2173 *Fax:* 315-443-3660 *Web Site:* english.syr.edu/creative_writing; www.syr.edu, pg 680

Kennedy, Daniel W, Whitehorse Press, 107 E Conway Rd, Center Conway, NH 03813-4012 *Tel:* 603-356-6556 *Toll Free Tel:* 800-531-1133 *Fax:* 603-356-6590 *E-mail:* customerservice@whitehorsepress.com *Web Site:* www.whitehorsebooks.com, pg 280

Kennedy, Frances, The Doe Coover Agency, PO Box 668, Winchester, MA 01890 *Tel:* 781-721-6000 *Fax:* 781-721-6727 *E-mail:* info@doecooveragency.com *Web Site:* www.doecooveragency.com, pg 567

Kennedy, Hank, AMACOM Books, 1601 Broadway, New York, NY 10019-7420 *Tel:* 212-586-8100; 518-891-5510 (orders) *Toll Free Tel:* 800-250-5308 (cust serv) *Fax:* 212-903-8083; 518-891-2372 (orders) *E-mail:* pubservice@amanet.org *Web Site:* www.amacombooks.org, pg 9

Kennedy, Judith M, Whitehorse Press, 107 E Conway Rd, Center Conway, NH 03813-4012 *Tel:* 603-356-6556 *Toll Free Tel:* 800-531-1133 *Fax:* 603-356-6590 *E-mail:* customerservice@whitehorsepress.com *Web Site:* www.whitehorsebooks.com, pg 280

Kennedy, Mary, Institute of Intergovernmental Relations, Queen's University, Robert Sutheland Hall, Rm 301, Kingston, ON K7L 3N6, Canada *Tel:* 613-533-2080 *Fax:* 613-533-6868 *E-mail:* iigr@queensu.ca *Web Site:* www.queensu.ca/iigr, pg 509

Kennedy, Megan, Rough Guides, 375 Hudson St, New York, NY 10014 *Toll Free Tel:* 800-631-8571 *E-mail:* mail@roughguides.com *Web Site:* www.roughguides.com, pg 221

Kennedy, Paul, F+W Media Inc, 10151 Carver Rd, Suite 200, Blue Ash, OH 45242 *Tel:* 513-531-2690 *Toll Free Tel:* 800-289-0963 (trade accts); 800-258-0929 (orders) *E-mail:* contact_us@fwmedia.com *Web Site:* www.fwmedia.com, pg 92

Kennedy, Shane, Lone Pine Publishing, 2311 96 St, Edmonton, AB T6N 1G3, Canada *Tel:* 780-433-9333 *Toll Free Tel:* 800-661-9017 *Fax:* 780-433-9646 *Toll Free Fax:* 800-424-7173 *E-mail:* info@lonepinepublishing.com *Web Site:* www.lonepinepublishing.com, pg 511

Kennedy, Susan Petersen, Riverhead Books (Hardcover), 375 Hudson St, New York, NY 10014 *Tel:* 212-366-2000 *E-mail:* online@penguinputnam.com *Web Site:* www.penguinputnam.com; us.penguingroup.com, pg 219

Kennedy, Tara, Oxford University Press USA, 198 Madison Ave, New York, NY 10016 *Tel:* 212-726-6000 *Toll Free Tel:* 800-451-7556 (orders); 800-445-9714 (cust serv) *Fax:* 919-677-1303 *E-mail:* custserv.us@oup.com *Web Site:* www.oup.com/us, pg 189

Kennedy, Terry, The Robert Watson Literary Prizes in Fiction & Poetry, MFA Writing Program, The Greensboro Review, UNC-Greensboro, 3302 MHRA Bldg, Greensboro, NC 27402-6170 *Tel:* 336-334-5459 *Fax:* 336-256-1470 *Web Site:* www.greensbororeview.org, pg 748

Kennedy, William, New York State Edith Wharton Citation of Merit for Fiction Writers, University at Albany, SL 320, Albany, NY 12222 *Tel:* 518-442-5620 *Fax:* 518-442-5621 *E-mail:* writers@uamail.albany.edu *Web Site:* www.albany.edu/writers-inst, pg 729

Kennedy, William, New York State Walt Whitman Citation of Merit for Poets, University at Albany, SL 320, Albany, NY 12222 *Tel:* 518-442-5620 *Fax:* 518-442-5621 *E-mail:* writers@uamail.albany.edu *Web Site:* www.albany.edu/writers-inst, pg 729

Kennedy, William, New York State Writers Institute, University at Albany, Science Library 320, Albany, NY 12222 *Tel:* 518-442-5620 *Fax:* 518-442-5621 *E-mail:* writers@uamail.albany.edu *Web Site:* www.albany.edu/writers-inst/, pg 671

Kenney, Verne, Zondervan, A HarperCollins Company, 5300 Patterson Ave SE, Grand Rapids, MI 49530 *Tel:* 616-698-6900 *Toll Free Tel:* 800-226-1122; 800-727-1309 (retail orders) *Fax:* 616-698-3350 *Toll Free Fax:* 800-698-3256 (retail orders) *E-mail:* zinfo@zondervan.com *Web Site:* www.zondervan.com, pg 289

Kenniff, Thomas, National Press Photographers Association Inc (NPPA), 3200 Croasdaile Dr, Suite 306, Durham, NC 27705 *Tel:* 919-383-7246 *Fax:* 919-383-7261 *E-mail:* info@nppa.org *Web Site:* www.nppa.org, pg 631

Kenny, Julia, Dunow, Carlson & Lerner Literary Agency Inc, 27 W 20 St, Suite 1107, New York, NY 10011 *Tel:* 212-645-7606 *E-mail:* mail@dclagency.com *Web Site:* www.dclagency.com, pg 569

Kenny, Maryanne, The Blackburn Press, PO Box 287, Caldwell, NJ 07006-0287 *Tel:* 973-228-7077 *Fax:* 973-228-7276 *Web Site:* www.blackburnpress.com, pg 39

Kenshole, Fiona, Transatlantic Agency, 2 Bloor St E, Ste 3500, Toronto, ON M4W-1A8, Canada *Tel:* 416-488-9214 *E-mail:* info@transatlanticagency.com *Web Site:* www.transatlanticagency.com, pg 597

Kent, Amy, Wm B Eerdmans Publishing Co, 2140 Oak Industrial Dr NE, Grand Rapids, MI 49505 *Tel:* 616-459-4591 *Toll Free Tel:* 800-253-7521 *Fax:* 616-459-6540 *E-mail:* customerservice@eerdmans.com; sales@eerdmans.com *Web Site:* www.eerdmans.com, pg 86

Kent, David, HarperCollins Canada Ltd, 2 Bloor St E, 20th fl, Toronto, ON M4W 1A8, Canada *Tel:* 416-975-9334 *Fax:* 416-975-9884 *E-mail:* hccanada@harpercollins.com *Web Site:* www.harpercollins.ca, pg 508

Kent, Holly, Marilyn Baillie Picture Book Award, 40 Orchard View Blvd, Suite 217, Toronto, ON M4R 1B9, Canada *Tel:* 416-975-0010 *Fax:* 416-975-8970 *E-mail:* info@bookcentre.ca *Web Site:* www.bookcentre.ca, pg 689

Kent, Holly, The Geoffrey Bilson Award for Historical Fiction for Young People, 40 Orchard View Blvd, Suite 217, Toronto, ON M4R 1B9, Canada *Tel:* 416-975-0010 *Fax:* 416-975-8970 *E-mail:* info@bookcentre.ca *Web Site:* www.bookcentre.ca, pg 691

Kent, Holly, Canadian Children's Book Centre, 40 Orchard View Blvd, Suite 217, Toronto, ON M4R 1B9, Canada *Tel:* 416-975-0010 *Fax:* 416-975-8970 *E-mail:* info@bookcentre.ca *Web Site:* www.bookcentre.ca, pg 620

Kent, Holly, Norma Fleck Award for Canadian Children's Non-Fiction, 40 Orchard View Blvd, Suite 217, Toronto, ON M4R 1B9, Canada *Tel:* 416-975-0010 *Fax:* 416-975-8970 *E-mail:* info@bookcentre.ca *Web Site:* www.bookcentre.ca, pg 704

Kent, Holly, Monica Hughes Award for Science Fiction & Fantasy, 40 Orchard View Blvd, Suite 217, Toronto, ON M4R 1B9, Canada *Tel:* 416-975-0010 *Fax:* 416-975-8970 *E-mail:* info@bookcentre.ca *Web Site:* www.bookcentre.ca, pg 711

Kent, Holly, John Spray Mystery Award, 40 Orchard View Blvd, Suite 217, Toronto, ON M4R 1B9, Canada *Tel:* 416-975-0010 *Fax:* 416-975-8970 *E-mail:* info@bookcentre.ca *Web Site:* www.bookcentre.ca, pg 744

Kent, Holly, TD Canadian Children's Literature Award, 40 Orchard View Blvd, Suite 217, Toronto, ON M4R 1B9, Canada *Tel:* 416-975-0010 *Fax:* 416-975-8970 *E-mail:* info@bookcentre.ca *Web Site:* www.bookcentre.ca, pg 745

Kent, Marie, Simon & Schuster, 1230 Avenue of the Americas, New York, NY 10020 *Tel:* 212-698-7000 *Toll Free Tel:* 800-223-2348 (cust serv); 800-223-2336 (orders) *Toll Free Fax:* 800-943-9831 (orders) *Web Site:* www.simonandschuster.com, pg 234

Kent, Norma G, Community College Press, One Dupont Circle NW, Suite 410, Washington, DC 20036 *Tel:* 202-728-0200; 301-490-8116 (orders) *Toll Free Tel:* 800-250-6557 *Fax:* 202-223-9390 (edit); 301-604-0158 (orders); 202-833-2467 *E-mail:* aaccpub@ebrightkey.net *Web Site:* www.aacc.nche.edu/bookstore, pg 66

Kent, Rachel, Books & Such, 52 Mission Circle, Suite 122, PMB 170, Santa Rosa, CA 95409-5370 *Tel:* 707-538-4184 *Web Site:* booksandsuch.com, pg 563

Kent, Rachel, New York Media Works, 112 Franklin St, New York, NY 10013 *Tel:* 646-369-5681 *Fax:* 646-810-4033 *E-mail:* info@nymediaworks.com *Web Site:* www.nymediaworks.com, pg 528

Kentwell, Richard, Reedswain Inc, 88 Wells Rd, Spring City, PA 19475 *Tel:* 610-495-9578 *Toll Free Tel:* 800-331-5191 *Fax:* 610-495-6632 *E-mail:* orders@reedswain.com *Web Site:* www.reedswain.com, pg 217

Kenworthy, Ann, Entomological Society of America, 10001 Derekwood Lane, Suite 100, Lanham, MD 20706-4876 *Tel:* 301-731-4535 *Fax:* 301-731-4538 *E-mail:* esa@entsoc.org *Web Site:* www.entsoc.org, pg 89

Keough, Matthew, Albert B Corey Prize, c/o American Historical Association, 400 "A" St SE, Washington, DC 20003-3889 *Tel:* 202-544-2422 *Fax:* 202-544-8307 *E-mail:* cha-shc@cha-shc.ca *Web Site:* www.historians.org/prizes; www.cha-shc.ca, pg 699

Kephart, Sheri, Easy Money Press, 5419 87 St, Lubbock, TX 79424 *Tel:* 806-543-5215 *E-mail:* easymoneypress@yahoo.com, pg 84

Kepner, Mr Chris, Victoria Sanders & Associates LLC, 241 Avenue of the Americas, Suite 11-H, New York, NY 10014 *Tel:* 212-633-8811 *Fax:* 212-633-0525 *E-mail:* queriesvsa@gmail.com *Web Site:* www.victoriasanders.com, pg 592

Kerber, Heather, Beaver's Pond Press Inc, 7108 Ohms Lane, Edina, MN 55439-2129 *Tel:* 952-829-8818 *Web Site:* www.beaverspondpress.com, pg 33

Kerber, Michael, Red Wheel/Weiser/Conari, 65 Parker St, Suite 7, Newburyport, MA 01950 *Tel:* 978-465-0504 *Toll Free Tel:* 800-423-7087 (orders) *Fax:* 978-465-0243 *E-mail:* info@rwwbooks.com *Web Site:* www.redwheelweiser.com, pg 216

Kerber, Tom, Beaver's Pond Press Inc, 7108 Ohms Lane, Edina, MN 55439-2129 *Tel:* 952-829-8818 *Web Site:* www.beaverspondpress.com, pg 33

Kerfoot, Karen, The Continuing Legal Education Society of British Columbia (CLEBC), 500-1155 W Pender St, Vancouver, BC V6E 2P4, Canada *Tel:* 604-669-3544; 604-893-2121 (cust serv) *Toll Free Tel:* 800-663-0437 (CN) *Fax:* 604-669-9260 *E-mail:* custserv@cle.bc.ca *Web Site:* www.cle.bc.ca, pg 499

Kerkstra, Allen R, Zondervan, A HarperCollins Company, 5300 Patterson Ave SE, Grand Rapids, MI 49530 *Tel:* 616-698-6900 *Toll Free Tel:* 800-226-1122; 800-727-1309 (retail orders) *Fax:* 616-698-3350 *Toll Free Fax:* 800-698-3256 (retail orders) *E-mail:* zinfo@zondervan.com *Web Site:* www.zondervan.com, pg 289

Kern, Athena, Natasha Kern Literary Agency Inc, PO Box 1069, White Salmon, WA 98672 *Tel:* 509-493-3803 *E-mail:* agent@natashakern.com *Web Site:* www.natashakern.com, pg 579

Kern, Natasha, Natasha Kern Literary Agency Inc, PO Box 1069, White Salmon, WA 98672 *Tel:* 509-493-3803 *E-mail:* agent@natashakern.com *Web Site:* www.natashakern.com, pg 579

Kerner, Diane, Scholastic Canada Ltd, 604 King St W, Toronto, ON M5V 1E1, Canada *Tel:* 905-887-7323 *Toll Free Tel:* 800-268-3848 (CN) *Fax:* 905-887-1131 *Toll Free Fax:* 866-346-1288 *Web Site:* www.scholastic.ca, pg 518

Kerr, Elisabeth, W W Norton & Company Inc, 500 Fifth Ave, New York, NY 10110-0017 *Tel:* 212-354-5500 *Toll Free Tel:* 800-233-4830 (orders & cust serv) *Fax:* 212-869-0856 *Toll Free Fax:* 800-458-6515 *Web Site:* www.wwnorton.com, pg 181

Kerr, Karen, Cornell University Press, Sage House, 512 E State St, Ithaca, NY 14850 *Tel:* 607-277-2338 *Fax:* 607-277-2374 *E-mail:* cupressinfo@cornell.edu; cupress-sales@cornell.edu *Web Site:* www.cornellpress.cornell.edu, pg 67

Kerr, Marianne, Oakstone Publishing LLC, 100 Corporate Pkwy, Suite 600, Birmingham, AL 35242 *Toll Free Tel:* 800-633-4743 *Fax:* 205-995-1926 *E-mail:* service@oakstonemedical.com *Web Site:* www.oakstonepublishing.com; www.cmeonly.com; www.cdeonly.com, pg 183

Kerwin, Donald, Center for Migration Studies of New York Inc (CMS), 27 Carmine St, New York, NY 10014-4423 *Tel:* 212-337-3080 *Fax:* 646-998-4625 *E-mail:* cms@cmsny.org *Web Site:* www.cmsny.org, pg 56

Kesling, Ashley, Allen Ginsberg Poetry Award, One College Blvd, Paterson, NJ 07505-1179 *Tel:* 973-684-6555 *Fax:* 973-523-6085 *Web Site:* www.pccc.edu/poetry, pg 707

Kesling, Ashley, The Paterson Fiction Prize, One College Blvd, Paterson, NJ 07505-1179 *Tel:* 973-684-6555 *Fax:* 973-523-6085 *Web Site:* www.pccc.edu/poetry, pg 732

Kesling, Ashley, The Paterson Poetry Prize, One College Blvd, Paterson, NJ 07505-1179 *Tel:* 973-684-6555 *Fax:* 973-523-6085 *Web Site:* www.pccc.edu/poetry, pg 732

Kesling, Ashley, The Paterson Prize for Books for Young People, One College Blvd, Paterson, NJ 07505-1179 *Tel:* 973-684-6555 *Fax:* 973-523-6085 *Web Site:* www.pccc.edu/poetry, pg 732

Kessel-Hendricks, Greer, Atria Books, 1230 Avenue of the Americas, New York, NY 10020 *Tel:* 212-698-7000 *Fax:* 212-698-7007 *Web Site:* www.simonandschuster.com, pg 26

Kessinger, Roger A, Kessinger Publishing LLC, PO Box 1404, Whitefish, MT 59937 *E-mail:* books@kessingerpub.com *Web Site:* www.kessinger.net, pg 140

Kessler, Ellen Terry, Kessler Communications, 280 W 86 St, New York, NY 10024 *Tel:* 212-724-8610 *E-mail:* lmp@etk.mailbolt.com *Web Site:* www.kesslercommunications.com, pg 549

Kessler, Erika, Contemporary Publishing Co of Raleigh Inc, 5849 Lease Lane, Raleigh, NC 27617 *Tel:* 919-851-8221 *Fax:* 919-851-6666 *E-mail:* questions@contemporarypublishing.com *Web Site:* www.contemporarypublishing.com, pg 66

Kessler, Joseph I, World Class Speakers & Entertainers, 5200 Kanan Rd, Suite 210, Agoura Hills, CA 91301 *Tel:* 818-991-5400 *Fax:* 818-991-2226 *E-mail:* wcse@wcspeakers.com *Web Site:* www.wcspeakers.com, pg 606

Kessler, Judy, Creative Homeowner, 24 Park Way, Upper Saddle River, NJ 07458-9960 *Tel:* 201-934-7100 *Toll Free Tel:* 800-631-7795 (cust serv) *Fax:* 201-934-7541; 201-934-8971 (orders) *E-mail:* info@creativehomeowner.com; customerservice@creativehomeowner.com *Web Site:* www.creativehomeowner.com, pg 71

Kessler, Liz, Hachette Digital, 237 Park Ave, New York, NY 10017 *Tel:* 212-364-0600, pg 110

Kessler, Fr Mathew, Liguori Publications, One Liguori Dr, Liguori, MO 63057-1000 *Tel:* 636-464-2500 *Toll Free Tel:* 866-848-2492; 800-325-9521 *Fax:* 636-464-8449 *Web Site:* www.liguori.org, pg 149

Kessler, Meredith, Milkweed Editions, 1011 Washington Ave S, Suite 300, Minneapolis, MN 55415-1246 *Tel:* 612-332-3192 *Toll Free Tel:* 800-520-6455 *Fax:* 612-215-2550 *Web Site:* www.milkweed.org, pg 166

Kessler, Meredith, Milkweed National Fiction Prize, 1011 Washington Ave S, Suite 300, Minneapolis, MN 55415-1246 *Tel:* 612-332-3192 *Toll Free Tel:* 800-520-6455 *Fax:* 612-215-2550 *E-mail:* submissions@milkweed.org *Web Site:* www.milkweed.org, pg 723

Kessler, Robert J, Pendragon Press, 52 White Hill Lane, Hillsdale, NY 12529-5839 *Tel:* 518-325-6100 *Toll Free Tel:* 877-656-6381 (orders) *Fax:* 518-325-6102 *E-mail:* editor@pendragonpress.com *Web Site:* www.pendragonpress.com, pg 196

Kettlewell, John, Adirondack Mountain Club, 814 Goggins Rd, Lake George, NY 12845-4117 *Tel:* 518-668-4447 *Toll Free Tel:* 800-395-8080 *Fax:* 518-668-3746 *E-mail:* adkinfo@adk.org *Web Site:* www.adk.org, pg 5

Kettner, Christine, Clarion Books, 215 Park Ave S, New York, NY 10003 *Tel:* 212-420-5883 *Toll Free Tel:* 800-225-3362 (orders) *Fax:* 212-420-5855 *Toll Free Fax:* 800-634-7568 (orders) *Web Site:* www.houghtonmifflinbooks.com, pg 62

Ketz, Louise B, Louise B Ketz Agency, 414 E 78 St, Suite 1-B, New York, NY 10075 *Tel:* 212-249-0668 *E-mail:* ketzagency@aol.com, pg 579

Keyishian, Harry, Fairleigh Dickinson University Press, M-GH2-01, 285 Madison Ave, Madison, NJ 07940 *Tel:* 973-443-8564 *Fax:* 974-443-8364 *E-mail:* fdupress@fdu.edu *Web Site:* www.fdupress.org, pg 92

Keyser, Christopher, Writers Guild of America Awards, 7000 W Third St, Los Angeles, CA 90048 *Tel:* 323-951-4000; 323-782-4569 *Fax:* 323-782-4800 *Web Site:* www.wga.org, pg 752

Keyser, Christopher, Writers Guild of America, West (WGAW), 7000 W Third St, Los Angeles, CA 90048 *Tel:* 323-951-4000 *Toll Free Tel:* 800-548-4532 *Fax:* 323-782-4800 *Web Site:* www.wga.org, pg 639

Khalfan, Aun Ali, Tahrike Tarsile Qur'an Inc, 80-08 51 Ave, Elmhurst, NY 11373 *Tel:* 718-446-6472 *Fax:* 718-446-4370 *E-mail:* read@koranusa.org *Web Site:* www.koranusa.org, pg 249

Khalil, Maha, Hyperion, 1500 Broadway, 3rd fl, New York, NY 10036 *Tel:* 212-536-6500 *Web Site:* hyperionbooks.com, pg 126

Khan, Ms Lakin, Napa Valley Writers' Conference, Upper Valley Campus, 1088 College Ave, St Helena, CA 94574 *Tel:* 707-967-2900 (ext 1611) *Fax:* 707-967-2909 *E-mail:* writecon@napavalley.edu *Web Site:* www.napawritersconf.org, pg 671

Khan, Olive, HarperCollins Canada Ltd, 2 Bloor St E, 20th fl, Toronto, ON M4W 1A8, Canada *Tel:* 416-975-9334 *Fax:* 416-975-9884 *E-mail:* hccanada@harpercollins.com *Web Site:* www.harpercollins.ca, pg 508

Khan, Roohana, Palgrave Macmillan, 175 Fifth Ave, Suite 200, New York, NY 10010 *Tel:* 646-307-5151 *Fax:* 212-777-6359 *E-mail:* firstname.lastname@palgrave-usa.com *Web Site:* us.macmillan.com/Palgrave.aspx, pg 191

Kharbanda, Sanj, Houghton Mifflin Harcourt Trade & Reference Division, 222 Berkeley St, Boston, MA 02116-3764 *Tel:* 617-351-5000 *Toll Free Tel:* 800-225-3362 *Web Site:* www.houghtonmifflinbooks.com, pg 124

Khatib, Kate, AK Press Distribution, 674-A 23 St, Oakland, CA 94612 *Tel:* 510-208-1700 *Fax:* 510-208-1701 *E-mail:* info@akpress.org; sales@akpress.org; orders@akpress.org *Web Site:* www.akpress.org, pg 7

Kheradi, Cyrus, Random House Publishing Group, 1745 Broadway, New York, NY 10019 *Toll Free Tel:* 800-200-3552 *Web Site:* atrandom.com, pg 214

Kheradi, Irene, Simon & Schuster, 1230 Avenue of the Americas, New York, NY 10020 *Tel:* 212-698-7000 *Toll Free Tel:* 800-223-2348 (cust serv); 800-223-2336 (orders) *Toll Free Fax:* 800-943-9831 (orders) *Web Site:* www.simonandschuster.com, pg 234

Kibby, Brian, McGraw-Hill Higher Education, 1333 Burr Ridge Pkwy, Burr Ridge, IL 60527 *Tel:* 630-789-4000 *Toll Free Tel:* 800-338-3987 (cust serv) *Fax:* 614-755-5645 (cust serv) *Web Site:* www.mhhe.com, pg 161

Kichler, Florrie Binford, Patria Press Inc, PO Box 752, Carmel, IN 46082 *Tel:* 317-577-1321 *Fax:* 413-215-8030 *E-mail:* moreinfo@patriapress.com *Web Site:* www.patriapress.com; www.facebook.com/YoungPatriotsBooks; twitter.com/#!/kidsbios, pg 194

Kichline, Linda, ImaJinn Books Inc, PO Box 74274, Phoenix, AZ 85087-4274 *Toll Free Tel:* 877-625-3592 *E-mail:* orders@imajinnbooks.com *Web Site:* www.imajinnbooks.com, pg 128

Kidd, Kenneth, Children's Literature Association Beiter Graduate Student Research Grants, 1301 W 22 St, Suite 202, Oak Brook, IL 60523 *Tel:* 630-571-4520 *Fax:* 708-876-5598 *E-mail:* info@childlitassn.org *Web Site:* www.childlitassn.org, pg 696

Kidd, Nancy PhD, National Communication Association, 1765 "N" St NW, Washington, DC 20036 *Tel:* 202-464-4622 *Fax:* 202-464-4600 *Web Site:* www.natcom.org, pg 629

Kiefer, Emily, Westminster John Knox Press, 100 Witherspoon St, Louisville, KY 40202-1396 *Tel:* 502-569-5052 *Toll Free Tel:* 800-227-2872 (US only) *Fax:* 502-569-8308 *Toll Free Fax:* 800-541-5113 (US & CN) *E-mail:* wjk@wjkbooks.com; customer_service@wjkbooks.com *Web Site:* www.wjkbooks.com, pg 279

Kielbicki, Eugenia, Puddingstone Literary, Authors' Agents, 11 Mabro Dr, Denville, NJ 07834-9607 *Tel:* 973-366-3622, pg 589

Kiely, Garrett P, University of Chicago Press, 1427 E 60 St, Chicago, IL 60637-2954 *Tel:* 773-702-7700; 773-702-7600 *Toll Free Tel:* 800-621-2736 (orders) *Fax:* 773-702-9756; 773-660-2235 (orders); 773-702-2708 *E-mail:* custserv@press.uchicago.edu; marketing@press.uchicago.edu *Web Site:* www.press.uchicago.edu, pg 265

Kier, Mary Alice, Cine/Lit Representation, PO Box 802918, Santa Clarita, CA 91380-2918 *Tel:* 661-513-0268 *Fax:* 661-513-0915 *E-mail:* cinelit@att.net, pg 566

Kietlinski, Teresa, Prospect Agency, 285 Fifth Ave, PMB 445, Brooklyn, NY 11215 *Tel:* 718-788-3217 *Fax:* 718-360-9582 *Web Site:* www.prospectagency.com, pg 589

Kihano, Desiree, Bess Press, 3565 Harding Ave, Honolulu, HI 96816 *Tel:* 808-734-7159; 808-734-7159 (ext 10, returns) *Toll Free Tel:* 800-910-2377 *Fax:* 808-732-3627 *E-mail:* sales@besspress.com *Web Site:* www.besspress.com, pg 36

Kilburg, Kathy, McGraw-Hill Create, 501 Bell St, Dubuque, IA 52001 *Tel:* 563-584-6000 *Fax:* 563-584-6600 *E-mail:* first_last@mcgraw-hill.com *Web Site:* www.mhhe.com, pg 160

Kilburn, Donald, Pearson Learning Solutions, 501 Boylston St, Suite 900, Boston, MA 02116 *Tel:* 617-848-6300 *Toll Free Tel:* 800-428-4466 (orders) *Fax:* 617-848-6358 *E-mail:* pcp@pearsoncustom.com *Web Site:* www.pearsoned.com, pg 196

Kilduff, Meghan, Objective Entertainment, 609 Greenwich St, 6th fl, New York, NY 10014 *Tel:* 212-431-5454 *Fax:* 917-464-6394 *Web Site:* www.objectiveent.com, pg 587

Kiley, Gus, Zone Books dba Urzone Inc, 1226 Prospect Ave, Brooklyn, NY 11218 *Tel:* 718-686-0048 *Toll Free Tel:* 800-405-1619 (orders & cust serv) *Fax:* 718-686-9045 *Toll Free Fax:* 800-406-9145 (orders) *E-mail:* orders@triliteral.org *Web Site:* www.zonebooks.org, pg 289

Kilgras, Heidi, Random House Children's Books, 1745 Broadway, New York, NY 10019 *Tel:* 212-782-9000 *Toll Free Tel:* 800-200-3552 *Fax:* 212-782-9452 *Web Site:* randomhousekids.com, pg 213

Kilkelly, Mary Beth, Random House Children's Books, 1745 Broadway, New York, NY 10019 *Tel:* 212-782-9000 *Toll Free Tel:* 800-200-3552 *Fax:* 212-782-9452 *Web Site:* randomhousekids.com, pg 213

Killeen, Brenna, Association of Writers & Writing Programs (AWP), George Mason University, 4400 University Dr, MSN 1E3, Fairfax, VA 22030 *Tel:* 703-993-4301 *Fax:* 703-993-4302 *E-mail:* awp@awpwriter.org *Web Site:* www.awpwriter.org, pg 617

Killeen, Brenna, AWP Award Series, George Mason University, 4400 University Dr, MSN 1E3, Fairfax, VA 22030 *Tel:* 703-993-4301 *Fax:* 703-993-4302 *E-mail:* awp@awpwriter.org *Web Site:* www.awpwriter.org, pg 688

Killoh, Kathy, Athabasca University Press, Edmonton Learning Ctr, Peace Hills Trust Tower, 1200, 10011-109 St, Edmonton, AB T5J 3S8, Canada *Tel:* 780-497-3412 *Fax:* 780-421-3298 *E-mail:* aupress@athabascau.ca *Web Site:* www.aupress.ca, pg 494

Kilmartin, Kerry, University of British Columbia Press, 2029 West Mall, Vancouver, BC V6T 1Z2, Canada *Tel:* 604-822-5959 *Toll Free Tel:* 877-377-9378 *Fax:* 604-822-6083 *Toll Free Fax:* 800-668-0821 *E-mail:* frontdesk@ubcpress.ca *Web Site:* www.ubcpress.ca, pg 523

Kim, Chae, Management Concepts Inc, 8230 Leesburg Pike, Suite 800, Vienna, VA 22182 *Tel:* 703-790-9595 *Toll Free Tel:* 800 506-4450 *Fax:* 703-790-1371 *E-mail:* publications@managementconcepts.com *Web Site:* www.managementconcepts.com, pg 155

Kim, Charles R, The Museum of Modern Art, 11 W 53 St, New York, NY 10019 *Tel:* 212-708-9443 *Fax:* 212-333-6575 *E-mail:* moma_publications@moma.org *Web Site:* www.moma.org, pg 171

Kim, Emily Sylvan, Prospect Agency, 285 Fifth Ave, PMB 445, Brooklyn, NY 11215 *Tel:* 718-788-3217 *Fax:* 718-360-9582 *Web Site:* www.prospectagency.com, pg 589

Kim, Gail, Judy Lopez Memorial Award For Children's Literature, 1225 Selby Ave, Los Angeles, CA 90024 *Tel:* 310-474-9917 *Fax:* 310-474-6436 *Web Site:* www.wnba-books.org/la; www.judylopezbookaward.org, pg 719

Kim, Jean H, Stanford University Press, 1450 Page Mill Rd, Palo Alto, CA 94304-1124 *Tel:* 650-723-9434 *Fax:* 650-725-3457 *E-mail:* info@sup.org *Web Site:* www.sup.org, pg 243

Kim, Luenna H, National Society of Newspaper Columnists (NSNC), 1345 Fillmore St, Suite 507, San Francisco, CA 94115 *Tel:* 415-488-NCNC (488-6762) *Toll Free Tel:* 866-440-NSNC (440-6762) *Fax:* 484-

297-0336 *Toll Free Fax:* 866-635-5759 *E-mail:* staff@columnists.com *Web Site:* www.columnists.com, pg 631

Kim, Luenna H, National Society of Newspaper Columnists Annual Conference, 1345 Fillmore St, Suite 507, San Francisco, CA 94115 *Tel:* 415-488-NCNC (488-6762) *Toll Free Tel:* 866-440-NSNC (440-6762) *Fax:* 484-297-0336 *Toll Free Fax:* 866-635-5759 *Web Site:* www.columnists.com, pg 671

Kim, Sally, Touchstone, 1230 Avenue of the Americas, New York, NY 10020, pg 256

Kim, Stephanie, Houghton Mifflin Harcourt, 222 Berkeley St, Boston, MA 02116-3764 *Tel:* 617-351-5000 *Toll Free Tel:* 800-225-5425 (Pre-K-8); 800-462-6595 (6–12; Advanced & Electives); 800-289-4490 (Specialized Curriculum: Great Source, Rigby, Saxon, Steck-Vaughn; Homeschool; Adult Ed); 800-323-9540 (Assessment: Riverside Publishing); 888-391-3245 (SkillsTutor); 888-242-6747 option 2 (Destination Series; Classroom Connect; Earobics; Edmark; Learning Village; Riverdeep); 800-225-3362 (Houghton Mifflin Harcourt Trade & Reference Publishers); 800-225-5800 (Heinemann) *Fax:* 617-351-1125 *Web Site:* www.hmhco.com, pg 123

Kimball, David, National Association of Real Estate Editors (NAREE), 1003 NW Sixth Terr, Boca Raton, FL 33486-3455 *Tel:* 561-391-3599 *Fax:* 561-391-0099 *Web Site:* www.naree.org, pg 629

Kimball, Gregg, Library of Virginia, 800 E Broad St, Richmond, VA 23219-8000 *Tel:* 804-692-3999; 804-692-3500 *Fax:* 804-692-3736 *Web Site:* www.lva.virginia.gov, pg 148

Kimball, James, Doubleday/Nan A Talese, c/o Random House Inc, 1745 Broadway, New York, NY 10019 *Tel:* 212-751-2600 *Toll Free Tel:* 800-638-6460 *Fax:* 212-572-2593 *Web Site:* www.knopfdoubleday.com, pg 81

Kimball, James, Alfred A Knopf/Everyman's Library, c/o Random House Inc, 1745 Broadway, New York, NY 10019 *Tel:* 212-751-2600 *Toll Free Tel:* 800-638-6460 *Fax:* 212-572-2593 *Web Site:* www.knopfdoubleday.com, pg 141

Kimball, Roger, Encounter Books, 900 Broadway, Suite 601, New York, NY 10003 *Tel:* 212-871-6310 *Toll Free Tel:* 800-786-3839 *Fax:* 212-871-6311 *Toll Free Fax:* 877-811-1461 *E-mail:* read@encounterbooks.com *Web Site:* www.encounterbooks.com, pg 88

Kimball, Tom, Signature Books Publishing LLC, 564 W 400 N, Salt Lake City, UT 84116-3411 *Tel:* 801-531-1483 *Toll Free Tel:* 800-356-5687 (orders) *Fax:* 801-531-1488 *E-mail:* people@signaturebooks.com *Web Site:* www.signaturebooks.com; www.signaturebookslibrary.org, pg 234

Kimberling, Clint, University Press of Mississippi, 3825 Ridgewood Rd, Jackson, MS 39211-6492 *Tel:* 601-432-6205 *Toll Free Tel:* 800-737-7788 (orders & cust serv) *Fax:* 601-432-6217 *E-mail:* press@mississippi.edu *Web Site:* www.upress.state.ms.us, pg 271

Kimmel, Janine L, Spring Tree Press, 571 Locust Point Rd, Locust, NJ 07760 *Tel:* 732-872-8002 *Fax:* 732-872-6967 *E-mail:* springtreepress@gmail.com *Web Site:* www.springtreepress.com; www.tyrrc.com, pg 529

Kimzey, Anne, Alabama Artists Fellowship Awards, 201 Monroe St, Suite 110, Montgomery, AL 36130-1800 *Tel:* 334-242-4076 *Fax:* 334-240-3269, pg 686

Kinard, Erin, Abrams Learning Trends, 16310 Bratton Lane, Suite 250, Austin, TX 78728-2403 *Toll Free Tel:* 800-227-9120 *Toll Free Fax:* 800-737-3322 *E-mail:* customerservice@abramslearningtrends.com (orders, cust serv) *Web Site:* www.abramslearningtrends.com (orders, cust serv), pg 3

Kincaid, Christen, New Women's Voices Chapbook Competition, PO Box 1626, Georgetown, KY 40324 *Tel:* 859-514-8966 *E-mail:* finishingbooks@aol.com; flpbookstore@aol.com *Web Site:* www.finishinglinepress.com, pg 728

Kincaid, Christen, Open Chapbook Competition, PO Box 1626, Georgetown, KY 40324 *Tel:* 859-514-8966 *E-mail:* finishingbooks@aol.com; flpbookstore@aol.com *Web Site:* www.finishinglinepress.com, pg 731

KinCannon, Mary, Interweave Press LLC, 201 E Fourth St, Loveland, CO 80537 *Tel:* 970-669-7672 *Toll Free Tel:* 800-272-2193 *Fax:* 970-667-8317 *E-mail:* interweaveservice@interweave.com *Web Site:* www.interweave.com, pg 134

Kind, Rachel, Random House Publishing Group, 1745 Broadway, New York, NY 10019 *Toll Free Tel:* 800-200-3552 *Web Site:* atrandom.com, pg 214

King, Amy, Jason Aronson Inc, 4501 Forbes Blvd, Suite 200, Lanham, MD 20706 *Tel:* 301-459-3366 *Toll Free Tel:* 800-462-6420 (orders) *Fax:* 301-429-5748 *Web Site:* www.jasonaronson.com, pg 22

King, Brenda, Yale University Press, 302 Temple St, New Haven, CT 06511-8909 *Tel:* 401-531-2800 (cust serv); 203-432-0960 *Toll Free Tel:* 800-405-1619 (cust serv) *Fax:* 203-432-0948; 401-531-2801 (cust serv) *Toll Free Fax:* 800-406-9145 (cust serv) *E-mail:* customer.care@trilateral.org (cust serv); language.yalepress@yale.edu *Web Site:* www.yalebooks.com, pg 287

King, Brian, The University of Arkansas Press, McIlroy House, 105 N McIlroy Ave, Fayetteville, AR 72701 *Tel:* 479-575-3246 *Toll Free Tel:* 800-626-0090 *Fax:* 479-575-6044 *E-mail:* uapress@uark.edu *Web Site:* www.uapress.com, pg 264

King, Brian B, Appalachian Trail Conservancy, 799 Washington St, Harpers Ferry, WV 25425 *Tel:* 304-535-6331 *Toll Free Tel:* 888-287-8673 (orders only) *Fax:* 304-535-2667 *E-mail:* info@appalachiantrail.org *Web Site:* www.appalachiantrail.org; www.atctrailstore.org, pg 20

King, Carolyn Dineen, American Law Institute, 4025 Chestnut St, Philadelphia, PA 19104-3099 *Tel:* 215-243-1600 *Toll Free Tel:* 800-253-6397 *Fax:* 215-243-1664; 215-243-1683 *Web Site:* www.ali.org, pg 14

King, Darrell, Ellora's Cave, 1056 Home Ave, Akron, OH 44310-3302 *Tel:* 330-253-3521 *E-mail:* service@ellorascave.com; comments@ellorascave.com *Web Site:* www.ellorascave.com, pg 86

King, Kristy, Writers House, 21 W 26 St, New York, NY 10010 *Tel:* 212-685-2400 *Fax:* 212-685-1781 *Web Site:* www.writershouse.com, pg 599

King, London, Random House Publishing Group, 1745 Broadway, New York, NY 10019 *Toll Free Tel:* 800-200-3552 *Web Site:* atrandom.com, pg 214

King, Lucia, Avery, 375 Hudson St, New York, NY 10014 *Tel:* 212-366-2000 *Fax:* 212-366-2643 *E-mail:* online@penguinputnam.com *Web Site:* www.penguinputnam.com; us.penguingroup.com, pg 28

King, Margaret J PhD, Cultural Studies & Analysis, 1123 Montrose St, Philadelphia, PA 19147-3721 *Tel:* 215-592-8544 *Fax:* 215-413-9041 *E-mail:* info@culturalanalysis.com *Web Site:* www.culturalanalysis.com, pg 544

King, Patricia, Berkley Books, 375 Hudson St, New York, NY 10014 *Tel:* 212-366-2000 *Fax:* 212-366-2666 *E-mail:* online@penguinputnam.com *Web Site:* www.penguinputnam.com; us.penguingroup.com, pg 35

King, Patricia, Berkley Publishing Group, 375 Hudson St, New York, NY 10014 *Tel:* 212-366-2000 *Fax:* 212-366-2385 *E-mail:* online@penguinputnam.com *Web Site:* us.penguingroup.com, pg 36

King, Rachel, West Virginia University Press, West Virginia University, PO Box 6295, Morgantown, WV 26506-6295 *Tel:* 304-293-8400 *Toll Free Tel:* 866-WVU-PRES (988-7737) *Fax:* 304-293-6585 *E-mail:* press@wvu.edu *Web Site:* www.wvupress.com, pg 278

King, Stacy, Federal Bar Association, 1220 N Filmore St, Suite 444, Arlington, VA 22201 *Tel:* 571-481-9100 *Fax:* 571-481-9090 *E-mail:* fba@fedbar.org *Web Site:* www.fedbar.org, pg 93

King, Stephen, W W Norton & Company Inc, 500 Fifth Ave, New York, NY 10110-0017 *Tel:* 212-354-5500 *Toll Free Tel:* 800-233-4830 (orders & cust serv) *Fax:* 212-869-0856 *Toll Free Fax:* 800-458-6515 *Web Site:* www.wwnorton.com, pg 181

King, Terry, The Authors Registry Inc, 31 E 32 St, 7th fl, New York, NY 10016 *Tel:* 212-563-6920 *Fax:* 212-564-5363 *E-mail:* staff@authorsregistry.org *Web Site:* www.authorsregistry.org, pg 617

King, Vicki, Psychological Assessment Resources Inc (PAR), 16204 N Florida Ave, Lutz, FL 33549 *Tel:* 813-968-3003; 813-449-4065 *Toll Free Tel:* 800-331-8378 *Fax:* 813-968-2598; 813-961-2196 *Toll Free Fax:* 800-727-9329 *E-mail:* custsup@parinc.com *Web Site:* www4.parinc.com, pg 208

Kingra, Mr Mahinder S, Cornell University Press, Sage House, 512 E State St, Ithaca, NY 14850 *Tel:* 607-277-2338 *Fax:* 607-277-2374 *E-mail:* cupressinfo@cornell.edu; cupress-sales@cornell.edu *Web Site:* www.cornellpress.cornell.edu, pg 67

Kings, Daisy, National Press Club (NPC), 529 14 St NW, 13th fl, Washington, DC 20045 *Tel:* 202-662-7500 *Fax:* 202-662-7569 *E-mail:* infocenter@npcpress.org *Web Site:* www.press.org, pg 630

Kinkaid, Asley McDonald, Phi Delta Kappa International®, 320 W Eighth St, Suite 216, Bloomington, IN 47405 *Tel:* 812-339-1156 *Toll Free Tel:* 800-766-1156 *Fax:* 812-339-0018 *E-mail:* customerservice@pdkintl.org *Web Site:* www.pdkintl.org, pg 200

Kinkel, Jessica, Brown Books Publishing Group, 16250 Knoll Trail, Suite 205, Dallas, TX 75248 *Tel:* 972-381-0009 *Fax:* 972-248-4336 *E-mail:* publishing@brownbooks.com *Web Site:* www.brownbooks.com, pg 49

Kinnear, Victoria, National Information Standards Organization, One N Charles St, Suite 1905, Baltimore, MD 21201 *Tel:* 301-654-2512 *Toll Free Tel:* 866-957-1593 *Fax:* 410-685-5278 *E-mail:* nisohq@niso.org *Web Site:* www.niso.org, pg 175, 630

Kinney, Erika, Brookes Publishing Co Inc, PO Box 10624, Baltimore, MD 21285-0624 *Tel:* 410-337-9580 (outside US & CN) *Toll Free Tel:* 800-638-3775 (US & CN) *Fax:* 410-337-8539 *E-mail:* custserv@brookespublishing.com *Web Site:* www.brookespublishing.com, pg 48

Kinney, Noreen, Cordon d'Or - Gold Ribbon International Annual Cook Book & Culinary Arts Culinary Academy Awards, 7312 Sixth Ave N, St Petersburg, FL 33710 *Tel:* 727-347-2437 *E-mail:* culinaryparadise@aol.com *Web Site:* www.cordondorcuisine.com; www.floridaamericasculinaryparadise.com, pg 698

Kinstler, Jake, Black Warrior Review Fiction, Nonfiction & Poetry Contest, Office of Student Media, University of Alabama, Tuscaloosa, AL 35486-0027 *Tel:* 205-348-4518 *Web Site:* www.bwr.ua.edu, pg 691

Kintigh, Cynthia, ANR Publications University of California, 1301 S 46 St, Bldg 478 - MC 3580, Richmond, CA 94804 *Tel:* 510-665-2195 (cust serv) *Toll Free Tel:* 800-994-8849 *Fax:* 510-665-3427 *E-mail:* anrcatalog@ucdavis.edu *Web Site:* anrcatalog.ucanr.edu, pg 19

Kintz, Dr Bruce G, Concordia Publishing House, 3558 S Jefferson Ave, St Louis, MO 63118-3968 *Tel:* 314-268-1000 *Toll Free Tel:* 800-325-3040 (cust serv) *Toll Free Fax:* 800-490-9889 (cust serv) *E-mail:* order@cph.org *Web Site:* www.cph.org, pg 66

Kiple, Cindy, InterVarsity Press, 430 Plaza Dr, Westmont, IL 60559-1234 *Tel:* 630-734-4000 *Toll Free Tel:* 800-843-9487 *Fax:* 630-734-4200 *E-mail:* email@ivpress.com *Web Site:* www.ivpress.com, pg 134

Kipp, Karin, Integra Software Services Inc, 1110 Jorie Blvd, Suite 200, Oak Brook, IL 60523 *Tel:* 630-586-2579 *Fax:* 630-586-2599 *Web Site:* www.integra.co.in, pg 548

Kiraz, George Anton PhD, Gorgias Press LLC, 954 River Rd, Piscataway, NJ 08854 *Tel:* 732-885-8900 *Fax:* 732-885-8908 *E-mail:* helpdesk@gorgiaspress.com *Web Site:* www.gorgiaspress.com, pg 105

Kleit, Micah, Temple University Press, 1852 N Tenth St, Philadelphia, PA 19122-6099 *Tel:* 215-926-2140 *Toll Free Tel:* 800-621-2736 *Fax:* 215-926-2141 *E-mail:* tempress@temple.edu *Web Site:* www.temple.edu/tempress, pg 251

Klika, Lynn, Ascension Press, PO Box 1990, West Chester, PA 19380 *Tel:* 610-696-7795 *Toll Free Tel:* 800-376-0520 (sales & cust serv) *Fax:* 610-696-7796; 608-565-2025 (sales & cust serv) *E-mail:* info@ascensionpress.com *Web Site:* www.ascensionpress.com, pg 23

Klim, Christopher, Eric Hoffer Award for Independent Books, PO Box 11, Titusville, NJ 08560 *Fax:* 609-964-1718 *E-mail:* info@hofferaward.com *Web Site:* www.hofferaward.com, pg 710

Klim, Christopher, Eric Hoffer Award for Short Prose, PO Box 11, Titusville, NJ 08560 *Fax:* 609-964-1718 *E-mail:* info@hofferaward.com *Web Site:* www.hofferaward.com, pg 710

Kline, Daisy, Scholastic Media, 524 Broadway, 5th fl, New York, NY 10012 *Tel:* 212-389-3900 *Fax:* 212-389-3886, pg 228

Kline, Missy, College & University Professional Association for Human Resources (CUPA-HR), 1811 Commons Point Dr, Knoxville, TN 37932 *Tel:* 865-637-7673 *Toll Free Tel:* 877-CUPA-HR4 (287-2474) *Fax:* 865-637-7674 *E-mail:* communications@cupahr.org *Web Site:* www.cupahr.org, pg 64

Klingborg, Brian, Kumon Publishing North America, 300 Frank Burr Blvd, Suite 6, Teaneck, NJ 07666 *Tel:* 201-836-2105 *Fax:* 201-836-1559 *E-mail:* books@kumon.com *Web Site:* www.kumonbooks.com, pg 142

Klinger, Harvey, Harvey Klinger Inc, 300 W 55 St, Suite 11-V, New York, NY 10019 *Tel:* 212-581-7068 *Fax:* 212-315-3823 *E-mail:* queries@harveyklinger.com *Web Site:* www.harveyklinger.com, pg 580

Klopper, E J, Palm Kids™, 50 Washington St, 12th fl, Norwalk, CT 06854 *Toll Free Tel:* 800-409-2457 *E-mail:* customercare@palmkids.com; sales@palmkids.com *Web Site:* www.palmkids.com, pg 191

Klose, Lisa, The Johns Hopkins University Press, 2715 N Charles St, Baltimore, MD 21218-4363 *Tel:* 410-516-6900; 410-516-6987 (journals outside US & CN) *Toll Free Tel:* 800-537-5487 (book orders & cust serv); 800-548-1784 (journal orders) *Fax:* 410-516-6968; 410-516-3866 (journal orders) *E-mail:* hfscustserv@press.jhu.edu (cust serv); jrnlcirc@press.jhu.edu (journal orders) *Web Site:* www.press.jhu.edu; muse.jhu.edu/about/subscriptions/index.html (Project Muse subns), pg 136

Klose, Tory, Viking, 375 Hudson St, New York, NY 10014 *Tel:* 212-366-2000 *E-mail:* online@penguinputnam.com *Web Site:* www.penguinputnam.com; us.penguingroup.com, pg 275

Kloske, Geoffrey, Riverhead Books (Hardcover), 375 Hudson St, New York, NY 10014 *Tel:* 212-366-2000 *E-mail:* online@penguinputnam.com *Web Site:* www.penguinputnam.com; us.penguingroup.com, pg 219

Kloss, Stephanie, Alfred A Knopf/Everyman's Library, c/o Random House Inc, 1745 Broadway, New York, NY 10019 *Tel:* 212-751-2600 *Toll Free Tel:* 800-638-6460 *Fax:* 212-572-2593 *Web Site:* www.knopfdoubleday.com, pg 141

Klunder, Sean, Bright Connections Media, A World Book Encyclopedia Company, 233 N Michigan Ave, Suite 2000, Chicago, IL 60601 *Tel:* 312-729-5800 *Fax:* 312-729-5610 *Web Site:* www.brightconnectionsmedia.com, pg 47

Kmit, Kate, AZ Books LLC, 245 Eighth Ave, Suite 180, New York, NY 10011 *Toll Free Tel:* 888-945-7723 *Toll Free Fax:* 888-945-7724 *Web Site:* www.azbooksusa.com, pg 28

Knapp, Lindsay, Green Sugar Press, 2200 E Devon Ave, Suite 340, Des Plaines, IL 60018-4503 *Tel:* 773-580-7780; 615-254-2402 (orders); 615-254-2488 (returns) *Fax:* 615-254-2405 (orders); 615-254-2405 (returns) *Toll Free Fax:* 866-270-4100 *E-mail:* order@greensugarpress.com *Web Site:* www.greensugarpress.com, pg 107

Knapp, Stephanie, Crown Publishing Group, c/o Random House Inc, 1745 Broadway, New York, NY 10019 *Tel:* 212-782-9000 *Toll Free Tel:* 888-264-1745 *Fax:* 212-940-7408 *Web Site:* www.randomhouse.com/crown, pg 72

Knauf, Sandra, Greenwoman Publishing LLC, 1823 W Pikes Peak Ave, Colorado Springs, CO 80904-3844 *Tel:* 719-473-9237 *Fax:* 719-473-9237 *Web Site:* www.greenwomanpublishing.com, pg 108

Knauf, Zora, Greenwoman Publishing LLC, 1823 W Pikes Peak Ave, Colorado Springs, CO 80904-3844 *Tel:* 719-473-9237 *Fax:* 719-473-9237 *Web Site:* www.greenwomanpublishing.com, pg 108

Knecht, Ashley, The Mountaineers Books, 1001 SW Klickitat Way, Suite 201, Seattle, WA 98134 *Tel:* 206-223-6303 *Toll Free Tel:* 800-553-4453 *Fax:* 206-223-6306 *Toll Free Fax:* 800-568-7604 *E-mail:* mbooks@mountaineersbooks.org *Web Site:* www.mountaineersbooks.org, pg 170

Kneerim, Jill, Kneerim, Williams & Bloom Agency, 90 Canal St, Boston, MA 02114 *Tel:* 617-303-1650 *Web Site:* www.kwlit.com, pg 580

Knerr, Jennifer, Paradigm Publishers, 5589 Arapahoe Ave, Suite 206A, Boulder, CO 80303 *Tel:* 303-245-9054 *Web Site:* www.paradigmpublishers.com, pg 193

Knezek, Don, International Society for Technology in Education, 180 W Eighth Ave, Suite 300, Eugene, OR 97401-2916 *Tel:* 541-302-3777 (intl) *Toll Free Tel:* 800-336-5191 (US & CN) *Fax:* 541-302-3778 *E-mail:* iste@iste.org *Web Site:* www.iste.org; www.iste.org/bookstore (orders), pg 133

Knight, Barb, Tiger Tales, 5 River Rd, Suite 128, Wilton, CT 06897 *Tel:* 920-387-2333 *Fax:* 920-387-9994 *Web Site:* www.tigertalesbooks.com, pg 255

Knight, Brenda, Cleis Press, 2246 Sixth St, Berkeley, CA 94710 *Tel:* 510-845-8000 *Toll Free Tel:* 800-780-2279 (US) *Fax:* 510-845-8001 *E-mail:* orders@cleispress.com *Web Site:* www.cleispress.com; www.vivaeditions.com, pg 63

Knight, Deidre, The Knight Agency Inc, 570 East Ave, Madison, GA 30650 *E-mail:* submissions@knightagency.net *Web Site:* www.knightagency.net, pg 580

Knight, Denise, Eagle's View Publishing, 6756 North Fork Rd, Liberty, UT 84310 *Tel:* 801-393-4555; 801-745-0905 (edit) *Toll Free Tel:* 800-547-3364 (orders over $100) *Fax:* 801-745-0903 (edit); 801-393-4647 *E-mail:* sales@eaglefeathertrading.com *Web Site:* www.eaglefeathertrading.com, pg 83

Knight, Dominic, Palgrave Macmillan, 175 Fifth Ave, Suite 200, New York, NY 10010 *Tel:* 646-307-5151 *Fax:* 212-777-6359 *E-mail:* firstname.lastname@palgrave-usa.com *Web Site:* us.macmillan.com/Palgrave.aspx, pg 191

Knight, Judson, The Knight Agency Inc, 570 East Ave, Madison, GA 30650 *E-mail:* submissions@knightagency.net *Web Site:* www.knightagency.net, pg 580

Knight, Margot, Djerassi Resident Artists Program, 2325 Bear Gulch Rd, Woodside, CA 94062 *Tel:* 650-747-1250 *Fax:* 650-747-0105 *E-mail:* drap@djerassi.org *Web Site:* www.djerassi.org, pg 668

Knight, Melissa, Kabbalah Publishing, 1100 S Robertson Blvd, Los Angeles, CA 90035 *Tel:* 310-601-1039; 310-657-7957 *E-mail:* kcla@kabbalah.com; customerservice@kabbalahpublishing.com *Web Site:* www.kabbalah.com; www.kabbalahpublishing.com, pg 138

Knight, Sarah, Simon & Schuster, 1230 Avenue of the Americas, New York, NY 10020 *Tel:* 212-698-7000 *Toll Free Tel:* 800-223-2348 (cust serv); 800-223-2336 (orders) *Toll Free Fax:* 800-943-9831 (orders) *Web Site:* www.simonandschuster.com, pg 234

Knill, Ellen, Bellerophon Books, PO Box 21307, Santa Barbara, CA 93121-1307 *Tel:* 805-965-7034 *Toll Free Tel:* 800-253-9943 *Fax:* 805-965-8286 *E-mail:* sales@bellerophonbooks.com *Web Site:* www.bellerophonbooks.com, pg 34

Knobloch, Jamie, Thorndike Press®, 10 Water St, Suite 310, Waterville, ME 04901 *Toll Free Tel:* 800-233-1244 (ext 4, cust serv/orders); 800-877-4253 (cust serv) *Toll Free Fax:* 877-363-4253 (cust serv); 800-558-4676 (orders) *E-mail:* gale.printorders@cengage.com; international@cengage.com (orders for customers outside US & CN) *Web Site:* thorndike.gale.com, pg 255

Knoll, Elizabeth, Harvard University Press, 79 Garden St, Cambridge, MA 02138-1499 *Tel:* 617-495-2600; 401-531-2800 (intl orders) *Toll Free Tel:* 800-405-1619 (orders) *Fax:* 617-495-5898 (general); 617-496-4677 (edit & rts); 401-531-2801 (intl orders) *Toll Free Fax:* 800-406-9145 (orders) *E-mail:* contact_hup@harvard.edu *Web Site:* www.hup.harvard.edu, pg 115

Knopf, Susan, American Book Producers Association (ABPA), 151 W 19 St, 3rd fl, New York, NY 10011 *Tel:* 212-675-1363 *Fax:* 212-675-1364 *E-mail:* office@abpaonline.org *Web Site:* www.abpaonline.org, pg 612

Knopf, Susan, WNBA Pannell Award for Excellence in Children's Bookselling, 435 W 23 St, Suite 8-C, New York, NY 10011 *Tel:* 212-242-6930 *E-mail:* pannellaward@gmail.com *Web Site:* www.wnba-books.org; www.NationalReadingGroupMonth.org; www.wnba-books.org/awards, pg 750

Knotek, George, Copper Canyon Press, Fort Worden State Park, Bldg 33, Port Townsend, WA 98368 *Tel:* 360-385-4925 *Toll Free Tel:* 877-501-1393 *Fax:* 360-385-4985 *E-mail:* poetry@coppercanyonpress.org *Web Site:* www.coppercanyonpress.org, pg 67

Knott, Ronald, Andrews University Press, Sutherland House, 8360 W Campus Circle Dr, Berrien Springs, MI 49104-1700 *Tel:* 269-471-6915; 269-471-6134 (orders) *Toll Free Tel:* 800-467-6369 (Visa, MC & American Express orders only) *Fax:* 269-471-6224 *E-mail:* aupo@andrews.edu *Web Site:* www.universitypress.andrews.edu, pg 18

Knowlton, Ginger, Curtis Brown Ltd, 10 Astor Place, New York, NY 10003 *Tel:* 212-473-5400 *Web Site:* www.curtisbrown.com, pg 565

Knowlton, Timothy F, Curtis Brown Ltd, 10 Astor Place, New York, NY 10003 *Tel:* 212-473-5400 *Web Site:* www.curtisbrown.com, pg 565

Knox, Doug, Tyndale House Publishers Inc, 351 Executive Dr, Carol Stream, IL 60188 *Tel:* 630-668-8300 *Toll Free Tel:* 800-323-9400 *Web Site:* www.tyndale.com, pg 261

Kobasa, Paul, Bright Connections Media, A World Book Encyclopedia Company, 233 N Michigan Ave, Suite 2000, Chicago, IL 60601 *Tel:* 312-729-5800 *Fax:* 312-729-5610 *Web Site:* www.brightconnectionsmedia.com, pg 47

Kobasa, Paul A, World Book Inc, 233 N Michigan, Suite 2000, Chicago, IL 60601 *Tel:* 312-729-5800 *Toll Free Tel:* 800-967-5325 (consumer sales, US); 800-463-8845 (consumer sales, CN); 800-975-3250 (school & lib sales, US); 800-837-5365 (school & lib sales, CN); 866-866-5200 (web sales) *Fax:* 312-729-5600; 312-729-5606 *Toll Free Fax:* 800-433-9330 (school & lib sales, US); 888-690-4002 (school lib sales, CN) *Web Site:* www.worldbook.com, pg 285

Koberstein, Teresa, National Coalition Against Censorship (NCAC), 19 Fulton St, Suite 407, New York, NY 10038 *Tel:* 212-807-6222 *Fax:* 212-807-6245 *E-mail:* ncac@ncac.org *Web Site:* www.ncac.org, pg 629

Koch, Laura, Penguin Group (USA) LLC Sales, 375 Hudson St, New York, NY 10014 *Tel:* 212-366-2000 *E-mail:* online@penguinputnam.com *Web Site:* us.penguingroup.com, pg 197

Koch, Pat, McGraw-Hill Create, 501 Bell St, Dubuque, IA 52001 *Tel:* 563-584-6000 *Fax:* 563-584-6600 *E-mail:* first_last@mcgraw-hill.com *Web Site:* www.mhhe.com, pg 160

Kochan, Susan, GP Putnam's Sons (Children's), 345 Hudson St, New York, NY 10014 *Tel:* 212-366-2000 *Fax:* 212-414-3393 *E-mail:* online@penguinputnam.com *Web Site:* us.penguingroup.com, pg 210

Kodak, Don, National Park Service Media Services, 67 Mather Place, Harpers Ferry, WV 25425 *Tel:* 304-535-5050 *Fax:* 304-535-6176 *Web Site:* www.nps.gov/hfc, pg 175

Kodat, Catherine, Hamilton College, English/Creative Writing, English/Creative Writing Dept, 198 College Hill Rd, Clinton, NY 13323 *Tel:* 315-859-4370 *Fax:* 315-859-4390 *E-mail:* english@hamilton.edu *Web Site:* www.hamilton.edu, pg 678

Koduvalil, Bobby, Hendrickson Publishers Inc, PO Box 3473, Peabody, MA 01961-3473 *Tel:* 978-532-6546 *Toll Free Tel:* 800-358-3111 *Fax:* 978-573-8111 *E-mail:* orders@hendrickson.com *Web Site:* www.hendrickson.com, pg 118

Koecher, Molly, CarTech Inc, 39966 Grand Ave, North Branch, MN 55056 *Tel:* 651-277-1200 *Toll Free Tel:* 800-551-4754 *Fax:* 651-277-1203 *E-mail:* info@cartechbooks.com *Web Site:* www.cartechbooks.com, pg 53

Koehler, H Dirk, World Bank Publications, Office of the Publisher, 1818 "H" St NW, U-11-1104, Washington, DC 20433 *Tel:* 202-458-4497 *Toll Free Tel:* 800-645-7247 (cust serv) *Fax:* 202-522-2631; 202-614-1237 *E-mail:* books@worldbank.org; pubrights@worldbank.org (foreign rts) *Web Site:* www.worldbank.org/publications; publications.worldbank.org, pg 285

Koenig, Stephen, Interweave Press LLC, 201 E Fourth St, Loveland, CO 80537 *Tel:* 970-669-7672 *Toll Free Tel:* 800-272-2193 *Fax:* 970-667-8317 *E-mail:* interweaveservice@interweave.com *Web Site:* www.interweave.com, pg 134

Koenig, Wade, Moody Publishers, 820 N La Salle Blvd, Chicago, IL 60610 *Tel:* 312-329-4000 *Toll Free Tel:* 800-678-8812 (cust serv) *Fax:* 312-329-2019 *Web Site:* www.moodypublishers.com, pg 169

Koeppel, Mary Sue, E M Koeppel Short Fiction Award, PO Box 140310, Gainesville, FL 32614 *Tel:* 352-338-7778 *E-mail:* contact@writecorner.com *Web Site:* www.writecorner.com, pg 715

Koerner, Darrell, Chelsea Green Publishing Co, 85 N Main St, Suite 120, White River Junction, VT 05001 *Tel:* 802-295-6300 *Toll Free Tel:* 800-639-4099 (cust serv, consumer & trade orders) *Fax:* 802-295-6444 *Web Site:* www.chelseagreen.com, pg 59

Koester, Robert J, dbS Productions, PO Box 94, Charlottesville, VA 22902 *Tel:* 434-293-5502 *Toll Free Tel:* 800-745-1581 *Fax:* 434-293-5502 *E-mail:* info@dbs-sar.com *Web Site:* www.dbs-sar.com, pg 76

Koetje, David, Christian Schools International, 3350 E Paris Ave SE, Grand Rapids, MI 49512-3054 *Tel:* 616-957-1070 *Toll Free Tel:* 800-635-8288 *Fax:* 616-957-5022 *E-mail:* info@csionline.org *Web Site:* www.csionline.org, pg 61

Koffler, Lionel, Firefly Books Ltd, 50 Staples Ave, Unit 1, Richmond Hill, ON L4B 0A7, Canada *Tel:* 416-499-8412 *Toll Free Tel:* 800-387-6192 (CN); 800-387-5085 (US) *Fax:* 416-499-8313 *Toll Free Fax:* 800-450-0391 (CN); 800-565-6034 (US) *E-mail:* service@fireflybooks.com *Web Site:* www.fireflybooks.com, pg 505

Kogan, Helen, Kogan Page Publishers, 1518 Walnut St, Suite 1100, Philadelphia, PA 19102 *Tel:* 215-928-9112 *Fax:* 215-928-9113 *E-mail:* info@koganpage.com *Web Site:* www.koganpageusa.com, pg 141

Koh, Becky, Black Dog & Leventhal Publishers Inc, 151 W 19 St, New York, NY 10011 *Tel:* 212-647-9336 *Toll Free Tel:* 800-722-7202 *Fax:* 212-647-9332 *E-mail:* info@blackdogandleventhal.com; orders@workman.com *Web Site:* www.blackdogandleventhal.com; blackdogonline.com, pg 39

Koheil, Ruth, The Mellen Poetry Press, 240 Portage Rd, Lewiston, NY 14092 *Tel:* 716-754-2266; 716-754-1400 (mktg); 716-754-2788 (order fulfillment) *Fax:* 716-754-4056; 716-754-1860 (fulfillment) *E-mail:* cservice@mellenpress.com *Web Site:* www.mellenpress.com, pg 164

Kohler, Frank, Academy of Television Arts & Sciences (ATAS), 5220 Lankershim Blvd, North Hollywood, CA 91601-3109 *Tel:* 818-754-2800 *Fax:* 818-761-2827 *Web Site:* www.emmys.tv, pg 611

Kohlmeier, Rob, Wilfrid Laurier University Press, 75 University Ave W, Waterloo, ON N2L 3C5, Canada *Tel:* 519-884-0710 (ext 6124) *Toll Free Tel:* 866-836-5551 *Fax:* 519-725-1399 *E-mail:* press@wlu.ca *Web Site:* www.wlupress.wlu.ca, pg 525

Kohn, Chris, Macmillan, 175 Fifth Ave, New York, NY 10010 *Tel:* 646-307-5151 *Fax:* 212-420-9314 *E-mail:* firstname.lastname@macmillan.com *Web Site:* www.macmillan.com, pg 154

Kok, John H, Dordt College Press, 498 Fourth Ave NE, Sioux Center, IA 51250-1606 *Tel:* 712-722-6420 *Toll Free Tel:* 800-343-6738 *Fax:* 712-722-1198 *E-mail:* dordtpress@dordt.edu; bookstore@dordt.edu *Web Site:* www.dordt.edu, pg 80

Koke, Elizabeth, The Feminist Press at The City University of New York, 365 Fifth Ave, Suite 5406, New York, NY 10016 *Tel:* 212-817-7915 *Fax:* 212-817-1593 *E-mail:* info@feministpress.org *Web Site:* www.feministpress.org, pg 94

Kolady, Nancy, H W Wilson, 10 Estes St, Ipswich, MA 01938 *Tel:* 978-356-6500 *Toll Free Tel:* 800-653-2726 (US & CN) *Fax:* 978-356-6565 *E-mail:* information@ebscohost.com *Web Site:* www.ebscohost.com, pg 282

Kolatch, Alfred J, Jonathan David Publishers Inc, 68-22 Eliot Ave, Middle Village, NY 11379 *Tel:* 718-456-8611 *Fax:* 718-894-2818 *E-mail:* info@jdbooks.com; customerservice@jdbooks.com *Web Site:* www.jdbooks.com, pg 136

Kolatch, David, Jonathan David Publishers Inc, 68-22 Eliot Ave, Middle Village, NY 11379 *Tel:* 718-456-8611 *Fax:* 718-894-2818 *E-mail:* info@jdbooks.com; customerservice@jdbooks.com *Web Site:* www.jdbooks.com, pg 136

Kolatch, Thelma R, Jonathan David Publishers Inc, 68-22 Eliot Ave, Middle Village, NY 11379 *Tel:* 718-456-8611 *Fax:* 718-894-2818 *E-mail:* info@jdbooks.com; customerservice@jdbooks.com *Web Site:* www.jdbooks.com, pg 136

Kolb, Patricia A, M E Sharpe Inc, 80 Business Park Dr, Suite 202, Armonk, NY 10504 *Tel:* 914-273-1800 *Toll Free Tel:* 800-541-6563 *Fax:* 914-273-2106 *E-mail:* info@mesharpe.com *Web Site:* www.mesharpe.com, pg 232

Kolbe, Kimberly, The Green Rose Prize in Poetry, Western Michigan University, 1903 W Michigan Ave, Kalamazoo, MI 49008-5463 *Tel:* 269-387-8185 *Fax:* 269-387-2562 *E-mail:* new-issues@wmich.edu *Web Site:* www.wmich.edu/newissues/greenroseprize.html, pg 708

Kolbe, Kimberly, New Issues Poetry & Prose, Western Michigan University, 1903 W Michigan Ave, Kalamazoo, MI 49008-5463 *Tel:* 269-387-8185 *Fax:* 269-387-2562 *E-mail:* new-issues@wmich.edu *Web Site:* www.wmich.edu/newissues, pg 178

Kolbe, Kimberly, New Issues Poetry Prize, Western Michigan University, 1903 W Michigan Ave, Kalamazoo, MI 49008-5463 *Tel:* 269-387-8185 *Fax:* 269-387-2562 *E-mail:* new-issues@wmich.edu *Web Site:* www.wmich.edu/newissues, pg 728

Kolby, Jeff, Nova Press, 9058 Lloyd Place, West Hollywood, CA 90069 *Tel:* 310-275-3513 *Toll Free Tel:* 800-949-6175 *Fax:* 310-281-5629 *E-mail:* novapress@aol.com *Web Site:* www.novapress.net, pg 182

Kole, Mary, Movable Type Management, 610 Fifth Ave, Suite 1220, New York, NY 10185 *Tel:* 917-289-1089 *Fax:* 646-810-5757 *Web Site:* www.mtmgmt.net, pg 586

Kolen, Kerri, GP Putnam's Sons (Hardcover), 375 Hudson St, New York, NY 10014 *Tel:* 212-366-2000 *E-mail:* online@penguinputnam.com *Web Site:* us.penguingroup.com, pg 210

Kolendo, Kate, PROSE Awards, 71 Fifth Ave, 2nd fl, New York, NY 10003-3004 *Tel:* 212-255-0200 *Fax:* 212-255-7007 *Web Site:* www.proseawards.com; www.publishers.org, pg 736

Kolkman, Tammy, Covenant Communications Inc, 920 E State Rd, Suite F, American Fork, UT 84003-0416 *Tel:* 801-756-9966 *Toll Free Tel:* 800-662-9545 *Fax:* 801-756-1049 *E-mail:* info@covenant-lds.com *Web Site:* www.covenant-lds.com, pg 70

Komie, Michelle, Yale University Press, 302 Temple St, New Haven, CT 06511-8909 *Tel:* 401-531-2800 (cust serv); 203-432-0960 *Toll Free Tel:* 800-405-1619 (cust serv) *Fax:* 203-432-0948; 401-531-2801 (cust serv) *Toll Free Fax:* 800-406-9145 (cust serv) *E-mail:* customer.care@trilateral.org (cust serv); language.yalepress@yale.edu *Web Site:* www.yalebooks.com, pg 287

Kondras, Holly, Wish Publishing, PO Box 10337, Terre Haute, IN 47801-0337 *Web Site:* www.wishpublishing.com, pg 284

Kondrick, Maureen, Marquette University Press, 1415 W Wisconsin Ave, Milwaukee, WI 53233 *Tel:* 414-288-1564 *Toll Free Tel:* 800-247-6553 (cust serv) *Fax:* 414-288-7813 *Web Site:* www.marquette.edu/mupress, pg 157

Konecke, Kaitlin, Health Professions Press, 409 Washington Ave, Suite 500, Towson, MD 21204 *Tel:* 410-337-9585 *Toll Free Tel:* 888-337-8808 *Fax:* 410-337-8539 *E-mail:* custserv@healthpropress.com *Web Site:* www.healthpropress.com, pg 117

Konecky, Edith, Hamilton Stone Editions, PO Box 43, Maplewood, NJ 07040 *Tel:* 973-378-8361 *E-mail:* hstone@hamiltonstone.org *Web Site:* www.hamiltonstone.org, pg 111

Konecky, Sean, Konecky & Konecky LLC, 72 Ayers Point Rd, Old Saybrook, CT 06475 *Tel:* 860-388-0878 *Fax:* 860-388-0273 *Web Site:* www.koneckyandkonecky.com, pg 142

Kong, Molly, Disney Press, 44 S Broadway, White Plains, NY 10601 *Tel:* 212-633-4400 *Fax:* 212-807-5432 *Web Site:* disney.go.com/index; disney.go.com/books/index, pg 79

Konner, Linda, Linda Konner Literary Agency, 10 W 15 St, Suite 1918, New York, NY 10011 *Tel:* 212-691-3419 *Fax:* 212-691-0935 *Web Site:* www.lindakonnerliteraryagency.com, pg 580

Konopka, Lauren, Association of School Business Officials International, 11401 N Shore Dr, Reston, VA 20190-4200 *Tel:* 703-478-0405 *Toll Free Tel:* 866-682-2729 *Fax:* 703-478-0205 *E-mail:* asboreq@asbointl.org; asbosba@asbointl.org *Web Site:* www.asbointl.org, pg 25

Konowitch, Paul, Sundance/Newbridge Publishing, 33 Boston Post Rd W, Suite 440, Marlborough, MA 01752 *Toll Free Tel:* 888-200-2720; 800-343-8204 (Sundance cust serv & orders); 800-867-0307 (Newbridge cust serv & orders) *Toll Free Fax:* 800-456-2419 (orders) *E-mail:* info@sundancepub.com; info@newbridgeonline.com *Web Site:* www.sundancepub.com; www.newbridgeonline.com, pg 247

Koohi-Kamali, Farideh, Palgrave Macmillan, 175 Fifth Ave, Suite 200, New York, NY 10010 *Tel:* 646-307-5151 *Fax:* 212-777-6359 *E-mail:* firstname.lastname@palgrave-usa.com *Web Site:* us.macmillan.com/Palgrave.aspx, pg 191

Kooij, Nina, Pelican Publishing Co, 1000 Burmaster St, Gretna, LA 70053-2246 *Tel:* 504-368-1175 *Toll Free Tel:* 800-843-1724 *Fax:* 504-368-1195 *E-mail:* sales@pelicanpub.com (sales); office@pelicanpub.com (permission); promo@pelicanpub.com (publicity) *Web Site:* www.pelicanpub.com, pg 196

Koors, Patrick, Thomas Nelson Inc, 501 Nelson Place, Nashville, TN 37214 *Tel:* 615-889-9000 *Toll Free Tel:* 800-251-4000 *Fax:* 615-902-1548 *E-mail:* publicity@thomasnelson.com *Web Site:* www.thomasnelson.com, pg 255

Kopb, Charles, The French-American Foundation & Florence Gould Foundation Annual Translation Prize, 28 W 44 St, Suite 1420, New York, NY 10036 *Tel:* 212-829-8800 *Fax:* 212-829-8810 *E-mail:* translation@frenchamerican.org *Web Site:* www.frenchamerican.org, pg 706

Kopelman, Charles, Abrams Artists Agency, 275 Seventh Ave, 26th fl, New York, NY 10001 *Tel:* 646-486-4600 *Fax:* 646-486-2358 *E-mail:* literary@abramsartny.com *Web Site:* www.abramsartists.com, pg 559

Kopf, Dorothy, Harlan Davidson Inc/Forum Press Inc, 773 Glenn Ave, Wheeling, IL 60090-6900 *Tel:* 847-541-9720 *Fax:* 847-541-9830 *E-mail:* harlandavidson@harlandavidson.com *Web Site:* www.harlandavidson.com, pg 112

Koppenhaver, Leslie, Graywolf Press, 250 Third Ave N, Suite 600, Minneapolis, MN 55401 *Tel:* 651-641-0077 *Fax:* 651-641-0036 *E-mail:* wolves@graywolfpress.org *Web Site:* www.graywolfpress.org, pg 106

Kopper, Philip, Posterity Press Inc, 4948 Saint Elmo Ave, 3rd fl, Bethesda, MD 20814 *Tel:* 301-652-2384 *Fax:* 301-652-2543 *Web Site:* www.posteritypress.com, pg 204

Kopprasch, Christine, Crown Publishing Group, c/o Random House Inc, 1745 Broadway, New York, NY 10019 *Tel:* 212-782-9000 *Toll Free Tel:* 888-264-1745 *Fax:* 212-940-7408 *Web Site:* www.randomhouse.com/crown, pg 72

Korleski, Allison, Interweave Press LLC, 201 E Fourth St, Loveland, CO 80537 *Tel:* 970-669-7672 *Toll Free Tel:* 800-272-2193 *Fax:* 970-667-8317 *E-mail:* interweaveservice@interweave.com *Web Site:* www.interweave.com, pg 134

Korlishin, Victoria, DK, 375 Hudson St, 2nd fl, New York, NY 10014-3672 *Tel:* 212-213-4800 *Toll Free Tel:* 877-342-5357 (cust serv) *Fax:* 212-213-5202 *Web Site:* us.dk.com, pg 80

Korman, Keith, Raines & Raines, 103 Kenyon Rd, Medusa, NY 12120 *Tel:* 518-239-8311 *Fax:* 518-239-6029, pg 590

Korman, Tom, DK, 375 Hudson St, 2nd fl, New York, NY 10014-3672 *Tel:* 212-213-4800 *Toll Free Tel:* 877-342-5357 (cust serv) *Fax:* 212-213-5202 *Web Site:* us.dk.com, pg 80

Korn, Adam, HarperCollins General Books Group, 10 E 53 St, New York, NY 10022 *Tel:* 212-207-7000 *Fax:* 212-207-7633 *Web Site:* www.harpercollins.com, pg 113

Kornelsen, Renita, Kindred Productions, 1310 Taylor Ave, Winnipeg, MB R3M 3Z6, Canada *Tel:* 204-669-6575 *Toll Free Tel:* 800-545-7322 *Fax:* 204-654-1865 *E-mail:* custserv@kindredproductions.com *Web Site:* www.kindredproductions.com, pg 510

Korte, Steven, EPS/School Specialty Literacy & Intervention, 625 Mount Auburn St, 3rd fl, Cambridge, MA 02138-4555 *Tel:* 617-547-6706 *Toll Free Tel:* 800-225-5750 *Fax:* 617-547-0412 *Toll Free Fax:* 888-440-2665 *E-mail:* customerservice.eps@schoolspecialty.com *Web Site:* eps.schoolspecialty.com, pg 89

Kortekamp, Jeanne, Franciscan Media, 28 W Liberty St, Cincinnati, OH 45202 *Tel:* 513-241-5615 *Toll Free Tel:* 800-488-0488 *Fax:* 513-241-0399 *E-mail:* books@americancatholic.org *Web Site:* www.americancatholic.org, pg 98

Korth, Bob, Standard Publishing, 8805 Governors Hill Dr, Suite 400, Cincinnati, OH 45249 *Tel:* 513-931-4050 *Toll Free Tel:* 800-543-1353 *Fax:* 513-931-0950 *Toll Free Fax:* 877-867-5751 *E-mail:* customerservice@standardpub.com *Web Site:* www.standardpub.com, pg 242

Kosiewska, Anthony, Scholastic Media, 524 Broadway, 5th fl, New York, NY 10012 *Tel:* 212-389-3900 *Fax:* 212-389-3886, pg 228

Kosman, Phoebe, Harvard University Press, 79 Garden St, Cambridge, MA 02138-1499 *Tel:* 617-495-2600; 401-531-2800 (intl orders) *Toll Free Tel:* 800-405-1619 (orders) *Fax:* 617-495-5898 (general); 617-496-4677 (edit & rts); 401-531-2801 (intl orders) *Toll Free Fax:* 800-406-9145 (orders) *E-mail:* contact_hup@harvard.edu *Web Site:* www.hup.harvard.edu, pg 115

Kosmicki, Greg, The Backwaters Press, 3502 N 52 St, Omaha, NE 68104-3506 *Tel:* 402-451-4052 *E-mail:* thebackwaterspress@gmail.com *Web Site:* www.thebackwaterspress.org, pg 29

Kosmoski, Anne, Avery, 375 Hudson St, New York, NY 10014 *Tel:* 212-366-2000 *Fax:* 212-366-2643 *E-mail:* online@penguinputnam.com *Web Site:* www.penguinputnam.com; us.penguingroup.com, pg 28

Kosowski, Mary Beth, Mercer University Press, 368 Orange St, Macon, GA 31201 *Tel:* 478-301-2880 *Toll Free Tel:* 866-895-1472 *Fax:* 478-301-2585 *E-mail:* mupressorders@mercer.edu *Web Site:* www.mupress.org, pg 164

Kostka, Leslie, Klutz, 450 Lambert Ave, Palo Alto, CA 94306 *Tel:* 650-857-0888 *Toll Free Tel:* 800-737-4123 *Fax:* 650-857-9110 *E-mail:* thefolks@klutz.com *Web Site:* www.klutz.com, pg 140

Kostman, Lynne, UCLA Fowler Museum of Cultural History, 308 Charles E Young Dr N, Los Angeles, CA 90095 *Tel:* 310-825-4361 *Fax:* 310-206-7007 *Web Site:* www.fmch.ucla.edu, pg 261

Kosztolnyik, Karen, Gallery Books, 1230 Avenue of the Americas, New York, NY 10020 *Toll Free Tel:* 800-456-6798 *Fax:* 212-698-7284 *E-mail:* consumer.customerservice@simonandschuster.com *Web Site:* www.simonsays.com, pg 101

Kot, Rick, Viking, 375 Hudson St, New York, NY 10014 *Tel:* 212-366-2000 *E-mail:* online@penguinputnam.com *Web Site:* www.penguinputnam.com; us.penguingroup.com, pg 275

Kotchman, Katie, Don Congdon Associates Inc, 110 William St, Suite 2202, New York, NY 10038-3914 *Tel:* 212-645-1229 *Fax:* 212-727-2688 *E-mail:* dca@doncongdon.com *Web Site:* www.doncongdon.com, pg 567

Kottke, Erin, Graywolf Press, 250 Third Ave N, Suite 600, Minneapolis, MN 55401 *Tel:* 651-641-0077 *Fax:* 651-641-0036 *E-mail:* wolves@graywolfpress.org *Web Site:* www.graywolfpress.org, pg 106

Kouma, Cecelia, Playwrights Project, 3675 Ruffin Rd, Suite 330, San Diego, CA 92123 *Tel:* 858-384-2970 *Fax:* 858-384-2974 *E-mail:* write@playwrightsproject.org *Web Site:* www.playwrightsproject.org, pg 734

Kouts, Barbara S, Barbara S Kouts Literary Agency LLC, PO Box 560, Bellport, NY 11713 *Tel:* 631-286-1278 *Fax:* 631-286-1538 *E-mail:* bkouts@aol.com, pg 580

Kovach, Ronnie, Marketscope Group Books LLC, PO Box 3118, Huntington Beach, CA 92605-3118 *Tel:* 562-343-5414 *Fax:* 562-343-5417 *E-mail:* info@marketscopegroup.com; fxtv@msn.com, pg 157

Kovacs, Kathryn, Association Media & Publishing, 12100 Sunset Hills Rd, Suite 130, Reston, VA 20190 *Tel:* 703-234-4063 *Fax:* 703-435-4390 *E-mail:* info@associationmediaandpublishing.org *Web Site:* www.associationmediaandpublishing.org, pg 615

Kowalchuk, Tavia, HarperCollins General Books Group, 10 E 53 St, New York, NY 10022 *Tel:* 212-207-7000 *Fax:* 212-207-7633 *Web Site:* www.harpercollins.com, pg 113

Kowalewski, Christina, Hackett Publishing Co Inc, 3333 Massachusetts Ave, Indianapolis, IN 46218 *Tel:* 317-635-9250 (orders & cust serv) *Fax:* 317-635-9292 *Toll Free Fax:* 800-783-9213 *E-mail:* customer@hackettpublishing.com *Web Site:* www.hackettpublishing.com, pg 110

Kowaluk, Lucia, Black Rose Books Ltd, CP 35788 Succ Leo Pariseau, Montreal, QC H2X 0A4, Canada *Tel:* 514-844-4076 *Toll Free Tel:* 800-565-9523 (orders) *Toll Free Fax:* 800-221-9985 (orders) *E-mail:* info@blackrosebooks.net *Web Site:* www.blackrosebooks.net, pg 494

Kozlowski, Darrell, DWJ BOOKS LLC, 22 Division St, 2nd fl, Sag Harbor, NY 11963 *Tel:* 631-899-4500 *Fax:* 631-899-4499 *E-mail:* info@dwjbooks.com *Web Site:* www.dwjbooks.com, pg 545

Kozlowski, Paul, Other Press LLC, 2 Park Ave, 24th fl, New York, NY 10016 *Tel:* 212-414-0054 *Toll Free Tel:* 877-843-6843 *Fax:* 212-414-0939 *E-mail:* editor@otherpress.com; rights@otherpress.com *Web Site:* www.otherpress.com, pg 188

Krach, Elizabeth, Kimberley Cameron & Associates, 1550 Tiburon Blvd, Suite 704, Tiburon, CA 94920 *Tel:* 415-789-9191 *Fax:* 415-789-9177 *E-mail:* info@kimberleycameron.com *Web Site:* www.kimberleycameron.com, pg 579

Kracht, Peter, University of Pittsburgh Press, Eureka Bldg, 5th fl, 3400 Forbes Ave, Pittsburgh, PA 15260 *Tel:* 412-383-2456 *Fax:* 412-383-2466 *E-mail:* info@upress.pitt.edu *Web Site:* www.upress.pitt.edu, pg 268

Kraft, Eric, Kraft & Kraft, 40 Memorial Hwy, Apt 23-C, New Rochelle, NY 10801 *Tel:* 914-319-3320 *Web Site:* www.erickraft.com, pg 549

Kraft, Madeline, Kraft & Kraft, 40 Memorial Hwy, Apt 23-C, New Rochelle, NY 10801 *Tel:* 914-319-3320 *Web Site:* www.erickraft.com, pg 549

Kral, Steve, Society for Mining, Metallurgy & Exploration, 12999 E Adam Aircraft Circle, Englewood, CO 80112 *Tel:* 303-948-4200 *Toll Free Tel:* 800-763-3132 *Fax:* 303-973-3845 *E-mail:* cs@smenet.org *Web Site:* www.smenet.org, pg 238

Kramer, Gary, Temple University Press, 1852 N Tenth St, Philadelphia, PA 19122-6099 *Tel:* 215-926-2140 *Toll Free Tel:* 800-621-2736 *Fax:* 215-926-2141 *E-mail:* tempress@temple.edu *Web Site:* www.temple.edu/tempress, pg 251

Kramer, Jill, Waterside Productions Inc, 2055 Oxford Ave, Cardiff, CA 92007 *Tel:* 760-632-9190 *Fax:* 760-632-9295 *E-mail:* admin@waterside.com *Web Site:* www.waterside.com, pg 598

Kramer, Linda, H J Kramer Inc, PO Box 1082, Tiburon, CA 94920 *Tel:* 415-884-2100 (ext 10) *Toll Free Tel:* 800-972-6657 *Fax:* 415-435-5364 *E-mail:* hjkramer@jps.net *Web Site:* www.hjkramer.com; www.newworldlibrary.com, pg 142

Kramer, Sidney B, Mews Books Ltd, 20 Bluewater Hill, Westport, CT 06880 *Tel:* 203-227-1836 *Fax:* 203-227-1144 *E-mail:* mewsbooks@aol.com, pg 585

Kramer, Sydelle, Susan Rabiner Literary Agency Inc, 315 W 39 St, Suite 1501, New York, NY 10018-3907 *Web Site:* RabinerLit.com, pg 589

Krank, Charlie, Chaosium Inc, 22568 Mission Blvd, Suite 423, Hayward, CA 94541-5116 *Tel:* 510-583-1000 *Fax:* 510-583-1101 *Web Site:* www.chaosium.com, pg 58

Krannich, Ronald PhD, Impact Publications/Development Concepts Inc, 9104 Manassas Dr, Suite N, Manassas Park, VA 20111-5211 *Tel:* 703-361-7300 *Toll Free Tel:* 800-361-1055 (cust serv) *Fax:* 703-335-9486 *E-mail:* query@impactpublications.com *Web Site:* www.impactpublications.com; www.ishoparoundtheworld.com; www.veteransworld.com; www.middleeasttravellover.com, pg 128

Kranz, Deb, Plexus Publishing, Inc, 143 Old Marlton Pike, Medford, NJ 08055 *Tel:* 609-654-6500 *Fax:* 609-654-4309 *E-mail:* info@plexuspublishing.com *Web Site:* www.plexuspublishing.com, pg 203

Krattenmaker, Kathleen, Philadelphia Museum of Art, 2525 Pennsylvania Ave, Philadelphia, PA 19130 *Tel:* 215-684-7250 *Fax:* 215-235-8715 *Web Site:* www.philamuseum.org, pg 200

Kraus, Jim, Tyndale House Publishers Inc, 351 Executive Dr, Carol Stream, IL 60188 *Tel:* 630-668-8300 *Toll Free Tel:* 800-323-9400 *Web Site:* www.tyndale.com, pg 261

Kraus, Maribeth T, Modern Language Association of America (MLA), 26 Broadway, 3rd fl, New York, NY 10004-1789 *Tel:* 646-576-5000 *Fax:* 646-458-0030 *E-mail:* info@mla.org *Web Site:* www.mla.org, pg 168

Kraus, Maribeth T, Modern Language Association of America (MLA), 26 Broadway, 3rd fl, New York, NY 10004-1789 *Tel:* 646-576-5000 *Fax:* 646-458-0030 *E-mail:* convention@mla.org *Web Site:* www.mla.org, pg 628

Kraus, Marisa Smith, Smith & Kraus Publishers Inc, 40 Walch Dr, Portland, ME 04103 *Tel:* 207-523-2585 *Toll Free Tel:* 877-668-8680 *Fax:* 207-699-3698 *E-mail:* editor@smithandkraus.com *Web Site:* www.smithandkraus.com, pg 237

Krause, Bill, Llewellyn Publications, 2143 Wooddale Dr, Woodbury, MN 55125 *Tel:* 651-291-1970 *Toll Free Tel:* 800-843-6666 *Fax:* 651-291-1908 *E-mail:* publicity@llewellyn.com *Web Site:* www.llewellyn.com, pg 151

Krause, Chester L, Krause Publications Inc, 700 E State St, Iola, WI 54990 *Tel:* 715-445-2214 *Toll Free Tel:* 800-258-0929 (cust serv); 888-457-2873 (orders) *Fax:* 715-445-4087 *E-mail:* bookorders@krause.com *Web Site:* www.krausebooks.com, pg 142

Krause, Katrina, Houghton Mifflin Harcourt Trade & Reference Division, 222 Berkeley St, Boston, MA 02116-3764 *Tel:* 617-351-5000 *Toll Free Tel:* 800-225-3362 *Web Site:* www.houghtonmifflinbooks.com, pg 124

Krauss, Pam, Clarkson Potter Publishers, c/o Random House Inc, 1745 Broadway, New York, NY 10019 *Tel:* 212-782-9000 *Toll Free Tel:* 888-264-1745 *Fax:* 212-572-6181 *Web Site:* www.clarksonpotter.com; www.randomhouse.com/crown/clarksonpotter, pg 62

Kraut, Diane, DK Research Inc, 14 Mohegan Lane, Commack, NY 11725 *Tel:* 631-543-5537 *Fax:* 631-543-5549, pg 544

Kravenas, Mary, Chicago Review Press, 814 N Franklin St, Chicago, IL 60610 *Tel:* 312-337-0747 *Toll Free Tel:* 800-888-4741 *Fax:* 312-337-5110 *E-mail:* frontdesk@chicagoreviewpress.com *Web Site:* www.chicagoreviewpress.com, pg 60

Kravitz, Jamie, Aspen Writers' Foundation, 110 E Hallam St, Suite 116, Aspen, CO 81611 *Tel:* 970-925-3122 *Fax:* 970-920-5700 *E-mail:* info@aspenwriters.org *Web Site:* www.aspenwriters.org, pg 615

Krebs, Gary, Brilliance Audio, 1704 Eaton Dr, Grand Haven, MI 49417 *Tel:* 616-846-5256 *Toll Free Tel:* 800-648-2312 (orders only) *Fax:* 616-846-0630 *E-mail:* customerservice@brillianceaudio.com *Web Site:* www.brillianceaudio.com, pg 48

Krefman, Adam, McSweeney's Publishing, 849 Valencia St, San Francisco, CA 94110 *Tel:* 415-642-5609 (cust serv) *Web Site:* www.mcsweeneys.net, pg 162

Kregel, James R, Editorial Portavoz, 733 Wealthy St SE, Grand Rapids, MI 49503-5553 *Toll Free Tel:* 877-733-2607 (ext 206) *Fax:* 616-493-1790 *E-mail:* portavoz@portavoz.com *Web Site:* www.portavoz.com, pg 85

Kregel, James R, Kregel Publications, 733 Wealthy St SE, Grand Rapids, MI 49503-5553 *Tel:* 616-451-4775 *Toll Free Tel:* 800-733-2607 *Fax:* 616-451-9330 *E-mail:* kregelbooks@kregel.com *Web Site:* www.kregel.com, pg 142

Kregel, Jerold W, Kregel Publications, 733 Wealthy St SE, Grand Rapids, MI 49503-5553 *Tel:* 616-451-4775 *Toll Free Tel:* 800-733-2607 *Fax:* 616-451-9330 *E-mail:* kregelbooks@kregel.com *Web Site:* www.kregel.com, pg 142

Krehbiel, Kenneth, National Council of Teachers of Mathematics (NCTM), 1906 Association Dr, Reston, VA 20191-1502 *Tel:* 703-620-9840 *Toll Free Tel:* 800-235-7566 *Fax:* 703-476-2970 *E-mail:* nctm@nctm.org *Web Site:* www.nctm.org, pg 174

Kreit, Eileen, Puffin Books, 345 Hudson St, New York, NY 10014 *Tel:* 212-366-2000 *E-mail:* online@penguinputnam.com *Web Site:* www.penguinputnam.com; us.penguingroup.com, pg 209

Krell, Henry, Springer, 233 Spring St, New York, NY 10013-1578 *Tel:* 212-460-1500 *Toll Free Tel:* 800-SPRINGER (777-4643) *Fax:* 212-460-1575 *E-mail:* service-ny@springer.com *Web Site:* www.springer.com, pg 241

Kreloff, Elliot, Blue Apple Books, 515 Valley St, Suite 170, Maplewood, NJ 07040 *Tel:* 973-763-8191 *Toll Free Tel:* 800-722-6657; 800-733-3000 (orders) *Fax:* 973-763-5944 *E-mail:* info@blueapplebooks.com *Web Site:* blueapplebooks.com, pg 41

Kremer, John, Open Horizons Publishing Co, PO Box 2887, Taos, NM 87571 *Tel:* 575-751-3398 *Fax:* 575-751-3100 *E-mail:* info@bookmarket.com *Web Site:* www.bookmarket.com, pg 186

Krempa, Julie, Baywood Publishing Co Inc, 26 Austin Ave, Amityville, NY 11701 *Tel:* 631-691-1270 *Toll Free Tel:* 800-638-7819 *Fax:* 631-691-1770 *E-mail:* baywood@baywood.com *Web Site:* www.baywood.com, pg 32

Kresan, Dawn, Palimpsest Press, 5 King St, Kingsville, ON N9Y 1H9, Canada *Tel:* 519-563-9981 *E-mail:* info@palimpsestpress.ca *Web Site:* www.palimpsestpress.ca, pg 515

Kress, Steven, The Pennsylvania State University Press, University Support Bldg 1, Suite C, 820 N University Dr, University Park, PA 16802-1003 *Tel:* 814-865-1327 *Toll Free Tel:* 800-326-9180 *Fax:* 814-863-1408 *Toll Free Fax:* 877-778-2665 *E-mail:* info@psupress.org *Web Site:* www.psupress.org, pg 198

Kress-Russick, Michael, Wisconsin Annual Fall Conferencee, PO Box 259303, Madison, WI 53725 *Tel:* 608-278-0692 *Web Site:* www.scbwi.org; www.scbwi-wi.com, pg 674

Kretchman, Julie, First Folio Resource Group Inc, 218 Adelaide St W, 2nd fl, Toronto, ON M5H 1W7, Canada *Tel:* 416-368-7668 *Fax:* 416-368-9363 *E-mail:* mail@firstfolio.com *Web Site:* www.firstfolio.com, pg 546

Kretzer, Marilyn, Sterling Publishing Co Inc, 387 Park Ave S, 11th fl, New York, NY 10016-8810 *Tel:* 212-532-7160 *Toll Free Tel:* 800-367-9692 *Fax:* 212-213-2495 *Web Site:* www.sterlingpub.com, pg 244

Krichevsky, Stuart, Stuart Krichevsky Literary Agency Inc, 381 Park Ave South, Suite 428, New York, NY 10016 *Tel:* 212-725-5288 *Fax:* 212-725-5275 *E-mail:* query@skagency.com *Web Site:* skagency.com, pg 581

Krieger, Donald E, Krieger Publishing Co, 1725 Krieger Dr, Malabar, FL 32950 *Tel:* 321-724-9542 *Toll Free Tel:* 800-724-0025 *Fax:* 321-951-3671 *E-mail:* info@krieger-publishing.com *Web Site:* www.krieger-publishing.com, pg 142

Krieger, Maxine D, Krieger Publishing Co, 1725 Krieger Dr, Malabar, FL 32950 *Tel:* 321-724-9542 *Toll Free Tel:* 800-724-0025 *Fax:* 321-951-3671 *E-mail:* info@krieger-publishing.com *Web Site:* www.krieger-publishing.com, pg 142

Krieger, Robert E, Krieger Publishing Co, 1725 Krieger Dr, Malabar, FL 32950 *Tel:* 321-724-9542 *Toll Free Tel:* 800-724-0025 *Fax:* 321-951-3671 *E-mail:* info@krieger-publishing.com *Web Site:* www.krieger-publishing.com, pg 142

Krinsky, Santosh, Lotus Press, PO Box 325, Twin Lakes, WI 53181-0325 *Tel:* 262-889-8561 *Toll Free Tel:* 800-824-6396 (orders) *Fax:* 262-889-2461 *E-mail:* lotuspress@lotuspress.com *Web Site:* www.lotuspress.com, pg 152

Kriss, Miriam, Irene Goodman Literary Agency, 27 W 24 St, Suite 700B, New York, NY 10010 *Tel:* 212-604-0330 *E-mail:* queries@irenegoodman.com *Web Site:* www.irenegoodman.com, pg 575

Krissoff, Derek, University of Nebraska Press, 1111 Lincoln Mall, Lincoln, NE 68588-0630 *Tel:* 402-472-3581; 919-966-7449 (cust serv & foreign orders) *Toll Free Tel:* 800-848-6224 (cust serv & US orders) *Fax:* 402-472-6214; 919-962-2704 (cust serv & foreign orders) *Toll Free Fax:* 800-526-2617 (cust serv & US orders) *E-mail:* pressmail@unl.edu *Web Site:* www.nebraskapress.unl.edu, pg 267

Kritzer, Eddie, Eddie Kritzer Productions, 1112 Montana Ave, Suite 449, Santa Monica, CA 90403 *Tel:* 310-702-5356 *Fax:* 310-394-5770 *E-mail:* producedby@aol.com *Web Site:* eddiekritzer.com, pg 605

Kritzmacher, John, John Wiley & Sons Inc, 111 River St, Hoboken, NJ 07030-5774 *Tel:* 201-748-6000 *Toll Free Tel:* 800-225-5945 (cust serv) *Fax:* 201-748-6088 *E-mail:* info@wiley.com *Web Site:* www.wiley.com, pg 281

Krivda, David, Simon & Schuster Digital, 1230 Avenue of the Americas, New York, NY 10020 *Tel:* 212-698-7547 *Web Site:* www.simonandschuster.com; kids.simonandschuster.com; www.simonandschuster.ca; www.simonandschuster.co.uk; www.simonandschuster.net; www.simonandschuster.biz; www.tipsoncareerandmoney.com; www.tipsonhealthyliving.com; www.tipsonhomeandstyle.com; www.tipsonlifeandlove.com, pg 235

Kroberger, Jonathan, Bloomsbury Publishing, 175 Fifth Ave, New York, NY 10010 *Tel:* 212-674-5151 *Toll Free Tel:* 800-221-7945 *Fax:* 212-780-0115; 212-982-2837 *E-mail:* marketingusa@bloomsbury.com; adultpublicityusa.@bloomsbury.com *Web Site:* www.bloomsbury.com, pg 41

Kroger, Rev Dan OFM, Franciscan Media, 28 W Liberty St, Cincinnati, OH 45202 *Tel:* 513-241-5615 *Toll Free Tel:* 800-488-0488 *Fax:* 513-241-0399 *E-mail:* books@americancatholic.org *Web Site:* www.americancatholic.org, pg 98

Krohn, Talia, Crown Publishing Group, c/o Random House Inc, 1745 Broadway, New York, NY 10019 *Tel:* 212-782-9000 *Toll Free Tel:* 888-264-1745 *Fax:* 212-940-7408 *Web Site:* www.randomhouse.com/crown, pg 72

Kroll, Edite, Edite Kroll Literary Agency Inc, 20 Cross St, Saco, ME 04072 *Tel:* 207-283-8797 *Fax:* 207-283-8799, pg 581

Kronzek, Lynn C, Lynn C Kronzek & Richard A Flom, 145 S Glenoaks Blvd, Suite 240, Burbank, CA 91502 *Tel:* 818-768-7688 *Fax:* 818-768-7648, pg 550

Krossing, Karen, Canadian Society of Children's Authors Illustrators & Performers (CANSCAIP), 104-40 Orchard View Blvd, Lower Level Entrance, Toronto, ON M4R 1B9, Canada *Tel:* 416-515-1559 *E-mail:* office@canscaip.org *Web Site:* www.canscaip.org, pg 620

Krotov, Mark, The Overlook Press, 141 Wooster St, Suite 4-B, New York, NY 10012 *Tel:* 212-673-2210; 845-679-6838 (orders & dist) *Fax:* 212-673-2296 *E-mail:* sales@overlookny.com (orders) *Web Site:* www.overlookpress.com, pg 189

Kroupa, Melanie, Words into Print, 131 Fifth Ave, Suite 501, New York, NY 10003 *Tel:* 212-741-1393 *Fax:* 419-441-1393 *E-mail:* query@wordsintoprint.org *Web Site:* www.wordsintoprint.org, pg 557

Krueger, Jo Ann, The Aaland Agency, PO Box 849, Inyokern, CA 93527-0849 *Tel:* 760-384-3910 *Web Site:* www.the-aaland-agency.com, pg 559

Krug, Susan, American Medical Writers Association (AMWA), 30 W Gude Dr, Suite 525, Rockville, MD 20850-1161 *Tel:* 240-238-0940 *Fax:* 301-294-9006 *E-mail:* amwa@amwa.org *Web Site:* www.amwa.org, pg 613

Kruggel, James, The Catholic University of America Press, 240 Leahy Hall, 620 Michigan Ave NE, Washington, DC 20064 *Tel:* 202-319-5052 *Toll Free Tel:* 800-537-5487 (orders only) *Fax:* 202-319-4985 *E-mail:* cua-press@cua.edu *Web Site:* cuapress.cua.edu, pg 54

Krule, Lawrence J, Jewish Book Council, 520 Eighth Ave, 4th fl, New York, NY 10018 *Tel:* 212-201-2920 *Fax:* 212-532-4952 *E-mail:* jbc@jewishbooks.org *Web Site:* www.jewishbookcouncil.org, pg 626

Krule, Lawrence J, National Jewish Book Award-Children's & Young Adult Literature, 520 Eighth Ave, 4th fl, New York, NY 10018 *Tel:* 212-201-2920 *Fax:* 212-532-4952 *E-mail:* jbc@jewishbooks.org *Web Site:* www.jewishbookcouncil.org, pg 726

Krule, Lawrence J, National Jewish Book Award-Contemporary Jewish Life & Practice, 520 Eighth Ave, 4th fl, New York, NY 10018 *Tel:* 212-201-2920 *Fax:* 212-532-4952 *E-mail:* jbc@jewishbooks.org *Web Site:* www.jewishbookcouncil.org, pg 726

Krule, Lawrence J, National Jewish Book Award-History, 520 Eighth Ave, 4th fl, New York, NY 10018 *Tel:* 212-201-2920 *Fax:* 212-532-4952 *E-mail:* jbc@jewishbooks.org *Web Site:* www.jewishbookcouncil.org, pg 726

Krule, Lawrence J, National Jewish Book Award-Illustrated Children's Book, 520 Eighth Ave, 4th fl, New York, NY 10018 *Tel:* 212-201-2920 *Fax:* 212-532-4952 *E-mail:* jbc@jewishbooks.org *Web Site:* www.jewishbookcouncil.org, pg 726

Krule, Lawrence J, National Jewish Book Award-Modern Jewish Thought & Experience, 520 Eighth Ave, 4th fl, New York, NY 10018 *Tel:* 212-201-2920 *Fax:* 212-532-4952 *E-mail:* jbc@jewishbooks.org *Web Site:* www.jewishbookcouncil.org, pg 726

Krule, Lawrence J, National Jewish Book Award-Scholarship, 520 Eighth Ave, 4th fl, New York, NY 10018 *Tel:* 212-201-2920 *Fax:* 212-532-4952 *E-mail:* jbc@jewishbooks.org *Web Site:* www.jewishbookcouncil.org, pg 726

Krule, Lawrence J, National Jewish Book Awards, 520 Eighth Ave, 4th fl, New York, NY 10018 *Tel:* 212-201-2920 *Fax:* 212-532-4952 *E-mail:* jbc@jewishbooks.org *Web Site:* www.jewishbookcouncil.org, pg 726

Krule, Lawrence J, Sami Rohr Prize for Jewish Literature, 520 Eighth Ave, 4th fl, New York, NY 10018 *Tel:* 212-201-2920 *Fax:* 212-532-4952 *E-mail:* jbc@jewishbooks.org *Web Site:* www.jewishbookcouncil.org, pg 738

Krump, Emily, HarperCollins General Books Group, 10 E 53 St, New York, NY 10022 *Tel:* 212-207-7000 *Fax:* 212-207-7633 *Web Site:* www.harpercollins.com, pg 113

Krumpe, Mr Kreig, Boyds Mills Press, 815 Church St, Honesdale, PA 18431 *Tel:* 570-253-1164 *Toll Free Tel:* 800-490-5111 *Fax:* 570-253-0179 *E-mail:* contact@boydsmillspress.com *Web Site:* www.boydsmillspress.com, pg 45

Krumpfer, Jorie, W W Norton & Company Inc, 500 Fifth Ave, New York, NY 10110-0017 *Tel:* 212-354-5500 *Toll Free Tel:* 800-233-4830 (orders & cust serv) *Fax:* 212-869-0856 *Toll Free Fax:* 800-458-6515 *Web Site:* www.wwnorton.com, pg 182

Krup, Agnes, Sanford J Greenburger Associates Inc, 55 Fifth Ave, 15th fl, New York, NY 10003 *Tel:* 212-206-5600 *Fax:* 212-463-8718 *Web Site:* www.greenburger.com, pg 575

Kruse, Katrina, Houghton Mifflin Harcourt, 222 Berkeley St, Boston, MA 02116-3764 *Tel:* 617-351-5000 *Toll Free Tel:* 800-225-5425 (Pre-K-8); 800-462-6595 (6–12; Advanced & Electives); 800-289-4490 (Specialized Curriculum: Great Source, Rigby, Saxon, Steck-Vaughn; Homeschool; Adult Ed); 800-323-9540 (Assessment: Riverside Publishing); 888-391-3245 (SkillsTutor); 888-242-6747 option 2 (Destination Series; Classroom Connect; Earobics; Edmark; Learning Village; Riverdeep); 800-225-3362 (Houghton Mifflin Harcourt Trade & Reference Publishers); 800-225-5800 (Heinemann) *Fax:* 617-351-1125 *Web Site:* www.hmhco.com, pg 123

Kruusi, John, Penguin Group (Canada), 90 Eglinton Ave E, Suite 700, Toronto, ON M4P 2Y3, Canada *Tel:* 416-925-2249 *Fax:* 416-925-0068 *Web Site:* www.penguin.ca, pg 515

Krysan, Alan, Astragal Press, 8075 215 St W, Lakeville, MN 55044 *Tel:* 952-469-6699 *Toll Free Tel:* 866-543-3045 *Fax:* 952-469-1968 *Toll Free Fax:* 800-330-6232 *E-mail:* info@astragalpress.com *Web Site:* www.astragalpress.com, pg 26

Krysan, Alan, Pogo Press Inc, 8075 215 St W, Lakeville, MN 55044 *Tel:* 952-469-6699 *Toll Free Tel:* 800-846-7027 *Fax:* 952-469-1968 *Toll Free Fax:* 800-330-6232 *E-mail:* info@finneyco.com *Web Site:* www.pogopress.com, pg 204

Krysan, Alan E, Ecopress, 8075 215 St W, Lakeville, MN 55044 *Tel:* 952-469-6699 *Toll Free Tel:* 800-846-7027 *Fax:* 952-469-1968 *Toll Free Fax:* 800-330-6232 *E-mail:* info@finneyco.com *Web Site:* www.ecopress.com, pg 84

Krysan, Alan E, Finney Company Inc, 8075 215 St W, Lakeville, MN 55044 *Tel:* 952-469-6699 *Toll Free Tel:* 800-846-7027 *Fax:* 952-469-1968 *Toll Free Fax:* 800-330-6232 *E-mail:* info@finneyco.com *Web Site:* www.finneyco.com, pg 95

Krysan, Alan E, Hobar Publications, 8075 215 St W, Lakeville, MN 55044 *Tel:* 952-469-6699 *Toll Free Tel:* 800-846-7027 *Fax:* 952-469-1968 *Toll Free Fax:* 800-330-6232 *E-mail:* info@finneyco.com *Web Site:* www.finney-hobar.com, pg 120

Krysan, Alan E, Windward Publishing, 8075 215 St W, Lakeville, MN 55044 *Tel:* 952-469-6699 *Toll Free Tel:* 800-846-7027 *Fax:* 952-469-1968 *Toll Free Fax:* 800-330-6232 *E-mail:* info@finneyco.com *Web Site:* www.finneyco.com, pg 283

Kubie, Greg, Random House Publishing Group, 1745 Broadway, New York, NY 10019 *Toll Free Tel:* 800-200-3552 *Web Site:* atrandom.com, pg 214

Kubik, John Milan, Foto Expression International (Toronto), 266 Charlotte St, Suite 297, Peterborough, ON K9J 2V4, Canada *Tel:* 705-745-5770 *E-mail:* operations@fotopressnews.org *Web Site:* www.fotopressnews.org, pg 601

Kuehl, Kathy, The Guilford Press, 72 Spring St, 4th fl, New York, NY 10012 *Tel:* 212-431-9800 *Toll Free Tel:* 800-365-7006 (ext 1, orders) *Fax:* 212-966-6708 *E-mail:* orders@guilford.com; info@guilford.com *Web Site:* www.guilford.com, pg 109

Kuerbis, Lisa, Syracuse University Press, 621 Skytop Rd, Suite 110, Syracuse, NY 13244-5290 *Tel:* 315-443-5534 *Toll Free Tel:* 800-365-8929 (cust serv) *Fax:* 315-443-5545 *E-mail:* supress@syr.edu *Web Site:* syracuseuniversitypress.syr.edu, pg 249

Kuhatschek, Jack, Baker Books, 6030 E Fulton Rd, Ada, MI 49301 *Tel:* 616-676-9185 *Toll Free Tel:* 800-877-2665; 800-679-1957 *Fax:* 616-676-9573 *Toll Free Fax:* 800-398-3111 *Web Site:* www.bakerpublishinggroup.com, pg 29

Kuhne, Barbara, Pacific Educational Press, c/o University of British Columbia, Faculty of Education, 411-2389 Health Sciences Mall, Vancouver, BC V6T 1Z4, Canada *Tel:* 604-822-5385 *Fax:* 604-822-6603 *E-mail:* pep.sales@ubc.ca *Web Site:* www.pacificedpress.ca, pg 514

Kuizenga, Sandra, Marick Press, PO Box 36253, Grosse Pointe Farms, MI 48236 *Tel:* 313-407-9236 *E-mail:* orders@marickpress.com *Web Site:* www.marickpress.com, pg 157

Kuizenga, Sandra, Marick Press Poetry Prize Competition, PO Box 36253, Grosse Pointe Farms, MI 48236 *Tel:* 313-407-9236 *Web Site:* www.marickpress.com, pg 721

Kuka, Ronald, Chris O'Malley Fiction Prize, University of Wisconsin, 6193 Helen C White Hall, English Dept, 600 N Park St, Madison, WI 53706 *Tel:* 608-263-0566 *E-mail:* madisonrevw@gmail.com *Web Site:* www.english.wisc.edu/madisonreview, pg 731

Kuka, Ronald, Phyllis Smart-Young Poetry Prize, University of Wisconsin, 6193 Helen C White Hall, English Dept, 600 N Park St, Madison, WI 53706 *Tel:* 608-263-0566 *E-mail:* madisonrevw@gmail.com *Web Site:* www.english.wisc.edu/madisonreview, pg 753

Kulick, Greg, Blue Rider Press, 375 Hudson St, New York, NY 10014 *Tel:* 212-366-2000, pg 42

Kulikowski, Katarzyna, W W Norton & Company Inc, 500 Fifth Ave, New York, NY 10110-0017 *Tel:* 212-354-5500 *Toll Free Tel:* 800-233-4830 (orders & cust serv) *Fax:* 212-869-0856 *Toll Free Fax:* 800-458-6515 *Web Site:* www.wwnorton.com, pg 182

Kull, Irene Imperio, Temple University Press, 1852 N Tenth St, Philadelphia, PA 19122-6099 *Tel:* 215-926-2140 *Toll Free Tel:* 800-621-2736 *Fax:* 215-926-2141 *E-mail:* tempress@temple.edu *Web Site:* www.temple.edu/tempress, pg 251

Kumangai, Miya, Touchstone, 1230 Avenue of the Americas, New York, NY 10020, pg 257

Kunde-Anderson, Mary Beth, Association of Catholic Publishers Inc, 4725 Dorsey Hall Dr, Suite A, PMB 709, Elliott City, MD 21042 *Tel:* 410-988-2926 *Fax:* 410-571-4946 *Web Site:* www.catholicsread.org; www.catholicpublishers.org; www.midatlanticcongress.org, pg 616

Kundert, Beth, McGraw-Hill Create, 501 Bell St, Dubuque, IA 52001 *Tel:* 563-584-6000 *Fax:* 563-584-6600 *E-mail:* first_last@mcgraw-hill.com *Web Site:* www.mhhe.com, pg 160

Kunjufu, Dr Jawanza PhD, African American Images, PO Box 1799, Chicago Heights, IL 60412 *Tel:* 708-672-4909 (cust serv) *Toll Free Tel:* 800-552-1991 (orders) *Fax:* 708-672-0466 *E-mail:* customer@africanamericanimages.com *Web Site:* www.africanamericanimages.com, pg 6

Kuny, Greg, American Psychiatric Publishing (APP), 1000 Wilson Blvd, Suite 1825, Arlington, VA 22209 *Tel:* 703-907-7322 *Toll Free Tel:* 800-368-5777 *Fax:* 703-907-1091 *E-mail:* appi@psych.org *Web Site:* www.appi.org; www.psychiatryonline.org, pg 15

Kunz, Jeannine, Society of Manufacturing Engineers, One SME Dr, Dearborn, MI 48121 *Tel:* 313-425-3000 *Toll Free Tel:* 800-733-4763 (cust serv) *Fax:* 313-425-3400 *E-mail:* publications@sme.org *Web Site:* www.sme.org, pg 238

Kuong, Jay, Management Advisory Services & Publications (MASP), PO Box 81151, Wellesley Hills, MA 02481-0001 *Tel:* 781-235-2895 *Fax:* 781-235-5446 *E-mail:* info@masp.com *Web Site:* www.masp.com, pg 155

Kurian, George, International Encyclopedia Society, PO Box 519, Baldwin Place, NY 10505-0519 *Tel:* 914-962-3287 *Fax:* 914-962-3287 *Web Site:* encyclopediasociety.com, pg 625

Kurian, George, George Kurian Reference Books, PO Box 519, Baldwin Place, NY 10505-0519 *Tel:* 914-962-3287 *Fax:* 914-962-3287, pg 142

Kurklis, Jackie, The Fairmont Press Inc, 700 Indian Trail, Lilburn, GA 30047 *Tel:* 770-925-9388 *Fax:* 770-381-9865 *Web Site:* www.fairmontpress.com, pg 92

Kurland, Midian, Scholastic Education, 524 Broadway, New York, NY 10012 *Tel:* 212-343-6100 *Fax:* 212-343-6189 *Web Site:* www.scholastic.com, pg 228

Kurmey, Bev, City of Toronto Book Award, Toronto Protocol City Clerks Office, City Hall, 100 Queen St W, 2nd fl West, Toronto, ON M5H 2N2, Canada *Tel:* 416-392-7805 *Fax:* 416-392-1247 *E-mail:* protocol@toronto.ca *Web Site:* www.toronto.ca/book_awards, pg 697

Kurtz, Gretchen, Prometheus Books, 59 John Glenn Dr, Amherst, NY 14228-2119 *Tel:* 716-691-0133 *Toll Free Tel:* 800-421-0351 *Fax:* 716-691-0137 *E-mail:* marketing@prometheusbooks.com; editorial@prometheusbooks.com *Web Site:* www.Prometheusbooks.com, pg 208

Kurtz, Jonathan, Prometheus Books, 59 John Glenn Dr, Amherst, NY 14228-2119 *Tel:* 716-691-0133 *Toll Free Tel:* 800-421-0351 *Fax:* 716-691-0137 *E-mail:* marketing@prometheusbooks.com; editorial@prometheusbooks.com *Web Site:* www.Prometheusbooks.com, pg 208

Kurtz, Paul, Prometheus Books, 59 John Glenn Dr, Amherst, NY 14228-2119 *Tel:* 716-691-0133 *Toll Free Tel:* 800-421-0351 *Fax:* 716-691-0137 *E-mail:* marketing@prometheusbooks.com; editorial@prometheusbooks.com *Web Site:* www.Prometheusbooks.com, pg 208

Kusler, Jack, Addicus Books Inc, PO Box 45327, Omaha, NE 68145 *Tel:* 402-330-7493 *Toll Free Tel:* 800-352-2873 (orders) *Fax:* 402-330-1707 *E-mail:* info@addicusbooks.com; addicusbks@aol.com *Web Site:* www.addicusbooks.com, pg 5

Kuster, Charles, DynaMinds Publishing, 6119 Nottingham Dr, Suite 1, Johnston, IA 50131 *Tel:* 515-270-5315 *Toll Free Tel:* 888-991-BOOK (991-2665) *Web Site:* www.dynamindspublishing.com, pg 83

Kutsko, John F, Society of Biblical Literature, The Luce Ctr, Suite 350, 825 Houston Mill Rd, Atlanta, GA 30329 *Tel:* 404-727-3100 *Fax:* 404-727-3101 (corp) *E-mail:* sbl@sbl-site.org *Web Site:* www.sbl-site.org, pg 238

Kutys, Ms Ronnie, Clerisy Press, 306 Greenup St, Covington, KY 41011 *Tel:* 513-861-4045 *Toll Free Tel:* 888-604-4537 *Fax:* 859-291-9111 *E-mail:* info@clerisypress.com *Web Site:* www.clerisypress.com, pg 63

Lam, Brian, Arsenal Pulp Press, 211 E Georgia St, No 101, Vancouver, BC V6A 1Z6, Canada *Tel:* 604-687-4233 *Toll Free Tel:* 888-600-PULP (600-7857) *Fax:* 604-687-4283 *E-mail:* info@arsenalpulp.com *Web Site:* www.arsenalpulp.com, pg 493

Lam, Francis, Clarkson Potter Publishers, c/o Random House Inc, 1745 Broadway, New York, NY 10019 *Tel:* 212-782-9000 *Toll Free Tel:* 888-264-1745 *Fax:* 212-572-6181 *Web Site:* www.clarksonpotter.com; www.randomhouse.com/crown/clarksonpotter, pg 62

Lamb, Beth, Vintage & Anchor Books, c/o Random House Inc, 1745 Broadway, New York, NY 10019 *Tel:* 212-572-2420 *E-mail:* vintageanchorpublicity@randomhouse.com *Web Site:* vintage-anchor.knopfdoubleday.com, pg 275

Lamb, Cynthia, Carnegie Mellon University Press, 5032 Forbes Ave, Pittsburgh, PA 15289-1021 *Tel:* 412-268-2861 *Toll Free Tel:* 800-666-2211 *Fax:* 412-268-8706 *E-mail:* carnegiemellonuniversitypress@gmail.com *Web Site:* www.cmu.edu/universitypress, pg 52

Lamb, John D, Springfed Writers' Retreat, PO Box 304, Royal Oak, MI 48068-0304 *Tel:* 248-589-3913 *Web Site:* www.springfed.org, pg 673

Lamb, Wendy, Random House Children's Books, 1745 Broadway, New York, NY 10019 *Tel:* 212-782-9000 *Toll Free Tel:* 800-200-3552 *Fax:* 212-782-9452 *Web Site:* randomhousekids.com, pg 213

Lamba, Marie, The Jennifer DeChiara Literary Agency, 31 E 32 St, Suite 300, New York, NY 10016 *Tel:* 212-481-8484 (ext 362) *Fax:* 212-481-9582 *Web Site:* www.jdlit.com, pg 568

Lambert, Joan, Online Training Solutions Inc (OTSI), 2217 152 Ave NE, Redmond, WA 98052 *Toll Free Tel:* 888-308-6874 *Toll Free Fax:* 888-308-6875 *Web Site:* www.otsi.com, pg 185

Lambert, Nancy, Harry N Abrams Inc, 115 W 18 St, 6th fl, New York, NY 10011 *Tel:* 212-206-7715 *Toll Free Tel:* 800-345-1359 *Fax:* 212-519-1210 *E-mail:* abrams@abramsbooks.com *Web Site:* www.abramsbooks.com, pg 3

Lambert, Patricia, David W & Beatrice C Evans Biography & Handcart Awards, 0735 Old Main Hill, Logan, UT 84322-0735 *Tel:* 435-797-0299 *Fax:* 435-797-1092 *E-mail:* mwc@usu.edu *Web Site:* www.mountainwest.usu.edu, pg 702

Lamberty, Laurena, American Society of Civil Engineers (ASCE), 1801 Alexander Bell Dr, Reston, VA 20191-4400 *Tel:* 703-295-6300 *Toll Free Tel:* 800-548-2723 *Fax:* 703-295-6278 *E-mail:* marketing@asce.org *Web Site:* www.asce.org, pg 16

Lambeth, Pike, Foundation Publications, 900 S Euclid St, La Habra, CA 90631 *Tel:* 714-879-2286 *Toll Free Tel:* 800-257-6272 *Fax:* 714-535-2164 *E-mail:* info@foundationpublications.com *Web Site:* www.foundationpublications.com, pg 98

LaMee, Maurice, Aspen Writers' Foundation, 110 E Hallam St, Suite 116, Aspen, CO 81611 *Tel:* 970-925-3122 *Fax:* 970-920-5700 *E-mail:* info@aspenwriters.org *Web Site:* www.aspenwriters.org, pg 615

Lamm, Gigi, Running Press Book Publishers, 2300 Chestnut St, Philadelphia, PA 19103-4399 *Tel:* 215-567-5080 *Toll Free Tel:* 800-343-4499 (cust serv & orders) *Fax:* 215-568-2919 *Toll Free Fax:* 800-453-2884 (cust serv & orders) *E-mail:* perseus.promos@perseusbooks.com *Web Site:* www.runningpress.com, pg 222

Lamolinara, Guy, The Center for the Book in the Library of Congress, The Library of Congress, 101 Independence Ave SE, Washington, DC 20540-4920 *Tel:* 202-707-5221 *Fax:* 202-707-0269 *E-mail:* cfbook@loc.gov *Web Site:* www.loc.gov/cfbook; www.read.gov.cfb, pg 621

Lampack, Andrew, Peter Lampack Agency Inc, 350 Fifth Ave, Suite 5300, New York, NY 10118 *Tel:* 212-687-9106 *Fax:* 212-687-9109 *Web Site:* peterlampackagency.com, pg 581

Lampack, Peter A, Peter Lampack Agency Inc, 350 Fifth Ave, Suite 5300, New York, NY 10118 *Tel:* 212-687-9106 *Fax:* 212-687-9109 *Web Site:* peterlampackagency.com, pg 581

Lampe, Betsy, Rainbow Books Inc, PO Box 430, Highland City, FL 33846 *Tel:* 863-648-4420 *Fax:* 863-647-5951 *E-mail:* info@rainbowbooksinc.com *Web Site:* www.rainbowbooksinc.com, pg 212

Lampe, C Marzen, Rainbow Books Inc, PO Box 430, Highland City, FL 33846 *Tel:* 863-648-4420 *Fax:* 863-647-5951 *E-mail:* info@rainbowbooksinc.com *Web Site:* www.rainbowbooksinc.com, pg 212

Lamplough, Jack, The Overlook Press, 141 Wooster St, Suite 4-B, New York, NY 10012 *Tel:* 212-673-2210; 845-679-6838 (orders & dist) *Fax:* 212-673-2296 *E-mail:* sales@overlookny.com (orders) *Web Site:* www.overlookpress.com, pg 189

Lampo, David, Cato Institute, 1000 Massachusetts Ave NW, Washington, DC 20001-5403 *Tel:* 202-842-0200 *Toll Free Tel:* 800-767-1241 *Fax:* 202-842-3490 *E-mail:* catostore@cato.org *Web Site:* www.cato.org, pg 54

Lamprich, Ed, Pearson Education/ELT, 10 Bank St, 9th fl, White Plains, NY 10606-1951 *Tel:* 914-287-8000 *Web Site:* www.pearsonelt.com, pg 195

Lamstein, Sarah, Boston Authors Club Inc, 45 Pine Crest Rd, Newton, MA 02459 *Tel:* 617-552-8457 *E-mail:* bostonauthors@aol.com *Web Site:* www.bostonauthorsclub.org, pg 619

Lamstein, Sarah, Julia Ward Howe Book Awards, 45 Pine Crest Rd, Newton, MA 02459 *Tel:* 617-552-8457 *E-mail:* bostonauthors@aol.com *Web Site:* www.bostonauthorsclub.org, pg 710

Lancaster, Brian, Africana Homestead Legacy Publishers Inc, 811 Church Rd, Suite 105, Cherry Hill, NJ 08002 *Tel:* 856-773-0694 *Toll Free Tel:* 866-250-8477 *Fax:* 856-486-1135 *Toll Free Fax:* 866-289-8681 *E-mail:* customer-service@ahlpub.com; sales@ahlpub.com (ordering info); editors@ahlpub.com (edit inquiries); public-relations@ahlpub.com *Web Site:* www.ahlpub.com, pg 6

Lance, Dan, Madavor Media, 21027 Crossroads Circle, Waukesha, WI 53187-1612 *Tel:* 262-796-8776 *Toll Free Tel:* 800-533-6644 (cust serv & orders) *Fax:* 262-796-1615 (sales & cust serv); 262-798-6468 (edit) *Web Site:* www.kalmbach.com, pg 155

Lance, Jim, Kumarian Press, 1800 30 St, Suite 314, Boulder, CO 80301 *Tel:* 303-444-6684 *Toll Free Tel:* 800-232-0223 (orders only) *Fax:* 303-444-0824 *E-mail:* questions@rienner.com *Web Site:* www.kpbooks.com, pg 142

Lance, Suzanne, New York State Walt Whitman Citation of Merit for Poets, University at Albany, SL 320, Albany, NY 12222 *Tel:* 518-442-5620 *Fax:* 518-442-5621 *E-mail:* writers@uamail.albany.edu *Web Site:* www.albany.edu/writers-inst, pg 729

Lance, Suzanne, New York State Writers Institute, University at Albany, Science Library 320, Albany, NY 12222 *Tel:* 518-442-5620 *Fax:* 518-442-5621 *E-mail:* writers@uamail.albany.edu *Web Site:* www.albany.edu/writers-inst/, pg 671

Land, Bob, Land on Demand, 20 Long Crescent Dr, Bristol, VA 24201 *Tel:* 276-642-0550 *E-mail:* landondemand@bvunet.net *Web Site:* boblandedits.blogspot.com, pg 550

Land, Dudley, McGraw-Hill Create, 501 Bell St, Dubuque, IA 52001 *Tel:* 563-584-6000 *Fax:* 563-584-6600 *E-mail:* first_last@mcgraw-hill.com *Web Site:* www.mhhe.com, pg 160

Landau, David, Harvard Square Editions, 2152 Beachwood Terr, Hollywood, CA 90068 *Tel:* 323-469-8932 *Fax:* 323-469-8932 *Web Site:* harvardsquareeditions.org, pg 114

Landau, David, Pureplay Press, 195 26 Ave, No 2, San Francisco, CA 94121 *Tel:* 310-597-0328 *E-mail:* info@pureplaypress.com *Web Site:* www.pureplaypress.com, pg 210

Landauer, Jeramy, Landauer Corp, 3100 101 St, Suite A, Urbandale, IA 50322 *Tel:* 515-287-2144 *Toll Free Tel:* 800-557-2144 *Fax:* 515-276-5102 *E-mail:* info@landauercorp.com *Web Site:* www.landauercorp.com, pg 143

Landes, Ronald, Landes Bioscience, 1806 Rio Grande St, Austin, TX 78701 *Tel:* 512-637-6050 *Toll Free Tel:* 800-736-9948 *Fax:* 512-637-6079 *E-mail:* info@landesbioscience.com *Web Site:* www.landesbioscience.com, pg 143

Landesman, Cliff, W W Norton & Company Inc, 500 Fifth Ave, New York, NY 10110-0017 *Tel:* 212-354-5500 *Toll Free Tel:* 800-233-4830 (orders & cust serv) *Fax:* 212-869-0856 *Toll Free Fax:* 800-458-6515 *Web Site:* www.wwnorton.com, pg 182

Landis, Sarah, HarperCollins Children's Books, 10 E 53 St, New York, NY 10022 *Tel:* 212-207-7000 *Web Site:* www.harpercollinschildrens.com, pg 113

Landon, Hut, Northern California Independent Booksellers Association (NCIBA), 1007 General Kennedy Ave, San Francisco, CA 94129 *Tel:* 415-561-7686 *Fax:* 415-561-7685 *E-mail:* office@nciba.com *Web Site:* www.nciba.com, pg 632

Landskroener, Marcia, Sophie Kerr Prize, c/o College Relations Office, 300 Washington Ave, Chestertown, MD 21620 *Tel:* 410-778-2800 *Toll Free Tel:* 800-422-1782 *Fax:* 410-810-7150 *Web Site:* www.washcoll.edu, pg 743

Landwehr, Kathy, Peachtree Publishers, 1700 Chattahoochee Ave, Atlanta, GA 30318-2112 *Tel:* 404-876-8761 *Toll Free Tel:* 800-241-0113 *Fax:* 404-875-2578 *Toll Free Fax:* 800-875-8909 *E-mail:* hello@peachtree-online.com *Web Site:* www.peachtree-online.com, pg 195

Lane, Fr Edmund C, St Pauls/Alba House, 2187 Victory Blvd, Staten Island, NY 10314-6603 *Tel:* 718-761-0047 (edit & prodn); 718-698-2759 (mktg & billing) *Toll Free Tel:* 800-343-2522 *Fax:* 718-761-0057 *E-mail:* sales@stpauls.us; marketing@stpauls.us *Web Site:* www.stpauls.us; www.albahouse.org, pg 225

Lane, Mary Ann, Harvard University Press, 79 Garden St, Cambridge, MA 02138-1499 *Tel:* 617-495-2600; 401-531-2800 (intl orders) *Toll Free Tel:* 800-405-1619 (orders) *Fax:* 617-495-5898 (general); 617-496-4677 (edit & rts); 401-531-2801 (intl orders) *Toll Free Fax:* 800-406-9145 (orders) *E-mail:* contact_hup@harvard.edu *Web Site:* www.hup.harvard.edu, pg 115

Lange, April, W W Norton & Company Inc, 500 Fifth Ave, New York, NY 10110-0017 *Tel:* 212-354-5500 *Toll Free Tel:* 800-233-4830 (orders & cust serv) *Fax:* 212-869-0856 *Toll Free Fax:* 800-458-6515 *Web Site:* www.wwnorton.com, pg 182

Lange, Barbara, Society of Motion Picture & Television Engineers (SMPTE), 3 Barker Ave, 5th fl, White Plains, NY 10601 *Tel:* 914-761-1100 *Fax:* 914-761-3115 *Web Site:* www.smpte.org, pg 637

Lange, Heide, Sanford J Greenburger Associates Inc, 55 Fifth Ave, 15th fl, New York, NY 10003 *Tel:* 212-206-5600 *Fax:* 212-463-8718 *Web Site:* www.greenburger.com, pg 575

Lange, Marty, McGraw-Hill Science, Engineering, Mathematics, 501 Bell St, Dubuque, IA 52001 *Tel:* 563-584-6000 *Toll Free Tel:* 800-338-3987 (cust serv) *Fax:* 614-755-5645 (cust serv) *Web Site:* www.mhhe.com, pg 162

Langenscheidt, Andreas, American Map Corp, 36-36 33 St, 4th fl, Long Island City, NY 11106 *Tel:* 718-784-0055 *Toll Free Tel:* 888-774-7979 *Fax:* 718-784-0640 (admin); 718-784-1216 (sales & orders) *E-mail:* sales@americanmap.com *Web Site:* www.americanmap.com, pg 14

Langenscheidt, Andreas, Hagstrom Map & Travel Center, 51 W 43 St, New York, NY 10036 *Toll Free Tel:* 800-432-MAPS (432-6277) *Fax:* 212-398-9856 *Web Site:* www.americanmap.com, pg 110

Langevin, David J, Houghton Mifflin Harcourt Trade & Reference Division, 222 Berkeley St, Boston, MA 02116-3764 *Tel:* 617-351-5000 *Toll Free Tel:* 800-225-3362 *Web Site:* www.houghtonmifflinbooks.com, pg 124

Langille, Donald, Palm Island Press, 411 Truman Ave, Key West, FL 33040 *Tel:* 305-296-3102 *E-mail:* pipress2@gmail.com, pg 191

Langley, Norris, Duke University Press, 905 W Main St, Suite 18B, Durham, NC 27701 *Tel:* 919-688-5134 *Toll Free Tel:* 888-651-0122 *Fax:* 919-688-2615 *Toll Free Fax:* 888-651-0124 *E-mail:* orders@dukeupress.edu *Web Site:* www.dukeupress.edu, pg 82

Langman, Joe, Schiffer Publishing Ltd, 4880 Lower Valley Rd, Atglen, PA 19310 *Tel:* 610-593-1777 *Fax:* 610-593-2002 *E-mail:* schifferbk@aol.com *Web Site:* www.schifferbooks.com, pg 227

Langman, Lucy, Fons Vitae, 49 Mockingbird Valley Dr, Louisville, KY 40207-1366 *Tel:* 502-897-3641 *Fax:* 502-893-7373 *E-mail:* fonsvitaeky@aol.com *Web Site:* www.fonsvitae.com, pg 97

Langsam, Karen, Oxford University Press USA, 198 Madison Ave, New York, NY 10016 *Tel:* 212-726-6000 *Toll Free Tel:* 800-451-7556 (orders); 800-445-9714 (cust serv) *Fax:* 919-677-1303 *E-mail:* custserv.us@oup.com *Web Site:* www.oup.com/us, pg 189

Langston, John, University Press of Mississippi, 3825 Ridgewood Rd, Jackson, MS 39211-6492 *Tel:* 601-432-6205 *Toll Free Tel:* 800-737-7788 (orders & cust serv) *Fax:* 601-432-6217 *E-mail:* press@mississippi.edu *Web Site:* www.upress.state.ms.us, pg 271

Langton, Dawn, Training Resource Network Inc (TRN), PO Box 439, St Augustine, FL 32085-0439 *Tel:* 904-823-9800 (cust serv) *Toll Free Tel:* 800-280-7010 (orders) *Fax:* 904-823-3554 *E-mail:* customerservice@trninc.com *Web Site:* www.trn-store.com, pg 257

Langum, David J Sr, Langum Prize in American Legal History or Biography, 2809 Berkeley Dr, Birmingham, AL 35242 *Tel:* 205-726-2424 *Fax:* 205-726-4216 *E-mail:* langumtrust@gmail.com *Web Site:* www.langumtrust.org, pg 716

Langum, David J Sr, Langum Prize in Historical Fiction, 2809 Berkeley Dr, Birmingham, AL 35242 *Tel:* 205-726-2424 *Fax:* 205-726-4216 *Web Site:* www.langumtrust.org, pg 716

Langum, David J Sr, Gene E & Adele R Malott Prize for Recording Community Activism, 2809 Berkeley Dr, Birmingham, AL 35242 *Tel:* 205-726-2424 *Fax:* 205-726-4216 *E-mail:* langumtrust@gmail.com *Web Site:* www.langumtrust.org, pg 721

Lanick, Colleen, The MIT Press, 55 Hayward St, Cambridge, MA 02142 *Tel:* 617-253-5255 *Toll Free Tel:* 800-207-8354 (orders) *Fax:* 617-258-6779; 617-577-1545 (orders) *Web Site:* mitpress.mit.edu, pg 167

Lansing, Jim, OMNI Publishers Inc, 29131 Bulverde Rd, San Antonio, TX 78260 *Tel:* 210-778-4437 *Fax:* 830-438-4645 *Web Site:* www.omnipublishers.com; www.educatorethicsseries.com, pg 185

Lansing, Richard, Springer, 233 Spring St, New York, NY 10013-1578 *Tel:* 212-460-1500 *Toll Free Tel:* 800-SPRINGER (777-4643) *Fax:* 212-460-1575 *E-mail:* service-ny@springer.com *Web Site:* www.springer.com, pg 241

Lansing, Ruth, OMNI Publishers Inc, 29131 Bulverde Rd, San Antonio, TX 78260 *Tel:* 210-778-4437 *Fax:* 830-438-4645 *Web Site:* www.omnipublishers.com; www.educatorethicsseries.com, pg 185

Lansky, Bruce, Meadowbrook Press, 6110 Blue Circle Dr, Suite 237, Minnetonka, MN 55343 *Toll Free Tel:* 800-338-2232 *Fax:* 952-930-1940 *E-mail:* info@meadowbrookpress.com *Web Site:* www.meadowbrookpress.com, pg 163

Lansky, Vicki, Book Peddlers, 2950 W Dean Pkwy, No 1602, Minneapolis, MN 55416 *Tel:* 952-544-1154 *E-mail:* bookpeddlers@aol.com *Web Site:* www.bookpeddlers.com; www.practicalparenting.com, pg 43

Lape, Todd, University Press of Mississippi, 3825 Ridgewood Rd, Jackson, MS 39211-6492 *Tel:* 601-432-6205 *Toll Free Tel:* 800-737-7788 (orders & cust serv) *Fax:* 601-432-6217 *E-mail:* press@mississippi.edu *Web Site:* www.upress.state.ms.us, pg 271

Laperriere, Ginette, Guerin Editeur Ltee, 4501 rue Drolet, Montreal, QC H2T 2G2, Canada *Tel:* 514-842-3481 *Toll Free Tel:* 800-398-8337 *Fax:* 514-842-4923 *Web Site:* www.guerin-editeur.qc.ca, pg 507

Laporte, Janine, Doubleday Canada, One Toronto St, Suite 300, Toronto, ON M5C 2V6, Canada *Tel:* 416-364-4449 *Fax:* 416-364-6863 *Web Site:* www.randomhouse.ca, pg 501

Laporte, Janine, Knopf Random Canada, One Toronto St, Suite 300, Toronto, ON M5C 2V6, Canada *Tel:* 416-364-4449 *Toll Free Tel:* 888-523-9292 *Fax:* 416-364-6863 *Web Site:* www.randomhouse.ca, pg 510

Laporte, Janine, Random House of Canada Limited, One Toronto St, Suite 300, Toronto, ON M5C 2V6, Canada *Tel:* 416-364-4449 *Toll Free Tel:* 888-523-9292 (cust serv) *Fax:* 416-364-6863; 416-364-6653 (subs rts) *Web Site:* www.randomhouse.ca, pg 517

Laporte, Janine, Seal Books, One Toronto St, Suite 300, Toronto, ON M5C 2V6, Canada *Tel:* 416-364-4449 *Toll Free Tel:* 888-523-9292 (order desk) *Fax:* 416-364-6863 *Web Site:* www.randomhouse.ca, pg 518

Laprairie, Dinah, BrainStorm Poetry Contest for Mental Health Consumers, 680 Kirkwood Dr, Bldg 1, Sudbury, ON P3E 1X3, Canada *Tel:* 705-222-6472 (ext 303) *E-mail:* openminds@nisa.on.ca *Web Site:* www.nisa.on.ca, pg 693

Larabell, David, David Black Agency, 335 Adams St, 27th fl, Suite 2707, Brooklyn, NY 11201 *Tel:* 718-852-5500 *Fax:* 718-852-5539 *Web Site:* www.davidblackagency.com, pg 562

Larcada, Marie Ellen, Teachers College Press, 1234 Amsterdam Ave, New York, NY 10027 *Tel:* 212-678-3929 *Toll Free Tel:* 800-575-6566 *Fax:* 212-678-4149; 802-864-7626 *E-mail:* tcpress@tc.columbia.edu; tcp.orders@aidcvt.com (orders) *Web Site:* www.teacherscollegepress.com, pg 251

Laredo, Sam, Laredo Publishing Co Inc, 465 Westview Ave, Englewood, NJ 07631 *Tel:* 201-408-4048 *Fax:* 201-408-5011 *E-mail:* info@laredopublishing.com *Web Site:* www.laredopublishing.com, pg 144

Laredo, Sam, Renaissance House, 465 Westview Ave, Englewood, NJ 07631 *Tel:* 201-408-4048 *Fax:* 201-408-5011 *E-mail:* info@renaissancehouse.net *Web Site:* www.renaissancehouse.net, pg 218

Large, Anita, Theytus Books Ltd, RR 2, Green Mountain Rd, Site 50, Comp 8, Lot 45, Penticton, BC V2A 6J7, Canada *Tel:* 250-493-7181 *Fax:* 250-493-5302 *E-mail:* info@theytus.com *Web Site:* www.theytus.com, pg 521

Larochelle, France, Guerin Editeur Ltee, 4501 rue Drolet, Montreal, QC H2T 2G2, Canada *Tel:* 514-842-3481 *Toll Free Tel:* 800-398-8337 *Fax:* 514-842-4923 *Web Site:* www.guerin-editeur.qc.ca, pg 507

Larouche, Jean-Claude, Les Editions JCL, 930 rue Jacques Cartier est, Chicoutimi, QC G7H 7K9, Canada *Tel:* 418-696-0536 *Fax:* 418-696-3132 *E-mail:* jcl@jcl.qc.ca *Web Site:* www.jcl.qc.ca, pg 503

Larrisey, Megan, Clinical Laboratory & Standards Institute (CLSI), 950 W Valley Rd, Suite 2500, Wayne, PA 19087 *Tel:* 610-688-0100 *Toll Free Tel:* 877-447-1888 (orders) *Fax:* 610-688-0700 *E-mail:* customerservice@clsi.org *Web Site:* www.clsi.org, pg 63

Larsen, Donna, Book Publicists of Southern California, 714 Crescent Dr, Beverly Hills, CA 90210 *Tel:* 323-461-3921 *Fax:* 323-461-0917, pg 618

Larsen, Elizabeth A, Tapestry Press Ltd, 19 Nashoba Rd, Littleton, MA 01460 *Tel:* 978-486-0200 *Toll Free Tel:* 800-535-2007 *Fax:* 978-486-0244 *E-mail:* publish@tapestrypress.com *Web Site:* www.tapestrypress.com, pg 250

Larsen, Emily, Book Industry Guild of New York, PO Box 2001, New York, NY 10113-2001 *E-mail:* admin@bookindustryguildofny.org *Web Site:* www.bookindustryguildofny.org, pg 618

Larsen, Prof Jeanne, Hollins University-Jackson Center for Creative Writing, PO Box 9677, Roanoke, VA 24020 *Tel:* 540-362-6317 *Fax:* 540-362-6097 *E-mail:* creative.writing@hollins.edu *Web Site:* www.hollins.edu, pg 678

Larsen, Michael, Indie Publishing Contest, 1029 Jones St, San Francisco, CA 94109 *Tel:* 415-673-0939 *E-mail:* sfwriterscon@aol.com *Web Site:* www.sfwriters.org, pg 711

Larsen, Michael, Michael Larsen/Elizabeth Pomada Literary Agents, 1029 Jones St, San Francisco, CA 94109 *Tel:* 415-673-0939 *E-mail:* larsenpoma@aol.com *Web Site:* www.larsenpomada.com, pg 581

Larsen, Michael, San Francisco Writers Conference, 1029 Jones St, San Francisco, CA 94109 *Tel:* 415-673-0939 *E-mail:* sfwriterscon@aol.com *Web Site:* www.sfwriters.org, pg 672

Larsen, Todd, EMC Publishing, 875 Montreal Way, St Paul, MN 55102 *Tel:* 651-290-2800 (corp) *Toll Free Tel:* 800-328-1452 *Fax:* 651-290-2899 *Toll Free Fax:* 800-328-4564 *E-mail:* educate@emcp.com *Web Site:* www.emcp.com, pg 87

Larson, Doran, Hamilton College, English/Creative Writing, English/Creative Writing Dept, 198 College Hill Rd, Clinton, NY 13323 *Tel:* 315-859-4370 *Fax:* 315-859-4390 *E-mail:* english@hamilton.edu *Web Site:* www.hamilton.edu, pg 678

Larson, Jeannette, Houghton Mifflin Harcourt Trade & Reference Division, 222 Berkeley St, Boston, MA 02116-3764 *Tel:* 617-351-5000 *Toll Free Tel:* 800-225-3362 *Web Site:* www.houghtonmifflinbooks.com, pg 124

Lasek, Ms Robin, Xlibris Corp, 1663 Liberty Dr, Suite 200, Bloomington, IN 47403 *Toll Free Tel:* 888-795-4274 *Fax:* 610-915-0294 *E-mail:* info@xlibris.com *Web Site:* www.xlibris.com, pg 287

Lasher, Eric, The LA Literary Agency, PO Box 46370, Los Angeles, CA 90046 *Tel:* 323-654-5288 *E-mail:* laliteraryagency@mac.com; mail@laliteraryagency.com *Web Site:* www.laliteraryagency.com, pg 581

Lasher, Maureen, The LA Literary Agency, PO Box 46370, Los Angeles, CA 90046 *Tel:* 323-654-5288 *E-mail:* laliteraryagency@mac.com; mail@laliteraryagency.com *Web Site:* www.laliteraryagency.com, pg 581

Laskowski-Caujolle, Dr Elvira Monika, ARTAMO Press, 11 W Anapamu St, Santa Barbara, CA 93101 *Tel:* 805-568-1400 *Fax:* 805-568-1400 *E-mail:* admin@artamopress.com *Web Site:* www.artamopress.com, pg 23

Lasky, Cynthia, Random House Publishing Group, 1745 Broadway, New York, NY 10019 *Toll Free Tel:* 800-200-3552 *Web Site:* atrandom.com, pg 214

Lasky, Karl, Ravenhawk™ Books, 7739 E Broadway Blvd, No 95, Tucson, AZ 85710 *Tel:* 520-296-4491 *Fax:* 520-296-4491 *E-mail:* ravenhawk6dof@yahoo.com *Web Site:* 6dofsolutions.com, pg 215

Lasner, Mark Samuels, William Morris Society in the United States Fellowships, PO Box 53263, Washington, DC 20009 *E-mail:* us@morrissociety.org *Web Site:* www.morrissociety.org, pg 725

Lassiter, Steve, APA Talent & Literary Agency, 405 S Beverly Dr, Beverly Hills, CA 90212 *Tel:* 310-888-4200 *Fax:* 310-888-4242 *Web Site:* www.apa-agency.com, pg 561

Last, Stanley, Fine Communications, 322 Eighth Ave, 15th fl, New York, NY 10001 *Tel:* 212-595-3500 *Fax:* 212-595-3779, pg 95

Latham, Adam, Sewanee Writers' Conference, Stamler Ctr, 119 Gailor Hall, 735 University Ave, Sewanee, TN 37383-1000 *Tel:* 931-598-1141 *E-mail:* swc@sewanee.edu *Web Site:* www.sewaneewriters.org, pg 673

Latham, Joyce Eileen, JL Communications, 10205 Green Holly Terr, Silver Spring, MD 20902 *Tel:* 301-593-0640, pg 549

Lathbury, Roger, Orchises Press, PO Box 320533, Alexandria, VA 22320-4533 *Tel:* 703-683-1243 *Web Site:* mason.gmu.edu/~lathbury/, pg 187

Lawson, Alan, Boston Authors Club Inc, 45 Pine Crest Rd, Newton, MA 02459 *Tel:* 617-552-8457 *E-mail:* bostonauthors@aol.com *Web Site:* www.bostonauthorsclub.org, pg 619

Lawson, Alan, Julia Ward Howe Book Awards, 45 Pine Crest Rd, Newton, MA 02459 *Tel:* 617-552-8457 *E-mail:* bostonauthors@aol.com *Web Site:* www.bostonauthorsclub.org, pg 710

Lawson, Vance, Thomas Nelson Inc, 501 Nelson Place, Nashville, TN 37214 *Tel:* 615-889-9000 *Toll Free Tel:* 800-251-4000 *Fax:* 615-902-1548 *E-mail:* publicity@thomasnelson.com *Web Site:* www.thomasnelson.com, pg 255

Lawton, Caryn, Washington State University Press, Cooper Publications Bldg, Grimes Way, Pullman, WA 99164 *Tel:* 509-335-3518; 509-335-7880 (order fulfillment) *Toll Free Tel:* 800-354-7360 *Fax:* 509-335-8568 *E-mail:* wsupress@wsu.edu *Web Site:* wsupress.wsu.edu, pg 276

Lawton, John, Penguin Group (USA) LLC Sales, 375 Hudson St, New York, NY 10014 *Tel:* 212-366-2000 *E-mail:* online@penguinputnam.com *Web Site:* us.penguingroup.com, pg 197

Lawton, Wendy, Books & Such, 52 Mission Circle, Suite 122, PMB 170, Santa Rosa, CA 95409-5370 *Tel:* 707-538-4184 *Web Site:* booksandsuch.com, pg 563

Lay, Kevin, Scepter Publishers, PO Box 1391, New York, NY 10802 *Tel:* 212-354-0670 *Toll Free Tel:* 800-322-8773 *Fax:* 212-354-0736 *Web Site:* www.scepterpublishers.org, pg 227

Lay, Tom, Fordham University Press, 2546 Belmont Ave, University Box L, Bronx, NY 10458 *Tel:* 718-817-4795 *Fax:* 718-817-4785 *Web Site:* www.fordhampress.com, pg 97

Laychur, Tina, The Pennsylvania State University Press, University Support Bldg 1, Suite C, 820 N University Dr, University Park, PA 16802-1003 *Tel:* 814-865-1327 *Toll Free Tel:* 800-326-9180 *Fax:* 814-863-1408 *Toll Free Fax:* 877-778-2665 *E-mail:* info@psupress.org *Web Site:* www.psupress.org, pg 198

Lazar, Dan, Writers House, 21 W 26 St, New York, NY 10010 *Tel:* 212-685-2400 *Fax:* 212-685-1781 *Web Site:* www.writershouse.com, pg 599

Lazare, Heather, Crown Publishing Group, c/o Random House Inc, 1745 Broadway, New York, NY 10019 *Tel:* 212-782-9000 *Toll Free Tel:* 888-264-1745 *Fax:* 212-940-7408 *Web Site:* www.randomhouse.com/crown, pg 72

Lazarus, Alison, Macmillan, 175 Fifth Ave, New York, NY 10010 *Tel:* 646-307-5151 *Fax:* 212-420-9314 *E-mail:* firstname.lastname@macmillan.com *Web Site:* www.macmillan.com, pg 154

Lazer, Jill, Houghton Mifflin Harcourt Trade & Reference Division, 222 Berkeley St, Boston, MA 02116-3764 *Tel:* 617-351-5000 *Toll Free Tel:* 800-225-3362 *Web Site:* www.houghtonmifflinbooks.com, pg 124

Lazin, Sarah, Sarah Lazin Books, 121 W 27 St, Suite 704, New York, NY 10001 *Tel:* 212-989-5757 *Fax:* 212-989-1393 *Web Site:* lazinbooks.com, pg 581

Lazipone, Lori, Syracuse University Press, 621 Skytop Rd, Suite 110, Syracuse, NY 13244-5290 *Tel:* 315-443-5534 *Toll Free Tel:* 800-365-8929 (cust serv) *Fax:* 315-443-5545 *E-mail:* supress@syr.edu *Web Site:* syracuseuniversitypress.syr.edu, pg 249

Le Blanc, Leslie, University Publishing Group, 219 W Washington St, Hagerstown, MD 21740 *Tel:* 240-420-0036 *Toll Free Tel:* 800-654-8188 *Fax:* 240-718-7100 *E-mail:* editorial@upgbooks.com; orders@upgbooks.com; sales@upgbooks.com *Web Site:* www.upgbooks.com, pg 272

Le Blanc, Nicole, Nicholas Brealey Publishing, 20 Park Plaza, Suite 610, Boston, MA 02116 *Tel:* 617-523-3801 *Toll Free Tel:* 888-BREALEY (273-2539) *Fax:* 617-523-3708 *E-mail:* info@nicholasbrealey.com *Web Site:* www.nicholasbrealey.com, pg 46

Le Blanc, Ondine E, The Massachusetts Historical Society, 1154 Boylston St, Boston, MA 02215-3695 *Tel:* 617-536-1608 *Fax:* 617-859-0074 *E-mail:* publications@masshist.org *Web Site:* www.masshist.org, pg 158

Le Coney, Elizabeth, Amon Carter Museum, 3501 Camp Bowie Blvd, Fort Worth, TX 76107-2695 *Tel:* 817-738-1933; 817-738-5065 (PR) *Toll Free Tel:* 800-573-1933 *Fax:* 817-336-1123 *E-mail:* pr@cartermuseum.org *Web Site:* www.cartermuseum.org, pg 53

Le May, Konnie, Lake Superior Port Cities Inc, 310 E Superior St, Suite 125, Duluth, MN 55802 *Tel:* 218-722-5002 *Toll Free Tel:* 888-BIG-LAKE (244-5253) *Fax:* 218-722-4096 *E-mail:* reader@lakesuperior.com *Web Site:* www.lakesuperior.com, pg 143

Le Pan, Don, Broadview Press, 280 Perry St, Unit 5, Peterborough, ON K9J 2J4, Canada *Tel:* 705-743-8990 *Fax:* 705-743-8353 *E-mail:* customerservice@broadviewpress.com *Web Site:* www.broadviewpress.com, pg 496

Le Peau, Andrew T, InterVarsity Press, 430 Plaza Dr, Westmont, IL 60559-1234 *Tel:* 630-734-4000 *Toll Free Tel:* 800-843-9487 *Fax:* 630-734-4200 *E-mail:* email@ivpress.com *Web Site:* www.ivpress.com, pg 134

Le, Thao, Sandra Dijkstra Literary Agency, 1155 Camino del Mar, PMB 515, Del Mar, CA 92014-2605 *Web Site:* dijkstraagency.com, pg 568

Leach, Michael, Orbis Books, Price Bldg, 85 Ryder Rd, Ossining, NY 10562 *Tel:* 914-941-7636 *Toll Free Tel:* 800-258-5838 (orders) *Fax:* 914-941-7005 *E-mail:* orbisbooks@maryknoll.org *Web Site:* www.orbisbooks.com, pg 186

Leahy, P Patrick PhD, American Geological Institute (AGI), 4220 King St, Alexandria, VA 22302-1502 *Tel:* 703-379-2480 *Fax:* 703-379-7563 *E-mail:* pubs@agiweb.org *Web Site:* www.agiweb.org, pg 13

Leaman, George, Philosophy Documentation Center, PO Box 7147, Charlottesville, VA 22906-7147 *Tel:* 434-220-3300 *Toll Free Tel:* 800-444-2419 *Fax:* 434-220-3301 *E-mail:* order@pdcnet.org *Web Site:* www.pdcnet.org, pg 201

Leandro, Sam, Bell Springs Publishing, PO Box 1240, Willits, CA 95490-1240 *Tel:* 707-459-6372 *Toll Free Tel:* 800-515-8050 *Fax:* 707-459-6372 *E-mail:* publisher@bellsprings.com *Web Site:* bellsprings.com; aboutpinball.com, pg 34

Leanza, Frank, Crystal Publishers Inc, 3460 Lost Hills Dr, Las Vegas, NV 89122 *Tel:* 702-434-3037 *Fax:* 702-434-3037 *Web Site:* www.crystalpub.com, pg 73

Leary, Sheila M, University of Wisconsin Press, 1930 Monroe St, 3rd fl, Madison, WI 53711-2059 *Tel:* 608-263-0668 *Toll Free Tel:* 800-621-2736 (orders) *Fax:* 608-263-1173 *Toll Free Fax:* 800-621-2736 (orders) *E-mail:* uwiscpress@uwpress.wisc.edu (main off) *Web Site:* www.wisc.edu/wisconsinpress, pg 270

Leavell, Byrd, Waxman Literary Agency, 80 Fifth Ave, Suite 1101, New York, NY 10011 *Tel:* 212-675-5556 *Fax:* 212-675-1381 *Web Site:* www.waxmanagency.com, pg 599

Leavitt, Ned, The Ned Leavitt Agency, 70 Wooster St, Suite 4-F, New York, NY 10012 *Tel:* 212-334-0999 *Web Site:* www.nedleavittagency.com, pg 581

Leber, Keith, University of Hawaii Press, 2840 Kolowalu St, Honolulu, HI 96822 *Tel:* 808-956-8255 *Toll Free Tel:* 888-UHPRESS (847-7377) *Fax:* 808-988-6052 *Toll Free Fax:* 800-650-7811 *E-mail:* uhpbooks@hawaii.edu *Web Site:* www.uhpress.hawaii.edu, pg 265

LeBien, Thomas, Simon & Schuster, 1230 Avenue of the Americas, New York, NY 10020 *Tel:* 212-698-7000 *Toll Free Tel:* 800-223-2348 (cust serv); 800-223-2336 (orders) *Toll Free Fax:* 800-943-9831 (orders) *Web Site:* www.simonandschuster.com, pg 234

Leblanc, Kieran, Alberta Book Awards, 10523 100 Ave, Edmonton, AB T5J 0A8, Canada *Tel:* 780-424-5060 *Fax:* 780-424-7943 *E-mail:* info@bookpublishers.ab.ca *Web Site:* www.bookpublishers.ab.ca, pg 686

Leblanc, Kieran, The Book Publishers Association of Alberta (BPAA), 10523 100 Ave, Edmonton, AB T5J 0A8, Canada *Tel:* 780-424-5060 *Fax:* 780-424-7943 *E-mail:* info@bookpublishers.ab.ca *Web Site:* www.bookpublishers.ab.ca, pg 618

LeBlanc, Tom, nSight Inc, One Van de Graaff Dr, Suite 202, Burlington, MA 01803 *Tel:* 781-273-6300 *Fax:* 781-273-6301 *E-mail:* nfritz@nsightworks.com *Web Site:* www.nsightworks.com, pg 552

Lebow, Jacqueline, Crown Publishing Group, c/o Random House Inc, 1745 Broadway, New York, NY 10019 *Tel:* 212-782-9000 *Toll Free Tel:* 888-264-1745 *Fax:* 212-940-7408 *Web Site:* www.randomhouse.com/crown, pg 72

LeCates, Justine, Doubleday/Nan A Talese, c/o Random House Inc, 1745 Broadway, New York, NY 10019 *Tel:* 212-751-2600 *Toll Free Tel:* 800-638-6460 *Fax:* 212-572-2593 *Web Site:* www.knopfdoubleday.com, pg 81

LeCates, Justine, Alfred A Knopf/Everyman's Library, c/o Random House Inc, 1745 Broadway, New York, NY 10019 *Tel:* 212-751-2600 *Toll Free Tel:* 800-638-6460 *Fax:* 212-572-2593 *Web Site:* www.knopfdoubleday.com, pg 141

LeCates, Justine, Pantheon Books/Schocken Books, c/o Random House Inc, 1745 Broadway, New York, NY 10019 *Tel:* 212-751-2600 *Toll Free Tel:* 800-638-6460 *Fax:* 212-572-6030, pg 192

Leckie, Ross, Goose Lane Editions, 500 Beaverbrook Ct, Suite 330, Fredericton, NB E3B 5X4, Canada *Tel:* 506-450-4251 *Toll Free Tel:* 888-926-8377 *Fax:* 506-459-4991 *E-mail:* info@gooselane.com *Web Site:* www.gooselane.com, pg 507

Leclerc, Richard PhD, Editions du Bois-de-Coulonge, 1140 de Montigny, Sillery, QC G1S 3T7, Canada *Tel:* 418-683-6332 *Fax:* 418-683-6332 *Web Site:* www.ebc.qc.ca, pg 495

Leczkowski, Jennifer, Running Press Book Publishers, 2300 Chestnut St, Philadelphia, PA 19103-4399 *Tel:* 215-567-5080 *Toll Free Tel:* 800-343-4499 (cust serv & orders) *Fax:* 215-568-2919 *Toll Free Fax:* 800-453-2884 (cust serv & orders) *E-mail:* perseus.promos@perseusbooks.com *Web Site:* www.runningpress.com, pg 222

Leder, Meg, Perigee Books, 375 Hudson St, New York, NY 10014 *Tel:* 212-366-2000 *Fax:* 212-366-2365 *E-mail:* perigeebooks@us.penguingroup.com *Web Site:* www.penguin.com, pg 199

Lee, Adam, Lasaria Creative Publishing, 4094 Majestic Lane, Suite 352, Fairfax, VA 22033 *E-mail:* submissions@lasariacreative.com *Web Site:* www.lasariacreative.com, pg 144

Lee, Arnie, Abacus, 3413 Roger B Chaffee SE, Suite 101, Grand Rapids, MI 49546 *Tel:* 616-241-3404 *Fax:* 616-698-0325 *E-mail:* info@abacuspub.com *Web Site:* www.abacuspub.com, pg 2

Lee, Ben, Fine Communications, 322 Eighth Ave, 15th fl, New York, NY 10001 *Tel:* 212-595-3500 *Fax:* 212-595-3779, pg 95

Lee, Calee, Xist Publishing, 16604 Sonora St, Tustin, CA 92782 *Tel:* 949-478-2568 *E-mail:* info@xistpublishing.com *Web Site:* www.xistpublishing.com, pg 287

Lee, Dan, Pearson Education Canada, 26 Prince Andrew Place, Don Mills, ON M3C 2T8, Canada *Tel:* 416-447-5101 *Toll Free Tel:* 800-263-9965 *Fax:* 416-443-0948 *Toll Free Fax:* 800-263-7733; 888-465-0536 *Web Site:* www.pearsoned.ca, pg 515

Lee, Fred, The Countryman Press, 43 Lincoln Corners Way, Woodstock, VT 05091 *Tel:* 802-457-4826 *Toll Free Tel:* 800-245-4151 *Fax:* 802-457-1678 *E-mail:* countrymanpress@wwnorton.com *Web Site:* www.countrymanpress.com, pg 70

Lee, Jacob, Xist Publishing, 16604 Sonora St, Tustin, CA 92782 *Tel:* 949-478-2568 *E-mail:* info@xistpublishing.com *Web Site:* www.xistpublishing.com, pg 287

Lee, Jeanne, Atria Books, 1230 Avenue of the Americas, New York, NY 10020 *Tel:* 212-698-7000 *Fax:* 212-698-7007 *Web Site:* www.simonandschuster.com, pg 26

Leslie, Nathan, Hamilton Stone Editions, PO Box 43, Maplewood, NJ 07040 *Tel:* 973-378-8361 *E-mail:* hstone@hamiltonstone.org *Web Site:* www.hamiltonstone.org, pg 111

Lesman, Robert G, The Sow's Ear Poetry Prize & The Sow's Ear Chapbook Prize, 217 Brookneill Dr, Winchester, VA 22602 *Tel:* 540-955-3955 *Web Site:* sows-ear.kitenet.net, pg 743

Lesperance, Pierre, VLB Editeur Inc, 1010 rue de la Gauchetiere E, Montreal, QC H2L 2N5, Canada *Tel:* 514-523-7993 *Fax:* 514-282-7530 *Web Site:* www.edvlb.com, pg 524

Lessiter, Frank, Lessiter Publications, 225 Regency Ct, Suite 200, Brookfield, WI 53045 *Tel:* 262-782-4480 *Toll Free Tel:* 800-645-8455 *Fax:* 262-782-1252 *E-mail:* info@lesspub.com *Web Site:* www.lesspub.com, pg 147

Lessiter, Mike, Lessiter Publications, 225 Regency Ct, Suite 200, Brookfield, WI 53045 *Tel:* 262-782-4480 *Toll Free Tel:* 800-645-8455 *Fax:* 262-782-1252 *E-mail:* info@lesspub.com *Web Site:* www.lesspub.com, pg 147

Lessne, Donald L, Frederick Fell Publishers Inc, 2131 Hollywood Blvd, Suite 305, Hollywood, FL 33020 *Tel:* 954-925-5242 *E-mail:* fellpub@aol.com (admin only) *Web Site:* www.fellpub.com, pg 98

Lester, Carmen, Enslow Publishers Inc, 40 Industrial Rd, Dept F-61, Berkeley Heights, NJ 07922 *Tel:* 908-771-9400 *Toll Free Tel:* 800-398-2504 *Fax:* 908-771-0925; 908-771-8400 (orders) *E-mail:* customerservice@enslow.com; orders@enslow.com *Web Site:* www.enslow.com; www.myreportlinks.com, pg 88

Letchworth, Lynne, Chalice Press, 483 E Lockwood Ave, Suite 100, St Louis, MO 63119 *Tel:* 314-231-8500 *Toll Free Tel:* 800-366-3383 *Fax:* 314-231-8524; 770-280-4039 (orders) *E-mail:* customerservice@chalicepress.com *Web Site:* www.chalicepress.com, pg 57

Letourneau, Helene, Association Nationale des Editeurs de Livres, 2514 boul Rosemont, Montreal, QC H1Y 1K4, Canada *Tel:* 514-273-8130 *Toll Free Tel:* 866-900-ANEL (900-2635) *Fax:* 514-273-9657 *E-mail:* info@anel.qc.ca *Web Site:* www.anel.qc.ca, pg 616

Lett, Ivan, Yale University Press, 302 Temple St, New Haven, CT 06511-8909 *Tel:* 401-531-2800 (cust serv); 203-432-0960 *Toll Free Tel:* 800-405-1619 (cust serv) *Fax:* 203-432-0948; 401-531-2801 (cust serv) *Toll Free Fax:* 800-406-9145 (cust serv) *E-mail:* customer.care@trilateral.org (cust serv); language.yalepress@yale.edu *Web Site:* www.yalebooks.com, pg 287

Letvin, Alice, Cricket Books, 70 E Lake St, Suite 300, Chicago, IL 60601 *Tel:* 603-924-7209 *Toll Free Tel:* 800-821-0115 *E-mail:* customerservice@caruspub.com *Web Site:* www.cricketmag.com, pg 71

Leung, Mona, McGraw-Hill Higher Education, 1333 Burr Ridge Pkwy, Burr Ridge, IL 60527 *Tel:* 630-789-4000 *Toll Free Tel:* 800-338-3987 (cust serv) *Fax:* 614-755-5645 (cust serv) *Web Site:* www.mhhe.com, pg 161

Levay, Rachael, University of Washington Press, 433 Brooklyn Ave NE, Seattle, WA 98195-9570 *Tel:* 206-543-4050 *Toll Free Tel:* 800-537-5487 (orders) *Fax:* 206-543-3932; 410-516-6998 (orders) *E-mail:* uwpress@u.washington.edu *Web Site:* www.washington.edu/uwpress/, pg 270

Levenberg, Rachel, HarperCollins Publishers Sales, 10 E 53 St, New York, NY 10022 *Fax:* 212-207-7000 *Web Site:* www.harpercollins.com, pg 114

Leventhal, J P, Black Dog & Leventhal Publishers Inc, 151 W 19 St, New York, NY 10011 *Tel:* 212-647-9336 *Toll Free Tel:* 800-722-7202 *Fax:* 212-647-9332 *E-mail:* info@blackdogandleventhal.com; orders@workman.com *Web Site:* www.blackdogandleventhal.com; blackdogonline.com, pg 39

Leverence, John, Academy of Television Arts & Sciences (ATAS), 5220 Lankershim Blvd, North Hollywood, CA 91601-3109 *Tel:* 818-754-2800 *Fax:* 818-761-2827 *Web Site:* www.emmys.tv, pg 611

Leverton, Yossi, Hachai Publishing, 527 Empire Blvd, Brooklyn, NY 11225 *Tel:* 718-633-0100 *Fax:* 718-633-0103 *E-mail:* info@hachai.com *Web Site:* www.hachai.com, pg 109

Levin, Janet, North Atlantic Books, 2526 Martin Luther King Jr Way, Berkeley, CA 94704 *Tel:* 510-549-4270 *Fax:* 510-549-4276 *Web Site:* www.northatlanticbooks.com, pg 180

Levine, Arthur A, Scholastic Trade Division, 557 Broadway, New York, NY 10012 *Tel:* 212-343-6100; 212-343-4685 (export sales) *Fax:* 212-343-4714 (export sales) *Web Site:* www.scholastic.com, pg 228

Levine, Barbara, Aslan Publishing, 857 Post Rd, Suite 302, Fairfield, CT 06824 *Tel:* 203-372-0300 *Fax:* 203-374-4766 *E-mail:* information@aslanpublishing.com *Web Site:* www.aslanpublishing.com, pg 24

Levine, Daniel, Empire Press Media/Avant-Guide, 244 Fifth Ave, Suite 2053, New York, NY 10001-7604 *Tel:* 917-512-3881 *Fax:* 212-202-7757 *E-mail:* info@avantguide.com; communications@avantguide.com; editor@avantguide.com *Web Site:* www.avantguide.com, pg 87

Levine, Deborah, The Jeff Herman Agency LLC, 29 Park St, Stockbridge, MA 01262 *Tel:* 413-298-0077 *Fax:* 413-298-8188 *E-mail:* submissions@jeffherman.com *Web Site:* www.jeffherman.com, pg 577

Levine, Ellen, Trident Media Group LLC, 41 Madison Ave, 36th fl, New York, NY 10010 *Tel:* 212-262-4810 *Fax:* 212-262-4849 *Web Site:* www.tridentmediagroup.com, pg 598

Levine, Ellie, Harry N Abrams Inc, 115 W 18 St, 6th fl, New York, NY 10011 *Tel:* 212-206-7715 *Toll Free Tel:* 800-345-1359 *Fax:* 212-519-1210 *E-mail:* abrams@abramsbooks.com *Web Site:* www.abramsbooks.com, pg 3

Levine, Harold, Aslan Publishing, 857 Post Rd, Suite 302, Fairfield, CT 06824 *Tel:* 203-372-0300 *Fax:* 203-374-4766 *E-mail:* information@aslanpublishing.com *Web Site:* www.aslanpublishing.com, pg 24

Levine, James, Levine|Greenberg Literary Agency Inc, 307 Seventh Ave, Suite 2407, New York, NY 10001 *Tel:* 212-337-0934 *Fax:* 212-337-0948 *Web Site:* www.levinegreenberg.com, pg 581

Levine, Jeffrey, Tupelo Press Inc, PO Box 1767, North Adams, MA 01247 *Tel:* 413-664-9611 *Fax:* 413-664-9711 *E-mail:* info@tupelopress.org *Web Site:* www.tupelopress.org, pg 260

Levine, Jonathan D, Prayer Book Press Inc, 1363 Fairfield Ave, Bridgeport, CT 06605 *Tel:* 203-384-2284 *Fax:* 203-579-9109, pg 205

Levine, Katie, HarperCollins Publishers, 10 E 53 St, New York, NY 10022 *Tel:* 212-207-7000 *Fax:* 212-207-7145 *Web Site:* www.harpercollins.com, pg 113

Levine, Michael, Westwood Creative Artists Ltd, 94 Harbord St, Toronto, ON M5S 1G6, Canada *Tel:* 416-964-3302 *Fax:* 416-975-9209 *E-mail:* wca_office@wcaltd.com *Web Site:* www.wcaltd.com, pg 599

Levine, Ronn, Specialized Information Publishers Association (SIPA), 1090 Vermont Ave NW, 6th fl, Washington, DC 20005 *Tel:* 202-289-7442 *Fax:* 202-289-7097 *E-mail:* sipa@siia.net *Web Site:* www.sipaonline.com, pg 637

Levins, Michael S, innovativeKids®, 50 Washington St, Suite 201, Norwalk, CT 06854 *Tel:* 203-838-6400 *E-mail:* info@innovativekids.com *Web Site:* www.innovativekids.com, pg 131

Levinson, Diane, Princeton Architectural Press, 37 E Seventh St, New York, NY 10003 *Tel:* 212-995-9620 *Toll Free Tel:* 800-722-6657 (dist); 800-759-0190 (sales) *Fax:* 212-995-9454 *E-mail:* sales@papress.com *Web Site:* www.papress.com, pg 206

Levitan, Jeanie, Bear & Co Inc, One Park St, Rochester, VT 05767 *Tel:* 802-767-3174 *Toll Free Tel:* 800-932-3277 *Fax:* 802-767-3726 *E-mail:* customerservice@InnerTraditions.com *Web Site:* InnerTraditions.com, pg 33

Levitan, Jeanie, Inner Traditions International Ltd, One Park St, Rochester, VT 05767 *Tel:* 802-767-3174 *Toll Free Tel:* 800-246-8648 *Fax:* 802-767-3726 *E-mail:* customerservice@InnerTraditions.com *Web Site:* www.InnerTraditions.com, pg 130

Levithan, David, Scholastic Trade Division, 557 Broadway, New York, NY 10012 *Tel:* 212-343-6100; 212-343-4685 (export sales) *Fax:* 212-343-4714 (export sales) *Web Site:* www.scholastic.com, pg 228

Levy, Donna, Business Marketing Association (BMA), 1833 Centre Point Circle, Suite 123, Naperville, IL 60563 *Tel:* 630-544-5054 *Fax:* 630-544-5055 *E-mail:* info@marketing.org *Web Site:* www.marketing.org, pg 619

Levy, Roanie, Access Copyright, The Canadian Copyright Licensing Agency, One Yonge St, Suite 800, Toronto, ON M5E 1E5, Canada *Tel:* 416-868-1620 *Toll Free Tel:* 800-893-5777 *Fax:* 416-868-1621 *E-mail:* info@accesscopyright.ca *Web Site:* www.accesscopyright.ca, pg 611

Lew, Cindy, Fine Communications, 322 Eighth Ave, 15th fl, New York, NY 10001 *Tel:* 212-595-3500 *Fax:* 212-595-3779, pg 95

Lewandoski, Joyce, University of Texas Press, 2100 Comal St, Austin, TX 78722 *Tel:* 512-471-7233 *Fax:* 512-232-7178 *E-mail:* utpress@uts.cc.utexas.edu *Web Site:* www.utexaspress.com, pg 253

Lewin, Arianne, GP Putnam's Sons (Children's), 345 Hudson St, New York, NY 10014 *Tel:* 212-366-2000 *Fax:* 212-414-3393 *E-mail:* online@penguinputnam.com *Web Site:* us.penguingroup.com, pg 210

Lewis, Amanda, Knopf Random Canada, One Toronto St, Suite 300, Toronto, ON M5C 2V6, Canada *Tel:* 416-364-4449 *Toll Free Tel:* 888-523-9292 *Fax:* 416-364-6863 *Web Site:* www.randomhouse.ca, pg 510

Lewis, Beth A, Augsburg Fortress Publishers, Publishing House of the Evangelical Lutheran Church in America, 100 S Fifth St, Suite 600, Minneapolis, MN 55402 *Tel:* 612-330-3300 *Toll Free Tel:* 800-426-0115 (ext 639, subns); 800-328-4648 (orders) *E-mail:* info@augsburgfortress.org; copyright@augsburgfortress.org (reprint permission requests); customercare@augsburgfortress.org *Web Site:* www.augsburgfortress.org, pg 27

Lewis, Brandi, Howard Books, 216 Centerview Dr, Suite 303, Brentwood, TN 37027 *Tel:* 615-873-2080 *Fax:* 615-370-3834 *E-mail:* howardbooks@simonandschuster.com (info) *Web Site:* www.howardpublishing.com, pg 124

Lewis, Brent, Harlequin Enterprises Ltd, 225 Duncan Mill Rd, Don Mills, ON M3B 3K9, Canada *Tel:* 416-445-5860 *Toll Free Tel:* 888-432-4879; 800-370-5838 (ebook inquiries) *Fax:* 416-445-8655 *E-mail:* CustomerService@harlequin.com *Web Site:* www.harlequin.com, pg 508

Lewis, Daniel, The Overmountain Press, PO Box 1261, Johnson City, TN 37605-1261 *Tel:* 423-926-2691 *Toll Free Tel:* 800-992-2691 (orders) *Fax:* 423-232-1252 *E-mail:* orders@overmtn.com *Web Site:* www.overmtn.com, pg 189

Lewis, Dave, Baker Books, 6030 E Fulton Rd, Ada, MI 49301 *Tel:* 616-676-9185 *Toll Free Tel:* 800-877-2665; 800-679-1957 *Fax:* 616-676-9573 *Toll Free Fax:* 800-398-3111 *Web Site:* www.bakerpublishinggroup.com, pg 29

Lewis, Dave, Bethany House Publishers, 11400 Hampshire Ave S, Bloomington, MN 55438 *Tel:* 952-829-2500 *Toll Free Tel:* 800-877-2665 (orders) *Fax:* 952-829-2568 *Toll Free Fax:* 800-398-3111 (orders) *Web Site:* www.bethanyhouse.com; www.bakerpublishinggroup.com, pg 36

Lewis, David, Don Buchwald & Associates Inc, 10 E 44 St, New York, NY 10017 *Tel:* 212-867-1200 *Fax:* 212-867-2434 *E-mail:* info@buchwald.com *Web Site:* www.buchwald.com, pg 565

Lewis, Dottie, National Academies Press (NAP), Lockbox 285, 500 Fifth St NW, Washington, DC 20001 *Tel:* 202-334-3313 *Toll Free Tel:* 888-624-8373 (cust serv) *Fax:* 202-334-2451 (cust serv); 202-334-2793 (mktg dept) *E-mail:* customer_service@nap.edu *Web Site:* www.nap.edu, pg 173

Lewis, George, Beyond Words Publishing Inc, 20827 NW Cornell Rd, Suite 500, Hillsboro, OR 97124-9808 *Tel:* 503-531-8700 *Fax:* 503-531-8773 *Web Site:* www.beyondword.com, pg 37

Lewis, Jacob, Crown Publishing Group, c/o Random House Inc, 1745 Broadway, New York, NY 10019 *Tel:* 212-782-9000 *Toll Free Tel:* 888-264-1745 *Fax:* 212-940-7408 *Web Site:* www.randomhouse.com/crown, pg 72

Lewis, Jennifer, Gryphon House Inc, 10770 Columbia Pike, Suite 201, Silver Spring, MD 20901 *Tel:* 301-595-9500 *Toll Free Tel:* 800-638-0928 *Fax:* 301-595-0051 *Toll Free Fax:* 877-638-7576 *E-mail:* info@ghbooks.com *Web Site:* www.gryphonhouse.com, pg 109

Lewis, Kevin, Disney-Hyperion Books, 44 S Broadway, White Plains, NY 10601 *Tel:* 212-633-4400 *Fax:* 212-807-5880 *Web Site:* disney.go.com/books/index, pg 79

Lewis, Kitty, Brick Books, Box 20081, 431 Boler Rd, London, ON N6K 4G6, Canada *Tel:* 519-657-8579 *E-mail:* brick.books@sympatico.ca *Web Site:* www.brickbooks.ca, pg 495

Lewis, Kristen, Upper Access Inc, 87 Upper Access Rd, Hinesburg, VT 05461 *Tel:* 802-482-2988 *Toll Free Tel:* 800-310-8320 *Fax:* 802-304-1005 *E-mail:* info@upperaccess.com *Web Site:* www.upperaccess.com, pg 272

Lewis, Marc, Presbyterian Publishing Corp, 100 Witherspoon St, Louisville, KY 40202 *Tel:* 502-569-5000 *Toll Free Tel:* 800-523-1631 (US only) *Fax:* 502-569-5113 *E-mail:* ppcmail@presbypub.com *Web Site:* www.wjkbooks.com, pg 205

Lewis, Marc, Westminster John Knox Press, 100 Witherspoon St, Louisville, KY 40202-1396 *Tel:* 502-569-5052 *Toll Free Tel:* 800-227-2872 (US only) *Fax:* 502-569-8308 *Toll Free Fax:* 800-541-5113 (US & CN) *E-mail:* wjk@wjkbooks.com; customer_service@wjkbooks.com *Web Site:* www.wjkbooks.com, pg 279

Lewis, Molly, ZOVA Books, PO Box 21833, Long Beach, CA 90801 *Tel:* 805-426-9682 *Fax:* 562-394-9568 *Web Site:* www.zovabooks.com, pg 290

Lewis, Mrs Morgan, Florida Individual Artist Fellowships, 500 S Bronough St, Tallahassee, FL 32399-0250 *Tel:* 850-245-6470 *Fax:* 850-245-6497 *E-mail:* info@florida-arts.org *Web Site:* www.florida-arts.org, pg 704

Lewis, Nora, College of Liberal & Professional Studies, University of Pennsylvania, 3440 Market St, Suite 100, Philadelphia, PA 19104-3335 *Tel:* 215-898-7326 *Fax:* 215-573-2053 *E-mail:* lps@sas.upenn.edu *Web Site:* www.sas.upenn.edu; www.sas.upenn.edu/lps, pg 677

Lewis, Sherry, The Overmountain Press, PO Box 1261, Johnson City, TN 37605-1261 *Tel:* 423-926-2691 *Toll Free Tel:* 800-992-2691 (orders) *Fax:* 423-232-1252 *E-mail:* orders@overmtn.com *Web Site:* www.overmtn.com, pg 189

Lewis, Stacey, City Lights Publishers, 261 Columbus Ave, San Francisco, CA 94133 *Tel:* 415-362-8193 *Fax:* 415-362-4921 *E-mail:* staff@citylights.com *Web Site:* www.citylights.com, pg 62

Lewis, Sylvia, APA Planners Press, 205 N Michigan Ave, Suite 1200, Chicago, IL 60601 *Tel:* 312-431-9100 *Fax:* 312-786-6700 *E-mail:* customerservice@planning.org *Web Site:* www.planning.org, pg 19

Li, Cherlynne, Touchstone, 1230 Avenue of the Americas, New York, NY 10020, pg 256

Li, Johanna, Simon & Schuster, 1230 Avenue of the Americas, New York, NY 10020 *Tel:* 212-698-7000 *Toll Free Tel:* 800-223-2348 (cust serv); 800-223-2336 (orders) *Toll Free Fax:* 800-943-9831 (orders) *Web Site:* www.simonandschuster.com, pg 234

Li, Karen, Owlkids Books Inc, 10 Lower Spadina Ave, Suite 400, Toronto, ON M5V 2Z2, Canada *Tel:* 416-340-3700 *Fax:* 416-340-9769 *E-mail:* owlkids@owlkids.com *Web Site:* www.owlkidsbooks.com, pg 514

Li, Philip, The Century Foundation, 41 E 70 St, New York, NY 10021 *Tel:* 212-535-4441; 212-879-9197 *Fax:* 212-879-9197 *E-mail:* info@tcf.org *Web Site:* www.tcf.org, pg 57, 641

Liberatore, Arlette, Society for Industrial & Applied Mathematics, 3600 Market St, 6th fl, Philadelphia, PA 19104-2688 *Tel:* 215-382-9800 *Toll Free Tel:* 800-447-7426 *Fax:* 215-386-7999 *E-mail:* siambooks@siam.org *Web Site:* www.siam.org, pg 238

Lichtenstadter, Jill, The Overlook Press, 141 Wooster St, Suite 4-B, New York, NY 10012 *Tel:* 212-673-2210; 845-679-6838 (orders & dist) *Fax:* 212-673-2296 *E-mail:* sales@overlookny.com (orders) *Web Site:* www.overlookpress.com, pg 189

Lidofsky, Norman, Penguin Group (USA) LLC, 375 Hudson St, New York, NY 10014 *Tel:* 212-366-2000 *Toll Free Tel:* 800-847-5515 (inside sales); 800-631-8571 (cust serv) *Fax:* 212-366-2666; 607-775-4829 (inside sales) *E-mail:* online@us.penguingroup.com *Web Site:* www.penguin.com; us.penguingroup.com, pg 197

Lidofsky, Norman, Penguin Group (USA) LLC Sales, 375 Hudson St, New York, NY 10014 *Tel:* 212-366-2000 *E-mail:* online@penguinputnam.com *Web Site:* us.penguingroup.com, pg 197

Lieberman, Beth, The Editors Circle, 462 Grove St, Montclair, NJ 07043 *Tel:* 973-783-5082 *E-mail:* query@theeditorscircle.com *Web Site:* www.theeditorscircle.com, pg 545

Lieberman, Robert H, Robert Lieberman Agency, 475 Nelson Rd, Ithaca, NY 14850 *Tel:* 607-273-8801 *Web Site:* www.kewgardensmovie.com/CUPeople/users/rhl10, pg 582

Lieberman, Sarah, Simon & Schuster Audio, 1230 Avenue of the Americas, New York, NY 10020 *Web Site:* audio.simonandschuster.com, pg 234

Lieberwirth, Meghan, Merriam-Webster Inc, 47 Federal St, Springfield, MA 01102 *Tel:* 413-734-3134 *Toll Free Tel:* 800-828-1880 (orders & cust serv) *Fax:* 413-731-5979 (sales) *E-mail:* support@merriam-webster.com *Web Site:* www.merriam-webster.com, pg 165

Liebling, Sara, Disney-Hyperion Books, 44 S Broadway, White Plains, NY 10601 *Tel:* 212-633-4400 *Fax:* 212-807-5880 *Web Site:* disney.go.com/books/index, pg 79

Liebling, Sara, Disney Publishing Worldwide, 44 S Broadway, 9th fl, White Plains, NY 10601-4411 *Tel:* 914-288-4100 *Web Site:* disney.go.com/books/index, pg 80

Liebman, Lance, American Law Institute, 4025 Chestnut St, Philadelphia, PA 19104-3099 *Tel:* 215-243-1600 *Toll Free Tel:* 800-253-6397 *Fax:* 215-243-1664; 215-243-1683 *Web Site:* www.ali.org, pg 14

Liebmann, Nicholas, St Herman Press, 10 Beegum Gorge Rd, Platina, CA 96076 *Tel:* 530-352-4430 *Fax:* 530-352-4432 *E-mail:* stherman@stherman.com *Web Site:* www.stherman.com, pg 224

Liffring-Zug Bourret, Joan, Penfield Books, 215 Brown St, Iowa City, IA 52245 *Tel:* 319-337-9998 *Toll Free Tel:* 800-728-9998 *Fax:* 319-351-6846 *E-mail:* penfield@penfieldbooks.com *Web Site:* www.penfieldbooks.com, pg 196

Liggett, Diane, National Park Service Media Services, 67 Mather Place, Harpers Ferry, WV 25425 *Tel:* 304-535-5050 *Fax:* 304-535-6176 *Web Site:* www.nps.gov/hfc, pg 175

Ligon, Linda, Interweave Press LLC, 201 E Fourth St, Loveland, CO 80537 *Tel:* 970-669-7672 *Toll Free Tel:* 800-272-2193 *Fax:* 970-667-8317 *E-mail:* interweaveservice@interweave.com *Web Site:* www.interweave.com, pg 134

Likoff, Laurie, Bloom's Literary Criticism, 132 W 31 St, 17th fl, New York, NY 10001 *Toll Free Tel:* 800-322-8755 *Toll Free Fax:* 800-678-3633 *E-mail:* custserv@factsonfile.com *Web Site:* www.infobasepublishing.com, pg 40

Likoff, Laurie, Chelsea House Publishers, 132 W 31 St, 17th fl, New York, NY 10001 *Tel:* 212-967-8800 *Toll Free Tel:* 800-322-8755 *Fax:* 917-339-0325; 917-339-0323 *Toll Free Fax:* 800-678-3633 *E-mail:* custserv@factsonfile.com *Web Site:* www.infobasepublishing.com; www.infobaselearning.com, pg 59

Likoff, Laurie, Facts On File, 132 W 31 St, 17th fl, New York, NY 10001 *Tel:* 212-967-8800 *Toll Free Tel:* 800-322-8755 *Fax:* 917-339-0323 *Toll Free Fax:* 800-678-3633 *E-mail:* custserv@factsonfile.com *Web Site:* infobasepublishing.com, pg 91

Likoff, Laurie, Ferguson Publishing, 132 W 31 St, 17th fl, New York, NY 10001 *Tel:* 212-967-8800 *Toll Free Tel:* 800-322-8755 *Fax:* 917-339-0323 *Toll Free Fax:* 800-678-3633 *E-mail:* custserv@factsonfile.com *Web Site:* infobasepublishing.com, pg 94

Lillie, Brandon, Beckett Media LLC, 22840 Savi Ranch Pkwy, Suite 200, Yorba Linda, CA 92887 *Tel:* 714-939-9991 *Toll Free Tel:* 800-332-3330 *Fax:* 714-939-9909 *Toll Free Fax:* 800-249-7761 *Web Site:* www.beckettmedia.com, pg 33

Limb, John, OCP, 5536 NE Hassalo St, Portland, OR 97213 *Tel:* 503-281-1191 *Toll Free Tel:* 800-548-8749 *Fax:* 503-282-3486 *Toll Free Fax:* 800-843-8181 *E-mail:* liturgy@ocp.org *Web Site:* www.ocp.org, pg 184

Limb, John, Pastoral Press, 5536 NE Hassalo, Portland, OR 97213-3638 *Tel:* 503-281-1191 *Toll Free Tel:* 800-548-8749 *Fax:* 503-282-3486 *Toll Free Fax:* 800-462-7329 *E-mail:* liturgy@ocp.org *Web Site:* www.ocp.org, pg 194

Limke, Fred, Franciscan Media, 28 W Liberty St, Cincinnati, OH 45202 *Tel:* 513-241-5615 *Toll Free Tel:* 800-488-0488 *Fax:* 513-241-0399 *E-mail:* books@americancatholic.org *Web Site:* www.americancatholic.org, pg 98

Lincoln, Mike, National Government Publishing Association, 629 N Main St, Hattiesburg, MS 39401 *Tel:* 601-582-3330 *Fax:* 601-582-3354 *E-mail:* info@govpublishing.org *Web Site:* www.govpublishing.org, pg 630

Lindeburg, Michael, Professional Publications Inc (PPI), 1250 Fifth Ave, Belmont, CA 94002 *Tel:* 650-593-9119 *Toll Free Tel:* 800-426-1178 (orders) *Fax:* 650-592-4519 *E-mail:* info@ppi2pass.com *Web Site:* www.ppi2pass.com, pg 207

Lindeman, Susan, Pennsylvania Historical & Museum Commission, Commonwealth Keystone Bldg, 400 North St, Harrisburg, PA 17120-0053 *Tel:* 717-783-2618 *Toll Free Tel:* 800-747-7790 *Fax:* 717-787-8312 *E-mail:* ra-pabookstore@state.pa.us *Web Site:* www.pabookstore.com; www.phmc.state.pa.us, pg 198

Lindemer, Christine R, Boston Road Communications, 227 Boston Rd, Groton, MA 01450-1959 *Tel:* 978-448-8133 *Web Site:* www.bostonroadcommunications.com, pg 542

Lindensmith, Chris, Bitingduck Press LLC, 1262 Sunnyoaks Cir, Altadena, CA 91001 *Tel:* 626-679-2494; 626-507-8033 *E-mail:* notifications@bitingduckpress.com *Web Site:* bitingduckpress.com, pg 38

Lindensmith, Chris, Boson Books, 1262 Sunnyoaks Circle, Altadena, CA 91001 *Tel:* 626-507-8033 *Web Site:* www.bosonbooks.com, pg 44

Lindensmith, Gretchen, Bitingduck Press LLC, 1262 Sunnyoaks Cir, Altadena, CA 91001 *Tel:* 626-679-2494; 626-507-8033 *E-mail:* notifications@bitingduckpress.com *Web Site:* bitingduckpress.com, pg 38

Linder, Bertram L, Educational Design Services LLC, 5750 Bou Ave, Suite 1508, North Bethesda, MD 20852 *Tel:* 301-881-8611 *Web Site:* www.educationaldesignservices.com, pg 570

Lindgren, Pat, Lindgren & Smith, 676-A Ninth Ave, New York, NY 10036 *Tel:* 212-397-7330 *E-mail:* representation@lindgrensmith.com *Web Site:* www.lindgrensmith.com; www.redpaintbox.com, pg 602

Livesey, Magdalen B, Cortina Institute of Languages, 7 Hollyhock Rd, Wilton, CT 06897 *Tel:* 203-762-2510 *Toll Free Tel:* 800-245-2145 *Fax:* 203-762-2514 *Web Site:* www.cortina-languages.com, pg 68

Livesey, Magdalen B, Cortina Learning International Inc (CLI), 7 Hollyhock Rd, Wilton, CT 06897-4414 *Tel:* 203-762-2510 *Toll Free Tel:* 800-245-2145 *Fax:* 203-762-2514 *E-mail:* info@cortinalearning.com *Web Site:* www.cortinalearning.com, pg 68

Livesey, Robert E, Cortina Institute of Languages, 7 Hollyhock Rd, Wilton, CT 06897 *Tel:* 203-762-2510 *Toll Free Tel:* 800-245-2145 *Fax:* 203-762-2514 *Web Site:* www.cortina-languages.com, pg 68

Livesey, Robert E, Cortina Learning International Inc (CLI), 7 Hollyhock Rd, Wilton, CT 06897-4414 *Tel:* 203-762-2510 *Toll Free Tel:* 800-245-2145 *Fax:* 203-762-2514 *E-mail:* info@cortinalearning.com *Web Site:* www.cortinalearning.com, pg 68

Livingstone, Donna, University of Calgary Press, 2500 University Dr NW, Calgary, AB T2N 1N4, Canada *Tel:* 403-220-7578 *Fax:* 403-282-0085 *Web Site:* www.uofcpress.com, pg 523

Lizzi, Marian, Perigee Books, 375 Hudson St, New York, NY 10014 *Tel:* 212-366-2000 *Fax:* 212-366-2365 *E-mail:* perigeebooks@us.penguingroup.com *Web Site:* www.penguin.com, pg 199

Llosa, Genoveva, HarperCollins General Books Group, 10 E 53 St, New York, NY 10022 *Tel:* 212-207-7000 *Fax:* 212-207-7633 *Web Site:* www.harpercollins.com, pg 113

Lloyd, Casey, Random House Children's Books, 1745 Broadway, New York, NY 10019 *Tel:* 212-782-9000 *Toll Free Tel:* 800-200-3552 *Fax:* 212-782-9452 *Web Site:* randomhousekids.com, pg 213

Lloyd, Dennis, University Press of Florida, 15 NW 15 St, Gainesville, FL 32603-2079 *Tel:* 352-392-1351 *Toll Free Tel:* 800-226-3822 (orders only) *Fax:* 352-392-0590 *Toll Free Fax:* 800-680-1955 (orders only) *E-mail:* info@upf.com *Web Site:* www.upf.com, pg 271

Lloyd, Tim, Alexander Street Press LLC, 3212 Duke St, Alexandria, VA 22314 *Tel:* 703-212-8520 *Toll Free Tel:* 800-889-5937 *Fax:* 703-940-6584 *E-mail:* sales@alexanderstreet.com; marketing@alexanderstreet.com *Web Site:* www.alexanderstreet.com, pg 7

Lloyd, Timothy, Opie Prize, Ohio State Univ, Mershon Ctr, 1501 Neil Ave, Columbus, OH 43201-2602 *Tel:* 614-292-3375 *Fax:* 614-292-2407 *Web Site:* www.afsnet.org/aboutAFS/AFSprizes.cfm, pg 731

Lloyd-Sidle, Elena, Fons Vitae, 49 Mockingbird Valley Dr, Louisville, KY 40207-1366 *Tel:* 502-897-3641 *Fax:* 502-893-7373 *E-mail:* fonsvitaeky@aol.com *Web Site:* www.fonsvitae.com, pg 97

Lo Frumento, John, American Society of Composers, Authors & Publishers (ASCAP), One Lincoln Plaza, New York City, NY 10023 *Tel:* 212-621-6000 *Toll Free Tel:* 800-952-7227 *Fax:* 212-612-8453 *E-mail:* info@ascap.com *Web Site:* www.ascap.com, pg 614

Lobdell, Jim, Balance Sports Publishing, 195 Lucero Way, Portola Valley, CA 94028 *Tel:* 650-561-9586 *Fax:* 650-391-9850 *E-mail:* info@balancesportspublishing.com *Web Site:* www.balancesportspublishing.com, pg 30

Lobynko, Anastasia, AZ Books LLC, 245 Eighth Ave, Suite 180, New York, NY 10011 *Toll Free Tel:* 888-945-7723 *Toll Free Fax:* 888-945-7724 *Web Site:* www.azbooksusa.com, pg 28

Lochner, Wendy, Columbia University Press, 61 W 62 St, New York, NY 10023 *Tel:* 212-459-0600 *Toll Free Tel:* 800-944-8648 *Fax:* 212-459-3678 *E-mail:* cup_book@columbia.edu (orders & cust serv) *Web Site:* cup.columbia.edu, pg 65

Lockard, Eric, Salina Bookshelf Inc, 3120 N Caden Ct, Suite 4, Flagstaff, AZ 86004 *Toll Free Tel:* 877-527-0070 *Fax:* 928-526-0386 *Web Site:* www.salinabookshelf.com, pg 225

Locke, Terry, Loyola Press, 3441 N Ashland Ave, Chicago, IL 60657 *Tel:* 773-281-1818 *Toll Free Tel:* 800-621-1008 *Fax:* 773-281-0555 (cust serv); 773-281-4129 (edit) *E-mail:* customerservice@loyolapress.com *Web Site:* www.loyolapress.com; www.spiritedtalk.org, pg 153

Locke, Tracy, The Penguin Press, 375 Hudson St, New York, NY 10014, pg 197

Lockhart, Matt, Standard Publishing, 8805 Governors Hill Dr, Suite 400, Cincinnati, OH 45249 *Tel:* 513-931-4050 *Toll Free Tel:* 800-543-1353 *Fax:* 513-931-0950 *Toll Free Fax:* 877-867-5751 *E-mail:* customerservice@standardpub.com *Web Site:* www.standardpub.com, pg 242

Lockhart, Robert, University of Pennsylvania Press, 3905 Spruce St, Philadelphia, PA 19104 *Tel:* 215-898-6261 *Fax:* 215-898-0404 *E-mail:* custserv@pobox.upenn.edu *Web Site:* www.pennpress.org, pg 268

Locks, Sueyun, Locks Art Publications/Locks Gallery, 600 Washington Sq S, Philadelphia, PA 19106 *Tel:* 215-629-1000 *E-mail:* info@locksgallery.com *Web Site:* www.locksgallery.com, pg 151

Lockwood, Karen, Syracuse University Press, 621 Skytop Rd, Suite 110, Syracuse, NY 13244-5290 *Tel:* 315-443-5534 *Toll Free Tel:* 800-365-8929 (cust serv) *Fax:* 315-443-5545 *E-mail:* supress@syr.edu *Web Site:* syracuseuniversitypress.syr.edu, pg 249

Lodwick, Kathleen, EastBridge, 70 New Canaan Ave, Norwalk, CT 06850 *Tel:* 203-855-9125 *Fax:* 203-857-0730 *E-mail:* asia@eastbridgebooks.org *Web Site:* www.eastbridgebooks.org, pg 84

Loeb, Sharon, McGraw-Hill/Irwin, 1333 Burr Ridge Pkwy, Burr Ridge, IL 60527 *Tel:* 630-789-4000 *Toll Free Tel:* 800-338-3987 (cust serv) *Fax:* 630-789-6942; 614-755-5645 (cust serv) *Web Site:* www.mhhe.com, pg 162

Loeding, Deborah V, H W Wilson, 10 Estes St, Ipswich, MA 01938 *Tel:* 978-356-6500 *Toll Free Tel:* 800-653-2726 (US & CN) *Fax:* 978-356-6565 *E-mail:* information@ebscohost.com *Web Site:* www.ebscohost.com, pg 282

Loehnen, Ben, Simon & Schuster, 1230 Avenue of the Americas, New York, NY 10020 *Tel:* 212-698-7000 *Toll Free Tel:* 800-223-2348 (cust serv); 800-223-2336 (orders) *Toll Free Fax:* 800-943-9831 (orders) *Web Site:* www.simonandschuster.com, pg 234

Loehr, Julie L, Michigan State University Press (MSU Press), 1405 S Harrison Rd, Suite 25, East Lansing, MI 48823 *Tel:* 517-355-9543 *Fax:* 517-432-2611 *Toll Free Fax:* 800-678-2120 *E-mail:* msupress@msu.edu *Web Site:* www.msupress.msu.edu, pg 165

Loehr, Mallory, Random House Children's Books, 1745 Broadway, New York, NY 10019 *Tel:* 212-782-9000 *Toll Free Tel:* 800-200-3552 *Fax:* 212-782-9452 *Web Site:* randomhousekids.com, pg 213

Loertscher, David V, Hi Willow Research & Publishing, PO Box 131266, Spring, TX 77393 *Toll Free Tel:* 800-873-3043 *Fax:* 936-271-4560 *E-mail:* lmcsourcesales@gmail.com *Web Site:* www.lmcsource.com, pg 119

Loerzel, Robert, The Society of Midland Authors (SMA), PO Box 10419, Chicago, IL 60610 *E-mail:* info@midlandauthors.com *Web Site:* www.midlandauthors.com, pg 636

Loerzel, Robert, The Society of Midland Authors Awards, 530 Michigan Ave, Evanston, IL 60202 *E-mail:* info@midlandauthors.com *Web Site:* www.midlandauthors.com, pg 743

Loesche, Kerri, Group Publishing Inc, 1515 Cascade Ave, Loveland, CO 80538 *Tel:* 970-669-3836 *Toll Free Tel:* 800-447-1070 *Fax:* 970-292-4373 *E-mail:* info@group.com *Web Site:* www.group.com, pg 108

Loewen, Darleen, PrairieView Press, PO Box 460, Rosenort, MB R0G 0W0, Canada *Tel:* 204-327-6543 *Toll Free Tel:* 800-477-7377 *Fax:* 204-327-6544 *Web Site:* www.prairieviewpress.com, pg 516

Loewenthal, Linda, David Black Agency, 335 Adams St, 27th fl, Suite 2707, Brooklyn, NY 11201 *Tel:* 718-852-5500 *Fax:* 718-852-5539 *Web Site:* www.davidblackagency.com, pg 562

Logan, Beverly, Pacific Press Publishing Association, 1350 N Kings Rd, Nampa, ID 83687-3193 *Tel:* 208-465-2500 *Toll Free Tel:* 800-447-7377 *Fax:* 208-465-2531 *Web Site:* www.pacificpress.com, pg 190

Loggia, Wendy, Random House Children's Books, 1745 Broadway, New York, NY 10019 *Tel:* 212-782-9000 *Toll Free Tel:* 800-200-3552 *Fax:* 212-782-9452 *Web Site:* randomhousekids.com, pg 213

Loh, Cindy, Bloomsbury Publishing, 175 Fifth Ave, New York, NY 10010 *Tel:* 212-674-5151 *Toll Free Tel:* 800-221-7945 *Fax:* 212-780-0115; 212-982-2837 *E-mail:* marketingusa@bloomsbury.com; adultpublicityusa.@bloomsbury.com *Web Site:* www.bloomsbury.com, pg 40

Loiselle, Louise, Flammarion Quebec, 375 Ave Laurier W, Montreal, QC H2V 2K3, Canada *Tel:* 514-277-8807 *Fax:* 514-278-2085 *E-mail:* info@flammarion.qc.ca *Web Site:* www.flammarion.qc.ca, pg 505

Lombardi, Terri, Hyperion, 1500 Broadway, 3rd fl, New York, NY 10036 *Tel:* 212-536-6500 *Web Site:* hyperionbooks.com, pg 126

Lombardo, Adrienne, Trident Media Group LLC, 41 Madison Ave, 36th fl, New York, NY 10010 *Tel:* 212-262-4810 *Fax:* 212-262-4849 *Web Site:* www.tridentmediagroup.com, pg 598

Loney, Brian, Canadian Institute of Chartered Accountants (L'Institut Canadien des Comptables Agrees), 277 Wellington St W, Toronto, ON M5V 3H2, Canada *Tel:* 416-977-3222 *Toll Free Tel:* 800-268-3793 (CN orders) *Fax:* 416-977-8585 *E-mail:* orders@cica.ca *Web Site:* www.cica.ca, pg 497

Long, Ben, Dancing Dakini Press, 77 Morning Sun Dr, Sedona, AZ 86336 *Tel:* 928-852-0129 *E-mail:* editor@dancingdakinipress.com *Web Site:* www.dancingdakinipress.com, pg 74

Long, Bob, Thinkers' Press Inc, 1524 Le Claire St, Davenport, IA 52803 *Tel:* 563-271-6657 *E-mail:* info@chessbutler.com *Web Site:* www.thinkerspressinc.com, pg 254

Long, Christopher G, ISI Books, 3901 Centerville Rd, Wilmington, DE 19807-1938 *Tel:* 302-652-4600 *Toll Free Tel:* 800-526-7022 *Fax:* 302-652-1760 *E-mail:* info@isi.org; isibooks@isi.org *Web Site:* www.isibooks.org, pg 134

Long, Donna, HRD Press, 22 Amherst Rd, Amherst, MA 01002-9709 *Tel:* 413-253-3488 *Toll Free Tel:* 800-822-2801 *Fax:* 413-253-3490 *E-mail:* info@hrdpress.com; customerservice@hrdpress.com *Web Site:* www.hrdpress.com, pg 125

Long, Karen R, The Anisfield-Wolf Book Awards, 1422 Euclid Ave, Suite 1300, Cleveland, OH 44115 *Tel:* 216-861-3810 *Fax:* 216-861-1729 *E-mail:* awinfo@clevefdn.org *Web Site:* www.anisfield-wolf.org; www.clevelandfoundation.org, pg 687

Long, Michael, Hendrick-Long Publishing Co, 10635 Tower Oaks, Suite D, Houston, TX 77070 *Tel:* 832-912-READ (912-7323) *Fax:* 832-912-7353 *E-mail:* hendrick-long@worldnet.att.net *Web Site:* www.hendricklongpublishing.com, pg 118

Long, Vilma, Hendrick-Long Publishing Co, 10635 Tower Oaks, Suite D, Houston, TX 77070 *Tel:* 832-912-READ (912-7323) *Fax:* 832-912-7353 *E-mail:* hendrick-long@worldnet.att.net *Web Site:* www.hendricklongpublishing.com, pg 118

Longert, Audra, Harvard Business Press, 300 N Beacon St, Watertown, MA 02472 *Tel:* 617-783-7400 *Fax:* 617-783-7489 *E-mail:* custserv@hbsp.harvard.edu *Web Site:* www.harvardbusiness.org, pg 114

Longino, Karen, Howard Books, 216 Centerview Dr, Suite 303, Brentwood, TN 37027 *Tel:* 615-873-2080 *Fax:* 615-370-3834 *E-mail:* howardbooks@simonandschuster.com (info) *Web Site:* www.howardpublishing.com, pg 124

Longmeyer, Michael, Gallopade International Inc, 611 Hwy 74 S, Suite 2000, Peachtree City, GA 30269 *Tel:* 770-631-4222 *Toll Free Tel:* 800-536-2GET

(536-2438) *Fax:* 770-631-4810 *Toll Free Fax:* 800-871-2979 *E-mail:* customerservice@gallopade.com *Web Site:* www.gallopade.com, pg 101

Longo, Edward, Recorded Books LLC, 270 Skipjack Rd, Prince Frederick, MD 20678 *Tel:* 410-535-5590 *Toll Free Tel:* 800-638-1304; 877-732-2898 *Fax:* 410-535-5499 *E-mail:* customerservice@recordedbooks.com *Web Site:* www.recordedbooks.com, pg 215

Longobardi, Cara, Empire State Award for Excellence in Literature for Young People, 6021 State Farm Rd, Guilderland, NY 12084 *Tel:* 518-432-6952 *Toll Free Tel:* 800-252-6952 *Fax:* 518-427-1697 *E-mail:* info@nyla.org *Web Site:* www.nyla.org, pg 702

Loomis, Gloria, Watkins/Loomis Agency Inc, PO Box 20925, New York, NY 10025 *Tel:* 212-532-0080 *Fax:* 646-383-2449 *E-mail:* assistant@watkinsloomis.com *Web Site:* www.watkinsloomis.com, pg 599

Loomis, Michael J, Graphic World Publishing Services, 11687 Adie Rd, St Louis, MO 63043 *Tel:* 314-567-9854 *Fax:* 314-567-7178 *E-mail:* quote@gwinc.com *Web Site:* www.gwinc.com, pg 547

Lopez-Franco, Edna, Morgan Kaufmann, 225 Wyman St, Waltham, MA 02451 *Toll Free Tel:* 866-607-1417 *Fax:* 619-699-6310 *Web Site:* www.mkp.com, pg 170

Lord, Sterling, Sterling Lord Literistic Inc, 65 Bleecker St, New York, NY 10012 *Tel:* 212-780-6050 *Fax:* 212-780-6095 *E-mail:* info@sll.com *Web Site:* www.sll.com, pg 595

Lore, Matthew, The Experiment, 260 Fifth Ave, Suite 3 South, New York, NY 10001-6425 *Tel:* 212-889-1659 *E-mail:* info@theexperimentpublishing.com *Web Site:* www.theexperimentpublishing.com, pg 91

Lorenz, Geoff, Show What You Know® Publishing, A Lorenz Company, 501 E Third St, Dayton, OH 45402 *Tel:* 614-764-1211; 937-228-6118 *Toll Free Tel:* 877-PASSING (727-7464) *Fax:* 937-233-2042 *E-mail:* info@swykonline.com *Web Site:* www.swykonline.com; www.lorenzeducationalpress.com, pg 233

Lorenz, Ken, Standard Publishing, 8805 Governors Hill Dr, Suite 400, Cincinnati, OH 45249 *Tel:* 513-931-4050 *Toll Free Tel:* 800-543-1353 *Fax:* 513-931-0950 *Toll Free Fax:* 877-867-5751 *E-mail:* customerservice@standardpub.com *Web Site:* www.standardpub.com, pg 242

Lorenz, Tom, Cottonwood Press, University of Kansas, Kansas Union, Rm 400, 1301 Jayhawk Blvd, Lawrence, KS 66045 *Tel:* 785-864-4520 *E-mail:* pwedge@ku.edu *Web Site:* www.cottonwoodmagazine.org, pg 69

Lorenz, Vera, Hagstrom Map & Travel Center, 51 W 43 St, New York, NY 10036 *Toll Free Tel:* 800-432-MAPS (432-6277) *Fax:* 212-398-9856 *Web Site:* www.americanmap.com, pg 110

Lorimer, James, James Lorimer & Co Ltd, Publishers, 317 Adelaide St W, Suite 1002, Toronto, ON M5V 1P9, Canada *Tel:* 416-362-4762 *Fax:* 416-362-3939 *Web Site:* www.lorimer.ca, pg 511

LoRusso, Michael, National Publishing Co, 11311 Roosevelt Blvd, Philadelphia, PA 19154-2105 *Tel:* 215-676-1863 *Toll Free Tel:* 888-333-1863 *Fax:* 215-673-8069 *Web Site:* www.courier.com, pg 175

Lotman, Lynda, A+ English LLC/Book-Editing.com, PO Box 1372, Mansfield, TX 76063 *Tel:* 469-789-3030 *E-mail:* editingnetwork@gmail.com *Web Site:* www.editing-writing.com; www.book-editing.com; www.HelpWithStatistics; www.medical-writing-editing.com; www.apawriting.com, pg 539

Lott, Peter, Lott Representatives, PO Box 3607, New York, NY 10163 *Tel:* 212-755-5737 *Web Site:* www.lottreps.com, pg 602

Lotz, Amy B, Alliance for Women in Media (AWM), 1760 Old Meadow Rd, Suite 500, McLean, VA 22102 *Tel:* 703-506-3290 *Fax:* 703-506-3266 *E-mail:* info@awrt.org *Web Site:* www.awrt.org, pg 611

Lotz, Amy B, The Gracies®, 1760 Old Meadow Rd, Suite 500, McLean, VA 22102 *Tel:* 703-506-3290 *Fax:* 703-506-3266 *E-mail:* info@awrt.org *Web Site:* www.awrt.org, pg 708

Lotz, Karen, Candlewick Press, 99 Dover St, Somerville, MA 02144-2825 *Tel:* 617-661-3330 *Fax:* 617-661-0565 *E-mail:* bigbear@candlewick.com *Web Site:* www.candlewick.com, pg 51

Lough, Loree, Lighthouse Publishing of the Carolinas, 2333 Barton Oaks Dr, Raleigh, NC 27614-7940 *E-mail:* lighthousepublishingcarolinas@gmail.com *Web Site:* lighthousepublishingofthecarolinas.com, pg 149

Loughlin, Thomas, American Society of Mechanical Engineers (ASME), 3 Park Ave, New York, NY 10016-5990 *Tel:* 212-591-7000 *Toll Free Tel:* 800-843-2763 (cust serv-US, CN & Mexico) *Fax:* 212-591-7674; 973-882-8113 (cust serv); 973-882-1717 (orders & inquiries) *E-mail:* infocentral@asme.org *Web Site:* www.asme.org, pg 17

Loughrey, Mary, Looseleaf Law Publications Inc, 43-08 162 St, Flushing, NY 11358 *Tel:* 718-359-5559 *Toll Free Tel:* 800-647-5547 *Fax:* 718-539-0941 *E-mail:* info@looseleaf.com *Web Site:* www.looseleaflaw.com, pg 152

Loughrey, Michael L, Looseleaf Law Publications Inc, 43-08 162 St, Flushing, NY 11358 *Tel:* 718-359-5559 *Toll Free Tel:* 800-647-5547 *Fax:* 718-539-0941 *E-mail:* info@looseleaf.com *Web Site:* www.looseleaflaw.com, pg 152

Louie, Karen, Harlequin Enterprises Ltd, 225 Duncan Mill Rd, Don Mills, ON M3B 3K9, Canada *Tel:* 416-445-5860 *Toll Free Tel:* 888-432-4879; 800-370-5838 (ebook inquiries) *Fax:* 416-445-8655 *E-mail:* CustomerService@harlequin.com *Web Site:* www.harlequin.com, pg 508

Lourie, Dick, Hanging Loose Press, 231 Wyckoff St, Brooklyn, NY 11217 *Tel:* 347-529-4738 *Fax:* 347-227-8215 *E-mail:* print225@aol.com *Web Site:* www.hangingloosepress.com, pg 111

Lourie, Iven, Gateways Books & Tapes, PO Box 370, Nevada City, CA 95959-0370 *Tel:* 530-271-2239 *Toll Free Tel:* 800-869-0658 *Fax:* 530-272-0184 *E-mail:* info@gatewaysbooksandtapes.com *Web Site:* www.gatewaysbooksandtapes.com; www.retrosf.com (Retro Science Fiction Imprint), pg 101

Lovaas, Eric, HarperCollins Publishers Sales, 10 E 53 St, New York, NY 10022 *Fax:* 212-207-7000 *Web Site:* www.harpercollins.com, pg 114

Love, Hannah, University of California Press, 2120 Berkeley Way, Berkeley, CA 94704-1012 *Tel:* 510-642-4247 *Fax:* 510-643-7127 *E-mail:* askucp@ucpress.edu (books); customerservice@ucpressjournals.com (journals) *Web Site:* www.ucpress.edu, pg 264

Love, Robert, Square One Publishers Inc, 115 Herricks Rd, Garden City Park, NY 11040 *Tel:* 516-535-2010 *Toll Free Tel:* 877-900-BOOK (900-2665) *Fax:* 516-535-2014 *E-mail:* sq1publish@aol.com *Web Site:* www.squareonepublishers.com, pg 242

Love, Shelby, Mill Mountain Theatre, Center in the Square, 2nd fl, One Market Sq SE, Roanoke, VA 24011-1437 *Tel:* 540-224-1250 (ext 7307) *Web Site:* www.millmountain.org, pg 723

Love, Stanley F, Love Publishing Co, 9101 E Kenyon Ave, Suite 2200, Denver, CO 80237 *Tel:* 303-221-7333 *Toll Free Tel:* 877-240-6396 *Fax:* 303-221-7444 *E-mail:* lpc@lovepublishing.com *Web Site:* www.lovepublishing.com, pg 153

Lovegrove, Stephanie, Janet B McCabe Poetry Prize, 140 N Roosevelt Ave, Collins, CO 80521 *Tel:* 970-449-2726 *E-mail:* editor@ruminatemagazine.org *Web Site:* www.ruminatemagazine.com, pg 722

Lovegrove, Stephanie, William Van Dyke Short Story Prize, 140 N Roosevelt Ave, Collins, CO 80521 *Tel:* 970-449-2726 *E-mail:* editor@ruminatemagazine.org *Web Site:* www.ruminatemagazine.com, pg 747

Lovegrove, Stephanie, VanderMey Nonfiction Prize, 140 N Roosevelt Ave, Collins, CO 80521 *Tel:* 970-449-2726 *E-mail:* editor@ruminatemagazine.org *Web Site:* www.ruminatemagazine.com, pg 747

Lovell, Deborah, Taylor & Francis Inc, 325 Chestnut St, Suite 800, Philadelphia, PA 20036-1802 *Tel:* 215-625-8900 *Toll Free Tel:* 800-354-1420 *Fax:* 215-625-2940 *E-mail:* customer.service@taylorandfrancis.com *Web Site:* www.taylorandfrancis.com, pg 250

Lovett, Tom, The Johns Hopkins University Press, 2715 N Charles St, Baltimore, MD 21218-4363 *Tel:* 410-516-6900; 410-516-6987 (journals outside US & CN) *Toll Free Tel:* 800-537-5487 (book orders & cust serv); 800-548-1784 (journal orders) *Fax:* 410-516-6968; 410-516-3866 (journal orders) *E-mail:* hfscustserv@press.jhu.edu (cust serv); jrnlcirc@press.jhu.edu (journal orders) *Web Site:* www.press.jhu.edu; muse.jhu.edu/about/subscriptions/index.html (Project Muse subns), pg 136

Lovette, Heidi Steinmetz, Cornell University Press, Sage House, 512 E State St, Ithaca, NY 14850 *Tel:* 607-277-2338 *Fax:* 607-277-2374 *E-mail:* cupressinfo@cornell.edu; cupress-sales@cornell.edu *Web Site:* www.cornellpress.cornell.edu, pg 67

Lovig, Gail, Company's Coming Publishing Ltd, 2311 96 St, Edmonton, AB T6N 1G3, Canada *Tel:* 780-450-6223 *Toll Free Tel:* 800-875-7108 (US & CN) *Fax:* 780-450-1857 *E-mail:* info@companyscoming.com *Web Site:* www.companyscoming.com, pg 499

Lovig, Grant, Company's Coming Publishing Ltd, 2311 96 St, Edmonton, AB T6N 1G3, Canada *Tel:* 780-450-6223 *Toll Free Tel:* 800-875-7108 (US & CN) *Fax:* 780-450-1857 *E-mail:* info@companyscoming.com *Web Site:* www.companyscoming.com, pg 499

Lovisi, Gary, Gryphon Books, PO Box 209, Brooklyn, NY 11228-0209 *E-mail:* gryphonbooks@att.net *Web Site:* www.gryphonbooks.com, pg 109

Lovito-Nelson, Joanne, University of Texas at Arlington School of Urban & Public Affairs, 511 University Hall, 5th fl, 601 S Nedderman Dr, Arlington, TX 76010 *Tel:* 817-272-3071 *Fax:* 817-272-3415 *E-mail:* supa@uta.edu *Web Site:* www.uta.edu/supa, pg 269

Low, Craig, Children's Book Press, 95 Madison Ave, Suite 1205, New York, NY 10016 *Tel:* 212-779-4400 *Fax:* 212-683-1894 *Web Site:* www.leeandlow.com, pg 60

Low, Craig, Lee & Low Books Inc, 95 Madison Ave, New York, NY 10016 *Tel:* 212-779-4400 *Toll Free Tel:* 888-320-3190 (ext 28, orders only) *Fax:* 212-683-1894 (orders only); 212-532-6035 *E-mail:* general@leeandlow.com *Web Site:* www.leeandlow.com, pg 146

Low, Jason, Lee & Low Books Inc, 95 Madison Ave, New York, NY 10016 *Tel:* 212-779-4400 *Toll Free Tel:* 888-320-3190 (ext 28, orders only) *Fax:* 212-683-1894 (orders only); 212-532-6035 *E-mail:* general@leeandlow.com *Web Site:* www.leeandlow.com, pg 146

Lowary, Nicole, Marianne Strong Literary Agency, 65 E 96 St, New York, NY 10128 *Tel:* 212-249-1000 *Fax:* 212-831-3241 *Web Site:* stronglit.com, pg 596

Lowe, Amy, Janet B McCabe Poetry Prize, 140 N Roosevelt Ave, Collins, CO 80521 *Tel:* 970-449-2726 *E-mail:* editor@ruminatemagazine.org *Web Site:* www.ruminatemagazine.com, pg 722

Lowe, Amy, William Van Dyke Short Story Prize, 140 N Roosevelt Ave, Collins, CO 80521 *Tel:* 970-449-2726 *E-mail:* editor@ruminatemagazine.org *Web Site:* www.ruminatemagazine.com, pg 747

Lowe, Amy, VanderMey Nonfiction Prize, 140 N Roosevelt Ave, Collins, CO 80521 *Tel:* 970-449-2726 *E-mail:* editor@ruminatemagazine.org *Web Site:* www.ruminatemagazine.com, pg 747

Lowenstein, Barbara, Lowenstein Associates Inc, 121 W 27 St, Suite 501, New York, NY 10001 *Tel:* 212-206-1630 *Fax:* 212-727-0280 *E-mail:* assistant@bookhaven.com (queries, no attachments) *Web Site:* www.lowensteinassociates.com, pg 582

Lowenstein, Carole, Random House Publishing Group, 1745 Broadway, New York, NY 10019 *Toll Free Tel:* 800-200-3552 *Web Site:* atrandom.com, pg 214

Lyman, Joe, Great Lakes Graphics Association, W232 N2950 Roundy Circle E, Suite 200, Pewaukee, WI 53072-4110 *Tel:* 262-522-2210 *Fax:* 262-522-2211 *E-mail:* info@piw.org *Web Site:* www.piw.org, pg 624

Lynch, Catharine, GP Putnam's Sons (Hardcover), 375 Hudson St, New York, NY 10014 *Tel:* 212-366-2000 *E-mail:* online@penguinputnam.com *Web Site:* us.penguingroup.com, pg 210

Lynch, Chris, Simon & Schuster Audio, 1230 Avenue of the Americas, New York, NY 10020 *Web Site:* audio.simonandschuster.com, pg 234

Lynch, Chris, Simon & Schuster, Inc, 1230 Avenue of the Americas, New York, NY 10020 *Tel:* 212-698-7000 *Fax:* 212-698-7007 *E-mail:* firstname.lastname@simonandschuster.com *Web Site:* www.simonandschuster.com, pg 235

Lynch, Desiree, BowTie Press®, 3 Burroughs, Irvine, CA 92618 *Tel:* 949-855-8822 *Toll Free Tel:* 888-738-2665 *Fax:* 949-458-3856 *E-mail:* bowtiepress@bowtieinc.com *Web Site:* www.bowtiepress.com, pg 44

Lynch, Kevin, The Globe Pequot Press, 246 Goose Lane, Guilford, CT 06437 *Tel:* 203-458-4500 *Toll Free Tel:* 800-243-0495 (orders only); 888-249-7586 (cust serv) *Fax:* 203-458-4601 *Toll Free Fax:* 800-820-2329 (orders & cust serv) *E-mail:* info@globepequot.com *Web Site:* www.globepequot.com, pg 104

Lynch, Megan, Riverhead Books (Hardcover), 375 Hudson St, New York, NY 10014 *Tel:* 212-366-2000 *E-mail:* online@penguinputnam.com *Web Site:* www.penguinputnam.com; us.penguingroup.com, pg 219

Lynch, Patrick, Oxford University Press USA, 198 Madison Ave, New York, NY 10016 *Tel:* 212-726-6000 *Toll Free Tel:* 800-451-7556 (orders); 800-445-9714 (cust serv) *Fax:* 919-677-1303 *E-mail:* custserv.us@oup.com *Web Site:* www.oup.com/us, pg 189

Lynch, William, ProChain Press, 3460 Commission Ct, No 301, Lake Ridge, VA 22192 *Tel:* 703-490-8821 *Fax:* 703-494-1414 *E-mail:* publishing@prochain.com *Web Site:* prochain.com, pg 529

Lynell, James, Multicultural Publications Inc, 936 Slosson St, Akron, OH 44320 *Tel:* 330-865-9578 *Fax:* 330-865-9578 *E-mail:* multiculturalpub@prodigy.net, pg 171

Lynley, Cason, Duke University Press, 905 W Main St, Suite 18B, Durham, NC 27701 *Tel:* 919-688-5134 *Toll Free Tel:* 888-651-0122 *Fax:* 919-688-2615 *Toll Free Fax:* 888-651-0124 *E-mail:* orders@dukeupress.edu *Web Site:* www.dukeupress.edu, pg 82

Lynn, Kira, Kane Miller Books, 4901 Morena Blvd, Suite 213, San Diego, CA 92117 *E-mail:* info@kanemiller.com *Web Site:* www.kanemiller.com, pg 138

Lyon, Kevan, Marsal Lyon Literary Agency LLC, 665 San Rodolfo Dr, Suite 124, PMB 121, Solana Beach, CA 92075 *Tel:* 760-814-8507 *Web Site:* www.marsallyonliteraryagency.com, pg 583

Lyons, Brad, Chalice Press, 483 E Lockwood Ave, Suite 100, St Louis, MO 63119 *Tel:* 314-231-8500 *Toll Free Tel:* 800-366-3383 *Fax:* 314-231-8524; 770-280-4039 (orders) *E-mail:* customerservice@chalicepress.com *Web Site:* www.chalicepress.com, pg 57

Lyons, Chris, Society for Technical Communication, 9401 Lee Hwy, Suite 300, Fairfax, VA 22031 *Tel:* 703-522-4114 *Fax:* 703-522-2075 *E-mail:* stc@stc.org *Web Site:* www.stc.org, pg 636

Lyons, Chris, Society for Technical Communication's Annual Conference, 9401 Lee Hwy, Suite 300, Fairfax, VA 22031 *Tel:* 703-522-4114 *Fax:* 703-522-2075 *E-mail:* stc@stc.org *Web Site:* www.stc.org, pg 673

Lyons, James E, University Press of America Inc, 4501 Forbes Blvd, Suite 200, Lanham, MD 20706 *Tel:* 301-459-3366 *Toll Free Tel:* 800-462-6420 *Fax:* 301-429-5748 *Toll Free Fax:* 800-338-4550 *Web Site:* www.univpress.com, pg 270

Lyons, Jed, Madison House Publishers, 4501 Forbes Blvd, Lanham, MD 20706 *Tel:* 301-459-3366 *Toll Free Tel:* 800-462-6420 *Fax:* 301-306-0941 *Web Site:* rlpgbooks.com, pg 155

Lyons, Jed, Rowman & Littlefield Publishers Inc, 4501 Forbes Blvd, Suite 200, Lanham, MD 20706 *Tel:* 301-459-3366 *Toll Free Tel:* 800-462-6420 (cust serv) *Fax:* 301-429-5748 *Web Site:* www.rowmanlittlefield.com, pg 221

Lyons, Jed, Scarecrow Press Inc, 4501 Forbes Blvd, Suite 200, Lanham, MD 20706 *Tel:* 301-459-3366 *Fax:* 301-429-5748 *Web Site:* www.scarecrowpress.com, pg 226

Lyons, Jonathan, Curtis Brown Ltd, 10 Astor Place, New York, NY 10003 *Tel:* 212-473-5400 *Web Site:* www.curtisbrown.com, pg 565

Lyons, Krista, Seal Press, 1700 Fourth St, Berkeley, CA 94710 *Tel:* 510-595-3664 *Fax:* 510-595-4228 *E-mail:* seal.press@perseusbooks.com *Web Site:* www.sealpress.com, pg 230

Lyons, Lisa, Kids Can Press Ltd, 25 Dockside Dr, Toronto, ON M5A 0B5, Canada *Tel:* 416-479-7000 *Toll Free Tel:* 800-265-0884 *Fax:* 416-960-5437 *E-mail:* info@kidscan.com; customerservice@kidscan.com *Web Site:* www.kidscanpress.com; www.kidscanpress.ca, pg 510

Lyons, Marjory D PhD, Telling Your Story Inc, PO Box 668485, Pompano Beach, FL 33069 *Tel:* 954-249-1333; 954-970-9333 *Web Site:* www.telling-your-story.com, pg 529

Lyons, Michael, Tower Publishing Co, 588 Saco Rd, Standish, ME 04084 *Tel:* 207-642-5400 *Toll Free Tel:* 800-969-8693 *Fax:* 207-264-3870 *E-mail:* info@towerpub.com *Web Site:* www.towerpub.com, pg 257

Lyons, Pat, Dutton, 375 Hudson St, New York, NY 10014 *Tel:* 212-366-2000 *Fax:* 212-366-2262 *E-mail:* online@penguinputnam.com *Web Site:* www.penguinputnam.com; us.penguingroup.com, pg 83

Lyons, Pat, NAL, 375 Hudson St, New York, NY 10014 *Tel:* 212-366-2000 *E-mail:* online@penguinputnam.com *Web Site:* www.penguinputnam.com; us.penguingroup.com, pg 172

Lyons, Pat, Plume, 375 Hudson St, New York, NY 10014 *Tel:* 212-366-2000 *Fax:* 212-366-2666 *E-mail:* online@penguinputnam.com *Web Site:* www.penguinputnam.com; us.penguingroup.com, pg 203

Lyons, Tony, Arcade Publishing Inc, 307 W 36 St, 11th fl, New York, NY 10018 *Tel:* 212-643-6816 *Fax:* 212-643-6819 *E-mail:* info@skyhorsepublishing.com (Subs & Foreign Rts) *Web Site:* www.arcadepub.com, pg 21

Ma, Amy, Immedium, 535 Rockdale Dr, San Francisco, CA 94127 *Tel:* 415-452-8546 *Fax:* 360-937-6272 *E-mail:* orders@immedium.com; sales@immedium.com *Web Site:* www.immedium.com, pg 128

Maass, Donald, Donald Maass Literary Agency, 121 W 27 St, Suite 801, New York, NY 10001 *Tel:* 212-727-8383 *Fax:* 212-727-3271 *E-mail:* info@maassagency.com; rights@maassagency.com (subs rights inquiries) *Web Site:* www.maassagency.com, pg 582

Mabie, Van, Riverside Publishing, 3800 Golf Rd, Suite 200, Rolling Meadows, IL 60008 *Tel:* 630-467-7000 *Toll Free Tel:* 800-323-9540 *Fax:* 630-467-7192 (cust serv) *E-mail:* rpc_customer_service@hmhpub.com (cust serv) *Web Site:* www.riversidepublishing.com, pg 219

Mabry, John R, The Apocryphile Press, 1700 Shattuck Ave, Suite 81, Berkeley, CA 94709 *Tel:* 510-290-4349 *E-mail:* apocryphile@earthlink.net *Web Site:* www.apocryphile.org, pg 20

Mabry, Vickie, IACP Cookbook Awards, 1100 Johnson Ferry Rd, Suite 300, Atlanta, GA 30342 *Tel:* 404-252-3663 *Fax:* 404-252-0774 *E-mail:* info@iacp.com *Web Site:* www.iacp.com, pg 711

MacBain, Teresa, American Atheist Press, PO Box 158, Cranford, NJ 07016 *Tel:* 908-276-7300 *Fax:* 908-276-7402 *E-mail:* info@atheists.org *Web Site:* www.atheists.org, pg 11

Macca, Joe, Scholastic International, 557 Broadway, New York, NY 10012 *Tel:* 212-343-6100; 646-330-5288 (intl cust serv) *Toll Free Tel:* 800-SCHOLASTIC (800-724-6527) *Fax:* 646-837-7878 *E-mail:* international@scholastic.com, pg 228

Maccarone, Grace, Holiday House Inc, 425 Madison Ave, New York, NY 10017 *Tel:* 212-688-0085 *Fax:* 212-421-6134 *E-mail:* holiday@holidayhouse.com *Web Site:* www.holidayhouse.com, pg 121

Macchiusi, Mary, Pembroke Publishers Ltd, 538 Hood Rd, Markham, ON L3R 3K9, Canada *Tel:* 905-477-0650 *Toll Free Tel.* 800-997-9807 *Fax:* 905-477-3691 *Toll Free Fax:* 800-339-5568 *Web Site:* www.pembrokepublishers.com, pg 515

Maccoby, Gina, Gina Maccoby Literary Agency, PO Box 60, Chappaqua, NY 10514-0060 *Tel:* 914-238-5630 *E-mail:* query@maccobylit.com *Web Site:* www.publishersmarketplace.com/members/GinaMaccoby, pg 583

MacDonald, Brian A, National Braille Press, 88 Saint Stephen St, Boston, MA 02115-4302 *Tel:* 617-266-6160 *Toll Free Tel:* 800-548-7323 (cust serv); 888-965-8965 *Fax:* 617-437-0456 *E-mail:* orders@nbp.org *Web Site:* www.nbp.org, pg 173

MacDonald, David, The National Underwriter Co, 5081 Olympic Blvd, Erlanger, KY 41018-3164 *Tel:* 859-692-2100 *Toll Free Tel:* 800-543-0874 *Fax:* 859-692-2289 *E-mail:* customerservice@nuco.com *Web Site:* www.nationalunderwriter.com, pg 176

MacDonald, Jane, The MIT Press, 55 Hayward St, Cambridge, MA 02142 *Tel:* 617-253-5255 *Toll Free Tel:* 800-207-8354 (orders) *Fax:* 617-258-6779; 617-577-1545 (orders) *Web Site:* mitpress.mit.edu, pg 167

MacDonald, Leo, HarperCollins Canada Ltd, 2 Bloor St E, 20th fl, Toronto, ON M4W 1A8, Canada *Tel:* 416-975-9334 *Fax:* 416-975-9884 *E-mail:* hccanada@harpercollins.com *Web Site:* www.harpercollins.ca, pg 508

MacDonald, Lindsay, University Press of America Inc, 4501 Forbes Blvd, Suite 200, Lanham, MD 20706 *Tel:* 301-459-3366 *Toll Free Tel:* 800-462-6420 *Fax:* 301-429-5748 *Toll Free Fax:* 800-338-4550 *Web Site:* www.univpress.com, pg 270

Macdonald, Meghan, Transatlantic Agency, 2 Bloor St E, Ste 3500, Toronto, ON M4W-1A8, Canada *Tel:* 416-488-9214 *E-mail:* info@transatlanticagency.com *Web Site:* www.transatlanticagency.com, pg 597

Macer-Story, Eugenia, Magick Mirror Communications, 511 Avenue of the Americas, PMB 173, New York, NY 10011-8436 *Tel:* 212-255-2111; 212-208-2951 (voice mail) *Toll Free Tel:* 800-356-6796 *Fax:* 212-208-2951 (e-fax) *E-mail:* MagickMirr@aol.com; Magickorders@aol.com *Web Site:* magickmirror.com, pg 528

MacFarlane, Fraser, One Act Play Depot, Box 335, 618 Memorial Dr, Spiritwood, SK S0J 2M0, Canada *E-mail:* plays@oneactplays.net; orders@oneactplays.net *Web Site:* oneactplays.net, pg 514

MacGregor, Rob, Crabtree Publishing Co Ltd, 616 Welland Ave, St Catharines, ON L2M-5V6, Canada *Tel:* 905-682-5221 *Toll Free Tel:* 800-387-7650 *Fax:* 905-682-7166 *Toll Free Fax:* 800-355-7166 *E-mail:* custserv@crabtreebooks.com; sales@crabtreebooks.com; orders@crabtreebooks.com *Web Site:* www.crabtreebooks.com, pg 500

MacGregor, Robert, Crabtree Publishing Co, 350 Fifth Ave, 59th fl, PMB 59051, New York, NY 10118 *Tel:* 212-496-5040 *Toll Free Tel:* 800-387-7650 *Toll Free Fax:* 800-355-7166 *E-mail:* custserv@crabtreebooks.com *Web Site:* www.crabtreebooks.com, pg 70

Machala, Asharaine, Whidbey Island Writers Conference, 5577 Vanbarr Place, Freeland, WA 98249 *Tel:* 360-331-0307 *E-mail:* nila@whidbey.com *Web Site:* www.nila.edu, pg 674

Machinist, Alexandra, Janklow & Nesbit Associates, 445 Park Ave, New York, NY 10022 *Tel:* 212-421-1700 *Fax:* 212-980-3671 *E-mail:* info@janklow.com *Web Site:* www.janklowandnesbit.com, pg 578

Maciag, Thomas, Hachette Book Group, 237 Park Ave, New York, NY 10017 *Tel:* 212-364-1100 *Toll Free Tel:* 800-759-0190 (cust serv) *Fax:* 212-364-0933 (intl orders) *Toll Free Fax:* 800-286-9471 (cust serv) *Web Site:* www.HachetteBookGroup.com, pg 110

MacIlwaine, Paula, American Water Works Association, 6666 W Quincy Ave, Denver, CO 80235 *Tel:* 303-794-7711 *Toll Free Tel:* 800-926-7337 *Fax:* 303-347-0804 *Web Site:* www.awwa.org, pg 17

Macintosh, Adrienne, Harlequin Enterprises Ltd, 225 Duncan Mill Rd, Don Mills, ON M3B 3K9, Canada *Tel:* 416-445-5860 *Toll Free Tel:* 888-432-4879; 800-370-5838 (ebook inquiries) *Fax:* 416-445-8655 *E-mail:* CustomerService@harlequin.com *Web Site:* www.harlequin.com, pg 508

MacIntyre, Mary, Canadian Bookbinders and Book Artists Guild (CBBAG), 80 Ward St, Suite 207, Toronto, ON M6H 4A6, Canada *Tel:* 416-581-1071 *E-mail:* cbbag@cbbag.ca *Web Site:* www.cbbag.ca, pg 619

MacIssac, Bonnie, Howard Books, 216 Centerview Dr, Suite 303, Brentwood, TN 37027 *Tel:* 615-873-2080 *Fax:* 615-370-3834 *E-mail:* howardbooks@simonandschuster.com (info) *Web Site:* www.howardpublishing.com, pg 124

Mack, Melissa, Kaplan Publishing, 395 Hudson St, 4th fl, New York, NY 10014 *Tel:* 212-618-2400 *Toll Free Tel:* 888-KAPLAN8 (527-5268) *Fax:* 917-344-2499 *Toll Free Fax:* 877-712-5487 *E-mail:* book.support@kaplan.com *Web Site:* www.kaplanpublishing.com, pg 138

MacKeen, Alison, Princeton University Press, 41 William St, Princeton, NJ 08540-5237 *Tel:* 609-258-4900 *Toll Free Tel:* 800-777-4726 (orders) *Fax:* 609-258-6305 *Toll Free Fax:* 800-999-1958 *E-mail:* orders@cpfsinc.com *Web Site:* press.princeton.edu, pg 206

Mackensie, Constance, Random House of Canada Limited, One Toronto St, Suite 300, Toronto, ON M5C 2V6, Canada *Tel:* 416-364-4449 *Toll Free Tel:* 888-523-9292 (cust serv) *Fax:* 416-364-6863; 416-364-6653 (subs rts) *Web Site:* www.randomhouse.ca, pg 517

MacKenzie, Joanna, Browne & Miller Literary Associates, 410 S Michigan Ave, Suite 460, Chicago, IL 60605 *Tel:* 312-922-3063 *Fax:* 312-922-1905 *E-mail:* mail@browneandmiller.com *Web Site:* www.browneandmiller.com, pg 565

Mackenzie, Leslie, Grey House Publishing Inc™, 4919 Rte 22, Amenia, NY 12501 *Tel:* 518-789-8700 *Toll Free Tel:* 800-562-2139 *Fax:* 518-789-0556 *E-mail:* books@greyhouse.com *Web Site:* www.greyhouse.com, pg 108

Mackey, Elliott, The Wine Appreciation Guild Ltd, 360 Swift Ave, Suites 30 & 34, South San Francisco, CA 94080 *Tel:* 650-866-3020 *Toll Free Tel:* 800-231-9463 *Fax:* 650-866-3513 *E-mail:* info@wineappreciation.com *Web Site:* www.wineappreciation.com, pg 283

Mackey, Zoe, Berrett-Koehler Publishers Inc, 235 Montgomery St, Suite 650, San Francisco, CA 94104 *Tel:* 415-288-0260 *Fax:* 415-362-2512 *E-mail:* bkpub@bkpub.com *Web Site:* www.bkconnection.com, pg 36

Mackinnon, Margo, Municipal Chapter of Toronto IODE Jean Throop Book Award, 40 Orchard View Blvd, Suite 219, Toronto, ON M4R 1B9, Canada *Tel:* 416-925-5078 *Fax:* 416-487-4417 *E-mail:* iodeontario@bellnet.ca *Web Site:* www.iodeontario.ca, pg 725

MacKlem, Ann, University of British Columbia Press, 2029 West Mall, Vancouver, BC V6T 1Z2, Canada *Tel:* 604-822-5959 *Toll Free Tel:* 877-377-9378 *Fax:* 604-822-6083 *Toll Free Fax:* 800-668-0821 *E-mail:* frontdesk@ubcpress.ca *Web Site:* www.ubcpress.ca, pg 523

Macklem, Michael, Oberon Press, 145 Spruce St, Suite 205, Ottawa, ON K1R 6P1, Canada *Tel:* 613-238-3275 *Fax:* 613-238-3275 *E-mail:* oberon@sympatico.ca *Web Site:* www.oberonpress.ca, pg 514

Macklem, Nicholas, Oberon Press, 145 Spruce St, Suite 205, Ottawa, ON K1R 6P1, Canada *Tel:* 613-238-3275 *Fax:* 613-238-3275 *E-mail:* oberon@sympatico.ca *Web Site:* www.oberonpress.ca, pg 514

Mackross, Valerie, Amsco School Publications Inc, 315 Hudson St, New York, NY 10013-1085 *Tel:* 212-886-6500; 212-886-6565 *Toll Free Tel:* 800-969-8398 *Fax:* 212-675-7010 *E-mail:* info@amscopub.com *Web Site:* www.amscopub.com, pg 18

Mackwood, Robert, Seventh Avenue Literary Agency, 2052 124 St, South Surrey, BC V4A 9K3, Canada *Tel:* 604-538-7252 *Fax:* 604-538-7252 *E-mail:* info@seventhavenuelit.com *Web Site:* www.seventhavenuelit.com, pg 593

MacLachlan, Allison, Kids Can Press Ltd, 25 Dockside Dr, Toronto, ON M5A 0B5, Canada *Tel:* 416-479-7000 *Toll Free Tel:* 800-265-0884 *Fax:* 416-960-5437 *E-mail:* info@kidscan.com; customerservice@kidscan.com *Web Site:* www.kidscanpress.com; www.kidscanpress.ca, pg 510

MacLachlan, Christina, Wildflower Press, Oakbrook Press, 3301 S Valley Dr, Rapid City, SD 57703 *Tel:* 605-381-6385 *Fax:* 605-343-8733 *E-mail:* info@wildflowerpress.org; bookorder@wildflowerpress.org *Web Site:* www.wildflowerpress.org, pg 281

MacLachlan, Sarah, Groundwood Books, 110 Spadina Ave, Suite 801, Toronto, ON M5V 2K4, Canada *Tel:* 416-363-4343 *Fax:* 416-363-1017 *E-mail:* genmail@groundwoodbooks.com *Web Site:* www.houseofanansi.com, pg 507

MacLachlan, Sarah, House of Anansi Press Ltd, 110 Spadina Ave, Suite 801, Toronto, ON M5V 2K4, Canada *Tel:* 416-363-4343 *Fax:* 416-363-1017 *E-mail:* customerservice@houseofanansi.com *Web Site:* www.anansi.ca, pg 509

Maclagan, Maral, Scholastic Canada Ltd, 604 King St W, Toronto, ON M5V 1E1, Canada *Tel:* 905-887-7323 *Toll Free Tel:* 800-268-3848 (CN) *Fax:* 905-887-1131 *Toll Free Fax:* 866-346-1288 *Web Site:* www.scholastic.ca, pg 518

MacLeod, Lauren E, Strothman Agency LLC, PO Box 231132, Boston, MA 02123 *E-mail:* info@strothmanagency.com *Web Site:* www.strothmanagency.com, pg 596

MacLeod, Nancy, Danuta Gleed Literary Award, 90 Richmond St E, Suite 200, Toronto, ON M5C 1P1, Canada *Tel:* 416-703-8982 *Fax:* 416-504-9090 *E-mail:* info@writersunion.ca *Web Site:* www.writersunion.ca, pg 707

MacLeod, Nancy, Postcard Story Competition, 90 Richmond St E, Suite 200, Toronto, ON M5C 1P1, Canada *Tel:* 416-703-8982 *Fax:* 416-504-9090 *E-mail:* info@writersunion.ca *Web Site:* www.writersunion.ca, pg 735

MacLeod, Nancy, Short Prose Competition for Developing Writers, 90 Richmond St E, Suite 200, Toronto, ON M5C 1P1, Canada *Tel:* 416-703-8982 *Fax:* 416-504-9090 *E-mail:* info@writersunion.ca *Web Site:* www.writersunion.ca, pg 741

MacLeod, Nancy, Writing for Children Competition, 90 Richmond St E, Suite 200, Toronto, ON M5C 1P1, Canada *Tel:* 416-703-8982 *Fax:* 416-504-9090 *E-mail:* info@writersunion.ca *Web Site:* www.writersunion.ca, pg 752

MacMahon, Ted, Newbury Street Press, 101 Newbury St, Boston, MA 02116 *Tel:* 617-536-5740 *Toll Free Tel:* 888-296-3447 (NEHGS membership) *Fax:* 617-536-7307 *E-mail:* sales@nehgs.org *Web Site:* www.newenglandancestors.org, pg 179

MacMillan, Colleen, Annick Press Ltd, 15 Patricia Ave, Toronto, ON M2M 1H9, Canada *Tel:* 416-221-4802 *Fax:* 416-221-8400 *E-mail:* annickpress@annickpress.com *Web Site:* www.annickpress.com, pg 493

Macnair, Randal, Oolichan Books, PO Box 2278, Fernie, BC V0B 1M0, Canada *Tel:* 250-423-6113 *E-mail:* info@oolichan.com *Web Site:* www.oolichan.com, pg 514

MacNamara, Elisabeth, League of Women Voters of the United States, 1730 "M" St NW, Suite 1000, Washington, DC 20036-4508 *Tel:* 202-429-1965 *Fax:* 202-429-0854; 202-429-4343 *E-mail:* lwv@lwv.org *Web Site:* www.lwv.org, pg 626

MacNeil, Mary, The University of Virginia Press, PO Box 400318, Charlottesville, VA 22904-4318 *Tel:* 434-924-3468 (cust serv); 434-924-3469 (cust serv) *Toll Free Tel:* 800-831-3406 (orders) *Fax:* 434-982-2655 *Toll Free Fax:* 877-288-6400 *E-mail:* vapress@virginia.edu *Web Site:* www.upress.virginia.edu, pg 270

MacNevin, James, McGill-Queen's University Press, 1010 Sherbrooke W, Suite 1720, Montreal, QC H3A 2R7, Canada *Tel:* 514-398-3750 *Fax:* 514-398-4333 *E-mail:* mqup@mqup.ca *Web Site:* www.mqup.ca, pg 512

Macrides, Kristine, HarperCollins Publishers Sales, 10 E 53 St, New York, NY 10022 *Fax:* 212-207-7000 *Web Site:* www.harpercollins.com, pg 114

Macris, Natalie, Solano Press Books, PO Box 773, Point Arena, CA 95468 *Tel:* 707-884-4508 *Toll Free Tel:* 800-931-9373 *Fax:* 707-884-4109 *E-mail:* spbooks@solano.com *Web Site:* www.solano.com, pg 239

MacRobert, Alan M, Sky Publishing, 90 Sherman St, Cambridge, MA 02140 *Tel:* 617-864-7360 *Toll Free Tel:* 866-644-1377 *Fax:* 617-864-6117 *E-mail:* info@skyandtelescope.com *Web Site:* www.skyandtelescope.com, pg 237

Madan, Neeti, Sterling Lord Literistic Inc, 65 Bleecker St, New York, NY 10012 *Tel:* 212-780-6050 *Fax:* 212-780-6095 *E-mail:* info@sll.com *Web Site:* www.sll.com, pg 595

Madan, Vineet, McGraw-Hill Education, 2 Penn Plaza, New York, NY 10121-2298 *Tel:* 212-904-2000 *E-mail:* customer.service@mcgraw-hill.com *Web Site:* www.mheducation.com; www.mheducation.com/custserv.html, pg 161

Madara, Dr James, American Medical Association, 515 N State St, Chicago, IL 60654 *Tel:* 312-464-5000 *Toll Free Tel:* 800-621-8335 *Fax:* 312-464-4184 *Web Site:* www.ama-assn.org, pg 15, 613

Madden, Patrick, United Nations Association of the United States of America, 801 Second Ave, 2nd fl, New York, NY 10017-4706 *Tel:* 212-907-1300 *Fax:* 212-682-9185 *E-mail:* unahq@unausa.org *Web Site:* www.unausa.org, pg 638

Maddex, John, Conciliar Press, 2747 Bond St, University Park, IL 60484 *Tel:* 219-728-2216 (outside US) *Toll Free Tel:* 800-967-7377 *Fax:* 708-534-7803 *Toll Free Fax:* 866-599-5208 *E-mail:* service@conciliarmedia.com *Web Site:* www.conciliarpress.com, pg 66

Maddox, Christine, The Fairmont Press Inc, 700 Indian Trail, Lilburn, GA 30047 *Tel:* 770-925-9388 *Fax:* 770-381-9865 *Web Site:* www.fairmontpress.com, pg 92

Madhubuti, Haki R, Third World Press, 7822 S Dobson Ave, Chicago, IL 60619 *Tel:* 773-651-0700 *Fax:* 773-651-7286 *E-mail:* twpress3@aol.com *Web Site:* www.twpbooks.com, pg 254

Madonia, Nena, Dupree, Miller & Associates Inc, 100 Highland Park Village, Suite 350, Dallas, TX 75205 *Tel:* 214-559-2665 *Fax:* 214-559-7243 *E-mail:* editorial@dupreemiller.com *Web Site:* www.dupreemiller.com, pg 569

Madrus, Ingel, Gerald Lampert Memorial Award, 192 Spadina Ave, Suite 312, Toronto, ON M5T 2C2, Canada *Tel:* 416-504-1657 *Fax:* 416-504-0096 *E-mail:* readings@poets.ca *Web Site:* www.poets.ca, pg 716

Madrus, Ingel, The League of Canadian Poets, 192 Spadina Ave, Suite 312, Toronto, ON M5T 2C2, Canada *Tel:* 416-504-1657 *Fax:* 416-504-0096 *E-mail:* readings@poets.ca *Web Site:* www.poets.ca, pg 626

Madrus, Ingel, Pat Lowther Memorial Award, 192 Spadina Ave, Suite 312, Toronto, ON M5T 2C2, Canada *Tel:* 416-504-1657 *Fax:* 416-504-0096 *E-mail:* readings@poets.ca *Web Site:* www.poets.ca, pg 719

Maner, Ron, The University of North Carolina Press, 116 S Boundary St, Chapel Hill, NC 27514-3808 *Tel:* 919-966-3561 *Fax:* 919-966-3829 *E-mail:* uncpress@unc.edu *Web Site:* www.uncpress.unc.edu, pg 267

Mangan, Joe, The Perseus Books Group, 387 Park Ave S, 12th fl, New York, NY 10016 *Tel:* 212-340-8100 *Toll Free Tel:* 800-343-4499 (cust serv) *Fax:* 212-340-8105 *Web Site:* www.perseusbooksgroup.com, pg 199

Mangan, Joe, Westview Press, 2465 Central Ave, Boulder, CO 80301 *Tel:* 303-444-3541 *Fax:* 720-406-7336 *E-mail:* westview.orders@perseusbooks.com *Web Site:* www.perseusbooksgroup.com; www.westviewpress.com, pg 279

Mangouni, Norman, Caravan Books, 6946 E Stevens Rd, Cave Creek, AZ 85331-8677 *Tel:* 480-575-9945 *E-mail:* sfandr@msn.com *Web Site:* www.scholarsbooklist.com, pg 52

Mangouni, Norman, Scholars' Facsimiles & Reprints, 6946 E Stevens Rd, Cave Creek, AZ 85331-8677 *Tel:* 480-575-9945 *E-mail:* sfandr@msn.com *Web Site:* www.scholarsbooklist.com, pg 228

Mangru, Akash, BookLogix, 1264 Old Alpharetta Rd, Alpharetta, GA 30005 *Tel:* 770-346-9979 *Toll Free Fax:* 888-564-7890 *E-mail:* sales@booklogix.com *Web Site:* www.booklogix.com, pg 43

Mangum, Lisa, Deseret Book Co, 57 W South Temple, Salt Lake City, UT 84101-1511 *Tel:* 801-517-3372; 801-534-1515 *Toll Free Tel:* 800-453-4532 (orders); 888-846-7302 (orders) *Fax:* 801-517-3126 *E-mail:* dbol@deseretbook.com *Web Site:* www.deseretbook.com, pg 78

Manion, Christopher, Productivity Press, c/o Routledge, 711 Third Ave, New York, NY 10017 *Tel:* 212-216-7800 *Toll Free Tel:* 800-634-7064 (orders) *Fax:* 212-563-2269 *Toll Free Fax:* 800-248-4724 (orders) *E-mail:* info@productivitypress.com; orders@taylorandfrancis.com *Web Site:* www.productivitypress.com, pg 207

Mann, Carol, Carol Mann Agency, 55 Fifth Ave, New York, NY 10003 *Tel:* 212-206-5635 *Fax:* 212-675-4809 *E-mail:* submissions@carolmannagency.com *Web Site:* www.carolmannagency.com, pg 583

Mann, Darlene, Apprentice Shop Books LLC, 18 Wentworth Dr, Bedford, NH 03110 *Tel:* 603-472-8741 *Fax:* 603-472-2323 *E-mail:* info@apprenticeshopbooks.com *Web Site:* www.apprenticeshopbooks.com, pg 21

Mann, Sue, Working With Words, 9720 SW Eagle Ct, Beaverton, OR 97008 *Tel:* 503-644-4317 *E-mail:* editor@zzz.com, pg 557

Mannheimer, Rachel, Bloomsbury Publishing, 175 Fifth Ave, New York, NY 10010 *Tel:* 212-674-5151 *Toll Free Tel:* 800-221-7945 *Fax:* 212-780-0115; 212-982-2837 *E-mail:* marketingusa@bloomsbury.com; adultpublicityusa.@bloomsbury.com *Web Site:* www.bloomsbury.com, pg 40

Manning, James, The Astronomical Society of the Pacific, 390 Ashton Ave, San Francisco, CA 94112 *Tel:* 415-337-1100 *Fax:* 415-337-5205 *Web Site:* www.astrosociety.org, pg 26

Manning, Linda, The University of Utah Press, J Willard Marriott Library, Suite 5400, 295 S 1500 E, Salt Lake City, UT 84112-0860 *Tel:* 801-581-6771 *Toll Free Tel:* 800-621-2736 (orders) *Fax:* 801-581-3365 *Toll Free Fax:* 800-621-8471 *E-mail:* info@upress.utah.edu *Web Site:* www.uofupress.com, pg 269

Manning, Paul, Apress Media LLC, 233 Spring St, New York, NY 10013 *Tel:* 212-460-1500 *Fax:* 212-460-1575 *E-mail:* editorial@apress.com *Web Site:* www.apress.com, pg 21

Manning, Paul, Springer, 233 Spring St, New York, NY 10013-1578 *Tel:* 212-460-1500 *Toll Free Tel:* 800-SPRINGER (777-4643) *Fax:* 212-460-1575 *E-mail:* service-ny@springer.com *Web Site:* www.springer.com, pg 241

Mano, Barry, Referee Books, 2017 Lathrop Ave, Racine, WI 53405 *Tel:* 262-632-8855 *Toll Free Tel:* 800-733-6100 *Fax:* 262-632-5460 *E-mail:* questions@referee.com *Web Site:* www.referee.com, pg 217

Manoogian, Daron, Harvard Art Museums, 32 Quincy St, Cambridge, MA 02138 *Tel:* 617-495-1440; 617-496-6529 (edit) *Fax:* 617-495-9985 *E-mail:* am_shop@harvard.edu *Web Site:* www.harvardartmuseums.org, pg 114

Manos, Wayne, Cold Spring Harbor Laboratory Press, 500 Sunnyside Blvd, Woodbury, NY 11797-2924 *Tel:* 516-422-4100; 516-422-4101 *Toll Free Tel:* 800-843-4388 *Fax:* 516-422-4097; 516-422-4092 (submissions) *E-mail:* cshpress@cshl.edu *Web Site:* www.cshlpress.com, pg 64

Mansoor, Leah, Encyclopaedia Britannica Inc, 331 N La Salle St, Chicago, IL 60654 *Tel:* 312-347-7159 (all other countries) *Toll Free Tel:* 800-323-1229 (US & CN) *Fax:* 312-294-2104 *E-mail:* editor@eb.com *Web Site:* www.eb.com; www.britannica.com, pg 88

Manston, Freya, Freya Manston Associates Inc, 145 W 58 St, New York, NY 10019 *Tel:* 212-247-3075, pg 583

Manston, Peter B, Travel Keys, PO Box 160691, Sacramento, CA 95816-0691 *Tel:* 916-452-5200 *Fax:* 916-452-5200, pg 258

Mantee, Duke, Wittenborn Art Books, 1109 Geary Blvd, San Francisco, CA 94109 *Tel:* 415-292-6500 *Toll Free Tel:* 800-660-6403 *Fax:* 415-292-6594 *E-mail:* wittenborn@art-books.com *Web Site:* www.art-books.com, pg 284

Mantilla, Jaime, Inter American Press Association (IAPA), Jules Dubois Bldg, 1801 SW Third Ave, Miami, FL 33129 *Tel:* 305-634-2465 *Fax:* 305-635-2272 *E-mail:* info@sipiapa.org *Web Site:* www.sipiapa.org, pg 625

Mantilla, Tito, Editorial Portavoz, 733 Wealthy St SE, Grand Rapids, MI 49503-5553 *Toll Free Tel:* 877-733-2607 (ext 206) *Fax:* 616-493-1790 *E-mail:* portavoz@portavoz.com *Web Site:* www.portavoz.com, pg 85

Manus, Jillian W, Manus & Associates Literary Agency Inc, 425 Sherman Ave, Suite 200, Palo Alto, CA 94306 *Tel:* 650-470-5151 *Fax:* 650-470-5159 *E-mail:* manuslit@manuslit.com *Web Site:* www.manuslit.com, pg 583

Manus, Ron, Alfred Publishing Company Inc, PO Box 10003, Van Nuys, CA 91410-0003 *Tel:* 818-891-5999 *Toll Free Tel:* 800-292-6122 (dealer sales) *Fax:* 818-892-9239; 818-893-5560 *Toll Free Fax:* 800-632-1928 (dealer sales) *E-mail:* customerservice@alfred.com; sales@alfred.com *Web Site:* www.alfred.com, pg 8

Maragni, Kelly, Health Communications Inc, 3201 SW 15 St, Deerfield Beach, FL 33442-8190 *Tel:* 954-360-0909 *Toll Free Tel:* 800-441-5569 (cust serv) *Fax:* 954-360-0034 *Web Site:* www.hcibooks.com; hci-online.com, pg 116

Marano, Lydia C, Babbage Press, 8939 Canby Ave, Northridge, CA 91325-2702 *Tel:* 818-341-3161 *E-mail:* books@babbagepress.com *Web Site:* www.babbagepress.com, pg 29

Marbach, Donna M, Poetry Chapbook Contest, 330 Knickerbocker Ave, Rochester, NY 14615 *Tel:* 585-458-0217 *E-mail:* palettesnquills@gmail.com *Web Site:* www.palettesnquills.com, pg 735

Marbury, Margaret, Harlequin Enterprises Ltd, 233 Broadway, Suite 1001, New York, NY 10279 *Tel:* 212-553-4200 *Fax:* 212-227-8969 *E-mail:* CustomerService@harlequin.com *Web Site:* www.harlequin.com, pg 112

Marcakis, Jason, Springer, 233 Spring St, New York, NY 10013-1578 *Tel:* 212-460-1500 *Toll Free Tel:* 800-SPRINGER (777-4643) *Fax:* 212-460-1575 *E-mail:* service-ny@springer.com *Web Site:* www.springer.com, pg 241

March, Joe, The American Legion Fourth Estate Award, 700 N Pennsylvania St, Indianapolis, IN 46204 *Tel:* 317-630-1253 *Fax:* 317-630-1368 *E-mail:* pr@legion.org *Web Site:* www.legion.org, pg 687

Marchand, Jesse, Whitecap Books Ltd, 314 W Cordova St, Suite 210, Vancouver, BC V6B 1E8, Canada *Tel:* 604-681-6181 *Toll Free Tel:* 800-387-9776 *Toll Free Fax:* 800-260-9777 *Web Site:* www.whitecap.ca, pg 524

Marchese, Shannon Hill, WaterBrook Multnomah Publishing Group, 12265 Oracle Blvd, Suite 200, Colorado Springs, CO 80921 *Tel:* 719-590-4999 *Toll Free Tel:* 800-603-7051 (orders) *Fax:* 719-590-8977 *Toll Free Fax:* 800-294-5686 (orders) *E-mail:* info@waterbrookmultnomah.com *Web Site:* waterbrookmultnomah.com, pg 277

Marcil, Denise, Denise Marcil Literary Agency Inc, 483 Westover Rd, Stamford, CT 06902 *Tel:* 203-327-9970 *E-mail:* dmla@denisemarcilagency.com *Web Site:* www.denisemarcilagency.com, pg 583

Marciniszyn, Alex, Palladium Books Inc, 39074 Webb Ct, Westland, MI 48185 *Tel:* 734-721-2903 (orders) *Fax:* 734-721-1238 *Web Site:* www.palladiumbooks.com, pg 191

Marcok, Vicki, Vehicule Press, PO Box 125, Place du Park Sta, Montreal, QC H2X 4A3, Canada *Tel:* 514-844-6073 *Fax:* 514-844-7543 *E-mail:* vp@vehiculepress.com; admin@vehiculepress.com *Web Site:* www.vehiculepress.com, pg 524

Marcus, Barbara, Random House Children's Books, 1745 Broadway, New York, NY 10019 *Tel:* 212-782-9000 *Toll Free Tel:* 800-200-3552 *Fax:* 212-782-9452 *Web Site:* randomhousekids.com, pg 213

Marcus, Barbara, Random House Inc, 1745 Broadway, New York, NY 10019 *Tel:* 212-782-9000 *Toll Free Tel:* 800-726-0600 *Web Site:* www.randomhouse.com, pg 213

Marcus, Bruce D, McGraw-Hill Education, 2 Penn Plaza, New York, NY 10121-2298 *Tel:* 212-904-2000 *E-mail:* customer.service@mcgraw-hill.com *Web Site:* www.mheducation.com; www.mheducation.com/custserv.html, pg 160

Marcus, James, Harper's Magazine Foundation, 666 Broadway, 11th fl, New York, NY 10012 *Tel:* 212-420-5720 *Toll Free Tel:* 800-444-4653 *Fax:* 212-228-5889 *E-mail:* harpers@harpers.org *Web Site:* www.harpers.org, pg 114

Marcus, Jim, Leadership Directories, 104 Fifth Ave, 3rd fl, New York, NY 10011 *Tel:* 212-627-4140 *Fax:* 212-645-0931 *E-mail:* info@leadershipdirectories.com *Web Site:* www.leadershipdirectories.com, pg 145

Marcus, Karyn, Simon & Schuster, 1230 Avenue of the Americas, New York, NY 10020 *Tel:* 212-698-7000 *Toll Free Tel:* 800-223-2348 (cust serv); 800-223-2336 (orders) *Toll Free Fax:* 800-943-9831 (orders) *Web Site:* www.simonandschuster.com, pg 234

Marcus, Kendra, BookStop Literary Agency LLC, 67 Meadow View Rd, Orinda, CA 94563 *E-mail:* info@bookstopliterary.com *Web Site:* www.bookstopliterary.com, pg 563

Marcus, Steven, American Academy of Arts & Sciences (AAAS), Norton's Woods, 136 Irving St, Cambridge, MA 02138-1996 *Tel:* 617-576-5000 *Fax:* 617-576-5050 *E-mail:* aaas@amacad.org *Web Site:* www.amacad.org, pg 612

Mardak, Keith, Hal Leonard Corp, 7777 W Bluemound Rd, Milwaukee, WI 53213 *Tel:* 414-774-3630 *Toll Free Tel:* 800-524-4425 *Fax:* 414-774-3259 *E-mail:* sales@halleonard.com *Web Site:* www.halleonard.com; twitter.com/#!/HalleonardBooks, pg 110

Mardon, Austin, Golden Meteorite Press, 126 Kingsway Garden, Edmonton, AB T5G 3G4, Canada *Tel:* 780-378-0063 *Web Site:* www.goldenmeteoritepress.com, pg 506

Marell, Zach, Carolrhoda Books, 241 First Ave N, Minneapolis, MN 55401 *Tel:* 612-332-3344 *Toll Free Tel:* 800-328-4929 *Fax:* 612-332-7615 *Toll Free Fax:* 800-332-1132 *E-mail:* info@lernerbooks.com *Web Site:* www.lernerbooks.com, pg 53

Marell, Zach, Carolrhoda Lab™, 241 First Ave N, Minneapolis, MN 55401 *Tel:* 612-332-3344 *Toll Free Tel:* 800-328-4929 *Fax:* 612-332-7615 *Toll Free Fax:* 800-332-1132 (US) *E-mail:* info@lernerbooks.com *Web Site:* www.lernerbooks.com, pg 53

Mathews, Richard, The Tampa Review Prize for Poetry, University of Tampa Press, 401 W Kennedy Blvd, Tampa, FL 33606 *Tel:* 813-253-6266 *E-mail:* utpress@ut.edu *Web Site:* tampareview.ut.edu, pg 745

Mathieson, Tim, Faith & Fellowship Press, 1020 W Alcott Ave, Fergus Falls, MN 56537 *Tel:* 218-736-7357; 218-736-2200 *Toll Free Tel:* 800-332-9232 *E-mail:* ffbooks@clba.org; ffpublishing@clba.org *Web Site:* www.faithandfellowship.org, pg 92

Mathieu, James R, University of Pennsylvania Museum of Archaeology & Anthropology, 3260 South St, Philadelphia, PA 19104-6324 *Tel:* 215-898-5723 *Fax:* 215-573-2497 *E-mail:* info@pennmuseum.org; publications@pennmuseum.org *Web Site:* www.penn.museum, pg 268

Matlins, Stuart M, GemStone Press, Sunset Farm Offices, Rte 4, Woodstock, VT 05091 *Tel:* 802-457-4000 *Toll Free Tel:* 800-962-4544 *Fax:* 802-457-4004 *E-mail:* sales@gemstonepress.com *Web Site:* www.gemstonepress.com, pg 102

Matlins, Stuart M, Jewish Lights Publishing, Sunset Farm Offices, Rte 4, Woodstock, VT 05091 *Tel:* 802-457-4000 *Toll Free Tel:* 800-962-4544 (orders only) *Fax:* 802-457-4004 *E-mail:* sales@jewishlights.com *Web Site:* www.jewishlights.com, pg 135

Matlins, Stuart M, SkyLight Paths Publishing, Sunset Farm Offices, Rte 4, Woodstock, VT 05091 *Tel:* 802-457-4000 *Toll Free Tel:* 800-962-4544 *Fax:* 802-457-4004 *E-mail:* sales@skylightpaths.com *Web Site:* www.skylightpaths.com, pg 237

Matloff, Robert, The Guilford Press, 72 Spring St, 4th fl, New York, NY 10012 *Tel:* 212-431-9800 *Toll Free Tel:* 800-365-7006 (ext 1, orders) *Fax:* 212-966-6708 *E-mail:* orders@guilford.com; info@guilford.com *Web Site:* www.guilford.com, pg 109

Matrisciani, Michele, Movable Type Management, 610 Fifth Ave, Suite 1220, New York, NY 10185 *Tel:* 917-289-1089 *Fax:* 646-810-5757 *Web Site:* www.mtmgmt.net, pg 586

Matson, Jonathan, Harold Matson Co Inc, 276 Fifth Ave, New York, NY 10001 *Tel:* 212-679-4490 *Fax:* 212-545-1224, pg 584

Matson, Katinka, Brockman Inc, 260 Fifth Ave, 10th fl, New York, NY 10001 *Tel:* 212-935-8900 *Fax:* 212-935-5535 *E-mail:* rights@brockman.com *Web Site:* www.brockman.com, pg 564

Matson, Peter, Sterling Lord Literistic Inc, 65 Bleecker St, New York, NY 10012 *Tel:* 212-780-6050 *Fax:* 212-780-6095 *E-mail:* info@sll.com *Web Site:* www.sll.com, pg 595

Matthews, Katherine, Lucky Marble Books, 2671 Bristol Rd, Columbus, OH 43221 *Tel:* 614-264-5588 *E-mail:* sales@pagespringpublishing.com *Web Site:* www.luckymarblebooks.com, pg 154

Mattingly, Laura Lee, Chronicle Books LLC, 680 Second St, San Francisco, CA 94107 *Tel:* 415-537-4200 *Toll Free Tel:* 800-759-0190 (cust serv) *Fax:* 415-537-4460 *Toll Free Fax:* 800-858-7787 (orders); 800-286-9471 (cust serv) *E-mail:* frontdesk@chroniclebooks.com *Web Site:* www.chroniclebooks.com, pg 61

Mattison, Zach, PRISM international Literary Non-Fiction Contest, University of British Columbia, Buch E462, 1866 Main Mall, Vancouver, BC V6T 1Z1, Canada *Tel:* 778-822-2514 *Fax:* 778-822-3616 *E-mail:* prismwritingcontest@gmail.com *Web Site:* www.prismmagazine.ca, pg 735

Mattison, Zach, PRISM international Poetry Contest, University of British Columbia, Buch E462, 1866 Main Mall, Vancouver, BC V6T 1Z1, Canada *Tel:* 778-822-2514 *Fax:* 778-822-3616 *E-mail:* prismwritingcontest@gmail.com *Web Site:* www.prismmagazine.ca, pg 736

Mattison, Zach, PRISM international Short Fiction Contest, University of British Columbia, Buch E462, 1866 Main Mall, Vancouver, BC V6T 1Z1, Canada *Tel:* 778-822-2514 *Fax:* 778-822-3616 *E-mail:* prismwritingcontest@gmail.com *Web Site:* www.prismmagazine.ca, pg 736

Mattos, Dominic, T&T Clark International, 1385 Broadway, 5th fl, New York, NY 10018 *Tel:* 212-953-5858 *Toll Free Tel:* 800-561-7704 (orders) *Fax:* 212-953-5944 *Web Site:* www.continuumbooks.com, pg 249

Mattson, Trilogy, Time Being Books, 10411 Clayton Rd, Suites 201-203, St Louis, MO 63131 *Tel:* 314-432-1771 *Fax:* 314-432-7939 *E-mail:* tbbooks@sbcglobal.net *Web Site:* www.timebeing.com, pg 255

Mattura, Cat, McGraw-Hill Create, 501 Bell St, Dubuque, IA 52001 *Tel:* 563-584-6000 *Fax:* 563-584-6600 *E-mail:* first_last@mcgraw-hill.com *Web Site:* www.mhhe.com, pg 160

Matuszak, Ashley, Ten Speed Press, 2625 Alcatraz Ave, Unit 505, Berkeley, CA 94705 *Tel:* 510-285-3000 *Toll Free Tel:* 800-841-BOOK (841-2665) *E-mail:* csorders@randomhouse.com *Web Site:* crownpublishing.com/imprint/ten-speed-press, pg 252

Matute, Silvia, Santillana USA Publishing Co Inc, 2023 NW 84 Ave, Doral, FL 33122 *Tel:* 305-591-9522 *Toll Free Tel:* 800-245-8584 *Fax:* 305-591-9145 *Toll Free Fax:* 888-248-9518 *E-mail:* customerservice@santillanausa.com *Web Site:* www.santillanausa.com; www.alfaguara.net, pg 226

Matwychuk, Paul, NeWest Press, 8540 109 St, No 201, Edmonton, AB T6G 1E6, Canada *Tel:* 780-432-9427 *Toll Free Tel:* 866-796-5473 *Fax:* 780-433-3179 *E-mail:* info@newestpress.com *Web Site:* www.newestpress.com, pg 513

Matysko, Harriet I, Mary Ann Liebert Inc, 140 Huguenot St, 3rd fl, New Rochelle, NY 10801-5215 *Tel:* 914-740-2100 *Toll Free Tel:* 800-654-3237 *Fax:* 914-740-2101 *E-mail:* info@liebertpub.com *Web Site:* www.liebertonline.com, pg 148

Mauer, Harry, Flashlight Press, 527 Empire Blvd, Brooklyn, NY 11225 *Tel:* 718-288-8300 *Fax:* 718-972-6307 *E-mail:* editor@flashlightpress.com *Web Site:* www.flashlightpress.com, pg 96

Mauer, Tzvi, Urim Publications, c/o Lambda Publications Inc, 527 Empire Blvd, Brooklyn, NY 11225-3121 *Tel:* 718-972-5449 *Fax:* 718-972-6307 *E-mail:* publisher@urimpublications.com *Web Site:* urimpublications.com, pg 273

Mauk, J T, The Perseus Books Group, 387 Park Ave S, 12th fl, New York, NY 10016 *Tel:* 212-340-8100 *Toll Free Tel:* 800-343-4499 (cust serv) *Fax:* 212-340-8105 *Web Site:* www.perseusbooksgroup.com, pg 199

Maurer, Rolf, New Star Books Ltd, 107-3477 Commercial St, Vancouver, BC V5N 4E8, Canada *Tel:* 604-738-9429 *Fax:* 604-738-9332 *E-mail:* info@newstarbooks.com; orders@newstarbooks.com *Web Site:* www.newstarbooks.com, pg 513

Maurin, Denise, Omnibus Press, 257 Park Ave S, 20th fl, New York, NY 10010 *Tel:* 212-254-2100 *Toll Free Tel:* 800-431-7187 *Fax:* 212-254-2013 *Toll Free Fax:* 800-345-6842 *E-mail:* info-us@omnibuspress.com *Web Site:* www.musicsales.com; omnibuspressusa.com, pg 185

Mausser, Therese, AMACOM Books, 1601 Broadway, New York, NY 10019-7420 *Tel:* 212-586-8100; 518-891-5510 (orders) *Toll Free Tel:* 800-250-5308 (cust serv) *Fax:* 212-903-8083; 518-891-2372 (orders) *E-mail:* pubservice@amanet.org *Web Site:* www.amacombooks.org, pg 9

Mautner, Stephen, National Academies Press (NAP), Lockbox 285, 500 Fifth St NW, Washington, DC 20001 *Tel:* 202-334-3313 *Toll Free Tel:* 888-624-8373 (cust serv) *Fax:* 202-334-2451 (cust serv); 202-334-2793 (mktg dept) *E-mail:* customer_service@nap.edu *Web Site:* www.nap.edu, pg 173

Mavjee, Maya, Crown Publishing Group, c/o Random House Inc, 1745 Broadway, New York, NY 10019 *Tel:* 212-782-9000 *Toll Free Tel:* 888-264-1745 *Fax:* 212-940-7408 *Web Site:* www.randomhouse.com/crown, pg 72

Mavjee, Maya, Random House Inc, 1745 Broadway, New York, NY 10019 *Tel:* 212-782-9000 *Toll Free Tel:* 800-726-0600 *Web Site:* www.randomhouse.com, pg 213

Max, P J, Easy Money Press, 5419 87 St, Lubbock, TX 79424 *Tel:* 806-543-5215 *E-mail:* easymoneypress@yahoo.com, pg 84

Maxick, Jill, Prometheus Books, 59 John Glenn Dr, Amherst, NY 14228-2119 *Tel:* 716-691-0133 *Toll Free Tel:* 800-421-0351 *Fax:* 716-691-0137 *E-mail:* marketing@prometheusbooks.com; editorial@prometheusbooks.com *Web Site:* www.Prometheusbooks.com, pg 208

Maxwell, Linda, Blue Dolphin Publishing Inc, 13340-D Grass Valley Ave, Grass Valley, CA 95945 *Tel:* 530-477-1503 *Toll Free Tel:* 800-643-0765 (orders) *Fax:* 530-477-8342 *E-mail:* bdolphin@bluedolphinpublishing.com *Web Site:* www.bluedolphinpublishing.com, pg 41

Maxwell, Mitchell, The Story Plant, PO Box 4331, Stamford, CT 06907 *Tel:* 203-722-7920 *E-mail:* thestoryplant@thestoryplant.com *Web Site:* www.thestoryplant.com, pg 246

Maxwell, Nancy, Ariel Press, 88 N Gate Station Dr, Suite 106, Marble Hill, GA 30148 *Tel:* 770-894-4226 *Fax:* 706-579-1274 *E-mail:* lig201@lightariel.com *Web Site:* www.lightariel.com, pg 22

May, Christopher, Dufour Editions Inc, PO Box 7, Chester Springs, PA 19425 *Tel:* 610-458-5005 *Toll Free Tel:* 800-869-5677 *Fax:* 610-458-7103 *E-mail:* info@dufoureditions.com *Web Site:* www.dufoureditions.com, pg 82

May, Duncan, Dufour Editions Inc, PO Box 7, Chester Springs, PA 19425 *Tel:* 610-458-5005 *Toll Free Tel:* 800-869-5677 *Fax:* 610-458-7103 *E-mail:* info@dufoureditions.com *Web Site:* www.dufoureditions.com, pg 82

May, Linda, The Apex Press, 4501 Forbes Blvd, Suite 200, Lanham, MD 20706 *Tel:* 301-459-3366 *Toll Free Tel:* 800-462-6420 *Toll Free Fax:* 800-388-4450 *E-mail:* customercare@rowman.com, pg 19

May, Linda, Scarecrow Press Inc, 4501 Forbes Blvd, Suite 200, Lanham, MD 20706 *Tel:* 301-459-3366 *Fax:* 301-429-5748 *Web Site:* www.scarecrowpress.com, pg 226

May, Louise, Lee & Low Books Inc, 95 Madison Ave, New York, NY 10016 *Tel:* 212-779-4400 *Toll Free Tel:* 888-320-3190 (ext 28, orders only) *Fax:* 212-683-1894 (orders only); 212-532-6035 *E-mail:* general@leeandlow.com *Web Site:* www.leeandlow.com, pg 146

May, Theresa, University of Texas Press, 2100 Comal St, Austin, TX 78722 *Tel:* 512-471-7233 *Fax:* 512-232-7178 *E-mail:* utpress@uts.cc.utexas.edu *Web Site:* www.utexaspress.com, pg 253

Mayer, Christie, Dissertation.com, 23331 Water Circle, Boca Raton, FL 33486-8540 *Tel:* 561-750-4344 *Toll Free Tel:* 800-636-8329 *Fax:* 561-750-6797 *Web Site:* www.dissertation.com, pg 80

Mayer, Dariel, Vanderbilt University Press, 2014 Broadway, Suite 320, Nashville, TN 37203 *Tel:* 615-322-3585 *Toll Free Tel:* 800-627-7377 (orders only) *Fax:* 615-343-8823 *Toll Free Fax:* 800-735-0476 (orders only) *E-mail:* vupress@vanderbilt.edu *Web Site:* www.vanderbiltuniversitypress.com, pg 274

Mayer, Karen, Penguin Group (USA) LLC, 375 Hudson St, New York, NY 10014 *Tel:* 212-366-2000 *Toll Free Tel:* 800-847-5515 (inside sales); 800-631-8571 (cust serv) *Fax:* 212-366-2666; 607-775-4829 (inside sales) *E-mail:* online@us.penguingroup.com *Web Site:* www.penguin.com; us.penguingroup.com, pg 197

Mayer, Liese, The Overlook Press, 141 Wooster St, Suite 4-B, New York, NY 10012 *Tel:* 212-673-2210; 845-679-6838 (orders & dist) *Fax:* 212-673-2296 *E-mail:* sales@overlookny.com (orders) *Web Site:* www.overlookpress.com, pg 189

Mayer, Loomis, Fordham University Press, 2546 Belmont Ave, University Box L, Bronx, NY 10458 *Tel:* 718-817-4795 *Fax:* 718-817-4785 *Web Site:* www.fordhampress.com, pg 97

Mayer, Margery, Scholastic Education, 524 Broadway, New York, NY 10012 *Tel:* 212-343-6100 *Fax:* 212-343-6189 *Web Site:* www.scholastic.com, pg 228

Mayer, Margery, Scholastic Inc, 557 Broadway, New York, NY 10012 *Tel:* 212-343-6100 *Toll Free Tel:* 800-scholastic *Web Site:* www.scholastic.com, pg 228

Mayer, Peter, The Overlook Press, 141 Wooster St, Suite 4-B, New York, NY 10012 *Tel:* 212-673-2210; 845-679-6838 (orders & dist) *Fax:* 212-673-2296 *E-mail:* sales@overlookny.com (orders) *Web Site:* www.overlookpress.com, pg 189

Mayer, Sr Sean Marie David, Pauline Books & Media, 50 Saint Paul's Ave, Boston, MA 02130 *Tel:* 617-522-8911 *Toll Free Tel:* 800-876-4463 (orders); 800-836-9723 (cust serv) *Fax:* 617-541-9805 *E-mail:* orderentry@pauline.org (cust serv); editorial@paulinemedia.com (ms submissions) *Web Site:* www.pauline.org, pg 194

Mayer, Tania, The Clarion Science Fiction & Fantasy Writers' Workshop, Dept of Literature, Mail Code 0410, UC San Diego, 9500 Gilman Dr, La Jolla, CA 92093-0410 *Tel:* 858-534-2115 *E-mail:* clarion@ucsd.edu *Web Site:* clarion.ucsd.edu, pg 668

Mayer, Tom, W W Norton & Company Inc, 500 Fifth Ave, New York, NY 10110-0017 *Tel:* 212-354-5500 *Toll Free Tel:* 800-233-4830 (orders & cust serv) *Fax:* 212-869-0856 *Toll Free Fax:* 800-458-6515 *Web Site:* www.wwnorton.com, pg 182

Mayers, Roy, Abrams Learning Trends, 16310 Bratton Lane, Suite 250, Austin, TX 78728-2403 *Toll Free Tel:* 800-227-9120 *Toll Free Fax:* 800-737-3322 *E-mail:* customerservice@abramslearningtrends.com (orders, cust serv) *Web Site:* www.abramslearningtrends.com (orders, cust serv), pg 3

Mayhew, Alice E, Simon & Schuster, 1230 Avenue of the Americas, New York, NY 10020 *Tel:* 212-698-7000 *Toll Free Tel:* 800-223-2348 (cust serv); 800-223-2336 (orders) *Toll Free Fax:* 800-943-9831 (orders) *Web Site:* www.simonandschuster.com, pg 234

Maynard, Audrey, Tilbury House Publishers, 103 Brunswick Ave, Gardiner, ME 04345 *Tel:* 207-582-1899 *Toll Free Tel:* 800-582-1899 (orders) *Fax:* 207-582-8227 *E-mail:* tilbury@tilburyhouse.com *Web Site:* www.tilburyhouse.com, pg 255

Maynard, Garret C, The Gary-Paul Agency, 1549 Main St, Stratford, CT 06615 *Tel:* 203-345-6167 *Fax:* 203-345-6167 *E-mail:* garret@thegarypaulagency.com *Web Site:* www.thegarypaulagency.com; www.nutmegpictures.com, pg 547

Maynard, Jim, Quicksilver Productions, PO Box 340, Ashland, OR 97520-0012 *Tel:* 541-482-5343 *Fax:* 508-590-0099 *E-mail:* celestialcalendars@email.com *Web Site:* www.quicksilverproductions.com, pg 211

Mayotte, Alain, Prise de Parole Inc, 109 Elm St, Suite 205, Sudbury, ON P3C 1T4, Canada *Tel:* 705-675-6491 *Fax:* 705-673-1817 *E-mail:* info@prisedeparole.ca *Web Site:* www.prisedeparole.ca, pg 516

Mays, Wendy, WendyLynn & Co, 504 Wilson Rd, Annapolis, MD 21401 *Tel:* 410-224-2729; 410-507-1059 *Web Site:* wendylynn.com, pg 603

Maze, Stephanie, Moonstone Press LLC, 4816 Carrington Circle, Sarasota, FL 34243 *Tel:* 301-765-1081 *Fax:* 301-765-0510 *E-mail:* mazeprod@erols.com *Web Site:* www.moonstonepress.net, pg 528

Mazer, Laura, Seal Press, 1700 Fourth St, Berkeley, CA 94710 *Tel:* 510-595-3664 *Fax:* 510-595-4228 *E-mail:* seal.press@perseusbooks.com *Web Site:* www.sealpress.com, pg 230

Mazia, Judith, Alan Wofsy Fine Arts, 1109 Geary Blvd, San Francisco, CA 94109 *Tel:* 415-292-6500 *Toll Free Tel:* 800-660-6403 *Fax:* 415-292-6594 (off & cust serv); 415-512-0130 (acctg) *E-mail:* order@art-books.com (orders); editeur@earthlink.net (edit); beauxarts@earthlink.net (cust serv) *Web Site:* www.art-books.com, pg 284

Mazur, Julie, Watson-Guptill Publications, c/o Random House Inc, 1745 Broadway, New York, NY 10019 *Tel:* 212-782-9000 *Fax:* 212-940-7381 *E-mail:* crownbiz@randomhouse.com *Web Site:* www.randomhouse.com/crown/watsonguptill, pg 277

Mazurkiewicz, Orchid, UCLA Latin American Center Publications, UCLA Latin American Institute, 10343 Bunche Hall, Los Angeles, CA 90095 *Tel:* 310-825-4571 *Fax:* 310-206-6859 *E-mail:* latinamctr@international.ucla.edu *Web Site:* www.international.ucla.edu/lai, pg 261

Mazza, Cris, University of Illinois at Chicago, Program for Writers, College of Liberal Arts & Sciences, 2027 University Hall, 601 S Morgan St, Chicago, IL 60607-7120 *Tel:* 312-413-2200 (Eng Dept) *Fax:* 312-413-1005 *Web Site:* www.uic.edu, pg 681

McAdam, Elena Goranescu, McGill-Queen's University Press, 1010 Sherbrooke W, Suite 1720, Montreal, QC H3A 2R7, Canada *Tel:* 514-398-3750 *Fax:* 514-398-4333 *E-mail:* mqup@mqup.ca *Web Site:* www.mqup.ca, pg 512

McAdam, Matthew, The Johns Hopkins University Press, 2715 N Charles St, Baltimore, MD 21218-4363 *Tel:* 410-516-6900; 410-516-6987 (journals outside US & CN) *Toll Free Tel:* 800-537-5487 (book orders & cust serv); 800-548-1784 (journal orders) *Fax:* 410-516-6968; 410-516-3866 (journal orders) *E-mail:* hfscustserv@press.jhu.edu (cust serv); jrnlcirc@press.jhu.edu (journal orders) *Web Site:* www.press.jhu.edu; muse.jhu.edu/about/subscriptions/index.html (Project Muse subns), pg 136

McAdams, Kevin, Schiavone Literary Agency Inc, 236 Trails End, West Palm Beach, FL 33413-2135 *Tel:* 561-966-9294 *Fax:* 561-966-9294 *E-mail:* profschia@aol.com *Web Site:* www.publishersmarketplace.com/members/profschia, pg 592

McAliley, Kevin, Haights Cross Communications Inc, 136 Madison Ave, 8th fl, New York, NY 10016 *Tel:* 212-209-0500 *Fax:* 212-209-0501 *E-mail:* info@haightscross.com *Web Site:* www.haightscross.com, pg 110

McAliley, Kevin, Triumph Learning, 136 Madison Ave, 7th fl, New York, NY 10016 *Tel:* 212-652-0200 *Toll Free Tel:* 800-221-9372 (cust serv) *Toll Free Fax:* 866-805-5723 *E-mail:* info@triumphlearning.com; customerservice@triumphlearning.com *Web Site:* www.triumphlearning.com, pg 259

McAllister, David, C & M Online Media Inc, 3905 Meadow Field Lane, Raleigh, NC 27606 *Tel:* 919-233-8164 *E-mail:* support@cmonline.com *Web Site:* www.cmonline.com, pg 50

McAllister, Lisa, The Apex Press, 4501 Forbes Blvd, Suite 200, Lanham, MD 20706 *Tel:* 301-459-3366 *Toll Free Tel:* 800-462-6420 *Toll Free Fax:* 800-388-4450 *E-mail:* customercare@rowman.com, pg 20

McAllister, Lisa, Bernan, 4501 Forbes Blvd, Suite 200, Lanham, MD 20706 *Tel:* 301-459-7666 (cust serv & orders) *Fax:* 301-459-0056 *E-mail:* customercare@bernan.com *Web Site:* www.bernan.com, pg 36

McAllister, Lisa, Government Institutes (GI), 4501 Forbes Blvd, Suite 200, Lanham, MD 20706 *Tel:* 301-459-3366 (ext 5622) *Toll Free Tel:* 800-462-6420 *Fax:* 301-429-5748 *Toll Free Fax:* 800-338-4550 *Web Site:* www.govinstpress.com, pg 105

McAllister, Nancy, C & M Online Media Inc, 3905 Meadow Field Lane, Raleigh, NC 27606 *Tel:* 919-233-8164 *E-mail:* support@cmonline.com *Web Site:* www.cmonline.com, pg 50

McAllister, Shawn, StarGroup International Inc, 1194 Old Dixie Hwy, Suite 201, West Palm Beach, FL 33413 *Tel:* 561-547-0667 *Fax:* 561-843-8530 *E-mail:* info@stargroupinternational.com *Web Site:* www.stargroupinternational.com, pg 243

McAloon, Hugh, Krause Publications Inc, 700 E State St, Iola, WI 54990 *Tel:* 715-445-2214 *Toll Free Tel:* 800-258-0929 (cust serv); 888-457-2873 (orders) *Fax:* 715-445-4087 *E-mail:* bookorders@krause.com *Web Site:* www.krausebooks.com, pg 142

McArdle, Moira, MDR, A D & B Co, 6 Armstrong Rd, Suite 301, Shelton, CT 06484 *Tel:* 203-926-4800 *Toll Free Tel:* 800-333-8802 *E-mail:* mdrinfo@dnb.com *Web Site:* www.schooldata.com, pg 162

McAuley, Scott, Angel City Press, 2118 Wilshire Blvd, Suite 880, Santa Monica, CA 90403 *Tel:* 310-395-9982 *Toll Free Tel:* 800-949-8039 *Fax:* 310-395-3353 *E-mail:* info@angelcitypress.com *Web Site:* www.angelcitypress.com, pg 18

McAweeney, Terry, MFA Publications, 465 Huntington Ave, Boston, MA 02115 *Tel:* 617-369-4233 *Fax:* 617-369-3459 *Web Site:* www.mfa.org/publications, pg 165

McBeath, Kasey, Texas Tech University Press, 2903 Fourth St, Suite 201, Lubbock, TX 79409 *Tel:* 806-742-2982 *Toll Free Tel:* 800-832-4042 *Fax:* 806-742-2979 *E-mail:* ttup@ttu.edu *Web Site:* www.ttupress.org, pg 253

McBride, David, Oxford University Press USA, 198 Madison Ave, New York, NY 10016 *Tel:* 212-726-6000 *Toll Free Tel:* 800-451-7556 (orders); 800-445-9714 (cust serv) *Fax:* 919-677-1303 *E-mail:* custserv.us@oup.com *Web Site:* www.oup.com/us, pg 189

McBride, Margret, Margret McBride Literary Agency, PO Box 9128, La Jolla, CA 92038 *Tel:* 858-454-1550 *Fax:* 858-454-2156 *E-mail:* staff@mcbridelit.com *Web Site:* www.mcbrideliterary.com, pg 584

McCabe, Don, AVKO Educational Research Foundation Inc, 3084 Willard Rd, Birch Run, MI 48415-9404 *Tel:* 810-686-9283 (orders & billing) *Toll Free Tel:* 866-AVKO612 (285-6612) *Fax:* 810-686-1101 *E-mail:* info@avko.org (gen inquiry) *Web Site:* www.avko.org; www.avko.blogspot.org, pg 28

McCabe, Kristin, American Association of Colleges for Teacher Education (AACTE), 1307 New York Ave NW, Suite 300, Washington, DC 20005-4701 *Tel:* 202-293-2450 *Fax:* 202-457-8095 *E-mail:* aacte@aacte.org *Web Site:* www.aacte.org, pg 11

McCabe, Robert, AVKO Educational Research Foundation Inc, 3084 Willard Rd, Birch Run, MI 48415-9404 *Tel:* 810-686-9283 (orders & billing) *Toll Free Tel:* 866-AVKO612 (285-6612) *Fax:* 810-686-1101 *E-mail:* info@avko.org (gen inquiry) *Web Site:* www.avko.org; www.avko.blogspot.org, pg 28

McCaffrey, Philip, W H Freeman and Co, 41 Madison Ave, 37th fl, New York, NY 10010 *Tel:* 212-576-9400 *Fax:* 212-689-2383 *Web Site:* www.whfreeman.com, pg 99

McCaffrey, Philip, Worth Publishers, 41 Madison Ave, 37th fl, New York, NY 10010 *Tel:* 212-576-9400 *Fax:* 212-561-8281 *Web Site:* www.worthpub.com, pg 286

McCaffrey, Roger A, Roman Catholic Books, PO Box 2286, Fort Collins, CO 80522-2286 *Tel:* 970-490-2735 *Fax:* 904-212-1287 *Web Site:* www.booksforcatholics.com, pg 220

McCahill, Kevin, Gallery Books, 1230 Avenue of the Americas, New York, NY 10020 *Toll Free Tel:* 800-456-6798 *Fax:* 212-698-7284 *E-mail:* consumer.customerservice@simonandschuster.com *Web Site:* www.simonsays.com, pg 101

McCahon, Kristin, The Fraser Institute, 1770 Burrard St, 4th fl, Vancouver, BC V6J 3G7, Canada *Tel:* 604-688-0221 *Toll Free Tel:* 800-665-3558 *Fax:* 604-688-8539 *E-mail:* info@fraserinstitute.org; sales@fraserinstitute.org *Web Site:* www.fraserinstitute.org, pg 506

McCain, Michelle, Comprehensive Health Education Foundation (CHEF), 159 S Jackson St, Suite 510, Seattle, WA 98104 *Tel:* 206-824-2907 *Toll Free Tel:* 800-323-2433 *Fax:* 206-824-3072 *E-mail:* info@chef.org *Web Site:* www.chef.org, pg 66

McCain, Rev Paul T, Concordia Publishing House, 3558 S Jefferson Ave, St Louis, MO 63118-3968 *Tel:* 314-268-1000 *Toll Free Tel:* 800-325-3040 (cust serv) *Toll Free Fax:* 800-490-9889 (cust serv) *E-mail:* order@cph.org *Web Site:* www.cph.org, pg 66

McCall, Linda, AAUP Book, Jacket & Journal Design Show, 28 W 36 St, Suite 602, New York, NY 10018 *Tel:* 212-989-1010 *Fax:* 212-989-0275 *E-mail:* info@aaupnet.org *Web Site:* www.aaupnet.org, pg 685

McCall, Linda, Association of American University Presses (AAUP), 28 W 36 St, Suite 602, New York, NY 10018 *Tel:* 212-989-1010 *Fax:* 212-989-0275 *E-mail:* info@aaupnet.org *Web Site:* www.aaupnet.org, pg 616

McCall, Timothy, Penguin Group (USA) LLC Sales, 375 Hudson St, New York, NY 10014 *Tel:* 212-366-2000 *E-mail:* online@penguinputnam.com *Web Site:* us.penguingroup.com, pg 197

McCann, Peg, American Society of Agricultural Engineers (ASABE), 2950 Niles Rd, St Joseph, MI 49085-9659 *Tel:* 269-429-0300 *Fax:* 269-429-3852 *E-mail:* hq@asabe.org *Web Site:* www.asabe.org, pg 16

McCardell, Michelle, Upstart Books™, 4810 Forest Run Rd, Madison, WI 53704 *Tel:* 608-241-1201 *Toll Free Tel:* 800-448-4887 (orders) *Toll Free Fax:* 800-448-5828 *E-mail:* custsvc@upstartpromotions.com *Web Site:* www.upstartbooks.com, pg 273

McCarter, Robert, Jodie Rhodes Literary Agency, 8840 Villa La Jolla Dr, Suite 315, La Jolla, CA 92037 *E-mail:* jrhodesl@san.rr.com *Web Site:* www.jodierhodesliterary.com, pg 590

McCarthy, Brian, The Library of America, 14 E 60 St, New York, NY 10022-1006 *Tel:* 212-308-3360 *Fax:* 212-750-8352 *E-mail:* info@loa.org *Web Site:* www.loa.org, pg 148

McCarthy, E J, E J McCarthy Agency, 1104 Shelter Bay Ave, Mill Valley, CA 94941 *Tel:* 415-383-6639 *Fax:* 415-383-6639 *E-mail:* ejmagency@gmail.com *Web Site:* www.publishersmarketplace.com/members/ejmccarthy, pg 585

McCarthy, Jim, Dystel & Goderich Literary Management, One Union Sq W, Suite 904, New York, NY 10003 *Tel:* 212-627-9100 *Fax:* 212-627-9313 *Web Site:* www.dystel.com, pg 569

McCarthy, Juliana M, The Johns Hopkins University Press, 2715 N Charles St, Baltimore, MD 21218-4363 *Tel:* 410-516-6900; 410-516-6987 (journals outside US & CN) *Toll Free Tel:* 800-537-5487 (book orders & cust serv); 800-548-1784 (journal orders) *Fax:* 410-516-6968; 410-516-3866 (journal orders) *E-mail:* hfscustserv@press.jhu.edu (cust serv); jrnlcirc@press.jhu.edu (journal orders) *Web Site:* www.press.jhu.edu; muse.jhu.edu/about/subscriptions/index.html (Project Muse subns), pg 136

McCarthy, Malachy R, Aggiornamento Award, 205 W Monroe, Suite 314, Chicago, IL 60606-5061 *Tel:* 312-739-1776; 312-739-1776 *Toll Free Tel:* 855-739-1776 *Fax:* 312-739-1778; 312-739-1778 *E-mail:* cla2@cathla.org *Web Site:* www.cathla.org, pg 685

McCarthy, Malachy R, Catholic Library Association, 205 W Monroe, Suite 314, Chicago, IL 60606-5061 *Tel:* 312-739-1776 *Toll Free Tel:* 855-739-1776 *Fax:* 312-739-1778 *E-mail:* cla2@cathla.org *Web Site:* www.cathla.org, pg 620

McCarthy, Malachy R, Saint Katharine Drexel Award, 205 W Monroe, Suite 314, Chicago, IL 60606-5061 *Tel:* 312-739-1776; 312-739-1776 *Toll Free Tel:* 855-739-1776 *Fax:* 312-739-1778; 312-739-1778 *E-mail:* cla2@cathla.org *Web Site:* www.cathla.org, pg 701

McCarthy, Malachy R, Jerome Award, 205 W Monroe, Suite 314, Chicago, IL 60606-5061 *Tel:* 312-739-1776; 312-739-1776 *Toll Free Tel:* 855-739-1776 *Fax:* 312-739-1778; 312-739-1778 *E-mail:* cla2@cathla.org *Web Site:* www.cathla.org, pg 714

McCarthy, Malachy R, Regina Medal Award, 205 W Monroe, Suite 314, Chicago, IL 60606-5061 *Tel:* 312-739-1776; 312-739-1776 *Toll Free Tel:* 855-739-1776 *Fax:* 312-739-1778; 312-739-1778 *E-mail:* cla2@cathla.org *Web Site:* www.cathla.org, pg 737

McCarthy, Pat, Cornell & McCarthy LLC, 2-D Cross Hwy, Westport, CT 06880 *Tel:* 203-454-4210 *E-mail:* contact@cmartreps.com *Web Site:* www.cmartreps.com, pg 601

McCarthy, Prof Paul D, McCarthy Creative Services, 625 Main St, Suite 834, New York, NY 10044-0035 *Tel:* 212-832-3428 *E-mail:* PaulMccarthy@MccarthyCreative.com *Web Site:* www.mccarthycreative.com, pg 551

McCarthy, Sabrina, The Perseus Books Group, 387 Park Ave S, 12th fl, New York, NY 10016 *Tel:* 212-340-8100 *Toll Free Tel:* 800-343-4499 (cust serv) *Fax:* 212-340-8105 *Web Site:* www.perseusbooksgroup.com, pg 199

McCarthy, Sarah, Center for Publishing Departmental Scholarships, Midtown Ctr, Rm 429, 11 W 42 St, New York, NY 10036 *Tel:* 212-992-3232 *Fax:* 212-992-3233 *E-mail:* pub.center@nyu.edu; ms.publishing@nyu.edu *Web Site:* www.scps.nyu.edu, pg 696

McCarthy, Sarah, New York University, Center for Publishing, Midtown Ctr, Rm 429, 11 W 42 St, New York, NY 10036 *Tel:* 212-992-3232 *Fax:* 212-992-3233 *E-mail:* pub.center@nyu.edu *Web Site:* www.scps.nyu.edu/publishing, pg 679

McCarthy, Sean, Sheldon Fogelman Agency Inc, 10 E 40 St, Suite 3205, New York, NY 10016 *Tel:* 212-532-7250 *Fax:* 212-685-8939 *E-mail:* info@sheldonfogelmanagency.com *Web Site:* sheldonfogelmanagency.com, pg 572

McCarthy, Vanessa, Centre for Reformation & Renaissance Studies (CRRS), EJ Pratt Library, Rm 301, 71 Queen's Park Crescent E, Toronto, ON M5S 1K7, Canada *Tel:* 416-585-4468 *Fax:* 416-585-4430 (attn: CRRS) *E-mail:* crrs.publications@utoronto.ca *Web Site:* www.crrs.ca, pg 498

McCaskey, Caitlin, Random House Speakers Bureau, 1745 Broadway, Mail Drop 13-1, New York, NY 10019 *Tel:* 212-572-2013 *E-mail:* rhspeakers@randomhouse.com *Web Site:* www.rhspeakers.com, pg 605

McCauley, Gerard, Gerard McCauley Agency Inc, PO Box 844, Katonah, NY 10536-0844 *Tel:* 914-232-5700 *Fax:* 914-232-1506, pg 585

McCauley, Kay, The Pimlico Agency Inc, PO Box 20490, New York, NY 10017 *Tel:* 212-628-9729 *Fax:* 212-535-7861, pg 588

McCauley, Kirby, The Pimlico Agency Inc, PO Box 20490, New York, NY 10017 *Tel:* 212-628-9729 *Fax:* 212-535-7861, pg 588

McCaull, June, The MIT Press, 55 Hayward St, Cambridge, MA 02142 *Tel:* 617-253-5255 *Toll Free Tel:* 800-207-8354 (orders) *Fax:* 617-258-6779; 617-577-1545 (orders) *Web Site:* mitpress.mit.edu, pg 168

McCay, Deanna, Syracuse University Press, 621 Skytop Rd, Suite 110, Syracuse, NY 13244-5290 *Tel:* 315-443-5534 *Toll Free Tel:* 800-365-8929 (cust serv) *Fax:* 315-443-5545 *E-mail:* supress@syr.edu *Web Site:* syracuseuniversitypress.syr.edu, pg 249

McClanahan, Pamela, Minnesota Historical Society Press, 345 Kellogg Blvd W, St Paul, MN 55102-1906 *Tel:* 651-259-3205; 651-259-3000 *Toll Free Tel:* 800-621-2736 (warehouse) *Fax:* 651-297-1345 *Toll Free Fax:* 800-621-8476 (warehouse) *E-mail:* info-mhspress@mnhs.org *Web Site:* www.mhspress.org, pg 167

McClellan, Anita, Anita D McClellan Associates, 464 Common St, Suite 142, Belmont, MA 02478-2704 *Tel:* 617-575-9203 *Fax:* 206-203-0829 *E-mail:* adm@anitamcclellan.com *Web Site:* www.anitamcclellan.com, pg 585

McClellan, Anita D, Anita D McClellan Associates, 464 Common St, Suite 142, Belmont, MA 02478-2704 *Tel:* 617-575-9203 *Fax:* 206-203-0829 *E-mail:* adm@anitamcclellan.com *Web Site:* www.anitamcclellan.com, pg 551

McClellan, Dennis, DC Press LLC, 750 Powderhorn Circle, Lake Mary, FL 32746 *Tel:* 407-688-1156 *Web Site:* www.dcpressbooks.com, pg 77

McClelland, Anne, Book & Periodical Council (BPC), 192 Spadina Ave, Suite 107, Toronto, ON M5T 2C2, Canada *Tel:* 416-975-9366 *Fax:* 416-975-1839 *E-mail:* info@thebpc.ca *Web Site:* www.thebpc.ca, pg 618

McClendon, Carole Jelen, Waterside Productions Inc, 2055 Oxford Ave, Cardiff, CA 92007 *Tel:* 760-632-9190 *Fax:* 760-632-9295 *E-mail:* admin@waterside.com *Web Site:* www.waterside.com, pg 598

McClure, Cameron, Donald Maass Literary Agency, 121 W 27 St, Suite 801, New York, NY 10001 *Tel:* 212-727-8383 *Fax:* 212-727-3271 *E-mail:* info@maassagency.com; rights@maassagency.com (subs rights inquiries) *Web Site:* www.maassagency.com, pg 582

McClure, Dr Donald E, American Mathematical Society, 201 Charles St, Providence, RI 02904-2294 *Tel:* 401-455-4000 *Toll Free Tel:* 800-321-4267 *Fax:* 401-331-3842; 401-455-4046 (cust serv) *E-mail:* ams@ams.org; cust-serv@ams.org *Web Site:* www.ams.org, pg 14

McClure, John, Signalman Publishing, 3700 Commerce Blvd, Kissimmee, FL 34741 *Tel:* 407-504-4103 *Toll Free Tel:* 888-907-4423 *E-mail:* info@signalmanpublishing.com *Web Site:* www.signalmanpublishing.com, pg 233

McClure, Urmila, Signalman Publishing, 3700 Commerce Blvd, Kissimmee, FL 34741 *Tel:* 407-504-4103 *Toll Free Tel:* 888-907-4423 *E-mail:* info@signalmanpublishing.com *Web Site:* www.signalmanpublishing.com, pg 233

McConnell, Christine, Margaret Mann Citation, 50 E Huron St, Chicago, IL 60611 *Tel:* 312-280-5037 *Toll Free Tel:* 800-545-2433 *Fax:* 312-280-5033 *E-mail:* alcts@ala.org *Web Site:* www.ala.org/alcts, pg 721

McConnell, David B, Hillsdale Educational Publishers Inc, 39 North St, Hillsdale, MI 49242 *Tel:* 517-437-3179 *Fax:* 517-437-0531 *E-mail:* davestory@aol.com *Web Site:* www.hillsdalepublishers.com; michbooks.com, pg 120

McConnell, Ted, Advertising Research Foundation (ARF), 432 Park Ave S, 6th fl, New York, NY 10016-8013 *Tel:* 212-751-5656 *Fax:* 212-319-5265 *E-mail:* info@thearf.org; jar@thearf.org (edit) *Web Site:* www.thearf.org; www.journalofadvertisingresearch.com, pg 611

McConville, Nicole, Lark Crafts, 67 Broadway, Asheville, NC 28801 *Tel:* 828-253-0467 *Fax:* 828-253-7952 *E-mail:* info@larkbooks.com *Web Site:* www.larkcrafts.com; www.larkbooks.com, pg 144

McCord, Jennifer, Epicenter Press Inc, 6524 NE 181 St, Suite 2, Kenmore, WA 98028 *Tel:* 425-485-6822 (edit, mktg, busn off) *Toll Free Tel:* 800-950-6663 (orders) *Fax:* 425-481-8253 *E-mail:* info@epicenterpress.com *Web Site:* www.epicenterpress.com, pg 89

McCoy, Anne, Columbia University Press, 61 W 62 St, New York, NY 10023 *Tel:* 212-459-0600 *Toll Free Tel:* 800-944-8648 *Fax:* 212-459-3678 *E-mail:* cup_book@columbia.edu (orders & cust serv) *Web Site:* cup.columbia.edu, pg 65

McCoy, Beverly, Eisenbrauns Inc, PO Box 275, Winona Lake, IN 46590-0275 *Tel:* 574-269-2011 *Fax:* 574-269-6788 *E-mail:* customer_service@eisenbrauns.com; publisher@eisenbrauns.com *Web Site:* www.eisenbrauns.com, pg 86

McCoy, James, Iowa Poetry Prize, 119 W Park Rd, 100 Kuhl House, Iowa City, IA 52242-1000 *Tel:* 319-335-2000 *Fax:* 319-335-2055 *E-mail:* uipress@uiowa.edu *Web Site:* www.uiowapress.org, pg 713

McCoy, James, Iowa Short Fiction Awards, 119 W Park Rd, 100 Kuhl House, Iowa City, IA 52242-1000 *Tel:* 319-335-2000 *Fax:* 319-335-2055 *E-mail:* uipress@uiowa.edu *Web Site:* www.uiowapress.org, pg 713

McCoy, James, University of Iowa Press, 119 W Park Rd, 100 Kuhl House, Iowa City, IA 52242-1000 *Tel:* 319-335-2000 *Toll Free Tel:* 800-621-2736 (orders only) *Fax:* 319-335-2055 *Toll Free Fax:* 800-621-8476 (orders only) *E-mail:* uipress@uiowa.edu *Web Site:* www.uiowapress.org, pg 266

McCoy, Melody, Jhpiego, 1615 Thames St, Baltimore, MD 21231-3492 *Tel:* 410-537-1800 *Fax:* 410-537-1473 *E-mail:* info@jhpiego.net; orders@jhpiego.net *Web Site:* www.jhpiego.org, pg 135

McCracken, Brad, Pauline Books & Media, 50 Saint Paul's Ave, Boston, MA 02130 *Tel:* 617-522-8911 *Toll Free Tel:* 800-876-4463 (orders); 800-836-9723 (cust serv) *Fax:* 617-541-9805 *E-mail:* orderentry@pauline.org (cust serv); editorial@paulinemedia.com (ms submissions) *Web Site:* www.pauline.org, pg 194

McCrae, Fiona, Graywolf Press, 250 Third Ave N, Suite 600, Minneapolis, MN 55401 *Tel:* 651-641-0077 *Fax:* 651-641-0036 *E-mail:* wolves@graywolfpress.org *Web Site:* www.graywolfpress.org, pg 106

McCreary, Courtney, University Press of Mississippi, 3825 Ridgewood Rd, Jackson, MS 39211-6492 *Tel:* 601-432-6205 *Toll Free Tel:* 800-737-7788 (orders & cust serv) *Fax:* 601-432-6217 *E-mail:* press@mississippi.edu *Web Site:* www.upress.state.ms.us, pg 271

McCreight, Tim, American Institute of Chemical Engineers (AIChE), 3 Park Ave, 19th fl, New York, NY 10016-5991 *Tel:* 203-702-7660 *Toll Free Tel:* 800-242-4363 *Fax:* 203-775-5177 *E-mail:* custserv@aiche.org *Web Site:* www.aiche.org, pg 14

McCullough, Mark S, Wyndham Hall Press, 5050 Kerr Rd, Lima, OH 45806 *Tel:* 419-648-9124 *Toll Free Tel:* 866-895-0977 *Fax:* 419-648-9124; 413-208-2409 *E-mail:* whpbooks@wyndhamhallbooks.com; orders@wyndhamhallbooks.com *Web Site:* www.wyndhamhallpress.com, pg 287

McCullough, Michael, Duke University Press, 905 W Main St, Suite 18B, Durham, NC 27701 *Tel:* 919-688-5134 *Toll Free Tel:* 888-651-0122 *Fax:* 919-688-2615 *Toll Free Fax:* 888-651-0124 *E-mail:* orders@dukeupress.edu *Web Site:* www.dukeupress.edu, pg 82

McCullough, Robert, Random House of Canada Limited, One Toronto St, Suite 300, Toronto, ON M5C 2V6, Canada *Tel:* 416-364-4449 *Toll Free Tel:* 888-523-9292 (cust serv) *Fax:* 416-364-6863; 416-364-6653 (subs rts) *Web Site:* www.randomhouse.ca, pg 517

McCully, Meredith, Beyond the Book, 222 Rosewood Dr, Danvers, MA 01923 *Tel:* 978-750-8400 *Fax:* 978-646-8600 *E-mail:* beyondthebook@copyright.com *Web Site:* www.copyright.com; beyondthebookcast.com, pg 668

McCune, Sara Miller, SAGE Publications, 2455 Teller Rd, Thousand Oaks, CA 91320 *Toll Free Tel:* 800-818-7243 *Toll Free Fax:* 800-583-2665 *E-mail:* info@sagepub.com *Web Site:* www.sagepub.com, pg 223

McCurdy, Wendy, Berkley Books, 375 Hudson St, New York, NY 10014 *Tel:* 212-366-2000 *Fax:* 212-366-2666 *E-mail:* online@penguinputnam.com *Web Site:* www.penguinputnam.com; us.penguingroup.com, pg 36

McCurdy, Wendy, Berkley Publishing Group, 375 Hudson St, New York, NY 10014 *Tel:* 212-366-2000 *Fax:* 212-366-2385 *E-mail:* online@penguinputnam.com *Web Site:* us.penguingroup.com, pg 36

McCutcheon, Clark, Jodie Rhodes Literary Agency, 8840 Villa La Jolla Dr, Suite 315, La Jolla, CA 92037 *E-mail:* jrhodesl@san.rr.com *Web Site:* www.jodierhodesliterary.com, pg 590

McDaniel, Ronald T, EDC Publishing, 10302 E 55 Place, Tulsa, OK 74146-6515 *Tel:* 918-622-4522 *Toll Free Tel:* 800-475-4522 *Fax:* 918-665-7919 *Toll Free Fax:* 800-743-5660 *E-mail:* edc@edcpub.com *Web Site:* www.edcpub.com, pg 84

McDermid, Val, Bywater Books, PO Box 3671, Ann Arbor, MI 48106-3671 *Tel:* 734-662-8815 *Web Site:* bywaterbooks.com, pg 50

McDermott, Diana, M E Sharpe Inc, 80 Business Park Dr, Suite 202, Armonk, NY 10504 *Tel:* 914-273-1800 *Toll Free Tel:* 800-541-6563 *Fax:* 914-273-2106 *E-mail:* info@mesharpe.com *Web Site:* www.mesharpe.com, pg 232

McDermott, Kathleen, Harvard University Press, 79 Garden St, Cambridge, MA 02138-1499 *Tel:* 617-495-2600; 401-531-2800 (intl orders) *Toll Free Tel:* 800-405-1619 (orders) *Fax:* 617-495-5898 (general); 617-496-4677 (edit & rts); 401-531-2801 (intl orders) *Toll Free Fax:* 800-406-9145 (orders) *E-mail:* contact_hup@harvard.edu *Web Site:* www.hup.harvard.edu, pg 115

McDevitt, Jo-Ann, PreK-12 Learning Group, 325 Chestnut St, Suite 1110, Philadelphia, PA 19106 *Tel:* 267-351-4310 *Fax:* 267-351-4317 *E-mail:* prek12learning@publishers.org *Web Site:* www.aepweb.org, pg 634

McDiarmid, Mark, Penguin Group (USA) LLC Sales, 375 Hudson St, New York, NY 10014 *Tel:* 212-366-2000 *E-mail:* online@penguinputnam.com *Web Site:* us.penguingroup.com, pg 197

McDonald, Erroll, Pantheon Books/Schocken Books, c/o Random House Inc, 1745 Broadway, New York, NY 10019 *Tel:* 212-751-2600 *Toll Free Tel:* 800-638-6460 *Fax:* 212-572-6030, pg 192

McDonald, Jerry N, The McDonald & Woodward Publishing Co, 431 E College St, Granville, OH 43023 *Tel:* 740-321-1140 *Toll Free Tel:* 800-233-8787 *Fax:* 740-321-1141 *E-mail:* mwpubco@mwpubco.com *Web Site:* www.mwpubco.com, pg 160

McDonald, Mark, Cambridge Educational, 132 W 31 St, 17th fl, New York, NY 10001 *Toll Free Tel:* 800-322-8755 *Fax:* 609-671-0266 *Toll Free Fax:* 800-329-6687 *E-mail:* custserve@films.com *Web Site:* cambridge.films.com, pg 51

McDonald, Mary, American Philosophical Society, 104 S Fifth St, Philadelphia, PA 19106 *Tel:* 215-440-3425 *Fax:* 215-440-3450 *E-mail:* dianepub@comcast.net *Web Site:* www.amphilsoc.org, pg 15

McDonald, Sean, Farrar, Straus & Giroux, LLC, 18 W 18 St, New York, NY 10011 *Tel:* 212-741-6900 *Fax:* 212-633-9385 *E-mail:* fsg.publicity@fsgbooks.com *Web Site:* us.macmillan.com/fsg.aspx, pg 93

McDonnell, Mark, Bloom's Literary Criticism, 132 W 31 St, 17th fl, New York, NY 10001 *Toll Free Tel:* 800-322-8755 *Toll Free Fax:* 800-678-3633 *E-mail:* custserv@factsonfile.com *Web Site:* www.infobasepublishing.com, pg 40

McDonnell, Mark, Chelsea House Publishers, 132 W 31 St, 17th fl, New York, NY 10001 *Tel:* 212-967-8800 *Toll Free Tel:* 800-322-8755 *Fax:* 917-339-0325; 917-339-0323 *Toll Free Fax:* 800-678-3633 *E-mail:* custserv@factsonfile.com *Web Site:* www.infobasepublishing.com; www.infobaselearning.com, pg 59

McDonnell, Mark, Facts On File, 132 W 31 St, 17th fl, New York, NY 10001 *Tel:* 212-967-8800 *Toll Free Tel:* 800-322-8755 *Fax:* 917-339-0323 *Toll Free Fax:* 800-678-3633 *E-mail:* custserv@factsonfile.com *Web Site:* infobasepublishing.com, pg 91

McDonnell, Mark, Ferguson Publishing, 132 W 31 St, 17th fl, New York, NY 10001 *Tel:* 212-967-8800 *Toll Free Tel:* 800-322-8755 *Fax:* 917-339-0323 *Toll Free Fax:* 800-678-3633 *E-mail:* custserv@factsonfile.com *Web Site:* infobasepublishing.com, pg 94

McDonough, Aileen, SDP Publishing Solutions LLC, 36 Captain's Way, East Bridgewater, MA 02333 *Tel:* 617-775-0656 *Web Site:* www.sdppublishingsolutions.com, pg 555

McDonough, Katie, National Book Awards, 90 Broad St, Suite 604, New York, NY 10004 *Tel:* 212-685-0261 *Fax:* 212-213-6570 *E-mail:* nationalbook@nationalbook.org *Web Site:* www.nationalbook.org, pg 726

McDonough, Liz, University of California Extension Professional Sequence in Copyediting & Courses in Publishing, 1995 University Ave, Suite 110, Berkeley, CA 94720-7000 *Tel:* 510-642-6362 *Fax:* 510-643-0216 *E-mail:* letters@unex.berkeley.edu *Web Site:* www.unex.berkeley.edu, pg 681

McDuffie, John, American Psychiatric Publishing (APP), 1000 Wilson Blvd, Suite 1825, Arlington, VA 22209 *Tel:* 703-907-7322 *Toll Free Tel:* 800-368-5777 *Fax:* 703-907-1091 *E-mail:* appi@psych.org *Web Site:* www.appi.org; www.psychiatryonline.org, pg 15

McElvene, Clyde, Hurston/Wright Award for College Writers, 12138 Central Ave, Suite 209, Bowie, MD 20721 *Tel:* 301-459-2108 *Fax:* 301-277-1262 *E-mail:* info@hurstonwright.org *Web Site:* www.hurstonwright.org, pg 711

McElvene, Clyde, Hurston/Wright Legacy Awards, 12138 Central Ave, Suite 209, Bowie, MD 20721 *Tel:* 301-459-2108 *Fax:* 301-277-1262 *E-mail:* info@hurstonwright.org *Web Site:* www.hurstonwright.org, pg 711

McElvene, Clyde, Hurston/Wright Writer's Week, 12138 Central Ave, Suite 209, Bowie, MD 20721 *Tel:* 301-459-2108 *Fax:* 301-277-1262 *E-mail:* info@hurstonwright.org *Web Site:* www.hurstonwright.org, pg 669

McEvoy, Nion, Chronicle Books LLC, 680 Second St, San Francisco, CA 94107 *Tel:* 415-537-4200 *Toll Free Tel:* 800-759-0190 (cust serv) *Fax:* 415-537-4460 *Toll Free Fax:* 800-858-7787 (orders); 800-286-9471 (cust serv) *E-mail:* frontdesk@chroniclebooks.com *Web Site:* www.chroniclebooks.com, pg 61

McEvoy, William, The Guilford Press, 72 Spring St, 4th fl, New York, NY 10012 *Tel:* 212-431-9800 *Toll Free Tel:* 800-365-7006 (ext 1, orders) *Fax:* 212-966-6708 *E-mail:* orders@guilford.com; info@guilford.com *Web Site:* www.guilford.com, pg 109

McFadden, Michael, Peter Lang Publishing Inc, 29 Broadway, 18th fl, New York, NY 10006-3223 *Tel:* 212-647-7706 *Toll Free Tel:* 800-770-5264 (cust serv) *Fax:* 212-647-7707 *Web Site:* www.peterlang.com, pg 143

McFadden, Wendy, Brethren Press, 1451 Dundee Ave, Elgin, IL 60120 *Tel:* 847-742-5100 *Toll Free Tel:* 800-323-8039 *Fax:* 847-742-6103 *Toll Free Fax:* 800-667-8188 *E-mail:* brethrenpress@brethren.org; cobweb@brethren.org *Web Site:* www.brethrenpress.com, pg 46

McFarlane, Megan, Scholastic Library/National Library Week Grant, 50 E Huron St, Chicago, IL 60611 *Tel:* 312-280-2148 *Toll Free Tel:* 800-545-2433 (ext 2148) *Fax:* 312-280-5274 *Web Site:* www.ala.org/nlwgrant, pg 740

McFarlin, James D, Palm Springs Writers Guild, PO Box 947, Rancho Mirage, CA 92270-0947 *Web Site:* www.palmspringswritersguild.org, pg 633

McFeely, W Drake, The Countryman Press, 43 Lincoln Corners Way, Woodstock, VT 05091 *Tel:* 802-457-4826 *Toll Free Tel:* 800-245-4151 *Fax:* 802-457-1678 *E-mail:* countrymanpress@wwnorton.com *Web Site:* www.countrymanpress.com, pg 70

McFeely, W Drake, W W Norton & Company Inc, 500 Fifth Ave, New York, NY 10110-0017 *Tel:* 212-354-5500 *Toll Free Tel:* 800-233-4830 (orders & cust serv) *Fax:* 212-869-0856 *Toll Free Fax:* 800-458-6515 *Web Site:* www.wwnorton.com, pg 181

McGahern, Liam, ABAC/ALAC, 368 Dalhousie St, Suite 301, Ottawa, ON K1N 7G3, Canada *Tel:* 416-364-2376 *E-mail:* info@abac.org *Web Site:* www.abac.org, pg 611

McGandy, Michael J, Cornell University Press, Sage House, 512 E State St, Ithaca, NY 14850 *Tel:* 607-277-2338 *Fax:* 607-277-2374 *E-mail:* cupressinfo@cornell.edu; cupress-sales@cornell.edu *Web Site:* www.cornellpress.cornell.edu, pg 67

McGarity, Todd, Hachette Book Group, 237 Park Ave, New York, NY 10017 *Tel:* 212-364-1100 *Toll Free Tel:* 800-759-0190 (cust serv) *Fax:* 212-364-0933 (intl orders) *Toll Free Fax:* 800-286-9471 (cust serv) *Web Site:* www.HachetteBookGroup.com, pg 110

McGeagh, Ellen, Lucent Books®, 27500 Drake Rd, Farmington Hills, MI 48331 *Tel:* 248-699-4253 *Fax:* 248-699-8004 *E-mail:* gale.customerservice@cengage.com *Web Site:* www.gale.com/greenhaven, pg 153

McGee, Linda, Bearport Publishing Co Inc, 45 W 21 St, Suite 3B, New York, NY 10010 *Tel:* 212-337-8577 *Toll Free Tel:* 877-337-8577 *Fax:* 212-337-8557 *Toll Free Fax:* 866-337-8557 *E-mail:* info@bearportpublishing.com *Web Site:* www.bearportpublishing.com, pg 33

McGee, Mary, Fire Engineering Books & Videos, 1421 S Sheridan Rd, Tulsa, OK 74112 *Tel:* 918-831-9410 *Toll Free Tel:* 800-752-9764 *Fax:* 918-831-9555 *E-mail:* sales@pennwell.com *Web Site:* www.pennwellbooks.com/fire.html, pg 95

McGee, Mary, PennWell Books, 1421 S Sheridan Rd, Tulsa, OK 74112 *Tel:* 918-831-9410 *Toll Free Tel:* 800-752-9764 *Fax:* 918-831-9555 *E-mail:* sales@pennwell.com *Web Site:* www.pennwellbooks.com, pg 198

McGeehon, Allison, Artisan Books, 225 Varick St, New York, NY 10014-4381 *Tel:* 212-254-5900 *Toll Free Tel:* 800-722-7202 *Fax:* 212-254-8098 *E-mail:* artisaninfo@workman.com; artisaninfo@artisanbooks.com *Web Site:* www.workman.com/artisanbooks/, pg 23

McGeehon, Priscilla, Fairchild Books, 1385 Broadway, New York, NY 10018 *Tel:* 212-419-5292 *Toll Free Tel:* 800-932-4724; 888-330-8477 (orders) *E-mail:* orders@mpsvirginia.com *Web Site:* www.fairchildbooks.com, pg 91

McGeehon, Priscilla, Westview Press, 2465 Central Ave, Boulder, CO 80301 *Tel:* 303-444-3541 *Fax:* 720-406-7336 *E-mail:* westview.orders@perseusbooks.com *Web Site:* www.perseusbooksgroup.com; www.westviewpress.com, pg 279

McGhee, Holly M, Pippin Properties Inc, 155 E 38 St, Suite 2-H, New York, NY 10016 *Tel:* 212-338-9310 *Fax:* 212-338-9579 *E-mail:* info@pippinproperties.com *Web Site:* www.pippinproperties.com, pg 588

McGinn, Patrick, Clinical Laboratory & Standards Institute (CLSI), 950 W Valley Rd, Suite 2500, Wayne, PA 19087 *Tel:* 610-688-0100 *Toll Free Tel:* 877-447-1888 (orders) *Fax:* 610-688-0700 *E-mail:* customerservice@clsi.org *Web Site:* www.clsi.org, pg 63

McGinnis, Claire, Riverhead Books (Hardcover), 375 Hudson St, New York, NY 10014 *Tel:* 212-366-2000 *E-mail:* online@penguinputnam.com *Web Site:* www.penguinputnam.com; us.penguingroup.com, pg 219

McGinnis, Meredith, Crown Publishing Group, c/o Random House Inc, 1745 Broadway, New York, NY 10019 *Tel:* 212-782-9000 *Toll Free Tel:* 888-264-1745 *Fax:* 212-940-7408 *Web Site:* www.randomhouse.com/crown, pg 72

McGinty, Kelly, Sylvan Dell Publishing, 612 Johnnie Dodds Blvd, Suite A-2, Mount Pleasant, SC 29464 *Tel:* 843-971-6722 *Toll Free Tel:* 877-243-3457 *Fax:* 843-216-3804 *E-mail:* customerservice@sylvandellpublishing.com; info@sylvandellpublishing.com *Web Site:* www.sylvandellpublishing.com, pg 248

McGovern, Donna, Allen D Bragdon Publishers Inc, 252 Great Western Rd, South Yarmouth, MA 02664-2210 *Tel:* 508-398-4440 *Toll Free Tel:* 877-876-2787 *Fax:* 508-760-2397 *E-mail:* admin@brainwaves.com *Web Site:* www.brainwaves.com, pg 8

McGowan, Gerald, The Melville Society, c/o Kent State Univ, Dept of English, Box 5190, Kent, OH 44242, pg 627

McGowan, Matt, Frances Goldin Literary Agency, Inc, 57 E 11 St, Suite 5-B, New York, NY 10003 *Tel:* 212-777-0047 *Fax:* 212-228-1660 *E-mail:* agency@goldinlit.com *Web Site:* www.goldinlit.com, pg 575

McGrane, Marilyn, Krause Publications Inc, 700 E State St, Iola, WI 54990 *Tel:* 715-445-2214 *Toll Free Tel:* 800-258-0929 (cust serv); 888-457-2873 (orders) *Fax:* 715-445-4087 *E-mail:* bookorders@krause.com *Web Site:* www.krausebooks.com, pg 142

McGrath, Erinn, Alfred A Knopf/Everyman's Library, c/o Random House Inc, 1745 Broadway, New York, NY 10019 *Tel:* 212-751-2600 *Toll Free Tel:* 800-638-6460 *Fax:* 212-572-2593 *Web Site:* www.knopfdoubleday.com, pg 141

McGrath, Mary, Penguin Group (USA) LLC Sales, 375 Hudson St, New York, NY 10014 *Tel:* 212-366-2000 *E-mail:* online@penguinputnam.com *Web Site:* us.penguingroup.com, pg 197

McGrath, Michael, LinguaText Ltd, 103 Walker Way, Newark, DE 19711 *Tel:* 302-453-8695 *Fax:* 302-453-8695 *Toll Free Fax:* 800-784-4935 *E-mail:* linguatextext@juno.com *Web Site:* www.linguatextltd.com, pg 149

McGrath, Sarah, Riverhead Books (Hardcover), 375 Hudson St, New York, NY 10014 *Tel:* 212-366-2000 *E-mail:* online@penguinputnam.com *Web Site:* www.penguinputnam.com; us.penguingroup.com, pg 219

McGraw, Harold W (Terry) III, McGraw-Hill Financial, 1221 Avenue of the Americas, 50th fl, New York, NY 10020 *Tel:* 212-512-2000 *Web Site:* www.mhfi.com, pg 161

McGraw, Mary, Bookhaven Press LLC, 302 Scenic Ct, Moon Township, PA 15108 *Tel:* 412-494-6926 *Toll Free Tel:* 800-782-7424 (orders only) *E-mail:* info@bookhavenpress.com; orders@bookhavenpress.com *Web Site:* bookhavenpress.com, pg 43

McGray, Jo Anne, Multimedia Larga, 900 S Boardman Dr, No G72, Gallup, NM 87301 *Tel:* 505-726-1720, pg 171

McGregor, Janet, National Association of Broadcasters (NAB), 1771 "N" St NW, Washington, DC 20036-2891 *Tel:* 202-429-5300 *Fax:* 202-429-4199 *E-mail:* nab@nab.org *Web Site:* www.nab.org, pg 173, 628

McGuire, Beverly, Coastside Editorial, PO Box 181, Moss Beach, CA 94038 *E-mail:* bevjoe@pacific.net, pg 543

McGuire, Libby, Random House Publishing Group, 1745 Broadway, New York, NY 10019 *Toll Free Tel:* 800-200-3552 *Web Site:* atrandom.com, pg 214

McGuire, Margaret, Quirk Books, 215 Church St, Philadelphia, PA 19106 *Tel:* 215-627-3581 *Fax:* 215-627-5220 *E-mail:* general@quirkbooks.com *Web Site:* www.quirkbooks.com, pg 211

McGuire, Marilyn, Nautilus Awards, 378 Bromley Dr, Eastsound, WA 98245 *Tel:* 360-376-2001 *Web Site:* www.nautilusbookawards.com, pg 727

McGuire, Tim, W W Norton & Company Inc, 500 Fifth Ave, New York, NY 10110-0017 *Tel:* 212-354-5500 *Toll Free Tel:* 800-233-4830 (orders & cust serv) *Fax:* 212-869-0856 *Toll Free Fax:* 800-458-6515 *Web Site:* www.wwnorton.com, pg 181

McGuirk, George, Pearson Education, 1900 E Lake Ave, Glenview, IL 60025 *Tel:* 847-729-3000 *Toll Free Tel:* 800-535-4391 (Midwest) *Fax:* 847-729-8910, pg 195

McGurgan, Diane, Council for the Advancement of Science Writing (CASW), PO Box 910, Hedgesville, WV 25427 *Tel:* 304-754-6786 *Web Site:* www.casw.org, pg 622

McGurk, John, Quirk Books, 215 Church St, Philadelphia, PA 19106 *Tel:* 215-627-3581 *Fax:* 215-627-5220 *E-mail:* general@quirkbooks.com *Web Site:* www.quirkbooks.com, pg 211

McHale, Joe, Rigby, 9205 Southpark Center Loop, Orlando, FL 32819 *Toll Free Tel:* 800-531-5015; 800-289-4490 *Toll Free Fax:* 800-289-3994 *Web Site:* rigby.hmhco.com/en/rigby.htm, pg 218

McHugh, Arianne, Saddleback Educational Publishing, 3120-A Pullman St, Costa Mesa, CA 92626 *Tel:* 714-640-5200 *Toll Free Tel:* 888-SDLBACK (735-2225); 800-637-8715 *Fax:* 714-640-5297 *Toll Free Fax:* 888-734-4010 *E-mail:* contact@sdlback.com *Web Site:* www.sdlback.com, pg 223

McHugh, Daniel, National Institute for Trial Advocacy (NITA), 1685 38 St, Suite 200, Boulder, CO 80301-2735 *Tel:* 720-890-4860 *Toll Free Tel:* 877-648-2632; 800-225-6482 (orders & returns) *Fax:* 720-890-7069 *E-mail:* info@nita.org *Web Site:* www.nita.org, pg 175

McHugh, John B, McHugh's Rights/Permissions Workshop™, PO Box 170665, Milwaukee, WI 53217-8056 *Tel:* 414-351-3056 *E-mail:* jack@johnbmchugh.com *Web Site:* www.johnbmchugh.com, pg 670

McIlroy, Randal, Pemmican Publications Inc, 150 Henry Ave, Winnipeg, MB R3B 0J7, Canada *Tel:* 204-589-6346 *Fax:* 204-589-2063 *E-mail:* pemmican@pemmican.mb.ca *Web Site:* www.pemmican.mb.ca, pg 515

McInerney, Paige, Penguin Group (USA) LLC, 375 Hudson St, New York, NY 10014 *Tel:* 212-366-2000 *Toll Free Tel:* 800-847-5515 (inside sales); 800-631-8571 (cust serv) *Fax:* 212-366-2666; 607-775-4829 (inside sales) *E-mail:* online@us.penguingroup.com *Web Site:* www.penguin.com; us.penguingroup.com, pg 197

McIntosh, Dorla, Columbia University School of the Arts, Creative Writing Program, 617 Kent Hall, New York, NY 10027 *Tel:* 212-854-3774 *Fax:* 212-854-7704 *E-mail:* writingprogram@columbia.edu *Web Site:* www.columbia.edu/cu/writing, pg 677

McIntosh, Joel, Prufrock Press, PO Box 8813, Waco, TX 76714-8813 *Tel:* 254-756-3337 *Toll Free Tel:* 800-998-2208 *Fax:* 254-756-3339 *Toll Free Fax:* 800-240-0333 *E-mail:* info@prufrock.com *Web Site:* www.prufrock.com, pg 208

McIntosh, Kelly, Barbour Publishing Inc, 1810 Barbour Dr, Uhrichsville, OH 44683 *Tel:* 740-922-6045 *Fax:* 740-922-5948 *E-mail:* info@barbourbooks.com *Web Site:* www.barbourbooks.com, pg 30

McIntosh, Madeline, Random House Inc, 1745 Broadway, New York, NY 10019 *Tel:* 212-782-9000 *Toll Free Tel:* 800-726-0600 *Web Site:* www.randomhouse.com, pg 213

McIntosh, Susan, McGill-Queen's University Press, 1010 Sherbrooke W, Suite 1720, Montreal, QC H3A 2R7, Canada *Tel:* 514-398-3750 *Fax:* 514-398-4333 *E-mail:* mqup@mqup.ca *Web Site:* www.mqup.ca, pg 512

McIntyre, Kheil, LearningExpress LLC, 2 Rector St, 26th fl, New York, NY 10006 *Tel:* 212-995-2566 *Toll Free Tel:* 800-295-9556 (ext 2) *Fax:* 212-995-5512 *E-mail:* customerservice@learningexpressllc.com (cust serv) *Web Site:* www.learningexpressllc.com, pg 145

McIntyre, Suzanne Ostiguy, The Institute for Research on Public Policy (IRPP), 1470 Peel, Suite 200, Montreal, QC H3A 1T1, Canada *Tel:* 514-985-2461 *Fax:* 514-985-2559 *E-mail:* irpp@irpp.org *Web Site:* www.irpp.org, pg 509

McKay, Matt PhD, New Harbinger Publications Inc, 5674 Shattuck Ave, Oakland, CA 94609 *Tel:* 510-652-0215 *Toll Free Tel:* 800-748-6273 (orders only) *Fax:* 510-652-5472 *Toll Free Fax:* 800-652-1613 *E-mail:* nhhelp@newharbinger.com; customerservice@newharbinger.com *Web Site:* www.newharbinger.com, pg 177

McKean, Kate, Howard Morhaim Literary Agency Inc, 30 Pierrepont St, Brooklyn, NY 11201-3371 *Tel:* 718-222-8400 *Fax:* 718-222-5056 *E-mail:* info@morhaimliterary.com *Web Site:* www.morhaimliterary.com, pg 586

McKee, Barney, Quail Ridge Press, 101 Brooks Dr, Brandon, MS 39042 *Tel:* 601-825-2063 *Toll Free Tel:* 800-343-1583 *Fax:* 601-825-3091 *Toll Free Fax:* 800-864-1082 *E-mail:* info@quailridge.com *Web Site:* quailridge.com, pg 211

McKee, Gwen, Quail Ridge Press, 101 Brooks Dr, Brandon, MS 39042 *Tel:* 601-825-2063 *Toll Free Tel:* 800-343-1583 *Fax:* 601-825-3091 *Toll Free Fax:* 800-864-1082 *E-mail:* info@quailridge.com *Web Site:* quailridge.com, pg 211

McKenna, Gwen, Mountain Press Publishing Co, 1301 S Third W, Missoula, MT 59801 *Tel:* 406-728-1900 *Toll Free Tel:* 800-234-5308 *Fax:* 406-728-1635 *E-mail:* info@mtnpress.com *Web Site:* www.mountain-press.com, pg 170

McKenna, Lauren, Gallery Books, 1230 Avenue of the Americas, New York, NY 10020 *Toll Free Tel:* 800-456-6798 *Fax:* 212-698-7284 *E-mail:* consumer.customerservice@simonandschuster.com *Web Site:* www.simonsays.com, pg 101

McKenna, Tiffany, Thames & Hudson, 500 Fifth Ave, New York, NY 10110 *Tel:* 212-354-3763 *Toll Free Tel:* 800-233-4830 *Fax:* 212-398-1252 *E-mail:* bookinfo@thames.wwnorton.com *Web Site:* www.thamesandhudsonusa.com, pg 253

McKeon, Hilary, Looseleaf Law Publications Inc, 43-08 162 St, Flushing, NY 11358 *Tel:* 718-359-5559 *Toll Free Tel:* 800-647-5547 *Fax:* 718-539-0941 *E-mail:* info@looseleaf.com *Web Site:* www.looseleaflaw.com, pg 152

McKernan, John, ABZ First Book Poetry Prize, PO Box 2746, Huntington, WV 25727-2746 *Tel:* 304-638-5701 *Web Site:* abzpress.sharepoint.com, pg 685

McKie, Ellen, University of Texas Press, 2100 Comal St, Austin, TX 78722 *Tel:* 512-471-7233 *Fax:* 512-232-7178 *E-mail:* utpress@uts.cc.utexas.edu *Web Site:* www.utexaspress.com, pg 253

McKiernan, Patricia, Graphic Artists Guild Inc, 32 Broadway, Suite 1114, New York, NY 10004-1612 *Tel:* 212-791-3400 *Fax:* 212-791-0333 *Web Site:* www.graphicartistsguild.org, pg 624, 678

McKinley, Robert B, Cardweb.com Inc®, 999 Vanderbilt Beach Rd, 2nd fl, Naples, FL 34108 *Tel:* 239-325-5300 *Toll Free Tel:* 800-874-8999 *Fax:* 239-236-0835 *Toll Free Fax:* 800-821-4627 *E-mail:* cardservices@cardweb.com; cardstaff@cardweb.com *Web Site:* www.cardweb.com, pg 52

McKinney, Anne, PREP Publishing, 1110 1/2 Hay St, Suite C, Fayetteville, NC 28305 *Tel:* 910-483-6611 *Toll Free Tel:* 800-533-2814 *E-mail:* preppub@aol.com *Web Site:* www.prep-pub.com, pg 205

McKinney, Betty, Alpine Publications Inc, 38262 Linman Rd, Crawford, CO 81415 *Tel:* 970-921-5005 *Toll Free Tel:* 800-777-7257 *Fax:* 970-921-5081 *E-mail:* editorial@alpinepub.com; customerservice@alpinepub.com *Web Site:* www.alpinepub.com, pg 9

McKinney, Charlie, Sophia Institute Press®, 522 Donald St, Unit 3, Bedford, NH 03110 *Tel:* 603-836-5505 *Toll Free Tel:* 800-888-9344 *Fax:* 603-641-8108 *Toll Free Fax:* 888-288-2259 *E-mail:* orders@sophiainstitute.com *Web Site:* www.sophiainstitute.com, pg 239

McKinnon, Tanya, Victoria Sanders & Associates LLC, 241 Avenue of the Americas, Suite 11-H, New York, NY 10014 *Tel:* 212-633-8811 *Fax:* 212-633-0525 *E-mail:* queriesvsa@gmail.com *Web Site:* www.victoriasanders.com, pg 592

McKinstry, Nancy, Wolters Kluwer US Corp, 2700 Lake Cook Rd, Riverwoods, IL 60015 *Tel:* 847-267-7000 *Fax:* 847-580-5192 *Web Site:* www.wolterskluwer.com, pg 284

McKitterick, Chris, John W Campbell Memorial Award, University of Kansas, Wescoe Hall, Rm 3001, Dept of English, 1445 Jayhawk Blvd, Lawrence, KS 66045-7590 *Tel:* 785-864-3380 *Fax:* 785-864-1159 *Web Site:* www.ku.edu/~sfcenter; ku.edu/campbell.htm, pg 694

McKitterick, Chris, Science Fiction Writers Workshop, University of Kansas, Wescoe Hall, Rm 3001, Dept of English, 1445 Jayhawk Blvd, Lawrence, KS 66045-7590 *Tel:* 785-864-3380 *Fax:* 785-864-1159 *Web Site:* www.ku.edu/~sfcenter, pg 673

McKnight, Linda, Westwood Creative Artists Ltd, 94 Harbord St, Toronto, ON M5S 1G6, Canada *Tel:* 416-964-3302 *Fax:* 416-975-9209 *E-mail:* wca_office@wcaltd.com *Web Site:* www.wcaltd.com, pg 599

McLain, Kevin, Avalon Travel Publishing, 1700 Fourth St, Berkeley, CA 94710-1711 *Tel:* 510-595-3664 *Fax:* 510-595-4228 *Web Site:* www.avalontravelbooks.com, pg 27

McLaughlin, Brenna, AAUP Book, Jacket & Journal Design Show, 28 W 36 St, Suite 602, New York, NY 10018 *Tel:* 212-989-1010 *Fax:* 212-989-0275 *E-mail:* info@aaupnet.org *Web Site:* www.aaupnet.org, pg 685

McLaughlin, Brenna, Association of American University Presses (AAUP), 28 W 36 St, Suite 602, New York, NY 10018 *Tel:* 212-989-1010 *Fax:* 212-989-0275 *E-mail:* info@aaupnet.org *Web Site:* www.aaupnet.org, pg 616

McLaughlin, Nancy, Solano Press Books, PO Box 773, Point Arena, CA 95468 *Tel:* 707-884-4508 *Toll Free Tel:* 800-931-9373 *Fax:* 707-884-4109 *E-mail:* spbooks@solano.com *Web Site:* www.solano.com, pg 239

McLean, Allison, Portfolio, 375 Hudson St, New York, NY 10014, pg 204

McLean, Christian, Southampton Writers' Conference, 239 Montauk Hwy, Southampton, NY 11968 *Tel:* 631-632-5007 *E-mail:* southamptonwriters@notes.cc.sunysb.edu *Web Site:* www.stonybrook.edu/writers, pg 673

McLean, George F, Council for Research in Values & Philosophy (RVP), The Catholic University of America, Gibbons Hall, Rm B-12, 620 Michigan Ave NE, Washington, DC 20064 *Tel:* 202-319-6089 *Fax:* 202-319-6089 *E-mail:* cua-rvp@cua.edu *Web Site:* www.crvp.org, pg 69

McLean, Laurie, Indie Publishing Contest, 1029 Jones St, San Francisco, CA 94109 *Tel:* 415-673-0939 *E-mail:* sfwriterscon@aol.com *Web Site:* www.sfwriters.org, pg 711

McLean, Laurie, Michael Larsen/Elizabeth Pomada Literary Agents, 1029 Jones St, San Francisco, CA 94109 *Tel:* 415-673-0939 *E-mail:* larsenpoma@aol.com *Web Site:* www.larsenpomada.com, pg 581

McLoughlin, Kate, Pearson Education/ELT, 10 Bank St, 9th fl, White Plains, NY 10606-1951 *Tel:* 914-287-8000 *Web Site:* www.pearsonelt.com, pg 195

McMahon, Daniel J, New York State Bar Association, One Elk St, Albany, NY 12207 *Tel:* 518-463-3200 *Toll Free Tel:* 800-582-2452 *Fax:* 518-487-5517 *Web Site:* www.nysba.org, pg 179

McMahon, Hilary, Westwood Creative Artists Ltd, 94 Harbord St, Toronto, ON M5S 1G6, Canada *Tel:* 416-964-3302 *Fax:* 416-975-9209 *E-mail:* wca_office@wcaltd.com *Web Site:* www.wcaltd.com, pg 599

McMahon, Maureen, Kaplan Publishing, 395 Hudson St, 4th fl, New York, NY 10014 *Tel:* 212-618-2400 *Toll Free Tel:* 888-KAPLAN8 (527-5268) *Fax:* 917-344-2499 *Toll Free Fax:* 877-712-5487 *E-mail:* book.support@kaplan.com *Web Site:* www.kaplanpublishing.com, pg 138

Mcmanus, Kerry, Boyds Mills Press, 815 Church St, Honesdale, PA 18431 *Tel:* 570-253-1164 *Toll Free Tel:* 800-490-5111 *Fax:* 570-253-0179 *E-mail:* contact@boydsmillspress.com *Web Site:* www.boydsmillspress.com, pg 45

McManus, Rosanne, The Reader's Digest Association Inc, 750 Third Ave, New York, NY 10017 *Tel:* 914-238-1000; 646-293-6284 *Toll Free Tel:* 800-310-6261 (cust serv) *Fax:* 914-238-4559 *Web Site:* www.rd.com; www.rda.com, pg 215

McManus, Rosanne, Reader's Digest Children's Books, 44 S Broadway, White Plains, NY 10601 *Tel:* 914-238-1000 *Toll Free Tel:* 800-934-0977 *Web Site:* www.rdtradepublishing.com, pg 215

McManus, Rosanne, Reader's Digest Trade Books, 44 S Broadway, White Plains, NY 10601 *Tel:* 914-244-7503 *Fax:* 914-244-4841 *Web Site:* www.rd.com, pg 215

McMeel, John P, Andrews McMeel Publishing LLC, 1130 Walnut St, Kansas City, MO 64106-2109 *Toll Free Tel:* 800-851-8923; 800-943-9839 (cust serv) *Toll Free Fax:* 800-943-9831 (orders) *Web Site:* www.andrewsmcmeel.com, pg 18

McMenamin, John, Princeton Book Co Publishers, 614 Rte 130, Hightstown, NJ 08520 *Tel:* 609-426-0602 *Toll Free Tel:* 800-220-7149 *Fax:* 609-426-1344 *E-mail:* pbc@dancehorizons.com; elysian@princetonbookcompany.com *Web Site:* www.dancehorizons.com, pg 206

McMillan, Sally Hill, Sally Hill McMillan LLC, 429 E Kingston Ave, Charlotte, NC 28203 *Tel:* 704-334-0897 *E-mail:* mcmagency@aol.com, pg 585

McMillen, Wendy, University of Notre Dame Press, 310 Flanner Hall, Notre Dame, IN 46556 *Tel:* 574-631-6346 *Fax:* 574-631-8148 *E-mail:* undpress@nd.edu *Web Site:* www.undpress.nd.edu, pg 268

McMullen, Shawn, Standard Publishing, 8805 Governors Hill Dr, Suite 400, Cincinnati, OH 45249 *Tel:* 513-931-4050 *Toll Free Tel:* 800-543-1353 *Fax:* 513-931-0950 *Toll Free Fax:* 877-867-5751 *E-mail:* customerservice@standardpub.com *Web Site:* www.standardpub.com, pg 242

McMurray, Debbie, Nilgiri Press, 3600 Tomales Rd, Tomales, CA 94971 *Tel:* 707-878-2369 *E-mail:* info@easwaran.org *Web Site:* www.easwaran.org, pg 179

McNabb, Stephen, Vintage & Anchor Books, c/o Random House Inc, 1745 Broadway, New York, NY 10019 *Tel:* 212-572-2420 *E-mail:* vintageanchorpublicity@randomhouse.com *Web Site:* vintage-anchor.knopfdoubleday.com, pg 275

McNair, Shanna, Knightville Poetry Contest, PO Box 866, Wells, ME 04094 *E-mail:* info@newguardreview.com *Web Site:* www.newguardreview.com, pg 715

McNair, Shanna, Machigonne Fiction Contest, PO Box 866, Wells, ME 04094 *E-mail:* info@newguardreview.com *Web Site:* www.newguardreview.com, pg 720

McNeal, A Phil II, The National Endowment for the Arts, Nancy Hanks Ctr, Rm 703, 1100 Pennsylvania Ave NW, Washington, DC 20506-0001 *Tel:* 202-682-5400 *Web Site:* www.arts.gov; www.nea.gov, pg 641

McNeely, Joe, Brilliance Audio, 1704 Eaton Dr, Grand Haven, MI 49417 *Tel:* 616-846-5256 *Toll Free Tel:* 800-648-2312 (orders only) *Fax:* 616-846-0630 *E-mail:* customerservice@brillianceaudio.com *Web Site:* www.brillianceaudio.com, pg 48

McNeil, Donna, Individual Artist Fellowships, 25 State House Sta, 193 State St, Augusta, ME 04333-0025 *Tel:* 207-287-2726 *Fax:* 207-287-2725 *Web Site:* www.mainearts.com, pg 712

McNeill, Doug, Wimmer Cookbooks, 4650 Shelby Air Dr, Memphis, TN 38118 *Tel:* 901-362-8900 *Toll Free Tel:* 800-363-1771 *E-mail:* wimmer@wimmerco.com *Web Site:* www.wimmerco.com, pg 282

McNeill, Timothy, Wisdom Publications Inc, 199 Elm St, Somerville, MA 02144 *Tel:* 617-776-7416 *Toll Free Tel:* 800-272-4050 (orders) *Fax:* 617-776-7841 *E-mail:* info@wisdompubs.org *Web Site:* www.wisdompubs.org, pg 283

McParland, Connie, Guernica Editions Inc, 2250 Military Rd, Tonawanda, NY 14150-6000 *Tel:* 416-576-9403 *Fax:* 716-693-2667; 716-692-7479 *Toll Free Fax:* 800-221-9985 (orders) *E-mail:* guernicaeditions@cs.com *Web Site:* www.guernicaeditions.com, pg 109

McParland, Connie Guzzo, Guernica Editions Inc, 489 Strathmore Blvd, Toronto, ON M4C 1N8, Canada *Tel:* 416-576-9403 (orders & cust serv); 416-285-4067 (edit) *Fax:* 416-981-7606 *Web Site:* guernicaeditions.com, pg 508

McPartland, Pat, Albert Whitman & Co, 250 S Northwest Hwy, Suite 320, Park Ridge, IL 60068 *Tel:* 847-232-2800 *Toll Free Tel:* 800-255-7675 *Fax:* 847-581-0039 *E-mail:* mail@awhitmanco.com *Web Site:* www.albertwhitman.com, pg 7

McPherson, Bruce R, McPherson & Co, 148 Smith Ave, Kingston, NY 12401 *Tel:* 845-331-5807 *Toll Free Tel:* 800-613-8219 *Fax:* 845-331-5807 *Toll Free Fax:* 800-613-8219 *E-mail:* bmcphersonco@gmail.com *Web Site:* www.mcphersonco.com, pg 162

McPherson, Rachel, Beacon Hill Press of Kansas City, PO Box 419527, Kansas City, MO 64141-6527 *Tel:* 816-931-1900 *Toll Free Tel:* 800-877-0700 (cust serv) *Fax:* 816-753-4071 *Web Site:* www.beaconhillbooks.com, pg 32

McQuagge, Cassie, ARE Press, 215 67 St, Virginia Beach, VA 23451 *Tel:* 757-428-3588 *Toll Free Tel:* 800-333-4499 *Fax:* 757-491-0689 *Web Site:* www.edgarcayce.org, pg 21

McQuilkin, Robert, Antrim House, 21 Goodrich Rd, Simsbury, CT 06070-1804 *Tel:* 860-217-0023 *Fax:* 860-217-0023 *E-mail:* eds@antrimhousebooks.com *Web Site:* www.antrimhousebooks.com, pg 19

McShane, Kevin D, Fifi Oscard Agency Inc, 110 W 40 St, 16th fl, New York, NY 10018 *Tel:* 212-764-1100 *Fax:* 212-840-5019 *E-mail:* agency@fifioscard.com *Web Site:* www.fifioscard.com, pg 587

McVay, Barry, Panoptic Enterprises, PO Box 11220, Burke, VA 22009-1220 *Tel:* 703-451-5953 *Toll Free Tel:* 800-594-4766 *Fax:* 703-451-5953 *E-mail:* panoptic@fedgovcontracts.com *Web Site:* www.fedgovcontracts.com, pg 191

McVay, Vivina H, Panoptic Enterprises, PO Box 11220, Burke, VA 22009-1220 *Tel:* 703-451-5953 *Toll Free Tel:* 800-594-4766 *Fax:* 703-451-5953 *E-mail:* panoptic@fedgovcontracts.com *Web Site:* www.fedgovcontracts.com, pg 191

McWilliams, Skip, Teacher's Discovery, 2741 Paldan Dr, Auburn Hills, MI 48326 *Toll Free Tel:* 800-832-2437 *Toll Free Fax:* 800-287-4509 *E-mail:* foreignlanguage@teachersdiscovery.com; worldlanguage@teachersdiscovery.com *Web Site:* www.teachersdiscovery.com, pg 251

Mdhlongwa, Ndaba, OUT OF YOUR MIND...AND INTO THE MARKETPLACE™, 13381 White Sand Dr, Tustin, CA 92780-4565 *Tel:* 714-544-0248 *Toll Free Tel:* 800-419-1513 *Fax:* 714-730-1414 *Web Site:* www.business-plan.com, pg 189

Meacham, Beth, Tom Doherty Associates, LLC, 175 Fifth Ave, 14th fl, New York, NY 10010 *Tel:* 646-307-5151 *Toll Free Tel:* 800-455-0340 *Fax:* 212-388-0191 *E-mail:* firstname.lastname@tor.com *Web Site:* www.tor-forge.com, pg 80

Meader, James, Picador, 175 Fifth Ave, 19th fl, New York, NY 10010 *Tel:* 646-307-5151 *Fax:* 212-253-9627 *E-mail:* firstname.lastname@picadorusa.com *Web Site:* www.picadorusa.com, pg 201

Meadows, Laura, Carl Vinson Institute of Government, University of Georgia, 201 N Milledge Ave, Athens, GA 30602 *Tel:* 706-542-2736 *Fax:* 706-542-9301 *Web Site:* www.cviog.uga.edu, pg 275

Meadows, Rob, Bear & Co Inc, One Park St, Rochester, VT 05767 *Tel:* 802-767-3174 *Toll Free Tel:* 800-932-3277 *Fax:* 802-767-3726 *E-mail:* customerservice@InnerTraditions.com *Web Site:* InnerTraditions.com, pg 33

Mecabe, Christen, PMA Literary & Film Management Inc, PO Box 1817, Old Chelsea Sta, New York, NY 10113 *Tel:* 212-929-1222 *Fax:* 212-206-0238 *E-mail:* queries@pmalitfilm.com *Web Site:* www.pmalitfilm.com, pg 588

Mecadon, Patricia, University of Scranton Press, 445 Madison Ave, Scranton, PA 18510 *Tel:* 570-941-4228 *Fax:* 570-941-7085 *E-mail:* salesoffice@scranton.edu *Web Site:* academic.scranton.edu/organization/upress, pg 269

Mechanic, Joline, Black Mountain Press, PO Box 9907, Asheville, NC 28815 *Tel:* 828-273-3332 *Web Site:* www.theblackmountainpress.com, pg 39

Mechlin, Elena, Pippin Properties Inc, 155 E 38 St, Suite 2-H, New York, NY 10016 *Tel:* 212-338-9310 *Fax:* 212-338-9579 *E-mail:* info@pippinproperties.com *Web Site:* www.pippinproperties.com, pg 588

Mecklenborg, Mark, The American Ceramic Society, 600 N Cleveland Ave, Suite 210, Westerville, OH 43082 *Tel:* 240-646-7054 *Toll Free Tel:* 866-721-3322 *Fax:* 614-794-5892 *E-mail:* customerservice@ceramics.org *Web Site:* www.ceramics.org, pg 12

Medeot, William, Orbis Books, Price Bldg, 85 Ryder Rd, Ossining, NY 10562 *Tel:* 914-941-7636 *Toll Free Tel:* 800-258-5838 (orders) *Fax:* 914-941-7005 *E-mail:* orbisbooks@maryknoll.org *Web Site:* www.orbisbooks.com, pg 186

Medina, Jose Antonio, Liguori Publications, One Liguori Dr, Liguori, MO 63057-1000 *Tel:* 636-464-2500 *Toll Free Tel:* 866-848-2492; 800-325-9521 *Fax:* 636-464-8449 *Web Site:* www.liguori.org, pg 149

Medina, Kate, Random House Publishing Group, 1745 Broadway, New York, NY 10019 *Toll Free Tel:* 800-200-3552 *Web Site:* atrandom.com, pg 214

Meehan, Larry, ALI-ABA Continuing Professional Education, 4025 Chestnut St, Philadelphia, PA 19104 *Tel:* 215-243-1600 *Toll Free Tel:* 800-CLE-NEWS (253-6397) *Fax:* 215-243-1664; 215-243-1683 *Web Site:* www.ali-aba.org, pg 8

Meerdink, Jan, The Russell Meerdink Co Ltd, 1555 S Park Ave, Neenah, WI 54956 *Tel:* 920-725-0955 *Toll Free Tel:* 800-635-6499 *Fax:* 920-725-0709 *E-mail:* questions@horseinfo.com *Web Site:* www.horseinfo.com, pg 163

Meere, Selina, Workman Publishing Co Inc, 225 Varick St, 9th fl, New York, NY 10014-4381 *Tel:* 212-254-5900 *Toll Free Tel:* 800-722-7202 *Fax:* 212-254-8098 *E-mail:* info@workman.com *Web Site:* www.workman.com, pg 285

Meeropol, Ellen, Mt Chocorua Writing Workshop, PO Box 2280, Conway, NH 03818-2280 *Tel:* 603-447-2280 *Fax:* 603-447-1820 *E-mail:* reservations@worldfellowship.org *Web Site:* www.worldfellowship.org, pg 670

Meese, Allan, Macmillan, 175 Fifth Ave, New York, NY 10010 *Tel:* 646-307-5151 *Fax:* 212-420-9314 *E-mail:* firstname.lastname@macmillan.com *Web Site:* www.macmillan.com, pg 154

Megargee, Moira, Interlink Publishing Group Inc, 46 Crosby St, Northampton, MA 01060 *Tel:* 413-582-7054 *Toll Free Tel:* 800-238-LINK (238-5465) *Fax:* 413-582-7057 *E-mail:* info@interlinkbooks.com *Web Site:* www.interlinkbooks.com, pg 132

Megged, Semadar, Philomel, 345 Hudson St, New York, NY 10014 *Tel:* 212-366-2000, pg 201

Megibow, Sara, Nelson Literary Agency LLC, 1732 Wazee St, Suite 207, Denver, CO 80202-1284 *Tel:* 303-292-2805 *E-mail:* query@nelsonagency.com *Web Site:* www.nelsonagency.com, pg 587

Meglin, Pat, Baldwin Literary Services, 935 Hayes St, Baldwin, NY 11510-4834 *Tel:* 516-546-8338 *Fax:* 516-546-8338, pg 541

Mehta, Sonny, Doubleday/Nan A Talese, c/o Random House Inc, 1745 Broadway, New York, NY 10019 *Tel:* 212-751-2600 *Toll Free Tel:* 800-638-6460 *Fax:* 212-572-2593 *Web Site:* www.knopfdoubleday.com, pg 81

Mehta, Sonny, Alfred A Knopf/Everyman's Library, c/o Random House Inc, 1745 Broadway, New York, NY 10019 *Tel:* 212-751-2600 *Toll Free Tel:* 800-638-6460 *Fax:* 212-572-2593 *Web Site:* www.knopfdoubleday.com, pg 141

Mehta, Sonny, Random House Inc, 1745 Broadway, New York, NY 10019 *Tel:* 212-782-9000 *Toll Free Tel:* 800-726-0600 *Web Site:* www.randomhouse.com, pg 213

Meier, Chris, The Plough Publishing House, PO Box 903, Rifton, NY 12471-0903 *E-mail:* info@plough.com *Web Site:* www.plough.com, pg 203

Meier, Rachel, Crown Publishing Group, c/o Random House Inc, 1745 Broadway, New York, NY 10019 *Tel:* 212-782-9000 *Toll Free Tel:* 888-264-1745 *Fax:* 212-940-7408 *Web Site:* www.randomhouse.com/crown, pg 72

Meinholz, Matt, American Society for Quality (ASQ), 600 N Plankinton Ave, Milwaukee, WI 53203 *Tel:* 414-272-8575 *Toll Free Tel:* 800-248-1946 (US & CN); 800-514-1564 (Mexico) *Fax:* 414-272-1734 *E-mail:* help@asq.org *Web Site:* www.asq.org, pg 16

Meisenheimer, Barbara, Pacific Northwest Young Reader's Choice Award, Vancouver Mall Community Library, 8700 NE Vancouver Mall Dr, Suite 285, Vancouver, WA 98662 *Tel:* 360-892-8256 *Web Site:* www.pnla.org/yrca, pg 731

Meisler, Dan, Inter-University Consortium for Political & Social Research (ICPSR), 330 Packard St, Ann Arbor, MI 48104 *Tel:* 734-647-5000 *Fax:* 734-647-8200 *E-mail:* netmail@icpsr.umich.edu *Web Site:* www.icpsr.umich.edu, pg 132

Meissner, Bill, Mississippi River Creative Writing Workshop, 720 Fourth Ave S, B-151, Rm 100, St Cloud, MN 56301-4498 *Tel:* 320-308-4947 *Fax:* 320-308-5524 *Web Site:* www.stcloudstate.edu, pg 670

Meizlik, Shelby, HarperCollins General Books Group, 10 E 53 St, New York, NY 10022 *Tel:* 212-207-7000 *Fax:* 212-207-7633 *Web Site:* www.harpercollins.com, pg 113

Melancon, Barry C, AICPA Professional Publications, 220 Leigh Farm Rd, Durham, NC 27707 *Tel:* 919-402-4500 *Toll Free Tel:* 888-777-7077 *Fax:* 919-402-4505 *E-mail:* acquisitions@aicpa.org *Web Site:* www.aicpa.org, pg 6

Melando, Edward J, John Wiley & Sons Inc, 111 River St, Hoboken, NJ 07030-5774 *Tel:* 201-748-6000 *Toll Free Tel:* 800-225-5945 (cust serv) *Fax:* 201-748-6088 *E-mail:* info@wiley.com *Web Site:* www.wiley.com, pg 281

Mell, Dr Donald C, University of Delaware Press, 200A Morris Library, 181 S College Ave, Newark, DE 19717-5267 *Tel:* 302-831-1149 *Fax:* 302-831-6549 *E-mail:* ud-press@udel.edu *Web Site:* www2.lib.udel.edu/udpress, pg 265

Mello, Felice, W W Norton & Company Inc, 500 Fifth Ave, New York, NY 10110-0017 *Tel:* 212-354-5500 *Toll Free Tel:* 800-233-4830 (orders & cust serv) *Fax:* 212-869-0856 *Toll Free Fax:* 800-458-6515 *Web Site:* www.wwnorton.com, pg 181

Meloche, Luc, LexisNexis Canada Inc, 123 Commerce Valley Dr E, Suite 700, Markham, ON L3T 7W8, Canada *Tel:* 905-479-2665 *Toll Free Tel:* 800-668-6481; 800-387-0899 (cust serv) *Fax:* 905-479-2826 *Toll Free Fax:* 800-461-3275 *E-mail:* orders@lexisnexis.ca; service@lexisnexis.ca (cust serv) *Web Site:* www.lexisnexis.ca, pg 511

Meltzer, Lauren, The Charles Press, Publishers, 230 N 21 St, Suite 202, Philadelphia, PA 19103 *Tel:* 215-561-2786 *Fax:* 215-561-0191 *E-mail:* mailbox@charlespresspub.com *Web Site:* www.charlespresspub.com, pg 58

Meltzer, Steve, Celebra, 375 Hudson St, New York, NY 10014 *Tel:* 212-366-2000 *Fax:* 212-366-2889, pg 55

Meltzer, Steve, Dial Books for Young Readers, 345 Hudson St, New York, NY 10014 *Tel:* 212-366-2000 *Fax:* 212-414-3396 *E-mail:* online@penguinputnam.com *Web Site:* www.penguinputnam.com; us.penguingroup.com, pg 79

Meltzer, Steven, Dutton Children's Books, 345 Hudson St, New York, NY 10014 *Tel:* 212-366-2000 *E-mail:* online@penguinputnam.com *Web Site:* www.penguinputnam.com; us.penguingroup.com, pg 83

Melville, Kirsty, Andrews McMeel Publishing LLC, 1130 Walnut St, Kansas City, MO 64106-2109 *Toll Free Tel:* 800-851-8923; 800-943-9839 (cust serv) *Toll Free Fax:* 800-943-9831 (orders) *Web Site:* www.andrewsmcmeel.com, pg 18

Melvin, Terrence, The Brookings Institution Press, 1775 Massachusetts Ave NW, Washington, DC 20036-2188 *Tel:* 202-536-3600 *Toll Free Tel:* 800-537-5487 *Fax:* 202-536-3623 *E-mail:* permissions@brookings.edu *Web Site:* www.brookings.edu, pg 48

Melynis, Ms Indre "Indy", The Guilford Press, 72 Spring St, 4th fl, New York, NY 10012 *Tel:* 212-431-9800 *Toll Free Tel:* 800-365-7006 (ext 1, orders) *Fax:* 212-966-6708 *E-mail:* orders@guilford.com; info@guilford.com *Web Site:* www.guilford.com, pg 109

Menchaca, Frank, Gale, 27500 Drake Rd, Farmington Hills, MI 48331-3535 *Tel:* 248-699-4253 *Toll Free Tel:* 800-877-4253 *Fax:* 248-699-8049 *Toll Free Fax:* 800-414-5043 (orders) *E-mail:* gale.salesassistance@cengage.com *Web Site:* www.gale.cengage.com, pg 100

Menchaca, Frank, Macmillan Reference USA™, 12 Lunar Dr, Woodbridge, CT 06525 *Tel:* 203-397-2600 *Toll Free Tel:* 800-444-0799 *Fax:* 203-397-8296 *Web Site:* www.gale.cengage.com/macmillan/, pg 155

Mendel, Scott, Mendel Media Group LLC, 115 W 30 St, Suite 800, New York, NY 10001 *Tel:* 646-239-9896 *Fax:* 212-685-4717 *Web Site:* www.mendelmedia.com, pg 585

Mendelson, John, Candlewick Press, 99 Dover St, Somerville, MA 02144-2825 *Tel:* 617-661-3330 *Fax:* 617-661-0565 *E-mail:* bigbear@candlewick.com *Web Site:* www.candlewick.com, pg 51

Menick, Jim, Reader's Digest USA Select Editions, 44 S Broadway, 7th fl, White Plains, NY 10601 *Tel:* 914-238-1000 *Toll Free Tel:* 800-304-2807 (cust serv) *Fax:* 914-831-1560 *Web Site:* www.rda.com/readers-digest-select-editions, pg 215

Menke, Dean, American Society of Health-System Pharmacists, 7272 Wisconsin Ave, Bethesda, MD 20814 *Tel:* 301-657-3000; 301-664-8700 *Toll Free Tel:* 866-279-0681 (orders) *Fax:* 301-657-1251 (orders) *E-mail:* custserv@ashp.org *Web Site:* www.ashp.org, pg 17

Menn, Don, Immedium, 535 Rockdale Dr, San Francisco, CA 94127 *Tel:* 415-452-8546 *Fax:* 360-937-6272 *E-mail:* orders@immedium.com; sales@immedium.com *Web Site:* www.immedium.com, pg 128

Mennel, Timothy, APA Planners Press, 205 N Michigan Ave, Suite 1200, Chicago, IL 60601 *Tel:* 312-431-9100 *Fax:* 312-786-6700 *E-mail:* customerservice@planning.org *Web Site:* www.planning.org, pg 19

Mennel, Timothy, University of Chicago Press, 1427 E 60 St, Chicago, IL 60637-2954 *Tel:* 773-702-7700; 773-702-7600 *Toll Free Tel:* 800-621-2736 (orders) *Fax:* 773-702-9756; 773-660-2235 (orders); 773-702-2708 *E-mail:* custserv@press.uchicago.edu; marketing@press.uchicago.edu *Web Site:* www.press.uchicago.edu, pg 265

Menon, Pooja, Kimberley Cameron & Associates, 1550 Tiburon Blvd, Suite 704, Tiburon, CA 94920 *Tel:* 415-789-9191 *Fax:* 415-789-9177 *E-mail:* info@kimberleycameron.com *Web Site:* www.kimberleycameron.com, pg 579

Menzies, Tracey, HarperCollins Children's Books, 10 E 53 St, New York, NY 10022 *Tel:* 212-207-7000 *Web Site:* www.harpercollinschildrens.com, pg 113

Menzies, Tracey, HarperCollins General Books Group, 10 E 53 St, New York, NY 10022 *Tel:* 212-207-7000 *Fax:* 212-207-7633 *Web Site:* www.harpercollins.com, pg 113

Menzies, Tracey, HarperCollins Publishers, 10 E 53 St, New York, NY 10022 *Tel:* 212-207-7000 *Fax:* 212-207-7145 *Web Site:* www.harpercollins.com, pg 113

Meradji, Ahmad, BookLogix, 1264 Old Alpharetta Rd, Alpharetta, GA 30005 *Tel:* 770-346-9979 *Toll Free Fax:* 888-564-7890 *E-mail:* sales@booklogix.com *Web Site:* www.booklogix.com, pg 43

Mercandetti, Susan, Random House Publishing Group, 1745 Broadway, New York, NY 10019 *Toll Free Tel:* 800-200-3552 *Web Site:* atrandom.com, pg 214

Merchant, Ann, National Academies Press (NAP), Lockbox 285, 500 Fifth St NW, Washington, DC 20001 *Tel:* 202-334-3313 *Toll Free Tel:* 888-624-8373 (cust serv) *Fax:* 202-334-2451 (cust serv); 202-334-2793 (mktg dept) *E-mail:* customer_service@nap.edu *Web Site:* www.nap.edu, pg 173

Merchant, Leigh, Random House Publishing Group, 1745 Broadway, New York, NY 10019 *Toll Free Tel:* 800-200-3552 *Web Site:* atrandom.com, pg 214

Mercy, Jon, ANR Publications University of California, 1301 S 46 St, Bldg 478 - MC 3580, Richmond, CA 94804 *Tel:* 510-665-2195 (cust serv) *Toll Free Tel:* 800-994-8849 *Fax:* 510-665-3427 *E-mail:* anrcatalog@ucdavis.edu *Web Site:* anrcatalog.ucanr.edu, pg 19

Meredith, Mimi, Society of Environmental Toxicology & Chemistry, 229 S Baylen St, 2nd fl, Pensacola, FL 32502 *Tel:* 850-469-1500 *Fax:* 850-469-9778 *E-mail:* setac@setac.org *Web Site:* www.setac.org, pg 238

Merkh, Jonathan, Howard Books, 216 Centerview Dr, Suite 303, Brentwood, TN 37027 *Tel:* 615-873-2080 *Fax:* 615-370-3834 *E-mail:* howardbooks@simonandschuster.com (info) *Web Site:* www.howardpublishing.com, pg 124

Merkh, Jonathan, Simon & Schuster, Inc, 1230 Avenue of the Americas, New York, NY 10020 *Tel:* 212-698-7000 *Fax:* 212-698-7007 *E-mail:* firstname.lastname@simonandschuster.com *Web Site:* www.simonandschuster.com, pg 235

Merkle, Dieter, Springer, 233 Spring St, New York, NY 10013-1578 *Tel:* 212-460-1500 *Toll Free Tel:* 800-SPRINGER (777-4643) *Fax:* 212-460-1575 *E-mail:* service-ny@springer.com *Web Site:* www.springer.com, pg 241

Merkle, Molly B, Menasha Ridge Press Inc, 2204 First Ave S, Suite 102, Birmingham, AL 35233 *Tel:* 205-322-0439 *Toll Free Tel:* 888-604-4537 *Fax:* 205-326-1012 *E-mail:* info@menasharidge.com *Web Site:* www.menasharidge.com, pg 164

Merola, Marianne, Brandt & Hochman Literary Agents Inc, 1501 Broadway, Suite 2310, New York, NY 10036 *Tel:* 212-840-5760 *Fax:* 212-840-5776 *Web Site:* brandthochman.com, pg 564

Merriam, Ray, Merriam Press, 133 Elm St, Suite 3R, Bennington, VT 05201-2250 *Tel:* 802-447-0313 *Web Site:* www.merriam-press.com, pg 165

Merrill, Deirdre, Chronicle Books LLC, 680 Second St, San Francisco, CA 94107 *Tel:* 415-537-4200 *Toll Free Tel:* 800-759-0190 (cust serv) *Fax:* 415-537-4460 *Toll Free Fax:* 800-858-7787 (orders); 800-286-9471 (cust serv) *E-mail:* frontdesk@chroniclebooks.com *Web Site:* www.chroniclebooks.com, pg 61

Merrill, Robert, Maisonneuve Press, 6423 Adelphi Rd, Hyattsville, MD 20782 *Tel:* 301-277-7505 *Fax:* 301-277-2467 *Web Site:* www.maisonneuvepress.com, pg 155

Merryman-Means, Marcia, Schlager Group Inc, 2501 Oak Lawn Ave, Suite 440, Dallas, TX 75219 *Toll Free Tel:* 888-416-5727 *Fax:* 214-347-9469 *E-mail:* info@schlagergroup.com *Web Site:* www.schlagergroup.com, pg 227

Merubia, Lilana, Lyndon B Johnson School of Public Affairs, University of Texas at Austin, 2315 Red River St, Austin, TX 78712-1536 *Tel:* 512-471-3200 *Fax:* 512-471-4697 *E-mail:* pubsinfo@uts.cc.utexas.edu; lbjdeansoffice@austin.utexas.edu *Web Site:* www.utexas.edu/lbj, pg 154

Mesecher, Kim, M Lee Smith Publishers LLC, 5201 Virginia Way, Brentwood, TN 37027 *Tel:* 615-373-7517 *Toll Free Tel:* 800-274-6774 *Fax:* 615-373-5183 *E-mail:* custserv@mleesmith.com *Web Site:* www.mleesmith.com, pg 237

Meskis, Joyce, University of Denver Publishing Institute, 2000 E Asbury Ave, Denver, CO 80208 *Tel:* 303-871-2570 *Fax:* 303-871-2501 *Web Site:* www.du.edu/pi, pg 681

Messer, Randy, Perfection Learning Corp, 2680 Berkshire Pkwy, Clive, IA 50325 *Tel:* 515-278-0133 *Toll Free Tel:* 800-762-2999 *Fax:* 515-278-2980 *Web Site:* perfectionlearning.com, pg 199

Messerli, Douglas, Green Integer, 6022 Wilshire Blvd, Suite 202-C, Los Angeles, CA 90036 *Tel:* 323-857-1115 *Fax:* 323-857-0143 *E-mail:* info@greeninteger.com *Web Site:* www.greeninteger.com, pg 107

Messick, Mary K, Schoolhouse Network Inc, PO Box 17676, Fountain Hills, AZ 85269 *Tel:* 973-206-1389 *E-mail:* info@schoolhousenetwork.com *Web Site:* www.schoolhousenetwork.com, pg 555

Messina, Scott, Fine Communications, 322 Eighth Ave, 15th fl, New York, NY 10001 *Tel:* 212-595-3500 *Fax:* 212-595-3779, pg 95

Messitte, Anne, Alfred A Knopf/Everyman's Library, c/o Random House Inc, 1745 Broadway, New York, NY 10019 *Tel:* 212-751-2600 *Toll Free Tel:* 800-638-6460 *Fax:* 212-572-2593 *Web Site:* www.knopfdoubleday.com, pg 141

Messitte, Anne, Vintage & Anchor Books, c/o Random House Inc, 1745 Broadway, New York, NY 10019 *Tel:* 212-572-2420 *E-mail:* vintageanchorpublicity@randomhouse.com *Web Site:* vintage-anchor.knopfdoubleday.com, pg 275

Metcalfe, Heidi, HarperCollins General Books Group, 10 E 53 St, New York, NY 10022 *Tel:* 212-207-7000 *Fax:* 212-207-7633 *Web Site:* www.harpercollins.com, pg 113

Meterval, Jeff, American Girl Publishing, 8400 Fairway Place, Middleton, WI 53562 *Tel:* 608-836-4848; 608-360-1861 (US & CN); 608-831-5210 (outside US & CN) *Toll Free Tel:* 800-233-0264; 800-360-1861 *Fax:* 608-836-1999 *Web Site:* www.americangirl.com, pg 13

Meth, David L, Writers' Productions, PO Box 630, Westport, CT 06881-0630 *Tel:* 203-227-8199, pg 600

Metro, Judy, National Gallery of Art, Fourth St & Pennsylvania Ave NW, Washington, DC 20565 *Tel:* 202-737-4215; 202-842-6480 *Fax:* 202-842-6733 *E-mail:* casva@nga.gov *Web Site:* www.nga.gov, pg 174

Metsch, Amy, Random House Large Print, 1745 Broadway, New York, NY 10019 *Tel:* 212-782-9000 *Fax:* 212-782-9484, pg 214

Metts, Shawn, North Light Books, 10151 Carver Rd, Suite 200, Blue Ash, OH 45242 *Tel:* 513-531-2690 *Toll Free Tel:* 800-666-0963 *Fax:* 513-891-7185 *Toll Free Fax:* 888-590-4082 *E-mail:* contact_us@fwmedia.com *Web Site:* www.fwmedia.com, pg 181

Metz, Isabel, University Press of Mississippi, 3825 Ridgewood Rd, Jackson, MS 39211-6492 *Tel:* 601-432-6205 *Toll Free Tel:* 800-737-7788 (orders & cust serv) *Fax:* 601-432-6217 *E-mail:* press@mississippi.edu *Web Site:* www.upress.state.ms.us, pg 271

Metz, Mary, The Mountaineers Books, 1001 SW Klickitat Way, Suite 201, Seattle, WA 98134 *Tel:* 206-223-6303 *Toll Free Tel:* 800-553-4453 *Fax:* 206-223-6306 *Toll Free Fax:* 800-568-7604 *E-mail:* mbooks@mountaineersbooks.org *Web Site:* www.mountaineersbooks.org, pg 170

Meyer, Amy, F+W Media Inc, 10151 Carver Rd, Suite 200, Blue Ash, OH 45242 *Tel:* 513-531-2690 *Toll Free Tel:* 800-289-0963 (trade accts); 800-258-0929 (orders) *E-mail:* contact_us@fwmedia.com *Web Site:* www.fwmedia.com, pg 92

Meyer, Kathleen, Duquesne University Press, 600 Forbes Ave, Pittsburgh, PA 15282 *Tel:* 412-396-6610 *Fax:* 412-396-5984 *E-mail:* dupress@duq.edu *Web Site:* www.dupress.duq.edu, pg 83

Meyer, Michael A, Hebrew Union College Press, 3101 Clifton Ave, Cincinnati, OH 45220 *Tel:* 513-221-1875 *Fax:* 513-221-0321 *E-mail:* hucpress@huc.edu *Web Site:* huc.edu, pg 117

Meyer, Steve, LAMA Books, 2381 Sleepy Hollow Ave, Hayward, CA 94545-3429 *Tel:* 510-785-1091 *Toll Free Tel:* 888-452-6244 *Fax:* 510-785-1099 *Web Site:* www.lamabooks.com, pg 143

Meyering, Michelle, PEN Center USA, PO Box 6037, Beverly Hills, CA 90212 *Tel:* 323-424-4939 *Fax:* 323-424-4944 *E-mail:* pen@penusa.org *Web Site:* www.penusa.org, pg 633

Meyers, Amy, Yale Center for British Art, 1080 Chapel St, New Haven, CT 06510-2302 *Tel:* 203-432-2800 *Toll Free Tel:* 877-274-8278 *Fax:* 203-432-9628 *E-mail:* ycba.info@yale.edu *Web Site:* www.yale.edu/ycba; britishart.yale.edu, pg 287

Meyers, Bob, The National Press Foundation, 1211 Connecticut Ave NW, Suite 310, Washington, DC 20036 *Tel:* 202-663-7280 *Web Site:* www.nationalpress.org, pg 631

Meyers, Dale, Standard Publishing, 8805 Governors Hill Dr, Suite 400, Cincinnati, OH 45249 *Tel:* 513-931-4050 *Toll Free Tel:* 800-543-1353 *Fax:* 513-931-0950 *Toll Free Fax:* 877-867-5751 *E-mail:* customerservice@standardpub.com *Web Site:* www.standardpub.com, pg 242

Meyers, Denise C, National Freedom of Information Coalition (NFOIC), 101 Reynolds Journalism Institute, Columbia, MO 65211-0012 *Tel:* 573-882-4856 *Fax:* 573-884-6204 *Web Site:* nfoic.org, pg 630

Meyers, Tona Pearce-, New World Library, 14 Pamaron Way, Novato, CA 94949 *Tel:* 415-884-2100 *Toll Free Tel:* 800-227-3900 (ext 52, retail orders); 800-972-6657 *Fax:* 415-884-2199 *E-mail:* escort@newworldlibrary.com *Web Site:* www.newworldlibrary.com, pg 178

Micallef, Joseph, McGraw-Hill Education, 2 Penn Plaza, New York, NY 10121-2298 *Tel:* 212-904-2000 *E-mail:* customer.service@mcgraw-hill.com *Web Site:* www.mheducation.com; www.mheducation.com/custserv.html, pg 160

Miceli, Jaya, Plume, 375 Hudson St, New York, NY 10014 *Tel:* 212-366-2000 *Fax:* 212-366-2666 *E-mail:* online@penguinputnam.com *Web Site:* www.penguinputnam.com; us.penguingroup.com, pg 203

Michaels, Doris S, Doris S Michaels Literary Agency Inc, 1841 Broadway, Suite 903, New York, NY 10023 *Tel:* 212-265-9474 *Fax:* 212-265-9480 *E-mail:* info@dsmagency.com *Web Site:* www.dsmagency.com, pg 585

Michaels, Ken, Hachette Book Group, 237 Park Ave, New York, NY 10017 *Tel:* 212-364-1100 *Toll Free Tel:* 800-759-0190 (cust serv) *Fax:* 212-364-0933 (intl orders) *Toll Free Fax:* 800-286-9471 (cust serv) *Web Site:* www.HachetteBookGroup.com, pg 110

Michalicek, Steven S, Heuer Publishing LLC, 211 First Ave SE, Suite 200, Cedar Rapids, IA 52401 *Tel:* 319-368-8008 *Toll Free Tel:* 800-950-7529 *Fax:* 319-368-8011 *E-mail:* editor@hitplays.com *Web Site:* www.hitplays.com, pg 119

Michel, Bob, Hachette Book Group, 237 Park Ave, New York, NY 10017 *Tel:* 212-364-1100 *Toll Free Tel:* 800-759-0190 (cust serv) *Fax:* 212-364-0933 (intl orders) *Toll Free Fax:* 800-286-9471 (cust serv) *Web Site:* www.HachetteBookGroup.com, pg 110

Michels, Dia L, Platypus Media LLC, 725 Eighth St SE, Washington, DC 20003 *Tel:* 202-546-1674 *Toll Free Tel:* 877-PLATYPS (752-8977) *Fax:* 202-546-2356 *E-mail:* info@platypusmedia.com *Web Site:* www.platypusmedia.com, pg 202

Michels, Dia L, Science, Naturally!™, 725 Eighth St SE, Washington, DC 20003 *Tel:* 202-465-4798 *Toll Free Tel:* 866-724-9876 *Fax:* 202-558-2132 *E-mail:* info@sciencenaturally.com *Web Site:* www.sciencenaturally.com, pg 229

Michels, Greg, Municipal Analysis Services Inc, PO Box 13453, Austin, TX 78711-3453 *Tel:* 512-327-3328 *Fax:* 413-740-1294 *E-mail:* munilysis@hotmail.com, pg 171

Miciak, Kate, Random House Publishing Group, 1745 Broadway, New York, NY 10019 *Toll Free Tel:* 800-200-3552 *Web Site:* atrandom.com, pg 214

Mickey, Kathy, Simba Information, 60 Long Ridge Rd, Suite 300, Stamford, CT 06902 *Tel:* 203-325-8193 *Toll Free Tel:* 888-297-4622 (cust serv) *Fax:* 203-325-8975 *E-mail:* customerservice@simbainformation.com *Web Site:* www.simbainformation.com, pg 234

Micklos, John, PreK-12 Learning Group, 325 Chestnut St, Suite 1110, Philadelphia, PA 19106 *Tel:* 267-351-4310 *Fax:* 267-351-4317 *E-mail:* prek12learning@publishers.org *Web Site:* www.aepweb.org, pg 634

Mickulas, Peter, Rutgers University Press, 106 Somerset St, 3rd fl, New Brunswick, NJ 08901 *Tel:* 858-445-7784 (edit); 848-445-7788 *Toll Free Tel:* 800-848-6224 (orders only) *Fax:* 732-745-4935 (acqs, edit, mktg, perms & prodn) *Toll Free Fax:* 800-272-6817 (fulfillment) *Web Site:* rutgerspress.rutgers.edu, pg 222

Middaugh, Dallas, Random House Publishing Group, 1745 Broadway, New York, NY 10019 *Toll Free Tel:* 800-200-3552 *Web Site:* atrandom.com, pg 214

Middendorf, Sandy, Augsburg Fortress Publishers, Publishing House of the Evangelical Lutheran Church in America, 100 S Fifth St, Suite 600, Minneapolis, MN 55402 *Tel:* 612-330-3300 *Toll Free Tel:* 800-426-0115 (ext 639, subns); 800-328-4648 (orders) *E-mail:* info@augsburgfortress.org; copyright@augsburgfortress.org (reprint permission requests); customercare@augsburgfortress.org *Web Site:* www.augsburgfortress.org, pg 27

Middlebrook, Ron, Centerstream Publishing LLC, PO Box 17878, Anaheim Hills, CA 92817-7878 *Tel:* 714-779-9390 *E-mail:* centerstrm@aol.com *Web Site:* www.centerstream-usa.com, pg 57

Middleton, Jean F, IndexEmpire Indexing Services, 16740 Orville Wright Dr, Riverside, CA 92518 *Tel:* 951-697-2819 *E-mail:* indexempire@gmail.com, pg 548

Middleton, Kathy, Crabtree Publishing Co, 350 Fifth Ave, 59th fl, PMB 59051, New York, NY 10118 *Tel:* 212-496-5040 *Toll Free Tel:* 800-387-7650 *Toll Free Fax:* 800-355-7166 *E-mail:* custserv@crabtreebooks.com *Web Site:* www.crabtreebooks.com, pg 70

Middleton, Kathy, Crabtree Publishing Co Ltd, 616 Welland Ave, St Catharines, ON L2M-5V6, Canada *Tel:* 905-682-5221 *Toll Free Tel:* 800-387-7650 *Fax:* 905-682-7166 *Toll Free Fax:* 800-355-7166 *E-mail:* custserv@crabtreebooks.com; sales@crabtreebooks.com; orders@crabtreebooks.com *Web Site:* www.crabtreebooks.com, pg 500

Middleton, Maria, Harry N Abrams Inc, 115 W 18 St, 6th fl, New York, NY 10011 *Tel:* 212-206-7715 *Toll Free Tel:* 800-345-1359 *Fax:* 212-519-1210 *E-mail:* abrams@abramsbooks.com *Web Site:* www.abramsbooks.com, pg 3

Midgley, Peter, University of Alberta Press, Ring House 2, Edmonton, AB T6G 2E1, Canada *Tel:* 780-492-3662 *Fax:* 780-492-0719 *Web Site:* www.uap.ualberta.ca, pg 522

Miers, Charles, Rizzoli International Publications Inc, 300 Park Ave S, 4th fl, New York, NY 10010-5399 *Tel:* 212-387-3400 *Toll Free Tel:* 800-522-6657 (orders only) *Fax:* 212-387-3535 *E-mail:* publicity@rizzoliusa.com *Web Site:* www.rizzoliusa.com, pg 219

Mihalick, Laura, Harry N Abrams Inc, 115 W 18 St, 6th fl, New York, NY 10011 *Tel:* 212-206-7715 *Toll Free Tel:* 800-345-1359 *Fax:* 212-519-1210 *E-mail:* abrams@abramsbooks.com *Web Site:* www.abramsbooks.com, pg 3

Mihavolic, Andrea, Visual Artists & Galleries Association Inc (VAGA), 350 Fifth Ave, Suite 2820, New York, NY 10118 *Tel:* 212-736-6666 *Fax:* 212-736-6767 *E-mail:* info@vagarights.com *Web Site:* www.vagarights.com, pg 638

Miholer, Sue, Oregon Christian Writers (OCW), 1075 Willow Lake Rd N, Keizer, OR 97303 *Tel:* 503-393-3356 *E-mail:* contact@oregonchristianwriters.org *Web Site:* www.oregonchristianwriters.org, pg 633

Miholer, Sue, Oregon Christian Writers Coaching Conference, 1075 Willow Lake Rd N, Keizer, OR 97303 *Tel:* 503-393-3356 *E-mail:* contact@oregonchristianwriters.org *Web Site:* www.oregonchristianwriters.org, pg 671

Miholer, Sue, Oregon Christian Writers Seminar, 1075 Willow Lake Rd N, Keizer, OR 97303 *Tel:* 503-393-3356 *E-mail:* contact@oregonchristianwriters.org *Web Site:* www.oregonchristianwriters.org, pg 671

Miklos, Lauren, Encounter Books, 900 Broadway, Suite 601, New York, NY 10003 *Tel:* 212-871-6310 *Toll Free Tel:* 800-786-3839 *Fax:* 212-871-6311 *Toll Free Fax:* 877-811-1461 *E-mail:* read@encounterbooks.com *Web Site:* www.encounterbooks.com, pg 88

Milanes, Sarah, Ruth & Sylvia Schwartz Children's Book Award, c/o Ontario Arts Council, 151 Bloor St W, 5th fl, Toronto, ON M5S 1T6, Canada *Tel:* 416-961-1660 *Toll Free Tel:* 800-387-0058 (ON) *Fax:* 416-961-7447 *E-mail:* info@arts.on.ca *Web Site:* www.arts.on.ca, pg 741

Milazzo, Richard, Edgewise Press Inc, 24 Fifth Ave, Suite 224, New York, NY 10011 *Tel:* 212-982-4818 *Fax:* 212-982-1364 *E-mail:* epinc@mindspring.com *Web Site:* www.edgewisepress.org, pg 84

Miles, Linda, George Freedley Memorial Award, Roundabout Theatre Co, 231 W 39 St, Suite 1200, New York, NY 10018 *Tel:* 212-719-9393 (ext 351) *E-mail:* info@tla-online.org; tlabookawards@gmail.com *Web Site:* www.tla-online.org, pg 705

Miles, Linda, Richard Wall Memorial Award, Roundabout Theatre Co, 231 W 39 St, Suite 1200, New York, NY 10018 *Tel:* 212-719-9393 (ext 351) *E-mail:* info@tla-online.org; tlabookawards@gmail.com *Web Site:* www.tla-online.org, pg 748

Miles, Stephen, Harlequin Enterprises Ltd, 225 Duncan Mill Rd, Don Mills, ON M3B 3K9, Canada *Tel:* 416-445-5860 *Toll Free Tel:* 888-432-4879; 800-370-5838 (ebook inquiries) *Fax:* 416-445-8655 *E-mail:* CustomerService@harlequin.com *Web Site:* www.harlequin.com, pg 508

Miley, Daniel, Rainbow Publishers, PO Box 261129, San Diego, CA 92196 *Tel:* 858-277-1167 *Toll Free Tel:* 800-323-7337 *Toll Free Fax:* 800-331-0297 *E-mail:* info@rainbowpublishers.com; editor@rainbowpublishers.com (edit dept) *Web Site:* www.rainbowpublishers.com, pg 212

Millar, Carla, The Press at California State University, Fresno, 2380 E Keats, M/S MB 99, Fresno, CA 93740-8024 *Tel:* 559-278-3056 *Fax:* 559-278-6758 *E-mail:* press@csufresno.edu *Web Site:* shop.thepressatcsufresno.com; thepressatcsufresno.com, pg 205

Millar, David, Simon & Schuster Canada, 166 King St E, Suite 300, Toronto, ON M5A 1J3, Canada *Tel:* 647-427-8882 *Toll Free Tel:* 800-387-0446; 800-268-3216 (orders) *Fax:* 647-430-9446 *Toll Free Fax:* 888-849-8151 (orders) *E-mail:* info@simonandschuster.ca *Web Site:* www.simonsayscanada.com, pg 519

Millard, Martha, Martha Millard Literary Agency, 420 Central Park W, Suite 5H, New York, NY 10025 *Tel:* 212-662-1030 *E-mail:* marmillink@aol.com, pg 586

Miller, Andrew, Alfred A Knopf/Everyman's Library, c/o Random House Inc, 1745 Broadway, New York, NY 10019 *Tel:* 212-751-2600 *Toll Free Tel:* 800-638-6460 *Fax:* 212-572-2593 *Web Site:* www.knopfdoubleday.com, pg 141

Miller, Anelle, Society of Illustrators (SI), 128 E 63 St, New York, NY 10065 *Tel:* 212-838-2560 *Fax:* 212-838-2561 *E-mail:* info@societyillustrators.org *Web Site:* www.societyillustrators.org, pg 636

Miller, Angela, The Miller Agency Inc, 630 Ninth Ave, Suite 1102, New York, NY 10036 *Tel:* 212-206-0913 *Fax:* 212-206-1473, pg 586

Miller, Anita, Academy Chicago Publishers, 363 W Erie St, Suite 4-W, Chicago, IL 60654 *Tel:* 312-751-7300 *Toll Free Tel:* 800-248-READ (248-7323) *Fax:* 312-751-7306 *E-mail:* info@academychicago.com *Web Site:* www.academychicago.com, pg 4

Miller, Avital, Crystal Clarity Publishers, 14618 Tyler Foote Rd, Nevada City, CA 95959 *Tel:* 530-478-7600 *Toll Free Tel:* 800-424-1055 *Fax:* 530-478-7610 *E-mail:* clarity@crystalclarity.com *Web Site:* www.crystalclarity.com, pg 73

Miller, Betsy, Robert Miller Gallery, 524 W 26 St, New York, NY 10001 *Tel:* 212-366-4774 *Fax:* 212-366-4454 *E-mail:* rmg@robertmillergallery.com *Web Site:* www.robertmillergallery.com, pg 167

Miller, Brenda, Annie Dillard Award for Creative Nonfiction, Mail Stop 9053, Western Washington University, Bellingham, WA 98225 *Tel:* 360-650-4863 *E-mail:* bhreview@wwu.edu *Web Site:* www.bhreview.org, pg 700

Miller, Brenda, 49th Parallel Poetry Award, Mail Stop 9053, Western Washington University, Bellingham, WA 98225 *Tel:* 360-650-4863 *E-mail:* bhreview@wwu.edu *Web Site:* www.bhreview.org, pg 705

Miller, Brenda, Tobias Wolff Award for Fiction, Mail Stop 9053, Western Washington University, Bellingham, WA 98225 *Tel:* 360-650-4863 *E-mail:* bhreview@wwu.edu *Web Site:* www.bhreview.org, pg 750

Miller, Bryan, The Art Institute of Chicago, 111 S Michigan Ave, Chicago, IL 60603-6404 *Tel:* 312-443-3600; 312-443-3540 (pubns) *Fax:* 312-443-1334 (pubns) *Web Site:* www.artic.edu; www.artinstituteshop.org, pg 22

Miller, Ceci, CeciBooks Editorial & Publishing Consultation, 7057 26 Ave NW, Seattle, WA 98117 *Tel:* 206-706-9565 *E-mail:* cecibooks@gmail.com *Web Site:* www.cecibooks.com, pg 543

Miller, Christopher, Liguori Publications, One Liguori Dr, Liguori, MO 63057-1000 *Tel:* 636-464-2500 *Toll Free Tel:* 866-848-2492; 800-325-9521 *Fax:* 636-464-8449 *Web Site:* www.liguori.org, pg 149

Miller, Connie, Standard International Media Holdings, 568 Ninth St S, Suite 201, Naples, FL 34102-7336 *Tel:* 239-649-7077 *Fax:* 239-649-5832 *E-mail:* sales@standardinternationalmedia.com *Web Site:* www.standardinternationalmedia.com, pg 242

Miller, Cynthia, University of Pittsburgh Press, Eureka Bldg, 5th fl, 3400 Forbes Ave, Pittsburgh, PA 15260 *Tel:* 412-383-2456 *Fax:* 412-383-2466 *E-mail:* info@upress.pitt.edu *Web Site:* www.upress.pitt.edu, pg 268

Miller, Dan, Utah State University Press, 3078 Old Main Hill, Logan, UT 84322-3078 *Tel:* 435-797-1362 *Fax:* 435-797-0313 *Web Site:* www.usupress.org, pg 274

Miller, David, Evan-Moor Educational Publishers, 18 Lower Ragsdale Dr, Monterey, CA 93940-5746 *Tel:* 831-649-5901 *Toll Free Tel:* 800-714-0971 (cust serv); 800-777-4362 (orders) *Fax:* 831-649-6256 *Toll Free Fax:* 800-777-4332 (orders) *E-mail:* sales@evan-moor.com; marketing@evan-moor.com *Web Site:* www.evan-moor.com, pg 90

Miller, David, The Garamond Agency Inc, 12 Horton St, Newburyport, MA 01950 *Fax:* 978-992-0265 *E-mail:* query@garamondagency.com *Web Site:* www.garamondagency.com, pg 574

Miller, David, Island Press, 1718 Connecticut Ave NW, Suite 300, Washington, DC 20009 *Tel:* 202-232-7933 *Toll Free Tel:* 800-828-1302 *Fax:* 202-234-1328 *E-mail:* info@islandpress.org *Web Site:* www.islandpress.org, pg 134

Miller, Diana, Palm Springs Writers Guild, PO Box 947, Rancho Mirage, CA 92270-0947 *Web Site:* www.palmspringswritersguild.org, pg 633

Miller, Diane M, Peoples Education Inc, 299 Market St, Suite 240, Saddle Brook, NJ 07663 *Tel:* 201-712-0090 *Toll Free Tel:* 800-822-1080 *Fax:* 201-712-0045; 201-712-1016 *Web Site:* www.peopleseducation.com; www.peoplescollegeprep.com; www.measuringuplive.com; www.brightpointliteracy.com, pg 199

Miller, Gary, Marshall & Swift, 777 S Fiqueroa St, 12th fl, Los Angeles, CA 90017 *Tel:* 213-683-9000 *Toll Free Tel:* 800-544-2678 *Fax:* 213-683-9043 *E-mail:* csinquiry@marshallswift.com *Web Site:* www.marshallswift.com, pg 158

Miller, Harold, Taylor-Dth Publishing, 108 Caribe Isle, Novato, CA 94949 *Tel:* 415-299-1087 *Web Site:* www.taylor-dth.com, pg 250

Miller, Irene, The Mellen Poetry Press, 240 Portage Rd, Lewiston, NY 14092 *Tel:* 716-754-2266; 716-754-1400 (mktg); 716-754-2788 (order fulfillment) *Fax:* 716-754-4056; 716-754-1860 (fulfillment) *E-mail:* cservice@mellenpress.com *Web Site:* www.mellenpress.com, pg 164

Miller, Jan, Dupree, Miller & Associates Inc, 100 Highland Park Village, Suite 350, Dallas, TX 75205 *Tel:* 214-559-2665 *Fax:* 214-559-7243 *E-mail:* editorial@dupreemiller.com *Web Site:* www.dupreemiller.com, pg 569

Miller, Jeffrey, Cadmus Editions, PO Box 126, Belvedere-Tiburon, CA 94920-0126 *Tel:* 707-762-0510 *Web Site:* www.cadmuseditions.com, pg 50

Miller, Jeffrey, Irwin Law Inc, 14 Duncan St, Suite 206, Toronto, ON M5H 3G8, Canada *Tel:* 416-862-7690 *Toll Free Tel:* 888-314-9014 *Fax:* 416-862-9236 *Web Site:* www.irwinlaw.com, pg 510

Miller, Jordan, Academy Chicago Publishers, 363 W Erie St, Suite 4-W, Chicago, IL 60654 *Tel:* 312-751-7300 *Toll Free Tel:* 800-248-READ (248-7323) *Fax:* 312-751-7306 *E-mail:* info@academychicago.com *Web Site:* www.academychicago.com, pg 4

Miller, Joseph MLS, PhD, H W Wilson, 10 Estes St, Ipswich, MA 01938 *Tel:* 978-356-6500 *Toll Free Tel:* 800-653-2726 (US & CN) *Fax:* 978-356-6565 *E-mail:* information@ebscohost.com *Web Site:* www.ebscohost.com, pg 282

Miller, Kevin, Atlantic Center for the Arts Artists-in-Residence Program, 1414 Art Center Ave, New Smyrna Beach, FL 32168 *Tel:* 386-427-6975 *Toll Free Tel:* 800-393-6975 *Fax:* 386-427-5669 *E-mail:* program@atlanticcenterforthearts.org *Web Site:* www.atlanticcenterforthearts.org, pg 667

Miller, Lauren, Thames & Hudson, 500 Fifth Ave, New York, NY 10110 *Tel:* 212-354-3763 *Toll Free Tel:* 800-233-4830 *Fax:* 212-398-1252 *E-mail:* bookinfo@thames.wwnorton.com *Web Site:* www.thamesandhudsonusa.com, pg 253

Miller, Lawton, M Lee Smith Publishers LLC, 5201 Virginia Way, Brentwood, TN 37027 *Tel:* 615-373-7517 *Toll Free Tel:* 800-274-6774 *Fax:* 615-373-5183 *E-mail:* custserv@mleesmith.com *Web Site:* www.mleesmith.com, pg 237

Miller, Leah, Crown Publishing Group, c/o Random House Inc, 1745 Broadway, New York, NY 10019 *Tel:* 212-782-9000 *Toll Free Tel:* 888-264-1745 *Fax:* 212-940-7408 *Web Site:* www.randomhouse.com/crown, pg 72

Miller, Matthew, The Toby Press LLC, 2 Great Pasture Rd, Danbury, CT 06810 *Tel:* 203-830-8508 *Fax:* 203-830-8512 *E-mail:* toby@tobypress.com *Web Site:* www.tobypress.com; www.korenpub.com, pg 256

Miller, Meg, Simon & Schuster, 1230 Avenue of the Americas, New York, NY 10020 *Tel:* 212-698-7000 *Toll Free Tel:* 800-223-2348 (cust serv); 800-223-2336 (orders) *Toll Free Fax:* 800-943-9831 (orders) *Web Site:* www.simonandschuster.com, pg 234

Miller, Peter, Bloomsbury Publishing, 175 Fifth Ave, New York, NY 10010 *Tel:* 212-674-5151 *Toll Free Tel:* 800-221-7945 *Fax:* 212-780-0115; 212-982-2837 *E-mail:* marketingusa@bloomsbury.com; adultpublicityusa.@bloomsbury.com *Web Site:* www.bloomsbury.com, pg 40

Miller, Peter, The Institutes™, 720 Providence Rd, Suite 100, Malvern, PA 19355-3433 *Tel:* 610-644-2100 *Toll Free Tel:* 800-644-2101 *Fax:* 610-640-9576 *E-mail:* customerservice@theinstitutes.org *Web Site:* www.theinstitutes.org, pg 131

Miller, Peter, PMA Literary & Film Management Inc, PO Box 1817, Old Chelsea Sta, New York, NY 10113 *Tel:* 212-929-1222 *Fax:* 212-206-0238 *E-mail:* queries@pmalitfilm.com *Web Site:* www.pmalitfilm.com, pg 588

Miller, Richard K, Richard K Miller Associates, 4132 Atlanta Hwy, Suite 110, Loganville, GA 30052 *Tel:* 770-466-9709 *Toll Free Tel:* 888-928-RKMA (928-7562) *Fax:* 770-466-6879 *Toll Free Fax:* 877-928-RKMA (928-7562) *Web Site:* rkma.com, pg 167

Miller, Sarah, Yale University Press, 302 Temple St, New Haven, CT 06511-8909 *Tel:* 401-531-2800 (cust serv); 203-432-0960 *Toll Free Tel:* 800-405-1619 (cust serv) *Fax:* 203-432-0948; 401-531-2801 (cust serv) *Toll Free Fax:* 800-406-9145 (cust serv) *E-mail:* customer.care@trilateral.org (cust serv); language.yalepress@yale.edu *Web Site:* www.yalebooks.com, pg 287

Miller, Scott, Trident Media Group LLC, 41 Madison Ave, 36th fl, New York, NY 10010 *Tel:* 212-262-4810 *Fax:* 212-262-4849 *Web Site:* www.tridentmediagroup.com, pg 598

Miller, Shannon, SDP Publishing Solutions LLC, 36 Captain's Way, East Bridgewater, MA 02333 *Tel:* 617-775-0656 *Web Site:* www.sdppublishingsolutions.com, pg 555

Miller, Sid, Burnside Review Fiction Chapbook Competition, PO Box 1782, Portland, OR 97207 *Web Site:* burnsidereview.org, pg 693

Miller, Stephen M, Stephen M Miller Inc, 15727 S Madison Dr, Olathe, KS 66062 *Tel:* 913-768-7997 *Web Site:* www.stephenmillerbooks.com, pg 551

Miller, Stuart, Federal Buyers Guide Inc, 324 Palm Ave, Santa Barbara, CA 93101 *Tel:* 805-963-6524 *Fax:* 805-963-7478 *E-mail:* info@gov-world.com; info@fbgglobal.com *Web Site:* www.gov-world.com; www.federalbuyersguideinc.com; www.digitalsubs.com, pg 93

Miller, Ted, Human Kinetics Inc, 1607 N Market St, Champaign, IL 61820 *Tel:* 217-351-5076 *Toll Free Tel:* 800-747-4457 *Fax:* 217-351-1549 (orders/cust serv) *E-mail:* info@hkusa.com *Web Site:* www.humankinetics.com, pg 125

Miller, Terri, Pentecostal Publishing House, 8855 Dunn Rd, Hazelwood, MO 63042 *Tel:* 314-837-7300 *Fax:* 314-336-1803 *E-mail:* pphordersdept@upci.org (orders) *Web Site:* www.pentecostalpublishing.com, pg 198

Miller, Tom, McGraw-Hill Professional, 1221 Avenue of the Americas, New York, NY 10020 *Tel:* 212-512-2000 *Web Site:* www.mhprofessional.com, pg 162

Miller, Dr Yvette E, Latin American Literary Review Press, PO Box 17660, Pittsburgh, PA 15235-0860 *Tel:* 412-824-7903 *Fax:* 412-824-7909 *E-mail:* lalrp.editor@gmail.com *Web Site:* www.lalrp.org, pg 144

Miller-Callihan, Courtney, Sanford J Greenburger Associates Inc, 55 Fifth Ave, 15th fl, New York, NY 10003 *Tel:* 212-206-5600 *Fax:* 212-463-8718 *Web Site:* www.greenburger.com, pg 576

Miller-Vincent, Kristin, D4EO Literary Agency, 7 Indian Valley Rd, Weston, CT 06883 *Tel:* 203-544-7180 *Fax:* 203-544-7160 *Web Site:* www.d4eoliteraryagency.com, pg 568

Millholland, Valerie, Duke University Press, 905 W Main St, Suite 18B, Durham, NC 27701 *Tel:* 919-688-5134 *Toll Free Tel:* 888-651-0122 *Fax:* 919-688-2615 *Toll Free Fax:* 888-651-0124 *E-mail:* orders@dukeupress.edu *Web Site:* www.dukeupress.edu, pg 82

Millichap, Paulette, Council Oak Books LLC, 2 W Sixth St, Suite 262, Tulsa, OK 74119 *Tel:* 918-743-BOOK (743-2665) *Toll Free Tel:* 800-247-8850 *Fax:* 918-743-4288 *E-mail:* publicity@counciloakbooks.com; order@counciloakbooks.com *Web Site:* www.counciloakbooks.com, pg 69

Milligan, Bryce, Wings Press, 627 E Guenther, San Antonio, TX 78210-1134 *Tel:* 210-271-7805 *Fax:* 210-271-7805 *E-mail:* press@wingspress.com *Web Site:* www.wingspress.com, pg 283

Milliken, Jean Mellichamp, Lyric Poetry Prizes, PO Box 110, Jericho, VT 05465 *Tel:* 802-899-3993 *Fax:* 802-899-3993 *E-mail:* themuse@thelyricmagazine.com *Web Site:* thelyricmagazine.com, pg 720

Milliken, Leif, University of Nebraska Press, 1111 Lincoln Mall, Lincoln, NE 68588-0630 *Tel:* 402-472-3581; 919-966-7449 (cust serv & foreign orders) *Toll Free Tel:* 800-848-6224 (cust serv & US orders) *Fax:* 402-472-6214; 919-962-2704 (cust serv & foreign orders) *Toll Free Fax:* 800-526-2617 (cust serv & US orders) *E-mail:* pressmail@unl.edu *Web Site:* www.nebraskapress.unl.edu, pg 267

Millman, Norman N, Summit University Press, 63 Summit Way, Gardiner, MT 59030-9314 *Tel:* 406-848-9742; 406-848-9500 *Toll Free Tel:* 800-245-5445 (retail orders) *Fax:* 406-848-9650 *Toll Free Fax:* 800-221-8307 *E-mail:* info@summituniversitypress.com *Web Site:* www.summituniversitypress.com, pg 246

Mills, Elizabeth M, Temporal Mechanical Press, 6760 Hwy 7, Estes Park, CO 80517-6404 *Tel:* 970-586-4706 *E-mail:* enosmillscbn@earthlink.net *Web Site:* www.enosmills.com, pg 252

Mills, Eryn, Temporal Mechanical Press, 6760 Hwy 7, Estes Park, CO 80517-6404 *Tel:* 970-586-4706 *E-mail:* enosmillscbn@earthlink.net *Web Site:* www.enosmills.com, pg 252

Mills, Kathleen, Kathleen Mills Editorial Services, PO Box 214, Chardon, OH 44024 *Tel:* 440-285-4347 *E-mail:* mills_edit@yahoo.com, pg 551

Mills, Kevin, The Tuesday Agency, 123 N Linn St, Suite 2-C, Iowa City, IA 52245 *Tel:* 319-338-7080 *E-mail:* trinity@tuesdayagency.com *Web Site:* tuesdayagency.com, pg 606

Mills, Nancy L, Pie in the Sky Publishing LLC, 8031 E Phillips Circle, Centennial, CO 80112 *Tel:* 303-773-0851 *Fax:* 303-773-0851 *E-mail:* pieintheskypublishing@msn.com *Web Site:* www.pieintheskypublishing.com, pg 201

Mills, Sharon, Texas A&M University Press, John H Lindsey Bldg, Lewis St, 4354 TAMU, College Station, TX 77843-4354 *Tel:* 979-845-1436 *Toll Free Tel:* 800-826-8911 (orders) *Fax:* 979-847-8752 *Toll Free Fax:* 888-617-2421 (orders) *E-mail:* upress@tamu.edu *Web Site:* www.tamupress.com, pg 252

Mitchem, Terri, TotalRecall Publications Inc, 1103 Middlecreek, Friendswood, TX 77546 *Tel:* 281-992-3131 *E-mail:* sales@totalrecallpress.com *Web Site:* www.totalrecallpress.com, pg 256

Mitchner, Leslie, Rutgers University Press, 106 Somerset St, 3rd fl, New Brunswick, NJ 08901 *Tel:* 858-445-7784 (edit); 848-445-7788 *Toll Free Tel:* 800-848-6224 (orders only) *Fax:* 732-745-4935 (acqs, edit, mktg, perms & prodn) *Toll Free Fax:* 800-272-6817 (fulfillment) *Web Site:* rutgerspress.rutgers.edu, pg 222

Mitnick, Audrey, Sleeping Bear Press™, 315 Eisenhower Pkwy, Suite 200, Ann Arbor, MI 48108 *Toll Free Tel:* 800-487-2323 *Fax:* 734-794-0004 *E-mail:* sleepingbearpress@cengage.com *Web Site:* www.sleepingbearpress.com, pg 237

Mittelstadt, David J, New Canaan Publishing Co LLC, 2384 N Hwy 341, Rossville, GA 30741 *Tel:* 423-285-8672 *E-mail:* djm@newcanaanpublishing.com *Web Site:* www.newcanaanpublishing.com, pg 177

Mlazgar, Brian, Canadian Plains Research Center, 2 Research Dr, Regina, SK S4S 7H9, Canada *Tel:* 306-585-4758 *Toll Free Tel:* 866-874-2257 *Fax:* 306-585-4699 *E-mail:* canadian.plains@uregina.ca *Web Site:* www.cprc.ca, pg 497

Moberg, David, Thomas Nelson Inc, 501 Nelson Place, Nashville, TN 37214 *Tel:* 615-889-9000 *Toll Free Tel:* 800-251-4000 *Fax:* 615-902-1548 *E-mail:* publicity@thomasnelson.com *Web Site:* www.thomasnelson.com, pg 255

Mock, Alishea, Dufour Editions Inc, PO Box 7, Chester Springs, PA 19425 *Tel:* 610-458-5005 *Toll Free Tel:* 800-869-5677 *Fax:* 610-458-7103 *E-mail:* info@dufoureditions.com *Web Site:* www.dufoureditions.com, pg 82

Mock, Barbara, AACC International, 3340 Pilot Knob Rd, St Paul, MN 55121 *Tel:* 651-454-7250 *Fax:* 651-454-0766 *E-mail:* aacc@scisoc.org *Web Site:* www.aaccnet.org, pg 2

Mock, Barbara, Eagan Press, 3340 Pilot Knob Rd, St Paul, MN 55121 *Tel:* 651-454-7250 *Toll Free Tel:* 800-328-7560 *Fax:* 651-454-0766 *E-mail:* aacc@scisoc.org *Web Site:* www.aaccnet.org, pg 83

Modugno, Maria, Random House Children's Books, 1745 Broadway, New York, NY 10019 *Tel:* 212-782-9000 *Toll Free Tel:* 800 200 3552 *Fax:* 212-782-9452 *Web Site:* randomhousekids.com, pg 213

Moe, Jack, Black Mountain Press, PO Box 9907, Asheville, NC 28815 *Tel:* 828-273-3332 *Web Site:* www.theblackmountainpress.com, pg 39

Moen, Jeff, University of Minnesota Press, 111 Third Ave S, Suite 290, Minneapolis, MN 55401-2520 *Tel:* 612-627-1970 *Fax:* 612-627-1980 *E-mail:* ump@umn.edu *Web Site:* www.upress.umn.edu, pg 267

Moench, Dan, Gibbs Smith Publisher, 1877 E Gentile St, Layton, UT 84041 *Tel:* 801-544-9800 *Toll Free Tel:* 800-748-5439; 800-835-4993 (orders) *Fax:* 801-544-5582 *Toll Free Fax:* 800-213-3023 (orders only) *E-mail:* info@gibbs-smith.com *Web Site:* www.gibbs-smith.com, pg 103

Moersch, Sarah, Southern Playwrights Competition, 700 Pelham Rd N, Jacksonville, AL 36265-1602 *Tel:* 256-782-5498 *Fax:* 256-782-5441 *Web Site:* www.jsu.edu/depart/english/southpla.htm, pg 743

Moffat, Christa, Oolichan Books, PO Box 2278, Fernie, BC V0B 1M0, Canada *Tel:* 250-423-6113 *E-mail:* info@oolichan.com *Web Site:* www.oolichan.com, pg 514

Moffett, Stephen A, FPMI Solutions Inc, 245 Business Park Rd, Suite A, Madison, AL 35758 *Tel:* 256-539-1850 *Toll Free Tel:* 888-644-3764 *Fax:* 256-539-0911 *E-mail:* info@fpmi.com *Web Site:* www.fpmisolutions.com; www.fpmi.com, pg 98

Moggy, Dianne, Harlequin Enterprises Ltd, 225 Duncan Mill Rd, Don Mills, ON M3B 3K9, Canada *Tel:* 416-445-5860 *Toll Free Tel:* 888-432-4879; 800-370-5838 (ebook inquiries) *Fax:* 416-445-8655 *E-mail:* CustomerService@harlequin.com *Web Site:* www.harlequin.com, pg 508

Moghari, Francesca, National Academies Press (NAP), Lockbox 285, 500 Fifth St NW, Washington, DC 20001 *Tel:* 202-334-3313 *Toll Free Tel:* 888-624-8373 (cust serv) *Fax:* 202-334-2451 (cust serv); 202-334-2793 (mktg dept) *E-mail:* customer_service@nap.edu *Web Site:* www.nap.edu, pg 173

Mogus, Mary Ann, Ligonier Valley Writers Conference, PO Box B, Ligonier, PA 15658-1602 *Tel:* 724-238-3692, pg 670

Mohammed, Feroze, Worldwide Library, 225 Duncan Mill Rd, Don Mills, ON M3B 3K9, Canada *Tel:* 416-445-5860 *Toll Free Tel:* 888-432-4879 *Fax:* 416-445-8655; 416-445-8736 *E-mail:* CustomerService@harlequin.com *Web Site:* www.harlequin.com, pg 525

Mohan, Joseph, The Art Institute of Chicago, 111 S Michigan Ave, Chicago, IL 60603-6404 *Tel:* 312-443-3600; 312-443-3540 (pubns) *Fax:* 312-443-1334 (pubns) *Web Site:* www.artic.edu; www.artinstituteshop.org, pg 22

Mohyde, Colleen, The Doe Coover Agency, PO Box 668, Winchester, MA 01890 *Tel:* 781-721-6000 *Fax:* 781-721-6727 *E-mail:* info@doecooveragency.com *Web Site:* www.doecooveragency.com, pg 567

Mokotoff, Gary, Avotaynu Inc, 155 N Washington Ave, Bergenfield, NJ 07621 *Tel:* 201-387-7200 *Toll Free Tel:* 800-286-8296 *Fax:* 201-387-2855 *E-mail:* info@avotaynu.com *Web Site:* www.avotaynu.com, pg 28

Moldow, Susan, Scribner, 1230 Avenue of the Americas, New York, NY 10020, pg 230

Moldow, Susan, Simon & Schuster, Inc, 1230 Avenue of the Americas, New York, NY 10020 *Tel:* 212-698-7000 *Fax:* 212-698-7007 *E-mail:* firstname.lastname@simonandschuster.com *Web Site:* www.simonandschuster.com, pg 235

Moldow, Susan, Touchstone, 1230 Avenue of the Americas, New York, NY 10020, pg 256

Mole, Alan, American Literacy Council, 1441 Mariposa Ave, Boulder, CO 80302 *Tel:* 303-440-7385 *E-mail:* presidentalc@americanliteracy.com *Web Site:* www.americanliteracy.com, pg 613

Molgat, Anne, Les Editions du Ble, 340 Provencher Blvd, St Boniface, MB R2H 0G7, Canada *Tel:* 204-237-8200 *Fax:* 204-233-8182 *E-mail:* direction@editionsduble.ca *Web Site:* www.livres-disques.ca/editions_ble/home/index.cfm, pg 502

Molina, Deidre, Knopf Random Canada, One Toronto St, Suite 300, Toronto, ON M5C 2V6, Canada *Tel:* 416-364-4449 *Toll Free Tel:* 888-523-9292 *Fax:* 416-364-6863 *Web Site:* www.randomhouse.ca, pg 510

Molish, John, Tantor Media Inc, 2 Business Park, Old Saybrook, CT 06475 *Toll Free Tel:* 877-782-6867 *Toll Free Fax:* 888-782-7821 *Web Site:* www.tantor.com, pg 250

Moller, Marilyn, W W Norton & Company Inc, 500 Fifth Ave, New York, NY 10110-0017 *Tel:* 212-354-5500 *Toll Free Tel:* 800-233-4830 (orders & cust serv) *Fax:* 212-869-0856 *Toll Free Fax:* 800-458-6515 *Web Site:* www.wwnorton.com, pg 182

Molnar, Szilvia, Sterling Lord Literistic Inc, 65 Bleecker St, New York, NY 10012 *Tel:* 212-780-6050 *Fax:* 212-780-6095 *E-mail:* info@sll.com *Web Site:* www.sll.com, pg 595

Moltke, Nina von, Random House Publishing Group, 1745 Broadway, New York, NY 10019 *Toll Free Tel:* 800-200-3552 *Web Site:* atrandom.com, pg 214

Molyneaux, David G, SATW Foundation Lowell Thomas Travel Journalism Competition, 6317 Crab Orchard Rd, Houston, TX 77057 *Tel:* 713-973-9985 *E-mail:* awards@satwf.com *Web Site:* www.satwfoundation.org, pg 739

Molyneux, Beverly, AAPG (American Association of Petroleum Geologists), 1444 S Boulder Ave, Tulsa, OK 74119 *Tel:* 918-584-2555 *Toll Free Tel:* 800-364-AAPG (364-2274) *Fax:* 918-580-2665 *Toll Free Fax:* 800-898-2274 *E-mail:* publications@aapg.org *Web Site:* www.aapg.org, pg 2

Mommer, Kerri, Open Court, 70 E Lake St, Suite 300, Chicago, IL 60601 *Tel:* 312-701-1720 *Toll Free Tel:* 800-815-2280 (orders only) *Fax:* 312-701-1728 *E-mail:* opencourt@caruspub.com *Web Site:* www.opencourtbooks.com, pg 185

Monacelli, Gianfranco, Crown Publishing Group, c/o Random House Inc, 1745 Broadway, New York, NY 10019 *Tel:* 212-782-9000 *Toll Free Tel:* 888-264-1745 *Fax:* 212-940-7408 *Web Site:* www.randomhouse.com/crown, pg 72

Monacelli, Gianfranco, The Monacelli Press, 236 W 27 St, 4th fl, New York, NY 10001 *Tel:* 212-229-9925 *E-mail:* contact@monacellipress.com *Web Site:* www.monacellipress.com, pg 168

Monachello, Melissa, Quirk Books, 215 Church St, Philadelphia, PA 19106 *Tel:* 215-627-3581 *Fax:* 215-627-5220 *E-mail:* general@quirkbooks.com *Web Site:* www.quirkbooks.com, pg 211

Monaghan, Katie, Scribner, 1230 Avenue of the Americas, New York, NY 10020, pg 230

Monaghan, Kelly, The Intrepid Traveler, 152 Saltonstall Pkwy, Rear Entrance, East Haven, CT 06512 *Tel:* 203-469-0214 *Fax:* 203-469-0430 *E-mail:* admin@intrepidtraveler.com *Web Site:* www.intrepidtraveler.com, pg 134

Monaghan, Timothy, The Ledge Press Fiction Awards Competition, 40 Maple Ave, Bellport, NY 11713 *E-mail:* info@theledgemagazine.com *Web Site:* theledgemagazine.com, pg 716

Monaghan, Timothy, The Ledge Press Poetry Awards Competition, 40 Maple Ave, Bellport, NY 11713 *E-mail:* info@theledgemagazine.com *Web Site:* theledgemagazine.com, pg 717

Monaghan, Timothy, The Ledge Press Poetry Chapbook Competition, 40 Maple Ave, Bellport, NY 11713 *E-mail:* info@theledgemagazine.com *Web Site:* theledgemagazine.com, pg 717

Monahan, Sherry, Spur Awards, 271 CR 219, Encampment, WY 82325 *Tel:* 307-329-8942 *Fax:* 307-327-5465 *E-mail:* wwa.moulton@gmail.com *Web Site:* www.westernwriters.org, pg 744

Monahan, Sherry, Western Writers of America Inc (WWA), 271 CR 219, Encampment, WY 82325 *Tel:* 307-329-8942 *Fax:* 307-327-5465 *Web Site:* www.westernwriters.org, pg 638

Monfried, Andrea, Crown Publishing Group, c/o Random House Inc, 1745 Broadway, New York, NY 10019 *Tel:* 212-782-9000 *Toll Free Tel:* 888-264-1745 *Fax:* 212-940-7408 *Web Site:* www.randomhouse.com/crown, pg 72

Monfried, Andrea, The Monacelli Press, 236 W 27 St, 4th fl, New York, NY 10001 *Tel:* 212-229-9925 *E-mail:* contact@monacellipress.com *Web Site:* www.monacellipress.com, pg 168

Monfried, Lucia, Dial Books for Young Readers, 345 Hudson St, New York, NY 10014 *Tel:* 212-366-2000 *Fax:* 212-414-3396 *E-mail:* online@penguinputnam.com *Web Site:* www.penguinputnam.com; us.penguingroup.com, pg 79

Monge, Sr Marlyn Evangelina, Pauline Books & Media, 50 Saint Paul's Ave, Boston, MA 02130 *Tel:* 617-522-8911 *Toll Free Tel:* 800-876-4463 (orders); 800-836-9723 (cust serv) *Fax:* 617-541-9805 *E-mail:* orderentry@pauline.org (cust serv); editorial@paulinemedia.com (ms submissions) *Web Site:* www.pauline.org, pg 194

Monitello, Maren, Living Language, c/o Random House Inc, 1745 Broadway, New York, NY 10019 *Tel:* 212-782-9000 *Toll Free Tel:* 800-733-3000 (orders) *Toll Free Fax:* 800-659-2436 *E-mail:* livinglanguage@randomhouse.com *Web Site:* www.livinglanguage.com, pg 151

Monk, Steve, CCH Canadian Limited, A Wolters Kluwer Company, 90 Sheppard Ave E, Suite 300, Toronto, ON M2N 6X1, Canada *Tel:* 416-224-2224 *Toll Free Tel:* 800-268-4522 (CN & US cust serv) *Fax:* 416-224-2243 *Toll Free Fax:* 800-461-4131 *E-mail:* cservice@cch.ca (cust serv) *Web Site:* www.cch.ca, pg 498

Monroe, Elvira, Wide World Publishing, PO Box 476, San Carlos, CA 94070-0476 *Tel:* 650-593-2839 *Fax:* 650-595-0802 *E-mail:* wwpbl@aol.com *Web Site:* wideworldpublishing.com, pg 280

Monson, Ander, Diagram Essay Contest, University of Arizona, ML-445, PO Box 210067, Tucson, AZ 85721 *E-mail:* editor@thediagram.com *Web Site:* www.thediagram.com/contest.html, pg 700

Monson, Cheryl, EMC Publishing, 875 Montreal Way, St Paul, MN 55102 *Tel:* 651-290-2800 (corp) *Toll Free Tel:* 800-328-1452 *Fax:* 651-290-2899 *Toll Free Fax:* 800-328-4564 *E-mail:* educate@emcp.com *Web Site:* www.emcp.com, pg 87

Montag, John, Institute of Jesuit Sources (IJS), 3601 Lindell Blvd, St Louis, MO 63108 *Tel:* 314-633-4622 *Fax:* 314-633-4623 *E-mail:* ijs@jesuitsources.com *Web Site:* www.jesuitsources.com, pg 131

Montagni, Patricia, International Council of Shopping Centers (ICSC), 1221 Avenue of the Americas, 41st fl, New York, NY 10020-1099 *Tel:* 646-728-3800 *Fax:* 732-694-1755 *E-mail:* icsc@icsc.org *Web Site:* www.icsc.org, pg 132

Montague, Michelle, Harry N Abrams Inc, 115 W 18 St, 6th fl, New York, NY 10011 *Tel:* 212-206-7715 *Toll Free Tel:* 800-345-1359 *Fax:* 212-519-1210 *E-mail:* abrams@abramsbooks.com *Web Site:* www.abramsbooks.com, pg 3

Montecel, Dr Maria "Cuca" Robledo, Intercultural Development Research Association (IDRA), 5815 Callaghan Rd, Suite 101, San Antonio, TX 78228 *Tel:* 210-444-1710 *Fax:* 210-444-1714 *E-mail:* contact@idra.org *Web Site:* www.idra.org, pg 132

Montefinise, Angela, New York Public Library, Publications Office, 2nd fl, 188 Madison Ave, New York, NY 10016-4314 *Tel:* 917-275-6975 *Web Site:* www.nypl.org, pg 179

Monteforte, Greg, Professional Publications Inc (PPI), 1250 Fifth Ave, Belmont, CA 94002 *Tel:* 650-593-9119 *Toll Free Tel:* 800-426-1178 (orders) *Fax:* 650-592-4519 *E-mail:* info@ppi2pass.com *Web Site:* www.ppi2pass.com, pg 207

Montgomery, Kathleen Brooks, American Book Publishing, 14435-C Big Basin Way, No 155, Saratoga, CA 95070 *Tel:* 415-935-5082 *Toll Free Tel:* 800-684-8746 *E-mail:* info@american-book.com; orders@american-book.com *Web Site:* www.americanbookpublishing.com, pg 11

Montgomery, Michelle, Society for Industrial & Applied Mathematics, 3600 Market St, 6th fl, Philadelphia, PA 19104-2688 *Tel:* 215-382-9800 *Toll Free Tel:* 800-447-7426 *Fax:* 215-386-7999 *E-mail:* siambooks@siam.org *Web Site:* www.siam.org, pg 238

Moody, Douglas, Educational Directories Inc (EDI), 1025 W Wise Rd, Suite 101, Schaumburg, IL 60193 *Tel:* 847-891-1250 *Toll Free Tel:* 800-357-6183 *Fax:* 847-891-0945 *E-mail:* info@ediusa.com *Web Site:* www.ediusa.com, pg 85

Moody, Jeanne C, Beaver Wood Associates, 655 Alstead Center Rd, Alstead, NH 03602 *Tel:* 603-835-7900 *Fax:* 603-835-6279 *Web Site:* www.beaverwood.com, pg 541

Moody, Jessica, Grey House Publishing Inc™, 4919 Rte 22, Amenia, NY 12501 *Tel:* 518-789-8700 *Toll Free Tel:* 800-562-2139 *Fax:* 518-789-0556 *E-mail:* books@greyhouse.com *Web Site:* www.greyhouse.com, pg 108

Moody, Rodger, Gerald Cable Book Award, PO Box 3541, Eugene, OR 97403 *Tel:* 541-344-5060 *E-mail:* sfrpress@earthlink.net *Web Site:* www.silverfishreviewpress.com, pg 694

Moog, Bob, BePuzzled, 2030 Harrison St, San Francisco, CA 94110 *Tel:* 415-503-1600 *Toll Free Tel:* 800-347-4818 *Fax:* 415-503-0085 *E-mail:* info@ugames.com *Web Site:* www.ugames.com, pg 35

Mooney, Robert, Etruscan Press, Wilkes University, 84 W South St, Wilkes-Barre, PA 18766 *Tel:* 570-408-4546 *Fax:* 570-408-3333 *E-mail:* books@etruscanpress.org *Web Site:* www.etruscanpress.org, pg 90

Moore, Amber, Chalice Press, 483 E Lockwood Ave, Suite 100, St Louis, MO 63119 *Tel:* 314-231-8500 *Toll Free Tel:* 800-366-3383 *Fax:* 314-231-8524; 770-280-4039 (orders) *E-mail:* customerservice@chalicepress.com *Web Site:* www.chalicepress.com, pg 57

Moore, Anne, Candlewick Press, 99 Dover St, Somerville, MA 02144-2825 *Tel:* 617-661-3330 *Fax:* 617-661-0565 *E-mail:* bigbear@candlewick.com *Web Site:* www.candlewick.com, pg 51

Moore, Berwyn, Gannon University's High School Poetry Contest, Gannon University, Dept of English, 109 University Sq, Erie, PA 16541 *Tel:* 814-871-7504 *Web Site:* www.gannon.edu/departmental/english/poetry.asp, pg 706

Moore, Brian, Houghton Mifflin Harcourt, 222 Berkeley St, Boston, MA 02116-3764 *Tel:* 617-351-5000 *Toll Free Tel:* 800-225-5425 (Pre-K-8); 800-462-6595 (6–12; Advanced & Electives); 800-289-4490 (Specialized Curriculum: Great Source, Rigby, Saxon, Steck-Vaughn; Homeschool; Adult Ed); 800-323-9540 (Assessment: Riverside Publishing); 888-391-3245 (SkillsTutor); 888-242-6747 option 2 (Destination Series; Classroom Connect; Earobics; Edmark; Learning Village; Riverdeep); 800-225-3362 (Houghton Mifflin Harcourt Trade & Reference Publishers); 800-225-5800 (Heinemann) *Fax:* 617-351-1125 *Web Site:* www.hmhco.com, pg 123

Moore, Brian, Houghton Mifflin Harcourt Trade & Reference Division, 222 Berkeley St, Boston, MA 02116-3764 *Tel:* 617-351-5000 *Toll Free Tel:* 800-225-3362 *Web Site:* www.houghtonmifflinbooks.com, pg 124

Moore, Claudette, Moore Literary Agency, 10 State St, Suite 210, Newburyport, MA 01950 *Tel:* 978-465-9015 *Fax:* 978-465-6653, pg 586

Moore, Declan, National Geographic Books, 1145 17 St NW, Washington, DC 20036-4688 *Tel:* 202-857-7000 *Fax:* 202-857-7670 *Web Site:* www.nationalgeographic.com, pg 174

Moore, Declan, National Geographic Society, 1145 17 St NW, Washington, DC 20036-4688 *Tel:* 202-857-7000 *Fax:* 202-429-5727 *Web Site:* www.nationalgeographic.com, pg 175

Moore, Dinty W, Ohio University, English Dept, Creative Writing Program, Ohio University, English Dept, Ellis Hall, Athens, OH 45701 *Tel:* 740-593-2838 (English Dept) *Fax:* 740-593-2832 *E-mail:* english.department@ohio.edu *Web Site:* english.ohiou.edu, pg 680

Moore, Heather, Sourcebooks Inc, 1935 Brookdale Rd, Suite 139, Naperville, IL 60563 *Tel:* 630-961-3900 *Toll Free Tel:* 800-432-7444 *Fax:* 630-961-2168 *E-mail:* info@sourcebooks.com; customersupport@sourcebooks.com *Web Site:* www.sourcebooks.com, pg 240

Moore, Kelly, Canadian Library Association (CLA) (Association Canadienne des bibliotheques), 1150 Morrison Dr, Suite 400, Ottawa, ON K2H 8S9, Canada *Tel:* 613-232-9625 *Fax:* 613-563-9895 *E-mail:* info@cla.ca *Web Site:* www.cla.ca, pg 620

Moore, Kelly, The Young Adult Book Award, 1150 Morrison Dr, Suite 400, Ottawa, ON K2H 8S9, Canada *Tel:* 613-232-9625 *Fax:* 613-563-9895 *E-mail:* info@cla.ca *Web Site:* www.cla.ca, pg 752

Moore, Kenneth, IEEE Press, 445 Hoes Lane, Piscataway, NJ 08854 *Tel:* 732-562-3418 *Fax:* 732-562-1746 *E-mail:* pressbooks@ieee.org (proposals & info) *Web Site:* www.ieee.org/press, pg 127

Moore, Leander, Marshall Cavendish Corp, 99 White Plains Rd, Tarrytown, NY 10591-9001 *Tel:* 914-332-8888 *Toll Free Tel:* 800-821-9881 *Fax:* 914-332-8102 *E-mail:* customerservice@marshallcavendish.com; mcc@marshallcavendish.com *Web Site:* marshallcavendish.us; marshallcavendishdigital.com; marshallcavendishebooks.com, pg 158

Moore, Lisa C, RedBone Press, PO Box 15571, Washington, DC 20003 *Tel:* 202-667-0392 *Fax:* 301-588-0588 *E-mail:* info@redbonepress.com *Web Site:* www.redbonepress.com, pg 216

Moore, Marie, Decker Publishing, 69 John St S, Suite 310, Hamilton, ON L8N 2B9, Canada *Tel:* 905-522-8526 *Toll Free Tel:* 855-647-6511 *Fax:* 905-522-9273 *E-mail:* customercare@deckerpublishing.com *Web Site:* www.deckerpublishing.com, pg 500

Moore, Marvin, Pacific Press Publishing Association, 1350 N Kings Rd, Nampa, ID 83687-3193 *Tel:* 208-465-2500 *Toll Free Tel:* 800-447-7377 *Fax:* 208-465-2531 *Web Site:* www.pacificpress.com, pg 190

Moore, Mary-Alice, Boyds Mills Press, 815 Church St, Honesdale, PA 18431 *Tel:* 570-253-1164 *Toll Free Tel:* 800-490-5111 *Fax:* 570-253-0179 *E-mail:* contact@boydsmillspress.com *Web Site:* www.boydsmillspress.com, pg 45

Moore, Mary-Alice, Front Street, 815 Church St, Honesdale, PA 18431 *Tel:* 570-253-1164 *Toll Free Tel:* 800-490-5111 *E-mail:* contact@boydsmillspress.com *Web Site:* www.frontstreetbooks.com, pg 100

Moore, Michael, Steerforth Press, 45 Lyme Rd, Suite 208, Hanover, NH 03755-1222 *Tel:* 603-643-4787 *Fax:* 603-643-4788 *E-mail:* info@steerforth.com *Web Site:* www.steerforth.com, pg 244

Moore, Nancy, Gerald & Cullen Rapp, 420 Lexington Ave, New York, NY 10170 *Tel:* 212-889-3337 *Fax:* 212-889-3341 *E-mail:* info@rappart.com *Web Site:* www.rappart.com, pg 602

Moore, Richard, Marshall Cavendish Corp, 99 White Plains Rd, Tarrytown, NY 10591-9001 *Tel:* 914-332-8888 *Toll Free Tel:* 800-821-9881 *Fax:* 914-332-8102 *E-mail:* customerservice@marshallcavendish.com; mcc@marshallcavendish.com *Web Site:* marshallcavendish.us; marshallcavendishdigital.com; marshallcavendishebooks.com, pg 158

Moore, Stacey, Zeig, Tucker & Theisen Inc, 3614 N 24 St, Phoenix, AZ 85016 *Tel:* 480-389-4342 *Toll Free Tel:* 800-666-2211 (orders) *Fax:* 602-944-8118 *E-mail:* marketing@zeigtucker.com *Web Site:* www.zeigtucker.com, pg 289

Moore, Stephen, Paul Kohner Agency, 9300 Wilshire Blvd, Suite 555, Beverly Hills, CA 90212 *Tel:* 310-550-1060 *Fax:* 310-276-1083, pg 580

Moore, Steve, Ram Publishing Co, 1881 W State St, Garland, TX 75042 *Tel:* 972-494-6151 *Toll Free Tel:* 800-527-4011 *Fax:* 972-494-1881 *E-mail:* sales@garrett.com *Web Site:* www.garrett.com, pg 212

Moore, Sylvia, Midmarch Arts Press, 300 Riverside Dr, New York, NY 10025-5239 *Tel:* 212-666-6990 *Web Site:* midmarchartspress.org, pg 166

Moore, Tim, Baha'i Publishing, 415 Linden Ave, Wilmette, IL 60091 *Tel:* 847-425-7950 *Fax:* 847-425-7951 *E-mail:* bpt@usbnc.org *Web Site:* books.bahai.us, pg 29

Moore, Tim, Financial Times Press & Wharton School Publishing, One Lake St, Upper Saddle River, NJ 07458 *Tel:* 201-236-7000 *Toll Free Tel:* 800-922-0579 (orders) *Web Site:* www.ftpress.com, pg 95

Moore-Anderson, Sheryl, HarperCollins Children's Books, 10 E 53 St, New York, NY 10022 *Tel:* 212-207-7000 *Web Site:* www.harpercollinschildrens.com, pg 113

Moore-Swafford, Angela, Southern Illinois University Press, 1915 University Press Dr, SIUC Mail Code 6806, Carbondale, IL 62901-4323 *Tel:* 618-453-2281 *Fax:* 618-453-1221 *E-mail:* custserv@press.uchicago.edu; rights@siu.edu *Web Site:* www.siupress.com, pg 240

Moorehead, Harold, Stanford University Press, 1450 Page Mill Rd, Palo Alto, CA 94304-1124 *Tel:* 650-723-9434 *Fax:* 650-725-3457 *E-mail:* info@sup.org *Web Site:* www.sup.org, pg 243

Mooser, Stephen, The Don Freeman Memorial Grant-In-Aid, 8271 Beverly Blvd, Los Angeles, CA 90048 *Tel:* 323-782-1010 *Fax:* 323-782-1892 *E-mail:* membership@scbwi.org; scbwi@scbwi.org *Web Site:* www.scbwi.org, pg 705

Morris, Candice E, Mercer University Press, 368 Orange St, Macon, GA 31201 *Tel:* 478-301-2880 *Toll Free Tel:* 866-895-1472 *Fax:* 478-301-2585 *E-mail:* mupressorders@mercer.edu *Web Site:* www.mupress.org, pg 164

Morris, David, Guideposts Book & Inspirational Media, 16 E 34 St, 12th fl, New York, NY 10016 *Tel:* 212-251-8100 *Toll Free Tel:* 800-431-2344 (cust serv) *Fax:* 212-684-0689 *Web Site:* guideposts.org, pg 109

Morris, Gary, David Black Agency, 335 Adams St, 27th fl, Suite 2707, Brooklyn, NY 11201 *Tel:* 718-852-5500 *Fax:* 718-852-5539 *Web Site:* www.davidblackagency.com, pg 562

Morris, Michael A, Cornell University Press, Sage House, 512 E State St, Ithaca, NY 14850 *Tel:* 607-277-2338 *Fax:* 607-277-2374 *E-mail:* cupressinfo@cornell.edu; cupress-sales@cornell.edu *Web Site:* www.cornellpress.cornell.edu, pg 67

Morris, Paul, PEN American Center, 588 Broadway, Suite 303, New York, NY 10012 *Tel:* 212-334-1660 *Fax:* 212-334-2181 *E-mail:* info@pen.org *Web Site:* www.pen.org, pg 633

Morris, Paul, The PEN Award for Poetry in Translation, 588 Broadway, Suite 303, New York, NY 10012 *Tel:* 212-334-1660 *Fax:* 212-334-2181 *E-mail:* awards@pen.org *Web Site:* www.pen.org, pg 732

Morris, Paul, PEN/Phyllis Naylor Working Writer Fellowship, 588 Broadway, Suite 303, New York, NY 10012 *Tel:* 212-334-1660 *Fax:* 212-334-2181 *E-mail:* awards@pen.org *Web Site:* www.pen.org, pg 733

Morris, Paul, PEN/Ralph Manheim Medal for Translation, 588 Broadway, Suite 303, New York, NY 10012 *Tel:* 212-334-1660 *Fax:* 212-334-2181 *E-mail:* awards@pen.org *Web Site:* www.pen.org, pg 733

Morris, Paul, PEN/Robert Bingham Fellowships for Writers, 588 Broadway, Suite 303, New York, NY 10012 *Tel:* 212-334-1660 *Fax:* 212-334-2181 *E-mail:* awards@pen.org *Web Site:* www.pen.org, pg 733

Morris, Paul, PEN Translation Prize, 588 Broadway, Suite 303, New York, NY 10012 *Tel:* 212-334-1660 *Fax:* 212-334-2181 *E-mail:* awards@pen.org *Web Site:* www.pen.org, pg 733

Morris, Richard, Janklow & Nesbit Associates, 445 Park Ave, New York, NY 10022 *Tel:* 212-421-1700 *Fax:* 212-980-3671 *E-mail:* info@janklow.com *Web Site:* www.janklowandnesbit.com, pg 578

Morris, Sherine, Mary Ann Liebert Inc, 140 Huguenot St, 3rd fl, New Rochelle, NY 10801-5215 *Tel:* 914-740-2100 *Toll Free Tel:* 800-654-3237 *Fax:* 914-740-2101 *E-mail:* info@liebertpub.com *Web Site:* www.liebertonline.com, pg 148

Morris-Babb, Meredith, University Press of Florida, 15 NW 15 St, Gainesville, FL 32603-2079 *Tel:* 352-392-1351 *Toll Free Tel:* 800-226-3822 (orders only) *Fax:* 352-392-0590 *Toll Free Fax:* 800-680-1955 (orders only) *E-mail:* info@upf.com *Web Site:* www.upf.com, pg 271

Morrisey, Stephenie, McLemore Prize, PO Box 571, Jackson, MS 39205-0571 *Tel:* 601-576-6850 *Fax:* 601-576-6975 *E-mail:* mhs@mdah.state.ms.us *Web Site:* www.mdah.state.ms.us, pg 723

Morrison, Charles, Prometheus Awards, 650 Castro St, Suite 120-433, Mountain View, CA 94041 *Tel:* 650-968-6319 *E-mail:* info@lfs.org *Web Site:* www.lfs.org, pg 736

Morrison, Henry, Henry Morrison Inc, PO Box 235, Bedford Hills, NY 10507-0235 *Tel:* 914-666-3500 *Fax:* 914-241-7846 *E-mail:* hmorrison1@aol.com, pg 586

Morrison, Jeff, LexisNexis Canada Inc, 123 Commerce Valley Dr E, Suite 700, Markham, ON L3T 7W8, Canada *Tel:* 905-479-2665 *Toll Free Tel:* 800-668-6481; 800-387-0899 (cust serv) *Fax:* 905-479-2826 *Toll Free Fax:* 800-461-3275 *E-mail:* orders@lexisnexis.ca; service@lexisnexis.ca (cust serv) *Web Site:* www.lexisnexis.ca, pg 511

Morrison, Marg Anne, Organization of Book Publishers of Ontario, 20 Maud St, No 401, Toronto, ON M5V 2M5, Canada *Tel:* 416-536-7584 *Fax:* 416-536-7692 *Web Site:* www.ontariobooks.ca, pg 633

Morrison, Margaret, Harlequin Enterprises Ltd, 225 Duncan Mill Rd, Don Mills, ON M3B 3K9, Canada *Tel:* 416-445-5860 *Toll Free Tel:* 888-432-4879; 800-370-5838 (ebook inquiries) *Fax:* 416-445-8655 *E-mail:* CustomerService@harlequin.com *Web Site:* www.harlequin.com, pg 508

Morrison, Michael, HarperCollins General Books Group, 10 E 53 St, New York, NY 10022 *Tel:* 212-207-7000 *Fax:* 212-207-7633 *Web Site:* www.harpercollins.com, pg 113

Morrison, Paula, Frog Books, 2526 Martin Luther King Jr Way, Berkeley, CA 94704 *Tel:* 510-549-4270 *Toll Free Tel:* 800-733-3000 (book orders only) *Fax:* 510-549-4276 *Toll Free Fax:* 800-659-2436 (orders) *E-mail:* orders@northatlanticbooks.com *Web Site:* www.northatlanticbooks.com, pg 99

Morrison, Paula, North Atlantic Books, 2526 Martin Luther King Jr Way, Berkeley, CA 94704 *Tel:* 510-549-4270 *Fax:* 510-549-4276 *Web Site:* www.northatlanticbooks.com, pg 180

Morrison, Richard, University of Minnesota Press, 111 Third Ave S, Suite 290, Minneapolis, MN 55401-2520 *Tel:* 612-627-1970 *Fax:* 612-627-1980 *E-mail:* ump@umn.edu *Web Site:* www.upress.umn.edu, pg 266

Morrison, Rusty, Omnidawn Publishing, 1632 Elm Ave, Richmond, CA 94805-1614 *Tel:* 510-237-5472 *Toll Free Tel:* 800-792-4957 *Fax:* 510-232-8525 *E-mail:* manager@omnidawn.com *Web Site:* www.omnidawn.com, pg 185

Morrison, Stephen, Picador, 175 Fifth Ave, 19th fl, New York, NY 10010 *Tel:* 646-307-5151 *Fax:* 212-253-9627 *E-mail:* firstname.lastname@picadorusa.com *Web Site:* www.picadorusa.com, pg 201

Morrison, William R, The Lieutenant-Governor's Medal for Historical Writing, PO Box 5254, Sta B, Victoria, BC V8R 6N4, Canada *E-mail:* writing@bchistory.ca *Web Site:* www.bchistory.ca, pg 717

Morrissey, Georgia A, Hyperion, 1500 Broadway, 3rd fl, New York, NY 10036 *Tel:* 212-536-6500 *Web Site:* hyperionbooks.com, pg 126

Morrissey, Jake, Riverhead Books (Hardcover), 375 Hudson St, New York, NY 10014 *Tel:* 212-366-2000 *E-mail:* online@penguinputnam.com *Web Site:* www.penguinputnam.com; us.penguingroup.com, pg 219

Morrow, Stephen, Dutton, 375 Hudson St, New York, NY 10014 *Tel:* 212-366-2000 *Fax:* 212-366-2262 *E-mail:* online@penguinputnam.com *Web Site:* www.penguinputnam.com; us.penguingroup.com, pg 83

Morse, John M, Merriam-Webster Inc, 47 Federal St, Springfield, MA 01102 *Tel:* 413-734-3134 *Toll Free Tel:* 800-828-1880 (orders & cust serv) *Fax:* 413-731-5979 (sales) *E-mail:* support@merriam-webster.com *Web Site:* www.merriam-webster.com, pg 165

Mortensen, Dee, Indiana University Press, 601 N Morton St, Bloomington, IN 47404-3797 *Tel:* 812-855-8817 *Toll Free Tel:* 800-842-6796 (orders only) *Fax:* 812-855-7931; 812-855-8507 *E-mail:* iupress@indiana.edu; iuporder@indiana.edu (orders) *Web Site:* www.iupress.indiana.edu, pg 129

Mortensen, Vivian, Friends of American Writers Awards, 506 Rose Ave, Des Plaines, IL 60016 *Tel:* 847-827-8339 *Web Site:* www.fawchicago.org, pg 706

Mortensen, Vivian, Juvenile Literary Awards/Young People's Literature Awards, 506 Rose Ave, Des Plaines, IL 60016 *Tel:* 847-827-8339 *Web Site:* www.fawchicago.org, pg 714

Mortimer, Frank, Oxford University Press USA, 198 Madison Ave, New York, NY 10016 *Tel:* 212-726-6000 *Toll Free Tel:* 800-451-7556 (orders); 800-445-9714 (cust serv) *Fax:* 919-677-1303 *E-mail:* custserv.us@oup.com *Web Site:* www.oup.com/us, pg 189

Mortimer, Lyle, Cedar Fort Inc, 2373 W 700 S, Springville, UT 84663 *Tel:* 801-489-4084 *Toll Free Tel:* 800-SKY-BOOK (759-2665) *Fax:* 801-489-1097 *Toll Free Fax:* 800-388-3727 *E-mail:* brycemortimer@cedarfort.com *Web Site:* www.cedarfort.com, pg 55

Mortimer, Michele, Darhansoff & Verrill, 236 W 26 St, Suite 802, New York, NY 10001-6736 *Tel:* 917-305-1300 *Fax:* 917-305-1400 *E-mail:* info@dvagency.com *Web Site:* www.dvagency.com, pg 567

Morton, David, Rizzoli International Publications Inc, 300 Park Ave S, 4th fl, New York, NY 10010-5399 *Tel:* 212-387-3400 *Toll Free Tel:* 800-522-6657 (orders only) *Fax:* 212-387-3535 *E-mail:* publicity@rizzoliusa.com *Web Site:* www.rizzoliusa.com, pg 219

Morton, Douglas, Morton Publishing Co, 925 W Kenyon Ave, Unit 12, Englewood, CO 80110 *Tel:* 303-761-4805 *Fax:* 303-762-9923 *E-mail:* contact@morton-pub.com *Web Site:* www.morton-pub.com, pg 170

Morton, Larry, Hal Leonard Corp, 7777 W Bluemound Rd, Milwaukee, WI 53213 *Tel:* 414-774-3630 *Toll Free Tel:* 800-524-4425 *Fax:* 414-774-3259 *E-mail:* sales@halleonard.com *Web Site:* www.halleonard.com; twitter.com/#!/HalleonardBooks, pg 111

Morton, Lisa, Horror Writers Association (HWA), 244 Fifth Ave, Suite 2767, New York, NY 10001 *E-mail:* hwa@horror.org *Web Site:* www.horror.org, pg 624

Mosberg, Stephen R, College Publishing, 12309 Lynwood Dr, Glen Allen, VA 23059 *Tel:* 804-364-8410 *Toll Free Tel:* 800-827-0723 *Fax:* 804-364-8408 *E-mail:* collegepub@mindspring.com *Web Site:* www.collegepublishing.us, pg 64

Mosbrook, Bill, Pathfinder Publishing Inc, 120 S Houghton Rd, Suite 138, Tucson, AZ 85748 *Tel:* 520-647-0158 *Toll Free Tel:* 800-977-2282 *Fax:* 520-647-0160 *Web Site:* www.pathfinderpublishing.com, pg 194

Mosbrook, Evelyn, Pathfinder Publishing Inc, 120 S Houghton Rd, Suite 138, Tucson, AZ 85748 *Tel:* 520-647-0158 *Toll Free Tel:* 800-977-2282 *Fax:* 520-647-0160 *Web Site:* www.pathfinderpublishing.com, pg 194

Moschovakis, Anna, Ugly Duckling Presse, The Old American Can Factory, 232 Third St, Suite E002, Brooklyn, NY 11215 *Tel:* 347-948-5170 *E-mail:* udp_mailbox@yahoo.com; info@uglyducklingpresse.org *Web Site:* www.uglyducklingpresse.org, pg 261

Moselle, Ben, Craftsman Book Co, 6058 Corte Del Cedro, Carlsbad, CA 92011 *Tel:* 760-438-7828 *Toll Free Tel:* 800-829-8123 *Fax:* 760-438-0398 *Web Site:* www.craftsman-book.com, pg 70

Moselle, Gary, Craftsman Book Co, 6058 Corte Del Cedro, Carlsbad, CA 92011 *Tel:* 760-438-7828 *Toll Free Tel:* 800-829-8123 *Fax:* 760-438-0398 *Web Site:* www.craftsman-book.com, pg 70

Moser, Margaret L, Editorial Freelancers Association (EFA), 71 W 23 St, 4th fl, New York, NY 10010-4102 *Tel:* 212-929-5400 *Toll Free Tel:* 866-929-5425 *Fax:* 212-929-5439 *Toll Free Fax:* 866-929-5439 *E-mail:* info@the-efa.org; office@the-efa.org *Web Site:* www.the-efa.org, pg 622

Moser, Philip, Biblo-Moser, PO Box 302, Cheshire, CT 06410-0302 *Tel:* 203-988-8100 *Fax:* 203-272-2308 *E-mail:* biblo.moser@snet.net, pg 37

Moses, James, Primary Research Group Inc, 2753 Broadway, Suite 156, New York, NY 10025 *Tel:* 212-736-2316 *Fax:* 212-412-9097 *E-mail:* primaryresearchgroup@gmail.com *Web Site:* www.primaryresearch.com, pg 206

Moskowitz, Kenneth, Practising Law Institute, 810 Seventh Ave, New York, NY 10019 *Tel:* 212-824-5700 *Toll Free Tel:* 800-260-4PLI (260-4754 cust serv) *Fax:* 212-265-4742 (intl) *Toll Free Fax:* 800-321-0093 (local) *E-mail:* info@pli.edu *Web Site:* www.pli.edu, pg 205

Mosley, Christine, Penguin Group (USA) LLC Sales, 375 Hudson St, New York, NY 10014 *Tel:* 212-366-2000 *E-mail:* online@penguinputnam.com *Web Site:* us.penguingroup.com, pg 197

Muzzarelli, Linda, Consumer Press, 13326 SW 28 St, Suite 102, Fort Lauderdale, FL 33330-1102 *Tel:* 954-370-9153 *Fax:* 954-472-1008 *E-mail:* info@consumerpress.com *Web Site:* consumerpress.com, pg 66

Myers, Charles T, University Press of Kansas, 2502 Westbrooke Circle, Lawrence, KS 66045-4444 *Tel:* 785-864-4154; 785-864-4155 (orders) *Fax:* 785-864-4586 *E-mail:* upress@ku.edu; upkorders@ku.edu (orders) *Web Site:* www.kansaspress.ku.edu, pg 271

Myers, Christopher S, Peter Lang Publishing Inc, 29 Broadway, 18th fl, New York, NY 10006-3223 *Tel:* 212-647-7706 *Toll Free Tel:* 800-770-5264 (cust serv) *Fax:* 212-647-7707 *Web Site:* www.peterlang.com, pg 143

Myers, Edward, Montemayor Press, 663 Hyland Hill Rd, Washington, VT 05675 *Tel:* 802-883-5081 *E-mail:* montepress@aol.com *Web Site:* www.montemayorpress.com, pg 169

Myers, Eric, The Spieler Agency, 154 W 57 St, Suite 135, New York, NY 10019 *Tel:* 212-757-4439 *Fax:* 212-333-2019 *E-mail:* spieleragency@spieleragency.com, pg 595

Myers, Janice, Wm B Eerdmans Publishing Co, 2140 Oak Industrial Dr NE, Grand Rapids, MI 49505 *Tel:* 616-459-4591 *Toll Free Tel:* 800-253-7521 *Fax:* 616-459-6540 *E-mail:* customerservice@eerdmans.com; sales@eerdmans.com *Web Site:* www.eerdmans.com, pg 86

Myers, Kaela, Random House Publishing Group, 1745 Broadway, New York, NY 10019 *Toll Free Tel:* 800-200-3552 *Web Site:* atrandom.com, pg 214

Myers, Katharine, Princeton Architectural Press, 37 E Seventh St, New York, NY 10003 *Tel:* 212-995-9620 *Toll Free Tel:* 800-722-6657 (dist); 800-759-0190 (sales) *Fax:* 212-995-9454 *E-mail:* sales@papress.com *Web Site:* www.papress.com, pg 206

Myers, Patricia, Stanford University Press, 1450 Page Mill Rd, Palo Alto, CA 94304-1124 *Tel:* 650-723-9434 *Fax:* 650-725-3457 *E-mail:* info@sup.org *Web Site:* www.sup.org, pg 243

Myers, Mrs Shawn, Bridge-Logos Inc, Bldg 200, Suite 220, 17750 NW 115 Ave, Alachua, FL 32615 *Tel:* 386-462-2525 *Toll Free Tel:* 800-631-5802 (orders) *Fax:* 386-462-2535 *Toll Free Fax:* 800-935-6467 *E-mail:* customerservice@bridgelogos.com; info@bridgelogos.com *Web Site:* www.bridgelogos.com, pg 47

Mylott, Paul M, Mill Mountain Theatre, Center in the Square, 2nd fl, One Market Sq SE, Roanoke, VA 24011-1437 *Tel:* 540-224-1250 (ext 7307) *Web Site:* www.millmountain.org, pg 723

Nachbaur, Fredric, Fordham University Press, 2546 Belmont Ave, University Box L, Bronx, NY 10458 *Tel:* 718-817-4795 *Fax:* 718-817-4785 *Web Site:* www.fordhampress.com, pg 97

Nackel, John, OptumInsight™, 12125 Technology Dr, Eden Prairie, MN 55334 *Tel:* 952-833-7100 *Toll Free Tel:* 888-445-8745; 800-765-6713 *Fax:* 952-833-7201 *E-mail:* insight@optum.com *Web Site:* www.optuminsight.com, pg 186

Naddaff, Ramona, Zone Books dba Urzone Inc, 1226 Prospect Ave, Brooklyn, NY 11218 *Tel:* 718-686-0048 *Toll Free Tel:* 800-405-1619 (orders & cust serv) *Fax:* 718-686-9045 *Toll Free Fax:* 800-406-9145 (orders) *E-mail:* orders@triliteral.org *Web Site:* www.zonebooks.org, pg 289

Nadeau, Jay, Bitingduck Press LLC, 1262 Sunnyoaks Cir, Altadena, CA 91001 *Tel:* 626-679-2494; 626-507-8033 *E-mail:* notifications@bitingduckpress.com *Web Site:* bitingduckpress.com, pg 38

Nadeau, Jay, Boson Books, 1262 Sunnyoaks Circle, Altadena, CA 91001 *Tel:* 626-507-8033 *Web Site:* www.bosonbooks.com, pg 44

Nadeau, Marie, Bitingduck Press LLC, 1262 Sunnyoaks Cir, Altadena, CA 91001 *Tel:* 626-679-2494; 626-507-8033 *E-mail:* notifications@bitingduckpress.com *Web Site:* bitingduckpress.com, pg 38

Nadell, Bonnie, Hill Nadell Literary Agency, 8899 Beverly Blvd, Suite 805, Los Angeles, CA 90048 *Tel:* 310-860-9605 *Fax:* 310-860-9672 *Web Site:* www.hillnadell.com, pg 577

Naeye, Robert, Sky Publishing, 90 Sherman St, Cambridge, MA 02140 *Tel:* 617-864-7360 *Toll Free Tel:* 866-644-1377 *Fax:* 617-864-6117 *E-mail:* info@skyandtelescope.com *Web Site:* www.skyandtelescope.com, pg 237

Nagel, Karen, Simon & Schuster Children's Publishing, 1230 Avenue of the Americas, New York, NY 10020 *Tel:* 212-698-7000 *Web Site:* KIDS.SimonandSchuster.com; TEEN.SimonandSchuster.com; simonandschuster.net; simonandschuster.biz, pg 235

Naggar, Jean V, Jean V Naggar Literary Agency Inc, 216 E 75 St, Suite 1-E, New York, NY 10021 *Tel:* 212-794-1082 *E-mail:* jvnla@jvnla.com *Web Site:* www.jvnla.com, pg 586

Nagler, Michelle, Random House Children's Books, 1745 Broadway, New York, NY 10019 *Tel:* 212-782-9000 *Toll Free Tel:* 800-200-3552 *Fax:* 212-782-9452 *Web Site:* randomhousekids.com, pg 213

Nagy, Sandor, CTB/McGraw-Hill, 20 Ryan Ranch Rd, Monterey, CA 93940-5703 *Tel:* 831-393-0700 *Toll Free Tel:* 800-538-9547 *Fax:* 831-393-7825 *Web Site:* www.ctb.com, pg 73

Naiburg, Irving B Jr, Ardent Media Inc, 522 E 82 St, Suite 1, New York, NY 10028 *Tel:* 212-861-1501 *Fax:* 212-861-0998 *E-mail:* ivyboxer@aol.com; ardentmedia@hotmail.com, pg 21

Nail, Dawson B, Warren Communications News Inc, 2115 Ward Ct NW, Washington, DC 20037 *Tel:* 202-872-9200 *Toll Free Tel:* 800-771-9202 *Fax:* 202-293-3435; 202-318-8350 *E-mail:* info@warren-news.com; newsroom@warren-news.com *Web Site:* www.warren-news.com, pg 276

Nail, Gaye, Warren Communications News Inc, 2115 Ward Ct NW, Washington, DC 20037 *Tel:* 202-872-9200 *Toll Free Tel:* 800-771-9202 *Fax:* 202-293-3435; 202-318-8350 *E-mail:* info@warren-news.com; newsroom@warren-news.com *Web Site:* www.warren-news.com, pg 276

Najar, Regeen Runes, Philosophical Library Inc, PO Box 251, New York, NY 10024 *Tel:* 212-886-1873; 212-873-6070 *Fax:* 212-873-6070 *E-mail:* editors@philosophicallibrary.com *Web Site:* philosophicallibrary.com, pg 201

Nakis, Aleka, Fun in the Sun, PO Box 430744, Miami, FL 33243 *Web Site:* www.frwriters.org, pg 669

Nalle, Sarah, Simon & Schuster, 1230 Avenue of the Americas, New York, NY 10020 *Tel:* 212-698-7000 *Toll Free Tel:* 800-223-2348 (cust serv); 800-223-2336 (orders) *Toll Free Fax:* 800-943-9831 (orders) *Web Site:* www.simonandschuster.com, pg 234

Nam, Helen, Sourcebooks Inc, 1935 Brookdale Rd, Suite 139, Naperville, IL 60563 *Tel:* 630-961-3900 *Toll Free Tel:* 800-432-7444 *Fax:* 630-961-2168 *E-mail:* info@sourcebooks.com; customersupport@sourcebooks.com *Web Site:* www.sourcebooks.com, pg 240

Nantier, Terry, NBM Publishing Inc, 40 Exchange Place, Suite 1308, New York, NY 10005 *Tel:* 212-643-5407 *Toll Free Tel:* 800-886-1223 *Fax:* 212-643-1545 *E-mail:* admin@nbmpub.com *Web Site:* www.nbmpub.com, pg 176

Nantier, Terry, Papercutz, 40 Exchange Place, Suite 1308, New York, NY 10005 *Tel:* 212-643-5407 *Toll Free Tel:* 800-886-1223 *Fax:* 212-643-1545 *E-mail:* papercutz@papercutz.com *Web Site:* www.papercutz.com, pg 192

Naples, Mary Ann, Rodale Books, 400 S Tenth St, Emmaus, PA 18098 *Tel:* 610-967-5171 *Toll Free Tel:* 800-848-4735 (cust serv) *E-mail:* customerservice@rodale.com *Web Site:* www.rodaleinc.com, pg 220

Napoli, Philip M, Fordham University, Graduate School of Business Administration, 113 W 60 St, New York, NY 10023 *Fax:* 212-636-7076 *Web Site:* www.bnet.fordham.edu, pg 705

Napp, Jessica, Rizzoli International Publications Inc, 300 Park Ave S, 4th fl, New York, NY 10010-5399 *Tel:* 212-387-3400 *Toll Free Tel:* 800-522-6657 (orders only) *Fax:* 212-387-3535 *E-mail:* publicity@rizzoliusa.com *Web Site:* www.rizzoliusa.com, pg 219

Nappi, Ralph J, Graphic Arts Education & Research Foundation (GAERF), 1899 Preston White Dr, Reston, VA 20191 *Tel:* 703-264-7200 *Toll Free Tel:* 866-381-9839 *Fax:* 703-620-3165 *E-mail:* gaerf@npes.org *Web Site:* www.gaerf.org, pg 641

Nappi, Ralph J, NPES The Association for Suppliers of Printing, Publishing & Converting Technologies, 1899 Preston White Dr, Reston, VA 20191 *Tel:* 703-264-7200 *Fax:* 703-620-0994 *E-mail:* npes@npes.org *Web Site:* www.npes.org, pg 632

Nardin, Theodore C, Demos Medical Publishing LLC, 11 W 42 St, New York, NY 10036 *Tel:* 212-683-0072 *Toll Free Tel:* 800-532-8663 *Fax:* 212-683-0118 *E-mail:* info@demosmedpub.com; orderdept@demosmedpub.com *Web Site:* www.demosmedpub.com, pg 78

Nardin, Theodore C, Springer Publishing Co LLC, 11 W 42 St, 15th fl, New York, NY 10036-8002 *Tel:* 212-431-4370 *Toll Free Tel:* 877-687-7476 *Fax:* 212-941-7842 *E-mail:* marketing@springerpub.com; cs@springerpub.com (orders); editorial@springerpub.com *Web Site:* www.springerpub.com, pg 241

Nasaw, David, James Fenimore Cooper Prize, 603 Fayerweather, MC 2538, New York, NY 10027 *Tel:* 212-854-6495 *E-mail:* amhistsociety@columbia.edu *Web Site:* sah.columbia.edu, pg 698

Nasaw, David, Allan Nevins Prize, 603 Fayerweather, MC 2538, New York, NY 10027 *Tel:* 212-854-6495 *E-mail:* amhistsociety@columbia.edu *Web Site:* sah.columbia.edu, pg 728

Nasaw, David, Francis Parkman Prize, 603 Fayerweather, MC 2538, New York, NY 10027 *Tel:* 212-854-6495 *E-mail:* amhistsociety@columbia.edu *Web Site:* sah.columbia.edu, pg 732

Nash, Leigh, Coach House Books, 80 bpNichol Lane, Toronto, ON M5S 3J4, Canada *Tel:* 416-979-2217 *Toll Free Tel:* 800-367-6360 (outside Toronto) *Fax:* 416-977-1158 *E-mail:* mail@chbooks.com *Web Site:* www.chbooks.com, pg 499

Nathan, Terry, Benjamin Franklin Awards™, 1020 Manhattan Beach Blvd, Suite 204, Manhattan Beach, CA 90266 *Tel:* 310-546-1818 *Fax:* 310-546-3939 *E-mail:* info@ibpa-online.org *Web Site:* www.ibpa-online.org; ibpabenjaminfranklinawards.com, pg 690

Nathan, Terry, IBPA, the Independent Book Publishers Association, 1020 Manhattan Beach Blvd, Suite 204, Manhattan Beach, CA 90266 *Tel:* 310-546-1818 *Fax:* 310-546-3939 *E-mail:* info@ibpa-online.org *Web Site:* www.ibpa-online.org, pg 624

Naughton, Diane, HarperCollins Children's Books, 10 E 53 St, New York, NY 10022 *Tel:* 212-207-7000 *Web Site:* www.harpercollinschildrens.com, pg 113

Nauman, April, Friends of American Writers Awards, 506 Rose Ave, Des Plaines, IL 60016 *Tel:* 847-827-8339 *Web Site:* www.fawchicago.org, pg 706

Navaretta, Cynthia, Midmarch Arts Press, 300 Riverside Dr, New York, NY 10025-5239 *Tel:* 212-666-6990 *Web Site:* midmarchartspress.org, pg 166

Navarre, Randy, Roncorp Music, PO Box 517, Glenmoore, PA 19343 *Tel:* 610-942-2370 *Fax:* 610-942-0660 *E-mail:* info@nemusicpub.com *Web Site:* www.nemusicpub.com, pg 220

Navratil, Christopher, Running Press Book Publishers, 2300 Chestnut St, Philadelphia, PA 19103-4399 *Tel:* 215-567-5080 *Toll Free Tel:* 800-343-4499 (cust serv & orders) *Fax:* 215-568-2919 *Toll Free Fax:* 800-453-2884 (cust serv & orders) *E-mail:* perseus.promos@perseusbooks.com *Web Site:* www.runningpress.com, pg 222

Nawalinski, Beth, Association of Library Trustees, Advocates, Friends & Foundations (ALTAFF), 109 S 13 St, Suite 3-N, Philadelphia, PA 19107 *Tel:* 312-280-2161 *Toll Free Tel:* 800-545-2433 (ext

2161) *Fax:* 215-545-3821 *E-mail:* altaff@ala.org *Web Site:* www.ala.org/ala/mgrps/divs/altaff/index.cfm, pg 617

Nawrocki, Sarah, Trinity University Press, One Trinity Place, San Antonio, TX 78212-7200 *Tel:* 210-999-8884 *Fax:* 210-999-8838 *E-mail:* books@trinity.edu *Web Site:* www.tupress.org, pg 259

Nayer, Rick, Berkley Books, 375 Hudson St, New York, NY 10014 *Tel:* 212-366-2000 *Fax:* 212-366-2666 *E-mail:* online@penguinputnam.com *Web Site:* www.penguinputnam.com; us.penguingroup.com, pg 35

Nayer, Rick, Berkley Publishing Group, 375 Hudson St, New York, NY 10014 *Tel:* 212-366-2000 *Fax:* 212-366-2385 *E-mail:* online@penguinputnam.com *Web Site:* us.penguingroup.com, pg 36

Nayer, Rick, NAL, 375 Hudson St, New York, NY 10014 *Tel:* 212-366-2000 *E-mail:* online@penguinputnam.com *Web Site:* www.penguinputnam.com; us.penguingroup.com, pg 172

Nayeri, Daniel, Houghton Mifflin Harcourt Trade & Reference Division, 222 Berkeley St, Boston, MA 02116-3764 *Tel:* 617-351-5000 *Toll Free Tel:* 800-225-3362 *Web Site:* www.houghtonmifflinbooks.com, pg 124

Nazarian, Vera, Norilana Books, PO Box 209, Highgate Center, VT 05459-0209 *E-mail:* service@norilana.com *Web Site:* www.norilana.com, pg 180

Neal, John Vincent, Neal-Schuman Publishers Inc, 100 William St, Suite 2004, New York, NY 10038 *Tel:* 212-925-8650 *Toll Free Tel:* 866-NS-BOOKS (672-6657) *Fax:* 212-219-8916 *Toll Free Fax:* 877-231-6980 *E-mail:* info@neal-schuman.com *Web Site:* www.neal-schuman.com, pg 176

Neal, Rae, Multicultural Publications Inc, 936 Slosson St, Akron, OH 44320 *Tel:* 330-865-9578 *Fax:* 330-865-9578 *E-mail:* multiculturalpub@prodigy.net, pg 171

Nealeigh, Robert, FaithWords, 12 Cadillac Dr, Suite 480, Brentwood, TN 37027 *Tel:* 615-221-0996 *Fax:* 615-221-0962 *Web Site:* www.hachettebookgroup.com, pg 92

Nealon, Terry, Houghton Mifflin Harcourt, 222 Berkeley St, Boston, MA 02116-3764 *Tel:* 617-351-5000 *Toll Free Tel:* 800-225-5125 (Pre-K-8), 800-462-6595 (6–12; Advanced & Electives); 800-289-4490 (Specialized Curriculum: Great Source, Rigby, Saxon, Steck-Vaughn; Homeschool; Adult Ed); 800-323-9540 (Assessment: Riverside Publishing); 888-391-3245 (SkillsTutor); 888-242-6747 option 2 (Destination Series; Classroom Connect; Earobics; Edmark; Learning Village; Riverdeep); 800-225-3362 (Houghton Mifflin Harcourt Trade & Reference Publishers); 800-225-5800 (Heinemann) *Fax:* 617-351-1125 *Web Site:* www.hmhco.com, pg 123

Neault, Sylvain, Groupe Sogides Inc, 955 rue Amherst, Montreal, QC H2L 3K4, Canada *Tel:* 514-523-1182 *Toll Free Tel:* 800-361-4806 *Fax:* 514-597-0370 *E-mail:* edhomme@sogides.com *Web Site:* www.sogides.com; www.edhomme.com, pg 507

Neaverth, Kathryn-Kingsbury, Amherst Media Inc, 175 Rano St, Suite 200, Buffalo, NY 14207 *Tel:* 716-874-4450 *Toll Free Tel:* 800-622-3278 *Fax:* 716-874-4508 *E-mail:* marketing@amherstmedia.com *Web Site:* www.amherstmedia.com, pg 17

Necarsulmer, Edward IV, Dunow, Carlson & Lerner Literary Agency Inc, 27 W 20 St, Suite 1107, New York, NY 10011 *Tel:* 212-645-7606 *E-mail:* mail@dclagency.com *Web Site:* www.dclagency.com, pg 569

Nedelcu, Maria, Teora USA LLC, 505 Hampton Park Blvd, Unit G, Capitol Heights, MD 20743 *Tel:* 301-986-6990 *Toll Free Tel:* 800-974-2105 *Fax:* 301-350-5480 *Toll Free Fax:* 800-358-3754 *E-mail:* 2010@teora.com *Web Site:* www.teora.com, pg 252

Neel, David, Texas A&M University Press, John H Lindsey Bldg, Lewis St, 4354 TAMU, College Station, TX 77843-4354 *Tel:* 979-845-1436 *Toll Free Tel:* 800-826-8911 (orders) *Fax:* 979-847-8752 *Toll Free Fax:* 888-617-2421 (orders) *E-mail:* upress@tamu.edu *Web Site:* www.tamupress.com, pg 253

Neel, Thomas Stephen, Ohio Genealogical Society, 611 State Rte 97 W, Bellville, OH 44813-8813 *Tel:* 419-886-1903 *Fax:* 419-886-0092 *E-mail:* ogs@ogs.org *Web Site:* www.ogs.org, pg 184

Neely, Judith Illov, F A Davis Co, 1915 Arch St, Philadelphia, PA 19103 *Tel:* 215-568-2270 *Toll Free Tel:* 800-523-4049 *Fax:* 215-568-5065 *E-mail:* info@fadavis.com *Web Site:* www.fadavis.com, pg 76

Neesemann, Cynthia, CS International Literary Agency, 43 W 39 St, New York, NY 10018 *Tel:* 212-921-1610; 212-391-9208 *E-mail:* query@csliterary.com; csliterary08@gmail.com *Web Site:* www.csliterary.com, pg 544

Neff, Amber, University of Chicago, Graham School of General Studies, 1427 E 60 St, Chicago, IL 60637 *Tel:* 773-702-1722 *Fax:* 773-702-6814 *Web Site:* www.grahamschool.uchicago.edu, pg 681

Nehmer, Kathy, Educators Progress Service Inc, 214 Center St, Randolph, WI 53956 *Tel:* 920-326-3126 *Toll Free Tel:* 888-951-4469 *Fax:* 920-326-3127 *E-mail:* epsinc@centurytel.net *Web Site:* www.freeteachingaids.com, pg 85

Neibauer, Nathan, Neibauer Press & Church Supplier, 20 Industrial Dr, Warminster, PA 18974 *Tel:* 215-322-6200 *Toll Free Tel:* 800-322-6203 *Fax:* 215-322-2495 *E-mail:* sales@neibauer.com; sales@churchsupplier.com *Web Site:* www.churchsupplier.com, pg 176

Neimark, Nina, Nina Neimark Editorial Services, 543 Third St, Brooklyn, NY 11215 *Tel:* 718-499-6804 *E-mail:* pneimark@hotmail.com, pg 552

Nellis, Muriel G, Literary & Creative Artists Inc, 3543 Albemarle St NW, Washington, DC 20008-4213 *Tel:* 202-362-4688 *Fax:* 202-362-8875 *E-mail:* lca9643@lcadc.com (queries, no attachments) *Web Site:* www.lcadc.com, pg 582

Nelson, Bonita K, BK Nelson Inc Lecture Bureau, 1565 Paseo Vida, Palm Springs, CA 92264 *Tel:* 760-778-8800 *Fax:* 760-778-6242 *E-mail:* bknelson4@cs.com *Web Site:* www.bknelsonlecturebureau.com; www.bknelson.com; www.bknelsonmovieproduction.com, pg 605

Nelson, Bonita K, BK Nelson Inc Literary Agency, 1565 Paseo Vida, Palm Springs, CA 92264 *Tel:* 760-778-8800 *Fax:* 760-778-6242 *E-mail:* bknelson4@cs.com *Web Site:* www.bknelson.com; www.bknelsonlecturebureau.com; www.bknelsonmovieproduction.com, pg 587

Nelson, Dan, Visual Media Alliance (VMA), 665 Third St, Suite 500, San Francisco, CA 94107-1926 *Tel:* 415-495-8242 *Toll Free Tel:* 800-659-3363 *Fax:* 415-543-7790 *Toll Free Fax:* 800-824-1911 *E-mail:* info@vma.bz *Web Site:* vma.bz; www.visualmediaalliance.org, pg 638

Nelson, Danielle, Spring Tree Press, 571 Locust Point Rd, Locust, NJ 07760 *Tel:* 732-872-8002 *Fax:* 732-872-6967 *E-mail:* springtreepress@gmail.com *Web Site:* www.springtreepress.com; www.tyrrc.com, pg 529

Nelson, David C, Waterside Productions Inc, 2055 Oxford Ave, Cardiff, CA 92007 *Tel:* 760-632-9190 *Fax:* 760-632-9295 *E-mail:* admin@waterside.com *Web Site:* www.waterside.com, pg 598

Nelson, Diane, DC Entertainment, 1700 Broadway, New York, NY 10019 *Tel:* 212-636-5400 *Toll Free Tel:* 800-887-6789 *Fax:* 212-636-5979 *E-mail:* dccomics@cambeywest.com *Web Site:* www.dccomics.com; www.madmag.com; www.dcentertainment.com, pg 76

Nelson, Eric, Susan Rabiner Literary Agency Inc, 315 W 39 St, Suite 1501, New York, NY 10018-3907 *Web Site:* RabinerLit.com, pg 589

Nelson, Jandy, Manus & Associates Literary Agency Inc, 425 Sherman Ave, Suite 200, Palo Alto, CA 94306 *Tel:* 650-470-5151 *Fax:* 650-470-5159 *E-mail:* manuslit@manuslit.com *Web Site:* www.manuslit.com, pg 583

Nelson, Jeffrey O, ISI Books, 3901 Centerville Rd, Wilmington, DE 19807-1938 *Tel:* 302-652-4600 *Toll Free Tel:* 800-526-7022 *Fax:* 302-652-1760 *E-mail:* info@isi.org; isibooks@isi.org *Web Site:* www.isibooks.org, pg 134

Nelson, Kristin, Nelson Literary Agency LLC, 1732 Wazee St, Suite 207, Denver, CO 80202-1284 *Tel:* 303-292-2805 *E-mail:* query@nelsonagency.com *Web Site:* www.nelsonagency.com, pg 587

Nelson, Stephen R, Sheffield Publishing Co, 9009 Antioch Rd, Salem, WI 53168 *Tel:* 262-843-2281 *Fax:* 262-843-3683 *E-mail:* info@spcbooks.com *Web Site:* www.spcbooks.com, pg 233

Nelson, Steve, APS PRESS, 3340 Pilot Knob Rd, St Paul, MN 55121 *Tel:* 651-454-7250 *Toll Free Tel:* 800-328-7560 *Fax:* 651-454-0766 *E-mail:* aps@scisoc.org *Web Site:* www.shopapspress.org, pg 21

Nelson, Steven, American Phytopathological Society (APS), 3340 Pilot Knob Rd, St Paul, MN 55121 *Tel:* 651-454-7250 *Toll Free Tel:* 800-328-7560 *Fax:* 651-454-0766 *E-mail:* aps@scisoc.org *Web Site:* www.apsnet.org, pg 15

Nelson, Steven C, AACC International, 3340 Pilot Knob Rd, St Paul, MN 55121 *Tel:* 651-454-7250 *Fax:* 651-454-0766 *E-mail:* aacc@scisoc.org *Web Site:* www.aaccnet.org, pg 2

Nelson, Steven C, Eagan Press, 3340 Pilot Knob Rd, St Paul, MN 55121 *Tel:* 651-454-7250 *Toll Free Tel:* 800-328-7560 *Fax:* 651-454-0766 *E-mail:* aacc@scisoc.org *Web Site:* www.aaccnet.org, pg 83

Nemeth, Terence, Theatre Communications Group, 520 Eighth Ave, 24th fl, New York, NY 10018-4156 *Tel:* 212-609-5900 *Fax:* 212-609-5901 *E-mail:* tcg@tcg.org *Web Site:* www.tcg.org, pg 254

Nephew, John, Trident Inc, 885 Pierce Butler Rte, St Paul, MN 55104 *Tel:* 651-638-0077 *Fax:* 651-638-0084 *E-mail:* info@atlas-games.com *Web Site:* www.atlas-games.com, pg 258

Nericcio, Dr Bill, San Diego State University Press, Arts & Letters 283, 5500 Campanile Dr, San Diego, CA 92182-6020 *Tel:* 619-594-6220 (orders) *Web Site:* sdsupress.sdsu.edu, pg 225

Nerya, Javier, McGraw-Hill International Publishing Group, 2 Penn Plaza, New York, NY 10121 *Tel:* 212-904-2000 *Web Site:* www.mcgraw-hill.com, pg 161

Nesbit, Lynn, Janklow & Nesbit Associates, 445 Park Ave, New York, NY 10022 *Tel:* 212-421-1700 *Fax:* 212-980-3671 *E-mail:* info@janklow.com *Web Site:* www.janklowandnesbit.com, pg 578

Nesbitt, Becky, Howard Books, 216 Centerview Dr, Suite 303, Brentwood, TN 37027 *Tel:* 615-873-2080 *Fax:* 615-370-3834 *E-mail:* howardbooks@simonandschuster.com (info) *Web Site:* www.howardpublishing.com, pg 124

Nesbitt, Bruce, Nesbitt Graphics Inc, 555 Virginia Dr, Fort Washington, PA 19034 *Tel:* 215-591-9125 *Fax:* 215-591-9093 *Web Site:* www.nesbittgraphics.com, pg 552

Nesbitt, Harry J III, Nesbitt Graphics Inc, 555 Virginia Dr, Fort Washington, PA 19034 *Tel:* 215-591-9125 *Fax:* 215-591-9093 *Web Site:* www.nesbittgraphics.com, pg 552

Nettleton, Kathleen Calhoun, Pelican Publishing Co, 1000 Burmaster St, Gretna, LA 70053-2246 *Tel:* 504-368-1175 *Toll Free Tel:* 800-843-1724 *Fax:* 504-368-1195 *E-mail:* sales@pelicanpub.com (sales); office@pelicanpub.com (permission); promo@pelicanpub.com (publicity) *Web Site:* www.pelicanpub.com, pg 196

Neubauer, Erica, Letterbox/Papyrus of London Publishers USA, 10501 Broom Hill Dr, Suite 1-F, Las Vegas, NV 89134-7339 *Tel:* 702-256-3838 *E-mail:* lb27383@cox.net, pg 147

Neubauer, Mrs H, Letterbox/Papyrus of London Publishers USA, 10501 Broom Hill Dr, Suite 1-F, Las Vegas, NV 89134-7339 *Tel:* 702-256-3838 *E-mail:* lb27383@cox.net, pg 147

Neuburger, Rebecca, Police Executive Research Forum, 1120 Connecticut Ave NW, Suite 930, Washington, DC 20036 *Tel:* 202-466-7820 *Fax:* 202-466-7826 *E-mail:* perf@policeforum.org *Web Site:* www.policeforum.org, pg 204

Neufeld, J, Safari Press, 15621 Chemical Lane, Bldg B, Huntington Beach, CA 92649 *Tel:* 714-894-9080 *Toll Free Tel:* 800-451-4788 *Fax:* 714-894-4949 *E-mail:* info@safaripress.com *Web Site:* www.safaripress.com, pg 223

Neumann, Rachel, Parallax Press, 2236-B Sixth St, Berkeley, CA 94710 *Tel:* 510-525-0101 *Toll Free Tel:* 800-863-5290 (orders) *Fax:* 510-525-7129 *E-mail:* info@parallax.org *Web Site:* www.parallax.org, pg 193

Neusner, Dena, Behrman House Inc, 11 Edison Place, Springfield, NJ 07081 *Tel:* 973-379-7200 *Toll Free Tel:* 800-221-2755 *Fax:* 973-379-7280 *E-mail:* behrmanhouse@gmail.com; customersupport@behrmanhouse.com *Web Site:* www.behrmanhouse.com, pg 34

Nevins, Alan, Renaissance Literary & Talent, PO Box 17379, Beverly Hills, CA 90209 *Tel:* 323-848-8305 *E-mail:* query@renaissancemgmt.net, pg 590

Nevins, Larry, HarperCollins Publishers, 10 E 53 St, New York, NY 10022 *Tel:* 212-207-7000 *Fax:* 212-207-7145 *Web Site:* www.harpercollins.com, pg 113

Nevraumont, Peter N, Nevraumont Publishing Co, 259 E 134 St, 2nd fl loft, Bronx, NY 10454-4405 *Tel:* 718-993-6192 *E-mail:* info@nevraumontpublishing.com *Web Site:* nevraumontpublishing.com, pg 177

Newbold, Robert, ProChain Press, 3460 Commission Ct, No 301, Lake Ridge, VA 22192 *Tel:* 703-490-8821 *Fax:* 703-494-1414 *E-mail:* publishing@prochain.com *Web Site:* prochain.com, pg 529

Newborn, Andrea, The Reader's Digest Association Inc, 750 Third Ave, New York, NY 10017 *Tel:* 914-238-1000; 646-293-6284 *Toll Free Tel:* 800-310-6261 (cust serv) *Fax:* 914-238-4559 *Web Site:* www.rd.com; www.rda.com, pg 215

Newborn, Ms Sasha "Birdie", Bandanna Books, 1212 Punta Gorda St, No 13, Santa Barbara, CA 93103 *Tel:* 805-899-2145 *E-mail:* bandanna@cox.net *Web Site:* www.bandannabooks.com; www.shakespeareplaybook.com; bookdoc.us, pg 30

Newbury, Saralinda, Whitaker House, 1030 Hunt Valley Circle, New Kensington, PA 15068 *Tel:* 724-334-7000 *Toll Free Tel:* 877-793-9800 *Fax:* 724-334-1200 *Toll Free Fax:* 800-765-1960 *E-mail:* publisher@whitakerhouse.com *Web Site:* whitakerhouse.com, pg 280

Newcomb, Doug, Special Libraries Association (SLA), 331 S Patrick St, Alexandria, VA 22314-3501 *Tel:* 703-647-4900 *Fax:* 703-647-4901 *E-mail:* sla@sla.org *Web Site:* www.sla.org, pg 637

Newcomb, Trish, The McDonald & Woodward Publishing Co, 431 E College St, Granville, OH 43023 *Tel:* 740-321-1140 *Toll Free Tel:* 800-233-8787 *Fax:* 740-321-1141 *E-mail:* mwpubco@mwpubco.com *Web Site:* www.mwpubco.com, pg 160

Newell, Patricia, North Country Press, 126 Main St, Unity, ME 04988 *Tel:* 207-948-2208 *Fax:* 207-948-9000 *E-mail:* info@northcountrypress.com *Web Site:* www.northcountrypress.com, pg 181

Newhouse, Ryan, Green Sugar Press, 2200 E Devon Ave, Suite 340, Des Plaines, IL 60018-4503 *Tel:* 773-580-7780; 615-254-2402 (orders); 615-254-2488 (returns) *Fax:* 615-254-2405 (orders); 615-254-2405 (returns) *Toll Free Fax:* 866-270-4100 *E-mail:* order@greensugarpress.com *Web Site:* www.greensugarpress.com, pg 107

Newlin, Bill, Avalon Travel Publishing, 1700 Fourth St, Berkeley, CA 94710-1711 *Tel:* 510-595-3664 *Fax:* 510-595-4228 *Web Site:* www.avalontravelbooks.com, pg 27

Newlin, Shanta, Penguin Young Readers Group, 345 Hudson St, New York, NY 10014 *Tel:* 212-366-2000 *E-mail:* online@penguinputnam.com *Web Site:* www.penguinputnam.com; us.penguingroup.com, pg 198

Newman, Ms Barbara, Frederick Fell Publishers Inc, 2131 Hollywood Blvd, Suite 305, Hollywood, FL 33020 *Tel:* 954-925-5242 *E-mail:* fellpub@aol.com (admin only) *Web Site:* www.fellpub.com, pg 98

Newman, Brent, Accuity, a SourceMedia Co, 4709 W Golf Rd, Suite 600, Skokie, IL 60076-1253 *Tel:* 847-676-9600 *Toll Free Tel:* 800-321-3373 *Fax:* 847-933-8101 *E-mail:* custserv@accuitysolutions.com; support@accuitysolutions.com; sales@accuitysolutions.com; general@accuitysolutions.com *Web Site:* www.accuitysolutions.com, pg 4

Newman, Dr Carey C, Baylor University Press, Baylor University, One Bear Place, Waco, TX 76798-7363 *Tel:* 254-710-3164 *Fax:* 254-710-3440 *Web Site:* www.baylorpress.com, pg 32

Newman, Carolyn, River City Publishing LLC, 1719 Mulberry St, Montgomery, AL 36106 *Tel:* 334-265-6753 *Fax:* 334-265-8880 *E-mail:* sales@rivercitypublishing.com *Web Site:* www.rivercitypublishing.com, pg 219

Newman, Eric, Fordham University Press, 2546 Belmont Ave, University Box L, Bronx, NY 10458 *Tel:* 718-817-4795 *Fax:* 718-817-4785 *Web Site:* www.fordhampress.com, pg 97

Newman, Felice, Cleis Press, 2246 Sixth St, Berkeley, CA 94710 *Tel:* 510-845-8000 *Toll Free Tel:* 800-780-2279 (US) *Fax:* 510-845-8001 *E-mail:* orders@cleispress.com *Web Site:* www.cleispress.com; www.vivaeditions.com, pg 63

Newman, Joy, Ozark Mountain Publishing Inc, PO Box 754, Huntsville, AR 72740-0754 *Tel:* 479-738-2348 *Toll Free Tel:* 800-935-0045 *Fax:* 479-738-2448 *E-mail:* info@ozarkmt.com *Web Site:* www.ozarkmt.com, pg 190

Newman, Judith A, Scholastic Inc, 557 Broadway, New York, NY 10012 *Tel:* 212-343-6100 *Toll Free Tel:* 800-scholastic *Web Site:* www.scholastic.com, pg 228

Newman, Megan, Avery, 375 Hudson St, New York, NY 10014 *Tel:* 212-366-2000 *Fax:* 212-366-2643 *E-mail:* online@penguinputnam.com *Web Site:* www.penguinputnam.com; us.penguingroup.com, pg 28

Newsome, Stuart, Unicor Medical Inc, 4160 Carmichael Rd, Montgomery, AL 36106 *Tel:* 334-260-8150 *Toll Free Tel:* 800-825-7421 *Toll Free Fax:* 800-305-8030 *E-mail:* sales@unicormed.com *Web Site:* www.unicormed.com, pg 262

Newton, Nigel, Bloomsbury Publishing, 175 Fifth Ave, New York, NY 10010 *Tel:* 212-674-5151 *Toll Free Tel:* 800-221-7945 *Fax:* 212-780-0115; 212-982-2837 *E-mail:* marketingusa@bloomsbury.com; adultpublicityusa.@bloomsbury.com *Web Site:* www.bloomsbury.com, pg 40

Ney, Alison, Radcliffe Fellowship, 8 Garden St, Cambridge, MA 02138 *Tel:* 617-495-8212; 617-496-1324 (application office) *Fax:* 617-495-8136 *Web Site:* www.radcliffe.harvard.edu, pg 737

Nicholaou, Mary, Eros Books, 463 Barlow Ave, Staten Island, NY 10308 *Tel:* 718-317-7484 *Web Site:* www.eros.thecraze.com, pg 89

Nicholas, Calliope, Residency, 454 E Hill Rd, Austerlitz, NY 12017 *Tel:* 518-392-3103; 518-392-4144 *E-mail:* apply@millaycolony.org *Web Site:* www.millaycolony.org, pg 737

Nicholl, Greg, The Johns Hopkins University Press, 2715 N Charles St, Baltimore, MD 21218-4363 *Tel:* 410-516-6900; 410-516-6987 (journals outside US & CN) *Toll Free Tel:* 800-537-5487 (book orders & cust serv); 800-548-1784 (journal orders) *Fax:* 410-516-6968; 410-516-3866 (journal orders) *E-mail:* hfscustserv@press.jhu.edu (cust serv); jrnlcirc@press.jhu.edu (journal orders) *Web Site:* www.press.jhu.edu; muse.jhu.edu/about/subscriptions/index.html (Project Muse subns), pg 136

Nichols, Bruce, Houghton Mifflin Harcourt Trade & Reference Division, 222 Berkeley St, Boston, MA 02116-3764 *Tel:* 617-351-5000 *Toll Free Tel:* 800-225-3362 *Web Site:* www.houghtonmifflinbooks.com, pg 124

Nichols, Dan, Indiana University Press, 601 N Morton St, Bloomington, IN 47404-3797 *Tel:* 812-855-8817 *Toll Free Tel:* 800-842-6796 (orders only) *Fax:* 812-855-7931; 812-855-8507 *E-mail:* iupress@indiana.edu; iuporder@indiana.edu (orders) *Web Site:* www.iupress.indiana.edu, pg 129

Nichols, Jenny, American Map Corp, 36-36 33 St, 4th fl, Long Island City, NY 11106 *Tel:* 718-784-0055 *Toll Free Tel:* 888-774-7979 *Fax:* 718-784-0640 (admin); 718-784-1216 (sales & orders) *E-mail:* sales@americanmap.com *Web Site:* www.americanmap.com, pg 14

Nichols, Mark, American Booksellers Association, 333 Westchester Ave, Suite S202, White Plains, NY 10604 *Tel:* 914-406-7500 *Toll Free Tel:* 800-637-0037 *Fax:* 914-410-6297 *E-mail:* info@bookweb.org *Web Site:* www.bookweb.org, pg 612

Nichols, Mark, Indies Choice Book Awards, 333 Westchester Ave, Suite S202, White Plains, NY 10604 *Tel:* 914-406-7500 *Toll Free Tel:* 800-637-0037 *Fax:* 914-410-6297 *Web Site:* www.bookweb.org, pg 712

Nichols, Robby, Covenant Communications Inc, 920 E State Rd, Suite F, American Fork, UT 84003-0416 *Tel:* 801-756-9966 *Toll Free Tel:* 800-662-9545 *Fax:* 801-756-1049 *E-mail:* info@covenant-lds.com *Web Site:* www.covenant-lds.com, pg 70

Nichols, Sally, University of Massachusetts Press, East Experiment Sta, 671 N Pleasant St, Amherst, MA 01003 *Tel:* 413-545-2217 *Fax:* 413-545-1226 *E-mail:* info@umpress.umass.edu *Web Site:* www.umass.edu/umpress, pg 266

Nichols, Suzanne, Russell Sage Foundation, 112 E 64 St, New York, NY 10065 *Tel:* 212-750-6000 *Toll Free Tel:* 800-524-6401 *Fax:* 212-371-4761 *E-mail:* info@rsage.org *Web Site:* www.russellsage.org, pg 222

Nicholson, George, Sterling Lord Literistic Inc, 65 Bleecker St, New York, NY 10012 *Tel:* 212-780-6050 *Fax:* 212-780-6095 *E-mail:* info@sll.com *Web Site:* www.sll.com, pg 595

Nicholson, Jim, Riverside Publishing, 3800 Golf Rd, Suite 200, Rolling Meadows, IL 60008 *Tel:* 630-467-7000 *Toll Free Tel:* 800-323-9540 *Fax:* 630-467-7192 (cust serv) *E-mail:* rpc_customer_service@hmhpub.com (cust serv) *Web Site:* www.riversidepublishing.com, pg 219

Nicholson, Leah, Jenkins Group Inc, 1129 Woodmere Ave, Suite B, Traverse City, MI 49686 *Tel:* 231-933-0445 *Toll Free Tel:* 800-706-4636 *Fax:* 231-933-0448 *E-mail:* info@bookpublishing.com *Web Site:* www.bookpublishing.com, pg 549

Nicholson, Sam, Random House Publishing Group, 1745 Broadway, New York, NY 10019 *Toll Free Tel:* 800-200-3552 *Web Site:* atrandom.com, pg 214

Nici, Joanne, Don Buchwald & Associates Inc, 10 E 44 St, New York, NY 10017 *Tel:* 212-867-1200 *Fax:* 212-867-2434 *E-mail:* info@buchwald.com *Web Site:* www.buchwald.com, pg 565

Nickelson, Ron, Standard Publishing, 8805 Governors Hill Dr, Suite 400, Cincinnati, OH 45249 *Tel:* 513-931-4050 *Toll Free Tel:* 800-543-1353 *Fax:* 513-931-0950 *Toll Free Fax:* 877-867-5751 *E-mail:* customerservice@standardpub.com *Web Site:* www.standardpub.com, pg 242

Nickless, Rachael, Colorado Geological Survey, Publications Section, 1313 Sherman St, Rm 715, Denver, CO 80203 *Tel:* 303-866-2611 *Fax:* 303-866-2461 (cust serv) *E-mail:* pubscgs@state.co.us (cust serv) *Web Site:* geosurvey.state.co.us, pg 65

Nicolajsen, Alex, Kensington Publishing Corp, 119 W 40 St, New York, NY 10018 *Tel:* 212-407-1500 *Toll Free Tel:* 800-221-2647 *Fax:* 212-935-0699 *Web Site:* www.kensingtonbooks.com, pg 139

Nieginski, Elizabeth, Springer Publishing Co LLC, 11 W 42 St, 15th fl, New York, NY 10036-8002 *Tel:* 212-431-4370 *Toll Free Tel:* 877-687-7476 *Fax:* 212-

941-7842 *E-mail:* marketing@springerpub.com; cs@springerpub.com (orders); editorial@springerpub.com *Web Site:* www.springerpub.com, pg 241

Nielsen, Margarete, Hay House Inc, 2776 Loker Ave W, Carlsbad, CA 92010 *Tel:* 760-431-7695 (ext 2, intl) *Toll Free Tel:* 800-654-5126 (ext 2, US) *Toll Free Fax:* 800 650-5115 *E-mail:* info@hayhouse.com, editorial@hayhouse.com *Web Site:* www.hayhouse.com, pg 115

Nieman, James, Standard Publishing, 8805 Governors Hill Dr, Suite 400, Cincinnati, OH 45249 *Tel:* 513-931-4050 *Toll Free Tel:* 800-543-1353 *Fax:* 513-931-0950 *Toll Free Fax:* 877-867-5751 *E-mail:* customerservice@standardpub.com *Web Site:* www.standardpub.com, pg 242

Nikitina, Elena, Corwin, a Sage Co, 2455 Teller Rd, Thousand Oaks, CA 91320 *Tel:* 805-499-9734 *Toll Free Tel:* 800-233-9936 *Fax:* 805-499-5323 *Toll Free Fax:* 800-417-2466 *E-mail:* info@corwin.com *Web Site:* www.corwin.com, pg 68

Nikolic, Maja, Writers House, 21 W 26 St, New York, NY 10010 *Tel:* 212-685-2400 *Fax:* 212-685-1781 *Web Site:* www.writershouse.com, pg 599

Nintzel, Katherine, HarperCollins General Books Group, 10 E 53 St, New York, NY 10022 *Tel:* 212-207-7000 *Fax:* 212-207-7633 *Web Site:* www.harpercollins.com, pg 113

Nirkind, Robert, AMACOM Books, 1601 Broadway, New York, NY 10019-7420 *Tel:* 212-586-8100; 518-891-5510 (orders) *Toll Free Tel:* 800-250-5308 (cust serv) *Fax:* 212-903-8083; 518-891-2372 (orders) *E-mail:* pubservice@amanet.org *Web Site:* www.amacombooks.org, pg 9

Nisbet, Lynette, Prometheus Books, 59 John Glenn Dr, Amherst, NY 14228-2119 *Tel:* 716-691-0133 *Toll Free Tel:* 800-421-0351 *Fax:* 716-691-0137 *E-mail:* marketing@prometheusbooks.com; editorial@prometheusbooks.com *Web Site:* www.Prometheusbooks.com, pg 208

Nishan, Rachel, Twin Oaks Indexing, 138 Twin Oaks Rd, Suite W, Louisa, VA 23093 *Tel:* 540-894-5126 *Fax:* 540-894-4112 *Web Site:* www.twinoaks.org, pg 556

Nitsche, David, TSI Graphics, 1300 S Raney St, Effingham, IL 62401-4206 *Tel:* 217-347-7733; 217-347-7734 *Fax:* 217-342-9611 *E-mail:* info@tsigraphics.com *Web Site:* www.tsigraphics.com, pg 556

Nittoli, Janice, The Century Foundation, 41 E 70 St, New York, NY 10021 *Tel:* 212-535-4441; 212-879-9197 *Fax:* 212-879-9197 *E-mail:* info@tcf.org *Web Site:* www.tcf.org, pg 57, 641

Niumata, Erin, Folio Literary Management LLC, The Film Center Bldg, 630 Ninth Ave, Suite 1101, New York, NY 10036 *Tel:* 212-400-1494 *Fax:* 212-967-0977 *Web Site:* www.foliolit.com, pg 572

Nixon, Cheri, Canadian Printing Industries Association, 151 Slater St, Suite 1110, Ottawa, ON K1P 5H3, Canada *Tel:* 613-236-7208 *Toll Free Tel:* 800-267-7280 *Fax:* 613-232-1334 *E-mail:* info@cpia-aci.ca *Web Site:* www.cpia-aci.ca, pg 620

Nixon, Tiffany, George Freedley Memorial Award, Roundabout Theatre Co, 231 W 39 St, Suite 1200, New York, NY 10018 *Tel:* 212-719-9393 (ext 351) *E-mail:* info@tla-online.org; tlabookawards@gmail.com *Web Site:* www.tla-online.org, pg 705

Nixon, Tiffany, Richard Wall Memorial Award, Roundabout Theatre Co, 231 W 39 St, Suite 1200, New York, NY 10018 *Tel:* 212-719-9393 (ext 351) *E-mail:* info@tla-online.org; tlabookawards@gmail.com *Web Site:* www.tla-online.org, pg 748

Noakes-Fry, Kristen, Rothstein Associates Inc, 4 Arapaho Rd, Brookfield, CT 06804-3104 *Tel:* 203-740-7400 *Toll Free Tel:* 888-768-4783 *Fax:* 203-740-7401 *E-mail:* info@rothstein.com *Web Site:* www.rothstein.com, pg 221

Noble, Claire, Naval Institute Press, 291 Wood Rd, Annapolis, MD 21402-5034 *Tel:* 410-268-6110 *Toll Free Tel:* 800-233-8764 *Fax:* 410-295-1084; 410-571-1703 (cust serv) *E-mail:* webmaster@navalinstitute.org; customer@navalinstitute.org (cust serv); trade@usni.org *Web Site:* www.nip.org; www.usni.org, pg 176

Noe, Courtney, Marshall Cavendish Corp, 99 White Plains Rd, Tarrytown, NY 10591-9001 *Tel:* 914-332-8888 *Toll Free Tel:* 800-821-9881 *Fax:* 914-332-8102 *E-mail:* customerservice@marshallcavendish.com; mcc@marshallcavendish.com *Web Site:* marshallcavendish.us; marshallcavendishdigital.com; marshallcavendishebooks.com, pg 158

Noel, Kaela, Mary Evans Inc, 242 E Fifth St, New York, NY 10003-8501 *Tel:* 212-979-0880 *Fax:* 212-979-5344 *E-mail:* info@maryevansinc.com *Web Site:* www.maryevansinc.com, pg 571

Nogas, Holly, American Society for Training & Development (ASTD), 1640 King St, Box 1443, Alexandria, VA 22313-1443 *Tel:* 703-683-8100 *Toll Free Tel:* 800-628-2783 *Fax:* 703-683-8103 *E-mail:* publications@astd.org *Web Site:* www.astd.org, pg 16

Noh, Chrissy, Simon & Schuster Children's Publishing, 1230 Avenue of the Americas, New York, NY 10020 *Tel:* 212-698-7000 *Web Site:* KIDS.SimonandSchuster.com; TEEN.SimonandSchuster.com; simonandschuster.net; simonandschuster.biz, pg 235

Nolan, Betsy, The Betsy Nolan Literary Agency, 214 W 29 St, Suite 1002, New York, NY 10001 *Tel:* 212-967-8200 *Fax:* 212-967-7292 *E-mail:* dblehr@cs.com, pg 587

Nolan, Debra S, Library Binding Institute, 4440 PGA Blvd, Suite 600, Palm Beach Gardens, FL 33410 *Tel:* 561-745-6821 *Fax:* 561-472-8401 *E-mail:* info@lbibinders.org *Web Site:* www.lbibinders.org, pg 626

Nolan, Elizabeth, OSA, The Optical Society, 2010 Massachusetts Ave NW, Washington, DC 20036-1023 *Tel:* 202-223-8130 *Toll Free Tel:* 800-766-4672 *E-mail:* custserv@osa.org *Web Site:* www.osa.org, pg 188

Nolan, Michael, The Foundation for Economic Education Inc, 30 S Broadway, Irvington-on-Hudson, NY 10533 *Tel:* 914-591-7230 *Toll Free Tel:* 800-960-4FEE (960-4333) *Fax:* 914-591-8910 *E-mail:* freeman@fee.org (query/submit: attention Sheldon Richman, all others: attention Michael Nolan) *Web Site:* www.thefreemanonline.org; www.fee.org, pg 98

Nolan, Patrick, Penguin Books, 375 Hudson St, New York, NY 10014 *Tel:* 212-366-2000 *E-mail:* online@penguinputnam.com *Web Site:* www.penguinputnam.com; www.penguinclassics.com; us.penguingroup.com, pg 196

Nolin, Leslie, Fairwinds Press, PO Box 668, Lions Bay, BC V0N 2E0, Canada *Tel:* 604-913-0649 *E-mail:* orders@fairwinds-press.com *Web Site:* www.fairwinds-press.com, pg 504

Nonbello, Michael, Andrews McMeel Publishing LLC, 1130 Walnut St, Kansas City, MO 64106-2109 *Toll Free Tel:* 800-851-8923; 800-943-9839 (cust serv) *Toll Free Fax:* 800-943-9831 (orders) *Web Site:* www.andrewsmcmeel.com, pg 18

Noonan, Margaret, Fordham University Press, 2546 Belmont Ave, University Box L, Bronx, NY 10458 *Tel:* 718-817-4795 *Fax:* 718-817-4785 *Web Site:* www.fordhampress.com, pg 97

Nora, Marianne Leslie, Mid-List Press, 6524 Brownlee Dr, Nashville, TN 37205-3038 *Tel:* 615-822-3777 *Fax:* 612-823-8387 *E-mail:* guide@midlist.org *Web Site:* www.midlist.org, pg 166

Nordal, Greg, Nelson Education Ltd, 1120 Birchmount Rd, Scarborough, ON M1K 5G4, Canada *Tel:* 416-752-9100 *Toll Free Tel:* 800-268-2222 (cust serv) *Fax:* 416-752-8101 *Toll Free Fax:* 800-430-4445 *E-mail:* inquire@nelson.com *Web Site:* www.nelson.com, pg 513

Nordling, Kerry, St Martin's Press, LLC, 175 Fifth Ave, New York, NY 10010 *Tel:* 646-307-5151 *Fax:* 212-420-9314 *E-mail:* firstname.lastname@macmillan.com *Web Site:* www.stmartins.com, pg 224

Nordstrom, Robyn, The Pilgrim Press/United Church Press, 700 Prospect Ave, Cleveland, OH 44115-1100 *Toll Free Tel:* 800-537-3394 (cust serv-indivs); 800-654-5129 (cust serv-commercial accts) *Fax:* 216-736-2206 (orders) *E-mail:* proposals@thepilgrimpress.com *Web Site:* www.thepilgrimpress.com; www.unitedchurchpress.com, pg 202

Nori, Don Jr, Destiny Image Inc, 167 Walnut Bottom Rd, Shippensburg, PA 17257-0310 *Tel:* 717-532-3040 *Toll Free Tel:* 800-722-6774 (orders only) *Fax:* 717-532-9291 *E-mail:* sales@destinyimage.com *Web Site:* www.destinyimage.com, pg 78

Norman, Adrian, Simon & Schuster Digital, 1230 Avenue of the Americas, New York, NY 10020 *Tel:* 212-698-7547 *Web Site:* www.simonandschuster.com; kids.simonandschuster.com; www.simonandschuster.ca; www.simonandschuster.co.uk; www.simonandschuster.net; www.simonandschuster.biz; www.tipsoncareerandmoney.com; www.tipsonhealthyliving.com; www.tipsonhomeandstyle.com; www.tipsonlifeandlove.com, pg 235

Norman, Nancy Lowden, Atlantic Center for the Arts Artists-in-Residence Program, 1414 Art Center Ave, New Smyrna Beach, FL 32168 *Tel:* 386-427-6975 *Toll Free Tel:* 800-393-6975 *Fax:* 386-427-5669 *E-mail:* program@atlanticcenterforthearts.org *Web Site:* www.atlanticcenterforthearts.org, pg 667

Norris, Fran, River City Publishing LLC, 1719 Mulberry St, Montgomery, AL 36106 *Tel:* 334-265-6753 *Fax:* 334-265-8880 *E-mail:* sales@rivercitypublishing.com *Web Site:* www.rivercitypublishing.com, pg 219

Norris, Jill S, Incentive Publications Inc, 2400 Crestmoor Rd, Suite 211, Nashville, TN 37215 *Tel:* 615-385-2934 *Toll Free Tel:* 800-421-2830 *Fax:* 615-385-2967 *E-mail:* comments@incentivepublications.com *Web Site:* www.incentivepublications.com, pg 128

Norris, Kevin, ProQuest LLC, 789 E Eisenhower Pkwy, Ann Arbor, MI 48108-3218 *Tel:* 734-761-4700 *Toll Free Tel:* 800-521-0600 *Fax:* 734-975-6486 *Toll Free Fax:* 800-864-0019 *E-mail:* info@proquest.com *Web Site:* www.proquest.com, pg 208

Norris, Laurie Glenn, Maritime Writers' Workshops, PO Box 4400, Fredericton, NB E3B 5A3, Canada *Tel:* 506-458-7106 *Toll Free Tel:* 866-599-4646 *Fax:* 506-458-5012 *E-mail:* extend@unb.ca *Web Site:* www.unb.ca/cel, pg 670

Norris, Mary, The Globe Pequot Press, 246 Goose Lane, Guilford, CT 06437 *Tel:* 203-458-4500 *Toll Free Tel:* 800-243-0495 (orders only); 888-249-7586 (cust serv) *Fax:* 203-458-4601 *Toll Free Fax:* 800-820-2329 (orders & cust serv) *E-mail:* info@globepequot.com *Web Site:* www.globepequot.com, pg 104

North, Samantha, Random House of Canada Limited, One Toronto St, Suite 300, Toronto, ON M5C 2V6, Canada *Tel:* 416-364-4449 *Toll Free Tel:* 888-523-9292 (cust serv) *Fax:* 416-364-6863; 416-364-6653 (subs rts) *Web Site:* www.randomhouse.ca, pg 517

Norton, Jennifer, The Pennsylvania State University Press, University Support Bldg 1, Suite C, 820 N University Dr, University Park, PA 16802-1003 *Tel:* 814-865-1327 *Toll Free Tel:* 800-326-9180 *Fax:* 814-863-1408 *Toll Free Fax:* 877-778-2665 *E-mail:* info@psupress.org *Web Site:* www.psupress.org, pg 198

Norton, Kim, Peace Hill Press, 18021 The Glebe Lane, Charles City, VA 23030 *Tel:* 804-829-5043 *Toll Free Tel:* 877-322-3445 (orders) *Fax:* 804-829-5704 *E-mail:* info@peacehillpress.com *Web Site:* www.peacehillpress.com, pg 195

Norton, Paul, AMMO Books LLC, 300 S Raymond Ave, Suite 3, Pasadena, CA 91105 *Tel:* 323-223-AMMO (223-2666) *Toll Free Tel:* 888-642-AMMO (642-2666) *Fax:* 323-978-4200 *Web Site:* www.ammobooks.com, pg 17

Norville, Valerie, United States Institute of Peace Press, 2301 Constitution Ave NW, Washington, DC 20037 *Tel:* 202-457-1700 (edit); 703-661-1590 (cust serv) *Toll Free Tel:* 800-868-8064 (cust serv) *Fax:* 202-429-6063; 703-661-1501 (cust serv) *Web Site:* bookstore.usip.org, pg 262

Nosowsky, Ethan, McSweeney's Publishing, 849 Valencia St, San Francisco, CA 94110 *Tel:* 415-642-5609 (cust serv) *Web Site:* www.mcsweeneys.net, pg 162

Nossel, Suzanne, PEN American Center, 588 Broadway, Suite 303, New York, NY 10012 *Tel:* 212-334-1660 *Fax:* 212-334-2181 *E-mail:* info@pen.org *Web Site:* www.pen.org, pg 633

Nossel, Suzanne, The PEN Award for Poetry in Translation, 588 Broadway, Suite 303, New York, NY 10012 *Tel:* 212-334-1660 *Fax:* 212-334-2181 *E-mail:* awards@pen.org *Web Site:* www.pen.org, pg 732

Nossel, Suzanne, PEN/Phyllis Naylor Working Writer Fellowship, 588 Broadway, Suite 303, New York, NY 10012 *Tel:* 212-334-1660 *Fax:* 212-334-2181 *E-mail:* awards@pen.org *Web Site:* www.pen.org, pg 733

Nossel, Suzanne, PEN/Ralph Manheim Medal for Translation, 588 Broadway, Suite 303, New York, NY 10012 *Tel:* 212-334-1660 *Fax:* 212-334-2181 *E-mail:* awards@pen.org *Web Site:* www.pen.org, pg 733

Nossel, Suzanne, PEN/Robert Bingham Fellowships for Writers, 588 Broadway, Suite 303, New York, NY 10012 *Tel:* 212-334-1660 *Fax:* 212-334-2181 *E-mail:* awards@pen.org *Web Site:* www.pen.org, pg 733

Nossel, Suzanne, PEN Translation Prize, 588 Broadway, Suite 303, New York, NY 10012 *Tel:* 212-334-1660 *Fax:* 212-334-2181 *E-mail:* awards@pen.org *Web Site:* www.pen.org, pg 733

Nossel, Suzanne, PEN Writers' Emergency Fund, 588 Broadway, Suite 303, New York, NY 10012 *Tel:* 212-334-1660 *Fax:* 212-334-2181 *Web Site:* www.pen.org, pg 733

Noudehou, Lisa, Barranca Press, 1450 Couse St, No 10, Taos, NM 87571 *Tel:* 575-613-1026 *E-mail:* editor@barrancapress.com *Web Site:* www.barrancapress.com, pg 31

Novack, Matt, Alan Wofsy Fine Arts, 1109 Geary Blvd, San Francisco, CA 94109 *Tel:* 415-292-6500 *Toll Free Tel:* 800-660-6403 *Fax:* 415-292-6594 (off & cust serv); 415-512-0130 (acctg) *E-mail:* order@art-books.com (orders); editeur@earthlink.net (edit); beauxarts@earthlink.net (cust serv) *Web Site:* www.art-books.com, pg 284

Novak, Alex, Regnery Publishing Inc, One Massachusetts Ave NW, Washington, DC 20001 *Tel:* 202-216-0600 *Toll Free Tel:* 888-219-4747 *Fax:* 202-216-0612 *Web Site:* www.regnery.com, pg 217

Novak, Eileen Kiley, Materials Research Society, 506 Keystone Dr, Warrendale, PA 15086-7537 *Tel:* 724-779-3003 *Fax:* 724-779-8313 *E-mail:* info@mrs.org *Web Site:* www.mrs.org, pg 159

Novakshonoff, Vasili, Synaxis Press, 37323 Hawkins Pickle Rd, Dewdney, BC V0M 1H0, Canada *Tel:* 604-826-9336 *E-mail:* synaxis@new-ostrog.org *Web Site:* synaxispress.ca, pg 520

November, Sharyn, Viking Children's Books, 345 Hudson St, New York, NY 10014 *Tel:* 212-366-2000 *E-mail:* online@penguinputnam.com *Web Site:* www.penguinputnam.com; us.penguingroup.com, pg 275

Nowak, Emily, Wayne State University Press, Leonard N Simons Bldg, 4809 Woodward Ave, Detroit, MI 48201-1309 *Tel:* 313-577-6120 *Toll Free Tel:* 800-978-7323 *Fax:* 313-577-6131 *Web Site:* www.wsupress.wayne.edu, pg 277

Nowak, Wanda, Wanda Nowak Creative Illustrators Agency, 231 E 76 St, Suite 5-D, New York, NY 10021 *Tel:* 212-535-0438 *E-mail:* wanda@wandanow.com *Web Site:* www.wandanow.com, pg 602

Nowicki, Lori, Painted-Words Inc, 310 W 97 St, Suite 24, New York, NY 10025 *Tel:* 212-663-2311 *Fax:* 212-663-2891 *E-mail:* info@painted-words.com *Web Site:* www.painted-words.com, pg 602

Noyes, Al, Walch Education, 40 Walch Dr, Portland, ME 04103-1286 *Tel:* 207-772-2846 *Toll Free Tel:* 800-558-2846 *Fax:* 207-772-3105 *Toll Free Fax:* 888-991-5755 *E-mail:* customerservice@walch.com *Web Site:* www.walch.com, pg 276

Nozari, Roshan, Houghton Mifflin Harcourt K-12 Publishers, 222 Berkeley St, Boston, MA 02116-3764 *Tel:* 617-351-5000 *Toll Free Tel:* 800-225-5425 (cust serv) *Web Site:* www.hmhco.com; www.hmheducation.com, pg 123

Nuchi, Adah, Houghton Mifflin Harcourt Trade & Reference Division, 222 Berkeley St, Boston, MA 02116-3764 *Tel:* 617-351-5000 *Toll Free Tel:* 800-225-3362 *Web Site:* www.houghtonmifflinbooks.com, pg 124

Nuding, Micki, Gallery Books, 1230 Avenue of the Americas, New York, NY 10020 *Toll Free Tel:* 800-456-6798 *Fax:* 212-698-7284 *E-mail:* consumer.customerservice@simonandschuster.com *Web Site:* www.simonsays.com, pg 101

Nugent, Cynthia, Tradewind Books, 202-1807 Maritime Mews, Vancouver, BC V6H 3W7, Canada *Fax:* 604-662-4405 *E-mail:* tradewindbooks@telus.net *Web Site:* www.tradewindbooks.com, pg 521

Nugent, Lynne, The Iowa Review Award, 308 EPB, Iowa City, IA 52242-1408 *E-mail:* iowa-review@uiowa.edu *Web Site:* www.iowareview.org, pg 713

Nugent, Rosemary, Canadian Museum of Civilization, 100 Laurier St, Gatineau, QC K1A 0M8, Canada *Tel:* 819-776-7000 *Toll Free Tel:* 800-555-5621 (North American orders only) *Fax:* 819-776-8393 *E-mail:* publications@civilization.ca *Web Site:* www.civilization.ca, pg 497

Nunez, Frank, Simon & Schuster, Inc, 1230 Avenue of the Americas, New York, NY 10020 *Tel:* 212-698-7000 *Fax:* 212-698-7007 *E-mail:* firstname.lastname@simonandschuster.com *Web Site:* www.simonandschuster.com, pg 235

Nurnberg, Charles, Charlesbridge Publishing Inc, 85 Main St, Watertown, MA 02472 *Tel:* 617-926-0329 *Toll Free Tel:* 800-225-3214 *Fax:* 617-926-5720 *Toll Free Fax:* 800-926-5775 *E-mail:* books@charlesbridge.com *Web Site:* www.charlesbridge.com, pg 58

Nurnberg, Jeremy, Charlesbridge Publishing Inc, 85 Main St, Watertown, MA 02472 *Tel:* 617-926-0329 *Toll Free Tel:* 800-225-3214 *Fax:* 617-926-5720 *Toll Free Fax:* 800-926-5775 *E-mail:* books@charlesbridge.com *Web Site:* www.charlesbridge.com, pg 58

Nussbaum, David, F+W Media Inc, 10151 Carver Rd, Suite 200, Blue Ash, OH 45242 *Tel:* 513-531-2690 *Toll Free Tel:* 800-289-0963 (trade accts); 800-258-0929 (orders) *E-mail:* contact_us@fwmedia.com *Web Site:* www.fwmedia.com, pg 92

Nuttall-Smith, Ben, Federation of BC Writers, PO Box 3887, Sta Terminal, Vancouver, BC V6B 3Z3, Canada *Tel:* 604-683-2057 *E-mail:* fedbcwriters@gmail.com *Web Site:* www.bcwriters.ca, pg 623

Nuwsbaum, David, Writer's Digest Books, 10151 Carver Rd, Suite 200, Blue Ash, OH 45242 *Tel:* 513-531-2690 *Toll Free Tel:* 800-289-0963 *Fax:* 513-531-7185 *E-mail:* writersdigest@fwmedia.com (edit) *Web Site:* www.writersdigest.com, pg 286

Nyborg, Randell, University Publishing House, PO Box 1664, Mannford, OK 74044 *Tel:* 918-865-4726 *E-mail:* upub3@juno.com *Web Site:* www.universitypublishinghouse.net, pg 272

Nyilassy, Marlene, Nelson Education Ltd, 1120 Birchmount Rd, Scarborough, ON M1K 5G4, Canada *Tel:* 416-752-9100 *Toll Free Tel:* 800-268-2222 (cust serv) *Fax:* 416-752-8101 *Toll Free Fax:* 800-430-4445 *E-mail:* inquire@nelson.com *Web Site:* www.nelson.com, pg 513

Nyren, Neil, GP Putnam's Sons (Hardcover), 375 Hudson St, New York, NY 10014 *Tel:* 212-366-2000 *E-mail:* online@penguinputnam.com *Web Site:* us.penguingroup.com, pg 210

Nys, Claudia, Lynn C Franklin Associates Ltd, 1350 Broadway, Suite 2015, New York, NY 10018 *Tel:* 212-868-6311 *Fax:* 212-868-6312 *E-mail:* agency@franklinandsiegal.com, pg 573

O'Boyle, Jamie, Cultural Studies & Analysis, 1123 Montrose St, Philadelphia, PA 19147-3721 *Tel:* 215-592-8544 *Fax:* 215-413-9041 *E-mail:* info@culturalanalysis.com *Web Site:* www.culturalanalysis.com, pg 544

O'Brien, Cindy L, National Council on Radiation Protection & Measurements (NCRP), 7910 Woodmont Ave, Suite 400, Bethesda, MD 20814-3095 *Tel:* 301-657-2652 *Toll Free Tel:* 800-229-2652 *Fax:* 301-907-8768 *E-mail:* ncrppubs@ncrponline.org *Web Site:* www.ncrponline.org; www.ncrppublications.org, pg 174

O'Brien, Colin D, T H Peek Publisher, PO Box 7406, Ann Arbor, MI 48107 *Tel:* 734-222-8205 *Fax:* 734-661-0136 *E-mail:* info@thpeekpublisher.com *Web Site:* www.thpeekpublisher.com, pg 196

O'Brien, Geoffrey, The Library of America, 14 E 60 St, New York, NY 10022-1006 *Tel:* 212-308-3360 *Fax:* 212-750-8352 *E-mail:* info@loa.org *Web Site:* www.loa.org, pg 148

O'Brien, John, Dalkey Archive Press, University of Illinois, 1805 S Wright St, MC-011, Champaign, IL 61820 *Tel:* 217-244-5700 *Fax:* 217-244-9142 *E-mail:* contact@dalkeyarchive.com *Web Site:* www.dalkeyarchive.com, pg 74

O'Brien, John, EEI Communications, 7240 Parkway Dr, Suite 250, Hanover, MD 21076-1364 *Tel:* 410-309-8200 *Toll Free Tel:* 888-253-2762 *Fax:* 410-630-3980 *E-mail:* info@eeicom.com *Web Site:* www.eeicom.com, pg 546, 678

O'Brien, Karin, The Overmountain Press, PO Box 1261, Johnson City, TN 37605-1261 *Tel:* 423-926-2691 *Toll Free Tel:* 800-992-2691 (orders) *Fax:* 423-232-1252 *E-mail:* orders@overmtn.com *Web Site:* www.overmtn.com, pg 189

O'Brien, Meg, Random House Children's Books, 1745 Broadway, New York, NY 10019 *Tel:* 212-782-9000 *Toll Free Tel:* 800-200-3552 *Fax:* 212-782-9452 *Web Site:* randomhousekids.com, pg 213

O'Brien, Samantha (Sam), Hyperion, 1500 Broadway, 3rd fl, New York, NY 10036 *Tel:* 212-536-6500 *Web Site:* hyperionbooks.com, pg 126

O'Brien-Nicholson, Kathleen, Fordham University Press, 2546 Belmont Ave, University Box L, Bronx, NY 10458 *Tel:* 718-817-4795 *Fax:* 718-817-4785 *Web Site:* www.fordhampress.com, pg 97

O'Callaghan, Katie, HarperCollins General Books Group, 10 E 53 St, New York, NY 10022 *Tel:* 212-207-7000 *Fax:* 212-207-7633 *Web Site:* www.harpercollins.com, pg 113

O'Carroll, Fiona, Houghton Mifflin Harcourt, 222 Berkeley St, Boston, MA 02116-3764 *Tel:* 617-351-5000 *Toll Free Tel:* 800-225-5425 (Pre-K-8); 800-462-6595 (6–12; Advanced & Electives); 800-289-4490 (Specialized Curriculum: Great Source, Rigby, Saxon, Steck-Vaughn; Homeschool; Adult Ed); 800-323-9540 (Assessment: Riverside Publishing); 888-391-3245 (SkillsTutor); 888-242-6747 option 2 (Destination Series; Classroom Connect; Earobics; Edmark; Learning Village; Riverdeep); 800-225-3362 (Houghton Mifflin Harcourt Trade & Reference Publishers); 800-225-5800 (Heinemann) *Fax:* 617-351-1125 *Web Site:* www.hmhco.com, pg 123

O'Connell, Maureen, Scholastic Inc, 557 Broadway, New York, NY 10012 *Tel:* 212-343-6100 *Toll Free Tel:* 800-scholastic *Web Site:* www.scholastic.com, pg 228

O'Connell, Tim, Vintage & Anchor Books, c/o Random House Inc, 1745 Broadway, New York, NY 10019 *Tel:* 212-572-2420 *E-mail:* vintageanchorpublicity@randomhouse.com *Web Site:* vintage-anchor.knopfdoubleday.com, pg 275

O'Connor, Brian, National Society of Newspaper Columnists Annual Conference, 1345 Fillmore St, Suite 507, San Francisco, CA 94115 *Tel:* 415-488-NCNC (488-6762) *Toll Free Tel:* 866-440-NSNC (440-6762) *Fax:* 484-297-0336 *Toll Free Fax:* 866-635-5759 *Web Site:* www.columnists.com, pg 671

Oakes, Roger B, Adams & Ambrose Publishing, PO Box 259684, Madison, WI 53725-9684 *Tel:* 608-257-5700 *Fax:* 608-257-5700 *E-mail:* info@adamsambrose.com, pg 4

Oakley, Eric, Haynes Manuals Inc, 861 Lawrence Dr, Newbury Park, CA 91320 *Tel:* 805-498-6703 *Toll Free Tel:* 800-4-HAYNES (442-9637) *Fax:* 805-498-2867 *E-mail:* cstn@haynes.com *Web Site:* www.haynes.com, pg 115

Oates, Steve, Bethany House Publishers, 11400 Hampshire Ave S, Bloomington, MN 55438 *Tel:* 952-829-2500 *Toll Free Tel:* 800-877-2665 (orders) *Fax:* 952-829-2568 *Toll Free Fax:* 800-398-3111 (orders) *Web Site:* www.bethanyhouse.com; www.bakerpublishinggroup.com, pg 36

Obeng, Samuel, Indiana University African Studies Program, Indiana University, 221 Woodburn Hall, Bloomington, IN 47405 *Tel:* 812-855-8284 *Fax:* 812-855-6734 *E-mail:* afrist@indiana.edu *Web Site:* www.indiana.edu/~afrist, pg 129

Oberhelman, David, Mythopoeic Awards, Oklahoma State University, 306 Edmon Low Library, Stillwater, OK 74078 *Tel:* 405-744-9773 *E-mail:* awards@mythsoc.org *Web Site:* www.mythsoc.org, pg 725

Oberweger, Lorin, Writers Retreat Workshop (WRW), PO Box 4236, Louisville, KY 40204 *E-mail:* wrw04@netscape.net *Web Site:* www.writersretreatworkshop.com, pg 675

Oblack, Linda, Indiana University Press, 601 N Morton St, Bloomington, IN 47404-3797 *Tel:* 812-855-8817 *Toll Free Tel:* 800-842-6796 (orders only) *Fax:* 812-855-7931; 812-855-8507 *E-mail:* iupress@indiana.edu; iuporder@indiana.edu (orders) *Web Site:* www.iupress.indiana.edu, pg 129

Obry, Carrie, Midwest Independent Booksellers Association (MIBA), 2355 Louisiana Ave N, Suite A, Golden Valley, MN 55427-3646 *Tel:* 763-544-2993 *Toll Free Tel:* 800-784-7522 *Fax:* 763-544-2266 *Web Site:* www.midwestbooksellers.org, pg 627

Ocampo, Patricia, Transatlantic Agency, 2 Bloor St E, Ste 3500, Toronto, ON M4W-1A8, Canada *Tel:* 416-488-9214 *E-mail:* info@transatlanticagency.com *Web Site:* www.transatlanticagency.com, pg 597

Ochsner, Daniel, University of Minnesota Press, 111 Third Ave S, Suite 290, Minneapolis, MN 55401-2520 *Tel:* 612-627-1970 *Fax:* 612-627-1980 *E-mail:* ump@umn.edu *Web Site:* www.upress.umn.edu, pg 266

Odiseos, Nikko, Shambhala Publications Inc, Horticultural Hall, 300 Massachusetts Ave, Boston, MA 02115 *Tel:* 617-424-0030 *Toll Free Tel:* 866-424-0030 (off); 888-424-2329 (cust serv) *Fax:* 617-236-1563 *E-mail:* customercare@shambhala.com *Web Site:* www.shambhala.com, pg 232

Odom, Monica, Liza Dawson Associates, 350 Seventh Ave, Suite 2003, New York, NY 10001 *Tel:* 212-465-9071 *Fax:* 212-947-0460 *Web Site:* www.lizadawsonassociates.com, pg 568

Odu, Jude, Decent Hill Publishers LLC, 6100 Oak Tree Blvd, Suite 200, Cleveland, OH 44131 *Toll Free Tel:* 866-688-5325 *Toll Free Fax:* 866-688-5325 *E-mail:* support@decenthill.com *Web Site:* www.decenthill.com, pg 77

Oerlemans, Onno, Hamilton College, English/Creative Writing, English/Creative Writing Dept, 198 College Hill Rd, Clinton, NY 13323 *Tel:* 315-859-4370 *Fax:* 315-859-4390 *E-mail:* english@hamilton.edu *Web Site:* www.hamilton.edu, pg 678

Oestreicher, Mark, Zondervan, A HarperCollins Company, 5300 Patterson Ave SE, Grand Rapids, MI 49530 *Tel:* 616-698-6900 *Toll Free Tel:* 800-226-1122; 800-727-1309 (retail orders) *Fax:* 616-698-3350 *Toll Free Fax:* 800-698-3256 (retail orders) *E-mail:* zinfo@zondervan.com *Web Site:* www.zondervan.com, pg 289

Oey, Eric, Tuttle Publishing, Airport Business Park, 364 Innovation Dr, North Clarendon, VT 05759-9436 *Tel:* 802-773-8930 *Toll Free Tel:* 800-526-2778 *Fax:* 802-773-6993 *Toll Free Fax:* 800-FAX-TUTL *E-mail:* info@tuttlepublishing.com *Web Site:* www.tuttlepublishing.com, pg 260

Offit, Sidney, The Authors League Fund, 31 E 32 St, 7th fl, New York, NY 10016 *Tel:* 212-268-1208 *Fax:* 212-564-5363 *E-mail:* staff@authorsleaguefund.org *Web Site:* www.authorsleaguefund.org, pg 617

Ogden, Abe, American Diabetes Association, 1701 N Beauregard St, Alexandria, VA 22311 *Toll Free Tel:* 800-342-2383 *E-mail:* booksinfo@diabetes.org *Web Site:* www.diabetes.org, pg 12

Ogden, Bree, D4EO Literary Agency, 7 Indian Valley Rd, Weston, CT 06883 *Tel:* 203-544-7180 *Fax:* 203-544-7160 *Web Site:* www.d4eoliteraryagency.com, pg 568

Ogilvie, June, Bookmakers Ltd, 32 Parkview Ave, Wolfville, NS B4P 2K8, Canada *Tel:* 575-776-5435 *Fax:* 505-776-2762, pg 601

Ogilvie, Reg, Bookmakers Ltd, 32 Parkview Ave, Wolfville, NS B4P 2K8, Canada *Tel:* 575-776-5435 *Fax:* 505-776-2762, pg 601

Ogle, Jim, F+W Media Inc, 10151 Carver Rd, Suite 200, Blue Ash, OH 45242 *Tel:* 513-531-2690 *Toll Free Tel:* 800-289-0963 (trade accts); 800-258-0929 (orders) *E-mail:* contact_us@fwmedia.com *Web Site:* www.fwmedia.com, pg 92

Ogle, Jim, Krause Publications Inc, 700 E State St, Iola, WI 54990 *Tel:* 715-445-2214 *Toll Free Tel:* 800-258-0929 (cust serv); 888-457-2873 (orders) *Fax:* 715-445-4087 *E-mail:* bookorders@krause.com *Web Site:* www.krausebooks.com, pg 142

Ognibene, Peter E, Breakthrough Publications Inc, 3 Iroquois St, Barn, Emmaus, PA 18049 *Tel:* 610-928-4061 (ext 12) *Toll Free Tel:* 800-824-5001 (ext 12) *Fax:* 610-928-4064 *E-mail:* dot@booksonhorses.com; ruth@booksonhorses.com *Web Site:* www.booksonhorses.com, pg 46

Ogorek, Keith, AuthorHouse, 1663 Liberty Dr, Bloomington, IN 47403 *Toll Free Tel:* 888-519-5121 *E-mail:* authorsupport@authorhouse.com *Web Site:* www.authorhouse.com, pg 27

Ogorek, Keith, iUniverse, 1663 Liberty Dr, Bloomington, IN 47403 *Toll Free Tel:* 800-AUTHORS (288-4677) *Fax:* 812-355-4085 *Web Site:* www.iuniverse.com, pg 135

Ogorek, Keith, Trafford, 1663 Liberty Dr, Bloomington, IN 47403 *Toll Free Tel:* 888-232-4444 *E-mail:* customersupport@trafford.com *Web Site:* www.trafford.com, pg 257

Ogorek, Keith, Xlibris Corp, 1663 Liberty Dr, Suite 200, Bloomington, IN 47403 *Toll Free Tel:* 888-795-4274 *Fax:* 610-915-0294 *E-mail:* info@xlibris.com *Web Site:* www.xlibris.com, pg 287

Ogren, Rhonda, Llewellyn Publications, 2143 Wooddale Dr, Woodbury, MN 55125 *Tel:* 651-291-1970 *Toll Free Tel:* 800-843-6666 *Fax:* 651-291-1908 *E-mail:* publicity@llewellyn.com *Web Site:* www.llewellyn.com, pg 151

Ohl, Helaine, Macmillan, 175 Fifth Ave, New York, NY 10010 *Tel:* 646-307-5151 *Fax:* 212-420-9314 *E-mail:* firstname.lastname@macmillan.com *Web Site:* www.macmillan.com, pg 154

Ohle, Heather, Encounter Books, 900 Broadway, Suite 601, New York, NY 10003 *Tel:* 212-871-6310 *Toll Free Tel:* 800-786-3839 *Fax:* 212-871-6311 *Toll Free Fax:* 877-811-1461 *E-mail:* read@encounterbooks.com *Web Site:* www.encounterbooks.com, pg 88

Ojakli, Sumya, Simon & Schuster Sales & Marketing, 1230 Avenue of the Americas, New York, NY 10020 *Tel:* 212-698-7000, pg 236

Okrent, Marilyn, Oxford University Press USA, 198 Madison Ave, New York, NY 10016 *Tel:* 212-726-6000 *Toll Free Tel:* 800-451-7556 (orders); 800-445-9714 (cust serv) *Fax:* 919-677-1303 *E-mail:* custserv.us@oup.com *Web Site:* www.oup.com/us, pg 189

Oldfield, James Jr, Abacus, 3413 Roger B Chaffee SE, Suite 101, Grand Rapids, MI 49546 *Tel:* 616-241-3404 *Fax:* 616-698-0325 *E-mail:* info@abacuspub.com *Web Site:* www.abacuspub.com, pg 2

Oldsey, William F, McGraw-Hill Education, 2 Penn Plaza, New York, NY 10121-2298 *Tel:* 212-904-2000 *E-mail:* customer.service@mcgraw-hill.com *Web Site:* www.mheducation.com; www.mheducation.com/custserv.html, pg 160

Olenick, Michelle, Emmaus Road Publishing Inc, 827 N Fourth St, Steubenville, OH 43952 *Tel:* 740-283-2880 (outside US) *Toll Free Tel:* 800-398-5470 (orders) *Fax:* 740-283-4011 (orders) *E-mail:* questions@emmausroad.org *Web Site:* www.emmausroad.org, pg 87

Olinger, Chauncey G Jr, Metropolitan Editorial & Writing Service, 4455 Douglas Ave, Riverdale, NY 10471 *Tel:* 718-549-5518, pg 551

Oliver, Lin, The Don Freeman Memorial Grant-In-Aid, 8271 Beverly Blvd, Los Angeles, CA 90048 *Tel:* 323-782-1010 *Fax:* 323-782-1892 *E-mail:* membership@scbwi.org; scbwi@scbwi.org *Web Site:* www.scbwi.org, pg 705

Oliver, Lin, Golden Kite Awards, 8271 Beverly Blvd, Los Angeles, CA 90048 *Tel:* 323-782-1010 *Fax:* 323-782-1892 *E-mail:* scbwi@scbwi.org; membership@scbwi.org *Web Site:* www.scbwi.org, pg 707

Oliver, Lin, Magazine Merit Awards, 8271 Beverly Blvd, Los Angeles, CA 90048 *Tel:* 323-782-1010 *Fax:* 323-782-1892 *E-mail:* membership@scbwi.org; scbwi@scbwi.org *Web Site:* www.scbwi.org, pg 720

Oliver, Lin, SCBWI Work-In-Progress Grants, 8271 Beverly Blvd, Los Angeles, CA 90048 *Tel:* 323-782-1010 *Fax:* 323-782-1892 *E-mail:* membership@scbwi.org; scbwi@scbwi.org *Web Site:* www.scbwi.org, pg 740

Oliver, Lin, Society of Children's Book Writers & Illustrators (SCBWI), 8271 Beverly Blvd, Los Angeles, CA 90048 *Tel:* 323-782-1010 *Fax:* 323-782-1892 *E-mail:* membership@scbwi.org; scbwi@scbwi.org *Web Site:* www.scbwi.org, pg 636

Oliver, Paul, Soho Press Inc, 853 Broadway, New York, NY 10003 *Tel:* 212-260-1900 *Fax:* 212-260-1902 *E-mail:* soho@sohopress.com; publicity@sohopress.com *Web Site:* www.sohopress.com, pg 239

Olivieri, John, Abbeville Publishing Group, 137 Varick St, Suite 504, New York, NY 10013 *Tel:* 212-366-5585 *Toll Free Tel:* 800-ART-BOOK (278-2665) *Fax:* 212-366-6966 *E-mail:* abbeville@abbeville.com; marketing@abbeville.com; sales@abbeville.com; rights@abbeville.com *Web Site:* www.abbeville.com, pg 2

Olivo, Jessica, Trident Media Group LLC, 41 Madison Ave, 36th fl, New York, NY 10010 *Tel:* 212-262-4810 *Fax:* 212-262-4849 *Web Site:* www.tridentmediagroup.com, pg 598

Olsen, Charlie, InkWell Management, 521 Fifth Ave, 26th fl, New York, NY 10175 *Tel:* 212-922-3500 *Fax:* 212-922-0535 *E-mail:* info@inkwellmanagement.com; submissions@inkwellmanagement.com *Web Site:* inkwellmanagement.com, pg 577

Olsen, Eric, Twilight Times Books, PO Box 3340, Kingsport, TN 37664-0340 *Tel:* 423-323-0183 *Fax:* 423-323-0183 *E-mail:* publisher@twilighttimes.com *Web Site:* www.twilighttimesbooks.com, pg 261

Olsen, Kevin, W W Norton & Company Inc, 500 Fifth Ave, New York, NY 10110-0017 *Tel:* 212-354-5500 *Toll Free Tel:* 800-233-4830 (orders & cust serv) *Fax:* 212-869-0856 *Toll Free Fax:* 800-458-6515 *Web Site:* www.wwnorton.com, pg 182

Olsen, Marilyn, Oak Tree Press, 140 E Palmer St, Taylorville, IL 62568 *Tel:* 217-824-6500 *E-mail:* publisher@oaktreebooks.com; info@oaktreebooks.com; query@oaktreebooks.com; pressdept@oaktreebooks.com; bookorders@oaktreebooks.com *Web Site:* www.oaktreebooks.com; www.otpblog.blogspot.com, pg 183

Olsen, William, The Green Rose Prize in Poetry, Western Michigan University, 1903 W Michigan Ave, Kalamazoo, MI 49008-5463 *Tel:* 269-387-8185 *Fax:* 269-387-2562 *E-mail:* new-issues@wmich.edu *Web Site:* www.wmich.edu/newissues/greenroseprize.html, pg 708

Ou, Michelle, Editors' Association of Canada (Association canadienne des reviseurs), 502-27 Carlton St, Toronto, ON M5B 1L2, Canada *Tel:* 416-975-1379 *Toll Free Tel:* 866-CAN-EDIT (226-3348) *Fax:* 416-975-1637 *E-mail:* info@editors.ca *Web Site:* www.editors.ca; www.reviseurs.ca, pg 622

Ou, Michelle, Tom Fairley Award for Editorial Excellence, 502-27 Carlton St, Toronto, ON M5B 1L2, Canada *Tel:* 416-975-1379 *Toll Free Tel:* 866-CAN-EDIT (226-3348) *Fax:* 416-975-1637 *E-mail:* fairley_award@editors.ca *Web Site:* www.editors.ca; www.reviseurs.ca, pg 703

Ouzounian, Matt, Columbia Books & Information Services, 8120 Woodmont Ave, Suite 110, Bethesda, MD 20814 *Tel:* 202-464-1662 *Toll Free Tel:* 888-265-0600 (cust serv) *Fax:* 202-464-1775 *E-mail:* info@columbiabooks.com *Web Site:* www.columbiabooks.com; www.lobbyists.info; www.associationexecs.com, pg 65

Ovedovitz, Nancy, Yale University Press, 302 Temple St, New Haven, CT 06511-8909 *Tel:* 401-531-2800 (cust serv); 203-432-0960 *Toll Free Tel:* 800-405-1619 (cust serv) *Fax:* 203-432-0948; 401-531-2801 (cust serv) *Toll Free Fax:* 800-406-9145 (cust serv) *E-mail:* customer.care@trilateral.org (cust serv); language.yalepress@yale.edu *Web Site:* www.yalebooks.com, pg 287

Overby, Jordan, Red Wheel/Weiser/Conari, 65 Parker St, Suite 7, Newburyport, MA 01950 *Tel:* 978-465-0504 *Toll Free Tel:* 800-423-7087 (orders) *Fax:* 978-465-0243 *E-mail:* info@rwwbooks.com *Web Site:* www.redwheelweiser.com, pg 216

Overstreet, Sheryl, Standard Publishing, 8805 Governors Hill Dr, Suite 400, Cincinnati, OH 45249 *Tel:* 513-931-4050 *Toll Free Tel:* 800-543-1353 *Fax:* 513-931-0950 *Toll Free Fax:* 877-867-5751 *E-mail:* customerservice@standardpub.com *Web Site:* www.standardpub.com, pg 242

Owen, Charlyce Jones, Pearson Humanities & Social Sciences, One Lake St, Upper Saddle River, NJ 07458 *Tel:* 201-236-7000 *Fax:* 201-236-3400, pg 196

Owen, Rebecca, Ingalls Publishing Group Inc (IPG), PO Box 2500, Banner Elk, NC 28604 *Tel:* 828-297-6884 *Fax:* 828-297-6880 *E-mail:* sales@ingallspublishinggroup.com *Web Site:* www.ingallspublishinggroup.com, pg 130

Owen, Richard C, Richard C Owen Publishers Inc, PO Box 585, Katonah, NY 10536-0585 *Tel:* 914-232-3903 *Toll Free Tel:* 800-336-5588 *Fax:* 914-232-3977 *E-mail:* rcostaff@rcowen.com *Web Site:* www.rcowen.com, pg 189

Owens, Alexandra, American Society of Journalists and Authors (ASJA), 1501 Broadway, Suite 403, New York, NY 10036 *Tel:* 212-997-0947 *Fax:* 212-937-2315 *Web Site:* asja.org, pg 614

Owens, Alexandra, American Society of Journalists and Authors Annual Writers Conference, 1501 Broadway, Suite 403, New York, NY 10036 *Tel:* 212-997-0947 *Fax:* 212-937-2315 *Web Site:* asja.org, pg 667

Owens, Alexandra, ASJA Freelance Writer Search, 1501 Broadway, Suite 403, New York, NY 10036 *Tel:* 212-997-0947 *Fax:* 212-937-2315 *E-mail:* fws@asja.org *Web Site:* www.freelancewritersearch.com, pg 540

Owens, Katherine, Potomac Books Inc, 22841 Quicksilver Dr, Dulles, VA 20166 *Tel:* 703-661-1548 *Fax:* 703-661-1547 *E-mail:* pbimail@presswarehouse.com *Web Site:* www.potomacbooksinc.com, pg 204

Owens, Nancy L, National One-Act Playwriting Competition, 600 Wolfe St, Alexandria, VA 22314 *Tel:* 703-683-5778 *Fax:* 703-683-1378 *E-mail:* asklta@thelittletheatre.com *Web Site:* www.thelittletheatre.com, pg 727

Owens, William A Jr, North Carolina Office of Archives & History, Historical Publications Section, 4622 Mail Service Ctr, Raleigh, NC 27699-4622 *Tel:* 919-733-7442 (ext 225) *Fax:* 919-733-1439 *Web Site:* www.ncpublications.com; nc-historical-publications.stores.yahoo.net (online store), pg 180

Owles, John Paul, Joshua Tree Publishing, 1016 W Jackson Blvd, Suite 500, Chicago, IL 60607 *Tel:* 312-893-7525 *E-mail:* info@joshuatreepublishing.com *Web Site:* www.joshuatreepublishing.com; www.centaurbooks.com (imprint); www.chiralhouse.com (imprint), pg 137

Oxenreider, Ken, Simon & Schuster Audio, 1230 Avenue of the Americas, New York, NY 10020 *Web Site:* audio.simonandschuster.com, pg 234

Pace, David, Utah Original Writing Competition, 617 E South Temple, Salt Lake City, UT 84102 *Tel:* 801-236-7555 *Fax:* 801-236-7556 *Web Site:* arts.utah.gov, pg 747

Pace, John, ASTM International, 100 Barr Harbor Dr, West Conshohocken, PA 19428 *Tel:* 610-832-9500 *Fax:* 610-832-9555 *E-mail:* service@astm.org *Web Site:* www.astm.org, pg 26

Pace, Kaye, John Wiley & Sons Inc Higher Education, 111 River St, Hoboken, NJ 07030-5774 *Tel:* 201-748-6000 *Toll Free Tel:* 800-225-5945 (cust serv) *Fax:* 201-748-6008 *E-mail:* info@wiley.com *Web Site:* www.wiley.com, pg 281

Pace, Steven, Workman Publishing Co Inc, 225 Varick St, 9th fl, New York, NY 10014-4381 *Tel:* 212-254-5900 *Toll Free Tel:* 800-722-7202 *Fax:* 212-254-8098 *E-mail:* info@workman.com *Web Site:* www.workman.com, pg 285

Padakis, Marina, Houghton Mifflin Harcourt Trade & Reference Division, 222 Berkeley St, Boston, MA 02116-3764 *Tel:* 617-351-5000 *Toll Free Tel:* 800-225-3362 *Web Site:* www.houghtonmifflinbooks.com, pg 124

Padberg, Fr John W, Institute of Jesuit Sources (IJS), 3601 Lindell Blvd, St Louis, MO 63108 *Tel:* 314-633-4622 *Fax:* 314-633-4623 *E-mail:* ijs@jesuitsources.com *Web Site:* www.jesuitsources.com, pg 131

Paddick, David, TSI Graphics, 1300 S Raney St, Effingham, IL 62401-4206 *Tel:* 217-347-7733; 217-347-7734 *Fax:* 217-342-9611 *E-mail:* info@tsigraphics.com *Web Site:* www.tsigraphics.com, pg 556

Paddio, Martin, Monthly Review Press, 146 W 29 St, Suite 6W, New York, NY 10001 *Tel:* 212-691-2555 *Toll Free Tel:* 800-670-9499 *Fax:* 212-727-3676 *E-mail:* mreview@igc.org *Web Site:* www.MonthlyReview.org, pg 169

Padgett, Marvin, P & R Publishing Co, 1102 Marble Hill Rd, Phillipsburg, NJ 08865 *Tel:* 908-454-0505 *Toll Free Tel:* 800-631-0094 *Fax:* 908-859-2390 *E-mail:* sales@prpbooks.com; generalinfo@prpbooks.com *Web Site:* prpbooks.com, pg 190

Padgett, Siobhan, Hachette Digital, 237 Park Ave, New York, NY 10017 *Tel:* 212-364-0600, pg 110

Pagan, Zena, Advertising Research Foundation (ARF), 432 Park Ave S, 6th fl, New York, NY 10016-8013 *Tel:* 212-751-5656 *Fax:* 212-319-5265 *E-mail:* info@thearf.org; jar@thearf.org (edit) *Web Site:* www.thearf.org; www.journalofadvertisingresearch.com, pg 611

Page, Lisa, Jenny McKean Moore Writer-in-Washington, English Dept, Rome Hall, 801 22 St NW, Suite 760, Washington, DC 20052 *Tel:* 202-994-6180 *Fax:* 202-994-7915 *E-mail:* engldept@gwu.edu *Web Site:* www.gwu.edu/~english; departments.columbian.gwu.edu/english/openings (position details), pg 725

Page, Robert, Zaner-Bloser Inc, 1201 Dublin Rd, Columbus, OH 43215-1026 *Tel:* 614-486-0221 *Toll Free Tel:* 800-421-3018 (cust serv) *Toll Free Fax:* 800-992-6087 (orders) *E-mail:* zbcsd@zaner-bloser.com; international@zaner-bloser.com *Web Site:* www.zaner-bloser.com, pg 289

Paine, John, Joelle Delbourgo Associates Inc, 101 Park St, Montclair, NJ 07042 *Tel:* 973-773-0836 (call only during standard business hours) *Web Site:* www.delbourgo.com, pg 568

Paine, John, The Editors Circle, 462 Grove St, Montclair, NJ 07043 *Tel:* 973-783-5082 *E-mail:* query@theeditorscircle.com *Web Site:* www.theeditorscircle.com, pg 545

Paine, Steven, CTB/McGraw-Hill, 20 Ryan Ranch Rd, Monterey, CA 93940-5703 *Tel:* 831-393-0700 *Toll Free Tel:* 800-538-9547 *Fax:* 831-393-7825 *Web Site:* www.ctb.com, pg 73

Painter, Benjamin, Schlager Group Inc, 2501 Oak Lawn Ave, Suite 440, Dallas, TX 75219 *Toll Free Tel:* 888-416-5727 *Fax:* 214-347-9469 *E-mail:* info@schlagergroup.com *Web Site:* www.schlagergroup.com, pg 227

Painter, Jeannie, Mountain Press Publishing Co, 1301 S Third W, Missoula, MT 59801 *Tel:* 406-728-1900 *Toll Free Tel:* 800-234-5308 *Fax:* 406-728-1635 *E-mail:* info@mtnpress.com *Web Site:* www.mountain-press.com, pg 170

Painton, Priscilla, Simon & Schuster, 1230 Avenue of the Americas, New York, NY 10020 *Tel:* 212-698-7000 *Toll Free Tel:* 800-223-2348 (cust serv); 800-223-2336 (orders) *Toll Free Fax:* 800-943-9831 (orders) *Web Site:* www.simonandschuster.com, pg 234

Pajak, Nina, Simon & Schuster, 1230 Avenue of the Americas, New York, NY 10020 *Tel:* 212-698-7000 *Toll Free Tel:* 800-223-2348 (cust serv); 800-223-2336 (orders) *Toll Free Fax:* 800-943-9831 (orders) *Web Site:* www.simonandschuster.com, pg 234

Pakalik, Eugenia, W W Norton & Company Inc, 500 Fifth Ave, New York, NY 10110-0017 *Tel:* 212-354-5500 *Toll Free Tel:* 800-233-4830 (orders & cust serv) *Fax:* 212-869-0856 *Toll Free Fax:* 800-458-6515 *Web Site:* www.wwnorton.com, pg 182

Palassis, Neketas S, Saint Nectarios Press, 10300 Ashworth Ave N, Seattle, WA 98133-9410 *Tel:* 206-522-4471 *Toll Free Tel:* 800-643-4233 *Fax:* 206-523-0550 *E-mail:* orders@stnectariospress.com *Web Site:* www.stnectariospress.com, pg 225

Palazzo, Norma, Marshall Cavendish Corp, 99 White Plains Rd, Tarrytown, NY 10591-9001 *Tel:* 914-332-8888 *Toll Free Tel:* 800-821-9881 *Fax:* 914-332-8102 *E-mail:* customerservice@marshallcavendish.com; mcc@marshallcavendish.com *Web Site:* marshallcavendish.us; marshallcavendishdigital.com; marshallcavendishebooks.com, pg 158

Palermo, Laura, Peachtree Publishers, 1700 Chattahoochee Ave, Atlanta, GA 30318-2112 *Tel:* 404-876-8761 *Toll Free Tel:* 800-241-0113 *Fax:* 404-875-2578 *Toll Free Fax:* 800-875-8909 *E-mail:* hello@peachtree-online.com *Web Site:* www.peachtree-online.com, pg 195

Palin, Marissa, ANR Publications University of California, 1301 S 46 St, Bldg 478 - MC 3580, Richmond, CA 94804 *Tel:* 510-665-2195 (cust serv) *Toll Free Tel:* 800-994-8849 *Fax:* 510-665-3427 *E-mail:* anrcatalog@ucdavis.edu *Web Site:* anrcatalog.ucanr.edu, pg 19

Palkovic, Mark, Miniature Book Society Inc, 702 Rosecrans St, San Diego, CA 92106-3013 *Tel:* 619-226-4441 *Fax:* 619-226-4441 *E-mail:* minibook@cox.net *Web Site:* www.mbs.org, pg 627

Palladino, Linda, Random House Children's Books, 1745 Broadway, New York, NY 10019 *Tel:* 212-782-9000 *Toll Free Tel:* 800-200-3552 *Fax:* 212-782-9452 *Web Site:* randomhousekids.com, pg 213

Pallot, Wendy, Bloomsbury Publishing, 175 Fifth Ave, New York, NY 10010 *Tel:* 212-674-5151 *Toll Free Tel:* 800-221-7945 *Fax:* 212-780-0115; 212-982-2837 *E-mail:* marketingusa@bloomsbury.com; adultpublicityusa.@bloomsbury.com *Web Site:* www.bloomsbury.com, pg 40

Palmer, Dr Gail, Smoky Mountain Publishers, PO Box 684, Alcoa, TN 37701 *Tel:* 865-724-4959 *Web Site:* smokymountainpublishers.com, pg 529

Palmer, Jack, The Experiment, 260 Fifth Ave, Suite 3 South, New York, NY 10001-6425 *Tel:* 212-889-1659 *E-mail:* info@theexperimentpublishing.com *Web Site:* www.theexperimentpublishing.com, pg 91

Palmer, Jojo, World Vision Resources, 800 W Chestnut Ave, Monrovia, CA 91016-3198 *Tel:* 626-303-8811; 909-463-2998 (intl orders) *Toll Free Tel:* 800-777-7752 (US only) *Fax:* 909-463-2999 *E-mail:* wvresources@worldvision.org *Web Site:* www.worldvisionresources.com, pg 286

Palmer, Judd, Bayeux Arts Inc, 119 Stratton Crescent SW, Calgary, AB T3H 1T7, Canada *E-mail:* mail@bayeux.com *Web Site:* www.bayeux.com, pg 494

Palmer, Paula, US Games Systems Inc, 179 Ludlow St, Stamford, CT 06902 *Tel:* 203-353-8400 *Toll Free Tel:* 800-54-GAMES (544-2637) *Fax:* 203-353-8431 *E-mail:* info@usgamesinc.com *Web Site:* www.usgamesinc.com, pg 273

Palmquist, Nancy K, W W Norton & Company Inc, 500 Fifth Ave, New York, NY 10110-0017 *Tel:* 212-354-5500 *Toll Free Tel:* 800-233-4830 (orders & cust serv) *Fax:* 212-869-0856 *Toll Free Fax:* 800-458-6515 *Web Site:* www.wwnorton.com, pg 181

Panara, David, Information Today, Inc, 143 Old Marlton Pike, Medford, NJ 08055-8750 *Tel:* 609-654-6266 *Toll Free Tel:* 800-300-9868 (cust serv) *Fax:* 609-654-4309 *E-mail:* custserv@infotoday.com *Web Site:* www.infotoday.com, pg 130

Panec, Don, Treasure Bay Inc, PO Box 119, Novato, CA 94948 *Tel:* 415-884-2888 *Fax:* 415-884-2840 *E-mail:* webothread@comcast.net *Web Site:* www.webothread.com, pg 258

Panepinto, Lauren, Orbit, 237 Park Ave, New York, NY 10017 *Tel:* 212-364-1100 *Toll Free Tel:* 800-759-0190 *Web Site:* www.orbitbooks.net, pg 186

Pangburn, Michael, Artist Grants, 711 E Wells Ave, Pierre, SD 57501-3369 *Tel:* 605-773-3301 *Fax:* 605-773-5977 *E-mail:* sdac@state.sd.us *Web Site:* www.artscouncil.sd.gov/grants, pg 688

Pangle, Noelle, Playhouse Publishing, PO Box 1962, Cleveland, OH 44106 *Tel:* 330-926-1313 *Fax:* 330-475-8579 *E-mail:* info@picturemepress.com *Web Site:* www.picturemepress.com, pg 203

Panico, Neil, The Dawn Horse Press, 10336 Loch Lomond Rd, No 305, Middletown, CA 95461 *Tel:* 707-928-6590 *Toll Free Tel:* 877-770-0772 *Fax:* 707-928-6590 *E-mail:* dhp@adidam.org *Web Site:* www.dawnhorsepress.com, pg 76

Pannasch, Jeanann, The Feminist Press at The City University of New York, 365 Fifth Ave, Suite 5406, New York, NY 10016 *Tel:* 212-817-7915 *Fax:* 212-817-1593 *E-mail:* info@feministpress.org *Web Site:* www.feministpress.org, pg 94

Pannek, Lisa, Penguin Group (USA) LLC Sales, 375 Hudson St, New York, NY 10014 *Tel:* 212-366-2000 *E-mail:* online@penguinputnam.com *Web Site:* us.penguingroup.com, pg 197

Pantelo, Pam, Humanix Books LLC, PO Box 20989, West Palm Beach, FL 33416 *Tel:* 561-459-5997 *Toll Free Tel:* 855-371-7810 *Fax:* 561-241-6448 *Toll Free Fax:* 855-371-7809 *E-mail:* info@humanixbooks.com *Web Site:* www.humanixbooks.com, pg 125

Panzer, Caite, Oxford University Press USA, 198 Madison Ave, New York, NY 10016 *Tel:* 212-726-6000 *Toll Free Tel:* 800-451-7556 (orders); 800-445-9714 (cust serv) *Fax:* 919-677-1303 *E-mail:* custserv.us@oup.com *Web Site:* www.oup.com/us, pg 189

Panzer, Robert, Visual Artists & Galleries Association Inc (VAGA), 350 Fifth Ave, Suite 2820, New York, NY 10118 *Tel:* 212-736-6666 *Fax:* 212-736-6767 *E-mail:* info@vagarights.com *Web Site:* www.vagarights.com, pg 638

Papademetriou, Dean, Somerset Hall Press, 416 Commonwealth Ave, Suite 612, Boston, MA 02215 *Tel:* 617-236-5126 *E-mail:* info@somersethallpress.com *Web Site:* www.somersethallpress.com, pg 239

Papadopoulos, Niki, Portfolio, 375 Hudson St, New York, NY 10014, pg 204

Papale, Richard, ASCD, 1703 N Beauregard St, Alexandria, VA 22311-1714 *Tel:* 703-578-9600 *Toll Free Tel:* 800-933-2723 *Fax:* 703-575-5400 *E-mail:* member@ascd.org *Web Site:* www.ascd.org, pg 23

Paparozzi, Andrew D, NAPL, One Meadowlands Plaza, Suite 1511, East Rutherford, NJ 07073 *Tel:* 201-634-9600 *Toll Free Tel:* 800-642-6275 *Fax:* 201-634-0324 *E-mail:* naplmemberservice@napl.org *Web Site:* www.napl.org, pg 628

Paperny, Laura R, Fifi Oscard Agency Inc, 110 W 40 St, 16th fl, New York, NY 10018 *Tel:* 212-764-1100 *Fax:* 212-840-5019 *E-mail:* agency@fifioscard.com *Web Site:* www.fifioscard.com, pg 587

Papin, Jessica, Dystel & Goderich Literary Management, One Union Sq W, Suite 904, New York, NY 10003 *Tel:* 212-627-9100 *Fax:* 212-627-9313 *Web Site:* www.dystel.com, pg 569

Pappas, Evangeline A, ASIS International, 1625 Prince St, Alexandria, VA 22314 *Tel:* 703-519-6200 *Fax:* 703-519-6299 *E-mail:* asis@asisonline.org *Web Site:* www.asisonline.org, pg 24

Pappas, Joseph J, Consumer Press, 13326 SW 28 St, Suite 102, Fort Lauderdale, FL 33330-1102 *Tel:* 954-370-9153 *Fax:* 954-472-1008 *E-mail:* info@consumerpress.com *Web Site:* consumerpress.com, pg 66

Pappenheimer, Andrea, HarperCollins Children's Books, 10 E 53 St, New York, NY 10022 *Tel:* 212-207-7000 *Web Site:* www.harpercollinschildrens.com, pg 113

Pappenheimer, Andrea, HarperCollins Publishers Sales, 10 E 53 St, New York, NY 10022 *Fax:* 212-207-7000 *Web Site:* www.harpercollins.com, pg 114

Paradis, Lucille, Paulines Editions, 5610 rue Beaubien est, Montreal, QC H1T 1X5, Canada *Tel:* 514-253-5610 *Fax:* 514-253-1907 *E-mail:* editions@paulines.qc.ca *Web Site:* www.editions.paulines.qc.ca, pg 515

Paraskevopoulos, D Jane, Forward Movement Publications, 412 Sycamore St, Cincinnati, OH 45202-4110 *Tel:* 513-721-6659 *Toll Free Tel:* 800-543-1813 *Fax:* 513-721-0729 (orders) *E-mail:* orders@forwardmovement.org (orders & cust serv) *Web Site:* www.forwardmovement.org, pg 97

Parchert, Shirley, John Deere Publishing, 5440 Corporate Park Dr, Davenport, IA 52807 *Tel:* 309-765-4951 *Toll Free Tel:* 800-522-7448 (orders) *Fax:* 563-355-3690; 309-748-4083 *E-mail:* johndeerepublishing@johndeere.com *Web Site:* www.deere.com, pg 136

Parello, Jennifer, Bright Connections Media, A World Book Encyclopedia Company, 233 N Michigan Ave, Suite 2000, Chicago, IL 60601 *Tel:* 312-729-5800 *Fax:* 312-729-5610 *Web Site:* www.brightconnectionsmedia.com, pg 47

Parfrey, Adam, Feral House, 1240 W Sims Way, Suite 124, Port Townsend, WA 98368 *Tel:* 323-666-3311 *Fax:* 323-297-4331 *E-mail:* info@feralhouse.com *Web Site:* feralhouse.com, pg 94

Paris, Shirley, Carroll Publishing, 4701 Sangamore Rd, Suite S-155, Bethesda, MD 20816 *Tel:* 301-263-9800 *Toll Free Tel:* 800-336-4240 *Fax:* 301-263-9801 *E-mail:* info@carrollpub.com *Web Site:* www.carrollpub.com, pg 53

Parisi, Christina, AMACOM Books, 1601 Broadway, New York, NY 10019-7420 *Tel:* 212-586-8100; 518-891-5510 (orders) *Toll Free Tel:* 800-250-5308 (cust serv) *Fax:* 212-903-8083; 518-891-2372 (orders) *E-mail:* pubservice@amanet.org *Web Site:* www.amacombooks.org, pg 9

Parisi, Ron, CQ Press, 2300 "N" St NW, Suite 800, Washington, DC 20037 *Tel:* 202-729-1900 *Toll Free Tel:* 866-4CQ-PRESS (427-7737) *Fax:* 202-729-1923 *Toll Free Fax:* 800-380-3810 *E-mail:* customerservice@cqpress.com *Web Site:* www.cqpress.com, pg 70

Park, Drew, WingSpread Publishers, 2020 State Rd, Camp Hill, PA 17011 *Tel:* 717-761-7044 *Toll Free Tel:* 800-884-4571 *Fax:* 717-761-7273 *E-mail:* customerservice@echurchdepot.com *Web Site:* wingspreadpublishers.com, pg 283

Park, Gilman, Hudson Park Press, 232 Madison Ave, Rm 1400, New York, NY 10016 *Tel:* 212-929-8898 *Fax:* 212-208-0946, pg 125

Park, Mi Mi Chloe, Glitterati Inc, 322 W 57 St, No 19T, New York, NY 10019 *Tel:* 212-362-9119 *Fax:* 646-607-4433 *E-mail:* info@glitteratiincorporated.com *Web Site:* glitteratiincorporated.com, pg 103

Park, Michael, ABAC/ALAC, 368 Dalhousie St, Suite 301, Ottawa, ON K1N 7G3, Canada *Tel:* 416-364-2376 *E-mail:* info@abac.org *Web Site:* www.abac.org, pg 611

Park, Rick, Newbury Street Press, 101 Newbury St, Boston, MA 02116 *Tel:* 617-536-5740 *Toll Free Tel:* 888 296 3447 (NEHGS membership) *Fax:* 617-536-7307 *E-mail:* sales@nehgs.org *Web Site:* www.newenglandancestors.org, pg 179

Parker, Beth, Avery, 375 Hudson St, New York, NY 10014 *Tel:* 212-366-2000 *Fax:* 212-366-2643 *E-mail:* online@penguinputnam.com *Web Site:* www.penguinputnam.com; us.penguingroup.com, pg 28

Parker, David, Business Expert Press, 222 E 46 St, New York, NY 10017-2906 *Tel:* 908-752-1257 *E-mail:* molly.hurford@businessexpertpress.com *Web Site:* www.businessexpertpress.com, pg 50

Parker, Harvey, ADD Warehouse, 300 NW 70 Ave, Suite 102, Plantation, FL 33317 *Tel:* 954-792-8100 *Toll Free Tel:* 800-233-9273 *Fax:* 954-792-8545 *E-mail:* websales@addwarehouse.com *Web Site:* addwarehouse.com, pg 5

Parker, J Blake, Incentive Publications Inc, 2400 Crestmoor Rd, Suite 211, Nashville, TN 37215 *Tel:* 615-385-2934 *Toll Free Tel:* 800-421-2830 *Fax:* 615-385-2967 *E-mail:* comments@incentivepublications.com *Web Site:* www.incentivepublications.com, pg 128

Parker, Kate, W H Freeman and Co, 41 Madison Ave, 37th fl, New York, NY 10010 *Tel:* 212-576-9400 *Fax:* 212-689-2383 *Web Site:* www.whfreeman.com, pg 99

Parker, Leslie, McKenna Publishing Group, 425 POA Place, San Luis Obispo, CA 93405 *Tel:* 805-550-1667 *Web Site:* www.mckennapubgrp.com, pg 162

Parker, Mary Elizabeth, Dana Awards, Literary Competition, 200 Fosseway Dr, Greensboro, NC 27455 *E-mail:* danaawards@gmail.com *Web Site:* www.danaawards.com, pg 699

Parker, Peyton, Parlay Press, 301 Central Ave, No 311, Hilton Head, SC 29926 *Toll Free Fax:* 888-301-3116 *E-mail:* mail@parlaypress.com *Web Site:* www.parlaypress.com, pg 194

Parkerson, Ami, New World Library, 14 Pamaron Way, Novato, CA 94949 *Tel:* 415-884-2100 *Toll Free Tel:* 800-227-3900 (ext 52, retail orders); 800-972-6657 *Fax:* 415-884-2199 *E-mail:* escort@newworldlibrary.com *Web Site:* www.newworldlibrary.com, pg 178

Parkerson, Donnie, Oakstone Publishing LLC, 100 Corporate Pkwy, Suite 600, Birmingham, AL 35242 *Toll Free Tel:* 800-633-4743 *Fax:* 205-995-1926 *E-mail:* service@oakstonemedical.com *Web Site:* www.oakstonepublishing.com; www.cmeonly.com; www.cdeonly.com, pg 183

Parkin, Laurie, Kensington Publishing Corp, 119 W 40 St, New York, NY 10018 *Tel:* 212-407-1500 *Toll Free Tel:* 800-221-2647 *Fax:* 212-935-0699 *Web Site:* www.kensingtonbooks.com, pg 139

Parkinson, Judy, Research Press, 2612 N Mattis Ave, Champaign, IL 61822 *Tel:* 217-352-3273 *Toll Free Tel:* 800-519-2707 *Fax:* 217-352-1221 *E-mail:* rp@researchpress.com; orders@researchpress.com *Web Site:* www.researchpress.com, pg 218

Parkinson, Matt, Dark Horse Comics, 10956 SE Main St, Milwaukie, OR 97222 *Tel:* 503-652-8815 *Fax:* 503-654-9440 *E-mail:* dhcomics@darkhorsecomics.com *Web Site:* www.darkhorse.com, pg 75

Parks, Richard, The Richard Parks Agency, PO Box 693, Salem, NY 12865 *Tel:* 518-854-9466 *Fax:* 518-854-9466 *E-mail:* rp@richardparksagency.com, pg 588

Parks, Walter, UnKnownTruths.com Publishing Co, 8815 Conroy Windermere Rd, Suite 190, Orlando, FL 32835 *Tel:* 407-929-9207 *Fax:* 407-876-3933 *E-mail:* info@unknowntruths.com *Web Site:* unknowntruths.com, pg 272

Parr, Roz, Alfred A Knopf/Everyman's Library, c/o Random House Inc, 1745 Broadway, New York, NY 10019 *Tel:* 212-751-2600 *Toll Free Tel:* 800-638-6460 *Fax:* 212-572-2593 *Web Site:* www.knopfdoubleday.com, pg 141

Parrish, Jim, Bethany House Publishers, 11400 Hampshire Ave S, Bloomington, MN 55438 *Tel:* 952-829-2500 *Toll Free Tel:* 800-877-2665 (orders) *Fax:* 952-829-2568 *Toll Free Fax:* 800-398-3111 (orders) *Web Site:* www.bethanyhouse.com; www.bakerpublishinggroup.com, pg 36

Parsons, Brad, Houghton Mifflin Harcourt Trade & Reference Division, 222 Berkeley St, Boston, MA 02116-3764 *Tel:* 617-351-5000 *Toll Free Tel:* 800-225-3362 *Web Site:* www.houghtonmifflinbooks.com, pg 124

Parsons, Heidi, Institute of Environmental Sciences and Technology - IEST, 2340 S Arlington Heights Rd, Suite 100, Arlington Heights, IL 60005-4516 *Tel:* 847-981-0100 *Fax:* 847-981-4130 *E-mail:* information@iest.org *Web Site:* www.iest.org, pg 131

Parsons, Jayne, Bloomsbury Publishing, 175 Fifth Ave, New York, NY 10010 *Tel:* 212-674-5151 *Toll Free Tel:* 800-221-7945 *Fax:* 212-780-0115; 212-982-2837 *E-mail:* marketingusa@bloomsbury.com; adultpublicityusa.@bloomsbury.com *Web Site:* www.bloomsbury.com, pg 40

Parsons, Sue, Canadian Institute of Resources Law (Institut Canadien du Droit des Resources), Faculty of Law, University of Calgary, 2500 University Dr NW, MFH 3353, Calgary, AB T2N 1N4, Canada *Tel:* 403-220-3200 *Fax:* 403-282-6182 *E-mail:* cirl@ucalgary.ca *Web Site:* www.cirl.ca, pg 497

Parsons, Tara, Harlequin Enterprises Ltd, 233 Broadway, Suite 1001, New York, NY 10279 *Tel:* 212-553-4200 *Fax:* 212-227-8969 *E-mail:* CustomerService@harlequin.com *Web Site:* www.harlequin.com, pg 112

Partland, J P, Editorial Freelancers Association (EFA), 71 W 23 St, 4th fl, New York, NY 10010-4102 *Tel:* 212-929-5400 *Toll Free Tel:* 866-929-5425 *Fax:* 212-929-5439 *Toll Free Fax:* 866-929-5439 *E-mail:* info@the-efa.org; office@the-efa.org *Web Site:* www.the-efa.org, pg 622

Parziale, Lucian A, H W Wilson, 10 Estes St, Ipswich, MA 01938 *Tel:* 978-356-6500 *Toll Free Tel:* 800-653-2726 (US & CN) *Fax:* 978-356-6565 *E-mail:* information@ebscohost.com *Web Site:* www.ebscohost.com, pg 282

Pascocello, Rick, Berkley Books, 375 Hudson St, New York, NY 10014 *Tel:* 212-366-2000 *Fax:* 212-366-2666 *E-mail:* online@penguinputnam.com *Web Site:* www.penguinputnam.com; us.penguingroup.com, pg 35

Pascocello, Rick, Berkley Publishing Group, 375 Hudson St, New York, NY 10014 *Tel:* 212-366-2000 *Fax:* 212-366-2385 *E-mail:* online@penguinputnam.com *Web Site:* us.penguingroup.com, pg 36

Pascocello, Rick, NAL, 375 Hudson St, New York, NY 10014 *Tel:* 212-366-2000 *E-mail:* online@penguinputnam.com *Web Site:* www.penguinputnam.com; us.penguingroup.com, pg 172

Pascocello, Rick, Riverhead Books (Trade Paperback), 375 Hudson St, New York, NY 10014 *Tel:* 212-366-2000 *E-mail:* online@penguinputnam.com *Web Site:* www.penguinputnam.com; us.penguingroup.com, pg 219

Passanante, Donna, Crown Publishing Group, c/o Random House Inc, 1745 Broadway, New York, NY 10019 *Tel:* 212-782-9000 *Toll Free Tel:* 888-264-1745 *Fax:* 212-940-7408 *Web Site:* www.randomhouse.com/crown, pg 72

Passannante, Donna, Crown Publishing Group, c/o Random House Inc, 1745 Broadway, New York, NY 10019 *Tel:* 212-782-9000 *Toll Free Tel:* 888-264-1745 *Fax:* 212-940-7408 *Web Site:* www.randomhouse.com/crown, pg 72

Passannante, Donna, Watson-Guptill Publications, c/o Random House Inc, 1745 Broadway, New York, NY 10019 *Tel:* 212-782-9000 *Fax:* 212-940-7381 *E-mail:* crownbiz@randomhouse.com *Web Site:* www.randomhouse.com/crown/watsonguptill, pg 277

Passarella, Lee, International Poetry Competition, PO Box 8248, Atlanta, GA 31106 *E-mail:* atlanta.review@yahoo.com *Web Site:* www.atlantareview.com, pg 712

Pasternak, Tricia, Random House Publishing Group, 1745 Broadway, New York, NY 10019 *Toll Free Tel:* 800-200-3552 *Web Site:* atrandom.com, pg 214

Pastore, Julia, Demos Medical Publishing LLC, 11 W 42 St, New York, NY 10036 *Tel:* 212-683-0072 *Toll Free Tel:* 800-532-8663 *Fax:* 212-683-0118 *E-mail:* info@demosmedpub.com; orderdept@demosmedpub.com *Web Site:* www.demosmedpub.com, pg 78

Pata, Janae, Camino E E & Book Co, PO Box 6400, Incline Village, NV 89450 *Tel:* 775-831-3078 *Fax:* 775-831-3078 *E-mail:* info@camino-books.com *Web Site:* www.camino-books.com, pg 51

Patchin, Richard R, Delta Publishing Co, 1400 Miller Pkwy, McHenry, IL 60050-7030 *Tel:* 815-363-3582 *Toll Free Tel:* 800-323-8270 (orders) *Fax:* 815-363-2948 *Toll Free Fax:* 800-909-9901 *E-mail:* custsvc@deltapublishing.com *Web Site:* www.deltapublishing.com, pg 78

Pate, Ginger, Women Who Write, PO Box 652, Madison, NJ 07940-0652 *E-mail:* info@womenwhowrite.org *Web Site:* www.womenwhowrite.org, pg 638

Patenaude, Jason, Cobblestone Publishing, 30 Grove St, Suite C, Peterborough, NH 03458 *Tel:* 603-924-7209 *Toll Free Tel:* 800-821-0115 *Fax:* 603-924-7380 *E-mail:* customerservice@caruspub.com *Web Site:* www.cobblestonepub.com, pg 64

Paterson, Shelagh, Ontario Library Association, 50 Wellington St E, Suite 201, Toronto, ON M5E 1C8, Canada *Tel:* 416-363-3388 *Toll Free Tel:* 866-873-9867 *Fax:* 416-941-9581 *Toll Free Fax:* 800-387-1181 *E-mail:* info@accessola.com *Web Site:* www.accessola.com, pg 633

Patnaik, Gayatri, Beacon Press, 25 Beacon St, Boston, MA 02108 *Tel:* 617-742-2110 *Fax:* 617-723-3097; 617-742-2290 *Web Site:* www.beacon.org, pg 32

Paton, Kathi J, Kathi J Paton Literary Agency, Box 2236, Radio City Sta, New York, NY 10101-2236 *Tel:* 212-265-6586 *Fax:* 908-647-2117 *E-mail:* kjplitbiz@optonline.net *Web Site:* www.patonliterary.com, pg 588

Paton, Ken, WingSpread Publishers, 2020 State Rd, Camp Hill, PA 17011 *Tel:* 717-761-7044 *Toll Free Tel:* 800-884-4571 *Fax:* 717-761-7273 *E-mail:* customerservice@echurchdepot.com *Web Site:* wingspreadpublishers.com, pg 283

Patota, Anne, The Guilford Press, 72 Spring St, 4th fl, New York, NY 10012 *Tel:* 212-431-9800 *Toll Free Tel:* 800-365-7006 (ext 1, orders) *Fax:* 212-966-6708 *E-mail:* orders@guilford.com; info@guilford.com *Web Site:* www.guilford.com, pg 109

Patrick, Harley B, Hellgate Press, PO Box 3531, Ashland, OR 97520 *Tel:* 541-973-5154 *Toll Free Tel:* 800-795-4059 *E-mail:* info@hellgatepress.com *Web Site:* www.hellgatepress.com, pg 117

Patrick, Julia, Chronicle Books LLC, 680 Second St, San Francisco, CA 94107 *Tel:* 415-537-4200 *Toll Free Tel:* 800-759-0190 (cust serv) *Fax:* 415-537-4460 *Toll Free Fax:* 800-858-7787 (orders); 800-286-9471 (cust serv) *E-mail:* frontdesk@chroniclebooks.com *Web Site:* www.chroniclebooks.com, pg 61

Patrusky, Ben, Council for the Advancement of Science Writing (CASW), PO Box 910, Hedgesville, WV 25427 *Tel:* 304-754-6786 *Web Site:* www.casw.org, pg 622

Patrusky, Ben, Rennie Taylor & Alton Blakeslee Fellowships in Science Writing, PO Box 910, Hedgesville, WV 25427 *Tel:* 304-754-6786 *Web Site:* www.casw.org, pg 745

Patterson, Elaine, Maryland History Press, PO Box 206, Fruitland, MD 21826-0206 *Tel:* 410-742-2682 *Toll Free Tel:* 877-742-2682 *Fax:* 410-505-4555 *E-mail:* sales@marylandhistorypress.com *Web Site:* www.marylandhistorypress.com, pg 158

Patterson, Emma, Brandt & Hochman Literary Agents Inc, 1501 Broadway, Suite 2310, New York, NY 10036 *Tel:* 212-840-5760 *Fax:* 212-840-5776 *Web Site:* brandthochman.com, pg 564

Patterson, Jean, Huntington Library Press, 1151 Oxford Rd, San Marino, CA 91108 *Tel:* 626-405-2172 *Fax:* 626-585-0794 *E-mail:* booksales@huntington.org *Web Site:* www.huntington.org, pg 126

Patterson, Karen, Adams Media, 57 Littlefield St, Avon, MA 02322 *Tel:* 508-427-7100 *Fax:* 508-427-6790 *Toll Free Fax:* 800-872-5627 *E-mail:* orders@adamsmedia.com *Web Site:* www.adamsmedia.com, pg 5

Patterson, Karen, F+W Media Inc, 10151 Carver Rd, Suite 200, Blue Ash, OH 45242 *Tel:* 513-531-2690 *Toll Free Tel:* 800-289-0963 (trade accts); 800-258-0929 (orders) *E-mail:* contact_us@fwmedia.com *Web Site:* www.fwmedia.com, pg 92

Patterson, Kathleen, Optometric Extension Program Foundation, 1921 E Carnegie Ave, Suite 3-L, Santa Ana, CA 92705-5510 *Tel:* 949-250-8070 *Fax:* 949-250-8157 *E-mail:* oep@oep.org *Web Site:* www.oepf.org, pg 186

Patterson, Monique, St Martin's Press, LLC, 175 Fifth Ave, New York, NY 10010 *Tel:* 646-307-5151 *Fax:* 212-420-9314 *E-mail:* firstname.lastname@macmillan.com *Web Site:* www.stmartins.com, pg 224

Patterson, Sarah, Association Media & Publishing, 12100 Sunset Hills Rd, Suite 130, Reston, VA 20190 *Tel:* 703-234-4063 *Fax:* 703-435-4390 *E-mail:* info@associationmediaandpublishing.org *Web Site:* www.associationmediaandpublishing.org, pg 615

Patterson, Sarah, EXCEL Awards, 12100 Sunset Hills Rd, Suite 130, Reston, VA 20190 *Tel:* 703-234-4063 *Fax:* 703-435-4390 *E-mail:* info@associationmediaandpublishing.org *Web Site:* www.associationmediaandpublishing.org, pg 703

Patterson, Tracy, Stackpole Books, 5067 Ritter Rd, Mechanicsburg, PA 17055 *Tel:* 717-796-0411 *Toll Free Tel:* 800-732-3669 *Fax:* 717-796-0412 *Web Site:* www.stackpolebooks.com, pg 242

Patz, Richard, CTB/McGraw-Hill, 20 Ryan Ranch Rd, Monterey, CA 93940-5703 *Tel:* 831-393-0700 *Toll Free Tel:* 800-538-9547 *Fax:* 831-393-7825 *Web Site:* www.ctb.com, pg 73

Paul, Beverly, Beautiful America Publishing Co, 2600 Progress Way, Woodburn, OR 97071 *Tel:* 503-982-4616 *Toll Free Tel:* 800-874-1233 *Fax:* 503-982-2825 *E-mail:* bapco@beautifulamericapub.com *Web Site:* www.beautifulamericapub.com, pg 33

Paul, Chris, Candlewick Press, 99 Dover St, Somerville, MA 02144-2825 *Tel:* 617-661-3330 *Fax:* 617-661-0565 *E-mail:* bigbear@candlewick.com *Web Site:* www.candlewick.com, pg 51

Paul, Nancy Gray, Woodbine House, 6510 Bells Mill Rd, Bethesda, MD 20817 *Tel:* 301-897-3570 *Toll Free Tel:* 800-843-7323 *Fax:* 301-897-5838 *E-mail:* info@woodbinehouse.com *Web Site:* www.woodbinehouse.com, pg 284

Paulding, Barbara, Peter Pauper Press, Inc, 202 Mamaroneck Ave, White Plains, NY 10601-5376 *Tel:* 914-681-0144 *Fax:* 914-681-0389 *E-mail:* customerservice@peterpauper.com; orders@peterpauper.com *Web Site:* www.peterpauper.com, pg 200

Pauls, Kris, Greenleaf Book Group LLC, 4005 Banister Lane, Suite B, Austin, TX 78704 *Tel:* 512-891-6100 *Toll Free Tel:* 800-932-5420 *Fax:* 512-891-6150 *E-mail:* contact@greenleafbookgroup.com *Web Site:* www.greenleafbookgroup.com, pg 107

Paulsen, Nancy, GP Putnam's Sons (Children's), 345 Hudson St, New York, NY 10014 *Tel:* 212-366-2000 *Fax:* 212-414-3393 *E-mail:* online@penguinputnam.com *Web Site:* us.penguingroup.com, pg 210

Paulson, Jamis, Turnstone Press, 100 Arthur St, Unit 206, Winnipeg, MB R3B 1H3, Canada *Tel:* 204-947-1555 *Toll Free Tel:* 888-363-7718 *Fax:* 204-942-1555 *E-mail:* info@turnstonepress.com *Web Site:* www.turnstonepress.com, pg 522

Paumen, Brandon, North Star Press of Saint Cloud Inc, PO Box 451, St Cloud, MN 56302-0451 *Tel:* 320-558-9062 *Toll Free Tel:* 888-820-1636 *Fax:* 320-558-9063 *E-mail:* info@northstarpress.com *Web Site:* www.northstarpress.com, pg 181

Pautz, Peter Dennis, World Fantasy Awards, PO Box 43, Mukilteo, WA 98275-0043 *Web Site:* www.worldfantasy.org, pg 751

Pavia, Julian, Crown Publishing Group, c/o Random House Inc, 1745 Broadway, New York, NY 10019 *Tel:* 212-782-9000 *Toll Free Tel:* 888-264-1745 *Fax:* 212-940-7408 *Web Site:* www.randomhouse.com/crown, pg 72

Pavlin, Jordan, Alfred A Knopf/Everyman's Library, c/o Random House Inc, 1745 Broadway, New York, NY 10019 *Tel:* 212-751-2600 *Toll Free Tel:* 800-638-6460 *Fax:* 212-572-2593 *Web Site:* www.knopfdoubleday.com, pg 141

Pawlak, Mark, Hanging Loose Press, 231 Wyckoff St, Brooklyn, NY 11217 *Tel:* 347-529-4738 *Fax:* 347-227-8215 *E-mail:* print225@aol.com *Web Site:* www.hangingloosepress.com, pg 111

Payette, Jacques, Les Editions Heritage Inc, 300 Rue Arran, St-Lambert, QC J4R 1K5, Canada *Tel:* 514-875-0327 *Toll Free Tel:* 800-561-3737 *Fax:* 450-672-5448, pg 503

Payette, Sylvie, Les Editions Heritage Inc, 300 Rue Arran, St-Lambert, QC J4R 1K5, Canada *Tel:* 514-875-0327 *Toll Free Tel:* 800-561-3737 *Fax:* 450-672-5448, pg 503

Payne, Jennifer, Bick Publishing House, 16 Marion Rd, Branford, CT 06405 *Tel:* 203-208-5253 *Fax:* 203-208-5253 *E-mail:* bickpubhse@aol.com *Web Site:* www.bickpubhouse.com, pg 37

Payne, Prof Johnny, University of Texas at El Paso, Dept Creative Writing, MFA/Dept Creative Writing, Liberal Arts 415 UTEP, 500 W University Ave, El Paso, TX 79968-9991 *Tel:* 915-747-5713 *Fax:* 915-747-5523 *Web Site:* www.utep.edu/cw, pg 682

Payne, Maribeth, W W Norton & Company Inc, 500 Fifth Ave, New York, NY 10110-0017 *Tel:* 212-354-5500 *Toll Free Tel:* 800-233-4830 (orders & cust serv) *Fax:* 212-869-0856 *Toll Free Fax:* 800-458-6515 *Web Site:* www.wwnorton.com, pg 182

Payton, Thomas, Trinity University Press, One Trinity Place, San Antonio, TX 78212-7200 *Tel:* 210-999-8884 *Fax:* 210-999-8838 *E-mail:* books@trinity.edu *Web Site:* www.tupress.org, pg 259

Pazdera, Todd, Llewellyn Publications, 2143 Wooddale Dr, Woodbury, MN 55125 *Tel:* 651-291-1970 *Toll Free Tel:* 800-843-6666 *Fax:* 651-291-1908 *E-mail:* publicity@llewellyn.com *Web Site:* www.llewellyn.com, pg 151

Pazour, Don, Dorland Healthcare Information, 4 Choke Cherry Rd, 2nd fl, Rockville, MD 20850 *Tel:* 301-354-2000 *Toll Free Tel:* 800-784-2332 *Fax:* 801-365-2300 *E-mail:* info@dorlandhealth.com *Web Site:* www.dorlandhealth.com, pg 81

Peabody, William, GP Putnam's Sons (Hardcover), 375 Hudson St, New York, NY 10014 *Tel:* 212-366-2000 *E-mail:* online@penguinputnam.com *Web Site:* us.penguingroup.com, pg 210

Peake, Leigh, Heinemann, 361 Hanover St, Portsmouth, NH 03801-3912 *Tel:* 603-431-7894 *Toll Free Tel:* 800-225-5800 (US) *Fax:* 603-431-2214 *Toll Free Fax:* 877-231-6980 (US) *E-mail:* custserv@heinemann.com *Web Site:* www.heinemann.com, pg 117

Pearce, Beth, The Fairmont Press Inc, 700 Indian Trail, Lilburn, GA 30047 *Tel:* 770-925-9388 *Fax:* 770-381-9865 *Web Site:* www.fairmontpress.com, pg 92

Pearce, John, Westwood Creative Artists Ltd, 94 Harbord St, Toronto, ON M5S 1G6, Canada *Tel:* 416-964-3302 *Fax:* 416-975-9209 *E-mail:* wca_office@wcaltd.com *Web Site:* www.wcaltd.com, pg 599

Pearce, Dr Scott, Center for East Asian Studies (CEAS), Western Washington University, 516 High St, Bellingham, WA 98225-9057 *Tel:* 360-650-3339 *Fax:* 360-650-6110 *E-mail:* easpress@wwu.edu *Web Site:* www.wwu.edu/eas, pg 56

Pearl, Allyson, Random House Publishing Group, 1745 Broadway, New York, NY 10019 *Toll Free Tel:* 800-200-3552 *Web Site:* atrandom.com, pg 214

Pearpoint, Jack, Inclusion Press International, 47 Indian Trail, Toronto, ON M6R 1Z8, Canada *Tel:* 416-658-5363 *Fax:* 416-658-5067 *E-mail:* inclusionpress@inclusion.com *Web Site:* www.inclusion.com, pg 509

Pearson, Gina, Energy Information Administration (EIA), 1000 Independence Ave SW, Washington, DC 20585 *Tel:* 202-586-8800 *Fax:* 202-586-0727 *E-mail:* infoctr@eia.doe.gov *Web Site:* www.eia.doe.gov, pg 88

Pearson, Lisa, Siglio, 2432 Medlow Ave, Los Angeles, CA 90041 *Tel:* 310-857-6935 *Fax:* 310-728-6844 *E-mail:* publisher@sigliopress.com *Web Site:* sigliopress.com, pg 233

Pearson, Michael, The Mathematical Association of America, 1529 18 St NW, Washington, DC 20036-1358 *Tel:* 202-387-5200 *Toll Free Tel:* 800-741-9415 *Fax:* 202-265-2384 *E-mail:* maahq@maa.org *Web Site:* www.maa.org, pg 159

Pearson, Nancy, Scholastic Canada Ltd, 604 King St W, Toronto, ON M5V 1E1, Canada *Tel:* 905-887-7323 *Toll Free Tel:* 800-268-3848 (CN) *Fax:* 905-887-1131 *Toll Free Fax:* 866-346-1288 *Web Site:* www.scholastic.ca, pg 518

Pease, Pamela, Paintbox Press, 275 Madison Ave, Suite 600, New York, NY 10016 *Tel:* 212-878-6610 *Fax:* 212-202-6157 *E-mail:* info@paintboxpress.com *Web Site:* www.paintboxpress.com, pg 191

Pease, Roland, Steerforth Press, 45 Lyme Rd, Suite 208, Hanover, NH 03755-1222 *Tel:* 603-643-4787 *Fax:* 603-643-4788 *E-mail:* info@steerforth.com *Web Site:* www.steerforth.com, pg 244

Peattie, Gary R, De Vorss & Co, 553 Constitution Ave, Camarillo, CA 93012-8510 *Tel:* 805-322-9010 *Toll Free Tel:* 800-843-5743 *Fax:* 805-322-9011 *E-mail:* service@devorss.com *Web Site:* www.devorss.com, pg 77

Peck, Alice, Words into Print, 131 Fifth Ave, Suite 501, New York, NY 10003 *Tel:* 212-741-1393 *Fax:* 419-441-1393 *E-mail:* query@wordsintoprint.org *Web Site:* www.wordsintoprint.org, pg 557

Peckous, Frank, Do It Now Foundation, PO Box 27568, Tempe, AZ 85285-7568 *Tel:* 480-736-0599 *Fax:* 480-736-0771 *Web Site:* www.doitnow.org, pg 80

Pedersen, Nadine, Pacific Educational Press, c/o University of British Columbia, Faculty of Education, 411-2389 Health Sciences Mall, Vancouver, BC V6T 1Z4, Canada *Tel:* 604-822-5385 *Fax:* 604-822-6603 *E-mail:* pep.sales@ubc.ca *Web Site:* www.pacificedpress.ca, pg 514

Peed, Sarah, Random House Inc, 1745 Broadway, New York, NY 10019 *Tel:* 212-782-9000 *Toll Free Tel:* 800-726-0600 *Web Site:* www.randomhouse.com, pg 213

Peel, Tim, CCAB Inc, One Concorde Gate, Suite 800, Toronto, ON M3C 3N6, Canada *Tel:* 416-487-2418 *Fax:* 416-487-6405 *E-mail:* info@bpaww.com *Web Site:* www.bpaww.com, pg 621

Peele, Rosie, Mary Evans Inc, 242 E Fifth St, New York, NY 10003-8501 *Tel:* 212-979-0880 *Fax:* 212-979-5344 *E-mail:* info@maryevansinc.com *Web Site:* www.maryevansinc.com, pg 571

Peeler, Denise, University of Illinois Press, 1325 S Oak St, MC-566, Champaign, IL 61820-6903 *Tel:* 217-333-0950 *Fax:* 217-244-8082 *E-mail:* uipress@uillinois.edu; journals@uillinois.edu *Web Site:* www.press.uillinois.edu, pg 266

Pelehach, Laura, Academy of Nutrition & Dietetics, 120 S Riverside Plaza, Suite 2000, Chicago, IL 60606-6995 *Tel:* 312-899-0040 *Toll Free Tel:* 800-877-1600 *Fax:* 312-899-4757 *E-mail:* sales@eatright.org *Web Site:* www.eatright.org, pg 4

Pelicano, Kara, Clerisy Press, 306 Greenup St, Covington, KY 41011 *Tel:* 513-861-4045 *Toll Free Tel:* 888-604-4537 *Fax:* 859-291-9111 *E-mail:* info@clerisypress.com *Web Site:* www.clerisypress.com, pg 63

Pelkey, Dean, The Fraser Institute, 1770 Burrard St, 4th fl, Vancouver, BC V6J 3G7, Canada *Tel:* 604-688-0221 *Toll Free Tel:* 800-665-3558 *Fax:* 604-688-8539 *E-mail:* info@fraserinstitute.org; sales@fraserinstitute.org *Web Site:* www.fraserinstitute.org, pg 506

Pellant, Daisy, Rada Press Inc, 1277 Fairmount Ave, St Paul, MN 55105 *Tel:* 651-645-3304 *E-mail:* info@radapress.com *Web Site:* www.radapress.com, pg 212

Pellant, Ron-Michael, Rada Press Inc, 1277 Fairmount Ave, St Paul, MN 55105 *Tel:* 651-645-3304 *E-mail:* info@radapress.com *Web Site:* www.radapress.com, pg 212

Peller, Allan W, Educational Impressions Inc, 350 Ramapo Valley Rd, Oakland, NJ 07436 *Tel:* 973-423-4666 *Toll Free Tel:* 800-451-7450 *Fax:* 973-423-5569 *Web Site:* www.edimpressions.com; www.awpeller.com, pg 85

Peller, Neil, Educational Impressions Inc, 350 Ramapo Valley Rd, Oakland, NJ 07436 *Tel:* 973-423-4666 *Toll Free Tel:* 800-451-7450 *Fax:* 973-423-5569 *Web Site:* www.edimpressions.com; www.awpeller.com, pg 85

Pellerin, Alexandra, Les Editions de Mortagne, CP 116, Boucherville, QC J4B 5E6, Canada *Tel:* 450-641-2387 *Fax:* 450-655-6092 *E-mail:* info@editionsdemortagne.com *Web Site:* www.editionsdemortagne.com, pg 502

Pellerin, Caroline, Les Editions de Mortagne, CP 116, Boucherville, QC J4B 5E6, Canada *Tel:* 450-641-2387 *Fax:* 450-655-6092 *E-mail:* info@editionsdemortagne.com *Web Site:* www.editionsdemortagne.com, pg 502

Pellerin, Sandy, Les Editions de Mortagne, CP 116, Boucherville, QC J4B 5E6, Canada *Tel:* 450-641-2387 *Fax:* 450-655-6092 *E-mail:* info@editionsdemortagne.com *Web Site:* www.editionsdemortagne.com, pg 502

Pelletier, James L, Marine Techniques Publishing, 126 Western Ave, Suite 266, Augusta, ME 04330-7249 *Tel:* 207-622-7984 *E-mail:* info@marinetechpublishing.com; sales@marinetechpublishing.com *Web Site:* marinetechpublishing.com; www.groups.yahoo.com/group/marinetechniquespublishing, pg 157

Pelletier, Liz, Entangled Publishing, 2614 S Timberline Rd, Suite 109, Fort Collins, CO 80525 *Tel:* 724-208-7888 (sales) *E-mail:* publisher@entangledpublishing.com *Web Site:* www.entangledpublishing.com, pg 89

Pelletier, Sharon, Dystel & Goderich Literary Management, One Union Sq W, Suite 904, New York, NY 10003 *Tel:* 212-627-9100 *Fax:* 212-627-9313 *Web Site:* www.dystel.com, pg 569

Peloquin, Ginette, Les Editions du Remue-Menage, La Maison Parent-Roback, 110 rue Ste-Therese, bureau 501, Montreal, QC H2Y 1E6, Canada *Tel:* 514-876-0097 *Fax:* 514-876-7951 *E-mail:* info@editions-remuemenage.qc.ca *Web Site:* www.editions-remuemenage.qc.ca, pg 503

Peltz, Amy, The Art Institute of Chicago, 111 S Michigan Ave, Chicago, IL 60603-6404 *Tel:* 312-443-3600; 312-443-3540 (pubns) *Fax:* 312-443-1334 (pubns) *Web Site:* www.artic.edu; www.artinstituteshop.org, pg 22

Peltz, James, Excelsior Editions, 22 Corporate Woods Blvd, 3rd fl, Albany, NY 12211-2504 *Tel:* 518-472-5000 *Toll Free Tel:* 877-204-6073 *Fax:* 518-472-5038 *Toll Free Fax:* 877-204-6074 *E-mail:* info@sunypress.edu *Web Site:* www.sunypress.edu, pg 90

Peltz, James, State University of New York Press, 22 Corporate Woods Blvd, 3rd fl, Albany, NY 12211-2504 *Tel:* 518-472-5000 *Toll Free Tel:* 877-204-6073 (orders) *Fax:* 518-472-5038 *Toll Free Fax:* 877-204-6074 (orders) *E-mail:* suny@presswarehouse.com (orders); info@sunypress.edu (edit off) *Web Site:* www.sunypress.edu, pg 243

Peluse, Michael, Cambridge University Press, 32 Avenue of the Americas, New York, NY 10013-2473 *Tel:* 212-924-3900; 212-337-5000 *Toll Free Tel:* 800-899-5222 *Fax:* 212-691-3239 *E-mail:* newyork@cambridge.org *Web Site:* www.cambridge.org/us, pg 51

Penalba, Ezra, White Cloud Press, 300 E Hersey St, Suite 11, Ashland, OR 97520 *Tel:* 541-488-6415 *Toll Free Tel:* 800-380-8286 *Fax:* 541-482-7708 *E-mail:* info@whitecloudpress.com *Web Site:* www.whitecloudpress.com, pg 280

Pendergast, Alison, Jones & Bartlett Learning LLC, 5 Wall St, Burlington, MA 01803 *Tel:* 978-443-5000 *Toll Free Tel:* 800-832-0034 *Fax:* 978-443-8000 *E-mail:* info@jblearning.com *Web Site:* www.jblearning.com, pg 137

Peng, Cindy, Allworth Press, 307 W 36 St, 11th fl, New York, NY 10018 *Tel:* 212-643-6816 *E-mail:* crawford@allworth.com *Web Site:* www.allworth.com, pg 9

Pennefeather, Shannon M, Minnesota Historical Society Press, 345 Kellogg Blvd W, St Paul, MN 55102-1906 *Tel:* 651-259-3205; 651-259-3000 *Toll Free Tel:* 800-621-2736 (warehouse) *Fax:* 651-297-1345 *Toll Free Fax:* 800-621-8476 (warehouse) *E-mail:* info-mhspress@mnhs.org *Web Site:* www.mhspress.org, pg 167

Penney, Beth, Beth Penney Editorial Services, PO Box 604, Pacific Grove, CA 93950-0604 *Tel:* 831-372-7625, pg 552

Pennington, Mikki, National Federation of State Poetry Societies Annual Poetry Contest, PO Box 7842, Moore, OK 73153 *E-mail:* connpoetry@comcast.net *Web Site:* www.NFSPS.com, pg 726

Penrose, Denise, University of California Press, 2120 Berkeley Way, Berkeley, CA 94704-1012 *Tel:* 510-642-4247 *Fax:* 510-643-7127 *E-mail:* askucp@ucpress.edu (books); customerservice@ucpressjournals.com (journals) *Web Site:* www.ucpress.edu, pg 264

Penry, Tara, Hemingway Western Studies Center, Boise State University, 1910 University Dr, Boise, ID 83725-1135 *Tel:* 208-426-1999; 208-426-1514 *Fax:* 208-426-4373 *E-mail:* books@booksboisestate.com *Web Site:* www.booksboisestate.com, pg 118

Pentes, Jennifer, Lonely Planet, 150 Linden St, Oakland, CA 94607 *Tel:* 510-893-8555 *Toll Free Tel:* 800-275-8555 (orders) *Fax:* 510-893-8563 *E-mail:* info@lonelyplanet.com *Web Site:* www.lonelyplanet.com, pg 152

Pepe, Christine, GP Putnam's Sons (Hardcover), 375 Hudson St, New York, NY 10014 *Tel:* 212-366-2000 *E-mail:* online@penguinputnam.com *Web Site:* us.penguingroup.com, pg 210

Pepe, Paolo, Random House Publishing Group, 1745 Broadway, New York, NY 10019 *Toll Free Tel:* 800-200-3552 *Web Site:* atrandom.com, pg 214

Pepper, Douglas, McClelland & Stewart Ltd, 75 Sherbourne St, 5th fl, Toronto, ON M5A 2P9, Canada *Tel:* 416-598-1114 *Fax:* 416-598-7764 *E-mail:* editorial@mcclelland.com *Web Site:* www.mcclelland.com, pg 512

Pepper, Eric, SPIE, 1000 20 St, Bellingham, WA 98225-6705 *Tel:* 360-676-3290 *Toll Free Tel:* 888-504-8171 *Fax:* 360-647-1445 *E-mail:* spie@spie.org *Web Site:* www.spie.org, pg 241

Pepper, Jeff, Apress Media LLC, 233 Spring St, New York, NY 10013 *Tel:* 212-460-1500 *Fax:* 212-460-1575 *E-mail:* editorial@apress.com *Web Site:* www.apress.com, pg 21

Peragine, Dan, Dan Peragine Literary Agency, 227 Beechwood Ave, Bogota, NJ 07603 *Tel:* 201-390-0468 *E-mail:* dpliterary@aol.com, pg 588

Peragine, Karen A, Dan Peragine Literary Agency, 227 Beechwood Ave, Bogota, NJ 07603 *Tel:* 201-390-0468 *E-mail:* dpliterary@aol.com, pg 588

Peranteau, Paul, John Benjamins Publishing Co, PO Box 27519, Philadelphia, PA 19118 *Tel:* 215-836-1200 *Toll Free Tel:* 800-562-5666 (orders) *Fax:* 215-836-1204 *E-mail:* service@benjamins.com *Web Site:* www.benjamins.com, pg 35

Perdue, Amy, Henrico Theatre Company One-Act Playwriting Competition, PO Box 90775, Richmond, VA 23273-0775 *Tel:* 804-501-5138 *Fax:* 804-501-5284, pg 709

Perdue, Charles, McFarland, 960 NC Hwy 88 W, Jefferson, NC 28640 *Tel:* 336-246-4460 *Toll Free Tel:* 800-253-2187 (orders) *Fax:* 336-246-5018; 336-246-4403 (orders) *E-mail:* info@mcfarlandpub.com *Web Site:* www.mcfarlandpub.com, pg 160

Pereira, Mark, Brilliance Audio, 1704 Eaton Dr, Grand Haven, MI 49417 *Tel:* 616-846-5256 *Toll Free Tel:* 800-648-2312 (orders only) *Fax:* 616-846-0630 *E-mail:* customerservice@brillianceaudio.com *Web Site:* www.brillianceaudio.com, pg 47

Perel, Kimberly, Wendy Sherman Associates Inc, 27 W 24 St, Suite 700-B, New York, NY 10010 *Tel:* 212-279-9027 *Fax:* 212-279-9027 *Web Site:* www.wsherman.com, pg 594

Perez, Danielle, NAL, 375 Hudson St, New York, NY 10014 *Tel:* 212-366-2000 *E-mail:* online@penguinputnam.com *Web Site:* www.penguinputnam.com; us.penguingroup.com, pg 172

Perez, Jaime, Information Gatekeepers Inc, 1340 Soldiers Field Rd, Suite 2, Boston, MA 02135 *Tel:* 617-782-5033 *Toll Free Tel:* 800-323-1088 *Fax:* 617-782-5735 *E-mail:* info@igigroup.com *Web Site:* www.igigroup.com, pg 130

Perez, Jeanette, HarperCollins General Books Group, 10 E 53 St, New York, NY 10022 *Tel:* 212-207-7000 *Fax:* 212-207-7633 *Web Site:* www.harpercollins.com, pg 113

Perez, Joe, Random House Publishing Group, 1745 Broadway, New York, NY 10019 *Toll Free Tel:* 800-200-3552 *Web Site:* atrandom.com, pg 214

Perez, Margie, The Amy Rennert Agency Inc, 1550 Tiburon Blvd, Suite 302, Tiburon, CA 94920 *Tel:* 415-789-8955 *E-mail:* queries@amyrennert.com *Web Site:* amyrennert.com, pg 590

Perez, Minh L, Multimedia Larga, 900 S Boardman Dr, No G72, Gallup, NM 87301 *Tel:* 505-726-1720, pg 171

Perez, Nanette, John Phillip Immroth Memorial Award, 50 E Huron St, Chicago, IL 60611 *Tel:* 312-280-4223 *Toll Free Tel:* 800-545-2433 *Fax:* 312-280-4227 *E-mail:* oif@ala.org *Web Site:* www.ala.org/ifrt, pg 711

Perez, Nanette, Eli M Oboler Memorial Award, 50 E Huron St, Chicago, IL 60611 *Tel:* 312-280-4223 *Toll Free Tel:* 800-545-2433 *Fax:* 312-280-4227 *E-mail:* oif@ala.org *Web Site:* www.ala.org/ifrt, pg 730

Perez, Peter, Chronicle Books LLC, 680 Second St, San Francisco, CA 94107 *Tel:* 415-537-4200 *Toll Free Tel:* 800-759-0190 (cust serv) *Fax:* 415-537-4460 *Toll Free Fax:* 800-858-7787 (orders); 800-286-9471 (cust serv) *E-mail:* frontdesk@chroniclebooks.com *Web Site:* www.chroniclebooks.com, pg 61

Perillo, Jennifer, Columbia University Press, 61 W 62 St, New York, NY 10023 *Tel:* 212-459-0600 *Toll Free Tel:* 800-944-8648 *Fax:* 212-459-3678 *E-mail:* cup_book@columbia.edu (orders & cust serv) *Web Site:* cup.columbia.edu, pg 65

Perkins, Dorothy, Diane Publishing Co, 330 Pusey Ave, Suite 3 (rear), Collingdale, PA 19023-0617 *Tel:* 610-461-6200 *Toll Free Tel:* 800-782-3833 *Fax:* 610-461-6130 *Web Site:* www.dianepublishing.net, pg 79

Perkins, Edie, Scholastic International, 557 Broadway, New York, NY 10012 *Tel:* 212-343-6100; 646-330-5288 (intl cust serv) *Toll Free Tel:* 800-SCHOLASTIC (800-724-6527) *Fax:* 646-837-7878 *E-mail:* international@scholastic.com, pg 228

Perkins, Gareth K, Berkeley Slavic Specialties, PO Box 3034, Oakland, CA 94609-0034 *Tel:* 510-653-8048 *Fax:* 510-653-6313 *E-mail:* 71034.456@compuserve.com *Web Site:* www.berkslav.com, pg 35

Perkins, Lori, Riverdale Avenue Books (RAB), 5676 Riverdale Ave, Bronx, NY 10471 *Tel:* 212-279-6418 *Web Site:* www.riverdaleavebooks.com, pg 219

Perkins, Mr Terry, Pflaum Publishing Group, 2621 Dryden Rd, Suite 300, Dayton, OH 45439 *Tel:* 937-293-1415 *Toll Free Tel:* 800-543-4383; 800-523-4625 (sales) *Fax:* 937-293-1310 *Toll Free Fax:* 800-370-4450 *E-mail:* service@pflaum.com *Web Site:* pflaum.com, pg 200

Perl, Liz, Simon & Schuster, Inc, 1230 Avenue of the Americas, New York, NY 10020 *Tel:* 212-698-7000 *Fax:* 212-698-7007 *E-mail:* firstname.lastname@simonandschuster.com *Web Site:* www.simonandschuster.com, pg 235

Perl, Liz, Simon & Schuster Sales & Marketing, 1230 Avenue of the Americas, New York, NY 10020 *Tel:* 212-698-7000, pg 236

Perlee, Chris, McGraw-Hill Create, 501 Bell St, Dubuque, IA 52001 *Tel:* 563-584-6000 *Fax:* 563-584-6600 *E-mail:* first_last@mcgraw-hill.com *Web Site:* www.mhhe.com, pg 160

Perlman Cohen, Susan, The Gersh Agency (TGA), 41 Madison Ave, 33rd fl, New York, NY 10010 *Tel:* 212-997-1818 *E-mail:* info@gershla.com *Web Site:* gershagency.com, pg 574

Perlman, Jim, Holy Cow! Press, PO Box 3170, Mount Royal Sta, Duluth, MN 55803 *Tel:* 218-724-1653 *Fax:* 218-724-1653 *E-mail:* holycow@holycowpress.org *Web Site:* www.holycowpress.org, pg 122

Perlman, Michael, Simon & Schuster Sales & Marketing, 1230 Avenue of the Americas, New York, NY 10020 *Tel:* 212-698-7000, pg 236

Perlstein, Jill, American Booksellers Association, 333 Westchester Ave, Suite S202, White Plains, NY 10604 *Tel:* 914-406-7500 *Toll Free Tel:* 800-637-0037 *Fax:* 914-410-6297 *E-mail:* info@bookweb.org *Web Site:* www.bookweb.org, pg 612

Permingeat, Max, Les Editions de Mortagne, CP 116, Boucherville, QC J4B 5E6, Canada *Tel:* 450-641-2387 *Fax:* 450-655-6092 *E-mail:* info@editionsdemortagne.com *Web Site:* www.editionsdemortagne.com, pg 502

Perreault, Russell, Vintage & Anchor Books, c/o Random House Inc, 1745 Broadway, New York, NY 10019 *Tel:* 212-572-2420 *E-mail:* vintageanchorpublicity@randomhouse.com *Web Site:* vintage-anchor.knopfdoubleday.com, pg 275

Perrin, Brian, HarperCollins General Books Group, 10 E 53 St, New York, NY 10022 *Tel:* 212-207-7000 *Fax:* 212-207-7633 *Web Site:* www.harpercollins.com, pg 113

Perrin, Christopher, Classical Academic Press, 2151 Market St, Camp Hill, PA 17011 *Tel:* 717-730-0711 *Fax:* 717-730-0721 *E-mail:* info@classicalsubjects.com *Web Site:* www.classicalacademicpress.com, pg 62

Perrin, Christopher, Plum Tree Books, 2151 Market St, Camp Hill, PA 17011 *Tel:* 717-730-0711 *Fax:* 717-730-0721 *E-mail:* info@classicalsubjects.com *Web Site:* www.plumtreebooks.com, pg 203

Perris, Alan, Academy of Television Arts & Sciences (ATAS), 5220 Lankershim Blvd, North Hollywood, CA 91601-3109 *Tel:* 818-754-2800 *Fax:* 818-761-2827 *Web Site:* www.emmys.tv, pg 611

Perritt, Megan, Crown Publishing Group, c/o Random House Inc, 1745 Broadway, New York, NY 10019 *Tel:* 212-782-9000 *Toll Free Tel:* 888-264-1745 *Fax:* 212-940-7408 *Web Site:* www.randomhouse.com/crown, pg 72

Perrizo, Mira, Johnson Books, 3005 Center Green Dr, Suite 225, Boulder, CO 80301 *Tel:* 303-443-9766 *Toll Free Tel:* 800-258-5830 *Fax:* 303-443-9687 *E-mail:* books@bigearthpublishing.com *Web Site:* www.bigearthpublishing.com; www.johnsonbooks.com, pg 136

Perrone, Madeline, Literary Artists Representatives, 575 West End Ave, Suite GRC, New York, NY 10024-2711 *Tel:* 212-679-7788 *Fax:* 212-595-2098 *E-mail:* litartists@aol.com, pg 582

Perry, Ava, Circlet Press Inc, 39 Hurlbut St, Cambridge, MA 02138 *Tel:* 617-864-0492 *Toll Free Tel:* 800-729-6423 (orders) *E-mail:* circletintern@gmail.com (edit queries); kjc@circlet.com (order fulfillment) *Web Site:* www.circlet.com, pg 61

Phelan, James F, H W Wilson, 10 Estes St, Ipswich, MA 01938 *Tel:* 978-356-6500 *Toll Free Tel:* 800-653-2726 (US & CN) *Fax:* 978-356-6565 *E-mail:* information@ebscohost.com *Web Site:* www.ebscohost.com, pg 282

Phelan, Sheila, DK, 375 Hudson St, 2nd fl, New York, NY 10014-3672 *Tel:* 212-213-4800 *Toll Free Tel:* 877-342-5357 (cust serv) *Fax:* 212-213-5202 *Web Site:* us.dk.com, pg 80

Phelps, Chad, F+W Media Inc, 10151 Carver Rd, Suite 200, Blue Ash, OH 45242 *Tel:* 513-531-2690 *Toll Free Tel:* 800-289-0963 (trade accts); 800-258-0929 (orders) *E-mail:* contact_us@fwmedia.com *Web Site:* www.fwmedia.com, pg 92

Phillips, Andrew, AuthorHouse, 1663 Liberty Dr, Bloomington, IN 47403 *Toll Free Tel:* 888-519-5121 *E-mail:* authorsupport@authorhouse.com *Web Site:* www.authorhouse.com, pg 27

Phillips, Andrew, iUniverse, 1663 Liberty Dr, Bloomington, IN 47403 *Toll Free Tel:* 800-AUTHORS (288-4677) *Fax:* 812-355-4085 *Web Site:* www.iuniverse.com, pg 135

Phillips, Andrew, Trafford, 1663 Liberty Dr, Bloomington, IN 47403 *Toll Free Tel:* 888-232-4444 *E-mail:* customersupport@trafford.com *Web Site:* www.trafford.com, pg 257

Phillips, Andrew, Xlibris Corp, 1663 Liberty Dr, Suite 200, Bloomington, IN 47403 *Toll Free Tel:* 888-795-4274 *Fax:* 610-915-0294 *E-mail:* info@xlibris.com *Web Site:* www.xlibris.com, pg 287

Phillips, Andrew V, Windhaven®, 68 Hunting Rd, Auburn, NH 03032 *Tel:* 603-483-0929 *Fax:* 603-483-8022 *E-mail:* info@windhaven.com *Web Site:* www.windhaven.com, pg 557

Phillips, Ashley, Clarkson Potter Publishers, c/o Random House Inc, 1745 Broadway, New York, NY 10019 *Tel:* 212-782-9000 *Toll Free Tel:* 888-264-1745 *Fax:* 212-572-6181 *Web Site:* www.clarksonpotter.com; www.randomhouse.com/crown/clarksonpotter, pg 62

Phillips, Barbara, Bridge Works Publishing, PO Box 1798, Bridgehampton, NY 11932-1798 *Tel:* 631-537-3418 *Web Site:* www.bridgeworksbooks.com, pg 47

Phillips, Betsy, Jackie White Memorial National Children's Playwriting Contest, 309 Parkade Blvd, Columbia, MO 65202 *Tel:* 573-874-5628 *Web Site:* www.cectheatre.org, pg 713

Phillips, Betsy, Vanderbilt University Press, 2014 Broadway, Suite 320, Nashville, TN 37203 *Tel:* 615-322-3585 *Toll Free Tel:* 800-627-7377 (orders only) *Fax:* 615-343-8823 *Toll Free Fax:* 800-735-0476 (orders only) *E-mail:* vupress@vanderbilt.edu *Web Site:* www.vanderbiltuniversitypress.com, pg 274

Phillips, Kathleen, North American Agricultural Journalists (NAAJ), 6434 Hurta Lane, Bryan, TX 77808 *Tel:* 979-845-2872 *Fax:* 979-862-1202 *Web Site:* www.naaj.net, pg 632

Phillips, Kirsten, Portage & Main Press, 318 McDermot, Suite 100, Winnipeg, MB R3A 0A2, Canada *Tel:* 204-987-3500 *Toll Free Tel:* 800-667-9673 *Fax:* 204-947-0080 *Toll Free Fax:* 866-734-8477 *E-mail:* books@portageandmainpress.com *Web Site:* www.portageandmainpress.com, pg 516

Phillips, Peter, The 25 Most "Censored" Stories Annual, PO Box 571, Cotati, CA 94931 *Tel:* 707-874-2695 *Web Site:* www.projectcensored.org, pg 747

Phillips, Ted, United States Holocaust Memorial Museum, 100 Raoul Wallenberg Place SW, Washington, DC 20024-2126 *Tel:* 202-314-7837; 202-488-6144 (orders) *Toll Free Tel:* 800-259-9998 (orders) *Fax:* 202-479-9726; 202-488-0438 (orders) *E-mail:* cahs_publications@ushmm.org *Web Site:* www.ushmm.org, pg 262

Phillips, Warren, Bridge Works Publishing, PO Box 1798, Bridgehampton, NY 11932-1798 *Tel:* 631-537-3418 *Web Site:* www.bridgeworksbooks.com, pg 47

Phillipson, Nicholas, Springer, 233 Spring St, New York, NY 10013-1578 *Tel:* 212-460-1500 *Toll Free Tel:* 800-SPRINGER (777-4643) *Fax:* 212-460-1575 *E-mail:* service-ny@springer.com *Web Site:* www.springer.com, pg 241

Philpott, Sandy, Dawn Publications Inc, 12402 Bitney Springs Rd, Nevada City, CA 95959 *Tel:* 530-274-7775 *Toll Free Tel:* 800-545-7475 *Fax:* 530-274-7778 *E-mail:* nature@dawnpub.com; orders@dawnpub.com *Web Site:* www.dawnpub.com, pg 76

Philps, Rebecca, Western Magazine Awards Foundation, 875 Prairie Ave, Port Coquitlam, BC V3B 1R9, Canada *Tel:* 604-945-3711 *E-mail:* wma@direct.ca *Web Site:* www.westernmagazineawards.ca, pg 748

Phirmam, James, Houghton Mifflin Harcourt, 222 Berkeley St, Boston, MA 02116-3764 *Tel:* 617-351-5000 *Toll Free Tel:* 800-225-5425 (Pre-K-8); 800-462-6595 (6–12; Advanced & Electives); 800-289-4490 (Specialized Curriculum: Great Source, Rigby, Saxon, Steck-Vaughn; Homeschool; Adult Ed); 800-323-9540 (Assessment: Riverside Publishing); 888-391-3245 (SkillsTutor); 888-242-6747 option 2 (Destination Series; Classroom Connect; Earobics; Edmark; Learning Village; Riverdeep); 800-225-3362 (Houghton Mifflin Harcourt Trade & Reference Publishers); 800-225-5800 (Heinemann) *Fax:* 617-351-1125 *Web Site:* www.hmhco.com, pg 123

Phuna, K K, World Scientific Publishing Co Inc, 27 Warren St, Suite 401-402, Hackensack, NJ 07601 *Tel:* 201-487-9655 *Toll Free Tel:* 800-227-7562 *Fax:* 201-487-9656 *Toll Free Fax:* 888-977-2665 *E-mail:* wspc@wspc.com *Web Site:* www.wspc.com, pg 285

Piazzi, Remo D, The United Educators Inc, 900 N Shore Dr, Suite 279, Lake Bluff, IL 60044-2210 *Tel:* 847-234-3700 *Toll Free Tel:* 800-323-5875 *Fax:* 847-234-8705 *E-mail:* uniteducators@yahoo.com *Web Site:* www.theunitededucatorsinc.com, pg 262

Pickett, Patty, Accuity, a SourceMedia Co, 4709 W Golf Rd, Suite 600, Skokie, IL 60076-1253 *Tel:* 847-676-9600 *Toll Free Tel:* 800-321-3373 *Fax:* 847-933-8101 *E-mail:* custserv@accuitysolutions.com; support@accuitysolutions.com; sales@accuitysolutions.com; general@accuitysolutions.com *Web Site:* www.accuitysolutions.com, pg 4

Pickett, Shumeca, John Phillip Immroth Memorial Award, 50 E Huron St, Chicago, IL 60611 *Tel:* 312-280-4223 *Toll Free Tel:* 800-545-2433 *Fax:* 312-280-4227 *E-mail:* oif@ala.org *Web Site:* www.ala.org/ifrt, pg 711

Pickett, Shumeca, Eli M Oboler Memorial Award, 50 E Huron St, Chicago, IL 60611 *Tel:* 312-280-4223 *Toll Free Tel:* 800-545-2433 *Fax:* 312-280-4227 *E-mail:* oif@ala.org *Web Site:* www.ala.org/ifrt, pg 730

Picott, Miryam, Casa Bautista de Publicaciones, 7000 Alabama Ave, El Paso, TX 79904 *Tel:* 915-566-9656 *Toll Free Tel:* 800-755-5958 (cust serv & orders) *Fax:* 915-562-6502; 915-565-9008 (orders) *Web Site:* www.casabautista.org; www.editorialmh.org, pg 53

Pierce, Gregory, ACTA Publications, 4848 N Clark St, Chicago, IL 60640 *Tel:* 773-271-1030 *Toll Free Tel:* 800-397-2282 *Fax:* 773-271-7399 *Toll Free Fax:* 800-397-0079 *E-mail:* info@actapublications.com *Web Site:* www.actapublications.com, pg 4

Pierce, Jesse, Albert B Corey Prize, c/o American Historical Association, 400 "A" St SE, Washington, DC 20003-3889 *Tel:* 202-544-2422 *Fax:* 202-544-8307 *E-mail:* cha-shc@cha-shc.ca *Web Site:* www.historians.org/prizes; www.cha-shc.ca, pg 699

Pierce, Valerie, Sourcebooks Inc, 1935 Brookdale Rd, Suite 139, Naperville, IL 60563 *Tel:* 630-961-3900 *Toll Free Tel:* 800-432-7444 *Fax:* 630-961-2168 *E-mail:* info@sourcebooks.com; customersupport@sourcebooks.com *Web Site:* www.sourcebooks.com, pg 240

Piergies, Mary, Manning Publications Co, 20 Baldwin Rd, Shelter Island, NY 11964 *Toll Free Tel:* 800-294-4747 (orders) *E-mail:* orders@manning.com *Web Site:* www.manning.com, pg 156

Pierpont, Amy, Grand Central Publishing, 237 Park Ave, New York, NY 10017 *Tel:* 212-364-1100 *Web Site:* www.hachettebookgroup.com, pg 106

Piersanti, Steven, Berrett-Koehler Publishers Inc, 235 Montgomery St, Suite 650, San Francisco, CA 94104 *Tel:* 415-288-0260 *Fax:* 415-362-2512 *E-mail:* bkpub@bkpub.com *Web Site:* www.bkconnection.com, pg 36

Pierson, Caryl K, Math Teachers Press Inc, 4850 Park Glen Rd, Minneapolis, MN 55416 *Tel:* 952-545-6535 *Toll Free Tel:* 800-852-2435 *Fax:* 952-546-7502 *E-mail:* info@movingwithmath.com *Web Site:* www.movingwithmath.com, pg 159

Pierson, Jean Marie, Hyperion, 1500 Broadway, 3rd fl, New York, NY 10036 *Tel:* 212-536-6500 *Web Site:* hyperionbooks.com, pg 126

Pierson, Jennifer, Rizzoli International Publications Inc, 300 Park Ave S, 4th fl, New York, NY 10010-5399 *Tel:* 212-387-3400 *Toll Free Tel:* 800-522-6657 (orders only) *Fax:* 212-387-3535 *E-mail:* publicity@rizzoliusa.com *Web Site:* www.rizzoliusa.com, pg 219

Pietsch, Michael, Hachette Book Group, 237 Park Ave, New York, NY 10017 *Tel:* 212-364-1100 *Toll Free Tel:* 800-759-0190 (cust serv) *Fax:* 212-364-0933 (intl orders) *Toll Free Fax:* 800-286-9471 (cust serv) *Web Site:* www.HachetteBookGroup.com, pg 110

Pietsch, Michael, Little, Brown and Company, 237 Park Ave, New York, NY 10017 *Tel:* 212-364-1100 *Fax:* 212-364-0952 *E-mail:* firstname.lastname@hbgusa.com *Web Site:* www.HachetteBookGroup.com, pg 150

Pike, Bryan, The BC Book Prizes, 207 W Hastings St, Suite 901, Vancouver, BC V6B 1H7, Canada *Tel:* 604-687-2405 *Fax:* 604-687-2435 *E-mail:* info@bcbookprizes.ca *Web Site:* www.bcbookprizes.ca, pg 690

Pikitch, Susan, Wolters Kluwer Law & Business, 76 Ninth Ave, 7th fl, New York, NY 10011-5201 *Tel:* 212-771-0600 *Toll Free Tel:* 800-234-1660 (cust serv); 800-638-8437 (orders); 800-317-3113 (bookstore sales) *Toll Free Fax:* 800-901-9075 (cust serv); 800-561-4845 (bookstore sales) *Web Site:* www.aspenpublishers.com, pg 141

Pikser, Jeremy, Writers Guild of America East (WGAE), 250 Hudson St, New York, NY 10013 *Tel:* 212-767-7800 *Fax:* 212-582-1909 *E-mail:* info@wgae.org *Web Site:* www.wgaeast.org, pg 638

Pilguy, Natalya, Workman Publishing Co Inc, 225 Varick St, 9th fl, New York, NY 10014-4381 *Tel:* 212-254-5900 *Toll Free Tel:* 800-722-7202 *Fax:* 212-254-8098 *E-mail:* info@workman.com *Web Site:* www.workman.com, pg 285

Pillai, Devi, Orbit, 237 Park Ave, New York, NY 10017 *Tel:* 212-364-1100 *Toll Free Tel:* 800-759-0190 *Web Site:* www.orbitbooks.net, pg 186

Pimlott, Philip, Gravure Association of America Inc, 8281 Pine Lake Rd, Denver, NC 28037 *Tel:* 201-523-6042 *Fax:* 201-523-6048 *E-mail:* gaa@gaa.org *Web Site:* www.gaa.org, pg 624

Pincich, Theresa, Liturgy Training Publications, 3949 S Racine Ave, Chicago, IL 60609-2523 *Tel:* 773-579-4900 *Toll Free Tel:* 800-933-1800 (US & CN only orders) *Fax:* 773-486-7094 *Toll Free Fax:* 800-933-7094 (US & CN only orders) *E-mail:* orders@ltp.org *Web Site:* www.ltp.org, pg 151

Pincus, Caroline, Caroline Pincus Book Midwife, 101 Wool St, San Francisco, CA 94110 *Tel:* 415-516-6206 *E-mail:* cpincus100@sbcglobal.net, pg 553

Pincus, Marilyn, Marilyn Pincus Inc, 1320 W Bloomington Place, Tucson, AZ 85755-8773 *Tel:* 520-742-6699 *E-mail:* mpscribe@aol.com *Web Site:* www.marilynpincus.info, pg 553

Pine, Barbra, MIT List Visual Arts Center, MIT E 15-109, 20 Ames St, Cambridge, MA 02139 *Tel:* 617-253-4400; 617-253-4680 *Fax:* 617-258-7265 *E-mail:* mlinga@mit.edu *Web Site:* listart.mit.edu, pg 167

Pine, Ralph, Quite Specific Media Group Ltd, 7373 Pyramid Place, Hollywood, CA 90046 *Tel:* 323-851-5797 *Fax:* 323-851-5798 *E-mail:* info@quitespecificmedia.com *Web Site:* www.quitespecificmedia.com, pg 211

*Fax:* 801-531-1488 *E-mail:* people@signaturebooks.com *Web Site:* www.signaturebooks.com; www.signaturebookslibrary.org, pg 233

Priddle, Clive, PublicAffairs, 250 W 57 St, Suite 1321, New York, NY 10107 *Tel:* 212-397-6666 *Toll Free Tel:* 800-343-4499 (orders) *Fax:* 212-397-4277 *E-mail:* publicaffairs@perseusbooks.com *Web Site:* www.publicaffairsbooks.com, pg 209

Pride, Jean, ASCD, 1703 N Beauregard St, Alexandria, VA 22311-1714 *Tel:* 703-578-9600 *Toll Free Tel:* 800-933-2723 *Fax:* 703-575-5400 *E-mail:* member@ascd.org *Web Site:* www.ascd.org, pg 23

Priest, Aaron M, The Aaron M Priest Literary Agency Inc, 708 Third Ave, 23rd fl, New York, NY 10017-4201 *Tel:* 212-818-0344 *Fax:* 212-573-9417 *E-mail:* info@aaronpriest.com *Web Site:* www.aaronpriest.com, pg 589

Priest, Arleen Gradinger, The Aaron M Priest Literary Agency Inc, 708 Third Ave, 23rd fl, New York, NY 10017-4201 *Tel:* 212-818-0344 *Fax:* 212-573-9417 *E-mail:* info@aaronpriest.com *Web Site:* www.aaronpriest.com, pg 589

Prieur, Richard, Association Nationale des Editeurs de Livres, 2514 boul Rosemont, Montreal, QC H1Y 1K4, Canada *Tel:* 514-273-8130 *Toll Free Tel:* 866-900-ANEL (900-2635) *Fax:* 514-273-9657 *E-mail:* info@anel.qc.ca *Web Site:* www.anel.qc.ca, pg 616

Primlani, Vijay, Science Publishers Inc, PO Box 699, Enfield, NH 03748-0699 *Tel:* 603-632-7377 *Fax:* 603-632-5611 *E-mail:* info@scipub.net *Web Site:* www.scipub.net, pg 229

Primont, Peter W, Cherry Lane Music Co, 315 Fifth Ave, Suite 801, New York, NY 10016 *Tel:* 646-470-3782 *Fax:* 212-251-0822 *Web Site:* www.cherrylaneprint.com, pg 59

Prince, Danforth, Blood Moon Productions Ltd, 75 Saint Marks Place, Staten Island, NY 10301-1606 *Tel:* 718-556-9410 *E-mail:* editors@bloodmoonproductions.com *Web Site:* bloodmoonproductions.com, pg 40

Pringle, Rebecca "Becky", National Education Association (NEA), 1201 16 St NW, Washington, DC 20036-3290 *Tel:* 202-833-4000 *Fax:* 202-822-7974 *Web Site:* www.nea.org, pg 174, 630

Prior, Robert, The MIT Press, 55 Hayward St, Cambridge, MA 02142 *Tel:* 617-253-5255 *Toll Free Tel:* 800-207-8354 (orders) *Fax:* 617-258-6779; 617-577-1545 (orders) *Web Site:* mitpress.mit.edu, pg 167

Proctor, Christopher, American Technical Publishers Inc, 10100 Orland Pkwy, Suite 200, Orland Park, IL 60467-5756 *Tel:* 708-957-1100 *Toll Free Tel:* 800-323-3471 *Fax:* 708-957-1101 *E-mail:* service@americantech.net *Web Site:* www.go2atp.com, pg 17

Proia, Brandon, PublicAffairs, 250 W 57 St, Suite 1321, New York, NY 10107 *Tel:* 212-397-6666 *Toll Free Tel:* 800-343-4499 (orders) *Fax:* 212-397-4277 *E-mail:* publicaffairs@perseusbooks.com *Web Site:* www.publicaffairsbooks.com, pg 209

Proia, Brandon, The University of North Carolina Press, 116 S Boundary St, Chapel Hill, NC 27514-3808 *Tel:* 919-966-3561 *Fax:* 919-966-3829 *E-mail:* uncpress@unc.edu *Web Site:* www.uncpress.unc.edu, pg 267

Pronk, Gord, Pronk Media Inc, PO Box 340, Beaverton, ON L0K 1A0, Canada *Tel:* 416-441-3760 *E-mail:* info@pronk.com *Web Site:* www.pronk.com, pg 553

Pronovost, Nina, Doubleday Canada, One Toronto St, Suite 300, Toronto, ON M5C 2V6, Canada *Tel:* 416-364-4449 *Fax:* 416-364-6863 *Web Site:* www.randomhouse.ca, pg 501

Prosser, Julia, Simon & Schuster, 1230 Avenue of the Americas, New York, NY 10020 *Tel:* 212-698-7000 *Toll Free Tel:* 800-223-2348 (cust serv); 800-223-2336 (orders) *Toll Free Fax:* 800-943-9831 (orders) *Web Site:* www.simonandschuster.com, pg 234

Prost, Jennifer, Joelle Delbourgo Associates Inc, 101 Park St, Montclair, NJ 07042 *Tel:* 973-773-0836 (call only during standard business hours) *Web Site:* www.delbourgo.com, pg 568

Protano, Generosa Gina, GGP Publishing Inc, 105 Calvert St, Suite 201, Harrison, NY 10528-3138 *Tel:* 914-834-8896 *Fax:* 914-834-7566 *Web Site:* www.ggppublishing.com, pg 547, 574

Provost, Cherry, Medal of Honor for Literature, 15 Gramercy Park S, New York, NY 10003 *E-mail:* literary@thenationalartsclub.org *Web Site:* www.nationalartsclub.org, pg 723

Pruett, Robert H, Brandylane Publishers Inc, 5 S First St, Richmond, VA 23219 *Tel:* 804-644-3090 *Fax:* 804-644-3092 *Web Site:* www.brandylanepublishers.com, pg 45

Prunty, Wyatt, Sewanee Writers' Conference, Stamler Ctr, 119 Gailor Hall, 735 University Ave, Sewanee, TN 37383-1000 *Tel:* 931-598-1141 *E-mail:* swc@sewanee.edu *Web Site:* www.sewaneewriters.org, pg 673

Prybylowski, Doug, Comex Systems Inc, 5 Cold Hill Rd, Suite 24, Mendham, NJ 07945 *Tel:* 973-543-2862 *Toll Free Tel:* 800-543-6959 *Fax:* 973-543-9644 *E-mail:* mail@comexsystems.com *Web Site:* www.comexsystems.com, pg 65

Pryor, Victoria Gould, Arcadia, 31 Lake Place N, Danbury, CT 06810 *Tel:* 203-797-0993 *E-mail:* arcadialit@sbcglobal.net, pg 561

Psaltis, Elizabeth, Gallery Books, 1230 Avenue of the Americas, New York, NY 10020 *Toll Free Tel:* 800-456-6798 *Fax:* 212-698-7284 *E-mail:* consumer.customerservice@simonandschuster.com *Web Site:* www.simonsays.com, pg 101

Pucillo, Ann-Marie, Houghton Mifflin Harcourt, 222 Berkeley St, Boston, MA 02116-3764 *Tel:* 617-351-5000 *Toll Free Tel:* 800-225-5425 (Pre-K-8); 800-462-6595 (6–12; Advanced & Electives); 800-289-4490 (Specialized Curriculum: Great Source, Rigby, Saxon, Steck-Vaughn; Homeschool; Adult Ed); 800-323-9540 (Assessment: Riverside Publishing); 888-391-3245 (SkillsTutor); 888-242-6747 option 2 (Destination Series; Classroom Connect; Earobics; Edmark; Learning Village; Riverdeep); 800-225-3362 (Houghton Mifflin Harcourt Trade & Reference Publishers); 800-225-5800 (Heinemann) *Fax:* 617-351-1125 *Web Site:* www.hmhco.com, pg 123

Pucillo, Ann-Marie, Houghton Mifflin Harcourt Trade & Reference Division, 222 Berkeley St, Boston, MA 02116-3764 *Tel:* 617-351-5000 *Toll Free Tel:* 800-225-3362 *Web Site:* www.houghtonmifflinbooks.com, pg 124

Puhalo, Lazar, Synaxis Press, 37323 Hawkins Pickle Rd, Dewdney, BC V0M 1H0, Canada *Tel:* 604-826-9336 *E-mail:* synaxis@new-ostrog.org *Web Site:* synaxispress.ca, pg 520

Pujic, Anja, DC Canada Education Publishing, 120 Slater St, Suite 960, Ottawa, ON K1P 6E2, Canada *Tel:* 613-565-8885 *Toll Free Tel:* 888-565-0262 *Fax:* 613-565-8881 *E-mail:* info@dc-canada.ca *Web Site:* www.dc-canada.ca, pg 500

Pulice, Mario, Little, Brown and Company, 237 Park Ave, New York, NY 10017 *Tel:* 212-364-1100 *Fax:* 212-364-0952 *E-mail:* firstname.lastname@hbgusa.com *Web Site:* www.HachetteBookGroup.com, pg 150

Pullano, Michelle, The MIT Press, 55 Hayward St, Cambridge, MA 02142 *Tel:* 617-253-5255 *Toll Free Tel:* 800-207-8354 (orders) *Fax:* 617-258-6779; 617-577-1545 (orders) *Web Site:* mitpress.mit.edu, pg 168

Pullen, Lindsey, The Perseus Books Group, 387 Park Ave S, 12th fl, New York, NY 10016 *Tel:* 212-340-8100 *Toll Free Tel:* 800-343-4499 (cust serv) *Fax:* 212-340-8105 *Web Site:* www.perseusbooksgroup.com, pg 199

Pullins, Ron, Focus Publishing/R Pullins Co Inc, PO Box 369, Newburyport, MA 01950 *Tel:* 978-462-7288 (edit) *Toll Free Tel:* 800-848-7236 (orders) *Fax:* 978-462-9035 (edit) *E-mail:* orders@pullins.com *Web Site:* www.pullins.com, pg 96

Pullman, Alyson, Chronicle Books LLC, 680 Second St, San Francisco, CA 94107 *Tel:* 415-537-4200 *Toll Free Tel:* 800-759-0190 (cust serv) *Fax:* 415-537-4460 *Toll Free Fax:* 800-858-7787 (orders); 800-286-9471 (cust serv) *E-mail:* frontdesk@chroniclebooks.com *Web Site:* www.chroniclebooks.com, pg 61

Puls, Eloise, Boydell & Brewer Inc, 668 Mount Hope Ave, Rochester, NY 14620-2731 *Tel:* 585-275-0419 *Fax:* 585-271-8778 *E-mail:* boydell@boydellusa.net *Web Site:* www.boydellandbrewer.com, pg 45

Puls, Eloise, University of Rochester Press, 668 Mount Hope Ave, Rochester, NY 14620-2731 *Tel:* 585-275-0419 *Fax:* 585-271-8778 *E-mail:* boydell@boydellusa.net *Web Site:* www.urpress.com, pg 269

Pult, Richard, University Press of New England, One Court St, Suite 250, Lebanon, NH 03766 *Tel:* 603-448-1533 *Toll Free Tel:* 800-421-1561 (orders only) *Fax:* 603-448-7006; 603-643-1540 *E-mail:* university.press@dartmouth.edu *Web Site:* www.upne.com, pg 271

Pulver, Sarah, Ten Speed Press, 2625 Alcatraz Ave, Unit 505, Berkeley, CA 94705 *Tel:* 510-285-3000 *Toll Free Tel:* 800-841-BOOK (841-2665) *E-mail:* csorders@randomhouse.com *Web Site:* crownpublishing.com/imprint/ten-speed-press, pg 252

Puopolo, Kristine, Doubleday/Nan A Talese, c/o Random House Inc, 1745 Broadway, New York, NY 10019 *Tel:* 212-751-2600 *Toll Free Tel:* 800-638-6460 *Fax:* 212-572-2593 *Web Site:* www.knopfdoubleday.com, pg 81

Puppa, Brian, TCP Press, Legacy Ctr, 9 Lobraico Lane, Whitchurch-Stouffville, ON L4A 7X5, Canada *Tel:* 905-640-8914 *Toll Free Tel:* 800-772-7765 *E-mail:* tcp@tcpnow.com *Web Site:* www.tcppress.com, pg 521

Purcell, Anita, Book & Periodical Council (BPC), 192 Spadina Ave, Suite 107, Toronto, ON M5T 2C2, Canada *Tel:* 416-975-9366 *Fax:* 416-975-1839 *E-mail:* info@thebpc.ca *Web Site:* www.thebpc.ca, pg 618

Purcell, Anita, CAA Award for Fiction, 6 West St N, Suite 203, Orillia, ON L3V 5B8, Canada *Tel:* 705-325-3926 *Toll Free Tel:* 866-216-6222 *E-mail:* admin@canauthors.org *Web Site:* www.canauthors.org, pg 694

Purcell, Anita, CAA Emerging Writer Award, 6 West St N, Suite 203, Orillia, ON L3V 5B8, Canada *Tel:* 705-325-3926 *Toll Free Tel:* 866-216-6222 *E-mail:* admin@canauthors.org *Web Site:* www.canauthors.org, pg 694

Purcell, Anita, CAA Lela Common Award for Canadian History, 6 West St N, Suite 203, Orillia, ON L3V 5B8, Canada *Tel:* 705-325-3926 *Toll Free Tel:* 866-216-6222 *E-mail:* admin@canauthors.org *Web Site:* www.canauthors.org, pg 694

Purcell, Anita, CAA Poetry Award, 6 West St N, Suite 203, Orillia, ON L3V 5B8, Canada *Tel:* 705-325-3926 *Toll Free Tel:* 866-216-6222 *E-mail:* admin@canauthors.org *Web Site:* www.canauthors.org, pg 694

Purcell, Anita, Canadian Authors Association (CAA), 6 West St N, Suite 203, Orillia, ON L3V 5B8, Canada *Tel:* 705-325-3926 *Toll Free Tel:* 866-216-6222 *Fax:* 705-653-0593 *E-mail:* admin@canauthors.org *Web Site:* www.canauthors.org, pg 619

Purdy, C, Oxford University Press USA, 198 Madison Ave, New York, NY 10016 *Tel:* 212-726-6000 *Toll Free Tel:* 800-451-7556 (orders); 800-445-9714 (cust serv) *Fax:* 919-677-1303 *E-mail:* custserv.us@oup.com *Web Site:* www.oup.com/us, pg 189

Purelis, Eileen, Springer, 233 Spring St, New York, NY 10013-1578 *Tel:* 212-460-1500 *Toll Free Tel:* 800-SPRINGER (777-4643) *Fax:* 212-460-1575 *E-mail:* service-ny@springer.com *Web Site:* www.springer.com, pg 241

Purich, Donald, Purich Publishing Ltd, PO Box 23032, Market Mall Postal Outlet, Saskatoon, SK S7J 5H3, Canada *Tel:* 306-373-5311 *Fax:* 306-373-5315 *E-mail:* purich@sasktel.net *Web Site:* www.purichpublishing.com, pg 517

Purple, Katherine, Purdue University Press, Stewart Ctr 370, 504 W State St, West Lafayette, IN 47907-2058 *Tel:* 765-494-2038 *Fax:* 765-496-2442 *E-mail:* pupress@purdue.edu *Web Site:* www.thepress.purdue.edu, pg 209

Purtell, April, Hewitt Homeschooling Resources, 2103 Main St, Washougal, WA 98671 *Tel:* 360-835-8708 *Toll Free Tel:* 800-348-1750 *Fax:* 360-835-8697 *E-mail:* info@hewitthomeschooling.com *Web Site:* hewitthomeschooling.com, pg 119

Pusey, Stacey, PreK-12 Learning Group, 325 Chestnut St, Suite 1110, Philadelphia, PA 19106 *Tel:* 267-351-4310 *Fax:* 267-351-4317 *E-mail:* prek12learning@publishers.org *Web Site:* www.aepweb.org, pg 634

Putnam, Marvin, PEN Center USA, PO Box 6037, Beverly Hills, CA 90212 *Tel:* 323-424-4939 *Fax:* 323-424-4944 *E-mail:* pen@penusa.org *Web Site:* www.penusa.org, pg 633

Putnam, Richelle, MWG Writer Workshops, PO Box 3845, Meridian, MS 39303-3845 *Tel:* 601-880-1089 *Web Site:* www.mississippiwritersguild.com, pg 671

Putt, Melodee, Adam Hill Publications, 2699 Stirling Rd, Suite B-301, Fort Lauderdale, FL 33312 *Tel:* 954-680-7639 *E-mail:* books@adamhilldesign.com *Web Site:* www.adamhilldesign.com, pg 4

Pye, Michael, The Career Press Inc, 220 W Parkway, Unit 12, Pompton Plains, NJ 07444 *Tel:* 201-848-0310 *Toll Free Tel:* 800-CAREER-1 (227-3371) *Fax:* 201-848-1727 *Web Site:* www.careerpress.com, pg 52

Pyette, Craig, Knopf Random Canada, One Toronto St, Suite 300, Toronto, ON M5C 2V6, Canada *Tel:* 416-364-4449 *Toll Free Tel:* 888-523-9292 *Fax:* 416-364-6863 *Web Site:* www.randomhouse.ca, pg 510

Pyster, Phil, National Cartoonists Society (NCS), 341 N Maitland Ave, Suite 130, Maitland, FL 32751 *Tel:* 407-647-8839 *Fax:* 407-629-2502 *E-mail:* crowsgal@crowsgal.com; info@reuben.org *Web Site:* www.reuben.org, pg 629

Qaimari, Mr Nader, Gale, 27500 Drake Rd, Farmington Hills, MI 48331-3535 *Tel:* 248-699-4253 *Toll Free Tel:* 800-877-4253 *Fax:* 248-699-8049 *Toll Free Fax:* 800-414-5043 (orders) *E-mail:* gale.salesassistance@cengage.com *Web Site:* www.gale.cengage.com, pg 100

Quach, Andrew, Standard Publishing, 8805 Governors Hill Dr, Suite 400, Cincinnati, OH 45249 *Tel:* 513-931-4050 *Toll Free Tel:* 800-543-1353 *Fax:* 513-931-0950 *Toll Free Fax:* 877-867-5751 *E-mail:* customerservice@standardpub.com *Web Site:* www.standardpub.com, pg 242

Qualben, Lois, LangMarc Publishing, PO Box 90488, Austin, TX 78709-0488 *Tel:* 512-394-0989 *Toll Free Tel:* 800-864-1648 (orders) *Fax:* 512-394-0829 *E-mail:* langmarc@booksails.com *Web Site:* www.langmarc.com, pg 143

Qualben, Michael, LangMarc Publishing, PO Box 90488, Austin, TX 78709-0488 *Tel:* 512-394-0989 *Toll Free Tel:* 800-864-1648 (orders) *Fax:* 512-394-0829 *E-mail:* langmarc@booksails.com *Web Site:* www.langmarc.com, pg 143

Quasha, George, Barrytown/Station Hill Press, 120 Station Hill Rd, Barrytown, NY 12507 *Tel:* 845-758-5293 *E-mail:* publishers@stationhill.org *Web Site:* www.stationhill.org, pg 31

Quattrocchi, John, Albert Whitman & Co, 250 S Northwest Hwy, Suite 320, Park Ridge, IL 60068 *Tel:* 847-232-2800 *Toll Free Tel:* 800-255-7675 *Fax:* 847-581-0039 *E-mail:* mail@awhitmanco.com *Web Site:* www.albertwhitman.com, pg 7

Quayle, Elaine, Business & Legal Reports Inc (BLR), 100 Winners Circle, Suite 300, Brentwood, CT 37027 *Tel:* 860-510-0100 *Toll Free Tel:* 800-727-5257 *E-mail:* service@blr.com *Web Site:* www.blr.com, pg 50

Quesnel-Lafontaine, Monique, Centre Franco-Ontarien de Ressources en Alphabetisation (Centre FORA), 432 Ave Westmount, Unit H, Sudbury, ON P3A 5Z8, Canada *Tel:* 705-524-3672 *Toll Free Tel:* 888-814-4422 (orders, CN only) *Fax:* 705-524-8535 *E-mail:* info@centrefora.on.ca *Web Site:* www.centrefora.on.ca, pg 498

Quigley, Colleen, PreK-12 Learning Group, 325 Chestnut St, Suite 1110, Philadelphia, PA 19106 *Tel:* 267-351-4310 *Fax:* 267-351-4317 *E-mail:* prek12learning@publishers.org *Web Site:* www.aepweb.org, pg 634

Quigley, James, Paulist Press, 997 MacArthur Blvd, Mahwah, NJ 07430-9990 *Tel:* 201-825-7300 *Toll Free Tel:* 800-218-1903 *Fax:* 201-825-8345 *Toll Free Fax:* 800-836-3161 *E-mail:* info@paulistpress.com *Web Site:* www.paulistpress.com, pg 195

Quillen, Lida E, Twilight Times Books, PO Box 3340, Kingsport, TN 37664-0340 *Tel:* 423-323-0183 *Fax:* 423-323-0183 *E-mail:* publisher@twilighttimes.com *Web Site:* www.twilighttimesbooks.com, pg 261

Quincannon, Alan, Quincannon Publishing Group, PO Box 8100, Glen Ridge, NJ 07028-8100 *Tel:* 973-380-9942 *E-mail:* editors@quincannongroup.com *Web Site:* www.quincannongroup.com, pg 211

Quinlan, Stephanie, Canadian Booksellers Association (CBA), 1255 Bay St, Suite 902, Toronto, ON M5R 2A9, Canada *Tel:* 416-467-7883 *Toll Free Tel:* 866-788-0790 *Fax:* 416-467-7886 *E-mail:* enquiries@cbabook.org *Web Site:* www.cbabook.org, pg 619

Quinlan, Stephanie, CBA Libris Award for Author of the Year, 1255 Bay St, Suite 902, Toronto, ON M5R 2A9, Canada *Tel:* 416-467-7883 *Toll Free Tel:* 866-788-0790 *Fax:* 416-467-7886 *E-mail:* enquiries@cbabook.org *Web Site:* www.cbabook.org, pg 695

Quinlan, Stephanie, CBA Libris Children's Picture Book of the Year, 1255 Bay St, Suite 902, Toronto, ON M5R 2A9, Canada *Tel:* 416-467-7883 *Toll Free Tel:* 866-788-0790 *Fax:* 416-467-7886 *E-mail:* enquiries@cbabook.org *Web Site:* www.cbabook.org, pg 695

Quinlan, Stephanie, CBA Libris Distributor of the Year, 1255 Bay St, Suite 902, Toronto, ON M5R 2A9, Canada *Tel:* 416-467-7883 *Toll Free Tel:* 866-788-0790 *Fax:* 416-467-7886 *E-mail:* enquiries@cbabook.org *Web Site:* www.cbabook.org, pg 695

Quinlan, Stephanie, CBA Libris Editor of the Year, 1255 Bay St, Suite 902, Toronto, ON M5R 2A9, Canada *Tel:* 416-467-7883 *Toll Free Tel:* 866-788-0790 *Fax:* 416-467-7886 *E-mail:* enquiries@cbabook.org *Web Site:* www.cbabook.org, pg 695

Quinlan, Stephanie, CBA Libris Fiction Book of the Year, 1255 Bay St, Suite 902, Toronto, ON M5R 2A9, Canada *Tel:* 416-467-7883 *Toll Free Tel:* 866-788-0790 *Fax:* 416-467-7886 *E-mail:* enquiries@cbabook.org *Web Site:* www.cbabook.org, pg 695

Quinlan, Stephanie, CBA Libris Publisher of the Year, 1255 Bay St, Suite 902, Toronto, ON M5R 2A9, Canada *Tel:* 416-467-7883 *Toll Free Tel:* 866-788-0790 *Fax:* 416-467-7886 *E-mail:* enquiries@cbabook.org *Web Site:* www.cbabook.org, pg 695

Quinlan, Stephanie, CBA Libris Sales Rep of the Year, 1255 Bay St, Suite 902, Toronto, ON M5R 2A9, Canada *Tel:* 416-467-7883 *Toll Free Tel:* 866-788-0790 *Fax:* 416-467-7886 *E-mail:* enquiries@cbabook.org *Web Site:* www.cbabook.org, pg 695

Quinlan, Stephanie, CBA Libris Small Press Publisher of the Year, 1255 Bay St, Suite 902, Toronto, ON M5R 2A9, Canada *Tel:* 416-467-7883 *Toll Free Tel:* 866-788-0790 *Fax:* 416-467-7886 *E-mail:* enquiries@cbabook.org *Web Site:* www.cbabook.org, pg 696

Quinn, Alice, George Bogin Memorial Award, 15 Gramercy Park S, New York, NY 10003 *Tel:* 212-254-9628 *Fax:* 212-673-2352 *Web Site:* www.poetrysociety.org, pg 692

Quinn, Alice, Alice Fay Di Castagnola Award, 15 Gramercy Park S, New York, NY 10003 *Tel:* 212-254-9628 *Fax:* 212-673-2352 *Web Site:* www.poetrysociety.org, pg 700

Quinn, Alice, Norma Farber First Book Award, 15 Gramercy Park S, New York, NY 10003 *Tel:* 212-254-9628 *Fax:* 212-673-2352 *Web Site:* www.poetrysociety.org, pg 703

Quinn, Alice, Cecil Hemley Memorial Award, 15 Gramercy Park S, New York, NY 10003 *Tel:* 212-254-9628 *Fax:* 212-673-2352 *Web Site:* www.poetrysociety.org, pg 709

Quinn, Alice, Louise Louis/Emily F Bourne Student Poetry Award, 15 Gramercy Park S, New York, NY 10003 *Tel:* 212-254-9628 *Fax:* 212-673-2352 *Web Site:* www.poetrysociety.org, pg 719

Quinn, Alice, Lyric Poetry Award, 15 Gramercy Park S, New York, NY 10003 *Tel:* 212-254-9628 *Fax:* 212-673-2352 *Web Site:* www.poetrysociety.org, pg 720

Quinn, Alice, Lucille Medwick Memorial Award, 15 Gramercy Park S, New York, NY 10003 *Tel:* 212-254-9628 *Fax:* 212-673-2352 *Web Site:* www.poetrysociety.org, pg 723

Quinn, Alice, Poetry Society of America (PSA), 15 Gramercy Park S, New York, NY 10003 *Tel:* 212-254-9628 *Fax:* 212-673-2352 *Web Site:* www.poetrysociety.org, pg 634

Quinn, Alice, William Carlos Williams Award, 15 Gramercy Park S, New York, NY 10003 *Tel:* 212-254-9628 *Fax:* 212-673-2352 *Web Site:* www.poetrysociety.org, pg 749

Quinn, Alice, The Writer Magazine/Emily Dickinson Award, 15 Gramercy Park S, New York, NY 10003 *Tel:* 212-254-9628 *Fax:* 212-673-2352 *Web Site:* www.poetrysociety.org, pg 751

Quinn, Ann, Annick Press Ltd, 15 Patricia Ave, Toronto, ON M2M 1H9, Canada *Tel:* 416-221-4802 *Fax:* 416-221-8400 *E-mail:* annickpress@annickpress.com *Web Site:* www.annickpress.com, pg 493

Quinn, Ann, Firefly Books Ltd, 50 Staples Ave, Unit 1, Richmond Hill, ON L4B 0A7, Canada *Tel:* 416-499-8412 *Toll Free Tel:* 800-387-6192 (CN); 800-387-5085 (US) *Fax:* 416-499-8313 *Toll Free Fax:* 800-450-0391 (CN); 800-565-6034 (US) *E-mail:* service@fireflybooks.com *Web Site:* www.fireflybooks.com, pg 505

Quinn, Kevin, Writer's Digest University, 10151 Carver Rd, Suite 200, Blue Ash, OH 45242-4760 *Tel:* 513-531-2690 *Toll Free Tel:* 800-759-0963 *Fax:* 513-531-0798 *E-mail:* contact_us@fwmedia.com *Web Site:* www.writersonlineworkshops.com, pg 682

Quinn, Lisa, Wilfrid Laurier University Press, 75 University Ave W, Waterloo, ON N2L 3C5, Canada *Tel:* 519-884-0710 (ext 6124) *Toll Free Tel:* 866-836-5551 *Fax:* 519-725-1399 *E-mail:* press@wlu.ca *Web Site:* www.wlupress.wlu.ca, pg 525

Quinn, Marysarah, Clarkson Potter Publishers, c/o Random House Inc, 1745 Broadway, New York, NY 10019 *Tel:* 212-782-9000 *Toll Free Tel:* 888-264-1745 *Fax:* 212-572-6181 *Web Site:* www.clarksonpotter.com; www.randomhouse.com/crown/clarksonpotter, pg 62

Quinn, Marysarah, Crown Publishing Group, c/o Random House Inc, 1745 Broadway, New York, NY 10019 *Tel:* 212-782-9000 *Toll Free Tel:* 888-264-1745 *Fax:* 212-940-7408 *Web Site:* www.randomhouse.com/crown, pg 72

Quinn, Meghan, Prometheus Books, 59 John Glenn Dr, Amherst, NY 14228-2119 *Tel:* 716-691-0133 *Toll Free Tel:* 800-421-0351 *Fax:* 716-691-0137 *E-mail:* marketing@prometheusbooks.com; editorial@prometheusbooks.com *Web Site:* www.Prometheusbooks.com, pg 208

Quinney, Nigel, Roaring Forties Press, 1053 Santa Fe Ave, Berkeley, CA 94706 *Tel:* 510-527-5461 *E-mail:* info@roaringfortiespress.com *Web Site:* www.roaringfortiespress.com, pg 220

Quintin, Michel, Editions Michel Quintin, 4770 rue Foster, Waterloo, QC J0E 2N0, Canada *Tel:* 450-539-3774 *Fax:* 450-539-4905 *E-mail:* info@editionsmichelquintin.ca *Web Site:* www.editionsmichelquintin.ca, pg 517

Quinton, Linda, Tom Doherty Associates, LLC, 175 Fifth Ave, 14th fl, New York, NY 10010 *Tel:* 646-307-5151 *Toll Free Tel:* 800-455-0340 *Fax:* 212-388-0191 *E-mail:* firstname.lastname@tor.com *Web Site:* www.tor-forge.com, pg 80

Quiring, Nichole, R Ross Annett Award for Children's Literature, 11759 Groat Rd, Edmonton, AB T5M 3K6, Canada *Tel:* 780-422-8174 *Toll Free Tel:* 800-665-5354 (AB only) *Fax:* 780-422-2663 (attn WGA) *E-mail:* mail@writersguild.ab.ca *Web Site:* www.writersguild.ab.ca, pg 687

Quiring, Nichole, Amber Bowerman Memorial Travel Writing Award, 11759 Groat Rd, Edmonton, AB T5M 3K6, Canada *Tel:* 780-422-8174 *Toll Free Tel:* 800-665-5354 (AB only) *Fax:* 780-422-2663 (attn WGA) *E-mail:* mail@writersguild.ab.ca *Web Site:* www.writersguild.ab.ca, pg 692

Quiring, Nichole, Georges Bugnet Award for Fiction, 11759 Groat Rd, Edmonton, AB T5M 3K6, Canada *Tel:* 780-422-8174 *Toll Free Tel:* 800-665-5354 (AB only) *Fax:* 780-422-2663 (attn WGA) *E-mail:* mail@writersguild.ab.ca *Web Site:* www.writersguild.ab.ca, pg 693

Quiring, Nichole, The City of Calgary W O Mitchell Book Prize, 11759 Groat Rd, Edmonton, AB T5M 3K6, Canada *Tel:* 780-422-8174 *Toll Free Tel:* 800-665-5354 (AB only) *Fax:* 780-422-2663 (attn WGA) *E-mail:* mail@writersguild.ab.ca *Web Site:* www.writersguild.ab.ca, pg 697

Quiring, Nichole, Wilfrid Eggleston Award for Nonfiction, 11759 Groat Rd, Edmonton, AB T5M 3K6, Canada *Tel:* 780-422-8174 *Toll Free Tel:* 800-665-5354 (AB only) *Fax:* 780-422-2663 (attn WGA) *E-mail:* mail@writersguild.ab.ca *Web Site:* www.writersguild.ab.ca, pg 702

Quiring, Nichole, James H Gray Award for Short Nonfiction, 11759 Groat Rd, Edmonton, AB T5M 3K6, Canada *Tel:* 780-422-8174 *Toll Free Tel:* 800-665-5354 (AB only) *Fax:* 780-422-2663 (attn WGA) *E-mail:* mail@writersguild.ab.ca *Web Site:* www.writersguild.ab.ca, pg 708

Quiring, Nichole, The Robert Kroetsch City of Edmonton Book Prize, 11759 Groat Rd, Edmonton, AB T5M 3K6, Canada *Tel:* 780-422-8174 *Toll Free Tel:* 800-665-5354 (AB only) *Fax:* 780-422-2663 (attn WGA) *E-mail:* mail@writersguild.ab.ca *Web Site:* www.writersguild.ab.ca, pg 716

Quiring, Nichole, Isabel Miller Young Writers Award, 11759 Groat Rd, Edmonton, AB T5M 3K6, Canada *Tel:* 780-422-8174 *Toll Free Tel:* 800-665-5354 (AB only) *Fax:* 780-422-2663 (attn WGA) *E-mail:* mail@writersguild.ab.ca *Web Site:* www.writersguild.ab.ca, pg 723

Quiring, Nichole, Howard O'Hagan Award for Short Story, 11759 Groat Rd, Edmonton, AB T5M 3K6, Canada *Tel:* 780-422-8174 *Toll Free Tel:* 800-665-5354 (AB only) *Fax:* 780-422-2663 (attn WGA) *E-mail:* mail@writersguild.ab.ca *Web Site:* www.writersguild.ab.ca, pg 730

Quiring, Nichole, Gwen Pharis Ringwood Award for Drama, 11759 Groat Rd, Edmonton, AB T5M 3K6, Canada *Tel:* 780-422-8174 *Toll Free Tel:* 800-665-5354 (AB only) *Fax:* 780-422-2663 (attn WGA) *E-mail:* mail@writersguild.ab.ca *Web Site:* www.writersguild.ab.ca, pg 738

Quiring, Nichole, Stephan G Stephansson Award for Poetry, 11759 Groat Rd, Edmonton, AB T5M 3K6, Canada *Tel:* 780-422-8174 *Toll Free Tel:* 800-665-5354 (AB only) *Fax:* 780-422-2663 (attn WGA) *E-mail:* mail@writersguild.ab.ca *Web Site:* www.writersguild.ab.ca, pg 744

Quiring, Nichole, Jon Whyte Memorial Essay Prize, 11759 Groat Rd, Edmonton, AB T5M 3K6, Canada *Tel:* 780-422-8174 *Toll Free Tel:* 800-665-5354 (AB only) *Fax:* 780-422-2663 (attn WGA) *E-mail:* mail@writersguild.ab.ca *Web Site:* www.writersguild.ab.ca, pg 749

Quiring, Nichole, Writers Guild of Alberta, 11759 Groat Rd, Edmonton, AB T5M 3K6, Canada *Tel:* 780-422-8174 *Toll Free Tel:* 800-665-5354 (AB only) *Fax:* 780-422-2663 (attn WGA) *E-mail:* mail@writersguild.ab.ca *Web Site:* www.writersguild.ab.ca, pg 638

Quist, Norman, University Publishing Group, 219 W Washington St, Hagerstown, MD 21740 *Tel:* 240-420-0036 *Toll Free Tel:* 800-654-8188 *Fax:* 240-718-7100 *E-mail:* editorial@upgbooks.com; orders@upgbooks.com; sales@upgbooks.com *Web Site:* www.upgbooks.com, pg 272

Quon, Felicia, Simon & Schuster Canada, 166 King St E, Suite 300, Toronto, ON M5A 1J3, Canada *Tel:* 647-427-8882 *Toll Free Tel:* 800-387-0446; 800-268-3216 (orders) *Fax:* 647-430-9446 *Toll Free Fax:* 888-849-8151 (orders) *E-mail:* info@simonandschuster.ca *Web Site:* www.simonsayscanada.com, pg 519

Qureshi, Amber, Seven Stories Press, 140 Watts St, New York, NY 10013 *Tel:* 212-226-8760 *Fax:* 212-226-1411 *E-mail:* info@sevenstories.com *Web Site:* www.sevenstories.com, pg 232

Raab, Jackie, Barron's Educational Series Inc, 250 Wireless Blvd, Hauppauge, NY 11788 *Tel:* 631-434-3311 *Toll Free Tel:* 800-645-3476 *Fax:* 631-434-3723 *E-mail:* barrons@barronseduc.com *Web Site:* www.barronseduc.com, pg 31

Raab, Jamie, Grand Central Publishing, 237 Park Ave, New York, NY 10017 *Tel:* 212-364-1100 *Web Site:* www.hachettebookgroup.com, pg 106

Raab, Jamie, Hachette Book Group, 237 Park Ave, New York, NY 10017 *Tel:* 212-364-1100 *Toll Free Tel:* 800-759-0190 (cust serv) *Fax:* 212-364-0933 (intl orders) *Toll Free Fax:* 800-286-9471 (cust serv) *Web Site:* www.HachetteBookGroup.com, pg 110

Raagas, Lorna, Financial Executives Research Foundation Inc (FERF), West Tower, 7th fl, 1250 Headquarters Plaza, Morristown, NJ 07960-6837 *Tel:* 973-765-1000 *Fax:* 973-765-1023 *Web Site:* www.financialexecutives.org, pg 95

Rab, Sharon, Dayton Literary Peace Prize, 25 Harman Terr, Dayton, OH 45419 *Tel:* 937-298-5072 *Web Site:* daytonliterarypeaceprize.org, pg 699

Rabberman, Kristine PhD, College of Liberal & Professional Studies, University of Pennsylvania, 3440 Market St, Suite 100, Philadelphia, PA 19104-3335 *Tel:* 215-898-7326 *Fax:* 215-573-2053 *E-mail:* lps@sas.upenn.edu *Web Site:* www.sas.upenn.edu; www.sas.upenn.edu/lps, pg 677

Rabiner, Susan, Susan Rabiner Literary Agency Inc, 315 W 39 St, Suite 1501, New York, NY 10018-3907 *Web Site:* RabinerLit.com, pg 589

Rabinowitch, Janet, Indiana University Press, 601 N Morton St, Bloomington, IN 47404-3797 *Tel:* 812-855-8817 *Toll Free Tel:* 800-842-6796 (orders only) *Fax:* 812-855-7931; 812-855-8507 *E-mail:* iupress@indiana.edu; iuporder@indiana.edu (orders) *Web Site:* www.iupress.indiana.edu, pg 129

Rabinowitz, Jonathan D, Turtle Point Press, 233 Broadway, Rm 946, New York, NY 10279 *Tel:* 212-945-6622 *E-mail:* countomega@aol.com *Web Site:* www.turtlepointpress.com, pg 260

Raccah, Dominique, Cumberland House, 1935 Brookdale Rd, Suite 139, Naperville, IL 60563 *Tel:* 630-961-3900 *Toll Free Tel:* 800-43-BRIGHT (432-7444) *Fax:* 630-961-2168 *E-mail:* info@sourcebooks.com *Web Site:* www.sourcebooks.com/products/cumberland.html, pg 73

Raccah, Dominique, Sourcebooks Inc, 1935 Brookdale Rd, Suite 139, Naperville, IL 60563 *Tel:* 630-961-3900 *Toll Free Tel:* 800-432-7444 *Fax:* 630-961-2168 *E-mail:* info@sourcebooks.com; customersupport@sourcebooks.com *Web Site:* www.sourcebooks.com, pg 240

Racette, A C, Northwestern University Press, 629 Noyes St, Evanston, IL 60208-4210 *Tel:* 847-491-2046 *Toll Free Tel:* 800-621-2736 (orders only) *Fax:* 847-491-8150 *E-mail:* nupress@northwestern.edu *Web Site:* www.nupress.northwestern.edu, pg 181

Racette, Dorothee, American Translators Association (ATA), 225 Reinekers Lane, Suite 590, Alexandria, VA 22314 *Tel:* 703-683-6100 *Fax:* 703-683-6122 *E-mail:* ata@atanet.org *Web Site:* www.atanet.org, pg 615

Rach, Beverly, Fernwood Publishing, 32 Oceanvista Lane, Black Point, NS B0J 1B0, Canada *Tel:* 902-857-1388 *Fax:* 902-857-1328 *E-mail:* info@fernpub.ca *Web Site:* www.fernwoodpublishing.ca, pg 504

Racz, Gary, American Literary Translators Association (ALTA), c/o The University of Texas at Dallas, 800 W Campbell Rd, Mail Sta JO51, Richardson, TX 75080-3021 *Tel:* 972-883-2093 *Fax:* 972-883-6303 *Web Site:* www.utdallas.edu/alta/, pg 613

Rada, Monica, OCP, 5536 NE Hassalo St, Portland, OR 97213 *Tel:* 503-281-1191 *Toll Free Tel:* 800-548-8749 *Fax:* 503-282-3486 *Toll Free Fax:* 800-843-8181 *E-mail:* liturgy@ocp.org *Web Site:* www.ocp.org, pg 184

Radant, Cyndi, Carolrhoda Books, 241 First Ave N, Minneapolis, MN 55401 *Tel:* 612-332-3344 *Toll Free Tel:* 800-328-4929 *Fax:* 612-332-7615 *Toll Free Fax:* 800-332-1132 *E-mail:* info@lernerbooks.com *Web Site:* www.lernerbooks.com, pg 53

Radant, Cyndi, ediciones Lerner, 241 First Ave N, Minneapolis, MN 55401 *Tel:* 612-332-3344 *Toll Free Tel:* 800-328-4929 *Fax:* 612-332-7615 *Toll Free Fax:* 800-332-1132 *E-mail:* info@lernerbooks.com *Web Site:* www.lernerbooks.com, pg 85

Radant, Cyndi, First Avenue Editions, 241 First Ave N, Minneapolis, MN 55401 *Tel:* 612-332-3344 *Toll Free Tel:* 800-328-4929 *Fax:* 612-332-7615 *Toll Free Fax:* 800-332-1132 *E-mail:* info@lernerbooks.com *Web Site:* www.lernerbooks.com, pg 95

Radant, Cyndi, Graphic Universe™, 241 First Ave N, Minneapolis, MN 55401 *Tel:* 612-332-3344 *Toll Free Tel:* 800-328-4929 *Fax:* 612-332-7615 *Toll Free Fax:* 800-332-1132 *E-mail:* info@lernerbooks.com *Web Site:* www.lernerbooks.com, pg 106

Radant, Cyndi, Lerner Publications, 241 First Ave N, Minneapolis, MN 55401 *Tel:* 612-332-3344 *Toll Free Tel:* 800-328-4929 *Fax:* 612-332-7615 *Toll Free Fax:* 800-332-1132 *E-mail:* info@lernerbooks.com *Web Site:* www.lernerbooks.com, pg 146

Radant, Cyndi, Lerner Publishing Group Inc, 241 First Ave N, Minneapolis, MN 55401 *Tel:* 612-332-3344 *Toll Free Tel:* 800-328-4929 *Fax:* 612-332-7615 *Toll Free Fax:* 800-332-1132 *E-mail:* info@lernerbooks.com *Web Site:* www.lernerbooks.com, pg 146

Radant, Cyndi, LernerClassroom, 241 First Ave N, Minneapolis, MN 55401 *Tel:* 612-332-3344 *Toll Free Tel:* 800-328-4929 *Fax:* 612-332-7615 *Toll Free Fax:* 800-332-1132 *E-mail:* info@lernerbooks.com *Web Site:* www.lernerbooks.com, pg 147

Radant, Cyndi, Millbrook Press, 241 First Ave N, Minneapolis, MN 55401 *Tel:* 612-332-3344 *Toll Free Tel:* 800-328-4929 (US only) *Fax:* 612-332-7615 *Toll Free Fax:* 800-332-1132, pg 167

Radant, Cyndi, Twenty-First Century Books, 241 First Ave N, Minneapolis, MN 55401 *Tel:* 612-332-3344 *Toll Free Tel:* 800-328-4929 *Fax:* 612-332-7615 *Toll Free Fax:* 800-332-1132 *E-mail:* info@lernerbooks.com *Web Site:* www.lernerbooks.com, pg 260

Radcliffe, Barbara, Developmental Studies Center, 2000 Embarcadero, Suite 305, Oakland, CA 94606-5300 *Tel:* 510-533-0213 *Toll Free Tel:* 800-666-7270 *Fax:* 510-464-3670 *E-mail:* pubs@devstu.org; info@devstu.org *Web Site:* www.devstu.org, pg 78

Rade, David, Swan Isle Press, 11030 S Langley Ave, Chicago, IL 60628 *Tel:* 773-728-3780 (edit); 773-702-7000 (cust serv) *Toll Free Tel:* 800-621-2736 (cust serv) *Fax:* 773-702-7212 (cust serv) *Toll Free Fax:* 800-621-8476 (cust serv) *E-mail:* info@swanislepress.com *Web Site:* www.swanislepress.com, pg 248

Radice, Neal, Maxim Mazumdar New Play Competition, One Curtain Up Alley, Buffalo, NY 14202-1911 *Tel:* 716-852-2600 *E-mail:* publicrelations@alleyway.com *Web Site:* alleyway.com, pg 722

Radich, Anthony, Western States Arts Federation, 1743 Wazee St, Suite 300, Denver, CO 80202 *Tel:* 303-629-1166 *Toll Free Tel:* 888-562-7232 *Fax:* 303-629-9717 *E-mail:* staff@westaf.org *Web Site:* www.westaf.org, pg 641

Radke, Linda F, Five Star Dragonfly Book Awards, 4696 W Tyson St, Chandler, AZ 85226 *Tel:* 480-940-8182 *Toll Free Tel:* 866-471-0777 *Fax:* 480-

940-8787 *E-mail:* info@fivestarpublications.com *Web Site:* www.fivestarpublications.com; www.fivestarmarketingsecrets.com, pg 704

Radke, Linda F, Five Star Publications Inc, 4696 W Tyson St, Chandler, AZ 85226 *Tel:* 480-940-8182 *Toll Free Tel:* 866-471-0777 *Fax:* 480-940-8787 *E-mail:* info@fivestarpublications.com *Web Site:* www.fivestarpublications.com, pg 96

Radke, Linda F, Five Star Publishing & Marketing Secrets, 4696 W Tyson St, Chandler, AZ 85226 *Tel:* 480-940-8182 *Toll Free Tel:* 866-471-0777 *Fax:* 480-940-8787 *E-mail:* info@fivestarpublications.com *Web Site:* www.fivestarpublications.com; www.fivestarmarketingsecrets.com, pg 669

Rados, Kate, Crown Publishing Group, c/o Random House Inc, 1745 Broadway, New York, NY 10019 *Tel:* 212-782-9000 *Toll Free Tel:* 888-264-1745 *Fax:* 212-940-7408 *Web Site:* www.randomhouse.com/crown, pg 72

Radovsky, Judy, Oregon State University Press, 121 The Valley Library, Corvallis, OR 97331-4501 *Tel:* 541-737-3166 *Toll Free Tel:* 800-621-2736 (orders) *Fax:* 541-737-3170 *Toll Free Fax:* 800-426-3797 (orders) *E-mail:* osu.press@oregonstate.edu *Web Site:* oregonstate.edu/dept/press; osupress.oregonstate.edu, pg 187

Raducanu, Teodor, Teora USA LLC, 505 Hampton Park Blvd, Unit G, Capitol Heights, MD 20743 *Tel:* 301-986-6990 *Toll Free Tel:* 800-974-2105 *Fax:* 301-350-5480 *Toll Free Fax:* 800-358-3754 *E-mail:* 2010@teora.com *Web Site:* www.teora.com, pg 252

Rae, Sonia, Vermont Arts Council Grants, 136 State St, Montpelier, VT 05602 *Tel:* 802-828-5425 *Fax:* 802-828-3363 *E-mail:* info@vermontartscouncil.org *Web Site:* www.vermontartscouncil.org, pg 747

Raeber, Rick, W W Norton & Company Inc, 500 Fifth Ave, New York, NY 10110-0017 *Tel:* 212-354-5500 *Toll Free Tel:* 800-233-4830 (orders & cust serv) *Fax:* 212-869-0856 *Toll Free Fax:* 800-458-6515 *Web Site:* www.wwnorton.com, pg 182

Rafal, Jane, Jane Rafal Editing Associates, 325 Forest Ridge Dr, Scottsville, VA 24590 *Tel:* 434-286-6949, pg 554

Rafer, Suzanne, Workman Publishing Co Inc, 225 Varick St, 9th fl, New York, NY 10014-4381 *Tel:* 212-254-5900 *Toll Free Tel:* 800-722-7202 *Fax:* 212-254-8098 *E-mail:* info@workman.com *Web Site:* www.workman.com, pg 285

Rafferty, Emily K, The Metropolitan Museum of Art, 1000 Fifth Ave, New York, NY 10028 *Tel:* 212-879-5500; 212-570-3725 *Fax:* 212-396-5062 *E-mail:* editorial@metmuseum.org *Web Site:* www.metmuseum.org, pg 165

Raffio, Michael, Pflaum Publishing Group, 2621 Dryden Rd, Suite 300, Dayton, OH 45439 *Tel:* 937-293-1415 *Toll Free Tel:* 800-543-4383; 800-523-4625 (sales) *Fax:* 937-293-1310 *Toll Free Fax:* 800-370-4450 *E-mail:* service@pflaum.com *Web Site:* pflaum.com, pg 200

Rafter, Katherine, Art of Living, PrimaMedia Inc, 1250 Bethlehem Pike, Suite 241, Hatfield, PA 19440 *Tel:* 215-660-5045 *Toll Free Tel:* 800-581-9020 *Fax:* 734-448-4125 *E-mail:* primamedia4@yahoo.com, pg 23

Ragan, Lise B, Course Crafters Inc, 3 Washington Sq, Haverhill, MA 01830 *Tel:* 978-372-3446 *Fax:* 978-372-3660 *E-mail:* info@coursecrafters.com *Web Site:* www.coursecrafters.com, pg 544

Ragasa, Christine, Hyperion, 1500 Broadway, 3rd fl, New York, NY 10036 *Tel:* 212-536-6500 *Web Site:* hyperionbooks.com, pg 126

Ragland, Kelley, St Martin's Press, LLC, 175 Fifth Ave, New York, NY 10010 *Tel:* 646-307-5151 *Fax:* 212-420-9314 *E-mail:* firstname.lastname@macmillan.com *Web Site:* www.stmartins.com, pg 224

Ragusa, Barbara, LAMA Books, 2381 Sleepy Hollow Ave, Hayward, CA 94545-3429 *Tel:* 510-785-1091 *Toll Free Tel:* 888-452-6244 *Fax:* 510-785-1099 *Web Site:* www.lamabooks.com, pg 143

Rahaeuser, Alice, Random House Children's Books, 1745 Broadway, New York, NY 10019 *Tel:* 212-782-9000 *Toll Free Tel:* 800-200-3552 *Fax:* 212-782-9452 *Web Site:* randomhousekids.com, pg 213

Rahill, Hannah, Ten Speed Press, 2625 Alcatraz Ave, Unit 505, Berkeley, CA 94705 *Tel:* 510-285-3000 *Toll Free Tel:* 800-841-BOOK (841-2665) *E-mail:* csorders@randomhouse.com *Web Site:* crownpublishing.com/imprint/ten-speed-press, pg 252

Rahm, Willi, Alan Wofsy Fine Arts, 1109 Geary Blvd, San Francisco, CA 94109 *Tel:* 415-292-6500 *Toll Free Tel:* 800-660-6403 *Fax:* 415-292-6594 (off & cust serv); 415-512-0130 (acctg) *E-mail:* order@art-books.com (orders); editeur@earthlink.net (edit); beauxarts@earthlink.net (cust serv) *Web Site:* www.art-books.com, pg 284

Rahr, Tim, The Taunton Press Inc, 63 S Main St, Newtown, CT 06470 *Tel:* 203-426-8171 *Toll Free Tel:* 800-477-8727 (cust serv); 800-888-8286 (orders) *Fax:* 203-426-3434 *E-mail:* booksales@taunton.com *Web Site:* www.taunton.com, pg 250

Raihofer, Susan, David Black Agency, 335 Adams St, 27th fl, Suite 2707, Brooklyn, NY 11201 *Tel:* 718-852-5500 *Fax:* 718-852-5539 *Web Site:* www.davidblackagency.com, pg 562

Raij, Emily, Maupin House Publishing, 2300 NW 71 Place, Gainesville, FL 32653 *Tel:* 352-373-5588 *Toll Free Tel:* 800-524-0634 *Fax:* 352-373-5546 *E-mail:* info@maupinhouse.com *Web Site:* www.maupinhouse.com, pg 159

Rainer, Tom, B&H Publishing Group, One Lifeway Plaza, Nashville, TN 37234-0114 *Tel:* 615-251-2520 *Fax:* 615-251-5004 *Web Site:* www.bhpublishinggroup.com, pg 30

Raines, Joan, Raines & Raines, 103 Kenyon Rd, Medusa, NY 12120 *Tel:* 518-239-8311 *Fax:* 518-239-6029, pg 590

Raines, Theron, Raines & Raines, 103 Kenyon Rd, Medusa, NY 12120 *Tel:* 518-239-8311 *Fax:* 518-239-6029, pg 590

Rains, H Montgomery, Oakstone Publishing LLC, 100 Corporate Pkwy, Suite 600, Birmingham, AL 35242 *Toll Free Tel:* 800-633-4743 *Fax:* 205-995-1926 *E-mail:* service@oakstonemedical.com *Web Site:* www.oakstonepublishing.com; www.cmeonly.com; www.cdeonly.com, pg 183

Raley, David, Halcyon Press Ltd, 2206 N Gordon St, Suite D, Alvin, TX 77511 *Tel:* 281-585-9559 *Toll Free Tel:* 866-774-5786 *E-mail:* info@halcyon-press.com; editor@halcyonpress.com *Web Site:* www.halcyonpress.com, pg 111

Ramelize, Yusef, BioTechniques Books, 52 Vanderbilt Ave, 7th fl, New York, NY 10017 *Tel:* 212-520-2777 *Fax:* 212-520-2705 *Web Site:* www.biotechniques.com, pg 38

Ramer, Susan, Don Congdon Associates Inc, 110 William St, Suite 2202, New York, NY 10038-3914 *Tel:* 212-645-1229 *Fax:* 212-727-2688 *E-mail:* dca@doncongdon.com *Web Site:* www.doncongdon.com, pg 567

Rameriz, Raquel, PhotoEdit Inc, 3505 Cadillac Ave, Suite P-101, Costa Mesa, CA 92626 *Tel:* 714-434-5925 *Toll Free Tel:* 800-860-2098 *Fax:* 714-434-5937 *Toll Free Fax:* 800-804-3707 *E-mail:* sales@photoeditinc.com *Web Site:* www.photoeditinc.com, pg 553

Ramin, Sue Berger, David R Godine Publisher Inc, 15 Court Sq, Suite 320, Boston, MA 02108-4715 *Tel:* 617-451-9600 *Fax:* 617-350-0250 *E-mail:* pub@godine.com *Web Site:* www.godine.com, pg 104

Ramirez, Alanna, Trident Media Group LLC, 41 Madison Ave, 36th fl, New York, NY 10010 *Tel:* 212-262-4810 *Fax:* 212-262-4849 *Web Site:* www.tridentmediagroup.com, pg 598

Ramirez, Bruce, Council for Exceptional Children (CEC), 2900 Crystal Dr, Suite 1000, Arlington, VA 22201 *Toll Free Tel:* 888-232-7733 (memb servs); 866-509-0219 *Fax:* 703-264-9494 *E-mail:* service@cec.sped.org *Web Site:* www.cec.sped.org, pg 69

Ramo, Roberta Cooper, American Law Institute, 4025 Chestnut St, Philadelphia, PA 19104-3099 *Tel:* 215-243-1600 *Toll Free Tel:* 800-253-6397 *Fax:* 215-243-1664; 215-243-1683 *Web Site:* www.ali.org, pg 14

Ramondo, Anthony, NAL, 375 Hudson St, New York, NY 10014 *Tel:* 212-366-2000 *E-mail:* online@penguinputnam.com *Web Site:* www.penguinputnam.com; us.penguingroup.com, pg 172

Ramos, Christine, American Map Corp, 36-36 33 St, 4th fl, Long Island City, NY 11106 *Tel:* 718-784-0055 *Toll Free Tel:* 888-774-7979 *Fax:* 718-784-0640 (admin); 718-784-1216 (sales & orders) *E-mail:* sales@americanmap.com *Web Site:* www.americanmap.com, pg 14

Ramos, Luis Arturo, University of Texas at El Paso, Dept Creative Writing, MFA/Dept Creative Writing, Liberal Arts 415 UTEP, 500 W University Ave, El Paso, TX 79968-9991 *Tel:* 915-747-5713 *Fax:* 915-747-5523 *Web Site:* www.utep.edu/cw, pg 682

Ramsey, Sherry, SF Canada, 7433 E River Rd, Washago, ON L0K 2B0, Canada *Web Site:* www.sfcanada.org, pg 636

Randall, Michele E, Bibliographical Society of America, PO Box 1537, Lenox Hill Sta, New York, NY 10021-0043 *Tel:* 212-452-2710 *Fax:* 212-452-2710 *E-mail:* bsa@bibsocamer.org *Web Site:* www.bibsocamer.org, pg 618

Randolph, Carol, Akin & Randolph Agency, Literary Div, One Gateway Ctr, Suite 2600, Newark, NJ 07102 *Tel:* 973-353-8409; 973-623-6834 *Fax:* 973-353-8417 *E-mail:* info@akinandrandolph.com *Web Site:* www.akinandrandolph.com, pg 560

Randolph, Ladette, Ploughshares, Emerson College, 120 Boylston St, Boston, MA 02116 *Tel:* 617-824-3757 *E-mail:* pshares@pshares.org *Web Site:* www.pshares.org, pg 203

Raney, Candace, Watson-Guptill Publications, c/o Random House Inc, 1745 Broadway, New York, NY 10019 *Tel:* 212-782-9000 *Fax:* 212-940-7381 *E-mail:* crownbiz@randomhouse.com *Web Site:* www.randomhouse.com/crown/watsonguptill, pg 277

Ranger, Abby, Disney-Hyperion Books, 44 S Broadway, White Plains, NY 10601 *Tel:* 212-633-4400 *Fax:* 212-807-5880 *Web Site:* disney.go.com/books/index, pg 79

Ranger, Abby, HarperCollins Children's Books, 10 E 53 St, New York, NY 10022 *Tel:* 212-207-7000 *Web Site:* www.harpercollinschildrens.com, pg 113

Rankin, Charles, University of Oklahoma Press, 2800 Venture Dr, Norman, OK 73069-8216 *Tel:* 405-325-2000 *Toll Free Tel:* 800-627-7377 (orders) *Fax:* 405-364-5798 (orders) *Toll Free Fax:* 800-735-0476 (orders) *E-mail:* presscs@ou.edu *Web Site:* www.oupress.com, pg 268

Rankin, Jada, Texas Tech University Press, 2903 Fourth St, Suite 201, Lubbock, TX 79409 *Tel:* 806-742-2982 *Toll Free Tel:* 800-832-4042 *Fax:* 806-742-2979 *E-mail:* ttup@ttu.edu *Web Site:* www.ttupress.org, pg 253

Rankin, Jenni, Annual Reviews, 4139 El Camino Way, Palo Alto, CA 94306 *Tel:* 650-493-4400 *Toll Free Tel:* 800-523-8635 *Fax:* 650-424-0910 *E-mail:* service@annualreviews.org *Web Site:* www.annualreviews.org, pg 18

Rankin, Margit, Artist Trust Fellowship, 1835 12 Ave, Seattle, WA 98122 *Tel:* 206-467-8734 (ext 11) *Toll Free Tel:* 866-218-7878 (ext 11) *Fax:* 206-467-9633 *E-mail:* info@artisttrust.org *Web Site:* www.artisttrust.org, pg 688

Rankin, Margit, Grants for Artist Projects, 1835 12 Ave, Seattle, WA 98122 *Tel:* 206-467-8734 (ext 11) *Toll Free Tel:* 866-218-7878 (ext 11) *Fax:* 206-467-9633 *E-mail:* info@artisttrust.org *Web Site:* www.artisttrust.org, pg 708

Reidy, Sarah, Other Press LLC, 2 Park Ave, 24th fl, New York, NY 10016 *Tel:* 212-414-0054 *Toll Free Tel:* 877-843-6843 *Fax:* 212-414-0939 *E-mail:* editor@otherpress.com; rights@otherpress.com *Web Site:* www.otherpress.com, pg 188

Reighard, Jessica, Brookes Publishing Co Inc, PO Box 10624, Baltimore, MD 21285-0624 *Tel:* 410-337-9580 (outside US & CN) *Toll Free Tel:* 800-638-3775 (US & CN) *Fax:* 410-337-8539 *E-mail:* custserv@brookespublishing.com *Web Site:* www.brookespublishing.com, pg 48

Reil, Doug, Frog Books, 2526 Martin Luther King Jr Way, Berkeley, CA 94704 *Tel:* 510-549-4270 *Toll Free Tel:* 800-733-3000 (book orders only) *Fax:* 510-549-4276 *Toll Free Fax:* 800-659-2436 (orders) *E-mail:* orders@northatlanticbooks.com *Web Site:* www.northatlanticbooks.com, pg 99

Reil, Doug, North Atlantic Books, 2526 Martin Luther King Jr Way, Berkeley, CA 94704 *Tel:* 510-549-4270 *Fax:* 510-549-4276 *Web Site:* www.northatlanticbooks.com, pg 180

Reilly, Edward T, American Management Association®, 1601 Broadway, New York, NY 10019-7420 *Tel:* 212-586-8100 *Toll Free Tel:* 877-566-9441 *Fax:* 212-903-8168; 518-891-0368 *E-mail:* customerservice@amanet.org *Web Site:* www.amanet.org, pg 613

Reilly, Jack, Pearson Higher Education, One Lake St, Upper Saddle River, NJ 07458 *Tel:* 201-236-7000 *Fax:* 201-236-3381 *Web Site:* www.pearsonhighered.com, pg 196

Reimer, John, IEEE Computer Society, 2001 "L" St NW, Suite 700, Washington, DC 20036-4928 *Tel:* 202-371-0101 *Toll Free Tel:* 800-272-6657 (memb info) *Fax:* 202-728-9614 *E-mail:* help@computer.org *Web Site:* www.computer.org, pg 127

Rein, Jody, Jody Rein Books Inc, 7741 S Ash Ct, Centennial, CO 80122 *Tel:* 303-694-9386 *Web Site:* www.jodyreinbooks.com, pg 578

Reinertsen, Claire, W W Norton & Company Inc, 500 Fifth Ave, New York, NY 10110-0017 *Tel:* 212-354-5500 *Toll Free Tel:* 800-233-4830 (orders & cust serv) *Fax:* 212-869-0856 *Toll Free Fax:* 800-458-6515 *Web Site:* www.wwnorton.com, pg 182

Reinhart, Julia, Library Association of Alberta (LAA), 80 Baker Crescent NW, Calgary, AB T2L 1R4, Canada *Tel:* 403-284-5818 *Toll Free Tel:* 877-522-5550 *Fax:* 403-282-6646 *E-mail:* info@laa.ca *Web Site:* www.laa.ca, pg 626

Reis, Mike, Kids Can Press Ltd, 25 Dockside Dr, Toronto, ON M5A 0B5, Canada *Tel:* 416-479-7000 *Toll Free Tel:* 800-265-0884 *Fax:* 416-960-5437 *E-mail:* info@kidscan.com; customerservice@kidscan.com *Web Site:* www.kidscanpress.com; www.kidscanpress.ca, pg 510

Reisdorff, James J, South Platte Press, PO Box 163, David City, NE 68632-0163 *Tel:* 402-367-3554 *E-mail:* railroads@windstream.net *Web Site:* www.southplattepress.net, pg 240

Reiser, Annie M, Morton N Cohen Award for a Distinguished Edition of Letters, 26 Broadway, 3rd fl, New York, NY 10004-1789 *Tel:* 646-576-5141 *Fax:* 646-458-0030 *E-mail:* awards@mla.org *Web Site:* www.mla.org, pg 698

Reiser, Annie M, Katherine Singer Kovacs Prize, 26 Broadway, 3rd fl, New York, NY 10004-1789 *Tel:* 646-576-5141 *Fax:* 646-458-0030 *E-mail:* awards@mla.org *Web Site:* www.mla.org, pg 715

Reiser, Annie M, Fenia & Yaakov Leviant Memorial Prize in Yiddish Studies, 26 Broadway, 3rd fl, New York, NY 10004-1789 *Tel:* 646-576-5141 *Fax:* 646-458-0030 *E-mail:* awards@mla.org *Web Site:* www.mla.org, pg 717

Reiser, Annie M, James Russell Lowell Prize, 26 Broadway, 3rd fl, New York, NY 10004-1789 *Tel:* 646-576-5141 *Fax:* 646-458-0030 *E-mail:* awards@mla.org *Web Site:* www.mla.org, pg 719

Reiser, Annie M, Howard R Marraro Prize, 26 Broadway, 3rd fl, New York, NY 10004-1789 *Tel:* 646-576-5141 *Fax:* 646-458-0030 *E-mail:* awards@mla.org *Web Site:* www.mla.org, pg 721

Reiser, Annie M, Kenneth W Mildenberger Prize, 26 Broadway, 3rd fl, New York, NY 10004-1789 *Tel:* 646-576-5141 *Fax:* 646-458-0030 *E-mail:* awards@mla.org *Web Site:* www.mla.org, pg 723

Reiser, Annie M, MLA Prize for a Bibliography, Archive or Digital Project, 26 Broadway, 3rd fl, New York, NY 10004-1789 *Tel:* 646-576-5141 *Fax:* 646-458-0030 *E-mail:* awards@mla.org *Web Site:* www.mla.org, pg 724

Reiser, Annie M, MLA Prize for a First Book, 26 Broadway, 3rd fl, New York, NY 10004-1789 *Tel:* 646-576-5141 *Fax:* 646-458-0030 *E-mail:* awards@mla.org *Web Site:* www.mla.org, pg 724

Reiser, Annie M, MLA Prize for a Scholarly Edition, 26 Broadway, 3rd fl, New York, NY 10004-1789 *Tel:* 646-576-5141 *Fax:* 646-458-0030 *E-mail:* awards@mla.org *Web Site:* www.mla.org, pg 724

Reiser, Annie M, MLA Prize for Independent Scholars, 26 Broadway, 3rd fl, New York, NY 10004-1789 *Tel:* 646-576-5141 *Fax:* 646-458-0030 *E-mail:* awards@mla.org *Web Site:* www.mla.org, pg 724

Reiser, Annie M, MLA Prize in United States Latina & Latino & Chicana & Chicano Literary & Cultural Studies, 26 Broadway, 3rd fl, New York, NY 10004-1789 *Tel:* 646-576-5141 *Fax:* 646-458-0030 *E-mail:* awards@mla.org *Web Site:* www.mla.org, pg 724

Reiser, Annie M, Lois Roth Award, 26 Broadway, 3rd fl, New York, NY 10004-1789 *Tel:* 646-576-5141 *Fax:* 646-458-0030 *E-mail:* awards@mla.org *Web Site:* www.mla.org, pg 738

Reiser, Annie M, Aldo & Jeanne Scaglione Prize for a Translation of a Literary Work, 26 Broadway, 3rd fl, New York, NY 10004-1789 *Tel:* 646-576-5141 *Fax:* 646-458-0030 *E-mail:* awards@mla.org *Web Site:* www.mla.org, pg 739

Reiser, Annie M, Aldo & Jeanne Scaglione Prize for a Translation of a Scholarly Study of Literature, 26 Broadway, 3rd fl, New York, NY 10004-1789 *Tel:* 646-576-5141 *Fax:* 646-458-0030 *E-mail:* awards@mla.org *Web Site:* www.mla.org, pg 739

Reiser, Annie M, Aldo & Jeanne Scaglione Prize for Comparative Literary Studies, 26 Broadway, 3rd fl, New York, NY 10004-1789 *Tel:* 646-576-5141 *Fax:* 646-458-0030 *E-mail:* awards@mla.org *Web Site:* www.mla.org, pg 740

Reiser, Annie M, Aldo & Jeanne Scaglione Prize for French & Francophone Studies, 26 Broadway, 3rd fl, New York, NY 10004-1789 *Tel:* 646-576-5141 *Fax:* 646-458-0030 *E-mail:* awards@mla.org *Web Site:* www.mla.org, pg 740

Reiser, Annie M, Aldo & Jeanne Scaglione Prize for Italian Studies, 26 Broadway, 3rd fl, New York, NY 10004-1789 *Tel:* 646-576-5141 *Fax:* 646-458-0030 *E-mail:* awards@mla.org *Web Site:* www.mla.org, pg 740

Reiser, Annie M, Aldo & Jeanne Scaglione Prize for Studies in Germanic Languages & Literature, 26 Broadway, 3rd fl, New York, NY 10004-1789 *Tel:* 646-576-5141 *Fax:* 646-458-0030 *E-mail:* awards@mla.org *Web Site:* www.mla.org, pg 740

Reiser, Annie M, Aldo & Jeanne Scaglione Prize for Studies in Slavic Languages & Literature, 26 Broadway, 3rd fl, New York, NY 10004-1789 *Tel:* 646-576-5141 *E-mail:* awards@mla.org *Web Site:* www.mla.org, pg 740

Reiser, Annie M, Aldo & Jeanne Scaglione Publication Award for a Manuscript in Italian Literary Studies, 26 Broadway, 3rd fl, New York, NY 10004-1789 *Tel:* 646-576-5141 *Fax:* 646-458-0030 *E-mail:* awards@mla.org *Web Site:* www.mla.org, pg 740

Reiser, Annie M, William Sanders Scarborough Prize, 26 Broadway, 3rd fl, New York, NY 10004-1789 *Tel:* 646-576-5141 *Fax:* 646-458-0030 *E-mail:* awards@mla.org *Web Site:* www.mla.org, pg 740

Reiser, Annie M, Mina P Shaughnessy Prize, 26 Broadway, 3rd fl, New York, NY 10004-1789 *Tel:* 646-576-5141 *Fax:* 646-458-0030 *E-mail:* awards@mla.org *Web Site:* www.mla.org, pg 741

Reiser, Marc A, National Notary Association (NNA), 9350 De Soto Ave, Chatsworth, CA 91311 *Tel:* 818-739-4000 *Toll Free Tel:* 800-876-6827 *Toll Free Fax:* 800-833-1211 *E-mail:* nna@nationalnotary.org *Web Site:* www.nationalnotary.org, pg 175

Reiss, William, John Hawkins & Associates Inc, 71 W 23 St, Suite 1600, New York, NY 10010 *Tel:* 212-807-7040 *Fax:* 212-807-9555 *E-mail:* jha@jhalit.com *Web Site:* jhalit.com, pg 576

Reiter, Jendi, Tom Howard/John H Reid Short Story Contest, 351 Pleasant St, PMB 222, Northampton, MA 01060-3961 *Tel:* 413-320-1847 *Toll Free Tel:* 866-WINWRIT (946-9748) *Fax:* 413-280-0539 *Web Site:* www.winningwriters.com, pg 710

Reiter, Jendi, Tom Howard/Margaret Reid Poetry Contest, 351 Pleasant St, PMB 222, Northampton, MA 01060-3961 *Tel:* 413-320-1847 *Toll Free Tel:* 866-WINWRIT (946-9748) *Fax:* 413-280-0539 *Web Site:* www.winningwriters.com, pg 710

Reiter, Jendi, Sports Fiction & Essay Contest, 351 Pleasant St, PMB 222, Northampton, MA 01060-3961 *Tel:* 413-320-1847 *Toll Free Tel:* 866-WINWRIT (946-9748) *Fax:* 413-280-0539 *Web Site:* www.winningwriters.com, pg 743

Reiter, Jendi, Wergle Flomp Humor Poetry Contest, 351 Pleasant St, PMB 222, Northampton, MA 01060-3961 *Tel:* 413-320-1847 *Toll Free Tel:* 866-WINWRIT (946-9748) *Fax:* 413-280-0539 *Web Site:* www.winningwriters.com, pg 748

Rekulak, Jason, Quirk Books, 215 Church St, Philadelphia, PA 19106 *Tel:* 215-627-3581 *Fax:* 215-627-5220 *E-mail:* general@quirkbooks.com *Web Site:* www.quirkbooks.com, pg 211

Remazeilles, Ingrid, Les Editions Goelette Inc, 1350 Marie-Victorin, St-Bruno-de-Montarville, Quebec, QC J3V 6B9, Canada *Tel:* 450-653-1337 *Toll Free Tel:* 800-463-4961 *Fax:* 450-653-9924 *Web Site:* www.editionsgoelette.com, pg 506

Renaldi, Joe, Writers' Haven Writers (WHW), 2244 Fourth Av, Suite A, San Diego, CA 92101-2119 *Tel:* 619-665-2712, pg 639

Renaud, Alain-Nicolas, Les Editions de l'Hexagone, 1010 rue de la Gauchetiere E, Montreal, QC H2L 2N5, Canada *Tel:* 514-523-7993 (ext 4201) *Fax:* 514-282-7530 *E-mail:* vml@sogides.com *Web Site:* www.edhexagone.com, pg 502

Renaud, Marie-Lyne, Innis-Gerin Medal, Walter House, 282 Somerset W, Ottawa, ON K2P 0J6, Canada *Tel:* 613-991-6990 *Fax:* 613-991-6996 *E-mail:* nominations@rsc-src.ca *Web Site:* www.rsc-src.ca, pg 712

Renaud, Marie-Lyne, Lorne Pierce Medal, Walter House, 282 Somerset W, Ottawa, ON K2P 0J6, Canada *Tel:* 613-991-6990 *Fax:* 613-991-6996 *E-mail:* nominations@rsc-src.ca *Web Site:* www.rsc-src.ca, pg 734

Renker, Jason, The Century Foundation, 41 E 70 St, New York, NY 10021 *Tel:* 212-535-4441; 212-879-9197 *Fax:* 212-879-9197 *E-mail:* info@tcf.org *Web Site:* www.tcf.org, pg 57, 641

Renner, Georgene, Society for Mining, Metallurgy & Exploration, 12999 E Adam Aircraft Circle, Englewood, CO 80112 *Tel:* 303-948-4200 *Toll Free Tel:* 800-763-3132 *Fax:* 303-973-3845 *E-mail:* cs@smenet.org *Web Site:* www.smenet.org, pg 238

Rinck, Gary M, John Wiley & Sons Inc, 111 River St, Hoboken, NJ 07030-5774 *Tel:* 201-748-6000 *Toll Free Tel:* 800-225-5945 (cust serv) *Fax:* 201-748-6088 *E-mail:* info@wiley.com *Web Site:* www.wiley.com, pg 281

Rinehart, Rick, Cooper Square Press, 5360 Manhattan Circle, Suite 101, Boulder, CO 80303 *Tel:* 303-543-7835 *Fax:* 303-543-0043 *Web Site:* www.rlpgbooks.com; www.rlpgtrade.com, pg 67

Ringold, Francine PhD, The Pablo Neruda Prize for Poetry, Nimrod International Journal, 800 S Tucker Dr, Tulsa, OK 74104 *Tel:* 918-631-3080 *Fax:* 918-631-3033 *E-mail:* nimrod@utulsa.edu *Web Site:* www.utulsa.edu/nimrod, pg 727

Ringold, Francine PhD, Katherine Anne Porter Prize for Fiction, Nimrod International Journal, 800 S Tucker Dr, Tulsa, OK 74104 *Tel:* 918-631-3080 *Fax:* 918-631-3033 *E-mail:* nimrod@utulsa.edu *Web Site:* www.utulsa.edu/nimrod, pg 735

Riordan, Caroline, Penguin Group (USA) LLC Sales, 375 Hudson St, New York, NY 10014 *Tel:* 212-366-2000 *E-mail:* online@penguinputnam.com *Web Site:* us.penguingroup.com, pg 197

Riordan, James C, Seven Locks Press, 3100 W Warner Ave, Suite 8, Santa Ana, CA 97204 *E-mail:* sevenlocks@aol.com *Web Site:* www.sevenlockspublishing.com, pg 232

Ripianzi, David, YMAA Publication Center, PO Box 480, Wolfeboro, NH 03894 *Tel:* 603-569-7988 *Toll Free Tel:* 800-669-8892 *Fax:* 603-569-1889 *E-mail:* ymaa@aol.com *Web Site:* www.ymaa.com, pg 288

Riske, Kris Brandt, American Federation of Astrologers Inc, 6535 S Rural Rd, Tempe, AZ 85283-3746 *Tel:* 480-838-1751 *Toll Free Tel:* 888-301-7630 *Fax:* 480-838-8293 *Web Site:* www.astrologers.com, pg 13

Riskey, Curtis, CBA: The Association for Christian Retail, 9240 Explorer Dr, Suite 200, Colorado Springs, CO 80920 *Tel:* 719-265-9895 *Toll Free Tel:* 800-252-1950 *Fax:* 719-272-3510 *E-mail:* info@cbaonline.org *Web Site:* www.cbaonline.org, pg 620

Risko, Allison, Kaplan Publishing, 395 Hudson St, 4th fl, New York, NY 10014 *Tel:* 212-618-2400 *Toll Free Tel:* 888-KAPLAN8 (527-5268) *Fax:* 917-344-2499 *Toll Free Fax:* 877-712-5487 *E-mail:* book.support@kaplan.com *Web Site:* www.kaplanpublishing.com, pg 138

Rissi, Anica, HarperCollins Children's Books, 10 E 53 St, New York, NY 10022 *Tel:* 212-207-7000 *Web Site:* www.harpercollinschildrens.com, pg 113

Ristau, Karen M PhD, National Catholic Educational Association, 1005 N Glebe Rd, Suite 525, Arlington, VA 22201 *Tel:* 571-257-0010 *Toll Free Tel:* 800-711-6232 *Fax:* 703-243-0025 *E-mail:* nceaadmin@ncea.org *Web Site:* www.ncea.org, pg 173

Ristau, Todd, Southeastern Theatre Conference New Play Project, 1175 Revolution Mill Dr, Suite 14, Greensboro, NC 27405 *Tel:* 336-272-3645 *Fax:* 336-272-8810 *E-mail:* info@setc.org *Web Site:* www.setc.org, pg 743

Ritchie, Adele, Canadian Newspaper Association, 890 Yonge St, Suite 200, Toronto, ON M4W 3P4, Canada *Tel:* 416-923-3567; 416-482-1090 *Toll Free Tel:* 877-305-2262 *Fax:* 416-923-7206; 416-482-1908 *E-mail:* info@cna-acj.ca *Web Site:* www.cna-acj.ca, pg 620

Ritchken, Deborah, Marsal Lyon Literary Agency LLC, 665 San Rodolfo Dr, Suite 124, PMB 121, Solana Beach, CA 92075 *Tel:* 760-814-8507 *Web Site:* www.marsallyonliteraryagency.com, pg 583

Ritt, Judith W, Professional Resource Press, 1891 Apex Rd, Sarasota, FL 34240-9386 *Tel:* 941-343-9601 *Toll Free Tel:* 800-443-3364 *Fax:* 941-343-9201 *Toll Free Fax:* 866-804-4843 (orders) *E-mail:* orders@prpress.com *Web Site:* www.prpress.com, pg 208

Ritt, Lawrence G, Professional Resource Press, 1891 Apex Rd, Sarasota, FL 34240-9386 *Tel:* 941-343-9601 *Toll Free Tel:* 800-443-3364 *Fax:* 941-343-9201 *Toll Free Fax:* 866-804-4843 (orders) *E-mail:* orders@prpress.com *Web Site:* www.prpress.com, pg 208

Rittenberg, Ann, Ann Rittenberg Literary Agency Inc, 15 Maiden Lane, Suite 206, New York, NY 10038 *Tel:* 212-684-6936 *Fax:* 212-684-6929 *Web Site:* www.rittlit.com, pg 591

Ritter, Carol, Romance Writers of America Awards, 14615 Benfer Rd, Houston, TX 77069 *Tel:* 832-717-5200 *Fax:* 832-717-5201 *E-mail:* info@rwa.org *Web Site:* www.rwa.org, pg 738

Ritter, Richard G, Gryphon Editions, PO Box 34461, Bethesda, MD 20827 *Tel:* 301-983-4171 *Toll Free Tel:* 800-633-8911 *Fax:* 301-983-8734 *E-mail:* gryphonedn@gmail.com *Web Site:* www.gryphoneditions.com, pg 109

Riva, Peter, International Transactions Inc, 28 Alope Way, Gila, NM 88038 *Tel:* 845-373-9696 *Fax:* 480-393-5162 *E-mail:* info@intltrans.com *Web Site:* www.intltrans.com, pg 577

Riva, Sandra Anne, International Transactions Inc, 28 Alope Way, Gila, NM 88038 *Tel:* 845-373-9696 *Fax:* 480-393-5162 *E-mail:* info@intltrans.com *Web Site:* www.intltrans.com, pg 577

Rivas-Smith, Alexandra, William H Sadlier Inc, 9 Pine St, New York, NY 10005 *Tel:* 212-227-2120 *Toll Free Tel:* 800-221-5175 (cust serv) *Fax:* 212-312-6080 *Web Site:* www.sadlier.com, pg 223

Riven, Judith, Judith Riven Literary Agent LLC, 250 W 16 St, Suite 4F, New York, NY 10011 *Tel:* 212-255-1009 *Fax:* 212-255-8547 *E-mail:* rivenlitqueries@gmail.com *Web Site:* rivenlit.com, pg 554, 591

Rivers, Shana R, University of Alabama Press, 200 Hackberry Lane, 2nd fl, Tuscaloosa, AL 35487 *Tel:* 205-348-5180 *Fax:* 205-348-9201 *Web Site:* www.uapress.ua.edu, pg 263

Rizzo, Joel, Writers' Haven Writers (WHW), 2244 Fourth Av, Suite A, San Diego, CA 92101-2119 *Tel:* 619-665-2712, pg 639

Rizzo, Mary, New Jersey Council for the Humanities Book Award, 28 W State St, 6th fl, Trenton, NJ 08608 *Tel:* 609-695-4838 *Toll Free Tel:* 888-FYI-NJCH (394-6524) *Fax:* 609-695-4929 *E-mail:* njch@njch.org *Web Site:* www.njch.org, pg 728

Roach, Brian, The Catholic University of America Press, 240 Leahy Hall, 620 Michigan Ave NE, Washington, DC 20064 *Tel:* 202-319-5052 *Toll Free Tel:* 800-537-5487 (orders only) *Fax:* 202-319-4985 *E-mail:* cua-press@cua.edu *Web Site:* cuapress.cua.edu, pg 54

Roach, Reginald, Palmetto Bug Books, 121 N Hibiscus Dr, Miami Beach, FL 33139 *Tel:* 305-531-9813 *Fax:* 305-604-1516 *E-mail:* palmettobugbooks@gmail.com, pg 191

Roane, Rick, Cherry Hill Publishing, 24344 Del Amo Rd, Ramona, CA 92065 *Tel:* 858-829-5550 *Toll Free Tel:* 800-407-1072 *Fax:* 760-203-1200 *E-mail:* operations@cherryhillpublishing.com; sales@cherryhillpublishing.com *Web Site:* www.cherryhillpublishing.com, pg 59

Roane, Sharon, Cherry Hill Publishing, 24344 Del Amo Rd, Ramona, CA 92065 *Tel:* 858-829-5550 *Toll Free Tel:* 800-407-1072 *Fax:* 760-203-1200 *E-mail:* operations@cherryhillpublishing.com; sales@cherryhillpublishing.com *Web Site:* www.cherryhillpublishing.com, pg 59

Robbins, B J, B J Robbins Literary Agency, 5130 Bellaire Ave, North Hollywood, CA 91607 *E-mail:* robbinsliterary@gmail.com, pg 591

Robbins, Caroline, Trafalgar Square Books, 388 Howe Hill Rd, North Pomfret, VT 05053 *Tel:* 802-457-1911 *Toll Free Tel:* 800-423-4525 *Fax:* 802-457-1913 *E-mail:* tsquare@sover.net; info@trafalgarbooks.com *Web Site:* www.trafalgarbooks.com; www.horseandriderbooks.com, pg 257

Robbins, Lara, Berkley Books, 375 Hudson St, New York, NY 10014 *Tel:* 212-366-2000 *Fax:* 212-366-2666 *E-mail:* online@penguinputnam.com *Web Site:* www.penguinputnam.com; us.penguingroup.com, pg 36

Robbins, Lara, Berkley Publishing Group, 375 Hudson St, New York, NY 10014 *Tel:* 212-366-2000 *Fax:* 212-366-2385 *E-mail:* online@penguinputnam.com *Web Site:* us.penguingroup.com, pg 36

Robbins-Butcher, Amanda, Jerome Fellowship, 2301 Franklin Ave E, Minneapolis, MN 55406-1099 *Tel:* 612-332-7481 *Fax:* 612-332-6037 *E-mail:* info@pwcenter.org *Web Site:* www.pwcenter.org, pg 714

Robbins-Butcher, Amanda, Many Voices Fellowships, 2301 Franklin Ave E, Minneapolis, MN 55406-1099 *Tel:* 612-332-7481 *Fax:* 612-332-6037 *E-mail:* info@pwcenter.org *Web Site:* www.pwcenter.org, pg 721

Robbins-Butcher, Amanda, McKnight Advancement Grants, 2301 Franklin Ave E, Minneapolis, MN 55406-1099 *Tel:* 612-332-7481 *Fax:* 612-332-6037 *E-mail:* info@pwcenter.org *Web Site:* www.pwcenter.org, pg 722

Robbins-Butcher, Amanda, McKnight National Residency & Commission, 2301 Franklin Ave E, Minneapolis, MN 55406-1099 *Tel:* 612-332-7481 *Fax:* 612-332-6037 *E-mail:* info@pwcenter.org *Web Site:* www.pwcenter.org, pg 722

Roberson, Nancy, Oxford University Press USA, 198 Madison Ave, New York, NY 10016 *Tel:* 212-726-6000 *Toll Free Tel:* 800-451-7556 (orders); 800-445-9714 (cust serv) *Fax:* 919-677-1303 *E-mail:* custserv.us@oup.com *Web Site:* www.oup.com/us, pg 189

Robert, Katie, American Industrial Hygiene Association - AIHA, 3141 Fairview Park Dr, Suite 777, Falls Church, VA 22042 *Tel:* 703-849-8888 *Fax:* 703-207-3561 *E-mail:* infonet@aiha.org *Web Site:* www.aiha.org, pg 13

Roberts, Benjamin C, Health Research Books, 62 Seventh St, Pomeroy, WA 99347 *Tel:* 509-843-2385 *Toll Free Tel:* 888-844-2386 *Fax:* 509-843-2387 *E-mail:* publish@pomeroy-wa.com *Web Site:* www.healthresearchbooks.com, pg 117

Roberts, Cathy, International Risk Management Institute Inc, 12222 Merit Dr, Suite 1450, Dallas, TX 75251-2276 *Tel:* 972-960-7693 *Fax:* 972-371-5120 *E-mail:* info27@irmi.com *Web Site:* www.irmi.com, pg 133

Roberts, Claire, Trident Media Group LLC, 41 Madison Ave, 36th fl, New York, NY 10010 *Tel:* 212-262-4810 *Fax:* 212-262-4849 *Web Site:* www.tridentmediagroup.com, pg 598

Roberts, Conrad, University Press of Kansas, 2502 Westbrooke Circle, Lawrence, KS 66045-4444 *Tel:* 785-864-4154; 785-864-4155 (orders) *Fax:* 785-864-4586 *E-mail:* upress@ku.edu; upkorders@ku.edu (orders) *Web Site:* www.kansaspress.ku.edu, pg 271

Roberts, Jane F, Literary & Creative Artists Inc, 3543 Albemarle St NW, Washington, DC 20008-4213 *Tel:* 202-362-4688 *Fax:* 202-362-8875 *E-mail:* lca9643@lcadc.com (queries, no attachments) *Web Site:* www.lcadc.com, pg 582

Roberts, Jennifer, Candlewick Press, 99 Dover St, Somerville, MA 02144-2825 *Tel:* 617-661-3330 *Fax:* 617-661-0565 *E-mail:* bigbear@candlewick.com *Web Site:* www.candlewick.com, pg 51

Roberts, Jill, Tachyon Publications, 1459 18 St, Suite 139, San Francisco, CA 94107 *Tel:* 415-285-5615 *E-mail:* tachyon@tachyonpublications.com *Web Site:* www.tachyonpublications.com, pg 249

Roberts, LaTisha, Texas Tech University Press, 2903 Fourth St, Suite 201, Lubbock, TX 79409 *Tel:* 806-742-2982 *Toll Free Tel:* 800-832-4042 *Fax:* 806-742-2979 *E-mail:* ttup@ttu.edu *Web Site:* www.ttupress.org, pg 253

Roberts, Megan, Sewanee Writers' Conference, Stamler Ctr, 119 Gailor Hall, 735 University Ave, Sewanee, TN 37383-1000 *Tel:* 931-598-1141 *E-mail:* swc@sewanee.edu *Web Site:* www.sewaneewriters.org, pg 673

Roberts, Michael, Fine Arts Work Center in Provincetown, 24 Pearl St, Provincetown, MA 02657 *Tel:* 508-487-9960 *Fax:* 508-487-8873 *E-mail:* general@fawc.org *Web Site:* www.fawc.org, pg 704

Roberts, Nancy, Pearson Humanities & Social Sciences, One Lake St, Upper Saddle River, NJ 07458 *Tel:* 201-236-7000 *Fax:* 201-236-3400, pg 196

Roberts, Nikki Jones, Health Research Books, 62 Seventh St, Pomeroy, WA 99347 *Tel:* 509-843-2385 *Toll Free Tel:* 888-844-2386 *Fax:* 509-843-2387 *E-mail:* publish@pomeroy-wa.com *Web Site:* www.healthresearchbooks.com, pg 117

Roberts, Sherry, The Roberts Group, 12803 Eastview Curve, Apple Valley, MN 55124 *Tel:* 952-322-4005 *E-mail:* info@editorialservice.com *Web Site:* www.editorialservice.com, pg 554

Roberts, Stacie, Sovereign Award for Writing, Woodbine Sales Pavilion, 555 Rexdale Blvd, Rexdale, ON M9W 5L2, Canada *Tel:* 416-675-7756 *Fax:* 416-675-6378 *E-mail:* jockeyclub@bellnet.ca *Web Site:* www.jockeyclubcanada.com, pg 743

Roberts, Tim, Counterpath Press, PO Box 18351, Denver, CO 80218 *E-mail:* editors@counterpathpress.org *Web Site:* www.counterpathpress.org, pg 69

Roberts, Tony, The Roberts Group, 12803 Eastview Curve, Apple Valley, MN 55124 *Tel:* 952-322-4005 *E-mail:* info@editorialservice.com *Web Site:* www.editorialservice.com, pg 554

Roberts, U D, Brentwood Christian Press, 4000 Beallwood Ave, Columbus, GA 31904 *Toll Free Tel:* 800-334-8861 *E-mail:* brentwood@aol.com *Web Site:* www.brentwoodbooks.com, pg 46

Robertson, Michael, Digital Printing & Imaging Association, 10015 Main St, Fairfax, VA 22031-3489 *Tel:* 703-385-1335 *Toll Free Tel:* 888-385-3588 *Fax:* 703-273-0456 *E-mail:* sgia@sgia.org *Web Site:* www.sgia.org, pg 622

Robertson, Randy, Susquehanna University, Dept of English, 514 University Ave, Selinsgrove, PA 17870 *Tel:* 570-372-0101, pg 680

Robey, Annelise, Jane Rotrosen Agency LLC, 318 E 51 St, New York, NY 10022 *Tel:* 212-593-4330 *Fax:* 212-935-6985 *Web Site:* janerotrosen.com, pg 591

Robichaud, Danielle, Tormont Publishing International, 3305 Pitfield Blvd, St-Laurent, QC H4S 1H3, Canada *Tel:* 514-954-1441 *Fax:* 514-954-1443, pg 521

Robins, Jennifer, Prufrock Press, PO Box 8813, Waco, TX 76714-8813 *Tel:* 254-756-3337 *Toll Free Tel:* 800-998-2208 *Fax:* 254-756-3339 *Toll Free Fax:* 800-240-0333 *E-mail:* info@prufrock.com *Web Site:* www.prufrock.com, pg 208

Robinson, Don, Penguin Group (Canada), 90 Eglinton Ave E, Suite 700, Toronto, ON M4P 2Y3, Canada *Tel:* 416-925-2249 *Fax:* 416-925-0068 *Web Site:* www.penguin.ca, pg 515

Robinson, James J, The Minerals, Metals & Materials Society (TMS), 184 Thorn Hill Rd, Warrendale, PA 15086 *Tel:* 724-776-9000 *Toll Free Tel:* 800-759-4867 *Fax:* 724-776-3770 *E-mail:* publications@tms.org (orders) *Web Site:* www.tms.org (orders), pg 167

Robinson, Jennifer, Gallery Books, 1230 Avenue of the Americas, New York, NY 10020 *Toll Free Tel:* 800-456-6798 *Fax:* 212-698-7284 *E-mail:* consumer.customerservice@simonandschuster.com *Web Site:* www.simonsays.com, pg 101

Robinson, Jim, Harlequin Enterprises Ltd, 225 Duncan Mill Rd, Don Mills, ON M3B 3K9, Canada *Tel:* 416-445-5860 *Toll Free Tel:* 888-432-4879; 800-370-5838 (ebook inquiries) *Fax:* 416-445-8655 *E-mail:* CustomerService@harlequin.com *Web Site:* www.harlequin.com, pg 508

Robinson, Joe, EEI Communications, 7240 Parkway Dr, Suite 250, Hanover, MD 21076-1364 *Tel:* 410-309-8200 *Toll Free Tel:* 888-253-2762 *Fax:* 410-630-3980 *E-mail:* info@eeicom.com *Web Site:* www.eeicom.com, pg 678

Robinson, Kim, University of California Press, 2120 Berkeley Way, Berkeley, CA 94704-1012 *Tel:* 510-642-4247 *Fax:* 510-643-7127 *E-mail:* askucp@ucpress.edu (books); customerservice@ucpressjournals.com (journals) *Web Site:* www.ucpress.edu, pg 264

Robinson, Marian, The Guilford Press, 72 Spring St, 4th fl, New York, NY 10012 *Tel:* 212-431-9800 *Toll Free Tel:* 800-365-7006 (ext 1, orders) *Fax:* 212-966-6708 *E-mail:* orders@guilford.com; info@guilford.com *Web Site:* www.guilford.com, pg 109

Robinson, Richard, Scholastic Inc, 557 Broadway, New York, NY 10012 *Tel:* 212-343-6100 *Toll Free Tel:* 800-scholastic *Web Site:* www.scholastic.com, pg 228

Robinson, Saunders, University of Pennsylvania Press, 3905 Spruce St, Philadelphia, PA 19104 *Tel:* 215-898-6261 *Fax:* 215-898-0404 *E-mail:* custserv@pobox.upenn.edu *Web Site:* www.pennpress.org, pg 268

Robinson, Sharon P, American Association of Colleges for Teacher Education (AACTE), 1307 New York Ave NW, Suite 300, Washington, DC 20005-4701 *Tel:* 202-293-2450 *Fax:* 202-457-8095 *E-mail:* aacte@aacte.org *Web Site:* www.aacte.org, pg 11

Robitaille, Roland, Jones Hutton Literary Associates, 160 N Compo Rd, Westport, CT 06880-2102 *Tel:* 203-226-2588 *Fax:* 203-226-2588 *E-mail:* huttonbooks@hotmail.com, pg 579

Robson, William B P, C D Howe Institute, 67 Yonge St, Suite 300, Toronto, ON M5E 1J8, Canada *Tel:* 416-865-1904 *Fax:* 416-865-1866 *E-mail:* cdhowe@cdhowe.org *Web Site:* www.cdhowe.org, pg 509

Roby, Theresa, Association of College & University Printers, Penn State University, 101 Hostetter Business Services Bldg, University Park, PA 16802 *Tel:* 814-865-7544 *Fax:* 814-863-6376 *Web Site:* www.multimediaprint.psu.edu, pg 616

Robyn, Mr Chris, Long River Press, 360 Swift Ave, Suite 48, South San Francisco, CA 94080 *Tel:* 650-872-7718 (ext 312) *Fax:* 650-872-7808 *E-mail:* info@longriverpress.com *Web Site:* www.chinabooks.com, pg 152

Roche, Art, Dubuque Fine Arts Players Annual One Act Play Festival, PO Box 1160, Dubuque, IA 52004-1160 *Tel:* 563-588-3438 *E-mail:* contact@dbqoneacts.org *Web Site:* www.dbqoneacts.org, pg 701

Roche, Mary Beth, Macmillan, 175 Fifth Ave, New York, NY 10010 *Tel:* 646-307-5151 *Fax:* 212-420-9314 *E-mail:* firstname.lastname@macmillan.com *Web Site:* www.macmillan.com, pg 154

Roche, Mary Beth, Macmillan Audio, 175 Fifth Ave, New York, NY 10010 *Tel:* 646-307-5151 *Toll Free Tel:* 888-330-8477 (cust serv) *Fax:* 917-534-0980 *E-mail:* firstname.lastname@macmillan.com *Web Site:* www.macmillanaudio.com, pg 154

Rochefort, Jacques, Cheneliere Education Inc, 5800 Saint Denis St, Montreal, QC H2S 3L5, Canada *Tel:* 514-273-1066 *Toll Free Tel:* 800-565-5531 *Fax:* 514-276-0324 *Toll Free Fax:* 800-814-0324 *E-mail:* info@cheneliere.ca *Web Site:* www.cheneliere.ca, pg 498

Rochefort, Jacques, Gaetan Morin Editeur, 5800 rue Ste-Denis, Bur 900, Montreal, QC H2S 3L5, Canada *Tel:* 514-273-1066 *Toll Free Tel:* 800-565-5531 *Fax:* 514-276-0324 *Toll Free Fax:* 800-814-0324 *E-mail:* info@cheneliere.ca *Web Site:* www.cheneliere.ca, pg 506

Rock, James A, James A Rock & Co Publishers, 900 S Irby St, Suite 508, Florence, SC 29501 *Toll Free Tel:* 800-411-2230 *Fax:* 843-395-5975 *E-mail:* jrock@rockpublishing.com *Web Site:* rockpublishing.com, pg 220

Rockefeller, Kirwan PhD, UCI Extension Writers' Program, PO Box 6050, Irvine, CA 92616-6050 *Tel:* 949-824-5990 *Fax:* 949-824-3651 *Web Site:* www.unex.uci.edu, pg 674

Rockey, Colleen, Brilliance Audio, 1704 Eaton Dr, Grand Haven, MI 49417 *Tel:* 616-846-5256 *Toll Free Tel:* 800-648-2312 (orders only) *Fax:* 616-846-0630 *E-mail:* customerservice@brillianceaudio.com *Web Site:* www.brillianceaudio.com, pg 47

Rockmill, Jayne, Rockmill & Company, 647 Warren St, Brooklyn, NY 11217 *Tel:* 718-638-3990 *E-mail:* agentrockmill@yahoo.com *Web Site:* www.rockmillandcompany.com, pg 591

Rockwell, Lew, Ludwig von Mises Institute, 518 W Magnolia Ave, Auburn, AL 36832 *Tel:* 334-321-2100 *Fax:* 334-321-2119 *E-mail:* info@mises.org *Web Site:* www.mises.org, pg 275

Roco, Mary, Krause Publications Inc, 700 E State St, Iola, WI 54990 *Tel:* 715-445-2214 *Toll Free Tel:* 800-258-0929 (cust serv); 888-457-2873 (orders) *Fax:* 715-445-4087 *E-mail:* bookorders@krause.com *Web Site:* www.krausebooks.com, pg 142

Rodale, Maria, Rodale Books, 400 S Tenth St, Emmaus, PA 18098 *Tel:* 610-967-5171 *Toll Free Tel:* 800-848-4735 (cust serv) *E-mail:* customerservice@rodale.com *Web Site:* www.rodaleinc.com, pg 220

Rodenberger, Jean, F A Davis Co, 1915 Arch St, Philadelphia, PA 19103 *Tel:* 215-568-2270 *Toll Free Tel:* 800-523-4049 *Fax:* 215-568-5065 *E-mail:* info@fadavis.com *Web Site:* www.fadavis.com, pg 76

Rodengen, Jeffrey L, Write Stuff Enterprises Inc, 1001 S Andrew Ave, Suite 120, Fort Lauderdale, FL 33316 *Tel:* 954-462-6657 *Toll Free Tel:* 800-900-2665 *Fax:* 954-462-6023 *E-mail:* legends@writestuffbooks.com *Web Site:* www.writestuffbooks.com, pg 286

Rodgers, Loren, National Center For Employee Ownership (NCEO), 1736 Franklin St, 8th fl, Oakland, CA 94612-3445 *Tel:* 510-208-1300 *Fax:* 510-272-9510 *E-mail:* customerservice@nceo.org *Web Site:* www.nceo.org, pg 174

Rodman, Howard, Writers Guild of America Awards, 7000 W Third St, Los Angeles, CA 90048 *Tel:* 323-951-4000; 323-782-4569 *Fax:* 323-782-4800 *Web Site:* www.wga.org, pg 752

Rodman, Howard, Writers Guild of America, West (WGAW), 7000 W Third St, Los Angeles, CA 90048 *Tel:* 323-951-4000 *Toll Free Tel:* 800-548-4532 *Fax:* 323-782-4800 *Web Site:* www.wga.org, pg 639

Rodmell, Emily, Love Inspired Books, 233 Broadway, Suite 1001, New York, NY 10279 *Tel:* 212-553-4200 *Fax:* 212-227-8969 *E-mail:* customer_service@harlequin.ca *Web Site:* www.loveinspiredbooks.com, pg 153

Rodovsky, Jayson, Transcontinental Music Publications, 633 Third Ave, New York, NY 10017 *Tel:* 212-650-4101; 212-650-4120 *Toll Free Tel:* 888-489-8242 (orders) *Fax:* 212-650-4119 *E-mail:* tmp@urj.org; press@urj.org *Web Site:* www.transcontinentalmusic.com, pg 258

Rodrick, Scott, National Center For Employee Ownership (NCEO), 1736 Franklin St, 8th fl, Oakland, CA 94612-3445 *Tel:* 510-208-1300 *Fax:* 510-272-9510 *E-mail:* customerservice@nceo.org *Web Site:* www.nceo.org, pg 174

Roe, Rosanne, nursesbooks.org, The Publishing Program of ANA, 8515 Georgia Ave, Suite 400, Silver Spring, MD 20910-3492 *Tel:* 301-628-5000 *Toll Free Tel:* 800-924-9053; 800-637-0323 (orders) *Fax:* 301-628-5001 *E-mail:* anp@ana.org *Web Site:* www.nursesbooks.org; www.nursingworld.org, pg 182

Roeder, Taryn, Houghton Mifflin Harcourt Trade & Reference Division, 222 Berkeley St, Boston, MA 02116-3764 *Tel:* 617-351-5000 *Toll Free Tel:* 800-225-3362 *Web Site:* www.houghtonmifflinbooks.com, pg 124

Roehrig, Fr Matthew, St Pauls/Alba House, 2187 Victory Blvd, Staten Island, NY 10314-6603 *Tel:* 718-761-0047 (edit & prodn); 718-698-2759 (mktg & billing) *Toll Free Tel:* 800-343-2522 *Fax:* 718-761-0057 *E-mail:* sales@stpauls.us; marketing@stpauls.us *Web Site:* www.stpauls.us; www.albahouse.org, pg 225

Roetzheim, William, Level 4 Press Inc, 13518 Jamul Dr, Jamul, CA 91935-1635 *Fax:* 619-374-7311 *E-mail:* sales@level4press.com *Web Site:* www.level4press.com, pg 147

Rogatz, Mitch, Triumph Books, 814 N Franklin St, Chicago, IL 60610 *Toll Free Tel:* 800-888-4741 (orders only) *Fax:* 312-663-3557 *Web Site:* www.triumphbooks.com, pg 259

Rose, Rebecca, Breakwater Books Ltd, One Stamp's Lane, St Johns, NL A1C 6E6, Canada *Tel:* 709-722-6680 *Toll Free Tel:* 800-563-3333 (orders) *Fax:* 709-753-0708 *E-mail:* info@breakwaterbooks.com *Web Site:* www.breakwaterbooks.com, pg 495

Rose, Rie Sheridan, Zumaya Publications LLC, 3209 S IH 35, Suite 1086, Austin, TX 78741 *Tel:* 512-402-5298 *Fax:* 253-660-2009 *E-mail:* acquisitions@zumayapublications.com *Web Site:* www.zumayapublications.com, pg 290

Rose, Verena, Agatha Awards, PO Box 8007, Gaithersburg, MD 20898-8007 *E-mail:* malicedomesticpr@gmail.com *Web Site:* www.malicedomestic.org, pg 685

Rosema, Randy, HarperCollins Children's Books, 10 E 53 St, New York, NY 10022 *Tel:* 212-207-7000 *Web Site:* www.harpercollinschildrens.com, pg 113

Roseman, Karl-Heinz, McFarland, 960 NC Hwy 88 W, Jefferson, NC 28640 *Tel:* 336-246-4460 *Toll Free Tel:* 800-253-2187 (orders) *Fax:* 336-246-5018; 336-246-4403 (orders) *E-mail:* info@mcfarlandpub.com *Web Site:* www.mcfarlandpub.com, pg 160

Rosen, Andrew S, Kaplan Publishing, 395 Hudson St, 4th fl, New York, NY 10014 *Tel:* 212-618-2400 *Toll Free Tel:* 888-KAPLAN8 (527-5268) *Fax:* 917-344-2499 *Toll Free Fax:* 877-712-5487 *E-mail:* book.support@kaplan.com *Web Site:* www.kaplanpublishing.com, pg 138

Rosen, Roger, The Rosen Publishing Group Inc, 29 E 21 St, New York, NY 10010 *Tel:* 212-777-3017 *Toll Free Tel:* 800-237-9932 *Toll Free Fax:* 888-436-4643 *E-mail:* info@rosenpub.com *Web Site:* www.rosenpublishing.com, pg 221

Rosen, Selina, Yard Dog Press, 710 W Redbud Lane, Alma, AR 72921-7247 *Tel:* 479-632-4693 *Fax:* 479-632-4693 *Web Site:* www.yarddogpress.com, pg 288

Rosen-Fine, Marlene, Fine Communications, 322 Eighth Ave, 15th fl, New York, NY 10001 *Tel:* 212-595-3500 *Fax:* 212-595-3779, pg 95

Rosenberg, Andrew, Rough Guides, 375 Hudson St, New York, NY 10014 *Toll Free Tel:* 800-631-8571 *E-mail:* mail@roughguides.com *Web Site:* www.roughguides.com, pg 221

Rosenberg, Barbara Collins, The Rosenberg Group, 23 Lincoln Ave, Marblehead, MA 01945 *Tel:* 781-990-1341 *Fax:* 781-990-1344 *Web Site:* www.rosenberggroup.com, pg 591

Rosenberg, Barr, Dorothy Sargent Rosenberg Poetry Prizes, PO Box 2306, Orinda, CA 94563 *Web Site:* www.dorothyprizes.org, pg 738

Rosenberg, Carol, Basic Health Publications Inc, 28812 Top of the World Dr, Laguna Beach, CA 92651 *Tel:* 949-715-7327 *Toll Free Tel:* 800-575-8890 (orders) *Fax:* 949-715-7328 *E-mail:* info@basichealthpub.com *Web Site:* www.basichealthpub.com, pg 32

Rosenberg, Gary, Basic Health Publications Inc, 28812 Top of the World Dr, Laguna Beach, CA 92651 *Tel:* 949-715-7327 *Toll Free Tel:* 800-575-8890 (orders) *Fax:* 949-715-7328 *E-mail:* info@basichealthpub.com *Web Site:* www.basichealthpub.com, pg 32

Rosenberg, Jessica, Harlequin Enterprises Ltd, 233 Broadway, Suite 1001, New York, NY 10279 *Tel:* 212-553-4200 *Fax:* 212-227-8969 *E-mail:* CustomerService@harlequin.com *Web Site:* www.harlequin.com, pg 112

Rosenberg, Leora, Objective Entertainment, 609 Greenwich St, 6th fl, New York, NY 10014 *Tel:* 212-431-5454 *Fax:* 917-464-6394 *Web Site:* www.objectiveent.com, pg 587

Rosenberg, Linda, GP Putnam's Sons (Hardcover), 375 Hudson St, New York, NY 10014 *Tel:* 212-366-2000 *E-mail:* online@penguinputnam.com *Web Site:* us.penguingroup.com, pg 210

Rosenberg, Liz, Binghamton University Creative Writing Program, c/o Dept of English, PO Box 6000, Binghamton, NY 13902-6000 *Tel:* 607-777-2168 *Fax:* 607-777-2408 *E-mail:* cwpro@binghamton.edu *Web Site:* english.binghamton.edu/cwpro, pg 677

Rosenberg, Mary, Dorothy Sargent Rosenberg Poetry Prizes, PO Box 2306, Orinda, CA 94563 *Web Site:* www.dorothyprizes.org, pg 738

Rosenberg, Shirley Sirota, SSR Inc, 116 Fourth St SE, Washington, DC 20003 *Tel:* 202-543-1800 *Fax:* 202-544-7432 *E-mail:* ssr@ssrinc.com *Web Site:* www.ssrinc.com, pg 555

Rosenberg, Tracy, Media Alliance, 1904 Franklin St, Suite 818, Oakland, CA 94612 *Tel:* 510-832-9000 *Fax:* 510-238-8557 *E-mail:* info@media-alliance.org *Web Site:* www.media-alliance.org, pg 627

Rosenblum, Bruce, Academy of Television Arts & Sciences (ATAS), 5220 Lankershim Blvd, North Hollywood, CA 91601-3109 *Tel:* 818-754-2800 *Fax:* 818-761-2827 *Web Site:* www.emmys.tv, pg 611

Rosenblum, Jill, Walch Education, 40 Walch Dr, Portland, ME 04103-1286 *Tel:* 207-772-2846 *Toll Free Tel:* 800-558-2846 *Fax:* 207-772-3105 *Toll Free Fax:* 888-991-5755 *E-mail:* customerservice@walch.com *Web Site:* www.walch.com, pg 276

Rosenbush, Ellen, Harper's Magazine Foundation, 666 Broadway, 11th fl, New York, NY 10012 *Tel:* 212-420-5720 *Toll Free Tel:* 800-444-4653 *Fax:* 212-228-5889 *E-mail:* harpers@harpers.org *Web Site:* www.harpers.org, pg 114

Rosencrans, Stephanie, QED Press, 155 Cypress St, Fort Bragg, CA 95437 *Tel:* 707-964-9520 *Toll Free Tel:* 800-773-7782 *Fax:* 707-964-7531 *E-mail:* qedpress@mcn.org *Web Site:* www.cypresshouse.com, pg 211

Rosenfeld, Dina, Hachai Publishing, 527 Empire Blvd, Brooklyn, NY 11225 *Tel:* 718-633-0100 *Fax:* 718-633-0103 *E-mail:* info@hachai.com *Web Site:* www.hachai.com, pg 109

Rosenfeld, Erv, BK Nelson Inc Lecture Bureau, 1565 Paseo Vida, Palm Springs, CA 92264 *Tel:* 760-778-8800 *Fax:* 760-778-6242 *E-mail:* bknelson4@cs.com *Web Site:* www.bknelsonlecturebureau.com; www.bknelson.com; www.bknelsonmovieproduction.com, pg 605

Rosenfeld, Erwin, BK Nelson Inc Literary Agency, 1565 Paseo Vida, Palm Springs, CA 92264 *Tel:* 760-778-8800 *Fax:* 760-778-6242 *E-mail:* bknelson4@cs.com *Web Site:* www.bknelson.com; www.bknelsonlecturebureau.com; www.bknelsonmovieproduction.com, pg 587

Rosenfeld, Nancy, AAA Books Unlimited, 88 Greenbriar E Dr, Deerfield, IL 60015 *Tel:* 847-444-1220 *Fax:* 847-607-8335 *Web Site:* www.aaabooksunlimited.com, pg 559

Rosenfeld, Theodore D, Taplinger Publishing Co Inc, PO Box 175, Marlboro, NJ 07746-0175 *Tel:* 305-256-7880 *Fax:* 305-256-7816 *E-mail:* taplingerpub@yahoo.com (rts & perms, edit, corp only), pg 250

Rosengard, Alice, Words into Print, 131 Fifth Ave, Suite 501, New York, NY 10003 *Tel:* 212-741-1393 *Fax:* 419-441-1393 *E-mail:* query@wordsintoprint.org *Web Site:* www.wordsintoprint.org, pg 557

Rosenheim, Kellye, Whiting Writers' Awards, 1133 Avenue of the Americas, 22nd fl, New York, NY 10036-6710 *Tel:* 212-336-2138 *E-mail:* info@whitingfoundation.org *Web Site:* www.whitingfoundation.org, pg 749

Rosenkranz, Rita, Rita Rosenkranz Literary Agency, 440 West End Ave, Suite 15D, New York, NY 10024-5358 *Tel:* 212-873-6333 *Fax:* 212-873-5225 *Web Site:* www.ritarosenkranzliteraryagency.com, pg 591

Rosenstein, Natalee, Berkley Books, 375 Hudson St, New York, NY 10014 *Tel:* 212-366-2000 *Fax:* 212-366-2666 *E-mail:* online@penguinputnam.com *Web Site:* www.penguinputnam.com; us.penguingroup.com, pg 35

Rosenstein, Natalee, Berkley Publishing Group, 375 Hudson St, New York, NY 10014 *Tel:* 212-366-2000 *Fax:* 212-366-2385 *E-mail:* online@penguinputnam.com *Web Site:* us.penguingroup.com, pg 36

Rosenthal, Carole, Hamilton Stone Editions, PO Box 43, Maplewood, NJ 07040 *Tel:* 973-378-8361 *E-mail:* hstone@hamiltonstone.org *Web Site:* www.hamiltonstone.org, pg 111

Rosenthal, David, Blue Rider Press, 375 Hudson St, New York, NY 10014 *Tel:* 212-366-2000, pg 42

Rosenthal, David, Penguin Group (USA) LLC, 375 Hudson St, New York, NY 10014 *Tel:* 212-366-2000 *Toll Free Tel:* 800-847-5515 (inside sales); 800-631-8571 (cust serv) *Fax:* 212-366-2666; 607-775-4829 (inside sales) *E-mail:* online@us.penguingroup.com *Web Site:* www.penguin.com; us.penguingroup.com, pg 197

Rosenthal, Elise, Rosenthal Represents, 3850 Eddingham Ave, Calabasas, CA 91302 *Tel:* 818-222-5445 *Fax:* 818-222-5650 *E-mail:* eliselicenses@earthlink.net *Web Site:* www.rosenthalrepresents.com, pg 602

Rosenthal, Tom, Morgan Kaufmann, 225 Wyman St, Waltham, MA 02451 *Toll Free Tel:* 866-607-1417 *Fax:* 619-699-6310 *Web Site:* www.mkp.com, pg 170

Rosenwald, Robert, Poisoned Pen Press Inc, 6962 E First Ave, Suite 103, Scottsdale, AZ 85251 *Tel:* 480-945-3375 *Toll Free Tel:* 1-800-421-3976 *Fax:* 480-949-1707 *E-mail:* info@poisonedpenpress.com *Web Site:* www.poisonedpenpress.com, pg 204

Rosenwasser, Rena, Kelsey Street Press, 2824 Kelsey St, Berkeley, CA 94705 *Tel:* 510-845-2260 *Fax:* 510-548-9185 *E-mail:* info@kelseyst.com *Web Site:* www.kelseyst.com, pg 139

Rosokoff, Sylvie, Trident Media Group LLC, 41 Madison Ave, 36th fl, New York, NY 10010 *Tel:* 212-262-4810 *Fax:* 212-262-4849 *Web Site:* www.tridentmediagroup.com, pg 598

Ross, Andy, Andy Ross Literary Agency, 767 Santa Ray Ave, Oakland, CA 94610 *Tel:* 510-238-8965 *E-mail:* andyrossagency@hotmail.com *Web Site:* www.andyrossagency.com, pg 561

Ross, Bob, Pilgrim Publications, PO Box 66, Pasadena, TX 77501-0066 *Tel:* 713-477-4261 *Fax:* 713-477-7561 *E-mail:* pilgrimpub@aol.com *Web Site:* members.aol.com/pilgrimpub/; www.pilgrimpublications.com, pg 202

Ross, Carol, Hachette Book Group, 237 Park Ave, New York, NY 10017 *Tel:* 212-364-1100 *Toll Free Tel:* 800-759-0190 (cust serv) *Fax:* 212-364-0933 (intl orders) *Toll Free Fax:* 800-286-9471 (cust serv) *Web Site:* www.HachetteBookGroup.com, pg 110

Ross, Franz H, Ross Books, PO Box 4340, Berkeley, CA 94704-0340 *Tel:* 510-841-2474 *Fax:* 510-295-2531 *E-mail:* sales@rossbooks.com *Web Site:* www.rossbooks.com, pg 221

Ross, Kim, Riverside Publishing, 3800 Golf Rd, Suite 200, Rolling Meadows, IL 60008 *Tel:* 630-467-7000 *Toll Free Tel:* 800-323-9540 *Fax:* 630-467-7192 (cust serv) *E-mail:* rpc_customer_service@hmhpub.com (cust serv) *Web Site:* www.riversidepublishing.com, pg 219

Ross, Marjory G, Regnery Publishing Inc, One Massachusetts Ave NW, Washington, DC 20001 *Tel:* 202-216-0600 *Toll Free Tel:* 888-219-4747 *Fax:* 202-216-0612 *Web Site:* www.regnery.com, pg 217

Ross, Michael, Encyclopaedia Britannica Inc, 331 N La Salle St, Chicago, IL 60654 *Tel:* 312-347-7159 (all other countries) *Toll Free Tel:* 800-323-1229 (US & CN) *Fax:* 312-294-2104 *E-mail:* editor@eb.com *Web Site:* www.eb.com; www.britannica.com, pg 88

Ross, Michael, Macmillan, 175 Fifth Ave, New York, NY 10010 *Tel:* 646-307-5151 *Fax:* 212-420-9314 *E-mail:* firstname.lastname@macmillan.com *Web Site:* www.macmillan.com, pg 154

Ross, Mimi, Henry Holt and Company, LLC, 175 Fifth Ave, New York, NY 10010 *Tel:* 646-307-5151 *Toll Free Tel:* 888-330-8477 (orders) *Fax:* 646-307-5285 *E-mail:* firstname.lastname@hholt.com *Web Site:* www.henryholt.com, pg 122

Rubie, Peter, FinePrint Literary Management, 115 W 29 St, 3rd fl, New York, NY 10001 *Tel:* 212-279-1282 *Web Site:* www.fineprintlit.com, pg 571

Rubin, Barry, Lederer Books, 6120 Day Long Lane, Clarksville, MD 21029 *Tel:* 410-531-6644 *Toll Free Tel:* 800-410-7367 (orders) *Fax:* 717-761-7273 *E-mail:* lederer@messianicjewish.net; customerservice@messianicjewish.net *Web Site:* www.messianicjewish.net, pg 146

Rubin, Barry, Messianic Jewish Publishers, 6120 Day Long Lane, Clarksville, MD 21029 *Tel:* 410-531-6644 *Toll Free Tel:* 800-410-7367 (orders) *Fax:* 410-531-9440 (no orders) *E-mail:* lederer@messianicjewish.net; rightsandpermissions@messianicjewish.net (rights & perms) *Web Site:* messianicjewish.net, pg 165

Rubin, Donald S, McGraw-Hill Financial, 1221 Avenue of the Americas, 50th fl, New York, NY 10020 *Tel:* 212-512-2000 *Web Site:* www.mhfi.com, pg 161

Rubin, Irene, Amsco School Publications Inc, 315 Hudson St, New York, NY 10013-1085 *Tel:* 212-886-6500; 212-886-6565 *Toll Free Tel:* 800-969-8398 *Fax:* 212-675-7010 *E-mail:* info@amscopub.com *Web Site:* www.amscopub.com, pg 18

Rubin, Lisa, Messianic Jewish Publishers, 6120 Day Long Lane, Clarksville, MD 21029 *Tel:* 410-531-6644 *Toll Free Tel:* 800-410-7367 (orders) *Fax:* 410-531-9440 (no orders) *E-mail:* lederer@messianicjewish.net; rightsandpermissions@messianicjewish.net (rights & perms) *Web Site:* messianicjewish.net, pg 165

Rubin, Lorna, Triad Publishing Co, PO Box 13355, Gainesville, FL 32604 *Tel:* 352-373-5800 *Fax:* 352-373-1488 *Toll Free Fax:* 800-854-4947 *E-mail:* orders@triadpublishing.com *Web Site:* www.triadpublishing.com, pg 258

Rubin, Melvin L, Triad Publishing Co, PO Box 13355, Gainesville, FL 32604 *Tel:* 352-373-5800 *Fax:* 352-373-1488 *Toll Free Fax:* 800-854-4947 *E-mail:* orders@triadpublishing.com *Web Site:* www.triadpublishing.com, pg 258

Rubin, Michele, Writers House, 21 W 26 St, New York, NY 10010 *Tel:* 212-685-2400 *Fax:* 212-685-1781 *Web Site:* www.writershouse.com, pg 599

Rubin, Stephen, Henry Holt and Company, LLC, 175 Fifth Ave, New York, NY 10010 *Tel:* 646-307-5151 *Toll Free Tel:* 888-330-8477 (orders) *Fax:* 646-307-5285 *E-mail:* firstname.lastname@hholt.com *Web Site:* www.henryholt.com, pg 122

Rubin, Stephen, Macmillan, 175 Fifth Ave, New York, NY 10010 *Tel:* 646-307-5151 *Fax:* 212-420-9314 *E-mail:* firstname.lastname@macmillan.com *Web Site:* www.macmillan.com, pg 154

Rubino, Victor J, Practising Law Institute, 810 Seventh Ave, New York, NY 10019 *Tel:* 212-824-5700 *Toll Free Tel:* 800-260-4PLI (260-4754 cust serv) *Fax:* 212-265-4742 (intl) *Toll Free Fax:* 800-321-0093 (local) *E-mail:* info@pli.edu *Web Site:* www.pli.edu, pg 205

Rubinstein, Elizabeth Winick, McIntosh & Otis Inc, 353 Lexington Ave, New York, NY 10016-0900 *Tel:* 212-687-7400 *Fax:* 212-687-6894 *E-mail:* info@mcintoshandotis.com *Web Site:* www.mcintoshandotis.com, pg 585

Ruby, Brenda A, Woodbine House, 6510 Bells Mill Rd, Bethesda, MD 20817 *Tel:* 301-897-3570 *Toll Free Tel:* 800-843-7323 *Fax:* 301-897-5838 *E-mail:* info@woodbinehouse.com *Web Site:* www.woodbinehouse.com, pg 284

Ruby-Strauss, Jeremie, Gallery Books, 1230 Avenue of the Americas, New York, NY 10020 *Toll Free Tel:* 800-456-6798 *Fax:* 212-698-7284 *E-mail:* consumer.customerservice@simonandschuster.com *Web Site:* www.simonsays.com, pg 101

Rucci, Marysue, Simon & Schuster, 1230 Avenue of the Americas, New York, NY 10020 *Tel:* 212-698-7000 *Toll Free Tel:* 800-223-2348 (cust serv); 800-223-2336 (orders) *Toll Free Fax:* 800-943-9831 (orders) *Web Site:* www.simonandschuster.com, pg 234

Rudes, Jerome, Fifi Oscard Agency Inc, 110 W 40 St, 16th fl, New York, NY 10018 *Tel:* 212-764-1100 *Fax:* 212-840-5019 *E-mail:* agency@fifioscard.com *Web Site:* www.fifioscard.com, pg 587

Rudick, Nicole, The Plimpton Prize, 62 White St, New York, NY 10013 *Tel:* 212-343-1333 *Fax:* 212-343-1988 *E-mail:* queries@theparisreview.org *Web Site:* www.theparisreview.org, pg 734

Rudin, Max, The Library of America, 14 E 60 St, New York, NY 10022-1006 *Tel:* 212-308-3360 *Fax:* 212-750-8352 *E-mail:* info@loa.org *Web Site:* www.loa.org, pg 148

Rudman, Michael P, National Learning Corp, 212 Michael Dr, Syosset, NY 11791 *Tel:* 516-921-8888 *Toll Free Tel:* 800-632-8888 *Fax:* 516-921-8743 *E-mail:* info@passbooks.com *Web Site:* www.passbooks.com, pg 175

Rudnick, Arnold, Paraphrase LLC, PO Box 56508, Sherman Oaks, CA 91413 *Tel:* 818-219-4377 *Toll Free Fax:* 888-863-4377 *E-mail:* books@paraphrasellc.com *Web Site:* www.paraphrasellc.com, pg 528

Rudnicki, Stefan, The Barbara Bova Literary Agency LLC, 3951 Gulf Shore Blvd N, Unit PH 1-B, Naples, FL 34103 *Tel:* 239-649-7237 *E-mail:* slushpile@yahoo.com *Web Site:* www.barbarabovaliteraryagency.com, pg 564

Rudolph, Janet, Macavity Award, 7155 Marlborough Terr, Berkeley, CA 94705 *Tel:* 510-845-3600 *Web Site:* www.mysteryreaders.org, pg 720

Rudolph, John, Dystel & Goderich Literary Management, One Union Sq W, Suite 904, New York, NY 10003 *Tel:* 212-627-9100 *Fax:* 212-627-9313 *Web Site:* www.dystel.com, pg 569

Rudy, Caryn Karmatz, DeFiore and Company, LLC, 47 E 19 St, 3rd fl, New York, NY 10003 *Tel:* 212-925-7744 *Fax:* 212-925-9803 *E-mail:* submissions@defioreandco.com; info@defioreandco.com *Web Site:* www.defioreandco.com, pg 568

Rudy, Catherine, Wolf Pirate Project Inc, 337 Lost Lake Dr, Divide, CO 80814 *Tel:* 305-333-3186 *E-mail:* contact@wolfpiratebooks.com; workshop@wolfpiratebooks.com *Web Site:* www.wolf-pirate.com, pg 557

Rudy, Gordon, University of Chicago Press, 1427 E 60 St, Chicago, IL 60637-2954 *Tel:* 773-702-7700; 773-702-7600 *Toll Free Tel:* 800-621-2736 (orders) *Fax:* 773-702-9756; 773-660-2235 (orders); 773-702-2708 *E-mail:* custserv@press.uchicago.edu; marketing@press.uchicago.edu *Web Site:* www.press.uchicago.edu, pg 265

Rue, Robin, Writers House, 21 W 26 St, New York, NY 10010 *Tel:* 212-685-2400 *Fax:* 212-685-1781 *Web Site:* www.writershouse.com, pg 599

Ruebel, Donny, Willow Creek Press, 9931 Hwy 70 W, Minocqua, WI 54548 *Tel:* 715-358-7010 *Toll Free Tel:* 800-850-9453 *Fax:* 715-358-2807 *E-mail:* info@willowcreekpress.com *Web Site:* www.willowcreekpress.com, pg 282

Ruenzel, Nancy, Peachpit Press, 1249 Eighth St, Berkeley, CA 94710 *Tel:* 510-524-2178 *Toll Free Tel:* 800-283-9444 *Fax:* 510-524-2221 *E-mail:* info@peachpit.com *Web Site:* www.peachpit.com, pg 195

Ruffner, Frederick G Jr, Omnigraphics Inc, 155 W Congress, Suite 200, Detroit, MI 48226 *Tel:* 313-961-1340 *Toll Free Tel:* 800-234-1340 (cust serv) *Fax:* 313-961-1383 *Toll Free Fax:* 800-875-1340 (cust serv) *E-mail:* info@omnigraphics.com *Web Site:* www.omnigraphics.com, pg 185

Ruffner, Peter E, Omnigraphics Inc, 155 W Congress, Suite 200, Detroit, MI 48226 *Tel:* 313-961-1340 *Toll Free Tel:* 800-234-1340 (cust serv) *Fax:* 313-961-1383 *Toll Free Fax:* 800-875-1340 (cust serv) *E-mail:* info@omnigraphics.com *Web Site:* www.omnigraphics.com, pg 185

Ruggiero, Anthony, Pauline Books & Media, 50 Saint Paul's Ave, Boston, MA 02130 *Tel:* 617-522-8911 *Toll Free Tel:* 800-876-4463 (orders); 800-836-9723 (cust serv) *Fax:* 617-541-9805 *E-mail:* orderentry@pauline.org (cust serv); editorial@paulinemedia.com (ms submissions) *Web Site:* www.pauline.org, pg 194

Ruggiero, Greg, City Lights Publishers, 261 Columbus Ave, San Francisco, CA 94133 *Tel:* 415-362-8193 *Fax:* 415-362-4921 *E-mail:* staff@citylights.com *Web Site:* www.citylights.com, pg 62

Ruggiero, Vincenzo, Penguin Group (USA) LLC, 375 Hudson St, New York, NY 10014 *Tel:* 212-366-2000 *Toll Free Tel:* 800-847-5515 (inside sales); 800-631-8571 (cust serv) *Fax:* 212-366-2666; 607-775-4829 (inside sales) *E-mail:* online@us.penguingroup.com *Web Site:* www.penguin.com; us.penguingroup.com, pg 197

Ruhl, Maria, Regnery Publishing Inc, One Massachusetts Ave NW, Washington, DC 20001 *Tel:* 202-216-0600 *Toll Free Tel:* 888-219-4747 *Fax:* 202-216-0612 *Web Site:* www.regnery.com, pg 217

Ruhl, Peter, American Catholic Press (ACP), 16565 S State St, South Holland, IL 60473 *Tel:* 708-331-5485 *Fax:* 708-331-5484 *E-mail:* acp@acpress.org *Web Site:* www.acpress.org, pg 12

Ruhlig, Steve, Human Kinetics Inc, 1607 N Market St, Champaign, IL 61820 *Tel:* 217-351-5076 *Toll Free Tel:* 800-747-4457 *Fax:* 217-351-1549 (orders/cust serv) *E-mail:* info@hkusa.com *Web Site:* www.humankinetics.com, pg 125

Ruiz, Jonathan, Velazquez Press, 9682 Telstar Ave, Suite 110, El Monte, CA 91731 *Tel:* 626-448-3448 *Fax:* 626-602-3817 *E-mail:* info@academiclearningcompany.com *Web Site:* www.velazquezpress.com, pg 274

Rukkila, Roy, Bagwyn Books, 975 S Myrtle Ave, Tempe, AZ 85281 *Tel:* 480-965-5900 *Fax:* 480-965-1681 *E-mail:* bagwynbooks@acmrs.org *Web Site:* acmrs.org/publications/bagwyn, pg 29

Rukkila, Roy, MRTS, PO Box 874402, Tempe, AZ 85287-4402 *Tel:* 480-727-6503 *Toll Free Tel:* 800-621-2736 (orders) *Fax:* 480-965-1681 *Toll Free Fax:* 800-621-8476 (orders) *E-mail:* mrts@asu.edu *Web Site:* www.acmrs.org/pubs, pg 171

Ruley, Meg, Jane Rotrosen Agency LLC, 318 E 51 St, New York, NY 10022 *Tel:* 212-593-4330 *Fax:* 212-935-6985 *Web Site:* janerotrosen.com, pg 592

Rumble, Brant, Scribner, 1230 Avenue of the Americas, New York, NY 10020, pg 230

Rundall, Nick, Whitecap Books Ltd, 314 W Cordova St, Suite 210, Vancouver, BC V6B 1E8, Canada *Tel:* 604-681-6181 *Toll Free Tel:* 800-387-9776 *Toll Free Fax:* 800-260-9777 *Web Site:* www.whitecap.ca, pg 524

Rundle, Lisa, HarperCollins Canada Ltd, 2 Bloor St E, 20th fl, Toronto, ON M4W 1A8, Canada *Tel:* 416-975-9334 *Fax:* 416-975-9884 *E-mail:* hccanada@harpercollins.com *Web Site:* www.harpercollins.ca, pg 508

Runge, Gailen, C & T Publishing Inc, 1651 Challenge Dr, Concord, CA 94520-5206 *Tel:* 925-677-0377 *Toll Free Tel:* 800-284-1114 *Fax:* 925-677-0373 *E-mail:* ctinfo@ctpub.com *Web Site:* www.ctpub.com, pg 50

Runk, David, FaithWalk Publishing, 5450 N Dixie Hwy, Lima, OH 45807 *Tel:* 419-227-1818 *Toll Free Tel:* 800-537-1030 (orders: non-bookstore mkts) *Fax:* 419-224-9184 *Web Site:* www.faithwalkpub.com, pg 92

Runyon, Joy, The New York Botanical Garden Press, 2900 Southern Blvd, Bronx, NY 10458-5126 *Tel:* 718-817-8721 *Fax:* 718-817-8842 *E-mail:* nybgpress@nybg.org *Web Site:* www.nybgpress.org, pg 179

Runyon, Nancy, McCutchan Publishing Corp, 3220 Blume Dr, Suite 197, Richmond, CA 94806 *Tel:* 510-758-5510 *Toll Free Tel:* 800-227-1540 *Fax:* 510-758-6078 *E-mail:* mccutchanpublish@sbcglobal.net *Web Site:* www.mccutchanpublishing.com, pg 160

Rupnow, Dr John, The Mellen Poetry Press, 240 Portage Rd, Lewiston, NY 14092 *Tel:* 716-754-2266; 716-754-1400 (mktg); 716-754-2788 (order fulfillment) *Fax:* 716-754-4056; 716-754-1860 (fulfillment) *E-mail:* cservice@mellenpress.com *Web Site:* www.mellenpress.com, pg 164

Ruppel, Philip R, McGraw-Hill Professional, 1221 Avenue of the Americas, New York, NY 10020 *Tel:* 212-512-2000 *Web Site:* www.mhprofessional.com, pg 162

Rusch, Robert D, Cadence Jazz Books, Cadence Bldg, Redwood, NY 13679 *Tel:* 315-287-2852 *Fax:* 315-287-2860 *E-mail:* cjb@cadencebuilding.com; cadence@cadencebuilding.com *Web Site:* www.cadencebuilding.com, pg 50

Rush, Tonda F, National Newspaper Association, 309 S Providence St, Columbia, MO 65203-4267 *Tel:* 573-882-5800 *Toll Free Tel:* 800-829-4NNA (829-4662) *Fax:* 573-884-5490 *E-mail:* info@nna.org *Web Site:* www.nnaweb.org, pg 630

Rushall, Kathleen, Marsal Lyon Literary Agency LLC, 665 San Rodolfo Dr, Suite 124, PMB 121, Solana Beach, CA 92075 *Tel:* 760-814-8507 *Web Site:* www.marsallyonliteraryagency.com, pg 583

Rusin, William F, W W Norton & Company Inc, 500 Fifth Ave, New York, NY 10110-0017 *Tel:* 212-354-5500 *Toll Free Tel:* 800-233-4830 (orders & cust serv) *Fax:* 212-869-0856 *Toll Free Fax:* 800-458-6515 *Web Site:* www.wwnorton.com, pg 182

Russ, Susan Fraysse, The Reader's Digest Association Inc, 750 Third Ave, New York, NY 10017 *Tel:* 914-238-1000; 646-293-6284 *Toll Free Tel:* 800-310-6261 (cust serv) *Fax:* 914-238-4559 *Web Site:* www.rd.com; www.rda.com, pg 215

Russell, Cheryl, New Strategist Publications Inc, 120 W State St, 4th fl, Ithaca, NY 14850 *Tel:* 607-273-0913 *Toll Free Tel:* 800-848-0842 *Fax:* 607-277-5009 *E-mail:* demographics@newstrategist.com *Web Site:* newstrategist.com, pg 178

Russell, Christie, Peter Lampack Agency Inc, 350 Fifth Ave, Suite 5300, New York, NY 10118 *Tel:* 212-687-9106 *Fax:* 212-687-9109 *Web Site:* peterlampackagency.com, pg 581

Russell, Jim, Amy Writing Awards, PO Box 16091, Lansing, MI 48901-6091 *Tel:* 517-323-6233 *Toll Free Tel:* 877-727-4262 *Fax:* 517-321-2572 *E-mail:* amyawards@worldmag.com *Web Site:* www.worldmag.com/amyawards, pg 687

Russell, Kenn, Henry Holt and Company, LLC, 175 Fifth Ave, New York, NY 10010 *Tel:* 646-307-5151 *Toll Free Tel:* 888-330-8477 (orders) *Fax:* 646-307-5285 *E-mail:* firstname.lastname@hholt.com *Web Site:* www.henryholt.com, pg 122

Russell, Pam, Council for Advancement & Support of Education (CASE), 1307 New York Ave NW, Suite 1000, Washington, DC 20005-4701 *Tel:* 202-328-CASE (328-2273) *Fax:* 202-387-4973 *E-mail:* info@case.org; memberservicecenter@case.org *Web Site:* www.case.org, pg 622

Russell, Rick, Naval Institute Press, 291 Wood Rd, Annapolis, MD 21402-5034 *Tel:* 410-268-6110 *Toll Free Tel:* 800-233-8764 *Fax:* 410-295-1084; 410-571-1703 (cust serv) *E-mail:* webmaster@navalinstitute.org; customer@navalinstitute.org (cust serv); trade@usni.org *Web Site:* www.nip.org; www.usni.org, pg 176

Russell, Robyn, The Amy Rennert Agency Inc, 1550 Tiburon Blvd, Suite 302, Tiburon, CA 94920 *Tel:* 415-789-8955 *E-mail:* queries@amyrennert.com *Web Site:* amyrennert.com, pg 590

Russell, Susan, The Aaland Agency, PO Box 849, Inyokern, CA 93527-0849 *Tel:* 760-384-3910 *Web Site:* www.the-aaland-agency.com, pg 559

Russell, Tom, The Princeton Review, c/o Random House Inc, 1745 Broadway, New York, NY 10019 *Toll Free Tel:* 800-733-3000 *Fax:* 212-782-9682 *E-mail:* princetonreview@randomhouse.com *Web Site:* www.princetonreview.com, pg 206

Russo, Cat, American Society for Training & Development (ASTD), 1640 King St, Box 1443, Alexandria, VA 22313-1443 *Tel:* 703-683-8100 *Toll Free Tel:* 800-628-2783 *Fax:* 703-683-8103 *E-mail:* publications@astd.org *Web Site:* www.astd.org, pg 16

Russo, Cat, ASCD, 1703 N Beauregard St, Alexandria, VA 22311-1714 *Tel:* 703-578-9600 *Toll Free Tel:* 800-933-2723 *Fax:* 703-575-5400 *E-mail:* member@ascd.org *Web Site:* www.ascd.org, pg 23

Russo, Dane, AMWA Annual Conference, 30 W Gude Dr, Suite 525, Rockville, MD 20850-1161 *Tel:* 240-238-0940 *Fax:* 301-294-9006 *E-mail:* amwa@amwa.org *Web Site:* www.amwa.org, pg 667

Russo, Nicole, Harry N Abrams Inc, 115 W 18 St, 6th fl, New York, NY 10011 *Tel:* 212-206-7715 *Toll Free Tel:* 800-345-1359 *Fax:* 212-519-1210 *E-mail:* abrams@abramsbooks.com *Web Site:* www.abramsbooks.com, pg 3

Russo, Mr Seth, Simon & Schuster Sales & Marketing, 1230 Avenue of the Americas, New York, NY 10020 *Tel:* 212-698-7000, pg 236

Rutledge, Nicole, Meriwether Publishing Ltd/ Contemporary Drama Service, 885 Elkton Dr, Colorado Springs, CO 80907-3522 *Tel:* 719-594-4422 *Toll Free Tel:* 800-937-5297 *Fax:* 719-594-9916 *Toll Free Fax:* 888-594-4436 *E-mail:* customerservice@meriwether.com *Web Site:* www.meriwether.com, pg 164

Rutman, Jim, Sterling Lord Literistic Inc, 65 Bleecker St, New York, NY 10012 *Tel:* 212-780-6050 *Fax:* 212-780-6095 *E-mail:* info@sll.com *Web Site:* www.sll.com, pg 595

Rutsky, Alan, Rizzoli International Publications Inc, 300 Park Ave S, 4th fl, New York, NY 10010-5399 *Tel:* 212-387-3400 *Toll Free Tel:* 800-522-6657 (orders only) *Fax:* 212-387-3535 *E-mail:* publicity@rizzoliusa.com *Web Site:* www.rizzoliusa.com, pg 219

Rutter, Sandy, American Society of Agricultural Engineers (ASABE), 2950 Niles Rd, St Joseph, MI 49085-9659 *Tel:* 269-429-0300 *Fax:* 269-429-3852 *E-mail:* hq@asabe.org *Web Site:* www.asabe.org, pg 16

Ryan, Amy, HarperCollins Children's Books, 10 E 53 St, New York, NY 10022 *Tel:* 212-207-7000 *Web Site:* www.harpercollinschildrens.com, pg 113

Ryan, Anthony J, Ignatius Press, 1348 Tenth Ave, San Francisco, CA 94122-2304 *Tel:* 415-387-2324 *Toll Free Tel:* 800-651-1531 (orders) *Fax:* 415-387-0896 *E-mail:* info@ignatius.com *Web Site:* www.ignatius.com, pg 127

Ryan, Becky, DawnSignPress, 6130 Nancy Ridge Dr, San Diego, CA 92121-3223 *Tel:* 858-625-0600 *Toll Free Tel:* 800-549-5350 *Fax:* 858-625-2336 *E-mail:* info@dawnsign.com *Web Site:* www.dawnsign.com, pg 76

Ryan, Becky, SDSU Writers' Conference, 5250 Campanile Dr, Rm 2503, San Diego, CA 92182-1920 *Tel:* 619-594-2517 *Fax:* 619-594-8566 *E-mail:* sdsuwritersconference@mail.sdsu.edu *Web Site:* www.neverstoplearning.net/writers, pg 673

Ryan, George, Printing Association of Florida Inc, 6275 Hazeltine National Dr, Orlando, FL 32822 *Tel:* 407-240-8009 *Toll Free Tel:* 800-331-0461 *Fax:* 407-240-8333 *Web Site:* www.pafgraf.org, pg 634

Ryan, Hampton, Abingdon Press, 201 Eighth Ave S, Nashville, TN 37203-3919 *Toll Free Tel:* 800-251-3320 *Toll Free Fax:* 800-836-7802 (orders) *E-mail:* orders@abingdonpress.com *Web Site:* www.abingdonpress.com, pg 3

Ryan, Jane, RAND Corp, 1776 Main St, Santa Monica, CA 90407-2138 *Tel:* 310-393-0411 *Fax:* 310-393-4818 *Web Site:* www.rand.org, pg 212

Ryan, John R, Center for Creative Leadership LLC, One Leadership Place, Greensboro, NC 27410-9427 *Tel:* 336-545-2810; 336-288-7210 *Fax:* 336-282-3284 *E-mail:* info@ccl.org *Web Site:* www.ccl.org/publications, pg 55

Ryan, Matt, Eric Hoffer Award for Short Prose, PO Box 11, Titusville, NJ 08560 *Fax:* 609-964-1718 *E-mail:* info@hofferaward.com *Web Site:* www.hofferaward.com, pg 710

Ryan, Mike, McGraw-Hill Humanities, Social Sciences, Languages, 2 Penn Plaza, 20th fl, New York, NY 10121 *Tel:* 212-904-2000 *Toll Free Tel:* 800-338-3987 (cust serv) *Fax:* 614-755-5645 (cust serv) *Web Site:* www.mhhe.com, pg 161

Ryan, Regina, Regina Ryan Books, 251 Central Park W, Suite 7-D, New York, NY 10024 *Tel:* 212 787-5589 *E-mail:* queries@reginaryanbooks.com *Web Site:* www.reginaryanbooks.com, pg 592

Ryan, Regina Sara, Hohm Press, PO Box 4410, Chino Valley, AZ 86323 *Tel:* 928-636-3331 *Toll Free Tel:* 800-381-2700 *Fax:* 928-636-7519 *E-mail:* hppublisher@cableone.net; hohmpresseditor@gmail.com *Web Site:* www.hohmpress.com, pg 121

Ryan, Suzanne, Oxford University Press USA, 198 Madison Ave, New York, NY 10016 *Tel:* 212-726-6000 *Toll Free Tel:* 800-451-7556 (orders); 800-445-9714 (cust serv) *Fax:* 919-677-1303 *E-mail:* custserv.us@oup.com *Web Site:* www.oup.com/us, pg 189

Ryan, Thomas, History Publishing Co LLC, 173 Rte 9W, Palisades, NY 10964 *Tel:* 845-398-8161 *Fax:* 845-231-6167 *E-mail:* historypublish@aol.com; info@historypublishingco.com *Web Site:* www.historypublishingco.com, pg 120

Saada, Yves, Disney Publishing Worldwide, 44 S Broadway, 9th fl, White Plains, NY 10601-4411 *Tel:* 914-288-4100 *Web Site:* disney.go.com/books/index, pg 80

Sabbagh, Julia, Reader's Digest Children's Books, 44 S Broadway, White Plains, NY 10601 *Tel:* 914-238-1000 *Toll Free Tel:* 800-934-0977 *Web Site:* www.rdtradepublishing.com, pg 215

Sabbagh, Julia, Reader's Digest Trade Books, 44 S Broadway, White Plains, NY 10601 *Tel:* 914-244-7503 *Fax:* 914-244-4841 *Web Site:* www.rd.com, pg 215

Sabia, Mary Ann, Charlesbridge Publishing Inc, 85 Main St, Watertown, MA 02472 *Tel:* 617-926-0329 *Toll Free Tel:* 800-225-3214 *Fax:* 617-926-5720 *Toll Free Fax:* 800-926-5775 *E-mail:* books@charlesbridge.com *Web Site:* www.charlesbridge.com, pg 58

Sablar, Christy, The AEI Press, 1150 17 St NW, Washington, DC 20036 *Tel:* 202-862-5800 *Fax:* 202-862-7177 *Web Site:* www.aei.org, pg 6

Sablik, Filip, Boom! Studios, 5670 Wilshire Blvd, Suite 450, Los Angeles, CA 90036 *Web Site:* www.boom-studios.com, pg 44

Sablone, Frank, Tag & Label Manufacturers Institute Inc (TLMI), One Blackburn Ctr, Gloucester, MA 01930 *Tel:* 978-282-1400 *Fax:* 978-282-3238 *E-mail:* office@tlmi.com *Web Site:* www.tlmi.com, pg 637

Sabol, Richard, Springer, 233 Spring St, New York, NY 10013-1578 *Tel:* 212-460-1500 *Toll Free Tel:* 800-SPRINGER (777-4643) *Fax:* 212-460-1575 *E-mail:* service-ny@springer.com *Web Site:* www.springer.com, pg 241

Sabol, Stephanie, Penguin Group (USA) LLC Sales, 375 Hudson St, New York, NY 10014 *Tel:* 212-366-2000 *E-mail:* online@penguinputnam.com *Web Site:* us.penguingroup.com, pg 197

Sachdev, Dr Rachana, Susquehanna University Press, 514 University Ave, Selinsgrove, PA 17870 *Tel:* 570-372-4175 *Fax:* 570-372-4021 *E-mail:* supress@susqu.edu *Web Site:* www.susqu.edu/su_press, pg 248

Sacilotto, Loriana, Harlequin Enterprises Ltd, 225 Duncan Mill Rd, Don Mills, ON M3B 3K9, Canada *Tel:* 416-445-5860 *Toll Free Tel:* 888-432-4879; 800-370-5838 (ebook inquiries) *Fax:* 416-445-8655 *E-mail:* CustomerService@harlequin.com *Web Site:* www.harlequin.com, pg 508

Sacilotto, Loriana, Love Inspired Books, 233 Broadway, Suite 1001, New York, NY 10279 *Tel:* 212-553-4200 *Fax:* 212-227-8969 *E-mail:* customer_service@harlequin.ca *Web Site:* www.loveinspiredbooks.com, pg 153

Sader, Pam, Scholastic Consumer & Professional Publishing, 557 Broadway, New York, NY 10012 *Tel:* 212-343-6100 *Toll Free Tel:* 800-621-1115 *Fax:* 800-621-1115 *Web Site:* www.scholastic.com, pg 228

Sadler, Kim Martin, The Pilgrim Press/United Church Press, 700 Prospect Ave, Cleveland, OH 44115-1100 *Toll Free Tel:* 800-537-3394 (cust serv-indivs); 800-654-5129 (cust serv-commercial accts) *Fax:* 216-736-2206 (orders) *E-mail:* proposals@thepilgrimpress.com *Web Site:* www.thepilgrimpress.com; www.unitedchurchpress.com, pg 202

Sadlon, Annie, Unicorn Writers' Conference, 17 Church Hill Rd, Redding, CT 06896 *Tel:* 203-938-7405 *Fax:* 203-938-7405 *E-mail:* unicornwritersconference@gmail.com *Web Site:* unicornwritersconference.com, pg 674

Sadowski, Cheryl, Newspaper Association of America (NAA), 4401 Wilson Blvd, Suite 900, Arlington, VA 22203 *Tel:* 571-366-1000 *Fax:* 571-366-1195 *Web Site:* www.naa.org, pg 631

Sadowski, Br Frank, St Pauls/Alba House, 2187 Victory Blvd, Staten Island, NY 10314-6603 *Tel:* 718-761-0047 (edit & prodn); 718-698-2759 (mktg & billing) *Toll Free Tel:* 800-343-2522 *Fax:* 718-761-0057 *E-mail:* sales@stpauls.us; marketing@stpauls.us *Web Site:* www.stpauls.us; www.albahouse.org, pg 225

Saenz, Benjamin Alire, University of Texas at El Paso, Dept Creative Writing, MFA/Dept Creative Writing, Liberal Arts 415 UTEP, 500 W University Ave, El Paso, TX 79968-9991 *Tel:* 915-747-5713 *Fax:* 915-747-5523 *Web Site:* www.utep.edu/cw, pg 682

Saffel, Than, West Virginia University Press, West Virginia University, PO Box 6295, Morgantown, WV 26506-6295 *Tel:* 304-293-8400 *Toll Free Tel:* 866-WVU-PRES (988-7737) *Fax:* 304-293-6585 *E-mail:* press@wvu.edu *Web Site:* www.wvupress.com, pg 278

Safyan, Susan, Arsenal Pulp Press, 211 E Georgia St, No 101, Vancouver, BC V6A 1Z6, Canada *Tel:* 604-687-4233 *Toll Free Tel:* 888-600-PULP (600-7857) *Fax:* 604-687-4283 *E-mail:* info@arsenalpulp.com *Web Site:* www.arsenalpulp.com, pg 493

Sagalyn, Raphael, ICM/Sagalyn, 4922 Fairmont Ave, Suite 200, Bethesda, MD 20814 *Tel:* 301-718-6440 *Fax:* 301-718-6444 *E-mail:* query@sagalyn.com *Web Site:* www.sagalyn.com, pg 577

Sagan, Raymond, William H Sadlier Inc, 9 Pine St, New York, NY 10005 *Tel:* 212-227-2120 *Toll Free Tel:* 800-221-5175 (cust serv) *Fax:* 212-312-6080 *Web Site:* www.sadlier.com, pg 223

Saidenberg, Julie, Shambhala Publications Inc, Horticultural Hall, 300 Massachusetts Ave, Boston, MA 02115 *Tel:* 617-424-0030 *Toll Free Tel:* 866-424-0030 (off); 888-424-2329 (cust serv) *Fax:* 617-236-1563 *E-mail:* customercare@shambhala.com *Web Site:* www.shambhala.com, pg 232

Saidenberg, Julie, Snow Lion Publications Inc, 300 Massachusetts Ave, Boston, MA 02115 *Tel:* 617-236-0030 *Fax:* 617-236-1563 *E-mail:* customercare@shambhala.com *Web Site:* www.shambhala.com/snowlion, pg 238

Saielli, Robert J, Young People's Press Inc (YPPI), 814 Morena Blvd, Suite 102, San Diego, CA 92110 *Tel:* 619-296-1297 (orders) *Toll Free Tel:* 800-231-9774 *E-mail:* admin@youngpeoplespress.com *Web Site:* www.youngpeoplespress.com, pg 288

Saikia-Wilson, Rebecca, Houghton Mifflin Harcourt Trade & Reference Division, 222 Berkeley St, Boston, MA 02116-3764 *Tel:* 617-351-5000 *Toll Free Tel:* 800-225-3362 *Web Site:* www.houghtonmifflinbooks.com, pg 124

Saint-Jean, Marie-Claire, Guy Saint-Jean Editeur Inc, 3440 Blvd Industriel, Laval, QC H7L 4R9, Canada *Tel:* 450-663-1777 *Fax:* 450-663-6666 *E-mail:* info@saint-jeanediteur.com *Web Site:* www.saint-jeanediteur.com, pg 518

Saint-Jean, Nicole, Guy Saint-Jean Editeur Inc, 3440 Blvd Industriel, Laval, QC H7L 4R9, Canada *Tel:* 450-663-1777 *Fax:* 450-663-6666 *E-mail:* info@saint-jeanediteur.com *Web Site:* www.saint-jeanediteur.com, pg 518

Sakamoto, Dawn, Watermark Publishing, 1088 Bishop St, Suite 310, Honolulu, HI 96813 *Tel:* 808-587-7766 *Toll Free Tel:* 866-900-BOOK (900-2665) *Fax:* 808-521-3461 *E-mail:* info@bookshawaii.net *Web Site:* www.bookshawaii.net, pg 277

Sakoian, Carol, Scholastic International, 557 Broadway, New York, NY 10012 *Tel:* 212-343-6100; 646-330-5288 (intl cust serv) *Toll Free Tel:* 800-SCHOLASTIC (800-724-6527) *Fax:* 646-837-7878 *E-mail:* international@scholastic.com, pg 228

Sakowski, Carolyn, John F Blair Publisher, 1406 Plaza Dr, Winston-Salem, NC 27103 *Tel:* 336-768-1374 *Toll Free Tel:* 800-222-9796 *Fax:* 336-768-9194 *Web Site:* www.blairpub.com, pg 40

Sakuda, Takashi, Kodansha USA Inc, 451 Park Ave S, 7th fl, New York, NY 10016 *Tel:* 917-322-6200 *Fax:* 212-935-6929 *E-mail:* info@kodansha-usa.com *Web Site:* www.kodansha-intl.com, pg 141

Salamie, David E, InfoWorks Development Group, 2801 Cook Creek Dr, Ann Arbor, MI 48103-8962 *Tel:* 734-327-9669 *Fax:* 734-327-9686, pg 548

Salazar, Kat, Red Wheel/Weiser/Conari, 65 Parker St, Suite 7, Newburyport, MA 01950 *Tel:* 978-465-0504 *Toll Free Tel:* 800-423-7087 (orders) *Fax:* 978-465-0243 *E-mail:* info@rwwbooks.com *Web Site:* www.redwheelweiser.com, pg 216

Salerno, Carey, Alice James Books, 238 Main St, Farmington, ME 04938 *Tel:* 207-778-7071 *Fax:* 207-778-7766 *E-mail:* info@alicejamesbooks.org *Web Site:* www.alicejamesbooks.org, pg 8

Sales, Bethany, Nicholas Brealey Publishing, 20 Park Plaza, Suite 610, Boston, MA 02116 *Tel:* 617-523-3801 *Toll Free Tel:* 888-BREALEY (273-2539) *Fax:* 617-523-3708 *E-mail:* info@nicholasbrealey.com *Web Site:* www.nicholasbrealey.com, pg 46

Saletan, Rebecca, Riverhead Books (Hardcover), 375 Hudson St, New York, NY 10014 *Tel:* 212-366-2000 *E-mail:* online@penguinputnam.com *Web Site:* www.penguinputnam.com; us.penguingroup.com, pg 219

Salicup, Jim, Papercutz, 40 Exchange Place, Suite 1308, New York, NY 10005 *Tel:* 212-643-5407 *Toll Free Tel:* 800-886-1223 *Fax:* 212-643-1545 *E-mail:* papercutz@papercutz.com *Web Site:* www.papercutz.com, pg 192

Salisbury, Leila W, University Press of Mississippi, 3825 Ridgewood Rd, Jackson, MS 39211-6492 *Tel:* 601-432-6205 *Toll Free Tel:* 800-737-7788 (orders & cust serv) *Fax:* 601-432-6217 *E-mail:* press@mississippi.edu *Web Site:* www.upress.state.ms.us, pg 271

Salk, Judy, Elsevier Engineering Information (Ei), 360 Park Ave S, New York, NY 10010-1710 *Tel:* 212-989-5800 *Toll Free Tel:* 800-221-1044 *Fax:* 212-633-6380 *E-mail:* eicustomersupport@elsevier.com *Web Site:* www.ei.org, pg 86

Salo, Gay, Piano Press, 1425 Ocean Ave, Suite 17, Del Mar, CA 92014 *Tel:* 619-884-1401 *Fax:* 858-755-1104 *E-mail:* pianopress@pianopress.com *Web Site:* www.pianopress.com, pg 201

Salome, Adam, The Harvard Common Press, 535 Albany St, Boston, MA 02118 *Tel:* 617-423-5803 *Toll Free Tel:* 888-657-3755 *Fax:* 617-695-9794 *E-mail:* orders@harvardcommonpress.com; info@harvardcommonpress.com *Web Site:* www.harvardcommonpress.com, pg 114

Salser, Mark R, National Book Co, PO Box 8795, Portland, OR 97207-8795 *Tel:* 503-228-6345 *Fax:* 810-885-5811 *E-mail:* info@eralearning.com *Web Site:* www.eralearning.com, pg 173

Saltz, Carole, Teachers College Press, 1234 Amsterdam Ave, New York, NY 10027 *Tel:* 212-678-3929 *Toll Free Tel:* 800-575-6566 *Fax:* 212-678-4149; 802-864-7626 *E-mail:* tcpress@tc.columbia.edu; tcp.orders@aidcvt.com (orders) *Web Site:* www.teacherscollegepress.com, pg 251

Saltzman, Glenn Lisa, American Society for Training & Development (ASTD), 1640 King St, Box 1443, Alexandria, VA 22313-1443 *Tel:* 703-683-8100 *Toll Free Tel:* 800-628-2783 *Fax:* 703-683-8103 *E-mail:* publications@astd.org *Web Site:* www.astd.org, pg 16

Salvador, Vanda, Paulines Editions, 5610 rue Beaubien est, Montreal, QC H1T 1X5, Canada *Tel:* 514-253-5610 *Fax:* 514-253-1907 *E-mail:* editions@paulines.qc.ca *Web Site:* www.editions.paulines.qc.ca, pg 515

Salvaille, Janick, Guerin Editeur Ltee, 4501 rue Drolet, Montreal, QC H2T 2G2, Canada *Tel:* 514-842-3481 *Toll Free Tel:* 800-398-8337 *Fax:* 514-842-4923 *Web Site:* www.guerin-editeur.qc.ca, pg 507

Salvat-Golik, Marta, Ediciones Universal, 3090 SW Eighth St, Miami, FL 33135 *Tel:* 305-642-3234 *Fax:* 305-642-7978 *E-mail:* ediciones@ediciones.com *Web Site:* www.ediciones.com, pg 85

Salvatore, Laurea, Oxford University Press USA, 198 Madison Ave, New York, NY 10016 *Tel:* 212-726-6000 *Toll Free Tel:* 800-451-7556 (orders); 800-445-9714 (cust serv) *Fax:* 919-677-1303 *E-mail:* custserv.us@oup.com *Web Site:* www.oup.com/us, pg 189

Salvatore, Ruth, Ucross Foundation Residency Program, 30 Big Red Lane, Clearmont, WY 82835 *Tel:* 307-737-2291 *Fax:* 307-737-2322 *E-mail:* info@ucross.org *Web Site:* www.ucrossfoundation.org, pg 747

Salyer, Kathy, De Vorss & Co, 553 Constitution Ave, Camarillo, CA 93012-8510 *Tel:* 805-322-9010 *Toll Free Tel:* 800-843-5743 *Fax:* 805-322-9011 *E-mail:* service@devorss.com *Web Site:* www.devorss.com, pg 77

Salzman, Richard, Salzman International, 1751 Charles Ave, Arcata, CA 95521 *Tel:* 415-285-8267; 212-997-0115 (NY) *Fax:* 707-822-5500 *Web Site:* www.salzint.com, pg 602

Salzmann, Oliver, Madison Press Books, PO Box 239, Cannington, ON L0E 1E0, Canada *Tel:* 416-360-0006 *E-mail:* info@madisonpressbooks.com *Web Site:* www.madisonpressbooks.com, pg 511

Samms, June, Kids Can Press Ltd, 25 Dockside Dr, Toronto, ON M5A 0B5, Canada *Tel:* 416-479-7000 *Toll Free Tel:* 800-265-0884 *Fax:* 416-960-5437 *E-mail:* info@kidscan.com; customerservice@kidscan.com *Web Site:* www.kidscanpress.com; www.kidscanpress.ca, pg 510

Samper, Marjorie, Lectorum Publications Inc, 205 Chubb Ave, Lyndhurst, NJ 07071 *Toll Free Tel:* 800-345-5946 *Fax:* 201-559-2201 *Toll Free Fax:* 877-532-8676 *E-mail:* lectorum@lectorum.com *Web Site:* www.lectorum.com, pg 145

Sample, Stephen, National Press Photographers Association Inc (NPPA), 3200 Croasdaile Dr, Suite 306, Durham, NC 27705 *Tel:* 919-383-7246 *Fax:* 919-383-7261 *E-mail:* info@nppa.org *Web Site:* www.nppa.org, pg 631

Samuel, Alicia, Simon & Schuster, 1230 Avenue of the Americas, New York, NY 10020 *Tel:* 212-698-7000 *Toll Free Tel:* 800-223-2348 (cust serv); 800-223-2336 (orders) *Toll Free Fax:* 800-943-9831 (orders) *Web Site:* www.simonandschuster.com, pg 234

Samuel, Martha, NBM Publishing Inc, 40 Exchange Place, Suite 1308, New York, NY 10005 *Tel:* 212-643-5407 *Toll Free Tel:* 800-886-1223 *Fax:* 212-643-1545 *E-mail:* admin@nbmpub.com *Web Site:* www.nbmpub.com, pg 176

Samuelson, Bruce, Bernan, 4501 Forbes Blvd, Suite 200, Lanham, MD 20706 *Tel:* 301-459-7666 (cust serv & orders) *Fax:* 301-459-0056 *E-mail:* customercare@bernan.com *Web Site:* www.bernan.com, pg 36

Sanchez, Irene, Liturgy Training Publications, 3949 S Racine Ave, Chicago, IL 60609-2523 *Tel:* 773-579-4900 *Toll Free Tel:* 800-933-1800 (US & CN only orders) *Fax:* 773-486-7094 *Toll Free Fax:* 800-933-7094 (US & CN only orders) *E-mail:* orders@ltp.org *Web Site:* www.ltp.org, pg 151

Sanchez, Wanda, Mary Ann Liebert Inc, 140 Huguenot St, 3rd fl, New Rochelle, NY 10801-5215 *Tel:* 914-740-2100 *Toll Free Tel:* 800-654-3237 *Fax:* 914-740-2101 *E-mail:* info@liebertpub.com *Web Site:* www.liebertonline.com, pg 148

Sandberg, Mark, The Ibsen Society of America, University of California, Dept of Scandinavian, 6303 Dwinelle Hall, No 2690, Berkeley, CA 94720-2690 *Tel:* 510-642-0927 *Fax:* 510-642-6220 *Web Site:* www.ibsensociety.liu.edu, pg 624

Sandell, Katie, Howard Books, 216 Centerview Dr, Suite 303, Brentwood, TN 37027 *Tel:* 615-873-2080 *Fax:* 615-370-3834 *E-mail:* howardbooks@simonandschuster.com (info) *Web Site:* www.howardpublishing.com, pg 124

Sanders, Bob, Mundania Press LLC, 6457 Glenway Ave, Suite 109, Cincinnati, OH 45211-5222 *Tel:* 513-490-2822 *Fax:* 513-598-9220 *Toll Free Fax:* 888-460-4752 *E-mail:* books@mundania.com; inquiry@mundania.com *Web Site:* www.mundania.com, pg 171

Sanders, Bonnie, ASM International, 9639 Kinsman Rd, Materials Park, OH 44073-0002 *Tel:* 440-338-5151 *Toll Free Tel:* 800-336-5152; 800-368-9800 (Europe) *Fax:* 440-338-4634 *E-mail:* memberservicecenter@asminternational.org *Web Site:* asmcommunity.asminternational.org, pg 25

Sanders, Keith P PhD, Frank Luther Mott-Kappa Tau Alpha Research Award, University of Missouri, School of Journalism, 76 Gannett Hall, Columbia, MO 65211-1200 *Tel:* 573-882-7685 *Fax:* 573-884-1720 *E-mail:* umcjourkta@missouri.edu *Web Site:* www.kapataualpha.org, pg 725

Sanders, Michael, Alpha, 375 Hudson St, New York, NY 10014 *Tel:* 212-366-2000, pg 9

Sanders, Patricia, Manitoba Arts Council, 525-93 Lombard Ave, Winnipeg, MB R3B 3B1, Canada *Tel:* 204-945-2237 *Toll Free Tel:* 866-994-2787 (in Manitoba) *Fax:* 204-945-5925 *E-mail:* info@artscouncil.mb.ca *Web Site:* www.artscouncil.mb.ca, pg 627

Sanders, Ray, Purple House Press, 8100 US Hwy 62 E, Cynthiana, KY 41031 *Tel:* 859-235-9970 *Web Site:* www.purplehousepress.com, pg 210

Sanders, Rob, Douglas & McIntyre, 2323 Quebec St, Suite 201, Vancouver, BC V5T 4S7, Canada *Tel:* 604-254-7191 *Toll Free Tel:* 800-667-6902 (orders) *Fax:* 604-254-9099 *Toll Free Fax:* 800-668-5788 (orders CN) *E-mail:* info@harbourpublishing.com, pg 501

Sanders, Rob, Greystone Books, 2323 Quebec St, Suite 201, Vancouver, BC V5T 4S7, Canada *Tel:* 604-254-9099 *Fax:* 604-254-9099 *E-mail:* info@greystonebooks.com *Web Site:* www.greystonebooks.com; www.dmpibooks.com, pg 507

Sanders, Victoria, Victoria Sanders & Associates LLC, 241 Avenue of the Americas, Suite 11-H, New York, NY 10014 *Tel:* 212-633-8811 *Fax:* 212-633-0525 *E-mail:* queriesvsa@gmail.com *Web Site:* www.victoriasanders.com, pg 592

Sandler, Neil, Rosenthal Represents, 3850 Eddingham Ave, Calabasas, CA 91302 *Tel:* 818-222-5445 *Fax:* 818-222-5650 *E-mail:* eliselicenses@earthlink.net *Web Site:* www.rosenthalrepresents.com, pg 602

Sands, Katharine, Sarah Jane Freymann Literary Agency LLC, 59 W 71 St, Suite 9-B, New York, NY 10023 *Tel:* 212-362-9277 *E-mail:* submissions@sarahjanefreymann.com *Web Site:* www.sarahjanefreymann.com, pg 573

Sanfilippo, Tony, The Pennsylvania State University Press, University Support Bldg 1, Suite C, 820 N University Dr, University Park, PA 16802-1003 *Tel:* 814-865-1327 *Toll Free Tel:* 800-326-9180 *Fax:* 814-863-1408 *Toll Free Fax:* 877-778-2665 *E-mail:* info@psupress.org *Web Site:* www.psupress.org, pg 198

Sanford, Kurt, ProQuest LLC, 789 E Eisenhower Pkwy, Ann Arbor, MI 48108-3218 *Tel:* 734-761-4700 *Toll Free Tel:* 800-521-0600 *Fax:* 734-975-6486 *Toll Free Fax:* 800-864-0019 *E-mail:* info@proquest.com *Web Site:* www.proquest.com, pg 208

Sanford, Linda, Triumph Learning, 136 Madison Ave, 7th fl, New York, NY 10016 *Tel:* 212-652-0200 *Toll Free Tel:* 800-221-9372 (cust serv) *Toll Free Fax:* 866-805-5723 *E-mail:* info@triumphlearning.com; customerservice@triumphlearning.com *Web Site:* www.triumphlearning.com, pg 259

Sankar, Siva, PJD Publications Ltd, PO Box 966, Westbury, NY 11590-0966 *Tel:* 516-626-0650 *Fax:* 516-626-4456 *Web Site:* www.pjdonline.com, pg 202

Sankel, Melanie, Bloomsbury Publishing, 175 Fifth Ave, New York, NY 10010 *Tel:* 212-674-5151 *Toll Free Tel:* 800-221-7945 *Fax:* 212-780-0115; 212-982-2837 *E-mail:* marketingusa@bloomsbury.com; adultpublicityusa.@bloomsbury.com *Web Site:* www.bloomsbury.com, pg 40

Sankel, Melanie, Fairchild Books, 1385 Broadway, New York, NY 10018 *Tel:* 212-419-5292 *Toll Free Tel:* 800-932-4724; 888-330-8477 (orders) *E-mail:* orders@mpsvirginia.com *Web Site:* www.fairchildbooks.com, pg 91

Sanmartin, Cristina, The MIT Press, 55 Hayward St, Cambridge, MA 02142 *Tel:* 617-253-5255 *Toll Free Tel:* 800-207-8354 (orders) *Fax:* 617-258-6779; 617-577-1545 (orders) *Web Site:* mitpress.mit.edu, pg 167

Sanny, Bob, Open Horizons Publishing Co, PO Box 2887, Taos, NM 87571 *Tel:* 575-751-3398 *Fax:* 575-751-3100 *E-mail:* info@bookmarket.com *Web Site:* www.bookmarket.com, pg 186

Sansevere, John, Rights Unlimited Inc, 6 W 37 St, New York, NY 10001 *Tel:* 212-246-0900 *Fax:* 212-246-2114 *E-mail:* rightsunlimited@gmail.com *Web Site:* rightsunlimited.com, pg 591

Sansone, Jill, Hyperion, 1500 Broadway, 3rd fl, New York, NY 10036 *Tel:* 212-536-6500 *Web Site:* hyperionbooks.com, pg 126

Santa, Shelley, Martingale®, 19021 120 Ave NE, Suite 102, Bothell, WA 98011 *Tel:* 425-483-3313 *Toll Free Tel:* 800-426-3126 *Fax:* 425-486-7596 *E-mail:* info@martingale-pub.com *Web Site:* www.martingale-pub.com, pg 158

Santana, Reina, Demos Medical Publishing LLC, 11 W 42 St, New York, NY 10036 *Tel:* 212-683-0072 *Toll Free Tel:* 800-532-8663 *Fax:* 212-683-0118 *E-mail:* info@demosmedpub.com; orderdept@demosmedpub.com *Web Site:* www.demosmedpub.com, pg 78

Santek, Jerod, Loft-Mentor Series in Poetry & Creative Prose, Open Book, Suite 200, 1011 Washington Ave S, Minneapolis, MN 55415 *Tel:* 612-215-2575 *Fax:* 612-215-2576 *E-mail:* loft@loft.org *Web Site:* www.loft.org, pg 718

Santek, Jerod, McKnight Artist Fellowship for Writers, Open Book, Suite 200, 1011 Washington Ave S, Minneapolis, MN 55415 *Tel:* 612-215-2575 *Fax:* 612-215-2576 *E-mail:* loft@loft.org *Web Site:* www.loft.org, pg 722

Santi, Pat, Dog Writers' Association of America Inc (DWAA), 173 Union Rd, Coatesville, PA 19320 *Tel:* 610-384-2436 *Fax:* 610-384-2471 *E-mail:* rhydowen@aol.com *Web Site:* www.dwaa.org, pg 622

Santi, Pat, Dog Writers' Association of America Inc (DWAA) Annual Awards, 173 Union Rd, Coatesville, PA 19320 *Tel:* 610-384-2436 *E-mail:* rhydowen@aol.com *Web Site:* www.dwaa.org, pg 700

Santini, Robert, Pearson Humanities & Social Sciences, One Lake St, Upper Saddle River, NJ 07458 *Tel:* 201-236-7000 *Fax:* 201-236-3400, pg 196

Santopolo, Jill, Philomel, 345 Hudson St, New York, NY 10014 *Tel:* 212-366-2000, pg 201

Santoro, Jed, Merriam-Webster Inc, 47 Federal St, Springfield, MA 01102 *Tel:* 413-734-3134 *Toll Free Tel:* 800-828-1880 (orders & cust serv) *Fax:* 413-731-5979 (sales) *E-mail:* support@merriam-webster.com *Web Site:* www.merriam-webster.com, pg 165

Santucci, Ernest, Agency Chicago, 332 S Michigan Ave, Suite 1032, No A600, Chicago, IL 60604 *E-mail:* ernsant@aol.com, pg 560

Sanzalone, Merrily, Society of Exploration Geophysicists, 8801 S Yale Ave, Tulsa, OK 74137 *Tel:* 918-497-5500 *Fax:* 918-497-5557 *E-mail:* web@seg.org *Web Site:* www.seg.org, pg 238

Sanzone, Donna, M E Sharpe Inc, 80 Business Park Dr, Suite 202, Armonk, NY 10504 *Tel:* 914-273-1800 *Toll Free Tel:* 800-541-6563 *Fax:* 914-273-2106 *E-mail:* info@mesharpe.com *Web Site:* www.mesharpe.com, pg 232

Sapir, Marc, The Museum of Modern Art, 11 W 53 St, New York, NY 10019 *Tel:* 212-708-9443 *Fax:* 212-333-6575 *E-mail:* moma_publications@moma.org *Web Site:* www.moma.org, pg 171

Sarantos, DeLacy, Theosophical Publishing House/Quest Books, 306 W Geneva Rd, Wheaton, IL 60187 *Tel:* 630-665-0130 (ext 347) *Toll Free Tel:* 800-669-9425 (ext 347) *Fax:* 630-665-8791 *E-mail:* customerservice@questbooks.net *Web Site:* www.questbooks.net, pg 254

Saraydarian, Gita, TSG Publishing Foundation Inc, 28641 N 63 Place, Cave Creek, AZ 85331 *Tel:* 480-502-1909 *Fax:* 480-502-0713 *E-mail:* info@tsgfoundation.org *Web Site:* www.tsgfoundation.org, pg 259

Sargent, Dave Jr, Ozark Publishing Inc, PO Box 228, Prairie Grove, AR 72753-0228 *Tel:* 479-595-9522 *Toll Free Tel:* 800-321-5671 *Fax:* 479-846-2843 *E-mail:* srg304@yahoo.com *Web Site:* www.ozarkpublishing.us, pg 190

Sargent, Dave, Ozark Publishing Inc, PO Box 228, Prairie Grove, AR 72753-0228 *Tel:* 479-595-9522 *Toll Free Tel:* 800-321-5671 *Fax:* 479-846-2843 *E-mail:* srg304@yahoo.com *Web Site:* www.ozarkpublishing.us, pg 190

Sargent, John, Bedford, Freeman & Worth Publishing Group, LLC, 41 Madison Ave, 37th fl, New York, NY 10010 *Tel:* 212-576-9400 *Fax:* 212-689-2383 *Web Site:* www.macmillanhighered.com, pg 33

Sargent, John, Macmillan, 175 Fifth Ave, New York, NY 10010 *Tel:* 646-307-5151 *Fax:* 212-420-9314 *E-mail:* firstname.lastname@macmillan.com *Web Site:* www.macmillan.com, pg 154

Sargent, Karen, Simon & Schuster Children's Publishing, 1230 Avenue of the Americas, New York, NY 10020 *Tel:* 212-698-7000 *Web Site:* KIDS.SimonandSchuster.com; TEEN.SimonandSchuster.com; simonandschuster.net; simonandschuster.biz, pg 235

Sargent, Michael, Tuttle Publishing, Airport Business Park, 364 Innovation Dr, North Clarendon, VT 05759-9436 *Tel:* 802-773-8930 *Toll Free Tel:* 800-526-2778 *Fax:* 802-773-6993 *Toll Free Fax:* 800-FAX-TUTL *E-mail:* info@tuttlepublishing.com *Web Site:* www.tuttlepublishing.com, pg 260

Sargent, Sara, HarperCollins Children's Books, 10 E 53 St, New York, NY 10022 *Tel:* 212-207-7000 *Web Site:* www.harpercollinschildrens.com, pg 113

Sari, Paula, Wadsworth Publishing, 20 Davis Dr, Belmont, CA 94002 *Tel:* 650-595-2350 *Fax:* 650-592-3022 *Toll Free Fax:* 800-522-4923 *Web Site:* www.cengage.com, pg 276

Sarot, Ellin, Golden Rose Award, 2 Farrar St, Cambridge, MA 02138 *Tel:* 617-744-6034 *E-mail:* contests@nepoetryclub.org *Web Site:* www.nepoetryclub.org, pg 707

Sarot, Ellin, New England Poetry Club, 2 Farrar St, Cambridge, MA 02138 *Tel:* 617-744-6034 *E-mail:* info@nepoetryclub.org *Web Site:* www.nepoetryclub.org, pg 631

Sarracino, Ross, Walter Foster Publishing Inc, 3 Wrigley, Suite A, Irvine, CA 92618 *Tel:* 949-380-7510 *Toll Free Tel:* 800-426-0099; 800-826-6600 (orders) *Fax:* 949-380-7575 *E-mail:* info@walterfoster.com *Web Site:* www.walterfoster.com, pg 97

Sartin, Sharon, Unity Books, 1901 NW Blue Pkwy, Unity Village, MO 64065-0001 *Tel:* 816-524-3550 (ext 3300); 816-251-3571 (sales) *Fax:* 816-251-3557 *Web Site:* www.unity.org, pg 263

Sarver, Melissa, Folio Literary Management LLC, The Film Center Bldg, 630 Ninth Ave, Suite 1101, New York, NY 10036 *Tel:* 212-400-1494 *Fax:* 212-967-0977 *Web Site:* www.foliolit.com, pg 572

Sassi, Lynda Zuber, Chronicle Books LLC, 680 Second St, San Francisco, CA 94107 *Tel:* 415-537-4200 *Toll Free Tel:* 800-759-0190 (cust serv) *Fax:* 415-537-4460 *Toll Free Fax:* 800-858-7787 (orders); 800-286-9471 (cust serv) *E-mail:* frontdesk@chroniclebooks.com *Web Site:* www.chroniclebooks.com, pg 61

Sattler, Maggie, University of Minnesota Press, 111 Third Ave S, Suite 290, Minneapolis, MN 55401-2520 *Tel:* 612-627-1970 *Fax:* 612-627-1980 *E-mail:* ump@umn.edu *Web Site:* www.upress.umn.edu, pg 267

Saul, John Ralston, PEN American Center, 588 Broadway, Suite 303, New York, NY 10012 *Tel:* 212-334-1660 *Fax:* 212-334-2181 *E-mail:* info@pen.org *Web Site:* www.pen.org, pg 633

Saunders, David, APA Talent & Literary Agency, 405 S Beverly Dr, Beverly Hills, CA 90212 *Tel:* 310-888-4200 *Fax:* 310-888-4242 *Web Site:* www.apa-agency.com, pg 561

Saunders, Marci, Storey Publishing LLC, 210 MASS MoCA Way, North Adams, MA 01247 *Tel:* 413-346-2100 *Toll Free Tel:* 800-441-5700 (orders); 800-793-9396 (edit) *Fax:* 413-346-2199; 413-346-2196 (edit) *E-mail:* sales@storey.com *Web Site:* www.storey.com, pg 246

Saunders, Mark, The University of Virginia Press, PO Box 400318, Charlottesville, VA 22904-4318 *Tel:* 434-924-3468 (cust serv); 434-924-3469 (cust serv) *Toll Free Tel:* 800-831-3406 (orders) *Fax:* 434-982-2655 *Toll Free Fax:* 877-288-6400 *E-mail:* vapress@virginia.edu *Web Site:* www.upress.virginia.edu, pg 270

Sauri, Frank, Your Culture Gifts, 12801 Old Columbia Pike, Apt 218, Silver Spring, MD 20904 *Tel:* 410-900-0184 *Fax:* 410-461-2415 *E-mail:* info@yourculturegifts.com *Web Site:* www.yourculturegifts.com, pg 288

Sauri, Trudy, Your Culture Gifts, 12801 Old Columbia Pike, Apt 218, Silver Spring, MD 20904 *Tel:* 410-900-0184 *Fax:* 410-461-2415 *E-mail:* info@yourculturegifts.com *Web Site:* www.yourculturegifts.com, pg 288

Savage, Roth, BizBest Media Corp, 881 Alma Real Dr, Suite 220, Pacific Palisades, CA 90272 *E-mail:* info@bizbest.com *Web Site:* www.bizbest.com, pg 38

Savarese, Anne, Princeton University Press, 41 William St, Princeton, NJ 08540-5237 *Tel:* 609-258-4900 *Toll Free Tel:* 800-777-4726 (orders) *Fax:* 609-258-6305 *Toll Free Fax:* 800-999-1958 *E-mail:* orders@cpfsinc.com *Web Site:* press.princeton.edu, pg 206

Savarese, Carolyn, Merloyd Lawrence Inc, 102 Chestnut St, Boston, MA 02108 *Tel:* 617-523-5895 *Fax:* 617-252-5285, pg 145

Savitt, Charles C, Island Press, 1718 Connecticut Ave NW, Suite 300, Washington, DC 20009 *Tel:* 202-232-7933 *Toll Free Tel:* 800-828-1302 *Fax:* 202-234-1328 *E-mail:* info@islandpress.org *Web Site:* www.islandpress.org, pg 134

Sawyer, Peter, Fifi Oscard Agency Inc, 110 W 40 St, 16th fl, New York, NY 10018 *Tel:* 212-764-1100 *Fax:* 212-840-5019 *E-mail:* agency@fifioscard.com *Web Site:* www.fifioscard.com, pg 588

Sayle, Kim, Hachette Digital, 237 Park Ave, New York, NY 10017 *Tel:* 212-364-0600, pg 110

Saylor, David, Scholastic Trade Division, 557 Broadway, New York, NY 10012 *Tel:* 212-343-6100; 212-343-4685 (export sales) *Fax:* 212-343-4714 (export sales) *Web Site:* www.scholastic.com, pg 228

Sayre, C B, Hudson Park Press, 232 Madison Ave, Rm 1400, New York, NY 10016 *Tel:* 212-929-8898 *Fax:* 212-208-0946, pg 125

Scagnetti, Jack, Jack Scagnetti Talent & Literary Agency, 5118 Vineland Ave, No 102, North Hollywood, CA 91601 *Tel:* 818-761-0580 *Web Site:* jackscagnettitalentandliteraryagency.books.officelive.com, pg 592

Scalerbio, Elena, ASM Press, 1752 "N" St NW, Washington, DC 20036-2904 *Tel:* 202-737-3600 *Toll Free Tel:* 800-546-2416 *Fax:* 202-942-9342 *E-mail:* books@asmusa.org *Web Site:* estore.asm.org, pg 25

Scanlan, Brian, Thieme Medical Publishers Inc, 333 Seventh Ave, 18th fl, New York, NY 10001 *Tel:* 212-760-0888 *Toll Free Tel:* 800-782-3488 *Fax:* 212-947-1112 *E-mail:* customerservice@thieme.com *Web Site:* www.thieme.com, pg 254

Scanlon, Elizabeth, Honickman First Book Prize, University of the Arts (UARTS), Hamilton Hall, 320 S Broad St, Rm 313, Philadelphia, PA 19102-4901 *Tel:* 215-717-6801 *Fax:* 215-717-6805 *Web Site:* www.aprweb.org, pg 710

Scanlon, Jim, IHS Jane's, 110 N Royal St, Suite 200, Alexandria, VA 22314-1651 *Tel:* 703-683-3700 *Toll Free Tel:* 800-824-0768 (sales) *Fax:* 703-836-0297 *Toll Free Fax:* 800-836-0297 *E-mail:* customercare@ihs.com *Web Site:* www.ihs.com, pg 127

Scanlon, Sally, The Intrepid Traveler, 152 Saltonstall Pkwy, Rear Entrance, East Haven, CT 06512 *Tel:* 203-469-0214 *Fax:* 203-469-0430 *E-mail:* admin@intrepidtraveler.com *Web Site:* www.intrepidtraveler.com, pg 134

Scarpelli, Elizabeth, Rutgers University Press, 106 Somerset St, 3rd fl, New Brunswick, NJ 08901 *Tel:* 858-445-7784 (edit); 848-445-7788 *Toll Free Tel:* 800-848-6224 (orders only) *Fax:* 732-745-4935 (acqs, edit, mktg, perms & prodn) *Toll Free Fax:* 800-272-6817 (fulfillment) *Web Site:* rutgerspress.rutgers.edu, pg 222

Scarpello, Jason, The Institutes™, 720 Providence Rd, Suite 100, Malvern, PA 19355-3433 *Tel:* 610-644-2100 *Toll Free Tel:* 800-644-2101 *Fax:* 610-640-9576 *E-mail:* customerservice@theinstitutes.org *Web Site:* www.theinstitutes.org, pg 131

Scarpulla, Zina, Bloom's Literary Criticism, 132 W 31 St, 17th fl, New York, NY 10001 *Toll Free Tel:* 800-322-8755 *Toll Free Fax:* 800-678-3633 *E-mail:* custserv@factsonfile.com *Web Site:* www.infobasepublishing.com, pg 40

Scarpulla, Zina, Chelsea House Publishers, 132 W 31 St, 17th fl, New York, NY 10001 *Tel:* 212-967-8800 *Toll Free Tel:* 800-322-8755 *Fax:* 917-339-0325; 917-339-0323 *Toll Free Fax:* 800-678-3633 *E-mail:* custserv@factsonfile.com *Web Site:* www.infobasepublishing.com; www.infobaselearning.com, pg 59

Scarpulla, Zina, Facts On File, 132 W 31 St, 17th fl, New York, NY 10001 *Tel:* 212-967-8800 *Toll Free Tel:* 800-322-8755 *Fax:* 917-339-0323 *Toll Free Fax:* 800-678-3633 *E-mail:* custserv@factsonfile.com *Web Site:* infobasepublishing.com, pg 91

Scarpulla, Zina, Ferguson Publishing, 132 W 31 St, 17th fl, New York, NY 10001 *Tel:* 212-967-8800 *Toll Free Tel:* 800-322-8755 *Fax:* 917-339-0323 *Toll Free Fax:* 800-678-3633 *E-mail:* custserv@factsonfile.com *Web Site:* infobasepublishing.com, pg 94

Scartz-Montesano, Sara, Teton NewMedia, 90 E Simpson, Suite 110, Jackson, WY 83001 *Tel:* 307-732-0028 *Toll Free Tel:* 877-306-9793 *Fax:* 307-734-0841 *E-mail:* sales@tetonnm.com *Web Site:* www.tetonnm.com, pg 252

Scavotto, Marie, Sinauer Associates Inc, 23 Plumtree Rd, Sunderland, MA 01375 *Tel:* 413-549-4300 *Fax:* 413-549-1118 *E-mail:* publish@sinauer.com; orders@sinauer.com *Web Site:* www.sinauer.com, pg 236

Schaefer, Leslye, Scholastic Media, 524 Broadway, 5th fl, New York, NY 10012 *Tel:* 212-389-3900 *Fax:* 212-389-3886, pg 228

Schaefer, Peggy, Ideals Publications, a Guideposts Co, 2630 Elm Hill Pike, Suite 100, Nashville, TN 37214 *Toll Free Tel:* 800-586-2572 (cust serv) *Fax:* 615-781-1447 *Web Site:* www.idealsbooks.com, pg 126

Schaefer, Rita, Houghton Mifflin Harcourt, 222 Berkeley St, Boston, MA 02116-3764 *Tel:* 617-351-5000 *Toll Free Tel:* 800-225-5425 (Pre-K-8); 800-462-6595 (6–12; Advanced & Electives); 800-289-4490 (Specialized Curriculum: Great Source, Rigby, Saxon, Steck-Vaughn; Homeschool; Adult Ed); 800-323-9540 (Assessment: Riverside Publishing); 888-391-3245 (SkillsTutor); 888-242-6747 option 2 (Destination Series; Classroom Connect; Earobics; Edmark; Learning Village; Riverdeep); 800-225-3362 (Houghton Mifflin Harcourt Trade & Reference Publishers); 800-225-5800 (Heinemann) *Fax:* 617-351-1125 *Web Site:* www.hmhco.com, pg 123

Schaeffer, Dave, Simon & Schuster, Inc, 1230 Avenue of the Americas, New York, NY 10020 *Tel:* 212-698-7000 *Fax:* 212-698-7007 *E-mail:* firstname.lastname@simonandschuster.com *Web Site:* www.simonandschuster.com, pg 235

Schaeffer, Rob, Blue Apple Books, 515 Valley St, Suite 170, Maplewood, NJ 07040 *Tel:* 973-763-8191 *Toll Free Tel:* 800-722-6657; 800-733-3000 (orders) *Fax:* 973-763-5944 *E-mail:* info@blueapplebooks.com *Web Site:* blueapplebooks.com, pg 41

Schaffer, Holly, The University of Arizona Press, 355 S Euclid Ave, Suite 103, Tucson, AZ 85719-6654 *Tel:* 520-621-1441 *Toll Free Tel:* 800-426-3797 (orders) *Fax:* 520-621-8899 *Toll Free Fax:* 800-426-3797 *E-mail:* uap@uapress.arizona.edu *Web Site:* www.uapress.arizona.edu, pg 264

Schanck, Denise, Garland Science Publishing, 711 Third Ave, 8th fl, New York, NY 10017 *Tel:* 212-216-7800 *Fax:* 212-281-4487 *E-mail:* science@garland.com *Web Site:* www.garlandscience.com, pg 101

Schang, Scott, Environmental Law Institute, 2000 "L" St NW, Suite 620, Washington, DC 20036 *Tel:* 202-939-3800 *Fax:* 202-939-3868 *E-mail:* law@eli.org *Web Site:* www.eli.org, pg 89

Schaps, Eric, Developmental Studies Center, 2000 Embarcadero, Suite 305, Oakland, CA 94606-5300 *Tel:* 510-533-0213 *Toll Free Tel:* 800-666-7270 *Fax:* 510-464-3670 *E-mail:* pubs@devstu.org; info@devstu.org *Web Site:* www.devstu.org, pg 78

Scharf, Dan, The Jim Henson Co, 1416 N La Brea Ave, Hollywood, CA 90028 *Tel:* 323-802-1500 *Fax:* 323-802-1825 *Web Site:* www.henson.com, pg 135

Scharfstein, Bernard, KTAV Publishing House Inc, 888 Newark Ave, Jersey City, NJ 07306 *Tel:* 201-963-9524 *Fax:* 201-963-0102 *E-mail:* orders@ktav.com *Web Site:* www.ktav.com, pg 142

Scharlatt, Elisabeth, Algonquin Books of Chapel Hill, 400 Silver Cedar Ct, Suite 300, Chapel Hill, NC 27514-1585 *Tel:* 919-967-0108 *Fax:* 919-933-0272 *E-mail:* inquiry@algonquin.com *Web Site:* www.workman.com/algonquin, pg 8

Schaub, Patricia, University of Texas at Austin, Creative Writing Program, Dept of English, PAR 108, One University Sta, Mailcode B5000, Austin, TX 78712-1164 *Tel:* 512-471-5132; 512-471-4991 *Fax:* 512-471-4909 *Web Site:* www.utexas.edu/cola/depts/english/creative-writing, pg 682

Schaub, Prof Thomas, Chris O'Malley Fiction Prize, University of Wisconsin, 6193 Helen C White Hall, English Dept, 600 N Park St, Madison, WI 53706 *Tel:* 608-263-0566 *E-mail:* madisonrevw@gmail.com *Web Site:* www.english.wisc.edu/madisonreview, pg 731

Schaub, Prof Thomas, Phyllis Smart-Young Poetry Prize, University of Wisconsin, 6193 Helen C White Hall, English Dept, 600 N Park St, Madison, WI 53706 *Tel:* 608-263-0566 *E-mail:* madisonrevw@gmail.com *Web Site:* www.english.wisc.edu/madisonreview, pg 753

Schauer, David A, National Council on Radiation Protection & Measurements (NCRP), 7910 Woodmont Ave, Suite 400, Bethesda, MD 20814-3095 *Tel:* 301-657-2652 *Toll Free Tel:* 800-229-2652 *Fax:* 301-907-8768 *E-mail:* ncrppubs@ncrponline.org *Web Site:* www.ncrponline.org; www.ncrppublications.org, pg 174

Schaumberg, Jean, The Tony Hillerman Prize, 1063 Willow Way, Santa Fe, NM 87507 *Tel:* 505-471-1565 *E-mail:* wordharvest@wordharvest.com *Web Site:* www.wordharvest.com, pg 710

Schaumberg, Jean, Tony Hillerman Writers Conference, 1063 Willow Way, Santa Fe, NM 87507 *Tel:* 505-471-1565 *E-mail:* wordharvest@wordharvest.com *Web Site:* www.wordharvest.com, pg 674

Schultz, Jonathan D, Concordia Publishing House, 3558 S Jefferson Ave, St Louis, MO 63118-3968 *Tel:* 314-268-1000 *Toll Free Tel:* 800-325-3040 (cust serv) *Toll Free Fax:* 800-490-9889 (cust serv) *E-mail:* order@cph.org *Web Site:* www.cph.org, pg 66

Schultz, Patricia, The Mellen Poetry Press, 240 Portage Rd, Lewiston, NY 14092 *Tel:* 716-754-2266; 716-754-1400 (mktg); 716-754-2788 (order fulfillment) *Fax:* 716-754-4056; 716-754-1860 (fulfillment) *E-mail:* cservice@mellenpress.com *Web Site:* www.mellenpress.com, pg 164

Schultz, Thom, Group Publishing Inc, 1515 Cascade Ave, Loveland, CO 80538 *Tel:* 970-669-3836 *Toll Free Tel:* 800-447-1070 *Fax:* 970-292-4373 *E-mail:* info@group.com *Web Site:* www.group.com, pg 108

Schumacher, George, Penguin Young Readers Group, 345 Hudson St, New York, NY 10014 *Tel:* 212-366-2000 *E-mail:* online@penguinputnam.com *Web Site:* www.penguinputnam.com; us.penguingroup.com, pg 198

Schumacher, Peg, RAND Corp, 1776 Main St, Santa Monica, CA 90407-2138 *Tel:* 310-393-0411 *Fax:* 310-393-4818 *Web Site:* www.rand.org, pg 212

Schumacher, Ryan, Texas State Historical Association, Stovall Hall 175, 1400 W Highland St, Denton, TX 76203 *Tel:* 940-369-5200 *Fax:* 940-369-5248 *Web Site:* www.tshaonline.org, pg 253

Schuman, Patricia Glass, Neal-Schuman Publishers Inc, 100 William St, Suite 2004, New York, NY 10038 *Tel:* 212-925-8650 *Toll Free Tel:* 866-NS-BOOKS (672-6657) *Fax:* 212-219-8916 *Toll Free Fax:* 877-231-6980 *E-mail:* info@neal-schuman.com *Web Site:* www.neal-schuman.com, pg 176

Schumer, Fran, Joelle Delbourgo Associates Inc, 101 Park St, Montclair, NJ 07042 *Tel:* 973-773-0836 (call only during standard business hours) *Web Site:* www.delbourgo.com, pg 568

Schuna, Jo Anne, The Schuna Group Inc, 1503 Briarknoll Dr, Arden Hills, MN 55112 *Tel:* 651-631-8480 *Web Site:* www.schunagroup.com, pg 603

Schuneman, Robert, ECS Publishing Corp, 615 Concord St, Framingham, MA 01702 *Tel:* 508-620-7400 *Toll Free Tel:* 800-777-1919 *Fax:* 508-620-7401 *E-mail:* office@ecspub.com *Web Site:* www.ecspublishing.com, pg 84

Schustack, Margie, John Wiley & Sons Inc Professional/Trade Group, 111 River St, Hoboken, NJ 07030 *Tel:* 201-748-6000 *Toll Free Tel:* 800-225-5945 (cust serv) *Fax:* 201-748-6088 *E-mail:* info@wiley.com *Web Site:* www.wiley.com, pg 282

Schuster, Jennifer, NAL, 375 Hudson St, New York, NY 10014 *Tel:* 212-366-2000 *E-mail:* online@penguinputnam.com *Web Site:* www.penguinputnam.com; us.penguingroup.com, pg 172

Schutt, David L, SAE (Society of Automotive Engineers International), 400 Commonwealth Dr, Warrendale, PA 15096-0001 *Tel:* 724-776-4841; 724-776-4970 (outside US & CN) *Toll Free Tel:* 877-606-7323 (cust serv) *Fax:* 724-776-0790 (cust serv) *E-mail:* publications@sae.org; customerservice@sae.org *Web Site:* www.sae.org, pg 223

Schwab, Ann, Black Rabbit Books, 123 S Broad St, Mankato, MN 56001 *Tel:* 507-388-1609 *Fax:* 507-388-1364 *E-mail:* info@blackrabbitbooks.com; orders@blackrabbitbooks.com *Web Site:* www.blackrabbitbooks.com, pg 39

Schwabinger, Jennifer, Penguin Group (USA) LLC Sales, 375 Hudson St, New York, NY 10014 *Tel:* 212-366-2000 *E-mail:* online@penguinputnam.com *Web Site:* us.penguingroup.com, pg 197

Schwacke, Susanna Sharp, Bottom Dog Press, c/o Firelands College of Bowling Green State Univ, PO Box 425, Huron, OH 44839-0425 *Tel:* 419-433-5560 (ext 20784) *Fax:* 419-616-3966 *Web Site:* smithdocs.net, pg 44

Schwartz, Andrew E, A E Schwartz & Associates, 13 Conversation Way, Stoughton, MA 02072 *Tel:* 781-436-5033 *E-mail:* info@aeschwartz.com *Web Site:* aeschwartz.com, pg 593

Schwartz, Anne, Random House Children's Books, 1745 Broadway, New York, NY 10019 *Tel:* 212-782-9000 *Toll Free Tel:* 800-200-3552 *Fax:* 212-782-9452 *Web Site:* randomhousekids.com, pg 213

Schwartz, Barry L, Jewish Publication Society, 2100 Arch St, 2nd fl, Philadelphia, PA 19103 *Tel:* 215-832-0600 *Toll Free Tel:* 800-234-3151 *Fax:* 215-568-2017 *E-mail:* jewishbook@jps.org *Web Site:* www.jps.org, pg 135

Schwartz, Diane, Dorland Healthcare Information, 4 Choke Cherry Rd, 2nd fl, Rockville, MD 20850 *Tel:* 301-354-2000 *Toll Free Tel:* 800-784-2332 *Fax:* 801-365-2300 *E-mail:* info@dorlandhealth.com *Web Site:* www.dorlandhealth.com, pg 81

Schwartz, J Alex, Northern Illinois University Press, 2280 Bethany Rd, DeKalb, IL 60115 *Tel:* 815-753-1826; 815-753-1075 *Fax:* 815-753-1845 *Web Site:* www.niupress.niu.edu, pg 181

Schwartz, Jamie, Council of Literary Magazines & Presses (CLMP), 154 Christopher St, Suite 3-C, New York, NY 10014-9110 *Tel:* 212-741-9110 *Fax:* 212-741-9112 *E-mail:* info@clmp.org *Web Site:* www.clmp.org, pg 622

Schwartz, Jenny Wesselmann, AMACOM Books, 1601 Broadway, New York, NY 10019-7420 *Tel:* 212-586-8100; 518-891-5510 (orders) *Toll Free Tel:* 800-250-5308 (cust serv) *Fax:* 212-903-8083; 518-891-2372 (orders) *E-mail:* pubservice@amanet.org *Web Site:* www.amacombooks.org, pg 9

Schwartz, Joan Brandt, The Joan Brandt Agency, 788 Wesley Dr NW, Atlanta, GA 30305 *Tel:* 404-351-8877 *Fax:* 404-351-0068, pg 564

Schwartz, Marilyn, University of California Press, 2120 Berkeley Way, Berkeley, CA 94704-1012 *Tel:* 510-642-4247 *Fax:* 510-643-7127 *E-mail:* askucp@ucpress.edu (books); customerservice@ucpressjournals.com (journals) *Web Site:* www.ucpress.edu, pg 264

Schwartz, Matt, Random House Inc, 1745 Broadway, New York, NY 10019 *Tel:* 212-782-9000 *Toll Free Tel:* 800-726-0600 *Web Site:* www.randomhouse.com, pg 213

Schwartz, Matt, Random House Publishing Group, 1745 Broadway, New York, NY 10019 *Toll Free Tel:* 800-200-3552 *Web Site:* atrandom.com, pg 214

Schwartz, Rick, HarperCollins Publishers, 10 E 53 St, New York, NY 10022 *Tel:* 212-207-7000 *Fax:* 212-207-7145 *Web Site:* www.harpercollins.com, pg 113

Schwartz, Russ, Thomas Nelson Inc, 501 Nelson Place, Nashville, TN 37214 *Tel:* 615-889-9000 *Toll Free Tel:* 800-251-4000 *Fax:* 615-902-1548 *E-mail:* publicity@thomasnelson.com *Web Site:* www.thomasnelson.com, pg 255

Schwartz, Sheryl, The Perseus Books Group, 387 Park Ave S, 12th fl, New York, NY 10016 *Tel:* 212-340-8100 *Toll Free Tel:* 800-343-4499 (cust serv) *Fax:* 212-340-8105 *Web Site:* www.perseusbooksgroup.com, pg 199

Schwartz, Steven, Sarah Jane Freymann Literary Agency LLC, 59 W 71 St, Suite 9-B, New York, NY 10023 *Tel:* 212-362-9277 *E-mail:* submissions@sarahjanefreymann.com *Web Site:* www.sarahjanefreymann.com, pg 573

Schwartz, Susan, Dutton, 375 Hudson St, New York, NY 10014 *Tel:* 212-366-2000 *Fax:* 212-366-2262 *E-mail:* online@penguinputnam.com *Web Site:* www.penguinputnam.com; us.penguingroup.com, pg 83

Schwartz, Susan, The Editors Circle, 462 Grove St, Montclair, NJ 07043 *Tel:* 973-783-5082 *E-mail:* query@theeditorscircle.com *Web Site:* www.theeditorscircle.com, pg 545

Schwartzentruber, Mike, Northstone Publishing, 9590 Jim Bailey Rd, Kelowna, BC V4V 1R2, Canada *Tel:* 250-766-2778 *Toll Free Tel:* 800-299-2926; 800-663-2775 (orders) *Fax:* 250-766-2736 *Toll Free Fax:* 888-841-9991 *E-mail:* info@woodlakebooks.com *Web Site:* www.woodlakebooks.com, pg 514

Schwartzentruber, Mike, Wood Lake Publishing Inc, 9590 Jim Bailey Rd, Kelowna, BC V4V 1R2, Canada *Tel:* 250-766-2778 *Toll Free Tel:* 800-663-2775 (orders) *Fax:* 250-766-2736 *Toll Free Fax:* 888-841-9991 (orders) *E-mail:* info@woodlake.com; customerservice@woodlake.com *Web Site:* www.woodlakebooks.com, pg 525

Schwartzman, Jill, Dutton, 375 Hudson St, New York, NY 10014 *Tel:* 212-366-2000 *Fax:* 212-366-2262 *E-mail:* online@penguinputnam.com *Web Site:* www.penguinputnam.com; us.penguingroup.com, pg 83

Schwarz, Helena, Susan Rabiner Literary Agency Inc, 315 W 39 St, Suite 1501, New York, NY 10018-3907 *Web Site:* RabinerLit.com, pg 589

Schwarz, Lisa, Business Marketing Association (BMA), 1833 Centre Point Circle, Suite 123, Naperville, IL 60563 *Tel:* 630-544-5054 *Fax:* 630-544-5055 *E-mail:* info@marketing.org *Web Site:* www.marketing.org, pg 619

Schwarze, Diane, Book Peddlers, 2950 W Dean Pkwy, No 1602, Minneapolis, MN 55416 *Tel:* 952-544-1154 *E-mail:* bookpeddlers@aol.com *Web Site:* www.bookpeddlers.com; www.practicalparenting.com, pg 43

Scinta, Sam, Fulcrum Publishing Inc, 4690 Table Mountain Dr, Suite 100, Golden, CO 80403 *Tel:* 303-277-1623 *Toll Free Tel:* 800-992-2908 *Fax:* 303-279-7111 *Toll Free Fax:* 800-726-7112 *E-mail:* info@fulcrumbooks.com; orders@fulcrumbooks.com *Web Site:* www.fulcrumbooks.com, pg 100

Scognamiglio, John, Kensington Publishing Corp, 119 W 40 St, New York, NY 10018 *Tel:* 212-407-1500 *Toll Free Tel:* 800-221-2647 *Fax:* 212-935-0699 *Web Site:* www.kensingtonbooks.com, pg 139

Scollans, Colleen, Oxford University Press USA, 198 Madison Ave, New York, NY 10016 *Tel:* 212-726-6000 *Toll Free Tel:* 800-451-7556 (orders); 800-445-9714 (cust serv) *Fax:* 919-677-1303 *E-mail:* custserv.us@oup.com *Web Site:* www.oup.com/us, pg 189

Scott, Alan, Wolters Kluwer Law & Business, 76 Ninth Ave, 7th fl, New York, NY 10011-5201 *Tel:* 212-771-0600 *Toll Free Tel:* 800-234-1660 (cust serv); 800-638-8437 (orders); 800-317-3113 (bookstore sales) *Toll Free Fax:* 800-901-9075 (cust serv); 800-561-4845 (bookstore sales) *Web Site:* www.aspenpublishers.com, pg 141

Scott, Angel, CODiE Awards, 1090 Vermont Ave NW, 6th fl, Washington, DC 20005-4095 *Tel:* 202-289-7442 *Fax:* 202-289-7097 *E-mail:* info@siia.net *Web Site:* www.siia.net, pg 697

Scott, Ardy M, Twilight Times Books, PO Box 3340, Kingsport, TN 37664-0340 *Tel:* 423-323-0183 *Fax:* 423-323-0183 *E-mail:* publisher@twilighttimes.com *Web Site:* www.twilighttimesbooks.com, pg 261

Scott, Craig R, Heritage Books Inc, 100 Railroad Ave, Suite 104, Westminster, MD 21157-4826 *Tel:* 410-876-6101 *Toll Free Tel:* 800-876-6103 *Fax:* 410-558-6574 *E-mail:* info@heritagebooks.com; orders@heritagebooks.com *Web Site:* www.heritagebooks.com, pg 118

Scott, Darryl, Thomas Allen Publishers, 390 Steelcase Rd E, Markham, ON L3R 1G2, Canada *Tel:* 905-475-9126 *Toll Free Tel:* 800-387-4333 (orders) *Fax:* 905-475-6747 *Toll Free Fax:* 800-458-5504 (orders) *E-mail:* info@t-allen.com *Web Site:* www.thomasallen.ca, pg 493

Scott, Debra Leigh, Hidden River Arts Playwriting Award, PO Box 63927, Philadelphia, PA 19147 *Tel:* 610-764-0813 *E-mail:* hiddenriverarts@gmail.com *Web Site:* www.hiddenriverarts.org, pg 709

Scott, Debra Leigh, The William Van Wert Memorial Fiction Award, PO Box 63927, Philadelphia, PA 19147 *Tel:* 610-764-0813 *E-mail:* hiddenriverarts@gmail.com *Web Site:* www.hiddenriverarts.org, pg 747

Scott, Katherine, The Canadian Council on Social Development, 190 O'Connor St, Suite 100, Ottawa, ON K2P 2R3, Canada *Tel:* 613-236-8977 *Fax:* 613-236-2750 *E-mail:* council@ccsd.ca *Web Site:* www.ccsd.ca, pg 496

Seldes, Marian, The Authors League Fund, 31 E 32 St, 7th fl, New York, NY 10016 *Tel:* 212-268-1208 *Fax:* 212-564-5363 *E-mail:* staff@authorsleaguefund.org *Web Site:* www.authorsleaguefund.org, pg 617

Selestow, Claire Ann, Harmonie Park Press, Liberty Professional Ctr, 35675 Mound Rd, Sterling Heights, MI 48310-4727 *Tel:* 586-979-2077; 586-979-1844 (cust serv) *Toll Free Tel.* 800-422-4880 *Fax:* 586-979-1786; 586-979-1863 (cust serv) *E-mail:* info@harmonieparkpress.com *Web Site:* harmonieparkpress.com, pg 113

Self, Robert, Baby Tattoo Books, 6045 Longridge Ave, Van Nuys, CA 91401 *Tel:* 818-416-5314 *E-mail:* info@babytattoo.com *Web Site:* www.babytattoo.com, pg 29

Self, Ron, Brick Road Poetry Book Contest, PO Box 751, Columbus, GA 31902-0751 *Tel:* 706-649-3080 *Web Site:* brickroadpoetrypress.com, pg 693

Seligman, Ellen, McClelland & Stewart Ltd, 75 Sherbourne St, 5th fl, Toronto, ON M5A 2P9, Canada *Tel:* 416-598-1114 *Fax:* 416-598-7764 *E-mail:* editorial@mcclelland.com *Web Site:* www.mcclelland.com, pg 512

Selleck, Carol, Society of Manufacturing Engineers, One SME Dr, Dearborn, MI 48121 *Tel:* 313-425-3000 *Toll Free Tel:* 800-733-4763 (cust serv) *Fax:* 313-425-3400 *E-mail:* publications@sme.org *Web Site:* www.sme.org, pg 238

Selleck, Michael, Simon & Schuster, Inc, 1230 Avenue of the Americas, New York, NY 10020 *Tel:* 212-698-7000 *Fax:* 212-698-7007 *E-mail:* firstname.lastname@simonandschuster.com *Web Site:* www.simonandschuster.com, pg 235

Selleck, Michael, Simon & Schuster Sales & Marketing, 1230 Avenue of the Americas, New York, NY 10020 *Tel:* 212-698-7000, pg 236

Seller, Shyla, Arsenal Pulp Press, 211 E Georgia St, No 101, Vancouver, BC V6A 1Z6, Canada *Tel:* 604-687-4233 *Toll Free Tel:* 888-600-PULP (600-7857) *Fax:* 604-687-4283 *E-mail:* info@arsenalpulp.com *Web Site:* www.arsenalpulp.com, pg 493

Sellers, Scott, Doubleday Canada, One Toronto St, Suite 300, Toronto, ON M5C 2V6, Canada *Tel:* 416-364-4449 *Fax:* 416-364-6863 *Web Site:* www.randomhouse.ca, pg 501

Sellers, Scott, Knopf Random Canada, One Toronto St, Suite 300, Toronto, ON M5C 2V6, Canada *Tel:* 416-364-4449 *Toll Free Tel:* 888-523-9292 *Fax:* 416-364-6863 *Web Site:* www.randomhouse.ca, pg 510

Sellers, Scott, Random House of Canada Limited, One Toronto St, Suite 300, Toronto, ON M5C 2V6, Canada *Tel:* 416-364-4449 *Toll Free Tel:* 888-523-9292 (cust serv) *Fax:* 416-364-6863; 416-364-6653 (subs rts) *Web Site:* www.randomhouse.ca, pg 517

Sellers, Scott, Seal Books, One Toronto St, Suite 300, Toronto, ON M5C 2V6, Canada *Tel:* 416-364-4449 *Toll Free Tel:* 888-523-9292 (order desk) *Fax:* 416-364-6863 *Web Site:* www.randomhouse.ca, pg 518

Sells, Dianna, Texas A&M University Press, John H Lindsey Bldg, Lewis St, 4354 TAMU, College Station, TX 77843-4354 *Tel:* 979-845-1436 *Toll Free Tel:* 800-826-8911 (orders) *Fax:* 979-847-8752 *Toll Free Fax:* 888-617-2421 (orders) *E-mail:* upress@tamu.edu *Web Site:* www.tamupress.com, pg 253

Selman, Edythea Ginis, Edythea Ginis Selman Literary Agency Inc, 14 Washington Place, New York, NY 10003 *Tel:* 212-473-1874 *Fax:* 212-473-1875, pg 593

Selman, Richard, Edythea Ginis Selman Literary Agency Inc, 14 Washington Place, New York, NY 10003 *Tel:* 212-473-1874 *Fax:* 212-473-1875, pg 593

Seltz, Martin, Augsburg Fortress Publishers, Publishing House of the Evangelical Lutheran Church in America, 100 S Fifth St, Suite 600, Minneapolis, MN 55402 *Tel:* 612-330-3300 *Toll Free Tel:* 800-426-0115 (ext 639, subns); 800-328-4648 (orders) *E-mail:* info@augsburgfortress.org; copyright@augsburgfortress.org (reprint permission requests); customercare@augsburgfortress.org *Web Site:* www.augsburgfortress.org, pg 27

Seltzer, Joyce, Harvard University Press, 79 Garden St, Cambridge, MA 02138-1499 *Tel:* 617-495-2600; 401-531-2800 (intl orders) *Toll Free Tel:* 800-405-1619 (orders) *Fax:* 617-495-5898 (general); 617-496-4677 (edit & rts); 401-531-2801 (intl orders) *Toll Free Fax:* 800-406-9145 (orders) *E-mail:* contact_hup@harvard.edu *Web Site:* www.hup.harvard.edu, pg 115

Semens, Jack, Integra Software Services Inc, 1110 Jorie Blvd, Suite 200, Oak Brook, IL 60523 *Tel:* 630-586-2579 *Fax:* 630-586-2599 *Web Site:* www.integra.co.in, pg 548

Semens, Zak, Goodheart-Willcox Publisher, 18604 W Creek Dr, Tinley Park, IL 60477-6243 *Tel:* 708-687-5000 *Toll Free Tel:* 800-323-0440 *Fax:* 708-687-0315 *Toll Free Fax:* 888-409-3900 *E-mail:* custserv@g-w.com *Web Site:* www.g-w.com, pg 105

Sen, Sharmila, Harvard University Press, 79 Garden St, Cambridge, MA 02138-1499 *Tel:* 617-495-2600; 401-531-2800 (intl orders) *Toll Free Tel:* 800-405-1619 (orders) *Fax:* 617-495-5898 (general); 617-496-4677 (edit & rts); 401-531-2801 (intl orders) *Toll Free Fax:* 800-406-9145 (orders) *E-mail:* contact_hup@harvard.edu *Web Site:* www.hup.harvard.edu, pg 115

Senftleben, Peter, Kensington Publishing Corp, 119 W 40 St, New York, NY 10018 *Tel:* 212-407-1500 *Toll Free Tel:* 800-221-2647 *Fax:* 212-935-0699 *Web Site:* www.kensingtonbooks.com, pg 139

Sengthavy, Khamla, Norma Epstein Foundation, 15 King's College Circle, UC 173, Toronto, ON M5S 3H7, Canada *Tel:* 416-978-8083 *Fax:* 416-971-2027 *Web Site:* www.utoronto.ca, pg 702

Sennholz, Lyn M, Center for Futures Education Inc, 345 Erie St, Grove City, PA 16127 *Tel:* 724-458-5860 *Fax:* 724-458-5962 *E-mail:* info@thectr.com *Web Site:* www.thectr.com, pg 56

Senturk, Huseyin, Tughra Books, 345 Clifton Ave, Clifton, NJ 07011 *Tel:* 973-777-2704 *Fax:* 973-457-7334 *E-mail:* info@tughrabooks.com *Web Site:* www.tughrabooks.com, pg 259

Senz, Lisa, St Martin's Press, LLC, 175 Fifth Ave, New York, NY 10010 *Tel:* 646-307-5151 *Fax:* 212-420-9314 *E-mail:* firstname.lastname@macmillan.com *Web Site:* www.stmartins.com, pg 224

Seo, Ginee, Chronicle Books LLC, 680 Second St, San Francisco, CA 94107 *Tel:* 415-537-4200 *Toll Free Tel:* 800-759-0190 (cust serv) *Fax:* 415-537-4460 *Toll Free Fax:* 800-858-7787 (orders); 800-286-9471 (cust serv) *E-mail:* frontdesk@chroniclebooks.com *Web Site:* www.chroniclebooks.com, pg 61

Seow, Jackie, Simon & Schuster, 1230 Avenue of the Americas, New York, NY 10020 *Tel:* 212-698-7000 *Toll Free Tel:* 800-223-2348 (cust serv); 800-223-2336 (orders) *Toll Free Fax:* 800-943-9831 (orders) *Web Site:* www.simonandschuster.com, pg 234

Sepehri, Amin, Mage Publishers Inc, 1032 29 St NW, Washington, DC 20007 *Tel:* 202-342-1642 *Toll Free Tel:* 800-962-0922 *Fax:* 202-342-9269 *Web Site:* www.mage.com, pg 155

Serafimidis, Sarah, Frog Books, 2526 Martin Luther King Jr Way, Berkeley, CA 94704 *Tel:* 510-549-4270 *Toll Free Tel:* 800-733-3000 (book orders only) *Fax:* 510-549-4276 *Toll Free Fax:* 800-659-2436 (orders) *E-mail:* orders@northatlanticbooks.com *Web Site:* www.northatlanticbooks.com, pg 99

Serafimidis, Sarah, North Atlantic Books, 2526 Martin Luther King Jr Way, Berkeley, CA 94704 *Tel:* 510-549-4270 *Fax:* 510-549-4276 *Web Site:* www.northatlanticbooks.com, pg 180

Serafini, Julie, The Texas Bluebonnet Award, 3355 Bee Cave Rd, Suite 401, Austin, TX 78746 *Tel:* 512-328-1518 *Toll Free Tel:* 800-580-2852 *Fax:* 512-328-8852 *Web Site:* www.txla.org, pg 745

Seraphim, Joshua, Leilah Publications, PO Box 1863, Tempe, AZ 85280-1863 *Tel:* 480-241-4120 *E-mail:* leilah@leilahpublications.com *Web Site:* leilahpublications.com, pg 146

Sergel, Christopher III, Dramatic Publishing Co, 311 Washington St, Woodstock, IL 60098-3308 *Tel:* 815-338-7170 *Toll Free Tel:* 800-448-7469 *Fax:* 815-338-8981 *Toll Free Fax:* 800-334-5302 *E-mail:* plays@dramaticpublishing.com *Web Site:* www.dramaticpublishing.com, pg 82

Sergel, Gayle, Dramatic Publishing Co, 311 Washington St, Woodstock, IL 60098-3308 *Tel:* 815-338-7170 *Toll Free Tel:* 800-448-7469 *Fax:* 815-338-8981 *Toll Free Fax:* 800-334-5302 *E-mail:* plays@dramaticpublishing.com *Web Site:* www.dramaticpublishing.com, pg 82

Sergel, Susan, Dramatic Publishing Co, 311 Washington St, Woodstock, IL 60098-3308 *Tel:* 815-338-7170 *Toll Free Tel:* 800-448-7469 *Fax:* 815-338-8981 *Toll Free Fax:* 800-334-5302 *E-mail:* plays@dramaticpublishing.com *Web Site:* www.dramaticpublishing.com, pg 82

Sergio, Christopher, Portfolio, 375 Hudson St, New York, NY 10014, pg 204

Seroy, Jeff, Faber & Faber Inc, 18 W 18 St, New York, NY 10011 *Tel:* 212-741-6900 *Fax:* 212-633-9385 *E-mail:* fsg.editorial@fsgbooks.com (edit inquiries) *Web Site:* us.macmillan.com/faberandfaber.aspx, pg 91

Seroy, Jeff, Farrar, Straus & Giroux, LLC, 18 W 18 St, New York, NY 10011 *Tel:* 212-741-6900 *Fax:* 212-633-9385 *E-mail:* fsg.publicity@fsgbooks.com *Web Site:* us.macmillan.com/fsg.aspx, pg 93

Seroy, Jeff, Hill & Wang, 18 W 18 St, New York, NY 10011 *Tel:* 212-741-6900 *Fax:* 212-633-9385 *E-mail:* fsg.publicity@fsgbooks.com; fsg.editorial@fsgbooks.com *Web Site:* us.macmillan.com/hillandwang.aspx, pg 119

Seroy, Jeff, North Point Press, 18 W 18 St, 8th fl, New York, NY 10011 *Tel:* 212-741-6900 *Toll Free Tel:* 888-330-8477 *Fax:* 212-633-9385 *Web Site:* www.fsgbooks.com, pg 181

Sery, Douglas, The MIT Press, 55 Hayward St, Cambridge, MA 02142 *Tel:* 617-253-5255 *Toll Free Tel:* 800-207-8354 (orders) *Fax:* 617-258-6779; 617-577-1545 (orders) *Web Site:* mitpress.mit.edu, pg 167

Settle, Alicia B, Per Annum Inc, 555 Eighth Ave, Suite 203, New York, NY 10018 *Tel:* 212-647-8700 *Toll Free Tel:* 800-548-1108 *Fax:* 212-647-8716 *E-mail:* info@perannum.com *Web Site:* www.perannum.com, pg 199

Seum, Rebecca, Cup of Tea Books, 2671 Bristol Rd, Columbus, OH 43221 *Tel:* 614-264-5588 *E-mail:* sales@pagespringpublishing.com *Web Site:* www.cupofteabooks.com, pg 73

Severini, Giorgia, R Ross Annett Award for Children's Literature, 11759 Groat Rd, Edmonton, AB T5M 3K6, Canada *Tel:* 780-422-8174 *Toll Free Tel:* 800-665-5354 (AB only) *Fax:* 780-422-2663 (attn WGA) *E-mail:* mail@writersguild.ab.ca *Web Site:* www.writersguild.ab.ca, pg 687

Severini, Giorgia, Amber Bowerman Memorial Travel Writing Award, 11759 Groat Rd, Edmonton, AB T5M 3K6, Canada *Tel:* 780-422-8174 *Toll Free Tel:* 800-665-5354 (AB only) *Fax:* 780-422-2663 (attn WGA) *E-mail:* mail@writersguild.ab.ca *Web Site:* www.writersguild.ab.ca, pg 692

Severini, Giorgia, Georges Bugnet Award for Fiction, 11759 Groat Rd, Edmonton, AB T5M 3K6, Canada *Tel:* 780-422-8174 *Toll Free Tel:* 800-665-5354 (AB only) *Fax:* 780-422-2663 (attn WGA) *E-mail:* mail@writersguild.ab.ca *Web Site:* www.writersguild.ab.ca, pg 693

Severini, Giorgia, The City of Calgary W O Mitchell Book Prize, 11759 Groat Rd, Edmonton, AB T5M 3K6, Canada *Tel:* 780-422-8174 *Toll Free Tel:* 800-665-5354 (AB only) *Fax:* 780-422-2663 (attn WGA) *E-mail:* mail@writersguild.ab.ca *Web Site:* www.writersguild.ab.ca, pg 697

Severini, Giorgia, Wilfrid Eggleston Award for Nonfiction, 11759 Groat Rd, Edmonton, AB T5M 3K6, Canada *Tel:* 780-422-8174 *Toll Free Tel:* 800-665-5354 (AB only) *Fax:* 780-422-2663 (attn WGA) *E-mail:* mail@writersguild.ab.ca *Web Site:* www.writersguild.ab.ca, pg 702

Severini, Giorgia, James H Gray Award for Short Nonfiction, 11759 Groat Rd, Edmonton, AB T5M 3K6, Canada *Tel:* 780-422-8174 *Toll Free Tel:* 800-665-5354 (AB only) *Fax:* 780-422-2663 (attn WGA) *E-mail:* mail@writersguild.ab.ca *Web Site:* www.writersguild.ab.ca, pg 708

Severini, Giorgia, The Robert Kroetsch City of Edmonton Book Prize, 11759 Groat Rd, Edmonton, AB T5M 3K6, Canada *Tel:* 780-422-8174 *Toll Free Tel:* 800-665-5354 (AB only) *Fax:* 780-422-2663 (attn WGA) *E-mail:* mail@writersguild.ab.ca *Web Site:* www.writersguild.ab.ca, pg 716

Severini, Giorgia, Isabel Miller Young Writers Award, 11759 Groat Rd, Edmonton, AB T5M 3K6, Canada *Tel:* 780-422-8174 *Toll Free Tel:* 800-665-5354 (AB only) *Fax:* 780-422-2663 (attn WGA) *E-mail:* mail@writersguild.ab.ca *Web Site:* www.writersguild.ab.ca, pg 723

Severini, Giorgia, Howard O'Hagan Award for Short Story, 11759 Groat Rd, Edmonton, AB T5M 3K6, Canada *Tel:* 780-422-8174 *Toll Free Tel:* 800-665-5354 (AB only) *Fax:* 780-422-2663 (attn WGA) *E-mail:* mail@writersguild.ab.ca *Web Site:* www.writersguild.ab.ca, pg 730

Severini, Giorgia, Gwen Pharis Ringwood Award for Drama, 11759 Groat Rd, Edmonton, AB T5M 3K6, Canada *Tel:* 780-422-8174 *Toll Free Tel:* 800-665-5354 (AB only) *Fax:* 780-422-2663 (attn WGA) *E-mail:* mail@writersguild.ab.ca *Web Site:* www.writersguild.ab.ca, pg 738

Severini, Giorgia, Stephan G Stephansson Award for Poetry, 11759 Groat Rd, Edmonton, AB T5M 3K6, Canada *Tel:* 780-422-8174 *Toll Free Tel:* 800-665-5354 (AB only) *Fax:* 780-422-2663 (attn WGA) *E-mail:* mail@writersguild.ab.ca *Web Site:* www.writersguild.ab.ca, pg 744

Severini, Giorgia, Jon Whyte Memorial Essay Prize, 11759 Groat Rd, Edmonton, AB T5M 3K6, Canada *Tel:* 780-422-8174 *Toll Free Tel:* 800-665-5354 (AB only) *Fax:* 780-422-2663 (attn WGA) *E-mail:* mail@writersguild.ab.ca *Web Site:* www.writersguild.ab.ca, pg 749

Severini, Giorgia, Writers Guild of Alberta, 11759 Groat Rd, Edmonton, AB T5M 3K6, Canada *Tel:* 780-422-8174 *Toll Free Tel:* 800-665-5354 (AB only) *Fax:* 780-422-2663 (attn WGA) *E-mail:* mail@writersguild.ab.ca *Web Site:* www.writersguild.ab.ca, pg 638

Sevier, Ben, Dutton, 375 Hudson St, New York, NY 10014 *Tel:* 212-366-2000 *Fax:* 212-366-2262 *E-mail:* online@penguinputnam.com *Web Site:* www.penguinputnam.com; us.penguingroup.com, pg 83

Sevig, Mike, Skandisk Inc, 6667 W Old Shakopee Rd, Suite 109, Bloomington, MN 55438-2622 *Tel:* 952-829-8998 *Toll Free Tel:* 800-468-2424 *Fax:* 952-829-8992 *E-mail:* tomten@skandisk.com *Web Site:* www.skandisk.com, pg 236

Sewell, Emily, Bull Publishing Co, PO Box 1377, Boulder, CO 80306 *Tel:* 303-545-6350 *Toll Free Tel:* 800-676-2855 *Fax:* 303-545-6354 *E-mail:* bullpublishing@msn.com *Web Site:* www.bullpub.com, pg 49

Sewell, Vicki, University of South Carolina Press, 1600 Hampton St, Suite 544, Columbia, SC 29208 *Tel:* 803-777-5245 *Toll Free Tel:* 800-768-2500 (orders) *Fax:* 803-777-0160 *Toll Free Fax:* 800-868-0740 (orders) *Web Site:* www.sc.edu/uscpress, pg 269

Sexton, Kim, SDP Publishing Solutions LLC, 36 Captain's Way, East Bridgewater, MA 02333 *Tel:* 617-775-0656 *Web Site:* www.sdppublishingsolutions.com, pg 555

Sexton, Phil, F+W Media Inc, 10151 Carver Rd, Suite 200, Blue Ash, OH 45242 *Tel:* 513-531-2690 *Toll Free Tel:* 800-289-0963 (trade accts); 800-258-0929 (orders) *E-mail:* contact_us@fwmedia.com *Web Site:* www.fwmedia.com, pg 92

Sexton, Phil, Writer's Digest Books, 10151 Carver Rd, Suite 200, Blue Ash, OH 45242 *Tel:* 513-531-2690 *Toll Free Tel:* 800-289-0963 *Fax:* 513-531-7185 *E-mail:* writersdigest@fwmedia.com (edit) *Web Site:* www.writersdigest.com, pg 286

Seymour, Mary Sue, Mary Sue Seymour, 475 Miner Street Rd, Canton, NY 13617 *Tel:* 315-386-1831 *Web Site:* www.theseymouragency.com, pg 593

Sgariat, Sara, Spring Tree Press, 571 Locust Point Rd, Locust, NJ 07760 *Tel:* 732-872-8002 *Fax:* 732-872-6967 *E-mail:* springtreepress@gmail.com *Web Site:* www.springtreepress.com; www.tyrrc.com, pg 529

Shaak, Teresa, Association of American Editorial Cartoonists, 3899 N Front St, Harrisburg, PA 17110 *Tel:* 717-703-3003 *Fax:* 717-703-3008 *E-mail:* aaec@pa-news.org *Web Site:* www.editorialcartoonists.com, pg 616

Shabelman, Doug, Burns Entertainment & Sports Marketing, 820 Davis St, Suite 222, Evanston, IL 60201 *Tel:* 847-866-9400 *Fax:* 847-491-9778 *E-mail:* burnsl@burnsent.com *Web Site:* burnsent.com, pg 605

Shadek, Ed, Wildlife Education Ltd, 2418 Noyes St, Evanston, IL 60201 *Toll Free Tel:* 800-477-5034 *E-mail:* owls5@zoobooks.com; helpdesk@zoobooks.com *Web Site:* www.zoobooks.com; wildlife-ed.com, pg 281

Shadid, Dina, The North-South Institute/Institut Nord-Sud, 55 Murray St, Suite 500, Ottawa, ON K1N 5M3, Canada *Tel:* 613-241-3535 *Fax:* 613-241-7435 *E-mail:* nsi@nsi-ins.ca *Web Site:* www.nsi-ins.ca, pg 514

Shafeyeva, Yelena, Begell House Inc Publishers, 50 Cross Hwy, Redding, CT 06896 *Tel:* 203-938-1300 *Fax:* 203-938-1304 *E-mail:* orders@begellhouse.com *Web Site:* www.begellhouse.com, pg 34

Shaffer, Bryan, Purdue University Press, Stewart Ctr 370, 504 W State St, West Lafayette, IN 47907-2058 *Tel:* 765-494-2038 *Fax:* 765-496-2442 *E-mail:* pupress@purdue.edu *Web Site:* www.thepress.purdue.edu, pg 209

Shaffer, Mike, New Readers Press, 1320 Jamesville Ave, Syracuse, NY 13210 *Tel:* 315-422-9121 *Toll Free Tel:* 800-448-8878 *Fax:* 315-422-6369 *Toll Free Fax:* 866-894-2100 *E-mail:* nrp@proliteracy.org *Web Site:* www.newreaderspress.com, pg 178

Shaine, Ilene, Foster City International Writer's Contest, 650 Shell Blvd, Foster City, CA 94404 *Tel:* 650-286-3386 *E-mail:* fostercity_writers@yahoo.com *Web Site:* www.fostercity.org, pg 705

Shakely, Lauren, Crown Publishing Group, c/o Random House Inc, 1745 Broadway, New York, NY 10019 *Tel:* 212-782-9000 *Toll Free Tel:* 888-264-1745 *Fax:* 212-940-7408 *Web Site:* www.randomhouse.com/crown, pg 72

Shaker, Anthony F PhD, AFS Wordstead, 1062 Vallee-a-Josaphat, Lac-des-Iles, QC J0W 1J0, Canada *Tel:* 819-597-4072 *Fax:* 819-597-4547 *Web Site:* www.wordstead.com, pg 539

Shakeshaft, Dominic, Apress Media LLC, 233 Spring St, New York, NY 10013 *Tel:* 212-460-1500 *Fax:* 212-460-1575 *E-mail:* editorial@apress.com *Web Site:* www.apress.com, pg 21

Shakhashiri, Bassam Z, The American Chemical Society, 1155 16 St NW, Washington, DC 20036 *Tel:* 202-872-4600 *Fax:* 202-872-6067 *E-mail:* help@acs.org *Web Site:* www.acs.org, pg 12

Shallcross, Andrea, Hachette Book Group, 237 Park Ave, New York, NY 10017 *Tel:* 212-364-1100 *Toll Free Tel:* 800-759-0190 (cust serv) *Fax:* 212-364-0933 (intl orders) *Toll Free Fax:* 800-286-9471 (cust serv) *Web Site:* www.HachetteBookGroup.com, pg 110

Shaloo, Sharon, Massachusetts Book Awards, Simons College - GSLIS, 300 The Fenway, Boston, MA 02115 *Tel:* 617-521-2719 *Fax:* 617-521-3035 *E-mail:* bookawards@massbook.org *Web Site:* www.massbook.org, pg 721

Shamroe, Amy, Axiom Business Book Awards, 1129 Woodmere Ave, Suite B, Traverse City, MI 49686 *Tel:* 231-933-0445 *Toll Free Tel:* 800-706-4636 *Fax:* 231-933-0448 *E-mail:* info@axiomawards.com *Web Site:* www.axiomawards.com, pg 689

Shamroe, Amy, The Independent Publisher Book Awards, 1129 Woodmere Ave, Suite B, Traverse City, MI 49686 *Tel:* 231-933-0445 *Toll Free Tel:* 800-706-4636 *Fax:* 231-933-0448 *Web Site:* www.independentpublisher.com/ipaward.lasso, pg 711

Shamroe, Amy, Moonbeam Children's Book Awards, 1129 Woodmere Ave, Suite B, Traverse City, MI 49686 *Tel:* 231-933-0445 *Toll Free Tel:* 800-706-4636 *Fax:* 231-933-0448 *E-mail:* info@axiomawards.com *Web Site:* www.moonbeamawards.com, pg 724

Shandler, Geoff, Little, Brown and Company, 237 Park Ave, New York, NY 10017 *Tel:* 212-364-1100 *Fax:* 212-364-0952 *E-mail:* firstname.lastname@hbgusa.com *Web Site:* www.HachetteBookGroup.com, pg 150

Shandler, Sara, Alloy Entertainment, 151 W 26 St, 11th fl, New York, NY 10001 *Tel:* 212-244-4307 *E-mail:* nycassistant@alloyentertainment.com *Web Site:* www.alloyentertainment.com, pg 9

Shangle, Barbara, American Products Publishing Co, 8260 SW Nimbus Ave, Beaverton, OR 97008 *Tel:* 503-672-7502 *Toll Free Tel:* 800-668-8181 *Fax:* 503-672-7104 *E-mail:* info@american-products.com *Web Site:* www.american-products.com, pg 15

Shangle, Robert, American Products Publishing Co, 8260 SW Nimbus Ave, Beaverton, OR 97008 *Tel:* 503-672-7502 *Toll Free Tel:* 800-668-8181 *Fax:* 503-672-7104 *E-mail:* info@american-products.com *Web Site:* www.american-products.com, pg 15

Shank, Merna B, Christian Light Publications Inc, 1050 Mount Clinton Pike, Harrisonburg, VA 22802 *Tel:* 540-434-1003 *Toll Free Tel:* 800-776-0478 *Fax:* 540-433-8896 *E-mail:* info@clp.org; orders@clp.org *Web Site:* www.clp.org, pg 61

Shanks, Tessa, PublicAffairs, 250 W 57 St, Suite 1321, New York, NY 10107 *Tel:* 212-397-6666 *Toll Free Tel:* 800-343-4499 (orders) *Fax:* 212-397-4277 *E-mail:* publicaffairs@perseusbooks.com *Web Site:* www.publicaffairsbooks.com, pg 209

Shannon, Katya, Penguin Group (USA) LLC Sales, 375 Hudson St, New York, NY 10014 *Tel:* 212-366-2000 *E-mail:* online@penguinputnam.com *Web Site:* us.penguingroup.com, pg 197

Shannon, Lizzy, Kay Snow Literary Contest, 2108 Buck St, West Linn, OR 97068 *Tel:* 503-305-6729 *Fax:* 503-344-6174 *E-mail:* wilwrite@willamettewriters.com *Web Site:* www.willamettewriters.com, pg 743

Shannon, Scott, Random House Inc, 1745 Broadway, New York, NY 10019 *Tel:* 212-782-9000 *Toll Free Tel:* 800-726-0600 *Web Site:* www.randomhouse.com, pg 213

Shannon, Scott, Random House Publishing Group, 1745 Broadway, New York, NY 10019 *Toll Free Tel:* 800-200-3552 *Web Site:* atrandom.com, pg 214

Shannon, Tom, Oxford University Press USA, 198 Madison Ave, New York, NY 10016 *Tel:* 212-726-6000 *Toll Free Tel:* 800-451-7556 (orders); 800-445-9714 (cust serv) *Fax:* 919-677-1303 *E-mail:* custserv.us@oup.com *Web Site:* www.oup.com/us, pg 189

Shantz, Kathy, Herald Press, 490 Dutton Dr, Unit C-8, Waterloo, ON N2L 6H7, Canada *Tel:* 519-747-5722 *Toll Free Tel:* 800-631-6535 *Fax:* 519-747-5721 *E-mail:* hpcan@mpn.net *Web Site:* www.heraldpress.com, pg 508

Shapiro, Amy, ALI-ABA Continuing Professional Education, 4025 Chestnut St, Philadelphia, PA 19104 *Tel:* 215-243-1600 *Toll Free Tel:* 800-CLE-NEWS (253-6397) *Fax:* 215-243-1664; 215-243-1683 *Web Site:* www.ali-aba.org, pg 8

Shapiro, Amy, American Law Institute, 4025 Chestnut St, Philadelphia, PA 19104-3099 *Tel:* 215-243-1600 *Toll Free Tel:* 800-253-6397 *Fax:* 215-243-1664; 215-243-1683 *Web Site:* www.ali.org, pg 14

Shapiro, Anita C, Practising Law Institute, 810 Seventh Ave, New York, NY 10019 *Tel:* 212-824-5700 *Toll Free Tel:* 800-260-4PLI (260-4754 cust serv)

*Fax:* 212-265-4742 (intl) *Toll Free Fax:* 800-321-0093 (local) *E-mail:* info@pli.edu *Web Site:* www.pli.edu, pg 205

Shapiro, Melvin, Book Sales Inc, 276 Fifth Ave, Suite 206, New York, NY 10001 *Tel:* 212-779-4972 *Toll Free Tel:* 866-483-5456 *Fax:* 212-779-6058 *E-mail:* sales@booksalesusa.com; customerservice@booksalesusa.com *Web Site:* www.booksalesusa.com, pg 43

Shapiro, Norman, Judaica Press Inc, 123 Ditmas Ave, Brooklyn, NY 11218 *Tel:* 718-972-6200 *Toll Free Tel:* 800-972-6201 *Fax:* 718-972-6204 *E-mail:* info@judaicapress.com; orders@judaicapress.com *Web Site:* www.judaicapress.com, pg 137

Shapiro, Norman, Soncino Press Ltd, 123 Ditmas Ave, Brooklyn, NY 11218 *Tel:* 718-972-6200 *Toll Free Tel:* 800-972-6201 *Fax:* 718-972-6204 *E-mail:* info@soncino.com *Web Site:* www.soncino.com, pg 239

Shapiro, Shelly, Random House Publishing Group, 1745 Broadway, New York, NY 10019 *Toll Free Tel:* 800-200-3552 *Web Site:* atrandom.com, pg 214

Shapland, Juliette, HarperCollins Publishers, 10 E 53 St, New York, NY 10022 *Tel:* 212-207-7000 *Fax:* 212-207-7145 *Web Site:* www.harpercollins.com, pg 113

Shareck, Michael, Macmillan, 175 Fifth Ave, New York, NY 10010 *Tel:* 646-307-5151 *Fax:* 212-420-9314 *E-mail:* firstname.lastname@macmillan.com *Web Site:* www.macmillan.com, pg 154

Sharma, Deven, McGraw-Hill Financial, 1221 Avenue of the Americas, 50th fl, New York, NY 10020 *Tel:* 212-512-2000 *Web Site:* www.mhfi.com, pg 161

Sharp, Robert V, The Art Institute of Chicago, 111 S Michigan Ave, Chicago, IL 60603-6404 *Tel:* 312-443-3600; 312-443-3540 (pubns) *Fax:* 312-443-1334 (pubns) *Web Site:* www.artic.edu; www.artinstituteshop.org, pg 22

Sharpe, Errol, Fernwood Publishing, 32 Oceanvista Lane, Black Point, NS B0J 1B0, Canada *Tel:* 902-857-1388 *Fax:* 902-857-1328 *E-mail:* info@fernpub.ca *Web Site:* www.fernwoodpublishing.ca, pg 504

Sharpe, Jack, Bethlehem Books, 10194 Garfield St S, Bathgate, ND 58216 *Toll Free Tel:* 800-757-6831 *Fax:* 701-265-3716 *E-mail:* contact@bethlehembooks.com *Web Site:* www.bethlehembooks.com, pg 36

Sharpe, Myron E, M E Sharpe Inc, 80 Business Park Dr, Suite 202, Armonk, NY 10504 *Tel:* 914-273-1800 *Toll Free Tel:* 800-541-6563 *Fax:* 914-273-2106 *E-mail:* info@mesharpe.com *Web Site:* www.mesharpe.com, pg 232

Sharrar, Kim, McCutchan Publishing Corp, 3220 Blume Dr, Suite 197, Richmond, CA 94806 *Tel:* 510-758-5510 *Toll Free Tel:* 800-227-1540 *Fax:* 510-758-6078 *E-mail:* mccutchanpublish@sbcglobal.net *Web Site:* www.mccutchanpublishing.com, pg 160

Sharrard, Robert, City Lights Publishers, 261 Columbus Ave, San Francisco, CA 94133 *Tel:* 415-362-8193 *Fax:* 415-362-4921 *E-mail:* staff@citylights.com *Web Site:* www.citylights.com, pg 62

Shaub, Ms Bobbett, Medical Physics Publishing Corp (MPP), 4513 Vernon Blvd, Madison, WI 53705-4964 *Tel:* 608-262-4021 *Toll Free Tel:* 800-442-5778 (cust serv) *Fax:* 608-265-2121 *E-mail:* mpp@medicalphysics.org *Web Site:* www.medicalphysics.org, pg 163

Shaughnessy, Sandy, Florida Individual Artist Fellowships, 500 S Bronough St, Tallahassee, FL 32399-0250 *Tel:* 850-245-6470 *Fax:* 850-245-6497 *E-mail:* info@florida-arts.org *Web Site:* www.florida-arts.org, pg 704

Shaw, Bruce P, The Harvard Common Press, 535 Albany St, Boston, MA 02118 *Tel:* 617-423-5803 *Toll Free Tel:* 888-657-3755 *Fax:* 617-695-9794 *E-mail:* orders@harvardcommonpress.com; info@harvardcommonpress.com *Web Site:* www.harvardcommonpress.com, pg 114

Shaw, Connie, Sentient Publications LLC, 1113 Spruce St, Boulder, CO 80302 *Tel:* 303-443-2188 *Fax:* 303-381-2538 *E-mail:* contact@sentientpublications.com *Web Site:* www.sentientpublications.com, pg 231

Shaw, Darren, Evangel Publishing House, 2000 Evangel Way, Nappanee, IN 46550 *Tel:* 574-773-3164 *Toll Free Tel:* 800-253-9315 (orders) *Fax:* 574-773-5934 *E-mail:* sales@evangelpublishing.com *Web Site:* www.evangelpublishing.com; www.evangelpress.com, pg 90

Shaw, Jeanette, Prentice Hall Press, 375 Hudson St, New York, NY 10014 *Tel:* 212-366-2000 *Fax:* 212-366-2666, pg 205

Shaw, Joe, Cypress House, 155 Cypress St, Fort Bragg, CA 95437 *Tel:* 707-964-9520 *Toll Free Tel:* 800-773-7782 *Fax:* 707-964-7531 *E-mail:* cypresshouse@cypresshouse.com *Web Site:* www.cypresshouse.com, pg 74, 544

Shaw, Joe, QED Press, 155 Cypress St, Fort Bragg, CA 95437 *Tel:* 707-964-9520 *Toll Free Tel:* 800-773-7782 *Fax:* 707-964-7531 *E-mail:* qedpress@mcn.org *Web Site:* www.cypresshouse.com, pg 211

Shaw, Lisa, Corwin, a Sage Co, 2455 Teller Rd, Thousand Oaks, CA 91320 *Tel:* 805-499-9734 *Toll Free Tel:* 800-233-9936 *Fax:* 805-499-5323 *Toll Free Fax:* 800-417-2466 *E-mail:* info@corwin.com *Web Site:* www.corwin.com, pg 68

Shaw, Liz, Shambhala Publications Inc, Horticultural Hall, 300 Massachusetts Ave, Boston, MA 02115 *Tel:* 617-424-0030 *Toll Free Tel:* 866-424-0030 (off); 888-424-2329 (cust serv) *Fax:* 617-236-1563 *E-mail:* customercare@shambhala.com *Web Site:* www.shambhala.com, pg 232

Shaw, Marjorie, Wildlife Education Ltd, 2418 Noyes St, Evanston, IL 60201 *Toll Free Tel:* 800-477-5034 *E-mail:* owls5@zoobooks.com; helpdesk@zoobooks.com *Web Site:* www.zoobooks.com; wildlife-ed.com, pg 281

Shay, Michael, Neltje Blanchan Memorial Award, 2320 Capitol Ave, Cheyenne, WY 82002 *Tel:* 307-777-5234 *Fax:* 307-777-5499 *Web Site:* wyoarts.state.wy.us, pg 691

Shay, Michael, Frank Nelson Doubleday Memorial Award, 2320 Capitol Ave, Cheyenne, WY 82002 *Tel:* 307-777-5234 *Fax:* 307-777-5499 *Web Site:* wyoarts.state.wy.us, pg 701

Shay, Michael, Wyoming Arts Council Literature Fellowships, 2320 Capitol Ave, Cheyenne, WY 82002 *Tel:* 307-777-5234 *Fax:* 307 777 5499 *Web Site:* wyoarts.state.wy.us, pg 752

Shea, John, R S Means, a Reed Construction Data Co, 700 Longwater Dr, Norwell, MA 02061 *Tel:* 781-422-5000 *Toll Free Tel:* 800-334-3509 *Fax:* 781-585-8814 *Toll Free Fax:* 800-632-6701 *Web Site:* rsmeans.reedconstructiondata.com, pg 163

Shea, Katie, Donald Maass Literary Agency, 121 W 27 St, Suite 801, New York, NY 10001 *Tel:* 212-727-8383 *Fax:* 212-727-3271 *E-mail:* info@maassagency.com; rights@maassagency.com (subs rights inquiries) *Web Site:* www.maassagency.com, pg 582

Shea, Samantha, Georges Borchardt Inc, 136 E 57 St, New York, NY 10022 *Tel:* 212-753-5785 *E-mail:* georges@gbagency.com *Web Site:* www.gbagency.com, pg 563

Shea, Tim, Yale University Press, 302 Temple St, New Haven, CT 06511-8909 *Tel:* 401-531-2800 (cust serv); 203-432-0960 *Toll Free Tel:* 800-405-1619 (cust serv) *Fax:* 203-432-0948; 401-531-2801 (cust serv) *Toll Free Fax:* 800-406-9145 (cust serv) *E-mail:* customer.care@trilateral.org (cust serv); language.yalepress@yale.edu *Web Site:* www.yalebooks.com, pg 287

Shea-Joyce, Tep, Appraisal Institute, 200 W Madison, Suite 1500, Chicago, IL 60606 *Tel:* 312-335-4100 *Toll Free Tel:* 888-756-4624 *Fax:* 312-335-4400 *Web Site:* www.appraisalinstitute.org, pg 21

Shealy, Dennis, Random House Children's Books, 1745 Broadway, New York, NY 10019 *Tel:* 212-782-9000 *Toll Free Tel:* 800-200-3552 *Fax:* 212-782-9452 *Web Site:* randomhousekids.com, pg 213

Sheanin, Wendy, Simon & Schuster Sales & Marketing, 1230 Avenue of the Americas, New York, NY 10020 *Tel:* 212-698-7000, pg 236

Shear, Donna, University of Nebraska Press, 1111 Lincoln Mall, Lincoln, NE 68588-0630 *Tel:* 402-472-3581; 919-966-7449 (cust serv & foreign orders) *Toll Free Tel:* 800-848-6224 (cust serv & US orders) *Fax:* 402-472-6214; 919-962-2704 (cust serv & foreign orders) *Toll Free Fax:* 800-526-2617 (cust serv & US orders) *E-mail:* pressmail@unl.edu *Web Site:* www.nebraskapress.unl.edu, pg 267

Shear, Matthew, Macmillan, 175 Fifth Ave, New York, NY 10010 *Tel:* 646-307-5151 *Fax:* 212-420-9314 *E-mail:* firstname.lastname@macmillan.com *Web Site:* www.macmillan.com, pg 154

Shear, Matthew, St Martin's Press, LLC, 175 Fifth Ave, New York, NY 10010 *Tel:* 646-307-5151 *Fax:* 212-420-9314 *E-mail:* firstname.lastname@macmillan.com *Web Site:* www.stmartins.com, pg 224

Shearer, Deborah, Braille Co Inc, 65-B Town Hall Sq, Falmouth, MA 02540-2754 *Tel:* 508-540-0800 *Fax:* 508-548-6116 *E-mail:* braillinc@capecod.net *Web Site:* home.capecod.net/~braillinc, pg 45

Sheedy, Charlotte, Charlotte Sheedy Literary Agency Inc, 928 Broadway, Suite 901, New York, NY 10010 *Tel:* 212-780-9800 *Fax:* 212-780-0308; 212-780-6095 *E-mail:* sheedy@sll.com *Web Site:* www.sheedylit.com, pg 593

Sheedy, Rachel, Don Buchwald & Associates Inc, 10 E 44 St, New York, NY 10017 *Tel:* 212-867-1200 *Fax:* 212-867-2434 *E-mail:* info@buchwald.com *Web Site:* www.buchwald.com, pg 565

Sheehan, Katie, Berrett-Koehler Publishers Inc, 235 Montgomery St, Suite 650, San Francisco, CA 94104 *Tel:* 415-288-0260 *Fax:* 415-362-2512 *E-mail:* bkpub@bkpub.com *Web Site:* www.bkconnection.com, pg 36

Sheinkopf, Barry, The Writing Center, 601 Palisade Ave, Englewood Cliffs, NJ 07632 *Tel:* 201-567-4017 *Fax:* 201-567-7202 *E-mail:* writingcenter@optonline.net *Web Site:* www.thewritingcenternj.com, pg 675

Shekari, Lauren, Other Press LLC, 2 Park Ave, 24th fl, New York, NY 10016 *Tel:* 212-414-0054 *Toll Free Tel:* 877-843-6843 *Fax:* 212-414-0939 *E-mail:* editor@otherpress.com; rights@otherpress.com *Web Site:* www.otherpress.com, pg 188

Shell, Nicole, Bridge Publications Inc, 5600 E Olympic Blvd, Commerce City, CA 90022 *Tel:* 323-888-6200 *Toll Free Tel:* 800-722-1733 *Fax:* 323-888-6202 *E-mail:* info@bridgepub.com *Web Site:* www.bridgepub.com, pg 47

Shelton, Darryl, Christian Schools International, 3350 E Paris Ave SE, Grand Rapids, MI 49512-3054 *Tel:* 616-957-1070 *Toll Free Tel:* 800-635-8288 *Fax:* 616-957-5022 *E-mail:* info@csionline.org *Web Site:* www.csionline.org, pg 61

Shenk, Steve, Herald Press, 1251 Virginia Ave, Harrisonburg, VA 22802-2434 *Toll Free Tel:* 800-245-7894 (orders-US); 800-999-3534; 800-631-6535 (orders-CN) *Toll Free Fax:* 877-271-0760 *E-mail:* info@MennoMedia.org *Web Site:* www.heraldpress.com; store.mennomedia.org, pg 118

Shepard, Aaron, Shepard Publications, PO Box 280, Friday Harbor, WA 98250 *Web Site:* www.shepardpub.com, pg 233

Shepard, Christopher, The Pimlico Agency Inc, PO Box 20490, New York, NY 10017 *Tel:* 212-628-9729 *Fax:* 212-535-7861, pg 588

Shepard, Diane, Bear & Co Inc, One Park St, Rochester, VT 05767 *Tel:* 802-767-3174 *Toll Free Tel:* 800-932-3277 *Fax:* 802-767-3726 *E-mail:* customerservice@InnerTraditions.com *Web Site:* InnerTraditions.com, pg 33

Shepard, Diane, Inner Traditions International Ltd, One Park St, Rochester, VT 05767 *Tel:* 802-767-3174 *Toll Free Tel:* 800-246-8648 *Fax:* 802-767-3726 *E-mail:* customerservice@InnerTraditions.com *Web Site:* www.InnerTraditions.com, pg 130

Shepard, Jean H, The Shepard Agency, 73 Kingswood Dr, Bethel, CT 06801 *Tel:* 203-790-4230; 203-790-1780 *Fax:* 203-798-2924 *E-mail:* shepardagcy@mindspring.com, pg 594

Shepard, Judith, The Permanent Press, 4170 Noyac Rd, Sag Harbor, NY 11963 *Tel:* 631-725-1101 *Fax:* 631-725-8215 *E-mail:* info@thepermanentpress.com *Web Site:* www.thepermanentpress.com, pg 199

Shepard, Judith, Second Chance Press, 4170 Noyac Rd, Sag Harbor, NY 11963 *Tel:* 631-725-1101 *E-mail:* info@thepermanentpress.com *Web Site:* www.thepermanentpress.com, pg 230

Shepard, Lance Hastings, The Shepard Agency, 73 Kingswood Dr, Bethel, CT 06801 *Tel:* 203-790-4230; 203-790-1780 *Fax:* 203-798-2924 *E-mail:* shepardagcy@mindspring.com, pg 594

Shepard, Martin, The Permanent Press, 4170 Noyac Rd, Sag Harbor, NY 11963 *Tel:* 631-725-1101 *Fax:* 631-725-8215 *E-mail:* info@thepermanentpress.com *Web Site:* www.thepermanentpress.com, pg 199

Shepard, Martin, Second Chance Press, 4170 Noyac Rd, Sag Harbor, NY 11963 *Tel:* 631-725-1101 *E-mail:* info@thepermanentpress.com *Web Site:* www.thepermanentpress.com, pg 230

Shepard, Robert E, The Robert E Shepard Agency, 4804 Laurel Canyon Blvd, Box 592, Valley Village, CA 91607-3717 *E-mail:* mail@shepardagency.com *Web Site:* www.shepardagency.com, pg 594

Sheppard, Christine, Library Association of Alberta (LAA), 80 Baker Crescent NW, Calgary, AB T2L 1R4, Canada *Tel:* 403-284-5818 *Toll Free Tel:* 877-522-5550 *Fax:* 403-282-6646 *E-mail:* info@laa.ca *Web Site:* www.laa.ca, pg 626

Sheppard, Nancy, Viking, 375 Hudson St, New York, NY 10014 *Tel:* 212-366-2000 *E-mail:* online@penguinputnam.com *Web Site:* www.penguinputnam.com; us.penguingroup.com, pg 275

Sherer, John, The University of North Carolina Press, 116 S Boundary St, Chapel Hill, NC 27514-3808 *Tel:* 919-966-3561 *Fax:* 919-966-3829 *E-mail:* uncpress@unc.edu *Web Site:* www.uncpress.unc.edu, pg 267

Sheridan, John, William Allen White Children's Book Awards, William Allen White Library, 1200 Commercial St, Emporia, KS 66801-5092 *Tel:* 620-341-5208 *Toll Free Tel:* 877-613-7323 *Fax:* 620-341-6208 *E-mail:* wawbookaward@emporia.edu *Web Site:* waw.emporia.edu, pg 749

Sherk, Mary Lou, Galen Press Ltd, PO Box 64400, Tucson, AZ 85728-4400 *Tel:* 520-577-8363 *Fax:* 520-529-6459 *E-mail:* sales@galenpress.com *Web Site:* www.galenpress.com, pg 100

Sherman, Brooks, FinePrint Literary Management, 115 W 29 St, 3rd fl, New York, NY 10001 *Tel:* 212-279-1282 *Web Site:* www.fineprintlit.com, pg 571

Sherman, Ken, Ken Sherman & Associates, 1275 N Hayworth, Suite 103, Los Angeles, CA 90046 *Tel:* 310-273-8840 *Fax:* 310-271-2875 *E-mail:* kenshermanassociates@gmail.com *Web Site:* www.kenshermanassociates.com, pg 594

Sherman, Laura, American Institute of Aeronautics & Astronautics, 1801 Alexander Bell Dr, Suite 500, Reston, VA 20191-4344 *Tel:* 703-264-7500 *Toll Free Tel:* 800-639-AIAA (639-2422) *Fax:* 703-264-7551 *E-mail:* custserv@aiaa.org *Web Site:* www.aiaa.org, pg 14

Sherman, Rebecca, Writers House, 21 W 26 St, New York, NY 10010 *Tel:* 212-685-2400 *Fax:* 212-685-1781 *Web Site:* www.writershouse.com, pg 599

Sherman, Stephen, Radix Press, 11715 Bandlon Dr, Houston, TX 77072 *Tel:* 281-879-5688 *Web Site:* www.specialforcesbooks.com, pg 212

Sherman, Susan, Charlesbridge Publishing Inc, 85 Main St, Watertown, MA 02472 *Tel:* 617-926-0329 *Toll Free Tel:* 800-225-3214 *Fax:* 617-926-5720 *Toll Free Fax:* 800-926-5775 *E-mail:* books@charlesbridge.com *Web Site:* www.charlesbridge.com, pg 58

Sherman, Wendy, Wendy Sherman Associates Inc, 27 W 24 St, Suite 700-B, New York, NY 10010 *Tel:* 212-279-9027 *Fax:* 212-279-9027 *Web Site:* www.wsherman.com, pg 594

Shern, David L PhD, Mental Health America (MHA), 2000 N Beauregard St, 6th fl, Alexandria, VA 22311 *Tel:* 703-684-7722 *Toll Free Tel:* 800-969-6642 *Fax:* 703-684-5968 *Web Site:* mentalhealthamerica.net, pg 627

Sherr, Roger, Genealogical Publishing Co, 3600 Clipper Mill Rd, Suite 260, Baltimore, MD 21211 *Tel:* 410-837-8271 *Toll Free Tel:* 800-296-6687 *Fax:* 410-752-8492 *Web Site:* www.genealogical.com, pg 102

Sherrod, Tracy, HarperCollins General Books Group, 10 E 53 St, New York, NY 10022 *Tel:* 212-207-7000 *Fax:* 212-207-7633 *Web Site:* www.harpercollins.com, pg 113

Sherry, Cassandra, National Association of Hispanic Publications Inc (NAHP), 529 14 St NW, Suite 1126, Washington, DC 20045 *Tel:* 202-662-7250 *Fax:* 202-662-7251 *Web Site:* www.nahp.org, pg 628

Sherry, Cynthia, Chicago Review Press, 814 N Franklin St, Chicago, IL 60610 *Tel:* 312-337-0747 *Toll Free Tel:* 800-888-4741 *Fax:* 312-337-5110 *E-mail:* frontdesk@chicagoreviewpress.com *Web Site:* www.chicagoreviewpress.com, pg 60

Sherry, Sophia, Other Press LLC, 2 Park Ave, 24th fl, New York, NY 10016 *Tel:* 212-414-0054 *Toll Free Tel:* 877-843-6843 *Fax:* 212-414-0939 *E-mail:* editor@otherpress.com; rights@otherpress.com *Web Site:* www.otherpress.com, pg 188

Shevlin, Eleanor F, Society for the History of Authorship, Reading & Publishing Inc (SHARP), c/o The Johns Hopkins University Press, Journals Publishing Div, PO Box 19966, Baltimore, MD 21211-0966 *Tel:* 910-254-0308 *E-mail:* members@sharpweb.org *Web Site:* www.sharpweb.org, pg 636

Shiel, Lisa, Slipdown Mountain Publications LLC, 28151 Quarry Lake Rd, Lake Linden, MI 49945 *Tel:* 906-523-4118 *Toll Free Tel:* 866-341-3705 *Toll Free Fax:* 866-341-3705 *E-mail:* books@jacobsvillebooks.com *Web Site:* www.jacobsvillebooks.com, pg 237

Shiel, Walt, Slipdown Mountain Publications LLC, 28151 Quarry Lake Rd, Lake Linden, MI 49945 *Tel:* 906-523-4118 *Toll Free Tel:* 866-341-3705 *Toll Free Fax:* 866-341-3705 *E-mail:* books@jacobsvillebooks.com *Web Site:* www.jacobsvillebooks.com, pg 237

Shields, Colin, Simon & Schuster Sales & Marketing, 1230 Avenue of the Americas, New York, NY 10020 *Tel:* 212-698-7000, pg 236

Shields, Duncan, Doubleday Canada, One Toronto St, Suite 300, Toronto, ON M5C 2V6, Canada *Tel:* 416-364-4449 *Fax:* 416-364-6863 *Web Site:* www.randomhouse.ca, pg 501

Shields, Duncan, Knopf Random Canada, One Toronto St, Suite 300, Toronto, ON M5C 2V6, Canada *Tel:* 416-364-4449 *Toll Free Tel:* 888-523-9292 *Fax:* 416-364-6863 *Web Site:* www.randomhouse.ca, pg 510

Shields, Duncan, Random House of Canada Limited, One Toronto St, Suite 300, Toronto, ON M5C 2V6, Canada *Tel:* 416-364-4449 *Toll Free Tel:* 888-523-9292 (cust serv) *Fax:* 416-364-6863; 416-364-6653 (subs rts) *Web Site:* www.randomhouse.ca, pg 517

Shields, Duncan, Seal Books, One Toronto St, Suite 300, Toronto, ON M5C 2V6, Canada *Tel:* 416-364-4449 *Toll Free Tel:* 888-523-9292 (order desk) *Fax:* 416-364-6863 *Web Site:* www.randomhouse.ca, pg 518

Shillingford, Gordon, J Gordon Shillingford Publishing Inc, PO Box 86, RPO Corydon Ave, Winnipeg, MB R3M 3S3, Canada *Tel:* 204-779-6967 *Fax:* 204-779-6970 *Web Site:* www.jgshillingford.com, pg 519

Shimkus, Tony, Concordia Publishing House, 3558 S Jefferson Ave, St Louis, MO 63118-3968 *Tel:* 314-268-1000 *Toll Free Tel:* 800-325-3040 (cust serv) *Toll Free Fax:* 800-490-9889 (cust serv) *E-mail:* order@cph.org *Web Site:* www.cph.org, pg 66

Shin, Ann, W W Norton & Company Inc, 500 Fifth Ave, New York, NY 10110-0017 *Tel:* 212-354-5500 *Toll Free Tel:* 800-233-4830 (orders & cust serv) *Fax:* 212-869-0856 *Toll Free Fax:* 800-458-6515 *Web Site:* www.wwnorton.com, pg 182

Shin, Jinna, Random House Children's Books, 1745 Broadway, New York, NY 10019 *Tel:* 212-782-9000 *Toll Free Tel:* 800-200-3552 *Fax:* 212-782-9452 *Web Site:* randomhousekids.com, pg 213

Shine, Deborah, Star Bright Books Inc, 13 Landsdowne St, Cambridge, MA 02139 *Tel:* 617-354-1300 *Fax:* 617-354-1399 *E-mail:* info@starbrightbooks.com; orders@starbrightbooks.com *Web Site:* www.starbrightbooks.com, pg 243

Shinker, William, Avery, 375 Hudson St, New York, NY 10014 *Tel:* 212-366-2000 *Fax:* 212-366-2643 *E-mail:* online@penguinputnam.com *Web Site:* www.penguinputnam.com; us.penguingroup.com, pg 28

Shinker, William, Gotham Books, 375 Hudson St, New York, NY 10014, pg 105

Shinker, William, Penguin Group (USA) LLC, 375 Hudson St, New York, NY 10014 *Tel:* 212-366-2000 *Toll Free Tel:* 800-847-5515 (inside sales); 800-631-8571 (cust serv) *Fax:* 212-366-2666; 607-775-4829 (inside sales) *E-mail:* online@us.penguingroup.com *Web Site:* www.penguin.com; us.penguingroup.com, pg 197

Shipman, Leslie, National Book Awards, 90 Broad St, Suite 604, New York, NY 10004 *Tel:* 212-685-0261 *Fax:* 212-213-6570 *E-mail:* nationalbook@nationalbook.org *Web Site:* www.nationalbook.org, pg 726

Shippy, Karen, Wm B Eerdmans Publishing Co, 2140 Oak Industrial Dr NE, Grand Rapids, MI 49505 *Tel:* 616-459-4591 *Toll Free Tel:* 800-253-7521 *Fax:* 616-459-6540 *E-mail:* customerservice@eerdmans.com; sales@eerdmans.com *Web Site:* www.eerdmans.com, pg 86

Shirzad, Mr Farhad, Ibex Publishers, PO Box 30087, Bethesda, MD 20824 *Tel:* 301-718-8188 *Toll Free Tel:* 888-718-8188 *Fax:* 301-907-8707 *E-mail:* info@ibexpub.com *Web Site:* www.ibexpublishers.com, pg 126

Shivers, Lottchen, Farrar, Straus & Giroux, LLC, 18 W 18 St, New York, NY 10011 *Tel:* 212-741-6900 *Fax:* 212-633-9385 *E-mail:* fsg.publicity@fsgbooks.com *Web Site:* us.macmillan.com/fsg.aspx, pg 93

Shnookal, Deborah, Ocean Press, 511 Avenue of the Americas, Suite 96, New York, NY 10011-8436 *Tel:* 212-260-3690 *E-mail:* info@oceanbooks.com.au; orders@oceanbooks.com.au (orders only) *Web Site:* www.oceanbooks.com.au, pg 183

Shoemaker, Jack, Counterpoint Press LLC, 1919 Fifth St, Berkeley, CA 94710 *Tel:* 510-704-0230 *Fax:* 510-704-0268 *E-mail:* info@counterpointpress.com *Web Site:* www.counterpointpress.com; www.sierraclub.org/books; www.softskull.com, pg 69

Shokoff, Elisa, Simon & Schuster Audio, 1230 Avenue of the Americas, New York, NY 10020 *Web Site:* audio.simonandschuster.com, pg 234

Shor, Deborah, Oxford University Press USA, 198 Madison Ave, New York, NY 10016 *Tel:* 212-726-6000 *Toll Free Tel:* 800-451-7556 (orders); 800-445-9714 (cust serv) *Fax:* 919-677-1303 *E-mail:* custserv.us@oup.com *Web Site:* www.oup.com/us, pg 189

Shorney, John, Hope Publishing Co, 380 S Main Place, Carol Stream, IL 60188 *Tel:* 630-665-3200 *Toll Free Tel:* 800-323-1049 *Fax:* 630-665-2552 *E-mail:* hope@hopepublishing.com *Web Site:* www.hopepublishing.com, pg 123

Shorney, Scott, Hope Publishing Co, 380 S Main Place, Carol Stream, IL 60188 *Tel:* 630-665-3200 *Toll Free Tel:* 800-323-1049 *Fax:* 630-665-2552 *E-mail:* hope@hopepublishing.com *Web Site:* www.hopepublishing.com, pg 123

Shorney, Steve, Hope Publishing Co, 380 S Main Place, Carol Stream, IL 60188 *Tel:* 630-665-3200 *Toll Free Tel:* 800-323-1049 *Fax:* 630-665-2552 *E-mail:* hope@hopepublishing.com *Web Site:* www.hopepublishing.com, pg 123

Silverstein, Clara, Chautauqua Writers' Workshop, PO Box 28, Chautauqua, NY 14722-0408 *Tel:* 716-357-6316; 716-357-6250 *Toll Free Tel:* 800-836-ARTS (836-2787) *Fax:* 716-269-7444 *Web Site:* writers.ciweb.org, pg 668

Silvestro, Denise, Berkley Books, 375 Hudson St, New York, NY 10014 *Tel:* 212-366-2000 *Fax:* 212-366-2666 *E-mail:* online@penguinputnam.com *Web Site:* www.penguinputnam.com; us.penguingroup.com, pg 36

Silvestro, Denise, Berkley Publishing Group, 375 Hudson St, New York, NY 10014 *Tel:* 212-366-2000 *Fax:* 212-366-2385 *E-mail:* online@penguinputnam.com *Web Site:* us.penguingroup.com, pg 36

Simard, Luc, Canadian Cataloguing in Publication Program, Library & Archives Canada, 395 Wellington St, Ottawa, ON K1A 0N4, Canada *Tel:* 613-996-5115 *Toll Free Tel:* 866-578-7777 (CN) *Fax:* 613-995-6274 *E-mail:* cip@lac-bac.gc.ca *Web Site:* www.collectionscanada.ca, pg 619

Simard, Luc, Canadian ISBN Agency, National Library of Canada, 395 Wellington St, Ottawa, ON K1A 0N4, Canada *Tel:* 613-996-5115 *Toll Free Tel:* 866-578-7777 *Fax:* 613-995-6274 *E-mail:* isbn@lac-bac.gc.ca *Web Site:* www.collectionscanada.ca, pg 620

Simmons, Ann, McLemore Prize, PO Box 571, Jackson, MS 39205-0571 *Tel:* 601-576-6850 *Fax:* 601-576-6975 *E-mail:* mhs@mdah.state.ms.us *Web Site:* www.mdah.state.ms.us, pg 723

Simmons, Ann, Pie in the Sky Publishing LLC, 8031 E Phillips Circle, Centennial, CO 80112 *Tel:* 303-773-0851 *Fax:* 303-773-0851 *E-mail:* pieintheskypublishing@msn.com *Web Site:* www.pieintheskypublishing.com, pg 201

Simmons, Carolyn, Getty Publications, 1200 Getty Center Dr, Suite 500, Los Angeles, CA 90049-1682 *Tel:* 310-440-7365 *Toll Free Tel:* 800-223-3431 (orders) *Fax:* 310-440-7758 *E-mail:* pubsinfo@getty.edu *Web Site:* www.getty.edu/publications, pg 103

Simmons, Karen, Harmonie Park Press, Liberty Professional Ctr, 35675 Mound Rd, Sterling Heights, MI 48310-4727 *Tel:* 586-979-2077; 586-979-1844 (cust serv) *Toll Free Tel:* 800-422-4880 *Fax:* 586-979-1786; 586-979-1863 (cust serv) *E-mail:* info@harmonieparkpress.com *Web Site:* harmonieparkpress.com, pg 113

Simmons, Zoe, PAGE International Screenwriting Awards, 7510 Sunset Blvd, Suite 610, Hollywood, CA 90046 *E-mail:* info@pageawards.com *Web Site:* www.pageawards.com, pg 732

Simms, Maria K, Starcrafts LLC, 334-A Calef Hwy, Epping, NH 03042 *Tel:* 603-734-4300 *Toll Free Tel:* 866-953-8458 (24 hr message ctr) *Fax:* 603-734-4311 *E-mail:* astrosales@astrocom.com; starcrafts@comcast.net *Web Site:* www.astrocom.com; starcraftspublishing.com; acspublications.com, pg 243

Simms, Michael, Autumn House Press, 87 1/2 Westwood St, Pittsburgh, PA 15211 *Tel:* 412-381-4261 *Web Site:* www.autumnhouse.org, pg 27

Simms, Michael, Coal Hill Review Poetry Chapbook Contest, c/o Autumn House Press, PO Box 60100, Pittsburgh, PA 15211 *E-mail:* reviewcoalhill@gmail.com *Web Site:* www.coalhillreview.com, pg 697

Simon, Daniel, Neustadt International Prize for Literature, University of Oklahoma, Suite 110, 630 Parrington Oval, Norman, OK 73019-4033 *Tel:* 405-325-4531 *Fax:* 405-325-7495 *Web Site:* www.worldliteraturetoday.org, pg 728

Simon, Daniel, NSK Neustadt Prize for Children's Literature, University of Oklahoma, Suite 110, 630 Parrington Oval, Norman, OK 73019-4033 *Tel:* 405-325-4531 *Fax:* 405-325-7495 *Web Site:* www.worldliteraturetoday.org, pg 729

Simon, Daniel, Seven Stories Press, 140 Watts St, New York, NY 10013 *Tel:* 212-226-8760 *Fax:* 212-226-1411 *E-mail:* info@sevenstories.com *Web Site:* www.sevenstories.com, pg 232

Simon, Elizabeth, Council on Social Work Education (CSWE), 1701 Duke St, Suite 200, Alexandria, VA 22314-3457 *Tel:* 703-683-8080 *Fax:* 703-683-8493 *E-mail:* publications@cswe.org; info@cswe.org *Web Site:* www.cswe.org, pg 69

Simon, Peter J, W W Norton & Company Inc, 500 Fifth Ave, New York, NY 10110-0017 *Tel:* 212-354-5500 *Toll Free Tel:* 800-233-4830 (orders & cust serv) *Fax:* 212-869-0856 *Toll Free Fax:* 800-458-6515 *Web Site:* www.wwnorton.com, pg 182

Simon, Rebecca, University of California Press, 2120 Berkeley Way, Berkeley, CA 94704-1012 *Tel:* 510-642-4247 *Fax:* 510-643-7127 *E-mail:* askucp@ucpress.edu (books); customerservice@ucpressjournals.com (journals) *Web Site:* www.ucpress.edu, pg 264

Simon, Robin, Berkley Books, 375 Hudson St, New York, NY 10014 *Tel:* 212-366-2000 *Fax:* 212-366-2666 *E-mail:* online@penguinputnam.com *Web Site:* www.penguinputnam.com; us.penguingroup.com, pg 36

Simon, Robin, Berkley Publishing Group, 375 Hudson St, New York, NY 10014 *Tel:* 212-366-2000 *Fax:* 212-366-2385 *E-mail:* online@penguinputnam.com *Web Site:* us.penguingroup.com, pg 36

Simon, Tami, Sounds True Inc, 413 S Arthur Ave, Louisville, CO 80027 *Tel:* 303-665-3151 *Toll Free Tel:* 800-333-9185 *E-mail:* customerservice@soundstrue.com *Web Site:* www.soundstrue.com, pg 240

Simonello, Loraine, Morehouse Publishing, 4775 Linglestown Rd, Harrisburg, PA 17112 *Tel:* 717-541-8130 *Toll Free Tel:* 800-877-0012 (orders only); 800-242-1918 (cust serv) *Fax:* 717-541-8136; 717-541-8128 (orders only) *Web Site:* www.morehousepublishing.com, pg 169

Simonoff, Eric, WME, 1325 Avenue of the Americas, New York, NY 10019 *Tel:* 212-586-5100 *Fax:* 212-246-3583 *E-mail:* wma@interport.net *Web Site:* www.wma.com, pg 599

Simons, D Brenton, Newbury Street Press, 101 Newbury St, Boston, MA 02116 *Tel:* 617-536-5740 *Toll Free Tel:* 888-296-3447 (NEHGS membership) *Fax:* 617-536-7307 *E-mail:* sales@nehgs.org *Web Site:* www.newenglandancestors.org, pg 179

Simpson, Amy, University of Alaska Press, 794 University Ave, Suite 220, Fairbanks, AK 99709 *Tel:* 907-474-5831 *Toll Free Tel:* 888-252-6657 (US only) *Fax:* 907-474-5502 *E-mail:* fypress@uaf.edu *Web Site:* www.uaf.edu/uapress, pg 264

Simpson, Fiona, Simon & Schuster Children's Publishing, 1230 Avenue of the Americas, New York, NY 10020 *Tel:* 212-698-7000 *Web Site:* KIDS.SimonandSchuster.com; TEEN.SimonandSchuster.com; simonandschuster.net; simonandschuster.biz, pg 235

Simpson, Michael, Carter G Woodson Book Awards, 8555 16 St, Suite 500, Silver Spring, MD 20910 *Tel:* 301-588-1800 *Toll Free Tel:* 800-296-7840; 800-683-0812 (pubn orders) *Fax:* 301-588-2049 *E-mail:* excellence@ncss.org; publications@ncss.org *Web Site:* www.socialstudies.org, pg 751

Simpson, Shayla, Western Heritage Awards (Wrangler Award), 1700 NE 63 St, Oklahoma City, OK 73111 *Tel:* 405-478-2250 *Fax:* 405-478-4714 *E-mail:* info@nationalcowboymuseum.org *Web Site:* www.nationalcowboymuseum.org, pg 748

Simpson-Vos, Mark, The University of North Carolina Press, 116 S Boundary St, Chapel Hill, NC 27514-3808 *Tel:* 919-966-3561 *Fax:* 919-966-3829 *E-mail:* uncpress@unc.edu *Web Site:* www.uncpress.unc.edu, pg 267

Simqu, Blaise, Pine Forge Press, 2455 Teller Rd, Thousand Oaks, CA 91320 *Tel:* 805-499-4224; 805-499-9774 (orders) *Fax:* 805-499-0871 (orders) *E-mail:* info@sagepub.com *Web Site:* www.sagepub.com; www.pineforge.com, pg 202

Simqu, Blaise R, SAGE Publications, 2455 Teller Rd, Thousand Oaks, CA 91320 *Toll Free Tel:* 800-818-7243 *Toll Free Fax:* 800-583-2665 *E-mail:* info@sagepub.com *Web Site:* www.sagepub.com, pg 223

Sims, Michael, The MIT Press, 55 Hayward St, Cambridge, MA 02142 *Tel:* 617-253-5255 *Toll Free Tel:* 800-207-8354 (orders) *Fax:* 617-258-6779; 617-577-1545 (orders) *Web Site:* mitpress.mit.edu, pg 167

Sims, Peter, Yale University Press, 302 Temple St, New Haven, CT 06511-8909 *Tel:* 401-531-2800 (cust serv); 203-432-0960 *Toll Free Tel:* 800-405-1619 (cust serv) *Fax:* 203-432-0948; 401-531-2801 (cust serv) *Toll Free Fax:* 800-406-9145 (cust serv) *E-mail:* customer.care@trilateral.org (cust serv); language.yalepress@yale.edu *Web Site:* www.yalebooks.com, pg 287

Sinasac, Joseph, Novalis Publishing, 10 Lower Spadina Ave, Suite 400, Toronto, ON M5V 2Z2, Canada *Tel:* 416-363-3303 *Toll Free Tel:* 877-702-7773 *Fax:* 416-363-9409 *Toll Free Fax:* 877-702-7775 *E-mail:* books@novalis.ca *Web Site:* www.novalis.ca, pg 514

Sinauer, Andrew D, Sinauer Associates Inc, 23 Plumtree Rd, Sunderland, MA 01375 *Tel:* 413-549-4300 *Fax:* 413-549-1118 *E-mail:* publish@sinauer.com; orders@sinauer.com *Web Site:* www.sinauer.com, pg 236

Sinclair, Vivian, Heritage House Publishing Co Ltd, 1105 Pandora Ave, Victoria, BC V8V 3P9, Canada *Tel:* 604-574-7067 *Toll Free Tel:* 800-665-3302 *Fax:* 604-574-9942 *Toll Free Fax:* 800-566-3336 *E-mail:* heritage@heritagehouse.ca; orders@heritagehouse.ca *Web Site:* www.heritagehouse.ca, pg 509

Sindler, Jessica, Random House Publishing Group, 1745 Broadway, New York, NY 10019 *Toll Free Tel:* 800-200-3552 *Web Site:* atrandom.com, pg 214

Singerman, Jerome E, University of Pennsylvania Press, 3905 Spruce St, Philadelphia, PA 19104 *Tel:* 215-898-6261 *Fax:* 215-898-0404 *E-mail:* custserv@pobox.upenn.edu *Web Site:* www.pennpress.org, pg 268

Singleton, Brett, Concordia Publishing House, 3558 S Jefferson Ave, St Louis, MO 63118-3968 *Tel:* 314-268-1000 *Toll Free Tel:* 800-325-3040 (cust serv) *Toll Free Fax:* 800-490-9889 (cust serv) *E-mail:* order@cph.org *Web Site:* www.cph.org, pg 66

Sinnett, Gina, Humanix Books LLC, PO Box 20989, West Palm Beach, FL 33416 *Tel:* 561-459-5997 *Toll Free Tel:* 855-371-7810 *Fax:* 561-241-6448 *Toll Free Fax:* 855-371-7809 *E-mail:* info@humanixbooks.com *Web Site:* www.humanixbooks.com, pg 125

Sinocchi, Michael, Productivity Press, c/o Routledge, 711 Third Ave, New York, NY 10017 *Tel:* 212-216-7800 *Toll Free Tel:* 800-634-7064 (orders) *Fax:* 212-563-2269 *Toll Free Fax:* 800-248-4724 (orders) *E-mail:* info@productivitypress.com; orders@taylorandfrancis.com *Web Site:* www.productivitypress.com, pg 207

Sinsheimer, Jessica, Sarah Jane Freymann Literary Agency LLC, 59 W 71 St, Suite 9-B, New York, NY 10023 *Tel:* 212-362-9277 *E-mail:* submissions@sarahjanefreymann.com *Web Site:* www.sarahjanefreymann.com, pg 573

Sioles, Lee Campbell, Louisiana State University Press, 3990 W Lakeshore Dr, Baton Rouge, LA 70808 *Tel:* 225-578-6666 *Fax:* 225-578-6461 *E-mail:* lsupress@lsu.edu *Web Site:* lsupress.org, pg 153

Sipe, Keith R, Carolina Academic Press, 700 Kent St, Durham, NC 27701 *Tel:* 919-489-7486 *Toll Free Tel:* 800-489-7486 *Fax:* 919-493-5668 *E-mail:* cap@cap-press.com *Web Site:* www.cap-press.com; www.caplaw.com, pg 52

Sipe, Scott, Carolina Academic Press, 700 Kent St, Durham, NC 27701 *Tel:* 919-489-7486 *Toll Free Tel:* 800-489-7486 *Fax:* 919-493-5668 *E-mail:* cap@cap-press.com *Web Site:* www.cap-press.com; www.caplaw.com, pg 52

Sippell, Kelly, University of Michigan Press, 839 Greene St, Ann Arbor, MI 48104-3209 *Tel:* 734-764-4388 *Fax:* 734-615-1540 *E-mail:* esladmin@umich.edu *Web Site:* www.press.umich.edu, pg 266

Sippola, Carlene, Whole Person Associates Inc, 210 W Michigan St, Duluth, MN 55802-1908 *Tel:* 218-727-0500 *Toll Free Tel:* 800-247-6789 *Fax:* 218-727-0505 *E-mail:* books@wholeperson.com *Web Site:* www.wholeperson.com, pg 280

Spring, Kathleen, Spring Time Writers Creative Writing & Journaling Workshop, PO Box 512, Lyons, CO 80540-0512 *Tel:* 303-823-0997 *E-mail:* writers@springtimewriters.com *Web Site:* www.springtimewriters.com, pg 673

Springer, Rebecca, Houghton Mifflin Harcourt Trade & Reference Division, 222 Berkeley St, Boston, MA 02116-3764 *Tel:* 617-351-5000 *Toll Free Tel:* 800-225-3362 *Web Site:* www.houghtonmifflinbooks.com, pg 124

Springstead, Phil, Triumph Books, 814 N Franklin St, Chicago, IL 60610 *Toll Free Tel:* 800-888-4741 (orders only) *Fax:* 312-663-3557 *Web Site:* www.triumphbooks.com, pg 259

Sproule-Jones, Megan, Institute of Public Administration of Canada, 1075 Bay St, Suite 401, Toronto, ON M5S 2B1, Canada *Tel:* 416-924-8787 *Fax:* 416-924-4992 *E-mail:* ntl@ipac.ca; ntl@iapc.ca *Web Site:* www.ipac.ca; www.iapc.ca, pg 509

Squires, Jeff, Riverside Publishing, 3800 Golf Rd, Suite 200, Rolling Meadows, IL 60008 *Tel:* 630-467-7000 *Toll Free Tel:* 800-323-9540 *Fax:* 630-467-7192 (cust serv) *E-mail:* rpc_customer_service@hmhpub.com (cust serv) *Web Site:* www.riversidepublishing.com, pg 219

St George, Linda, Bilingual Review Press/Editorial Bilingue, Arizona State Univ, Hispanic Research Ctr, Tempe, AZ 85287-2702 *Tel:* 480-965-3867 *Toll Free Tel:* 866-965-3867 *Fax:* 480-965-0315 *E-mail:* brp@asu.edu *Web Site:* www.asu.edu/brp, pg 37

St Germain, Elizabeth, nSight Inc, One Van de Graaff Dr, Suite 202, Burlington, MA 01803 *Tel:* 781-273-6300 *Fax:* 781-273-6301 *E-mail:* nfritz@nsightworks.com *Web Site:* www.nsightworks.com, pg 552

St John, David W, Elderberry Press Inc, 1393 Old Homestead Dr, Mezzanine, Oakland, OR 97462-9506 *Tel:* 541-459-6043 *Web Site:* www.elderberrypress.com, pg 86

St John, Max, Ransom Note Press, PO Box 419, Ridgewood, NJ 07451 *Tel:* 201-835-2790 *E-mail:* editorial@ransomnotepress.com *Web Site:* www.ransomnotepress.com, pg 529

St Lifer, Evan, Scholastic Consumer & Professional Publishing, 557 Broadway, New York, NY 10012 *Tel:* 212-343-6100 *Toll Free Tel:* 800-621-1115 *Fax:* 800-621-1115 *Web Site:* www.scholastic.com, pg 228

St Pierre, Louisa, Bernstein & Andriulli Inc, 58 W 40 St, 6th fl, New York, NY 10018 *Tel:* 212-682-1490 *Fax:* 212-286-1890 *E-mail:* info@ba-reps.com *Web Site:* www.ba-reps.com, pg 601

St Thomasino, Carol, Palgrave Macmillan, 175 Fifth Ave, Suite 200, New York, NY 10010 *Tel:* 646-307-5151 *Fax:* 212-777-6359 *E-mail:* firstname.lastname@palgrave-usa.com *Web Site:* us.macmillan.com/Palgrave.aspx, pg 191

Stackler, Ed, Stackler Editorial Agency, 555 Lincoln Ave, Alameda, CA 94501 *Tel:* 510-814-9694 *Fax:* 510-814-9694 *E-mail:* stackler@aol.com *Web Site:* www.fictioneditor.com, pg 555

Stackpole, Kerry C, Printing & Graphing Association MidAtlantic, 9685 Gerwig Lane, Columbia, MD 21046 *Tel:* 410-319-0900 *Toll Free Tel:* 877-319-0906 *Fax:* 410-319-0905 *E-mail:* info@pgama.com *Web Site:* www.pgama.com, pg 634

Staff, Bruce, Blue Poppy Press, 1990 57 Ct, Unit A, Boulder, CO 80301 *Tel:* 303-447-8372 *Toll Free Tel:* 800-487-9296 *Fax:* 303-245-8362 *E-mail:* info@bluepoppy.com *Web Site:* www.bluepoppy.com, pg 41

Stafford, John, Writers' Haven Writers (WHW), 2244 Fourth Av, Suite A, San Diego, CA 92101-2119 *Tel:* 619-665-2712, pg 639

Staib, Erich, Duke University Press, 905 W Main St, Suite 18B, Durham, NC 27701 *Tel:* 919-688-5134 *Toll Free Tel:* 888-651-0122 *Fax:* 919-688-2615 *Toll Free Fax:* 888-651-0124 *E-mail:* orders@dukeupress.edu *Web Site:* www.dukeupress.edu, pg 82

Staines, Gail M PhD, Saint Louis Literary Award, Pius XII Memorial Library, 3650 Lindell Blvd, St Louis, MO 63108 *Tel:* 314-977-3100 *Fax:* 314-977-3587 *E-mail:* slula@slu.edu *Web Site:* www.slu.edu/libraries/associates, pg 739

Stakes, Robert, Texas Western Press, c/o University of Texas at El Paso, 500 W University Ave, El Paso, TX 79968-0633 *Tel:* 915-747-5688 *Toll Free Tel:* 800-488-3798 (orders only) *Fax:* 915-747-7515 *E-mail:* twpress@utep.edu *Web Site:* twp.utep.edu, pg 253

Stakes, Robert L, Carl Hertzog Book Design Award, c/o Dir of the Library, University of Texas at El Paso, University Library, El Paso, TX 79968-0582 *Tel:* 915-747-5683 *Fax:* 915-747-5345 *Web Site:* libraryweb.utep.edu, pg 709

Staklo, Vadim, Yale University Press, 302 Temple St, New Haven, CT 06511-8909 *Tel:* 401-531-2800 (cust serv); 203-432-0960 *Toll Free Tel:* 800-405-1619 (cust serv) *Fax:* 203-432-0948; 401-531-2801 (cust serv) *Toll Free Fax:* 800-406-9145 (cust serv) *E-mail:* customer.care@trilateral.org (cust serv); language.yalepress@yale.edu *Web Site:* www.yalebooks.com, pg 287

Stallings, A E, International Poetry Competition, PO Box 8248, Atlanta, GA 31106 *E-mail:* atlanta.review@yahoo.com *Web Site:* www.atlantareview.com, pg 712

Stallings, Lisa, The University of Arizona Press, 355 S Euclid Ave, Suite 103, Tucson, AZ 85719-6654 *Tel:* 520-621-1441 *Toll Free Tel:* 800-426-3797 (orders) *Fax:* 520-621-8899 *Toll Free Fax:* 800-426-3797 *E-mail:* uap@uapress.arizona.edu *Web Site:* www.uapress.arizona.edu, pg 264

Stamathis, George S, Brookes Publishing Co Inc, PO Box 10624, Baltimore, MD 21285-0624 *Tel:* 410-337-9580 (outside US & CN) *Toll Free Tel:* 800-638-3775 (US & CN) *Fax:* 410-337-8539 *E-mail:* custserv@brookespublishing.com *Web Site:* www.brookespublishing.com, pg 48

Stambaugh, Doug, Simon & Schuster, Inc, 1230 Avenue of the Americas, New York, NY 10020 *Tel:* 212-698-7000 *Fax:* 212-698-7007 *E-mail:* firstname.lastname@simonandschuster.com *Web Site:* www.simonandschuster.com, pg 235

Stampfel, Peter, DAW Books Inc, 375 Hudson St, 3rd fl, New York, NY 10014 *Tel:* 212-366-2096 *Fax:* 212-366-2090 *E-mail:* daw@us.penguingroup.com *Web Site:* us.penguingroup.com; www.dawbooks.com, pg 76

Stanczyk, Ms Soki, New City Press, 202 Comforter Blvd, Hyde Park, NY 12538 *Tel:* 845-229-0335 *Toll Free Tel:* 800-462-5980 (orders only) *Fax:* 845-229-0351 *E-mail:* info@newcitypress.com *Web Site:* www.newcitypress.com, pg 177

Standley, Will, Wescott Cove Publishing Co, 1227 S Florida Ave, Rockledge, FL 32955 *Tel:* 321-690-2224 *Fax:* 321-690-0853 *E-mail:* customerservice@farhorizonsmedia.com *Web Site:* www.farhorizonsmedia.com, pg 278

Stanford, Elisa, Edit Resource LLC, 3578-E Hartsel Dr, Suite 387, Colorado Springs, CO 80920 *Tel:* 719-290-0757 *E-mail:* info@editresource.com (main) *Web Site:* www.editresource.com (main); www.inspirationalghostwriting.com, pg 545

Stanford, Eric, Edit Resource LLC, 3578-E Hartsel Dr, Suite 387, Colorado Springs, CO 80920 *Tel:* 719-290-0757 *E-mail:* info@editresource.com (main) *Web Site:* www.editresource.com (main); www.inspirationalghostwriting.com, pg 545

Stanford, Halle, The Jim Henson Co, 1416 N La Brea Ave, Hollywood, CA 90028 *Tel:* 323-802-1500 *Fax:* 323-802-1825 *Web Site:* www.henson.com, pg 135

Stanish, Charles, Cotsen Institute of Archaeology Press, 308 Charles E Young Dr N, Fowler A163, Box 951510, Los Angeles, CA 90024 *Tel:* 310-206-9384 *Fax:* 310-206-4723 *E-mail:* ioapubs@ioa.ucla.edu *Web Site:* www.ioa.ucla.edu, pg 68

Stanley, Cullen, Janklow & Nesbit Associates, 445 Park Ave, New York, NY 10022 *Tel:* 212-421-1700 *Fax:* 212-980-3671 *E-mail:* info@janklow.com *Web Site:* www.janklowandnesbit.com, pg 578

Stanley, George, John Wiley & Sons Inc Professional/Trade Group, 111 River St, Hoboken, NJ 07030 *Tel:* 201-748-6000 *Toll Free Tel:* 800-225-5945 (cust serv) *Fax:* 201-748-6088 *E-mail:* info@wiley.com *Web Site:* www.wiley.com, pg 282

Stanley, James, Xlibris Corp, 1663 Liberty Dr, Suite 200, Bloomington, IN 47403 *Toll Free Tel:* 888-795-4274 *Fax:* 610-915-0294 *E-mail:* info@xlibris.com *Web Site:* www.xlibris.com, pg 287

Stanley, Rex, Unicor Medical Inc, 4160 Carmichael Rd, Montgomery, AL 36106 *Tel:* 334-260-8150 *Toll Free Tel:* 800-825-7421 *Toll Free Fax:* 800-305-8030 *E-mail:* sales@unicormed.com *Web Site:* www.unicormed.com, pg 262

Stanton, Cheryl, Krieger Publishing Co, 1725 Krieger Dr, Malabar, FL 32950 *Tel:* 321-724-9542 *Toll Free Tel:* 800-724-0025 *Fax:* 321-951-3671 *E-mail:* info@krieger-publishing.com *Web Site:* www.krieger-publishing.com, pg 142

Stanton, Sarah, Cowley Publications, 4501 Forbes Blvd, Suite 200, Lanham, MD 20706 *Tel:* 301-459-3366 *Toll Free Tel:* 800-462-6420 *Fax:* 301-429-5748 *Toll Free Fax:* 800-338-4550 *E-mail:* custserv@rowman.com *Web Site:* rowman.com, pg 70

Stanton, Steve, SF Canada, 7433 E River Rd, Washago, ON L0K 2B0, Canada *Web Site:* www.sfcanada.org, pg 636

Staples, Debra, SynergEbooks, 948 New Hwy 7, Columbia, TN 38401 *Tel:* 931-223-5990 *E-mail:* synergebooks@aol.com *Web Site:* www.synergebooks.com, pg 249

Stapleton, Janet, Beacon Hill Press of Kansas City, PO Box 419527, Kansas City, MO 64141-6527 *Tel:* 816-931-1900 *Toll Free Tel:* 800-877-0700 (cust serv) *Fax:* 816-753-4071 *Web Site:* www.beaconhillbooks.com, pg 32

Stapleton, Jay, Law Tribune Books, 201 Ann Uccello St, 4th fl, Hartford, CT 06103 *Tel:* 860-527-7900 *Fax:* 860-527-7433 *E-mail:* lawtribune@alm.com *Web Site:* www.ctlawtribune.com, pg 144

Stapleton, Victoria, Little, Brown Books for Young Readers, 237 Park Ave, New York, NY 10017 *Tel:* 212-364-1100 *Toll Free Tel:* 800-759-0190 (cust serv) *Web Site:* www.HachetteBookGroup.com, pg 150

Star, Alexander, Farrar, Straus & Giroux, LLC, 18 W 18 St, New York, NY 10011 *Tel:* 212-741-6900 *Fax:* 212-633-9385 *E-mail:* fsg.publicity@fsgbooks.com *Web Site:* us.macmillan.com/fsg.aspx, pg 93

Star, Brenda, StarGroup International Inc, 1194 Old Dixie Hwy, Suite 201, West Palm Beach, FL 33413 *Tel:* 561-547-0667 *Fax:* 561-843-8530 *E-mail:* info@stargroupinternational.com *Web Site:* www.stargroupinternational.com, pg 243

Staral, Christian, Springer, 233 Spring St, New York, NY 10013-1578 *Tel:* 212-460-1500 *Toll Free Tel:* 800-SPRINGER (777-4643) *Fax:* 212-460-1575 *E-mail:* service-ny@springer.com *Web Site:* www.springer.com, pg 241

Stark, Kate, GP Putnam's Sons (Hardcover), 375 Hudson St, New York, NY 10014 *Tel:* 212-366-2000 *E-mail:* online@penguinputnam.com *Web Site:* us.penguingroup.com, pg 210

Stark, Kate, Riverhead Books (Hardcover), 375 Hudson St, New York, NY 10014 *Tel:* 212-366-2000 *E-mail:* online@penguinputnam.com *Web Site:* www.penguinputnam.com; us.penguingroup.com, pg 219

Stark, Patty, John Wiley & Sons Inc Higher Education, 111 River St, Hoboken, NJ 07030-5774 *Tel:* 201-748-6000 *Toll Free Tel:* 800-225-5945 (cust serv) *Fax:* 201-748-6008 *E-mail:* info@wiley.com *Web Site:* www.wiley.com, pg 281

Stark, Sheldon, Institute of Continuing Legal Education, 1020 Greene St, Ann Arbor, MI 48109-1444 *Tel:* 734-764-0533 *Toll Free Tel:* 877-229-4350 *Fax:* 734-763-2412 *Toll Free Fax:* 877-229-4351 *E-mail:* icle@umich.edu *Web Site:* www.icle.org, pg 131

Starke, Alexis, History Publishing Co LLC, 173 Rte 9W, Palisades, NY 10964 *Tel:* 845-398-8161 *Fax:* 845-231-6167 *E-mail:* historypublish@aol.com; info@historypublishingco.com *Web Site:* www.historypublishingco.com, pg 120

Starkman, Jennifer, Transatlantic Agency, 2 Bloor St E, Ste 3500, Toronto, ON M4W-1A8, Canada *Tel:* 416-488-9214 *E-mail:* info@transatlanticagency.com *Web Site:* www.transatlanticagency.com, pg 597

Starkman, Stanley, Chestnut Publishing Group Inc, 4005 Bayview Ave, Suite 610, Toronto, ON M2M 3Z9, Canada *Tel:* 416-224-5824 *Fax:* 416-224-0595 *Web Site:* www.chestnutpublishing.com, pg 499

Starnino, Carmine, Vehicule Press, PO Box 125, Place du Park Sta, Montreal, QC H2X 4A3, Canada *Tel:* 514-844-6073 *Fax:* 514-844-7543 *E-mail:* vp@vehiculepress.com; admin@vehiculepress.com *Web Site:* www.vehiculepress.com, pg 524

Starr, Leslie, Wesleyan University Press, 215 Long Lane, Middletown, CT 06459-0433 *Tel:* 860-685-7711 *Fax:* 860-685-7712 *Web Site:* www.wesleyan.edu/wespress, pg 278

Starrett, Margaret, Branden Books, PO Box 812094, Wellesley, MA 02482-0013 *Tel:* 781-235-3634 *E-mail:* branden@brandenbooks.com *Web Site:* www.brandenbooks.com, pg 45

Starsia, Victor, LaChance Publishing LLC, 120 Bond St, Brooklyn, NY 11217 *Tel:* 917-855-7537 *Fax:* 646-390-1326 *E-mail:* info@lachancepublishing.com *Web Site:* www.lachancepublishing.com, pg 143

Stascavage, Anne, University Press of Mississippi, 3825 Ridgewood Rd, Jackson, MS 39211-6492 *Tel:* 601-432-6205 *Toll Free Tel:* 800-737-7788 (orders & cust serv) *Fax:* 601-432-6217 *E-mail:* press@mississippi.edu *Web Site:* www.upress.state.ms.us, pg 271

Staton, Cecil P Jr, Smyth & Helwys Publishing Inc, 6316 Peake Rd, Macon, GA 31210-3960 *Tel:* 478-757-0564 *Toll Free Tel:* 800-747-3016 (orders only); 800-568-1248 (orders only) *Fax:* 478-757-1305 *E-mail:* information@helwys.com *Web Site:* www.helwys.com, pg 238

Stebbins, Dr Chad, International Society of Weekly Newspaper Editors, Missouri Southern State University, 3950 E Newman Rd, Joplin, MO 64801-1595 *Tel:* 417-625-9736 *Fax:* 417-659-4445 *Web Site:* www.mssu.edu/iswne, pg 625

Stech, Marko R, Canadian Institute of Ukrainian Studies Press, University of Toronto, Rm 308, 256 McCaul St, Toronto, ON M5T 1W5, Canada *Tel:* 416-946-7326 *Fax:* 416-978-2672 *E-mail:* cius@ualberta.ca *Web Site:* www.ciuspress.com, pg 497

Steele, David Ramsay, Open Court, 70 E Lake St, Suite 300, Chicago, IL 60601 *Tel:* 312-701-1720 *Toll Free Tel:* 800-815-2280 (orders only) *Fax:* 312-701-1728 *E-mail:* opencourt@caruspub.com *Web Site:* www.opencourtbooks.com, pg 185

Steelman, Cheryl, Charles C Thomas Publisher Ltd, 2600 S First St, Springfield, IL 62704 *Tel:* 217-789-8980 *Toll Free Tel:* 800-258-8980 *Fax:* 217-789-9130 *E-mail:* books@ccthomas.com *Web Site:* www.ccthomas.com, pg 254

Steere, Michael, Down East Books, 680 Commercial St (US Rte 1), Rockport, ME 04856 *Tel:* 207-594-9544 *Toll Free Tel:* 800-685-7962 (US only orders); 800-766-1670 *Fax:* 207-594-7215 *E-mail:* submissions@downeast.com *Web Site:* www.downeast.com, pg 81

Steffen, Zach, North Country Books Inc, 220 Lafayette St, Utica, NY 13502-4312 *Tel:* 315-735-4877 *Toll Free Tel:* 800-342-7409 (orders) *Fax:* 315-738-4342 *E-mail:* ncbooks@verizon.net *Web Site:* www.northcountrybooks.com, pg 180

Stehlik, Liate, HarperCollins General Books Group, 10 E 53 St, New York, NY 10022 *Tel:* 212-207-7000 *Fax:* 212-207-7633 *Web Site:* www.harpercollins.com, pg 113

Steidel, Lauren, Society for Industrial & Applied Mathematics, 3600 Market St, 6th fl, Philadelphia, PA 19104-2688 *Tel:* 215-382-9800 *Toll Free Tel:* 800-447-7426 *Fax:* 215-386-7999 *E-mail:* siambooks@siam.org *Web Site:* www.siam.org, pg 238

Steiger, Bill, American College of Physician Executives, 400 N Ashley Dr, Suite 400, Tampa, FL 33602 *Tel:* 813-287-2000 *Toll Free Tel:* 800-562-8088 *Fax:* 813-287-8993 *E-mail:* acpe@acpe.org *Web Site:* www.acpe.org, pg 12

Stein, Anna, Aitken Alexander Associates LLC, 30 Vandam St, Suite 5A, New York, NY 10013 *Tel:* 212-929-4100 *Web Site:* www.aitkenalexander.co.uk, pg 560

Stein, Anne Marie, Massachusetts College of Art & Design Writing Children's Literature, 621 Huntington Ave, Boston, MA 02115 *Tel:* 617-879-7200 *Fax:* 617-879-7171 *E-mail:* ce@massart.edu *Web Site:* www.massart.edu/ce, pg 679

Stein, Erin, Little, Brown Books for Young Readers, 237 Park Ave, New York, NY 10017 *Tel:* 212-364-1100 *Toll Free Tel:* 800-759-0190 (cust serv) *Web Site:* www.HachetteBookGroup.com, pg 150

Stein, Jonathan, Central Conference of American Rabbis/CCAR Press, 355 Lexington Ave, 18th fl, New York, NY 10017 *Tel:* 212-972-3636 *Toll Free Tel:* 800-935-2227 *Fax:* 212-692-0819 *E-mail:* info@ccarnet.org *Web Site:* www.ccarnet.org/ccar-press, pg 57

Stein, Jonathan, Open Road Publishing, PO Box 284, Cold Spring Harbor, NY 11724-0284 *Tel:* 631-692-7172 *E-mail:* jopenroad@aol.com *Web Site:* www.openroadguides.com, pg 186

Stein, Judith, The Author's Friend, 548 Ocean Blvd, No 12, Long Branch, NJ 07740 *Tel:* 732-571-8051 *Toll Free Tel:* 877-485-7689 *Toll Free Fax:* 877-485-7689, pg 541

Stein, Kathy, American Psychiatric Publishing (APP), 1000 Wilson Blvd, Suite 1825, Arlington, VA 22209 *Tel:* 703-907-7322 *Toll Free Tel:* 800-368-5777 *Fax:* 703-907-1091 *E-mail:* appi@psych.org *Web Site:* www.appi.org; www.psychiatryonline.org, pg 15

Stein, Lonny R, Barron's Educational Series Inc, 250 Wireless Blvd, Hauppauge, NY 11788 *Tel:* 631-434-3311 *Toll Free Tel:* 800-645-3476 *Fax:* 631-434-3723 *E-mail:* barrons@barronseduc.com *Web Site:* www.barronseduc.com, pg 31

Stein, Sherry, The Fraser Institute, 1770 Burrard St, 4th fl, Vancouver, BC V6J 3G7, Canada *Tel:* 604-688-0221 *Toll Free Tel:* 800-665-3558 *Fax:* 604-688-8539 *E-mail:* info@fraserinstitute.org; sales@fraserinstitute.org *Web Site:* www.fraserinstitute.org, pg 506

Steinberg, Andrew, Modern Publishing, 155 E 55 St, New York, NY 10022 *Tel:* 212-826-0850 *Fax:* 212-759-9069 *Web Site:* www.modernpublishing.com, pg 168

Steinberg, Michael, Michael Steinberg Literary Agent, PO Box 274, Glencoe, IL 60022-0274 *Tel:* 847-626-1000 *Fax:* 847-626-1002 *E-mail:* michael14steinberg@comcast.net, pg 595

Steinberger, David, Basic Books, 250 W 57 St, 15th fl, New York, NY 10107 *Tel:* 212-340-8164 *Fax:* 212-340-8135 *E-mail:* perseus.promos@perseusbooks.com *Web Site:* www.basicbooks.com; perseusbooks.com, pg 31

Steinberger, David, The Perseus Books Group, 387 Park Ave S, 12th fl, New York, NY 10016 *Tel:* 212-340-8100 *Toll Free Tel:* 800-343-4499 (cust serv) *Fax:* 212-340-8105 *Web Site:* www.perseusbooksgroup.com, pg 199

Steinberger, David, Westview Press, 2465 Central Ave, Boulder, CO 80301 *Tel:* 303-444-3541 *Fax:* 720-406-7336 *E-mail:* westview.orders@perseusbooks.com *Web Site:* www.perseusbooksgroup.com; www.westviewpress.com, pg 279

Steinbock, Steven, International Association of Crime Writers Inc, North American Branch, 328 Eighth Ave, Suite 114, New York, NY 10001 *Tel:* 212-243-8966 *Fax:* 815-361-1477 *E-mail:* info@crimewritersna.org *Web Site:* www.crimewritersna.org, pg 625

Steinecke, Anke, Random House Inc, 1745 Broadway, New York, NY 10019 *Tel:* 212-782-9000 *Toll Free Tel:* 800-726-0600 *Web Site:* www.randomhouse.com, pg 213

Steiner, Karen, Research Press, 2612 N Mattis Ave, Champaign, IL 61822 *Tel:* 217-352-3273 *Toll Free Tel:* 800-519-2707 *Fax:* 217-352-1221 *E-mail:* rp@researchpress.com; orders@researchpress.com *Web Site:* www.researchpress.com, pg 218

Steinert, Frank, Random House Inc, 1745 Broadway, New York, NY 10019 *Tel.* 212-782-9000 *Toll Free Tel:* 800-726-0600 *Web Site:* www.randomhouse.com, pg 213

Steinhardt, David J, IDEAlliance®, 1600 Duke St, Suite 420, Alexandria, VA 22314 *Tel:* 703-837-1070 *Fax:* 703-837-1072 *E-mail:* info@idealliance.org; registrar@idealliance.org *Web Site:* www.idealliance.org, pg 624

Steinmetz, Andrew, Vehicule Press, PO Box 125, Place du Park Sta, Montreal, QC H2X 4A3, Canada *Tel:* 514-844-6073 *Fax:* 514-844-7543 *E-mail:* vp@vehiculepress.com; admin@vehiculepress.com *Web Site:* www.vehiculepress.com, pg 524

Stelzig, Christopher, Entomological Society of America, 10001 Derekwood Lane, Suite 100, Lanham, MD 20706-4876 *Tel:* 301-731-4535 *Fax:* 301-731-4538 *E-mail:* esa@entsoc.org *Web Site:* www.entsoc.org, pg 89

Stender, Dr Uwe, TriadaUS Literary Agency, PO Box 561, Sewickley, PA 15143 *Tel:* 412-401-3376 *Fax:* 412-749-0842 *Web Site:* www.triadaus.com, pg 598

Stenger, Lisa, Kaeden Corp, PO Box 16190, Rocky River, OH 44116-0190 *Tel:* 440-617-1400 *Toll Free Tel:* 800-890-7323 *Fax:* 440-617-1403 *E-mail:* info@kaeden.com *Web Site:* www.kaeden.com, pg 138

Stephanides, Myrsini, Carol Mann Agency, 55 Fifth Ave, New York, NY 10003 *Tel:* 212-206-5635 *Fax:* 212-675-4809 *E-mail:* submissions@carolmannagency.com *Web Site:* www.carolmannagency.com, pg 583

Stephens, Christopher P, Ultramarine Publishing Co Inc, 12 Washington Ave, Hastings-on-Hudson, NY 10706 *Tel:* 914-478-1339, pg 262

Stephens, Gavin, Presbyterian Publishing Corp, 100 Witherspoon St, Louisville, KY 40202 *Tel:* 502-569-5000 *Toll Free Tel:* 800-523-1631 (US only) *Fax:* 502-569-5113 *E-mail:* ppcmail@presbypub.com *Web Site:* www.wjkbooks.com, pg 205

Stephens, Gavin, Westminster John Knox Press, 100 Witherspoon St, Louisville, KY 40202-1396 *Tel:* 502-569-5052 *Toll Free Tel:* 800-227-2872 (US only) *Fax:* 502-569-8308 *Toll Free Fax:* 800-541-5113 (US & CN) *E-mail:* wjk@wjkbooks.com; customer_service@wjkbooks.com *Web Site:* www.wjkbooks.com, pg 279

Stephens, Michael, Manning Publications Co, 20 Baldwin Rd, Shelter Island, NY 11964 *Toll Free Tel:* 800-294-4747 (orders) *E-mail:* orders@manning.com *Web Site:* www.manning.com, pg 156

Stephens, R David, Tradewind Books, 202-1807 Maritime Mews, Vancouver, BC V6H 3W7, Canada *Fax:* 604-662-4405 *E-mail:* tradewindbooks@telus.net *Web Site:* www.tradewindbooks.com, pg 521

Stephenson, Heather, Appalachian Mountain Club Books, 5 Joy St, Boston, MA 02108 *Tel:* 617-523-0655 *Fax:* 617-523-0722 *Web Site:* www.outdoors.org, pg 20

Sterbenz, Carol Endler, Creative Homeowner, 24 Park Way, Upper Saddle River, NJ 07458-9960 *Tel:* 201-934-7100 *Toll Free Tel:* 800-631-7795 (cust serv) *Fax:* 201-934-7541; 201-934-8971 (orders) *E-mail:* info@creativehomeowner.com; customerservice@creativehomeowner.com *Web Site:* www.creativehomeowner.com, pg 71

Sterling, John, Macmillan, 175 Fifth Ave, New York, NY 10010 *Tel:* 646-307-5151 *Fax:* 212-420-9314 *E-mail:* firstname.lastname@macmillan.com *Web Site:* www.macmillan.com, pg 154

Stern, Amy, Sheldon Fogelman Agency Inc, 10 E 40 St, Suite 3205, New York, NY 10016 *Tel:* 212-532-7250 *Fax:* 212-685-8939 *E-mail:* info@sheldonfogelmanagency.com *Web Site:* sheldonfogelmanagency.com, pg 572

Stern, Greg, Hoover's, Inc, 5800 Airport Blvd, Austin, TX 78752 *Tel:* 512-374-4500 *Toll Free Tel:* 866-307-3812 *Fax:* 512-374-4501 *E-mail:* info@hoovers.com *Web Site:* www.hoovers.com, pg 123

Stern, Ina, Algonquin Books of Chapel Hill, 400 Silver Cedar Ct, Suite 300, Chapel Hill, NC 27514-1585 *Tel:* 919-967-0108 *Fax:* 919-933-0272 *E-mail:* inquiry@algonquin.com *Web Site:* www.workman.com/algonquin, pg 8

Stern, Janet, Markus Wiener Publishers Inc, 231 Nassau St, Princeton, NJ 08542 *Tel:* 609-921-1141 *Fax:* 609-921-1140 *E-mail:* publisher@markuswiener.com *Web Site:* www.markuswiener.com, pg 280

Stern, Molly, Crown Publishing Group, c/o Random House Inc, 1745 Broadway, New York, NY 10019 *Tel:* 212-782-9000 *Toll Free Tel:* 888-264-1745 *Fax:* 212-940-7408 *Web Site:* www.randomhouse.com/crown, pg 72

Stern, Peter, Marick Press, PO Box 36253, Grosse Pointe Farms, MI 48236 *Tel:* 313-407-9236 *E-mail:* orders@marickpress.com *Web Site:* www.marickpress.com, pg 157

Stern, Walter B, Prayer Book Press Inc, 1363 Fairfield Ave, Bridgeport, CT 06605 *Tel:* 203-384-2284 *Fax:* 203-579-9109, pg 205

Sternlicht, Moshe, Moznaim Publishing Corp, 4304 12 Ave, Brooklyn, NY 11219 *Tel:* 718-438-7680 *Fax:* 718-438-1305 *E-mail:* sales@moznaim.com, pg 171

Stets, Mary Anne, Mystic Seaport Museum Inc, PO Box 6000, Mystic, CT 06355-0990 *Tel:* 860-572-5302; 860-572-0711 (visitor serv) *Toll Free Tel:* 800-248-1066 (wholesale orders only); 800-331-2665 (retail orders only) *Fax:* 860-572-5321 *E-mail:* info@mysticseaport.org *Web Site:* www.mysticseaport.org, pg 172

Stetz, Jeffrey, Transaction Publishers Inc, 10 Corporate Place S, 35 Berrue Circle, Piscataway, NJ 08854 *Tel:* 732-445-2280; 732-445-1245 (orders) *Toll Free Tel:* 888-999-6778 (dist ctr) *Fax:* 732-445-3138 *E-mail:* trans@transactionpub.com; orders@transactionpub.om *Web Site:* www.transactionpub.com, pg 258

Steve, Betsy, New York University Press, 838 Broadway, 3rd fl, New York, NY 10003-4812 *Tel:* 212-998-2575 (edit) *Toll Free Tel:* 800-996-6987 (orders) *Fax:* 212-995-3833 (orders) *E-mail:* information@nyupress.org; customerservice@nyupress.org; orders@nyupress.org *Web Site:* www.nyupress.org, pg 179

Stevens, Drew, The Feminist Press at The City University of New York, 365 Fifth Ave, Suite 5406, New York, NY 10016 *Tel:* 212-817-7915 *Fax:* 212-817-1593 *E-mail:* info@feministpress.org *Web Site:* www.feministpress.org, pg 94

Stevens, Jacob, Verso, 20 Jay St, Suite 1010, Brooklyn, NY 11201 *Tel:* 718-246-8160 *Fax:* 718-246-8165 *E-mail:* verso@versobooks.com *Web Site:* www.versobooks.com, pg 274

Stevens, Lavonne, Literary Management Group LLC, 613 Crieve Rd, Nashville, TN 37220 *Tel:* 615-832-7231 *Web Site:* www.literarymanagementgroup.com; www.brucebarbour.com, pg 582

Stevens, Martin, Forum Publishing Co, 383 E Main St, Centerport, NY 11721 *Tel:* 631-754-5000 *Toll Free Tel:* 800-635-7654 *Fax:* 631-754-0630 *E-mail:* forumpublishing@aol.com *Web Site:* www.forum123.com, pg 97

Stevens, Megan, American Council on Education, One Dupont Circle NW, Washington, DC 20036-1193 *Tel:* 202-939-9300; 301-632-6757 (orders) *Fax:* 202-939-9302 *E-mail:* pubs@acenet.edu *Web Site:* www.acenet.edu, pg 12

Stevens, R Blake, Collector Grade Publications Inc, PO Box 1046, Cobourg, ON K9A 4W5, Canada *Tel:* 905-342-3434 *Fax:* 905-342-3688 *E-mail:* info@collectorgrade.com *Web Site:* www.collectorgrade.com, pg 499

Stevenson, Deborah, Scott O'Dell Award for Historical Fiction, Hornbook, Suite 200, 56 Roland St, Boston, MA 02129 *Tel:* 617-628-8471 *Toll Free Tel:* 800-325-1170 *Web Site:* www.scottodell.com/odellaward.html, pg 730

Stevenson, Dinah, Clarion Books, 215 Park Ave S, New York, NY 10003 *Tel:* 212-420-5883 *Toll Free Tel:* 800-225-3362 (orders) *Fax:* 212-420-5855 *Toll Free Fax:* 800-634-7568 (orders) *Web Site:* www.houghtonmifflinbooks.com, pg 62

Stevenson, Dinah, Houghton Mifflin Harcourt Trade & Reference Division, 222 Berkeley St, Boston, MA 02116-3764 *Tel:* 617-351-5000 *Toll Free Tel:* 800-225-3362 *Web Site:* www.houghtonmifflinbooks.com, pg 124

Steward, Carlos, Black Mountain Press, PO Box 9907, Asheville, NC 28815 *Tel:* 828-273-3332 *Web Site:* www.theblackmountainpress.com, pg 39

Steward, Scott C, Newbury Street Press, 101 Newbury St, Boston, MA 02116 *Tel:* 617-536-5740 *Toll Free Tel:* 888-296-3447 (NEHGS membership) *Fax:* 617-536-7307 *E-mail:* sales@nehgs.org *Web Site:* www.newenglandancestors.org, pg 179

Stewart, Amy, University of Texas at Austin, Creative Writing Program, Dept of English, PAR 108, One University Sta, Mailcode B5000, Austin, TX 78712-1164 *Tel:* 512-471-5132; 512-471-4991 *Fax:* 512-471-4909 *Web Site:* www.utexas.edu/cola/depts/english/creative-writing, pg 682

Stewart, Douglas, Sterling Lord Literistic Inc, 65 Bleecker St, New York, NY 10012 *Tel:* 212-780-6050 *Fax:* 212-780-6095 *E-mail:* info@sll.com *Web Site:* www.sll.com, pg 595

Stewart, James B, The Authors League Fund, 31 E 32 St, 7th fl, New York, NY 10016 *Tel:* 212-268-1208 *Fax:* 212-564-5363 *E-mail:* staff@authorsleaguefund.org *Web Site:* www.authorsleaguefund.org, pg 617

Stewart, Jenna, Chelsea Green Publishing Co, 85 N Main St, Suite 120, White River Junction, VT 05001 *Tel:* 802-295-6300 *Toll Free Tel:* 800-639-4099 (cust serv, consumer & trade orders) *Fax:* 802-295-6444 *Web Site:* www.chelseagreen.com, pg 59

Stewart, Joan, The Joan Stewart Agency, 885 Second Ave, 35th fl, New York, NY 10017 *Tel:* 212-418-7255 *Fax:* 212-832-3809, pg 596

Stewart, Robert, BkMk Press - University of Missouri-Kansas City, 5101 Rockhill Rd, Kansas City, MO 64110-2499 *Tel:* 816-235-2558 *Fax:* 816-235-2611 *E-mail:* bkmk@umkc.edu *Web Site:* www.umkc.edu/bkmk, pg 38

Stewart, Robert, G S Sharat Chandra Prize for Short Fiction, 5101 Rockhill Rd, Kansas City, MO 64110-2499 *Tel:* 816-235-2558 *Fax:* 816-235-2611 *E-mail:* bkmk@umkc.edu *Web Site:* www.umkc.edu/bkmk, pg 696

Stewart, Robert, John Ciardi Prize for Poetry, 5101 Rockhill Rd, Kansas City, MO 64110-2499 *Tel:* 816-235-2558 *Fax:* 816-235-2611 *E-mail:* bkmk@umkc.edu *Web Site:* www.umkc.edu/bkmk, pg 697

Stewart, Robert, Mark Twain Creative Writing Workshop, UMKC, University House, 5101 Rockhill Rd, Kansas City, MO 64110-2499 *Tel:* 816-235-1168 *Fax:* 816-235-2611 *E-mail:* newletters@umkc.edu *Web Site:* www.newletters.org, pg 670

Sticco, Maria, University of Pittsburgh Press, Eureka Bldg, 5th fl, 3400 Forbes Ave, Pittsburgh, PA 15260 *Tel:* 412-383-2456 *Fax:* 412-383-2466 *E-mail:* info@upress.pitt.edu *Web Site:* www.upress.pitt.edu, pg 268

Stiles, Lane, Mid-List Press, 6524 Brownlee Dr, Nashville, TN 37205-3038 *Tel:* 615-822-3777 *Fax:* 612-823-8387 *E-mail:* guide@midlist.org *Web Site:* www.midlist.org, pg 166

Stillwell, Cynthia Fritts, Big Apple Conference, 317 Madison Ave, Suite 1704, New York, NY 10017 *Tel:* 917-720-6959 *E-mail:* iwwgquestions@gmail.com *Web Site:* www.iwwg.org, pg 668

Stillwell, Cynthia Fritts, The International Women's Writing Guild (IWWG), 317 Madison Ave, Suite 1704, New York, NY 10017 *Tel:* 917-720-6959 *E-mail:* iwwgquestions@gmail.com *Web Site:* www.iwwg.org, pg 625

Stillwell, Cynthia Fritts, ReIMAGINE the MAGIC Annual Summer Conference, 317 Madison Ave, Suite 1704, New York, NY 10017 *Tel:* 917-720-6959 *E-mail:* iwwgquestions@gmail.com *Web Site:* www.iwwg.org, pg 672

Stilson, Joyce, Maxim Mazumdar New Play Competition, One Curtain Up Alley, Buffalo, NY 14202-1911 *Tel:* 716-852-2600 *E-mail:* publicrelations@alleyway.com *Web Site:* alleyway.com, pg 722

Stimola, Rosemary B, Stimola Literary Studio Inc, 308 Livingston Ct, Edgewater, NJ 07020 *Tel:* 201-945-9353 *Fax:* 201-945-9353 *E-mail:* info@stimolaliterarystudio.com *Web Site:* www.stimolaliterarystudio.com, pg 596

Stimson, Theresa, Marquette Books, 3107 E 62 Ave, Spokane, WA 99223 *Tel:* 509-290-9240 *Fax:* 509-448-2191 *E-mail:* books@marquettebooks.com *Web Site:* www.marquettebooks.com, pg 157

Stine, Jane, Parachute Publishing LLC, 322 Eighth Ave, Suite 702, New York, NY 10001 *Tel:* 212-691-1422 *Fax:* 212-645-8769 *E-mail:* tlabreglia@parachutepublishing.com *Web Site:* www.parachutepublishing.com, pg 192

Stinnett, Barbara, St Johann Press, 315 Schraalenburgh Rd, Haworth, NJ 07641 *Tel:* 201-387-1529 *Fax:* 201-501-0698 *Web Site:* www.stjohannpress.com, pg 224

Stio, Stephanie, National Poetry Series Open Competition, 57 Mountain Ave, Princeton, NJ 08540 *Tel:* 609-430-0999 *Fax:* 609-430-9933 *Web Site:* www.pw.org/content/open_competition, pg 727

Stiver, Kim, DeLorme Publishing Co Inc, 2 DeLorme Dr, Yarmouth, ME 04096 *Tel:* 207-846-7000; 207-846-7111 (sales) *Toll Free Tel:* 800-561-5105; 800-511-2459 (cust serv) *Fax:* 207-846-7051 *Toll Free Fax:* 800-575-2244 *E-mail:* reseller@delorme.com *Web Site:* www.delorme.com, pg 77

Stix, John, Cherry Lane Music Co, 315 Fifth Ave, Suite 801, New York, NY 10016 *Tel:* 646-470-3782 *Fax:* 212-251-0822 *Web Site:* www.cherrylaneprint.com, pg 59

Stocke, Todd, Sourcebooks Inc, 1935 Brookdale Rd, Suite 139, Naperville, IL 60563 *Tel:* 630-961-3900 *Toll Free Tel:* 800-432-7444 *Fax:* 630-961-2168 *E-mail:* info@sourcebooks.com; customersupport@sourcebooks.com *Web Site:* www.sourcebooks.com, pg 240

Stocke, Todd, Sphinx Publishing, 1935 Brookdale Rd, Suite 139, Naperville, IL 60563 *Tel:* 630-961-3900 *Toll Free Tel:* 800-43-bright (432-7448) *Fax:* 630-961-2168 *E-mail:* info@sourcebooks.com *Web Site:* www.sourcebooks.com, pg 241

Stockfield, Mindy, Hyperion, 1500 Broadway, 3rd fl, New York, NY 10036 *Tel:* 212-536-6500 *Web Site:* hyperionbooks.com, pg 126

Stockland, Patricia M, Carolrhoda Books, 241 First Ave N, Minneapolis, MN 55401 *Tel:* 612-332-3344 *Toll Free Tel:* 800-328-4929 *Fax:* 612-332-7615 *Toll Free Fax:* 800-332-1132 *E-mail:* info@lernerbooks.com *Web Site:* www.lernerbooks.com, pg 53

Stockland, Patricia M, Carolrhoda Lab™, 241 First Ave N, Minneapolis, MN 55401 *Tel:* 612-332-3344 *Toll Free Tel:* 800-328-4929 *Fax:* 612-332-7615 *Toll Free Fax:* 800-332-1132 (US) *E-mail:* info@lernerbooks.com *Web Site:* www.lernerbooks.com, pg 53

Stockland, Patricia M, ediciones Lerner, 241 First Ave N, Minneapolis, MN 55401 *Tel:* 612-332-3344 *Toll Free Tel:* 800-328-4929 *Fax:* 612-332-7615 *Toll Free Fax:* 800-332-1132 *E-mail:* info@lernerbooks.com *Web Site:* www.lernerbooks.com, pg 85

Stockland, Patricia M, First Avenue Editions, 241 First Ave N, Minneapolis, MN 55401 *Tel:* 612-332-3344 *Toll Free Tel:* 800-328-4929 *Fax:* 612-332-7615 *Toll Free Fax:* 800-332-1132 *E-mail:* info@lernerbooks.com *Web Site:* www.lernerbooks.com, pg 95

Stockland, Patricia M, Graphic Universe™, 241 First Ave N, Minneapolis, MN 55401 *Tel:* 612-332-3344 *Toll Free Tel:* 800-328-4929 *Fax:* 612-332-7615 *Toll Free Fax:* 800-332-1132 *E-mail:* info@lernerbooks.com *Web Site:* www.lernerbooks.com, pg 106

Stockland, Patricia M, Lerner Publications, 241 First Ave N, Minneapolis, MN 55401 *Tel:* 612-332-3344 *Toll Free Tel:* 800-328-4929 *Fax:* 612-332-7615 *Toll Free Fax:* 800-332-1132 *E-mail:* info@lernerbooks.com *Web Site:* www.lernerbooks.com, pg 146

Stockland, Patricia M, Lerner Publishing Group Inc, 241 First Ave N, Minneapolis, MN 55401 *Tel:* 612-332-3344 *Toll Free Tel:* 800-328-4929 *Fax:* 612-332-7615 *Toll Free Fax:* 800-332-1132 *E-mail:* info@lernerbooks.com *Web Site:* www.lernerbooks.com, pg 146

Stockland, Patricia M, LernerClassroom, 241 First Ave N, Minneapolis, MN 55401 *Tel:* 612-332-3344 *Toll Free Tel:* 800-328-4929 *Fax:* 612-332-7615 *Toll Free Fax:* 800-332-1132 *E-mail:* info@lernerbooks.com *Web Site:* www.lernerbooks.com, pg 147

Stockland, Patricia M, Millbrook Press, 241 First Ave N, Minneapolis, MN 55401 *Tel:* 612-332-3344 *Toll Free Tel:* 800-328-4929 (US only) *Fax:* 612-332-7615 *Toll Free Fax:* 800-332-1132, pg 167

Stockland, Patricia M, Twenty-First Century Books, 241 First Ave N, Minneapolis, MN 55401 *Tel:* 612-332-3344 *Toll Free Tel:* 800-328-4929 *Fax:* 612-332-7615 *Toll Free Fax:* 800-332-1132 *E-mail:* info@lernerbooks.com *Web Site:* www.lernerbooks.com, pg 260

Stocks, John C, National Education Association (NEA), 1201 16 St NW, Washington, DC 20036-3290 *Tel:* 202-833-4000 *Fax:* 202-822-7974 *Web Site:* www.nea.org, pg 174, 630

Stockwell, Diane, Globo Libros Literary Agency, 402 E 64 St, Suite 6-C, New York, NY 10065 *Tel:* 212-888-4655 *Web Site:* www.globo-libros.com; publishersmarketplace.com/members/dstockwell, pg 574

Stockwell, Gail Provost, Writers Retreat Workshop (WRW), PO Box 4236, Louisville, KY 40204 *E-mail:* wrw04@netscape.net *Web Site:* www.writersretreatworkshop.com, pg 675

Stoddard, Bill, Prometheus Awards, 650 Castro St, Suite 120-433, Mountain View, CA 94041 *Tel:* 650-968-6319 *E-mail:* info@lfs.org *Web Site:* www.lfs.org, pg 736

Stoddard, Rebecca, Omnidawn Publishing, 1632 Elm Ave, Richmond, CA 94805-1614 *Tel:* 510-237-5472 *Toll Free Tel:* 800-792-4957 *Fax:* 510-232-8525 *E-mail:* manager@omnidawn.com *Web Site:* www.omnidawn.com, pg 185

Stoddard, Rob, National Cable & Telecommunications Association (NCTA), 25 Massachusetts Ave NW, Suite 100, Washington, DC 20001-1413 *Tel:* 202-222-2300 *Fax:* 202-222-2514 *Web Site:* www.ncta.com, pg 629

Stoker, Leslie, Stewart, Tabori & Chang, 115 W 18 St, 6th fl, New York, NY 10011 *Tel:* 212-519-1200 *Fax:* 212-519-1210 *Web Site:* www.abramsbooks.com, pg 245

Stokes, Susan S, Woodbine House, 6510 Bells Mill Rd, Bethesda, MD 20817 *Tel:* 301-897-3570 *Toll Free Tel:* 800-843-7323 *Fax:* 301-897-5838 *E-mail:* info@woodbinehouse.com *Web Site:* www.woodbinehouse.com, pg 284

Stolls, Amy, The National Endowment for the Arts, Nancy Hanks Ctr, Rm 703, 1100 Pennsylvania Ave NW, Washington, DC 20506-0001 *Tel:* 202-682-5400 *Web Site:* www.arts.gov; www.nea.gov, pg 641

Stoloff, Sam, Frances Goldin Literary Agency, Inc, 57 E 11 St, Suite 5-B, New York, NY 10003 *Tel:* 212-777-0047 *Fax:* 212-228-1660 *E-mail:* agency@goldinlit.com *Web Site:* www.goldinlit.com, pg 575

Stoltz, Jamison, Grove/Atlantic Inc, 841 Broadway, 4th fl, New York, NY 10003-4793 *Tel:* 212-614-7850 *Toll Free Tel:* 800-521-0178 *Fax:* 212-614-7886 *E-mail:* info@groveatlantic.com *Web Site:* www.groveatlantic.com, pg 108

Stoltzfus, Alison, The Princeton Review, c/o Random House Inc, 1745 Broadway, New York, NY 10019 *Toll Free Tel:* 800-733-3000 *Fax:* 212 782 9682 *E-mail:* princetonreview@randomhouse.com *Web Site:* www.princetonreview.com, pg 206

Stone, Ivy Fischer, Fifi Oscard Agency Inc, 110 W 40 St, 16th fl, New York, NY 10018 *Tel:* 212-764-1100 *Fax:* 212-840-5019 *E-mail:* agency@fifioscard.com *Web Site:* www.fifioscard.com, pg 588

Stone, John W, Artech House Inc, 685 Canton St, Norwood, MA 02062 *Tel:* 781-769-9750 *Toll Free Tel:* 800-225-9977 *Fax:* 781-769-6334 *E-mail:* artech@artechhouse.com *Web Site:* www.artechhouse.com, pg 23

Stone, Judi, Artech House Inc, 685 Canton St, Norwood, MA 02062 *Tel:* 781-769-9750 *Toll Free Tel:* 800-225-9977 *Fax:* 781-769-6334 *E-mail:* artech@artechhouse.com *Web Site:* www.artechhouse.com, pg 23

Stone, Kevin, Cengage Learning, 200 First Stamford Place, Suite 400, Stamford, CT 06902 *Tel:* 203-965-8600 *Toll Free Tel:* 800-354-9706 *Fax:* 203-965-8599 *Toll Free Fax:* 800-487-8488 *E-mail:* esales@cengage.com *Web Site:* www.cengage.com, pg 55

Stone, Kris, Piano Press, 1425 Ocean Ave, Suite 17, Del Mar, CA 92014 *Tel:* 619-884-1401 *Fax:* 858-755-1104 *E-mail:* pianopress@pianopress.com *Web Site:* www.pianopress.com, pg 201

Stone, Michelle, McClanahan Publishing House Inc, 88 Cedar St, Kuttawa, KY 42055-0100 *Tel:* 270-388-9388 *Toll Free Tel:* 800-544-6959 *Fax:* 270-388-6186 *E-mail:* books@kybooks.com *Web Site:* www.kybooks.com, pg 160

Stone, Suezen, H J Kramer Inc, PO Box 1082, Tiburon, CA 94920 *Tel:* 415-884-2100 (ext 10) *Toll Free Tel:* 800-972-6657 *Fax:* 415-435-5364 *E-mail:* hjkramer@jps.net *Web Site:* www.hjkramer.com; www.newworldlibrary.com, pg 142

Stonefield, Jeff, Apress Media LLC, 233 Spring St, New York, NY 10013 *Tel:* 212-460-1500 *Fax:* 212-460-1575 *E-mail:* editorial@apress.com *Web Site:* www.apress.com, pg 21

Storch, Maury, Gefen Books, 11 Edison Place, Springfield, NJ 07081 *Tel:* 516-593-1234 *Toll Free Tel:* 800-477-5257 *Fax:* 516-295-2739 *E-mail:* info@gefenpublishing.com; gefenny@gefenpublishing.com *Web Site:* www.israelbooks.com, pg 102

Stordahl, Derek, Bloomsbury Academic, 80 Maiden Lane, Suite 704, New York, NY 10038 *Tel:* 212-953-5858 *Toll Free Tel:* 800-561-7704 *Fax:* 212-953-5944 *E-mail:* info@continuum-books.com *Web Site:* www.continuumbooks.com, pg 40

Stordahl, Derek, Bloomsbury Publishing, 175 Fifth Ave, New York, NY 10010 *Tel:* 212-674-5151 *Toll Free Tel:* 800-221-7945 *Fax:* 212-780-0115; 212-982-2837 *E-mail:* marketingusa@bloomsbury.com; adultpublicityusa.@bloomsbury.com *Web Site:* www.bloomsbury.com, pg 40

Storrings, Michael, St Martin's Press, LLC, 175 Fifth Ave, New York, NY 10010 *Tel:* 646-307-5151 *Fax:* 212-420-9314 *E-mail:* firstname.lastname@macmillan.com *Web Site:* www.stmartins.com, pg 224

Story, Elizabeth, Tachyon Publications, 1459 18 St, Suite 139, San Francisco, CA 94107 *Tel:* 415-285-5615 *E-mail:* tachyon@tachyonpublications.com *Web Site:* www.tachyonpublications.com, pg 249

Story, Karin, Amber Quill Press LLC, PO Box 265, Indian Hills, CO 80454 *E-mail:* business@amberquill.com *Web Site:* www.amberquill.com; www.amberheat.com (imprint); www.amberallure.com (imprint), pg 10

Stoshak, Joe, Public Citizen, 1600 20 St NW, Washington, DC 20009 *Tel:* 202-588-1000 *Fax:* 202-588-7798 *E-mail:* public_citizen@citizen.org *Web Site:* www.citizen.org, pg 209

Stott, Phil, Vault.com Inc, 75 Varick St, 8th fl, New York, NY 10013 *Tel:* 212-366-4212 *Fax:* 212-366-6117 *E-mail:* feedback@staff.vault.com *Web Site:* www.vault.com, pg 274

Stouras, Tom, Macmillan, 175 Fifth Ave, New York, NY 10010 *Tel:* 646-307-5151 *Fax:* 212-420-9314 *E-mail:* firstname.lastname@macmillan.com *Web Site:* www.macmillan.com, pg 154

Stout, Christina, Penguin Group (USA) LLC Sales, 375 Hudson St, New York, NY 10014 *Tel:* 212-366-2000 *E-mail:* online@penguinputnam.com *Web Site:* us.penguingroup.com, pg 197

Stout, Rachel, Dystel & Goderich Literary Management, One Union Sq W, Suite 904, New York, NY 10003 *Tel:* 212-627-9100 *Fax:* 212-627-9313 *Web Site:* www.dystel.com, pg 569

Stovall, Dennis, Ooligan Press, Portland State University, 369 Neuberger Hall, 724 SW Harrison St, Portland, OR 97201 *Tel:* 503-725-9748 *Fax:* 503-725-3561 *E-mail:* ooligan@ooliganpress.pdx.edu *Web Site:* ooligan.pdx.edu, pg 185

Stowe, Shanon, Center Street, 12 Cadillac Dr, Suite 480, Brentwood, TN 37027 *Tel:* 615-221-0996 *Web Site:* www.centerstreet.com, pg 56

Stowe, Shanon, FaithWords, 12 Cadillac Dr, Suite 480, Brentwood, TN 37027 *Tel:* 615-221-0996 *Fax:* 615-221-0962 *Web Site:* www.hachettebookgroup.com, pg 92

Stoykova-Klemer, Katerina, Poetry Book Contest, PO Box 910456, Lexington, KY 40591-0456 *Web Site:* www.accents-publishing.com/contest.html, pg 735

Straatmann, Michael, Mari Sandoz Award, PO Box 21756, Lincoln, NE 68542-1756 *Tel:* 402-216-0727 *E-mail:* nebraskalibraries@gmail.com *Web Site:* www.nebraskalibraries.org, pg 739

Strachan, Glenn R, Jhpiego, 1615 Thames St, Baltimore, MD 21231-3492 *Tel:* 410-537-1800 *Fax:* 410-537-1473 *E-mail:* info@jhpiego.net; orders@jhpiego.net *Web Site:* www.jhpiego.org, pg 135

Strads, Gundars, American Book Award, The Raymond House, Suite 302, 655 13 St, Oakland, CA 94612 *Tel:* 510-268-9775 *E-mail:* info@beforecolumbusfoundation.com *Web Site:* www.beforecolumbusfoundation.org, pg 687

Strads, Gundars, Before Columbus Foundation, The Raymond House, Suite 302, 655 13 St, Oakland, CA 94612 *Tel:* 510-268-9775 *E-mail:* info@beforecolumbusfoundation.com *Web Site:* www.beforecolumbusfoundation.org, pg 618

Stranathan, Lynn, Yard Dog Press, 710 W Redbud Lane, Alma, AR 72921-7247 *Tel:* 479-632-4693 *Fax:* 479-632-4693 *Web Site:* www.yarddogpress.com, pg 288

Strand, Kurt, McGraw-Hill Contemporary Learning Series, 501 Bell St, Dubuque, IA 52001 *Toll Free Tel:* 800-243-6532 *Web Site:* www.mhcls.com, pg 160

Strand, Kurt, McGraw-Hill Higher Education, 1333 Burr Ridge Pkwy, Burr Ridge, IL 60527 *Tel:* 630-789-4000 *Toll Free Tel:* 800-338-3987 (cust serv) *Fax:* 614-755-5645 (cust serv) *Web Site:* www.mhhe.com, pg 161

Strand, Kurt, McGraw-Hill Humanities, Social Sciences, Languages, 2 Penn Plaza, 20th fl, New York, NY 10121 *Tel:* 212-904-2000 *Toll Free Tel:* 800-338-3987 (cust serv) *Fax:* 614-755-5645 (cust serv) *Web Site:* www.mhhe.com, pg 161

Strand, Kurt, McGraw-Hill Science, Engineering, Mathematics, 501 Bell St, Dubuque, IA 52001 *Tel:* 563-584-6000 *Toll Free Tel:* 800-338-3987 (cust serv) *Fax:* 614-755-5645 (cust serv) *Web Site:* www.mhhe.com, pg 162

Strand, Lisa K, Notable Wisconsin Authors, 4610 S Biltmore Lane, Madison, WI 53718 *Tel:* 608-245-3640 *Fax:* 608-245-3646 *Web Site:* www.wla.lib.wi.us, pg 729

Strand, Lisa K, WLA Literary Award, 4610 S Biltmore Lane, Madison, WI 53718 *Tel:* 608-245-3640 *Fax:* 608-245-3646 *Web Site:* www.wla.lib.wi.us, pg 750

Strandberg, Neil, American Booksellers Association, 333 Westchester Ave, Suite S202, White Plains, NY 10604 *Tel:* 914-406-7500 *Toll Free Tel:* 800-637-0037 *Fax:* 914-410-6297 *E-mail:* info@bookweb.org *Web Site:* www.bookweb.org, pg 612

Strang, Stephen, Charisma Media, 600 Rinehart Rd, Lake Mary, FL 32746 *Tel:* 407-333-0600 (all imprints) *Toll Free Tel:* 800-283-8494 (Charisma Media, Siloam Press, Creation House); 800-665-1468 *Fax:* 407-333-7100 (all imprints) *E-mail:* charisma@charismamedia.com *Web Site:* www.charismamedia.com, pg 58

Strang, Stephen, CharismaLife Publishers, 600 Rinehart Rd, Lake Mary, FL 32746 *Tel:* 407-333-0600 *Toll Free Tel:* 800-451-4598 *Fax:* 407-333-7100 *E-mail:* charismalife@charismamedia.com *Web Site:* www.charismamedia.com, pg 58

Strange, Nancy, Tudor Publishers Inc, 3109 Shady Lawn Dr, Greensboro, NC 27408 *Tel:* 336-288-5395 *E-mail:* tudorpublishers@triad.rr.com, pg 259

Stranges, Dr Julie Ann PhD, International Evangelism Crusades Inc, 9101 Topanga Canyon Blvd, Unit 209, Chatsworth, CA 91311-5763 *Tel:* 818-882-0039 *Fax:* 818-998-6712, pg 132

Strasbaugh, Joan, Abbeville Press, 137 Varick St, Suite 504, New York, NY 10013-1105 *Tel:* 212-366-5585 *Toll Free Tel:* 800-ARTBOOK (278-2665) *Fax:* 212-366-6966 *E-mail:* abbeville@abbeville.com *Web Site:* www.abbeville.com, pg 2

Stratton, Philippa, Stenhouse Publishers, 480 Congress St, Portland, ME 04101-3451 *Tel:* 207-253-1600 *Toll Free Tel:* 888-363-0566 *Fax:* 207-253-5121 *Toll Free Fax:* 800-833-9164 *E-mail:* customerservice@stenhouse.com *Web Site:* www.stenhouse.com, pg 244

Stratton, W K, Carr P Collins Award, PO Box 609, Round Rock, TX 78680 *Tel:* 512-683-5640 *E-mail:* tilsecretary@yahoo.com *Web Site:* www.texasinstituteofletters.org, pg 698

Stratton, W K, Soeurette Diehl Fraser Translation Award, PO Box 609, Round Rock, TX 78680 *Tel:* 512-683-5640 *E-mail:* tilsecretary@yahoo.com *Web Site:* www.texasinstituteofletters.org, pg 705

Stratton, W K, Jesse H Jones Award, PO Box 609, Round Rock, TX 78680 *Tel:* 512-683-5640 *E-mail:* tilsecretary@yahoo.com *Web Site:* www.texasinstituteofletters.org, pg 714

Stratton, W K, Most Significant Scholarly Book Award, PO Box 609, Round Rock, TX 78680 *Tel:* 512-683-5640 *E-mail:* tilsecretary@yahoo.com *Web Site:* www.texasinstituteofletters.org, pg 725

Stratton, W K, Edwin "Bud" Shrake Award for Best Short Nonfiction, PO Box 609, Round Rock, TX 78680 *Tel:* 512-683-5640 *E-mail:* tilsecretary@yahoo.com *Web Site:* www.texasinstituteofletters.org, pg 741

Stratton, W K, Helen C Smith Memorial Award, PO Box 609, Round Rock, TX 78680 *Tel:* 512-683-5640 *E-mail:* tilsecretary@yahoo.com *Web Site:* www.texasinstituteofletters.org, pg 742

Stratton, W K, Texas Institute of Letters (TIL), PO Box 609, Round Rock, TX 78680 *Tel:* 512-683-5640 *E-mail:* tilsecretary@yahoo.com *Web Site:* www.texasinstituteofletters.org, pg 637

Stratton, W K, Texas Institute of Letters Awards, PO Box 609, Round Rock, TX 78680 *Tel:* 512-683-5640 *E-mail:* tilsecretary@yahoo.com *Web Site:* www.texasinstituteofletters.org, pg 745

Straus, Jonah, Straus Literary, 319 Lafayette St, Suite 220, New York, NY 10012 *Tel:* 646-843-9950 *Fax:* 646-390-3320 *Web Site:* www.strausliterary.com, pg 596

Straus, Robin, Robin Straus Agency Inc, 229 E 79 St, Suite 5-A, New York, NY 10075 *Tel:* 212-472-3282 *Fax:* 212-472-3833 *E-mail:* info@robinstrausagency.com *Web Site:* www.robinstrausagency.com, pg 596

Strauss, Leslie R, Housing Assistance Council, 1025 Vermont Ave NW, Suite 606, Washington, DC 20005 *Tel:* 202-842-8600 *Fax:* 202-347-3441 *E-mail:* hac@ruralhome.org *Web Site:* www.ruralhome.org, pg 124

Strauss, Mark, Springer, 233 Spring St, New York, NY 10013-1578 *Tel:* 212-460-1500 *Toll Free Tel:* 800-SPRINGER (777-4643) *Fax:* 212-460-1575 *E-mail:* service-ny@springer.com *Web Site:* www.springer.com, pg 241

Strauss, Myra, Management Concepts Inc, 8230 Leesburg Pike, Suite 800, Vienna, VA 22182 *Tel:* 703-790-9595 *Toll Free Tel:* 800 506-4450 *Fax:* 703-790-1371 *E-mail:* publications@managementconcepts.com *Web Site:* www.managementconcepts.com, pg 155

Strauss, Rebecca, DeFiore and Company, LLC, 47 E 19 St, 3rd fl, New York, NY 10003 *Tel:* 212-925-7744 *Fax:* 212-925-9803 *E-mail:* submissions@defioreandco.com; info@defioreandco.com *Web Site:* www.defioreandco.com, pg 568

Strauss, Russell H, National Federation of State Poetry Societies Annual Poetry Contest, PO Box 7842, Moore, OK 73153 *E-mail:* connpoetry@comcast.net *Web Site:* www.NFSPS.com, pg 726

Strauss-Gabel, Julie, Dutton Children's Books, 345 Hudson St, New York, NY 10014 *Tel:* 212-366-2000 *E-mail:* online@penguinputnam.com *Web Site:* www.penguinputnam.com; us.penguingroup.com, pg 83

Streckfus, Peter, University of Alabama Program in Creative Writing, PO Box 870244, Tuscaloosa, AL 35487-0244 *Tel:* 205-348-5065 *Fax:* 205-348-1388 *E-mail:* english@ua.edu *Web Site:* www.as.ua.edu/english, pg 681

Streetman, Ms Burgin, Trinity University Press, One Trinity Place, San Antonio, TX 78212-7200 *Tel:* 210-999-8884 *Fax:* 210-999-8838 *E-mail:* books@trinity.edu *Web Site:* www.tupress.org, pg 259

Streitfeld, Linda Topping, The National Press Foundation, 1211 Connecticut Ave NW, Suite 310, Washington, DC 20036 *Tel:* 202-663-7280 *Web Site:* www.nationalpress.org, pg 631

Strick, Louis, Taplinger Publishing Co Inc, PO Box 175, Marlboro, NJ 07746-0175 *Tel:* 305-256-7880 *Fax:* 305-256-7816 *E-mail:* taplingerpub@yahoo.com (rts & perms, edit, corp only), pg 250

Strickland, Albert Lee, Pacific Publishing Services, PO Box 1150, Capitola, CA 95010-1150 *Tel:* 831-476-8284 *Fax:* 831-476-8294 *E-mail:* pacpub@attglobal.net, pg 552

Strickland, Jonathan, Amicus, PO Box 1329, Mankato, MN 56002 *Tel:* 507-388-9357 *Fax:* 507-388-1779 *E-mail:* info@amicuspublishing.us; orders@amicuspublishing.us *Web Site:* www.amicuspublishing.us, pg 17

Strickland, Jonathan, Black Rabbit Books, 123 S Broad St, Mankato, MN 56001 *Tel:* 507-388-1609 *Fax:* 507-388-1364 *E-mail:* info@blackrabbitbooks.com; orders@blackrabbitbooks.com *Web Site:* www.blackrabbitbooks.com, pg 39

Strickland, Kate, Milkweed Editions, 1011 Washington Ave S, Suite 300, Minneapolis, MN 55415-1246 *Tel:* 612-332-3192 *Toll Free Tel:* 800-520-6455 *Fax:* 612-215-2550 *Web Site:* www.milkweed.org, pg 166

Strickland, Kate, Milkweed National Fiction Prize, 1011 Washington Ave S, Suite 300, Minneapolis, MN 55415-1246 *Tel:* 612-332-3192 *Toll Free Tel:* 800-520-6455 *Fax:* 612-215-2550 *E-mail:* submissions@milkweed.org *Web Site:* www.milkweed.org, pg 723

Strickland, Sherri, University Press of New England, One Court St, Suite 250, Lebanon, NH 03766 *Tel:* 603-448-1533 *Toll Free Tel:* 800-421-1561 (orders only) *Fax:* 603-448-7006; 603-643-1540 *E-mail:* university.press@dartmouth.edu *Web Site:* www.upne.com, pg 271

Strickland, Tessa, Barefoot Books, 2067 Massachusetts Ave, 5th fl, Cambridge, MA 02140 *Tel:* 617-576-0660 *Toll Free Tel:* 866-215-1756 (cust serv); 866-417-2369 (orders) *Fax:* 617-576-0049 *E-mail:* ussales@barefootbooks.com; help@barefootbooks.com *Web Site:* www.barefootbooks.com, pg 30

Strickler, Sarah A, Woodbine House, 6510 Bells Mill Rd, Bethesda, MD 20817 *Tel:* 301-897-3570 *Toll Free Tel:* 800-843-7323 *Fax:* 301-897-5838 *E-mail:* info@woodbinehouse.com *Web Site:* www.woodbinehouse.com, pg 284

Strittmatter, Aimee, ALSC BWI/Summer Reading Program Grant, 50 E Huron St, Chicago, IL 60611-2795 *Tel:* 312-280-2163 *Toll Free Tel:* 800-545-2433 *Fax:* 312-440-9374 *E-mail:* alsc@ala.org *Web Site:* www.ala.org/alsc, pg 687

Strittmatter, Aimee, The May Hill Arbuthnot Honor Lecture Award, 50 E Huron St, Chicago, IL 60611-2795 *Tel:* 312-280-2163 *Toll Free Tel:* 800-545-2433 *Fax:* 312-440-9374 *E-mail:* alsc@ala.org *Web Site:* www.ala.org/alsc, pg 688

Strittmatter, Aimee, The Mildred L Batchelder Award, 50 E Huron St, Chicago, IL 60611-2795 *Tel:* 312-280-2163 *Toll Free Tel:* 800-545-2433 *Fax:* 312-440-9374 *E-mail:* alsc@ala.org *Web Site:* www.ala.org/alsc, pg 689

Strittmatter, Aimee, The Pura Belpre Award, 50 E Huron St, Chicago, IL 60611-2795 *Tel:* 312-280-2163 *Toll Free Tel:* 800-545-2433 *Fax:* 312-440-9374 *E-mail:* alsc@ala.org *Web Site:* www.ala.org/alsc, pg 690

Strittmatter, Aimee, Bound to Stay Bound Books Scholarship, 50 E Huron St, Chicago, IL 60611-2795 *Tel:* 312-280-2163 *Toll Free Tel:* 800-545-2433 *Fax:* 312-440-9374 *E-mail:* alsc@ala.org *Web Site:* www.ala.org/alsc, pg 692

Strittmatter, Aimee, The Randolph Caldecott Medal, 50 E Huron St, Chicago, IL 60611-2795 *Tel:* 312-280-2163 *Toll Free Tel:* 800-545-2433 *Fax:* 312-440-9374 *E-mail:* alsc@ala.org *Web Site:* www.ala.org/alsc, pg 694

Strittmatter, Aimee, Frederic G Melcher Scholarship, 50 E Huron St, Chicago, IL 60611-2795 *Tel:* 312-280-2163 *Toll Free Tel:* 800-545-2433 *Fax:* 312-440-9374 *E-mail:* alsc@ala.org *Web Site:* www.ala.org/alsc, pg 723

Strittmatter, Aimee, John Newbery Medal, 50 E Huron St, Chicago, IL 60611-2795 *Tel:* 312-280-2163 *Toll Free Tel:* 800-545-2433 *Fax:* 312-440-9374 *E-mail:* alsc@ala.org *Web Site:* www.ala.org/alsc, pg 729

Strittmatter, Aimee, Robert F Sibert Informational Book Award, 50 E Huron St, Chicago, IL 60611-2795 *Tel:* 312-280-2163 *Toll Free Tel:* 800-545-2433 *Fax:* 312-440-9374 *E-mail:* alsc@ala.org *Web Site:* www.ala.org/alsc, pg 742

Strittmatter, Aimee, The Laura Ingalls Wilder Medal, 50 E Huron St, Chicago, IL 60611-2795 *Tel:* 312-280-2163 *Toll Free Tel:* 800-545-2433 *Fax:* 312-440-9374 *E-mail:* alsc@ala.org *Web Site:* www.ala.org/alsc, pg 749

Strohle, Lisa, Association of Opinion Journalists (AOJ), 3899 N Front St, Harrisburg, PA 17110 *Tel:* 717-703-3015 *Fax:* 717-703-3014 *E-mail:* ncew@pa-news.org *Web Site:* www.ncew.org, pg 617

Stromberg, Elizabeth, Ten Speed Press, 2625 Alcatraz Ave, Unit 505, Berkeley, CA 94705 *Tel:* 510-285-3000 *Toll Free Tel:* 800-841-BOOK (841-2665) *E-mail:* csorders@randomhouse.com *Web Site:* crownpublishing.com/imprint/ten-speed-press, pg 252

Strone, Daniel, Trident Media Group LLC, 41 Madison Ave, 36th fl, New York, NY 10010 *Tel:* 212-262-4810 *Fax:* 212-262-4849 *Web Site:* www.tridentmediagroup.com, pg 598

Strong, Marianne, Marianne Strong Literary Agency, 65 E 96 St, New York, NY 10128 *Tel:* 212-249-1000 *Fax:* 212-831-3241 *Web Site:* stronglit.com, pg 596

Stroschein, Steven, IBFD North America Inc (International Bureau of Fiscal Documentation), 8100 Boone Blvd, Suite 210, Vienna, VA 22182 *Tel:* 703-442-7757 *Fax:* 703-442-7758 *E-mail:* americas@ibfd.org *Web Site:* www.ibfd.org, pg 126

941-7842 *E-mail:* marketing@springerpub.com; cs@springerpub.com (orders); editorial@springerpub.com *Web Site:* www.springerpub.com, pg 241

Sussman, Steven, Dover Publications Inc, 31 E Second St, Mineola, NY 11501-3852 *Tel:* 516-294-7000 *Toll Free Tel:* 800-223-3130 (orders) *Fax:* 516-742-6953; 516-742-5049 (orders) *Web Site:* store.doverdirect.com, pg 81

Suter, Cathy, The Permanent Press, 4170 Noyac Rd, Sag Harbor, NY 11963 *Tel:* 631-725-1101 *Fax:* 631-725-8215 *E-mail:* info@thepermanentpress.com *Web Site:* www.thepermanentpress.com, pg 199

Suter, Cathy, Second Chance Press, 4170 Noyac Rd, Sag Harbor, NY 11963 *Tel:* 631-725-1101 *E-mail:* info@thepermanentpress.com *Web Site:* www.thepermanentpress.com, pg 230

Sutherland, Victoria, ForeWord Reviews Book of the Year Awards, 425 Boardman Ave, Suite B, Traverse City, MI 49684 *Tel:* 231-933-3699 *Fax:* 231-933-3899 *Web Site:* www.bookoftheyearawards.com, pg 705

Sutker, Catherine, New Harbinger Publications Inc, 5674 Shattuck Ave, Oakland, CA 94609 *Tel:* 510-652-0215 *Toll Free Tel:* 800-748-6273 (orders only) *Fax:* 510-652-5472 *Toll Free Fax:* 800-652-1613 *E-mail:* nhhelp@newharbinger.com; customerservice@newharbinger.com *Web Site:* www.newharbinger.com, pg 177

Sutton, Caroline, Penguin Group (USA) LLC, 375 Hudson St, New York, NY 10014 *Tel:* 212-366-2000 *Toll Free Tel:* 800-847-5515 (inside sales); 800-631-8571 (cust serv) *Fax:* 212-366-2666; 607-775-4829 (inside sales) *E-mail:* online@us.penguingroup.com *Web Site:* www.penguin.com; us.penguingroup.com, pg 197

Sutton, Jo Ann, Morton Publishing Co, 925 W Kenyon Ave, Unit 12, Englewood, CO 80110 *Tel:* 303-761-4805 *Fax:* 303-762-9923 *E-mail:* contact@morton-pub.com *Web Site:* www.morton-pub.com, pg 170

Sutton, Roger, Boston Globe-Horn Book Award, 56 Roland St, Suite 200, Boston, MA 02129 *Tel:* 617-628-0225 *Toll Free Tel:* 800-325-1170 *Fax:* 617-628-0882 *E-mail:* info@hbook.com *Web Site:* www.hbook.com, pg 692

Sutton, Roger, Scott O'Dell Award for Historical Fiction, Hornbook, Suite 200, 56 Roland St, Boston, MA 02129 *Tel:* 617-628-8471 *Toll Free Tel:* 800-325-1170 *Web Site:* www.scottodell.com/odellaward.html, pg 730

Suvikapakornkul, Shane, Serindia Publications, PO Box 10335, Chicago, IL 60610-0335 *Tel:* 312-664-5531 *Fax:* 312-664-4389 *E-mail:* info@serindia.com *Web Site:* www.serindia.com, pg 231

Suzanne, Claudia, Wambtac Communications, 2323 N Tustin Ave, Suite C-202, Santa Ana, CA 92705 *Tel:* 714-954-0580 *Toll Free Tel:* 800-641-3936 *Fax:* 714-954-0793 (orders) *E-mail:* wambtac@wambtac.com *Web Site:* www.wambtac.com; claudiasuzanne.com (prof servs), pg 556

Svehla, Gary, Midnight Marquee Press Inc, 9721 Britinay Lane, Baltimore, MD 21234 *Tel:* 410-665-1198 *E-mail:* mmarquee@aol.com *Web Site:* www.midmar.com, pg 166

Svehla, Susan, Midnight Marquee Press Inc, 9721 Britinay Lane, Baltimore, MD 21234 *Tel:* 410-665-1198 *E-mail:* mmarquee@aol.com *Web Site:* www.midmar.com, pg 166

Sverdrup, Christina, Hunter House Publishers, 1515 1/2 Park St, Alameda, CA 94501 *Tel:* 510-865-5282 *Toll Free Tel:* 800-266-5592 *Fax:* 510-865-4295 *E-mail:* ordering@hunterhouse.com *Web Site:* www.hunterhouse.com, pg 126

Svetcov, Danielle, Levine|Greenberg Literary Agency Inc, 307 Seventh Ave, Suite 2407, New York, NY 10001 *Tel:* 212-337-0934 *Fax:* 212-337-0948 *Web Site:* www.levinegreenberg.com, pg 581

Swail, David, McGraw-Hill International Publishing Group, 2 Penn Plaza, New York, NY 10121 *Tel:* 212-904-2000 *Web Site:* www.mcgraw-hill.com, pg 161

Swail, David, McGraw-Hill Ryerson Limited, 300 Water St, Whitby, ON L1N 9B6, Canada *Tel:* 905-430-5000 *Toll Free Tel:* 800-565-5758 (cust serv) *Fax:* 905-430-5020 *Web Site:* www.mcgrawhill.ca, pg 512

Swaim, Dennis, Penguin Books, 375 Hudson St, New York, NY 10014 *Tel:* 212-366-2000 *E-mail:* online@penguinputnam.com *Web Site:* www.penguinputnam.com; www.penguinclassics.com; us.penguingroup.com, pg 197

Swaim, Dennis, Viking, 375 Hudson St, New York, NY 10014 *Tel:* 212-366-2000 *E-mail:* online@penguinputnam.com *Web Site:* www.penguinputnam.com; us.penguingroup.com, pg 275

Swain, Neal, Wales Literary Agency Inc, PO Box 9426, Seattle, WA 98109-0426 *Tel:* 206-284-7114 *E-mail:* waleslit@waleslit.com *Web Site:* www.waleslit.com, pg 598

Swaney, Charlie, Tyndale House Publishers Inc, 351 Executive Dr, Carol Stream, IL 60188 *Tel:* 630-668-8300 *Toll Free Tel:* 800-323-9400 *Web Site:* www.tyndale.com, pg 261

Swank, Linda, PreK-12 Learning Group, 325 Chestnut St, Suite 1110, Philadelphia, PA 19106 *Tel:* 267-351-4310 *Fax:* 267-351-4317 *E-mail:* prek12learning@publishers.org *Web Site:* www.aepweb.org, pg 634

Swanson, O'Ryin, Light Technology Publishing, 4030 E Huntington Dr, Flagstaff, AZ 86004 *Tel:* 928-526-1345 *Toll Free Tel:* 800-450-0985 *Fax:* 928-714-1132 *E-mail:* publishing@lighttechnology.net *Web Site:* www.lighttechnology.com, pg 148

Swanson-Davies, Linda, Glimmer Train Press Inc, PO Box 80430, Portland, OR 97280 *Tel:* 503-221-0836 *Fax:* 503-221-0837 *E-mail:* editors@glimmertrain.org *Web Site:* www.glimmertrain.org, pg 103

Swauger, Amy, Teachers & Writers Collaborative, 520 Eighth Ave, Suite 2020, New York, NY 10018-4165 *Tel:* 212-691-6590 *Toll Free Tel:* 888-BOOKS-TW (266-5789) *Fax:* 212-675-0171 *E-mail:* info@twc.org; books@twc.org *Web Site:* www.twc.org, pg 637

Swayze, Carolyn, Carolyn Swayze Literary Agency Ltd, 15927 Pacific Place, White Rock, BC V4B 1S9, Canada *Tel:* 604-538-3478 *Web Site:* www.swayzeagency.com, pg 596

Sweany, Brian, Recorded Books LLC, 270 Skipjack Rd, Prince Frederick, MD 20678 *Tel:* 410-535-5590 *Toll Free Tel:* 800-638-1304; 877-732-2898 *Fax:* 410-535-5499 *E-mail:* customerservice@recordedbooks.com *Web Site:* www.recordedbooks.com, pg 215

Sweeney, Frances, PREP Publishing, 1110 1/2 Hay St, Suite C, Fayetteville, NC 28305 *Tel:* 910-483-6611 *Toll Free Tel:* 800-533-2814 *E-mail:* preppub@aol.com *Web Site:* www.prep-pub.com, pg 205

Sweeney, Jillian, The Ned Leavitt Agency, 70 Wooster St, Suite 4-F, New York, NY 10012 *Tel:* 212-334-0999 *Web Site:* www.nedleavittagency.com, pg 581

Sweeney, Jon, Paraclete Press Inc, 36 Southern Eagle Cartway, Brewster, MA 02631 *Tel:* 508-255-4685 *Toll Free Tel:* 800-451-5006 *Fax:* 508-255-5705 *E-mail:* mail@paracletepress.com *Web Site:* www.paracletepress.com, pg 192

Sweeney, Katie, Fordham University Press, 2546 Belmont Ave, University Box L, Bronx, NY 10458 *Tel:* 718-817-4795 *Fax:* 718-817-4785 *Web Site:* www.fordhampress.com, pg 97

Sweet, Beth, Lark Crafts, 67 Broadway, Asheville, NC 28801 *Tel:* 828-253-0467 *Fax:* 828-253-7952 *E-mail:* info@larkbooks.com *Web Site:* www.larkcrafts.com; www.larkbooks.com, pg 144

Sweet, Christopher, Thames & Hudson, 500 Fifth Ave, New York, NY 10110 *Tel:* 212-354-3763 *Toll Free Tel:* 800-233-4830 *Fax:* 212-398-1252 *E-mail:* bookinfo@thames.wwnorton.com *Web Site:* www.thamesandhudsonusa.com, pg 253

Sweetland, Helen, Sierra Club Books, 85 Second St, 2nd fl, San Francisco, CA 94105 *Tel:* 415-977-5500 *Fax:* 415-977-5794 *E-mail:* books.publishing@sierraclub.org *Web Site:* www.sierraclubbooks.org, pg 233

Swensen, Evan, Publication Consultants, 8370 Eleusis Dr, Anchorage, AK 99502 *Tel:* 907-349-2424 *Fax:* 907-349-2426 *E-mail:* books@publicationconsultants.com *Web Site:* www.publicationconsultants.com, pg 209

Swenson, Bruce, PhotoSource International, Pine Lake Farm, 1910 35 Rd, Osceola, WI 54020-5602 *Tel:* 715-248-3800 (ext 21) *Toll Free Tel:* 800-624-0266 (ext 21) *Fax:* 715-248-3800 *Toll Free Fax:* 800-223-3860 *E-mail:* info@photosource.com; psi2@photosource.com *Web Site:* www.photosource.com, pg 553

Swenson, Emily, Pearson Education, 1900 E Lake Ave, Glenview, IL 60025 *Tel:* 847-729-3000 *Toll Free Tel:* 800-535-4391 (Midwest) *Fax:* 847-729-8910, pg 195

Swenson, Jamie, Wisconsin Annual Fall Conferencee, PO Box 259303, Madison, WI 53725 *Tel:* 608-278-0692 *Web Site:* www.scbwi.org; www.scbwi-wi.com, pg 674

Swenson, Tree, The Academy of American Poets Inc, 75 Maiden Lane, Suite 901, New York, NY 10038 *Tel:* 212-274-0343 *Fax:* 212-274-9427 *E-mail:* academy@poets.org *Web Site:* www.poets.org, pg 611

Swenson, Tree, Raiziss/de Palchi Fellowship, 75 Maiden Lane, Suite 901, New York, NY 10038 *Tel:* 212-274-0343 *Fax:* 212-274-9427 *E-mail:* academy@poets.org *Web Site:* www.poets.org, pg 737

Swenson, Tree, Walt Whitman Award, 75 Maiden Lane, Suite 901, New York, NY 10038 *Tel:* 212-274-0343 *Fax:* 212-274-9427 *E-mail:* academy@poets.org *Web Site:* www.poets.org, pg 749

Swerdloff, Carolyn, Simon & Schuster Children's Publishing, 1230 Avenue of the Americas, New York, NY 10020 *Tel:* 212-698-7000 *Web Site:* KIDS.SimonandSchuster.com; TEEN.SimonandSchuster.com; simonandschuster.net; simonandschuster.biz, pg 235

Swetonic, Carrie, Dutton, 375 Hudson St, New York, NY 10014 *Tel:* 212-366-2000 *Fax:* 212-366-2262 *E-mail:* online@penguinputnam.com *Web Site:* www.penguinputnam.com; us.penguingroup.com, pg 83

Swinwood, Craig, Harlequin Enterprises Ltd, 225 Duncan Mill Rd, Don Mills, ON M3B 3K9, Canada *Tel:* 416-445-5860 *Toll Free Tel:* 888-432-4879; 800-370-5838 (ebook inquiries) *Fax:* 416-445-8655 *E-mail:* CustomerService@harlequin.com *Web Site:* www.harlequin.com, pg 508

Swinwood, Susan, Harlequin Enterprises Ltd, 225 Duncan Mill Rd, Don Mills, ON M3B 3K9, Canada *Tel:* 416-445-5860 *Toll Free Tel:* 888-432-4879; 800-370-5838 (ebook inquiries) *Fax:* 416-445-8655 *E-mail:* CustomerService@harlequin.com *Web Site:* www.harlequin.com, pg 508

Swirsky, Rachel, Science Fiction & Fantasy Writers of America Inc (SFWA), PO Box 3238, Enfield, CT 06083-3238 *E-mail:* office@sfwa.org *Web Site:* www.sfwa.org, pg 635

Swirsky, Rachel, SFWA Nebula Awards, PO Box 3238, Enfield, CT 06083-3238 *E-mail:* office@sfwa.org *Web Site:* www.sfwa.org, pg 741

Switzer, Kristi, Brewers Publications, 736 Pearl St, Boulder, CO 80302 *Tel:* 303-447-0816 *Toll Free Tel:* 888-822-6273 (CN & US) *Fax:* 303-447-2825 *E-mail:* info@brewersassociation.org *Web Site:* www.brewersassociation.org, pg 46

Swope, Pamela K, Philosophy Documentation Center, PO Box 7147, Charlottesville, VA 22906-7147 *Tel:* 434-220-3300 *Toll Free Tel:* 800-444-2419 *Fax:* 434-220-3301 *E-mail:* order@pdcnet.org *Web Site:* www.pdcnet.org, pg 201

Sygall, Susan, Mobility International USA, 132 E Broadway, Suite 343, Eugene, OR 97401 *Tel:* 541-343-1284 *Fax:* 541-343-6812 *E-mail:* info@miusa.org *Web Site:* www.miusa.org, pg 168

Sylbert, John, American Institute for Economic Research (AIER), 250 Division St, Great Barrington, MA 01230 *Tel:* 413-528-1216 *Toll Free Tel:* 888-528-0103; 888-528-1216 (orders) *Fax:* 413-528-0103 *E-mail:* info@aier.org *Web Site:* www.aier.org, pg 13

281-0373 *E-mail:* info@harperarringtonmedia.com *Web Site:* www.thelittlee.com; www.harperarringtonmedia.com, pg 150

Thomas, John A, Liturgy Training Publications, 3949 S Racine Ave, Chicago, IL 60609-2523 *Tel:* 773-579-4900 *Toll Free Tel:* 800-933-1800 (US & CN only orders) *Fax:* 773-486-7094 *Toll Free Fax:* 800-933-7094 (US & CN only orders) *E-mail:* orders@ltp.org *Web Site:* www.ltp.org, pg 151

Thomas, Kelly, Society for Industrial & Applied Mathematics, 3600 Market St, 6th fl, Philadelphia, PA 19104-2688 *Tel:* 215-382-9800 *Toll Free Tel:* 800-447-7426 *Fax:* 215-386-7999 *E-mail:* siambooks@siam.org *Web Site:* www.siam.org, pg 238

Thomas, Luke, David Black Agency, 335 Adams St, 27th fl, Suite 2707, Brooklyn, NY 11201 *Tel:* 718-852-5500 *Fax:* 718-852-5539 *Web Site:* www.davidblackagency.com, pg 562

Thomas, Mark B, Review & Herald Publishing Association, 55 W Oak Ridge Dr, Hagerstown, MD 21740 *Tel:* 301-393-3000 *Toll Free Tel:* 800-234-7630 *Fax:* 301-393-4055 (edit); 301-393-3222 (book div) *E-mail:* editorial@rhpa.org *Web Site:* www.reviewandherald.com, pg 218

Thomas, Mary Beth, HarperCollins Publishers Sales, 10 E 53 St, New York, NY 10022 *Fax:* 212-207-7000 *Web Site:* www.harpercollins.com, pg 114

Thomas, Michael Donald, Pflaum Publishing Group, 2621 Dryden Rd, Suite 300, Dayton, OH 45439 *Tel:* 937-293-1415 *Toll Free Tel:* 800-543-4383; 800-523-4625 (sales) *Fax:* 937-293-1310 *Toll Free Fax:* 800-370-4450 *E-mail:* service@pflaum.com *Web Site:* pflaum.com, pg 200

Thomas, Michael Payne, Charles C Thomas Publisher Ltd, 2600 S First St, Springfield, IL 62704 *Tel:* 217-789-8980 *Toll Free Tel:* 800-258-8980 *Fax:* 217-789-9130 *E-mail:* books@ccthomas.com *Web Site:* www.ccthomas.com, pg 254

Thomas, Nicole, Central Recovery Press (CRP), 3321 N Buffalo Dr, Suite 275, Las Vegas, NV 89129 *Tel:* 702-868-5830 *Fax:* 702-868-5831 *E-mail:* info@centralrecovery.com *Web Site:* centralrecoverypress.com, pg 57

Thomas, Patrick, Milkweed Editions, 1011 Washington Ave S, Suite 300, Minneapolis, MN 55415-1246 *Tel:* 612-332-3192 *Toll Free Tel:* 800-520-6455 *Fax:* 612-215-2550 *Web Site:* www.milkweed.org, pg 166

Thomas, Patrick, Milkweed National Fiction Prize, 1011 Washington Ave S, Suite 300, Minneapolis, MN 55415-1246 *Tel:* 612-332-3192 *Toll Free Tel:* 800-520-6455 *Fax:* 612-215-2550 *E-mail:* submissions@milkweed.org *Web Site:* www.milkweed.org, pg 723

Thomas, Randolph, Louisiana State University Creative Writing Program MFA, English Dept, 260 Allen Hall, Baton Rouge, LA 70803 *Tel:* 225-578-5922 *Fax:* 225-578-4129 *Web Site:* www.lsu.edu; www.english.lsu.edu/dept/programs/grad/creative_writing, pg 679

Thomas, Trisha, Evan-Moor Educational Publishers, 18 Lower Ragsdale Dr, Monterey, CA 93940-5746 *Tel:* 831-649-5901 *Toll Free Tel:* 800-714-0971 (cust serv); 800-777-4362 (orders) *Fax:* 831-649-6256 *Toll Free Fax:* 800-777-4332 (orders) *E-mail:* sales@evan-moor.com; marketing@evan-moor.com *Web Site:* www.evan-moor.com, pg 90

Thomas, Wayne, The Tusculum Review Prize for Fiction, 60 Shiloh Rd, PO Box 5113, Greeneville, TN 37743 *Web Site:* www.tusculum.edu/tusculumreview, pg 747

Thomas, William, Abrams Learning Trends, 16310 Bratton Lane, Suite 250, Austin, TX 78728-2403 *Toll Free Tel:* 800-227-9120 *Toll Free Fax:* 800-737-3322 *E-mail:* customerservice@abramslearningtrends.com (orders, cust serv) *Web Site:* www.abramslearningtrends.com (orders, cust serv), pg 3

Thomas, William, Doubleday/Nan A Talese, c/o Random House Inc, 1745 Broadway, New York, NY 10019 *Tel:* 212-751-2600 *Toll Free Tel:* 800-638-6460 *Fax:* 212-572-2593 *Web Site:* www.knopfdoubleday.com, pg 81

Thompson, Andrew, Alice James Books, 238 Main St, Farmington, ME 04938 *Tel:* 207-778-7071 *Fax:* 207-778-7766 *E-mail:* info@alicejamesbooks.org *Web Site:* www.alicejamesbooks.org, pg 8

Thompson, Jeana, Oak Tree Press, 140 E Palmer St, Taylorville, IL 62568 *Tel:* 217-824-6500 *E-mail:* publisher@oaktreebooks.com; info@oaktreebooks.com; query@oaktreebooks.com; pressdept@oaktreebooks.com; bookorders@oaktreebooks.com *Web Site:* www.oaktreebooks.com; www.otpblog.blogspot.com, pg 183

Thompson, John, B&H Publishing Group, One Lifeway Plaza, Nashville, TN 37234-0114 *Tel:* 615-251-2520 *Fax:* 615-251-5004 *Web Site:* www.bhpublishinggroup.com, pg 30

Thompson, John, Illumination Arts Publishing, 808 Sixth St S, Suite 200, Kirkland, WA 98033 *Tel:* 425-968-5097 *Fax:* 425-968-5634 *E-mail:* liteinfo@illumin.com *Web Site:* www.illumin.com, pg 128

Thompson, Judy, The Briar Cliff Review Fiction, Poetry & Creative Nonfiction Contest, 3303 Rebecca St, Sioux City, IA 51104-2100 *Tel:* 712-279-1651 *Fax:* 712-279-5486 *Web Site:* www.briarcliff.edu/bcreview, pg 693

Thompson, Keith, Thompson Educational Publishing Inc, 20 Ripley Ave, Toronto, ON M6S 3N9, Canada *Tel:* 416-766-2763 (admin & orders) *Toll Free Tel:* 877-366-2763 *Fax:* 416-766-0398 (admin & orders) *E-mail:* publisher@thompsonbooks.com *Web Site:* www.thompsonbooks.com, pg 521

Thompson, Liz, Phaidon Press Inc, 180 Varick St, 14th fl, New York, NY 10014 *Tel:* 212-652-5400 *Toll Free Tel:* 800-759-0190 (cust serv) *Fax:* 212-652-5410 *Toll Free Fax:* 800-286-9471 (cust serv) *E-mail:* ussales@phaidon.com *Web Site:* www.phaidon.com, pg 200

Thompson, MaryAnn, Tradewind Books, 202-1807 Maritime Mews, Vancouver, BC V6H 3W7, Canada *Fax:* 604-662-4405 *E-mail:* tradewindbooks@telus.net *Web Site:* www.tradewindbooks.com, pg 521

Thompson, Myles, Columbia University Press, 61 W 62 St, New York, NY 10023 *Tel:* 212-459-0600 *Toll Free Tel:* 800-944-8648 *Fax:* 212-459-3678 *E-mail:* cup_book@columbia.edu (orders & cust serv) *Web Site:* cup.columbia.edu, pg 65

Thompson, Richelle, Forward Movement Publications, 412 Sycamore St, Cincinnati, OH 45202-4110 *Tel:* 513-721-6659 *Toll Free Tel:* 800-543-1813 *Fax:* 513-721-0729 (orders) *E-mail:* orders@forwardmovement.org (orders & cust serv) *Web Site:* www.forwardmovement.org, pg 97

Thompson, Theresa, Sterling Publishing Co Inc, 387 Park Ave S, 11th fl, New York, NY 10016-8810 *Tel:* 212-532-7160 *Toll Free Tel:* 800-367-9692 *Fax:* 212-213-2495 *Web Site:* www.sterlingpub.com, pg 244

Thompson, Tommy, Florida Outdoor Writers Association Inc, 24 NW 33 Ct, Suite A, Gainesville, FL 32607 *E-mail:* info@fowa.org *Web Site:* www.fowa.org, pg 623

Thomson, John, Antiquarian Booksellers' Association of America (ABAA), 20 W 44 St, Suite 507, New York, NY 10036 *Tel:* 212-944-8291 *Fax:* 212-944-8293 *E-mail:* hq@abaa.org *Web Site:* www.abaa.org, pg 615

Thomson, Keith, American Philosophical Society, 104 S Fifth St, Philadelphia, PA 19106 *Tel:* 215-440-3425 *Fax:* 215-440-3450 *E-mail:* dianepub@comcast.net *Web Site:* www.amphilsoc.org, pg 15

Thomson, Ryan J, Captain Fiddle Music & Publications, 94 Wiswall Rd, Lee, NH 03824 *Tel:* 603-659-2658 *E-mail:* cfiddle@tiac.net *Web Site:* captainfiddle.com, pg 52

Thomson, Sue, Art of Living, PrimaMedia Inc, 1250 Bethlehem Pike, Suite 241, Hatfield, PA 19440 *Tel:* 215-660-5045 *Toll Free Tel:* 800-581-9020 *Fax:* 734-448-4125 *E-mail:* primamedia4@yahoo.com, pg 22

Thomson-Black, Jean E, Yale University Press, 302 Temple St, New Haven, CT 06511-8909 *Tel:* 401-531-2800 (cust serv); 203-432-0960 *Toll Free Tel:* 800-405-1619 (cust serv) *Fax:* 203-432-0948; 401-531-2801 (cust serv) *Toll Free Fax:* 800-406-9145 (cust serv) *E-mail:* customer.care@trilateral.org (cust serv); language.yalepress@yale.edu *Web Site:* www.yalebooks.com, pg 287

Thorne, Troy, Fox Chapel Publishing Co Inc, 1970 Broad St, East Petersburg, PA 17520 *Tel:* 717-560-4703 *Toll Free Tel:* 800-457-9112 *Fax:* 717-560-4702 *E-mail:* customerservice@foxchapelpublishing.com *Web Site:* www.foxchapelpublishing.com, pg 98

Thornton, Allen, Susan Thornton, 6090 Liberty Ave, Vermilion, OH 44089 *Tel:* 440-967-1757 *E-mail:* allenthornton@earthlink.net, pg 556

Thornton, Carrie, HarperCollins General Books Group, 10 E 53 St, New York, NY 10022 *Tel:* 212-207-7000 *Fax:* 212-207-7633 *Web Site:* www.harpercollins.com, pg 113

Thornton, Greg, Moody Publishers, 820 N La Salle Blvd, Chicago, IL 60610 *Tel:* 312-329-4000 *Toll Free Tel:* 800-678-8812 (cust serv) *Fax:* 312-329-2019 *Web Site:* www.moodypublishers.com, pg 169

Thornton, Jennifer, National Geographic Books, 1145 17 St NW, Washington, DC 20036-4688 *Tel:* 202-857-7000 *Fax:* 202-857-7670 *Web Site:* www.nationalgeographic.com, pg 174

Thornton, Kim, Random House Speakers Bureau, 1745 Broadway, Mail Drop 13-1, New York, NY 10019 *Tel:* 212-572-2013 *E-mail:* rhspeakers@randomhouse.com *Web Site:* www.rhspeakers.com, pg 605

Thornton, Susan, Susan Thornton, 6090 Liberty Ave, Vermilion, OH 44089 *Tel:* 440-967-1757 *E-mail:* allenthornton@earthlink.net, pg 556

Thorpe, Andrea, Sarah Josepha Hale Award, 58 N Main, Newport, NH 03773 *Tel:* 603-863-3430 *E-mail:* rfl@newport.lib.nh.us *Web Site:* www.newport.lib.nh.us, pg 708

Threadgill, Carolyn, Parenting Press Inc, 11065 Fifth Ave NE, Suite F, Seattle, WA 98125 *Tel:* 206-364-2900 *Toll Free Tel:* 800-99-BOOKS (992-6657) *Fax:* 206-364-0702 *E-mail:* office@parentingpress.com; marketing@parentingpress.com *Web Site:* www.parentingpress.com, pg 193

Thresher, Tanya, The Ibsen Society of America, University of California, Dept of Scandinavian, 6303 Dwinelle Hall, No 2690, Berkeley, CA 94720-2690 *Tel:* 510-642-0927 *Fax:* 510-642-6220 *Web Site:* www.ibsensociety.liu.edu, pg 624

Thrombly, J, Wittenborn Art Books, 1109 Geary Blvd, San Francisco, CA 94109 *Tel:* 415-292-6500 *Toll Free Tel:* 800-660-6403 *Fax:* 415-292-6594 *E-mail:* wittenborn@art-books.com *Web Site:* www.art-books.com, pg 284

Tierney, P J, Beacon Press, 25 Beacon St, Boston, MA 02108 *Tel:* 617-742-2110 *Fax:* 617-723-3097; 617-742-2290 *Web Site:* www.beacon.org, pg 32

Tierney, Peggy, Tanglewood Press, PO Box 3009, Terre Haute, IN 47803 *Tel:* 812-877-9488; 412-741-1579 (orders) *Toll Free Tel:* 800-836-4994 (orders) *Fax:* 412-741-0609 (orders) *Web Site:* www.tanglewoodbooks.com, pg 250

Tigay, Alan M, The Harold U Ribalow Prize, 50 W 58 St, 4th fl, New York, NY 10019 *Tel:* 212-451-6289 *Fax:* 212-451-6257 *E-mail:* ribalowprize@hadassah.org *Web Site:* www.hadassah.org/magazine, pg 738

Tigunait, Pandit Rajmani PhD, Himalayan Institute Press, 952 Bethany Tpke, Honesdale, PA 18431-9706 *Tel:* 570-253-5551 *Toll Free Tel:* 800-822-4547 *Fax:* 570-253-4500 *E-mail:* info@himalayaninstitute.org *Web Site:* www.himalayaninstitute.org, pg 120

Tijerina, Andres, Carr P Collins Award, PO Box 609, Round Rock, TX 78680 *Tel:* 512-683-5640 *E-mail:* tilsecretary@yahoo.com *Web Site:* www.texasinstituteofletters.org, pg 698

Tomasino, Christine K, The Tomasino Agency Inc, 70 Chestnut St, Dobbs Ferry, NY 10522 *Tel:* 914-674-9659 *Fax:* 914-693-0381 *E-mail:* info@tomasinoagency.com *Web Site:* www.tomasinoagency.com, pg 597

Tomassi, Noreen, The Center for Fiction, 17 E 47 St, New York, NY 10017 *Tel:* 212-755-6710 *Fax:* 212-826-0831 *E-mail:* info@centerforfiction.org *Web Site:* www.centerforfiction.org, pg 621

Tomb, Lynn Stowe, Merriam-Webster Inc, 47 Federal St, Springfield, MA 01102 *Tel:* 413-734-3134 *Toll Free Tel:* 800-828-1880 (orders & cust serv) *Fax:* 413-731-5979 (sales) *E-mail:* support@merriam-webster.com *Web Site:* www.merriam-webster.com, pg 165

Tombs, Greg, David C Cook, 4050 Lee Vance View, Colorado Springs, CO 80918 *Tel:* 719-536-0100 *Toll Free Tel:* 800-708-5550 *Fax:* 519-536-3269 *Web Site:* www.davidccook.com, pg 67

Tomkins, Paul, The Reader's Digest Association Inc, 750 Third Ave, New York, NY 10017 *Tel:* 914-238-1000; 646-293-6284 *Toll Free Tel:* 800-310-6261 (cust serv) *Fax:* 914-238-4559 *Web Site:* www.rd.com; www.rda.com, pg 215

Tomlinson, Mark, Society of Manufacturing Engineers, One SME Dr, Dearborn, MI 48121 *Tel:* 313-425-3000 *Toll Free Tel:* 800-733-4763 (cust serv) *Fax:* 313-425-3400 *E-mail:* publications@sme.org *Web Site:* www.sme.org, pg 238

Tompkins, Amy, Transatlantic Agency, 2 Bloor St E, Ste 3500, Toronto, ON M4W-1A8, Canada *Tel:* 416-488-9214 *E-mail:* info@transatlanticagency.com *Web Site:* www.transatlanticagency.com, pg 597

Tonegutti, Marta, University of Chicago Press, 1427 E 60 St, Chicago, IL 60637-2954 *Tel:* 773-702-7700; 773-702-7600 *Toll Free Tel:* 800-621-2736 (orders) *Fax:* 773-702-9756; 773-660-2235 (orders); 773-702-2708 *E-mail:* custserv@press.uchicago.edu; marketing@press.uchicago.edu *Web Site:* www.press.uchicago.edu, pg 265

Toner, Joel, Sky Publishing, 90 Sherman St, Cambridge, MA 02140 *Tel:* 617-864-7360 *Toll Free Tel:* 866-644-1377 *Fax:* 617-864-6117 *E-mail:* info@skyandtelescope.com *Web Site:* www.skyandtelescope.com, pg 237

Toole, Jenny, Mercer University Press, 368 Orange St, Macon, GA 31201 *Tel:* 478-301-2880 *Toll Free Tel:* 866-895-1472 *Fax:* 478-301-2585 *E-mail:* mupressorders@mercer.edu *Web Site:* www.mupress.org, pg 164

Toraason, John O, Wildlife Education Ltd, 2418 Noyes St, Evanston, IL 60201 *Toll Free Tel:* 800-477-5034 *E-mail:* owls5@zoobooks.com; helpdesk@zoobooks.com *Web Site:* www.zoobooks.com; wildlife-ed.com, pg 281

Torr, Jolene, City Lights Publishers, 261 Columbus Ave, San Francisco, CA 94133 *Tel:* 415-362-8193 *Fax:* 415-362-4921 *E-mail:* staff@citylights.com *Web Site:* www.citylights.com, pg 62

Toto, Cheryl Cramer, Houghton Mifflin Harcourt Trade & Reference Division, 222 Berkeley St, Boston, MA 02116-3764 *Tel:* 617-351-5000 *Toll Free Tel:* 800-225-3362 *Web Site:* www.houghtonmifflinbooks.com, pg 124

Totten, Shay, Chelsea Green Publishing Co, 85 N Main St, Suite 120, White River Junction, VT 05001 *Tel:* 802-295-6300 *Toll Free Tel:* 800-639-4099 (cust serv, consumer & trade orders) *Fax:* 802-295-6444 *Web Site:* www.chelseagreen.com, pg 59

Touchie, Rodger, Heritage House Publishing Co Ltd, 1105 Pandora Ave, Victoria, BC V8V 3P9, Canada *Tel:* 604-574-7067 *Toll Free Tel:* 800-665-3302 *Fax:* 604-574-9942 *Toll Free Fax:* 800-566-3336 *E-mail:* heritage@heritagehouse.ca; orders@heritagehouse.ca *Web Site:* www.heritagehouse.ca, pg 509

Tourtlotte, Alan N, OSA, The Optical Society, 2010 Massachusetts Ave NW, Washington, DC 20036-1023 *Tel:* 202-223-8130 *Toll Free Tel:* 800-766-4672 *E-mail:* custserv@osa.org *Web Site:* www.osa.org, pg 188

Touvell, Anne, Thurber Prize for American Humor, 77 Jefferson Ave, Columbus, OH 43215 *Tel:* 614-464-1032 *Fax:* 614-280-3645 *E-mail:* thurberhouse@thurberhouse.org *Web Site:* www.thurberhouse.org, pg 746

Tower, Carol, Society of Manufacturing Engineers, One SME Dr, Dearborn, MI 48121 *Tel:* 313-425-3000 *Toll Free Tel:* 800-733-4763 (cust serv) *Fax:* 313-425-3400 *E-mail:* publications@sme.org *Web Site:* www.sme.org, pg 238

Tower, Lois, Wolf Pirate Project Inc, 337 Lost Lake Dr, Divide, CO 80814 *Tel:* 305-333-3186 *E-mail:* contact@wolfpiratebooks.com; workshop@wolfpiratebooks.com *Web Site:* www.wolf-pirate.com, pg 557

Towers, Cheryl R, The Local History Co, 112 N Woodland Rd, Pittsburgh, PA 15232-2849 *Tel:* 412-362-2294 *Toll Free Tel:* 866-362-0789 (orders) *Fax:* 412-362-8192 *E-mail:* info@thelocalhistorycompany.com; sales@thelocalhistorycomany.com *Web Site:* www.thelocalhistorycompany.com, pg 151

Townsend, Robert B, American Historical Association, 400 "A" St SE, Washington, DC 20003-3889 *Tel:* 202-544-2422 *Fax:* 202-544-8307 *E-mail:* aha@historians.org; awards@historians.org *Web Site:* www.historians.org, pg 13

Townsley, Dave, Hendrickson Publishers Inc, PO Box 3473, Peabody, MA 01961-3473 *Tel:* 978-532-6546 *Toll Free Tel:* 800-358-3111 *Fax:* 978-573-8111 *E-mail:* orders@hendrickson.com *Web Site:* www.hendrickson.com, pg 118

Townson, Donald, Townson Publishing Co Ltd, PO Box 1404, Sta A, Vancouver, BC V6C 2P7, Canada *Tel:* 604-886-0594 (CN) *E-mail:* townsonpublishing@gmail.com *Web Site:* generalpublishing.co.uk, pg 521

Tozzi, Ryan, Bloomsbury Publishing, 175 Fifth Ave, New York, NY 10010 *Tel:* 212-674-5151 *Toll Free Tel:* 800-221-7945 *Fax:* 212-780-0115; 212-982-2837 *E-mail:* marketingusa@bloomsbury.com; adultpublicityusa.@bloomsbury.com *Web Site:* www.bloomsbury.com, pg 40

Tracten, Mark, Crown House Publishing Co LLC, 6 Trowbridge Dr, Bethel, CT 06801 *Tel:* 203-778-1300 *Toll Free Tel:* 877-925-1213 (cust serv); 866-272-8497 *Fax:* 203-778-9100 *E-mail:* info@chpus.com *Web Site:* www.crownhousepublishing.com, pg 72

Tracy, Bruce, Workman Publishing Co Inc, 225 Varick St, 9th fl, New York, NY 10014-4381 *Tel:* 212-254-5900 *Toll Free Tel:* 800-722-7202 *Fax:* 212-254-8098 *E-mail:* info@workman.com *Web Site:* www.workman.com, pg 285

Tracy, Reid, Hay House Inc, 2776 Loker Ave W, Carlsbad, CA 92010 *Tel:* 760-431-7695 (ext 2, intl) *Toll Free Tel:* 800-654-5126 (ext 2, US) *Toll Free Fax:* 800-650-5115 *E-mail:* info@hayhouse.com; editorial@hayhouse.com *Web Site:* www.hayhouse.com, pg 115

Trager, Katherine, Random House Inc, 1745 Broadway, New York, NY 10019 *Tel:* 212-782-9000 *Toll Free Tel:* 800-726-0600 *Web Site:* www.randomhouse.com, pg 213

Trandem, Bryan, Quayside Publishing Group, 400 First Ave N, Suite 300, Minneapolis, MN 55401 *Tel:* 612-344-8100 *Toll Free Tel:* 800-328-0590 (sales); 800-458-0454 *Fax:* 612-344-8691 *E-mail:* sales@creativepub.com *Web Site:* www.qbookshop.com, pg 211

Tranfaglia, Frank, Piano Press, 1425 Ocean Ave, Suite 17, Del Mar, CA 92014 *Tel:* 619-884-1401 *Fax:* 858-755-1104 *E-mail:* pianopress@pianopress.com *Web Site:* www.pianopress.com, pg 201

Trank, Megan, Beaufort Books, 27 W 20 St, Suite 1102, New York, NY 10011 *Tel:* 212-727-0222 *Fax:* 212-727-0195 *E-mail:* info@beaufortbooks.com *Web Site:* www.beaufortbooks.com, pg 33

Trautner, Cris, Infusionmedia, 140 N Eighth St, Suite 214, The Apothecary, Lincoln, NE 68508-1353 *Tel:* 402-477-2065 *E-mail:* info@infusionmediadesign.com *Web Site:* www.infusionmediadesign.com, pg 527

Traversy, Nancy, Barefoot Books, 2067 Massachusetts Ave, 5th fl, Cambridge, MA 02140 *Tel:* 617-576-0660 *Toll Free Tel:* 866-215-1756 (cust serv); 866-417-2369 (orders) *Fax:* 617-576-0049 *E-mail:* ussales@barefootbooks.com; help@barefootbooks.com *Web Site:* www.barefootbooks.com, pg 30

Traynor, Karen, Tralco-Lingo Fun, 3909 Witmer Rd, Suite 856, Niagara Falls, NY 14305 *Tel:* 905-575-5717 *Toll Free Tel:* 888-487-2526 *Fax:* 905-575-1783 *Toll Free Fax:* 866-487-2527 *E-mail:* contact@tralco.com *Web Site:* www.tralco.com, pg 257

Treco, Stacy, Pearson Benjamin Cummings, 1301 Sansome St, San Francisco, CA 94111-1122 *Tel:* 415-402-2500 *Toll Free Tel:* 800-922-0579 (orders) *Fax:* 415-402-2590 *E-mail:* question@aol.com *Web Site:* www.pearsonhighered.com, pg 195

Treimel, Scott, S©ott Treimel NY, 434 Lafayette St, New York, NY 10003-6943 *Tel:* 212-505-8353 *Web Site:* scotttreimelny.com; scotttreimelny.blogspot.com, pg 593

Treistman, Ann, The Countryman Press, 43 Lincoln Corners Way, Woodstock, VT 05091 *Tel:* 802-457-4826 *Toll Free Tel:* 800-245-4151 *Fax:* 802-457-1678 *E-mail:* countrymanpress@wwnorton.com *Web Site:* www.countrymanpress.com, pg 70

Trelstad, Julie, Writers House, 21 W 26 St, New York, NY 10010 *Tel:* 212-685-2400 *Fax:* 212-685-1781 *Web Site:* www.writershouse.com, pg 599

Tremblay, Diana Thistle, Angel Publications, 3169 Quail Dr, Gloucester, ON K1T 1T9, Canada *Tel:* 613-791-0979, pg 540

Tress, Neil, Recorded Books LLC, 270 Skipjack Rd, Prince Frederick, MD 20678 *Tel:* 410-535-5590 *Toll Free Tel:* 800-638-1304; 877-732-2898 *Fax:* 410-535-5499 *E-mail:* customerservice@recordedbooks.com *Web Site:* www.recordedbooks.com, pg 215

Trevorrow, Elaine, Random House Speakers Bureau, 1745 Broadway, Mail Drop 13-1, New York, NY 10019 *Tel:* 212-572-2013 *E-mail:* rhspeakers@randomhouse.com *Web Site:* www.rhspeakers.com, pg 605

Tribbey, Deb, Elite Books, PO Box 442, Fulton, CA 95439 *Tel:* 707-525-9292 *Toll Free Fax:* 800-330-9798 *Web Site:* www.elitebooks.biz, pg 86

Tribbey, Deb, Energy Psychology Press, 1490 Mark West Springs Rd, Santa Rosa, CA 95404 *Tel:* 707-237-6951 *Toll Free Fax:* 800-330-9798 *Web Site:* www.energypsychologypress.com, pg 88

Tribble, Jessica, Poisoned Pen Press Inc, 6962 E First Ave, Suite 103, Scottsdale, AZ 85251 *Tel:* 480-945-3375 *Toll Free Tel:* 1-800-421-3976 *Fax:* 480-949-1707 *E-mail:* info@poisonedpenpress.com *Web Site:* www.poisonedpenpress.com, pg 204

Tribelli, Angela, HarperCollins General Books Group, 10 E 53 St, New York, NY 10022 *Tel:* 212-207-7000 *Fax:* 212-207-7633 *Web Site:* www.harpercollins.com, pg 113

Tricarico, Joy Elton, Carol Bancroft & Friends, PO Box 2030, Danbury, CT 06813 *Tel:* 203-730-8270 *Fax:* 203-730-8275 *E-mail:* cbfriends@sbcglobal.net *Web Site:* www.carolbancroft.com, pg 601

Trimmer, Christian, Simon & Schuster Children's Publishing, 1230 Avenue of the Americas, New York, NY 10020 *Tel:* 212-698-7000 *Web Site:* KIDS.SimonandSchuster.com; TEEN.SimonandSchuster.com; simonandschuster.net; simonandschuster.biz, pg 235

Tripathi, Namrata, Simon & Schuster Children's Publishing, 1230 Avenue of the Americas, New York, NY 10020 *Tel:* 212-698-7000 *Web Site:* KIDS.SimonandSchuster.com; TEEN.SimonandSchuster.com; simonandschuster.net; simonandschuster.biz, pg 235

Triplett, Rick, Prometheus Awards, 650 Castro St, Suite 120-433, Mountain View, CA 94041 *Tel:* 650-968-6319 *E-mail:* info@lfs.org *Web Site:* www.lfs.org, pg 736

Vaccaro, Claire, GP Putnam's Sons (Hardcover), 375 Hudson St, New York, NY 10014 *Tel:* 212-366-2000 *E-mail:* online@penguinputnam.com *Web Site:* us.penguingroup.com, pg 210

Vacha, Brigitte Rupp, Notable Wisconsin Authors, 4610 S Biltmore Lane, Madison, WI 53718 *Tel:* 608-245-3640 *Fax:* 608-245-3646 *Web Site:* www.wla.lib.wi.us, pg 729

Vacha, Brigitte Rupp, WLA Literary Award, 4610 S Biltmore Lane, Madison, WI 53718 *Tel:* 608-245-3640 *Fax:* 608-245-3646 *Web Site:* www.wla.lib.wi.us, pg 750

Vachon, Chris, The Society of Professional Journalists, Eugene S Pulliam National Journalism Ctr, 3909 N Meridian St, Indianapolis, IN 46208 *Tel:* 317-927-8000 *Fax:* 317-920-4789 *E-mail:* spj@spj.org *Web Site:* www.spj.org, pg 637

Vacin, Aaron, Infusionmedia, 140 N Eighth St, Suite 214, The Apothecary, Lincoln, NE 68508-1353 *Tel:* 402-477-2065 *E-mail:* info@infusionmediadesign.com *Web Site:* www.infusionmediadesign.com, pg 527

Vagstad, Marit, Palgrave Macmillan, 175 Fifth Ave, Suite 200, New York, NY 10010 *Tel:* 646-307-5151 *Fax:* 212-777-6359 *E-mail:* firstname.lastname@palgrave-usa.com *Web Site:* us.macmillan.com/Palgrave.aspx, pg 191

Vaillancourt, Claude, Brault & Bouthillier, 700 ave Beaumont, Montreal, QC H3N 1V5, Canada *Tel:* 514-273-9186 *Toll Free Tel:* 800-361-0378 *Fax:* 514-273-8627 *Toll Free Fax:* 800-361-0378 *E-mail:* ventes@bb.ca *Web Site:* www.braultbouthillier.com, pg 495

Vajda, Prof Edward, Center for East Asian Studies (CEAS), Western Washington University, 516 High St, Bellingham, WA 98225-9057 *Tel:* 360-650-3339 *Fax:* 360-650-6110 *E-mail:* easpress@wwu.edu *Web Site:* www.wwu.edu/eas, pg 56

Valaitis, Maryellen, McGraw-Hill Education, 2 Penn Plaza, New York, NY 10121-2298 *Tel:* 212-904-2000 *E-mail:* customer.service@mcgraw-hill.com *Web Site:* www.mheducation.com; www.mheducation.com/custserv.html, pg 161

Valdez, Jason, Museum of New Mexico Press, 725 Camino Lejo, Suite C, Santa Fe, NM 87505 *Tel:* 505-476-1155; 505-272-7777 (orders) *Toll Free Tel:* 800-249-7737 (orders) *Fax:* 505-476-1156 *Toll Free Fax:* 800-622-8667 (orders) *Web Site:* www.mnmpress.org, pg 171

Valenta, Rose A, National Society of Newspaper Columnists (NSNC), 1345 Fillmore St, Suite 507, San Francisco, CA 94115 *Tel:* 415-488-NCNC (488-6762) *Toll Free Tel:* 866-440-NSNC (440-6762) *Fax:* 484-297-0336 *Toll Free Fax:* 866-635-5759 *E-mail:* staff@columnists.com *Web Site:* www.columnists.com, pg 631

Valenta, Rose A, National Society of Newspaper Columnists Annual Conference, 1345 Fillmore St, Suite 507, San Francisco, CA 94115 *Tel:* 415-488-NCNC (488-6762) *Toll Free Tel:* 866-440-NSNC (440-6762) *Fax:* 484-297-0336 *Toll Free Fax:* 866-635-5759 *Web Site:* www.columnists.com, pg 671

Valentine, Andrea, Teaching Strategies, 7101 Wisconsin Ave, Suite 700, Bethesda, MD 20814 *Tel:* 301-634-0818 *Toll Free Tel:* 800-637-3652 *Fax:* 301-657-0250 *E-mail:* customerrelations@teachingstrategies.com *Web Site:* www.teachingstrategies.com, pg 251

Valentine, Ansley, Mildred & Albert Panowski Playwriting Award, Forest Roberts Theatre, 1401 Presque Isle Ave, Marquette, MI 49855-5364 *Tel:* 906-227-2553 *Fax:* 906-227-2567 *Web Site:* www.nmu.edu/theatre, pg 732

Valentino, Michael, Cambridge Literary Associates, 135 Beach Rd, Unit C-3, Salisbury, MA 01952 *Tel:* 978-499-0374 *Fax:* 978-499-9774 *Web Site:* www.cambridgeliterary.com, pg 565

Valentino, Ralph, Cambridge Literary Associates, 135 Beach Rd, Unit C-3, Salisbury, MA 01952 *Tel:* 978-499-0374 *Fax:* 978-499-9774 *Web Site:* www.cambridgeliterary.com, pg 565

Valentino, Russell, The Iowa Review Award, 308 EPB, Iowa City, IA 52242-1408 *E-mail:* iowa-review@uiowa.edu *Web Site:* www.iowareview.org, pg 713

Valenzuela, Pamela, The Association for Women In Communications, 3337 Duke St, Alexandria, VA 22314 *Tel:* 703-370-7436 *Fax:* 703-342-4311 *E-mail:* info@womcom.org *Web Site:* www.womcom.org, pg 667

Valenzuela, Pamela, The Clarion Awards, 3337 Duke St, Alexandria, VA 22314 *Tel:* 703-370-7436 *Fax:* 703-342-4311 *E-mail:* clarion@womcom.org *Web Site:* www.womcom.org, pg 697

Valenzuela, Tony, Lambda Literary Awards (Lammys), 5482 Wilshire Blvd, Suite 1595, Los Angeles, CA 90036 *Tel:* 213-568-3570 *Fax:* 213-568-3570 *E-mail:* info@lambdaliterary.org *Web Site:* www.lambdaliterary.org, pg 716

Valera, Milton G, National Notary Association (NNA), 9350 De Soto Ave, Chatsworth, CA 91311 *Tel:* 818-739-4000 *Toll Free Tel:* 800-876-6827 *Toll Free Fax:* 800-833-1211 *E-mail:* nna@nationalnotary.org *Web Site:* www.nationalnotary.org, pg 175

Valko-Warner, Mary Jo Anne, Scott Meredith Literary Agency LP, 200 W 57 St, Suite 904, New York, NY 10019-3211 *Tel:* 646-274-1970 *Fax:* 212-977-5997 *E-mail:* info@scottmeredith.com *Web Site:* www.scottmeredith.com, pg 585

Vallely, Janis, Flaming Star Literary Enterprises LLC, 111 Raup Rd, Chatham, NY 12037 *Web Site:* www.janisvallely.com, pg 572

Vallely, Joseph B, Flaming Star Literary Enterprises LLC, 111 Raup Rd, Chatham, NY 12037 *Web Site:* www.janisvallely.com, pg 572

Vallimont, Candice, Chronicle Books LLC, 680 Second St, San Francisco, CA 94107 *Tel:* 415-537-4200 *Toll Free Tel:* 800-759-0190 (cust serv) *Fax:* 415-537-4460 *Toll Free Fax:* 800-858-7787 (orders); 800-286-9471 (cust serv) *E-mail:* frontdesk@chroniclebooks.com *Web Site:* www.chroniclebooks.com, pg 61

Valois, Rob, Grosset & Dunlap, 345 Hudson St, New York, NY 10014 *Tel:* 212-366-2000 *E-mail:* online@penguinputnam.com *Web Site:* www.penguinputnam.com; us.penguingroup.com, pg 108

Valvano, Al, Microsoft Press, One Microsoft Way, Redmond, WA 98052-6399 *Tel:* 425-882-8080 *Toll Free Tel:* 800-677-7377 *Fax:* 425-936-7329 *Web Site:* www.microsoft.com/learning/books, pg 166

Van Altine, Michael, East Asian Legal Studies Program (EALSP), 500 W Baltimore St, Suite 411, Baltimore, MD 21201-1786 *Tel:* 410-706-3870 *Fax:* 410-706-1516 *E-mail:* eastasia@law.umaryland.edu *Web Site:* www.law.umaryland.edu/programs/international/eastasia, pg 83

Van Andel, Cheryl, Baker Books, 6030 E Fulton Rd, Ada, MI 49301 *Tel:* 616-676-9185 *Toll Free Tel:* 800-877-2665; 800-679-1957 *Fax:* 616-676-9573 *Toll Free Fax:* 800-398-3111 *Web Site:* www.bakerpublishinggroup.com, pg 29

Van Arkel, Meeuwis, Elsevier, Health Sciences Division, 1600 John F Kennedy Blvd, Suite 1800, Philadelphia, PA 19103-2899 *Tel:* 215-239-3900 *Toll Free Tel:* 800-523-1649 *Fax:* 215-239-3990 *Web Site:* www.elsevierhealth.com, pg 87

van Beek, Emily, Folio Literary Management LLC, The Film Center Bldg, 630 Ninth Ave, Suite 1101, New York, NY 10036 *Tel:* 212-400-1494 *Fax:* 212-967-0977 *Web Site:* www.foliolit.com, pg 572

Van Beuren, Victor, American Diabetes Association, 1701 N Beauregard St, Alexandria, VA 22311 *Toll Free Tel:* 800-342-2383 *E-mail:* booksinfo@diabetes.org *Web Site:* www.diabetes.org, pg 12

van Breen, Kristen, Hudson Hills Press LLC, 3556 Main St, Manchester, VT 05254 *Tel:* 802-362-6450 *Fax:* 802-362-6459 *E-mail:* artbooks@hudsonhills.com; editorial@hudsonhills.com (submissions) *Web Site:* www.hudsonhills.com, pg 125

Van de Water, Kara, Ten Speed Press, 2625 Alcatraz Ave, Unit 505, Berkeley, CA 94705 *Tel:* 510-285-3000 *Toll Free Tel:* 800-841-BOOK (841-2665) *E-mail:* csorders@randomhouse.com *Web Site:* crownpublishing.com/imprint/ten-speed-press, pg 252

van der Plas, Rob, Cycle Publishing, 1282 Seventh Ave, San Francisco, CA 94122-2526 *Tel:* 415-665-8214 *Toll Free Tel:* 877-353-1207 *Fax:* 415-753-8572 *E-mail:* contact@cyclepublishing.com *Web Site:* www.cyclepublishing.com, pg 74

Van der Veer, Laura, Random House Publishing Group, 1745 Broadway, New York, NY 10019 *Toll Free Tel:* 800-200-3552 *Web Site:* atrandom.com, pg 214

Van Derwater, Peter, Fulbright Scholar Program, 1400 "K" St NW, Washington, DC 20005 *Tel:* 202-686-4000 *Fax:* 202-362-3442 *E-mail:* scholars@iie.org *Web Site:* www.iie.org/cies, pg 706

Van Doren, Elizabeth, Boyds Mills Press, 815 Church St, Honesdale, PA 18431 *Tel:* 570-253-1164 *Toll Free Tel:* 800-490-5111 *Fax:* 570-253-0179 *E-mail:* contact@boydsmillspress.com *Web Site:* www.boydsmillspress.com, pg 45

Van Doren, Liz, Highlights for Children, 1800 Watermark Dr, Columbus, OH 43215-1060 *Tel:* 614-486-0631 *Toll Free Tel:* 800-962-3661 (Highlights Club cust serv); 800-255-9517 (Highlights Magazine cust serv) *Web Site:* www.highlights.com, pg 119

Van Dyck, Craig, John Wiley & Sons Inc Scientific, Technical, Medical & Scholarly (STMS), 111 River St, Hoboken, NJ 07030 *Tel:* 201-748-6000 *Toll Free Tel:* 800-225-5945 (cust serv) *Fax:* 201-748-6088 *E-mail:* info@wiley.com *Web Site:* www.wiley.com, pg 282

Van Dyke, Brianna, Janet B McCabe Poetry Prize, 140 N Roosevelt Ave, Collins, CO 80521 *Tel:* 970-449-2726 *E-mail:* editor@ruminatemagazine.org *Web Site:* www.ruminatemagazine.com, pg 722

Van Dyke, Brianna, William Van Dyke Short Story Prize, 140 N Roosevelt Ave, Collins, CO 80521 *Tel:* 970-449-2726 *E-mail:* editor@ruminatemagazine.org *Web Site:* www.ruminatemagazine.com, pg 747

Van Dyke, Brianna, VanderMey Nonfiction Prize, 140 N Roosevelt Ave, Collins, CO 80521 *Tel:* 970-449-2726 *E-mail:* editor@ruminatemagazine.org *Web Site:* www.ruminatemagazine.com, pg 747

Van Hoof-Haines, Kristine, Hazelden Publishing, 15251 Pleasant Valley Rd, Center City, MN 55012-0011 *Tel:* 651-213-4200 *Toll Free Tel:* 800-257-7810 *Fax:* 651-213-4590 *E-mail:* info@hazelden.org *Web Site:* www.hazelden.org, pg 116

Van Hooft, Karen, Bilingual Review Press/Editorial Bilingue, Arizona State Univ, Hispanic Research Ctr, Tempe, AZ 85287-2702 *Tel:* 480-965-3867 *Toll Free Tel:* 866-965-3867 *Fax:* 480-965-0315 *E-mail:* brp@asu.edu *Web Site:* www.asu.edu/brp, pg 37

Van Meeuwen, Frank, Diamond Farm Book Publishers, Bailey Settlement Rd, Alexandria Bay, NY 13607 *Tel:* 613-475-1771 *Toll Free Tel:* 800-481-1353 *Fax:* 613-475-3748 *Toll Free Fax:* 800-305-5138 *E-mail:* info@diamondfarm.com *Web Site:* www.diamondfarm.com; www.yesteryeartoys.com, pg 79

Van Meeuwen, Shawn, Diamond Farm Book Publishers, Bailey Settlement Rd, Alexandria Bay, NY 13607 *Tel:* 613-475-1771 *Toll Free Tel:* 800-481-1353 *Fax:* 613-475-3748 *Toll Free Fax:* 800-305-5138 *E-mail:* info@diamondfarm.com *Web Site:* www.diamondfarm.com; www.yesteryeartoys.com, pg 79

Van Orman, Mark, LexisNexis/Martindale-Hubbell, 121 Chanlon Rd, New Providence, NJ 07974 *Tel:* 908-464-6800 *Toll Free Tel:* 800-526-4902 *Fax:* 908-464-3553 *E-mail:* info@martindale.com *Web Site:* www.martindale.com, pg 147

van Rheinberg, Brigitta, Princeton University Press, 41 William St, Princeton, NJ 08540-5237 *Tel:* 609-258-4900 *Toll Free Tel:* 800-777-4726 (orders) *Fax:* 609-258-6305 *Toll Free Fax:* 800-999-1958 *E-mail:* orders@cpfsinc.com *Web Site:* press.princeton.edu, pg 206

Van Roekel, Dennis, National Education Association (NEA), 1201 16 St NW, Washington, DC 20036-3290 *Tel:* 202-833-4000 *Fax:* 202-822-7974 *Web Site:* www.nea.org, pg 174, 630

Van Sant, Jules, Pacific Printing Industries Association, 6825 SW Sandburg St, Portland, OR 97223 *Tel:* 503-221-3944 *Toll Free Tel:* 877-762-7742 *Fax:* 503-221-5691 *E-mail:* info@ppiassociation.org *Web Site:* www.ppiassociation.org, pg 633

van Straaten, Tracy, Scholastic Trade Division, 557 Broadway, New York, NY 10012 *Tel:* 212-343-6100; 212-343-4685 (export sales) *Fax:* 212-343-4714 (export sales) *Web Site:* www.scholastic.com, pg 229

Van Thornout, Steve, EMC Publishing, 875 Montreal Way, St Paul, MN 55102 *Tel:* 651-290-2800 (corp) *Toll Free Tel:* 800-328-1452 *Fax:* 651-290-2899 *Toll Free Fax:* 800-328-4564 *E-mail:* educate@emcp.com *Web Site:* www.emcp.com, pg 87

Van Thornout, Steve, JIST Publishing, 875 Montreal Way, St Paul, MN 55102 *Tel:* 317-613-4200 *Toll Free Tel:* 800-328-1452 *Toll Free Fax:* 800-328-4564 *E-mail:* educate@emcp.com *Web Site:* jist.emcpublishingllc.com, pg 135

Van Wagner, CJ, Tyndale House Publishers Inc, 351 Executive Dr, Carol Stream, IL 60188 *Tel:* 630-668-8300 *Toll Free Tel:* 800-323-9400 *Web Site:* www.tyndale.com, pg 261

Van Wie, Pat, BelleBooks, PO Box 300921, Memphis, TN 38130 *Tel:* 901-344-9024 *Fax:* 901-344-9068 *E-mail:* bellebooks@bellebooks.com *Web Site:* www.bellebooks.com, pg 34

Van't Haaf, Corey, Western Magazine Awards Foundation, 875 Prairie Ave, Port Coquitlam, BC V3B 1R9, Canada *Tel:* 604-945-3711 *E-mail:* wma@direct.ca *Web Site:* www.westernmagazineawards.ca, pg 748

Vanasse, Andre, Les Editions XYZ inc, 1815 Ave de Lorimier, Montreal, QC H2K 3W6, Canada *Tel:* 514-525-2170 *Fax:* 514-525-7537 *E-mail:* info@editionsxyz.com *Web Site:* www.editionsxyz.com, pg 504

Vance, Lisa Erbach, The Aaron M Priest Literary Agency Inc, 708 Third Ave, 23rd fl, New York, NY 10017-4201 *Tel:* 212-818-0344 *Fax:* 212-573-9417 *E-mail:* info@aaronpriest.com *Web Site:* www.aaronpriest.com, pg 589

Vance, V Ellis, Hans Christian Andersen Award, 5503 N El Adobe Dr, Fresno, CA 93711-2363 *Tel:* 559-351-6119 *E-mail:* executive.director@usbby.org *Web Site:* www.usbby.org, pg 687

Vance, V Ellis, US Board on Books For Young People (USBBY), 5503 N El Adobe Dr, Fresno, CA 93711-2363 *Tel:* 559-351-6119 *E-mail:* executive.director@usbby.org *Web Site:* www.usbby.org, pg 638

VanDam, Stephan C, VanDam Inc, 11 W 20 St, 4th fl, New York, NY 10011-3704 *Tel:* 212-929-0416 *Toll Free Tel:* 800-UNFOLDS (863-6537) *Fax:* 212-929-0426 *E-mail:* info@vandam.com *Web Site:* www.vandam.com, pg 274

Vanden Bos, Gary R PhD, American Psychological Association, 750 First St NE, Washington, DC 20002-4242 *Tel:* 202-336-5500 *Toll Free Tel:* 800-374-2721 *Fax:* 202-336-5620 *E-mail:* order@apa.org *Web Site:* www.apa.org/books, pg 16

Vanden Bos, Gary R PhD, American Psychological Association, 750 First St NE, Washington, DC 20002-4242 *Tel:* 202-336-5500 *Toll Free Tel:* 800-374-2721 *Fax:* 202-336-5620 *E-mail:* order@apa.org *Web Site:* www.apa.org, pg 614

Vander Kam, Claire, Wm B Eerdmans Publishing Co, 2140 Oak Industrial Dr NE, Grand Rapids, MI 49505 *Tel:* 616-459-4591 *Toll Free Tel:* 800-253-7521 *Fax:* 616-459-6540 *E-mail:* customerservice@eerdmans.com; sales@eerdmans.com *Web Site:* www.eerdmans.com, pg 85

Vanderhart, Ruth, Faith Alive Christian Resources, 2850 Kalamazoo Ave SE, Grand Rapids, MI 49560 *Tel:* 616-224-0728 *Toll Free Tel:* 800-333-8300 *Fax:* 616-224-0834 *Toll Free Fax:* 888-642-8606 *E-mail:* info@faithaliveresources.org; sales@faithaliveresources.org; editors@faithaliveresources.org *Web Site:* www.faithaliveresources.org, pg 92

Vanderkooy, Diane, Firefly Books Ltd, 50 Staples Ave, Unit 1, Richmond Hill, ON L4B 0A7, Canada *Tel:* 416-499-8412 *Toll Free Tel:* 800-387-6192 (CN); 800-387-5085 (US) *Fax:* 416-499-8313 *Toll Free Fax:* 800-450-0391 (CN); 800-565-6034 (US) *E-mail:* service@fireflybooks.com *Web Site:* www.fireflybooks.com, pg 505

Vandervoort, Kathy, Harlequin Enterprises Ltd, 225 Duncan Mill Rd, Don Mills, ON M3B 3K9, Canada *Tel:* 416-445-5860 *Toll Free Tel:* 888-432-4879; 800-370-5838 (ebook inquiries) *Fax:* 416-445-8655 *E-mail:* CustomerService@harlequin.com *Web Site:* www.harlequin.com, pg 508

Vanderwilt, Dirk, Channel Lake Inc, 238 E 30 St, No 1F, New York, NY 10016 *Tel:* 347-329-5576 *Toll Free Tel:* 800-592-1566 (orders) *Toll Free Fax:* 866-794-5507 *E-mail:* info@channellake.com *Web Site:* www.channellake.com; www.touristtown.com, pg 58

VanMeter, Joann, Standard Publishing, 8805 Governors Hill Dr, Suite 400, Cincinnati, OH 45249 *Tel:* 513-931-4050 *Toll Free Tel:* 800-543-1353 *Fax:* 513-931-0950 *Toll Free Fax:* 877-867-5751 *E-mail:* customerservice@standardpub.com *Web Site:* www.standardpub.com, pg 242

Vanterpool, Lisa, InkWell Management, 521 Fifth Ave, 26th fl, New York, NY 10175 *Tel:* 212-922-3500 *Fax:* 212-922-0535 *E-mail:* info@inkwellmanagement.com; submissions@inkwellmanagement.com *Web Site:* inkwellmanagement.com, pg 577

Vardigan, Mary, Inter-University Consortium for Political & Social Research (ICPSR), 330 Packard St, Ann Arbor, MI 48104 *Tel:* 734-647-5000 *Fax:* 734-647-8200 *E-mail:* netmail@icpsr.umich.edu *Web Site:* www.icpsr.umich.edu, pg 132

Varga, Lisa R, Jefferson Cup Award, c/o Virginia Library Association (VLA), PO Box 56312, Virginia Beach, VA 23456 *Tel:* 757-689-0594 *Fax:* 757-447-3478 *Web Site:* www.vla.org, pg 714

Vargas, Allison Astor, Nuestras Voces National Playwriting Competition, 138 E 27 St, New York, NY 10016 *Tel:* 212-225-9950 *Fax:* 212-225-9085 *Web Site:* www.repertorio.org, pg 730

Vargo, Linda, National Association of College Stores (NACS), 500 E Lorain St, Oberlin, OH 44074 *Tel:* 440-775-7777 *Toll Free Tel:* 800-622-7498 *Fax:* 440-775-4769 *Web Site:* www.nacs.org, pg 628

Varma, Sarita, Farrar, Straus & Giroux, LLC, 18 W 18 St, New York, NY 10011 *Tel:* 212-741-6900 *Fax:* 212-633-9385 *E-mail:* fsg.publicity@fsgbooks.com *Web Site:* us.macmillan.com/fsg.aspx, pg 93

Varma, Sarita, North Point Press, 18 W 18 St, 8th fl, New York, NY 10011 *Tel:* 212-741-6900 *Toll Free Tel:* 888-330-8477 *Fax:* 212-633-9385 *Web Site:* www.fsgbooks.com, pg 181

Varnum, Keith, New Dimensions Publishing, 11248 N 11 St, Phoenix, AZ 85020 *Tel:* 602-861-2631 *Toll Free Tel:* 800-736-7367 *Fax:* 602-944-1235 *E-mail:* info@thedream.com *Web Site:* www.thedream.com, pg 177

Varrette, Dan, Insomniac Press, 520 Princess Ave, London, ON N6B 2B8, Canada *Tel:* 416-504-6270 *Web Site:* www.insomniacpress.com, pg 509

Vasquez, Cynthia, Mike Murach & Associates Inc, 4340 N Knoll Ave, Fresno, CA 93722 *Tel:* 559-440-9071 *Toll Free Tel:* 800-221-5528 *Fax:* 559-440-0963 *E-mail:* murachbooks@murach.com *Web Site:* www.murach.com, pg 166

Vassallo, Nadine, Book Industry Study Group Inc (BISG), 145 W 45 St, Suite 601, New York, NY 10036 *Tel:* 646-336-7141 *Fax:* 646-336-6214 *E-mail:* info@bisg.org *Web Site:* www.bisg.org, pg 618

Vaugeois, Denis, Les Editions du Septentrion, 1300 Maguire Ave, Sillery, QC G1T 1Z3, Canada *Tel:* 418-688-3556 *Fax:* 418-527-4978 *E-mail:* sept@septentrion.qc.ca *Web Site:* www.septentrion.qc.ca, pg 503

Vaugeois, Mary Ellen, Association des Libraires du Quebec, 407, blvd de Sainte Laurent Est, Bureau 801, Montreal, QC H2Y 2Y5, Canada *Tel:* 514-526-3349 *Fax:* 514-526-3340 *E-mail:* info@alq.qc.ca *Web Site:* www.alq.qc.ca, pg 615

Vaughan, Jeanne, Paladin Press, Gunbarrel Tech Ctr, 7077 Winchester Circle, Boulder, CO 80301 *Tel:* 303-443-7250 *Toll Free Tel:* 800-392-2400 *Fax:* 303-442-8741 *E-mail:* service@paladin-press.com *Web Site:* www.paladin-press.com, pg 191

Vaughn, Ethan, Kimberley Cameron & Associates, 1550 Tiburon Blvd, Suite 704, Tiburon, CA 94920 *Tel:* 415-789-9191 *Fax:* 415-789-9177 *E-mail:* info@kimberleycameron.com *Web Site:* www.kimberleycameron.com, pg 579

Vaughn, Patrika, A Cappela Publishing, PO Box 3691, Sarasota, FL 34230-3691 *Tel:* 941-351-2050 *Fax:* 941-351-4735 *E-mail:* acappub@aol.com *Web Site:* www.acappela.com, pg 1

Vayo, Rick A, PreMediaGlobal, 4 Collins Ave, Plymouth, MA 02360 *Tel:* 508-746-0300 *Fax:* 508-746-3233 *E-mail:* info@premediaglobal.com *Web Site:* www.premediaglobal.com, pg 553

Vaysbeyn, Elina, Simon & Schuster, 1230 Avenue of the Americas, New York, NY 10020 *Tel:* 212-698-7000 *Toll Free Tel:* 800-223-2348 (cust serv); 800-223-2336 (orders) *Toll Free Fax:* 800-943-9831 (orders) *Web Site:* www.simonandschuster.com, pg 234

Veach, Dan, International Poetry Competition, PO Box 8248, Atlanta, GA 31106 *E-mail:* atlanta.review@yahoo.com *Web Site:* www.atlantareview.com, pg 712

Vega, Javier, School of Visual Arts, 209 E 23 St, New York, NY 10010-3994 *Tel:* 212-592-2100 *Fax:* 212-592-2116 *Web Site:* www.sva.edu, pg 680

Vegso, Peter, Health Communications Inc, 3201 SW 15 St, Deerfield Beach, FL 33442-8190 *Tel:* 954-360-0909 *Toll Free Tel:* 800-441-5569 (cust serv) *Fax:* 954-360-0034 *Web Site:* www.hcibooks.com; hci-online.com, pg 116

Velez, Wendy, National Institute for Trial Advocacy (NITA), 1685 38 St, Suite 200, Boulder, CO 80301-2735 *Tel:* 720-890-4860 *Toll Free Tel:* 877-648-2632; 800-225-6482 (orders & returns) *Fax:* 720-890-7069 *E-mail:* info@nita.org *Web Site:* www.nita.org, pg 175

Veltre, J Joseph III, The Gersh Agency (TGA), 41 Madison Ave, 33rd fl, New York, NY 10010 *Tel:* 212-997-1818 *E-mail:* info@gershla.com *Web Site:* gershagency.com, pg 574

Venditti, Michelle, Harlequin Enterprises Ltd, 225 Duncan Mill Rd, Don Mills, ON M3B 3K9, Canada *Tel:* 416-445-5860 *Toll Free Tel:* 888-432-4879; 800-370-5838 (ebook inquiries) *Fax:* 416-445-8655 *E-mail:* CustomerService@harlequin.com *Web Site:* www.harlequin.com, pg 508

Venema, Gerard, The Mathematical Association of America, 1529 18 St NW, Washington, DC 20036-1358 *Tel:* 202-387-5200 *Toll Free Tel:* 800-741-9415 *Fax:* 202-265-2384 *E-mail:* maahq@maa.org *Web Site:* www.maa.org, pg 159

Veney, Beth, The Association for Women In Communications, 3337 Duke St, Alexandria, VA 22314 *Tel:* 703-370-7436 *Fax:* 703-342-4311 *E-mail:* info@womcom.org *Web Site:* www.womcom.org, pg 667

Veney, Beth, The Clarion Awards, 3337 Duke St, Alexandria, VA 22314 *Tel:* 703-370-7436 *Fax:* 703-342-4311 *E-mail:* clarion@womcom.org *Web Site:* www.womcom.org, pg 697

Venezia, Angie, Vintage & Anchor Books, c/o Random House Inc, 1745 Broadway, New York, NY 10019 *Tel:* 212-572-2420 *E-mail:* vintageanchorpublicity@randomhouse.com *Web Site:* vintage-anchor.knopfdoubleday.com, pg 275

Verburg, Bonnie, Scholastic Trade Division, 557 Broadway, New York, NY 10012 *Tel:* 212-343-6100; 212-343-4685 (export sales) *Fax:* 212-343-4714 (export sales) *Web Site:* www.scholastic.com, pg 228

Verdick, Dan, ABDO Publishing Group, 8000 W 78 St, Suite 310, Edina, MN 55439 *Tel:* 952-831-2120 (ext 223) *Toll Free Tel:* 800-800-1312 *Toll Free Fax:* 800-862-3480 *E-mail:* info@abdopublishing.com *Web Site:* www.abdopub.com, pg 2

Verdick, Dan, Mid-List Press, 6524 Brownlee Dr, Nashville, TN 37205-3038 *Tel:* 615-822-3777 *Fax:* 612-823-8387 *E-mail:* guide@midlist.org *Web Site:* www.midlist.org, pg 166

Verkuilen, Michelle, Liturgical Press, PO Box 7500, St John's Abbey, Collegeville, MN 56321-7500 *Tel:* 320-363-2213 *Toll Free Tel:* 800-858-5450 *Fax:* 320-363-3299 *Toll Free Fax:* 800-445-5899 *E-mail:* sales@litpress.org *Web Site:* www.litpress.org, pg 151

Verma, Monika, Levine|Greenberg Literary Agency Inc, 307 Seventh Ave, Suite 2407, New York, NY 10001 *Tel:* 212-337-0934 *Fax:* 212-337-0948 *Web Site:* www.levinegreenberg.com, pg 581

Vernon, John, Binghamton University Creative Writing Program, c/o Dept of English, PO Box 6000, Binghamton, NY 13902-6000 *Tel:* 607-777-2168 *Fax:* 607-777-2408 *E-mail:* cwpro@binghamton.edu *Web Site:* english.binghamton.edu/cwpro, pg 677

Verrill, Chuck, Darhansoff & Verrill, 236 W 26 St, Suite 802, New York, NY 10001-6736 *Tel:* 917-305-1300 *Fax:* 917-305-1400 *E-mail:* info@dvagency.com *Web Site:* www.dvagency.com, pg 567

Victor, Nomi, W W Norton & Company Inc, 500 Fifth Ave, New York, NY 10110-0017 *Tel:* 212-354-5500 *Toll Free Tel:* 800-233-4830 (orders & cust serv) *Fax:* 212-869-0856 *Toll Free Fax:* 800-458-6515 *Web Site:* www.wwnorton.com, pg 182

Victorson, Emily, Allium Press of Chicago, 1530 Elgin Ave, Forest Park, IL 60130 *Tel:* 708-689-9323 *E-mail:* info@alliumpress.com *Web Site:* www.alliumpress.com, pg 8

Vidourek, Chris, Oxford University Press USA, 198 Madison Ave, New York, NY 10016 *Tel:* 212-726-6000 *Toll Free Tel:* 800-451-7556 (orders); 800-445-9714 (cust serv) *Fax:* 919-677-1303 *E-mail:* custserv.us@oup.com *Web Site:* www.oup.com/us, pg 189

Vieder, Deborah, NPES The Association for Suppliers of Printing, Publishing & Converting Technologies, 1899 Preston White Dr, Reston, VA 20191 *Tel:* 703-264-7200 *Fax:* 703-620-0994 *E-mail:* npes@npes.org *Web Site:* www.npes.org, pg 632

Viehman, John, Down East Books, 680 Commercial St (US Rte 1), Rockport, ME 04856 *Tel:* 207-594-9544 *Toll Free Tel:* 800-685-7962 (US only orders); 800-766-1670 *Fax:* 207-594-7215 *E-mail:* submissions@downeast.com *Web Site:* www.downeast.com, pg 81

Viera, Carmen, Institute of Puerto Rican Culture, PO Box 9024184, San Juan, PR 00902-1484 *Tel:* 787-724-0700 *Fax:* 787-724-8393 *E-mail:* www@icp.gobierno.pr *Web Site:* www.icp.gobierno.pr, pg 712

Vilarello, Meredith, Touchstone, 1230 Avenue of the Americas, New York, NY 10020, pg 256

Villegas, Teresa, Heart and Mind Press, 3135 E Palo Verde Dr, Phoenix, AZ 85016 *Tel:* 602-790-4009 *E-mail:* info@heartandmindpress.com *Web Site:* heartandmindpress.com, pg 527

Villeneuve, Nicole, Sourcebooks Inc, 1935 Brookdale Rd, Suite 139, Naperville, IL 60563 *Tel:* 630-961-3900 *Toll Free Tel:* 800-432-7444 *Fax:* 630-961-2168 *E-mail:* info@sourcebooks.com; customersupport@sourcebooks.com *Web Site:* www.sourcebooks.com, pg 240

Vinarub, Vanessa, Harvard University Press, 79 Garden St, Cambridge, MA 02138-1499 *Tel:* 617-495-2600; 401-531-2800 (intl orders) *Toll Free Tel:* 800-405-1619 (orders) *Fax:* 617-495-5898 (general); 617-496-4677 (edit & rts); 401-531-2801 (intl orders) *Toll Free Fax:* 800-406-9145 (orders) *E-mail:* contact_hup@harvard.edu *Web Site:* www.hup.harvard.edu, pg 115

Vincent, Heidi, National Geographic Books, 1145 17 St NW, Washington, DC 20036-4688 *Tel:* 202-857-7000 *Fax:* 202-857-7670 *Web Site:* www.nationalgeographic.com, pg 174

Vincent, Randi, Harmonie Park Press, Liberty Professional Ctr, 35675 Mound Rd, Sterling Heights, MI 48310-4727 *Tel:* 586-979-2077; 586-979-1844 (cust serv) *Toll Free Tel:* 800-422-4880 *Fax:* 586-979-1786; 586-979-1863 (cust serv) *E-mail:* info@harmonieparkpress.com *Web Site:* harmonieparkpress.com, pg 113

Vineis, Mark, Mondo Publishing, 200 Sherwood Ave, Farmingdale, NY 11735 *Tel:* 212-268-3560 *Toll Free Tel:* 888-88-MONDO (886-6636) *Toll Free Fax:* 888-532-4492 *E-mail:* info@mondopub.com *Web Site:* www.mondopub.com, pg 168

Vines, Jason, Zondervan, A HarperCollins Company, 5300 Patterson Ave SE, Grand Rapids, MI 49530 *Tel:* 616-698-6900 *Toll Free Tel:* 800-226-1122; 800-727-1309 (retail orders) *Fax:* 616-698-3350 *Toll Free Fax:* 800-698-3256 (retail orders) *E-mail:* zinfo@zondervan.com *Web Site:* www.zondervan.com, pg 289

Vines Verlin, Nicole, Sterling Publishing Co Inc, 387 Park Ave S, 11th fl, New York, NY 10016-8810 *Tel:* 212-532-7160 *Toll Free Tel:* 800-367-9692 *Fax:* 212-213-2495 *Web Site:* www.sterlingpub.com, pg 244

Vining, Peggy, Arkansas Writers' Conference, 13005 Misty Creek Dr, Little Rock, AR 72211 *Tel:* 501-224-5823 *Fax:* 501-224-5823 *Web Site:* www.arkansaswritersconference.org, pg 667

Vinter, Becky, FinePrint Literary Management, 115 W 29 St, 3rd fl, New York, NY 10001 *Tel:* 212-279-1282 *Web Site:* www.fineprintlit.com, pg 572

Viola, Juliet, Northern California Translators Association, PO Box 14015, Berkeley, CA 94712-5015 *Tel:* 510-845-8712 *Fax:* 510-845-8712 *E-mail:* ncta@ncta.org *Web Site:* www.ncta.org, pg 632

Vipperman Cohen, Melissa, Touchstone, 1230 Avenue of the Americas, New York, NY 10020, pg 257

Vitanza, Dianna, Baylor University, Writing Program, One Bear Place, Unit 97404, Waco, TX 76798-7404 *Tel:* 254-710-1768 *Fax:* 254-710-3894 *Web Site:* www.baylor.edu, pg 677

Vitek, John M, Saint Mary's Press, 702 Terrace Heights, Winona, MN 55987-1318 *Tel:* 507-457-7900 *Toll Free Tel:* 800-533-8095 *Fax:* 507-457-7990 *Toll Free Fax:* 800-344-9225 *E-mail:* smpress@smp.org *Web Site:* www.smp.org, pg 224

Vitelli, Lisa, Penguin Group (USA) LLC Sales, 375 Hudson St, New York, NY 10014 *Tel:* 212-366-2000 *E-mail:* online@penguinputnam.com *Web Site:* us.penguingroup.com, pg 197

Vitkovski, Vlad, United Nations Publications, 2 United Nations Plaza, Rm DC2-0853, New York, NY 10017 *Tel:* 212-963-8302 *Toll Free Tel:* 800-253-9646 *Fax:* 212-963-3489 *E-mail:* publications@un.org *Web Site:* unp.un.org, pg 262

Vlahos, Len, Book Industry Study Group Inc (BISG), 145 W 45 St, Suite 601, New York, NY 10036 *Tel:* 646-336-7141 *Fax:* 646-336-6214 *E-mail:* info@bisg.org *Web Site:* www.bisg.org, pg 618

Vogel, Chris, National Gallery of Art, Fourth St & Pennsylvania Ave NW, Washington, DC 20565 *Tel:* 202-737-4215; 202-842-6480 *Fax:* 202-842-6733 *E-mail:* casva@nga.gov *Web Site:* www.nga.gov, pg 174

Vogel, James, Angelus Press, 2915 Forest Ave, Kansas City, MO 64109 *Tel:* 816-753-3150 *Toll Free Tel:* 800-966-7337 *Fax:* 816-753-3557 *E-mail:* info@angeluspress.org *Web Site:* www.angeluspress.org, pg 18

Vogel, Rachel, Waxman Literary Agency, 80 Fifth Ave, Suite 1101, New York, NY 10011 *Tel:* 212-675-5556 *Fax:* 212-675-1381 *Web Site:* www.waxmanagency.com, pg 599

Volkman, Victor R, Loving Healing Press Inc, 5145 Pontiac Trail, Ann Arbor, MI 48105 *Tel:* 734-417-4266 *Toll Free Tel:* 888-761-6268 (US & CN) *Fax:* 734-663-6861 *E-mail:* info@lovinghealing.com *Web Site:* www.lovinghealing.com; www.modernhistorypress.com (imprint), pg 153

Voltz, Gunnar, Abrams Learning Trends, 16310 Bratton Lane, Suite 250, Austin, TX 78728-2403 *Toll Free Tel:* 800-227-9120 *Toll Free Fax:* 800-737-3322 *E-mail:* customerservice@abramslearningtrends.com (orders, cust serv) *Web Site:* www.abramslearningtrends.com (orders, cust serv), pg 3

Voltz, Gunnar, Haights Cross Communications Inc, 136 Madison Ave, 8th fl, New York, NY 10016 *Tel:* 212-209-0500 *Fax:* 212-209-0501 *E-mail:* info@haightscross.com *Web Site:* www.haightscross.com, pg 110

Von Beoczy, Stefanie, Random House Speakers Bureau, 1745 Broadway, Mail Drop 13-1, New York, NY 10019 *Tel:* 212-572-2013 *E-mail:* rhspeakers@randomhouse.com *Web Site:* www.rhspeakers.com, pg 605

von der Linn, Michael PhD, The Lawbook Exchange Ltd, 33 Terminal Ave, Clark, NJ 07066-1321 *Tel:* 732-382-1800 *Toll Free Tel:* 800-422-6686 *Fax:* 732-382-1887 *E-mail:* law@lawbookexchange.com *Web Site:* www.lawbookexchange.com, pg 145

von der Lippe, Angela, W W Norton & Company Inc, 500 Fifth Ave, New York, NY 10110-0017 *Tel:* 212-354-5500 *Toll Free Tel:* 800-233-4830 (orders & cust serv) *Fax:* 212-869-0856 *Toll Free Fax:* 800-458-6515 *Web Site:* www.wwnorton.com, pg 182

von Grebner, Klaus, International Food Policy Research Institute, 2033 "K" St NW, Washington, DC 20006-1002 *Tel:* 202-862-5600 *Fax:* 202-467-4439 *E-mail:* ifpri@cgiar.org *Web Site:* www.ifpri.org, pg 133

Von Hertsenberg, Kurt, Wildlife Education Ltd, 2418 Noyes St, Evanston, IL 60201 *Toll Free Tel:* 800-477-5034 *E-mail:* owls5@zoobooks.com; helpdesk@zoobooks.com *Web Site:* www.zoobooks.com; wildlife-ed.com, pg 281

Von Hoelscher, Russ, North American Bookdealers Exchange (NABE), PO Box 606, Cottage Grove, OR 97424-0026 *Tel:* 541-942-7455 *E-mail:* nabe@bookmarketingprofits.com *Web Site:* www.bookmarketingprofits.com, pg 632

von Knorring, John, Stylus Publishing LLC, 22883 Quicksilver Dr, Sterling, VA 20166-2012 *Tel:* 703-661-1504 (edit & sales) *Toll Free Tel:* 800-232-0223 (orders & cust serv) *Fax:* 703-661-1547 *E-mail:* stylusmail@presswarehouse.com (orders & cust serv); stylusinfo@styluspub.com *Web Site:* www.styluspub.com, pg 246

von Knorring, Robin, Stylus Publishing LLC, 22883 Quicksilver Dr, Sterling, VA 20166-2012 *Tel:* 703-661-1504 (edit & sales) *Toll Free Tel:* 800-232-0223 (orders & cust serv) *Fax:* 703-661-1547 *E-mail:* stylusmail@presswarehouse.com (orders & cust serv); stylusinfo@styluspub.com *Web Site:* www.styluspub.com, pg 246

von Schilling, Claire, Random House Publishing Group, 1745 Broadway, New York, NY 10019 *Toll Free Tel:* 800-200-3552 *Web Site:* atrandom.com, pg 214

Vondeling, Johanna, Berrett-Koehler Publishers Inc, 235 Montgomery St, Suite 650, San Francisco, CA 94104 *Tel:* 415-288-0260 *Fax:* 415-362-2512 *E-mail:* bkpub@bkpub.com *Web Site:* www.bkconnection.com, pg 36

Vorenberg, Bonnie L, ArtAge Publications, PO Box 19955, Portland, OR 97280 *Tel:* 503-246-3000 *Toll Free Tel:* 800-858-4998 *Fax:* 503-246-3006 *Web Site:* www.seniortheatre.com, pg 23

Voros, Stephanie, Simon & Schuster Children's Publishing, 1230 Avenue of the Americas, New York, NY 10020 *Tel:* 212-698-7000 *Web Site:* KIDS.SimonandSchuster.com; TEEN.SimonandSchuster.com; simonandschuster.net; simonandschuster.biz, pg 235

Vosburgh, Andrew R, Graphic World Publishing Services, 11687 Adie Rd, St Louis, MO 63043 *Tel:* 314-567-9854 *Fax:* 314-567-7178 *E-mail:* quote@gwinc.com *Web Site:* www.gwinc.com, pg 547

Walker, David, Oberlin College Press, 50 N Professor St, Oberlin, OH 44074-1091 *Tel:* 440-775-8408 *Fax:* 440-775-8124 *E-mail:* oc.press@oberlin.edu *Web Site:* www.oberlin.edu/ocpress, pg 183

Walker, James R Jr, Walch Education, 40 Walch Dr, Portland, ME 04103-1286 *Tel:* 207-772-2846 *Toll Free Tel:* 800-558-2846 *Fax:* 207-772-3105 *Toll Free Fax:* 888-991-5755 *E-mail:* customerservice@walch.com *Web Site:* www.walch.com, pg 276

Walker, Janet, The Brookings Institution Press, 1775 Massachusetts Ave NW, Washington, DC 20036-2188 *Tel:* 202-536-3600 *Toll Free Tel:* 800-537-5487 *Fax:* 202-536-3623 *E-mail:* permissions@brookings.edu *Web Site:* www.brookings.edu, pg 48

Walker, Jayne, Jayne Walker Literary Services, 1406 Euclid Ave, Suite 1, Berkeley, CA 94708 *Tel:* 510-843-8265, pg 556

Walker, Jerald, Emerson College Dept of Writing, Literature & Publishing, 180 Tremont St, 10th fl, Boston, MA 02116 *Tel:* 617-824-8750 *Fax:* 617-824-7856 *Web Site:* www.emerson.edu, pg 678

Walker, Kathy, MidWest Plan Service (MWPS), Iowa State University, 122 Davidson Hall, Ames, IA 50011-3080 *Tel:* 515-294-4337 *Toll Free Tel:* 800-562-3618 *Fax:* 515-294-9589 *E-mail:* mwps@iastate.edu *Web Site:* www.mwps.org, pg 166

Walker, Laura, University of Alaska Press, 794 University Ave, Suite 220, Fairbanks, AK 99709 *Tel:* 907-474-5831 *Toll Free Tel:* 888-252-6657 (US only) *Fax:* 907-474-5502 *E-mail:* fypress@uaf.edu *Web Site:* www.uaf.edu/uapress, pg 264

Walker, Margaret, Taylor & Francis Inc, 325 Chestnut St, Suite 800, Philadelphia, PA 20036-1802 *Tel:* 215-625-8900 *Toll Free Tel:* 800-354-1420 *Fax:* 215-625-2940 *E-mail:* customer.service@taylorandfrancis.com *Web Site:* www.taylorandfrancis.com, pg 250

Walker, Matthew, Recorded Books LLC, 270 Skipjack Rd, Prince Frederick, MD 20678 *Tel:* 410-535-5590 *Toll Free Tel:* 800-638-1304; 877-732-2898 *Fax:* 410-535-5499 *E-mail:* customerservice@recordedbooks.com *Web Site:* www.recordedbooks.com, pg 215

Walker, Rick, Canadian Scholars' Press Inc, 180 Bloor St W, Suite 801, Toronto, ON M5S 2V6, Canada *Tel:* 416-929-2774 *Toll Free Tel:* 800-463-1998 *Fax:* 416-929-1926 *E-mail:* info@cspi.org; editorial@cspi.org *Web Site:* cspi.org; www.womenspress.ca, pg 497

Walker, Tara, Tundra Books, One Toronto St, Suite 300, Toronto, ON M5C 2V6, Canada *Tel:* 416-364-4449 *Toll Free Tel:* 888-523-9292 (orders); 800-588-1074 *Fax:* 416-598-0247 *Toll Free Fax:* 888-562-9924 (orders) *E-mail:* tundra@mcclelland.com *Web Site:* www.tundrabooks.com, pg 522

Walker, Teresa, The Catholic University of America Press, 240 Leahy Hall, 620 Michigan Ave NE, Washington, DC 20064 *Tel:* 202-319-5052 *Toll Free Tel:* 800-537-5487 (orders only) *Fax:* 202-319-4985 *E-mail:* cua-press@cua.edu *Web Site:* cuapress.cua.edu, pg 54

Wall, Marcia K, Evan-Moor Educational Publishers, 18 Lower Ragsdale Dr, Monterey, CA 93940-5746 *Tel:* 831-649-5901 *Toll Free Tel:* 800-714-0971 (cust serv); 800-777-4362 (orders) *Fax:* 831-649-6256 *Toll Free Fax:* 800-777-4332 (orders) *E-mail:* sales@evan-moor.com; marketing@evan-moor.com *Web Site:* www.evan-moor.com, pg 90

Wall, Melanie, The Center for Learning, 29313 Clemens Rd, Suite 2-E, Westlake, OH 44145 *Tel:* 440-250-9341 *Fax:* 440-250-9715 *E-mail:* customerservice@centerforlearning.org *Web Site:* www.centerforlearning.org, pg 56

Wall, Patrick, A-R Editions Inc, 8551 Research Way, Suite 180, Middleton, WI 53562 *Tel:* 608-836-9000 *Toll Free Tel:* 800-736-0070 (US book orders only) *Fax:* 608-831-8200 *E-mail:* info@areditions.com *Web Site:* www.areditions.com, pg 1

Wallace, Dan, Gallaudet University Press, 800 Florida Ave NE, Washington, DC 20002-3695 *Tel:* 202-651-5488 *Fax:* 202-651-5489 *E-mail:* gupress@gallaudet.edu *Web Site:* gupress.gallaudet.edu, pg 101

Wallace, Ivey P, Gallaudet University Press, 800 Florida Ave NE, Washington, DC 20002-3695 *Tel:* 202-651-5488 *Fax:* 202-651-5489 *E-mail:* gupress@gallaudet.edu *Web Site:* gupress.gallaudet.edu, pg 101

Wallace, Kristen, Fun in the Sun, PO Box 430744, Miami, FL 33243 *Web Site:* www.frwriters.org, pg 669

Wallace, Lois, Wallace Literary Agency Inc, 301 E 79 St, No 14-J, New York, NY 10075-0951 *Tel:* 212-570-9090 *Fax:* 212-772-8979 *E-mail:* walliter@aol.com, pg 598

Wallace, Robert, PEN Center USA, PO Box 6037, Beverly Hills, CA 90212 *Tel:* 323-424-4939 *Fax:* 323-424-4944 *E-mail:* pen@penusa.org *Web Site:* www.penusa.org, pg 633

Wallace, Ronald, Brittingham & Pollak Prizes in Poetry, Dept of English, 600 N Park St, Madison, WI 53706 *Web Site:* www.wisc.edu/wisconsinpress, pg 693

Wallace, Sharah, Hospital & Healthcare Compensation Service, 3 Post Rd FL, Suite 3, Oakland, NJ 07436 *Tel:* 201-405-0075 *Fax:* 201-405-2110 *E-mail:* allinfo@hhcsinc.com *Web Site:* www.hhcsinc.com, pg 123

Wallek, Dan, Carolrhoda Lab™, 241 First Ave N, Minneapolis, MN 55401 *Tel:* 612-332-3344 *Toll Free Tel:* 800-328-4929 *Fax:* 612-332-7615 *Toll Free Fax:* 800-332-1132 (US) *E-mail:* info@lernerbooks.com *Web Site:* www.lernerbooks.com, pg 53

Wallek, Dan, ediciones Lerner, 241 First Ave N, Minneapolis, MN 55401 *Tel:* 612-332-3344 *Toll Free Tel:* 800-328-4929 *Fax:* 612-332-7615 *Toll Free Fax:* 800-332-1132 *E-mail:* info@lernerbooks.com *Web Site:* www.lernerbooks.com, pg 85

Wallek, Dan, First Avenue Editions, 241 First Ave N, Minneapolis, MN 55401 *Tel:* 612-332-3344 *Toll Free Tel:* 800-328-4929 *Fax:* 612-332-7615 *Toll Free Fax:* 800-332-1132 *E-mail:* info@lernerbooks.com *Web Site:* www.lernerbooks.com, pg 95

Wallek, Dan, Graphic Universe™, 241 First Ave N, Minneapolis, MN 55401 *Tel:* 612-332-3344 *Toll Free Tel:* 800-328-4929 *Fax:* 612-332-7615 *Toll Free Fax:* 800-332-1132 *E-mail:* info@lernerbooks.com *Web Site:* www.lernerbooks.com, pg 106

Wallek, Dan, Lerner Publications, 241 First Ave N, Minneapolis, MN 55401 *Tel:* 612-332-3344 *Toll Free Tel:* 800-328-4929 *Fax:* 612-332-7615 *Toll Free Fax:* 800-332-1132 *E-mail:* info@lernerbooks.com *Web Site:* www.lernerbooks.com, pg 146

Wallek, Dan, Lerner Publishing Group Inc, 241 First Ave N, Minneapolis, MN 55401 *Tel:* 612-332-3344 *Toll Free Tel:* 800-328-4929 *Fax:* 612-332-7615 *Toll Free Fax:* 800-332-1132 *E-mail:* info@lernerbooks.com *Web Site:* www.lernerbooks.com, pg 146

Wallek, Dan, LernerClassroom, 241 First Ave N, Minneapolis, MN 55401 *Tel:* 612-332-3344 *Toll Free Tel:* 800-328-4929 *Fax:* 612-332-7615 *Toll Free Fax:* 800-332-1132 *E-mail:* info@lernerbooks.com *Web Site:* www.lernerbooks.com, pg 147

Wallek, Dan, Millbrook Press, 241 First Ave N, Minneapolis, MN 55401 *Tel:* 612-332-3344 *Toll Free Tel:* 800-328-4929 (US only) *Fax:* 612-332-7615 *Toll Free Fax:* 800-332-1132, pg 167

Wallek, Dan, Twenty-First Century Books, 241 First Ave N, Minneapolis, MN 55401 *Tel:* 612-332-3344 *Toll Free Tel:* 800-328-4929 *Fax:* 612-332-7615 *Toll Free Fax:* 800-332-1132 *E-mail:* info@lernerbooks.com *Web Site:* www.lernerbooks.com, pg 260

Wallentine, Lois, Carolrhoda Books, 241 First Ave N, Minneapolis, MN 55401 *Tel:* 612-332-3344 *Toll Free Tel:* 800-328-4929 *Fax:* 612-332-7615 *Toll Free Fax:* 800-332-1132 *E-mail:* info@lernerbooks.com *Web Site:* www.lernerbooks.com, pg 53

Wallentine, Lois, Carolrhoda Lab™, 241 First Ave N, Minneapolis, MN 55401 *Tel:* 612-332-3344 *Toll Free Tel:* 800-328-4929 *Fax:* 612-332-7615 *Toll Free Fax:* 800-332-1132 (US) *E-mail:* info@lernerbooks.com *Web Site:* www.lernerbooks.com, pg 53

Wallentine, Lois, ediciones Lerner, 241 First Ave N, Minneapolis, MN 55401 *Tel:* 612-332-3344 *Toll Free Tel:* 800-328-4929 *Fax:* 612-332-7615 *Toll Free Fax:* 800-332-1132 *E-mail:* info@lernerbooks.com *Web Site:* www.lernerbooks.com, pg 85

Wallentine, Lois, First Avenue Editions, 241 First Ave N, Minneapolis, MN 55401 *Tel:* 612-332-3344 *Toll Free Tel:* 800-328-4929 *Fax:* 612-332-7615 *Toll Free Fax:* 800-332-1132 *E-mail:* info@lernerbooks.com *Web Site:* www.lernerbooks.com, pg 95

Wallentine, Lois, Graphic Universe™, 241 First Ave N, Minneapolis, MN 55401 *Tel:* 612-332-3344 *Toll Free Tel:* 800-328-4929 *Fax:* 612-332-7615 *Toll Free Fax:* 800-332-1132 *E-mail:* info@lernerbooks.com *Web Site:* www.lernerbooks.com, pg 106

Wallentine, Lois, Lerner Publications, 241 First Ave N, Minneapolis, MN 55401 *Tel:* 612-332-3344 *Toll Free Tel:* 800-328-4929 *Fax:* 612-332-7615 *Toll Free Fax:* 800-332-1132 *E-mail:* info@lernerbooks.com *Web Site:* www.lernerbooks.com, pg 146

Wallentine, Lois, Lerner Publishing Group Inc, 241 First Ave N, Minneapolis, MN 55401 *Tel:* 612-332-3344 *Toll Free Tel:* 800-328-4929 *Fax:* 612-332-7615 *Toll Free Fax:* 800-332-1132 *E-mail:* info@lernerbooks.com *Web Site:* www.lernerbooks.com, pg 146

Wallentine, Lois, LernerClassroom, 241 First Ave N, Minneapolis, MN 55401 *Tel:* 612-332-3344 *Toll Free Tel:* 800-328-4929 *Fax:* 612-332-7615 *Toll Free Fax:* 800-332-1132 *E-mail:* info@lernerbooks.com *Web Site:* www.lernerbooks.com, pg 147

Wallentine, Lois, Millbrook Press, 241 First Ave N, Minneapolis, MN 55401 *Tel:* 612-332-3344 *Toll Free Tel:* 800-328-4929 (US only) *Fax:* 612-332-7615 *Toll Free Fax:* 800-332-1132, pg 167

Wallentine, Lois, Twenty-First Century Books, 241 First Ave N, Minneapolis, MN 55401 *Tel:* 612-332-3344 *Toll Free Tel:* 800-328-4929 *Fax:* 612-332-7615 *Toll Free Fax:* 800-332-1132 *E-mail:* info@lernerbooks.com *Web Site:* www.lernerbooks.com, pg 260

Waller, Samantha, Prestel Publishing, 900 Broadway, Suite 603, New York, NY 10003 *Tel:* 212-995-2720 *Toll Free Tel:* 888-463-6110 (cust serv) *Fax:* 212-995-2733 *E-mail:* sales@prestel-usa.com *Web Site:* www.prestel.com, pg 205

Walling, Bonnie, OPIS/STALSBY Directories & Databases, 3349 Hwy 138, Bldg D, Suite D, Wall, NJ 07719 *Tel:* 732-901-8800 *Toll Free Tel:* 800-275-0950 *Toll Free Fax:* 800-450-5864 *E-mail:* opisstalsbylistings@opisnet.com *Web Site:* www.opisnet.com, pg 186

Walling, Lori, Tyndale House Publishers Inc, 351 Executive Dr, Carol Stream, IL 60188 *Tel:* 630-668-8300 *Toll Free Tel:* 800-323-9400 *Web Site:* www.tyndale.com, pg 261

Walls, Kathleen, Global Authors Publications (GAP), 38 Bluegrass, Middleberg, FL 32068 *Tel:* 904-425-1608 *E-mail:* gapbook@yahoo.com, pg 104

Walsh, Barbara A, Holiday House Inc, 425 Madison Ave, New York, NY 10017 *Tel:* 212-688-0085 *Fax:* 212-421-6134 *E-mail:* holiday@holidayhouse.com *Web Site:* www.holidayhouse.com, pg 121

Walsh, Jennifer Rudolph, WME, 1325 Avenue of the Americas, New York, NY 10019 *Tel:* 212-586-5100 *Fax:* 212-246-3583 *E-mail:* wma@interport.net *Web Site:* www.wma.com, pg 599

Walsh, Karen, Houghton Mifflin Harcourt Trade & Reference Division, 222 Berkeley St, Boston, MA 02116-3764 *Tel:* 617-351-5000 *Toll Free Tel:* 800-225-3362 *Web Site:* www.houghtonmifflinbooks.com, pg 124

Walsh, Lillie, HarperCollins Publishers Sales, 10 E 53 St, New York, NY 10022 *Fax:* 212-207-7000 *Web Site:* www.harpercollins.com, pg 114

Walsh, Mark, Artech House Inc, 685 Canton St, Norwood, MA 02062 *Tel:* 781-769-9750 *Toll Free Tel:* 800-225-9977 *Fax:* 781-769-6334 *E-mail:* artech@artechhouse.com *Web Site:* www.artechhouse.com, pg 23

Weber, John, Welcome Rain Publishers LLC, 217 Thompson St, Suite 473, New York, NY 10012 *Tel:* 212-686-1909 *Web Site:* welcomerain.com, pg 278

Weber, Judith, Sobel Weber Associates Inc, 146 E 19 St, New York, NY 10003-2404 *Tel:* 212-420-8585 *Fax:* 212-505-1017 *E-mail:* info@sobelweber.com *Web Site:* www.sobelweber.com, pg 595

Weber, Louis, Publications International Ltd, 7373 N Cicero Ave, Lincolnwood, IL 60712 *Tel:* 847-676-3470 *Fax:* 847-676-3671 *Web Site:* www.pilbooks.com, pg 209

Weber, Mark, The Noontide Press, PO Box 2719, Newport Beach, CA 92659-1319 *Tel:* 714-593-9725 *Fax:* 714-593-9731 *E-mail:* orders@noontidepress.com *Web Site:* www.noontidepress.com, pg 180

Weberg, Inga, Redleaf Press, 10 Yorkton Ct, St Paul, MN 55117 *Tel:* 651-641-0508 *Toll Free Tel:* 800-423-8309 *Toll Free Fax:* 800-641-0115 *Web Site:* www.redleafpress.org, pg 216

Weberman, Alisa, Listen & Live Audio Inc, PO Box 817, Roseland, NJ 07068-0817 *Tel:* 201-558-9000 *Toll Free Tel:* 800-653-9400 (orders) *Fax:* 201-558-9800 *Web Site:* www.listenandlive.com, pg 150

Weckbaugh, Patty, Book Publicists of Southern California, 714 Crescent Dr, Beverly Hills, CA 90210 *Tel:* 323-461-3921 *Fax:* 323-461-0917, pg 618

Wedin, Neil, Heritage House Publishing Co Ltd, 1105 Pandora Ave, Victoria, BC V8V 3P9, Canada *Tel:* 604-574-7067 *Toll Free Tel:* 800-665-3302 *Fax:* 604-574-9942 *Toll Free Fax:* 800-566-3336 *E-mail:* heritage@heritagehouse.ca; orders@heritagehouse.ca *Web Site:* www.heritagehouse.ca, pg 509

Weed, Susun, Ash Tree Publishing, PO Box 64, Woodstock, NY 12498 *Tel:* 845-246-8081 *Fax:* 845-246-8081 *E-mail:* info@ashtreepublishing.com *Web Site:* www.ashtreepublishing.com, pg 24

Weeks, Kevin M, The Street Life Series, c/o Xlibris Corp, 1663 Liberty Dr, Suite 200, Bloomington, IN 47403 *Toll Free Tel:* 888-795-4274 (orders thru Xlibris) *Fax:* 610-915-0294 (orders thru Xlibris) *E-mail:* info@kevinmweeks.com *Web Site:* www.kevinmweeks.com, pg 529

Weeks, Robin, Dancing Dakini Press, 77 Morning Sun Dr, Sedona, AZ 86336 *Tel:* 928-852-0129 *E-mail:* editor@dancingdakinipress.com *Web Site:* www.dancingdakinipress.com, pg 74

Weese, Brian, Island Press, 1718 Connecticut Ave NW, Suite 300, Washington, DC 20009 *Tel:* 202-232-7933 *Toll Free Tel:* 800-828-1302 *Fax:* 202-234-1328 *E-mail:* info@islandpress.org *Web Site:* www.islandpress.org, pg 134

Wegendt, Sr Christina, Pauline Books & Media, 50 Saint Paul's Ave, Boston, MA 02130 *Tel:* 617-522-8911 *Toll Free Tel:* 800-876-4463 (orders); 800-836-9723 (cust serv) *Fax:* 617-541-9805 *E-mail:* orderentry@pauline.org (cust serv); editorial@paulinemedia.com (ms submissions) *Web Site:* www.pauline.org, pg 194

Weggel, Anna, Milkweed Editions, 1011 Washington Ave S, Suite 300, Minneapolis, MN 55415-1246 *Tel:* 612-332-3192 *Toll Free Tel:* 800-520-6455 *Fax:* 612-215-2550 *Web Site:* www.milkweed.org, pg 166

Weggel, Anna, Milkweed National Fiction Prize, 1011 Washington Ave S, Suite 300, Minneapolis, MN 55415-1246 *Tel:* 612-332-3192 *Toll Free Tel:* 800-520-6455 *Fax:* 612-215-2550 *E-mail:* submissions@milkweed.org *Web Site:* www.milkweed.org, pg 723

Wegner, Gregory R, GLCA New Writers Awards, 535 W William St, Suite 301, Ann Arbor, MI 48103 *Tel:* 734-661-2350 *Fax:* 734-661-2349 *Web Site:* www.glca.org, pg 707

Wehmueller, Jacqueline C, The Johns Hopkins University Press, 2715 N Charles St, Baltimore, MD 21218-4363 *Tel:* 410-516-6900; 410-516-6987 (journals outside US & CN) *Toll Free Tel:* 800-537-5487 (book orders & cust serv); 800-548-1784 (journal orders) *Fax:* 410-516-6968; 410-516-3866 (journal orders) *E-mail:* hfscustserv@press.jhu.edu (cust serv); jrnlcirc@press.jhu.edu (journal orders) *Web Site:* www.press.jhu.edu; muse.jhu.edu/about/subscriptions/index.html (Project Muse subns), pg 136

Wehner, Aaron, Crown Publishing Group, c/o Random House Inc, 1745 Broadway, New York, NY 10019 *Tel:* 212-782-9000 *Toll Free Tel:* 888-264-1745 *Fax:* 212-940-7408 *Web Site:* www.randomhouse.com/crown, pg 72

Wehner, Aaron, Ten Speed Press, 2625 Alcatraz Ave, Unit 505, Berkeley, CA 94705 *Tel:* 510-285-3000 *Toll Free Tel:* 800-841-BOOK (841-2665) *E-mail:* csorders@randomhouse.com *Web Site:* crownpublishing.com/imprint/ten-speed-press, pg 252

Weidinger, Lilo, A Cappela Publishing, PO Box 3691, Sarasota, FL 34230-3691 *Tel:* 941-351-2050 *Fax:* 941-351-4735 *E-mail:* acappub@aol.com *Web Site:* www.acappela.com, pg 1

Weidknecht, Katrina, Harry N Abrams Inc, 115 W 18 St, 6th fl, New York, NY 10011 *Tel:* 212-206-7715 *Toll Free Tel:* 800-345-1359 *Fax:* 212-519-1210 *E-mail:* abrams@abramsbooks.com *Web Site:* www.abramsbooks.com, pg 3

Weidknecht, Katrina, Stewart, Tabori & Chang, 115 W 18 St, 6th fl, New York, NY 10011 *Tel:* 212-519-1200 *Fax:* 212-519-1210 *Web Site:* www.abramsbooks.com, pg 245

Weidman, Anna, University of California Press, 2120 Berkeley Way, Berkeley, CA 94704-1012 *Tel:* 510-642-4247 *Fax:* 510-643-7127 *E-mail:* askucp@ucpress.edu (books); customerservice@ucpressjournals.com (journals) *Web Site:* www.ucpress.edu, pg 264

Weight, Alden PhD, Sourced Media Books, 29 Via Regalo, San Clemente, CA 92673 *Tel:* 949-813-0182 *E-mail:* info@sourcemediabooks.com *Web Site:* sourcedmediabooks.com, pg 240

Weigl, Linda, Weigl Educational Publishers Ltd, 6325 Tenth St SE, Calgary, AB T2H 2Z9, Canada *Tel:* 403-233-7747 *Toll Free Tel:* 800-668-0766 *Fax:* 403-233-7769 *Toll Free Fax:* 866-449-3445 *E-mail:* info@weigl.com; orders@weigl.com *Web Site:* www.weigl.ca; www.weigl.com, pg 524

Weikart, Jim, International Association of Crime Writers Inc, North American Branch, 328 Eighth Ave, Suite 114, New York, NY 10001 *Tel:* 212-243-8966 *Fax:* 815-361-1477 *E-mail:* info@crimewritersna.org *Web Site:* www.crimewritersna.org, pg 625

Weikersheimer, Joshua R, ASCP Press, 33 W Monroe St, Suite 1600, Chicago, IL 60603 *Tel:* 312-541-4999 *Toll Free Tel:* 800-267-2727 *Fax:* 312-541-4998 *Web Site:* www.ascp.org, pg 24

Weil, Gideon, HarperCollins General Books Group, 10 E 53 St, New York, NY 10022 *Tel:* 212-207-7000 *Fax:* 212-207-7633 *Web Site:* www.harpercollins.com, pg 113

Weil, Joe, Binghamton University Creative Writing Program, c/o Dept of English, PO Box 6000, Binghamton, NY 13902-6000 *Tel:* 607-777-2168 *Fax:* 607-777-2408 *E-mail:* cwpro@binghamton.edu *Web Site:* english.binghamton.edu/cwpro, pg 677

Weil, Robert, W W Norton & Company Inc, 500 Fifth Ave, New York, NY 10110-0017 *Tel:* 212-354-5500 *Toll Free Tel:* 800-233-4830 (orders & cust serv) *Fax:* 212-869-0856 *Toll Free Fax:* 800-458-6515 *Web Site:* www.wwnorton.com, pg 182

Weil, Steve, Farrar, Straus & Giroux, LLC, 18 W 18 St, New York, NY 10011 *Tel:* 212-741-6900 *Fax:* 212-633-9385 *E-mail:* fsg.publicity@fsgbooks.com *Web Site:* us.macmillan.com/fsg.aspx, pg 93

Weiland, Matt, W W Norton & Company Inc, 500 Fifth Ave, New York, NY 10110-0017 *Tel:* 212-354-5500 *Toll Free Tel:* 800-233-4830 (orders & cust serv) *Fax:* 212-869-0856 *Toll Free Fax:* 800-458-6515 *Web Site:* www.wwnorton.com, pg 182

Weimann, Frank, Folio Literary Management LLC, The Film Center Bldg, 630 Ninth Ave, Suite 1101, New York, NY 10036 *Tel:* 212-400-1494 *Fax:* 212-967-0977 *Web Site:* www.foliolit.com, pg 572

Wein, Lauren, Houghton Mifflin Harcourt Trade & Reference Division, 222 Berkeley St, Boston, MA 02116-3764 *Tel:* 617-351-5000 *Toll Free Tel:* 800-225-3362 *Web Site:* www.houghtonmifflinbooks.com, pg 124

Weinberg, Bill, Grove/Atlantic Inc, 841 Broadway, 4th fl, New York, NY 10003-4793 *Tel:* 212-614-7850 *Toll Free Tel:* 800-521-0178 *Fax:* 212-614-7886 *E-mail:* info@groveatlantic.com *Web Site:* www.groveatlantic.com, pg 108

Weinberg, Jeffrey H, Water Row Press, PO Box 438, Sudbury, MA 01776 *Tel:* 508-485-8515 *Fax:* 508-229-0885 *E-mail:* contact@waterrowbooks.com *Web Site:* www.waterrowbooks.com, pg 277

Weinberg, Susan, Basic Books, 250 W 57 St, 15th fl, New York, NY 10107 *Tel:* 212-340-8164 *Fax:* 212-340-8135 *E-mail:* perseus.promos@perseusbooks.com *Web Site:* www.basicbooks.com; perseusbooks.com, pg 31

Weinberg, Susan, Nation Books, 116 E 16 St, 8th fl, New York, NY 10003 *Tel:* 212-822-0264 *Fax:* 212-253-5356 *E-mail:* submissions@nationbooks.org *Web Site:* www.nationbooks.org, pg 172

Weinberg, Susan, PublicAffairs, 250 W 57 St, Suite 1321, New York, NY 10107 *Tel:* 212-397-6666 *Toll Free Tel:* 800-343-4499 (orders) *Fax:* 212-397-4277 *E-mail:* publicaffairs@perseusbooks.com *Web Site:* www.publicaffairsbooks.com, pg 209

Weinberger, Russell, Brockman Inc, 260 Fifth Ave, 10th fl, New York, NY 10001 *Tel:* 212-935-8900 *Fax:* 212-935-5535 *E-mail:* rights@brockman.com *Web Site:* www.brockman.com, pg 565

Weiner, Cherry, Cherry Weiner Literary Agency, 28 Kipling Way, Manalapan, NJ 07726 *Tel:* 732-446-2096 *Fax:* 732-792-0506 *E-mail:* cherry8486@aol.com, pg 599

Weiner, Deborah, Georgetown University Press, 3240 Prospect St NW, Suite 250, Washington, DC 20007 *Tel:* 202-687-5889 (busn) *Toll Free Tel:* 800-537-5487 *Fax:* 202-687-6340 (edit) *E-mail:* gupress@georgetown.edu *Web Site:* press.georgetown.edu, pg 102

Weiner, Eric J, Information Publications Inc, 2995 Woodside Rd, Suite 400-182, Woodside, CA 94062 *Tel:* 650-568-6170 *Toll Free Tel:* 877-544-4636 *Fax:* 650-568-6150 *Toll Free Fax:* 877-544-4635 *E-mail:* info@informationpublications.com *Web Site:* www.informationpublications.com, pg 130

Weiner, Ruth, Seven Stories Press, 140 Watts St, New York, NY 10013 *Tel:* 212-226-8760 *Fax:* 212-226-1411 *E-mail:* info@sevenstories.com *Web Site:* www.sevenstories.com, pg 232

Weiner, Samantha, Harry N Abrams Inc, 115 W 18 St, 6th fl, New York, NY 10011 *Tel:* 212-206-7715 *Toll Free Tel:* 800-345-1359 *Fax:* 212-519-1210 *E-mail:* abrams@abramsbooks.com *Web Site:* www.abramsbooks.com, pg 3

Weinfeld, Rodger, Disney Press, 44 S Broadway, White Plains, NY 10601 *Tel:* 212-633-4400 *Fax:* 212-807-5432 *Web Site:* disney.go.com/index; disney.go.com/books/index, pg 79

Weingarten, Seymour, The Guilford Press, 72 Spring St, 4th fl, New York, NY 10012 *Tel:* 212-431-9800 *Toll Free Tel:* 800-365-7006 (ext 1, orders) *Fax:* 212-966-6708 *E-mail:* orders@guilford.com; info@guilford.com *Web Site:* www.guilford.com, pg 109

Weingarten, Simone, Harvard Square Editions, 2152 Beachwood Terr, Hollywood, CA 90068 *Tel:* 323-469-8932 *Fax:* 323-469-8932 *Web Site:* harvardsquareeditions.org, pg 114

Weingel-Fidel, Loretta, The Weingel-Fidel Agency, 310 E 46 St, Suite 21-E, New York, NY 10017 *Tel:* 212-599-2959 *Fax:* 212-286-1986 *E-mail:* queries@theweingel-fidelagency.com, pg 599

Weinstein, Mark, Rodale Books, 400 S Tenth St, Emmaus, PA 18098 *Tel:* 610-967-5171 *Toll Free Tel:* 800-848-4735 (cust serv) *E-mail:* customerservice@rodale.com *Web Site:* www.rodaleinc.com, pg 220

Wentworth, K D, L Ron Hubbard's Writers of the Future Contest, PO Box 1630, Los Angeles, CA 90078 *Tel:* 323-466-3310 *Fax:* 323-466-6474 *E-mail:* contests@authorservicesinc.com *Web Site:* www.writersofthefuture.com, pg 711

Werk, Dawn, Alpha, 375 Hudson St, New York, NY 10014 *Tel:* 212-366-2000, pg 9

Werksman, Deb, Sourcebooks Inc, 1935 Brookdale Rd, Suite 139, Naperville, IL 60563 *Tel:* 630-961-3900 *Toll Free Tel:* 800-432-7444 *Fax:* 630-961-2168 *E-mail:* info@sourcebooks.com; customersupport@sourcebooks.com *Web Site:* www.sourcebooks.com, pg 240

Werner, George, Pearson Higher Education, One Lake St, Upper Saddle River, NJ 07458 *Tel:* 201-236-7000 *Fax:* 201-236-3381 *Web Site:* www.pearsonhighered.com, pg 196

Werner, Rich, F+W Media Inc, 10151 Carver Rd, Suite 200, Blue Ash, OH 45242 *Tel:* 513-531-2690 *Toll Free Tel:* 800-289-0963 (trade accts); 800-258-0929 (orders) *E-mail:* contact_us@fwmedia.com *Web Site:* www.fwmedia.com, pg 92

Werner, Theresa, National Press Club (NPC), 529 14 St NW, 13th fl, Washington, DC 20045 *Tel:* 202-662-7500 *Fax:* 202-662-7569 *E-mail:* infocenter@npcpress.org *Web Site:* www.press.org, pg 630

Werstler, Larisa, Dufour Editions Inc, PO Box 7, Chester Springs, PA 19425 *Tel:* 610-458-5005 *Toll Free Tel:* 800-869-5677 *Fax:* 610-458-7103 *E-mail:* info@dufoureditions.com *Web Site:* www.dufoureditions.com, pg 82

Wertheimer, Neil, The Reader's Digest Association Inc, 750 Third Ave, New York, NY 10017 *Tel:* 914-238-1000; 646-293-6284 *Toll Free Tel:* 800-310-6261 (cust serv) *Fax:* 914-238-4559 *Web Site:* www.rd.com; www.rda.com, pg 215

Werts, Lynn, University Press of Florida, 15 NW 15 St, Gainesville, FL 32603-2079 *Tel:* 352-392-1351 *Toll Free Tel:* 800-226-3822 (orders only) *Fax:* 352-392-0590 *Toll Free Fax:* 800-680-1955 (orders only) *E-mail:* info@upf.com *Web Site:* www.upf.com, pg 271

Werz, Ed, JayJo Books LLC, 303 Crossways Park Dr, Woodbury, NY 11797 *Tel:* 516-496-8492 *Toll Free Tel:* 800-999-6884 *Fax:* 516-496-4050 *Toll Free Fax:* 800-262-1886 *E-mail:* jayjobooks@guidance-group.com *Web Site:* www.guidance-group.com; www.jayjo.com, pg 135

Werz, Edward, The Bureau For At-Risk Youth, 303 Crossways Park Dr, Woodbury, NY 11797 *Tel:* 516-496-4863 *Fax:* 516-496-4050 *Web Site:* www.at-risk.com; www.guidance-group.com, pg 49

Weschcke, Carl L, Llewellyn Publications, 2143 Wooddale Dr, Woodbury, MN 55125 *Tel:* 651-291-1970 *Toll Free Tel:* 800-843-6666 *Fax:* 651-291-1908 *E-mail:* publicity@llewellyn.com *Web Site:* www.llewellyn.com, pg 151

Wesley, Mark, me+mi publishing inc, 400 S Knoll St, Suite B, Wheaton, IL 60187 *Tel:* 630-752-9951 *Toll Free Tel:* 888-251-1444 *Fax:* 630-588-9804 *E-mail:* rw@rosawesley.com *Web Site:* www.memima.com, pg 163

Wessels, Cindy, University of Pittsburgh Press, Eureka Bldg, 5th fl, 3400 Forbes Ave, Pittsburgh, PA 15260 *Tel:* 412-383-2456 *Fax:* 412-383-2466 *E-mail:* info@upress.pitt.edu *Web Site:* www.upress.pitt.edu, pg 268

Wessler, Derek, McGraw-Hill Education, 2 Penn Plaza, New York, NY 10121-2298 *Tel:* 212-904-2000 *E-mail:* customer.service@mcgraw-hill.com *Web Site:* www.mheducation.com; www.mheducation.com/custserv.html, pg 161

West, Ann, Mazda Publishers Inc, One Park Plaza, Suite 600, Irvine, CA 92614 *Tel:* 714-751-5252 *Fax:* 714-751-4805 *E-mail:* mazdapub@aol.com *Web Site:* www.mazdapub.com, pg 159

West, Douglas, Advertising Research Foundation (ARF), 432 Park Ave S, 6th fl, New York, NY 10016-8013 *Tel:* 212-751-5656 *Fax:* 212-319-5265 *E-mail:* info@thearf.org; jar@thearf.org (edit) *Web Site:* www.thearf.org; www.journalofadvertisingresearch.com, pg 611

West, J C, Abaris Books, 70 New Canaan Ave, Norwalk, CT 06850 *Tel:* 203-838-8402 *Fax:* 203-857-0730 *E-mail:* abaris@abarisbooks.com *Web Site:* abarisbooks.com, pg 2

West, J C, EastBridge, 70 New Canaan Ave, Norwalk, CT 06850 *Tel:* 203-855-9125 *Fax:* 203-857-0730 *E-mail:* asia@eastbridgebooks.org *Web Site:* www.eastbridgebooks.org, pg 84

West, Miriam, Abaris Books, 70 New Canaan Ave, Norwalk, CT 06850 *Tel:* 203-838-8402 *Fax:* 203-857-0730 *E-mail:* abaris@abarisbooks.com *Web Site:* abarisbooks.com, pg 2

Westberg, Phyllis, Harold Ober Associates Inc, 425 Madison Ave, New York, NY 10017 *Tel:* 212-759-8600 *Fax:* 212-759-9428 *Web Site:* www.haroldober.com, pg 587

Westfall, William, Barbour Publishing Inc, 1810 Barbour Dr, Uhrichsville, OH 44683 *Tel:* 740-922-6045 *Fax:* 740-922-5948 *E-mail:* info@barbourbooks.com *Web Site:* www.barbourbooks.com, pg 30

Westlund, Laura, University of Minnesota Press, 111 Third Ave S, Suite 290, Minneapolis, MN 55401-2520 *Tel:* 612-627-1970 *Fax:* 612-627-1980 *E-mail:* ump@umn.edu *Web Site:* www.upress.umn.edu, pg 266

Westmoreland, Lisa, Ten Speed Press, 2625 Alcatraz Ave, Unit 505, Berkeley, CA 94705 *Tel:* 510-285-3000 *Toll Free Tel:* 800-841-BOOK (841-2665) *E-mail:* csorders@randomhouse.com *Web Site:* crownpublishing.com/imprint/ten-speed-press, pg 252

Westmoreland, Phillip, American Institute of Chemical Engineers (AIChE), 3 Park Ave, 19th fl, New York, NY 10016-5991 *Tel:* 203-702-7660 *Toll Free Tel:* 800-242-4363 *Fax:* 203-775-5177 *E-mail:* custserv@aiche.org *Web Site:* www.aiche.org, pg 14

Weston, Pamela, Research & Education Association (REA), 61 Ethel Rd W, Piscataway, NJ 08854 *Tel:* 732-819-8880 *Fax:* 732-819-8808 (orders) *E-mail:* info@rea.com *Web Site:* www.rea.com, pg 218

Westwood, Bruce, Westwood Creative Artists Ltd, 94 Harbord St, Toronto, ON M5S 1G6, Canada *Tel:* 416-964-3302 *Fax:* 416-975-9209 *E-mail:* wca_office@wcaltd.com *Web Site:* www.wcaltd.com, pg 599

Wetherbee, Kerri, Focus Publishing/R Pullins Co Inc, PO Box 369, Newburyport, MA 01950 *Tel:* 978-462-7288 (edit) *Toll Free Tel:* 800-848-7236 (orders) *Fax:* 978-462-9035 (edit) *E-mail:* orders@pullins.com *Web Site:* www.pullins.com, pg 96

Wetstein, Rachel, Transcontinental Music Publications, 633 Third Ave, New York, NY 10017 *Tel:* 212-650-4101; 212-650-4120 *Toll Free Tel:* 888-489-8242 (orders) *Fax:* 212-650-4119 *E-mail:* tmp@urj.org; press@urj.org *Web Site:* www.transcontinentalmusic.com, pg 258

Wexler, David, Carolrhoda Books, 241 First Ave N, Minneapolis, MN 55401 *Tel:* 612-332-3344 *Toll Free Tel:* 800-328-4929 *Fax:* 612-332-7615 *Toll Free Fax:* 800-332-1132 *E-mail:* info@lernerbooks.com *Web Site:* www.lernerbooks.com, pg 53

Wexler, David, Carolrhoda Lab™, 241 First Ave N, Minneapolis, MN 55401 *Tel:* 612-332-3344 *Toll Free Tel:* 800-328-4929 *Fax:* 612-332-7615 *Toll Free Fax:* 800-332-1132 (US) *E-mail:* info@lernerbooks.com *Web Site:* www.lernerbooks.com, pg 53

Wexler, David, ediciones Lerner, 241 First Ave N, Minneapolis, MN 55401 *Tel:* 612-332-3344 *Toll Free Tel:* 800-328-4929 *Fax:* 612-332-7615 *Toll Free Fax:* 800-332-1132 *E-mail:* info@lernerbooks.com *Web Site:* www.lernerbooks.com, pg 85

Wexler, David, First Avenue Editions, 241 First Ave N, Minneapolis, MN 55401 *Tel:* 612-332-3344 *Toll Free Tel:* 800-328-4929 *Fax:* 612-332-7615 *Toll Free Fax:* 800-332-1132 *E-mail:* info@lernerbooks.com *Web Site:* www.lernerbooks.com, pg 95

Wexler, David, Graphic Universe™, 241 First Ave N, Minneapolis, MN 55401 *Tel:* 612-332-3344 *Toll Free Tel:* 800-328-4929 *Fax:* 612-332-7615 *Toll Free Fax:* 800-332-1132 *E-mail:* info@lernerbooks.com *Web Site:* www.lernerbooks.com, pg 106

Wexler, David, Lerner Publications, 241 First Ave N, Minneapolis, MN 55401 *Tel:* 612-332-3344 *Toll Free Tel:* 800-328-4929 *Fax:* 612-332-7615 *Toll Free Fax:* 800-332-1132 *E-mail:* info@lernerbooks.com *Web Site:* www.lernerbooks.com, pg 146

Wexler, David, Lerner Publishing Group Inc, 241 First Ave N, Minneapolis, MN 55401 *Tel:* 612-332-3344 *Toll Free Tel:* 800-328-4929 *Fax:* 612-332-7615 *Toll Free Fax:* 800-332-1132 *E-mail:* info@lernerbooks.com *Web Site:* www.lernerbooks.com, pg 146

Wexler, David, LernerClassroom, 241 First Ave N, Minneapolis, MN 55401 *Tel:* 612-332-3344 *Toll Free Tel:* 800-328-4929 *Fax:* 612-332-7615 *Toll Free Fax:* 800-332-1132 *E-mail:* info@lernerbooks.com *Web Site:* www.lernerbooks.com, pg 147

Wexler, David, Millbrook Press, 241 First Ave N, Minneapolis, MN 55401 *Tel:* 612-332-3344 *Toll Free Tel:* 800-328-4929 (US only) *Fax:* 612-332-7615 *Toll Free Fax:* 800-332-1132, pg 167

Wexler, David, Twenty-First Century Books, 241 First Ave N, Minneapolis, MN 55401 *Tel:* 612-332-3344 *Toll Free Tel:* 800-328-4929 *Fax:* 612-332-7615 *Toll Free Fax:* 800-332-1132 *E-mail:* info@lernerbooks.com *Web Site:* www.lernerbooks.com, pg 260

Wexler, Pearl, Paul Kohner Agency, 9300 Wilshire Blvd, Suite 555, Beverly Hills, CA 90212 *Tel:* 310-550-1060 *Fax:* 310-276-1083, pg 580

Weyenberg, Patricia, Penguin Group (USA) LLC Sales, 375 Hudson St, New York, NY 10014 *Tel:* 212-366-2000 *E-mail:* online@penguinputnam.com *Web Site:* us.penguingroup.com, pg 197

Whalen, Bill, BCFL, 4806 Martinique Way, Naples, FL 34119 *Tel:* 908-447-3553 *Fax:* 239-596-8611 *E-mail:* BCFLGroup@gmail.com *Web Site:* judgingfloraldesign.com, pg 527

Whalen, John F Jr, Cider Mill Press Book Publishers LLC, 12 Port Farm Rd, Kennebunkport, ME 04046 *Tel:* 207-967-8232 *Fax:* 207-967-8233 *Web Site:* www.cidermillpress.com, pg 61

Whalen, Kimberly, Trident Media Group LLC, 41 Madison Ave, 36th fl, New York, NY 10010 *Tel:* 212-262-4810 *Fax:* 212-262-4849 *Web Site:* www.tridentmediagroup.com, pg 598

Whalen, Lindsay, The Penguin Press, 375 Hudson St, New York, NY 10014, pg 197

Whaley, Glenn, STM Learning Inc, 8045 Big Bend Blvd, Suite 202, St Louis, MO 63119-2714 *Tel:* 314-993-2728 *Toll Free Tel:* 800-600-0330 *Fax:* 314-993-2281 *E-mail:* info@stmlearning.com; orders@stmlearning.com *Web Site:* www.stmlearning.com, pg 245

Whaley, Marianne, STM Learning Inc, 8045 Big Bend Blvd, Suite 202, St Louis, MO 63119-2714 *Tel:* 314-993-2728 *Toll Free Tel:* 800-600-0330 *Fax:* 314-993-2281 *E-mail:* info@stmlearning.com; orders@stmlearning.com *Web Site:* www.stmlearning.com, pg 245

Whaley, Marika, Harvard Ukrainian Research Institute, 34 Kirkland St, Cambridge, MA 02138 *Tel:* 617-495-4053 *Fax:* 617-495-8097 *E-mail:* huri@fas.harvard.edu *Web Site:* www.huri.harvard.edu, pg 114

Whaling, Penn, Ann Rittenberg Literary Agency Inc, 15 Maiden Lane, Suite 206, New York, NY 10038 *Tel:* 212-684-6936 *Fax:* 212-684-6929 *Web Site:* www.rittlit.com, pg 591

Wharton, Campbell, Crown Publishing Group, c/o Random House Inc, 1745 Broadway, New York, NY 10019 *Tel:* 212-782-9000 *Toll Free Tel:* 888-264-1745 *Fax:* 212-940-7408 *Web Site:* www.randomhouse.com/crown, pg 72

Wheaton, Robert, Random House of Canada Limited, One Toronto St, Suite 300, Toronto, ON M5C 2V6, Canada *Tel:* 416-364-4449 *Toll Free Tel:* 888-523-9292 (cust serv) *Fax:* 416-364-6863; 416-364-6653 (subs rts) *Web Site:* www.randomhouse.ca, pg 517

Wheeler, Betsy, Juniper Summer Writing Institute, c/o University Conference Services, 810 Campus Ctr, One Campus Ctr Way, Amherst, MA 01003 *Tel:* 413-545-5510 *E-mail:* juniperinstitute@hfa.umass.edu *Web Site:* www.umass.edu/juniperinstitute, pg 670

Wheeler, Diane, Madavor Media, 21027 Crossroads Circle, Waukesha, WI 53187-1612 *Tel:* 262-796-8776 *Toll Free Tel:* 800-533-6644 (cust serv & orders) *Fax:* 262-796-1615 (sales & cust serv); 262-798-6468 (edit) *Web Site:* www.kalmbach.com, pg 155

Wheeler, Paige, Folio Literary Management LLC, The Film Center Bldg, 630 Ninth Ave, Suite 1101, New York, NY 10036 *Tel:* 212-400-1494 *Fax:* 212-967-0977 *Web Site:* www.foliolit.com, pg 572

Whelan, Michael F, The Baker Street Irregulars (BSI), 7938 Mill Stream Circle, Indianapolis, IN 46278 *Tel:* 317-293-2212; 317-384-4728 (cell) *Web Site:* bakerstreetjournal.com, pg 29, 617

Whelchel, Sandy, Associated Business Writers of America Inc, 10940 S Parker Rd, Suite 508, Parker, CO 80134 *Tel:* 303-841-0246 *E-mail:* natlwritersassn@hotmail.com *Web Site:* www.nationalwriters.com, pg 615

Whelchel, Sandy, National Writers Association, 10940 S Parker Rd, Suite 508, Parker, CO 80134 *Tel:* 303-841-0246 *E-mail:* natlwritersassn@hotmail.com *Web Site:* www.nationalwriters.com, pg 631

Whelchel, Sandy, National Writers Association Novel Contest, 10940 S Parker Rd, Suite 508, Parker, CO 80134 *Tel:* 303-841-0246 *E-mail:* natlwritersassn@hotmail.com *Web Site:* www.nationalwriters.com, pg 727

Whitaker, Christine, Whitaker House, 1030 Hunt Valley Circle, New Kensington, PA 15068 *Tel:* 724-334-7000 *Toll Free Tel:* 877-793-9800 *Fax:* 724-334-1200 *Toll Free Fax:* 800-765-1960 *E-mail:* publisher@whitakerhouse.com *Web Site:* whitakerhouse.com, pg 280

Whitaker, Laura, Bloomsbury Publishing, 175 Fifth Ave, New York, NY 10010 *Tel:* 212-674-5151 *Toll Free Tel:* 800-221-7945 *Fax:* 212-780-0115; 212-982-2837 *E-mail:* marketingusa@bloomsbury.com; adultpublicityusa.@bloomsbury.com *Web Site:* www.bloomsbury.com, pg 41

Whitbread, Thomas, University of Texas at Austin, Creative Writing Program, Dept of English, PAR 108, One University Sta, Mailcode B5000, Austin, TX 78712-1164 *Tel:* 512-471-5132; 512-471-4991 *Fax:* 512-471-4909 *Web Site:* www.utexas.edu/cola/depts/english/creative-writing, pg 682

White, Carol, The Helen Brann Agency Inc, 94 Curtis Rd, Bridgewater, CT 06752 *Tel:* 860-354-9580 *Fax:* 860-355-2572, pg 564

White, Craig M, EDC Publishing, 10302 E 55 Place, Tulsa, OK 74146-6515 *Tel:* 918-622-4522 *Toll Free Tel:* 800-475-4522 *Fax:* 918-665-7919 *Toll Free Fax:* 800-743-5660 *E-mail:* edc@edcpub.com *Web Site:* www.edcpub.com, pg 84

White, Darrin, Milton Acorn Poetry Award, 115 Richmond St, Charlottetown, PE C1A 1H7, Canada *Tel:* 902-368-4410 *Toll Free Tel:* 888-734-2784 *Fax:* 902-368-4418 *E-mail:* peiwritersguild@gmail.com *Web Site:* www.peiwritersguild.com, pg 685

White, Darrin, The Aliant Creative Writing Award for Young People, 115 Richmond St, Charlottetown, PE C1A 1H7, Canada *Tel:* 902-368-4410 *Toll Free Tel:* 888-734-2784 *Fax:* 902-368-4418 *E-mail:* peiwritersguild@gmail.com *Web Site:* www.peiwritersguild.com, pg 686

White, Darrin, Lucy Maud Montgomery Literature for Children Prize, 115 Richmond St, Charlottetown, PE C1A 1H7, Canada *Tel:* 902-368-4410 *Toll Free Tel:* 888-734-2784 *Fax:* 902-368-4418 *E-mail:* peiwritersguild@gmail.com *Web Site:* www.peiwritersguild.com, pg 724

White, Darrin, Short Story Award, 115 Richmond St, Charlottetown, PE C1A 1H7, Canada *Tel:* 902-368-4410 *Toll Free Tel:* 888-734-2784 *Fax:* 902-368-4418 *E-mail:* peiwritersguild@gmail.com *Web Site:* www.peiwritersguild.com, pg 741

White, Donna, Alberta Book Awards, 10523 100 Ave, Edmonton, AB T5J 0A8, Canada *Tel:* 780-424-5060 *Fax:* 780-424-7943 *E-mail:* info@bookpublishers.ab.ca *Web Site:* www.bookpublishers.ab.ca, pg 686

White, Donna, The Book Publishers Association of Alberta (BPAA), 10523 100 Ave, Edmonton, AB T5J 0A8, Canada *Tel:* 780-424-5060 *Fax:* 780-424-7943 *E-mail:* info@bookpublishers.ab.ca *Web Site:* www.bookpublishers.ab.ca, pg 618

White, Doug, Bloomsbury Publishing, 175 Fifth Ave, New York, NY 10010 *Tel:* 212-674-5151 *Toll Free Tel:* 800-221-7945 *Fax:* 212-780-0115; 212-982-2837 *E-mail:* marketingusa@bloomsbury.com; adultpublicityusa.@bloomsbury.com *Web Site:* www.bloomsbury.com, pg 40

White, Elizabeth, The Monacelli Press, 236 W 27 St, 4th fl, New York, NY 10001 *Tel:* 212-229-9925 *E-mail:* contact@monacellipress.com *Web Site:* www.monacellipress.com, pg 168

White, Emily, The Mountaineers Books, 1001 SW Klickitat Way, Suite 201, Seattle, WA 98134 *Tel:* 206-223-6303 *Toll Free Tel:* 800-553-4453 *Fax:* 206-223-6306 *Toll Free Fax:* 800-568-7604 *E-mail:* mbooks@mountaineersbooks.org *Web Site:* www.mountaineersbooks.org, pg 170

White, Howard, Harbour Publishing Co Ltd, PO Box 219, Madeira Park, BC V0N 2H0, Canada *Tel:* 604-883-2730 *Toll Free Tel:* 800-667-2988 *Fax:* 604-883-9451 *E-mail:* info@harbourpublishing.com *Web Site:* www.harbourpublishing.com, pg 508

White, Hudson, Ocean Tree Books, 1325 Cerro Gordo Rd, Santa Fe, NM 87501 *Tel:* 505-983-1412 *Fax:* 505-983-0899 *Web Site:* www.oceantree.com, pg 183

White, Jodi, Canadian Booksellers Association (CBA), 1255 Bay St, Suite 902, Toronto, ON M5R 2A9, Canada *Tel:* 416-467-7883 *Toll Free Tel:* 866-788-0790 *Fax:* 416-467-7886 *E-mail:* enquiries@cbabook.org *Web Site:* www.cbabook.org, pg 619

White, Jodi, CBA Libris Award for Author of the Year, 1255 Bay St, Suite 902, Toronto, ON M5R 2A9, Canada *Tel:* 416-467-7883 *Toll Free Tel:* 866-788-0790 *Fax:* 416-467-7886 *E-mail:* enquiries@cbabook.org *Web Site:* www.cbabook.org, pg 695

White, Jodi, CBA Libris Children's Picture Book of the Year, 1255 Bay St, Suite 902, Toronto, ON M5R 2A9, Canada *Tel:* 416-467-7883 *Toll Free Tel:* 866-788-0790 *Fax:* 416-467-7886 *E-mail:* enquiries@cbabook.org *Web Site:* www.cbabook.org, pg 695

White, Jodi, CBA Libris Distributor of the Year, 1255 Bay St, Suite 902, Toronto, ON M5R 2A9, Canada *Tel:* 416-467-7883 *Toll Free Tel:* 866-788-0790 *Fax:* 416-467-7886 *E-mail:* enquiries@cbabook.org *Web Site:* www.cbabook.org, pg 695

White, Jodi, CBA Libris Editor of the Year, 1255 Bay St, Suite 902, Toronto, ON M5R 2A9, Canada *Tel:* 416-467-7883 *Toll Free Tel:* 866-788-0790 *Fax:* 416-467-7886 *E-mail:* enquiries@cbabook.org *Web Site:* www.cbabook.org, pg 695

White, Jodi, CBA Libris Fiction Book of the Year, 1255 Bay St, Suite 902, Toronto, ON M5R 2A9, Canada *Tel:* 416-467-7883 *Toll Free Tel:* 866-788-0790 *Fax:* 416-467-7886 *E-mail:* enquiries@cbabook.org *Web Site:* www.cbabook.org, pg 695

White, Jodi, CBA Libris Publisher of the Year, 1255 Bay St, Suite 902, Toronto, ON M5R 2A9, Canada *Tel:* 416-467-7883 *Toll Free Tel:* 866-788-0790 *Fax:* 416-467-7886 *E-mail:* enquiries@cbabook.org *Web Site:* www.cbabook.org, pg 695

White, Jodi, CBA Libris Sales Rep of the Year, 1255 Bay St, Suite 902, Toronto, ON M5R 2A9, Canada *Tel:* 416-467-7883 *Toll Free Tel:* 866-788-0790 *Fax:* 416-467-7886 *E-mail:* enquiries@cbabook.org *Web Site:* www.cbabook.org, pg 695

White, Jodi, CBA Libris Small Press Publisher of the Year, 1255 Bay St, Suite 902, Toronto, ON M5R 2A9, Canada *Tel:* 416-467-7883 *Toll Free Tel:* 866-788-0790 *Fax:* 416-467-7886 *E-mail:* enquiries@cbabook.org *Web Site:* www.cbabook.org, pg 696

White, Lisa, IET, c/o Inspec Inc, 379 Thornall St, Edison, NJ 08837-2225 *Tel:* 732-321-5575; 732-321-5579 *Fax:* 732-321-5702 *E-mail:* iee@inspecinc.com *Web Site:* www.theiet.org/inspec, pg 127

White, Martin L, Martin L White, 10511 Preston St, Westchester, IL 60154-5311 *Tel:* 708-492-1253 *Fax:* 708-492-1253 *E-mail:* mlw@mlwindexing.com *Web Site:* www.mlwindexing.com, pg 557

White, Nancy, Word Works Washington Prize, Adirondack Community College, Dearlove Hall, 640 Bay Rd, Queensbury, NY 12804 *Fax:* 301-581-9443 *E-mail:* editor@wordworksbooks.org *Web Site:* www.wordworksbooks.org, pg 751

White, Pam, Random House Children's Books, 1745 Broadway, New York, NY 10019 *Tel:* 212-782-9000 *Toll Free Tel:* 800-200-3552 *Fax:* 212-782-9452 *Web Site:* randomhousekids.com, pg 213

White, Peter, Begell House Inc Publishers, 50 Cross Hwy, Redding, CT 06896 *Tel:* 203-938-1300 *Fax:* 203-938-1304 *E-mail:* orders@begellhouse.com *Web Site:* www.begellhouse.com, pg 34

White, Randall, EDC Publishing, 10302 E 55 Place, Tulsa, OK 74146-6515 *Tel:* 918-622-4522 *Toll Free Tel:* 800-475-4522 *Fax:* 918-665-7919 *Toll Free Fax:* 800-743-5660 *E-mail:* edc@edcpub.com *Web Site:* www.edcpub.com, pg 84

White, Stephen C, Mystic Seaport Museum Inc, PO Box 6000, Mystic, CT 06355-0990 *Tel:* 860-572-5302; 860-572-0711 (visitor serv) *Toll Free Tel:* 800-248-1066 (wholesale orders only); 800-331-2665 (retail orders only) *Fax:* 860-572-5321 *E-mail:* info@mysticseaport.org *Web Site:* www.mysticseaport.org, pg 172

White, Todd, Regal Books, 1957 Eastman Ave, Ventura, CA 93003 *Tel:* 805-644-9721 *Toll Free Tel:* 800-446-7735 (orders) *Web Site:* www.regalbooks.com; www.gospellight.com, pg 217

White, Travis, Psychological Assessment Resources Inc (PAR), 16204 N Florida Ave, Lutz, FL 33549 *Tel:* 813-968-3003; 813-449-4065 *Toll Free Tel:* 800-331-8378 *Fax:* 813-968-2598; 813-961-2196 *Toll Free Fax:* 800-727-9329 *E-mail:* custsup@parinc.com *Web Site:* www4.parinc.com, pg 208

White, Trena, Douglas & McIntyre, 2323 Quebec St, Suite 201, Vancouver, BC V5T 4S7, Canada *Tel:* 604-254-7191 *Toll Free Tel:* 800-667-6902 (orders) *Fax:* 604-254-9099 *Toll Free Fax:* 800-668-5788 (orders CN) *E-mail:* info@harbourpublishing.com, pg 501

White, William, The Colonial Williamsburg Foundation, PO Box 1776, Williamsburg, VA 23187-1776 *Tel:* 757-229-1000 *Toll Free Tel:* 800-HISTORY (447-8679) *Fax:* 757-220-7325 *E-mail:* cwres@cwf.org; geninfo@cwf.org *Web Site:* www.colonialwilliamsburg.org/publications, pg 64

Whitehouse, Susan, Society for Industrial & Applied Mathematics, 3600 Market St, 6th fl, Philadelphia, PA 19104-2688 *Tel:* 215-382-9800 *Toll Free Tel:* 800-447-7426 *Fax:* 215-386-7999 *E-mail:* siambooks@siam.org *Web Site:* www.siam.org, pg 238

Whiteman, Doug, Penguin Group (USA) LLC, 375 Hudson St, New York, NY 10014 *Tel:* 212-366-2000 *Toll Free Tel:* 800-847-5515 (inside sales); 800-631-8571 (cust serv) *Fax:* 212-366-2666; 607-775-4829 (inside sales) *E-mail:* online@us.penguingroup.com *Web Site:* www.penguin.com; us.penguingroup.com, pg 197

Whiteside, David, Penguin Group (Canada), 90 Eglinton Ave E, Suite 700, Toronto, ON M4P 2Y3, Canada *Tel:* 416-925-2249 *Fax:* 416-925-0068 *Web Site:* www.penguin.ca, pg 515

Whiteside, Kay, Venture Publishing Inc, 1999 Cato Ave, State College, PA 16801 *Tel:* 814-234-4561 *Fax:* 814-234-1651 *E-mail:* vpublish@venturepublish.com *Web Site:* www.venturepublish.com, pg 274

Whitethorne, Baje Jr, Salina Bookshelf Inc, 3120 N Caden Ct, Suite 4, Flagstaff, AZ 86004 *Toll Free Tel:* 877-527-0070 *Fax:* 928-526-0386 *Web Site:* www.salinabookshelf.com, pg 225

Williams, John Taylor "Ike", Kneerim, Williams & Bloom Agency, 90 Canal St, Boston, MA 02114 *Tel:* 617-303-1650 *Web Site:* www.kwlit.com, pg 580

Williams, Laura, Oak Knoll Press, 310 Delaware St, New Castle, DE 19720 *Tel:* 302-328-7232 *Toll Free Tel:* 800-996-2556 *Fax:* 302-328-7274 *E-mail:* oakknoll@oakknoll.com *Web Site:* www.oakknoll.com, pg 183

Williams, Laurencia, Consumertronics, 8400 Menaul NE, Suite A-199, Albuquerque, NM 87112 *Tel:* 505-321-1034 *E-mail:* wizguru@consumertronics.net *Web Site:* www.consumertronics.net, pg 66

Williams, Leslie, Twenty-Third Publications, One Montauk Ave, Suite 200, New London, CT 06320 *Tel:* 860-437-3012 *Toll Free Tel:* 800-321-0411 (orders) *Toll Free Fax:* 800-572-0788 *E-mail:* 23ppweb@bayard-inc.com *Web Site:* www.twentythirdpublications.com, pg 260

Williams, Margaret K, Standard Publishing, 8805 Governors Hill Dr, Suite 400, Cincinnati, OH 45249 *Tel:* 513-931-4050 *Toll Free Tel:* 800-543-1353 *Fax:* 513-931-0950 *Toll Free Fax:* 877-867-5751 *E-mail:* customerservice@standardpub.com *Web Site:* www.standardpub.com, pg 242

Williams, Matt, Groundwood Books, 110 Spadina Ave, Suite 801, Toronto, ON M5V 2K4, Canada *Tel:* 416-363-4343 *Fax:* 416-363-1017 *E-mail:* genmail@groundwoodbooks.com *Web Site:* www.houseofanansi.com, pg 507

Williams, Matt, House of Anansi Press Ltd, 110 Spadina Ave, Suite 801, Toronto, ON M5V 2K4, Canada *Tel:* 416-363-4343 *Fax:* 416-363-1017 *E-mail:* customerservice@houseofanansi.com *Web Site:* www.anansi.ca, pg 509

Williams, Paul, American Society of Composers, Authors & Publishers (ASCAP), One Lincoln Plaza, New York City, NY 10023 *Tel:* 212-621-6000 *Toll Free Tel:* 800-952-7227 *Fax:* 212-612-8453 *E-mail:* info@ascap.com *Web Site:* www.ascap.com, pg 614

Williams, R Scott, Haights Cross Communications Inc, 136 Madison Ave, 8th fl, New York, NY 10016 *Tel:* 212-209-0500 *Fax:* 212-209-0501 *E-mail:* info@haightscross.com *Web Site:* www.haightscross.com, pg 110

Williams, Rachel A, Mount Hermon Christian Writers Conference, c/o Mount Hermon Association Inc, 37 Conference Dr, Mount Hermon, CA 95041 *Tel:* 831-335-4466 *Toll Free Tel:* 888-MH-CAMPS (642-2677 - registration) *Fax:* 831-335-9218 *E-mail:* info@mhcamps.org *Web Site:* www.mounthermon.org/writers, pg 670

Williams, Randall, NewSouth Books, 105 S Court St, Montgomery, AL 36104 *Tel:* 334-834-3556 *Fax:* 334-834-3557 *E-mail:* info@newsouthbooks.com *Web Site:* www.newsouthbooks.com, pg 179

Williams, Ric, Dalton Publishing, PO Box 242, Austin, TX 78767 *Tel:* 512-567-4955 *Fax:* 512-879-6814 *E-mail:* dpquery@daltonpublishing.com *Web Site:* www.daltonpublishing.com, pg 74

Williams, Rob, Mountain Press Publishing Co, 1301 S Third W, Missoula, MT 59801 *Tel:* 406-728-1900 *Toll Free Tel:* 800-234-5308 *Fax:* 406-728-1635 *E-mail:* info@mtnpress.com *Web Site:* www.mountain-press.com, pg 170

Williams, Robert A, Optometric Extension Program Foundation, 1921 E Carnegie Ave, Suite 3-L, Santa Ana, CA 92705-5510 *Tel:* 949-250-8070 *Fax:* 949-250-8157 *E-mail:* oep@oep.org *Web Site:* www.oepf.org, pg 186

Williams, Roberta, American Printing House for the Blind Inc, 1839 Frankfort Ave, Louisville, KY 40206 *Tel:* 502-895-2405 *Toll Free Tel:* 800-223-1839 (cust serv) *Fax:* 502-899-2274 *E-mail:* info@aph.org *Web Site:* www.aph.org; shop.aph.org, pg 15

Williams, Dr Roger L MD, United States Pharmacopeia, 12601 Twinbrook Pkwy, Rockville, MD 20852-1790 *Tel:* 301-881-0666 *Toll Free Tel:* 800-227-8772 *Fax:* 301-816-8237 (mktg) *E-mail:* marketing@usp.org *Web Site:* www.usp.org, pg 263

Williams, Roger S, New England Publishing Associates Inc, One Carver Place, Lawrenceville, GA 08648 *Tel:* 860-973-2439 *E-mail:* nepa@nepa.com; info@nepa.com; queries@nepa.com *Web Site:* www.nepa.com, pg 587

Williams, Ryan L, National Association of Black Journalists (NABJ), 1100 Knight Hall, Suite 3100, College Park, MD 20742 *Tel:* 301-405-0248 *Fax:* 301-314-1714 *E-mail:* nabj@nabj.org *Web Site:* www.nabj.org, pg 628

Williams, Sandra, Mountain Writers Series, 2804 SE 27 Ave, Suite 2, Portland, OR 97202 *Tel:* 503-232-4517 *Fax:* 503-232-4517 *E-mail:* pdxmws@mountainwriters.org *Web Site:* www.mountainwriters.org, pg 671

Williams, Sarah, Chronicle Books LLC, 680 Second St, San Francisco, CA 94107 *Tel:* 415-537-4200 *Toll Free Tel:* 800-759-0190 (cust serv) *Fax:* 415-537-4460 *Toll Free Fax:* 800-858-7787 (orders); 800-286-9471 (cust serv) *E-mail:* frontdesk@chroniclebooks.com *Web Site:* www.chroniclebooks.com, pg 61

Williams, Suzanne, The Canadian Writers' Foundation Inc (La Fondation des Ecrivains Canadiens), PO Box 13281, Kanata Sta, Ottawa, ON K2K 1X4, Canada *Tel:* 613-256-6937 *Fax:* 613-256-5457 *E-mail:* info@canadianwritersfoundation.org *Web Site:* www.canadianwritersfoundation.org, pg 641

Williams, Thomas A PhD, Williams & Company Book Publishers, 1317 Pine Ridge Dr, Savannah, GA 31406 *Tel:* 912-352-0404 *E-mail:* bookpub@comcast.net *Web Site:* www.pubmart.com, pg 282

Williams, Tracy, Little, Brown and Company, 237 Park Ave, New York, NY 10017 *Tel:* 212-364-1100 *Fax:* 212-364-0952 *E-mail:* firstname.lastname@hbgusa.com *Web Site:* www.HachetteBookGroup.com, pg 150

Williams, Troy, Bedford, Freeman & Worth Publishing Group, LLC, 41 Madison Ave, 37th fl, New York, NY 10010 *Tel:* 212-576-9400 *Fax:* 212-689-2383 *Web Site:* www.macmillanhighered.com, pg 33

Williamson, Alain, Editions Le Dauphin Blanc Inc, 825, boul Lebourgneuf, Suite 125, Quebec, QC G2J 0B9, Canada *Tel:* 418-845-4045 *Fax:* 418-845-1933 *E-mail:* info@dauphinblanc.com *Web Site:* www.dauphinblanc.com, pg 500

Williamson, Iain, Productive Publications, 7-B Pleasant Blvd, Unit 1210, Toronto, ON M4T 1K2, Canada *Tel:* 416-483-0634 *Fax:* 416-322-7434 *Web Site:* www.productivepublications.com, pg 516

Williamson, Kent, National Council of Teachers of English (NCTE), 1111 W Kenyon Rd, Urbana, IL 61801-1096 *Tel:* 217-328-3870 *Toll Free Tel:* 877-369-6283 (cust serv) *Fax:* 217-328-9645 *E-mail:* orders@ncte.org *Web Site:* www.ncte.org, pg 174

Williamson, Kent, National Council of Teachers of English (NCTE), 1111 W Kenyon Rd, Urbana, IL 61801-1096 *Tel:* 217-328-3870 *Toll Free Tel:* 877-369-6283 (cust serv) *Fax:* 217-328-9645 *E-mail:* public_info@ncte.org *Web Site:* www.ncte.org, pg 629

Williamson, Lesley, Artists & Writers Summer Fellowships, 435 Ellis Hollow Creek Rd, Ithaca, NY 14850 *Tel:* 607-539-3146 *E-mail:* artscolony@saltonstall.org *Web Site:* www.saltonstall.org, pg 667

Williamson, Maureen, Roman Catholic Books, PO Box 2286, Fort Collins, CO 80522-2286 *Tel:* 970-490-2735 *Fax:* 904-212-1287 *Web Site:* www.booksforcatholics.com, pg 220

Williford, Lex, University of Texas at El Paso, Dept Creative Writing, MFA/Dept Creative Writing, Liberal Arts 415 UTEP, 500 W University Ave, El Paso, TX 79968-9991 *Tel:* 915-747-5713 *Fax:* 915-747-5523 *Web Site:* www.utep.edu/cw, pg 682

Willig, Alan, Don Buchwald & Associates Inc, 10 E 44 St, New York, NY 10017 *Tel:* 212-867-1200 *Fax:* 212-867-2434 *E-mail:* info@buchwald.com *Web Site:* www.buchwald.com, pg 565

Willig, Christine, Math Solutions®, 150 Gate 5 Rd, Suite 101, Sausalito, CA 94965 *Tel:* 415-332-4181 *Toll Free Tel:* 800-868-9092 *Fax:* 415-331-1931 *Toll Free Fax:* 877-942-8837 *E-mail:* info@mathsolutions.com; orders@mathsolutions.com *Web Site:* www.mathsolutions.com, pg 159

Willing, Meg, Alice James Books, 238 Main St, Farmington, ME 04938 *Tel:* 207-778-7071 *Fax:* 207-778-7766 *E-mail:* info@alicejamesbooks.org *Web Site:* www.alicejamesbooks.org, pg 8

Willinger, James L, Wide World of Maps Inc, 2626 W Indian School Rd, Phoenix, AZ 85017 *Tel:* 602-279-2324 *Toll Free Tel:* 800-279-7654 *Fax:* 602-279-2350 *E-mail:* sales@maps4u.com *Web Site:* www.maps4u.com, pg 280

Willis, Clarissa, Gryphon House Inc, 10770 Columbia Pike, Suite 201, Silver Spring, MD 20901 *Tel:* 301-595-9500 *Toll Free Tel:* 800-638-0928 *Fax:* 301-595-0051 *Toll Free Fax:* 877-638-7576 *E-mail:* info@ghbooks.com *Web Site:* www.gryphonhouse.com, pg 109

Willis, Meredith Sue, Hamilton Stone Editions, PO Box 43, Maplewood, NJ 07040 *Tel:* 973-378-8361 *E-mail:* hstone@hamiltonstone.org *Web Site:* www.hamiltonstone.org, pg 111

Willkomm, Anne, Rosemont College, Graduate Publg Prog, 1400 Montgomery Ave, Rosemont, PA 19010 *Tel:* 610-527-0200 (ext 2336) *Fax:* 610-526-2964 *Web Site:* www.rosemont.edu, pg 680

Willmes, Karen L, The Johns Hopkins University Press, 2715 N Charles St, Baltimore, MD 21218-4363 *Tel:* 410-516-6900; 410-516-6987 (journals outside US & CN) *Toll Free Tel:* 800-537-5487 (book orders & cust serv); 800-548-1784 (journal orders) *Fax:* 410-516-6968; 410-516-3866 (journal orders) *E-mail:* hfscustserv@press.jhu.edu (cust serv); jrnlcirc@press.jhu.edu (journal orders) *Web Site:* www.press.jhu.edu; muse.jhu.edu/about/subscriptions/index.html (Project Muse subns), pg 136

Willoughby, Bruce E, University of Michigan Center for Japanese Studies, 1007 E Huron St, Ann Arbor, MI 48104-1690 *Tel:* 734-647-8885 *Fax:* 734-647-8886 *E-mail:* ii.cjspubs@umich.edu *Web Site:* www.cjspubs.lsa.umich.edu, pg 266

Willoughby, John, Leadership Ministries Worldwide/OBR, 3755 Pilot Point, Chattanooga, TN 37416 *Tel:* 423-855-2181 *Toll Free Tel:* 800-987-8790 *Fax:* 423-855-8616 *E-mail:* info@outlinebible.org *Web Site:* www.outlinebible.org, pg 145

Willoughby-Harris, H Lee, Duke University Press, 905 W Main St, Suite 18B, Durham, NC 27701 *Tel:* 919-688-5134 *Toll Free Tel:* 888-651-0122 *Fax:* 919-688-2615 *Toll Free Fax:* 888-651-0124 *E-mail:* orders@dukeupress.edu *Web Site:* www.dukeupress.edu, pg 82

Wilmot, Andrew, NeWest Press, 8540 109 St, No 201, Edmonton, AB T6G 1E6, Canada *Tel:* 780-432-9427 *Toll Free Tel:* 866-796-5473 *Fax:* 780-433-3179 *E-mail:* info@newestpress.com *Web Site:* www.newestpress.com, pg 513

Wilmot, Jodie, National Association of College Stores (NACS), 500 E Lorain St, Oberlin, OH 44074 *Tel:* 440-775-7777 *Toll Free Tel:* 800-622-7498 *Fax:* 440-775-4769 *Web Site:* www.nacs.org, pg 628

Wilson, Adam, Gallery Books, 1230 Avenue of the Americas, New York, NY 10020 *Toll Free Tel:* 800-456-6798 *Fax:* 212-698-7284 *E-mail:* consumer.customerservice@simonandschuster.com *Web Site:* www.simonsays.com, pg 101

Wilson, Amy, GemStone Press, Sunset Farm Offices, Rte 4, Woodstock, VT 05091 *Tel:* 802-457-4000 *Toll Free Tel:* 800-962-4544 *Fax:* 802-457-4004 *E-mail:* sales@gemstonepress.com *Web Site:* www.gemstonepress.com, pg 102

Wilson, Amy M, SkyLight Paths Publishing, Sunset Farm Offices, Rte 4, Woodstock, VT 05091 *Tel:* 802-457-4000 *Toll Free Tel:* 800-962-4544 *Fax:* 802-457-4004 *E-mail:* sales@skylightpaths.com *Web Site:* www.skylightpaths.com, pg 237

Wiseman, Le Anne, National Freedom of Information Coalition (NFOIC), 101 Reynolds Journalism Institute, Columbia, MO 65211-0012 *Tel:* 573-882-4856 *Fax:* 573-884-6204 *Web Site:* nfoic.org, pg 630

Wiseman, Paula, Simon & Schuster Children's Publishing, 1230 Avenue of the Americas, New York, NY 10020 *Tel:* 212-698-7000 *Web Site:* KIDS. SimonandSchuster.com; TEEN.SimonandSchuster.com; simonandschuster.net; simonandschuster.biz, pg 235

Wisenthal, Paul, The Professional Writer, 175 W 12 St, Suite 6D, New York, NY 10011 *Tel:* 212-414-0188; 917-658-1946 (cell) *E-mail:* paul@theprofessionalwriter.com *Web Site:* www.theprofessionalwriter.com, pg 553

Wishard, Tammy, Anson Jones MD Award, 401 W 15 St, Austin, TX 78701 *Tel:* 512-370-1300 *Fax:* 512-370-1630 *Web Site:* www.texmed.org, pg 714

Wispelwey, June C, American Institute of Chemical Engineers (AIChE), 3 Park Ave, 19th fl, New York, NY 10016-5991 *Tel:* 203-702-7660 *Toll Free Tel:* 800-242-4363 *Fax:* 203-775-5177 *E-mail:* custserv@aiche.org *Web Site:* www.aiche.org, pg 14

Wissman, Pamela, F+W Media Inc, 10151 Carver Rd, Suite 200, Blue Ash, OH 45242 *Tel:* 513-531-2690 *Toll Free Tel:* 800-289-0963 (trade accts); 800-258-0929 (orders) *E-mail:* contact_us@fwmedia.com *Web Site:* www.fwmedia.com, pg 92

Wissoker, Ken, Duke University Press, 905 W Main St, Suite 18B, Durham, NC 27701 *Tel:* 919-688-5134 *Toll Free Tel:* 888-651-0122 *Fax:* 919-688-2615 *Toll Free Fax:* 888-651-0124 *E-mail:* orders@dukeupress.edu *Web Site:* www.dukeupress.edu, pg 82

Witcraft, Stacey, Random House Publishing Group, 1745 Broadway, New York, NY 10019 *Toll Free Tel:* 800-200-3552 *Web Site:* atrandom.com, pg 214

Witherell, Jennifer, InkWell Management, 521 Fifth Ave, 26th fl, New York, NY 10175 *Tel:* 212-922-3500 *Fax:* 212-922-0535 *E-mail:* info@inkwellmanagement.com; submissions@inkwellmanagement.com *Web Site:* inkwellmanagement.com, pg 577

Withers, Laurel, Playwrights Project, 3675 Ruffin Rd, Suite 330, San Diego, CA 92123 *Tel:* 858-384-2970 *Fax:* 858-384-2974 *E-mail:* write@playwrightsproject.org *Web Site:* www.playwrightsproject.org, pg 734

Witherspoon, Kim, InkWell Management, 521 Fifth Ave, 26th fl, New York, NY 10175 *Tel:* 212-922-3500 *Fax:* 212-922-0535 *E-mail:* info@inkwellmanagement.com; submissions@inkwellmanagement.com *Web Site:* inkwellmanagement.com, pg 577

Withgott, James W, Merriam-Webster Inc, 47 Federal St, Springfield, MA 01102 *Tel:* 413-734-3134 *Toll Free Tel:* 800-828-1880 (orders & cust serv) *Fax:* 413-731-5979 (sales) *E-mail:* support@merriam-webster.com *Web Site:* www.merriam-webster.com, pg 165

Withington, Marcy, Mystic Seaport Museum Inc, PO Box 6000, Mystic, CT 06355-0990 *Tel:* 860-572-5302; 860-572-0711 (visitor serv) *Toll Free Tel:* 800-248-1066 (wholesale orders only); 800-331-2665 (retail orders only) *Fax:* 860-572-5321 *E-mail:* info@mysticseaport.org *Web Site:* www.mysticseaport.org, pg 172

Withycombe, Amber, Association of Writers & Writing Programs (AWP), George Mason University, 4400 University Dr, MSN 1E3, Fairfax, VA 22030 *Tel:* 703-993-4301 *Fax:* 703-993-4302 *E-mail:* awp@awpwriter.org *Web Site:* www.awpwriter.org, pg 617

Withycombe, Amber, AWP Award Series, George Mason University, 4400 University Dr, MSN 1E3, Fairfax, VA 22030 *Tel:* 703-993-4301 *Fax:* 703-993-4302 *E-mail:* awp@awpwriter.org *Web Site:* www.awpwriter.org, pg 688

Witlox, Cathy, WordWitlox, 70 Grainger Crescent, Ajax, ON L1T 4Y6, Canada *Tel:* 647-505-9673 *Fax:* 905-239-3604 *Web Site:* www.wordwitlox.com, pg 557

Witman, Mark, Integra Software Services Inc, 1110 Jorie Blvd, Suite 200, Oak Brook, IL 60523 *Tel:* 630-586-2579 *Fax:* 630-586-2599 *Web Site:* www.integra.co.in, pg 548

Witmore, Dr Michael, National Endowment for the Humanities, Mellon Foundation & Folger Long-term Fellowships, c/o Fellowship Committee, 201 E Capitol St SE, Washington, DC 20003 *Tel:* 202-544-4600 *Fax:* 202-544-4623 *E-mail:* institute@folger.edu *Web Site:* www.folger.edu, pg 726

Witt, Joseph W, Empire Publishing Service, PO Box 1344, Studio City, CA 91614-0344 *Tel:* 818-784-8918 *E-mail:* empirepubsvc@att.net *Web Site:* www.ppeps.com, pg 87

Witte, George, St Martin's Press, LLC, 175 Fifth Ave, New York, NY 10010 *Tel:* 646-307-5151 *Fax:* 212-420-9314 *E-mail:* firstname.lastname@macmillan.com *Web Site:* www.stmartins.com, pg 224

Witter, Karen, Illinois State Museum Society, 502 S Spring St, Springfield, IL 62706-5000 *Tel:* 217-782-7386 *Fax:* 217-782-1254 *E-mail:* editor@museum.state.il.us *Web Site:* www.museum.state.il.us, pg 127

Wittfeld, Kathi, University of Missouri-Kansas City, New Letters Weekend Writers Conference, College of Arts & Sciences, Continuing Education Div, 5300 Rockhill Rd, Kansas City, MO 64110 *Tel:* 816-235-2736 *Fax:* 816-235-5279 *Web Site:* www.umkc.edu, pg 681

Woehlbier, Fred, Trans Tech Publications, c/o Enfield Distribution Co, 234 May St, Enfield, NH 03748 *Tel:* 603-632-7377 *Fax:* 603-632-5611 *E-mail:* usa-ttp@ttp.net; info@enfieldbooks.com *Web Site:* www.ttp.net, pg 257

Woehlbier, Thomas, Trans Tech Publications, c/o Enfield Distribution Co, 234 May St, Enfield, NH 03748 *Tel:* 603-632-7377 *Fax:* 603-632-5611 *E-mail:* usa-ttp@ttp.net; info@enfieldbooks.com *Web Site:* www.ttp.net, pg 257

Woerheide, Walt PhD, American College, 270 S Bryn Mawr Ave, Bryn Mawr, PA 19010 *Tel:* 610-526-1000 *Toll Free Tel:* 888-263-7265 *Fax:* 610-526-1310 *Web Site:* www.theamericancollege.edu, pg 12

Woessner, Steve, Brilliance Audio, 1704 Eaton Dr, Grand Haven, MI 49417 *Tel:* 616-846-5256 *Toll Free Tel:* 800-648-2312 (orders only) *Fax:* 616-846-0630 *E-mail:* customerservice@brillianceaudio.com *Web Site:* www.brillianceaudio.com, pg 48

Wofsy, Alan, Alan Wofsy Fine Arts, 1109 Geary Blvd, San Francisco, CA 94109 *Tel:* 415-292-6500 *Toll Free Tel:* 800-660-6403 *Fax:* 415-292-6594 (off & cust serv); 415-512-0130 (acctg) *E-mail:* order@art-books.com (orders); editeur@earthlink.net (edit); beauxarts@earthlink.net (cust serv) *Web Site:* www.art-books.com, pg 284

Wojcik, Paul, BNA Books, 1801 S Bell St, Arlington, VA 22202 *Toll Free Tel:* 800-372-1033 *Fax:* 732-346-1624 *E-mail:* books@bna.com *Web Site:* www.bnabooks.com, pg 42

Wojcik, Tim, Levine|Greenberg Literary Agency Inc, 307 Seventh Ave, Suite 2407, New York, NY 10001 *Tel:* 212-337-0934 *Fax:* 212-337-0948 *Web Site:* www.levinegreenberg.com, pg 581

Wojtyla, Karen, Simon & Schuster Children's Publishing, 1230 Avenue of the Americas, New York, NY 10020 *Tel:* 212-698-7000 *Web Site:* KIDS.SimonandSchuster.com; TEEN.SimonandSchuster.com; simonandschuster.net; simonandschuster.biz, pg 235

Wolf, Carol, Rigby, 9205 Southpark Center Loop, Orlando, FL 32819 *Toll Free Tel:* 800-531-5015; 800-289-4490 *Toll Free Fax:* 800-289-3994 *Web Site:* rigby.hmhco.com/en/rigby.htm, pg 218

Wolf, Jamie, PEN Center USA, PO Box 6037, Beverly Hills, CA 90212 *Tel:* 323-424-4939 *Fax:* 323-424-4944 *E-mail:* pen@penusa.org *Web Site:* www.penusa.org, pg 633

Wolf, Maria, Institute of Governmental Studies, 109 Moses Hall, Suite 2370, Berkeley, CA 94720-2370 *Tel:* 510-642-1428 *Fax:* 510-642-3020; 510-642-5537 (orders) *E-mail:* igspress@berkeley.edu *Web Site:* www.igs.berkeley.edu, pg 131

Wolf, Wendy, Viking, 375 Hudson St, New York, NY 10014 *Tel:* 212-366-2000 *E-mail:* online@penguinputnam.com *Web Site:* www.penguinputnam.com; us.penguingroup.com, pg 275

Wolfe, Alexander, University of Pittsburgh Press, Eureka Bldg, 5th fl, 3400 Forbes Ave, Pittsburgh, PA 15260 *Tel:* 412-383-2456 *Fax:* 412-383-2466 *E-mail:* info@upress.pitt.edu *Web Site:* www.upress.pitt.edu, pg 268

Wolfe, Honora, Blue Poppy Press, 1990 57 Ct, Unit A, Boulder, CO 80301 *Tel:* 303-447-8372 *Toll Free Tel:* 800-487-9296 *Fax:* 303-245-8362 *E-mail:* info@bluepoppy.com *Web Site:* www.bluepoppy.com, pg 41

Wolfe, Jaymie Stuart, Pauline Books & Media, 50 Saint Paul's Ave, Boston, MA 02130 *Tel:* 617-522-8911 *Toll Free Tel:* 800-876-4463 (orders); 800-836-9723 (cust serv) *Fax:* 617-541-9805 *E-mail:* orderentry@pauline.org (cust serv); editorial@paulinemedia.com (ms submissions) *Web Site:* www.pauline.org, pg 194

Wolfe, Lesley, Dancing Lemur Press LLC, PO Box 383, Pikeville, NC 27863-0383 *Tel:* 919-273-0939 *E-mail:* inquiries@dancinglemurpress.com *Web Site:* www.dancinglemurpress.com, pg 75

Wolfe, Leslie R PhD, Center for Women Policy Studies, 1776 Massachusetts Ave NW, Suite 450, Washington, DC 20036 *Tel:* 202-872-1770 *Fax:* 202-296-8962 *E-mail:* cwps@centerwomenpolicy.org *Web Site:* www.centerwomenpolicy.org, pg 56

Wolfe, Margie, Second Story Feminist Press, 20 Maud St, Suite 401, Toronto, ON M5V 2M5, Canada *Tel:* 416-537-7850 *Fax:* 416-537-0588 *E-mail:* info@secondstorypress.ca *Web Site:* www.secondstorypress.ca, pg 518

Wolfenberg, Todd, Himalayan Institute Press, 952 Bethany Tpke, Honesdale, PA 18431-9706 *Tel:* 570-253-5551 *Toll Free Tel:* 800-822-4547 *Fax:* 570-253-4500 *E-mail:* info@himalayaninstitute.org *Web Site:* www.himalayaninstitute.org, pg 120

Wolff, Doug, Workman Publishing Co Inc, 225 Varick St, 9th fl, New York, NY 10014-4381 *Tel:* 212-254-5900 *Toll Free Tel:* 800-722-7202 *Fax:* 212-254-8098 *E-mail:* info@workman.com *Web Site:* www.workman.com, pg 285

Wolff, Rebecca, Fence Books, University at Albany, Science Library 320, 1400 Washington Ave, Albany, NY 12222 *Tel:* 518-591-8162 *E-mail:* fence.fencebooks@gmail.com *Web Site:* www.fenceportal.org, pg 94

Wolff, Rebecca, Fence Modern Poets Series, University at Albany, Science Library 320, 1400 Washington Ave, Albany, NY 12222 *Tel:* 518-591-8162 *E-mail:* fence.fencebooks@gmail.com *Web Site:* www.fenceportal.org, pg 704

Wolff, Rebecca, Ottoline Morrell Prize, University at Albany, Science Library 320, 1400 Washington Ave, Albany, NY 12222 *Tel:* 518-591-8162 *E-mail:* fence.fencebooks@gmail.com *Web Site:* www.fenceportal.org, pg 725

Wolff, Rick, Grand Central Publishing, 237 Park Ave, New York, NY 10017 *Tel:* 212-364-1100 *Web Site:* www.hachettebookgroup.com, pg 106

Wolford, Henry, Easy Money Press, 5419 87 St, Lubbock, TX 79424 *Tel:* 806-543-5215 *E-mail:* easymoneypress@yahoo.com, pg 84

Wolfson, Robin, Random House Speakers Bureau, 1745 Broadway, Mail Drop 13-1, New York, NY 10019 *Tel:* 212-572-2013 *E-mail:* rhspeakers@randomhouse.com *Web Site:* www.rhspeakers.com, pg 605

Wolfsthal, Bill, Arcade Publishing Inc, 307 W 36 St, 11th fl, New York, NY 10018 *Tel:* 212-643-6816 *Fax:* 212-643-6819 *E-mail:* info@skyhorsepublishing.com (Subs & Foreign Rts) *Web Site:* www.arcadepub.com, pg 21

Wollheim, Elizabeth R, DAW Books Inc, 375 Hudson St, 3rd fl, New York, NY 10014 *Tel:* 212-366-2096 *Fax:* 212-366-2090 *E-mail:* daw@us.penguingroup.com *Web Site:* us.penguingroup.com; www.dawbooks.com, pg 76

Wolny, Karen, Palgrave Macmillan, 175 Fifth Ave, Suite 200, New York, NY 10010 *Tel:* 646-307-5151 *Fax:* 212-777-6359 *E-mail:* firstname.lastname@palgrave-usa.com *Web Site:* us.macmillan.com/Palgrave.aspx, pg 191

Worchte, Allison, Random House Children's Books, 1745 Broadway, New York, NY 10019 *Tel:* 212-782-9000 *Toll Free Tel:* 800-200-3552 *Fax:* 212-782-9452 *Web Site:* randomhousekids.com, pg 213

Wordsworth, Franklin, Wordsworth Communication, PO Box 9781, Alexandria, VA 22304-0468 *Tel:* 703-642-8775 *Fax:* 703-642-8775, pg 557

Workman, Jim, Orientation to the Graphic Arts, 200 Deer Run Rd, Sewickley, PA 15143-2600 *Tel:* 412-259-1711 *Toll Free Tel:* 800-910-4283 *Fax:* 412-741-2311 *E-mail:* printing@printing.org *Web Site:* www.printing.org, pg 671

Workman, Peter, Yale University Press, 302 Temple St, New Haven, CT 06511-8909 *Tel:* 401-531-2800 (cust serv); 203-432-0960 *Toll Free Tel:* 800-405-1619 (cust serv) *Fax:* 203-432-0948; 401-531-2801 (cust serv) *Toll Free Fax:* 800-406-9145 (cust serv) *E-mail:* customer.care@trilateral.org (cust serv); language.yalepress@yale.edu *Web Site:* www.yalebooks.com, pg 287

Worley, Amy, Andrews McMeel Publishing LLC, 1130 Walnut St, Kansas City, MO 64106-2109 *Toll Free Tel:* 800-851-8923; 800-943-9839 (cust serv) *Toll Free Fax:* 800-943-9831 (orders) *Web Site:* www.andrewsmcmeel.com, pg 18

Wormald, Colleen, Canadian Scholars' Press Inc, 180 Bloor St W, Suite 801, Toronto, ON M5S 2V6, Canada *Tel:* 416-929-2774 *Toll Free Tel:* 800-463-1998 *Fax:* 416-929-1926 *E-mail:* info@cspi.org; editorial@cspi.org *Web Site:* cspi.org; www.womenspress.ca, pg 497

Worrell, Greg, Scholastic Classroom & Community Group, 524 Broadway, New York, NY 10012 *Tel:* 212-343-6100 *Web Site:* www.scholastic.com, pg 228

Worrell, Greg, Scholastic Inc, 557 Broadway, New York, NY 10012 *Tel:* 212-343-6100 *Toll Free Tel:* 800-scholastic *Web Site:* www.scholastic.com, pg 228

Worrell, Ray, W W Norton & Company Inc, 500 Fifth Ave, New York, NY 10110-0017 *Tel:* 212-354-5500 *Toll Free Tel:* 800-233-4830 (orders & cust serv) *Fax:* 212-869-0856 *Toll Free Fax:* 800-458-6515 *Web Site:* www.wwnorton.com, pg 182

Worrell, Raymond E, W W Norton & Company Inc, 500 Fifth Ave, New York, NY 10110-0017 *Tel:* 212-354-5500 *Toll Free Tel:* 800-233-4830 (orders & cust serv) *Fax:* 212-869-0856 *Toll Free Fax:* 800-458-6515 *Web Site:* www.wwnorton.com, pg 181

Worthington, Dr Pepper, Mount Olive College Press, 634 Henderson St, Mount Olive, NC 28365 *Tel:* 252-286-6851 *Fax:* 919-658-7180 *Web Site:* www.mountolivecollege.edu, pg 170

Wowk, Mary, Harry N Abrams Inc, 115 W 18 St, 6th fl, New York, NY 10011 *Tel:* 212-206-7715 *Toll Free Tel:* 800-345-1359 *Fax:* 212-519-1210 *E-mail:* abrams@abramsbooks.com *Web Site:* www.abramsbooks.com, pg 3

Wren, Jill Robinson, Adams & Ambrose Publishing, PO Box 259684, Madison, WI 53725-9684 *Tel:* 608-257-5700 *Fax:* 608-257-5700 *E-mail:* info@adamsambrose.com, pg 4

Wright, Andrew, Harlequin Enterprises Ltd, 225 Duncan Mill Rd, Don Mills, ON M3B 3K9, Canada *Tel:* 416-445-5860 *Toll Free Tel:* 888-432-4879; 800-370-5838 (ebook inquiries) *Fax:* 416-445-8655 *E-mail:* CustomerService@harlequin.com *Web Site:* www.harlequin.com, pg 508

Wright, Betty, Rainbow Books Inc, PO Box 430, Highland City, FL 33846 *Tel:* 863-648-4420 *Fax:* 863-647-5951 *E-mail:* info@rainbowbooksinc.com *Web Site:* www.rainbowbooksinc.com, pg 212

Wright, Brett, Bloomsbury Publishing, 175 Fifth Ave, New York, NY 10010 *Tel:* 212-674-5151 *Toll Free Tel:* 800-221-7945 *Fax:* 212-780-0115; 212-982-2837 *E-mail:* marketingusa@bloomsbury.com; adultpublicityusa.@bloomsbury.com *Web Site:* www.bloomsbury.com, pg 41

Wright, Elizabeth L, The Overmountain Press, PO Box 1261, Johnson City, TN 37605-1261 *Tel:* 423-926-2691 *Toll Free Tel:* 800-992-2691 (orders) *Fax:* 423-232-1252 *E-mail:* orders@overmtn.com *Web Site:* www.overmtn.com, pg 189

Wright, Jan C, Wright Information Indexing Services, PO Box 658, Sandia Park, NM 87047 *Tel:* 505-281-2600 *Web Site:* www.wrightinformation.com, pg 557

Wright, John, National Government Publishing Association, 629 N Main St, Hattiesburg, MS 39401 *Tel:* 601-582-3330 *Fax:* 601-582-3354 *E-mail:* info@govpublishing.org *Web Site:* www.govpublishing.org, pg 630

Wright, Ken, Viking Children's Books, 345 Hudson St, New York, NY 10014 *Tel:* 212-366-2000 *E-mail:* online@penguinputnam.com *Web Site:* www.penguinputnam.com; us.penguingroup.com, pg 275

Wright, Kenya, Dragonfairy Press, 4355 Cobb Pkwy, Suite J116, Atlanta, GA 30339 *Tel:* 404-955-8150 *E-mail:* info@dragonfairypress.com *Web Site:* www.dragonfairypress.com, pg 81

Wright, Michael, W W Norton & Company Inc, 500 Fifth Ave, New York, NY 10110-0017 *Tel:* 212-354-5500 *Toll Free Tel:* 800-233-4830 (orders & cust serv) *Fax:* 212-869-0856 *Toll Free Fax:* 800-458-6515 *Web Site:* www.wwnorton.com, pg 182

Wright-Lampe, Betsy, The Florida Publishers Association Inc (FPA), PO Box 916383, Longwood, FL 32791-6383 *Tel:* 863-647-5951 *Fax:* 863-647-5951 *E-mail:* fpabooks@gmail.com *Web Site:* www.floridapublishersassociation.com, pg 623

Wrinn, Julie Kuzneski, Kentucky Women Writers Conference, 232 E Maxwell St, Lexington, KY 40506-0344 *Tel:* 859-257-2874 *E-mail:* kentuckywomenwriters@gmail.com *Web Site:* www.uky.edu/wwk, pg 670

Wrinn, Stephen M, The University Press of Kentucky, 663 S Limestone St, Lexington, KY 40508-4008 *Tel:* 859-257-8400 *Fax:* 859-257-8481 *Web Site:* www.kentuckypress.com, pg 271

Wrubel, Kim, Random House Children's Books, 1745 Broadway, New York, NY 10019 *Tel:* 212-782-9000 *Toll Free Tel:* 800-200-3552 *Fax:* 212-782-9452 *Web Site:* randomhousekids.com, pg 213

Wrzesinski, Julie, Michigan State University Press (MSU Press), 1405 S Harrison Rd, Suite 25, East Lansing, MI 48823 *Tel:* 517-355-9543 *Fax:* 517-432-2611 *Toll Free Fax:* 800-678-2120 *E-mail:* msupress@msu.edu *Web Site:* www.msupress.msu.edu, pg 165

Wu, Chih-Yu T, East Asian Legal Studies Program (EALSP), 500 W Baltimore St, Suite 411, Baltimore, MD 21201-1786 *Tel:* 410-706-3870 *Fax:* 410-706-1516 *E-mail:* eastasia@law.umaryland.edu *Web Site:* www.law.umaryland.edu/programs/international/eastasia, pg 83

Wu, Nancy, Oxford University Press USA, 198 Madison Ave, New York, NY 10016 *Tel:* 212-726-6000 *Toll Free Tel:* 800-451-7556 (orders); 800-445-9714 (cust serv) *Fax:* 919-677-1303 *E-mail:* custserv.us@oup.com *Web Site:* www.oup.com/us, pg 189

Wuerker, Matt, Association of American Editorial Cartoonists, 3899 N Front St, Harrisburg, PA 17110 *Tel:* 717-703-3003 *Fax:* 717-703-3008 *E-mail:* aaec@pa-news.org *Web Site:* www.editorialcartoonists.com, pg 616

Wulf, Karen, The Hemingway Foundation/PEN Award, Massachusetts Institute of Technology, 77 Massachusetts Ave, 14-N-221A, Cambridge, MA 02139 *Tel:* 617-324-1729 *E-mail:* pen-newengland@mit.edu *Web Site:* www.pen-ne.org, pg 709

Wulf, Karen, PEN New England, Massachusetts Institute of Technology, 77 Massachusetts Ave, 14-N-221A, Cambridge, MA 02139 *Tel:* 617-324-1729 *E-mail:* pen-newengland@mit.edu *Web Site:* www.pen-ne.org, pg 633

Wulf, Karen, The Laurence L & Thomas Winship/PEN New England Award, MIT 14N-221A, 77 Massachusetts Ave, Cambridge, MA 02139 *Tel:* 617-324-1729 *E-mail:* pen-ne@lesley.edu *Web Site:* www.pen-ne.org, pg 750

Wulf, Karin A, Jamestown Prize, Swem Library, Ground fl, 400 Landrum Dr, Williamsburg, VA 23185 *Tel:* 757-221-1114 *Fax:* 757-221-1047 *E-mail:* ieahc1@wm.edu *Web Site:* oieahc.wm.edu, pg 714

Wulf, Karin A, Omohundro Institute of Early American History & Culture, Swem Library, Ground fl, 400 Landrum Dr, Williamsburg, VA 23185 *Tel:* 757-221-1110 *Fax:* 757-221-1047 *E-mail:* ieahc1@wm.edu *Web Site:* oieahc.wm.edu, pg 185

Wunderlich, Margaret, Carolrhoda Books, 241 First Ave N, Minneapolis, MN 55401 *Tel:* 612-332-3344 *Toll Free Tel:* 800-328-4929 *Fax:* 612-332-7615 *Toll Free Fax:* 800-332-1132 *E-mail:* info@lernerbooks.com *Web Site:* www.lernerbooks.com, pg 53

Wunderlich, Margaret, Carolrhoda Lab™, 241 First Ave N, Minneapolis, MN 55401 *Tel:* 612-332-3344 *Toll Free Tel:* 800-328-4929 *Fax:* 612-332-7615 *Toll Free Fax:* 800-332-1132 (US) *E-mail:* info@lernerbooks.com *Web Site:* www.lernerbooks.com, pg 53

Wunderlich, Margaret, ediciones Lerner, 241 First Ave N, Minneapolis, MN 55401 *Tel:* 612-332-3344 *Toll Free Tel:* 800-328-4929 *Fax:* 612-332-7615 *Toll Free Fax:* 800-332-1132 *E-mail:* info@lernerbooks.com *Web Site:* www.lernerbooks.com, pg 85

Wunderlich, Margaret, First Avenue Editions, 241 First Ave N, Minneapolis, MN 55401 *Tel:* 612-332-3344 *Toll Free Tel:* 800-328-4929 *Fax:* 612-332-7615 *Toll Free Fax:* 800-332-1132 *E-mail:* info@lernerbooks.com *Web Site:* www.lernerbooks.com, pg 95

Wunderlich, Margaret, Graphic Universe™, 241 First Ave N, Minneapolis, MN 55401 *Tel:* 612-332-3344 *Toll Free Tel:* 800-328-4929 *Fax:* 612-332-7615 *Toll Free Fax:* 800-332-1132 *E-mail:* info@lernerbooks.com *Web Site:* www.lernerbooks.com, pg 106

Wunderlich, Margaret, Lerner Publications, 241 First Ave N, Minneapolis, MN 55401 *Tel:* 612-332-3344 *Toll Free Tel:* 800-328-4929 *Fax:* 612-332-7615 *Toll Free Fax:* 800-332-1132 *E-mail:* info@lernerbooks.com *Web Site:* www.lernerbooks.com, pg 146

Wunderlich, Margaret, Lerner Publishing Group Inc, 241 First Ave N, Minneapolis, MN 55401 *Tel:* 612-332-3344 *Toll Free Tel:* 800-328-4929 *Fax:* 612-332-7615 *Toll Free Fax:* 800-332-1132 *E-mail:* info@lernerbooks.com *Web Site:* www.lernerbooks.com, pg 146

Wunderlich, Margaret, LernerClassroom, 241 First Ave N, Minneapolis, MN 55401 *Tel:* 612-332-3344 *Toll Free Tel:* 800-328-4929 *Fax:* 612-332-7615 *Toll Free Fax:* 800-332-1132 *E-mail:* info@lernerbooks.com *Web Site:* www.lernerbooks.com, pg 147

Wunderlich, Margaret, Millbrook Press, 241 First Ave N, Minneapolis, MN 55401 *Tel:* 612-332-3344 *Toll Free Tel:* 800-328-4929 (US only) *Fax:* 612-332-7615 *Toll Free Fax:* 800-332-1132, pg 167

Wunderlich, Margaret, Twenty-First Century Books, 241 First Ave N, Minneapolis, MN 55401 *Tel:* 612-332-3344 *Toll Free Tel:* 800-328-4929 *Fax:* 612-332-7615 *Toll Free Fax:* 800-332-1132 *E-mail:* info@lernerbooks.com *Web Site:* www.lernerbooks.com, pg 260

Wurfbain, Ludo J, Safari Press, 15621 Chemical Lane, Bldg B, Huntington Beach, CA 92649 *Tel:* 714-894-9080 *Toll Free Tel:* 800-451-4788 *Fax:* 714-894-4949 *E-mail:* info@safaripress.com *Web Site:* www.safaripress.com, pg 223

Wurzbacher, Eric, nursesbooks.org, The Publishing Program of ANA, 8515 Georgia Ave, Suite 400, Silver Spring, MD 20910-3492 *Tel:* 301-628-5000 *Toll Free Tel:* 800-924-9053; 800-637-0323 (orders) *Fax:* 301-628-5001 *E-mail:* anp@ana.org *Web Site:* www.nursesbooks.org; www.nursingworld.org, pg 182

Wyatt, John, The Mathematical Association of America, 1529 18 St NW, Washington, DC 20036-1358 *Tel:* 202-387-5200 *Toll Free Tel:* 800-741-9415 *Fax:* 202-265-2384 *E-mail:* maahq@maa.org *Web Site:* www.maa.org, pg 159

Wyatt, Rich, The Backwaters Press, 3502 N 52 St, Omaha, NE 68104-3506 *Tel:* 402-451-4052 *E-mail:* thebackwaterspress@gmail.com *Web Site:* www.thebackwaterspress.org, pg 29

Wybraniec, Barbara, Oscar Williams/Gene Derwood Award, 909 Third Ave, New York, NY 10022 *Tel:* 212-686-0010 *Fax:* 212-532-8528 *E-mail:* info@nycommunitytrust.org *Web Site:* www.nycommunitytrust.org, pg 749

Wyckoff, Joanne, Carol Mann Agency, 55 Fifth Ave, New York, NY 10003 *Tel:* 212-206-5635 *Fax:* 212-675-4809 *E-mail:* submissions@carolmannagency.com *Web Site:* www.carolmannagency.com, pg 583

Wydra, Denise, Bedford/St Martin's, 75 Arlington St, Boston, MA 02116 *Tel:* 617-399-4000 *Toll Free Tel:* 800-779-7440 *Fax:* 617-426-8582 *Web Site:* www.bedfordstmartins.com, pg 34

Wylie, Andrew, The Wylie Agency Inc, 250 W 57 St, Suite 2114, New York, NY 10107 *Tel:* 212-246-0069 *Fax:* 212-586-8953 *E-mail:* mail@wylieagency.com *Web Site:* www.wylieagency.com, pg 600

Wyman, Pilar, Wyman Indexing, 8526 Foxborough Dr, Suite 2-C, Savage, MD 20763 *Tel:* 443-336-5497 *Web Site:* www.wymanindexing.com, pg 558

Wynn, Mychal, Rising Sun Publishing, PO Box 70906, Marietta, GA 30007-0906 *Tel:* 770-518-0369 *Toll Free Tel:* 800-524-2813 *Fax:* 770-587-0862 *E-mail:* info@rspublishing.com *Web Site:* www.rspublishing.com, pg 219

Wypych, Anna, ChemTec Publishing, 38 Earswick Dr, Toronto, ON M1E 1C6, Canada *Tel:* 416-265-2603 *Fax:* 416-265-1399 *E-mail:* orderdesk@chemtec.org *Web Site:* www.chemtec.org, pg 498

Wyrwa, Richard, W E Upjohn Institute for Employment Research, 300 S Westnedge Ave, Kalamazoo, MI 49007-4686 *Tel:* 269-343-5541; 269-343-4330 (pubns) *Toll Free Tel:* 888-227-8569 *Fax:* 269-343-7310 *E-mail:* publications@upjohninstitute.org *Web Site:* www.upjohn.org, pg 272

Yaged, Jonathan, Macmillan, 175 Fifth Ave, New York, NY 10010 *Tel:* 646-307-5151 *Fax:* 212-420-9314 *E-mail:* firstname.lastname@macmillan.com *Web Site:* www.macmillan.com, pg 154

Yager, Dr Jan, Hannacroix Creek Books Inc, 1127 High Ridge Rd, No 110-B, Stamford, CT 06905-1203 *Tel:* 203-968-8098 *Fax:* 203-968-0193 *E-mail:* hannacroix@aol.com *Web Site:* www.hannacroixcreekbooks.com, pg 112

Yager, Raymond, McGraw-Hill International Publishing Group, 2 Penn Plaza, New York, NY 10121 *Tel:* 212-904-2000 *Web Site:* www.mcgraw-hill.com, pg 161

Yake, Sarah, Frances Collin Literary Agent, PO Box 33, Wayne, PA 19087 *E-mail:* queries@francescollin.com *Web Site:* www.francescollin.com, pg 567

Yamada, Miki, Integra Software Services Inc, 1110 Jorie Blvd, Suite 200, Oak Brook, IL 60523 *Tel:* 630-586-2579 *Fax:* 630-586-2599 *Web Site:* www.integra.co.in, pg 548

Yamaguchi, Jeffrey, Harry N Abrams Inc, 115 W 18 St, 6th fl, New York, NY 10011 *Tel:* 212-206-7715 *Toll Free Tel:* 800-345-1359 *Fax:* 212-519-1210 *E-mail:* abrams@abramsbooks.com *Web Site:* www.abramsbooks.com, pg 3

Yamamoto, Ken, Scholastic Media, 524 Broadway, 5th fl, New York, NY 10012 *Tel:* 212-389-3900 *Fax:* 212-389-3886, pg 228

Yamashita, Brianna, Jeremy P Tarcher, 375 Hudson St, New York, NY 10014 *Tel:* 212-366-2000 *E-mail:* online@penguinputnam.com *Web Site:* www.penguinputnam.com; us.penguingroup.com, pg 250

Yambert, Karl, Westview Press, 2465 Central Ave, Boulder, CO 80301 *Tel:* 303-444-3541 *Fax:* 720-406-7336 *E-mail:* westview.orders@perseusbooks.com *Web Site:* www.perseusbooksgroup.com; www.westviewpress.com, pg 279

Yammer, Channi, Simon & Schuster Children's Publishing, 1230 Avenue of the Americas, New York, NY 10020 *Tel:* 212-698-7000 *Web Site:* KIDS.SimonandSchuster.com; TEEN.SimonandSchuster.com; simonandschuster.net; simonandschuster.biz, pg 235

Yang, Caren, Saint Mary's Press, 702 Terrace Heights, Winona, MN 55987-1318 *Tel:* 507-457-7900 *Toll Free Tel:* 800-533-8095 *Fax:* 507-457-7990 *Toll Free Fax:* 800-344-9225 *E-mail:* smpress@smp.org *Web Site:* www.smp.org, pg 224

Yang, Kichoon, National Council of Teachers of Mathematics (NCTM), 1906 Association Dr, Reston, VA 20191-1502 *Tel:* 703-620-9840 *Toll Free Tel:* 800-235-7566 *Fax:* 703-476-2970 *E-mail:* nctm@nctm.org *Web Site:* www.nctm.org, pg 174

Yankech, Andrew, Loyola Press, 3441 N Ashland Ave, Chicago, IL 60657 *Tel:* 773-281-1818 *Toll Free Tel:* 800-621-1008 *Fax:* 773-281-0555 (cust serv); 773-281-4129 (edit) *E-mail:* customerservice@loyolapress.com *Web Site:* www.loyolapress.com; www.spiritedtalk.org, pg 153

Yankelevich, Matvei, Ugly Duckling Presse, The Old American Can Factory, 232 Third St, Suite E002, Brooklyn, NY 11215 *Tel:* 347-948-5170 *E-mail:* udp_mailbox@yahoo.com; info@uglyducklingpresse.org *Web Site:* www.uglyducklingpresse.org, pg 261

Yankelevitz, Harold, Printing Association of Florida Inc, 6275 Hazeltine National Dr, Orlando, FL 32822 *Tel:* 407-240-8009 *Toll Free Tel:* 800-331-0461 *Fax:* 407-240-8333 *Web Site:* www.pafgraf.org, pg 634

Yanosey, Robert J, Morning Sun Books Inc, PO Box 326, Kutztown, PA 19530-0326 *Tel:* 610-683-8566 *Fax:* 610-683-3287 *Web Site:* www.morningsunbooks.com, pg 170

Yao, Mei C, Chinese Connection Agency, 67 Banksville Rd, Armonk, NY 10504 *Tel:* 914-765-0296 *Fax:* 914-765-0297 *E-mail:* info@yaollc.com *Web Site:* www.yaollc.com, pg 566

Yarbrough, Courtney, Carl Vinson Institute of Government, University of Georgia, 201 N Milledge Ave, Athens, GA 30602 *Tel:* 706-542-2736 *Fax:* 706-542-9301 *Web Site:* www.cviog.uga.edu, pg 275

Yarshater, Prof Ehsan, Bibliotheca Persica Press, 450 Riverside Dr, Suite 4, New York, NY 10027 *Tel:* 212-851-5723 *Fax:* 212-749-9524 *E-mail:* ey4@columbia.edu, pg 37

Yates, Gary, The Alexander Graham Bell Association for the Deaf & Hard of Hearing, 3417 Volta Place NW, Washington, DC 20007-2778 *Tel:* 202-337-5220 *Toll Free Tel:* 866-337-5220 (orders) *Fax:* 202-337-8314 *E-mail:* info@agbell.org; publications@agbell.org *Web Site:* www.agbell.org, pg 7

Yates, John, University of Toronto Press Inc, 10 Saint Mary St, Suite 700, Toronto, ON M4Y 2W8, Canada *Tel:* 416-978-2239 *Fax:* 416-978-4738 *E-mail:* utpbooks@utpress.utoronto.ca *Web Site:* www.utpress.utoronto.ca; www.utppublishing.com, pg 524

Yates, Steve, University Press of Mississippi, 3825 Ridgewood Rd, Jackson, MS 39211-6492 *Tel:* 601-432-6205 *Toll Free Tel:* 800-737-7788 (orders & cust serv) *Fax:* 601-432-6217 *E-mail:* press@mississippi.edu *Web Site:* www.upress.state.ms.us, pg 271

Yaverski, Aaron, Wolters Kluwer Law & Business, 76 Ninth Ave, 7th fl, New York, NY 10011-5201 *Tel:* 212-771-0600 *Toll Free Tel:* 800-234-1660 (cust serv); 800-638-8437 (orders); 800-317-3113 (bookstore sales) *Toll Free Fax:* 800-901-9075 (cust serv); 800-561-4845 (bookstore sales) *Web Site:* www.aspenpublishers.com, pg 141

Yazell, Suzanne, Oak Tree Press, 140 E Palmer St, Taylorville, IL 62568 *Tel:* 217-824-6500 *E-mail:* publisher@oaktreebooks.com; info@oaktreebooks.com; query@oaktreebooks.com; pressdept@oaktreebooks.com; bookorders@oaktreebooks.com *Web Site:* www.oaktreebooks.com; www.otpblog.blogspot.com, pg 183

Ye, Shawn, Homa & Sekey Books, 140 E Ridgewood Ave, Paramus, NJ 07652 *Tel:* 201-261-8810 *Toll Free Tel:* 800-870-HOMA (870-4662 orders) *Fax:* 201-261-8890 *E-mail:* info@homabooks.com *Web Site:* www.homabooks.com, pg 122

Yeager, Tristra Newyear, The Mongolia Society Inc, Indiana University, 322 Goodbody Hall, 1011 E Third St, Bloomington, IN 47405-7005 *Tel:* 812-855-4078 *Fax:* 812-855-4078 *E-mail:* monsoc@indiana.edu *Web Site:* www.mongoliasociety.org, pg 169

Yee, Henry, Picador, 175 Fifth Ave, 19th fl, New York, NY 10010 *Tel:* 646-307-5151 *Fax:* 212-253-9627 *E-mail:* firstname.lastname@picadorusa.com *Web Site:* www.picadorusa.com, pg 201

Yee, Jennifer, Book Sales Inc, 276 Fifth Ave, Suite 206, New York, NY 10001 *Tel:* 212-779-4972 *Toll Free Tel:* 866-483-5456 *Fax:* 212-779-6058 *E-mail:* sales@booksalesusa.com; customerservice@booksalesusa.com *Web Site:* www.booksalesusa.com, pg 43

Yeffeth, Glenn, BenBella Books Inc, 10300 N Central Expwy, Suite 400, Dallas, TX 75231 *Tel:* 214-750-3600 *Fax:* 214-750-3645 *E-mail:* feedback@benbellabooks.com *Web Site:* www.benbellabooks.com; www.smartpopbooks.com, pg 35

Yeh, Phoebe, Random House Children's Books, 1745 Broadway, New York, NY 10019 *Tel:* 212-782-9000 *Toll Free Tel:* 800-200-3552 *Fax:* 212-782-9452 *Web Site:* randomhousekids.com, pg 213

Yeh, Phoebe, Random House Inc, 1745 Broadway, New York, NY 10019 *Tel:* 212-782-9000 *Toll Free Tel:* 800-726-0600 *Web Site:* www.randomhouse.com, pg 213

Yelavich, John, American Society of Mechanical Engineers (ASME), 3 Park Ave, New York, NY 10016-5990 *Tel:* 212-591-7000 *Toll Free Tel:* 800-843-2763 (cust serv-US, CN & Mexico) *Fax:* 212-591-7674; 973-882-8113 (cust serv); 973-882-1717 (orders & inquiries) *E-mail:* infocentral@asme.org *Web Site:* www.asme.org, pg 17

Yelton, Richard, Hanley-Wood LLC, One Thomas Circle NW, Suite 600, Washington, DC 20005 *Tel:* 202-452-0800 *Fax:* 202-785-1974 *Web Site:* www.hanleywood.com, pg 112

Yentus, Helen, Riverhead Books (Hardcover), 375 Hudson St, New York, NY 10014 *Tel:* 212-366-2000 *E-mail:* online@penguinputnam.com *Web Site:* www.penguinputnam.com; us.penguingroup.com, pg 219

Yentus, Helen, Riverhead Books (Trade Paperback), 375 Hudson St, New York, NY 10014 *Tel:* 212-366-2000 *E-mail:* online@penguinputnam.com *Web Site:* www.penguinputnam.com; us.penguingroup.com, pg 219

Yeping, Hu, Council for Research in Values & Philosophy (RVP), The Catholic University of America, Gibbons Hall, Rm B-12, 620 Michigan Ave NE, Washington, DC 20064 *Tel:* 202-319-6089 *Fax:* 202-319-6089 *E-mail:* cua-rvp@cua.edu *Web Site:* www.crvp.org, pg 69

Yersak, John, Information Today, Inc, 143 Old Marlton Pike, Medford, NJ 08055-8750 *Tel:* 609-654-6266 *Toll Free Tel:* 800-300-9868 (cust serv) *Fax:* 609-654-4309 *E-mail:* custserv@infotoday.com *Web Site:* www.infotoday.com, pg 130

Yess, Mary E, The Electrochemical Society (ECS), 65 S Main St, Bldg D, Pennington, NJ 08534-2839 *Tel:* 609-737-1902 *Fax:* 609-737-2743 *E-mail:* ecs@electrochem.org *Web Site:* www.electrochem.org, pg 86

Yoars, Marcus, Charisma Media, 600 Rinehart Rd, Lake Mary, FL 32746 *Tel:* 407-333-0600 (all imprints) *Toll Free Tel:* 800-283-8494 (Charisma Media, Siloam Press, Creation House); 800-665-1468 *Fax:* 407-333-7100 (all imprints) *E-mail:* charisma@charismamedia.com *Web Site:* www.charismamedia.com, pg 58

Yocum, Richard, Venture Publishing Inc, 1999 Cato Ave, State College, PA 16801 *Tel:* 814-234-4561 *Fax:* 814-234-1651 *E-mail:* vpublish@venturepublish.com *Web Site:* www.venturepublish.com, pg 274

Yoke, Beth, Baker & Taylor/YALSA Conference Grants, 50 E Huron St, Chicago, IL 60611 *Tel:* 312-280-4390 *Toll Free Tel:* 800-545-2433 *Fax:* 312-280-5276; 312-664-7459 *E-mail:* yalsa@ala.org *Web Site:* www.ala.org/yalsa/, pg 689

Zion, Claire, NAL, 375 Hudson St, New York, NY 10014 *Tel:* 212-366-2000 *E-mail:* online@penguinputnam.com *Web Site:* www.penguinputnam.com; us.penguingroup.com, pg 172

Zissimos, Mary Ann, Harry N Abrams Inc, 115 W 18 St, 6th fl, New York, NY 10011 *Tel:* 212-206-7715 *Toll Free Tel:* 800-345-1359 *Fax:* 212-519-1210 *E-mail:* abrams@abramsbooks.com *Web Site:* www.abramsbooks.com, pg 3

Zitwer, Barbara J, Barbara J Zitwer Agency, 525 West End Ave, Unit 11-H, New York, NY 10024 *Tel:* 212-501-8423 *Fax:* 646-514-0497 *E-mail:* zitwer@gmail.com, pg 600

Ziv, Maya, HarperCollins General Books Group, 10 E 53 St, New York, NY 10022 *Tel:* 212-207-7000 *Fax:* 212-207-7633 *Web Site:* www.harpercollins.com, pg 113

Zline, Patricia, Jason Aronson Inc, 4501 Forbes Blvd, Suite 200, Lanham, MD 20706 *Tel:* 301-459-3366 *Toll Free Tel:* 800-462-6420 (orders) *Fax:* 301-429-5748 *Web Site:* www.jasonaronson.com, pg 22

Zlotowitz, Meir, Mesorah Publications Ltd, 4401 Second Ave, Brooklyn, NY 11232 *Tel:* 718-921-9000 *Toll Free Tel:* 800-637-6724 *Fax:* 718-680-1875 *E-mail:* artscroll@mesorah.com *Web Site:* www.artscroll.com; www.mesorah.com, pg 165

Zock, Jim, Atlantic Center for the Arts Artists-in-Residence Program, 1414 Art Center Ave, New Smyrna Beach, FL 32168 *Tel:* 386-427-6975 *Toll Free Tel:* 800-393-6975 *Fax:* 386-427-5669 *E-mail:* program@atlanticcenterforthearts.org *Web Site:* www.atlanticcenterforthearts.org, pg 667

Zollshan, Ronald P, Kirchoff/Wohlberg Inc, 897 Boston Post Rd, Madison, CT 06443 *Tel:* 203-245-7308 *Fax:* 203-245-3218 *Web Site:* www.kirchoffwohlberg.com, pg 579

Zorn, Paul Manthey, The Mathematical Association of America, 1529 18 St NW, Washington, DC 20036-1358 *Tel:* 202-387-5200 *Toll Free Tel:* 800-741-9415 *Fax:* 202-265-2384 *E-mail:* maahq@maa.org *Web Site:* www.maa.org, pg 159

Zoro, Theresa, Random House Publishing Group, 1745 Broadway, New York, NY 10019 *Toll Free Tel:* 800-200-3552 *Web Site:* atrandom.com, pg 214

Zoss, Bernadette, Indiana University Press, 601 N Morton St, Bloomington, IN 47404-3797 *Tel:* 812-855-8817 *Toll Free Tel:* 800-842-6796 (orders only) *Fax:* 812-855-7931; 812-855-8507 *E-mail:* iupress@indiana.edu; iuporder@indiana.edu (orders) *Web Site:* www.iupress.indiana.edu, pg 129

Zschock, Heather, Peter Pauper Press, Inc, 202 Mamaroneck Ave, White Plains, NY 10601-5376 *Tel:* 914-681-0144 *Fax:* 914-681-0389 *E-mail:* customerservice@peterpauper.com; orders@peterpauper.com *Web Site:* www.peterpauper.com, pg 200

Zubal, John T, USBE: United States Book Exchange, 2969 W 25 St, Cleveland, OH 44113 *Tel:* 216-241-6960 *Fax:* 216-241-6966 *E-mail:* usbe@usbe.com *Web Site:* www.usbe.com, pg 638

Zubal, Marilyn, USBE: United States Book Exchange, 2969 W 25 St, Cleveland, OH 44113 *Tel:* 216-241-6960 *Fax:* 216-241-6966 *E-mail:* usbe@usbe.com *Web Site:* www.usbc.com, pg 638

Zucca, Damon, Oxford University Press USA, 198 Madison Ave, New York, NY 10016 *Tel:* 212-726-6000 *Toll Free Tel:* 800-451-7556 (orders); 800-445-9714 (cust serv) *Fax:* 919-677-1303 *E-mail:* custserv.us@oup.com *Web Site:* www.oup.com/us, pg 189

Zuccarello, Dasya Anthony, Hohm Press, PO Box 4410, Chino Valley, AZ 86323 *Tel:* 928-636-3331 *Toll Free Tel:* 800-381-2700 *Fax:* 928-636-7519 *E-mail:* hppublisher@cableone.net; hohmpresseditor@gmail.com *Web Site:* www.hohmpress.com, pg 121

Zuccarello, Joe Bala, Hohm Press, PO Box 4410, Chino Valley, AZ 86323 *Tel:* 928-636-3331 *Toll Free Tel:* 800-381-2700 *Fax:* 928-636-7519 *E-mail:* hppublisher@cableone.net; hohmpresseditor@gmail.com *Web Site:* www.hohmpress.com, pg 121

Zuccarini, Margaret, Springer Publishing Co LLC, 11 W 42 St, 15th fl, New York, NY 10036-8002 *Tel:* 212-431-4370 *Toll Free Tel:* 877-687-7476 *Fax:* 212-941-7842 *E-mail:* marketing@springerpub.com; cs@springerpub.com (orders); editorial@springerpub.com *Web Site:* www.springerpub.com, pg 241

Zucchi, John, McGill-Queen's University Press, 1010 Sherbrooke W, Suite 1720, Montreal, QC H3A 2R7, Canada *Tel:* 514-398-3750 *Fax:* 514-398-4333 *E-mail:* mqup@mqup.ca *Web Site:* www.mqup.ca, pg 512

Zuch, Franklin Jon, George T Bisel Co Inc, 710 S Washington Sq, Philadelphia, PA 19106-3519 *Tel:* 215-922-5760 *Toll Free Tel:* 800-247-3526 *Fax:* 215-922-2235 *E-mail:* gbisel@bisel.com *Web Site:* www.bisel.com, pg 38

Zucker, Irwin, Book Publicists of Southern California, 714 Crescent Dr, Beverly Hills, CA 90210 *Tel:* 323-461-3921 *Fax:* 323-461-0917, pg 618

Zucker, Joel, Harcourt Achieve, 6277 Sea Harbor Dr, Orlando, FL 32887 *Tel:* 407-345-2000 *Toll Free Tel:* 800-531-5015 (cust serv/orders) *Toll Free Fax:* 800-699-9459 (cust serv/orders) *Web Site:* www.harcourtachieve.com, pg 112

Zucker, Joel, Harcourt Inc, 6277 Sea Harbor Dr, Orlando, FL 32887 *Tel:* 407-345-2000 *Toll Free Tel:* 800-225-5425 (cust serv/orders) *Toll Free Fax:* 800-269-5232 (cust serv/orders) *Web Site:* www.hmhco.com, pg 112

Zuckerman, Kathryn, Alfred A Knopf/Everyman's Library, c/o Random House Inc, 1745 Broadway, New York, NY 10019 *Tel:* 212-751-2600 *Toll Free Tel:* 800-638-6460 *Fax:* 212-572-2593 *Web Site:* www.knopfdoubleday.com, pg 141

Zuckerman, Phil, Applewood Books Inc, One River Rd, Carlisle, MA 01741 *Tel:* 781-271-0055 *Fax:* 781-271-0056 *E-mail:* applewood@awb.com *Web Site:* www.awb.com, pg 20

Zuckerman, Philip, Commonwealth Editions, One River Rd, Carlisle, MA 01741 *Tel:* 781-271-0055 *Toll Free Tel:* 800-277-5312 *Fax:* 781-271-0056 *E-mail:* customercare@awb.com *Web Site:* www.awb.com, pg 65

Zukowski, Steve, Great Source Education Group, 181 Ballardvale St, Wilmington, MA 01887 *Tel:* 978-661-1471 *Toll Free Tel:* 800-289-4490 *Toll Free Fax:* 800-289-3994 *Web Site:* www.greatsource.com, pg 107

Zulli, Jessica, Sourcebooks Inc, 1935 Brookdale Rd, Suite 139, Naperville, IL 60563 *Tel:* 630-961-3900 *Toll Free Tel:* 800-432-7444 *Fax:* 630-961-2168 *E-mail:* info@sourcebooks.com; customersupport@sourcebooks.com *Web Site:* www.sourcebooks.com, pg 240

Zwarenstein, Lianne, Editors' Association of Canada (Association canadienne des reviseurs), 502-27 Carlton St, Toronto, ON M5B 1L2, Canada *Tel:* 416-975-1379 *Toll Free Tel:* 866-CAN-EDIT (226-3348) *Fax:* 416-975-1637 *E-mail:* info@editors.ca *Web Site:* www.editors.ca; www.reviseurs.ca, pg 622

Zwarenstein, Lianne, Tom Fairley Award for Editorial Excellence, 502-27 Carlton St, Toronto, ON M5B 1L2, Canada *Tel:* 416-975-1379 *Toll Free Tel:* 866-CAN-EDIT (226-3348) *Fax:* 416-975-1637 *E-mail:* fairley_award@editors.ca *Web Site:* www.editors.ca; www.reviseurs.ca, pg 703

Zychowicz, James L, A-R Editions Inc, 8551 Research Way, Suite 180, Middleton, WI 53562 *Tel:* 608-836-9000 *Toll Free Tel:* 800-736-0070 (US book orders only) *Fax:* 608-831-8200 *E-mail:* info@areditions.com *Web Site:* www.areditions.com, pg 1

# Publishers Toll Free Directory

A-R Editions Inc, Middleton, WI *Toll Free Tel:* 800-736-0070 (US book orders only), pg 1

AAPG (American Association of Petroleum Geologists), Tulsa, OK *Toll Free Tel:* 800-364-AAPG (364-2274) *Toll Free Fax:* 800-898-2274, pg 2

Abbeville Press, New York, NY *Toll Free Tel:* 800-ARTBOOK (278-2665), pg 2

Abbeville Publishing Group, New York, NY *Toll Free Tel:* 800-ART-BOOK (278-2665), pg 2

ABC-CLIO, Santa Barbara, CA *Toll Free Tel:* 800-368-6868 *Toll Free Fax:* 866-270-3856, pg 2

ABDO Publishing Group, Edina, MN *Toll Free Tel:* 800-800-1312 *Toll Free Fax:* 800-862-3480, pg 2

Abingdon Press, Nashville, TN *Toll Free Tel:* 800-251-3320 *Toll Free Fax:* 800-836-7802 (orders), pg 3

Harry N Abrams Inc, New York, NY *Toll Free Tel:* 800-345-1359, pg 3

Abrams Learning Trends, Austin, TX *Toll Free Tel:* 800-227-9120 *Toll Free Fax:* 800-737-3322, pg 3

Absey & Co Inc, Spring, TX *Toll Free Tel:* 888-41-ABSEY (412-2739), pg 3

Academic Press, San Diego, CA *Toll Free Tel:* 800-321-5068 (cust serv), pg 3

Academy Chicago Publishers, Chicago, IL *Toll Free Tel:* 800-248-READ (248-7323), pg 4

Academy of Nutrition & Dietetics, Chicago, IL *Toll Free Tel:* 800-877-1600, pg 4

Accent Publications, Colorado Springs, CO *Toll Free Tel:* 800-708-5550; 800-535-2905 (cust serv); 800-323-7543 (main); 800-426-6596 (sales) *Toll Free Fax:* 800-430-0726, pg 4

Accuity, a SourceMedia Co, Skokie, IL *Toll Free Tel:* 800-321-3373, pg 4

Acres USA, Austin, TX *Toll Free Tel:* 800-355-5313, pg 4

ACTA Publications, Chicago, IL *Toll Free Tel:* 800-397-2282 *Toll Free Fax:* 800-397-0079, pg 4

ACU Press, Abilene, TX *Toll Free Tel:* 877-816-4455, pg 4

Adams Media, Avon, MA *Toll Free Fax:* 800-872-5627, pg 5

Adams-Pomeroy Press, Albany, WI *Toll Free Tel:* 877-862-3645, pg 527

ADD Warehouse, Plantation, FL *Toll Free Tel:* 800-233-9273, pg 5

Addicus Books Inc, Omaha, NE *Toll Free Tel:* 800-352-2873 (orders), pg 5

Adirondack Mountain Club, Lake George, NY *Toll Free Tel:* 800-395-8080, pg 5

Adler Publishing Inc, Parker, CO *Toll Free Tel:* 800-660-5107 (sales & orders), pg 5

Advance Publishing Inc, Houston, TX *Toll Free Tel:* 800-917-9630, pg 5

Adventure Publications, Cambridge, MN *Toll Free Tel:* 800-678-7006 *Toll Free Fax:* 877-374-9016, pg 5

Aegean Park Press, Walnut Creek, CA *Toll Free Tel:* 800-736-3587 (orders only), pg 6

African American Images, Chicago Heights, IL *Toll Free Tel:* 800-552-1991 (orders), pg 6

Africana Homestead Legacy Publishers Inc, Cherry Hill, NJ *Toll Free Tel:* 866-250-8477 *Toll Free Fax:* 866-289-8681, pg 6

AHA Press, Chicago, IL *Toll Free Tel:* 800-242-4890 *Toll Free Fax:* 866-516-5817 (orders), pg 6

AICPA Professional Publications, Durham, NC *Toll Free Tel:* 888-777-7077, pg 6

AIMS Education Foundation, Fresno, CA *Toll Free Tel:* 888-733-2467, pg 7

Alban Publishing, Herndon, VA *Toll Free Tel:* 800-486-1318, pg 7

Albert Whitman & Co, Park Ridge, IL *Toll Free Tel:* 800-255-7675, pg 7

The Alexander Graham Bell Association for the Deaf & Hard of Hearing, Washington, DC *Toll Free Tel:* 866-337-5220 (orders), pg 7

Alexander Street Press LLC, Alexandria, VA *Toll Free Tel:* 800-889-5937, pg 7

Alfred Publishing Company Inc, Van Nuys, CA *Toll Free Tel:* 800-292-6122 (dealer sales) *Toll Free Fax:* 800-632-1928 (dealer sales), pg 7

ALI-ABA Continuing Professional Education, Philadelphia, PA *Toll Free Tel:* 800-CLE-NEWS (253-6397), pg 8

Allen D Bragdon Publishers Inc, South Yarmouth, MA *Toll Free Tel:* 877-876-2787, pg 8

Thomas Allen Publishers, Markham, ON Canada *Toll Free Tel:* 800-387-4333 (orders) *Toll Free Fax:* 800-458-5504 (orders), pg 493

Allyn & Bacon, Boston, MA *Toll Free Tel:* 800-526-0485, pg 9

ALPHA Publications of America Inc, Tucson, AZ *Toll Free Tel:* 800-528-3494 *Toll Free Fax:* 800-770-4329, pg 9

Alpine Publications Inc, Crawford, CO *Toll Free Tel:* 800-777-7257, pg 9

AltaMira Press, Lanham, MD *Toll Free Tel:* 800-462-6420 (cust serv), pg 9

AMACOM Books, New York, NY *Toll Free Tel:* 800-250-5308 (cust serv), pg 9

Amadeus Press/Hal Leonard Performing Arts Publishing Group, Montclair, NJ *Toll Free Tel:* 800-524-4425, pg 10

Frank Amato Publications Inc, Portland, OR *Toll Free Tel:* 800-541-9498, pg 10

Amber Lotus Publishing, Portland, OR *Toll Free Tel:* 800-326-2375 (orders only), pg 10

America West Publishers, Hayden, ID *Toll Free Tel:* 800-729-4131, pg 10

American Academy of Orthopaedic Surgeons, Rosemont, IL *Toll Free Tel:* 800-346-2267 *Toll Free Fax:* 800-999-2939, pg 10

American Academy of Pediatrics, Elk Grove Village, IL *Toll Free Tel:* 888-227-1770, pg 10

American Association for Vocational Instructional Materials, Winterville, GA *Toll Free Tel:* 800-228-4689, pg 11

American Association of Blood Banks, Bethesda, MD *Toll Free Tel:* 866-222-2498 (sales), pg 11

American Bar Association, Chicago, IL *Toll Free Tel:* 800-285-2221 (orders), pg 11

American Bible Society, New York, NY *Toll Free Tel:* 800-322-4253, pg 11

American Book Publishing, Saratoga, CA *Toll Free Tel:* 800-684-8746, pg 11

American Carriage House Publishing, Nevada City, CA *Toll Free Tel:* 866-986-2665, pg 11

The American Ceramic Society, Westerville, OH *Toll Free Tel:* 866-721-3322, pg 12

American College, Bryn Mawr, PA *Toll Free Tel:* 888-263-7265, pg 12

American College of Physician Executives, Tampa, FL *Toll Free Tel:* 800-562-8088, pg 12

American Correctional Association, Alexandria, VA *Toll Free Tel:* 800-222-5646, pg 12

American Counseling Association, Alexandria, VA *Toll Free Tel:* 800-422-2648 (ext 222, book orders); 800-347-6647 *Toll Free Fax:* 800-473-2329, pg 12

American Diabetes Association, Alexandria, VA *Toll Free Tel:* 800-342-2383, pg 12

American Federation of Arts, New York, NY *Toll Free Tel:* 800-232-0270, pg 12

American Federation of Astrologers Inc, Tempe, AZ *Toll Free Tel:* 888-301-7630, pg 13

American Foundation for the Blind (AFB Press), New York, NY *Toll Free Tel:* 800-232-3044 (orders) *Toll Free Fax:* 888-545-8331, pg 13

American Geophysical Union (AGU), Washington, DC *Toll Free Tel:* 800-966-2481 (North America), pg 13

American Girl Publishing, Middleton, WI *Toll Free Tel:* 800-233-0264; 800-360-1861, pg 13

American Institute for Economic Research (AIER), Great Barrington, MA *Toll Free Tel:* 888-528-0103; 888-528-1216 (orders), pg 13

American Institute of Aeronautics & Astronautics, Reston, VA *Toll Free Tel:* 800-639-AIAA (639-2422), pg 14

American Institute of Chemical Engineers (AIChE), New York, NY *Toll Free Tel:* 800-242-4363, pg 14

American Institute of Physics, Melville, NY *Toll Free Tel:* 800-777-4643 (hardcover books), pg 14

American Law Institute, Philadelphia, PA *Toll Free Tel:* 800-253-6397, pg 14

The American Library Association (ALA), Chicago, IL *Toll Free Tel:* 800-545-2433, pg 14

American Map Corp, Long Island City, NY *Toll Free Tel:* 888-774-7979, pg 14

American Marketing Association, Chicago, IL *Toll Free Tel:* 800-AMA-1150 (262-1150), pg 14

American Mathematical Society, Providence, RI *Toll Free Tel:* 800-321-4267, pg 14

American Medical Association, Chicago, IL *Toll Free Tel:* 800-621-8335, pg 15

American Occupational Therapy Association Inc, Bethesda, MD *Toll Free Tel:* 800-377-8555, pg 15

American Phytopathological Society (APS), St Paul, MN *Toll Free Tel:* 800-328-7560, pg 15

American Printing House for the Blind Inc, Louisville, KY *Toll Free Tel:* 800-223-1839 (cust serv), pg 15

American Products Publishing Co, Beaverton, OR *Toll Free Tel:* 800-668-8181, pg 15

American Psychiatric Publishing (APP), Arlington, VA *Toll Free Tel:* 800-368-5777, pg 15

American Psychological Association, Washington, DC *Toll Free Tel:* 800-374-2721, pg 16

American Public Works Association, Kansas City, MO *Toll Free Tel:* 800-848-2792, pg 16

American Quilter's Society, Paducah, KY *Toll Free Tel:* 800-626-5420 (orders), pg 16

American Society for Nondestructive Testing, Columbus, OH *Toll Free Tel:* 800-222-2768, pg 16

American Society for Quality (ASQ), Milwaukee, WI *Toll Free Tel:* 800-248-1946 (US & CN); 800-514-1564 (Mexico), pg 16

American Society for Training & Development (ASTD), Alexandria, VA *Toll Free Tel:* 800-628-2783, pg 16

American Society of Civil Engineers (ASCE), Reston, VA *Toll Free Tel:* 800-548-2723, pg 16

American Society of Health-System Pharmacists, Bethesda, MD *Toll Free Tel:* 866-279-0681 (orders), pg 17

American Society of Mechanical Engineers (ASME), New York, NY *Toll Free Tel:* 800-843-2763 (cust serv-US, CN & Mexico), pg 17

American Technical Publishers Inc, Orland Park, IL *Toll Free Tel:* 800-323-3471, pg 17

American Water Works Association, Denver, CO *Toll Free Tel:* 800-926-7337, pg 17

Amherst Media Inc, Buffalo, NY *Toll Free Tel:* 800-622-3278, pg 17

AMMO Books LLC, Pasadena, CA *Toll Free Tel:* 888-642-AMMO (642-2666), pg 17

Amsco School Publications Inc, New York, NY *Toll Free Tel:* 800-969-8398, pg 18

Andrews McMeel Publishing LLC, Kansas City, MO *Toll Free Tel:* 800-851-8923; 800-943-9839 (cust serv) *Toll Free Fax:* 800-943-9831 (orders), pg 18

Andrews University Press, Berrien Springs, MI *Toll Free Tel:* 800-467-6369 (Visa, MC & American Express orders only), pg 18

Angel City Press, Santa Monica, CA *Toll Free Tel:* 800-949-8039, pg 18

Angelus Press, Kansas City, MO *Toll Free Tel:* 800-966-7337, pg 18

Annual Reviews, Palo Alto, CA *Toll Free Tel:* 800-523-8635, pg 18

ANR Publications University of California, Richmond, CA *Toll Free Tel:* 800-994-8849, pg 19

Antion & Associates, Virginia Beach, VA *Toll Free Tel:* 800-448-6280, pg 19

Antique Collectors Club Ltd, East Hampton, MA *Toll Free Tel:* 800-252-5231, pg 19

Antique Trader Books, Iola, WI *Toll Free Tel:* 888-457-2873, pg 19

Aperture Books, New York, NY *Toll Free Tel:* 800-929-2323, pg 19

The Apex Press, Lanham, MD *Toll Free Tel:* 800-462-6420 *Toll Free Fax:* 800-388-4450, pg 19

Appalachian Trail Conservancy, Harpers Ferry, WV *Toll Free Tel:* 888-287-8673 (orders only), pg 20

Applause Theatre & Cinema Books, Montclair, NJ *Toll Free Tel:* 800-637-2852, pg 20

Appletree Press Inc, Mankato, MN *Toll Free Tel:* 800-322-5679, pg 20

Appraisal Institute, Chicago, IL *Toll Free Tel:* 888-756-4624, pg 21

APS PRESS, St Paul, MN *Toll Free Tel:* 800-328-7560, pg 21

Aqua Quest Publications Inc, Locust Valley, NY *Toll Free Tel:* 800-933-8989, pg 21

Aquila Communications Inc, St-Laurent, QC Canada *Toll Free Tel:* 800-667-7071 *Toll Free Fax:* 866-338-1948, pg 493

Arcadia Publishing Inc, Mount Pleasant, SC *Toll Free Tel:* 888-313-2665 (orders only), pg 21

ARE Press, Virginia Beach, VA *Toll Free Tel:* 800-333-4499, pg 21

Jason Aronson Inc, Lanham, MD *Toll Free Tel:* 800-462-6420 (orders), pg 22

Arsenal Pulp Press, Vancouver, BC Canada *Toll Free Tel:* 888-600-PULP (600-7857), pg 493

Art Image Publications, Derby Line, VT *Toll Free Tel:* 800-361-2598 *Toll Free Fax:* 800-559-2598, pg 22

Art of Living, PrimaMedia Inc, Hatfield, PA *Toll Free Tel:* 800-581-9020, pg 22

ArtAge Publications, Portland, OR *Toll Free Tel:* 800-858-4998, pg 23

Arte Publico Press, Houston, TX *Toll Free Tel:* 800-633-2783, pg 23

Artech House Inc, Norwood, MA *Toll Free Tel:* 800-225-9977, pg 23

Artisan Books, New York, NY *Toll Free Tel:* 800-722-7202, pg 23

ASCD, Alexandria, VA *Toll Free Tel:* 800-933-2723, pg 23

Ascension Press, West Chester, PA *Toll Free Tel:* 800-376-0520 (sales & cust serv), pg 23

ASCP Press, Chicago, IL *Toll Free Tel:* 800-267-2727, pg 24

Ashgate Publishing Co, Burlington, VT *Toll Free Tel:* 800-535-9544, pg 24

ASM International, Materials Park, OH *Toll Free Tel:* 800-336-5152; 800-368-9800 (Europe), pg 25

ASM Press, Washington, DC *Toll Free Tel:* 800-546-2416, pg 25

Aspatore Books, Boston, MA *Toll Free Tel:* 866-ASPATORE (277-2867), pg 25

Association for Computing Machinery, New York, NY *Toll Free Tel:* 800-342-6626, pg 25

Association of College & Research Libraries (ACRL), Chicago, IL *Toll Free Tel:* 800-545-2433 (ext 2523), pg 25

Association of School Business Officials International, Reston, VA *Toll Free Tel:* 866-682-2729, pg 25

Asta Publications LLC, Stockbridge, GA *Toll Free Tel:* 800-482-4190, pg 25

Astragal Press, Lakeville, MN *Toll Free Tel:* 866-543-3045 *Toll Free Fax:* 800-330-6232, pg 26

Athletic Guide Publishing, Flagler Beach, FL *Toll Free Tel:* 800-255-1050, pg 26

Atlantic Publishing Group Inc, Ocala, FL *Toll Free Tel:* 800-814-1132, pg 26

Atwood Publishing, Madison, WI *Toll Free Tel:* 888-242-7101, pg 26

AudioGO, North Kingstown, RI *Toll Free Tel:* 800-621-0182 *Toll Free Fax:* 877-492-0873, pg 26

Augsburg Fortress Publishers, Publishing House of the Evangelical Lutheran Church in America, Minneapolis, MN *Toll Free Tel:* 800-426-0115 (ext 639, subns); 800-328-4648 (orders), pg 27

August House Inc, Atlanta, GA *Toll Free Tel:* 800-284-8784, pg 27

AuthorHouse, Bloomington, IN *Toll Free Tel:* 888-519-5121, pg 27

Authorlink Press, Irving, TX *Toll Free Fax:* 866-381-1587, pg 27

Autism Asperger Publishing Co, Overland Park, KS *Toll Free Tel:* 877-277-8254, pg 27

Ave Maria Press, Notre Dame, IN *Toll Free Tel:* 800-282-1865 *Toll Free Fax:* 800-282-5681, pg 28

Avery Color Studios, Gwinn, MI *Toll Free Tel:* 800-722-9925, pg 28

AVKO Educational Research Foundation Inc, Birch Run, MI *Toll Free Tel:* 866-AVKO612 (285-6612), pg 28

Avotaynu Inc, Bergenfield, NJ *Toll Free Tel:* 800-286-8296, pg 28

Awe-Struck Publishing, Cincinnati, OH *Toll Free Tel:* 888-232-0808, pg 28

AZ Books LLC, New York, NY *Toll Free Tel:* 888-945-7723 *Toll Free Fax:* 888-945-7724, pg 28

Babalu Inc, Santa Barbara, CA *Toll Free Tel:* 877-522-2258, pg 28

Backbeat Books, Montclair, NJ *Toll Free Tel:* 800-637-2852 (Music Dispatch), pg 29

Baker Books, Ada, MI *Toll Free Tel:* 800-877-2665; 800-679-1957 *Toll Free Fax:* 800-398-3111, pg 29

Baker's Plays, New York, NY *Toll Free Tel:* 866-598-8449, pg 29

Banner of Truth, Carlisle, PA *Toll Free Tel:* 800-263-8085 (orders), pg 30

Barefoot Books, Cambridge, MA *Toll Free Tel:* 866-215-1756 (cust serv); 866-417-2369 (orders), pg 30

Barnhardt & Ashe Publishing, Miami, FL *Toll Free Tel:* 800-283-6360 (orders), pg 31

Barron's Educational Series Inc, Hauppauge, NY *Toll Free Tel:* 800-645-3476, pg 31

Bartleby Press, Savage, MD *Toll Free Tel:* 800-953-9929, pg 31

Basic Health Publications Inc, Laguna Beach, CA *Toll Free Tel:* 800-575-8890 (orders), pg 32

Bay Tree Publishing LLC, Point Richmond, CA *Toll Free Fax:* 866-552-7329, pg 32

Baywood Publishing Co Inc, Amityville, NY *Toll Free Tel:* 800-638-7819, pg 32

Beach Lloyd Publishers LLC, Wayne, PA *Toll Free Tel:* 866-218-3253 (pin 8668), pg 32

Beacon Hill Press of Kansas City, Kansas City, MO *Toll Free Tel:* 800-877-0700 (cust serv), pg 32

Bear & Co Inc, Rochester, VT *Toll Free Tel:* 800-932-3277, pg 33

Beard Books Inc, Frederick, MD *Toll Free Tel:* 888-563-4573 (book orders), pg 33

Bearport Publishing Co Inc, New York, NY *Toll Free Tel:* 877-337-8577 *Toll Free Fax:* 866-337-8557, pg 33

Beautiful America Publishing Co, Woodburn, OR *Toll Free Tel:* 800-874-1233, pg 33

Beckett Media LLC, Yorba Linda, CA *Toll Free Tel:* 800-332-3330 *Toll Free Fax:* 800-249-7761, pg 33

Bedford/St Martin's, Boston, MA *Toll Free Tel:* 800-779-7440, pg 34

Behrman House Inc, Springfield, NJ *Toll Free Tel:* 800-221-2755, pg 34

Bell Springs Publishing, Willits, CA *Toll Free Tel:* 800-515-8050, pg 34

Bella Books, Tallahassee, FL *Toll Free Tel:* 800-729-4992, pg 34

Bellerophon Books, Santa Barbara, CA *Toll Free Tel:* 800-253-9943, pg 34

Ben Yehuda Press, Teaneck, NJ *Toll Free Tel:* 800-809-3505, pg 34

John Benjamins Publishing Co, Philadelphia, PA *Toll Free Tel:* 800-562-5666 (orders), pg 35

Bentley Publishers, Cambridge, MA *Toll Free Tel:* 800-423-4595, pg 35

BePuzzled, San Francisco, CA *Toll Free Tel:* 800-347-4818, pg 35

Bess Press, Honolulu, HI *Toll Free Tel:* 800-910-2377, pg 36

Bethany House Publishers, Bloomington, MN *Toll Free Tel:* 800-877-2665 (orders) *Toll Free Fax:* 800-398-3111 (orders), pg 36

Bethlehem Books, Bathgate, ND *Toll Free Tel:* 800-757-6831, pg 36

Betterway Books, Blue Ash, OH *Toll Free Tel:* 800-666-0963 *Toll Free Fax:* 888-590-4082, pg 36

Between the Lines, Toronto, ON Canada *Toll Free Tel:* 800-718-7201, pg 494

Bhaktivedanta Book Trust (BBT), Los Angeles, CA *Toll Free Tel:* 800-927-4152, pg 37

Big Guy Books Inc, Encinitas, CA *Toll Free Tel:* 800-536-3030 (booksellers' cust serv), pg 37

Bilingual Review Press/Editorial Bilingue, Tempe, AZ *Toll Free Tel:* 866-965-3867, pg 37

George T Bisel Co Inc, Philadelphia, PA *Toll Free Tel:* 800-247-3526, pg 38

Bisk Education, Tampa, FL *Toll Free Tel:* 800-874-7877, pg 38

BJU Press, Greenville, SC *Toll Free Tel:* 800-845-5731, pg 38

Black Classic Press, Baltimore, MD *Toll Free Tel:* 800-476-8870, pg 39

Black Dog & Leventhal Publishers Inc, New York, NY *Toll Free Tel:* 800-722-7202, pg 39

Black Dome Press Corp, Delmar, NY *Toll Free Tel:* 800-513-9013 (orders), pg 39

Black Rose Books Ltd, Montreal, QC Canada *Toll Free Tel:* 800-565-9523 (orders) *Toll Free Fax:* 800-221-9985 (orders), pg 494

John F Blair Publisher, Winston-Salem, NC *Toll Free Tel:* 800-222-9796, pg 40

Bloch Publishing Co, Jacksonville, FL *Toll Free Tel:* 866-532-3977, pg 40

Bloom's Literary Criticism, New York, NY *Toll Free Tel:* 800-322-8755 *Toll Free Fax:* 800-678-3633, pg 40

Bloomsbury Academic, New York, NY *Toll Free Tel:* 800-561-7704, pg 40

Bloomsbury Publishing, New York, NY *Toll Free Tel:* 800-221-7945, pg 40

Blue Apple Books, Maplewood, NJ *Toll Free Tel:* 800-722-6657; 800-733-3000 (orders), pg 41

Blue Book Publications Inc, Minneapolis, MN *Toll Free Tel:* 800-877-4867, pg 41

Blue Dolphin Publishing Inc, Grass Valley, CA *Toll Free Tel:* 800-643-0765 (orders), pg 41

Blue Mountain Arts Inc, Boulder, CO *Toll Free Tel:* 800-525-0642 *Toll Free Fax:* 800-545-8573, pg 41

Blue Note Publications Inc, Melbourne, FL *Toll Free Tel:* 800-624-0401 (orders), pg 41

Blue Poppy Press, Boulder, CO *Toll Free Tel:* 800-487-9296, pg 41

Bluestocking Press, Placerville, CA *Toll Free Tel:* 800-959-8586, pg 42

BNA Books, Arlington, VA *Toll Free Tel:* 800-372-1033, pg 42

BNi Building News, Vista, CA *Toll Free Tel:* 888-264-2665, pg 42

BoardSource, Washington, DC *Toll Free Tel:* 877-892-6273, pg 42

Bolchazy-Carducci Publishers Inc, Mundelein, IL *Toll Free Tel:* 800-392-6453, pg 42

Book Sales Inc, New York, NY *Toll Free Tel:* 866-483-5456, pg 43

The Book Tree, San Diego, CA *Toll Free Tel:* 800-700-8733 (orders), pg 43

Bookhaven Press LLC, Moon Township, PA *Toll Free Tel:* 800-782-7424 (orders only), pg 43

BookLogix, Alpharetta, GA *Toll Free Fax:* 888-564-7890, pg 43

Books In Motion, Spokane Valley, WA *Toll Free Tel:* 800-752-3199, pg 43

Books on Tape®, Costa Mesa, CA *Toll Free Tel:* 800-733-3000 (cust serv) *Toll Free Fax:* 800-940-7046, pg 44

Borealis Press Ltd, Nepean, ON Canada *Toll Free Tel:* 877-696-2585, pg 495

The Boston Mills Press, Richmond Hill, ON Canada *Toll Free Tel:* 800-387-6192 *Toll Free Fax:* 800-450-0391, pg 495

Eddie Bowers Publishing Co Inc, Peosta, IA *Toll Free Tel:* 800-747-2411, pg 44

R R Bowker LLC, New Providence, NJ *Toll Free Tel:* 888-269-5372 (edit & cust serv, press 2 for returns) *Toll Free Fax:* 877-337-7015 (domestic/US & CN), pg 44

BowTie Press®, Irvine, CA *Toll Free Tel:* 888-738-2665, pg 44

Boyds Mills Press, Honesdale, PA *Toll Free Tel:* 800-490-5111, pg 45

Boynton/Cook Publishers, Portsmouth, NH *Toll Free Tel:* 800-225-5800 *Toll Free Fax:* 877-231-6980, pg 45

Boys Town Press, Boys Town, NE *Toll Free Tel:* 800-282-6657, pg 45

Bradford Publishing Co, Denver, CO *Toll Free Tel:* 800-446-2831, pg 45

BradyGames, Indianapolis, IN *Toll Free Tel:* 800-545-5912; 800-571-5840 (cust serv), pg 45

Brault & Bouthillier, Montreal, QC Canada *Toll Free Tel:* 800-361-0378 *Toll Free Fax:* 800-361-0378, pg 495

Breakaway Books, Halcottsville, NY *Toll Free Tel:* 800-548-4348 (voicemail), pg 46

Breakthrough Publications Inc, Emmaus, PA *Toll Free Tel:* 800-824-5001 (ext 12), pg 46

Breakwater Books Ltd, St Johns, NL Canada *Toll Free Tel:* 800-563-3333 (orders), pg 495

Nicholas Brealey Publishing, Boston, MA *Toll Free Tel:* 888-BREALEY (273-2539), pg 46

Brenner Information Group, San Diego, CA *Toll Free Tel:* 800-811-4337 (orders), pg 46

Brentwood Christian Press, Columbus, GA *Toll Free Tel:* 800-334-8861, pg 46

Brethren Press, Elgin, IL *Toll Free Tel:* 800-323-8039 *Toll Free Fax:* 800-667-8188, pg 46

Brewers Publications, Boulder, CO *Toll Free Tel:* 888-822-6273 (CN & US), pg 46

Brick Tower Press, New York, NY *Toll Free Tel:* 800-68-BRICK (682-7425), pg 46

Bridge-Logos Inc, Alachua, FL *Toll Free Tel:* 800-631-5802 (orders) *Toll Free Fax:* 800-935-6467, pg 47

Bridge Publications Inc, Commerce City, CA *Toll Free Tel:* 800-722-1733, pg 47

Bright Mountain Books Inc, Fairview, NC *Toll Free Tel:* 800-437-3959, pg 47

Brill Inc, Boston, MA *Toll Free Tel:* 800-962-4406, pg 47

Brilliance Audio, Grand Haven, MI *Toll Free Tel:* 800-648-2312 (orders only), pg 47

Brookes Publishing Co Inc, Baltimore, MD *Toll Free Tel:* 800-638-3775 (US & CN), pg 48

Brookhaven Press, La Crosse, WI *Toll Free Tel:* 800-236-0850, pg 48

The Brookings Institution Press, Washington, DC *Toll Free Tel:* 800-537-5487, pg 48

Brookline Books, Northampton, MA *Toll Free Tel:* 800-666-2665 (orders), pg 48

Brooklyn Publishers LLC, Cedar Rapids, IA *Toll Free Tel:* 888-473-8521, pg 48

BuilderBooks.com, Washington, DC *Toll Free Tel:* 800-223-2665, pg 49

Bull Publishing Co, Boulder, CO *Toll Free Tel:* 800-676-2855, pg 49

Burford Books, Ithaca, NY *Toll Free Fax:* 866-212-7750, pg 49

Business & Legal Reports Inc (BLR), Brentwood, CT *Toll Free Tel:* 800-727-5257, pg 50

Business Research Services Inc, Bethesda, MD *Toll Free Tel:* 800-845-8420, pg 50

Butte Publications Inc, Hillsboro, OR *Toll Free Tel:* 866-312-8883 *Toll Free Fax:* 866-412-8883 (orders only), pg 50

C & T Publishing Inc, Concord, CA *Toll Free Tel:* 800-284-1114, pg 50

Cambridge Educational, New York, NY *Toll Free Tel:* 800-322-8755 *Toll Free Fax:* 800-329-6687, pg 51

Cambridge University Press, New York, NY *Toll Free Tel:* 800-899-5222, pg 51

Campfield & Campfield Publishing, Philadelphia, PA *Toll Free Tel:* 888-518-2440, pg 51

Canada Law Book®, Toronto, ON Canada *Toll Free Tel:* 800-387-5351 (cust rel, CN & US only); 866-614-7033 (tech support, CN & US only); 800-347-5164 (CN & US) *Toll Free Fax:* 877-750-9041 (cust rel, CN only), pg 496

Canadian Bible Society, Toronto, ON Canada *Toll Free Tel:* 866-946-1711, pg 496

Canadian Government Publishing, Ottawa, ON Canada *Toll Free Tel:* 800-635-7943 *Toll Free Fax:* 800-565-7757, pg 497

Canadian Institute of Chartered Accountants (L'Institut Canadien des Comptables Agrees), Toronto, ON Canada *Toll Free Tel:* 800-268-3793 (CN orders), pg 497

Canadian Museum of Civilization, Gatineau, QC Canada *Toll Free Tel:* 800-555-5621 (North American orders only), pg 497

Canadian Plains Research Center, Regina, SK Canada *Toll Free Tel:* 866-874-2257, pg 497

Canadian Scholars' Press Inc, Toronto, ON Canada *Toll Free Tel:* 800-463-1998, pg 497

Capital Enquiry Inc, South Lake Tahoe, CA *Toll Free Tel:* 800-922-7486, pg 51

Capstone Publishers™, North Mankato, MN *Toll Free Tel:* 800-747-4992 (cust serv) *Toll Free Fax:* 888-262-0705, pg 51

Cardiotext Publishing, Minneapolis, MN *Toll Free Tel:* 888-999-9174, pg 52

Cardoza Publishing, Las Vegas, NV *Toll Free Tel:* 800-577-WINS (577-9467), pg 52

Cardweb.com Inc®, Naples, FL *Toll Free Tel:* 800-874-8999 *Toll Free Fax:* 800-821-4627, pg 52

The Career Press Inc, Pompton Plains, NJ *Toll Free Tel:* 800-CAREER-1 (227-3371), pg 52

Caribe Betania Editores, Nashville, TN *Toll Free Tel:* 800-322-7423 (ext 1893), pg 52

Carlisle Press - Walnut Creek, Sugarcreek, OH *Toll Free Tel:* 800-852-4482, pg 52

Carnegie Mellon University Press, Pittsburgh, PA *Toll Free Tel:* 800-666-2211, pg 52

Carolina Academic Press, Durham, NC *Toll Free Tel:* 800-489-7486, pg 52

Carolrhoda Books, Minneapolis, MN *Toll Free Tel:* 800-328-4929 *Toll Free Fax:* 800-332-1132, pg 53

Carolrhoda Lab™, Minneapolis, MN *Toll Free Tel:* 800-328-4929 *Toll Free Fax:* 800-332-1132 (US), pg 53

Carroll Publishing, Bethesda, MD *Toll Free Tel:* 800-336-4240, pg 53

Carson-Dellosa Publishing LLC, Greensboro, NC *Toll Free Tel:* 800-321-0943 *Toll Free Fax:* 800-535-2669, pg 53

Carstens Publications Inc, Newton, NJ *Toll Free Tel:* 888-526-5365, pg 53

Carswell, Toronto, ON Canada *Toll Free Tel:* 800-387-5164 (cust serv CN & US) *Toll Free Fax:* 877-750-9041 (CN only), pg 498

CarTech Inc, North Branch, MN *Toll Free Tel:* 800-551-4754, pg 53

Amon Carter Museum, Fort Worth, TX *Toll Free Tel:* 800-573-1933, pg 53

Casa Bautista de Publicaciones, El Paso, TX *Toll Free Tel:* 800-755-5958 (cust serv & orders), pg 53

Cascade Pass Inc, Marina Del Rey, CA *Toll Free Tel:* 888-837-0704, pg 54

Castle Connolly Medical Ltd, New York, NY *Toll Free Tel:* 800-339-DOCS (339-3627), pg 54

Catholic Book Publishing Corp, Totowa, NJ *Toll Free Tel:* 877-228-2665, pg 54

The Catholic University of America Press, Washington, DC *Toll Free Tel:* 800-537-5487 (orders only), pg 54

Cato Institute, Washington, DC *Toll Free Tel:* 800-767-1241, pg 54

Caxton Press, Caldwell, ID *Toll Free Tel:* 800-657-6465, pg 54

CCH, a Wolters Kluwer business, Riverwoods, IL *Toll Free Tel:* 800-525-3335, pg 55

CCH Canadian Limited, A Wolters Kluwer Company, Toronto, ON Canada *Toll Free Tel:* 800-268-4522 (CN & US cust serv) *Toll Free Fax:* 800-461-4131, pg 498

Cedar Fort Inc, Springville, UT *Toll Free Tel:* 800-SKY-BOOK (759-2665) *Toll Free Fax:* 800-388-3727, pg 55

CEF Press, Warrenton, MO *Toll Free Tel:* 800-748-7710 (cust serv); 800-300-4033 (USA ministries), pg 55

Celestial Arts Publishing Co, Berkeley, CA *Toll Free Tel:* 800-841-2665; 800-733-3000 (orders & cust serv), pg 55

Cengage Learning, Stamford, CT *Toll Free Tel:* 800-354-9706 *Toll Free Fax:* 800-487-8488, pg 55

Centering Corp, Omaha, NE *Toll Free Tel:* 866-218-0101, pg 56

Central Conference of American Rabbis/CCAR Press, New York, NY *Toll Free Tel:* 800-935-2227, pg 57

Centre Franco-Ontarien de Ressources en Alphabetisation (Centre FORA), Sudbury, ON Canada *Toll Free Tel:* 888-814-4422 (orders, CN only), pg 498

Chain Store Guide (CSG), Tampa, FL *Toll Free Tel:* 800-927-9292 (orders), pg 57

Chalice Press, St Louis, MO *Toll Free Tel:* 800-366-3383, pg 57

Channel Lake Inc, New York, NY *Toll Free Tel:* 800-592-1566 (orders) *Toll Free Fax:* 866-794-5507, pg 58

Charisma Media, Lake Mary, FL *Toll Free Tel:* 800-283-8494 (Charisma Media, Siloam Press, Creation House); 800-665-1468, pg 58

CharismaLife Publishers, Lake Mary, FL *Toll Free Tel:* 800-451-4598, pg 58

Charles River Media, Boston, MA *Toll Free Tel:* 800-354-9706 *Toll Free Fax:* 800-487-8488, pg 58

Charles Scribner's Sons®, Farmington Hills, MI *Toll Free Tel:* 800-877-4253 *Toll Free Fax:* 800-414-5043, pg 58

Charlesbridge Publishing Inc, Watertown, MA *Toll Free Tel:* 800-225-3214 *Toll Free Fax:* 800-926-5775, pg 58

The Charlton Press, North York, ON Canada *Toll Free Tel:* 800-442-6042 (North America) *Toll Free Fax:* 800-442-1542 (North America), pg 498

Chelsea Green Publishing Co, White River Junction, VT *Toll Free Tel:* 800-639-4099 (cust serv, consumer & trade orders), pg 59

Chelsea House Publishers, New York, NY *Toll Free Tel:* 800-322-8755 *Toll Free Fax:* 800-678-3633, pg 59

Chemical Education Resources Inc, Belmont, CA *Toll Free Tel:* 800-543-0487 (ext 1308, orders); 800-355-9983 (cust serv) *Toll Free Fax:* 800-451-3661 (orders), pg 59

Cheneliere Education Inc, Montreal, QC Canada *Toll Free Tel:* 800-565-5531 *Toll Free Fax:* 800-814-0324, pg 498

Cheng & Tsui Co Inc, Boston, MA *Toll Free Tel:* 800-554-1963, pg 59

Cherry Hill Publishing, Ramona, CA *Toll Free Tel:* 800-407-1072, pg 59

Chicago Review Press, Chicago, IL *Toll Free Tel:* 800-888-4741, pg 59

Chicago Spectrum Press, Louisville, KY *Toll Free Tel:* 800-594-5190; 888-BOOKS-80 (266-5780), pg 60

Child's Play®, Auburn, ME *Toll Free Tel:* 800-472-0099; 800-639-6404 *Toll Free Fax:* 800-854-6989, pg 60

The Child's World Inc, Mankato, MN *Toll Free Tel:* 800-599-READ (599-7323) *Toll Free Fax:* 888-320-2329, pg 60

Childswork/Childsplay LLC, Woodbury, NY *Toll Free Tel:* 800-962-1141 (cust serv) *Toll Free Fax:* 800-262-1886 (orders), pg 60

China Books, South San Francisco, CA *Toll Free Tel:* 800-818-2017 (US only), pg 60

Chosen Books, Grand Rapids, MI *Toll Free Tel:* 800-877-2665 (orders only) *Toll Free Fax:* 800-398-3111 (orders only), pg 60

Christian Liberty Press, Arlington Heights, IL *Toll Free Tel:* 800-832-2741 (cust serv), pg 60

Christian Light Publications Inc, Harrisonburg, VA *Toll Free Tel:* 800-776-0478, pg 60

Christian Schools International, Grand Rapids, MI *Toll Free Tel:* 800-635-8288, pg 61

The Christian Science Publishing Society, Boston, MA *Toll Free Tel:* 800-288-7090, pg 61

Chronicle Books LLC, San Francisco, CA *Toll Free Tel:* 800-759-0190 (cust serv) *Toll Free Fax:* 800-858-7787 (orders); 800-286-9471 (cust serv), pg 61

Chronicle Guidance Publications Inc, Moravia, NY *Toll Free Tel:* 800-622-7284, pg 61

Cinco Puntos Press, El Paso, TX *Toll Free Tel:* 800-566-9072, pg 61

Circlet Press Inc, Cambridge, MA *Toll Free Tel:* 800-729-6423 (orders), pg 61

Cistercian Publications Inc, Editorial Office, Collegeville, MN *Toll Free Tel:* 800-436-8431 *Toll Free Fax:* 800-445-5899, pg 62

Clarion Books, New York, NY *Toll Free Tel:* 800-225-3362 (orders) *Toll Free Fax:* 800-634-7568 (orders), pg 62

Clarity Press Inc, Atlanta, GA *Toll Free Tel:* 877-613-1495 (edit) *Toll Free Fax:* 877-613-7868, pg 62

Clarkson Potter Publishers, New York, NY *Toll Free Tel:* 888-264-1745, pg 62

Classroom Connect, Boston, MA *Toll Free Tel:* 800-638-1639 (cust support), pg 62

CLC Ministries, Fort Washington, PA *Toll Free Tel:* 800-659-1240, pg 62

Clear Light Publishers, Santa Fe, NM *Toll Free Tel:* 800-253-2747 (orders), pg 63

Clearfield Co Inc, Baltimore, MD *Toll Free Tel:* 800-296-6687 (orders & cust serv), pg 63

Cleis Press, Berkeley, CA *Toll Free Tel:* 800-780-2279 (US), pg 63

Clerisy Press, Covington, KY *Toll Free Tel:* 888-604-4537, pg 63

Clinical Laboratory & Standards Institute (CLSI), Wayne, PA *Toll Free Tel:* 877-447-1888 (orders), pg 63

Close Up Publishing, Alexandria, VA *Toll Free Tel:* 800-CLOSE-UP (256-7387), pg 63

Clovernook Printing House for the Blind & Visually Impaired, Cincinnati, OH *Toll Free Tel:* 888-234-7156, pg 63

Coach House Books, Toronto, ON Canada *Toll Free Tel:* 800-367-6360 (outside Toronto), pg 499

Coaches Choice, Marina, CA *Toll Free Tel:* 888-229-5745, pg 63

Cobblestone Publishing, Peterborough, NH *Toll Free Tel:* 800-821-0115, pg 64

Cold Spring Harbor Laboratory Press, Woodbury, NY *Toll Free Tel:* 800-843-4388, pg 64

College & University Professional Association for Human Resources (CUPA-HR), Knoxville, TN *Toll Free Tel:* 877-CUPA-HR4 (287-2474), pg 64

College Press Publishing Co, Joplin, MO *Toll Free Tel:* 800-289-3300, pg 64

College Publishing, Glen Allen, VA *Toll Free Tel:* 800-827-0723, pg 64

The Colonial Williamsburg Foundation, Williamsburg, VA *Toll Free Tel:* 800-HISTORY (447-8679), pg 64

Columbia Books & Information Services, Bethesda, MD *Toll Free Tel:* 888-265-0600 (cust serv), pg 65

Columbia University Press, New York, NY *Toll Free Tel:* 800-944-8648, pg 65

Comex Systems Inc, Mendham, NJ *Toll Free Tel:* 800-543-6959, pg 65

Common Courage Press, Monroe, ME *Toll Free Tel:* 800-497-3207, pg 65

Commonwealth Editions, Carlisle, MA *Toll Free Tel:* 800-277-5312, pg 65

Communication Creativity, Highlands Ranch, CO *Toll Free Fax:* 866-685-0307, pg 65

Community College Press, Washington, DC *Toll Free Tel:* 800-250-6557, pg 66

Company's Coming Publishing Ltd, Edmonton, AB Canada *Toll Free Tel:* 800-875-7108 (US & CN), pg 499

Comprehensive Health Education Foundation (CHEF), Seattle, WA *Toll Free Tel:* 800-323-2433, pg 66

Conciliar Press, University Park, IL *Toll Free Tel:* 800-967-7377 *Toll Free Fax:* 866-599-5208, pg 66

Concordia Publishing House, St Louis, MO *Toll Free Tel:* 800-325-3040 (cust serv) *Toll Free Fax:* 800-490-9889 (cust serv), pg 66

The Continuing Legal Education Society of British Columbia (CLEBC), Vancouver, BC Canada *Toll Free Tel:* 800-663-0437 (CN), pg 499

David C Cook, Colorado Springs, CO *Toll Free Tel:* 800-708-5550, pg 67

Copley Custom Textbooks, Acton, MA *Toll Free Tel:* 800-562-2147, pg 67

Copper Canyon Press, Port Townsend, WA *Toll Free Tel:* 877-501-1393, pg 67

Cornell University Southeast Asia Program Publications, Ithaca, NY *Toll Free Tel:* 800-666-2211 *Toll Free Fax:* 800-688-2877, pg 68

Cortina Institute of Languages, Wilton, CT *Toll Free Tel:* 800-245-2145, pg 68

Cortina Learning International Inc (CLI), Wilton, CT *Toll Free Tel:* 800-245-2145, pg 68

Corwin, a Sage Co, Thousand Oaks, CA *Toll Free Tel:* 800-233-9936 *Toll Free Fax:* 800-417-2466, pg 68

Coteau Books, Regina, SK Canada *Toll Free Tel:* 800-440-4471 (CN only), pg 500

Council for Exceptional Children (CEC), Arlington, VA *Toll Free Tel:* 888-232-7733 (memb servs); 866-509-0219, pg 69

Council Oak Books LLC, Tulsa, OK *Toll Free Tel:* 800-247-8850, pg 69

Council of State Governments, Lexington, KY *Toll Free Tel:* 800-800-1910, pg 69

The Countryman Press, Woodstock, VT *Toll Free Tel:* 800-245-4151, pg 70

Course Technology, Boston, MA *Toll Free Tel:* 800-354-9706 (cust serv), pg 70

La Courte Echelle, Montreal, QC Canada *Toll Free Tel:* 800-387-6192 (orders only) *Toll Free Fax:* 800-450-0391 (orders only), pg 500

Covenant Communications Inc, American Fork, UT *Toll Free Tel:* 800-662-9545, pg 70

Cowley Publications, Lanham, MD *Toll Free Tel:* 800-462-6420 *Toll Free Fax:* 800-338-4550, pg 70

CQ Press, Washington, DC *Toll Free Tel:* 866-4CQ-PRESS (427-7737) *Toll Free Fax:* 800-380-3810, pg 70

Crabtree Publishing Co, New York, NY *Toll Free Tel:* 800-387-7650 *Toll Free Fax:* 800-355-7166, pg 70

Crabtree Publishing Co Ltd, St Catharines, ON Canada *Toll Free Tel:* 800-387-7650 *Toll Free Fax:* 800-355-7166, pg 500

Craftsman Book Co, Carlsbad, CA *Toll Free Tel:* 800-829-8123, pg 70

CRC Press LLC, Boca Raton, FL *Toll Free Tel:* 800-272-7737 *Toll Free Fax:* 800-643-9428 (sales); 800-374-3401 (orders), pg 71

The Creative Co, Mankato, MN *Toll Free Tel:* 800-445-6209, pg 71

Creative Homeowner, Upper Saddle River, NJ *Toll Free Tel:* 800-631-7795 (cust serv), pg 71

Cricket Books, Chicago, IL *Toll Free Tel:* 800-821-0115, pg 71

The Crossroad Publishing Co, Chestnut Ridge, NY *Toll Free Tel:* 800-888-4741 (orders), pg 72

Crossway, Wheaton, IL *Toll Free Tel:* 800-635-7993 (orders); 800-543-1659 (cust serv), pg 72

Crown House Publishing Co LLC, Bethel, CT *Toll Free Tel:* 877-925-1213 (cust serv); 866-272-8497, pg 72

Crown Publishing Group, New York, NY *Toll Free Tel:* 888-264-1745, pg 72

Crystal Clarity Publishers, Nevada City, CA *Toll Free Tel:* 800-424-1055, pg 73

Crystal Productions, Glenview, IL *Toll Free Tel:* 800-255-8629 *Toll Free Fax:* 800-657-8149, pg 73

CTB/McGraw-Hill, Monterey, CA *Toll Free Tel:* 800-538-9547, pg 73

Cumberland House, Naperville, IL *Toll Free Tel:* 800-43-BRIGHT (432-7444), pg 73

Current Medicine Group (CMG), Philadelphia, PA *Toll Free Tel:* 800-427-1796, pg 73

Cycle Publishing, San Francisco, CA *Toll Free Tel:* 877-353-1207, pg 74

Cypress House, Fort Bragg, CA *Toll Free Tel:* 800-773-7782, pg 74

Da Capo Press Inc & Lifelong Books, Boston, MA *Toll Free Tel:* 800-343-4499 (orders), pg 74

Damron Co, San Francisco, CA *Toll Free Tel:* 800-462-6654, pg 74

John Daniel & Co, McKinleyville, CA *Toll Free Tel:* 800-662-8351, pg 75

The Dartnell Corporation, Durham, NC *Toll Free Tel:* 800-223-8720; 800-472-0148 (cust serv) *Toll Free Fax:* 800-508-2592, pg 75

The Darwin Press Inc, Princeton, NJ *Toll Free Tel:* 866-772-9817, pg 75

Data Trace Publishing Co (DTP), Towson, MD *Toll Free Tel:* 800-342-0454 (orders only), pg 75

Davies Publishing Inc, Pasadena, CA *Toll Free Tel:* 877-792-0005, pg 75

F A Davis Co, Philadelphia, PA *Toll Free Tel:* 800-523-4049, pg 76

The Dawn Horse Press, Middletown, CA *Toll Free Tel:* 877-770-0772, pg 76

Dawn Publications Inc, Nevada City, CA *Toll Free Tel:* 800-545-7475, pg 76

DawnSignPress, San Diego, CA *Toll Free Tel:* 800-549-5350, pg 76

Day Owl Press Corp, Lantana, FL *Toll Free Tel:* 866-806-6981 *Toll Free Fax:* 866-854-4375, pg 76

dbS Productions, Charlottesville, VA *Toll Free Tel:* 800-745-1581, pg 76

DC Canada Education Publishing, Ottawa, ON Canada *Toll Free Tel:* 888-565-0262, pg 500

DC Entertainment, New York, NY *Toll Free Tel:* 800-887-6789, pg 76

De Vorss & Co, Camarillo, CA *Toll Free Tel:* 800-843-5743, pg 77

Decent Hill Publishers LLC, Cleveland, OH *Toll Free Tel:* 866-688-5325 *Toll Free Fax:* 866-688-5325, pg 77

Decker Publishing, Hamilton, ON Canada *Toll Free Tel:* 855-647-6511, pg 500

Ivan R Dee Publisher, Lanham, MD *Toll Free Tel:* 800-462-6420 (cust serv) *Toll Free Fax:* 800-338-4550 (orders), pg 77

Delmar, Clifton Park, NY *Toll Free Tel:* 800-347-7707 (cust serv); 800-998-7498 *Toll Free Fax:* 800-487-8488 (cust serv), pg 77

DeLorme Publishing Co Inc, Yarmouth, ME *Toll Free Tel:* 800-561-5105; 800-511-2459 (cust serv) *Toll Free Fax:* 800-575-2244, pg 77

Delphi Books, Lee's Summit, MO *Toll Free Tel:* 800-431-1579 (orders), pg 77

Delta Publishing Co, McHenry, IL *Toll Free Tel:* 800-323-8270 (orders) *Toll Free Fax:* 800-909-9901, pg 78

Demos Medical Publishing LLC, New York, NY *Toll Free Tel:* 800-532-8663, pg 78

Deseret Book Co, Salt Lake City, UT *Toll Free Tel:* 800-453-4532 (orders); 888-846-7302 (orders), pg 78

DEStech Publications Inc, Lancaster, PA *Toll Free Tel:* 877-500-4337, pg 78

Destiny Image Inc, Shippensburg, PA *Toll Free Tel:* 800-722-6774 (orders only), pg 78

Developmental Studies Center, Oakland, CA *Toll Free Tel:* 800-666-7270, pg 78

Dharma Publishing, Cazadero, CA *Toll Free Tel:* 800-873-4276, pg 78

Diamond Farm Book Publishers, Alexandria Bay, NY *Toll Free Tel:* 800-481-1353 *Toll Free Fax:* 800-305-5138, pg 79

Diane Publishing Co, Collingdale, PA *Toll Free Tel:* 800-782-3833, pg 79

Discipleship Publications International (DPI), Spring Hill, TN *Toll Free Tel:* 888-DPI-BOOK (374-2665, orders only), pg 79

Discovery House Publishers, Grand Rapids, MI *Toll Free Tel:* 800-653-8333 (cust serv), pg 79

Dissertation.com, Boca Raton, FL *Toll Free Tel:* 800-636-8329, pg 80

DK, New York, NY *Toll Free Tel:* 877-342-5357 (cust serv), pg 80

Dogwise Publishing, Wenatchee, WA *Toll Free Tel:* 800-776-2665, pg 80

Tom Doherty Associates, LLC, New York, NY *Toll Free Tel:* 800-455-0340, pg 80

Dominie Press Inc, Lebanon, IN *Toll Free Tel:* 800-321-3106 (Pearson Cust Serv); 800-848-9500 *Toll Free Fax:* 877-260-2530, pg 80

The Donning Company Publishers, Virginia Beach, VA *Toll Free Tel:* 800-296-8572, pg 80

Dordt College Press, Sioux Center, IA *Toll Free Tel:* 800-343-6738, pg 80

Dorland Healthcare Information, Rockville, MD *Toll Free Tel:* 800-784-2332, pg 81

Dorrance Publishing Co Inc, Pittsburgh, PA *Toll Free Tel:* 800-695-9599; 800-788-7654 (gen cust orders); 888-840-8581 (bookstore orders & returns), pg 81

Dorset House Publishing Co Inc, New York, NY *Toll Free Tel:* 800-DHBOOKS (342-6657, orders only), pg 81

Doubleday/Nan A Talese, New York, NY *Toll Free Tel:* 800-638-6460, pg 81

Doug Butler Enterprises, Inc, Crawford, NE *Toll Free Tel:* 800-728-3826, pg 527

Douglas & McIntyre, Vancouver, BC Canada *Toll Free Tel:* 800-667-6902 (orders) *Toll Free Fax:* 800-668-5788 (orders CN), pg 501

Dover Publications Inc, Mineola, NY *Toll Free Tel:* 800-223-3130 (orders), pg 81

Down East Books, Rockport, ME *Toll Free Tel:* 800-685-7962 (US only orders); 800-766-1670, pg 81

Dragon Door Publications, Little Canada, MN *Toll Free Tel:* 800-899-5111 (orders & cust serv), pg 81

Dramatic Publishing Co, Woodstock, IL *Toll Free Tel:* 800-448-7469 *Toll Free Fax:* 800-334-5302, pg 82

Dream Catcher Publishing Inc, Decatur, GA *Toll Free Tel:* 888-771-2800 *Toll Free Fax:* 888-771-2800, pg 82

Dufour Editions Inc, Chester Springs, PA *Toll Free Tel:* 800-869-5677, pg 82

Duke University Press, Durham, NC *Toll Free Tel:* 888-651-0122 *Toll Free Fax:* 888-651-0124, pg 82

Dun & Bradstreet, Short Hills, NJ *Toll Free Tel:* 800-526-0651; 800-234-3867 (cust serv), pg 82

Dustbooks, Paradise, CA *Toll Free Tel:* 800-477-6110, pg 83

DynaMinds Publishing, Johnston, IA *Toll Free Tel:* 888-991-BOOK (991-2665), pg 83

Eagan Press, St Paul, MN *Toll Free Tel:* 800-328-7560, pg 83

Eagle's View Publishing, Liberty, UT *Toll Free Tel:* 800-547-3364 (orders over $100), pg 83

Eakin Press, Waco, TX *Toll Free Tel:* 800-880-8642, pg 83

Eastland Press, Vista, CA *Toll Free Tel:* 800-453-3278 (orders) *Toll Free Fax:* 800-241-3329 (orders), pg 84

Eckankar, Chanhassen, MN *Toll Free Tel:* 800-275-2606 *Toll Free Fax:* 800-510-3650, pg 84

Eclipse Press, Lexington, KY *Toll Free Tel:* 800-866-2361, pg 84

Ecopress, Lakeville, MN *Toll Free Tel:* 800-846-7027 *Toll Free Fax:* 800-330-6232, pg 84

ECS Publishing Corp, Framingham, MA *Toll Free Tel:* 800-777-1919, pg 84

EDC Publishing, Tulsa, OK *Toll Free Tel:* 800-475-4522 *Toll Free Fax:* 800-743-5660, pg 84

ediciones Lerner, Minneapolis, MN *Toll Free Tel:* 800-328-4929 *Toll Free Fax:* 800-332-1132, pg 85

Editions Marcel Didier Inc, Montreal, QC Canada *Toll Free Tel:* 800-361-1664 (Ontario to Maritimes), pg 502

Editions du renouveau Pedagogique Inc (ERPI), St-Laurent, QC Canada *Toll Free Tel:* 800-263-3678 *Toll Free Fax:* 800-643-4720, pg 503

Les Editions Fides, Montreal, QC Canada *Toll Free Tel:* 800-363-1451 (CN), pg 503

Editions FouLire, Charlesbourg, QC Canada *Toll Free Tel:* 877-628-4029, pg 503

Les Editions Heritage Inc, St-Lambert, QC Canada *Toll Free Tel:* 800-561-3737, pg 503

Editions Hurtubise, Montreal, QC Canada *Toll Free Tel:* 800-361-1664 (CN only), pg 503

Editions Marie-France, Montreal, QC Canada *Toll Free Tel:* 800-563-6644 (Canada), pg 504

Les Editions Phidal Inc, Montreal, QC Canada *Toll Free Tel:* 800-738-7349, pg 504

Les Editions Un Monde Different Itee, Brossand, QC Canada *Toll Free Tel:* 800-443-2582, pg 504

Editions Yvon Blais, Cowansville, QC Canada *Toll Free Tel:* 800-363-3047, pg 504

Editorial Bautista Independiente, Sebring, FL *Toll Free Tel:* 800-398-7187 (US), pg 85

Editorial Portavoz, Grand Rapids, MI *Toll Free Tel:* 877-733-2607 (ext 206), pg 85

Editorial Unilit, Miami, FL *Toll Free Tel:* 800-767-7726, pg 85

Educational Directories Inc (EDI), Schaumburg, IL *Toll Free Tel:* 800-357-6183, pg 85

Educational Impressions Inc, Oakland, NJ *Toll Free Tel:* 800-451-7450, pg 85

Educational Insights Inc, Gardena, CA *Toll Free Tel:* 800-933-3277 *Toll Free Fax:* 800-995-0506, pg 85

Educators Progress Service Inc, Randolph, WI *Toll Free Tel:* 888-951-4469, pg 85

Edupress Inc, Madison, WI *Toll Free Tel:* 800-694-5827 *Toll Free Fax:* 800-835-2329, pg 85

Wm B Eerdmans Publishing Co, Grand Rapids, MI *Toll Free Tel:* 800-253-7521, pg 85

Edward Elgar Publishing Inc, Northampton, MA *Toll Free Tel:* 800-390-3149 (orders), pg 86

Elite Books, Fulton, CA *Toll Free Fax:* 800-330-9798, pg 86

Elsevier Engineering Information (Ei), New York, NY *Toll Free Tel:* 800-221-1044, pg 86

Elsevier, Health Sciences Division, Philadelphia, PA *Toll Free Tel:* 800-523-1649, pg 86

EMC Publishing, St Paul, MN *Toll Free Tel:* 800-328-1452 *Toll Free Fax:* 800-328-4564, pg 87

Emerald Books, Seattle, WA *Toll Free Tel:* 800-922-2143, pg 87

Emmaus Road Publishing Inc, Steubenville, OH *Toll Free Tel:* 800-398-5470 (orders), pg 87

Emond Montgomery Publications, Toronto, ON Canada *Toll Free Tel:* 888-837-0815, pg 504

Encounter Books, New York, NY *Toll Free Tel:* 800-786-3839 *Toll Free Fax:* 877-811-1461, pg 88

Encyclopaedia Britannica Inc, Chicago, IL *Toll Free Tel:* 800-323-1229 (US & CN), pg 88

Energy Psychology Press, Santa Rosa, CA *Toll Free Fax:* 800-330-9798, pg 88

Enslow Publishers Inc, Berkeley Heights, NJ *Toll Free Tel:* 800-398-2504, pg 88

Ephemera Bound Publishing, Fargo, ND *Toll Free Tel:* 888-642-3043 *Toll Free Fax:* 888-291-4052 (orders), pg 89

Epicenter Press Inc, Kenmore, WA *Toll Free Tel:* 800-950-6663 (orders), pg 89

EPS/School Specialty Literacy & Intervention, Cambridge, MA *Toll Free Tel:* 800-225-5750 *Toll Free Fax:* 888-440-2665, pg 89

Ernst Publishing Co LLC, Albany, NY *Toll Free Tel:* 800-345-3822 *Toll Free Fax:* 800-252-0906, pg 89

ETC Publications, Palm Springs, CA *Toll Free Tel:* 866-514-9969, pg 89

Evan-Moor Educational Publishers, Monterey, CA *Toll Free Tel:* 800-714-0971 (cust serv); 800-777-4362 (orders) *Toll Free Fax:* 800-777-4332 (orders), pg 90

Evangel Publishing House, Nappanee, IN *Toll Free Tel:* 800-253-9315 (orders), pg 90

Evanston Publishing Inc, Louisville, KY *Toll Free Tel:* 888-BOOKS80 (266-5780), pg 90

Excelsior Editions, Albany, NY *Toll Free Tel:* 877-204-6073 *Toll Free Fax:* 877-204-6074, pg 90

Eye in the Ear Children's Audio, Portland, ME *Toll Free Tel:* 877-99-STORY (997-8679), pg 91

Eye On Education, Larchmont, NY *Toll Free Tel:* 888-299-5350, pg 91

Facts On File, New York, NY *Toll Free Tel:* 800-322-8755 *Toll Free Fax:* 800-678-3633, pg 91

Fair Winds Press, Beverly, MA *Toll Free Tel:* 800-328-0590 (sales), pg 91

Fairchild Books, New York, NY *Toll Free Tel:* 800-932-4724; 888-330-8477 (orders), pg 91

Faith Alive Christian Resources, Grand Rapids, MI *Toll Free Tel:* 800-333-8300 *Toll Free Fax:* 888-642-8606, pg 92

Faith & Fellowship Press, Fergus Falls, MN *Toll Free Tel:* 800-332-9232, pg 92

Faith & Life Resources, Harrisonburg, VA *Toll Free Tel:* 800-245-7894 (orders & cust serv US); 800-631-6535 (orders & cust serv CN) *Toll Free Fax:* 877-271-0760, pg 92

Faith Library Publications, Tulsa, OK *Toll Free Tel:* 888-258-0999 (orders), pg 92

FaithWalk Publishing, Lima, OH *Toll Free Tel:* 800-537-1030 (orders: non-bookstore mkts), pg 92

F+W Media Inc, Blue Ash, OH *Toll Free Tel:* 800-289-0963 (trade accts); 800-258-0929 (orders), pg 92

Farrar, Straus & Giroux Books for Young Readers, New York, NY *Toll Free Tel:* 888-330-8477 (sales), pg 93

Father & Son Publishing Inc, Tallahassee, FL *Toll Free Tel:* 800-741-2712 (orders only), pg 93

Favorable Impressions, Pleasant Ridge, MI *Toll Free Tel:* 800-206-9513, pg 93

FC&A Publishing, Peachtree City, GA *Toll Free Tel:* 800-226-8024, pg 93

Federal Street Press, Darien, CT *Toll Free Tel:* 877-886-2830, pg 93

Feldheim Publishers (Philipp Feldheim Inc), Nanuet, NY *Toll Free Tel:* 800-237-7149 (orders), pg 94

Ferguson Publishing, New York, NY *Toll Free Tel:* 800-322-8755 *Toll Free Fax:* 800-678-3633, pg 94

Fifth Estate Publishing, Blounstville, AL *Toll Free Tel:* 855-299-2160, pg 94

Fifth House Publishers, Markham, ON Canada *Toll Free Tel:* 800-387-9776 *Toll Free Fax:* 800-260-9777, pg 505

Filter Press LLC, Palmer Lake, CO *Toll Free Tel:* 888-570-2663, pg 95

Financial Times Press & Wharton School Publishing, Upper Saddle River, NJ *Toll Free Tel:* 800-922-0579 (orders), pg 95

Finney Company Inc, Lakeville, MN *Toll Free Tel:* 800-846-7027 *Toll Free Fax:* 800-330-6232, pg 95

Fire Engineering Books & Videos, Tulsa, OK *Toll Free Tel:* 800-752-9764, pg 95

Firefly Books Ltd, Richmond Hill, ON Canada *Toll Free Tel:* 800-387-6192 (CN); 800-387-5085 (US) *Toll Free Fax:* 800-450-0391 (CN); 800-565-6034 (US), pg 505

First Avenue Editions, Minneapolis, MN *Toll Free Tel:* 800-328-4929 *Toll Free Fax:* 800-332-1132, pg 95

Fitzhenry & Whiteside Limited, Markham, ON Canada *Toll Free Tel:* 800-387-9776 *Toll Free Fax:* 800-260-9777, pg 505

Five Star Publications Inc, Chandler, AZ *Toll Free Tel:* 866-471-0777, pg 96

FJH Music Co Inc, Fort Lauderdale, FL *Toll Free Tel:* 800-262-8744, pg 96

Flanker Press Ltd, Paradise, NL Canada *Toll Free Tel:* 866-739-4420, pg 506

FleetSeek, Fredericksburg, VA *Toll Free Tel:* 888-ONLY-TTS (665-9887), pg 96

Focus on the Family, Colorado Springs, CO *Toll Free Tel:* 800-A-FAMILY (232-6459), pg 96

Focus Publishing/R Pullins Co Inc, Newburyport, MA *Toll Free Tel:* 800-848-7236 (orders), pg 96

Fodor's Travel Publications, New York, NY *Toll Free Tel:* 800-733-3000, pg 96

Forum Publishing Co, Centerport, NY *Toll Free Tel:* 800-635-7654, pg 97

Forward Movement Publications, Cincinnati, OH *Toll Free Tel:* 800-543-1813, pg 97

Walter Foster Publishing Inc, Irvine, CA *Toll Free Tel:* 800-426-0099; 800-826-6600 (orders), pg 97

The Foundation Center, New York, NY *Toll Free Tel:* 800-424-9836, pg 97

The Foundation for Economic Education Inc, Irvington-on-Hudson, NY *Toll Free Tel:* 800-960-4FEE (960-4333), pg 97

Foundation Press Inc, New York, NY *Toll Free Tel:* 877-888-1330, pg 98

Foundation Publications, La Habra, CA *Toll Free Tel:* 800-257-6272, pg 98

Fox Chapel Publishing Co Inc, East Petersburg, PA *Toll Free Tel:* 800-457-9112, pg 98

FPMI Solutions Inc, Madison, AL *Toll Free Tel:* 888-644-3764, pg 98

Franciscan Media, Cincinnati, OH *Toll Free Tel:* 800-488-0488, pg 98

Franklin, Beedle & Associates Inc, Sherwood, OR *Toll Free Tel:* 800-322-2665, pg 98

The Fraser Institute, Vancouver, BC Canada *Toll Free Tel:* 800-665-3558, pg 506

Free Spirit Publishing Inc, Minneapolis, MN *Toll Free Tel:* 800-735-7323 *Toll Free Fax:* 866-419-5199, pg 99

Samuel French Inc, New York, NY *Toll Free Tel:* 866-598-8449, pg 99

Fresh Air Books, Nashville, TN *Toll Free Tel:* 800-972-0433 (orders), pg 99

Friends United Press, Richmond, IN *Toll Free Tel:* 800-537-8839, pg 99

Frog Books, Berkeley, CA *Toll Free Tel:* 800-733-3000 (book orders only) *Toll Free Fax:* 800-659-2436 (orders), pg 99

Front Street, Honesdale, PA *Toll Free Tel:* 800-490-5111, pg 100

Fulcrum Publishing Inc, Golden, CO *Toll Free Tel:* 800-992-2908 *Toll Free Fax:* 800-726-7112, pg 100

Future Horizons Inc, Arlington, TX *Toll Free Tel:* 800-489-0727, pg 100

Gaetan Morin Editeur, Montreal, QC Canada *Toll Free Tel:* 800-565-5531 *Toll Free Fax:* 800-814-0324, pg 506

Galaxy Press, Hollywood, CA *Toll Free Tel:* 877-8GALAXY (842-5299), pg 100

Galde Press Inc, Lakeville, MN *Toll Free Tel:* 800-777-3454, pg 100

Gale, Farmington Hills, MI *Toll Free Tel:* 800-877-4253 *Toll Free Fax:* 800-414-5043 (orders), pg 100

Gallery Books, New York, NY *Toll Free Tel:* 800-456-6798, pg 101

Gallopade International Inc, Peachtree City, GA *Toll Free Tel:* 800-536-2GET (536-2438) *Toll Free Fax:* 800-871-2979, pg 101

Gareth Stevens Publishing, New York, NY *Toll Free Tel:* 800-542-2595 *Toll Free Fax:* 877-542-2596 (cust serv), pg 101

Gateways Books & Tapes, Nevada City, CA *Toll Free Tel:* 800-869-0658, pg 101

Gefen Books, Springfield, NJ *Toll Free Tel:* 800-477-5257, pg 102

Gem Guides Book Co, Upland, CA *Toll Free Tel:* 800-824-5118 (orders), pg 102

GemStone Press, Woodstock, VT *Toll Free Tel:* 800-962-4544, pg 102

Genealogical Publishing Co, Baltimore, MD *Toll Free Tel:* 800-296-6687, pg 102

General Store Publishing House, Renfrew, ON Canada *Toll Free Tel:* 800-465-6072, pg 506

Genesis Press Inc, Columbus, MS *Toll Free Tel:* 888-463-4461 (orders only), pg 102

Geolytics Inc, East Brunswick, NJ *Toll Free Tel:* 800-577-6717, pg 102

Georgetown University Press, Washington, DC *Toll Free Tel:* 800-537-5487, pg 102

Gestalt Journal Press, Gouldsboro, ME *Toll Free Fax:* 866-460-8795, pg 103

Getty Publications, Los Angeles, CA *Toll Free Tel:* 800-223-3431 (orders), pg 103

GIA Publications Inc, Chicago, IL *Toll Free Tel:* 800-GIA-1358 (442-1358), pg 103

Gibbs Smith Publisher, Layton, UT *Toll Free Tel:* 800-748-5439; 800-835-4993 (orders) *Toll Free Fax:* 800-213-3023 (orders only), pg 103

Gilpin Publishing, Alliston, ON Canada *Toll Free Tel:* 800-867-3281, pg 506

Glenbridge Publishing Ltd, Centennial, CO *Toll Free Tel:* 800-986-4135 (orders), pg 103

Peter Glenn Publications, Delray Beach, FL *Toll Free Tel:* 888-332-6700, pg 103

Global Training Center Inc, El Paso, TX *Toll Free Tel:* 800-860-5030, pg 104

The Globe Pequot Press, Guilford, CT *Toll Free Tel:* 800-243-0495 (orders only); 888-249-7586 (cust serv) *Toll Free Fax:* 800-820-2329 (orders & cust serv), pg 104

Les Editions Goelette Inc, Quebec, QC Canada *Toll Free Tel:* 800-463-4961, pg 506

Golden West Cookbooks, Phoenix, AZ *Toll Free Tel:* 800-521-9221, pg 104

Good Books, Intercourse, PA *Toll Free Tel:* 800-762-7171 *Toll Free Fax:* 888-768-3433, pg 105

Good Parent Inc, Providence, RI *Toll Free Fax:* 866-718-0344, pg 105

Goodheart-Willcox Publisher, Tinley Park, IL *Toll Free Tel:* 800-323-0440 *Toll Free Fax:* 888-409-3900, pg 105

Goose Lane Editions, Fredericton, NB Canada *Toll Free Tel:* 888-926-8377, pg 507

Goosebottom Books, Foster City, CA *Toll Free Fax:* 888-407-5286, pg 105

Gospel Publishing House (GPH), Springfield, MO *Toll Free Tel:* 800-641-4310 *Toll Free Fax:* 800-328-0294, pg 105

Government Institutes (GI), Lanham, MD *Toll Free Tel:* 800-462-6420 *Toll Free Fax:* 800-338-4550, pg 105

Grade Finders Inc, Exton, PA *Toll Free Tel:* 877-524-7080, pg 105

The Graduate Group/Booksellers, West Hartford, CT *Toll Free Tel:* 800-484-7280 ext 3579, pg 106

Grafco Productions, Marietta, GA *Toll Free Tel:* 800-381-9169, pg 106

Graphic Universe™, Minneapolis, MN *Toll Free Tel:* 800-328-4929 *Toll Free Fax:* 800-332-1132, pg 106

Gray & Company Publishers, Cleveland, OH *Toll Free Tel:* 800-915-3609, pg 106

Great Potential Press Inc, Scottsdale, AZ *Toll Free Tel:* 877-954-4200, pg 106

Great Quotations Inc, Woodridge, IL *Toll Free Tel:* 800-830-3020, pg 107

Great Source Education Group, Wilmington, MA *Toll Free Tel:* 800-289-4490 *Toll Free Fax:* 800-289-3994, pg 107

Green Dragon Books, Lake Worth, FL *Toll Free Tel:* 800-874-8844 *Toll Free Fax:* 888-874-8844, pg 107

Green Sugar Press, Des Plaines, IL *Toll Free Fax:* 866-270-4100, pg 107

Greenhaven Press®, Farmington Hills, MI *Toll Free Tel:* 800-877-4253 (cust serv & orders) *Toll Free Fax:* 800-414-5043 (orders only), pg 107

Greenleaf Book Group LLC, Austin, TX *Toll Free Tel:* 800-932-5420, pg 107

Grey House Publishing Inc™, Amenia, NY *Toll Free Tel:* 800-562-2139, pg 108

Griffin Publishing LLC, Santa Ana, CA *Toll Free Tel:* 800-472-9741, pg 108

Group Publishing Inc, Loveland, CO *Toll Free Tel:* 800-447-1070, pg 108

Groupe Educalivres Inc, Laval, QC Canada *Toll Free Tel:* 800-567-3671 (info serv), pg 507

Groupe Sogides Inc, Montreal, QC Canada *Toll Free Tel:* 800-361-4806, pg 507

Grove/Atlantic Inc, New York, NY *Toll Free Tel:* 800-521-0178, pg 108

Gryphon Editions, Bethesda, MD *Toll Free Tel:* 800-633-8911, pg 109

Gryphon House Inc, Silver Spring, MD *Toll Free Tel:* 800-638-0928 *Toll Free Fax:* 877-638-7576, pg 109

Guerin Editeur Ltee, Montreal, QC Canada *Toll Free Tel:* 800-398-8337, pg 507

Guernica Editions Inc, Tonawanda, NY *Toll Free Fax:* 800-221-9985 (orders), pg 109

Guideposts Book & Inspirational Media, New York, NY *Toll Free Tel:* 800-431-2344 (cust serv), pg 109

The Guilford Press, New York, NY *Toll Free Tel:* 800-365-7006 (ext 1, orders), pg 109

Hachette Book Group, New York, NY *Toll Free Tel:* 800-759-0190 (cust serv) *Toll Free Fax:* 800-286-9471 (cust serv), pg 110

Hackett Publishing Co Inc, Indianapolis, IN *Toll Free Fax:* 800-783-9213, pg 110

Hagstrom Map & Travel Center, New York, NY *Toll Free Tel:* 800-432-MAPS (432-6277), pg 110

Hal Leonard Corp, Milwaukee, WI *Toll Free Tel:* 800-524-4425, pg 110

Halcyon Press Ltd, Alvin, TX *Toll Free Tel:* 866-774-5786, pg 111

Half Halt Press Inc, Boonsboro, MD *Toll Free Tel:* 800-822-9635 (orders), pg 111

Hamilton Books, Lanham, MD *Toll Free Tel:* 800-462-6420 (cust serv) *Toll Free Fax:* 800-388-4550 (cust serv), pg 111

Hampton Press Inc, New York, NY *Toll Free Tel:* 800-894-8955, pg 111

Hampton Roads Publishing Co Inc, Charlottesville, VA *Toll Free Tel:* 800-423-7087 (orders), pg 111

Hancock House Publishers, Blaine, WA *Toll Free Tel:* 800-938-1114 *Toll Free Fax:* 800-983-2262, pg 111

Hancock House Publishers Ltd, Surrey, BC Canada *Toll Free Tel:* 800-938-1114 *Toll Free Fax:* 800-983-2262, pg 508

Handprint Books Inc, Brooklyn, NY *Toll Free Tel:* 800-722-6657 (orders) *Toll Free Fax:* 800-858-7787 (orders), pg 111

Hanser Publications LLC, Cincinnati, OH *Toll Free Tel:* 800-950-8977; 877-751-5052 (orders) *Toll Free Fax:* 800-527-8801, pg 112

Harbour Publishing Co Ltd, Madeira Park, BC Canada *Toll Free Tel:* 800-667-2988, pg 508

Harcourt Achieve, Orlando, FL *Toll Free Tel:* 800-531-5015 (cust serv/orders) *Toll Free Fax:* 800-699-9459 (cust serv/orders), pg 112

Harcourt Inc, Orlando, FL *Toll Free Tel:* 800-225-5425 (cust serv/orders) *Toll Free Fax:* 800-269-5232 (cust serv/orders), pg 112

Harcourt Mifflin School Publishers, Orlando, FL *Toll Free Tel:* 800-225-5425 (cust serv) *Toll Free Fax:* 800-874-6418; 800-269-5232 (cust serv), pg 112

Hard Shell Word Factory, Cincinnati, OH *Toll Free Tel:* 888-232-0808 *Toll Free Fax:* 888-460-4752, pg 112

Harlequin Enterprises Ltd, Don Mills, ON Canada *Toll Free Tel:* 888-432-4879; 800-370-5838 (ebook inquiries), pg 508

Harmonie Park Press, Sterling Heights, MI *Toll Free Tel:* 800-422-4880, pg 113

Harper's Magazine Foundation, New York, NY *Toll Free Tel:* 800-444-4653, pg 114

Harrison House Publishers, Tulsa, OK *Toll Free Tel:* 800-888-4126 *Toll Free Fax:* 800-830-5688, pg 114

Hartman Publishing Inc, Albuquerque, NM *Toll Free Tel:* 800-999-9534 *Toll Free Fax:* 800-474-6106, pg 114

The Harvard Common Press, Boston, MA *Toll Free Tel:* 888-657-3755, pg 114

Harvard Education Publishing Group, Cambridge, MA *Toll Free Tel:* 800-513-0763 (subns); 888-437-1437 (orders), pg 114

Harvard University Press, Cambridge, MA *Toll Free Tel:* 800-405-1619 (orders) *Toll Free Fax:* 800-406-9145 (orders), pg 114

Harvest Hill Press, Salisbury Cove, ME *Toll Free Tel:* 888-288-8900, pg 115

Harvest House Publishers Inc, Eugene, OR *Toll Free Tel:* 888-501-6991, pg 115

Hatherleigh Press, Long Island City, NY *Toll Free Tel:* 800-367-2550 *Toll Free Fax:* 800-733-3000 (orders), pg 115

Hay House Inc, Carlsbad, CA *Toll Free Tel:* 800-654-5126 (ext 2, US) *Toll Free Fax:* 800-650-5115, pg 115

Haynes Manuals Inc, Newbury Park, CA *Toll Free Tel:* 800-4-HAYNES (442-9637), pg 115

Hazelden Publishing, Center City, MN *Toll Free Tel:* 800-257-7810, pg 116

HCPro Inc, Marblehead, MA *Toll Free Tel:* 800-650-6787 *Toll Free Fax:* 800-639-8511, pg 116

Health Communications Inc, Deerfield Beach, FL *Toll Free Tel:* 800-441-5569 (cust serv), pg 116

Health Forum Inc, Chicago, IL *Toll Free Tel:* 800-242-2626, pg 116

Health InfoNet Inc, San Ramon, CA *Toll Free Tel:* 800-446-1121, pg 116

Health Press NA Inc, Albuquerque, NM *Toll Free Tel:* 877-411-0707, pg 116

Health Professions Press, Towson, MD *Toll Free Tel:* 888-337-8808, pg 117

Health Research Books, Pomeroy, WA *Toll Free Tel:* 888-844-2386, pg 117

HeartMath LLC, Boulder Creek, CA *Toll Free Tel:* 800-450-9111, pg 117

Hearts & Tummies Cookbook Co, Wever, IA *Toll Free Tel:* 800-571-2665, pg 117

Heian International Inc, Berkeley, CA *Toll Free Tel:* 800-947-7271 *Toll Free Fax:* 888-411-8527, pg 117

William S Hein & Co Inc, Getzville, NY *Toll Free Tel:* 800-828-7571, pg 117

Heinemann, Portsmouth, NH *Toll Free Tel:* 800-225-5800 (US) *Toll Free Fax:* 877-231-6980 (US), pg 117

Hellgate Press, Ashland, OR *Toll Free Tel:* 800-795-4059, pg 117

Hendrickson Publishers Inc, Peabody, MA *Toll Free Tel:* 800-358-3111, pg 118

Hensley Publishing, Tulsa, OK *Toll Free Tel:* 800-288-8520 (orders only), pg 118

Herald Press, Harrisonburg, VA *Toll Free Tel:* 800-245-7894 (orders-US); 800-999-3534; 800-631-6535 (orders-CN) *Toll Free Fax:* 877-271-0760, pg 118

Herald Press, Waterloo, ON Canada *Toll Free Tel:* 800-631-6535, pg 508

Herald Publishing House, Independence, MO *Toll Free Tel:* 800-767-8181, pg 118

Heritage Books Inc, Westminster, MD *Toll Free Tel:* 800-876-6103, pg 118

The Heritage Foundation, Washington, DC *Toll Free Tel:* 800-544-4843, pg 118

Heritage House Publishing Co Ltd, Victoria, BC Canada *Toll Free Tel:* 800-665-3302 *Toll Free Fax:* 800-566-3336, pg 509

Heuer Publishing LLC, Cedar Rapids, IA *Toll Free Tel:* 800-950-7529, pg 119

Hewitt Homeschooling Resources, Washougal, WA *Toll Free Tel:* 800-348-1750, pg 119

Hi Willow Research & Publishing, Spring, TX *Toll Free Tel:* 800-873-3043, pg 119

High Plains Press, Glendo, WY *Toll Free Tel:* 800-552-7819, pg 119

Highlights for Children, Columbus, OH *Toll Free Tel:* 800-962-3661 (Highlights Club cust serv); 800-255-9517 (Highlights Magazine cust serv), pg 119

Hillsdale College Press, Hillsdale, MI *Toll Free Tel:* 800-437-2268, pg 120

Himalayan Institute Press, Honesdale, PA *Toll Free Tel:* 800-822-4547, pg 120

Hobar Publications, Lakeville, MN *Toll Free Tel:* 800-846-7027 *Toll Free Fax:* 800-330-6232, pg 120

Hogrefe Publishing, Boston, MA *Toll Free Tel:* 866-823-4726, pg 121

Hohm Press, Chino Valley, AZ *Toll Free Tel:* 800-381-2700, pg 121

Henry Holt and Company, LLC, New York, NY *Toll Free Tel:* 888-330-8477 (orders), pg 122

Holt McDougal, Geneva, IL *Toll Free Tel:* 800-462-6595 *Toll Free Fax:* 888-872-8380, pg 122

Homa & Sekey Books, Paramus, NJ *Toll Free Tel:* 800-870-HOMA (870-4662 orders), pg 122

Home Planners LLC, Tucson, AZ *Toll Free Tel:* 800-521-6797 *Toll Free Fax:* 800-224-6699, pg 122

Hoover Institution Press, Stanford, CA *Toll Free Tel:* 800-935-2882, pg 122

Hoover's, Inc, Austin, TX *Toll Free Tel:* 866-307-3812, pg 122

Hope Publishing Co, Carol Stream, IL *Toll Free Tel:* 800-323-1049, pg 123

Houghton Mifflin Harcourt, Boston, MA *Toll Free Tel:* 800-225-5425 (Pre-K-8); 800-462-6595 (6–12; Advanced & Electives); 800-289-4490 (Specialized Curriculum: Great Source, Rigby, Saxon, Steck-Vaughn; Homeschool; Adult Ed); 800-323-9540 (Assessment: Riverside Publishing); 888-391-3245 (SkillsTutor); 888-242-6747 option 2 (Destination Series; Classroom Connect; Earobics; Edmark; Learning Village; Riverdeep); 800-225-3362 (Houghton Mifflin Harcourt Trade & Reference Publishers); 800-225-5800 (Heinemann), pg 123

Houghton Mifflin Harcourt K-12 Publishers, Boston, MA *Toll Free Tel:* 800-225-5425 (cust serv), pg 123

Houghton Mifflin Harcourt Trade & Reference Division, Boston, MA *Toll Free Tel:* 800-225-3362, pg 123

House to House Publications, Lititz, PA *Toll Free Tel:* 800-848-5892, pg 124

HRD Press, Amherst, MA *Toll Free Tel:* 800-822-2801, pg 125

Hudson Institute, Washington, DC *Toll Free Tel:* 888-554-1325 (bookstore inquiries), pg 125

Human Kinetics Inc, Champaign, IL *Toll Free Tel:* 800-747-4457, pg 125

Humanix Books LLC, West Palm Beach, FL *Toll Free Tel:* 855-371-7810 *Toll Free Fax:* 855-371-7809, pg 125

Hunter House Publishers, Alameda, CA *Toll Free Tel:* 800-266-5592, pg 125

Huntington Press Publishing, Las Vegas, NV *Toll Free Tel:* 800-244-2224, pg 126

Ibex Publishers, Bethesda, MD *Toll Free Tel:* 888-718-8188, pg 126

Iconografix Inc, Hudson, WI *Toll Free Tel:* 800-289-3504 (orders only), pg 126

Idaho Center for the Book, Boise, ID *Toll Free Tel:* 800-992-8398 (outside ID), pg 126

Ideals Publications, a Guideposts Co, Nashville, TN *Toll Free Tel:* 800-586-2572 (cust serv), pg 126

IEEE Computer Society, Washington, DC *Toll Free Tel:* 800-272-6657 (memb info), pg 127

Ignatius Press, San Francisco, CA *Toll Free Tel:* 800-651-1531 (orders), pg 127

IHS Jane's, Alexandria, VA *Toll Free Tel:* 800-824-0768 (sales) *Toll Free Fax:* 800-836-0297, pg 127

IHS Press, Norfolk, VA *Toll Free Tel:* 877-447-7737 *Toll Free Fax:* 877-447-7737, pg 127

Imagination Publishing Group, Dunedin, FL *Toll Free Tel:* 888-701-6481, pg 128

ImaJinn Books Inc, Phoenix, AZ *Toll Free Tel:* 877-625-3592, pg 128

Impact Publications/Development Concepts Inc, Manassas Park, VA *Toll Free Tel:* 800-361-1055 (cust serv), pg 128

Impact Publishers Inc, Atascadero, CA *Toll Free Tel:* 800-246-7228 (orders), pg 128

Incentive Publications Inc, Nashville, TN *Toll Free Tel:* 800-421-2830, pg 128

Independent Institute, Oakland, CA *Toll Free Tel:* 800-927-8733, pg 129

Indiana Historical Society Press (IHS Press), Indianapolis, IN *Toll Free Tel:* 800-447-1830 (orders), pg 129

Indiana University Press, Bloomington, IN *Toll Free Tel:* 800-842-6796 (orders only), pg 129

Industrial Press Inc, New York, NY *Toll Free Tel:* 888-528-7852, pg 129

Information Gatekeepers Inc, Boston, MA *Toll Free Tel:* 800-323-1088, pg 129

Information Publications Inc, Woodside, CA *Toll Free Tel:* 877-544-4636 *Toll Free Fax:* 877-544-4635, pg 130

Information Today, Inc, Medford, NJ *Toll Free Tel:* 800-300-9868 (cust serv), pg 130

Inner Traditions International Ltd, Rochester, VT *Toll Free Tel:* 800-246-8648, pg 130

Insight Editions, San Rafael, CA *Toll Free Tel:* 800-809-3792, pg 131

Institute of Continuing Legal Education, Ann Arbor, MI *Toll Free Tel:* 877-229-4350 *Toll Free Fax:* 877-229-4351, pg 131

Institute of Psychological Research, Inc., Montreal, QC Canada *Toll Free Tel:* 800-363-7800 *Toll Free Fax:* 888-382-3007, pg 509

The Institutes™, Malvern, PA *Toll Free Tel:* 800-644-2101, pg 131

Intercultural Press Inc, Boston, MA *Toll Free Tel:* 888-273-2539, pg 132

Interlink Publishing Group Inc, Northampton, MA *Toll Free Tel:* 800-238-LINK (238-5465), pg 132

International City/County Management Association (ICMA), Washington, DC *Toll Free Tel:* 800-745-8780, pg 132

International Code Council Inc, Whittier, CA *Toll Free Tel:* 888-422-7233, pg 132

International Foundation of Employee Benefit Plans, Brookfield, WI *Toll Free Tel:* 888-334-3327, pg 133

International Linguistics Corp, Grandview, MO *Toll Free Tel:* 800-237-1830 (orders), pg 133

International Reading Association, Newark, DE *Toll Free Tel:* 800-336-7323 (US & CN), pg 133

International Society for Technology in Education, Eugene, OR *Toll Free Tel:* 800-336-5191 (US & CN), pg 133

International Wealth Success Inc, Merrick, NY *Toll Free Tel:* 800-323-0548, pg 134

InterVarsity Press, Westmont, IL *Toll Free Tel:* 800-843-9487, pg 134

Interweave Press LLC, Loveland, CO *Toll Free Tel:* 800-272-2193, pg 134

Irwin Law Inc, Toronto, ON Canada *Toll Free Tel:* 888-314-9014, pg 510

ISI Books, Wilmington, DE *Toll Free Tel:* 800-526-7022, pg 134

Island Press, Washington, DC *Toll Free Tel:* 800-828-1302, pg 134

iUniverse, Bloomington, IN *Toll Free Tel:* 800-AUTHORS (288-4677), pg 135

Richard Ivey School of Business, London, ON Canada *Toll Free Tel:* 800-649-6355, pg 510

JayJo Books LLC, Woodbury, NY *Toll Free Tel:* 800-999-6884 *Toll Free Fax:* 800-262-1886, pg 135

Jewish Lights Publishing, Woodstock, VT *Toll Free Tel:* 800-962-4544 (orders only), pg 135

Jewish Publication Society, Philadelphia, PA *Toll Free Tel:* 800-234-3151, pg 135

JIST Publishing, St Paul, MN *Toll Free Tel:* 800-328-1452 *Toll Free Fax:* 800-328-4564, pg 135

John Deere Publishing, Davenport, IA *Toll Free Tel:* 800-522-7448 (orders), pg 136

The Johns Hopkins University Press, Baltimore, MD *Toll Free Tel:* 800-537-5487 (book orders & cust serv); 800-548-1784 (journal orders), pg 136

Johnson Books, Boulder, CO *Toll Free Tel:* 800-258-5830, pg 136

Jones & Bartlett Learning LLC, Burlington, MA *Toll Free Tel:* 800-832-0034, pg 136

Jones McClure Publishing, Houston, TX *Toll Free Tel:* 800-626-6667, pg 137

Jossey-Bass, San Francisco, CA *Toll Free Tel:* 800-956-7739, pg 137

Joy Publishing Co, Fountain Valley, CA *Toll Free Tel:* 800-454-8228, pg 137

Judaica Press Inc, Brooklyn, NY *Toll Free Tel:* 800-972-6201, pg 137

Judson Press, King of Prussia, PA *Toll Free Tel:* 800-458-3766, pg 137

Kaeden Corp, Rocky River, OH *Toll Free Tel:* 800-890-7323, pg 138

Kamehameha Publishing, Honolulu, HI *Toll Free Tel:* 800-523-6200, pg 138

Kaplan Publishing, New York, NY *Toll Free Tel:* 888-KAPLAN8 (527-5268) *Toll Free Fax:* 877-712-5487, pg 138

Kar-Ben Publishing, Minneapolis, MN *Toll Free Tel:* 800-4-KARBEN (452-7236) *Toll Free Fax:* 800-332-1132, pg 138

J J Keller & Associates, Inc, Neenah, WI *Toll Free Tel:* 877-564-2333 *Toll Free Fax:* 800-727-7516, pg 139

Kendall/Hunt Publishing Co, Dubuque, IA *Toll Free Tel:* 800-228-0810 (orders) *Toll Free Fax:* 800-772-9165, pg 139

Kennedy Information Inc, Peterborough, NH *Toll Free Tel:* 800-531-0007, pg 139

Kensington Publishing Corp, New York, NY *Toll Free Tel:* 800-221-2647, pg 139

Key Curriculum, A McGraw-Hill Education Company, Emeryville, CA *Toll Free Tel:* 800-995-6284 *Toll Free Fax:* 800-541-2442, pg 140

Kids Can Press Ltd, Toronto, ON Canada *Toll Free Tel:* 800-265-0884, pg 510

Kindred Productions, Winnipeg, MB Canada *Toll Free Tel:* 800-545-7322, pg 510

Jessica Kingsley Publishers Inc, Philadelphia, PA *Toll Free Tel:* 866-416-1078 (cust serv), pg 140

Kirk House Publishers, Minneapolis, MN *Toll Free Tel:* 888-696-1828, pg 140

Kirkbride Bible Co Inc, Indianapolis, IN *Toll Free Tel:* 800-428-4385, pg 140

Klutz, Palo Alto, CA *Toll Free Tel:* 800-737-4123, pg 140

Wolters Kluwer Law & Business, New York, NY *Toll Free Tel:* 800-234-1660 (cust serv); 800-638-8437 (orders); 800-317-3113 (bookstore sales) *Toll Free Fax:* 800-901-9075 (cust serv); 800-561-4845 (bookstore sales), pg 141

Allen A Knoll Publishers, Santa Barbara, CA *Toll Free Tel:* 800-777-7623, pg 141

Alfred A Knopf/Everyman's Library, New York, NY *Toll Free Tel:* 800-638-6460, pg 141

Knopf Random Canada, Toronto, ON Canada *Toll Free Tel:* 888-523-9292, pg 510

Koho Pono LLC, Clackamas, OR *Toll Free Tel:* 800-937-8000 (orders) *Toll Free Fax:* 800-876-0186 (orders), pg 141

H J Kramer Inc, Tiburon, CA *Toll Free Tel:* 800-972-6657, pg 142

Krause Publications Inc, Iola, WI *Toll Free Tel:* 800-258-0929 (cust serv); 888-457-2873 (orders), pg 142

Kregel Publications, Grand Rapids, MI *Toll Free Tel:* 800-733-2607, pg 142

Krieger Publishing Co, Malabar, FL *Toll Free Tel:* 800-724-0025, pg 142

Kumarian Press, Boulder, CO *Toll Free Tel:* 800-232-0223 (orders only), pg 142

LadybugPress, Sonora, CA *Toll Free Tel:* 888-892-5000, pg 143

Lake Superior Port Cities Inc, Duluth, MN *Toll Free Tel:* 888-BIG-LAKE (244-5253), pg 143

LAMA Books, Hayward, CA *Toll Free Tel:* 888-452-6244, pg 143

Lanahan Publishers Inc, Baltimore, MD *Toll Free Tel:* 866-345-1949 *Toll Free Fax:* 888-345-7257, pg 143

Landauer Corp, Urbandale, IA *Toll Free Tel:* 800-557-2144, pg 143

Landes Bioscience, Austin, TX *Toll Free Tel:* 800-736-9948, pg 143

Peter Lang Publishing Inc, New York, NY *Toll Free Tel:* 800-770-5264 (cust serv), pg 143

LangMarc Publishing, Austin, TX *Toll Free Tel:* 800-864-1648 (orders), pg 143

Larson Publications, Burdett, NY *Toll Free Tel:* 800-828-2197, pg 144

Laughing Elephant, Seattle, WA *Toll Free Tel:* 800-354-0400, pg 144

The Lawbook Exchange Ltd, Clark, NJ *Toll Free Tel:* 800-422-6686, pg 144

Lawyers & Judges Publishing Co Inc, Tucson, AZ *Toll Free Tel:* 800-209-7109 *Toll Free Fax:* 800-330-8795, pg 145

Leadership Ministries Worldwide/OBR, Chattanooga, TN *Toll Free Tel:* 800-987-8790, pg 145

THE Learning Connection®, Orlando, FL *Toll Free Tel:* 800-218-8489, pg 145

Learning Links Inc, Cranbury, NJ *Toll Free Tel:* 800-724-2616, pg 145

LearningExpress LLC, New York, NY *Toll Free Tel:* 800-295-9556 (ext 2), pg 145

Lectorum Publications Inc, Lyndhurst, NJ *Toll Free Tel:* 800-345-5946 *Toll Free Fax:* 877-532-8676, pg 145

Lederer Books, Clarksville, MD *Toll Free Tel:* 800-410-7367 (orders), pg 146

Lee & Low Books Inc, New York, NY *Toll Free Tel:* 888-320-3190 (ext 28, orders only), pg 146

Leisure Arts Inc, Little Rock, AR *Toll Free Tel:* 800-643-8030, pg 146

The Lentz Leadership Institute, Las Vegas, NV *Toll Free Fax:* 877-298-5172, pg 146

Lerner Publications, Minneapolis, MN *Toll Free Tel:* 800-328-4929 *Toll Free Fax:* 800-332-1132, pg 146

Lerner Publishing Group Inc, Minneapolis, MN *Toll Free Tel:* 800-328-4929 *Toll Free Fax:* 800-332-1132, pg 146

LernerClassroom, Minneapolis, MN *Toll Free Tel:* 800-328-4929 *Toll Free Fax:* 800-332-1132, pg 147

Lessiter Publications, Brookfield, WI *Toll Free Tel:* 800-645-8455, pg 147

LexisNexis®, Charlottesville, VA *Toll Free Tel:* 800-446-3410, pg 147

LexisNexis Canada Inc, Markham, ON Canada *Toll Free Tel:* 800-668-6481; 800-387-0899 (cust serv) *Toll Free Fax:* 800-461-3275, pg 511

LexisNexis/Martindale-Hubbell, New Providence, NJ *Toll Free Tel:* 800-526-4902, pg 147

LexisNexis® Matthew Bender®, Albany, NY *Toll Free Tel:* 800-424-4200, pg 148

Liberty Fund Inc, Indianapolis, IN *Toll Free Tel:* 800-955-8335; 800-866-3520; 800-368-7897 ext 6069 (cust serv), pg 148

Libraries Unlimited, Santa Barbara, CA *Toll Free Tel:* 800-368-6868 *Toll Free Fax:* 866-270-3856, pg 148

Lidec Inc, Montreal, QC Canada *Toll Free Tel:* 800-350-5991 (CN only), pg 511

Mary Ann Liebert Inc, New Rochelle, NY *Toll Free Tel:* 800-654-3237, pg 148

Life Cycle Books, Fort Collins, CO *Toll Free Tel:* 800-214-5849 *Toll Free Fax:* 888-690-8532, pg 148

Life Cycle Books Ltd, Toronto, ON Canada *Toll Free Tel:* 866-880-5860 *Toll Free Fax:* 866-690-8532, pg 511

Light-Beams Publishing, Lee, NH *Toll Free Tel:* 800-397-7641, pg 148

Light Technology Publishing, Flagstaff, AZ *Toll Free Tel:* 800-450-0985, pg 148

Liguori Publications, Liguori, MO *Toll Free Tel:* 866-848-2492; 800-325-9521, pg 149

Linden Publishing Co Inc, Fresno, CA *Toll Free Tel:* 800-345-4447 (orders), pg 149

LinguaText Ltd, Newark, DE *Toll Free Fax:* 800-784-4935, pg 149

LinguiSystems Inc, East Moline, IL *Toll Free Tel:* 800-776-4332 *Toll Free Fax:* 800-577-4555, pg 149

Linworth Publishing, Santa Barbara, CA *Toll Free Tel:* 800-368-6868 *Toll Free Fax:* 866-270-3856, pg 149

LionHearted Publishing Inc, Zephyr Cove, NV *Toll Free Tel:* 888-546-6478 *Toll Free Fax:* 888-546-6478, pg 149

Lipper Marketplace, New York, NY *Toll Free Tel:* 800-782-5555 (orders), pg 150

Lippincott Williams & Wilkins, Philadelphia, PA *Toll Free Tel:* 800-638-3030 (orders & cust serv), pg 150

Listen & Live Audio Inc, Roseland, NJ *Toll Free Tel:* 800-653-9400 (orders), pg 150

Little, Brown Books for Young Readers, New York, NY *Toll Free Tel:* 800-759-0190 (cust serv), pg 150

The Little Entrepreneur, Detroit, MI *Toll Free Tel:* 888-435-9234, pg 150

Little Pickle Press LLC, Belvedere, CA *Toll Free Tel:* 877-415-4488, pg 528

Liturgical Press, Collegeville, MN *Toll Free Tel:* 800-858-5450 *Toll Free Fax:* 800-445-5899, pg 150

Liturgy Training Publications, Chicago, IL *Toll Free Tel:* 800-933-1800 (US & CN only orders) *Toll Free Fax:* 800-933-7094 (US & CN only orders), pg 151

Living Language, New York, NY *Toll Free Tel:* 800-733-3000 (orders) *Toll Free Fax:* 800-659-2436, pg 151

Llewellyn Publications, Woodbury, MN *Toll Free Tel:* 800-843-6666, pg 151

The Local History Co, Pittsburgh, PA *Toll Free Tel:* 866-362-0789 (orders), pg 151

Logos Bible Software, Bellingham, WA *Toll Free Tel:* 800-875-6467, pg 152

Lone Pine Publishing, Edmonton, AB Canada *Toll Free Tel:* 800-661-9017 *Toll Free Fax:* 800-424-7173, pg 511

Lonely Planet, Oakland, CA *Toll Free Tel:* 800-275-8555 (orders), pg 152

Looseleaf Law Publications Inc, Flushing, NY *Toll Free Tel:* 800-647-5547, pg 152

Lorenz Educational Press, Dayton, OH *Toll Free Tel:* 800-444-1144, pg 152

Lotus Press, Twin Lakes, WI *Toll Free Tel:* 800-824-6396 (orders), pg 152

Love Publishing Co, Denver, CO *Toll Free Tel:* 877-240-6396, pg 153

Loving Healing Press Inc, Ann Arbor, MI *Toll Free Tel:* 888-761-6268 (US & CN), pg 153

Loyola Press, Chicago, IL *Toll Free Tel:* 800-621-1008, pg 153

LRP Publications, Palm Beach Gardens, FL *Toll Free Tel:* 800-341-7874, pg 153

LRS, Los Angeles, CA *Toll Free Tel:* 800-255-5002, pg 153

Macmillan Audio, New York, NY *Toll Free Tel:* 888-330-8477 (cust serv), pg 154

Macmillan Reference USA™, Woodbridge, CT *Toll Free Tel:* 800-444-0799, pg 155

Madavor Media, Waukesha, WI *Toll Free Tel:* 800-533-6644 (cust serv & orders), pg 155

Madison House Publishers, Lanham, MD *Toll Free Tel:* 800-462-6420, pg 155

Madonna House Publications, Combermere, ON Canada *Toll Free Tel:* 888-703-7110 *Toll Free Fax:* 877-717-2888, pg 511

Mage Publishers Inc, Washington, DC *Toll Free Tel:* 800-962-0922, pg 155

Magick Mirror Communications, New York, NY *Toll Free Tel:* 800-356-6796, pg 528

Maharishi University of Management Press, Fairfield, IA *Toll Free Tel:* 800-831-6523, pg 155

Management Concepts Inc, Vienna, VA *Toll Free Tel:* 800 506-4450, pg 155

Mandala Publishing, San Rafael, CA *Toll Free Fax:* 866-509-0515, pg 156

Manning Publications Co, Shelter Island, NY *Toll Free Tel:* 800-294-4747 (orders), pg 156

MapEasy Inc, Wainscott, NY *Toll Free Tel:* 888-627-3279, pg 156

MAR*CO Products Inc, Warminster, PA *Toll Free Tel:* 800-448-2197, pg 156

Marathon Press, Norfolk, NE *Toll Free Tel:* 800-228-0629, pg 156

Maren Green Publishing Inc, Oak Park Heights, MN *Toll Free Tel:* 800-287-1512, pg 156

Marion Street Press Inc, Portland, OR *Toll Free Fax:* 866-571-8359, pg 157

Marquette University Press, Milwaukee, WI *Toll Free Tel:* 800-247-6553 (cust serv), pg 157

Marquis Who's Who LLC, Berkeley Heights, NJ *Toll Free Tel:* 800-473-7020, pg 157

Marshall & Swift, Los Angeles, CA *Toll Free Tel:* 800-544-2678, pg 158

Marshall Cavendish Corp, Tarrytown, NY *Toll Free Tel:* 800-821-9881, pg 158

Martingale®, Bothell, WA *Toll Free Tel:* 800-426-3126, pg 158

Maryland History Press, Fruitland, MD *Toll Free Tel:* 877-742-2682, pg 158

Mason Crest Publishers, Broomall, PA *Toll Free Tel:* 866-MCP-BOOK (627-2665), pg 158

Math Solutions®, Sausalito, CA *Toll Free Tel:* 800-868-9092 *Toll Free Fax:* 877-942-8837, pg 159

Math Teachers Press Inc, Minneapolis, MN *Toll Free Tel:* 800-852-2435, pg 159

The Mathematical Association of America, Washington, DC *Toll Free Tel:* 800-741-9415, pg 159

Maupin House Publishing, Gainesville, FL *Toll Free Tel:* 800-524-0634, pg 159

MBI Publishing Co, Minneapolis, MN *Toll Free Tel:* 800-328-0590, pg 159

McClanahan Publishing House Inc, Kuttawa, KY *Toll Free Tel:* 800-544-6959, pg 160

McCutchan Publishing Corp, Richmond, CA *Toll Free Tel:* 800-227-1540, pg 160

The McDonald & Woodward Publishing Co, Granville, OH *Toll Free Tel:* 800-233-8787, pg 160

McFarland, Jefferson, NC *Toll Free Tel:* 800-253-2187 (orders), pg 160

McGraw-Hill Career Education, Burr Ridge, IL *Toll Free Tel:* 800-338-3987 (cust serv), pg 160

McGraw-Hill Contemporary Learning Series, Dubuque, IA *Toll Free Tel:* 800-243-6532, pg 160

McGraw-Hill Higher Education, Burr Ridge, IL *Toll Free Tel:* 800-338-3987 (cust serv), pg 161

McGraw-Hill Humanities, Social Sciences, Languages, New York, NY *Toll Free Tel:* 800-338-3987 (cust serv), pg 161

McGraw-Hill/Irwin, Burr Ridge, IL *Toll Free Tel:* 800-338-3987 (cust serv), pg 161

McGraw-Hill Ryerson Limited, Whitby, ON Canada *Toll Free Tel:* 800-565-5758 (cust serv), pg 512

McGraw-Hill School Education Group, Columbus, OH *Toll Free Tel:* 800-848-1567, pg 162

McGraw-Hill Science, Engineering, Mathematics, Dubuque, IA *Toll Free Tel:* 800-338-3987 (cust serv), pg 162

McPherson & Co, Kingston, NY *Toll Free Tel:* 800-613-8219 *Toll Free Fax:* 800-613-8219, pg 162

MDR, A D & B Co, Shelton, CT *Toll Free Tel:* 800-333-8802, pg 162

Meadowbrook Press, Minnetonka, MN *Toll Free Tel:* 800-338-2232, pg 163

me+mi publishing inc, Wheaton, IL *Toll Free Tel:* 888-251-1444, pg 163

R S Means, a Reed Construction Data Co, Norwell, MA *Toll Free Tel:* 800-334-3509 *Toll Free Fax:* 800-632-6701, pg 163

Medals of America, Fountain Inn, SC *Toll Free Tel:* 800-605-4001 *Toll Free Fax:* 800-407-8640, pg 163

MedBooks, Richardson, TX *Toll Free Tel:* 800-443-7397, pg 163

Medical Group Management Association (MGMA), Englewood, CO *Toll Free Tel:* 877-275-6462, pg 163

Medical Physics Publishing Corp (MPP), Madison, WI *Toll Free Tel:* 800-442-5778 (cust serv), pg 163

MedMaster Inc, Fort Lauderdale, FL *Toll Free Tel:* 800-335-3480, pg 163

The Russell Meerdink Co Ltd, Neenah, WI *Toll Free Tel:* 800-635-6499, pg 163

Mel Bay Publications Inc, Pacific, MO *Toll Free Tel:* 800-863-5229 *Toll Free Fax:* 800-660-9818, pg 164

Menasha Ridge Press Inc, Birmingham, AL *Toll Free Tel:* 888-604-4537, pg 164

Mercer University Press, Macon, GA *Toll Free Tel:* 866-895-1472, pg 164

Meriwether Publishing Ltd/Contemporary Drama Service, Colorado Springs, CO *Toll Free Tel:* 800-937-5297 *Toll Free Fax:* 888-594-4436, pg 164

Merriam-Webster Inc, Springfield, MA *Toll Free Tel:* 800-828-1880 (orders & cust serv), pg 165

Mesorah Publications Ltd, Brooklyn, NY *Toll Free Tel:* 800-637-6724, pg 165

Messianic Jewish Publishers, Clarksville, MD *Toll Free Tel:* 800-410-7367 (orders), pg 165

MGI Management Institute Inc, Hawthorne, NY *Toll Free Tel:* 800-932-0191, pg 165

Michelin Maps & Guides, Greenville, SC *Toll Free Fax:* 866-297-0914; 888-773-7979, pg 165

Michigan Municipal League, Ann Arbor, MI *Toll Free Tel:* 800-653-2483, pg 165

Michigan State University Press (MSU Press), East Lansing, MI *Toll Free Fax:* 800-678-2120, pg 165

Microsoft Press, Redmond, WA *Toll Free Tel:* 800-677-7377, pg 166

MidWest Plan Service (MWPS), Ames, IA *Toll Free Tel:* 800-562-3618, pg 166

Mike Murach & Associates Inc, Fresno, CA *Toll Free Tel:* 800-221-5528, pg 166

Milady, Clifton Park, NY *Toll Free Tel:* 800-998-7498, pg 166

Military Living Publications, Vienna, VA *Toll Free Tel:* 877-363-4677 (ext 1), pg 166

Milkweed Editions, Minneapolis, MN *Toll Free Tel:* 800-520-6455, pg 166

Millbrook Press, Minneapolis, MN *Toll Free Tel:* 800-328-4929 (US only) *Toll Free Fax:* 800-332-1132, pg 167

Richard K Miller Associates, Loganville, GA *Toll Free Tel:* 888-928-RKMA (928-7562) *Toll Free Fax:* 877-928-RKMA (928-7562), pg 167

Milliken Publishing Co, Dayton, OH *Toll Free Tel:* 800-444-1144, pg 167

The Minerals, Metals & Materials Society (TMS), Warrendale, PA *Toll Free Tel:* 800-759-4867, pg 167

Minnesota Historical Society Press, St Paul, MN *Toll Free Tel:* 800-621-2736 (warehouse) *Toll Free Fax:* 800-621-8476 (warehouse), pg 167

The MIT Press, Cambridge, MA *Toll Free Tel:* 800-207-8354 (orders), pg 167

Mitchell Lane Publishers Inc, Hockessin, DE *Toll Free Tel:* 800-814-5484 *Toll Free Fax:* 866-834-4164, pg 168

Mondo Publishing, Farmingdale, NY *Toll Free Tel:* 888-88-MONDO (886-6636) *Toll Free Fax:* 888-532-4492, pg 168

Money Market Directories, Charlottesville, VA *Toll Free Tel:* 800-446-2810, pg 169

Montana Historical Society Press, Helena, MT *Toll Free Tel:* 800-243-9900, pg 169

Monthly Review Press, New York, NY *Toll Free Tel:* 800-670-9499, pg 169

Moody Publishers, Chicago, IL *Toll Free Tel:* 800-678-8812 (cust serv), pg 169

Morehouse Publishing, Harrisburg, PA *Toll Free Tel:* 800-877-0012 (orders only); 800-242-1918 (cust serv), pg 169

Morgan James Publishing, New York, NY *Toll Free Tel:* 800-485-4943, pg 169

Morgan Kaufmann, Waltham, MA *Toll Free Tel:* 866-607-1417, pg 170

Morgan Reynolds Publishing, Greensboro, NC *Toll Free Tel:* 800-535-1504 *Toll Free Fax:* 800-535-5725, pg 170

Mountain n' Air Books, La Crescenta, CA *Toll Free Tel:* 800-446-9696 *Toll Free Fax:* 800-303-5578, pg 170

Mountain Press Publishing Co, Missoula, MT *Toll Free Tel:* 800-234-5308, pg 170

The Mountaineers Books, Seattle, WA *Toll Free Tel:* 800-553-4453 *Toll Free Fax:* 800-568-7604, pg 170

MRTS, Tempe, AZ *Toll Free Tel:* 800-621-2736 (orders) *Toll Free Fax:* 800-621-8476 (orders), pg 171

Editions MultiMondes, Quebec, QC Canada *Toll Free Tel:* 800-840-3029 *Toll Free Fax:* 888-303-5931, pg 512

Mundania Press LLC, Cincinnati, OH *Toll Free Fax:* 888-460-4752, pg 171

Museum of New Mexico Press, Santa Fe, NM *Toll Free Tel:* 800-249-7737 (orders) *Toll Free Fax:* 800-622-8667 (orders), pg 171

Mystic Seaport Museum Inc, Mystic, CT *Toll Free Tel:* 800-248-1066 (wholesale orders only); 800-331-2665 (retail orders only), pg 172

NACE International, Houston, TX *Toll Free Tel:* 800-797-NACE (797-6223), pg 172

National Academies Press (NAP), Washington, DC *Toll Free Tel:* 888-624-8373 (cust serv), pg 172

The National Alliance Research Academy, Austin, TX *Toll Free Tel:* 800-633-2165, pg 173

National Association for Music Education, Reston, VA *Toll Free Tel:* 800-462-6420 (orders & returns); 800-336-3768, pg 173

National Association of Secondary School Principals (NASSP), Reston, VA *Toll Free Tel:* 800-253-7746, pg 173

National Braille Press, Boston, MA *Toll Free Tel:* 800-548-7323 (cust serv); 888-965-8965, pg 173

National Catholic Educational Association, Arlington, VA *Toll Free Tel:* 800-711-6232, pg 173

National Council of Teachers of English (NCTE), Urbana, IL *Toll Free Tel:* 877-369-6283 (cust serv), pg 174

National Council of Teachers of Mathematics (NCTM), Reston, VA *Toll Free Tel:* 800-235-7566, pg 174

National Council on Radiation Protection & Measurements (NCRP), Bethesda, MD *Toll Free Tel:* 800-229-2652, pg 174

National Golf Foundation, Jupiter, FL *Toll Free Tel:* 888-275-4643, pg 175

National Information Standards Organization, Baltimore, MD *Toll Free Tel:* 866-957-1593, pg 175

National Institute for Trial Advocacy (NITA), Boulder, CO *Toll Free Tel:* 877-648-2632; 800-225-6482 (orders & returns), pg 175

National Learning Corp, Syosset, NY *Toll Free Tel:* 800-632-8888, pg 175

National Notary Association (NNA), Chatsworth, CA *Toll Free Tel:* 800-876-6827 *Toll Free Fax:* 800-833-1211, pg 175

National Publishing Co, Philadelphia, PA *Toll Free Tel:* 888-333-1863, pg 175

National Register Publishing, Berkeley Heights, NJ *Toll Free Tel:* 800-473-7020, pg 175

National Resource Center for Youth Services (NRCYS), Tulsa, OK *Toll Free Tel:* 800-274-2687, pg 175

National Science Teachers Association (NSTA), Arlington, VA *Toll Free Tel:* 800-722-NSTA; 800-277-5300 (orders) *Toll Free Fax:* 888-433-0526 (orders), pg 176

The National Underwriter Co, Erlanger, KY *Toll Free Tel:* 800-543-0874, pg 176

Naval Institute Press, Annapolis, MD *Toll Free Tel:* 800-233-8764, pg 176

NavPress Publishing Group, Colorado Springs, CO *Toll Free Tel:* 800-366-7788 *Toll Free Fax:* 800-343-3902, pg 176

NBM Publishing Inc, New York, NY *Toll Free Tel:* 800-886-1223, pg 176

Neal-Schuman Publishers Inc, New York, NY *Toll Free Tel:* 866-NS-BOOKS (672-6657) *Toll Free Fax:* 877-231-6980, pg 176

Neibauer Press & Church Supplier, Warminster, PA *Toll Free Tel:* 800-322-6203, pg 176

Nelson Education Ltd, Scarborough, ON Canada *Toll Free Tel:* 800-268-2222 (cust serv) *Toll Free Fax:* 800-430-4445, pg 513

New City Press, Hyde Park, NY *Toll Free Tel:* 800-462-5980 (orders only), pg 177

New Dimensions Publishing, Phoenix, AZ *Toll Free Tel:* 800-736-7367, pg 177

New Forums Press Inc, Stillwater, OK *Toll Free Tel:* 800-606-3766, pg 177

New Harbinger Publications Inc, Oakland, CA *Toll Free Tel:* 800-748-6273 (orders only) *Toll Free Fax:* 800-652-1613, pg 177

New Horizon Press, Far Hills, NJ *Toll Free Tel:* 800-533-7978 (orders only), pg 177

New Leaf Press Inc, Green Forest, AR *Toll Free Tel:* 800-999-3777, pg 178

The New Press, New York, NY *Toll Free Tel:* 800-343-4489 (orders) *Toll Free Fax:* 800-351-5073 (orders), pg 178

New Readers Press, Syracuse, NY *Toll Free Tel:* 800-448-8878 *Toll Free Fax:* 866-894-2100, pg 178

New Strategist Publications Inc, Ithaca, NY *Toll Free Tel:* 800-848-0842, pg 178

New Victoria Publishers, Chicago, IL *Toll Free Tel:* 888-530-4588, pg 178

New World Library, Novato, CA *Toll Free Tel:* 800-227-3900 (ext 52, retail orders); 800-972-6657, pg 178

New World Publishing, Halifax, NS Canada *Toll Free Tel:* 877-211-3334 (orders), pg 513

New York Academy of Sciences, New York, NY *Toll Free Tel:* 800-843-6927, pg 179

New York State Bar Association, Albany, NY *Toll Free Tel:* 800-582-2452, pg 179

New York University Press, New York, NY *Toll Free Tel:* 800-996-6987 (orders), pg 179

Newbury Street Press, Boston, MA *Toll Free Tel:* 888-296-3447 (NEHGS membership), pg 179

NeWest Press, Edmonton, AB Canada *Toll Free Tel:* 866-796-5473, pg 513

Nightingale-Conant, Niles, IL *Toll Free Tel:* 800-572-2770; 800-557-1660 (sales); 800-560-6081 (cust serv), pg 179

Nimbus Publishing Ltd, Halifax, NS Canada *Toll Free Tel:* 800-NIMBUS9 (646-2879) *Toll Free Fax:* 888-253-3133, pg 513

No Starch Press Inc, San Francisco, CA *Toll Free Tel:* 800-420-7240, pg 180

North Country Books Inc, Utica, NY *Toll Free Tel:* 800-342-7409 (orders), pg 180

North Light Books, Blue Ash, OH *Toll Free Tel:* 800-666-0963 *Toll Free Fax:* 888-590-4082, pg 181

North Point Press, New York, NY *Toll Free Tel:* 888-330-8477, pg 181

North River Press Publishing Corp, Great Barrington, MA *Toll Free Tel:* 800-486-2665 *Toll Free Fax:* 800-BOOK-FAX (266-5329), pg 181

North Star Press of Saint Cloud Inc, St Cloud, MN *Toll Free Tel:* 888-820-1636, pg 181

Northstone Publishing, Kelowna, BC Canada *Toll Free Tel:* 800-299-2926; 800-663-2775 (orders) *Toll Free Fax:* 888-841-9991, pg 514

Northwestern University Press, Evanston, IL *Toll Free Tel:* 800-621-2736 (orders only), pg 181

W W Norton & Company Inc, New York, NY *Toll Free Tel:* 800-233-4830 (orders & cust serv) *Toll Free Fax:* 800-458-6515, pg 181

Norwood House Press, Chicago, IL *Toll Free Tel:* 866-565-2900 *Toll Free Fax:* 866-565-2901, pg 182

Nova Press, West Hollywood, CA *Toll Free Tel:* 800-949-6175, pg 182

Nova Publishing Co, Carbondale, IL *Toll Free Tel:* 800-748-1175 (cust serv), pg 182

Novalis Publishing, Toronto, ON Canada *Toll Free Tel:* 877-702-7773 *Toll Free Fax:* 877-702-7775, pg 514

nursesbooks.org, The Publishing Program of ANA, Silver Spring, MD *Toll Free Tel:* 800-924-9053; 800-637-0323 (orders), pg 182

Nystrom Herff Jones Education Division, Indianapolis, IN *Toll Free Tel:* 800-621-8086 (cust serv), pg 182

OAG Worldwide, Downers Grove, IL *Toll Free Tel:* 800-342-5624 (cust serv), pg 182

Oak Knoll Press, New Castle, DE *Toll Free Tel:* 800-996-2556, pg 183

Oakstone Publishing LLC, Birmingham, AL *Toll Free Tel:* 800-633-4743, pg 183

Oceana®, New York, NY *Toll Free Tel:* 800-451-7556 (orders only), pg 184

OCP, Portland, OR *Toll Free Tel:* 800-548-8749 *Toll Free Fax:* 800-843-8181, pg 184

Ohio State University Foreign Language Publications, Columbus, OH *Toll Free Tel:* 800-678-6999, pg 184

Ohio State University Press, Columbus, OH *Toll Free Fax:* 800-621-8476, pg 184

The Oliver Press Inc, Minneapolis, MN *Toll Free Tel:* 800-8-OLIVER (865-4837), pg 185

Omnibus Press, New York, NY *Toll Free Tel:* 800-431-7187 *Toll Free Fax:* 800-345-6842, pg 185

Omnidawn Publishing, Richmond, CA *Toll Free Tel:* 800-792-4957, pg 185

Omnigraphics Inc, Detroit, MI *Toll Free Tel:* 800-234-1340 (cust serv) *Toll Free Fax:* 800-875-1340 (cust serv), pg 185

OneSource, Concord, MA *Toll Free Tel:* 866-354-6936, pg 185

Online Training Solutions Inc (OTSI), Redmond, WA *Toll Free Tel:* 888-308-6874 *Toll Free Fax:* 888-308-6875, pg 185

Open Court, Chicago, IL *Toll Free Tel:* 800-815-2280 (orders only), pg 185

OPIS/STALSBY Directories & Databases, Wall, NJ *Toll Free Tel:* 800-275-0950 *Toll Free Fax:* 800-450-5864, pg 186

OptumInsight™, Eden Prairie, MN *Toll Free Tel:* 888-445-8745; 800-765-6713, pg 186

Orange Frazer Press Inc, Wilmington, OH *Toll Free Tel:* 800-852-9332 (orders), pg 186

Orbis Books, Ossining, NY *Toll Free Tel:* 800-258-5838 (orders), pg 186

Orbit, New York, NY *Toll Free Tel:* 800-759-0190, pg 186

Orca Book Publishers, Custer, WA *Toll Free Tel:* 800-210-5277 *Toll Free Fax:* 877-408-1551, pg 186

Oregon State University Press, Corvallis, OR *Toll Free Tel:* 800-621-2736 (orders) *Toll Free Fax:* 800-426-3797 (orders), pg 187

O'Reilly Media Inc, Sebastopol, CA *Toll Free Tel:* 800-998-9938; 800-889-8969, pg 187

Organization for Economic Cooperation & Development, Washington, DC *Toll Free Tel:* 800-456-6323 (dist ctr/pubns orders), pg 187

Original Publications, Old Beth Page, NY *Toll Free Tel:* 888-622-8581, pg 188

OSA, The Optical Society, Washington, DC *Toll Free Tel:* 800-766-4672, pg 188

Other Press LLC, New York, NY *Toll Free Tel:* 877-843-6843, pg 188

OTTN Publishing, Stockton, NJ *Toll Free Tel:* 866-356-6886, pg 188

Our Sunday Visitor Publishing, Huntington, IN *Toll Free Tel:* 800-348-2440 (orders) *Toll Free Fax:* 800-498-6709, pg 188

OUT OF YOUR MIND...AND INTO THE MARKETPLACE™, Tustin, CA *Toll Free Tel:* 800-419-1513, pg 189

The Overmountain Press, Johnson City, TN *Toll Free Tel:* 800-992-2691 (orders), pg 189

Richard C Owen Publishers Inc, Katonah, NY *Toll Free Tel:* 800-336-5588, pg 189

Oxbridge® Communications Inc, New York, NY *Toll Free Tel:* 800-955-0231, pg 189

Oxford University Press USA, New York, NY *Toll Free Tel:* 800-451-7556 (orders); 800-445-9714 (cust serv), pg 189

Oxmoor House Inc, Birmingham, AL *Toll Free Tel:* 800-366-4712; 888-891-8935 (cust serv); 800-765-6400 (orders), pg 190

Ozark Mountain Publishing Inc, Huntsville, AR *Toll Free Tel:* 800-935-0045, pg 190

Ozark Publishing Inc, Prairie Grove, AR *Toll Free Tel:* 800-321-5671, pg 190

P & R Publishing Co, Phillipsburg, NJ *Toll Free Tel:* 800-631-0094, pg 190

P S M J Resources Inc, Newton, MA *Toll Free Tel:* 800-537-7765, pg 190

Pacific Press Publishing Association, Nampa, ID *Toll Free Tel:* 800-447-7377, pg 190

Painted Pony Inc, Fort Washakie, WY *Toll Free Tel:* 877-253-3824, pg 191

Paladin Press, Boulder, CO *Toll Free Tel:* 800-392-2400, pg 191

Palm Kids™, Norwalk, CT *Toll Free Tel:* 800-409-2457, pg 191

Panoptic Enterprises, Burke, VA *Toll Free Tel:* 800-594-4766, pg 191

Pantheon Books/Schocken Books, New York, NY *Toll Free Tel:* 800-638-6460, pg 191

Papercutz, New York, NY *Toll Free Tel:* 800-886-1223, pg 192

Para Publishing LLC, Santa Barbara, CA *Toll Free Tel:* 800-727-2782, pg 192

Parabola Books, New York, NY *Toll Free Tel:* 800-592-2521 (subns), pg 192

Paraclete Press Inc, Brewster, MA *Toll Free Tel:* 800-451-5006, pg 192

Paradigm Publications, Taos, NM *Toll Free Tel:* 800-873-3946 (US); 888-873-3947 (CN), pg 192

Paradise Cay Publications Inc, Arcata, CA *Toll Free Tel:* 800-736-4509, pg 193

Paragon House, St Paul, MN *Toll Free Tel:* 800-447-3709, pg 193

Parallax Press, Berkeley, CA *Toll Free Tel:* 800-863-5290 (orders), pg 193

Paramount Market Publishing Inc, Ithaca, NY *Toll Free Tel:* 888-787-8100, pg 193

Paraphrase LLC, Sherman Oaks, CA *Toll Free Fax:* 888-863-4377, pg 528

Parenting Press Inc, Seattle, WA *Toll Free Tel:* 800-99-BOOKS (992-6657), pg 193

Park Place Publications, Pacific Grove, CA *Toll Free Tel:* 888-702-4500, pg 193

Parlay Press, Hilton Head, SC *Toll Free Fax:* 888-301-3116, pg 194

Pastoral Press, Portland, OR *Toll Free Tel:* 800-548-8749 *Toll Free Fax:* 800-462-7329, pg 194

Pathfinder Publishing Inc, Tucson, AZ *Toll Free Tel:* 800-977-2282, pg 194

Pauline Books & Media, Boston, MA *Toll Free Tel:* 800-876-4463 (orders); 800-836-9723 (cust serv), pg 194

Paulist Press, Mahwah, NJ *Toll Free Tel:* 800-218-1903 *Toll Free Fax:* 800-836-3161, pg 194

Peace Hill Press, Charles City, VA *Toll Free Tel:* 877-322-3445 (orders), pg 195

Peachpit Press, Berkeley, CA *Toll Free Tel:* 800-283-9444, pg 195

Peachtree Publishers, Atlanta, GA *Toll Free Tel:* 800-241-0113 *Toll Free Fax:* 800-875-8909, pg 195

Pearson Benjamin Cummings, San Francisco, CA *Toll Free Tel:* 800-922-0579 (orders), pg 195

Pearson Education, Glenview, IL *Toll Free Tel:* 800-535-4391 (Midwest), pg 195

Pearson Education Canada, Don Mills, ON Canada *Toll Free Tel:* 800-263-9965 *Toll Free Fax:* 800-263-7733; 888-465-0536, pg 515

Pearson Learning Solutions, Boston, MA *Toll Free Tel:* 800-428-4466 (orders), pg 196

Peel Productions Inc, Vancouver, WA *Toll Free Tel:* 800-345-6665, pg 196

Pelican Publishing Co, Gretna, LA *Toll Free Tel:* 800-843-1724, pg 196

Pembroke Publishers Ltd, Markham, ON Canada *Toll Free Tel:* 800-997-9807 *Toll Free Fax:* 800-339-5568, pg 515

Pendragon Press, Hillsdale, NY *Toll Free Tel:* 877-656-6381 (orders), pg 196

Penfield Books, Iowa City, IA *Toll Free Tel:* 800-728-9998, pg 196

Penguin Group (USA) LLC, New York, NY *Toll Free Tel:* 800-847-5515 (inside sales); 800-631-8571 (cust serv), pg 197

Pennsylvania Historical & Museum Commission, Harrisburg, PA *Toll Free Tel:* 800-747-7790, pg 198

The Pennsylvania State University Press, University Park, PA *Toll Free Tel:* 800-326-9180 *Toll Free Fax:* 877-778-2665, pg 198

PennWell Books, Tulsa, OK *Toll Free Tel:* 800-752-9764, pg 198

Penton Media, Overland Park, KS *Toll Free Tel:* 800-262-1954 (cust serv) *Toll Free Fax:* 800-633-6219, pg 198

Peoples Education Inc, Saddle Brook, NJ *Toll Free Tel:* 800-822-1080, pg 199

Per Annum Inc, New York, NY *Toll Free Tel:* 800-548-1108, pg 199

Perfection Learning Corp, Clive, IA *Toll Free Tel:* 800-762-2999, pg 199

The Perseus Books Group, New York, NY *Toll Free Tel:* 800-343-4499 (cust serv), pg 199

Peterson Institute for International Economics, Washington, DC *Toll Free Tel:* 800-522-9139 (orders), pg 200

Petroleum Extension Service (PETEX), Austin, TX *Toll Free Tel:* 800-687-4132 *Toll Free Fax:* 800-687-7839, pg 200

Pflaum Publishing Group, Dayton, OH *Toll Free Tel:* 800-543-4383; 800-523-4625 (sales) *Toll Free Fax:* 800-370-4450, pg 200

Phaidon Press Inc, New York, NY *Toll Free Tel:* 800-759-0190 (cust serv) *Toll Free Fax:* 800-286-9471 (cust serv), pg 200

Phi Delta Kappa International®, Bloomington, IN *Toll Free Tel:* 800-766-1156, pg 200

Philosophy Documentation Center, Charlottesville, VA *Toll Free Tel:* 800-444-2419, pg 201

Phoenix Society for Burn Survivors, Grand Rapids, MI *Toll Free Tel:* 800-888-BURN (888-2876), pg 201

Pictorial Histories Publishing Co, Missoula, MT *Toll Free Tel:* 888-763-8350, pg 201

Pieces of Learning, Marion, IL *Toll Free Tel:* 800-729-5137 *Toll Free Fax:* 800-844-0455, pg 201

The Pilgrim Press/United Church Press, Cleveland, OH *Toll Free Tel:* 800-537-3394 (cust serv-indivs); 800-654-5129 (cust serv-commercial accts), pg 202

Pineapple Press Inc, Sarasota, FL *Toll Free Tel:* 866-766-3850 (orders) *Toll Free Fax:* 800-838-1149 (orders), pg 202

Pippin Publishing Corp, Don Mills, ON Canada *Toll Free Tel:* 888-889-0001, pg 515

Platypus Media LLC, Washington, DC *Toll Free Tel:* 877-PLATYPS (752-8977), pg 202

Pleasure Boat Studio: A Literary Press, New York, NY *Toll Free Tel:* 888-810-5308 *Toll Free Fax:* 888-810-5308, pg 203

Pocket Press Inc, Portland, OR *Toll Free Tel:* 888-237-2110 *Toll Free Fax:* 877-643-3732, pg 203

Pogo Press Inc, Lakeville, MN *Toll Free Tel:* 800-846-7027 *Toll Free Fax:* 800-330-6232, pg 204

Poisoned Pen Press Inc, Scottsdale, AZ *Toll Free Tel:* 1-800-421-3976, pg 204

Pomegranate Communications Inc, Portland, OR *Toll Free Tel:* 800-227-1428 *Toll Free Fax:* 800-848-4376, pg 204

Portage & Main Press, Winnipeg, MB Canada *Toll Free Tel:* 800-667-9673 *Toll Free Fax:* 866-734-8477, pg 516

Pottersfield Press, East Lawrencetown, NS Canada *Toll Free Fax:* 888-253-3133, pg 516

Practice Management Information Corp (PMIC), Los Angeles, CA *Toll Free Fax:* 800-633-6556 (orders), pg 205

Practising Law Institute, New York, NY *Toll Free Tel:* 800-260-4PLI (260-4754 cust serv) *Toll Free Fax:* 800-321-0093 (local), pg 205

PrairieView Press, Rosenort, MB Canada *Toll Free Tel:* 800-477-7377, pg 516

PREP Publishing, Fayetteville, NC *Toll Free Tel:* 800-533-2814, pg 205

Presbyterian Publishing Corp, Louisville, KY *Toll Free Tel:* 800-523-1631 (US only), pg 205

Prestel Publishing, New York, NY *Toll Free Tel:* 888-463-6110 (cust serv), pg 205

Price World Publishing LLC, Chicago, IL *Toll Free Tel:* 888-234-6896, pg 206

Princeton Architectural Press, New York, NY *Toll Free Tel:* 800-722-6657 (dist); 800-759-0190 (sales), pg 206

Princeton Book Co Publishers, Hightstown, NJ *Toll Free Tel:* 800-220-7149, pg 206

The Princeton Review, New York, NY *Toll Free Tel:* 800-733-3000, pg 206

Princeton University Press, Princeton, NJ *Toll Free Tel:* 800-777-4726 (orders) *Toll Free Fax:* 800-999-1958, pg 206

PRO-ED Inc, Austin, TX *Toll Free Tel:* 800-897-3202 *Toll Free Fax:* 800-397-7633, pg 207

Pro Lingua Associates Inc, Brattleboro, VT *Toll Free Tel:* 800-366-4775, pg 207

Productivity Press, New York, NY *Toll Free Tel:* 800-634-7064 (orders) *Toll Free Fax:* 800-248-4724 (orders), pg 207

Professional Communications Inc, Caddo, OK *Toll Free Tel:* 800-337-9838, pg 207

The Professional Education Group Inc (PEG), Minnetonka, MN *Toll Free Tel:* 800-229-2531, pg 207

Professional Publications Inc (PPI), Belmont, CA *Toll Free Tel:* 800-426-1178 (orders), pg 207

Professional Resource Press, Sarasota, FL *Toll Free Tel:* 800-443-3364 *Toll Free Fax:* 866-804-4843 (orders), pg 208

Prometheus Books, Amherst, NY *Toll Free Tel:* 800-421-0351, pg 208

ProQuest LLC, Ann Arbor, MI *Toll Free Tel:* 800-521-0600 *Toll Free Fax:* 800-864-0019, pg 208

ProStar Publications Inc, Annapolis, MD *Toll Free Tel:* 800-481-6277 *Toll Free Fax:* 800-487-6277, pg 208

Prufrock Press, Waco, TX *Toll Free Tel:* 800-998-2208 *Toll Free Fax:* 800-240-0333, pg 208

Psychological Assessment Resources Inc (PAR), Lutz, FL *Toll Free Tel:* 800-331-8378 *Toll Free Fax:* 800-727-9329, pg 208

Psychology Press, New York, NY *Toll Free Tel:* 800-634-7064, pg 209

PublicAffairs, New York, NY *Toll Free Tel:* 800-343-4499 (orders), pg 209

Les Publications du Quebec, Quebec, QC Canada *Toll Free Tel:* 800-463-2100 (Quebec province only) *Toll Free Fax:* 800-561-3479, pg 517

Purple Mountain Press Ltd, Fleischmanns, NY *Toll Free Tel:* 800-325-2665 (orders), pg 210

The Putnam Publishing Group, New York, NY *Toll Free Tel:* 800-631-8571, pg 210

QED Press, Fort Bragg, CA *Toll Free Tel:* 800-773-7782, pg 210

Quackenworth Publishing, Culver City, CA *Toll Free Tel:* 888-701-4991 *Toll Free Fax:* 888-892-6339, pg 211

Quail Ridge Press, Brandon, MS *Toll Free Tel:* 800-343-1583 *Toll Free Fax:* 800-864-1082, pg 211

Quality Medical Publishing Inc, St Louis, MO *Toll Free Tel:* 800-348-7808, pg 211

Quayside Publishing Group, Minneapolis, MN *Toll Free Tel:* 800-328-0590 (sales); 800-458-0454, pg 211

Quintessence Publishing Co Inc, Hanover Park, IL *Toll Free Tel:* 800-621-0387, pg 211

Quixote Press, Wever, IA *Toll Free Tel:* 800-571-2665, pg 212

Rainbow Publishers, San Diego, CA *Toll Free Tel:* 800-323-7337 *Toll Free Fax:* 800-331-0297, pg 212

Ram Publishing Co, Garland, TX *Toll Free Tel:* 800-527-4011, pg 212

Rand McNally, Skokie, IL *Toll Free Tel:* 800-678-7263, pg 212

Random House Children's Books, New York, NY *Toll Free Tel:* 800-200-3552, pg 212

Random House Inc, New York, NY *Toll Free Tel:* 800-726-0600, pg 213

Random House of Canada Limited, Toronto, ON Canada *Toll Free Tel:* 888-523-9292 (cust serv), pg 517

Random House Publishing Group, New York, NY *Toll Free Tel:* 800-200-3552, pg 214

Random House Reference/Random House Puzzles & Games/House of Collectibles, New York, NY *Toll Free Tel:* 800-733-3000 *Toll Free Fax:* 800-659-2436, pg 214

Raven Publishing Inc, Norris, MT *Toll Free Tel:* 866-685-3545, pg 214

Raven Tree Press, McHenry, IL *Toll Free Tel:* 800-323-8270 *Toll Free Fax:* 800-909-9901, pg 214

Rayve Productions Inc, Windsor, CA *Toll Free Tel:* 800-852-4890, pg 215

Reader's Digest Association Canada ULC (Selection du Reader's Digest Canada SRL), Montreal, QC Canada *Toll Free Tel:* 866-236-7789 (cust serv), pg 517

The Reader's Digest Association Inc, New York, NY *Toll Free Tel:* 800-310-6261 (cust serv), pg 215

Reader's Digest Children's Books, White Plains, NY *Toll Free Tel:* 800-934-0977, pg 215

Reader's Digest General Books, Pleasantville, NY *Toll Free Tel:* 800-304-2807 (cust serv), pg 215

Reader's Digest USA Select Editions, White Plains, NY *Toll Free Tel:* 800-304-2807 (cust serv), pg 215

Recorded Books LLC, Prince Frederick, MD *Toll Free Tel:* 800-638-1304; 877-732-2898, pg 215

Red Chair Press, South Egremont, MA *Toll Free Tel:* 888-327-2141 (ext 110) *Toll Free Fax:* 888-533-4037, pg 216

Red Deer Press, Markham, ON Canada *Toll Free Tel:* 800-387-9776 (orders) *Toll Free Fax:* 800-260-9777 (orders), pg 517

Red Wheel/Weiser/Conari, Newburyport, MA *Toll Free Tel:* 800-423-7087 (orders), pg 216

Redleaf Press, St Paul, MN *Toll Free Tel:* 800-423-8309 *Toll Free Fax:* 800-641-0115, pg 216

Reedswain Inc, Spring City, PA *Toll Free Tel:* 800-331-5191, pg 217

Referee Books, Racine, WI *Toll Free Tel:* 800-733-6100, pg 217

ReferencePoint Press Inc, San Diego, CA *Toll Free Tel:* 888-479-6436, pg 217

Regal Books, Ventura, CA *Toll Free Tel:* 800-446-7735 (orders), pg 217

Regal Crest Enterprises LLC, Belton, TX *Toll Free Fax:* 866-294-9628, pg 217

Regnery Publishing Inc, Washington, DC *Toll Free Tel:* 888-219-4747, pg 217

Regular Baptist Press, Schaumburg, IL *Toll Free Tel:* 800-727-4440 (orders only); 888-588-1600, pg 217

Research Press, Champaign, IL *Toll Free Tel:* 800-519-2707, pg 218

Fleming H Revell, Grand Rapids, MI *Toll Free Tel:* 800-877-2665; 800-679-1957, pg 218

Review & Herald Publishing Association, Hagerstown, MD *Toll Free Tel:* 800-234-7630, pg 218

Rigby, Orlando, FL *Toll Free Tel:* 800-531-5015; 800-289-4490 *Toll Free Fax:* 800-289-3994, pg 218

Rio Nuevo Publishers, Tucson, AZ *Toll Free Tel:* 800-969-9558 *Toll Free Fax:* 800-715-5888, pg 218

Rising Sun Publishing, Marietta, GA *Toll Free Tel:* 800-524-2813, pg 219

Riverside Publishing, Rolling Meadows, IL *Toll Free Tel:* 800-323-9540, pg 219

Rizzoli International Publications Inc, New York, NY *Toll Free Tel:* 800-522-6657 (orders only), pg 219

James A Rock & Co Publishers, Florence, SC *Toll Free Tel:* 800-411-2230, pg 220

Rod & Staff Publishers Inc, Crockett, KY *Toll Free Fax:* 800-643-1244 (ordering in US), pg 220

Rodale Books, Emmaus, PA *Toll Free Tel:* 800-848-4735 (cust serv), pg 220

Ronsdale Press Ltd, Vancouver, BC Canada *Toll Free Tel:* 855-738-4688, pg 518

The Rosen Publishing Group Inc, New York, NY *Toll Free Tel:* 800-237-9932 *Toll Free Fax:* 888-436-4643, pg 221

Rothstein Associates Inc, Brookfield, CT *Toll Free Tel:* 888-768-4783, pg 221

Rough Guides, New York, NY *Toll Free Tel:* 800-631-8571, pg 221

The Rough Notes Co Inc, Carmel, IN *Toll Free Tel:* 800-428-4384 (cust serv) *Toll Free Fax:* 800-321-1909, pg 221

Routledge/Taylor & Francis, New York, NY *Toll Free Tel:* 800-634-7064 (orders), pg 221

Rowman & Littlefield Publishers Inc, Lanham, MD *Toll Free Tel:* 800-462-6420 (cust serv), pg 221

Roxbury Publishing Co, Cary, NC *Toll Free Tel:* 800-280-0280; 800-451-7556 (orders); 800-455-9714, pg 222

Running Press Book Publishers, Philadelphia, PA *Toll Free Tel:* 800-343-4499 (cust serv & orders) *Toll Free Fax:* 800-453-2884 (cust serv & orders), pg 222

Russell Sage Foundation, New York, NY *Toll Free Tel:* 800-524-6401, pg 222

Rutgers University Press, New Brunswick, NJ *Toll Free Tel:* 800-848-6224 (orders only) *Toll Free Fax:* 800-272-6817 (fulfillment), pg 222

Saddleback Educational Publishing, Costa Mesa, CA *Toll Free Tel:* 888-SDLBACK (735-2225); 800-637-8715 *Toll Free Fax:* 888-734-4010, pg 222

William H Sadlier Inc, New York, NY *Toll Free Tel:* 800-221-5175 (cust serv), pg 223

SAE (Society of Automotive Engineers International), Warrendale, PA *Toll Free Tel:* 877-606-7323 (cust serv), pg 223

Safari Press, Huntington Beach, CA *Toll Free Tel:* 800-451-4788, pg 223

Sagamore Publishing LLC, Urbana, IL *Toll Free Tel:* 800-327-5557 (orders), pg 223

SAGE Publications, Thousand Oaks, CA *Toll Free Tel:* 800-818-7243 *Toll Free Fax:* 800-583-2665, pg 223

St Augustine's Press Inc, South Bend, IN *Toll Free Tel:* 888-997-4994, pg 223

St James Press®, Farmington Hills, MI *Toll Free Tel:* 800-877-4253 (orders) *Toll Free Fax:* 800-414-5043 (orders), pg 224

Saint Mary's Press, Winona, MN *Toll Free Tel:* 800-533-8095 *Toll Free Fax:* 800-344-9225, pg 224

Saint Nectarios Press, Seattle, WA *Toll Free Tel:* 800-643-4233, pg 225

St Pauls/Alba House, Staten Island, NY *Toll Free Tel:* 800-343-2522, pg 225

Salem Press Inc, Hackensack, NJ *Toll Free Tel:* 800-221-1592; 866-550-8122, pg 225

Salina Bookshelf Inc, Flagstaff, AZ *Toll Free Tel:* 877-527-0070, pg 225

Samhain Publishing Ltd, Cincinnati, OH *Toll Free Tel:* 800-509-4158 (orders), pg 225

Sams Technical Publishing LLC, Indianapolis, IN *Toll Free Tel:* 800-428-7267 *Toll Free Fax:* 800-552-3910, pg 225

Sandlapper Publishing Inc, Orangeburg, SC *Toll Free Tel:* 800-849-7263 (orders only) *Toll Free Fax:* 800-337-9420, pg 225

Santa Monica Press LLC, Solana Beach, CA *Toll Free Tel:* 800-784-9553, pg 226

Santillana USA Publishing Co Inc, Doral, FL *Toll Free Tel:* 800-245-8584 *Toll Free Fax:* 888-248-9518, pg 226

Sara Jordan Publishing, St Catharines, ON Canada *Toll Free Tel:* 800-567-7733 *Toll Free Fax:* 800-229-3855, pg 518

Sasquatch Books, Seattle, WA *Toll Free Tel:* 800-775-0817, pg 226

Saxon Publishers, Orlando, FL *Toll Free Tel:* 800-289-4490 *Toll Free Fax:* 800-289-3994, pg 226

Scepter Publishers, New York, NY *Toll Free Tel:* 800-322-8773, pg 227

Schiel & Denver Book Publishers, Houston, TX *Toll Free Tel:* 888-629-4449 *Toll Free Fax:* 888-224-2721, pg 227

Schirmer Trade Books, New York, NY *Toll Free Tel:* 800-431-7187 (orders), pg 227

Schlager Group Inc, Dallas, TX *Toll Free Tel:* 888-416-5727, pg 227

Scholastic Canada Ltd, Toronto, ON Canada *Toll Free Tel:* 800-268-3848 (CN) *Toll Free Fax:* 866-346-1288, pg 518

Scholastic Consumer & Professional Publishing, New York, NY *Toll Free Tel:* 800-621-1115, pg 228

Scholastic Inc, New York, NY *Toll Free Tel:* 800-scholastic, pg 228

Scholastic International, New York, NY *Toll Free Tel:* 800-SCHOLASTIC (800-724-6527), pg 228

Schonfeld & Associates Inc, Libertyville, IL *Toll Free Tel:* 800-205-0030, pg 229

School for Advanced Research Press, Santa Fe, NM *Toll Free Tel:* 888-390-6070, pg 229

School Guide Publications, New Rochelle, NY *Toll Free Tel:* 800-433-7771, pg 229

School Zone Publishing Co, Grand Haven, MI *Toll Free Tel:* 800-253-0564 *Toll Free Fax:* 800-550-4618 (orders only), pg 229

Schreiber Publishing Inc, Rockville, MD *Toll Free Tel:* 800-296-1961 (sales), pg 229

Science, Naturally!™, Washington, DC *Toll Free Tel:* 866-724-9876, pg 229

Scobre Press Corp, La Jolla, CA *Toll Free Tel:* 877-726-2734, pg 230

Scott Publishing Co, Sidney, OH *Toll Free Tel:* 800-572-6885 (cust serv) *Toll Free Fax:* 800-488-5349, pg 230

Scurlock Publishing Co Inc, Texarkana, TX *Toll Free Tel:* 800-228-6389 (US & CN), pg 230

Seal Books, Toronto, ON Canada *Toll Free Tel:* 888-523-9292 (order desk), pg 518

Search Institute Press®, Minneapolis, MN *Toll Free Tel:* 800-888-7828, pg 230

Seedling Publications Inc, Elizabethtown, PA *Toll Free Tel:* 800-233-0759 *Toll Free Fax:* 888-834-1303, pg 231

Self-Counsel Press Ltd, Bellingham, WA *Toll Free Tel:* 800-663-3007, pg 231

Self-Realization Fellowship Publishers, Los Angeles, CA *Toll Free Tel:* 888-773-8680, pg 231

Shambhala Publications Inc, Boston, MA *Toll Free Tel:* 866-424-0030 (off); 888-424-2329 (cust serv), pg 232

M E Sharpe Inc, Armonk, NY *Toll Free Tel:* 800-541-6563, pg 232

Shen's Books, Walnut Creek, CA *Toll Free Tel:* 800-456-6660 *Toll Free Fax:* 888-269-9092, pg 233

Show What You Know® Publishing, A Lorenz Company, Dayton, OH *Toll Free Tel:* 877-PASSING (727-7464), pg 233

Signalman Publishing, Kissimmee, FL *Toll Free Tel:* 888-907-4423, pg 233

Signature Books Publishing LLC, Salt Lake City, UT *Toll Free Tel:* 800-356-5687 (orders), pg 233

Silman-James Press, Los Angeles, CA *Toll Free Tel:* 877-SJP-BOOK (757-2665), pg 234

Silver Moon Press, New York, NY *Toll Free Tel:* 800-874-3320, pg 234

Simba Information, Stamford, CT *Toll Free Tel:* 888-297-4622 (cust serv), pg 234

Simcha Press, Deerfield Beach, FL *Toll Free Tel:* 800-851-9100 ext 212 *Toll Free Fax:* 800-424-7652, pg 234

Simon & Schuster, New York, NY *Toll Free Tel:* 800-223-2348 (cust serv); 800-223-2336 (orders) *Toll Free Fax:* 800-943-9831 (orders), pg 234

Simon & Schuster Canada, Toronto, ON Canada *Toll Free Tel:* 800-387-0446; 800-268-3216 (orders) *Toll Free Fax:* 888-849-8151 (orders), pg 519

Skandisk Inc, Bloomington, MN *Toll Free Tel:* 800-468-2424, pg 236

SkillPath Publications, Mission, KS *Toll Free Tel:* 800-873-7545, pg 236

Sky Publishing, Cambridge, MA *Toll Free Tel:* 866-644-1377, pg 236

SkyLight Paths Publishing, Woodstock, VT *Toll Free Tel:* 800-962-4544, pg 237

Slack Incorporated, Thorofare, NJ *Toll Free Tel:* 800-257-8290, pg 237

Sleeping Bear Press™, Ann Arbor, MI *Toll Free Tel:* 800-487-2323, pg 237

Slipdown Mountain Publications LLC, Lake Linden, MI *Toll Free Tel:* 866-341-3705 *Toll Free Fax:* 866-341-3705, pg 237

Smith & Kraus Publishers Inc, Portland, ME *Toll Free Tel:* 877-668-8680, pg 237

M Lee Smith Publishers LLC, Brentwood, TN *Toll Free Tel:* 800-274-6774, pg 237

Smyth & Helwys Publishing Inc, Macon, GA *Toll Free Tel:* 800-747-3016 (orders only); 800-568-1248 (orders only), pg 237

Society for Human Resource Management (SHRM), Alexandria, VA *Toll Free Tel:* 800-444-5006 (orders), pg 238

Society for Industrial & Applied Mathematics, Philadelphia, PA *Toll Free Tel:* 800-447-7426, pg 238

Society for Mining, Metallurgy & Exploration, Englewood, CO *Toll Free Tel:* 800-763-3132, pg 238

Society of American Archivists, Chicago, IL *Toll Free Tel:* 866-722-7858, pg 238

Society of Manufacturing Engineers, Dearborn, MI *Toll Free Tel:* 800-733-4763 (cust serv), pg 238

The Society of Naval Architects & Marine Engineers, Jersey City, NJ *Toll Free Tel:* 800-798-2188, pg 238

Solano Press Books, Point Arena, CA *Toll Free Tel:* 800-931-9373, pg 239

Solution Tree, Bloomington, IN *Toll Free Tel:* 800-733-6786, pg 239

Soncino Press Ltd, Brooklyn, NY *Toll Free Tel:* 800-972-6201, pg 239

Sophia Institute Press®, Bedford, NH *Toll Free Tel:* 800-888-9344 *Toll Free Fax:* 888-288-2259, pg 239

Sopris West Educational Services, Dallas, TX *Toll Free Tel:* 800-547-6747 *Toll Free Fax:* 888-819-7767, pg 239

Sounds True Inc, Louisville, CO *Toll Free Tel:* 800-333-9185, pg 239

Sourcebooks Inc, Naperville, IL *Toll Free Tel:* 800-432-7444, pg 240

South Carolina Bar, Columbia, SC *Toll Free Tel:* 800-768-7787, pg 240

South End Press, Cambridge, MA *Toll Free Fax:* 800-960-0078, pg 240

Southern Historical Press Inc, Greenville, SC *Toll Free Tel:* 800-233-0152, pg 240

Sphinx Publishing, Naperville, IL *Toll Free Tel:* 800-43-bright (432-7448), pg 241

SPIE, Bellingham, WA *Toll Free Tel:* 888-504-8171, pg 241

Spizzirri Publishing Inc, Rapid City, SD *Toll Free Tel:* 800-325-9819 *Toll Free Fax:* 800-322-9819, pg 241

Springer, New York, NY *Toll Free Tel:* 800-SPRINGER (777-4643), pg 241

Springer Publishing Co LLC, New York, NY *Toll Free Tel:* 877-687-7476, pg 241

Spry Publishing, Ann Arbor, MI *Toll Free Tel:* 877-722-2264, pg 241

Square One Publishers Inc, Garden City Park, NY *Toll Free Tel:* 877-900-BOOK (900-2665), pg 241

SSPC: The Society for Protective Coatings, Pittsburgh, PA *Toll Free Tel:* 877-281-7772 (US only), pg 242

ST Media Group Book Division, Cincinnati, OH *Toll Free Tel:* 866-265-0954, pg 242

Stackpole Books, Mechanicsburg, PA *Toll Free Tel:* 800-732-3669, pg 242

Standard Publishing, Cincinnati, OH *Toll Free Tel:* 800-543-1353 *Toll Free Fax:* 877-867-5751, pg 242

Standard Publishing Corp, Boston, MA *Toll Free Tel:* 800-682-5759, pg 242

Starcrafts LLC, Epping, NH *Toll Free Tel:* 866-953-8458 (24 hr message ctr), pg 243

Stargazer Publishing Co, Corona, CA *Toll Free Tel:* 800-606-7895 (orders), pg 243

State University of New York Press, Albany, NY *Toll Free Tel:* 877-204-6073 (orders) *Toll Free Fax:* 877-204-6074 (orders), pg 243

Statistics Canada, Ottawa, ON Canada *Toll Free Tel:* 800-263-1136 (CN & US, gen inquiries); 800-267-6677 (prods & servs) *Toll Free Fax:* 877-287-4369 (orders), pg 520

Stemmer House Publishers Inc, Gilsum, NH *Toll Free Tel:* 800-345-6665, pg 244

Stenhouse Publishers, Portland, ME *Toll Free Tel:* 888-363-0566 *Toll Free Fax:* 800-833-9164, pg 244

Stephens Press™, Las Vegas, NV *Toll Free Tel:* 888-951-2665, pg 244

Sterling Publishing Co Inc, New York, NY *Toll Free Tel:* 800-367-9692, pg 244

STM Learning Inc, St Louis, MO *Toll Free Tel:* 800-600-0330, pg 245

Stone Bridge Press Inc, Albany, CA *Toll Free Tel:* 800-947-7271 (orders), pg 245

Stoneydale Press Publishing Co, Stevensville, MT *Toll Free Tel:* 800-735-7006, pg 245

Storey Publishing LLC, North Adams, MA *Toll Free Tel:* 800-441-5700 (orders); 800-793-9396 (edit), pg 245

Strategic Book Publishing & Rights Agency (SBPRA), Houston, TX *Toll Free Tel:* 888-808-6190, pg 246

The Street Life Series, Bloomington, IN *Toll Free Tel:* 888-795-4274 (orders thru Xlibris), pg 529

Stress Free Kids®, Marietta, GA *Toll Free Tel:* 800-841-4204 *Toll Free Fax:* 866-302-2759, pg 246

Stylus Publishing LLC, Sterling, VA *Toll Free Tel:* 800-232-0223 (orders & cust serv), pg 246

Summerthought Publishing, Banff, AB Canada *Toll Free Fax:* 800-762-3095 (orders), pg 520

Summit University Press, Gardiner, MT *Toll Free Tel:* 800-245-5445 (retail orders) *Toll Free Fax:* 800-221-8307, pg 246

Sun Books - Sun Publishing Co, Santa Fe, NM *Toll Free Tel:* 877-849-0051, pg 247

Sunbelt Publications Inc, El Cajon, CA *Toll Free Tel:* 800-626-6579 (cust serv), pg 247

Sunburst Digital Inc, Hoffman Estates, IL *Toll Free Tel:* 800-321-7511 *Toll Free Fax:* 888-800-3028, pg 247

Sundance/Newbridge Publishing, Marlborough, MA *Toll Free Tel:* 888-200-2720; 800-343-8204 (Sundance cust serv & orders); 800-867-0307 (Newbridge cust serv & orders) *Toll Free Fax:* 800-456-2419 (orders), pg 247

Sunrise River Press, North Branch, MN *Toll Free Tel:* 800-895-4585, pg 247

Sunstone Press, Santa Fe, NM *Toll Free Tel:* 800-243-5644, pg 247

Surrey Books, Evanston, IL *Toll Free Tel:* 800-326-4430, pg 247

Swan Isle Press, Chicago, IL *Toll Free Tel:* 800-621-2736 (cust serv) *Toll Free Fax:* 800-621-8476 (cust serv), pg 248

Swedenborg Foundation Press, West Chester, PA *Toll Free Tel:* 800-355-3222 (cust serv), pg 248

Sylvan Dell Publishing, Mount Pleasant, SC *Toll Free Tel:* 877-243-3457, pg 248

Synapse Information Resources Inc, Endicott, NY *Toll Free Tel:* 888-SYN-CHEM (796-2436), pg 249

Syracuse University Press, Syracuse, NY *Toll Free Tel:* 800-365-8929 (cust serv), pg 249

TAN Books, Charlotte, NC *Toll Free Tel:* 800-437-5876, pg 249

T&T Clark International, New York, NY *Toll Free Tel:* 800-561-7704 (orders), pg 249

Tanglewood Press, Terre Haute, IN *Toll Free Tel:* 800-836-4994 (orders), pg 249

Tantor Media Inc, Old Saybrook, CT *Toll Free Tel:* 877-782-6867 *Toll Free Fax:* 888-782-7821, pg 250

Tapestry Press Ltd, Littleton, MA *Toll Free Tel:* 800-535-2007, pg 250

Taschen America, Los Angeles, CA *Toll Free Tel:* 888-TASCHEN (827-2436), pg 250

The Taunton Press Inc, Newtown, CT *Toll Free Tel:* 800-477-8727 (cust serv); 800-888-8286 (orders), pg 250

Taylor & Francis Inc, Philadelphia, PA *Toll Free Tel:* 800-354-1420, pg 250

TCP Press, Whitchurch-Stouffville, ON Canada *Toll Free Tel:* 800-772-7765, pg 521

Teach Me Tapes Inc, Minnetonka, MN *Toll Free Tel:* 800-456-4656, pg 251

Teacher Created Resources Inc, Westminster, CA *Toll Free Tel:* 800-662-4321; 888-343-4335 *Toll Free Fax:* 800-525-1254, pg 251

Teachers College Press, New York, NY *Toll Free Tel:* 800-575-6566, pg 251

Teacher's Discovery, Auburn Hills, MI *Toll Free Tel:* 800-832-2437 *Toll Free Fax:* 800-287-4509, pg 251

Teachers of English to Speakers of Other Languages Inc (TESOL), Alexandria, VA *Toll Free Tel:* 888-547-3369, pg 251

Teaching & Learning Co, Dayton, OH *Toll Free Tel:* 800-444-1144, pg 251

Teaching Strategies, Bethesda, MD *Toll Free Tel:* 800-637-3652, pg 251

Temple University Press, Philadelphia, PA *Toll Free Tel:* 800-621-2736, pg 251

Templegate Publishers, Springfield, IL *Toll Free Tel:* 800-367-4844 (orders only), pg 252

Ten Speed Press, Berkeley, CA *Toll Free Tel:* 800-841-BOOK (841-2665), pg 252

Teora USA LLC, Capitol Heights, MD *Toll Free Tel:* 800-974-2105 *Toll Free Fax:* 800-358-3754, pg 252

Teton NewMedia, Jackson, WY *Toll Free Tel:* 877-306-9793, pg 252

Tetra Press, Blacksburg, VA *Toll Free Tel:* 800-526-0650, pg 252

Texas A&M University Press, College Station, TX *Toll Free Tel:* 800-826-8911 (orders) *Toll Free Fax:* 888-617-2421 (orders), pg 252

Texas Christian University Press, Fort Worth, TX *Toll Free Tel:* 800-826-8911, pg 253

Texas Tech University Press, Lubbock, TX *Toll Free Tel:* 800-832-4042, pg 253

Texas Western Press, El Paso, TX *Toll Free Tel:* 800-488-3798 (orders only), pg 253

TFH Publications Inc, Neptune City, NJ *Toll Free Tel:* 800-631-2188, pg 253

Thames & Hudson, New York, NY *Toll Free Tel:* 800-233-4830, pg 253

Theosophical Publishing House/Quest Books, Wheaton, IL *Toll Free Tel:* 800-669-9425 (ext 347), pg 254

Thieme Medical Publishers Inc, New York, NY *Toll Free Tel:* 800-782-3488, pg 254

Charles C Thomas Publisher Ltd, Springfield, IL *Toll Free Tel:* 800-258-8980, pg 254

Thomas Geale Publications Inc, Montara, CA *Toll Free Tel:* 800-554-5457, pg 254

Thomas Nelson Inc, Nashville, TN *Toll Free Tel:* 800-251-4000, pg 254

Thomas Nelson Publishers, Nashville, TN *Toll Free Tel:* 800-251-4000, pg 255

Thomas Publications, Gettysburg, PA *Toll Free Tel:* 800-840-6782, pg 255

Thompson Educational Publishing Inc, Toronto, ON Canada *Toll Free Tel:* 877-366-2763, pg 521

Thomson Groupe Modulo, Montreal, QC Canada *Toll Free Tel:* 888-738-9818 *Toll Free Fax:* 888-273-5247, pg 521

Thomson Reuters Westlaw™, Eagan, MN *Toll Free Tel:* 800-328-9352 (sales); 800-328-4880 (cust serv), pg 255

Thorndike Press®, Waterville, ME *Toll Free Tel:* 800-233-1244 (ext 4, cust serv/orders); 800-877-4253 (cust serv) *Toll Free Fax:* 877-363-4253 (cust serv); 800-558-4676 (orders), pg 255

Tide-mark Press, Windsor, CT *Toll Free Tel:* 888-461-4619, pg 255

Tilbury House Publishers, Gardiner, ME *Toll Free Tel:* 800-582-1899 (orders), pg 255

Timber Press Inc, Portland, OR *Toll Free Tel:* 800-327-5680, pg 255

TJ Publishers Inc, Dallas, TX *Toll Free Tel:* 800-999-1168, pg 530

Tommy Nelson, Nashville, TN *Toll Free Tel:* 800-251-4000, pg 256

Torah Aura Productions, Los Angeles, CA *Toll Free Tel:* 800-238-6724, pg 256

Tortuga Press, Santa Rosa, CA *Toll Free Tel:* 866-4TORTUGA (486-7884), pg 256

Tower Publishing Co, Standish, ME *Toll Free Tel:* 800-969-8693, pg 257

Tracks Publishing, Chula Vista, CA *Toll Free Tel:* 800-443-3570, pg 257

Trafalgar Square Books, North Pomfret, VT *Toll Free Tel:* 800-423-4525, pg 257

Trafford, Bloomington, IN *Toll Free Tel:* 888-232-4444, pg 257

Trails Books, Boulder, CO *Toll Free Tel:* 800-258-5830, pg 257

Training Resource Network Inc (TRN), St Augustine, FL *Toll Free Tel:* 800-280-7010 (orders), pg 257

Tralco-Lingo Fun, Niagara Falls, NY *Toll Free Tel:* 888-487-2526 *Toll Free Fax:* 866-487-2527, pg 257

Transaction Publishers Inc, Piscataway, NJ *Toll Free Tel:* 888-999-6778 (dist ctr), pg 257

Transcontinental Music Publications, New York, NY *Toll Free Tel:* 888-489-8242 (orders), pg 258

Treehaus Communications Inc, Loveland, OH *Toll Free Tel:* 800-638-4287 (orders), pg 258

Triad Publishing Co, Gainesville, FL *Toll Free Fax:* 800-854-4947, pg 258

TripBuilder Media Inc, Westport, CT *Toll Free Tel:* 800-525-9745, pg 259

TriQuarterly Books, Evanston, IL *Toll Free Tel:* 800-621-2736 (orders only), pg 259

TRISTAN Publishing, Minneapolis, MN *Toll Free Tel:* 866-545-1383, pg 259

Triumph Books, Chicago, IL *Toll Free Tel:* 800-888-4741 (orders only), pg 259

Triumph Learning, New York, NY *Toll Free Tel:* 800-221-9372 (cust serv) *Toll Free Fax:* 866-805-5723, pg 259

Truman State University Press, Kirksville, MO *Toll Free Tel:* 800-916-6802, pg 259

Tundra Books, Toronto, ON Canada *Toll Free Tel:* 888-523-9292 (orders); 800-588-1074 *Toll Free Fax:* 888-562-9924 (orders), pg 522

Turnstone Press, Winnipeg, MB Canada *Toll Free Tel:* 888-363-7718, pg 522

Tuttle Publishing, North Clarendon, VT *Toll Free Tel:* 800-526-2778 *Toll Free Fax:* 800-FAX-TUTL, pg 260

Twayne Publishers™, Farmington Hills, MI *Toll Free Tel:* 800-877-4253; 800-363-4253 *Toll Free Fax:* 800-414-5043, pg 260

Twenty-First Century Books, Minneapolis, MN *Toll Free Tel:* 800-328-4929 *Toll Free Fax:* 800-332-1132, pg 260

Twenty-Third Publications, New London, CT *Toll Free Tel:* 800-321-0411 (orders) *Toll Free Fax:* 800-572-0788, pg 260

Twin Peaks Press, Vancouver, WA *Toll Free Tel:* 800-637-2256, pg 261

Tyndale House Publishers Inc, Carol Stream, IL *Toll Free Tel:* 800-323-9400, pg 261

Type & Archetype Press, Charleston, SC *Toll Free Tel:* 800-447-8973, pg 261

UBM Global Trade, Newark, NJ *Toll Free Tel:* 800-221-5488 (ext 7841), pg 261

ULI-The Urban Land Institute, Washington, DC *Toll Free Tel:* 800-321-5011 (cust serv) *Toll Free Fax:* 800-248-4585, pg 262

Ulysses Press, Berkeley, CA *Toll Free Tel:* 800-377-2542, pg 262

Unarius Academy of Science Publications, El Cajon, CA *Toll Free Tel:* 800-475-7062, pg 262

Unicor Medical Inc, Montgomery, AL *Toll Free Tel:* 800-825-7421 *Toll Free Fax:* 800-305-8030, pg 262

The United Educators Inc, Lake Bluff, IL *Toll Free Tel:* 800-323-5875, pg 262

United Nations Publications, New York, NY *Toll Free Tel:* 800-253-9646, pg 262

United States Holocaust Memorial Museum, Washington, DC *Toll Free Tel:* 800-259-9998 (orders), pg 262

United States Institute of Peace Press, Washington, DC *Toll Free Tel:* 800-868-8064 (cust serv), pg 262

United States Pharmacopeia, Rockville, MD *Toll Free Tel:* 800-227-8772, pg 263

United Synagogue Book Service, New York, NY *Toll Free Tel:* 800-594-5617 (warehouse only), pg 263

Universal-Publishers Inc, Boca Raton, FL *Toll Free Tel:* 800-636-8329, pg 263

The University of Akron Press, Akron, OH *Toll Free Tel:* 800-247-6553 (orders), pg 263

University of Alaska Press, Fairbanks, AK *Toll Free Tel:* 888-252-6657 (US only), pg 264

The University of Arizona Press, Tucson, AZ *Toll Free Tel:* 800-426-3797 (orders) *Toll Free Fax:* 800-426-3797, pg 264

The University of Arkansas Press, Fayetteville, AR *Toll Free Tel:* 800-626-0090, pg 264

University of British Columbia Press, Vancouver, BC Canada *Toll Free Tel:* 877-377-9378 *Toll Free Fax:* 800-668-0821, pg 523

University of Chicago Press, Chicago, IL *Toll Free Tel:* 800-621-2736 (orders), pg 265

University of Hawaii Press, Honolulu, HI *Toll Free Tel:* 888-UHPRESS (847-7377) *Toll Free Fax:* 800-650-7811, pg 265

University of Iowa Press, Iowa City, IA *Toll Free Tel:* 800-621-2736 (orders only) *Toll Free Fax:* 800-621-8476 (orders only), pg 266

University of Missouri Press, Columbia, MO *Toll Free Tel:* 800-621-2736 (orders), pg 267

University of Nebraska Press, Lincoln, NE *Toll Free Tel:* 800-848-6224 (cust serv & US orders) *Toll Free Fax:* 800-526-2617 (cust serv & US orders), pg 267

University of New Mexico, Albuquerque, NM *Toll Free Tel:* 800-249-7737 (orders only) *Toll Free Fax:* 800-622-8667 (orders only), pg 267

University of Oklahoma Press, Norman, OK *Toll Free Tel:* 800-627-7377 (orders) *Toll Free Fax:* 800-735-0476 (orders), pg 268

University of Puerto Rico Press, San Juan, PR *Toll Free Tel:* 877-338-7788, pg 269

University of South Carolina Press, Columbia, SC *Toll Free Tel:* 800-768-2500 (orders) *Toll Free Fax:* 800-868-0740 (orders), pg 269

University of Tennessee Press, Knoxville, TN *Toll Free Tel:* 800-621-2736 (orders) *Toll Free Fax:* 800-621-8476 (orders), pg 269

The University of Utah Press, Salt Lake City, UT *Toll Free Tel:* 800-621-2736 (orders) *Toll Free Fax:* 800-621-8471, pg 269

The University of Virginia Press, Charlottesville, VA *Toll Free Tel:* 800-831-3406 (orders) *Toll Free Fax:* 877-288-6400, pg 269

University of Washington Press, Seattle, WA *Toll Free Tel:* 800-537-5487 (orders), pg 270

University of Wisconsin Press, Madison, WI *Toll Free Tel:* 800-621-2736 (orders) *Toll Free Fax:* 800-621-2736 (orders), pg 270

University Press of America Inc, Lanham, MD *Toll Free Tel:* 800-462-6420 *Toll Free Fax:* 800-338-4550, pg 270

University Press of Colorado, Boulder, CO *Toll Free Tel:* 800-621-2736 (orders), pg 270

University Press of Florida, Gainesville, FL *Toll Free Tel:* 800-226-3822 (orders only) *Toll Free Fax:* 800-680-1955 (orders only), pg 271

University Press of Mississippi, Jackson, MS *Toll Free Tel:* 800-737-7788 (orders & cust serv), pg 271

University Press of New England, Lebanon, NH *Toll Free Tel:* 800-421-1561 (orders only), pg 271

University Publishing Group, Hagerstown, MD *Toll Free Tel:* 800-654-8188, pg 272

W E Upjohn Institute for Employment Research, Kalamazoo, MI *Toll Free Tel:* 888-227-8569, pg 272

Upper Access Inc, Hinesburg, VT *Toll Free Tel:* 800-310-8320, pg 272

Upper Room Books, Nashville, TN *Toll Free Tel:* 800-972-0433, pg 273

Upstart Books™, Madison, WI *Toll Free Tel:* 800-448-4887 (orders) *Toll Free Fax:* 800-448-5828, pg 273

The Urban Institute Press, Washington, DC *Toll Free Tel:* 877-UIPRESS (847-7377); 800-537-5487 (orders), pg 273

Urban Land Institute, Washington, DC *Toll Free Tel:* 800-321-5011 (cust serv), pg 273

US Conference of Catholic Bishops, Washington, DC *Toll Free Tel:* 800-235-8722 (orders only), pg 273

US Games Systems Inc, Stamford, CT *Toll Free Tel:* 800-54-GAMES (544-2637), pg 273

US Government Printing Office, Washington, DC *Toll Free Tel:* 866-512-1800 (orders), pg 273

Utah Geological Survey, Salt Lake City, UT *Toll Free Tel:* 888-UTAH-MAP (882-4627 bookstore), pg 273

VanDam Inc, New York, NY *Toll Free Tel:* 800-UNFOLDS (863-6537), pg 274

Vandamere Press, St Petersburg, FL *Toll Free Tel:* 800-551-7776, pg 274

Vanderbilt University Press, Nashville, TN *Toll Free Tel:* 800-627-7377 (orders only) *Toll Free Fax:* 800-735-0476 (orders only), pg 274

Vedanta Press, Hollywood, CA *Toll Free Tel:* 800-816-2242, pg 274

Victory in Grace Printing, Lake Zurich, IL *Toll Free Tel:* 800-78-GRACE (784-7223), pg 274

Volcano Press, Volcano, CA *Toll Free Tel:* 800-879-9636, pg 275

Wadsworth Publishing, Belmont, CA *Toll Free Fax:* 800-522-4923, pg 275

Walch Education, Portland, ME *Toll Free Tel:* 800-558-2846 *Toll Free Fax:* 888-991-5755, pg 276

Warren Communications News Inc, Washington, DC *Toll Free Tel:* 800-771-9202, pg 276

Washington State University Press, Pullman, WA *Toll Free Tel:* 800-354-7360, pg 276

Water Environment Federation, Alexandria, VA *Toll Free Tel:* 800-666-0206, pg 276

Water Resources Publications LLC, Highlands Ranch, CO *Toll Free Tel:* 800-736-2405 *Toll Free Fax:* 800-616-1971, pg 277

WaterBrook Multnomah Publishing Group, Colorado Springs, CO *Toll Free Tel:* 800-603-7051 (orders) *Toll Free Fax:* 800-294-5686 (orders), pg 277

Watermark Publishing, Honolulu, HI *Toll Free Tel:* 866-900-BOOK (900-2665), pg 277

Wayne State University Press, Detroit, MI *Toll Free Tel:* 800-978-7323, pg 277

Wayside Publishing, Sandwich, MA *Toll Free Tel:* 888-302-2519, pg 277

Weigl Educational Publishers Ltd, Calgary, AB Canada *Toll Free Tel:* 800-668-0766 *Toll Free Fax:* 866-449-3445, pg 524

Wesleyan Publishing House, Fishers, IN *Toll Free Tel:* 800-493-7539 *Toll Free Fax:* 800-788-3535, pg 278

West Academic Publishing, Eagan, MN *Toll Free Tel:* 800-328-2209 (bookstore orders); 800-313-WEST (313-9378) *Toll Free Fax:* 800-213-2323 (bookstore orders), pg 278

West Virginia University Press, Morgantown, WV *Toll Free Tel:* 866-WVU-PRES (988-7737), pg 278

Westcliffe Publishers Inc, Boulder, CO *Toll Free Tel:* 800-258-5830, pg 279

Western Reflections Publishing Co, Lake City, CO *Toll Free Tel:* 800-993-4490, pg 279

Westminster John Knox Press, Louisville, KY *Toll Free Tel:* 800-227-2872 (US only) *Toll Free Fax:* 800-541-5113 (US & CN), pg 279

Whitaker House, New Kensington, PA *Toll Free Tel:* 877-793-9800 *Toll Free Fax:* 800-765-1960, pg 280

White Cloud Press, Ashland, OR *Toll Free Tel:* 800-380-8286, pg 280

White Wolf Publishing Inc, Decatur, GA *Toll Free Tel:* 800-454-9653, pg 280

Whitecap Books Ltd, Vancouver, BC Canada *Toll Free Tel:* 800-387-9776 *Toll Free Fax:* 800-260-9777, pg 524

Whitehorse Press, Center Conway, NH *Toll Free Tel:* 800-531-1133, pg 280

Whittier Publications Inc, Oceanside, NY *Toll Free Tel:* 800-897-TEXT (897-8398), pg 280

Whole Person Associates Inc, Duluth, MN *Toll Free Tel:* 800-247-6789, pg 280

Wide World of Maps Inc, Phoenix, AZ *Toll Free Tel:* 800-279-7654, pg 280

Michael Wiese Productions, Studio City, CA *Toll Free Tel:* 800-833-5738 (orders), pg 281

Wilderness Adventures Press Inc, Belgrade, MT *Toll Free Tel:* 866-400-2012, pg 281

Wildlife Education Ltd, Evanston, IL *Toll Free Tel:* 800-477-5034, pg 281

John Wiley & Sons Canada Ltd, Toronto, ON Canada *Toll Free Tel:* 800-467-4797 (orders only) *Toll Free Fax:* 800-565-6802 (orders), pg 525

John Wiley & Sons Inc, Hoboken, NJ *Toll Free Tel:* 800-225-5945 (cust serv), pg 281

John Wiley & Sons Inc Higher Education, Hoboken, NJ *Toll Free Tel:* 800-225-5945 (cust serv), pg 281

John Wiley & Sons Inc Professional/Trade Group, Hoboken, NJ *Toll Free Tel:* 800-225-5945 (cust serv), pg 281

John Wiley & Sons Inc Scientific, Technical, Medical & Scholarly (STMS), Hoboken, NJ *Toll Free Tel:* 800-225-5945 (cust serv), pg 282

Wilfrid Laurier University Press, Waterloo, ON Canada *Toll Free Tel:* 866-836-5551, pg 525

William Carey Library Publishers, Pasadena, CA *Toll Free Tel:* 866-732-6657 (orders & cust serv), pg 282

William K Bradford Publishing Co Inc, Maynard, MA *Toll Free Tel:* 800-421-2009, pg 282

Willow Creek Press, Minocqua, WI *Toll Free Tel:* 800-850-9453, pg 282

H W Wilson, Ipswich, MA *Toll Free Tel:* 800-653-2726 (US & CN), pg 282

Wimmer Cookbooks, Memphis, TN *Toll Free Tel:* 800-363-1771, pg 282

Wind Canyon Books, Stockton, CA *Toll Free Tel:* 800-952-7007 *Toll Free Fax:* 888-289-7086, pg 282

Windsor Books, Bayshore, NY *Toll Free Tel:* 800-321-5934, pg 282

Windward Publishing, Lakeville, MN *Toll Free Tel:* 800-846-7027 *Toll Free Fax:* 800-330-6232, pg 282

The Wine Appreciation Guild Ltd, South San Francisco, CA *Toll Free Tel:* 800-231-9463, pg 283

WinePress Publishing, Enumclaw, WA *Toll Free Tel:* 800-326-4674, pg 283

WingSpread Publishers, Camp Hill, PA *Toll Free Tel:* 800-884-4571, pg 283

Winters Publishing, Greensburg, IN *Toll Free Tel:* 800-457-3230 *Toll Free Fax:* 800-457-3230, pg 283

Winterthur Museum & Country Estate, Wilmington, DE *Toll Free Tel:* 800-448-3883, pg 283

Wisconsin Dept of Public Instruction, Madison, WI *Toll Free Tel:* 800-441-4563, pg 283

Wisdom Publications Inc, Somerville, MA *Toll Free Tel:* 800-272-4050 (orders), pg 283

Wittenborn Art Books, San Francisco, CA *Toll Free Tel:* 800-660-6403, pg 284

Alan Wofsy Fine Arts, San Francisco, CA *Toll Free Tel:* 800-660-6403, pg 284

Wood Lake Publishing Inc, Kelowna, BC Canada *Toll Free Tel:* 800-663-2775 (orders) *Toll Free Fax:* 888-841-9991 (orders), pg 525

Woodbine House, Bethesda, MD *Toll Free Tel:* 800-843-7323, pg 284

Woodland Publishing Inc, Salt Lake City, UT *Toll Free Tel:* 800-277-3243, pg 284

Workman Publishing Co Inc, New York, NY *Toll Free Tel:* 800-722-7202, pg 285

World Almanac®, New York, NY *Toll Free Tel:* 800-322-8755, pg 285

World Bank Publications, Washington, DC *Toll Free Tel:* 800-645-7247 (cust serv), pg 285

World Book Inc, Chicago, IL *Toll Free Tel:* 800-967-5325 (consumer sales, US); 800-463-8845 (consumer sales, CN); 800-975-3250 (school & lib sales, US); 800-837-5365 (school & lib sales, CN); 866-866-5200 (web sales) *Toll Free Fax:* 800-433-9330 (school & lib sales, US); 888-690-4002 (school lib sales, CN), pg 285

World Citizens, Mill Valley, CA *Toll Free Tel:* 800-247-6553 (orders only), pg 285

World Scientific Publishing Co Inc, Hackensack, NJ *Toll Free Tel:* 800-227-7562 *Toll Free Fax:* 888-977-2665, pg 285

World Trade Press, Petaluma, CA *Toll Free Tel:* 800-833-8586, pg 286

World Vision Resources, Monrovia, CA *Toll Free Tel:* 800-777-7752 (US only), pg 286

WorldTariff, San Francisco, CA *Toll Free Tel:* 800-556-9334, pg 286

Worldwide Library, Don Mills, ON Canada *Toll Free Tel:* 888-432-4879, pg 525

Wright Group/McGraw-Hill, Columbus, OH *Toll Free Tel:* 800-537-4740, pg 286

Write Stuff Enterprises Inc, Fort Lauderdale, FL *Toll Free Tel:* 800-900-2665, pg 286

Writer's Digest Books, Blue Ash, OH *Toll Free Tel:* 800-289-0963, pg 286

Wyndham Hall Press, Lima, OH *Toll Free Tel:* 866-895-0977, pg 287

Xlibris Corp, Bloomington, IN *Toll Free Tel:* 888-795-4274, pg 287

Yale Center for British Art, New Haven, CT *Toll Free Tel:* 877-274-8278, pg 287

Yale University Press, New Haven, CT *Toll Free Tel:* 800-405-1619 (cust serv) *Toll Free Fax:* 800-406-9145 (cust serv), pg 287

YMAA Publication Center, Wolfeboro, NH *Toll Free Tel:* 800-669-8892, pg 288

York Press, Spring Grove, PA *Toll Free Tel:* 888-317-5571, pg 530

Young People's Press Inc (YPPI), San Diego, CA *Toll Free Tel:* 800-231-9774, pg 288

YWAM Publishing, Seattle, WA *Toll Free Tel:* 800-922-2143, pg 289

Zagat Survey LLC, New York, NY *Toll Free Tel:* 866-817-9947 (orders); 800-540-9609, pg 289

Zaner-Bloser Inc, Columbus, OH *Toll Free Tel:* 800-421-3018 (cust serv) *Toll Free Fax:* 800-992-6087 (orders), pg 289

Zeig, Tucker & Theisen Inc, Phoenix, AZ *Toll Free Tel:* 800-666-2211 (orders), pg 289

Zondervan, A HarperCollins Company, Grand Rapids, MI *Toll Free Tel:* 800-226-1122; 800-727-1309 (retail orders) *Toll Free Fax:* 800-698-3256 (retail orders), pg 289

Zone Books dba Urzone Inc, Brooklyn, NY *Toll Free Tel:* 800-405-1619 (orders & cust serv) *Toll Free Fax:* 800-406-9145 (orders), pg 289

# Index to Sections

## D



## E



## F

## U

# Index to Advertisers